HOLT McDOUGAL

CLASSZONE

Visit classzone.com and get connected.

ClassZone resources provide instruction, planning and assessment support for teachers.

State-Specific Resources

- Select your state and access state-specific resources.

Algebra

- Engaging activities with animated problem-solving graphics support each lesson.

Help with the Math

- @HomeTutor prepares students for class, with animated examples and instruction.
- Extra examples similar to those in the book provide additional support.

Practice, Practice, Practice

- eWorkbook includes interactive worksheets with additional practice problems.

Games and Activities

- Crossword puzzles, memory games, and other activities help students connect to essential math concepts.
- Math Vocabulary Flipcards are a fun way to learn math terminology.

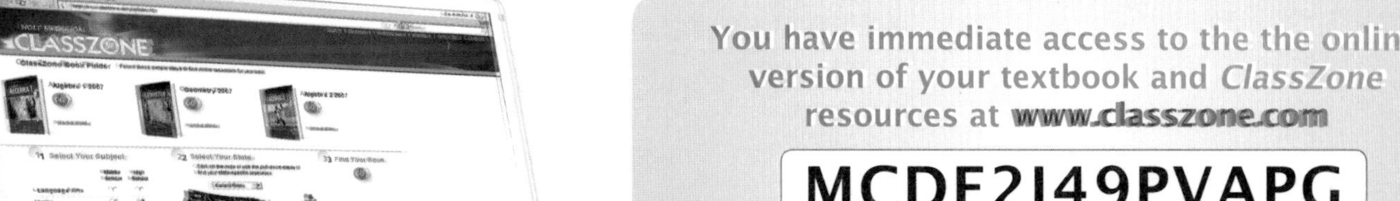

You have immediate access to the the online version of your textbook and *ClassZone* resources at www.classzone.com

MCDE2I49PVAPG

Use this code to create your own user name and password.

HOLT McDOUGAL

LARSON ALGEBRA 1

Ron Larson

Laurie Boswell

Timothy D. Kanold

Lee Stiff

HOLT McDOUGAL

HOUGHTON MIFFLIN HARCOURT

About *Larson Algebra 1*

The content of *Algebra 1* is organized around families of functions, with special emphasis on linear and quadratic functions. As students learn about each family of functions, they will learn to represent them in multiple ways—as verbal descriptions, equations, tables, and graphs. They will also learn to model real-world situations using functions in order to solve problems arising from those situations.

In addition to its algebra content, *Algebra 1* includes lessons on probability and data analysis as well as numerous examples and exercises involving geometry. These math topics often appear on standardized tests, so maintaining students' familiarity with them is important. To help students prepare for standardized tests, *Algebra 1* provides instruction and practice on standardized test questions in a variety of formats—multiple choice, short response, extended response, and so on. Technology support for both learning algebra and preparing for standardized tests is available at classzone.com.

Printed in the U.S.A.

ISBN-13 978-0-547-31539-3
ISBN-10 0-547-31539-2

2 3 4 5 6 7 8 9 10 0914 18 17 16 15 14 13 12 11 4500283209

LARSON

ALGEBRA 1

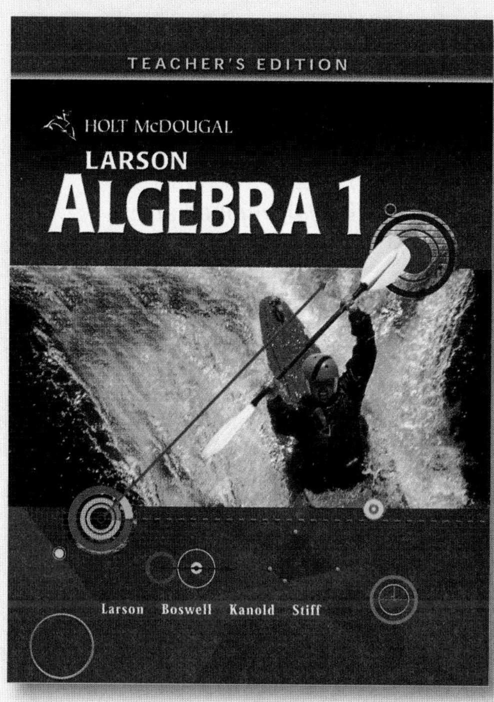

© Amy and Chuck Wiley/Wales/
Index Stock Imagery/Photolibrary

Contents

A Letter from the Authors

Dear Colleagues,

We wanted to create a program that would help your students succeed in mathematics and make your teaching job easier. To achieve these objectives, we reviewed and addressed the curriculum and assessment guidelines of many states and of the National Council of Teachers of Mathematics. We also developed an extensive collection of teacher resources to assist you in the classroom. Our overall goal was to prepare your students both for important assessments and for future mathematics courses.

Our commitment has always been to writing books that contain accurate mathematics, sound pedagogy, and student-friendly presentations. We believe that a balance of teaching approaches is generally most effective. Therefore, we combine clear, straightforward instruction in concepts and skills with thought-provoking student activities, relevant real-life applications, and powerful strategies for problem solving and communication. We have also incorporated feedback from many teachers and students nationwide who have used earlier editions or pilot materials in the classroom.

During more than 20 years of working together as an author team, we have remained dedicated to helping students at all levels achieve high mathematics standards. Our textbooks provide differentiated instruction for struggling students, carefully constructed examples and practice for the majority of students, and demanding challenge exercises for more advanced students.

We wish you success as you strive to give every student in your classroom a quality mathematics education.

Ron Larson

Laurie Boswell

Tim Kanold

Lee Stiff

About the Authors

Ron Larson is a professor of mathematics at Penn State University in Erie, where he has taught since receiving his Ph.D. in mathematics from the University of Colorado. His activities and accomplishments include:

- Author of a comprehensive program for mathematics that spans middle school, high school, and college courses
- Active member of the National Council of Teachers of Mathematics, the American Mathematical Association of Two-Year Colleges, and the Mathematical Association of America
- Stays in close contact with mathematics teachers and supervisors through numerous speaking engagements ranging in size from school districts to national conferences

Laurie Boswell is a mathematics teacher at The Riverside School in Lyndonville, Vermont, as well as a Regional Director for the National Council of Supervisors of Mathematics. Her activities and accomplishments include:

- Recipient of the Presidential Award for Excellence in Mathematics and Science Teaching, and a past president of the Council of Presidential Awardees in Mathematics
- Served on the NCTM Board of Directors for the years 2002–2005
- Frequent speaker at regional and national NCTM conferences

Timothy D. Kanold is a former superintendent of Adlai E. Stevenson High School District 125 in Lincolnshire, Illinois, where he also served as a teacher and director of mathematics and science for 22 years. His activities and accomplishments include:

- President of the National Council of Supervisors of Mathematics for the years 2007–2009
- Recipient of the Presidential Award for Excellence in Mathematics and Science Teaching, and a past president of the Council of Presidential Awardees in Mathematics
- Has presented hundreds of mathematics leadership seminars worldwide for the past 20 years

Lee Stiff is a professor of mathematics education in the College of Education of North Carolina State University at Raleigh and has taught mathematics at the high school and middle school levels. His activities and accomplishments include:

- Served on the NCTM Board of Directors and was elected President of NCTM for the years 2000–2002
- Fulbright Scholar to the University of Ghana
- Recipient of the W.W. Rankin Award for Excellence in Mathematics Education presented by the North Carolina Council of Teachers of Mathematics

A Program You Can Trust

Larson Algebra 1 is a program you can count on to teach the mathematical concepts and methods your students need to know to meet curriculum standards and succeed on high-stakes tests. Including the appropriate content, however, is not enough. The math must be presented in a way that students can understand and that will motivate them to learn. The distinguished author team of *Larson Algebra 1* and the thorough, research-based planning and development process ensure that students gain conceptual understanding and achieve success on important assessments.

Distinguished Author Team

The experienced, expert author team of Ron Larson, Laurie Boswell, Timothy Kanold, and Lee Stiff brings a wealth of mathematical expertise, writing talent, and classroom teaching and curriculum planning experience from middle school through college to the creation of this program. Lead author Ron Larson has been writing highly-respected and widely-used textbooks for more than 20 years, and each new book benefits from the comments of the many teachers and students who used earlier editions.

Standards-Based Instruction and Assessment

In planning the outline and writing the textbook, the authors paid careful attention to state curriculum standards and state assessment objectives from all states to make sure that the important mathematical concepts and skills were included and given appropriate emphasis. The authors also made sure that the outline and course content fully addressed the standards of national organizations such as the National Council of Teachers of Mathematics and the National Assessment of Educational Progress.

Supporting Best Practices from Research

Recent research studies have confirmed strategies for increasing student achievement. These strategies, which reflect the best practices of successful teachers, can help all students learn more effectively. The authors kept this research in mind as they planned and wrote *Algebra 1,* so that the content, organization, and instructional strategies in the program would make it easy for you to implement best-practice instruction in your classroom.

Comprehensive Research and Review

Several years prior to publication, the authors and teams of editors, consultants, graphic designers, professional researchers, and experts in content, instruction, and technology began gathering and analyzing the extensive data on which this program is based. The chart on the next page summarizes the research.

. . . Validated by Research

✓ **CLASSROOM VISITS**	Discussions and classroom observations took place in schools throughout the country to determine the key needs of teachers and students, the obstacles that they face in achieving their goals, and the types of materials that can help them achieve success.
✓ **NATIONWIDE RESEARCH SURVEYS**	Comprehensive mail surveys on Algebra 1 curriculum needs, instructional practices, student achievement levels, and teacher preferences regarding instructional materials were conducted early in the development process to guide the planning of the program.
✓ **TEACHER PANELS**	Panels of expert teachers from different areas of the country participated in the development of the program by identifying instructional and curriculum needs, reviewing prototype outlines and sample materials for both print and electronic materials, and providing suggestions for teaching-support publications.
✓ **STUDENT DISCUSSION GROUPS**	Discussion groups were held with Algebra 1 students to determine the textbook characteristics that make it easy or hard for them to learn and the extent to which they have access to and feel comfortable using electronic products.
✓ **FOCUS TESTS**	Focus tests in which teachers discussed their instructional goals and evaluated sample student and teacher materials were held in different areas of the country. The teachers were chosen to represent the wide range of types of schools, philosophies of instruction, and teacher characteristics (like number of years of teaching) in the teaching population. The feedback from these diverse groups was used to revise and refine the project plans.
✓ **CURRICULUM ADVISERS AND REVIEWERS**	The Curriculum Advisers and Reviewers listed on page T8 participated in planning the program and read all the proof for the student edition in detail with regard to clarity, accuracy, and appropriateness for classroom use. Other teacher reviewers read selected chapters for these characteristics.
✓ **LEARNER VERIFICATION**	The *Algebra 1, Geometry, Algebra 2 Research-Based Framework and Learner Verification* book provides information about the instructional research on which the program was based as well as classroom research demonstrating the effectiveness of the program.

Advisers and Reviewers

Curriculum Advisers and Reviewers

Cindy Branson
Mathematics Teacher
Creekview High School
Carrollton, TX

Rhonda Foote
Secondary Math Resource Specialist
North Kansas City School District
Kansas City, MO

Michael J. Klein
Educational Consultant
Macomb ISD
Clinton Township, MI

Fizza Munaim
Mathematics Teacher
Riverside Middle School
El Paso, TX

Dr. Anne Papakonstantinou
Director, School Mathematics Project
Rice University
Houston, TX

Richard Parr
Director, School Mathematics Project
and Instructional Programs,
School Mathematics Project
Rice University
Houston, TX

Rebecca S. Poe
Mathematics Teacher
Winnsboro High School
Winnsboro, TX

Teacher Panels

Leticia Alvarado
Mathematics Department Chair
Hornedo Middle School
El Paso, TX

Arlene Banks
Mathematics Teacher
Westridge Middle School
Overland Park, KS

Monette Bartel
Associate Adjunct Professor
College of the Canyons
Valencia, CA

Janice Beauchamp
Mathematics Teacher
Buchanan High School
Clovis, CA

Jan Berghaus
Mathematics Teacher
Shawnee Mission West High School
Overland Park, KS

Dennis Dickson
Mathematics Teacher
Leavenworth High School
Leavenworth, KS

Teacher Panels *(continued)*

Pauline Embree
Mathematics Department Chair
Rancho San Joaquin Middle School
Irvine, CA

Coleen Floberg
Mathematics Teacher
Highland Park High School
Topeka, KS

Phillip Gegen
Mathematics Teacher
Oak Park High School
Kansas City, MO

Jason Godfrey
Mathematics Teacher
Grandview High School
Grandview, MO

Leticia Gonzales-Reynolds
Mathematics Teacher
Crockett High School
Austin, TX

Maria Gossett
Mathematics Department Chair
E.M. Daggett Middle School
Fort Worth, TX

Tom Griffith
Mathematics Department Chair
Scripps Ranch High School
San Diego, CA

Alberto Hernandez Galindo
Mathematics Department Chair
San Jose High Academy
San Jose, CA

Debra Konvalin
Mathematics Teacher
Hiram W. Johnson High School
Sacramento, CA

William Lee Littles
Mathematics Teacher
Central High School
Beaumont, TX

Maria Magdalena Lucio
Lead Teacher for Algebra 1
Homer Hanna High School
Brownsville, TX

Deborah Reilly
Mathematics Teacher
West Middle School
Leavenworth, KS

Jon Simon
National Board Certified
Mathematics Teacher
Casa Grande High School
Petaluma, CA

Karen S. Skinner
Mathematics Teacher
New Mark Middle School
Kansas City, MO

Steve Snider
Mathematics Teacher
Benton High School
St. Joseph, MO

Bertha Stimac
Instructional Specialist
Elsik High School
Houston, TX

Karen Stohlmann
Mathematics Teacher
Blue Valley Northwest High School
Overland Park, KS

Deborah Sylvester
Mathematics Teacher
Wamego High School
Wamego, KS

Tommie L. Walsh
Mathematics Teacher (retired)
Smylie Wilson Junior High School
Lubbock, TX

Mary Warner
Mathematics Teacher
Richard King High School
Corpus Christi, TX

Maureen Williams
Mathematics Department Chair
Southwest Junior High School
Lawrence, KS

Chapter 1 Summary

Chapter 1 focuses on the basics of algebra, showing how **variables** are used in forming **algebraic expressions** and how expressions are used in forming **equations and inequalities**. Along the way, students evaluate expressions using the **order of operations** and solve equations and inequalities using **mental math**. Students also use equations to solve real-world problems as part of the four-step **problem solving plan**. The chapter concludes by looking at the dependence of one variable on another in the form of **functional relationships**. Students see that functions have **multiple representations**: verbal descriptions, rules, tables, and graphs.

CHAPTER 1

Unit 1
Equations in One Variable

Problem Solving, p. 29
$0.1s + 0.6 = 2$

Expressions, Equations, and Functions

Chapter 1 Highlights

PROBLEM SOLVING

- Mixed Review of Problem Solving, 27, 51
- Multiple Representations, 33, 39
- Multi-Step Problems, 6, 11, 19, 27, 40, 51
- Using Alternative Methods, 34
- Real-World Problem Solving Examples, 4, 10, 17, 23, 28, 30, 35, 37, 45

★ ASSESSMENT

- Standardized Test Practice Examples, 10, 30
- Multiple Choice, 5, 6, 11, 18, 24, 25, 31, 38, 46
- Short Response/Extended Response, 7, 12, 20, 26, 27, 32, 33, 40, 48, 51, 58
- Writing/Open-Ended, 5, 10, 12, 18, 19, 24, 25, 27, 31, 38, 39, 46, 47, 51, 53

TECHNOLOGY

At classzone.com:

- Animated Algebra 1, 7, 9, 14, 21, 29, 34, 37, 50
- @Home Tutor, xxii, 6, 11, 13, 19, 25, 32, 39, 41, 47, 53
- Online Quiz, 7, 12, 20, 26, 33, 40, 48
- Electronic Function Library, 52
- State Test Practice, 27, 51, 61

FOCUS ON MATHEMATICAL UNDERSTANDING AND REASONING

Conceptual Understanding

Opportunities for developing students' conceptual understanding in this chapter include:

- **Investigating Algebra** activities, pp. 14, 42
- **Animated Algebra** activities, pp. 1, 7, 9, 14, 21, 29, 34, 37, 50
- **Problem Solving Workshop**, p. 34

Critical Thinking

Opportunities for developing students' critical thinking skills in this chapter include:

- **Error Analysis** exercises, pp. 5, 11, 18, 24, 31, 34, 38, 46
- **Challenge** exercises, pp. 6, 7, 11, 12, 19, 20, 25, 26, 31, 33, 39, 40, 47, 48,
- **Reasoning** exercises, pp. 45, 50

CHAPTER

2

Unit 1

Equations in One Variable

Multiplying Real Numbers, p. 90

Elevation = $6416 + (-0.12)(50)$

Properties of Real Numbers

Chapter 2 Highlights

PROBLEM SOLVING

- **Mixed Review of Problem Solving,** 86, 119
- **Multiple Representations,** 83, 93, 116
- **Multi-Step Problems,** 69, 78, 86, 107, 115, 119
- **Using Alternative Methods,** 102
- **Real-World Problem Solving Examples,** 65, 76, 81, 90, 98, 104, 111

★ ASSESSMENT

- **Standardized Test Practice Examples,** 98
- **Multiple Choice,** 68, 69, 78, 82, 92, 99, 106, 107, 108, 114
- **Short Response/Extended Response,** 70, 79, 83, 86, 92, 93, 100, 101, 108, 115, 119, 126
- **Writing/Open-Ended,** 67, 77, 82, 83, 86, 91, 99, 106, 107, 113, 114, 119

TECHNOLOGY

At classzone.com:

- Animated Algebra 63, 73, 80, 90, 93, 98
- **@Home Tutor,** 62, 69, 78, 83, 92, 100, 107, 115, 121
- **Online Quiz,** 70, 79, 84, 93, 101, 108, 116
- **State Test Practice,** 86, 119, 129

Chapter 2 Summary

Chapter 2 focuses on the set of **real numbers** and its various subsets, including integers, rational numbers, and irrational numbers. Students become proficient at **comparing and ordering** real numbers and **performing operations** on them. Students also learn the **properties** of real-number addition and multiplication, including the **distributive property,** which students use to simplify expressions. The chapter emphasizes logical reasoning by asking students to write **conditional statements** and to determine whether those statements are true or false. Students learn to provide **justifications** for true statements and **counterexamples** for false statements.

FOCUS ON MATHEMATICAL UNDERSTANDING AND REASONING

Conceptual Understanding

Opportunities for developing students' conceptual understanding in this chapter include:

- **Investigating Algebra** activities, pp. 73, 87, 109
- **Animated Algebra** activities, pp. 63, 73, 80, 90, 93, 98
- **Problem Solving Workshop,** p. 102

Critical Thinking

Opportunities for developing students' critical thinking skills in this chapter include:

- **Error Analysis** exercises, pp. 40, 77, 82, 91, 99, 102, 106
- **Challenge** exercises, pp. 68, 70, 78, 79, 83, 84, 92, 93, 100, 101, 107, 108, 114, 116
- **Reasoning** exercises, p. 92

Chapter 3 Summary

Chapter 3 focuses on **solving linear equations** in one variable. In the first half of the chapter, students learn the **properties of equality** in the course of solving simple one-step equations, and they employ those properties to solve increasingly complex multi-step equations. In the second half of the chapter, students solve **proportions** using the multiplication property of equality as well as the cross products property, and they solve **percent problems** by using proportions as well as the percent equation. The chapter concludes by asking students to **rewrite functions and formulas** by solving for one variable in terms of the other(s).

CHAPTER

3

Unit 1
Equations in One Variable

Solving Equations, p. 143
$8517 = 2117 + 64d$

Solving Linear Equations

Chapter 3 Highlights

PROBLEM SOLVING

- **Mixed Review of Problem Solving,** 161, 190
- **Multiple Representations,** 139, 146, 147, 153, 159, 166, 172, 188
- **Multi-Step Problems,** 140, 146, 161, 167, 190
- **Using Alternative Methods,** 147
- **Real-World Problem Solving Examples,** 137, 143, 150, 155, 164, 170, 178, 186

★ ASSESSMENT

- **Standardized Test Practice Examples,** 149, 169
- **Multiple Choice,** 138, 144, 145, 151, 157, 165, 171, 179, 187, 198
- **Short Response/Extended Response,** 139, 140, 145, 146, 151, 152, 159, 161, 166, 167, 172, 173, 180, 181, 189, 190
- **Writing/Open-Ended,** 137, 139, 144, 150, 151, 157, 161, 165, 171, 179, 180, 181, 187, 188, 190

TECHNOLOGY

At classzone.com:

- Animated Algebra 131, 133, 139, 154, 176, 185, 187
- **@Home Tutor,** 130, 139, 145, 152, 158, 160, 166, 172, 180, 188, 192
- **Online Quiz,** 140, 146, 153, 159, 167, 173, 181, 189
- **State Test Practice,** 161, 190, 201

FOCUS ON MATHEMATICAL UNDERSTANDING AND REASONING

Conceptual Understanding

Opportunities for developing students' conceptual understanding in this chapter include:

- **Investigating Algebra** activities, p. 132
- **Animated Algebra** activities, pp. 131, 133, 139, 154, 176, 185, 187
- **Problem Solving Workshop,** p. 147

Critical Thinking

Opportunities for developing students' critical thinking skills in this chapter include:

- **Error Analysis** exercises, pp. 144, 151, 157, 165, 171, 179, 187
- **Challenge** exercises, pp. 138, 140, 145, 146, 151, 153, 158, 159, 166, 167, 172, 173, 180, 181, 188, 189
- **Reasoning** exercises, pp. 114, 172

Graphing Linear Equations, p. 231
$2x + y = 128$

Graphing Linear Equations and Functions

Chapter 4 Highlights

PROBLEM SOLVING

- **Mixed Review of Problem Solving,** 233, 269
- **Multiple Representations,** 211, 221, 230, 259, 260
- **Multi-Step Problems,** 211, 220, 231, 233, 241, 269
- **Using Alternative Methods,** 260, 261
- **Real-World Problem Solving Examples,** 208, 218, 227, 228, 237, 238, 245, 246, 255, 256, 265

★ ASSESSMENT

- **Standardized Test Practice Examples,** 215, 262
- **Multiple Choice,** 209, 219, 220, 230, 239, 247, 257, 266, 276
- **Short Response/Extended Response,** 212, 221, 231, 232, 233, 242, 249, 258, 259, 267, 268, 269
- **Writing/Open-Ended,** 209, 210, 214, 219, 229, 230, 233, 239, 241, 247, 248, 256, 257, 265, 266, 269, 271

TECHNOLOGY

At classzone.com:

- Animated Algebra 205, 207, 216, 226, 238, 245, 254, 267
- **@Home Tutor,** 204, 210, 211, 220, 222, 230, 241, 248, 249, 258, 267, 271
- **Online Quiz,** 212, 221, 232, 242, 250, 259, 268
- **Electronic Function Library,** 270
- **State Test Practice,** 233, 269, 279

Chapter 4 Summary

Chapter 4 focuses on **graphing linear equations** in two variables. Students learn a variety of graphing techniques, including making a table of values and plotting points, identifying and using just the ***x*- and *y*-intercepts**, and identifying and using just the **slope** and *y*-intercept. Students recognize that the slope of a line is constant and that slope can be interpreted as a **rate of change** in real-world graphs. Students examine a special type of linear relationship known as **direct variation**, and they use direct variation models to solve real-world problems. The chapter concludes by introducing students to **function notation** while examining the effects of *m* and *b* on the graph of $f(x) = mx + b$.

FOCUS ON MATHEMATICAL UNDERSTANDING AND REASONING

Conceptual Understanding

Opportunities for developing students' conceptual understanding in this chapter include:

- **Investigating Algebra** activities, pp. 234, 243
- **Animated Algebra** activities, pp. 205, 207, 216, 226, 238, 245, 254, 267
- **Problem Solving Workshop,** p. 260

Critical Thinking

Opportunities for developing students' critical thinking skills in this chapter include:

- **Error Analysis** exercises, pp. 209, 219, 229, 239, 247, 257, 261, 265
- **Challenge** exercises, pp. 210, 211, 220, 221, 230, 232, 241, 242, 248, 250, 257, 259, 266, 268
- **Reasoning** exercises, pp. 210, 230, 241, 248, 261, 266

Chapter 5 Summary

Chapter 5 focuses on **writing linear equations** in two variables. Students learn to write equations in a various forms: **slope-intercept form, point-slope form**, and **standard form**. Students then solve real-world problems using these forms. For instance, given a real-world situation involving a starting value and a constant rate of change, students model the situation using a linear equation in slope-intercept form. Students also examine the relationships among slopes of **parallel and perpendicular lines** and write equations based on those relationships. The chapter concludes by showing students how to **fit lines to data** and **make predictions** from the resulting linear models.

Focus On Mathematical Understanding and Reasoning

Conceptual Understanding

Opportunities for developing students' conceptual understanding in this chapter include:

- **Investigating Algebra** activities, pp. 282, 334
- **Animated Algebra** activities, pp. 281, 283, 303, 307, 311, 326, 335
- **Problem Solving Workshop,** p. 300

Critical Thinking

Opportunities for developing students' critical thinking skills in this chapter include:

- **Error Analysis** exercises, pp. 286, 296, 301, 305, 306, 314, 322, 328, 339
- **Challenge** exercises, pp. 287, 289, 297, 299, 306, 308, 314, 316, 322, 323, 328, 339, 341
- **Reasoning** exercises, pp. 297, 310, 322, 333

CHAPTER 5

Unit 2
Equations in Two Variables

Slopes of Lines, p. 320
$12y = -7x + 42$

Writing Linear Equations

Chapter 5 Highlights

PROBLEM SOLVING

- **Mixed Review of Problem Solving,** 317, 343
- **Multiple Representations,** 288, 299, 315, 340
- **Multi-Step Problems,** 317, 343
- **Using Alternative Methods,** 300
- **Real-World Problem Solving Examples,** 285, 294, 295, 304, 313, 320, 325, 326, 337

★ ASSESSMENT

- **Standardized Test Practice Examples,** 293
- **Multiple Choice,** 286, 297, 305, 306, 321, 322, 328, 339
- **Short Response/Extended Response,** 288, 289, 297, 298, 306, 307, 315, 317, 321, 322, 323, 328, 329, 340, 343, 350
- **Writing/Open-Ended,** 286, 287, 296, 297, 305, 314, 317, 321, 322, 327, 328, 338, 339, 343, 345

TECHNOLOGY

At classzone.com:

- Animated Algebra 281, 283, 303, 307, 311, 326, 335
- **@Home Tutor,** 280, 288, 291, 298, 307, 315, 322, 329, 332, 339, 340, 342, 345
- **Online Quiz,** 289, 299, 308, 316, 323, 330, 341
- **State Test Practice,** 317, 343, 353

CHAPTER 6

Unit 2
Equations in Two Variables

Graphing Inequalities, p. 356
$T \leq 134$

Solving and Graphing Linear Inequalities

Chapter 6 Highlights

PROBLEM SOLVING
- **Mixed Review of Problem Solving,** 389, 413
- **Multiple Representations,** 361, 367, 374, 386, 402, 411
- **Multi-Step Problems,** 360, 389, 403, 411, 413
- **Using Alternative Methods,** 375, 376
- **Real-World Problem Solving Examples,** 358, 365, 371, 383, 392, 400, 408

★ ASSESSMENT
- **Standardized Test Practice Examples,** 365, 405
- **Multiple Choice,** 360, 372, 373, 385, 386, 393, 394, 401, 409, 411
- **Short Response/Extended Response,** 361, 368, 373, 374, 387, 389, 395, 402, 403, 411, 412, 413, 420
- **Writing/Open-Ended,** 359, 360, 366, 372, 384, 389, 393, 401, 409, 410, 413

TECHNOLOGY

At classzone.com:
- Animated Algebra 355, 358, 364, 382, 387, 390, 391, 399, 407
- **@Home Tutor,** 354, 360, 367, 373, 385, 388, 394, 402, 410, 415
- **Online Quiz,** 361, 368, 374, 387, 395, 403, 412
- **State Test Practice,** 389, 413, 423

Chapter 6 Summary

Chapter 6 focuses on **solving linear inequalities** in one variable and **graphing linear inequalities** in two variables. Paralleling the development of Chapter 3, students use the **properties of inequality** to solve inequalities, starting with simple one-step inequalities and progressing to more complicated multi-step inequalities. Students then solve **compound inequalities** involving *and* and *or*, and students extend this skill to solving **absolute value equations and inequalities.** The chapter concludes by showing students how to graph a linear inequality in two variables by graphing the related equation (using techniques from Chapter 4) and shading the appropriate half-plane.

Additional Lesson

When teaching Chapter 6, you may want to use the additional lesson **Use Piecewise Functions** starting on page A1 at the back of the book.

FOCUS ON MATHEMATICAL UNDERSTANDING AND REASONING

Conceptual Understanding

Opportunities for developing students' conceptual understanding in this chapter include:
- **Investigating Algebra** activities, pp. 362, 379, 404
- **Animated Algebra** activities, pp. 355, 358, 364, 382, 387, 390, 391, 399, 407
- **Problem Solving Workshop,** p. 375

Critical Thinking

Opportunities for developing students' critical thinking skills in this chapter include:
- **Error Analysis** exercises, pp. 359, 366, 372, 384, 393, 401, 409
- **Challenge** exercises, pp. 360, 361, 367, 368, 373, 374, 385, 387, 394, 395, 402, 403, 410, 412
- **Reasoning** exercises, pp. 379, 385, 394, 402

Chapter 7 Summary

Chapter 7 focuses on **solving systems of linear equations** and inequalities in two variables. Students learn various methods for solving systems of equations: by graphing and finding the point where the lines intersect (**graphing method**), by solving one equation for one of the variables and substituting into the other equation (**substitution method**), and by combining the equations to eliminate one of the variables (**elimination method**). Students also examine **special cases** where a system has no solution or has infinitely many solutions. The chapter concludes by showing students how to graph a system of inequalities using the method for graphing single inequalities from Chapter 6.

CHAPTER 7

Unit 2
Equations in Two Variables

Solving Linear Systems, p. 446
$x - y = 4, x + y = 6$

Systems of Equations and Inequalities

Chapter 7 Highlights

PROBLEM SOLVING

- **Mixed Review of Problem Solving,** 458, 473
- **Multiple Representations,** 433, 442, 449, 456
- **Multi-Step Problems,** 440, 450, 458, 465, 473
- **Using Alternative Methods,** 442
- **Real-World Problem Solving Examples,** 430, 438, 446, 453, 461, 468

★ ASSESSMENT

- **Standardized Test Practice Examples,** 429, 453
- **Multiple Choice,** 431, 432, 439, 447, 455, 463, 469, 470, 480
- **Short Response/Extended Response,** 432, 440, 441, 448, 450, 456, 458, 465, 470, 471, 473
- **Writing/Open-Ended,** 430, 431, 439, 440, 447, 454, 455, 456, 458, 462, 464, 469, 473

TECHNOLOGY

At classzone.com:

- Animated Algebra 425, 428, 435, 441, 446, 452, 459, 466
- **@Home Tutor,** 424, 432, 434, 440, 449, 456, 464, 471, 475
- **Online Quiz,** 433, 441, 450, 457, 465, 472
- **State Test Practice,** 458, 473, 483

FOCUS ON MATHEMATICAL UNDERSTANDING AND REASONING

Conceptual Understanding

Opportunities for developing students' conceptual understanding in this chapter include:

- **Investigating Algebra** activities, pp. 426, 443
- **Animated Algebra** activities, pp. 425, 428, 435, 441, 446, 452, 459, 466
- **Problem Solving Workshop,** p. 442

Critical Thinking

Opportunities for developing students' critical thinking skills in this chapter include:

- **Error Analysis** exercises, pp. 431, 439, 448, 455, 463, 470
- **Challenge** exercises, pp. 432, 433, 440, 441, 448, 450, 455, 457, 464, 465, 470, 472
- **Reasoning** exercises, p. 464

CHAPTER

8

Unit 3
Exponential and Quadratic Functions

Scientific Notation, p. 516
9.065×10^9 miles

Exponents and Exponential Functions

Chapter 8 Highlights

PROBLEM SOLVING

- **Mixed Review of Problem Solving,** 511, 541
- **Multiple Representations,** 493, 500, 507, 517, 524, 525, 528, 537
- **Multi-Step Problems,** 493, 511, 517, 525, 538, 541
- **Using Alternative Methods,** 528, 529
- **Real-World Problem Solving Examples,** 491, 498, 505, 514, 522, 523, 534

★ ASSESSMENT

- **Standardized Test Practice Examples,** 505, 523
- **Multiple Choice,** 492, 499, 506, 515, 516, 526, 535, 536, 548
- **Short Response/Extended Response,** 494, 501, 507, 508, 511, 516, 517, 526, 537, 541
- **Writing/Open-Ended,** 492, 493, 498, 499, 506, 511, 515, 516, 523, 524, 527, 535, 536, 541, 543

TECHNOLOGY

At *classzone.com*:

- Animated Algebra 487, 491, 505, 512, 522, 534, 536
- **@Home Tutor,** 486, 493, 500, 507, 516, 519, 525, 537, 543
- **Online Quiz,** 494, 501, 508, 518, 527, 538
- **State Test Practice,** 511, 541, 551

Chapter 8 Summary

Chapter 8 focuses on **working with exponents** and **graphing exponential functions**. Students learn the **properties of exponents** while working with positive exponents, then they extend the properties to **zero and negative exponents**. Students also learn to write numbers in **scientific notation** using positive, negative, and zero exponents and to compare and perform operations with numbers written in scientific notation. With an understanding of exponents, students are prepared to examine exponential functions, their first encounter with **nonlinear functions**. Students write and graph exponential functions and then use **exponential growth and decay models** to solve real-world problems.

Additional Lesson

When teaching Chapter 8, you may want to use the additional lesson **Define Sequences Recursively** starting on page A3 at the back of the book.

FOCUS ON MATHEMATICAL UNDERSTANDING AND REASONING

Conceptual Understanding

Opportunities for developing students' conceptual understanding in this chapter include:

- **Investigating Algebra** activities, pp. 488, 502, 530
- **Animated Algebra** activities, pp. 487, 491, 505, 512, 522, 534, 536
- **Problem Solving Workshop,** p. 528

Critical Thinking

Opportunities for developing students' critical thinking skills in this chapter include:

- **Error Analysis** exercises, pp. 492, 499, 506, 515, 524, 529, 536
- **Challenge** exercises, pp. 493, 494, 499, 501, 507, 508, 516, 518, 524, 527, 536, 538
- **Reasoning** exercises, pp. 499, 507, 510, 536

Chapter 9 Summary

Chapter 9 focuses on **working with polynomials** and **solving polynomial equations**. In the first half of the chapter, students learn to **classify polynomials** by degree and by the number of terms and to **add, subtract, and multiply polynomials**, including recognizing patterns for **special products**. In the second half of the chapter, students learn to **factor polynomials** using several techniques: factoring out a common monomial factor, factoring a trinomial into a product of binomials, and factoring special products. Students then use factoring and the **zero product property** to solve polynomial equations, with particular emphasis on solving quadratic equations.

Focus On Mathematical Understanding and Reasoning

Conceptual Understanding

Opportunities for developing students' conceptual understanding in this chapter include:

- **Investigating Algebra** activities, pp. 561, 582, 592
- **Animated Algebra** activities, pp. 553, 555, 582, 592, 598, 601
- **Problem Solving Workshop**, p. 590

Critical Thinking

Opportunities for developing students' critical thinking skills in this chapter include:

- **Error Analysis** exercises, pp. 557, 565, 572, 578, 586, 591, 597, 603, 610
- **Challenge** exercises, pp. 558, 559, 566, 568, 572, 574, 579, 580, 587, 589, 597, 599, 604, 605, 611, 613
- **Reasoning** exercises, pp. 561, 566, 582, 592

CHAPTER 9

Unit 3
Exponential and Quadratic Functions

Subtracting Polynomials, p. 558
$B = -0.0262t^3 + 0.376t^2 - 0.574t + 9.67$

Polynomials and Factoring

Chapter 9 Highlights

PROBLEM SOLVING

- **Mixed Review of Problem Solving,** 581, 614
- **Multiple Representations,** 573, 580, 589, 598
- **Multi-Step Problems,** 581, 614
- **Using Alternative Methods,** 590
- **Real-World Problem Solving Examples,** 556, 564, 571, 577, 585, 595, 602, 609

★ ASSESSMENT

- **Standardized Test Practice Examples,** 564, 596
- **Multiple Choice,** 557, 566, 572, 578, 580, 586, 589, 597, 603, 610
- **Short Response/Extended Response,** 558, 559, 567, 568, 573, 574, 579, 581, 587, 588, 597, 598, 604, 612, 614, 622
- **Writing/Open-Ended,** 557, 565, 572, 578, 581, 586, 596, 603, 610, 611, 614, 616

TECHNOLOGY

At classzone.com:

- Animated Algebra 553, 555, 582, 592, 598, 601
- **@Home Tutor,** 552, 558, 560, 567, 573, 579, 588, 598, 604, 612, 616
- **Online Quiz,** 559, 568, 574, 580, 589, 599, 605, 613
- **State Test Practice,** 581, 614, 625

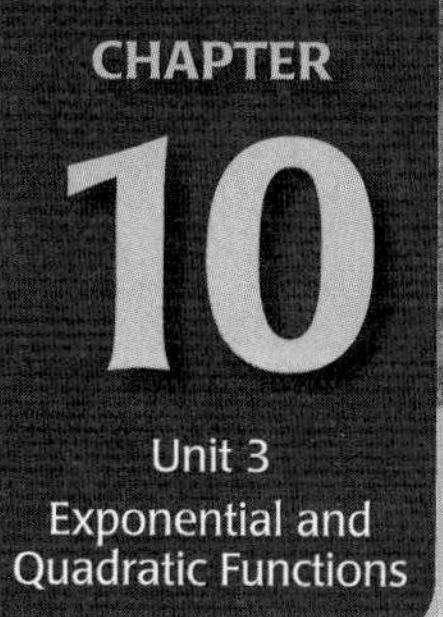

Unit 3
Exponential and Quadratic Functions

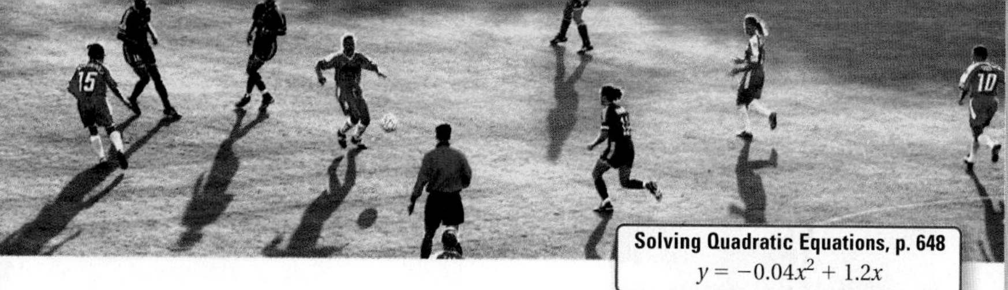

Solving Quadratic Equations, p. 648
$y = -0.04x^2 + 1.2x$

Quadratic Equations and Functions

Chapter 10 Highlights

PROBLEM SOLVING

- **Mixed Review of Problem Solving,** 661, 694
- **Multiple Representations,** 658, 659, 667, 676, 690
- **Multi-Step Problems,** 658, 661, 668, 675, 683, 694
- **Using Alternative Methods,** 659
- **Real-World Problem Solving Examples,** 631, 637, 646, 654, 665, 672, 680, 687

★ ASSESSMENT

- **Standardized Test Practice Examples,** 631, 671
- **Multiple Choice,** 632, 633, 638, 647, 655, 657, 666, 674, 681, 688, 690
- **Short Response/Extended Response,** 634, 640, 648, 649, 656, 657, 661, 668, 676, 682, 690, 694
- **Writing/Open-Ended,** 632, 638, 639, 647, 655, 656, 661, 666, 667, 674, 681, 682, 688, 694

TECHNOLOGY

At classzone.com:

- Animated Algebra 627, 634, 636, 642, 662, 668, 672, 684
- **@Home Tutor,** 626, 633, 639, 648, 651, 657, 667, 675, 682, 689, 690, 692, 696
- **Online Quiz,** 634, 640, 649, 658, 668, 676, 683, 691
- **Electronic Function Library,** 695
- **State Test Practice,** 661, 694, 705

Chapter 10 Summary

Chapter 10 focuses on **graphing quadratic functions** and **solving quadratic equations**. Students learn the effects of a and c on the graph of $y = ax^2 + c$ and then extend their understanding of quadratic graphs to $y = ax^2 + bx + c$. Students are able to solve quadratic equations graphically by interpreting the solutions as the x-intercepts of related graphs. Students also solve quadratic equations by **completing the square**, and this method leads to the **quadratic formula** when applied to the general equation $ax^2 + bx + c = 0$. Students see that the **discriminant** in the quadratic formula determines the number of solutions that a quadratic equation has. The chapter concludes by comparing linear models (from Chapter 5), exponential models (from Chapter 8), and **quadratic models** and asking students to choose an appropriate model for a given set of data.

Additional Lesson

When teaching Chapter 10, you may want to use the additional lesson **Solve Quadratic Inequalities** starting on page A6 at the back of the book.

FOCUS ON MATHEMATICAL UNDERSTANDING AND REASONING

Conceptual Understanding

Opportunities for developing students' conceptual understanding in this chapter include:

- **Investigating Algebra** activities, pp. 662, 677
- **Animated Algebra** activities, pp. 627, 634, 636, 642, 662, 668, 672, 684
- **Problem Solving Workshop,** p. 659

Critical Thinking

Opportunities for developing students' critical thinking skills in this chapter include:

- **Error Analysis** exercises, pp. 632, 638, 647, 656, 660, 666, 674, 681, 689
- **Challenge** exercises, pp. 633, 634, 639, 640, 648, 649, 656, 658, 667, 668, 675, 676, 682, 683, 689, 691
- **Reasoning** exercises, pp. 639, 656, 681, 689

Chapter 11 Summary

Chapter 11 focuses on **working with radicals** and **connections to geometry**. In the first half of the chapter, students learn to **graph square root functions**. Students then **simplify square root expressions** using the properties of radicals and **solve square root equations** by squaring both sides. In the second half of the chapter, students look at geometric situations involving square roots. In particular, students solve right-triangle problems using the **Pythagorean theorem and its converse**, and they solve coordinate-plane problems using the **distance and midpoint formulas**.

Focus On Mathematical Understanding and Reasoning

Conceptual Understanding

Opportunities for developing students' conceptual understanding in this chapter include:

- **Investigating Algebra** activities, pp. 718, 736, 743
- **Animated Algebra** activities, pp. 709, 711, 719, 722, 731, 737, 746
- **Problem Solving Workshop,** p. 751

Critical Thinking

Opportunities for developing students' critical thinking skills in this chapter include:

- **Error Analysis** exercises, pp. 714, 723, 732, 740, 748
- **Challenge** exercises, pp. 714, 716, 724, 726, 733, 734, 741, 742, 748, 750
- **Reasoning** exercises, pp. 718, 724, 736, 741, 743

CHAPTER 11

Unit 4 Radical and Rational Functions

Solving Radical Equations, p. 731
$s = 1.34\sqrt{\ell}$

Radicals and Geometry Connections

Chapter 11 Highlights

PROBLEM SOLVING

- Mixed Review of Problem Solving, 735, 752
- Multiple Representations, 725
- Multi-Step Problems, 715, 725, 733, 735, 748, 752
- Using Alternative Methods, 751
- Real-World Problem Solving Examples, 713, 722, 731, 738, 739, 746

★ ASSESSMENT

- Standardized Test Practice Examples, 738, 746
- Multiple Choice, 713, 714, 723, 732, 740, 741, 747, 748, 758
- Short Response/Extended Response, 716, 726, 734, 735, 742, 749, 752
- Writing/Open-Ended, 713, 723, 724, 732, 733, 735, 740, 741, 747, 748, 752

TECHNOLOGY

At classzone.com:

- Animated Algebra 709, 711, 719, 722, 731, 737, 746
- @Home Tutor, 708, 715, 717, 725, 733, 741, 748, 749, 754, 755
- Online Quiz, 716, 726, 734, 742, 750
- State Test Practice, 735, 752, 761

CHAPTER

12

Unit 4
Radical and Rational Functions

Dividing Rational Expressions, p. 807
$T = \frac{100 + 2.2x}{1 - 0.014x}$

Rational Equations and Functions

Chapter 12 Highlights

PROBLEM SOLVING

- **Mixed Review of Problem Solving,** 801, 829
- **Multiple Representations,** 771, 781, 790, 808
- **Multi-Step Problems,** 801, 818, 825, 829
- **Using Alternative Methods,** 827
- **Real-World Problem Solving Examples,** 768, 778, 787, 797, 805, 815, 822

★ ASSESSMENT

- **Multiple Choice,** 769, 779, 788, 789, 791, 798, 806, 807, 817, 824, 836
- **Short Response/Extended Response,** 771, 772, 781, 790, 791, 800, 801, 808, 809, 818, 819, 825, 829
- **Writing/Open-Ended,** 769, 779, 780, 788, 789, 797, 798, 801, 806, 807, 816, 823, 829

TECHNOLOGY

At classzone.com:

- Animated Algebra 763, 766, 777, 783, 791, 804, 814
- **@Home Tutor,** 762, 770, 780, 789, 793, 799, 807, 808, 817, 824, 831
- **Online Quiz,** 772, 782, 791, 800, 809, 819, 826
- **State Test Practice,** 801, 829, 839

Chapter 12 Summary

Chapter 12 focuses on **rational expressions and equations**. In the first half of the chapter, students learn to **graph rational functions** whose numerators and denominators have degree 0 or 1, including the special case of **inverse variation**. Students also extend their work with polynomials in Chapter 9 by using **polynomial division** to put rational functions in a form for graphing. In the second half of the chapter, students learn to **simplify and perform operations** on rational expressions, and they use graphs to check their work visually. Students then learn to **solve rational equations** and check for extraneous solutions.

FOCUS ON MATHEMATICAL UNDERSTANDING AND REASONING

Conceptual Understanding

Opportunities for developing students' conceptual understanding in this chapter include:

- **Investigating Algebra** activities, pp. 764, 773, 783
- **Animated Algebra** activities, pp. 763, 766, 777, 783, 791, 804, 814
- **Problem Solving Workshop,** p. 827

Critical Thinking

Opportunities for developing students' critical thinking skills in this chapter include:

- **Error Analysis** exercises, pp. 769, 780, 788, 798, 806, 816, 823, 828
- **Challenge** exercises, pp. 770, 772, 780, 782, 789, 791, 798, 800, 807, 809, 817, 819, 824, 826
- **Reasoning** exercises, pp. 770, 783, 789, 824

Chapter 13 Summary

Chapter 13 focuses on **probability and combinatorics** as well as **data analysis**. In the first half of the chapter, students learn to find probabilities of **simple and compound events**. Students also learn to calculate **permutations and combinations**, which are in turn used to find probabilities. In the second half of the chapter, students learn to recognize potential bias in **sampling methods and survey questions**. Students also learn to find **measures of central tendency and dispersion** and to display data using **stem-and-leaf plots, histograms,** and **box-and-whisker plots**.

CHAPTER 13

Unit 4 Radical and Rational Functions

Using Permutations, p. 855

$$\text{Probability} = \frac{{}_5P_5}{{}_7P_7}$$

Probability and Data Analysis

Chapter 13 Highlights

PROBLEM SOLVING
- Mixed Review of Problem Solving, 870, 894
- Multiple Representations, 854, 866
- Multi-Step Problems, 870, 894
- Using Alternative Methods, 868
- Real-World Problem Solving Examples, 844, 852, 853, 857, 863, 871, 872, 876, 882, 888, 889

★ ASSESSMENT
- Standardized Test Practice Examples, 845, 889
- Multiple Choice, 846, 847, 854, 858, 864, 865, 873, 877, 883, 890
- Short Response/Extended Response, 847, 848, 855, 858, 859, 866, 870, 874, 877, 878, 885, 891, 894, 902
- Writing/Open-Ended, 846, 853, 858, 864, 865, 870, 873, 877, 883, 884, 889, 894, 896

TECHNOLOGY

At classzone.com:
- Animated Algebra 841, 845, 848, 856, 875, 887
- @Home Tutor, 840, 847, 854, 859, 860, 866, 874, 877, 878, 884, 886, 890, 891, 893, 896
- Online Quiz, 848, 855, 859, 867, 874, 878, 885, 892
- State Test Practice, 870, 894, 905

Focus On Mathematical Understanding and Reasoning

Conceptual Understanding

Opportunities for developing students' conceptual understanding in this chapter include:
- **Investigating Algebra** activities, p. 842
- **Animated Algebra** activities, pp. 841, 845, 848, 856, 875, 887
- **Problem Solving Workshop,** p. 868

Critical Thinking

Opportunities for developing students' critical thinking skills in this chapter include:
- **Error Analysis** exercises, pp. 846, 854, 858, 864, 865, 869, 873, 877, 883, 884, 890
- **Challenge** exercises, pp. 847, 848, 854, 855, 858, 859, 865, 867, 873, 874, 877, 878, 884, 885, 890, 892
- **Reasoning** exercises, pp. 842, 858, 880, 881

Contents of Student Resources

Additional Lessons

You can teach these additional lessons with the indicated chapters.

Additional Lesson	For Chapter	On Page
Use Piecewise Functions	6	A1
Define Sequences Recursively	8	A3
Solve Quadratic Inequalities	10	A6

LARSON ALGEBRA 1

Where great lessons begin

- Engages students in active learning
- Adaptable to different teaching styles and student abilities
- Ongoing assessment integrated with instruction

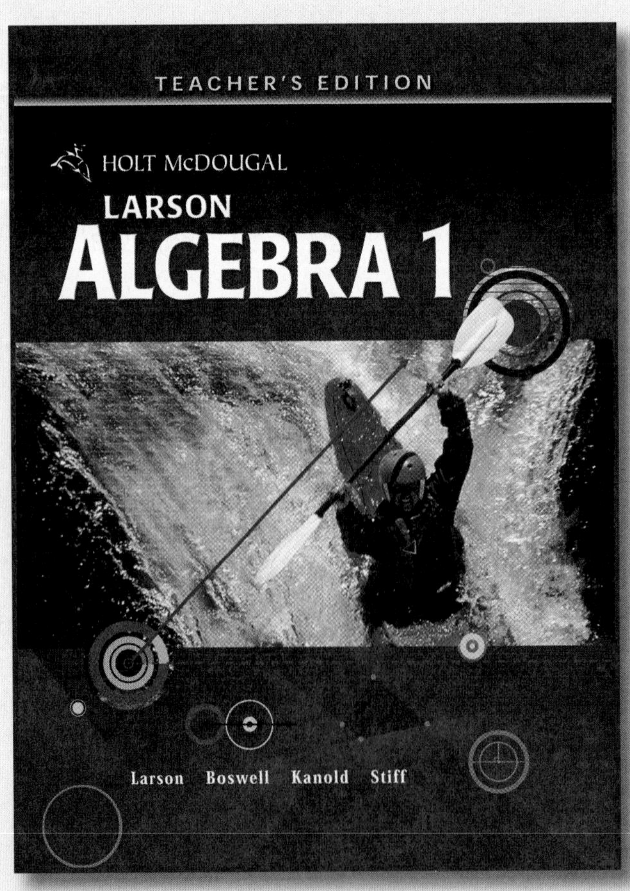

1

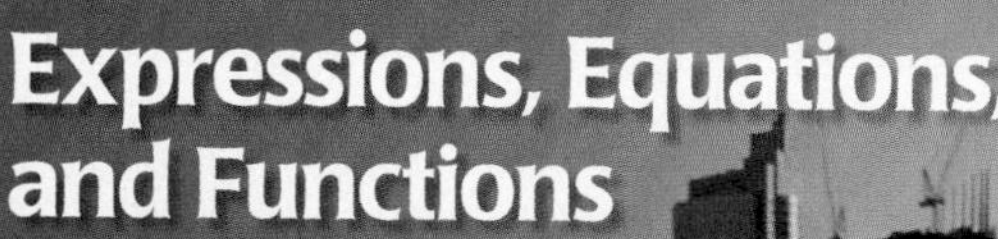

aking Sense Chapter 1
oughout your dy of algebra you l be working with ctions. By the end his chapter, you will able to represent ple functions as bal rules, equations, les, and graphs.

Before

Previously, you learned the following skills, which you'll use in Chapter 1: using fractions and percents, and finding area.

Prerequisite Skills

VOCABULARY CHECK

Copy and complete the statement.

1. In the fraction $\frac{2}{3}$, _?_ is the numerator and _?_ is the denominator.
2. Two fractions that represent the same number are called _?_ fractions.
3. The word *percent* (%) means "divided by _?_."

SKILLS CHECK

Perform the indicated operation. *(Prerequisite skill for 1.1, 1.2)*

4. $\frac{3}{5} \times \frac{2}{3}$ 5. $1\frac{1}{4} \times \frac{3}{5}$ 6. $\frac{1}{2} \div \frac{5}{8}$ 7. $6 \div \frac{3}{4}$

Write the percent as a decimal. *(Prerequisite skill for 1.5)*

8. 4% 9. 23% 10. 1.5% 11. 2.5%

12. Find the area of the rectangle. *(Prerequisite skill for 1.5)*

$4\frac{1}{2}$ in.
11 in.

@HomeTutor Prerequisite skills practice at classzone.com

Now

In Chapter 1, you will apply the big ideas listed below and reviewed in the Chapter Summary on page 52. You will also use the key vocabulary listed below.

Big Ideas

1. **Writing and evaluating algebraic expressions**
2. **Using expressions to write equations and inequalities**
3. **Representing functions as verbal rules, equations, tables, and graphs**

KEY VOCABULARY

- variable, *p. 2*
- algebraic expression, *p. 2*
- power, exponent, base, *p. 3*
- order of operations, *p. 8*
- verbal model, *p. 16*
- rate, unit rate, *p. 17*
- open sentence, *p. 21*
- equation, inequality, *p. 21*
- solution of an equation or inequality, *p. 22*
- formula, *p. 30*
- function, *p. 35*
- domain, range, *p. 35*
- independent variable, *p. 36*
- dependent variable, *p. 36*

Why?

You can use multiple representations to describe a real-world situation. For example, you can solve an equation, make a table, or draw a diagram to determine a running route.

Animated Algebra

The animation illustrated below for Example 1 on page 28 helps you answer this question: How does the number of blocks you run affect the total distance?

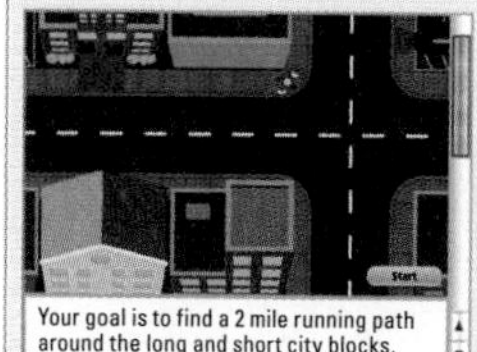

Your goal is to find a 2 mile running path around the long and short city blocks.

Click on a point on the graph to move the runner and see the distance covered.

Animated Algebra at classzone.com

Other animations for Chapter 1: pages 7, 9, 14, 21, 37, 50, and 52

1

Animated Algebra

Animated Algebra includes interactive electronic activities that provide insights into both the how and the why of math.

- Each chapter opens with an animated activity related to a real-world problem in the chapter. Throughout the chapter, additional activities support and extend specific examples and exercises.
- The Electronic Function Library allows students to explore the properties of functions and their graphs.

Clear Instruction

New concepts and methods are presented using clear, student-friendly language and visuals, and examples are carefully stepped out for easier understanding. Vocabulary and key ideas are highlighted.

Connect
New topics are related to what students have already learned and are applied to real-world problems.

Teach
Concepts and procedures that students need to know are presented concisely.

Model
Students can easily follow the step-by-step approach of the examples.

Check
Students are encouraged to check their work.

7.2 Solve Linear Systems by Substitution

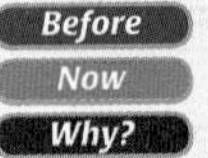

Before You solved systems of linear equations by graphing.
Now You will solve systems of linear equations by substitution.
Why? So you can find tubing costs, as in Ex. 32.

Key Vocabulary
- system of linear equations, *p. 427*

KEY CONCEPT *For Your Notebook*

Solving a Linear System Using the Substitution Method

STEP 1 **Solve** one of the equations for one of its variables. When possible, solve for a variable that has a coefficient of 1 or −1.

STEP 2 **Substitute** the expression from Step 1 into the other equation and solve for the other variable.

STEP 3 **Substitute** the value from Step 2 into the revised equation from Step 1 and solve.

EXAMPLE 1 **Use the substitution method**

Solve the linear system: $y = 3x + 2$ Equation 1
$x + 2y = 11$ Equation 2

Solution

STEP 1 **Solve** for y. Equation 1 is already solved for y.

STEP 2 **Substitute** $3x + 2$ for y in Equation 2 and solve for x.

$x + 2y = 11$ Write Equation 2.
$x + 2(3x + 2) = 11$ Substitute $3x + 2$ for y.
$7x + 4 = 11$ Simplify.
$7x = 7$ Subtract 4 from each side.
$x = 1$ Divide each side by 7.

STEP 3 **Substitute** 1 for x in the original Equation 1 to find the value of y.

$y = 3x + 2 = 3(1) + 2 = 3 + 2 = 5$

▶ The solution is (1, 5).

CHECK Substitute 1 for x and 5 for y in each of the original equations.

$y = 3x + 2$	$x + 2y = 11$
$5 \stackrel{?}{=} 3(1) + 2$	$1 + 2(5) \stackrel{?}{=} 11$
$5 = 5$ ✓	$11 = 11$ ✓

Animated Algebra at classzone.com

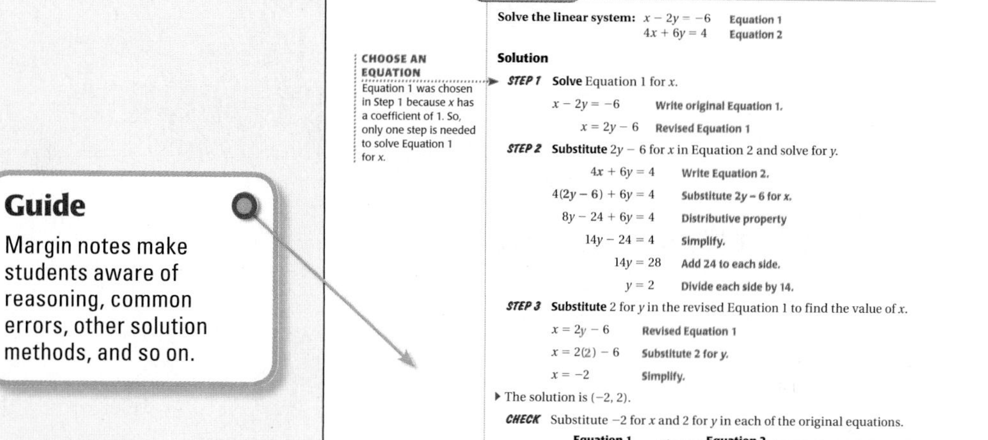

EXAMPLE 2 **Use the substitution method**

Solve the linear system: $x - 2y = -6$ Equation 1
$4x + 6y = 4$ Equation 2

CHOOSE AN EQUATION
Equation 1 was chosen in Step 1 because x has a coefficient of 1. So, only one step is needed to solve Equation 1 for x.

Solution

STEP 1 **Solve** Equation 1 for x.

$x - 2y = -6$ **Write original Equation 1.**

$x = 2y - 6$ **Revised Equation 1**

STEP 2 **Substitute** $2y - 6$ for x in Equation 2 and solve for y.

$4x + 6y = 4$ **Write Equation 2.**

$4(2y - 6) + 6y = 4$ **Substitute $2y - 6$ for x.**

$8y - 24 + 6y = 4$ **Distributive property**

$14y - 24 = 4$ **Simplify.**

$14y = 28$ **Add 24 to each side.**

$y = 2$ **Divide each side by 14.**

STEP 3 **Substitute** 2 for y in the revised Equation 1 to find the value of x.

$x = 2y - 6$ **Revised Equation 1**

$x = 2(2) - 6$ **Substitute 2 for y.**

$x = -2$ **Simplify.**

▶ The solution is $(-2, 2)$.

CHECK Substitute -2 for x and 2 for y in each of the original equations.

Equation 1 **Equation 2**

$x - 2y = -6$

$-2 - 2(2) \stackrel{?}{=} -6$

$-6 = -6$ ✓

CHECK REASONABLENESS Whe
a linear system using the subst
method, you can use a graph to
the reasonableness of your solu
example, the graph at the right
$(-2, 2)$ is a solution of the linea
Example 2.

✓ **GUIDED PRACTICE** for Examp

Solve the linear system using

1. $y = 2x + 5$
$3x + y = 10$

EXAMPLE 3 **Solve a multi-step problem**

ANOTHER WAY
For an alternative method for solving the problem in Example 3, turn to page 442 for the **Problem Solving Workshop**.

WEBSITES Many businesses pay website hosting companies to store and maintain the computer files that make up their websites. Internet service providers also offer website hosting. The costs for website hosting offered by a website hosting company and an Internet service provider are shown in the table. Find the number of months after which the total cost for website hosting will be the same for both companies.

Company	Set-up fee (dollars)	Cost per month (dollars)
Internet service provider	10	21.95
Website hosting company	None	22.45

Solution

STEP 1 **Write** a system of equations. Let y be the total cost after x months.

Equation 1: Internet service provider

Total cost = Set-up fee + Cost per month · Number of months

$y = 10 + 21.95 \cdot x$

Equation 2: Website hosting company

Total cost = Cost per month · Number of months

$y = 22.45 \cdot x$

The system of equations is: $y = 10 + 21.95x$ **Equation 1**
$y = 22.45x$ **Equation 2**

STEP 2 **Substitute** $22.45x$ for y in Equation 1 and solve for x.

$y = 10 + 21.95x$ **Write Equation 1.**

$22.45x = 10 + 21.95x$ **Substitute $22.45x$ for y.**

$0.5x = 10$ **Subtract $21.95x$ from each side.**

$x = 20$ **Divide each side by 0.5.**

▶ The total cost will be the same for both companies after 20 months.

✓ **GUIDED PRACTICE** for Example 3

4. In Example 3, what is the total cost for website hosting for each company after 20 months?

5. **WHAT IF?** In Example 3, suppose the Internet service provider offers \$5 off the set-up fee. After how many months will the total cost for website hosting be the same for both companies?

Guide

Margin notes make students aware of reasoning, common errors, other solution methods, and so on.

Practice

Students have the opportunity to immediately practice and apply the new skills they are learning.

Apply

A verbal model helps students make the transition from the statement of a problem to the symbols used to solve the problem.

Extend

"What if" questions challenge students to extend newly acquired concepts and skills to a variety of situations.

Varied, Leveled Practice

The wide variety of skill and problem solving exercises is carefully paced, ensuring that students build skills and feel confident about their work. The @HomeTutor and Animated Algebra features provide additional support.

Communicate

"Vocabulary" and "Writing" exercises encourage students to talk and write about their understanding of the mathematics.

Support

Exercises are correlated to examples, providing homework support and fostering independent student learning.

Analyze

"Error Analysis" exercises give students the opportunity to recognize mistakes and correct them.

Represent

By representing problems in more than one way, students make important mathematical connections.

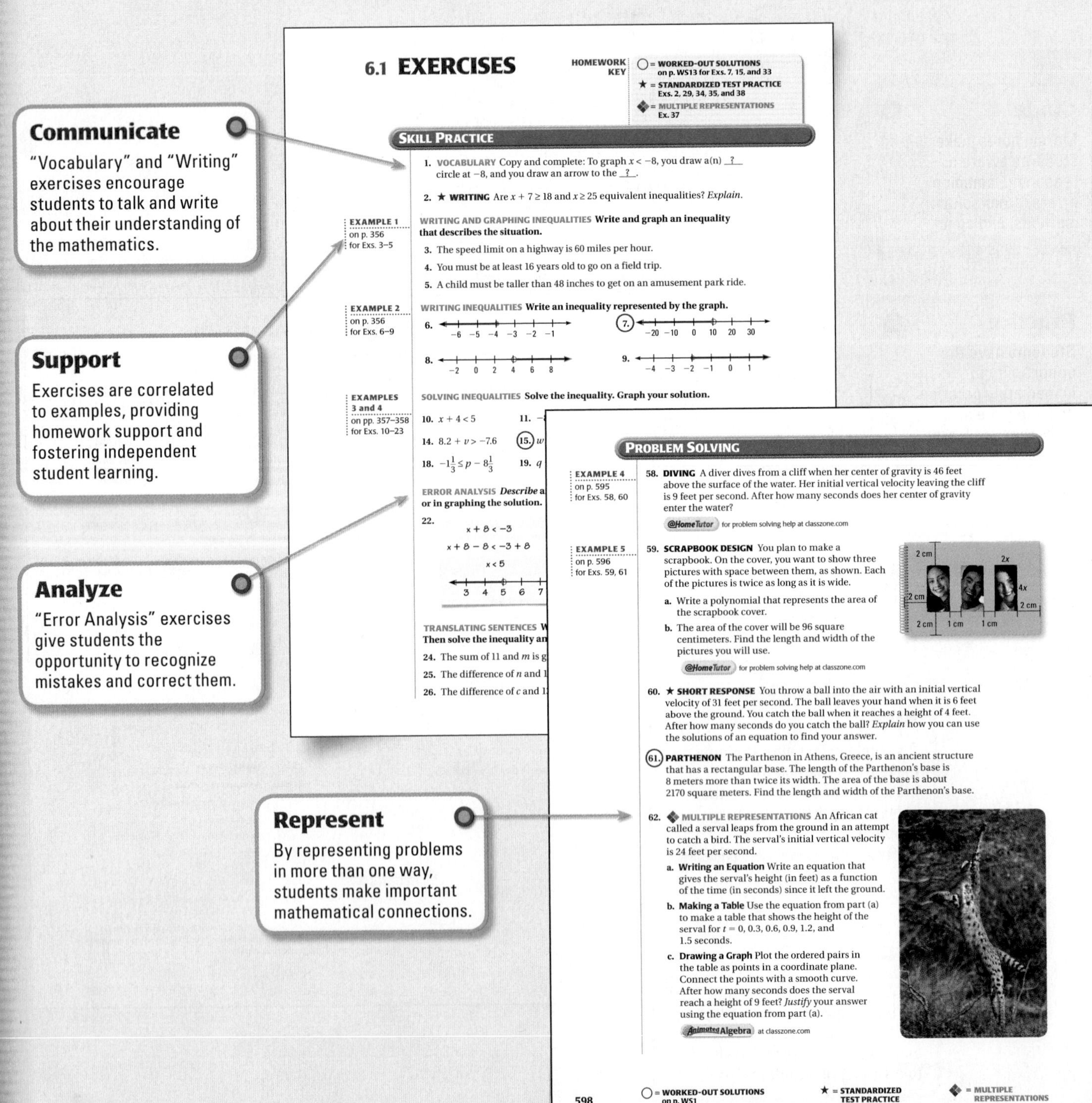

Challenge

Students with strong mathematical abilities find challenging skill and problem solving exercises in every lesson.

Intervene

The @HomeTutor provides additional explanation and guided practice so that students have access to immediate help for every lesson.

Reason

Concepts and writing skills are developed through exercises that ask students to explain their reasoning.

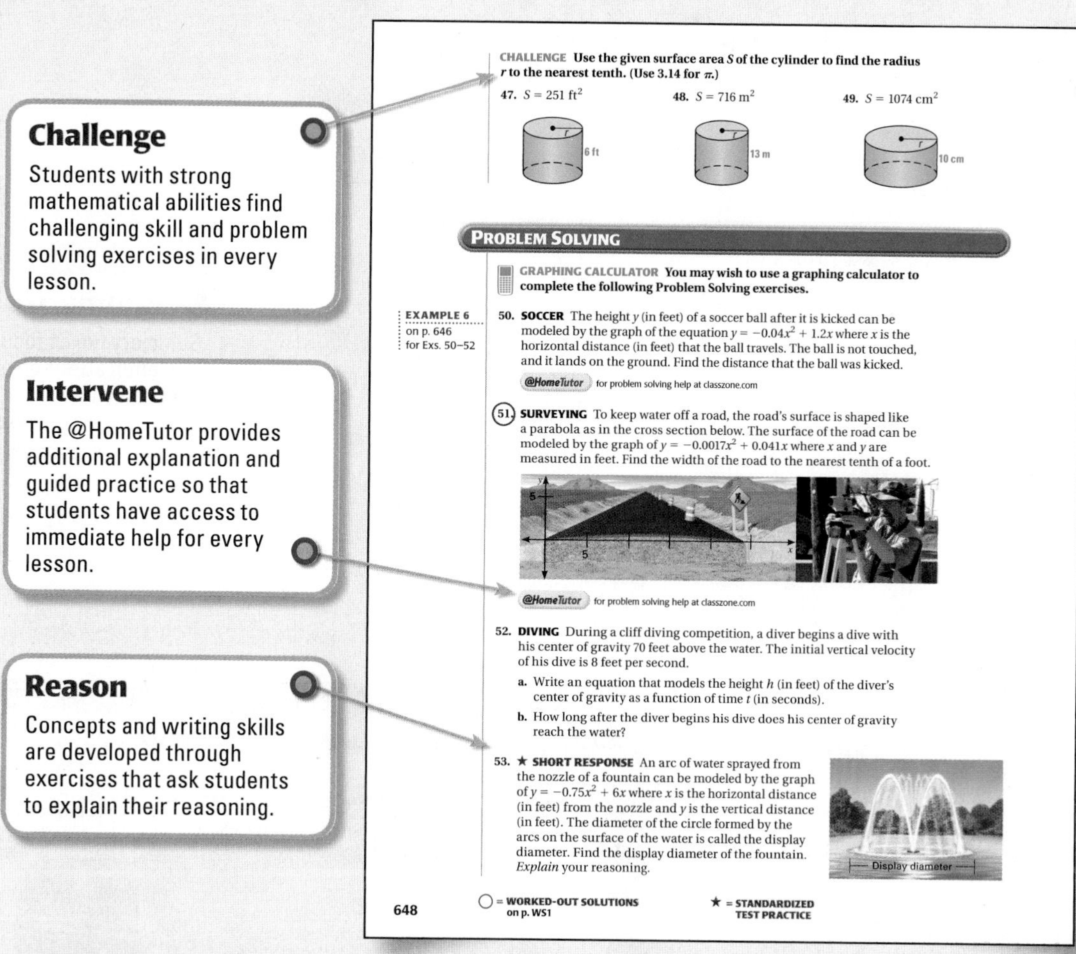

CHALLENGE **Use the given surface area S of the cylinder to find the radius r to the nearest tenth. (Use 3.14 for π.)**

47. $S = 251\text{ ft}^2$ **48.** $S = 716\text{ m}^2$ **49.** $S = 1074\text{ cm}^2$

PROBLEM SOLVING

GRAPHING CALCULATOR **You may wish to use a graphing calculator to complete the following Problem Solving exercises.**

EXAMPLE 6 on p. 646 for Exs. 50–52

50. SOCCER The height y (in feet) of a soccer ball after it is kicked can be modeled by the graph of the equation $y = -0.04x^2 + 1.2x$ where x is the horizontal distance (in feet) that the ball travels. The ball is not touched, and it lands on the ground. Find the distance that the ball was kicked.

@HomeTutor for problem solving help at classzone.com

51. SURVEYING To keep water off a road, the road's surface is shaped like a parabola as in the cross section below. The surface of the road can be modeled by the graph of $y = -0.0017x^2 + 0.041x$ where x and y are measured in feet. Find the width of the road to the nearest tenth of a foot.

@HomeTutor for problem solving help at classzone.com

52. DIVING During a cliff diving competition, a diver begins a dive with his center of gravity 70 feet above the water. The initial vertical velocity of his dive is 8 feet per second.

a. Write an equation that models the height h (in feet) of the diver's center of gravity as a function of time t (in seconds).

b. How long after the diver begins his dive does his center of gravity reach the water?

53. ★ SHORT RESPONSE An arc of water sprayed from the nozzle of a fountain can be modeled by the graph of $y = -0.75x^2 + 6x$ where x is the horizontal distance (in feet) from the nozzle and y is the vertical distance (in feet). The diameter of the circle formed by the arcs on the surface of the water is called the display diameter. Find the display diameter of the fountain. *Explain* your reasoning.

648 ◯ = WORKED-OUT SOLUTIONS on p. WS1 ★ = STANDARDIZED TEST PRACTICE

eWorkbook on classzone.com

Provides additional practice with feedback on the correctness of answers

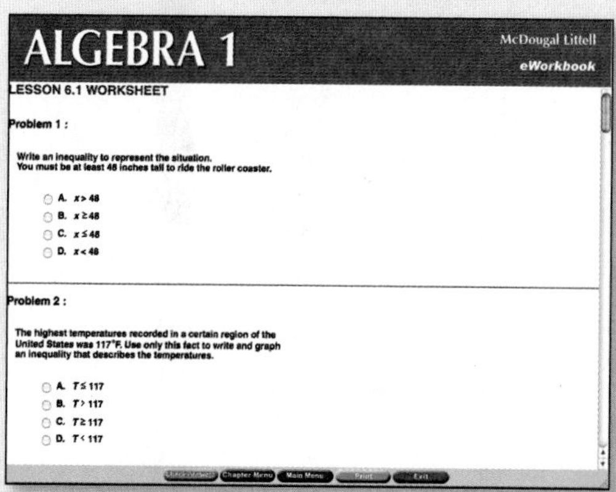

ALGEBRA 1 McDougal Littell eWorkbook

LESSON 6.1 WORKSHEET

Problem 1 :

Write an inequality to represent the situation. You must be at least 48 inches tall to ride the roller coaster.

A. $x > 48$
B. $x \geq 48$
C. $x \leq 48$
D. $x < 48$

Problem 2 :

The highest temperatures recorded in a certain region of the United States was 117°F. Use only this fact to write and graph an inequality that describes the temperatures.

A. $T \leq 117$
B. $T > 117$
C. $T \geq 117$
D. $T < 117$

Chapter Menu Main Menu Exit

Practice Workbook

Consumable workbook that provides convenient practice for every lesson

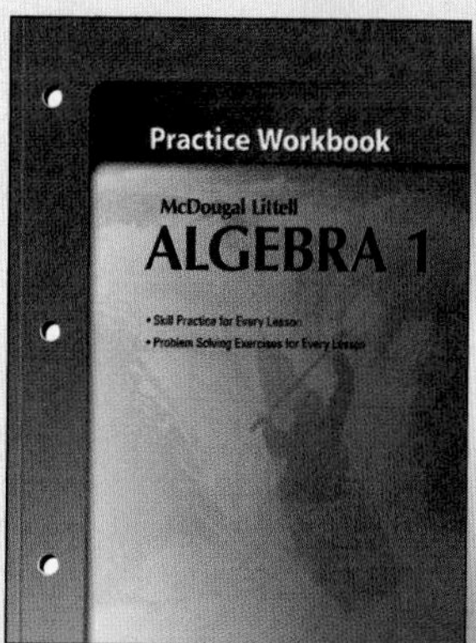

Leveled Practice

Three levels of practice for every lesson in the Chapter Resource Book

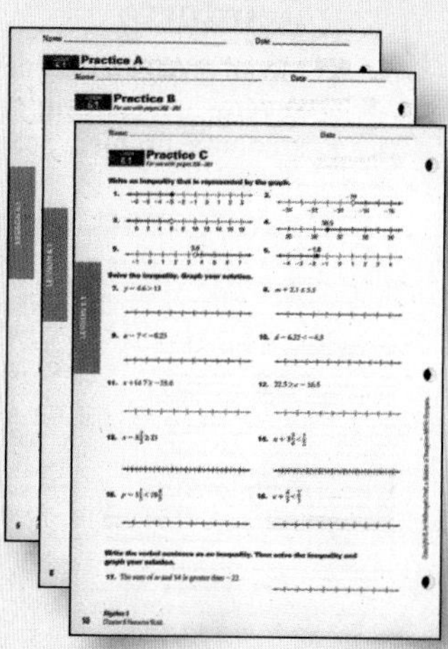

Focused Summary and Review

Throughout each chapter, carefully coordinated summaries and reviews focus on key concepts, vocabulary, and problem solving skills.

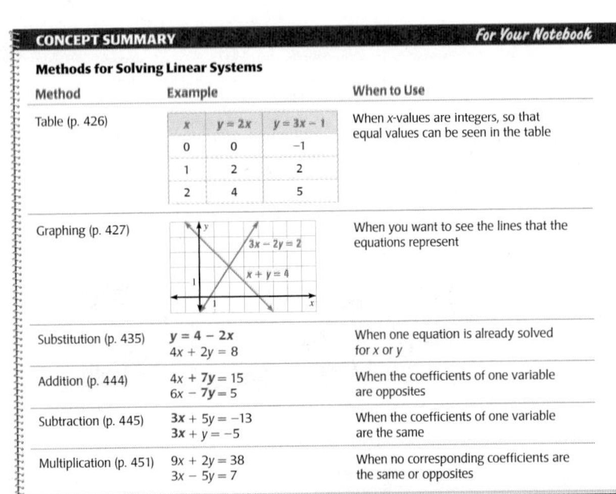

CONCEPT SUMMARY *For Your Notebook*

Methods for Solving Linear Systems

Method	Example	When to Use
Table (p. 426)	x: 0, 1, 2; $y = 2x$: 0, 2, 4; $y = 3x - 1$: −1, 2, 5	When x-values are integers, so that equal values can be seen in the table
Graphing (p. 427)	Graph of $3x - 2y = 2$ and $x + y = 4$	When you want to see the lines that the equations represent
Substitution (p. 435)	$y = 4 - 2x$ $4x + 2y = 8$	When one equation is already solved for x or y
Addition (p. 444)	$4x + 7y = 15$ $6x - 7y = 5$	When the coefficients of one variable are opposites
Subtraction (p. 445)	$3x + 5y = -13$ $3x + y = -5$	When the coefficients of one variable are the same
Multiplication (p. 451)	$9x + 2y = 38$ $3x - 5y = 7$	When no corresponding coefficients are the same or opposites

Summarize

Summary boxes focus students' attention on the important ideas running through several lessons.

7.4 EXERCISES

SKILL PRACTICE

1. VOCABULARY What is the least c
2. ★ WRITING *Explain* how to solve system using the elimination me

EXAMPLE 1 on p. 451 for Exs. 3–8

SOLVING LINEAR SYSTEMS Solve the

3. $x + y = 2$; $2x + 7y = 9$
4. 3x
6. $10x - 9y = 46$; $-2x + 3y = 10$
7. 8x

454 Chapter 7 Systems of Equations and Inequalities

MIXED REVIEW of Problem Solving STATE TEST PRACTICE classzone.com

Lessons 5.5–5.7

1. **MULTI-STEP PROBLEM** The table shows the value of primary and secondary schools built in the U.S. each year from 1995 to 2000.

Year	Value (millions of dollars)
1995	1245
1996	1560
1997	2032
1998	2174
1999	2420
2000	2948

   a. Make a scatter plot of the data.
   b. Write an equation that models the value (in millions of dollars) of the schools built as a function of the number of years since 1995.
   c. At approximately what rate did the value change from 1995 to 2000?
   d. In what year would you predict the value of the schools built in the U.S. to be $3,600,000,000?

2. **GRIDDED ANSWER** A map of a city shows streets as lines on a coordinate grid. State Street has a slope of $-\frac{1}{2}$. Park Street runs perpendicular to State Street. What is the slope of Park Street on the map?

3. **OPEN-ENDED** The graph represents the cost for one kayak owner for storing a kayak at a marina over time. The total cost includes a standard initial fee and a monthly storage fee. Suppose a different kayak owner pays a lower initial fee during a special promotion. Write an equation that could give the total cost as a function of the number of months of storage for this kayak owner.

4. **SHORT RESPONSE** The table shows the heights and corresponding lengths of horses in a stable. Make a scatter plot of the data. *Describe* the correlation of the data.

Height (hands)	Length (inches)
17.0	76
16.0	72
16.2	74
15.3	71
15.1	69
16.3	75

5. **EXTENDED RESPONSE** The table shows the percent of revenue from U.S. music sales made through music clubs from 1998 through 2003.

Year	Percent of revenue
1998	9
1999	7.9
2000	7.6
2001	6.1
2002	4
2003	4.1

   a. Find an equation that models the percent of revenue from music clubs as a function of the number of years since 1998.
   b. At approximately what rate did the percent of revenue from music clubs change from 1998 to 2003?
   c. Find the zero of the function. *Explain* what the zero means in this situation.

6. **SHORT RESPONSE** The cost of bowling includes a $4.00 fee per game and a shoe rental fee. Shoes for adults cost $2.25. Shoes for children cost $1.75. Write equations that give the total cost of bowling for an adult and for a child as functions of the number of games bowled. How are the graphs of the equations related? *Explain.*

Mixed Review of Problem Solving 343

Reinforce

Mixed problem sets covering several lessons reinforce students' problem solving skills.

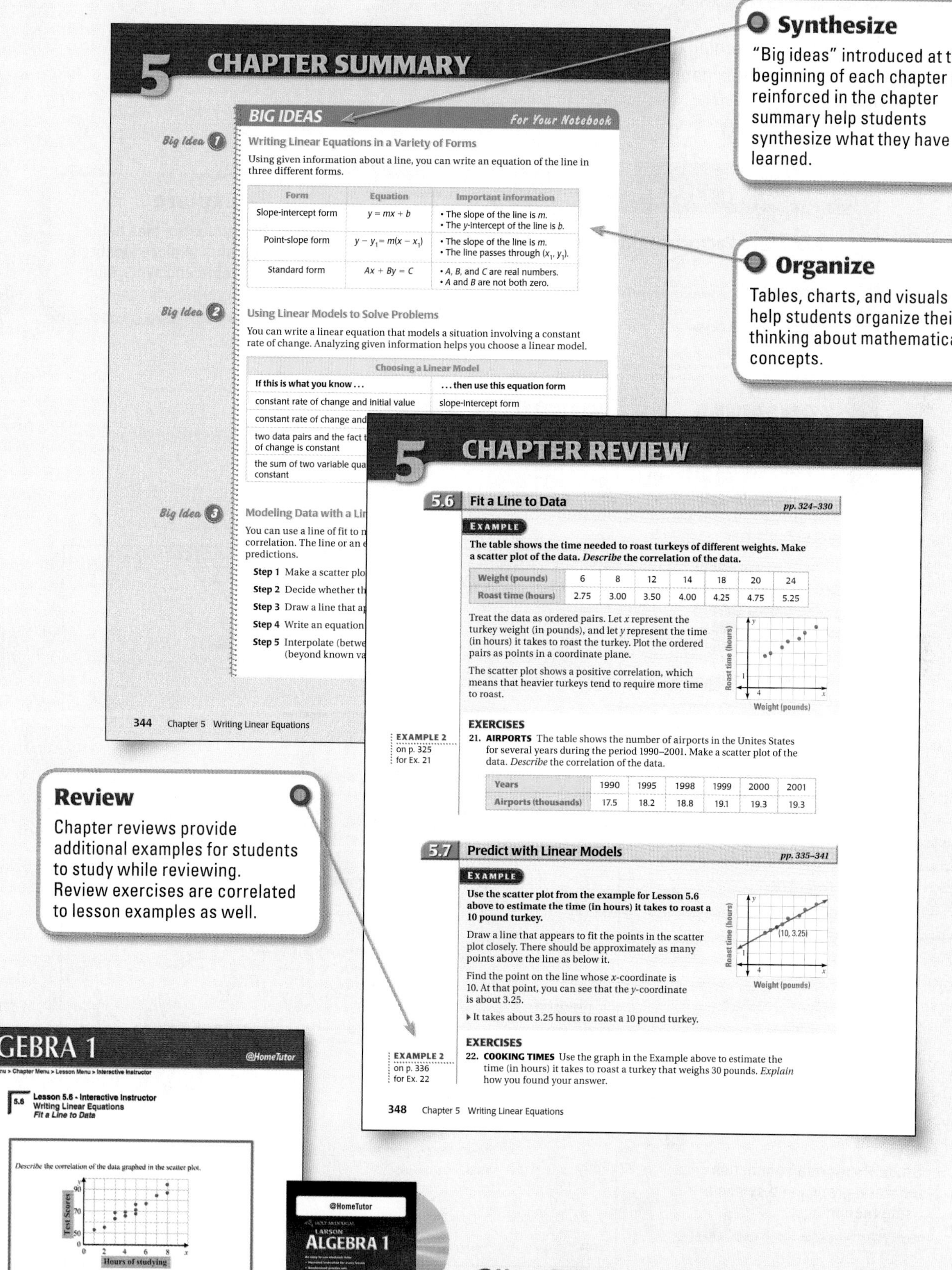

5 CHAPTER SUMMARY

BIG IDEAS *For Your Notebook*

Big Idea 1 **Writing Linear Equations in a Variety of Forms**

Using given information about a line, you can write an equation of the line in three different forms.

Form	Equation	Important information
Slope-intercept form	$y = mx + b$	• The slope of the line is m. • The y-intercept of the line is b.
Point-slope form	$y - y_1 = m(x - x_1)$	• The slope of the line is m. • The line passes through (x_1, y_1).
Standard form	$Ax + By = C$	• A, B, and C are real numbers. • A and B are not both zero.

Big Idea 2 **Using Linear Models to Solve Problems**

You can write a linear equation that models a situation involving a constant rate of change. Analyzing given information helps you choose a linear model.

Choosing a Linear Model	
If this is what you know . . .	**. . . then use this equation form**
constant rate of change and initial value	slope-intercept form
constant rate of change and	
two data pairs and the fact t of change is constant	
the sum of two variable qua constant	

Big Idea 3 **Modeling Data with a Lin**

You can use a line of fit to m correlation. The line or an e predictions.

Step 1 Make a scatter plo

Step 2 Decide whether th

Step 3 Draw a line that a

Step 4 Write an equation

Step 5 Interpolate (betwe (beyond known va

344 Chapter 5 Writing Linear Equations

5 CHAPTER REVIEW

5.6 Fit a Line to Data *pp. 324–330*

EXAMPLE

The table shows the time needed to roast turkeys of different weights. Make a scatter plot of the data. *Describe* the correlation of the data.

Weight (pounds)	6	8	12	14	18	20	24
Roast time (hours)	2.75	3.00	3.50	4.00	4.25	4.75	5.25

Treat the data as ordered pairs. Let x represent the turkey weight (in pounds), and let y represent the time (in hours) it takes to roast the turkey. Plot the ordered pairs as points in a coordinate plane.

The scatter plot shows a positive correlation, which means that heavier turkeys tend to require more time to roast.

EXERCISES

EXAMPLE 2 on p. 325 for Ex. 21

21. AIRPORTS The table shows the number of airports in the Unites States for several years during the period 1990–2001. Make a scatter plot of the data. *Describe* the correlation of the data.

Years	1990	1995	1998	1999	2000	2001
Airports (thousands)	17.5	18.2	18.8	19.1	19.3	19.3

5.7 Predict with Linear Models *pp. 335–341*

EXAMPLE

Use the scatter plot from the example for Lesson 5.6 above to estimate the time (in hours) it takes to roast a 10 pound turkey.

Draw a line that appears to fit the points in the scatter plot closely. There should be approximately as many points above the line as below it.

Find the point on the line whose x-coordinate is 10. At that point, you can see that the y-coordinate is about 3.25.

▸ It takes about 3.25 hours to roast a 10 pound turkey.

EXERCISES

EXAMPLE 2 on p. 336 for Ex. 22

22. COOKING TIMES Use the graph in the Example above to estimate the time (in hours) it takes to roast a turkey that weighs 30 pounds. *Explain* how you found your answer.

348 Chapter 5 Writing Linear Equations

Synthesize

"Big ideas" introduced at the beginning of each chapter and reinforced in the chapter summary help students synthesize what they have learned.

Organize

Tables, charts, and visuals help students organize their thinking about mathematical concepts.

Review

Chapter reviews provide additional examples for students to study while reviewing. Review exercises are correlated to lesson examples as well.

ALGEBRA 1
@HomeTutor
Lesson 5.6 - Interactive Instructor
Writing Linear Equations
Fit a Line to Data
Describe the correlation of the data graphed in the scatter plot.
Test Scores
Hours of studying
This means that as the hours of studying increased, the test scores tended to increase.
@HomeTutor
LARSON
ALGEBRA 1

@HomeTutor Provides animated examples for every lesson as well as self-scoring exercises for independent review

Motivating Students

Larson Algebra 1 supports teaching in a variety of ways, including direct instruction, hands-on activities, paper-and-pencil explorations, and calculator-assisted solutions.

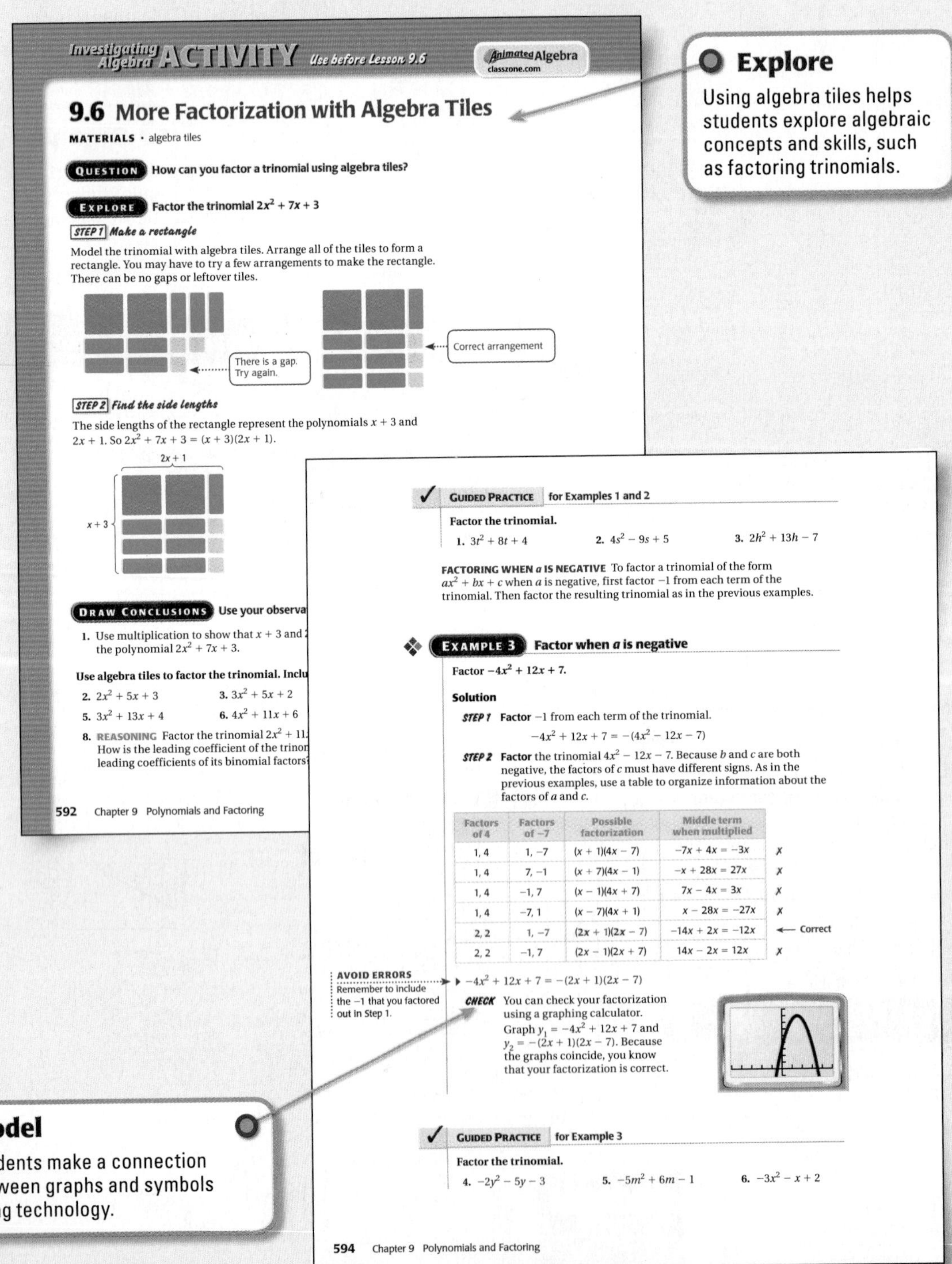

Investigating Algebra ACTIVITY Use before Lesson 9.6 — Animated Algebra classzone.com

9.6 More Factorization with Algebra Tiles

MATERIALS • algebra tiles

QUESTION How can you factor a trinomial using algebra tiles?

EXPLORE Factor the trinomial $2x^2 + 7x + 3$

STEP 1 *Make a rectangle*

Model the trinomial with algebra tiles. Arrange all of the tiles to form a rectangle. You may have to try a few arrangements to make the rectangle. There can be no gaps or leftover tiles.

STEP 2 *Find the side lengths*

The side lengths of the rectangle represent the polynomials $x + 3$ and $2x + 1$. So $2x^2 + 7x + 3 = (x + 3)(2x + 1)$.

DRAW CONCLUSIONS Use your observa

1. Use multiplication to show that $x + 3$ and 2 the polynomial $2x^2 + 7x + 3$.

Use algebra tiles to factor the trinomial. Inclu

2. $2x^2 + 5x + 3$
3. $3x^2 + 5x + 2$
5. $3x^2 + 13x + 4$
6. $4x^2 + 11x + 6$
8. **REASONING** Factor the trinomial $2x^2 + 11$ How is the leading coefficient of the trinor leading coefficients of its binomial factors

592 Chapter 9 Polynomials and Factoring

✓ **GUIDED PRACTICE** for Examples 1 and 2

Factor the trinomial.

1. $3t^2 + 8t + 4$
2. $4s^2 - 9s + 5$
3. $2h^2 + 13h - 7$

FACTORING WHEN *a* IS NEGATIVE To factor a trinomial of the form $ax^2 + bx + c$ when *a* is negative, first factor −1 from each term of the trinomial. Then factor the resulting trinomial as in the previous examples.

EXAMPLE 3 Factor when *a* is negative

Factor $-4x^2 + 12x + 7$.

Solution

STEP 1 **Factor** −1 from each term of the trinomial.

$$-4x^2 + 12x + 7 = -(4x^2 - 12x - 7)$$

STEP 2 **Factor** the trinomial $4x^2 - 12x - 7$. Because *b* and *c* are both negative, the factors of *c* must have different signs. As in the previous examples, use a table to organize information about the factors of *a* and *c*.

Factors of 4	Factors of −7	Possible factorization	Middle term when multiplied	
1, 4	1, −7	$(x + 1)(4x - 7)$	$-7x + 4x = -3x$	✗
1, 4	7, −1	$(x + 7)(4x - 1)$	$-x + 28x = 27x$	✗
1, 4	−1, 7	$(x - 1)(4x + 7)$	$7x - 4x = 3x$	✗
1, 4	−7, 1	$(x - 7)(4x + 1)$	$x - 28x = -27x$	✗
2, 2	1, −7	$(2x + 1)(2x - 7)$	$-14x + 2x = -12x$	← Correct
2, 2	−1, 7	$(2x - 1)(2x + 7)$	$14x - 2x = 12x$	✗

AVOID ERRORS Remember to include the −1 that you factored out in Step 1.

$$-4x^2 + 12x + 7 = -(2x + 1)(2x - 7)$$

CHECK You can check your factorization using a graphing calculator. Graph $y_1 = -4x^2 + 12x + 7$ and $y_2 = -(2x + 1)(2x - 7)$. Because the graphs coincide, you know that your factorization is correct.

✓ **GUIDED PRACTICE** for Example 3

Factor the trinomial.

4. $-2y^2 - 5y - 3$
5. $-5m^2 + 6m - 1$
6. $-3x^2 - x + 2$

594 Chapter 9 Polynomials and Factoring

Explore

Using algebra tiles helps students explore algebraic concepts and skills, such as factoring trinomials.

Model

Students make a connection between graphs and symbols using technology.

Connect

Students use mathematical models to solve real-life problems.

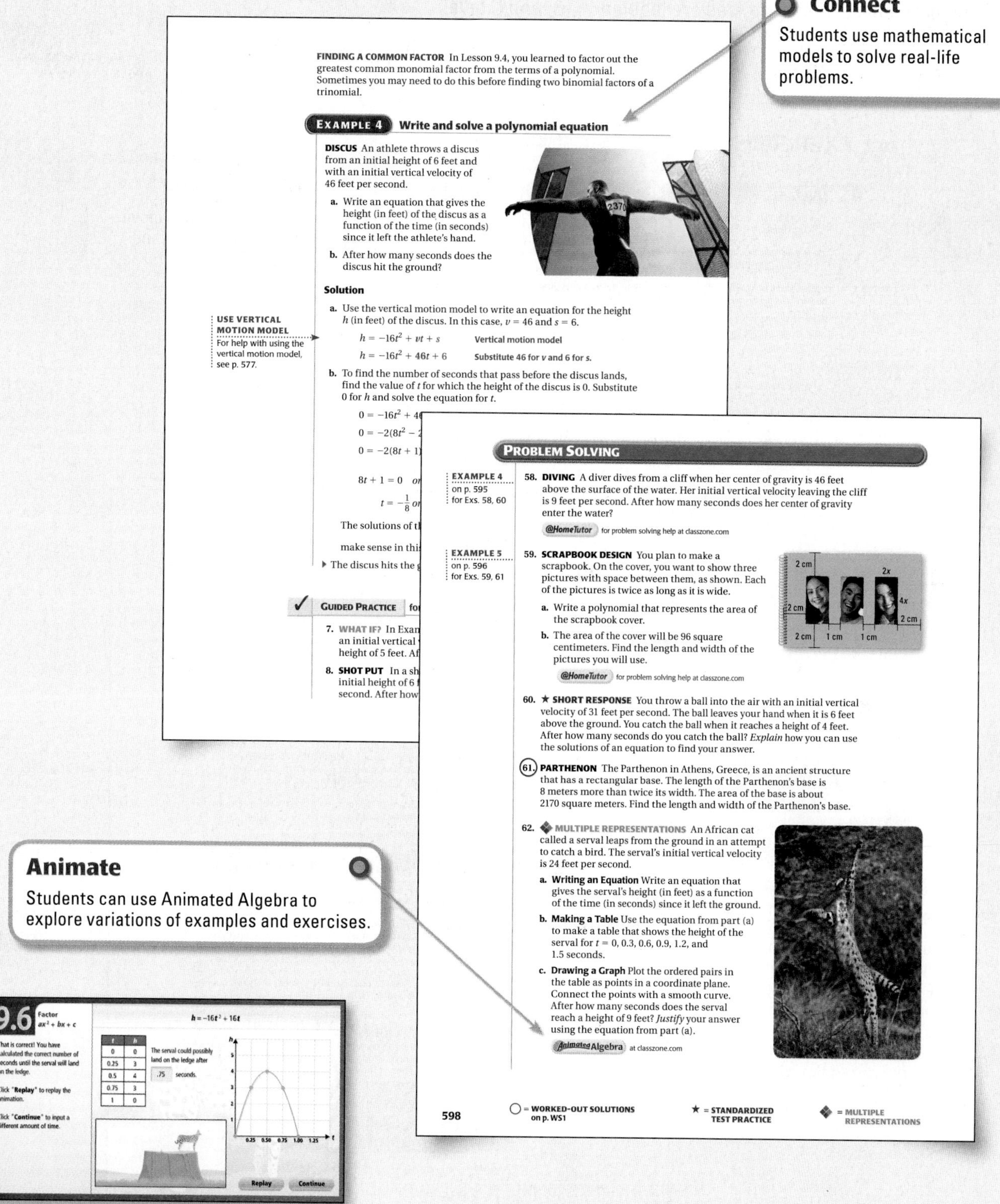

FINDING A COMMON FACTOR In Lesson 9.4, you learned to factor out the greatest common monomial factor from the terms of a polynomial. Sometimes you may need to do this before finding two binomial factors of a trinomial.

EXAMPLE 4 **Write and solve a polynomial equation**

DISCUS An athlete throws a discus from an initial height of 6 feet and with an initial vertical velocity of 46 feet per second.

a. Write an equation that gives the height (in feet) of the discus as a function of the time (in seconds) since it left the athlete's hand.

b. After how many seconds does the discus hit the ground?

Solution

USE VERTICAL MOTION MODEL For help with using the vertical motion model, see p. 577.

a. Use the vertical motion model to write an equation for the height h (in feet) of the discus. In this case, $v = 46$ and $s = 6$.

$h = -16t^2 + vt + s$ Vertical motion model

$h = -16t^2 + 46t + 6$ Substitute 46 for v and 6 for s.

b. To find the number of seconds that pass before the discus lands, find the value of t for which the height of the discus is 0. Substitute 0 for h and solve the equation for t.

$0 = -16t^2 + 4$

$0 = -2(8t^2 -$

$0 = -2(8t + 1$

$8t + 1 = 0$ o

$t = -\frac{1}{8}$ o

The solutions of t

make sense in thi

▸ The discus hits the

GUIDED PRACTICE fo

7. **WHAT IF?** In Exam an initial vertical height of 5 feet. Af

8. **SHOT PUT** In a sh initial height of 6 second. After how

PROBLEM SOLVING

EXAMPLE 4 on p. 595 for Exs. 58, 60

58. **DIVING** A diver dives from a cliff when her center of gravity is 46 feet above the surface of the water. Her initial vertical velocity leaving the cliff is 9 feet per second. After how many seconds does her center of gravity enter the water?

@HomeTutor for problem solving help at classzone.com

EXAMPLE 5 on p. 596 for Exs. 59, 61

59. **SCRAPBOOK DESIGN** You plan to make a scrapbook. On the cover, you want to show three pictures with space between them, as shown. Each of the pictures is twice as long as it is wide.

a. Write a polynomial that represents the area of the scrapbook cover.

b. The area of the cover will be 96 square centimeters. Find the length and width of the pictures you will use.

@HomeTutor for problem solving help at classzone.com

60. ★ **SHORT RESPONSE** You throw a ball into the air with an initial vertical velocity of 31 feet per second. The ball leaves your hand when it is 6 feet above the ground. You catch the ball when it reaches a height of 4 feet. After how many seconds do you catch the ball? *Explain* how you can use the solutions of an equation to find your answer.

(61.) **PARTHENON** The Parthenon in Athens, Greece, is an ancient structure that has a rectangular base. The length of the Parthenon's base is 8 meters more than twice its width. The area of the base is about 2170 square meters. Find the length and width of the Parthenon's base.

62. ◆ **MULTIPLE REPRESENTATIONS** An African cat called a serval leaps from the ground in an attempt to catch a bird. The serval's initial vertical velocity is 24 feet per second.

a. **Writing an Equation** Write an equation that gives the serval's height (in feet) as a function of the time (in seconds) since it left the ground.

b. **Making a Table** Use the equation from part (a) to make a table that shows the height of the serval for $t = 0, 0.3, 0.6, 0.9, 1.2,$ and 1.5 seconds.

c. **Drawing a Graph** Plot the ordered pairs in the table as points in a coordinate plane. Connect the points with a smooth curve. After how many seconds does the serval reach a height of 9 feet? *Justify* your answer using the equation from part (a).

Animated Algebra at classzone.com

598

○ = WORKED-OUT SOLUTIONS on p. WS1 ★ = STANDARDIZED TEST PRACTICE ◆ = MULTIPLE REPRESENTATIONS

Animate

Students can use Animated Algebra to explore variations of examples and exercises.

9.6 Factor $ax^2 + bx + c$
$h = -16t^2 + 16t$
That is correct! You have calculated the correct number of seconds until the serval will land on the ledge.
Click "Replay" to replay the animation.
Click "Continue" to input a different amount of time.
t | h
0 | 0
0.25 | 3
0.5 | 4
0.75 | 3
1 | 0
The serval could possibly land on the ledge after .75 seconds.
Replay
Continue

Animated Algebra Provides interactive activities that support and extend what's taught in the book

Differentiating Instruction

Exercises are easily adapted to a range of abilities. For each lesson, both skill and problem solving exercises are labeled A, B, and C level in the Teacher's Edition.

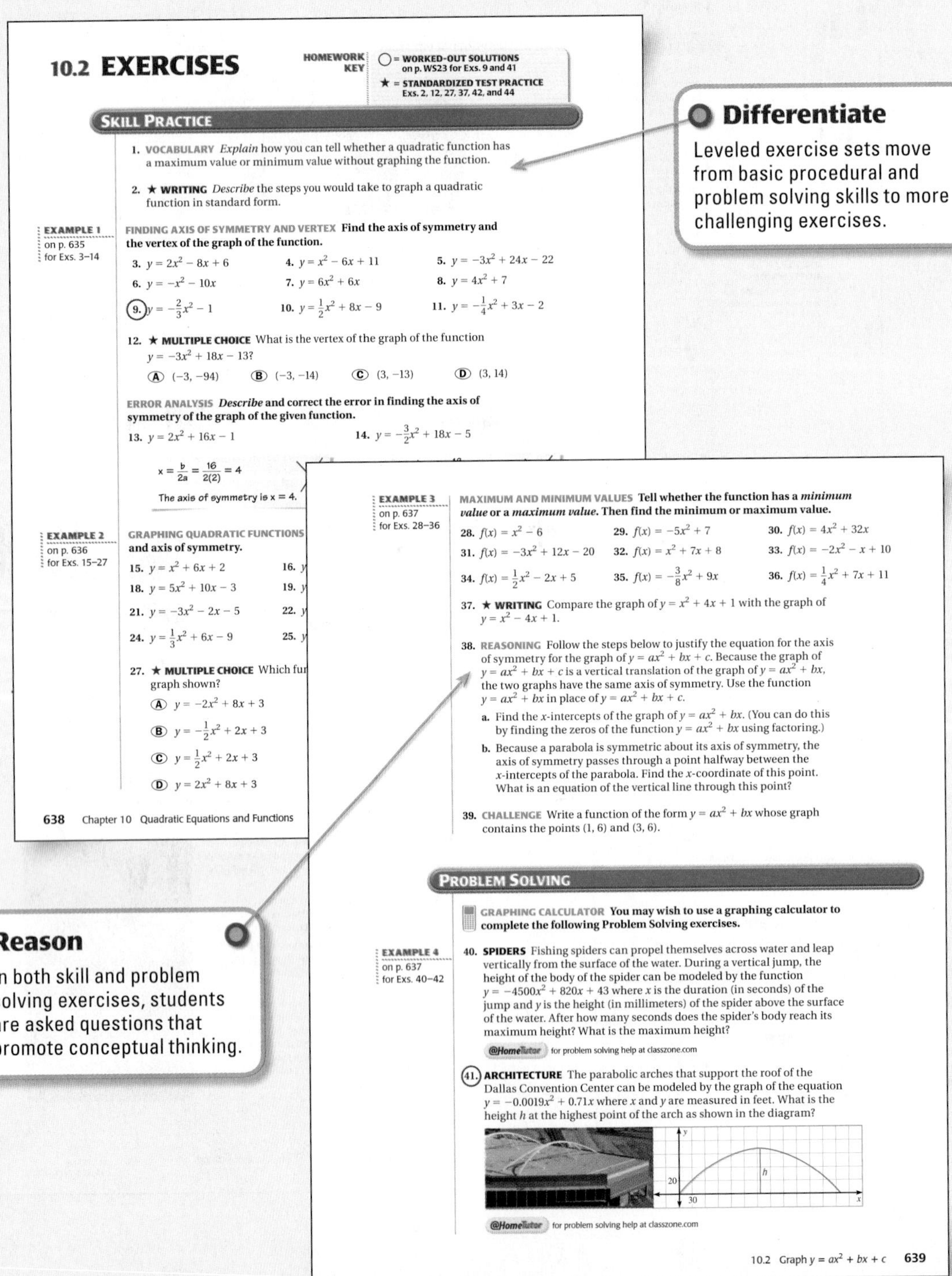

10.2 EXERCISES

HOMEWORK KEY
○ = WORKED-OUT SOLUTIONS on p. WS23 for Exs. 9 and 41
★ = STANDARDIZED TEST PRACTICE Exs. 2, 12, 27, 37, 42, and 44

SKILL PRACTICE

1. **VOCABULARY** *Explain* how you can tell whether a quadratic function has a maximum value or minimum value without graphing the function.

2. ★ **WRITING** *Describe* the steps you would take to graph a quadratic function in standard form.

EXAMPLE 1 on p. 635 for Exs. 3–14

FINDING AXIS OF SYMMETRY AND VERTEX Find the axis of symmetry and the vertex of the graph of the function.

3. $y = 2x^2 - 8x + 6$
4. $y = x^2 - 6x + 11$
5. $y = -3x^2 + 24x - 22$
6. $y = -x^2 - 10x$
7. $y = 6x^2 + 6x$
8. $y = 4x^2 + 7$
9. $y = -\frac{2}{3}x^2 - 1$
10. $y = \frac{1}{2}x^2 + 8x - 9$
11. $y = -\frac{1}{4}x^2 + 3x - 2$

12. ★ **MULTIPLE CHOICE** What is the vertex of the graph of the function $y = -3x^2 + 18x - 13$?
Ⓐ (−3, −94) Ⓑ (−3, −14) Ⓒ (3, −13) Ⓓ (3, 14)

ERROR ANALYSIS ***Describe*** **and correct the error in finding the axis of symmetry of the graph of the given function.**

13. $y = 2x^2 + 16x - 1$

$x = \frac{b}{2a} = \frac{16}{2(2)} = 4$

The axis of symmetry is x = 4.

14. $y = -\frac{3}{2}x^2 + 18x - 5$

EXAMPLE 2 on p. 636 for Exs. 15–27

GRAPHING QUADRATIC FUNCTIONS ... **and axis of symmetry.**

15. $y = x^2 + 6x + 2$
16. ...
18. $y = 5x^2 + 10x - 3$
19. ...
21. $y = -3x^2 - 2x - 5$
22. ...
24. $y = \frac{1}{3}x^2 + 6x - 9$
25. ...

27. ★ **MULTIPLE CHOICE** Which fu... graph shown?
Ⓐ $y = -2x^2 + 8x + 3$
Ⓑ $y = -\frac{1}{2}x^2 + 2x + 3$
Ⓒ $y = \frac{1}{2}x^2 + 2x + 3$
Ⓓ $y = 2x^2 + 8x + 3$

638 Chapter 10 Quadratic Equations and Functions

EXAMPLE 3 on p. 637 for Exs. 28–36

MAXIMUM AND MINIMUM VALUES Tell whether the function has a ***minimum value*** **or a** ***maximum value.*** **Then find the minimum or maximum value.**

28. $f(x) = x^2 - 6$
29. $f(x) = -5x^2 + 7$
30. $f(x) = 4x^2 + 32x$
31. $f(x) = -3x^2 + 12x - 20$
32. $f(x) = x^2 + 7x + 8$
33. $f(x) = -2x^2 - x + 10$
34. $f(x) = \frac{1}{2}x^2 - 2x + 5$
35. $f(x) = -\frac{3}{8}x^2 + 9x$
36. $f(x) = \frac{1}{4}x^2 + 7x + 11$

37. ★ **WRITING** Compare the graph of $y = x^2 + 4x + 1$ with the graph of $y = x^2 - 4x + 1$.

38. **REASONING** Follow the steps below to justify the equation for the axis of symmetry for the graph of $y = ax^2 + bx + c$. Because the graph of $y = ax^2 + bx + c$ is a vertical translation of the graph of $y = ax^2 + bx$, the two graphs have the same axis of symmetry. Use the function $y = ax^2 + bx$ in place of $y = ax^2 + bx + c$.
a. Find the *x*-intercepts of the graph of $y = ax^2 + bx$. (You can do this by finding the zeros of the function $y = ax^2 + bx$ using factoring.)
b. Because a parabola is symmetric about its axis of symmetry, the axis of symmetry passes through a point halfway between the *x*-intercepts of the parabola. Find the *x*-coordinate of this point. What is an equation of the vertical line through this point?

39. **CHALLENGE** Write a function of the form $y = ax^2 + bx$ whose graph contains the points (1, 6) and (3, 6).

PROBLEM SOLVING

GRAPHING CALCULATOR You may wish to use a graphing calculator to complete the following Problem Solving exercises.

EXAMPLE 4 on p. 637 for Exs. 40–42

40. **SPIDERS** Fishing spiders can propel themselves across water and leap vertically from the surface of the water. During a vertical jump, the height of the body of the spider can be modeled by the function $y = -4500x^2 + 820x + 43$ where x is the duration (in seconds) of the jump and y is the height (in millimeters) of the spider above the surface of the water. After how many seconds does the spider's body reach its maximum height? What is the maximum height?

@HomeTutor for problem solving help at classzone.com

41. **ARCHITECTURE** The parabolic arches that support the roof of the Dallas Convention Center can be modeled by the graph of the equation $y = -0.0019x^2 + 0.71x$ where x and y are measured in feet. What is the height h at the highest point of the arch as shown in the diagram?

@HomeTutor for problem solving help at classzone.com

10.2 Graph $y = ax^2 + bx + c$ 639

Differentiate
Leveled exercise sets move from basic procedural and problem solving skills to more challenging exercises.

Reason
In both skill and problem solving exercises, students are asked questions that promote conceptual thinking.

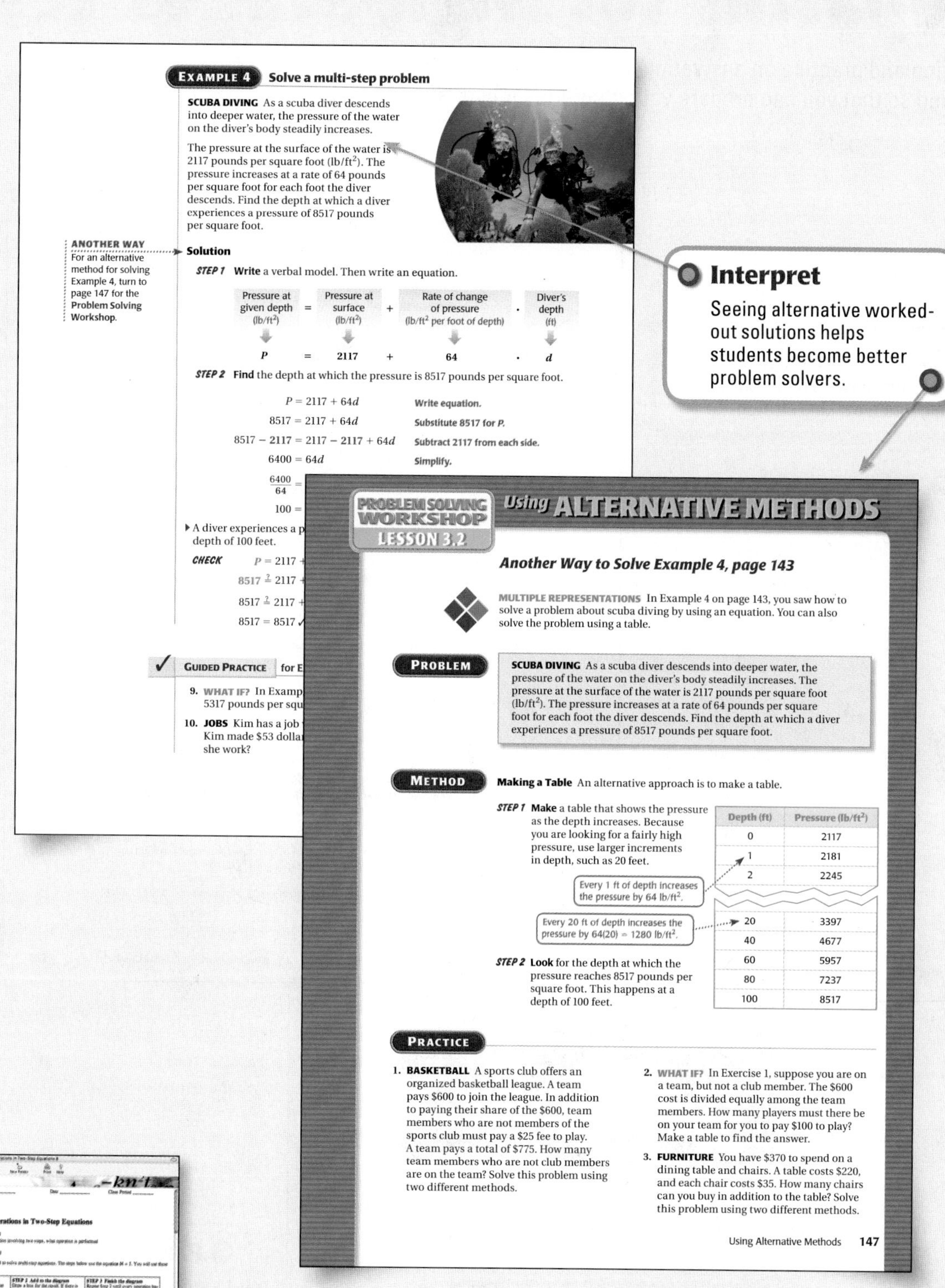

EXAMPLE 4 Solve a multi-step problem

SCUBA DIVING As a scuba diver descends into deeper water, the pressure of the water on the diver's body steadily increases.

The pressure at the surface of the water is 2117 pounds per square foot (lb/ft^2). The pressure increases at a rate of 64 pounds per square foot for each foot the diver descends. Find the depth at which a diver experiences a pressure of 8517 pounds per square foot.

ANOTHER WAY For an alternative method for solving Example 4, turn to page 147 for the **Problem Solving Workshop**.

Solution

STEP 1 **Write** a verbal model. Then write an equation.

Pressure at given depth (lb/ft^2)	=	Pressure at surface (lb/ft^2)	+	Rate of change of pressure (lb/ft^2 per foot of depth)	·	Diver's depth (ft)
P	=	2117	+	64	·	d

STEP 2 **Find** the depth at which the pressure is 8517 pounds per square foot.

$P = 2117 + 64d$ Write equation.

$8517 = 2117 + 64d$ Substitute 8517 for P.

$8517 - 2117 = 2117 - 2117 + 64d$ Subtract 2117 from each side.

$6400 = 64d$ Simplify.

$\frac{6400}{64} =$

$100 =$

▶ A diver experiences a p... depth of 100 feet.

CHECK $P = 2117$ ...

$8517 \stackrel{?}{=} 2117$ ...

$8517 \stackrel{?}{=} 2117$ ...

$8517 = 8517$ ✓

✓ **GUIDED PRACTICE** for E...

9. **WHAT IF?** In Examp... 5317 pounds per squ...

10. **JOBS** Kim has a job ... Kim made $53 dolla... she work?

Interpret

Seeing alternative worked-out solutions helps students become better problem solvers.

PROBLEM SOLVING WORKSHOP LESSON 3.2 *Using* **ALTERNATIVE METHODS**

Another Way to Solve Example 4, page 143

MULTIPLE REPRESENTATIONS In Example 4 on page 143, you saw how to solve a problem about scuba diving by using an equation. You can also solve the problem using a table.

PROBLEM

SCUBA DIVING As a scuba diver descends into deeper water, the pressure of the water on the diver's body steadily increases. The pressure at the surface of the water is 2117 pounds per square foot (lb/ft^2). The pressure increases at a rate of 64 pounds per square foot for each foot the diver descends. Find the depth at which a diver experiences a pressure of 8517 pounds per square foot.

METHOD

Making a Table An alternative approach is to make a table.

STEP 1 **Make** a table that shows the pressure as the depth increases. Because you are looking for a fairly high pressure, use larger increments in depth, such as 20 feet.

Depth (ft)	Pressure (lb/ft^2)
0	2117
1	2181
2	2245
20	3397
40	4677
60	5957
80	7237
100	8517

Every 1 ft of depth increases the pressure by 64 lb/ft^2.

Every 20 ft of depth increases the pressure by 64(20) = 1280 lb/ft^2.

STEP 2 **Look** for the depth at which the pressure reaches 8517 pounds per square foot. This happens at a depth of 100 feet.

PRACTICE

1. **BASKETBALL** A sports club offers an organized basketball league. A team pays $600 to join the league. In addition to paying their share of the $600, team members who are not members of the sports club must pay a $25 fee to play. A team pays a total of $775. How many team members who are not club members are on the team? Solve this problem using two different methods.

2. **WHAT IF?** In Exercise 1, suppose you are on a team, but not a club member. The $600 cost is divided equally among the team members. How many players must there be on your team for you to pay $100 to play? Make a table to find the answer.

3. **FURNITURE** You have $370 to spend on a dining table and chairs. A table costs $220, and each chair costs $35. How many chairs can you buy in addition to the table? Solve this problem using two different methods.

Using Alternative Methods 147

Activity Generator Provides leveled activities (A, B, C) for every lesson

Preparing for High-Stakes Tests

Instruction and practice on answering standardized test questions are embedded so that you can prepare your students for high-stake tests.

Strategize

Standardized Test Practice examples develop math skills and suggest test-taking strategies.

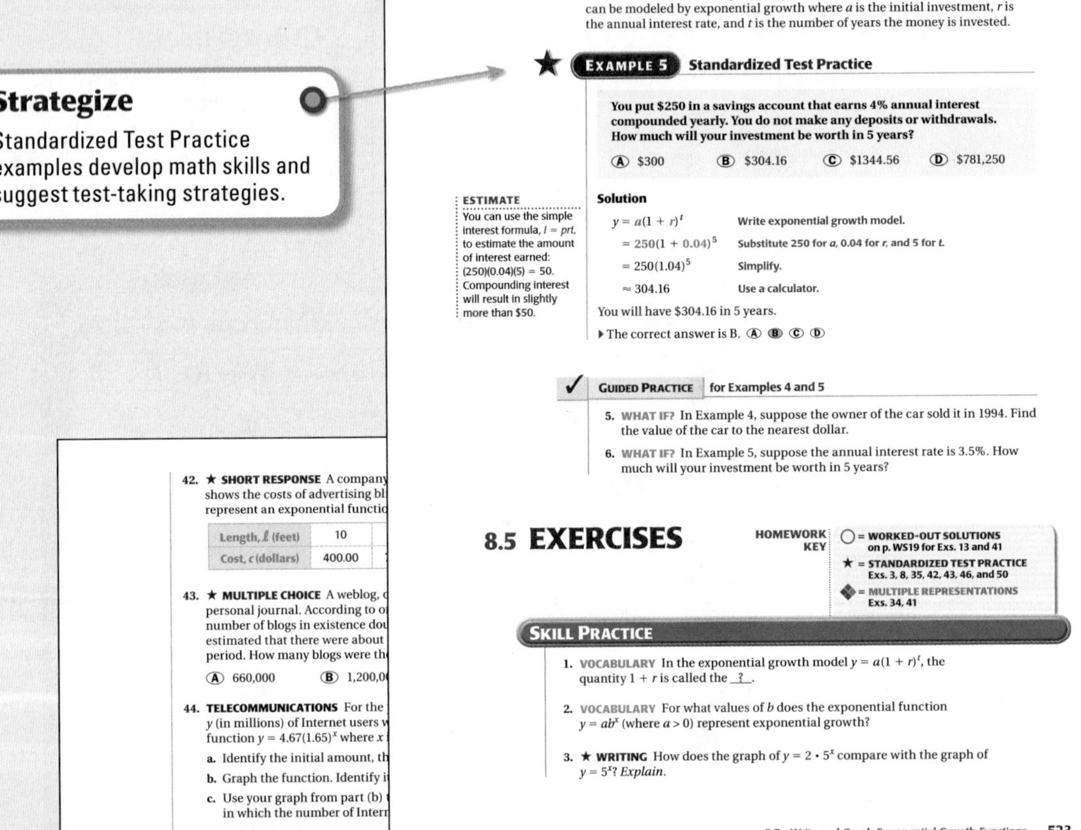

COMPOUND INTEREST **Compound interest** is interest earned on both an initial investment and on previously earned interest. Compounding of interest can be modeled by exponential growth where a is the initial investment, r is the annual interest rate, and t is the number of years the money is invested.

★ **EXAMPLE 5** **Standardized Test Practice**

You put $250 in a savings account that earns 4% annual interest compounded yearly. You do not make any deposits or withdrawals. How much will your investment be worth in 5 years?

Ⓐ $300 Ⓑ $304.16 Ⓒ $1344.56 Ⓓ $781,250

ESTIMATE
You can use the simple interest formula, $I = prt$, to estimate the amount of interest earned: $(250)(0.04)(5) = 50$. Compounding interest will result in slightly more than $50.

Solution

$y = a(1 + r)^t$ Write exponential growth model.

$= 250(1 + 0.04)^5$ Substitute 250 for a, 0.04 for r, and 5 for t.

$= 250(1.04)^5$ Simplify.

≈ 304.16 Use a calculator.

You will have $304.16 in 5 years.

▸ The correct answer is B. Ⓐ Ⓑ Ⓒ Ⓓ

✓ **GUIDED PRACTICE** for Examples 4 and 5

5. **WHAT IF?** In Example 4, suppose the owner of the car sold it in 1994. Find the value of the car to the nearest dollar.
6. **WHAT IF?** In Example 5, suppose the annual interest rate is 3.5%. How much will your investment be worth in 5 years?

8.5 EXERCISES

HOMEWORK KEY
○ = WORKED-OUT SOLUTIONS on p. WS19 for Exs. 13 and 41
★ = STANDARDIZED TEST PRACTICE Exs. 3, 8, 35, 42, 43, 46, and 50
◆ = MULTIPLE REPRESENTATIONS Exs. 34, 41

SKILL PRACTICE

1. **VOCABULARY** In the exponential growth model $y = a(1 + r)^t$, the quantity $1 + r$ is called the _?_.
2. **VOCABULARY** For what values of b does the exponential function $y = ab^x$ (where $a > 0$) represent exponential growth?
3. ★ **WRITING** How does the graph of $y = 2 \cdot 5^x$ compare with the graph of $y = 5^x$? *Explain.*

8.5 Write and Graph Exponential Growth Functions 523

42. ★ **SHORT RESPONSE** A company shows the costs of advertising bl represent an exponential functio

Length, ℓ (feet)	10
Cost, c (dollars)	400.00

43. ★ **MULTIPLE CHOICE** A weblog, personal journal. According to o number of blogs in existence dou estimated that there were about period. How many blogs were th

Ⓐ 660,000 Ⓑ 1,200,0

44. **TELECOMMUNICATIONS** For the y (in millions) of Internet users function $y = 4.67(1.65)^x$ where x
a. Identify the initial amount, th
b. Graph the function. Identify i
c. Use your graph from part (b) in which the number of Intern

45. **GRAPHING CALCULATOR** The fre piano is a function of the positio position of some piano keys and the frequencies of the notes created by the keys are shown below. Use the exponential regression feature on a graphing calculator to find an exponential model for the frequency of piano notes. What is the frequency of the note created by the 30th key?

Key	1	3	4	6	8	9	11	13	15	16	18	20
Frequency (in hertz)	29.14	32.70	36.71	41.20	46.25	51.91	58.27	65.41	73.42	82.41		

46. ★ **EXTENDED RESPONSE** In 1830, the population of the United States was 12,866,020. By 1890, the population was 62,947,714.
a. **Model** Assume the population growth from 1830 to 1890 was linear. Write a linear model for the U.S. population from 1830 to 1890. By about how much did the population grow per year from 1830 to 1890?
b. **Model** Assume the population growth from 1830 to 1890 was exponential. Write an exponential model for the U.S. population from 1830 to 1890. By approximately what percent did the population grow per year from 1830 to 1890?
c. **Explain** The U.S. population was 23,191,876 in 1850 and 38,558,371 in 1870. Which of the models in parts (a) and (b) is a better approximation of actual U.S. population for the time period 1850–1890? *Explain.*

526 ★ = STANDARDIZED TEST PRACTICE

Prepare

Lesson exercises include a variety of test-format questions, such as multiple choice, short response, and extended response.

4 ★ Standardized TEST PREPARATION

CONTEXT-BASED MULTIPLE CHOICE QUESTIONS

Some of the information you need to solve a context-based multiple choice question may appear in a table, a diagram, or a graph.

PROBLEM 1

A recipe from a box of pancake mix is shown. The number p of pancakes you can make varies directly with the number m of cups of mix you use. A full box of pancake mix contains 9 cups of mix. How many pancakes can you make when you use the full box?

Ⓐ 63 Ⓑ 65
Ⓒ 126 Ⓓ 131

2 cups pancake mix
1 cup milk
2 eggs
Combine ingredients. Pour batter on hot greased griddle. Flip when edges are dry. Makes 14 pancakes.

Plan

INTERPRET THE INFORMATION Use the number of pancakes and the number of cups of mix given in the recipe to write a direct variation equation. Then use the equation to find the number of pancakes that you can make when you use 9 cups of mix.

Solution

STEP 1 Use the values given in the recipe to find a direct variation equation.

Because the number p of … number m of cups of mix … the recipe, you know tha…

$p = am$ Write direc…

$14 = a(2)$ Substitute.

$7 = a$ Solve for a.

So, a direct variation equ…

STEP 2 Substitute 9 for m in the direct variation equation and solve for p.

Use the direct variation … make when you use a ful…

$p = 7m$ Write direc…

$p = 7(9)$ Substitute …

$p = 63$ Simplify.

You can make 63 pancak…

The correct answer is A. …

Interpret

Learning how to interpret information is a critical problem solving skill.

4 ★ Standardized TEST PRACTICE

MULTIPLE CHOICE

In Exercises 1 and 2, use the graph below.

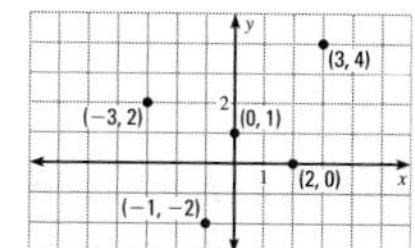

1. The graph represents a function. Which number is in the domain of the function?
   Ⓐ 22 Ⓑ −1
   Ⓒ 1 Ⓓ 4

2. The graph would no longer represent a function if which point were included?
   Ⓐ (−4, −2) Ⓑ (−2, 0)
   Ⓒ (1, 3) Ⓓ (3, −1)

In Exercises 3 and 4, use the graph below, which shows a traveler's movements through an airport to a terminal. The traveler has to walk and take a shuttle bus to get to the terminal.

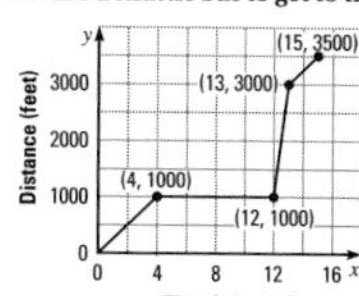

3. For how many minutes does the traveler wait for the shuttle bus?
   Ⓐ 1 min Ⓑ 2 min
   Ⓒ 4 min Ⓓ 8 min

4. For about what distance does the traveler ride on the shuttle bus?
   Ⓐ 100 ft Ⓑ 100 ft
   Ⓒ 2000 ft Ⓓ 3000 ft

In Exercises 5–7, use the following information.

At a yoga studio, new members pay a sign-up fee of \$50 plus a monthly fee of \$25. The total cost C (in dollars) of a new membership is given by $C = 25m + 50$ where m is the number of months of membership. The owner of the studio is considering changing the cost of a new membership. A graph of four different options for changing the cost is shown.

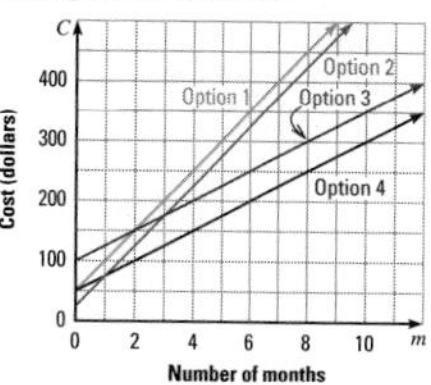

5. For which option are the sign-up fee and monthly fee kept the same?
   Ⓐ Option 1 Ⓑ Option 2
   Ⓒ Option 3 Ⓓ Option 4

6. For which option is the sign-up fee kept the same and the monthly fee raised?
   Ⓐ Option 1 Ⓑ Option 2
   Ⓒ Option 3 Ⓓ Option 4

7. For which option is the monthly fee kept the same and the sign-up fee raised?
   Ⓐ Option 1 Ⓑ Option 2
   Ⓒ Option 3 Ⓓ Option 4

8. The table shows the cost of a therapeutic massage for a given amount of time. What is the cost per minute?

Time (minutes)	30	45	60
Cost (dollars)	42.00	63.00	84.00

   Ⓐ \$.71 Ⓑ \$1.40
   Ⓒ \$2.80 Ⓓ \$14.00

Practice

Thorough practice builds students' confidence and skills.

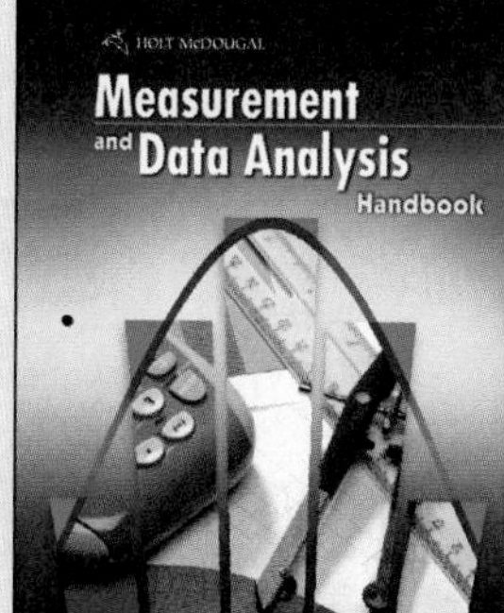

Measurement and Data Analysis Handbook

Provides lessons and labs on topics from measurement, probability, and data analysis commonly assessed on state tests

PROGRAM OVERVIEW

The *Larson Algebra 1* program provides a complete set of resources organized for ease of use.

eEdition
DVD-ROM and online

DAILY RESOURCES

EasyPlanner
HOLT McDOUGAL
LARSON
ALGEBRA 1

DIFFERENTIATING INSTRUCTION

ASSESSMENT AND INTERVENTION

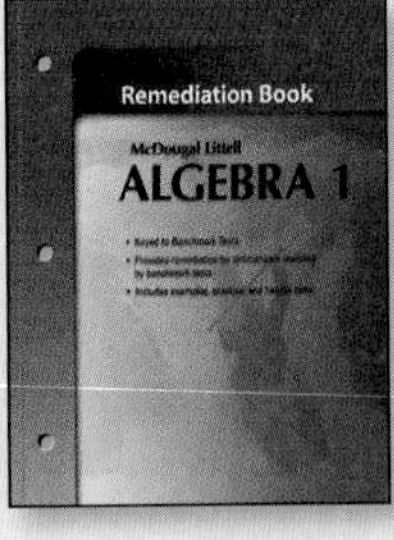

ENGLISH LEARNERS

PLANNING AND TEACHING RESOURCES

Flexible, easy-to-navigate resources for planning, motivation, instruction, and assessment

EasyPlanner

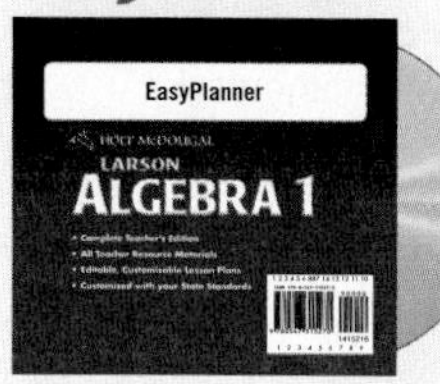

- Lesson plans that you can customize
- Includes all print teaching resources
- Also includes Skills Readiness: Intervention and Enrichment

eEdition

- Electronic version of the text
- Interactivity through Animated Algebra

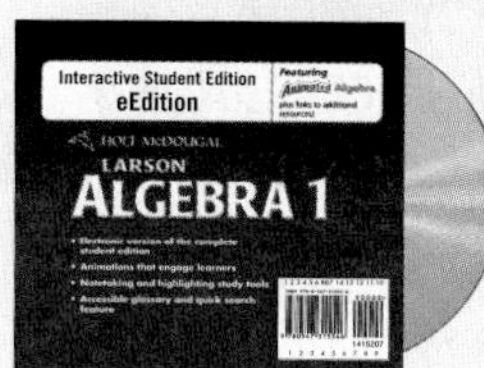

Animated Algebra

Engaging, interactive activities that support textbook lessons and exercises

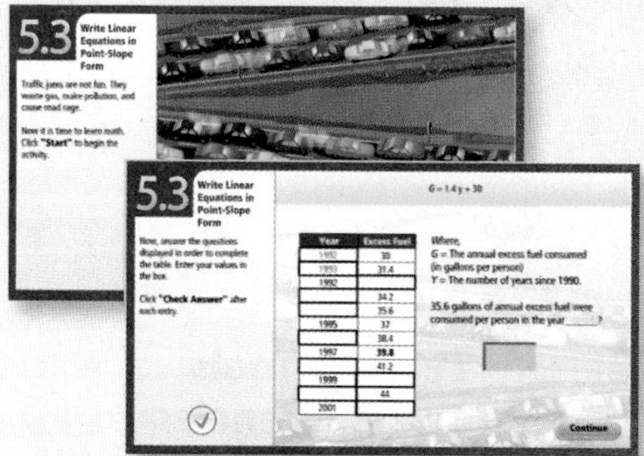

Power Presentations: The Electronic Classroom

All the classroom resources you need to teach an interactive lesson

Activity Generator

- Leveled activities (A, B, C) for each lesson
- Teaching commentary to help you guide students from concrete to abstract

classzone.com

Holt McDougal's companion website provides full support for the student at home.

- Extra examples
- Animations
- Quizzes
- Vocabulary support
- eWorkbook

ASSESSMENT AND INTERVENTION RESOURCES

Test Generator powered by ExamView®* Assessment Suite

Develop customized tests, practice sheets, and answer keys

*ExamView is a registered trademark of eInstruction, Corp.

@HomeTutor

- Animated examples and instruction
- Self-scoring exercises
- Customized student progress reports

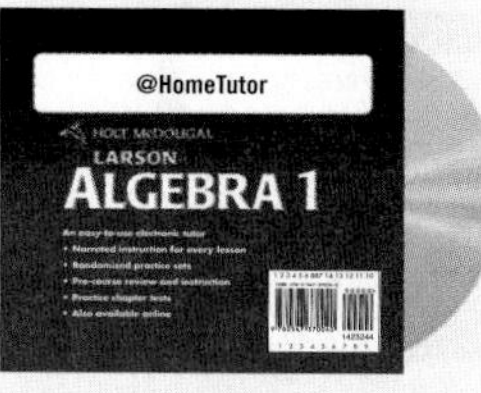

McDougal Littell Assessment System

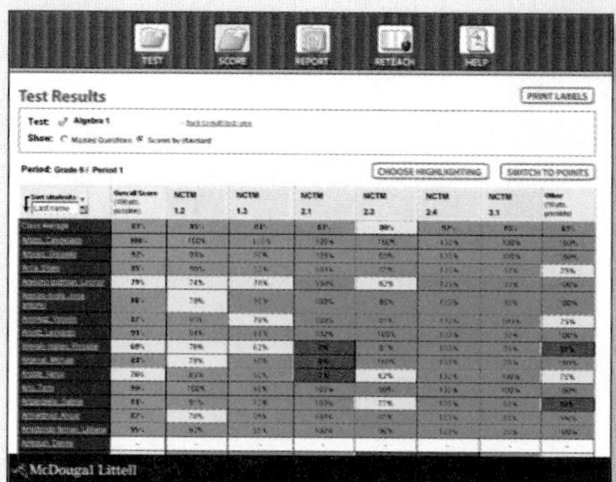

- Innovative standards-based system
- Helps you test, score, report, and reteach
- Tests and answer sheets can be printed on plain paper

DAILY RESOURCES

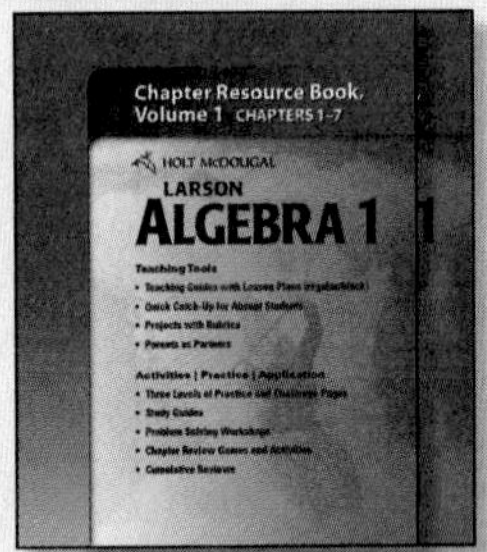

Chapter Resource Book

Includes teaching guides with lesson plans, three levels of practice, study guides, and more

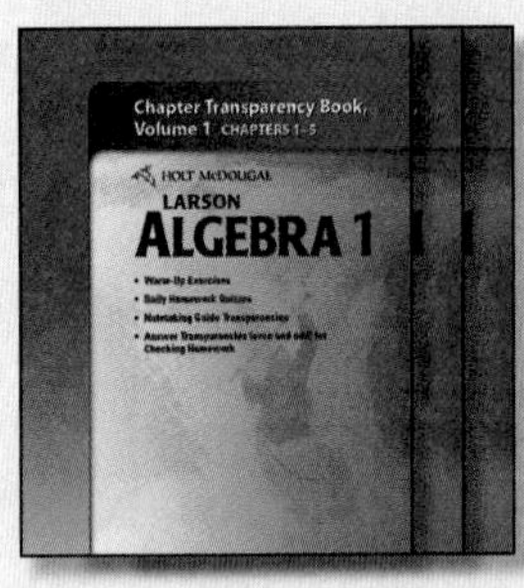

Chapter Transparency Book

Includes warm-up exercises and daily homework quizzes as well as answers for checking homework

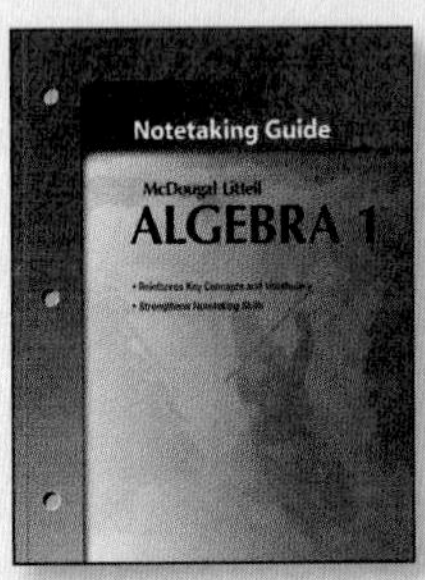

Notetaking Guide

Consumable workbook that helps students develop notetaking skills, review vocabulary, and prepare for tests

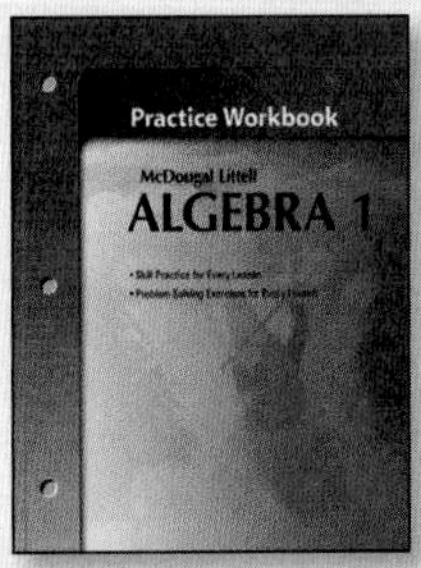

Practice Workbook

Consumable workbook that provides additional practice for every lesson

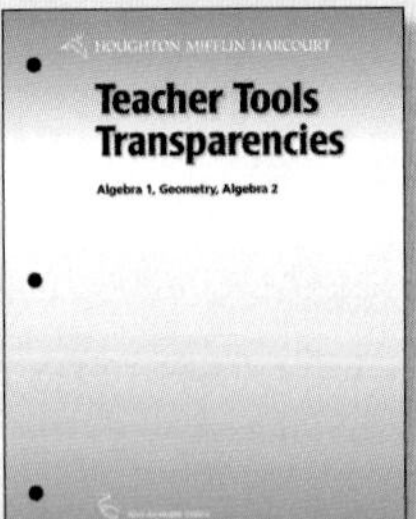

Teacher Tools Transparencies

Includes number lines, coordinate grids, and more

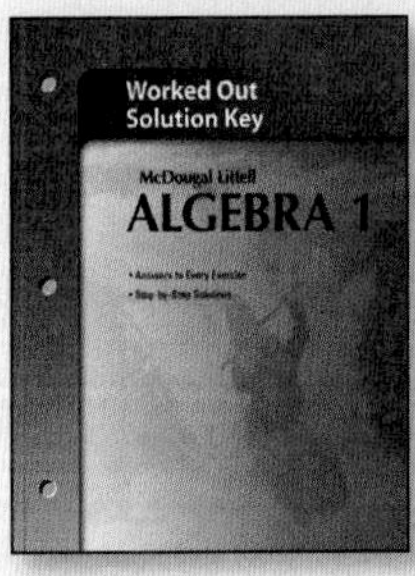

Worked-Out Solution Key

Provides complete solutions for all textbook exercises

DIFFERENTIATING INSTRUCTION RESOURCES

Differentiated Instruction Resources

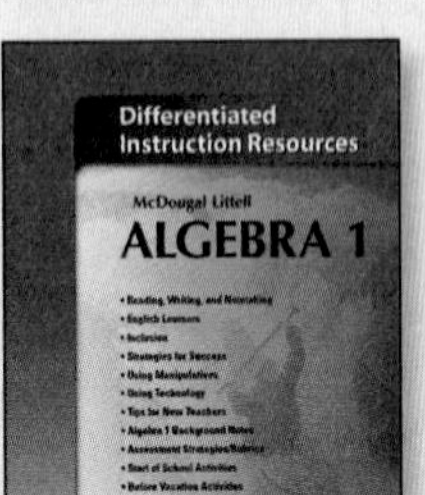

- Strategies for Reading Mathematics
- Differentiated Instruction Lesson Notes
- English Learner Lesson Notes
- Inclusion Lesson Notes
- Teaching Strategies and Worksheets
- Using Technology in the Classroom
- Tips for New Teachers
- Math Background Notes
- Teacher Survival Activities
- Bulletin Board Ideas

Pre-AP®* Resources

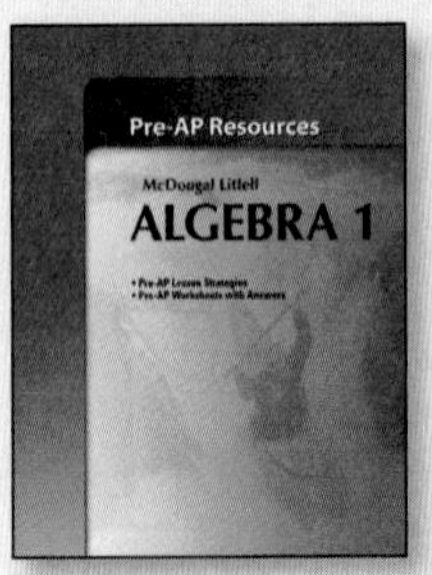

- Pre-AP Overview
- Pre-AP Pacing and Assignment Guide
- Pre-AP Best Practices
- Pre-AP Copymasters

*Pre-AP is a registered trademark of the College Board, which was not involved in the production of, and does not endorse, this product.

Activity Generator

- Leveled activities (A, B, C) for each lesson
- Teaching commentary to help you guide students from concrete to abstract

ENGLISH LEARNERS RESOURCES

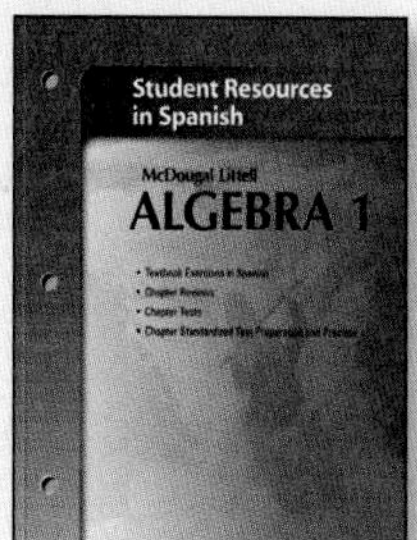

Student Resources in Spanish

Textbook exercises, chapter reviews and tests, and chapter standardized test preparation and practice pages in Spanish

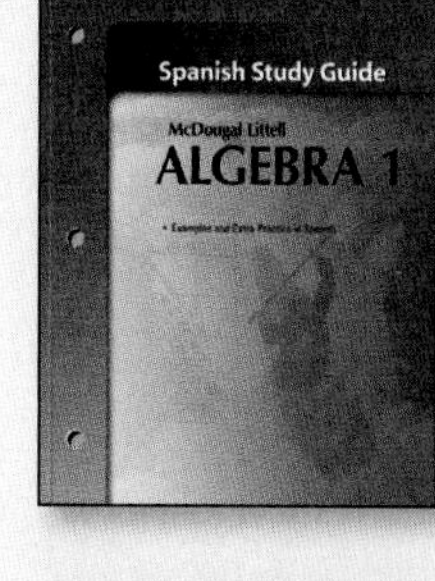

Spanish Study Guide

Examples and extra practice in Spanish

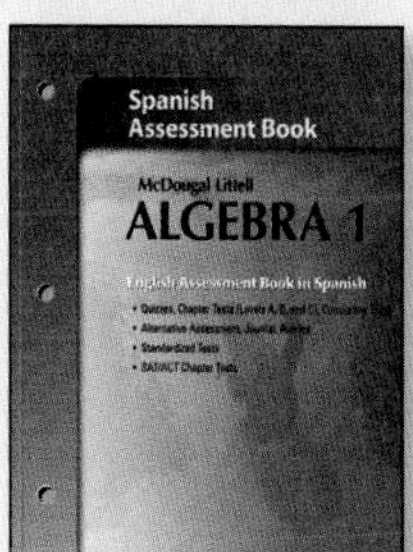

Spanish Assessment Book

English Assessment Book in Spanish

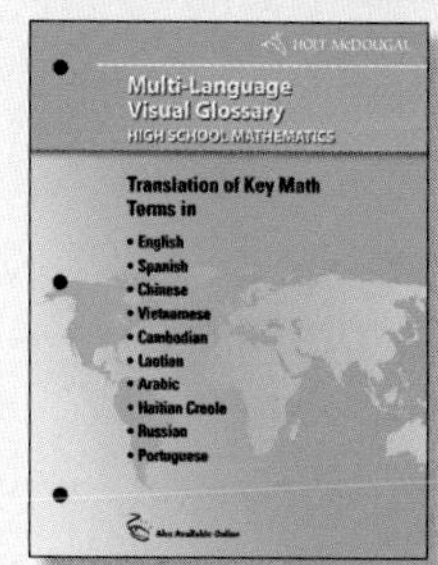

Multi-Language Visual Glossary

A visual math glossary translated into nine languages

ASSESSMENT AND INTERVENTION RESOURCES

Assessment Book

Quizzes and tests in various formats

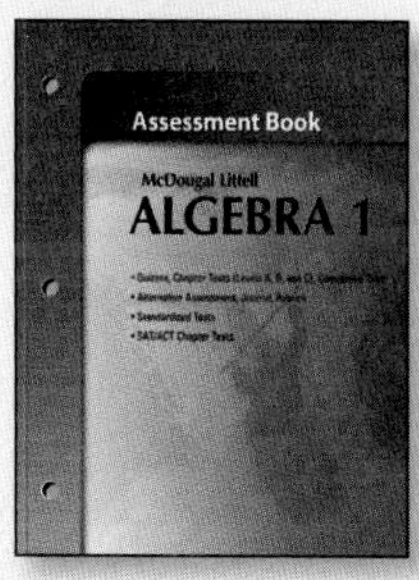

Benchmark Tests

Tests correlated to the Remediation Book

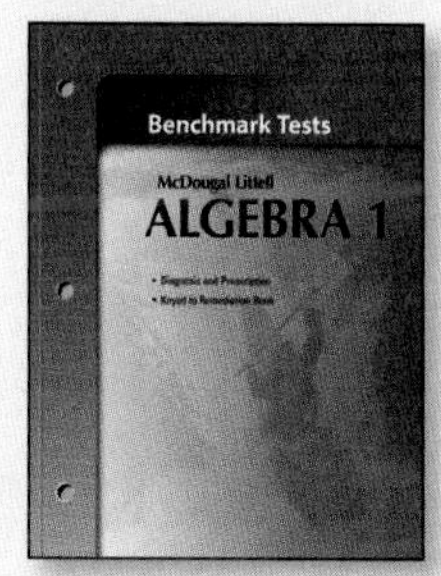

Remediation Book

Remediation lessons and quizzes

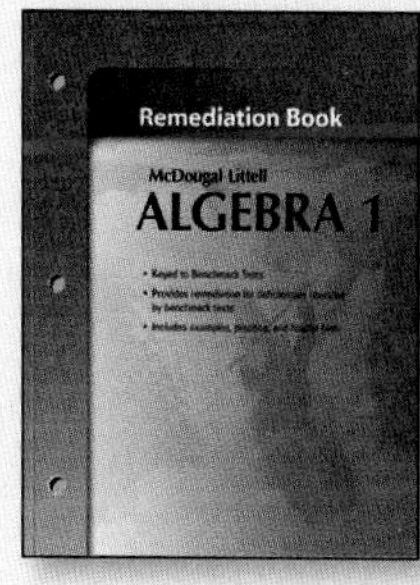

Activity Generator

- Leveled activities (A, B, C) for each lesson
- Teaching commentary to help you guide students from concrete to abstract

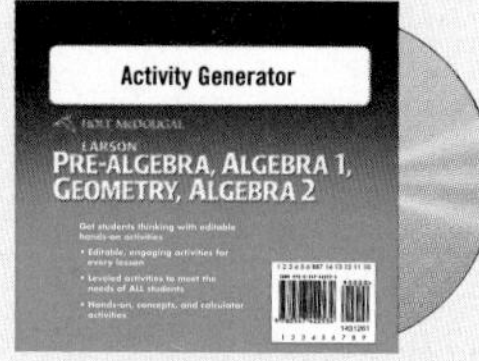

Test Generator

Develop customized tests, practice sheets, and answer keys

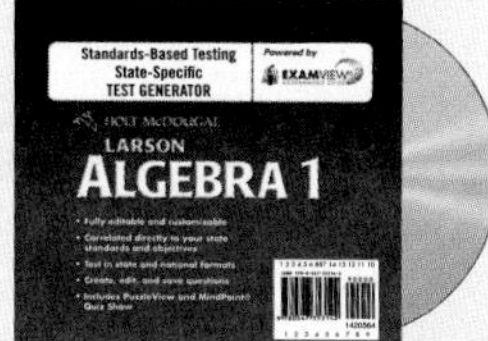

@HomeTutor

- Animated examples and instruction
- Self-scoring exercises
- Customized student progress reports

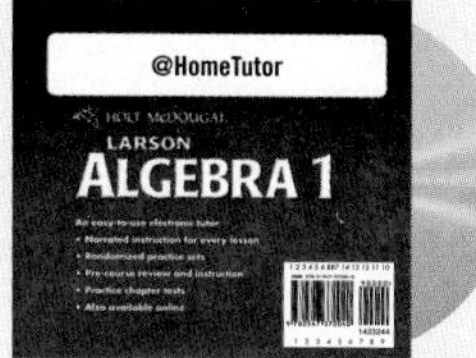

McDougal Littell Assessment System

- Innovative standards-based system
- Helps you test, score, report, and reteach
- Tests and answer sheets can be printed on plain paper

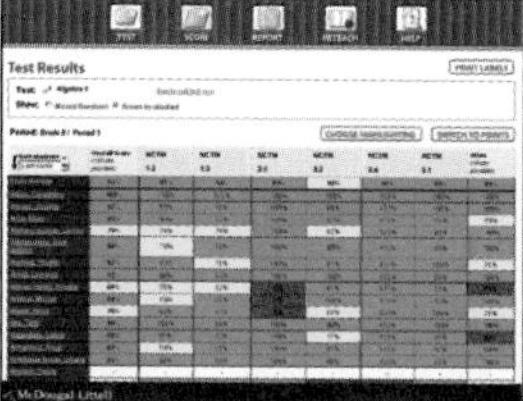

Planning the Chapter

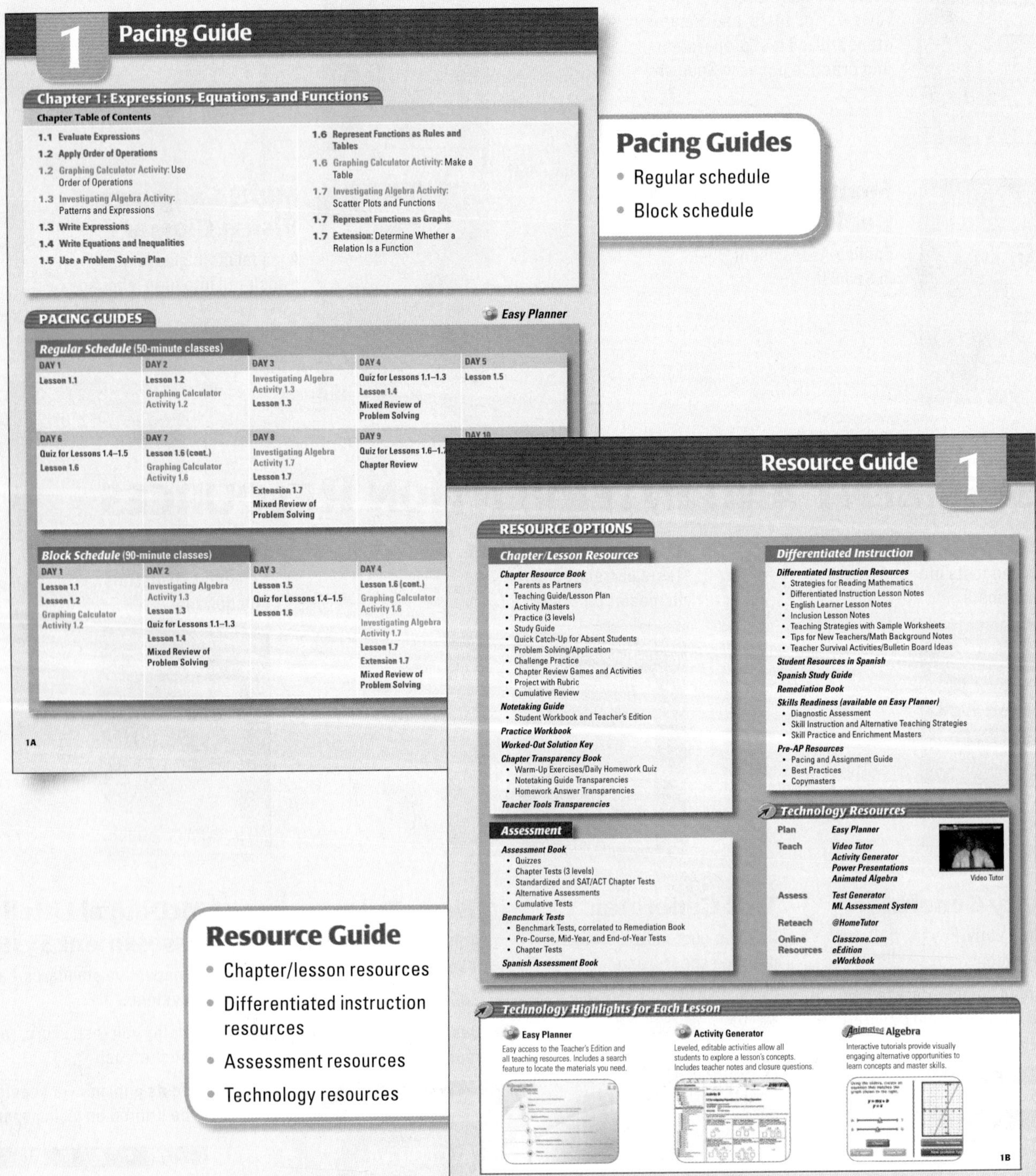

1 Pacing Guide

Chapter 1: Expressions, Equations, and Functions

Chapter Table of Contents

PACING GUIDES Easy Planner

Regular Schedule (50-minute classes)

DAY 1	DAY 2	DAY 3	DAY 4	DAY 5
Lesson 1.1	Lesson 1.2 Graphing Calculator Activity 1.2	Investigating Algebra Activity 1.3 Lesson 1.3	Quiz for Lessons 1.1–1.3 Lesson 1.4 Mixed Review of Problem Solving	Lesson 1.5
DAY 6	**DAY 7**	**DAY 8**	**DAY 9**	**DAY 10**
Quiz for Lessons 1.4–1.5 Lesson 1.6	Lesson 1.6 (cont.) Graphing Calculator Activity 1.6	Investigating Algebra Activity 1.7 Lesson 1.7 Extension 1.7 Mixed Review of Problem Solving	Quiz for Lessons 1.6–1.7 Chapter Review	

Block Schedule (90-minute classes)

DAY 1	DAY 2	DAY 3	DAY 4
Lesson 1.1 Lesson 1.2 Graphing Calculator Activity 1.2	Investigating Algebra Activity 1.3 Lesson 1.3 Quiz for Lessons 1.1–1.3 Lesson 1.4 Mixed Review of Problem Solving	Lesson 1.5 Quiz for Lessons 1.4–1.5 Lesson 1.6	Lesson 1.6 (cont.) Graphing Calculator Activity 1.6 Investigating Algebra Activity 1.7 Lesson 1.7 Extension 1.7 Mixed Review of Problem Solving

1A

Resource Guide 1

RESOURCE OPTIONS

Chapter/Lesson Resources

Chapter Resource Book
- Parents as Partners
- Teaching Guide/Lesson Plan
- Activity Masters
- Practice (3 levels)
- Study Guide
- Quick Catch-Up for Absent Students
- Problem Solving/Application
- Challenge Practice
- Chapter Review Games and Activities
- Project with Rubric
- Cumulative Review

Notetaking Guide
- Student Workbook and Teacher's Edition

Practice Workbook

Worked-Out Solution Key

Chapter Transparency Book
- Warm-Up Exercises/Daily Homework Quiz
- Notetaking Guide Transparencies
- Homework Answer Transparencies

Teacher Tools Transparencies

Assessment

Assessment Book
- Quizzes
- Chapter Tests (3 levels)
- Standardized and SAT/ACT Chapter Tests
- Alternative Assessments
- Cumulative Tests

Benchmark Tests
- Benchmark Tests, correlated to Remediation Book
- Pre-Course, Mid-Year, and End-of-Year Tests
- Chapter Tests

Spanish Assessment Book

Differentiated Instruction

Differentiated Instruction Resources
- Strategies for Reading Mathematics
- Differentiated Instruction Lesson Notes
- English Learner Lesson Notes
- Inclusion Lesson Notes
- Teaching Strategies with Sample Worksheets
- Tips for New Teachers/Math Background Notes
- Teacher Survival Activities/Bulletin Board Ideas

Student Resources in Spanish

Spanish Study Guide

Remediation Book

Skills Readiness (available on Easy Planner)
- Diagnostic Assessment
- Skill Instruction and Alternative Teaching Strategies
- Skill Practice and Enrichment Masters

Pre-AP Resources
- Pacing and Assignment Guide
- Best Practices
- Copymasters

Technology Resources

Plan	*Easy Planner*
Teach	*Video Tutor* *Activity Generator* *Power Presentations* *Animated Algebra*
Assess	*Test Generator* *ML Assessment System*
Reteach	*@HomeTutor*
Online Resources	*Classzone.com* *eEdition* *eWorkbook*

Video Tutor

Technology Highlights for Each Lesson

Easy Planner Easy access to the Teacher's Edition and all teaching resources. Includes a search feature to locate the materials you need.

Activity Generator Leveled, editable activities allow all students to explore a lesson's concepts. Includes teacher notes and closure questions.

Animated Algebra Interactive tutorials provide visually engaging alternative opportunities to learn concepts and master skills.

1B

Pacing Guides
- Regular schedule
- Block schedule

Resource Guide
- Chapter/lesson resources
- Differentiated instruction resources
- Assessment resources
- Technology resources

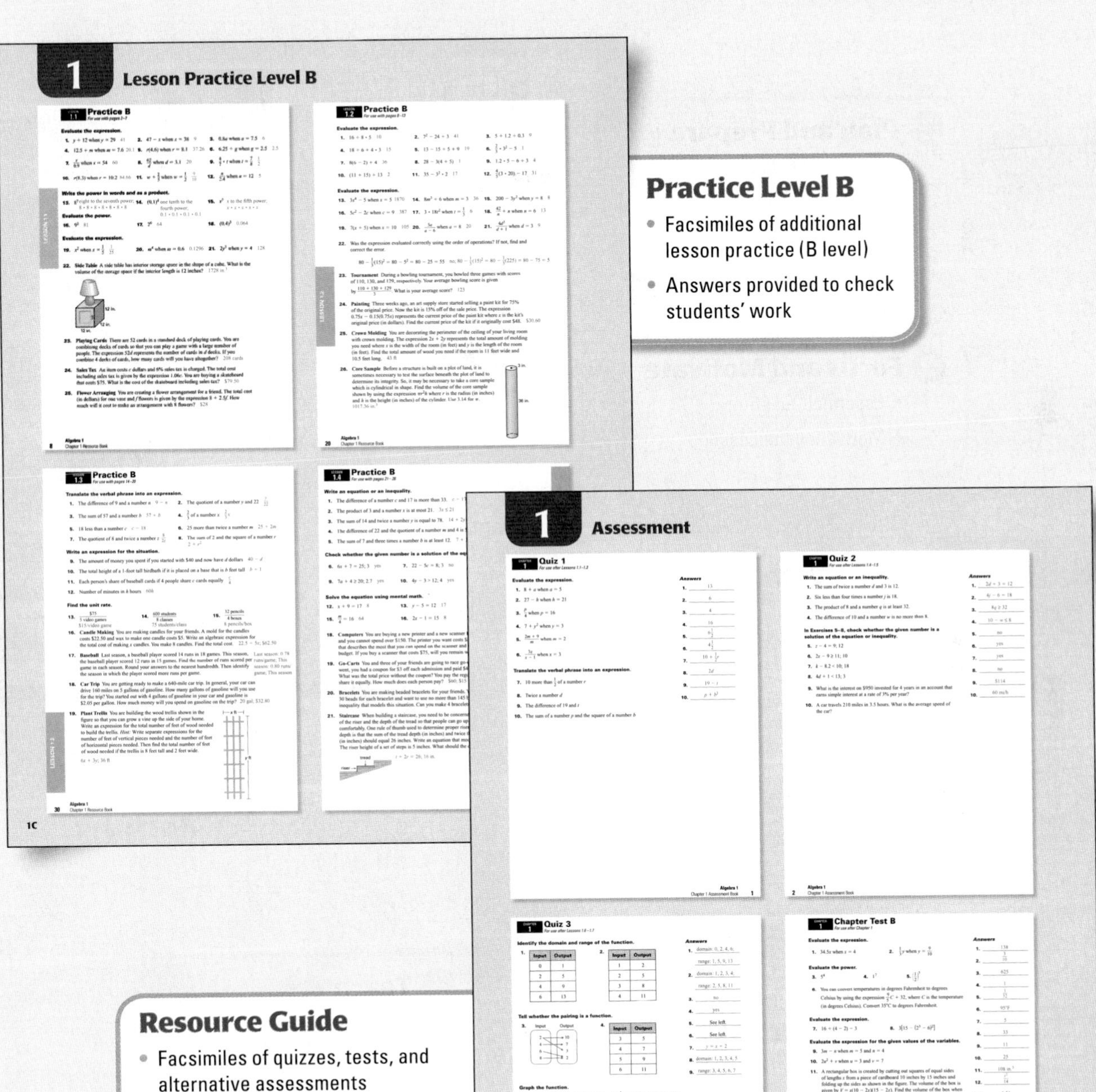

Practice Level B

- Facsimiles of additional lesson practice (B level)
- Answers provided to check students' work

Resource Guide

- Facsimiles of quizzes, tests, and alternative assessments
- Answers provided for easy grading

Planning the Lesson

1 Plan and Prepare

- Warm-Up Exercises
- Notetaking Guide
- Pacing summary

2 Focus and Motivate

- Essential Question
- Motivating the Lesson

3 Teach

- Extra Example for each example in the book
- Key Questions to Ask for examples in the book
- Closing the Lesson summary and Essential Question at the end of each lesson
- Differentiated Instruction notes

4.3 Graph Using Intercepts

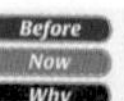

Before: You graphed a linear equation using a table of values.
Now: You will graph a linear equation using intercepts.
Why: So you can find a submersible's location, as in Example 5.

Key Vocabulary
- *x*-intercept
- *y*-intercept

You can use the fact that two points determine a line to graph a linear equation. Two convenient points are the points where the graph crosses the axes.

An ***x*-intercept** of a graph is the *x*-coordinate of a point where the graph crosses the *x*-axis. A ***y*-intercept** of a graph is the *y*-coordinate of a point where the graph crosses the *y*-axis.

To find the *x*-intercept of the graph of a linear equation, find the value of *x* when $y = 0$. To find the *y*-intercept of the graph, find the value of *y* when $x = 0$.

EXAMPLE 1 Find the intercepts of the graph of an equation

Find the *x*-intercept and the *y*-intercept of the graph of $2x + 7y = 28$.

Solution

To find the *x*-intercept, substitute 0 for *y* and solve for *x*.

$2x + 7y = 28$ Write original equation.
$2x + 7(0) = 28$ Substitute 0 for *y*.
$x = \frac{28}{2} = 14$ Solve for *x*.

To find the *y*-intercept, substitute 0 for *x* and solve for *y*.

$2x + 7y = 28$ Write original equation.
$2(0) + 7y = 28$ Substitute 0 for *x*.
$y = \frac{28}{7} = 4$ Solve for *y*.

…intercept is 14. The *y*-intercept is 4.

…PRACTICE for Example 1

…*x*-intercept and the *y*-intercept of the graph of the equation.

…$+ 2y = 6$ 2, 3   2. $4x - 2y = 10$ 2.5, −5   3. $-3x + 5y = -15$ 5, −3

4.3 Graph Using Intercepts 225

1 PLAN AND PREPARE

Warm-Up Exercises
Transparency Available
Evaluate the expression when $x = -3$.
1. $3x + 4$ −5
2. $-2x + 6$ 12
3. $4x - 3$ −15
4. The amount *a* that a taxi service charges is given by $a = 1.5m$ where *m* is the number of miles. Find *a* when *m* is 7. $10.50

Notetaking Guide
Transparency Available
Promotes interactive learning and notetaking skills.

Pacing
Basic: 1 day
Average: 1 day
Advanced: 1 day
Block: 0.5 block with 4.2
- See *Teaching Guide/Lesson Plan.*

2 FOCUS AND MOTIVATE

Essential Question
Big Idea 1, p. 205
How do you use intercepts to graph equations? **Tell students they will learn how to answer this question by finding and using the *x*- and *y*-intercepts of the graph of an equation.**

NCTM STANDARDS
Standard 3: Specify locations using coordinate geometry
Standard 10: Use representations to communicate mathematical ideas

Guide

Workbooks
- Notetaking Guide
- Practice Workbook

Teaching Options
- **Power Presentations** provides dynamic electronic teaching resources for the classroom.
- **Activity Generator** provides editable activities for all ability levels.

Interactive Technology
- Easy Planner
- Power Presentations
- Activity Generator
- Animated Algebra
- Test Generator
- Online Quiz
- eWorkbook
- eEdition
- @HomeTutor

Resources for English Learners
- Spanish Study Guide
- Multi-Language Visual Glossary
- Student Resources in Spanish

See also the *Differentiated Instruction Resources* for more strategies for meeting individual needs.

225

Motivating the Lesson
You know that your school sells T-shirts and sweatshirts with the school name on them. T-shirts cost $9 and sweatshirts cost $12. You have $144. By writing an equation and finding the intercepts of the graph of the equation, you can find the possible numbers of T-shirts and sweatshirts you can buy.

3 TEACH

Extra Example 1
Find the *x*-intercept and the *y*-intercept of the graph of $3x - 4y = 12$. ***x*-intercept: 4, *y*-intercept: −3**

Key Question to Ask for Example 1
- What coordinates are associated with the *x*-intercept and the *y*-intercept? **(14, 0), (0, 4)**

Extra Example 2
Graph the equation $4x + 8y = 24$.

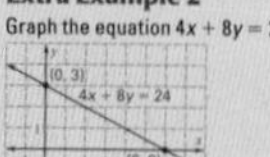

Key Question to Ask for Example 2
- Why is using intercepts an efficient way to graph an equation? **Since $x = 0$ and $y = 0$, it is easier to find the intercepts than other points on the line.**

Animated Algebra classzone.com

An **Animated Algebra** activity is available online for **Example 2.** This activity is also part of **Power Presentations.**

EXAMPLE 2 Use intercepts to graph an equation

Graph the equation $x + 2y = 4$.

Solution

STEP 1 Find the intercepts.

$x + 2y = 4$ $x + 2y = 4$
$x + 2(0) = 4$ $0 + 2y = 4$
$x = 4$ ← *x*-intercept $y = 2$ ← *y*-intercept

STEP 2 Plot points. The *x*-intercept is 4, so plot the point (4, 0). The *y*-intercept is 2, so plot the point (0, 2). Draw a line through the points.

Animated Algebra at classzone.com

CHECK A GRAPH Be sure to check the graph by finding a third solution of the equation and checking to see that the corresponding point is on the graph.

EXAMPLE 3 Use a graph to find intercepts

The graph crosses the *x*-axis at (2, 0). The *x*-intercept is 2. The graph crosses the *y*-axis at (0, −1). The *y*-intercept is −1.

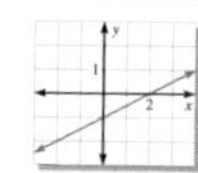

GUIDED PRACTICE for Examples 2 and 3

4. Graph $6x + 7y = 42$. Label the points where the line crosses the axes. **See margin.**
5. Identify the *x*-intercept and the *y*-intercept of the graph shown at the right. **−4, 2**

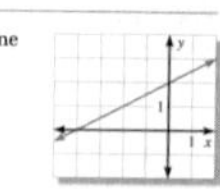

KEY CONCEPT *For Your Notebook*

Relating Intercepts, Points, and Graphs

Intercepts	Points
The *x* intercept of a graph is *a*.	The graph crosses the *x*-axis at (*a*, 0).
The *y*-intercept of a graph is *b*.	The graph crosses the *y*-axis at (0, *b*).

226 Chapter 4 Graphing Linear Equations and Functions

Differentiated Instruction

Visual Learners To help students remember how to find the intercepts in problems similar to Example 2, have them make the following table.

x-intercept	$x = 0$
y-intercept	$y = 0$

Have them connect the entries in this table with an "X," pairing "*x*-intercept" with "$y = 0$" and pairing "*y*-intercept" with "$x = 0$." See also the *Differentiated Instruction Resources* for more strategies.

226

④ Practice and Apply

- Assignment Guide
- Differentiated Instruction
- Homework Check exercises
- Extra Practice references

4.3 EXERCISES

HOMEWORK KEY
- ○ = WORKED-OUT SOLUTIONS on p. WS8 for Exs. 21 and 47
- ★ = STANDARDIZED TEST PRACTICE Exs. 2, 37, 41, 49, and 50
- ◆ = MULTIPLE REPRESENTATIONS Ex. 44

SKILL PRACTICE

A

1. **VOCABULARY** Copy and complete: The _?_ of the graph of an equation is the value of x when y is zero. *x*-intercept

2. ★ **WRITING** What are the x-intercept and the y-intercept of the line passing through the points $(0, 3)$ and $(-4, 0)$? *Explain.*

2. -4, 3; the x-intercept is when y is 0, so the point $(-4, 0)$ gives the x-intercept. The y-intercept is when x is 0, so the point $(0, 3)$ gives the y-intercept.

3. **ERROR ANALYSIS** *Describe* and correct the error in finding the intercepts of the line shown. The intercepts are switched around; the x-intercept is -2, and the y-intercept is 1.

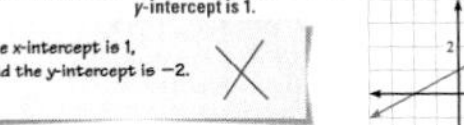

EXAMPLE 1 on p. 225 for Exs. 4–15

FINDING INTERCEPTS Find the x-intercept and the y-intercept of the graph of the equation.

4. $5x - y = 35$ 7, -35
5. $3x - 3y = 9$ 3, -3
6. $-3x + 9y = -18$ 6, -2
7. $4x + y = 4$ 1, 4
8. $2x + y = 10$ 5, 10
9. $2x - 8y = 24$ 12, -3
10. $3x + 0.5y = 6$ 2, 12
11. $0.2x + 3.2y = 12.8$ 64, 4
12. $y = 2x + 24$ -12, 24
13. $y = -14x + 7$ $\frac{1}{2}$, 7
14. $y = -4.8x + 1.2$ 0.25, 1.2
15. $y = \frac{3}{5}x - 12$ 20, -12

EXAMPLE 2 on p. 226 for Exs. 16–27

GRAPHING LINES Graph the equation. Label the points where the line crosses the axes. 16–27. See margin.

16. $y = x + 3$
17. $y = x - 2$
18. $y = 4x - 8$
19. $y = 5 + 10x$
20. $y = -2 + 8x$
21. (circled) $y = -4x + 3$
22. $3x + y = 15$
23. $x - 4y = 18$
24. $8x - 5y = 80$
25. $-2x + 5y = 15$
26. $0.5x + 3y = 9$
27. $y = \frac{1}{2}x + \frac{1}{4}$

EXAMPLE 3 on p. 226 for Exs. 28–30

USING GRAPHS TO FIND INTERCEPTS Identify the x-intercept and the y-intercept of the graph.

28. 29. 30.

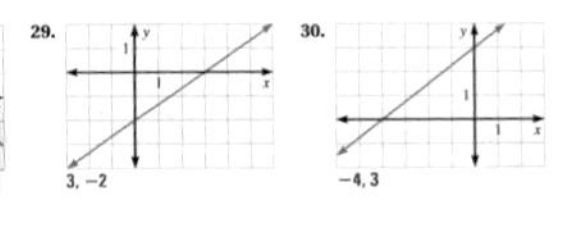

29. 3, -2 30. -4, 3

④ PRACTICE AND APPLY

Assignment Guide

Answer Transparencies available for all exercises

Basic:
Day 1: EP p. 940 Exs. 1–7 odd
pp. 229–232
Exs. 1–10, 16–21, 28–33, 37, 44–47, 51–56

Average:
Day 1: pp. 229–232
Exs. 1–3, 10–15, 22–27, 29, 30, 34–41, 44–49, 51–55 odd

Advanced:
Day 1: pp. 229–232
Exs. 1, 2, 12–15, 24–27, 29, 30, 35–37, 39–43*, 46–50*, 52–56 even

Block:
pp. 229–232
Exs. 1–3, 10–15, 22–27, 29, 30, 34–41, 44–49, 51–55 odd (with 4.2)

Differentiated Instruction

See *Differentiated Instruction Resources* for suggestions on addressing the needs of a diverse classroom.

Homework Check

For a quick check of student understanding of key concepts, go over the following exercises:

Basic: 6, 17, 28, 44, 45
Average: 11, 24, 29, 46, 48
Advanced: 13, 26, 30, 48, 49

Extra Practice

- Student Edition, p. 941
- Chapter Resource Book: Practice levels A, B, C

Practice Worksheet

An easily-readable reduced practice page (with answers) for this lesson can be found on p. 204D.

16–27. See Additional Answers beginning on p. AA1.

⑤ ASSESS AND RETEACH

Daily Homework Quiz

Transparency Available

1. Find the x-intercept and the y-intercept of the graph of $3x - y = 3$. x-int: 1, y-int: -3
2. A recycling company pays \$1 per used ink jet cartridge and \$2 per used laser cartridge. The company paid a customer \$14. This situation is given by $x + 2y = 14$ where x is the number of ink jet cartridges and y the number of laser cartridges. Use intercepts to graph the equation. Give four possibilities for the number of each type of cartridge that could have been recycled. (0, 7), (6, 4), (10, 2), (14, 0)

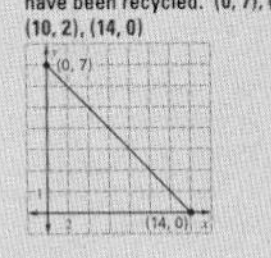

Online Quiz

Available at **classzone.com**

Diagnosis/Remediation

- Practice A, B, C in Chapter Resource Book
- Study Guide in Chapter Resource Book
- Practice Workbook
- @HomeTutor

Challenge

Additional challenge is available in the Chapter Resource Book.

Quiz

An easily-readable reduced copy of the quiz (with answers) on Lessons 4.1–4.3 from the Assessment Book can be found on p. 204G.

50b, Quiz 1–6, 13. See Additional Answers beginning on p. AA1.

C

50. ★ **EXTENDED RESPONSE** You borrow \$180 from a friend who doesn't charge you interest. You work out a payment schedule in which you will make weekly payments to your friend. The balance B (in dollars) of the loan is given by the function $B = 180 - pn$ where p is the weekly payment and n is the number of weeks you make payments.
    a. **Interpret** Without finding the intercepts, state what they represent.
    b. **Graph** Graph the function if you make weekly payments of \$20. See margin.
    c. **Identify** Find the domain and range of the function in part (b). How long will it take to pay back your friend? domain: $0 \le n \le 9$, range: $0 \le B \le 180$; 9 wk
    d. **CHALLENGE** Suppose you make payments of \$20 for three weeks. Then you make payments of \$15 until you have paid your friend back. How does this affect the graph? How many payments do you make? The graph is two line segments; 11 payments.

50a. The B-intercept is the balance of the loan after 0 weeks, the n-intercept is the amount of time it takes to pay off the loan.

MIXED REVIEW

REVIEW GRAPHS For help with line graphs, see p. 933.

In Exercises 51–53, use the line graph, which shows the number of points Alex scored in five basketball games. *(p. 933)*

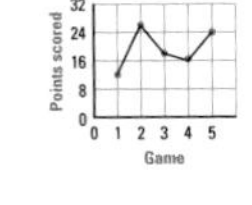

51. How many points did Alex score in game 4? 16 points
52. In which game did Alex score the most points? game 2
53. How many more points did Alex score in game 5 than in game 1? 12 more points

PREVIEW Prepare for Lesson 4.4 in Exs. 54–56.

Solve the proportion. *(p. 168)*

54. $\frac{3}{5} = \frac{x}{30}$ 18
55. $\frac{x}{x+6} = \frac{7}{6}$ -42
56. $\frac{t-3}{12} = \frac{2t-2}{9}$ $-\frac{1}{5}$

QUIZ for Lessons 4.1–4.3

Plot the point in a coordinate plane. *Describe* the location of the point. *(p. 206)* 1–3. See margin for art.

1. $(-7, 2)$ Quadrant II
2. $(0, -5)$ y-axis
3. $(2, -6)$ Quadrant IV

Graph the equation. *(p. 215)* 4–6. See margin.

4. $-4x - 2y = 12$
5. $y = -5$
6. $x = 6$

Find the x-intercept and the y-intercept of the graph of the equation. *(p. 225)*

7. $y = x + 7$ -7, 7
8. $y = x - 3$ 3, -3
9. $y = -5x + 2$ $\frac{2}{5}$, 2
10. $x + 3y = 15$ 15, 5
11. $3x - 6y = 36$ 12, -6
12. $-2x - 5y = 22$ -11, $-4\frac{2}{5}$

13. **SWIMMING POOLS** A public swimming pool that holds 45,000 gallons of water is going to be drained for maintenance at a rate of 100 gallons per minute. The amount of water w (in gallons) in the pool after t minutes is given by the function $w = 45{,}000 - 100t$. Graph the function. Identify its domain and range. How much water is in the pool after 60 minutes? How many minutes will it take to empty the pool? *(p. 225)* See margin for art; domain: $0 \le t \le 450$, range: $0 \le w \le 45{,}000$; 39,000 gal; 450 min.

⑤ Assess and Reteach

- Daily Homework Quiz
- Online Quiz for each lesson
- Diagnosis/Remediation
- Challenge

Pacing the Course

Pacing Chart The Pacing Chart below shows the number of days allotted for each chapter. The Regular Schedule requires 160 days. The Block Schedule requires 80 days. These time frames include days for review and assessment: 2 days per chapter for the Regular Schedule and 1 day per chapter for the Block Schedule. Semester and trimester divisions are indicated by blue and green rules, respectively.

	SEMESTER 1							SEMESTER 2					
CHAPTER	1	2	3	4	5	6	7	8	9	10	11	12	13
Regular Schedule	10	12	12	12	12	12	10	12	14	16	10	14	14
Block Schedule	5	6	6	6	6	6	5	6	7	8	5	7	7
	Trimester 1					Trimester 2				Trimester 3			

State Test Chapters 1–10 of *Algebra 1* focus on linear and quadratic equations in one and two variables and therefore provide the core content for the course. Chapter 11, on radical expressions and equations, prepares students for Geometry, while Chapter 12, on rational expressions and equations, looks ahead to Algebra 2. Chapter 13 provides instruction on probability and data analysis topics commonly assessed on state tests. The chart below shows two of the ways that you can pace the course in relation to your state test.

	BEFORE THE TEST	AFTER THE TEST
Option 1	**Chapters 1–10 and 13** (136 days on Regular Schedule; 68 days on Block Schedule)	**Chapters 11 and 12** (24 days on Regular Schedule; 12 days on Block Schedule)
Option 2	**Chapters 1–11** (132 days on Regular Schedule; 66 days on Block Schedule)	**Chapters 12 and 13** (28 days on Regular Schedule; 14 days on Block Schedule)

Pacing Guides The Pacing Guides for each chapter are located on the interleaved pages preceding the chapter. Portions of Chapter 1's Pacing Guides are shown below. Lessons and extensions are in blue, activities are in green, and reviews and assessments are in red.

Regular Schedule **(50-minute classes)**

DAY 1	DAY 2
Lesson 1.1	Lesson 1.2 Graphing Calculator Activity 1.2
DAY 6	**DAY 7**
Quiz for Lessons 1.4–1.5 Lesson 1.6	Lesson 1.6 (cont.) Graphing Calculator Activity 1.6

Block Schedule **(90-minute classes)**

DAY 1	DAY 2
Lesson 1.1 Lesson 1.2 Graphing Calculator Activity 1.2	Investigating Algebra Activity 1.3 Lesson 1.3 Quiz for Lessons 1.1–1.3 Lesson 1.4 Mixed Review of Problem Solving

Assignment Guides An Assignment Guide for each lesson is provided at the beginning of the lesson's exercise set. Assignments are given for four courses: basic, average, advanced, and block schedule. Lesson 1.1's Assignment Guide is shown below along with descriptions of the four courses.

Basic Course

The basic course is intended for students who enter with below-average mathematical and problem solving skills. Assignments include:

- spiral review of pre-course and on-level topics using the Skills Review Handbook and Extra Practice
- substantial work with the skills and concepts presented in the lesson
- straightforward applications of these skills and concepts
- test preparation and mixed review exercises

Average Course

The average course is intended for students who enter with typical mathematical and problem solving skills. Assignments include:

- substantial work with the skills and concepts presented in the lesson
- applications of these skills and concepts
- test preparation and mixed review exercises

Advanced Course

The advanced course is intended for students who enter with above-average mathematical and problem solving skills. Assignments include:

- substantial work with the skills and concepts presented in the lesson
- more complex applications and challenge exercises
- test preparation and mixed review exercises
- optional extra challenge exercises provided in the Chapter Resource Book ancillary

Block-Schedule Course

The block-schedule course is intended for schools that use a block schedule. It covers the same content as the regular-schedule course. The exercises assigned are comparable to the exercises for the average course.

Assignment Guide

Answer Transparencies available for all exercises

Basic:
Day 1: SRH p. 914 Exs. 11–15
pp. 5–7
Exs. 1, 2, 3–13 odd, 15–25, 27–41 odd, 48–52, 56–65

Average:
Day 1: pp. 5–7
Exs. 1, 2, 4–14 even, 15, 16–22 even, 24, 25, 26–44 even, 45, 46, 49–54, 57–65

Advanced:
Day 1: pp. 5–7
Exs. 1, 2, 10–14, 15–23 odd, 32–44 even, 45–47*, 50–63*

Block:
pp. 5–7
Exs. 1, 2, 4–14 even, 15, 16–22 even, 24, 25, 26–44 even, 45, 46, 49–54, 57–65 (with 1.2)

An exercise range marked with an asterisk (*) contains a Challenge exercise.

National Council of Teachers of Mathematics

The chart below lists the lessons and other features in the textbook that address the NCTM Content Standards. These five standards cover the content areas of number and operations, algebra, geometry, measurement, and data analysis and probability.

Content Standards

Standard	Lessons and Features
1. NUMBER AND OPERATIONS Understand numbers, ways of representing numbers, relationships among numbers, and number systems; understand meanings of operations and how they relate to one another; compute fluently and make reasonable estimates.	1.1 through 1.2 Tech. Act., 2.1, 2.2 Act. through 2.4, 2.5, 2.6, 2.7, 3.1 through 3.4 Tech. Act., 3.7, 3.7 Ext., 6.2 Act., 8.1 Act. through 8.4 Tech. Act., 8.6 Act., 11.2 Act., 11.2, 13.2 through 13.3 Tech. Act., 13.6, 13.6 Ext., Skills Review Handbook
2. ALGEBRA Understand patterns, relations, and functions; represent and analyze mathematical situations and structures using algebraic symbols; use mathematical models to represent and understand quantitative relationships; analyze change in various contexts.	1.3 Act. through 1.6, 1.7, 1.7 Ext., 2.1 Ext., 2.4 through 2.5, 3.1 Act. through 3.3, 3.5 through 3.6 Ext., 3.8, 4.2, 4.2 Ext. through 4.7, 5.1, 5.3, 5.4, 5.5, 6.1 through 6.3 Ext., 6.4 through 6.6, 6.7, 7.1 Act., 7.1, 7.2 through 7.6, 8.1 Act. through 8.2, 8.3 Act., 8.3, 8.4, 8.5 through 8.6 Ext., 9.1 through 9.8, 10.1 through 10.6, 10.7 through 10.8 Tech. Act., 11.1 through 11.4 Act., 11.5, 12.1 Act. through 12.7
3. GEOMETRY Analyze characteristics and properties of two- and three-dimensional geometric shapes and develop mathematical arguments about geometric relationships; specify locations and describe spatial relationships using coordinate geometry and other representational systems; apply transformations and use symmetry to analyze mathematical situations; use visualization, spatial reasoning, and geometric modeling to solve problems.	3.6 Ext., 4.1 through 4.2 Tech. Act., 4.3, 4.4, 4.6, 4.7, 5.1 through 5.3, 5.5, 6.3 Ext., 6.5, 6.5 Ext., 6.6, 6.7 Act., 6.7, 7.1, 7.1 Tech. Act., 7.5, 7.6, 8.5, 8.6, 9.1 Tech. Act., 10.1 through 10.3 Tech. Act., 10.5 Ext., 10.7 Act., 10.8 Tech. Act., 11.1, 11.1 Tech. Act., 11.4 Act. through 11.5, 12.1 Act. through 12.2, 12.3 Tech. Act., Skills Review Handbook
4. MEASUREMENT Understand measurable attributes of objects and the units, systems, and processes of measurement; apply appropriate techniques, tools, and formulas to determine measurements.	1.5, 3.6, 3.6 Ext., 3.8, 4.4 Act., 4.4, 5.1 Act., 5.1, Skills Review Handbook
5. DATA ANALYSIS AND PROBABILITY Formulate questions that can be addressed with data and collect, organize, and display relevant data to answer them; select and use appropriate statistical methods to analyze data; develop and evaluate inferences and predictions that are based on data; understand and apply basic concepts of probability.	1.7 Act., 2.6, 5.6 through 5.7 Tech. Act., 10.8, 10.8 Tech. Act., 13.1 Act. through 13.3, 13.4 through 13.8 Tech. Act., Skills Review Handbook

The chart below lists the lessons and other features in the textbook that address the NCTM Process Standards. These five standards cover the processes of problem solving, reasoning and proof, communication, connections, and representation.

Process Standards

Standard	Lessons and features
6. PROBLEM SOLVING Build new mathematical knowledge through problem solving; solve problems that arise in mathematics and in other contexts; apply and adapt a variety of appropriate strategies to solve problems; monitor and reflect on the process of mathematical problem solving.	Occurs throughout. E.g.: 1.3 through 1.5, 2.4, 2.5, 2.5 PSW, 3.2, 3.5, 3.8, 4.2, 4.3, 4.6, 5.1, 5.2, 5.3, 5.4, 5.7, 6.3, 6.3 PSW, 6.4, 7.2, 7.3, 7.6, 8.2, 8.4, 9.2, 9.4, 9.5, 9.6 through 9.8, 10.3, 10.4, 10.5, 10.7, 10.8, 11.2, 11.3, 11.4, 11.5 PSW, 12.1, 12.3, 12.5, 12.7, 13.1, 13.2, 13.3, 13.4, 13.5, Skills Review Handbook
7. REASONING AND PROOF Recognize reasoning and proof as fundamental aspects of mathematics; make and investigate mathematical conjectures; develop and evaluate mathematical arguments and proofs; select and use various types of reasoning and methods of proof.	Occurs throughout. E.g.: 2.1, 2.7 Act., 2.7 Ext., 4.7, 5.5 Act., 6.4 Act., 6.4, 7.3, 11.2 Ext., 13.1 Act.; Reasoning exs.: 2.4, 4.1, 5.2, 8.2, 10.2, 13.3; Error analysis exs.: 1.6, 3.3, 6.5, 7.2, 9.6, 11.1, 12.4
8. COMMUNICATION Organize and consolidate their mathematical thinking through communication; communicate their mathematical thinking coherently and clearly to peers, teachers, and others; analyze and evaluate the mathematical thinking and strategies of others; use the language of mathematics to express mathematical ideas precisely.	Occurs throughout. E.g.: 1.5, 1.7 Act., 2.7 Act., 4.5, 4.6, 4.7, 5.1 Tech. Act., 5.2, 7.6, 8.3, 9.2, 9.3, 10.6, 12.3 Act., 13.1 Ext., 13.5, 13.7, 13.8; Explain exs.: 2.4, 3.6, 5.3, 6.1, 8.1, 10.1, 11.4, 12.7; Writing exs.: 1.7, 3.3, 4.1, 6.6, 7.4, 9.8, 11.2, 13.7
9. CONNECTIONS Recognize and use connections among mathematical ideas; understand how mathematical ideas interconnect and build on one another to produce a coherent whole; recognize and apply mathematics in contexts outside of mathematics.	Occurs throughout. E.g.: 1.7 Act., 1.7, 2.3, 2.4 Ext., 3.3, 3.4, 3.5 through 3.6 Ext., 4.5, 4.6, 5.3 Ext., 5.5 through 5.7 Tech. Act., 6.7, 7.1, 7.1 Tech. Act., 7.5, 8.3 Ext., 8.5 through 8.6 Ext., 10.7 Act. through 10.8 Tech. Act., 11.4 Act., 11.4, 11.5, 12.2, 12.7
10. REPRESENTATION Create and use representations to organize, record, and communicate mathematical ideas; select, apply, and translate among mathematical representations to solve problems; use representations to model and interpret physical, social, and mathematical phenomena.	Occurs throughout. E.g.: 1.3, 1.4, 1.6 through 1.7 Ext., 2.1 Ext., 2.3 Tech. Act., 3.1 Act., 3.4, 3.4 Tech. Act., 4.1 through 4.3, 4.4, 4.5 Ext. through 4.7, 5.1, 5.3 Ext., 5.6 through 5.7 Tech. Act., 6.1, 6.2, 6.3 Ext., 6.4 Act., 6.4 Tech. Act., 6.5 Ext., 6.7 Act., 6.7, 7.1 Act. through 7.1 Tech. Act., 7.4, 7.5, 8.5 through 8.6, 9.1, 9.2, 9.3, 9.5 Act., 9.6 Act. through 9.8, 10.1, 10.3, 10.5 Act., 10.8 Act. through 10.8 Tech. Act., 11.1, 12.2 Act., 12.2, 12.3 Tech. Act., 12.7, 13.4, 13.7 through 13.8 Tech. Act.; Multiple Representations examples and exercises: 3.4, 5.7, 8.5, 10.8, 11.1, 13.4

Achieve's ADP Algebra I End-of-Course Exam

Operations on Numbers and Expressions

Standard	Objective	Correlation
O1. NUMBER SENSE AND OPERATIONS	a. Reasoning with real numbers	Lessons 2.1, 2.7; Extension 2.7
	b. Using ratios, rates and proportions	Lessons 1.3, 3.5, 3.6, 3.7; Extensions 3.6, 3.7
	c. Using numerical exponential expressions	Lessons 8.1–8.4
	d. Using numerical radical expressions	Lessons 11.2, 11.4, 11.5
O2. ALGEBRAIC EXPRESSIONS	a. Using algebraic exponential expressions	Lessons 8.1–8.3, 12.3, 12.4
	b. Operating with polynomial expressions	Lessons 9.1–9.3
	c. Factoring polynomial expressions	Lessons 9.4–9.8
	d. Using algebraic radical expressions	Lesson 11.2

Linear Relationships

Standard	Objective	Correlation
L1. LINEAR FUNCTIONS	a. Representing linear functions in multiple ways	Chapters 4, 5
	b. Analyzing linear functions	Chapters 4, 5
	c. Graphing linear functions involving absolute value	Extension 6.5
	d. Using linear models	Chapters 4, 5
L2. LINEAR EQUATIONS AND INEQUALITIES	a. Solving linear equations and inequalities	Lessons 3.1–3.4, 6.1–6.4
	b. Solving equations involving absolute value	Lesson 6.5
	c. Graphing linear inequalities	Lesson 6.7
	d. Solving systems of linear equations	Lessons 7.1–7.5
	e. Modeling with single-variable linear equations, one- or two-variable inequalities or systems of equations	Lessons 3.1–3.4, 6.1–6.5, 6.7, 7.1–7.5

Non-Linear Relationships

Standard	Objective	Correlation
N1. NON-LINEAR FUNCTIONS	a. Representing quadratic functions in multiple ways	Lessons 10.1–10.3, 10.8; Extensions 10.2, 10.5
	b. Distinguishing between function types	Lessons 5.1–5.3, 5.4, 8.5, 8.6, 10.1–10.3, 10.5; Extensions 5.3, 8.6, 10.2, 10.5
	c. Using quadratic models	Chapter 10
N2. NON-LINEAR EQUATIONS	a. Solving literal equations	Lessons 3.8, 11.2
	b. Solving quadratic equations	Lessons 9.4–9.7, 10.3–10.6

Data, Statistics and Probability

Standard	Objective	Correlation
D1. DATA AND STATISTICAL ANALYSIS	a. Interpreting linear trends in data	Lessons 5.6, 5.7
	b. Comparing data using summary statistics	Lessons 13.6–13.8; Extension 13.6; Skills Review Handbook
	c. Evaluating data-based reports in the media	Lessons 13.5, 13.6; Skills Review Handbook
D2. PROBABILITY	a. Using counting principles	Lessons 13.2, 13.3; Skills Review Handbook
	b. Determining probability	Lessons 13.1–13.4

National Assessment of Educational Progress

The chart below lists the lessons and features in the textbook that address the topics assessed by NAEP.

Number Properties and Operations

Topic	Lessons and features
1. Number sense	2.1, 2.2 Act., 2.2, 2.7, 6.1, 6.2, 8.4, 11.5, 11.5 Act., 13.1–13.3, Skills Review Handbook
2. Estimation	1.4, 1.5, 2.7, 3.1, 3.2, 5.6, 5.7, 8.2, 10.7 Act., 10.7, Skills Review Handbook
3. Number operations	1.1–1.3, 1.5, 2.1–2.4, 2.6, 3.6 Ext., 3.7, 4.4, 7.3, 7.4, 8.1, 8.2, 9.1, 9.2, 11.4, 11.4 Act., 13.1–13.6
4. Ratios and proportional reasoning	3.5–3.7, 13.3–13.6, Skills Review Handbook
5. Properties of number and operations	1.1, 2.1–2.6, 9.5 Act.–9.8
6. Mathematical reasoning using number	2.5 (Ex. 49), 2.7 Ext., 3.6 (Ex. 31), 8.1 (Ex. 51), 8.2 (Ex. 47)

Measurement

Topic	Lessons and features
1. Measuring physical attributes	1.5, 3.3 (Exs. 33, 34), 3.4 (Exs. 44–46), 3.5, 3.8, 8.5, 8.6, 10.3 (Exs. 47–49), 10.4 (Exs. 47–49), 11.4 Act.
2. Systems of measurement	1.5, 3.1 (Ex. 60), 11.4, 11.5, Skills Review Handbook
3. Measurement in triangles	3.6 Ext.

Geometry

Topic	Lessons and features
1. Dimension and shape	1.5, 11.5, 12.1 Act., Skills Review Handbook
2. Transformation of shapes and preservation of properties	3.6, 9.2 Act., 9.5 Act., 9.6 Act., 11.4 Act., 10.5 Ext., Skills Review Handbook
3. Relationships between geometric figures	5.5, 7.1 Act.–7.6, 11.4 Act., 11.4, Skills Review Handbook
4. Position, direction, and coordinate geometry	5.5, 7.5, 10.1 (Ex. 40), 11.4, 11.5 Act., 11.5
5. Mathematical reasoning in geometry	11.4 Act., 11.4, 11.5 (Ex. 51)

Data Analysis, Statistics, and Probability

Topic	Lessons and features
1. Data representation	1.7 Act., 1.7, 4.1, 5.6 Act., 5.6, 5.7 Act., 5.7, 13.7 Act., 13.7, 13.8 Act., 13.8
2. Characteristics of data sets	6.6, 10.8 Act., 13.4–13.8
3. Experiments and samples	13.5, 13.6
4. Probability	13.1–13.6
5. Mathematical reasoning with data	1.5, 5.6 Ext., 13.6 (Ex. 22), Skills Review Handbook

Algebra

Topic	Lessons and features
1. Patterns, relations, and functions	1.6, 1.7, 1.7 Ext., 4.1–4.7, 5.3, 5.3 Ext., 5.5–5.7, 10.8, 11.4 Act.
2. Algebraic representations	1.3, 1.5–1.7, 4.1, 4.3, 7.1–7.5, 8.5, 8.6, 10.8, 11.1, 12.2
3. Variables, expressions, and operations	1.1–1.6, 3.1–3.8, 5.1–5.3, 7.1–7.6, 8.1–8.6
4. Equations and inequalities	1.4, 3.1–3.4, 3.6–3.8, 4.3–4.5, 5.1–5.5, 6.1–6.6, 7.1–7.6
5. Mathematical reasoning in algebra	2.1–2.7 Ext., 6.4 Act.–6.6

1

Pacing Guide

Chapter 1: Expressions, Equations, and Functions

Chapter Table of Contents

PACING GUIDES

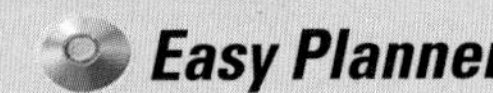

Regular Schedule (50-minute classes)

DAY 1	DAY 2	DAY 3	DAY 4	DAY 5
Lesson 1.1	Lesson 1.2 Graphing Calculator Activity 1.2	Investigating Algebra Activity 1.3 Lesson 1.3	Quiz for Lessons 1.1–1.3 Lesson 1.4 Mixed Review of Problem Solving	Lesson 1.5
DAY 6	**DAY 7**	**DAY 8**	**DAY 9**	**DAY 10**
Quiz for Lessons 1.4–1.5 Lesson 1.6	Lesson 1.6 (cont.) Graphing Calculator Activity 1.6	Investigating Algebra Activity 1.7 Lesson 1.7 Extension 1.7 Mixed Review of Problem Solving	Quiz for Lessons 1.6–1.7 Chapter Review	Chapter Test

Block Schedule (90-minute classes)

DAY 1	DAY 2	DAY 3	DAY 4	DAY 5
Lesson 1.1 Lesson 1.2 Graphing Calculator Activity 1.2	Investigating Algebra Activity 1.3 Lesson 1.3 Quiz for Lessons 1.1–1.3 Lesson 1.4 Mixed Review of Problem Solving	Lesson 1.5 Quiz for Lessons 1.4–1.5 Lesson 1.6	Lesson 1.6 (cont.) Graphing Calculator Activity 1.6 Investigating Algebra Activity 1.7 Lesson 1.7 Extension 1.7 Mixed Review of Problem Solving	Quiz for Lessons 1.6–1.7 Chapter Review Chapter Test

RESOURCE OPTIONS

Chapter/Lesson Resources

Chapter Resource Book
- Parents as Partners
- Teaching Guide/Lesson Plan
- Activity Masters
- Practice (3 levels)
- Study Guide
- Quick Catch-Up for Absent Students
- Problem Solving/Application
- Challenge Practice
- Chapter Review Games and Activities
- Project with Rubric
- Cumulative Review

Notetaking Guide
- Student Workbook and Teacher's Edition

Practice Workbook

Worked-Out Solution Key

Chapter Transparency Book
- Warm-Up Exercises/Daily Homework Quiz
- Notetaking Guide Transparencies
- Homework Answer Transparencies

Teacher Tools Transparencies

Assessment

Assessment Book
- Quizzes
- Chapter Tests (3 levels)
- Standardized and SAT/ACT Chapter Tests
- Alternative Assessments
- Cumulative Tests

Benchmark Tests
- Benchmark Tests, correlated to Remediation Book
- Pre-Course, Mid-Year, and End-of-Year Tests
- Chapter Tests

Spanish Assessment Book

Differentiated Instruction

Differentiated Instruction Resources
- Strategies for Reading Mathematics
- Differentiated Instruction Lesson Notes
- English Learner Lesson Notes
- Inclusion Lesson Notes
- Teaching Strategies with Sample Worksheets
- Tips for New Teachers/Math Background Notes
- Teacher Survival Activities/Bulletin Board Ideas

Student Resources in Spanish

Spanish Study Guide

Remediation Book

Skills Readiness (available on Easy Planner)
- Diagnostic Assessment
- Skill Instruction and Alternative Teaching Strategies
- Skill Practice and Enrichment Masters

Pre-AP Resources
- Pacing and Assignment Guide
- Best Practices
- Copymasters

Technology Resources

Plan	*Easy Planner*
Teach	*Video Tutor* *Activity Generator* *Power Presentations* *Animated Algebra*
Assess	*Test Generator* *ML Assessment System*
Reteach	*@HomeTutor*
Online Resources	*Classzone.com* *eEdition* *eWorkbook*

Video Tutor

Technology Highlights for Each Lesson

Easy Planner

Easy access to the Teacher's Edition and all teaching resources. Includes a search feature to locate the materials you need.

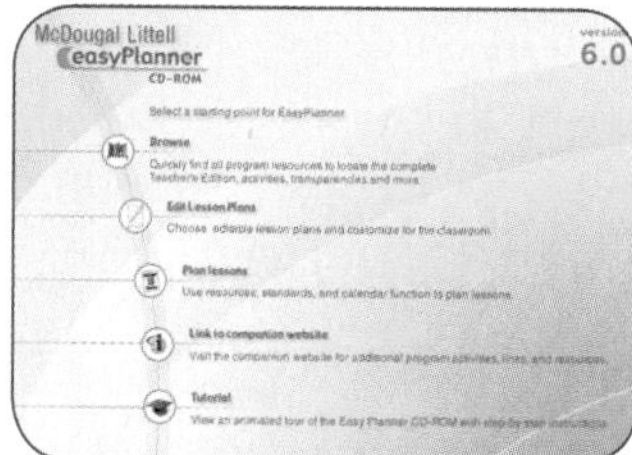

Activity Generator

Leveled, editable activities allow all students to explore a lesson's concepts. Includes teacher notes and closure questions.

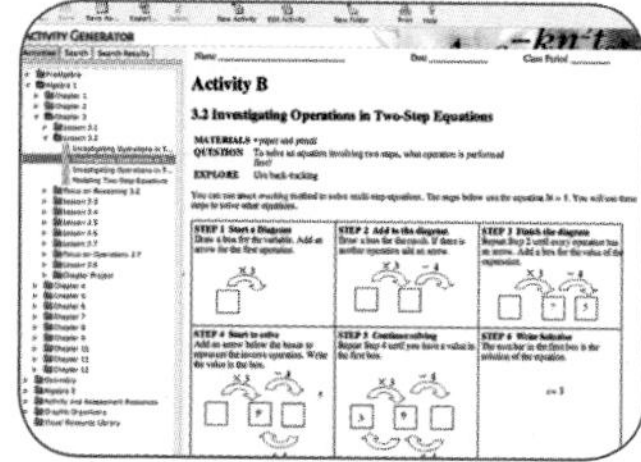

Animated Algebra

Interactive tutorials provide visually engaging alternative opportunities to learn concepts and master skills.

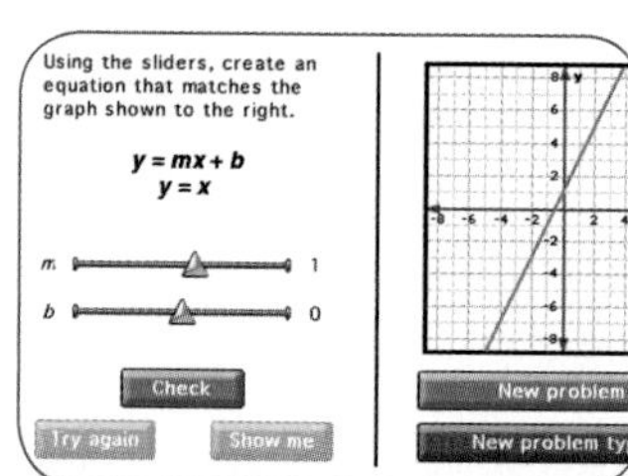

1 Lesson Practice Level B

LESSON 1.1 Practice B
For use with pages 2–7

Evaluate the expression.

1. $y + 12$ when $y = 29$ 41
2. $47 - x$ when $x = 38$ 9
3. $0.8a$ when $a = 7.5$ 6
4. $12.5 + m$ when $m = 7.6$ 20.1
5. $r(4.6)$ when $r = 8.1$ 37.26
6. $6.25 \div g$ when $g = 2.5$ 2.5
7. $\frac{x}{0.9}$ when $x = 54$ 60
8. $\frac{62}{d}$ when $d = 3.1$ 20
9. $\frac{4}{7} \cdot t$ when $t = \frac{7}{8}$ $\frac{1}{2}$
10. $r(8.3)$ when $r = 10.2$ 84.66
11. $w + \frac{2}{5}$ when $w = \frac{1}{2}$ $\frac{9}{10}$
12. $\frac{n}{2.4}$ when $n = 12$ 5

Write the power in words and as a product.

13. 8^7 eight to the seventh power; $8 \cdot 8 \cdot 8 \cdot 8 \cdot 8 \cdot 8 \cdot 8$
14. $(0.1)^4$ one tenth to the fourth power; $0.1 \cdot 0.1 \cdot 0.1 \cdot 0.1$
15. x^5 x to the fifth power; $x \cdot x \cdot x \cdot x \cdot x$

Evaluate the power.

16. 9^2 81
17. 2^6 64
18. $(0.4)^3$ 0.064

Evaluate the expression.

19. x^2 when $x = \frac{1}{5}$ $\frac{1}{25}$
20. m^4 when $m = 0.6$ 0.1296
21. $2y^3$ when $y = 4$ 128

22. **Side Table** A side table has interior storage space in the shape of a cube. What is the volume of the storage space if the interior length is 12 inches?   1728 in.[3]

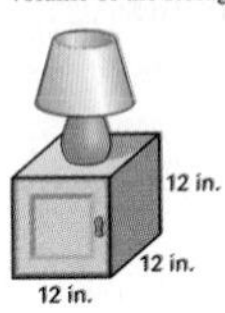

23. **Playing Cards** There are 52 cards in a standard deck of playing cards. You are combining decks of cards so that you can play a game with a large number of people. The expression $52d$ represents the number of cards in d decks. If you combine 4 decks of cards, how many cards will you have altogether?   208 cards

24. **Sales Tax** An item costs c dollars and 6% sales tax is charged. The total cost including sales tax is given by the expression $1.06c$. You are buying a skateboard that costs \$75. What is the cost of the skateboard including sales tax?   \$79.50

25. **Flower Arranging** You are creating a flower arrangement for a friend. The total cost (in dollars) for one vase and f flowers is given by the expression $8 + 2.5f$. How much will it cost to make an arrangement with 8 flowers?   \$28

LESSON 1.1

LESSON 1.2 Practice B
For use with pages 8–13

Evaluate the expression.

1. $16 \div 8 \cdot 5$ 10
2. $7^2 - 24 \div 3$ 41
3. $5 + 1.2 \div 0.3$ 9
4. $18 \div 6 + 4 \cdot 3$ 15
5. $13 - 15 \div 5 + 9$ 19
6. $\frac{2}{3} \cdot 3^2 - 5$ 1
7. $8(6 - 2) + 4$ 36
8. $28 - 3(4 + 5)$ 1
9. $1.2 \cdot 5 - 6 \div 3$ 4
10. $(11 + 15) \div 13$ 2
11. $35 - 3^2 \cdot 2$ 17
12. $\frac{4}{5}(3 \cdot 20) - 17$ 31

Evaluate the expression.

13. $3x^4 - 5$ when $x = 5$ 1870
14. $8m^3 \div 6$ when $m = 3$ 36
15. $200 - 3y^2$ when $y = 8$ 8
16. $5c^2 - 2c$ when $c = 9$ 387
17. $3 \cdot 18t^2$ when $t = \frac{1}{3}$ 6
18. $\frac{42}{n} + n$ when $n = 6$ 13
19. $7(x + 5)$ when $x = 10$ 105
20. $\frac{5a}{a - 6}$ when $a = 8$ 20
21. $\frac{4d^2}{d + 1}$ when $d = 3$ 9

22. Was the expression evaluated correctly using the order of operations? If not, find and correct the error.

$$80 - \frac{1}{3}(15)^2 = 80 - 5^2 = 80 - 25 = 55$$ no; $80 - \frac{1}{3}(15)^2 = 80 - \frac{1}{3}(225) = 80 - 75 = 5$

23. **Tournament** During a bowling tournament, you bowled three games with scores of 110, 130, and 129, respectively. Your average bowling score is given by $\frac{110 + 130 + 129}{3}$. What is your average score?   123

24. **Painting** Three weeks ago, an art supply store started selling a paint kit for 75% of the original price. Now the kit is 15% off of the sale price. The expression $0.75x - 0.15(0.75x)$ represents the current price of the paint kit where x is the kit's original price (in dollars). Find the current price of the kit if it originally cost \$48.   \$30.60

25. **Crown Molding** You are decorating the perimeter of the ceiling of your living room with crown molding. The expression $2x + 2y$ represents the total amount of molding you need where x is the width of the room (in feet) and y is the length of the room (in feet). Find the total amount of wood you need if the room is 11 feet wide and 10.5 feet long.   43 ft

26. **Core Sample** Before a structure is built on a plot of land, it is sometimes necessary to test the surface beneath the plot of land to determine its integrity. So, it may be necessary to take a core sample which is cylindrical in shape. Find the volume of the core sample shown by using the expression $\pi r^2 h$ where r is the radius (in inches) and h is the height (in inches) of the cylinder. Use 3.14 for π.   1017.36 in.[3]

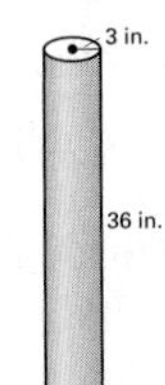

LESSON 1.2

LESSON 1.3 Practice B
For use with pages 14–20

Translate the verbal phrase into an expression.

1. The difference of 9 and a number n $9 - n$
2. The quotient of a number y and 22 $\frac{y}{22}$
3. The sum of 57 and a number b $57 + b$
4. $\frac{2}{3}$ of a number x $\frac{2}{3}x$
5. 18 less than a number c $c - 18$
6. 25 more than twice a number m $25 + 2m$
7. The quotient of 8 and twice a number z $\frac{8}{2z}$
8. The sum of 2 and the square of a number r $2 + r^2$

Write an expression for the situation.

9. The amount of money you spent if you started with \$40 and now have d dollars $40 - d$
10. The total height of a 1-foot tall birdbath if it is placed on a base that is b feet tall $b + 1$
11. Each person's share of baseball cards if 4 people share c cards equally $\frac{c}{4}$
12. Number of minutes in h hours $60h$

Find the unit rate.

13. $\frac{\$75}{5 \text{ video games}}$ \$15/video game
14. $\frac{600 \text{ students}}{8 \text{ classes}}$ 75 students/class
15. $\frac{32 \text{ pencils}}{4 \text{ boxes}}$ 8 pencils/box

16. **Candle Making** You are making candles for your friends. A mold for the candles costs \$22.50 and wax to make one candle costs \$5. Write an algebraic expression for the total cost of making x candles. You make 8 candles. Find the total cost. $22.5 + 5x$; \$62.50

17. **Baseball** Last season, a baseball player scored 14 runs in 18 games. This season, the baseball player scored 12 runs in 15 games. Find the number of runs scored per game in each season. Round your answers to the nearest hundredth. Then identify the season in which the player scored more runs per game.   Last season: 0.78 runs/game; This season: 0.80 runs/game; This season

18. **Car Trip** You are getting ready to make a 640-mile car trip. In general, your car can drive 160 miles on 5 gallons of gasoline. How many gallons of gasoline will you need for the trip? You started out with 4 gallons of gasoline in your car and gasoline is \$2.05 per gallon. How much money will you spend on gasoline on the trip?   20 gal; \$32.80

19. **Plant Trellis** You are building the wood trellis shown in the figure so that you can grow a vine up the side of your home. Write an expression for the total number of feet of wood needed to build the trellis. *Hint:* Write separate expressions for the number of feet of vertical pieces needed and the number of feet of horizontal pieces needed. Then find the total number of feet of wood needed if the trellis is 8 feet tall and 2 feet wide.

$6x + 3y$; 36 ft

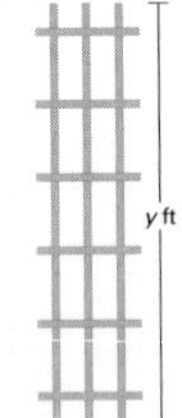

LESSON 1.3

LESSON 1.4 Practice B
For use with pages 21–26

Write an equation or an inequality.

1. The difference of a number c and 17 is more than 33. $c - 17 > 33$
2. The product of 3 and a number x is at most 21. $3x \le 21$
3. The sum of 14 and twice a number y is equal to 78. $14 + 2y = 78$
4. The difference of 22 and the quotient of a number m and 4 is 54. $22 - \frac{m}{4} = 54$
5. The sum of 7 and three times a number b is at least 12. $7 + 3b \ge 12$

Check whether the given number is a solution of the equation or inequality.

6. $6x + 7 = 25$; 3   yes
7. $22 - 5c = 8$; 3   no
8. $\frac{b}{4} - 7 = 1$; 36   no
9. $7a + 4 \ge 20$; 2.7   yes
10. $4y - 3 > 12$; 4   yes
11. $\frac{m}{3} + 14 < 33$; 9   yes

Solve the equation using mental math.

12. $x + 9 = 17$ 8
13. $y - 5 = 12$ 17
14. $8w = 48$ 6
15. $\frac{m}{4} = 16$ 64
16. $2x - 1 = 15$ 8
17. $3x + 2 = 20$ 6

18. **Computers** You are buying a new printer and a new scanner for your computer, and you cannot spend over \$150. The printer you want costs \$80. Write an inequality that describes the most that you can spend on the scanner and still stay within your budget. If you buy a scanner that costs \$75, will you remain within your budget? $80 + x \le 150$; no

19. **Go-Carts** You and three of your friends are going to race go-carts. The last time you went, you had a coupon for \$3 off each admission and paid \$48 for the 4 admissions. What was the total price without the coupon? You pay the regular price this time and share it equally. How much does each person pay?   \$60; \$15

20. **Bracelets** You are making beaded bracelets for your friends. You want to use 30 beads for each bracelet and want to use no more than 145 beads. Write an inequality that models this situation. Can you make 4 bracelets? $30x \le 145$; yes

21. **Staircase** When building a staircase, you need to be concerned with the height of the riser and the depth of the tread so that people can go up and down the stairs comfortably. One rule of thumb used to determine proper riser height and tread depth is that the sum of the tread depth (in inches) and twice the riser height (in inches) should equal 26 inches. Write an equation that models this situation. The riser height of a set of steps is 5 inches. What should the depth be?

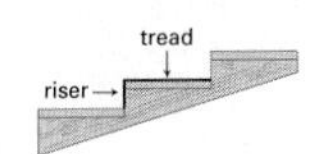

$t + 2r = 26$; 16 in.

LESSON 1.4

LESSON 1.5

Practice B

For use with pages 28–34

In Exercises 1 and 2, identify what you know and what you need to find out. You do *not* need to solve the problem. See below.

1. You are making cookies for a bake sale and need to make enough cookies to fill 24 boxes containing 6 cookies each. How many dozen cookies do you need to make?

2. The cellular phone plan you signed up for gives you 400 minutes a month for \$35 and charges \$.15 for each additional minute over 400 minutes. How long can you talk on the phone each month and stay within a budget of \$45?

In Exercises 3 and 4, state the formula that is needed to solve the problem. You do *not* need to solve the problem.

3. You invest \$200 into a savings account that earns 2% simple interest. How long will it take to earn \$50 in interest? $I = Prt$

4. It takes you half an hour to travel 26 miles to work. What is your average speed? $d = rt$

5. **Sticker Collection** Your sticker collection consists of 175 stickers. Each sticker is either an animated cartoon character or an animal. There are 43 less stickers that are animated characters than stickers that are animals. Let x be the number of stickers that are animals. Which equation correctly models this situation? c

   a. $x - 43 = 175$
   b. $x + (x + 43) = 175$
   c. $x + (x - 43) = 175$

6. **Bookshelf** You installed a bookshelf on the wall to organize some of your books. The books that you absolutely want on the shelf weigh a total of $6\frac{3}{4}$ pounds. The bookshelf can handle no more than 9 pounds. You plan on filling the rest of the shelf with your paperbacks that each weigh about $\frac{1}{8}$ pound. Assuming you won't run out of room, how many paperback books can you add to the shelf? 18

7. **Camping** You are responsible for buying supplies for an upcoming camping trip. You can buy packages of stew that just need water added and then are heated. Each package costs \$4.95 and contains enough stew for 2 people. You need to buy enough packages so that you can have stew for 3 days of the trip. There will be 8 people on the trip. How many packages do you need? What is the total cost? 12; \$59.40

8. **Banking** You are going to open a certificate of deposit (CD) that earns simple interest. One bank offers a CD in which you must deposit \$500 for 3 years with 2% interest. Another bank offers a CD in which you must deposit \$250 for 4 years with 3% interest. Which CD will earn more interest?
   Neither; they both earn the same amount.

1. Know: Number of boxes and number of cookies in one box; Need to find out: How many dozen cookies need made

2. Know: Charge for 400 minutes of service, charge per minute over 400 minutes, and amount you can spend; Need to find out: How many minutes over 400 you can talk

LESSON 1.6

Practice B

For use with pages 35–41

Complete the sentence.

1. The input variable is called the __?__ variable. independent

2. The output variable is called the __?__ variable. dependent

6.

Domain	1	2	3	4
Range	2	6	10	14

Tell whether the pairing is a function.

3.

Input	Output
1	15
3	20
5	15
7	20

function

4.

Input	Output
5	5
6	5
7	5
8	5

function

5.

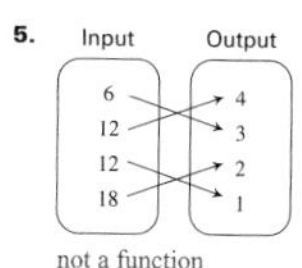

not a function

Make a table for the function. Identify the range of the function.

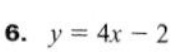

6. $y = 4x - 2$
   Domain: 1, 2, 3, 4
   See above.

7. $y = 0.1x + 3$
   Domain: 10, 20, 30, 40
   See below.

8. $y = \frac{1}{2}x + 2$
   Domain: 6, 7, 8, 9
   See below.

Write a rule for the function.

9.

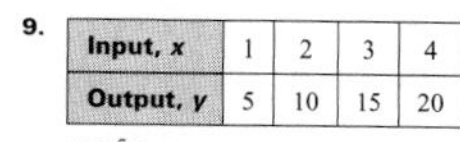

Input, x	1	2	3	4
Output, y	5	10	15	20

$y = 5x$

10.

Input, x	10	11	12	13
Output, y	3	4	5	6

$y = x - 7$

11. **Shoe Sizes** The table shows men's shoe sizes in the United States and Australia. Write a rule for the Australian size as a function of the United States' size.

U.S. size	5	6	7	8	9	10
Australian size	3	4	5	6	7	8

$y = x - 2$

7.

Domain	10	20	30	40
Range	4	5	6	7

12. **Balloon Bunches** You are making balloon bunches to attach to tables for a charity event. You plan on using 8 balloons in each bunch. Write a rule for the total number of balloons used as a function of the number of bunches created. Identify the independent and dependent variables. How many balloons will you use if you make 10 bunches? $y = 8x$; independent: number of balloon bunches; dependent: number of balloons; 80 balloons

13. **Baking** A baker has baked 10 loaves of bread so far today and plans on baking 3 loaves more each hour for the rest of his shift. Write a rule for the total number of loaves baked as a function of the number of hours left in the baker's shift. Identify the independent and dependent variables. How many loaves will the baker make if he has 4 hours left in his shift?
    $y = 10 + 3x$; independent: number of hours left in shift; dependent: number of loaves baked; 22 loaves

8.

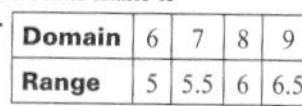

Domain	6	7	8	9
Range	5	5.5	6	6.5

LESSON 1.7

Practice B

For use with pages 42–48

Graph the ordered pairs.

1. (3, 4), (4, 7), (5, 10), (6, 13), (7, 16)

2. (2, 5), (6, 7), (4, 6), (12, 10), (10, 9)

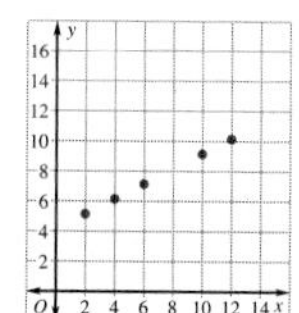

Complete the input-output table for the function.

3. $y = 3x + 2$

x	0	1	2	3
y	2	5	8	11

4. $y = 4x - 1$

x	1	2	3	4
y	3	7	11	15

Graph the function.

5. $y = 6 - x$
   Domain: 6, 5, 4, 3, 2

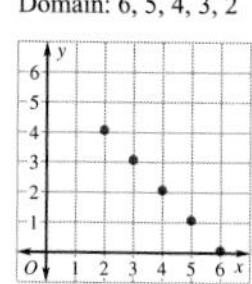

6. $y = \frac{1}{3}x$
   Domain: 6, 9, 12, 15, 18

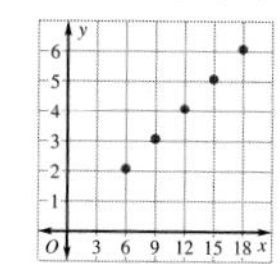

7. $y = 4x - 3$
   Domain: 1, 2, 3, 4, 5

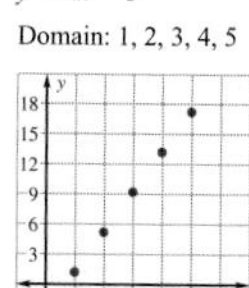

8. $y = 1.2x$
   Domain: 1, 2, 3, 4, 5

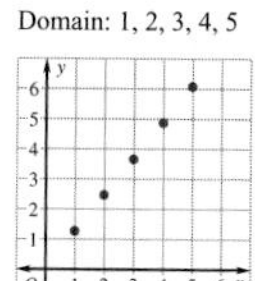

LESSON 1.7

Practice B *continued*

For use with pages 42–48

Write a rule for the function represented by the graph. Identify the domain and range of the function. **10.** $y = 4x - 1$; Domain: 1, 2, 3, 4; Range: 3, 7, 11, 15

9.

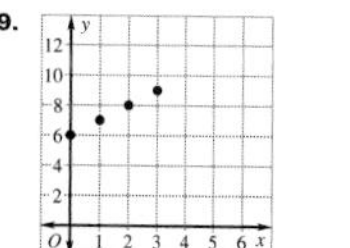

10.

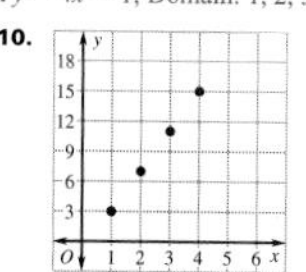

11.

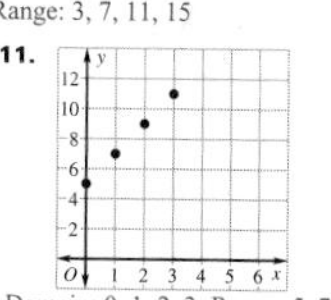

9. $y = x + 6$; Domain: 0, 1, 2, 3; Range: 6, 7, 8, 9 **11.** $y = 2x + 5$; Domain: 0, 1, 2, 3; Range: 5, 7, 9, 11

12. **13.**

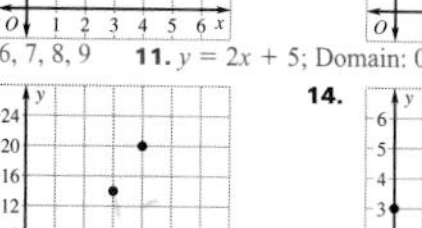

14.

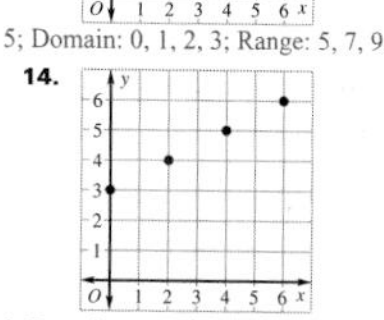

12. $y = \frac{1}{3}x$; Domain: 3, 6, 9, 12; Range: 1, 2, 3, 4 **13.** $y = 6x - 4$; Domain: 1, 2, 3, 4; Range: 2, 8, 14, 20

15. **High Temperatures** The table shows the high temperature H (in degrees Fahrenheit) in a city during the week as a function of the number of days d since Monday. Graph the function. Describe how the high temperatures change as the week progresses. **15.** Answers will vary.

Number of days since Monday, d	0	1	2	3	4	5
High temperature (degrees Fahrenheit), H	24	34	41	39	37	39

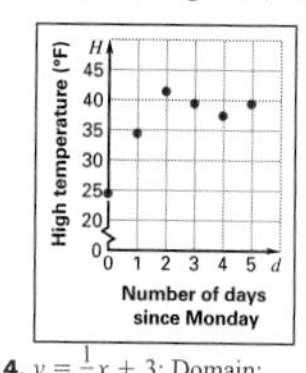

14. $y = \frac{1}{2}x + 3$; Domain: 0, 2, 4, 6; Range: 3, 4, 5, 6

16. **Metal Screws** The table shows the number of threads per inch on a screw as a function of screw size.

Screw size number, x	0	1	2	3	4	5	6
Number of threads per inch, y	80	72	64	56	48	44	40

   a. Graph the function.
   b. Describe how the number of threads per inch changes as the screw size increases.
   c. Would it be reasonable to expect a #8 screw to have 32 threads per inch? *Explain.* **16. c.** Yes. Answers will vary.

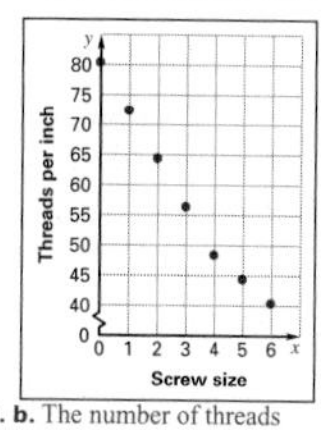

16. b. The number of threads decrease as the screw size increases.

1 Assessment

CHAPTER 1 Quiz 1

For use after Lessons 1.1–1.3

Evaluate the expression.

1. $8 + a$ when $a = 5$
2. $27 - h$ when $h = 21$
3. $\frac{p}{4}$ when $p = 16$
4. $7 + y^2$ when $y = 3$
5. $\frac{2m + 9}{m}$ when $m = 2$
6. $\frac{3x}{x - 1}$ when $x = 3$

Translate the verbal phrase into an expression.

7. 10 more than $\frac{1}{2}$ of a number r
8. Twice a number d
9. The difference of 19 and t
10. The sum of a number p and the square of a number b

Answers

1. 13
2. 6
3. 4
4. 16
5. $6\frac{1}{2}$
6. $4\frac{1}{2}$
7. $10 + \frac{1}{2}r$
8. $2d$
9. $19 - t$
10. $p + b^2$

CHAPTER 1 Quiz 2

For use after Lessons 1.4–1.5

Write an equation or an inequality.

1. The sum of twice a number d and 3 is 12.
2. Six less than four times a number j is 18.
3. The product of 8 and a number q is at least 32.
4. The difference of 10 and a number w is no more than 8.

In Exercises 5–8, check whether the given number is a solution of the equation or inequality.

5. $z - 4 = 9$; 12
6. $2x - 9 \geq 11$; 10
7. $k - 8.2 < 10$; 18
8. $4d + 1 < 13$; 3
9. What is the interest on $950 invested for 4 years in an account that earns simple interest at a rate of 3% per year?
10. A car travels 210 miles in 3.5 hours. What is the average speed of the car?

Answers

1. $2d + 3 = 12$
2. $4j - 6 = 18$
3. $8q \geq 32$
4. $10 - w \leq 8$
5. no
6. yes
7. yes
8. no
9. $114
10. 60 mi/h

CHAPTER 1 Quiz 3

For use after Lessons 1.6–1.7

Identify the domain and range of the function.

1.

Input	Output
0	1
2	5
4	9
6	13

2.

Input	Output
1	2
2	5
3	8
4	11

Tell whether the pairing is a function.

3. Input: 2, 4, 6, 8; Output: 10, 7, 3, 2

4.

Input	Output
3	5
4	7
5	9
6	11

Graph the function.

5. $y = x - 2$; Domain: 2, 3, 4, 5, 6

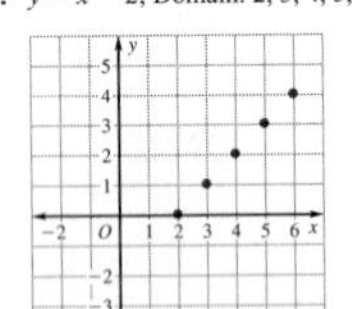

6. $y = \frac{1}{2}x + 3$; Domain: 0, 2, 4, 6, 8

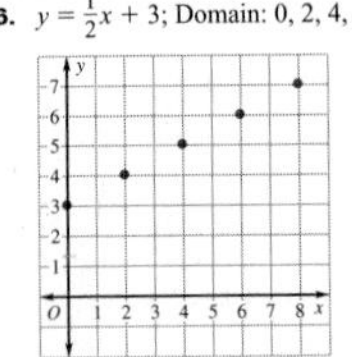

In Exercises 7–9, use the graph at the right.

7. Write a rule for the function represented by the graph.
8. Identify the domain of the function.
9. Identify the range of the function.

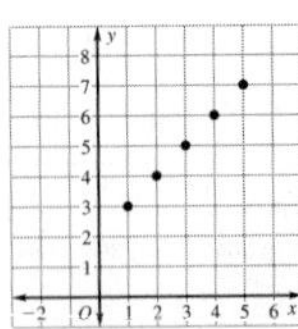

Answers

1. domain: 0, 2, 4, 6; range: 1, 5, 9, 13
2. domain: 1, 2, 3, 4; range: 2, 5, 8, 11
3. no
4. yes
5. See left.
6. See left.
7. $y = x + 2$
8. domain: 1, 2, 3, 4, 5
9. range: 3, 4, 5, 6, 7

CHAPTER 1 Chapter Test B

For use after Chapter 1

Evaluate the expression.

1. $34.5x$ when $x = 4$
2. $\frac{1}{3}y$ when $y = \frac{9}{10}$

Evaluate the power.

3. 5^4
4. 1^7
5. $\left(\frac{1}{2}\right)^5$
6. You can convert temperatures in degrees Fahrenheit to degrees Celsius by using the expression $\frac{9}{5}C + 32$, where C is the temperature (in degrees Celsius). Convert 35°C to degrees Fahrenheit.

Evaluate the expression.

7. $16 \div (4 - 2) - 3$
8. $3[15 - (2^3 - 6)^2]$

Evaluate the expression for the given values of the variables.

9. $3m - n$ when $m = 5$ and $n = 4$
10. $2u^2 + v$ when $u = 3$ and $v = 7$
11. A rectangular box is created by cutting out squares of equal sides of lengths x from a piece of cardboard 10 inches by 15 inches and folding up the sides as shown in the figure. The volume of the box is given by $V = x(10 - 2x)(15 - 2x)$. Find the volume of the box when the side length of the square is 3 inches.

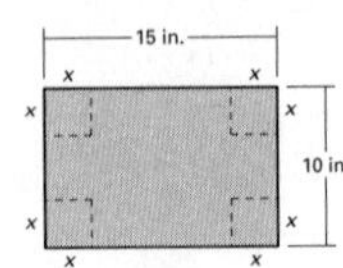

Write an algebraic expression, an equation, or an inequality.

12. The quotient of the square of a number t and 14
13. Amount you earn if you make 6.5 dollars an hour for h hours
14. The product of 6 and the quantity 2 more than a number x is at least 45.
15. The sum of 4 and the quotient of a number k and 9 is 12.

Answers

1. 138
2. $\frac{3}{10}$
3. 625
4. 1
5. $\frac{1}{32}$
6. 95°F
7. 5
8. 33
9. 11
10. 25
11. 108 in.^{3}
12. $\frac{t^2}{14}$
13. $6.5h$
14. $6(2 + x) \geq 45$
15. $4 + \frac{k}{9} = 12$

CHAPTER 1 **Chapter Test B** *continued*
For use after Chapter 1

Check whether the given number is a solution of the equation or the inequality.

16. $7z + 8 > 20; 2$ **17.** $\frac{r}{5} + 15 = 20; 25$

18. A carpet outlet advertises a price of \$470.40 to carpet a 12-foot by 16-foot room. If a customer was given a price of \$725.20 for carpeting a room that is 16 feet wide, what is the length of the room?

Write a rule for the function.

19.

Input, x	1	3	5	7
Output, y	2	6	10	14

20.

Input, x	12	15	18	21
Output, y	4	5	6	7

Find the range of the function. Then graph the function.

21. $y = \frac{1}{2}x + 3$ Domain: 0, 1, 2, 3, 4

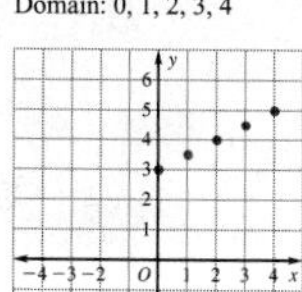

22. $y = x - 6$ Domain: 10, 12, 14, 16, 18

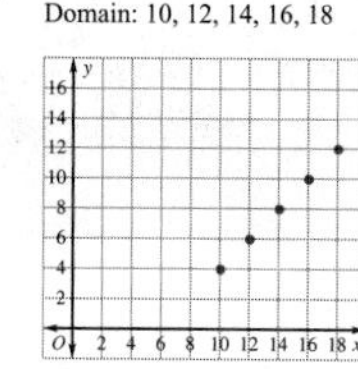

Answers

16. yes
17. yes
18. $18\frac{1}{2}$ ft
19. $y = 2x$
20. $y = \frac{x}{3}$
21. Range: 3, 3.5, 4, 4.5, 5; See left.
22. Range: 4, 6, 8, 10, 12; See left.

CHAPTER 1 **Standardized Test**
For use after Chapter 1

Multiple Choice

1. What is the value of $3.2n$ when $n = 5$? C
Ⓐ 0.16 Ⓑ 1.6 Ⓒ 16 Ⓓ 161

2. What is the value of 5^4? C
Ⓐ 20 Ⓑ 54 Ⓒ 625 Ⓓ 1024

3. Let d be the number of dollars you spent on gas and let g be the number of gallons you purchased. Which expression represents the price you paid per gallon? D
Ⓐ $d + g$ Ⓑ $\frac{g}{d}$
Ⓒ dg Ⓓ $\frac{d}{g}$

4. What is the value of $3[1^2(5 - 3 + 1)^3 \div 9]$? B
Ⓐ $\frac{1}{3}$ Ⓑ 9 Ⓒ 18 Ⓓ 6

5. What is the value of $\frac{108}{x^2} + 4x$ when $x = 6$? A
Ⓐ 27 Ⓑ 33 Ⓒ 42 Ⓓ 55

6. Which expression represents the phrase "twice the quotient of 5 less than a number m and 6"? B
Ⓐ $2\left(\frac{5 - m}{6}\right)$ Ⓑ $2\left(\frac{m - 5}{6}\right)$
Ⓒ $\frac{2m - 5}{6}$ Ⓓ $\frac{2(5) - m}{6}$

7. Which inequality corresponds to the sentence "Five less than the product of a number n and -6 is at least 8."? D
Ⓐ $5 - (-6n) \ge 8$ Ⓑ $-6n - 5 \le 8$
Ⓒ $-\frac{n}{6} - 5 \ge 8$ Ⓓ $-6n - 5 \ge 8$

8. What is the solution of the equation $\frac{x}{4} - 12 = -4$? C
Ⓐ -64 Ⓑ -32 Ⓒ 32 Ⓓ 64

9. A car travels an average speed of 45 miles per hour. How many hours would it take to travel 540 miles? A
Ⓐ 12 hours Ⓑ 12.5 hours
Ⓒ 13 hours Ⓓ 14 hours

10. The temperature is 77°F. What is the temperature in degrees Celsius? B
Ⓐ 11°C Ⓑ 25°C
Ⓒ 61°C Ⓓ 225°C

11. The range of the function $y = 3x - 2$ is 1, 7, 13, 16, and 19. Which number is in the domain of the function? C
Ⓐ 2 Ⓑ 4 Ⓒ 6 Ⓓ 8

12. Each output of a function is 0.25 greater than the corresponding input. Which equation is a rule for the function? A
Ⓐ $y = x + 0.25$ Ⓑ $y = x - 0.25$
Ⓒ $y = 0.25x$ Ⓓ $y = \frac{x}{0.25}$

13. Which set of numbers represents the domain of the function in the table? D

Input	Output
−2	6
0	0
2	−6
4	−12

Ⓐ −12, −6, 0, 6
Ⓑ −12, −6, −2, 0, 2, 4, 6
Ⓒ −2, 2, 4
Ⓓ −2, 0, 2, 4

CHAPTER 1 **Standardized Test** *continued*
For use after Chapter 1

14. Which ordered pair is a solution of the function $y = 2x + 5$? B
Ⓐ (7, 1) Ⓑ (0, 5)
Ⓒ (−2, 9) Ⓓ (0, 0)

15. The relation in the table is a function. Which ordered pair can be included with this relation to form a new relation that is also a function? D

Input	−5	0	5	10
Output	12	15	18	21

Ⓐ (5, 7) Ⓑ (0, 2)
Ⓒ (−5, 5) Ⓓ (2, 16)

16. The graph of what function is shown? A

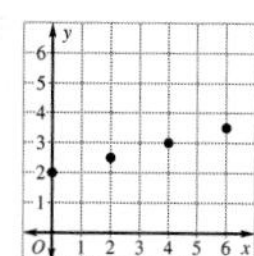

Ⓐ $y = \frac{1}{4}x + 2$ Ⓑ $y = \frac{1}{4}x + 4$
Ⓒ $y = 2x + \frac{1}{4}$ Ⓓ $y = 4x + 2$

Gridded Answer

17. What is the value of the expression $\frac{1}{3}x^2 + 4$ when $x = 9$?

Answer grid: 31

19. b.

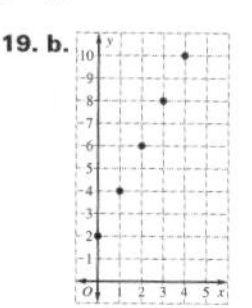

Short Response

18. You need to buy school supplies. Notebooks are \$1.95 each and folders are \$1.25 each. You only have \$7.35 to spend.

a. Write an inequality for this situation. Let n represent the number of notebooks you can buy and let f represent the number of folders you can buy. $1.95n + 1.25f \le 7.35$

b. What is the maximum number of notebooks you can buy if you want to buy one folder? 3

c. Would you have enough money left to buy a binder for \$2.49 if you purchased two notebooks and one folder? *Explain.* See below.

Extended Response

19. Use the table to complete parts a–c.

Input	Output
0	2
1	4
2	6
3	8
4	10

19. a. $y = 2x + 2$; domain: 0, 1, 2, 3, 4; range: 2, 4, 6, 8, 10

a. Write a rule for the function represented by the table. Identify the domain and range of the function.

b. Graph the function. See left.

c. Write a problem that involves a real-world situation that can be solved using the rule for the function you wrote in part a. *Explain.*

Sample answer: I have one \$2-bill in my money collection. My aunt gives me 7 more \$2-bills. How much is my \$2-bill collection worth? The input, x, is 7, so the output, y, is 16. \$16

18. c. No; If you buy 2 notebooks and 1 folder, you only have \$2.20 left, which is not enough to buy a binder.

CHAPTER 1 **Alternative Assessment and Math Journal**
For use after Chapter 1

Journal **1.** Explain the difference between an algebraic expression and an equation. Write an example of each, and explain what it means to evaluate an algebraic expression.

Multi-Step Problem **2.** A local pizza shop offers the following special every Tuesday: buy one large pizza with one topping at regular price, and get as many medium one topping pizza as you would like for \$6.25 each.

a. If the cost of a large pizza with one topping is \$13.50, how much would it cost to purchase one large and five medium pizzas?

b. Complete the table by calculating the total cost of purchasing one large pizzas and the indicated number of medium pizzas.

Number of medium pizzas	0	1	2	3	4
Total cost	?	?	?	?	?

c. Graph the function for total cost using your work in the table above.

d. Write a rule for the function representing the total cost T of purchasing one large pizza with one topping and m medium pizzas.

e. You and a group of friends decide to pool your money to have a pizza party. If you have a total of \$100 and purchase one large pizza, how many medium pizzas can you buy?

f. Your parents decide to purchase one large pizza and five medium pizzas. Determine the total area (in square inches) of pizza if a large pizza has a radius of 8 inches and a medium pizza has a radius of 5 inches. (*Hint:* $A = \pi r^2$) Use 3.14 for π. Round your answer to the nearest square inch.

g. What is the cost per square inch of pizza if one large and five medium pizzas are purchased?

1. Complete answers should include: a clear distinction that an equation contains the equal sign and algebraic expressions do not; one example of an algebraic expression and one example of an equation; a written explanation describing how to replace the variable(s) in the expression with particular values to evaluate the expression.

2. a. \$44.75 **b.** \$13.50; \$19.75; \$26.00; \$32.25; \$38.50

c.

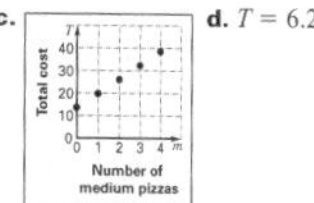

d. $T = 6.25m + 13.50$

e. 13 medium pizzas **f.** about 594 in.^{2} **g.** about \$.08 per square inch

PLAN AND PREPARE

Main Ideas

In Chapter 1, students write and evaluate expressions, equations, and inequalities. They learn to apply the order of operations and to use a problem solving plan to solve real-world problems. Students represent functions as rules and as tables. They also graph functions given a rule or table of values.

Prerequisite Skills

Skills Readiness, available on the *Easy Planner*, provides review and practice for the Skills Check portion of the Prerequisite Skills quiz.

How student answers the exercises	What to assign from *Skills Readiness*
Any of Exs. 4–7 answered incorrectly	**Skill 47** Multiply and divide fractions
Any of Exs. 8–11 answered incorrectly	**Skill 14** Write percents as decimals
Ex. 12 answered incorrectly	**Skill 37** Find the area of a rectangle
All exercises answered correctly	Chapter 1 Enrichment

Additional skills review and practice is available in the Skills Review Handbook, pp. 909–937, and the @HomeTutor.

1 Expressions, Equations, and Functions

Making Sense of Chapter 1

Throughout your study of algebra you will be working with functions. By the end of this chapter, you will be able to represent simple functions as verbal rules, equations, tables, and graphs.

Before

Previously, you learned the following skills, which you'll use in Chapter 1: using fractions and percents, and finding area.

Prerequisite Skills

VOCABULARY CHECK

Copy and complete the statement.

1. In the fraction $\frac{2}{3}$, __?__ is the numerator and __?__ is the denominator. **2, 3**
2. Two fractions that represent the same number are called __?__ fractions. **equivalent**
3. The word *percent* (%) means "divided by __?__." **100**

SKILLS CHECK

Perform the indicated operation. *(Prerequisite skill for 1.1, 1.2)*

4. $\frac{3}{5} \times \frac{2}{3}$ $\frac{2}{5}$
5. $1\frac{1}{4} \times \frac{3}{5}$ $\frac{3}{4}$
6. $\frac{1}{2} \div \frac{5}{8}$ $\frac{4}{5}$
7. $6 \div \frac{3}{4}$ **8**

Write the percent as a decimal. *(Prerequisite skill for 1.5)*

8. 4% **0.04**
9. 23% **0.23**
10. 1.5% **0.015**
11. 2.5% **0.025**

12. Find the area of the rectangle. *(Prerequisite skill for 1.5)* $49\frac{1}{2}$ **in.**^{2}

$4\frac{1}{2}$ in.

11 in.

@HomeTutor Prerequisite skills practice at classzone.com

Chapter Planning Guide

Chapter Resource Book
- Teaching Guide/Lesson Plan
- Project with Rubric

Assessment and Intervention
- Assessment Book
- Benchmark Tests
- Remediation Book
- Skills Readiness

Interactive Technology
- Easy Planner
- Power Presentations
- Activity Generator
- Animated Algebra
- Test Generator
- Online Quizzes
- eWorkbook
- eEdition
- @HomeTutor

Resources for English Learners
- Spanish Study Guide
- Multi-Language Visual Glossary
- Student Resources in Spanish

Now

In Chapter 1, you will apply the big ideas listed below and reviewed in the Chapter Summary on page 52. You will also use the key vocabulary listed below.

Big Ideas

1. **Writing and evaluating algebraic expressions**
2. **Using expressions to write equations and inequalities**
3. **Representing functions as verbal rules, equations, tables, and graphs**

KEY VOCABULARY

- variable, *p. 2*
- algebraic expression, *p. 2*
- power, exponent, base, *p. 3*
- order of operations, *p. 8*
- verbal model, *p. 16*
- rate, unit rate, *p. 17*
- open sentence, *p. 21*
- equation, inequality, *p. 21*
- solution of an equation or inequality, *p. 22*
- formula, *p. 30*
- function, *p. 35*
- domain, range, *p. 35*
- independent variable, *p. 36*
- dependent variable, *p. 36*

Why?

You can use multiple representations to describe a real-world situation. For example, you can solve an equation, make a table, or draw a diagram to determine a running route.

Animated Algebra

The animation illustrated below for Example 1 on page 28 helps you answer this question: How does the number of blocks you run affect the total distance?

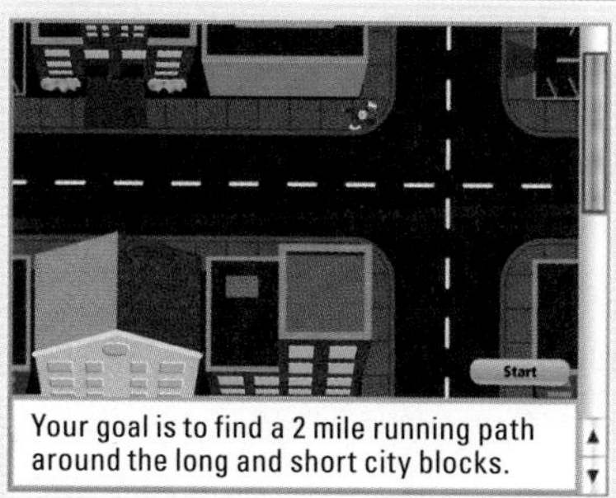

Start
Your goal is to find a 2 mile running path around the long and short city blocks.

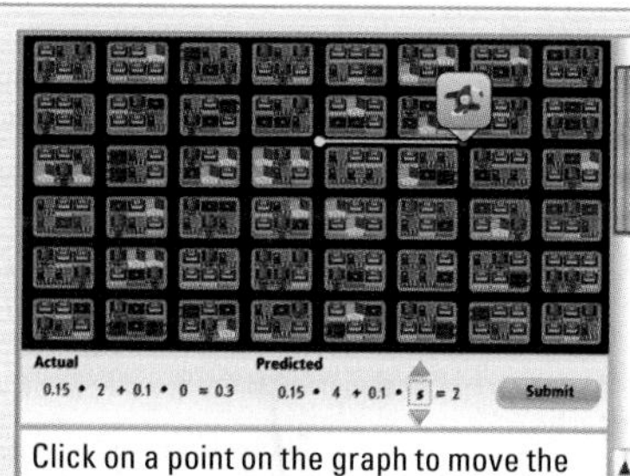

Animated Algebra at classzone.com

Other animations for Chapter 1: pages 7, 9, 14, 21, 37, 50, and 52

1

Differentiated Instruction Resources

- Reading Strategies for Chapter 1
- Differentiated Instruction Lesson Notes
- English Learners Lesson Notes
- Inclusion Lesson Notes
- Teaching Strategies with Sample Worksheets
- Using Technology in the Classroom
- Tips for New Teachers
- Math Background Notes
- Assessment Strategies
- Teacher Survival Activities
- Bulletin Board Idea

1 PLAN AND PREPARE

Warm-Up Exercises

Transparency Available

Perform the indicated operation.

1. $12 \div 1.5$ **8**
2. 3.3×7 **23.1**
3. $11.6 - 5.9$ **5.7**
4. Julia ran $10\frac{2}{3}$ miles last week and $8\frac{5}{6}$ miles this week. How many more miles did she run last week? **$1\frac{5}{6}$ mi**

Notetaking Guide

Transparency Available

Promotes interactive learning and notetaking skills.

Pacing

Basic: 1 day

Average: 1 day

Advanced: 1 day

Block: 0.5 block with 1.2

- See *Teaching Guide/Lesson Plan.*

2 FOCUS AND MOTIVATE

Essential Question

Big Idea 1, p. 1

How do you evaluate algebraic expressions and powers? **Tell students they will learn how to answer this question by substituting values for the variables in an expression and then performing the operation.**

NCTM STANDARDS

Standard 1: Understand ways of representing numbers; Compute fluently

1.1 Evaluate Expressions

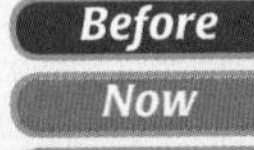

Before	You used whole numbers, fractions, and decimals.
Now	You will evaluate algebraic expressions and use exponents.
Why	So you can calculate sports statistics, as in Ex. 50.

Key Vocabulary
- **variable**
- **algebraic expression**
- **power**
- **base**
- **exponent**

A **variable** is a letter used to represent one or more numbers. The numbers are the values of the variable. *Expressions* consist of numbers, variables, and operations. An **algebraic expression**, or *variable expression*, is an expression that includes at least one variable.

Algebraic expression			Meaning	Operation
$5(n)$	$5 \cdot n$	$5n$	5 times n	Multiplication
$\frac{14}{y}$	$14 \div y$		14 divided by y	Division
$6 + c$			6 plus c	Addition
$8 - x$			8 minus x	Subtraction

To **evaluate an algebraic expression**, substitute a number for each variable, perform the operation(s), and simplify the result, if necessary.

EXAMPLE 1 Evaluate algebraic expressions

USE A PROPERTY
Part (a) of Example 1 illustrates the transitive property of equality: If $a = b$ and $b = c$, then $a = c$. Because $13 \cdot n = 13 \cdot 3$ and $13 \cdot 3 = 39$, $13 \cdot n = 39$. Two other properties of equality are the reflexive property ($a = a$) and the symmetric property (if $a = b$, then $b = a$).

Evaluate the expression when $n = 3$.

a. $13 \cdot n = 13 \cdot 3$ — Substitute 3 for n.
$= 39$ — Multiply.

b. $\frac{9}{n} = \frac{9}{3}$ — Substitute 3 for n.
$= 3$ — Divide.

c. $n - 1 = 3 - 1$ — Substitute 3 for n.
$= 2$ — Subtract.

d. $n + 8 = 3 + 8$ — Substitute 3 for n.
$= 11$ — Add.

✓ GUIDED PRACTICE for Example 1

Evaluate the expression when $y = 2$.

1. $6y$ **12** **2.** $\frac{8}{y}$ **4** **3.** $y + 4$ **6** **4.** $11 - y$ **9**

Resource Planning Guide

Chapter Resource Book
- Teaching Guide/Lesson Plan
- Activity Master
- Practice levels A, B, C
- Study Guide
- Catch-up for Absent Students
- Application
- Challenge

Workbooks
- Notetaking Guide
- Practice Workbook

Teaching Options
- **Power Presentations** provides dynamic electronic teaching resources for the classroom.
- **Activity Generator** provides editable activities for all ability levels.

Interactive Technology
- Easy Planner
- Power Presentations
- Activity Generator
- Animated Algebra
- Test Generator
- Online Quiz
- eWorkbook
- eEdition
- @HomeTutor

Resources for English Learners
- Spanish Study Guide
- Multi-Language Visual Glossary
- Student Resources in Spanish

See also the *Differentiated Instruction Resources* for more strategies for meeting individual needs.

EXAMPLE 2 Evaluate an expression

MOVIES The total cost of seeing a movie at a theater can be represented by the expression $a + r$ where a is the cost (in dollars) of admission and r is the cost (in dollars) of refreshments. Suppose you pay \$7.50 for admission and \$7.25 for refreshments. Find the total cost.

Solution

Total cost $= a + r$	**Write expression.**
$= 7.50 + 7.25$	**Substitute 7.50 for a and 7.25 for r.**
$= 14.75$	**Add.**

▶ The total cost is \$14.75.

EXPRESSIONS USING EXPONENTS A **power** is an expression that represents repeated multiplication of the same factor. For example, 81 is a power of 3 because $81 = 3 \cdot 3 \cdot 3 \cdot 3$. A power can be written in a form using two numbers, a **base** and an **exponent**. The exponent represents the number of times the base is used as a factor, so 81 can be written as 3^4.

base, exponent

$$3^4 = 3 \cdot 3 \cdot 3 \cdot 3$$

power — 4 factors of 3

EXAMPLE 3 Read and write powers

Write the power in words and as a product.

WRITE EXPONENTS
For a number raised to the first power, you usually do not write the exponent 1. For instance, you write 7^1 simply as 7.

Power	Words	Product
a. 7^1	seven to the first power	7
b. 5^2	five to the second power, or five *squared*	$5 \cdot 5$
c. $\left(\frac{1}{2}\right)^3$	one half to the third power, or one half *cubed*	$\frac{1}{2} \cdot \frac{1}{2} \cdot \frac{1}{2}$
d. z^5	z to the fifth power	$z \cdot z \cdot z \cdot z \cdot z$

✓ **GUIDED PRACTICE** for Examples 2 and 3

5. **WHAT IF?** In Example 2, suppose you go back to the theater with a friend to see an afternoon movie. You pay for both admissions. Your total cost (in dollars) can be represented by the expression $2a$. If each admission costs \$4.75, what is your total cost? **\$9.50**

Write the power in words and as a product.

6. 9^5 **nine to the fifth power, $9 \cdot 9 \cdot 9 \cdot 9 \cdot 9$**
7. 2^8 **two to the eighth power, $2 \cdot 2 \cdot 2 \cdot 2 \cdot 2 \cdot 2 \cdot 2 \cdot 2$**
8. n^4 **n to the fourth power, $n \cdot n \cdot n \cdot n$**

Motivating the Lesson

You want to save money to buy a digital music player. If you know how much it costs, you can determine how much you need to save each week depending on whether you want to purchase it in 2, 3, 4, or more weeks. You can do this by evaluating an expression that involves a variable.

3 TEACH

Extra Example 1

Evaluate the expression when $c = 4$.

a. $4c$ **16**

b. $\frac{8}{c}$ **2**

c. $15 + c$ **19**

Extra Example 2

You are ordering a skateboard and a helmet from an on-line store. The total weight of the two items can be represented by $s + h$, where s is the weight of the skateboard and h is the weight of the helmet. Find the total weight if the helmet weighs 1.3 kilograms and the skateboard weighs 5.4 kilograms. **6.7 kg**

Key Question to Ask for Example 2

- How are the letters used as variables appropriate for this situation? **The first letter in the word *admission* is a and the first letter in the word *refreshments* is r.**

Extra Example 3

Write the power in words and as a product.

a. $\left(\frac{1}{5}\right)^1$ **one fifth to the first power; $\frac{1}{5}$**

b. 6^2 **six squared; $6 \cdot 6$**

c. 3^4 **three to the fourth power; $3 \cdot 3 \cdot 3 \cdot 3$**

d. p^3 **p to the third power or p cubed; $p \cdot p \cdot p$**

Differentiated Instruction

English Learners Some mathematical terms can be associated with more common English definitions. For example, the *base* is the lower part or bottom of something. Therefore, in any power expression, the base is the number at the bottom (and the exponent is the number at the top).

See also the *Differentiated Instruction Resources* for more strategies.

Extra Example 4

Evaluate the expression.

a. n^5 when $n = 3$ **243**

b. d^2 when $d = \frac{9}{5}$ **$\frac{81}{25}$**

Extra Example 5

Each side of a square garden measures 22 feet. You are going to buy fertilizer for the garden before you begin planting and you need to determine its area. Find the area of the garden. **484 ft^2**

Key Question to Ask for Example 5

- Why is 14 substituted for s? **The variable s represents the length of an edge of the cube, and this length is given as 14 inches.**

Avoiding Common Errors

When evaluating a power, students sometimes make the mistake of multiplying the base of the power by the exponent. For example, they would evaluate 14^3 as $14 \times 3 = 42$. Stress that the exponent in a power indicates how many times to multiply the base by itself.

Closing the Lesson

Have students summarize the major points of the lesson and answer the Essential Question: How do you evaluate algebraic expressions and powers?

- **Algebraic expressions can be used to represent a situation in which the actual numerical value used may change.**
- **A power is written using a base and an exponent. The exponent is the number of times you multiply the base by itself.**

To evaluate an algebraic expression, substitute the given value for the variable and then perform the operation. To evaluate a power, multiply the base by itself the number of times indicated by exponent.

EXAMPLE 4 Evaluate powers

USE A PROPERTY
Example 4 illustrates the substitution property of equality: If $a = b$, then a can be substituted for b in any expression or equation. Because $x = 2$, $x^4 = 2^4$.

Evaluate the expression.

a. x^4 when $x = 2$

b. n^3 when $n = 1.5$

Solution

a. $x^4 = 2^4$

$= 2 \cdot 2 \cdot 2 \cdot 2$

$= 16$

b. $n^3 = 1.5^3$

$= (1.5)(1.5)(1.5)$

$= 3.375$

✓ **GUIDED PRACTICE** for Example 4

Evaluate the expression.

9. x^3 when $x = 8$ **512**

10. k^2 when $k = 2.5$ **6.25**

11. d^4 when $d = \frac{1}{3}$ **$\frac{1}{81}$**

REVIEW AREA AND VOLUME
For help with area and volume, see pp. 922 and 925.

AREA AND VOLUME Exponents are used in the formulas for the area of a square and the volume of a cube. In fact, the words *squared* and *cubed* come from the formula for the area of a square and the formula for the volume of a cube.

$A = s^2$

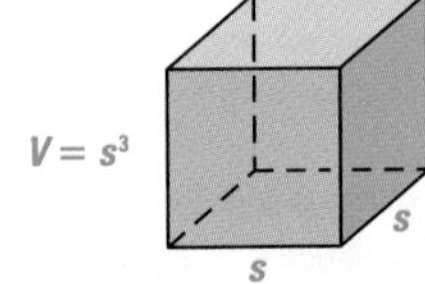

EXAMPLE 5 Evaluate a power

STORAGE CUBES Each edge of the medium-sized pop-up storage cube shown is 14 inches long. The storage cube is made so that it can be folded flat when not in use. Find the volume of the storage cube.

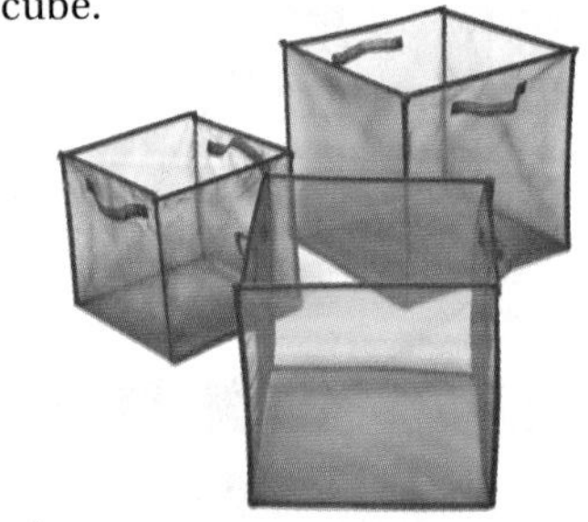

Solution

$V = s^3$	Write formula for volume.
$= 14^3$	Substitute 14 for s.
$= 2744$	Evaluate power.

▶ The volume of the storage cube is 2744 cubic inches.

✓ **GUIDED PRACTICE** for Example 5

12. WHAT IF? In Example 5, suppose the storage cube is folded flat to form a square. Find the area of the square. **196 in.^{2}**

1.1 EXERCISES

HOMEWORK KEY

○ = **WORKED-OUT SOLUTIONS** on p. WS1 for Exs. 19, 35, and 51

★ = **STANDARDIZED TEST PRACTICE** Exs. 2, 15, 44, 45, 52, and 54

SKILL PRACTICE

A

1. **VOCABULARY** Identify the exponent and the base in the expression 6^{12}. **exponent: 12, base: 6**

2. ★ **WRITING** *Describe* the steps you would take to evaluate the expression n^5 when $n = 3$. Then evaluate the expression. **Substitute 3 for n. Then write 3^5 as the product 3 • 3 • 3 • 3 • 3 and multiply; 243.**

EXAMPLE 1 on p. 2 for Exs. 3–15

EVALUATING EXPRESSIONS Evaluate the expression.

3. $15x$ when $x = 4$ **60**
4. $0.4r$ when $r = 6$ **2.4**
5. $w - 8$ when $w = 20$ **12**
6. $1.6 - g$ when $g = 1.2$ **0.4**
7. $5 + m$ when $m = 7$ **12**
8. $0.8 + h$ when $h = 3.7$ **4.5**
9. $\frac{24}{f}$ when $f = 8$ **3**
10. $\frac{t}{5}$ when $t = 4.5$ **0.9**
11. $2.5m$ when $m = 4$ **10**
12. $\frac{1}{2}k$ when $k = \frac{2}{3}$ $\mathbf{\frac{1}{3}}$
13. $y - \frac{1}{2}$ when $y = \frac{5}{6}$ $\mathbf{\frac{1}{3}}$
14. $h + \frac{1}{3}$ when $h = 1\frac{1}{3}$ $\mathbf{1\frac{2}{3}}$

15. ★ **MULTIPLE CHOICE** What is the value of $2.5m$ when $m = 10$? **D**

Ⓐ 0.25 Ⓑ 2.5 Ⓒ 12.5 Ⓓ 25

EXAMPLE 3 on p. 3 for Exs. 16–25

WRITING POWERS Write the power in words and as a product. **16, 18–20. See margin.**

16. 12^5
17. 7^3 **seven to the third power, 7 • 7 • 7**
18. $(3.2)^2$
19. $(0.3)^4$
20. $\left(\frac{1}{2}\right)^8$
21. n^7 **n to the seventh power, $n \cdot n \cdot n \cdot n \cdot n \cdot n \cdot n$**
22. y^6 **y to the sixth power, $y \cdot y \cdot y \cdot y \cdot y \cdot y$**
23. t^4 **t to the fourth power, $t \cdot t \cdot t \cdot t$**

ERROR ANALYSIS *Describe* and correct the error in evaluating the power. **24, 25. See margin.**

24. $(0.4)^2 = 2(0.4) = 0.8$ 

25. $5^4 = 4 \cdot 4 \cdot 4 \cdot 4 \cdot 4 = 1024$ 

EXAMPLE 4 on p. 4 for Exs. 26–37

EVALUATING POWERS Evaluate the power.

26. 3^2 **9**
27. 10^2 **100**
28. 1^5 **1**
29. 11^3 **1331**
30. 5^3 **125**
31. 3^5 **243**
32. 2^6 **64**
33. 6^4 **1296**
34. $\left(\frac{1}{4}\right)^2$ $\mathbf{\frac{1}{16}}$
35. $\left(\frac{3}{5}\right)^3$ $\mathbf{\frac{27}{125}}$
36. $\left(\frac{2}{3}\right)^4$ $\mathbf{\frac{16}{81}}$
37. $\left(\frac{1}{6}\right)^3$ $\mathbf{\frac{1}{216}}$

B

EVALUATING EXPRESSIONS Evaluate the expression.

38. x^2 when $x = \frac{3}{4}$ $\mathbf{\frac{9}{16}}$
39. p^2 when $p = 1.1$ **1.21**
40. $x + y$ when $x = 11$ and $y = 6.4$ **17.4**
41. kn when $k = 9$ and $n = 4.5$ **40.5**
42. $w - z$ when $w = 9.5$ and $z = 2.8$ **6.7**
43. $\frac{b}{c}$ when $b = 24$ and $c = 2.5$ **9.6**

44. ★ **MULTIPLE CHOICE** Which expression has the greatest value when $x = 10$ and $y = 0.5$? **C**

Ⓐ xy Ⓑ $x - y$ Ⓒ $\frac{x}{y}$ Ⓓ $\frac{y}{x}$

16. twelve to the fifth power, 12 • 12 • 12 • 12 • 12

18. three and two tenths squared, 3.2 • 3.2

19. three tenths to the fourth power, 0.3 • 0.3 • 0.3 • 0.3

20. one half to the eighth power, $\frac{1}{2} \cdot \frac{1}{2} \cdot \frac{1}{2} \cdot \frac{1}{2} \cdot \frac{1}{2} \cdot \frac{1}{2} \cdot \frac{1}{2} \cdot \frac{1}{2}$

24. 0.4 was multiplied by 2 instead of squared; $(0.4)^2 = (0.4)(0.4) = 0.16$.

25. The base was used as the exponent and the exponent was used as the base; $5^4 = 5 \cdot 5 \cdot 5 \cdot 5 = 625$.

4 PRACTICE AND APPLY

Assignment Guide

Answer Transparencies available for all exercises

Basic:
Day 1: SRH p. 914 Exs. 11–15
pp. 5–7
Exs. 1, 2, 3–13 odd, 15–25, 27–41 odd, 48–52, 56–65

Average:
Day 1: pp. 5–7
Exs. 1, 2, 4–14 even, 15, 16–22 even, 24, 25, 26–44 even, 45, 46, 49–54, 57–65

Advanced:
Day 1: pp. 5–7
Exs. 1, 2, 10–14, 15–23 odd, 32–44 even, 45–47*, 50–63*

Block:
pp. 5–7
Exs. 1, 2, 4–14 even, 15, 16–22 even, 24, 25, 26–44 even, 45, 46, 49–54, 57–65 (with 1.2)

Differentiated Instruction

See *Differentiated Instruction Resources* for suggestions on addressing the needs of a diverse classroom.

Homework Check

For a quick check of student understanding of key concepts, go over the following exercises:

Basic: 5, 18, 31, 48, 51
Average: 10, 20, 32, 49, 51
Advanced: 12, 21, 34, 50, 52

Extra Practice

- Student Edition, p. 938
- Chapter Resource Book: Practice levels A, B, C

Practice Worksheet

An easily-readable reduced practice page (with answers) for this lesson can be found on p. 1C.

Differentiated Instruction

Auditory Learners For students who begin learning algebra, the concept of a variable is a new idea. When saying the word *variable* out loud to students, stress the sounds "vary" and "able" as in "able to vary." Explain that letters such as x are called variables because they represent a number that varies, or changes. For example, in **Exercise 3**, $x = 4$; but in **Exercise 38**, $x = \frac{3}{4}$.

See also the *Differentiated Instruction Resources* for more strategies.

Study Strategy

Exercise 45 For students who have difficulty with this problem, suggest that they replace the variables with numbers in order to determine the mathematical operation to be used. For example, *I bought 12 tokens and used 2 of them. What operation should I use to determine how many tokens I have left?*

Reading Strategy

Exercise 47 Suggest that the following might be an alternative reading of the problem. *When is the value of the square of a whole number greater than the value of 2 raised to that whole number power?*

Teaching Strategy

Exercise 53 You may wish to step out this exercise into parts as was done in Exercises 50 and 51. For example, part a might be finding the Patriots' net score, part b would be finding the Panthers' net score, and part c would be the comparison of the net scores. Point out that breaking problems into parts helps to clarify the solution process and can help students avoid incomplete solutions.

An **Animated Algebra** activity is available online for **Exercise 54**. This activity is also part of **Power Presentations**.

Exercise 53 Additional statistical information about teams in the National Football League can be found at www.nfl.com/stats.

---

45. ★ **MULTIPLE CHOICE** Let b be the number of tokens you bought at an arcade, and let u be the number you have used. Which expression represents the number of tokens remaining? **B**

Ⓐ $b + u$ Ⓑ $b - u$ Ⓒ bu Ⓓ $\frac{b}{u}$

[C] **46. COMPARING POWERS** Let x and y be whole numbers greater than 0 with $y > x$. Which has the greater value, 3^x or 3^y? *Explain.* **3^y; if $y > x$, then 3^y is raised to a higher power than 3^x.**

47. CHALLENGE For which whole number value(s) of x greater than 0 is the value of x^2 greater than the value of 2^x? *Explain.* **3; $3^2 = 9$ and $2^3 = 8$. For $x = 1$ and $x > 4$, $x^2 < 2^x$. For $x = 2$ and $x = 4$, $x^2 = 2^x$.**

PROBLEM SOLVING

EXAMPLE 2 [A] on p. 3 for Exs. 48–50

48. **GEOMETRY** The perimeter of a square with a side length of s is given by the expression $4s$. What is the perimeter of the square shown? **30 m**

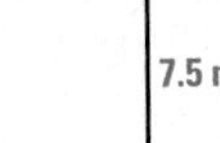

@HomeTutor for problem solving help at classzone.com

49. LEOPARD FROG You can estimate the distance (in centimeters) that a leopard frog can jump using the expression 13ℓ where ℓ is the frog's length (in centimeters). What distance can a leopard frog that is 12.5 centimeters long jump? **162.5 cm**

@HomeTutor for problem solving help at classzone.com

50. MULTI-STEP PROBLEM Jen was the leading scorer on her soccer team. She scored 120 goals and had 20 assists in her high school career.

a. The number n of points awarded for goals is given by $2g$ where g is the number of goals scored. How many points did Jen earn for goals? **240 points**

b. The point total is given by $n + a$ where a is the number of assists. Use your answer from part (a) to find Jen's point total. **260 points**

EXAMPLE 5 on p. 4 for Exs. 51–52

(51.) MULTI-STEP PROBLEM You are buying a tank for three fish. You have a flame angel that is 3.5 inches long, a yellow sailfin tang that is 5.5 inches long, and a coral beauty that is 3 inches long. The area (in square inches) of water surface the fish need is given by the expression $12f$ where f is the sum of the lengths (in inches) of all the fish in the tank.

a. What is the total length of the three fish? **12 in.**

b. How many square inches of water surface do the fish need? **144 in.^{2}**

[B] **52.** ★ **MULTIPLE CHOICE** For a snow sculpture contest, snow is packed into a cube-shaped box with an edge length of 8 feet. The box is frozen and removed, leaving a cube of snow. One cubic foot of the snow weighs about 30 pounds. You can estimate the weight (in pounds) of the cube using the expression $30V$ where V is the volume (in cubic feet) of the snow. About how much does the uncarved cube weigh? **C**

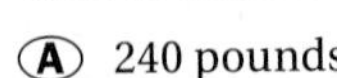

Ⓐ 240 pounds Ⓑ 1920 pounds
Ⓒ 15,360 pounds Ⓓ 216,000 pounds

○ = WORKED-OUT SOLUTIONS on p. WS1 ★ = STANDARDIZED TEST PRACTICE

53. **FOOTBALL** A football team's net score for the regular season is given by the expression $a - b$ where a is the total number of points the team scored and b is the total number of points scored against the team. The table shows the point totals for the 2003 National Football League Conference Champions. Which team's net score was greater? **New England Patriots**

Team	Points scored, a	Points scored against, b
New England Patriots	336	238
Carolina Panthers	325	304

C 54. ★ **EXTENDED RESPONSE** A manufacturer produces three different sizes of cube-shaped stacking bins with edge lengths as shown.

Bin A 6 in.

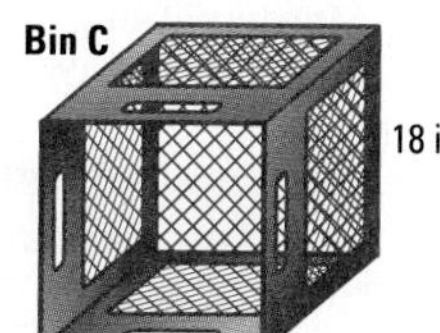

a. **Evaluate** Find the volume of each bin. **216 in.^{3}; 1728 in.^{3}; 5832 in.^{3}**

b. **Compare** How many times greater is the edge length of bin B than the edge length of bin A? How many times greater is the volume of bin B than the volume of bin A? **2; 8**

c. **Compare** Answer the questions in part (b) for bin A and bin C. **3; 27**

d. CHALLENGE *Explain* how multiplying the edge length of a cube by a number n affects the volume of the cube. *Justify* your explanation.

54d. ***Sample answer:*** **The volume of the cube is multiplied by n^3. The edge length of Bin B is 2 times the edge length of Bin A, so the volume of Bin B is 2^3 or 8 times the volume of Bin A. The edge length of Bin C is 3 times the edge length of Bin A, so the volume of Bin C is 3^3 or 27 times the volume of Bin A.**

Animated Algebra at classzone.com

55. CHALLENGE You purchase a set of 100 cube-shaped miniature magnets, each with an edge length of $\frac{1}{8}$ inch. You arrange the cubes to form larger cubes, each one with a different edge length. How many cubes can you form? What is their total volume? **3 cubes; about 0.1934 in.^{3}**

MIXED REVIEW

PREVIEW Prepare for Lesson 1.2 in Exs. 56–59.

Perform the indicated operation.

56. $\frac{13}{16} - \frac{1}{8}$ *(p. 914)* $\frac{11}{16}$ 57. $\frac{3}{4} + \frac{1}{3}$ *(p. 914)* $1\frac{1}{12}$ 58. $\frac{4}{7} \times \frac{7}{9}$ *(p. 915)* $\frac{4}{9}$ 59. $\frac{3}{20} \div \frac{5}{8}$ *(p. 915)* $\frac{6}{25}$

Write the percent as a decimal and as a fraction. *(p. 916)*

60. 37% $0.37, \frac{37}{100}$ 61. 15% $0.15, \frac{3}{20}$ 62. 125% $1.25, 1\frac{1}{4}$ 63. 0.2% $0.002, \frac{1}{500}$

Find the perimeter of the rectangle or square. *(p. 922)*

64. 3.5 m, 9.1 m **25.2 m**

65. 14 in., 14 in. **56 in.**

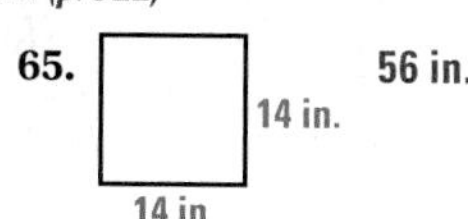

5 ASSESS AND RETEACH

Daily Homework Quiz

Transparency Available

Evaluate the expression or power.

1. $13g$ when $g = 7$ **91**
2. $1.65 - a$ when $a = 0.75$ **0.9**
3. 5^4 **625**
4. $\left(\frac{1}{3}\right)^3$ $\frac{1}{27}$
5. Emily is saving for a $300 bicycle. She has saved $128.25. The amount she still needs to save is given by the expression $c - s$, where c is the cost of the bicycle and s is the amount she has saved. How much does she have left to save? **$171.75**

Available at **classzone.com**

Diagnosis/Remediation

- Practice A, B, C in Chapter Resource Book
- Study Guide in Chapter Resource Book
- Practice Workbook
- @HomeTutor

Challenge

Additional challenge is available in the Chapter Resource Book.

1.2 Apply Order of Operations

Before You evaluated algebraic expressions and used exponents.
Now You will use the order of operations to evaluate expressions.
Why? So you can determine online music costs, as in Ex. 35.

Key Vocabulary
• **order of operations**

Mathematicians have established an **order of operations** to evaluate an expression involving more than one operation.

KEY CONCEPT *For Your Notebook*

Order of Operations

STEP 1 **Evaluate** expressions inside grouping symbols.

STEP 2 **Evaluate** powers.

STEP 3 **Multiply** and **divide** from left to right.

STEP 4 **Add** and **subtract** from left to right.

EXAMPLE 1 Evaluate expressions

Evaluate the expression $27 \div 3^2 \times 2 - 3$.

STEP 1 There are no grouping symbols, so go to Step 2.

STEP 2 **Evaluate** powers.

$27 \div 3^2 \times 2 - 3 = 27 \div 9 \times 2 - 3$ **Evaluate power.**

STEP 3 **Multiply** and **divide** from left to right.

$27 \div 9 \times 2 - 3 = 3 \times 2 - 3$ **Divide.**

$3 \times 2 - 3 = 6 - 3$ **Multiply.**

STEP 4 **Add** and **subtract** from left to right.

$6 - 3 = 3$ **Subtract.**

▶ The value of the expression $27 \div 3^2 \times 2 - 3$ is 3.

✓ **GUIDED PRACTICE** for Example 1

Evaluate the expression.

1. $20 - 4^2$ **4** **2.** $2 \cdot 3^2 + 4$ **22** **3.** $32 \div 2^3 + 6$ **10** **4.** $15 + 6^2 - 4$ **47**

1 PLAN AND PREPARE

Warm-Up Exercises

Transparency Available

Evaluate the expression.

1. $a + 5.7$ when $a = 1.3$ **7**

2. b^3 when $b = 4$ **64**

3. The number of weeks it takes you to read a novel is given by $\frac{n}{p}$, where n is total pages in the novel and p is pages read per week. How long will it take you to read a 340-page novel if you read 85 pages per week? **4 weeks**

Notetaking Guide

Transparency Available

Promotes interactive learning and notetaking skills.

Pacing

Basic: 1 day
Average: 1 day
Advanced: 1 day
Block: 0.5 block with 1.1
• See *Teaching Guide/Lesson Plan.*

2 FOCUS AND MOTIVATE

Essential Question

Big Idea 1, p. 1

How do you use the order of operations to evaluate an expression? **Tell students they will learn how to answer this question by using an algorithm (an ordered series of steps).**

NCTM STANDARDS

Standard 1: Understand how operations are related; Compute fluently

Resource Planning Guide

Chapter Resource Book
• Teaching Guide/Lesson Plan
• Activity Master
• Practice levels A, B, C
• Study Guide
• Catch-up for Absent Students
• Application
• Challenge

Workbooks
• Notetaking Guide
• Practice Workbook

Teaching Options
• **Power Presentations** provides dynamic electronic teaching resources for the classroom.
• **Activity Generator** provides editable activities for all ability levels.

Interactive Technology
• Easy Planner
• Power Presentations
• Activity Generator
• Animated Algebra
• Test Generator
• Online Quiz
• eWorkbook
• eEdition
• @HomeTutor

Resources for English Learners
• Spanish Study Guide
• Multi-Language Visual Glossary
• Student Resources in Spanish

See also the *Differentiated Instruction Resources* for more strategies for meeting individual needs.

GROUPING SYMBOLS Grouping symbols such as parentheses ( ) and brackets [ ] indicate that operations inside the grouping symbols should be performed first. For example, to evaluate $2 \cdot 4 + 6$, you multiply first, then add. To evaluate $2(4 + 6)$, you add first, then multiply.

EXAMPLE 2 Evaluate expressions with grouping symbols

Evaluate the expression.

a. $7(\mathbf{13 - 8}) = 7(5)$ — Subtract within parentheses.

$= 35$ — Multiply.

b. $24 - (\mathbf{3^2} + 1) = 24 - (\mathbf{9 + 1})$ — Evaluate power.

$= 24 - 10$ — Add within parentheses.

$= 14$ — Subtract.

c. $2[30 - (\mathbf{8 + 13})] = 2[\mathbf{30 - 21}]$ — Add within parentheses.

$= 2[9]$ — Subtract within brackets.

$= 18$ — Multiply.

AVOID ERRORS
When grouping symbols appear inside other grouping symbols, work from the innermost grouping symbols outward.

FRACTION BARS A fraction bar can act as a grouping symbol. Evaluate the numerator and denominator before you divide:

$$\frac{8 + 4}{5 - 2} = (8 + 4) \div (5 - 2) = 12 \div 3 = 4$$

EXAMPLE 3 Evaluate an algebraic expression

Evaluate the expression when $x = 4$.

$\frac{9x}{3(x + 2)} = \frac{9 \cdot 4}{3(4 + 2)}$ — Substitute 4 for x.

$= \frac{9 \cdot 4}{3 \cdot 6}$ — Add within parentheses.

$= \frac{36}{18}$ — Multiply.

$= 2$ — Divide.

Animated Algebra at classzone.com

✓ **GUIDED PRACTICE** for Examples 2 and 3

Evaluate the expression.

5. $4(3 + 9)$ **48** **6.** $3(8 - 2^2)$ **12** **7.** $2[(9 + 3) \div 4]$ **6**

Evaluate the expression when $y = 8$.

8. $y^2 - 3$ **61** **9.** $12 - y - 1$ **3** **10.** $\frac{10y + 1}{y + 1}$ **9**

Motivating the Lesson

On a 3-day trip, the Browns drove 186 miles the first day, 168 miles the second day, and 255 miles the third day. Ask students what series of calculations they would use to find the average number of miles driven each day. Then ask them how they would write a single numerical expression to calculate this average.

3 TEACH

Extra Example 1

Evaluate the expression $6 + 12 \div 3 \times 4^2$. **70**

Extra Example 2

Evaluate the expression.

a. $24 \div (4 - 1)$ **8**

b. $48 - (6 + 5^2)$ **17**

c. $3[32 \div (2 + 6)]$ **12**

Key Questions to Ask for Example 2

- How are the expressions in Example 2 different from those in Example 1? **The expressions in Example 2 involve grouping symbols.**
- In part c, why is the addition done first? **You evaluate the expression in the innermost grouping symbols first.**

Extra Example 3

Evaluate the expression $\frac{10x}{2(x + 2)}$ when $x = 3$. **3**

An **Animated Algebra** activity is available online for **Example 3.** This activity is also part of **Power Presentations.**

Differentiated Instruction

Inclusion Students having difficulty using basic arithmetic operations may be allowed to rely on calculators. Have students work in groups with a variety of calculators. Include a calculator that does *not* follow the order of operations. Present each group with a simple expression to evaluate on the calculator, such as $2 + 3 \cdot 4$. For different calculators, the answer will be 14 or 20. Help students understand how to use their own calculator to evaluate numerical expressions.

See also the *Differentiated Instruction Resources* for more strategies.

Extra Example 4

John had 4 copies of a science report made to give to his lab partners. In each copied report there were 20 black-and-white pages and 5 color pages. He paid a copy center to make and bind the copies. His cost in dollars is given by the expression $4(5c + 20b)$, where c is the cost of a color page and b is the cost of a black-and-white page. What is the total cost if a color page costs $2 and a black-and-white page costs $.05? **D**

Ⓐ $23 Ⓑ $26
Ⓒ $41 Ⓓ $44

Key Questions to Ask for Example 4

- Why must the value of the expression inside the parentheses be found first? **Parentheses are one type of grouping symbol and evaluating expressions inside grouping symbols is the first step of the order of operations.**
- What is the order of operations within the parentheses? **Multiply from left to right and then add the products.**

Closing the Lesson

Have students summarize the major points of the lesson and answer the Essential Question: How do you use the order of operations to evaluate an expression?

- **The order of operations is a series of steps to use when evaluating expressions.**
- **Parentheses, brackets, and fraction bars act as grouping symbols.**

Always evaluate expressions using the following order: evaluate expressions inside grouping symbols, evaluate powers, multiply and divide from left to right, and then add and subtract from left to right.

 **EXAMPLE 4** Standardized Test Practice

A group of 12 students volunteers to collect litter for one day. A sponsor provides 3 juice drinks and 2 sandwiches for each student and pays $30 for trash bags. The sponsor's cost (in dollars) is given by the expression $12(3j + 2s) + 30$ where j is the cost of a juice drink and s is the cost of a sandwich. A juice drink costs $1.25. A sandwich costs $2. What is the sponsor's cost?

Ⓐ $79 Ⓑ $123 Ⓒ $129 Ⓓ $210

ELIMINATE CHOICES
You can eliminate choices A and D by estimating. When j is about 1 and s is 2, the value of the expression is about $12(3 + 4) + 30$, or $114.

Solution

$12(3j + 2s) + 30 = 12(3 \cdot \mathbf{1.25} + 2 \cdot \mathbf{2}) + 30$	**Substitute 1.25 for *j* and 2 for *s*.**
$= 12(3.75 + 4) + 30$	**Multiply within parentheses.**
$= 12(7.75) + 30$	**Add within parentheses.**
$= 93 + 30$	**Multiply.**
$= 123$	**Add.**

▶ The sponsor's cost is $123. The correct answer is B. Ⓐ Ⓑ Ⓒ Ⓓ.

 **GUIDED PRACTICE** for Example 4

11. **WHAT IF?** In Example 4, suppose the number of volunteers doubles. Does the sponsor's cost double as well? *Explain.* **No; the total cost of the juice drinks and sandwiches will double, but the cost of the trash bags will not.**

1.2 EXERCISES

HOMEWORK KEY
○ = **WORKED-OUT SOLUTIONS** on p. WS1 for Exs. 16 and 35
★ = **STANDARDIZED TEST PRACTICE** Exs. 2, 19, 31, 37, 39, and 40

SKILL PRACTICE

A

1. **VOCABULARY** According to the order of operations, which operation would you perform first in simplifying $50 - 5 \times 4^2 \div 2$? **Square 4.**

2. ★ **WRITING** *Describe* the steps you would use to evaluate the expression $2(3x + 1)^2$ when $x = 3$. **Substitute 3 for *x*; multiply 3 • 3; add 9 + 1; square 10; multiply 2 • 100. The result is 200.**

EXAMPLES 1 and 2 on pp. 8–9 for Exs. 3–21

EVALUATING EXPRESSIONS Evaluate the expression.

3. $13 - 8 + 3$ **8**
4. $8 - 2^2$ **4**
5. $3 \cdot 6 - 4$ **14**
6. $5 \cdot 2^3 + 7$ **47**
7. $48 \div 4^2 + \frac{3}{5}$ $\mathbf{3\frac{3}{5}}$
8. $1 + 5^2 \div 50$ $\mathbf{1\frac{1}{2}}$
9. $2^4 \cdot 4 - 2 \div 8$ $\mathbf{63\frac{3}{4}}$
10. $4^3 \div 8 + 8$ **16**
11. $(12 + 72) \div 4$ **21**
12. $24 + 4(3 + 1)$ **40**
13. $12(6 - 3.5)^2 - 1.5$ **73.5**
14. $24 \div (8 + 4^2)$ **1**
15. $\frac{1}{2}(21 + 2^2)$ $\mathbf{12\frac{1}{2}}$
16. $\frac{1}{6}(6 + 18) - 2^2$ **0**
17. $\frac{3}{4}[13 - (2 + 3)]^2$ **48**
18. $8[20 - (9 - 5)^2]$ **32**

19. ★ **MULTIPLE CHOICE** What is the value of $3[20 - (7 - 5)^2]$? **A**

Ⓐ 48　Ⓑ 56　Ⓒ 192　Ⓓ 972

20. 7 + 7 was added before dividing 14 by 7; (1 + 13) ÷ 7 + 7 = 14 ÷ 7 + 7 = 2 + 7 = 9

ERROR ANALYSIS *Describe* **and correct the error in evaluating the expression.** **20, 21. See margin.**

20. $(1 + 13) \div 7 + 7 = 14 \div 7 + 7$
$= 14 \div 14$
$= 1$

21. $20 - \frac{1}{2} \cdot 6^2 = 20 - 3^2$
$= 20 - 9$
$= 11$

21. $\frac{1}{2}$ was multiplied by 6 before squaring 6; $20 - \frac{1}{2} \cdot 6^2 = 20 - \frac{1}{2} \cdot 36 = 20 - 18 = 2$.

EXAMPLE 3 B on p. 9 for Exs. 22–31

EVALUATING EXPRESSIONS **Evaluate the expression.**

22. $4n - 12$ when $n = 7$ **16**

23. $2 + 3x^2$ when $x = 3$ **29**

24. $6t^2 - 13$ when $t = 2$ **11**

25. $11 + r^3 - 2r$ when $r = 5$ **126**

26. $5(w - 4)$ when $w = 7$ **15**

27. $3(m^2 - 2)$ when $m = 1.5$ **0.75**

28. $\frac{9x + 4}{3x + 1}$ when $x = 7$ $3\frac{1}{22}$

29. $\frac{k^2 - 1}{k + 3}$ when $k = 5$ **3**

30. $\frac{b^3 - 21}{5b + 9}$ when $b = 3$ $\frac{1}{4}$

31. ★ **MULTIPLE CHOICE** What is the value of $\frac{x^2}{25} + 3x$ when $x = 10$? **B**

Ⓐ 26　Ⓑ 34　Ⓒ 43　Ⓓ 105

C **CHALLENGE** **Insert grouping symbols in the expression so that the value of the expression is 14.**

32. $9 + 39 + 22 \div 11 - 9 + 3$
$(9 + 39 + 22) \div (11 - 9 + 3)$

33. $2 \times 2 + 3^2 - 4 + 3 \times 5$
$(2 \times 2 + 3)^2 - (4 + 3) \times 5$

PROBLEM SOLVING

EXAMPLE 4 A on p. 10 for Exs. 34–37

34. SALES Your school's booster club sells school T-shirts. Half the T-shirts come from one supplier at a cost of \$5.95 each, and half from another supplier at a cost of \$6.15 each. The average cost (in dollars) of a T-shirt is given by the expression $\frac{5.95 + 6.15}{2}$. Find the average cost. **\$6.05**

@HomeTutor for problem solving help at classzone.com

35. MULTI-STEP PROBLEM You join an online music service. The total cost (in dollars) of downloading 3 singles at \$.99 each and 2 albums at \$9.95 each is given by the expression $3 \cdot 0.99 + 2 \cdot 9.95$.

a. Find the total cost. **\$22.87**

b. You have \$25 to spend. How much will you have left? **\$2.13**

@HomeTutor for problem solving help at classzone.com

36. PHYSIOLOGY If you know how tall you were at the age of 2, you can estimate your adult height (in inches). Girls can use the expression $25 + 1.17h$ where h is the height (in inches) at the age of 2. Boys can use the expression $22.7 + 1.37h$. Estimate the adult height of each person to the nearest inch.

a. A girl who was 34 inches tall at age 2 **65 in.**

b. A boy who was 33 inches tall at age 2 **68 in.**

4 PRACTICE AND APPLY

Assignment Guide

Answer Transparencies available for all exercises

Basic:
Day 1: SRH p. 915 Exs. 11–15
pp. 10–12
Exs. 1, 2, 3–17 odd, 19–26, 28–30, 34–38, 41–52

Average:
Day 1: pp. 10–12
Exs. 1, 2, 8–18 even, 20–39, 41–52

Advanced:
Day 1: pp. 10–12
Exs. 1, 2, 13–19, 25–33*, 36–40*, 43–52

Block:
pp. 10–12
Exs. 1, 2, 8–18 even, 20–39, 41–52 (with 1.1)

Differentiated Instruction

See *Differentiated Instruction Resources* for suggestions on addressing the needs of a diverse classroom.

Homework Check

For a quick check of student understanding of key concepts, go over the following exercises:

Basic: 5, 10, 22, 34, 35
Average: 10, 16, 24, 35, 36
Advanced: 13, 18, 28, 36, 37

Extra Practice

- Student Edition, p. 938
- Chapter Resource Book: Practice levels A, B, C

Practice Worksheet

An easily-readable reduced practice page (with answers) for this lesson can be found on p. 1C.

Differentiated Instruction

Below Level Point out that the fraction bars appearing in **Exercises 28–30** are grouping symbols. To help students evaluate the expressions in these exercises, suggest that they use this algorithm: *evaluate the numerator, then evaluate the denominator, and divide the value of the numerator by the value of the denominator.* You might suggest that they remember *numerator/denominator/divide* as a shortened version of the algorithm.

See also the *Differentiated Instruction Resources* for more strategies.

5 ASSESS AND RETEACH

Daily Homework Quiz

Transparency Available

Evaluate the expression.

1. $3^3 \div 9 + 4 \cdot 3$ **15**
2. $12 + (5 - 3)^2$ **16**
3. $2(c^2 + 4)$ when $c = 4$ **40**
4. $\frac{g^2 - 8}{2g - 5}$ when $g = 6$ **4**
5. The cost (in dollars) to buy p posters at the Posters Plus online store is given by the expression $3.5p + 6.75$. At the More Posters online store, the cost is given by $4.25p + 2.55$. Which store has the lower cost for 5 posters? **More Posters**

Online Quiz

Available at **classzone.com**

Diagnosis/Remediation

- Practice A, B, C in Chapter Resource Book
- Study Guide in Chapter Resource Book
- Practice Workbook
- @HomeTutor

Challenge

Additional challenge is available in the Chapter Resource Book.

---

37. ★ OPEN-ENDED Write a numerical expression including parentheses that has the same value when you remove the parentheses. ***Sample answer:*** **$(3 \times 4) + 5$**

B **38. ONLINE SHOPPING** The regular shipping fee (in dollars) for an online computer store is given by the expression $0.5w + 4.49$ where w is the weight (in pounds) of the item. The fee (in dollars) for rush delivery is given by $0.99w + 6.49$. You purchase a 26.5 pound computer. How much do you save using regular shipping instead of rush delivery? **$14.99**

39. ★ SHORT RESPONSE You make and sell flags for $10 each. Each flag requires $4.50 worth of fabric. You pay $12.99 for a kit to punch holes to hang the flags. Your expenses (in dollars) are given by the expression $4.50m + 12.99$ where m is the number of flags you make. Your income is given by the expression $10s$ where s is the number of flags you sell. Your profit is equal to the difference of your income and your expenses.

a. You make 50 flags and sell 38 of them. Find your income and your expenses. Then find your profit. **$380, $237.99; $142.01**

b. *Explain* how you could use a single expression to determine your profit. ***Sample answer:*** **You could write an expression showing the difference of your income and expenses as $10s - (4.50m + 12.99)$.**

40a. ***Sample answer:*** **First place votes are worth 3 points which is $3f$, second place votes are worth 2 points which is $2s$, third place votes are worth 1 point which is $1t$. A player's point total is $3f + 2s + t$.**

C **40. ★ EXTENDED RESPONSE** Each year Heisman Trophy voters select the outstanding college football player. Each voter selects three players ranked first to third. A first place vote is worth 3 points, a second place vote is worth 2 points, and a third place vote is worth 1 point. Let f, s, and t be, respectively, the number of first place, second place, and third place votes a player gets. The table shows the votes for the winner and the runner-up in 2003.

Player	First place	Second place	Third place
Jason White	319	204	116
Larry Fitzgerald	253	233	128

a. Analyze *Explain* why the expression $3f + 2s + t$ represents a player's point total. **See margin.**

b. Calculate Use the expression in part (a) to determine how many more points Jason White got than Larry Fitzgerald got. **128 points**

c. CHALLENGE Can you rearrange the order of the votes for each player in such a way that Larry Fitzgerald would have won? *Explain.*

40c. Yes. ***Sample answer:*** **Change each of the first place votes to third place votes, change each of the second place votes to first place votes, and change each of the third place votes to second place votes.**

MIXED REVIEW

PREVIEW
Prepare for Lesson 1.3 in Exs. 41–48.

Copy and complete. *(p. 927)*

41. 360 in. = ? ft **30**
42. 250 g = ? kg **0.25**
43. 8 ft^2 = ? in.^{2} **1152**
44. 80 L = ? mL **80,000**

Find the value of the expression when $x = 5$. *(p. 2)*

45. $x + 4.7$ **9.7**
46. $19.3 - x$ **14.3**
47. $\frac{1}{2}x$ **$2\frac{1}{2}$**
48. $x - \frac{3}{4}$ **$4\frac{1}{4}$**

Evaluate the power. *(p. 2)*

49. 6^2 **36**
50. 10^4 **10,000**
51. $(0.2)^2$ **0.04**
52. $\left(\frac{2}{3}\right)^3$ **$\frac{8}{27}$**

@HomeTutor
classzone.com
Keystrokes

1.2 Use Order of Operations

QUESTION **How can you use a graphing calculator to evaluate an expression?**

You can use a graphing calculator to evaluate an expression. When you enter the expression, it is important to use grouping symbols so that the calculator performs operations in the correct order.

EXAMPLE **Evaluate an expression**

Use a graphing calculator to evaluate an expression.

Lean body mass is the mass of the skeleton, muscles, and organs. Physicians use lean body mass to determine dosages of medicine.

Scientists have developed separate formulas for the lean body masses of men and women based on their mass m (in kilograms) and height h (in meters). Lean body mass in measured in units called BMI (Body Mass Index) units.

Men: $1.10m - \frac{128m^2}{10{,}000h^2}$ **Women:** $1.07m - \frac{148m^2}{10{,}000h^2}$

Find the lean body mass (in BMI units) of a man who is 1.8 meters tall and has a mass of 80 kilograms.

Solution

Enter the expression for men in the calculator. Substitute 80 for m and 1.8 for h. Because the fraction bar is a grouping symbol, enter the denominator using parentheses.

Use the following keystrokes.

1.10 [×] 80 [−] 128 [×] 80 [x²] [÷] [(] 10000 [×] 1.8 [x²] [)]

▶ The lean body mass of a man who is 1.8 meters tall and has a mass of 80 kilograms is about 62.7 BMI units.

PRACTICE

Use a calculator to evaluate the expression for $n = 4$. Round to the nearest thousandth.

1. $3 + 5 \cdot n \div 10$ **5**
2. $2 + \frac{3n^2}{4}$ **14**
3. $\frac{83}{3n^2} - 1.3$ **0.429**
4. $\frac{14.2n}{8 + n^3}$ **0.789**
5. $\frac{7 - n}{n^2}$ **0.188**
6. $5n^2 + \frac{4n^3 + 1}{3}$ **165.667**
7. Find the lean body mass (to the nearest tenth of a BMI unit) of a woman who is 1.6 meters tall and has a mass of 54 kilograms. **40.9 BMI units**

1 PLAN AND PREPARE

Learn the Method

- Students will learn how to use a graphing calculator to evaluate an algebraic expression.
- After completing the activity, students can use their graphing calculators to check their answers for Exercises 3–19 and 22–31 in Lesson 1.2. They can also use their calculators to test various placements of grouping symbols in the expressions given in Exercises 32 and 33.

Keystroke Help

Keystrokes for several models of calculators are available in blackline format in the *Chapter Resource Book*.

2 TEACH

Tips for Success

In the keystroking shown, point out the use of parentheses around the denominator since the expression involves a fraction bar. Stress that the right parenthesis comes after the second x^2 key.

Extra Example

A person's body mass index (BMI) indicates if they are overweight and at risk for health problems. BMI is calculated using the formula $\frac{w}{h^2} \cdot 703$, where w is the person's weight in pounds and h is their height in inches. Calculate the BMI for a person who weighs 120 pounds and is 64.5 inches tall. **about 20.3**

3 ASSESS AND RETEACH

Use a calculator to evaluate the expression for $b = 2$. Round to the nearest thousandth.

1. $7 + \frac{9b^2}{3}$ **19**
2. $\frac{83}{4b^3 - 7.4}$ **3.374**

Animated Algebra classzone.com

1 PLAN AND PREPARE

Explore the Concept

- Students will describe a pattern.
- This activity leads into the study of writing an algebraic expression in Example 2 in Lesson 1.3.

Materials

Each student or pair of students will need graph paper.

Recommended Time

Work activity: 10 min

Discuss results: 5 min

Grouping

Students can work individually or in pairs. If students work in pairs, one student can draw and label the figures and the other can write the numerical expression.

2 TEACH

Tips for Success

To visually reinforce the pattern, in Figures 2 and 3 have students shade those squares that appeared in the previous figure. Students should readily see that four new squares are added at each stage.

An **Animated Algebra** activity is available online. This activity is also part of **Power Presentations**.

Key Discovery

Algebraic expressions can be used to determine the *n*th number in a pattern.

3 ASSESS AND RETEACH

Without drawing it, how can you find the number of squares in the 15th figure of the pattern? **Multiply 4 × 15 and add 1.**

1.3 Patterns and Expressions

MATERIALS • graph paper

QUESTION How can you use an algebraic expression to describe a pattern?

EXPLORE Create and describe a pattern

STEP 1

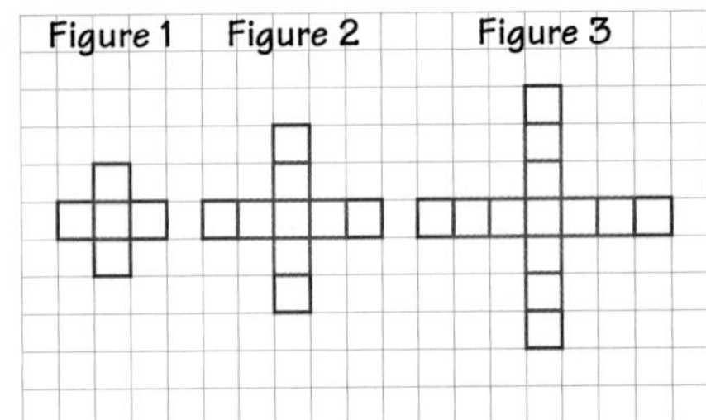

Draw a figure Draw a unit square on graph paper. Then draw a unit square against each side of the first square to form figure 1.

Copy figure 1 and draw a square on each "arm" to form figure 2. Use the same method to form figure 3.

STEP 2

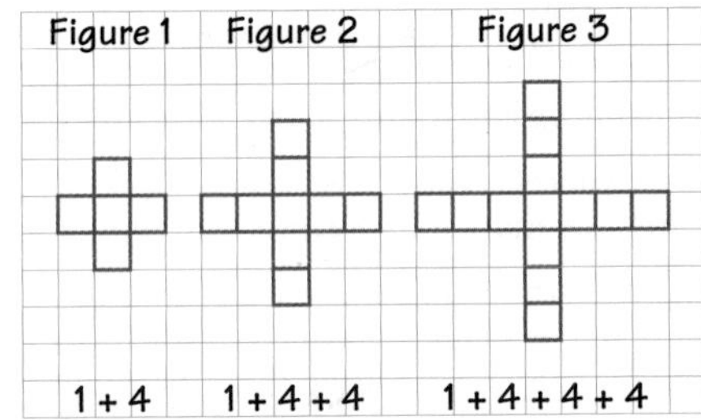

Write expressions For each figure, write a numerical expression that describes the number of squares in the figure.

DRAW CONCLUSIONS Use your observations to complete these exercises

In Exercises 1–3, use the pattern in Steps 1 and 2 above.

1. How is the figure number related to the number of times 4 is added in the numerical expression? Predict the number of squares in the fourth figure. Create figure 4 and check your prediction. **The figure number is equal to the number of times 4 is added in the numerical expression; 17 squares; see margin.**
2. *Describe* how to calculate the number of squares in the *n*th figure. **Find the sum of 1 and the quantity 4 times *n*.**
3. Write an algebraic expression for the number of squares in the *n*th figure. (*Hint:* Remember that repeated addition can be written as multiplication.) $1 + 4n$
4. **a.** Write an algebraic expression for the number of squares in the *n*th figure of the pattern shown. $2n$

   b. *Explain* why the expression n^2 is not an appropriate answer to part (a). Create a pattern that can be described by the expression n^2. **See margin**

Figure 1 Figure 2 Figure 3 Figure 4

1.

4b. For the figures in the pattern shown, the length is the figure number and the width is 2, so the number of squares in the *n*th figure is $2n$. If both the length and the width equal the figure number (that is, the figure is a square), then the number of small squares is $n \cdot n$, or n^2.

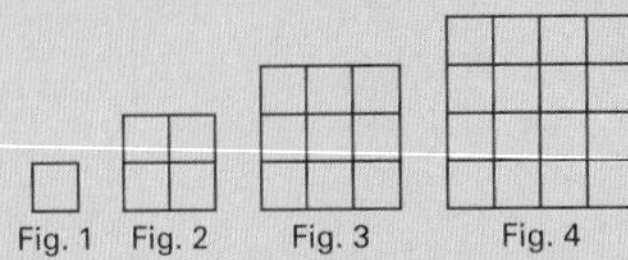

1.3 Write Expressions

Before You evaluated expressions.
Now You will translate verbal phrases into expressions.
Why? So you can find a bicycling distance, as in Ex. 36.

Key Vocabulary
- verbal model
- rate
- unit rate

To translate verbal phrases into expressions, look for words that indicate mathematical operations.

KEY CONCEPT *For Your Notebook*

Translating Verbal Phrases

Operation	Verbal Phrase	Expression
Addition: sum, plus, total, more than, increased by	The sum of 2 and a number x	$2 + x$
	A number n plus 7	$n + 7$
Subtraction: difference, less than, minus, decreased by	The difference of a number n and 6	$n - 6$
	A number y minus 5	$y - 5$
Multiplication: times, product, multiplied by, of	12 times a number y	$12y$
	$\frac{1}{3}$ of a number x	$\frac{1}{3}x$
Division: quotient, divided by, divided into	The quotient of a number k and 2	$\frac{k}{2}$

Order is important when writing subtraction and division expressions. For instance, "the difference of a number n and 6" is written $n - 6$, *not* $6 - n$, and "the quotient of a number k and 2" is written $\frac{k}{2}$, *not* $\frac{2}{k}$.

AVOID ERRORS
When you translate verbal phrases, the words "the quantity" tell you what to group. In part (a), you write $6n - 4$, *not* $(6 - 4)n$.

EXAMPLE 1 Translate verbal phrases into expressions

	Verbal Phrase	Expression
a.	4 less than the quantity 6 times a number n	$6n - 4$
b.	3 times the sum of 7 and a number y	$3(7 + y)$
c.	The difference of 22 and the square of a number m	$22 - m^2$

GUIDED PRACTICE for Example 1

1. Translate the phrase "the quotient when the quantity 10 plus a number x is divided by 2" into an expression. $\frac{10 + x}{2}$

1 PLAN AND PREPARE

Warm-Up Exercises

Transparency Available

1. Evaluate $2[54 \div (4^2 + 2)]$. **6**
2. Evaluate $\frac{5x}{x + 2}$ when $x = 3$. **3**
3. Eight students each ordered 2 drawing kits and 4 drawing pencils. The expression $8(2k + 4p)$ gives the total cost, where k is the cost of a kit and p is the cost of a pencil. Find the total cost if a kit costs $25 and a pencil costs $1.25. **$440**

Notetaking Guide

Transparency Available

Promotes interactive learning and notetaking skills.

Pacing

Basic: 1 day
Average: 1 day
Advanced: 1 day
Block: 0.5 block with 1.4
- See *Teaching Guide/Lesson Plan.*

2 FOCUS AND MOTIVATE

Essential Question

Big Idea 1, p. 1
How do you write an expression to represent a real-world situation?
Tell students they will learn how to answer this question by using variables, symbols, and a verbal model to describe the situation.

NCTM STANDARDS

Standard 2: Represent situations using algebraic symbols

Standard 10: Use representations to solve problems

Resource Planning Guide

Chapter Resource Book
- Teaching Guide/Lesson Plan
- Practice levels A, B, C
- Study Guide
- Catch-up for Absent Students
- Problem Solving Workshop
- Challenge

Workbooks
- Notetaking Guide
- Practice Workbook

Teaching Options
- **Power Presentations** provides dynamic electronic teaching resources for the classroom.
- **Activity Generator** provides editable activities for all ability levels.

Interactive Technology
- Easy Planner
- Power Presentations
- Activity Generator
- Animated Algebra
- Test Generator
- Online Quiz
- eWorkbook
- eEdition
- @HomeTutor

Resources for English Learners
- Spanish Study Guide
- Multi-Language Visual Glossary
- Student Resources in Spanish

See also the *Differentiated Instruction Resources* for more strategies for meeting individual needs.

Motivating the Lesson

You want to invite some friends to a football game. You know tickets cost $4 each. If you translate the situation into an expression, you can use it to find the cost of inviting different numbers of friends to the game.

3 TEACH

Extra Example 1

Translate the verbal phrase into an expression.

a. 8 times the quantity 4 plus a number n **$8(4 + n)$**

b. 12 decreased by a number x **$12 - x$**

c. The quotient of the square of a number w and 5 **$\frac{w^2}{5}$**

Extra Example 2

The length of a building is 20 feet more than its width w. Write an expression for the length of the building. **$w + 20$**

Extra Example 3

You and 4 friends meet to have dinner at a restaurant. Everyone decides to order the nightly special. Write an expression for the total cost of the meals. **$5s$, where s is the cost of the nightly special**

Key Questions to Ask for Example 3

- Why is the amount of money in the jar represented by a variable? **The amount changes each day.**
- What phrase in the problem indicates division? **"share the amount in the jar equally"**
- Why is the number of people given as 6 and not 5? **You need to include yourself in the total.**

CHOOSE A VARIABLE
To write an expression for a real-world problem, choose a letter that reminds you of the quantity represented, such as ℓ for length.

EXAMPLE 2 Write an expression

CUTTING A RIBBON A piece of ribbon ℓ feet long is cut from a ribbon 8 feet long. Write an expression for the length (in feet) of the remaining piece.

Solution

Draw a diagram and use a specific case to help you write the expression.

Suppose the piece cut is 2 feet long.	Suppose the piece cut is ℓ feet long.
8 ft; $(8 - 2)$ ft, 2 ft	8 ft; $(8 - \ell)$ ft, ℓ ft
The remaining piece is $(8 - 2)$ feet long.	The remaining piece is $(8 - \ell)$ feet long.

▶ The expression $8 - \ell$ represents the length (in feet) of the remaining piece.

VERBAL MODEL A **verbal model** describes a real-world situation using words as labels and using math symbols to relate the words. You can replace the words with numbers and variables to create a *mathematical model*, such as an expression, for the real-world situation.

EXAMPLE 3 Use a verbal model to write an expression

TIPS You work with 5 other people at an ice cream stand. All the workers put their tips into a jar and share the amount in the jar equally at the end of the day. Write an expression for each person's share (in dollars) of the tips.

Solution

STEP 1 **Write** a verbal model.

STEP 2 **Translate** the verbal model into an algebraic expression. Let a represent the amount (in dollars) in the jar.

Amount in jar	÷	Number of people
a	÷	6

▶ An expression that represents each person's share (in dollars) is $\frac{a}{6}$.

AVOID ERRORS
Read the statement of the problem carefully. The number of people sharing tips is 6.

✓ GUIDED PRACTICE for Examples 2 and 3

2. **WHAT IF?** In Example 2, suppose that you cut the original ribbon into p pieces of equal length. Write an expression that represents the length (in feet) of each piece. **$\frac{8}{p}$**

3. **WHAT IF?** In Example 3, suppose that each of the 6 workers contributes an equal amount for an after-work celebration. Write an expression that represents the total amount (in dollars) contributed. **$6d$, where d represents the amount contributed by each worker.**

Differentiated Instruction

Inclusion Students with conceptual processing difficulties may have a hard time with the many verbal descriptions and symbolic notations for expressing the same operation. For example, "k divided by 2" or "the quotient of k and 2" can be written as $\frac{k}{2}$, $k/2$, and $k \div 2$. Students with such difficulties should be provided with resource sheets listing as many possible descriptions and notations for each standard operation. See also the *Differentiated Instruction Resources* for more strategies.

RATES A **rate** is a fraction that compares two quantities measured in different units. If the denominator of the fraction is 1 unit, the rate is called a **unit rate**.

EXAMPLE 4 Find a unit rate

READING
Per means "for each" or "for every" and can also be represented using the symbol /, as in mi/h.

A car travels 120 miles in 2 hours. Find the unit rate in feet per second.

$$\frac{120 \text{ miles}}{2 \text{ hours}} = \frac{120 \text{ miles}}{2 \text{ hours}} \cdot \frac{5280 \text{ feet}}{1 \text{ mile}} \cdot \frac{1 \text{ hour}}{60 \text{ minutes}} \cdot \frac{1 \text{ minute}}{60 \text{ seconds}} = \frac{88 \text{ feet}}{1 \text{ second}}$$

▶ The unit rate is 88 feet per second.

EXAMPLE 5 Solve a multi-step problem

TRAINING For a training program, each day you run a given distance and then walk to cool down. One day you run 2 miles and then walk for 20 minutes at a rate of 0.1 mile per 100 seconds. What total distance do you cover?

Solution

STEP 1 **Convert** your walking rate to miles per minute.

$$\frac{0.1 \text{ mile}}{100 \text{ seconds}} \cdot \frac{60 \text{ seconds}}{1 \text{ minute}} = \frac{6 \text{ miles}}{100 \text{ minutes}} = \frac{0.06 \text{ mile}}{1 \text{ minute}}$$

STEP 2 **Write** a verbal model and then an expression. Let m be the number of minutes you walk.

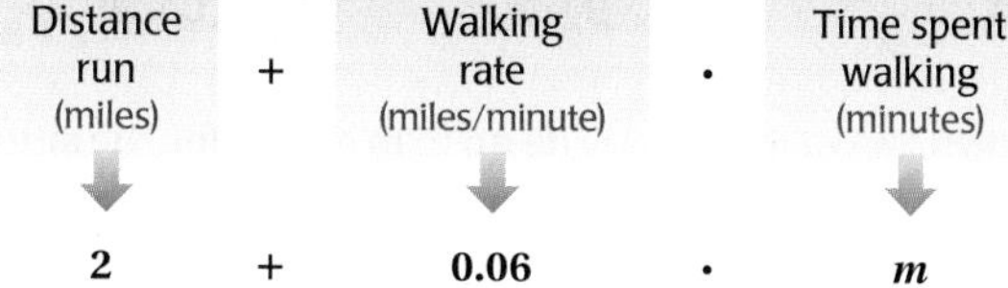

2 + **0.06** • ***m***

USE UNIT ANALYSIS
You expect the answer to be a distance in miles. You can use unit analysis, also called *dimensional analysis,* to check that the expression produces an answer in miles.

Use *unit analysis* to check that the expression $2 + 0.06m$ is reasonable.

$$\text{miles} + \frac{\text{miles}}{\text{minute}} \cdot \text{minutes} = \text{miles} + \text{miles} = \text{miles}$$

Because the units are miles, the expression is reasonable.

STEP 3 **Evaluate** the expression when $m = 20$.

$2 + 0.06(20) = 3.2$

▶ You cover a total distance of 3.2 miles.

✓ **GUIDED PRACTICE** for Examples 4 and 5

4. **WHAT IF?** In Example 5, suppose tomorrow you run 3 miles and then walk for 15 minutes at a rate of 0.1 mile per 90 seconds. What total distance will you cover? **4 mi**

Extra Example 4

A runner travels 730 yards in 5 minutes. Find the unit rate in feet per second. **7.3 ft/sec**

Key Questions to Ask for Example 4

- Why do you multiply by $\frac{5280 \text{ feet}}{1 \text{ mile}}$? **So you can convert miles to feet.**

Extra Example 5

You are teaching your friend how to drive a boat. You drive 4 miles to an open location and then let your friend drive for 15 minutes at a rate of 1.25 miles per 15 seconds. What total distance do you and your friend cover? **15.25 mi**

Key Question to Ask for Example 5

- Why do you convert your walking rate to miles per minute? **So you can find the distance walked by multiplying the walking rate by the number of minutes walked.**

Closing the Lesson

Have students summarize the major points of the lesson and answer the Essential Question: How do you write an expression to represent a real-world situation?

- **Certain words and phrases indicate the operation(s) to be used in a real-world situation.**
- **A verbal model can be used to write an expression that models a real-world situation.**
- **Use unit analysis to check that the expression is reasonable.**

Translate the verbal phrases in the problem into operations and variables, create a verbal model, and then translate the verbal model into an expression.

4 PRACTICE AND APPLY

Assignment Guide

Answer Transparencies available for all exercises

Basic:
Day 1: SRH p. 929 Exs. 1–6
pp. 18–20
Exs. 1, 2, 3–11 odd, 13, 14, 15–21 odd, 22–27, 31–35, 38–46 even

Average:
Day 1: pp. 18–20
Exs. 1, 2, 4–12 even, 13–29, 32–37, 41–46

Advanced:
Day 1: pp. 18–20
Exs. 1, 2, 9–14, 18–25, 28–30*, 33–37*, 44–46

Block:
pp. 18–20
Exs. 1, 2, 3–11 odd, 13–29, 32–37, 41–46 (with 1.4)

Differentiated Instruction

See *Differentiated Instruction Resources* for suggestions on addressing the needs of a diverse classroom.

Homework Check

For a quick check of student understanding of key concepts, go over the following exercises:

Basic: 7, 15, 19, 23, 31
Average: 9, 17, 20, 24, 32
Advanced: 11, 18, 21, 25, 33

Extra Practice

- Student Edition, p. 938
- Chapter Resource Book: Practice levels A, B, C

Practice Worksheet

An easily-readable reduced practice page (with answers) for this lesson can be found on p. 1C.

1.3 EXERCISES

HOMEWORK KEY
○ = **WORKED-OUT SOLUTIONS on p. WS1 for Exs. 11, 21, and 33**
★ = **STANDARDIZED TEST PRACTICE Exs. 2, 13, 14, 34, and 37**

SKILL PRACTICE

A

1. **VOCABULARY** Copy and complete: A(n) __?__ is a fraction that compares two quantities measured in different units. **rate**

2. ★ **WRITING** *Explain* how to write $\frac{20 \text{ miles}}{4 \text{ hours}}$ as a unit rate. **See margin.**

EXAMPLE 1 on p. 15 for Exs. 3–14

2. Divide the numerator and the denominator by 4; $\frac{20 \text{ miles} \div 4}{4 \text{ hours} \div 4} = \frac{5 \text{ mi}}{1 \text{h}}$ or 5 mi/h.

9. $\frac{2t}{12}$

TRANSLATING PHRASES **Translate the verbal phrase into an expression.**

3. 8 more than a number x **$x + 8$**
4. The product of 6 and a number y **$6y$**
5. $\frac{1}{2}$ of a number m **$\frac{1}{2}m$**
6. 50 divided by a number h **$\frac{50}{h}$**
7. The difference of 7 and a number n **$7 - n$**
8. The sum of 15 and a number x **$15 + x$**
9. The quotient of twice a number t and 12
10. 3 less than the square of a number p **$p^2 - 3$**
11. 7 less than twice a number k **$2k - 7$**
12. 5 more than 3 times a number w **$3w + 5$**

13. ★ **MULTIPLE CHOICE** Which expression represents the phrase "the product of 15 and the quantity 12 more than a number x"? **C**

Ⓐ $15 + 12 \cdot x$ Ⓑ $(15 + 12)x$ Ⓒ $15(x + 12)$ Ⓓ $15 \cdot 12 + x$

14. ★ **MULTIPLE CHOICE** Which expression represents the phrase "twice the quotient of 50 and the sum of a number y and 8"? **C**

Ⓐ $\frac{2 \cdot 50}{y} + 8$ Ⓑ $2\left(\frac{50 + y}{8}\right)$ Ⓒ $2\left(\frac{50}{y + 8}\right)$ Ⓓ $\frac{2}{50} + (y + 8)$

EXAMPLES 2 and 3 on p. 16 for Exs. 15–21

WRITING EXPRESSIONS **Write an expression for the situation.**

15. Number of tokens needed for v video games if each game takes 4 tokens **$4v$**
16. Number of pages of a 5 page article left to read if you've read p pages **$5 - p$**
17. Each person's share if p people share 16 slices of pizza equally **$\frac{16}{p}$**
18. Amount you spend if you buy a shirt for \$20 and jeans for j dollars **$20 + j$**
19. Number of days left in the week if d days have passed so far **$7 - d$**
20. Number of hours in m minutes **$\frac{m}{60}$**
21. Number of months in y years **$12y$**

EXAMPLE 4 on p. 17 for Exs. 22–27

UNIT RATES **Find the unit rate in feet per second.**

22. $\frac{300 \text{ yards}}{1 \text{ minute}}$ **15 ft/sec**
23. $\frac{240 \text{ yards}}{1 \text{ hour}}$ **0.2 ft/sec**
24. $\frac{180 \text{ miles}}{2 \text{ hours}}$ **132 ft/sec**
25. $\frac{171 \text{ miles}}{3 \text{ hours}}$ **83.6 ft/sec**

B

ERROR ANALYSIS ***Describe*** **and correct the error in the units.**

26. $\frac{\$2}{\text{foot}} \cdot 24 \text{ feet} = \frac{\$48}{\text{ft}^2}$

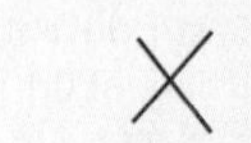

Feet should cancel out, not be squared; \$48.

27. $9 \text{ yards} \cdot \frac{3 \text{ feet}}{1 \text{ yard}} \cdot \frac{\$2}{\text{foot}} = \frac{\$54}{\text{ft}}$

Feet should cancel out; \$54.

COMPARING RATES In Exercises 28 and 29, tell which rate is greater.

28. $1\frac{1}{4}$ miles in 2 minutes and 4 seconds, or $1\frac{3}{16}$ miles in 1 minute and 55 seconds **$1\frac{3}{16}$ mi in 1 min 55 sec**

29. $1.60 for 5 minutes, or $19.50 for 1 hour **$19.50 for 1 h**

C 30. **CHALLENGE** Look for a pattern in the expressions shown below. Use the pattern to write an expression for the sum of the whole numbers from 1 to n. Then find the sum of the whole numbers from 1 to 50.

$1 + 2 = \frac{2 \cdot 3}{2}$ $\quad 1 + 2 + 3 = \frac{3 \cdot 4}{2}$ $\quad 1 + 2 + 3 + 4 = \frac{4 \cdot 5}{2}$ $\quad$ **$\frac{n \cdot (n + 1)}{2}$; 1275**

PROBLEM SOLVING

EXAMPLE 5 A on p. 17 for Exs. 31–34

A 31. **TICKET PRICES** Tickets to a science museum cost $19.95 each. There is a $3 charge for each order no matter how many tickets are ordered. Write an expression for the cost (in dollars) of ordering tickets. Then find the total cost if you order 5 tickets. **$19.95t + 3$; $102.75**

@HomeTutor for problem solving help at classzone.com

32. **FOSSIL FUELS** Fossil fuels are produced by the decay of organic material over millions of years. To make one gallon of gas, it takes about 98 tons of organic material, roughly the amount of wheat that could be harvested in a 40 acre field. Write an expression for the amount (in tons) of organic material it takes to make g gallons of gas. How many tons would it take to make enough gas to fill a car's 20 gallon gas tank? **$98g$; 1960 tons**

@HomeTutor for problem solving help at classzone.com

33. **MULTI-STEP PROBLEM** A 48 ounce container of juice costs $2.64. A 64 ounce container of the same juice costs $3.84.

a. Find the cost per ounce of each container. **$.055, $.06**

b. Which size container costs less per ounce? **48 oz container**

c. You want to buy 192 ounces of juice. How much do you save using the container size from your answer to part (b)? **$.96**

34. ★ **OPEN-ENDED** *Describe* a real-world situation that can be modeled by the rate $\frac{30}{x}$ where x is a period of time (in hours). Identify the units for 30. Choose a value for x and find the unit rate.

34. *Sample answer:* You earn 30 dollars for shoveling driveways in a certain amount of time. If $x =$ 4 hours, the unit rate is $7.50 per hour.

35. **WILDLIFE EDUCATION** A wildlife center presents a program about birds of prey. The center charges a basic fee of $325 and an additional fee for each bird exhibited. If 5 birds are exhibited, the additional fee is $125. What is the total cost if 7 birds are exhibited? **$500**

B 36. **CYCLING** To prepare for a bicycling event, you warm up each day at a moderate pace and then you ride hard for a number of miles. One day, you warm up for 15 minutes at a rate of 0.1 mile per 25 seconds and then you ride hard for 12 miles. What total distance do you cover? **15.6 mi**

Avoiding Common Errors

Exercises 28–29 In Exercise 28, watch for students who convert 2 minutes and 4 seconds to 2.4 minutes, and 1 minute and 55 seconds to 1.55 minutes. Show them that $2.4 \times 60 = 144$ seconds, but the correct calculation is $2(60) + 4 =$ 124 seconds. In Exercise 29, point out that one rate involves minutes and the other uses hours.

Graphing Calculator

Exercise 28 Encourage students to use their calculators to compare rates. Point out that it will be necessary to convert the fractions $\frac{1}{4}$ and $\frac{3}{16}$ to decimals before calculating the unit rates.

Reading Strategy

Exercise 32 Caution students to read the problem carefully and to use only relevant information to write their expression. If necessary, point out that the information about how much wheat can be harvested from a 40 acre field is not needed to find the answer.

Internet Reference

Exercise 32 For more information on energy sources, including fossil fuels, visit the U.S. Department of Energy's website at www.energy.gov.

Teaching Strategy

Exercise 35 To help students solve this problem, instruct them to write out a detailed solution like the one shown in Example 5.

5 ASSESS AND RETEACH

Daily Homework Quiz

Transparency Available

1. Write an expression for the situation: The number of miles left in a 425-mile trip after m miles have been traveled. **$425 - m$**
2. Find the unit rate for the rate $\frac{18 \text{ figurines}}{6 \text{ boxes}}$. **3 figurines per box**
3. A video store charges \$5 per game rental plus \$12 to rent the game system. Write an expression for renting the game system and a number of games. Then find the total cost if you rent 6 games. **$5g + 12$, where g is the number of games; \$42**

Online Quiz

Available at **classzone.com**

Diagnosis/Remediation

- Practice A, B, C in Chapter Resource Book
- Study Guide in Chapter Resource Book
- Practice Workbook
- @HomeTutor

Challenge

Additional challenge is available in the Chapter Resource Book.

Quiz

An easily-readable reduced copy of the quiz (with answers) on Lessons 1.1–1.3 from the Assessment Book can be found on p. 1E.

C 37. ★ **EXTENDED RESPONSE** A national survey determines the champion tree in a species. The champion is the tree with the greatest score, based on the tree's girth, its height, and its crown spread as shown.

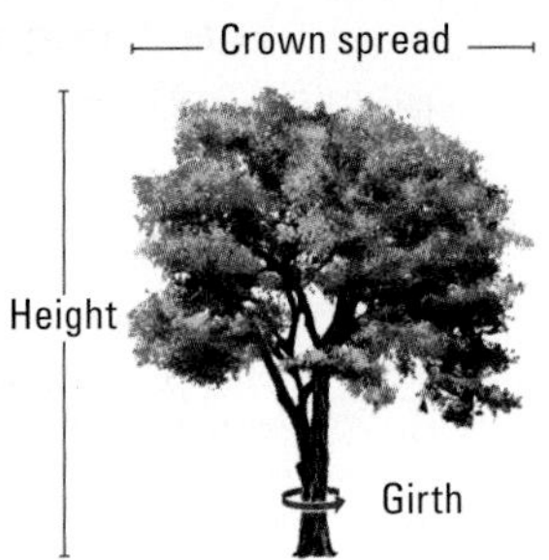

A tree's score is the sum of the girth in inches, the height in feet, and $\frac{1}{4}$ the crown spread in feet. The data for three champion trees are given. Note that the girth is given in feet.

Species	Girth (ft)	Height (ft)	Crown spread (ft)
Narrowleaf cottonwood	12	97	24
Green ash	21.5	95	95
Green buttonwood	14.5	51	68

a. **Write** Write an expression for a tree's score. **$12g + h + \frac{1}{4}c$**

b. **Evaluate** Find the score for each tree in the table. **247; 376.75; 242**

c. **CHALLENGE** Let n be any number greater than 0. Which change would have the greatest effect on a tree's score, an increase of n feet in the girth, in the height, or in the crown spread? *Explain* your reasoning. **Girth; because it is multiplied by 12.**

MIXED REVIEW

Find the area of the rectangle. *(p. 922)*

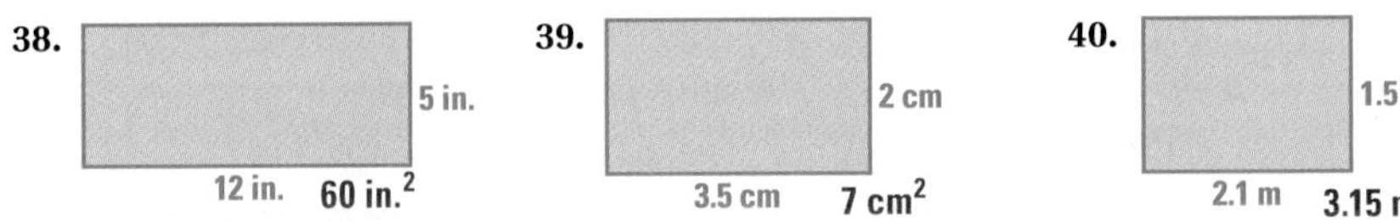

38. **60 in.^{2}** 39. **7 cm^2** 40. **3.15 m^2**

PREVIEW Prepare for Lesson 1.4 in Exs. 41–46.

Evaluate the expression.

41. $18x$ when $x = 5$ *(p. 2)* **90**
42. $y - 6$ when $y = 22$ *(p. 2)* **16**
43. $5 + z$ when $z = 11$ *(p. 2)* **16**
44. $\frac{g}{7} + 2$ when $g = 35$ *(p. 10)* **7**
45. $5 - 2y^2$ when $y = 1$ *(p. 10)* **3**
46. $\frac{a + 9}{2}$ when $a = 4$ *(p. 10)* **6.5**

QUIZ for Lessons 1.1–1.3

Evaluate the expression.

1. $y + 10$ when $y = 43$ *(p. 2)* **53**
2. $15 - b$ when $b = 9$ *(p. 2)* **6**
3. t^2 when $t = 20$ *(p. 2)* **400**
4. $3n - 5$ when $n = 8$ *(p. 8)* **19**
5. $2y^2 - 1$ when $y = 5$ *(p. 8)* **49**
6. $\frac{3x - 6}{8}$ when $x = 8$ *(p. 8)* **$2\frac{1}{4}$**

Translate the verbal phrase into an expression. *(p. 15)*

7. 7 less than a number y **$y - 7$**
8. 5 more than a number t **$t + 5$**
9. Twice a number k **$2k$**
10. **CAMPING** The rental cost for a campsite is \$25 plus \$2 per person. Write an expression for the total cost. Then find the total cost for 5 people. *(p. 15)* **$25 + 2p$; \$35**

EXTRA PRACTICE for Lesson 1.3, p. 938

ONLINE QUIZ at classzone.com

1.4 Write Equations and Inequalities

Before You translated verbal phrases into expressions.
Now You will translate verbal sentences into equations or inequalities.
Why So you can calculate team competition statistics, as in Ex. 41.

Key Vocabulary
- **equation**
- **inequality**
- **open sentence**
- **solution of an equation**
- **solution of an inequality**

An **equation** is a mathematical sentence formed by placing the symbol = between two expressions. An **inequality** is a mathematical sentence formed by placing one of the symbols <, ≤, >, or ≥ between two expressions.

An **open sentence** is an equation or an inequality that contains an algebraic expression.

KEY CONCEPT *For Your Notebook*

Symbol	Meaning	Associated Words
=	is equal to	the same as
<	is less than	fewer than
≤	is less than or equal to	at most, no more than
>	is greater than	more than
≥	is greater than or equal to	at least, no less than

COMBINING INEQUALITIES Sometimes two inequalities are combined. For example, the inequalities $x > 4$ and $x < 9$ can be combined to form the inequality $4 < x < 9$, which is read "x is greater than 4 and less than 9."

EXAMPLE 1 Write equations and inequalities

	Verbal Sentence	Equation or Inequality
a.	The difference of twice a number k and 8 is 12.	$2k - 8 = 12$
b.	The product of 6 and a number n is at least 24.	$6n \geq 24$
c.	A number y is no less than 5 and no more than 13.	$5 \leq y \leq 13$

Animated Algebra at classzone.com

✓ **GUIDED PRACTICE** for Example 1

1. Write an equation or an inequality: The quotient of a number p and 12 is at least 30. $\frac{p}{12} \geq 30$

1 PLAN AND PREPARE

Warm-Up Exercises

Transparency Available

1. Write an expression for the phrase: 4 times the difference of 6 and a number y. **$4(6 - y)$**
2. A museum charges $50 for an annual membership and then a reduced price of $2 per ticket. Write an expression to represent the situation. Then find the total cost to join the museum and buy 9 tickets. **$50 + 2t$, where t is the number of tickets; $68**

Notetaking Guide

Transparency Available

Promotes interactive learning and notetaking skills.

Pacing

Basic: 1 day
Average: 1 day
Advanced: 1 day
Block: 0.5 block with 1.3
- See *Teaching Guide/Lesson Plan.*

2 FOCUS AND MOTIVATE

Essential Question

Big Idea 2, p. 1

How do you write equations and inequalities? **Tell students they will learn how to answer this question by translating sentences into equations or inequalities.**

NCTM STANDARDS

Standard 2: Represent situations using algebraic symbols

Standard 6: Solve problems in math and other contexts

Resource Planning Guide

Chapter Resource Book
- Teaching Guide/Lesson Plan
- Activity Master
- Practice levels A, B, C
- Study Guide
- Catch-up for Absent Students
- Problem Solving Workshop
- Challenge

Workbooks
- Notetaking Guide
- Practice Workbook

Teaching Options
- **Power Presentations** provides dynamic electronic teaching resources for the classroom.
- **Activity Generator** provides editable activities for all ability levels.

Interactive Technology
- Easy Planner
- Power Presentations
- Activity Generator
- Animated Algebra
- Test Generator
- Online Quiz
- eWorkbook
- eEdition
- @HomeTutor

Resources for English Learners
- Spanish Study Guide
- Multi-Language Visual Glossary
- Student Resources in Spanish

See also the *Differentiated Instruction Resources* for more strategies for meeting individual needs.

Motivating the Lesson

Planning an event, such as a school dance, is a major undertaking. One issue to be decided is the price of a ticket. Do you want to at least break even, or do you want to make at least a specific profit? By writing an inequality, you can represent either of these situations and then find the amount you need to charge for a ticket.

3 TEACH

Extra Example 1

Write an equation or an inequality.

a. The sum of twice a number r and 3 is 11. $2r + 3 = 11$

b. The quotient of a number n and 2 is at most 16. $\frac{n}{2} \le 16$

c. A number q is at least 5 and less than 17. $5 \le q < 17$

An **Animated Algebra** activity is available online for **Example 1**. This activity is also part of **Power Presentations**.

Extra Example 2

Check whether 5 is a solution of the equation or inequality.

a. $24 - 3d = 9$ $9 = 9$; 5 is a solution.

b. $3x + 4 = 18$ $19 \ne 18$; 5 is *not* a solution.

c. $2w - 7 \le 3$ $3 \le 3$; 5 is a solution.

d. $4 + 3p > 19$ $19 \not> 19$; 5 is *not* a solution.

Key Question to Ask for Example 2

- In part c, what is the least whole number solution? Explain. 4; $2(4) + 5 = 13$ and 13 is greater than 12.

SOLUTIONS When you substitute a number for the variable in an open sentence like $x + 2 = 5$ or $2y > 6$, the resulting statement is either true or false. If the statement is true, the number is a **solution of the equation** or a **solution of the inequality**.

READING
A question mark above a symbol indicates a question. For instance, $8 - 2(3) \stackrel{?}{=} 2$ means "Is $8 - 2(3)$ equal to 2?"

EXAMPLE 2 Check possible solutions

Check whether 3 is a solution of the equation or inequality.

Equation/Inequality	Substitute	Conclusion
a. $8 - 2x = 2$	$8 - 2(3) \stackrel{?}{=} 2$	$2 = 2$ ✓ 3 is a solution.
b. $4x - 5 = 6$	$4(3) - 5 \stackrel{?}{=} 6$	$7 = 6$ ✗ 3 is *not* a solution.
c. $2z + 5 > 12$	$2(3) + 5 \stackrel{?}{>} 12$	$11 > 12$ ✗ 3 is *not* a solution.
d. $5 + 3n \le 20$	$5 + 3(3) \stackrel{?}{\le} 20$	$14 \le 20$ ✓ 3 is a solution.

USING MENTAL MATH Some equations are simple enough to solve using mental math. Think of the equation as a question. Once you answer the question, check the solution.

EXAMPLE 3 Use mental math to solve an equation

Equation	Think	Solution	Check
a. $x + 4 = 10$	What number plus 4 equals 10?	6	$6 + 4 = 10$ ✓
b. $20 - y = 8$	20 minus what number equals 8?	12	$20 - 12 = 8$ ✓
c. $6n = 42$	6 times what number equals 42?	7	$6(7) = 42$ ✓
d. $\frac{a}{5} = 9$	What number divided by 5 equals 9?	45	$\frac{45}{5} = 9$ ✓

✓ GUIDED PRACTICE for Examples 2 and 3

Check whether the given number is a solution of the equation or inequality.

2. $9 - x = 4$; 5 **solution** **3.** $b + 5 < 15$; 7 **solution** **4.** $2n + 3 \ge 21$; 9 **solution**

Solve the equation using mental math.

5. $m + 6 = 11$ **5** **6.** $5x = 40$ **8** **7.** $\frac{r}{4} = 10$ **40**

EXAMPLE 4 Solve a multi-step problem

MOUNTAIN BIKING The last time you and 3 friends went to a mountain bike park, you had a coupon for \$10 off and paid \$17 for 4 tickets. What is the regular price of 4 tickets? If you pay the regular price this time and share it equally, how much does each person pay?

Solution

STEP 1 **Write** a verbal model. Let p be the regular price of 4 tickets. Write an equation.

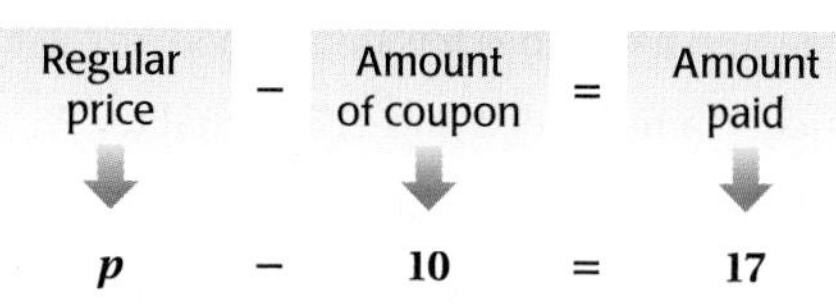

$$p - 10 = 17$$

STEP 2 **Use** mental math to solve the equation $p - 10 = 17$. Think: 10 less than what number is 17? Because $27 - 10 = 17$, the solution is 27.

▶ The regular price for 4 tickets is \$27.

STEP 3 **Find** the cost per person: $\frac{\$27}{4 \text{ people}} = \$6.75$ per person

▶ Each person pays \$6.75.

EXAMPLE 5 Write and check a solution of an inequality

BASKETBALL A basketball player scored 351 points last year. If the player plays 18 games this year, will an average of 20 points per game be enough to beat last year's total?

Solution

STEP 1 **Write** a verbal model. Let p be the average number of points per game. Write an inequality.

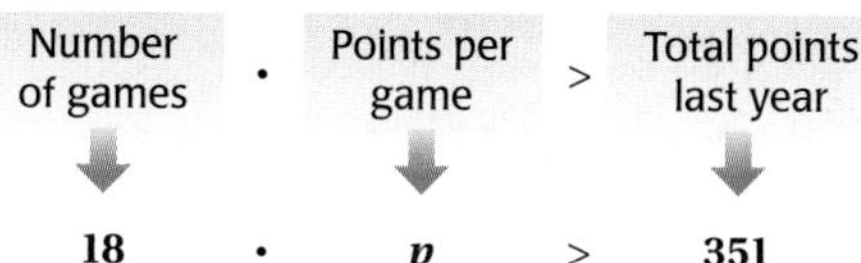

$$18 \cdot p > 351$$

USE UNIT ANALYSIS
Unit analysis shows that games $\cdot \frac{\text{points}}{\text{games}}$ = points, so the inequality is reasonable.

STEP 2 **Check** that 20 is a solution of the inequality $18p > 351$. Because $18(20) = 360$ and $360 > 351$, 20 is a solution. ✓

▶ An average of 20 points per game will be enough.

✓ **GUIDED PRACTICE** for Examples 4 and 5

8. **WHAT IF?** In Example 4, suppose that the price of 4 tickets with a half-off coupon is \$15. What is each person's share if you pay full price? **\$7.50**

9. **WHAT IF?** In Example 5, suppose that the player plays 16 games. Would an average of 22 points per game be enough to beat last year's total? **yes**

Extra Example 3

Solve the equation using mental math.

a. $y + 8 = 13$ **5** **b.** $a - 6 = 3$ **9**
c. $8c = 32$ **4** **d.** $\frac{h}{7} = 4$ **28**

Extra Example 4

Sarah enrolled in a guitar class. The enrollment fee was \$25. She paid a total of \$70 for the enrollment fee and 3 lessons. What is the cost of 3 lessons? How much did each lesson cost? **\$45; \$15**

Key Questions to Ask for Example 4

- How did you know to subtract 10 in Step 1? **Having a \$10 discount coupon means you subtract \$10.**
- What phrase indicates that you need to divide? **share it equally**

Extra Example 5

Tyler would like to make no less than \$610 selling coffee mugs online. If he sells 28 mugs for \$22 each, will he achieve his goal? **yes**

Closing the Lesson

Have students summarize the major points of the lesson and answer the Essential Question: How do you write equations and inequalities?

- **An equation is two expressions related by an equal sign, and an inequality is two expressions related by an inequality symbol.**
- **Substitute numbers for the variables and solve to find solutions for equations and inequalities.**

Use the verbal phrases associated with an equal sign and with each type of inequality symbol to determine whether to write an equation or an inequality. Then use the techniques for writing expressions learned in Lesson 1.3 to write the expressions on each side of the equal sign or inequality symbol.

4 PRACTICE AND APPLY

Assignment Guide

Answer Transparencies available for all exercises

Basic:
Day 1: pp. 24–26
Exs. 1, 2, 3–13 odd, 14–16, 17–35 odd, 39–45, 49–57 odd

Average:
Day 1: pp. 24–26
Exs. 1, 2, 7–11, 13–16, 21–28, 32–38, 41–46, 50–56 even

Advanced:
Day 1: pp. 24–26
Exs. 1, 2, 9–13, 16, 22–28 even, 32–38*, 42–48*, 50, 51, 56, 57

Block:
pp. 24–26
Exs. 1, 2, 7–11, 13–16, 21–28, 32–38, 41–46, 50–56 even (with 1.3)

Differentiated Instruction

See *Differentiated Instruction Resources* for suggestions on addressing the needs of a diverse classroom.

Homework Check

For a quick check of student understanding of key concepts, go over the following exercises:

Basic: 5, 19, 31, 39, 40
Average: 8, 22, 33, 41, 42
Advanced: 10, 26, 34, 42, 43

Extra Practice

- Student Edition, p. 938
- Chapter Resource Book: Practice levels A, B, C

Practice Worksheet

An easily-readable reduced practice page (with answers) for this lesson can be found on p. 1C.

1.4 EXERCISES

HOMEWORK KEY
○ = **WORKED-OUT SOLUTIONS** on p. WS1 for Exs. 7 and 41
★ = **STANDARDIZED TEST PRACTICE** Exs. 2, 16, 37, 44, 45, and 46

SKILL PRACTICE

A

1. **VOCABULARY** Give an example of an open sentence. ***Sample answer:*** $3x + 5 = 20$

2. ★ **WRITING** *Describe* the difference between an expression and an equation. **An expression does not contain an equal sign but an equation does.**

EXAMPLE 1 on p. 21 for Exs. 3–16

WRITING OPEN SENTENCES **Write an equation or an inequality.**

3. The sum of 42 and a number n is equal to 51. $42 + n = 51$
4. The difference of a number z and 11 is equal to 35. $z - 11 = 35$
5. The difference of 9 and the quotient of a number t and 6 is 5. $9 - \frac{t}{6} = 5$
6. The sum of 12 and the quantity 8 times a number k is equal to 48. $12 + 8k = 48$
7. The product of 9 and the quantity 5 more than a number t is less than 6. $9(t + 5) < 6$
8. The product of 4 and a number w is at most 51. $4w \le 51$
9. The sum of a number b and 3 is greater than 8 and less than 12. $8 < b + 3 < 12$
10. The product of 8 and a number k is greater than 4 and no more than 16. $4 < 8k \le 16$
11. The difference of a number t and 7 is greater than 10 and less than 20. $10 < t - 7 < 20$

STORE SALES **Write an inequality for the price p (in dollars) described.**

12. 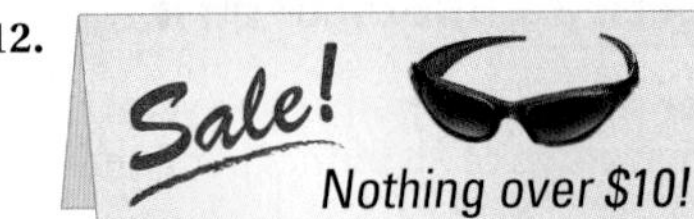
Sale!
Nothing over $10!
$p \le 10$

13.
Prices start at $12.99
$p \ge 12.99$

ERROR ANALYSIS ***Describe*** **and correct the error in writing the verbal sentence as an equation or an inequality.**

14. The sum of a number n and 4 is no more than 13.

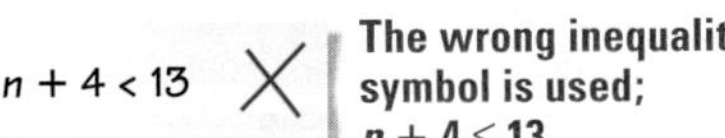
$n + 4 < 13$ ✗

The wrong inequality symbol is used; $n + 4 \le 13$.

15. The quotient of a number t and 4.2 is at most 15.

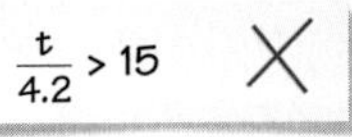
$\frac{t}{4.2} > 15$ ✗

The wrong inequality symbol is used; $\frac{t}{4.2} \le 15$.

16. ★ **MULTIPLE CHOICE** Which inequality corresponds to the sentence "The product of a number b and 3 is no less than 12"? **D**

Ⓐ $3b < 12$ Ⓑ $3b \le 12$ Ⓒ $3b > 12$ Ⓓ $3b \ge 12$

EXAMPLE 2 on p. 22 for Exs. 17–28

CHECK POSSIBLE SOLUTIONS **Check whether the given number is a solution of the equation or inequality.**

17. $x + 9 = 17$; 8 **solution**
18. $9 + 4y = 17$; 1 **not a solution**
19. $6f - 7 = 29$; 5 **not a solution**
20. $\frac{k}{5} + 9 = 11$; 10 **solution**
21. $\frac{r}{3} - 4 = 4$; 12 **not a solution**
22. $\frac{x - 5}{3} \ge 2.8$; 11 **not a solution**
23. $15 - 4y > 6$; 2 **solution**
24. $y - 3.5 < 6$; 9 **solution**
25. $2 + 3x \le 8$; 2 **solution**
26. $2p - 1 \ge 7$; 3 **not a solution**
27. $4z - 5 < 3$; 2 **not a solution**
28. $3z + 7 > 20$; 4 **not a solution**

Differentiated Instruction

Kinesthetic Learners To assist students in **Exercises 3–11**, have students associate "less than" with their left hand and "greater than" with their right hand. Then if they open the associated hand as if it is "eating" something, they can identify the correct inequality symbol.

See also the *Differentiated Instruction Resources* for more strategies.

EXAMPLE 3 on p. 22 for Exs. 29–34

MENTAL MATH **Solve the equation using mental math.**

29. $x + 8 = 13$ **5**
30. $y + 16 = 25$ **9**
31. $z - 11 = 1$ **12**
32. $5w = 20$ **4**
33. $8b = 72$ **9**
34. $\frac{f}{6} = 4$ **24**

EQUATIONS AND INEQUALITIES **In Exercises 35 and 36, write an open sentence. Then check whether $3\frac{1}{2}$ is a solution of the open sentence.**

B

35. 2 less than the product of 3 and a number x is equal to the sum of x and 5. **$3x - 2 = x + 5$; solution**

36. 4 more than twice a number k is no greater than the sum of k and 11. **$2k + 4 \le k + 11$; solution**

37. ★ **MULTIPLE CHOICE** Which equation has the same solution as $z - 9 = 3$? **C**

Ⓐ $z - 4 = 16$ Ⓑ $\frac{1}{2}z = 7$ Ⓒ $z + 15 = 27$ Ⓓ $5z = 45$

C

38. **CHALLENGE** Use mental math to solve the equation $3x + 4 = 19$. *Explain* your thinking. **5; ask what number times 3 plus 4 equals 19.**

PROBLEM SOLVING

EXAMPLES 4 and 5 on p. 23 for Exs. 39–43

A

39. **CHARITY WALK** You are taking part in a charity walk, and you have walked 12.5 miles so far. Your goal is to walk 20 miles. How many more miles do you need to walk to meet your goal? **7.5 mi**

@HomeTutor for problem solving help at classzone.com

40. **COMPACT DISCS** You buy a storage rack that holds 40 CDs. You have 27 CDs. Write an inequality that describes how many more CDs you can buy and still have no more CDs than the rack can hold. You buy 15 CDs. Will they all still fit? **$27 + c \le 40$; no**

@HomeTutor for problem solving help at classzone.com

41. **ECO-CHALLENGE** Eco-Challenge Fiji was a competition that included jungle trekking, ocean swimming, mountain biking, and river kayaking. In 2002, the U.S. team finished second about 6 hours after the winning team from New Zealand. The U.S. team finished in about 173 hours. What was the winning team's time? **167 h**

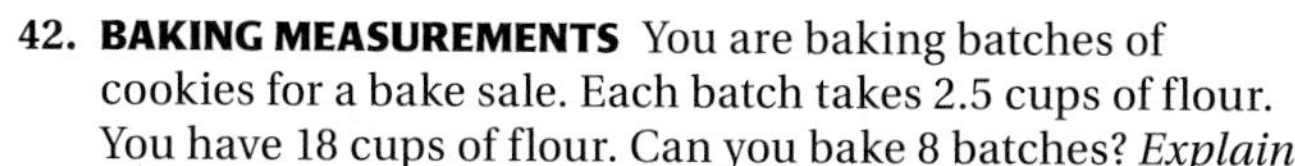

42. **BAKING MEASUREMENTS** You are baking batches of cookies for a bake sale. Each batch takes 2.5 cups of flour. You have 18 cups of flour. Can you bake 8 batches? *Explain.*

42. No. ***Sample answer*: Since each batch of cookies takes 2.5 cups of flour and you want to make 8 batches, you need to multiply 2.5 by 8, which gives you 20 cups. Since you only have 18 cups, you do not have enough.**

43. **EMPLOYMENT** Your friend takes a job cleaning up a neighbor's yard and mowing the grass, and asks you and two other friends to help. Your friend divides the amount the neighbor pays equally among all the members of the group. Each of you got $25. How much did the neighbor pay? **$100**

44. ★ **OPEN-ENDED** Describe a real-world situation you could model using the equation $5x = 50$. Use mental math to solve the equation. *Explain* what the solution means in this situation. **See margin.**

Vocabulary

Exercise 35 Some students may be confused by the words "less" and "less than" since they both indicate subtraction. Point out that "less than" means "subtracted from" while "less" means "minus." So, "2 less than the product of 3 and a number x" means 2 subtracted from $3x$, or $3x - 2$.

Mathematical Reasoning

Exercise 38 Point out that $3x$ must have a value of 15 in order for x to be a solution of the equation. Students should then see that the solution of the equation $3x = 15$ is the solution of the given equation.

Reading Strategy

Exercise 40 Students may want to reword the third sentence of this exercise. The following sentence may be easier for students to decipher: *Write an inequality that describes the number of additional CDs you can buy without having too many to fit in the storage rack.*

Avoiding Common Errors

Exercise 43 Watch for students who use 3 as the number of workers in the group. Suggest they give names to each of the persons discussed in the problem as they read it. Then ask them to count the number of workers; they will discover that there are 4 workers.

44. ***Sample answer:* You want to buy $5 gift certificates to a music store for your friends. If you have $50, how many certificates can you buy? 10 certificates; you can buy 10 $5 gift certificates for $50.**

5 ASSESS AND RETEACH

Daily Homework Quiz

Transparency Available

Write an equation or an inequality.

1. 3 less than twice a number n is 12. **$2n - 3 = 12$**
2. The product of 5 and a number k is no more than 30. **$5k \le 30$**
3. Check whether 2 is a solution of the inequality $3p + 2 > 8$. **$8 \not> 8$; 2 is *not* a solution.**
4. You need to practice a gymnastic routine for at least 25 hours. You have already practiced 8.5 hours. If you practice for another 16.5 hours, will you reach your goal? Explain. **Yes; the inequality $h + 8.5 \ge 25$ represents the situation. If you substitute 16.5 for h, $16.5 + 8.5 = 25$ and $25 \ge 25$.**

Available at **classzone.com**

Diagnosis/Remediation

- Practice A, B, C in Chapter Resource Book
- Study Guide in Chapter Resource Book
- Practice Workbook
- @HomeTutor

Challenge

Additional challenge is available in the Chapter Resource Book.

B

45. ★ **SHORT RESPONSE** You have two part-time jobs. You earn \$6 per hour running errands and \$5 per hour walking dogs. You can work a total of 10 hours this weekend and hope to earn at least \$55. Let r be the number of hours you spend running errands.

    a. Write an inequality that describes the situation. Your inequality should involve only one variable, r. **$6r + 5(10 - r) \ge 55$**

    b. If you spend the same amount of time at each job, will you meet your goal? *Explain.* **Yes; you will earn \$30 running errands and \$25 walking dogs; $30 + 25 = 55$.**

    c. Can you meet your goal by working all 10 hours at only one job? *Explain.* **Yes; if you work 10 hours running errands, you will earn \$60. You will not meet your goal if you work all 10 hours walking dogs.**

46. ★ **EXTENDED RESPONSE** Your school's service club is sponsoring a dance in the school gym to raise money for a local charity. The expenses will be \$600. The club members will sell tickets for \$10. They hope to raise enough money to cover the expenses and have enough left to donate \$1000 to the charity.

    a. How many tickets must they sell to cover their expenses? **60 tickets**

    b. How many tickets must they sell to cover their expenses and meet their goal? **160 tickets**

    c. The school allows no more than 200 students in the gymnasium for a dance. Can the club members sell enough tickets to exceed their goal? What is the greatest possible amount by which they can exceed their goal? *Explain* your reasoning. **Yes; \$400; if they sell 200 tickets they will bring in \$2000, which is \$400 over their goal.**

C

47. **CHALLENGE** You and your friend are reading the same series of science fiction books. You tell your friend, "I've read 3 times as many books as you have." Your friend replies, "You've read only 4 more books than I have." How many books have each of you read? **friend: 2 books; you: 6 books**

48. **CHALLENGE** Each of the long sides of a rectangle has a length of x inches. Each of the other sides is 1 inch shorter than the long sides. The perimeter of the rectangle is 22 inches. Find the length and the width of the rectangle. *Justify* your answer. **6 in., 5 in.; $P = 2\ell + 2w$, $2(6) + 2(5) = 12 + 10 = 22$**

MIXED REVIEW

PREVIEW
Prepare for Lesson 1.5 in Exs. 49–54.

Write the percent as a decimal. *(p. 916)*

49. 3% **0.03**
50. 3.5% **0.035**
51. 5.25% **0.0525**

Find the perimeter of the triangle or rectangle. *(p. 922)*

52. Triangle with sides $1\frac{3}{4}$ in., $1\frac{3}{4}$ in., $1\frac{3}{4}$ in. **$5\frac{1}{4}$ in.**

53. Rectangle 1.6 m by 0.9 m **5 m**

54. Rectangle $4\frac{1}{2}$ ft by 7 ft **23 ft**

Evaluate the expression. *(p. 8)*

55. $9 \cdot 3^2 - 2$ **79**
56. $4 \div 2^2 + \frac{1}{7}$ **$1\frac{1}{7}$**
57. $5 \div 0.25 \cdot 3$ **60**

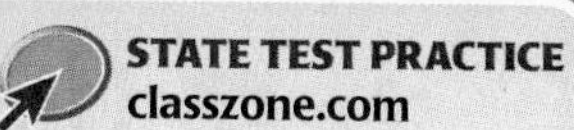

MIXED REVIEW of Problem Solving

STATE TEST PRACTICE classzone.com

Lessons 1.1–1.4

1. **MULTI-STEP PROBLEM** You are making a photo quilt by transferring photos to squares of fabric. Each square should be big enough so that you can turn over an edge $\frac{5}{8}$ inch long on each side and have a finished square with a side length of $5\frac{3}{4}$ inches.

   a. What are the dimensions of each fabric square? **7 in. by 7 in.**

   b. How many square inches of fabric do you need if you want to include 48 squares? **2352 in.^{2}**

   c. The fabric you buy is 36 inches wide. How long a piece of fabric do you need? **70 in.**

   d. You buy a piece of fabric that has the length you found in part (c). Once you've cut all the squares, how many square inches of fabric are left over? **168 in.^{2}**

2. **MULTI-STEP PROBLEM** A rule of thumb states that the ideal weight (in ounces) of a baseball bat for a high school baseball player is 5 ounces more than one third of the player's height (in inches).

   a. Write an expression that describes the ideal weight (in ounces) of a bat for a high school baseball player who is h inches tall. **$\frac{1}{3}h + 5$**

   b. One player was 66 inches tall last year. This year the player is 69 inches tall. How much heavier should the player's new bat be than the bat used last year? **1 oz**

3. **SHORT RESPONSE** You collect miniature cars and display them on shelves that hold 20 cars each.

   a. Which expression would you evaluate to find the number of shelves you need for x cars: $20x$, $\frac{x}{20}$, or $\frac{20}{x}$? *Justify* your choice. **See margin.**

   b. Find the number of shelves you need to display 120 cars. **6 shelves**

4. **OPEN-ENDED** *Describe* a real-world situation that you could model with the inequality $3x < 15$. *Explain* what a solution of the inequality means in this situation. **See margin.**

5. **SHORT RESPONSE** You pay \$7.50 for 3 quarts of strawberries. You realize that you need more strawberries for your recipe. You return to the store with \$4.50. Will you have enough money to buy 2 more quarts of strawberries? *Explain* your reasoning. **No; each quart cost \$2.50, so you will need \$5 for 2 quarts.**

6. **EXTENDED RESPONSE** The number of calories in one serving of any food is the sum of the calories from fat, protein, and carbohydrate. The table shows the calories in 1 gram of each of the three food components.

Component	Calories in 1 gram
Fat	9
Protein	4
Carbohydrate	4

   a. Write an expression for the total number of calories in a serving of food that contains f grams of fat, p grams of protein, and c grams of carbohydrate. **$9f + 4p + 4c$**

   b. A serving of cheddar cheese contains 14 grams of fat, 11 grams of protein, and 1 gram of carbohydrate. How many calories are in a serving of cheddar cheese? **174 calories**

   c. A 100 pound teenager requires about 45 grams of protein per day. If the teenager tried to get all the required protein for one day from cheddar cheese, how many calories would the teenager consume? *Explain.* **See margin.**

7. **GRIDDED ANSWER** You are comparing two dorm-size refrigerators, both with cube-shaped interiors. One model has an interior edge length of 14 inches. Another model has an interior edge length of 16 inches. How many more cubic inches of storage space does the larger model have? **1352 in.^{3}**

3a. $\frac{x}{20}$; **if you divide the number of cars you have by 20 you will know how many shelves you need.**

4. ***Sample answer:*** **A basketball player scores less than 15 points in a game. What is the most 3-point field goals the player could have scored? The solution $x < 5$ means the player scored less than 5 3-point field goals.**

6c. About 713 calories; the teenager would need about 4.1 servings of cheese to get 45 grams of protein. So, 4.1 times 174 calories per serving is about 713 calories.

1.5 Use a Problem Solving Plan

Before You used problem solving strategies.
Now You will use a problem solving plan to solve problems.
Why? So you can determine a route, as in Example 1.

Key Vocabulary
• formula

KEY CONCEPT *For Your Notebook*

A Problem Solving Plan

STEP 1 **Read and Understand** Read the problem carefully. Identify what you know and what you want to find out.

STEP 2 **Make a Plan** Decide on an approach to solving the problem.

STEP 3 **Solve the Problem** Carry out your plan. Try a new approach if the first one isn't successful.

STEP 4 **Look Back** Once you obtain an answer, check that it is reasonable.

EXAMPLE 1 **Read a problem and make a plan**

RUNNING You run in a city. Short blocks are north-south and are 0.1 mile long. Long blocks are east-west and are 0.15 mile long. You will run 2 long blocks east, a number of short blocks south, 2 long blocks west, and back to your start. You want to run 2 miles at a rate of 7 miles per hour. How many short blocks must you run?

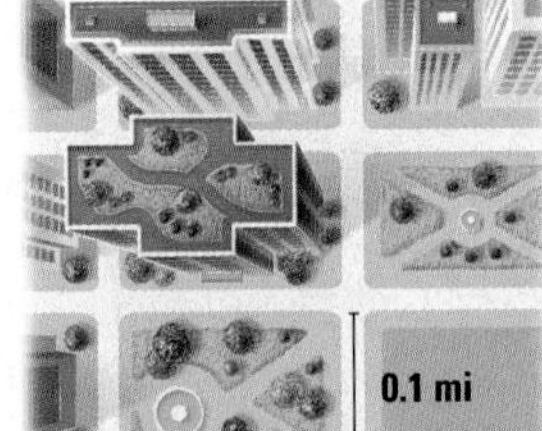

Solution

ANOTHER WAY
For an alternative method for solving the problem in Example 1, turn to page 34 for the **Problem Solving Workshop**.

STEP 1 **Read and Understand**

What do you know?

You know the length of each size block, the number of long blocks you will run, and the total distance you want to run.

You can conclude that you must run an even number of short blocks because you run the same number of short blocks in each direction.

What do you want to find out?

You want to find out the number of short blocks you should run so that, along with the 4 long blocks, you run 2 miles.

STEP 2 **Make a Plan** Use what you know to write a verbal model that represents what you want to find out. Then write an equation and solve it, as in Example 2.

1 PLAN AND PREPARE

Warm-Up Exercises

Transparency Available

1. Mr. Lu is planting trees around the perimeter of a rectangular park. The park measures 72 feet by 48 feet. The trees need to be spaced 12 feet apart. A tree is to be planted in each corner. How many trees are needed? **20 trees**
2. In an aviary, there are three times as many finches as mockingbirds. If there are 48 birds, how many mockingbirds are there? **12 mockingbirds**

Notetaking Guide

Transparency Available

Promotes interactive learning and notetaking skills.

Pacing

Basic: 1 day
Average: 1 day
Advanced: 1 day
Block: 0.5 block with 1.6
• See *Teaching Guide/Lesson Plan.*

2 FOCUS AND MOTIVATE

Essential Question

Big Idea 2, p. 1

How can you use a problem solving plan to solve a problem? **Tell students they will learn how to answer this question by working through the steps of a problem solving plan.**

NCTM STANDARDS

Standard 6: Solve problems in math and other contexts; Apply/adapt strategies to solve problems

Resource Planning Guide

Chapter Resource Book
• Teaching Guide/Lesson Plan
• Practice levels A, B, C
• Study Guide
• Catch-up for Absent Students
• Problem Solving Workshop
• Challenge

Workbooks
• Notetaking Guide
• Practice Workbook

Teaching Options
• **Power Presentations** provides dynamic electronic teaching resources for the classroom.
• **Activity Generator** provides editable activities for all ability levels.

Interactive Technology
• Easy Planner
• Power Presentations
• Activity Generator
• Animated Algebra
• Test Generator
• Online Quiz
• eWorkbook
• eEdition
• @HomeTutor

Resources for English Learners
• Spanish Study Guide
• Multi-Language Visual Glossary
• Student Resources in Spanish

See also the *Differentiated Instruction Resources* for more strategies for meeting individual needs.

EXAMPLE 2 Solve a problem and look back

Solve the problem in Example 1 by carrying out the plan. Then check your answer.

Solution

IDENTIFY IRRELEVANT INFORMATION

The rate at which you run is given, but it is not needed to solve the problem. That information is irrelevant. All other given information is relevant, and no information needed to solve the problem is missing.

STEP 3 **Solve the Problem** Write a verbal model. Then write an equation. Let s be the number of short blocks you run.

Length of short block (miles/block)	·	Number of short blocks (blocks)	+	Length of long block (miles/block)	·	Number of long blocks (blocks)	=	Total distance (miles)
0.1	·	s	+	0.15	·	4	=	2

The equation is $0.1s + 0.6 = 2$. One way to solve the equation is to use the strategy *guess, check, and revise.*

Guess an even number that is easily multiplied by 0.1. Try 20.

Check whether 20 is a solution.

$0.1s + 0.6 = 2$ **Write equation.**

$0.1(20) + 0.6 \stackrel{?}{=} 2$ **Substitute 20 for *s*.**

$2.6 = 2$ ✗ **Simplify; 20 does not check.**

Revise. Because $2.6 > 2$, try an even number less than 20. Try 14.

Check whether 14 is a solution.

$0.1s + 0.6 = 2$ **Write equation.**

$0.1(14) + 0.6 \stackrel{?}{=} 2$ **Substitute 14 for *s*.**

$2 = 2$ ✓ **Simplify.**

▶ To run 2 miles, you should run 14 short blocks along with the 4 long blocks you run.

STEP 4 **Look Back** Check your answer by making a table. You run 0.6 mile on long blocks. Each two short blocks add 0.2 mile.

Short blocks	0	2	4	6	8	10	12	14
Total distance	0.6	0.8	1.0	1.2	1.4	1.6	1.8	2.0

The total distance is 2 miles when you run 4 long blocks and 14 short blocks. The answer in Step 3 is correct.

at classzone.com

✓ **GUIDED PRACTICE** for Examples 1 and 2

1. **WHAT IF?** In Example 1, suppose that you want to run a total distance of 3 miles. How many short blocks should you run? **24 short blocks**

Differentiated Instruction

Below Level In Step 1 of **Example 1**, some students may not be able to conclude that there must be an even number of short blocks. Have these students draw a diagram of the route and label it using the information in the problem. The diagram should enable them to see that the number of short blocks must be even. Suggest they use the diagram to create a verbal model for the problem.

See also the *Differentiated Instruction Resources* for more strategies.

Motivating the Lesson

Ask students to recount a complex situation they have had to resolve, such as allocating time for homework, activities, and chores after school each day. After they share some problems, tell them that this lesson offers a plan for solving complex math problems.

3 TEACH

Extra Example 1

You are designing the layout for a newspaper about teen issues. The newspaper will be $22\frac{1}{2}$ inches wide and 30 inches high. You plan to have 5 columns with $\frac{1}{8}$-inch gaps between them and $\frac{3}{8}$-inch margins on the left and right sides. How wide will each column be? **Step 1: I know the width of the newspaper, the number of columns, the size of the margins, and the size of the gaps between the columns. I want to find out how many gaps there are, so I can determine the width of each column. The height of the newspaper is irrelevant. Step 2: I can use a diagram to find the number of gaps and then use what I know to make a verbal model. Next, I can write an equation and solve it.**

Extra Example 2

Solve the problem in Extra Example 1 by carrying out the plan. Then check your answer. **Step 3: Let w be the width of each column. There are two margins and four gaps. The problem is modeled by $5w + 2\left(\frac{3}{8}\right) + 4\left(\frac{1}{8}\right) = 22\frac{1}{2}$. Using the guess, check, and revise strategy, the width of each column should be $4\frac{1}{4}$ inches. Step 4: Substituting $4\frac{1}{4}$ into the equation for w results in a true statement.**

An **Animated Algebra** activity is available online for **Example 2** on page 29. This activity is also part of **Power Presentations**.

Extra Example 3

A builder lays sod on the lawns of new homes. The installed cost for sod is $.38 per square foot. What is the cost of installing sod on a rectangular lawn that is 32 feet long and 18 feet wide? **D**

Ⓐ $19.00 Ⓑ $38.00
Ⓒ $184.32 Ⓓ $218.88

Key Question to Ask for Example 3

- Why do you use the formula $A = \ell w$? **The piece of leather is described as being rectangular and the words *square inches* indicate area, so the formula $A = \ell w$ is needed to solve the problem.**

Closing the Lesson

Have students summarize the major points of the lesson and answer the Essential Question: How can you use a problem solving plan to solve a problem?

- **A problem solving plan is a guide that helps you organize the steps of the work necessary to solve a problem.**
- **Any problem solving strategy can be utilized within the problem solving plan.**

By following the steps in the plan, you can identify what you need to know, decide on a strategy to use, carry out the strategy, and then check that the answer you calculate is reasonable.

FORMULAS A **formula** is an equation that relates two or more quantities. You may find it helpful to use formulas in problem solving.

REVIEW FORMULAS
For additional formulas, see pp. 924–928 and the Table of Formulas on pp. 952–953.

KEY CONCEPT — *For Your Notebook*

Formulas

Temperature

$C = \frac{5}{9}(F - 32)$ where F = degrees Fahrenheit and C = degrees Celsius

Simple interest

$I = Prt$ where I = interest, P = principal, r = interest rate (as a decimal), and t = time

Distance traveled

$d = rt$ where d = distance traveled, r = rate (constant or average speed), and t = time

Profit

$P = I - E$ where P = profit, I = income, and E = expenses

★ EXAMPLE 3 Standardized Test Practice

You are making a leather book cover. You need a rectangular piece of leather as shown. Find the cost of the piece if leather costs $.25 per square inch.

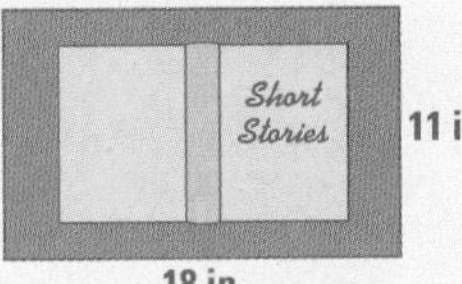

Ⓐ $14.50 Ⓑ $49.50
Ⓒ $58.00 Ⓓ $198.00

ELIMINATE CHOICES
You can eliminate choices A and D by estimating. The area of the piece of leather is about 200 square inches, and $.25(200) is about $50.

Solution

Use the formula for the area of a rectangle, $A = \ell w$, with ℓ = 18 inches and w = 11 inches.

$A = \ell w$ **Write area formula.**

$= 18(11)$ **Substitute 18 for ℓ and 11 for w.**

$= 198$ **Simplify.**

The area is 198 square inches, so the total cost is $.25(198) = $49.50.

▸ The correct answer is B. Ⓐ Ⓑ Ⓒ Ⓓ

✓ GUIDED PRACTICE for Example 3

2. **GARDENING** A gardener determines the cost of planting daffodil bulbs to be $2.40 per square foot. How much will it cost to plant daffodil bulbs in a rectangular garden that is 12 feet long and 5 feet wide? **D**

Ⓐ $40.80 Ⓑ $60 Ⓒ $81.60 Ⓓ $144

Differentiated Instruction

Visual Learners A diagram is often the most helpful way to solve a word problem. If a diagram such as the one in **Example 3** is given, that is a sign to use it. Encourage visual learners to construct diagrams whenever possible. Have them construct a similar diagram for **Guided Practice Exercise 2**.

See also the *Differentiated Instruction Resources* for more strategies.

1.5 EXERCISES

HOMEWORK KEY
○ = **WORKED-OUT SOLUTIONS** on p. WS2 for Exs. 5 and 17
★ = **STANDARDIZED TEST PRACTICE** Exs. 2, 11, 12, 20, and 22
◆ = **MULTIPLE REPRESENTATIONS** Ex. 21

SKILL PRACTICE

A

1. **VOCABULARY** Give an example of a formula. ***Sample answer:*** $d = rt$

2. ★ **WRITING** *Describe* how you can use a formula to solve the following problem: The inner edges of a cube-shaped pot have a length of 1.5 feet. How much does it cost to fill the planter if soil costs $4 per cubic foot? **See margin.**

EXAMPLES 1 and 2 on pp. 28–29 for Exs. 3–5

READING AND UNDERSTANDING In Exercises 3–5, identify what you know and what you need to find out. Identify any missing or irrelevant information. You do *not* need to solve the problem.

3. **CRAFT SHOW** You make dog collars and anticipate selling all of them at a craft fair. You spent $85 for materials and hope to make a profit of $90. How much should you charge for each collar? **See margin.**

4. **DISTANCE RUNNING** One day Paul ran at a rate of 0.15 mile per minute for 40 minutes. The next day Paul and Jen ran together at a rate of 0.16 mile per minute for 50 minutes. How far did Paul run altogether? **See margin.**

5. **TEMPERATURE** One day, the temperature in Rome, Italy, was 30°C. The temperature in Dallas, Texas, was 83°F. Which temperature was higher? **See margin.**

ERROR ANALYSIS *Describe* and correct the error in solving the problem.

A town is fencing a rectangular field that is 200 feet long and 150 feet wide. At $10 per foot, how much will it cost to fence the field? **6, 7. See margin.**

6. $P = 200 + 150 = 350$
$\$10(350) = \$3500$

7. $A = (200)(150) = 30{,}000$
$\$10(30{,}000) = \$300{,}000$

EXAMPLE 3 on p. 30 for Exs. 8–12

B

CHOOSING A FORMULA In Exercises 8–10, state the formula that is needed to solve the problem. You do *not* need to solve the problem.

8. The temperature is 68°F. What is the temperature in degrees Celsius? $C = \frac{5}{9}(F - 32)$

9. A store buys a baseball cap for $5 and sells it for $20. What is the profit? $P = I - E$

10. Find the area of a triangle with a base of 25 feet and a height of 8 feet. $A = \frac{1}{2}bh$

11. ★ **MULTIPLE CHOICE** What is the interest on $1200 invested for 2 years in an account that earns simple interest at a rate of 5% per year? **C**

Ⓐ $12 Ⓑ $60 Ⓒ $120 Ⓓ $240

12. ★ **MULTIPLE CHOICE** A car travels at an average speed of 55 miles per hour. How many miles does the car travel in 2.5 hours? **D**

Ⓐ 22 miles Ⓑ 57.5 miles Ⓒ 110 miles Ⓓ 137.5 miles

C

13. **CHALLENGE** Write a formula for the length ℓ of a rectangle given its perimeter P and its width w. *Justify* your thinking.
$\ell = \frac{P}{2} - w$. ***Sample answer:*** **Dividing the perimeter by 2 will give the sum of the length and the width. Subtracting the width will give the length.**

4 PRACTICE AND APPLY

Assignment Guide

Answer Transparencies available for all exercises

Basic:
Day 1: SRH p. 937 Exs. 1–4
pp. 31–33
Exs. 1–10, 14–20, 24–32

Average:
Day 1: pp. 31–33
Exs. 1, 2, 4–13, 16–22, 24–32

Advanced:
Day 1: pp. 31–33
Exs. 1, 2, 4, 5, 8–13*, 17–23*, 25–31 odd

Block:
pp. 31–33
Exs. 1, 2, 4–13, 16–22, 24–32 (with 1.6)

Differentiated Instruction

See *Differentiated Instruction Resources* for suggestions on addressing the needs of a diverse classroom.

Homework Check

For a quick check of student understanding of key concepts, go over the following exercises:

Basic: 3, 4, 8, 14, 16
Average: 4, 5, 9, 16, 17
Advanced: 4, 5, 10, 17, 18

Extra Practice

- Student Edition, p. 938
- Chapter Resource Book: Practice levels A, B, C

Practice Worksheet

An easily-readable reduced practice page (with answers) for this lesson can be found on p. 1D.

Differentiated Instruction

Advanced You may wish to pair advanced students with other students who are struggling with the word problems in the exercises of this lesson. Both students will benefit from this interaction—the advanced student must follow the steps of the problem solving plan for each problem when they often might not while working on their own, and the assisted student receives the guidance they need to succeed.

See also the *Differentiated Instruction Resources* for more strategies.

2. *Sample answer:* Since you are filling a cubic container, you need to use the volume formula $V = s^3$ where s is the length of an edge. Substituting 1.5 for s gives $V = 1.5^3 = 3.375$ cubic feet. If the soil costs $4 per cubic foot, $3.375 \cdot 4 = \$13.50$ to fill the planter.

3. You know the cost of the materials and the amount you hope to make. You need to find the amount you should charge for each collar. The number of collars, which is necessary for solving the problem, is missing.

4–7. See Additional Answers beginning on p. AA1.

Teaching Strategy

Exercises 14–19 Some students may feel they can solve these problems without needing to follow a plan. Encourage them to use the 4-step plan in order to gain practice using it. Stress that when they encounter a problem they find to be more difficult, they will know how to use the steps to simplify their work.

Study Strategy

Exercises 15, 17 Some students may find it easier to work with decimals than fractions. Suggest they convert the fractions to decimals as part of Step 3 in the problem solving plan.

Exercises 15, 19 For students who find these problems difficult, suggest they draw a diagram to help visualize the problem.

20c. 120; $382.80; The perimeter of the park is 150 + 200 + 250 = 600 feet. A post is placed every 5 feet so divide 600 by 5, which is 120 posts. Multiply 120 by the cost per post, 120 • 3.19 = $382.80.

PROBLEM SOLVING

EXAMPLES [A] **1, 2, and 3** on pp. 28–30 for Exs. 14–18

14. **DVD STORAGE** A stackable storage rack holds 22 DVDs and costs $21. How much would it cost to buy enough racks to hold 127 DVDs? **$126**

    @HomeTutor for problem solving help at classzone.com

15. **FRAMING** For an art project, you make a square print with a side length of 8 inches. You make a frame using strips of wood $1\frac{1}{4}$ inches wide. What is the area of the frame? **46.25 in.^{2}**

    @HomeTutor for problem solving help at classzone.com

16. **MOUNTAIN BOARDS** You have saved $70 to buy a mountain board that costs $250. You plan to save $10 each week. How many weeks will it take to save for the mountain board? **18 wk**

17. **HIKING** You are hiking. The total weight of your backpack and its contents is $13\frac{3}{8}$ pounds. You want to carry no more than 15 pounds. How many extra water bottles can you add to your backpack if each bottle weighs $\frac{3}{4}$ pound? **2 water bottles**

18. **PIZZA** Thick crust pizza requires about 0.15 ounce of dough per square inch of surface area. You have two rectangular pans, one that is 16 inches long and 14 inches wide, and one that is 15.5 inches long and 10 inches wide. How much more dough do you need to make a thick crust pizza in the larger pan than in the smaller one? **10.35 oz**

19. **SONAR** A diver uses a sonar device to determine the distance to her diving partner. The device sends a sound wave and records the time it takes for the wave to reach the diving partner and return to the device. Suppose the wave travels at a rate of about 4800 feet per second.

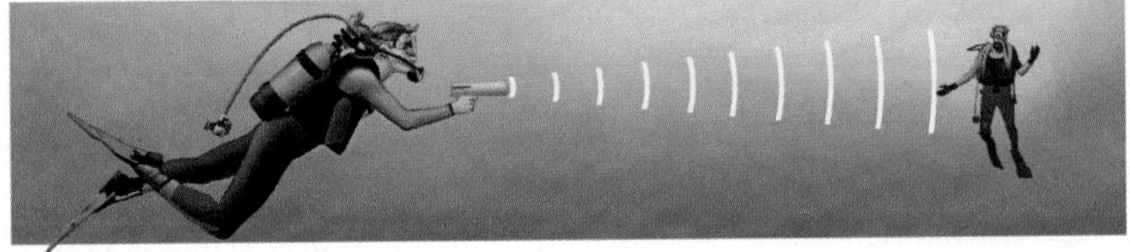

   a. The wave returns 0.2 second after it was sent. How far did the wave travel? **960 ft**

   b. How far away is the diving partner? **480 ft**

[B] 20. ★ **EXTENDED RESPONSE** A gardener is reseeding a city park that has the shape of a right triangle with a base of 150 feet and a height of 200 feet. The third side of the park is 250 feet long.

   a. One bag of grass seed covers 3750 square feet and costs $27.50. How many bags are needed? What is the total cost? **4 bags; $110**

   b. Wire fencing costs $23.19 for each 50 foot roll. How much does it cost to buy fencing to enclose the area? **$278.28**

   c. Fence posts cost $3.19 each and should be placed every 5 feet. How many posts are needed, and how much will they cost altogether? *Explain.* **See margin.**

○ = WORKED-OUT SOLUTIONS on p. WS1 ★ = STANDARDIZED TEST PRACTICE

= MULTIPLE REPRESENTATIONS

21a.

Room size (feet)	1 by 1	2 by 2	3 by 3	4 by 4	5 by 5
Remaining area (square feet)	431	428	423	416	407

21. **MULTIPLE REPRESENTATIONS** Homeowners are building a square closet in a rectangular room that is 24 feet long and 18 feet wide. They want the remaining floor area to be at least 400 square feet. Because they don't want to cut any of the 1 foot by 1 foot square floor tiles, the side length of the closet floor should be a whole number of feet.

   a. **Making a Table** Make a table showing possible side lengths of the closet floor and the remaining area for each side length. **See margin.**

   b. **Writing an Inequality** Write an inequality to describe the situation. Use your table to find the greatest possible side length of the closet floor. **$1 \le s \le 5$; 5 ft**

22. ★ **SHORT RESPONSE** A farmer plans to build a fence around a rectangular pen that is 16 feet long. The area of the pen is 80 square feet. Is 40 feet of fencing enough to fence in the pen? *Explain.* **No. *Sample answer:* The width of the pen is 5 feet long. The farmer would need $2(5) + 2(16) = 42$ feet of fencing.**

C 23. **CHALLENGE** You and your friend live 12 miles apart. You leave home at the same time and travel toward each other. You walk at a rate of 4 miles per hour and your friend bicycles at a rate of 11 miles per hour.

   a. How long after you leave home will you meet? How far from home will each of you be? **48 min; you: 3.2 mi, your friend: 8.8 mi**

   b. Suppose your friend bicycles at a rate of 12 miles per hour. How much sooner will you meet? How far from home will each of you be? **3 min; you: 3 mi, your friend: 9 mi**

MIXED REVIEW

Write the decimal as a fraction and as a percent. *(p. 916)*

24. 0.85 **$\frac{17}{20}$; 85%** 25. 1.25 **$1\frac{1}{4}$; 125%** 26. 0.245 **$\frac{49}{200}$; 24.5%** 27. 0.007 **$\frac{7}{1000}$; 0.7%**

28. Find the surface area and volume of the rectangular prism. *(p. 925)* **52 ft^2, 24 ft^3**

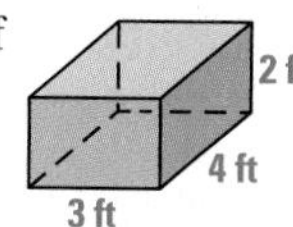

PREVIEW
Prepare for Lesson 1.6 in Exs. 29–32.

Translate the verbal phrase into an expression. *(p. 15)*

29. $\frac{1}{3}$ multiplied by a number v **$\frac{1}{3}v$**

30. 22 divided by a number h **$\frac{22}{h}$**

31. 7 more than twice a number m **$2m + 7$**

32. Twice the sum of a number y and 3 **$2(y + 3)$**

QUIZ for Lessons 1.4–1.5

Write an equation or an inequality. *(p. 21)*

1. 4 more than twice a number n is equal to 25. **$2n + 4 = 25$**
2. The quotient of a number x and 2 is no more than 9. **$\frac{x}{2} \le 9$**

Check whether the given number is a solution of the equation or inequality. *(p. 21)*

3. $13 - 2x = 5$; 4 **solution**
4. $5d - 4 \ge 16$; 4 **solution**
5. $4y + 3 \ge 15$; 3 **solution**
6. **CAR TRAVEL** One car travels about 28.5 miles on each gallon of gas. Suppose the average price of gas is \$2 per gallon. About how much would the gas for a 978 mile trip cost? *(p. 28)* **about \$68.63**

5 ASSESS AND RETEACH

Daily Homework Quiz

Transparency Available

1. Gerry is borrowing money from a friend at a simple interest rate of 4%. If she borrows \$2000 and plans to pay it back in 2 years, how much interest will she owe? **\$160**
2. A migrating whale is traveling at an average speed of 5.4 kilometers per hour. How far will the whale travel in 18 hours at this rate? **97.2 km**
3. Skye sells baskets that she weaves from sweet grass. She makes a profit of \$68 per basket and her expenses are \$2.50 per basket. How much does she charge a customer for 3 baskets? **\$211.50**

Available at **classzone.com**

Diagnosis/Remediation

- Practice A, B, C in Chapter Resource Book
- Study Guide in Chapter Resource Book
- Practice Workbook
- @HomeTutor

Challenge

Additional challenge is available in the Chapter Resource Book.

Quiz

An easily-readable reduced copy of the quiz (with answers) on Lessons 1.4–1.5 from the Assessment Book can be found on p. 1E.

PROBLEM SOLVING WORKSHOP
LESSON 1.5

Using ALTERNATIVE METHODS

Alternative Strategy

Example 1 on page 28 can be solved by drawing a diagram. This method allows students to visualize the solution and will help them to better understand the algebraic solution given in Example 2 on page 29.

Teaching Strategy

Stress that each pair of rectangles represents running 4 long blocks and 2 short blocks. Point out how each figure is labeled to indicate the total distance along its outer edges. Emphasize that carefully drawing an accurate diagram improves one's chances of avoiding errors and solving the problem correctly.

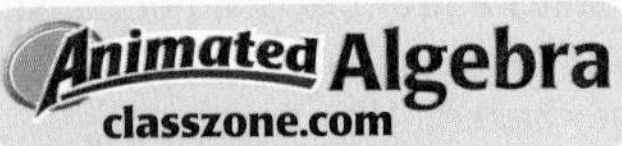

An **Animated Algebra** activity is available online for the **Problem**. This activity is also part of **Power Presentations**.

Another Way to Solve Example 1, page 28

MULTIPLE REPRESENTATIONS In Example 1 on page 28, you saw how to solve a problem about running using an equation. You can also solve the problem by using the strategy *draw a diagram*.

PROBLEM

RUNNING You run in a city. Short blocks are north-south and are 0.1 mile long. Long blocks are east-west and are 0.15 mile long. You will run 2 long blocks east, a number of short blocks south, 2 long blocks west, and back to your start. You want to run 2 miles at a rate of 7 miles per hour. How many short blocks must you run?

METHOD

Drawing a Diagram You can draw a diagram to solve the problem.

STEP 1 **Read** the problem carefully. It tells you the lengths of a short block and a long block. You plan to run 4 long blocks and a distance of 2 miles.

STEP 2 **Draw** a pair of rectangles to represent running 1 short block in each direction. The total distance is $4(0.15) + 2(0.1) = 0.8$ mile. Continue adding pairs of rectangles until the total distance run is 2 miles.

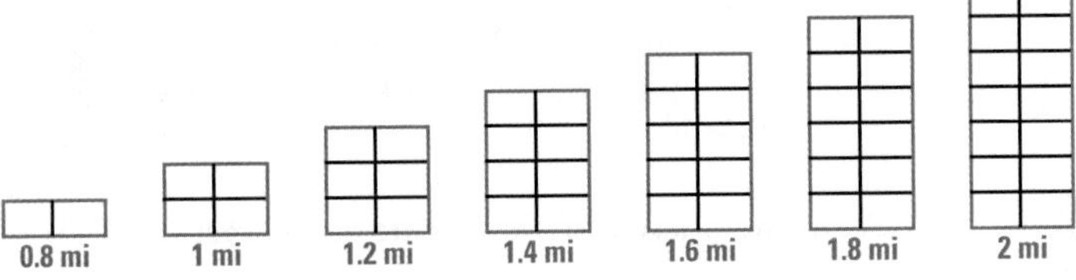

▶ You should run 14 short blocks.

Animated Algebra at classzone.com

PRACTICE

1–4. See margin.

1. **BAKING** A cake pan is 9 inches wide and 11 inches long. How many 3 inch by 3 inch square pieces can you cut? Solve this problem using an equation. Then draw a diagram. *Explain* why a diagram is useful.

2. **SWIMMING** A 12 foot rope strung through 4 floats marks off the deep end of a pool. Each end of the rope is 3 feet from a float. The floats are equally spaced. How far apart are they? Solve this problem using two different methods.

3. **ERROR ANALYSIS** *Describe* and correct the error in solving Exercise 2.

$4x + 6 = 12$
$4(1.5) + 6 = 12$ ✗
The floats are 1.5 feet apart.

4. **GEOMETRY** The length of a rectangle is twice its width. The perimeter is 72 inches. What is its length? Solve this problem using two different methods.

1. 9 pieces of cake; Draw a diagram of a 9 inch by 11 inch pan and divide it into 3 inch by 3 inch pieces. From the diagram you see that the cake can be divided into 9 pieces of cake.

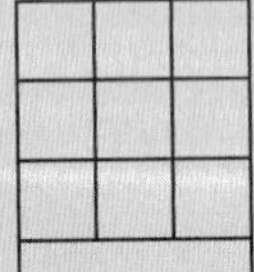

2. 2 ft. *Sample answer:* Method 1: Draw a diagram of the rope showing two of the floats 3 feet from each end. Divide the remaining rope so that the 4 floats are equally spaced. From the diagram you can see that there is 2 feet between consecutive floats.

3 ft | 2 ft | 2 ft | 2 ft | 3 ft

Method 2: Use the equation $3x + 6 = 12$ where 3 is the number of spaces between the floats, x is the length of space in between the floats, 6 is the total space at each end of the rope, and 12 is the total length of the rope. Solving the equation gives $x = 2$.

3. The equation should be $3x + 6 = 12$ because there are only 3 spaces between the 4 floats; $3(2) + 6 = 12$.

4. 24 in. *Sample answer:* Method 1: Use the formula $P = 2\ell + 2w$ to find the length. Substitute 72 for P and $2w$ for ℓ to get the equation $72 = 2(2w) + 2w$. Solving the equation gives $w = 12$. If the length is $2w$, the length is 24 inches. Method 2: Draw a diagram of the rectangle. Label the width, w, and the length, $2w$. If you add up the sides to find the perimeter you will get the equation $6w = 72$. Solving the equation gives $w = 12$, so the length must be 24 inches.

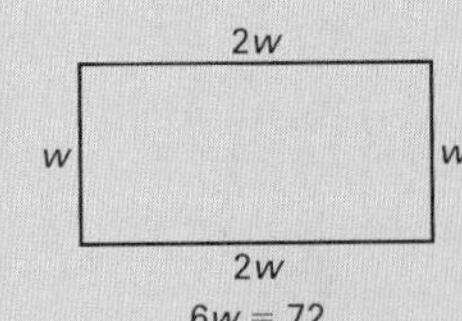

1.6 Represent Functions as Rules and Tables

Before You wrote algebraic expressions and equations.

Now You will represent functions as rules and as tables.

Why? So you can describe consumer costs, as in Example 1.

Key Vocabulary
- function
- domain
- range
- independent variable
- dependent variable

When you pump gas, the total cost depends on the number of gallons pumped. The total cost is a *function* of the number of gallons pumped.

A **function** consists of:

- A set called the **domain** containing numbers called **inputs**, and a set called the **range** containing numbers called **outputs**.
- A pairing of inputs with outputs such that each input is paired with exactly one output.

EXAMPLE 1 Identify the domain and range of a function

The input-output table shows the cost of various amounts of regular unleaded gas from the same pump. Identify the domain and range of the function.

Input (gallons)	10	12	13	17
Output (dollars)	19.99	23.99	25.99	33.98

19.99
THIS SALE $
10.000
GALLONS
1.999
PRICE PER GALLON $
ALL TAXES INCLUDED

Solution

▶ The domain is the set of inputs: 10, 12, 13, and 17. The range is the set of outputs: 19.99, 23.99, 25.99, and 33.98.

GUIDED PRACTICE for Example 1

1. Identify the domain and range of the function.
domain: 0, 1, 2, and 4, range: 1, 2, and 5

Input	0	1	2	4
Output	5	2	2	1

MAPPING DIAGRAMS A function may be represented by a *mapping diagram*. Notice that an output may be paired with more than one input, but no input is paired with more than one output.

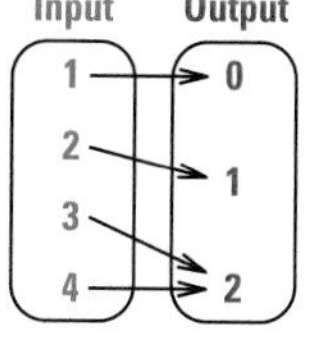

1 PLAN AND PREPARE

Warm-Up Exercises

Transparency Available

1. Write an expression: 7 more than a number x. **$x + 7$**
2. Determine if 3 is a solution of $2x - 4 = 2$. **$2 = 2$; 3 is a solution.**
3. Gae spent $4 more than twice as much as Casey at a store. If Casey spent $6, how much did Gae spend? **$16**

Notetaking Guide

Transparency Available

Promotes interactive learning and notetaking skills.

Pacing

Basic: 2 days
Average: 2 days
Advanced: 2 days
Block: 0.5 block with 1.5
0.5 block with 1.7

- See *Teaching Guide/Lesson Plan.*

2 FOCUS AND MOTIVATE

Essential Question

Big Idea 3, p. 1

How do you represent functions as tables and rules? **Tell students they will learn how to answer this question by describing the relationships between domain and range, between input and output, and between independent and dependent variables.**

NCTM STANDARDS

Standard 2: Understand functions; Use models to understand relationships

Resource Planning Guide

Chapter Resource Book
- Teaching Guide/Lesson Plan
- Activity Master
- Practice levels A, B, C
- Study Guide
- Catch-up for Absent Students
- Application
- Challenge

Workbooks
- Notetaking Guide
- Practice Workbook

Teaching Options
- **Power Presentations** provides dynamic electronic teaching resources for the classroom.
- **Activity Generator** provides editable activities for all ability levels.

Interactive Technology
- Easy Planner
- Power Presentations
- Activity Generator
- Animated Algebra
- Test Generator
- Online Quiz
- eWorkbook
- eEdition
- @HomeTutor

Resources for English Learners
- Spanish Study Guide
- Multi-Language Visual Glossary
- Student Resources in Spanish

See also the *Differentiated Instruction Resources* for more strategies for meeting individual needs.

Motivating the Lesson

Students have already encountered situations where numerical data is presented in a table, such as the shipping costs for various package weights when ordering from a catalog. Ask them about other real-world situations where they have encountered data given in a table.

3 TEACH

Extra Example 1

The input-output table shows the amount of money Miguel earns at his job for several numbers of hours. Identify the domain and range of the function.

Input (hours)	2	5	7	8
Output (dollars)	14	35	49	56

domain: 2, 5, 7, 8
range: 14, 35, 49, 56

Extra Example 2

Tell whether the pairing is a function.

a.

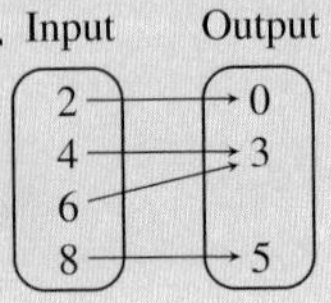

The pairing is a function, because each input is paired with exactly one output.

b.

Input	1	2	2	4
Output	2	3	4	6

The pairing is *not* a function, because the input 2 is paired with both 3 and 4.

Extra Example 3

The domain of the function $y = x + 4$ is 0, 2, 3, 6, and 7. Make a table for the function. Identify the range. **range: 4, 6, 7, 10, 11**

x	0	2	3	6	7
$y = x + 4$	4	6	7	10	11

EXAMPLE 2 Identify a function

Tell whether the pairing is a function.

a.

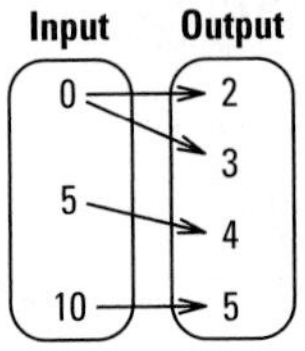

The pairing is *not* a function because the input 0 is paired with both 2 and 3.

b.

Input	Output
0	0
1	2
4	8
6	12

The pairing is a function because each input is paired with exactly one output.

✓ GUIDED PRACTICE for Example 2

Tell whether the pairing is a function.

2.

Input	3	6	9	12
Output	1	2	2	1

function

3.

Input	2	2	4	7
Output	0	1	2	3

not a function

FUNCTION RULES A function may be represented using a rule that relates one variable to another. The input variable is called the **independent variable.** The output variable is called the **dependent variable** because its value depends on the value of the input variable.

READING
Function rules typically give the dependent variable in terms of the independent variable. In an equation like $y = x + 3$, you know that y is the dependent variable.

KEY CONCEPT *For Your Notebook*

Functions

Verbal Rule
The output is 3 more than the input.

Equation
$y = x + 3$

Table

Input, x	0	1	2	3	4
Output, y	3	4	5	6	7

EXAMPLE 3 Make a table for a function

The domain of the function $y = 2x$ is 0, 2, 5, 7, and 8. Make a table for the function, then identify the range of the function.

Solution

x	0	2	5	7	8
$y = 2x$	$2(0) = 0$	$2(2) = 4$	$2(5) = 10$	$2(7) = 14$	$2(8) = 16$

The range of the function is 0, 4, 10, 14, and 16.

Differentiated Instruction

Visual Learners To help students remember that the input is the domain and the output is the range, show that the word pairings (domain, range) and (input, output) are both in alphabetical order. Emphasize that the first words in each pairing are associated with each other, as are the second words. This type of association can also be shown later in Lesson 1.7 with ordered pairs (x, y).

See also the *Differentiated Instruction Resources* for more strategies.

EXAMPLE 4 Write a function rule

Write a rule for the function.

Input	0	1	4	6	10
Output	2	3	6	8	12

Solution

Let x be the input, or independent variable, and let y be the output, or dependent variable. Notice that each output is 2 more than the corresponding input. So, a rule for the function is $y = x + 2$.

EXAMPLE 5 Write a function rule for a real-world situation

CONCERT TICKETS You are buying concert tickets that cost \$15 each. You can buy up to 6 tickets. Write the amount (in dollars) you spend as a function of the number of tickets you buy. Identify the independent and dependent variables. Then identify the domain and the range of the function.

Solution

CHOOSE A VARIABLE
To write a function rule for a real-world situation, choose letters for the variables that remind you of the quantities represented.

Write a verbal model. Then write a function rule. Let n represent the number of tickets purchased and A represent the amount spent (in dollars).

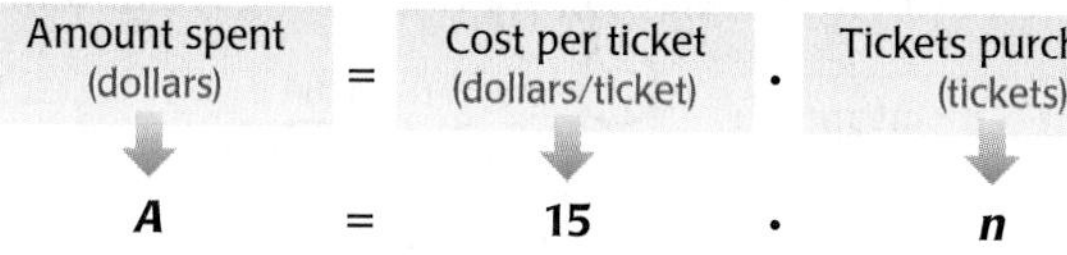

$$A = 15 \cdot n$$

So, the function rule is $A = 15n$. The amount spent depends on the number of tickets bought, so n is the independent variable and A is the dependent variable.

Because you can buy up to 6 tickets, the domain of the function is 0, 1, 2, 3, 4, 5, and 6. Make a table to identify the range.

Number of tickets, n	0	1	2	3	4	5	6
Amount (dollars), A	0	15	30	45	60	75	90

The range of the function is 0, 15, 30, 45, 60, 75, and 90.

Animated Algebra at classzone.com

✓ GUIDED PRACTICE for Examples 3, 4, and 5

4. Make a table for the function $y = x - 5$ with domain 10, 12, 15, 18, and 29. Then identify the range of the function. **See margin.**

5. Write a rule for the function. Identify the domain and the range.
$y = 8x$; domain: 1, 2, 3, and 4, range: 8, 16, 24, and 32

Time (hours)	1	2	3	4
Pay (dollars)	8	16	24	32

4.

x	10	12	15	18	29
$y = x - 5$	5	7	10	13	24

range: 5, 7, 10, 13, 24

Extra Example 4

Write a rule for the function.

Input	1	2	4	7	9
Output	0	1	3	6	8

$y = x - 1$

Extra Example 5

At a community center, art lessons are offered at night. The fee is \$12 per lesson. You plan to attend up to 5 lessons. Write the amount you will spend as a function of the number of lessons you attend. Identify the independent and dependent variables. Then identify the domain and the range of the function. **$A = 12n$; independent variable: n; dependent variable: A; domain: 0, 1, 2, 3, 4, 5; range: 0, 12, 24, 36, 48, 60**

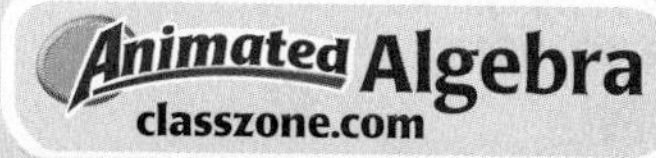

An **Animated Algebra** activity is available online for **Example 5**. This activity is also part of **Power Presentations**.

Closing the Lesson

Have students summarize the major points of the lesson and answer the Essential Question: How do you represent functions as tables and as rules?

- **For a function, no input value is paired with more than one output value.**
- **A function rule describes what must be done to the input to obtain the output.**

To create a table for a function, use the domain of the function as the input values and apply the function rule to each input to find its corresponding output. To write a rule for a function, determine the pattern that links each dependent variable (output y) to its corresponding independent variable (input x).

4 PRACTICE AND APPLY

Assignment Guide

Answer Transparencies available for all exercises

Basic:
Day 1: pp. 38–40
Exs. 1–15
Day 2: pp. 38–40
Exs. 16–20, 23–27, 30–36

Average:
Day 1: pp. 38–40
Exs. 1, 2, 4, 5, 7–16
Day 2: pp. 38–40
Exs. 17–28, 30–36

Advanced:
Day 1: pp. 38–40
Exs. 1, 2, 5, 8, 11–13, 18, 19, 22*
Day 2: pp. 38–40
Exs. 23–36*

Block:
pp. 38–40
Exs. 1, 2, 4, 5, 7–16 (with 1.5)
pp. 38–40
Exs. 17–28, 30–36 (with 1.7)

Differentiated Instruction

See *Differentiated Instruction Resources* for suggestions on addressing the needs of a diverse classroom.

Homework Check

For a quick check of student understanding of key concepts, go over the following exercises:

Basic: 3, 6, 15, 20, 23
Average: 4, 7, 16, 21, 24
Advanced: 5, 8, 18, 19, 25

Extra Practice

- Student Edition, p. 938
- Chapter Resource Book: Practice levels A, B, C

Practice Worksheet

An easily-readable reduced practice page (with answers) for this lesson can be found on p. 1D.

1.6 EXERCISES

HOMEWORK KEY
○ = **WORKED-OUT SOLUTIONS** on p. WS2 for Exs. 7 and 23
★ = **STANDARDIZED TEST PRACTICE** Exs. 2, 11, 12, 13, 26, and 27
◆ = **MULTIPLE REPRESENTATIONS** Exs. 23 and 24

SKILL PRACTICE

A

1. **VOCABULARY** Copy and complete: A(n) _?_ is a number in the domain of a function. A(n) _?_ is a number in the range of a function. **input; output**

2. ★ **WRITING** In the equation $b = a - 2$, which variable is the independent variable and which is the dependent variable? *Explain.* **a, b; the value of b depends on a.**

EXAMPLES 1 and 2 on pp. 35–36 for Exs. 3–11

DOMAIN AND RANGE **Identify the domain and range of the function.**

3.

Input	Output
0	5
1	7
2	15
3	44

domain: 0, 1, 2, and 3, range: 5, 7, 15, and 44

4. Input: 3, 5, 7, 8; Output: 7, 5, 3, 2 (3 → 7, 5 → 5, 7 → 3, 8 → 2)

domain: 3, 5, 7, and 8, range: 2, 3, 5, and 7

5.

Input	Output
6	5
12	7
21	10
42	17

domain: 6, 12, 21, and 42, range: 5, 7, 10, and 17

IDENTIFYING FUNCTIONS **Tell whether the pairing is a function.**

6.

Input	Output
0	7.5
1	9.5
2	11.5
3	13.5

function

7.

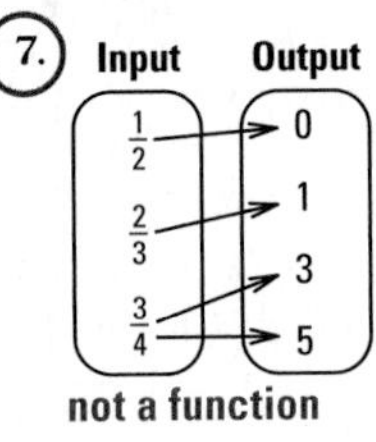

not a function

8.

Input	Output
7	13
11	8
21	13
35	20

function

ERROR ANALYSIS **In Exercises 9 and 10, describe and correct the error related to the function represented by the table.**

Input, x	1	2	3	4	5
Output, y	6	7	8	6	9

9, 10. See margin.

9. The pairing is not a function. One output is paired with two inputs. ✗

10. The pairing is a function. The range is 1, 2, 3, 4, and 5.

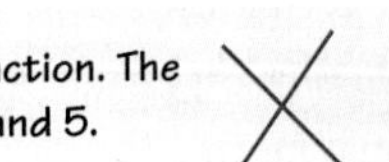

11. ★ **OPEN-ENDED** Draw a mapping diagram for a function with 6 inputs. Then make a table to represent the function. **See margin.**

EXAMPLES 3 and 4 on pp. 36–37 for Exs. 12–21

12. ★ **MULTIPLE CHOICE** The domain of the function $y = 5x - 1$ is 1, 3, 4, 5, and 6. Which number is in the range of the function? **B**

Ⓐ 0 Ⓑ 4 Ⓒ 9 Ⓓ 15

13. ★ **MULTIPLE CHOICE** Each output of a function is 0.5 less than the corresponding input. Which equation is a rule for the function? **A**

Ⓐ $y = x - 0.5$ Ⓑ $y = x + 0.5$ Ⓒ $y = 0.5 - x$ Ⓓ $y = 0.5x$

9. The pairing is a function. Each input is paired with only one output.

10. The numbers listed are the domain, not the range. The range of the function is 6, 7, 8, and 9.

11. *Sample:*

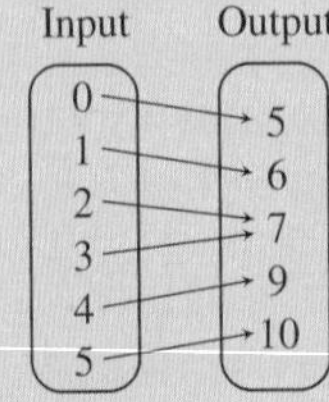

Input	Output
0	5
1	6
2	7
3	7
4	9
5	10

B **TABLES** **Make a table for the function. Identify the range of the function.**
14–19. See margin.

14. $y = x - 3$
Domain: 12, 15, 22, 30

15. $y = x + 3.5$
Domain: 4, 5, 7, 8, 12

16. $y = 3x + 4$
Domain: 0, 5, 7, 10

17. $y = \frac{1}{2}x + 3$
Domain: 4, 6, 9, 11

18. $y = \frac{2}{3}x + \frac{1}{3}$
Domain: 4, 6, 8, 12

19. $y = \frac{0.5x + 1}{2}$
Domain: 0, 2, 4, 6

FUNCTION RULES **Write a rule for the function.**

20.

Input, x	0	1	2	3
Output, y	2.2	3.2	4.2	5.2

$y = x + 2.2$

21.

Input, x	15	20	21	30	42
Output, y	7	12	13	22	34

$y = x - 8$

C 22. **CHALLENGE** Fill in the table in such a way that when t is the independent variable, the pairing is a function, and when t is the dependent variable, the pairing is not a function.

Sample answer:

t	? 1	? 2	? 3	? 4
v	? 2	? 2	? 3	? 3

PROBLEM SOLVING

EXAMPLE 5 A on p. 37 for Exs. 23–26

23a. the number of quarters left; the number of quarters used

23. **MULTIPLE REPRESENTATIONS** You have 10 quarters that you can use for a parking meter.

a. **Describing in Words** Copy and complete: Each time you put 1 quarter in the meter, you have 1 less quarter, so _?_ is a function of _?_.

b. **Writing a Rule** Write a rule for the number y of quarters that you have left as a function of the number x of quarters you have used so far. Identify the domain of the function. **$y = 10 - x$; domain: 0, 1, 2, 3, 4, 5, 6, 7, 8, 9, and 10**

c. **Making a Table** Make a table and identify the range of the function.
@HomeTutor for problem solving help at classzone.com **Range: 0, 1, 2, 3, 4, 5, 6, 7, 8, 9, and 10; see margin.**

24. **MULTIPLE REPRESENTATIONS** At a yard sale, you find 5 paperback books by your favorite author. Each book is priced at \$.75.

a. **Describing in Words** Copy and complete: For each book you buy, you spend \$.75, so _?_ is a function of _?_. **amount of money you spend; the number of books you buy**

b. **Writing a Rule** Write a rule for the amount (in dollars) you spend as a function of the number of books you buy. Identify the domain of the function. **$y = \$.75x$; domain: 0, 1, 2, 3, 4, and 5**

c. **Making a Table** Make a table and identify the range of the function.
@HomeTutor for problem solving help at classzone.com **Range: 0, 0.75, 1.5, 2.25, 3, and 3.75; see margin.**

25. **SAVINGS** You have \$100 saved and plan to save \$20 each month. Write a rule for the amount saved (in dollars) as a function of the number of months from now. Identify the independent and dependent variables, the domain, and the range. How much will you have saved altogether 12 months from now? **$y = 100 + 20m$; independent variable: m, the number of months; dependent variable: y, the amount of money saved; domain: 0, 1, 2, 3, . . ., range: 100, 120, 140, . . . ; \$340**

26. ★ **OPEN-ENDED** Write a function rule that models a real-world situation. Identify the independent variable and the dependent variable.
Sample answer: **$W = 8h$, where W is wages and h is hours worked; the independent variable is h, the dependent variable is W.**

Vocabulary

Exercises 3–8 For students who confuse the connection between the terms *input* and *domain* and between the terms *output* and *range*, suggest they use the memory clue "*i* comes before *o* like *d* comes before *r*, so *input* goes with *domain* and *output* goes with *range*."

Avoiding Common Errors

Exercises 20–21 Some students may write the input as a function of the output. Remind them that the output is always a result of having done something with the input. Stress that they need to look at what must be done with the input value in order to obtain the corresponding output value.

Study Strategy

Exercise 25 To help students solve this problem, suggest they use Example 5 as a model. Point out that the problem states \$100 is already saved, so students will need to show the addition of this amount in their rule.

14.

Input	12	15	22	30
Output	9	12	19	27

range: 9, 12, 19, and 27

15. See below.

16.

Input	0	5	7	10
Output	4	19	25	34

range: 4, 19, 25, and 34

17.

Input	4	6	9	11
Output	5	6	7.5	8.5

range: 5, 6, 7.5, and 8.5

18.

Input	4	6	8	12
Output	3	$4\frac{1}{3}$	$5\frac{2}{3}$	$8\frac{1}{3}$

range: 3, $4\frac{1}{3}$, $5\frac{2}{3}$, and $8\frac{1}{3}$

19.

Input	0	2	4	6
Output	$\frac{1}{2}$	1	$1\frac{1}{2}$	2

range: $\frac{1}{2}$, 1, $1\frac{1}{2}$, and 2

15.

Input	4	5	7	8	12
Output	7.5	8.5	10.5	11.5	15.5

range: 7.5, 8.5, 10.5, 11.5, and 15.5

23c.

Input	0	1	2	3	4	5	6	7	8	9	10
Output	10	9	8	7	6	5	4	3	2	1	0

24c.

Input	0	1	2	3	4	5
Output	0	0.75	1.5	2.25	3	3.75

5 ASSESS AND RETEACH

Daily Homework Quiz

Transparency Available

1. The domain of the function $y = \frac{2}{3}x + 1$ is 0, 3, 6, and 9. Make a table for the function. Identify the range of the function.

x	0	3	6	9
y	1	3	5	7

range: 1, 3, 5, 7

2. Write a rule for the function.

Input, x	2	3	4	5
Output, y	3	4.5	6	7.5

$y = 1.5x$

3. Jasmine sells bracelets. Her profit on each bracelet is $8. Write a rule that shows her total profit p as a function of the number of bracelets b she sells. Write the range of the function if the domain is 5, 10, 15, 20, and 25. **$p = 8b$; range: 40, 80, 120, 160, 200**

Available at **classzone.com**

Diagnosis/Remediation

- Practice A, B, C in Chapter Resource Book
- Study Guide in Chapter Resource Book
- Practice Workbook
- @HomeTutor

Challenge

Additional challenge is available in the Chapter Resource Book.

27a–b. See Additional Answers beginning on p. AA1.

30–33.

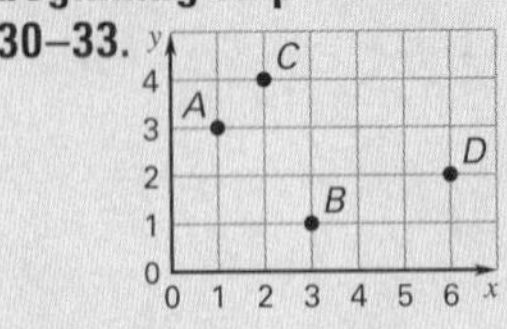

27a, b. See margin.

27. ★ **SHORT RESPONSE** Consider a pairing of the digits 2 through 9 on a telephone keypad with the associated letters.

a. Make a table showing the pairing with the digits as inputs and the letters as outputs. Is the pairing a function? *Explain.*

b. Make a table showing the pairing with the letters as inputs and the digits as outputs. Is the pairing a function? *Explain.*

28. **MULTI-STEP PROBLEM** The table shows the fuel efficiency of four compact cars from one manufacturer for model year 2004.

City fuel efficiency (mi/gal), *c*	24	26	27	28
Highway fuel efficiency (mi/gal), *h*	32	34	35	36

a. **Write a Rule** Use the table to write a rule for the cars' highway fuel efficiency as a function of their city fuel efficiency. **$h = c + 8$**

b. **Predict** Another of the manufacturer's compact cars has a city fuel efficiency of 30 miles per gallon. Predict the highway fuel efficiency. **38 mi/gal**

c. **Calculate** A study found that if gas costs $2 per gallon, you can use the expression $\frac{11{,}550}{c} + \frac{9450}{h}$ to estimate a car's annual fuel cost (in dollars) for a typical driver. Evaluate the expression for the car in part (b). **about $634**

C 29. **CHALLENGE** Each week you spend a total of 5 hours exercising. You swim part of the time and bike the rest.

300 calories per hour

440 calories per hour

a. Write a rule for the total number of calories you burn for the whole 5 hours as a function of the time you spend swimming. **$c = 300s + 440(5 - s)$**

b. One week you spend half the time swimming. How many calories do you burn during the whole 5 hours? **1850 cal**

MIXED REVIEW

PREVIEW Prepare for Lesson 1.7 in Exs. 30–33.

Plot the point in a coordinate plane. *(p. 919)* **30–33. See margin.**

30. $A(1, 3)$ 31. $B(3, 1)$ 32. $C(2, 4)$ 33. $D(6, 2)$

Write an equation or an inequality. *(p. 21)*

34. The difference of 13 and a number w is 5. **$13 - w = 5$**

35. The quotient of 21 and a number d is no less than 7. **$\frac{21}{d} \geq 7$**

36. **TRAVEL** On a 1375 mile flight, an airplane's average speed is 550 miles per hour. The flight is within a single time zone and leaves at 10 A.M. What time will the airplane arrive at its destination? *(p. 28)* **12:30 P.M.**

@HomeTutor
classzone.com
Keystrokes

1.6 Make a Table

QUESTION **How can you use a graphing calculator to create a table for a function?**

You can use a graphing calculator to create a table for a function when you want to display many pairs of input values and output values or when you want to find the input value that corresponds to a given output value.

In the example below, you will make a table to compare temperatures in degrees Celsius and temperatures in degrees Fahrenheit for temperatures at or above the temperature at which water freezes, 32°F.

EXAMPLE **Use a graphing calculator to make a table**

The formula $C = \frac{5}{9}(F - 32)$ gives the temperature in degrees Celsius as a function of the temperature in degrees Fahrenheit. Make a table for the function.

STEP 1 ***Enter equation***

Rewrite the function using x for F and y for C. Press Y= and enter $\frac{5}{9}(x - 32)$.

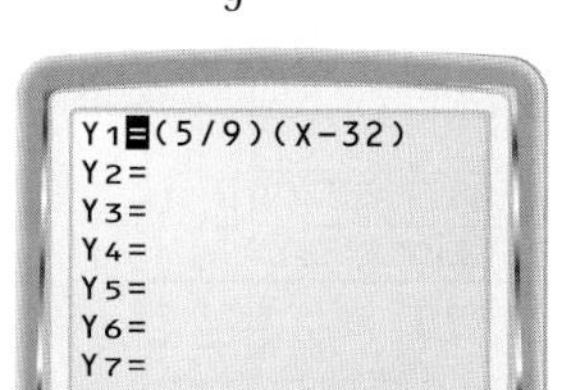

STEP 2 ***Set up table***

Go to the TABLE SETUP screen. Use a starting value (TblStart) of 32 and an increment (△Tbl) of 1.

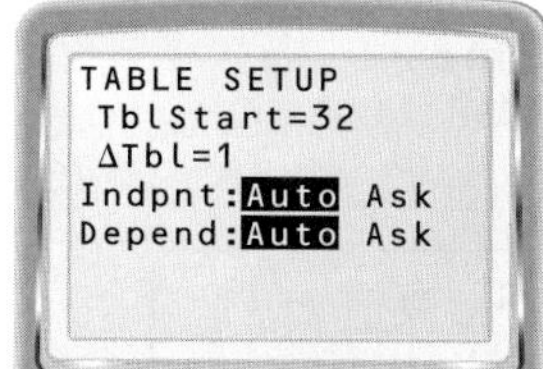

STEP 3 ***View table***

Display the table. Scroll down to see pairs of inputs and outputs.

X	Y1	Y2
32	0	
33	.55556	
34	1.1111	
35	1.6667	
36	2.2222	
37	2.7778	

PRACTICE

1. You see a sign that indicates that the outdoor temperature is 10°C. Find the temperature in degrees Fahrenheit. *Explain* how you found your answer. **50°F; scroll down until you see the output 10, look to see that the input is 50.**
2. Water boils at 100°C. What is the temperature in degrees Fahrenheit? **212°F**

Make a table for the function. Use the given starting value and increment. **3–6. See margin.**

3. $y = \frac{3}{4}x + 5$
   TblStart = 0, △Tbl = 1
4. $y = 4x + 2$
   TblStart = 0, △Tbl = 0.5
5. $y = 7.5x - 0.5$
   TblStart = 1, △Tbl = 1
6. $y = 0.5x + 6$
   TblStart = 3, △Tbl = 3

3.

Input	0	1	2	3
Output	5	5.75	6.5	7.25

4.

Input	0	0.5	1	1.5
Output	2	4	6	8

5.

Input	1	2	3	4
Output	7	14.5	22	29.5

6.

Input	3	6	9	12
Output	7.5	9	10.5	12

1 PLAN AND PREPARE

Learn the Method

- Students will use a graphing calculator to make a table for a function.
- Students can use the skills learned in this activity to check their tables in Exercises 14–19 in Lesson 1.6.

Keystroke Help

Keystrokes for several models of calculators are available in blackline format in the *Chapter Resource Book.*

2 TEACH

Tips for Success

When discussing Step 3, point out to students that the values for x and y are shown in the columns labeled X and Y_1, respectively. You may also wish to point out the unused column labeled Y_2. Remind students that the values in the X column are those for the variable F in the formula, and the values in the Y_1 column are those for the variable C.

Extra Example

Use your calculator to make a table for the function $y = 2x + 4$. Use a starting value of 4 and an increment of 0.25. Use your table to find the output when the input is 8.75. **21.5**

3 ASSESS AND RETEACH

1. What are the key items you need to enter into the calculator to have it set up a table? **the function, the starting value, and the increment**
2. Explain how you would use the table in Step 3 to find the Celsius temperature that is equivalent to 98°F. **Scroll down the table until you locate the value 98 in the X-column, and read the corresponding value in the Y_1-column.**

1.7 Scatter Plots and Functions

MATERIALS • tape measure • graph paper

QUESTION **How can you tell whether a graph represents a function?**

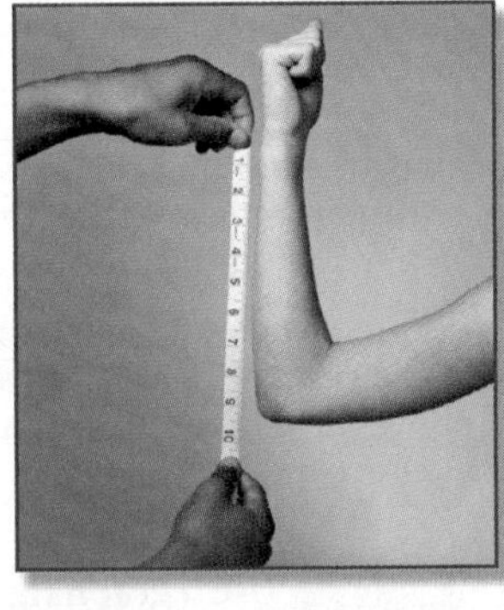

A *scatter plot* is a type of display for paired data. Each data pair is plotted as a point. In this activity, you will work in a group to make a scatter plot. You will measure the height of each student in your group and the length of his or her forearm. The length of the forearm is the distance from the elbow to the wrist.

EXPLORE **Collect data and make a scatter plot**

STEP 1 ***Collect data*** Measure the height of each student in your group and the length of his or her forearm. Record the results for each student in one row of a table like the one shown.

Height (inches)	Forearm length (inches)
63	10
?	?

STEP 2 ***Make a scatter plot*** Use graph paper to draw axes labeled as shown. Then plot the data pairs (*height, forearm length*). For example, plot the point (63, 10) for a student with a height of 63 inches and a forearm length of 10 inches.

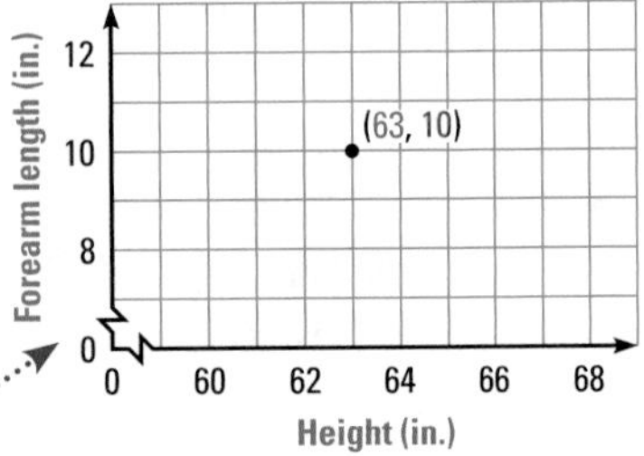

The symbol ⌇ on an axis represents a break in the axis.

DRAW CONCLUSIONS **Use your observations to complete these exercises**

1. Examine your scatter plot. What does it suggest about the relationship between a person's height and the person's forearm length?
   Sample answer: **The greater the person's height, the greater the length of the forearm.**
2. Compare your table with those of the other groups in your class. Determine which of the tables represent functions and which do not.
   Answers will vary. Tables that are functions should have only one forearm length for each height.
3. Is it possible to determine whether a table represents a function by looking at the corresponding scatter plot? *Explain.*
   Yes; if there is more than one *y* for an *x* it is not a function.

1 PLAN AND PREPARE

Explore the Concept

- Students will collect data and make a scatter plot.
- This activity leads into the study of graphing data in Example 2 in Lesson 1.7.

Materials

Each group of students will need:

- tape measure
- graph paper

Recommended Time

Work activity: 15 min
Discuss results: 5 min

Grouping

Students can work in groups of 6–8. Students should take turns doing the measurements, recording the results, and plotting the points. All students should check the accuracy of the graph against the recorded results.

2 TEACH

Tips for Success

Exercise 3 hints at the vertical line test to determine if a relation is a function. If students are having trouble discovering this, you should lead them to seeing it. The vertical line test will be covered in the Extension on pages 49–50.

Key Discovery

You can plot points on a graph to show the relationship between two sets of data and to see if that relationship is a function.

3 ASSESS AND RETEACH

Do all scatter plots represent functions? Explain. **No. Some scatter plots do not represent a function because there are some inputs that have more than one output associated with them.**

1.7 Represent Functions as Graphs

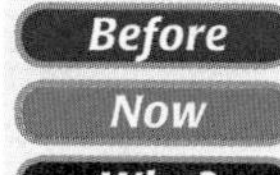

Before You represented functions as rules and tables.
Now You will represent functions as graphs.
Why? So you can describe sales trends, as in Example 4.

Key Vocabulary
- **function,** *p. 35*
- **domain,** *p. 35*
- **range,** *p. 35*

REVIEW THE COORDINATE PLANE
For help with the coordinate plane, see p. 919.

You can use a graph to represent a function. Given a table that represents a function, each corresponding pair of input and output values forms an ordered pair of numbers that can be plotted as a point. The *x*-coordinate is the input. The *y*-coordinate is the output.

Table

Input, *x*	Output, *y*
1	2
2	3
4	5

Ordered Pairs

(input, output)
(1, 2)
(2, 3)
(4, 5)

Graph

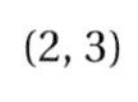

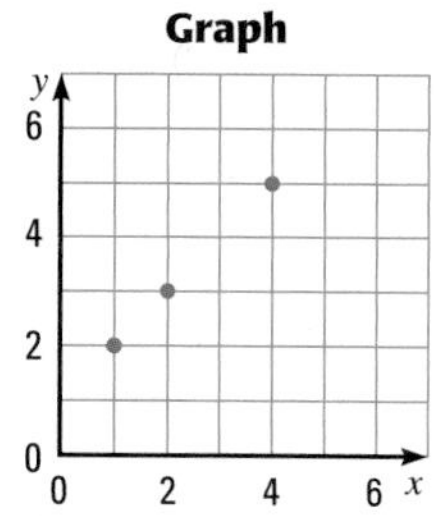

The horizontal axis of the graph is labeled with the input variable. The vertical axis is labeled with the output variable.

EXAMPLE 1 Graph a function

Graph the function $y = \frac{1}{2}x$ with domain 0, 2, 4, 6, and 8.

Solution

STEP 1 **Make** an input-output table.

x	0	2	4	6	8
y	0	1	2	3	4

STEP 2 **Plot** a point for each ordered pair (x, y).

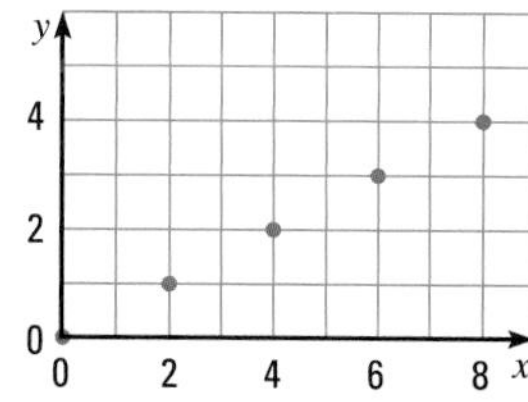

GUIDED PRACTICE for Example 1

1. Graph the function $y = 2x - 1$ with domain 1, 2, 3, 4, and 5. **See margin on p. 45.**

1 PLAN AND PREPARE

Warm-Up Exercises

Transparency Available

1. Make a table for $y = 2x + 3$ with domain 0, 3, 6, and 9.

x	0	3	6	9
y	3	9	15	21

2. Write a rule for the function.

Input, *x*	0	2	4	9
Output, *y*	1	7	13	28

$y = 3x + 1$

Notetaking Guide

Transparency Available

Promotes interactive learning and notetaking skills.

Pacing

Basic: 1 day
Average: 1 day
Advanced: 1 day
Block: 0.5 block with 1.6
- See *Teaching Guide/Lesson Plan.*

2 FOCUS AND MOTIVATE

Essential Question

Big Idea 3, p. 1

How do you represent functions as graphs? **Tell students they will learn how to answer this question by using the function's domain, range, and a table of values.**

NCTM STANDARDS

Standard 2: Understand functions; Use models to understand relationships

Resource Planning Guide

Chapter Resource Book
- Teaching Guide/Lesson Plan
- Practice levels A, B, C
- Study Guide
- Catch-up for Absent Students
- Problem Solving Workshop
- Challenge

Workbooks
- Notetaking Guide
- Practice Workbook

Teaching Options
- **Power Presentations** provides dynamic electronic teaching resources for the classroom.
- **Activity Generator** provides editable activities for all ability levels.

Interactive Technology
- Easy Planner
- Power Presentations
- Activity Generator
- Animated Algebra
- Test Generator
- Online Quiz
- eWorkbook
- eEdition
- @HomeTutor

Resources for English Learners
- Spanish Study Guide
- Multi-Language Visual Glossary
- Student Resources in Spanish

See also the *Differentiated Instruction Resources* for more strategies for meeting individual needs.

Motivating the Lesson

Tell students that graphs help to visualize the relationships between data values and that makes these relationships easier to recognize. Ask students to share instances where graphs have helped them to more easily visualize relationships.

3 TEACH

Extra Example 1

Graph the function $y = 2x - 3$ with domain 2, 3, 4, and 5.

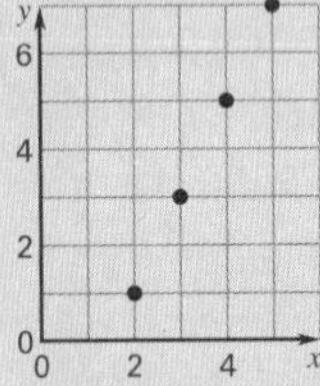

Extra Example 2

The table shows the profit p (in thousands of dollars) at a small toy store each year from 2000 to 2004 as a function of the time t in years since 2000. Graph the function.

t	0	1	2	3	4
p	19.5	20.3	22.7	21.1	21.8

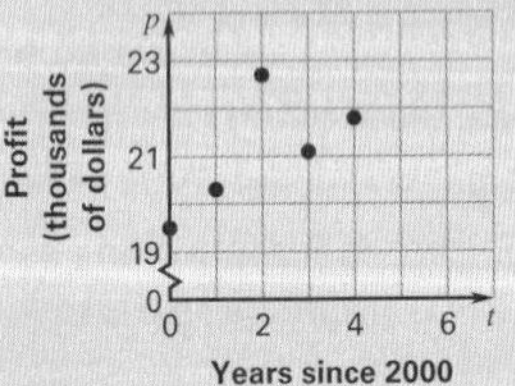

Extra Example 3

Write a rule for the function represented by the graph. Identify the domain and the range of the function.

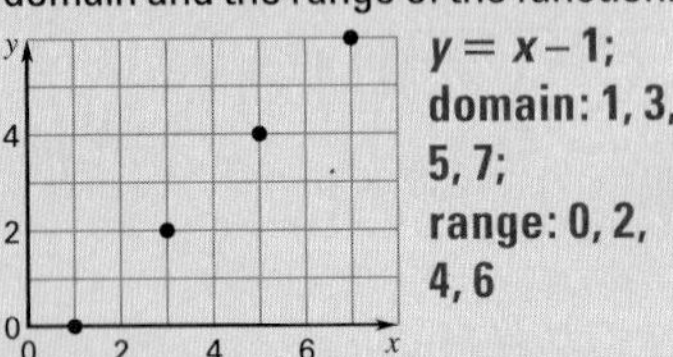

$y = x - 1$; domain: 1, 3, 5, 7; range: 0, 2, 4, 6

EXAMPLE 2 Graph a function

SAT SCORES The table shows the average score s on the mathematics section of the Scholastic Aptitude Test (SAT) in the United States from 1997 to 2003 as a function of the time t in years since 1997. In the table, 0 corresponds to the year 1997, 1 corresponds to 1998, and so on. Graph the function.

Years since 1997, t	0	1	2	3	4	5	6
Average score, s	511	512	511	514	514	516	519

READING
The symbol ⏚ on the vertical number line represents a break in the axis.

Solution

STEP 1 **Choose** a scale. The scale should allow you to plot all the points on a graph that is a reasonable size.

- The t-values range from 0 to 6, so label the t-axis from 0 to 6 in increments of 1 unit.
- The s-values range from 511 to 519, so label the s-axis from 510 to 520 in increments of 2 units.

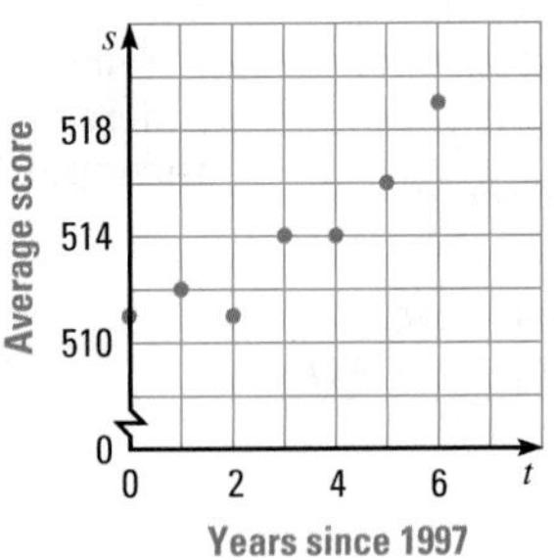

STEP 2 **Plot** the points.

✓ **GUIDED PRACTICE** for Example 2

2. **WHAT IF?** In Example 2, suppose that you use a scale on the s-axis from 0 to 520 in increments of 1 unit. *Describe* the appearance of the graph. ***Sample answer*: The graph would be very large with all the points near the top of the graph.**

EXAMPLE 3 Write a function rule for a graph

Write a rule for the function represented by the graph. Identify the domain and the range of the function.

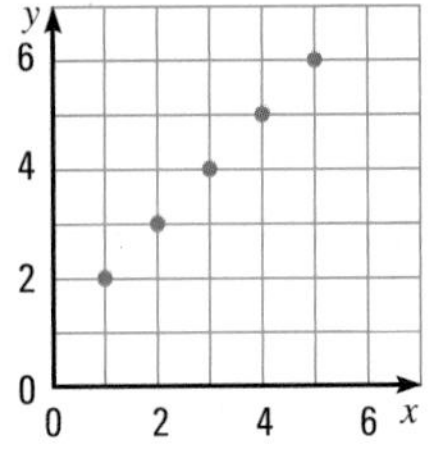

Solution

STEP 1 **Make** a table for the graph.

x	1	2	3	4	5
y	2	3	4	5	6

STEP 2 **Find** a relationship between the inputs and the outputs. Notice from the table that each output value is 1 more than the corresponding input value.

STEP 3 **Write** a function rule that describes the relationship: $y = x + 1$.

▶ A rule for the function is $y = x + 1$. The domain of the function is 1, 2, 3, 4, and 5. The range is 2, 3, 4, 5, and 6.

Differentiated Instruction

Inclusion Some students may find it counterintuitive to think of x-values increasing to the right and y-values increasing upward. Due to this, they may have difficulty constructing graphs on a coordinate plane. Have these students draw coordinate planes by first drawing the x- and y-axes with the arrows properly indicating the increasing direction of the x- and y-values.

See also the *Differentiated Instruction Resources* for more strategies.

GUIDED PRACTICE for Example 3

Write a rule for the function represented by the graph. Identify the domain and the range of the function.

3.

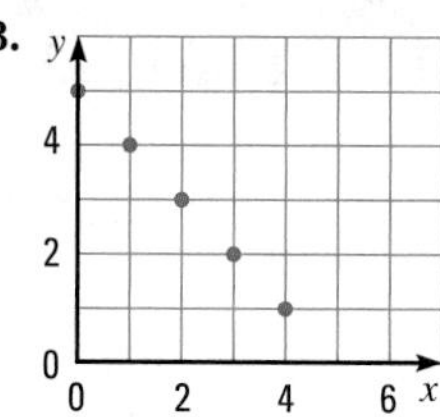

$y = 5 - x$; domain: 0, 1, 2, 3, and 4, range: 1, 2, 3, 4, and 5

4.

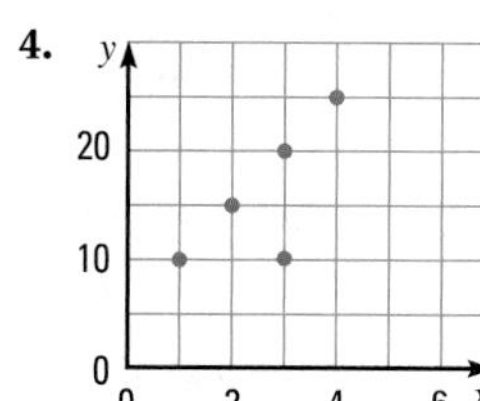

$y = 5x + 5$; domain: 1, 2, 3, and 4, range: 10, 15, 20, and 25

EXAMPLE 4 Analyze a graph

GUITAR SALES The graph shows guitar sales (in millions of dollars) for a chain of music stores for the period 1999–2005. Identify the independent variable and the dependent variable. Describe how sales changed over the period and how you would expect sales in 2006 to compare to sales in 2005.

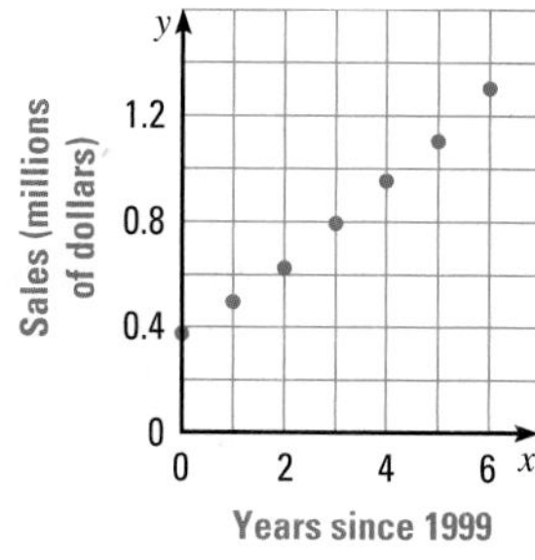

Solution

The independent variable is the number of years since 1999. The dependent variable is the sales (in millions of dollars). The graph shows that sales were increasing. If the trend continued, sales would be greater in 2006 than in 2005.

GUIDED PRACTICE for Example 4

5. **REASONING** Based on the graph in Example 4, is \$1.4 million a reasonable prediction of the chain's sales for 2006? *Explain.*
Yes; the graph seems to increase about \$0.2 million every two years.

CONCEPT SUMMARY *For Your Notebook*

Ways to Represent a Function

You can use a verbal rule, an equation, a table, or a graph to represent a function.

Verbal Rule

The output is 1 less than twice the input.

Equation

$y = 2x - 1$

Table

x	y
1	1
2	3
3	5
4	7

Graph

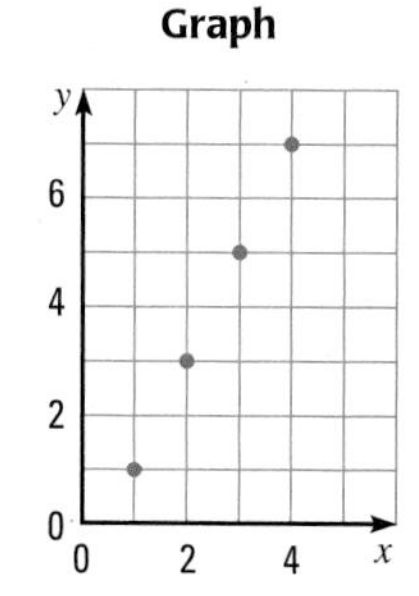

Extra Example 4

The graph shows the average number of video rentals per month at a video store for the years 2000–2006. Identify the independent variable and the dependent variable. Describe how the average number of rentals changed over the period and how you would expect the average number of rentals in 2006 to compare to the number in 2007.

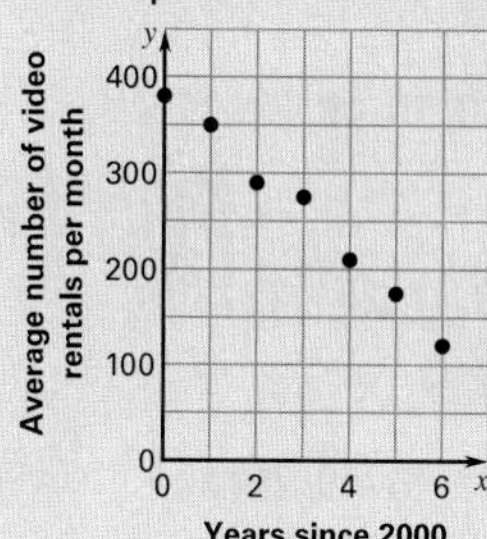

independent variable: years since 2000; dependent variable: average number of video rentals per month; The graph shows that the average number of video rentals per month was decreasing. If the trend continued, the average number of rentals in 2007 would be less than in 2006.

Closing the Lesson

Have students summarize the major points of the lesson and answer the Essential Question: How do you represent functions as graphs?

- **You can use a graph to represent a function.**
- **An input-output table can be used to write a rule for a function whose graph is given.**

You can graph a function by using its domain and function rule to create an input-output table, and then by graphing points for each ordered pair in the table.

p. 43

1.

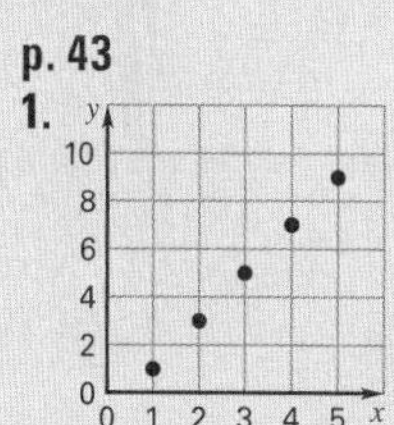

1.7 EXERCISES

HOMEWORK KEY ○ = **WORKED-OUT SOLUTIONS** on p. WS2 for Exs. 3 and 17
★ = **STANDARDIZED TEST PRACTICE** Exs. 2, 13, 18, 19, and 20

4 PRACTICE AND APPLY

Assignment Guide

Answer Transparencies available for all exercises

Basic:
Day 1: pp. 46–48
Exs. 1–11, 15–19, 21–30

Average:
Day 1: pp. 46–48
Exs. 1, 2, 4–13, 15–19, 21–30

Advanced:
Day 1: pp. 46–48
Exs. 1, 2, 6–8, 11–20*, 23–30

Block:
pp. 46–48
Exs. 1, 2, 4–13, 15–19, 21–30 (with 1.6)

Differentiated Instruction

See *Differentiated Instruction Resources* for suggestions on addressing the needs of a diverse classroom.

Homework Check

For a quick check of student understanding of key concepts, go over the following exercises:

Basic: 3, 6, 10, 15, 18
Average: 5, 11, 16, 18, 19
Advanced: 6, 12, 17, 18, 19

Extra Practice

- Student Edition, p. 938
- Chapter Resource Book: Practice levels A, B, C

Practice Worksheet

An easily-readable reduced practice page (with answers) for this lesson can be found on p. 1D.

SKILL PRACTICE

A

1. **VOCABULARY** Copy and complete: Each point on the graph of a function corresponds to an ordered pair (x, y) where x is in the _?_ of the function and y is in the _?_ of the function. **domain; range**

2. ★ **WRITING** Given the graph of a function, describe how to write a rule for the function. **Find a relationship between the input values and the output values.**

EXAMPLE 1 on p. 43 for Exs. 3–9

GRAPHING FUNCTIONS **Graph the function.** **3–8. See margin.**

3. $y = x + 3$; domain: 0, 1, 2, 3, 4, and 5
4. $y = \frac{1}{2}x + 1$; domain: 0, 1, 2, 3, 4, and 5
5. $y = 2x + 2$; domain: 0, 2, 5, 7, and 10
6. $y = 3x - 1$; domain: 1, 2, 3, 4, and 5
7. $y = x + 5$; domain: 0, 2, 4, 6, 8, and 10
8. $y = 2.5x$; domain: 0, 1, 2, 3, and 4

9. **ERROR ANALYSIS** *Describe* and correct the error in graphing the function $y = x - 1$ with domain 1, 2, 3, 4, and 5.
The domain and range are graphed backwards; see margin.

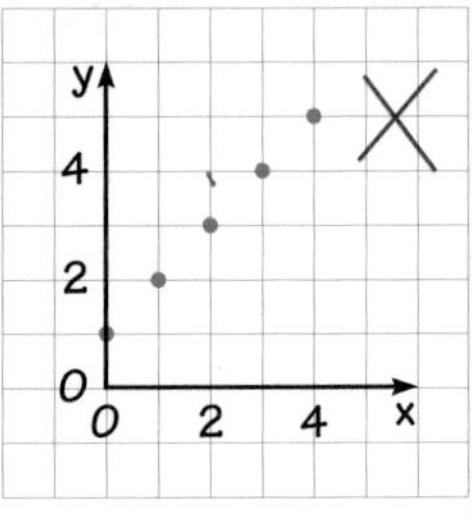

EXAMPLE 3 on p. 44 for Exs. 10–12

B

WRITING FUNCTION RULES **Write a rule for the function represented by the graph. Identify the domain and the range of the function.** **10–12. See margin.**

10. 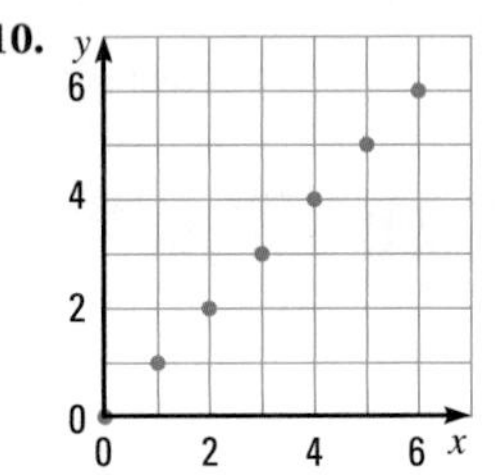

11. 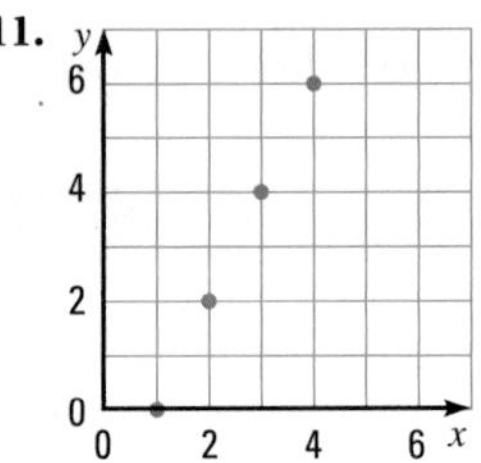

12. 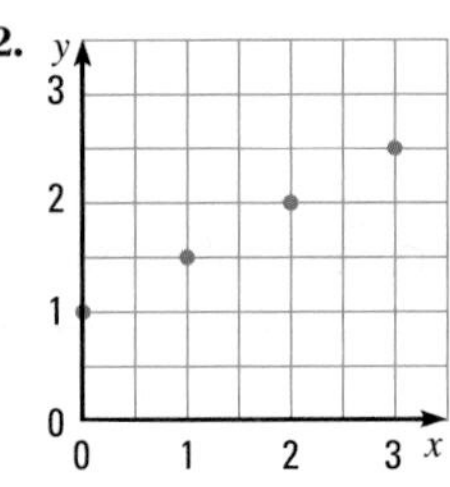

13. ★ **MULTIPLE CHOICE** The graph of which function is shown? **C**

(A) $y = \frac{1}{2}x + \frac{1}{2}$
(B) $y = x + \frac{1}{2}$
(C) $y = \frac{3}{2}x + \frac{1}{2}$
(D) $y = 2x + \frac{1}{2}$

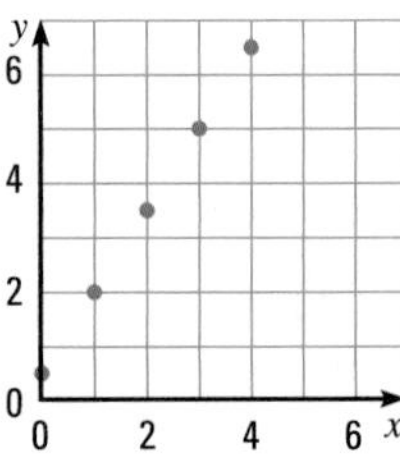

3–8. See Additional Answers beginning on p. AA1.

9. 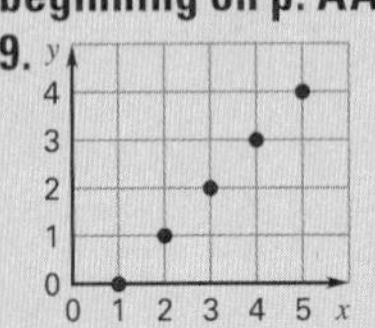

10. $y = x$; **domain: 0, 1, 2, 3, 4, 5, and 6, range: 0, 1, 2, 3, 4, 5, and 6**

11. $y = 2x - 2$; **domain: 1, 2, 3, and 4, range: 0, 2, 4, and 6**

12. $y = \frac{1}{2}x + 1$; **domain: 0, 1, 2, and 3, range: 1, $1\frac{1}{2}$, 2, $2\frac{1}{2}$**

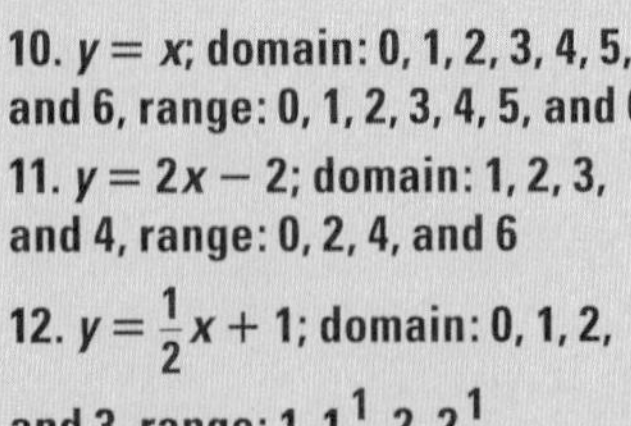

15. 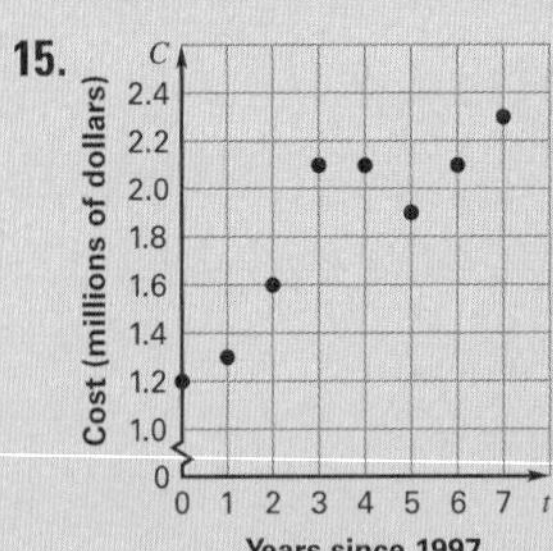

C 14. **CHALLENGE** The graph represents a function.

a. Write a rule for the function. $y = \frac{1}{2}x^2$

b. Find the value of y so that (1.5, y) is on the graph of the function. **1.125**

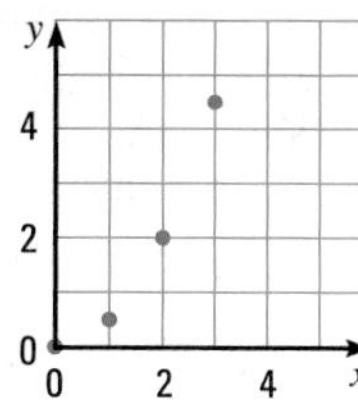

PROBLEM SOLVING

EXAMPLE 2 A on p. 44 for Exs. 15–17

15. **ADVERTISING** The table shows the cost C (in millions of dollars) of a 30 second Super Bowl ad on TV as a function of the time t (in years) since 1997. Graph the function. **See margin.**

Years since 1997, t	0	1	2	3	4	5	6	7
Cost (millions of dollars), C	1.2	1.3	1.6	2.1	2.1	1.9	2.1	2.3

@HomeTutor for problem solving help at classzone.com

16. **CONGRESS** The table shows the number r of U.S. representatives for Texas as a function of the time t (in years) since 1930. Graph the function. **See margin.**

Years since 1930, t	0	10	20	30	40	50	60	70
Number of representatives, r	21	21	22	23	24	27	30	32

@HomeTutor for problem solving help at classzone.com

17. **ELECTIONS** The table shows the number v of voters in U.S. presidential elections as a function of the time t (in years) since 1984. First copy and complete the table. Round to the nearest million. Then graph the function represented by the first and third columns. **See margin for art.**

Years since 1984	Voters	Voters (millions)
0	92,652,680	? 93
4	91,594,693	? 92
8	104,405,155	? 104
12	96,456,345	? 96
16	105,586,274	? 106

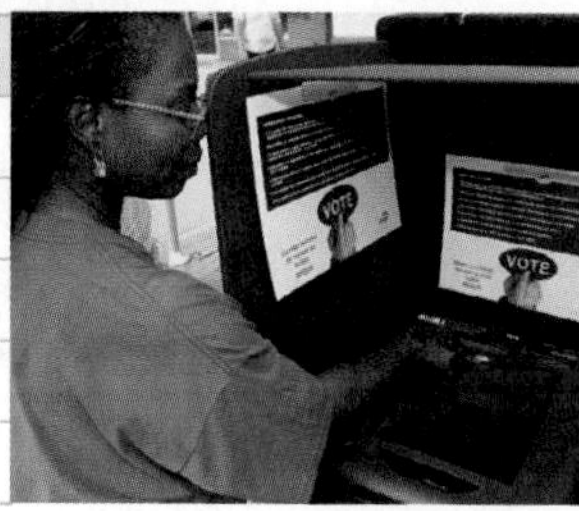

EXAMPLE 4 on p. 45 for Exs. 18–19

18. ★ **WRITING** The graph shows the number of hours of daylight in Houston, Texas, on the fifteenth day of the month, with 1 representing January, and so on. Identify the independent variable and the dependent variable. *Describe* how the number of hours of daylight changes over a year. **Independent variable: the month, dependent variable: the hours of daylight; the number of daylight hours increases from January to May and then decreases through December.**

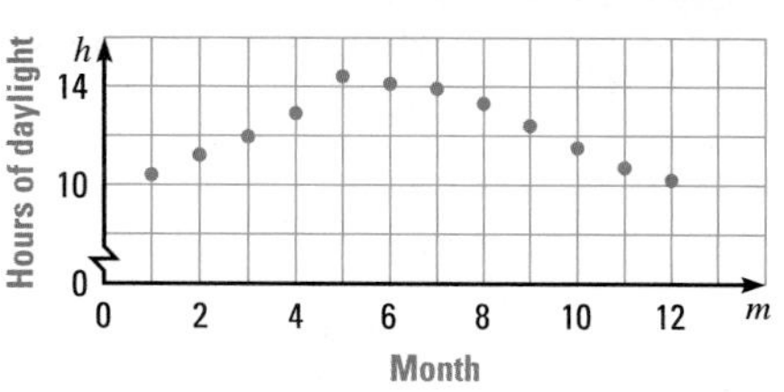

Avoiding Common Errors

Exercises 3–8 Students sometimes mistakenly reverse the x- and y-coordinates of a point when they plot it. Remind them that the domain values of a function are the x-coordinates of the points. Point out that they can quickly compare the given domain values to the labels of the vertical grid lines that have plotted points located on them.

Study Strategy

Exercises 10–12 Instruct students to use the solution steps shown in Example 3. Emphasize that a table will help them identify the relationship between the corresponding values of x and y.

Exercises 15–17 Suggest that students review Step 1 in Example 2 before graphing the functions. This will remind them to choose an appropriate scale and uniform increments for their graphs.

Mathematical Reasoning

Exercise 13 Lead students to see that the points are rising by $1\frac{1}{2}\left(\text{or } \frac{3}{2}\right)$ units on the y-axis for each increase of 1 unit on the x-axis. This suggests that answer C may be correct and should be checked first.

Exercise 15 Additional information about the Super Bowl, including a link to commercials, can be found at the official Super Bowl website www.nfl.com/superbowl.

Exercise 16 For information about the number of U.S. Representatives from other states, visit the official website for the U.S. House of Representatives at www.house.gov.

Differentiated Instruction

Advanced Ask students if it is possible to write a rule for the functions given in **Exercises 15 and 16**. Challenge them to explain why they can write rules for some functions and not for others. Suggest they graph a real-world situation in which they can write a rule for the function and then compare it to their graphs in Exercise 15 and 16. This will lead them into thinking about the differences between functions and prepare them for the concept of linear functions.

See also the *Differentiated Instruction Resources* for more strategies.

16.

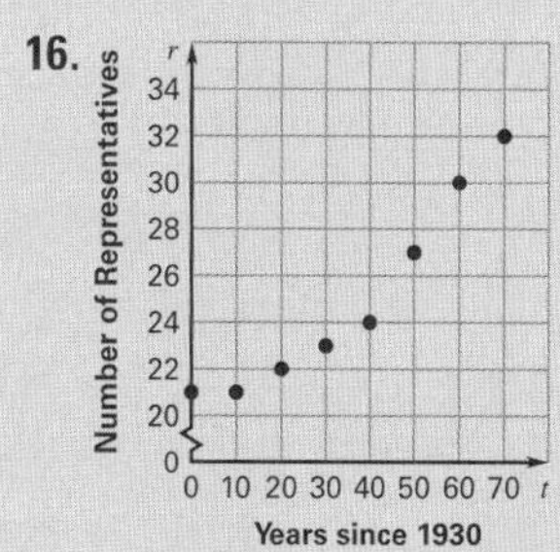

17.

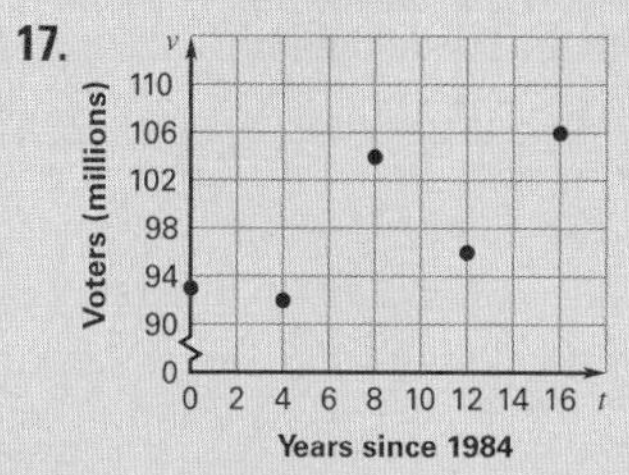

5 ASSESS AND RETEACH

Daily Homework Quiz

Transparency Available

1. Graph the function $y = \frac{1}{2}x + 2$ with domain 2, 4, 6, and 8.

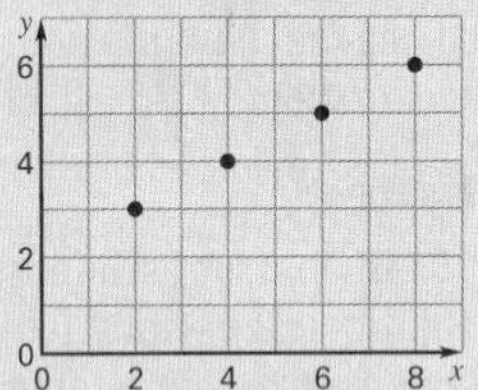

2. Write a rule for the function represented by the graph. Identify the domain and the range of the function.

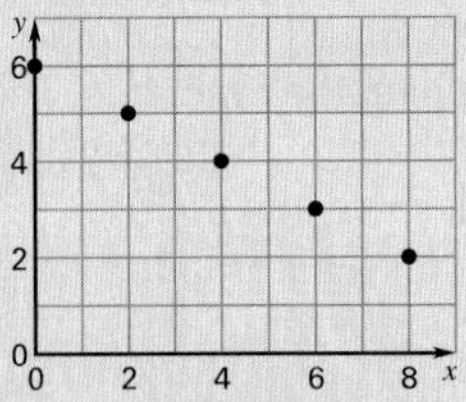

$y = -\frac{1}{2}x + 6$; domain: 0, 2, 4, 6, 8; range: 2, 3, 4, 5, 6

Online Quiz

Available at **classzone.com**

Diagnosis/Remediation

- Practice A, B, C in Chapter Resource Book
- Study Guide in Chapter Resource Book
- Practice Workbook
- @HomeTutor

Challenge

Additional challenge is available in the Chapter Resource Book.

Quiz

An easily-readable reduced copy of the quiz (with answers) on Lessons 1.6–1.7 from the Assessment Book can be found on p. 1E.

20a, Quiz 1, 4, 5. See Additional Answers beginning on p. AA1.

B 19. ★ **SHORT RESPONSE** A field biologist collected and measured alligator snapping turtle eggs. The graph shows the mass m (in grams) of an egg as a function of its length ℓ (in millimeters).

Mass (g); Length (mm)

a. **Describe** As the lengths of the eggs increase, what happens to the masses of the eggs? **increases**

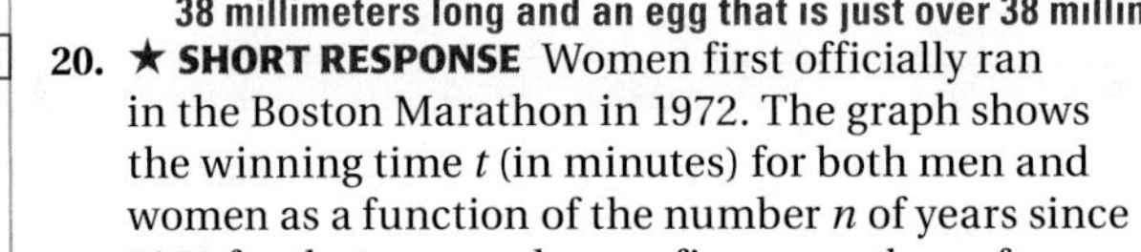

b. **Estimate** Is 27.5 g a reasonable estimate for the mass of an egg that is 38 mm long? *Explain.*
Yes; 27.5 grams is between the mass of an egg that is just under 38 millimeters long and an egg that is just over 38 millimeters long.

C 20. ★ **SHORT RESPONSE** Women first officially ran in the Boston Marathon in 1972. The graph shows the winning time t (in minutes) for both men and women as a function of the number n of years since 1972 for that year and every five years thereafter.

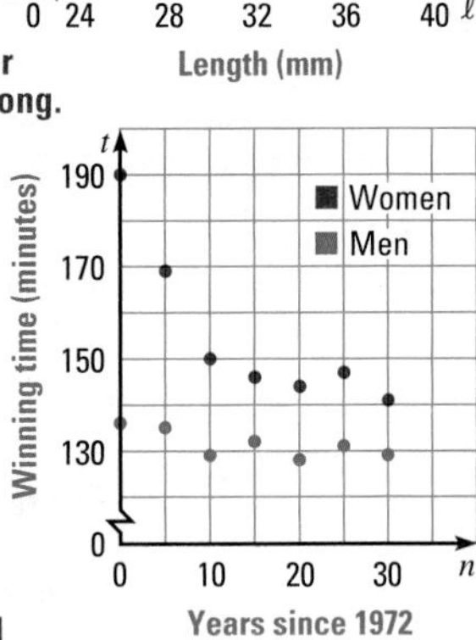

a. **CHALLENGE** *Explain* how you can estimate the difference in the men's and women's winning time for any year shown. **See margin.**

b. **CHALLENGE** *Compare* any trends you see in the graphs.
Sample answer: **Between 1982 and 2002 the men's times are all within about 5 minutes of each other and the women's times are all within about 10 minutes of each other.**

MIXED REVIEW

PREVIEW Prepare for Lesson 2.1 in Exs. 21–24.

Copy and complete the statement using <, >, or =. *(p. 909)*

21. 0.53 _?_ 0.5 >
22. 3.9 _?_ 4.0 <
23. 1.64 _?_ 1.66 <
24. 0.80 _?_ 0.8 =

Solve the equation using mental math. *(p. 21)*

25. $x + 12 = 20$ **8**
26. $12z = 480$ **40**
27. $x - 8 = 5$ **13**
28. $\frac{n}{2} = 32$ **64**

Write a rule for the function. *(p. 35)*

29.

Input, x	2	3	7	10
Ouput, y	8	7	3	0

$y = 10 - x$

30.

Input, x	0	4	8	12
Ouput, y	5	7	9	11

$y = \frac{1}{2}x + 5$

QUIZ for Lessons 1.6–1.7

1. The domain of the function $y = 12 - 2x$ is 0, 2, 3, 4, and 5. Make a table for the function, then identify the range of the function. *(p. 35)*
Range: 2, 4, 6, 8, and 12; see margin.

Tell whether the pairing is a function. *(p. 35)*

2.

x	5	6	7	11
y	1	2	3	7

function

3.

x	4	6	9	15
y	1	3	6	3

function

Graph the function. *(p. 43)* **4, 5. See margin.**

4. $y = 2x - 5$; domain: 5, 6, 7, 8, and 9
5. $y = 7 - x$; domain: 1, 2, 3, 4, and 5

EXTRA PRACTICE for Lesson 1.7, p. 938

 **ONLINE QUIZ** at classzone.com

Determine Whether a Relation Is a Function

GOAL Determine whether a relation is a function when the relation is represented by a table or a graph.

Key Vocabulary
- **relation,** *p. 49*

A **relation** is any pairing of a set of inputs with a set of outputs. Every function is a relation, but not every relation is a function. A relation is a function if for every input there is exactly one output.

EXAMPLE 1 Determine whether a relation is a function

Determine whether the relation is a function.

a.

Input	4	4	5	6	7
Output	0	1	2	3	4

b.

Input	3	5	7	9
Output	1	2	3	2

Solution

a. The input 4 has two different outputs, 0 and 1. So, the relation is *not* a function.

b. Every input has exactly one output, so the relation is a function.

USING THE GRAPH OF A RELATION You can use the *vertical line test* to determine whether a relation represented by a graph is a function. When a relation is *not* a function, its graph contains at least two points with the same x-coordinate and different y-coordinates. Those points lie on a vertical line.

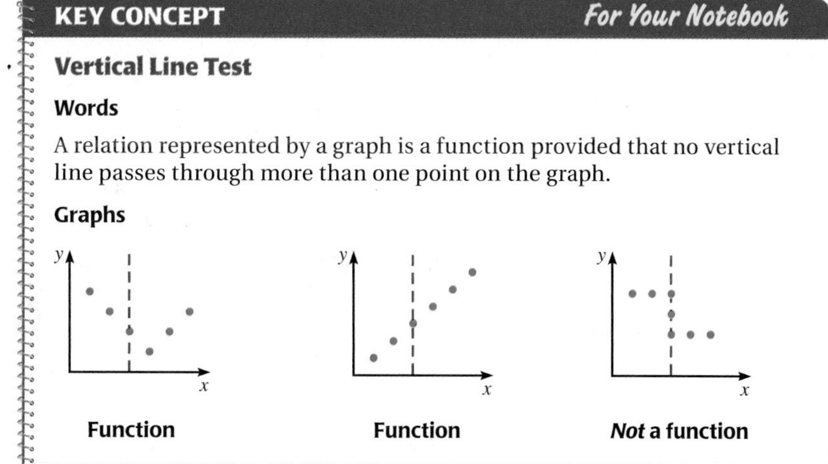

KEY CONCEPT
For Your Notebook
Vertical Line Test
Words
A relation represented by a graph is a function provided that no vertical line passes through more than one point on the graph.
Graphs
y
x
y
x
y
x
Function
Function
Not a function

1 PLAN AND PREPARE

Warm-Up Exercises

1. Identify the domain and range.

Input	0	2	6	7	8
Output	1	4	5	9	11

domain: 0, 2, 6, 7, 8; range: 1, 4, 5, 9, 11

Tell whether the pairing is a function.

2. Input Output

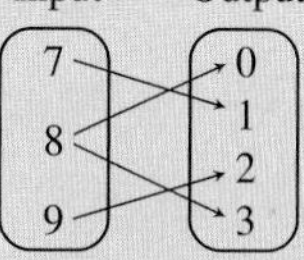

The pairing is *not* a function, because the input 8 is paired with both 0 and 3.

3. Input Output

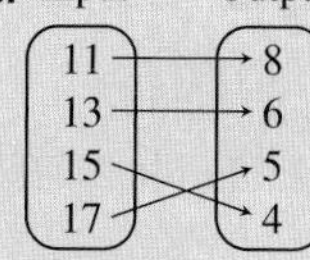

The pairing is a function, because each input is paired with exactly one output.

2 FOCUS AND MOTIVATE

Essential Question

Big Idea 3, p. 1

How do you determine whether a relation shown in a table or a graph is a function? **Tell students they will learn how to answer this question by examining input-output tables and by using the vertical line test on graphs.**

NCTM STANDARDS

Standard 2: Understand relations; Understand functions

3 TEACH

Extra Example 1

Determine whether the relation is a function. **yes**

Input	2	3	4	5	6
Output	9	4	1	0	1

Extra Example 2

Determine whether the graph represents a function. **no**

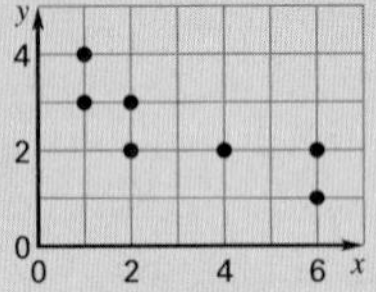

Animated Algebra classzone.com

An **Animated Algebra** activity is available online for **Example 2**. This activity is also part of **Power Presentations**.

Closing the Lesson

Have students summarize the major points of the lesson and answer the Essential Question: How do you determine whether a relation shown in a table or a graph is a function?

- **A relation is a function if for every input there is exactly one output.**
- **A relation is a function if no vertical line passes through more than one point when the relation is graphed.**

In a table, check that each input has exactly one output; in a graph, check that no vertical line passes through more than one point.

EXAMPLE 2 Use the vertical line test

Determine whether the graph represents a function.

a.

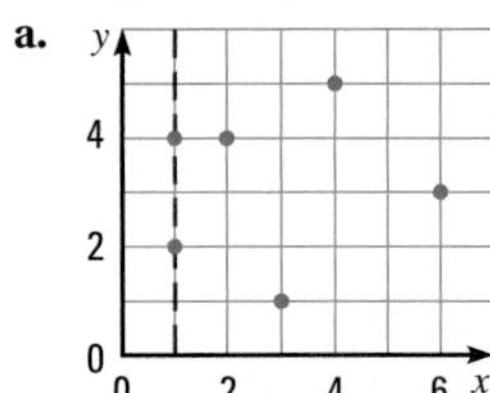

You can draw a vertical line through the points (1, 2) and (1, 4). The graph does *not* represent a function.

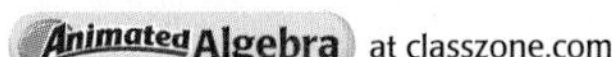

Animated Algebra at classzone.com

b.

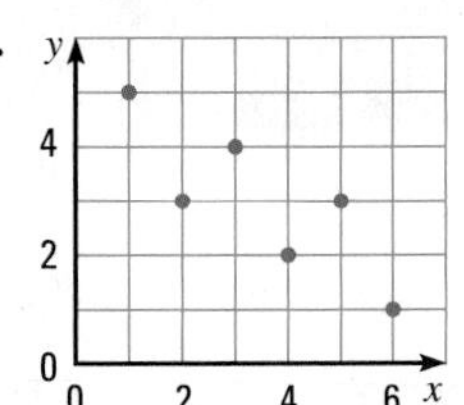

No vertical line can be drawn through more than one point. The graph represents a function.

PRACTICE

EXAMPLE 1 on p. 49 for Exs. 1–3

IDENTIFYING FUNCTIONS **Determine whether the relation is a function.**

1.

Input	Output
0	1
2	6
5	12
7	5
8	4

function

2.

Input	Output
3	7
4	8
4	9
5	10
6	11

not a function

3.

Input	Output
0.7	1.9
1.2	2.4
3.5	4.7
7.5	8.7
7.5	9.7

not a function

EXAMPLE 2 on p. 50 for Exs. 4–6

IDENTIFYING FUNCTIONS **Determine whether the graph represents a function.**

4.

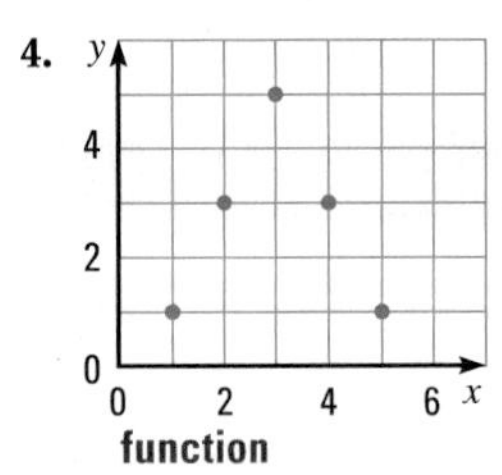

function

5.

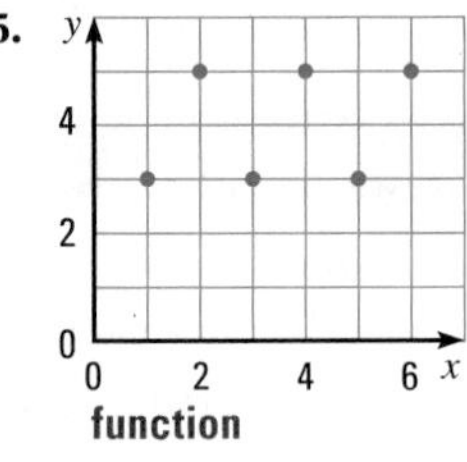

function

6.

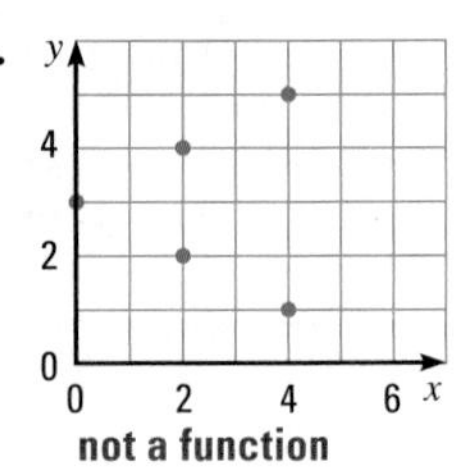

not a function

REASONING **Tell whether the pairing of x-values and y-values is necessarily a function. *Explain* your reasoning.** **7, 8. See margin.**

7. A teacher makes a table that lists the number x of letters in the first name and the number y of letters in the last name of each student in the class.

8. Your doctor records your height x (in inches) and your weight y (in pounds) each time you have a medical exam.

9. You have a record of your age x (in years) and your height y (in inches) on each of your birthdays since you were born.
Function; for each of your birthdays, you have only one height.

4 PRACTICE AND APPLY

Teaching Strategy

Exercises 8–9 Have students work in groups to create tables of realistic values and then have them graph them. Working with actual values may help students see the relationships more readily.

7. Not a function. *Sample answer:* There could be many students whose first names have 4 letters, for instance, but their last names could all have a different number of letters.

8. Not a function. *Sample answer:* If your height stays the same, you could lose or gain weight, giving more than one output for an input.

MIXED REVIEW of Problem Solving

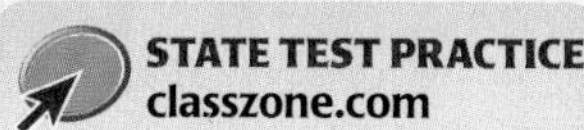

Lessons 1.5–1.7

1. **MULTI-STEP PROBLEM** A pizza shop charges \$7 for a large cheese pizza plus \$.95 for each topping.

   a. Use a verbal model to write an equation for the total cost C (in dollars) of a pizza with n toppings. **1a, b. See margin.**

   b. The pizza shop offers 10 toppings. Write an input-output table for the total cost (in dollars) of a pizza as a function of the number n of toppings. *Explain* why the table represents a function and describe the domain and range of the function.

   c. You have \$15 to spend on a large pizza. What is the greatest number of toppings you can afford? **8 toppings**

2. **SHORT RESPONSE** Your class is planning a car wash. You need \$75 worth of materials.

   a. Use a verbal model to write an equation that relates your profit to the number of cars you wash. Find your profit if you wash 120 cars. **2a, b. See margin.**

   b. Does doubling the number of cars you wash double your profit? *Explain.*

3. **MULTI-STEP PROBLEM** You are painting a room in a community center. The room has four walls that are each 9 feet high and 25 feet long. There are two rectangular windows and two rectangular doors that do not need to be painted. Each window is 3.5 feet wide and 4 feet high. Each door is 3.5 feet wide and 7 feet high.

   a. Find the combined area of the windows and doors. **77 ft²**

   b. Find the combined area of all four walls, excluding the windows and the doors. **823 ft²**

   c. A gallon of paint covers about 400 square feet. How many one-gallon cans of paint will you need in order to give the room one coat of paint? **3 one-gallon cans**

   d. The paint costs \$24.95 per gallon. How much will it cost for one coat of paint? **\$74.85**

4. **GRIDDED ANSWER** You consider 68°F to be a comfortable room temperature. The temperature in a room is 18°C. How many degrees Celsius should you raise the temperature so that it will be 68°F? **2°C**

5. **SHORT RESPONSE** Your family is driving from Charleston, South Carolina, to Jacksonville, Florida, a total distance of about 250 miles. You leave Charleston at 1:00 P.M. You travel at an average speed of 55 miles per hour without stopping. Will you get to Jacksonville before the 5:00 P.M. rush hour? *Explain.* **See margin.**

6. **GRIDDED ANSWER** A person invests \$1200 in an account earning 3% simple annual interest. How much will be in the account after 2 years? **\$1272**

7. **OPEN-ENDED** Write a problem that involves a real-world situation and that can be solved using the formula for distance traveled. Solve the problem and explain what the solution means in the situation. **See margin.**

8. **EXTENDED RESPONSE** You pay \$40 per hour for windsurfing lessons and rent equipment for \$20 per hour. The cost (in dollars) of lessons and the cost (in dollars) of rentals are both functions of the time (in hours).

   a. Write a rule for each function. **$c = 40t$, $c = 20t$**

   b. Let the domains of the functions be the whole numbers from 0 to 6. Graph each function. **See margin.**

   c. You rent equipment for every lesson you take. What function gives your total cost? How would the graph of this function compare with the graphs in part (b)?
   $c = 60t$; this graph would be steeper.

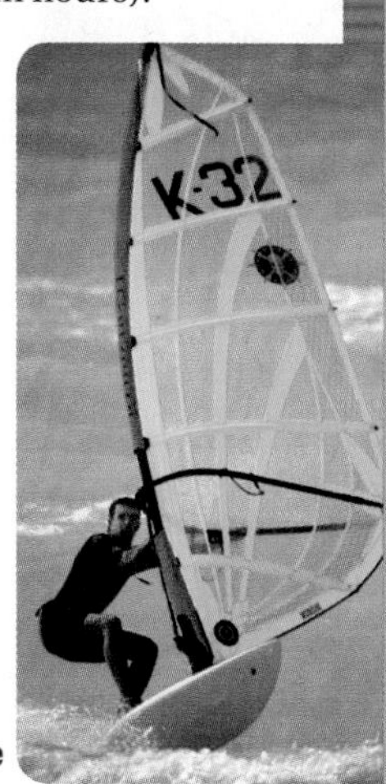

1a. total cost = cost of cheese + (number of toppings)(cost of each topping)

1b. See below.

2a. profit = (number of cars) • (price per car) − cost of materials; \$525

2b. No; your materials cost is the same. Only the income doubled, not the profit.

5. No; it will take your family about $4\frac{1}{2}$ hours to get to Jacksonville, so it will be after 5:30 P.M.

7. *Sample answer:* You are riding your bike to your friend's house, 5 miles away. You need to be there in a half hour. What should your average speed be to get there in time? $r = 10$, you must ride your bike at 10 miles per hour to get to your friend's house in a half hour.

8b.

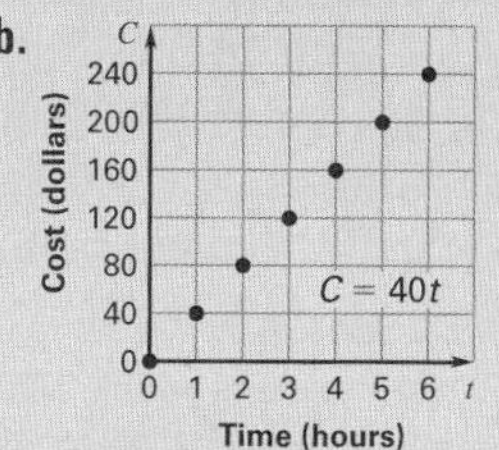

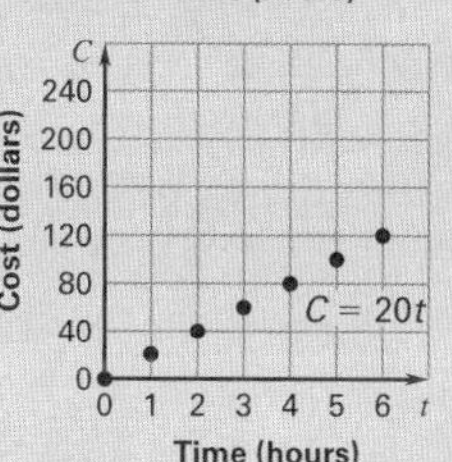

1b.

Toppings	0	1	2	3	4	5
Cost (dollars)	7	7.95	8.90	9.85	10.80	11.75

Toppings	6	7	8	9	10
Cost (dollars)	12.70	13.65	14.60	15.55	16.50

There is exactly one cost for each number of toppings, so the table represents a function. The domain is 0, 1, 2, 3, 4, 5, 6, 7, 8, 9, and 10. The range is 7, 7.95, 8.90, 9.85, 10.80, 11.75, 12.70, 13.65, 14.60, 15.55, and 16.50.

1 CHAPTER SUMMARY

Animated Algebra
classzone.com
Electronic Function Library

Additional Resources

The following resources are available to help review the materials in this chapter.

Chapter Resource Book

- Chapter Review Games and Activities
- Cumulative Practice, Ch. 1

Student Resources in Spanish

eWorkbook

@HomeTutor

Vocabulary Practice

Vocabulary practice is available at **classzone.com**

BIG IDEAS *For Your Notebook*

Big Idea 1 Writing and Evaluating Algebraic Expressions

The cost of admission for one student at a planetarium is \$6. You can use a verbal model to write an expression for the total cost of admission for any number of students.

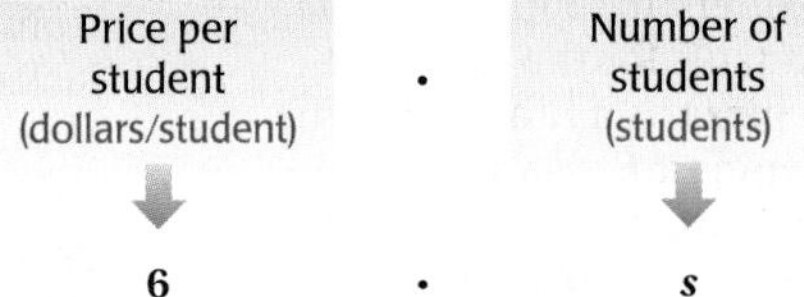

6 • s

An expression is $6s$. Because $\frac{\text{dollars}}{\cancel{\text{student}}} \cdot \cancel{\text{students}} = \text{dollars}$, the expression produces an answer in dollars. The expression is reasonable.

Big Idea 2 Using Expressions to Write Equations and Inequalities

You can use symbols to write an equation or inequality that compares the expression $6s$ to another expression.

The total cost of admission to the planetarium for s students at a rate of \$6 per student is \$150.

$6s = 150$ **Equation**

The total cost of admission to the planetarium for s students at a rate of \$6 per student is no more than \$150.

$6s \leq 150$ **Inequality**

Big Idea 3 Representing Functions as Verbal Rules, Equations, Tables, and Graphs

You can use a verbal description, an equation, a table, or a graph to represent a function.

Words The total cost (in dollars) of admission to the planetarium is 6 times the number of students.

Equation

$C = 6s$

Table

Input, s	Output, C
0	0
1	6
2	12
3	18

Graph

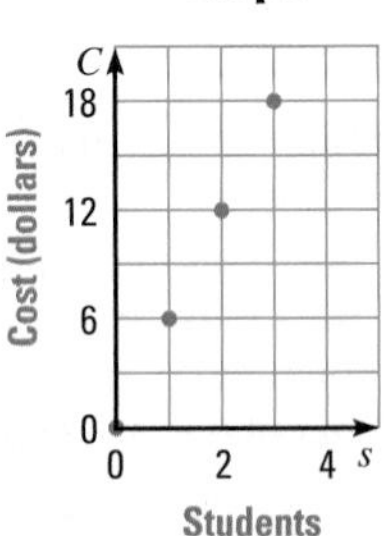

CHAPTER REVIEW

@HomeTutor
classzone.com
- Multi-Language Glossary
- Vocabulary practice

REVIEW KEY VOCABULARY

- variable, *p. 2*
- algebraic expression, *p. 2*
- evaluate an algebraic expression, *p. 2*
- power, exponent, base, *p. 3*
- order of operations, *p. 8*
- verbal model, *p. 16*
- rate, unit rate, *p. 17*
- equation, inequality, *p. 21*
- open sentence, *p. 21*
- solution of an equation or inequality, *p. 22*
- formula, *p. 30*
- function, *p. 35*
- input, output, *p. 35*
- domain, range, *p. 35*
- independent variable, *p. 36*
- dependent variable, *p. 36*

VOCABULARY EXERCISES

In Exercises 1–3, copy and complete the statement.

1. In the power 7^{12}, _?_ is the base and _?_ is the exponent. **7, 12**
2. A(n) _?_ is a statement that contains the symbol =. **equation**
3. A(n) _?_ is an expression that includes at least one variable. **algebraic expression**
4. **WRITING** *Describe* how you can tell by looking at the graph of a function which variable is the input variable and which is the output variable.
When looking at the graph of a function the variable along the *x*-axis is the input variable and the variable along the *y*-axis is the output variable.

REVIEW EXAMPLES AND EXERCISES

Use the review examples and exercises below to check your understanding of the concepts you have learned in each lesson of Chapter 1.

1.1 Evaluate Expressions *pp. 2–7*

EXAMPLE

Evaluate $6 - n$ when $n = 4$.

$6 - n = 6 - 4$ **Substitute 4 for *n*.**

$= 2$ **Simplify.**

EXERCISES

EXAMPLES 1, 4, and 5 on pp. 2–4 for Exs. 5–12

Evaluate the expression.

5. $3 + x$ when $x = 13$ **16**
6. $y - 2$ when $y = 18$ **16**
7. $\frac{20}{k}$ when $k = 2$ **10**
8. $40w$ when $w = 0.5$ **20**
9. z^2 when $z = 20$ **400**
10. w^3 when $w = 0.1$ **0.001**
11. **DVD STORAGE** A DVD storage sleeve has the shape of a square with an edge length of 5 inches. What is the area of the front of the sleeve? **25 in.^{2}**
12. **NOTEPAPER** You store square notepaper in a cube-shaped box with an inside edge length of 3 inches. What is the volume of the box? **27 in.^{3}**

Extra Example 1.1

Evaluate $\frac{36}{g}$ when $g = 4$. **9**

Extra Example 1.2

Evaluate $32 - (4^2 + 8) \div 4$. **26**

Extra Example 1.3

Write an expression for the height of a tree over time if the tree was 2.5 feet tall when planted and it grows at an average rate of 2 feet per year. **$2t + 2.5$, where t represents the time in years**

1 CHAPTER REVIEW

1.2 Apply Order of Operations

pp. 8–12

EXAMPLE

Evaluate $(5 + 3)^2 \div 2 \times 3$.

$(5 + 3)^2 \div 2 \times 3 = 8^2 \div 2 \times 3$	Add within parentheses.
$= 64 \div 2 \times 3$	Evaluate power.
$= 32 \times 3$	Divide.
$= 96$	Multiply.

EXERCISES

EXAMPLES 1, 2, and 3 on pp. 8–9 for Exs. 13–21

Evaluate the expression.

13. $12 - 6 \div 2$ **9**

14. $1 + 2 \cdot 9^2$ **163**

15. $3 + 2^3 - 6 \div 2$ **8**

16. $15 - (4 + 3^2)$ **2**

17. $\frac{20 - 12}{5^2 - 1}$ $\mathbf{\frac{1}{3}}$

18. $50 - [7 + (3^2 \div 2)]$ $\mathbf{38\frac{1}{2}}$

Evaluate the expression when $x = 4$.

19. $15x - 8$ **52**

20. $3x^2 + 4$ **52**

21. $2(x - 1)^2$ **18**

1.3 Write Expressions

pp. 15–20

EXAMPLE

Write an expression for the entry fee in a jazz band competition if there is a base fee of \$50 and a charge of \$1 per member.

Write a verbal model. Then translate the verbal model into an algebraic expression. Let n represent the number of band members.

Base fee (dollars)	+	Cost per member (dollars/member)	•	Number of members (members)
50	+	**1**	•	***n***

▸ An expression for the entry fee (in dollars) is $50 + n$.

EXERCISES

EXAMPLES 1, 2, and 3 on pp. 15–16 for Exs. 22–27

Translate the verbal phrase into an expression.

22. The sum of a number k and 7 $\mathbf{k + 7}$

23. 5 less than a number z $\mathbf{z - 5}$

24. The quotient of a number k and 12 $\mathbf{\frac{k}{12}}$

25. 3 times the square of a number x $\mathbf{3x^2}$

26. TOLL ROADS A toll road charges trucks a toll of \$3 per axle. Write an expression for the total toll for a truck. $\mathbf{3a}$

27. SCHOOL SUPPLIES You purchase some notebooks for \$2.95 each and a package of pens for \$2.19. Write an expression for the total amount (in dollars) that you spend. $\mathbf{2.95n + 2.19}$

1.4 Write Equations and Inequalities

pp. 21–26

EXAMPLE

Write an inequality for the sentence "The sum of 3 and twice a number k is no more than 15". Then check whether 4 is a solution of the inequality.

An inequality is $3 + 2k \le 15$.

To check whether 4 is a solution of the inequality, substitute 4 for k.

$3 + 2(4) \overset{?}{\le} 15$ **Substitute 4 for k.**

$11 \le 15$ ✓ **The solution checks. So, 4 is a solution.**

EXERCISES

EXAMPLES 1 and 2 on pp. 21–22 for Exs. 28–32

Write an equation or an inequality.

28. The product of a number z and 12 is 60. **$12z = 60$**

29. The sum of 13 and a number t is at least 24. **$13 + t \ge 24$**

Check whether the given number is a solution of the equation or inequality.

30. $3x - 4 = 10$; 5 **not a solution**

31. $4y - 2 \ge 2$; 3 **solution**

32. $2d + 4 < 9d - 7$; 3 **solution**

1.5 Use a Problem Solving Plan

pp. 28–33

EXAMPLE

A rectangular banner is 12 feet long and has an area of 60 square feet. What is the perimeter of the banner?

STEP 1 **Read and Understand** You know the length of the rectangular banner and its area. You want to find the perimeter.

STEP 2 **Make a Plan** Use the area formula for a rectangle to find the width. Then use the perimeter formula for a rectangle.

STEP 3 **Solve the Problem** Substituting 12 for ℓ in the formula $A = \ell w$, $60 = 12w$. Because $12 \cdot 5 = 60$, $w = 5$. Then substituting 12 for ℓ and 5 for w in the formula $P = 2\ell + 2w$, $P = 2(12) + 2(5) = 34$ feet.

STEP 4 **Look Back** Use estimation. Since $\ell \approx 10$ and $A = 60$, $w \approx 6$. Then $P \approx 2(10) + 2(6) = 32$ feet, so your answer is reasonable.

EXERCISES

EXAMPLES 1, 2, and 3 on p. 28–30 for Exs. 33–34

33. U.S. HISTORY The flag that inspired the national anthem was a rectangle 30 feet wide and 42 feet long. Pieces of the flag have been lost. It is now 30 feet wide and 34 feet long. How many square feet have been lost? **240 ft^2**

34. PATTERNS A grocery clerk stacks three rows of cans of fruit for a display. Each of the top two rows has 2 fewer cans than the row beneath it. There are 30 cans altogether. How many cans are there in each row? **8 cans, 10 cans, and 12 cans**

Extra Example 1.4

Write an equation for the sentence "Nine more than the quantity 6 less than a number n is 18." Then check whether 10 is a solution of the equation. **$9 + (n - 6) = 18$; 10 is not a solution since $9 + (10 - 6) = 13$ and $13 \neq 18$.**

Extra Example 1.5

The floor of a rectangular building is 52 feet long and has a perimeter of 174 feet. What is the area of the floor? **1820 ft^2**

Extra Example 1.6

The domain of the function $y = 4x + 1$ is 0, 2, 4, and 6. Make a table for the function, then identify the range of the function.

x	0	2	4	6
$y = 4x + 1$	1	9	17	25

range: 1, 9, 17, 25

Extra Example 1.7

Write a rule for the function represented by the graph. Identify the domain and the range of the function.

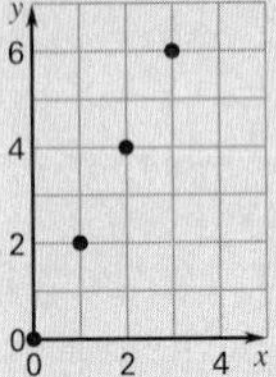

A rule for the function is $y = 2x$. The domain is 0, 1, 2, and 3. The range is 0, 2, 4, and 6.

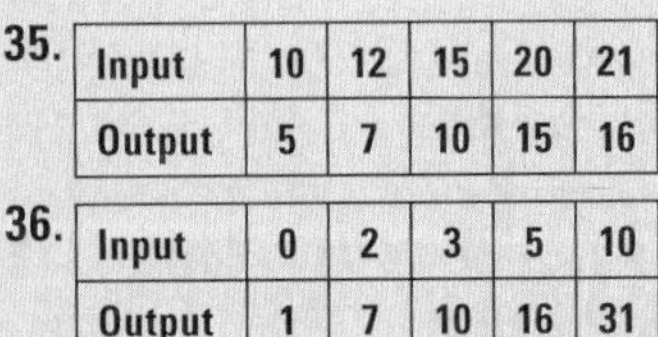

35.

Input	10	12	15	20	21
Output	5	7	10	15	16

36.

Input	0	2	3	5	10
Output	1	7	10	16	31

39.

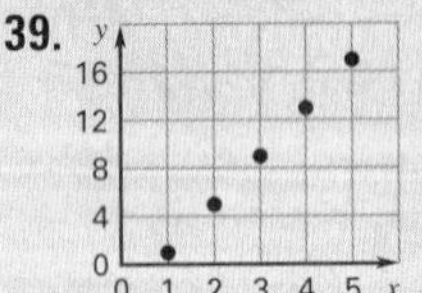

1 CHAPTER REVIEW

1.6 Represent Functions as Rules and Tables

pp. 35–40

EXAMPLE

The domain of the function $y = 3x - 5$ is 2, 3, 4, and 5. Make a table for the function, then identify the range of the function.

x	2	3	4	5
$y = 3x - 5$	$3(2) - 5 = 1$	$3(3) - 5 = 4$	$3(4) - 5 = 7$	$3(5) - 5 = 10$

The range of the function is 1, 4, 7, and 10.

EXERCISES

EXAMPLES 1, 3, and 4 on p. 35–37 for Exs. 35–38

Make a table for the function. Identify the range of the function.

35. $y = x - 5$
Domain: 10, 12, 15, 20, 21
Range: 5, 7, 10, 15, and 16; see margin.

36. $y = 3x + 1$
Domain: 0, 2, 3, 5, 10
Range: 1, 7, 10, 16, and 31; see margin.

Write a rule for the function.

37.

Input, x	0	2	4	5
Output, y	4	6	8	9

$y = x + 4$

38.

Input, x	0	3	4	6
Output, y	0	15	20	30

$y = 5x$

1.7 Represent Functions as Graphs

pp. 43–48

EXAMPLE

Write a rule for the function represented by the graph. Identify the domain and the range of the function.

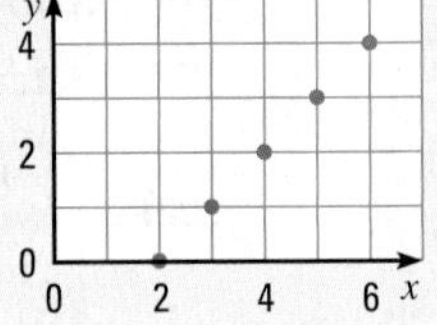

Make a table for the graph.

x	2	3	4	5	6
y	0	1	2	3	4

Each y-value is 2 less than the corresponding x-value. A rule for the function is $y = x - 2$. The domain is 2, 3, 4, 5, and 6. The range is 0, 1, 2, 3, and 4.

EXERCISES

EXAMPLES 1, 3, and 4 on pp. 43–45 for Exs. 39–40

39. Graph the function $y = 4x - 3$ with domain 1, 2, 3, 4, and 5. **See margin.**

40. Write a rule for the function represented by the graph. Identify the domain and the range of the function.

$\frac{1}{2}x + \frac{1}{2}$; domain: 1, 3, 5, and 7, range: 1, 2, 3, and 4

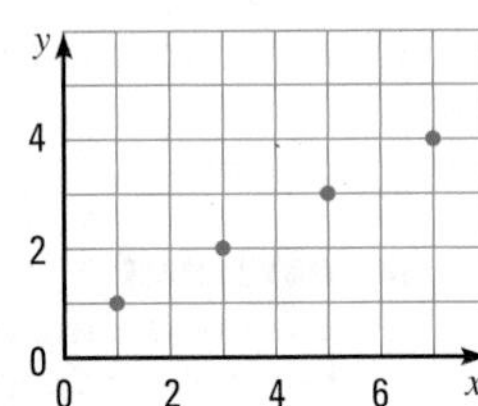

Evaluate the expression.

1. $7 + 3^2 \cdot 2$ **25**
2. $(5^2 + 17) \div 7$ **6**
3. $(24 - 11) - (3 + 2) \div 4$ **11.75**
4. $\frac{x}{5}$ when $x = 30$ **6**
5. n^3 when $n = 20$ **8000**
6. $15 - t$ when $t = 11$ **4**
7. $12 + 4x$ when $x = 1\frac{1}{2}$ **18**
8. $3z^2 - 7$ when $z = 6$ **101**
9. $2(4n + 5)$ when $n = 2$ **26**

Write an expression, an equation, or an inequality.

10. The sum of 19 and the cube of a number x **$19 + x^3$**
11. The product of 3 and a number y is no more than 21. **$3y \le 21$**
12. Twice the difference of a number z and 12 is equal to 10. **$2(z - 12) = 10$**

Check whether the given number is a solution of the equation or inequality.

13. $2 + 3x = 10$; 2 **not a solution**
14. $8 + 3b > 15$; 2 **not a solution**
15. $11y - 5 \le 30$; 3 **solution**

16. Refer to the graph.

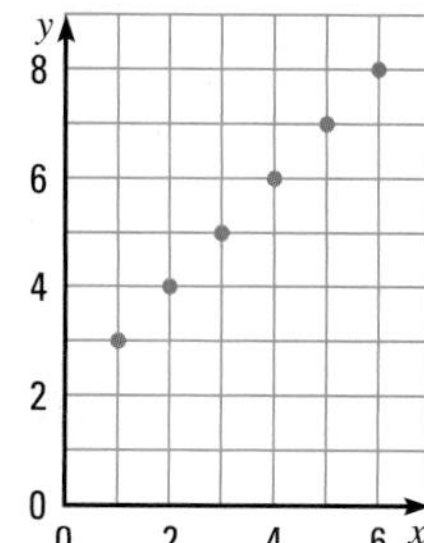

a. *Explain* why the graph represents a function.

b. Identify the domain and the range.

c. Write a rule for the function. **$y = x + 2$**

16a. There is exactly one output for each input.

16b. domain: 1, 2, 3, 4, 5, and 6, range: 3, 4, 5, 6, 7, and 8

17. **FOOD PREPARATION** You buy tomatoes at \$1.29 per pound and peppers at \$3.99 per pound to make salsa. Write an expression for the total cost of the ingredients. Then find the total cost of 5 pounds of tomatoes and 2 pounds of peppers. **$c = 1.29t + 3.99p$; \$14.43**

18. **CAR EXPENSES** A family determined the average cost of maintaining and operating the family car to be about \$.30 per mile. On one trip, the family drove at an average rate of 50 miles per hour for a total of 6.5 hours. On a second trip, they drove at an average rate of 55 miles per hour for a total of 6 hours. Which trip cost more? How much more? **the second trip; \$1.50**

19. **SHOE SIZES** A man's size 6 shoe is the same size as a woman's size $7\frac{1}{2}$. The table shows other corresponding sizes of men's and women's shoes.

Men's size, x	6	$6\frac{1}{2}$	7	$7\frac{1}{2}$	8	$8\frac{1}{2}$	9
Women's size, y	$7\frac{1}{2}$	8	$8\frac{1}{2}$	9	$9\frac{1}{2}$	10	$10\frac{1}{2}$

a. Using the data in the table, write a rule for women's shoe size as a function of men's shoe size. Identify the domain and the range.

b. Graph the function. **See margin.**

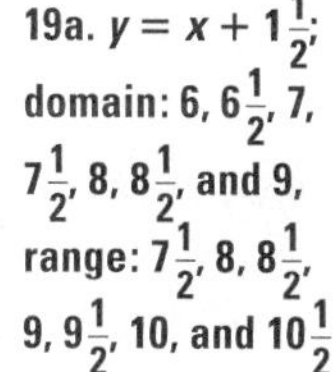

19a. $y = x + 1\frac{1}{2}$; domain: 6, $6\frac{1}{2}$, 7, $7\frac{1}{2}$, 8, $8\frac{1}{2}$, and 9, range: $7\frac{1}{2}$, 8, $8\frac{1}{2}$, 9, $9\frac{1}{2}$, 10, and $10\frac{1}{2}$

Additional Resources

Assessment Book

- Chapter Test, Levels A, B, C
- Standardized Chapter Test
- SAT/ACT Chapter Test
- Alternative Assessment

Test Generator

Chapter Test

Easily-readable reduced copies (with answers) of Chapter Test B, the Standardized Chapter Test, and the Alternative Assessment from the Assessment Book can be found on pp. 1E–1F.

19b.

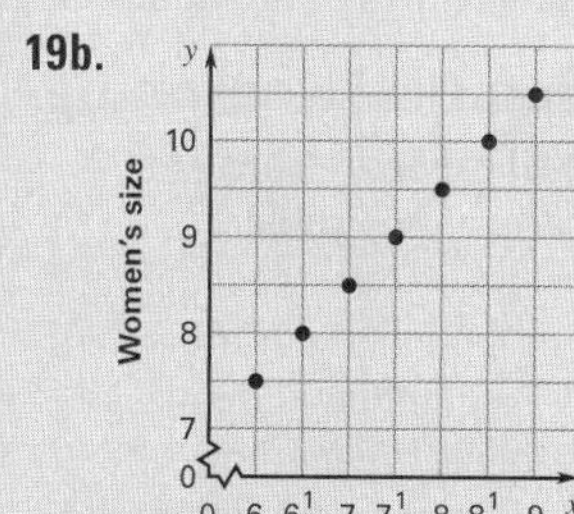

Using Rubrics

The rubric given on the pupil page is a sample of a three-level rubric. Other rubrics may contain four, five, or six levels. For more information on rubrics, see the *Differentiated Instruction Resources*.

Test-Taking Strategy

Encourage students to read short response questions carefully as they often contain more than one part, but the parts generally are not labeled. Suggest that they underline or circle each part of the question that must be answered. When they finish, they can refer back to the underlined or circled parts to verify that they have answered all parts of the question.

Mathematical Reasoning

Multiple Representations As shown here in the Problem, students may be able to use algebra, a graph, or a table to determine a solution to a question. Encourage students to use the method with which they are most proficient. If they should encounter difficulty using one method, suggest that they switch to another. Remind students that whatever method they use, they should be sure to include explanations of all the steps they followed in order to arrive at the solution.

Avoiding Common Errors

Students may arrive at a correct solution to a question, but if a table or graph they used contains errors, they will not receive full credit for their work. Caution students who use tables or graphs to check that these representations are free of errors and that the representations support their answer.

SHORT RESPONSE QUESTIONS

Scoring Rubric

Full Credit
- solution is complete and correct

Partial Credit
- solution is complete but has errors,

or
- solution is without error but incomplete

No Credit
- no solution is given,

or
- solution makes no sense

PROBLEM

Mike and Aaron are inflating helium balloons for a graduation party. Mike can inflate 3 balloons per minute, and Aaron can inflate 2 balloons per minute. If Mike and Aaron start inflating balloons at the same time, how many minutes will it take them to inflate a total of 30 balloons? *Explain* your answer.

Below are sample solutions to the problem. Read each solution and the comments on the left to see why the sample represents full credit, partial credit, or no credit.

SAMPLE 1: Full credit solution

For each person, the number of balloons inflated is a function of the number of minutes. Let t be the time (in minutes) that Mike and Aaron have been inflating balloons, and let b be the number of balloons inflated.

The function rules are correct. The tables and explanation show how the problem was solved.

Mike: $b = 3t$

t	1	2	3	4	5	6
b	3	6	9	12	15	18

Aaron: $b = 2t$

t	1	2	3	4	5	6
b	2	4	6	8	10	12

The tables show that in 6 minutes Mike will have inflated 18 balloons, and Aaron will have inflated 12 balloons.

The solution is correct.

Since $18 + 12 = 30$, it will take Mike and Aaron 6 minutes to inflate a total of 30 balloons.

SAMPLE 2: Partial credit solution

The reasoning and the function rule are correct.

Since Mike can inflate 3 balloons per minute and Aaron can inflate 2 balloons per minute, together they can inflate 5 balloons per minute.

Use the function $b = 5t$ where t is the time (in minutes) and b is the number of balloons inflated.

The solution is incorrect. The student substituted 30 for t instead of for b.

$b = 5t$

$= 5(30)$

$= 150$

So, it will take 150 minutes, or 2.5 hours, to inflate 30 balloons.

SAMPLE 3: Partial credit solution

The solution is without error but incomplete. There is no explanation of how the graph was used to find the answer.

Mike can inflate 3 balloons per minute, and Aaron can inflate 2 balloons per minute. Let t represent the time in minutes and b represent the total number of balloons the friends inflate. Graph the function $b = 5t$.

It will take 6 minutes to inflate 30 balloons.

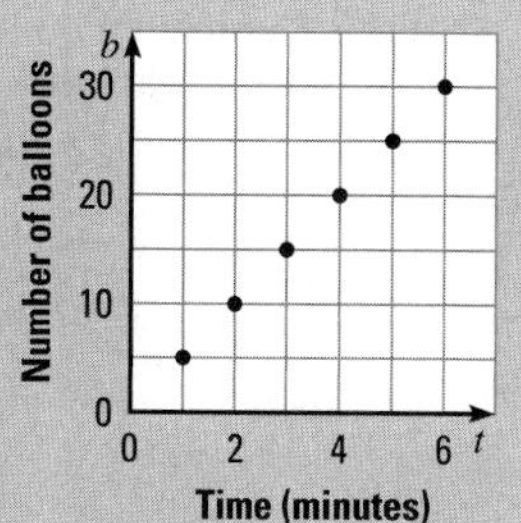

SAMPLE 4: No credit solution

The solution makes no sense. Each boy takes less time working alone.

Mike takes $30 \div 3 = 10$ minutes to inflate 30 balloons. Aaron takes $30 \div 2 = 15$ minutes to inflate 30 balloons. Because $10 + 15 = 25$, it will take Mike and Aaron 25 minutes to inflate 30 balloons.

PRACTICE Apply the Scoring Rubric

Score the solution to the problem below as *full credit, partial credit,* or *no credit. Explain* your reasoning.

PROBLEM Jessica and Graciela start exercising at the same time. Jessica jogs at a rate of 600 feet per minute. Graciela walks in the same direction at a rate of 400 feet per minute. If the girls start at the same time, in how many minutes will they be 4000 feet apart? *Explain.*

1. Because $4000 \div 200 = 20$, Jessica and Graciela will be 4000 feet apart after 20 minutes.

2. For every minute they exercise, the girls travel a total of 1000 feet. Let t be time (in minutes) and d be distance (in feet). Then $d = 1000t$, and when $t = 4$, $d = 4000$. The answer is 4 minutes.

3. Let t be the time (in minutes) and d be the distance (in feet). For Jessica, $d = 600t$. For Graciela, $d = 400t$.

t	5	10	15	20
d	3000	6000	9000	12,000

t	5	10	15	20
d	2000	4000	6000	8000

When $t = 20$, $600t = 12{,}000$ and $400t = 8000$, so the girls are 4000 feet apart. The answer is 20 minutes.

Answers

1. Partial credit; the calculation $4000 \div 200$ is the correct one to use, and the answer is correct, but the solution does not explain why the calculation $4000 \div 200$ produces the correct answer.

2. No credit; the answer is incorrect and the student's reasoning is incorrect. The equation $d = 1000t$ is a valid equation but it cannot be used to answer the question.

3. Full credit; the function rules are correct, and the student has explained what the variables represent. The tables and explanation show how the problem was solved, and the question is answered correctly.

Answers

1. Between 120 and 140 calories; 128 calories. *Sample answer:* The punch is $\frac{2}{5}$ pineapple juice and $\frac{3}{5}$ apple juice, so the number of calories in 1 cup of punch is $\frac{2}{5}(140) + \frac{3}{5}(120) = 56 + 72 =$ 128 calories.

2. A and B. *Sample answer:* Ming will spend at least 100($.99) = $99 on songs, so she has $340 − $99 = $241 to spend on the MP3 player. Models C and D cost more than $241, so she should not consider purchasing those.

3a. $12. *Sample answer:* The price per calendar should be (cost per calendar) + (profit per calendar). For a profit of $1800, the profit per calendar must be $1800 ÷ 200 = $9, so the price should be $9 + $3 = $12.

3b. $13. *Sample answer:* For a profit of $2000, the profit per calendar must be $2000 ÷ 200 = $10, so the price should be $10 + $3 = $13.

4. $408. *Sample answer:* On a weekday Mark earns $8.50 per hour, or $8.50(8) = $68 per day. On a weekend day Mark earns 1.5($8.50) = $12.75 per hour, or $12.75(8) = $102 per day. The most weekend days he can work in a week is 2, so he will earn the maximum amount by working 2 weekend days and 3 weekdays. The maximum amount is 2($102) + 3($68) = $408.

5. *Sample answer:* Option 1 is preferable if the child's current allowance is more than $6 per week; Option 2 is preferable if the child's current allowance is not more than $6 per week. For Option 1 to be preferable one-half of the current allowance must be more than $3, so the current allowance must be more than 2($3) = $6.

SHORT RESPONSE

1. A punch recipe uses 2 parts pineapple juice to 3 parts apple juice. The table shows the number of calories in each type of juice.

Juice	Calories in one cup
pineapple	140
apple	120

Would you expect there to be fewer than 120 calories, between 120 and 140 calories, or more than 140 calories in 1 cup of the punch? Exactly how many calories are there in 1 cup of the punch? *Explain.*

2. Ming has saved $340 to spend on an MP3 player and music. Music for the MP3 player costs $.99 per song, and Ming wants to buy at least 100 songs. Which models of MP3 player should she consider purchasing? *Explain* your reasoning.

Model	Price (dollars)
A	230
B	241
C	275
D	299

3. An animal shelter has 200 calendars to sell at a fair as a fundraiser. Each of the calendars costs $3 to make. The shelter hopes to sell all the calendars and make a total profit of $1800.
   a. What should the selling price of each calendar be?
   b. If the shelter hopes to make a profit of $2000, what should the selling price of each calendar be? *Explain* your reasoning.

4. Mark works at a grocery store where employees make one and a half times their regular hourly wage when they work on a Saturday or a Sunday. Mark works an 8 hour shift 5 days per week, sometimes including weekends. His regular hourly wage is $8.50. What is the maximum amount that he could earn in one week? *Explain* your reasoning.

5. The Ruizes offer each of their children two different options for increasing the child's weekly allowance.

   Option 1: Increase the allowance by one half of the current allowance.

   Option 2: Increase the allowance by $3 per week.

   Describe under what conditions each option is preferable. *Justify* your answers.

6. A pizzeria charges $11 for a large cheese pizza. The pizzeria is offering a special deal. If you buy 3 large cheese pizzas, you can choose to get a fourth cheese pizza free.
   a. Make a table showing the cost (in dollars) of 1, 2, 3, or 4 pizzas.
   b. Is the cost of the pizzas a function of the number of pizzas purchased? *Explain.*
   c. Is the number of pizzas purchased a function of the cost (in dollars)? *Explain.*

7. You buy 5 feet of ribbon to decorate the edge of a rectangular placemat. You have 6 inches of ribbon left over after you decorate the placemat. What is the width of the placemat? *Explain* your method.

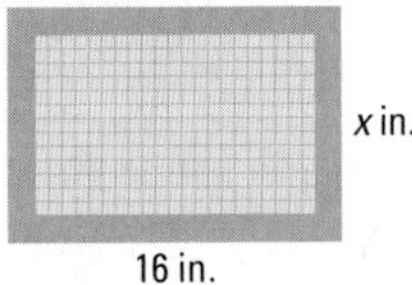

8. Two buses leave the same stop at the same time and travel the same route. One is an express bus and doesn't make any stops along the way. The other is a local bus and makes stops along the way.

   The express bus travels at an average speed of 40 miles per hour, and the local bus travels at an average speed of 30 miles per hour. The route is 10 miles long and the local bus makes 5 two-minute stops. How many minutes do you save by taking the express bus instead of the local bus? *Explain.*

6a.

Number of pizzas	1	2	3	4
Cost (dollars)	11	22	33	33

6b. Yes. *Sample answer:* When "number of pizzas" is the input, each input is paired with exactly one output.

6c. No; when "cost" is the input, there is an input, $33, that is paired with two different outputs, 3 and 4.

MULTIPLE CHOICE

9. Which is a rule for the function given by the input-output table?

Input, x	8	10	12	14
Output, y	5	7	9	11

Ⓐ $y = x - 3$ Ⓑ $y = x - 2$

Ⓒ $y = x + 3$ Ⓓ $y = x + 2$

10. The number of adult tickets sold at a school talent show is 5 less than 3 times the number c of children's tickets sold. Which expression represents the number of adult tickets sold?

Ⓐ $3c + 5$ Ⓑ $5 - 3c$

Ⓒ $5c + 3$ Ⓓ $3c - 5$

11. The function $y = 2x + 4$ has a domain of 2, 3, 5, 7, and 8. Which number is *not* in the range of the function?

Ⓐ 8 Ⓑ 12

Ⓒ 18 Ⓓ 20

GRIDDED ANSWER

12. What is the value of the expression $202 - 2(2 + 3)^2$?

13. What is the value of $x^2 - 2x + 7$ when $x = 3$?

14. What is the solution of the equation $54 = 9x$?

15. What is the volume (in cubic inches) of the cube?

9 in. 9 in. 9 in.

16. A rectangular field is twice as long as it is wide. A golf cart traveling at 12 miles per hour takes 7.5 minutes to travel the perimeter of the field. What is the length (in miles) of the field?

17. The table represents a function that can also be represented by a rule. What is the missing value in the table?

Input, x	7	8	11	12
Output, y	0	?	4	5

EXTENDED RESPONSE

18. Mario deposits \$140 in an account that earns simple interest at a rate of 5% per year. On the same day, Andy deposits \$150 in an account that earns simple interest at a rate of 3% per year. Mario and Andy plan to keep the accounts for at least 5 years, but make no additional deposits.

a. For each account, write a rule for the the amount I (in dollars) of interest as a function of the time t (in years) that the account has been open.

b. Let the domain of each function in part (a) be 1, 2, 3, 4, and 5. Make a table for each function.

c. After how many years will the total amount in each account be the same? How much will be in each account? *Justify* your answer.

19. A dance floor is made from square wooden tiles with a side length of 1 foot. The floor can be laid out as a square or as a rectangle. The width of the rectangular floor is 10 feet less than the width of the square floor, and its length is 15 feet greater than the length of the square floor.

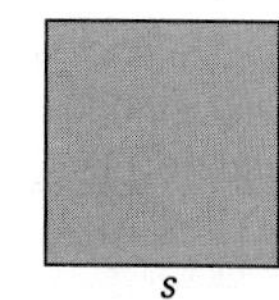

a. How much greater is the length of the rectangular dance floor than the width? *Justify* your answer.

b. The perimeter of the rectangular dance floor is 130 feet. What are the length and width of the dance floor? *Explain* your reasoning.

c. How many square tiles make up the dance floor?

7. 11 in. ***Sample answer:*** **The perimeter is 6 inches less than 5 feet, or $5(12) - 6 = 54$ inches. Length plus width equals one-half the perimeter, so $16 + x = 27$ inches. Using mental math to solve the equation, the value of x is $27 - 16 = 11$ inches.**

8. 15 min. ***Sample answer:*** **Since 10 miles $= \frac{1}{4}$(40 miles), the express bus takes $\frac{1}{4}$(60 minutes) = 15 minutes to travel the route. Because 10 miles $= \frac{1}{3}$(30 miles), the local bus takes $\frac{1}{3}$(60 minutes) = 20 minutes to travel the route. The local bus is stopped for $5(2) = 10$ minutes, so its total trip time is $20 + 10 = 30$ minutes; thus, taking the express bus saves $30 - 15 = 15$ minutes.**

9. A

10. D

11. B

12. 152

13. 10

14. 6

15. 729 in.^{3}

16. 0.5 mi

17. 1

18a. Mario's account: $I = 7t$, Andy's account: $I = 4.5t$

18b–c. See below.

19a. 25 ft. ***Sample answer:*** **If s feet is the length of the side of the square dance floor, then the length and the width of the rectangular dance floor are $(s + 15)$ feet and $(s - 10)$ feet. The difference is $(s + 15) - (s - 10) = s + 15 - s + 10 = 25$ feet.**

19b. 45 ft, 20 ft. ***Sample answer:*** **Length plus width equals one-half the perimeter, so $(s - 10) + (s + 15) = \frac{1}{2}(130)$, or $2s + 5 = 65$. Using the guess, check, and revise strategy to solve the equation, the value of s is 30 feet, so the length is $30 + 15 = 45$ feet and the width is $30 - 10 = 20$ feet.**

19c. 900 tiles

18b. Mario's account:

t (years)	1	2	3	4	5
I (dollars)	7	14	21	28	35

Andy's account:

t (years)	1	2	3	4	5
I (dollars)	4.5	9	13.5	18	22.5

18c. 4 yr. ***Sample answer:*** **Mario's account begins with \$10 less than Andy's account. The tables show that after the fourth year Mario's account has earned \$10 more in interest than Andy's account has. After four years, Mario's account has \$140 + \$28 = \$168, and Andy's account has \$150 + \$18 = \$168.**

2 Pacing Guide

Chapter 2: Properties of Real Numbers

Chapter Table of Contents

PACING GUIDES

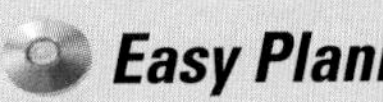
Easy Planner

Regular Schedule (50-minute classes)

DAY 1	DAY 2	DAY 3	DAY 4	DAY 5	DAY 6
Lesson 2.1	Lesson 2.1 (cont.) Extension 2.1	Investigating Algebra Activity 2.2 Lesson 2.2	Lesson 2.3 Spreadsheet Activity 2.3 Mixed Review of Problem Solving	Quiz for Lessons 2.1–2.3 Investigating Algebra Activity 2.4 Lesson 2.4 Extension 2.4	Lesson 2.5
DAY 7	**DAY 8**	**DAY 9**	**DAY 10**	**DAY 11**	**DAY 12**
Lesson 2.5 (cont.)	Quiz for Lessons 2.4–2.5 Lesson 2.6	Investigating Algebra Activity 2.7 Lesson 2.7	Lesson 2.7 (cont.) Extension 2.7 Mixed Review of Problem Solving	Quiz for Lessons 2.6–2.7 Chapter Review	Chapter Test

Block Schedule (90-minute classes)

DAY 1	DAY 2	DAY 3	DAY 4	DAY 5	DAY 6
Lesson 2.1 Extension 2.2	Investigating Algebra Activity 2.2 Lesson 2.2 Lesson 2.3 Spreadsheet Activity 2.3 Mixed Review of Problem Solving	Quiz for Lessons 2.1–2.3 Investigating Algebra Activity 2.4 Lesson 2.4 Extension 2.4 Lesson 2.5	Lesson 2.5 (cont.) Quiz for Lessons 2.4–2.5 Lesson 2.6	Investigating Algebra Activity 2.7 Lesson 2.7 Extension 2.7 Mixed Review of Problem Solving	Quiz for Lessons 2.6–2.7 Chapter Review Chapter Test

RESOURCE OPTIONS

Chapter/Lesson Resources

Chapter Resource Book
- Parents as Partners
- Teaching Guide/Lesson Plan
- Activity Masters
- Practice (3 levels)
- Study Guide
- Quick Catch-Up for Absent Students
- Problem Solving/Application
- Challenge Practice
- Chapter Review Games and Activities
- Project with Rubric
- Cumulative Review

Notetaking Guide
- Student Workbook and Teacher's Edition

Practice Workbook

Worked-Out Solution Key

Chapter Transparency Book
- Warm-Up Exercises/Daily Homework Quiz
- Notetaking Guide Transparencies
- Homework Answer Transparencies

Teacher Tools Transparencies

Assessment

Assessment Book
- Quizzes
- Chapter Tests (3 levels)
- Standardized and SAT/ACT Chapter Tests
- Alternative Assessments
- Cumulative Tests

Benchmark Tests
- Benchmark Tests, correlated to Remediation Book
- Pre-Course, Mid-Year, and End-of-Year Tests
- Chapter Tests

Spanish Assessment Book

Differentiated Instruction

Differentiated Instruction Resources
- Strategies for Reading Mathematics
- Differentiated Instruction Lesson Notes
- English Learner Lesson Notes
- Inclusion Lesson Notes
- Teaching Strategies with Sample Worksheets
- Tips for New Teachers/Math Background Notes
- Teacher Survival Activities/Bulletin Board Ideas

Student Resources in Spanish

Spanish Study Guide

Remediation Book

Skills Readiness (available on Easy Planner)
- Diagnostic Assessment
- Skill Instruction and Alternative Teaching Strategies
- Skill Practice and Enrichment Masters

Pre-AP Resources
- Pacing and Assignment Guide
- Best Practices
- Copymasters

Technology Resources

Plan	***Easy Planner***
Teach	***Video Tutor*** ***Activity Generator*** ***Power Presentations*** ***Animated Algebra***
Assess	***Test Generator*** ***ML Assessment System***
Reteach	***@HomeTutor***
Online Resources	***Classzone.com*** ***eEdition*** ***eWorkbook***

Video Tutor

Technology Highlights for Each Lesson

Easy Planner

Easy access to the Teacher's Edition and all teaching resources. Includes a search feature to locate the materials you need.

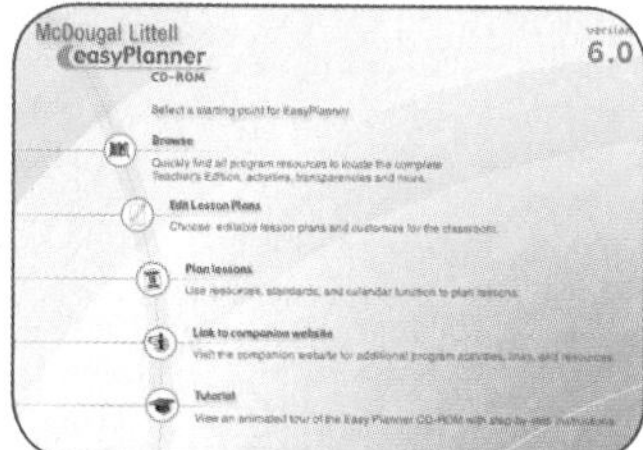

Activity Generator

Leveled, editable activities allow all students to explore a lesson's concepts. Includes teacher notes and closure questions.

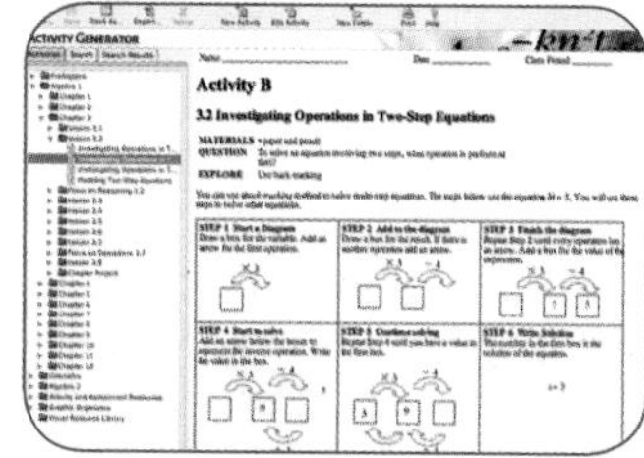

Algebra

Interactive tutorials provide visually engaging alternative opportunities to learn concepts and master skills.

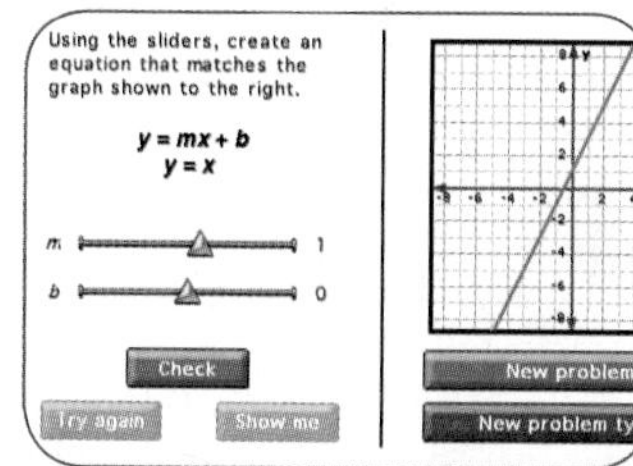

2 Lesson Practice Level B

LESSON 2.1 Practice B

For use with pages 64–70

Graph the numbers on a number line. Then order the numbers from least to greatest.

1. 2, −3, and 0   −3, 0, 2
2. −5, 7, and −8   −8, −5, 7
3. −9, −12, and 6   −12, −9, 6

Tell whether each number in the list is a whole number, an integer, or a rational number. Then order the numbers from least to greatest.

4. $-1.9, \frac{3}{4}, 0.8, -3$
5. $1.3, -2, \frac{1}{2}, 0$
6. $2.5, -\frac{7}{8}, -0.5, \frac{1}{3}$

4. whole number: none; integer: −3; rational number: $-1.9, \frac{3}{4}, 0.8, -3$; $-3, -1.9, \frac{3}{4}, 0.8$
5. whole number: 0; integer: 0, −2; rational number: $1.3, -2, \frac{1}{2}, 0$; $-2, 0, \frac{1}{2}, 1.3$
6. whole number: none; integer: none; rational number: $2.5, -\frac{7}{8}, -0.5, \frac{1}{3}$; $-\frac{7}{8}, -0.5, \frac{1}{3}, 2.5$

For the given value of *a*, find −*a* and |*a*|.

7. $a = 10.2$ −10.2; 10.2
8. $a = -14$ 14; 14
9. $a = \frac{1}{2}$ $-\frac{1}{2}; \frac{1}{2}$

Identify the hypothesis and conclusion of the conditional statement. Tell whether the statement is *true* or *false*. If it is false, give a counterexample.

10. If a number is negative, then its opposite is positive.
11. If a number is even, then its opposite is a whole number.

10. hypothesis: a number is negative; conclusion: its opposite is positive; true
11. hypothesis: a number is even; conclusion: its opposite is a whole number; false; 2

Evaluate the expression when *x* = −2.5.

12. $-x$ 2.5
13. $|x| + 3$ 5.5
14. $|x| - 4$ −1.5

15. **Fairbanks, Alaska** The table shows the monthly normal temperatures in Fairbanks, Alaska, during the winter months. Which monthly temperature is the lowest? Which months had temperatures below −5°F?   January; December and January

Month	December	January	February	March
Temperature (°F)	−7°	−10°	−4°	11°

16. **Stock Market** The gains and losses of a stock for a week are shown in the table. Which day showed the greatest gain? Which day showed the greatest loss?   Monday; Wednesday

Day	Monday	Tuesday	Wednesday	Thursday	Friday
Gain or loss	+0.02	−0.05	−0.12	−0.08	−0.01

17. **Class Enrollment** The table shows the growth in enrollment of the senior class at a high school between 1999 and 2004. Which year showed the greatest increase in class size? Which year showed the greatest decrease in class size?   2000; 2002

Year	1999	2000	2001	2002	2003	2004
Increase	15	22	−7	−12	10	18

LESSON 2.2 Practice B

For use with pages 71–77

Use a number line to find the sum.

1. $-8 + 9$ 1
2. $13 + (-4)$ 9
3. $-5 + (-11)$ −16
4. $-6 + (-7)$ −13
5. $-15 + 6$ −9
6. $-21 + 10$ −11

Find the sum.

7. $-4.2 + 6.5$ 2.3
8. $14.2 + (-9.1)$ 5.1
9. $7.8 + (-3.9)$ 3.9
10. $2\frac{2}{3} + \left(-1\frac{1}{3}\right)$ $1\frac{1}{3}$
11. $-7\frac{1}{2} + 10\frac{3}{4}$ $3\frac{1}{4}$
12. $8\frac{2}{3} + \left(-9\frac{1}{6}\right)$ $-\frac{1}{2}$
13. $-10 + (-23) + 18$ −15
14. $-1.25 + 2.5 + 3.5$ 4.75
15. $-2.6 + 7.5 + 5.6$ 10.5

Evaluate the expression for the given value of *x*.

16. $6 + x + (-11); x = 8$ 3
17. $-14 + x + 14; x = 9$ 9
18. $2.2 + x + (-3.4); x = -2.5$ −3.7
19. $-4.3 + (-x) + 1.5; x = 3.1$ −5.9
20. $-2.8 + (-x) + 8.1; x = -3.6$ 8.9
21. $-6.8 + |x| + 2.6; x = -3.2$ −1

Solve the equation.

22. $x + 15 + (-15) = 6$ $x = 6$
23. $6 + x + (-3) = 0$ $x = -3$
24. $x + (-2.5) + 6.8 = 0$ $x = -4.3$

25. **Delivery Driver** A furniture delivery driver is given three deliveries for the morning. The first delivery is 7 miles west of the furniture store. The second delivery is 14 miles east of the first house, and the last delivery before lunch is 3 miles west of the second house. How far is the delivery driver from the store after the last delivery?   4 miles

1st House   Furniture store   3nd House   2nd House
7 miles west
14 miles east
3 miles west
Not drawn to scale

26. **Homework** Your history teacher gives you an extra credit question on each homework assignment. You've been keeping track of how many points you are above or below the number of regular points you can earn on each assignment. How many total points do you have if there are 125 regular homework points for the five assignments?   128 points

Assignment	1	2	3	4	5
Number of points above and below	−2	4	−1	5	−3

27. **Company Profits** The table shows the profits earned by a small company during the first six months of the year. Did the company make a positive profit for the first six months? If so, how much?   yes; $500

Month	January	February	March	April	May	June
Profit	$1500	−$2000	$1000	$3000	−$2000	−$1000

LESSON 2.3 Practice B

For use with pages 78–83

Find the difference.

1. $12 - (-7)$ 19
2. $22 - (-28)$ 50
3. $-6 - (-13)$ 7
4. $-15 - (-9)$ −6
5. $5.8 - (-7.9)$ 13.7
6. $-4.1 - (-3.6)$ −0.5
7. $-6.2 - (-3.6)$ −2.6
8. $3.8 - (-5.9)$ 9.7
9. $-2.6 - (-10.2)$ 7.6
10. $\frac{1}{3} - \frac{4}{9}$ $-\frac{1}{9}$
11. $\frac{1}{2} - \left(-\frac{7}{8}\right)$ $1\frac{3}{8}$
12. $-\frac{2}{3} - \left(-\frac{3}{8}\right)$ $-\frac{7}{24}$

Evaluate the expression when *x* = −6.4 and *y* = 10.8.

13. $y - x$ 17.2
14. $x - (-y)$ 4.4
15. $x - y$ −17.2
16. $-y - x$ −4.4
17. $x - y - 2.6$ −19.8
18. $y - 5.4 - x$ 11.8
19. $-7.3 - x + y$ 9.9
20. $6.4 + y - x$ 23.6
21. $10.8 - x - y$ 6.4
22. $y - (-x) + 6.4$ 10.8
23. $7.2 + y - x$ 24.4
24. $4.25 - x - y$ −0.15

Find the change in temperature or elevation.

25. From 15°C to −5°C   −20°C
26. From −250 meters to 175 meters   425 m

27. **Planet Temperatures** The average temperature on the surface of Venus is 480°C and the average temperature on the surface of Mars is −65°C. How many degrees hotter is the temperature on Venus' surface than on Mars' surface?   545°C

28. **Manned Submersibles** Alvin, a manned submersible used in deep-sea exploration, has a maximum depth of −14,764 feet. Its first untethered dive was −35 feet. How many feet deeper is Alvin's maximum depth than the depth of its first dive?   14,729 ft

29. **Banana Prices** The table shows the weekly prices (in dollars) of a pound of bananas during a month at a local supermarket. Determine the change in the price per pound each week. Find the total of these changes to determine the total change in the price per pound over the 4 weeks.

Week	1	2	3	4
Price per pound (dollars)	0.49	0.49	0.39	0.49

Week 1 to Week 2: $0; Week 2 to Week 3: −$.10; Week 3 to Week 4: $.10; $0

30. **State Temperatures** The table shows the record high and low temperatures for several states. Find the difference between the record high and low temperatures for each state. Which state has the greatest temperature difference?

State	Alaska	North Dakota	Wyoming	Virginia	Nevada
High temperature (°F)	100°	121°	115°	110°	125°
Low temperature (°F)	−80°	−60°	−66°	−30°	−50°

Alaska: 180°; North Dakota: 181°; Wyoming: 181°; Virginia: 140°; Nevada: 175°; North Dakota and Wyoming

LESSON 2.4 Practice B

For use with pages 86–91

Find the product.

1. $10(-9)$ −90
2. $-12(-3)$ 36
3. $-11(7)$ −77
4. $2.6(-8)$ −20.8
5. $-3.2(15)$ −48
6. $-9.5(5)$ −47.5
7. $-\frac{1}{2}(28)$ −14
8. $-\frac{2}{3}(-21)$ 14
9. $\frac{4}{5}(-20)$ −16
10. $-6(4)(-3.5)$ 84
11. $-2.1(-10)(-5)$ −105
12. $-6.5(21)(-6)$ 819

Identify the property illustrated.

13. $5.6 \cdot (-3.2) = -3.2 \cdot 5.6$ Commutative prop. of mult.
14. $0 \cdot 2.1 = 0$ Multiplicative property of 0
15. $-1 \cdot (-1.5) = 1.5$ Multiplicative property of −1

Find the product. Justify your steps. See below.

16. $-3(-5)(-4x)$
17. $-\frac{3}{4}(-20)(7y)$
18. $8x(4.2)(-5)$

Evaluate the expression when *x* = −3 and *y* = 4.1.

19. $x + 2y$ 5.2
20. $y - 4x$ 16.1
21. $5.2x - y$ −19.7
22. $xy - 10.1$ −22.4
23. $14.3 - xy$ 26.6
24. $3x - |y|$ −13.1

25. **Death Valley** The lowest point in North America is Death Valley, California. Its elevation is at −86 meters. What is this elevation in feet? *Hint:* Use the fact that 1 meter ≈ 3.281 feet.   −282.166 m

26. **Lava Flow** A kind of lava, block lava, is moving away from the base of a volcano at a rate of 1.5 meters per day. If the lava continues to flow at this rate, how far away has the lava flowed from the base of the volcano in 30 days?   45 m

27. **Snow Melt** After a recent snowfall, the snow on the ground in a shaded area is melting at a rate of 0.01 inch per minute. Currently, there are 4 inches of snow on the ground. If the snow continues melting at this rate, how much snow will be on the ground in 6 hours? How much snow has melted?   0.4 in.; 3.6 in.

28. **City Population** In 1990, the population of Pittsburgh, Pennsylvania was 2468 thousand people. The table shows the average rate of change in the population for two periods of time. Find the total population in 2000 and 2002.   1990 to 2000: 2431 thousand people; 2000 to 2002: 2418 thousand people

Time period	Rate of change (thousand people/yr)
1990–2000	−3.7
2000–2002	−6.5

16. $-3(-5)(-4x)$
$= 15(-4x)$ Product of −3 and −5 is 15.
$= [15(-4)]x$ Assoc. prop. of mult.
$= -60x$ Product of 15 and −4 is −60.

17. $-\frac{3}{4}(-20)(7y)$
$= 15(7y)$ Product of $-\frac{3}{4}$ and −20 is 15.
$= (15 \cdot 7)y$ Assoc. prop. of mult.
$= 105y$ Product of 15 and 7 is 105.

18. $8x(4.2)(-5)$
$= 8x(-21)$ Product of 4.2 and −5 is −21.
$= 8(-21)x$ Comm. prop. of mult.
$= -168x$ Product of 8 and −21 is −168.

LESSON 2.5

Practice B

For use with pages 94–100

Use the distributive property to write an equivalent expression.

1. $5(x + 11)$ $5x + 55$　**2.** $3(x - 12)$ $3x - 36$　**3.** $-4(x + 8)$ $-4x - 32$

4. $9(2x + 1)$ $18x + 9$　**5.** $(x - 7)(-10)$ $-10x + 70$　**6.** $(4x + 3)5$ $20x + 15$

7. $x(4x - 1)$ $4x^2 - x$　**8.** $2x(x - 1)$ $2x^2 - 2x$　**9.** $-x(5x + 2)$ $-5x^2 - 2x$

Identify the terms, like terms, coefficients, and constant terms of the expression.

10. $-8 + 2x + 5 + 11x$　**11.** $4x^2 + 1 - 3x^2 + 5$

12. $7y^2 - 6 + 3y^2 - 15$ See below.　**13.** $3xy + 5 - 2xy + 10$ See below.

10. Terms: -8, $2x$, 5, $11x$; Like terms: $2x$ and $11x$, -8 and 5; Coefficients: 2, 11; Constant terms: -8, 5

11. Terms: $4x^2$, 1, $-3x^2$, 5; Like terms: $4x^2$ and $-3x^2$, 1 and 5; Coefficients: 4, -3; Constant terms: 1, 5

Simplify the expression.

14. $6 + 10x + 3$ $10x + 9$　**15.** $2(3x + 1) + 4x$ $10x + 2$　**16.** $6(5 - x) + 12x$ $6x + 30$

17. $7(x - 1) - 5$ $7x - 12$　**18.** $8x + 3(2x - 1)$ $14x - 3$　**19.** $-2(x + 4) - 3$ $-2x - 11$

20. $11x - (x + 7)$ $10x - 7$　**21.** $9 - 2(x - 4)$ $-2x + 17$　**22.** $7x - 3(4 - 2x)$ $13x - 12$

23. Curtains You are making curtains by alternating strips of solid colored fabric and patterned fabric. The solid colored fabric costs \$.99 per strip and the patterned fabric costs \$1.25 per strip. You need 7 strips for one curtain. Write an equation that gives the total cost c as a function of the number n of solid colored strips used. Then find the total cost if you use 3 solid colored strips. $c = 0.99n + 1.25(7 - n)$; \$7.97

24. Shoe Boxes A department store is selling its plastic shoe boxes for \$1.50 off the regular price of a shoe box. You buy 4 shoe boxes. Write an equation that gives the total cost t as a function of the regular cost r of a shoe box. Then find the total cost if the boxes regularly cost \$3.59 each. $t = 4(r - 1.5)$; \$8.36

25. Delivering Papers You and your friend share a paper route. You can deliver 4 papers in one minute and your friend can deliver 3 papers in one minute. Seventy-five papers have to be delivered each day on the route. Let n be the number of papers you deliver.

a. Use the verbal model to write an equation that you can use to find out how long it will take the both of you together to deliver the papers. $t = \frac{1}{4}n + \frac{1}{3}(75 - n)$

Total amount of time (min)	=	Your rate (min/paper)	•	Number of papers you deliver (papers)	+	Friend's rate (min/papers)	•	Number of papers friend delivers (papers)

b. How long will it take the both of you to deliver the papers if you deliver 38 papers? 50 papers? about 21.8 min; about 20.8 min

12. Terms: $7y^2$, -6, $3y^2$, -15; Like terms: $7y^2$ and $3y^2$, -6 and -15; Coefficients: 7, 3; Constant terms: -6, -15

13. Terms: $3xy$, 5, $-2xy$, 10; Like terms: $3xy$ and $-2xy$, 5 and 10; Coefficients: 3, -2; Constant terms: 5, 10

LESSON 2.5

LESSON 2.6

Practice B

For use with pages 101–106

Find the multiplicative inverse of the number.

1. -7 $-\frac{1}{7}$　**2.** $-\frac{1}{5}$ -5　**3.** $-\frac{7}{8}$ $-\frac{8}{7}$

Find the quotient.

4. $-32 \div (-2)$ 16　**5.** $-1 \div \left(-\frac{6}{5}\right)$ $\frac{5}{6}$　**6.** $14 \div \left(-\frac{2}{7}\right)$ -49

7. $17 \div \left(-2\frac{1}{8}\right)$ -8　**8.** $-\frac{3}{4} \div 4$ $-\frac{3}{16}$　**9.** $-\frac{1}{3} \div \frac{1}{5}$ $-1\frac{2}{3}$

10. $-\frac{1}{9} \div (-8)$ $\frac{1}{72}$　**11.** $-\frac{6}{11} \div (-3)$ $\frac{2}{11}$　**12.** $\frac{5}{8} \div \left(-2\frac{1}{2}\right)$ $-\frac{1}{4}$

Find the mean of the numbers.

13. 1, -3, -10 -4　**14.** -15, 4, -22 -11　**15.** -7.5, 3, -6.5 $-3\frac{2}{3}$

Simplify the expression.

16. $\frac{-8x + 27}{9}$ $-\frac{8}{9}x + 3$　**17.** $\frac{15x - 5}{-5}$ $1 - 3x$　**18.** $\frac{12x - 20}{-4}$ $5 - 3x$

19. Melting Point The melting point of the element fluorine is $-219.62°C$. The melting point of the element bromine is $-7.2°C$. How many times lower is the melting point of fluorine than the melting point of bromine? Round your answer to the nearest tenth. about 30.5

20. Website Traffic During a 3-month period, the traffic to a website dropped by 126,000 visitors. Find the average rate of change in the traffic to the website (in visitors per month) over the 3-month period. $-42{,}000$ visitors/month

21. Average Velocity The velocity of an object indicates the object's speed and the direction in which the object is traveling. A negative velocity indicates that the object is moving downward or backward. A hawk is diving downward at a rate of 50 feet in 28 seconds. Find the hawk's average velocity (in feet per second). Round your answer to the nearest tenth. -1.8 ft/sec

22. Health Club The table below shows change in the number of memberships at a health club. What is the average change in the number of memberships (in members per month)? 5.6 memberships/month

Month	Nov.	Dec.	Jan.	Feb.	Mar.
Change in number of memberships	18	10	40	−25	−15

23. Bank Account Activity During a 14-day period, there is the following activity on your bank account. You deposit \$100, withdraw \$75, deposit \$85, and withdraw \$150. What is the rate of change (in dollars per day) in your bank account? Round your answer to the nearest cent. about $-\$2.86$/day

LESSON 2.6

LESSON 2.7

Practice B

For use with pages 107–114

Evaluate the expression.

1. $\pm\sqrt{81}$ ± 9　**2.** $\pm\sqrt{25}$ ± 5　**3.** $-\sqrt{400}$ -20

4. $\sqrt{625}$ 25　**5.** $\sqrt{4900}$ 70　**6.** $\pm\sqrt{169}$ ± 13

Approximate the square root to the nearest integer.

7. $-\sqrt{29}$ -5　**8.** $\sqrt{108}$ 10　**9.** $-\sqrt{53}$ -7

10. $\sqrt{138}$ 12　**11.** $-\sqrt{55}$ -7　**12.** $\sqrt{640}$ 25

Tell whether each number in the list is a real number, a rational number, an irrational number, an integer, or a whole number. Then order the numbers from least to greatest. See below.

13. $-\sqrt{16}, 3.2, -\frac{3}{2}, \sqrt{9}$　**14.** $\sqrt{5}, -6, 2.5, -\frac{24}{5}$

Evaluate the expression for the given value of *x*.

15. $14 + \sqrt{x}$ when $x = 16$ 18　**16.** $\sqrt{x} - 5.5$ when $x = 4$ -3.5

17. $-9 \cdot \sqrt{x}$ when $x = 25$ -45　**18.** $2\sqrt{x} - 1$ when $x = 100$ 19

19. Park A local park is in the shape of a square and covers an area of 3600 square feet. Find the side length of the park. 60 ft

20. Wall Poster You are considering buying a square wall poster that has an area of 6.25 square feet. Find the side length of the wall poster. 2.5 ft

21. Road Sign The U.S. Department of Transportation determines the sizes of the traffic control signs that you see along the roadways. The square Pennsylvania state route sign at the right has an area of 1296 square inches. Find the side length of the sign. 36 in.

22. Flower Bed You are building the square flower bed shown using railroad ties. You want to place another railroad tie on the diagonal to form two triangular beds. Find the length of the diagonal by using the expression $\sqrt{2s^2}$ where s is the side length of the flower bed. Round your answer to the nearest tenth. about 7.1 ft

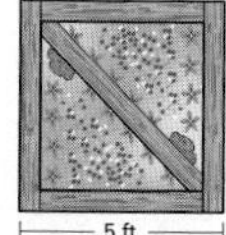

13. real number: $-\sqrt{16}, 3.2, -\frac{3}{2}, \sqrt{9}$; rational number: $-\sqrt{16}, 3.2, -\frac{3}{2}, \sqrt{9}$; irrational number: none; integer: $-\sqrt{16}, \sqrt{9}$; whole number: $\sqrt{9}$; $-\sqrt{16}, -\frac{3}{2}, \sqrt{9}, 3.2$

14. real number: $-6, -\frac{24}{5}, \sqrt{5}, 2.5$; rational number: $-6, -\frac{24}{5}, 2.5$; irrational number: $\sqrt{5}$; integer: -6; whole number: none; $-6, -\frac{24}{5}, \sqrt{5}, 2.5$

LESSON 2.7

2 Assessment

CHAPTER 2 Quiz 1

For use after Lessons 2.1–2.3

Identify the property illustrated.

1. $x + (-7) = -7 + x$
2. $5 + (-5) = 0$
3. $(3 + 2) + 9 = 3 + (2 + 9)$
4. $0 + 12 = 12$

Find the sum or difference.

5. $2.7 + (-5.2)$
6. $18 - (-4)$
7. $-3 - (-5)$

Evaluate the expression when $x = 10$ and $y = -3$.

8. $-x + y + 4$
9. $y + |y| - 7$
10. $6 - x - y$

Answers

1. Commutative property of addition
2. Inverse property of addition
3. Associative property of addition
4. Identity property of addition
5. -2.5
6. 22
7. 2
8. -9
9. -7
10. -1

CHAPTER 2 Quiz 2

For use after Lessons 2.4–2.5

Identify the property illustrated.

1. $(-8 \cdot 2) \cdot 3 = -8 \cdot (2 \cdot 3)$
2. $5 \cdot (-1) = -5$
3. $3 \cdot (-6) = -6 \cdot 3$
4. $14 \cdot 0 = 0$

Find the product.

5. $3(-8)$
6. $-4(-5)$
7. $2(3)(-1)$
8. $(-6x) \cdot (-5)$
9. $-\frac{3}{4}x \cdot 28$
10. $1.8 \cdot x \cdot (-4.6)$

Use the distributive property to write an equivalent expression.

11. $-(3x + 1)$
12. $-9(y - 7)$
13. $(4x + 3)3$

Answers

1. Associative property of multiplication
2. Property of -1
3. Commutative property of multiplication
4. Property of zero
5. -24
6. 20
7. -6
8. $30x$
9. $-21x$
10. $-8.28x$
11. $-3x - 1$
12. $-9y + 63$
13. $12x + 9$

CHAPTER 2 Quiz 3

For use after Lessons 2.6–2.7

Find the multiplicative inverse of the number.

1. $-\frac{1}{3}$
2. 8

Find the quotient.

3. $-30 \div 3$
4. $-24 \div (-4)$
5. $-\frac{3}{4} \div 2$

Simplify the expression.

6. $\frac{35 - 14x}{7}$
7. $\frac{-16x + 8}{-4}$

Evaluate the expression.

8. $\sqrt{49}$
9. $\pm\sqrt{4}$
10. $-\sqrt{16}$

Answers

1. -3
2. $\frac{1}{8}$
3. -10
4. 6
5. $-\frac{3}{8}$
6. $5 - 2x$
7. $4x - 2$
8. 7
9. 2 and -2
10. -4

CHAPTER 2 Chapter Test B

For use after Chapter 2

Tell whether each number is a real number, a rational number, an irrational number, an integer, or a whole number.

1. -0.75
2. $\sqrt{12}$
3. 10

Tell whether the statement is *true* or *false*. If it is false, give a counterexample.

4. If a number is positive, then its opposite is negative.
5. If a number is an integer, then the number is an irrational number.

Order the numbers in the list from least to greatest.

6. $-\frac{1}{5}, -0.25, \frac{1}{3}, 1$
7. $-\frac{14}{3}, -4.6, -4.07, -4\frac{1}{3}$

Identify the property being illustrated.

8. $(x \cdot 0.5) \cdot 8 = x \cdot (0.5 \cdot 8)$
9. $x + (-y) = -y + x$
10. $2(5z - 9) = 10z - 18$
11. $3a + (-3a) = 0$

Find the sum or the difference.

12. $3 - (-12)$
13. $-22 + 16$
14. $-0.8 + (-8.9)$
15. $-16 - (-25.2)$
16. $\frac{1}{2} - \frac{7}{10}$
17. $7\frac{4}{5} + \left(-2\frac{1}{4}\right)$

In Exercises 18 and 19, use the table below.

Name	Double eagle	Eagle	Birdie	Par	Bogey	Double bogey
Score	−3	−2	−1	0	1	2

18. In golf, the best total score is the lowest score. In 4 holes, you score a birdie, a par, a double eagle, and a double bogey. Your friend scores an eagle, a double eagle, a bogey, and a par. Who has the better total score?
19. What is the difference between your friend's total score and your total score?

Answers

1. real number, rational number
2. real number, irrational number
3. real number, rational number, integer, whole number
4. true
5. false; 5
6. $-0.25, -\frac{1}{5}, \frac{1}{3}, 1$
7. $-\frac{14}{3}, -4.6, -4\frac{1}{3}, -4.07$
8. Assoc. prop. of mult.
9. Commutative property of addition
10. Distributive prop.
11. Inverse prop. of add.
12. 15
13. -6
14. -9.7
15. 9.2
16. $-\frac{1}{5}$
17. $5\frac{11}{20}$
18. your friend
19. -2

CHAPTER 2 **Chapter Test B** *continued*

For use after Chapter 2

Evaluate the expression when $x = -5.4$ and $y = 2.8$.

20. $y - x - 1.4$

21. $x + |y - 10|$

Find the product or the quotient.

22. $-6(-12)$

23. $45 \div (-3)$

24. $\frac{5}{9}\left(-\frac{3}{4}\right)$

25. $-7.2 \div 8$

26. $-4 \div \left(-\frac{2}{9}\right)$

27. $-\frac{2}{3}(18)\left(-\frac{1}{4}\right)$

28. A person buys items and sells them on a website. The table shows the profit earned for each item. Suppose that in one week the person sells 8 mantel clocks, 5 framed mirrors, and 3 candles. Find the average daily profit.

Item	Mantel clock	Framed mirror	Candle
Profit	$4.13	−$1.65	$2.36

Simplify the expression.

29. $10x - (x + 3)$

30. $-2x(x - 6)$

31. $\frac{-6x + 15}{-10}$

32. Use the distributive property and mental math to find the total cost of 6 notebooks at $3.95 each.

33. Find the perimeter and area of the rectangle with the given dimensions.

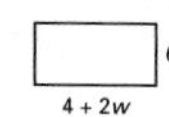

Approximate the square root to the nearest integer.

34. $\sqrt{35}$

35. $-\sqrt{150}$

36. $\sqrt{18}$

37. The area of a town's square is 14,400 square feet. Find the side length of the square.

Evaluate the expression for the given value of x.

38. $2 - \sqrt{x}$ when $x = 25$

39. $4\sqrt{x} + 9$ when $x = 1$

Answers

20. 6.8
21. 1.8
22. 72
23. −15
24. $-\frac{5}{12}$
25. −0.9
26. 18
27. 3
28. $4.55
29. $9x - 3$
30. $-2x^2 + 12x$
31. $\frac{3}{5}x - \frac{3}{2}$
32. $6(4 - 0.05) = \$23.70$
33. $P = 20 + 4w$; $A = 24 + 12w$
34. 6
35. −12
36. 4
37. 120 ft
38. −3
39. 13

CHAPTER 2 **Standardized Test**

For use after Chapter 2

Multiple Choice

1. Which list of numbers is ordered from least to greatest? C

Ⓐ $-\frac{1}{2}, -1, \frac{3}{8}, 5$ Ⓑ $\frac{1}{2}, \frac{1}{3}, \frac{1}{4}, \frac{1}{5}$

Ⓒ $-\frac{1}{2}, 0.66, \frac{2}{3}, \frac{7}{8}$ Ⓓ $-0.16, -\frac{1}{6}, 0, 3$

2. Which number is an integer? A

Ⓐ $-\frac{32}{8}$ Ⓑ $\frac{1}{5}$

Ⓒ $|-3.8|$ Ⓓ $\left|\frac{24}{5}\right|$

3. What is the value of $5(-x)$ when $x = -\frac{1}{10}$? C

Ⓐ $-2\frac{1}{2}$ Ⓑ $\frac{4}{5}$

Ⓒ $\frac{1}{2}$ Ⓓ $4\frac{9}{10}$

4. Which number is a solution of $5 + |m| = 7.3$? B

Ⓐ −12.3 Ⓑ −2.3

Ⓒ 7.3 Ⓓ 12.3

5. What is the value of $-5.06 + -2.3$? B

Ⓐ −7.9 Ⓑ −7.36

Ⓒ 3.3 Ⓓ 3.76

6. What property is being illustrated in the equation $-12 + 12 = 0$? D

Ⓐ Associative Property

Ⓑ Commutative Property

Ⓒ Identity Property

Ⓓ Inverse Property

7. What is the solution of the equation $-9.7 + x - 5.4 = 12.1$? D

Ⓐ −3 Ⓑ 3 Ⓒ 16.5 Ⓓ 27.2

8. What is the value of $-\frac{5}{6} - \left(-\frac{2}{3}\right)$? C

Ⓐ $-1\frac{1}{2}$ Ⓑ $-\frac{7}{9}$

Ⓒ $-\frac{1}{6}$ Ⓓ $1\frac{1}{2}$

9. What is the change in temperature from −26°F to 78°F? D

Ⓐ −104°F Ⓑ −52°F

Ⓒ 52°F Ⓓ 104°F

10. What is the value of $|z - y| - x$ where $x = 25.3, y = -7.2, z = 15.8$? B

Ⓐ −16.7 Ⓑ −2.3

Ⓒ 2.3 Ⓓ 16.7

11. What property is being illustrated in the equation $-2 \cdot (5 \cdot 2) = (-2 \cdot 5) \cdot 2$? A

Ⓐ Associative Property

Ⓑ Commutative Property

Ⓒ Identity Property

Ⓓ Inverse Property

12. What is the product of $-\frac{1}{5}(-a)(-a)\left(\frac{5}{9}\right)$? A

Ⓐ $-\frac{1}{9} \cdot a^2$ Ⓑ $\frac{1}{9} \cdot a^2$

Ⓒ $-\frac{2}{9} \cdot a$ Ⓓ $\frac{2}{9} \cdot a$

13. What is the value of $|n| + m^2$ where $m = -2.4$ and $n = -3.8$? C

Ⓐ −1 Ⓑ 1.96

Ⓒ 9.56 Ⓓ 16.84

14. Which pair of terms are like terms? D

Ⓐ $2x, 2y$ Ⓑ $3x, 2x^2$

Ⓒ $-4, -4y$ Ⓓ $x^3, 5x^3$

CHAPTER 2 **Standardized Test** *continued*

For use after Chapter 2

15. Simplify the expression $4(n - 3) - 2(-3 + n)$. A

Ⓐ $2n - 6$ Ⓑ $2n + 6$

Ⓒ $4n - 18$ Ⓓ $6n - 2$

16. What is the perimeter of the rectangle? D

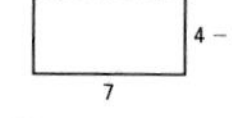

Ⓐ $-3y + 11$ Ⓑ $-21y + 28$

Ⓒ $-3y + 28$ Ⓓ $-6y + 22$

17. If $-\frac{4}{5}x = 1$, what is the value of x? B

Ⓐ $-1\frac{2}{5}$ Ⓑ $-1\frac{1}{4}$

Ⓒ $\frac{4}{5}$ Ⓓ $-1\frac{1}{5}$

18. Simplify the expression $\frac{27 - 6y}{-3}$. C

Ⓐ $-6y - 9$ Ⓑ $2y + 27$

Ⓒ $2y - 9$ Ⓓ $-7y$

19. Which number is between −20 and −15? C

Ⓐ $-\sqrt{1089}$ Ⓑ $-\sqrt{441}$

Ⓒ $-\sqrt{289}$ Ⓓ $-\sqrt{196}$

20. Which expression is a perfect square if $x = 81$? A

Ⓐ $2 \cdot \sqrt{x} + 31$ Ⓑ $\sqrt{x} + 3 \cdot 3$

Ⓒ $9 - 5\sqrt{x}$ Ⓓ $2 + 6\sqrt{x}$

21. Which number is irrational? D

Ⓐ $-\frac{5}{3}$ Ⓑ −2.4

Ⓒ $\sqrt{16}$ Ⓓ $\sqrt{18}$

Gridded Answer

22. What is the value of $\frac{5(2x - 6)}{x}$ when $x = -2$?

2 5

Short Response

23. Suppose you have a pre-paid cell phone where you pay a certain amount up front and the amount used is deducted. You pay $.15 per minute and $.10 per text message.

a. Write an equation for the total cost C where t represents each minute used and m represents each text message sent.

b. You have pre-paid $20 on your phone. If you have used 104 minutes and have sent 7 text messages, what is your remaining balance? *Explain.* $3.70

23. a. $C = 0.15t + 0.10m$

Extended Response

24. A gardener has a square garden with an area of 5476 square feet.

a. How many feet of fencing would the gardener need to fence around his garden? 296 ft

b. Fencing is sold in 50 feet rolls. Partial rolls cannot be purchased. How many rolls of fencing must the gardener purchase? *Explain.* 6 rolls

c. How many feet of fencing will the gardener have leftover? Explain. 4 ft

d. Each roll of fencing costs $45.65 plus 6% tax. How much will the gardener pay for the fencing? Round to the nearest cent. *Explain.* $290.33

CHAPTER 2 **Alternative Assessment and Math Journal**

For use after Chapter 2

Journal

1. Describe the relationship between integers and rational numbers. Explain the difference between rational numbers and irrational numbers, and provide an example of each type of number.

Multi-Step Problem

2. To discourage random guessing on a multiple-choice exam, a professor assigns 7 points for a correct answer, −3 points for an incorrect answer, and −1 point for leaving the question blank.

a. What is the score for a student who had 19 correct answers, 4 incorrect answers, and 2 questions left blank?

b. What is the maximum number of points available on the exam from part (a)?

c. The following calculation was used to compute Pete's score on the exam: $17(7) + 2(-1) + 6(-3)$. Determine the score for this student and describe Pete's performance on the exam.

d. Katie took the exam and had 19 correct answers, 3 incorrect answers, and left 3 questions blank. Katie calculated her score on the exam as shown.

$19(7) + 3(-3) + 3(-1) = 19(7) + 3(-3 - 1)$

Verify that both sides of this equation result in the same score and name the property that guarantees the equality.

e. Jason answered 20 questions correctly and 5 questions incorrectly. What fraction of the total points did Jason earn? Write your answer in simplest form.

f. Erin answered 18 questions correctly, 1 incorrectly, and left 6 blank. Stephen answered 19 questions correctly, 5 incorrectly, and left 1 blank. Who had the higher score on the exam?

g. If a student answers every question on the exam, the following expression can be used to calculate the number of points earned, where x represents the number of questions answered correctly.

$7x + (25 - x)(-3)$

Explain why this expression can be used to calculate the total number of points earned. Then simplify the expression.

h. Evaluate your expression from part (g) to determine the points earned by a student who answered all of the questions and had 16 correct answers.

1. Complete answers should include: an explanation that a rational number is a ratio of two integers; an explanation that irrational numbers cannot be expressed as a ratio of two integers, or a discussion of the differences between the decimal representations of rational numbers and irrational numbers; an example of a rational number and an example of an irrational number.

2. a. 119 points **b.** 175 points **c.** 99 points; 17 correct answers, 6 incorrect answers, 2 left blank **d.** 121 points; distributive property **e.** $\frac{5}{7}$ **f.** Neither; both scored 117 points. **g.** Explanations may vary; $10x - 75$ **h.** 85 points

PLAN AND PREPARE

Main Ideas

In Chapter 2, students will learn about the real number system. They will classify real numbers, compare and order integers and rational numbers, perform basic operations, find square roots, apply properties to evaluate and simplify expressions, and use the Distributive Property to write equivalent expressions. Students will use conditional statements and logical reasoning to reason with real numbers.

Prerequisite Skills

Skills Readiness, available on the *Easy Planner*, provides review and practice for the Skills Check portion of the Prerequisite Skills quiz.

How student answers the exercises	What to assign from *Skills Readiness*
Any of Exs. 4–7 answered incorrectly	**Skill 16** Compare real numbers
Any of Exs. 8–11 answered incorrectly	**Skill 60** Evaluate expressions
Any of Exs. 12–13 answered incorrectly	**Skill 55** Order of operations
All exercises answered correctly	Chapter 1 Enrichment

Additional skills review and practice is available in the Skills Review Handbook, pp. 909–937, and the @HomeTutor.

2 Properties of Real Numbers

Making Sense of Chapter 2

In this chapter you will learn the properties of real numbers and of operations, as well as the basics of logical reasoning. By the end of this chapter, you will have the tools you need to solve equations.

Before

Previously, you learned the following skills, which you'll use in Chapter 2: comparing and ordering numbers, evaluating expressions, and applying the order of operations.

Prerequisite Skills

VOCABULARY CHECK

In Exercises 1 and 2, copy and complete the statement.

1. The **least common denominator** of the fractions $\frac{3}{8}$ and $\frac{5}{12}$ is __?__. **24**
2. The **variable** in the expression $5x - 3$ is __?__. ***x***
3. According to the **order of operations**, what is the first step in simplifying the expression $(3 + 4)^2 - 8$? **Add 3 + 4.**

SKILLS CHECK

Copy and complete the statement using <, >, or =. ***(Prerequisite skill for 2.1, 2.7)***

4. 26.70 __?__ 29.69 **<**
5. 15.09 __?__ 15.1 **<**
6. 0.333 __?__ 0.34 **<**
7. 2.5 __?__ 2.500 **=**

Evaluate the expression when $x = 5$. ***(Prerequisite skill for 2.2–2.4, 2.6)***

8. $52 - x$ **47**
9. $1.7x$ **8.5**
10. $x + 39$ **44**
11. $\frac{125}{x}$ **25**

Evaluate the expression. ***(Prerequisite skill for 2.5)***

12. $5m - 9$ when $m = 6$ **21**
13. $16 - r - 3$ when $r = 10$ **3**

@HomeTutor Prerequisite skills practice at classzone.com

Chapter Planning Guide

Chapter Resource Book
- Teaching Guide/Lesson Plan
- Project with Rubric

Assessment and Intervention
- Assessment Book
- Benchmark Tests
- Remediation Book
- Skills Readiness

Interactive Technology
- Easy Planner
- Power Presentations
- Activity Generator
- Animated Algebra
- Test Generator
- Online Quizzes
- eWorkbook
- eEdition
- @HomeTutor

Resources for English Learners
- Spanish Study Guide
- Multi-Language Visual Glossary
- Student Resources in Spanish

Now

In Chapter 2, you will apply the big ideas listed below and reviewed in the Chapter Summary on page 120. You will also use the key vocabulary listed below.

Big Ideas

1. **Performing operations with real numbers**
2. **Applying properties of real numbers**
3. **Classifying and reasoning with real numbers**

KEY VOCABULARY

- whole numbers, integers, *p. 64*
- rational number, *p. 64*
- opposites, absolute value, *p. 66*
- conditional statement, *p. 66*
- additive identity, *p. 76*
- additive inverse, *p. 76*
- multiplicative identity, *p. 89*
- equivalent expressions, *p. 96*
- distributive property, *p. 96*
- term, coefficient, constant term, like terms, *p. 97*
- multiplicative inverse, *p. 103*
- square root, radicand, *p. 110*
- perfect square, *p. 111*
- irrational number, *p. 111*
- real numbers, *p. 112*

Why?

You can use multiple representations to solve a problem about a real-world situation. For example, you can write an equation and make a table to find a skydiver's altitude over time.

Animated Algebra

The animation illustrated below for Exercise 54 on page 93 helps you answer this question: How does the time spent in free fall after a skydiver reaches terminal velocity affect the altitude of the skydiver?

A skydiver in freefall wants to open the parachute at an altitude of 2500 feet.

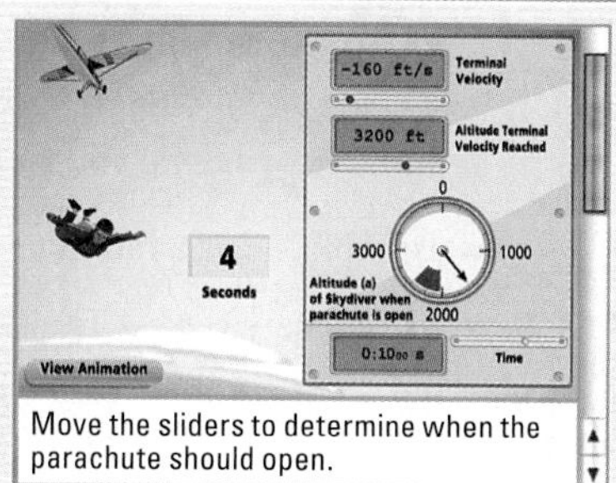

Move the sliders to determine when the parachute should open.

Animated Algebra at classzone.com

Other animations for Chapter 2: pages 73, 80, 90, and 98

63

Differentiated Instruction Resources

- Reading Strategies for Chapter 2
- Differentiated Instruction Lesson Notes
- English Learners Lesson Notes
- Inclusion Lesson Notes
- Teaching Strategies with Sample Worksheets
- Using Technology in the Classroom
- Tips for New Teachers
- Math Background Notes
- Assessment Strategies
- Teacher Survival Activities
- Bulletin Board Idea

1 PLAN AND PREPARE

Warm-Up Exercises

Transparency Available

Complete the statement using <, >, or =.

1. 1.3 ? 1.03 **>**
2. $\frac{5}{8}$? $\frac{6}{9}$ **<**
3. Order from least to greatest: $\frac{1}{2}$, 0.04, $\frac{3}{7}$, 0.45 **0.04, $\frac{3}{7}$, 0.45, $\frac{1}{2}$**
4. A hobby store has balsa wood strips in three thicknesses (in inches): $\frac{3}{16}$, $\frac{5}{32}$, and $\frac{1}{8}$. Which strip is the thickest? **$\frac{3}{16}$-inch strip**

Notetaking Guide

Transparency Available

Promotes interactive learning and notetaking skills.

Pacing

Basic: 2 days

Average: 2 days

Advanced: 2 days

Block: 1 block

- See *Teaching Guide/Lesson Plan.*

2 FOCUS AND MOTIVATE

Essential Question

Big Idea 3, p. 63

How do you compare positive and negative numbers? **Tell students they will learn how to answer this question by graphing integers.**

NCTM STANDARDS

Standard 1: Understand relationships among numbers; Understand number systems

2.1 Use Integers and Rational Numbers

Before You performed operations with whole numbers.

Now You will graph and compare positive and negative numbers.

Why? So you can compare temperatures, as in Ex. 58.

Key Vocabulary
- whole numbers
- integers
- rational number
- opposites
- absolute value
- conditional statement

Whole numbers are the numbers 0, 1, 2, 3, . . . and **integers** are the numbers . . . , −3, −2, −1, 0, 1, 2, 3, ... (The dots indicate that the numbers continue without end in both directions.) **Positive integers** are integers that are greater than 0. **Negative integers** are integers that are less than 0. The integer 0 is neither negative nor positive.

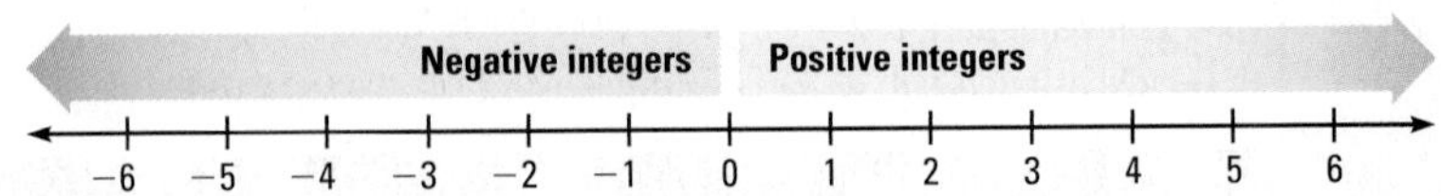

Zero is neither negative nor positive.

EXAMPLE 1 Graph and compare integers

Graph −3 and −4 on a number line. Then tell which number is greater.

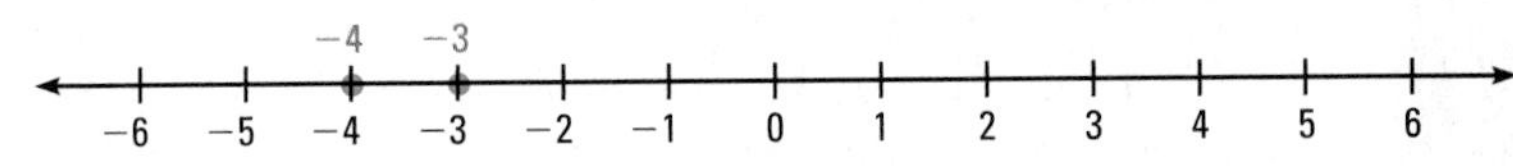

▶ On the number line, −3 is to the right of −4. So, −3 > −4.

RATIONAL NUMBERS The integers belong to the set of *rational numbers.* A **rational number** is a number $\frac{a}{b}$ where a and b are integers and $b \neq 0$. For example, $-\frac{1}{2}$ is a rational number because it can be written as $\frac{-1}{2}$ or $\frac{1}{-2}$. The rational numbers belong to the set of numbers called the *real numbers.*

READING Although you can write a negative fraction in different ways, you usually write it with the negative sign in front of the fraction.

Real numbers
Rational numbers
Integers
Whole numbers

✓ GUIDED PRACTICE for Example 1

1–3. Check students' graphs.

Graph the numbers on a number line. Then tell which number is greater.

1. 4 and 0 **4**
2. 2 and −5 **2**
3. −1 and −6 **−1**

Resource Planning Guide

Chapter Resource Book
- Teaching Guide/Lesson Plan
- Practice levels A, B, C
- Study Guide
- Catch-up for Absent Students
- Application
- Challenge

Workbooks
- Notetaking Guide
- Practice Workbook

Teaching Options
- **Power Presentations** provides dynamic electronic teaching resources for the classroom.
- **Activity Generator** provides editable activities for all ability levels.

Interactive Technology
- Easy Planner
- Power Presentations
- Activity Generator
- Animated Algebra
- Test Generator
- Online Quiz
- eWorkbook
- eEdition
- @HomeTutor

Resources for English Learners
- Spanish Study Guide
- Multi-Language Visual Glossary
- Student Resources in Spanish

See also the *Differentiated Instruction Resources* for more strategies for meeting individual needs.

REVIEW FRACTIONS
For help with writing fractions as decimals, see p. 916.

DECIMALS In decimal form, a rational number either terminates or repeats. For example, $\frac{3}{4} = 0.75$ is a *terminating decimal,* and $\frac{1}{3} = 0.333...$ is a *repeating decimal.*

EXAMPLE 2 Classify numbers

Tell whether each of the following numbers is a whole number, an integer, or a rational number: 5, 0.6, $-2\frac{2}{3}$, and −24.

Number	Whole number?	Integer?	Rational number?
5	Yes	Yes	Yes
0.6	No	No	Yes
$-2\frac{2}{3}$	No	No	Yes
−24	No	Yes	Yes

JUSTIFY AN ANSWER
The number 0.6 is a rational number because it can be written as a quotient of two integers: $\frac{3}{5}$.

EXAMPLE 3 Order rational numbers

ASTRONOMY A star's color index is a measure of the temperature of the star. The greater the color index, the cooler the star. Order the stars in the table from hottest to coolest.

Star	Rigel	Arneb	Denebola	Shaula
Color index	−0.03	0.21	0.09	−0.22

Solution

Begin by graphing the numbers on a number line.

Read the numbers from left to right: −0.22, −0.03, 0.09, 0.21.

▶ From hottest to coolest, the stars are Shaula, Rigel, Denebola, and Arneb.

GUIDED PRACTICE for Examples 2 and 3

Tell whether each number in the list is a whole number, an integer, or a rational number. Then order the numbers from least to greatest.
4–7. See margin.

4. 3, −1.2, −2, 0

5. 4.5, $-\frac{3}{4}$, −2.1, 0.5

6. 3.6, −1.5, −0.31, −2.8

7. $\frac{1}{6}$, 1.75, $-\frac{2}{3}$, 0

4. 3: whole number, integer, rational number, −1.2: rational number, −2: integer, rational number, 0: whole number, integer, rational number; −2, −1.2, 0, 3

5. 4.5: rational number, $-\frac{3}{4}$: rational number, −2.1: rational number, 0.5: rational number; −2.1, $-\frac{3}{4}$, 0.5, 4.5

6. 3.6: rational number, −1.5: rational number, −0.31: rational number, −2.8: rational number; −2.8, −1.5, −0.31, 3.6

7. $\frac{1}{6}$: rational number, 1.75: rational number, $-\frac{2}{3}$: rational number, 0: whole number, integer, rational number; $-\frac{2}{3}$, 0, $\frac{1}{6}$, 1.75

Motivating the Lesson

Ask students to give examples of situations where they might use negative numbers. Tell them by learning to compare positive and negative numbers they can determine who has a lower golf score.

3 TEACH

Extra Example 1

Graph 0 and −2 on a number line. Then tell which number is greater.

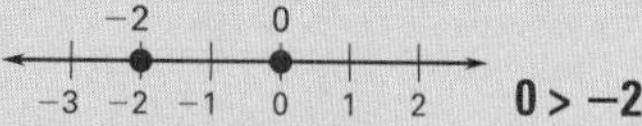

0 > −2

Extra Example 2

Tell whether each of the following numbers is a whole number, an integer, or a rational number: −19, 7, 0.3, and $-1\frac{1}{5}$. **−19: integer, rational number; 7: whole number, integer, rational number; 0.3: rational number; $-1\frac{1}{5}$: rational number**

Key Question to Ask for Example 2

- Why are all the numbers rational numbers? **They can all be written in the form $\frac{a}{b}$. $5 = \frac{5}{1}$; $0.6 = \frac{3}{5}$; $-2\frac{2}{3} = \frac{-8}{3}$; $-24 = \frac{-24}{1}$**

Extra Example 3

The apparent magnitude of a star is its brightness as observed from Earth. The greater the magnitude, the dimmer the star. Order the stars from brightest to dimmest.

Star	Magnitude
Arcturus	−0.06
Sirius	−1.47
Vega	0.03

Sirius, Arcturus, Vega

Differentiated Instruction

Below Level Students performing below level may not realize that all the numbers in **Guided Practice Exercises 4–7** are rational numbers. To help them see this fact, have these students write each of the numbers as a quotient of two integers. You may wish to do this as an activity in which below level students are paired with advanced students. If so, advanced students can give help where needed.

See also the *Differentiated Instruction Resources* for more strategies.

Extra Example 4

For the given value of a, find $-a$.

a. $a = \frac{3}{8}$ $-\frac{3}{8}$

b. $a = -0.65$ **0.65**

Avoiding Common Errors

Tell students to get into the habit of reading $-a$ as "the opposite of a" to avoid mistaking $-a$ as a negative number when it may be positive. Have them practice reading Examples 4a and 4b aloud.

Extra Example 5

For the given value of a, find $|a|$.

a. $a = -16.2$ **16.2**

b. $a = \frac{2}{3}$ $\frac{2}{3}$

Key Question to Ask for Example 5

- What do you know about the absolute values of a number and its opposite? Explain. **The absolute values are the same. Both a number and its opposite are the same distance from 0 on a number line, and absolute value is defined as the distance from a number to 0 on a number line.**

OPPOSITES Two numbers that are the same distance from 0 on a number line but are on opposite sides of 0 are called **opposites**. For example, 4 and -4 are opposites because they are both 4 units from 0 but are on opposite sides of 0. The opposite of 0 is 0. You read the expression $-a$ as "the opposite of a."

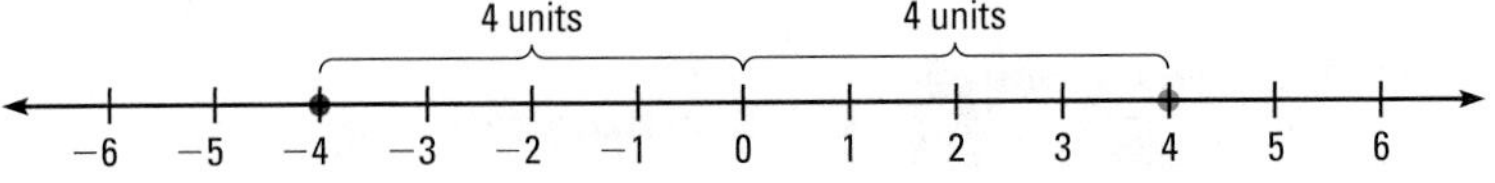

EXAMPLE 4 Find opposites of numbers

a. If $a = -2.5$, then $-a = -(-2.5) = 2.5$.

b. If $a = \frac{3}{4}$, then $-a = -\frac{3}{4}$.

READING
The absolute value of a number is also called its *magnitude*.

ABSOLUTE VALUE The **absolute value** of a number a is the distance between a and 0 on a number line. The symbol $|a|$ represents the absolute value of a.

KEY CONCEPT *For Your Notebook*

Absolute Value of a Number

Words If a is positive, then $|a| = a$.	**Example** $|2| = 2$
Words If a is 0, then $|a| = 0$.	**Example** $|0| = 0$
Words If a is negative, then $|a| = -a$.	**Example** $|-2| = -(-2) = 2$

EXAMPLE 5 Find absolute values of numbers

AVOID ERRORS
The absolute value of a number is never negative. If a number a is negative, then its absolute value, $-a$, is positive.

a. If $a = -\frac{2}{3}$, then $|a| = \left|-\frac{2}{3}\right| = -\left(-\frac{2}{3}\right) = \frac{2}{3}$.

b. If $a = 3.2$, then $|a| = |3.2| = 3.2$.

CONDITIONAL STATEMENTS A **conditional statement** has a hypothesis and a conclusion. An **if-then statement** is a form of a conditional statement. The *if* part contains the hypothesis. The *then* part contains the conclusion.

conditional statement

If a is a positive number, then $|a| = a$.

hypothesis **conclusion**

In mathematics, if-then statements are either true or false. An if-then statement is true if the conclusion is always true when the hypothesis is satisfied. An if-then statement is false if for just one example, called a **counterexample**, the conclusion is false when the hypothesis is satisfied.

Differentiated Instruction

Visual Learners Some students may not remember the distinction between whole numbers and integers. Whole numbers are integers greater than or equal to 0, and "0 ≥" looks like the letters "OL" in "WHOLE."

See also the *Differentiated Instruction Resources* for more strategies.

EXAMPLE 6 Analyze a conditional statement

Identify the hypothesis and the conclusion of the statement "If a number is a rational number, then the number is an integer." Tell whether the statement is *true* or *false*. If it is false, give a counterexample.

Solution

Hypothesis: a number is a rational number

Conclusion: the number is an integer

The statement is false. The number 0.5 is a counterexample, because 0.5 is a rational number but not an integer.

GUIDED PRACTICE for Examples 4, 5, and 6

For the given value of a, find $-a$ and $|a|$.

8. $a = 5.3$ **−5.3, 5.3**
9. $a = -7$ **7, 7**
10. $a = -\frac{4}{9}$ **$\frac{4}{9}, \frac{4}{9}$**

Identify the hypothesis and the conclusion of the statement. Tell whether the statement is *true* or *false*. If it is false, give a counterexample.

11. If a number is a rational number, then the number is positive.

11. Hypothesis: a number is a rational number, conclusion: the number is positive; false. *Sample answer:* −1 is rational, but not positive.

12. If the absolute value of a number is positive, then the number is positive. **Hypothesis: the absolute value of a number is positive, conclusion: the number is positive; false. *Sample answer:* The absolute value of −2 is 2, but −2 is negative.**

2.1 EXERCISES

HOMEWORK KEY
◯ = **WORKED-OUT SOLUTIONS** on p. WS3 for Exs. 7, 29, and 53
★ = **STANDARDIZED TEST PRACTICE** Exs. 3, 4, 39, 50, 56, and 59

SKILL PRACTICE

A

1. **VOCABULARY** Copy and complete: A number is a(n) _?_ if it can be written in the form $\frac{a}{b}$ where a and b are integers and $b \neq 0$. **rational number**
2. **VOCABULARY** What is the opposite of −2? **2**
3. ★ **WRITING** *Describe* the difference between whole numbers and positive integers. **Zero is in the set of whole numbers, but not in the set of positive integers.**
4. ★ **WRITING** For a negative number x, is the absolute value of x a *positive number* or a *negative number*? *Explain.* **Positive number; the absolute value of a negative number is always positive.**

EXAMPLE 1 on p. 64 for Exs. 5–13

GRAPHING AND COMPARING INTEGERS **Graph the numbers on a number line. Then tell which number is greater.** **5–13. Check students' graphs.**

5. 0 and 7 **7**
6. 0 and −4 **0**
7. −5 and −6 **−5**
8. −2 and −3 **−2**
9. 5 and −2 **5**
10. −12 and 8 **8**
11. −1 and −5 **−1**
12. 3 and −13 **3**
13. −20 and −2 **−2**

Extra Example 6

Identify the hypothesis and conclusion of the statement "If a number is an integer, then the number is either positive or negative." Then tell whether the statement is *true* or *false*. If it is false, give a counterexample. **Hypothesis: a number is an integer; Conclusion: the number is positive or negative; false: 0 is an integer and it is neither positive nor negative.**

Key Question to Ask for Example 6

- If you switch the hypothesis and conclusion so that the statement reads "If a number is an integer, then it is a rational number," is the statement true or false? Why? **True; an integer can be written as the quotient of two integers.**

Closing the Lesson

Have students summarize the major points of the lesson and answer the Essential Question: How do you compare positive and negative numbers?

- **A rational number can be written as the quotient of two integers.**
- **The absolute value of a number is the distance between the number and 0 on a number line. Opposites are the same distance from 0, but on opposite sides.**
- **Conditional statements contain a hypothesis and a conclusion, and can be either true or false.**

Graph numbers on a number line so you can compare them and order them from least to greatest.

4 PRACTICE AND APPLY

Assignment Guide

Answer Transparencies available for all exercises

Basic:
Day 1: SRH p. 930 Exs. 1–4
pp. 67–70
Exs. 1, 3, 5–10, 14–19, 53, 54, 57, 67–75
Day 2: pp. 67–70
Exs. 2, 4, 23–30, 35–44, 55, 56, 58, 61–66

Average:
Day 1: pp. 67–70
Exs. 1, 3, 8–13, 17–22, 53, 54, 57–59, 67–75 odd
Day 2: pp. 67–70
Exs. 2, 4, 27–39 odd, 40–51, 55, 56, 61–66

Advanced:
Day 1: pp. 67–70
Exs. 1, 3, 10–13, 19–22, 53, 54, 57–60*, 68–74 even
Day 2: pp. 67–70
Exs. 2, 4, 28–38 even, 39, 41–52*, 55, 56, 63, 65, 66

Block:
pp. 67–70
Exs. 1–4, 8–13, 17–22, 27–39 odd, 40–51, 53–59, 61–66, 67–75 odd

Differentiated Instruction

See *Differentiated Instruction Resources* for suggestions on addressing the needs of a diverse classroom.

Homework Check

For a quick check of student understanding of key concepts, go over the following exercises:

Basic: 16, 25, 35, 53, 55
Average: 18, 31, 37, 53, 56
Advanced: 20, 32, 38, 56, 57

Extra Practice

- Student Edition, p. 939
- Chapter Resource Book: Practice levels A, B, C

Practice Worksheet

An easily-readable reduced practice page (with answers) for this lesson can be found on p. 62C.

EXAMPLES 2 and 3 on p. 65 for Exs. 14–22

CLASSIFYING AND ORDERING NUMBERS **Tell whether each number in the list is a whole number, an integer, or a rational number. Then order the numbers from least to greatest.** **14–22. See margin.**

14. 3, −5, −2.4, 1 **15.** 1.6, 1, −4, 0 **16.** 0.25, −0.5, 0.2, −2

17. $-\frac{2}{3}, -0.6, -1, \frac{1}{3}$ **18.** $-0.01, 0.1, 0, -\frac{1}{10}$ **19.** $16, -1.66, \frac{5}{3}, -1.6$

20. $-2.7, \frac{1}{2}, 0.3, -7$ **21.** $-4.99, 5, \frac{16}{3}, -5.1$ **22.** $-\frac{3}{5}, -0.4, -1, -0.5$

EXAMPLES 4 and 5 on p. 66 for Exs. 23–34

FINDING OPPOSITES AND ABSOLUTE VALUES **For the given value of a, find $-a$ and $|a|$.**

23. $a = 6$ **−6, 6** **24.** $a = -3$ **3, 3** **25.** $a = -18$ **18, 18** **26.** $a = 0$ **0, 0**

27. $a = 13.4$ **−13.4, 13.4** **28.** $a = 2.7$ **−2.7, 2.7** **(29.)** $a = -6.1$ **6.1, 6.1** **30.** $a = -7.9$ **7.9, 7.9**

31. $a = -1\frac{1}{9}$ **$1\frac{1}{9}, 1\frac{1}{9}$** **32.** $a = -\frac{5}{6}$ **$\frac{5}{6}, \frac{5}{6}$** **33.** $a = \frac{3}{4}$ **$-\frac{3}{4}, \frac{3}{4}$** **34.** $a = 1\frac{1}{3}$ **$-1\frac{1}{3}, 1\frac{1}{3}$**

EXAMPLE 6 on p. 67 for Exs. 35–38

ANALYZING CONDITIONAL STATEMENTS **Identify the hypothesis and the conclusion of the conditional statement. Tell whether the statement is *true* or *false*. If it is false, give a counterexample.**

35. If a number is a positive integer, then the number is a whole number.
Hypothesis: a number is a positive integer, conclusion: the number is a whole number; true.

36. If a number is negative, then its absolute value is negative.

37. If a number is positive, then its opposite is positive.

38. If a number is an integer, then the number is a rational number.
Hypothesis: a number is an integer, conclusion: the number is a rational number; true.

39. ★ **MULTIPLE CHOICE** Which number is a whole number? **A**

Ⓐ $\left|-\frac{18}{9}\right|$ Ⓑ $-\frac{4}{3}$ Ⓒ 1.6 Ⓓ $-(-7.963)$

36. Hypothesis: a number is negative, conclusion: its absolute value is negative; false. *Sample answer:* |−3| is 3, a positive integer.

37. Hypothesis: a number is positive, conclusion: its opposite is positive; false. *Sample answer:* The opposite of 2 is −2, a negative number.

B **ERROR ANALYSIS** ***Describe*** **and correct the error in the statement.** **40, 41. See margin.**

40.

The numbers −(−2), −4, −|8|, and −0.3 are negative numbers.

41.

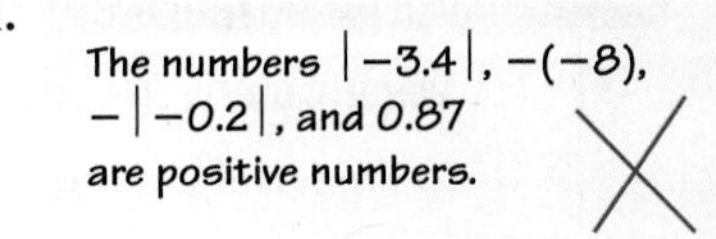

The numbers |−3.4|, −(−8), −|−0.2|, and 0.87 are positive numbers.

40. −(−2) is not negative. *Sample answer:* In the number −(−2), replace the parentheses with absolute value bars.

41. −|−0.2| is a negative number. *Sample answer:* In the number −|−0.2|, remove both negative signs.

EVALUATING EXPRESSIONS **Evaluate the expression when $x = -0.75$.**

42. $-x$ **0.75** **43.** $|x| + 0.25$ **1** **44.** $|x| - 0.75$ **0** **45.** $1 + |-x|$ **1.75**

46. $2 \cdot (-x)$ **1.5** **47.** $(-x) \cdot 3$ **2.25** **48.** $|x| + |x|$ **1.5** **49.** $-x + |x|$ **1.5**

50. ★ **MULTIPLE CHOICE** Which number is a solution of $|x| + 1 = 1.3$? **B**

Ⓐ −2.3 Ⓑ −0.3 Ⓒ 1.3 Ⓓ 2.3

C **51.** **CHALLENGE** What can you conclude about the opposite of the opposite of a number? *Explain* your reasoning. **It is the original number. *Sample answer:* The opposite of a is $-a$ and the opposite of $-a$ is a, which is the original number.**

52. **CHALLENGE** For what values of a is the opposite of a greater than a? less than a? equal to a? **See margin.**

○ = WORKED-OUT SOLUTIONS on p. WS1 ★ = STANDARDIZED TEST PRACTICE

---

14. 3: whole number, integer, rational number, −5: integer, rational number, −2.4: rational number, 1: whole number, integer, rational number; −5, −2.4, 1, 3

15. 1.6: rational number, 1: whole number, integer, rational number, −4: integer, rational number, 0: whole number, integer, rational number; −4, 0, 1, 1.6

16. 0.25: rational number, −0.5: rational number, 0.2: rational number, −2: integer, rational number; −2, −0.5, 0.2, 0.25

PROBLEM SOLVING

EXAMPLE 3 A
on p. 65
for Exs. 53, 57

53. Fondo, Frink, Alamorio, Calexico, Date City

53. **GEOGRAPHY** The map shows various locations in Imperial County, California, and their elevations above or below sea level. Order the locations from lowest elevation to highest elevation.

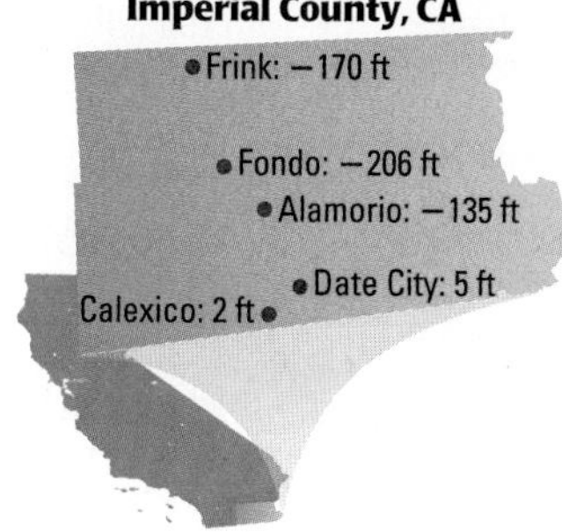

@HomeTutor for problem solving help at classzone.com

54. **SPORTS** In golf, the goal is to have the least score among all the players. Which golf score, −8 or −12, is the better score? **−12**

@HomeTutor for problem solving help at classzone.com

EXAMPLE 5
on p. 66
for Exs. 55–56

55. **MUSIC** A guitar tuner is a device that tunes a guitar string to its exact pitch. Some tuners use the measure *cents* to indicate how far above or below the exact pitch, marked as 0 cents, the string tone is. Suppose that one string tone measures −3.4 cents, and a second string tone measures −3.8 cents. Which string tone is closer to the exact pitch? *Explain.* **−3.4; the absolute value of −3.4 is less than the absolute value of −3.8, so it is closer to 0, the exact pitch.**

56. ★ **MULTIPLE CHOICE** The change in value of a share of a stock was −\$.45 on Monday, −\$1.32 on Tuesday, \$.27 on Wednesday, and \$1.03 on Thursday. On which day was the absolute value of the change the greatest? **B**

Ⓐ Monday Ⓑ Tuesday Ⓒ Wednesday Ⓓ Thursday

57. **MULTI-STEP PROBLEM** An equalizer on a stereo system is used to increase or decrease the intensity of sounds at different frequencies. The intensity is measured in decibels (dB), and the frequencies are measured in hertz (Hz). The table shows the intensity at different frequencies on a stereo system.

Frequency (Hz)	32	64	125	250	500	1000	2000	4000	8000
Intensity (dB)	8.8	7.1	5.8	1.5	−2.8	−1.5	2.7	2.8	2.9

a. Which frequency has the least sound intensity? **500 Hz**

b. *Describe* the change in sound intensity as the frequency increases from 32 hertz to 8000 hertz. **The intensity decreases until 500 Hz and then increases.**

B

58. **WEATHER** A wind chill index describes how much colder it feels outside when wind speed is considered with air temperature. The table shows the wind chill temperatures for given pairs of air temperature and wind speed.

Wind Chill Temperatures (°F)					
Wind speed (mi/h)	Air temperature (°F)				
	20	10	0	−10	−20
0	20	10	0	−10	−20
10	9	−4	−16	−28	−41
20	4	−9	−22	−35	−48
30	1	−12	−26	−39	−53

58a. −10°F with a wind speed of 10 miles per hour

a. **Compare** Which feels colder, an air temperature of 0°F with a wind speed of 30 miles per hour, or an air temperature of −10°F with a wind speed of 10 miles per hour?

b. **Analyze** How does the wind chill temperature change under constant wind speed and decreasing air temperature? under constant air temperature and increasing wind speed? **decreases; decreases**

Study Strategy

Exercises 23–34 Remind students that $-a$ is read "the opposite of a." Give an example such as, "if a is −1, then the opposite of a is the opposite of −1."

Avoiding Common Errors

Exercises 42–49 Some students may read $-x$ as −0.75 rather than −(−0.75). Suggest that students use parentheses around x to avoid this error.

Exercises 53–55 You may want to mention that students can avoid errors by graphing the numbers in these problems on a number line.

Reading Strategy

Exercise 56 Tell students to look for key words when they are reading a problem. Point out that this exercise asks for the day on which the *absolute value* of the change was the greatest.

Vocabulary

Exercise 58b Some students may need help with the word "constant." Tell these students that constant means that something does not change. Direct their attention to the chart so they can see that constant wind speed and decreasing air temperature are read in rows across the chart and constant air temperature and increasing wind speed are read in columns down the chart.

17. $-\frac{2}{3}$**: rational number, −0.6: rational number, −1: integer, rational number,** $\frac{1}{3}$**: rational number; −1,** $-\frac{2}{3}$**, −0.6,** $\frac{1}{3}$

18. −0.01: rational number, 0.1: rational number, 0: whole number, integer, rational number, $-\frac{1}{10}$**: rational number;** $-\frac{1}{10}$**, −0.01, 0, 0.1**

19. 16: whole number, integer, rational number, −1.66: rational number, $\frac{5}{3}$**: rational number, −1.6: rational number; −1.66, −1.6,** $\frac{5}{3}$**, 16**

20. −2.7: rational number, $\frac{1}{2}$**: rational number, 0.3: rational number, −7: integer, rational number; −7, −2.7, 0.3,** $\frac{1}{2}$

21. −4.99: rational number, 5: whole number, integer, rational number, $\frac{16}{3}$**: rational number, −5.1: rational number; −5.1, −4.99, 5,** $\frac{16}{3}$

22. $-\frac{3}{5}$**: rational number, −0.4: rational number, −1: integer, rational number, −0.5: rational number; −1,** $-\frac{3}{5}$**, −0.5, −0.4**

52. See Additional Answers beginning on p. AA1.

5 ASSESS AND RETEACH

Daily Homework Quiz

Transparency Available

1. Graph −3 and −5 on a number line. Then tell which number is greater. **−3 > −5**

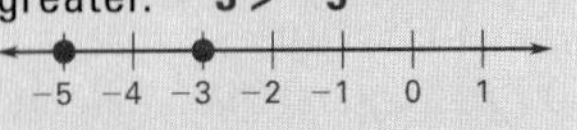

2. Tell whether each number is a whole number, an integer, or a rational number: −2.24, 6, $3\frac{1}{4}$, −16. **−2.24: rational number; 6: whole number, integer, rational number; $3\frac{1}{4}$: rational number; −16: integer, rational number**

3. The table shows the boiling-point temperatures of some elements. Order the elements from lowest boiling-point temperature to highest.

Element	Temperature
Hydrogen	−2593°C
Mercury	357°C
Nitrogen	−196°C
Oxygen	−183°C

Hydrogen, Nitrogen, Oxygen, Mercury

Online Quiz

Available at **classzone.com**

Diagnosis/Remediation

- Practice A, B, C in Chapter Resource Book
- Study Guide in Chapter Resource Book
- Practice Workbook
- @HomeTutor

Challenge

Additional challenge is available in the Chapter Resource Book.

59b. Rigel's apparent magnitude is greater than the Sun's apparent magnitude, so it is dimmer than the Sun; Rigel's absolute magnitude is less than the Sun's absolute magnitude, so it is brighter than the Sun.

59c. No. *Sample answer*: The apparent magnitude of Arcturus is less than the apparent magnitude of Achernar, but the absolute magnitude of Arcturus is greater than the absolute magnitude of Achernar.

59. ★ **EXTENDED RESPONSE** A star's apparent magnitude measures how bright the star appears to a person on Earth. A star's absolute magnitude measures its brightness if it were a distance of 33 light-years, or about 194 trillion miles, from Earth. The greater the magnitude, the dimmer the star.

Star	Arcturus	Achernar	Canopus	Capella	Sirius	Sun
Apparent magnitude	−0.04	0.46	−0.72	0.08	−1.46	−26.72
Absolute magnitude	0.2	−1.3	−2.5	0.4	1.4	4.8

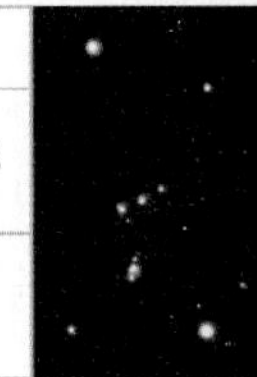

Orion Constellation

a. **Order** Order the stars in the table from brightest to dimmest when viewed from Earth. Then order the stars from brightest to dimmest if they were 33 light-years from Earth.

b. **Compare** The star Rigel has an apparent magnitude of 0.12 and an absolute magnitude of −8.1. *Compare* its brightness with the Sun's brightness using both apparent magnitude and absolute magnitude.

c. **Analyze** Can you use the apparent magnitudes of two stars to predict which star is brighter in terms of absolute magnitude? *Explain* your answer using a comparison of the apparent and absolute magnitudes of two stars in the table.

59a. Sun, Sirius, Canopus, Arcturus, Capella, Achernar; Canopus, Achernar, Arcturus, Capella, Sirius, Sun

C 60. **CHALLENGE** In an academic contest, the point values of the questions are given by the expression $50x$ where $x = 1, 2, 3,$ and 4. You earn $50x$ points for a correct answer to a question and $-(50x)$ points for an incorrect answer. Order from least to greatest all the possible points you can earn when answering a question. **−200, −150, −100, −50, 50, 100, 150, 200**

MIXED REVIEW

PREVIEW Prepare for Lesson 2.2 in Exs. 61–66.

Add. *(p. 914)*

61. $\frac{1}{2} + \frac{1}{3}$ **$\frac{5}{6}$**
62. $\frac{5}{6} + \frac{1}{6}$ **1**
63. $2\frac{1}{2} + 1\frac{3}{4}$ **$4\frac{1}{4}$**

Find the perimeter of the triangle or rectangle. *(p. 922)*

64. 5.8 cm, 4.2 cm, 6.3 cm **16.3 cm**

65.

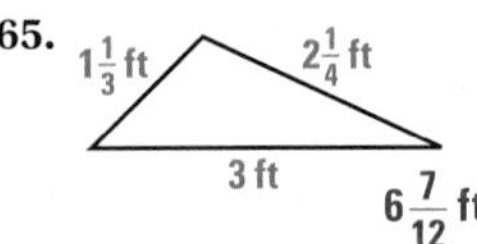

$6\frac{7}{12}$ ft

66.

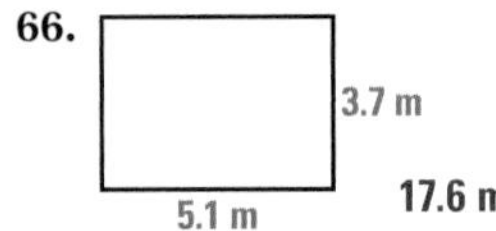

17.6 m

Check whether the given number is a solution of the inequality. *(p. 21)*

67. $x + 2 < 3$; 2 **not a solution**
68. $y - 8 < 6$; 13 **solution**
69. $9 - 2z \le 3$; 3 **solution**
70. $2y + 3 \ge 14$; 5 **not a solution**
71. $3 < 7x - 4$; 1 **not a solution**
72. $2a \ge 15$; 7 **not a solution**

Make a table for the function. Identify the range of the function. *(p. 43)* **73–75. See margin.**

73. $y = x - 3$
Domain: 5, 8, 14, 30

74. $y = 1.5x$
Domain: 0, 2, 6, 10

75. $y = 2x - 3$
Domain: 2, 4, 7, 11

EXTRA PRACTICE for Lesson 2.1, p. 939 **ONLINE QUIZ** at classzone.com

73. range: 2, 5, 11, 27

x	y
5	2
8	5
14	11
30	27

74. range: 0, 3, 9, 15

x	y
0	0
2	3
6	9
10	15

75. range: 1, 5, 11, 19

x	y
2	1
4	5
7	11
11	19

Apply Sets to Numbers and Functions

GOAL Apply set theory to numbers and functions.

Key Vocabulary
- set
- element
- empty set
- universal set
- union
- intersection

A **set** is a collection of distinct objects. Each object in a set is called an **element** or *member* of the set. You can use *set notation* to write a set by enclosing the elements of the set in braces. For example, if A is the set of whole numbers less than 6, then $A = \{0, 1, 2, 3, 4, 5\}$.

Two special sets are the *empty set* and the *universal set*. The set with no elements is called the **empty set** and is written as $\emptyset$. The set of all elements under consideration is called the **universal set** and is written as U.

KEY CONCEPT *For Your Notebook*

Union and Intersection of Two Sets

The **union** of two sets A and B is the set of all elements in *either* A or B and is written as $A \cup B$.

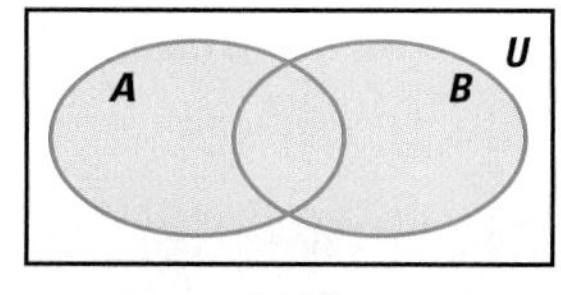

The **intersection** of two sets A and B is the set of all elements in *both* A and B and is written as $A \cap B$.

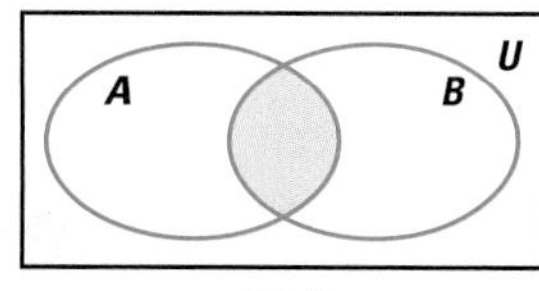

EXAMPLE 1 Find the union and intersection of two sets

Let U be the set of integers from 1 to 9. Let $A = \{2, 4, 6, 8\}$ and $B = \{2, 3, 5, 7\}$. Find (a) $A \cup B$ and (b) $A \cap B$.

Solution

a. The union of A and B consists of the elements that are in either set.

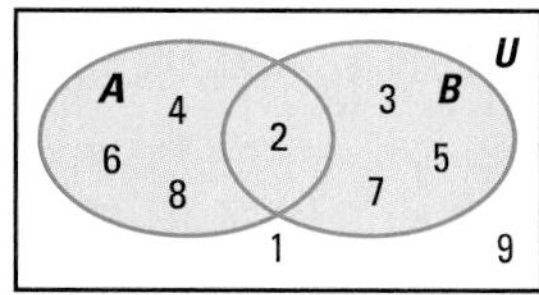

▶ $A \cup B = \{2, 3, 4, 5, 6, 7, 8\}$

b. The intersection of A and B consists of the elements that are in both sets.

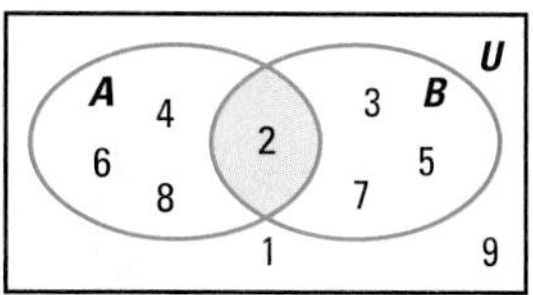

▶ $A \cap B = \{2\}$

1 PLAN AND PREPARE

Warm-Up Exercises

Find the range of the given function with the given domain.

1. $y = 2x$; Domain: 3, 5, 7 **6, 10, 14**
2. $y = x + 5$; Domain: 2, 5, 8 **7, 10, 13**
3. $y = x - 2$; Domain: 2, 4, 6 **0, 2, 4**

2 FOCUS AND MOTIVATE

Essential Question

Big Idea 3, p. 63

How do you apply sets to numbers and functions? **Tell students they will learn how to answer this question by finding the union and intersection of two sets of numbers and by using set notation to write a function and its range.**

3 TEACH

Extra Example 1

Let U be the set of rational numbers from -3 to 6.5. Let $A = \{-3, 1, 5\frac{1}{4}, 6.2\}$ and $B = \{-2, 1.5, 4, 6\}$. Find (a) $A \cup B$ and (b) $A \cap B$.

a. $A \cup B = \{-3, -2, 1, 1.5, 4, 5\frac{1}{4}, 6, 6.2\}$
b. $A \cap B = \emptyset$

NCTM STANDARDS

Standard 2: Understand functions; Use models to understand relationships

Extra Example 2

Consider the function $y = x - 4$ with domain $D = \{6, 7, 8, 9\}$. Write the range and function using set notation. **The range is $R = \{2, 3, 4, 5\}$. The function is $f = \{(6, 2), (7, 3), (8, 4), (9, 5)\}$.**

Key Question to Ask for Example 2

- How are the ordered pairs in f related to D and R? **The elements if D are the first coordinates and the elements of R are the second coordinates of the ordered pairs.**

Closing the Lesson

Have students summarize the major points of the lesson and answer the Essential Question: How do you apply sets to numbers and functions?

- **Enclose the elements of a set in braces when using set notation.**
- **A function can be written as a set of ordered pairs.**

The union of two sets of numbers is the set of all of the elements in either set. The intersection is the set of all of the numbers common to both sets. Write a function as a set of ordered pairs.

4 PRACTICE AND APPLY

Avoiding Common Errors

Exercises 1–10 Some students may confuse the symbols for union and intersection. Tell them to remember that union starts with the letter U and the symbol for union looks like the letter U.

FUNCTIONS AND SETS You can write the domain and range of a function as sets of input values and output values and the function as a set of ordered pairs, as illustrated for the mapping diagram below.

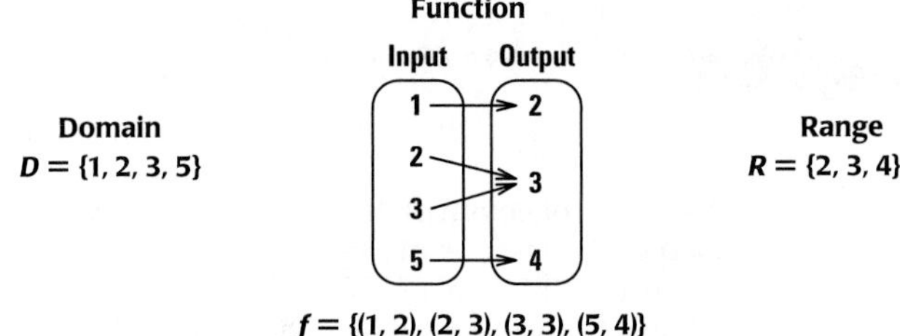

$f = \{(1, 2), (2, 3), (3, 3), (5, 4)\}$

EXAMPLE 2 Write a function and its range as sets

Consider the function $y = x + 2$ with domain $D = \{0, 1, 2, 3\}$. Write the range and function using set notation.

Solution

x	0	1	2	3
y	$0 + 2 = 2$	$1 + 2 = 3$	$2 + 2 = 4$	$3 + 2 = 5$

▶ The range is $R = \{2, 3, 4, 5\}$.
The function is $f = \{(0, 2), (1, 3), (2, 4), (3, 5)\}$.

PRACTICE

EXAMPLE 1 on p. 71 for Exs. 1–4

Let U be the set of whole numbers from 0 to 10. Find $A \cup B$ and $A \cap B$ for the specified sets A and B.

1. $A = \{1, 3, 5, 7, 9\}$ and $B = \{3, 6, 9\}$ **$\{1, 3, 5, 6, 7, 9\}, \{3, 9\}$**
2. $A = \{1, 2, 3, 4, 5, 6\}$ and $B = \{4, 5, 6, 7, 8\}$ **$\{1, 2, 3, 4, 5, 6, 7, 8\}, \{4, 5, 6\}$**
3. $A = \{0, 2, 4, 6, 8, 10\}$ and $B = \{1, 3, 5, 7, 9\}$ **$\{0, 1, 2, 3, 4, 5, 6, 7, 8, 9, 10\}, \emptyset$**
4. $A = \{0, 5, 10\}$ and $B = \{1, 4, 7, 10\}$ **$\{0, 1, 4, 5, 7, 10\}, \{10\}$**

EXAMPLE 2 on p. 72 for Exs. 5–8

In Exercises 5–8, consider the specified function and domain. Write the range and function using set notation.

5. $y = 2x$ with domain $D = \{1, 2, 3, 4, 5\}$ **$R = \{2, 4, 6, 8, 10\}, f = \{(1, 2), (2, 4), (3, 6), (4, 8), (5, 10)\}$**
6. $y = x - 1$ with domain $D = \{2, 4, 6, 8, 10\}$ **$R = \{1, 3, 5, 7, 9\}, f = \{(2, 1), (4, 3), (6, 5), (8, 7), (10, 9)\}$**
7. $y = x + 3$ with domain $D = \{1, 5, 9, 13, 17\}$
8. $y = 3x + 2$ with domain $D = \{1, 2, 3, 4, 5\}$ **$R = \{5, 8, 11, 14, 17\}, f = \{(1, 5), (2, 8), (3, 11), (4, 14), (5, 17)\}$**
9. Let A be the set of positive integers, and let B be the set of negative integers and 0. Find $A \cup B$ and $A \cap B$. **the set of integers, $\emptyset$**
10. Let A be the set of integers, and let B be the set of rational numbers. Find $A \cup B$ and $A \cap B$. **the set of rational numbers, the set of integers**

7. $R = \{4, 8, 12, 16, 20\}, f = \{(1, 4), (5, 8), (9, 12), (13, 16), (17, 20)\}$

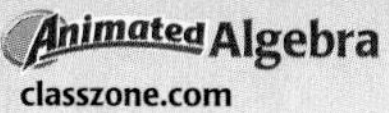

2.2 Addition of Integers

MATERIALS • algebra tiles

QUESTION How can you use algebra tiles to find the sum of two integers?

You can use algebra tiles to model addition of integers. Each + represents 1, and each − represents −1. Pairing a + with a − results in a sum of 0.

EXPLORE Find the sum of two integers

Find the sum −7 + 4.

STEP 1 Model −7 and 4 using algebra tiles.

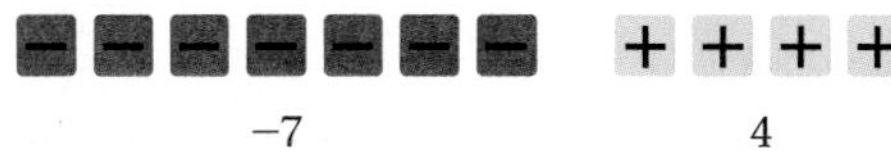

STEP 2 Group pairs of positive and negative tiles. Count the remaining tiles.

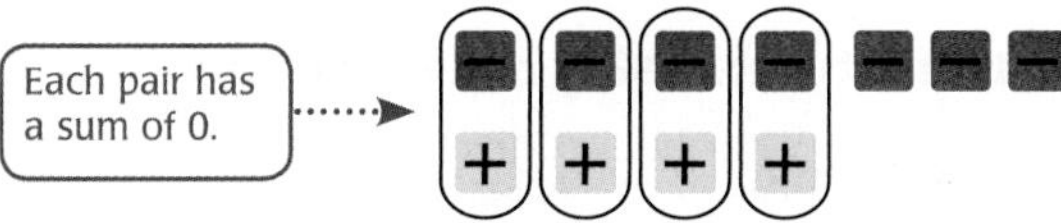

STEP 3 Copy and complete the statement: −7 + 4 = __?__. **−3**

DRAW CONCLUSIONS Use your observations to complete these exercises

Use algebra tiles to find the sum.

1. 3 + 8 **11**
2. 5 + (−1) **4**
3. −9 + 6 **−3**
4. −2 + (−3) **−5**
5. −4 + 4 **0**
6. −7 + 5 **−2**
7. 5 + (−7) **−2**
8. −6 + 0 **−6**

REASONING **In Exercises 9–13, answer the question and give an example from Exercises 1–8 to support your answer.**

9. Is the sum of two positive integers *positive* or *negative?* **positive, Ex. 1**
10. Is the sum of two negative integers *positive* or *negative?* **negative, Ex. 4**
11. Is the sum of a positive integer and a negative integer *always* positive? **no, Ex. 6**
12. What is the sum of an integer and its opposite? **0, Ex. 5**
13. What is the sum of an integer and 0? **the integer, Ex. 8**
14. In Exercises 6 and 7, the two integers being added are the same, but the order is reversed. What does this suggest about the sums $a + b$ and $b + a$ where a and b are integers? **It does not affect the answer.**

1 PLAN AND PREPARE

Explore the Concept

- Students will model integer addition with algebra tiles.
- This activity leads into the study of adding integers in Example 1 in Lesson 2.2.

Materials

Each student will need:

- algebra tiles
- Activity Support Master (*Chapter Resource Book*)

Recommended Time

Work activity: 10 min

Discuss results: 5 min

Grouping

Students should work individually.

2 TEACH

Tips for Success

Tell students that since the sum of a negative tile and a positive tile is zero, each such pair of tiles has no effect on the actual sum. Explain that this is why they need to pair one positive tile with one negative tile, and that they need to continue doing this until there are no pairs left.

Key Discovery

Students should see that the sum of an integer and its opposite is 0, the sum of two integers with the same sign has that same sign, and the sum of two integers with different signs has the sign of the integer modeled by the greater number of tiles.

3 ASSESS AND RETEACH

1. How many zero pairs can you make if you want to find the sum of 2 + (−5)? **2**
2. Can you make zero pairs if you want to find the sum of −2 + (−3)? Explain. **No, only one negative and one positive tile form a zero pair.**

2.2 Add Real Numbers

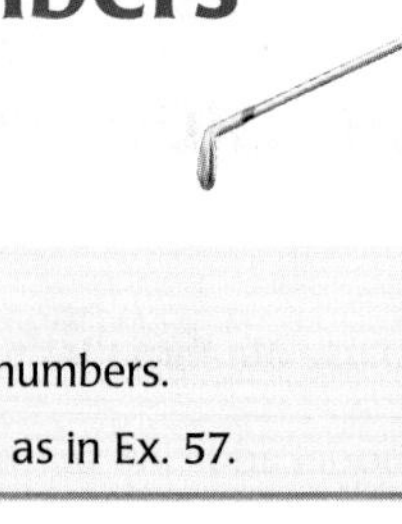

Before You added positive numbers.
Now You will add positive and negative numbers.
Why? So you can calculate a sports score, as in Ex. 57.

Key Vocabulary
- **additive identity**
- **additive inverse**

One way to add two real numbers is to use a number line. Start at the first number. Use the sign of the second number to decide whether to move left or right. Then use the absolute value of the second number to decide how many units to move. The number where you stop is the sum of the two numbers.

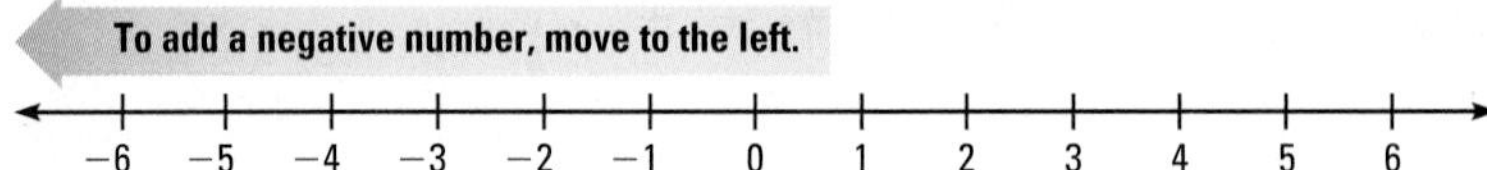

EXAMPLE 1 Add two integers using a number line

Use a number line to find the sum.

a. $-3 + 6$

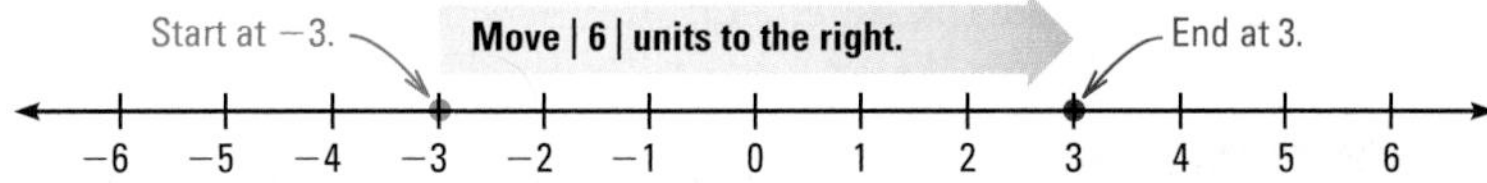

▶ The final position is 3. So, $-3 + 6 = 3$.

b. $-4 + (-5)$

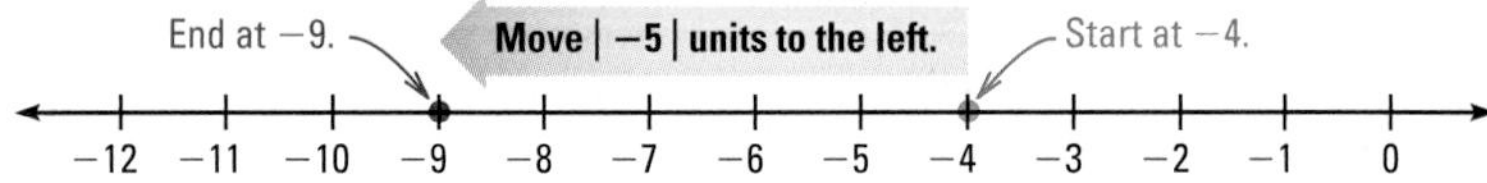

▶ The final position is −9. So, $-4 + (-5) = -9$.

GUIDED PRACTICE for Example 1

Use a number line to find the sum.

1. $7 + (-2)$ **5** **2.** $8 + (-11)$ **−3** **3.** $-8 + 4$ **−4** **4.** $-1 + (-4)$ **−5**

1 PLAN AND PREPARE

Warm-Up Exercises

Transparency Available

1. $0.43 + 1.27 = \underline{?}$ **1.7**

2. $4\frac{5}{6} + 2\frac{2}{3} = \underline{?}$ $7\frac{1}{2}$

3. Ned wants to ship 3 books in a box with a weight limit of 25 pounds. The books weigh 8.4 pounds, 7.9 pounds, and 9.2 pounds. Can he ship them in the box? Explain. **No; the total weight of the books is 25.5 pounds and 25.5 > 25.**

Notetaking Guide

Transparency Available

Promotes interactive learning and notetaking skills.

Pacing

Basic: 1 day
Average: 1 day
Advanced: 1 day
Block: 0.5 block with 2.3
- See *Teaching Guide/Lesson Plan*.

2 FOCUS AND MOTIVATE

Essential Question

Big Idea 1, p. 63

How do you add positive and negative numbers? **Tell students they will learn how to answer this question by using a number line, rules of addition, and properties of addition of real numbers.**

NCTM STANDARDS

Standard 1: Understand meanings of operations; Compute fluently

Resource Planning Guide

Chapter Resource Book
- Teaching Guide/Lesson Plan
- Practice levels A, B, C
- Study Guide
- Catch-up for Absent Students
- Application
- Challenge

Workbooks
- Notetaking Guide
- Practice Workbook

Teaching Options
- **Power Presentations** provides dynamic electronic teaching resources for the classroom.
- **Activity Generator** provides editable activities for all ability levels.

Interactive Technology
- Easy Planner
- Power Presentations
- Activity Generator
- Animated Algebra
- Test Generator
- Online Quiz
- eWorkbook
- eEdition
- @HomeTutor

Resources for English Learners
- Spanish Study Guide
- Multi-Language Visual Glossary
- Student Resources in Spanish

See also the *Differentiated Instruction Resources* for more strategies for meeting individual needs.

KEY CONCEPT *For Your Notebook*

Rules of Addition

Words To add two numbers with the *same* sign, add their absolute values. The sum has the same sign as the numbers added.

Examples $8 + 7 = 15$ $\quad -6 + (-10) = -16$

Words To add two numbers with *different* signs, subtract the lesser absolute value from the greater absolute value. The sum has the same sign as the number with the greater absolute value.

Examples $-12 + 7 = -5$ $\quad 18 + (-4) = 14$

EXAMPLE 2 Add real numbers

Find the sum.

a. $-5.3 + (-4.9) = -(|-5.3| + |-4.9|)$ **Rule of same signs**

$= -(5.3 + 4.9)$ **Take absolute values.**

$= -10.2$ **Add.**

b. $19.3 + (-12.2) = |19.3| - |-12.2|$ **Rule of different signs**

$= 19.3 - 12.2$ **Take absolute values.**

$= 7.1$ **Subtract.**

PROPERTIES OF ADDITION Notice that both $3 + (-2)$ and $-2 + 3$ have the same sum, 1. So, $3 + (-2) = -2 + 3$. This is an example of the *commutative property of addition*. The properties of addition are listed below.

KEY CONCEPT *For Your Notebook*

Properties of Addition

COMMUTATIVE PROPERTY The order in which you add two numbers does not change the sum.

Algebra $a + b = b + a$ **Example** $3 + (-2) = -2 + 3$

ASSOCIATIVE PROPERTY The way you group three numbers in a sum does not change the sum.

Algebra $(a + b) + c = a + (b + c)$ **Example** $(-3 + 2) + 1 = -3 + (2 + 1)$

IDENTITY PROPERTY The sum of a number and 0 is the number.

Algebra $a + 0 = 0 + a = a$ **Example** $-5 + 0 = -5$

INVERSE PROPERTY The sum of a number and its opposite is 0.

Algebra $a + (-a) = -a + a = 0$ **Example** $-6 + 6 = 0$

Motivating the Lesson

Have students imagine that they need to balance a checkbook, track a club's finances, or monitor a fund-raiser. Explain that learning how to add positive and negative numbers in this lesson will help them oversee activities that have money coming in and money going out.

3 TEACH

Extra Example 1

Use a number line to find the sum.

a. $-4 + 2$ **-2**

b. $3 + (-4)$ **-1**

Key Questions to Ask for Example 1

- In Example 1a, why do you start at -3? **-3 is the first number in the sum $-3 + 6$.**
- How do you know whether to move left or right? **Move right when the sign of the second number is positive and left when the sign is negative.**

Extra Example 2

Find the sum.

a. $-8.4 + (-0.7)$ **-9.1**

b. $-12.6 + 7.3$ **-5.3**

Key Question to Ask for Example 2

- In Example 2b, will $-12.2 + 19.3$ have the same answer as $19.3 + (-12.2)$? Why? **Yes, to add two numbers with different signs, you subtract the lesser absolute value from the greater absolute value, so for both, you will subtract 12.2 from 19.3.**

Extra Example 3

Identify the property being illustrated.

a. $-11.9 + 11.9 = 0$ **Inverse property of addition**

b. $-8 + (-x) = -x + (-8)$ **Commutative property of addition**

c. $-2 + 0 = -2$ **Identity property of addition**

Extra Example 4

The table shows how much weight two dieters lost or gained per month. Which dieter had the greater weight loss at the end of three months? **dieter A**

Month	Dieter A	Dieter B
1	−3.3	−7.8
2	−5.1	+1.2
3	+0.5	−0.8

Closing the Lesson

Have students summarize the major points of the lesson and answer the Essential Question: How do you add positive and negative numbers?

- **Use the rules for like signs and different signs to add real numbers.**
- **Use the properties of addition to make adding easier, such as using the associative property to associate numbers that are easy to add.**

Using the rules of addition, add the absolute value of two numbers with the same sign and use the sign of the numbers for the sum. If two numbers have different signs, subtract the lesser absolute value from the greater absolute value and use the sign of the greater absolute value for the sum.

The identity property states that the sum of a number a and 0 is a. The number 0 is the **additive identity**. The inverse property states that the sum of a number a and its opposite is 0. The opposite of a is its **additive inverse**.

EXAMPLE 3 Identify properties of addition

	Statement	Property illustrated
a.	$(x + 9) + 2 = x + (9 + 2)$	Associative property of addition
b.	$8.3 + (-8.3) = 0$	Inverse property of addition
c.	$-y + 0.7 = 0.7 + (-y)$	Commutative property of addition

EXAMPLE 4 Solve a multi-step problem

BUSINESS The table shows the annual profits of two piano manufacturers. Which manufacturer had the greater total profit for the three years?

Year	Profit (millions) for manufacturer A	Profit (millions) for manufacturer B
1	−\$5.8	−\$6.5
2	\$8.7	\$7.9
3	\$6.8	\$8.2

Solution

STEP 1 **Calculate** the total profit for each manufacturer.

Manufacturer A:

$$\text{Total profit} = -5.8 + 8.7 + 6.8 = -5.8 + (8.7 + 6.8) = -5.8 + 15.5 = 9.7$$

Manufacturer B:

$$\text{Total profit} = -6.5 + 7.9 + 8.2 = -6.5 + (7.9 + 8.2) = -6.5 + 16.1 = 9.6$$

STEP 2 **Compare** the total profits: $9.7 > 9.6$.

▸ Manufacturer A had the greater total profit.

CHECK REASONABLENESS
Use estimation to check reasonableness. Manufacturer A: about $-6 + 9 + 7$, or 10. Manufacturer B: about $-7 + 8 + 8$, or 9. Because $10 > 9$, the solution is reasonable.

✓ **GUIDED PRACTICE** for Examples 2, 3, and 4

Find the sum.

5. $-0.6 + (-6.7)$ **−7.3**

6. $10.1 + (-16.2)$ **−6.1**

7. $-13.1 + 8.7$ **−4.4**

Identify the property being illustrated.

8. $7 + (-7) = 0$ **Inverse property of addition**

9. $-12 + 0 = -12$ **Identity property of addition**

10. $4 + 8 = 8 + 4$ **Commutative property of addition**

11. **WHAT IF?** In Example 4, suppose that the profits for year 4 are −\$1.7 million for manufacturer A and −\$2.1 million for manufacturer B. Which manufacturer has the greater total profit for the four years? **manufacturer A**

2.2 EXERCISES

HOMEWORK KEY
○ = **WORKED-OUT SOLUTIONS** on p. WS3 for Exs. 13, 35, and 55
★ = **STANDARDIZED TEST PRACTICE** Exs. 2, 50, 56, 57, and 58

SKILL PRACTICE

A

1. **VOCABULARY** What number is called the additive identity? **0**
2. ★ **WRITING** Without actually adding, how can you tell if the sum of two numbers will be zero? **If they are opposites, their sum will be zero.**

EXAMPLE 1 on p. 74 for Exs. 3–11

USING A NUMBER LINE **Use a number line to find the sum.**

3. $-11 + 3$ **−8**
4. $-1 + 6$ **5**
5. $13 + (-7)$ **6**
6. $5 + (-10)$ **−5**
7. $-9 + (-4)$ **−13**
8. $-8 + (-2)$ **−10**
9. $-14 + 8$ **−6**
10. $6 + (-12)$ **−6**
11. $-11 + (-9)$ **−20**

EXAMPLE 2 on p. 75 for Exs. 12–25

FINDING SUMS **Find the sum.**

12. $-2.4 + 3.9$ **1.5**
13. $-8.7 + 4.2$ **−4.5**
14. $4.3 + (-10.2)$ **−5.9**
15. $9.1 + (-2.5)$ **6.6**
16. $-6.5 + (-7.1)$ **−13.6**
17. $-11.4 + (-3.8)$ **−15.2**
18. $4\frac{1}{5} + \left(-9\frac{1}{2}\right)$ $\mathbf{-5\frac{3}{10}}$
19. $8\frac{2}{3} + \left(-1\frac{3}{5}\right)$ $\mathbf{7\frac{1}{15}}$
20. $-12\frac{3}{4} + 6\frac{9}{10}$ $\mathbf{-5\frac{17}{20}}$
21. $-\frac{4}{9} + 1\frac{4}{5}$ $\mathbf{1\frac{16}{45}}$
22. $-3\frac{3}{7} + \left(-14\frac{3}{4}\right)$ $\mathbf{-18\frac{5}{28}}$
23. $-7\frac{1}{12} + \left(-13\frac{7}{8}\right)$ $\mathbf{-20\frac{23}{24}}$

ERROR ANALYSIS ***Describe*** **and correct the error in finding the sum.**

24. $-13 + (-15) = 28$ ✗
The answer should be negative, $-13 + (-15) = -28$.

25. $17 + (-31) = -48$ ✗
The numbers have different signs, so their absolute values should have been subtracted, $17 + (-31) = -14$.

EXAMPLE 3 on p. 76 for Exs. 26–31

IDENTIFYING PROPERTIES **Identify the property being illustrated.**

26. $-3 + 3 = 0$ **Inverse property of addition**
27. $(-6 + 1) + 7 = -6 + (1 + 7)$ **Associate property of addition**
28. $9 + (-1) = -1 + 9$ **Commutative property of addition**
29. $-8 + 0 = -8$ **Identity property of addition**
30. $(x + 2) + 3 = x + (2 + 3)$ **Associative property of addition**
31. $y + (-4) = -4 + y$ **Commutative property of addition**

EXAMPLE 4 on p. 76 for Exs. 32–37

FINDING SUMS **Find the sum.**

32. $-13 + 5 + (-7)$ **−15**
33. $-18 + (-12) + (-19)$ **−49**
34. $0.47 + (-1.8) + (-3.8)$ **−5.13**
35. $-2.6 + (-3.4) + 7.6$ **1.6**
36. $-3\frac{1}{2} + \left(-7\frac{2}{5}\right) + \left(-9\frac{3}{10}\right)$ $\mathbf{-20\frac{1}{5}}$
37. $8\frac{2}{3} + \left(-6\frac{3}{5}\right) + 3\frac{1}{4}$ $\mathbf{5\frac{19}{60}}$

B

EVALUATING EXPRESSIONS **Evaluate the expression for the given value of** x**.**

38. $3 + x + (-7); x = 6$ **2**
39. $x + (-5) + 5; x = -3$ **−3**
40. $9.6 + (-x) + 2.3; x = -8.5$ **20.4**
41. $-1.7 + (-5.4) + (-x); x = 2.4$ **−9.5**
42. $1\frac{1}{4} + |x| + \left(-3\frac{1}{2}\right); x = -8\frac{2}{5}$ $\mathbf{6\frac{3}{20}}$
43. $|x| + \left(-3\frac{1}{4}\right) + \left(7\frac{3}{10}\right); x = -3\frac{1}{3}$ $\mathbf{7\frac{23}{60}}$

Differentiated Instruction

Kinesthetic Learners While working on **Exercises 3–11**, some students may need to trace their fingertip along a number line in order to complete the exercises. Have them begin at the starting number, and trace to the right to add a positive number or to the left to add a negative number.

See also the *Differentiated Instruction Resources* for more strategies.

4 PRACTICE AND APPLY

Assignment Guide

Answer Transparencies available for all exercises

Basic:
Day 1: SRH p. 914 Exs. 21–25
pp. 77–79
Exs. 1, 2, 3–23 odd, 24–31, 33–43 odd, 53–57, 60–66

Average:
Day 1: pp. 77–79
Exs. 1, 2, 6–22 even, 24–31, 34–50 even, 53–59, 60–66 even

Advanced:
Day 1: pp. 77–79
Exs. 1, 2, 8–22 even, 27–49 odd, 51–53*, 55–59*, 61–65 odd

Block:
pp. 77–79
Exs. 1, 2, 6–22 even, 24–31, 34–50 even, 53–59, 60–66 even (with 2.3)

Differentiated Instruction

See *Differentiated Instruction Resources* for suggestions on addressing the needs of a diverse classroom.

Homework Check

For a quick check of student understanding of key concepts, go over the following exercises:

Basic: 7, 15, 28, 37, 54
Average: 8, 18, 30, 36, 54
Advanced: 10, 31, 37, 55, 57

Extra Practice

- Student Edition, p. 939
- Chapter Resource Book: Practice levels A, B, C

Practice Worksheet

An easily-readable reduced practice page (with answers) for this lesson can be found on p. 62C.

Teaching Strategy

Exercises 3–11 Some students may prefer using algebra tiles or the rules of addition to find the sums. Have these students find the sums using a number line and then check their answers using algebra tiles or the rules of addition.

Exercise 50 Tell students it may be easier to determine the answer if they first substitute real numbers for *a* and *b*.

Avoiding Common Errors

Exercises 12–23 Watch for students who add the greater absolute value to the lesser absolute value when adding numbers of different signs. Remind them that when the numbers have different signs, they need to subtract the lesser absolute value from the greater absolute value. This means if the lesser absolute value is the first number, it will become the second number when they subtract, such that $2.5 + (-8.2)$ becomes $8.2 - 2.5$ when they take the absolute values and subtract.

Mathematical Reasoning

Exercise 56 Suggest that students first look for ways to eliminate answers before adding the numbers. Point out that the answers for A and B overlap for the years 2000 and 2001. To determine which three-year period had the greater profit, all they need to do is compare profits for 1999 and 2002. They can do the same for answers C and D. After they eliminate two of the answers, they can add and then compare the profits for the remaining three-year periods.

Internet Reference

Exercise 58 For more information about atoms, visit the Jefferson Lab website at http://education.jlab.org/atomtour/index.html

FINDING SOLUTIONS **Solve the equation using mental math.**

44. $x + (-9) + 9 = 8$ **8**

45. $(-8) + x + (-2) = -10$ **0**

46. $x + (-2.8) + 9.2 = 0$ **−6.4**

47. $-8.7 + x + 1.3 = 0$ **7.4**

TRANSLATING PHRASES **In Exercises 48 and 49, translate the verbal phrase into an addition expression. Then find the sum.**

48. The sum of the absolute value of −4 and the additive identity **$|-4| + 0$; 4**

49. The sum of the opposite of −18 and its additive inverse **$-(-18) + (-18)$; 0**

50. ★ **MULTIPLE CHOICE** If $a + b$ is negative, which statement must be true? **D**

Ⓐ $a < 0, b < 0$ Ⓑ $a < 0$ Ⓒ $a < 0, b > 0$ Ⓓ $a < -b$

51. **CHALLENGE** Consider the expression $|x| + (-x)$. Write a simplified expression for the sum if x is positive. Then write a simplified expression for the sum if x is negative. Give examples to support your answers.

51. 0; $|2x|$. ***Sample answer:*** **If $x = 2$, then $|2| + (-2) = 2 + (-2) = 0$. If $x = -2$, then $|-2| + (-(-2)) = 2 + 2 = 4$.** C

52. **CHALLENGE** Evaluate $-50 + (-49) + (-48) + \cdots + 48 + 49 + 50$. *Explain* how you can use the properties of addition to obtain the sum.
0; use the commutative property of addition to add each negative number and its opposite. By the additive inverse property, it will equal 0.

PROBLEM SOLVING

EXAMPLE 1 A on p. 74 for Ex. 53

53. **WEATHER** The temperature in your city at 6 A.M. was −8°F and increased by 15°F by noon. What was the temperature at noon? **7°F**

@HomeTutor for problem solving help at classzone.com

EXAMPLE 2 on p. 75 for Exs. 54–55

54. **PARKING GARAGES** The bottom level of a parking garage has an elevation of −45 feet. The top level of the garage is 100 feet higher. What is the elevation of the top level? **55 ft**

@HomeTutor for problem solving help at classzone.com

(55.) **MULTI-STEP PROBLEM** In optometry, the strength of an eyeglass lens is measured in diopters. Two lenses can be combined to create a new lens, and the sum of their strengths is the strength of the new lens.

a. A lens of −4.75 diopters is combined with a lens of 6.25 diopters to form a new lens. What is the strength of the new lens? **1.5 diopters**

b. A lens of −2.5 diopters is combined with a lens of −1.25 diopters to form a new lens. What is the strength of the new lens? **−3.75 diopters**

c. The greater the absolute value of the strength of a lens, the stronger the lens. Which new lens is stronger, the one in part (a) or in part (b)? **part (b)**

EXAMPLE 4 on p. 76 for Exs. 56–57

56. ★ **MULTIPLE CHOICE** The table shows the profits for a company from 1999 to 2004. Which three-year period had the greatest total profit? **C**

Year	1999	2000	2001	2002	2003	2004
Profit (millions of dollars)	−13.76	54.91	38.54	−21.33	123.90	−14.82

Ⓐ 1999–2001 Ⓑ 2000–2002 Ⓒ 2001–2003 Ⓓ 2002–2004

◯ = WORKED-OUT SOLUTIONS on p. WS1 ★ = STANDARDIZED TEST PRACTICE

B 57. ★ **SHORT RESPONSE** In golf, your score on a hole is the number of strokes above or below an expected number of strokes needed to hit a ball into the hole. As shown in the table, each score has a name. When you compare two scores, the lesser score is the better score.

Name	Double eagle	Eagle	Birdie	Par	Bogey	Double bogey
Score	−3	−2	−1	0	1	2

a. **Compare** For three holes, you score an eagle, a double bogey, and a birdie. Your friend scores a double eagle, a bogey, and a par. Who has the better total score? **your friend**

b. **Explain** Your friend scores a double eagle and an eagle for the next two holes. Is it possible for you to have a better score on all five holes after your next two holes? *Explain* your reasoning. **No, if you score 2 double eagles, you will have the same score.**

58. ★ **EXTENDED RESPONSE** Atoms consist of protons, electrons, and neutrons. A group of x protons has a charge of x. A group of x electrons has a charge of $-x$. Neutrons have a charge of 0.

58c. 5 electrons should be added. *Sample answer*: $5 + x = 0$. For the expression to equal 0, add the additive inverse of 5, which is −5.

a. **Calculate** The total charge of an atom is the sum of the charges of its protons and electrons. Find the total charge of an atom that has 13 protons, 10 electrons, and 14 neutrons. **3**

b. **Interpret** An atom is an ion only when it has a positive or a negative total charge. Is the atom in part (a) an ion? **yes**

c. **Explain** In an atom, only the number of electrons can change. Suppose an atom has a total charge of 5. For the atom not to be an ion, how should the number of electrons change? Your answer should include an algebraic equation that models the situation and an explanation of how you solved the equation.

C 59. **CHALLENGE** You sold three items in an Internet auction. The table shows the profit earned for each item. You now plan to sell a floor lamp. What is the least profit that you can earn on the lamp and have a positive total profit for the four items? *Explain* your answer. Use estimation to check that your answer is reasonable. **\$12.40; the sum of the profits is −\$12.39; the total profit (in dollars) of the three items is about 4 + (−11) + (−6), or −13, and −13 + 13 = 0, so the answer \$12.40 is reasonable.**

Item	Profit (dollars)
Mantel clock	4.13
Framed mirror	−10.65
Metal lunch box	−5.87

MIXED REVIEW

PREVIEW
Prepare for Lesson 2.3 in Exs. 60–63.

Evaluate the expression.

60. $t - 7$ when $t = 21$ *(p. 2)* **14**

61. $1.7 - y$ when $y = 0.8$ *(p. 2)* **0.9**

62. $-a$ when $a = -13.5$ *(p. 64)* **13.5**

63. $|c|$ when $c = -9.6$ *(p. 64)* **9.6**

State the formula that is needed to solve the problem. Then solve the problem. *(p. 28)*

64. What is the interest on \$800 invested for 3 years in an account that earns simple interest at a rate of 1.5% per year? **$I = prt$; \$36**

65. Find the perimeter of a rectangle that is 28 feet wide and 40 feet long. **$P = 2\ell + 2w$; 136 ft**

66. The temperature is 50°F. What is the temperature in degrees Celsius? **$C = \frac{5}{9}(F - 32)$; 10°C**

5 ASSESS AND RETEACH

Daily Homework Quiz

Transparency Available

Find the sum.

1. 7.6 + (−9) **−1.4**
2. −23.7 + 28.2 + 8.3 **12.8**
3. What property is illustrated by $(-y + 3) + 6 = -y + (3 + 6)$? **Associative property of addition**
4. The table shows the account ledgers for the Science Club and the Astronomy Club. Which club has the greater assets at the end of 3 weeks?

Week	Science Club	Astronomy Club
1	−\$44.50	\$106.00
2	\$150.55	−\$48.50
3	−\$15.50	\$35.00

The Astronomy Club has greater assets since \$92.50 > \$90.55.

Available at **classzone.com**

Diagnosis/Remediation

- Practice A, B, C in Chapter Resource Book
- Study Guide in Chapter Resource Book
- Practice Workbook
- @HomeTutor

Challenge

Additional challenge is available in the Chapter Resource Book.

2.3 Subtract Real Numbers

Before You added real numbers.
Now You will subtract real numbers.
Why? So you can find a change in temperature, as in Ex. 43.

Key Vocabulary
- **opposites,** *p. 66*

Because the expressions $12 - 3$ and $12 + (-3)$ have the same value, 9, you can conclude that $12 - 3 = 12 + (-3)$. Subtracting 3 from 12 is equivalent to adding the opposite of 3 to 12. This example illustrates the *subtraction rule.*

KEY CONCEPT *For Your Notebook*

Subtraction Rule

Words To subtract b from a, add the opposite of b to a.

Algebra $a - b = a + (-b)$ **Example** $14 - 8 = 14 + (-8)$

EXAMPLE 1 Subtract real numbers

Find the difference.

a. $-12 - 19 = -12 + (-19)$
$= -31$

b. $18 - (-7) = 18 + 7$
$= 25$

Animated Algebra at classzone.com

GUIDED PRACTICE for Example 1

Find the difference.

1. $-2 - 7$ **-9**
2. $11.7 - (-5)$ **16.7**
3. $\frac{1}{3} - \frac{1}{2}$ **$-\frac{1}{6}$**

EXAMPLE 2 Evaluate a variable expression

Evaluate the expression $y - x + 6.8$ when $x = -2$ and $y = 7.2$.

$y - x + 6.8 = 7.2 - (-2) + 6.8$ Substitute -2 for x and 7.2 for y.
$= 7.2 + 2 + 6.8$ Add the opposite of -2.
$= 16$ Add.

1 PLAN AND PREPARE

Warm-Up Exercises

Transparency Available

Find the sum.

1. $-14 + 5$ **-9**
2. $6.4 + (-3.5)$ **2.9**

Evaluate the expression when $x = 6$.

3. $x - 4.8$ **1.2**
4. $6.3 - x$ **0.3**
5. The temperature was $-3°F$ in the morning and then rose $2°F$ by noon. What was the temperature at noon? **$-1°F$**

Notetaking Guide

Transparency Available

Promotes interactive learning and notetaking skills.

Pacing

Basic: 1 day
Average: 1 day
Advanced: 1 day
Block: 0.5 block with 2.2
- See *Teaching Guide/Lesson Plan.*

2 FOCUS AND MOTIVATE

Essential Question

Big Idea 1, p. 63

How do you subtract real numbers? **Tell students they will learn how to answer this question by using a subtraction rule that relates subtraction to addition.**

NCTM STANDARDS

Standard 1: Understand meanings of operations

Standard 9: Apply math in contexts outside of mathematics

Resource Planning Guide

Chapter Resource Book
- Teaching Guide/Lesson Plan
- Activity Master
- Practice levels A, B, C
- Study Guide
- Catch-up for Absent Students
- Problem Solving Workshop
- Challenge

Workbooks
- Notetaking Guide
- Practice Workbook

Teaching Options
- **Power Presentations** provides dynamic electronic teaching resources for the classroom.
- **Activity Generator** provides editable activities for all ability levels.

Interactive Technology
- Easy Planner
- Power Presentations
- Activity Generator
- Animated Algebra
- Test Generator
- Online Quiz
- eWorkbook
- eEdition
- @HomeTutor

Resources for English Learners
- Spanish Study Guide
- Multi-Language Visual Glossary
- Student Resources in Spanish

See also the *Differentiated Instruction Resources* for more strategies for meeting individual needs.

EVALUATING CHANGE You can use subtraction to find the change in a quantity, such as elevation or temperature. The change in a quantity is the difference of the new amount and the original amount. If the new amount is greater than the original amount, the change is positive. If the new amount is less than the original amount, the change is negative.

EXAMPLE 3 Evaluate change

TEMPERATURES One of the most extreme temperature changes in United States history occurred in Fairfield, Montana, on December 24, 1924. At noon, the temperature was 63°F. By midnight, the temperature fell to −21°F. What was the change in temperature?

Solution

The change C in temperature is the difference of the temperature m at midnight and the temperature n at noon.

STEP 1 **Write** a verbal model. Then write an equation.

Change in temperature	=	Temperature at midnight	−	Temperature at noon
C	=	m	−	n

AVOID ERRORS
When a quantity decreases, the change is negative. So, the change found in Example 3 should be a negative number.

STEP 2 **Find** the change in temperature.

$C = m - n$	**Write equation.**
$= -21 - 63$	**Substitute values.**
$= -21 + (-63)$	**Add the opposite of 63.**
$= -84$	**Add −21 and −63.**

▶ The change in temperature was −84°F.

USING A CALCULATOR To enter a negative number on a calculator, use the (−) key. To enter a subtraction sign, use the − key. You can use a calculator to check your answer in Example 3 using the following keystrokes.

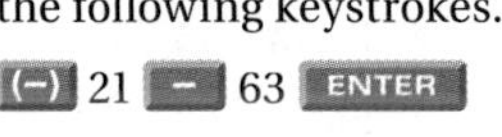

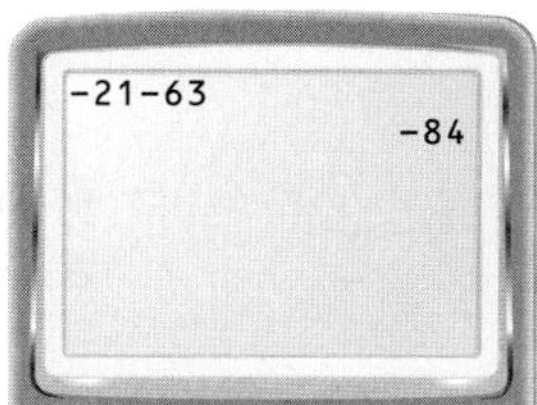

✓ GUIDED PRACTICE for Examples 2 and 3

Evaluate the expression when $x = -3$ and $y = 5.2$.

4. $x - y + 8$ **−0.2**
5. $y - (x - 2)$ **10.2**
6. $(y - 4) - x$ **4.2**

7. **CAR VALUES** A new car is valued at $15,000. One year later, the car is valued at $12,300. What is the change in the value of the car? **−$2700**

Motivating the Lesson

Tell students that learning to subtract real numbers allows them to evaluate changes in quantities, such as the change in value of a $1500 computer that is valued at $975 after two years.

3 TEACH

Extra Example 1

Find the difference.

a. −18 − 3 **−21** **b.** −9 − (−12) **3**

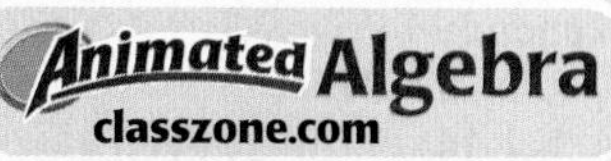

An **Animated Algebra** activity is available online for **Example 1**. This activity is also part of **Power Presentations**.

Extra Example 2

Evaluate the expression $x - y + 2.3$ when $x = 8.8$ and $y = -1.4$. **12.5**

Extra Example 3

The temperature one morning was 14°C. By midday, the temperature was −3°C. What was the change in temperature? **−17°C**

Closing the Lesson

Have students summarize the major points of the lesson and answer the Essential Question: How do you subtract real numbers?

- **Subtracting b from a is the same as adding the opposite of b to a, so $a - b = a + (-b)$.**
- **The change in a quantity is the difference of the new amount and the original amount. If the quantity increases, the change is positive and if it decreases, the change is negative.**

To subtract two numbers, add the opposite of the second number to the first number.

Differentiated Instruction

Visual Learners On a calculator, some students may confuse the subtraction key with the negation key. Show them that the four operation keys (+, −, ×, ÷) are always together in a group. The negation key is not only set apart from the other keys, but it is often a different color.

See also the *Differentiated Instruction Resources* for more strategies.

2.3 EXERCISES

HOMEWORK KEY
○ = WORKED-OUT SOLUTIONS on p. WS4 for Exs. 3, 21, and 43
★ = STANDARDIZED TEST PRACTICE Exs. 2, 38, 39, 40, and 46
◆ = MULTIPLE REPRESENTATIONS Ex. 45

4 PRACTICE AND APPLY

Assignment Guide

Answer Transparencies available for all exercises

Basic:
Day 1: pp. 82–84
Exs. 1–16, 17–35 odd, 42–46, 49–55 odd

Average:
Day 1: pp. 82–84
Exs. 1, 2, 6–14 even, 15, 16, 20–30 even, 32–46, 50–56 even

Advanced:
Day 1: pp. 82–84
Exs. 1, 2, 10–14, 20–30 even, 32–41*, 43–48*, 52, 56

Block:
pp. 82–84
Exs. 1, 2, 6–14 even, 15, 16, 20–30 even, 32–46, 50–56 even (with 2.2)

Differentiated Instruction

See *Differentiated Instruction Resources* for suggestions on addressing the needs of a diverse classroom.

Homework Check

For a quick check of student understanding of key concepts, go over the following exercises:

Basic: 7, 19, 23, 27, 42
Average: 10, 22, 28, 32, 42
Advanced: 13, 24, 30, 35, 43

Extra Practice

- Student Edition, p. 939
- Chapter Resource Book: Practice levels A, B, C

Practice Worksheet

An easily-readable reduced practice page (with answers) for this lesson can be found on p. 62C.

SKILL PRACTICE

A

1. **VOCABULARY** Use the subtraction rule to rewrite the expression $-3 - 6$ as an addition expression. **$-3 + (-6)$**

2. ★ **WRITING** Without actually subtracting, how can you tell whether a change in a quantity will be negative? **If the second number is greater than the first number.**

EXAMPLE 1 on p. 80 for Exs. 3–14

FINDING DIFFERENCES **Find the difference.**

3. $13 - (-5)$ **18**
4. $16 - 32$ **-16**
5. $-11 - (-3)$ **-8**
6. $-15 - 29$ **-44**
7. $-35.9 - (-50)$ **14.1**
8. $14.7 - (-2.3)$ **17**
9. $-3.6 - 22.2$ **-25.8**
10. $-18.2 - (-15.4)$ **-2.8**
11. $\frac{1}{2} - \frac{5}{6}$ **$-\frac{1}{3}$**
12. $-\frac{5}{3} - \frac{8}{3}$ **$-4\frac{1}{3}$**
13. $\frac{1}{2} - \left(-\frac{1}{4}\right)$ **$\frac{3}{4}$**
14. $-\frac{7}{10} - \left(-\frac{2}{5}\right)$ **$-\frac{3}{10}$**

EXAMPLE 2 on p. 80 for Exs. 15–25

ERROR ANALYSIS ***Describe*** **and correct the error in evaluating the expression when $x = 3$ and $y = -8$.**

15.
$$x - y + 2 = 3 - 8 + 2$$
$$= 3 + (-8) + 2$$
$$= -5 + 2$$
$$= -3$$

16.
$$x - (-4 + y) = 3 - [-4 + (-8)]$$
$$= 3 - (-12)$$
$$= 3 - 12$$
$$= -9$$

15. 8 was substituted for y instead of -8; $3 - (-8) + 2 = 3 + 8 + 2 = 13$.

16. The opposite of -12 was not added in step 3; $3 - [-4 + (-8)] = 3 - (-12) = 3 + 12 = 15$.

EVALUATING EXPRESSIONS **Evaluate the expression when $x = 7.1$ and $y = -2.5$.**

17. $x - (-y)$ **4.6**
18. $y - x - 12$ **-21.6**
19. $x - (-6) + y$ **10.6**
20. $x - (y - 13)$ **22.6**
21. $-y - (1.9 - x)$ **7.7**
22. $-y - x$ **-4.6**
23. $x - y - 2$ **7.6**
24. $5.3 - (y - x)$ **14.9**
25. $x + y - 2.8$ **1.8**

EXAMPLE 3 on p. 81 for Exs. 26–31

EVALUATING CHANGE **Find the change in temperature or elevation.**

26. From −5°C to −13°C **−8°C**
27. From −45°F to 62°F **107°F**
28. From −300 feet to −100 feet **200 ft**
29. From 1200 meters to −80 meters **−1280 m**
30. From 4.8°F to −12.6°F **−17.4°F**
31. From −90.7 miles to 36.4 miles **127.1 mi**

B

EVALUATING EXPRESSIONS **Evaluate the expression when $x = 3.6$, $y = 6.6$, and $z = -11$.**

32. $(x - y) - |z|$ **-14**
33. $(x - |-y|) - z$ **8**
34. $x - |y - z|$ **-14**
35. $(-x - y) - z - 5$ **-4.2**
36. $x + y - z + 12.9$ **34.1**
37. $-z + y - x - (-2.4)$ **16.4v**

38. ★ **MULTIPLE CHOICE** If the value of the expression $a - b$ is negative, which statement must be true? **C**

Ⓐ $a > b$ Ⓑ $a = 0$ Ⓒ $a < b$ Ⓓ $b = 0$

39. ★ **WRITING** Tell whether the associative property and the commutative property hold for subtraction. Give examples to support your answers. **No. *Sample answer*: $(2 - 3) - 4 \neq 2 - (3 - 4)$, $2 - 5 \neq 5 - 2$**

C 40. ★ **WRITING** If $a > b$, then the expression $a - b$ gives the distance between a and b on a number line. What expression gives the distance between a and b regardless of whether $a > b$ or $b > a$? *Explain* your thinking. **See margin.**

HINT
Add half the distance between a and b to b.

41. **CHALLENGE** Let $a > b$. *Explain* why $\frac{a+b}{2}$ lies between a and b on a number line for any two numbers a and b. **See margin.**

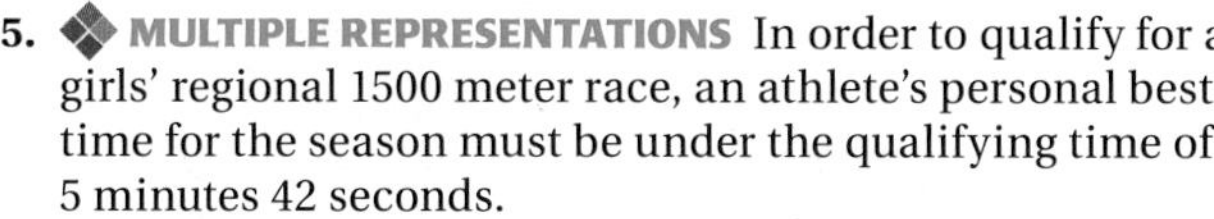

PROBLEM SOLVING

EXAMPLE 3 A
on p. 81 for Exs. 42–43

42. **VOLCANOES** Mahukona is a Hawaiian volcano whose summit has an elevation of −3600 feet. The summit once had an elevation of 800 feet. What was the change in elevation of the volcano's summit? **−4400 ft**

@HomeTutor for problem solving help at classzone.com

43. **CAVES** The temperature inside Mammoth Cave in Kentucky is about 12.2°C year round. If the temperature outside the cave is −2.4°C, what is the change in temperature from outside to inside the cave? **14.6°C**

@HomeTutor for problem solving help at classzone.com

44. **FOOTBALL** In four plays a football team gains 3 yards, loses 7 yards, loses 2 yards, and gains 15 yards. How many yards did the team gain after four plays? **9 yd**

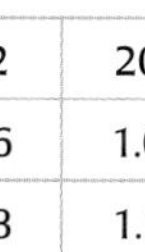

45. ◆ **MULTIPLE REPRESENTATIONS** In order to qualify for a girls' regional 1500 meter race, an athlete's personal best time for the season must be under the qualifying time of 5 minutes 42 seconds.

a. **Writing an Equation** Write an equation that expresses d as the difference of the athlete's personal best time t (in seconds) and the qualifying time (in seconds).

b. **Making a Table** Make a table that gives the values of d for $t = 341.7$, 343.8, 340.9, and 342.7. Which values of t in the table are under the qualifying time? How can you tell from the differences?

45a. $d = t - 342$

45b.

t	d
341.7	−0.3
343.8	1.8
340.9	−1.1
342.7	0.7

341.7 and 340.9; you can tell if $t - 342$ is negative.

B 46. ★ **SHORT RESPONSE** A trade surplus or deficit is the difference of the value of all exports and the value of all imports. A positive difference is a surplus, and a negative difference is a deficit. The table shows the values of the United States' imports and exports for the period 2000–2003.

Year	2000	2001	2002	2003
Value of exports (trillions of dollars)	1.071	1.007	0.976	1.021
Value of imports (trillions of dollars)	1.449	1.369	1.398	1.517

a. **Calculate** Find the trade surplus or deficit for each year. **−\$.378 trillion; −\$.362 trill… −\$.422 trillion; −\$…**

b. **Describe** *Describe* any trends in the surplus or deficit over the years… ***Sample answer:*** **There is a deficit each year; the deficit decreased b… and then increased each year in the next two years.**

Avoiding Common Errors

Exercises 26–31 Remind students that a change is positive if the new amount is greater than the original and negative if the new amount is less than the original. Point out that the new amount could be greater than the original amount and still be a negative number.

Graphing Calculator

Exercises 26–31, 46 Students can use their calculators to check their answers for exercises 26–31 and to calculate trade surpluses and deficits for exercise 46. Tell them to use the instructions for the calculator in Example 3. Note that they do not need to use negative numbers for exercise 46.

Internet Reference

Exercise 42 Additional information about volcanoes can be found at http://www.geology.sdsu.edu/how_volcanoes_work

Study Strategy

Exercises 42–43 Instruct students to write out detailed solutions for these exercises using Example 3 as a model. This will help them determine the original quantity and the new quantity and avoid confusing the two.

Reading Strategy

Exercise 45 Point out to students that part a on writing an equ… states that the best ti… qualifying tim… Exe…

40. $|a - b|$; ***Sample answer:*** **Consider $a = 7$ and $b = 3$. The distance between them is $7 - 3 = 4$. Now consider $a = b$ and $b = 7$. The distance between them is still 4, but $a - b$… $3 - 7 = -4$. Note that $|a - b| = 4$. Regardless of whether $a > b$ or $b > a$, the distance between a and b is $|a - b|$.**

41. Because $a > b$, the distance between a and b is $a - b$. If you add half that distance, $\frac{a-b}{2}$, to b, you get the midpoint between a and b. So, the midpoint is $b + \frac{a-b}{2} = \frac{2b}{2} + \frac{a-b}{2} = \frac{2b}{2} + \frac{a-b}{2} = \frac{b+a}{2} = \frac{a+b}{2}$. Then $\frac{a+b}{2}$ is between a and b.

5 ASSESS AND RETEACH

Daily Homework Quiz

 **Transparency Available**

Find the difference.

1. 37.5 − (−4.6) **42.1**

2. −12 − (−8.5) **−3.5**

Evaluate the expression when $x = -2.5$ and $y = 6.2$.

3. $y - x + 2$ **10.7**

4. $x - 4.7 - (-y)$ **−1**

5. On a hike through Benedict Canyon, Emma started at an elevation of 128 feet and then descended to −375 feet. What was Emma's change in elevation? **−503 ft**

Online Quiz

Available at **classzone.com**

Diagnosis/Remediation

- Practice A, B, C in Chapter Resource Book
- Study Guide in Chapter Resource Book
- Practice Workbook
- @HomeTutor

Challenge

Additional challenge is available in the Chapter Resource Book.

Quiz

An easily-readable reduced copy of the quiz (with answers) on Lessons 2.1–2.3 from the Assessment Book can be found on p. 62E.

47. SNOWBOARDS Snowboarders can rotate the shoe bindings on their snowboards. The binding setup shown below is written +24°/−18°. This means that the front angle is 24° counterclockwise from vertical, and the rear angle is 18° clockwise from vertical.

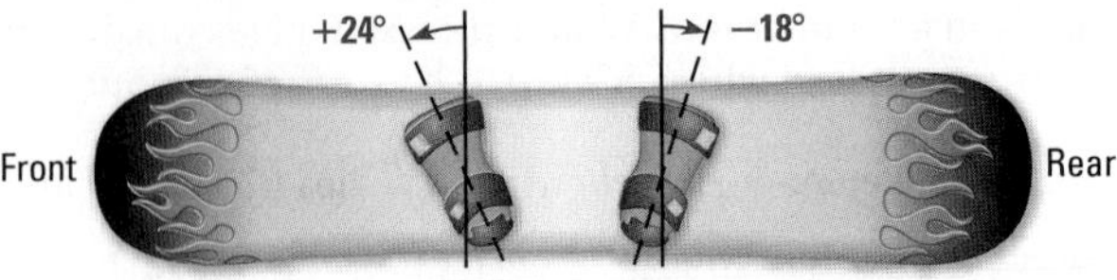

a. An instructor suggests a binding setup of +30°/+15° for beginners. Your setup is initially +24°/−4°. Find the changes in angle measures needed to match the instructor's suggestion. **6°; 19°**

b. A mirror setup is a setup of $+n°/-n°$ where n is between 0 and 90. Your setup is initially +13°/−6°. You change the front angle measure by −3°. Find the change in the rear angle measure needed for a mirror setup. **−4°**

C **48. CHALLENGE** Greenwich Mean Time (GMT) is the time at the Royal Observatory in Greenwich, England. A location that is $+n$ hours from GMT is n hours ahead of GMT, and a location that is $-n$ hours from GMT is n hours behind GMT. Costa Rica is −6 hours from GMT, and India is +5.5 hours from GMT. If it is 7:45 A.M. in India, what time is it in Costa Rica? **8:15 P.M.**

MIXED REVIEW

Evaluate the expression.

49. $20x$ when $x = 15$ *(p. 2)* **300**

50. $3x + 8$ when $x = 12$ *(p. 8)* **44**

51. $15.5 + x$ when $x = -30.2$ *(p. 74)* **−14.7**

52. $-x + 19.4$ when $x = 8.2$ *(p. 74)* **11.2**

PREVIEW
Prepare for Lesson 2.4 in Exs. 53–56.

Identify the property illustrated. *(p. 74)*

53. $1 + 7 = 7 + 1$ **Commutative property of addition**

54. $-4.8 + 4.8 = 0$ **Inverse property of addition**

55. $0 + (-9) = -9$ **Identity property of addition**

56. $(2 + 3) + 4 = 2 + (3 + 4)$ **Associative property of addition**

QUIZ *for Lessons 2.1–2.3*

1. Tell whether each of the following numbers is a whole number, an integer, or a rational number: $-\frac{5}{6}$, −8.2, 0, −9. Then order the numbers from least to greatest. *(p. 64)* **$-\frac{5}{6}$: rational number, −8.2: rational number, 0: whole number, integer, rational number, −9: integer, rational number; −9, −8.2, $-\frac{5}{6}$, 0**

Find the sum or difference.

2. $5 + (-36)$ *(p. 74)* **−31**

3. $-8.2 + (-2.3)$ *(p. 74)* **−10.5**

4. $3\frac{1}{2} + (-2)$ *(p. 74)* **$1\frac{1}{2}$**

5. $-18 - (-9)$ *(p. 80)* **−9**

6. $-11.2 - 21.7$ *(p. 80)* **−32.9**

7. $4\frac{1}{2} - \left(-\frac{1}{5}\right)$ *(p. 80)* **$4\frac{7}{10}$**

Evaluate the expression when $x = 2.5$ and $y = -3.4$. *(p. 80)*

8. $x + y - 9$ **−9.9**

9. $x - (y - 5.1)$ **11**

10. $12.1 - (y - x)$ **18**

EXTRA PRACTICE for Lesson 2.3, p. 939

ONLINE QUIZ at classzone.com

Spreadsheet **ACTIVITY** *Use after Lesson 2.3*

@HomeTutor
classzone.com
Keystrokes

2.3 Subtract Real Numbers

QUESTION **How can you use a spreadsheet to subtract the same number from various numbers?**

In a spreadsheet, the columns are identified by letters, and the rows are identified by numbers. Each cell has a name that is made up of a letter and a number. For example, B2 is the cell in column B and row 2. A cell can contain a label, a number, or a formula.

	A	B
1		
2		

EXAMPLE **Find the difference of two numbers**

A manufacturing company is making foam hand grips for bicycles and jump ropes. The ideal length of a hand grip is 5 inches. In a batch of ten hand grips, the actual lengths (in inches) are 4.878, 4.902, 5.115, 5.13, 4.877, 4.874, 4.799, 4.819, 4.879, and 5.124. Create a spreadsheet to find the difference of the actual length and the ideal length for each hand grip.

Solution

STEP 1 ***Enter data***

Enter the labels in the first row of the spreadsheet. Then enter the grip numbers and grip lengths in successive rows.

	A	B	C
1	Grip	Length (inches)	Difference
2	1	4.878	
3	2	4.902	

STEP 2 ***Calculate differences***

For each hand grip, enter the formula for the difference of the actual and ideal lengths in the appropriate cell in column C. **See margin.**

	A	B	C
1	Grip	Length (inches)	Difference
2	1	4.878	=B2−5
3	2	4.902	=B3−5

After you enter a formula, the cell should display the difference of the length of the grip and the ideal length. For example, C2 should display −0.122, and C3 should display −0.098.

DRAW CONCLUSIONS

1. The manufacturer will consider a hand grip acceptable if the absolute value of the difference of the actual length and the ideal length is at most 0.125 inch. How many hand grips from the batch are acceptable? **6 hand grips**
2. What are the least and greatest possible lengths that a hand grip can have and still be acceptable? *Explain* your reasoning. **4.875 in., 5.125 in.; adding and subtracting 0.125 from 5 will give the greatest and least acceptable lengths of a hand grip.**
3. For which of the ten hand grips is the length closest to the ideal length? How can you tell from the differences in column C? **4.902; the difference in the lengths has the smallest absolute value.**
4. In another batch of ten hand grips, the actual lengths (in inches) are 4.871, 5.019, 5.112, 4.987, 5.067, 4.899, 4.859, 5.132, 5.126, and 5.093. Create a spreadsheet to find the difference of the actual length and the ideal length for each hand grip. **See margin.**

1 PLAN AND PREPARE

Learn the Method

- Students will use a spreadsheet to subtract real numbers.
- After the activity, students can use a spreadsheet to check their table calculations in Exercise 46, Lesson 2.3.

2 TEACH

Alternative Strategy

Show students that they do not need to enter the formula in each cell in Step 2. Demonstrate that they can enter the formula for cell C2, click on the cell, move the cursor to the bottom right corner of the cell until the plus icon appears, click on the icon, and then move the cursor to the bottom of row 11. Students can check that the correct formula is entered by clicking on a cell. The formula will appear in the *fx* box at the top of the page. Warn that this works only if they have already entered all of the grip lengths in column B.

Extra Example

A manufacturing plant fills boxes with dog biscuits. The ideal weight per box is 12 ounces. In a batch of ten boxes, the actual weights (in ounces) are 11.025, 11.280, 11.275, 12.024, 11.685, 12.3, 11.45, 12.54, 11.955, and 12.2. Create a spreadsheet to find the difference of the actual weight and the ideal weight for each box of dog biscuits. **Enter box numbers in column A, actual weights in column B, and the formulas =B2–12, =B3–12, and so on in column C.**

3 ASSESS AND RETEACH

Suppose you made a spreadsheet to find the differences of the ideal and actual lengths of the grips. What would be the formula? Would the results be the same? **=5−B2, =5−B3, =5−B4, . . . ; yes**

Step 2, 4. See Additional Answers beginning on p. AA1.

4. *Sample answer:* You start a babysitting service. It costs you $35.50 for a training course and then you spend $12.43 on games to bring with you. After your first week, you've earned $50.43. The expression −35.50 + (−12.43) + 50.43 represents the profit or loss from the first week of business; $2.50.

5. −14; −444; −579; −515; −222. *Sample answer:* Each year more people migrate out of the city than migrate into it.

STATE TEST PRACTICE classzone.com

Lessons 2.1–2.3

1. **MULTI-STEP PROBLEM** The table shows the record low temperatures for several states in the United States.

State	Temperature (°F)
Alaska	−80
Arkansas	−29
California	−45
Hawaii	12
Kentucky	−37

   a. Order the temperatures from least to greatest. **−80°F, −45°F, −37°F, −29°F, 12°F**

   b. The record low temperature in Arizona is −40°F. Which states in the table have record low temperatures less than −40°F? **Alaska and California**

2. **MULTI-STEP PROBLEM** Your bank account incurs a $35 fee for each withdrawal that either results in a negative balance or occurs while your account balance is negative. You have a balance of $150. You withdraw $165.

   a. What will the balance in your account be after the fee is charged? **−$50**

   b. How much money do you need to deposit into the account so that the balance is $0? **$50**

3. **GRIDDED ANSWER** At the close of trading on the New York Stock Exchange on Monday, the value of a share of a certain stock was $10.65. Over the next three days, the change in value of a share was −$.56, then −$1.09, and then $.89. What was the value of a share of the stock at the end of the three days? **$9.89**

4. **OPEN-ENDED** *Describe* a real-world situation that can be modeled by the expression −35.50 + (−12.43) + 50.43. Then find the value of the expression. **See margin.**

5. **SHORT RESPONSE** Net migration flow is the difference of the number of people migrating into a place and the number of people migrating out of a place. The table shows the number of people who migrated into and out of a certain city during the period 2001–2005.

Year	Number migrating into city	Number migrating out of city
2001	3302	3316
2002	3179	3623
2003	3053	3632
2004	3180	3695
2005	3174	3396

Find the net migration flow for each year. Then describe any trends in the city's net migration flow during this period. **See margin.**

6. **EXTENDED RESPONSE** In meteorology, the lifted index measures the likelihood of a thunderstorm. The greater the lifted index, the less likely a storm will occur. The table shows the lifted index for two cities at various times during a day.

Time	Lifted index for city A	Lifted index for city B
12 A.M.	−5.6	−0.8
4 A.M.	−4.3	−1.8
8 A.M.	−3.8	−2.3
12 P.M.	−2.5	−2.6
4 P.M.	−3.0	−1.4
8 P.M.	−4.5	0.8

   a. At what time during that day is a storm least likely to occur in city A? **12 P.M.**

   b. Compare the likelihood of a storm between 12 A.M. and 8 P.M. for the two cities on that day. ***Sample answer:* A storm is less likely in city B except at 12 P.M.**

   c. Would you expect a storm in city B but not in city A at 8 P.M. that day? *Explain.* **No, because the lifted index is greater in city B.**

Investigating Algebra ACTIVITY *Use before Lesson 2.4*

2.4 Multiplication by –1

MATERIALS • paper and pencil

QUESTION **What is the product of any integer *a* and –1?**

You can rewrite a multiplication expression as repeated addition. For example, 3 • 8 can be rewritten as 8 + 8 + 8. Because the sum is 24, you can conclude that 3 • 8 = 24.

EXPLORE **Find the product of an integer and –1**

STEP 1 Copy and complete the table.

Multiplication Expression	Addition Expression	Sum	
5 • (–1)	–1 + (–1) + (–1) + (–1) + (–1)	–5	
4 • (–1)	?	?	**–1 + (–1) + (–1) + (–1); –4**
3 • (–1)	?	?	**–1 + (–1) + (–1); –3**
2 • (–1)	?	?	**–1 + (–1); –2**

STEP 2 Copy and complete the multiplication equations below.

5 • (–1) = ? **–5**
4 • (–1) = ? **–4**
3 • (–1) = ? **–3**
2 • (–1) = ? **–2**

Complete using the table from Step 1.

1 • (–1) = ? **–1**
0 • (–1) = ? **0**
–1 • (–1) = ? **1**
–2 • (–1) = ? **2**
–3 • (–1) = ? **3**

Complete by extending the pattern in the first four products.

DRAW CONCLUSIONS **Use your observations to complete these exercises**

1. Copy and complete: For any integer *a*, *a* • (–1) = ?. **–*a***

Find the product.

2. 12 • (–1) **–12**
3. 10 • (–1) **–10**
4. –23 • (–1) **23**
5. –47 • (–1) **47**
6. –18 • (–1) **18**
7. 15 • (–1) **–15**

1 PLAN AND PREPARE

Explore the Concept

- Students will multiply an integer by –1.
- This activity leads into the study of properties of multiplication in Example 2 in Lesson 2.4.

Recommended Time

Work activity: 10 min
Discuss results: 5 min

Grouping

Students can work individually or in pairs. If students work in pairs, one student can copy and complete the table in Step 1 and the other student can copy and complete the multiplication equations in Step 2. Each student can check the work of the other.

2 TEACH

Key Questions

- What can you conclude from the table in Step 1? **The product of a positive integer and –1 is the opposite of the integer.**
- What is the pattern in Step 2? **At each step, add 1 to the product from the step before.**

Key Discovery

The product of an integer and –1 is the opposite of the integer.

3 ASSESS AND RETEACH

1. What is the sign of *a* • (–1) if *a* is a negative integer? **positive**
2. What is the sign of *a* • (–1) if *a* is a positive integer? **negative**

2.4 Multiply Real Numbers

Before You added and subtracted real numbers.

Now You will multiply real numbers.

Why So you can calculate an elevation, as in Example 4.

Key Vocabulary
- **multiplicative identity**

In the activity on page 87, you saw that $a \cdot (-1) = -a$ for any integer a. This rule not only lets you write the product of a and -1 as $-a$, but it also lets you write $-a$ as $(-1)a$ and $a(-1)$. Using this rule, you can multiply any two real numbers. Here are two examples:

$$-2(3) = -1(2)(3) = -1(6) = -6 \qquad (-2)(-3) = -2(3)(-1) = -6(-1) = 6$$

KEY CONCEPT *For Your Notebook*

The Sign of a Product

Words The product of two real numbers with the *same* sign is positive.

Examples $3(4) = 12$ $\quad -6(-3) = 18$

Words The product of two real numbers with *different* signs is negative.

Examples $2(-5) = -10$ $\quad -7(2) = -14$

EXAMPLE 1 Multiply real numbers

MULTIPLY NEGATIVES
- A product is negative if it has an *odd* number of negative numbers.
- A product is positive if it has an *even* number of negative numbers.

Find the product.

a. $-3(6) = -18$ — Different signs; product is negative.

b. $2(-5)(-4) = (-10)(-4)$ — Multiply 2 and -5.
$= 40$ — Same signs; product is positive.

c. $-\frac{1}{2}(-4)(-3) = 2(-3)$ — Multiply $-\frac{1}{2}$ and -4.
$= -6$ — Different signs; product is negative.

 **GUIDED PRACTICE** for Example 1

Find the product.

1. $-2(-7)$ **14** **2.** $-0.5(-4)(-9)$ **−18** **3.** $\frac{4}{3}(-3)(7)$ **−28**

1 PLAN AND PREPARE

Warm-Up Exercises

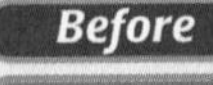 **Transparency Available**

1. $-17.3 + 6.2 = \underline{?}$ **−11.1**
2. $26.9 - (-5.8) = \underline{?}$ **32.7**

Identify the property illustrated.

3. $(12 + 14) + 82 = 12 + (14 + 82)$ **Associative property of addition**
4. $-3 + 0 = -3$ **Identity property of addition**
5. A company had a profit of −\$8.6 million in 2005 and \$1.4 million in 2006. What is the change in profit? **\$10 million**

Notetaking Guide

Transparency Available

Promotes interactive learning and notetaking skills.

Pacing

Basic: 1 day
Average: 1 day
Advanced: 1 day
Block: 0.5 block wi[illegible] 2.5
- See *Teaching Guide[illegible]son Plan.*

2 FOCUS AND MOTIVATE

Essential Question

Big Idea 1, p. 63

How do you multiply real numbers? **Tell students they will learn how to answer this question by using sign rules and properties of multiplication.**

NCTM STANDARDS

Standard 1: Understand meanings of operations

Standard 2: Represent situations using algebraic symbols

Resource Planning Guide

Chapter Resource Book
- Teaching Guide/Lesson Plan
- Practice levels A, B, C
- Study Guide
- Catch-up for Absent Students
- Problem Solving Workshop
- Challenge

Workbooks
- Notetaking Guide
- Practice Workbook

Teaching Options
- **Power Presentations** provides dynamic electronic teaching resources for the classroom.
- **Activity Generator** provides editable activities for all ability levels.

Interactive Technology
- Easy Planner
- Power Presentations
- Activity Generator
- Animated Algebra
- Test Generator
- Online Quiz
- eWorkbook
- eEdition
- @HomeTutor

Resources for English Learners
- Spanish Study Guide
- Multi-Language Visual Glossary
- Student Resources in Spanish

See also the *Differentiated Instruction Resources* for more strategies for meeting individual needs.

PROPERTIES OF MULTIPLICATION Notice that both $4(-5)$ and $-5(4)$ have a product of -20, so $4(-5) = -5(4)$. This equation is an example of the *commutative property of multiplication*. Properties of multiplication are listed below.

KEY CONCEPT *For Your Notebook*

Properties of Multiplication

COMMUTATIVE PROPERTY The order in which you multiply two numbers does not change the product.

Algebra $a \cdot b = b \cdot a$ **Example** $4 \cdot (-5) = -5 \cdot 4$

ASSOCIATIVE PROPERTY The way you group three numbers in a product does not change the product.

Algebra $(a \cdot b) \cdot c = a \cdot (b \cdot c)$ **Example** $(-2 \cdot 7) \cdot 4 = -2 \cdot (7 \cdot 4)$

IDENTITY PROPERTY The product of a number and 1 is that number.

Algebra $a \cdot 1 = 1 \cdot a = a$ **Example** $(-5) \cdot 1 = -5$

PROPERTY OF ZERO The product of a number and 0 is 0.

Algebra $a \cdot 0 = 0 \cdot a = 0$ **Example** $-3 \cdot 0 = 0$

PROPERTY OF −1 The product of a number and −1 is the opposite of the number.

Algebra $a \cdot (-1) = -1 \cdot a = -a$ **Example** $-2 \cdot (-1) = 2$

The identity property states that the product of a number a and 1 is a. The number 1 is called the **multiplicative identity**.

EXAMPLE 2 Identify properties of multiplication

	Statement	Property illustrated
a.	$(x \cdot 7) \cdot 0.5 = x \cdot (7 \cdot 0.5)$	Associative property of multiplication
b.	$8 \cdot 0 = 0$	Multiplicative property of zero
c.	$-6 \cdot y = y \cdot (-6)$	Commutative property of multiplication
d.	$9 \cdot (-1) = -9$	Multiplicative property of −1
e.	$1 \cdot v = v$	Identity property of multiplication

GUIDED PRACTICE for Example 2

Identify the property illustrated.

4. $-1 \cdot 8 = -8$
Multiplicative property of −1

5. $12 \cdot x = x \cdot 12$
Commutative property of multiplication

6. $(y \cdot 4) \cdot 9 = y \cdot (4 \cdot 9)$
Associative property of multiplication

7. $0 \cdot (-41) = 0$
Multiplicative property of zero

8. $-5 \cdot (-6) = -6 \cdot (-5)$
Commutative property of multiplication

9. $-13 \cdot (-1) = 13$
Multiplicative property of −1

Differentiated Instruction

Below Level To help students learn the properties of multiplication, have them write two of their own examples for each of the properties in the key concept box. Then have them use **Example 2** as a model to write statements that illustrate the properties. Ask them to exchange their statements with other students to see if they can identify the illustrated property. This will also help students justify their steps in **Example 3** and **Exercises 28–36**.

See also the *Differentiated Instruction Resources* for more strategies.

Motivating the Lesson

By learning to multiply real numbers, students can calculate the increase (or decrease) in a savings account if a fixed amount is added (or taken out) each week.

3 TEACH

Extra Example 1

Find the product.

a. $-8(-6)$ **48**

b. $-2(3.5)(-4)$ **28**

c. $\frac{1}{4}(-12)(3)$ **−9**

Key Question to Ask for Example 1

- How can you tell whether a product is positive or negative without multiplying? **If the number of negative factors is even, the product is positive. If the number of negative factors is odd, the product is negative.**

Extra Example 2

Identify the property illustrated.

a. $-7 \cdot 0 = 0$ **Multiplicative property of zero**

b. $b \cdot 1 = b$ **Identity property of multiplication**

c. $-1 \cdot (-13) = 13$ **Multiplicative property of −1**

d. $-a \cdot b = b \cdot (-a)$ **Commutative property of multiplication**

e. $(-2.5 \cdot y) \cdot (-4) = -2.5 \cdot (y \cdot (-4))$ **Associative property of multiplication**

Key Question to Ask for Example 2

- What is the difference between parts d and e? **In part d, the product of −1 and a number is the opposite of the number, while in part e, the product of 1 and the number is the number.**

Extra Example 3

Find the product $-2 \cdot (c \cdot (-0.5))$. Justify your steps.

$$-2 \cdot (c \cdot (-0.5)) = (c \cdot (-0.5)) \cdot (-2)$$
$$= c(-0.5 \cdot (-2))$$
$$= c \cdot 1$$
$$= c$$

Justifications: Commutative property, Associative property, the product of −0.5 and −2 is 1, and the Identity property.

Animated Algebra classzone.com

An **Animated Algebra** activity is available online for **Example 3**. This activity is also part of **Power Presentations**.

Extra Example 4

From 1900 to 1940, a 250-foot wide beach on the Atlantic coast was eroding at a rate of about −0.02 feet per year. From 1940 to 2000, it was eroding at a rate of about −0.12 feet per year. Approximate the width of the beach in 2000. **about 242 ft**

Closing the Lesson

Have students summarize the major points of the lesson and answer the Essential Question: How do you multiply real numbers?

- **The signs of the factors determine the sign of a product.**
- **The properties of multiplication hold for all real numbers.**

When multiplying real numbers, you use the properties of multiplication listed on page 89. The sign of the product of two numbers is positive if they have the same sign and negative if they have different signs.

10. $\frac{3}{2}y$; $\left(\frac{3}{10} \cdot 5\right)y$, **associative property of multiplication;** $\frac{3}{2} \cdot y$, **product of** $\frac{3}{10}$ **and 5 is** $\frac{3}{2}$; $\frac{3}{2}y$, **multiply.**

11. $0.8x$; $0.8(-1)(-x)$, **commutative property of multiplication;** $-0.8(-x)$, **multiplicative property of −1;** $0.8x$, **multiply**

12. $-3y$; $(-y)(3)$, **product of −0.5 and −6 is 3;** $-3y$, **commutative property of multiplication.**

EXAMPLE 3 Use properties of multiplication

JUSTIFY STEPS To justify a step, you name the property used. Sometimes a step is a calculation, as when you multiply 0.25 and −4 in Example 3.

Find the product $(-4x) \cdot 0.25$. Justify your steps.

$(-4x) \cdot 0.25 = 0.25 \cdot (-4x)$	**Commutative property of multiplication**
$= [0.25 \cdot (-4)]x$	**Associative property of multiplication**
$= -1 \cdot x$	**Product of 0.25 and −4 is −1.**
$= -x$	**Multiplicative property of −1**

Animated Algebra at classzone.com

EXAMPLE 4 Solve a multi-step problem

READING The average rate of change in elevation is the total change in elevation divided by the number of years that have passed.

LAKES In 1900 the elevation of Mono Lake in California was about 6416 feet. From 1900 to 1950, the average rate of change in elevation was about −0.12 foot per year. From 1950 to 2000, the average rate of change was about −0.526 foot per year. Approximate the elevation in 2000.

Solution

STEP 1 **Write** a verbal model.

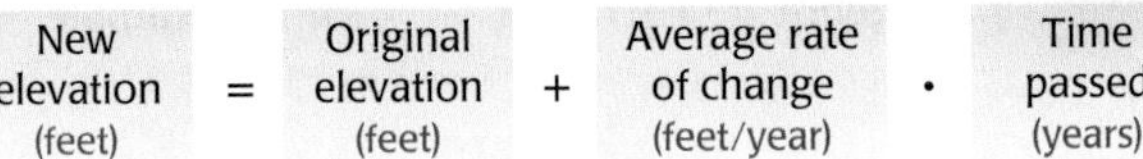

STEP 2 **Calculate** the elevation in 1950. Use the elevation in 1900 as the original elevation. The time span is 1950 − 1900 = 50 years.

New elevation $= 6416 + (-0.12)(50)$	**Substitute values.**
$= 6416 + (-6)$	**Multiply −0.12 and 50.**
$= 6410$	**Add 6416 and −6.**

CHECK REASONABLENESS In Step 2, note that $-0.12(50) \approx -0.1(50) = -5$, and $6416 + (-5) = 6411$, so 6410 is reasonable. In Step 3, $-0.526(50) \approx -0.5(50) = -25$, and $6410 + (-25) = 6385$, so 6383.7 is reasonable.

STEP 3 **Calculate** the elevation in 2000. Use the elevation in 1950 as the original elevation. The time span is 2000 − 1950 = 50 years.

New elevation $= 6410 + (-0.526)(50)$	**Substitute values.**
$= 6410 + (-26.3)$	**Multiply −0.526 and 50.**
$= 6383.7$	**Add 6410 and −26.3.**

▶ The elevation in 2000 was about 6383.7 feet above sea level.

✓ **GUIDED PRACTICE** for Examples 3 and 4

Find the product. *Justify* your steps. **10–12. See margin.**

10. $\frac{3}{10}(5y)$ **11.** $0.8(-x)(-1)$ **12.** $(-y)(-0.5)(-6)$

13. Using the data in Example 4, approximate the elevation of Mono Lake in 1925 and in 1965. **about 6413 ft; about 6402.11 ft**

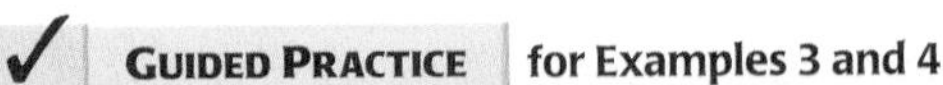

Differentiated Instruction

Advanced When discussing **Example 4,** have advanced students use the average rate of change from 1950 to 2000 to predict when the elevation of Lake Mono will be about 6300 feet. Suggest they use a spreadsheet to make their prediction. They can write a formula for the spreadsheet using the information in the example. Some students may be interested in learning about the environmental effects of the change in elevation. They can share their research with the class.

See also the *Differentiated Instruction Resources* for more strategies.

2.4 EXERCISES

HOMEWORK KEY

○ = **WORKED-OUT SOLUTIONS** on p. WS4 for Exs. 11, 31, and 51

★ = **STANDARDIZED TEST PRACTICE** Exs. 2, 48, 52, 53, and 55

◆ = **MULTIPLE REPRESENTATIONS** Ex. 54

SKILL PRACTICE

A

1. **VOCABULARY** What number is called the multiplicative identity? **1**

2. ★ **WRITING** *Describe* the difference between the identity property of multiplication and the multiplicative property of -1. **See margin.**

EXAMPLE 1 on p. 88 for Exs. 3–18

FINDING PRODUCTS **Find the product.**

3. $-4(7)$ **−28**
4. $11(-2)$ **−22**
5. $-9(-10)$ **90**
6. $-8(-11)$ **88**
7. $5(-7.2)$ **−36**
8. $(-2.5)(-1.3)$ **3.25**
9. $-42\left(-\frac{1}{6}\right)$ **7**
10. $-\frac{1}{2}(-32)$ **16**
11. $-1.9(3.3)(7)$ **−43.89**
12. $0.5(-20)(-3)$ **30**
13. $-\frac{5}{6}(-12)(-4)$ **−40**
14. $-\frac{3}{4}(2)(-6)$ **9**
15. $-8(-4)(-2.5)$ **−80**
16. $-1.6(-2)(-10)$ **−32**
17. $18\left(-\frac{2}{3}\right)\left(-\frac{1}{5}\right)$ $\mathbf{2\frac{2}{5}}$
18. $-\frac{3}{4}\left(-\frac{1}{3}\right)\left(-\frac{8}{9}\right)$ $\mathbf{-\frac{2}{9}}$

EXAMPLE 2 on p. 89 for Exs. 19–27

IDENTIFYING PROPERTIES **Identify the property illustrated.** **19–27. See margin.**

19. $-\frac{2}{5} \cdot 0 = 0$
20. $0.3 \cdot (-3) = -3 \cdot 0.3$
21. $-143 \cdot 1 = -143$
22. $-1 \cdot (-6) = 6$
23. $(-2 \cdot 5) \cdot 4 = -2 \cdot (5 \cdot 4)$
24. $0 \cdot (-76.3) = 0$
25. $1 \cdot (ab) = ab$
26. $(3x)y = 3(xy)$
27. $s \cdot (-1) = -s$

EXAMPLE 3 on p. 90 for Exs. 28–36

USING PROPERTIES **Find the product. *Justify* your steps.** **28–36. See margin.**

28. $y(-2)(-8)$
29. $-18(-x)$
30. $\frac{3}{5}(-5q)$
31. $-2(-6)(-7z)$
32. $-5(-4)(-2.1)(-z)$
33. $-\frac{1}{5}(-10)(4)(-5c)$
34. $-5t(-t)$
35. $-6r(-2.8r)$
36. $\frac{1}{3}\left(-\frac{9}{10}\right)(-m)(-m)$

B

EVALUATING EXPRESSIONS **Evaluate the expression when $x = -2$ and $y = 3.6$.**

37. $2x + y$ **−0.4**
38. $-x - 3y$ **−8.8**
39. $xy - 5.4$ **−12.6**
40. $|y| - 4x$ **11.6**
41. $1.5x - |-y|$ **−6.6**
42. $x^2 - y^2$ **−8.96**

ERROR ANALYSIS ***Describe*** **and correct the error in finding the product.**

43.
$$-1(7)(-3)(-2x) = 7(-3)(-2x)$$
$$= -21(-2x)$$
$$= [-21 \cdot (-2)]x$$
$$= 42x$$

44.
$$(-5z)(-8)(z) = (-8)(-5z)(z)$$
$$= (-8)(-5)(z)(z)$$
$$= -40(z \cdot z)$$
$$= -40z^2$$

43. $-1(7) = -7$, not 7; $-1(7)(-3)(-2x) = -7(-3)(-2x) = 21(-2x) = [21 \cdot (-2)]x = -42x$

44. $(-8)(-5) = 40$, not -40; $(-8)(-5)(z)(z) = 40(z \cdot z) = 40z^2$

4 PRACTICE AND APPLY

Assignment Guide

Answer Transparencies available for all exercises

Basic:
Day 1: pp. 91–93
Exs. 1–11, 19–41 odd, 43, 44, 50–54, 58–64 even

Average:
Day 1: pp. 91–93
Exs. 1, 2, 10–42 even, 43–48, 50–55, 58–64 even

Advanced:
Day 1: pp. 91–93
Exs. 1, 2, 12–42 even, 43–49*, 51–56*, 57–63 odd

Block:
pp. 91–93
Exs. 1, 2, 10–42 even, 43–48, 50–55, 58–64 even (with 2.5)

Differentiated Instruction

See *Differentiated Instruction Resources* for suggestions on addressing the needs of a diverse classroom.

Homework Check

For a quick check of student understanding of key concepts, go over the following exercises:

Basic: 7, 21, 29, 37, 50
Average: 12, 22, 32, 38, 51
Advanced: 16, 26, 34, 40, 52

Extra Practice

- Student Edition, p. 939
- Chapter Resource Book: Practice levels A, B, C

Practice Worksheet

An easily-readable reduced practice page (with answers) for this lesson can be found on p. 62C.

2. ***Sample answer:*** **The identity property of multiplication states that the product of a number and 1 is the number. The multiplicative property of −1 states that the product of a number and −1 is the *opposite* of the number.**

19. Multiplicative property of zero
20. Commutative property of multiplication
21. Identity property of multiplication
22. Multiplicative property of −1
23. Associative property of multiplication
24. Multiplicative property of zero
25. Identity property of multiplication
26. Associative property of multiplication
27. Multiplicative property of −1
28–36. See Additional Answers beginning on p. AA1.

Mathematical Reasoning

Exercise 48 Suggest that students use numbers to help them determine which statement must be true. Ask "If *a* is –1, what must be the signs of *b* and *c* for the product of *abc* to be positive?" Lead students to see that one of the factors must be positive and one must be negative. They can then test their reasoning against each of the statements.

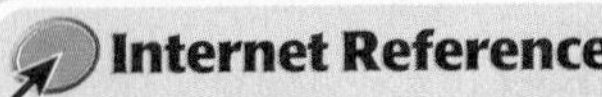

Exercise 52 Students may want to use their calculators to find the volume of the glaciers. Remind them to use the negative key to enter the rates of change.

Internet Reference

Exercise 52 Additional information about Mount Rainier can be found on the National Park Service website at http://www.nps.gov/mora.

Avoiding Common Errors

Exercise 53 Some students may use –2 as the rate of change. Point out that the rate of change is in millimeters and the maximum clearance between the water and the Rialto Bridge is in meters. Students need to change millimeters to meters.

Study Strategy

Exercises 54–55 Suggest that students create spreadsheets for both of these exercises. They can use the equations from part a of the exercises to write a formula for the spreadsheet. This will enable them to find their answers quickly, particularly for parts b and c in Exercise 55.

An **Animated Algebra** activity is available online for **Exercise 54**. This activity is also part of **Power Presentations**.

REASONING **In Exercises 45–47, tell whether the statement is *true* or *false*. If it is false, give a counterexample.**

45. If x is negative, then x^2 is positive. **true**

46. If the product abc is positive, then a, b, and c are all positive. **False. *Sample answer:* $(-1)(-2)(3) = 6$**

47. If the product of four numbers is 0, then at least one of the numbers is 0. **true**

48. ★ **MULTIPLE CHOICE** If $a < 0$ and $abc > 0$, which statement must be true? **B**

Ⓐ $bc > 0$ Ⓑ $bc < 0$ Ⓒ $ac > 0$ Ⓓ $ab < 0$

C 49. **CHALLENGE** For $x \neq 0$, compare the values of the expressions for each case described. Give examples to support your answers. **See margin.**

a. $|x|$ and $|kx|$ when $-1 < k < 1$, when $k < -1$, and when $k > 1$

b. x and x^2 when $x < 0$, when $0 < x < 1$, and when $x > 1$

PROBLEM SOLVING

EXAMPLE 4 A on p. 90 for Exs. 50–53

50. **DEAD SEA** In 1940 the surface area of the Dead Sea was about 980 square kilometers. From 1940 to 2001, the average rate of change in surface area was about -5.7 square kilometers per year. Find the surface area of the Dead Sea in 2001. **about 632.3 km^2**

@HomeTutor for problem solving help at classzone.com

51. **STOCKS** An investor purchases 50 shares of a stock at \$3.50 per share. The next day, the change in value of a share of the stock is $-\$.25$. What is the total value of the shares the next day? **\$162.50**

@HomeTutor for problem solving help at classzone.com

52b. about -0.47658 km^3; find the total change in the volume of the glaciers between 1913 and 1994, then multiply the change by $\frac{1}{3}$.

52. ★ **SHORT RESPONSE** In 1913 the total volume of glaciers on Mount Rainier was 5.62 km^3. The table shows the average rate of change in the volume for two time periods.

Time period	Rate of change (km^3/yr)
1913–1971	-0.02241
1971–1994	-0.00565

a. Find the total volume of the glaciers in 1971 and in 1994. Use estimation to check that your answer is reasonable. **See margin.**

b. About one third of the change in volume during the period 1913–1994 took place in the northeastern glaciers. Find the change in the volume of the northeastern glaciers. *Explain* your steps.

53. ★ **MULTIPLE CHOICE** The Rialto Bridge in Venice, Italy, is a footbridge built in the late 16th century. The maximum clearance between the water and the bridge is about 7.32 meters. Because of a rising sea level and a gradual sinking of the city, the clearance changes at an average rate of about -2 millimeters per year. Approximate the clearance after 15 years. **C**

Ⓐ 5.32 meters Ⓑ 7.02 meters

Ⓒ 7.29 meters Ⓓ 7.318 meters

○ = WORKED-OUT SOLUTIONS on p. WS1 ★ = STANDARDIZED TEST PRACTICE ◆ = MULTIPLE REPRESENTATIONS

49a. If $x \neq 0$, then $|x| > |kx|$ when $-1 < k < 0$ or when $0 < k < 1$. If $x \neq 0$, then $|x| < |kx|$ when $k < -1$ or when $k > 1$.

49b. If $x < 0$, or if $x > 1$, then $x < x^2$. If $0 < x < 1$, then $x > x^2$.

52a. 4.32022 km^3; 4.19027 km^3; $5.62 \approx 5.6$, the period 1913–1971 is about 60 years, and $-0.02241 \approx -0.02$, so the volume of the glaciers in 1971 was about $5.6 + 60(-0.02) = 4.4$ km^3, which suggests that 4.32022 km^3 is reasonable. $4.32022 \approx 4.3$, the period 1971–1994 is about 20 years, and $-0.00565 \approx -0.006$, so the volume of the glaciers in 1994 was about $4.3 + 20(-0.006) = 4.18$ km^3, which suggests that 4.19027 km^3 is reasonable.

B **54.** **MULTIPLE REPRESENTATIONS** A skydiver in free fall will eventually reach a constant velocity, called terminal velocity. A skydiver reaches a terminal velocity of −160 feet per second at an altitude of 3200 feet.

4400 feet: Plane flies at this altitude.
3200 feet: Skydiver reaches terminal velocity.
2500 feet: Parachute opens.

a. Writing an Equation Write an equation for the altitude a (in feet) of the skydiver as a function of the time t (in seconds) after reaching terminal velocity. **$a = 3200 + (-160t)$**

b. Making a Table Make a table of values for $t = 1, 2, 3, 4$, and 5 seconds. The skydiver wants to open the parachute after reaching an altitude of about 2500 feet. After how many seconds should the skydiver open the parachute? **See margin.**

Animated Algebra at classzone.com

55. ★ **EXTENDED RESPONSE** The table shows the fuel capacities of two ferries in Puget Sound, Washington, and the average rates of change in tank fuel when the ferries are burning fuel.

Ferry	Fuel capacity (gal)	Rate of change (gal/h)
Rhododendron	11,250	−30
Spokane	135,000	−240

a. Model For each ferry, write an equation that gives the amount of tank fuel f (in gallons) as a function of the time t (in hours) that fuel is burned. **$f = 11{,}250 + (-30t)$, $f = 135{,}000 + (-240t)$**

b. Calculate Both ferries start with a full tank. How many gallons of fuel will each ferry have left after 3 hours? **11,160 gal, 134,280 gal**

c. Explain If both ferries continue to burn fuel without refueling, which ferry will run out of fuel first? How many gallons will the other ferry have at that time? Your answer should include the following: **See margin.**

- the number of hours that each ferry will take to burn all of its fuel
- an explanation of how you used the equations in part (a)

C **56.** **CHALLENGE** Due to soil erosion, the surface area of Dongting Lake in China is decreasing. Its surface area was about 2626.5 square kilometers in 1995. From 1950 to 1995, the average rate of change in surface area was about −38.3 square kilometers per year. From 1825 to 1950, the average rate of change was about −13.2 square kilometers per year. Approximate the surface area in 1825. **6000 km²**

MIXED REVIEW

PREVIEW Prepare for Lesson 2.5 in Exs. 57–60.

Evaluate the expression for the given value of the variable. *(p. 8)*

57. $1 + 9y^2$ when $y = 3$ **82**

58. $z^2 \cdot 2$ when $z = 6$ **72**

59. $2(x - 19)$ when $x = 24$ **10**

60. $9(17 + w)$ when $w = 8$ **225**

Find the sum or difference.

61. $-3 + (-6)$ *(p. 74)* **−9**

62. $7.8 + (-6.4) + (-9.4)$ *(p. 74)* **−8**

63. $-19.4 - (-6.4)$ *(p. 80)* **−13**

64. $-\frac{4}{7} - \frac{3}{14}$ *(p. 80)* **$-\frac{11}{14}$**

54b.

t	$3200 + (-160t)$
1	3040
2	2880
3	2720
4	2560
5	2400

4 sec

5 ASSESS AND RETEACH

Daily Homework Quiz

Transparency Available

Find the product.

1. $-6.5(4)(-2)$ **52**

2. $7.4(-1.2)(3)$ **−26.64**

Identify the property illustrated.

3. $r \cdot 0 = 0$ **Multiplicative property of zero**

4. $-y \cdot (-1) = y$ **Multiplicative property of −1**

5. Since Javier began setting his thermostat lower, his energy bills have been declining at a rate of −0.88 dollar per year. If his average bill was $130 in 1990, estimate his average bill in 2005. **$116.80**

Available at **classzone.com**

Diagnosis/Remediation

- Practice A, B, C in Chapter Resource Book
- Study Guide in Chapter Resource Book
- Practice Workbook
- @HomeTutor

Challenge

Additional challenge is available in the Chapter Resource Book.

55c. Rhododendron; 45,000 gal; the Rhododendron takes 375 hours to burn all of its fuel; the Spokane takes 562.5 hours to burn all of its fuel; to find the number of hours the Rhododendron will take to burn all its fuel, use the equations in part (a) and find the additive inverse of 11,250, then divide it by −30; to find the number of hours the Spokane will take to burn all its fuel, use the equations in part (a) and find the additive inverse of 135,000, then divide it by −240.

1 PLAN AND PREPARE

Warm-Up Exercises

Perform the indicated operation.

1. $12.1 + (-15.2)$ **−3.1**
2. $-6 - (-9.8)$ **3.8**
3. $-15(-2.4)$ **36**
4. $4.8 \cdot (-5.5)(3)$ **−79.2**

2 FOCUS AND MOTIVATE

Essential Question

Big Idea 1, p. 63

How do you perform operations on matrices? **Tell students they will learn how to answer this question by adding and subtracting two matrices and by performing scalar multiplication.**

3 TEACH

Extra Example 1

Perform the indicated operation, if possible.

a. $\begin{bmatrix} 10 & -4 & -2 \\ 4 & -6 & 5 \end{bmatrix} - \begin{bmatrix} 11 & -1 & 3 \\ -4 & 0 & -8 \end{bmatrix}$ $\begin{bmatrix} -1 & -3 & -5 \\ 8 & -6 & 13 \end{bmatrix}$

b. $\begin{bmatrix} -5 & 14 & 0 \\ 6 & -7 & -4 \end{bmatrix} + \begin{bmatrix} -5 & -11 & -3 \\ -3 & -1 & 4 \end{bmatrix}$ $\begin{bmatrix} -10 & 3 & -3 \\ 3 & -8 & 0 \end{bmatrix}$

NCTM STANDARDS

Standard 2: Understand patterns

Standard 9: Use connections among mathematical ideas

Extension

Use after Lesson 2.4

Perform Matrix Addition, Subtraction, Scalar Multiplication

GOAL Perform operations on matrices.

Key Vocabulary
- matrix
- dimensions of a matrix
- element
- scalar multiplication
- scalar

A **matrix** is a rectangular arrangement of numbers in rows and columns. If a matrix has m rows and n columns, the **dimensions of the matrix** are written as $m \times n$. For example, matrix A below has two rows and three columns. The dimensions of matrix A are 2×3 (read "2 by 3"). Each number in a matrix is called an **element**, or *entry*. In matrix A, the element in the first row and second column is 4.

$$A = \begin{bmatrix} 0 & 4 & -1 \\ -3 & 2 & 5 \end{bmatrix} \text{ 2 rows}$$

3 columns

MATRIX ADDITION AND SUBTRACTION To add or subtract matrices (the plural of *matrix*), you add or subtract corresponding elements. You can add or subtract matrices only if they have the same dimensions.

EXAMPLE 1 **Add or subtract two matrices**

Perform the indicated operation, if possible.

a. $$\begin{bmatrix} 0 & 4 & -1 \\ -3 & 2 & 5 \end{bmatrix} + \begin{bmatrix} 2 & 1 & 3 \\ -2 & -6 & 4 \end{bmatrix} = \begin{bmatrix} 0+2 & 4+1 & -1+3 \\ -3+(-2) & 2+(-6) & 5+4 \end{bmatrix}$$

$$= \begin{bmatrix} 2 & 5 & 2 \\ -5 & -4 & 9 \end{bmatrix}$$

b. $$\begin{bmatrix} -10 & 2 \\ -4 & 7 \\ 7 & -13 \end{bmatrix} - \begin{bmatrix} 9 & -2 \\ 4 & 8 \\ -5 & -11 \end{bmatrix} = \begin{bmatrix} -10-9 & 2-(-2) \\ -4-4 & 7-8 \\ 7-(-5) & -13-(-11) \end{bmatrix}$$

$$= \begin{bmatrix} -10+(-9) & 2+2 \\ -4+(-4) & 7+(-8) \\ 7+5 & -13+11 \end{bmatrix}$$

$$= \begin{bmatrix} -19 & 4 \\ -8 & -1 \\ 12 & -2 \end{bmatrix}$$

c. You can't perform the subtraction $\begin{bmatrix} 6 & -4 & -8 \end{bmatrix} - \begin{bmatrix} 1 \\ 12 \\ -6 \end{bmatrix}$ because the first matrix is a 1×3 matrix and the second matrix is a 3×1 matrix.

SCALAR MULTIPLICATION In **scalar multiplication**, every element in a matrix is multiplied by a real number called a **scalar**.

EXAMPLE 2 Perform scalar multiplication

Perform the indicated operation.

a. $6\begin{bmatrix}-7 & -\frac{1}{3}\\ \frac{1}{2} & 11\end{bmatrix} = \begin{bmatrix}6(-7) & 6\left(-\frac{1}{3}\right)\\ 6\left(\frac{1}{2}\right) & 6(11)\end{bmatrix} = \begin{bmatrix}-42 & -2\\ 3 & 66\end{bmatrix}$

b. $-2\begin{bmatrix}0.5\\ -3.2\\ 8.1\end{bmatrix} = \begin{bmatrix}-2(0.5)\\ -2(-3.2)\\ -2(8.1)\end{bmatrix} = \begin{bmatrix}-1\\ 6.4\\ -16.2\end{bmatrix}$

PRACTICE

EXAMPLES 1 and 2 on pp. 94–95 for Exs. 1–10

Perform the indicated operation, if possible.

1. $\begin{bmatrix}7 & 6\\ 3 & 2\end{bmatrix} + \begin{bmatrix}9 & -2\\ 5 & 10\end{bmatrix}$ $\begin{bmatrix}16 & 4\\ 8 & 12\end{bmatrix}$

2. $\begin{bmatrix}-8\\ -4\\ 1\end{bmatrix} + \begin{bmatrix}11\\ -9\\ -6\end{bmatrix}$ $\begin{bmatrix}3\\ -13\\ -5\end{bmatrix}$

3. $\begin{bmatrix}-8 & -1 & -9\\ -4 & -3 & 2\end{bmatrix} - \begin{bmatrix}7 & 3 & 0\\ -2 & -5 & 7\end{bmatrix}$ See margin.

4. $\begin{bmatrix}11 & -12\\ 15 & -22\end{bmatrix} - \begin{bmatrix}7\\ 8\end{bmatrix}$ Cannot be performed.

5. $\begin{bmatrix}-9.1 & 5.4 & 3.7\end{bmatrix} + \begin{bmatrix}1.3 & -6.7\end{bmatrix}$ Cannot be performed.

6. $\begin{bmatrix}\frac{3}{4} & -2\\ 6 & -3\end{bmatrix} - \begin{bmatrix}8 & -2\\ 6 & -\frac{5}{6}\end{bmatrix}$ $\begin{bmatrix}-7\frac{1}{4} & 0\\ 0 & -2\frac{1}{6}\end{bmatrix}$

7. $7\begin{bmatrix}-4 & -7\\ \frac{1}{2} & \frac{4}{9}\end{bmatrix}$ $\begin{bmatrix}-28 & -49\\ 3\frac{1}{2} & 3\frac{1}{9}\end{bmatrix}$

8. $2\begin{bmatrix}1.5 & -6\\ -4.5 & 0\end{bmatrix}$ $\begin{bmatrix}3 & -12\\ -9 & 0\end{bmatrix}$

9. $-6\begin{bmatrix}12\\ -3.4\\ -0.7\end{bmatrix}$ $\begin{bmatrix}-72\\ 20.4\\ 4.2\end{bmatrix}$

10. $-\frac{1}{2}\begin{bmatrix}18 & -26 & \frac{7}{4}\\ -\frac{2}{3} & 20 & -2\end{bmatrix}$ $\begin{bmatrix}-9 & 13 & -\frac{7}{8}\\ \frac{1}{3} & -10 & 1\end{bmatrix}$

11. **NUTRITION** The matrix shows the amounts (in milligrams) of calcium and potassium in one ounce of different types of milk. Write a matrix for the amounts of calcium and potassium in 8 ounces of each type of milk.

	Calcium (mg)	Potassium (mg)	Calcium (mg)	Potassium (mg)
Lowfat milk	32.940	36.295	263.52	290.36
Reduced fat milk	33.855	42.700	270.84	341.6
Whole milk	30.805	40.565	246.44	324.52

CHALLENGE Perform the indicated operations.

12. $9\left(\begin{bmatrix}1 & -12 & 8\\ -7 & 10 & -4\end{bmatrix} + \begin{bmatrix}3 & -3 & -7\\ -5 & -21 & -12\end{bmatrix}\right)$ See margin.

13. $\begin{bmatrix}-6 & -8\\ 8 & 14\end{bmatrix} - 7\begin{bmatrix}5 & 13\\ -10 & -11\end{bmatrix}$ $\begin{bmatrix}-41 & -99\\ 78 & 91\end{bmatrix}$

Extra Example 2

Perform the indicated operation.

a. $4\begin{bmatrix}-8 & 0.5\\ \frac{1}{4} & -\frac{1}{2}\end{bmatrix}$ $\begin{bmatrix}-32 & 2\\ 1 & -2\end{bmatrix}$

b. $-2\begin{bmatrix}-1.6\\ 2.4\\ -5.5\end{bmatrix}$ $\begin{bmatrix}3.2\\ -4.8\\ 11\end{bmatrix}$

Closing the Lesson

Have students summarize the major points of the lesson and answer the Essential Question: How do you perform operations on matrices?

- **Matrices must have the same dimensions to add or subtract.**
- **To perform scalar multiplication, multiply each element in the matrix by the scalar.**

To add or subtract matrices with the same dimensions, add or subtract corresponding elements. For scalar multiplication, multiply all elements in the matrix by the scalar.

4 PRACTICE AND APPLY

Avoiding Common Errors

Exercises 1–10 Instruct students to write out the solutions, using Examples 1 and 2 as models. This will help them avoid adding, subtracting, or multiplying the wrong elements. It will also help them tell when two matrices do not have the same dimensions.

Reading Strategy

Exercise 11 For students who are having trouble solving this problem, ask whether it would make sense to add 8 ounces to find the number of milligrams of calcium and potassium, to subtract 8 ounces, or to multiply by 8 ounces.

3. $\begin{bmatrix}-15 & -4 & -9\\ -2 & 2 & -5\end{bmatrix}$

12. $\begin{bmatrix}36 & -135 & 9\\ -108 & -99 & -144\end{bmatrix}$

2.5 Apply the Distributive Property

Before You used properties to add and multiply real numbers.
Now You will apply the distributive property.
Why? So you can find calories burned, as in Example 5.

1 PLAN AND PREPARE

Warm-Up Exercises

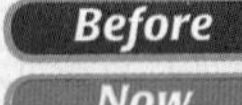

Transparency Available

1. $-15 + (-19) + 16 = \underline{?}$ **-18**
2. $6(-x)(-4) = \underline{?}$ **$24x$**
3. $-9(-2)(-4b) = \underline{?}$ **$-72b$**
4. Kristin paid \$1.90 per black-and-white photo b and \$6.80 per color photo c to have some photos restored. What was the total amount A that she paid if she had 8 black-and-white and 12 color photos restored? **\$96.80**

Notetaking Guide

Transparency Available

Promotes interactive learning and notetaking skills.

Pacing

Basic: 2 days
Average: 2 days
Advanced: 2 days
Block: 0.5 block with 2.4
0.5 block with 2.6

- See *Teaching Guide/Lesson Plan*.

2 FOCUS AND MOTIVATE

Essential Question

Big Idea 2, p. 63

How do you use the distributive property to simplify expressions? **Tell students they will learn how to answer this question by rewriting expressions.**

NCTM STANDARDS

Standard 1: Understand how operations are related

Standard 2: Represent situations using algebraic symbols

Key Vocabulary
- **equivalent expressions**
- **distributive property**
- **term**
- **coefficient**
- **constant term**
- **like terms**

The models below show two methods for finding the area of a rectangle that has a length of $(x + 2)$ units and a width of 3 units.

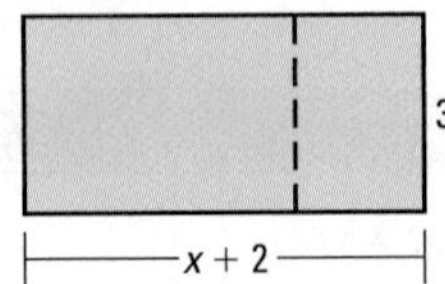

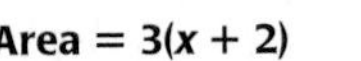

Area = 3(x + 2)

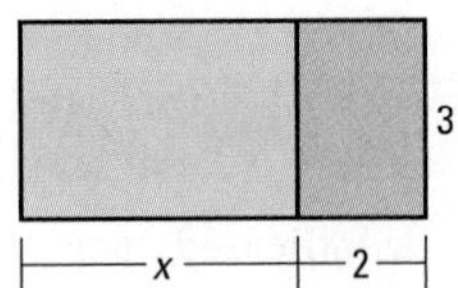

Area = 3(x) + 3(2)

The expressions $3(x + 2)$ and $3(x) + 3(2)$ are equivalent because they represent the same area. Two expressions that have the same value for all values of the variable are called **equivalent expressions**. The equation $3(x + 2) = 3(x) + 3(2)$ illustrates the **distributive property**, which can be used to find the product of a number and a sum or difference.

KEY CONCEPT *For Your Notebook*

The Distributive Property

Let a, b, and c be real numbers.

Words	Algebra	Examples
The product of a and $(b + c)$:	$a(b + c) = ab + ac$	$3(4 + 2) = 3(4) + 3(2)$
	$(b + c)a = ba + ca$	$(3 + 5)2 = 3(2) + 5(2)$
The product of a and $(b - c)$:	$a(b - c) = ab - ac$	$5(6 - 4) = 5(6) - 5(4)$
	$(b - c)a = ba - ca$	$(8 - 6)4 = 8(4) - 6(4)$

EXAMPLE 1 Apply the distributive property

AVOID ERRORS
Be sure to distribute the factor outside of the parentheses to *all* of the numbers inside the parentheses, not just to the first number.

Use the distributive property to write an equivalent expression.

a. $4(y + 3) = 4y + 12$

b. $(y + 7)y = y^2 + 7y$

c. $n(n - 9) = n^2 - 9n$

d. $(2 - n)8 = 16 - 8n$

Resource Planning Guide

Chapter Resource Book
- Teaching Guide/Lesson Plan
- Activity Master
- Practice levels A, B, C
- Study Guide
- Catch-up for Absent Students
- Problem Solving Workshop
- Challenge

Workbooks
- Notetaking Guide
- Practice Workbook

Teaching Options
- **Power Presentations** provides dynamic electronic teaching resources for the classroom.
- **Activity Generator** provides editable activities for all ability levels.

Interactive Technology
- Easy Planner
- Power Presentations
- Activity Generator
- Animated Algebra
- Test Generator
- Online Quiz
- eWorkbook
- eEdition
- @HomeTutor

Resources for English Learners
- Spanish Study Guide
- Multi-Language Visual Glossary
- Student Resources in Spanish

See also the *Differentiated Instruction Resources* for more strategies for meeting individual needs.

EXAMPLE 2 Distribute a negative number

Use the distributive property to write an equivalent expression.

a. $-2(x+7) = -2(x) + (-2)(7)$ — **Distribute −2.**

$= -2x - 14$ — **Simplify.**

b. $(5-y)(-3y) = 5(-3y) - y(-3y)$ — **Distribute −3y.**

$= -15y + 3y^2$ — **Simplify.**

c. $-(2x-11) = (-1)(2x-11)$ — **Multiplicative property of −1**

$= (-1)(2x) - (-1)(11)$ — **Distribute −1.**

$= -2x + 11$ — **Simplify.**

TERMS AND COEFFICIENTS The parts of an expression that are added together are called **terms**. The number part of a term with a variable part is called the **coefficient** of the term.

READING Note that $-x$ has a coefficient of −1 even though the 1 isn't written. Similarly, x has a coefficient of 1.

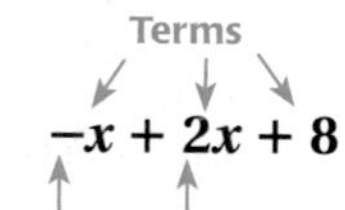

A **constant term** has a number part but no variable part, such as 8 in the expression above. **Like terms** are terms that have the same variable parts, such as $-x$ and $2x$ in the expression above. Constant terms are also like terms.

EXAMPLE 3 Identify parts of an expression

Identify the terms, like terms, coefficients, and constant terms of the expression $3x - 4 - 6x + 2$.

Solution

Write the expression as a sum: $3x + (-4) + (-6x) + 2$

Terms: $3x, -4, -6x, 2$ — **Like terms:** $3x$ and $-6x$; −4 and 2

Coefficients: 3, −6 — **Constant terms:** −4, 2

✓ GUIDED PRACTICE for Examples 1, 2, and 3

Use the distributive property to write an equivalent expression.

1. $2(x+3)$ $2x + 6$

2. $-(4-y)$ $-4 + y$

3. $(m-5)(-3m)$ $-3m^2 + 15m$

4. $(2n+6)\left(\frac{1}{2}\right)$ $n + 3$

5. Identify the terms, like terms, coefficients, and constant terms of the expression $-7y + 8 - 6y - 13$.
terms: $-7y, 8, -6y, -13$; like terms: $-7y$ and $-6y$, 8 and −13; coefficients: −7, −6; constant terms: 8, −13

COMBINING LIKE TERMS The distributive property allows you to combine like terms that have variable parts. For example, $5x + 6x = (5+6)x = 11x$. A quick way to combine like terms with variable parts is to mentally add the coefficients and use the common variable part. An expression is *simplified* if it has no grouping symbols and if all of the like terms have been combined.

Differentiated Instruction

Kinesthetic Learners When students apply the distributive property, some of them may find it helpful to draw arrows as shown in **Example 1**. Furthermore, students may find it helpful to place one fingertip on the page and trace the arrows.

See also the *Differentiated Instruction Resources* for more strategies.

Motivating the Lesson

Knowing how to use the distributive property can make calculations easier. For example, suppose the coach of the swim team buys 12 T-shirts for \$11.96 each. By learning how to use the distributive property, you will be able to use mental math to find that the T-shirts cost \$143.52.

3 TEACH

Extra Example 1

Use the distributive property to write an equivalent expression.

a. $3(x+6)$ **$3x + 18$**

b. $(n+5)n$ **$n^2 + 5n$**

c. $y(y-12)$ **$y^2 - 12y$**

d. $(8-x)9$ **$72 - 9x$**

Reading Strategy

When discussing Example 1, have students read "Avoid Errors." Point out that the arrows in each part of the example show where to distribute the factor that is outside the parentheses.

Extra Example 2

Use the distributive property to write an equivalent expression.

a. $(y-2)(-4)$ **$-4y + 8$**

b. $-5x(4-x)$ **$-20x + 5x^2$**

c. $-(3y-9)$ **$-3y + 9$**

Key Question to Ask for Example 2

- When you distribute −1, what happens to the signs in the parentheses? **They change to their opposites.**

Extra Example 3

Identify the terms, like terms, coefficients, and constant terms of the expression $-2x - 8 + 6x + 5$. **Terms: $-2x, -8, 6x, 5$; Like terms: $-2x$ and $6x$, −8 and 5; Coefficients: −2, 6; Constant terms: −8, 5**

Extra Example 4

Which expression is equivalent to $6(x + 3) - 2(8 + x)$? A

Ⓐ $4x + 2$ Ⓑ $4x + 34$

Ⓒ $8x + 2$ Ⓓ $8x + 34$

Extra Example 5

Ms. Jenkins rented a rototiller from a garden shop. The rental charge is \$28 per day for the first two days and then \$15 per day for each additional day. If Ms. Jenkins kept the rototiller for 13 days, what was the total rental charge? **\$221**

Key Question to Ask for Example 5

- Why is the swimming time represented by $50 - r$? **The swimming time is the time left from the total time after running. Since the total time is 50 minutes and the running time is *r* minutes, the swimming time must be $(50 - r)$ minutes.**

An **Animated Algebra** activity is available online for **Example 5**. This activity is also part of **Power Presentations**.

Closing the Lesson

Have students summarize the major points of the lesson and answer the Essential Question: How do you use the distributive property to simplify expressions?

- **Distribute the outside factor in expressions to all of the terms inside the parentheses.**
- **Expressions are sums of variables and constant terms.**

Use the distributive property to write equivalent expressions without parentheses. Then combine like terms to simplify expressions.

EXAMPLE 4 Standardized Test Practice

Simplify the expression $4(n + 9) - 3(2 + n)$.

Ⓐ $5n + 30$ Ⓑ $n + 30$ Ⓒ $5n + 3$ Ⓓ $n + 3$

ANOTHER WAY
In Example 4, you can rewrite the expression $4(n + 9) - 3(2 + n)$ as $4(n + 9) + (-3)(2 + n)$ and then distribute -3 to the terms in $2 + n$.

$4(n + 9) - 3(2 + n) = 4n + 36 - 6 - 3n$ **Distributive property**

$= n + 30$ **Combine like terms.**

▶ The correct answer is B. Ⓐ Ⓑ Ⓒ Ⓓ

EXAMPLE 5 Solve a multi-step problem

EXERCISING Your daily workout plan involves a total of 50 minutes of running and swimming. You burn 15 calories per minute when running and 9 calories per minute when swimming. Let *r* be the number of minutes that you run. Find the number of calories you burn in your 50 minute workout if you run for 20 minutes.

ANOTHER WAY
For an alternative method for solving the problem in Example 5, turn to page 102 for the **Problem Solving Workshop**.

Solution

The workout lasts 50 minutes, and your running time is *r* minutes. So, your swimming time is $(50 - r)$ minutes.

STEP 1 **Write** a verbal model. Then write an equation.

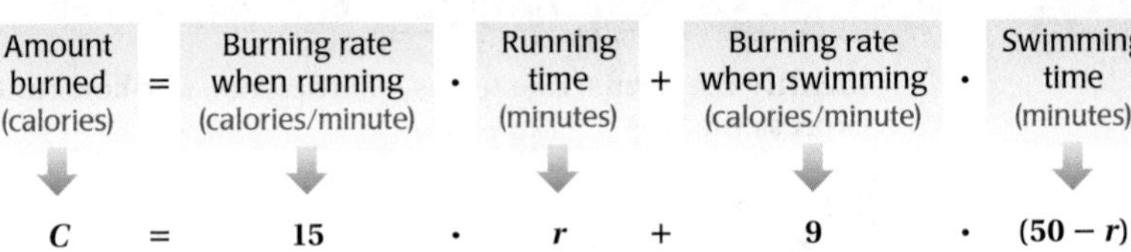

$C \quad = \quad 15 \quad \cdot \quad r \quad + \quad 9 \quad \cdot \quad (50 - r)$

$C = 15r + 9(50 - r)$ **Write equation.**

$= 15r + 450 - 9r$ **Distributive property**

$= 6r + 450$ **Combine like terms.**

STEP 2 **Find** the value of *C* when $r = 20$.

$C = 6r + 450$ **Write equation.**

$= 6(20) + 450 = 570$ **Substitute 20 for *r*. Then simplify.**

▶ You burn 570 calories in your 50 minute workout if you run for 20 minutes.

Animated Algebra at classzone.com

✓ **GUIDED PRACTICE** for Examples 4 and 5

6. Simplify the expression $5(6 + n) - 2(n - 2)$. **$34 + 3n$**

7. **WHAT IF?** In Example 5, suppose your workout lasts 45 minutes. How many calories do you burn if you run for 20 minutes? 30 minutes? **525 calories; 585 calories**

21. terms: $-7, 13x, 2x, 8$; like terms: -7 and 8, $13x$ and $2x$; coefficients: 13, 2; constant terms: $-7, 8$

22. terms: $9, 7y, -2, -5y$; like terms: 9 and -2, $7y$ and $-5y$; coefficients: 7, -5; constant terms: 9, -2

2.5 EXERCISES

HOMEWORK KEY
○ = **WORKED-OUT SOLUTIONS** on p. WS4 for Exs. 9, 23, and 51
★ = **STANDARDIZED TEST PRACTICE** Exs. 2, 27, 52, and 54

SKILL PRACTICE

A

1. **VOCABULARY** What are the coefficients of the expression $4x + 8 - 9x + 2$? **4, −9**

2. ★ **WRITING** Are the expressions $2(x + 1)$ and $2x + 1$ equivalent? *Explain.*
No; the 2 was not distributed to the 1, $2(x + 1) = 2x + 2$.

ERROR ANALYSIS ***Describe* and correct the error in simplifying the expression.**

3. The negative was not distributed to the −8; $5y - (2y - 8) = 5y - 2y + 8 = 3y + 8$.

3.
$5y - (2y - 8) = 5y - 2y - 8$
$= 3y - 8$ ✗

4.
$8 + 2(4 + 3x) = 8 + 8 + 6x$
$= 22x$ ✗

4. Unlike terms cannot be combined; $8 + 2(4 + 3x) = 8 + 8 + 6x = 16 + 6x$.

EXAMPLES 1 and 2 on pp. 96–97 for Exs. 5–20

USING THE DISTRIBUTIVE PROPERTY **Use the distributive property to write an equivalent expression.**

5. $4(x + 3)$ **$4x + 12$**
6. $8(y + 2)$ **$8y + 16$**
7. $(m + 5)5$ **$5m + 25$**
8. $(n + 6)3$ **$3n + 18$**
9. $(p - 3)(-8)$ **$-8p + 24$**
10. $-4(q - 4)$ **$-4q + 16$**
11. $2(2r - 3)$ **$4r - 6$**
12. $(s - 9)9$ **$9s - 81$**
13. $6v(v + 1)$ **$6v^2 + 6v$**
14. $-w(2w + 7)$ **$-2w^2 - 7w$**
15. $-2x(3 - x)$ **$2x^2 - 6x$**
16. $3y(y - 6)$ **$3y^2 - 18y$**
17. $\frac{1}{2}\left(\frac{1}{2}m - 4\right)$ **$\frac{1}{4}m - 2$**
18. $-\frac{3}{4}(p - 1)$ **$-\frac{3}{4}p + \frac{3}{4}$**
19. $\frac{2}{3}(6n - 9)$ **$4n - 6$**
20. $\frac{5}{6}r(r - 1)$ **$\frac{5}{6}r^2 - \frac{5}{6}r$**

EXAMPLE 3 on p. 97 for Exs. 21–26

IDENTIFYING PARTS OF AN EXPRESSION **Identify the terms, like terms, coefficients, and constant terms of the expression.** **21–26. See margin.**

21. $-7 + 13x + 2x + 8$
22. $9 + 7y - 2 - 5y$
23. $7x^2 - 10 - 2x^2 + 5$
24. $-3y^2 + 3y^2 - 7 + 9$
25. $2 + 3xy - 4xy + 6$
26. $6xy - 11xy + 2xy - 4xy + 7xy$

27. ★ **MULTIPLE CHOICE** Which two terms are like terms? **B**

Ⓐ $-2, -5x$ Ⓑ $4x, -x$ Ⓒ $-2, -2y$ Ⓓ $5x, -3y$

EXAMPLE 4 on p. 98 for Exs. 28–39

SIMPLIFYING EXPRESSIONS **Simplify the expression.**

28. $7x + (-11x)$ **$-4x$**
29. $6y - y$ **$5y$**
30. $5 + 2n + 2$ **$2n + 7$**
31. $(4a - 1)2 + a$ **$9a - 2$**
32. $3(2 - c) - c$ **$6 - 4c$**
33. $6r + 2(r + 4)$ **$8r + 8$**
34. $15t - (t - 4)$ **$14t + 4$**
35. $3(m + 5) - 10$ **$3m + 5$**
36. $-6(v + 1) + v$ **$-5v - 6$**
37. $7(w - 5) + 3w$ **$10w - 35$**
38. $6(5 - z) + 2z$ **$30 - 4z$**
39. $(s - 3)(-2) + 17s$ **$15s + 6$**

B

GEOMETRY **Find the perimeter and area of the rectangle.**

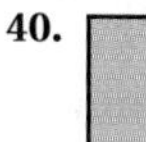

40.
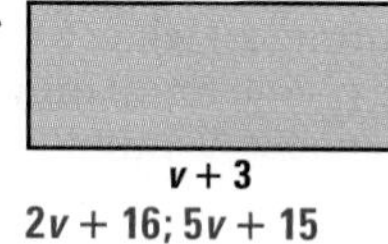
Width: 5; length: $v + 3$
$2v + 16$; $5v + 15$

41.
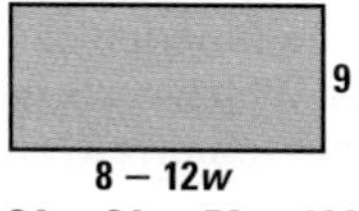
Width: 9; length: $8 - 12w$
$34 - 24w$; $72 - 108w$

42.
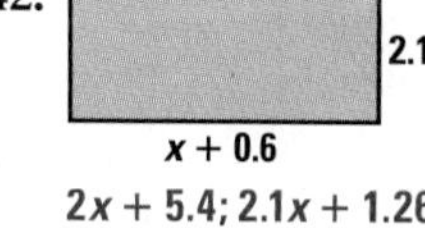
Width: 2.1; length: $x + 0.6$
$2x + 5.4$; $2.1x + 1.26$

23. terms: $7x^2$, −10, $-2x^2$, 5; like terms: $7x^2$ and $-2x^2$, −10 and 5; coefficients: 7, −2; constant terms: −10, 5

24. terms: $-3y^2$, $3y^2$, −7, 9; like terms: $-3y^2$ and $3y^2$, −7 and 9; coefficients: −3, 3; constant terms: −7, 9

25. terms: 2, $3xy$, $-4xy$, 6; like terms: 2 and 6, $3xy$ and $-4xy$; coefficients: 3, −4; constant terms: 2, 6

26. terms: $6xy$, $-11xy$, $2xy$, $-4xy$, $7xy$; like terms: $6xy$, $-11xy$, $2xy$, $-4xy$, and $7xy$; coefficients: 6, −11, 2, −4, 7; constant terms: none

4 PRACTICE AND APPLY

Assignment Guide

Answer Transparencies available for all exercises

Basic:
Day 1: SRH p. 925 Exs. 1, 2, 4, 5, 12
pp. 99–101
Exs. 1–15, 21–24, 62–67
Day 2: pp. 99–101
Exs. 27–42, 50–53, 56–61

Average:
Day 1: pp. 99–101
Exs. 1–4, 9–20, 23–27, 62–67
Day 2: pp. 99–101
Exs. 32–48, 50–54, 56–61

Advanced:
Day 1: pp. 99–101
Exs. 1, 2, 11–20, 23–27, 65–67
Day 2: pp. 99–101
Exs. 34–49*, 51–61*

Block:
pp. 99–101
Exs. 1–4, 9–20, 23–27, 62–67 (with 2.4)
pp. 99–101
Exs. 32–48, 50–54, 56–61 (with 2.6)

Differentiated Instruction

See *Differentiated Instruction Resources* for suggestions on addressing the needs of a diverse classroom.

Homework Check

For a quick check of student understanding of key concepts, go over the following exercises:
Basic: 6, 10, 22, 31, 50
Average: 11, 15, 24, 35, 51
Advanced: 16, 18, 25, 37, 52

Extra Practice

- Student Edition, p. 939
- Chapter Resource Book: Practice levels A, B, C

Practice Worksheet

An easily-readable reduced practice page (with answers) for this lesson can be found on p. 62D.

Avoiding Common Errors

Exercises 28–39 Some students may forget that x and $-x$ have a coefficient of 1 and -1, respectively. Encourage them to write x as "$1x$" and $-x$ as "$-1x$" so they do not overlook these variables when they combine like terms.

Study Strategy

Exercises 43–46 Suggest that students use the Example at the top of the page to write out the exercises in the same way. Tell them that once they become familiar with the method, they may no longer need to write out the steps.

Internet Reference

Exercise 50 For more information about archery in the United States, visit http://www.usarchery.org

Teaching Strategy

Exercises 50, 54 You may want to refer students to Example 5 before they begin solving these problems. Step 1 is particularly useful and may help them write a verbal model and an equation. Note for students that in Exercise 54, parts a and b correspond to Steps 1 and 2 in Example 5.

Reading Strategy

Exercise 51 Some students may write the equation incorrectly. Tell them that the problem states the coupon for \$2 off is for *each* movie rental.

Mathematical Reasoning

Exercise 54 Encourage students to create a spreadsheet for part c. They can adapt the equation in part a for the formula and then generate a table of values.

USING MENTAL MATH In Exercises 43–46, use the example below to find the total cost.

EXAMPLE **Use the distributive property and mental math**

Use the distributive property and mental math to find the total cost of 5 picture frames at \$1.99 each.

Total cost $= 5(1.99)$	**Write expression for total cost.**
$= 5(2 - 0.01)$	**Rewrite 1.99 as 2 − 0.01.**
$= 5(2) - 5(0.01)$	**Distributive property**
$= 10 - 0.05$	**Multiply using mental math.**
$= 9.95$	**Subtract. The total cost is \$9.95.**

43. 3 CDs at \$12.99 each **\$38.97**

44. 5 magazines at \$3.99 each **\$19.95**

45. 6 pairs of socks at \$1.98 per pair **\$11.88**

46. 25 baseballs at \$2.98 each **\$74.50**

TRANSLATING PHRASES In Exercises 47 and 48, translate the verbal phrase into an expression. Then simplify the expression.

47. Twice the sum of 6 and x, increased by 5 less than x
$2(6 + x) + (x - 5); 3x + 7$

48. Three times the difference of x and 2, decreased by the sum of x and 10
$3(x - 2) - (x + 10); 2x - 16$

C **49.** **CHALLENGE** How can you use $a(b + c) = ab + ac$ to show that $(b + c)a = ba + ca$ is also true? *Justify* your steps.
$(b + c)a = a(b + c)$, Commutative property of multiplication; $= ab + ac$, Given statement; $= ba + ca$, Commutative property of multiplication

PROBLEM SOLVING

EXAMPLE 5 A on p. 98 for Exs. 50–52

50. **SPORTS** An archer shoots 6 arrows at a target. Some arrows hit the 9 point ring, and the rest hit the 10 point bull's-eye. Write an equation that gives the score s as a function of the number a of arrows that hit the 9 point ring. Then find the score if 2 arrows hit the 9 point ring. **$s = -a + 60$; 58**

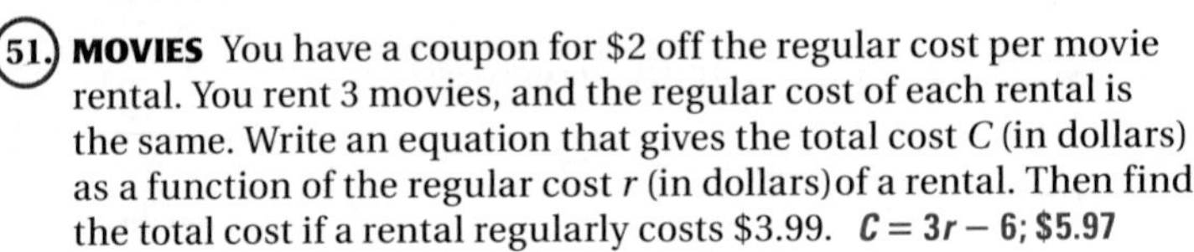

@HomeTutor for problem solving help at classzone.com

51. **MOVIES** You have a coupon for \$2 off the regular cost per movie rental. You rent 3 movies, and the regular cost of each rental is the same. Write an equation that gives the total cost C (in dollars) as a function of the regular cost r (in dollars) of a rental. Then find the total cost if a rental regularly costs \$3.99. **$C = 3r - 6$; \$5.97**

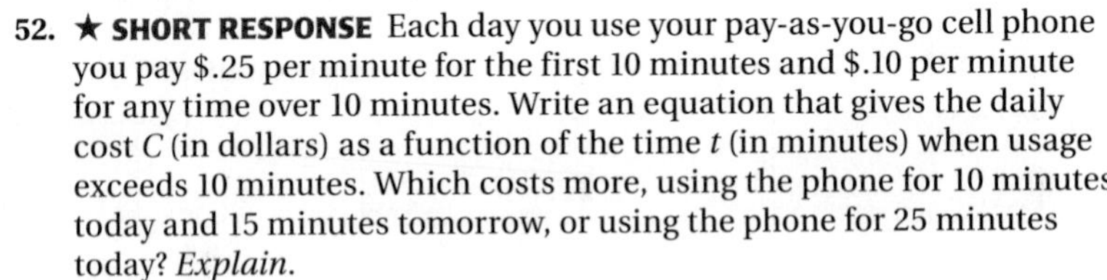

9 points
10 points

@HomeTutor for problem solving help at classzone.com

52. ★ **SHORT RESPONSE** Each day you use your pay-as-you-go cell phone you pay \$.25 per minute for the first 10 minutes and \$.10 per minute for any time over 10 minutes. Write an equation that gives the daily cost C (in dollars) as a function of the time t (in minutes) when usage exceeds 10 minutes. Which costs more, using the phone for 10 minutes today and 15 minutes tomorrow, or using the phone for 25 minutes today? *Explain.*

52. $C = 2.5 + 0.1(t - 10)$; 10 minutes today and 15 minutes tomorrow; the cost of using the phone 10 minutes today and 15 minutes tomorrow is $2.5 + 2.5 + 0.1(5) =$ \$5.50; the cost of using the phone for 25 minutes today is $2.5 + 0.1(15) =$ \$4.

○ = **WORKED-OUT SOLUTIONS on p. WS1**

★ = **STANDARDIZED TEST PRACTICE**

B 53. **DIVING** In a diving competition, a diver's score is the product of the difficulty level d of a dive and the sum of the scores x, y, and z of 3 judges. Write a simplified expression that represents the diver's score. $s = d(x + y + z) = dx + dy + dz$

54. ★ **EXTENDED RESPONSE** During the summer you give one hour saxophone lessons to 20 students each week. Use the information in the advertisement.

a. **Model** Write an equation that gives your weekly earnings y (in dollars) as a function of the number x of beginning students that you teach. $y = -15x + 700$

b. **Calculate** Find your weekly earnings if 15 of your 20 students are beginners. **$475**

c. **Explain** Suppose that you plan to teach for 10 weeks and want to earn $4000 for the summer. How many advanced students should you teach? Your answer should include the following:

- a table of values generated by the equation in part (a)
- an explanation of your method for answering the question **See margin.**

C 55. **CHALLENGE** A drama club plans to sell 100 tickets to a school musical. An adult ticket costs $6, and a student ticket costs $4. Students who attend the school get a $1 discount. The club expects two thirds of the student tickets to be discounted. Write an equation that gives the total revenue r (in dollars) as a function of the number a of adult tickets sold. $r = \frac{8}{3}a + \frac{1000}{3}$

MIXED REVIEW

PREVIEW Prepare for Lesson 2.6 in Exs. 56–61.

Multiply or divide. *(p. 915)*

56. $\frac{1}{2} \cdot \frac{2}{5}$ $\frac{1}{5}$
57. $\frac{4}{7} \cdot \frac{1}{8}$ $\frac{1}{14}$
58. $1\frac{2}{3} \cdot 2\frac{3}{10}$ $3\frac{5}{6}$
59. $\frac{1}{5} \div \frac{3}{10}$ $\frac{2}{3}$
60. $\frac{2}{3} \div \frac{4}{9}$ $1\frac{1}{2}$
61. $2\frac{3}{4} \div 1\frac{5}{8}$ $1\frac{9}{13}$

Find the sum, difference, or product.

62. $-7 + (-4)$ *(p. 74)* **−11**
63. $8 + (-11)$ *(p. 74)* **−3**
64. $12 - 23$ *(p. 80)* **−11**
65. $-9 - 6$ *(p. 80)* **−15**
66. $(-11)(-2.1)$ *(p. 88)* **23.1**
67. $15(3.5)$ *(p. 88)* **52.5**

QUIZ *for Lessons 2.4–2.5*

Find the product. *(p. 88)*

1. $-5 \cdot (-5)$ **25**
2. $18 \cdot \left(-\frac{7}{6}\right)$ **−21**
3. $8 \cdot \frac{4}{5} \cdot (-10)$ **−64**
4. $9 \cdot (-7) \cdot (-1.2)$ **75.6**
5. $(-3x) \cdot (-4)$ $12x$
6. $-\frac{2}{3}x \cdot 15$ $-10x$
7. $x \cdot 1.5 \cdot (-6.4)$ $-9.6x$
8. $(-2)(13x)$ $-26x$

Use the distributive property to write an equivalent expression. *(p. 96)*

9. $7(x + 14)$ $7x + 98$
10. $-4(5x + 9)$ $-20x - 36$
11. $-5(2x - 6)$ $-10x + 30$
12. $(3 - x)6$ $18 - 6x$

5 ASSESS AND RETEACH

Daily Homework Quiz

Transparency Available

Use the distributive property to write an equivalent expression.

1. $6(2 - x)$ $12 - 6x$
2. $-x(3x + 2)$ $-3x^2 - 2x$

Simplify the expression.

3. $4x - 5 + 3 - x$ $3x - 2$
4. $(3x - 2)4 + x$ $13x - 8$
5. You burn 18 calories per minute on an elliptical trainer and 7 calories per minute weight training. Suppose you work out at these two activities for 45 minutes. How many calories do you burn if you lift weights for 30 minutes? **480 calories**

Online Quiz

Available at **classzone.com**

Diagnosis/Remediation

- Practice A, B, C in Chapter Resource Book
- Study Guide in Chapter Resource Book
- Practice Workbook
- @HomeTutor

Challenge

Additional challenge is available in the Chapter Resource Book.

Quiz

An easily-readable reduced copy of the quiz (with answers) on Lessons 2.4–2.5 from the Assessment Book can be found on p. 62E.

54c. You do not need to teach any advanced students.

Number of beginner students	Weekly pay (dollars)
15	475
16	460
17	445
18	430
19	415
20	400

You need to earn $4000 ÷ 10 = $400 a week. A table of values shows how much you can earn based on the number of beginner students you teach.

PROBLEM SOLVING WORKSHOP LESSON 2.5

Using ALTERNATIVE METHODS

Alternative Strategy

Example 5 on page 98 can be solved by breaking the problem into parts. This method allows students to see the components of the problem and will help them better understand the algebraic solution given in Lesson 2.5.

Avoiding Common Errors

Students may confuse the time spent running with the time swimming or the number of calories burned per minute running with the number of calories burned per minute swimming. Have them check that their calculations match the numbers in the problem.

Teaching Strategy

Students may want to use this strategy for Exercises 50–55 in Lesson 2.5.

1. \$330; method 1: write an equation for c, the total cost as a function of n, the number of nights you spend at a campground; $c = 15n + 60(10 - n)$ or $c = -45n + 600$. Substitute 6 for n, giving you $c =$ \$330; method 2: break the problem into parts. Find the cost of staying at the campground for 6 nights: \$15 per night • 6 nights = \$90. Find the number of nights spent at the motel: 10 − 6 = 4 nights. Find the cost of staying at the motel for 4 nights: \$60 per night • 4 nights = \$240. Add the cost of the campground to the cost of the motel: \$90 + \$240 = \$330.

2. \$450; method 1: write an equation for c, the total cost, as a function of n, the number of nights you spend at a campground; $c = 15n + 60(12 - n)$ or $c = -45n + 720$. Substitute 6 for n, giving you $c =$ \$450; method 2: break the problem into parts. Find the cost of staying at the campground for 6 nights: \$15 per night • 6 nights = \$90. Find the number of nights spent at the motel: 12 − 6 = 6 nights. Find the cost of staying at the motel for 6 nights: \$60 per night • 6 nights = \$360. Add the cost of the campground to the cost of the motel: \$90 + \$360 = \$450.

Another Way to Solve Example 5, page 98

MULTIPLE REPRESENTATIONS In Example 5 on page 98, you saw how to solve a problem about exercising using a verbal model and an equation. You can also solve the problem by breaking it into parts.

PROBLEM

EXERCISING Your daily workout plan involves a total of 50 minutes of running and swimming. You burn 15 calories per minute when running and 9 calories per minute when swimming. Find the number of calories you burn in your 50 minute workout if you run for 20 minutes.

METHOD

Breaking into Parts You can solve the problem by breaking it into parts.

STEP 1 **Find** the number of calories you burn when running.

15 calories per minute • 20 minutes = 300 calories

Your running time is 20 minutes, so your swimming time is 50 − 20 = 30 minutes.

STEP 2 **Find** the calories you burn when swimming.

9 calories per minute • 30 minutes = 270 calories

STEP 3 **Add** the calories you burn when doing each activity. You burn a total of 570 calories.

300 calories + 270 calories = 570 calories

PRACTICE

1–4. See margin.

1. **VACATIONING** Your family is taking a vacation for 10 nights. You will spend some nights at a campground and the rest of the nights at a motel. A campground stay costs \$15 per night, and a motel stay costs \$60 per night. Find the total cost of lodging if you stay at a campground for 6 nights. Solve this problem using two different methods.

2. **WHAT IF?** In Exercise 1, suppose the vacation lasts 12 days. Find the total cost of lodging if you stay at the campground for 6 nights. Solve this problem using two different methods.

3. **FLORIST** During the summer, you work 35 hours per week at a florist shop. You get paid \$8 per hour for working at the register and \$9.50 per hour for making deliveries. Find the total amount you earn this week if you spend 5 hours making deliveries. Solve this problem using two different methods.

4. **ERROR ANALYSIS** *Describe* and correct the error in solving Exercise 3.

\$8 per hour • 5 hours = \$40

\$9.50 per hour • 30 hours = \$285

\$40 + \$285 = \$325

3. See Additional Answers beginning on p. AA1.

4. You earn \$9.50 per hour making deliveries, not working at the register; \$9.50 per hour • 5 hours = \$47.50; \$8 per hour • 30 hours = \$240; \$47.50 + \$240 = \$287.50.

2.6 Divide Real Numbers

Before You multiplied real numbers.
Now You will divide real numbers.
Why? So you can calculate volleyball statistics, as in Ex. 57.

Key Vocabulary
- **multiplicative inverse**
- **reciprocal,** *p. 915*
- **mean,** *p. 918*

Reciprocals like $\frac{2}{3}$ and $\frac{3}{2}$ have the property that their product is 1:

$$\frac{2}{3} \cdot \frac{3}{2} = 1$$

The reciprocal of a nonzero number a, written $\frac{1}{a}$, is called the **multiplicative inverse** of a. Zero does not have a multiplicative inverse because there is no number a such that $0 \cdot a = 1$.

READING
The symbol $\neq$ is read "is not equal to."

KEY CONCEPT *For Your Notebook*

Inverse Property of Multiplication

Words The product of a nonzero number and its multiplicative inverse is 1.

Algebra $a \cdot \frac{1}{a} = \frac{1}{a} \cdot a = 1, a \neq 0$ **Example** $8 \cdot \frac{1}{8} = 1$

EXAMPLE 1 Find multiplicative inverses of numbers

a. The multiplicative inverse of $-\frac{1}{5}$ is -5 because $-\frac{1}{5} \cdot (-5) = 1$.

b. The multiplicative inverse of $-\frac{6}{7}$ is $-\frac{7}{6}$ because $-\frac{6}{7} \cdot \left(-\frac{7}{6}\right) = 1$.

WRITE INVERSES
You can find the inverse of $-\frac{6}{7}$ as follows:

$$\frac{1}{-\frac{6}{7}} \cdot 1 = \frac{1}{-\frac{6}{7}} \cdot \frac{7}{7} = -\frac{7}{6}$$

DIVISION Because the expressions $6 \div 3$ and $6 \cdot \frac{1}{3}$ have the same value, 2, you can conclude that $6 \div 3 = 6 \cdot \frac{1}{3}$. This example illustrates the *division rule.*

KEY CONCEPT *For Your Notebook*

Division Rule

Words To divide a number a by a nonzero number b, multiply a by the multiplicative inverse of b.

Algebra $a \div b = a \cdot \frac{1}{b}, b \neq 0$ **Example** $5 \div 2 = 5 \cdot \frac{1}{2}$

1 PLAN AND PREPARE

Warm-Up Exercises

Transparency Available

Find the quotient.

1. $84 \div 14$ **6**

2. $1.2 \div 5$ **0.24**

3. $\frac{2}{3} \div 3$ $\mathbf{\frac{2}{9}}$

4. $\frac{5}{8} \div \frac{1}{5}$ $\mathbf{3\frac{1}{8}}$

5. The points Jeri scored in her last five basketball games were 28, 34, 19, 26, and 38. How many points did she average per game? **29 points**

Notetaking Guide

Transparency Available

Promotes interactive learning and notetaking skills.

Pacing

Basic: 1 day
Average: 1 day
Advanced: 1 day
Block: 0.5 block with 2.5
- See *Teaching Guide/Lesson Plan.*

2 FOCUS AND MOTIVATE

Essential Question

Big Idea 1, p. 63

How do you divide real numbers? **Tell students they will learn how to answer this question by using the division rule and sign rules for products and quotients.**

NCTM STANDARDS

Standard 1: Understand meanings of operations; Understand how operations are related

Resource Planning Guide

Chapter Resource Book
- Teaching Guide/Lesson Plan
- Activity Master
- Practice levels A, B, C
- Study Guide
- Catch-up for Absent Students
- Application
- Challenge

Workbooks
- Notetaking Guide
- Practice Workbook

Teaching Options
- **Power Presentations** provides dynamic electronic teaching resources for the classroom.
- **Activity Generator** provides editable activities for all ability levels.

Interactive Technology
- Easy Planner
- Power Presentations
- Activity Generator
- Animated Algebra
- Test Generator
- Online Quiz
- eWorkbook
- eEdition
- @HomeTutor

Resources for English Learners
- Spanish Study Guide
- Multi-Language Visual Glossary
- Student Resources in Spanish

See also the *Differentiated Instruction Resources* for more strategies for meeting individual needs.

Motivating the Lesson

A top golfer has scores of −4, −3, −6 and −3 in four rounds of golf on a new course. In this lesson, you will learn how to find the average score on this course.

3 TEACH

Extra Example 1

Find the multiplicative inverse of the number.

a. $-\frac{1}{7}$ −7 b. $-\frac{5}{3}$ $-\frac{3}{5}$

Key Question to Ask for Example 1

- What is the multiplicative inverse of $\frac{a}{b}$, where $a \neq 0$ and $b \neq 0$? $\frac{b}{a}$

Extra Example 2

Find the quotient

a. $18 \div (-3)$ −6 b. $-16 \div \left(-\frac{8}{3}\right)$ 6

Extra Example 3

Andy recorded the low temperature each night at his home during January. Over five consecutive nights, he recorded the temperatures −2°C, −10°C, 6°C, −1°C, and 2°C. What was the mean low temperature at his home for these nights? **−1°C**

Key Question to Ask for Example 3

- Why do you divide by 5 in Example 3? **because there are 5 values in the data set, one for each day**

Vocabulary

In Example 3, remind students that the mean is sometimes referred to as the "average" of a set of data.

SIGN OF A QUOTIENT Because division can be expressed as multiplication, the sign rules for division are the same as the sign rules for multiplication.

AVOID ERRORS
You cannot divide a real number by 0, because 0 does not have a multiplicative inverse.

KEY CONCEPT *For Your Notebook*

The Sign of a Quotient

- The quotient of two real numbers with the *same* sign is positive.
- The quotient of two real numbers with *different* signs is negative.
- The quotient of 0 and any nonzero real number is 0.

EXAMPLE 2 Divide real numbers

Find the quotient.

a. $-16 \div 4 = -16 \cdot \frac{1}{4}$
$= -4$

b. $-20 \div \left(-\frac{5}{3}\right) = -20 \cdot \left(-\frac{3}{5}\right)$
$= 12$

✓ GUIDED PRACTICE for Examples 1 and 2

Find the multiplicative inverse of the number.

1. −27 $-\frac{1}{27}$ **2.** −8 $-\frac{1}{8}$ **3.** $-\frac{4}{7}$ $-\frac{7}{4}$ **4.** $-\frac{1}{3}$ −3

Find the quotient.

5. $-64 \div (-4)$ 16 **6.** $-\frac{3}{8} \div \left(\frac{3}{10}\right)$ $-1\frac{1}{4}$ **7.** $18 \div \left(-\frac{2}{9}\right)$ −81 **8.** $-\frac{2}{5} \div 18$ $-\frac{1}{45}$

EXAMPLE 3 Find the mean

TEMPERATURES The table gives the daily minimum temperatures (in degrees Fahrenheit) in Barrow, Alaska, for the first 5 days of February 2004. Find the mean daily minimum temperature.

Day in February	1	2	3	4	5
Minimum temperature (°F)	−21	−29	−39	−39	−22

Point Barrow Observatory

Solution

To find the mean daily minimum temperature, find the sum of the minimum temperatures for the 5 days and then divide the sum by 5.

$$\text{Mean} = \frac{-21 + (-29) + (-39) + (-39) + (-22)}{5}$$

$$= -\frac{150}{5} = -30$$

▸ The mean daily minimum temperature was −30°F.

CHECK REASONABLENESS
The sum of the temperatures is about −20 + (−30) + (−40) + (−40) + (−20) = −150, and −150 ÷ 5 = −30, so the solution is reasonable.

Differentiated Instruction

Inclusion Some students may find it easier to divide real numbers by first determining the sign of the final answer and then proceeding with the division of the numbers without regard to the sign. Give grouped examples like the following: −4 ÷ 2 = −(4 ÷ 2) = −2, 4 ÷ (−2) = −(4 ÷ 2) = −2, −4 ÷ (−2) = +(4 ÷ 2) = 2. In these examples, once the sign was determined, the problem was reduced to dividing 4 by 2.

See also the *Differentiated Instruction Resources* for more strategies.

EXAMPLE 4 Simplify an expression

Simplify the expression $\frac{36x - 24}{6}$.

ANOTHER WAY
You can simplify the expression by first rewriting it as a difference of two fractions: $\frac{36x - 24}{6} = \frac{36x}{6} - \frac{24}{6} = 6x - 4$.

$\frac{36x - 24}{6} = (36x - 24) \div 6$ Rewrite fraction as division.

$= (36x - 24) \cdot \frac{1}{6}$ Division rule

$= 36x \cdot \frac{1}{6} - 24 \cdot \frac{1}{6}$ Distributive property

$= 6x - 4$ Simplify.

✓ GUIDED PRACTICE for Examples 3 and 4

9. Find the mean of the numbers −3, 4, 2.8, and −1.5. **0.575**

10. **TEMPERATURES** Find the mean daily maximum temperature (in degrees Fahrenheit) in Barrow, Alaska, for the first 5 days of February 2004. **−16.8°F**

Day in February	1	2	3	4	5
Maximum temperature (°F)	−3	−20	−21	−22	−18

Simplify the expression.

11. $\frac{2x - 8}{-4}$ $-\frac{1}{2}x + 2$

12. $\frac{-6y + 18}{3}$ $-2y + 6$

13. $\frac{-10z - 20}{-5}$ $2z + 4$

OPERATIONS ON REAL NUMBERS In this chapter, you saw how to find the sum, difference, product, and quotient of two real numbers a and b. You can use the values of a and b to determine whether the result is positive, negative, or 0.

CONCEPT SUMMARY *For Your Notebook*

Rules for Addition, Subtraction, Multiplication, and Division

Let a and b be real numbers.

Expression	$a + b$	$a - b$	$a \cdot b$	$a \div b$
Positive if...	the number with the greater absolute value is positive.	$a > b$.	a and b have the same sign ($a \neq 0, b \neq 0$).	a and b have the same sign ($a \neq 0, b \neq 0$).
Negative if...	the number with the greater absolute value is negative.	$a < b$.	a and b have different signs ($a \neq 0, b \neq 0$).	a and b have different signs ($a \neq 0, b \neq 0$).
Zero if...	a and b are additive inverses.	$a = b$.	$a = 0$ or $b = 0$.	$a = 0$ and $b \neq 0$.

Extra Example 4

Simplify the expression $\frac{40x + 32}{8}$. $5x + 4$

Reading Strategy

Be certain that students read and understand the Another Way note next to Example 4. This note presents another approach to simplifying expressions that some students may find preferable to use.

Closing the Lesson

Have students summarize the major points of the lesson and answer the Essential Question: How do you divide real numbers?

- **To divide a number a by a nonzero number b, find the product $a \cdot \frac{1}{b}$.**
- **The sign rules for division are the same as for multiplication.**
- **The product of a nonzero number and its multiplicative inverse is 1.**

To divide two real numbers, multiply the first number by the multiplicative inverse of the second number.

4 PRACTICE AND APPLY

Assignment Guide

Answer Transparencies available for all exercises

Basic:
Day 1: pp. 106–108
Exs. 1, 2, 3–23 odd, 24–28, 33–37, 42–45, 52–55, 59–63 odd

Average:
Day 1: pp. 106–108
Exs. 1, 2, 7–10, 15–23 odd, 28–32, 37–49, 53, 60–64 even

Advanced:
Day 1: pp. 106–108
Exs. 1, 2, 8–10, 19–23, 29–32, 38–41, 44–52*, 54–58*

Block:
pp. 106–108
Exs. 1, 2, 7–10, 15–23 odd, 28–32, 37–49, 60–64 even (with 2.5)

Differentiated Instruction

See *Differentiated Instruction Resources* for suggestions on addressing the needs of a diverse classroom.

Homework Check

For a quick check of student understanding of key concepts, go over the following exercises:

Basic: 5, 15, 25, 34, 52
Average: 8, 17, 30, 38, 53
Advanced: 9, 20, 31, 40, 54

Extra Practice

- Student Edition, p. 939
- Chapter Resource Book: Practice levels A, B, C

Practice Worksheet

An easily-readable reduced practice page (with answers) for this lesson can be found on p. 62D.

2.6 EXERCISES

HOMEWORK KEY ○ = **WORKED-OUT SOLUTIONS** on p. WS4 for Exs. 13, 35, and 53
★ = **STANDARDIZED TEST PRACTICE** Exs. 2, 23, 48, 49, 55, 56, and 57

SKILL PRACTICE

A

1. **VOCABULARY** Copy and complete: The product of a nonzero number and its _?_ is 1. **multiplicative inverse**

2. ★ **WRITING** How can you tell whether the mean of n numbers is negative without actually dividing the sum of the numbers by n? *Explain.*
If their sum is negative, the mean will be negative.

EXAMPLE 1 on p. 103 for Exs. 3–10, 23

FINDING INVERSES **Find the multiplicative inverse of the number.**

3. -18 $\mathbf{-\frac{1}{18}}$
4. -9 $\mathbf{-\frac{1}{9}}$
5. -1 $\mathbf{-1}$
6. $-\frac{1}{2}$ $\mathbf{-2}$
7. $-\frac{3}{4}$ $\mathbf{-1\frac{1}{3}}$
8. $-\frac{5}{9}$ $\mathbf{-1\frac{4}{5}}$
9. $-4\frac{1}{3}$ $\mathbf{-\frac{3}{13}}$
10. $-2\frac{2}{5}$ $\mathbf{-\frac{5}{12}}$

EXAMPLE 2 on p. 104 for Exs. 11–22

FINDING QUOTIENTS **Find the quotient.**

11. $-21 \div 3$ $\mathbf{-7}$
12. $-18 \div (-6)$ $\mathbf{3}$
13. (○) $-1 \div \left(-\frac{7}{2}\right)$ $\mathbf{\frac{2}{7}}$
14. $15 \div \left(-\frac{3}{4}\right)$ $\mathbf{-20}$
15. $13 \div \left(-4\frac{1}{3}\right)$ $\mathbf{-3}$
16. $-\frac{2}{3} \div 2$ $\mathbf{-\frac{1}{3}}$
17. $-\frac{1}{2} \div \frac{1}{5}$ $\mathbf{-2\frac{1}{2}}$
18. $-\frac{1}{5} \div (-6)$ $\mathbf{\frac{1}{30}}$
19. $-\frac{4}{7} \div (-2)$ $\mathbf{\frac{2}{7}}$
20. $-1 \div \left(-\frac{6}{5}\right)$ $\mathbf{\frac{5}{6}}$
21. $8 \div \left(-\frac{4}{11}\right)$ $\mathbf{-22}$
22. $-\frac{1}{3} \div \frac{5}{3}$ $\mathbf{-\frac{1}{5}}$

23. ★ **MULTIPLE CHOICE** If $-\frac{5}{7}x = 1$, what is the value of x? **A**

Ⓐ $-1\frac{2}{5}$ Ⓑ $\frac{5}{7}$ Ⓒ 1 Ⓓ $\frac{12}{5}$

EXAMPLE 3 on p. 104 for Exs. 24–32

FINDING MEANS **Find the mean of the numbers.**

24. $-10, -8, 3$ $\mathbf{-5}$
25. $12, -8, -9$ $\mathbf{-1\frac{2}{3}}$
26. $18, -9, 0, -5$ $\mathbf{1}$
27. $-2, 9, -3, 5$ $\mathbf{2\frac{1}{4}}$
28. $-1, -4, -5, 10$ $\mathbf{0}$
29. $7, -4, 1, -9, -6$ $\mathbf{-2\frac{1}{5}}$
30. $-5.3, -2, 1.3$ $\mathbf{-2}$
31. $0.25, -4, -0.75, -1, 6$ $\mathbf{0.1}$
32. $-0.6, 0.18, -2, 5, -0.5$ $\mathbf{0.416}$

EXAMPLE 4 on p. 105 for Exs. 33–43

SIMPLIFYING EXPRESSIONS **Simplify the expression.**

33. $\frac{6x - 14}{2}$ $\mathbf{3x - 7}$
34. $\frac{12y - 8}{-4}$ $\mathbf{-3y + 2}$
35. (○) $\frac{9z - 6}{-3}$ $\mathbf{-3z + 2}$
36. $\frac{-6p + 15}{6}$ $\mathbf{-p + 2\frac{1}{2}}$
37. $\frac{5 - 25q}{10}$ $\mathbf{\frac{1}{2} - \frac{5}{2}q}$
38. $\frac{-18 - 21r}{-12}$ $\mathbf{\frac{3}{2} + \frac{7}{4}r}$
39. $\frac{-24a - 10}{-8}$ $\mathbf{3a + 1\frac{1}{4}}$
40. $\frac{-20b + 12}{-5}$ $\mathbf{4b - 2\frac{2}{5}}$
41. $\frac{36 - 27c}{9}$ $\mathbf{4 - 3c}$

ERROR ANALYSIS ***Describe*** **and correct the error in simplifying the expression.** **42, 43. See margin.**

42.
$$\frac{12 - 18x}{6} = (12 - 18x) \cdot \left(-\frac{1}{6}\right)$$
$$= 12\left(-\frac{1}{6}\right) - 18x\left(-\frac{1}{6}\right)$$
$$= -2 + 3x$$

43.
$$\frac{-15x - 10}{-5} = (-15x - 10) \cdot \left(-\frac{1}{5}\right)$$
$$= -15x\left(-\frac{1}{5}\right) - 10\left(-\frac{1}{5}\right)$$
$$= 3x - 2$$

42. The multiplicative inverse of 6 is $\frac{1}{6}$, not $-\frac{1}{6}$. $\frac{12 - 18x}{6} = (12 - 18x) \cdot \left(\frac{1}{6}\right) = 12\left(\frac{1}{6}\right) - 18x\left(\frac{1}{6}\right) = 2 - 3x$.

43. −2 was added instead of subtracted; $\frac{-15x - 10}{-5} = (-15x - 10) \cdot \left(-\frac{1}{5}\right) = -15x\left(-\frac{1}{5}\right) - 10\left(-\frac{1}{5}\right) = 3x + 2$.

B **EVALUATING EXPRESSIONS** **Evaluate the expression.**

44. $\frac{2y - x}{x}$ when $x = 1$ and $y = -4$ **−9**

45. $\frac{4x}{3y + x}$ when $x = 6$ and $y = -8$ $\mathbf{-1\frac{1}{3}}$

46. $\frac{-9x}{y^2 - 1}$ when $x = -3$ and $y = -2$ **9**

47. $\frac{y - x}{xy}$ when $x = -6$ and $y = -2$ $\mathbf{\frac{1}{3}}$

48. No; no. ***Sample answer:*** $4 \div 2 = 2$ **but** $2 \div 4 = \frac{1}{2}$, $(20 \div 4) \div 2 = 2\frac{1}{2}$ **but** $20 \div (4 \div 2) = 10$.

48. ★ **WRITING** Tell whether division is commutative and associative. Give examples to support your answer.

49. ★ **MULTIPLE CHOICE** Let a and b be positive numbers, and let c and d be negative numbers. Which quotient has a value that is always negative? **C**

Ⓐ $\frac{a}{b} \div \frac{c}{d}$ Ⓑ $\frac{a}{c} \div \frac{b}{d}$ Ⓒ $\frac{c^2}{a} \div \frac{b}{d}$ Ⓓ $\frac{a}{cd} \div b$

C **50.** **CHALLENGE** Find the mean of the integers from −410 to 400. *Explain* how you got your answer. **See margin.**

51. **CHALLENGE** What is the mean of a number and three times its opposite? *Explain* your reasoning. **The opposite of the number; if you add x and 3 times $-x$, you get $-2x$; $-2x \div 2 = -x$.**

PROBLEM SOLVING

EXAMPLE 2 A on p. 104 for Ex. 52

52. SPORTS Free diving means diving without the aid of breathing equipment. Suppose that an athlete free dives to an elevation of −42 meters in 60 seconds. Find the average rate of change in the diver's elevation. $\mathbf{-\frac{7}{10}}$ **m/sec**

@HomeTutor for problem solving help at classzone.com

EXAMPLE 3 on p. 104 for Exs. 53–54

53. WEATHER The daily mean temperature is the mean of the high and low temperatures for a given day. The high temperature for Boston, Massachusetts, on January 10, 2004, was −10.6°C. The low temperature was −18.9°C. Find the daily mean temperature for that day. **−14.75°C**

@HomeTutor for problem solving help at classzone.com

54. MULTI-STEP PROBLEM The table shows the changes in the values of one share of stock A and one share of stock B over 5 days.

Day of week	Monday	Tuesday	Wednesday	Thursday	Friday
Change in share value for stock A (dollars)	−0.45	−0.32	0.66	−1.12	1.53
Change in share value for stock B (dollars)	−0.37	0.14	0.59	−0.53	1.02

a. Find the average daily change in share value for each stock. Use estimation to check that your answers are reasonable. **See margin.**

b. Which stock performed better over the 5 days? How much more money did the better performing stock earn, on average, per day? **stock B; $.11**

c. Can you conclude that the stock that performed better over all 5 days also performed better over the first 4 days of the week? *Explain* your reasoning.

54c. Yes. ***Sample answer:*** **Over the first four days, stock A's average change in value was −0.3075 whereas stock B's was −0.0425.**

Study Strategy

Exercises 33–41 In preparation for these exercises, students may want to review Example 4. Note that some students may find it easier to use the alternative method for simplifying expressions that is mentioned in "Another Way."

Avoiding Common Errors

Exercises 44–47 Students often substitute incorrectly when replacement values involve a negative sign. Encourage them to use parentheses to insert the values. This will help them avoid computational errors.

Reading Strategy

Exercise 56 Urge students to read all parts of the question carefully before completing part b. Note that the original prediction was off by 3.5 meters, which changes the rate of change for the whole period.

50. −5. ***Sample answer:*** **Using additive inverses you can determine that the sum of the integers −400 to 400 is 0. The sum of the integers from −410 to −401 is −4055. Divide this sum by the number of integers from −410 to 400, which is 811; −4055 ÷ 811 = −5.**

54a. $.06; $.17; Round the values to the nearest tenth. For stock A, −0.5 + (−0.3) + 0.7 + (−1.1) + 1.5 = 0.3, and 0.3 ÷ 5 = 0.06, which happens to be the exact answer. For stock B, (−0.4) + 0.1 + 0.6 + (−0.5) + 1.0 = 0.8 and 0.8 ÷ 5 = 0.16, and 0.16 is close to 0.17. The answers are reasonable.

5 ASSESS AND RETEACH

Daily Homework Quiz

 Transparency Available

Find the quotient.

1. $-14 \div 2\frac{1}{2}$ $-5\frac{3}{5}$
2. $-\frac{3}{4} \div (-4)$ $\frac{3}{16}$

Simplify the expression.

3. $\frac{9x - 15}{-3}$ $-3x + 5$
4. $\frac{-8x + 12}{5}$ $-1.6x + 2.4$
5. Ethan's team scored the following numbers of points in six rounds of a statewide History Quiz Contest: 86, −14, 58, −26, 74, and 20. What was the team's mean score? **33**

Online Quiz

Available at **classzone.com**

Diagnosis/Remediation

- Practice A, B, C in Chapter Resource Book
- Study Guide in Chapter Resource Book
- Practice Workbook
- @HomeTutor

Challenge

Additional challenge is available in the Chapter Resource Book.

57c. If the player had the same number of aces as service errors, then $a = e$, so $f = \frac{a-a}{s} = 0$; if all the serves were aces, a would be equal to s and e would be 0, so $f = \frac{s-0}{s} = \frac{s}{s} = 1$; if all the serves were errors, then $e = s$ and $a = 0$, so $f = \frac{0-s}{s} = \frac{-s}{s} = -1$.

B

55. ★ **MULTIPLE CHOICE** In a trivia competition, your team earned 60, −100, 300, 120, and −80 points on 5 questions. The sixth question has a value of 300 points. By how many points will your team's mean score per question change if you answer the sixth question correctly? **A**

 Ⓐ 40 points Ⓑ 50 points Ⓒ 60 points Ⓓ 100 points

56. ★ **SHORT RESPONSE** The South Aral Sea in Russia was about 57 meters above sea level in 1965. Scientists once predicted that the elevation would be about 34 meters above sea level in 2002.

 a. Estimate the average rate of change in elevation for the period 1965–2002 using the scientists' prediction. Round to the nearest hundredth of a meter per year. **−0.62 meter per year**

 b. More recent research suggests that the elevation decreased to about 30.5 meters above sea level in 2002. Use this information to predict the elevation in 2010. *Explain* the steps of your solution. **About 24.74 m. *Sample answer:* Find the average rate of change based on the actual elevation in 2002, −0.72; use the equation 30.5 + (−0.72)(8) to predict the elevation on 2010.**

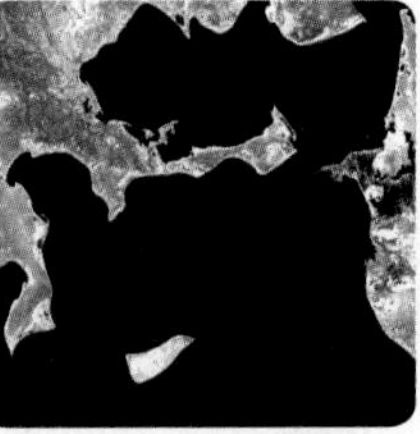
South Aral Sea, 1973

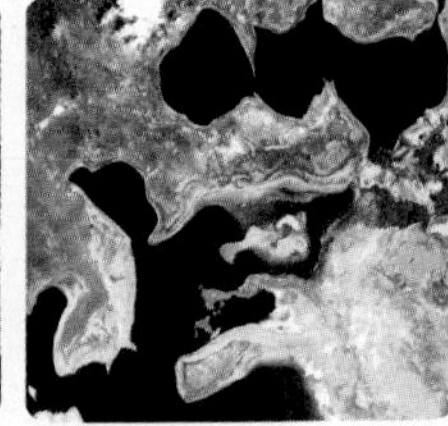
South Aral Sea, 2000

57. ★ **EXTENDED RESPONSE** In volleyball, an ace is a serve that the opponent doesn't hit. Ace efficiency is a measure of a player's ability to hit aces while minimizing service errors. The ace efficiency f is given by the formula $f = \frac{a-e}{s}$ where a is the number of aces, e is the number of service errors, and s is the total number of serves.

 a. **Calculate** Find the ace efficiency for a player who has 108 aces and 125 service errors in 500 serves. **−0.034**

 b. **Compare** If the player makes 30 more aces and 20 more service errors in the next 100 serves, will the ace efficiency improve? *Explain.* **Yes; it will improve to −0.012.**

 c. **Justify** Under what conditions would a player's ace efficiency be 0? 1? −1? *Justify* your answers algebraically. **See margin.**

C

58. **CHALLENGE** The average daily balance of a checking account is the sum of the daily balances in a given period divided by the number of days in the period. Suppose that a period has 30 days. Find the average daily balance of an account that has a balance of $110 for 18 days, −$300 for 10 days, and $100 for the rest of the period. **−$27.33**

MIXED REVIEW

Evaluate the expression.

59. $6x$ when $x = 15$ *(p. 2)* **90**

60. $4x + 2y$ when $x = 3$ and $y = 7$ *(p. 8)* **26**

61. $x - y - 2$ when $x = 3$ and $y = -4$ *(p. 80)* **5**

62. $-4xy$ when $x = -2$ and $y = -1.4$ *(p. 88)* **−11.2**

PREVIEW
Prepare for Lesson 2.7 in Exs. 63–64.

Identify the hypothesis and the conclusion of the statement. Tell whether the statement is *true* or *false*. If it is false, give a counterexample. *(p. 64)* **63, 64. See margin.**

63. If a number is a whole number, then the number is a rational number.

64. If a number is a rational number, then the number is an integer.

63. Hypothesis: a number is a whole number, conclusion: the number is a rational number; true.

64. Hypothesis: a number is a rational number, conclusion: the number is an integer; false. *Sample answer:* $\frac{2}{3}$ is a rational number, but not an integer.

2.7 Writing Statements in If-Then Form

MATERIALS • paper and pencil

QUESTION How can you write an *all* or *none* statement in if-then form?

EXPLORE Tell whether certain statements are true about a group

STEP 1 ***Answer questions*** Copy the questions below and write your answers beside them.

1. Do you play an instrument?
2. Do you participate in a school sport?
3. Are you taking an art class?
4. Do you walk to school?

STEP 2 ***Write if-then statements*** Each of the *all* or *none* statements below can be written in if-then form. Copy each statement and complete its equivalent if-then form. The first one is done for you as an example.

1. All of the students in our group play an instrument.
   If a student is in our group, then the student plays an instrument.
2. None of the students in our group participates in a school sport.
   If ? , then ? . **a student is in our group; the student doesn't participate in a school sport**
3. None of the students in our group is taking an art class.
   If ? , then ? . **a student is in our group; the student is not taking an art class**
4. All of the students in our group walk to school.
   If ? , then ? . **if a student is in our group; the student walks to school**

STEP 3 ***Analyze statements*** Form a group with 2 or 3 classmates. Tell whether each if-then statement in Step 2 is *true* or *false* for your group. If the statement is false, give a counterexample.

DRAW CONCLUSIONS Use your observations to complete these exercises

1. *Describe* the similarity and difference in the if-then forms of the following statements: **Both statements begin with "If a student is in our group" but the conclusion of the statement containing the word "all" is positive and the conclusion of the statement containing the word "none" is negative.**

   All of the students in our group listen to rock music.

   None of the students in our group listens to rock music.

Rewrite the given conditional statement in if-then form. Then tell whether the statement is *true* or *false*. If it is false, give a counterexample.

2. All of the positive numbers are integers. **If a number is positive, then it is an integer; false.** ***Sample answer***: $\frac{2}{3}$ **is a positive number, but it is not an integer.**
3. All of the rational numbers can be written as fractions.
   If a number is rational, then it can be written as a fraction; true.
4. None of the negative numbers is a whole number.
   If a number is negative, then it is not a whole number; true.
5. None of the rational numbers has an opposite equal to itself.
   If a number is rational, then it does not have an opposite equal to itself; false; 0 is a rational number and its opposite is 0.

1 PLAN AND PREPARE

Explore the Concept

- Students will write statements in if-then form.
- This activity leads into the study of rewriting conditional statements in Example 5 in Lesson 2.7.

Recommended Time

Work activity: 10 min

Discuss results:5 min

Grouping

Students should work in groups of 3–4. All students should answer the questions in Step 1. In Step 2, all students should write the if-then statements and then check that all the statements are written correctly. Students should complete Step 3 as a group.

2 TEACH

Tips for Success

In Step 2, point out that the "if" part of the if-then statement is the same for all of the statements and the "then" part of the if-then statement begins with "then the student."

Key Discovery

Generalizations that are true for all members of a set or for no members of a set can be written in if-then form.

3 ASSESS AND RETEACH

How many counterexamples does it take to prove that an if-then statement is false? **one**

1 PLAN AND PREPARE

Warm-Up Exercises

Transparency Available

Find the square of the number.

1. 14 **196** **2.** 16 **256**

Complete the statements using <, >, or =.

3. $-2.5 \ ? \ -\frac{19}{8}$ **<** **4.** $\frac{5}{6} \ ? \ \frac{21}{25}$ **<**

5. A square room has a side length of 25 feet. What is its area? **625 ft^2**

Notetaking Guide

Transparency Available

Promotes interactive learning and notetaking skills.

Pacing

Basic: 2 days

Average: 2 days

Advanced: 2 days

Block: 1 block

- See *Teaching Guide/Lesson Plan.*

2 FOCUS AND MOTIVATE

Essential Question

Big Idea 3, p. 63

How do you evaluate a square root and compare real numbers? **Tell students they will learn how to answer this question by finding and approximating square roots and graphing numbers on a number line.**

NCTM STANDARDS

Standard 1: Understand relationships among numbers; Understand number systems

2.7 Find Square Roots and Compare Real Numbers

Before You found squares of numbers and compared rational numbers.

Now You will find square roots and compare real numbers.

Why? So you can find side lengths of geometric shapes, as in Ex. 52.

Key Vocabulary
- **square root**
- **radicand**
- **perfect square**
- **irrational number**
- **real numbers**

Recall that the square of 4 is $4^2 = 16$ and the square of -4 is $(-4)^2 = 16$. The numbers 4 and -4 are called the *square roots* of 16. In this lesson, you will find the square roots of nonnegative numbers.

KEY CONCEPT *For Your Notebook*

Square Root of a Number

Words If $b^2 = a$, then b is a **square root** of a.

Example $3^2 = 9$ and $(-3)^2 = 9$, so 3 and -3 are square roots of 9.

All positive real numbers have two square roots, a positive square root (or *principal* square root) and a negative square root. A square root is written with the radical symbol $\sqrt{\ }$. The number or expression inside a radical symbol is the **radicand.**

radical symbol → $\sqrt{a}$ ← radicand

Zero has only one square root, 0. Negative real numbers do not have real square roots because the square of every real number is either positive or 0.

EXAMPLE 1 Find square roots

Evaluate the expression.

READING
The symbol ± is read as "plus or minus" and refers to both the positive square root and the negative square root.

a. $\pm\sqrt{36} = \pm 6$ **The positive and negative square roots of 36 are 6 and −6.**

b. $\sqrt{49} = 7$ **The positive square root of 49 is 7.**

c. $-\sqrt{4} = -2$ **The negative square root of 4 is −2.**

GUIDED PRACTICE for Example 1

Evaluate the expression.

1. $-\sqrt{9}$ **−3** **2.** $\sqrt{25}$ **5** **3.** $\pm\sqrt{64}$ **±8** **4.** $-\sqrt{81}$ **−9**

Resource Planning Guide

Chapter Resource Book
- Teaching Guide/Lesson Plan
- Practice levels A, B, C
- Study Guide
- Catch-up for Absent Students
- Problem Solving Workshop
- ...llenge

Workbooks
- Notetaking Guide
- Practice Workbook

Teaching Options
- **Power Presentations** provides dynamic electronic teaching resources for the classroom.
- **Activity Generator** provides editable activities for all ability levels.

Interactive Technology
- Easy Planner
- Power Presentations
- Activity Generator
- Animated Algebra
- Test Generator
- Online Quiz
- eWorkbook
- eEdition
- @HomeTutor

Resources for English Learners
- Spanish Study Guide
- Multi-Language Visual Glossary
- Student Resources in Spanish

See also the *Differentiated Instruction Resources* for more strategies for meeting individual needs.

PERFECT SQUARES The square of an integer is called a **perfect square**. As shown in Example 1, the square root of a perfect square is an integer. As you will see in Example 2, you need to approximate a square root if the radicand is a whole number that is *not* a perfect square.

EXAMPLE 2 Approximate a square root

FURNITURE The top of a folding table is a square whose area is 945 square inches. Approximate the side length of the tabletop to the nearest inch.

Solution

You need to find the side length s of the tabletop such that $s^2 = 945$. This means that s is the positive square root of 945. You can use a table to determine whether 945 is a perfect square.

Number	28	29	30	31	32
Square of number	784	841	900	961	1024

As shown in the table, 945 is *not* a perfect square. The greatest perfect square less than 945 is 900. The least perfect square greater than 945 is 961.

$900 < 945 < 961$ **Write a compound inequality that compares 945 with both 900 and 961.**

$\sqrt{900} < \sqrt{945} < \sqrt{961}$ **Take positive square root of each number.**

$30 < \sqrt{945} < 31$ **Find square root of each perfect square.**

The average of 30 and 31 is 30.5, and $(30.5)^2 = 930.25$. Because $945 > 930.25$, $\sqrt{945}$ is closer to 31 than to 30.

▶ The side length of the tabletop is about 31 inches.

USING A CALCULATOR In Example 2, you can use a calculator to obtain a better approximation of the side length of the tabletop.

The value shown can be rounded to the nearest hundredth, 30.74, or to the nearest tenth, 30.7. In either case, the length is closer to 31 than to 30.

GUIDED PRACTICE for Example 2

Approximate the square root to the nearest integer.

5. $\sqrt{32}$ **6** **6.** $\sqrt{103}$ **10** **7.** $-\sqrt{48}$ **−7** **8.** $-\sqrt{350}$ **−19**

IRRATIONAL NUMBERS The square root of a whole number that is not a perfect square is an example of an *irrational number*. An **irrational number**, such as $\sqrt{945} = 30.74085\ldots$, is a number that cannot be written as a quotient of two integers. The decimal form of an irrational number neither terminates nor repeats.

Motivating the Lesson

A square garden has an area of 225 square feet. You want to know how much fencing you should buy to go around the garden without measuring. By knowing how to find square roots, you can find the side length and then determine how much fencing you should buy.

3 TEACH

Extra Example 1

Evaluate the expression.

a. $\pm\sqrt{100}$ **±10**

b. $\sqrt{121}$ **11**

c. $-\sqrt{400}$ **−20**

Key Questions to Ask for Example 1

- How is Example 1a different from Examples 1b and 1c? **The symbol ± in Example 1a means that the expression represents *both* the positive and negative square roots. In Examples 1b and 1c, only a *single* square root is indicated.**
- In Example 1c, how is $-\sqrt{4}$ different from $\sqrt{-4}$? **$-\sqrt{4}$ means the negative square root of 4; $\sqrt{-4}$ means the square root of −4, which is not a real number.**

Extra Example 2

The top of a square box has an area of 320 square inches. Approximate the side length of the box top to the nearest inch. **18 in.**

Teaching Strategy

When discussing Example 2, suggest that students make a list of the squares of numbers to 50 to use as a reference in approximating square roots.

Differentiated Instruction

Visual Learners Mathematicians chose the symbol $\sqrt{\ }$ for a square root because it is a distorted letter *r*, which is the first letter of the word "root." Be sure that students do not confuse it with the symbol $\overline{)\ }$ used in long division.

See also the *Differentiated Instruction Resources* for more strategies.

Extra Example 3

Tell whether each of the following numbers is a real number, a rational number, an irrational number, an integer, or a whole number: $-\sqrt{25}$, $\sqrt{361}$, $\sqrt{30}$. **$-\sqrt{25}$: real number, rational number, integer; $\sqrt{361}$: real number, rational number, integer, whole number; $\sqrt{30}$: real number, irrational number**

Extra Example 4

Order the numbers from least to greatest: $-\sqrt{10}$, $\frac{19}{5}$, -3, $\sqrt{12}$, $\sqrt{16}$. **$-\sqrt{10}$, -3, $\sqrt{12}$, $\frac{19}{5}$, $\sqrt{16}$**

Teaching Strategy

In Example 4, remind students to use a calculator, as shown on page 111, to approximate square roots that are irrational numbers.

9. **$-\frac{9}{2}$: real number, rational number, 5.2: real number, rational number, 0: real number, rational number, integer, whole number, $\sqrt{7}$: real number, irrational number, 4.1: real number, rational number, $-\sqrt{20}$: real number, irrational number; $-\frac{9}{2}$, $-\sqrt{20}$, 0, $\sqrt{7}$, 4.1, 5.2**

REAL NUMBERS The set of **real numbers** is the set of all rational and irrational numbers, as illustrated in the Venn diagram below. Every point on the real number line represents a real number.

READING
If you exclude 0 from the whole numbers, the resulting set is called the *natural numbers*.

REAL NUMBERS

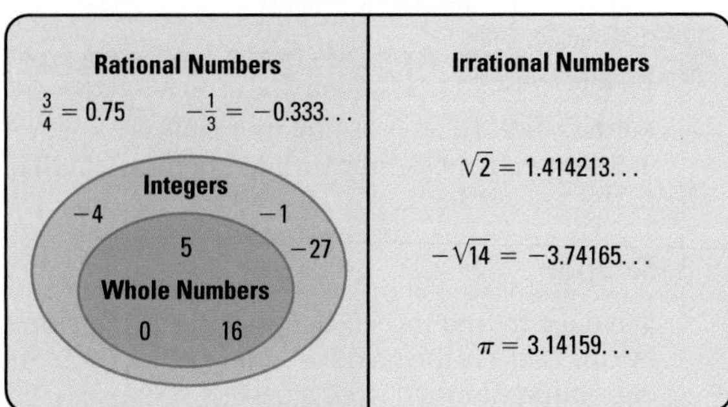

EXAMPLE 3 Classify numbers

Tell whether each of the following numbers is a real number, a rational number, an irrational number, an integer, or a whole number: $\sqrt{24}$, $\sqrt{100}$, $-\sqrt{81}$.

Number	Real number?	Rational number?	Irrational number?	Integer?	Whole number?
$\sqrt{24}$	Yes	No	Yes	No	No
$\sqrt{100}$	Yes	Yes	No	Yes	Yes
$-\sqrt{81}$	Yes	Yes	No	Yes	No

EXAMPLE 4 Graph and order real numbers

Order the numbers from least to greatest: $\frac{4}{3}$, $-\sqrt{5}$, $\sqrt{13}$, -2.5, $\sqrt{9}$.

Solution

Begin by graphing the numbers on a number line.

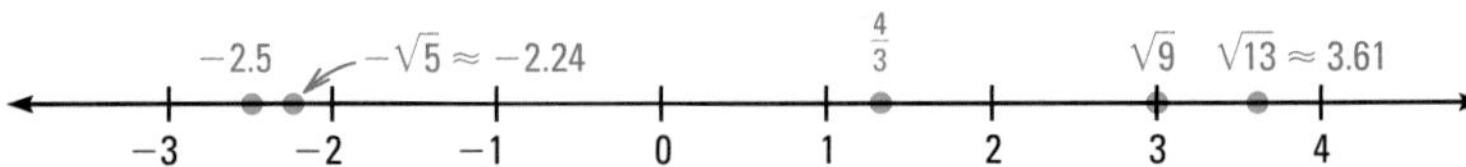

▸ Read the numbers from left to right: -2.5, $-\sqrt{5}$, $\frac{4}{3}$, $\sqrt{9}$, $\sqrt{13}$.

✓ **GUIDED PRACTICE** for Examples 3 and 4

9. Tell whether each of the following numbers is a real number, a rational number, an irrational number, an integer, or a whole number: $-\frac{9}{2}$, 5.2, 0, $\sqrt{7}$, 4.1, $-\sqrt{20}$. Then order the numbers from least to greatest. **See margin.**

CONDITIONAL STATEMENTS In the activity on page 109, you saw that a conditional statement not in if-then form can be written in that form.

EXAMPLE 5 Rewrite a conditional statement in if-then form

Rewrite the given conditional statement in if-then form. Then tell whether the statement is *true* or *false*. If it is false, give a counterexample.

Solution

a. Given: No fractions are irrational numbers.

If-then form: If a number is a fraction, then it is not an irrational number.

The statement is true.

b. Given: All real numbers are rational numbers.

If-then form: If a number is a real number, then it is a rational number.

The statement is false. For example, $\sqrt{2}$ is a real number but *not* a rational number.

✓ GUIDED PRACTICE for Example 5

Rewrite the conditional statement in if-then form. Then tell whether the statement is *true* or *false*. If it is false, give a counterexample.

10. All square roots of perfect squares are rational numbers.
If a number is the square root of a perfect square, then it is a rational number; true.

11. All repeating decimals are irrational numbers.

12. No integers are irrational numbers.
If a number is an integer, then it is not an irrational number; true.

1. If a number is a epeating decimal, hen it is an irrational umber; false. *Sample nswer:* 0.333... is a epeating decimal and can be written as $\frac{1}{3}$, so t is a rational number.

2.7 EXERCISES

HOMEWORK KEY
○ = **WORKED-OUT SOLUTIONS** on p. WS5 for Exs. 9, 19, and 47
★ = **STANDARDIZED TEST PRACTICE** Exs. 2, 23, 41, 42, 48, and 51
◆ = **MULTIPLE REPRESENTATIONS** Ex. 52

SKILL PRACTICE

1. VOCABULARY Copy and complete: The set of all rational and irrational numbers is called the set of __?__. **real numbers**

2. ★ WRITING Without calculating, how can you tell whether the square root of a whole number is rational or irrational?
If it is not a perfect square, the square root is irrational.

EXAMPLE 1 on p. 110 for Exs. 3–14

EVALUATING SQUARE ROOTS Evaluate the expression.

3. $\sqrt{4}$ **2**
4. $-\sqrt{49}$ **−7**
5. $-\sqrt{9}$ **−3**
6. $\pm\sqrt{1}$ **±1**
7. $\sqrt{196}$ **14**
8. $\pm\sqrt{121}$ **±11**
9. $\pm\sqrt{2500}$ **±50**
10. $-\sqrt{256}$ **−16**
11. $-\sqrt{225}$ **−15**
12. $\sqrt{361}$ **19**
13. $\pm\sqrt{169}$ **±13**
14. $-\sqrt{1600}$ **−40**

Extra Example 5

Rewrite the given conditional statement in if-then form. Then tell whether the statement is true or false. If it is false, give a counterexample.

a. Given: No square roots are rational numbers. **If a number is a square root, then it is not a rational number. False; $\sqrt{16}$ is a rational number.**

b. Given: All integers are rational numbers. **If a number is an integer, then it is a rational number. True.**

Closing the Lesson

Have students summarize the major points of the lesson and answer the Essential Question: How do you evaluate a square root and compare real numbers?

- **All positive numbers have a positive and a negative square root.**
- **Square roots of positive integers or rational numbers that are not perfect squares are irrational numbers that can be approximated by nonrepeating decimals.**

To evaluate the square root of *a*, you need to find the number *b* such that $b^2 = a$. To compare real numbers, you can graph the numbers on a number line, using approximations for any square roots that are irrational numbers.

4 PRACTICE AND APPLY

Assignment Guide

Answer Transparencies available for all exercises

Basic:
Day 1: SRH p. 909 Exs. 11–17 odd
pp. 113–116
Exs. 1–10, 15–20, 23, 45–48, 54–61
Day 2: pp. 113–116
Exs. 24–37, 49–51, 62–69

Average:
Day 1: pp. 113–116
Exs. 1, 2, 7–14, 17–23, 45–48, 54–61
Day 2: pp. 113–116
Exs. 24–32 even, 34–43, 49–52, 63–69 odd

Advanced:
Day 1: pp. 113–116
Exs. 1, 2, 9–14, 19–23, 45–50, 54–60 even
Day 2: pp. 113–116
Exs. 26–32 even, 36–44*, 51–53*, 62–68 even

Block:
pp. 113–116
Exs. 1, 2, 7–14, 17–23, 24–32 even, 34–43, 45–52, 54–61, 63–69 odd

Differentiated Instruction

See *Differentiated Instruction Resources* for suggestions on addressing the needs of a diverse classroom.

Homework Check

For a quick check of student understanding of key concepts, go over the following exercises:

Basic: 4, 16, 25, 30, 45
Average: 10, 20, 26, 30, 46
Advanced: 11, 21, 28, 32, 48

Extra Practice

- Student Edition, p. 939
- Chapter Resource Book: Practice levels A, B, C

Practice Worksheet

An easily-readable reduced practice page (with answers) for this lesson can be found on p. 62D.

EXAMPLE 2 on p. 111 for Exs. 15–22

APPROXIMATING SQUARE ROOTS Approximate the square root to the nearest integer.

15. $\sqrt{10}$ **3**
16. $-\sqrt{18}$ **−4**
17. $-\sqrt{3}$ **−2**
18. $\sqrt{150}$ **12**
(19.) $-\sqrt{86}$ **−9**
20. $\sqrt{40}$ **6**
21. $\sqrt{200}$ **14**
22. $-\sqrt{65}$ **−8**

23. ★ **MULTIPLE CHOICE** Which number is between −30 and −25? **B**

Ⓐ $-\sqrt{1610}$ Ⓑ $-\sqrt{680}$ Ⓒ $-\sqrt{410}$ Ⓓ $-\sqrt{27}$

EXAMPLES 3 and 4 on p. 112 for Exs. 24–29

CLASSIFYING AND ORDERING REAL NUMBERS Tell whether each number in the list is a real number, a rational number, an irrational number, an integer, or a whole number. Then order the numbers from least to greatest.

24. $\sqrt{49}$, 8, $-\sqrt{4}$, −3 **24–29. See margin.**
25. $-\sqrt{12}$, −3.7, $\sqrt{9}$, 2.9
26. −11.5, $-\sqrt{121}$, −10, $\frac{25}{2}$, $\sqrt{144}$
27. $\sqrt{8}$, $-\frac{2}{5}$, −1, 0.6, $\sqrt{6}$
28. $-\frac{8}{3}$, $-\sqrt{5}$, 2.6, −1.5, $\sqrt{5}$
29. −8.3, $-\sqrt{80}$, $-\frac{17}{2}$, −8.25, $-\sqrt{100}$

EXAMPLE 5 on p. 113 for Exs. 30–33

ANALYZING CONDITIONAL STATEMENTS Rewrite the conditional statement in if-then form. Then tell whether the statement is *true* or *false*. If it is false, give a counterexample. **30–33. See margin.**

30. All whole numbers are real numbers.
31. All real numbers are irrational numbers.
32. No perfect squares are whole numbers.
33. No irrational numbers are whole numbers.

B **EVALUATING EXPRESSIONS** Evaluate the expression for the given value of x.

34. $3 + \sqrt{x}$ when $x = 9$ **6**
35. $11 - \sqrt{x}$ when $x = 81$ **2**
36. $4 \cdot \sqrt{x}$ when $x = 49$ **28**
37. $-7 \cdot \sqrt{x}$ when $x = 36$ **−42**
38. $-3 \cdot \sqrt{x} - 7$ when $x = 121$ **−40**
39. $6 \cdot \sqrt{x} + 3$ when $x = 100$ **63**

40. **REASONING** Tell whether each of the following sets of numbers has an additive identity, additive inverses, a multiplicative identity, and multiplicative inverses: whole numbers, integers, rational numbers, real numbers. Use a table similar to the one on page 112 to display your results. **See margin.**

41. ★ **MULTIPLE CHOICE** If $x = 36$, the value of which expression is a perfect square? **B**

Ⓐ $\sqrt{x} + 17$ Ⓑ $87 - \sqrt{x}$ Ⓒ $5 \cdot \sqrt{x}$ Ⓓ $8 \cdot \sqrt{x} + 2$

42. ★ **WRITING** Let $x > 0$. Compare the values of x and $\sqrt{x}$ for $0 < x < 1$ and for $x > 1$. Give examples to justify your thinking.

42. For $0 < x < 1$, $x < \sqrt{x}$; for example, if $x = \frac{1}{4}$, $\sqrt{x} = \frac{1}{2}$, and $\frac{1}{4} < \frac{1}{2}$. For $x > 1$, $x > \sqrt{x}$; for example, if $x = 9$, $\sqrt{x} = 3$, and $9 > 3$.

C 43. **CHALLENGE** Find the first five perfect squares x such that $2 \cdot \sqrt{x}$ is also a perfect square. *Describe* your method. **4, 64, 324, 1024, 2500; take $\frac{1}{2}$ of an even perfect square, and then square it.**

44. **CHALLENGE** Let n be any whole number from 1 to 1000. For how many values of n is $\sqrt{n}$ a rational number? *Explain* your reasoning. **31; the square root of 1000 is between 31 and 32, so there are 31 perfect squares less than 1000.**

○ = WORKED-OUT SOLUTIONS on p. WS1 ★ = STANDARDIZED TEST PRACTICE

24–29. See Additional Answers beginning on p. AA1.
30. If a number is a whole number, then it is a real number; true.
31. If a number is a real number, then it is an irrational number; false. ***Sample answer:*** **3 is a real number and a rational number.**
32. If a number is a perfect square, then it is not a whole number; false. ***Sample answer:*** **9 is a perfect square and a whole number.**
33. If a number is an irrational number, then it is not a whole number; true.

PROBLEM SOLVING

EXAMPLE 1 A
on p. 110
for Exs. 45, 47

45. **ART** The area of a square painting is 3600 square inches. Find the side length of the painting. **60 in.**

@HomeTutor for problem solving help at classzone.com

EXAMPLE 2
on p. 111
for Exs. 46, 48

46. **SOCCER** Some soccer drills are practiced in a square section of a field. If the section of a field for a soccer drill is 1620 square yards, find the side length of the section. Round your answer to the nearest yard. **40 yd**

@HomeTutor for problem solving help at classzone.com

47. **MAZES** The table shows the locations and areas of various life-size square mazes. Find the side lengths of the mazes. Then tell whether the side lengths are *rational* or *irrational* numbers.
35 ft; 24 ft; 48 ft; 30 ft; they are all rational numbers.

Location of maze	Area (ft^2)
Dallas, Texas	1225
San Francisco, California	576
Corona, New York	2304
Waterville, Maine	900

Maze at Corona, New York

48. ★ **SHORT RESPONSE** You plan to use a square section of a park for a small outdoor concert. The section should have an area of 1450 square feet. You have 150 feet of rope to use to surround the section. Do you have enough rope? *Explain* your reasoning. **No; each side is a little more than 38 feet. 38 feet times 4 is 152 feet, which is more than 150 feet.**

49. **STORAGE CUBES** If $b^3 = a$, then b is called the *cube root* of a, written $\sqrt[3]{a}$. For instance, in Example 5 on page 4, $14^3 = 2744$, so 14 is the cube root of 2744, or $14 = \sqrt[3]{2744}$. Suppose a storage cube is advertised as having a volume of 10 cubic feet. Use a calculator to approximate the edge length of the storage cube to the nearest tenth of a foot. **2.2 feet**

B

50. **MULTI-STEP PROBLEM** The Kelvin temperature scale was invented by Lord Kelvin in the 19th century and is often used for scientific measurements. To convert a temperature from degrees Celsius (°C) to kelvin (K), you add 273 to the temperature in degrees Celsius.

    a. Convert 17°C to kelvin. **290 K**

    b. The speed s (in meters per second) of sound in air is given by the formula $s = 20.1 \cdot \sqrt{K}$ where K is the temperature in kelvin. Find the speed of sound in air at 17°C. Round your answer to the nearest meter per second. **342 m/sec**

51. ★ **SHORT RESPONSE** A homeowner is building a square patio and will cover the patio with square tiles. Each tile has an area of 256 square inches and costs $3.45. The homeowner has $500 to spend on tiles.

    a. **Calculate** How many tiles can the homeowner buy? **144 tiles**

    b. **Explain** Find the side length (in feet) of the largest patio that the homeowner can build. *Explain* how you got your answer. **See margin.**

Graphing Calculator

Exercises 15–23 It may be helpful for students to use calculators to approximate the square roots. Tell them to use the instructions on how to approximate square roots on page 111.

Study Strategy

Exercise 46 Students may be tempted to use their calculators to solve this problem. Encourage them to use their calculators to check their answers, but use the solution model for Example 2 to solve the problem. Explain that by using the model, they will develop a better understanding of square roots. By learning to approximate the square root of a number, they will develop estimation skills that can help them judge whether they entered numbers in their calculators incorrectly.

Avoiding Common Errors

Exercise 50 Some students overlook the different parts of a problem and then make errors because they lack information necessary to solve the problem. Some students may use 17°C for K in part b of this exercise. Remind students to read all parts of a problem before proceeding.

51b. 16 ft. *Sample answer:* If the homeowner can buy 144 tiles that are each 256 square inches, then the total area is (144 tiles) • (256 square inches per tile) = 36,864 square inches. Divide 36,864 square inches by 144 square inches to find the number of square feet, 256 square feet. If the area of the square is 256 square feet, take the square root of 256 to find the side length, 16 feet.

40.

Set	Additive identity?	Additive inverses?	Multiplicative identity?	Multiplicative inverses?
Whole numbers	Yes	No (except 0)	Yes	No (except 1)
Integers	Yes	Yes	Yes	No (except 1)
Rational numbers	Yes	Yes	Yes	Yes (except 0)
Real numbers	Yes	Yes	Yes	Yes (except 0)

5 ASSESS AND RETEACH

Daily Homework Quiz

Transparency Available

Evaluate the expression.

1. $\pm\sqrt{289}$ **±17**

2. $-\sqrt{36}$ **−6**

Approximate the square root to the nearest integer.

3. $-\sqrt{21}$ **−5**

4. $\sqrt{620}$ **25**

5. A square courtyard has an area of 272 square feet. What is the side length of the courtyard to the nearest foot? **16 ft**

Online Quiz

Available at **classzone.com**

Diagnosis/Remediation

- Practice A, B, C in Chapter Resource Book
- Study Guide in Chapter Resource Book
- Practice Workbook
- @HomeTutor

Challenge

Additional challenge is available in the Chapter Resource Book.

Quiz

An easily-readable reduced copy of the quiz (with answers) on Lessons 2.6–2.7 from the Assessment Book can be found on p. 62E.

52a. See Additional Answers beginning on p. AA1.

Quiz

6. −3: real number, rational number, integer, $-\sqrt{5}$: real number, irrational number, −3.7: real number, rational number, $\sqrt{3}$: real number, rational number; −3.7, −3, $-\sqrt{5}$, $\sqrt{3}$

52. ◆ **MULTIPLE REPRESENTATIONS** The diagram shows the approximate areas (in square meters) of the square bases for the pyramids of Giza. **See margin.**

a. Making a Table Make a table that gives the following quotients (rounded to the nearest tenth) for each of the 3 pairs of pyramids:

- (area of larger base) ÷ (area of smaller base)
- (side length of larger base) ÷ (side length of smaller base)

For each pair of pyramids, how are the two quotients related?

b. Writing an Equation Write an equation that gives the quotient q of the side lengths as a function of the quotient r of the areas. $q = \sqrt{r}$

C **53. CHALLENGE** Write an equation that gives the edge length ℓ of a cube as a function of the surface area A of the cube. $\ell = \sqrt{\frac{A}{6}}$

MIXED REVIEW

Evaluate the expression. *(p. 8)*

54. $11 + 6 - 3$ **14** **55.** $18 - 3^2$ **9** **56.** $9 \cdot 2^2 - 1$ **35** **57.** $6(4^2 + 4)$ **120**

58. $12 \cdot 3 + 15$ **51** **59.** $6 \cdot 4 + 7 \cdot 5$ **59** **60.** $9(15 - 2 \cdot 4)$ **63** **61.** $5^2 - 2^3$ **17**

PREVIEW Prepare for Lesson 3.1 in Exs. 62–69.

Solve the equation using mental math. *(p. 21)*

62. $8 + x = 13$ **5** **63.** $x - 20 = 15$ **35** **64.** $4x = 32$ **8** **65.** $\frac{x}{7} = 5$ **35**

66. $x - 14 = 30$ **44** **67.** $x + 11 = 27$ **16** **68.** $\frac{x}{9} = 10$ **90** **69.** $6x = 48$ **8**

QUIZ for Lessons 2.6–2.7

Find the quotient. *(p. 103)*

1. $-20 \div (-5)$ **4** **2.** $-12 \div \frac{2}{3}$ **−18** **3.** $\frac{4}{5} \div \left(-\frac{3}{10}\right)$ **$-2\frac{2}{3}$** **4.** $-18.2 \div (-3)$ **$6\frac{1}{15}$**

5. Simplify the expression $\frac{15x - 6}{3}$. *(p. 103)* **5x −2**

6. Tell whether each of the following numbers is a real number, a rational number, an irrational number, an integer, or a whole number: -3, $-\sqrt{5}$, -3.7, $\sqrt{3}$. Then order the numbers from least to greatest. *(p. 110)* **See margin.**

7. Rewrite the following conditional statement in if-then form: "No irrational numbers are negative numbers." Tell whether the statement is *true* or *false*. If it is false, give a counterexample. *(p. 110)*

7. If a number is irrational, then it is not a negative number; false. *Sample answer*: $-\sqrt{5}$ is an irrational number and it is negative.

EXTRA PRACTICE for Lesson 2.7, p. 939 **ONLINE QUIZ** at classzone.com

Use after Lesson 2.7

Use Logical Reasoning

GOAL Use inductive and deductive reasoning.

Key Vocabulary
- **inductive reasoning**
- **conjecture**
- **closure**
- **deductive reasoning**

When you make a conclusion based on several examples, you are using **inductive reasoning**. A conclusion reached using inductive reasoning is an example of a *conjecture*. A **conjecture** is a statement that is believed to be true but not yet shown to be true.

EXAMPLE 1 Use inductive reasoning

Let *a* and *b* be even integers. Make a conjecture about the product *ab*.

Solution

Consider pairs of integer values of *a* and *b*, including combinations of positive, negative, and 0 values.

a	*b*	*ab*	*ab* even or odd?
−8	−4	32	Even
−4	6	−24	Even
20	−2	−40	Even
0	2	0	Even
−14	0	0	Even
10	12	120	Even

Conjecture: For even integers *a* and *b*, the product *ab* is an even integer.

CLOSURE The conjecture in Example 1 is true. The product of any two even integers is an even integer. The set of even integers has *closure* or is *closed* under multiplication.

KEY CONCEPT — For Your Notebook

Closure

A set has **closure** or is *closed* under a given operation if the number that results from performing the operation on any two numbers in the set is also in the set.

Example: The product of any two integers is an integer. The set of integers is closed under multiplication.

Non-example: The quotient of two integers is not necessarily an integer. The set of integers is not closed under division.

1 PLAN AND PREPARE

Warm-Up Exercises

Tell whether each statement is *true* or *false*. If it is false, give a counterexample.

1. If a number is negative, then it is a rational number. **False; $-\sqrt{20}$ is a negative number and it is not rational.**
2. If a number is an integer, then it is not a whole number. **False; 7 is an integer and also a whole number.**

2 FOCUS AND MOTIVATE

Essential Question

Big Idea 3, p. 63

How do you use reasoning with real numbers? **Tell students they will learn how to answer this question by analyzing and proving conjectures.**

3 TEACH

Extra Example 1

Let *a* and *b* be even integers. Make a conjecture about the difference $a - b$.

Consider pairs of integer values of *a* and *b*: $-2 - 4 = -6$ (even); $-6 - 2 = -8$ (even); $4 - 6 = -2$ (even). Conjecture: For even integers *a* and *b*, the difference $a - b$ is an even integer.

NCTM STANDARDS

Standard 7: Make mathematical conjectures; Investigate mathematical conjectures

Extra Example 2

Prove that the set of even integers is closed under subtraction.

Let x and y be even integers. Then $x = 2m$ for some integer m, and $y = 2n$ for some integer n. So, $x - y = 2m - 2n$ by the substitution property of equality, and $2m - 2n = 2(m - n)$ by the distributive property. Also, $2(m - n) = 2[m + (-n)]$ by the subtraction rule. Because the set of integers is closed under addition, $m + (-n)$ is an integer, and $x - y$ is the product of 2 and another integer. By definition, $x - y$ is an even integer. So, the set of even integers is closed under subtraction.

Closing the Lesson

Have students summarize the major points of the lesson and answer the Essential Question: How do you use reasoning with real numbers?

- **Inductive reasoning uses examples to draw conclusions.**
- **Deductive reasoning uses true statements, whether assumed true or shown to be true, to draw conclusions.**
- **A conjecture is a conclusion based on inductive reasoning.**

You can use inductive and deductive methods to analyze statements about real numbers and determine if they are true or false.

4 PRACTICE AND APPLY

Teaching Strategy

Exercise 4 For students who have difficulty with this exercise, suggest they reread Example 2 carefully and use it as a guide to proving their conjectures.

DEDUCTIVE REASONING When you make a conclusion based on statements that are assumed or shown to be true, you are using deductive reasoning. An argument based on **deductive reasoning** is called a *proof.* The following example gives a proof, or *proves,* that the set of even integers is closed under multiplication. It uses the fact that an even integer is an integer that can be written as the product of 2 and another integer.

EXAMPLE 2 Use deductive reasoning

Prove that the set of even integers is closed under multiplication.

Solution

Let x and y be even integers. Then $x = 2m$ for some integer m, and $y = 2n$ for some integer n.

$xy = (2m)(2n)$	Substitution property of equality
$= 2[m(2n)]$	Associative property of multiplication

Because the set of integers is closed under multiplication, $m(2n)$ is an integer, and xy is the product of 2 and another integer. By definition, xy is an even integer. So, the set of even integers is closed under multiplication.

PRACTICE

EXAMPLE 1 on p. 117 for Exs. 1–3

Make a conjecture about the number. In Exercises 2 and 3, use the fact that an odd integer is an integer that can be written as the sum of an even integer and 1. That is, the integer x is odd if $x = 2m + 1$ for some integer m.

1. The sum of two even integers x and y **The sum is even.**
2. The sum of an odd integer x and an even integer y **The sum is odd.**
3. The sum of two odd integers x and y **The sum is even.**

EXAMPLE 2 on p. 118 for Exs. 4, 7

4. **REASONING** Prove your conjecture from Exercise 1.

Tell whether the set is closed under the indicated operation.

5. The set of negative integers; multiplication **Not closed**
6. The set of whole numbers; addition **Closed**
7. **REASONING** The following is a proof that for any real number a, $a + a \cdot (-1) = 0$, which shows that $a \cdot (-1)$ is the opposite of a. Justify each step. The proof uses the addition property of equality: If $a = b$, then $a + c = b + c$. You will learn about this property in Lesson 3.1.

$a = a \cdot 1$	? **Ident. prop. of mult.**
$a + a \cdot (-1) = a \cdot 1 + a \cdot (-1)$	Addition property of equality
$a + a \cdot (-1) = a[1 + (-1)]$	? **Dist. prop.**
$a + a \cdot (-1) = a \cdot 0$	? **Inv. prop. of add.**
$a + a \cdot (-1) = 0$	? **Prop. of zero**

4. Let x and y be even integers. Then $x = 2m$ for some integer m, and $y = 2n$ for some integer n. So, $x + y = 2m + 2n$ by the substitution property of equality, and $2m + 2n = 2(m + n)$ by the distributive property. Because the set of integers is closed under addition, $m + n$ is an integer, and $x + y$ is the product of 2 and another integer. By definition, $x + y$ is an even integer.

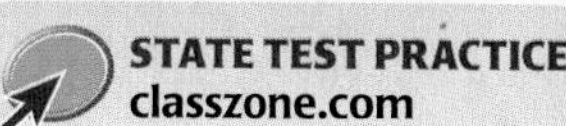

Lessons 2.4–2.7

1. **MULTI-STEP PROBLEM** The modern pentathlon consists of 5 events, including a distance run. For the men's run, every athlete starts with 1000 points. The athlete earns 2 points for every 0.5 second under a finishing time of 10 minutes and −2 points for every 0.5 second over 10 minutes.

   a. An athlete finishes the race in 9 minutes 34 seconds. How many points does he have now? **1104 points**

   b. His competitor finishes in 11 minutes 2.5 seconds. How many more points than his competitor does he have? **354 points**

2. **MULTI-STEP PROBLEM** The troposphere is the lowest layer of the atmosphere. It extends to a height of 11,000 meters. On average, the temperature is 15°C at the bottom of the troposphere and changes by about −0.0065°C for every meter of increase in elevation.

   a. Write an equation that gives the temperature T (in degrees Celsius) as a function of the elevation e (in meters) within the troposphere. $T = 15 + (-0.0065)e$

   b. Find the temperature at the top of the troposphere. **−56.5°C**

3. **GRIDDED ANSWER** The table shows the areas of two square rugs that a store sells. How many inches longer is the sorrel rug than the shaw rug? **3 in.**

Type of rug	Area (in.^{2})
Sorrel rug	8281
Shaw rug	7744

4. **SHORT RESPONSE** Your friend is comparing two 6-sided cubic storage bins. The yellow bin has a surface area of 9600 square centimeters and costs \$25. The blue bin has a surface area of 7350 square centimeters and costs \$20.

   a. Find the edge length of each bin. **40 cm; 35 cm**

   b. Which bin costs less per cubic centimeter? *Explain* your reasoning. **See margin.**

5. **SHORT RESPONSE** The table shows the costs of three items at a baseball stadium in 2002 and 2004.

Item	Cost in 2002	Cost in 2004
Ticket	\$20.44	\$17.90
Soda	\$2.75	\$2.00
Hot dog	\$2.75	\$2.75

   a. Write an equation that gives the change c in the total amount spent from 2002 to 2004 when buying x of each item. Then find the value of c when $x = 4$. $c = -3.29x$; **−\$13.16**

   b. Suppose that from 2004 to 2006 the cost of a ticket decreases, and the costs of the other two items increase. Can you conclude that the change in the total amount spent from 2004 to 2006 is positive? *Explain.* **No; it depends on the amount of change for each item.**

6. **EXTENDED RESPONSE** A farmer is planting corn and soybeans in the rectangular field shown. The farmer spends \$.09 per square yard to plant corn and \$.07 per square yard to plant soybeans.

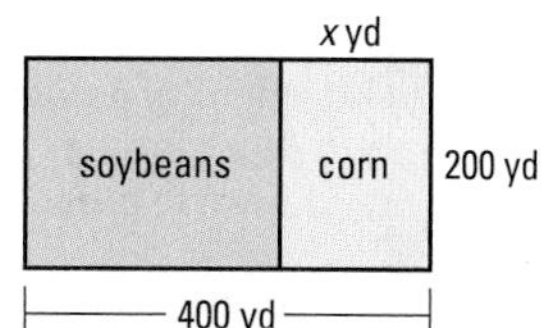

   a. Write an equation that gives the cost C of planting the field as a function of the length x (in yards) of the corn section. $C = 4x + 5600$

   b. How much money will the farmer spend on planting the field if the corn section has a length of 100 yards? **\$6000**

   c. Suppose that the farmer has \$6500 to plant the entire field. Will the farmer have enough money if the soybean section has a length of 250 yards? *Explain.* **Yes; the cost will be \$6200.**

7. **OPEN-ENDED** *Describe* a real-world situation that can be modeled by the expression $\frac{8.90 + (-2.34) + (-1.15)}{3}$. Then find the value of the expression. **See margin.**

4b. The yellow bin. ***Sample answer:*** **For each bin, divide the cost by the surface area; the yellow bin costs less per cubic centimeter.**

7. ***Sample answer:*** **A stock increases in value by \$8.90 one week, decreases by \$2.34 the next week and decreases \$1.15 the following week. The expression** $\frac{8.90 + (-2.34) + (-1.15)}{3}$ **represents the stock's average change over 3 weeks; \$1.80.**

Additional Resources

The following resources are available to help review the materials in this chapter.

Chapter Resource Book

- Chapter Review Games and Activities
- Cumulative Practice, Chs. 1–2

Student Resources in Spanish

eWorkbook

@HomeTutor

Vocabulary Practice

Vocabulary practice is available at **classzone.com**

2 CHAPTER SUMMARY

BIG IDEAS — For Your Notebook

Big Idea 1

Performing Operations with Real Numbers

To add or multiply two real numbers a and b, you can use the following rules:

Expression	Rule when a and b have the same sign	Rule when a and b have different signs
$a + b$	Add $\lvert a\rvert$ and $\lvert b\rvert$. The sum has the same sign as a and b.	Subtract the lesser absolute value from the greater absolute value. The sum has the same sign as the number with the greater absolute value.
ab	The product is positive.	The product is negative.

You can use these rules to subtract or divide numbers, but first you rewrite the difference or quotient using the subtraction rule or the division rule.

Big Idea 2

Applying Properties of Real Numbers

You can apply the properties of real numbers to evaluate and simplify expressions. Many of the properties of addition and multiplication are similar.

Property	Addition	Multiplication
Commutative property	$a + b = b + a$	$ab = ba$
Associative property	$(a + b) + c = a + (b + c)$	$(ab)c = a(bc)$
Identity property	$a + 0 = 0 + a = a$	$a \cdot 1 = 1 \cdot a = a$
Inverse property	$a + (-a) = -a + a = 0$	$a \cdot \frac{1}{a} = \frac{1}{a} \cdot a = 1, a \neq 0$
Distributive property	$a(b + c) = ab + ac$ (and three variations)	

Big Idea 3

Classifying and Reasoning with Real Numbers

Being able to classify numbers can help you tell whether a conditional statement about real numbers is true or false. For example, the following statement is false: "All real numbers are integers." A counterexample is 3.5.

Numbers	Description
Whole numbers	The numbers 0, 1, 2, 3, 4, . . .
Integers	The numbers . . . , −3, −2, −1, 0, 1, 2, 3, . . .
Rational numbers	Numbers of the form $\frac{a}{b}$ where a and b are integers and $b \neq 0$
Irrational numbers	Numbers that cannot be written as a quotient of two integers
Real numbers	All rational and irrational numbers

2 CHAPTER REVIEW

@HomeTutor
classzone.com
- Multi-Language Glossary
- Vocabulary practice

REVIEW KEY VOCABULARY

- whole numbers, integers, positive integer, negative integer, *p. 64*
- rational number, *p. 64*
- opposites, absolute value, *p. 66*
- conditional statement, *p. 66*
- if-then statement, *p. 66*
- counterexample, *p. 66*
- additive identity, *p. 76*
- additive inverse, *p. 76*
- multiplicative identity, *p. 89*
- equivalent expressions, *p. 96*
- distributive property, *p. 96*
- term, coefficient, constant term, like terms, *p. 97*
- multiplicative inverse, *p. 103*
- square root, radicand, *p. 110*
- perfect square, *p. 111*
- irrational number, *p. 111*
- real numbers, *p. 112*
- closure, *p. 117*

VOCABULARY EXERCISES

Identify the terms, coefficients, constant terms, and like terms of the expression. **1, 2. See margin.**

1. $-3x - 5 - 7x - 9$
2. $-10c - 6 + c$

Tell whether the number is a real number, a rational number, an irrational number, an integer, or a whole number.

3. 0.3 **real number, rational number**
4. $-\sqrt{8}$ **real number, irrational number**
5. -15 **real number, rational number, integer**
6. $\sqrt{49}$ **real number, rational number, integer, whole number**

REVIEW EXAMPLES AND EXERCISES

Use the review examples and exercises below to check your understanding of the concepts you have learned in each lesson of Chapter 2.

2.1 Use Integers and Rational Numbers *pp. 64–67*

EXAMPLE

Order the following numbers from least to greatest: $\frac{1}{5}$, −0.10, 0.25, $-\frac{1}{6}$.

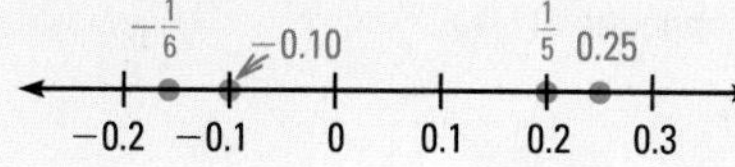

From least to greatest, the numbers are $-\frac{1}{6}$, −0.10, $\frac{1}{5}$, and 0.25.

EXERCISES

EXAMPLES 3, 4, and 5 on pp. 65–66 for Exs. 7–12

Order the numbers in the list from least to greatest.

7. $-5.2, -\frac{3}{8}, -6, 0.3, -\frac{1}{4}$ **$-6, -5.2, -\frac{3}{8}, -\frac{1}{4}, 0.3$**
8. $2.1, 0, -\frac{13}{10}, -1.38, \frac{3}{5}$ **$-1.38, -\frac{13}{10}, 0, \frac{3}{5}, 2.1$**

For the given value of a, find $-a$ and $|a|$.

9. $a = -0.2$ **0.2, 0.2**
10. $a = 3$ **−3, 3**
11. $a = \frac{7}{8}$ **$-\frac{7}{8}, \frac{7}{8}$**
12. $a = -\frac{6}{11}$ **$\frac{6}{11}, \frac{6}{11}$**

Extra Example 2.1
Order the following numbers from least to greatest: −1.3, 0.15, $-\frac{1}{3}, \frac{1}{8}$, −0.2. **$-1.3, -\frac{1}{3}, -0.2, \frac{1}{8}, 0.15$**

1. terms: $-3x$, −5, $-7x$, −9; coefficients: −3, −7; constant terms: −5, −9; like terms: $-3x$ and $-7x$, −5 and −9

2. terms: $-10c$, −6, c; coefficients: −10, 1; constant terms: −6; like terms: $-10c$ and c

Extra Example 2.2

Find the sum.

a. $-12.8 + 6$ **-6.8**

b. $\frac{5}{8} + \left(-\frac{3}{4}\right)$ **$-\frac{1}{8}$**

Extra Example 2.3

Find the difference.

a. $-14 - 8$ **-22**

b. $6.3 - (-2.9)$ **9.2**

2 CHAPTER REVIEW

2.2 Add Real Numbers

pp. 74–76

EXAMPLE

Find the sum.

a. $-3.6 + (-5.5) = -(|-3.6| + |-5.5|)$ **Rule of same signs**

$= -(3.6 + 5.5)$ **Take absolute values.**

$= -9.1$ **Add.**

b. $16.1 + (-9.3) = |16.1| - |-9.3|$ **Rule of different signs**

$= 16.1 - 9.3$ **Take absolute values.**

$= 6.8$ **Subtract.**

EXERCISES

EXAMPLES 1, 2, and 4 on pp. 74–76 for Exs. 13–19

Find the sum.

13. $-2 + 5$ **3**
14. $-6 + (-4)$ **-10**
15. $6.2 + (-9.7)$ **-3.5**
16. $-4.61 + (-0.79)$ **-5.4**
17. $-\frac{4}{7} + \left(-\frac{9}{14}\right)$ **$-1\frac{3}{14}$**
18. $-\frac{4}{5} + \frac{11}{12}$ **$\frac{7}{60}$**
19. **BUSINESS** A company has a profit of \$2.07 million in its first year, $-\$1.54$ million in its second year, and $-\$.76$ million in its third year. Find the company's total profit for the three years. **$-\$.23$ million**

2.3 Subtract Real Numbers

pp. 80–81

EXAMPLE

Find the difference.

a. $12 - 19 = 12 + (-19)$ **Add the opposite of 19.**

$= -7$ **Simplify.**

b. $8.2 - (-1.6) = 8.2 + 1.6$ **Add the opposite of -1.6.**

$= 9.8$ **Simplify.**

EXERCISES

EXAMPLES 1 and 2 on p. 80 for Exs. 20–28

Find the difference.

20. $-8 - 3$ **-11**
21. $1 - 11$ **-10**
22. $7.7 - 16.3$ **-8.6**
23. $-20.3 - (-14.2)$ **-6.1**
24. $\frac{7}{3} - \frac{11}{3}$ **$-1\frac{1}{3}$**
25. $-\frac{4}{9} - \frac{5}{12}$ **$-\frac{31}{36}$**

Evaluate the expression when $x = 2$ and $y = -3$.

26. $(x - 7) + y$ **-8**
27. $\frac{3}{2} - x - y$ **$2\frac{1}{2}$**
28. $y - (2.4 - x)$ **-3.4**

@HomeTutor
classzone.com
Chapter Review Practice

2.4 Multiply Real Numbers

pp. 88–90

EXAMPLE

Find the product.

a. $-4(12) = -48$ Different signs; product is negative.

b. $\frac{1}{2}(-6)(-3) = -3(-3)$ Multiply $\frac{1}{2}$ and -6.

$= 9$ Same signs; product is positive.

EXERCISES

EXAMPLES 1, 3, and 4 on pp. 88–90 for Exs. 29–35

Find the product.

29. $15(-4)$ **−60**

30. $-7.5(-8)$ **60**

31. $-\frac{2}{5}(-5)(-9)$ **−18**

Find the product. *Justify* your steps. 32–34. See margin.

32. $-4(-y)(-7)$

33. $-\frac{1}{3}x \cdot (-18)$

34. $2.5(-4z)(-2)$

35. SWIMMING POOLS The water level of a swimming pool is 3.3 feet and changes at an average rate of −0.14 feet per day due to water evaporation. What will the water level of the pool be after 4 days? **2.74 ft**

2.5 Apply the Distributive Property

pp. 96–98

EXAMPLE

Use the distributive property to write an equivalent expression.

a. $5(x + 3) = 5(x) + 5(3)$ Distribute 5.

$= 5x + 15$ Simplify.

b. $(7 - y)(-2y) = 7(-2y) - y(-2y)$ Distribute $-2y$.

$= -14y + 2y^2$ Simplify.

EXERCISES

EXAMPLES 1, 2, 4, and 5 on pp. 96–98 for Exs. 36–42

Use the distributive property to write an equivalent expression.

36. $8(5 - x)$ **$40 - 8x$**

37. $-3(y + 9)$ **$-3y - 27$**

38. $(z - 4)(-z)$ **$-z^2 + 4z$**

Simplify the expression.

39. $3(x - 2) + 14$ **$3x + 8$**

40. $9.1 - 4(m + 3.2)$ **$-3.7 - 4m$**

41. $5n + \frac{1}{2}(8n - 7)$ **$9n - 3\frac{1}{2}$**

42. PARTY COSTS You are buying 10 pizzas for a party. Cheese pizzas cost \$11 each, and single topping pizzas cost \$13 each. Write an equation that gives the total cost C (in dollars) as a function of the number p of cheese pizzas that you buy. Then find the total cost if you buy 4 cheese pizzas. **$C = -2p + 130$; \$122**

Extra Example 2.4

Find the product.

a. $-8(-2.5)$ 20

b. $-\frac{1}{3}(9)(2)$ −6

Extra Example 2.5

Use the distributive property to write an equivalent expression.

a. $-6(y - 2)$ $-6y + 12$

b. $(5 - x)(-x)$ $-5x + x^2$

32. $-28y$; $-4(-y)(-7) = -4(-7)(-y)$, commutative property of multiplication; $28(-y)$, product of −4 and −7; $-28y$, multiply

33. $6x$; $-\frac{1}{3}x \cdot (-18) = -\frac{1}{3}(-18)(x)$, commutative property of multiplication; $6(x)$, product of $-\frac{1}{3}$ and −18; $6x$, multiply

34. $20z$; $2.5(-4z)(-2) = 2.5(-2)(-4z)$, commutative property of multiplication, $-5(-4z)$, product of 2.5 and −2; $[(-5)(-4)]z$, associative property of multiplication, $20z$, multiply

Extra Example 2.6

Find the quotient.

a. $-112 \div (-8)$ **14**

b. $\frac{12}{21} \div \left(-\frac{6}{7}\right)$ **$-\frac{2}{3}$**

Extra Example 2.7

Order the following numbers from least to greatest: $\sqrt{12}$, 3.8, $-\sqrt{64}$, -8.2, 3. **-8.2, $-\sqrt{64}$, 3, $\sqrt{12}$, 3.8**

2.6 Divide Real Numbers

pp. 103–105

EXAMPLE

Find the quotient.

a. $196 \div (-7) = 196 \cdot \left(-\frac{1}{7}\right)$

$= -28$

b. $-\frac{14}{15} \div \left(-\frac{7}{3}\right) = -\frac{14}{15} \cdot \left(-\frac{3}{7}\right)$

$= \frac{2}{5}$

EXERCISES

EXAMPLES 2, 3, and 4 on pp. 104–105 for Exs. 43–49

Find the quotient.

43. $56 \div (-4)$ **-14**

44. $-6 \div \frac{3}{13}$ **-26**

45. $-\frac{4}{9} \div \left(-\frac{2}{3}\right)$ **$\frac{2}{3}$**

46. SCIENCE A scientist studies the diving abilities of three seals and records the elevations they reach before swimming back up to the surface. Find the mean of the following elevations (in meters) recorded: -380, -307, -354. **-347 m**

Simplify the expression.

47. $\frac{24x - 40}{8}$ **$3x - 5$**

48. $\frac{-36m + 18}{6}$ **$-6m + 3$**

49. $\frac{-18n - 9}{-9}$ **$2n + 1$**

2.7 Find Square Roots and Compare Real Numbers

pp. 110–113

EXAMPLE

Order the following numbers from least to greatest: $\sqrt{25}$, $-\sqrt{18}$, -4, 3.2.

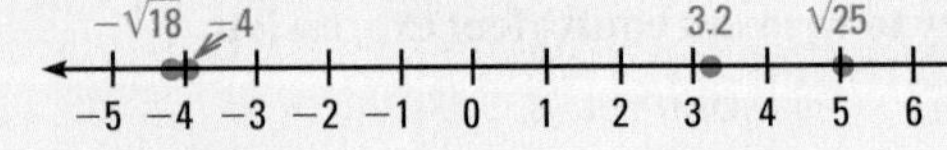

From least to greatest, the numbers are $-\sqrt{18}$, -4, 3.2, and $\sqrt{25}$.

EXERCISES

EXAMPLES 1, 2, 4, and 5 on pp. 110–113 for Exs. 50–60

Evaluate the expression.

50. $\sqrt{121}$ **11**

51. $-\sqrt{36}$ **-6**

52. $\pm\sqrt{81}$ **± 9**

53. $\pm\sqrt{225}$ **± 15**

Approximate the square root to the nearest integer.

54. $\sqrt{97}$ **10**

55. $-\sqrt{48}$ **-7**

56. $-\sqrt{142}$ **-12**

57. $\sqrt{300}$ **17**

Order the numbers in the list from least to greatest.

58. $-\sqrt{49}$, -6.8, 2, $\sqrt{3}$, 1.58
$-\sqrt{49}$, -6.8, 1.58, $\sqrt{3}$, 2

59. 1.25, $\sqrt{11}$, -0.3, 0, $-\sqrt{4}$
$-\sqrt{4}$, -0.3, 0, 1.25, $\sqrt{11}$

60. Rewrite the following conditional statement in if-then form: "All real numbers are irrational numbers." Tell whether the statement is *true* or *false*. If it is false, give a counterexample. **If a number is a real number, then it is irrational; false. *Sample answer:* 5 is a real number and it is rational.**

2 CHAPTER TEST

Tell whether the number is a real number, a rational number, an irrational number, an integer, or a whole number.

1. $-\frac{1}{4}$ **real number, rational number**
2. $\sqrt{90}$ **real number, irrational number**
3. $-\sqrt{144}$ **real number, rational number, integer**
4. 8.95 **real number, rational number**

Order the numbers in the list from least to greatest.

5. $-\frac{5}{3}, -2, 3, \frac{1}{2}, -1.07$ $\mathbf{-2, -\frac{5}{3}, -1.07, \frac{1}{2}, 3}$
6. $\sqrt{15}, -4.3, 4.2, 0, -\sqrt{25}$ $\mathbf{-\sqrt{25}, -4.3, 0, \sqrt{15}, 4.2}$

Find the sum, difference, product, or quotient.

7. $-5 + 2$ **−3**
8. $1.3 + (-10.4)$ **−9.1**
9. $-\frac{1}{3} + \frac{1}{6}$ $\mathbf{-\frac{1}{6}}$
10. $-\frac{2}{7} - \frac{5}{14}$ $\mathbf{-\frac{9}{14}}$
11. $-41 - 32$ **−73**
12. $7.2 - (-11.6)$ **18.8**
13. $-11(-7)$ **77**
14. $-4.5(20)(2)$ **−180**
15. $-\frac{1}{5}(-20)(-5)$ **−20**
16. $-36 \div (-6)$ **6**
17. $-\frac{3}{5} \div 12$ $\mathbf{-\frac{1}{20}}$
18. $5 \div \left(-\frac{10}{11}\right)$ $\mathbf{-5\frac{1}{2}}$

Evaluate the expression when $x = -6$ and $y = -10$.

19. $-x$ **6**
20. $|y|$ **10**
21. $8 - (x - y)$ **4**
22. $-4x + y$ **14**

Simplify the expression.

23. $-9(y - 7)$ $\mathbf{-9y + 63}$
24. $8(x - 4) - 10x$ $\mathbf{-2x - 32}$
25. $\frac{-7w - 21}{7}$ $\mathbf{-w - 3}$
26. $\frac{-16v + 8}{-4}$ $\mathbf{4v - 2}$

In Exercises 27 and 28, rewrite the conditional statement in if-then form. Then tell whether the statement is *true* or *false*. If it is false, give a counterexample.

27. No rational numbers are integers. **If a number is rational, then it is not an integer; false. *Sample answer:* −2 is a rational number and an integer.**
28. All irrational numbers are real numbers. **If a number is irrational, then it is a real number; true.**
29. **MUSIC** The revenue from sales of digital pianos in the United States was \$152.4 million in 2001 and \$149.0 million in 2002. Find the change in revenue from 2001 to 2002. **−\$3.4 million**
30. **ELEVATORS** An elevator moves at a rate of −5.8 feet per second from a height of 300 feet above the ground. It takes 3 seconds for the elevator to make its first stop. How many feet above the ground is the elevator now? **282.6 ft**
31. **SUMMER JOBS** You plan to work a total of 25 hours per week at two summer jobs. You will earn \$8.75 per hour working at a cafe and \$10.50 per hour working at an auto shop. Write an equation that gives your weekly pay p (in dollars) as a function of the time t (in hours) spent working at the cafe. Then find your weekly pay if you work 10 hours at the cafe. $\mathbf{p = -1.75t + 262.5}$**; \$245**
32. **TEMPERATURES** The low temperatures for Montreal, Quebec, in Canada on February 12 for each year during the period 2000–2004 are −6.7°F, −4.2°F, 4.1°F, −3.6°F, and 0.3°F. Find the mean of the temperatures. **−2.02°F**

Additional Resources

Assessment Book

- Chapter Test, Levels A, B, C
- Standardized Chapter Test
- SAT/ACT Chapter Test
- Alternative Assessment

Test Generator

Chapter Test

Easily-readable reduced copies (with answers) of Chapter Test B, the Standardized Chapter Test, and the Alternative Assessment from the Assessment Book can be found on pp. 62E–62F.

Using Rubrics

The rubric given on the pupil pages is a sample of a three-level rubric. Other rubrics may contain four, five, or six levels. For more information on rubrics, see the *Differentiated Instruction Resources*.

Test-Taking Strategy

Encourage students to read the question fully before beginning their work on a solution. Suggest that they take a few moments to organize the steps in their mind before starting to write down their work. This approach will help organize their solution into a logical sequence of steps leading to their answer.

Avoiding Common Errors

When using more than one equation, students often transpose numbers in the equations. Caution students to check their equations for the correct numbers before they begin their calculations.

Study Strategy

Remind students to label their answers according to the labels given in the extended response question. Tell them that reviewers expect the same organization in the answers as in the questions. Similarly, tell students to organize each part of the answer so that the answer is clear and the reviewer does not have to look in several places to put the answer together. If one part of an answer has multiple steps, such as part (c) in the Practice, suggest that students write a summary statement at the end that ties the steps together and shows the relationship between the steps.

EXTENDED RESPONSE QUESTIONS

Scoring Rubric

Full Credit
- solution is complete and correct

Partial Credit
- solution is complete but errors are made, *or*
- solution is without error but incomplete

No Credit
- no solution is given, *or*
- solution makes no sense

PROBLEM

The *Alvin* is an HOV (human-operated vehicle) used to explore the ocean. A new HOV is being built that will carry explorers deeper and faster. The table shows the capabilities of the two vehicles.

Vehicle	Lowest elevation (m)	Velocity (m/sec)
Alvin	−4500	−30
New HOV	−6500	−44

a. For each vehicle, write an equation that gives the elevation e (in meters) to which the vehicle dives as a function of the elapsed time t (in seconds) of the dive.

b. If both vehicles begin diving from the surface of the ocean at the same time, what will their elevations be after 90 seconds?

c. If both vehicles continue diving, which vehicle will reach its lowest elevation first? *Explain* how you can use the equations you wrote in part (a) to find the answer.

Below are sample solutions to the problem. Read each solution and the comments on the left to see why the sample represents full credit, partial credit, or no credit.

Full credit solution

a. Alvin: $e = -30t$ **New HOV:** $e = -44t$

The correct equations are given.

b. Alvin: $e = -30t$ **New HOV:** $e = -44t$

$= -30(90)$ $= -44(90)$

$= -2700$ $= -3960$

Alvin will be at an elevation of −2700 meters, and the new HOV will be at an elevation of −3960 meters.

The correct calculations are performed, and the correct elevations are given.

c. t **(sec)**	**Elevation of Alvin (m)**	**Elevation of new HOV (m)**
100	$e = -30(100) = -3000$	$e = -44(100) = -4400$
125	$e = -30(125) = -3750$	$e = -44(125) = -5500$
150	$e = -30(150) = -4500$	$e = -44(150) = -6600$

After 150 seconds, Alvin reaches its lowest elevation, −4500 feet. Because $-6600 < -6500$, the new HOV has reached its lowest elevation in less than 150 seconds. So, the new HOV reaches its lowest elevation first.

The reasoning is correct, and it includes use of the equations. The answer is correct.

Partial credit solution

The correct equations and elevations are given.

a. **Alvin:** $e = -30t$ **New HOV:** $e = -44t$

b. **Alvin:** $e = -30(90)$ **New HOV:** $e = -44(90)$

$= -2700$ $= -3960$

Alvin will be at an elevation of −2700 meters, and the new HOV will be at an elevation of −3960 meters.

The answer is correct, but the reasoning is incorrect. The lowest elevations were not considered.

c. The velocity of Alvin is −30 meters per second, and the velocity of the new HOV is −44 meters per second. So, each second the new HOV descends 14 meters more than Alvin. This means that the new HOV will reach its lowest elevation first.

No credit solution

The equations are incorrect and the elevations are incorrect.

a. **Alvin:** $e = \frac{-4500}{t}$ **New HOV:** $e = \frac{-6500}{t}$

b. **Alvin:** $e = \frac{-4500}{90} = -50$ **New HOV:** $e = \frac{-6500}{90} \approx -72$

Alvin will be at an elevation of −50 meters, and the new HOV will be at an elevation of about −72 meters.

The student's reasoning is incorrect and does not use the equations. The answer is incorrect.

c. Alvin has to travel only to −4500 meters, while the new HOV has to travel to −6500 meters. So, Alvin will reach its lowest elevation first.

PRACTICE Apply the Scoring Rubric

1. A student's solution to the problem on the previous page is given below. Score the solution as *full credit, partial credit,* or *no credit. Explain* your reasoning. If you choose *partial credit* or *no credit,* explain how you would change the solution so that it earns a score of full credit.

a. Alvin: $e = -30t$ New HOV: $e = -44t$

b. Alvin: $e = -30(90)$ New HOV: $e = -44(90)$

$= -2700$ meters $= -3960$ meters

c. The time it takes Alvin to reach its lowest elevation can be found by solving $-4500 = -30t$. Using mental math, I found that $t = 150$ seconds.

The time it takes the new HOV to reach its lowest elevation can be found by solving $-6500 = -44t$.

Try $t = 145$: $-44(145) = -6380$

Try $t = 150$: $-44(150) = -6600$

The new HOV reaches its lowest elevation, −6500 feet, after more than 145 seconds but less than 150 seconds. So, the new HOV will reach its lowest elevation first.

Answers

1. Full credit; for part (a), the correct equations are given. For part (b), the correct calculations are performed, and the correct elevations are given. For part (c), the reasoning is correct and includes use of the equations from part (b). The solution is correct.

Answers

1a. $1400; gain

1b. year 2; year 4

1c. No. *Sample answer:* Since profit = income − expenses, many different incomes and expenses can produce the same profit.

2a. $s = \sqrt{A}$

2b. 2 in. *Sample answer:* The side length *s* of the playing region is $\sqrt{256} = 16$ inches. Eight small squares fit along each side, so the side length of each small square is $16 \div 8 = 2$ inches.

2c. No;

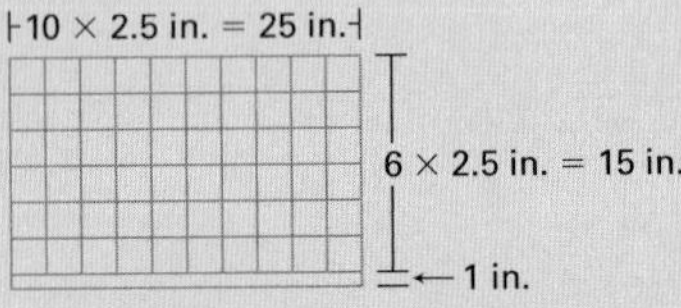

***Sample answer:* From the diagram, you can see that sixty 2.5-inch squares can be cut from the 16 inch by 25 inch piece of wood. The leftover 1 inch by 25 inch piece contains enough area to cover the remaining four 2.5 inch squares that are needed, but no square 2.5 inches on a side can be cut from this piece.**

3a. trail A: 1584 ft, trail B: 1865 ft; trail B

3b. Trail B. *Sample answer:* The average trail grade for trail A is $\frac{1584}{6} = 264$ feet per mile, and the average trail grade for trail B is $\frac{1865}{8} \approx 233$ feet per mile. Since trail B has a lesser average trail grade, it is the easier trail to hike.

EXTENDED RESPONSE

1. Your friend owns a business designing and selling personalized greeting cards. The table shows the profits for the first five years of the business.

Year	1	2	3	4	5
Profit (dollars)	−680	−1259	−963	2795	1507

   a. Find the total profit for the five years. Then tell whether the profit was a *gain* or a *loss*.

   b. In which year did the business have the least profit? the greatest profit?

   c. Can you use the table to determine the year with the greatest expenses and the year with the greatest income? *Justify* your answer.

2. The area of the playing region of a checkerboard has 64 small squares of equal size arranged as shown.

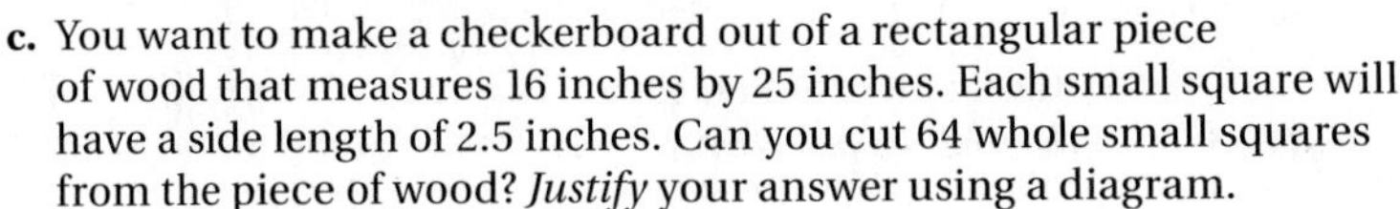

   a. Write an equation that gives the side length *s* of the playing region as a function of the area *A* of the playing region.

   b. The area of the playing region of a certain checkerboard is 256 square inches. What is the side length of a small square on the checkerboard? *Explain* your answer.

   c. You want to make a checkerboard out of a rectangular piece of wood that measures 16 inches by 25 inches. Each small square will have a side length of 2.5 inches. Can you cut 64 whole small squares from the piece of wood? *Justify* your answer using a diagram.

3. The table shows the changes in elevation from one mile marker to the next mile marker on each of two trails. Trail A is 6 miles long, and trail B is 8 miles long.

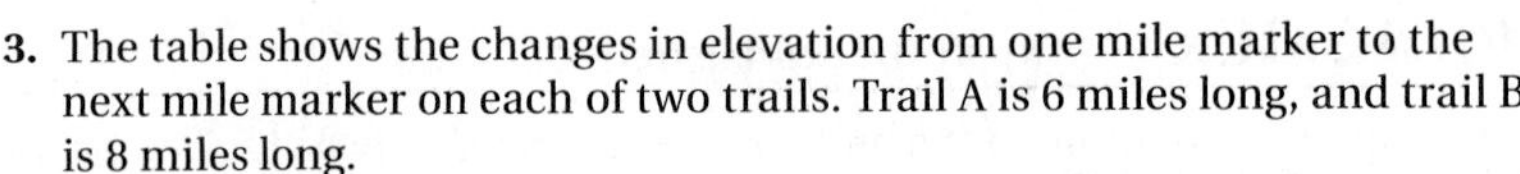

Mile markers	0 to 1	1 to 2	2 to 3	3 to 4	4 to 5	5 to 6	6 to 7	7 to 8
Elevation change on trail A (ft)	420	−60	−16	425	470	345	—	—
Elevation change on trail B (ft)	−135	430	465	410	390	−40	−60	405

   a. Find the total change in elevation for each trail. Which trail has the greater total change in elevation?

   b. The average trail grade is the total elevation change (in feet) divided by the trail length (in feet). The lesser the average trail grade is, the easier it is to hike the trail. Which is easier to hike, *trail A* or *trail B*? *Explain.*

   c. If trail B is extended by 1 mile, is it possible for trail B to have the same average trail grade as trail A? Your answer should include the following:
      - a table of values that gives the average trail grade of trail B for various elevation changes from mile 8 to mile 9
      - an explanation of how you used the table to answer the question

3c. Yes; for elevation change *x* from mile 8 to 9, the average trail grade will be $\frac{1865 + x}{9}$ feet per mile. Make a table of values showing the average trail grades for values of *x*, and look for an average trail grade value of 264 feet per mile, the average trail grade of trail A.

Elevation change (ft)	450	475	500	525
Average trail grade (ft/mi)	about 257	about 260	about 263	about 266

Since 264 is between 263 and 266, there is an elevation change between 500 and 525 feet that will give an average trail grade of 264 feet per mile.

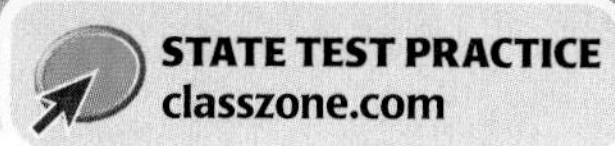

MULTIPLE CHOICE

4. Which description does not apply to $-\sqrt{9}$?

   (A) Real number (B) Whole number
   (C) Integer (D) Rational number

5. Which list of numbers is in order from least to greatest?

   (A) $-\frac{10}{3}, -\sqrt{16}, -\sqrt{20}, -4.5$
   (B) $-4.5, -\frac{10}{3}, -\sqrt{16}, -\sqrt{20}$
   (C) $-4.5, -\sqrt{20}, -\sqrt{16}, -\frac{10}{3}$
   (D) $-\sqrt{20}, -4.5, -\sqrt{16}, -\frac{10}{3}$

6. Which statement illustrates the associative property of multiplication?

   (A) $(-5 \cdot 3) + 7 = 7 + (-5 \cdot 3)$
   (B) $8 + (9 + 10) = (8 + 9) + 10$
   (C) $4 \cdot (2 \cdot 12) = (2 \cdot 12) \cdot 4$
   (D) $11 \cdot (4 \cdot 7) = (11 \cdot 4) \cdot 7$

GRIDDED ANSWER

7. The table shows the change in the balance of your bank account when you withdraw money from an automated teller machine (ATM).

Change in Balance after Withdrawal of $x	
Your bank's ATM	Another bank's ATM
$-x$	$-x - 1.50$

You have $230 in your bank account. You make 8 ATM withdrawals of $20 each, 4 of which are made from your bank's ATM. What is the amount (in dollars) in your account now?

8. The table shows the scores earned by two teams in each of three rounds of an academic contest. What is the difference of the greater total score and the lesser total score?

Round	Team A's score	Team B's score
1	−125	100
2	300	−75
3	150	−50

SHORT RESPONSE

9. A homeowner is dividing a rectangular room into two rooms as shown. The homeowner plans to install carpet in the living room and wood flooring in the dining room. Carpet costs $2.50 per square foot, and wood flooring costs $4.25 per square foot.

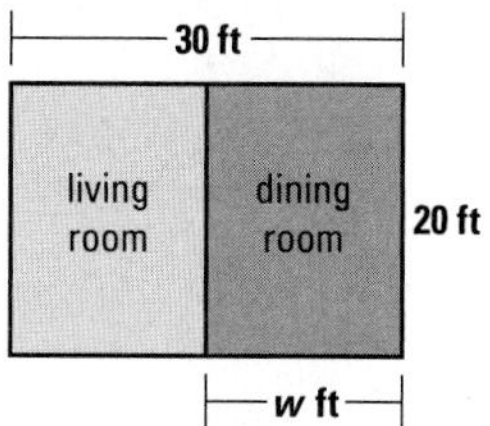

   a. Write an equation that gives the total cost C (in dollars) of the project as a function of the width w (in feet) of the dining room.

   b. How much money will the homeowner save by making the width of the dining room 12 feet instead of making the rooms the same size? *Explain* your answer.

10. A certain swimming pool contains 22,900 gallons of water when full. Due to evaporation, the amount of water in the pool changes at a rate of about −160 gallons per week.

   a. If water is not added to the pool, find the approximate amount of water that will be left in the pool after 12 weeks.

   b. A garden hose adds 2 gallons of water to the pool per minute. Estimate the time (in minutes) each day that the hose would need to add water in order to make up for the daily loss of water. *Explain* how you estimated the time.

4. B

5. C

6. D

7. $64

8. 350

9a. $C = 35w + 1500$

9b. $105. Sample answer: If the rooms are the same size, they both have a width of $30 \div 2 = 15$ feet. For $w = 15$, $C = 35(15) + 1500 = \$2025$. For $w = 12$, $C = 35(12) + 1500 = \$1920$. The difference in cost is $\$2025 - \$1920 = \$105$.

10a. about 20,980 gal

10b. About 11.5 min. *Sample answer:* Divide the loss per week by 7 to get the daily loss: $\frac{-160}{7} \approx -23$ gallons per day. The garden hose adds 2 gallons per minute, so to add 23 gallons, the hose will need to add water for $\frac{23 \text{ gal}}{2 \text{ gal/min}} = 11.5$ minutes.

3 Pacing Guide

Chapter 3: Solving Linear Equations

Chapter Table of Contents

PACING GUIDES

Regular Schedule (50-minute classes)

DAY 1	DAY 2	DAY 3	DAY 4	DAY 5	DAY 6
Investigating Algebra Activity 3.1 Lesson 3.1	Lesson 3.2	Lesson 3.3	Lesson 3.3 (cont.)	Quiz for Lessons 3.1–3.3 Lesson 3.4 Spreadsheet Activity 3.4 Mixed Review of Problem Solving	Lesson 3.5
DAY 7	**DAY 8**	**DAY 9**	**DAY 10**	**DAY 11**	**DAY 12**
Lesson 3.6 Extension 3.6	Quiz for Lessons 3.4–3.6 Lesson 3.7	Lesson 3.7 (cont.) Extension 3.7	Lesson 3.8 Mixed Review of Problem Solving	Quiz for Lessons 3.7–3.8 Chapter Review	Chapter Test

Block Schedule (90-minute classes)

DAY 1	DAY 2	DAY 3	DAY 4	DAY 5	DAY 6
Investigating Algebra Activity 3.1 Lesson 3.1 Lesson 3.2	Lesson 3.3	Quiz for Lessons 3.1–3.3 Lesson 3.4 Spreadsheet Activity 3.4 Mixed Review of Problem Solving Lesson 3.5	Lesson 3.6 Extension 3.6 Quiz for Lessons 3.4–3.6 Lesson 3.7	Lesson 3.7 (cont.) Extension 3.7 Lesson 3.8 Mixed Review of Problem Solving	Quiz for Lessons 3.7–3.8 Chapter Review Chapter Test

RESOURCE OPTIONS

Chapter/Lesson Resources

Chapter Resource Book
- Parents as Partners
- Teaching Guide/Lesson Plan
- Activity Masters
- Practice (3 levels)
- Study Guide
- Quick Catch-Up for Absent Students
- Problem Solving/Application
- Challenge Practice
- Chapter Review Games and Activities
- Project with Rubric
- Cumulative Review

Notetaking Guide
- Student Workbook and Teacher's Edition

Practice Workbook

Worked-Out Solution Key

Chapter Transparency Book
- Warm-Up Exercises/Daily Homework Quiz
- Notetaking Guide Transparencies
- Homework Answer Transparencies

Teacher Tools Transparencies

Assessment

Assessment Book
- Quizzes
- Chapter Tests (3 levels)
- Standardized and SAT/ACT Chapter Tests
- Alternative Assessments
- Cumulative Tests

Benchmark Tests
- Benchmark Tests, correlated to Remediation Book
- Pre-Course, Mid-Year, and End-of-Year Tests
- Chapter Tests

Spanish Assessment Book

Differentiated Instruction

Differentiated Instruction Resources
- Strategies for Reading Mathematics
- Differentiated Instruction Lesson Notes
- English Learner Lesson Notes
- Inclusion Lesson Notes
- Teaching Strategies with Sample Worksheets
- Tips for New Teachers/Math Background Notes
- Teacher Survival Activities/Bulletin Board Ideas

Student Resources in Spanish

Spanish Study Guide

Remediation Book

Skills Readiness (available on Easy Planner)
- Diagnostic Assessment
- Skill Instruction and Alternative Teaching Strategies
- Skill Practice and Enrichment Masters

Pre-AP Resources
- Pacing and Assignment Guide
- Best Practices
- Copymasters

Technology Resources

Plan	***Easy Planner***
Teach	***Video Tutor*** ***Activity Generator*** ***Power Presentations*** ***Animated Algebra***
Assess	***Test Generator*** ***ML Assessment System***
Reteach	***@HomeTutor***
Online Resources	***Classzone.com*** ***eEdition*** ***eWorkbook***

Video Tutor

Technology Highlights for Each Lesson

 **Easy Planner**

Easy access to the Teacher's Edition and all teaching resources. Includes a search feature to locate the materials you need.

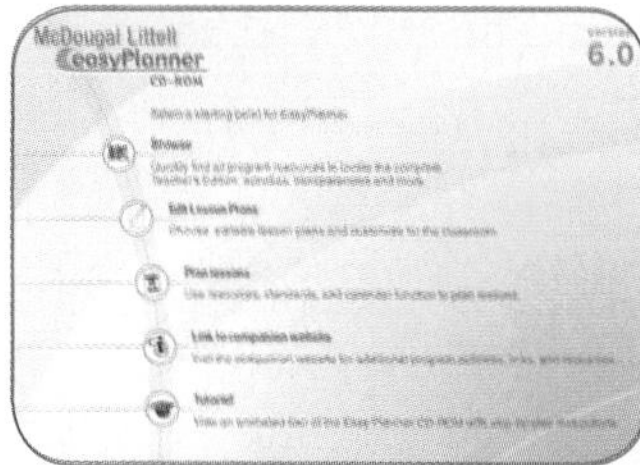

 **Activity Generator**

Leveled, editable activities allow all students to explore a lesson's concepts. Includes teacher notes and closure questions.

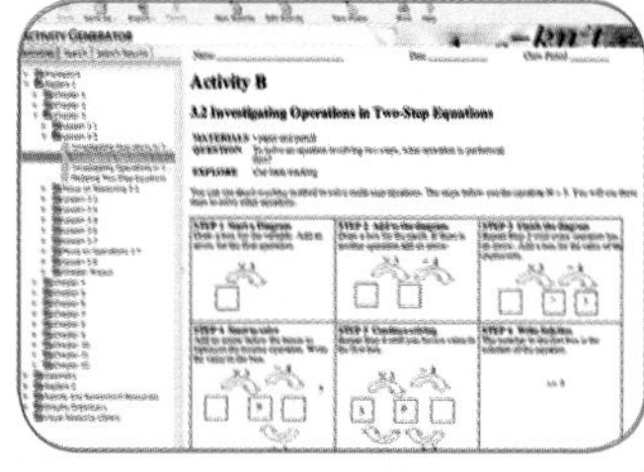

Animated Algebra

Interactive tutorials provide visually engaging alternative opportunities to learn concepts and master skills.

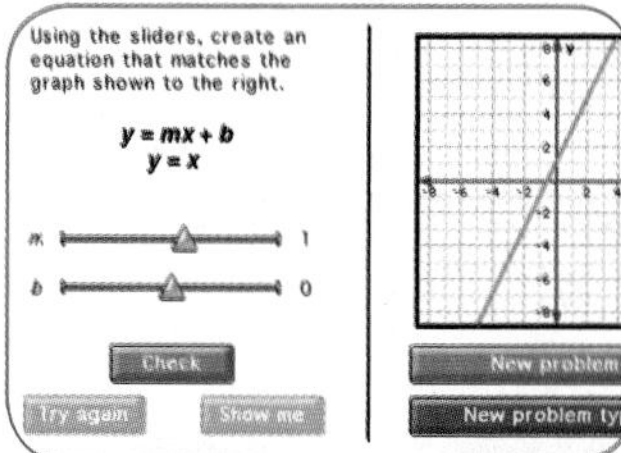

3 Lesson Practice Level B

LESSON 3.1
Practice B
For use with pages 134–140

Solve the equation.

1. $x + 16 = 25$ $x = 9$
2. $n - 9 = 17$ $n = 26$
3. $-30 = w + 8$ $w = -38$
4. $y + 5 = -13$ $y = -18$
5. $a - 17 = -10$ $a = 7$
6. $41 = 52 + m$ $m = -11$
7. $c - 2.4 = 1.8$ $c = 4.2$
8. $z + 4.1 = 9.6$ $z = 5.5$
9. $-3.2 = 4.5 + p$ $p = -7.7$
10. $9x = 54$ $x = 6$
11. $-5b = 55$ $b = -11$
12. $-42 = 3m$ $m = -14$
13. $-52 = -4y$ $y = 13$
14. $\frac{1}{3}n = 36$ $n = 108$
15. $-\frac{3}{4}a = 12$ $a = -16$
16. $0.5y = 17$ $y = 34$
17. $-1.4a = 2.8$ $a = -2$
18. $-6.5 = -1.3m$ $m = 5$

The rectangle or triangle has area *A*. Write and solve an equation to find the value of *x*.

19. $A = 70 \text{ in.}^2$ $10x = 70; x = 7$ in.
20. $A = 30 \text{ in.}^2$ $\frac{1}{2}(12x) = 30; x = 5$ in.

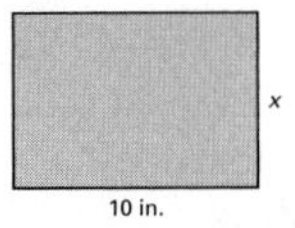

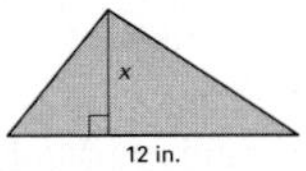

21. **Caves** Cumberland Caverns in Tennessee is 44.4 kilometers long. This cave is 10.9 kilometers longer than Carlsbad Caverns in New Mexico. How long is Carlsbad Caverns? 33.5 km

22. **Bocce** Bocce is a lawn bowling game that originated in Italy. The bocce court below has an area of 1032 square feet. The width of the court is 12 feet. What is the length of the court? 86 ft

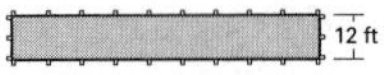

23. **Olympics** In the 2002 Winter Olympics, Cartriona LeMay Doan won the 500-meter race. Her winning time was 74.75 seconds. Find her average speed to the nearest tenth of a meter per second. 6.7 m/sec

24. **Part-Time Job** You work at a grocery store part-time. You estimate that you spend $\frac{3}{5}$ of your time stocking shelves. You work 20 hours each week. How many hours of your work week do you spend stocking shelves? 12 h

LESSON 3.1

LESSON 3.2
Practice B
For use with pages 141–146

Solve the equation.

1. $3n + 14 = 35$ $n = 7$
2. $7y - 10 = 11$ $y = 3$
3. $14 = 9 - x$ $x = -5$
4. $9c - 5 = 13$ $c = 2$
5. $4.6 = 4m - 3.4$ $m = 2$
6. $1.2 = 2.4 - 3b$ $b = 0.4$
7. $\frac{p}{6} + 9 = 14$ $p = 30$
8. $\frac{w}{7} - 2 = 9$ $w = 77$
9. $\frac{z}{3} - 8 = -4$ $z = 12$

Write an equation for the function described. Then find the input.

10. The output of a function is 5 more than 2 times the input. Find the input when the output is 17. $y = 2x + 5$; 6
11. The output of a function is 10 more than 4 times the input. Find the input when the output is −26. $y = 4x + 10$; −9
12. The output of a function is 14 less than 6 times the input. Find the input when the output is 22. $y = 6x - 14$; 6

Solve the equation.

13. $9a + 4a = 26$ $a = 2$
14. $14y - 6y = 48$ $y = 6$
15. $38 = 26x - 7x$ $x = 2$
16. $16x - 3x = -52$ $x = -4$
17. $-9 = 11m - 8m$ $m = -3$
18. $4.5z - 2.5z = 24$ $z = 12$

19. **Yoga Class** A fitness center offers yoga classes for \$10 per class and sells yoga mats for \$19.95. A person paid a total of \$139.95 to the fitness center for yoga classes and a mat. Find the number of yoga classes the person took. 12 classes

20. **Library Books** Your school has a \$1200 grant to buy books and magazine subscriptions for the school library. The average cost of a magazine subscription is \$30. Your school decides to spend \$870 on books and the remaining amount on magazine subscriptions. How many magazine subscriptions can the school buy? 11 subscriptions

21. **Walking** You have already walked 5 miles of an 18-mile trail. If you walk the rest of the trail at a pace of 1 mile in 17 minutes, how many hours will it take you to finish the trail? Use the following verbal model to answer the question. Round your answer to the nearest tenth. about 3.7 h

Walking rate (mi/min)	·	Number of minutes (min)	+	Number of miles already walked (mi)	=	Total number of miles walked (mi)

22. **Swimming Pool** The capacity of a small children's swimming pool is 106 gallons of water. There are currently 15 gallons of water in the pool. You are filling the pool with water at a rate of 2 gallons per minute.
   a. Write an equation that gives the amount *y* (in gallons) of water in the pool as a function of the number *x* of minutes from now. $y = 15 + 2x$
   b. After how many minutes will the pool be full? 45.5 min

LESSON 3.2

LESSON 3.3
Practice B
For use with pages 148–153

Solve the equation.

1. $16x - 15 - 9x = 13$ $x = 4$
2. $15m + 4 - 9m = -32$ $m = -6$
3. $3b - 9 - 8b = 11$ $b = -4$
4. $-31 = 8 - 6p - 7p$ $p = 3$
5. $9 + 4(x + 1) = 25$ $x = 3$
6. $7(d - 5) + 12 = 5$ $d = 4$
7. $10a + 5(a - 3) = 15$ $a = 2$
8. $19a - 3(a - 6) = 66$ $a = 3$
9. $\frac{1}{4}(x - 8) = 7$ $x = 36$
10. $\frac{1}{3}(d + 9) = -12$ $d = -45$
11. $\frac{3}{4}(n + 3) = 9$ $n = 9$
12. $-\frac{5}{2}(w - 1) = 15$ $w = -5$
13. $6.4 + 2.1(z - 2) = 8.5$ $z = 3$
14. $4.5 - 1.5(6m + 2) = 6$ $m = -0.5$
15. $15 = 4.3n - 2.1(n - 4)$ $n = 3$

Find the value of *x* for the triangle or rectangle.

16. Perimeter = 23 feet $x = 5$
17. Perimeter = 24 meters $x = 3$

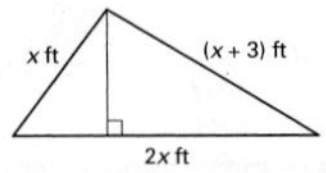

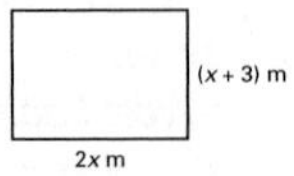

18. **Wrapping a Package** It takes 70 inches of ribbon to make a bow and wrap the ribbon around a box. The bow takes 32 inches of ribbon. The width of the box is 14 inches. What is the height of the box? 5 in.

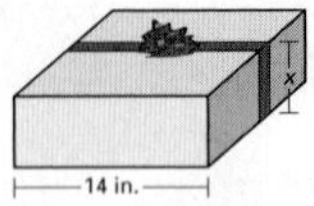

19. **Vacation** You are driving to a vacation spot that is 1500 miles away. Including rest stops, it takes you 42 hours to get to the vacation spot. You estimate that you drove at an average speed of 50 miles per hour. How many hours were you *not* driving? 12 h

20. **Moving** You helped a friend move a short distance recently. The friend rented a truck for \$15 an hour and rented a dolly for \$5. Your friend paid a total of \$80 for the rental. How long did your friend rent the truck for? 5 h

21. **Painting** You and your friend are painting the walls in your apartment. You estimate that there is 1000 square feet of space to be painted. You paint at a rate of 4 square feet per minute and your friend paints at a rate of 3 square feet per minute. Your friend shows up to help you paint 45 minutes after you have already started painting.
   a. Write an equation that gives the total number of square feet *y* as a function of the number of minutes *x* it takes to paint all of the walls. $y = 4(x + 45) + 3x$
   b. How long will it take you and your friend to finish painting? Round your answer to the nearest minute. about 117 min

LESSON 3.3

LESSON 3.4
Practice B
For use with pages 154–159

Solve the equation and describe each step you use.

1. $5x + 11 = 4x + 18$
2. $11p - 4 = 6p + 1$ See below.
3. $-6 = 2(w + 5)$ See below.

1. $5x + 11 = 4x + 18$
   $x + 11 = 18$ Subtract $4x$ from each side.
   $x = 7$ Subtract 11 from each side.

Solve the equation, if possible.

4. $15x - 8 = 14x + 13$ $x = 21$
5. $9n - 7 = 5n + 5$ $n = 3$
6. $4z - 15 = 4z + 11$ no solution
7. $-7a + 9 = 3a + 49$ $a = -4$
8. $4(w + 3) = w - 15$ $w = -9$
9. $8(y - 5) = 6y - 18$ $y = 11$
10. $14m - 10 = 3(4 + m)$ $m = 2$
11. $7 + x = \frac{1}{2}(4x - 2)$ $x = 8$
12. $8b + 11 - 3b = 2b + 2$ $b = -3$
13. $10d - 6 = 4d - 15 - 3d$ $d = -1$
14. $16p - 4 = 4(2p - 3)$ $p = -1$
15. $0.25(8z - 4) = z + 8 - 2z$ $z = 3$

Write an expression for the perimeter of the square.

16. $16x - 16$
17. $32x + 16$
18. $18x - 30$

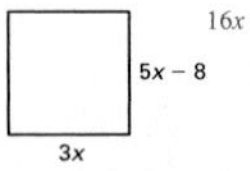

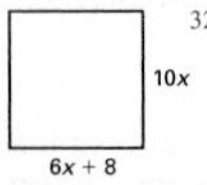

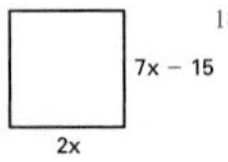

19. **Saving and Spending** Currently, you have \$80 and your sister has \$145. You decide to save \$6 of your allowance each week, while your sister decides to spend her whole allowance plus \$7 each week. How long will it be before you have as much money as your sister? 5 weeks

20. **Botanical Gardens** The membership fee for joining a gardening association is \$24 per year. A local botanical garden charges members of the gardening association \$3 for admission to the garden. Nonmembers of the association are charged \$6. After how many visits to the garden is the total cost for members, including the membership fee, the same as the total cost for nonmembers? 8 visits

21. **College Enrollment** Information about students' choices of majors at a small college is shown in the table. In how many years will there be 2 times as many students majoring in engineering than in business? In how many years will there be 2 times as many students majoring in engineering than in biology? 3 years; 7.6 years

Major	Number of students enrolled in major	Average rate of change
Engineering	120	22 more students each year
Business	105	4 fewer students each year
Biology	98	6 more students each year

2. $11p - 4 = 6p + 1$
   $5p - 4 = 1$ Subtract $6p$ from each side.
   $5p = 5$ Add 4 to each side.
   $p = 1$ Divide each side by 5.

3. $-6 = 2(w + 5)$
   $-6 = 2w + 10$ Distribute 2 to $(w + 5)$.
   $-16 = 2w$ Subtract 10 from each side.
   $-8 = w$ Divide each side by 2.

LESSON 3.4

LESSON 3.5

Practice B

For use with pages 162–167

Tell whether the ratio is in simplest form. If not, write it in simplest form.

1. 16 to 34 no; 8 to 17 **2.** 17 : 65 yes **3.** $\frac{33}{108}$ no; $\frac{11}{36}$

Solve the proportion.

4. $\frac{1}{2} = \frac{p}{14}$ $p = 7$ **5.** $\frac{2}{3} = \frac{x}{21}$ $x = 14$ **6.** $\frac{14}{8} = \frac{y}{20}$ $y = 35$

7. $\frac{y}{6} = \frac{15}{9}$ $y = 10$ **8.** $\frac{10}{15} = \frac{m}{39}$ $m = 26$ **9.** $\frac{b}{8} = \frac{50}{20}$ $b = 20$

10. $\frac{8}{2.5} = \frac{d}{0.5}$ $d = 1.6$ **11.** $\frac{1.4}{1.6} = \frac{z}{10}$ $z = 8.75$ **12.** $\frac{n}{4} = \frac{0.3}{1.5}$ $n = 0.8$

Write the sentence as a proportion. Then solve the proportion.

13. 5 is to 12 as x is to 48. $\frac{5}{12} = \frac{x}{48}$; $x = 20$ **14.** w is to 9 as 7 is to 36. $\frac{w}{9} = \frac{7}{36}$; $w = \frac{7}{4}$

15. d is to 4 as 32 is to 56. $\frac{d}{4} = \frac{32}{56}$; $d = \frac{16}{7}$ **16.** 22 is to 50 as x is to 500. $\frac{22}{50} = \frac{x}{500}$; $x = 220$

17. 10 is to 45 as b is to 225. $\frac{10}{45} = \frac{b}{225}$; $b = 50$ **18.** n is to 18 as 64 is to 72. $\frac{n}{18} = \frac{64}{72}$; $n = 16$

19. **Books** Over the summer, you read 20 books. Eight of these books were biographies.

a. Find the ratio of biographies to the total number of books. $\frac{2}{5}$

b. Find the ratio of non-biographies to biographies. $\frac{3}{2}$

c. Find the ratio of non-biographies to the total number of books. $\frac{3}{5}$

20. **Fitness Center** The table shows the number of people attending classes at a fitness center during a recent evening.

Class	Aerobics	Spinning	Yoga
Number of people	32	28	16

a. Find the ratio of the number of people taking yoga to the number of people taking spinning class. $\frac{4}{7}$

b. Find the ratio of the number of people taking aerobics to the total number of people taking classes. $\frac{8}{19}$

21. **Mailroom** You work in the local mailroom at a college. One of your duties is to sort local mail from all of the other mail. You can sort 8 pieces of mail in 10 seconds. How many pieces of mail should you be able to sort in 45 minutes? 2160 pieces of mail

22. **Music** A music downloading website reports that nearly 5 out of every 7 songs downloaded are classified as pop music. According to this information, predict how many of the next 500 songs downloaded will be pop songs. Round your answer to the nearest whole number. about 357 songs

LESSON 3.5

LESSON 3.6

Practice B

For use with pages 168–173

Name the cross products of the proportion.

1. $\frac{n}{11} = \frac{40}{55}$ $55n$ and $11(40)$ **2.** $\frac{4}{9} = \frac{1}{x}$ $4x$ and $9(1)$ **3.** $\frac{1.8}{1.9} = \frac{b}{3.8}$ $1.8(3.8)$ and $1.9b$

4. $\frac{a+6}{21} = \frac{4}{7}$ $7(a + 6)$ and $21(4)$ **5.** $\frac{5x}{x+1} = \frac{30}{9}$ $9(5x)$ and $30(x + 1)$ **6.** $\frac{2.2}{3.3} = \frac{a-2}{a-1}$ $2.2(a - 1)$ and $3.3(a - 2)$

Solve the proportion.

7. $\frac{3}{5} = \frac{21}{m}$ $m = 35$ **8.** $\frac{12}{7} = \frac{60}{d}$ $d = 35$ **9.** $\frac{24}{x} = \frac{48}{60}$ $x = 30$

10. $\frac{5}{7} = \frac{3w}{21}$ $w = 5$ **11.** $\frac{2w}{16} = \frac{30}{80}$ $w = 3$ **12.** $\frac{2z}{24} = \frac{6}{8}$ $z = 9$

13. $\frac{8}{9} = \frac{30+a}{45}$ $a = 10$ **14.** $\frac{9-y}{44} = \frac{5}{22}$ $y = -1$ **15.** $\frac{26}{15} = \frac{104}{70-w}$ $w = 10$

16. $\frac{35}{16} = \frac{c-8}{2}$ $c = 12.375$ **17.** $\frac{1}{9} = \frac{a}{a+24}$ $a = 3$ **18.** $\frac{2}{n} = \frac{14}{n+30}$ $n = 5$

A map has a scale of 1 in. : 38 ft. Use the given map distance to find the actual distance.

19. 5.5 in. 209 ft **20.** 2.25 in. 85.5 ft **21.** 1.75 in. 66.5 ft

22. **Concrete** You are making up your own mix of concrete to patch a set of stairs. In order to have the proper mix, you need to mix 1 part of Portland cement with 2 parts of sand and 3 parts of gravel.

a. How many total parts are in one batch of concrete? 6

b. You make a mix with 4 parts of sand. How many total parts of cement, sand, and gravel are in your mix? 12 parts

23. **Architectural Firm** An architectural firm makes a model of a science center they are building. The ratio of the model to the actual size is 1 in. : 85 ft. Estimate the height of the building if the model is 1.5 inches tall. 127.5 ft

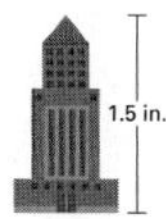

24. **Tall Buildings** You made a model of the Space Needle in Seattle, Washington, for a report on architecture in the United States. You used a scale of 1 in. : 50 ft. Your model is 12.1 inches tall. Estimate the actual height of the Space Needle. 605 ft

LESSON 3.6

LESSON 3.7

Practice B

For use with pages 176–181

Use a proportion to answer the question.

1. What percent of 125 is 25? 20% **2.** What percent of 70 is 14? 20%

3. What number is 15% of 80? 12 **4.** What number is 65% of 180? 117

5. 3 is 2% of what number? 150 **6.** 384 is 64% of what number? 600

Use the percent equation to answer the question.

7. What percent of 64 is 16? 25% **8.** What percent of 160 is 128? 80%

9. What number is 12% of 225? 27 **10.** What number is 85% of 360? 306

11. 4.8 is 8% of what number? 60 **12.** 25.8 is 86% of what number? 30

Find the percent. Round your answer to the nearest whole percent when necessary.

13. \$6 tip for a \$40 dinner 15% **14.** \$8.10 tax on an item priced at \$135 6%

15. 46 musicians out of 230 people 20% **16.** 18 action movies out of 45 movies 40%

17. **Antarctica** Antarctica comprises about 10.5% of the total land area on Earth. Antarctica has a surface area of about 5,400,000 square miles. What is the total land area on Earth? 51,000,000 mi^2

18. **Part-Time Job** So far this week, you have worked 10 hours at your part-time job. This is 80% of the number of hours you work each week. How many hours do you work each week? 12.5 h

19. **Class Times** The circle graph shows the results of a survey in which 500 college students were asked which time they preferred to start classes for the day.

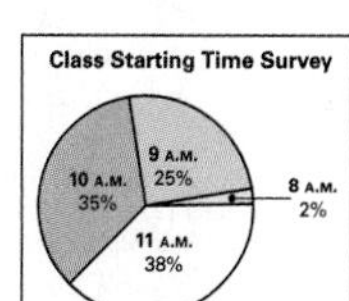

a. How many students who participated in the survey want to start classes at 8 A.M.? 10 students

b. How many students who participated in the survey want to start classes at 9 A.M.? 125 students

c. How many students who participated in the survey want to start classes at either 10 or 11 A.M.? 365 students

20. **Boots** Last year you bought a pair of designer boots on sale for \$84. Your friend bought the same boots this year for \$120. Which statements are correct? a and c

a. You paid 30% less than your friend paid.

b. Your friend paid 50% more than you did.

c. You paid 70% of what your friend paid.

LESSON 3.7

LESSON 3.8

Practice B

For use with pages 184–189

Write the equation in function form.

1. $4x + y = -10$ $y = -4x - 10$ **2.** $6 - y = 17x$ $y = 6 - 17x$ **3.** $y - 3x - 11 = 0$ $y = 3x + 11$

4. $2x + 2y = 8$ $y = 4 - x$ **5.** $6x - 3y = 12$ $y = 2x - 4$ **6.** $16 - 8y = 4x$ $y = 2 - \frac{1}{2}x$

7. $5x - 7y = 14$ $y = \frac{5}{7}x - 2$ **8.** $9y - 4x - 9 = 0$ $y = \frac{4}{9}x + 1$ **9.** $15 + 3y = -24x$ $y = -8x - 5$

10. $4 + 6y = 12x - 2$ $y = 2x - 1$ **11.** $4 - 10y = 22 - 6x$ $y = \frac{3}{5}x - \frac{9}{5}$ **12.** $8x - 2y - 5 = 11$ $y = 4x - 8$

Solve the literal equation.

13. Solve $R = R_1 + R_2$ for R_2. $R_2 = R - R_1$ **14.** Solve $I = Prt$ for r. $r = \frac{I}{Pt}$

15. Solve $C = \frac{Q}{V}$ for V. $V = \frac{Q}{C}$ **16.** Solve $y = mx + b$ for m. $m = \frac{y-b}{x}$

Solve the formula for the indicated variable.

17. Area of a trapezoid: $A = \frac{h}{2}(a + b)$. Solve for h. $h = \frac{2A}{a+b}$

18. Area of a rhombus: $A = \frac{1}{2}d_1d_2$. Solve for d_1. $d_1 = \frac{2A}{d_2}$

19. **Guitar Practice** You practice playing your guitar every day. You spend 15 minutes practicing chords and the rest of the time practicing a new song. So the total number of minutes y you practice for the week is given by $y = 7(15 + x)$, where x is the number of minutes you spend on practicing a new song.

a. Solve the equation for x. $x = \frac{y}{7} - 15$

b. How many minutes did you spend on a new song if you practiced 210 minutes last week? 245 minutes? 315 minutes? 15 min; 20 min; 30 min

20. **Discounts** Solve for r in the formula $S = L - rL$ where S is the sale price, L is the list price, and r is the discount rate. $r = \frac{L-S}{L}$

a. An item with a list price of \$128 goes on sale for \$51.20. Find the discount rate. 60%

b. An item with a list price of \$56.80 goes on sale for \$36.92. Find the discount rate. 35%

21. **Cookbook** You bought a cookbook while on a recent trip overseas. All of the oven temperatures are in degrees Celsius and the only formula you can remember for temperature is how to convert Fahrenheit to Celsius: $C = \frac{5}{9}(F - 32)$.

a. Solve the equation for F. $F = \frac{9}{5}C + 32$

b. A recipe tells you to bake a pie in the oven at 149°C. What is this temperature in degrees Fahrenheit? Round your answer to the nearest whole degree. about 300°F

LESSON 3.8

3 Assessment

CHAPTER 3 Quiz 1
For use after Lessons 3.1–3.3

Solve the equation. Check your solution.

1. $-112 = 7n$
2. $\frac{2}{3}t = 18$
3. $\frac{f}{-3} = -30$
4. $-28 = 10w - 3w$
5. $\frac{d}{5} + 1 = 7$
6. $\frac{9}{4}y - 2 = 25$
7. $24 = 13z - 4z + 6$
8. $7(h + 3) + 4 = -3$
9. $\frac{2}{3}(4x - 7) = -2$
10. A contractor purchases ceramic tile to remodel a kitchen floor. Each tile costs \$4, and the adhesive and grouting material costs \$17.82. If the contractor is charged a total of \$545.82, how many ceramic tiles did the contractor purchase?

Answers

1. $n = -16$
2. $t = 27$
3. $f = 90$
4. $w = -4$
5. $d = 30$
6. $y = 12$
7. $z = 2$
8. $h = -4$
9. $x = 1$
10. 132 tiles

CHAPTER 3 Quiz 2
For use after Lessons 3.4–3.6

Solve the equation, if possible.

1. $6 - 11x = 7x - 12$
2. $2y + 5 = 3(4y - 5)$
3. $12(x + 3) = 24 + 12x$

Solve the proportion. Check your solution.

4. $\frac{t}{65} = \frac{5}{13}$
5. $\frac{1.9}{2.1} = \frac{b}{8.4}$
6. $\frac{j + 4}{6} = \frac{18}{12}$
7. $\frac{m + 18}{m} = \frac{5}{2}$
8. $\frac{d + 4}{2d + 2} = \frac{3}{4}$
9. $\frac{f - 9}{-3} = \frac{11 - f}{5}$
10. At a pet show, the ratio of dogs to cats is 4 : 3. If the number of cats is 45, find the number of dogs at the show.

Answers

1. $x = 1$
2. $y = 2$
3. no solution
4. $t = 25$
5. $b = 7.6$
6. $j = 5$
7. $m = 12$
8. $d = 5$
9. $f = 6$
10. 60 dogs

CHAPTER 3 Quiz 3
For use after Lessons 3.7–3.8

Use the percent equation to answer the question.

1. 9 is 36 percent of what number?
2. What percent of 125 is 65?
3. What number is 15% of 120?
4. What percent of 110 is 8.8?
5. 62.4 is 48% of what number?
6. What number is 118% of 80?

Write the equation in function form.

7. $4 = 8x + 5y$
8. $2y - 10x = 16$
9. $10 + 7x = 19 - 3y$
10. The formula for simple interest is $I = Prt$ where P is the principal, r is the interest rate, and t is time. Solve the formula for r.

Answers

1. 25
2. 52%
3. 18
4. 8%
5. 130
6. 94.4
7. $y = -\frac{8}{5}x + \frac{4}{5}$
8. $y = 5x + 8$
9. $y = -\frac{7}{3}x + 3$
10. $r = \frac{I}{Pt}$

CHAPTER 3 Chapter Test B
For use after Chapter 3

Solve the equation, if posssible.

1. $-7 = -2 + x$
2. $b - \frac{2}{5} = \frac{3}{5}$
3. $-\frac{2}{3}d = 8$
4. $17 = 14 + 6y$
5. $2t - 5t = 9$
6. $13 - 9w = -14$
7. $7m - 4 - 2m = 6$
8. $\frac{3}{4}(c + 4) = 3$
9. $5(3 - 2y) + 4y = 3$
10. $4x - 1 = 2(2x + 3)$
11. $7a - 3.9a = 6.2$
12. $9 - 5z = 12 - (6z + 7)$
13. A new plasma-screen television costs \$5250. A family makes a down payment of \$552 and pays off the balance in 24 equal monthly payments. Write and solve an equation to find the monthly payment.
14. On a class trip, there were 45 more girls than boys. The total number of students on the trip was 211. Write and solve an equation to find the number of girls and the number of boys on the class trip.

Solve the proportion.

15. $\frac{4}{5} = \frac{12}{y}$
16. $\frac{1.1}{1.2} = \frac{w}{3.6}$
17. $\frac{16}{9} = \frac{-4t}{27}$
18. $\frac{8}{m + 3} = \frac{4}{m}$
19. $\frac{6}{x + 4} = \frac{12}{5x - 13}$
20. $\frac{5}{3z - 4} = \frac{-3}{1 - 2z}$
21. On Monday, biologists tagged 150 sunfish from a lake. On Friday, the biologists counted 12 tagged fish out of a sample of 400 sunfish from the same lake. Estimate the total number of sunfish in the lake.

Answers

1. $x = -5$
2. $b = 1$
3. $d = -12$
4. $y = \frac{1}{2}$
5. $t = -3$
6. $w = 3$
7. $m = 2$
8. $c = 0$
9. $y = 2$
10. no solution
11. $a = 2$
12. $z = -4$
13. $24x + 552 = 5250$; \$195.75
14. $x + x + 45 = 211$; 128 girls; 83 boys
15. $y = 15$
16. $w = 3.3$
17. $t = -12$
18. $m = 3$
19. $x = 7$
20. $z = -7$
21. 5000 sunfish

CHAPTER 3

Chapter Test B *continued*

For use after Chapter 3

22. A recipe for oatmeal raisin cookies calls for $1\frac{2}{3}$ cups of flour to make 4 dozen cookies. How many cups of flour are needed to make 6 dozen cookies?

Solve the percent problem.

23. 3 is 1.5% of what number? **24.** 9 is what percent of 6?

25. What is 26.5% of 46? **26.** 70 is 200% of what number?

27. In a renovation project, a football stadium increased its 60,000-seat capacity by 15%. How many seats will be available when the project is completed?

Write the equation in function form.

28. $5x - y = 7$ **29.** $10x + 3y + 2 = 9x + 8$

In Exercises 30–32, use the following information. Anthropologists can estimate the height of a woman by measuring the length of her radius bone (from the wrist to the elbow). The length (in centimeters) of the radius bone *b* is given by $b = 0.26h - 18.85$ where *h* is the height (in centimeters) of the woman.

30. Solve the equation for *h*.

31. If the length of a woman's radius bone is 25 centimeters, estimate the height of the woman. Round your answer to the nearest centimeter.

32. If 1 in. = 2.54 cm, convert the woman's height to inches. Round your answer to the nearest inch.

Answers

22. $2\frac{1}{2}$ cups of flour

23. 200

24. 150%

25. 12.19

26. 35

27. 69,000 seats

28. $y = 5x - 7$

29. $y = -\frac{1}{3}x + 2$

30. $h = \frac{b + 18.85}{0.26}$

31. about 169 cm

32. about 67 in.

CHAPTER 3

Standardized Test

For use after Chapter 3

Multiple Choice

1. What is the solution of the equation $-25 = x - 12$? B

Ⓐ −37 Ⓑ −13 Ⓒ 13 Ⓓ 37

2. What is the solution of the equation $\frac{m}{3.6} = -1.2$? A

Ⓐ −4.32 Ⓑ −3
Ⓒ 2.4 Ⓓ 4.8

3. What is the solution of the equation $15 = \frac{3}{5}n$? D

Ⓐ 5 Ⓑ 9 Ⓒ $15\frac{3}{5}$ Ⓓ 25

4. What is the solution of the equation $\frac{2}{3}c + 6 = -12$? A

Ⓐ −27 Ⓑ −18
Ⓒ −9 Ⓓ 3

5. What is the first step in solving the equation $5 + \frac{12}{x} = -1$? C

Ⓐ Add 1 to each side.
Ⓑ Divide each side by 12.
Ⓒ Subtract 5 from each side.
Ⓓ Add 5 to each side.

6. Examine the problem below. Which line contains an error? A

$6x - 2(x - 5) = 22$	Line 1
$6x - 2x - 10 = 22$	Line 2
$4x - 10 = 22$	Line 3
$4x = 32$	Line 4
$x = 8$	Line 5

Ⓐ Line 2 Ⓑ Line 3
Ⓒ Line 4 Ⓓ Line 5

7. What is the solution of the equation $8x - 4(5 - x) = -44$? B

Ⓐ −6 Ⓑ −2 Ⓒ 5 Ⓓ 8

8. The perimeter of the triangle is 37 centimeters. What is the value of *x*? B

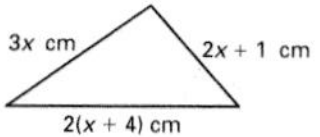

Ⓐ $2\frac{1}{4}$ Ⓑ 4
Ⓒ $4\frac{3}{7}$ Ⓓ 25

9. What is the solution of the equation $5t - 3(t - 2) = t + 6$? D

Ⓐ −16 Ⓑ −9
Ⓒ −7 Ⓓ 0

10. What equation does *not* have a solution? D

Ⓐ $3y - 2 = \frac{y}{2}$
Ⓑ $5(x - 3) = 2x + 7$
Ⓒ $4m - 15 = m - 15$
Ⓓ $3(6 - n) = -3(n - 8)$

11. What is the value of *r* in the proportion $\frac{2}{5} = \frac{18}{r}$? C

Ⓐ 10 Ⓑ 40
Ⓒ 45 Ⓓ 90

12. What is the value of *p* in the proportion $\frac{2}{3} = \frac{p}{35}$? A

Ⓐ $23\frac{1}{3}$ Ⓑ $52\frac{1}{2}$
Ⓒ 70 Ⓓ 105

CHAPTER 3

Standardized Test *continued*

For use after Chapter 3

13. Which proportion represents the statement 5 is to 4 as *x* is to 24? B

Ⓐ $\frac{5}{x} = \frac{24}{4}$ Ⓑ $\frac{5}{4} = \frac{x}{24}$
Ⓒ $\frac{5}{24} = \frac{4}{x}$ Ⓓ $\frac{4}{5} = \frac{x}{24}$

14. Which ratio represents the number of dogs to birds? C

Dogs	Cats	Birds
243	372	195

Ⓐ $\frac{81}{124}$ Ⓑ $\frac{65}{81}$
Ⓒ $\frac{81}{65}$ Ⓓ $\frac{124}{65}$

15. What is the value of *y* in the proportion $\frac{6}{y - 5} = \frac{18}{y + 1}$? C

Ⓐ $\frac{1}{2}$ Ⓑ 5
Ⓒ 8 Ⓓ 23

16. What number is 65% of 92? B

Ⓐ 5.98 Ⓑ 59.8
Ⓒ 598 Ⓓ 5980

17. What percent of 150 is 30? C

Ⓐ 2% Ⓑ 5%
Ⓒ 20% Ⓓ 500%

18. Which equation is *not* equivalent to the formula $C = \frac{5}{9}(F - 32)$? A

Ⓐ $C - \frac{5}{9}F = -32$ Ⓑ $C = \frac{5}{9}F - \frac{160}{9}$
Ⓒ $\frac{9}{5}C = F - 32$ Ⓓ $C + 17\frac{7}{9} = \frac{5}{9}F$

Gridded Answer

19. What is the solution of the equation $15t - 3(t - 7) = 57$?

[Answer grid: 3]

Short Response

20. a. $C = 0.65P$ or $C = P - 0.35P$

20. You are shopping for a new jacket and find that your favorite store has jackets 35% off.

a. Write an equation representing the cost *C* before taxes where *P* represents the original price.

b. If the sale price of the jacket you want is \$55.25, what was the original price? *Explain.* \$85; Solve the equation $55.25 = 0.65P$.

Extended Response

21. The formula for simple interest is $I = Prt$ where *I* is the interest, *P* is the principal, *r* is the interest rate, and *t* is time in years.

a. Calculate the amount of interest you would pay if you borrowed \$15,000 at a rate of 7.25% for 5 years. \$5437.50

b. Calculate the *total* amount you would pay back on a \$25,000 loan at a rate of 5.25% for 5 years. *Explain.*

c. Rewrite the formula for simple interest so that you can easily calculate the principal given the interest, rate, and time. $P = \frac{I}{rt}$

d. If the simple interest on a loan at a rate of 6.5% for 4 years is \$3250, what was the principal? \$12,500

21. b. \$31,562.50; The simple interest calculates to be \$6562.50. This amount must be added to the original \$25,000 borrowed for a total of \$31,562.50.

CHAPTER 3

Alternative Assessment and Math Journal

For use after Chapter 3

Journal **1.** Explain the difference between a ratio and a proportion. Write an example of each, and explain how to solve a proportion.

Multi-Step Problem **2.** A car rental agency charges \$25 per day to rent an economy class car, and also charges \$.08 per mile for each mile that the car is driven.

a. Write an equation that gives the cost *C* of a 3 day car rental as a function of the number of miles *m* that the car is driven.

b. Juanita needs to rent a car for a 3 day period. If she has \$150 budgeted to pay for the rental car, how many miles can she drive the car and not go over her budget? Write your answer in whole numbers of miles.

c. If Juanita changes her plans so that her rental is for 2 days, how many more miles can she drive the rental car and still stay within her \$150 budget? Write your answer in whole numbers of miles.

d. Write an equation that gives the cost *C* of a car rental for which 1000 miles were driven as a function of the number of days *d* that the car is rented.

e. Stephen needs to rent a car and knows that he will need to drive a total of 1000 miles. If Stephen has \$250 to spend on the rental car, how many days is he able to rent the car? Write your answer in whole numbers of days.

f. If Stephen decides to reduce the number of miles he drives to 800, how many more days is he able to rent the car? Write your answer in whole numbers of days.

1. Complete answers should include: an explanation that a ratio is a relationship between two quantities; an explanation that a proportion is created by equating two ratios; one example of a ratio and one example of a proportion; a written explanation describing how to solve a proportion.

2. a. $C = 75 + 0.08m$ **b.** 937 miles **c.** 313 more miles
d. $C = 25d + 80$ **e.** 6 days **f.** 1 more day

PLAN AND PREPARE

Main Ideas

In Chapter 3, students use properties of equality to solve one-step, two-step, and multi-step equations in one variable. They also use properties of equality and the distributive property to solve equations with variables on both sides. Students write ratios and proportions, solve proportions using cross products, and solve percent problems, such as finding the percent of a number, a base, and part of a base. Finally, students rewrite equations in function form and solve formulas and literal equations for a given variable.

Prerequisite Skills

Skills Readiness, available on the *Easy Planner*, provides review and practice for the Skills Check portion of the Prerequisite Skills quiz.

How student answers the exercises	What to assign from *Skills Readiness*
Any of Exs. 3–6 answered incorrectly	**Skill 56** Apply distributive property
Any of Exs. 7–10 answered incorrectly	**Skill 14** Write percents as decimals
Any of Exs. 11–13 answered incorrectly	**Skill 36** Find perimeter of a rectangle
All exercises answered correctly	Chapter 3 Enrichment

Additional skills review and practice is available in the Skills Review Handbook, pp. 909–937, and the @HomeTutor.

3 Solving Linear Equations

Making Sense of Chapter 3

In this chapter you will solve equations in one variable using properties of numbers and operations. By the end of this chapter, you will be prepared to work with linear equations in two variables.

Before

Previously, you learned the following skills, which you'll use in Chapter 3: simplifying expressions, writing percents as decimals, and using formulas.

Prerequisite Skills

VOCABULARY CHECK

Copy and complete the statement.

1. In the expression $3x + 7 + 7x$, __?__ and __?__ are like terms. **3x, 7x**
2. The reciprocal of $\frac{5}{8}$ is __?__. $\mathbf{\frac{8}{5}}$

SKILLS CHECK

Simplify the expression. *(Prerequisite skill for 3.2–3.6)*

3. $5x - (6 - x)$ **6x − 6**
4. $3(x - 9) - 16$ **3x − 43**
5. $23 + 4(x + 2)$ **4x + 31**
6. $x(7 + x) + 9x^2$ $\mathbf{10x^2 + 7x}$

Write the percent as a decimal. *(Prerequisite skill for 3.7)*

7. 54% **0.54**
8. 99% **0.99**
9. 12.5% **0.125**
10. 150% **1.5**

Find the perimeter of the rectangle. *(Prerequisite skill for 3.8)*

11. Rectangle: 16 ft by 7 ft. **46 ft**
12. Rectangle: 20 cm by 14 cm. **68 cm**
13. Rectangle: 11 in. by 4 in. **30 in.**

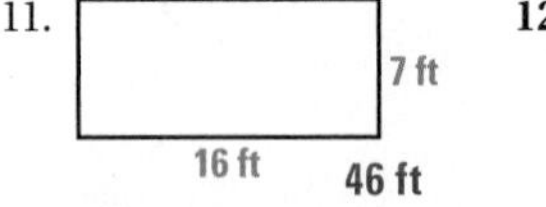

Prerequisite skills practice at classzone.com

Chapter Planning Guide

Chapter Resource Book
- Teaching Guide/Lesson Plan)
- Project with Rubric

Assessment and Intervention
- Assessment Book
- Benchmark Tests
- Remediation Book
- Skills Readiness

Interactive Technology
- Easy Planner
- Power Presentations
- Activity Generator
- Animated Algebra
- Test Generator
- Online Quizzes
- eWorkbook
- eEdition
- @HomeTutor

Resources for English Learners
- Spanish Study Guide
- Multi-Language Visual Glossary
- Student Resources in Spanish

Now

In Chapter 3, you will apply the big ideas listed below and reviewed in the Chapter Summary on page 191. You will also use the key vocabulary listed below.

Big Ideas

1. **Solving equations in one variable**
2. **Solving proportion and percent problems**
3. **Rewriting equations in two or more variables**

KEY VOCABULARY

- inverse operations, *p. 134*
- equivalent equations, *p. 134*
- identity, *p. 156*
- ratio, *p. 162*
- proportion, *p. 163*
- cross product, *p. 168*
- scale drawing, *p. 170*
- scale model, *p. 170*
- scale, *p. 170*
- literal equation, *p. 184*

Why?

Knowing how to solve a linear equation can help you solve problems involving distance, rate, and time. For example, you can solve an equation to find the time it takes a jellyfish to travel a given distance at a given rate.

Animated Algebra

The animation illustrated below for Exercise 59 on page 139 helps you answer this question: How long does it take the jellyfish to travel 26 feet?

Start
You have to find the time it takes for the jellyfish to travel 26 feet.

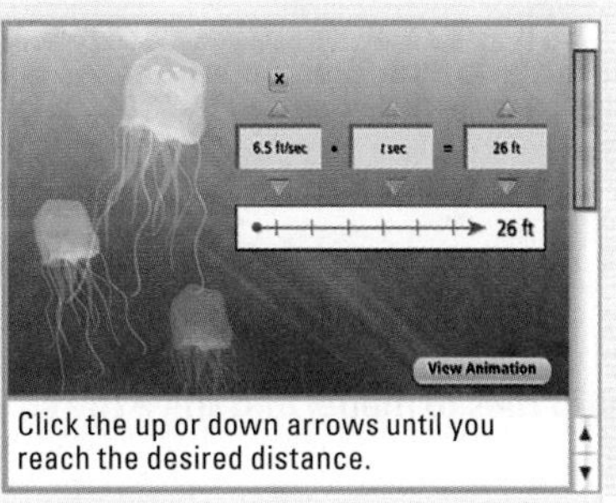
6.5 ft/sec
t sec
26 ft
26 ft
View Animation
Click the up or down arrows until you reach the desired distance.

Animated Algebra at classzone.com

Other animations for Chapter 3: pages 133, 154, 176, 185, and 187

Differentiated Instruction Resources

- Reading Strategies for Chapter 3
- Differentiated Instruction Lesson Notes
- English Learners Lesson Notes
- Inclusion Lesson Notes
- Teaching Strategies with Sample Worksheets
- Using Technology in the Classroom
- Tips for New Teachers
- Math Background Notes
- Assessment Strategies
- Teacher Survival Activities
- Bulletin Board Idea

1 PLAN AND PREPARE

Explore the Concept

- Students will use algebra tiles to model and solve one-step equations.
- This activity leads into the study of solving equations in Example 1 in Lesson 3.1.

Materials

Each student will need:

- algebra tiles
- Activity Support Master (*Chapter Resource Book*)

Recommended Time

Work activity: 10 min

Discuss results: 5 min

Grouping

Students should work individually.

2 TEACH

Tips for Success

In Explore 1, some students may think they should remove one 1-tile from each side of the equation since $1 + 1 = 2$. Point out that since there are two 1-tiles on the left side of the equation, they need to remove two 1-tiles to isolate the *x*-tile.

Key Questions

- In Explore 1, why do you remove the same number of 1-tiles from each side of the equation? **to keep the equation balanced**
- In Explore 2, why do you divide the 1-tiles into equal groups according to the number of *x*-tiles? **Since you want to isolate the *x*-tile, you need to find how many 1-tiles correspond to each *x*-tile.**

3.1 Modeling One-Step Equations

MATERIALS • algebra tiles

QUESTION **How can you use algebra tiles to solve one-step equations?**

You can model one-step equations using algebra tiles.

1-tile **x-tile**

A 1-tile represents the number 1. An x-tile represents the variable x.

EXPLORE 1 **Solve an equation using subtraction**

Solve $x + 2 = 5$.

STEP 1 Model $x + 2 = 5$ using algebra tiles.

STEP 2 To find the value of x, isolate the x-tile on one side of the equation. You can do this by removing two 1-tiles from each side.

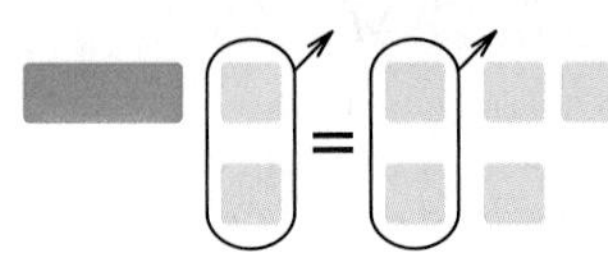

STEP 3 The x-tile is equal to three 1-tiles. So, the solution of $x + 2 = 5$ is 3.

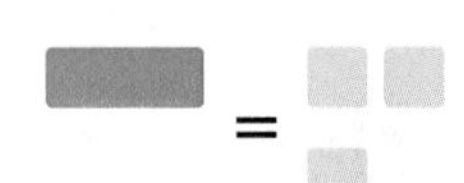

PRACTICE

Write the equation modeled by the algebra tiles.

1. 

$x + 2 = 6$

2. 

$7 = x + 6$

Use algebra tiles to model and solve the equation.

3. $x + 3 = 9$ **6** **4.** $x + 2 = 7$ **5** **5.** $x + 8 = 8$ **0** **6.** $x + 3 = 7$ **4**

7. $x + 2 = 12$ **10** **8.** $x + 7 = 12$ **5** **9.** $15 = x + 5$ **10** **10.** $13 = x + 10$ **3**

Animated Algebra
classzone.com

EXPLORE 2 **Solve an equation using division**

Solve $2x = 12$.

STEP 1 Model $2x = 12$ using algebra tiles.

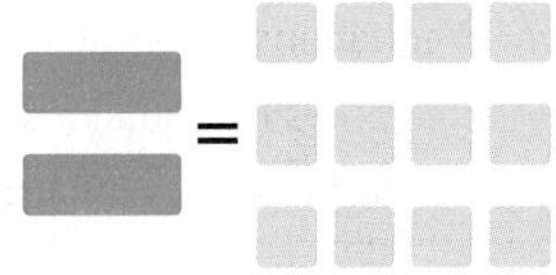

STEP 2 There are two x-tiles, so divide the x-tiles and 1-tiles into two equal groups.

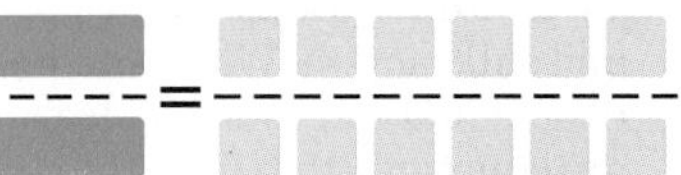

STEP 3 An x-tile is equal to six 1-tiles. So, the solution of $2x = 12$ is 6.

PRACTICE

Write the equation modeled by the algebra tiles.

11.

$4x = 4$

12.

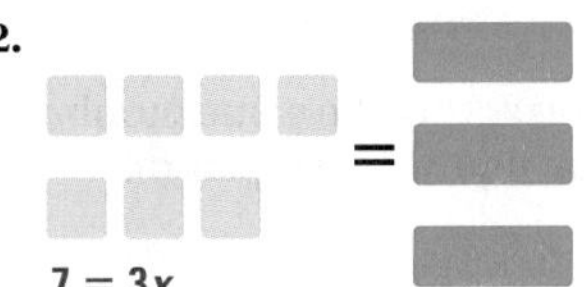

$7 = 3x$

Use algebra tiles to model and solve the equation.

13. $2x = 10$ **5** **14.** $3x = 12$ **4** **15.** $3x = 18$ **6** **16.** $4x = 16$ **4**

17. $6 = 2x$ **3** **18.** $12 = 4x$ **3** **19.** $20 = 5x$ **4** **20.** $21 = 7x$ **3**

DRAW CONCLUSIONS **Use your observations to complete these exercises**

21. An equation and explanation that correspond to each step in Explore 1 are shown below. Copy and complete the equations and explanations.

$x + 2 = 5$	Original equation
$x + 2 - \underline{?}\ (2) = 5 - \underline{?}\ (2)$	Subtract $\underline{?}$ (2) from each side.
$x = \underline{?}\ (3)$	Simplify. Solution is $\underline{?}$ (3).

22. Write an equation that corresponds to the algebra tile equation in each step of Explore 2. Based on your results, describe an algebraic method that you can use to solve $12x = 180$. Then use your method to find the solution. **$2x = 12$, $\frac{2x}{2} = \frac{12}{2}$, $x = 6$; divide each side by 12; 15.**

Animated Algebra
classzone.com

An **Animated Algebra** activity is available online. This activity is also part of **Power Presentations**.

Key Discovery

Subtract to isolate the variable in a one-step addition equation and divide to isolate the variable in a one-step multiplication equation.

3 ASSESS AND RETEACH

1. If you were modeling the solution of $x + 7 = 12$, how many 1-tiles would you remove from each side of the equation? **7**
2. How many equal groups do you form when using algebra tiles to model and solve the equation $4x = 12$? Explain. **Form 4 equal groups since there are 4 x-tiles.**

3.1 Solve One-Step Equations

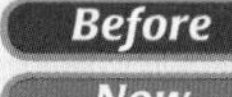

Before You solved equations using mental math.

Now You will solve one-step equations using algebra.

Why? So you can determine a weight limit, as in Ex. 56.

Key Vocabulary
- **inverse operations**
- **equivalent equations**
- **reciprocal,** *p. 915*

Inverse operations are two operations that undo each other, such as addition and subtraction. When you perform the same inverse operation on each side of an equation, you produce an *equivalent equation.* **Equivalent equations** are equations that have the same solution(s).

KEY CONCEPT — *For Your Notebook*

Addition Property of Equality

Words Adding the same number to each side of an equation produces an equivalent equation.

Algebra If $x - a = b$, then $x - a + a = b + a$, or $x = b + a$.

Subtraction Property of Equality

Words Subtracting the same number from each side of an equation produces an equivalent equation.

Algebra If $x + a = b$, then $x + a - a = b - a$, or $x = b - a$.

EXAMPLE 1 Solve an equation using subtraction

Solve $x + 7 = 4$.

$x + 7 = 4$	**Write original equation.**
$x + 7 - 7 = 4 - 7$	**Use subtraction property of equality: Subtract 7 from each side.**
$x = -3$	**Simplify.**

▶ The solution is -3.

AVOID ERRORS
To obtain an equivalent equation, be sure to subtract the same number from each side.

CHECK Substitute -3 for x in the original equation.

$x + 7 = 4$	**Write original equation.**
$-3 + 7 \stackrel{?}{=} 4$	**Substitute −3 for *x*.**
$4 = 4$ ✓	**Simplify. Solution checks.**

1 PLAN AND PREPARE

Warm-Up Exercises

Transparency Available

Solve using mental math.

1. $x + 2 = 17$ **15**
2. $\frac{x}{6} = 4$ **24**
3. $x - 7 = 3$ **10**
4. $9x = 54$ **6**
5. Katrina divided her photos into three albums. Each album contains 26 photos. How many photos did Katrina have to begin with? **78 photos**

Notetaking Guide

Transparency Available

Promotes interactive learning and notetaking skills.

Pacing

Basic: 1 day
Average: 1 day
Advanced: 1 day
Block: 0.5 block with 3.2
- See *Teaching Guide/Lesson Plan.*

2 FOCUS AND MOTIVATE

Essential Question

Big Idea 1, p. 131

How do you solve one-step equations using subtraction, addition, division, and multiplication? **Tell students they will learn how to answer this question by using properties of equality and reciprocals to solve equations.**

NCTM STANDARDS

Standard 1: Understand meanings of operations; Understand how operations are related

Resource Planning Guide

Chapter Resource Book
- Teaching Guide/Lesson Plan
- Practice levels A, B, C
- Study Guide
- Catch-up for Absent Students
- Application
- Challenge

Workbooks
- Notetaking Guide
- Practice Workbook

Teaching Options
- **Power Presentations** provides dynamic electronic teaching resources for the classroom.
- **Activity Generator** provides editable activities for all ability levels.

Interactive Technology
- Easy Planner
- Power Presentations
- Activity Generator
- Animated Algebra
- Test Generator
- Online Quiz
- eWorkbook
- eEdition
- @HomeTutor

Resources for English Learners
- Spanish Study Guide
- Multi-Language Visual Glossary
- Student Resources in Spanish

See also the *Differentiated Instruction Resources* for more strategies for meeting individual needs.

EXAMPLE 2 Solve an equation using addition

USE HORIZONTAL FORMAT
In Example 2, both horizontal and vertical formats are used. In the rest of the book, equations will be solved using the horizontal format.

Solve $x - 12 = 3$.

Horizontal format		Vertical format
$x - 12 = 3$	Write original equation.	$x - 12 = \quad 3$
$x - 12 + 12 = 3 + 12$	Add 12 to each side.	$+12 \quad +12$
$x = 15$	Simplify.	$x \quad = \quad 15$

MULTIPLICATION AND DIVISION EQUATIONS Multiplication and division are inverse operations. So, the multiplication property of equality can be used to solve equations involving division, and the division property of equality can be used to solve equations involving multiplication.

KEY CONCEPT *For Your Notebook*

Multiplication Property of Equality

Words Multiplying each side of an equation by the same nonzero number produces an equivalent equation.

Algebra If $\frac{x}{a} = b$ and $a \neq 0$, then $a \cdot \frac{x}{a} = a \cdot b$, or $x = ab$.

Division Property of Equality

Words Dividing each side of an equation by the same nonzero number produces an equivalent equation.

Algebra If $ax = b$ and $a \neq 0$, then $\frac{ax}{a} = \frac{b}{a}$, or $x = \frac{b}{a}$.

EXAMPLE 3 Solve an equation using division

Solve $-6x = 48$.

$-6x = 48$ Write original equation.

$\frac{-6x}{-6} = \frac{48}{-6}$ Divide each side by -6.

$x = -8$ Simplify.

GUIDED PRACTICE for Examples 1, 2, and 3

Solve the equation. Check your solution.

1. $y + 7 = 10$ **3**
2. $x - 5 = 3$ **8**
3. $q - 11 = -5$ **6**
4. $6 = t - 2$ **8**
5. $4x = 48$ **12**
6. $-65 = -5y$ **13**
7. $6w = -54$ **−9**
8. $24 = -8n$ **−3**

Differentiated Instruction

Visual Learners The variable in an equation can be any letter, not just *x*. Instead of a letter, it may be easier for some students to use a box or a blank to be filled in with a number. After completing a few problems in this way, they can use a variable.

See also the *Differentiated Instruction Resources* for more strategies.

Motivating the Lesson

In 1979, Susan Montgomery set a world's record for blowing the biggest gum bubble—48.2 centimeters in diameter. She broke that record in 1994 by blowing a bubble with a 58.4-centimeter diameter. By knowing how to solve equations, you can compare and determine world records in feats such as Susan's or in sports and other activities.

3 TEACH

Extra Example 1

Solve $x + 9 = 3$. **−6**

Extra Example 2

Solve $x - 2 = 11$. **13**

Key Questions to Ask for Example 2

- How are Examples 1 and 2 alike and how are they different? **Both use inverse operations of addition and subtraction. In Example 1 you subtract to obtain an equivalent equation, while in Example 2 you add.**
- Why do you perform the same operation on both sides of the equation? Explain. **You need to produce an equation equivalent to the original equation so they have the same solution.**

Extra Example 3

Solve $-4x = -28$. **7**

Key Questions to Ask for Example 3

- Which property of equality do you use to solve the equation? Why? **You use the division property of equality to undo multiplication of −6 times *x*.**
- Why do you divide by −6? **You want *x* to have a coefficient of 1.**

Extra Example 4

Solve $\frac{x}{3} = 7$. **21**

Key Question to Ask for Example 4

- Could you solve the equation by multiplying by 5? Explain. **No. If you multiply each side of the equation by 5, the new coefficient of *x* will be $\frac{5}{4}$. To isolate the variable, you have to multiply $\frac{x}{4}$ by 4.**

Extra Example 5

Solve $\frac{3}{5}x = -9$. **−15**

Avoiding Common Errors

Students may overlook the negative sign when working with reciprocals. In Guided Practice for Examples 4 and 5, suggest they do an additional check by determining the sign of the solution before solving the problem.

Mathematical Reasoning

To help students understand the algebraic concepts in the Key Concept boxes on pages 134 and 135, provide a concrete demonstration by using numbers for the variables. On the board, you can show an algebraic and number version of the properties side-by-side or one underneath the other. By seeing how the concepts work with numbers, students will be able to make the connection to algebraic thinking. In discussing the multiplication and division properties of equality, show that *a* cannot equal 0 by giving the example that you can divide 8 into 2 groups but you cannot divide 8 into 0 groups.

EXAMPLE 4 Solve an equation using multiplication

Solve $\frac{x}{4} = 5$.

Solution

$\frac{x}{4} = 5$ Write original equation.

$4 \cdot \frac{x}{4} = 4 \cdot 5$ Multiply each side by 4.

$x = 20$ Simplify.

✓ GUIDED PRACTICE for Example 4

Solve the equation. Check your solution.

9. $\frac{t}{-3} = 9$ **−27** **10.** $6 = \frac{c}{7}$ **42** **11.** $13 = \frac{z}{-2}$ **−26** **12.** $\frac{a}{5} = -11$ **−55**

USING RECIPROCALS Recall that the product of a number and its reciprocal is 1. You can isolate a variable with a fractional coefficient by multiplying each side of the equation by the reciprocal of the fraction.

EXAMPLE 5 Solve an equation by multiplying by a reciprocal

Solve $-\frac{2}{7}x = 4$.

Solution

REVIEW RECIPROCALS
For help with finding reciprocals, see p. 915.

The coefficient of x is $-\frac{2}{7}$. The reciprocal of $-\frac{2}{7}$ is $-\frac{7}{2}$.

$-\frac{2}{7}x = 4$ Write original equation.

$-\frac{7}{2}\left(-\frac{2}{7}x\right) = -\frac{7}{2}(4)$ Multiply each side by the reciprocal, $-\frac{7}{2}$.

$x = -14$ Simplify.

▶ The solution is −14. Check by substituting −14 for x in the original equation.

CHECK $-\frac{2}{7}x = 4$ Write original equation.

$-\frac{2}{7}(-14) \stackrel{?}{=} 4$ Substitute −14 for *x*.

$4 = 4$ ✓ Simplify. Solution checks.

GUIDED PRACTICE for Example 5

Solve the equation. Check your solution.

13. $\frac{5}{6}w = 10$ **12** **14.** $\frac{2}{3}p = 14$ **21** **15.** $9 = -\frac{3}{4}m$ **−12** **16.** $-8 = -\frac{4}{5}v$ **10**

Differentiated Instruction

Below Level Some students may find it difficult working with reciprocals in **Example 5**. Have these students use the stepped-out solution in Example 5 as a model to solve each of the exercises in the **Guided Practice**. In the second step of the solution, it may be useful to write 4 as $\frac{4}{1}$ to more easily discern that $-\frac{7}{2}(4)$ is −14. The same holds true for substituting −14 for *x* in checking the solution.

Advanced You may want to ask advanced students how they would solve **Example 5** if they did not use the reciprocal of $-\frac{2}{7}$. Have them write a stepped-out solution and justify each step. Ask them to share their solutions and explain the advantages and disadvantages of using the reciprocal.

See also the *Differentiated Instruction Resources* for more strategies.

EXAMPLE 6 Write and solve an equation

OLYMPICS In the 2004 Olympics, Shawn Crawford won the 200 meter dash. His winning time was 19.79 seconds. Find his average speed to the nearest tenth of a meter per second.

Solution

Let r represent Crawford's speed in meters per second. Write a verbal model. Then write and solve an equation.

Distance (meters)	=	Rate (meters/second)	·	Time (seconds)
↓		↓		↓
200	=	r	·	**19.79**

$$\frac{200}{19.79} = \frac{19.79r}{19.79}$$

$$10.1 \approx r$$

▶ Crawford's average speed was about 10.1 meters per second.

✓ **GUIDED PRACTICE** for Example 6

17. **WHAT IF?** In Example 6, suppose Shawn Crawford ran 100 meters at the same average speed he ran the 200 meters. How long would it take him to run 100 meters? Round your answer to the nearest tenth of a second. **9.9 sec**

3.1 EXERCISES

HOMEWORK KEY

○ = **WORKED-OUT SOLUTIONS** on p. WS5 for Exs. 13 and 55

★ = **STANDARDIZED TEST PRACTICE** Exs. 2, 15, 16, 57, 58, and 61

 = **MULTIPLE REPRESENTATIONS** Ex. 59

SKILL PRACTICE

A

1. **VOCABULARY** Copy and complete: Two operations that undo each other are called _?_. **inverse operations**

2. ★ **WRITING** Which property of equality would you use to solve the equation $14x = 35$? *Explain.* **Division property of equality; to solve $14x = 35$, you need to divide each side by 14.**

EXAMPLES 1 and 2 on pp. 134–135 for Exs. 3–14

SOLVING ADDITION AND SUBTRACTION EQUATIONS **Solve the equation. Check your solution.**

3. $x + 5 = 8$ **3**
4. $m + 9 = 2$ **−7**
5. $11 = f + 6$ **5**
6. $13 = 7 + z$ **6**
7. $6 = 9 + h$ **−3**
8. $-3 = 5 + a$ **−8**
9. $y - 4 = 3$ **7**
10. $t - 5 = 7$ **12**
11. $14 = k - 3$ **17**
12. $6 = w - 7$ **13**
13. $-2 = n - 6$ **4**
14. $-11 = b - 9$ **−2**

Extra Example 6

In the 2004 Summer Olympics, Inge de Bruijn won the women's 50-meter freestyle. Her winning time was 24.58 seconds. Find her average swimming speed to the nearest hundredth of a meter per second. **about 2.03 m/sec**

Key Question to Ask for Example 6

- If you knew Crawford's average speed and wanted to find how long it took him to run 200 meters, would you use a different property of equality to solve the equation? Explain. **No, you would still use the division property of equality, and divide each side by the rate.**

Reading Strategy

In Guided Practice for Example 6, tell students to make sure they understand the question. Point out that they will use the solution to Example 6 to determine the answer to Exercise 17, which uses Crawford's average rate of speed.

Closing the Lesson

Have students summarize the major points of the lesson and answer the Essential Question: How do you solve one-step equations using subtraction, addition, division, and multiplication?

- **Use inverse operations and properties of equality to produce equivalent equations and isolate variables.**
- **Use reciprocals to isolate a variable with a fractional coefficient.**

Solve one-step equations by using inverse operations to isolate the variable, for example, use addition to undo subtraction. If a coefficient is a fraction, multiply by its reciprocal to produce a coefficient of 1. Always perform the same operation on each side of the equation.

4 PRACTICE AND APPLY

Assignment Guide

Answer Transparencies available for all exercises

Basic:
Day 1: SRH p. 915 Exs. 16–20
pp. 137–140
Exs. 1, 2, 3–13 odd, 15, 16, 17–27 odd, 29–42, 53–59, 64–75

Average:
Day 1: pp. 137–140
Exs. 1, 2, 8–14 even, 15, 16, 20–28 even, 29, 30, 32–50 even, 54–61, 64–75 even

Advanced:
Day 1: pp. 137–140
Exs. 1, 2, 11–16, 20–26 even, 34–48 even, 49–52*, 56–63*, 69–75 odd

Block:
pp. 137–140
Exs. 1, 2, 8–14 even, 15, 16, 20–28 even, 29, 30, 32–50 even, 54–61, 64–75 even (with 3.2)

Differentiated Instruction

See *Differentiated Instruction Resources* for suggestions on addressing the needs of a diverse classroom.

Homework Check

For a quick check of student understanding of key concepts, go over the following exercises:

Basic: 5, 19, 25, 40, 53
Average: 10, 20, 26, 44, 55
Advanced: 13, 22, 26, 46, 56

Extra Practice

- Student Edition, p. 940
- Chapter Resource Book: Practice levels A, B, C

Practice Worksheet

An easily-readable reduced practice page (with answers) for this lesson can be found on p. 130C.

EXAMPLES 1 and 2 on pp. 134–135 for Exs. 15, 16

15. ★ **MULTIPLE CHOICE** What is the solution of $-8 = d - 13$? **C**

Ⓐ -21 Ⓑ -5 Ⓒ 5 Ⓓ 21

16. ★ **MULTIPLE CHOICE** What is the solution of $22 + v = -65$? **A**

Ⓐ -87 Ⓑ -43 Ⓒ 43 Ⓓ 87

EXAMPLES 3 and 4 on pp. 135–136 for Exs. 17–30

SOLVING MULTIPLICATION AND DIVISION EQUATIONS **Solve the equation. Check your solution.**

17. $5g = 20$ **4**
18. $-4q = 52$ **−13**
19. $48 = 8c$ **6**
20. $-108 = 9j$ **−12**
21. $15 = -h$ **−15**
22. $187 = -17r$ **−11**
23. $\frac{y}{3} = 5$ **15**
24. $\frac{m}{2} = 14$ **28**
25. $8 = \frac{x}{6}$ **48**
26. $7 = \frac{t}{-7}$ **−49**
27. $-11 = \frac{z}{-2}$ **22**
28. $-3 = \frac{d}{14}$ **−42**

In Exercises 29 and 30, refer to the method shown, which a student used to write a repeating decimal as a fraction.

Let $x = 0.\overline{63}$. Then $100x = 63.\overline{63}$.
Subtract: $100x = 63.636363\ldots$
$-x = -0.636363\ldots$
$99x = 63$
$x = \frac{63}{99} = \frac{7}{11}$

29. *Explain* the student's method.

30. Write the repeating decimal as a fraction.

a. $0.\overline{7}$ b. $0.\overline{18}$

29. The student multiplied *x* by 100 to produce a number with a decimal part identical to the decimal part of *x*. When the student subtracted, the result was a whole number.

30. a. $\frac{7}{9}$; b. $\frac{2}{11}$

B

SOLVING EQUATIONS **Solve the equation. Check your solution.**

31. $b - 0.4 = 3.1$ **3.5**
32. $-3.2 + z = -7.4$ **−4.2**
33. $-5.7 = w - 4.6$ **−1.1**
34. $-6.1 = p + 2.2$ **−8.3**
35. $8.2 = -4g$ **−2.05**
36. $-3.3a = 19.8$ **−6**
37. $\frac{3}{4} = \frac{1}{8} + v$ **$\frac{5}{8}$**
38. $\frac{n}{4.6} = -2.5$ **−11.5**
39. $-0.12 = \frac{y}{-0.5}$ **0.06**

EXAMPLE 5 on p. 136 for Exs. 40–48

40. $\frac{1}{2}m = 21$ **42**
41. $\frac{1}{3}c = 32$ **96**
42. $-7 = \frac{1}{5}x$ **−35**
43. $\frac{3}{2}k = 18$ **12**
44. $-21 = -\frac{3}{5}t$ **35**
45. $-\frac{2}{7}v = 16$ **−56**
46. $\frac{8}{5}x = \frac{4}{15}$ **$\frac{1}{6}$**
47. $\frac{1}{3}y = \frac{1}{5}$ **$\frac{3}{5}$**
48. $-\frac{4}{3} = \frac{2}{3}z$ **−2**

C

GEOMETRY **The rectangle or triangle has area *A*. Write and solve an equation to find the value of *x*.**

49. $A = 54 \text{ in.}^2$

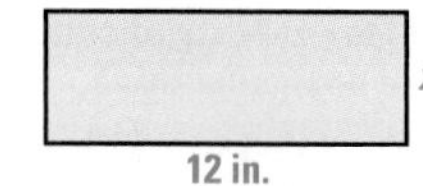

50. $A = 72 \text{ cm}^2$

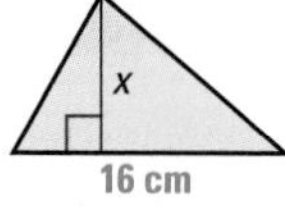

49. $54 = 12x$; 4.5 in.

50. $72 = \frac{1}{2}(16)x$; 9 cm

CHALLENGE **Find the value of *b* using the given information.**

51. $4a = 6$ and $b = a - 2$ **−0.5**

52. $a - 6.7 = 3.1$ and $b = 5a$ **49**

○ = WORKED-OUT SOLUTIONS on p. WS1 ★ = STANDARDIZED TEST PRACTICE

= MULTIPLE REPRESENTATIONS

PROBLEM SOLVING

EXAMPLE 6 A on p. 137 for Exs. 53–57

53. THE DEAD SEA For the period 1999–2004, the maximum depth of the Dead Sea decreased by 9.9 feet. The maximum depth in 2004 was 1036.7 feet. What was the maximum depth in 1999? **1046.6 ft**

@HomeTutor for problem solving help at classzone.com

54. CRAFTS You purchase a cane of polymer clay to make pendants for necklaces. The cane is 50 millimeters long. How thick should you make each pendant so that you will have 20 pendants of uniform thickness? **2.5 mm**

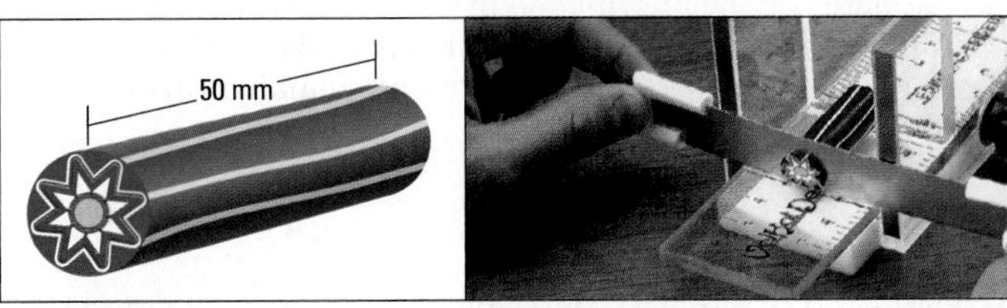

@HomeTutor for problem solving help at classzone.com

55. TRAMPOLINES A rectangular trampoline has an area of 187 square feet. The length of the trampoline is 17 feet. What is its width? **11 ft**

56. WHEELCHAIRS The van used to transport patients to and from a rehabilitation facility is equipped with a wheelchair lift. The maximum lifting capacity for the lift is 300 pounds. The wheelchairs used by the facility weigh 55 pounds each. What is the maximum weight of a wheelchair occupant who can use the lift? **245 lb**

57. ★ SHORT RESPONSE In Everglades National Park in Florida, there are 200 species of birds that migrate. This accounts for $\frac{4}{7}$ of all the species of birds sighted in the park.

a. Write an equation to find the number of species of birds that have been sighted in Everglades National Park. **$\frac{4}{7}x = 200$**

b. There are 600 species of plants in Everglades National Park. Are there more species of birds or of plants in the park? *Explain.* **Plants; if you solve the equation in part (a) you find that there are 350 species of birds.**

B **58. ★ OPEN-ENDED** *Describe* a real-world situation that can be modeled by the equation $15x = 135$. Solve the equation and explain what the solution means in this situation.

58. *Sample answer:* Each member of the drama club needs to sell tickets to the upcoming play. If there are 15 members and you want to sell 135 tickets, how many tickets should each member sell? $x = 9$; each member should sell 9 tickets.

59. ◆ MULTIPLE REPRESENTATIONS A box jellyfish can travel at a rate of 6.5 feet per second.

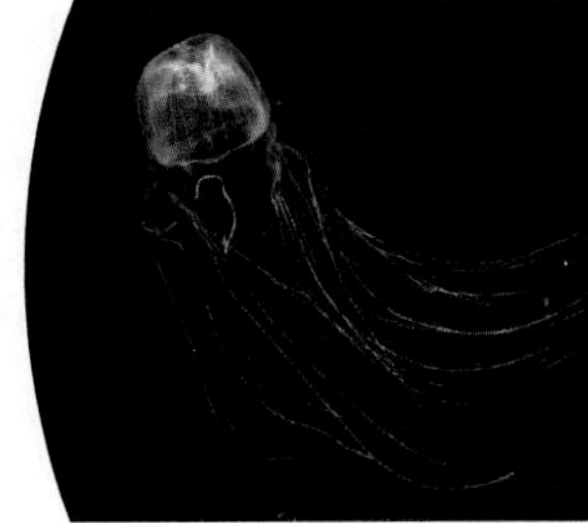

a. **Making a Table** Make a table that shows the distance d the jellyfish can travel after 1, 2, 3, 4, and 5 seconds. **See margin.**

b. **Drawing a Graph** Graph the ordered pairs from the table in a coordinate plane. How long does it take the jellyfish to travel 26 feet? **See margin for art.;4 sec.**

c. **Writing an Equation** Write and solve an equation to find the time it takes the jellyfish to travel 26 feet. **$26 = 6.5t$; 4 sec**

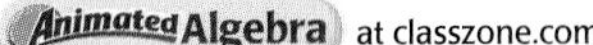 at classzone.com

Reading Strategy

Exercises 3–48 Some students may be confused when the variable is on the right side of the equation. Explain that the solution is the same whether the variable is on the right or the left side. If students find it distracting, they can rewrite the equation so that the variable is on the left side.

Exercises 47–48 Tell students to make sure they multiply by the reciprocal of the coefficient.

Avoiding Common Errors

Exercises 31–34 Remind students to align decimals when they add or subtract. They may want to use a vertical model for these exercises.

Study Strategy

Exercises 53–57 Encourage students to write a verbal model for each of these exercises using the model in Example 6 as a guide. This will help them organize all of the information in the problems so they write appropriate equations to solve the problems.

Internet Reference

Exercise 53 To learn more about the Dead Sea, visit i-cias.com/e.o/dead_sea.htm.

Exercise 57 More information about Everglades National Park can be found on the National Park Service's website www.nps.gov/ever.

An **Animated Algebra** activity is available online for **Exercise 59.** This activity is also part of **Power Presentations.**

59a.

t	D
1	6.5
2	13
3	19.5
4	26
5	32.5

59b.

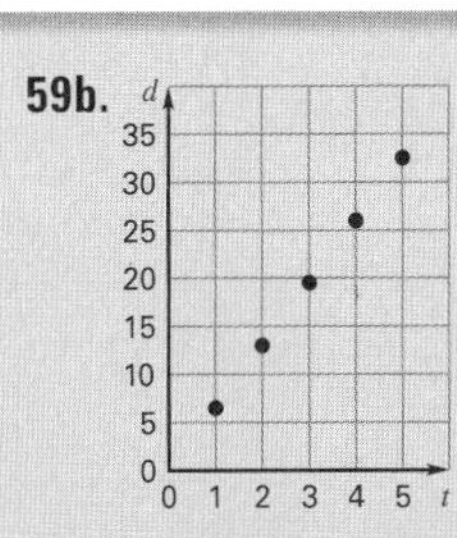

5 ASSESS AND RETEACH

Daily Homework Quiz

 **Transparency Available**

Solve the equation. Check your solution.

1. $-6 + a = -2$ **4**

2. $8 = m - 7$ **15**

3. $9k = -72$ **−8**

4. $12 = \frac{x}{-5}$ **−60**

5. Earth orbits the Sun at an average speed of 29.79 kilometers per second. Find how long it takes, to the nearest hundredth of a second, for Earth to travel 500 kilometers. **16.78 sec**

Online Quiz

Available at **classzone.com**

Diagnosis/Remediation

- Practice A, B, C in Chapter Resource Book
- Study Guide in Chapter Resource Book
- Practice Workbook
- @HomeTutor

Challenge

Additional challenge is available in the Chapter Resource Book.

60. MULTI-STEP PROBLEM Tatami mats are a floor covering used in Japan. Tatami mats are equal in size, unless they are cut in half. The floor shown has an area of 81 square feet and is covered with 4.5 tatami mats.

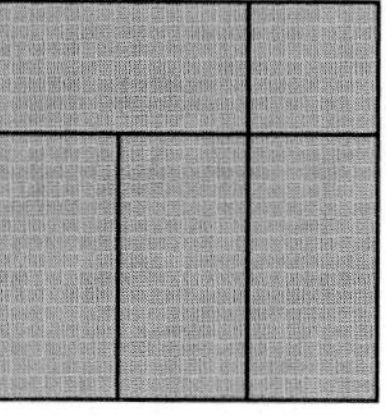

a. What is the area of one tatami mat? **18 ft²**

b. What is the length of one tatami mat if it has a width of 3 feet? **6 ft**

61. ★ EXTENDED RESPONSE In baseball, a player's batting average is calculated by dividing the number of hits by the number of at bats.

a. Calculate Use the information in the table to find the number of hits Bill Mueller had in the 2003 Major League Baseball regular season. Round your answer to the nearest whole number. **171 hits**

Player	Team	Batting average	At bats
Bill Mueller	Boston Red Sox	0.326	524

b. Calculate The number of hits Bill Mueller had was 44 less than the number of hits Vernon Wells of the Toronto Blue Jays had in the 2003 regular season. How many hits did Vernon Wells have? **215 hits**

c. Compare In the 2003 regular season, Mueller had a higher batting average than Wells. Did Wells have fewer at bats than Mueller? *Explain* your reasoning. **No; if Mueller had fewer hits than Wells but had a higher batting average, he must have had fewer at bats than Wells.**

C **62. AMERICAN FLAGS** An American flag has a length that is 1.9 times its width. What is the area of a flag that has a length of 9.5 feet? **47.5 ft²**

63. CHALLENGE At a farm where you can pick your own strawberries, the cost of picked strawberries is calculated using only the weight of the strawberries. The total weight of a container full of strawberries is 2.1 pounds. The cost of the strawberries is $4.68. The weight of the container is 0.3 pound. What is the cost per pound for strawberries? **$2.60**

MIXED REVIEW

Translate the verbal phrase into an expression. *(p. 15)*

64. 4 more than a number k **$k + 4$**

65. The product of 8 and a number x **$8x$**

66. 40 divided by a number y **$\frac{40}{y}$**

67. 10 less than twice a number w **$2w - 10$**

PREVIEW Prepare for Lesson 3.2 in Exs. 68–75.

A verbal description for a function and its domain are given. Write an equation for the function. Then describe the range. *(p. 35)*

68. The output is 9 more than the input.
Domain: −1, 0, 1, 2
$y = x + 9$; range: 8, 9, 10, 11

69. The output is 3 times the input.
Domain: −4, −2, 0, 2
$y = 3x$; range: −12, −6, 0, 6

Simplify the expression. *(p. 103)*

70. $-9x + 15x$ **$6x$**

71. $5x - 4x$ **x**

72. $12 + 3x - 3x$ **12**

73. $5x + 8 - x - 2$ **$4x + 6$**

74. $7.1x - 2.6x$ **$4.5x$**

75. $-0.7x + 11.3x$ **$10.6x$**

3.2 Solve Two-Step Equations

Before You solved one-step equations.
Now You will solve two-step equations.
Why? So you can find a scuba diver's depth, as in Example 4.

Key Vocabulary
- **like terms,** *p. 97*
- **input,** *p. 35*
- **output,** *p. 35*

The equation $\frac{x}{2} + 5 = 11$ involves two operations performed on x: division by 2 and addition by 5. You typically solve such an equation by applying the inverse operations in the reverse order of the order of operations. This is shown in the table below.

Operations performed on x	Operations to isolate x
1. Divide by 2. 2. Add 5.	1. Subtract 5. 2. Multiply by 2.

EXAMPLE 1 Solve a two-step equation

Solve $\frac{x}{2} + 5 = 11$.

$\frac{x}{2} + 5 = 11$ Write original equation.

$\frac{x}{2} + 5 - 5 = 11 - 5$ Subtract 5 from each side.

$\frac{x}{2} = 6$ Simplify.

$2 \cdot \frac{x}{2} = 2 \cdot 6$ Multiply each side by 2.

$x = 12$ Simplify.

▶ The solution is 12. Check by substituting 12 for x in the original equation.

CHECK $\frac{x}{2} + 5 = 11$ Write original equation.

$\frac{12}{2} + 5 \stackrel{?}{=} 11$ Substitute 12 for x.

$11 = 11$ ✓ Simplify. Solution checks.

GUIDED PRACTICE for Example 1

Solve the equation. Check your solution.

1. $5x + 9 = 24$ **3**
2. $4y - 4 = 16$ **5**
3. $-1 = \frac{z}{3} - 7$ **18**

1 PLAN AND PREPARE

Warm-Up Exercises

Transparency Available

Solve the equation.

1. $3x = -18$ **−6**

2. $b + 21 = 11$ **−10**

3. Simplify the expression $3(x + 2) - 4x + 1$. **$-x + 7$**

4. There are three times as many goats as sheep in a petting zoo. Find the number of sheep if the total number of goats and sheep is 28. **7 sheep**

Notetaking Guide

Transparency Available

Promotes interactive learning and notetaking skills.

Pacing

Basic: 1 day
Average: 1 day
Advanced: 1 day
Block: 0.5 block with 3.1
- See *Teaching Guide/Lesson Plan.*

2 FOCUS AND MOTIVATE

Essential Question

Big Idea 1, p. 131

How do you solve two-step equations? **Tell students they will learn how to answer this question by solving equations with more than one operation or with like terms.**

NCTM STANDARDS

Standard 1: Understand meanings of operations; Understand how operations are related

Resource Planning Guide

Chapter Resource Book
- Teaching Guide/Lesson Plan
- Activity Master
- Practice levels A, B, C
- Study Guide
- Catch-up for Absent Students
- Application
- Challenge

Workbooks
- Notetaking Guide
- Practice Workbook

Teaching Options
- **Power Presentations** provides dynamic electronic teaching resources for the classroom.
- **Activity Generator** provides editable activities for all ability levels.

Interactive Technology
- Easy Planner
- Power Presentations
- Activity Generator
- Animated Algebra
- Test Generator
- Online Quiz
- eWorkbook
- eEdition
- @HomeTutor

Resources for English Learners
- Spanish Study Guide
- Multi-Language Visual Glossary
- Student Resources in Spanish

See also the *Differentiated Instruction Resources* for more strategies for meeting individual needs.

Motivating the Lesson

Ask students if they have shipped a package at a shipping outlet or bought items online. Tell them that outlets or online stores often charge handling fees, such as $.37 per ounce, on top of the cost of the items or the cost of shipping the package. Invite students to share some of their experiences. Tell them that these are examples of two-step equations that they will be solving in Lesson 3.2.

3 TEACH

Extra Example 1

Solve $\frac{x}{4} - 3 = 2$. **20**

Key Questions to Ask for Example 1

- Could you multiply by 2 first? If so, what else would change? **Yes, you could multiply by 2 first to get $x + 10 = 22$. Then you would subtract 10 from each side.**
- Why is it simpler to subtract and then multiply? **There are fewer steps. If you multiply first, you have to multiply all of the terms of the equation by 2, which adds a step.**

Extra Example 2

Solve $5b - 7b = 4$. **−2**

Key Question to Ask for Example 2

- How do you use the distributive property to combine like terms? **Add the coefficients mentally, and then write the common variable.**

Extra Example 3

The output of a function is 7 more than 2 times the input. Write an equation for the function and then find the input when the output is 15. **$y = 2x + 7$; 4**

EXAMPLE 2 Solve a two-step equation by combining like terms

REVIEW LIKE TERMS
For help with combining like terms, see p. 97.

Solve $7x - 4x = 21$.

$7x - 4x = 21$	**Write original equation.**
$3x = 21$	**Combine like terms.**
$\frac{3x}{3} = \frac{21}{3}$	**Divide each side by 3.**
$x = 7$	**Simplify.**

EXAMPLE 3 Find an input of a function

The output of a function is 3 less than 5 times the input. Find the input when the output is 17.

Solution

STEP 1 **Write** an equation for the function. Let x be the input and y be the output.

$y = 5x - 3$	**y is 3 less than 5 times x.**

STEP 2 **Solve** the equation for x when $y = 17$.

$y = 5x - 3$	**Write original function.**
$17 = 5x - 3$	**Substitute 17 for y.**
$17 + 3 = 5x - 3 + 3$	**Add 3 to each side.**
$20 = 5x$	**Simplify.**
$\frac{20}{5} = \frac{5x}{5}$	**Divide each side by 5.**
$4 = x$	**Simplify.**

▸ An input of 4 produces an output of 17.

CHECK

$y = 5x - 3$	**Write original function.**
$17 \stackrel{?}{=} 5(4) - 3$	**Substitute 17 for y and 4 for x.**
$17 \stackrel{?}{=} 20 - 3$	**Multiply 5 and 4.**
$17 = 17$ ✓	**Simplify. Solution checks.**

✓ GUIDED PRACTICE for Examples 2 and 3

Solve the equation. Check your solution.

4. $4w + 2w = 24$ **4**
5. $8t - 3t = 35$ **7**
6. $-16 = 5d - 9d$ **4**
7. The output of a function is 5 more than −2 times the input. Find the input when the output is 11. **−3**
8. The output of a function is 4 less than 4 times the input. Find the input when the output is 3. **$1\frac{3}{4}$**

EXAMPLE 4 Solve a multi-step problem

SCUBA DIVING As a scuba diver descends into deeper water, the pressure of the water on the diver's body steadily increases.

The pressure at the surface of the water is 2117 pounds per square foot (lb/ft^2). The pressure increases at a rate of 64 pounds per square foot for each foot the diver descends. Find the depth at which a diver experiences a pressure of 8517 pounds per square foot.

ANOTHER WAY For an alternative method for solving Example 4, turn to page 147 for the **Problem Solving Workshop**.

Solution

STEP 1 **Write** a verbal model. Then write an equation.

Pressure at given depth (lb/ft^2)	=	Pressure at surface (lb/ft^2)	+	Rate of change of pressure (lb/ft^2 per foot of depth)	·	Diver's depth (ft)
P	=	2117	+	64	·	d

STEP 2 **Find** the depth at which the pressure is 8517 pounds per square foot.

$P = 2117 + 64d$	**Write equation.**
$8517 = 2117 + 64d$	**Substitute 8517 for *P*.**
$8517 - \mathbf{2117} = 2117 - \mathbf{2117} + 64d$	**Subtract 2117 from each side.**
$6400 = 64d$	**Simplify.**
$\frac{6400}{\mathbf{64}} = \frac{64d}{\mathbf{64}}$	**Divide each side by 64.**
$100 = d$	**Simplify.**

▶ A diver experiences a pressure of 8517 pounds per square foot at a depth of 100 feet.

CHECK

$P = 2117 + 64d$	**Write original equation.**
$8517 \stackrel{?}{=} 2117 + 64(100)$	**Substitute 8517 for *P* and 100 for *d*.**
$8517 \stackrel{?}{=} 2117 + 6400$	**Multiply 64 and 100.**
$8517 = 8517$ ✓	**Simplify. Solution checks.**

GUIDED PRACTICE for Example 4

9. **WHAT IF?** In Example 4, suppose the diver experiences a pressure of 5317 pounds per square foot. Find the diver's depth. **50 ft**

10. **JOBS** Kim has a job where she makes $8 per hour plus tips. Yesterday, Kim made $53 dollars, $13 of which was from tips. How many hours did she work? **5 h**

Extra Example 4

To rent a booth at the county fairgrounds costs $42 per day plus a one-time equipment fee of $85. Find the number of days Mr. Batzle rented a booth if he paid a total of $337. **6 days**

Key Questions to Ask for Example 4

- How is Example 4 like the output and input of the function in Example 3? **The output is *P*, the pressure at a given depth, and the input is *d*, the diver's depth.**
- Which are the dependent and independent variables? ***P* is the dependent variable and *d* is the independent variable.**
- Why do you subtract and then divide to solve the equation? **This is using inverse operations in the reverse order of the operations performed on *d*. Since you multiplied *d* by 64 and then added 2117, you subtract 2117 and then divide by 64 to apply inverse operations in the reverse order.**

Closing the Lesson

Have students summarize the major points of the lesson and answer the Essential Question: How do you solve two-step equations?

- **To solve equations efficiently, apply inverse operations in the reverse order of the operations performed on the variable.**
- **Combine like terms before solving equations.**

First look for like terms and combine them when solving two-step equations. For equations with two operations, look at the original equation and apply the inverse operations in the reverse order.

Differentiated Instruction

Inclusion Students need to organize their solution steps. It may be helpful to refer to a mnemonic device such as "My Dear Aunt Sally" to remember the order of operations Multiplication, Division, Addition, and Subtraction. For the method of solving linear equations, the mnemonic is reversed; to isolate the variable, first do Subtraction or Addition, then do Division or Multiplication.

See also the *Differentiated Instruction Resources* for more strategies.

3.2 EXERCISES

HOMEWORK KEY

○ = **WORKED-OUT SOLUTIONS** on p. WS5 for Exs. 13, 19, and 39

★ = **STANDARDIZED TEST PRACTICE** Exs. 2, 21, 40, 41, and 44

◆ = **MULTIPLE REPRESENTATIONS** Ex. 43

4 PRACTICE AND APPLY

Assignment Guide

Answer Transparencies available for all exercises

Basic:
Day 1: SRH p. 938 Exs. 21–24
pp. 144–146
Exs. 1, 2, 3–21 odd, 22–29, 37–41, 46–60

Average:
Day 1: pp. 144–146
Exs. 1, 2, 6–20 even, 21–26, 30–36, 38–44, 46–60

Advanced:
Day 1: pp. 144–146
Exs. 1, 2, 8–14 even, 19–21, 24–26, 32–36*, 39–45*, 49–51, 54–60 even

Block:
pp. 144–146
Exs. 1, 2, 6–20 even, 21–26, 30–36, 38–44, 46–60 (with 3.1)

Differentiated Instruction

See *Differentiated Instruction Resources* for suggestions on addressing the needs of a diverse classroom.

Homework Check

For a quick check of student understanding of key concepts, go over the following exercises:

Basic: 7, 13, 17, 24, 37

Average: 8, 14, 18, 25, 38

Advanced: 10, 14, 20, 26, 39

Extra Practice

- Student Edition, p. 940
- Chapter Resource Book: Practice levels A, B, C

Practice Worksheet

An easily-readable reduced practice page (with answers) for this lesson can be found on p. 130C.

SKILL PRACTICE

A

1. **VOCABULARY** Copy and complete: To solve the equation $2x + 3x = 20$, you would begin by combining $2x$ and $3x$ because they are _?_. **like terms**

2. ★ **WRITING** *Describe* the steps you would use to solve the equation $4x + 7 = 15$. **First, subtract 7 from each side to get $4x = 8$, then divide each side by 4 to get $x = 2$.**

EXAMPLE 1 on p. 141 for Exs. 3–14

SOLVING TWO-STEP EQUATIONS **Solve the equation. Check your solution.**

3. $3x + 7 = 19$ **4**
4. $5h + 4 = 19$ **3**
5. $7d - 1 = 13$ **2**
6. $2g - 13 = 3$ **8**
7. $10 = 7 - m$ **−3**
8. $11 = 12 - q$ **1**
9. $\frac{a}{3} + 4 = 6$ **6**
10. $17 = \frac{w}{5} + 13$ **20**
11. $\frac{b}{2} - 9 = 11$ **40**
12. $-6 = \frac{z}{4} - 3$ **−12**
13. $7 = \frac{5}{6}c - 8$ **18**
14. $10 = \frac{2}{7}n + 4$ **21**

EXAMPLE 2 on p. 142 for Exs. 15–23

COMBINING LIKE TERMS **Solve the equation. Check your solution.**

15. $8y + 3y = 44$ **4**
16. $2p + 7p = 54$ **6**
17. $11x - 9x = 18$ **9**
18. $36 = 9x - 3x$ **6**
19. $-32 = -5k + 13k$ **−4**
20. $6 = -7f + 4f$ **−2**

21. ★ **MULTIPLE CHOICE** What is the first step you can take to solve the equation $6 + \frac{x}{3} = -2$? **D**

Ⓐ Subtract 2 from each side.
Ⓑ Add 6 to each side.
Ⓒ Divide each side by 3.
Ⓓ Subtract 6 from each side.

ERROR ANALYSIS ***Describe*** **and correct the error in solving the equation.**

22.
$7 - 3x = 12$
$4x = 12$
$x = 3$

Unlike terms were combined; $-3x = 5$, $x = -\frac{5}{3}$.

23.
$-2x + x = 10$
$\frac{-2x + x}{-2} = \frac{10}{-2}$
$x = -5$

See margin.

EXAMPLE 3 on p. 142 for Exs. 24–26

FINDING AN INPUT OF A FUNCTION **Write an equation for the function described. Then find the input.**

24. The output of a function is 7 more than 3 times the input. Find the input when the output is −8. **$y = 3x + 7$; −5**

25. The output of a function is 4 more than 2 times the input. Find the input when the output is −10. **$y = 2x + 4$; −7**

26. The output of a function is 9 less than 10 times the input. Find the input when the output is 11. **$y = 10x - 9$; 2**

23. The division of $-2x + x$ by -2 is done incorrectly. *Sample answer:* If like terms are combined as the first step, the second line would be $-x = 10$ and the final result would be $x = -10$.

B **SOLVING EQUATIONS** **Solve the equation. Check your solution.**

27. $5.6 = 1.1p + 1.2$ **4**
28. $7.2y + 4.7 = 62.3$ **8**
29. $1.2j - 4.3 = 1.7$ **5**
30. $16 - 2.4d = -8$ **10**
31. $14.4m - 5.1 = 2.1$ **0.5**
32. $-5.3 = 2.2v - 8.6$ **1.5**
33. $\frac{c}{5.3} + 8.3 = 11.3$ **15.9**
34. $3.2 + \frac{x}{2.5} = 4.6$ **3.5**
35. $-1.2 = \frac{z}{4.6} - 2.7$ **6.9**

C 36. **CHALLENGE** Solve the equations $3x + 2 = 5$, $3x + 2 = 8$, and $3x + 2 = 11$. Predict the solution of the equation $3x + 2 = 14$. *Explain.* **1, 2, 3; 4; the output of each equation is increased by 3 because x is multiplied by 3, each solution increases by 1.**

PROBLEM SOLVING

EXAMPLE 4 A on p. 143 for Exs. 37–40

37. **DANCE CLASSES** A dance academy charges $24 per class and a one-time registration fee of $15. A student paid a total of $687 to the academy. Find the number of classes the student took. **28 classes**

@HomeTutor for problem solving help at classzone.com

38. **CAR REPAIR** Tyler paid $124 to get his car repaired. The total cost for the repairs was the sum of the amount paid for parts and the amount paid for labor. Tyler was charged $76 for parts and $32 per hour for labor. Find the amount of time it took to repair his car. **1.5 h**

@HomeTutor for problem solving help at classzone.com

(39.) **ADVERTISING** A science museum wants to promote an upcoming exhibit by advertising on city buses for one month. The costs of the two types of advertisements being considered are shown. The museum has budgeted $6000 for the advertisements. The museum decides to have 1 full bus wrap advertisement. How many half-side advertisements can the museum have? **5 half-side advertisements**

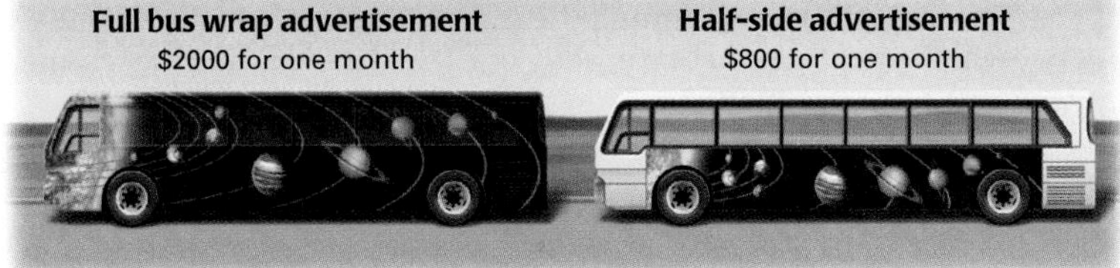

41. Yes; the equation $542 = 50 + 6x$ gives the monthly cost of a guitar that costs $542. Solving the equation gives $x = \$82$ per month, so you can afford the guitar.

40. ★ **MULTIPLE CHOICE** A skateboarding park charges $7 per session to skate and $4 per session to rent safety equipment. Jared rents safety equipment every time he skates. During one year, he spends $99 for skating charges and equipment rentals. Which equation can be used to find x, the number of sessions Jared attended? **B**

Ⓐ $99 = 7x$ Ⓑ $99 = 7x + 4x$ Ⓒ $99 = 7x + 4$ Ⓓ $99 = 4x + 7$

B 41. ★ **SHORT RESPONSE** A guitar store offers a finance plan where you give a $50 down payment on a guitar and pay the remaining balance in 6 equal monthly payments. You have $50 and you can afford to pay up to $90 per month for a guitar. Can you afford a guitar that costs $542? *Explain.*

Avoiding Common Errors

Exercises 3–14 Students often use the wrong operation when solving an equation. Suggest they work with a partner prior to solving the equations to go over the operations they should use in each of the exercises. Refer them to the box in the explanation before Example 1. Have them go through each of the exercises using the box as a model to determine which operations they should use and in which order.

Reading Strategy

Exercises 13–14 Caution students to read these exercises carefully. Note that the coefficients are slightly different than those in Exercises 9–12.

Teaching Strategy

Exercises 24–26 It may be useful to review Example 3 and functions in general before students work on these exercises. Remind students that functions typically give the output y in terms of the input x.

Exercise 36 For students who request help on this exercise, tell them to look for a pattern in the equations and for a pattern in the value of x. They may want to line up the equations, one underneath the other, to visualize the pattern. Tell them to use the patterns to explain their prediction.

Exercises 37–40 Suggest that students first determine the variable in the problem. This will help them determine the coefficient of the variable and the constant.

5 ASSESS AND RETEACH

Daily Homework Quiz

Transparency Available

Solve the equation.

1. $\frac{a}{4} + 6 = -14$ **−80**
2. $6r - 12 = 6$ **3**
3. $-36 = 7y + 2y$ **−4**
4. The output of a function is 9 less than 3 times the input. Write an equation for the function and then find the input when the output is −6. **$y = 3x - 9$; 1**
5. A bank charges $5.00 per month plus $.30 per check for a standard checking account. Find the number of checks Justine wrote if she paid $8.30 in fees last month. **11 checks**

Online Quiz

Available at **classzone.com**

Diagnosis/Remediation

- Practice A, B, C in Chapter Resource Book
- Study Guide in Chapter Resource Book
- Practice Workbook
- @HomeTutor

Challenge

Additional challenge is available in the Chapter Resource Book.

43b. See Additional Answers beginning on p. AA1.

43c.

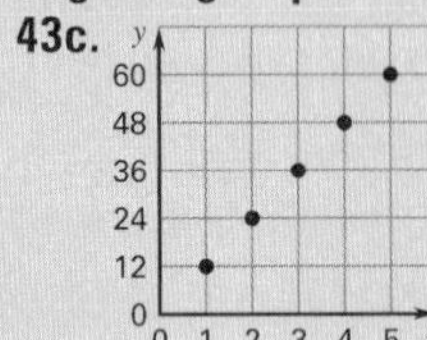

42. ***Sample answer:*** **Estimate the number of days to be about 1200; 3,000,000 + 1600(1200) = 3,000,000 + 1,920,000 = 4,920,000 so the solution makes sense.**

42. MULTI-STEP PROBLEM The capacity of a landfill is 4,756,505 tons. The landfill currently holds 2,896,112 tons. A cell is added to the landfill every day, and each cell averages 1600 tons.

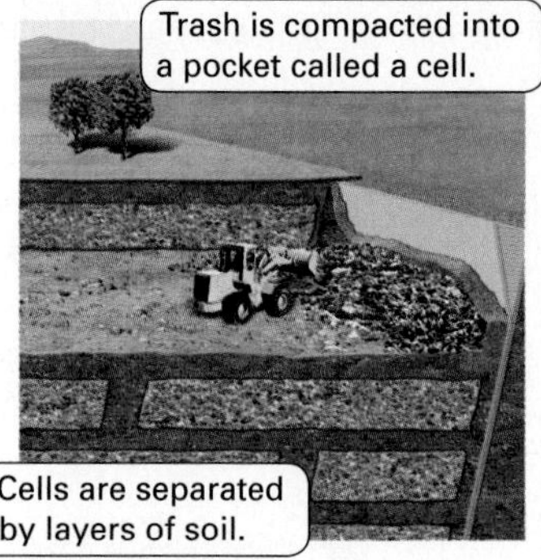

a. Write an equation that gives the amount y (in tons) in the landfill as a function of the number x of days from now. **$y = 2{,}896{,}112 + 1600x$**

b. After how many days will the landfill reach capacity? Round your answer to the nearest day. **1163 days**

c. Use estimation to check your answer to part (b).

43. MULTIPLE REPRESENTATIONS Two computer technicians are upgrading the software on the 54 computers in a school. On average, Marissa upgrades 5 computers in 1 hour and Ryan upgrades 7 computers in 1 hour.

a. Writing an Equation Write an equation that gives the total number y of computers upgraded as a function of the number x of hours worked. **$y = 12x$**

b. Making a Table Make a table that shows the number of computers upgraded by each technician and the total number of computers upgraded after 1, 2, 3, 4, and 5 hours. **See margin.**

c. Drawing a Graph Graph the ordered pairs that represent the total number y of computers upgraded after x hours. Use the graph to estimate the number of hours it took to upgrade all of the computers. **See margin for art; about 4.5 h.**

44. ★ SHORT RESPONSE At a restaurant, customers can dine inside the restaurant or pick up food at the take-out window. On an average day, 400 customers are served inside the restaurant, and 120 customers pick up food at the take-out window. After how many days will the restaurant have served 2600 customers? *Explain.* **5 days; the restaurant serves 400 + 120 = 520 customers each day, use the equation $2600 = 520x$ to find $x = 5$.**

C **45. CHALLENGE** During a 1 mile race, one runner is running at a rate of 14.6 feet per second, and another runner is running at a rate of 11.3 feet per second. One lap around the track is 660 feet. After how many seconds will the faster runner be exactly one lap ahead of the other runner? **200 sec**

MIXED REVIEW

Find the sum, difference, or product.

46. $14 + (-6)$ *(p. 74)* **8**
47. $-7 + (-13)$ *(p. 74)* **−20**
48. $16 - 21$ *(p. 80)* **−5**
49. $-9 - (-10)$ *(p. 80)* **1**
50. $(3a)(-3a)(a)$ *(p. 88)* **$-9a^3$**
51. $-2(-12)(2t)$ *(p. 88)* **$48t$**

Use the distributive property to write an equivalent expression. *(p. 96)*

52. $2(9z + 4)$ **$18z + 8$**
53. $-3(5b - 8)$ **$-15b + 24$**
54. $(2k - 7)(-5)$ **$-10k + 35$**

PREVIEW Prepare for Lesson 3.3 in Exs. 55–60.

Solve the equation. Check your solution. *(p. 134)*

55. $x + 9 = 2$ **−7**
56. $m + 2 = 5$ **3**
57. $y - 18 = 12$ **30**
58. $-7r = 56$ **−8**
59. $30s = 1200$ **40**
60. $-\frac{1}{9}c = -8$ **72**

Using ALTERNATIVE METHODS

Another Way to Solve Example 4, page 143

MULTIPLE REPRESENTATIONS In Example 4 on page 143, you saw how to solve a problem about scuba diving by using an equation. You can also solve the problem using a table.

PROBLEM

SCUBA DIVING As a scuba diver descends into deeper water, the pressure of the water on the diver's body steadily increases. The pressure at the surface of the water is 2117 pounds per square foot (lb/ft^2). The pressure increases at a rate of 64 pounds per square foot for each foot the diver descends. Find the depth at which a diver experiences a pressure of 8517 pounds per square foot.

METHOD

Making a Table An alternative approach is to make a table.

STEP 1 **Make** a table that shows the pressure as the depth increases. Because you are looking for a fairly high pressure, use larger increments in depth, such as 20 feet.

Every 1 ft of depth increases the pressure by 64 lb/ft^2.

Every 20 ft of depth increases the pressure by 64(20) = 1280 lb/ft^2.

Depth (ft)	Pressure (lb/ft^2)
0	2117
1	2181
2	2245
20	3397
40	4677
60	5957
80	7237
100	8517

STEP 2 **Look** for the depth at which the pressure reaches 8517 pounds per square foot. This happens at a depth of 100 feet.

PRACTICE

1. **BASKETBALL** A sports club offers an organized basketball league. A team pays $600 to join the league. In addition to paying their share of the $600, team members who are not members of the sports club must pay a $25 fee to play. A team pays a total of $775. How many team members who are not club members are on the team? Solve this problem using two different methods. **See margin.**

2. **WHAT IF?** In Exercise 1, suppose you are on a team, but not a club member. The $600 cost is divided equally among the team members. How many players must there be on your team for you to pay $100 to play? Make a table to find the answer. **8 players; see margin for table.**

3. **FURNITURE** You have $370 to spend on a dining table and chairs. A table costs $220, and each chair costs $35. How many chairs can you buy in addition to the table? Solve this problem using two different methods. **See margin.**

Alternative Strategy

Example 4 on page 143 can be solved using a table. This method allows the student to grasp and solve a complex problem in which the numbers are large and the measurements are most likely unfamiliar. The table can also be used to help the student understand the algebraic solution given in Lesson 3.2.

Mathematical Reasoning

Multiple Representations Using a table to solve a problem is a useful strategy when students have a difficult time writing an equation. It is particularly helpful in Example 4 because students may feel overwhelmed by the numbers or the concepts and may be discouraged in finding a solution. By using the table alongside the algebraic solution, students are more likely to see the relationships in the equation between pressure at the surface, the rate of change, and the diver's depth. Once they see these interconnections, it could help them write an equation to model the problem. Have students discuss advantages and disadvantages of using tables to solve problems. One advantage is they can see how the pressure changes at different depths and thereby get a sense for a reasonable solution to the problem. Some disadvantages include more possibilities for making errors in calculations and missing the actual depth because they are using an increment that misses the target pressure.

1. See Additional Answers beginning on p. AA1.

2.

Team members	Your cost (dollars)
1	625
2	325
3	225
4	175
5	145
6	125
7	110.71
8	100

3. See Additional Answers beginning on p. AA1.

3.3 Solve Multi-Step Equations

Before	You solved one-step and two-step equations.
Now	You will solve multi-step equations.
Why?	So you can solve a problem about lifeguarding, as in Ex. 40.

Key Vocabulary
- **like terms,** *p. 97*
- **distributive property,** *p. 96*
- **reciprocal,** *p. 915*

Solving a linear equation may take more than two steps. Start by simplifying one or both sides of the equation, if possible. Then use inverse operations to isolate the variable.

EXAMPLE 1 Solve an equation by combining like terms

Solve $8x - 3x - 10 = 20$.

$8x - 3x - 10 = 20$	Write original equation.
$5x - 10 = 20$	Combine like terms.
$5x - 10 + 10 = 20 + 10$	Add 10 to each side.
$5x = 30$	Simplify.
$\frac{5x}{5} = \frac{30}{5}$	Divide each side by 5.
$x = 6$	Simplify.

EXAMPLE 2 Solve an equation using the distributive property

Solve $7x + 2(x + 6) = 39$.

Solution

When solving an equation, you may feel comfortable doing some steps mentally. Method 2 shows a solution where some steps are done mentally.

REVIEW PROPERTIES
For help with using the distributive property, see p. 96.

METHOD 1 Show All Steps	METHOD 2 Do Some Steps Mentally
$7x + 2(x + 6) = 39$	$7x + 2(x + 6) = 39$
$7x + 2x + 12 = 39$	$7x + 2x + 12 = 39$
$9x + 12 = 39$	$9x + 12 = 39$
$9x + 12 - 12 = 39 - 12$	$9x = 27$
$9x = 27$	$x = 3$
$\frac{9x}{9} = \frac{27}{9}$	
$x = 3$	

1 PLAN AND PREPARE

Warm-Up Exercises
Transparency Available

1. Simplify the expression $9x + 2(x - 1) + 7$. **$11x + 5$**

Solve the equation.

2. $5g - 7 = 58$ **13**
3. $\frac{2}{3}x = 18$ **27**
4. A surf shop charges $85 for surfing lessons and $35 per hour to rent a surfboard. Anna paid $225. Find the number of hours she spent surfing. **4 h**

Notetaking Guide
Transparency Available

Promotes interactive learning and notetaking skills.

Pacing
Basic: 2 days
Average: 2 days
Advanced: 2 days
Block: 1 block
- See *Teaching Guide/Lesson Plan.*

2 FOCUS AND MOTIVATE

Essential Question
Big Idea 1, p. 131

How do you solve multi-step equations? **Tell students they will learn how to answer this question by combining like terms, using the distributive property, and multiplying by a reciprocal.**

NCTM STANDARDS
Standard 1: Understand how operations are related

Standard 9: Understand how mathematical ideas build on one another

Resource Planning Guide

Chapter Resource Book
- Teaching Guide/Lesson Plan
- Activity Master
- Practice levels A, B, C
- Study Guide
- Catch-up for Absent Students
- Problem Solving Workshop
- Challenge

Workbooks
- Notetaking Guide
- Practice Workbook

Teaching Options
- **Power Presentations** provides dynamic electronic teaching resources for the classroom.
- **Activity Generator** provides editable activities for all ability levels.

Interactive Technology
- Easy Planner
- Power Presentations
- Activity Generator
- Animated Algebra
- Test Generator
- Online Quiz
- eWorkbook
- eEdition
- @HomeTutor

Resources for English Learners
- Spanish Study Guide
- Multi-Language Visual Glossary
- Student Resources in Spanish

See also the *Differentiated Instruction Resources* for more strategies for meeting individual needs.

EXAMPLE 3 Standardized Test Practice

Which equation represents Step 2 in the solution process?

Step 1 $5x - 4(x - 3) = 17$

Step 2 ☐

Step 3 $x + 12 = 17$

Step 4 $x = 5$

ELIMINATE CHOICES
You can eliminate choices B and C because −4 has not been distributed to *both* terms in the parentheses.

Ⓐ $5x - 4x - 12 = 17$ Ⓑ $5x - 4x - 3 = 17$

Ⓒ $5x - 4x + 3 = 17$ Ⓓ $5x - 4x + 12 = 17$

Solution

In Step 2, the distributive property is used to simplify the left side of the equation. Because $-4(x - 3) = -4x + 12$, Step 2 should be $5x - 4x + 12 = 17$.

▶ The correct answer is D. Ⓐ Ⓑ Ⓒ Ⓓ

GUIDED PRACTICE for Examples 1, 2, and 3

Solve the equation. Check your solution.

1. $9d - 2d + 4 = 32$ **4**
2. $2w + 3(w + 4) = 27$ **3**
3. $6x - 2(x - 5) = 46$ **9**

USING RECIPROCALS Although you can use the distributive property to solve an equation such as $\frac{3}{2}(3x + 5) = -24$, it is easier to multiply each side of the equation by the reciprocal of the fraction.

EXAMPLE 4 Multiply by a reciprocal to solve an equation

Solve $\frac{3}{2}(3x + 5) = -24$.

$\frac{3}{2}(3x + 5) = -24$	Write original equation.
$\frac{2}{3} \cdot \frac{3}{2}(3x + 5) = \frac{2}{3}(-24)$	Multiply each side by $\frac{2}{3}$, the reciprocal of $\frac{3}{2}$.
$3x + 5 = -16$	Simplify.
$3x = -21$	Subtract 5 from each side.
$x = -7$	Divide each side by 3.

GUIDED PRACTICE for Example 4

Solve the equation. Check your solution.

4. $\frac{3}{4}(z - 6) = 12$ **22**
5. $\frac{2}{5}(3r + 4) = 10$ **7**
6. $-\frac{4}{5}(4a - 1) = 28$ **−8.5**

Motivating the Lesson

Inform students that real-world problems often involve many parts. For example, you might want to know how long it takes to ride one section of a bike trail if you ride the whole trail in 55 minutes, pedaling at 14 miles per hour for part of the trail and 8 miles per hour for the rest. Tell students that this lesson offers several methods to solve problems such as this and others with many steps.

3 TEACH

Extra Example 1

Solve $9x + x - 7 = 13$. **2**

Extra Example 2

Solve $4x - 7(x - 2) = 26$. **−4**

Key Question to Ask for Example 2

- Suppose you use Method 2 to solve Example 1. Which steps might you do mentally? **Add 10 to each side; divide each side by 5.**

Extra Example 3

Which equation represents Step 2 in the solution process? **C**

Step 1 $-3x + 4(x - 2) = 15$

Step 2 ☐

Step 3 $x - 8 = 15$

Step 4 $x = 23$

Ⓐ $-3x + 4x - 2 = 15$

Ⓑ $-3x + 4x + 2 = 15$

Ⓒ $-3x + 4x - 8 = 15$

Ⓓ $-3x + 4x + 8 = 15$

Extra Example 4

Solve $\frac{3}{5}(2x - 4) = 18$. **17**

Extra Example 5

Edmund and Roberto took a 7-day (168 hours), 90-mile canoe trip down the Allagash River. If they paddled at an average rate of 2.5 miles per hour, how many hours did they spend *not* paddling? Write and solve an equation to find the answer. **$90 = 2.5(168 - x)$; 132 h**

Key Question to Ask for Example 5

- Why does $1 + s$ represent the total number of campers on each team? **Each team has 1 recorder and s searchers, so the total number of campers on each team is represented by $1 + s$.**

Closing the Lesson

Have students summarize the major points of the lesson and answer the Essential Question: How do you solve multi-step equations?

- **To solve multi-step equations, first simplify one or both sides and then use inverse operations.**
- **If a fraction is being multiplied by a quantity, use reciprocals to simplify instead of the distributive property.**

To solve a multi-step equation, first simplify and combine like terms. After simplifying, use inverse operations to isolate the variable.

EXAMPLE 5 Write and solve an equation

SUMMER CAMP You are planning a scavenger hunt for 21 campers. You plan to have 5 teams. One camper from each team will be the recorder and the rest will be searchers. How many searchers will each team have?

Solution

Let s be the number of searchers on each team. Then $1 + s$ is the total number of campers on each team.

Number of campers	=	Number of teams	•	Number of campers on each team
21	=	5	•	$(1 + s)$

$21 = 5(1 + s)$ **Write equation.**

$21 = 5 + 5s$ **Distributive property**

$16 = 5s$ **Subtract 5 from each side.**

$3.2 = s$ **Divide each side by 5.**

CHECK REASONABLENESS
The number of searchers must be a whole number.

▶ Because 4 searchers per team would require a total of $5(1 + 4) =$ 25 campers, 4 teams will have 3 searchers and 1 team will have 4 searchers.

✓ **GUIDED PRACTICE** for Example 5

7. **WHAT IF?** In Example 5, suppose you decide to use only 4 teams. How many searchers should there be on each team? **5 searchers on one team and 4 searchers on the other teams**

3.3 EXERCISES

HOMEWORK KEY

○ = **WORKED-OUT SOLUTIONS** on p. WS6 for Exs. 17 and 39

★ = **STANDARDIZED TEST PRACTICE** Exs. 2, 18, 35, 36, and 41

 = **MULTIPLE REPRESENTATIONS** Ex. 42

SKILL PRACTICE

A

1. **VOCABULARY** What is the reciprocal of the fraction in the equation $\frac{3}{5}(2x + 8) = 18$? $\frac{5}{3}$

2. ★ **WRITING** *Describe* the steps you would use to solve the equation $3(4y - 7) = 6$. **Use the distributive property to get $12y - 21 = 6$, then add 21 to each side to get $12y = 27$, divide each side by 12 to get $y = 2.25$.**

EXAMPLE 1 on p. 148 for Exs. 3–11

COMBINING LIKE TERMS **Solve the equation. Check your solution.**

3. $p + 2p - 3 = 6$ **3**
4. $12v + 14 + 10v = 80$ **3**
5. $11w - 9 - 7w = 15$ **6**
6. $5a + 3 - 3a = -7$ **−5**
7. $6c - 8 - 2c = -16$ **−2**
8. $9 = 7z - 13z - 21$ **−5**
9. $-2 = 3y - 18 - 5y$ **−8**
10. $23 = -4m + 2 + m$ **−7**
11. $35 = -5 + 2x - 7x$ **−8**

EXAMPLES 2 and 3 on pp. 148–149 for Exs. 12–18, 25

USING THE DISTRIBUTIVE PROPERTY **Solve the equation. Check your solution.**

12. $3 + 4(z + 5) = 31$ **2**
13. $14 + 2(4g - 3) = 40$ **4**
14. $5m + 2(m + 1) = 23$ **3**
15. $5h + 2(11 - h) = -5$ **−9**
16. $27 = 3c - 3(6 - 2c)$ **5**
17. $-3 = 12y - 5(2y - 7)$ **−19**

18. ★ **MULTIPLE CHOICE** What is the solution of $7v - (6 - 2v) = 12$? **C**

Ⓐ −3.6 Ⓑ −2 Ⓒ 2 Ⓓ 3.6

EXAMPLE 4 on p. 149 for Exs. 19–24, 26

MULTIPLYING BY A RECIPROCAL **Solve the equation. Check your solution.**

19. $\frac{1}{3}(d + 3) = 5$ **12**
20. $\frac{3}{2}(x - 5) = -6$ **1**
21. $\frac{4}{3}(7 - n) = 12$ **−2**
22. $4 = \frac{2}{9}(4y - 2)$ **5**
23. $-32 = \frac{8}{7}(3w - 1)$ **−9**
24. $-14 = \frac{2}{5}(9 - 2b)$ **22**

ERROR ANALYSIS ***Describe*** **and correct the error in solving the equation.**

25. 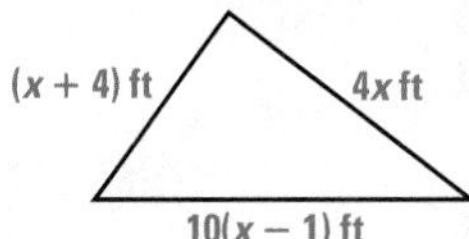

25. −3 times −6 is 18, not −18; $5x - 3x + 18 = 2$, $2x + 18 = 2$, $2x = -16$, $x = -8$.

26. 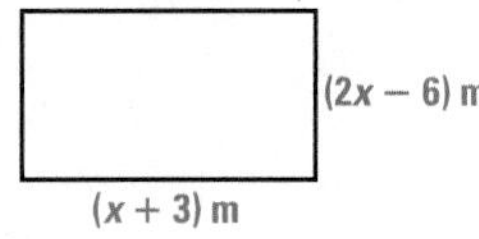

Multiply each side by 2, not $\frac{1}{2}$; $2x - 10 = 8$, $2x = 18$, $x = 9$.

B **SOLVING EQUATIONS** **Solve the equation. Check your solution.**

27. $8.9 + 1.2(3a - 1) = 14.9$ **2**
28. $-11.2 + 4(2.1 + q) = -0.8$ **0.5**
29. $1.3t + 3(t + 8.2) = 37.5$ **3**
30. $1.6 = 7.6 - 5(k + 1.1)$ **0.1**
31. $0.5 = 4.1x - 2(1.3x - 4)$ **−5**
32. $8.7 = 3.5m - 2.5(5.4 - 6m)$ **1.2**

REVIEW CONVERTING UNITS For help with converting units of measurement, see p. 927.

GEOMETRY **Find the value of *x* for the triangle or rectangle. Be sure to use the same units for the side lengths and the perimeters.**

33. Perimeter = 288 inches **2**

$(x + 4)$ ft, $4x$ ft, $10(x - 1)$ ft

34. Perimeter = 2600 centimeters **$5\frac{1}{3}$**

$(2x - 6)$ m, $(x + 3)$ m

35. ★ **WRITING** The length of a rectangle is 3.5 inches more than its width. The perimeter of the rectangle is 31 inches. Find the length and the width of the rectangle. *Explain* your reasoning. **9.5 in., 6 in.; if you use the perimeter formula $P = 2\ell + 2w$ and substitute $3.5 + w$ for ℓ, the solution is $w = 6$.**

36. ★ **SHORT RESPONSE** Solve each equation by first dividing each side of the equation by the number outside the parentheses. When would you recommend using this method to solve an equation? *Explain.*

a. $9(x - 4) = 72$ **12**
b. $8(x + 5) = 60$ **2.5**

36. You should divide each side of the equation by the number outside the parentheses when the number is a factor of the number on the other side of the equals sign or it is a fraction.

C 37. **CHALLENGE** An even integer can be represented by the expression $2n$. Find three consecutive even integers that have a sum of 54. **16, 18, 20**

4 PRACTICE AND APPLY

Assignment Guide

Answer Transparencies available for all exercises

Basic:
Day 1: pp. 150–153
Exs. 1–18, 27, 28, 44–47
Day 2: pp. 150–153
Exs. 19–26, 29, 30, 38–41, 48–56

Average:
Day 1: pp. 150–153
Exs. 1, 2, 4–10 even, 12–18, 27–32, 35, 45, 46
Day 2: pp. 150–153
Exs. 19–26, 33, 34, 36, 38–42, 49–55 odd

Advanced:
Day 1: pp. 150–153
Exs. 1, 9–11, 15–18, 29–32, 35, 37*, 45, 46
Day 2: pp. 150–153
Exs. 22–24, 33, 34, 36, 38–43*, 54–56

Block:
pp. 150–153
Exs. 1, 2, 4–10 even, 12–36, 38–42, 45, 46, 49–55 odd

Differentiated Instruction

See *Differentiated Instruction Resources* for suggestions on addressing the needs of a diverse classroom.

Homework Check

For a quick check of student understanding of key concepts, go over the following exercises:

Basic: 4, 13, 18, 20, 38
Average: 8, 14, 18, 22, 39
Advanced: 11, 16, 18, 23, 40

Extra Practice

- Student Edition, p. 940
- Chapter Resource Book: Practice levels A, B, C

Practice Worksheet

An easily-readable reduced practice page (with answers) for this lesson can be found on p. 130C.

Differentiated Instruction

English Learners While discussing **Exercise 37**, point out that the word "consecutive" comes from a Latin word meaning "to follow." Students may be more familiar with the related word "sequence," which is an ordered list. Show them examples of a list of consecutive integers, a list of consecutive even integers, and a list of consecutive odd integers.

See also the *Differentiated Instruction Resources* for more strategies.

Avoiding Common Errors

Exercises 3–11 Some students may overlook variables such as p in Exercise 3 when combining terms. Students should realize that these variables have a coefficient of 1.

Teaching Strategy

Exercise 18 For students who cannot solve this equation, suggest they rewrite it as an addition equation so that the equation reads $7v + (-1)(6 - 2v) = 12$.

Reading Strategy

Exercises 33–34 Point out to students that the known measurement for these exercises is perimeter, not area. Also, in Exercise 34 some students may think "m" is a variable. Note that x is the variable and the letter "m" stands for meters.

Study Strategy

Exercise 38 Some students may be confused by all the different dollar amounts. Suggest they look for like terms that can be combined to use the same variable.

Internet Reference

Exercise 41 For more information about the Colorado Midland Railway and the Busk-Ivanhoe Tunnel, visit www.daeunert.de/html/colorado_midland.html.

PROBLEM SOLVING

EXAMPLE 5 A on p. 150 for Exs. 38–40

38. BASKETBALL A ticket agency sells tickets to a professional basketball game. The agency charges \$32.50 for each ticket, a convenience charge of \$3.30 for each ticket, and a processing fee of \$5.90 for the entire order. The total charge for an order is \$220.70. How many tickets were purchased? **6 tickets**

@HomeTutor for problem solving help at classzone.com

39. HANGING POSTERS You want to hang 3 equally-sized travel posters on the wall in your room so that the posters on the ends are each 3 feet from the end of the wall. You want the spacing between posters to be equal. How much space should you leave between the posters? **0.75 ft**

@HomeTutor for problem solving help at classzone.com

40. LIFEGUARD TRAINING To qualify for a lifeguard training course, you have to swim continuously for 500 yards using either the front crawl or the breaststroke. You swim the front crawl at a rate of 45 yards per minute and the breaststroke at a rate of 35 yards per minute. You take 12 minutes to swim 500 yards. How much time did you spend swimming the front crawl? Use the verbal model below. **8 min**

Distance = Rate for front crawl · Time for front crawl + Rate for breaststroke (Total time − Time for front crawl)

B

41. ★ EXTENDED RESPONSE The Busk-Ivanhoe Tunnel on the Colorado Midland Railway was built in the 1890s with separate work crews starting on opposite ends at different times. The crew working from Ivanhoe started 0.75 month later than the crew working from Busk.

Cutaway of Busk-Ivanhoe Tunnel

a. Starting at the time construction began on the Busk end, find the time it took to complete a total of 8473 feet of the tunnel. Round your answer to the nearest month. **34 mo**

b. After 8473 feet were completed, the work crews merged under the same supervision. The combined crew took 3 months to complete the remaining 921 feet of the tunnel. Find the rate at which the remainder of the tunnel was completed. **307 ft per mo**

c. Was the tunnel being completed more rapidly before or after the work crews merged? *Explain* your reasoning.

41c. After the work crews merged; before the work crews merged they were working at a rate of 115 + 137 = 252 feet per month, and after merging at a rate of 307 feet per month.

○ = WORKED-OUT SOLUTIONS on p. WS1 ★ = STANDARDIZED TEST PRACTICE ◆ = MULTIPLE REPRESENTATIONS

42. ◆ **MULTIPLE REPRESENTATIONS** A roofing contractor gives estimates for shingling a roof in cost per square, where a square is a 10 foot by 10 foot section of roof. The contractor estimates \$27.50 per square for materials, \$17 per square for labor, \$30 per square for overhead and profit, and a total of \$750 for miscellaneous expenses.

a. **Writing an Equation** Write an equation that gives the estimate y (in dollars) as a function of the number x of squares of a roof. The contractor gives an estimate of \$2314.50. About how many squares does the roof have? **$y = 74.5x + 750$; 21 squares**

b. **Making a Table** Make a table that shows the estimates for shingling a roof that has 5, 10, 15, 20, or 25 squares. Use your table to check your answer to part (a). **See margin.**

C 43. **CHALLENGE** Jan says that she has quarters and dimes that total \$2.80, and that the number of dimes is 8 more than the number of quarters. Demonstrate algebraically that Jan must be mistaken. **See margin.**

MIXED REVIEW

Evaluate the expression for the given value(s) of the variable(s).

44. $x - y$ when $x = -7$ and $y = 2$ *(p. 80)* **−9**

45. $x - (-y)$ when $x = -4$ and $y = 5$ *(p. 80)* **1**

46. $\frac{x-9}{4}$ when $x = 9$ *(p. 103)* **0**

47. $\frac{4y+7}{3}$ when $y = 5$ *(p. 103)* **9**

PREVIEW
Prepare for Lesson 3.4 in Exs. 48–56.

Solve the equation. Check your solution. *(p. 141)*

48. $5x + 1 = 26$ **5**

49. $-x + 4 = 13$ **−9**

50. $3x - 5 = -14$ **−3**

51. $3 - 2x = 19$ **−8**

52. $\frac{x}{3} - 4 = 1$ **15**

53. $8 + \frac{x}{4} = -\frac{3}{4}$ **−35**

54. $11x + 5x = 48$ **3**

55. $-4x + 11x = -28$ **−4**

56. $\frac{2}{5}x - \frac{3}{5}x = -7$ **35**

QUIZ *for Lessons 3.1–3.3*

Solve the equation. Check your solution.

1. $x + 9 = 7$ *(p. 134)* **−2**

2. $y - 5 = -11$ *(p. 134)* **−6**

3. $-7b = -56$ *(p. 134)* **8**

4. $\frac{z}{4} = 6$ *(p. 134)* **24**

5. $-\frac{4}{3}t = -12$ *(p. 134)* **9**

6. $9w - 4 = 14$ *(p. 141)* **2**

7. $23 = 1 - d$ *(p. 141)* **−22**

8. $66 = 4m + 7m$ *(p. 141)* **6**

9. $-104 = -5p - 3p$ *(p. 141)* **13**

10. $2v + 5v - 8 = 13$ *(p. 148)* **3**

11. $2a - 6(a - 4) = -4$ *(p. 148)* **7**

12. $\frac{6}{5}(5 - 4g) = -18$ *(p. 148)* **5**

13. **INTERNET SHOPPING** Dan purchases DVDs from a website. Each DVD costs \$11, and the shipping and handling fees are \$6.95. Dan is charged a total of \$50.95. How many DVDs did he purchase? *(p. 141)* **4 DVDs**

5 ASSESS AND RETEACH

Daily Homework Quiz

Transparency Available

Solve the equation.

1. $8g - 2 + g = 16$ **2**
2. $3b + 2(b - 4) = 47$ **11**
3. $-6 + 4(2c + 1) = -34$ **−4**
4. $\frac{2}{3}(x - 6) = 12$ **24**
5. Joe drove 405 miles in 7 hours. He drove at a rate of 55 miles per hour during the first part of the trip and 60 miles per hour during the second part. How many hours did he drive at a rate of 55 miles per hour? **3 h**

Online Quiz

Available at **classzone.com**

Diagnosis/Remediation

- Practice A, B, C in Chapter Resource Book
- Study Guide in Chapter Resource Book
- Practice Workbook
- @HomeTutor

Challenge

Additional challenge is available in the Chapter Resource Book.

Quiz

An easily-readable reduced copy of the quiz (with answers) on Lessons 3.1–3.3 from the Assessment Book can be found on p. 130E.

42b.

Squares	Cost (dollars)
5	1122.50
10	1495
15	1867.50
20	2240
25	2612.50

43. Let q be the number of quarters, then $q + 8$ is the number of dimes. The equation $25q + 10(q + 8) = 280$ represents the situation, but the solution of the equation is $5\frac{5}{7}$. The number of quarters must be a whole number, so Jan must be mistaken.

1 PLAN AND PREPARE

Warm-Up Exercises

Transparency Available

Solve the equation.

1. $2m - 6 + 4m = 12$ **3**
2. $6a - 5(a - 1) = 11$ **6**
3. A charter bus company charges \$11.25 per ticket plus a handling charge of \$.50 per ticket, and a \$15 fee for booking the bus. If a group pays \$297 to charter a bus, how many tickets did they buy? **24 tickets**

Notetaking Guide

Transparency Available

Promotes interactive learning and notetaking skills.

Pacing

Basic: 1 day
Average: 1 day
Advanced: 1 day
Block: 0.5 block with 3.5
- See *Teaching Guide/Lesson Plan.*

2 FOCUS AND MOTIVATE

Essential Question

Big Idea 1, p. 131

How do you solve equations with variables on both sides? **Tell students they will learn how to answer this question by collecting variable terms on one side and constants on the other.**

NCTM STANDARDS

Standard 1: Understand how operations are related

Standard 9: Recognize math in contexts outside of mathematics

3.4 Solve Equations with Variables on Both Sides

Before You solved equations with variables on one side.
Now You will solve equations with variables on both sides.
Why? So you can find the cost of a gym membership, as in Ex. 52.

Key Vocabulary
- **identity**

Some equations have variables on both sides. To solve such equations, you can collect the variable terms on one side of the equation and the constant terms on the other side of the equation.

EXAMPLE 1 Solve an equation with variables on both sides

Solve $7 - 8x = 4x - 17$.

$7 - 8x = 4x - 17$	**Write original equation.**
$7 - 8x + 8x = 4x - 17 + 8x$	**Add 8x to each side.**
$7 = 12x - 17$	**Simplify each side.**
$24 = 12x$	**Add 17 to each side.**
$2 = x$	**Divide each side by 12.**

ANOTHER WAY You could also begin solving the equation by subtracting $4x$ from each side to obtain $7 - 12x = -17$. When you solve this equation for x, you get the same solution, 2.

▶ The solution is 2. Check by substituting 2 for x in the original equation.

CHECK	$7 - 8x = 4x - 17$	**Write original equation.**
	$7 - 8(2) \stackrel{?}{=} 4(2) - 17$	**Substitute 2 for x.**
	$-9 \stackrel{?}{=} 4(2) - 17$	**Simplify left side.**
	$-9 = -9$ ✓	**Simplify right side. Solution checks.**

 Animated Algebra at classzone.com

EXAMPLE 2 Solve an equation with grouping symbols

Solve $9x - 5 = \frac{1}{4}(16x + 60)$.

$9x - 5 = \frac{1}{4}(16x + 60)$	**Write original equation.**
$9x - 5 = 4x + 15$	**Distributive property**
$5x - 5 = 15$	**Subtract 4x from each side.**
$5x = 20$	**Add 5 to each side.**
$x = 4$	**Divide each side by 5.**

Resource Planning Guide

Chapter Resource Book
- Teaching Guide/Lesson Plan
- Activity Master
- Practice levels A, B, C
- Study Guide
- Catch-up for Absent Students
- Problem Solving Workshop
- Challenge

Workbooks
- Notetaking Guide
- Practice Workbook

Teaching Options
- **Power Presentations** provides dynamic electronic teaching resources for the classroom.
- **Activity Generator** provides editable activities for all ability levels.

Interactive Technology
- Easy Planner
- Power Presentations
- Activity Generator
- Animated Algebra
- Test Generator
- Online Quiz
- eWorkbook
- eEdition
- @HomeTutor

Resources for English Learners
- Spanish Study Guide
- Multi-Language Visual Glossary
- Student Resources in Spanish

See also the *Differentiated Instruction Resources* for more strategies for meeting individual needs.

GUIDED PRACTICE for Examples 1 and 2

Solve the equation. Check your solution.

1. $24 - 3m = 5m$ **3**

2. $20 + c = 4c - 7$ **9**

3. $9 - 3k = 17 - 2k$ **−8**

4. $5z - 2 = 2(3z - 4)$ **6**

5. $3 - 4a = 5(a - 3)$ **2**

6. $8y - 6 = \frac{2}{3}(6y + 15)$ **4**

EXAMPLE 3 Solve a real-world problem

CAR SALES A car dealership sold 78 new cars and 67 used cars this year. The number of new cars sold by the dealership has been increasing by 6 cars each year. The number of used cars sold by the dealership has been decreasing by 4 cars each year. If these trends continue, in how many years will the number of new cars sold be twice the number of used cars sold?

Solution

Let x represent the number of years from now. So, $6x$ represents the increase in the number of new cars sold over x years and $-4x$ represents the decrease in the number of used cars sold over x years. Write a verbal model.

New cars sold this year + Increase in new cars sold over x years = 2 (Used cars sold this year + Decrease in used cars sold over x years)

$$78 + 6x = 2(67 + (-4x))$$

$78 + 6x = 2(67 - 4x)$ **Write equation.**

$78 + 6x = 134 - 8x$ **Distributive property**

$78 + 14x = 134$ **Add $8x$ to each side.**

$14x = 56$ **Subtract 78 from each side.**

$x = 4$ **Divide each side by 14.**

▶ The number of new cars sold will be twice the number of used cars sold in 4 years.

CHECK You can use a table to check your answer.

Year	0	1	2	3	4
Used cars sold	67	63	59	55	51
New cars sold	78	84	90	96	102

The number of new cars sold is twice the number of used cars sold in 4 years.

GUIDED PRACTICE for Example 3

7. WHAT IF? In Example 3, suppose the car dealership sold 50 new cars this year instead of 78. In how many years will the number of new cars sold be twice the number of used cars sold? **6 yr**

Motivating the Lesson

Learning how to write and solve equations with variables on both sides allows you to determine when two quantities equal each other. Suppose you offer a dog grooming service to earn money during the summer. One plan could be to charge customers a flat fee of \$150 for two months of service, plus \$5 per comb out and shampoo. Another plan could be to charge \$10 per comb out and \$5 per shampoo. By setting these options equal to each other, you can find when the earnings from the two plans would be the same. This can help you decide which plan to use.

3 TEACH

Extra Example 1

Solve $13 + 5x = 2x - 8$. **−7**

An **Animated Algebra** activity is available online for **Example 1**. This activity is also part of **Power Presentations**.

Extra Example 2

Solve $4x - 5 = \frac{1}{5}(5x + 20)$. **3**

Key Question to Ask for Example 2

- Another way is suggested for solving the equation in Example 1. What is another way to solve the equation in Example 2? **You could start by mutiplying each side by 4 to get $36x - 20 = 16x + 60$. Then $20x = 80$ and $x = 4$.**

Extra Example 3

A music website sold 94 single songs and 67 albums today. The number of single downloads has been increasing by 22 each day. The number of album downloads has been decreasing by 5 each day. If these trends continue, in how many days will the number of single downloads be ten times the number of album downloads? Write and solve an equation to find the number of days. **$94 + 22x = 10(67 - 5x)$; 8**

Extra Example 4

Solve the equation, if possible.

a. $5x - 6 = 5(x - 1)$ **The equation has no solution.**

b. $4(3x + 2) = 2(6x + 4)$ **The equation is an identity.**

Closing the Lesson

Have students summarize the major points of the lesson and answer the Essential Question: How do you solve equations with variables on both sides?

- **To solve equations with variables on both sides, collect the variable terms on one side and the constant terms on the other.**
- **Some equations, called identities, are true for all values of the variable. Other equations have no solutions.**

To solve equations with variables on both sides, first simplify the expressions on each side of the equation by using the distributive property to remove grouping symbols and then combining like terms. Next, use properties of equality to collect variable terms on one side of the equation and constants on the other. Then solve the equation by isolating the variable.

NUMBER OF SOLUTIONS Equations do not always have one solution. An equation that is true for all values of the variable is an **identity**. So, the solution of an identity is all real numbers. Some equations have no solution.

EXAMPLE 4 Identify the number of solutions of an equation

Solve the equation, if possible.

a. $3x = 3(x + 4)$ **b.** $2x + 10 = 2(x + 5)$

Solution

a. $3x = 3(x + 4)$ **Original equation**

$3x = 3x + 12$ **Distributive property**

The equation $3x = 3x + 12$ is not true because the number $3x$ cannot be equal to 12 more than itself. So, the equation has no solution. This can be demonstrated by continuing to solve the equation.

$3x - 3x = 3x + 12 - 3x$ **Subtract 3x from each side.**

$0 = 12$ ✗ **Simplify.**

▶ The statement $0 = 12$ is not true, so the equation has no solution.

b. $2x + 10 = 2(x + 5)$ **Original equation**

$2x + 10 = 2x + 10$ **Distributive property**

▶ Notice that the statement $2x + 10 = 2x + 10$ is true for all values of x. So, the equation is an identity, and the solution is all real numbers.

✓ GUIDED PRACTICE for Example 4

Solve the equation, if possible.

8. $9z + 12 = 9(z + 3)$ **no solution** **9.** $7w + 1 = 8w + 1$ **0** **10.** $3(2a + 2) = 2(3a + 3)$ **identity**

SOLVING LINEAR EQUATIONS You have learned several ways to transform an equation to an equivalent equation. These methods are combined in the steps listed below.

CONCEPT SUMMARY *For Your Notebook*

Steps for Solving Linear Equations

STEP 1 **Use** the distributive property to remove any grouping symbols.

STEP 2 **Simplify** the expression on each side of the equation.

STEP 3 **Use** properties of equality to collect the variable terms on one side of the equation and the constant terms on the other side of the equation.

STEP 4 **Use** properties of equality to solve for the variable.

STEP 5 **Check** your solution in the original equation.

Differentiated Instruction

Below Level As you discuss **Example 4**, it may be difficult for students to understand the concept of no solution or a solution that is true for all values of the variable. Have these students substitute 5 to 10 different values for *x* in the equations in parts a and b. After they have done this, ask them to describe why the equation in part a has no solution and why any value satisfies the equation in part b. Check their understanding by asking them to explain the solutions to **Guided Practice Exercises 8 and 10**.

Advanced For some students, the equations in **Example 4** and the **Guided Practice** may seem obvious. Challenge these students to create complicated equations with no solution, one solution, or infinitely many solutions. Ask them to create five of each and then exchange them with other students to solve. Remind them to mix the equations.

See also the *Differentiated Instruction Resources* for more strategies.

3.4 EXERCISES

HOMEWORK KEY
- ○ = **WORKED-OUT SOLUTIONS** on p. WS6 for Exs. 13 and 51
- ★ = **STANDARDIZED TEST PRACTICE** Exs. 2, 15, 16, 17, 29, and 53
- ◆ = **MULTIPLE REPRESENTATIONS** Ex. 52

SKILL PRACTICE

A

1. **VOCABULARY** Copy and complete: An equation that is true for all values of the variable is called a(n) ___?___. **identity**

2. ★ **WRITING** *Explain* why the equation $4x + 3 = 4x + 1$ has no solution.
A number plus 3 can't be equal to itself plus 1. If you solve the equation, you get 0 = 2.

EXAMPLES 1 and 2 on p. 154 for Exs. 3–17

SOLVING EQUATIONS **Solve the equation. Check your solution.**

3. $8t + 5 = 6t + 1$ **−2**
4. $k + 1 = 3k - 1$ **1**
5. $8c + 5 = 4c - 11$ **−4**
6. $8 + 4m = 9m - 7$ **3**
7. $10b + 18 = 8b + 4$ **−7**
8. $19 - 13p = -17p - 5$ **−6**
9. $9a = 6(a + 4)$ **8**
10. $5h - 7 = 2(h + 1)$ **3**
11. $3(d + 12) = 8 - 4d$ **−4**
12. $7(r + 7) = 5r + 59$ **5**
13. $40 + 14j = 2(-4j - 13)$ **−3**
14. $5(n + 2) = \frac{3}{5}(5 + 10n)$ **7**

15. ★ **MULTIPLE CHOICE** What is the solution of the equation $8x + 2x = 15x - 10$? **C**

Ⓐ −2 Ⓑ 0.4 Ⓒ 2 Ⓓ 5

16. ★ **MULTIPLE CHOICE** What is the solution of the equation $4y + y + 1 = 7(y - 1)$? **D**

Ⓐ −4 Ⓑ −3 Ⓒ 3 Ⓓ 4

17. ★ **WRITING** *Describe* the steps you would use to solve the equation $3(2z - 5) = 2z + 13$.

17. *Sample answer:* Distribute the 3 to get $6z - 15 = 2z + 13$, then subtract $2z$ from each side to get $4z - 15 = 13$, next add 15 to each side to get $4z = 28$, finally divide each side by 4 to get $z = 7$.

EXAMPLE 4 on p. 156 for Exs. 18–28

SOLVING EQUATIONS **Solve the equation, if possible.**

18. $w + 3 = w + 6$ **no solution**
19. $16d = 22 + 5d$ **2**
20. $8z = 4(2z + 1)$ **no solution**
21. $12 + 5v = 2v - 9$ **−7**
22. $22x + 70 = 17x - 95$ **−33**
23. $2 - 15n = 5(-3n + 2)$ **no solution**
24. $12y + 6 = 6(2y + 1)$ **identity**
25. $5(1 + 4m) = 2(3 + 10m)$ **no solution**
26. $2(3g + 2) = \frac{1}{2}(12g + 8)$ **identity**

ERROR ANALYSIS ***Describe*** **and correct the error in solving the equation.**

27.

$3(x + 5) = 3x + 15$
$3x + 5 = 3x + 15$
$5 = 15$
The equation has no solution.

28.

$6(2y + 6) = 4(9 + 3y)$
$12y + 36 = 36 + 12y$
$12y = 12y$
$0 = 0$
The solution is $y = 0$.

27. The 3 was not distributed to both terms; $3x + 15 = 3x + 15$, $15 = 15$, so the equation is an identity.

28. When the equation is $0 = 0$, it means that it is true for all values of y, not just 0; the equation is an identity.

B

29. ★ **OPEN-ENDED** Give an example of an equation that has no solution. *Explain* why your equation does not have a solution.
Sample answer: **$5x + 4 = 5x$; the number $5x$ cannot be equal to 4 more than itself.**

4 PRACTICE AND APPLY

Assignment Guide

Answer Transparencies available for all exercises

Basic:
Day 1: EP p. 939 Exs. 38–41
pp. 157–159
Exs. 1, 2, 3–13 odd, 15–37, 49–52, 56–64 even

Average:
Day 1: pp. 157–159
Exs. 1, 2, 7–13 odd, 15–29, 31–43 odd, 44–47, 49–53, 56–64 odd

Advanced:
Day 1: pp. 157–159
Exs. 1, 7, 8, 12–17, 18–26, 29, 38–48*, 50–55*, 58–64 even

Block:
pp. 157–159
Exs. 1, 2, 7–13 odd, 15–29, 31–43 odd, 44–47, 49–53, 56–64 odd (with 3.5)

Differentiated Instruction

See *Differentiated Instruction Resources* for suggestions on addressing the needs of a diverse classroom.

Homework Check

For a quick check of student understanding of key concepts, go over the following exercises:

Basic: 5, 11, 19, 31, 49
Average: 7, 13, 22, 37, 50
Advanced: 8, 14, 24, 39, 51

Extra Practice

- Student Edition, p. 940
- Chapter Resource Book: Practice levels A, B, C

Practice Worksheet

An easily-readable reduced practice page (with answers) for this lesson can be found on p. 130C.

Avoiding Common Errors

Exercises 9–14 Students sometimes fail to distribute a factor to both terms in parentheses. Suggest that students confirm they distributed a factor to both terms if their solutions do not check.

Reading Strategy

Exercises 18–20, 30–43 Advise students that they may be able to solve some of these equations even though they are based on Example 4, which shows an equation with no solution and an equation that is an identity. Direct their attention to the instruction line, which indicates that an equation may or may not have a solution.

Teaching Strategy

Exercises 47–48 Before students try to solve these problems, you may want to review the meaning of an identity.

Study Strategy

Exercises 49–51 Suggest that students make a table to check their answers. This will also give them an opportunity to compare algebraic and tabular solutions to problems and gain facility in using each.

Internet Reference

Exercise 53 More information about flyball can be found at the website www.flyballdogs.com/FAQ.html#flyball_is

SOLVING EQUATIONS **Solve the equation, if possible.**

30. $8w - 8 - 6w = 4w - 7$ **$-\frac{1}{2}$**

31. $3x - 4 = 2x + 8 - 5x$ **2**

32. $-15c + 7c + 1 = 3 - 8c$ **no solution**

33. $\frac{3}{2} + \frac{3}{4}a = \frac{1}{4}a - \frac{1}{2}$ **−4**

34. $\frac{5}{8}m - \frac{3}{8} = \frac{1}{2}m + \frac{7}{8}$ **10**

35. $n - 10 = \frac{5}{6}n - 7 - \frac{1}{3}n$ **6**

36. $3.7b + 7 = 8.1b - 19.4$ **6**

37. $6.2h + 5 - 1.4h = 4.8h + 5$ **identity**

38. $0.7z + 1.9 + 0.1z = 5.5 - 0.4z$ **3**

39. $5.4t + 14.6 - 10.1t = 12.8 - 3.5t - 0.6$ **2**

40. $\frac{1}{8}(5y + 64) = \frac{1}{4}(20 + 2y)$ **−24**

41. $14 - \frac{1}{5}(j - 10) = \frac{2}{5}(25 + j)$ **10**

42. $5(1.2k + 6) = 7.1k + 34.4$ **−4**

43. $-0.25(4v - 8) = 0.5(4 - 2v)$ **identity**

GEOMETRY **Find the perimeter of the square.**

44. 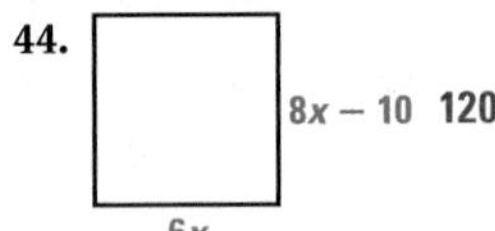

120

45. 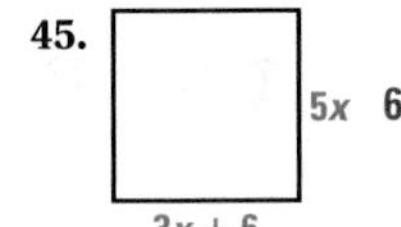

60

46. 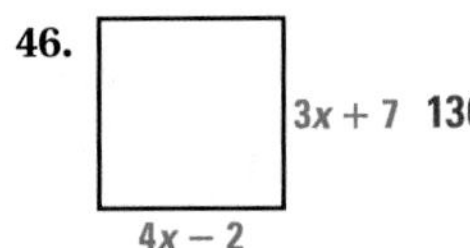

136

C **CHALLENGE** **Find the value(s) of a for which the equation is an identity.**

47. $a(2x + 3) = 9x + 12 - x$ **4**

48. $10x - 35 + 3ax = 5ax - 7a$ **5**

PROBLEM SOLVING

EXAMPLE 3 A
on p. 155
for Exs. 49–51

49. CAMPING The membership fee for joining a camping association is \$45. A local campground charges members of the camping association \$35 per night for a campsite and nonmembers \$40 per night for a campsite. After how many nights of camping is the total cost for members, including the membership fee, the same as the total cost for nonmembers? **9 nights**

@HomeTutor for problem solving help at classzone.com

50. HIGH-SPEED INTERNET Dan and Sydney are getting high-speed Internet access at the same time. Dan's provider charges \$60 for installation and \$42.95 per month. Sydney's provider has free installation and charges \$57.95 per month. After how many months will Dan and Sydney have paid the same amount for high-speed Internet service? **4 mo**

@HomeTutor for problem solving help at classzone.com

(51.) LANGUAGES Information about students who take Spanish and students who take French at a high school is shown in the table. If the trends continue, in how many years will there be 3 times as many students taking Spanish as French? **about 4 yr**

Language	Students enrolled this year	Average rate of change
Spanish	555	33 more students each year
French	230	2 fewer students each year

○ = WORKED-OUT SOLUTIONS on p. WS1 ★ = STANDARDIZED TEST PRACTICE ◆ = MULTIPLE REPRESENTATIONS

Differentiated Instruction

English Learners When solving **Exercises 49–55**, students will need to select their own variables. Students almost always create variables by using the first letter that a quantity represents (h for height, A for area, and so on). English learners may be more comfortable choosing variables from words in their native language. Explain that this still leads to a correct mathematical result, because the choice of variable is arbitrary.

See also the *Differentiated Instruction Resources* for more strategies.

B 52. MULTIPLE REPRESENTATIONS For $360, a rock-climbing gym offers a yearly membership where members can climb as many days as they want and pay $4 per day for equipment rental. Nonmembers pay $10 per day to use the gym and $6 per day for equipment rental.

a. **Writing an Equation** Write an equation to find the number of visits after which the total cost for a member and the total cost for a nonmember are the same. Then solve the equation. **$360 + 4x = 16x$; 30 visits**

b. **Making a Table** Make a table for the costs of members and nonmembers after 5, 10, 15, 20, 25, 30, and 35 visits. Use the table to check your answer to part (a). **See margin.**

53. ★ **EXTENDED RESPONSE** Flyball is a relay race for dogs. In each of the four legs of the relay, a dog jumps over hurdles, retrieves a ball from a flybox, and runs back over the hurdles. The last leg of a relay is shown below. The collie starts the course 0.3 second before the sheepdog.

flybox
The collie is running 23.4 feet per second.
51 ft
The sheepdog is running 24 feet per second.

53c. No; it would take 12 seconds for the sheepdog to catch up to the collie and it only takes 4.4 seconds for the collie to complete the last leg.

a. Let t represent the time (in seconds) it takes the collie to run the last leg. Write and solve an equation to find the number of seconds after which the sheepdog would catch up with the collie. **$23.4t = 24(t - 0.3)$; 12 sec**

b. How long does it take the collie to run the last leg? **about 4.4 sec**

c. Use your answers from parts (a) and (b) to determine whether the sheepdog catches up and passes the collie during the last leg of the relay. *Explain* your reasoning.

C **CHALLENGE** **Find the length and the width of the rectangle described.**

54. The length is 12 units more than the width. The perimeter is 7 times the width. **20, 8**

55. The length is 4 units less than 3 times the width. The perimeter is 22 units more than twice the width. **11, 5**

MIXED REVIEW

PREVIEW Prepare for Lesson 3.5 in Exs. 56–64.

Write the fraction in simplest form. *(p. 912)*

56. $\frac{5}{15}$ **$\frac{1}{3}$**
57. $\frac{10}{12}$ **$\frac{5}{6}$**
58. $\frac{4}{14}$ **$\frac{2}{7}$**
59. $\frac{18}{48}$ **$\frac{3}{8}$**

Solve the equation. *(p. 134)*

60. $\frac{w}{3} = 6$ **18**
61. $\frac{x}{18} = 2$ **36**
62. $-11 = \frac{m}{4}$ **−44**
63. $12 = \frac{z}{-9}$ **−108**

64. **FOOTBALL** The average rushing yards per game for a football player is found by dividing the total rushing yards for the season by the number of games played. How many total rushing yards did a player have if he played in 12 games and averaged 22 yards per game? *(p. 134)* **264 rushing yards**

5 ASSESS AND RETEACH

Daily Homework Quiz

Transparency Available

Solve the equation, if possible.

1. $3(3x + 6) = 9(x + 2)$ **The equation is an identity.**
2. $7(h - 4) = 2h + 17$ **9**
3. $8 - 2w = 6w - 8$ **2**
4. $4g + 3 = 2(2g + 3)$ **The equation has no solution.**
5. Bryson is looking for a repair service for general household maintenance. One service charges $75 to join the service and $30 per hour. Another service charges $45 per hour. After how many hours of service is the total cost for the two services the same? **5 h**

Online Quiz

Available at **classzone.com**

Diagnosis/Remediation

- Practice A, B, C in Chapter Resource Book
- Study Guide in Chapter Resource Book
- Practice Workbook
- @HomeTutor

Challenge

Additional challenge is available in the Chapter Resource Book.

52b. See Additional Answers beginning on p. AA1.

@HomeTutor
classzone.com
Keystrokes

1 PLAN AND PREPARE

Learn the Method

- Students will use a spreadsheet to solve equations with variables on both sides.
- After the activity, students can use a spreadsheet to check their solutions in Exercises 3–16 and 49–53 in Lesson 3.4.

2 TEACH

Tips for Success

Make sure students enter an asterisk to indicate multiplication in columns b and c in Step 1. Point out that in Exercise 1 they need to place an asterisk in the spreadsheet between 15 and x for the left side of the equation and between 6 and x for the right side of the equation. It may be helpful for students to go through each of the exercises and mark where they need to place asterisks.

As students are working, point out that they do not need to simplify the sides of the equations to use a spreadsheet.

Extra Example

Solve $-9(x + 4) + 56 = -3x - 4$.
4

3 ASSESS AND RETEACH

Use a spreadsheet to solve the equation.

1. $7x + 12 = 6(x + 3)$ **6**
2. $-4 + 3x = -3 + 2x$ **1**

4a–b. See Additional Answers beginning on p. AA1.

3.4 Solve Equations Using Tables

QUESTION **How can you use a spreadsheet to solve an equation with variables on both sides?**

You can use a spreadsheet to solve an equation with variables on both sides by evaluating the left side of the equation and the right side of the equation using the same value of the variable. If the left side and right side are equal, then the value of the variable is a solution.

EXAMPLE **Solve an equation using a spreadsheet**

Solve $19(x - 1) - 72 = 6x$.

STEP 1 ***Enter data and formulas***

Label columns for possible solutions, left side, and right side in row 1. Enter the integers from 0 through 10 as possible solutions in column A. Then enter the formulas for the left side and the right side of the equation in columns B and C.

	A	B	C
1	Possible solutions	Left side	Right side
2	0	=19*(A2−1)−72	=6*A2
3	1	=19*(A3−1)−72	=6*A3
...	...	...	...
12	10	=19*(A12−1)−72	=6*A12

STEP 2 ***Compare columns***

Compare the values of the left side and the values of the right side. The left side and right side values are equal when $x = 7$. So, the solution is 7.

	A	B	C
1	Possible solutions	Left side	Right side
...	...	...	...
8	6	23	36
9	7	42	42
10	8	61	48

DRAW CONCLUSIONS **Use your observations to complete these exercises**

In Exercises 1–3, use a spreadsheet to solve the equation.

1. $15x + 6 = 6x + 24$ **2**
2. $8x - 17 = 5x + 70$ **29**
3. $18 - 2(x + 3) = x$ **4**
4. Not all equations have integer solutions. Consider the equation $4.9 + 4.8(7 - x) = 6.2x$.
   a. Follow Step 1 above using $4.9 + 4.8(7 - x) = 6.2x$. **See answer to part (b).**
   b. Add a fourth column that shows the difference of the value of the left side and the value of the right side. Find consecutive possible solutions between which the differences of the values of the left side and right side change sign. **See margin for spreadsheet; 3 and 4.**
   c. Repeat Step 1. This time use the lesser of the two possible solutions from part (b) as the first possible solution, and increase each possible solution by 0.1. Can you identify a solution now? If so, what is it? **yes; 3.5**

MIXED REVIEW of Problem Solving

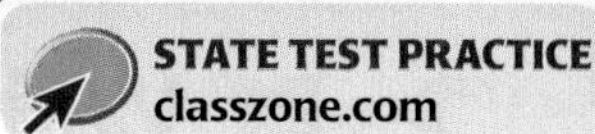

Lessons 3.1–3.4

1. **MULTI-STEP PROBLEM** A phone company charges \$.25 for the first minute of a long-distance call and \$.07 for each additional minute.
   a. Write an equation that gives the cost C of a long-distance call as a function of the length t (in minutes) of the call. **$C = 0.25 + 0.07(t - 1)$**
   b. Find the duration of a long-distance call that costs \$2. **26 min**

2. **GRIDDED ANSWER** A veterinary assistant steps on a scale while holding a cat. The weight of the cat and assistant is 175 pounds. The assistant weighs 162 pounds. Find the weight (in pounds) of the cat. **13 lb**

3. **EXTENDED RESPONSE** A bowling alley charges \$1.50 for bowling shoes and \$3.75 for each game. Paul and Brandon each have \$15 to spend at the bowling alley.
   a. Paul brings his own bowling shoes. How many games can he bowl? **4 games**
   b. Brandon needs to pay for bowling shoes. How many games can he bowl? Round your answer down to the nearest whole number. **3 games**
   c. Both Paul and Brandon decide to bowl the number of games that Brandon can afford to bowl. Does Paul have enough money to buy a slice of pizza and a soda that cost a total of \$3.25? *Explain* your reasoning. **See margin.**

4. **GRIDDED ANSWER** The triangle has a perimeter of 82 inches. What is x? **4**

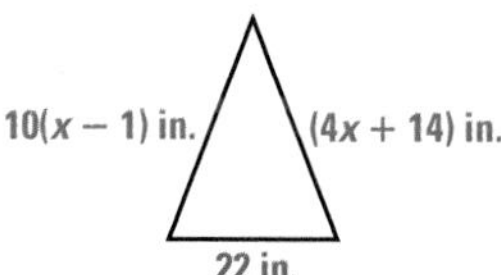

5. **SHORT RESPONSE** You are folding origami cranes that will be used as decorations at a wedding. If you make cranes for 1 hour without a break, you can make 40 cranes. During a 3 hour period, you make 100 cranes. How much time did you spend *not* making cranes? *Explain* your reasoning. **See margin.**

6. **SHORT RESPONSE** A ski resort offers a super-saver pass for \$90. The lift ticket rates with and without the super-saver pass are listed below.

Pass	Weekday lift ticket	Weekend/holiday lift ticket
With	\$22.50	\$36.00
Without	\$45.00	\$48.00

Suppose a skier skis only on weekdays. After how many visits to the ski resort will the cost for the super-saver pass and the lift tickets be equal to the cost of the lift tickets without the pass? *Explain* your reasoning. **See margin.**

7. **SHORT RESPONSE** The eruption of Mount St. Helens in 1980 decreased its elevation by 1313 feet. The current elevation is 8364 feet. What was the elevation of the volcano before the eruption? *Explain* your reasoning. **See margin.**

8. **EXTENDED RESPONSE** A garden supply store sells daffodil bulbs for \$.60 per bulb.
   a. Jen spends \$24 on daffodil bulbs. How many daffodil bulbs did she purchase? **40 daffodil bulbs**
   b. Jen decides to plant the daffodil bulbs along one side of her house that is 30 feet long. How many inches apart should she plant the bulbs so that they are equally spaced? **9 in.**
   c. Jen thinks that the daffodils will look better if the bulbs are planted 6 inches apart. How many more bulbs does she need? *Explain* your reasoning. **See margin.**

9. **OPEN-ENDED** *Describe* a real-world situation that can be modeled by the equation $4x + 15 = 47$. Then solve the equation and explain what your solution means in this situation. **See margin.**

3c. Yes; if Paul bowls only 3 games, he will have \$3.75 left over.

5. 30 min; if you make 40 cranes in an hour, it will take 2.5 hours to make 100 cranes, so you spent 30 minutes not making cranes.

6. 4 visits; use an equation to find when the cost of skiing with a pass is the same as skiing without a pass. Solve $90 + 22.50x = 45x$ to find that $x = 4$.

7. 9677 ft; if you add 1313 feet to the current elevation, you will get the elevation before the eruption.

8c. 20 daffodil bulbs. *Sample answer:* If she plants bulbs 6 inches apart she will need 360 inches ÷ 6 inches = 60, so she needs 60 − 40 = 20 more bulbs.

9. *Sample answer:* You want to buy a video game for \$47, if you have \$15 and plan on saving money from a paper route each week for 4 weeks, how much money should you save each week? $x = 8$; you need to save \$8 each week for 4 weeks to have enough money to buy the video game.

3.5 Write Ratios and Proportions

Before You solved equations involving division.

Now You will find ratios and write and solve proportions.

Why? So you can find a ratio involving a contest, as in Ex. 46.

Key Vocabulary
- ratio
- proportion
- simplest form, *p. 912*

Throughout this book you have been using rates, such as 50 miles per hour. A rate is a special type of *ratio.*

KEY CONCEPT *For Your Notebook*

Ratios

A **ratio** uses division to compare two quantities. You can write the ratio of two quantities a and b, where b is not equal to 0, in three ways.

a to b $\qquad a:b \qquad \frac{a}{b}$

Each ratio is read "the ratio of a to b." Ratios should be written in simplest form.

EXAMPLE 1 Write a ratio

VOLLEYBALL A volleyball team plays 14 home matches and 10 away matches.

a. Find the ratio of home matches to away matches.

b. Find the ratio of home matches to all matches.

Solution

a. $\frac{\text{home matches}}{\text{away matches}} = \frac{14}{10} = \frac{7}{5}$

b. $\frac{\text{home matches}}{\text{all matches}} = \frac{14}{14 + 10} = \frac{14}{24} = \frac{7}{12}$

GUIDED PRACTICE for Example 1

Derek and his brother decide to combine their CD collections. Derek has 44 CDs, and his brother has 52 CDs. Find the specified ratio.

1. The number of Derek's CDs to the number of his brother's CDs **$\frac{11}{13}$**

2. The number of Derek's CDs to the number of CDs in the entire collection **$\frac{11}{24}$**

1 PLAN AND PREPARE

Warm-Up Exercises

Solve the equation.

1. $\frac{5}{6}x = 25$ **30**
2. $\frac{2}{3}(6x + 3) = 14$ **3**
3. $\frac{g}{5} - 7 = 12$ **95**
4. You buy three identical polyester film balloons and a birthday card. The card costs \$3.95. Find the cost of each balloon if your total bill before tax was \$33.80. **\$9.95**

Notetaking Guide

Transparency Available

Promotes interactive learning and notetaking skills.

Pacing

Basic: 1 day

Average: 1 day

Advanced: 1 day

Block: 0.5 block with 3.4

- See *Teaching Guide/Lesson Plan.*

2 FOCUS AND MOTIVATE

Essential Question

Big Idea 2, p. 131

How do you find ratios and write and solve proportions? **Tell students they will learn how to answer this question by comparing quantities in the real world and by learning to recognize and set up proportions.**

NCTM STANDARDS

Standard 2: Represent situations using algebraic symbols

Standard 9: Recognize math in contexts outside of mathematics

Resource Planning Guide

Chapter Resource Book
- Teaching Guide/Lesson Plan
- Practice levels A, B, C
- Study Guide
- Catch-up for Absent Students
- Problem Solving Workshop
- Challenge

Workbooks
- Notetaking Guide
- Practice Workbook

Teaching Options
- **Power Presentations** provides dynamic electronic teaching resources for the classroom.
- **Activity Generator** provides editable activities for all ability levels.

Interactive Technology
- Easy Planner
- Power Presentations
- Activity Generator
- Animated Algebra
- Test Generator
- Online Quiz
- eWorkbook
- eEdition
- @HomeTutor

Resources for English Learners
- Spanish Study Guide
- Multi-Language Visual Glossary
- Student Resources in Spanish

See also the *Differentiated Instruction Resources* for more strategies for meeting individual needs.

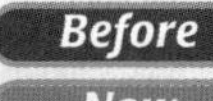

PROPORTIONS A **proportion** is an equation that states that two ratios are equivalent. The general form of a proportion is given below.

READING This proportion is read "*a* is to *b* as *c* is to *d*."

$$\frac{a}{b} = \frac{c}{d} \text{ where } b \neq 0, d \neq 0$$

If one of the numbers in a proportion is unknown, you can solve the proportion to find the unknown number. To solve a proportion with a variable in the numerator, you can use the same methods you used to solve equations.

EXAMPLE 2 Solve a proportion

Solve the proportion $\frac{11}{6} = \frac{x}{30}$.

$\frac{11}{6} = \frac{x}{30}$	Write original proportion.
$30 \cdot \frac{11}{6} = 30 \cdot \frac{x}{30}$	Multiply each side by 30.
$\frac{330}{6} = x$	Simplify.
$55 = x$	Divide.

✓ GUIDED PRACTICE for Example 2

Solve the proportion. Check your solution.

3. $\frac{w}{35} = \frac{4}{7}$ 20
4. $\frac{9}{2} = \frac{m}{12}$ 54
5. $\frac{z}{54} = \frac{5}{9}$ 30

SETTING UP A PROPORTION There are different ways to set up a proportion. Consider the following problem.

A recipe for tomato salsa calls for 30 tomatoes to make 12 pints of salsa. How many tomatoes are needed to make 4 pints of salsa?

The tables below show two ways of arranging the information from the problem. In each table, x represents the number of tomatoes needed to make 4 pints of salsa. The proportions follow from the tables.

AVOID ERRORS You cannot write a proportion that compares pints to tomatoes and tomatoes to pints.

$$\frac{\text{pints}}{\text{tomatoes}} \neq \frac{\text{tomatoes}}{\text{pints}}$$

	Tomatoes	Pints
Smaller recipe	x	4
Normal recipe	30	12

Proportion: $\frac{x}{30} = \frac{4}{12}$

	Smaller recipe	Normal recipe
Tomatoes	x	30
Pints	4	12

Proportion: $\frac{x}{4} = \frac{30}{12}$

Motivating the Lesson

Tell students that ratios and proportions are used to solve a wide range of problems in which the relationship between quantities is important. For example, you can use ratios to compare the number of math books to English books in the library, the number of boys to girls in drama classes, and the number of airplanes to cars at an airfield. Proportions can be used to find distance, time, speed, and cost, among other things.

3 TEACH

Extra Example 1

At a carwash fund raiser, 18 ninth grade students and 14 tenth grade students worked the first shift.

a. Find the ratio of ninth grade students to tenth grade students. $\frac{9}{7}$

b. Find the ratio of ninth grade students to all students. $\frac{9}{16}$

Key Question to Ask for Example 1

- Is the ratio of away matches to home matches the same as the ratio of home matches to away matches? Explain. **No, the ratio of away matches to home matches is 10 to 14 or 5 to 7, while the ratio of home matches to away matches is 7 to 5.**

Extra Example 2

Solve the proportion $\frac{12}{h} = \frac{3}{17}$. 68

Key Question to Ask for Example 2

- Why do you multiply by 30 and not by the reciprocal of $\frac{11}{6}$? **Multiplying by 30 isolates the variable.**

Differentiated Instruction

English Learners The similarities of the words *ratio* and *rational* may confuse some students. Explain that a rational number is the ratio of two integers. For instance, they can write the ratio 7 to 12 as 7 : 12 or as the rational number $\frac{7}{12}$. However, a ratio does not necessarily involve rational numbers. For example, the ratio of the area of a circle with radius r to a square with side length r is $\pi : 1$.

See also the *Differentiated Instruction Resources* for more strategies.

Extra Example 3

A backpacker in the Sierras hikes 5.5 miles in 2 hours. If the hiking rate remains the same, how far will the backpacker hike in 7 hours? Write and solve a proportion to find the answer. $\frac{5.5}{2} = \frac{x}{7}$; **19.25 mi**

Key Questions to Ask for Example 3

- What is another way to set up the proportion? Explain. $\frac{5}{x} = \frac{150}{1029}$; **it compares 5 seconds to 150 feet and the unknown number of seconds to 1029 feet.**
- What is an incorrect way to set up the proportion? Explain. $\frac{5}{x} = \frac{1029}{150}$; **it compares 5 seconds to 1029 feet and the unknown number of seconds to 150 feet.**

Closing the Lesson

Have students summarize the major points of the lesson and answer the Essential Question: How do you find ratios and write and solve proportions?

- **Ratios compare two quantities.**
- **A proportion states that two ratios are equivalent. When writing a proportion, put like quantities in the same location in each ratio, such as $\frac{\text{nuts}}{\text{ounces}} = \frac{\text{nuts}}{\text{ounces}}$.**

A ratio is an expression that relates one quantity to another by division, while a proportion is an equation of two ratios. Solve proportions with unknown numbers in the same way as you solve equations, by isolating the variable.

EXAMPLE 3 Solve a multi-step problem

ELEVATORS The elevator that takes passengers from the lobby of the John Hancock Center in Chicago to the observation level travels 150 feet in 5 seconds. The observation level is located on the 94th floor, at 1029 feet above the ground. Find the time it takes the elevator to travel from the lobby to the observation level.

Solution

STEP 1 **Write** a proportion involving two ratios that compare the amount of time the elevator has ascended with the distance traveled.

$$\frac{5}{150} = \frac{x}{1029} \begin{array}{l} \leftarrow \textbf{seconds} \\ \leftarrow \textbf{feet} \end{array}$$

STEP 2 **Solve** the proportion.

$\frac{5}{150} = \frac{x}{1029}$ — **Write proportion.**

$1029 \cdot \frac{5}{150} = 1029 \cdot \frac{x}{1029}$ — **Multiply each side by 1029.**

$\frac{5145}{150} = x$ — **Simplify.**

$34.3 = x$ — **Use a calculator.**

▶ The elevator travels from the lobby to the observation level in 34.3 seconds.

CHECK You can use a table to check the reasonableness of your answer.

GENERATE TABLE
As the amount of time increases by 5 seconds, the distance traveled increases by 150 feet.

Time (sec)	5	10	15	20	25	30	35
Distance traveled (ft)	150	300	450	600	750	900	1050

The solution, 34.3 seconds, is slightly less than 35 seconds, and 1029 feet is slightly less than 1050 feet. So, the solution is reasonable.

GUIDED PRACTICE for Example 3

6. **WHAT IF?** In Example 3, suppose the elevator travels 125 feet in 5 seconds. Find the time it will take for the elevator to travel from the lobby to the observation level. **41.16 sec**

7. **ASTRONOMY** When two full moons appear in the same month, the second full moon is called a blue moon. On average, 2 blue moons occur every 5 years. Find the number of blue moons that are likely to occur in the next 25 years. **10 blue moons**

3.5 EXERCISES

HOMEWORK KEY
○ = WORKED-OUT SOLUTIONS on p. WS6 for Exs. 17 and 49
★ = STANDARDIZED TEST PRACTICE Exs. 2, 19, 20, 43, and 54
◆ = MULTIPLE REPRESENTATIONS Ex. 52

SKILL PRACTICE

A

1. **VOCABULARY** Copy and complete: A proportion is an equation that states that two _?_ are equivalent. **ratios**

2. ★ **WRITING** Write a ratio of two quantities in three different ways. ***Sample answer:*** $\frac{2}{5}$, **2:5, 2 to 5**

SIMPLIFYING RATIOS **Tell whether the ratio is in simplest form. If not, write it in simplest form.**

3. 14 to 18 **no; 7 to 9**
4. 5 : 13 **yes**
5. $\frac{24}{25}$ **yes**
6. 28 to 32 **no; 7 to 8**

EXAMPLE 2 on p. 163 for Exs. 7–22

SOLVING PROPORTIONS **Solve the proportion. Check your solution.**

7. $\frac{2}{5} = \frac{x}{3}$ $\frac{6}{5}$
8. $\frac{4}{1} = \frac{z}{16}$ **64**
9. $\frac{c}{8} = \frac{11}{4}$ **22**
10. $\frac{36}{12} = \frac{x}{2}$ **6**
11. $\frac{16}{7} = \frac{m}{21}$ **48**
12. $\frac{k}{9} = \frac{10}{18}$ **5**
13. $\frac{5}{8} = \frac{t}{24}$ **15**
14. $\frac{d}{5} = \frac{80}{100}$ **4**
15. $\frac{v}{20} = \frac{8}{4}$ **40**
16. $\frac{r}{60} = \frac{40}{50}$ **48**
17. $\frac{16}{48} = \frac{n}{36}$ **12**
18. $\frac{49}{98} = \frac{s}{112}$ **56**

19. ★ **MULTIPLE CHOICE** What is the value of x in the proportion $\frac{8}{5} = \frac{x}{20}$? **C**

Ⓐ 2 Ⓑ 23 Ⓒ 32 Ⓓ 40

20. ★ **MULTIPLE CHOICE** What is the value of z in the proportion $\frac{z}{15} = \frac{28}{35}$? **B**

Ⓐ 8 Ⓑ 12 Ⓒ 18.75 Ⓓ 425

ERROR ANALYSIS ***Describe*** **and correct the error in solving the proportion.** **21, 22. See margin.**

21.
$$\frac{3}{4} = \frac{x}{6}$$
$$\frac{1}{6} \cdot \frac{3}{4} = \frac{1}{6} \cdot \frac{x}{6}$$
$$\frac{1}{8} = x$$
✗

22.
$$\frac{m}{10} = \frac{50}{20}$$
$$10 \cdot \frac{m}{10} = 20 \cdot \frac{50}{20}$$
$$m = 50$$
✗

B

WRITING AND SOLVING PROPORTIONS **Write the sentence as a proportion. Then solve the proportion.**

23. 3 is to 8 as x is to 32. $\frac{3}{8} = \frac{x}{32}$; **12**
24. 5 is to 7 as a is to 49. $\frac{5}{7} = \frac{a}{49}$; **35**
25. x is to 4 as 8 is to 16. $\frac{x}{4} = \frac{8}{16}$; **2**
26. y is to 20 as 9 is to 5. $\frac{y}{20} = \frac{9}{5}$; **36**
27. b is to 10 as 7 is to 2. $\frac{b}{10} = \frac{7}{2}$; **35**
28. 4 is to 12 as n is to 3. $\frac{4}{12} = \frac{n}{3}$; **1**
29. 12 is to 18 as d is to 27. $\frac{12}{18} = \frac{d}{27}$; **18**
30. t is to 21 as 40 is to 28. $\frac{t}{21} = \frac{40}{28}$; **30**

4 PRACTICE AND APPLY

Assignment Guide

Answer Transparencies available for all exercises

Basic:
Day 1: SRH p. 912 Exs. 6–10
pp. 165–167
Exs. 1–6, 7–17 odd, 19–26, 45–52, 56–66

Average:
Day 1: pp. 165–167
Exs. 1, 2, 5, 6, 10–18 even, 19–22, 23–43 odd, 47–54, 56–66 even

Advanced:
Day 1: pp. 165–167
Exs. 1, 2, 15–20, 27–30, 32–42 even, 43–55*, 57–65 odd

Block:
pp. 165–167
Exs. 1, 2, 5, 6, 10–18 even, 19–22, 23–43 odd, 47–54, 56–66 even (with 3.4)

Differentiated Instruction

See *Differentiated Instruction Resources* for suggestions on addressing the needs of a diverse classroom.

Homework Check

For a quick check of student understanding of key concepts, go over the following exercises:

Basic: 11, 13, 45, 47, 50
Average: 12, 16, 47, 48, 51
Advanced: 15, 20, 47, 48, 52

Extra Practice

- Student Edition, p. 940
- Chapter Resource Book: Practice levels A, B, C

Practice Worksheet

An easily-readable reduced practice page (with answers) for this lesson can be found on p. 130D.

21. Multiply each side by 6, not $\frac{1}{6}$; $6 \cdot \frac{3}{4} = 6 \cdot \frac{x}{6}$, $4\frac{1}{2} = x$.

22. Multiply each side by 10, not one side by 10 and the other side by 20; $10 \cdot \frac{m}{10} = 10 \cdot \frac{50}{20}$, $m = 25$.

Study Strategy

Exercises 7–18 Remind students that they solve proportions in the same way they solve equations, by isolating the variable. Also note that the variable can be on either side of the equation.

Exercises 34–42 Even though these proportions are more complex than those in the previous exercises, students should stay focused on isolating the variable.

Reading Strategy

Exercises 23–30 Before beginning these exercises, you may want to refer students to the reading note on page 163. Students can use this model to help them write the sentences as proportions.

Avoiding Common Errors

Exercises 45–49 Students often compare the wrong quantities when they write ratios. Point out that they should compare quantities in the same order as the words. For example, if they want to find the ratio between medium pizzas and small pizzas, the number for medium pizzas is first in the ratio and the number for small pizzas is second.

Exercises 50–52 Caution students to be sure to set up each proportion correctly. Suggest they reread the section on setting up proportions on page 163. They can then look over their proportions to make sure they are writing like quantities in the same location in each ratio.

SOLVING PROPORTIONS **Solve the proportion. Check your solution.**

31. $\frac{b}{0.5} = \frac{9}{2.5}$ **1.8**
32. $\frac{1.1}{1.2} = \frac{n}{3.6}$ **3.3**
33. $\frac{2.1}{7.7} = \frac{v}{8.8}$ **2.4**
34. $\frac{36}{54} = \frac{2x}{6}$ **2**
35. $\frac{3a}{4} = \frac{36}{12}$ **4**
36. $\frac{10h}{108} = \frac{5}{9}$ **6**
37. $\frac{6r}{10} = \frac{36}{15}$ **4**
38. $\frac{12}{42} = \frac{4w}{56}$ **4**
39. $\frac{m+3}{8} = \frac{40}{64}$ **2**
40. $\frac{5}{13} = \frac{k-4}{39}$ **19**
41. $\frac{7}{112} = \frac{c-3}{8}$ **3.5**
42. $\frac{6+n}{60} = \frac{15}{90}$ **4**

43. ★ **SHORT RESPONSE** Is it possible to write a proportion using the numbers 3, 4, 6, and 8? *Explain* your reasoning. **Yes.** ***Sample answer:*** $\frac{3}{6} = \frac{4}{8}$

C 44. **CHALLENGE** If $\frac{a}{b} = \frac{c}{d}$ for nonzero numbers *a*, *b*, *c*, and *d*, is it also true that $\frac{a}{c} = \frac{b}{d}$? *Explain.* **Yes; multiply each side by *b* to get the equation $a = \frac{cb}{d}$, then divide each side by *c* to get $\frac{a}{c} = \frac{b}{d}$.**

PROBLEM SOLVING

EXAMPLE 1 A on p. 162 for Exs. 45–49

45. **GOVERNMENT** There are 435 representatives in the U.S. House of Representatives. Of the 435 representatives, 6 are from Kentucky. Find the ratio of the number of representatives from Kentucky to the total number of representatives. $\frac{2}{145}$

@HomeTutor for problem solving help at classzone.com

46. **CONTEST** Of the 30 champions of the National Spelling Bee from 1974 to 2003, 16 are boys. Find the ratio of the number of champions who are girls to the number who are boys. $\frac{7}{8}$

@HomeTutor for problem solving help at classzone.com

PIZZA SALES **The table shows the number of pizzas sold at a pizzeria during a week. Use the information to find the specified ratio.**

47. Small pizzas to large pizzas $\frac{2}{5}$
48. Medium pizzas to large pizzas $\frac{3}{5}$
49. Large pizzas to all pizzas $\frac{1}{2}$

Size	Small	Medium	Large
Pizzas	96	144	240

EXAMPLE 3 on p. 164 for Exs. 50–52

50. **READING** A student can read 7 pages of a book in 10 minutes. How many pages of the book can the student read in 30 minutes? **21 pages**

51. **SOCCER** In the first 4 games of the season, a soccer team scored a total of 10 goals. If this trend continues, how many goals will the team score in the 18 remaining games of the season? **45 goals**

B 52. ◆ **MULTIPLE REPRESENTATIONS** A movie is filmed so that the ratio of the length to the width of the image on the screen is 1.85 : 1.
   a. **Writing a Proportion** Write and solve a proportion to find the length of the image on the screen when the width of the image is 38 feet. ***Sample answer:*** $\frac{1.85}{1} = \frac{x}{38}$**, 70.3 ft**
   b. **Making a Table** Make a table that shows the length of an image when the width of the image is 20, 25, 30, 35, and 40 feet. Use your table to check the reasonableness of your answer to part (a). **See margin.**

○ = WORKED-OUT SOLUTIONS on p. WS1 ★ = STANDARDIZED TEST PRACTICE ◆ = MULTIPLE REPRESENTATIONS

52b.

Width (ft)	Length (ft)
20	37
25	46.25
30	55.5
35	64.75
40	74

53. **MULTI-STEP PROBLEM** One day, the ratio of skiers to snowboarders on the mountain at a ski resort was 13 : 10. The resort sold a total of 253 lift tickets during the day.

a. Find the ratio of snowboarders on the mountain to all of the skiers and snowboarders on the mountain. **$\frac{10}{23}$**

b. Use the ratio from part (a) to find the number of lift tickets sold to snowboarders during the day. **110 lift tickets**

c. During the same day, the ratio of snowboarders who rented snowboards to snowboarders that have their own snowboards is 4 : 7. Find the number of snowboarders who rented a snowboard. **40 snowboarders**

54. ★ **EXTENDED RESPONSE** You and a friend are waiting in separate lines to purchase concert tickets.

a. **Interpret** Every 10 minutes, the cashier at the head of your line helps 3 people. There are 11 people in line in front of you. Write a proportion that can be used to determine how long you will have to wait to purchase tickets. ***Sample answer:*** **$\frac{10}{3} = \frac{x}{11}$**

b. **Interpret** Every 5 minutes, the cashier at the head of your friend's line helps 2 people. There are 14 people in line in front of your friend. Write a proportion that can be used to determine how long your friend will have to wait to purchase tickets. ***Sample answer:*** **$\frac{5}{2} = \frac{x}{14}$**

c. **Compare** Will you or your friend be able to purchase concert tickets first? *Explain.* **Your friend; you will wait in line for $36\frac{2}{3}$ minutes and your friend will wait only 35 minutes.**

C 55. **CHALLENGE** A car traveling 50 miles per hour goes 15 miles farther in the same amount of time as a car traveling 30 miles per hour. Find the distance that each car travels. **37.5 mi, 22.5 mi**

MIXED REVIEW

Tell whether the pairing is a function. *(p. 35)*

56.

Input	−4	−2	0	2	2
Output	2	2	0	−1	−2

not a function

57.

Input	−1	0	1	2	3
Output	5	5	5	5	5

function

Write a rule for the function represented by the graph. Identify the domain and range of the function. *(p. 43)* **58–60. See margin.**

58. 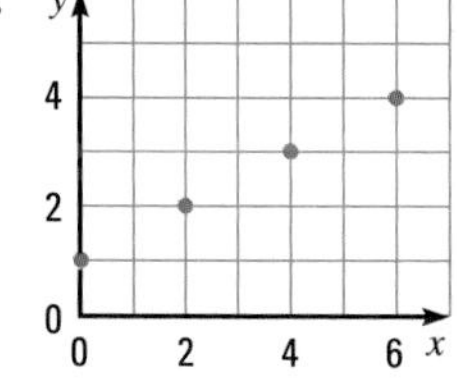

59. 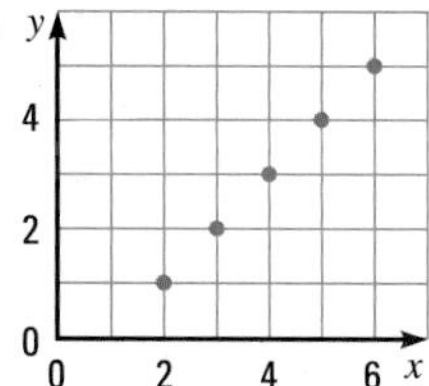

60. 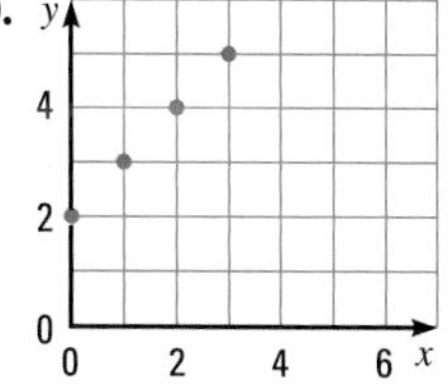

PREVIEW
Prepare for Lesson 3.6 in Exs. 61–66.

Solve the equation. Check your solution.

61. $-2y = 18$ *(p. 134)* **−9**

62. $20x = 40$ *(p. 134)* **2**

63. $56 = 7(z + 5)$ *(p. 148)* **3**

64. $16(r + 3) = -48$ *(p. 148)* **−6**

65. $5(c - 12) = 2c$ *(p. 154)* **20**

66. $b + 11 = 3(b - 1)$ *(p. 154)* **7**

5 ASSESS AND RETEACH

Daily Homework Quiz

Transparency Available

1. A chocolate chip cookie recipe calls for $2\frac{1}{4}$ cups of flour and $\frac{3}{4}$ cup of brown sugar. Find the ratio of brown sugar to flour. **$\frac{1}{3}$**

Solve the proportion.

2. $\frac{a}{7} = \frac{9}{21}$ **3**

3. $\frac{32}{28} = \frac{m}{14}$ **16**

4. A printer can print 12 color pages in 3 minutes. How many color pages can the printer print in 9 minutes? Write and solve a proportion to find the answer. **$\frac{12}{3} = \frac{x}{9}$; 36 color pages**

Online Quiz

Available at **classzone.com**

Diagnosis/Remediation

- Practice A, B, C in Chapter Resource Book
- Study Guide in Chapter Resource Book
- Practice Workbook
- @HomeTutor

Challenge

Additional challenge is available in the Chapter Resource Book.

58. $y = \frac{1}{2}x + 1$; **domain: 0, 2, 4, and 6, range: 1, 2, 3, and 4**

59. $y = x - 1$; **domain: 2, 3, 4, 5, and 6, range: 1, 2, 3, 4, and 5**

60. $y = x + 2$; **domain: 0, 1, 2, and 3, range: 2, 3, 4, and 5**

3.6 Solve Proportions Using Cross Products

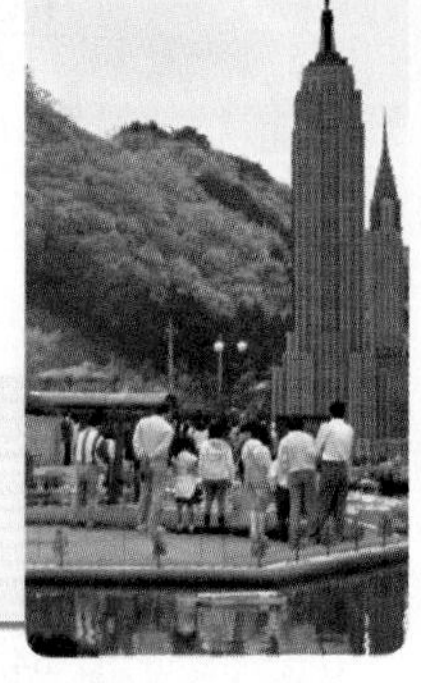

Before You solved proportions using the multiplication property of equality.

Now You will solve proportions using cross products.

Why? So you can find the height of a scale model, as in Ex. 39.

1 PLAN AND PREPARE

Warm-Up Exercises

Transparency Available

Solve the proportion.

1. $\frac{t}{32} = \frac{7}{16}$ **14**
2. $\frac{18}{24} = \frac{b}{12}$ **9**
3. $\frac{21}{n} = \frac{28}{32}$ **24**
4. $\frac{4}{12} = \frac{11}{p}$ **33**
5. It takes 30 tomatillos to make 8 ounces of enchilada sauce. How many tomatillos does it take to make 12 ounces of enchilada sauce? **45 tomatillos**

Notetaking Guide

Transparency Available

Promotes interactive learning and notetaking skills.

Pacing

Basic: 1 day

Average: 1 day

Advanced: 1 day

Block: 0.5 block with 3.7

• See *Teaching Guide/Lesson Plan.*

2 FOCUS AND MOTIVATE

Essential Question

Big Idea 2, p. 131

How do you solve proportions using cross products? **Tell students they will learn how to answer this question by using the cross products property.**

NCTM STANDARDS

Standard 2: Represent situations using algebraic symbols

Standard 9: Recognize math in contexts outside of mathematics

Key Vocabulary
- cross product
- scale drawing
- scale model
- scale

In a proportion, a **cross product** is the product of the numerator of one ratio and the denominator of the other ratio. The following property involving cross products can be used to solve proportions.

KEY CONCEPT *For Your Notebook*

Cross Products Property

Words The cross products of a proportion are equal.

Example $\frac{3}{4} = \frac{6}{8}$ $\quad 4 \cdot 6 = 24$, $\quad 3 \cdot 8 = 24$

Algebra If $\frac{a}{b} = \frac{c}{d}$ where $b \neq 0$ and $d \neq 0$, then $ad = bc$.

The proportion $\frac{3}{4} = \frac{6}{8}$ can be written as $3:4 = 6:8$. In this form, 4 and 6 are called the *means* of the proportion, and 3 and 8 are called the *extremes* of the proportion. This is why the cross products property is also called the *means-extremes property.*

EXAMPLE 1 Use the cross products property

Solve the proportion $\frac{8}{x} = \frac{6}{15}$.

$\frac{8}{x} = \frac{6}{15}$	Write original proportion.
$8 \cdot 15 = x \cdot 6$	Cross products property
$120 = 6x$	Simplify.
$20 = x$	Divide each side by 6.

▶ The solution is 20. Check by substituting 20 for x in the original proportion.

CHECK $\frac{8}{20} \stackrel{?}{=} \frac{6}{15}$	Substitute 20 for x.
$8 \cdot 15 \stackrel{?}{=} 20 \cdot 6$	Cross products property
$120 = 120$ ✓	Simplify. Solution checks.

Resource Planning Guide

Chapter Resource Book
- Teaching Guide/Lesson Plan
- Practice levels A, B, C
- Study Guide
- Catch-up for Absent Students
- Application
- Challenge

Workbooks
- Notetaking Guide
- Practice Workbook

Teaching Options
- **Power Presentations** provides dynamic electronic teaching resources for the classroom.
- **Activity Generator** provides editable activities for all ability levels.

Interactive Technology
- Easy Planner
- Power Presentations
- Activity Generator
- Animated Algebra
- Test Generator
- Online Quiz
- eWorkbook
- eEdition
- @HomeTutor

Resources for English Learners
- Spanish Study Guide
- Multi-Language Visual Glossary
- Student Resources in Spanish

See also the *Differentiated Instruction Resources* for more strategies for meeting individual needs.

 **EXAMPLE 2** Standardized Test Practice

What is the value of x in the proportion $\frac{4}{x} = \frac{8}{x-3}$?

Ⓐ -6 Ⓑ -3 Ⓒ 3 Ⓓ 6

Solution

ANOTHER WAY
Because 8 is twice 4, you can reason that $x - 3$ must be twice x:
$x - 3 = 2x$
$-3 = x$

$\frac{4}{x} = \frac{8}{x-3}$ Write original proportion.

$4(x - 3) = x \cdot 8$ Cross products property

$4x - 12 = 8x$ Simplify.

$-12 = 4x$ Subtract $4x$ from each side.

$-3 = x$ Divide each side by 4.

▸ The value of x is -3. The correct answer is B. Ⓐ Ⓑ Ⓒ Ⓓ

EXAMPLE 3 Write and solve a proportion

SEALS Each day, the seals at an aquarium are each fed 8 pounds of food for every 100 pounds of their body weight. A seal at the aquarium weighs 280 pounds. How much food should the seal be fed per day?

Solution

STEP 1 **Write** a proportion involving two ratios that compare the amount of food with the weight of the seal.

$\frac{8}{100} = \frac{x}{280}$ ← amount of food / ← weight of seal

STEP 2 **Solve** the proportion.

ANOTHER WAY
You can also solve the proportion by multiplying each side of the equation by 280.

$\frac{8}{100} = \frac{x}{280}$ Write proportion.

$8 \cdot 280 = 100 \cdot x$ Cross products property

$2240 = 100x$ Simplify.

$22.4 = x$ Divide each side by 100.

▸ A 280 pound seal should be fed 22.4 pounds of food per day.

 **GUIDED PRACTICE** for Examples 1, 2, and 3

Solve the proportion. Check your solution.

1. $\frac{4}{a} = \frac{24}{30}$ **5**
2. $\frac{3}{x} = \frac{2}{x-6}$ **18**
3. $\frac{m}{5} = \frac{m-6}{4}$ **30**
4. **WHAT IF?** In Example 3, suppose the seal weighs 260 pounds. How much food should the seal be fed per day? **20.8 lb**

Motivating the Lesson

Tell students that using cross products to solve proportions is useful in estimating actual distances on maps. Ask students to recount various times they have used the scale on a map to find the distance between two points. After a brief discussion, tell them they will learn how to use cross products to find map distances.

3 TEACH

Extra Example 1

Solve the proportion $\frac{4}{x} = \frac{12}{24}$. **8**

Key Questions to Ask for Example 1

- What are the means of the proportion? **x and 6**
- What are the extremes of the proportion? **8 and 15**

Extra Example 2

What is the value of x in the proportion $\frac{3}{x} = \frac{9}{x-4}$? **C**

Ⓐ 4 Ⓑ 2
Ⓒ -2 Ⓓ -4

Extra Example 3

Georgia is making her own potting soil. For every 4 buckets of peat moss, she mixes in 3 buckets of perlite. Suppose she uses 10 buckets of peat moss. How many buckets of perlite should she use? Write and solve a proportion to find the answer. **$\frac{4}{3} = \frac{10}{x}$; she should use 7.5 buckets of perlite.**

Differentiated Instruction

Visual Learners To solve problems like the one in **Example 3**, students may want to organize the information in a table first.

	100-lb seal	280-lb seal
Amount of food (lb)	8	?
Weight of seal (lb)	100	280

Then the students can set up ratios vertically, $\frac{8}{100}$ and $\frac{x}{280}$, or horizontally, $\frac{8}{x}$ and $\frac{100}{280}$, to write a proportion.

See also the *Differentiated Instruction Resources* for more strategies.

Extra Example 4

On a map, the distance between Red River Gorge and Pine Bluff is 3.8 centimeters. If the map scale is 1 cm = 25 km, estimate the actual distance between Red River Gorge and Pine Bluff. **about 95 km**

Key Question to Ask for Example 4

- If the distance between Columbus and Cincinnati is about 170 kilometers, could you use the proportion in Example 4 to find the distance between the two cities on the map? Explain. **Yes, you could use the proportion $\frac{1}{85} = \frac{x}{170}$ to find the distance on the map.**

Vocabulary

You may want to discuss the many meanings of the word "scale." You could have students look up *scale* in the dictionary and then have the class discuss the meanings. Finish by focusing on the meaning of scale in Example 4 as a ratio of map distance to actual distance.

Closing the Lesson

Have students summarize the major points of the lesson and answer the Essential Question: How do you solve proportions using cross products?

- **Cross products of a proportion are equal.**
- **The scale of a scale drawing or model relates the drawing's or model's dimensions to the actual dimensions.**

To use cross products, multiply the numerator of each ratio by the denominator of the other ratio, and write an equal sign between the two products. Then solve for the variable.

SCALE DRAWINGS AND SCALE MODELS The floor plan below is an example of a *scale drawing*. A **scale drawing** is a two-dimensional drawing of an object in which the dimensions of the drawing are in proportion to the dimensions of the object. A **scale model** is a three-dimensional model of an object in which the dimensions of the model are in proportion to the dimensions of the object.

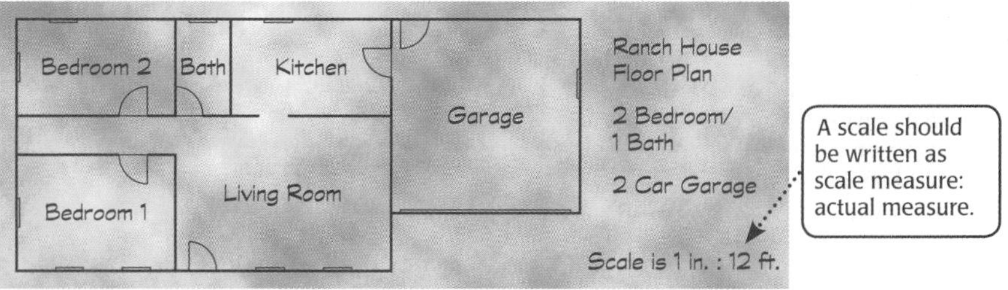

A scale should be written as scale measure: actual measure.

The **scale** of a scale drawing or scale model relates the drawing's or model's dimensions and the actual dimensions. For example, the scale 1 in. : 12 ft on the floor plan means that 1 inch in the floor plan represents an actual distance of 12 feet.

EXAMPLE 4 Use the scale on a map

MAPS Use a metric ruler and the map of Ohio to estimate the distance between Cleveland and Cincinnati.

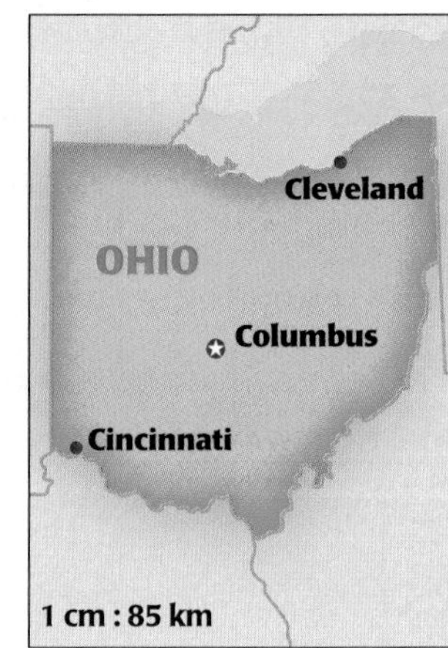

Solution

From the map's scale, 1 centimeter represents 85 kilometers. On the map, the distance between Cleveland and Cincinnati is about 4.2 centimeters.

Write and solve a proportion to find the distance d between the cities.

$$\frac{1}{85} = \frac{4.2}{d} \quad \begin{matrix}\leftarrow \text{centimeters} \\ \leftarrow \text{kilometers}\end{matrix}$$

$1 \cdot d = 85 \cdot 4.2$ **Cross products property**

$d = 357$ **Simplify.**

▶ The actual distance between Cleveland and Cincinnati is about 357 kilometers.

✓ **GUIDED PRACTICE** for Example 4

5. Use a metric ruler and the map in Example 4 to estimate the distance (in kilometers) between Columbus and Cleveland. **about 212.5 km**

6. **MODEL SHIPS** The ship model kits sold at a hobby store have a scale of 1 ft : 600 ft. A completed model of the *Queen Elizabeth II* is 1.6 feet long. Estimate the actual length of the *Queen Elizabeth II*. **about 960 ft**

3.6 EXERCISES

HOMEWORK KEY
- ○ = **WORKED-OUT SOLUTIONS** on p. WS7 for Exs. 13 and 39
- ★ = **STANDARDIZED TEST PRACTICE** Exs. 2, 15, 16, 41, and 42
- ◆ = **MULTIPLE REPRESENTATIONS** Ex. 40

SKILL PRACTICE

A

1. **VOCABULARY** Copy and complete: In a proportion, a(n) __?__ is the product of the numerator of one ratio and the denominator of the other ratio. **cross product**

2. ★ **WRITING** A scale drawing has a scale of 1 cm : 3 m. *Explain* how the scale can be used to find the actual distance between objects in the drawing. **Measure the distance in centimeters, in the drawing and then substitute the value in the proportion, $\frac{1}{3} = \frac{\text{distance in drawing}}{\text{actual distance}}$.**

EXAMPLES 1 and 2 on pp. 168–169 for Exs. 3–18

SOLVING PROPORTIONS **Solve the proportion. Check your solution.**

3. $\frac{2}{3} = \frac{4}{x}$ **6**
4. $\frac{3}{y} = \frac{15}{35}$ **7**
5. $\frac{13}{6} = \frac{52}{z}$ **24**
6. $\frac{10}{45} = \frac{v}{27}$ **6**
7. $\frac{5m}{6} = \frac{10}{12}$ **1**
8. $\frac{3k}{27} = \frac{2}{3}$ **6**
9. $\frac{-49}{7} = \frac{a+7}{6}$ **−49**
10. $\frac{6}{t+4} = \frac{42}{77}$ **7**
11. $\frac{8}{12} = \frac{r}{r+1}$ **2**
12. $\frac{n}{n-12} = \frac{9}{5}$ **27**
13. ○ $\frac{11}{w} = \frac{33}{w+24}$ **12**
14. $\frac{18}{d+13} = \frac{6}{d-13}$ **26**

15. ★ **MULTIPLE CHOICE** What is the value of h in the proportion $\frac{15}{-2h} = \frac{5}{12}$? **B**

   Ⓐ −36　　Ⓑ −18　　Ⓒ 18　　Ⓓ 36

16. ★ **MULTIPLE CHOICE** What is the value of s in the proportion $\frac{7}{s-14} = \frac{21}{s+18}$? **D**

   Ⓐ −48　　Ⓑ −16　　Ⓒ 3　　Ⓓ 30

ERROR ANALYSIS ***Describe*** **and correct the error in solving the proportion.**

17.
$$\frac{4}{3} = \frac{16}{x}$$
$$4 \cdot 16 = 4 \cdot x$$
$$64 = 4x$$
$$16 = x$$

Use the cross products property to multiply 4 by x and 16 by 3; $4 \cdot x = 3 \cdot 16$, $4x = 48$, $x = 12$.

18.
$$\frac{18}{14} = \frac{b+2}{b}$$
$$18b = 14b + 2$$
$$4b = 2$$
$$b = 0.5$$

Distribute the 14 to both b and 2; $18b = 14b + 28$, $4b = 28$, $b = 7$.

B

SOLVING PROPORTIONS **Solve the proportion. Check your solution.**

19. $\frac{7}{3} = \frac{2x+5}{x}$ **15**
20. $\frac{a}{9a-2} = \frac{1}{8}$ **2**
21. $\frac{24}{5z+4} = \frac{4}{z-1}$ **10**
22. $\frac{c-8}{-2} = \frac{11-4c}{11}$ **22**
23. $\frac{k-8}{7+k} = \frac{-1}{5}$ **5.5**
24. $\frac{2}{-3} = \frac{4v+4}{2v+14}$ **−2.5**
25. $\frac{m+1}{4} = \frac{3m+6}{7}$ **−3.4**
26. $\frac{6}{4+2w} = \frac{-2}{w-10}$ **5.2**
27. $\frac{n+0.3}{n-3.2} = \frac{9}{2}$ **4.2**
28. $\frac{-3}{11} = \frac{5-h}{h+1.4}$ **7.4**
29. $\frac{4}{b-3.9} = \frac{2}{b+1}$ **−5.9**
30. $\frac{16.5+3t}{3} = \frac{0.9-t}{-5}$ **−7.1**

4 PRACTICE AND APPLY

Assignment Guide

Answer Transparencies available for all exercises

Basic:
Day 1: pp. 171–173
Exs. 1–18, 19–25 odd, 33–39 odd, 40, 44–54 even

Average:
Day 1: pp. 171–173
Exs. 1, 2, 4–14 even, 15–18, 19–29 odd, 31–42, 44–54 even

Advanced:
Day 1: pp. 171–173
Exs. 1, 2, 11–16, 24–30 even, 31–34*, 37–43*, 46, 47, 53–55

Block:
pp. 171–173
Exs. 1, 2, 4–14 even, 15–18, 19–29 odd, 31–42, 44–54 even (with 3.7)

Differentiated Instruction

See *Differentiated Instruction Resources* for suggestions on addressing the needs of a diverse classroom.

Homework Check

For a quick check of student understanding of key concepts, go over the following exercises:

Basic: 7, 13, 15, 33, 35
Average: 10, 15, 23, 34, 37
Advanced: 12, 16, 30, 34, 39

Extra Practice

- Student Edition, p. 940
- Chapter Resource Book: Practice levels A, B, C

Practice Worksheet

An easily-readable reduced practice page (with answers) for this lesson can be found on p. 130D.

Avoiding Common Errors

Exercises 3–30 Students sometimes multiply numerator by numerator and denominator by denominator when solving a proportion. Remind them that they find the cross products by multiplying the numerator of each ratio by the denominator of the other.

Study Strategy

Exercises 3–30 Tell students they can solve the proportions using the method with which they are most comfortable. Suggest they try a different method if they become stuck on a problem.

Teaching Strategy

Exercise 40 You may want to point out that the table in part (b) can be used to check the reasonableness of the answer in part (a) given that the diameter of the shell is between 4 and 5 inches.

Reading Strategy

Exercise 41 Urge students to read this problem carefully and to note that there are two steps to solving this problem: one using the ratio 3 : 2 and the other using the ratio 1 in. : 20 yd.

31. REASONING The statements below justify the cross products property. Copy and complete the justification.

$\frac{a}{b} = \frac{c}{d}$	**Given**
$bd \cdot \frac{a}{b} = bd \cdot \frac{c}{d}$	**a.** ___?___ **Multiplication property of equality**
$\frac{bd \cdot a}{b} = \frac{bd \cdot c}{d}$	**b.** ___?___ **Multiply**
$ad = cb$	**c.** ___?___ **Simplify**

C **32. CHALLENGE** In the proportion $\frac{5}{h} = \frac{k}{14}$, what happens to the value of h as the value of k increases? *Explain.* **Decreases; as k gets larger, the value of $\frac{k}{14}$ increases, so for the value of $\frac{5}{h}$ to increase, h must decrease.**

PROBLEM SOLVING

EXAMPLE 3 A on p. 169 for Exs. 33–34

33. RECIPES A recipe that yields 12 buttermilk biscuits calls for 2 cups of flour. How much flour is needed to make 30 biscuits? **5 c**

@HomeTutor for problem solving help at classzone.com

34. DIGITAL PHOTOGRAPHS It took 7.2 minutes to upload 8 digital photographs from your computer to a website. At this rate, how long will it take to upload 20 photographs? **18 min**

@HomeTutor for problem solving help at classzone.com

EXAMPLE 4 on p. 170 for Exs. 35–39

MAPS A map has a scale of 1 cm : 15 km. Use the given map distance to find the actual distance.

35. 6 cm **90 km** **36.** 3.2 cm **48 km** **37.** 0.5 cm **7.5 km** **38.** 4.7 cm **70.5 km**

(39.) SCALE MODEL An exhibit at Tobu World Square in Japan includes a scale model of the Empire State Building. The model was built using a scale of 1 m : 25 m. The height of the actual Empire State Building is 443.2 meters. What is the height of the model? **17.728 m**

B **40. MULTIPLE REPRESENTATIONS** The diameter of the burst of a firework is proportional to the diameter of the shell of the firework.

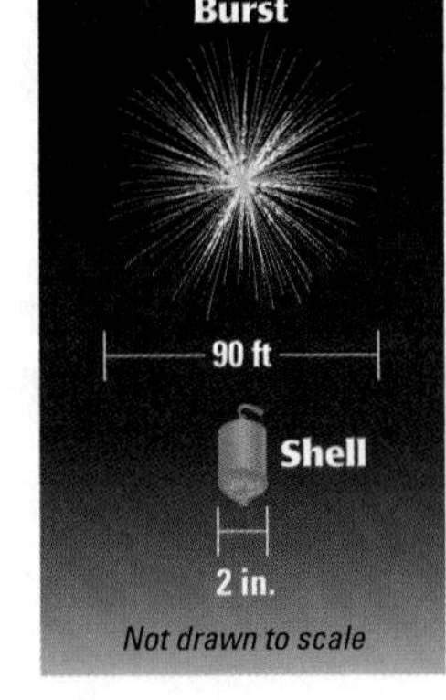

a. Writing a Proportion Use the information in the diagram to find the burst diameter for a 4.75 inch shell. **213.75 ft**

b. Making a Table Make a table of burst diameters for 2, 3, 4, 5, and 6 inch shells. Use the table to check your answer to part (a). **See margin.**

41. ★ SHORT RESPONSE The ratio of the length of a soccer field to the width of the field is 3 : 2. A scale drawing of a soccer field has a scale of 1 in. : 20 yd. The length of the field in the drawing is 6 inches. What is the actual width of the field? *Explain* your reasoning. **80 yd; find the actual length of the field by using the ratio 1 in. : 20 yd, then use that number to find the width of the soccer field by using the ratio 3 : 2.**

◯ = WORKED-OUT SOLUTIONS on p. WS1 ★ = STANDARDIZED TEST PRACTICE

= MULTIPLE REPRESENTATIONS

40b.

Shell diameter (in.)	Burst diameter (ft)
2	90
3	135
4	180
5	225
6	270

42c. Nearly equal. *Sample answer:* The ratio of moles of hydrogen to moles of carbon is about 1.33 to 1, the ratio of moles of hydrogen to moles of oxygen is about 1.32 to 1. The two ratios are nearly the same.

42. ★ **EXTENDED RESPONSE** A mole is a unit of measurement used in chemistry. The masses of one mole of three elements are in the table.

Element	Mass of 1 mole
Hydrogen	1.008 grams
Carbon	12.011 grams
Oxygen	15.999 grams

a. A 100 gram sample of ascorbic acid contains 4.58 grams of hydrogen. To the nearest tenth, find the number of moles of hydrogen. **4.5 moles**

b. A 100 gram sample of ascorbic acid contains 54.5 grams of oxygen. To the nearest tenth, find the number of moles of oxygen in the sample. **3.4 moles**

c. The ratio of moles of hydrogen to moles of carbon in ascorbic acid is 4:3. How does this ratio compare with the ratio of moles of hydrogen to moles of oxygen in ascorbic acid? *Explain.*

C 43. **CHALLENGE** In one high school, there are 90 seniors, 142 juniors, 175 sophomores, and 218 freshmen. Ideally, in the apportionment of the 30 seats on the student council, the number of seats each class has is proportional to the number of class members. Assign a number of seats on the council to each class. *Explain* your reasoning. **See margin.**

MIXED REVIEW

Evaluate the expression for the given value of *x*. *(p. 110)*

44. $16 + \sqrt{x}$ when $x = 16$ **20**

45. $27 - \sqrt{x}$ when $x = 81$ **18**

46. $-3 \cdot \sqrt{x}$ when $x = 25$ **−15**

47. $2 \cdot \sqrt{x} + 11$ when $x = 144$ **35**

PREVIEW Prepare for Lesson 3.7 in Exs. 48–55.

Solve the proportion. Check your solution. *(p. 162)*

48. $\frac{2}{3} = \frac{x}{21}$ **14**

49. $\frac{m}{6} = \frac{9}{2}$ **27**

50. $\frac{z}{11} = \frac{-10}{22}$ **−5**

51. $\frac{12}{5} = \frac{b}{25}$ **60**

52. $\frac{12}{36} = \frac{2c}{6}$ **1**

53. $\frac{9}{-8} = \frac{3w}{24}$ **−9**

54. $\frac{n-2}{50} = \frac{6}{30}$ **12**

55. $\frac{4}{13} = \frac{a+4}{39}$ **8**

QUIZ for Lessons 3.4–3.6

Solve the equation, if possible. *(p. 154)*

1. $y - 2 = y + 2$ **no solution**

2. $2x - 14 = -3x + 6$ **4**

3. $10z - 4 = 2(5z - 2)$ **identity**

4. $6m + 5 - 3m = 7(m - 1)$ **3**

5. $2(7 - g) = 9g + 14 - 11g$ **identity**

6. $13k + 3(k + 11) = 8k - 7$ **−5**

7. $\frac{1}{4}(8j - 3) = 2j - 3$ **no solution**

8. $8 - 4w = \frac{1}{3}(6w - 12)$ **2**

9. $\frac{2}{5}(10t - 50) = 4(9 - 6t)$ **2**

Solve the proportion. Check your solution. *(pp. 162, 168)*

10. $\frac{24}{20} = \frac{x}{5}$ **6**

11. $\frac{6}{-7} = \frac{3z}{42}$ **−12**

12. $\frac{14}{12} = \frac{w+11}{18}$ **10**

13. $\frac{18}{5a} = \frac{3}{-5}$ **−6**

14. $\frac{10}{17} = \frac{k}{2k-3}$ **10**

15. $\frac{h-1}{3} = \frac{2h+1}{9}$ **4**

16.  **GEOMETRY** The ratio of the length to the width of a rectangle is 5:4. The length of the rectangle is 60 inches. What is the width? *(p. 168)* **48 in.**

5 ASSESS AND RETEACH

Daily Homework Quiz

Transparency Available

Solve the proportion.

1. $\frac{10}{35} = \frac{y}{42}$ **12**
2. $\frac{13}{h} = \frac{26}{16}$ **8**
3. $\frac{5r}{6} = \frac{15}{2}$ **9**
4. $\frac{9}{d+3} = \frac{6}{17}$ **22.5**
5. A figurine of a ballerina is based on a scale of 0.5 in.:4 in. If the real ballerina used as a model for the figurine is 68 inches tall, what is the height of the figurine? **8.5 in.**

Online Quiz

Available at **classzone.com**

Diagnosis/Remediation

- Practice A, B, C in Chapter Resource Book
- Study Guide in Chapter Resource Book
- Practice Workbook
- @HomeTutor

Challenge

Additional challenge is available in the Chapter Resource Book.

Quiz

An easily-readable reduced copy of the quiz (with answers) on Lessons 3.4–3.6 from the Assessment Book can be found on p. 130E.

43. ***Sample answer:*** **I would assign 11 seats to the freshmen, 8 seats to the sophomores, 7 seats to the juniors, and 4 seats to the seniors. The actual numbers obtained from the proportions are 10.464, 8.4, 6.816, and 4.32. If I round each of those numbers in the traditional way, the sum is only 29. I rounded 10.464 up to 11 to get a total of 30 seats. I chose 10.464 because of the three numbers with decimal parts less than 0.5, its decimal part is the greatest.**

1 PLAN AND PREPARE

Warm-Up Exercises

Solve the proportions.

1. $\frac{8}{k} = \frac{15}{6}$ 3.2
2. $\frac{46}{25} = \frac{h}{35}$ 64.4
3. $\frac{m}{2.5} = \frac{12}{6}$ 5
4. $\frac{0.5}{13} = \frac{6.5}{x}$ 169
5. The scale on a map is given as 1.5 cm : 8 km. The distance on the map between two cities is 2.25 centimeters. What is the actual distance between the cities? **12 km**

2 FOCUS AND MOTIVATE

Essential Question

Big Idea 2, p. 131

How do you use similar figures to solve problems? **Tell students they will learn how to answer this question by using similar figures to find unknown lengths of geometric figures and other objects that are difficult to measure.**

3 TEACH

Extra Example 1

Given $\triangle EFG \sim \triangle QRS$, find GE. **12 m**

S 24 m Q; 10 m; R; F; 5 m; E x G

NCTM STANDARDS

Standard 2: Analyze situations using algebraic symbols

Standard 9: Grasp how mathematical ideas interconnect

Extension

Use after Lesson 3.6

Apply Proportions to Similar Figures

GOAL Use similar figures to solve problems.

Key Vocabulary
- **congruent figures**
- **similar figures**
- **corresponding parts**

Two figures are **congruent figures** if they have the same shape and size. The symbol $\cong$ indicates congruence. Of the triangles shown, $\triangle ABC \cong \triangle DEF$.

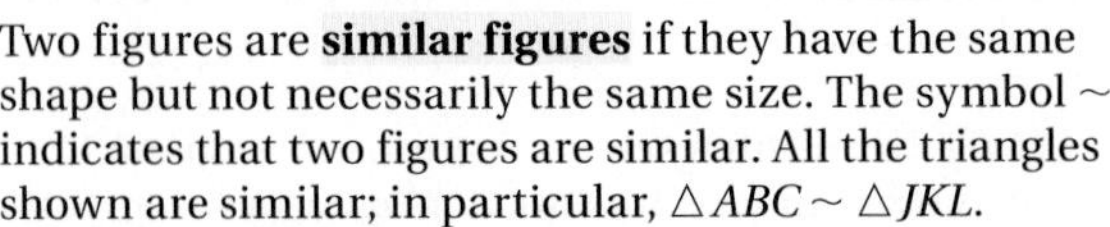

Two figures are **similar figures** if they have the same shape but not necessarily the same size. The symbol $\sim$ indicates that two figures are similar. All the triangles shown are similar; in particular, $\triangle ABC \sim \triangle JKL$.

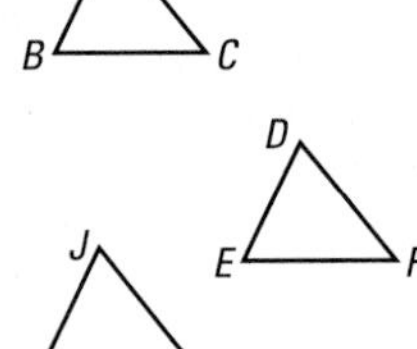

The sides or angles that have the same relative position within two figures are called **corresponding parts**.

NAME SIMILAR FIGURES
When naming similar figures, list the letters of the corresponding vertices (corner points) in the same order.

KEY CONCEPT *For Your Notebook*

Properties of Similar Figures

In the diagram, $\triangle ABC \sim \triangle DEF$.

1. Corresponding angles of similar figures are congruent.
$\angle A \cong \angle D$, $\angle B \cong \angle E$, $\angle C \cong \angle F$
2. The ratios of the lengths of corresponding sides of similar figures are equal.
$\frac{AB}{DE} = \frac{BC}{EF} = \frac{AC}{DF} = \frac{1}{2}$

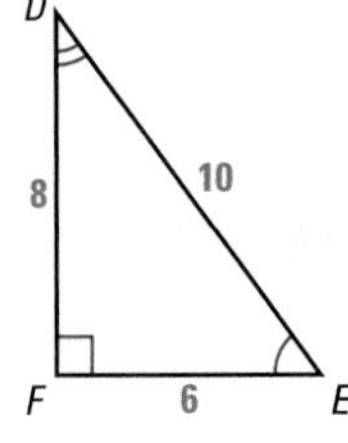

NAME LENGTHS OF SIDES
AB represents the length of the side whose endpoints are *A* and *B*.

EXAMPLE 1 **Find an unknown side length**

Given $\triangle JKL \sim \triangle QRS$, find QR.

Solution

Use the ratios of the lengths of corresponding sides to write a proportion.

$\frac{JK}{QR} = \frac{KL}{RS}$ Write proportion involving *QR*.

$\frac{18}{x} = \frac{8}{12}$ Substitute.

$216 = 8x$ Cross products property

$27 = x$ Divide each side by 8.

▸ *QR* is 27 centimeters.

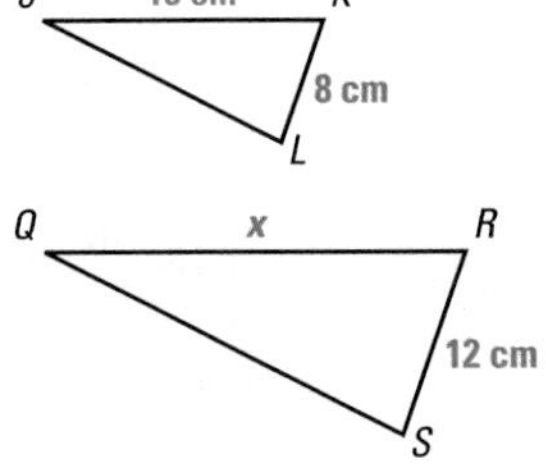

INDIRECT MEASUREMENT You can use similar figures to find lengths that are difficult to measure directly.

EXAMPLE 2 Use similar figures to measure indirectly

CAPE HATTERAS LIGHTHOUSE A man stands next to the Cape Hatteras Lighthouse in North Carolina. The lighthouse and the man are perpendicular to the ground. The sun's rays strike the lighthouse and the man at the same angle, forming two similar triangles. Use indirect measurement to approximate the height of the lighthouse.

83.2 ft

5.8 ft

2.5 ft

Not drawn to scale

Solution

Write and solve a proportion to find the height h (in feet) of the lighthouse.

ANOTHER WAY
You can also use the proportion below to find the height of the lighthouse.

$\frac{5.8}{2.5} = \frac{h}{83.2}$

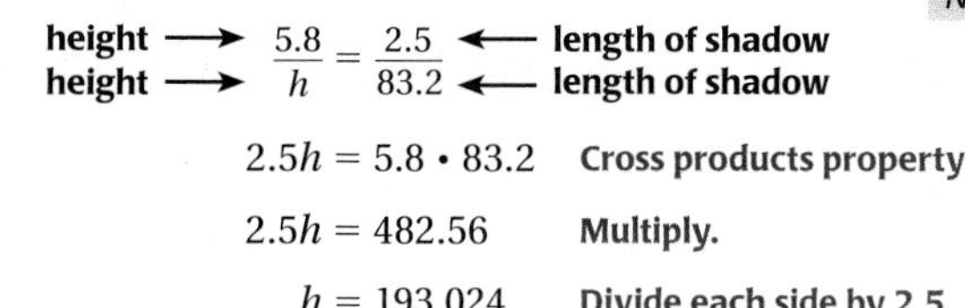

height ⟶ $\frac{5.8}{h} = \frac{2.5}{83.2}$ ⟵ **length of shadow**
height ⟶ ⟵ **length of shadow**

$2.5h = 5.8 \cdot 83.2$ **Cross products property**

$2.5h = 482.56$ **Multiply.**

$h = 193.024$ **Divide each side by 2.5.**

▶ The height of the lighthouse is about 193 feet.

PRACTICE

EXAMPLE 1 on p. 174 for Exs. 1–4

1. Given $\triangle JKL \sim \triangle MNP$, find JL. **24 in.**

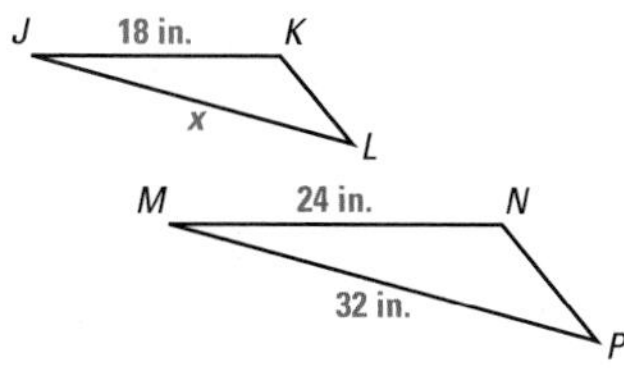

2. Given $\triangle EFG \sim \triangle UVW$, find UV. **10 cm**

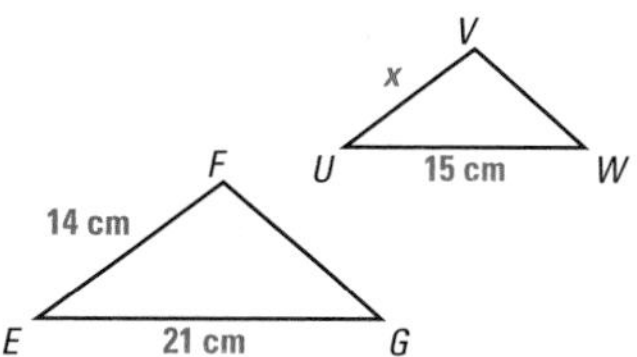

3. Given $ABCD \sim FGHJ$, find AD. **16 m**

C D x B 40 m A H J 14 m G 35 m F

4. Given $JKLM \sim QRST$, find QT. **40 ft**

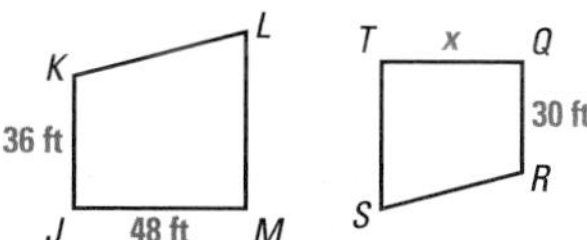

EXAMPLE 2 on p. 175 for Ex. 5

5. FLAGPOLES A 5 foot tall student stands near a flagpole. The flagpole and the student are perpendicular to the ground. The sun's rays strike the flagpole and the student at the same angle, forming two similar triangles. The flagpole casts a 15 foot shadow, and the student casts a 2 foot shadow. Use indirect measurement to find the height of the flagpole. **37.5 ft**

Key Questions to Ask for Example 1

- How do you know that $\overline{JK}$ corresponds to $\overline{QR}$? **The vertices appear in corresponding locations in the statement $\triangle JKL \sim \triangle QRS$.**
- Can you find JL? Explain. **No, you do not know the corresponding length QS in $\triangle QRS$.**

Extra Example 2

A woman 5.5 feet tall stands next to a lamp post. The woman and the lamp post are perpendicular to the ground. The Sun's rays strike the lamp post and the woman at the same angle, forming two similar triangles. The woman casts a 2.2-foot shadow, and the lamppost casts a 6.4-foot shadow. Use indirect measurement to find the height of the lamp post. **16 ft**

Closing the Lesson

Have students summarize the major points of the lesson and answer the Essential Question: How do you use similar figures to solve problems?

- **In similar triangles, the ratios of the lengths of corresponding sides are equal.**
- **You can use similar figures to find unknown lengths.**

If two figures are similar, you can use the ratios of corresponding side lengths to determine missing side lengths or to measure objects that are difficult to measure.

4 PRACTICE AND APPLY

Avoiding Common Errors

Exercises 1–4 Some students may try to determine corresponding sides in similar figures visually. Explain that this is difficult to do and often leads to inaccurate results. Remind them that the statement of similarity indicates how the vertices correspond. When they are setting up proportions, they should use the similarity statement to determine the corresponding sides.

1 PLAN AND PREPARE

Warm-Up Exercises

Transparency Available

Write the percent as a decimal.

1. 27% **0.27** **2.** 54.5% **0.545**

Solve the proportion.

3. $\frac{6}{25} = \frac{12}{n}$ **50** **4.** $\frac{y}{18} = \frac{5}{8}$ **11.25**

5. A tennis ball machine throws 2 balls every 3 seconds. How many balls will the machine throw in 18 seconds? **12 balls**

Notetaking Guide

Transparency Available

Promotes interactive learning and notetaking skills.

Pacing

Basic: 2 days

Average: 2 days

Advanced: 2 days

Block: 0.5 block with 3.6
0.5 block with 3.8

• See *Teaching Guide/Lesson Plan.*

2 FOCUS AND MOTIVATE

Essential Question

Big Idea 2, p. 131

How do you solve percent problems? **Tell students they will learn how to answer this question by using proportions and the percent equation to find a percent or a part of a base.**

NCTM STANDARDS

Standard 1: Understand numbers; Compute fluently

3.7 Solve Percent Problems

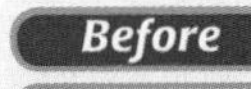

Before	You solved proportions.
Now	You will solve percent problems.
Why?	So you can solve a problem about racing, as in Ex. 34.

Key Vocabulary
- **percent,** *p. 916*
- **proportion,** *p. 163*

Recall that *percent* means "divided by 100." For example $27\% = \frac{27}{100}$.

By writing a percent as a fraction, you can use a proportion to solve a percent problem.

KEY CONCEPT *For Your Notebook*

Solving Percent Problems Using Proportions

You can represent "*a* is *p* percent of *b*" using the proportion

$$\frac{a}{b} = \frac{p}{100}$$

where *a* is a part of the base *b* and $\frac{p}{100}$, or *p*%, is the percent.

EXAMPLE 1 Find a percent using a proportion

What percent of 25 is 17?

Solution

Write a proportion where 25 is the base and 17 is a part of the base.

$\frac{a}{b} = \frac{p}{100}$ **Write proportion.**

$\frac{17}{25} = \frac{p}{100}$ **Substitute 17 for *a* and 25 for *b*.**

$1700 = 25p$ **Cross products property**

$68 = p$ **Divide each side by 25.**

▶ 17 is 68% of 25.

AVOID ERRORS
You can also solve for *p* by multiplying each side of the equation by 100.

 Animated Algebra at classzone.com

✓ **GUIDED PRACTICE** for Example 1

Use a proportion to answer the question.

1. What percent of 20 is 15? **75%** **2.** What number is 30% of 90? **27**

Resource Planning Guide

Chapter Resource Book
- Teaching Guide/Lesson Plan
- Practice levels A, B, C
- Study Guide
- Catch-up for Absent Students
- Application
- Challenge

Workbooks
- Notetaking Guide
- Practice Workbook

Teaching Options
- **Power Presentations** provides dynamic electronic teaching resources for the classroom.
- **Activity Generator** provides editable activities for all ability levels.

Interactive Technology
- Easy Planner
- Power Presentations
- Activity Generator
- Animated Algebra
- Test Generator
- Online Quiz
- eWorkbook
- eEdition
- @HomeTutor

Resources for English Learners
- Spanish Study Guide
- Multi-Language Visual Glossary
- Student Resources in Spanish

See also the *Differentiated Instruction Resources* for more strategies for meeting individual needs.

THE PERCENT EQUATION In Example 1, the proportion $\frac{a}{b} = \frac{p}{100}$ is used to find a percent. When you write $\frac{p}{100}$ as $p\%$ and solve for a, you get the equation $a = p\% \cdot b$.

KEY CONCEPT *For Your Notebook*

The Percent Equation

You can represent "a is p percent of b" using the equation

$$a = p\% \cdot b$$

where a is a part of the base b and $p\%$ is the percent.

EXAMPLE 2 Find a percent using the percent equation

What percent of 136 is 51?

$a = p\% \cdot b$	**Write percent equation.**
$51 = p\% \cdot 136$	**Substitute 51 for *a* and 136 for *b*.**
$0.375 = p\%$	**Divide each side by 136.**
$37.5\% = p\%$	**Write decimal as percent.**

▶ 51 is 37.5% of 136.

DETERMINE THE BASE
When a problem talks about the percent *of* a number, the number is the base b, which is multiplied by the percent.

CHECK Substitute 0.375 for $p\%$ in the original equation.

$51 = p\% \cdot 136$	**Write original equation.**
$51 \stackrel{?}{=} 0.375 \cdot 136$	**Substitute 0.375 for *p*%.**
$51 = 51$ ✓	**Multiply. Solution checks.**

EXAMPLE 3 Find a part of a base using the percent equation

What number is 15% of 88?

$a = p\% \cdot b$	**Write percent equation.**
$= 15\% \cdot 88$	**Substitute 15 for *p* and 88 for *b*.**
$= 0.15 \cdot 88$	**Write percent as decimal.**
$= 13.2$	**Multiply.**

▶ 13.2 is 15% of 88.

GUIDED PRACTICE for Examples 2 and 3

Use the percent equation to answer the question.

3. What percent of 56 is 49? **87.5%**
4. What percent of 55 is 11? **20%**
5. What number is 45% of 92? **41.4**
6. What number is 140% of 50? **70**

Differentiated Instruction

Visual Learners Remind students that "percent" means hundredths by writing familiar words like "centimeter" $\left(\frac{1}{100}\text{ of a meter}\right)$ and "centipede" (hundred legs). Circle the word stem "centi-" to emphasize hundred (the "cent" in percent). Also note the resemblance of the percent sign (%) to one of the symbols for division (÷) to remind students that percent means to divide, not multiply, by 100.

See also the *Differentiated Instruction Resources* for more strategies.

Motivating the Lesson

Ask students to give examples of surveys they have participated in or surveys they have taken. After discussing real-world surveys, point out that a common theme of all of these surveys is determining some kind of percent. For example, what percent of respondents prefer to travel by bicycle? Ask students to give other examples of survey percents. Close the discussion by telling students that this lesson will prepare them for solving problems that involve percents.

3 TEACH

Extra Example 1

What percent of 60 is 9? **15%**

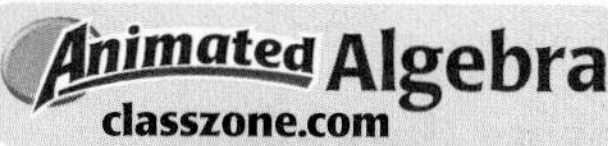

An **Animated Algebra** activity is available online for **Example 1**. This activity is also part of **Power Presentations**.

Extra Example 2

What percent of 20 is 13? **65%**

Key Questions to Ask for Example 2

- What is another way to write $p\%$? $\frac{p}{100}$**, as in Example 1**
- How would you write Example 2 as a proportion? $\frac{51}{136} = \frac{p}{100}$
- How do you know that 136 is the base, rather than 51? **136 follows the words "percent of".**

Extra Example 3

What number is 12% of 85? **10.2**

Extra Example 4

75 is 62.5% of what number? **120**

Key Question to Ask for Example 4

- How can you represent this problem as a proportion? $\frac{20}{b} = \frac{12.5}{100}$

Extra Example 5

A survey asked 180 students how much they would tip for a $28 meal. Find the percent of students who would tip the given amount.

Amount of tip	Students
$2.00	16
$2.80	28
$3.00	45
$4.20	36
$5.00	47
$5.60	8

a. $4.20 **20%**

b. $5.60 **about 4%**

Closing the Lesson

Have students summarize the major points of the lesson and answer the Essential Question: How do you solve percent problems?

- **Use "*a* is *p* percent of *b*" to represent percent problems, where *a* is part of a base, *b* is the base, and $\frac{p}{100}$ or $p\%$ is the percent.**
- **For proportions, use $\frac{a}{b} = \frac{p}{100}$.**
- **For equations, use $a = p\% \cdot b$.**

Solve percent problems using the percent equation or a proportion. Of the three quantities—the percent, the base, and the part of the base—two will be known and one is unknown. The value that follows "percent of," in words or symbols, is the base.

EXAMPLE 4 Find a base using the percent equation

CHECK REASONABLENESS

Use 10%, or $\frac{1}{10}$, to check your answer:

$160 \cdot \frac{1}{10} = 16$

Because 16 is slightly less than 20, the solution is reasonable.

20 is 12.5% of what number?

$a = p\% \cdot b$ **Write percent equation.**

$20 = 12.5\% \cdot b$ **Substitute 20 for *a* and 12.5 for *p*.**

$20 = 0.125 \cdot b$ **Write percent as decimal.**

$160 = b$ **Divide each side by 0.125.**

▸ 20 is 12.5% of 160.

EXAMPLE 5 Solve a real-world percent problem

SURVEY A survey asked 220 students to name their favorite pasta dish. Find the percent of students who chose the given pasta dish.

a. macaroni and cheese

b. lasagna

Type of Pasta	Students
Spaghetti	83
Lasagna	40
Macaroni and cheese	33
Fettucine alfredo	22
Baked ziti	16
Pasta primavera	15
Other	11

Solution

a. The survey results show that 33 of the 220 students chose macaroni and cheese.

$a = p\% \cdot b$ **Write percent equation.**

$33 = p\% \cdot 220$ **Substitute 33 for *a* and 220 for *b*.**

$0.15 = p\%$ **Divide each side by 220.**

$15\% = p\%$ **Write decimal as percent.**

▸ 15% of the students chose macaroni and cheese as their favorite dish.

b. The survey results show that 40 of the 220 students chose lasagna.

$a = p\% \cdot b$ **Write percent equation.**

$40 = p\% \cdot 220$ **Substitute 40 for *a* and 220 for *b*.**

$0.18 \approx p\%$ **Divide each side by 220.**

$18\% \approx p\%$ **Write decimal as percent.**

▸ About 18% of the students chose lasagna as their favorite dish.

✓ **GUIDED PRACTICE** for Examples 4 and 5

In Exercises 7 and 8, use the percent equation to answer the question.

7. 65 is 62.5% of what number? **104**

8. 50 is 125% of what number? **40**

9. In Example 5, what percent of students chose fettucine alfredo? **10%**

CONCEPT SUMMARY — For Your Notebook

Types of Percent Problems

Percent problem	Example	Equation
Find a percent.	What percent of 136 is 51?	$51 = p\% \cdot 136$
Find part of a base.	What number is 15% of 88?	$a = 15\% \cdot 88$
Find a base.	20 is 12.5% of what number?	$20 = 12.5\% \cdot b$

3.7 EXERCISES

HOMEWORK KEY
○ = **WORKED-OUT SOLUTIONS** on p. WS7 for Exs. 13 and 35
★ = **STANDARDIZED TEST PRACTICE** Exs. 2, 19, 30, 31, 38, and 39

SKILL PRACTICE

A

1. **VOCABULARY** Identify the percent, the base, and the part of the base in the following statement: 54 is 15% of 360. **percent: 15, base: 360, part: 54**

2. ★ **WRITING** Rewrite the statement "28 is 35% of 80" in the form $\frac{a}{b} = \frac{p}{100}$. *Explain* how you identified the values of *a*, *b*, and *p*. $\frac{28}{80} = \frac{35}{100}$; **the statement identifies 28 as part of 80 so 28 is the part, *a*, and 80 is the base, *b*; 35 is *p* because it is a percent.**

EXAMPLE 1 on p. 176 for Exs. 3–8

USING PROPORTIONS Use a proportion to answer the question.

3. What percent of 75 is 27? **36%**
4. What percent of 120 is 66? **55%**
5. What number is 35% of 80? **28**
6. What number is 60% of 85? **51**
7. 81 is 54% of what number? **150**
8. 42 is 200% of what number? **21**

EXAMPLES 2, 3, and 4 on pp. 177–178 for Exs. 9–21

USING THE PERCENT EQUATION Use the percent equation to answer the question.

9. What percent of 80 is 56? **70%**
10. What percent of 225 is 99? **44%**
11. What percent of 153 is 9.18? **6%**
12. What number is 18% of 150? **27**
13. What number is 115% of 60? **69**
14. What number is 82% of 215? **176.3**
15. 7 is 28% of what number? **25**
16. 189 is 90% of what number? **210**
17. 41.8 is 44% of what number? **95**
18. 71.5 is 52% of what number? **137.5**

19. ★ **MULTIPLE CHOICE** What number is 87.5% of 512? **B**

(A) 5.85 (B) 448 (C) 585 (D) 4480

ERROR ANALYSIS *Describe* and correct the error in answering the question.

20. What percent of 95 is 19? ***p*% should be multiplied by 95; 19 = *p*% • 95, *p*% = 20%.**

$95 = p\% \cdot 19$
$5 = p\%$
$500\% = p\%$

21. 153 is 76.5% of what number? **76.5% needs to be changed to 0.765; 153 = 0.765 • *b*, *b* = 200.**

$153 = 76.5\% \cdot b$
$153 = 76.5 \cdot b$
$2 = b$

4 PRACTICE AND APPLY

Assignment Guide

Answer Transparencies available for all exercises

Basic:
Day 1: SRH p. 917 Exs. 11–17 odd
pp. 179–181
Exs. 1–14, 22, 23, 47–52
Day 2: pp. 179–181
Exs. 15–21, 24, 25, 33–37, 41–46

Average:
Day 1: pp. 179–181
Exs. 1, 2, 3–13 odd, 22, 23, 26–29, 47–52
Day 2: pp. 179–181
Exs. 16, 19–21, 24, 25, 30, 31, 35–39, 41–46

Advanced:
Day 1: pp. 179–181
Exs. 1, 6–8, 12–14, 22, 23, 26–29
Day 2: pp. 179–181
Exs. 17–19, 24, 25, 30–32*, 35–40*, 42, 46

Block:
pp. 179–181
Exs. 1, 2, 3–13 odd, 22, 23, 26–29, 47–52 (with 3.6)
pp. 179–181
Exs. 16, 19–21, 24, 25, 30, 31, 35–39, 41–46 (with 3.8)

Differentiated Instruction

See *Differentiated Instruction Resources* for suggestions on addressing the needs of a diverse classroom.

Homework Check

For a quick check of student understanding of key concepts, go over the following exercises:
Basic: 5, 10, 13, 16, 33
Average: 7, 11, 13, 16, 36
Advanced: 8, 12, 14, 18, 35

Extra Practice

- Student Edition, p. 940
- Chapter Resource Book: Practice levels A, B, C

Practice Worksheet

An easily-readable reduced practice page (with answers) for this lesson can be found on p. 130D.

Avoiding Common Errors

Exercises 3–18 To avoid confusing the base and part of a base, suggest that students reread the note "determine the base" for Example 2 on page 177 on how to determine a base. Students can write this information on a 3 × 5 card to use until they become proficient in distinguishing between a base and a part of a base.

Exercise 35 Caution students that errors can occur when many categories and percents are used in a problem. Urge them to double check that they used the correct category and the correct percent when solving parts (a) and (b).

Exercise 36 You may want to suggest that students identify the base and the part of a base for years 2001 and 2002.

Teaching Strategy

Exercises 8, 13 Both of these exercises require using percents greater than 1. You may want to review how to write such percents before students begin these exercises. Point out that in Exercise 8, the base will be less than 42 since 42 is 200% of a number, and that in Exercise 13, a part of the base will be greater than 60 since it is 115% of 60. In Exercise 8, some students may recognize that 200% of a number is twice the number, and use the fact that 42 is twice 21.

Study Strategy

Exercise 19 Point out that students can eliminate two choices because the exercise asks for a part of the base, which in this exercise must be less than the base 512.

Reading Strategy

Exercises 22–25 For students who ask for help on these problems, point out that the direction line gives them the value for n, and they need to substitute for n before solving the percent problem.

B **SOLVING PERCENT PROBLEMS Answer the question when $n = 25$.**

22. What percent of 140 is $(n + 94)$? **85%**

23. What percent of $(4n)$ is 96? **96%**

24. What number is 52% of $(2n + 15)$? **33.8**

25. 25.5 is $(n - 8)$% of what number? **150**

SOLVING PERCENT PROBLEMS Find the percent. Round your answer to the nearest whole percent, if necessary.

26. $3.00 tip for a $18.70 taxi fare **16%**

27. $1.44 tax on an item priced at $24.00 **6%**

28. 90 rock CDs out of 125 CDs **72%**

29. 241 freshmen out of 804 students **30%**

30. ★ **WRITING** Would you use a proportion or the percent equation to solve the following problem: What number is 25% of 600? *Explain.* ***Sample answer:*** **Percent equation; you just need to multiply the percent by the base to find the part.**

31. ★ **SHORT RESPONSE** The side length of a square is 40% of the side length of another square. Is the area of the smaller square 40% of the area of the larger square? *Explain.* **No. *Sample answer:* The area of the smaller square would be 16% of the area of the larger square because the percent needs to be squared.**

C **32.** **CHALLENGE** Let y be 10% of a number. What is 50% of the number? Write your answer in terms of y. **5y**

PROBLEM SOLVING

EXAMPLE 5 A on p. 178 for Exs. 33–36

33. **SCHOOL TRANSPORTATION** In a school transportation survey of 225 students, 18 of the students surveyed said that they walk to school. What percent of the students surveyed walk to school? **8%**

@HomeTutor for problem solving help at classzone.com

34. **DAYTONA 500** After completing 10 laps in the Daytona 500, a driver has completed 5% of the race. How many laps does the race have? **200 laps**

@HomeTutor for problem solving help at classzone.com

REVIEW CIRCLE GRAPHS For help with using a circle graph, see p. 934.

(35.) **MUSIC** The circle graph shows the results of a radio survey in which 250 listeners were asked to rate a song.

a. How many of the listeners who participated in the survey are "tired of" the song? **90 listeners**

b. How many of the listeners who participated in the survey "love" the song? **35 listeners**

Radio Survey

- Tired of 36%
- Like 26%
- Love 14%
- Dislike 13%
- Not familiar with 11%

36. **HIKING** The table gives data about the number of people who started hiking the Appalachian Trail in Georgia and the number of those people who completed the trail in Maine. Copy and complete the table.

Year	Hikers who started	Hikers who completed	Percent completion
2001	2380	? **395**	16.6%
2002	? **1880**	376	20%
2003	1750	352	? **20%**

○ = **WORKED-OUT SOLUTIONS on p. WS1**   ★ = **STANDARDIZED TEST PRACTICE**

B 37. **ART** The Louvre Museum, which is an art museum in France, has virtual tours of its exhibits on its website. The website can be viewed in four different languages. The table shows the number of hits received by each version of the website during one day. Find the percent of hits for each version of the website. **59.3%; 16.5%; 13.2%; 11.0%**

Version	English	French	Spanish	Japanese
Number of hits	4860	1350	1080	900

38. ★ **OPEN-ENDED** Write a real-world percent problem that can be solved using the proportion $\frac{x}{75} = \frac{15}{100}$. Then find the value of x and explain what the solution means in this situation. ***Sample answer:*** **You want to leave a 15% tip at a restaurant. If the bill came to \$75, what tip should you leave? $x = 11.25$; you should leave \$11.25 for a tip.**

39. ★ **EXTENDED RESPONSE** Two different stores are selling a bicycle that you want to buy.

 a. **Solve** At one store, the bicycle is on sale for 20% off the original price of \$240. How much money will you save by purchasing the bicycle on sale at this store? **\$48**

 b. **Solve** At the other store, the bicycle is on sale for 25% off the original price of \$265. How much money will you save by purchasing the bicycle on sale at this store? **\$66.25**

 c. **Compare** Which bicycle should you buy? *Explain.* **The bicycle in part (a); it will cost \$192, the bicycle in part (b) will cost \$198.75.**

C 40. **CHALLENGE** Julia deposits 20% of her paycheck in her savings account. Then she deposits 60% of the remaining money in her checking account. She deposits \$108.24 in her checking account. How much money did she deposit in her savings account? **\$45.10**

MIXED REVIEW

PREVIEW Prepare for Lesson 3.8 in Exs. 41–46.

Find the area of the triangle or rectangle. *(p. 922)*

41. 

120 cm²

42. 

143 in.²

Make a table for the function. Identify the range of the function. *(p. 35)*
43–46. See margin for tables.

43. $y = x - 7$
Domain: −5, −2, 1, 4 **−12, −9, −6, −3**

44. $y = x + 4$
Domain: −6, −4, −2, 0 **−2, 0, 2, 4**

45. $y = 6x + 3$
Domain: −1, 1, 3, 5 **−3, 9, 21, 33**

46. $y = 5x - 5$
Domain: −2, −1, 0, 1 **−15, −10, −5, 0**

Find the sum or difference.

47. $-65 + (-27)$ *(p. 74)* **−92**

48. $33 + (-58)$ *(p. 74)* **−25**

49. $-43.9 + 89.4$ *(p. 74)* **45.5**

50. $91.2 - (-20.3)$ *(p. 80)* **111.5**

51. $-13 - 78$ *(p. 80)* **−91**

52. $28 - (-35)$ *(p. 80)* **63**

5 ASSESS AND RETEACH

Daily Homework Quiz

Transparency Available

Solve the percent problem.

1. What percent of 50 is 1? **2%**
2. What percent of 128 is 48? **37.5%**
3. What number is 16% of 45? **7.2**
4. 12 is 12.5% of what number? **96**
5. Leonard has read 1001 pages out of 1456 of Tolstoy's *War and Peace*. What percent of the novel has he read? **68.75%**

Online Quiz

Available at **classzone.com**

Diagnosis/Remediation

- Practice A, B, C in Chapter Resource Book
- Study Guide in Chapter Resource Book
- Practice Workbook
- @HomeTutor

Challenge

Additional challenge is available in the Chapter Resource Book.

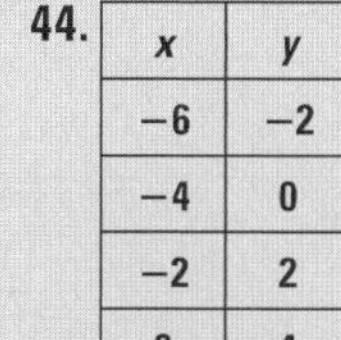

43.

x	y
−5	−12
−2	−9
1	−6
4	−3

44.

x	y
−6	−2
−4	0
−2	2
0	4

45.

x	y
−1	−3
1	9
3	21
5	33

46.

x	y
−2	−15
−1	10
0	−5
1	0

1 PLAN AND PREPARE

Warm-Up Exercises

1. What percent of 75 is 18? **24%**
2. What number is 45% of 180? **81**
3. 28 is 16% percent of what number? **175**
4. A particular Goliath Frog has a body that is 12 inches long. With its legs extended, it is 30 inches long. What percent of the frog's total length is its body? **40%**

2 FOCUS AND MOTIVATE

Essential Question

Big Idea 2, p. 131

How do you solve percent of change problems? **Tell students they will learn how to answer this question by finding the percent by which an amount increases or decreases from an original amount, and by finding a new amount when given an original amount and a percent of change.**

3 TEACH

Extra Example 1

Identify the percent of change as an *increase* or *decrease*. Then find the percent of change.

a. Original: 90
New: 126 **increase; 40%**

b. Original: 160
New: 72 **decrease; 55%**

NCTM STANDARDS

Standard 1: Understand numbers; Compute fluently

Extension Find Percent of Change

Use after Lesson 3.7

GOAL Solve percent of change problems.

Key Vocabulary
- **percent of change**
- **percent of increase**
- **percent of decrease**

A **percent of change** indicates how much a quantity increases or decreases with respect to the original amount. If the new amount is greater than the original amount, the percent of change is called a **percent of increase**. If the new amount is less than the original amount, the percent of change is called a **percent of decrease**.

KEY CONCEPT *For Your Notebook*

Percent of Change

The percent of change is the ratio of the amount of increase or decrease to the original amount.

$$\text{Percent of change, } p\% = \frac{\text{Amount of increase or decrease}}{\text{Original amount}}$$

The amount of increase is the new amount minus the original amount. The amount of decrease is the original amount minus the new amount.

EXAMPLE 1 Find a percent of change

Identify the percent of change as an *increase* or *decrease*. Then find the percent of change.

a. Original: 140
New: 189

b. Original: 70
New: 59.5

Solution

a. Because the new amount is greater than the original amount, the percent of change is an increase.

$$p\% = \frac{\text{Amount of increase}}{\text{Original amount}} = \frac{189 - 140}{140} = \frac{49}{140} = 0.35 = 35\%$$

▸ The percent of increase is 35%.

b. Because the new amount is less than the original amount, the percent of change is a decrease.

$$p\% = \frac{\text{Amount of decrease}}{\text{Original amount}} = \frac{70 - 59.5}{70} = \frac{10.5}{70} = 0.15 = 15\%$$

▸ The percent of decrease is 15%.

CHECK REASONABLENESS
Because 50 is one third (about 33%) of 150, it is reasonable that 49 is 35% of 140.

FINDING A NEW AMOUNT If you know the original amount and the percent of change, you can find the new amount.

- For a $p\%$ increase, multiply the original amount by $(100\% + p\%)$.
- For a $p\%$ decrease, multiply the original amount by $(100\% - p\%)$.

EXAMPLE 2 Find a new amount

SHOPPING Find the sale price of the pair of jeans described in the table.

Original price	$48.00
Discount	40%
Sale price	?

Solution

ANOTHER WAY
You can also find the sale price by first finding the change in price:
$0.4 \cdot 48 = 19.2$.
Then subtract the change in price from the original price:
$\$48.00 - \$19.20 = \$28.80$.

The sale price is a decrease from the original price, so multiply the original price by $(100\% - p\%)$.

Sale price = **Original price** $\cdot$ $(100\% - p\%)$

$= 48 \cdot (100\% - 40\%)$ **Substitute.**

$= 48 \cdot 0.6$ **Subtract percents. Then write as a decimal.**

$= 28.8$ **Multiply.**

▶ The sale price of the pair of jeans is $28.80.

PRACTICE

EXAMPLE 1 on p. 182 for Exs. 1–6

Identify the percent of change as an *increase* or *decrease*. Then find the percent of change.

1. Original: 16 New: 20 **increase; 25%**
2. Original: 35 New: 49 **increase; 40%**
3. Original: 80 New: 44 **decrease; 45%**
4. Original: 120 New: 78 **decrease; 35%**
5. Original: 360 New: 241.2 **decrease; 33%**
6. Original: 170 New: 283.9 **increase; 67%**

EXAMPLE 2 on p. 183 for Exs. 7–14

Find the new amount.

7. Increase 14 by 45%. **20.3**
8. Increase 78 by 80%. **140.4**
9. Decrease 44 by 20%. **35.2**
10. Decrease 108 by 90%. **10.8**

11. **SUBWAY** The price for a token to ride a city's subway system is changing from $1.25 to $1.50. Find the percent of change. **20% increase**

12. **DVDS** The average price of a new DVD in 1998 was $24. In 2003, the average price was $21.12. Find the percent of change. **12% decrease**

13. **POPULATION** In Arizona, the population increased by 48.6% from 1990 to 2002. Use the information in the table to find the population density in Arizona in 2002. **48.0 people per square mile**

Year	Population density
1990	32.3 people per square mile
2002	?

14. **DEPRECIATION** A new car is valued at $14,500. In one year, the car's value will depreciate, or decrease, by 15%. Find the value of the car after one year. **$12,325**

Key Question to Ask for Example 1

- How can you check that the answers are correct? **Multiply the original amount by the percent. Then add or subtract that amount to or from the original to obtain the new amount.**

Extra Example 2

An adventure company discounted an Australian tour by 30%. The original price for the tour was $3500. Find the sale price. **$2450**

Closing the Lesson

Have students summarize the major points of the lesson and answer the Essential Question: How do you solve percent of change problems?

- **Solve percent of change problems by dividing the amount of increase or decrease by the original amount.**
- **To find a new amount, multiply the original amount by $100\% + p\%$ for an increase or by $100\% - p\%$ for a decrease.**

To find percent of change, first find the amount of change by subtracting the lesser number from the greater number and then dividing that difference by the original amount. To find new amounts, add or subtract the percent of change to or from 100% and then multiply that percent by the original number.

4 PRACTICE AND APPLY

Avoiding Common Errors

Exercises 1–6 Watch for students who divide the original amount by the new amount for a decrease and the new amount by the original amount for an increase. Remind students that they have to divide the *amount* of increase or decrease by the original amount.

1 PLAN AND PREPARE

Warm-Up Exercises

Transparency Available

1. Write an equation for "3 more than twice a is 24." $2a + 3 = 24$
2. A square has a side length of 8 feet. Find the area of the square using the formula $A = s^2$. **64 ft²**
3. A rectangular serving tray is 26 inches long and 18 inches wide. What is the tray's serving area? **468 in.²**

Notetaking Guide

Transparency Available

Promotes interactive learning and notetaking skills.

Pacing

Basic: 1 day
Average: 1 day
Advanced: 1 day
Block: 0.5 block with 3.7

- See *Teaching Guide/Lesson Plan.*

2 FOCUS AND MOTIVATE

Essential Question

Big Idea 3, p. 131

How do you rewrite equations? **Tell students they will learn how to answer this question by rewriting equations and formulas with two or more variables so that any given variable is a function of the other variables.**

NCTM STANDARDS

Standard 2: Represent situations using algebraic symbols; Analyze situations using algebraic symbols

3.8 Rewrite Equations and Formulas

Before	You wrote functions and used formulas.
Now	You will rewrite equations and formulas.
Why?	So you can solve a problem about bowling, as in Ex. 33.

Key Vocabulary
- **literal equation**
- **formula,** *p. 30*

The equations $2x + 5 = 11$ and $6x + 3 = 15$ have the general form $ax + b = c$. The equation $ax + b = c$ is called a **literal equation** because the coefficients and constants have been replaced by letters. When you solve a literal equation, you can use the result to solve any equation that has the same form as the literal equation.

EXAMPLE 1 Solve a literal equation

Solve $ax + b = c$ for x. Then use the solution to solve $2x + 5 = 11$.

Solution

STEP 1 **Solve** $ax + b = c$ for x.

$ax + b = c$ — Write original equation.

$ax = c - b$ — Subtract b from each side.

$x = \frac{c - b}{a}$ — Assume $a \neq 0$. Divide each side by a.

STEP 2 **Use** the solution to solve $2x + 5 = 11$.

$x = \frac{c - b}{a}$ — Solution of literal equation

$= \frac{11 - 5}{2}$ — Substitute 2 for a, 5 for b, and 11 for c.

$= 3$ — Simplify.

▶ The solution of $2x + 5 = 11$ is 3.

VARIABLES IN DENOMINATORS In Example 1, you must assume that $a \neq 0$ in order to divide by a. In general, if you have to divide by a variable when solving a literal equation, you should assume that the variable does not equal 0.

GUIDED PRACTICE for Example 1

Solve the literal equation for x. Then use the solution to solve the specific equation.

1. $a - bx = c$; $12 - 5x = -3$ $x = \frac{a - c}{b}$; 3
2. $ax = bx + c$; $11x = 6x + 20$ $x = \frac{c}{a - b}$; 4

Resource Planning Guide

Chapter Resource Book
- Teaching Guide/Lesson Plan
- Practice levels A, B, C
- Study Guide
- Catch-up for Absent Students
- Problem Solving Workshop
- Challenge

Workbooks
- Notetaking Guide
- Practice Workbook

Teaching Options
- **Power Presentations** provides dynamic electronic teaching resources for the classroom.
- **Activity Generator** provides editable activities for all ability levels.

Interactive Technology
- Easy Planner
- Power Presentations
- Activity Generator
- Animated Algebra
- Test Generator
- Online Quiz
- eWorkbook
- eEdition
- @HomeTutor

Resources for English Learners
- Spanish Study Guide
- Multi-Language Visual Glossary
- Student Resources in Spanish

See also the *Differentiated Instruction Resources* for more strategies for meeting individual needs.

TWO OR MORE VARIABLES An equation in two variables, such as $3x + 2y = 8$, or a formula in two or more variables, such as $A = \frac{1}{2}bh$, can be rewritten so that one variable is a function of the other variable(s).

EXAMPLE 2 Rewrite an equation

Write $3x + 2y = 8$ so that y is a function of x.

$3x + 2y = 8$ — **Write original equation.**

$2y = 8 - 3x$ — **Subtract $3x$ from each side.**

$y = 4 - \frac{3}{2}x$ — **Divide each side by 2.**

EXAMPLE 3 Solve and use a geometric formula

The area A of a triangle is given by the formula $A = \frac{1}{2}bh$ where b is the base and h is the height.

a. Solve the formula for the height h.

b. Use the rewritten formula to find the height of the triangle shown, which has an area of 64.4 square meters.

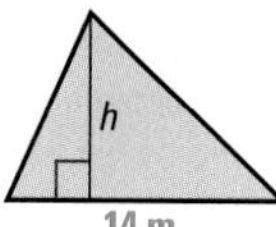

Solution

a. $A = \frac{1}{2}bh$ — **Write original formula.**

$2A = bh$ — **Multiply each side by 2.**

$\frac{2A}{b} = h$ — **Divide each side by b.**

b. Substitute 64.4 for A and 14 for b in the rewritten formula.

$h = \frac{2A}{b}$ — **Write rewritten formula.**

$= \frac{2(64.4)}{14}$ — **Substitute 64.4 for A and 14 for b.**

$= 9.2$ — **Simplify.**

▸ The height of the triangle is 9.2 meters.

USE UNIT ANALYSIS
When area is measured in square meters and the base is measured in meters, dividing twice the area by the base gives a result measured in meters.

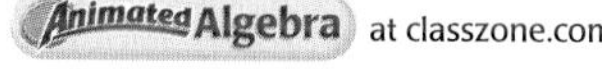 at classzone.com

GUIDED PRACTICE for Examples 2 and 3

3. Write $5x + 4y = 20$ so that y is a function of x. **$y = 5 - \frac{5}{4}x$**

4. The perimeter P of a rectangle is given by the formula $P = 2\ell + 2w$ where ℓ is the length and w is the width.

   a. Solve the formula for the width w.

   b. Use the rewritten formula to find the width of the rectangle shown. **2.4 ft**

P = 19.2 ft; w; 7.2 ft

4a. $w = \frac{P - 2\ell}{2}$ or $w = \frac{P}{2} - \ell$

Motivating the Lesson

Tell students that in this lesson they will learn how to rewrite formulas to isolate different variables. Explain that often it is easier to solve a problem if they isolate a variable before they substitute numbers for the other variables. As an example, suppose they want to find how long it will take to drive to the beach. Instead of substituting values for the formula $d = rt$ and then isolating the variable t, they can isolate t as $t = \frac{d}{r}$ and then substitute values for d and r.

3 TEACH

Extra Example 1

Solve $p + qx = r$ for x. Then use the solution to solve $3 + 5x = -7$. **$x = \frac{r - p}{q}$; -2**

Key Question to Ask for Example 1

- How would you solve $2x + 5 = 11$ directly? **Subtract 5 from both sides and then divide by 2.**

Extra Example 2

Write $-2x + 3y = 6$ so that y is a function of x. **$y = \frac{2}{3}x + 2$**

Extra Example 3

The area for a rectangle is given by the formula $A = \ell w$, where ℓ is the length and w is the width.

a. Solve the formula for the length ℓ. **$\ell = \frac{A}{w}$**

b. Use the rewritten formula to find the length of this rectangle.

A = 351 cm²; 13 cm

27 cm

An **Animated Algebra** activity is available online for **Example 3**. This activity is also part of **Power Presentations**.

Extra Example 4

Irina deposited $650 in a savings account. After two years her account balance was $682.50. Find the rate of interest for the two years. Use the formula $A = P(1 + rt)$, where A is the account balance, P is principal, r is rate, and t is time. Rewrite the formula to isolate r and then solve. **$r = \frac{A - P}{Pt}$; $r = 0.025$ or 2.5%**

Key Question to Ask for Example 4

- Do you have to rewrite the formula to find the low temperatures in degrees Fahrenheit? Explain. **No, you can use the given formula but the calculations are easier if you solve the given formula for F before you substitute 14°C or 10°C.**

Closing the Lesson

Have students summarize the major points of the lesson and answer the Essential Question: How do you rewrite equations?

- **In a literal equation, coefficients and constants have been replaced by letters. You can solve a literal equation for any variable.**
- **Use inverse operations when solving a formula or equation for a given variable.**

To rewrite an equation so that y is a function of x, rewrite the equation so that y is isolated on one side of the equation. For all literal equations, solve for the given variable by using properties of equality and inverse operations.

EXAMPLE 4 Solve a multi-step problem

TEMPERATURE You are visiting Toronto, Canada, over the weekend. A website gives the forecast shown. Find the low temperatures for Saturday and Sunday in degrees Fahrenheit. Use the formula $C = \frac{5}{9}(F - 32)$ where C is the temperature in degrees Celsius and F is the temperature in degrees Fahrenheit.

3 Day Forecast for Toronto
Friday
Sunny
High 21°C
Low 13°C
Saturday
Sunny
High 22°C
Low 14°C
Sunday
Partly Cloudy
High 16°C
Low 10°C

REWRITE FORMULAS
When using a formula for multiple calculations, you may find it easier to rewrite the formula first.

Solution

STEP 1 **Rewrite** the formula. In the problem, degrees Celsius are given and degrees Fahrenheit need to be calculated. The calculations will be easier if the formula is written so that F is a function of C.

$C = \frac{5}{9}(F - 32)$ **Write original formula.**

$\frac{9}{5} \cdot C = \frac{9}{5} \cdot \frac{5}{9}(F - 32)$ **Multiply each side by $\frac{9}{5}$, the reciprocal of $\frac{5}{9}$.**

$\frac{9}{5}C = F - 32$ **Simplify.**

$\frac{9}{5}C + 32 = F$ **Add 32 to each side.**

▶ The rewritten formula is $F = \frac{9}{5}C + 32$.

STEP 2 **Find** the low temperatures for Saturday and Sunday in degrees Fahrenheit.

Saturday (low of 14°C)

$F = \frac{9}{5}C + 32$

$= \frac{9}{5}(14) + 32$

$= 25.2 + 32$

$= 57.2$

▶ The low for Saturday is 57.2°F.

Sunday (low of 10°C)

$F = \frac{9}{5}C + 32$

$= \frac{9}{5}(10) + 32$

$= 18 + 32$

$= 50$

▶ The low for Sunday is 50°F.

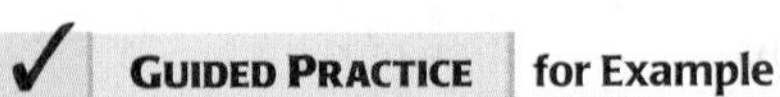
GUIDED PRACTICE for Example 4

5. Use the information in Example 4 to find the high temperatures for Saturday and Sunday in degrees Fahrenheit. **71.6°F, 60.8°F**

3.8 EXERCISES

HOMEWORK KEY
 = **WORKED-OUT SOLUTIONS** on p. WS7 for Exs. 17 and 33
★ = **STANDARDIZED TEST PRACTICE** Exs. 2, 23, 29, 35, and 36
◆ = **MULTIPLE REPRESENTATIONS** Ex. 34

SKILL PRACTICE

A

1. **VOCABULARY** Copy and complete: When you write the equation $3x + 2 = 8$ as $ax + b = c$, the equation $ax + b = c$ is called a(n) __?__ because the coefficients and constants have been replaced by letters. **literal equation**

2. ★ **WRITING** *Describe* the steps you would take to solve $I = prt$ for t. **Divide each side by pr to get $\frac{I}{pr} = t$.**

EXAMPLE 1 on p. 184 for Exs. 3–10

LITERAL EQUATIONS **Solve the literal equation for x. Then use the solution to solve the specific equation.**

3. $ax = bx - c$; $8x = 3x - 10$ $x = \frac{c}{b - a}$; -2
4. $a(x + b) = c$; $2(x + 1) = 9$ $x = \frac{c}{a} - b$; 3.5
5. $c = \frac{x + a}{b}$; $2 = \frac{x + 5}{7}$ $x = bc - a$; 9
6. $\frac{x}{a} = \frac{b}{c}$; $\frac{x}{8} = \frac{4.5}{12}$ $x = \frac{ab}{c}$; 3
7. $\frac{x}{a} + b = c$; $\frac{x}{4} + 6 = 13$ $x = a(c - b)$; 28
8. $ax + b = cx - d$; $2x + 9 = 7x - 1$ $x = \frac{b + d}{c - a}$; 2

ERROR ANALYSIS ***Describe*** **and correct the error in solving the equation for x.**

9.
$ax + b = 0$
$ax = b$
$x = \frac{b}{a}$

10.
$c = ax - bx$
$c = (a - b)x$
$c(a - b) = x$

9. b should have been subtracted from both sides, not added; $ax = -b$, $x = \frac{-b}{a}$.

10. Both sides should have been divided by $(a - b)$, not multiplied; $x = \frac{c}{a - b}$.

EXAMPLE 2 on p. 185 for Exs. 11–19

REWRITING EQUATIONS **Write the equation so that y is a function of x.**

11. $2x + y = 7$ $y = 7 - 2x$
12. $5x + 4y = 10$ $y = \frac{5}{2} - \frac{5}{4}x$
13. $12 = 9x + 3y$ $4 - 3x = y$
14. $18x - 2y = 26$ $y = -13 + 9x$
15. $14 = 7y - 6x$ $2 + \frac{6}{7}x = y$
16. $8x - 8y = 5$ $y = x - \frac{5}{8}$
17. $30 = 9x - 5y$ $\frac{9}{5}x - 6 = y$
18. $3 + 6x = 11 - 4y$ $2 - \frac{3}{2}x = y$
19. $2 + 6y = 3x + 4$ $y = \frac{1}{2}x + \frac{1}{3}$

EXAMPLE 3 on p. 185 for Exs. 20–23

REWRITING FORMULAS **Solve the formula for the indicated variable.**

20. Volume of a rectangular prism: $V = \ell wh$. Solve for w. $w = \frac{V}{\ell h}$
21. Surface area of a prism: $S = 2B + Ph$. Solve for h. $h = \frac{S - 2B}{P}$
22. Length of movie projected at 24 frames per second: $\ell = 24f$. Solve for f. $f = \frac{\ell}{24}$

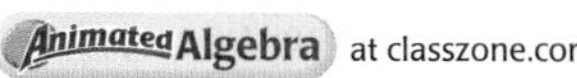 at classzone.com

23. ★ **MULTIPLE CHOICE** The formula for the area of a trapezoid is $A = \frac{1}{2}(b_1 + b_2)h$. Which equation is *not* equivalent to the formula? **C**

Ⓐ $h = \frac{2A}{b_1 + b_2}$ Ⓑ $b_1 = \frac{2A}{h} - b_2$ Ⓒ $b_2 = \frac{2A}{b_1} - h$ Ⓓ $b_2 = \frac{2A}{h} - b_1$

B

REWRITING EQUATIONS **Write the equation so that y is a function of x.**

24. $4.2x - 2y = 16.8$ $y = 2.1x - 8.4$
25. $9 - 0.5y = 2.5x$ $y = 18 - 5x$
26. $8x - 5x + 21 = 36 - 6y$ $y = -\frac{1}{2}x + \frac{5}{2}$

Differentiated Instruction

Auditory Learners While working on **Exercises 20–23**, students may benefit from reading the formulas aloud, including their meaning, in order to solve for a given variable. For example, in **Exercise 21**, students could read "Surface area is equal to twice the base area plus the product of the perimeter and the height" instead of just reading the formula as "*S* equals 2*B* plus *Ph*."

See also the *Differentiated Instruction Resources* for more strategies.

4 PRACTICE AND APPLY

Assignment Guide

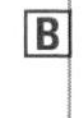 **Answer Transparencies available for all exercises**

Basic:
Day 1: pp. 187–189
Exs. 1–10, 11–19 odd, 20–25, 32–35, 38–45

Average:
Day 1: pp. 187–189
Exs. 1, 2, 4, 6, 8–10, 12–18 even, 20–30, 32–36, 38–45

Advanced:
Day 1: pp. 187–189
Exs. 1, 7, 8, 16–31*, 34–37*, 38–44 even

Block:
pp. 187–189
Exs. 1, 2, 4, 6, 8–10, 12–18 even, 20–30, 32–36, 38–45 (with 3.7)

Differentiated Instruction

See *Differentiated Instruction Resources* for suggestions on addressing the needs of a diverse classroom.

Homework Check

For a quick check of student understanding of key concepts, go over the following exercises:

Basic: 3, 6, 13, 20, 32
Average: 6, 16, 21, 24, 33
Advanced: 8, 18, 22, 26, 34

Extra Practice

- Student Edition, p. 940
- Chapter Resource Book: Practice levels A, B, C

Practice Worksheet

An easily-readable reduced practice page (with answers) for this lesson can be found on p. 130D.

Avoiding Common Errors

Exercises 3–8, 11–19, 27–28
Caution students to check that they used inverse operations when solving for a given variable. One way to check is to list the operations used in the original equation and then to check that the operations in the new equation are inverses of the operations in that list.

An **Animated Algebra** activity is available online for **Exercise 22.** This activity is also part of **Power Presentations**.

Vocabulary

Exercise 32 "Penny size" is an interesting term and it may lead to confusion between the length of a nail in inches *n* and the penny size *d*. Have a student look up the meaning of *penny size* and then discuss its meaning with the class.

34b.

r	x
50	173
51	170
52	167
53	164

34c.

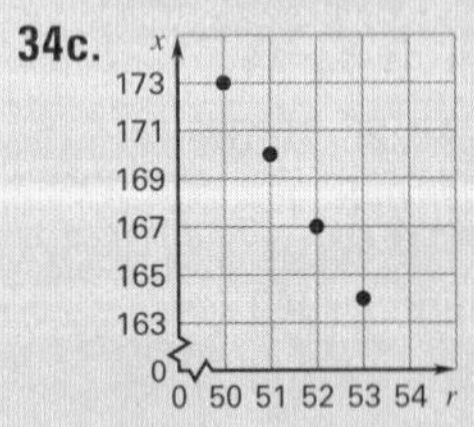

GEOMETRY Solve the formula for the indicated variable. Then evaluate the rewritten formula for the given values. (Use 3.14 for π.)

27. Surface area of a cone: $S = \pi r\ell + \pi r^2$. Solve for ℓ. Find ℓ when $S = 283\text{ cm}^2$ and $r = 5$ cm. $\ell = \frac{S}{\pi r} - r$; **13.03 cm**

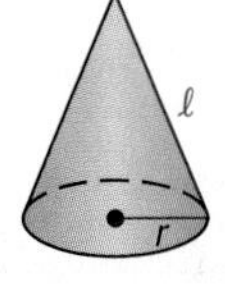

28. Area of a circular ring: $A = 4\pi pw$. Solve for p. Find p when $A = 905\text{ ft}^2$ and $w = 9$ ft. $p = \frac{A}{4\pi w}$; **8.01 ft**

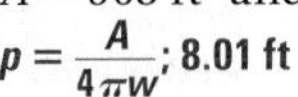

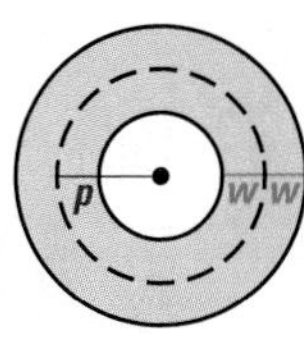

29. ★ **OPEN-ENDED** *Describe* a real-world situation where you would want to solve the distance traveled formula $d = rt$ for t. ***Sample answer:*** **You want to find how long it will take to drive 150 miles if you drive at an average rate of 55 miles per hour.**

C **CHALLENGE Solve the literal equation for a.**

30. $x = \frac{a + b + c}{ab}$ $a = \frac{b + c}{bx - 1}$

31. $y = x\left(\frac{ab}{a - b}\right)$ $a = \frac{by}{y - bx}$

PROBLEM SOLVING

EXAMPLE 4 on p. 186 for Exs. 32–34

A 32. **CARPENTRY** The penny size d of a nail is given by $d = 4n - 2$ where n is the length (in inches) of the nail.

a. Solve the formula for n. $n = \frac{d + 2}{4}$

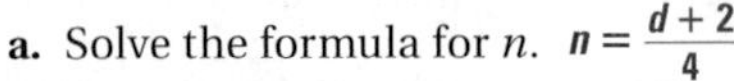

b. Use the new formula to find the lengths of nails with the following penny sizes: 5, 12, 16, and 20. **1.75 in., 3.5 in., 4.5 in., 5.5 in.**

@HomeTutor for problem solving help at classzone.com

33. **BOWLING** To participate in a bowling league, you pay a \$25 sign-up fee and \$12 for each league night that you bowl. So, the total cost C (in dollars) is given by the equation $C = 12x + 25$ where x is the number of league nights you bowled.

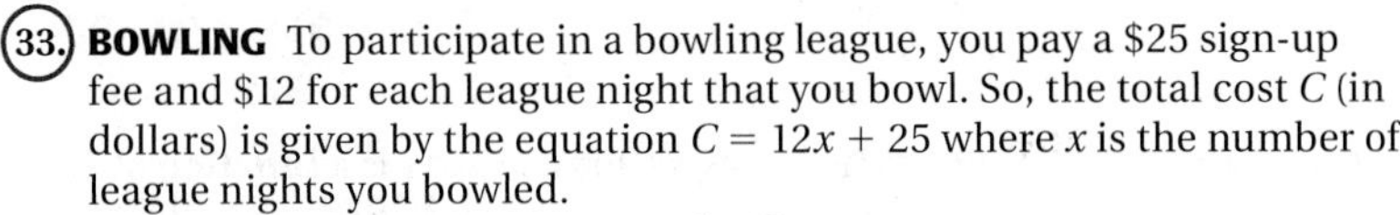

a. Solve the equation for x. $x = \frac{C - 25}{12}$

b. How many league nights have you bowled if you spent a total of \$145? \$181? \$205? **10 league nights; 13 league nights; 15 league nights**

@HomeTutor for problem solving help at classzone.com

34. **MULTIPLE REPRESENTATIONS** An athletic facility is building an indoor track like the one shown. The perimeter P (in feet) of the track is given by $P = 2\pi r + 2x$.

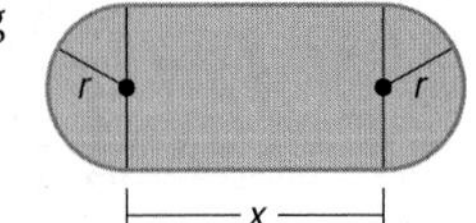

a. **Writing an Equation** Solve the formula for x. $x = \frac{P - 2\pi r}{2}$

b. **Making a Table** The perimeter of the track will be 660 feet. Use the rewritten formula to make a table that shows values of x to the nearest foot when r is 50 feet, 51 feet, 52 feet, and 53 feet. (Use 3.14 for π.) **See margin.**

c. **Drawing a Graph** Plot the ordered pairs from your table. Look for a pattern in the points. Use the pattern to find x when r is 54 feet. **See margin for art; 161 ft**

B 35. ★ **WRITING** You work as a server at a restaurant. During your shift, you keep track of the bills that you give the tables you serve and the tips you receive from the tables. You want to calculate the tip received from each table as a percent of the bill. *Explain* how to rewrite the percent equation to make it easier to calculate the percent tip from each table. **Divide each side by the total bill, b, to get $\frac{a}{b} = p\%$.**

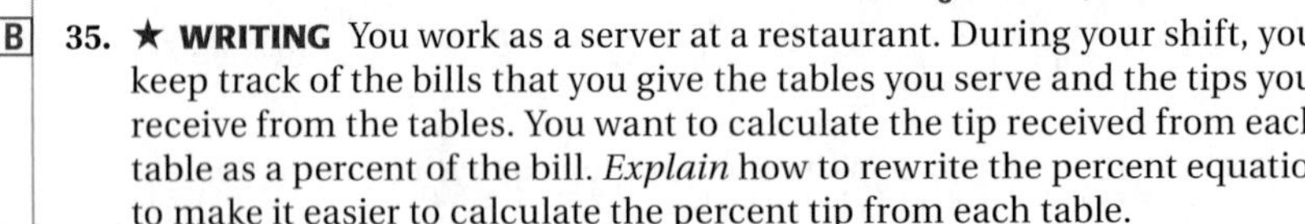

○ = WORKED-OUT SOLUTIONS on p. WS1 ★ = STANDARDIZED TEST PRACTICE ◆ = MULTIPLE REPRESENTATIONS

36b. 1.1 ft; 1.3 ft; 1.4 ft

36. ★ **EXTENDED RESPONSE** One type of stone formation found in Carlsbad Caverns in New Mexico is called a column. This cylindrical stone formation is connected to the ceiling and the floor of a cave.

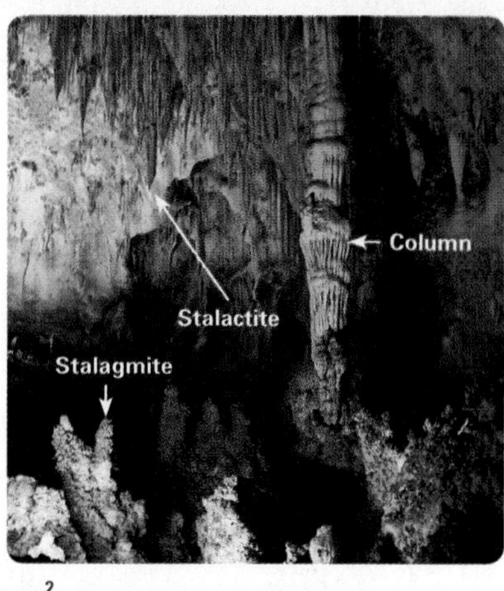

a. Rewrite the formula for the circumference of a circle, $C = 2\pi r$, so that you can easily calculate the radius of a column given its circumference. $r = \frac{C}{2\pi}$

b. What is the radius, to the nearest tenth of a foot, of a column that has a circumference of 7 feet? 8 feet? 9 feet? (Use 3.14 for π.)

c. *Explain* how you can find the *area* of a cross section of a column if you know its circumference. **Solve for r using $\frac{C}{2\pi} = r$, then substitute r into the equation $A = \pi r^2$.**

C 37. **CHALLENGE** The distance d (in miles) traveled by a car is given by $d = 55t$ where t is the time (in hours) the car has traveled. The distance d (in miles) traveled is also given by $d = 20g$ where g is the number of gallons of gasoline used by the car. Write an equation that expresses g as a function of t. $g = \frac{11t}{4}$

MIXED REVIEW

PREVIEW Prepare for Lesson 4.1 in Exs. 38–39.

Graph the function. *(p. 43)* **38, 39. See margin.**

38. $y = x + 4$; domain: 0, 2, 4, 6, and 8

39. $y = 2x - 1$; domain: 1, 2, 3, 4, and 5

Use the distributive property to write an equivalent expression. *(p. 96)*

40. $3(2x + 3)$ $\mathbf{6x + 9}$

41. $-2(x + 5)$ $\mathbf{-2x - 10}$

42. $(3x - 5)(-5)$ $\mathbf{-15x + 25}$

43. $(7x + 6)2$ $\mathbf{14x + 12}$

Use the percent equation to answer the question. *(p. 176)*

44. What percent of 80 is 64? **80%**

45. What number is 95% of 120? **114**

QUIZ for Lessons 3.7–3.8

Use the percent equation to answer the question. *(p. 176)*

1. What percent of 150 is 72? **48%**
2. What percent of 310 is 93? **30%**
3. 31 is 5% of what number? **620**
4. What number is 46% of 55? **25.3**

Write the equation so that y is a function of x. *(p. 184)*

5. $5x - 3y = 9$ $y = \frac{5}{3}x - 3$
6. $3x + 2y + 5x = 12$ $y = 6 - 4x$
7. $4(2x - y) = 6$ $y = 2x - \frac{3}{2}$

8. **GEOMETRY** The volume V of a cylinder is given by the formula $V = \pi r^2 h$ where r is the radius of the cylinder and h is the height of the cylinder. Solve the formula for h. *(p. 184)* $h = \frac{V}{\pi r^2}$

38.
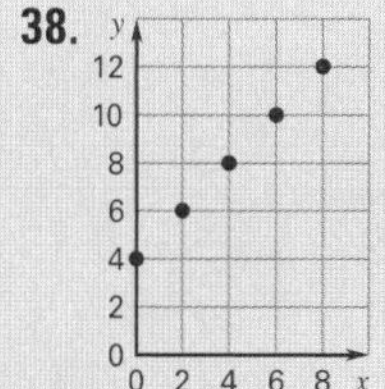

39.
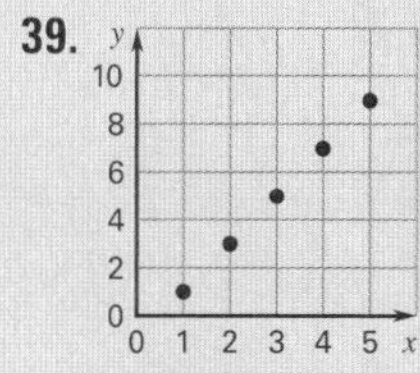

5 ASSESS AND RETEACH

Daily Homework Quiz

Transparency Available

1. Write the equation $15 = 5y - 4x$ so that y is a function of x. $y = \frac{4}{5}x + 3$
2. Solve $C = 2\pi r$ for r. $r = \frac{C}{2\pi}$
3. Solve $V = \frac{1}{3}Bh$ for B. $B = \frac{3V}{h}$
4. On a round-trip bicycle trip from Santa Barbara to Canada, Phil rode 2850 miles in 63 days. Find his average miles per day for the trip. Use the formula $d = rt$ where d is distance, r is rate, and t is time. Solve for r to find the rate in miles per day to the nearest mile. **about 45 miles per day**

 **Online Quiz**

Available at **classzone.com**

Diagnosis/Remediation

- Practice A, B, C in Chapter Resource Book
- Study Guide in Chapter Resource Book
- Practice Workbook
- @HomeTutor

Challenge

Additional challenge is available in the Chapter Resource Book.

Quiz

An easily-readable reduced copy of the quiz (with answers) on Lessons 3.7–3.8 from the Assessment Book can be found on p. 130E.

3. \$70. *Sample answer:* Use the proportion $\frac{7}{154} = \frac{x}{700}$ to find that you will need about 35 gallons of gas. Multiply 35 by \$2 per gallon.

4. Solve $Q = \frac{3}{r}$ for r to get $r = \frac{3}{Q}$; substitute $\frac{3}{Q}$ for r in the formula $d = 2r$ to get $d = \frac{6}{Q}$.

7. Multiply each side by 2 and divide each side by d_2 to get $d_1 = \frac{2A}{d_2}$.

Lessons 3.5–3.8

1. **MULTI-STEP PROBLEM** The table below shows the results of a survey in which students at a school were asked to name their favorite sport to watch on TV.

Sport	Students
Baseball	7
Basketball	6
Football	10
Other	8

   a. There are 1209 students at the school. Write a proportion that you can use to predict the number of students at the school who would name baseball as their favorite sport to watch on TV. *Sample answer:* $\frac{7}{31} = \frac{x}{1209}$

   b. Solve the proportion. **273 students**

2. **MULTI-STEP PROBLEM** The ratio of male students to female students in the freshman class at a high school is 4 : 5. There are 216 students in the freshman class.

   a. Find the ratio of female students to all students. $\frac{5}{9}$

   b. Use the ratio to find the number of female students in the freshman class. **120 females**

3. **SHORT RESPONSE** During a vacation, your family's car used 7 gallons of gasoline to travel 154 miles. Your family is planning another vacation in which you will travel 770 miles by car. If gasoline costs about \$2 per gallon, how much money should your family budget for gasoline for this vacation? *Explain* your reasoning. **See margin.**

4. **SHORT RESPONSE** In biology, the surface-area-to-volume quotient Q of a single spherical cell is given by the formula $Q = \frac{3}{r}$ where r is the radius of the cell. Suppose you need to calculate the diameters of cells given the surface-area-to-volume quotients of the cells. Given that $d = 2r$, explain how to write a formula for the diameter d of a cell given its surface-area-to-volume quotient. **See margin.**

5. **GRIDDED ANSWER** A basketball player made 60% of his free-throws during a season. The player made 84 free-throws. How many free-throw attempts did he have? **140 attempts**

6. **EXTENDED RESPONSE** When a real estate agent sells a house, the agent receives 6% of the sale price as a commission. The agent lists the sale price for a house as \$208,000.

   a. How much of a commission should the agent expect to receive for selling this house at full price? **\$12,480**

   b. The house actually sells for \$205,000. How much of a commission does the agent receive? **\$12,300**

   c. The real estate agent gives 10% of her commission to her assistant. What percent of the selling price does the agent's assistant receive? *Explain* your reasoning. **0.6%; find what number a is 10% of 6%; $a = 0.10 \cdot 0.06 = 0.006 = 0.6\%$.**

7. **SHORT RESPONSE** The area A of a rhombus is given by the formula $A = \frac{1}{2}d_1d_2$ where d_1 and d_2 are the lengths of the diagonals.

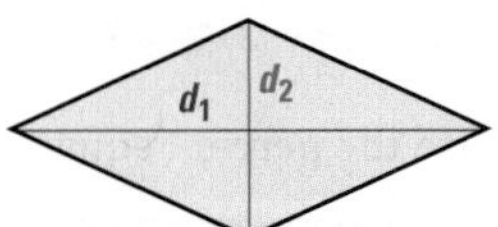

Suppose you need to find d_1 for different values of A and d_2. *Explain* how to rewrite the area formula to make it easier to find values for d_1. **See margin.**

8. **OPEN-ENDED** *Describe* how the dimensions of the rectangular garden below can be altered to increase the area of the garden by 25%. ***Sample answer:* Increase the length, 16 feet, by 4 feet.**

BIG IDEAS *For Your Notebook*

Big Idea 1

Solving Equations in One Variable

You can solve equations in one variable by adding, subtracting, multiplying by, or dividing by the same number on each side.

Property	Words	Algebra
Addition Property of Equality	Add the same number to each side.	If $x - a = b$, then $x - a + a = b + a$, or $x = b + a$.
Subtraction Property of Equality	Subtract the same number from each side.	If $x + a = b$, then $x + a - a = b - a$, or $x = b - a$.
Multiplication Property of Equality	Multiply each side by the same nonzero number.	If $\frac{x}{a} = b$ and $a \neq 0$, then $a \cdot \frac{x}{a} = a \cdot b$, or $x = ab$.
Division Property of Equality	Divide each side by the same nonzero number.	If $ax = b$ and $a \neq 0$, then $\frac{ax}{a} = \frac{b}{a}$, or $x = \frac{b}{a}$.

Big Idea 2

Solving Proportion and Percent Problems

When solving a proportion, you can take the cross products, then use properties of equality.

$\frac{x-3}{40} = \frac{4}{5}$ **Original proportion**

$5(x - 3) = 40 \cdot 4$ **Cross products property**

$5x - 15 = 160$ **Simplify.**

$5x = 175$ **Addition property of equality: Add 15 to each side.**

$x = 35$ **Division property of equality: Divide each side by 5.**

Big Idea 3

Rewriting Equations in Two or More Variables

If you have an equation in two or more variables, you can solve for one variable in terms of the others using properties of equality. For example, the formula for the perimeter P of a rectangle can be solved for the length ℓ.

$P = 2\ell + 2w$

w

ℓ

$P = 2\ell + 2w$ **Original formula**

$P - 2w = 2\ell$ **Subtraction property of equality: Subtract 2*w* from each side.**

$\frac{P - 2w}{2} = \ell$ **Division property of equality: Divide each side by 2.**

Additional Resources

The following resources are available to help review the materials in this chapter.

Chapter Resource Book

- Chapter Review Games and Activities
- Cumulative Practice, Ch. 1–3

Student Resources in Spanish

eWorkbook

@HomeTutor

Vocabulary Practice

Vocabulary practice is available at **classzone.com**

Extra Example 3.1
Solve $6x = -96$. **-16**

3 CHAPTER REVIEW

@HomeTutor
classzone.com
- Multi-Language Glossary
- Vocabulary practice

REVIEW KEY VOCABULARY

- inverse operations, *p. 134*
- equivalent equations, *p. 134*
- identity, *p. 156*
- ratio, *p. 162*
- proportion, *p. 163*
- cross product, *p. 168*
- scale drawing, *p. 170*
- scale model, *p. 170*
- scale, *p. 170*
- literal equation, *p. 184*

VOCABULARY EXERCISES

1. Copy and complete: A(n) __?__ is a two-dimensional drawing of an object in which the dimensions of the drawing are in proportion to the dimensions of the object. **scale drawing**
2. Copy and complete: When you perform the same inverse operation on each side of an equation, you produce a(n) __?__ equation. **equivalent**
3. *Explain* why the equation $2x + 8x = 3x + 7x$ is an identity.
If you collect like terms you get $10x = 10x$, so any value of x will make it true.
4. Copy and complete: In the proportion $\frac{7}{8} = \frac{28}{32}$, $7 \cdot 32$ and $8 \cdot 28$ are __?__. **cross products**
5. *Describe* the steps you would take to write the equation $6x - 2y = 16$ in function form. **Subtract $6x$ from each side, then divide each side by -2.**

REVIEW EXAMPLES AND EXERCISES

Use the review examples and exercises below to check your understanding of the concepts you have learned in each lesson of Chapter 3.

3.1 Solve One-Step Equations *pp. 134–140*

EXAMPLE

Solve $\frac{x}{5} = 14$.

$\frac{x}{5} = 14$	**Write original equation.**
$5 \cdot \frac{x}{5} = 5 \cdot 14$	**Multiply each side by 5.**
$x = 70$	**Simplify.**

EXERCISES

EXAMPLES 1, 2, 3, 4 and 5 on pp. 134–136 for Exs. 6–12

Solve the equation. Check your solution.

6. $x - 4 = 3$ **7**
7. $-8 + a = 5$ **13**
8. $4m = -84$ **-21**
9. $-5z = 75$ **-15**
10. $11 = \frac{r}{6}$ **66**
11. $-27 = \frac{3}{4}w$ **-36**
12. **PARKS** A rectangular city park has an area of 211,200 square feet. If the length of the park is 660 feet, what is the width of the park? **320 ft**

3.2 Solve Two-Step Equations

pp. 141–146

EXAMPLE

Solve $4x - 9 = 3$.

$4x - 9 = 3$	Write original equation.
$4x - 9 + 9 = 3 + 9$	Add 9 to each side.
$4x = 12$	Simplify.
$\frac{4x}{4} = \frac{12}{4}$	Divide each side by 4.
$x = 3$	Simplify.

EXERCISES

EXAMPLES 1 and 2 on pp. 141–142 for Exs. 13–18

Solve the equation. Check your solution.

13. $9b + 5 = 23$ **2**
14. $11 = 5y - 4$ **3**
15. $\frac{n}{3} - 4 = 2$ **18**
16. $\frac{3}{2}v + 2 = 20$ **12**
17. $3t + 9t = 60$ **5**
18. $-110 = -4c - 6c$ **11**

3.3 Solve Multi-Step Equations

pp. 148–153

EXAMPLE

Solve $5x - 2(4x + 3) = 9$.

$5x - 2(4x + 3) = 9$	Write original equation.
$5x - 8x - 6 = 9$	Distributive property
$-3x - 6 = 9$	Combine like terms.
$-3x = 15$	Add 6 to each side.
$x = -5$	Divide each side by -3.

EXERCISES

EXAMPLES 1, 2, 3 and 4 on pp. 148–149 for Exs. 19–28

Solve the equation. Check your solution.

19. $3w + 4w - 2 = 12$ **2**
20. $z + 5 - 4z = 8$ **−1**
21. $c + 2c - 5 - 5c = 7$ **−6**
22. $4y - (y - 4) = -20$ **−8**
23. $8a - 3(2a + 5) = 13$ **14**
24. $16h - 4(5h - 7) = 4$ **6**
25. $\frac{3}{2}(b + 1) = 3$ **1**
26. $\frac{4}{3}(2x - 1) = -12$ **−4**
27. $\frac{6}{5}(8k + 2) = -36$ **−4**

28. **FOOTBALL** You purchase 5 tickets to a football game from an Internet ticket agency. In addition to the cost per ticket, the agency charges a convenience charge of \$2.50 per ticket. You choose to pay for rush delivery, which costs \$15. The total cost of your order is \$352.50. What is the price per ticket not including the convenience charge? **\$65**

Extra Example 3.2

Solve $\frac{a}{3} - 8 = 4$. **36**

Extra Example 3.3

Solve $4b + 3(b - 2) = 15$. **3**

Extra Example 3.4

Solve the equation, if possible.

a. $6(w - 4) = -2(12 - 3w)$ **The equation is an identity.**

b. $4a + 3 = 4(a + 3)$ **The equation has no solution.**

Extra Example 3.5

You know you can buy 6 tickets to the county fair for $18. How many tickets can you buy for $51?
17 tickets

3 CHAPTER REVIEW

3.4 Solve Equations with Variables on Both Sides *pp. 154–159*

EXAMPLE

Solve the equation, if possible.

a. $-2(x - 5) = 7 - 2x$ — **Original equation**

$-2x + 10 = 7 - 2x$ — **Distributive property**

$-2x + 3 = -2x$ — **Subtract 7 from each side.**

▸ The equation $-2x + 3 = -2x$ is not true because the number $-2x$ cannot be equal to 3 more than itself. So, the equation has no solution.

b. $5(3 - 2x) = -(10x - 15)$ — **Original equation**

$15 - 10x = -10x + 15$ — **Distributive property**

$15 - 10x = 15 - 10x$ — **Rearrange terms.**

▸ The statement $15 - 10x = 15 - 10x$ is true for all values of x. So, the equation is an identity.

EXERCISES

EXAMPLES 1, 2, and 4 on pp. 154–156 for Exs. 29–37

Solve the equation, if possible.

29. $-3z - 1 = 8 - 3z$ **no solution**

30. $16 - 2m = 5m + 9$ **1**

31 $2.9w + 5 = 4.7w - 7.6$ **7**

32. $2y + 11.4 = 2.6 - 0.2y$ **−4**

33. $4(x - 3) = -2(6 - 2x)$ **identity**

34. $6(2a + 10) = 5(a + 5)$ **−5**

35. $\frac{1}{12}(48 + 24b) = 2(17 - 4b)$ **3**

36. $1.5(n + 20) = 0.5(3n + 60)$ **identity**

37. **GEOMETRY** Refer to the square shown.

a. Find the value of x. **4**

b. Find the perimeter of the square. **116**

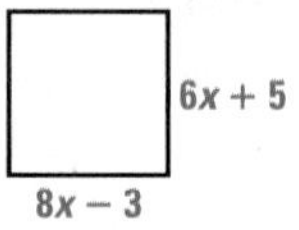

3.5 Write Ratios and Proportions *pp. 162–167*

EXAMPLE

You know that 5 pizzas will feed 20 people. How many pizzas do you need to order to feed 88 people?

$\frac{5}{20} = \frac{x}{88}$ ← number of pizzas / ← number of people

$88 \cdot \frac{5}{20} = 88 \cdot \frac{x}{88}$ — **Multiply each side by 88.**

$22 = x$ — **Simplify.**

▸ You need to order 22 pizzas.

EXERCISES

EXAMPLES 2 and 3 on pp. 163–164 for Exs. 38–44

Solve the proportion. Check your solution.

38. $\frac{56}{16} = \frac{x}{2}$ **7**

39. $\frac{y}{9} = \frac{25}{15}$ **15**

40. $\frac{2}{7} = \frac{m}{91}$ **26**

41. $\frac{5z}{3} = \frac{105}{6}$ **10.5**

42. $\frac{9}{4} = \frac{3a}{20}$ **15**

43. $\frac{c+2}{45} = \frac{8}{5}$ **70**

44. **PAINTING** The label on a can of paint states that one gallon of the paint will cover 560 square feet. How many gallons of that paint are needed to cover 1400 square feet? **2.5 gal**

3.6 Solve Proportions Using Cross Products

pp. 168–173

EXAMPLE

Solve the proportion $\frac{3}{10} = \frac{12}{x}$.

$\frac{3}{10} = \frac{12}{x}$	Write original proportion.
$3 \cdot x = 10 \cdot 12$	Cross products property
$3x = 120$	Simplify.
$x = 40$	Divide each side by 3.

EXAMPLE

A map has a scale of 1 cm : 15 km. The distance between two cities on the map is 7.2 centimeters. Estimate the actual distance between the cites.

$\frac{1}{15} = \frac{7.2}{d}$ ← centimeters / ← kilometers

$1 \cdot d = 15 \cdot 7.2$	Cross products property
$d = 108$	Simplify.

▶ The distance between the two cities is about 108 kilometers.

EXERCISES

EXAMPLES 1, 3, and 4 on pp. 168–170 for Exs. 45–52

Solve the proportion. Check your solution.

45. $\frac{5}{7} = \frac{20}{r}$ **28**

46. $\frac{6}{z} = \frac{12}{5}$ **2.5**

47. $\frac{126}{56} = \frac{9}{4b}$ **1**

48. $\frac{10}{3m} = \frac{-5}{6}$ **−4**

49. $\frac{n+8}{5n-2} = \frac{3}{8}$ **10**

50. $\frac{5-c}{3} = \frac{2c+2}{-4}$ **−13**

51. **TYPING RATES** A student can type 65 words in 2 minutes. How many words can the student type in 20 minutes? **650 words**

52. **MAPS** A map has a scale of 1 cm : 12 km. The distance between two cities on the map is 6.8 centimeters. Estimate the actual distance between the cities. **about 81.6 km**

Extra Examples 3.6

1. Solve the proportion $\frac{3}{5} = \frac{s}{4}$. **2.4**

2. A map has a scale of 1 cm : 8 km. The distance between 2 cities on the map is 6.5 centimeters. Estimate the actual distance between the cities. **The distance between the two cities is about 52 kilometers.**

Extra Example 3.7

What percent of 45 is 18? **40%**

Extra Example 3.8

Write $ax + by = c$ so that y is a function of x. $y = \frac{c - ax}{b}$ or $y = -\frac{a}{b}x + \frac{c}{b}$

3 CHAPTER REVIEW

3.7 Solve Percent Problems

pp. 176–181

EXAMPLE

42 is 40% of what number?

$a = p\% \cdot b$	**Write percent equation.**
$42 = 40\% \cdot b$	**Substitute 42 for a and 40 for p.**
$42 = 0.4 \cdot b$	**Write percent as decimal.**
$105 = b$	**Divide each side by 0.4.**

▸ 42 is 40% of 105.

EXERCISES

EXAMPLES 2, 3, 4, and 5 on pp. 177–179 for Exs. 53–57

Use the percent equation to answer the question.

53. What number is 30% of 55? **16.5**

54. 117 is 78% of what number? **150**

55. What percent of 56 is 21? **37.5%**

56. What percent of 60 is 18? **30%**

57. CONCERTS There were 7500 tickets sold for a concert, 20% of which were general admission tickets. How many general admission tickets were sold? **1500 general admission tickets**

3.8 Rewrite Equations and Formulas

pp. 184–189

EXAMPLE

Write $5x + 4y - 7 = 5$ so that y is a function of x.

$5x + 4y - 7 = 5$	**Write original equation.**
$5x + 4y = 12$	**Add 7 to each side.**
$4y = 12 - 5x$	**Subtract $5x$ from each side.**
$y = 3 - \frac{5}{4}x$	**Divide each side by 4.**

EXERCISES

EXAMPLES 2 and 3 on p. 185 for Exs. 58–61

Write the equation so that y is a function of x.

58. $x + 7y = 0$ $y = \frac{-x}{7}$

59. $3x = 2y - 18$ $y = \frac{3}{2}x + 9$

60. $4y - x = 20 - y$ $y = \frac{1}{5}x + 4$

61. AQUARIUMS A pet store sells aquariums that are rectangular prisms. The volume V of an aquarium is given by the formula $V = \ell wh$ where ℓ is the length, w is the width, and h is the height.

a. Solve the formula for h. $h = \frac{V}{\ell w}$

b. Use the rewritten formula to find the height of the aquarium shown, which has a volume of 5850 cubic inches. **15 in.**

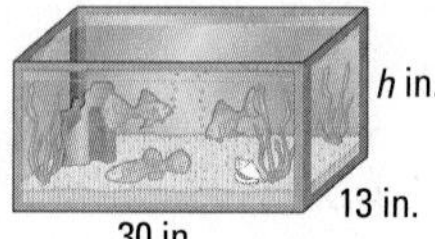

3 CHAPTER TEST

Solve the equation. Check your solution.

1. $5 + r = -19$ **−24**
2. $z - 8 = -12$ **−4**
3. $-11x = -77$ **7**
4. $\frac{a}{9} = 6$ **54**
5. $15q - 17 = 13$ **2**
6. $3y + 2 = 26$ **8**
7. $\frac{b}{4} + 5 = 14$ **36**
8. $\frac{m}{10} - 6 = 20$ **260**
9. $6j + 5j = 33$ **3**
10. $4k - 9k = 10$ **−2**
11. $14c - 8c + 7 = 37$ **5**
12. $4w - 21 + 5w = 51$ **8**
13. $-19.4 - 15d + 22d = 4.4$ **3.4**
14. $-12h + 39 = -4h - 17$ **7**
15. $-5.7v - 44.2 = -8.3v$ **17**
16. $-6.5t + 15 = -9.7t + 43.8$ **9**
17. $3(3n + 4) = 54 + 6n$ **14**
18. $\frac{1}{3}(24p - 66) = 3p + 43$ **13**

Solve the proportion. Check your solution.

19. $\frac{3}{4} = \frac{z}{16}$ **12**
20. $\frac{72}{45} = \frac{8}{w}$ **5**
21. $\frac{k}{9} = \frac{63}{81}$ **7**
22. $\frac{-5n}{4} = \frac{15}{2}$ **−6**
23. $\frac{34}{6} = \frac{2x + 1}{3}$ **8**
24. $\frac{-4a - 1}{-10a} = \frac{3}{8}$ **−4**

Use the percent equation to answer the question.

25. What percent of 84 is 21? **25%**
26. What percent of 124 is 93? **75%**
27. What number is 15% of 64? **9.6**
28. What number is 44% of 24.5? **10.78**
29. 90 is what percent of 250? **36%**
30. 79.8 is what percent of 95? **84%**

Write the equation so that *y* is a function of *x*.

31. $8x + y = 14$ **$y = 14 - 8x$**
32. $-9x + 3y = 18$ **$y = 3x + 6$**
33. $4x = -2y + 26$ **$13 - 2x = y$**

34. **MOVIES** The ticket prices at a movie theater are shown in the table. A family purchases tickets for 2 adults and 3 children, and the family purchases 3 boxes of popcorn of the same size. The family spent a total of $40.25. How much did each box of popcorn cost? **$2.25**

Ticket	Price
Adults	$8.50
Children	$5.50

35. **ICE SKATING** To become a member of an ice skating rink, you have to pay a $30 membership fee. The cost of admission to the rink is $5 for members and $7 for nonmembers. After how many visits to the rink is the total cost for members, including the membership fee, the same as the total cost for nonmembers? **15 visits**

36. **SCALE DRAWING** You are making a scale drawing of your classroom using the scale 1 inch : 3 feet. The floor of your classroom is a rectangle with a length of 21 feet and a width of 18 feet. What should the length and width of the floor in your drawing be? **7 in., 6 in.**

37. **SURVEYS** A survey asks high school seniors whether they would be willing to pay $5 for their yearbook. Out of the 225 seniors surveyed, 198 said "yes." What percent of the seniors said "yes"? **88%**

Additional Resources

Assessment Book

- Chapter Test, Levels A, B, C
- Standardized Chapter Test
- SAT/ACT Chapter Test
- Alternative Assessment

Test Generator

Chapter Test

Easily-readable reduced copies (with answers) of Chapter Test B, the Standardized Chapter Test, and the Alternative Assessment from the Assessment Book can be found on pp. 130E–130F.

Test-Taking Strategy

When students are unsure about how to solve a problem, encourage them to use estimation and number sense to eliminate some of the choices. Estimation may allow them to identify some choices that are not close to their estimate. Number sense can help them determine the possible range of answers, allowing them to eliminate any answers that are outside of this range. Point out that sometimes estimation and number sense will even eliminate all but one possible answer.

Avoiding Common Errors

When taking a standardized test, students may encounter questions that they cannot answer quickly, such as Problem 1. If students use the strategy of bypassing such questions, they may forget to return to some or all of them after reaching the end of the test. Remind students that if they bypass questions, they must have some method or list to remind themselves to return to each one.

Avoiding Common Errors

When students solve equations, recommend that they check their solutions using substitution in the original equation. This will help them avoid choosing answers that result from calculation errors.

Teaching Strategy

After students complete Exercises 2 and 3, you may want to use these exercises to demonstrate the advantages of using estimation and number sense to eliminate choices.

MULTIPLE CHOICE QUESTIONS

If you have difficulty solving a multiple choice problem directly, you may be able to use another approach to eliminate incorrect answer choices and obtain the correct answer.

PROBLEM 1

Sid's car gets 34 miles per gallon when driven on the highway and 26 miles per gallon when driven in the city. If Sid drove 414 miles on 13 gallons of gas, how many highway miles and how many city miles did Sid drive?

Ⓐ 91 highway miles, 323 city miles

Ⓑ 182 highway miles, 232 city miles

Ⓒ 232 highway miles, 182 city miles

Ⓓ 323 highway miles, 91 city miles

METHOD 1

SOLVE DIRECTLY Write and solve an equation for the situation.

STEP 1 **Write** an equation. Let x represent the amount of gas (in gallons) used for highway driving. Then $13 - x$ represents the amount of gas used for city driving.

$$414 = 34x + 26(13 - x)$$

STEP 2 **Solve** the equation.

$$414 = 34x + 338 - 26x$$

$$414 = 8x + 338$$

$$76 = 8x$$

$$9.5 = x$$

STEP 3 **Calculate** the number of highway miles driven.

$$34(9.5) = 323$$

STEP 4 **Calculate** the number of city miles driven.

$$26(13 - 9.5) = 91$$

Sid drove 323 highway miles and 91 city miles.

The correct answer is D. Ⓐ Ⓑ Ⓒ Ⓓ

METHOD 2

ELIMINATE CHOICES Another method is to consider the extremes to eliminate incorrect answer choices.

STEP 1 **Consider** driving all highway miles and all city miles.

All highway: $13 \text{ gal} \cdot \frac{34 \text{ mi}}{1 \text{ gal}} = 442 \text{ mi}$

All city: $13 \text{ gal} \cdot \frac{26 \text{ mi}}{1 \text{ gal}} = 338 \text{ mi}$

Because 414 is closer to 442 than to 338, you know that more highway miles were driven than city miles. So, you can eliminate choices A and B.

STEP 2 **Calculate** the gallons of gas that would be used for the remaining choices.

Choice C: $232 \text{ mi} \cdot \frac{1 \text{ gal}}{34 \text{ mi}} \approx 6.8 \text{ gal}$

$182 \text{ mi} \cdot \frac{1 \text{ gal}}{26 \text{ mi}} = 7 \text{ gal}$

Choice D: $323 \text{ mi} \cdot \frac{1 \text{ gal}}{34 \text{ mi}} = 9.5 \text{ gal}$

$91 \text{ mi} \cdot \frac{1 \text{ gal}}{26 \text{ mi}} = 3.5 \text{ gal}$

In choice D, the total number of gallons of gas is 13.

The correct answer is D. Ⓐ Ⓑ Ⓒ Ⓓ

PROBLEM 2

What is the value of x in the proportion $\frac{3}{2x - 10} = \frac{12}{x + 9}$?

Ⓐ 4 Ⓑ 6 Ⓒ 7 Ⓓ 8

METHOD 1

SOLVE DIRECTLY Find the value of x by using the cross products property to solve the proportion.

$$\frac{3}{2x - 10} = \frac{12}{x + 9}$$

$$3(x + 9) = (2x - 10) \cdot 12$$

$$3x + 27 = 24x - 120$$

$$147 = 21x$$

$$7 = x$$

The correct answer is C. Ⓐ Ⓑ Ⓒ Ⓓ

METHOD 2

ELIMINATE CHOICES Substitute each answer choice for x in the proportion and simplify.

Choice A: $\frac{3}{2(4) - 10} \stackrel{?}{=} \frac{12}{4 + 9}$

$\frac{3}{-2} = \frac{12}{13}$ ✗

Choice B: $\frac{3}{2(6) - 10} \stackrel{?}{=} \frac{12}{6 + 9}$

$\frac{3}{2} = \frac{4}{5}$ ✗

Choice C: $\frac{3}{2(7) - 10} \stackrel{?}{=} \frac{12}{7 + 9}$

$\frac{3}{4} = \frac{3}{4}$ ✓

The correct answer is C. Ⓐ Ⓑ Ⓒ Ⓓ

PRACTICE

Explain why you can eliminate the highlighted answer choice.

1. What is the solution of the equation $5(x + 13) = 8(4 + x)$?

   Ⓐ −11 Ⓑ −4 Ⓒ ✗ 0 Ⓓ 11

2. 45 is 80% of what number?

   Ⓐ ✗ 36 Ⓑ 56.25 Ⓒ 60 Ⓓ 64.5

3. A grocery store sells apples by the pound. A 3 pound bag of apples costs \$2.99. About how much does a 5 pound bag of apples cost?

   Ⓐ \$3.24 Ⓑ \$3.45 Ⓒ \$4.98 Ⓓ ✗ \$5.98

4. The surface area S of a cylinder is given by the formula $S = 2\pi rh + 2\pi r^2$ where r is the radius and h is the height of the cylinder. Which of the given formulas is *not* equivalent to the original formula?

   Ⓐ $S = 2\pi r(h + r)$ Ⓑ $h = 2\pi rS + 2\pi r^2$

   Ⓒ ✗ $h = \frac{S - 2\pi r^2}{2\pi r}$ Ⓓ $h = \frac{S}{2\pi r} - r$

Answers

1. Substituting 0 for x into the equation gives 65 = 32, which is not true.
2. 36 is less than 45, because 45 is only 80% of the number, the number must be greater than 45.
3. \$5.98 is two times \$2.99. Because 5 pounds is less than two times 3 pounds, the cost of the 5 pound bag should be less than two times the cost of the 3 pound bag.
4. Subtract $2\pi r^2$ from both sides of $S = 2\pi rh + 2\pi r^2$, and then divide both sides by $2\pi r$. The result is the formula given in answer C.

Answers
1. A
2. D
3. B
4. B
5. C
6. B
7. A
8. C
9. B
10. D
11. 1.9 ft
12. 13
13. 2.5
14. 1200 prints
15a. $24w + 28(5 - w) = 132$, $w = 2$, 2 cans of white paint and 3 cans of blue paint
15b. \$4; Kendra would have bought 2 cans of blue paint and 3 cans of white paint for a total of 2(\$28) + 3(\$24) = \$128. The difference in cost is \$132 − \$128 = \$4.

MULTIPLE CHOICE

1. How many solutions does the equation $3(x - 3) = 3x - 6$ have?

Ⓐ None Ⓑ 1
Ⓒ 2 Ⓓ Infinitely many

2. A karate studio offers a 6 week session for \$175. How much would you expect to pay for a 9 week session?

Ⓐ \$117 Ⓑ \$200
Ⓒ \$229 Ⓓ \$262.50

3. Andrew decides to get cable TV for \$43 per month. Doug buys a satellite dish for \$104 and pays \$30 per month for satellite TV. After how many months will Andrew and Doug have paid the same amount for their TV services?

Ⓐ 7 Ⓑ 8
Ⓒ 9 Ⓓ 10

4. The rates for using a swimming facility are given below. After how many visits will a family of 4 save money by having a membership rather than paying for all 4 family members for each visit?

Admission Prices	
One-day visit	\$3 per person
Family membership (unlimited visits)	\$150

Ⓐ 12 Ⓑ 13
Ⓒ 38 Ⓓ 50

5. The record for the longest distance and longest time ever flown by a model airplane was set in 2003 by Maynard Hill. The airplane flew 1888 miles from Canada to Ireland in 38 hours and 53 minutes. What was the plane's average speed?

Ⓐ About 36 mi/h Ⓑ About 45 mi/h
Ⓒ About 49 mi/h Ⓓ About 71,744 mi/h

6. The perimeter of the triangle shown is 16.5 inches. What is the length of the shortest side?

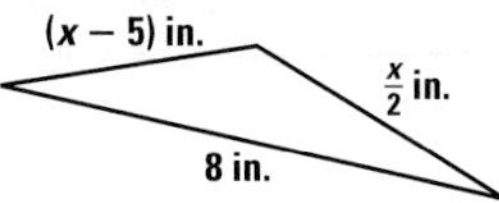

Ⓐ 3.5 in. Ⓑ 4 in.
Ⓒ 4.5 in. Ⓓ 9 in.

7. Jeanie completed a 27 mile duathlon (a race that is a combination of running and biking) in exactly 2 hours. She ran an average speed of 8.5 miles per hour and biked an average speed of 16 miles per hour. For how long did Jeanie bike during the race?

Ⓐ 1 hour 20 minutes
Ⓑ 1 hour 15 minutes
Ⓒ 45 minutes
Ⓓ 40 minutes

8. A model of the Gateway Arch in St. Louis, Missouri, was built using a scale of 1 ft : 500 ft. The model is 1.26 feet tall. What is the actual height of the Gateway Arch?

Ⓐ 75.6 ft Ⓑ 396.8 ft
Ⓒ 630 ft Ⓓ 7560 ft

9. A mountain biking park has a total of 48 trails, 37.5% of which are beginner trails. The rest are divided evenly between intermediate and expert trails. How many of each kind of trail is there?

Ⓐ 12 beginner, 18 intermediate, 18 expert
Ⓑ 18 beginner, 15 intermediate, 15 expert
Ⓒ 18 beginner, 12 intermediate, 18 expert
Ⓓ 30 beginner, 9 intermediate, 9 expert

10. What percent of 256 is 140.8?

Ⓐ 45% Ⓑ 50%
Ⓒ 52.5% Ⓓ 55%

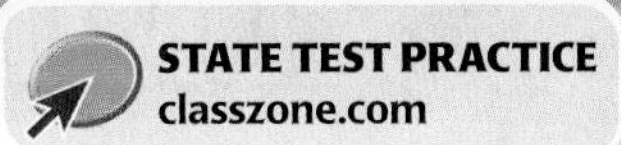

GRIDDED ANSWER

11. The circumference of a circle is 12 feet. What is the radius (in feet) of the circle? Round your answer to the nearest tenth.

12. What is the value of x in the equation $75 = 15x - 6(x + 7)$?

13. The perimeter of the rectangle shown is 41 centimeters. What is the value of x?

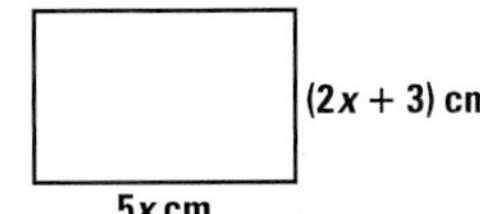

14. Chris pays $.29 for each digital photo he has printed. Debbie buys a photo printer for $180. It costs $.14 per photo for ink and paper to print a photo using the printer. After how many prints will Chris and Debbie have paid the same amount?

SHORT RESPONSE

15. Kendra is painting her dining room white and her living room blue. She spends a total of $132 on 5 cans of paint. The white paint costs $24 per can, and the blue paint costs $28 per can.

    a. Write and solve an equation to find the number of cans of each color paint that Kendra bought.

    b. How much would Kendra have saved by switching the colors of the dining room and living room? *Explain.*

16. Kim and Sandy are each knitting a scarf. Kim can knit 3 rows in 5 minutes. Sandy can knit 4 rows in 6 minutes. They start knitting at the same time and do not take any breaks. Kim wants her scarf to be 84 rows long. Sandy wants her scarf to be 88 rows long. Who will finish her scarf first? *Explain.*

EXTENDED RESPONSE

17. You are shopping for tools. You find two stores at which the regular prices of the tools are the same. Store A is currently offering $30 off any purchase of $100 or more. Store B is currently offering 12% off any purchase.

    a. Compare the costs of buying $200 worth of tools from each store.

    b. Compare the costs of buying $300 worth of tools from each store.

    c. Let x be the regular price (in dollars) of your purchase, and assume that x is greater than 100. Write an equation you could use to find the value of x for which the costs of the tools after the discounts are the same. *Explain* how you wrote the equation.

    d. Solve the equation from part (c). How can the solution help you to decide from which store you should buy the tools? *Explain.*

18. The circle graph shows the results of a survey that asked 225 randomly selected people how they get driving directions.

    a. How many people said that they get directions from the Internet?

    b. Suppose 15 more people were surveyed, and all 15 said that they get directions from the Internet. Calculate the new percent for the "From the Internet" category. *Explain* how you found your answer.

    c. Instead of 15 more people, suppose x more people are surveyed and they all said that they get directions from the Internet. What value of x would make the percent for the "From the Internet" category be 70%? Your response should include a proportion and an explanation of how you used the proportion to find your answer.

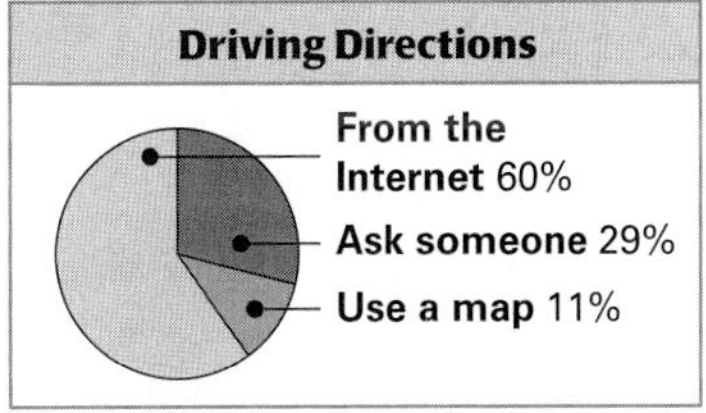

16. Sandy; Sandy knits 40 rows per hour, or $\frac{2}{3}$ row per minute. It takes her $88 \div \frac{2}{3} = 132$ minutes to knit 88 rows. Kim knits 36 rows per hour, or $\frac{3}{5}$ row per minute. It takes her $84 \div \frac{3}{5} = 140$ minutes to knit 84 rows. Sandy finishes $140 - 132 = 8$ minutes ahead of Kim.

17a. The cost of buying from the website, $109.99, is about $4 more than the cost of buying from the store, $106.

17b. The cost of buying from the website, $209.99, is about $2 less than the cost of buying from the store, $212.

17c. $x + 9.99 = x + 0.06x$; write an expression in terms of x for each cost and then set the two cost expressions equal to each other.

17d. 166.5; the solution $x = 166.5$ means that if you want to buy $166.50 worth of tools, the cost will be the same whether you buy them from the website or from the store. Combining this information with the results of parts (a) and (b), we know that if you are buying less than $166.50 worth of tools it is better to buy them from the store, and if you are buying more than $166.50 worth of tools it is better to buy them from the website.

18a. 135 people

18b. 62.5%; from part (a), 135 out of 225 people get directions from the Internet. The new number of people who get directions from the Internet is $135 + 15 = 150$ people, and the new total number of people surveyed is $225 + 15 = 240$ people. The new percent of people who get directions from the Internet is $\frac{150}{240} = 0.625$, or 62.5%.

18c. 75 people; following the method described in part (b), write the proportion $\frac{135 + x}{225 + x} = \frac{70}{100}$. Solve the proportion for x, the number of additional people surveyed.

3 CUMULATIVE REVIEW Chapters 1–3

Additional Resources

A Cumulative Review for each of Chapters 1–3 is available in the *Chapter Resource Book.*

Evaluate the expression. *(p. 8)*

1. $3 \cdot 4^2 - 21$ **27**
2. $4 + 4^2 \div 8$ **6**
3. $77 \div (11 - 4)$ **11**
4. $\frac{1}{2}(8 \cdot 6) - 4^2$ **8**
5. $3[50 - (13 - 7)^2]$ **42**
6. $\frac{3}{4}[(6 + 4)^2 - 40]$ **45**

Check whether the given number is a solution of the equation or inequality. *(p. 21)*

7. $7t - 11 = 52; 9$ **solution**
8. $3b - 2 = 2b + 3; 4$ **not a solution**
9. $8z - 11 > 21; 4$ **not a solution**
10. $5a + 3 \le 13; 2$ **solution**
11. $5 - y \ge 5; 3$ **not a solution**
12. $8x - 15 < 8; 7$ **not a solution**

Find the sum or difference.

13. $-2\frac{1}{6} + \left(-4\frac{2}{3}\right)$ *(p. 74)* **$-6\frac{5}{6}$**
14. $2.5 - (-2.05)$ *(p. 80)* **4.55**
15. $-24.6 - (-5.5)$ *(p. 80)* **−19.1**

Find the product or quotient.

16. $\frac{5}{2}(-8)(-5)$ *(p. 88)* **100**
17. $9 \div \left(-\frac{3}{7}\right)$ *(p. 103)* **−21**
18. $-\frac{7}{8} \div \frac{1}{2}$ *(p. 103)* **$-1\frac{3}{4}$**

Evaluate the expression for the given value of the variable(s).

19. $\frac{32}{w} - 2$ when $w = 4$ *(p. 8)* **6**
20. $7 + 3m^2 - 8m$ when $m = 5$ *(p. 8)* **42**
21. $\frac{5y}{32 - y^3}$ when $y = 3$ *(p. 8)* **3**
22. $5.15 + (-h) + 6.6$ when $h = 4.3$ *(p. 74)* **7.45**
23. $17.4 - |-p|$ when $p = 3.5$ *(p. 80)* **13.9**
24. $k^2 - 12.2k$ when $k = -1.6$ *(p. 88)* **22.08**
25. $8.3x - (-y)$ when $x = 6$ and $y = 9$ *(p. 88)* **58.8**
26. $\frac{y}{5x - y}$ when $x = 2$ and $y = 4$ *(p. 103)* **$\frac{2}{3}$**

Solve the equation. Check your solution.

27. $m + 16 = 5$ *(p. 134)* **−11**
28. $-4 = \frac{w}{7}$ *(p. 134)* **−28**
29. $5 + 3x = 23$ *(p. 141)* **6**
30. $\frac{a}{3} - 4 = 29$ *(p. 141)* **99**
31. $-4 = -2b - 18 + 5b$ *(p. 148)* **$4\frac{2}{3}$**
32. $\frac{3}{8}(16n + 48) = 72$ *(p. 148)* **9**
33. $-8z + 18 = 2(2z - 9)$ *(p. 154)* **3**
34. $(15c + 30) = \frac{1}{3}(102 - 12c)$ *(p. 154)* **$\frac{4}{19}$**

Solve the proportion. *(p. 168)*

35. $\frac{6}{d} = \frac{12}{17}$ **8.5**
36. $\frac{4}{7} = \frac{20}{m}$ **35**
37. $\frac{1}{9} = \frac{5}{3x}$ **15**
38. $\frac{3}{6h} = \frac{12}{72}$ **3**
39. $\frac{2}{11} = \frac{4}{t - 1}$ **23**
40. $\frac{12}{a + 1} = \frac{132}{35}$ **$2\frac{2}{11}$**
41. $\frac{w + 2}{8} = \frac{w}{3}$ **1.2**
42. $\frac{4}{9} = \frac{z}{z + 10}$ **8**

43. GARDENS You want to put edging around a rectangular flower garden that is 15 feet long and 12 feet wide. The edging comes in 3 foot pieces, as shown. How many pieces of edging do you need to buy? *(p. 28)* **18 pieces**

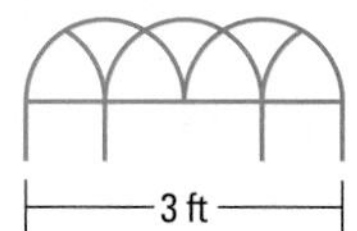

44. MUSIC The table shows the amount of time m (in hours per person per year) that adults listened to recorded music as a function of the time t (in years) since 1996. Graph the function. *(p. 43)* **See margin.**

Years since 1996, t	0	1	2	3	4	5
Hours listening to music, m	292	270	283	289	263	250

44.

45. STOCKS The daily change in the price of a share of stock is the difference of the price of a share when trading closes and the price of a share when trading opened earlier that day. The table shows the prices of a share of stock during a 5 day period. Find the change in price for each day. *(p. 80)* **−$.34; −$.45; −$.25; $1.02; $.08**

Day	1	2	3	4	5
Opening price (dollars)	39.16	38.82	38.37	38.12	39.14
Closing price (dollars)	38.82	38.37	38.12	39.14	39.22

46. CRAFTS You want to make a square mirror by applying silver leaf to a piece of glass. You have enough silver leaf to cover 854 square inches. Determine the side length of the square piece of glass you need to have cut for this project. Round your answer to the nearest inch. *(p. 110)* **29 in.**

47. BANQUETS The senior class at your high school has its prom at a banquet facility. The banquet facility charges $15.95 per person for a dinner buffet and $400 to rent the banquet hall for an evening. The class paid the banquet facility a total of $2633 for the dinner buffet and use of the banquet hall. How many people attended the prom? *(p. 141)* **140 people**

48. TELEVISIONS The ratio of the length to the width of two different television screens is shown. The width of each screen is 16.2 inches. Find the length of each screen. *(p. 162)* **21.6 in., 28.8 in.**

Standard

Wide screen

49. BASKETBALL The circle graph shows the positions of the 20 players on a basketball team. *(p. 176)*

a. How many players on the team play center? **2 players**

b. How many players on the team play guard? **7 players**

c. How many players on the team play forward? **11 players**

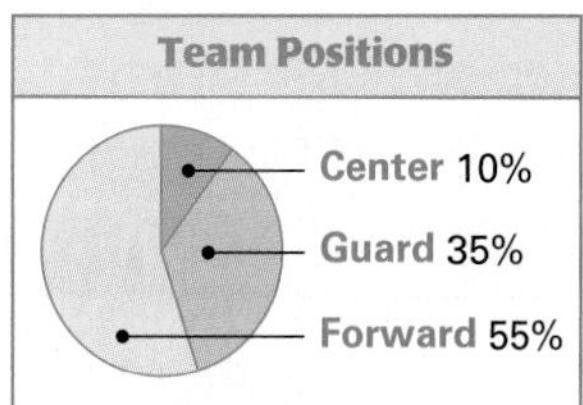

203

4 Pacing Guide

Chapter 4: Graphing Linear Equations and Functions

Chapter Table of Contents

PACING GUIDES

 ***Easy Planner***

Regular Schedule (50-minute classes)

DAY 1	DAY 2	DAY 3	DAY 4	DAY 5	DAY 6
Lesson 4.1 Extension 4.1	Lesson 4.2	Lesson 4.2 (cont.) Graphing Calculator Activity 4.2 Extension 4.2	Lesson 4.3 Mixed Review of Problem Solving	Quiz for Lessons 4.1–4.3 Investigating Algebra Activity 4.4 Lesson 4.4	Lesson 4.4 (cont.)
DAY 7	**DAY 8**	**DAY 9**	**DAY 10**	**DAY 11**	**DAY 12**
Investigating Algebra Activity 4.5 Lesson 4.5 Extension 4.5	Quiz for Lessons 4.4–4.5 Lesson 4.6	Lesson 4.7	Lesson 4.7 (cont.) Mixed Review of Problem Solving	Quiz for Lessons 4.6–4.7 Chapter Review	Chapter Test

Block Schedule (90-minute classes)

DAY 1	DAY 2	DAY 3	DAY 4	DAY 5	DAY 6
Lesson 4.1 Extension 4.1 Lesson 4.2	Lesson 4.2 (cont.) Graphing Calculator Activity 4.2 Extension 4.2 Lesson 4.3 Mixed Review of Problem Solving	Quiz for Lessons 4.1–4.3 Investigating Algebra Activity 4.4 Lesson 4.4	Investigating Algebra Activity 4.5 Lesson 4.5 Extension 4.5 Quiz for Lessons 4.4–4.5 Lesson 4.6	Lesson 4.7 Mixed Review of Problem Solving	Quiz for Lessons 4.6–4.7 Chapter Review Chapter Test

RESOURCE OPTIONS

Chapter/Lesson Resources

Chapter Resource Book
- Parents as Partners
- Teaching Guide/Lesson Plan
- Activity Masters
- Practice (3 levels)
- Study Guide
- Quick Catch-Up for Absent Students
- Problem Solving/Application
- Challenge Practice
- Chapter Review Games and Activities
- Project with Rubric
- Cumulative Review

Notetaking Guide
- Student Workbook and Teacher's Edition

Practice Workbook

Worked-Out Solution Key

Chapter Transparency Book
- Warm-Up Exercises/Daily Homework Quiz
- Notetaking Guide Transparencies
- Homework Answer Transparencies

Teacher Tools Transparencies

Assessment

Assessment Book
- Quizzes
- Chapter Tests (3 levels)
- Standardized and SAT/ACT Chapter Tests
- Alternative Assessments
- Cumulative Tests

Benchmark Tests
- Benchmark Tests, correlated to Remediation Book
- Pre-Course, Mid-Year, and End-of-Year Tests
- Chapter Tests

Spanish Assessment Book

Differentiated Instruction

Differentiated Instruction Resources
- Strategies for Reading Mathematics
- Differentiated Instruction Lesson Notes
- English Learner Lesson Notes
- Inclusion Lesson Notes
- Teaching Strategies with Sample Worksheets
- Tips for New Teachers/Math Background Notes
- Teacher Survival Activities/Bulletin Board Ideas

Student Resources in Spanish

Spanish Study Guide

Remediation Book

Skills Readiness (available on Easy Planner)
- Diagnostic Assessment
- Skill Instruction and Alternative Teaching Strategies
- Skill Practice and Enrichment Masters

Pre-AP Resources
- Pacing and Assignment Guide
- Best Practices
- Copymasters

Technology Resources

Plan	***Easy Planner***
Teach	***Video Tutor*** ***Activity Generator*** ***Power Presentations*** ***Animated Algebra***
Assess	***Test Generator*** ***ML Assessment System***
Reteach	***@HomeTutor***
Online Resources	***Classzone.com*** ***eEdition*** ***eWorkbook***

Video Tutor

Technology Highlights for Each Lesson

 **Easy Planner**

Easy access to the Teacher's Edition and all teaching resources. Includes a search feature to locate the materials you need.

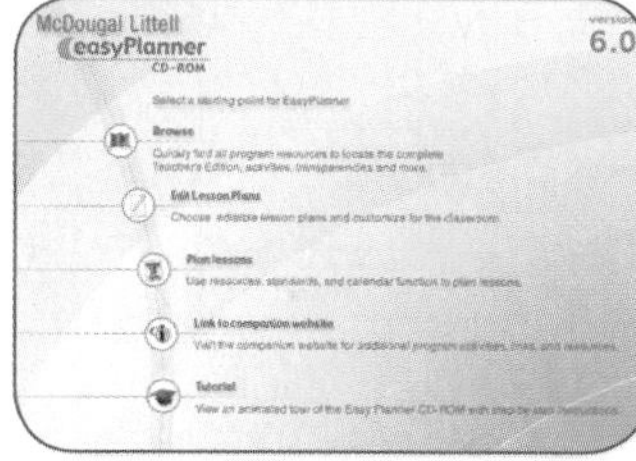

 **Activity Generator**

Leveled, editable activities allow all students to explore a lesson's concepts. Includes teacher notes and closure questions.

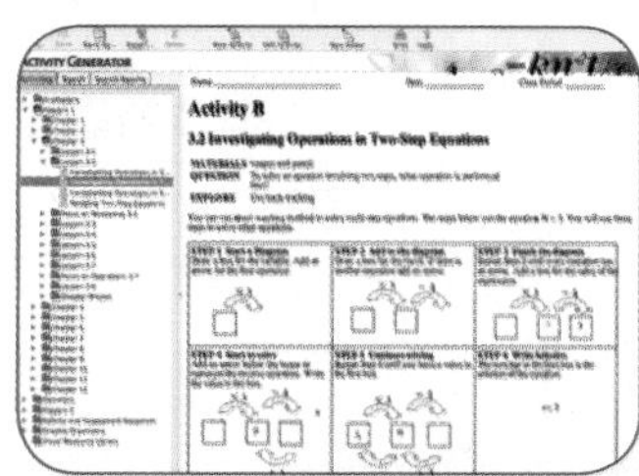

Interactive tutorials provide visually engaging alternative opportunities to learn concepts and master skills.

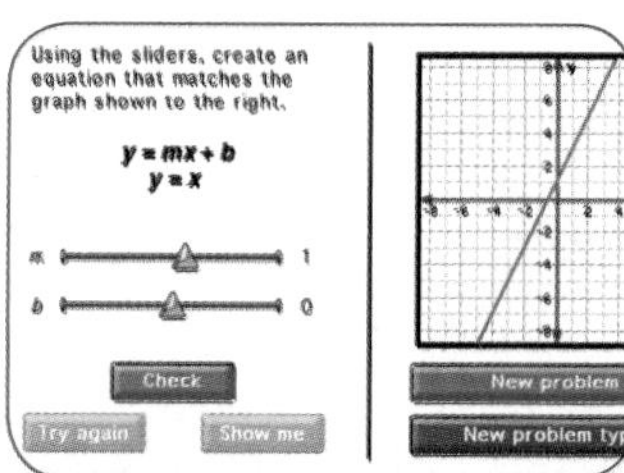

Lesson Practice Level B

LESSON 4.1

Practice B

For use with pages 206–212

Give the coordinates of the points labeled *A, B, C,* and *D*.

1.

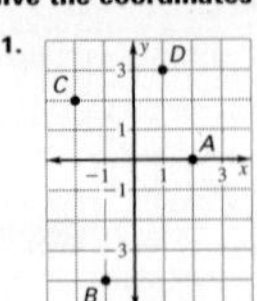

$A(2, 0), B(-1, -4), C(-2, 2), D(1, 3)$

2.

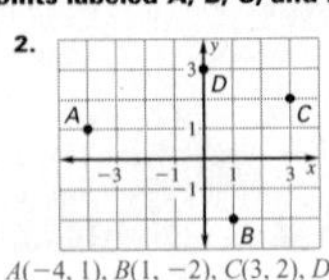

$A(-4, 1), B(1, -2), C(3, 2), D(0, 3)$

3.

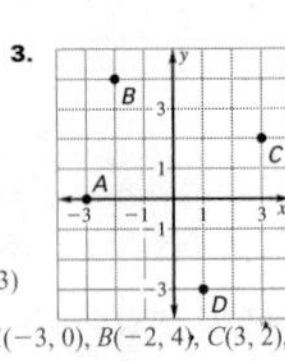

$A(-3, 0), B(-2, 4), C(3, 2), D(1, -3)$

Plot the point in a coordinate plane. *Describe* the location of the point.

4. $A(-4, 3)$

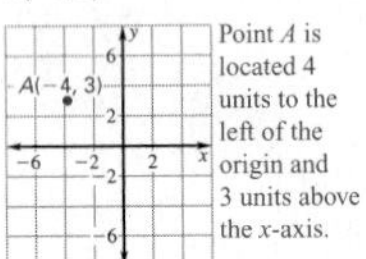

Point A is located 4 units to the left of the origin and 3 units above the x-axis.

5. $P(5, -6)$

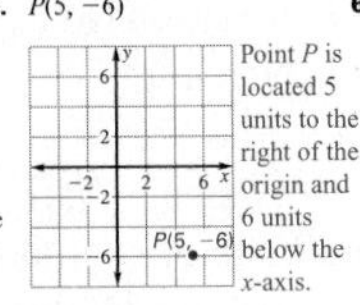

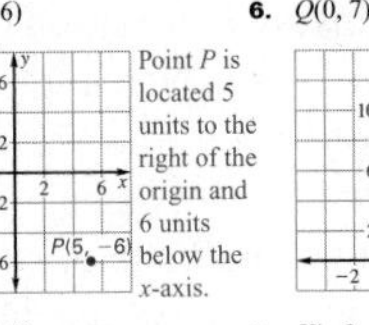

Point P is located 5 units to the right of the origin and 6 units below the x-axis.

6. $Q(0, 7)$

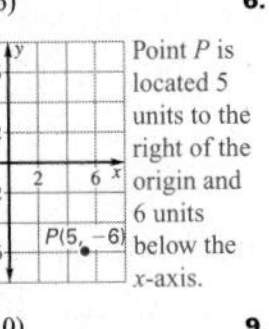

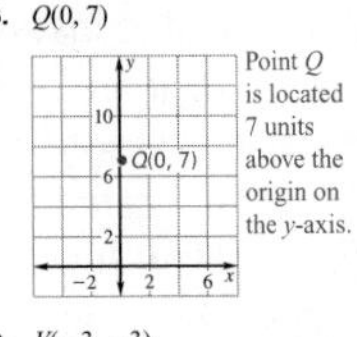

Point Q is located 7 units above the origin on the y-axis.

7. $B(-7, -5)$

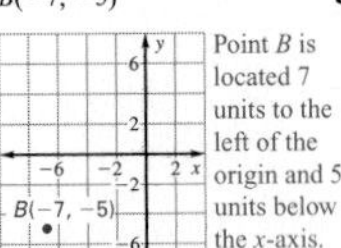

Point B is located 7 units to the left of the origin and 5 units below the x-axis.

8. $W(-5, 0)$

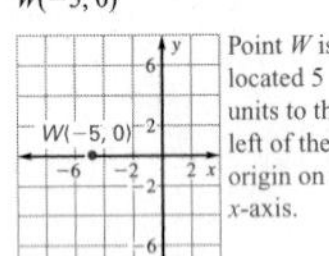

Point W is located 5 units to the left of the origin on the x-axis.

9. $V(-3, -3)$

Point V is located 3 units to the left of the origin and 3 units below the x-axis.

Graph the function with the given domain. Then identify the range of the function.

10. $y = x + 4$; domain: $-2, -1, 0, 1, 2$

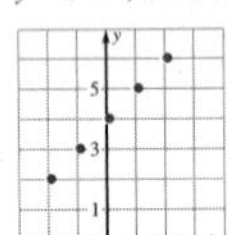

Range: 2, 3, 4, 5, 6

11. $y = 2x - 5$; domain: $-2, -1, 0, 1, 2$

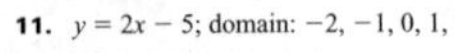

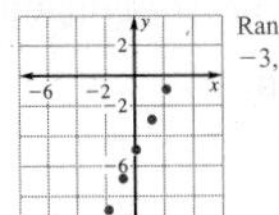

Range: $-9, -7, -5, -3, -1$

LESSON 4.1

LESSON 4.1

Practice B *continued*

For use with pages 206–212

12. $y = 3x - 1$; domain: $-2, -1, 0, 1, 2$

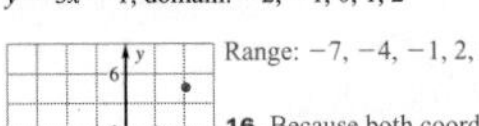

Range: $-7, -4, -1, 2, 5$

16. Because both coordinates are negative, $(-4, -2)$ lies in Quadrant III.

13. $y = 6x - 2$; domain: $-2, -1, 0, 1, 2$

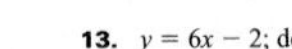

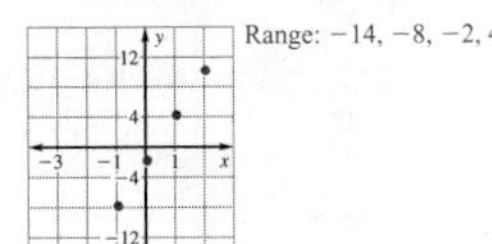

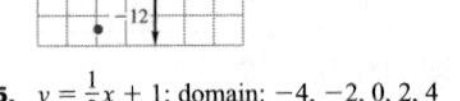

Range: $-14, -8, -2, 4, 10$

14. $y = 4x + 3$; domain: $-2, -1, 0, 1, 2$

Range: $-5, -1, 3, 7, 11$

17. Because the first coordinate is positive and the second coordinate is negative, $(9, -2)$ lies in Quadrant IV.

15. $y = \frac{1}{2}x + 1$; domain: $-4, -2, 0, 2, 4$

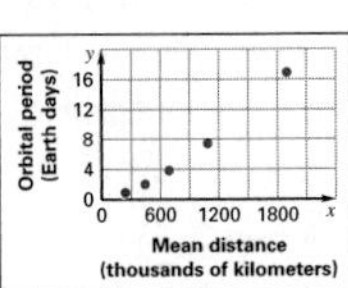

Range: $-1, 0, 1, 2, 3$

18. Because the first coordinate is negative and the second coordinate is positive, $(-1, 8)$ lies in Quadrant II.

Without plotting the point, tell whether it is in Quadrant I, Quadrant II, Quadrant III, or Quadrant IV. *Explain* your reasoning. See above.

16. $(-4, -2)$ **17.** $(9, -2)$ **18.** $(-1, 8)$

19. Jupiter's Moons The table shows some of the moons of Jupiter, their mean distances from Jupiter (in thousand kilometers), and their orbital periods (in Earth days). Graph the data from the table. Does the graph represent a function? Why or why not?

Moon	Io	Thebe	Ganymede	Callisto	Europa
Mean distance (thousand kilometers)	422	222	1070	1883	671
Orbital period (Earth days)	1.8	0.7	7.2	16.7	3.6

The graph represents a function because each input has exactly one output.

20. Cell Phone Use The table shows the number of cellular telephone subscribers in the United States since 1998.

Years since 1998	0	1	2	3	4
Subscribers (millions)	69	86	109	128	141

a. Graph the data from the table. Does the graph represent a function? Why or why not?

The graph represents a function because each input has exactly one output.

b. *Describe* any trend in the change in the number of subscribers.

The number of subscribers keeps increasing as time goes on.

LESSON 4.2

Practice B

For use with pages 215–221

Decide which of the two points lies on the graph of the line.

1. $2x + y = 10$ b
a. $(4, 3)$ **b.** $(-4, 18)$

2. $x - 3y = 12$ b
a. $(9, 1)$ **b.** $(6, -2)$

3. $2y - x = 9$ b
a. $(5, 1)$ **b.** $(1, 5)$

Solve the equation for *y*.

4. $-6x + y = 11$ $y = 6x + 11$

5. $8x + 2y = 10$ $y = -4x + 5$

6. $6x - 3y = -9$ $y = 2x + 3$

7. $-4x + 2y = 16$ $y = 2x + 8$

8. $10x - 5y = 25$ $y = 2x - 5$

9. $3x + 2y = -8$ $y = -\frac{3}{2}x - 4$

Graph the equation.

10. $y + x = 14$

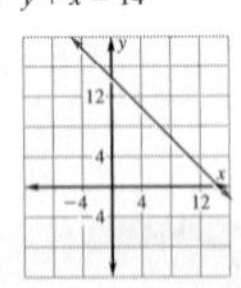

11. $y - 5x = 2$

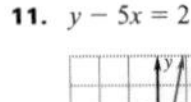

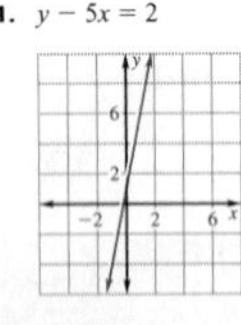

12. $2y - 4x = 10$

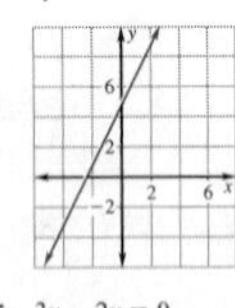

13. $x = -6$

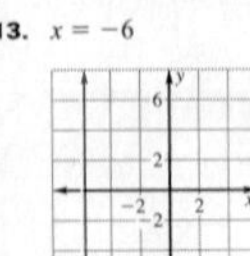

14. $y = 4$

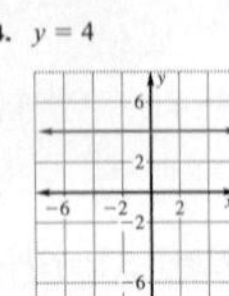

15. $3x - 2y = 0$

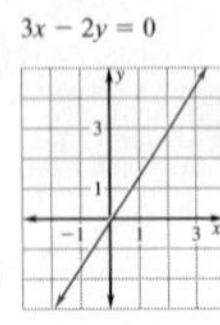

LESSON 4.2

Graph the function with the given domain. Then identify the range of the function.

16. $y = 2x - 2$; domain: $x \geq 0$

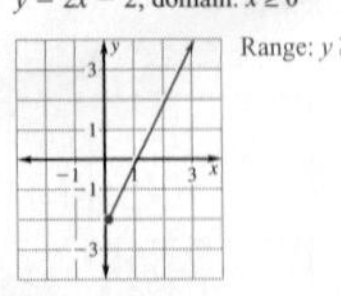

Range: $y \geq -2$

17. $y = -3x + 1$; domain: $x \leq 0$

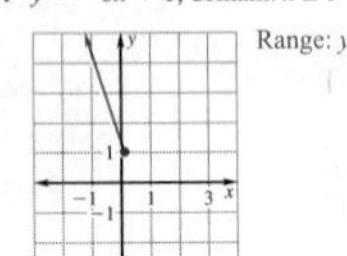

Range: $y \geq 1$

LESSON 4.2

Practice B *continued*

For use with pages 215–221

18. $y = 3$; domain: $x \leq 2$

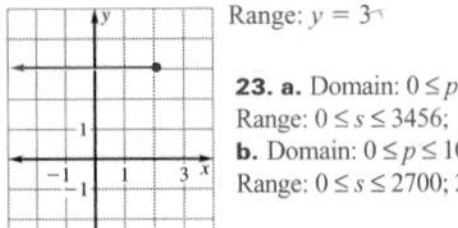

Range: $y = 3$

23. a. Domain: $0 \leq p \leq 128$; Range: $0 \leq s \leq 3456$; 128 pots
b. Domain: $0 \leq p \leq 100$; Range: $0 \leq s \leq 2700$; 2700 in.^{3}

19. $y = -1$; domain: $x \geq -1$

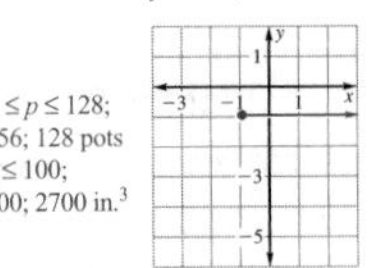

Range: $y = -1$

Identify the range of the function with the given domain.

20. $x + 3y = -8$; domain $x > 0$ $y < -\frac{8}{3}$

21. $6x - 3y = 9$; domain: $x < 1$ $y < -1$

22. Bicycle Rental A bicycle rental shop rents bicycles for \$8 per hour. The total cost c (in dollars) for renting a bicycle h hours is given by the function $c = 8h$. Once you get to the rental shop, you figure you can rent a bicycle for at most 5 hours. Graph the function and identify its domain and range. What is the most that you will pay for renting the bicycle? Domain: $0 \leq h \leq 5$; Range: $0 \leq c \leq 40$; \$40

24. Domain: $m \geq 0$; Range: $C \geq 700$; Rent for one year: Domain: $0 \leq m \leq 12$; Range: $700 \leq C \leq 6700$; The original graph was a ray. By restricting the domain, the graph becomes a line segment.

23. Plant Nursery A gardener at a nursery is filling pots with soil to prepare to transplant seedlings into these larger pots. Each new pot needs about 27 cubic inches of soil. The amount of soil s (in cubic inches) it takes to fill p pots is given by the function $s = 27p$. See above.

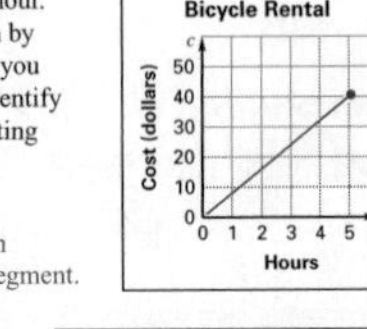

a. The gardener is filling the pots from a bag of soil that contains 3456 cubic inches of soil. Graph the function and identify its domain and range. How many pots can be filled from the bag?

b. Suppose the gardener needs to fill at most 100 pots. Graph the function on the coordinate plane in part (a). Identify its domain and range. How much soil (in cubic inches) will the gardener need?

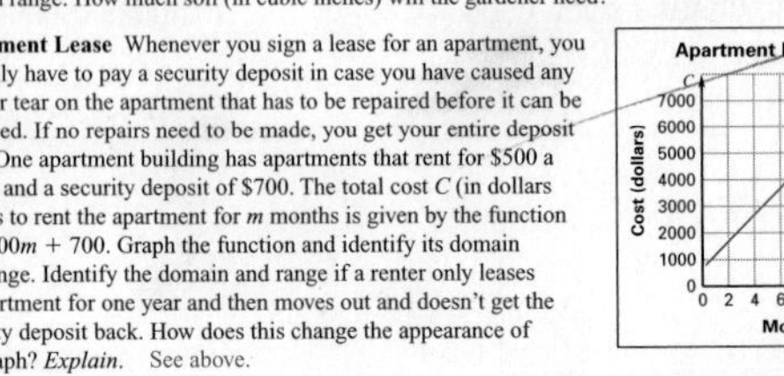

24. Apartment Lease Whenever you sign a lease for an apartment, you typically have to pay a security deposit in case you have caused any wear or tear on the apartment that has to be repaired before it can be re-leased. If no repairs need to be made, you get your entire deposit back. One apartment building has apartments that rent for \$500 a month and a security deposit of \$700. The total cost C (in dollars it costs to rent the apartment for m months is given by the function $C = 500m + 700$. Graph the function and identify its domain and range. Identify the domain and range if a renter only leases an apartment for one year and then moves out and doesn't get the security deposit back. How does this change the appearance of the graph? *Explain.* See above.

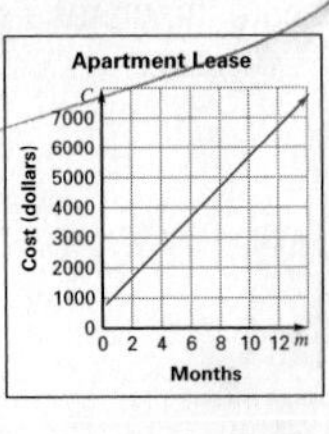

LESSON 4.2

LESSON 4.3

Practice B

For use with pages 225–232

Find the x-intercept and the y-intercept of the graph of the equation.

1. $x + y = 1$ $x = 1; y = 1$ **2.** $x - y = -5$ $x = -5; y = 5$ **3.** $6x - 3y = -3$ $x = -\frac{1}{2}; y = 1$

4. $5x + 10y = 30$ $x = 6; y = 3$ **5.** $9y - 5x = 20$ $x = -4; y = \frac{20}{9}$ **6.** $8x - 2y = 16$ $x = 2; y = -8$

7. $7x + 8y = 18$ $x = \frac{18}{7}; y = \frac{9}{4}$ **8.** $2y - 12x = -6$ $x = \frac{1}{2}; y = -3$ **9.** $2x - 0.5y = 8$ $x = 4; y = -16$

Draw the line that has the given intercepts.

10. x-intercept: 5, y-intercept: 4 **11.** x-intercept: −1, y-intercept: 6 **12.** x-intercept: 2, y-intercept: −3

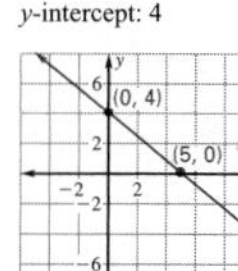
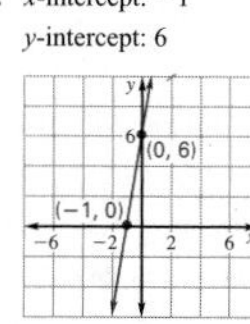
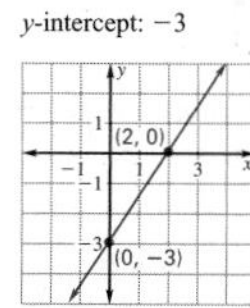

Graph the equation. Label the points where the line crosses the axes.

13. $y = -x - 4$ **14.** $y = 6 + 3x$ **15.** $y = 8x - 7$

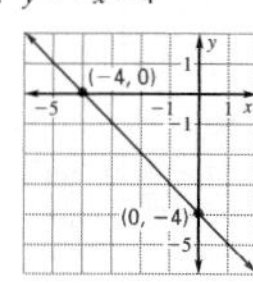
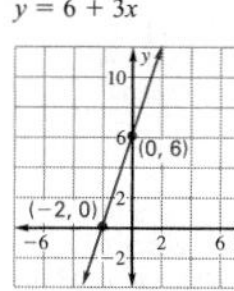
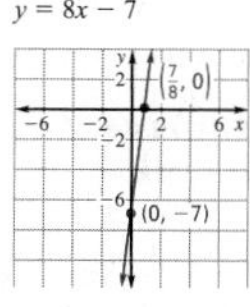

16. $y = 1 - 3x$ **17.** $7x - 7y = 42$ **18.** $3y + 2x = -5$

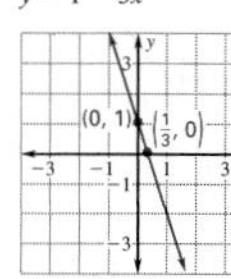
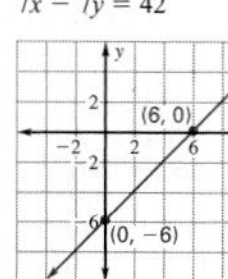
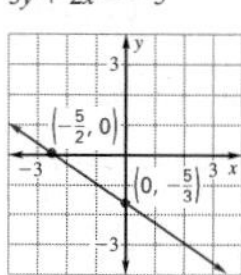

LESSON 4.3

Practice B *continued*

For use with pages 225–232

19. $4x - 9y = 16$ **20.** $y = 0.5x - 2$ **21.** $y = 3x + 0.2$

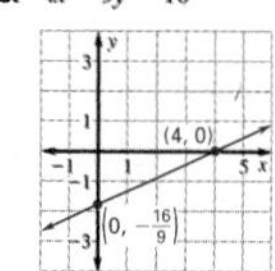
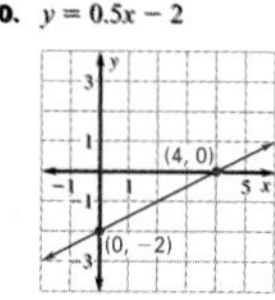
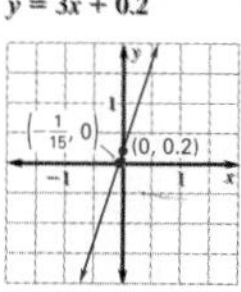

Match the equation with its intercepts.

22. $7y = 28 - 4x$ C **23.** $7x = 4y + 28$ A **24.** $4y = 7x + 28$ B

A. x-intercept: 4, y-intercept: −7 **B.** x-intercept: −4, y-intercept: 7 **C.** x-intercept: 7, y-intercept: 4

25. Rabbit Hutch The bottom of a rabbit cage is a rectangle with a perimeter of 118 inches. Let x be the cage's width (in inches) and let y be its length (in inches).

a. Write an equation for the perimeter. $2x + 2y = 118$

b. Find the intercepts of the graph of the equation you wrote. Then graph the equation. $x = 59; y = 59$

27. b. x-intercept: number of calories burnt when the man only bikes; y-intercept: number of calories burnt when the man only skates.

26. Home and Garden Show Admission to a home and garden show costs $7 per person during the week and $9 per person on the weekend. During one week of the show, a total of $142,506 was paid in admissions. This situation can be represented by the equation $7x + 9y = 142{,}506$ where x is the number of tickets sold during the week and y is the number of tickets sold on the weekend.

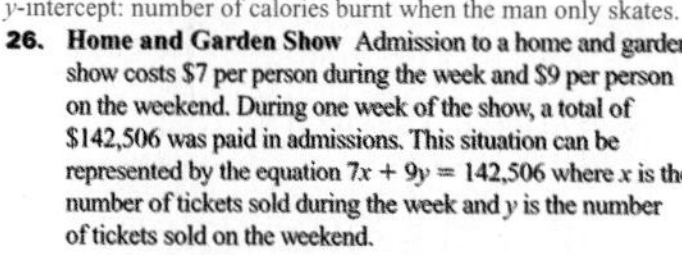

a. Find the intercepts of the graph of the equation. Graph the equation. $x = 20{,}358; y = 15{,}834$

b. Give three possibilities for the number of each kind of ticket that could have been sold for the week. Answers will vary.

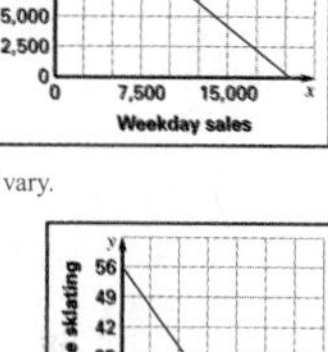

27. Burning Calories A man burns 10 calories per minute mountain biking and 7.5 calories per minute in-line skating. His goal is to burn approximately 420 calories daily. This situation can be represented by the equation $10x + 7.5y = 420$ where x is the number of minutes spent mountain biking and y is the number of minutes spent in-line skating.

a. Find the intercepts of the graph of the equation. Graph the equation. $x = 42; y = 56$

b. What do the intercepts mean in this situation? See above.

c. What are three possible numbers of minutes of biking and skating the man could do to reach his goal? Answers will vary.

LESSON 4.3

LESSON 4.4

Practice B

For use with pages 235–242

Plot the points and draw a line through them. Without calculating, tell whether the slope of the line is *positive, negative, zero,* or *undefined.*

1. (1, −4) and (5, −8) negative **2.** (−3, 6) and (−3, 0) undefined **3.** (−3, 3) and (7, −1) negative

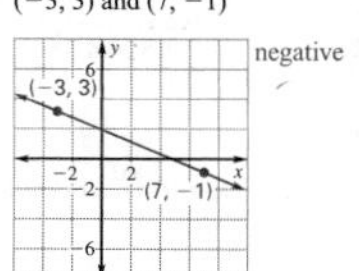

4. (0, −2) and (9, −5) negative **5.** (7, 1) and (−2, 1) zero **6.** (−3, −1) and (6, −2) negative

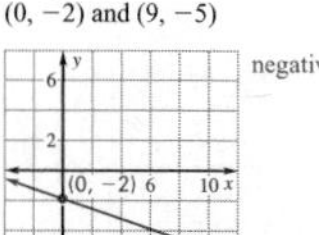
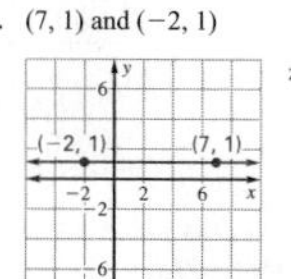
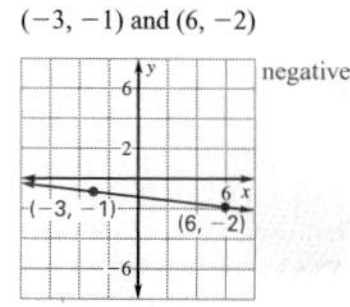

7. (−4, −5) and (−3, −2) positive **8.** (−7, 1) and (−7, −8) undefined **9.** (2, −10) and (12, 10) positive

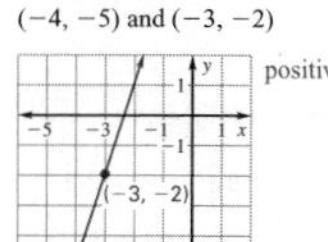
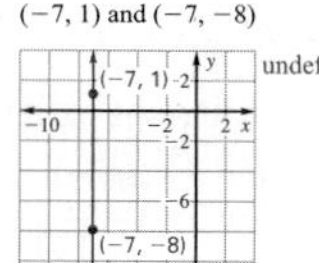
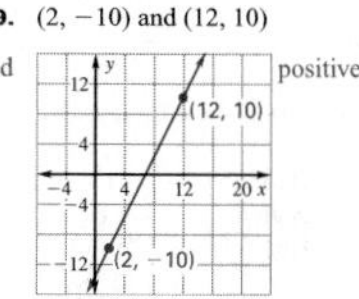

Find the slope of the line that passes through the points.

10. $\frac{2}{3}$ **11.** $-\frac{4}{5}$ **12.** 0

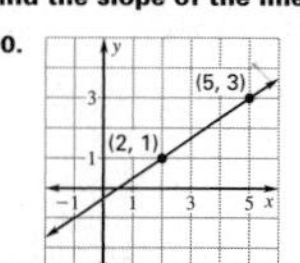

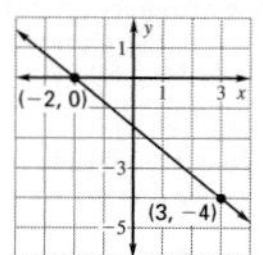
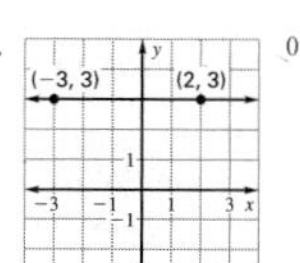

LESSON 4.4

LESSON 4.4

Practice B *continued*

For use with pages 235–242

13. $-\frac{3}{5}$ **14.** $\frac{3}{5}$ **15.** undefined

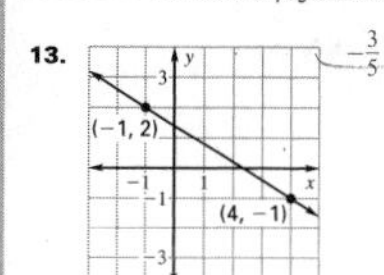
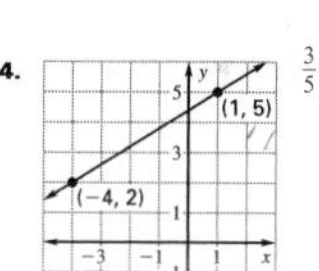
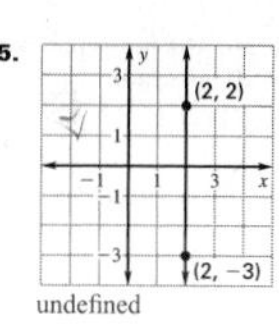

Find the slope of the line that passes through the points.

16. (1, 2) and (7, 7) $\frac{5}{6}$ **17.** (3, 4) and (−5, 0) $\frac{1}{2}$ **18.** (5, −2) and (5, 8) undefined

19. (3, 1) and (−5, 3) $-\frac{1}{4}$ **20.** (−7, 1) and (1, 5) $\frac{1}{2}$ **21.** (2, −5) and (5, −2) 1

22. (3, 0) and (8, 0) 0 **23.** (−6, −6) and (−2, −2) 1 **24.** (−5, −4) and (1, −2) $\frac{1}{3}$

Find the value of x or y so that the line passing through the two points has the given slope.

25. $(-3, y), (-9, -2); m = 1$ 4 **26.** $(-1, 4), (x, 3); m = \frac{1}{5}$ −6 **27.** $(8, 1), (1, y); m = -1$ 8

28. $(x, -7), (1, 2); m = 3$ −2 **29.** $(9, y), (3, 2); m = \frac{2}{3}$ 6 **30.** $(7, 5), (x, 2); m = \frac{3}{4}$ 3

31. Trolley Bus The table shows the number of trolley buses in operation in the United States during certain years.

Year	1980	1985	1990	1995	2000
Number of buses	823	676	832	885	951

a. *Describe* the rates of change in the number of buses during the time period. See below.

b. Determine the time intervals during which the number of trolley buses showed the greatest and least rates of change. Greatest: From 1985 to 1990; Least: From 1990 to 1995

32. Postage Rate The graph shows the cost (in dollars) (in dollars) to mail a letter that weighs one ounce during certain years.

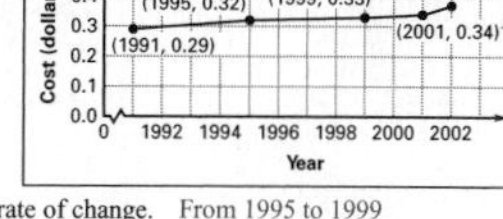

a. Determine the time interval during which the cost to mail a one-ounce letter showed the greatest rate of change. From 2001 to 2002

b. Determine the time interval during which the cost to mail a one-ounce letter showed the least rate of change. From 1995 to 1999

33. Heart Rate The graph shows the heart rate of a person during 30 minutes of exercise. Give a verbal description of the workout. The person's heartrate increased for 0 to 12 minutes, then it slowly decreased until the end of the workout.

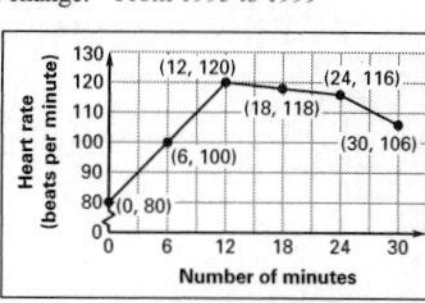

31. a. From 1980 to 1985: −29.4 buses per year; From 1985 to 1990: 31.2 buses per year; From 1990 to 1995: 10.6 buses per year; From 1995 to 2000: 13.2 buses per year; From 1980 to 1985, the number of buses decreased, but then the number of buses increased after that.

4 Lesson Practice Level B

LESSON 4.5 **Practice B**
For use with pages 244–250

Identify the slope and y-intercept of the line with the given equation. See below.

1. $y = 5x - 4$
2. $y = 10 - 4x$
3. $9x + y = 8$
4. $12x + 3y = 9$
5. $6x - 2y = 2$
6. $2x + 5y = 10$
7. $9x - 3y = -1$
8. $4y + 6x = 2$
9. $8y - 2x = 5$
10. $5x + 5y = 3$
11. $-4y = 16$
12. $6x = 12$

Match the equation with its graph.

13. $3x + 4y = 12$ C
14. $3x + 4y = -12$ B
15. $3x - 4y = 12$ A

A. 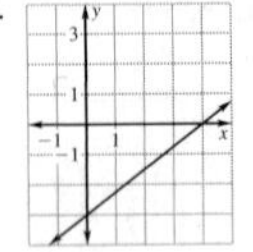

B. 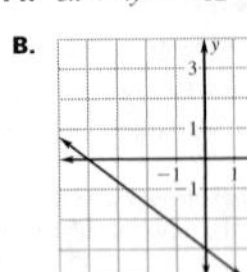

C. 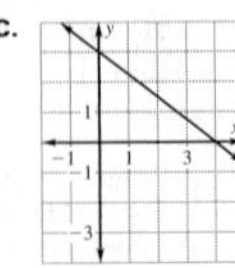

Graph the equation.

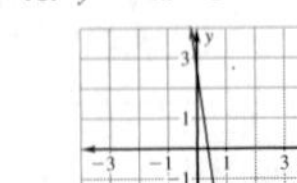

16. $y = -7x + 2$

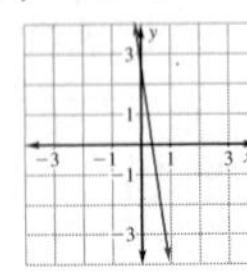

17. $y = 5x + 4$

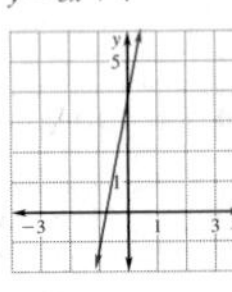

18. $y = -x + 9$

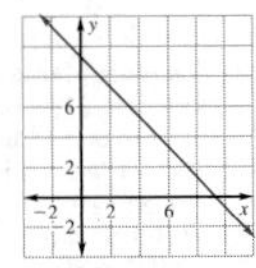

19. $y = \frac{1}{5}x$

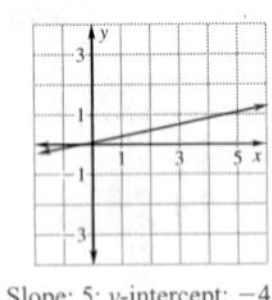

20. $y = -\frac{2}{3}x + 1$

21. $y = \frac{4}{3}x - 5$

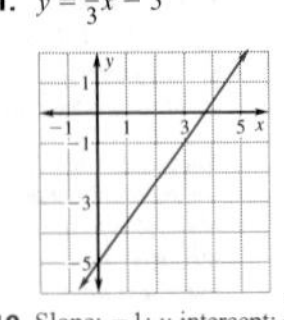

1. Slope: 5; y-intercept: -4
2. Slope: -4; y-intercept: 10
3. Slope: -9; y-intercept: 8
4. Slope: -4; y-intercept: 3
5. Slope: 3; y-intercept: -1
6. Slope: $-\frac{2}{5}$; y-intercept: 2
7. Slope: 3, y-intercept: $\frac{1}{3}$
8. Slope: $-\frac{3}{2}$; y-intercept: $\frac{1}{2}$
9. Slope: $\frac{1}{4}$; y-intercept: $\frac{5}{8}$
10. Slope: -1; y-intercept: $\frac{3}{5}$
11. Slope: 0; y-intercept: -4
12. Slope: undefined; y-intercept: none

LESSON 4.5 **Practice B** *continued*
For use with pages 244–250

Determine which lines are parallel.

22. 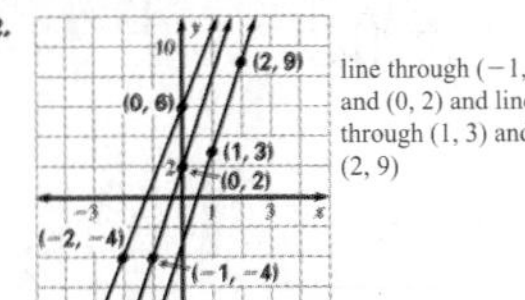

line through $(-1, -4)$ and $(0, 2)$ and line through $(1, 3)$ and $(2, 9)$

23. 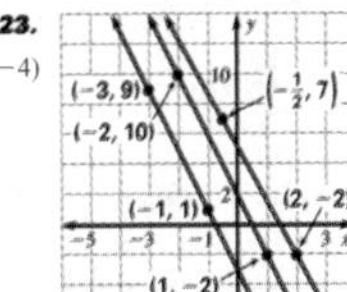

line through $(-3, 9)$ and $(-1, 1)$ and line through $(-2, 10)$ and $(1, -2)$

Tell whether the graphs of the two equations are parallel lines.

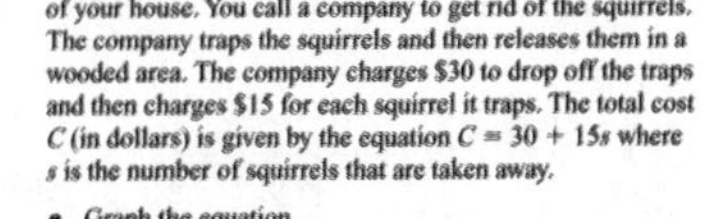

24. $y = 8x - 3, 8x + y = 3$ no
25. $2x + y = 5, -6 + 2x = y$ no
26. $2x + y = 5, y = 0.5x - 3$ no
27. $y = -0.6x + 2, 5y + 3x = 8$ yes
28. $8x + 3y = 9, 3y - 4 = 8x$ no
29. $10x + 2y = 7, 5x - y = 6$ no

30. **Squirrels** A family of squirrels takes up residence in the roof of your house. You call a company to get rid of the squirrels. The company traps the squirrels and then releases them in a wooded area. The company charges \$30 to drop off the traps and then charges \$15 for each squirrel it traps. The total cost C (in dollars) is given by the equation $C = 30 + 15s$ where s is the number of squirrels that are taken away.
    a. Graph the equation.
    b. Suppose the company raises its fee to \$18 to take away each squirrel so that the total cost for s squirrels is given by the equation $C = 30 + 18s$. Graph the equation in the same coordinate plane as the equation in part (a).
    c. How much more does it cost for the company to trap 4 squirrels after the fee is raised? \$12

31. **Water Usage** A new toilet model has two different flush settings in order to conserve water. One setting uses 1.6 gallons of water per flush and the other setting uses 0.8 gallon of water per flush. The total amount w (in gallons) of water used in the first setting is given by the equation $w = 1.6f$ where f is the number of times the toilet is flushed. The total amount of water used in the second setting is given by the equation $w = 0.8f$.
    a. Graph both equations in the same coordinate plane. What do the slopes and the w-intercepts mean in this situation?
    b. How much more water is used by the first setting if the toilet is flushed 10 times? 8 gal

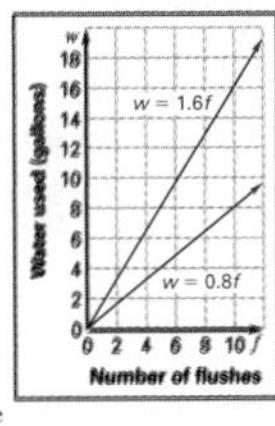

31. a. The slopes indicate the number of gallons of water used per flush. The w-intercepts show how much water is used when the toilet is not flushed at all.

LESSON 4.6 **Practice B**
For use with pages 253–259

Tell whether the equation represents direct variation. If so, identify the constant of variation.

1. $y = 8x$ yes; 8
2. $y = 2x + 1$ no
3. $3x + y = 6$ no

Graph the direct variation equation.

4. $y = 9x$

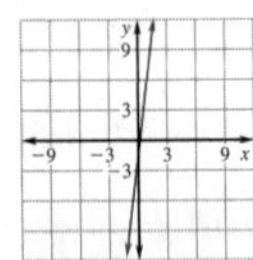

5. $y = -7x$

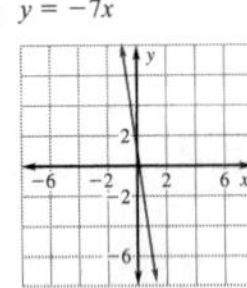

6. $3y = 4x$

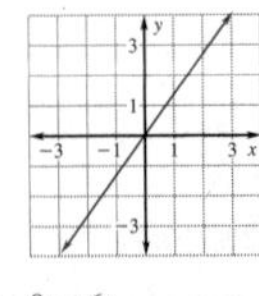

7. $4y = -12x$

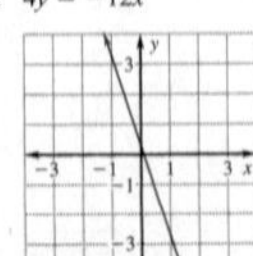

8. $8y = x$

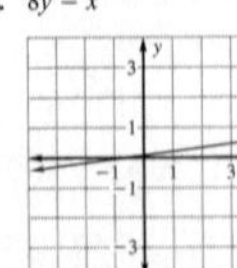

9. $8y = 6x$

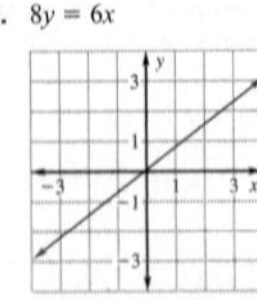

The graph of a direct variation equation is shown. Write the direct variation equation. Then find the value of y when x = 10.

10. 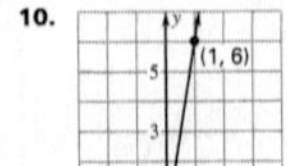
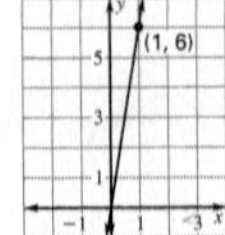

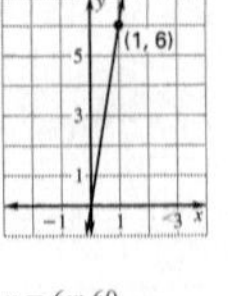

$y = 6x$; 60

11. 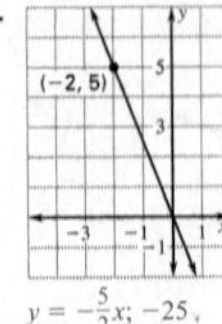

$y = -\frac{5}{2}x$; -25

12. 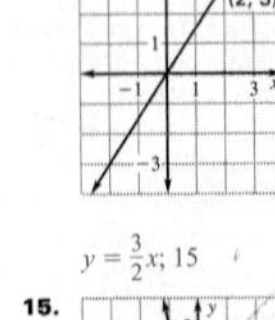

$y = \frac{3}{2}x$; 15

13. 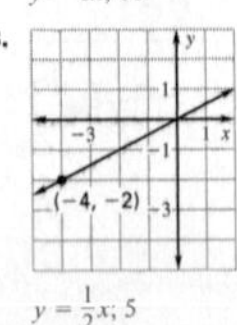

$y = \frac{1}{2}x$; 5

14. 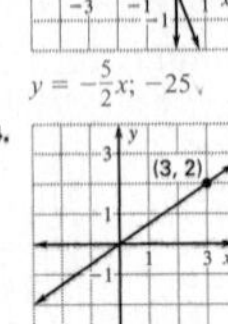
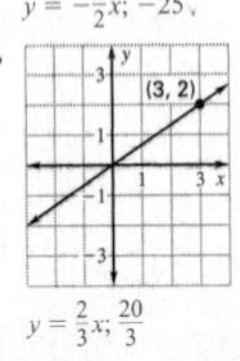

$y = \frac{2}{3}x$; $\frac{20}{3}$

15. 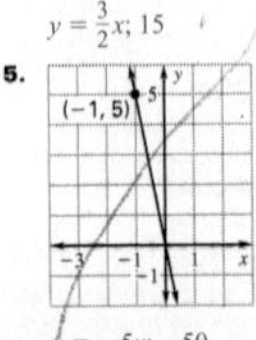

$y = -5x$; -50

LESSON 4.6 **Practice B** *continued*
For use with pages 253–259

16. 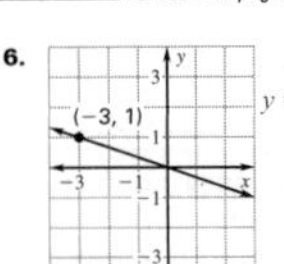

$y = -\frac{1}{3}x$; $-\frac{10}{3}$

17. 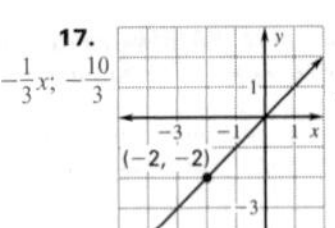

$y = x$; 10

18. 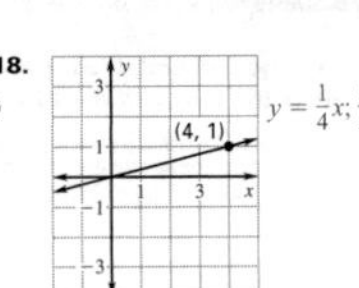

$y = \frac{1}{4}x$; $\frac{5}{2}$

Tell whether the table represents direct variation. If so, write the direct variation equation.

19.

x	0.5	3	−2	1	−8
y	9	54	−36	18	−144

yes; $y = 18x$

20.

x	−5	3	−2	10	20
y	−2	1.2	−0.8	4	8

yes; $y = 0.4x$

21.

x	8	2	−4	−0.5	14
y	7	28	7	−112	4

no

22.

x	−0.2	−2	1	12	18
y	30	3	−6	−0.5	3

no

Given that y varies directly with x, use the specified values to write a direct variation equation that relates x and y.

23. $x = 24, y = 3$ $y = \frac{1}{8}x$
24. $x = -16, y = -4$ $y = \frac{1}{4}x$
25. $x = 28, y = -4$ $y = -\frac{1}{7}x$
26. $x = 5, y = -30$ $y = -6x$
27. $x = \frac{1}{6}, y = 1$ $y = 6x$
28. $x = 8, y = -3$ $y = -\frac{3}{8}x$
29. $x = 6, y = 102$ $y = 17x$
30. $x = -8, y = 64$ $y = -8x$
31. $x = 15, y = 9$ $y = \frac{3}{5}x$

32. **Hooke's Law** The force F required to stretch a spring varies directly with the amount the spring is stretched s. Eight pounds is needed to stretch a spring 8 inches.
    a. Write a direct variation equation that relates F and s. $F = s$
    b. How much force is required to stretch a spring 25 inches? 25 lb

33. **Basement Waterproofing** One way to keep moisture out of your basement is to paint the walls with a waterproof paint. The number g (of gallons) of paint you need varies directly with the area A of the basement. One gallon of paint covers 100 square feet.
    a. Write a direct variation equation that relates g and A. $g = 0.01A$
    b. How many gallons do you need to cover 530 square feet? 5.3 gal
    c. How many square feet does 8.5 gallons of paint cover? 850 ft²

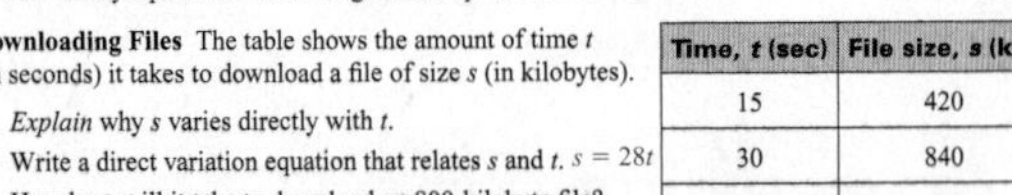

34. **Downloading Files** The table shows the amount of time t (in seconds) it takes to download a file of size s (in kilobytes).
    a. *Explain* why s varies directly with t.
    b. Write a direct variation equation that relates s and t. $s = 28t$
    c. How long will it take to download an 800-kilobyte file? Round your answer to the nearest second. about 29 sec

Time, t (sec)	File size, s (kb)
15	420
30	840
45	1260

34. a. Because the ratios for each data pair is 28, s varies directly with t.

LESSON 4.7
Practice B
For use with pages 262–268

Evaluate the function when $x = -3, 0,$ and 2.

1. $f(x) = 15x + 4$ $-41; 4; 34$
2. $g(x) = -9x + 1$ $28; 1; -17$
3. $p(x) = -7x - 5$ $16; -5; -19$
4. $h(x) = 3.25x$ $-9.75; 0; 6.5$
5. $m(x) = -4.4x$ $13.2; 0; -8.8$
6. $f(x) = 6.1x - 3.3$ $-21.6; -3.3; 8.9$
7. $s(x) = \frac{4}{5}x - 2$ $-\frac{22}{5}; -2; -\frac{2}{5}$
8. $d(x) = -\frac{5}{3}x + 4$ $9; 4; \frac{2}{3}$
9. $h(x) = \frac{3}{8}x - 6$ $-\frac{57}{8}; -6; -\frac{21}{4}$
10. $f(x) = -2.5x + 7$ $14.5; 7; 2$
11. $h(x) = 4.2x - 3$ $-15.6; -3; 5.4$
12. $g(x) = 6.1x - 2.2$ $-20.5; -2.2; 10$

Find the value of x so that the function has the given value.

13. $f(x) = 4x - 2; 18$ 5
14. $n(x) = 7x + 4; 39$ 5
15. $q(x) = 6 - 5x; 21$ -3
16. $g(x) = -3x + 8; 14$ -2
17. $h(x) = 9x - 13; 23$ 4
18. $m(x) = 12x - 30; 30$ 5
19. $s(x) = -4x - 9; 3$ -3
20. $m(x) = 8.5x - 3; 82$ 10
21. $p(x) = -2.4x + 6; 18$ -5
21. $d(x) = 3.3x - 1.1; 31.9$ 10

Graph the function. *Compare* your graph to the graph of $f(x) = x$.

23. $h(x) = x - 4$
24. $g(x) = x + 7$
25. $m(x) = 5x$

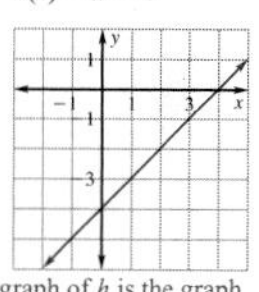

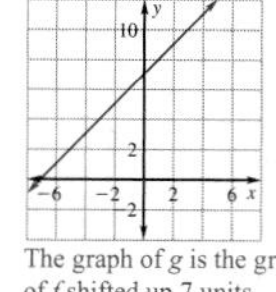
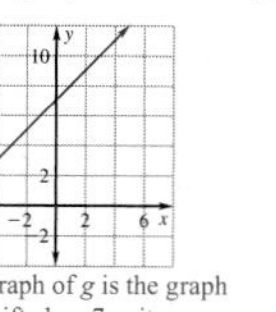
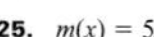
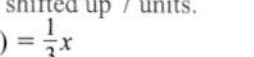

The graph of h is the graph of f shifted down 4 units.

The graph of g is the graph of f shifted up 7 units.

The graph of m is a dilation of the graph of f using a scale factor of 5.

26. $m(x) = 8x$
27. $p(x) = \frac{1}{3}x$
28. $n(x) = -2x$

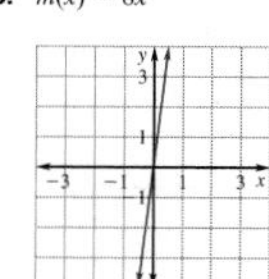
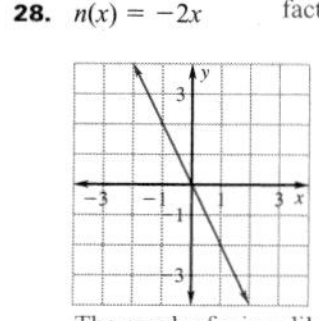

The graph of m is a dilation of the graph of f using a scale factor of 8.

The graph of p is a dilation of the graph of f using a scale factor of $\frac{1}{3}$.

The graph of n is a dilation of the graph of f using a scale factor of 2 and a reflection in the x-axis.

LESSON 4.7

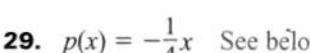

LESSON 4.7
Practice B *continued*
For use with pages 262–268

29. $p(x) = -\frac{1}{4}x$ See below.
30. $d(x) = x - 1.5$ See below.
31. $g(x) = x + 4.5$ See below.

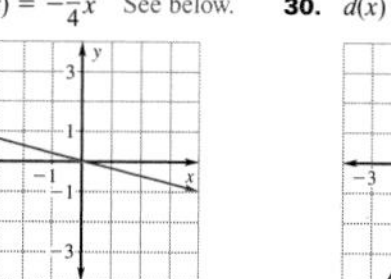
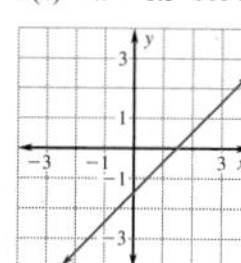
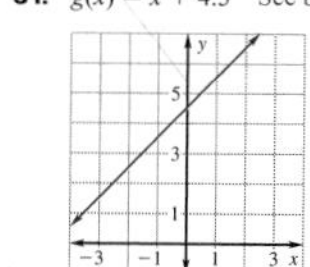

Match the function with the description of its graph in relation to the graph of $f(x) = x$.

32. $g(x) = 4x$ C
33. $g(x) = x + 4$ A
34. $g(x) = x - 4$ B

A. graph of f shifted up 4 units

B. graph of f shifted down 4 units

C. graph of f dilated by factor of 4

35. **Video Games** The number of hours people in the United States spend playing video games each year from 1998 to 2001 can be modeled by the function $f(x) = 11.9x + 46.4$ where x is the number of years since 1998. **a.** Domain: $0 \le x \le 3$ Range: $46.4 \le f(x) \le 82.1$
    - **a.** Graph the function and identify its domain and range.
    - **b.** Find the value of $f(x)$ when $x = 2$. *Explain* what the solution means in this situation.
    - **c.** Find the value of x so that $f(x) = 60$. *Explain* what the solution means in this situation. See below.

b. $f(2) = 70.2$; In 2000, people spent 70.2 hours each year playing video games.

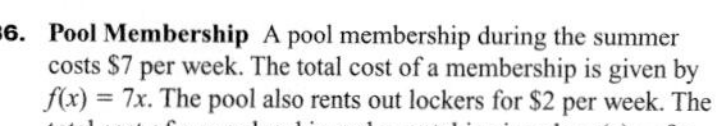

36. **Pool Membership** A pool membership during the summer costs \$7 per week. The total cost of a membership is given by $f(x) = 7x$. The pool also rents out lockers for \$2 per week. The total cost of a membership and a rental is given by $g(x) = 9x$.
    - **a.** Graph both functions. How is the graph of f related to the graph of g? See below.
    - **b.** What is the difference between a 12-week membership if you get a locker and if you don't? *Explain* how you got your answer. \$24; Because the difference is \$2 per week, multiply 2 by 12.

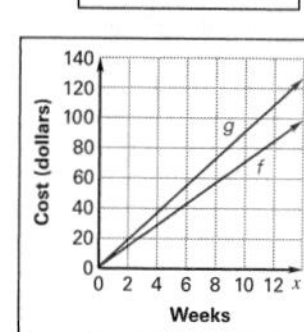

29. The graph of p is a dilation of the graph of f using a scale factor of $\frac{1}{4}$ and the reflection of f in the x-axis.

30. The graph of d is the graph of f shifted down 1.5 units.

31. The graph of g is the graph of f shifted up 4.5 units.

35. c. $f(1.1) \approx 60$; Near the beginning of 1999, people spent 60 hours each year playing video games.

36. a. The graphs have the same y-intercept but the slope of g is steeper than the slope of f.

LESSON 4.7

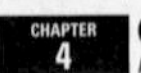

4 Assessment

CHAPTER 4 Quiz 1
For use after Lessons 4.1–4.3

Plot the point in a coordinate plane. Describe the location of the point.

1. $(1, -4)$
2. $(-3, -2)$

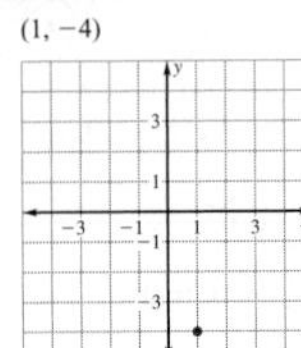

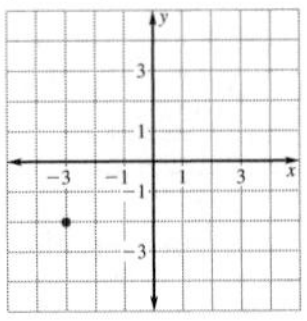

Graph the equation.

3. $x = 3$
4. $y = -3$

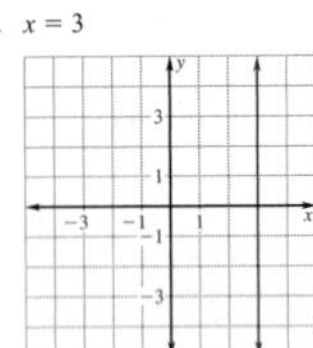

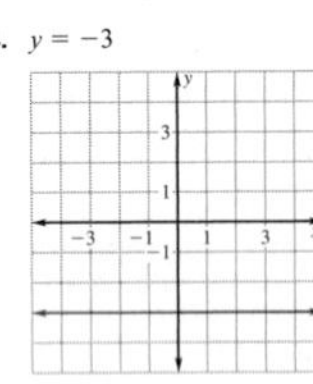

5. $y - 3x = 1$

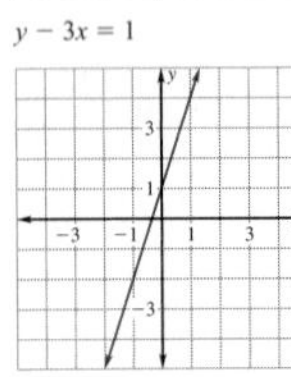

Find the *x*-intercept and the *y*-intercept of the graph of the equation.

6. $y = 7x - 3$
7. $-4y + x = 8$
8. $2x - 5y = 20$
9. Your school is selling tickets for a student concert. The total ticket sales can be modeled by the equation $90 = 6a + 3s$ where a is the number of adult tickets sold and s is the number of student tickets sold. Find the intercepts of the graph of the equation.

Answers

1. See left. Quadrant IV
2. See left. Quadrant III
3. See left.
4. See left.
5. See left.
6. x-intercept: $\left(\frac{3}{7}, 0\right)$; y-intercept: $(0, -3)$
7. x-intercept: $(8, 0)$; y-intercept: $(0, -2)$
8. x-intercept: $(10, 0)$; y-intercept: $(0, -4)$
9. a-intercept: $(15, 0)$; s-intercept: $(0, 30)$

CHAPTER 4 Quiz 2
For use after Lessons 4.4–4.5

Find the slope of the line that passes through the points.

1. $(-4, 3)$ and $(7, 5)$
2. $(1, 2)$ and $(-2, 2)$
3. $(4, -1)$ and $(4, 3)$

Identify the slope and the *y*-intercept of the line with the given equation.

4. $y = 7x + 2$
5. $10x - 5y = 30$
6. $3x - 8y = -24$

Graph the equation.

7. $y = -\frac{7}{2}x - 1$
8. $-4x + 6y = 12$

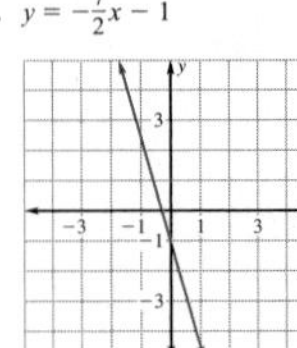

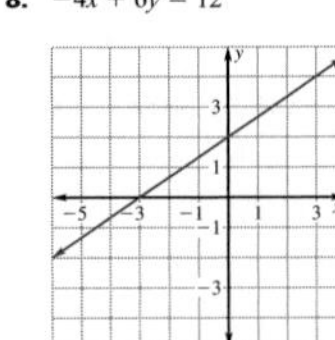

9. $9x + 2y = -7$

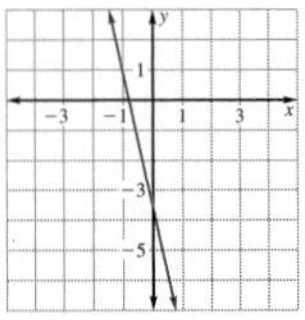

10. A campsite charges \$12 per day for the site rental and \$8 for parking. The total campsite charge C (in dollars) is given by $C = 12d + 8$ where d is the number of days that the site is rented. Graph the equation for $d \geq 0$.

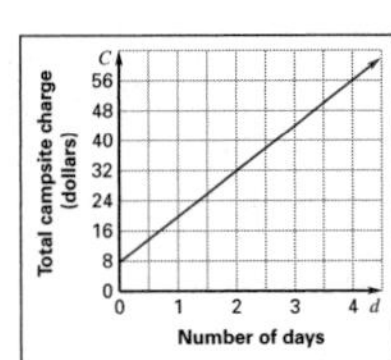

Answers

1. $\frac{2}{11}$
2. 0
3. undefined
4. 7; (0, 2)
5. 2; (0, −6)
6. $\frac{3}{8}$; (0, 3)
7. See left.
8. See left.
9. See left.
10. See left.

CHAPTER 4 Quiz 3
For use after Lessons 4.6–4.7

Given that *y* varies directly with *x*, use the specified values to write a direct variation equation that relates *x* and *y*.

1. $x = 4, y = 12$
2. $x = 6, y = 8$
3. $x = 3, y = -6$

Evaluate the function.

4. $f(x) = 7x + 2$ when $x = 5$
5. $h(x) = 0.3x + 9.7$ when $x = 15$
6. $p(x) = \frac{2}{5}x + \frac{1}{2}$ when $x = 3$

Graph the function. Compare the graph to the graph of $f(x) = x$.

7. $p(x) = x + 4$
8. $g(x) = 3x$

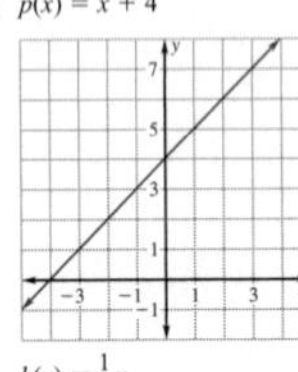

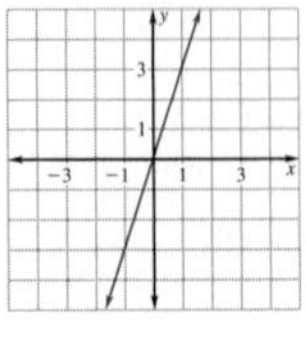

9. $h(x) = \frac{1}{2}x$

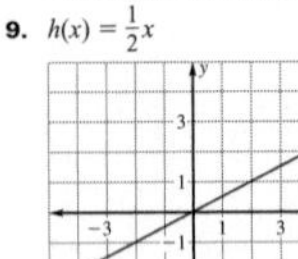

10. The area A of a square varies directly as the square of the side s. Write a direct variation equation that relates s and A.

Answers

1. $y = 3x$
2. $y = \frac{4}{3}x$
3. $y = -2x$
4. 37
5. 14.2
6. $\frac{17}{10}$
7. See left. Have the same slope; lines are parallel; the y-intercept of the graph of p is 4 more than the y-intercept of the graph of f.
8. See left. Slope of the graph of g > the slope of the graph of f; graph of g rises faster from left to right; the y-intercept for both graphs is 0; both lines pass through the origin.
9. See left. Slope of the graph of h < the slope of the graph of f; graph of h rises more slowly from left to right; the y-intercept for both graphs is 0; both lines pass through the origin.
10. $A = ks^2$

CHAPTER 4 Chapter Test
For use after Chapter 4

Plot the point in the coordinate plane. Describe the location of the point.

1. $A(-1, 3)$
2. $B(4, 0)$
3. $C(2, -2)$
4. $D(-1, -1)$

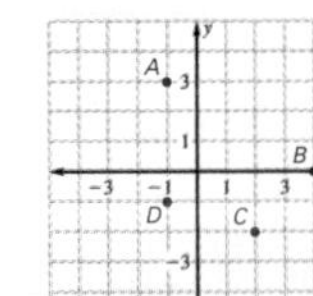

Graph the equation.

5. $3x - y = 5$
6. $3y - 2x = -3$
7. $y = -3$

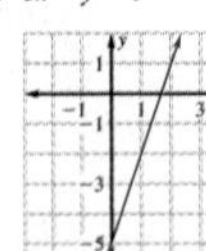

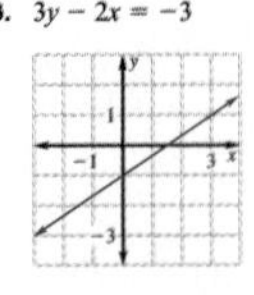

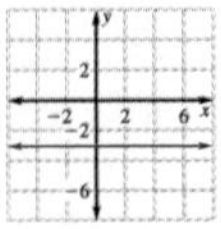

Find the *x*-intercept and the *y*-intercept of the graph of the equation.

8. $6x - 4y = 12$
9. $-2x + 5y = -10$
10. $y = \frac{1}{2}x - 2$

In Exercises 11–16, use the following information.

The graph shows the distance of a car traveling along a straight road for 8 hours. A positive velocity is motion to the right, and a negative velocity is motion to the left.

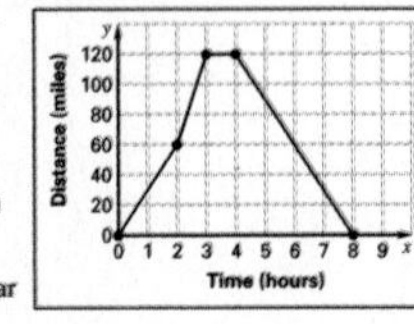

11. Determine the rates of change in distance with respect to time.
12. Between what two times is the car not moving?
13. Between what two times is the car traveling to the right?
14. Between what two times is the car traveling to the left?
15. Between what two times is the car traveling the fastest?
16. What does the x-intercept $(8, 0)$ represent in this situation?

Answers

1. See left. Quadrant II
2. See left. x-axis
3. See left. Quadrant IV
4. See left. Quadrant III
5. See left.
6. See left.
7. See left.
8. x-intercept = 2, y-intercept = −3
9. x-intercept = 5, y-intercept = −2
10. x-intercept = 4, y-intercept = −2
11. 30 mi/h, 60 mi/h, 0 mi/h, −30 mi/h
12. hours 3 and 4
13. hours 0 to 3
14. hours 4 and 8
15. hours 2 and 3
16. After 8 hours, the car returns to its starting position.

CHAPTER 4
Chapter Test B *continued*
For use after Chapter 4

Identify the slope and y-intercept of the line with the given equation.

17. $y = 8x - 3$ **18.** $2x + 9y = 9$ **19.** $-3x - 4y = -16$

Determine whether the equation represents direct variation. If so, identify the constant of variation.

20. $y = -x$ **21.** $4x - 3y = 0$ **22.** $2x + y = 4$

Complete the table for the function.

23. $f(x) = 6 + x$

x	-1	-4	0
$f(x)$	5	2	6

24. $f(x) = -\frac{7}{2}x$

x	0	2	-4
$f(x)$	0	-7	14

In Exercises 25–27, use the following information.

An advertising company charges \$150,000 each time a 30-second commercial is aired. The cost (in thousands of dollars) to produce the commercial and air it x times is given by the function $C(x) = 150x + 300$.

25. Graph the function.

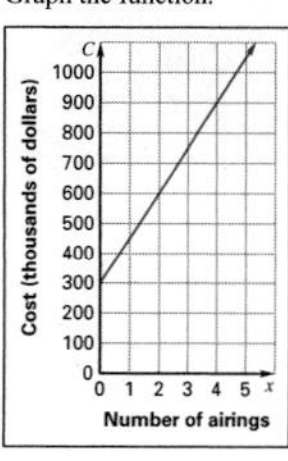

26. Identify the domain and the range of the function.

27. How many times could the station air the commercial if it wants to spend \$900,000?

Answers

17. $m = 8, b = -3$

18. $m = -\frac{2}{9}, b = 1$

19. $m = -\frac{3}{4}, b = 4$

20. yes; $a = -1$

21. yes; $a = \frac{4}{3}$

22. no

23. See left.

24. See left.

25. See left.

26. domain: $x \geq 0$; range: $C \geq 300$

27. 4 times

CHAPTER 4
Standardized Test
For use after Chapter 4

Multiple Choice

1. A point is located 5 units to the right of the origin and 4 units down. What are the coordinates of the point? D

Ⓐ (5, 4) Ⓑ (−4, 5)
Ⓒ (4, 5) Ⓓ (5, −4)

2. In which quadrant is the point (−2, 3) located? B

Ⓐ Quadrant I Ⓑ Quadrant II
Ⓒ Quadrant III Ⓓ Quadrant IV

3. Which ordered pair is a solution of $5x + 4y = 18$? A

Ⓐ (−2, 7) Ⓑ (8, 2)
Ⓒ (−3, 6) Ⓓ (2, 4)

4. Which statement is true for the function whose graph is shown? B

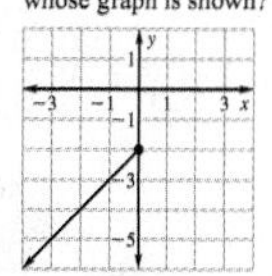

Ⓐ The domain is unrestricted.
Ⓑ The domain is $x \leq 0$.
Ⓒ The range is unrestricted.
Ⓓ The range is $y \leq 0$.

5. What is the x-intercept of the equation $3x - 2y = -12$? C

Ⓐ (0, 6) Ⓑ (0, −4)
Ⓒ (−4, 0) Ⓓ (6, 0)

6. The slope of the line that passes through the points (−2, 4) and (−3, 7) is __?__. A

Ⓐ negative Ⓑ positive
Ⓒ undefined Ⓓ zero

7. What is the slope of the line that passes through the points (5, −3) and (−7, 5)? B

Ⓐ $-\frac{1}{6}$ Ⓑ $-\frac{2}{3}$ Ⓒ -1 Ⓓ $-\frac{3}{2}$

8. What is the value of y for the line that has a slope of $-\frac{3}{2}$ and passes through the points (3, 5) and (7, y)? C

Ⓐ −11 Ⓑ −10
Ⓒ −1 Ⓓ 20

9. What is the slope of the line $y = \frac{1}{2}x + 2$? C

Ⓐ −2 Ⓑ $-\frac{1}{2}$ Ⓒ $\frac{1}{2}$ Ⓓ 2

10. What is the y-intercept of the line $5x - 4y = -12$? D

Ⓐ −3 Ⓑ $-\frac{5}{4}$ Ⓒ $\frac{5}{4}$ Ⓓ 3

11. Which line is parallel to the line $y = 4x - 2$? B

Ⓐ $12x - 4y = 8$ Ⓑ $4y - 16x = 10$
Ⓒ $5y - 25x = -10$ Ⓓ $-x + 4y = -8$

12. What is the value of m if Lines 1 and 2 are parallel? A

Line 1: (−2, −5) and (0, 0)
Line 2: (m, 12) and (−3, 2)

Ⓐ 1 Ⓑ 5 Ⓒ 7 Ⓓ 22

13. Which equation represents direct variation? A

Ⓐ $-2x = 3y$ Ⓑ $5y - x = 4$
Ⓒ $12x - 3 = 4y$ Ⓓ $5x - 2y + 3 = 0$

14. What is the constant of variation in the equation $5x + 3y = 0$? B

Ⓐ −3 Ⓑ $-\frac{5}{3}$ Ⓒ $-\frac{3}{5}$ Ⓓ 5

CHAPTER 4
Standardized Test *continued*
For use after Chapter 4

15. The graph of which function is shown? A

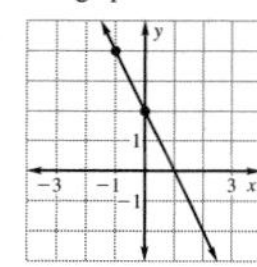

Ⓐ $f(x) = -2x + 2$ Ⓑ $f(x) = 2x + 2$
Ⓒ $f(x) = -2x - 2$ Ⓓ $f(x) = 2x - 2$

16. Examine the problem below. Which line first contains an error? B

$g(x) = -\frac{2}{3}x - \frac{5}{6}$

$g(36) = -\frac{2}{3}(36) - \frac{5}{6}$ Line 1

$g(36) = -24 - \frac{5}{6}$ Line 2

$g(36) = -\frac{152}{6} - \frac{5}{6}$ Line 3

$g(36) = -\frac{157}{6}$ Line 4

$g(36) = -26\frac{1}{6}$ Line 5

Ⓐ Line 2 Ⓑ Line 3
Ⓒ Line 4 Ⓓ Line 5

Gridded Answer

17. What is the value of $f(-3)$ if $f(x) = -4.2x + 6$?

1	8	.	6

18. a.

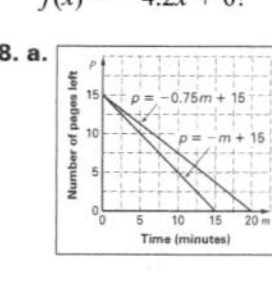

Short Response

18. You and a classmate are reading a short story that is 15 pages long. You read at a rate of 1 page per minute. Your classmate reads at a rate of 0.75 page per minute. The models below give the number of pages p you and your classmate have left to read after reading for m minutes.

You: $p = -m + 15$
Classmate: $p = -0.75m + 15$

a. Graph both equations on the same coordinate plane. See below.

b. How many more minutes would it take your classmate to read the short story than you? *Explain* how you used the graph to determine this information. 5 min

Extended Response

19. The table shows the difference d (in cents) of this year's average monthly gas price and the previous year's average monthly gas price. For example, in month 1, $d = -2$. So, the average gas price was 2 cents below the previous year's average gas price that month.

Month M	1	2	3	4	5	6
Difference d (in cents)	−2	5	10	5	0	9

a. *Explain* how you know the table represents a function.

b. Graph the function and identify its domain and range.

c. What does a point in Quadrant IV mean in terms of this situation?

19. a. This table represents a function because for every month M there is exactly one difference d. **b.** Domain = 1, 2, 3, 4, 5, and 6; Range = −2, 0, 5, 9, and 10 **c.** A point in Quadrant IV represents a decrease in the price of gas as compared to the average price that same month in the previous year.

CHAPTER 4
Alternative Assessment and Math Journal
For use after Chapter 4

Journal **1.** List the three different methods that can be used to graph a linear equation. Then briefly describe how to graph $2x + y = 3$ using each method.

Multi-Step Problem **2.** You are planning an ornamental garden that has a total area of 200 square feet. There are two sizes of ornamental plants you have chosen for your garden. Each small plant requires 2.5 square feet of space and each large plant requires 8 square feet of space. This situation can be modeled by the equation $2.5x + 8y = 200$ where x is the number of small plants and y is the number of large plants to be placed in the garden.

a. Find the intercepts of the graph of the equation.

b. Graph the equation.

c. What do the intercepts mean in this situation?

d. What are three possible numbers of small plants and large plants that you can plant in the garden?

e. What is the slope of this line?

f. Write the equation in slope-intercept form.

g. You decide to enlarge the space for the garden to a total of 240 square feet which means the new model will be $2.5x + 8y = 240$. Graph this equation on the same coordinate plane you used in part (b).

h. As you compare the two graphs, did increasing the size of the garden change the slope or y-intercept? Describe any changes that occurred.

1. Complete answers should include: a list of the three methods that can be used to graph a linear equation: make a table, use intercepts, and use the slope and y-intercept; an explanation of how to graph $2x + y = 3$ using each method. **2. a.** x-intercept: 80; y-intercept: 25 **b.**

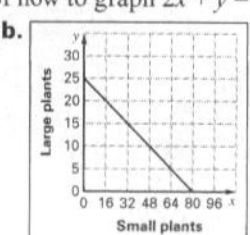

c. The x-intercept represents the number of small plants that can be placed in the garden if no large plants are used. The y-intercept represents the number of large plants that can be placed in the garden if no small plants are used. **d.** *Sample answer:* 16 small and 20 large; 32 small and 15 large; 48 small and 10 large **e.** $-\frac{5}{16}$ **f.** $y = -\frac{5}{16}x + 25$

g.

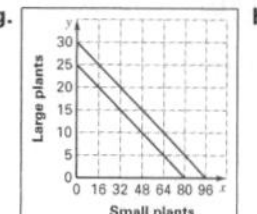

h. The slope remained the same, but the y-intercept increased by 5 units.

PLAN AND PREPARE

Main Ideas

In Chapter 4, students learn how to plot points in a coordinate plane and use tables, *x*- and *y*-intercepts, and the slope and *y*-intercept to graph linear equations and functions. They interpret slope as a rate of change in real-world situations and explore how changing the slope and *y*-intercept changes the graph. They use slope to identify parallel lines. They write and graph direct variation equations and use them to solve real-world problems. They learn how to use function notation and they compare families of graphs.

Prerequisite Skills

Skills Readiness, available on the *Easy Planner*, provides review and practice for the Skills Check portion of the Prerequisite Skills quiz.

How student answers the exercises	What to assign from *Skills Readiness*
Any of Exs. 3–8 answered incorrectly	**Skill 80** Graph functions
Any Exs. 8–11 answered incorrectly	**Skill 72** Solve for a variable
All exercises answered correctly	Chapter 4 Enrichment

Additional skills review and practice is available in the Skills Review Handbook, pp. 909–937, and the @HomeTutor.

4 Graphing Linear Equations and Functions

Making Sense of Chapter 4

In this chapter you will graph linear equations and functions. By the end of this chapter, you will be able to use slopes and *y*-intercepts to compare graphs of families of linear functions.

Before

Previously, you learned the following skills, which you'll use in Chapter 4: graphing functions and writing equations and functions.

Prerequisite Skills

VOCABULARY CHECK

Copy and complete the statement.

1. The set of inputs of a function is called the __?__ of the function. The set of outputs of a function is called the __?__ of the function. **domain; range**
2. A(n) __?__ uses division to compare two quantities. **ratio**

SKILLS CHECK

Graph the function. ***(Prerequisite skill for 4.1–4.7)*** **3–8. See margin.**

3. $y = x + 6$; domain: 0, 2, 4, 6, and 8
4. $y = 2x + 1$; domain: 0, 1, 2, 3, and 4
5. $y = \frac{2}{3}x$; domain: 0, 3, 6, 9, and 12
6. $y = x - \frac{1}{2}$; domain: 1, 2, 3, 4, and 5
7. $y = x - 4$; 5, 6, 7, and 9
8. $y = \frac{1}{2}x + 1$; 2, 4, 6, and 8

Write the equation so that *y* is a function of *x*. ***(Prerequisite skill for 4.5)***

9. $6x + 4y = 16$ **$y = -\frac{3}{2}x + 4$**
10. $x + 2y = 5$ **$y = -\frac{1}{2}x + \frac{5}{2}$**
11. $-12x + 6y = -12$ **$y = 2x - 2$**

@HomeTutor Prerequisite skills practice at classzone.com

Chapter Planning Guide

Chapter Resource Book
- Teaching Guide/Lesson Plan
- Project with Rubric

Assessment and Intervention
- Assessment Book
- Benchmark Tests
- Remediation Book
- Skills Readiness

Interactive Technology
- Easy Planner
- Power Presentations
- Activity Generator
- Animated Algebra
- Test Generator
- Online Quizzes
- eWorkbook
- eEdition
- @HomeTutor

Resources for English Learners
- Spanish Study Guide
- Multi-Language Visual Glossary
- Student Resources in Spanish

Now

In Chapter 4, you will apply the big ideas listed below and reviewed in the Chapter Summary on page 270. You will also use the key vocabulary listed below.

Big Ideas

1. **Graphing linear equations and functions using a variety of methods**
2. **Recognizing how changes in linear equations and functions affect their graphs**
3. **Using graphs of linear equations and functions to solve real-world problems**

KEY VOCABULARY

- quadrant, *p. 206*
- standard form of a linear equation, *p. 216*
- linear function, *p. 217*
- *x*-intercept, *p. 225*
- *y*-intercept, *p. 225*
- slope, *p. 235*
- rate of change, *p. 237*
- slope-intercept form, *p. 244*
- parallel, *p. 246*
- direct variation, *p. 253*
- constant of variation, *p. 253*
- function notation, *p. 262*
- family of functions, *p. 263*
- parent linear function, *p. 263*

Why?

You can graph linear functions to solve problems involving distance. For example, you can graph a linear function to find the time it takes and in-line skater to travel a particular distance at a particular speed.

Animated Algebra

The animation illustrated below for Exercise 41 on page 267 helps you answer this question: How can you graph a function that models the distance an in-line skater travels over time?

Start
You want to graph a function that gives the distance traveled by an in-line skater.

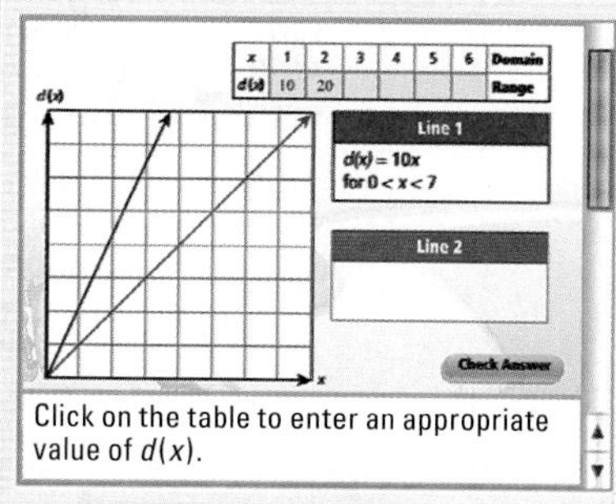

Animated Algebra at classzone.com

Other animations for Chapter 4: pages 207, 216, 226, 238, 245, and 254

Differentiated Instruction Resources

- Reading Strategies for Chapter 4
- Differentiated Instruction Lesson Notes
- English Learners Lesson Notes
- Inclusion Lesson Notes
- Teaching Strategies with Sample Worksheets
- Using Technology in the Classroom
- Tips for New Teachers
- Math Background Notes
- Assessment Strategies
- Teacher Survival Activities
- Bulletin Board Idea

5. 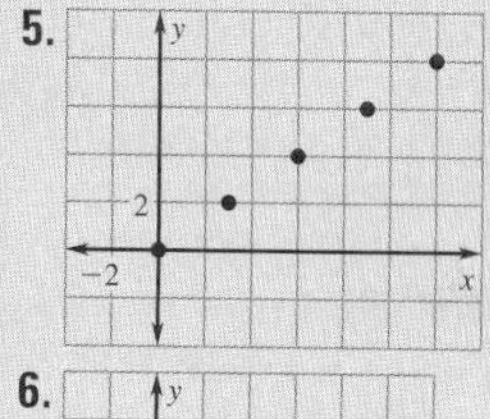

6. 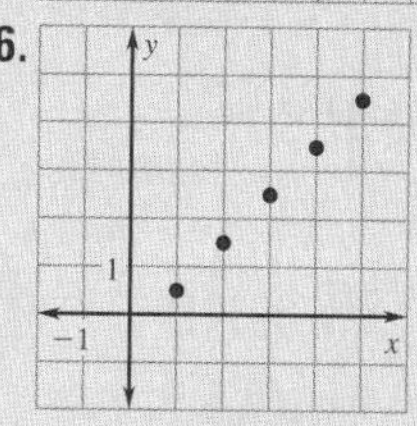

7. 8. 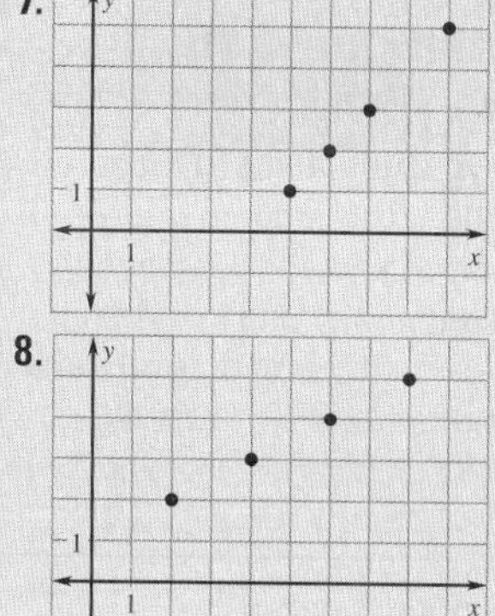

3. 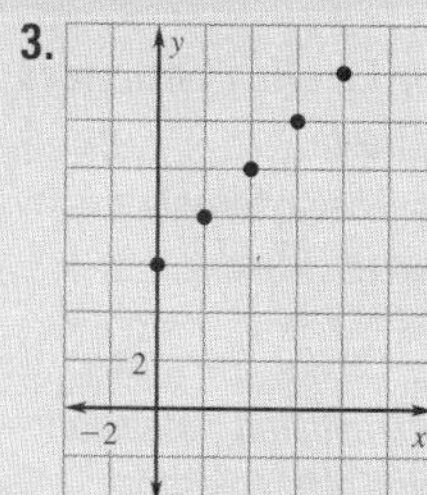

4. 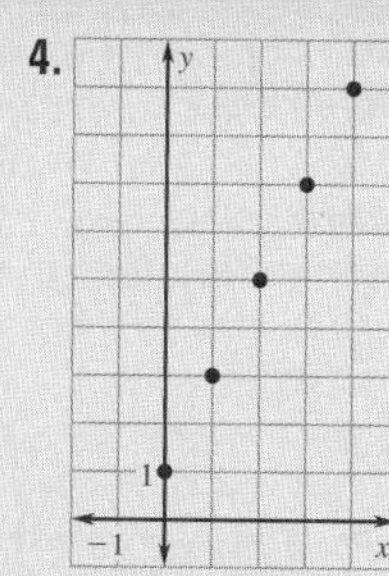

1 PLAN AND PREPARE

Warm-Up Exercises

Transparency Available

Plot the numbers on a number line.

1. −4, −2, 1, 3
2. −3, 0, 2, 5
3. 0.4, 0.9, 1.3, 1.6

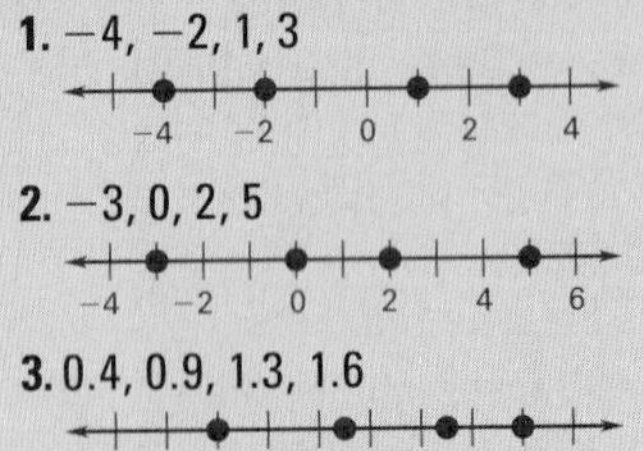

Notetaking Guide

Transparency Available

Promotes interactive learning and notetaking skills.

Pacing

Basic: 1 day

Average: 1 day

Advanced: 1 day

Block: 0.5 block with 4.2

- See *Teaching Guide/Lesson Plan.*

2 FOCUS AND MOTIVATE

Essential Question

Big Idea 1, p. 205

How do you plot points in a coordinate plane? **Tell students they will learn how to answer this question by locating points and graphing functions in all four quadrants of a coordinate plane.**

NCTM STANDARDS

Standard 3: Specify locations using coordinate geometry

Standard 10: Use representations to communicate mathematical ideas

4.1 Plot Points in a Coordinate Plane

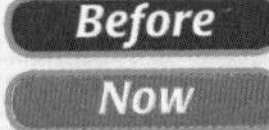

Before You graphed numbers on a number line.

Now You will identify and plot points in a coordinate plane.

Why? So you can interpret photos of Earth taken from space, as in Ex. 36.

Key Vocabulary
- **quadrants**
- **coordinate plane,** *p. 921*
- **ordered pair,** *p. 921*

In Chapter 1, you used a coordinate plane to graph ordered pairs whose coordinates were nonnegative. If you extend the x-axis and y-axis to include negative values, you divide the coordinate plane into four regions called **quadrants**, labeled I, II, III, and IV as shown.

Points in Quadrant I have two positive coordinates. Points in the other three quadrants have at least one negative coordinate.

For example, point P is in Quadrant IV and has an x-coordinate of 3 and a y-coordinate of −2. A point on an axis, such as point Q, is not considered to be in any of the four quadrants.

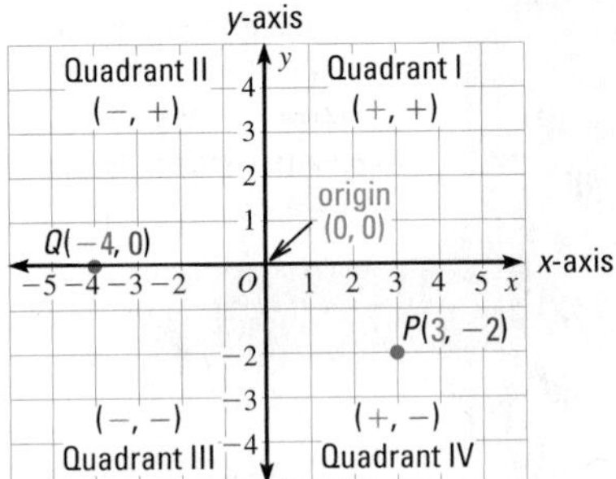

READING The x-coordinate of a point is sometimes called the *abscissa*. The y-coordinate of a point is sometimes called the *ordinate*.

EXAMPLE 1 Name points in a coordinate plane

Give the coordinates of the point.

a. A **b.** B

Solution

a. Point A is 3 units to the left of the origin and 4 units up. So, the x-coordinate is −3, and the y-coordinate is 4. The coordinates are (−3, 4).

b. Point B is 2 units to the right of the origin and 3 units down. So, the x-coordinate is 2, and the y-coordinate is −3. The coordinates are (2, −3).

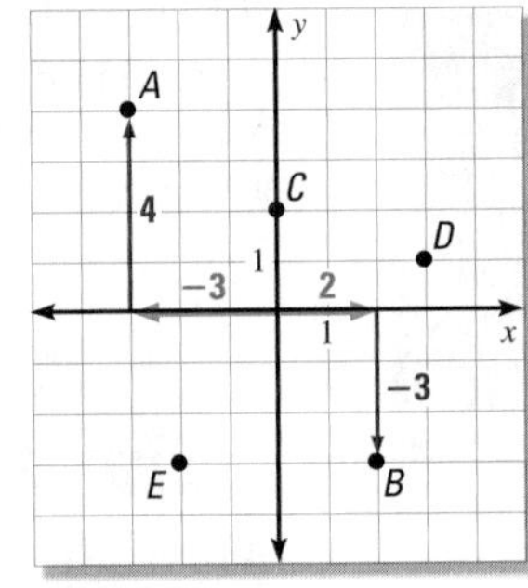

✓ GUIDED PRACTICE for Example 1

1. Use the coordinate plane in Example 1 to give the coordinates of points C, D, and E. **C(0,2), D(3, 1), E(−2, −3)**
2. What is the y-coordinate of any point on the x-axis? **0**

Resource Planning Guide

Chapter Resource Book
- Teaching Guide/Lesson Plan
- Practice levels A, B, C
- Study Guide
- Catch-up for Absent Students
- Application
- Challenge

Workbooks
- Notetaking Guide
- Practice Workbook

Teaching Options
- **Power Presentations** provides dynamic electronic teaching resources for the classroom.
- **Activity Generator** provides editable activities for all ability levels.

Interactive Technology
- Easy Planner
- Power Presentations
- Activity Generator
- Animated Algebra
- Test Generator
- Online Quiz
- eWorkbook
- eEdition
- @HomeTutor

Resources for English Learners
- Spanish Study Guide
- Multi-Language Visual Glossary
- Student Resources in Spanish

See also the *Differentiated Instruction Resources* for more strategies for meeting individual needs.

EXAMPLE 2 Plot points in a coordinate plane

Plot the point in a coordinate plane. Describe the location of the point.

a. $A(-4, 4)$ **b.** $B(3, -2)$ **c.** $C(0, -4)$

Solution

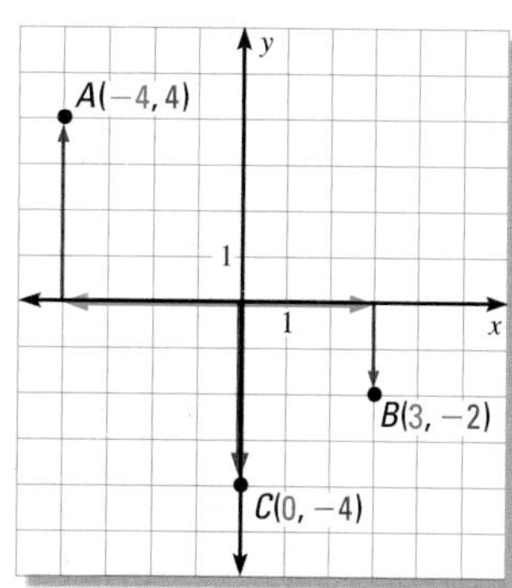

a. Begin at the origin. First move 4 units to the left, then 4 units up. Point A is in Quadrant II.

b. Begin at the origin. First move 3 units to the right, then 2 units down. Point B is in Quadrant IV.

c. Begin at the origin and move 4 units down. Point C is on the y-axis.

at classzone.com

EXAMPLE 3 Graph a function

Graph the function $y = 2x - 1$ with domain −2, −1, 0, 1, and 2. Then identify the range of the function.

Solution

STEP 1 **Make** a table by substituting the domain values into the function.

x	$y = 2x - 1$
−2	$y = 2(-2) - 1 = -5$
−1	$y = 2(-1) - 1 = -3$
0	$y = 2(0) - 1 = -1$
1	$y = 2(1) - 1 = 1$
2	$y = 2(2) - 1 = 3$

STEP 2 **List** the ordered pairs: (−2, −5), (−1, −3), (0, −1), (1, 1), (2, 3). Then graph the function.

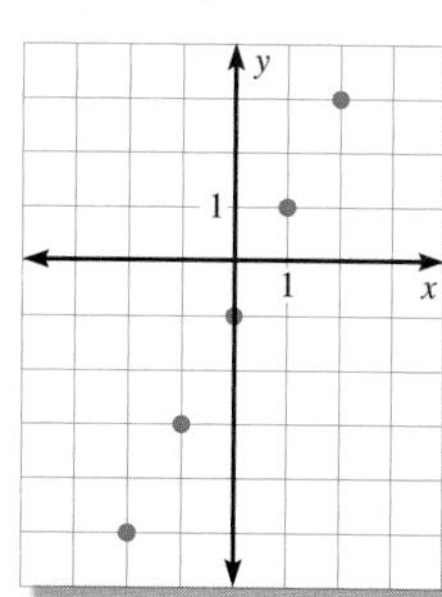

STEP 3 **Identify** the range. The range consists of the y-values from the table: −5, −3, −1, 1, and 3.

ANALYZE A FUNCTION
The function in Example 3 is called a *discrete* function. To learn about discrete functions, see p. 223.

✓ GUIDED PRACTICE for Examples 2 and 3

Plot the point in a coordinate plane. *Describe* the location of the point.

3–6. See margin for art.

3. $A(2, 5)$ **Quadrant I**
4. $B(-1, 0)$ **x-axis**
5. $C(-2, -1)$ **Quadrant III**
6. $D(-5, 3)$ **Quadrant II**
7. Graph the function $y = -\frac{1}{3}x + 2$ with domain −6, −3, 0, 3, and 6. Then identify the range of the function. **See margin for art; range: 0, 1, 2, 3, and 4.**

Motivating the Lesson

You can use graphs in a coordinate plane to analyze trends that include negative quantities. For example, a member of the school golf team could plot her score above or below par for each round she plays, with round 0 being the first day of competition and rounds −1, −2, −3, . . . being earlier practice rounds

3 TEACH

Extra Example 1

Give the coordinates of the point.

a. A **(−2, 1)** **b.** B **(4, −2)**

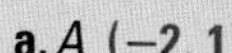

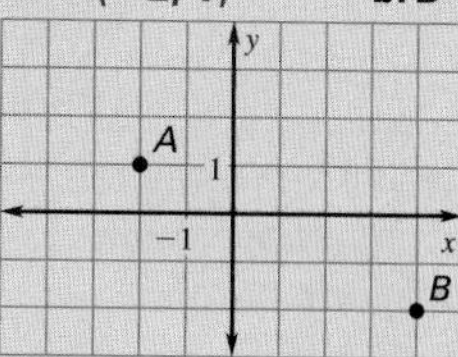

Extra Example 2

Plot the point in a coordinate plane. Describe the location of the point.

a. $A(-3, 0)$ **b.** $B(1, -4)$ **c.** $C(-4, -3)$

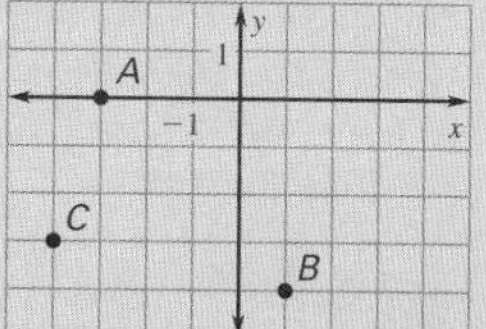

a. Point A is on the x-axis.
b. Point B is in Quadrant IV.
c. Point C is in Quadrant III.

Animated Algebra classzone.com

An **Animated Algebra** activity is available online for **Example 2.** This activity is also part of **Power Presentations.**

3–7. See Additional Answers beginning on p. AA1.

Differentiated Instruction

Below Level Students who confuse x- and y-coordinates and quadrants may want to create a note card with a model of a coordinate plane and instructions on how to plot points. Suggest they show the four quadrants, the origin, and the signs of the x- and y-coordinates in each quadrant. Instructions should indicate that they start at the origin, move right for positive x-coordinates and left for negative, and then up for positive y-coordinates and down for negative.

See also the *Differentiated Instruction Resources* for more strategies.

Extra Example 3

Graph the function $y = -\frac{1}{2}x + 1$ with domain −4, −2, 0, 2, and 4. Then identify the range.

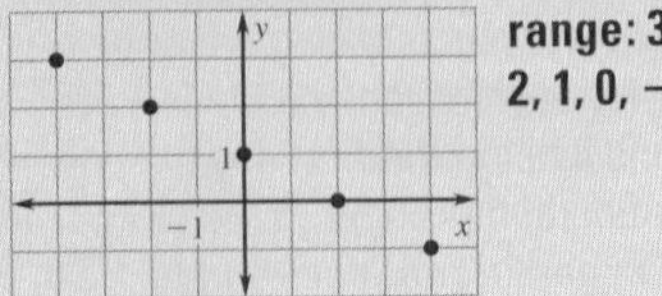

range: 3, 2, 1, 0, −1

Extra Example 4

The table shows attendance at a school carnival before and after the school added game booths in 2002.

Years, *x*, before or since 2002	−2	−1	0	1
Attendance, *y* (hundreds)	2.6	2.2	3.1	3.5

a. Explain how you know the table represents a function. **Each input has only one output.**

b. Graph the function.

c. Describe any trends. **Before 2002, attendance was below 300 and decreasing. After 2002, it increased to over 300 and it continued to climb in 2003.**

Closing the Lesson

Have students summarize the major points of the lesson and answer the Essential Question: How do you plot points in a coordinate plane?

- **A coordinate plane consists of four regions called quadrants.**
- **You plot points in a coordinate plane by moving left or right from the origin and then up or down from the x-axis.**

Begin at the origin and move to the right if the x-coordinate is positive and left if negative. Then move up if the y-coordinate is positive and down if negative.

EXAMPLE 4 Graph a function represented by a table

VOTING In 1920 the ratification of the 19th amendment to the United States Constitution gave women the right to vote. The table shows the number (to the nearest million) of votes cast in presidential elections both before and since women were able to vote.

Presidential campaign button

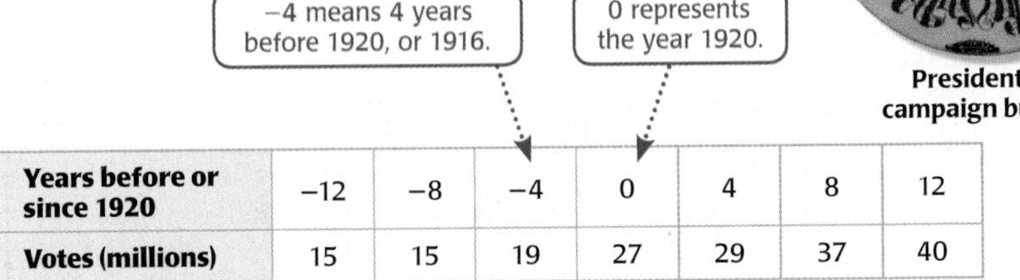

−4 means 4 years before 1920, or 1916.
0 represents the year 1920.

Years before or since 1920	−12	−8	−4	0	4	8	12
Votes (millions)	15	15	19	27	29	37	40

a. Explain how you know that the table represents a function.

b. Graph the function represented by the table.

c. Describe any trend in the number of votes cast.

Solution

a. The table represents a function because each input has exactly one output.

b. To graph the function, let *x* be the number of years before or since 1920. Let *y* be the number of votes cast (in millions).

The graph of the function is shown.

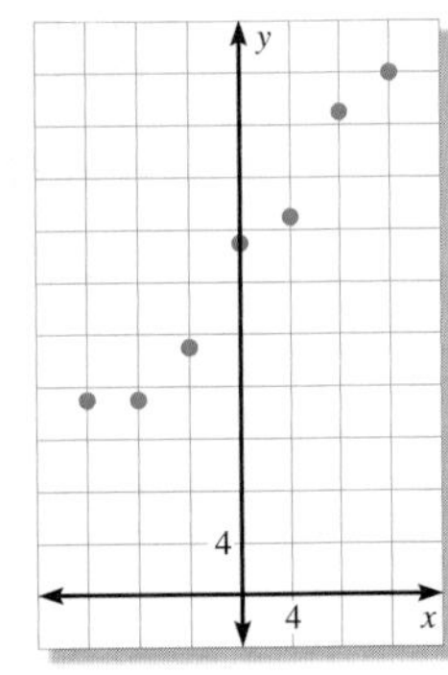

c. In the three election years before 1920, the number of votes cast was less than 20 million. In 1920, the number of votes cast was greater than 20 million. The number of votes cast continued to increase in the three election years since 1920.

✓ GUIDED PRACTICE for Example 4

8. **VOTING** The presidential election in 1972 was the first election in which 18-year-olds were allowed to vote. The table shows the number (to the nearest million) of votes cast in presidential elections both before and since 1972.

Years before or since 1972	−12	−8	−4	0	4	8	12
Votes (millions)	69	71	73	78	82	87	93

a. *Explain* how you know the graph represents a function.

b. Graph the function represented by the table. **See margin.**

c. *Describe* any trend in the number of votes cast. ***Sample answer:*** **Before 1972 the number of voters increased by 2 million every 4 years. In 1972 the number increased by 5 million and continued to increase by more than 2 million every 4 years since 1972.**

8a. The table represents a function because each input has exactly one output.

8b.

Differentiated Instruction

Inclusion If you use the words *abscissa* and *ordinate*, students sometimes cannot remember which coordinate is the ordinate and which is the abscissa. One way to avoid confusion is to point out that the words in the ordered pair (abscissa, ordinate) and the letters in the ordered pair (*x*, *y*) are both in alphabetical order.

See also the *Differentiated Instruction Resources* for more strategies.

4.1 EXERCISES

HOMEWORK KEY
○ = **WORKED-OUT SOLUTIONS** on p. WS7 for Exs. 15, 25, and 37
★ = **STANDARDIZED TEST PRACTICE** Exs. 2, 13, 23, 33, and 41
◆ = **MULTIPLE REPRESENTATIONS** Ex. 40

SKILL PRACTICE

A

1. **VOCABULARY** What is the *x*-coordinate of the point (5, −3)? What is the *y*-coordinate? **5; −3**

2. ★ **WRITING** One of the coordinates of a point is negative while the other is positive. Can you determine the quadrant in which the point lies? *Explain.* **No; the point could lie in either Quadrant II or Quadrant IV.**

EXAMPLE 1 on p. 206 for Exs. 3–13

NAMING POINTS **Give the coordinates of the point.**

3. *A* **(3, −2)**
4. *B* **(0, −1)**
5. *C* **(4, 4)**
6. *D* **(−4, 3)**
7. *E* **(4, −1)**
8. *F* **(3, 0)**
9. *G* **(−5, 4)**
10. *H* **(−3, −2)**
11. *J* **(−4, −1)**
12. *K* **(−1, 2)**

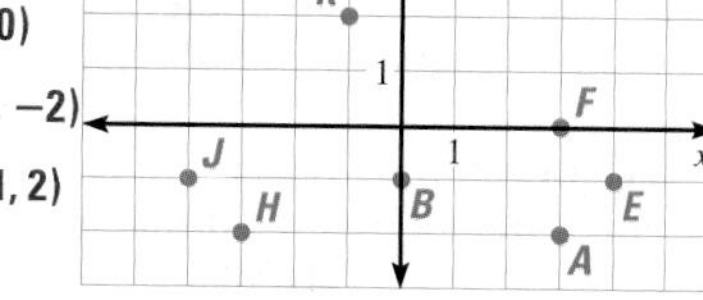

13. ★ **MULTIPLE CHOICE** A point is located 3 units to the left of the origin and 6 units up. What are the coordinates of the point? **B**

Ⓐ (3, 6) Ⓑ (−3, 6) Ⓒ (6, 3) Ⓓ (6, −3)

EXAMPLE 2 on p. 207 for Exs. 14–22

PLOTTING POINTS **Plot the point in a coordinate plane. *Describe* the location of the point.** **14–21. See margin for art.**

14. *P*(5, 5) **Quadrant I**
15. *Q*(−1, 5) **Quadrant II**
16. *R*(−3, 0) **x-axis**
17. *S*(0, 0) **origin**
18. *T*(−3, −4) **Quadrant III**
19. *U*(0, 6) **y-axis**
20. *V*(1.5, 4) **Quadrant I**
21. *W*(3, −2.5) **Quadrant IV**

22. **ERROR ANALYSIS** *Describe* and correct the error in describing the location of the point *W*(6, −6). **The description of the location is backwards, the point is 6 units to the right of the origin and 6 units down.**

> Point W(6, −6) is 6 units to the left of the origin and 6 units up. ✗

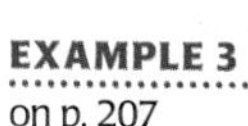

EXAMPLE 3 on p. 207 for Exs. 23–27

23. ★ **MULTIPLE CHOICE** Which number is in the range of the function whose graph is shown? **B**

Ⓐ −2 Ⓑ −1
Ⓒ 0 Ⓓ 2

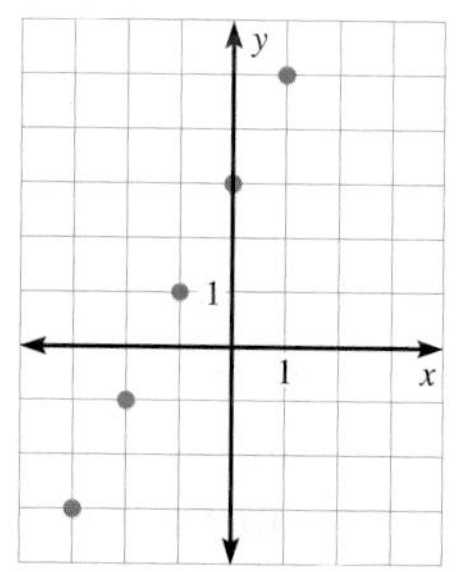

14–21. U(0, 6), P(5, 5), Q(−1, 5), V(1.5, 4), R(−3, 0), S(0, 0), W(3, −2.5), T(−3, −4)

4 PRACTICE AND APPLY

Assignment Guide

Answer Transparencies available for all exercises

Basic:
Day 1: SRH p. 919 Exs. 7–21 odd
pp. 209–212
Exs. 1, 2, 3–11 odd, 13–17, 22–30, 36–39, 42–54 even

Average:
Day 1: pp. 209–212
Exs. 1, 2, 7–13 odd, 16–22 even, 23, 24–32 even, 33–40, 43–53 odd

Advanced:
Day 1: pp. 209–212
Exs. 1, 2, 10–13, 19–23, 26–28, 31–35*, 38–41*, 43–53 odd

Block:
pp. 209–212
Exs. 1, 2, 7–13 odd, 16–22 even, 23, 24–32 even, 33–40, 43–53 odd (with 4.2)

Differentiated Instruction

See *Differentiated Instruction Resources* for suggestions on addressing the needs of a diverse classroom.

Homework Check

For a quick check of student understanding of key concepts, go over the following exercises:
Basic: 7, 16, 24, 36, 37
Average: 9, 18, 26, 36, 38
Advanced: 12, 20, 27, 38, 39

Extra Practice

- Student Edition, p. 941
- Chapter Resource Book: Practice levels A, B, C

Practice Worksheet

An easily-readable reduced practice page (with answers) for this lesson can be found on p. 204C.

Avoiding Common Errors

Exercises 3–21 Since students may switch x- and y-coordinates, you may want to remind them that the x-coordinate is the first number in an ordered pair and the y-coordinate the second.

Study Strategy

Exercise 23 Remind students that the range represents the y-values of the function. Have them rephrase the question as "Which y-value below is shown on the graph?"

Teaching Strategy

Exercise 35 Encourage students to create and use a visual model, such as the model of the coordinate plane shown in the introduction on page 206, to help determine the quadrant of each of the points.

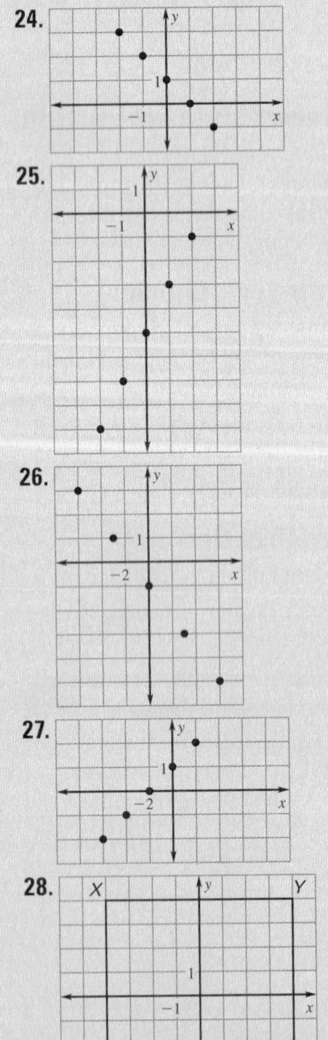

GRAPHING FUNCTIONS **Graph the function with the given domain. Then identify the range of the function.** **24–27. See margin for art.**

24. $y = -x + 1$; domain: −2, −1, 0, 1, 2 **−1, 0, 1, 2, 3**

25. $y = 2x - 5$; domain: −2, −1, 0, 1, 2 **−9, −7, −5, −3, −1**

26. $y = -\frac{2}{3}x - 1$; domain: −6, −3, 0, 3, 6 **−5, −3, −1, 1, 3**

27. $y = \frac{1}{2}x + 1$; domain: −6, −4, −2, 0, 2 **−2, −1, 0, 1, 2**

B 28. **GEOMETRY** Plot the points $W(-4, -2)$, $X(-4, 4)$, $Y(4, 4)$, and $Z(4, -2)$ in a coordinate plane. Connect the points in order. Connect point Z to point W. Identify the resulting figure. Find its perimeter and area. **See margin for art; rectangle; perimeter: 28 units, area: 48 square units.**

REASONING **Without plotting the point, tell whether it is in Quadrant I, II, III, or IV. *Explain* your reasoning.** **29–32. See margin.**

29. (4, −11) 30. (40, −40) 31. (−18, 15) 32. (−32, −22)

33. ★ **WRITING** *Explain* how can you tell by looking at the coordinates of a point whether the point is on the x-axis or on the y-axis.

33. If the x-coordinate is 0, then the point is on the y-axis. If the y-coordinate is 0, then the point is on the x-axis.

C 34. **REASONING** Plot the point $J(-4, 3)$ in a coordinate plane. Plot three additional points in the same coordinate plane so that each of the four points lies in a different quadrant and the figure formed by connecting the points is a square. *Explain* how you located the points. **See margin.**

35. **CHALLENGE** Suppose the point (a, b) lies in Quadrant IV. *Describe* the location of the following points: (b, a), $(2a, -2b)$, and $(-b, -a)$. *Explain* your reasoning. **See margin.**

PROBLEM SOLVING

A 36. **ASTRONAUT PHOTOGRAPHY** Astronauts use a coordinate system to describe the locations of objects they photograph from space. The x-axis is the equator, 0° latitude. The y-axis is the prime meridian, 0° longitude. The names and coordinates of some lakes photographed from space are given. Use the map to determine on which continent each lake is located.

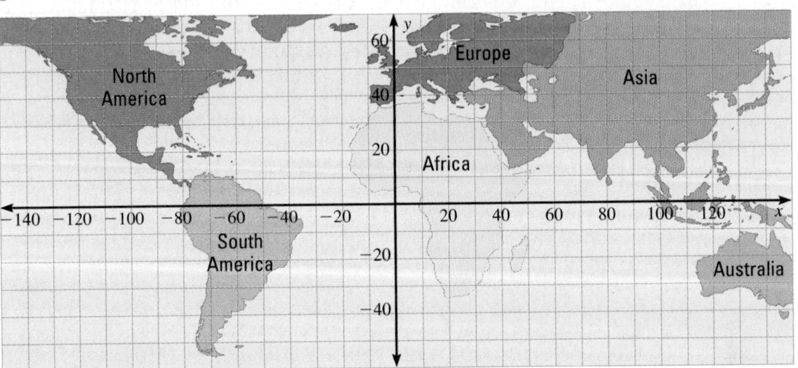

a. Lake Kulundinskoye: (80, 53) **Asia**

b. Lake Champlain: (−73, 45) **North America**

c. Lake Van: (43, 39) **Asia**

d. Lake Viedma: (−73, −50) **South America**

e. Lake Saint Clair: (−83, 43) **North America**

f. Starnberger Lake: (12, 48) **Europe**

@HomeTutor for problem solving help at classzone.com

○ = WORKED-OUT SOLUTIONS on p. WS1 ★ = STANDARDIZED TEST PRACTICE ◆ = MULTIPLE REPRESENTATIONS

29–32. See Additional Answers beginning on p. AA1.

34. *Sample answer:*

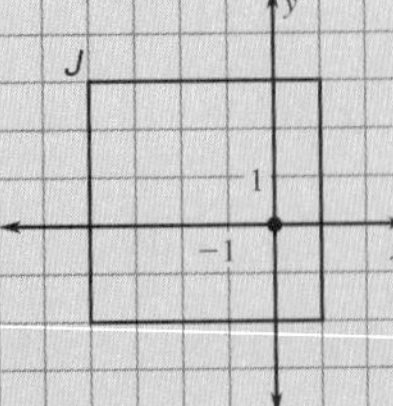

Decide on a side length of a square that is greater than 4, like 5, so the other points will be in different quadrants. Add 5 to the x-coordinate of J, −4, to find the point (1, 3) in Quadrant I. Then subtract 5 from the y-coordinate of J to find the point (−4, −2) in Quadrant 3. Then add 5 to the x-coordinate of (−4, −2) and subtract 5 to the y-coordinate of (1, 3) to find the point (1, −2) in Quadrant IV.

EXAMPLE 4
on p. 208
for Exs. 37–39

37. There is exactly one low temperature for each day in February; see margin for art.

37. **RECORD TEMPERATURES** The table shows the record low temperatures (in degrees Fahrenheit) for Odessa, Texas, for each day in the first week of February. *Explain* how you know the table represents a function. Graph the data from the table.

Day in February	1	2	3	4	5	6	7
Record low (degrees Fahrenheit)	−8	−11	10	8	10	9	11

@HomeTutor for problem solving help at classzone.com

38. **STOCK VALUE** The table shows the change in value (in dollars) of a stock over five days.

Day	1	2	3	4	5
Change in value (dollars)	−0.30	0.10	0.15	0.35	0.11

a. *Explain* how you know the table represents a function. Graph the data from the table. **There is exactly one change in value for each day; see margin for art.**

b. *Describe* any trend in the change in value of the stock.
***Sample answer:* The change in value increases until day 4, and then decreases.**

B 39. **MULTI-STEP PROBLEM** The difference between what the federal government collects and what it spends during a fiscal year is called the federal surplus or deficit. The table shows the federal surplus or deficit (in billions of dollars) in the 1990s. (A negative number represents a deficit.)

Years since 1990	0	1	2	3	4	5	6	7	8	9
Surplus or deficit (billions)	−221	−269	−290	−255	−203	−164	−108	−22	69	126

a. Graph the function represented by the table. **See margin.**

b. What conclusions can you make from the graph?
***Sample answer:* From 1992 to 1999 the federal deficit was decreasing.**

40. **MULTIPLE REPRESENTATIONS** Low-density lipoproteins (LDL) transport cholesterol in the bloodstream throughout the body. A high LDL number is associated with an increased risk of cardiovascular disease. A patient's LDL number in 1999 was 189 milligrams per deciliter (mg/dL). To lower that number, the patient went on a diet. The annual LDL numbers for the patient in years after 1999 are 169, 154, 145, 139, and 136

Years since 1999	1	2	? 3	? 4	? 5
Annual changes in LDL (mg/dL)	−20	−15	? −9	? −6	? −3

a. **Making a Table** Use the given information to copy and complete the table that shows the annual change in the patient's LDL number since 1999.

b. **Drawing a Graph** Graph the ordered pairs from the table. **See margin.**

c. **Describing in Words** Based on the graph, what can you conclude about the diet's effectiveness in lowering the patient's LDL number?
***Sample answer:* The diet is lowering the patient's LDL number.**

Vocabulary

Exercise 39 Students may be confused by the term "fiscal year." Tell them that a fiscal year refers to an accounting period of 12 months or 365 days, but the period may or may not correspond to the calendar year. The federal fiscal year runs from October through September.

Mathematical Reasoning

Exercises 39, 40 You may want to point out that both tables show years since a certain date, but the table in Exercise 39 begins with year 0, whereas the table in Exercise 40 begins with year 1. Lead students to see why the table in Exercise 40 must begin with year 1 and not year 0.

Internet Reference

Exercise 40 For more information about low-density lipoproteins, visit www.webmd.com/cholesterol-management/cholesterol-and-triglycerides-tests

37.
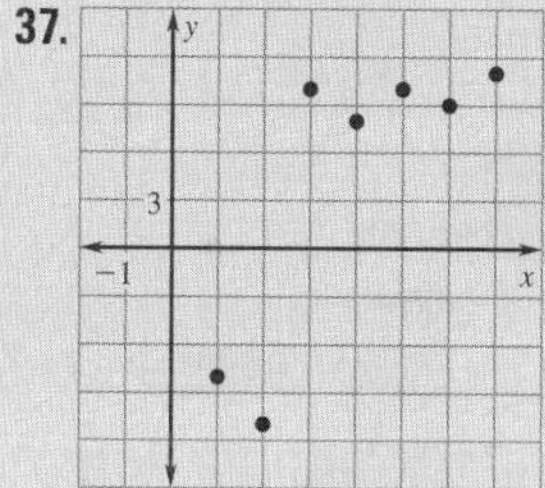

38a.
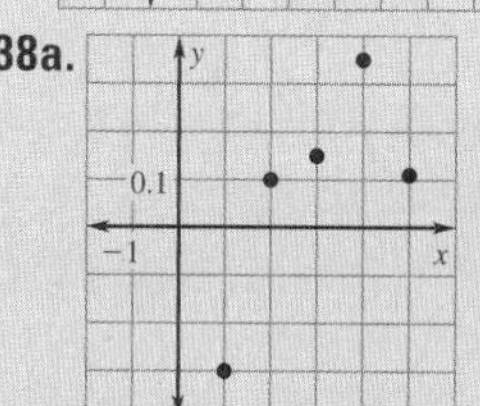

39a.
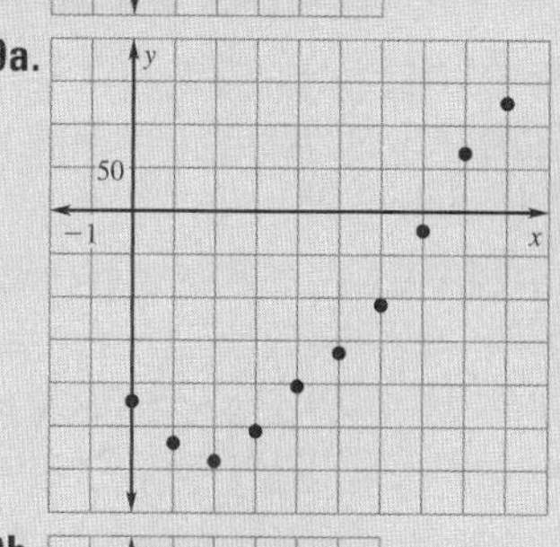

40b.
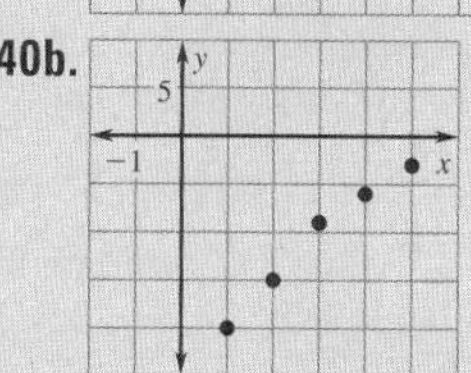

35. For (b, a): Quadrant II; since (a, b) is in Quadrant IV, a must be positive and b must be negative, so the coordinates of (b, a) must be negative and positive. For $(2a, -2b)$: Quadrant I; since (a, b) is in Quadrant IV, a must be positive and b must be negative, so the coordinates of $(2a, -2b)$ must both be positive. For $(-b, -a)$: Quadrant IV; since (a, b) is in Quadrant IV, a must be positive and b must be negative, so the coordinates of $(-b, -a)$ must be positive and negative.

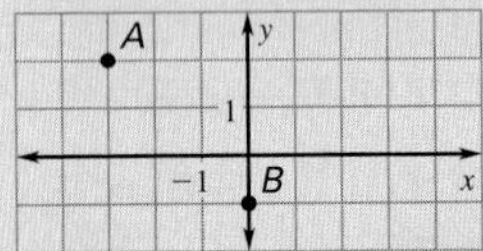

5 ASSESS AND RETEACH

Daily Homework Quiz

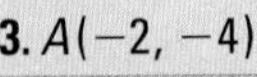

Transparency Available

Give the coordinates of the points.

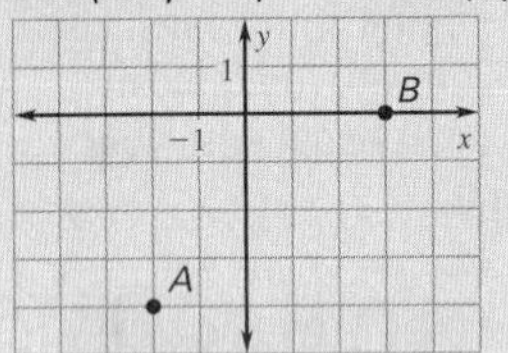

1. *A* (−3, 2) **2.** *B* (0, −1)

Plot the points in a coordinate plane.

3. *A*(−2, −4) **4.** *B*(3, 0)

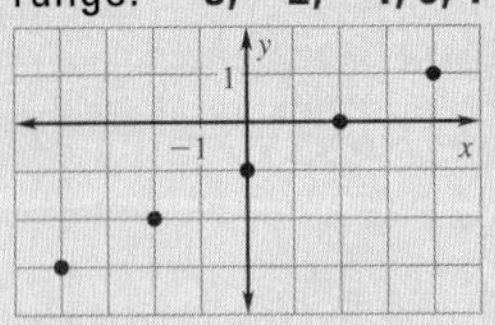

5. Graph $y = \frac{1}{2}x - 1$ with domain −4, −2, 0, 2, 4. Then identify the range. **−3, −2, −1, 0, 1**

Online Quiz

Available at **classzone.com**

Diagnosis/Remediation

- Practice A, B, C in Chapter Resource Book
- Study Guide in Chapter Resource Book
- Practice Workbook
- @HomeTutor

Challenge

Additional challenge is available in the Chapter Resource Book.

41b.

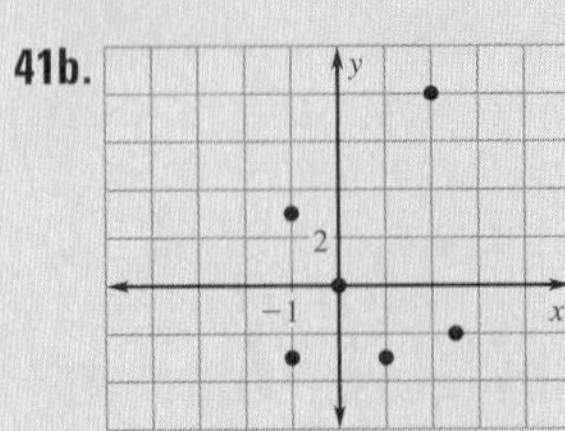

C **41.** ★ **EXTENDED RESPONSE** In a scientific study, researchers asked men to report their heights and weights. Then the researchers measured the actual heights and weights of the men. The data for six men are shown in the table. One row of the table represents the data for one man.

Height (inches)			Weight (pounds)		
Reported	**Measured**	**Difference**	**Reported**	**Measured**	**Difference**
70	68	70 − 68 = 2	154	146	154 − 146 = 8
70	67.5	? **2.5**	141	143	? **−2**
78.5	77.5	? **1**	165	168	? **−3**
68	69	? **−1**	146	143	? **3**
71	72	? **−1**	220	223	? **−3**
70	70	? **0**	176	176	? **0**

a. **Calculate** Copy and complete the table.

b. **Graph** For each participant, write an ordered pair (*x*, *y*) where *x* is the difference of the reported and measured heights and *y* is the difference of the reported and measured weights. Then plot the ordered pairs in a coordinate plane. **(2, 8), (2.5, −2), (1, −3), (−1, 3), (−1, −3), (0, 0); see margin for art.**

c. **CHALLENGE** What does the origin represent in this situation?

d. **CHALLENGE** Which quadrant has the greatest number of points? *Explain* what it means for a point to be in that quadrant. **Quadrant IV; the person reported a greater height than was measured and a lesser weight than was measured.**

41c. ***Sample answer:*** **A person who reported the same information that was measured.**

MIXED REVIEW

Evaluate the expression.

42. $4 + 2x^2$ when $x = 6$ *(p. 2)* **76**

43. $6 \cdot 2a^2$ when $a = 3$ *(p. 2)* **108**

44. $4 + 2(-7) + 3$ *(p. 8)* **−7**

45. $3(35 - 18)$ *(p. 8)* **51**

Use the distributive property to write an equivalent expression. *(p. 96)*

46. $6(x + 20)$ **6x + 120**

47. $3x(x + 9)$ **$3x^2 + 27x$**

48. $-(4 - 5y)$ **−4 + 5y**

49. TRAVEL You are traveling on the highway at an average speed of 55 miles per hour. How long will it take you to drive 66 miles? *(p. 168)* **1.2 h or 1 h 12 min**

PREVIEW Prepare for Lesson 4.2 in Exs. 50–54.

Write the equation so that *y* is a function of *x*. *(p. 184)*

50. $4x + y = 6$ **$y = -4x + 6$**

51. $x + 7y = 14$ **$y = -\frac{1}{7}x + 2$**

52. $4(y - 6x) = 12$ **$y = 6x + 3$**

Tell whether the pairing is a function. *(p. 35)*

53.

Input	−5	−4	−3	−2
Output	−2	0	2	4

function

54.

Input	−1	0	1	2
Output	10	10	4	1

function

EXTRA PRACTICE for Lesson 4.1, p. 941 **ONLINE QUIZ** at classzone.com

Extension Perform Transformations

Use after Lesson 4.1

GOAL Perform and describe transformations in a coordinate plane.

Key Vocabulary
- **transformation**
- **translation**
- **vertical stretch or shrink**
- **reflection**

For a given set of points, a **transformation** produces an image by applying a rule to the coordinates of the points. Some types of transformations are *translations, vertical stretches, vertical shrinks,* and *reflections.*

A **translation** moves every point in a figure the same distance in the same direction either horizontally, vertically, or both. You can describe translations algebraically.

Horizontal translation: $(x, y) \to (x + h, y)$ **Vertical translation:** $(x, y) \to (x, y + k)$

EXAMPLE 1 Perform a translation

READ TRANSFORMATIONS
If a transformation is performed on a point A, the new location of point A is indicated by A' (read "A prime").

The transformation $(x, y) \to (x, y + 3)$ moves $\triangle ABC$ up 3 units.

Original		Image
$A(3, 0)$	$\to$	$A'(3, 3)$
$B(4, 2)$	$\to$	$B'(4, 5)$
$C(5, 0)$	$\to$	$C'(5, 3)$

The result of the transformation is $\triangle A'B'C'$.

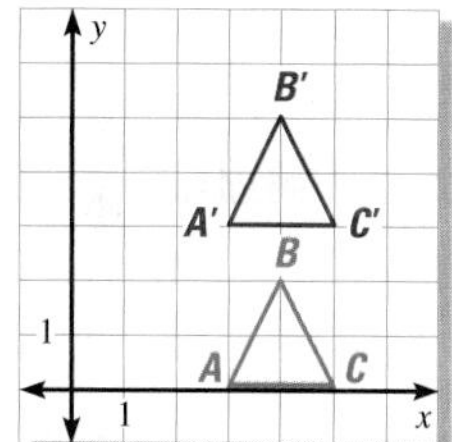

A **vertical stretch or shrink** moves every point in a figure away from the x-axis (a vertical stretch) or toward the x-axis (a vertical shrink), while points on the x-axis remain fixed. A **reflection** flips a figure in a line. You can describe vertical stretches and shrinks with or without reflection in the x-axis algebraically.

Vertical stretch:
$(x, y) \to (x, ay)$ where $a > 1$

Vertical shrink:
$(x, y) \to (x, ay)$ where $0 < a < 1$

Vertical stretch with reflection in the x-axis:
$(x, y) \to (x, ay)$ where $a < -1$

Vertical shrink with reflection in the x-axis:
$(x, y) \to (x, ay)$ where $-1 < a < 0$

EXAMPLE 2 Perform a vertical stretch with reflection

The transformation $(x, y) \to (x, -2y)$ vertically stretches $\triangle ABC$ and reflects it in the x-axis.

Original		Image
$A(3, 0)$	$\to$	$A'(3, 0)$
$B(4, 2)$	$\to$	$B'(4, -4)$
$C(5, 0)$	$\to$	$C'(5, 0)$

The result of the transformation is $\triangle A'B'C'$.

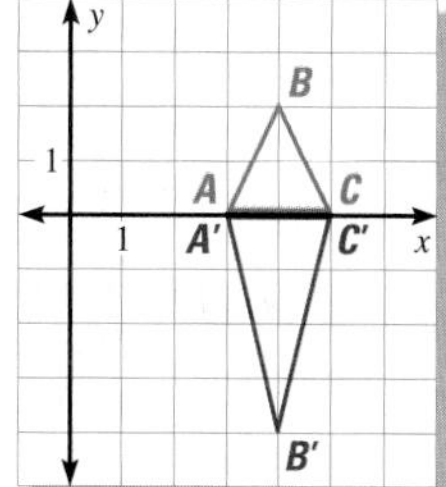

1 PLAN AND PREPARE

Warm-Up Exercises

Plot the points in a coordinate plane.

1. $A(-2, 1)$ **2.** $B(-1, -3)$
3. $C(4, -2)$ **4.** $D(1, 0)$

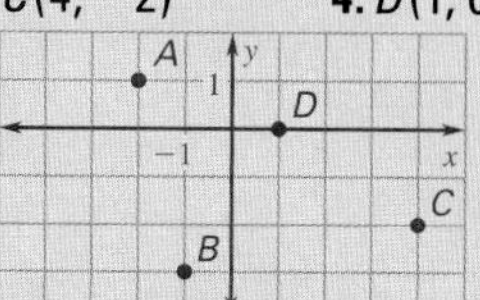

2 FOCUS AND MOTIVATE

Essential Question

Big Idea 2, p. 205

How do you transform figures in the coordinate plane? **Tell students they will learn how to answer this question by describing and performing translations, dilations, and reflections on figures in the coordinate plane.**

3 TEACH

Extra Example 1

Describe the transformation of $\triangle ABC$ to $\triangle A'B'C'$. **The transformation is $(x, y) \to (x - 4, y)$. $\triangle ABC$ is moved left 4 units.**

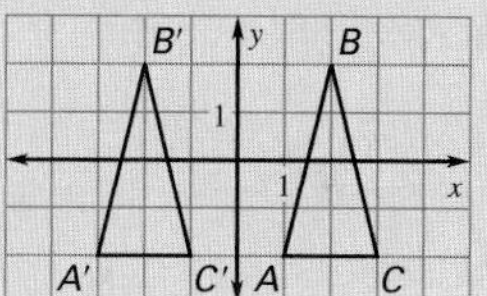

NCTM STANDARDS

Standard 3: Apply transformations to math situations

Standard 10: Use representations to communicate mathematical ideas

Extra Example 2

Describe the transformation of $\triangle ABC$ to $\triangle A'B'C'$. **The transformation is $(x, y) \rightarrow \left(x, -\frac{1}{2}y\right)$. $\triangle A'B'C'$ shows a vertical shrink and reflection in the x-axis of $\triangle ABC$.**

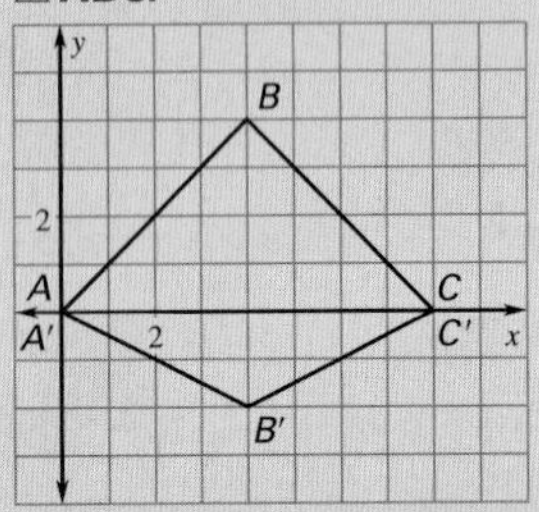

Closing the Lesson

Have students summarize the major points of the lesson and answer the Essential Question: How do you transform figures in the coordinate plane?

- **A translation moves a figure horizontally or vertically.**
- **If a figure has one side along the x-axis, a vertical stretch or shrink moves a figure away from or towards the x-axis.**
- **A reflection flips a figure in a line.**

Translate figures horizontally or vertically by adding to or subtracting from each x- or y-coordinate, respectively. Multiply the y-coordinates by positive numbers for stretches and shrinks and by negative numbers for reflections.

4 PRACTICE AND APPLY

Study Strategy

Exercises 9–11 Encourage students to check the indicated transformations against the descriptions of vertical stretches and shrinks and reflections on page 213. This allows them to anticipate the resulting transformation and to check that their calculations are correct.

CONCEPT SUMMARY *For Your Notebook*

Identifying Transformations

Translation		Vertical stretch or shrink	
Horizontal	**Vertical**	**Without reflection**	**With reflection**
$(x, y) \rightarrow (x + h, y)$	$(x, y) \rightarrow (x, y + k)$	$(x, y) \rightarrow (x, ay)$ where $a > 0$	$(x, y) \rightarrow (x, ay)$ where $a < 0$

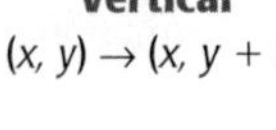
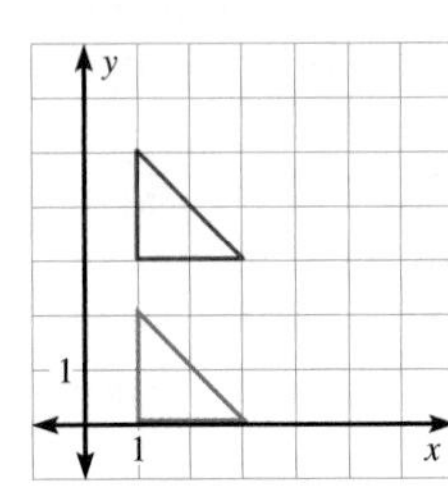
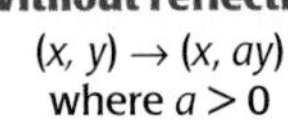
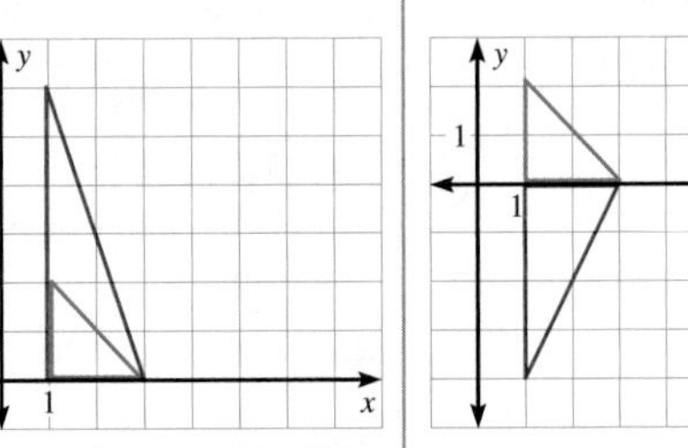

PRACTICE

1. **VOCABULARY** Does a translation or a vertical stretch always produce a figure that is the same size and shape as the original figure? *Explain.* **See margin.**

2. ★ **WRITING** *Describe* the vertical shrink $(x, y) \rightarrow (x, \frac{1}{2}y)$ in words. **Multiply each y-coordinate by $\frac{1}{2}$.**

EXAMPLES 1 and 2 on p. 213 for Exs. 3–14

1. Translation; a translation moves every point the same distance in the same direction so it will have the same shape and size as the original figure.

DESCRIBING TRANSFORMATIONS **Use words to describe the transformation of the blue figure to the red figure.**

3. **Subtract 4 from each y-coordinate.**

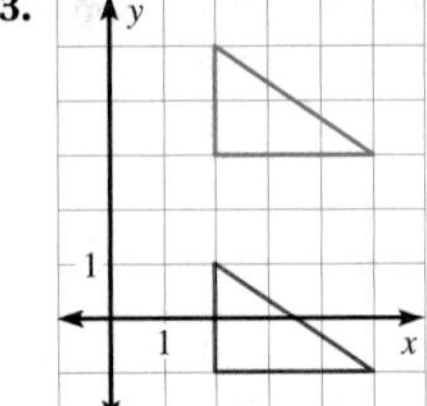

4. **Multiply each y-coordinate by $-\frac{1}{2}$.**

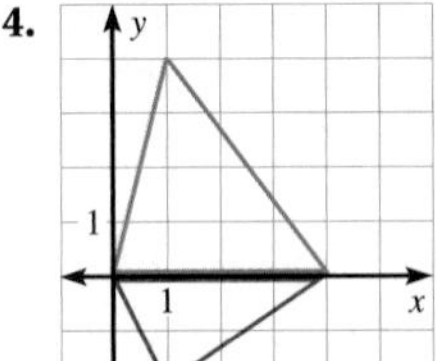

5. **Add 2 to each y-coordinate.**

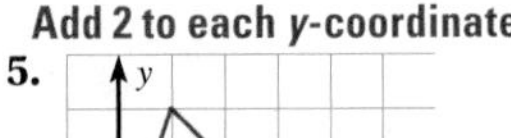
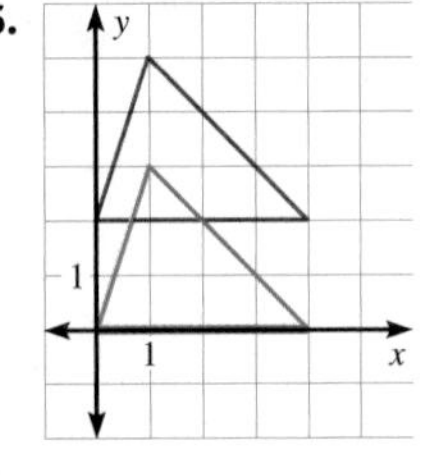

PERFORMING TRANSFORMATIONS **Square $ABCD$ has vertices at (0, 0), (0, 2), (2, 2), and (2, 0). Perform the indicated transformation. Then give the coordinates of figure $A'B'C'D'$.**

6. $(x, y) \rightarrow (x, y - 5)$ **(0, −5), (0, −3), (2, −3), (2, −5)**
7. $(x, y) \rightarrow (x, y + 1)$ **(0, 1), (0, 3), (2, 3), (2, 1)**
8. $(x, y) \rightarrow (x, y - 7)$ **(0, −7), (0, −5), (2, −5), (2, −7)**
9. $(x, y) \rightarrow (x, -y)$ **(0, 0), (0, −2), (2, −2), (2, 0)**
10. $(x, y) \rightarrow (x, 4y)$ **(0, 0), (0, 8), (2, 8), (2, 0)**
11. $(x, y) \rightarrow (x, -\frac{1}{2}y)$ **(0, 0), (0, −1), (2, −1), (2, 0)**
12. $(x, y) \rightarrow (x + 2, y + 3)$ **(2, 3), (2, 5), (4, 5), (4, 3)**
13. $(x, y) \rightarrow (x - 1, y + 4)$ **(−1, 4), (−1, 6), (1, 6), (1, 4)**
14. $(x, y) \rightarrow (x + 3, y)$ **(3, 0), (3, 2), (5, 2), (5, 0)**

15. ★ **WRITING** A square has vertices at (0, 0), (0, 3), (3, 3), and (3, 0). Tell how you could use a transformation to move the square so that it has new vertices at (0, 0), (0, −3), (3, −3), and (3, 0). **Use the transformation $(x, y) \rightarrow (x, -y)$.**

4.2 Graph Linear Equations

Before	You plotted points in a coordinate plane.
Now	You will graph linear equations in a coordinate plane.
Why?	So you can find how meteorologists collect data, as in Ex. 40.

Key Vocabulary
- **standard form of a linear equation**
- **linear function**

An example of an equation in two variables is $2x + 5y = 8$. A **solution of an equation in two variables**, x and y, is an ordered pair (x, y) that produces a true statement when the values of x and y are substituted into the equation.

EXAMPLE 1 Standardized Test Practice

Which ordered pair is a solution of $3x - y = 7$?

Ⓐ (3, 4) Ⓑ (1, −4) Ⓒ (5, −3) Ⓓ (−1, −2)

Solution

Check whether each ordered pair is a solution of the equation.

Test (3, 4):	$3x - y = 7$	**Write original equation.**
	$3(3) - 4 \stackrel{?}{=} 7$	**Substitute 3 for x and 4 for y.**
	$5 = 7$ ✗	**Simplify.**
Test (1, −4):	$3x - y = 7$	**Write original equation.**
	$3(1) - (-4) \stackrel{?}{=} 7$	**Substitute 1 for x and −4 for y.**
	$7 = 7$ ✓	**Simplify.**

So, (3, 4) is *not* a solution, but (1, −4) is a solution of $3x - y = 7$.

▶ The correct answer is B. Ⓐ Ⓑ Ⓒ Ⓓ

GUIDED PRACTICE for Example 1

1. Tell whether $\left(4, -\frac{1}{2}\right)$ is a solution of $x + 2y = 5$. **not a solution**

GRAPHS The **graph of an equation in two variables** is the set of points in a coordinate plane that represent all solutions of the equation. If the variables in an equation represent real numbers, one way to graph the equation is to make a table of values, plot enough points to recognize a pattern, and then connect the points. When making a table of values, choose convenient values of x that include negative values, zero, and positive values.

1 PLAN AND PREPARE

Warm-Up Exercises
Transparency Available

1. Graph $y = -x - 2$ with domain −2, −1, 0, 1, and 2.

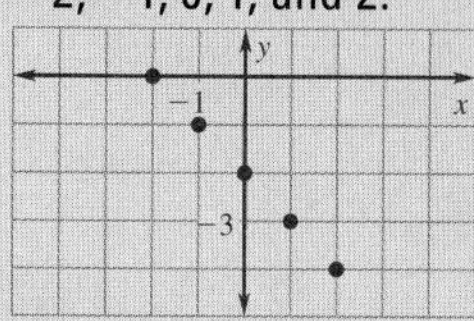

Rewrite the equation so y is a function of x.

2. $3x + 4y = 16$ $y = -\frac{3}{4}x + 4$
3. $-6x - 2y = -12$ $y = -3x + 6$

Notetaking Guide
Transparency Available
Promotes interactive learning and notetaking skills.

Pacing
Basic: 2 days
Average: 2 days
Advanced: 2 days
Block: 0.5 block with 4.1
0.5 block with 4.3
- See *Teaching Guide/Lesson Plan.*

2 FOCUS AND MOTIVATE

Essential Question
Big Idea 1, p. 205
How do you graph linear equations? **Tell students they will learn how to answer this question by using tables to graph linear equations.**

NCTM STANDARDS
Standard 2: Use models to understand relationships
Standard 10: Use representations to communicate mathematical ideas

Resource Planning Guide

Chapter Resource Book
- Teaching Guide/Lesson Plan
- Activity Master
- Practice levels A, B, C
- Study Guide
- Catch-up for Absent Students
- Problem Solving Workshop
- Challenge

Workbooks
- Notetaking Guide
- Practice Workbook

Teaching Options
- **Power Presentations** provides dynamic electronic teaching resources for the classroom.
- **Activity Generator** provides editable activities for all ability levels.

Interactive Technology
- Easy Planner
- Power Presentations
- Activity Generator
- Animated Algebra
- Test Generator
- Online Quiz
- eWorkbook
- eEdition
- @HomeTutor

Resources for English Learners
- Spanish Study Guide
- Multi-Language Visual Glossary
- Student Resources in Spanish

See also the *Differentiated Instruction Resources* for more strategies for meeting individual needs.

Motivating the Lesson

You can use graphs of linear equations to determine information about real-world situations. For example, if you paid $25 to join a skating rink and then $15 per lesson, you could use a graph of the situation to find the cost after a specific number of lessons.

3 TEACH

Extra Example 1

Which ordered pair is a solution of $-x + 2y = 8$? **D**

Ⓐ (2, 3) Ⓑ (−2, 5)
Ⓒ (−1, 4) Ⓓ (−2, 3)

Key Questions to Ask for Example 1

- Are there other solutions of the equation? Explain. **Yes. Any ordered pair that produces a true statement is a solution.**
- What are some other solutions? **(3, 2), (2, −1), (0, −7)**

Extra Example 2

Graph the equation $2x + y = 2$.

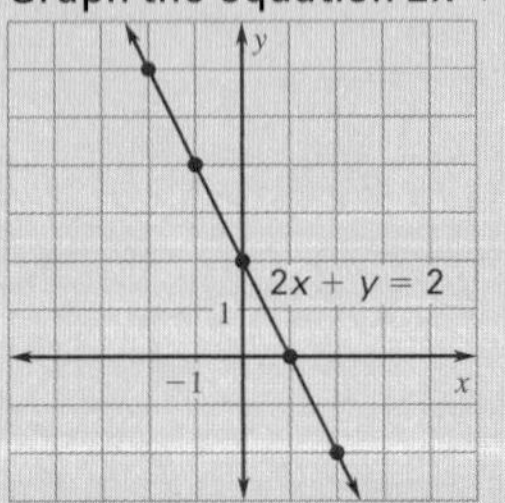

Key Question to Ask for Example 2

- How many points on the line represent solutions of the equation? Explain. **Every point on the line is a solution of the equation, so there are an infinite number of solutions.**

EXAMPLE 2 Graph an equation

Graph the equation $-2x + y = -3$.

Solution

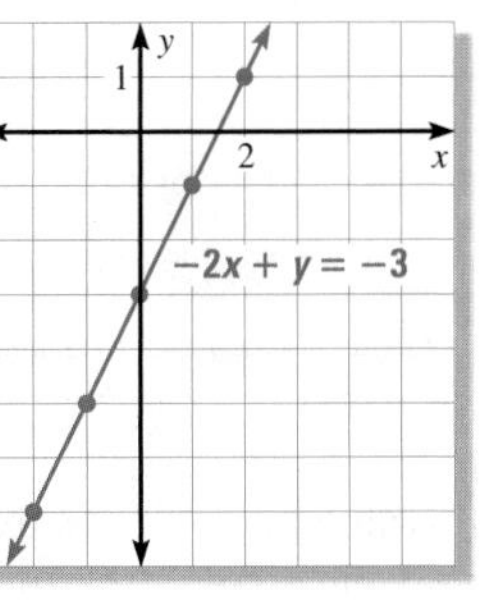

STEP 1 **Solve** the equation for y.

$$-2x + y = -3$$

$$y = 2x - 3$$

DRAW A GRAPH
If you continued to find solutions of the equation and plotted them, the line would fill in.

STEP 2 **Make** a table by choosing a few values for x and finding the values of y.

x	−2	−1	0	1	2
y	−7	−5	−3	−1	1

STEP 3 **Plot** the points. Notice that the points appear to lie on a line.

STEP 4 **Connect** the points by drawing a line through them. Use arrows to indicate that the graph goes on without end.

LINEAR EQUATIONS A **linear equation** is an equation whose graph is a line, such as the equation in Example 2. The **standard form** of a linear equation is

$$Ax + By = C$$

where A, B, and C are real numbers and A and B are not both zero.

Consider what happens when $A = 0$ or when $B = 0$. When $A = 0$, the equation becomes $By = C$, or $y = \frac{C}{B}$. Because $\frac{C}{B}$ is a constant, you can write $y = b$. Similarly, when $B = 0$, the equation becomes $Ax = C$, or $x = \frac{C}{A}$, and you can write $x = a$.

EXAMPLE 3 Graph $y = b$ and $x = a$

Graph (a) $y = 2$ and (b) $x = -1$.

Solution

FIND A SOLUTION
The equations $y = 2$ and $0x + 1y = 2$ are equivalent. For any value of x, the ordered pair $(x, 2)$ is a solution of $y = 2$.

a. For every value of x, the value of y is 2. The graph of the equation $y = 2$ is a horizontal line 2 units above the x-axis.

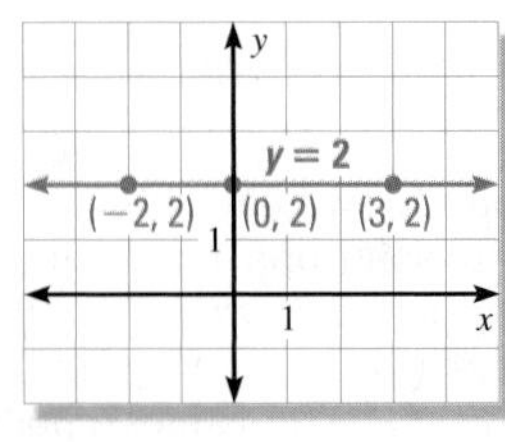

b. For every value of y, the value of x is −1. The graph of the equation $x = -1$ is a vertical line 1 unit to the left of the y-axis.

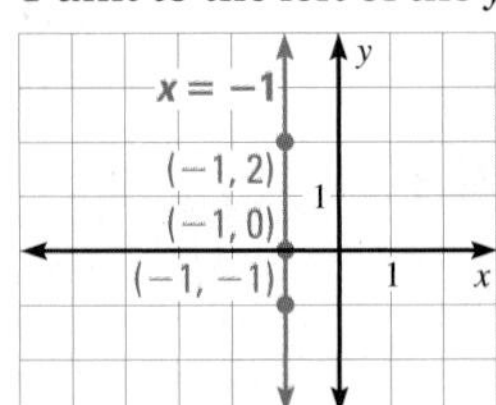

Animated Algebra at classzone.com

Differentiated Instruction

English Learners In Example 2, caution students that the figure is called a "graph of a line," and should not be confused with a *line graph* (p. 933). A line graph is a graph that uses line segments to connect data points. A graph of a line is a graph of a linear equation.

See also the *Differentiated Instruction Resources* for more strategies.

KEY CONCEPT *For Your Notebook*

Equations of Horizontal and Vertical Lines

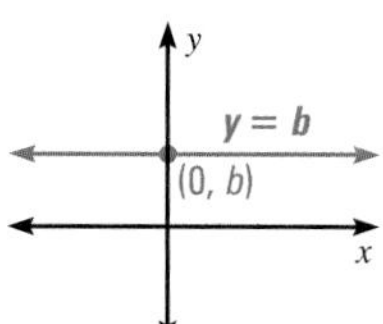

The graph of $y = b$ is a horizontal line. The line passes through the point $(0, b)$.

The graph of $x = a$ is a vertical line. The line passes through the point $(a, 0)$.

GUIDED PRACTICE for Examples 2 and 3

Graph the equation. **2–4. See margin.**

2. $y + 3x = -2$ **3.** $y = 2.5$ **4.** $x = -4$

IDENTIFY A FUNCTION
The function $y = 2$ is a *constant function*. The graph of a constant function is a horizontal line.

LINEAR FUNCTIONS In Example 3, $y = 2$ is a function, while $x = -1$ is not a function. The equation $Ax + By = C$ represents a **linear function** provided $B \neq 0$ (that is, provided the graph of the equation is not a vertical line). If the domain of a linear function is not specified, it is understood to be all real numbers. The domain can be restricted, as shown in Example 4.

EXAMPLE 4 Graph a linear function

Graph the function $y = -\frac{1}{2}x + 4$ with domain $x \geq 0$. Then identify the range of the function.

Solution

STEP 1 **Make** a table.

x	0	2	4	6	8
y	4	3	2	1	0

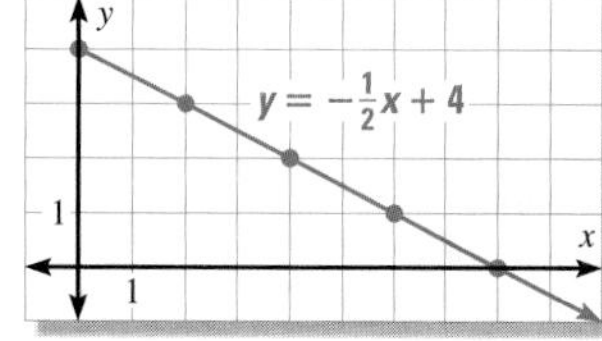

ANALYZE A FUNCTION
The function in Example 4 is called a *continuous* function. To learn about continuous functions, see p. 223.

STEP 2 **Plot** the points.

STEP 3 **Connect** the points with a ray because the domain is restricted.

STEP 4 **Identify** the range. From the graph, you can see that all points have a y-coordinate of 4 or less, so the range of the function is $y \leq 4$.

GUIDED PRACTICE for Example 4

5. Graph the function $y = -3x + 1$ with domain $x \leq 0$. Then identify the range of the function. **See margin for art; $y \geq 1$.**

Extra Example 3

Graph (a) $y = -3$ and (b) $x = 2$.

a.

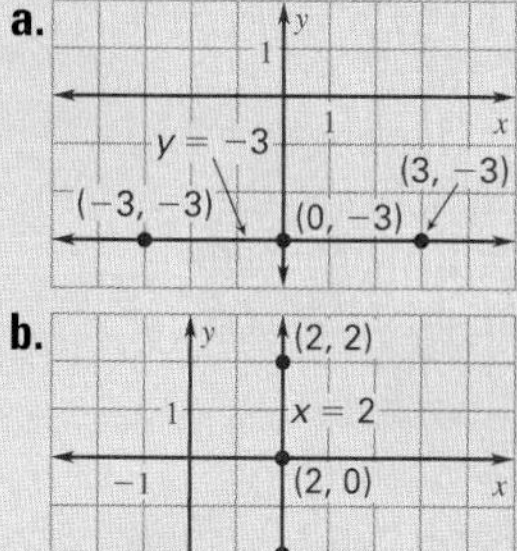

b. (2, 2) x = 2 (2, 0) (2, −2)

Key Question to Ask for Example 3

- Why is the graph of $y = b$ a horizontal line for any value of b? **All the y-coordinates are the same, so a line connecting points on the graph is horizontal.**

An **Animated Algebra** activity is available online for **Example 3**. This activity is also part of **Power Presentations**.

Extra Example 4

Graph the function $y = \frac{1}{2}x - 1$ with domain $x \leq 0$. Then identify the range of the function. **range: $y \leq -1$**

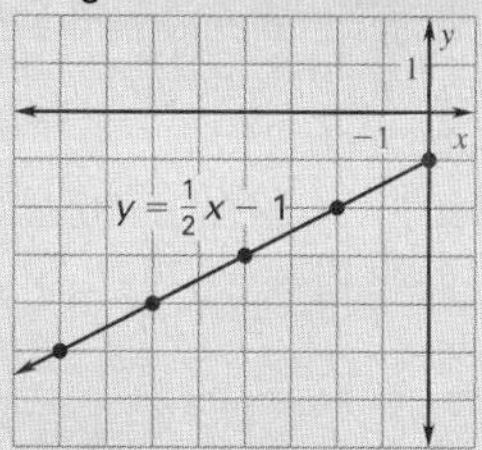

Key Questions to Ask for Example 4

- Why do the x-values in the table begin with 0? **It is the least value in the domain $x \geq 0$.**
- Does the range include negative numbers? Explain. **Yes; when $x > 8$, the values of y are negative.**

Differentiated Instruction

Kinesthetic Learners Some students may find it confusing that the y-axis is vertical line, but the graph of $y = b$ is a horizontal line, and that x-axis is horizontal line, but the graph of $x = a$ is a vertical line. Have students graph the equations $x = 0$ and $y = 0$ to identify them with the y- and x-axes, respectively, using an uncooked piece of spaghetti. Then have them graph $x = a$ and $y = b$ by sliding the spaghetti horizontally or vertically from the proper axis.

See also the *Differentiated Instruction Resources* for more strategies.

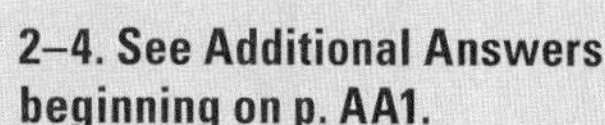

2–4. See Additional Answers beginning on p. AA1.

5.

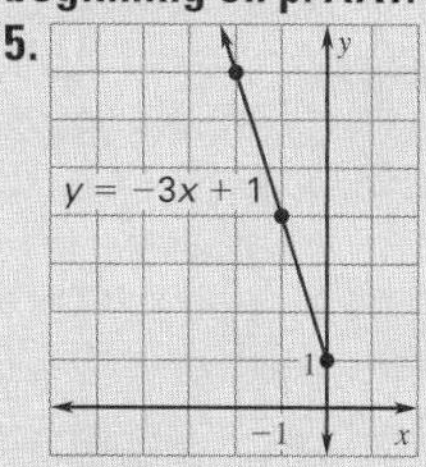

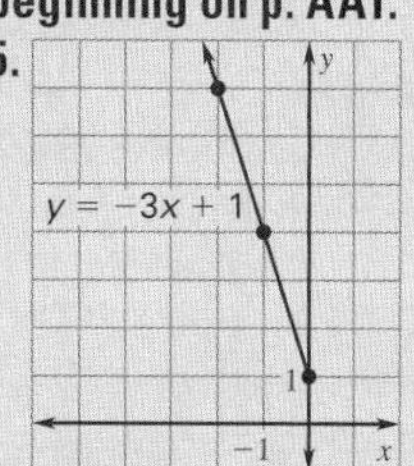

Extra Example 5

The number of pages a student types is given by $p = 4t$ where t is the time (in hours) spent typing. The student plans to type for at most 2.5 hours. Graph the function and identify its domain and range. **domain: $0 \le t \le 2.5$; range: $0 \le p \le 10$**

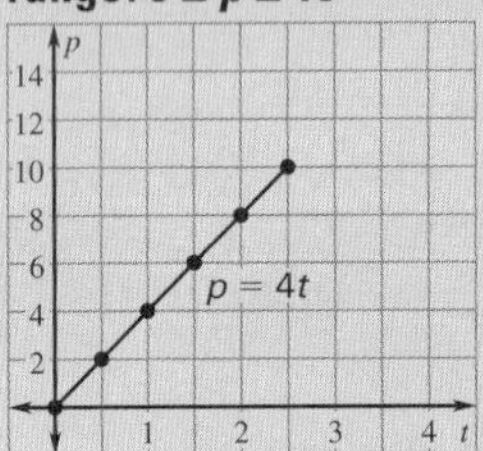

Extra Example 6

Suppose the student in Extra Example 5 plans to type at most 14 pages. Graph the function and identify its domain and range. **domain: $0 \le t \le 3.5$; range: $0 \le p \le 14$**

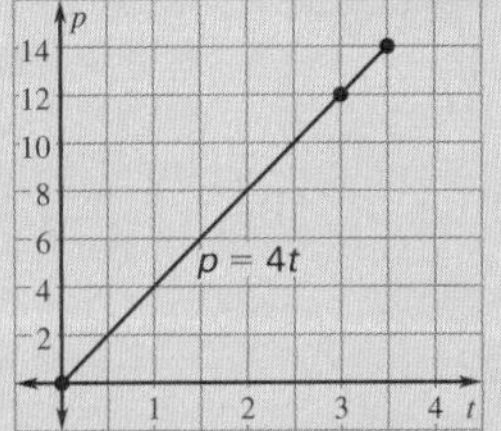

Closing the Lesson

Have students summarize the major points of the lesson and answer the Essential Question: How do you graph linear equations?

- **All points on the graph of a linear equation are solutions of the equation.**
- **Use a line to connect points when the domain is unrestricted, a ray when it is restricted, and a segment when both domain and range are restricted.**

Make a table of appropriate x-values, determine corresponding y-values, plot the points from the table, and connect the points with a line.

EXAMPLE 5 Solve a multi-step problem

RUNNING The distance d (in miles) that a runner travels is given by the function $d = 6t$ where t is the time (in hours) spent running. The runner plans to go for a 1.5 hour run. Graph the function and identify its domain and range.

Solution

STEP 1 **Identify** whether the problem specifies the domain or the range. You know the amount of time the runner plans to spend running. Because time is the independent variable, the domain is specified in this problem. The domain of the function is $0 \le t \le 1.5$.

STEP 2 **Graph** the function. Make a table of values. Then plot and connect the points.

t (hours)	0	0.5	1	1.5
d (miles)	0	3	6	9

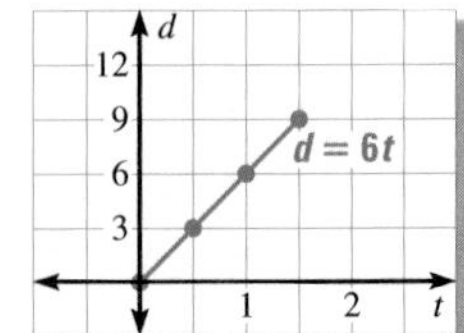

STEP 3 **Identify** the unspecified domain or range. From the table or graph, you can see that the range of the function is $0 \le d \le 9$.

ANALYZE GRAPHS
In Example 2, the domain is unrestricted, and the graph is a *line*. In Example 4, the domain is restricted to $x \ge 0$, and the graph is a *ray*. Here, the domain is restricted to $0 \le t \le 1.5$, and the graph is a *line segment*.

EXAMPLE 6 Solve a related problem

WHAT IF? Suppose the runner in Example 5 instead plans to run 12 miles. Graph the function and identify its domain and range.

Solution

STEP 1 **Identify** whether the problem specifies the domain or the range. You are given the distance that the runner plans to travel. Because distance is the dependent variable, the range is specified in this problem. The range of the function is $0 \le d \le 12$.

STEP 2 **Graph** the function. To make a table, you can substitute d-values (be sure to include 0 and 12) into the function $d = 6t$ and solve for t.

t (hours)	0	1	2
d (miles)	0	6	12

d
12
9
6
3
d = 6t
1
2
t

STEP 3 **Identify** the unspecified domain or range. From the table or graph, you can see that the domain of the function is $0 \le t \le 2$.

SOLVE FOR t
To find the time it takes the runner to run 12 miles, solve the equation $6t = 12$ to get $t = 2$.

✓ **GUIDED PRACTICE** for Examples 5 and 6

6. **GAS COSTS** For gas that costs \$2 per gallon, the equation $C = 2g$ gives the cost C (in dollars) of pumping g gallons of gas. You plan to pump \$10 worth of gas. Graph the function and identify its domain and range. **See margin for art; domain: $0 \le g \le 5$, range: $0 \le C \le 10$.**

6.

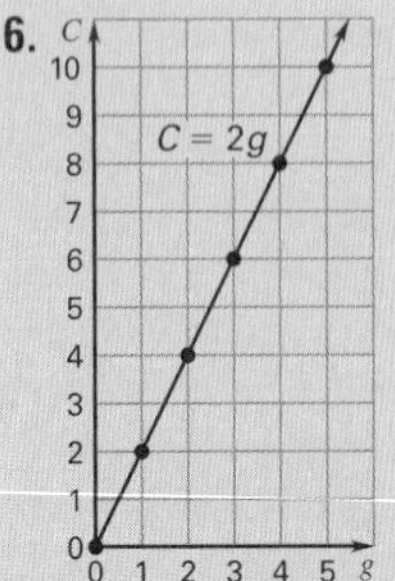

4.2 EXERCISES

HOMEWORK KEY

○ = **WORKED-OUT SOLUTIONS** on p. WS8 for Exs. 3, 11, and 37

★ = **STANDARDIZED TEST PRACTICE** Exs. 2, 10, 32, 33, 39, and 41

◆ = **MULTIPLE REPRESENTATIONS** Ex. 40

SKILL PRACTICE

A

1. **VOCABULARY** The equation $Ax + By = C$ represents a(n) _?_ provided $B \neq 0$. **linear function**

2. ★ **WRITING** Is the equation $y = 6x + 4$ in standard form? *Explain.*
No, to be in standard form it should be in the form $Ax + By = C$, so it should be $-6x + y = 4$.

EXAMPLE 1 on p. 215 for Exs. 3–10

CHECKING SOLUTIONS **Tell whether the ordered pair is a solution of the equation.**

3. $2y + x = 4$; $(-2, 3)$ **solution**
4. $3x - 2y = -5$; $(-1, 1)$ **solution**
5. $x = 9$; $(9, 6)$ **solution**
6. $y = -7$; $(-7, 0)$ **not a solution**
7. $-7x - 4y = 1$; $(-3, -5)$ **not a solution**
8. $-5y - 6x = 0$; $(-6, 5)$ **not a solution**

9. **ERROR ANALYSIS** *Describe* and correct the error in determining whether (8, 11) is a solution of $y - x = -3$.
The 8 should be substituted for x and 11 for y, $11 - 8 \neq -3$, so (8, 11) is not a solution.

$y - x = -3$

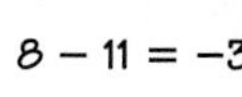

$-3 = -3$

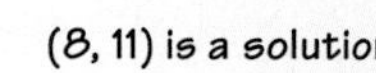

10. ★ **MULTIPLE CHOICE** Which ordered pair is a solution of $6x + 3y = 18$? **B**

Ⓐ $(-2, -10)$ Ⓑ $(-2, 10)$ Ⓒ $(2, 10)$ Ⓓ $(10, -2)$

EXAMPLES 2 and 3 on p. 216 for Exs. 11–25

GRAPHING EQUATIONS **Graph the equation.** **11–22. See margin.**

11. $y + x = 2$
12. $y - 2x = 5$
13. $y - 3x = 0$
14. $y + 4x = 1$
15. $2y - 6x = 10$
16. $3y + 4x = 12$
17. $x - 2y = 3$
18. $3x + 2y = 8$
19. $x = 0$
20. $y = 0$
21. $y = -4$
22. $x = 2$

MATCHING EQUATIONS WITH GRAPHS **Match the equation with its graph.**

23. $y - x = 0$ **C**
24. $x = -2$ **A**
25. $y = -1$ **B**

A.
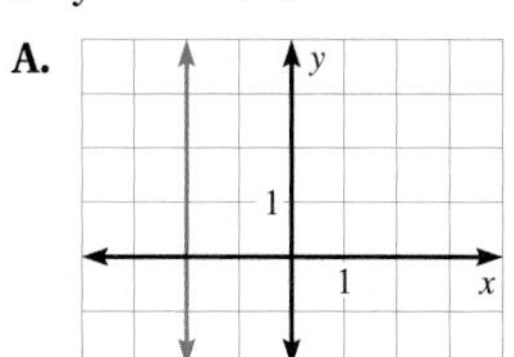

B.
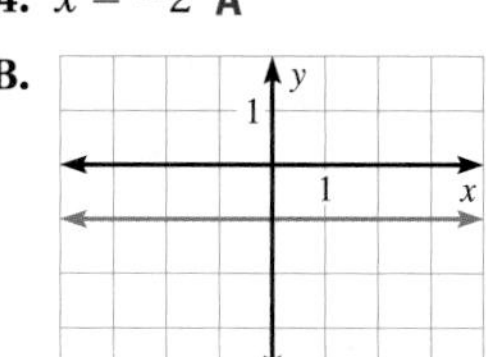

C.
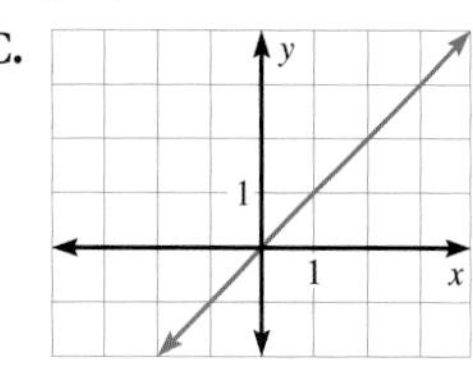

EXAMPLE 4 on p. 217 for Exs. 26–31

B

GRAPHING FUNCTIONS **Graph the function with the given domain. Then identify the range of the function.** **26–31. See margin for art.**

26. $y = 3x - 2$; domain: $x \geq 0$ $y \geq -2$
27. $y = -5x + 3$; domain: $x \leq 0$ $y \geq 3$
28. $y = 4$; domain: $x \leq 5$ $y = 4$
29. $y = -6$; domain: $x \geq 5$ $y = -6$
30. $y = 2x + 3$; domain: $-4 \leq x \leq 0$ $-5 \leq y \leq 3$
31. $y = -x - 1$; domain: $-1 \leq x \leq 3$ $-4 \leq y \leq 0$

32. ★ **OPEN-ENDED** Graph $x - y = 3$ and $2x - 2y = 6$. *Explain* why the equations look different but have the same graph. Find another equation that looks different from the two given equations but has the same graph.
See margin for art; the equations are the same, each term in the first equation was multiplied by 2 to get the second equation. ***Sample answer:*** **$3x - 3y = 9$**

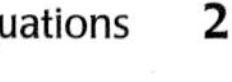

11–22, 26–31. See Additional Answers beginning on p. AA1.

32.
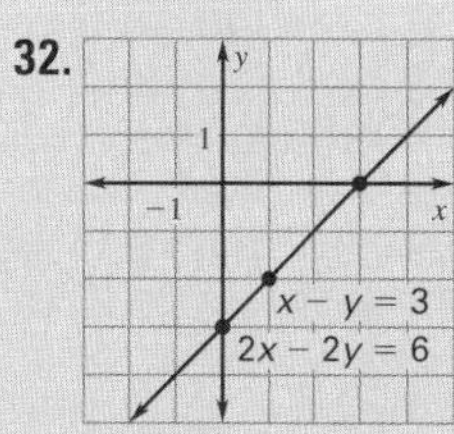

4 PRACTICE AND APPLY

Assignment Guide

Answer Transparencies available for all exercises

Basic:
Day 1: EP p. 938 Exs. 33–36
pp. 219–221
Exs. 1–10, 11–21 odd, 23–25, 42–47
Day 2: pp. 219–221
Exs. 26–29, 35–39, 48–55

Average:
Day 1: pp. 219–221
Exs. 1–10, 16–25, 42–47
Day 2: pp. 219–221
Exs. 26–32 even, 33, 35–40, 48–55

Advanced:
Day 1: pp. 219–221
Exs. 1, 2, 5–10, 17–25, 34*, 42–47
Day 2: pp. 219–221
Exs. 29–33, 36–41*, 48–55

Block:
pp. 219–221
Exs. 1–10, 16–25, 42–47 (with 4.1)
pp. 219–221
Exs. 26–32 even, 33, 35–40, 48–55 (with 4.3)

Differentiated Instruction

See *Differentiated Instruction Resources* for suggestions on addressing the needs of a diverse classroom.

Homework Check

For a quick check of student understanding of key concepts, go over the following exercises:

Basic: 4, 13, 21, 26, 35
Average: 6, 17, 22, 28, 36
Advanced: 7, 18, 30, 37, 38

Extra Practice

- Student Edition, p. 941
- Chapter Resource Book: Practice levels A, B, C

Practice Worksheet

An easily-readable reduced practice page (with answers) for this lesson can be found on p. 204C.

Avoiding Common Errors

Exercises 19–22 Since the y-axis is vertical and the x-axis is horizontal, some students may confuse axes with the graphs of equations. Watch for students who graph Exercises 19 and 22 as horizontal lines and 20 and 21 as vertical lines. Suggest they write ordered pairs for the equations before they begin to graph them. This should help students distinguish axes and graphs of equations.

Vocabulary

Exercise 33 Remind students that "unrestricted domain" means that the domain includes all the real numbers. A graph with an unrestricted domain therefore has an arrow on each end to show that the graph includes all the real numbers.

Mathematical Reasoning

Exercises 35, 36 Tell students that it makes sense to determine the domain or the range of the function before graphing it because that will help them decide what numbers to use in making a table of values. Ask students if values less than 0 make sense in these situations and how that affects the values they will use in their tables. Point out that upper limits on the domain or range also affect the values students use in their tables.

Internet Reference

Exercise 40 To find more information about the weather balloons used by the National Weather Service, visit www.srh.noaa.gov/elp/kids/balloon.shtml

35. 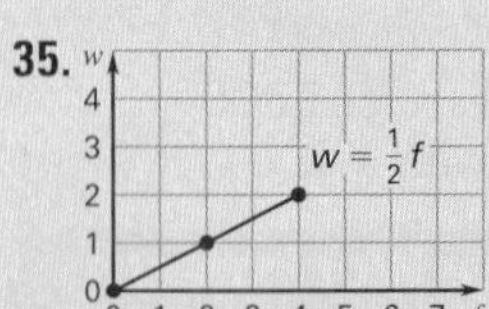

36. 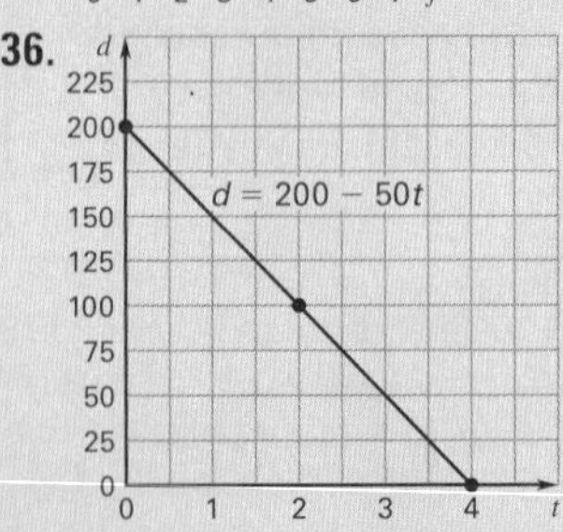

37a. 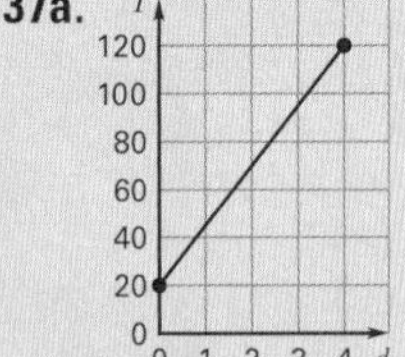

37b. 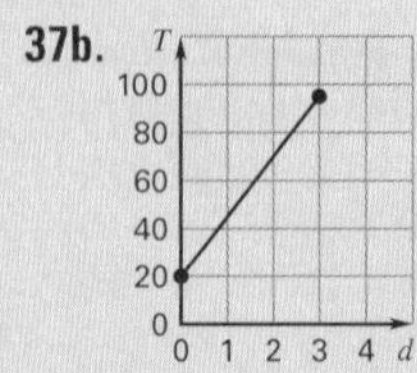

C

33. ★ **MULTIPLE CHOICE** Which statement is true for the function whose graph is shown? **D**

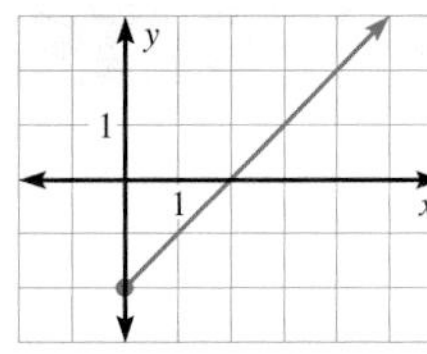

Ⓐ The domain is unrestricted.

Ⓑ The domain is $x \le -2$.

Ⓒ The range is $y \le -2$.

Ⓓ The range is $y \ge -2$.

34. CHALLENGE If $(3, n)$ is a solution of $Ax + 3y = 6$ and $(n, 5)$ is a solution of $5x + y = 20$, what is the value of A? **−1**

PROBLEM SOLVING

EXAMPLES 5 and 6 on p. 218 for Exs. 35–39

A

35. BAKING The weight w (in pounds) of a loaf of bread that a recipe yields is given by the function $w = \frac{1}{2}f$ where f is the number of cups of flour used. You have 4 cups of flour. Graph the function and identify its domain and range. What is the weight of the largest loaf of bread you can make?

@HomeTutor for problem solving help at classzone.com

See margin for art; domain: $0 \le f \le 4$, range: $0 \le w \le 2$; 2 lb.

36. TRAVEL After visiting relatives who live 200 miles away, your family drives home at an average speed of 50 miles per hour. Your distance d (in miles) from home is given by $d = 200 - 50t$ where t is the time (in hours) spent driving. Graph the function and identify its domain and range. What is your distance from home after driving for 1.5 hours?

@HomeTutor for problem solving help at classzone.com

See margin for art; domain: $0 \le t \le 4$, range: $0 \le d \le 200$; 125 mi.

37. EARTH SCIENCE The temperature T (in degrees Celsius) of Earth's crust can be modeled by the function $T = 20 + 25d$ where d is the distance (in kilometers) from the surface.

a. A scientist studies organisms in the first 4 kilometers of Earth's crust. Graph the function and identify its domain and range. What is the temperature at the deepest part of the section of crust?
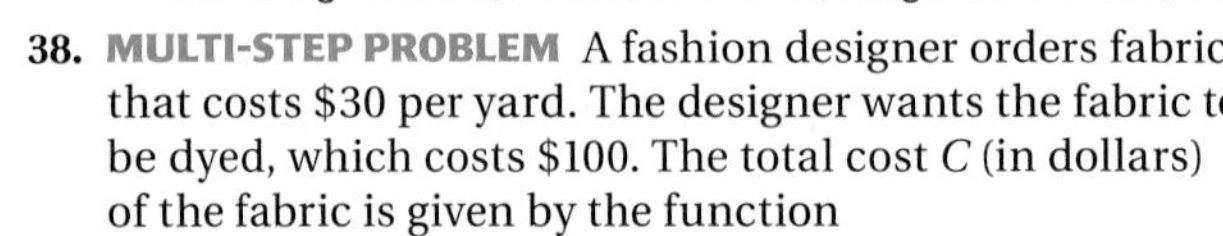
See margin for art; domain: $0 \le d \le 4$, range: $20 \le T \le 120$; 120°C.

b. Suppose the scientist studies organisms in a section of the crust where the temperature is between 20°C and 95°C. Graph the function and identify its domain and range. How many kilometers deep is the section of crust? **See margin for art; domain: $0 \le d \le 3$, range: $20 \le T \le 95$; 3 km.**

B

38. MULTI-STEP PROBLEM A fashion designer orders fabric that costs \$30 per yard. The designer wants the fabric to be dyed, which costs \$100. The total cost C (in dollars) of the fabric is given by the function

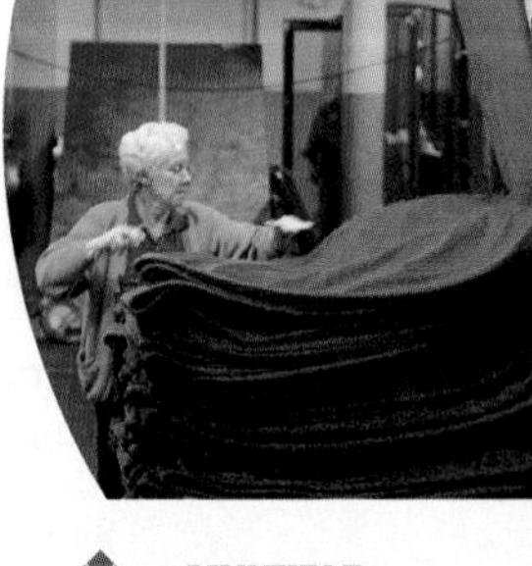

$$C = 30f + 100$$

where f is the number of yards of fabric.

a. The designer orders 3 yards of fabric. How much does the fabric cost? *Explain.* **\$190; substitute 3 in for f and solve.**

b. Suppose the designer can spend \$500 on fabric. How many yards of fabric can the designer buy? *Explain.*

38b. $13\frac{1}{3}$ yd; substitute 500 in for C and solve for f.

○ = WORKED-OUT SOLUTIONS on p. WS1 ★ = STANDARDIZED TEST PRACTICE ◆ = MULTIPLE REPRESENTATIONS

39a. See margin for art; domain: $t \geq 0$, range: $r \geq 0$.

39b. Domain: $0 \leq t \leq 4$, range: $0 \leq r \leq 480$; the graph was a ray, but is now a segment.

39. ★ **SHORT RESPONSE** An emergency cell phone charger requires you to turn a small crank in order to create the energy needed to recharge the phone's battery. If you turn the crank 120 times per minute, the total number r of revolutions that you turn the crank is given by

$$r = 120t$$

where t is the time (in minutes) spent turning the crank.

a. Graph the function and identify its domain and range.

b. Identify the domain and range if you stop turning the crank after 4 minutes. *Explain* how this affects the appearance of the graph.

40. ◆ **MULTIPLE REPRESENTATIONS** The National Weather Service releases weather balloons twice daily at over 90 locations in the United States in order to collect data for meteorologists. The height h (in feet) of a balloon is a function of the time t (in seconds) after the balloon is released, as shown.

a. Making a Table Make a table showing the height of a balloon after t seconds for $t = 0$ through $t = 10$. **See margin.**

b. Drawing a Graph A balloon bursts after a flight of about 7200 seconds. Graph the function and identify the domain and range.
See margin for art; domain: $0 \leq t \leq 7200$, range: $5 \leq h \leq 100,805$.

C **41.** ★ **EXTENDED RESPONSE** Students can pay for lunch at a school in one of two ways. Students can either make a payment of \$30 per month or they can buy lunch daily for \$2.50 per lunch.

a. Graph Graph the function $y = 30$ to represent the monthly payment plan. Using the same coordinate plane, graph the function $y = 2.5x$ to represent the daily payment plan. **See margin.**

41b. (12, 30); at 12 days the cost is the same for both payment plans.

b. CHALLENGE What are the coordinates of the point that is a solution of both functions? What does that point mean in this situation?

c. CHALLENGE A student eats an average of 15 school lunches per month. How should the student pay, daily or monthly? *Explain*.
Monthly; if he pays daily it will cost \$37.50, if he pays monthly it will cost only \$30.

MIXED REVIEW

Solve the equation.

42. $12x = 144$ *(p. 134)* **12**

43. $-4x = 30$ *(p. 134)* **−7.5**

44. $5.7x - 2x = 14.8$ *(p. 141)* **4**

45. $x - 4(x + 13) = 26$ *(p. 148)* **−26**

46. $6x - 4x + 13 = 27 - 2x$ *(p. 154)* **3.5**

47. $5x - \frac{1}{4}(24 + 8x) = 2x - 5$ *(p. 154)* **1**

PREVIEW Prepare for Lesson 4.3 in Exs. 48–55.

Plot the point in a coordinate plane. *Describe* the location of the point. *(p. 206)*
48–55. See margin for art.

48. (3, 5) **Quadrant I**

49. (−3, 2) **Quadrant II**

50. (0, −2) ***y*-axis**

51. (−5, 0) ***x*-axis**

52. (−2, −2) **Quadrant III**

53. $\left(\frac{1}{3}, 0\right)$ ***x*-axis**

54. $\left(-\frac{1}{2}, \frac{3}{4}\right)$ **Quadrant II**

55. (0, 6.2) ***y*-axis**

48–55.

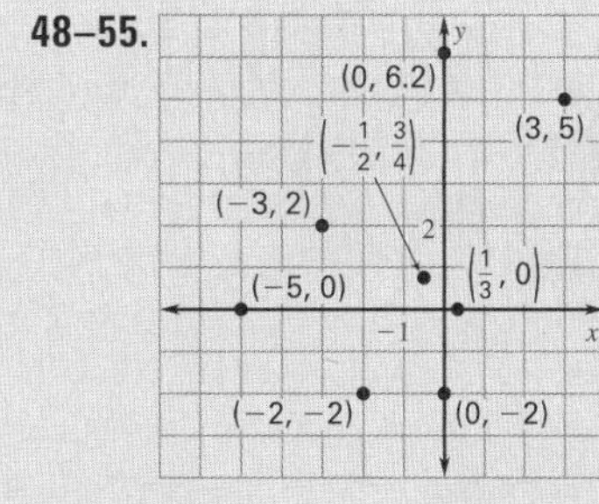

5 ASSESS AND RETEACH

Daily Homework Quiz

Transparency Available

1. Graph $y + 2x = 4$.

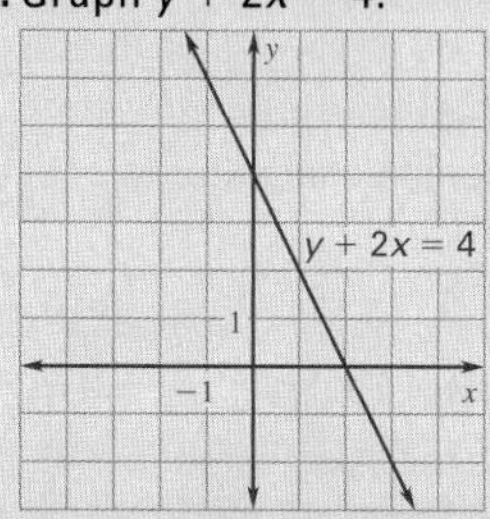

2. The distance in miles an elephant walks in t hours is given by $d = 5t$. The elephant walks for 2.5 hours. Graph the function and identify its domain and range. **domain: $0 \leq t \leq 2.5$; range: $0 \leq d \leq 12.5$**

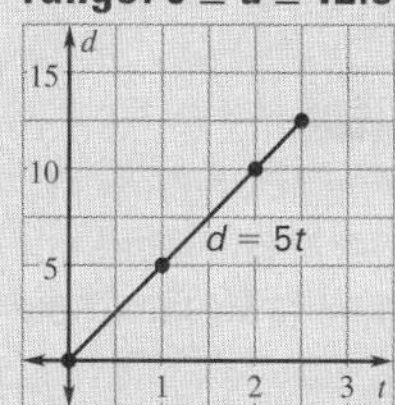

Available at **classzone.com**

Diagnosis/Remediation

- Practice A, B, C in Chapter Resource Book
- Study Guide in Chapter Resource Book
- Practice Workbook
- @HomeTutor

Challenge

Additional challenge is available in the Chapter Resource Book.

39a.

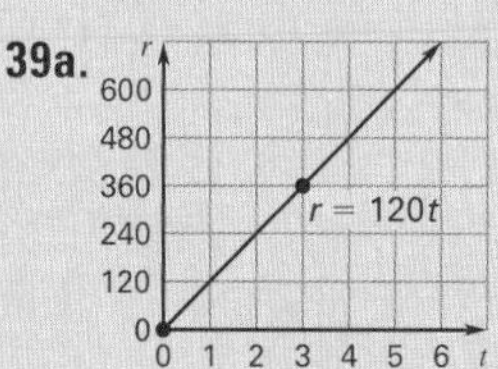

40a, 40b, 41a. See Additional Answers beginning on p. AA1.

@HomeTutor classzone.com Keystrokes

1 PLAN AND PREPARE

Learn the Method

- Students will graph an equation on a graphing calculator and use the equation to solve a problem.
- After the activity, students can use a graphing calculator to check their solutions in Exercises 35–40 in Lesson 4.2.

Keystroke Help

Keystrokes for several models of calculators are available in blackline format in the *Chapter Resource Book*.

2 TEACH

Tips for Success

As students are working on Step 2, mention that they can change existing minimums and maximums of a window by entering new data or by using the zoom feature on their calculators.

Extra Example

The total cost C to buy a water cooler and bottles of water can be modeled by $C = 115 + 5.65b$ where b is the number of bottles. Graph the equation. Estimate the total cost when the number of bottles is 18. **about $217**

3 ASSESS AND RETEACH

The fee f to use a photo lab can be modeled by $f = 12 + 4.25v$ where v is the number of visits.

1. Find the fee after 15 visits. **$75.75**
2. Find the number of visits if the fee is $63. **12 visits**

4.2 Graphing Linear Equations

QUESTION How do you graph an equation on a graphing calculator?

EXAMPLE Use a graph to solve a problem

The formula to convert temperature from degrees Fahrenheit to degrees Celsius is $C = \frac{5}{9}(F - 32)$. Graph the equation. At what temperature are degrees Fahrenheit and degrees Celsius equal?

STEP 1 ***Rewrite and enter equation***

Rewrite the equation using x for F and y for C. Enter the equation into the Y= screen. Put parentheses around the fraction $\frac{5}{9}$.

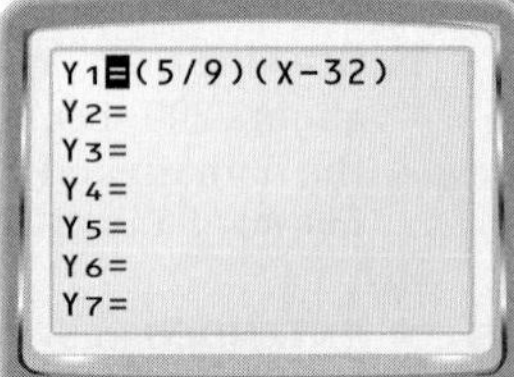

STEP 2 ***Set window***

The screen is a "window" that lets you look at part of a coordinate plane. Press WINDOW to set the borders of the graph. A friendly window for this equation is $-94 \le x \le 94$ and $-100 \le y \le 100$.

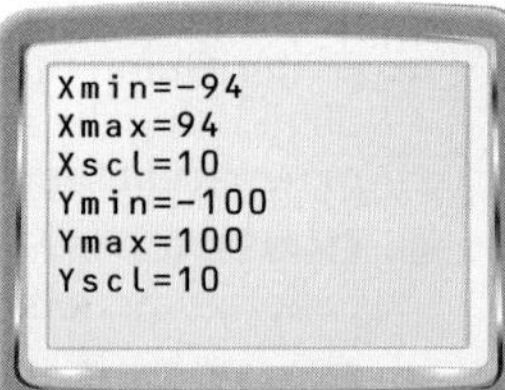

STEP 3 ***Graph and trace equation***

Press TRACE and use the left and right arrows to move the cursor along the graph until the x-coordinate and y-coordinate are equal. From the graph, you can see that degrees Fahrenheit and degrees Celsius are equal at -40.

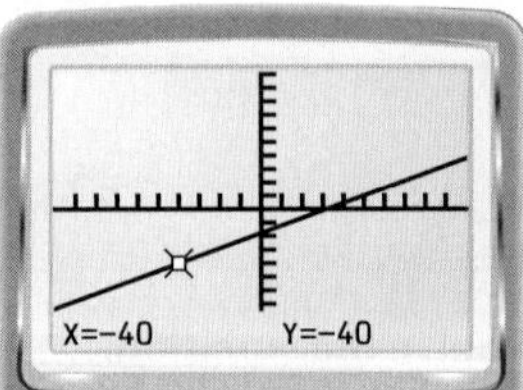

PRACTICE

Graph the equation. Find the unknown value in the ordered pair.

1. $y = 8 - x$; (2.4, ?) **5.6**
2. $y = 2x + 3$; (?, 0.8) **−1.1**
3. $y = -4.5x + 1$; (1.4, ?) **−5.3**
4. **SPEED OF SOUND** The speed s (in meters per second) of sound in air can be modeled by $s = 331.1 + 0.61T$ where T is the air temperature in degrees Celsius. Graph the equation. Estimate the speed of sound when the temperature is 20°C. **343.3 m/sec**

Identify Discrete and Continuous Functions

GOAL Graph and classify discrete and continuous functions.

Key Vocabulary
- **discrete function**
- **continuous function**

The graph of a function can consist of individual points, as in the graph in Example 3 on page 207. The graph of a function can also be a line or a part of a line with no breaks, as in the graph in Example 4 on page 217.

KEY CONCEPT *For Your Notebook*

Identifying Discrete and Continuous Functions

A **discrete function** has a graph that consists of isolated points.

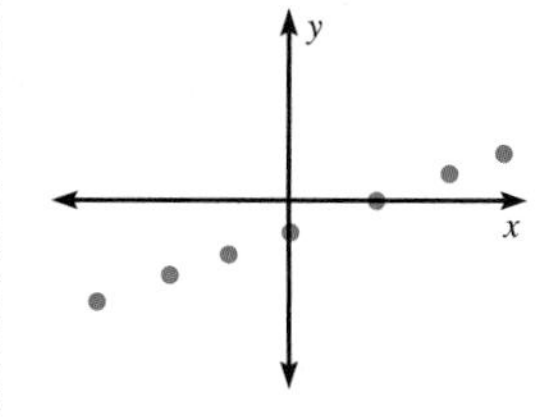

A **continuous function** has a graph that is unbroken.

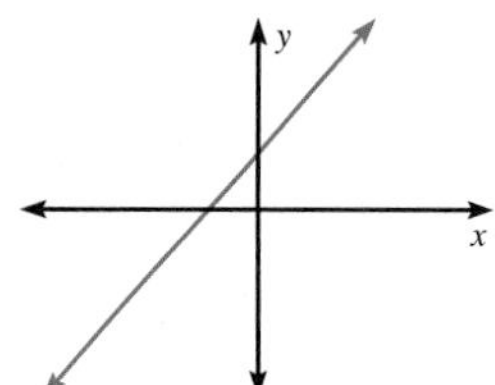

EXAMPLE 1 **Graph and classify a function**

Graph the function $y = 2x - 1$ with the given domain. Classify the function as discrete or continuous.

a. Domain: $x = 0, 1, 2, 3$

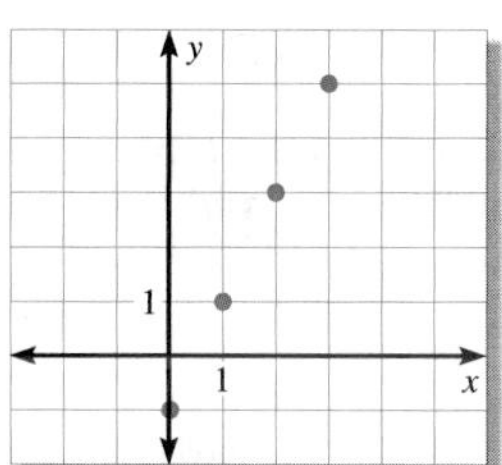

The graph consists of individual points, so the function is discrete.

b. Domain: $x \geq 0$

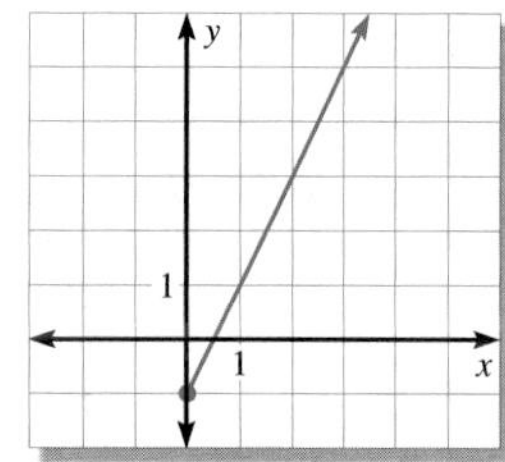

The graph is unbroken, so the function is continuous.

GRAPHS As a general rule, you can tell that a function is continuous if you do not have to lift your pencil from the paper to draw its graph, as in part (b) of Example 1.

1 PLAN AND PREPARE

Warm-Up Exercises

1. What is the range of $y = -x + 3$ with domain 0, 1, 2, and 4. **3, 2, 1, −1**
2. Graph $y = \frac{1}{3}x + 1$.

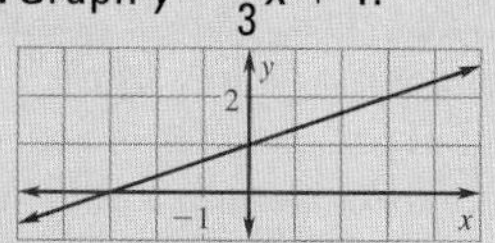

2 FOCUS AND MOTIVATE

Essential Question

Big Idea 1, p. 205

How do you tell if a function is discrete or continuous? **Tell students they will learn how to answer this question by graphing functions with individual points and lines or parts of lines.**

3 TEACH

Extra Example 1

Graph the function $y = \frac{1}{2}x + 1$ with the domain $x \geq 0$. Classify the function as discrete or continuous.

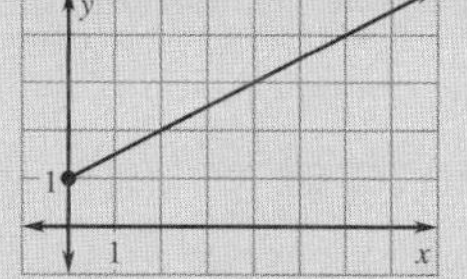

continuous

NCTM STANDARDS

Standard 2: Understand functions

Standard 10: Use representations to communicate mathematical ideas

Extra Example 2

Tell whether the function represented by the table is discrete or continuous. Explain. If continuous, graph the function and find the value of y when $x = 2.5$.

Hours hiked, x	1	2	3
Distance (mi), y	2.5	5	7.5

Since it makes sense to talk about the number of miles hiked after any amount of time, the table represents a continuous function. The distance hiked after 2.5 hours is about 6.25 miles.

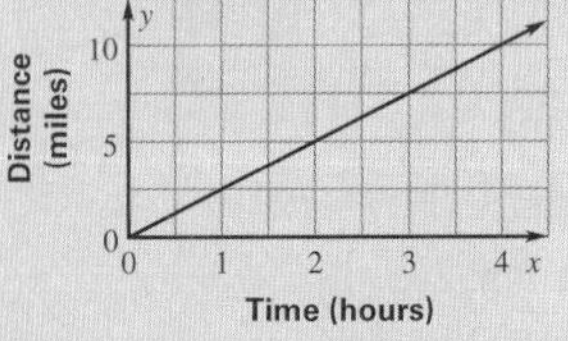

Closing the Lesson

Have students summarize the major points of the lesson and answer the Essential Question: How do you identify discrete and continuous functions?

- **A discrete function has a graph consisting of isolated points.**
- **A continuous function has a graph with no breaks in it.**

Given a situation or domain, determine whether you should represent the function with individual points or an unbroken line or part of a line.

4 PRACTICE AND APPLY

Study Strategy

Exercises 7–9 Instruct students to think in terms of what makes sense, as in Example 2, when considering whether the functions are discrete or continuous.

1–6. See Additional Answers beginning on p. AA1.

EXAMPLE 2 Classify and graph a real-world function

Tell whether the function represented by the table is discrete or continuous. Explain. If continuous, graph the function and find the value of y when $x = 1.5$.

Duration of storm (hours), x	1	2	3
Amount of rain (inches), y	0.5	1	1.5

Solution

Although the table shows the amount of rain that has fallen after whole numbers of hours only, it makes sense to talk about the amount of rain after any amount of time during the storm. So, the table represents a continuous function.

The graph of the function is shown. To find the value of y when $x = 1.5$, start at 1.5 on the x-axis, move up to the graph, and move over to the y-axis. The y-value is about 0.75. So, about 0.75 inch of rain has fallen after 1.5 hours.

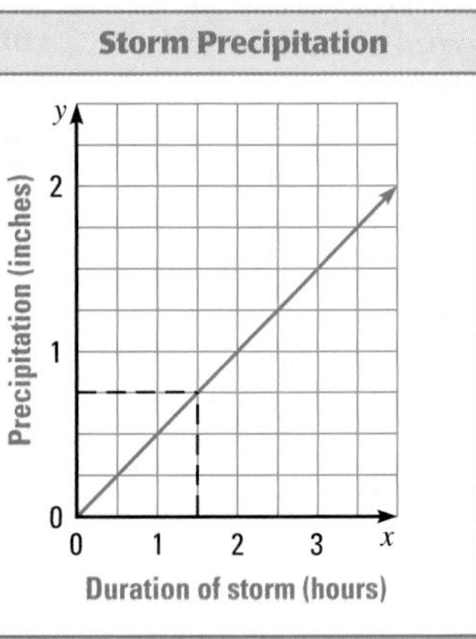

PRACTICE

EXAMPLE 1 on p. 223 for Exs. 1–6

Graph the function with the given domain. Classify the function as discrete or continuous. **1–6. See margin for art.**

1. $y = -2x + 3$; domain: $-2, -1, 0, 1, 2$ **discrete**
2. $y = x$; domain: all real numbers **continuous**
3. $y = -\frac{1}{3}x + 1$; domain: $-12, -6, 0, 6, 12$ **discrete**
4. $y = 0.5x$; domain: $-2, -1, 0, 1, 2$ **discrete**
5. $y = 3x - 4$; domain: $x \le 0$ **continuous**
6. $y = \frac{2}{3}x + \frac{1}{3}$; domain: $x \ge -2$ **continuous**

EXAMPLE 2 on p. 224 for Exs. 7–9

Tell whether the function represented by the table is discrete or continuous. *Explain.* If continuous, graph the function and find the value of y when $x = 3.5$. Round your answer to the nearest hundredth.

7.

Number of DVD rentals, x	1	2	3	4
Cost of rentals (dollars), y	4.50	9.00	13.50	18.00

Discrete; you can only rent a whole number of DVDs.

8.

Hours since 12 P.M., x	2	4	6	8
Distance driven (miles), y	100	200	300	400

8. Continuous; it makes sense to talk about the distance driven for any amount of time during the drive; 175.

9.

Volume of water (cubic inches), x	3	6	9	12
Approximate weight of water (pounds), y	0.1	0.2	0.3	0.4

Continuous; it makes sense to talk about the weight of water for any volume of water; about 0.12.

8.
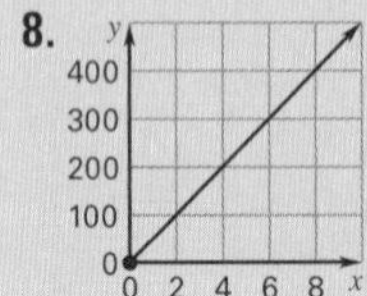

9.
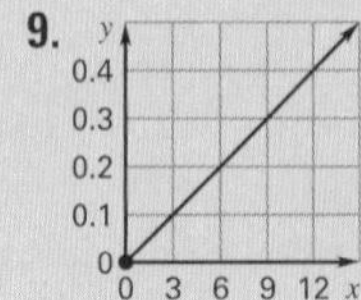

4.3 Graph Using Intercepts

Before You graphed a linear equation using a table of values.

Now You will graph a linear equation using intercepts.

Why So you can find a submersible's location, as in Example 5.

Key Vocabulary
- *x*-intercept
- *y*-intercept

You can use the fact that two points determine a line to graph a linear equation. Two convenient points are the points where the graph crosses the axes.

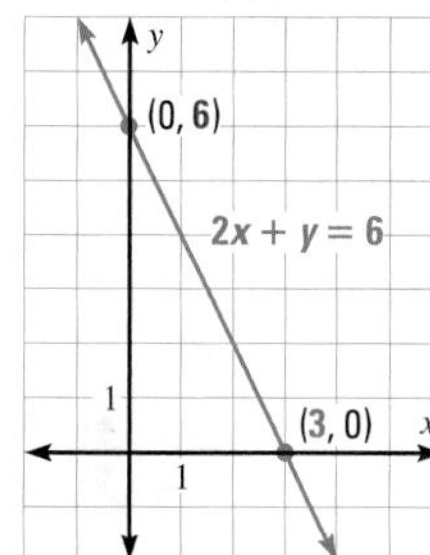

An ***x*-intercept** of a graph is the x-coordinate of a point where the graph crosses the x-axis. A ***y*-intercept** of a graph is the y-coordinate of a point where the graph crosses the y-axis.

To find the x-intercept of the graph of a linear equation, find the value of x when $y = 0$. To find the y-intercept of the graph, find the value of y when $x = 0$.

EXAMPLE 1 **Find the intercepts of the graph of an equation**

Find the x-intercept and the y-intercept of the graph of $2x + 7y = 28$.

Solution

To find the x-intercept, substitute 0 for y and solve for x.

$2x + 7y = 28$ **Write original equation.**

$2x + 7(\mathbf{0}) = 28$ **Substitute 0 for *y*.**

$x = \frac{28}{2} = 14$ **Solve for *x*.**

To find the y-intercept, substitute 0 for x and solve for y.

$2x + 7y = 28$ **Write original equation.**

$2(\mathbf{0}) + 7y = 28$ **Substitute 0 for *x*.**

$y = \frac{28}{7} = 4$ **Solve for *y*.**

▶ The x-intercept is 14. The y-intercept is 4.

GUIDED PRACTICE for Example 1

Find the x-intercept and the y-intercept of the graph of the equation.

1. $3x + 2y = 6$ **2, 3**
2. $4x - 2y = 10$ **2.5, −5**
3. $-3x + 5y = -15$ **5, −3**

1 PLAN AND PREPARE

Warm-Up Exercises

Transparency Available

Evaluate the expression when $x = -3$.

1. $3x + 4$ **−5**
2. $-2x + 6$ **12**
3. $4x - 3$ **−15**
4. The amount a that a taxi service charges is given by $a = 1.5m$ where m is the number of miles. Find a when m is 7. **$10.50**

Notetaking Guide

Transparency Available

Promotes interactive learning and notetaking skills.

Pacing

Basic: 1 day
Average: 1 day
Advanced: 1 day
Block: 0.5 block with 4.2
- See *Teaching Guide/Lesson Plan.*

2 FOCUS AND MOTIVATE

Essential Question

Big Idea 1, p. 205

How do you use intercepts to graph equations? **Tell students they will learn how to answer this question by finding and using the *x*- and *y*-intercepts of the graph of an equation.**

NCTM STANDARDS

Standard 3: Specify locations using coordinate geometry

Standard 10: Use representations to communicate mathematical ideas

Resource Planning Guide

Chapter Resource Book
- Teaching Guide/Lesson Plan
- Practice levels A, B, C
- Study Guide
- Catch-up for Absent Students
- Problem Solving Workshop
- Challenge

Workbooks
- Notetaking Guide
- Practice Workbook

Teaching Options
- **Power Presentations** provides dynamic electronic teaching resources for the classroom.
- **Activity Generator** provides editable activities for all ability levels.

Interactive Technology
- Easy Planner
- Power Presentations
- Activity Generator
- Animated Algebra
- Test Generator
- Online Quiz
- eWorkbook
- eEdition
- @HomeTutor

Resources for English Learners
- Spanish Study Guide
- Multi-Language Visual Glossary
- Student Resources in Spanish

See also the *Differentiated Instruction Resources* for more strategies for meeting individual needs.

Motivating the Lesson

You know that your school sells T-shirts and sweatshirts with the school name on them. T-shirts cost \$9 and sweatshirts cost \$12. You have \$144. By writing an equation and finding the intercepts of the graph of the equation, you can find the possible numbers of T-shirts and sweatshirts you can buy.

3 TEACH

Extra Example 1

Find the x-intercept and the y-intercept of the graph of $3x - 4y = 12$. **x-intercept: 4, y-intercept: −3**

Key Question to Ask for Example 1

- What coordinates are associated with the x-intercept and the y-intercept? **(14, 0), (0, 4)**

Extra Example 2

Graph the equation $4x + 8y = 24$.

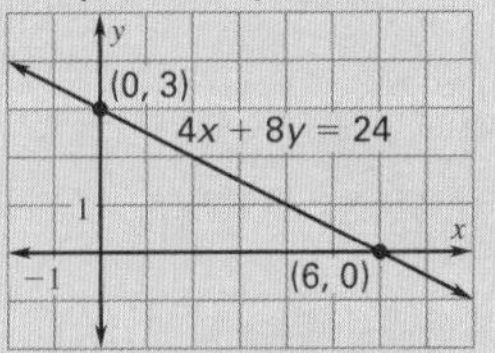

Key Question to Ask for Example 2

- Why is using intercepts an efficient way to graph an equation? **Since $x = 0$ and $y = 0$, it is easier to find the intercepts than other points on the line.**

An **Animated Algebra** activity is available online for **Example 2**. This activity is also part of **Power Presentations**.

EXAMPLE 2 Use intercepts to graph an equation

Graph the equation $x + 2y = 4$.

Solution

STEP 1 **Find** the intercepts.

$x + 2y = 4$	$x + 2y = 4$
$x + 2(0) = 4$	$0 + 2y = 4$
$x = 4$ ← **x-intercept**	$y = 2$ ← **y-intercept**

STEP 2 **Plot** points. The x-intercept is 4, so plot the point (4, 0). The y-intercept is 2, so plot the point (0, 2). Draw a line through the points.

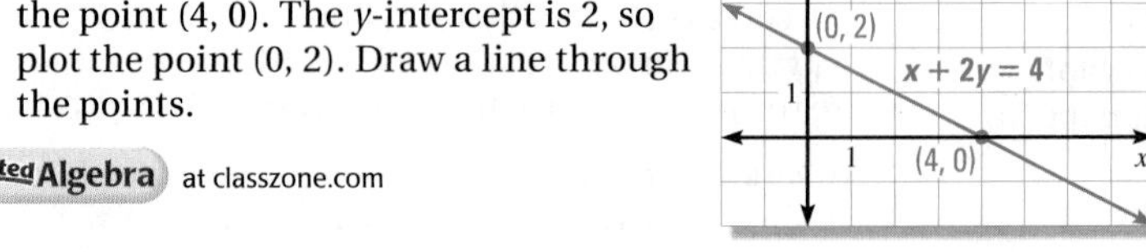

Animated Algebra at classzone.com

CHECK A GRAPH
Be sure to check the graph by finding a third solution of the equation and checking to see that the corresponding point is on the graph.

EXAMPLE 3 Use a graph to find intercepts

The graph crosses the x-axis at (2, 0). The x-intercept is 2. The graph crosses the y-axis at (0, −1). The y-intercept is −1.

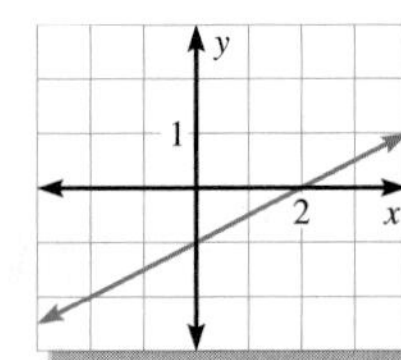

✓ **GUIDED PRACTICE** for Examples 2 and 3

4. Graph $6x + 7y = 42$. Label the points where the line crosses the axes. **See margin.**
5. Identify the x-intercept and the y-intercept of the graph shown at the right. **−4, 2**

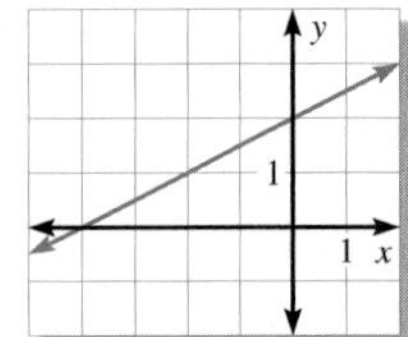

KEY CONCEPT *For Your Notebook*

Relating Intercepts, Points, and Graphs

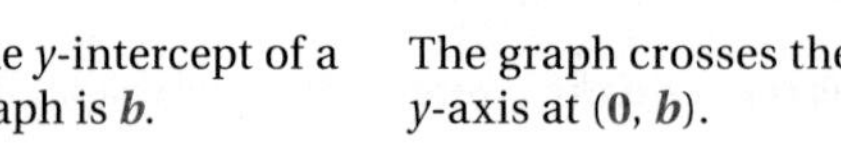

Intercepts	**Points**
The x intercept of a graph is a.	The graph crosses the x-axis at $(a, 0)$.
The y-intercept of a graph is b.	The graph crosses the y-axis at $(0, b)$.

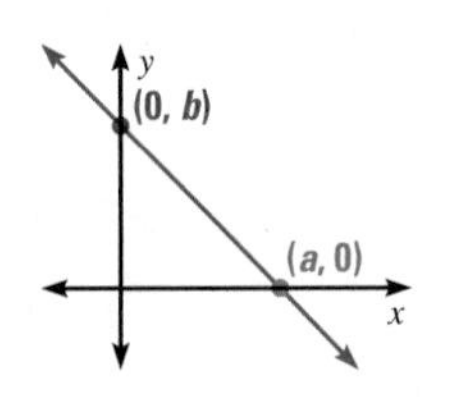

Differentiated Instruction

Visual Learners To help students remember how to find the intercepts in problems similar to Example 2, have them make the following table.

x-intercept	$x = 0$
y-intercept	$y = 0$

Have them connect the entries in this table with an "X," pairing "x-intercept" with "$y = 0$" and pairing "y-intercept" with "$x = 0$."

See also the *Differentiated Instruction Resources* for more strategies.

EXAMPLE 4 Solve a multi-step problem

EVENT PLANNING You are helping to plan an awards banquet for your school, and you need to rent tables to seat 180 people. Tables come in two sizes. Small tables seat 4 people, and large tables seat 6 people. This situation can be modeled by the equation

$$4x + 6y = 180$$

where x is the number of small tables and y is the number of large tables.

- Find the intercepts of the graph of the equation.
- Graph the equation.
- Give four possibilities for the number of each size table you could rent.

Solution

STEP 1 **Find** the intercepts.

$4x + 6y = 180$	$4x + 6y = 180$
$4x + 6(0) = 180$	$4(0) + 6y = 180$
$x = 45 \leftarrow$ ***x*-intercept**	$y = 30 \leftarrow$ ***y*-intercept**

STEP 2 **Graph** the equation.

The x-intercept is 45, so plot the point (45, 0). The y-intercept is 30, so plot the point (0, 30).

Since x and y both represent numbers of tables, neither x nor y can be negative. So, instead of drawing a line, draw the part of the line that is in Quadrant I.

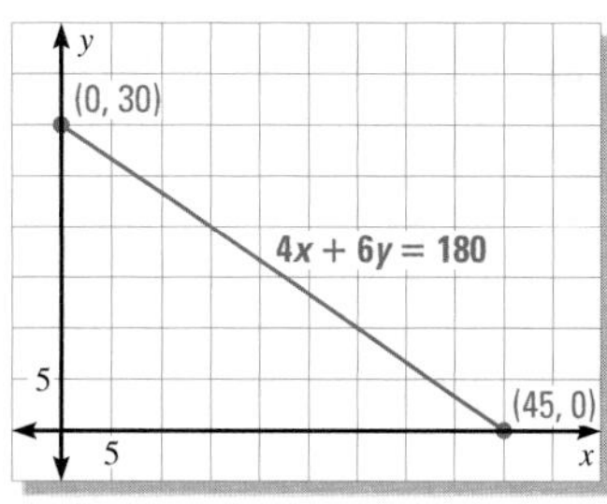

STEP 3 **Find** the number of tables. For this problem, only whole-number values of x and y make sense. You can see that the line passes through the points **(0, 30)**, **(15, 20)**, **(30, 10)**, and **(45, 0)**.

So, four possible combinations of tables that will seat 180 people are: 0 small and 30 large, 15 small and 20 large, 30 small and 10 large, and 45 small and 0 large.

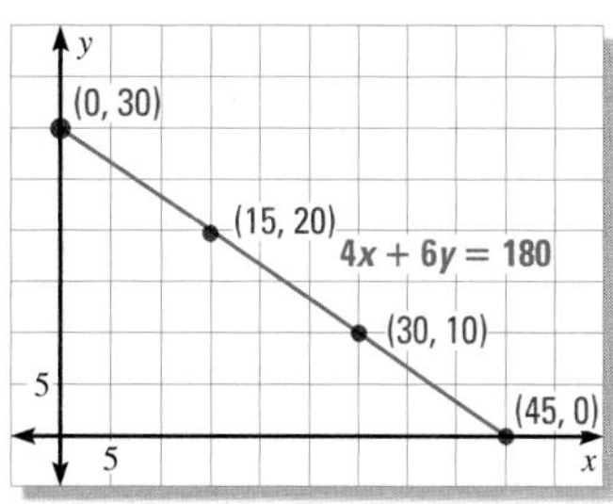

DRAW A GRAPH
Although x and y represent whole numbers, it is convenient to draw an unbroken line segment that includes points whose coordinates are not whole numbers.

FIND SOLUTIONS
Other points, such as (12, 22), are also on the graph but are not as obvious as the points shown here because their coordinates are not multiples of 5.

GUIDED PRACTICE for Example 4

6. **WHAT IF?** In Example 4, suppose the small tables cost \$9 to rent and the large tables cost \$14. Of the four possible combinations of tables given in the example, which rental is the least expensive? *Explain.* **45 small tables and no large tables; if you rent 45 small tables it costs \$405, all other combinations are more expensive.**

4. 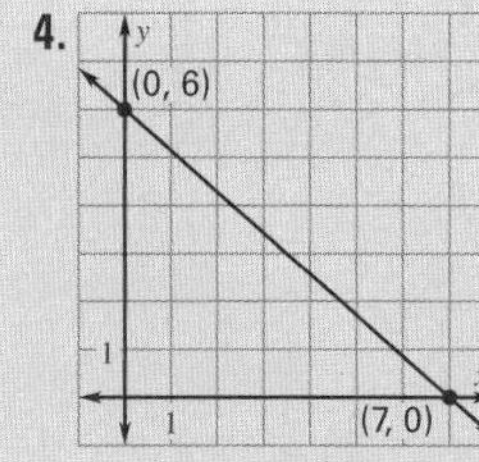

Extra Example 3

Identify the x-intercept and y-intercept of the graph.

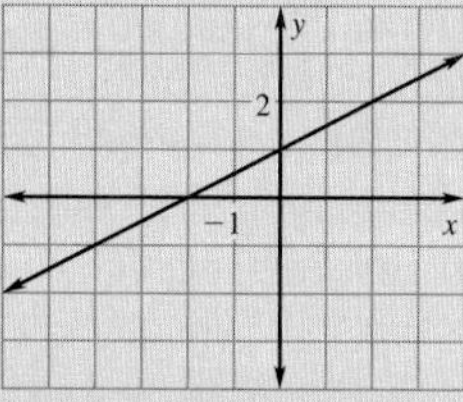

***x*-intercept: −2, *y*-intercept: 1**

Extra Example 4

You make and sell decorative bows. You sell small bows for \$3 and large bows for \$5. You want to earn \$60 per week. This situation can be modeled by $3x + 5y = 60$ where x is the number of small bows and y is the number of large bows.

- Find the intercepts of the graph.
- Graph the equation.
- Give three possibilities for the number of each type of bow you can sell to earn \$60.

***x*-intercept: 20, *y*-intercept: 12**

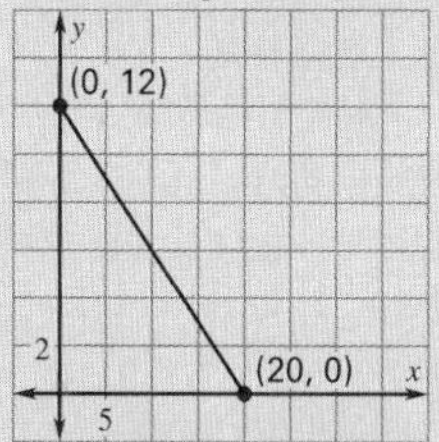

Possible combinations: 0 small and 12 large, 10 small and 6 large, 20 small and 0 large

Key Questions to Ask for Example 4

- How can you check the graph of the equation? Explain. **Test another point on the graph, such as (15, 20). If you substitute the values in the equation and they check, the graph is correct.**
- The point (10.5, 23) is a solution of the equation. Is it a solution of the problem? Explain. **No; you cannot rent 10.5 small tables.**

Teaching Strategy

In Step 2 of Example 5 on page 228, remind students that the scales on the x- and y-axes do not have to be the same and that it would be better in some situations to have two different scales.

Extra Example 5

You borrow \$1800 from your parents. To repay your debt, you give them \$150 per month. Your debt d (in dollars) is given by the function $d = 150t - 1800$ where t represents time (in months).

- Find the intercepts of the graph of the function and state what they represent. **t-intercept: 12, d-intercept: -1800; The t-intercept represents the number of months it takes to reduce the debt to 0 dollars. The d-intercept represents the amount of your debt at the time you begin to repay it.**
- Graph the function and identify its domain and range. **domain: $0 \le t \le 12$; range: $-1800 \le d \le 0$**

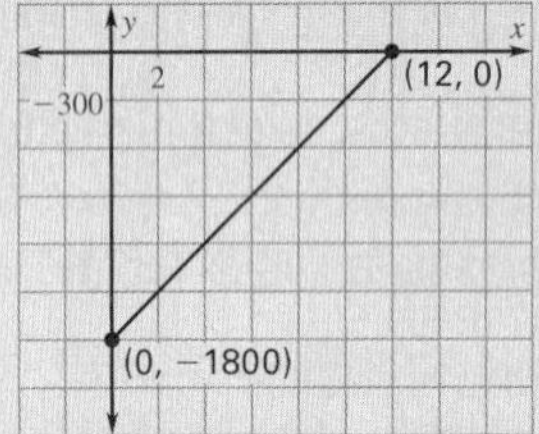

Closing the Lesson

Have students summarize the major points of the lesson and answer the Essential Question: How do you use intercepts to graph equations?

- **The x-intercept is the x-coordinate of the point where the graph crosses the x-axis.**
- **The y-intercept is the y-coordinate of the point where the graph crosses the y-axis.**

Find the x- and y-intercepts by substituting 0 for y in the equation and solving for x and then 0 for x and solving for y. Plot the points that correspond to the intercepts and then connect the points by drawing a line or part of a line through them.

EXAMPLE 5 Use a linear model

SUBMERSIBLES A submersible designed to explore the ocean floor is at an elevation of $-13{,}000$ feet (13,000 feet below sea level). The submersible ascends to the surface at an average rate of 650 feet per minute. The elevation e (in feet) of the submersible is given by the function

$$e = 650t - 13{,}000$$

where t is the time (in minutes) since the submersible began to ascend.

- Find the intercepts of the graph of the function and state what the intercepts represent.
- Graph the function and identify its domain and range.

Solution

STEP 1 **Find** the intercepts.

$0 = 650t - 13{,}000$	$e = 650(0) - 13{,}000$
$13{,}000 = 650t$	$e = -13{,}000 \leftarrow$ ***e*-intercept**
$20 = t \leftarrow$ ***t*-intercept**	

NAME INTERCEPTS
Because t is the independent variable, the horizontal axis is the t-axis, and you refer to the "t-intercept" of the graph of the function. Similarly, the vertical axis is the e-axis, and you refer to the "e-intercept."

The t-intercept represents the number of minutes the submersible takes to reach an elevation of 0 feet (sea level). The e-intercept represents the elevation of the submersible after 0 minutes (the time the ascent begins).

STEP 2 **Graph** the function using the intercepts.

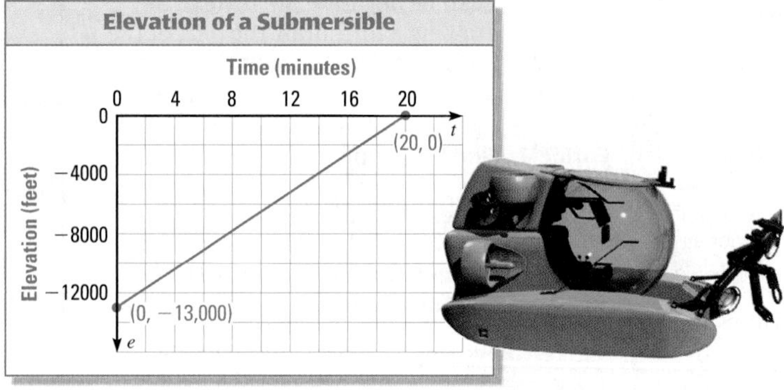

The submersible starts at an elevation of $-13{,}000$ feet and ascends to an elevation of 0 feet. So, the range of the function is $-13{,}000 \le e \le 0$. From the graph, you can see that the domain of the function is $0 \le t \le 20$.

✓ **GUIDED PRACTICE** for Example 5

7. **WHAT IF?** In Example 5, suppose the elevation of a second submersible is given by $e = 500t - 10{,}000$. Graph the function and identify its domain and range. **See margin for art; domain: $0 \le t \le 20$, range: $-10{,}000 \le e \le 0$.**

7.

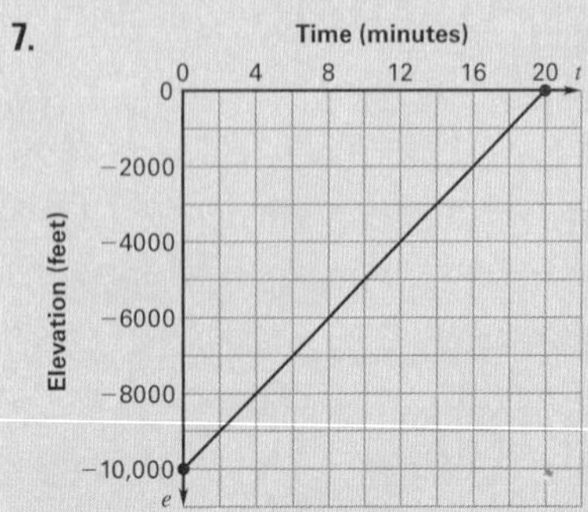

4.3 EXERCISES

HOMEWORK KEY

○ = **WORKED-OUT SOLUTIONS** on p. WS8 for Exs. 21 and 47

★ = **STANDARDIZED TEST PRACTICE** Exs. 2, 37, 41, 49, and 50

◆ = **MULTIPLE REPRESENTATIONS** Ex. 44

SKILL PRACTICE

A

1. **VOCABULARY** Copy and complete: The _?_ of the graph of an equation is the value of x when y is zero. **x-intercept**

2. ★ **WRITING** What are the x-intercept and the y-intercept of the line passing through the points (0, 3) and (−4, 0)? *Explain.*

2. −4, 3; the x-intercept is when y is 0, so the point (−4, 0) gives the x-intercept. The y-intercept is when x is 0, so the point (0, 3) gives the y-intercept.

3. **ERROR ANALYSIS** *Describe* and correct the error in finding the intercepts of the line shown. **The intercepts are switched around; the x-intercept is −2, and the y-intercept is 1.**

The x-intercept is 1, and the y-intercept is −2.

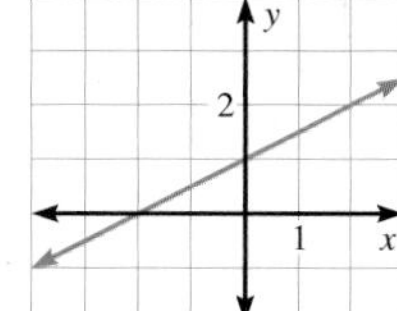

EXAMPLE 1 on p. 225 for Exs. 4–15

FINDING INTERCEPTS **Find the x-intercept and the y-intercept of the graph of the equation.**

4. $5x - y = 35$ **7, −35**
5. $3x - 3y = 9$ **3, −3**
6. $-3x + 9y = -18$ **6, −2**
7. $4x + y = 4$ **1, 4**
8. $2x + y = 10$ **5, 10**
9. $2x - 8y = 24$ **12, −3**
10. $3x + 0.5y = 6$ **2, 12**
11. $0.2x + 3.2y = 12.8$ **64, 4**
12. $y = 2x + 24$ **−12, 24**
13. $y = -14x + 7$ **$\frac{1}{2}$, 7**
14. $y = -4.8x + 1.2$ **0.25, 1.2**
15. $y = \frac{3}{5}x - 12$ **20, −12**

EXAMPLE 2 on p. 226 for Exs. 16–27

GRAPHING LINES **Graph the equation. Label the points where the line crosses the axes.** **16–27. See margin.**

16. $y = x + 3$
17. $y = x - 2$
18. $y = 4x - 8$
19. $y = 5 + 10x$
20. $y = -2 + 8x$
21. $y = -4x + 3$
22. $3x + y = 15$
23. $x - 4y = 18$
24. $8x - 5y = 80$
25. $-2x + 5y = 15$
26. $0.5x + 3y = 9$
27. $y = \frac{1}{2}x + \frac{1}{4}$

EXAMPLE 3 on p. 226 for Exs. 28–30

USING GRAPHS TO FIND INTERCEPTS **Identify the x-intercept and the y-intercept of the graph.**

28. 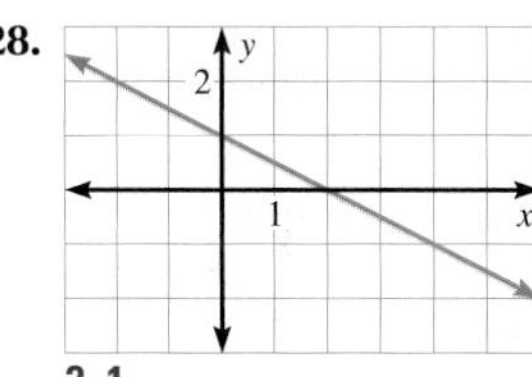
2, 1

29. 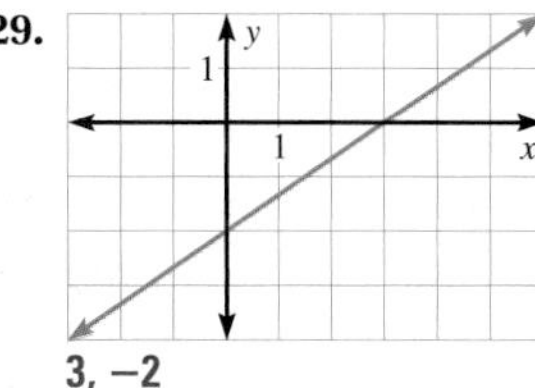
3, −2

30. 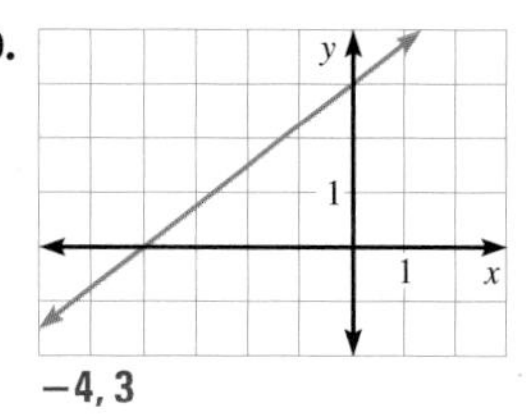
−4, 3

4 PRACTICE AND APPLY

Assignment Guide

Answer Transparencies available for all exercises

Basic:
Day 1: EP p. 940 Exs. 1–7 odd
pp. 229–232
Exs. 1–10, 16–21, 28–33, 37, 44–47, 51–56

Average:
Day 1: pp. 229–232
Exs. 1–3, 10–15, 22–27, 29, 30, 34–41, 44–49, 51–55 odd

Advanced:
Day 1: pp. 229–232
Exs. 1, 2, 12–15, 24–27, 29, 30, 35–37, 39–43*, 46–50*, 52–56 even

Block:
pp. 229–232
Exs. 1–3, 10–15, 22–27, 29, 30, 34–41, 44–49, 51–55 odd (with 4.2)

Differentiated Instruction

See *Differentiated Instruction Resources* for suggestions on addressing the needs of a diverse classroom.

Homework Check

For a quick check of student understanding of key concepts, go over the following exercises:

Basic: 6, 17, 28, 44, 45
Average: 11, 24, 29, 46, 48
Advanced: 13, 26, 30, 48, 49

Extra Practice

- Student Edition, p. 941
- Chapter Resource Book: Practice levels A, B, C

Practice Worksheet

An easily-readable reduced practice page (with answers) for this lesson can be found on p. 204D.

16–27. See Additional Answers beginning on p. AA1.

Avoiding Common Errors

Exercises 4–15 You may want to remind students before they begin these exercises that an intercept is either the x-coordinate or the y-coordinate of an ordered pair and therefore written as a number, not as an ordered pair.

Teaching Strategy

Exercises 31–36 Before students begin these exercises, suggest they write the ordered pairs that correspond to the intercepts.

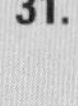

31\.

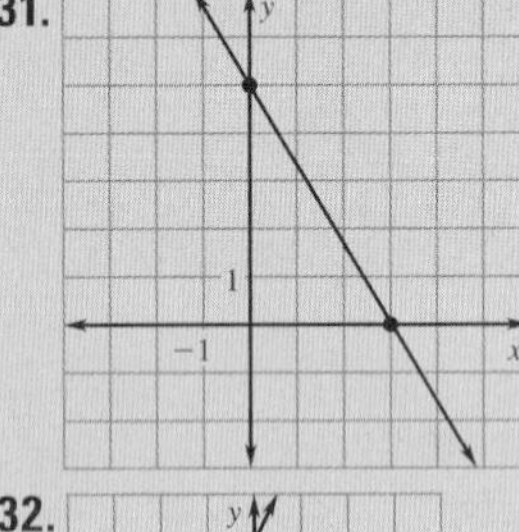

32\.

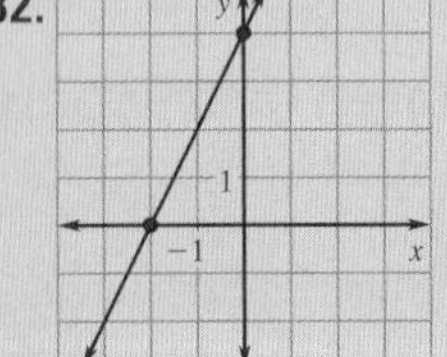

33\.

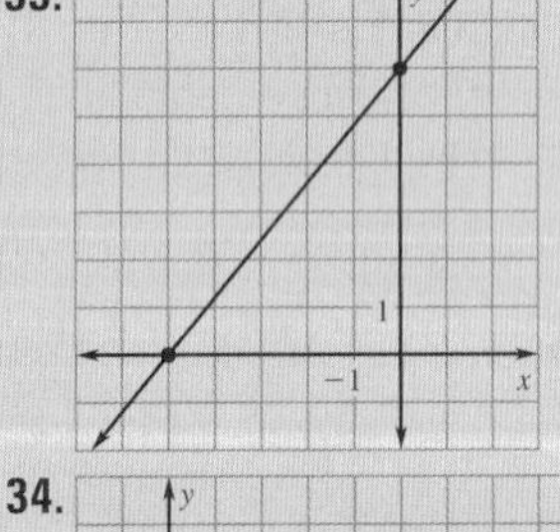

34\.

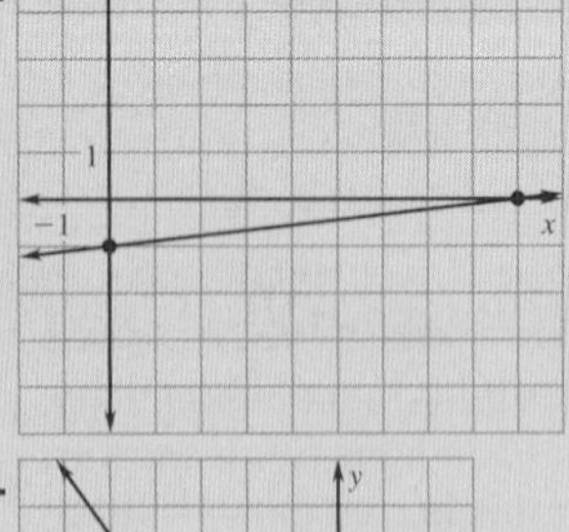

35\.

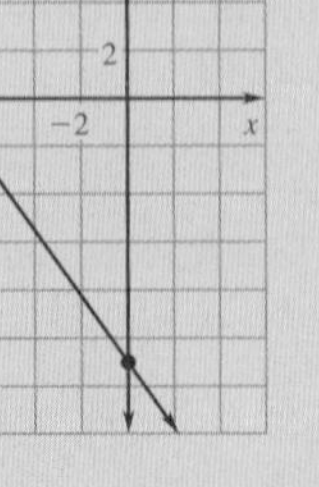

B **USING INTERCEPTS** **Draw the line that has the given intercepts.** **31–36. See margin.**

31. x-intercept: 3
y-intercept: 5

32. x-intercept: −2
y-intercept: 4

33. x-intercept: −5
y-intercept: 6

34. x-intercept: 9
y-intercept: −1

35. x-intercept: −8
y-intercept: −11

36. x-intercept: −2
y-intercept: −6

37. ★ **MULTIPLE CHOICE** The x-intercept of the graph of $Ax + 5y = 20$ is 2. What is the value of A? **D**

Ⓐ 2 Ⓑ 5 Ⓒ 7.5 Ⓓ 10

MATCHING EQUATIONS WITH GRAPHS **Match the equation with its graph.**

38. $2x - 6y = 6$ **C**

39. $2x - 6y = -6$ **B**

40. $2x - 6y = 12$ **A**

A.

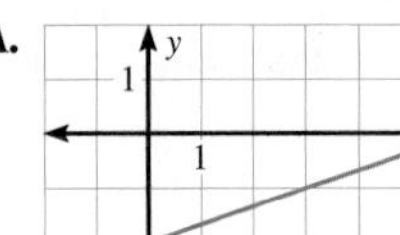

B.

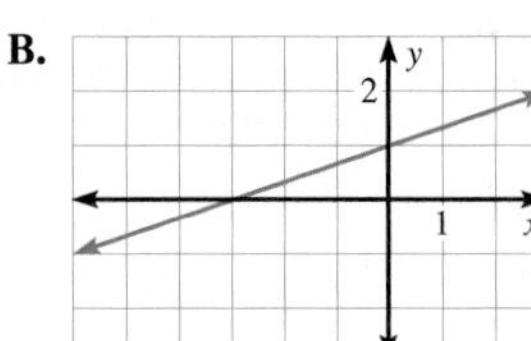

C.

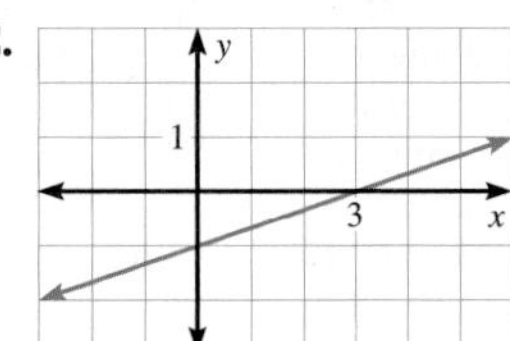

C **41.** ★ **WRITING** Is it possible for a line *not* to have an x-intercept? Is it possible for a line *not* to have a y-intercept? *Explain.* **Yes; yes; a horizontal line does not have an x-intercept if $y \neq 0$, a vertical line does not have a y-intercept if $x \neq 0$.**

42. **REASONING** Consider the equation $3x + 5y = k$. What values could k have so that the x-intercept and the y-intercept of the equation's graph would both be integers? *Explain.* ***Sample answer:*** **15 and 30; k can be any multiple of both 3 and 5.**

43. **CHALLENGE** If $a \neq 0$, find the intercepts of the graph of $y = ax + b$ in terms of a and b. $x = -\frac{b}{a}$, $y = b$

PROBLEM SOLVING

EXAMPLES A 4 and 5 on pp. 227–228 for Exs. 44–47

44. ◆ **MULTIPLE REPRESENTATIONS** The perimeter of a rectangular park is 72 feet. Let x be the park's width (in feet) and let y be its length (in feet).

a. **Writing an Equation** Write an equation for the perimeter. $2x + 2y = 72$

b. **Drawing a Graph** Find the intercepts of the graph of the equation you wrote. Then graph the equation. **36, 36; see margin for art.**

@HomeTutor for problem solving help at classzone.com

45. **RECYCLING** In one state, small bottles have a refund value of \$.04 each, and large bottles have a refund value of \$.08 each. Your friend returns both small and large bottles and receives \$.56. This situation is given by $4x + 8y = 56$ where x is the number of small bottles and y is the number of large bottles. **$x = 14$, $y = 7$; see margin for art.**

a. Find the intercepts of the graph of the equation. Graph the equation.

b. Give three possibilities for the number of each size bottle your friend could have returned. ***Sample answer:*** **2 and 6, 4 and 5, 6 and 4**

@HomeTutor for problem solving help at classzone.com

230 ○ = **WORKED-OUT SOLUTIONS** on p. WS1 ★ = **STANDARDIZED TEST PRACTICE**

= **MULTIPLE REPRESENTATIONS**

36\.

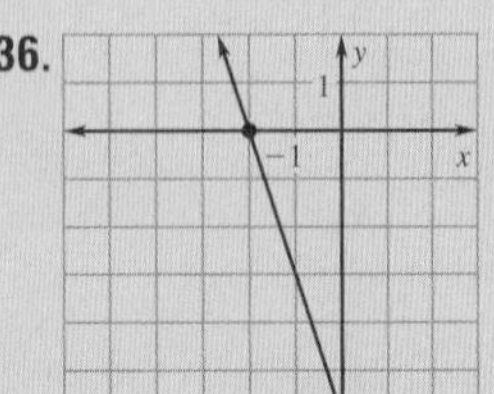

44b.

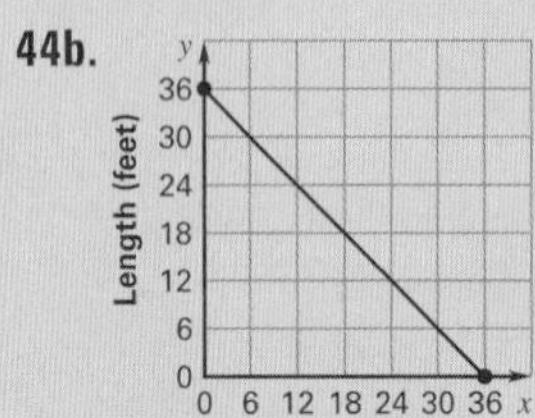

45a.

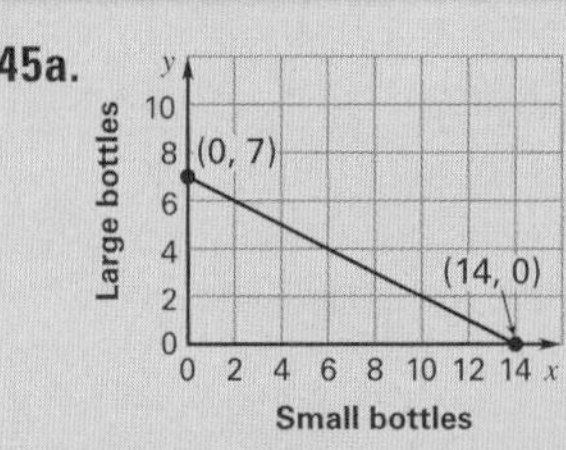

46b. The x-intercept means 64 field goals were scored and no free throws were scored. The y-intercept means that no field goals were scored and 128 free throws were scored.

46c. *Sample answer:* 40 field goals and 48 free throws, 50 field goals and 28 free throws, 60 field goals and 8 free throws

47a. v-intercept: 120, f-intercept: 180; the v-intercept means there are no flowers planted, the f-intercept means there are no vegetables planted.

47b. See margin for art; domain: $0 \le v \le 120$, range: $0 \le f \le 180$.

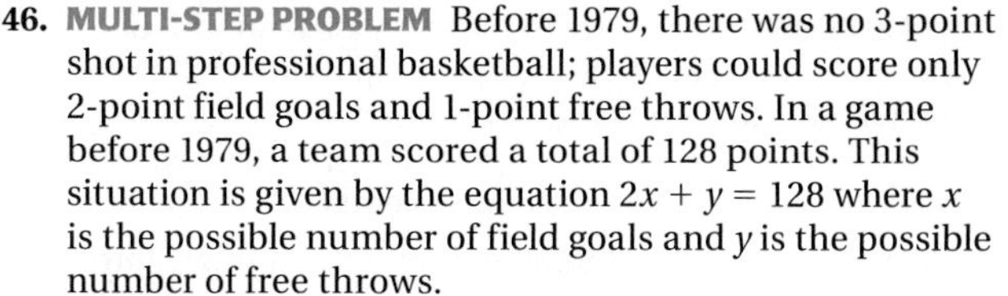

46. MULTI-STEP PROBLEM Before 1979, there was no 3-point shot in professional basketball; players could score only 2-point field goals and 1-point free throws. In a game before 1979, a team scored a total of 128 points. This situation is given by the equation $2x + y = 128$ where x is the possible number of field goals and y is the possible number of free throws.

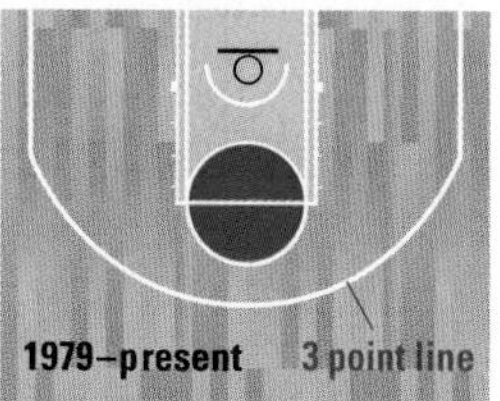

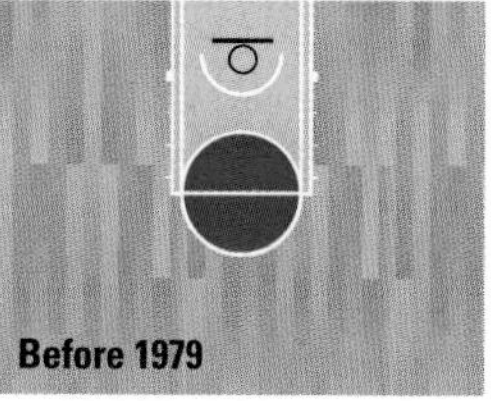

a. Find the intercepts of the graph of the equation. Graph the equation. **$x = 64$, $y = 128$; see margin for art.**

b. What do the intercepts mean in this situation?

c. What are three possible numbers of field goals and free throws the team could have scored?

d. If the team made 24 free throws, how many field goals were made? **52 field goals**

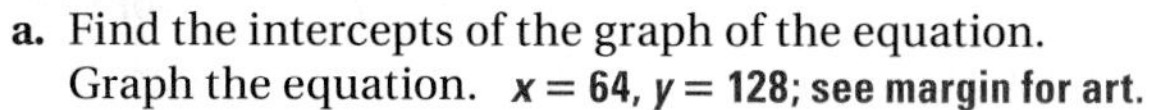

(47.) COMMUNITY GARDENS A family has a plot in a community garden. The family is going to plant vegetables, flowers, or both. The diagram shows the area used by one vegetable plant and the area of the entire plot. The area f (in square feet) of the plot left for flowers is given by $f = 180 - 1.5v$ where v is the number of vegetable plants the family plants.

a. Find the intercepts of the graph of the function and state what the intercepts represent.

b. Graph the function and identify its domain and range.

c. The family decides to plant 80 vegetable plants. How many square feet are left to plant flowers? **60 ft²**

B **48. CAR SHARING** A member of a car-sharing program can use a car for \$6 per hour and \$.50 per mile. The member uses the car for one day and is charged \$44. This situation is given by

$$6t + 0.5d = 44$$

where t is the time (in hours) the car is used and d is the distance (in miles) the car is driven. Give three examples of the number of hours the member could have used the car and the number of miles the member could have driven the car. ***Sample answer:* 1 h and 76 mi, 2 h and 64 mi, 3 h and 52 mi**

49. ★ SHORT RESPONSE A humidifier is a device used to put moisture into the air by turning water to vapor. A humidifier has a tank that can hold 1.5 gallons of water. The humidifier can disperse the water at a rate of 0.12 gallon per hour. The amount of water w (in gallons) left in the humidifier after t hours of use is given by the function

$$w = 1.5 - 0.12t.$$

After how many hours of use will you have to refill the humidifier? *Explain* how you found your answer. **12.5 h. *Sample answer:* Since the tank will be empty when it needs to be refilled, replace w in the function with 0 and then solve the resulting equation for t.**

Graphing Calculator

Exercises 44–49 Students can use their graphing calculators to check their graphs. They can enter the equation using the y= key, set parameters for the window using the Window key, and then graph using the Graph key. They can use the Table key to check x-intercepts, y-intercepts, and possible solutions for each of the exercises.

46a.

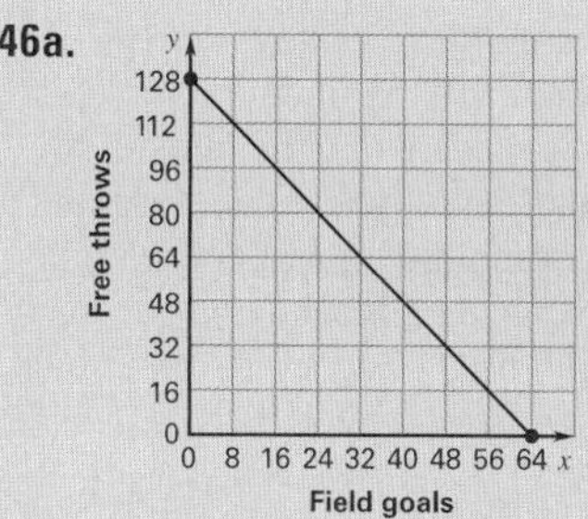

47b.

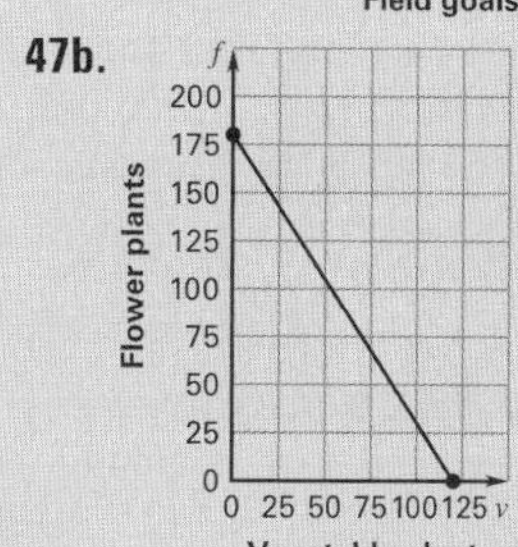

5 ASSESS AND RETEACH

Daily Homework Quiz

Transparency Available

1. Find the x-intercept and the y-intercept of the graph of $3x - y = 3$. **x-int: 1, y-int: −3**
2. A recycling company pays \$1 per used ink jet cartridge and \$2 per used laser cartridge. The company paid a customer \$14. This situation is given by $x + 2y = 14$ where x is the number of ink jet cartridges and y the number of laser cartridges. Use intercepts to graph the equation. Give four possibilities for the number of each type of cartridge that could have been recycled. **(0, 7), (6, 4), (10, 2), (14, 0)**

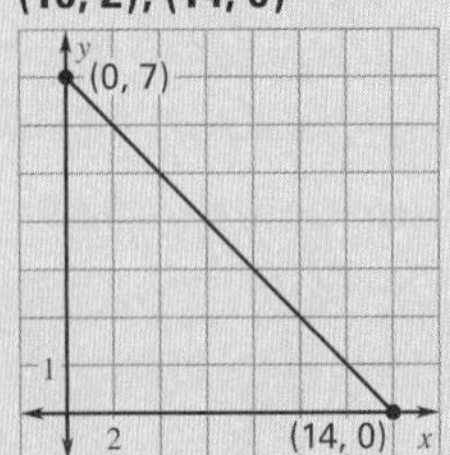

Available at **classzone.com**

Diagnosis/Remediation

- Practice A, B, C in Chapter Resource Book
- Study Guide in Chapter Resource Book
- Practice Workbook
- @HomeTutor

Challenge

Additional challenge is available in the Chapter Resource Book.

Quiz

An easily-readable reduced copy of the quiz (with answers) on Lessons 4.1–4.3 from the Assessment Book can be found on p. 204G.

50b, Quiz 1–6, 13. See Additional Answers beginning on p. AA1.

C **50.** ★ **EXTENDED RESPONSE** You borrow \$180 from a friend who doesn't charge you interest. You work out a payment schedule in which you will make weekly payments to your friend. The balance B (in dollars) of the loan is given by the function $B = 180 - pn$ where p is the weekly payment and n is the number of weeks you make payments.

50a. The B-intercept is the balance of the loan after 0 weeks, the n-intercept is the amount of time it takes to pay off the loan.

a. **Interpret** Without finding the intercepts, state what they represent.

b. **Graph** Graph the function if you make weekly payments of \$20. **See margin.**

c. **Identify** Find the domain and range of the function in part (b). How long will it take to pay back your friend? **domain: $0 \le n \le 9$, range: $0 \le B \le 180$; 9 wk**

d. **CHALLENGE** Suppose you make payments of \$20 for three weeks. Then you make payments of \$15 until you have paid your friend back. How does this affect the graph? How many payments do you make? **The graph is two line segments; 11 payments.**

MIXED REVIEW

REVIEW GRAPHS For help with line graphs, see p. 933.

In Exercises 51–53, use the line graph, which shows the number of points Alex scored in five basketball games. *(p. 933)*

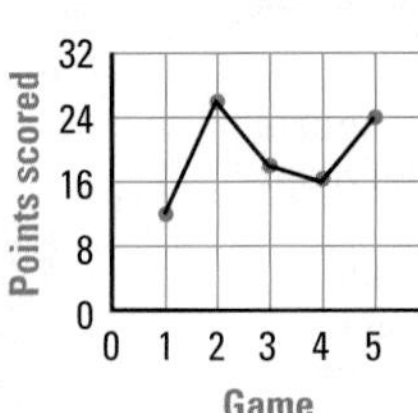

51. How many points did Alex score in game 4? **16 points**
52. In which game did Alex score the most points? **game 2**
53. How many more points did Alex score in game 5 than in game 1? **12 more points**

PREVIEW Prepare for Lesson 4.4 in Exs. 54–56.

Solve the proportion. *(p. 168)*

54. $\frac{3}{5} = \frac{x}{30}$ **18**
55. $\frac{x}{x+6} = \frac{7}{6}$ **−42**
56. $\frac{t-3}{12} = \frac{2t-2}{9}$ **$-\frac{1}{5}$**

QUIZ *for Lessons 4.1–4.3*

Plot the point in a coordinate plane. *Describe* the location of the point. *(p. 206)* **1–3. See margin for art.**

1. $(-7, 2)$ **Quadrant II**
2. $(0, -5)$ **y-axis**
3. $(2, -6)$ **Quadrant IV**

Graph the equation. *(p. 215)* **4–6. See margin.**

4. $-4x - 2y = 12$
5. $y = -5$
6. $x = 6$

Find the x-intercept and the y-intercept of the graph of the equation. *(p. 225)*

7. $y = x + 7$ **−7, 7**
8. $y = x - 3$ **3, −3**
9. $y = -5x + 2$ **$\frac{2}{5}$, 2**
10. $x + 3y = 15$ **15, 5**
11. $3x - 6y = 36$ **12, −6**
12. $-2x - 5y = 22$ **−11, $-4\frac{2}{5}$**

13. **SWIMMING POOLS** A public swimming pool that holds 45,000 gallons of water is going to be drained for maintenance at a rate of 100 gallons per minute. The amount of water w (in gallons) in the pool after t minutes is given by the function $w = 45{,}000 - 100t$. Graph the function. Identify its domain and range. How much water is in the pool after 60 minutes? How many minutes will it take to empty the pool? *(p. 225)* **See margin for art; domain: $0 \le t \le 450$, range: $0 \le w \le 45{,}000$; 39,000 gal; 450 min.**

MIXED REVIEW of Problem Solving

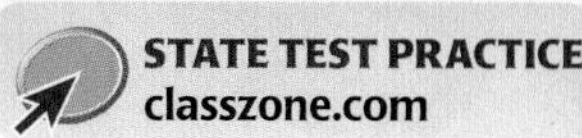

Lessons 4.1–4.3

1. **MULTI-STEP PROBLEM** An amusement park charges $20 for an all-day pass and $10 for a pass after 5 P.M. On Wednesday the amusement park collected $1000 in pass sales. This situation can be modeled by the equation $1000 = 20x + 10y$ where x is the number of all-day passes sold and y is the number of passes sold after 5 P.M. **a–c. See margin.**
   a. Find the x-intercept of the graph of the equation. What does it represent?
   b. Find the y-intercept of the graph of the equation. What does it represent?
   c. Graph the equation using a scale of 10 on the x- and y-axes.

2. **MULTI-STEP PROBLEM** A violin player who plays every day received a violin with new strings. Players who play every day should replace the strings on their violins every 6 months. A particular brand of strings costs $24 per pack. The table shows the total spent a (in dollars) on replacement strings with respect to time t (in months).

t (months)	*a* (dollars)
6	24
12	48
18	72
24	96
30	120

   a. *Explain* how you know the table represents a function. **There is exactly one cost for each time.**
   b. Graph the function. **See margin.**

3. **OPEN-ENDED** Create a table that shows the number of minutes you think you will spend watching TV next week. Let Monday be day 1, Tuesday be day 2, and so on. Graph the data. Does the graph represent a function? *Explain.* **See margin for art; yes; there is exactly one number of minutes for each day.**

4. **SHORT RESPONSE** You can hike at an average rate of 3 miles per hour. Your total hiking distance d (in miles) can be modeled by the function $d = 3t$ where t is the time (in hours) you hike. You plan on hiking for 10 hours this weekend.
   a. Is the domain or range specified in the problem? *Explain.* **Yes; the domain is specified because you plan on hiking for 10 hours.**
   b. Graph the function and identify its domain and range. Use the graph to find how long it takes to hike 6 miles. **See margin for art; domain: $0 \le t \le 10$, range: $0 \le d \le 30$; 2 h.**

5. **EXTENDED RESPONSE** The table shows the departure d (in degrees Fahrenheit) from the normal monthly temperature in New England for the first six months of 2004. For example, in month 1, $d = -3$. So, the average temperature was 3 degrees below the normal temperature for January.

M (month)	1	2	3	4	5	6
d (°F)	−3	−1	2	2	4	−1

   a. *Explain* how you know the table represents a function. **There is exactly one temperature departure for each month.**
   b. Graph the function and identify its domain and range. **See margin for art; domain: 1, 2, 3, 4, 5, and 6, range: −3, −1, 2, and 4.**
   c. What does a point in Quadrant IV mean in terms of this situation? **The temperature is below normal.**

6. **GRIDDED ANSWER** The graph shows the possible combinations of T-shirts and tank tops that you can buy with the amount of money you have. If you buy only T-shirts, how many can you buy? **6 T–shirts**

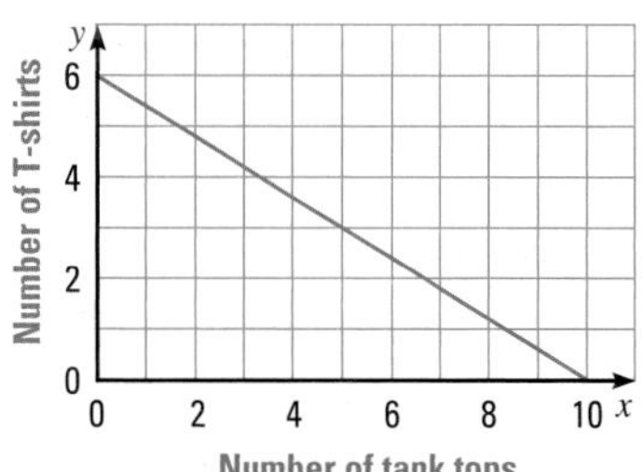

1a. 50; the number of all-day passes sold when no passes after 5 P.M. were sold

1b. 100; the number of passes sold after 5 P.M. when no all-day passes were sold

1c.

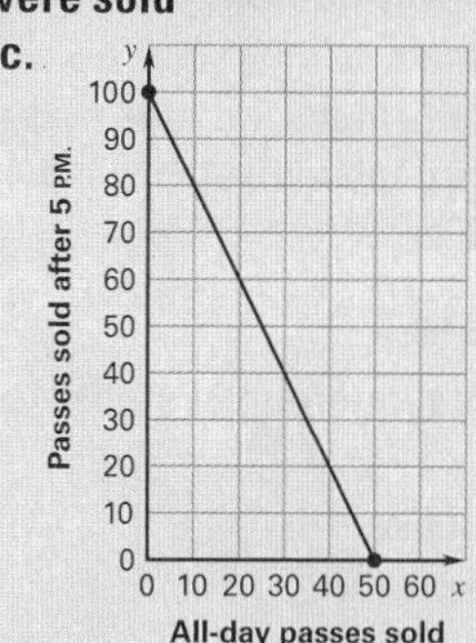

2b.

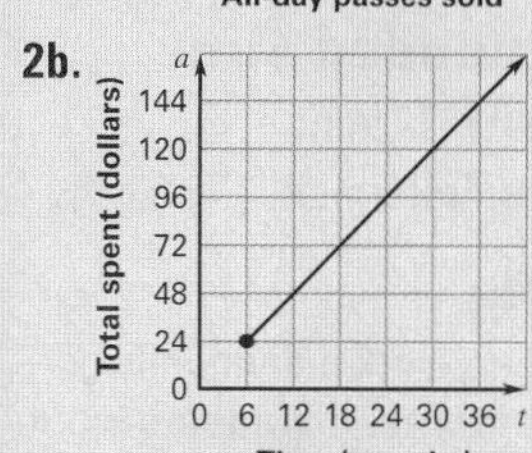

3.

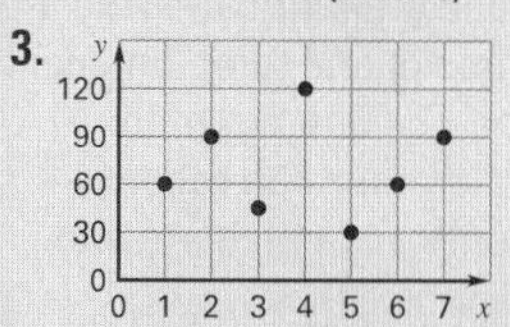

4b.

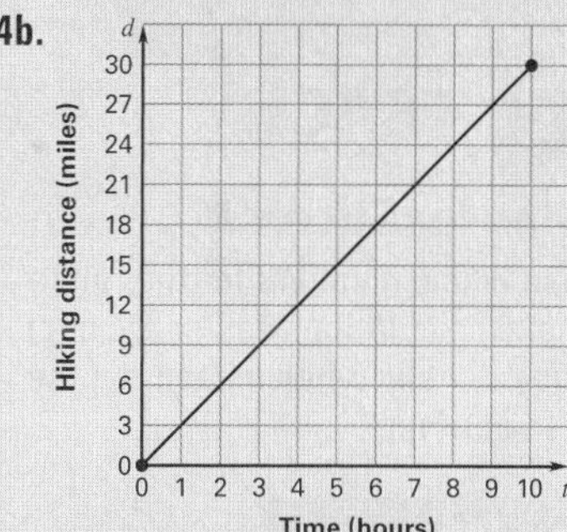

5b.

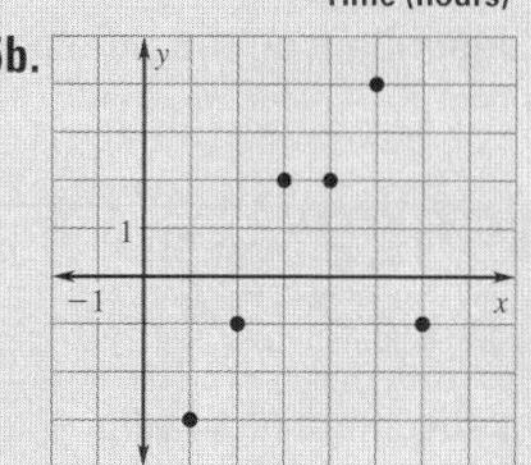

1 PLAN AND PREPARE

Explore the Concept

- Students will measure the slope of a ramp.
- This activity leads into the study of finding slope in Example 1 in Lesson 4.4.

Materials

Each student or group of students will need:

- several books
- two rulers

Recommended Time

Work activity: 10 min
Discuss results: 5 min

Grouping

Students can work individually or in groups of three. If students work in groups, one student can make a ramp with books and ruler, one can measure the rise and run of the ramp, and the other can record measurements and calculate and record the slope.

2 TEACH

Tips for Success

Use whole numbers for the run to make calculations easier. Do not let the ruler slip when measuring the rise and run.

Key Discovery

Slope is dependent on the ratio of rise to run.

3 ASSESS AND RETEACH

How does the slope of a ramp change if the rise of the ramp decreases and the run increases? **The slope decreases.**

4.4 Slopes of Lines

MATERIALS • several books • two rulers

QUESTION **How can you use algebra to describe the slope of a ramp?**

You can use the ratio of the vertical rise to the horizontal run to describe the *slope* of a ramp.

$$\text{slope} = \frac{\text{rise}}{\text{run}}$$

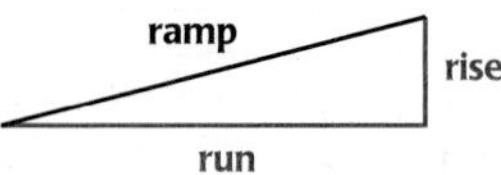

EXPLORE **Calculate the slopes of ramps**

STEP 1

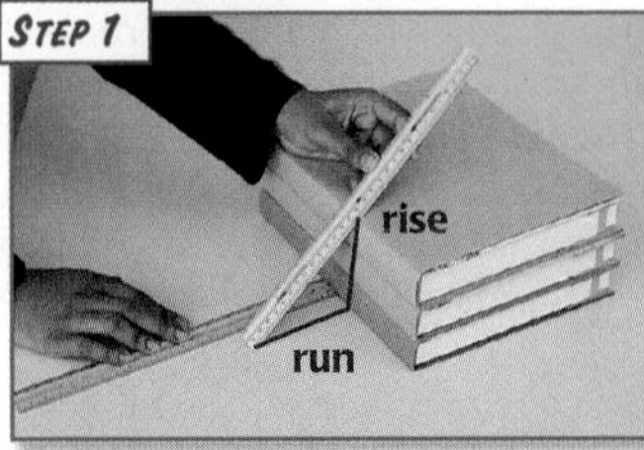

Make a ramp Make a stack of three books. Use a ruler as a ramp. Measure the rise and run of the ramp, and record them in a table. Calculate and record the slope of the ramp in your table.

STEP 2

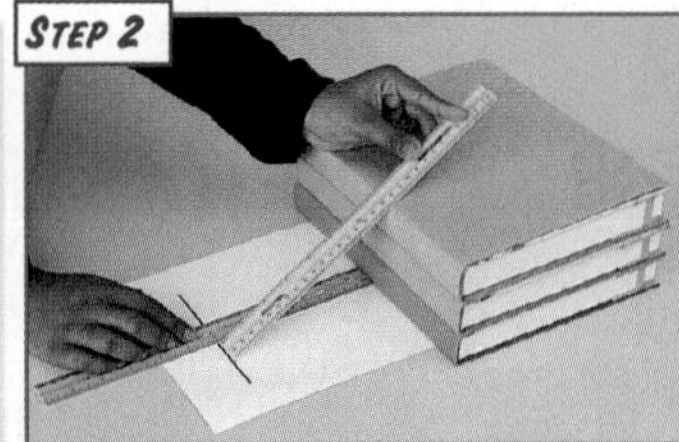

Change the run Without changing the rise, make three ramps with different runs by moving the lower end of the ruler. Measure and record the rise and run of each ramp. Calculate and record each slope.

STEP 3

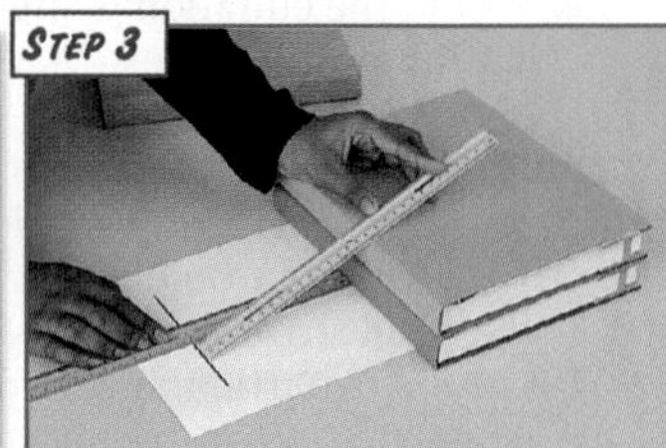

Change the rise Without changing the run, make three ramps with different rises by adding or removing books. Measure and record the rise and run of each ramp. Calculate and record each slope.

DRAW CONCLUSIONS **Use your observations to complete these exercises**

Describe **how the slope of the ramp changes given the following conditions. Give three examples that support your answer.**

1. The run of the ramp increases, and the rise stays the same. **The slope gets smaller. *Sample answer:* $\frac{1}{4}, \frac{1}{5}, \frac{1}{6}$**
2. The rise of the ramp increases, and the run stays the same. **The slope gets larger. *Sample answer:* $\frac{1}{5}, \frac{2}{5}, \frac{3}{5}$**

In Exercises 3–5, describe the relationship between the rise and the run of the ramp.

3. A ramp with a slope of 1 **The rise and the run are the same.**
4. A ramp with a slope greater than 1 **The rise is greater than the run.**
5. A ramp with a slope less than 1 **The rise is less than the run.**
6. Ramp A has a rise of 6 feet and a run of 2 feet. Ramp B has a rise of 10 feet and a run of 4 feet. Which ramp is steeper? How do you know? **Ramp A; the slope of ramp A is 3 while the slope of ramp B is $\frac{5}{2}$ or 2.5, and 3 > 2.5.**

4.4 Find Slope and Rate of Change

Before You graphed linear equations.

Now You will find the slope of a line and interpret slope as a rate of change.

Why? So you can find the slope of a boat ramp, as in Ex. 23.

Key Vocabulary
- **slope**
- **rate of change**

The **slope** of a nonvertical line is the ratio of the vertical change (the *rise*) to the horizontal change (the *run*) between any two points on the line. The slope of a line is represented by the letter m.

READING
Read x_1 as "x sub one." Think "x-coordinate of the first point."
Read y_1 as "y sub one." Think "y-coordinate of the first point."

KEY CONCEPT *For Your Notebook*

Finding the Slope of a Line

Words

The slope m of the nonvertical line passing through the two points (x_1, y_1) and (x_2, y_2) is the ratio of the rise (change in y) to the run (change in x).

$$\text{slope} = \frac{\text{rise}}{\text{run}} = \frac{\text{change in } y}{\text{change in } x}$$

Symbols

$$m = \frac{y_2 - y_1}{x_2 - x_1}$$

Graph

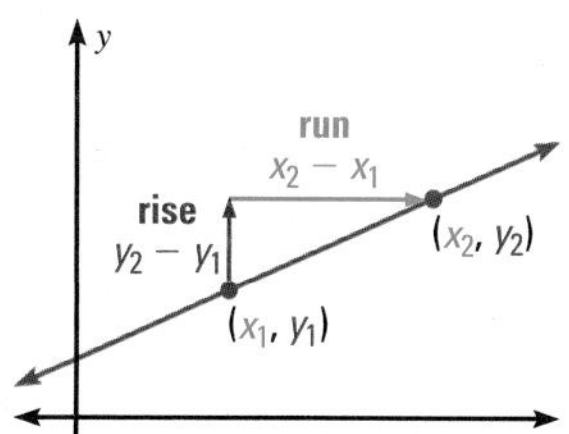

EXAMPLE 1 Find a positive slope

Find the slope of the line shown.

Let $(x_1, y_1) = (-4, 2)$ and $(x_2, y_2) = (2, 6)$.

$m = \frac{y_2 - y_1}{x_2 - x_1}$ **Write formula for slope.**

$= \frac{6 - 2}{2 - (-4)}$ **Substitute.**

$= \frac{4}{6} = \frac{2}{3}$ **Simplify.**

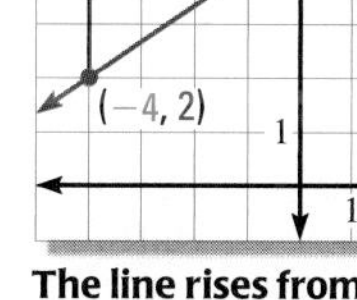

The line rises from left to right. The slope is positive.

AVOID ERRORS
Be sure to keep the x- and y-coordinates in the same order in both the numerator and denominator when calculating slope.

✓ **GUIDED PRACTICE** for Example 1

Find the slope of the line that passes through the points.

1. (5, 2) and (4, −1) **3**
2. (−2, 3) and (4, 6) $\frac{1}{2}$
3. $\left(\frac{9}{2}, 5\right)$ and $\left(\frac{1}{2}, -3\right)$ **2**

1 PLAN AND PREPARE

Warm-Up Exercises

Transparency Available

Evaluate and simplify the ratios when $x = 2$ and $y = -2$.

1. $\frac{y + 3}{x - 5}$ $-\frac{1}{3}$
2. $\frac{1 - y}{x - 6}$ $-\frac{3}{4}$
3. A cross-country skier traveled 14 miles in 3.5 hours. Use the formula $d = rt$ where d is distance, r is rate, and t is time, to find the average rate of speed. **4 mi/h**

Notetaking Guide

Transparency Available

Promotes interactive learning and notetaking skills.

Pacing

Basic: 2 days
Average: 2 days
Advanced: 2 days
Block: 1 block
- See *Teaching Guide/Lesson Plan*.

2 FOCUS AND MOTIVATE

Essential Question

Big Idea 3, p. 205

How do you find the slope of a line and interpret slope as a rate of change? **Tell students they will learn how to answer this question by using the slope formula to find slope and to describe changes in a real-world situation.**

NCTM STANDARDS

Standard 2: Use models to understand relationships

Standard 4: Understand the units of measurement

Resource Planning Guide

Chapter Resource Book
- Teaching Guide/Lesson Plan
- Practice levels A, B, C
- Study Guide
- Catch-up for Absent Students
- Application
- Challenge

Workbooks
- Notetaking Guide
- Practice Workbook

Teaching Options
- **Power Presentations** provides dynamic electronic teaching resources for the classroom.
- **Activity Generator** provides editable activities for all ability levels.

Interactive Technology
- Easy Planner
- Power Presentations
- Activity Generator
- Animated Algebra
- Test Generator
- Online Quiz
- eWorkbook
- eEdition
- @HomeTutor

Resources for English Learners
- Spanish Study Guide
- Multi-Language Visual Glossary
- Student Resources in Spanish

See also the *Differentiated Instruction Resources* for more strategies for meeting individual needs.

Motivating the Lesson

By learning how to use the slope formula, you can discover rates of change in real-world situations. For example, you are training for a marathon. After one hour, you have run 7 miles and after four hours, you have run 22 miles. By using the slope formula, you can find your average rate of change in distance with respect to time.

3 TEACH

Extra Example 1

Find the slope of the line shown. $\frac{3}{4}$

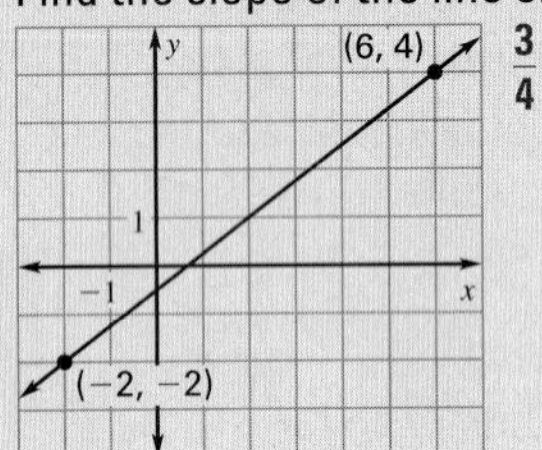

Extra Example 2

Find the slope of the line shown. $-\frac{1}{5}$

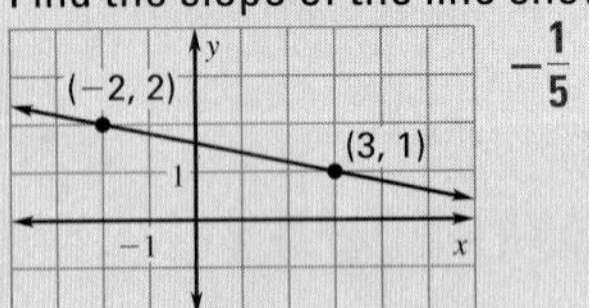

Key Question to Ask for Example 2

- If you let (6, −1) be (x_1, y_1) and (3, 5) be (x_2, y_2), will it change the slope? Explain. **No, the slope will be −2 regardless of the order of the points.**

Avoiding Common Errors

Example 2 Stress that the coordinates of the point chosen as (x_1, y_1) must be subtracted from the coordinates of (x_2, y_2) in the correct order in the numerator and the denominator.

EXAMPLE 2 Find a negative slope

FIND SLOPE

In Example 2, if you used two other points on the line, such as (4, 3) and (5, 1), in the slope formula, the slope would still be −2.

Find the slope of the line shown.

Let $(x_1, y_1) = (3, 5)$ and $(x_2, y_2) = (6, -1)$.

$m = \frac{y_2 - y_1}{x_2 - x_1}$ **Write formula for slope.**

$= \frac{-1 - 5}{6 - 3}$ **Substitute.**

$= \frac{-6}{3} = -2$ **Simplify.**

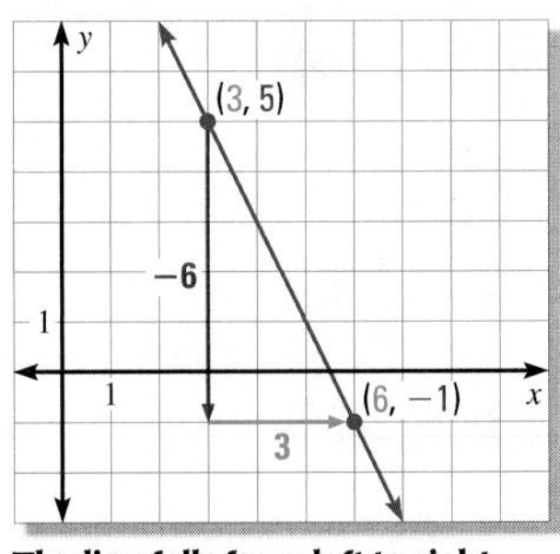

The line falls from left to right. The slope is negative.

EXAMPLE 3 Find the slope of a horizontal line

Find the slope of the line shown.

Let $(x_1, y_1) = (-2, 4)$ and $(x_2, y_2) = (4, 4)$.

$m = \frac{y_2 - y_1}{x_2 - x_1}$ **Write formula for slope.**

$= \frac{4 - 4}{4 - (-2)}$ **Substitute.**

$= \frac{0}{6} = 0$ **Simplify.**

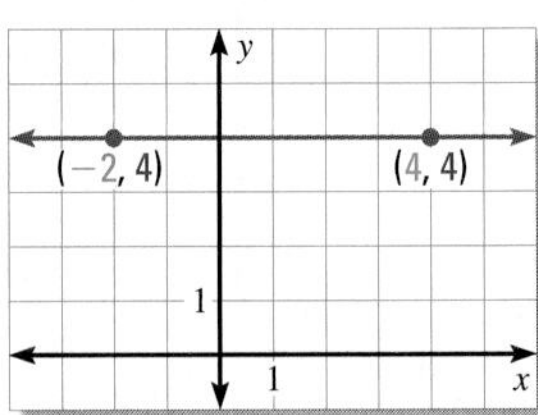

The line is horizontal. The slope is zero.

EXAMPLE 4 Find the slope of a vertical line

Find the slope of the line shown.

Let $(x_1, y_1) = (3, 5)$ and $(x_2, y_2) = (3, 1)$.

$m = \frac{y_2 - y_1}{x_2 - x_1}$ **Write formula for slope.**

$= \frac{1 - 5}{3 - 3}$ **Substitute.**

$= \frac{-4}{0}$ (crossed out) **Division by zero is undefined.**

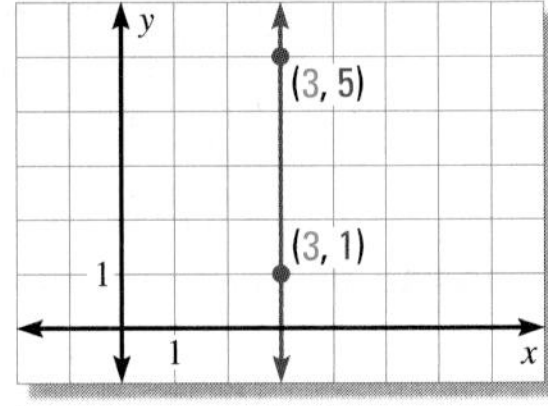

The line is vertical. The slope is undefined.

▶ Because division by zero is undefined, the slope of a vertical line is undefined.

✓ GUIDED PRACTICE for Examples 2, 3, and 4

Find the slope of the line that passes through the points.

4. (5, 2) and (5, −2) **undefined**
5. (0, 4) and (−3, 4) **0**
6. (0, 6) and (5, −4) **−2**

Differentiated Instruction

English Learners Some students may need to be reminded that the small numbers in the formula $m = \frac{y_2 - y_1}{x_2 - x_1}$ are *not* exponents; they are called *subscripts* because they rest below the base line of the text. Tell students to remember that a submarine goes below the surface of the ocean. Remind students to read x_1 as "*x* sub one."

See also the *Differentiated Instruction Resources* for more strategies.

CONCEPT SUMMARY *For Your Notebook*

Classification of Lines by Slope

A line with positive slope ($m > 0$) *rises* from left to right.

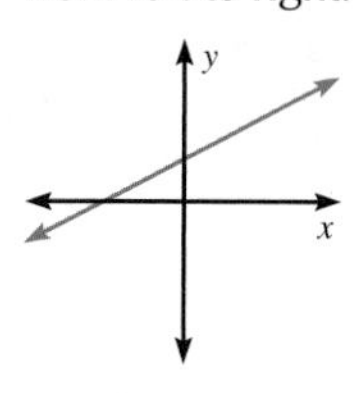

A line with negative slope ($m < 0$) *falls* from left to right.

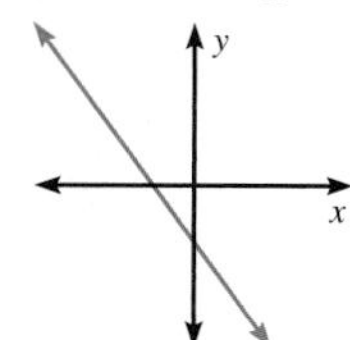

A line with zero slope ($m = 0$) is *horizontal.*

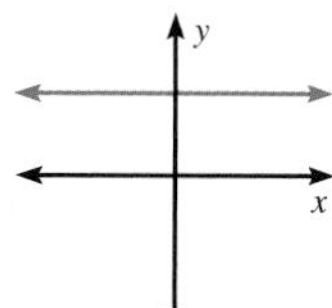

A line with undefined slope is *vertical.*

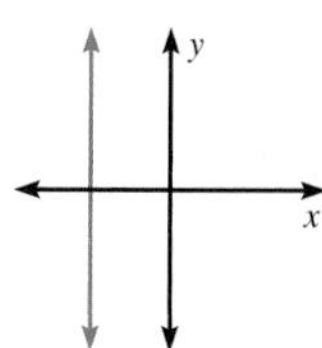

RATE OF CHANGE A **rate of change** compares a change in one quantity to a change in another quantity. For example, if you are paid \$60 for working 5 hours, then your hourly wage is \$12 per hour, a rate of change that describes how your pay increases with respect to time spent working.

EXAMPLE 5 Find a rate of change

INTERNET CAFE The table shows the cost of using a computer at an Internet cafe for a given amount of time. Find the rate of change in cost with respect to time.

Time (hours)	2	4	6
Cost (dollars)	7	14	21

Solution

ANALYZE UNITS
Because the cost is in dollars and time is in hours, the rate of change in cost with respect to time is expressed in dollars per hour.

$$\text{Rate of change} = \frac{\text{change in cost}}{\text{change in time}}$$

$$= \frac{14 - 7}{4 - 2} = \frac{7}{2} = 3.5$$

▶ The rate of change in cost is \$3.50 per hour.

✓ **GUIDED PRACTICE** for Example 5

7. **EXERCISE** The table shows the distance a person walks for exercise. Find the rate of change in distance with respect to time. **0.05 mi/min**

Time (minutes)	Distance (miles)
30	1.5
60	3
90	4.5

Differentiated Instruction

Below Level After discussing **Example 5**, have students determine the rate of change using two sets of quantities different from the set used in the example. Ask what would be the rise and run if they graphed the data. Then ask them to describe the slope of the line in terms of the rise and run.

Advanced Have students explore rates of change that are averages as well as constants. In **Example 5**, ask students to consider that the cost for 6 hours at the café is \$18 rather than \$21. Have them describe how this affects the rate of change by comparing rates at 2 hours and 4 hours, 2 hours and 6 hours, and 4 hours and 6 hours.

See also the *Differentiated Instruction Resources* for more strategies.

Extra Example 3

Find the slope of the line shown. **0**

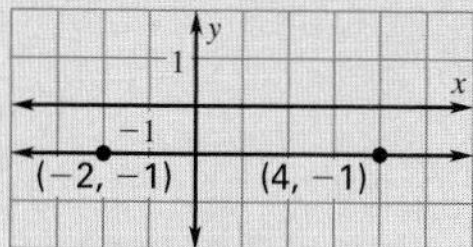

Key Question to Ask for Example 3

- What can you conclude about a line if the slope of the line is zero? **The y-coordinates of the points on the line are the same and the line is horizontal.**

Extra Example 4

Find the slope of the line shown. **undefined**

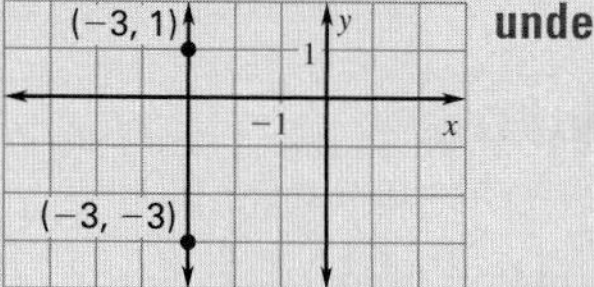

Key Question to Ask for Example 4

- What can you conclude about the slope of a line if two points on the line have the same x-coordinates? **The slope is undefined and the line is vertical.**

Extra Example 5

The table shows the cost to paint a house for a given number of hours. Find the rate of change in cost with respect to time. **\$22.50 per hour**

Time (hours)	4	6	8
Cost (\$)	90	135	180

Extra Example 6

The graph shows the number of computer games sold day 1, day 4, day 7, and day 9 of a sale. Describe the rates of change in sales with respect to time.

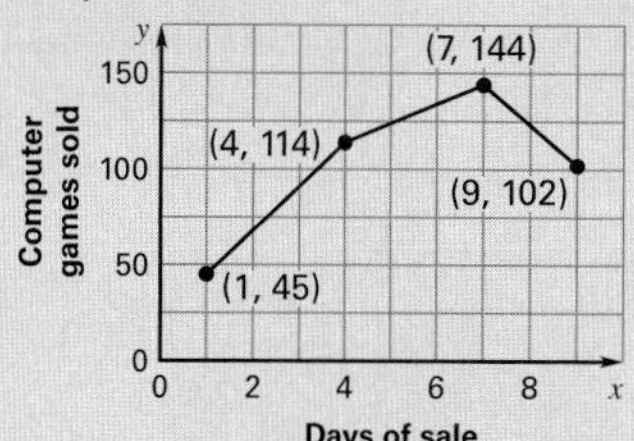

Sales increased at a fast rate, then at a slower rate, and finally decreased at a moderate rate.

SLOPE AND RATE OF CHANGE You can interpret the slope of a line as a rate of change. When given graphs of real-world data, you can compare rates of change by comparing slopes of lines.

EXAMPLE 6 Use a graph to find and compare rates of change

COMMUNITY THEATER A community theater performed a play each Saturday evening for 10 consecutive weeks. The graph shows the attendance for the performances in weeks 1, 4, 6, and 10. Describe the rates of change in attendance with respect to time.

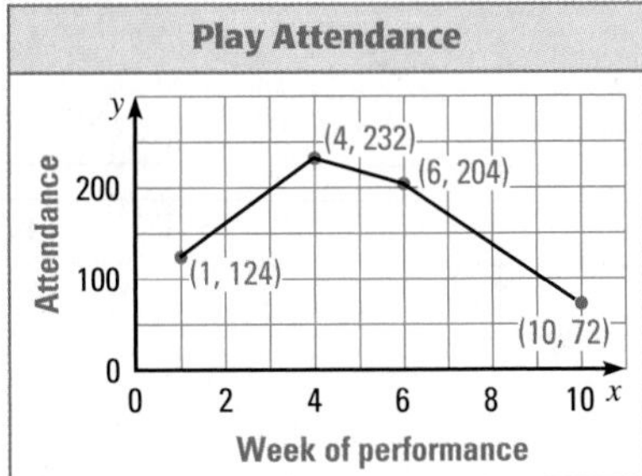

Solution

Find the rates of change using the slope formula.

Weeks 1–4: $\frac{232 - 124}{4 - 1} = \frac{108}{3} = 36$ people per week

INTERPRET RATE OF CHANGE
A negative rate of change indicates a decrease.

Weeks 4–6: $\frac{204 - 232}{6 - 4} = \frac{-28}{2} = -14$ people per week

Weeks 6–10: $\frac{72 - 204}{10 - 6} = \frac{-132}{4} = -33$ people per week

▶ Attendance increased during the early weeks of performing the play. Then attendance decreased, slowly at first, then more rapidly.

EXAMPLE 7 Interpret a graph

COMMUTING TO SCHOOL A student commutes from home to school by walking and by riding a bus. Describe the student's commute in words.

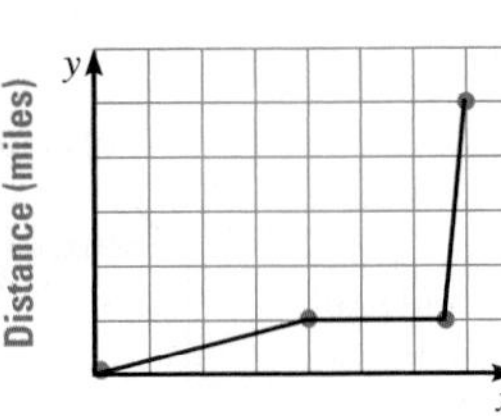

Solution

The first segment of the graph is not very steep, so the student is not traveling very far with respect to time. The student must be walking. The second segment has a zero slope, so the student must not be moving. He or she is waiting for the bus. The last segment is steep, so the student is traveling far with respect to time. The student must be riding the bus.

Animated Algebra at classzone.com

✓ **GUIDED PRACTICE** for Examples 6 and 7

8. **WHAT IF?** How would the answer to Example 6 change if you knew that attendance was 70 people in week 12? ***Sample answer:*** **The attendance did not decrease as rapidly between weeks 10 and 12.**
9. **WHAT IF?** Using the graph in Example 7, draw a graph that represents the student's commute from school to home. **See margin.**

Extra Example 7

The graph shows a ferry's trip across a lake. Describe the trip in words.

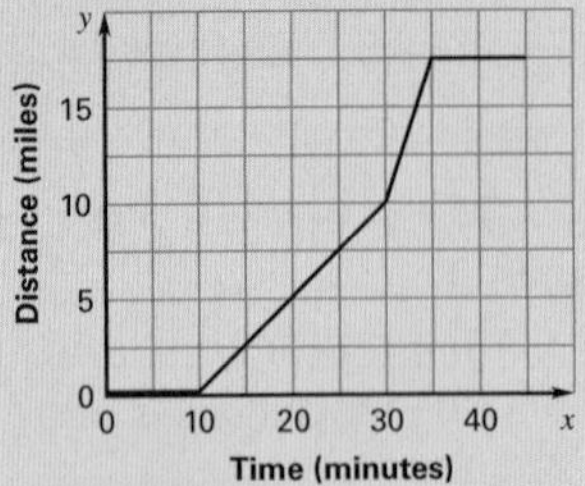

The slope is 0 at first, so the ferry must be loading. The ferry begins moving at a steady speed, picks up speed, and then unloads when the slope is 0 again.

An **Animated Algebra** activity is available online for **Example 7**. This activity is also part of **Power Presentations**.

Closing the Lesson

Have students summarize the major points of the lesson and answer the Essential Question: How do you find the slope of a line and interpret slope as a rate of change?

- **The slope of a line is the ratio of the change in *y* (rise) to the change in *x* (the run). The slope is positive if the line slants upward and negative if the line slants downward.**
- **For real-world data, interpret slope as a rate of change.**

Use two points on a graph and the slope formula to find the slope of a line. In graphs of real-world data, use slope to describe the rate of change in the data.

9.

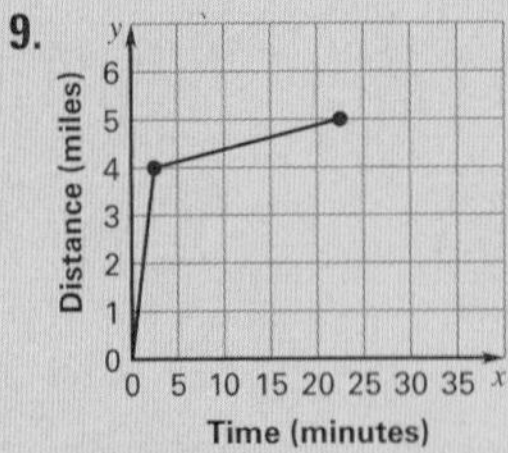

4.4 EXERCISES

HOMEWORK KEY
○ = **WORKED-OUT SOLUTIONS** on p. WS9 for Exs. 11 and 37
★ = **STANDARDIZED TEST PRACTICE** Exs. 2, 17, 18, 34, and 40

SKILL PRACTICE

A

1. **VOCABULARY** Copy and complete: The __?__ of a nonvertical line is the ratio of the vertical change to the horizontal change between any two points on the line. **slope**

2. ★ **WRITING** Without calculating the slope, how can you tell that the slope of the line that passes through the points (−5, −3) and (2, 4) is positive? **The line between the two points rises from left to right.**

3. **ERROR ANALYSIS** *Describe* and correct the error in calculating the slope of the line passing through the points (5, 3) and (2, 6). **The denominator should be 2 − 5, not 5 − 2;** $m = \frac{6-3}{2-5} = \frac{3}{-3} = -1.$

$$m = \frac{6-3}{5-2} = \frac{3}{3} = 1 \quad \times$$

EXAMPLES 1,2,3, and 4 on pp. 235–236 for Exs. 4–18

FINDING SLOPE **Tell whether the slope of the line is *positive, negative, zero,* or *undefined*. Then find the slope if it exists.**

4. 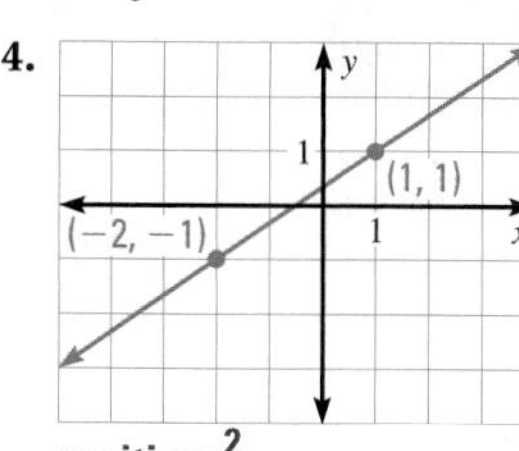

positive; $\frac{2}{3}$

5. 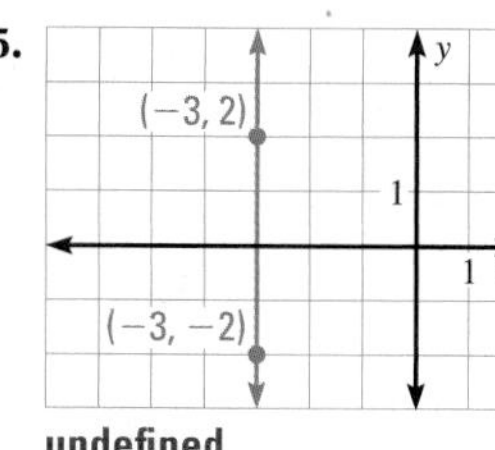

undefined

6. 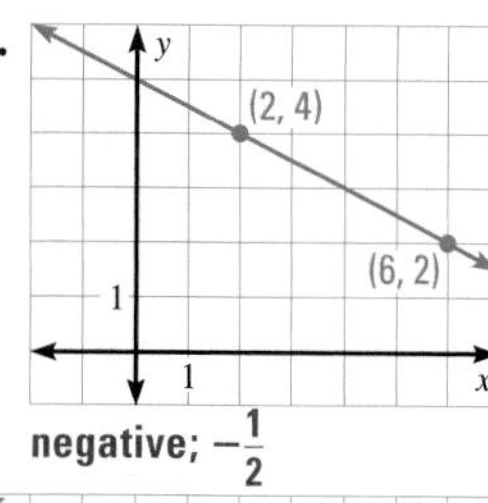

negative; $-\frac{1}{2}$

7. **ERROR ANALYSIS** *Describe* and correct the error in calculating the slope of the line shown.

$$m = \frac{12-6}{0-3} = \frac{6}{-3} = -2 \quad \times$$

(6, 3) (12, 0)

The slope was calculated using $\frac{\text{run}}{\text{rise}}$, **not** $\frac{\text{rise}}{\text{run}}$; $m = \frac{0-3}{12-6} = \frac{-3}{6} = -\frac{1}{2}.$

FINDING SLOPE **Find the slope of the line that passes through the points.**

8. (−2, −1) and (4, 5) **1**
9. (−3, −2) and (−3, 6) **undefined**
10. (5, −3) and (−5, −3) **0**
11. (1, 3) and (3, −2) $-\frac{5}{2}$
12. (−3, 4) and (4, 1) $-\frac{3}{7}$
13. (1, −3) and (7, 3) **1**
14. (0, 0) and (0, −6) **undefined**
15. (−9, 1) and (1, 1) **0**
16. (−10, −2) and (−8, 8) **5**

17. ★ **MULTIPLE CHOICE** The slope of the line that passes through the points (−2, −3) and (8, −3) is __?__. **C**

Ⓐ positive Ⓑ negative Ⓒ zero Ⓓ undefined

18. ★ **MULTIPLE CHOICE** What is the slope of the line that passes through the points (7, −9) and (−13, −6)? **A**

Ⓐ $-\frac{3}{20}$ Ⓑ $\frac{3}{20}$ Ⓒ $\frac{3}{4}$ Ⓓ $\frac{5}{2}$

4 PRACTICE AND APPLY

Assignment Guide

Answer Transparencies available for all exercises

Basic:
Day 1: SRH p. 933 Exs. 6–14
pp. 239–242
Exs. 1–18, 42–56 even
Day 2: pp. 239–242
Exs. 19–27, 36–39, 57–62

Average:
Day 1: pp. 239–242
Exs. 1–7, 11–18, 24–28, 43–55 odd
Day 2: pp. 239–242
Exs. 19–23, 31–33, 36–40, 57–62

Advanced:
Day 1: pp. 239–242
Exs. 1, 2, 12–18, 24–32, 43–55 odd
Day 2: pp. 239–242
Exs. 19–23, 35–41*, 57–62

Block:
pp. 239–242
Exs. 1–7, 11–28, 31–33, 36–40, 43–55 odd, 57–62

Differentiated Instruction

See *Differentiated Instruction Resources* for suggestions on addressing the needs of a diverse classroom.

Homework Check

For a quick check of student understanding of key concepts, go over the following exercises:
Basic: 4, 9, 19, 36, 38
Average: 11, 14, 20, 36, 39
Advanced: 12, 15, 20, 37, 39

Extra Practice

- Student Edition, p. 941
- Chapter Resource Book: Practice levels A, B, C

Practice Worksheet

An easily-readable reduced practice page (with answers) for this lesson can be found on p. 204D.

Avoiding Common Errors

Exercises 3, 8–16 Students often switch the order of the x- and y-coordinates when finding slope. Caution students to double-check their calculations to make sure the coordinates are in the right order.

Vocabulary

Exercise 17 To help students understand the difference between 0 slope and undefined slope, point out that 0 slope implies identical y-coordinates, while undefined slope implies identical x-coordinates.

Teaching Strategy

Exercises 24–32 You may want to point out to students that the example for these exercises skips the step of adding 6 to each side and then dividing by 3. Also, encourage students to check their answers by substituting their solutions in the slope formula.

EXAMPLE 5 on p. 237 for Exs. 19–20

19. MOVIE RENTALS The table shows the number of days you keep a rented movie before returning it and the total cost of renting the movie. Find the rate of change in cost with respect to time and interpret its meaning.

Time (days)	4	5	6	7
Total cost (dollars)	6.00	8.25	10.50	12.75

$2.25 per day, it costs $2.25 per day to rent a movie.

20. AMUSEMENT PARK The table shows the amount of time spent at an amusement park and the admission fee the park charges. Find the rate of change in the fee with respect to time spent at the park and interpret its meaning.

Time (hours)	4	5	6
Admission fee (dollars)	34.99	34.99	34.99

0, it does not matter how long a person stays at the park, the admission is the same.

FINDING SLOPE **Find the slope of the object. Round to the nearest tenth.**

21. Skateboard ramp **0.3** **22.** Pet ramp **0.4** **23.** Boat ramp **0.1**

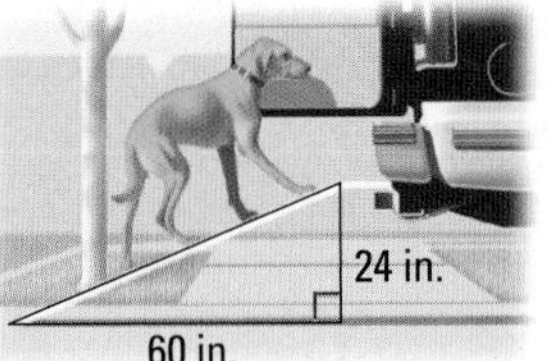

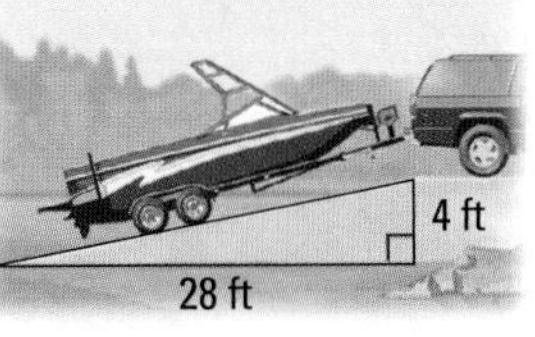

B **In Exercises 24–32, use the example below to find the value of x or y so that the line passing through the given points has the given slope.**

> **EXAMPLE** **Find a coordinate given the slope of a line**
>
> Find the value of x so that the line that passes through the points (2, 3) and $(x, 9)$ has a slope of $\frac{3}{2}$.
>
> **Solution**
>
> Let $(x_1, y_1) = (2, 3)$ and $(x_2, y_2) = (x, 9)$.
>
> $m = \frac{y_2 - y_1}{x_2 - x_1}$ **Write formula for slope.**
>
> $\frac{3}{2} = \frac{9-3}{x-2}$ **Substitute values.**
>
> $3(x-2) = 2(9-3)$ **Cross products property**
>
> $3x - 6 = 12$ **Simplify.**
>
> $x = 6$ **Solve for x.**

24. $(x, 4), (6, -1); m = \frac{5}{6}$ **12** **25.** $(0, y), (-2, 1); m = -8$ **−15** **26.** $(8, 1), (x, 7); m = -\frac{1}{2}$ **−4**

27. $(5, 4), (-5, y); m = \frac{3}{5}$ **−2** **28.** $(-9, y), (0, -3); m = -\frac{7}{9}$ **4** **29.** $(x, 9), (-1, 19); m = 5$ **−3**

30. $(9, 3), (-6, 7y); m = 3$ **−6** **31.** $(-3, y + 1), (0, 4); m = 6$ **−15** **32.** $\left(\frac{x}{2}, 7\right), (-10, 15); m = 4$ **−24**

○ = WORKED-OUT SOLUTIONS on p. WS1 ★ = STANDARDIZED TEST PRACTICE

C 33. **REASONING** The point (−1, 8) is on a line that has a slope of −3. Is the point (4, −7) on the same line? *Explain* your reasoning.
Yes; the slope of the line containing both points is −3.

34. ★ **WRITING** Is a line with undefined slope the graph of a function? *Explain.*
No; a line with an undefined slope is a vertical line, which is not the graph of a function.

35. **CHALLENGE** Given two points (x_1, y_1) and (x_2, y_2) such that $x_1 \neq x_2$, show that $\frac{y_2 - y_1}{x_2 - x_1} = \frac{y_1 - y_2}{x_1 - x_2}$. What does this result tell you about calculating the slope of a line? **See margin.**

PROBLEM SOLVING

EXAMPLE 6 A on p. 238 for Exs. 36–37

36. **OCEANOGRAPHY** Ocean water levels are measured hourly at a monitoring station. The table shows the water level (in meters) on one particular morning. *Describe* the rates of change in water levels throughout the morning. ***Sample answer:* The water level decreases until 8 A.M. and then it increases until 12 P.M.**

Hours since 12:00 A.M.	1	3	8	10	12
Water level (meters)	2	1.4	0.5	1	1.8

@HomeTutor for problem solving help at classzone.com

37. **MULTI-STEP PROBLEM** Firing a piece of pottery in a kiln takes place at different temperatures for different amounts of time. The graph shows the temperatures in a kiln while firing a piece of pottery (after the kiln is preheated to 250°F).

a. Determine the time interval during which the temperature in the kiln showed the greatest rate of change. **0 h to 1.5 h**

b. Determine the time interval during which the temperature in the kiln showed the least rate of change. **4.65 h to 8.95 h**

@HomeTutor for problem solving help at classzone.com

EXAMPLE 7 on p. 238 for Exs. 38–39

38. **FLYING** The graph shows the altitude of a plane during 4 hours of a flight. Give a verbal description of the flight. **See margin.**

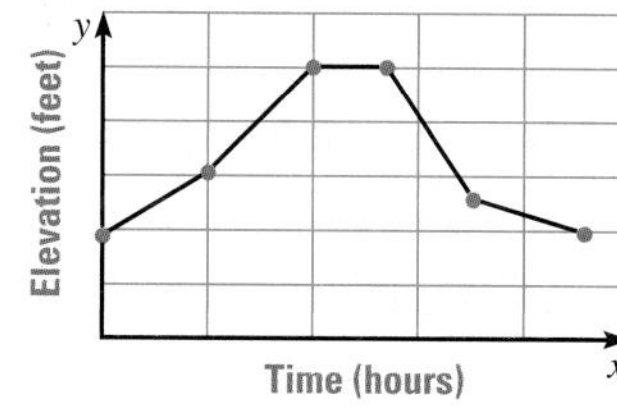

39. **HIKING** The graph shows the elevation of a hiker walking on a mountain trail. Give a verbal description of the hike. **See margin.**

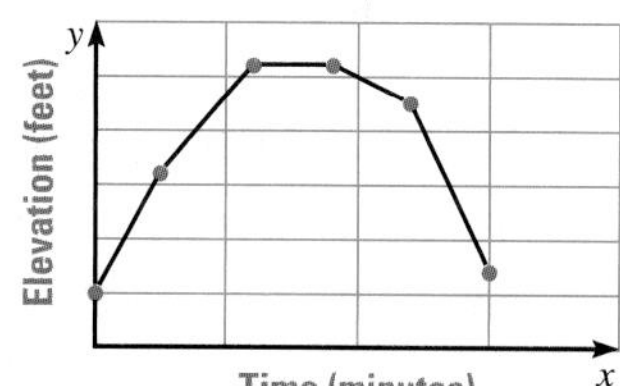

Study Strategy

Exercise 36 Tell students they can set up this problem using the solution in Example 6 as a model. Point out that instead of 3 intervals of time over weeks, there will be 4 intervals of time over hours for Exercise 36. Note that the independent variable is time and the dependent variable is water level. Ask students how this affects the use of the slope formula.

Exercises 38, 39 Suggest that students use Example 7 as a model for their descriptions. Note that the example describes the slope in each segment of the graph independently.

Internet Reference

Exercise 36 Additional information about oceanography can be found at the Office of Naval Research website at www.onr.navy.mil/focus/ocean

35. Multiply $\frac{y_2 - y_1}{x_2 - x_1}$ by $\frac{-1}{-1}$ to get $\frac{-y_2 + y_1}{-x_2 + x_1}$, which, by the commutative property of addition, is equal to $\frac{y_1 - y_2}{x_1 - x_2}$; it does not matter which point you choose to be (x_2, y_2) and which point is (x_1, y_1).

38. ***Sample answer:*** The altitude of the plane increases during the first 2 hours of the flight, then stays the same for about 45 minutes, and then decreases during the last hour and 45 minutes.

39. ***Sample answer:*** The elevation of the hiker increases for about 60 minutes, then stays the same for about 30 minutes, then decreases for the last 60 minutes.

5 ASSESS AND RETEACH

Daily Homework Quiz

Transparency Available

Find the slope of the line that passes through the points.

1. (12, −1) and (−3, −1) **0**
2. (−2, 6) and (4, −3) $-\frac{3}{2}$
3. The graph shows the ticket sales for a school dance on day 1, day 3, day 6, and day 9 of ticket sales. Describe the rates of change in ticket sales with respect to time.

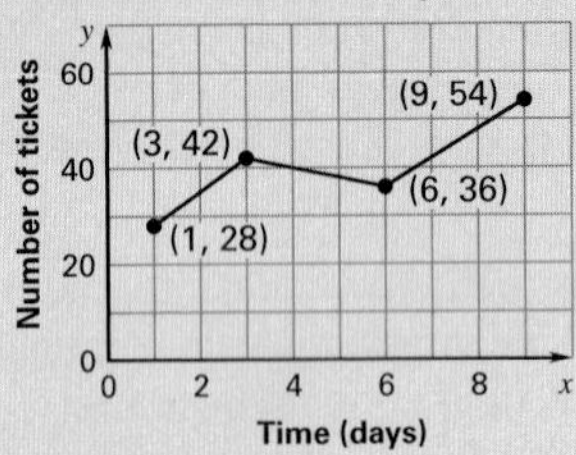

Ticket sales grew moderately, declined slightly, and then had another moderate rate of increase.

Online Quiz

Available at **classzone.com**

Diagnosis/Remediation

- Practice A, B, C in Chapter Resource Book
- Study Guide in Chapter Resource Book
- Practice Workbook
- @HomeTutor

Challenge

Additional challenge is available in the Chapter Resource Book.

41a–c. See Additional Answers beginning on p. AA1.

40a. 1996 to 1998; about −1500 students per year

40b. 1998 to 2000; about 1500 students per year

40c. It increased. *Sample answer:* Although the number of engineering majors decreased, the decrease was more than offset by the increase in the number of biological science majors and liberal arts majors.

B **40.** ★ **EXTENDED RESPONSE** The graph shows the number (in thousands) of undergraduate students who majored in biological science, engineering, or liberal arts in the United States from 1990 to 2000.

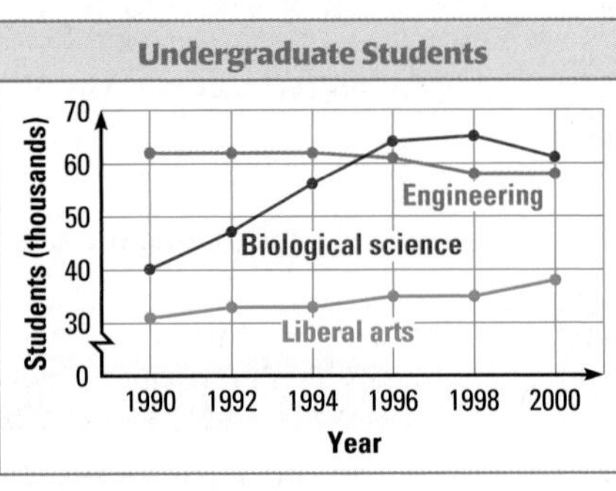

a. During which two-year period did the number of engineering students decrease the most? Estimate the rate of change for this time period.

b. During which two-year period did the number of liberal arts students increase the most? Estimate the rate of change for this time period.

c. How did the total number of students majoring in biological science, engineering, and liberal arts change in the 10 year period? *Explain* your thinking.

C **41. CHALLENGE** Imagine the containers below being filled with water at a constant rate. Sketch a graph that shows the water level for each container during the time it takes to fill the container with water. **See margin.**

a. 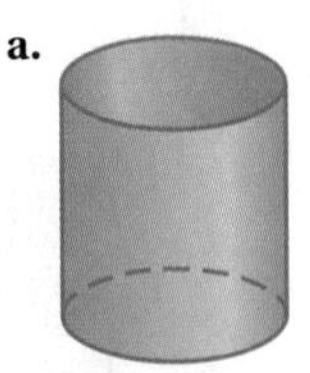

b. 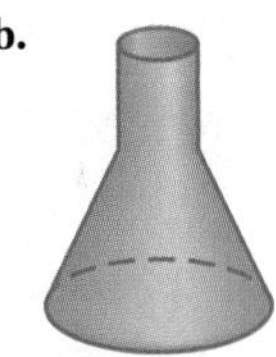

c. 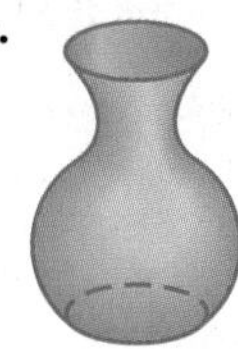

MIXED REVIEW

Check whether the given number is a solution of the equation or inequality. *(p. 21)*

42. $4b - 7 = b + 11; 6$ **solution**

43. $x - 8 = -2x - 14; -1$ **not a solution**

44. $\frac{t}{4} + 9 = 13; 16$ **solution**

45. $a + 9 > 20; 3$ **not a solution**

46. $\frac{y+3}{2} < 13; 23$ **not a solution**

47. $2(p + 5) \le 75; 4$ **solution**

Evaluate the expression. Approximate the square root to the nearest integer, if necessary. *(p. 110)*

48. $\sqrt{16}$ **4**

49. $-\sqrt{9}$ **−3**

50. $\pm\sqrt{45}$ **±7**

51. $\sqrt{136}$ **12**

52. $\pm\sqrt{64}$ **±8**

53. $-\sqrt{33}$ **−6**

54. $\pm\sqrt{154}$ **±12**

55. $\pm\sqrt{256}$ **±16**

56. $\sqrt{4761}$ **69**

PREVIEW
Prepare for Lesson 4.5 in Exs. 57–62.

Find the *x*-intercept and the *y*-intercept of the graph of the equation. *(p. 225)*

57. $y = x + 7$ **−7, 7**

58. $y = -x - 1$ **−1, −1**

59. $y = 8 - 2x$ **4, 8**

60. $y = 3x + 5$ $-1\frac{2}{3}$, **5**

61. $y = 4x - 10$ $2\frac{1}{2}$, **−10**

62. $y = -9 + 6x$ $1\frac{1}{2}$, **−9**

 EXTRA PRACTICE for Lesson 4.4, p. 941  **ONLINE QUIZ** at classzone.com

4.5 Slope and y-Intercept

QUESTION How can you use the equation of a line to find its slope and y-intercept?

EXPLORE Find the slopes and the y-intercepts of lines

STEP 1 *Find y when x = 0*
Copy the table below. Let $x_1 = 0$ and find y_1 for each equation. Use your answers to complete the second and fifth columns in the table.

STEP 2 *Find y when x = 2*
Let $x_2 = 2$ and find y_2 for each equation. Use your answers to complete the third column in the table.

STEP 3 *Compute the slope*
Use the slope formula and the ordered pairs you found in the second and third columns to complete the fourth column.

Line	$(0, y_1)$	$(2, y_2)$	Slope	y-intercept
$y = 4x + 3$	(0, 3)	(2, 11)	$\frac{11-3}{2-0} = 4$	3
$y = -2x + 3$	(0, ?) 3	(2, ?) −1	? −2	? 3
$y = \frac{1}{2}x + 4$	(0, ?) 4	(2, ?) 5	? $\frac{1}{2}$	? 4
$y = -4x - 3$	(0, ?) −3	(2, ?) −11	? −4	? −3
$y = -\frac{1}{4}x - 3$	(0, ?) −3	(2, ?) $-3\frac{1}{2}$	? $-\frac{1}{4}$	? −3

DRAW CONCLUSIONS Use your observations to complete these exercises

1. *Compare* the slope of each line with the equation of the line. What do you notice? **It is the same as the coefficient of *x* in each equation.**
2. *Compare* the y-intercept of each line with the equation of the line. What do you notice? **It is the same as the constant in each equation.**

Predict the slope and the y-intercept of the line with the given equation. Then check your predictions by finding the slope and y-intercept as you did in the table above.

3. $y = -5x + 1$ **−5, 1**
4. $y = \frac{3}{4}x + 2$ **$\frac{3}{4}$, 2**
5. $y = -\frac{3}{2}x - 1$ **$-\frac{3}{2}$, −1**

6. **REASONING** Use the procedure you followed to complete the table above to show that the y-intercept of the graph of $y = mx + b$ is b and the slope of the graph is m. **If you substitute 0 for *x* you get $y = b$, giving the point (0, *b*). This shows the y-intercept is *b*. Substitute 2 in for *x* giving the point (2, 2*m* + *b*). Use the points (0, *b*) and (2, 2*m* + *b*) to find the slope. $\frac{(2m + b) - b}{2 - 0} = m$.**

1 PLAN AND PREPARE

Explore the Concept
- Students will use the equation of a line to find the slope and y-intercept of the line.
- This activity leads into the study of finding the slope and y-intercept of a line in Example 1 in Lesson 4.5.

Materials
Each student will need:
- Activity Support Master (*Chapter Resource Book*)

Recommended Time
Work activity: 10 min
Discuss results: 5 min

Grouping
Students should work individually.

2 TEACH

Key Question
- What is the relationship between columns 2 and 5? **Column 2 gives the coordinates of the y-intercept in column 5.**

Key Discovery
The slope of a line written in the form $y = mx + b$ is m, the coefficient of x, and the y-intercept is the constant b.

3 ASSESS AND RETEACH

Predict the slope and y-intercept of the graph of $y = x$. Explain. **Since the coefficient of *x* is 1, the slope is 1. Since the equation is equivalent to $y = x + 0$, the constant is 0, and the y-intercept is 0.**

Warm-Up Exercises

Transparency Available

1. Rewrite $5x + y = 8$ so y is a function of x. $y = -5x + 8$
2. Find the slope of the line that passes through $(-5, 6)$ and $(0, 8)$. $\frac{2}{5}$
3. Find the intercepts of the graph of the function $a = 20t - 600$. **a-intercept: -600, t-intercept: 30**

Notetaking Guide

Transparency Available

Promotes interactive learning and notetaking skills.

Pacing

Basic: 1 day
Average: 1 day
Advanced: 1 day
Block: 0.5 block with 4.6
- See *Teaching Guide/Lesson Plan.*

2 FOCUS AND MOTIVATE

Essential Question

Big Idea 1, p. 205

How do you graph linear equations given in slope-intercept form? **Tell students they will learn how to answer this question by using the y-intercept and the slope to determine two points on the graph.**

NCTM STANDARDS

Standard 2: Use models to understand relationships

Standard 8: Use the language of math to express ideas

4.5 Graph Using Slope-Intercept Form

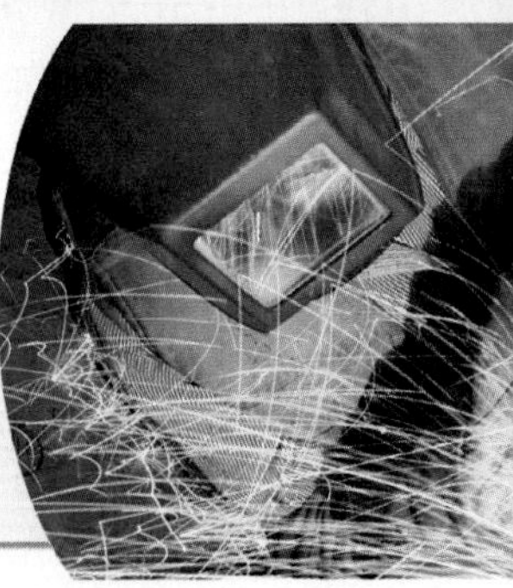

Before You found slopes and graphed equations using intercepts.
Now You will graph linear equations using slope-intercept form.
Why? So you can model a worker's earnings, as in Ex. 43.

Key Vocabulary
- slope-intercept form
- parallel

In the activity on page 243, you saw how the slope and y-intercept of the graph of a linear equation in the form $y = mx + b$ are related to the equation.

KEY CONCEPT *For Your Notebook*

Finding the Slope and y-Intercept of a Line

Words	Symbols	Graph
A linear equation of the form $y = mx + b$ is written in **slope-intercept form** where m is the slope and b is the y-intercept of the equation's graph.	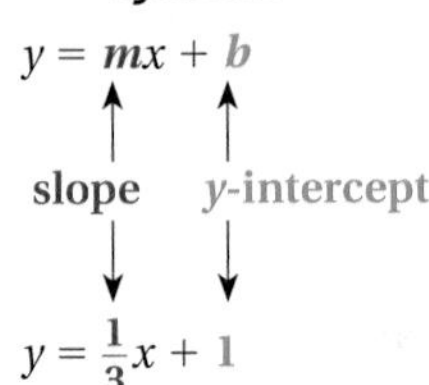	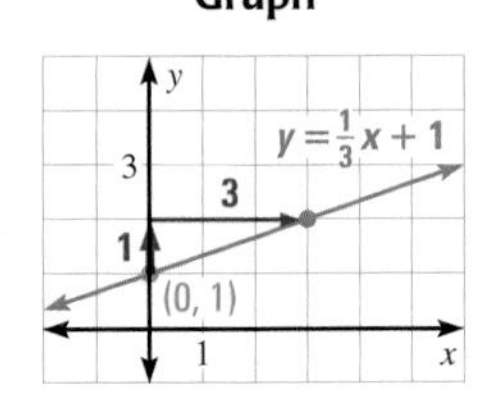

EXAMPLE 1 Identify slope and y-intercept

Identify the slope and y-intercept of the line with the given equation.

a. $y = 3x + 4$ **b.** $3x + y = 2$

Solution

a. The equation is in the form $y = mx + b$. So, the slope of the line is 3, and the y-intercept is 4.

b. Rewrite the equation in slope-intercept form by solving for y.

$3x + y = 2$ Write original equation.

$y = -3x + 2$ Subtract $3x$ from each side.

▸ The line has a slope of -3 and a y-intercept of 2.

REWRITE EQUATIONS
When you rewrite a linear equation in slope-intercept form, you are expressing y as a function of x.

GUIDED PRACTICE for Example 1

Identify the slope and y-intercept of the line with the given equation.

1. $y = 5x - 3$ **5, −3**
2. $3x - 3y = 12$ **1, −4**
3. $x + 4y = 6$ $-\frac{1}{4}, 1\frac{1}{2}$

Resource Planning Guide

Chapter Resource Book
- Teaching Guide/Lesson Plan
- Activity Master
- Practice levels A, B, C
- Study Guide
- Catch-up for Absent Students
- Problem Solving Workshop
- Challenge

Workbooks
- Notetaking Guide
- Practice Workbook

Teaching Options
- **Power Presentations** provides dynamic electronic teaching resources for the classroom.
- **Activity Generator** provides editable activities for all ability levels.

Interactive Technology
- Easy Planner
- Power Presentations
- Activity Generator
- Animated Algebra
- Test Generator
- Online Quiz
- eWorkbook
- eEdition
- @HomeTutor

Resources for English Learners
- Spanish Study Guide
- Multi-Language Visual Glossary
- Student Resources in Spanish

See also the *Differentiated Instruction Resources* for more strategies for meeting individual needs.

EXAMPLE 2 Graph an equation using slope-intercept form

Graph the equation $2x + y = 3$.

Solution

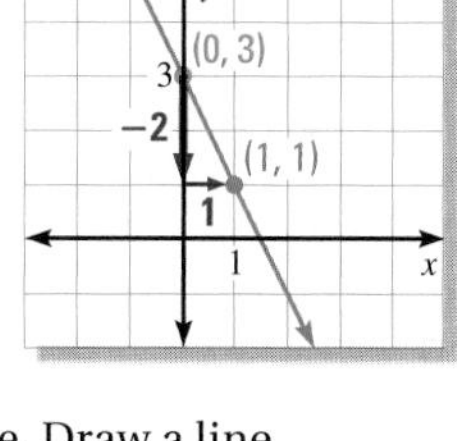

STEP 1 **Rewrite** the equation in slope-intercept form.

$y = -2x + 3$

STEP 2 **Identify** the slope and the y-intercept.

$m = -2$ and $b = 3$

STEP 3 **Plot** the point that corresponds to the y-intercept, $(0, 3)$.

STEP 4 **Use** the slope to locate a second point on the line. Draw a line through the two points.

CHECK REASONABLENESS
To check the line drawn in Example 2, substitute the coordinates of the second point into the original equation. You should get a true statement.

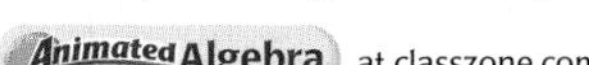

at classzone.com

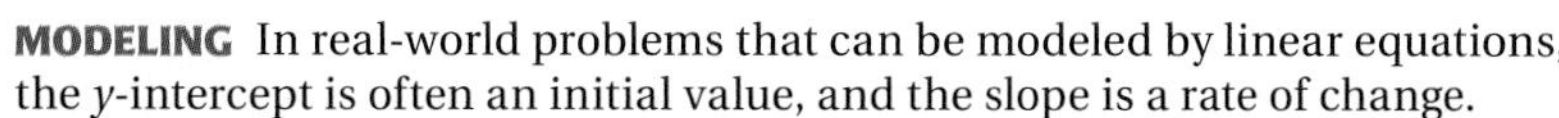

MODELING In real-world problems that can be modeled by linear equations, the y-intercept is often an initial value, and the slope is a rate of change.

EXAMPLE 3 Change slopes of lines

ESCALATORS To get from one floor to another at a library, you can take either the stairs or the escalator. You can climb stairs at a rate of 1.75 feet per second, and the escalator rises at a rate of 2 feet per second. You have to travel a vertical distance of 28 feet. The equations model the vertical distance d (in feet) you have left to travel after t seconds.

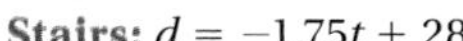

Stairs: $d = -1.75t + 28$ **Escalator:** $d = -2t + 28$

a. Graph the equations in the same coordinate plane.

b. How much time do you save by taking the escalator?

Solution

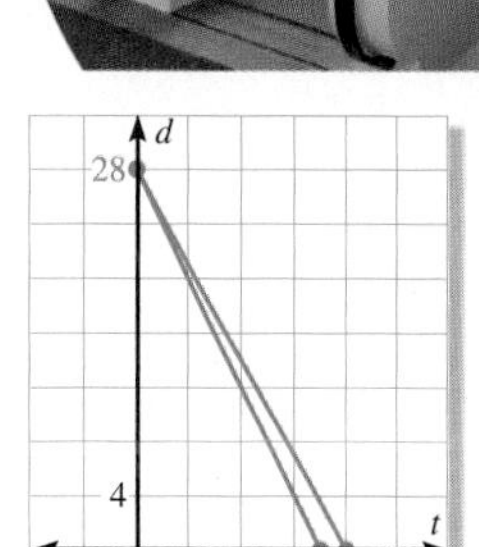
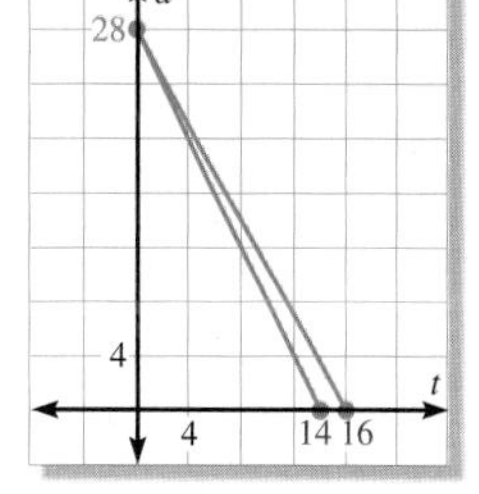

a. Draw the graph of $d = -1.75t + 28$ using the fact that the d-intercept is 28 and the slope is -1.75. Similarly, draw the graph of $d = -2t + 28$. The graphs make sense only in the first quadrant.

b. The equation $d = -1.75t + 28$ has a t-intercept of **16**. The equation $d = -2t + 28$ has a t-intercept of **14**. So, you save $16 - 14 = 2$ seconds by taking the escalator.

✓ GUIDED PRACTICE for Examples 2 and 3

4. Graph the equation $y = -2x + 5$. **See margin.**

5. **WHAT IF?** In Example 3, suppose a person can climb stairs at a rate of 1.4 feet per second. How much time does taking the escalator save? **6 sec**

Differentiated Instruction

Visual Learners Show students that if they let $x = 0$ in the slope-intercept form, $y = mx + b$, to find the y-intercept as they did in Section 4.3, they immediately find that the y-intercept is $y = b$.

See also the *Differentiated Instruction Resources* for more strategies.

Motivating the Lesson

Which is cheaper, paying a certain fee to join an art museum and then paying $5 for each special exhibit, or not joining and paying $10 for each special exhibit? This lesson will help you decide.

3 TEACH

Extra Example 1

Identify the slope and y-intercept of the line $x + 3y = 9$. **slope:** $-\frac{1}{3}$, **y-intercept: 3**

Extra Example 2

Graph $x + 2y = 4$.

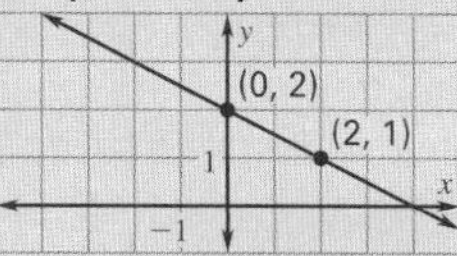

Animated Algebra classzone.com

An **Animated Algebra** activity is available online for **Example 2**. This activity is also part of **Power Presentations**.

Extra Example 3

You can use a laser or inkjet printer to print an 18-page report. The laser printer prints 6 pages/min and the inkjet printer prints 4.5 pages/min. The models give the number of pages p left to print after t minutes.
laser: $p = -6t + 18$
inkjet: $p = -4.5t + 18$

a. Graph both models in the same coordinate plane.

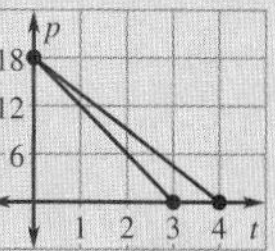

b. How many minutes do you save by using the laser printer? **1 min**

4. See Additional Answers beginning on p. AA1.

Extra Example 4

A violin teacher charges a one-time sheet-music fee of $20 for adults and no fee for children. The charge per hour is $20 for both children and adults. The cost C for children for n lessons is given by $C = 20n$ and for adults by $C = 20n + 20$.

a. Graph both equations in the same coordinate plane.

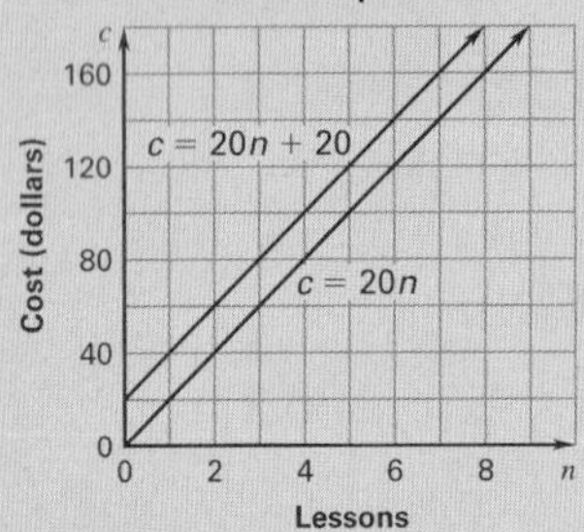

b. Based on the graphs, what is the difference in the costs? **$20, no matter how many lessons**

Extra Example 5

Determine which of the lines are parallel. **lines *a* and *b***

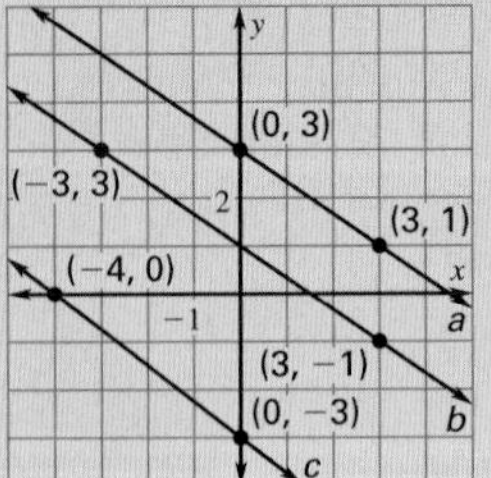

Closing the Lesson

Have students summarize the major points of the lesson and answer the Essential Question: How do you graph linear equations given in slope-intercept form?

- **The slope-intercept form of a linear equation is $y = mx + b$.**
- **In the slope-intercept form of the equation, m is slope and b is the y-intercept.**

Write the equation in slope-intercept form. Then plot the point that corresponds to the y-intercept, and use the slope to locate a second point.

EXAMPLE 4 Change intercepts of lines

TELEVISION A company produced two 30 second commercials, one for $300,000 and the second for $400,000. Each airing of either commercial on a particular station costs $150,000. The cost C (in thousands of dollars) to produce the first commercial and air it n times is given by $C = 150n + 300$. The cost to produce the second and air it n times is given by $C = 150n + 400$.

a. Graph both equations in the same coordinate plane.

b. Based on the graphs, what is the difference of the costs to produce each commercial and air it 2 times? 4 times? What do you notice about the differences of the costs?

Solution

a. The graphs of the equations are shown.

b. You can see that the vertical distance between the lines is $100,000 when $n = 2$ and $n = 4$.

The difference of the costs is $100,000 no matter how many times the commercials are aired.

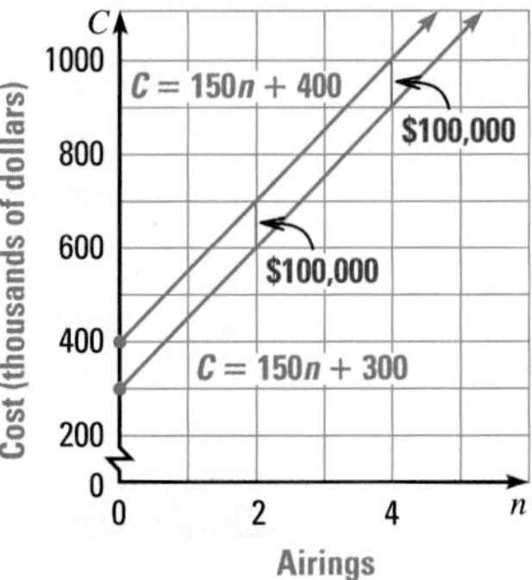

PARALLEL LINES Two lines in the same plane are **parallel** if they do not intersect. Because slope gives the rate at which a line rises or falls, two nonvertical lines with the same slope are parallel.

EXAMPLE 5 Identify parallel lines

Determine which of the lines are parallel.

Find the slope of each line.

Line *a*: $m = \frac{-1 - 0}{-1 - 2} = \frac{-1}{-3} = \frac{1}{3}$

Line *b*: $m = \frac{-3 - (-1)}{0 - 5} = \frac{-2}{-5} = \frac{2}{5}$

Line *c*: $m = \frac{-5 - (-3)}{-2 - 4} = \frac{-2}{-6} = \frac{1}{3}$

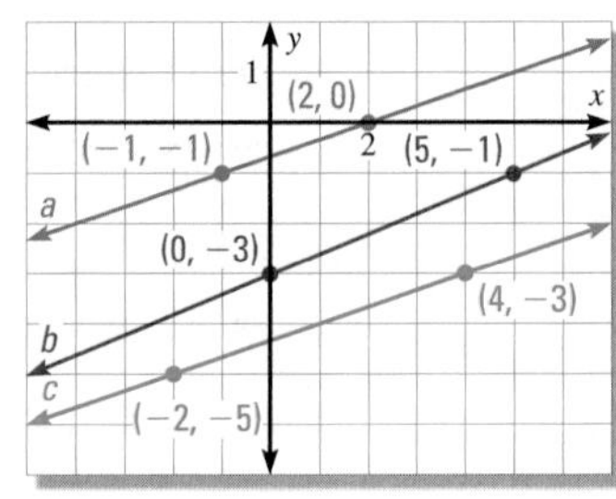

▶ Line a and line c have the same slope, so they are parallel.

✓ **GUIDED PRACTICE** for Examples 4 and 5

6. **WHAT IF?** In Example 4, suppose that the cost of producing and airing a third commercial is given by $C = 150n + 200$. Graph the equation. Find the difference of the costs of the second commercial and the third. **See margin for art; $200,000.**
7. Determine which lines are parallel: line a through $(-1, 2)$ and $(3, 4)$; line b through $(2, 2)$ and $(5, 8)$; line c through $(-9, -2)$ and $(-3, 1)$. ***a* and *c***

6.

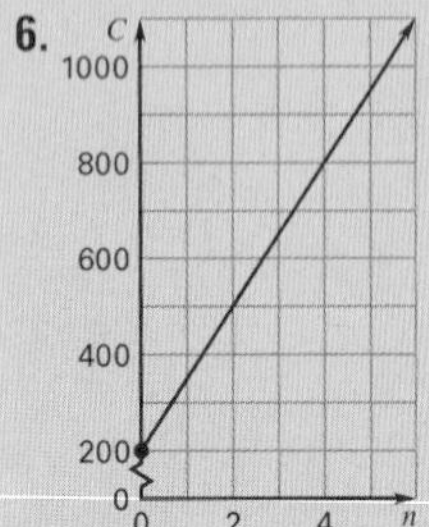

4.5 EXERCISES

HOMEWORK KEY

○ = WORKED-OUT SOLUTIONS on p. WS9 for Exs. 11, 21, and 41

★ = STANDARDIZED TEST PRACTICE Exs. 2, 9, 10, 36, 42, and 44

SKILL PRACTICE

A

1. **VOCABULARY** Copy and complete: Two lines in the same plane are _?_ if they do not intersect. **parallel**

2. ★ **WRITING** What is the slope-intercept form of a linear equation? *Explain* why this form is called slope-intercept form. **$y = mx + b$; because m is the slope and b is the y-intercept.**

EXAMPLE 1 on p. 244 for Exs. 3–16

SLOPE AND y-INTERCEPT Identify the slope and y-intercept of the line with the given equation.

3. $y = 2x + 1$ **2, 1**
4. $y = -x$ **−1, 0**
5. $y = 6 - 3x$ **−3, 6**
6. $y = -7 + 5x$ **5, −7**
7. $y = \frac{2}{3}x - 1$ **$\frac{2}{3}$, −1**
8. $y = -\frac{1}{4}x + 8$ **$-\frac{1}{4}$, 8**

9. ★ **MULTIPLE CHOICE** What is the slope of the line with the equation $y = -18x - 9$? **A**

Ⓐ −18 Ⓑ −9 Ⓒ 9 Ⓓ 18

10. ★ **MULTIPLE CHOICE** What is the y-intercept of the line with the equation $x - 3y = -12$? **C**

Ⓐ −12 Ⓑ −4 Ⓒ 4 Ⓓ 12

REWRITING EQUATIONS Rewrite the equation in slope-intercept form. Then identify the slope and the y-intercept of the line.

11. $4x + y = 1$ **$y = -4x + 1$; −4, 1**
12. $x - y = 6$ **$y = x - 6$; 1, −6**
13. $6x - 3y = -9$ **$y = 2x + 3$; 2, 3**
14. $-12x - 4y = 2$ **$y = -3x - \frac{1}{2}$; −3, $-\frac{1}{2}$**
15. $2x + 5y = -10$ **$y = -\frac{2}{5}x - 2$; $-\frac{2}{5}$, −2**
16. $-x - 10y = 20$ **$y = -\frac{1}{10}x - 2$; $-\frac{1}{10}$, −2**

EXAMPLE 2 on p. 245 for Exs. 17–29

MATCHING EQUATIONS WITH GRAPHS Match the equation with its graph.

17. $2x + 3y = 6$ **B**
18. $2x + 3y = -6$ **A**
19. $2x - 3y = 6$ **C**

A.
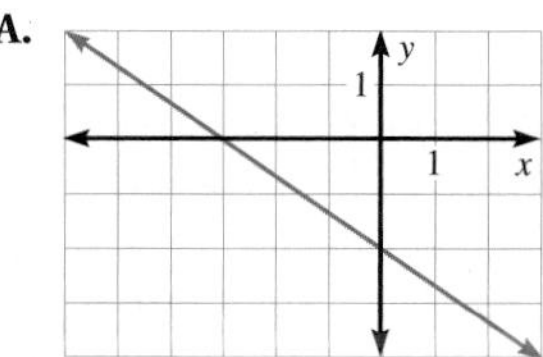

B.
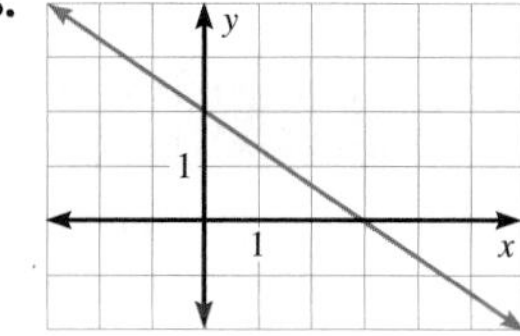

C.
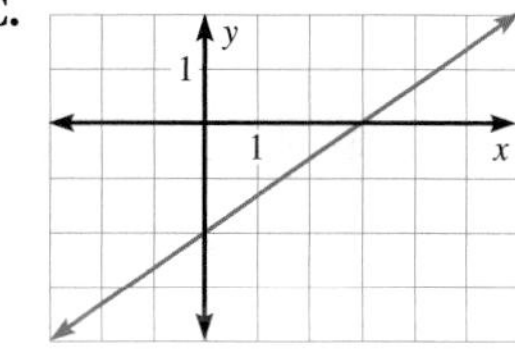

20. **ERROR ANALYSIS** *Describe* and correct the error in graphing the equation $y = 4x - 1$. **The y-intercept is −1, not 1; see margin for art.**

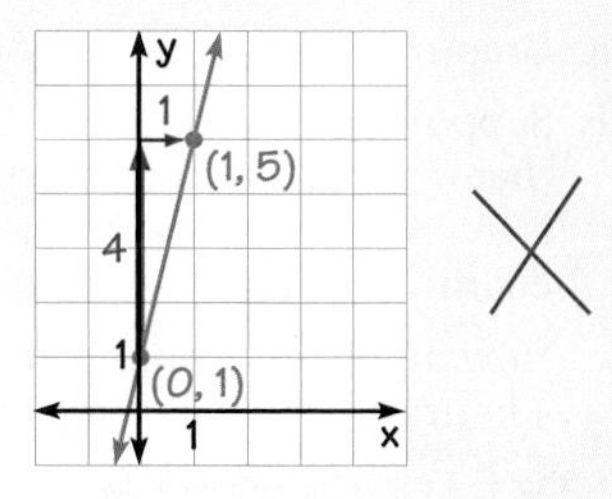

4 PRACTICE AND APPLY

Assignment Guide

Answer Transparencies available for all exercises

Basic:
Day 1: pp. 247–250
Exs. 1–13, 17–24, 30–33, 40–43, 46–56 even

Average:
Day 1: pp. 247–250
Exs. 1–5, 9, 10, 13–20, 25–31, 32–38 even, 40–44, 46–56 even

Advanced:
Day 1: pp. 247–250
Exs. 1, 2, 6–10, 14–19, 27–39*, 41–45*, 47–57 odd

Block:
pp. 247–250
Exs. 1–5, 9, 10, 13–20, 25–31, 32–38 even, 40–44, 46–56 even (with 4.6)

Differentiated Instruction

See *Differentiated Instruction Resources* for suggestions on addressing the needs of a diverse classroom.

Homework Check

For a quick check of student understanding of key concepts, go over the following exercises:

Basic: 12, 22, 30, 40, 42
Average: 15, 26, 32, 41, 43
Advanced: 16, 29, 34, 41, 44

Extra Practice

- Student Edition, p. 941
- Chapter Resource Book: Practice levels A, B, C

Practice Worksheet

An easily-readable reduced practice page (with answers) for this lesson can be found on p. 204E.

20.
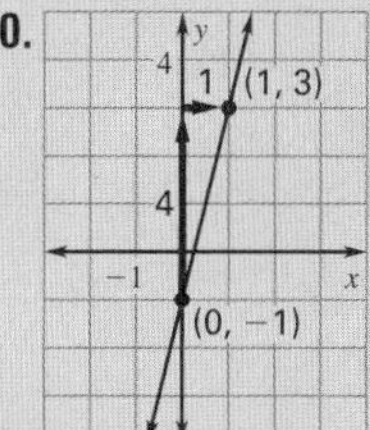

Avoiding Common Errors

Exercises 17–19 Caution students that the equation needs to be in slope-intercept form so they can visually match the equation with the graph.

Exercises 27–29, 32–35 Some students may think that the coefficient of x is the slope of the line of the equation regardless of the form of the equation. Remind them that the equation must be in the form $y = mx + b$.

Study Strategy

Exercises 37, 38 Students may want to review the slope formula before beginning these exercises. Remind them to pay attention to negative and positive numbers, especially when they replace k with a number.

21.
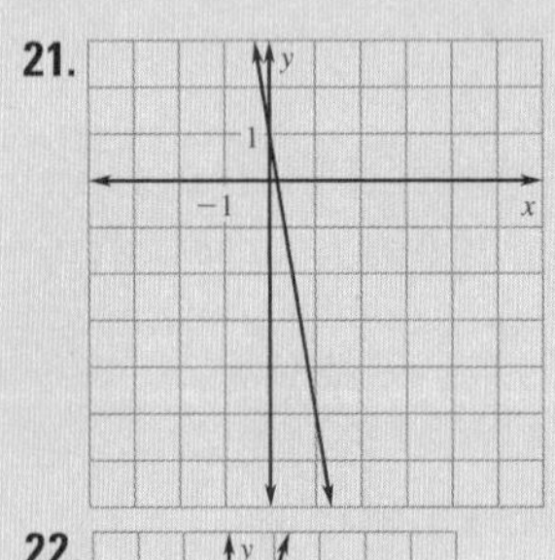

22.
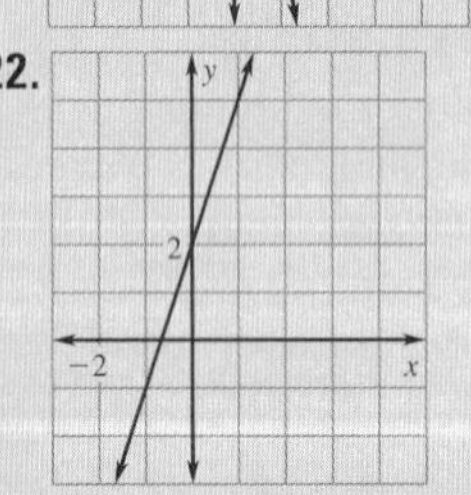

23.
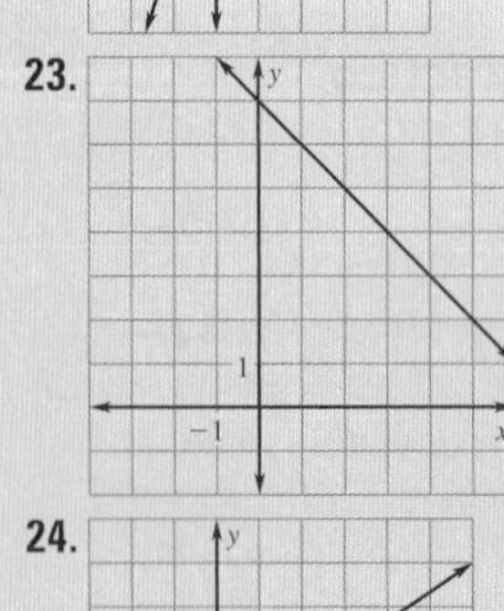

24.

GRAPHING EQUATIONS **Graph the equation.** **21–29. See margin.**

(21.) $y = -6x + 1$	22. $y = 3x + 2$	23. $y = -x + 7$
24. $y = \frac{2}{3}x$	25. $y = \frac{1}{4}x - 5$	26. $y = -\frac{5}{2}x + 2$
27. $7x - 2y = -11$	28. $-8x - 2y = 32$	29. $-x - 0.5y = 2.5$

EXAMPLE 5 on p. 246 for Exs. 30–35

PARALLEL LINES **Determine which lines are parallel.**

30.
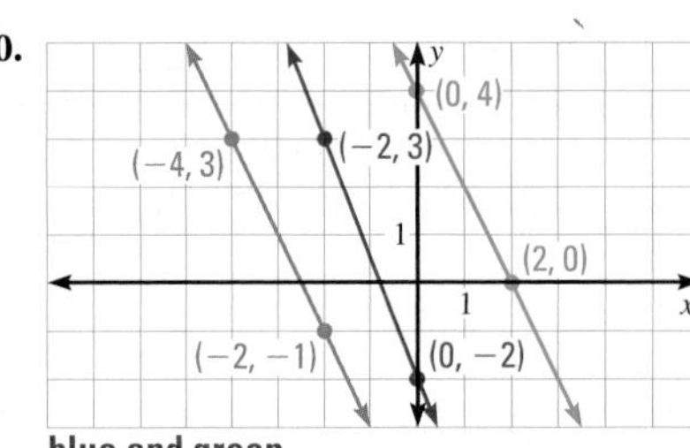

blue and green

31.
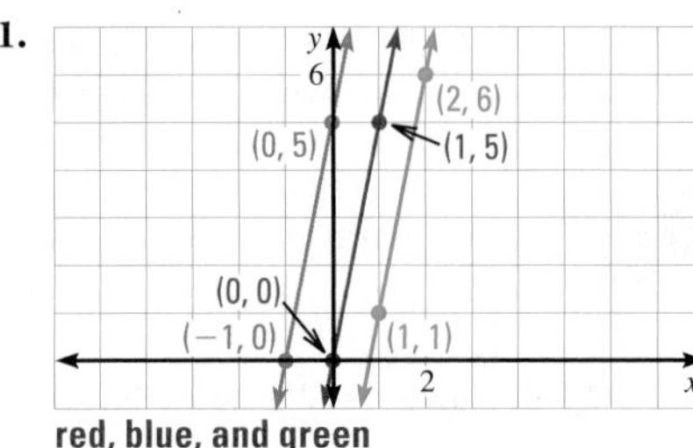

red, blue, and green

B **PARALLEL LINES** **Tell whether the graphs of the two equations are parallel lines. *Explain* your reasoning.**

32. $y = 5x - 7$, $5x + y = 7$ **Not parallel; the slopes are 5 and −5.**

33. $y = 3x + 2$, $-7 + 3x = y$ **Parallel; the slopes are both 3.**

34. $y = -0.5x$, $x + 2y = 18$ **Parallel; the slopes are both −0.5.**

35. $4x + y = 3$, $x + 4y = 3$ **Not parallel; the slopes are −4 and $-\frac{1}{4}$.**

36. ★ **OPEN-ENDED** Write the equation of a line that is parallel to $6x + y = 24$. *Explain* your reasoning. ***Sample answer:*** **$y = -6x + 5$; the equation has the same slope as $6x + y = 24$, but a different y-intercept.**

REASONING **Find the value of k so that the lines through the given points are parallel.**

37. Line 1: $(-4, -2)$ and $(0, 0)$
Line 2: $(2, 7)$ and $(k, 5)$ **−2**

38. Line 1: $(-1, 9)$ and $(-6, -6)$
Line 2: $(-7, k)$ and $(0, -2)$ **−23**

C 39. **CHALLENGE** To show that the slope of a line is constant, let (x_1, y_1) and (x_2, y_2) be any two points on the line $y = mx + b$. Use the equation of the line to express y_1 in terms of x_1 and y_2 in terms of x_2. Then show that the slope between the two points is m. **See margin.**

PROBLEM SOLVING

EXAMPLES 3 and 4 on pp. 245–246 for Exs. 40–44

A 40. **HOCKEY** Your family spends \$60 on tickets to a hockey game and \$4 per hour for parking. The total cost C (in dollars) is given by $C = 60 + 4t$ where t is the time (in hours) your family's car is parked.

a. Graph the equation. **a–b. See margin.**

b. Suppose the parking fee is raised to \$5.50 per hour so that the total cost of tickets and parking for t hours is $C = 60 + 5.5t$. Graph the equation in the same coordinate plane as the equation in part (a).

c. How much more does it cost to go to a game for 4 hours after the parking fee is raised? **\$6**

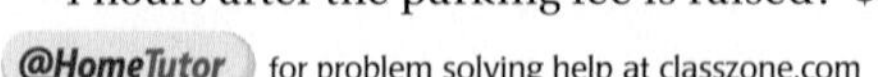

○ = WORKED-OUT SOLUTIONS on p. WS1 ★ = STANDARDIZED TEST PRACTICE

25.
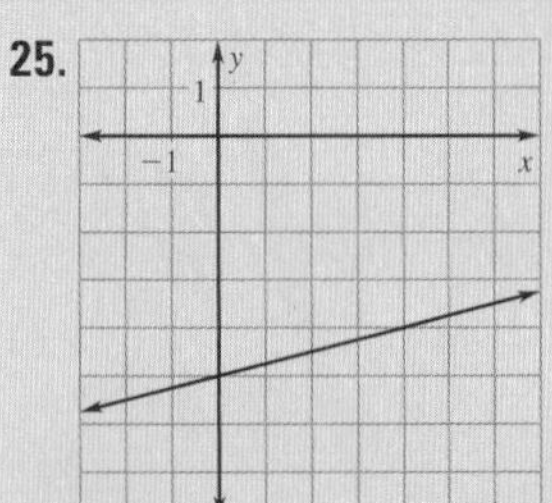

26.
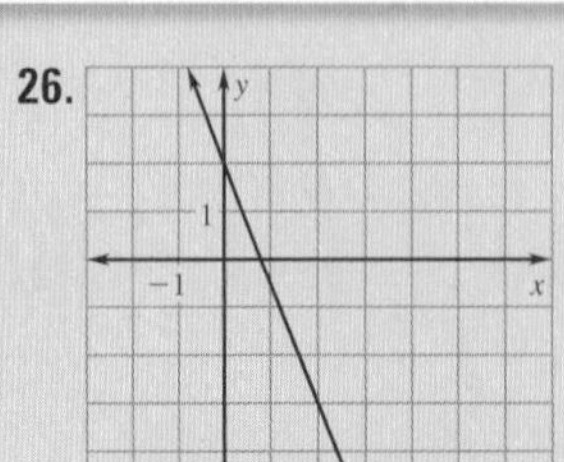

27.
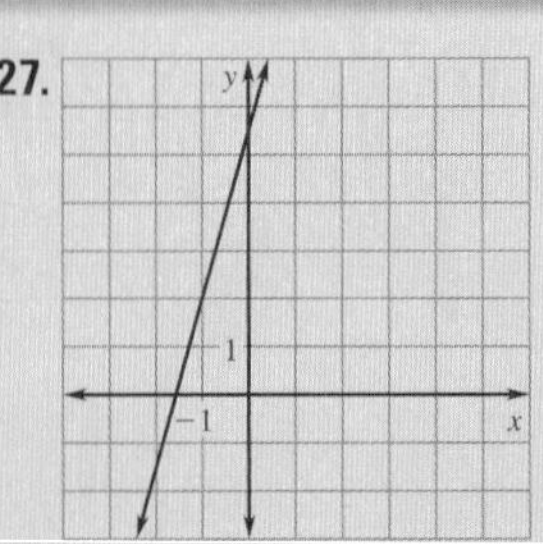

41. **SPEED LIMITS** In 1995 Pennsylvania changed its maximum speed limit on rural interstate highways, as shown below. The diagram also shows the distance d (in miles) a person could travel driving at the maximum speed limit for t hours both before and after 1995.

a. Graph both equations in the same coordinate plane. **See margin.**

b. Use the graphs to find the difference of the distances a person could drive in 3 hours before and after the speed limit was changed. **30 mi**

@HomeTutor for problem solving help at classzone.com

42. ★ **SHORT RESPONSE** A service station charges $40 per hour for labor plus the cost of parts to repair a car. Parts can either be ordered from the car dealership for $250 or from a warehouse for $200. The equations below give the total repair cost C (in dollars) for a repair that takes t hours using parts from the dealership or from the warehouse.

Dealership: $C = 40t + 250$ **Warehouse:** $C = 40t + 200$

a. Graph both equations in the same coordinate plane. **See margin.**

b. Use the graphs to find the difference of the costs if the repair takes 3 hours. What if the repair takes 4 hours? What do you notice about the differences of the costs? *Explain.* **$50; $50; the difference is $50 no matter how many hours it takes to repair a car because the slopes are the same.**

B **43.** **FACTORY SHIFTS** Welders at a factory can work one of two shifts. Welders on the first shift earn $12 per hour while workers on the second shift earn $14 per hour. The total amount a (in dollars) a first-shift worker earns is given by $a = 12t$ where t is the time (in hours) worked. The total amount a second-shift worker earns is given by $a = 14t$.

a. Graph both equations in the same coordinate plane. What do the slopes and the a-intercepts of the graphs mean in this situation?

43a. See margin for art; the slopes are the amount of money earned per hour, the a-intercepts show the amount of money made at 0 hours.

b. How much more money does a welder earn for a 40 hour week if he or she works the second shift rather than the first shift? **$80**

44. ★ **EXTENDED RESPONSE** An artist is renting a booth at an art show. A small booth costs $350 to rent. The artist plans to sell framed pictures for $50 each. The profit P (in dollars) the artist makes after selling p pictures is given by $P = 50p - 350$.

a. Graph the equation. **a–b. See margin for art.**

b. If the artist decides to rent a larger booth for $500, the profit is given by $P = 50p - 500$. Graph this equation on the same coordinate plane you used in part (a).

c. The artist can display 80 pictures in the small booth and 120 in the larger booth. If the artist is able to sell all of the pictures, which booth should the artist rent? *Explain.* **Larger booth; if the artist rents the larger booth and sells all the paintings, the artist will make $5500, if the artist rents the smaller booth and sells all the paintings, the artist will make only $3650.**

Exercise 41 To find a map showing the maximum speed limit on interstate highways for the entire United States, visit www.fhwa.dot.gov/policy/ohpi/speeds.htm

41a.

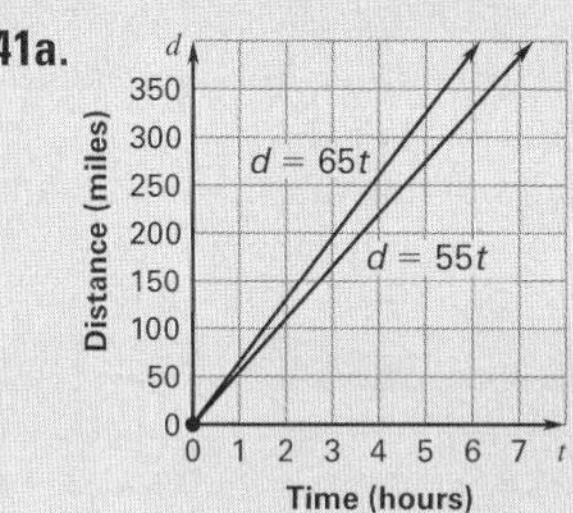

42a.

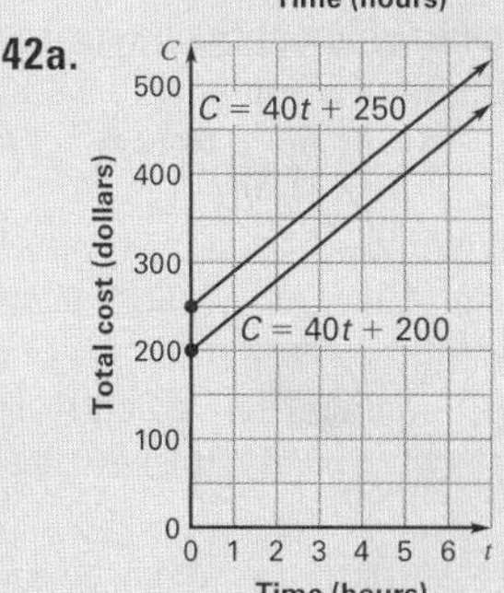

43a.

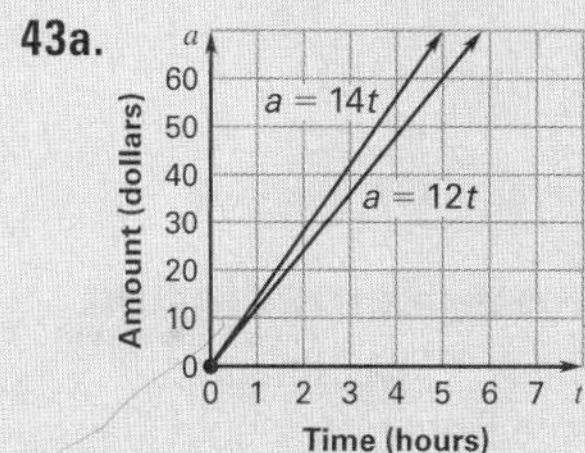

44a–b.

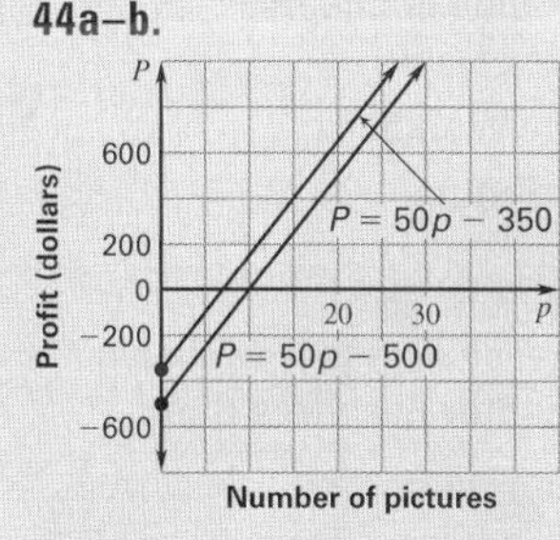

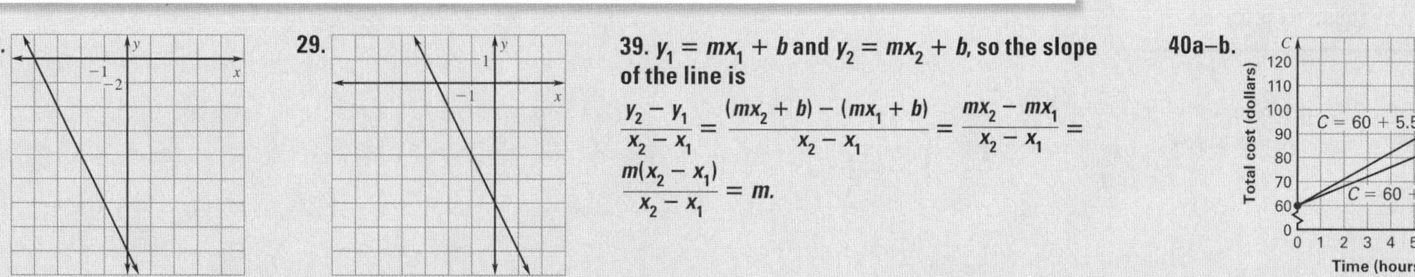

28.

29.

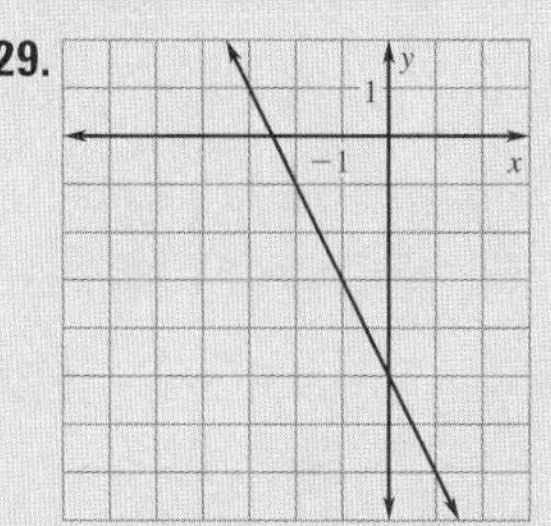

39. $y_1 = mx_1 + b$ and $y_2 = mx_2 + b$, so the slope of the line is

$$\frac{y_2 - y_1}{x_2 - x_1} = \frac{(mx_2 + b) - (mx_1 + b)}{x_2 - x_1} = \frac{mx_2 - mx_1}{x_2 - x_1} = \frac{m(x_2 - x_1)}{x_2 - x_1} = m.$$

40a–b.

5 ASSESS AND RETEACH

Daily Homework Quiz

Transparency Available

1. Identify the slope and y-intercept of the line $2x + 4y = -16$.
slope: $-\frac{1}{2}$, y-intercept: -4

2. Graph $y = \frac{2}{3}x + 1$.

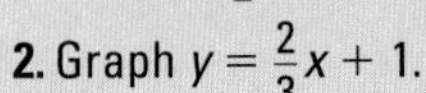

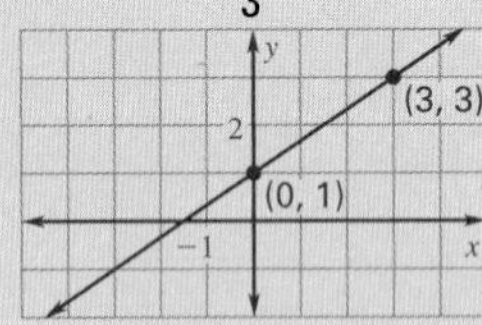

3. Determine which of the lines are parallel. **lines a and c**

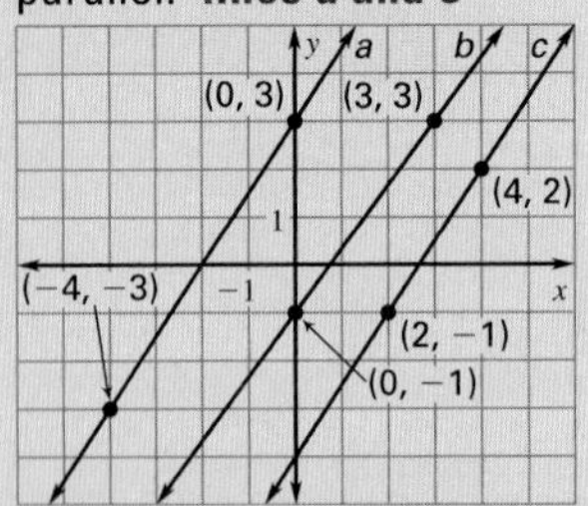

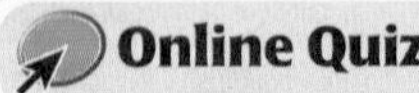

Online Quiz

Available at **classzone.com**

Diagnosis/Remediation

- Practice A, B, C in Chapter Resource Book
- Study Guide in Chapter Resource Book
- Practice Workbook
- @HomeTutor

Challenge

Additional challenge is available in the Chapter Resource Book.

Quiz

An easily-readable reduced copy of the quiz (with answers) on Lessons 4.4–4.5 from the Assessment Book can be found on p. 204G.

45a, Quiz 7–9, 10a. See Additional Answers beginning on p. AA1.

C 45. **CHALLENGE** To use a rock climbing wall at a college, a person who does not attend the college has to pay a \$5 certification fee plus \$3 per visit. The total cost C (in dollars) for a person who does not attend the college is given by $C = 3v + 5$ where v is the number of visits to the rock climbing wall. A student at the college pays only an \$8 certification fee, so the total cost for a student is given by $C = 8$.

a. Graph both equations in the same coordinate plane. At what point do the lines intersect? What does the point of intersection represent? **See margin for art; (1, 8); the point represents when the costs are equal.**

b. When will a nonstudent pay more than a student? When will a student pay more than a nonstudent? *Explain.* **A nonstudent pays more than a student after the first visit; a student pays more than a nonstudent when getting certified.**

MIXED REVIEW

PREVIEW
Prepare for Lesson 4.6 in Exs. 52–57.

Simplify the expression. *(p. 96)*

46. $3(x + 24)$ **$3x + 72$**
47. $5(x - 5)$ **$5x - 25$**
48. $8(x - 6)$ **$8x - 48$**

Solve the equation.

49. $3x + x = 8$ *(p. 141)* **2**
50. $5(x - 3x) = 15$ *(p. 148)* **−1.5**
51. $\frac{4}{3}(8x - 3) = 16$ *(p. 148)* **1.875**

Find the slope of the line that passes through the points. *(p. 235)*

52. (3, 4) and (9, 5) **$\frac{1}{6}$**
53. (4, −4) and (−2, 2) **−1**
54. (−3, −7) and (0, −7) **0**

Solve the proportion. Check your solution. *(p. 168)*

55. $\frac{4}{5} = \frac{x}{50}$ **40**
56. $\frac{2x}{x + 4} = \frac{8}{9}$ **3.2**
57. $\frac{7t - 2}{8} = \frac{3t - 4}{5}$ **−2**

QUIZ for Lessons 4.4–4.5

Find the slope of the line that passes through the points. *(p. 235)*

1. (3, −11) and (0, 4) **−5**
2. (2, 1) and (8, 4) **$\frac{1}{2}$**
3. (−4, −1) and (−1, −1) **0**

Identify the slope and y-intercept of the line with the given equation. *(p. 244)*

4. $y = -x + 9$ **−1, 9**
5. $2x + 9y = -18$ **$-\frac{2}{9}$, −2**
6. $-x + 6y = 21$ **$\frac{1}{6}$, $3\frac{1}{2}$**

Graph the equation. *(p. 244)* **7–9. See margin.**

7. $y = -2x + 11$
8. $y = \frac{5}{3}x - 8$
9. $-3x - 4y = -12$

10. **RED OAKS** Red oak trees grow at a rate of about 2 feet per year. You buy and plant two red oak trees, one that is 6 feet tall and one that is 8 feet tall. The height h (in feet) of the shorter tree can be modeled by $h = 2t + 6$ where t is the time (in years) since you planted the tree. The height of the taller tree can be modeled by $h = 2t + 8$. *(p. 244)*

a. Graph both equations in the same coordinate plane. **See margin.**

b. Use the graphs to find the difference of the heights of the trees 5 years after you plant them. What is the difference after 10 years? What do you notice about the difference of the heights of the two trees? **2 ft; 2 ft; it is always 2 feet.**

EXTRA PRACTICE for Lesson 4.5, p. 941

ONLINE QUIZ at classzone.com

Solve Linear Equations by Graphing

GOAL Use graphs to solve linear equations.

In Chapter 3, you learned how to solve linear equations in one variable algebraically. You can also solve linear equations graphically.

KEY CONCEPT *For Your Notebook*

Steps for Solving Linear Equations Graphically

Use the following steps to solve a linear equation in one variable graphically.

STEP 1 **Write** the equation in the form $ax + b = 0$.

STEP 2 **Write** the related function $y = ax + b$.

STEP 3 **Graph** the equation $y = ax + b$.

The solution of $ax + b = 0$ is the x-intercept of the graph of $y = ax + b$.

EXAMPLE 1 Solve an equation graphically

Solve $\frac{5}{2}x + 2 = 3x$ graphically. Check your solution algebraically.

Solution

STEP 1 **Write** the equation in the form $ax + b = 0$.

$\frac{5}{2}x + 2 = 3x$ **Write original equation.**

$-\frac{1}{2}x + 2 = 0$ **Subtract 3x from each side.**

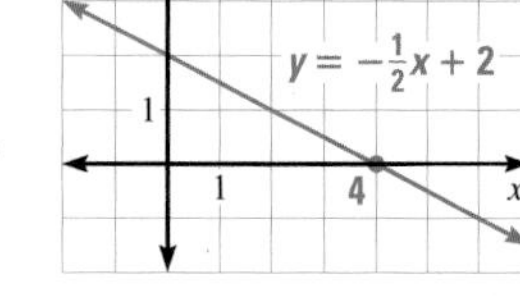

STEP 2 **Write** the related function $y = -\frac{1}{2}x + 2$.

STEP 3 **Graph** the equation $y = -\frac{1}{2}x + 2$. The x-intercept is 4.

▶ The solution of $\frac{5}{2}x + 2 = 3x$ is 4.

CHECK Use substitution.

$\frac{5}{2}x + 2 = 3x$ **Write original equation.**

$\frac{5}{2}(4) + 2 \stackrel{?}{=} 3(4)$ **Substitute 4 for x.**

$10 + 2 = 12$ **Simplify.**

$12 = 12$ ✓ **Solution checks.**

1 PLAN AND PREPARE

Warm-Up Exercises

Solve the equation.

1. $-3n + 13 = 7$ **2**
2. $\frac{3}{4}x + 2 = -10$ **−16**
3. $-6 + 4d = 2d + 2$ **4**
4. You buy a petrified rock and 6 postcards on a trip to the Petrified Forest. The petrified rock costs \$6.75. Find the cost of each postcard if your total cost is \$14.25 before tax and all the postcards cost the same. **\$1.25**

2 FOCUS AND MOTIVATE

Essential Question

Big Idea 1, p. 205

How do you use graphs to solve linear equations in one variable? **Tell students they will learn how to answer this question by writing equations and their related functions to find the *x*-intercept of a graph.**

3 TEACH

Extra Example 1

Solve $\frac{4}{3}x + 5 = 1$ graphically. **−3**

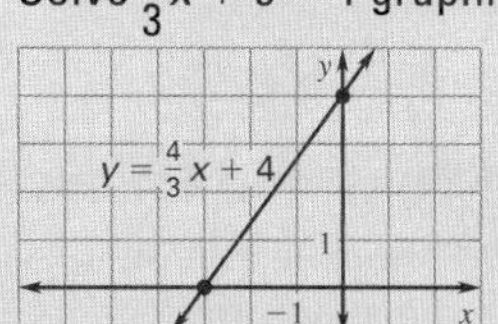

NCTM STANDARDS

Standard 2: Use models to understand relationships

Standard 10: Use representations to communicate mathematical ideas

Extra Example 2

The number s (in thousands) of subscribers to a local magazine can be modeled by the function $s = 3.128t + 12.58$ where t is the number of years since 1990. Use a graphing calculator to approximate the year when the number of subscribers will be 80 thousand.

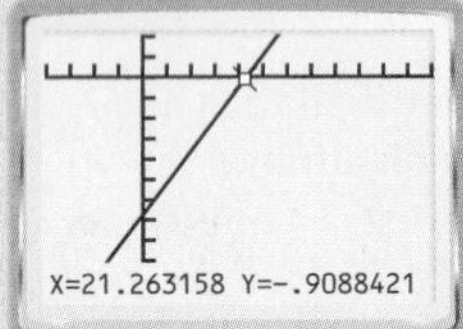

about 21 years after 1990, or 2011

Closing the Lesson

Have students summarize the major points of the lesson and answer the Essential Question: How do you use graphs to solve linear equations in one variable?

- **To solve a linear equation in one variable by graphing, first find a related function.**
- **The x-intercept of the graph of the related function is the solution of the original equation.**

Rewrite the given equation so it is equal to zero. Then write and graph the related function. The x-intercept of the graph is the solution of the equation.

4 PRACTICE AND APPLY

Avoiding Common Errors

Exercises 7–9 Remind students to substitute the appropriate numbers for s, b, and m in the equations and then write each equation in $ax + b = 0$ form.

EXAMPLE 2 Approximate a real-world solution

POPULATION The United States population P (in millions) can be modeled by the function $P = 2.683t + 213.1$ where t is the number of years since 1975. In approximately what year will the population be 350 million?

Solution

Substitute 350 for P in the linear model. You can answer the question by solving the resulting linear equation $350 = 2.683t + 213.1$.

STEP 1 **Write** the equation in the form $ax + b = 0$.

$350 = 2.683t + 213.1$	**Write equation.**
$0 = 2.683t - 136.9$	**Subtract 350 from each side.**
$0 = 2.683x - 136.9$	**Substitute x for t.**

STEP 2 **Write** the related function: $y = 2.683x - 136.9$.

SET THE WINDOW
Use the following viewing window for Example 2.
Xmin=−5
Xmax=60
Xscl=5
Ymin=−150
Ymax=10
Yscl=10

STEP 3 **Graph** the related function on a graphing calculator. Use the *trace* feature to approximate the x-intercept. You will know that you've crossed the x-axis when the y-values change from negative to positive. The x-intercept is about 51.

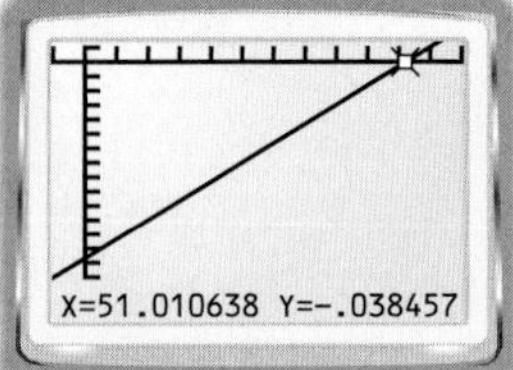

▶ Because x is the number of years since 1975, you can estimate that the population will be 350 million about 51 years after 1975, or in 2026.

PRACTICE

EXAMPLE 1
on p. 251
for Exs. 1–6

Solve the equation graphically. Then check your solution algebraically.

1. $6x + 5 = -7$ **−2**
2. $-7x + 18 = -3$ **3**
3. $2x - 4 = 3x$ **−4**
4. $\frac{1}{2}x - 3 = 2x$ **−2**
5. $-4 + 9x = -3x + 2$ **$\frac{1}{2}$**
6. $10x - 18x = 4x - 6$ **$\frac{1}{2}$**

EXAMPLE 2
on p. 252
for Exs. 7–9

7. **CABLE TELEVISION** The number s (in millions) of cable television subscribers can be modeled by the function $s = 1.79t + 51.1$ where t is the number of years since 1990. Use a graphing calculator to approximate the year when the number of subscribers was 70 million. **2000**

8. **EDUCATION** The number b (in thousands) of bachelor's degrees in Spanish earned in the U.S. can be modeled by the function $b = 0.281t + 4.26$ where t is the number of years since 1990. Use a graphing calculator to approximate the year when the number of degrees will be 9000. **2006**

9. **TRAVEL** The number of miles m (in billions) traveled by vehicles in New York can be modeled by $m = 2.56t + 113$ where t is the number of years since 1994. Use a graphing calculator to approximate the year in which the number of vehicle miles of travel in New York was 130 billion. **2000**

4.6 Model Direct Variation

Before	You wrote and graphed linear equations.
Now	You will write and graph direct variation equations.
Why?	So you can model distance traveled, as in Ex. 40.

Key Vocabulary
- **direct variation**
- **constant of variation**

Two variables x and y show **direct variation** provided $y = ax$ and $a \neq 0$. The nonzero number a is called the **constant of variation**, and y is said to *vary directly* with x.

The equation $y = 5x$ is an example of direct variation, and the constant of variation is 5. The equation $y = x + 5$ is *not* an example of direct variation.

EXAMPLE 1 Identify direct variation equations

Tell whether the equation represents direct variation. If so, identify the constant of variation.

a. $2x - 3y = 0$ **b.** $-x + y = 4$

Solution

To tell whether an equation represents direct variation, try to rewrite the equation in the form $y = ax$.

a. $2x - 3y = 0$ **Write original equation.**

$-3y = -2x$ **Subtract $2x$ from each side.**

$y = \frac{2}{3}x$ **Simplify.**

▶ Because the equation $2x - 3y = 0$ can be rewritten in the form $y = ax$, it represents direct variation. The constant of variation is $\frac{2}{3}$.

b. $-x + y = 4$ **Write original equation.**

$y = x + 4$ **Add x to each side.**

▶ Because the equation $-x + y = 4$ cannot be rewritten in the form $y = ax$, it does not represent direct variation.

GUIDED PRACTICE for Example 1

Tell whether the equation represents direct variation. If so, identify the constant of variation.

1. $-x + y = 1$ **not direct variation**
2. $2x + y = 0$ **direct variation; -2**
3. $4x - 5y = 0$ **direct variation; $\frac{4}{5}$**

1 PLAN AND PREPARE

Warm-Up Exercises

Transparency Available

Rewrite the equation so y is a function of x.

1. $4x - 2y = -8$ **$y = 2x + 4$**
2. $-9x + 3y = 21$ **$y = 3x + 7$**
3. You are traveling by bus. After 4.5 hours, the bus has traveled 234 miles. Use the formula $d = rt$ where d is distance, r is rate, and t is time to find the average rate of speed of the bus. **52 mi/h**

Notetaking Guide

Transparency Available

Promotes interactive learning and notetaking skills.

Pacing

Basic: 1 day
Average: 1 day
Advanced: 1 day
Block: 0.5 block with 4.5
- See *Teaching Guide/Lesson Plan.*

2 FOCUS AND MOTIVATE

Essential Question

Big Idea 3, p. 205

How do you write and graph direct variation equations? **Tell students they will learn how to answer this question by recognizing situations that represent direct variation and identifying the constant of variation.**

NCTM STANDARDS

Standard 2: Use models to understand relationships

Standard 8: Communicate thinking clearly to others

Resource Planning Guide

Chapter Resource Book
- Teaching Guide/Lesson Plan
- Practice levels A, B, C
- Study Guide
- Catch-up for Absent Students
- Application
- Challenge

Workbooks
- Notetaking Guide
- Practice Workbook

Teaching Options
- **Power Presentations** provides dynamic electronic teaching resources for the classroom.
- **Activity Generator** provides editable activities for all ability levels.

Interactive Technology
- Easy Planner
- Power Presentations
- Activity Generator
- Animated Algebra
- Test Generator
- Online Quiz
- eWorkbook
- eEdition
- @HomeTutor

Resources for English Learners
- Spanish Study Guide
- Multi-Language Visual Glossary
- Student Resources in Spanish

See also the *Differentiated Instruction Resources* for more strategies for meeting individual needs.

Motivating the Lesson

Suppose an object that weighs 150 pounds on Earth would weigh 165 pounds on Neptune and that the weight of an object on Neptune varies directly with the weight of an object on Earth. You can use this information to determine an equation that relates the two weights. Then you can determine your weight, and the weight of your friends on Neptune.

3 TEACH

Extra Example 1

Tell whether the equation represents direct variation. If so, identify the constant of variation.

a. $4x + 5y = 0$ **yes,** $-\frac{4}{5}$

b. $2x - y = 3$ **no**

Extra Example 2

Graph the direct variation equation.

a. $y = \frac{2}{5}x$

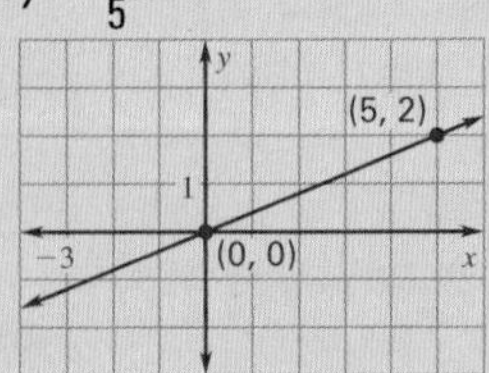

b. $y = -\frac{1}{2}x$

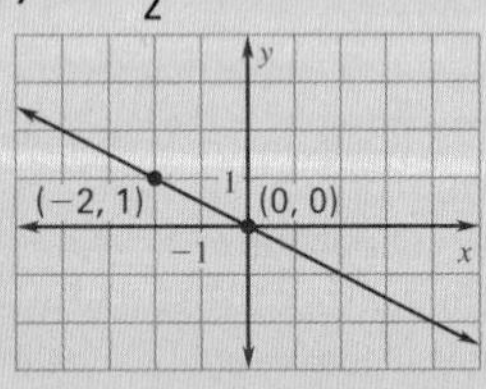

An **Animated Algebra** activity is available online for **Example 2**. This activity is also part of **Power Presentations**.

DIRECT VARIATION GRAPHS Notice that a direct variation equation, $y = ax$, is a linear equation in slope-intercept form, $y = mx + b$, with $m = a$ and $b = 0$. The graph of a direct variation equation is a line with a slope of a and a y-intercept of 0. So, the line passes through the origin.

EXAMPLE 2 Graph direct variation equations

Graph the direct variation equation.

a. $y = \frac{2}{3}x$

b. $y = -3x$

Solution

DRAW A GRAPH
If the constant of variation is positive, the graph of $y = ax$ passes through Quadrants I and III. If the constant of variation is negative, the graph of $y = ax$ passes through Quadrants II and IV.

a. Plot a point at the origin. The slope is equal to the constant of variation, or $\frac{2}{3}$. Find and plot a second point, then draw a line through the points.

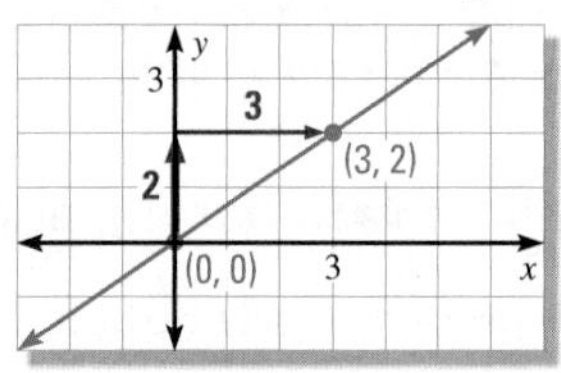

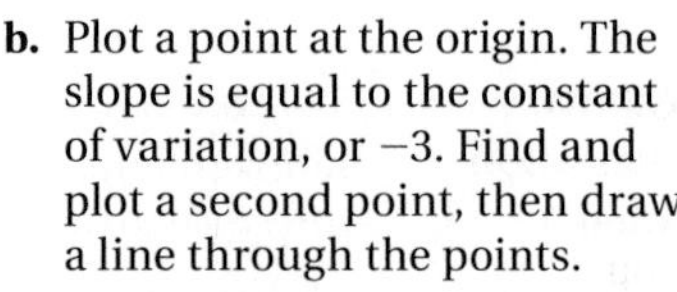

b. Plot a point at the origin. The slope is equal to the constant of variation, or −3. Find and plot a second point, then draw a line through the points.

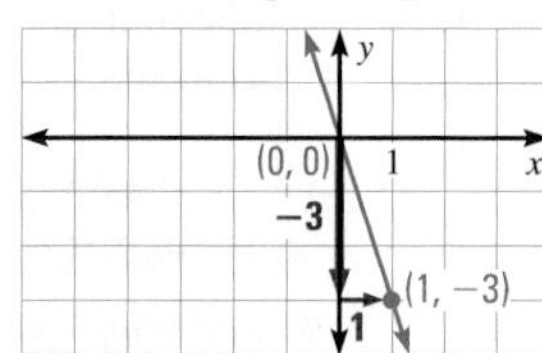

Animated Algebra at classzone.com

EXAMPLE 3 Write and use a direct variation equation

The graph of a direct variation equation is shown.

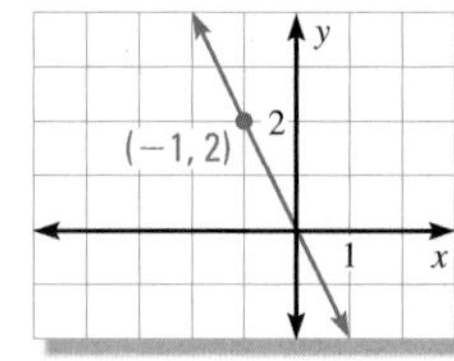

a. Write the direct variation equation.

b. Find the value of y when $x = 30$.

Solution

a. Because y varies directly with x, the equation has the form $y = ax$. Use the fact that $y = 2$ when $x = -1$ to find a.

$y = ax$	Write direct variation equation.
$2 = a(-1)$	Substitute.
$-2 = a$	Solve for a.

▶ A direct variation equation that relates x and y is $y = -2x$.

b. When $x = 30$, $y = -2(30) = -60$.

✓ **GUIDED PRACTICE** for Examples 2 and 3

4. Graph the direct variation equation $y = 2x$. **See margin.**

5. The graph of a direct variation equation passes through the point (4, 6). Write the direct variation equation and find the value of y when $x = 24$. $y = \frac{3}{2}x$, **36**

KEY CONCEPT *For Your Notebook*

Properties of Graphs of Direct Variation Equations

- The graph of a direct variation equation is a line through the origin.
- The slope of the graph of $y = ax$ is a.

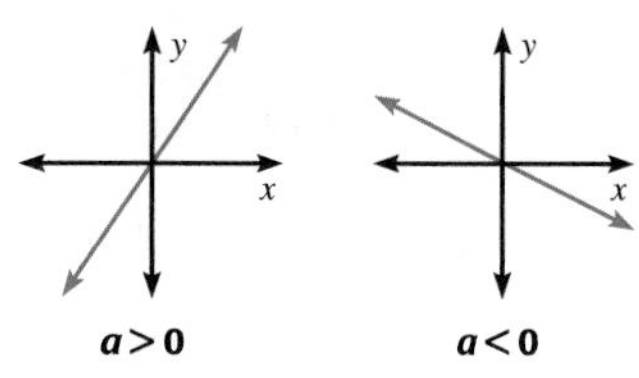

EXAMPLE 4 Solve a multi-step problem

ANOTHER WAY
For alternative methods for solving Example 4, turn to page 260 for the **Problem Solving Workshop**.

SALTWATER AQUARIUM The number s of tablespoons of sea salt needed in a saltwater fish tank varies directly with the number w of gallons of water in the tank. A pet shop owner recommends adding 100 tablespoons of sea salt to a 20 gallon tank.

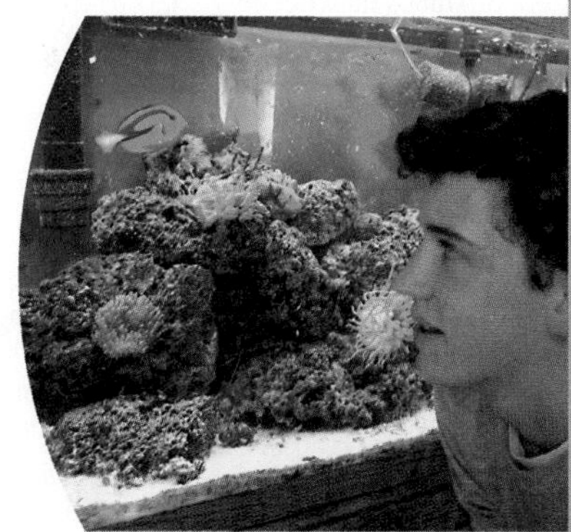

- Write a direct variation equation that relates w and s.
- How many tablespoons of salt should be added to a 30 gallon saltwater fish tank?

Solution

STEP 1 **Write** a direct variation equation. Because s varies directly with w, you can use the equation $s = aw$. Also use the fact that $s = 100$ when $w = 20$.

$s = aw$ — Write direct variation equation.

$100 = a(20)$ — Substitute.

$5 = a$ — Solve for a.

RECOGNIZE RATE OF CHANGE
The value of a in Example 4 is a rate of change: 5 tablespoons of sea salt per gallon of water.

▶ A direct variation equation that relates w and s is $s = 5w$.

STEP 2 **Find** the number of tablespoons of salt that should be added to a 30 gallon saltwater fish tank. Use your direct variation equation from Step 1.

$s = 5w$ — Write direct variation equation.

$s = 5(30)$ — Substitute 30 for w.

$s = 150$ — Simplify.

▶ You should add 150 tablespoons of salt to a 30 gallon fish tank.

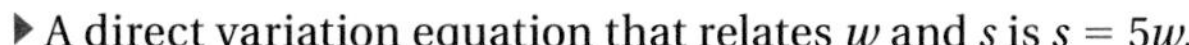

GUIDED PRACTICE for Example 4

6. **WHAT IF?** In Example 4, suppose the fish tank is a 25 gallon tank. How many tablespoons of salt should be added to the tank? **125 tbsp**

4.

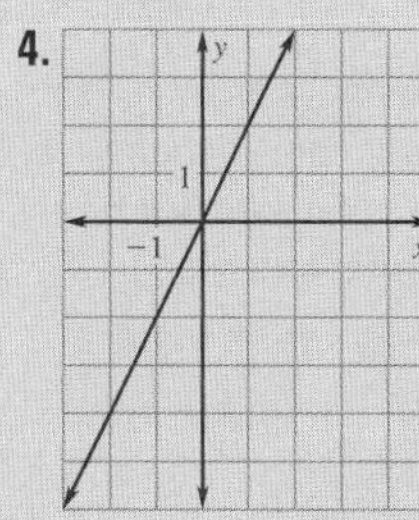

Key Questions to Ask for Example 2

- Can the y-intercept for the graph of a direct variation equation be a number other than zero? Explain. **No; a direct variation equation is of the form $y = ax + 0$, so the line must pass through the origin.**
- What is the relationship of slope to the constant of variation? **They are the same.**

Extra Example 3

The graph of a direct variation equation is shown.

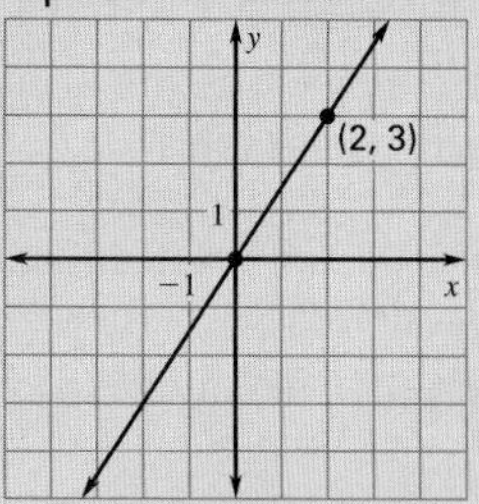

a. Write the direct variation equation. $y = \frac{3}{2}x$

b. Find the value of y when $x = 14$. **21**

Key Questions to Ask for Example 3

- What do you need from a graph to write a direct variation equation? **the coordinates of one point on the graph, other than the origin**
- What can you tell about the constant of variation from looking at the graph? Explain. **The constant of variation must be negative, because the graph slants downward from left to right.**

Extra Example 4

An object that weighs 100 pounds on Earth would weigh just 6 pounds on Pluto. Assume that weight P on Pluto varies directly with weight E on Earth.

- Write a direct variation equation that relates P and E. $P = 0.06E$
- What would a boulder weighing 750 pounds on Earth weigh on Pluto? **45 lb**

Extra Example 5

The table shows the cost of buying used DVDs at a music store.

Number of DVDs, d	Cost, c
3	\$25.77
6	\$51.54
9	\$77.31

a. Explain why C varies directly with d. **All of the data pairs have the same ratio, 8.59.**

b. Write a direct variation equation that relates d and C. **$C = 8.59d$**

Closing the Lesson

Have students summarize the major points of the lesson and answer the Essential Question: How do you write and graph direct variation equations?

- **A direct variation equation is of the form $y = ax$, with a not equal to 0.**
- **The graph of a direct variation equation is a line through the origin with slope a.**

Use facts in a real-world situation or the coordinates of a point for the values of x and y in the direct variation equation $y = ax$. Then solve for the constant of variation. To graph a direct variation equation, plot a point at the origin and then use the constant of variation, which is the slope, to plot a second point.

RATIOS The direct variation equation $y = ax$ can be rewritten as $\frac{y}{x} = a$ for $x \neq 0$. So, in a direct variation, the ratio of y to x is constant for all nonzero data pairs (x, y).

EXAMPLE 5 Use a direct variation model

ONLINE MUSIC The table shows the cost C of downloading s songs at an Internet music site.

Number of songs, s	Cost, C (dollars)
3	2.97
5	4.95
7	6.93

a. Explain why C varies directly with s.

b. Write a direct variation equation that relates s and C.

CHECK RATIOS
For real-world data, the ratios may not be exactly equal. You may still be able to use a direct variation model when the ratios are approximately equal.

Solution

a. To explain why C varies directly with s, compare the ratios $\frac{C}{s}$ for all data pairs (s, C): $\frac{2.97}{3} = \frac{4.95}{5} = \frac{6.93}{7} = 0.99$.

Because the ratios all equal 0.99, C varies directly with s.

b. A direct variation equation is $C = 0.99s$.

GUIDED PRACTICE for Example 5

7. **WHAT IF?** In Example 5, suppose the website charges a total of \$1.99 for the first 5 songs you download and \$.99 for each song after the first 5. Is it reasonable to use a direct variation model for this situation? *Explain.*
No; the equation that models this situation does not have the form $y = ax$.

4.6 EXERCISES

HOMEWORK KEY
○ = **WORKED-OUT SOLUTIONS** on p. WS9 for Exs. 7, 21, and 43
★ = **STANDARDIZED TEST PRACTICE** Exs. 2, 9, 28, 38, 43, 44, and 46
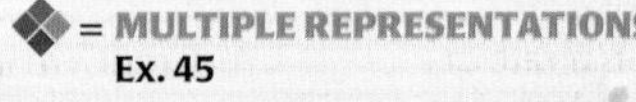
= **MULTIPLE REPRESENTATIONS** Ex. 45

SKILL PRACTICE

1. **VOCABULARY** Copy and complete: Two variables x and y show _?_ provided $y = ax$ and $a \neq 0$. **direct variation**

2. ★ **WRITING** A line has a slope of -3 and a y-intercept of 4. Is the equation of the line a direct variation equation? *Explain.* **No; a direct variation equation has a y-intercept of 0.**

EXAMPLE 1 on p. 253 for Exs. 3–10

IDENTIFYING DIRECT VARIATION EQUATIONS **Tell whether the equation represents direct variation. If so, identify the constant of variation.**

3. $y = x$ **direct variation; 1**
4. $y = 5x - 1$ **not direct variation**
5. $2x + y = 3$ **not direct variation**
6. $x - 3y = 0$ **direct variation; $\frac{1}{3}$**
7. $8x + 2y = 0$ **direct variation; -4**
8. $2.4x + 6 = 1.2y$ **not direct variation**

Differentiated Instruction

English Learners The word *variation* means "a change," so students may be confused by the term *constant of variation* for a in the direct variation equation $y = ax$. Stress that a does not vary, but rather stays constant, in a given direct variation equation.

See also the *Differentiated Instruction Resources* for more strategies.

9. ★ **MULTIPLE CHOICE** Which equation is a direct variation equation? **C**

Ⓐ $y = 7 - 3x$ Ⓑ $3x - 7y = 1$ Ⓒ $3x - 7y = 0$ Ⓓ $3y = 7x - 1$

10. **ERROR ANALYSIS** *Describe* and correct the error in identifying the constant of variation for the direct variation equation $-5x + 3y = 0$. **The coefficient of y should be 1, not 3; $y = \frac{5}{3}x$, the constant of variation is $\frac{5}{3}$.**

$-5x + 3y = 0$
$3y = 5x$
The constant of variation is 5. ✗

EXAMPLE 2 on p. 254 for Exs. 11–22

GRAPHING EQUATIONS **Graph the direct variation equation.** **11–22. See margin.**

11. $y = x$ 12. $y = 3x$ 13. $y = -4x$ 14. $y = 5x$

15. $y = \frac{4}{3}x$ 16. $y = \frac{1}{2}x$ 17. $y = -\frac{1}{3}x$ 18. $y = -\frac{3}{2}x$

19. $12y = -24x$ 20. $10y = 25x$ (21.) $4x + y = 0$ 22. $y - 1.25x = 0$

EXAMPLE 3 on p. 254 for Exs. 23–25

WRITING EQUATIONS **The graph of a direct variation equation is shown. Write the direct variation equation. Then find the value of y when $x = 8$.**

23. 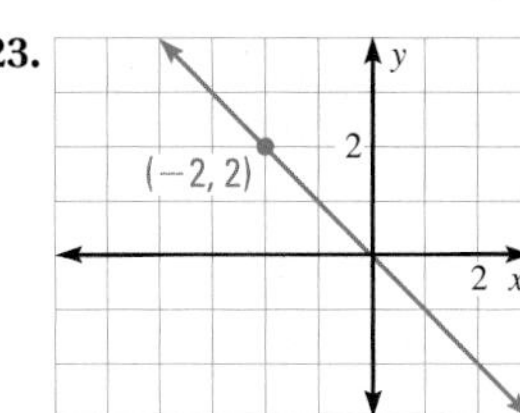

$y = -x; -8$

24. 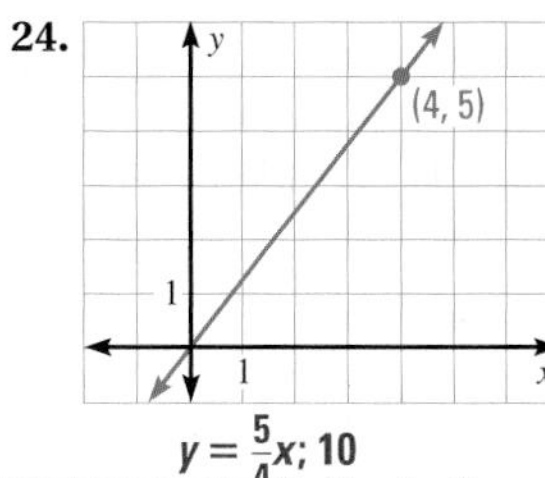

$y = \frac{5}{4}x; 10$

25. 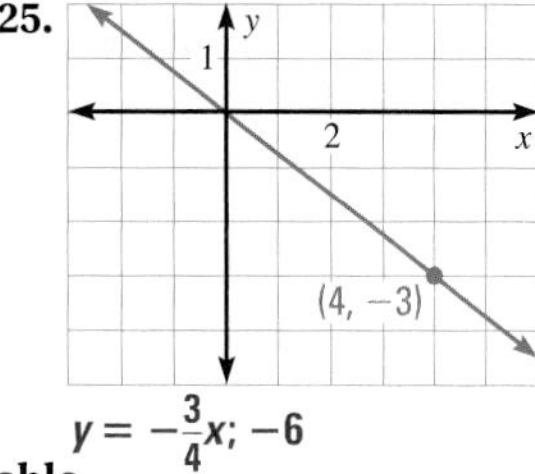

$y = -\frac{3}{4}x; -6$

B **IDENTIFYING DIRECT VARIATION EQUATIONS** **Tell whether the table represents direct variation. If so, write the direct variation equation.**

26.

x	1	2	3	4	6
y	5	10	15	20	30

direct variation; $y = 5x$

27.

x	−3	−1	1	3	5
y	−2	0	2	4	6

not a direct variation

28. ★ **WRITING** A student says that a direct variation equation can be used to model the data in the table. *Explain* why the student is mistaken.

x	2	4	8	16
y	1	2	4	6

Sample answer: **Each of the ratios $\frac{y}{x}$ should be equal, $\frac{4}{8} \neq \frac{6}{16}$, so y does not vary directly with x.**

WRITING EQUATIONS **Given that y varies directly with x, use the specified values to write a direct variation equation that relates x and y.**

29. $x = 3, y = 9$ **$y = 3x$** 30. $x = 2, y = 26$ **$y = 13x$** 31. $x = 14, y = 7$ **$y = \frac{1}{2}x$**

32. $x = 15, y = -5$ **$y = -\frac{1}{3}x$** 33. $x = -2, y = -2$ **$y = x$** 34. $x = -18, y = -4$ **$y = \frac{2}{9}x$**

35. $x = \frac{1}{4}, y = 1$ **$y = 4x$** 36. $x = -6, y = 15$ **$y = -\frac{5}{2}x$** 37. $x = -5.2, y = 1.4$ **$y = -\frac{7}{26}x$**

C 38. ★ **WRITING** If y varies directly with x, does x vary directly with y? If so, what is the relationship between the constants of variation? *Explain.*

38. Yes; the constants of variation are reciprocals of each other; if $y = a_1x$, then $a_1 = \frac{y}{x}$ and if $x = a_2y$, then $a_2 = \frac{x}{y}$, which shows the constants of variation, a_1 and a_2 are reciprocals of each other.

39. **CHALLENGE** The slope of a line is $-\frac{1}{3}$, and the point $(-6, 2)$ lies on the line. Use the formula for the slope of a line to determine if the equation of the line is a direct variation equation. **direct variation**

4 PRACTICE AND APPLY

Assignment Guide

Answer Transparencies available for all exercises

Basic:
Day 1: pp. 256–259
Exs. 1, 2, 3–9 odd, 10–22 even, 23–28, 40–45, 48–62 even

Average:
Day 1: pp. 256–259
Exs. 1, 2, 6–10, 18–28, 29–35 odd, 40–46, 53–56, 60–62

Advanced:
Day 1: pp. 256–259
Exs. 1, 2, 7–9, 19–22, 24–28, 33–39*, 41–47*, 54–56, 60–62

Block:
pp. 256–259
Exs. 1, 2, 6–10, 18–28, 29–35 odd, 40–46, 53–56, 60–62 (with 4.5)

Differentiated Instruction

See *Differentiated Instruction Resources* for suggestions on addressing the needs of a diverse classroom.

Homework Check

For a quick check of student understanding of key concepts, go over the following exercises:

Basic: 5, 14, 23, 40, 43
Average: 7, 19, 24, 41, 43
Advanced: 8, 20, 25, 42, 44

Extra Practice

- Student Edition, p. 941
- Chapter Resource Book: Practice levels A, B, C

Practice Worksheet

An easily-readable reduced practice page (with answers) for this lesson can be found on p. 204E.

11–22. See Additional Answers beginning on p. AA1.

Avoiding Common Errors

Exercises 19–22 Some students may forget to rewrite the equations in the form $y = ax$. Remind them to do this before graphing.

Exercises 23–25 Caution students to substitute the coordinates correctly in the direct variation equation.

Exercises 26–28 Some students may notice that the increments in the table are not equal and assume that the ratios are not the same for all the data pairs. Tell students they need to test all the data pairs to see if the ratios are equal.

Exercise 46 More statistical information for NCAA women's basketball can be found at www.ncaasports.com/basketball/womens/stats

PROBLEM SOLVING

EXAMPLE 4 A on p. 255 for Exs. 40–42

40. BICYCLES The distance d (in meters) you travel on a bicycle varies directly with the number r of revolutions that the rear tire completes. You travel about 2 meters on a mountain bike for every revolution of the tire.

a. Write a direct variation equation that relates r and d. **$d = 2r$**

b. How many meters do you travel in 1500 tire revolutions? **3000 m**

@HomeTutor for problem solving help at classzone.com

41. VACATION TIME At one company, the amount of vacation v (in hours) an employee earns varies directly with the amount of time t (in weeks) he or she works. An employee who works 2 weeks earns 3 hours of vacation.

a. Write a direct variation equation that relates t and v. $v = \frac{3}{2}t$

b. How many hours of vacation time does an employee earn in 8 weeks? **12 h**

@HomeTutor for problem solving help at classzone.com

42. LANDSCAPING Landscapers plan to spread a layer of stone on a path. The number s of bags of stone needed depends on the depth d (in inches) of the layer. They need 10 bags to spread a layer of stone that is 2 inches deep. Write a direct variation equation that relates d and s. Then find the number of bags needed to spread a layer that is 3 inches deep. **$s = 5d$; 15 bags**

EXAMPLE 5 on p. 256 for Exs. 43–44

43a. Compare the ratios, $\frac{f}{w}$, for all data pairs (w, f). Since the ratios all equal 0.25, f varies directly with w.

44a. Compare the ratios, $\frac{p}{\ell}$, for all data pairs (ℓ, p). Since the ratios all equal 1.25, p varies directly with ℓ.

(43.) ★ SHORT RESPONSE At a recycling center, computers and computer accessories can be recycled for a fee f based on weight w, as shown in the table.

Weight, w (pounds)	Fee, f (dollars)
10	2.50
15	3.75
30	7.50

a. *Explain* why f varies directly with w.

b. Write a direct variation equation that relates w and f, and identify the rate of change that the constant of variation represents. Find the total recycling fee for an 18 pound computer and a 10 pound printer. **$f = 0.25w$; \$.25 per pound; \$7**

44. ★ SHORT RESPONSE You can buy gold chain by the inch. The table shows the price of gold chain for various lengths.

Length, ℓ (inches)	7	9	16	18
Price, p (dollars)	8.75	11.25	20.00	22.50

a. *Explain* why p varies directly with ℓ.

b. Write a direct variation equation that relates ℓ and p, and identify the rate of change that the constant of variation represents. If you have \$30, what is the longest chain that you can buy? **$p = 1.25\ell$; \$1.25 per inch; 24 in.**

○ = WORKED-OUT SOLUTIONS on p. WS1 ★ = STANDARDIZED TEST PRACTICE ◆ = MULTIPLE REPRESENTATIONS

B 45. **MULTIPLE REPRESENTATIONS** The total cost of riding the subway to and from school every day is $1.50.

a. **Making a Table** Make a table that shows the number d of school days and the total cost C (in dollars) for trips to and from school for some values of d. Assume you travel to school once each school day and home from school once each school day. **See margin.**

b. **Drawing a Graph** Graph the ordered pairs from the table and draw a ray through them. **See margin.**

c. **Writing an Equation** Write an equation of the graph from part (b). Is it a direct variation equation? *Explain.* If there are 22 school days in one month, what will it cost to ride the subway to and from school for that month? **$C = 1.5d$; yes; it's in the form $y = ax$; $33.**

46. ★ **EXTENDED RESPONSE** The table shows the average number of field goals attempted t and the average number of field goals made m per game for all NCAA Division I women's basketball teams for 9 consecutive seasons.

Attempted field goals, t	61.8	61.9	61.8	60.8	59.5	59.0	58.9	59.2	58.4
Field goals made, m	25.7	25.6	25.6	25.2	24.5	24.6	24.5	24.3	24.0

a. **Write** Why is it reasonable to use a direct variation model for this situation? Write a direct variation equation that relates t and m. Find the constant of variation to the nearest tenth. **All of the ratios, $\frac{m}{t}$, are approximately equal to 0.4; $m = 0.4t$; 0.4.**

b. **Estimate** The highest average number of attempted field goals in one season was 66.2. Estimate the number of field goals made that season. **about 26 field goals**

c. **Explain** If the average number of field goals made was increasing rather than decreasing and the number of attempted field goals continued to decrease, would the data show direct variation? *Explain.* **No; the ratios, $\frac{m}{t}$, for each season would not be equal to each other.**

C 47. **CHALLENGE** In Exercise 40, you found an equation showing that the distance traveled on a bike varies directly with the number of revolutions that the rear tire completes. The number r of tire revolutions varies directly with the number p of pedal revolutions. In a particular gear, you travel about 1.3 meters for every 5 revolutions of the pedals. Show that distance traveled varies directly with pedal revolutions.

47. Because $d = 2r$ and r varies directly with p, you can write the equation $r = ap$. When $d = 1.3$ meters, $r = 0.65$. Substitute 0.65 for r when $p = 5$ to get $0.65 = 5a$. Solve to find $a = 0.13$. If you substitute ap for r into the equation $d = 2r$, you get $d = 2(0.13)p$, giving the direct variation equation $d = 0.26p$.

MIXED REVIEW

Graph the equation. **48–56. See margin.**

48. $y = -8$ *(p. 215)*
49. $x = 6$ *(p. 215)*
50. $2x + y = 4$ *(p. 225)*
51. $-2x + 5y = -30$ *(p. 225)*
52. $0.4x + 2y = 6$ *(p. 225)*
53. $y = 2x - 5$ *(p. 244)*
54. $y = \frac{1}{3}x$ *(p. 244)*
55. $y = -x + 3$ *(p. 244)*
56. $y = -\frac{3}{2}x + 2$ *(p. 244)*

PREVIEW
Prepare for Lesson 4.7 in Exs. 57–62.

Identify the slope and y-intercept of the line with the given equation. *(p. 244)*

57. $y = 3x + 5$ **3, 5**
58. $y = -3x$ **−3, 0**
59. $y = 2x - 5$ **2, −5**
60. $y = 4x - 11$ **4, −11**
61. $y = \frac{4}{5}x - 3$ **$\frac{4}{5}$, −3**
62. $y = \frac{5}{4}x + 3.1$ **$\frac{5}{4}$, 3.1**

48–56. See Additional Answers beginning on p. AA1.

5 ASSESS AND RETEACH

Daily Homework Quiz

Transparency Available

Tell whether the equation represents direct variation. If so, identify the constant of variation.

1. $5x - 6y = 2$ **no**
2. $x + y = 0$ **yes, −1**
3. The number p of parts a machine produces varies directly with the time t (in minutes) the machine is in operation. The machine produces 84 parts in 14 minutes. Write a direct variation equation that relates t and p. How many parts does the machine produce in 25 minutes? **$p = 6t$; 150 parts**

Online Quiz

Available at **classzone.com**

Diagnosis/Remediation

- Practice A, B, C in Chapter Resource Book
- Study Guide in Chapter Resource Book
- Practice Workbook
- @HomeTutor

Challenge

Additional challenge is available in the Chapter Resource Book.

45a. *Sample answer:*

d	C (dollars)
1	1.5
2	3
3	4.5

45b.

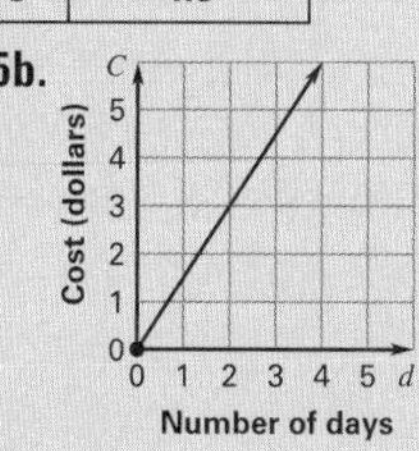

Alternative Strategy

Example 4 on page 255 can be solved by using a graph or by writing and solving a proportion. The method of using a graph allows students to visualize the solution. The method of using a proportion is useful when students cannot remember the direct variation equation. Both methods can help students understand the algebraic solution given in Lesson 4.6.

Reading Strategy

In Method 1, point out to students that the x-coordinates and x-values are color-coded blue and the y-coordinates and y-values are color-coded red for all three steps.

PROBLEM SOLVING WORKSHOP LESSON 4.6

Using ALTERNATIVE METHODS

Another Way to Solve Example 4, page 255

MULTIPLE REPRESENTATIONS In Example 4 on page 255, you saw how to solve the problem about how much salt to add to a saltwater fish tank by writing and using a direct variation equation. You can also solve the problem using a graph or a proportion.

PROBLEM

SALTWATER AQUARIUM The number s of tablespoons of sea salt needed in a saltwater fish tank varies directly with the number w of gallons of water in the tank. A pet shop owner recommends adding 100 tablespoons of sea salt to a 20 gallon tank. How many tablespoons of salt should be added to a 30 gallon saltwater fish tank?

METHOD 1

Using a Graph An alternative approach is to use a graph.

STEP 1 **Read** the problem. It tells you an amount of salt for a certain size fish tank. You can also assume that if a fishtank has no water, then no salt needs to be added. Write ordered pairs for this information.

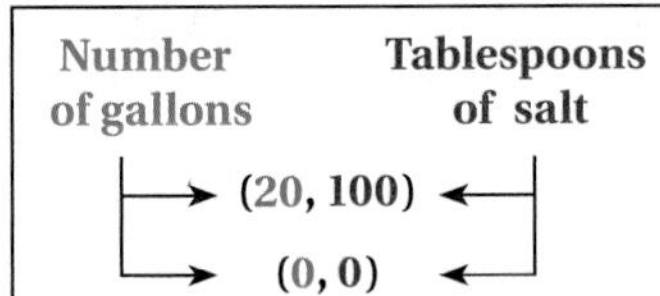

STEP 2 **Graph** the ordered pairs. Draw a line through the points.

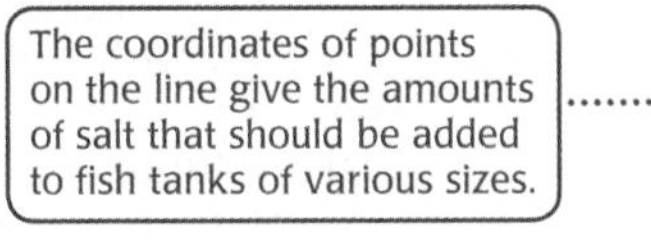

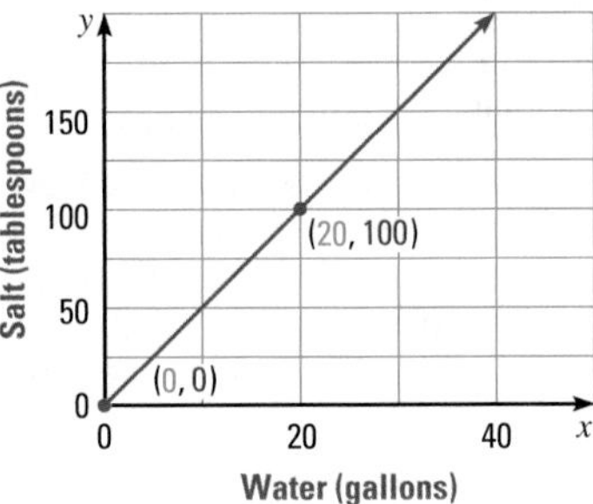

STEP 3 **Find** the point on the graph that has an x-coordinate of 30. The y-coordinate of this point is 150, so 150 tablespoons of salt should be added to a 30 gallon tank.

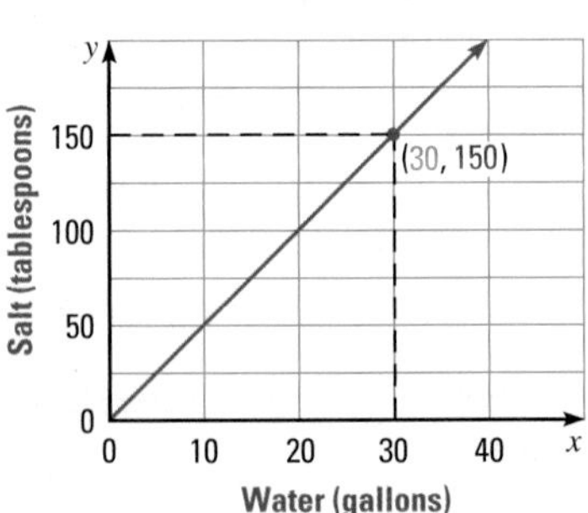

METHOD 2 **Writing a Proportion** Another alternative approach is to write and solve a proportion.

STEP 1 **Write** a proportion involving two ratios that each compare the amount of water (in gallons) to the amount of salt (in tablespoons).

$$\frac{20}{100} = \frac{30}{s}$$ ← amount of water (gallons) ← amount of salt (tablespoons)

STEP 2 **Solve** the proportion.

$\frac{20}{100} = \frac{30}{s}$	Write proportion.
$20s = 100 \cdot 30$	Cross products property
$20s = 3000$	Simplify.
$s = 150$	Divide each side by 20.

▸ You should add 150 tablespoons of salt to a 30 gallon tank.

CHECK Check your answer by writing each ratio in simplest form.

$$\frac{20}{100} = \frac{1}{5} \text{ and } \frac{30}{150} = \frac{1}{5}$$

Because each ratio simplifies to $\frac{1}{5}$, the answer is correct.

PRACTICE

1. **WHAT IF?** Suppose the fish tank in the problem above is a 22 gallon tank. How many tablespoons of salt should be added to the tank? *Describe* which method you used to solve this problem. **See margin.**

2. **ADVERTISING** A local newspaper charges by the word for printing classified ads. A 14 word ad costs \$5.88. How much would a 21 word ad cost? Solve this problem using two different methods. **See margin.**

3. **REASONING** In Exercise 2, how can you quickly determine the cost of a 7 word ad? *Explain* how you could use the cost of a 7 word ad to solve the problem. **See margin.**

4. **NUTRITION** A company sells fruit smoothies in two sizes of bottles: 6 fluid ounces and 10 fluid ounces. You know that a 6 ounce bottle contains 96 milligrams of sodium. How many milligrams of sodium does a 10 ounce bottle contain? **160 mg**

5. **ERROR ANALYSIS** A student solved the problem in Exercise 4 as shown. *Describe* and correct the error made.

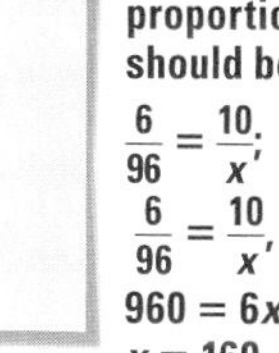

Let x = the number of milligrams of sodium in a 10 ounce bottle.
6/x = 10/96
576 = 10x
57.6 = x

The proportion should be $\frac{6}{96} = \frac{10}{x}$, $\frac{6}{96} = \frac{10}{x}$, $960 = 6x$, $x = 160$.

6. **SLEEPING** You find an online calculator that calculates the number of calories you burn while sleeping. The results for various sleeping times are shown. About how many more calories would you burn by sleeping for 9.5 hours than for 8 hours? Choose any method for solving the problem. **90 calories**

Hours of sleep	6.5	7	8.5	9
Calories burned	390	420	510	540

Avoiding Common Errors

In Method 2, point out to students that units of water are compared to units of salt. Caution students to check that their proportions in the Practice exercises are set up correctly. When using a graph to solve a Practice exercise, tell students to make sure they do not switch x- and y-coordinates. Suggest they use the algebraic or proportion method to check the reasonableness of their answer.

Teaching Strategy

You may want to discuss the relationship of dependent and independent variables before students solve Exercise 6.

1. 110 tbsp. *Sample answer:* Use the proportion $\frac{20}{100} = \frac{22}{x}$.

2. \$8.82; Method 1: Use a graph. Graph the points (0, 0) and (14, 5.88) and draw a line through the points. Find the point on the graph that has an x-coordinate of 21. The y-coordinate is about 8.82, so it costs \$8.82 for 21 words.

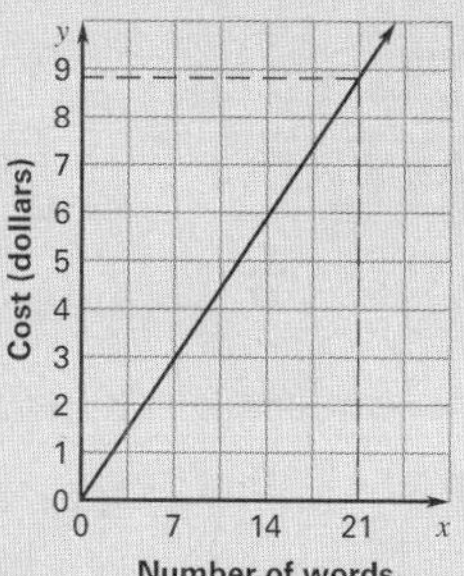

Method 2: Write a proportion. $\frac{14}{5.88} = \frac{21}{x}$, solve the proportion to find $x = 8.82$, so it costs \$8.82 for 21 words.

3. Because 7 is half of 14, you can take half of 5.88 to find 7 words cost \$2.94. Because 21 is 3 times 7, multiply \$2.94 by 3 to get \$8.82.

4.7 Graph Linear Functions

Before You graphed linear equations and functions.
Now You will use function notation.
Why? So you can model an animal population, as in Example 3.

Key Vocabulary
- **function notation**
- **family of functions**
- **parent linear function**

You have seen linear functions written in the form $y = mx + b$. By naming a function f, you can write it using **function notation**.

$$f(x) = mx + b \quad \text{Function notation}$$

The symbol $f(x)$ is another name for y and is read as "the value of f at x," or simply as "f of x." It does *not* mean f times x. You can use letters other than f, such as g or h, to name functions.

EXAMPLE 1 Standardized Test Practice

What is the value of the function $f(x) = 3x - 15$ when $x = -3$?

Ⓐ −24 Ⓑ −6 Ⓒ −2 Ⓓ 8

Solution

$f(x) = 3x - 15$ Write original function.

$f(-3) = 3(-3) - 15$ Substitute −3 for x.

$= -24$ Simplify.

▶ The correct answer is A. Ⓐ Ⓑ Ⓒ Ⓓ

GUIDED PRACTICE for Example 1

1. Evaluate the function $h(x) = -7x$ when $x = 7$. **−49**

EXAMPLE 2 Find an x-value

For the function $f(x) = 2x - 10$, find the value of x so that $f(x) = 6$.

$f(x) = 2x - 10$ Write original function.

$6 = 2x - 10$ Substitute 6 for $f(x)$.

$8 = x$ Solve for x.

▶ When $x = 8$, $f(x) = 6$.

1 PLAN AND PREPARE

Warm-Up Exercises

Transparency Available

Tell whether the ordered pair is a solution of the equation.

1. $2x + 3y = 2$; $(3, -2)$ **no**
2. $-x - 4y = -3$; $(-5, 2)$ **yes**
3. The weight of a person on Mars is given by the function $y = 0.371x$ where x is the weight of a person on Earth. A person weighs 130 pounds on Earth. Find the weight of the person on Mars. **48.23 lb**

Notetaking Guide

Transparency Available

Promotes interactive learning and notetaking skills.

Pacing

Basic: 2 days
Average: 2 days
Advanced: 2 days
Block: 1 block
- See *Teaching Guide/Lesson Plan.*

2 FOCUS AND MOTIVATE

Essential Question

Big Idea 3, p. 205

What is function notation? **Tell students they will learn how to answer this question by finding values of a function for given x-values, by finding x-values for given function values, and by graphing.**

NCTM STANDARDS

Standard 2: Use models to understand relationships

Standard 7: Investigate mathematical conjectures

Resource Planning Guide

Chapter Resource Book
- Teaching Guide/Lesson Plan
- Activity Master
- Practice levels A, B, C
- Study Guide
- Catch-up for Absent Students
- Problem Solving Workshop
- Challenge

Workbooks
- Notetaking Guide
- Practice Workbook

Teaching Options
- **Power Presentations** provides dynamic electronic teaching resources for the classroom.
- **Activity Generator** provides editable activities for all ability levels.

Interactive Technology
- Easy Planner
- Power Presentations
- Activity Generator
- Animated Algebra
- Test Generator
- Online Quiz
- eWorkbook
- eEdition
- @HomeTutor

Resources for English Learners
- Spanish Study Guide
- Multi-Language Visual Glossary
- Student Resources in Spanish

See also the *Differentiated Instruction Resources* for more strategies for meeting individual needs.

DOMAIN AND RANGE The domain of a function consists of the values of x for which the function is defined. The range consists of the values of $f(x)$ where x is in the domain of f. The graph of a function f is the set of all points $(x, f(x))$.

EXAMPLE 3 Graph a function

GRAY WOLF The gray wolf population in central Idaho was monitored over several years for a project aimed at boosting the number of wolves. The number of wolves can be modeled by the function $f(x) = 37x + 7$ where x is the number of years since 1995. Graph the function and identify its domain and range.

INTERPRET MODELS The rate of change in the wolf population actually varied over time. The model simplifies the situation by assuming a steady rate of change.

Solution

To graph the function, make a table.

x	$f(x)$
0	$37(0) + 7 = 7$
1	$37(1) + 7 = 44$
2	$37(2) + 7 = 81$

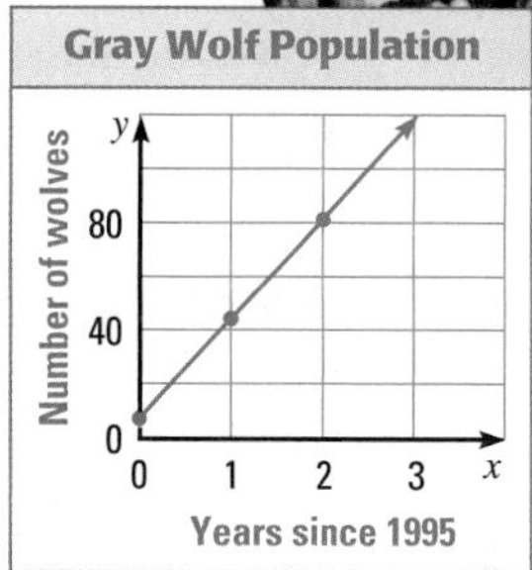

The domain of the function is $x \geq 0$. From the graph or table, you can see that the range of the function is $f(x) \geq 7$.

✓ GUIDED PRACTICE for Examples 2 and 3

2. **WOLF POPULATION** Use the model from Example 3 to find the value of x so that $f(x) = 155$. *Explain* what the solution means in this situation.
4; in 1999, 4 years after 1995, the wolf population will be 155.

FAMILIES OF FUNCTIONS A **family of functions** is a group of functions with similar characteristics. For example, functions that have the form $f(x) = mx + b$ constitute the family of *linear* functions.

IDENTIFY PARAMETERS Particular members of the family of linear functions are determined by the values of m and b, called *parameters*, in the general form $y = mx + b$.

KEY CONCEPT *For Your Notebook*

Parent Function for Linear Functions

The most basic linear function in the family of all linear functions, called the **parent linear function**, is:

$$f(x) = x$$

The graph of the parent linear function is shown.

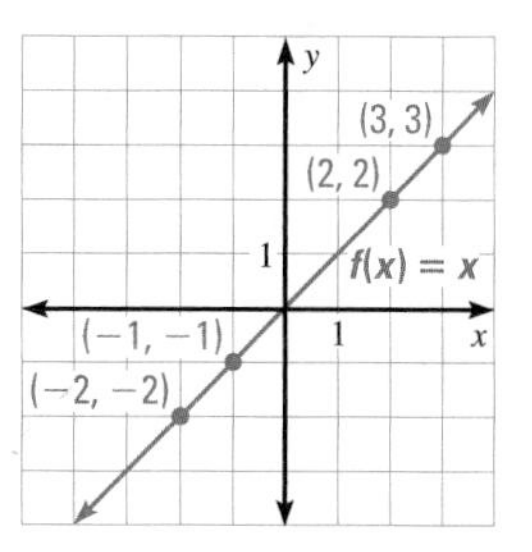

READING The parent linear function is also called the *identity function*.

Motivating the Lesson

You are comparing the costs of two veterinarians for the care of your horses. One veterinarian charges \$50 per house call plus \$25 per hour. Another charges \$25 per house call plus \$45 per hour. By learning how to use function notation, you can compare the two rates by graphing both functions on the same coordinate plane.

3 TEACH

Extra Example 1

What is the value of the function $f(x) = 2x + 12$ when $x = -8$? **B**

Ⓐ -12 Ⓑ -4
Ⓒ 4 Ⓓ 28

Extra Example 2

For the function $f(x) = -2x + 4$, find the value of x so that $f(x) = 16$. **−6**

Key Question to Ask for Example 2

- How is Example 2 different from Example 1? **In Example 1, x is replaced with a number to find $f(x)$; and in Example 2, $f(x)$ is replaced with a number to find x.**

Extra Example 3

A bowling alley charges \$5 to rent shoes and \$4 per game. The cost after playing x games is given by $f(x) = 4x + 5$. Graph the function and identify its domain and range.

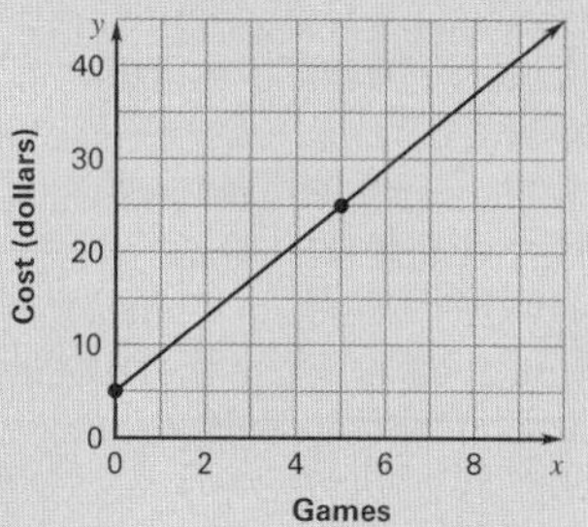

domain: $x \geq 0$; range: $f(x) \geq 5$

Differentiated Instruction

Kinesthetic Learners Explain that $y = x$ is called the *parent function* because any linear function can be obtained by changing the slope from 1 and moving the y-intercept from 0. Changing m and b in the linear function $f(x) = mx + b$ generates the family of linear functions. Draw a line on a transparency and place it on a grid to show the graph of $y = x$. Then show how this can be used to create any line on the coordinate plane by moving the transparency.

See also the *Differentiated Instruction Resources* for more strategies.

Extra Example 4

Graph the function. Compare the graph with the graph of $f(x) = x$.

a. $g(x) = -2x$

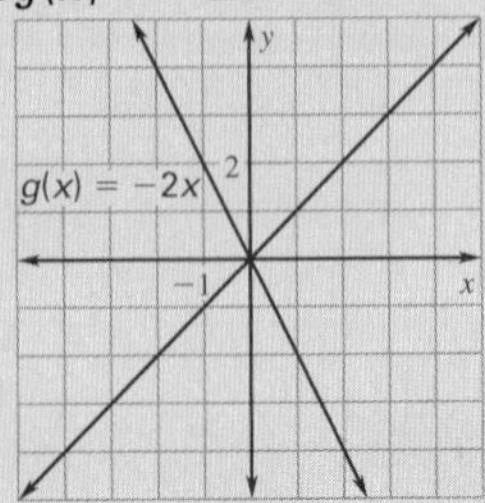

The graph of f has a positive slope, whereas the graph of g has a negative slope. The y-intercept for both graphs is 0, so both lines of pass through the origin.

b. $h(x) = \frac{1}{2}x$

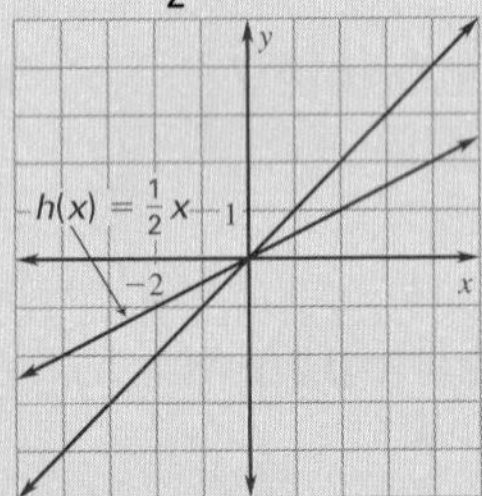

Because the slope of the graph of h is less than the slope of the graph of f, the graph of h is less steep than the graph of f. The lines of both graphs pass through the origin, since they have the same y-intercept of 0.

Key Questions to Ask for Example 4

- How can you describe the graphs of g and h in parts a and b in terms of changes in m and b from the graph of $f(x) = mx + b$? **For g, m remains the same, while b changes. For h, m changes and b remains the same.**
- What is another graph that would be parallel to the graph of f in part a? ***Sample answer:* $k(x) = x - 3$**

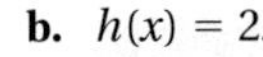

EXAMPLE 4 Compare graphs with the graph $f(x) = x$

Graph the function. Compare the graph with the graph of $f(x) = x$.

a. $g(x) = x + 3$ **b.** $h(x) = 2x$

Solution

a.

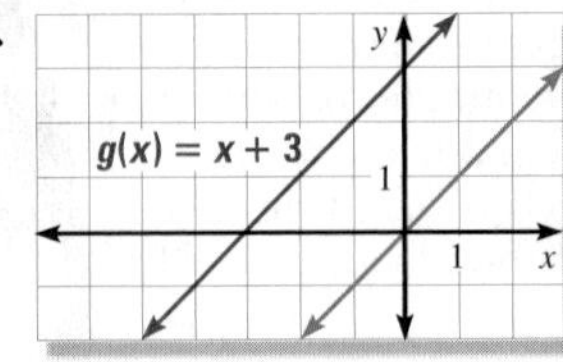

Because the graphs of g and f have the same slope, $m = 1$, the lines are parallel. Also, the y-intercept of the graph of g is 3 more than the y-intercept of the graph of f.

b.

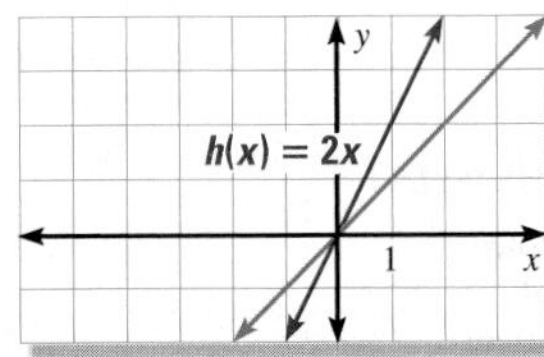

Because the slope of the graph of h is greater than the slope of the graph of f, the graph of h rises faster from left to right. The y-intercept for both graphs is 0, so both lines pass through the origin.

GUIDED PRACTICE for Example 4

3. Graph $h(x) = -3x$. Compare the graph with the graph of $f(x) = x$.
See margin for art; since the slope of the graph of h is negative the graph of h falls from left to right. The y-intercept for both graphs is 0, so both lines pass through the origin.

CONCEPT SUMMARY — For Your Notebook

Comparing Graphs of Linear Functions with the Graph of $f(x) = x$

Changing m or b in the general linear function $g(x) = mx + b$ creates families of linear functions whose graphs are related to the graph of $f(x) = x$.

$g(x) = x + b$

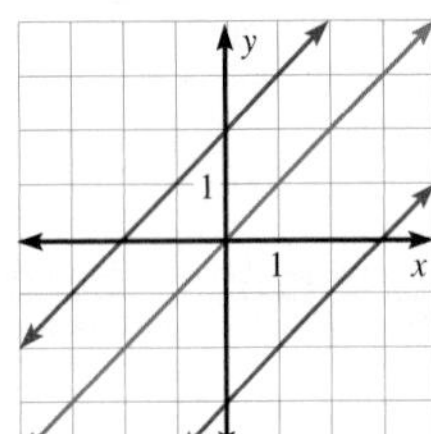

- The graphs have the same slope, but different y-intercepts.
- Graphs of this family are vertical translations of the graph of $f(x) = x$.

$g(x) = mx$ where $m > 0$

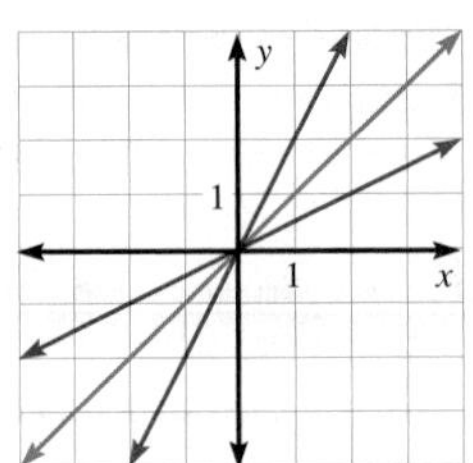

- The graphs have different (positive) slopes, but the same y-intercept.
- Graphs of this family are vertical stretches or shrinks of the graph of $f(x) = x$.

$g(x) = mx$ where $m < 0$

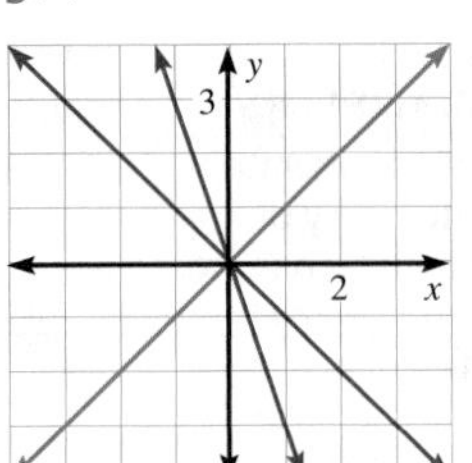

- The graphs have different (negative) slopes, but the same y-intercept.
- Graphs of this family are vertical stretches or shrinks with reflections in the x-axis of the graph of $f(x) = x$.

3.

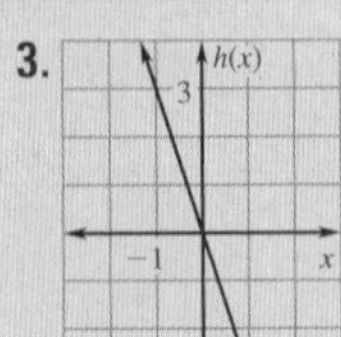

EXAMPLE 5 Graph real-world functions

CABLE A cable company charges new customers $40 for installation and $60 per month for its service. The cost to the customer is given by the function $f(x) = 60x + 40$ where x is the number of months of service. To attract new customers, the cable company reduces the installation fee to $5. A function for the cost with the reduced installation fee is $g(x) = 60x + 5$. Graph both functions. How is the graph of g related to the graph of f?

Solution

The graphs of both functions are shown. Both functions have a slope of 60, so they are parallel. The y-intercept of the graph of g is 35 less than the graph of f. So, the graph of g is a vertical translation of the graph of f.

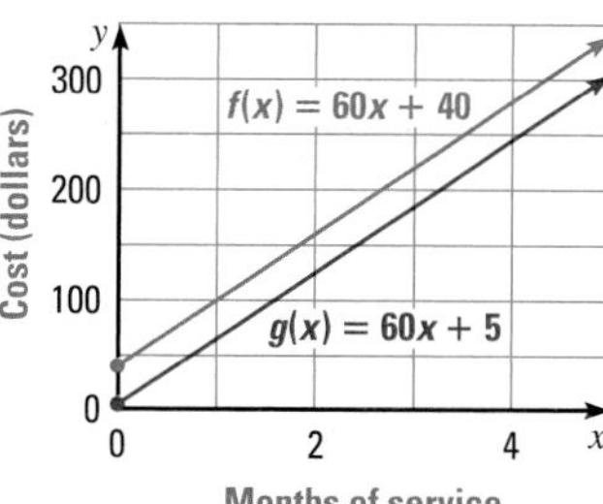

REVIEW TRANSFORMATIONS
For help with transformations, see pp. 922–923.

GUIDED PRACTICE for Example 5

4. **WHAT IF?** In Example 5, suppose the monthly fee is $70 so that the cost to the customer is given by $h(x) = 70x + 40$. Graph f and h in the same coordinate plane. How is the graph of h related to the graph of f?
See margin for art; since the slope of the graph of h is greater than the slope of the graph of f, the graph of h rises faster from left to right. The y-intercept for both graphs is 40, so both lines pass through (0, 40).

4.7 EXERCISES

HOMEWORK KEY
○ = **WORKED-OUT SOLUTIONS** on p. WS10 for Exs. 3, 17, and 39
★ = **STANDARDIZED TEST PRACTICE** Exs. 2, 13, 22, 35, 36, 44, and 45

SKILL PRACTICE

A

1. **VOCABULARY** When you write the function $y = 3x + 12$ as $f(x) = 3x + 12$, you are using __?__. **function notation**

2. ★ **WRITING** Would the functions $f(x) = -9x + 12$, $g(x) = -9x - 2$, and $h(x) = -9x$ be considered a family of functions? *Explain.* **Yes; they are all linear functions.**

EXAMPLE 1 on p. 262 for Exs. 3–13

EVALUATING FUNCTIONS Evaluate the function when $x = -2, 0,$ and 3.

3. $f(x) = 12x + 1$ **−23, 1, 37**
4. $g(x) = -3x + 5$ **11, 5, −4**
5. $p(x) = -8x - 2$ **14, −2, −26**
6. $h(x) = 2.25x$ **−4.5, 0, 6.75**
7. $m(x) = -6.5x$ **13, 0, −19.5**
8. $f(x) = -0.75x - 1$ **0.5, −1, −3.25**
9. $s(x) = \frac{2}{5}x + 3$ **$2\frac{1}{5}, 3, 4\frac{1}{5}$**
10. $d(x) = -\frac{3}{2}x + 5$ **$8, 5, \frac{1}{2}$**
11. $h(x) = \frac{3}{4}x - 6$ **$-7\frac{1}{2}, -6, -3\frac{3}{4}$**

12. **ERROR ANALYSIS** *Describe* and correct the error in evaluating the function $g(x) = -5x + 3$ when $x = -3$. **$g(-3)$ does not mean multiply −3 and g, it means to find the value of the function when $g = -3$, $g(-3) = 18$.**

$g(-3) = -5(-3) + 3$
$-3g = 18$
$g = -6$

Extra Example 5

A state park charges $5 per car as an entrance fee. The amount collected is given by the function $f(x) = 5x$. The park recently restructured its fees and now charges $10 per car. The function for the new fee is $g(x) = 10x$. Graph both functions. How is the graph of g related to the graph of f?

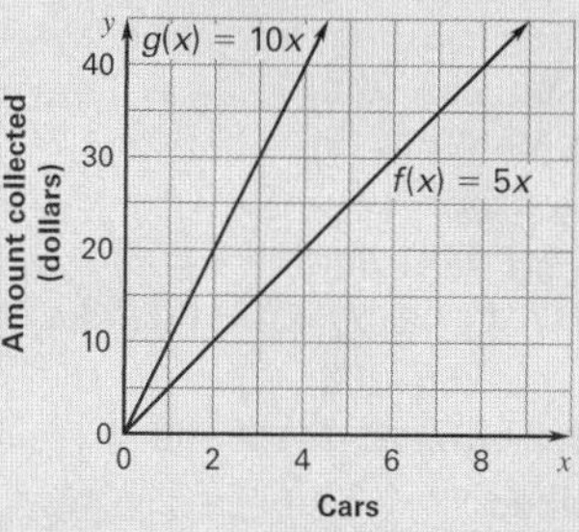

Both functions have the same y-intercept of 0. They have different slopes. The slope of the graph of g is steeper than the graph of f, so the graph of g is a vertical stretch of the graph of f.

Closing the Lesson

Have students summarize the major points of the lesson and answer the Essential Question: What is function notation?

- **$f(x)$ means "the value of f at x" and is function notation for y.**
- **Graphs of linear functions can be analyzed and categorized in terms of their relation to the graph of $f(x) = x$.**

Function notation is the use of $f(x)$ to replace y in functions. $f(x)$ represents the range of the function f for all values of x in its domain, so $f(3)$ represents the value of the function when $x = 3$. You can use g, h, and other letters to name functions.

4.
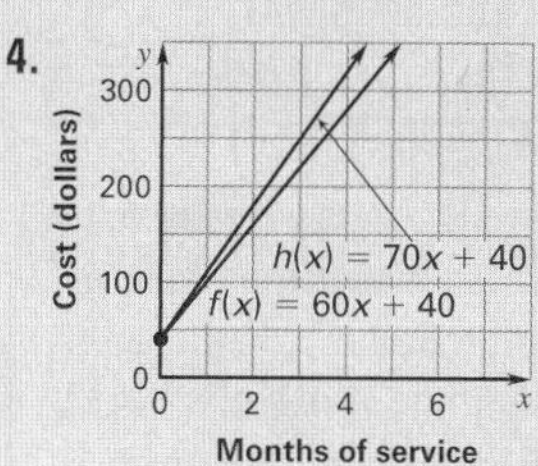

4 PRACTICE AND APPLY

Assignment Guide

Answer Transparencies available for all exercises

Basic:
Day 1: pp. 265–268
Exs. 1, 3–11 odd, 12–18, 39–41, 46–54
Day 2: pp. 265–268
Exs. 2, 19–29, 42, 55–60

Average:
Day 1: pp. 265–268
Exs. 1, 7–13, 16–22, 39–41, 46–54
Day 2: pp. 265–268
Exs. 2, 27–37, 42–44, 55–60

Advanced:
Day 1: pp. 265–268
Exs. 1, 7–11, 13, 17–22, 37–41*, 46–54 even
Day 2: pp. 265–268
Exs. 2, 28–36, 42–45*, 55–60

Block:
pp. 265–268
Exs. 1, 2, 7–13, 16–22, 27–37, 39–44, 46–60

Differentiated Instruction

See *Differentiated Instruction Resources* for suggestions on addressing the needs of a diverse classroom.

Homework Check

For a quick check of student understanding of key concepts, go over the following exercises:

Basic: 5, 16, 24, 39, 42
Average: 8, 18, 28, 40, 42
Advanced: 9, 20, 31, 41, 43

Extra Practice

- Student Edition, p. 941
- Chapter Resource Book: Practice levels A, B, C

Practice Worksheet

An easily-readable reduced practice page (with answers) for this lesson can be found on p. 204F.

23–34, 36a–c. See Additional Answers beginning on p. AA1.

---

13. ★ **MULTIPLE CHOICE** Given $f(x) = -6.8x + 5$, what is the value of $f(-2)$? **D**

Ⓐ -18.6 Ⓑ -8.6 Ⓒ 8.6 Ⓓ 18.6

EXAMPLE 2 on p. 262 for Exs. 14–22

FINDING X-VALUES Find the value of x so that the function has the given value.

14. $f(x) = 6x + 9;\ 3$ **−1**
15. $g(x) = -x + 5;\ 2$ **3**
16. $h(x) = -7x + 12;\ -9$ **3**
(17.) $j(x) = 4x + 11;\ -13$ **−6**
18. $m(x) = 9x - 5;\ -2$ **$\frac{1}{3}$**
19. $n(x) = -2x - 21;\ -6$ **−7.5**
20. $p(x) = -12x - 36;\ -3$ **−2.75**
21. $q(x) = 8x - 32;\ -4$ **3.5**

22. ★ **MULTIPLE CHOICE** What value of x makes $f(x) = 5$ if $f(x) = -2x + 25$? **C**

Ⓐ -15 Ⓑ -10 Ⓒ 10 Ⓓ 15

EXAMPLE 4 on p. 264 for Exs. 23–34

B **TRANSFORMATIONS OF LINEAR FUNCTIONS Graph the function. Compare the graph with the graph of $f(x) = x$.** **23–34. See margin.**

23. $g(x) = x + 5$
24. $h(x) = 6 + x$
25. $q(x) = x - 1$
26. $m(x) = x - 6$
27. $d(x) = x + 7$
28. $t(x) = x - 3$
29. $r(x) = 4x$
30. $w(x) = 5x$
31. $h(x) = -3x$
32. $k(x) = -6x$
33. $g(x) = \frac{1}{3}x$
34. $m(x) = -\frac{7}{2}x$

35. ★ **MULTIPLE CHOICE** The graph of which function is shown? **B**

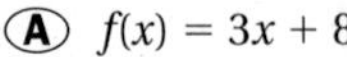

Ⓐ $f(x) = 3x + 8$
Ⓑ $f(x) = 3x - 8$
Ⓒ $f(x) = 8x + 3$
Ⓓ $f(x) = 8x - 3$

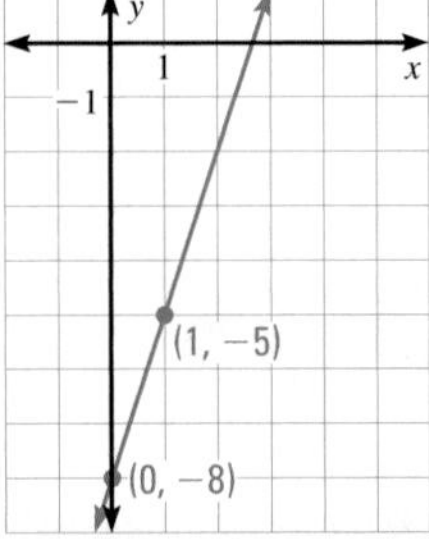

36. ★ **OPEN-ENDED** In this exercise you will compare the graphs of linear functions when their slopes and y-intercepts are changed.

a. Choose a linear function of the form $f(x) = mx + b$ where $m \neq 0$. Then graph the function. ***Sample answer:* $f(x) = 2x + 3$; see margin for art.**

b. Using the same m and b values as in part (a), graph the function $g(x) = 2mx + b$. How are the slope and y-intercept of the graph of g related to the slope and y-intercept of the graph of f? **See margin.**

c. Using the same m and b values as in part (a), graph the function $h(x) = mx + (b - 3)$. How are the slope and y-intercept of the graph of h related to the slope and y-intercept of the graph of f? **See margin.**

C 37. **REASONING** How is the graph of $g(x) = 1$ related to the graph of $h(x) = -1$? **Since the graphs of g and h have the same slope, $m = 0$, the lines are parallel. The y-intercept of the graph of h is 2 less than the y-intercept of the graph of g.**

38. **CHALLENGE** Suppose that $f(x) = 4x + 7$ and $g(x) = 2x$. What is a rule for $g(f(x))$? What is a rule for $f(g(x))$? **$8x + 14$; $8x + 7$**

○ = **WORKED-OUT SOLUTIONS on p. WS1**   ★ = **STANDARDIZED TEST PRACTICE**

PROBLEM SOLVING

EXAMPLE 3 A on p. 263 for Exs. 39–41

39a. See margin for art; domain: $0 \le x \le 20$, range: $2.75 \le f(x) \le 4.75$.

39b. 18; in 1998, 18 years after 1980, the price of a movie ticket was $4.55.

39. **MOVIE TICKETS** The average price of a movie ticket in the United States from 1980 to 2000 can be modeled by the function $f(x) = 0.10x + 2.75$ where x is the number of years since 1980.

    a. Graph the function and identify its domain and range.

    b. Find the value of x so that $f(x) = 4.55$. *Explain* what the solution means in this situation.

@HomeTutor for problem solving help at classzone.com

40a. See margin for art; domain: $0 \le x \le 5$, range: $330 \le f(x) \le 21{,}580$

40. **DVD PLAYERS** The number (in thousands) of DVD players sold in the United States from 1998 to 2003 can be modeled by $f(x) = 4250x + 330$ where x is the number of years since 1998.

    a. Graph the function and identify its domain and range.

    b. Find the value of x so that $f(x) = 13{,}080$. *Explain* what the solution means in this situation.

@HomeTutor for problem solving help at classzone.com

3; in 2001, 3 years after 1998, the number of DVD players sold was 13,080,000.

41. See margin for art; domain: $x \ge 0$, range: $d(x) \ge 0$; 1.5 h; substitute 15 for $d(x)$ to get the equation $15 = 10x$, solve for x.

41. **IN-LINE SKATING** An in-line skater's average speed is 10 miles per hour. The distance traveled after skating for x hours is given by the function $d(x) = 10x$. Graph the function and identify its domain and range. How long did it take the skater to travel 15 miles? *Explain.*

Animated Algebra at classzone.com

EXAMPLE 5 B on p. 265 for Exs. 42–43

42. **HOME SECURITY** A home security company charges new customers $155 for the installation of security equipment and a monthly fee of $40. To attract more customers, the company reduces its installation fee to $75. The functions below give the total cost for x months of service:

    Regular fee: $f(x) = 40x + 155$ **Reduced fee:** $g(x) = 40x + 75$

    Graph both functions. How is the graph of g related to the graph of f? **See margin.**

43. **THEATERS** A ticket for a play at a theater costs $16. The revenue (in dollars) generated from the sale of x tickets is given by $s(x) = 16x$. The theater managers raise the cost of tickets to $20. The revenue generated from the sale of x tickets at that price is given by $r(x) = 20x$. Graph both functions. How is the graph of r related to the graph of s? **See margin.**

C

44. ★ **EXTENDED RESPONSE** The cost of supplies, such as mustard and napkins, a pretzel vendor needs for one day is $75. Each pretzel costs the vendor $.50 to make. The total daily cost to the vendor is given by $C(x) = 0.5x + 75$ where x is the number of pretzels the vendor makes.

    a. **Graph** Graph the cost function. **See margin.**

    b. **Graph** The vendor sells each pretzel for $3. The revenue is given by $R(x) = 3x$ where x is the number of pretzels sold. Graph the function. **See margin.**

    c. **Explain** The vendor's profit is the difference of the revenue and the cost. *Explain* how you could use the graphs to find the vendor's profit for any given number of pretzels made and sold.
    ***Sample answer:* Find the values of y on each graph for any value of x. Subtract $C(x)$ from $R(x)$ to find the vendor's profit.**

Teaching Strategy

Exercises 3–11 To remind students that $f(x)$ does not mean f times x, you may wish to have them write the function name with x replaced by -2, 0, and 3. For example, students would write $f(-2) = -23$, $f(0) = 1$, and $f(3) = 37$ when answering Exercise 3.

Exercises 23–34 You may want to review the concept box on page 264 before the students begin these exercises. Ask students to give examples of vertical stretches and shrinks with and without reflections.

Reading Strategy

Exercises 14–21 Tell students to read the instruction line for the exercises carefully. They may want to review Examples 1 and 2 so they are clear on the difference between finding an x-value and finding the value of a function for a given x-value.

An **Animated Algebra** activity is available online for **Exercise 41**. This activity is also part of **Power Presentations**.

42, 43. See Additional Answers beginning on p. AA1.

44a.

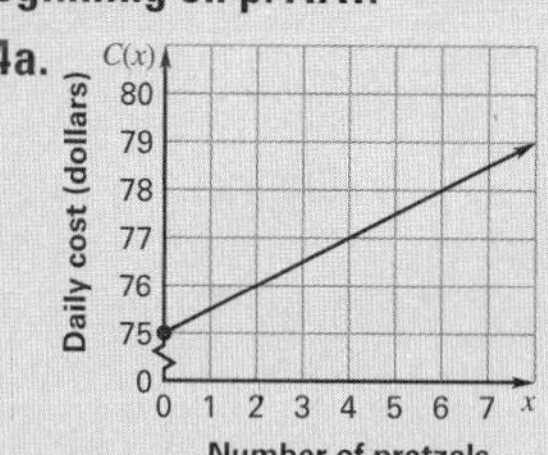

44b.

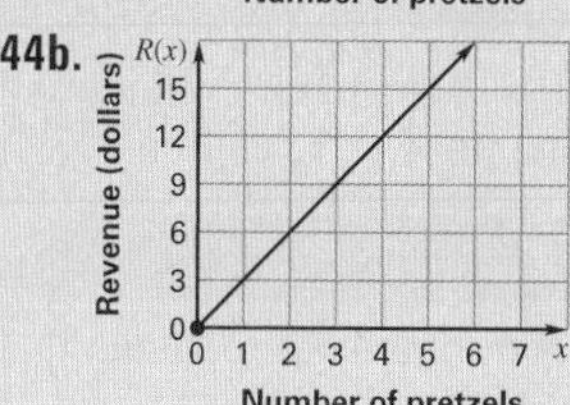

39a.

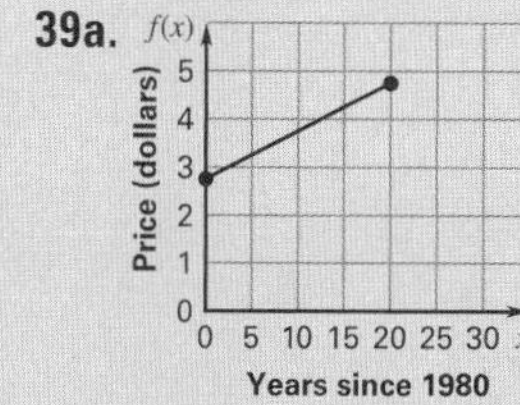

40a.

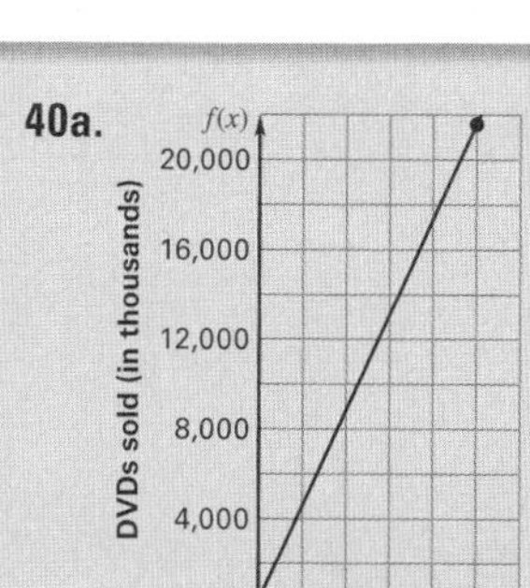

41.

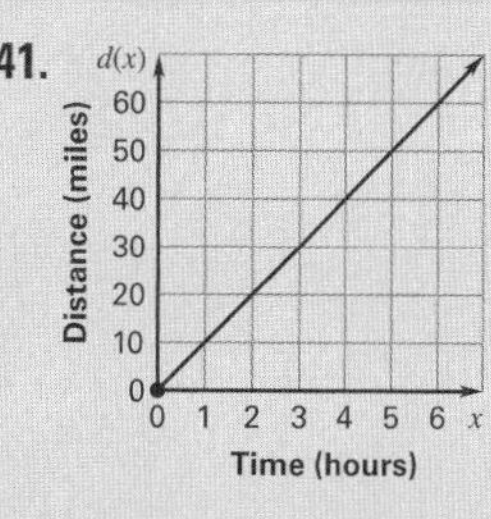

5 ASSESS AND RETEACH

Daily Homework Quiz

Transparency Available

1. Evaluate $f(x) = 8x - 4$ when $x = -3, 0,$ and 2. **−28, −4, 12**
2. Find the value of x so $g(x) = -2x + 1$ has the value -3. **2**
3. A stable charges $25 for feed and $50 per day to stable horses. The cost is given by $f(x) = 50x + 25$. Recently, the stable raised its fee for food to $50. The new fee is given by $g(x) = 50x + 50$. Graph the functions and then compare the two graphs.

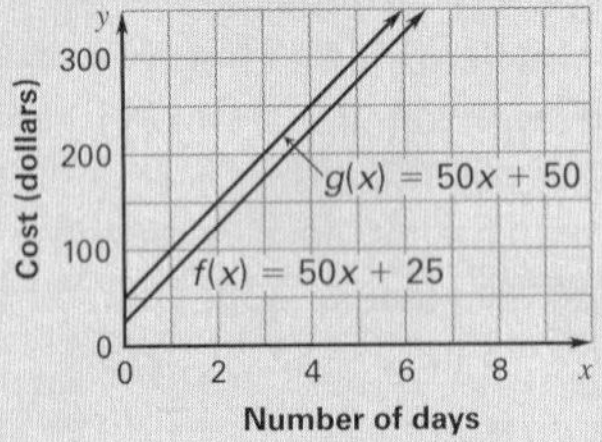

The graphs have the same slope. The y-intercept of g is 25 units greater than that of f, so g is a vertical translation.

Available at **classzone.com**

Diagnosis/Remediation

- Practice A, B, C in Chapter Resource Book
- Study Guide in Chapter Resource Book
- Practice Workbook
- @HomeTutor

Challenge

Additional challenge is available in the Chapter Resource Book.

Quiz

An easily-readable reduced copy of the quiz (with answers) on Lessons 4.6–4.7 from the Assessment Book can be found on p. 204G.

45b, Quiz 8, 9. See Additional Answers beginning on p. AA1.

45. ★ **EXTENDED RESPONSE** The number of hours of daylight in Austin, Texas, during the month of March can be modeled by the function $\ell(x) = 0.03x + 11.5$ where x is the day of the month.

 a. **Graph** Graph the function and identify its domain and range. **See graph in part (b); domain: $1 \le x \le 31$, range: $11.53 \le \ell(x) \le 12.43$**

 b. **Graph** The number of hours of darkness can be modeled by the function $d(x) = 24 - \ell(x)$. Graph the function on the same coordinate plane as you used in part (a). Identify its domain and range. **See margin for art; domain: $11.53 \le \ell(x) \le 12.43$, range: $11.57 \le d(x) \le 12.47$**

 c. **CHALLENGE** *Explain* how you could have obtained the graph of d from the graph of ℓ using translations and reflections. **The graph of d is a reflection of the line ℓ.**

 d. **CHALLENGE** What does the point where the graphs intersect mean in terms of the number of hours of daylight and darkness?
 The number of hours of daylight equals the number of hours of darkness.

MIXED REVIEW

Solve the equation or proportion.

46. $y - 7 = -3$ *(p. 134)* **4**
47. $4.5m = 49.5$ *(p. 134)* **11**
48. $4z + 5z = -36$ *(p. 141)* **−4**
49. $5(x - 4) = 20$ *(p. 148)* **8**
50. $3t + 4 + 5t = -4$ *(p. 148)* **−1**
51. $-5g = 3(g - 8)$ *(p. 154)* **3**
52. $9n = 4(2n + 1)$ *(p. 154)* **4**
53. $\frac{7}{6} = \frac{t}{42}$ *(p. 168)* **49**
54. $\frac{5}{6} = \frac{p}{15}$ *(p. 168)* **12.5**

PREVIEW
Prepare for Lesson 5.1 in Exs. 55–60.

Write the equation in slope-intercept form. Then graph the equation. *(p. 244)* **55–60. See margin for art.**

55. $x + 6y = 12$ **$y = -\frac{1}{6}x + 2$**
56. $5x + y = -10$ **$y = -5x - 10$**
57. $2x - 2y = 3$ **$y = x - \frac{3}{2}$**
58. $-2x - 3y = 21$ **$y = -\frac{2}{3}x - 7$**
59. $-4x - 3y = -18$ **$y = -\frac{4}{3}x + 6$**
60. $2x - y = 10$ **$y = 2x - 10$**

QUIZ for Lessons 4.6–4.7

Given that y varies directly with x, use the specified values to write a direct variation equation that relates x and y. *(p. 253)*

1. $x = 5, y = 10$ **$y = 2x$**
2. $x = 4, y = 6$ **$y = \frac{3}{2}x$**
3. $x = 2, y = -16$ **$y = -8x$**

Evaluate the function. *(p. 262)*

4. $g(x) = 6x - 5$ when $x = 4$ **19**
5. $h(x) = 14x + 7$ when $x = 2$ **35**
6. $j(x) = 0.2x + 12.2$ when $x = 244$ **61**
7. $k(x) = \frac{5}{6}x + \frac{1}{3}$ when $x = 4$ **$3\frac{2}{3}$**

Graph the function. Compare the graph to the graph of $f(x) = x$. *(p. 262)* **8–9. See margin.**

8. $g(x) = -4x$
9. $h(x) = x - 2$

10. **HOURLY WAGE** The table shows the number of hours that you worked for each of three weeks and the amount that you were paid. What is your hourly wage? *(p. 253)* **$7/h**

Hours	12	16	14
Pay (dollars)	84	112	98

55–60. See Additional Answers beginning on p. AA1.

MIXED REVIEW of Problem Solving

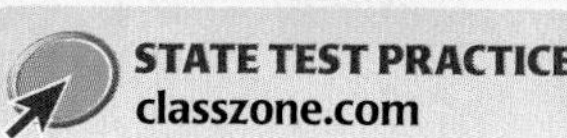

Lessons 4.4–4.7

1. **MULTI-STEP PROBLEM** The amount of drink mix d (in tablespoons) that you need to add to w fluid ounces of water is given by $d = \frac{1}{4}w$.
   a. Graph the equation. **See margin.**
   b. Use the graph to find the amount of drink mix you need if you want to make enough drinks to serve 4 people. Assume 1 serving is 8 fluid ounces. **8 tbsp**

2. **MULTI-STEP PROBLEM** A water park charges \$25 per ticket for adults. Let s be the amount of money the park receives from adult ticket sales, and let t be the number of adult tickets sold.
   a. Write a direct variation equation that relates t and s. **$s = 25t$**
   b. How much money does the park earn when 90 adult tickets are sold? **\$2250**
   c. The park collected \$3325 in adult ticket sales in one day. How many tickets did the park sell? **133 adult tickets**

3. **SHORT RESPONSE** You and your friend are each reading an essay that is 10 pages long. You read at a rate of 1 page per minute. Your friend reads at a rate of $\frac{2}{3}$ page per minute. The models below give the number p of pages you and your friend have left to read after reading for m minutes.

   You: $p = -m + 10$

   Your friend: $p = -\frac{2}{3}m + 10$

   Graph both equations in the same coordinate plane. *Explain* how you can use the graphs to find how many more minutes it took your friend to read the essay than it took you to read the essay. **See margin.**

4. **OPEN-ENDED** Draw a graph that represents going to a movie theater, watching a movie, and returning home from the theater. Let the x-axis represent time and the y-axis represent your distance from home. **See margin.**

5. **EXTENDED RESPONSE** A central observatory averages and then reports the number of sunspots recorded by various observatories. The table shows the average number of sunspots reported by the central observatory in years since 1995.

Years since 1995	Average number of sunspots
0	17.5
2	21.0
4	93.2
6	110.9

   a. Draw a line graph of the data. **See margin.**
   b. During which two-year period was the increase in sunspots the greatest? Find the rate of change for this time period. **1997 to 1999; 36.1 sunspots per year**
   c. During which two-year period was the increase in sunspots the least? Find the rate of change for this time period. **1995 to 1997; 1.75 sunspots per year**
   d. *Explain* how you could find the overall rate of change for the time period shown. **See margin.**

6. **GRIDDED ANSWER** To become a member at a gym, you have to pay a sign-up fee of \$125 and a monthly fee of \$40. To attract new customers, the gym lowers the sign-up fee to \$75. The function f gives the total cost with the regular sign-up fee. The function g gives the total cost with the reduced sign-up fee. The graphs of f and g are shown. The graph of g is a vertical translation of the graph of f by how many units down? **50**

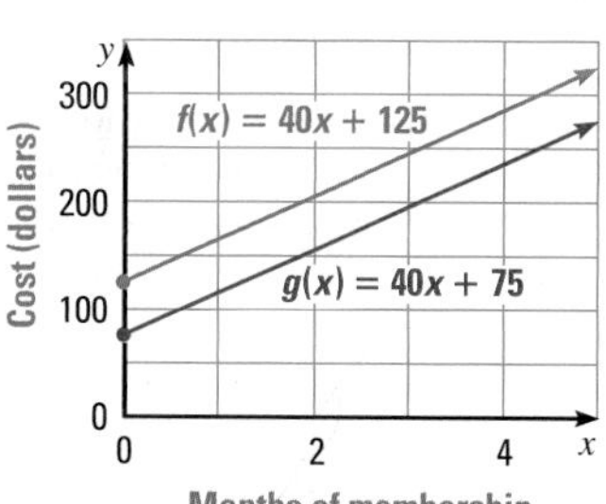

1a.

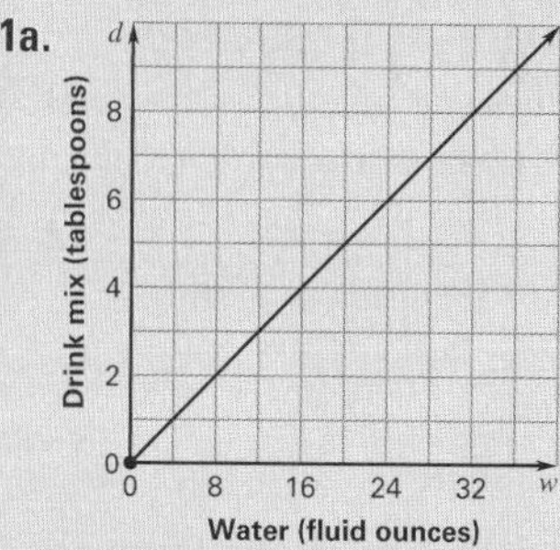

3. See below.

4. *Sample:*

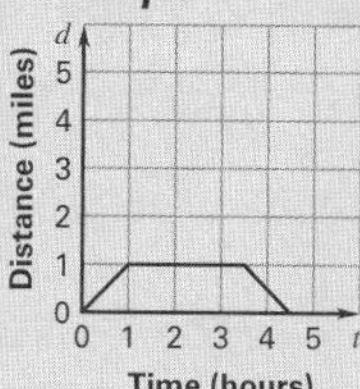

5a.

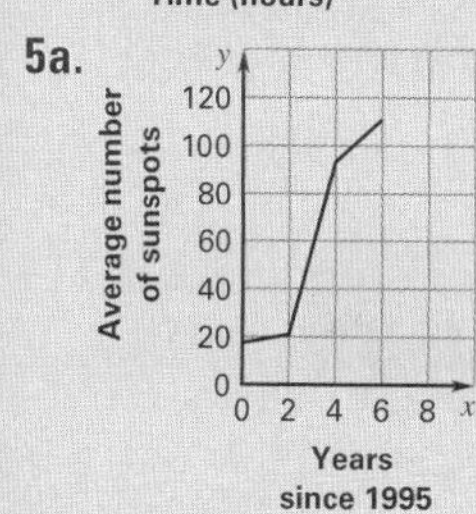

5d. Subtract 17.5 from 110.9 and divide by 6 to find 15.6 sunspots per year.

3.

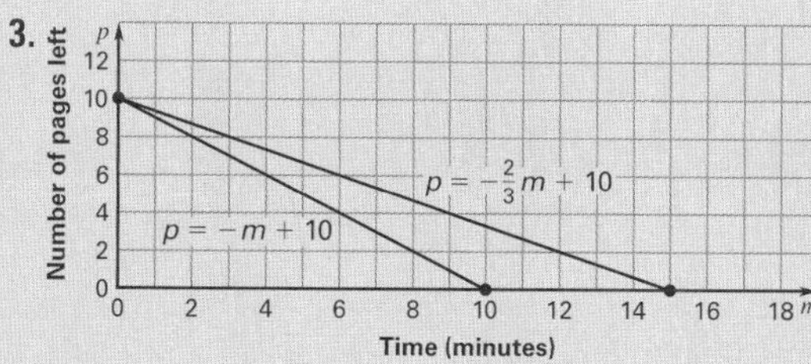

Find the m-intercepts of each line and subtract the m-intercept of your friend's line from the m-intercept of your line to find your friend takes 5 more minutes to read the essay.

4 CHAPTER SUMMARY

Animated Algebra
classzone.com
Electronic Function Library

Additional Resources

The following resources are available to help review the materials in this chapter.

Chapter Resource Book
- Chapter Review Games and Activities
- Cumulative Practice, Ch. 1–4

Student Resources in Spanish

eWorkbook

@HomeTutor

Vocabulary Practice

Vocabulary practice is available at **classzone.com**

BIG IDEAS

For Your Notebook

Big Idea 1

Graphing Linear Equations and Functions Using a Variety of Methods

You can graph a linear equation or function by making a table, using intercepts, or using the slope and *y*-intercept.

A taxi company charges a \$2 fee to pick up a customer plus \$1 per mile to drive to the customer's destination. The total cost *C* (in dollars) that a customer pays to travel *d* miles is given by $C = d + 2$. Graph this function.

Method: Make a table.

d	*C*
0	2
1	3
2	4
3	5

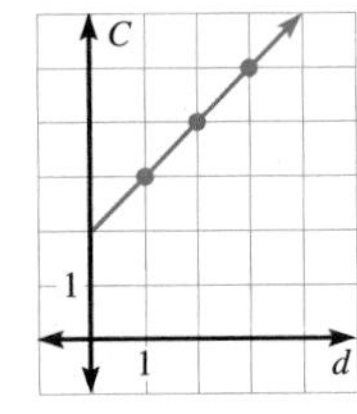

Method: Use slope and *C*-intercept.

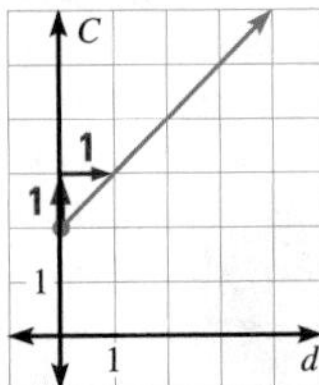

Big Idea 2

Recognizing How Changes in Linear Equations and Functions Affect Their Graphs

When you change the value of *m* or *b* in the equation $y = mx + b$, you produce an equation whose graph is related to the graph of the original equation.

Suppose the taxi company raises its rate to \$1.50 per mile. The total amount that a customer pays is given by $C = 1.5d + 2$. Graph the function.

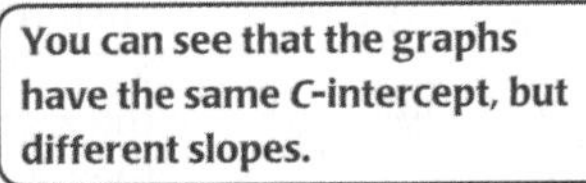

You can see that the graphs have the same C-intercept, but different slopes.

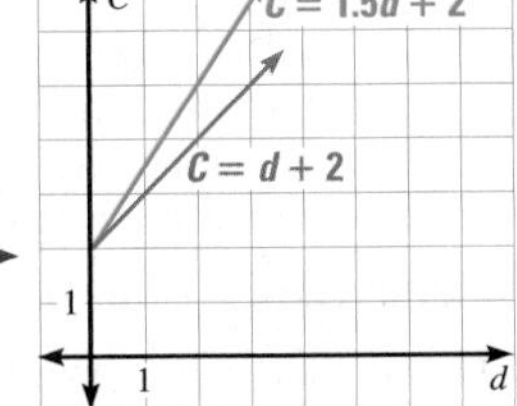

Big Idea 3

Using Graphs of Linear Equations and Functions to Solve Real-world Problems

You can use the graphs of $C = d + 2$ and $C = 1.5d + 2$ to find out how much more a customer pays to travel 4 miles at the new rate than at the old rate.

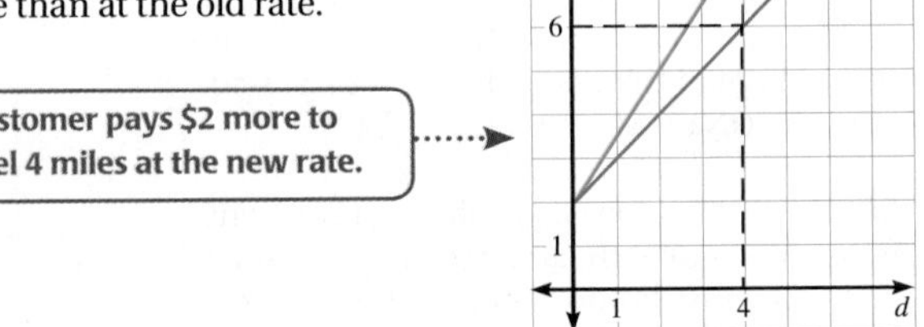

A customer pays $2 more to travel 4 miles at the new rate.
C
8
6
2
1
1
4
d

CHAPTER REVIEW

@HomeTutor
classzone.com
- Multi-Language Glossary
- Vocabulary practice

REVIEW KEY VOCABULARY

- quadrant, *p. 206*
- solution of an equation in two variables, *p. 215*
- graph of an equation in two variables, *p. 215*
- linear equation, *p. 216*
- standard form of a linear equation, *p. 216*
- linear function, *p. 217*
- *x*-intercept, *p. 225*
- *y*-intercept, *p. 225*
- slope, *p. 235*
- rate of change, *p. 237*
- slope-intercept form, *p. 244*
- parallel, *p. 246*
- direct variation, *p. 253*
- constant of variation, *p. 253*
- function notation, *p. 262*
- family of functions, *p. 263*
- parent linear function, *p. 263*

VOCABULARY EXERCISES

1. Copy and complete: The _?_ of a nonvertical line is the ratio of vertical change to horizontal change. **slope**
2. Copy and complete: When you write $y = 2x + 3$ as $f(x) = 2x + 3$, you use _?_. **function notation**
3. **WRITING** *Describe* three different methods you could use to graph the equation $5x + 3y = 12$. ***Sample answer:* Make a table, use intercepts, and use the slope and *y*-intercept.**
4. Tell whether the equation is written in slope-intercept form. If the equation is not in slope-intercept form, write it in slope-intercept form.

   a. $3x + y = 6$ **not slope-intercept form; $y = -3x + 6$**
   b. $y = 5x + 2$ **slope-intercept form**
   c. $x = 4y - 1$ **not slope-intercept form; $y = \frac{1}{4}x + \frac{1}{4}$**
   d. $y = -x + 6$ **slope-intercept form**

REVIEW EXAMPLES AND EXERCISES

Use the review examples and exercises below to check your understanding of the concepts you have learned in each lesson of Chapter 4.

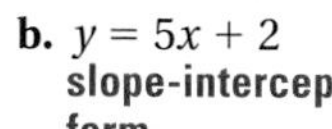

4.1 Plot Points in a Coordinate Plane

pp. 206–212

EXAMPLE

Plot the points $A(-2, 3)$ and $B(0, -2)$ in a coordinate plane. Describe the location of the points.

Point $A(-2, 3)$: Begin at the origin and move 2 units to the left, then 3 units up. Point *A* is in Quadrant II.

Point $B(0, -2)$: Begin at the origin and move 2 units down. Point *B* is on the *y*-axis.

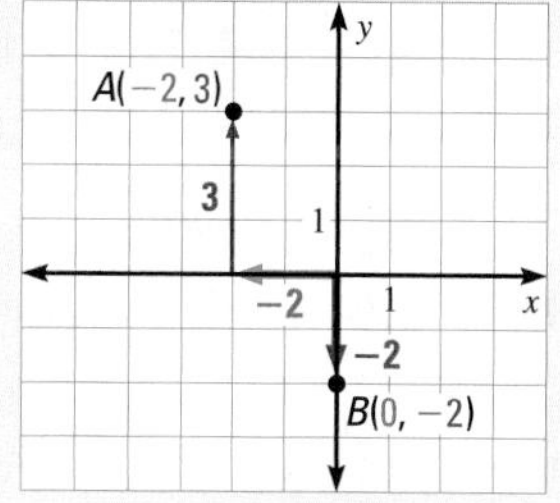

EXERCISES

EXAMPLE 2 on p. 207 for Exs. 5–7

Plot the point in a coordinate plane. *Describe* the location of the point. **5–7. See margin for art.**

5. $A(3, 4)$ **Quadrant I**
6. $B(-5, 0)$ ***x*-axis**
7. $C(-7, -2)$ **Quadrant III**

Extra Example 4.1

Plot the points $A(0, 3)$ and $B(-2, -1)$ in a coordinate plane. Describe the location of the points.

Point $A(0, 3)$: Begin at the origin and move 3 units up. Point *A* is on the *y*-axis.
Point *B*: Begin at the origin and move to the left 2 points, then 1 unit down. Point *B* is in Quadrant III.

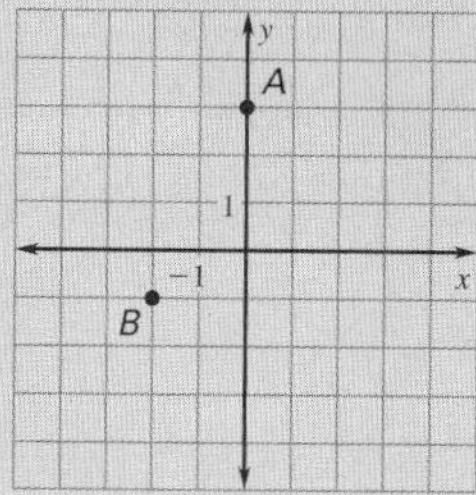

5–7.

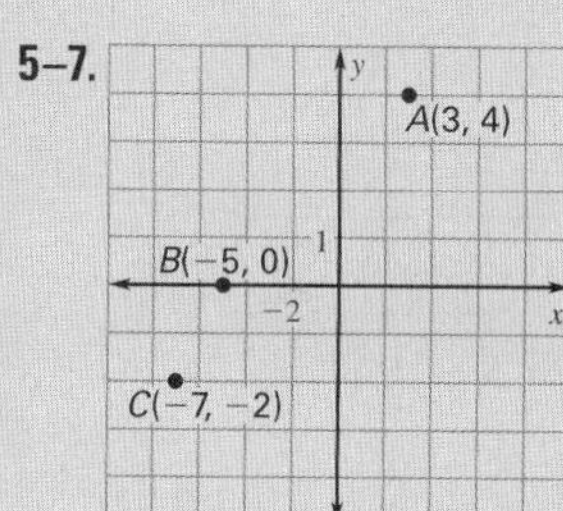

Extra Example 4.2

Graph the equation $y + 2x = -3$.

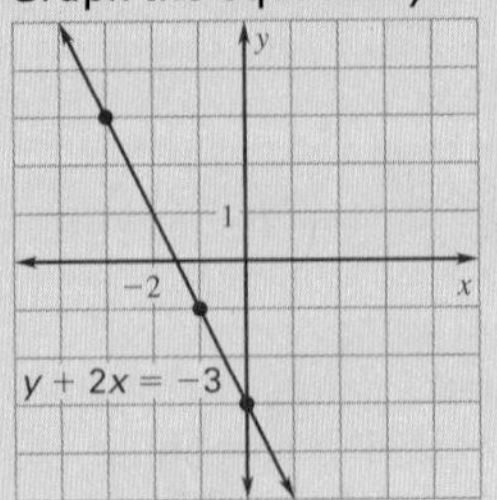

Extra Example 4.3

Graph the equation $-2x + 4y = 12$ using intercepts.

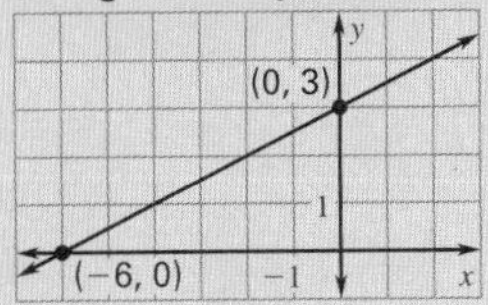

4 CHAPTER REVIEW

4.2 Graph Linear Equations

pp. 215–221

EXAMPLE

Graph the equation $y + 3x = 1$.

STEP 1 **Solve** the equation for y.

$$y + 3x = 1$$

$$y = -3x + 1$$

STEP 2 **Make** a table by choosing a few values for x and finding the values for y.

x	−1	0	1
y	4	1	−2

STEP 3 **Plot** the points.

STEP 4 **Connect** the points by drawing a line through them.

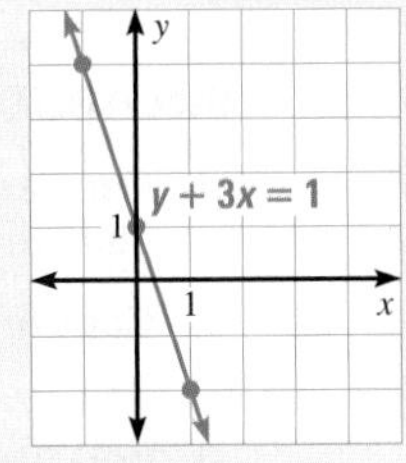

EXERCISES

EXAMPLE 2 on p. 216 for Exs. 8–10

Graph the equation. **8–10. See margin.**

8. $y + 5x = -5$ **9.** $2x + 3y = 9$ **10.** $2y - 14 = 4$

4.3 Graph Using Intercepts

pp. 225–232

EXAMPLE

Graph the equation $-0.5x + 2y = 4$.

STEP 1 **Find** the intercepts.

$$-0.5x + 2y = 4 \qquad -0.5x + 2y = 4$$

$$-0.5x + 2(0) = 4 \qquad -0.5(0) + 2y = 4$$

$$x = -8 \leftarrow x\text{-intercept} \qquad y = 2 \leftarrow y\text{-intercept}$$

STEP 2 **Plot** the points that correspond to the intercepts: $(-8, 0)$ and $(0, 2)$.

STEP 3 **Connect** the points by drawing a line through them.

EXERCISES

EXAMPLES 2 and 4 on pp. 226–227 for Exs. 11–14

Graph the equation. **11–13. See margin.**

11. $-x + 5y = 15$ **12.** $4x + 4y = -16$ **13.** $2x - 6y = 18$

14. CRAFT FAIR You sell necklaces for \$10 and bracelets for \$5 at a craft fair. You want to earn \$50. This situation is modeled by the equation $10n + 5b = 50$ where n is the number of necklaces you sell and b is the number of bracelets you sell. Find the intercepts of the graph of the equation. Then graph the equation. Give three possibilities for the number of bracelets and necklaces that you could sell. ***n*-intercept: 5, *b*-intercept: 10; see margin for art. *Sample answer:* 1 necklace and 8 bracelets, 2 necklaces and 6 bracelets, 3 necklaces and 4 bracelets**

8.–9.

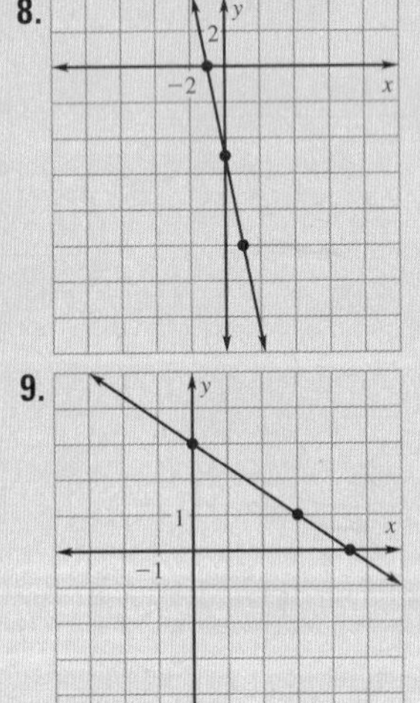

10.–11.

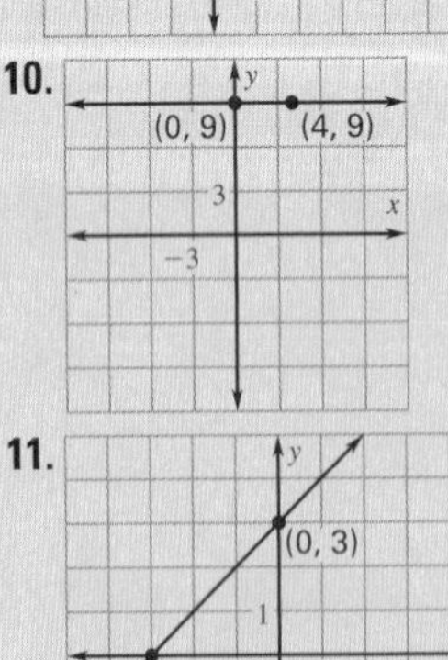

12.

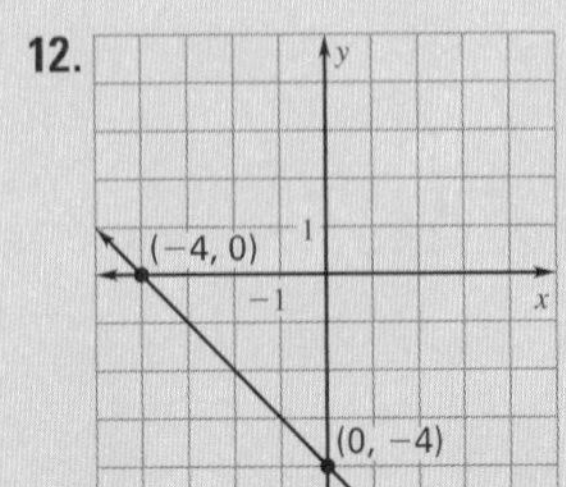

13.

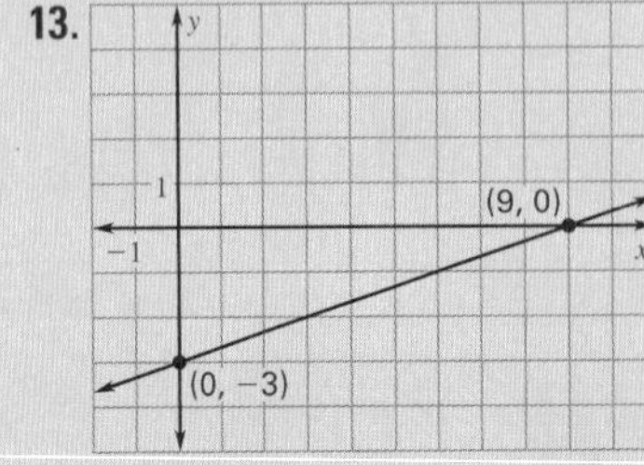

14.

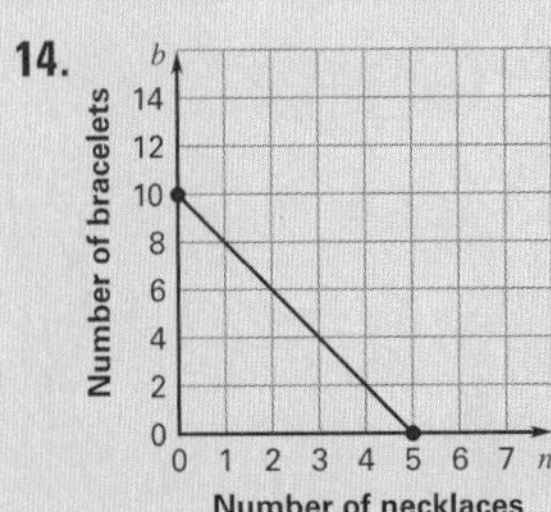

@HomeTutor
classzone.com
Chapter Review Practice

4.4 Find Slope and Rate of Change

pp. 235–242

EXAMPLE

Find the slope of the line shown.

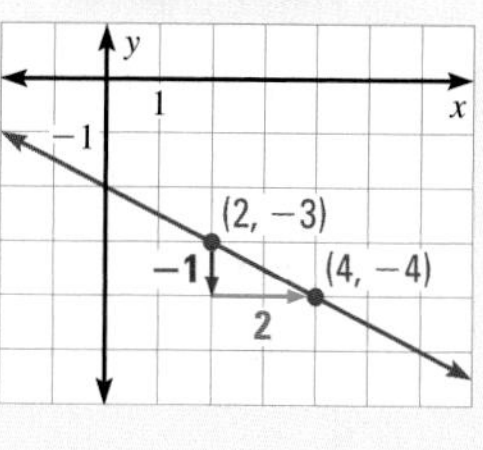

Let $(x_1, y_1) = (2, -3)$ and $(x_2, y_2) = (4, -4)$.

$m = \frac{y_2 - y_1}{x_2 - x_1}$ Write formula for slope.

$= \frac{-4 - (-3)}{4 - 2}$ Substitute values.

$= -\frac{1}{2}$ Simplify.

EXAMPLES 1,2,3, and 4 on pp. 235–236 for Exs. 15–17

EXERCISES

Find the slope of the line that passes through the points.

15. (−1, 11) and (2, 10) $-\frac{1}{3}$
16. (−2, 0) and (4, 9) $\frac{3}{2}$
17. (−5, 4) and (1, −8) −2

4.5 Graph Using Slope-Intercept Form

pp. 244–250

EXAMPLE

Graph the equation $2x + y = -1$.

STEP 1 **Rewrite** the equation in slope-intercept form.

$2x + y = -1 \rightarrow y = -2x - 1$

STEP 2 **Identify** the slope and the y-intercept.

$m = -2$ and $b = -1$

STEP 3 **Plot** the point that corresponds to the y-intercept, (0, −1).

STEP 4 **Use** the slope to locate a second point on the line. Draw a line through the two points.

EXAMPLES 2 and 3 on p. 245 for Exs. 18–21

EXERCISES

Graph the equation. 18–20. See margin.

18. $4x - y = 3$
19. $3x - 6y = 9$
20. $-3x + 4y - 12 = 0$

21. **RUNNING** One athlete can run a 60 meter race at an average rate of 7 meters per second. A second athlete can run the race at an average rate of 6 meters per second. The distance d (in meters) the athletes have left to run after t seconds is given by the following equations:

Athlete 1: $d = -7t + 60$ **Athlete 2:** $d = -6t + 60$

Graph both models in the same coordinate plane. About how many seconds faster does the first athlete finish the race than the second athlete? See margin for art; about 1.4 sec.

Extra Example 4.4

Find the slope of the line shown. $\frac{3}{2}$

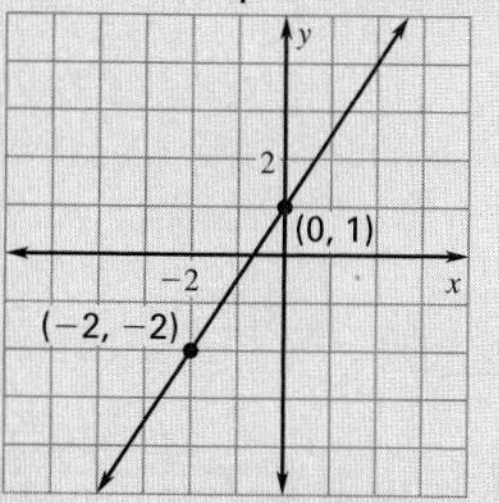

Extra Example 4.5

Graph the equation $3x + y = 2$ using slope-intercept form.

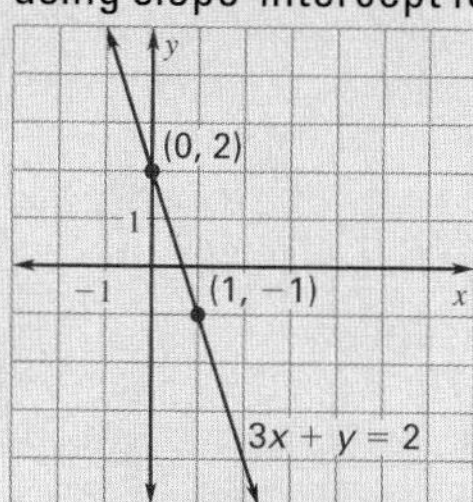

18.
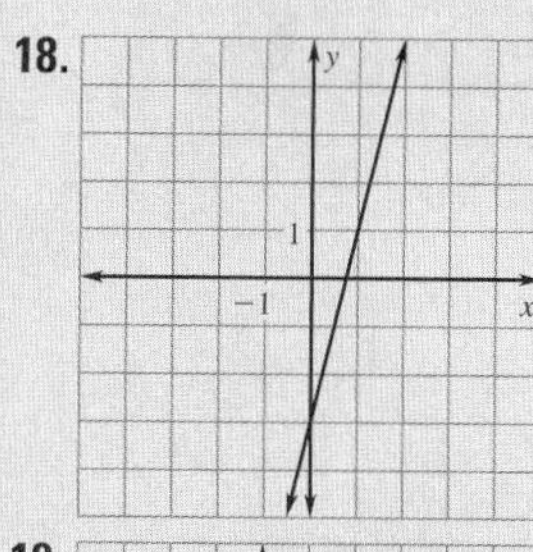

19.
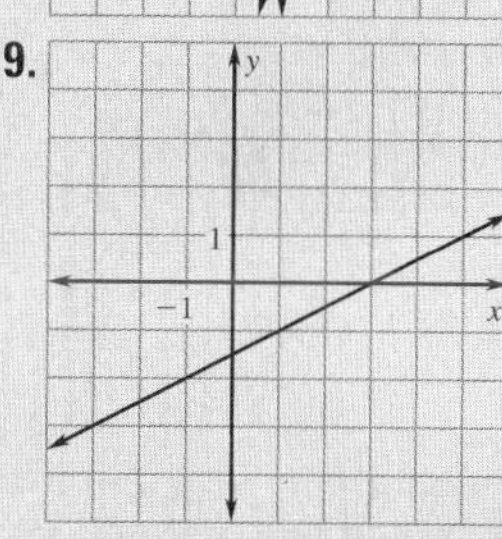

20.
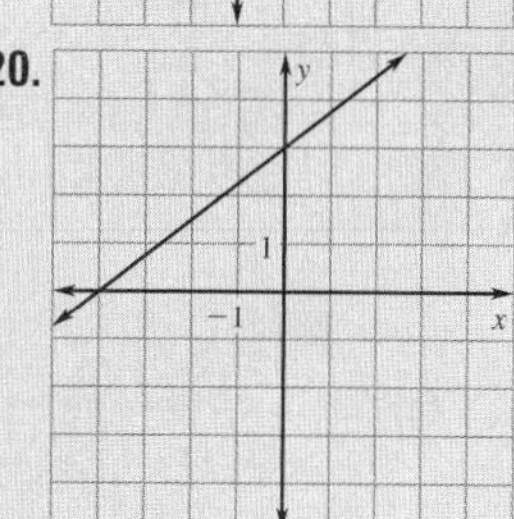

21.
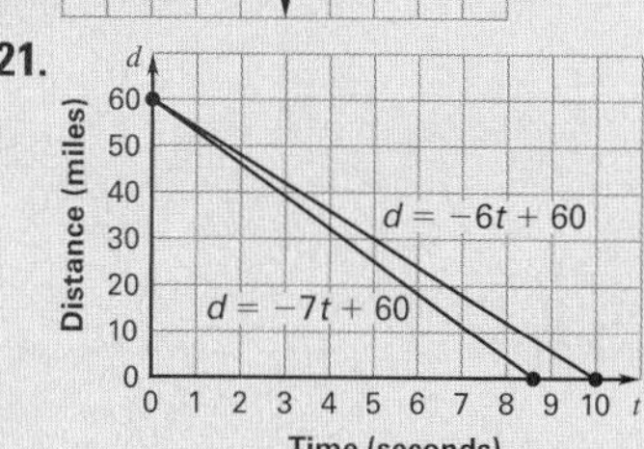

Extra Example 4.6

Graph the direct variation equation $y = \frac{1}{4}x$.

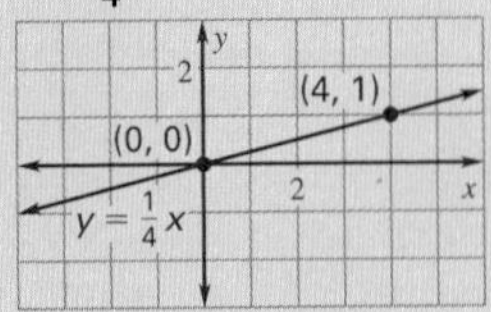

Extra Example 4.7

Evaluate the function $f(x) = 3x + 5$ when $x = -2$. **−1**

25.

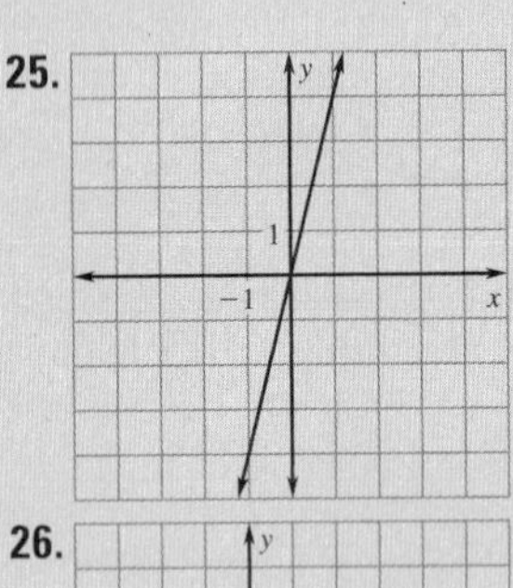

26.

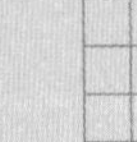

27.

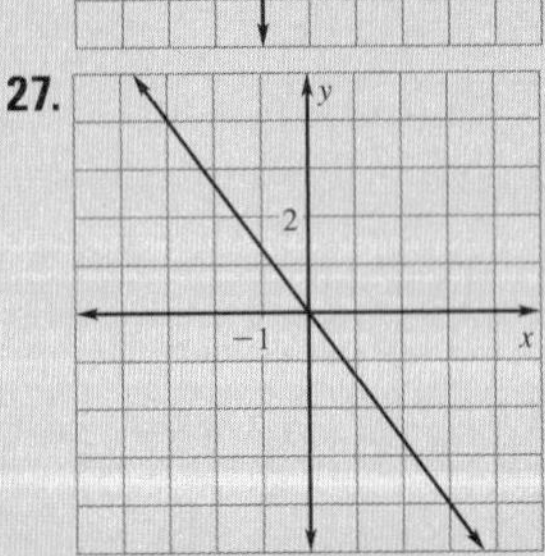

31–33. See Additional Answers beginning on p. AA1.

34.

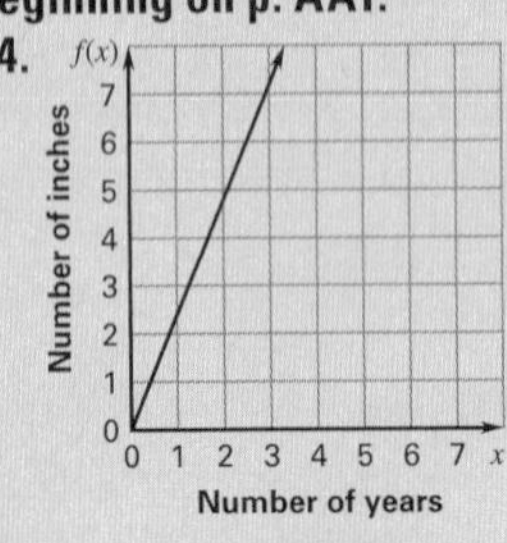

4.6 Model Direct Variation *pp. 253–259*

EXAMPLE

Graph the direct variation equation $y = -\frac{2}{3}x$.

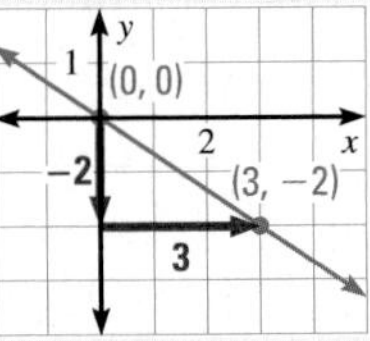

Plot a point at the origin. The slope is equal to the constant of variation, $-\frac{2}{3}$. Find and plot a second point, then draw a line through the points.

EXERCISES

EXAMPLES 1, 2, and 4 on pp. 253–255 for Exs. 22–28

Tell whether the equation represents direct variation. If so, identify the constant of variation.

22. $x - y = 3$ **not direct variation**

23. $x + 2y = 0$ **direct variation; $-\frac{1}{2}$**

24. $8x - 2y = 0$ **direct variation; 4**

Graph the direct variation equation. **25–27. See margin.**

25. $y = 4x$

26. $-5y = 3x$

27. $4x + 3y = 0$

28. SNOWSTORMS The amount s (in inches) of snow that fell during a snowstorm varied directly with the duration d (in hours) of the storm. In the first 2 hours of the storm 5 inches of snow fell. Write a direct variation equation that relates d and s. How many inches of snow fell in 6 hours? **$s = \frac{5}{2}d$; 15 in.**

4.7 Graph Linear Functions *pp. 262–268*

EXAMPLE

Evaluate the function $f(x) = -6x + 5$ when $x = 3$.

$f(x) = -6x + 5$	Write function.
$f(3) = -6(3) + 5$	Substitute 3 for x.
$= -13$	Simplify.

EXERCISES

EXAMPLES 1 and 3 on pp. 262–263 for Exs. 29–34

Evaluate the function.

29. $g(x) = 2x - 3$ when $x = 7$ **11**

30. $h(x) = -\frac{1}{2}x - 7$ when $x = -6$ **−4**

Graph the function. Compare the graph with the graph of $f(x) = x$. **31–33. See margin.**

31. $j(x) = x - 6$

32. $k(x) = -2.5x$

33. $t(x) = 2x + 1$

34. MOUNT EVEREST Mount Everest is rising at a rate of 2.4 inches per year. The number of inches that Mount Everest rises in x years is given by the function $f(x) = 2.4x$. Graph the function and identify its domain and range. Find the value of x so that $f(x) = 250$. *Explain* what the solution means in this situation. **See margin for art; domain: $x \geq 0$, range: $f(x) \geq 0$; about 104; Mount Everest will have grown 250 inches in 104 years.**

Plot the point in a coordinate plane. ***Describe*** **the location of the point.** **1–3. See margin for art.**

1. $A(7, 1)$ **Quadrant I**
2. $B(-4, 0)$ ***x*-axis**
3. $C(3, -9)$ **Quadrant IV**

Draw the line that has the given intercepts. **4–6. See margin.**

4. x-intercept: 2
   y-intercept: -6
5. x-intercept: -1
   y-intercept: 8
6. x-intercept: -3
   y-intercept: -5

Find the slope of the line that passes through the points.

7. (2, 1) and (8, 4) $\frac{1}{2}$
8. $(-2, 7)$ and $(0, -1)$ **−4**
9. (3, 5) and (3, 14) **undefined**

Identify the slope and *y*-intercept of the line with the given equation.

10. $y = -\frac{3}{2}x - 10$ $-\frac{3}{2}, -10$
11. $7x + 2y = -28$ $-\frac{7}{2}, -14$
12. $3x - 8y = 48$ $\frac{3}{8}, -6$

Tell whether the equation represents direct variation. If so, identify the constant of variation.

13. $x + 4y = 4$ **not direct variation**
14. $-\frac{1}{3}x - y = 0$ **direct variation;** $-\frac{1}{3}$
15. $3x - 3y = 0$ **direct variation; 1**

Graph the equation. **16–18. See margin.**

16. $x = 3$
17. $y + x = 6$
18. $2x + 8y = -32$

Evaluate the function for the given value.

19. $f(x) = -4x$ when $x = 2.5$ **−10**
20. $g(x) = \frac{5}{2}x - 6$ when $x = -2$ **−11**

21. **BUSINESS** To start a dog washing business, you invest $300 in supplies. You charge $10 per hour for your services. Your profit P (in dollars) for working t hours is given by $P = 10t - 300$. Graph the equation. You will break even when your profit is $0. Use the graph to find the number of hours you must work in order to break even. **See margin for art; 30 h.**

22. **PEDIATRICS** The dose d (in milligrams) of a particular medicine that a pediatrician prescribes for a patient varies directly with the patient's mass m (in kilograms). The pediatrician recommends a dose of 150 mg of medicine for a patient whose mass is 30 kg.
    a. Write a direct variation equation that relates m and d. $d = 5m$
    b. What would the dose of medicine be for a patient whose mass is 50 kg? **250 mg**

23. **SCISSOR LIFT** The scissor lift is a device that can lower and raise a platform. The maximum and minimum heights of the platform of a particular scissor lift are shown. The scissor lift can raise the platform at a rate of 3.5 inches per second. The height of the platform after t seconds is given by $h(t) = 3.5t + 48$. Graph the function and identify its domain and range. **See margin for art; domain:** $0 \le t \le 58.3$, **range:** $48 \le h(t) \le 252$.

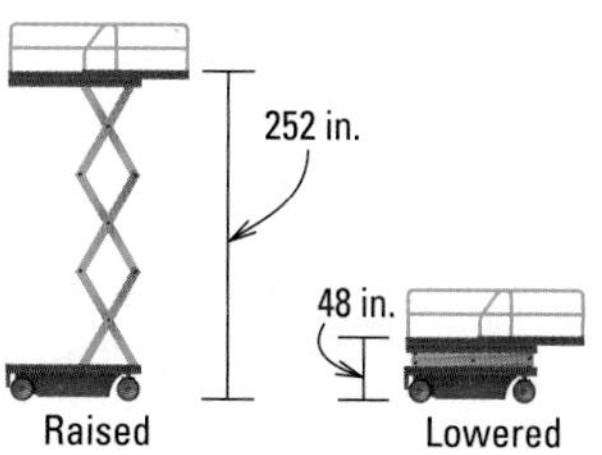

Additional Resources

Assessment Book

- Chapter Test, Levels A, B, C
- Standardized Chapter Test
- SAT/ACT Chapter Test
- Alternative Assessment

Test Generator

Chapter Test

Easily-readable reduced copies (with answers) of Chapter Test B, the Standardized Chapter Test, and the Alternative Assessment from the Assessment Book can be found on pp. 204G–204H.

5. **6.**

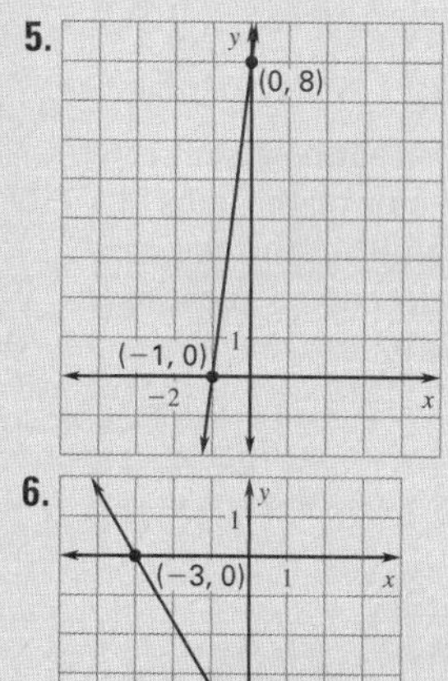

16–18. See Additional Answers beginning on p. AA1.

21.

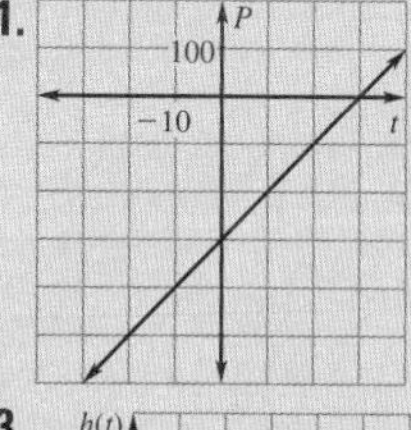

23.

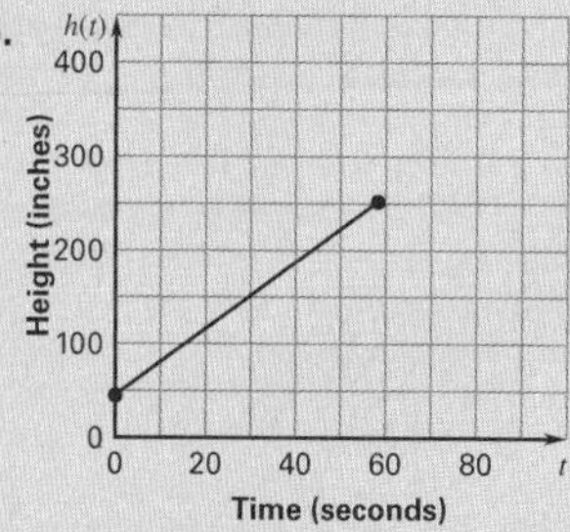

1–3.

A(7, 1)
B(−4, 0)
C(3, −9)

4.

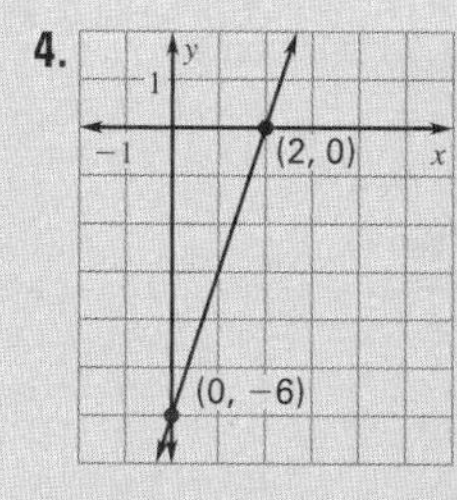

Test-Taking Strategy

Point out to students that graphs, tables, and diagrams may contain all of the information they need to solve a problem or they may contain only some of the information. Encourage students to examine the graphic in a question to determine how the given information will help them solve the problem.

Teaching Strategy

You may want to stress that students can solve problems in more than one way, and they should choose the strategy with which they are most comfortable. In Problem 1, for example, they could solve the problem using a proportion.

Avoiding Common Errors

Exercise 1 Caution students to read the labels on the axes of a graph carefully as the answers to a multiple-choice question often include values that appear on both axes.

CONTEXT-BASED MULTIPLE CHOICE QUESTIONS

Some of the information you need to solve a context-based multiple choice question may appear in a table, a diagram, or a graph.

PROBLEM 1

A recipe from a box of pancake mix is shown. The number p of pancakes you can make varies directly with the number m of cups of mix you use. A full box of pancake mix contains 9 cups of mix. How many pancakes can you make when you use the full box?

Ⓐ 63 Ⓑ 65

Ⓒ 126 Ⓓ 131

2 cups pancake mix
1 cup milk
2 eggs
Combine ingredients. Pour batter on hot greased griddle. Flip when edges are dry. Makes 14 pancakes.

Plan

INTERPRET THE INFORMATION Use the number of pancakes and the number of cups of mix given in the recipe to write a direct variation equation. Then use the equation to find the number of pancakes that you can make when you use 9 cups of mix.

Solution

STEP 1 Use the values given in the recipe to find a direct variation equation.

Because the number p of pancakes you can make varies directly with the number m of cups of mix you use, you can write the equation $p = am$. From the recipe, you know that $p = 14$ when $m = 2$.

$p = am$ **Write direct variation equation.**

$\mathbf{14} = a(\mathbf{2})$ **Substitute.**

$7 = a$ **Solve for *a*.**

So, a direct variation equation that relates p and m is $p = 7m$.

STEP 2 Substitute 9 for m in the direct variation equation and solve for p.

Use the direct variation equation to find the number of pancakes you can make when you use a full box of mix.

$p = 7m$ **Write direct variation equation.**

$p = 7(\mathbf{9})$ **Substitute 9 for *m*.**

$p = 63$ **Simplify.**

You can make 63 pancakes when you use a full box of mix.

The correct answer is A. Ⓐ Ⓑ Ⓒ Ⓓ

PROBLEM 2

At a yard sale, Jack made $54 selling cassettes for $1 each and CDs for $3 each. This situation is modeled by the equation $x + 3y = 54$ where x is the number of cassettes and y is the number of CDs that Jack sold. The graph of the equation is shown. Which is a possible combination of cassettes and CDs that Jack sold?

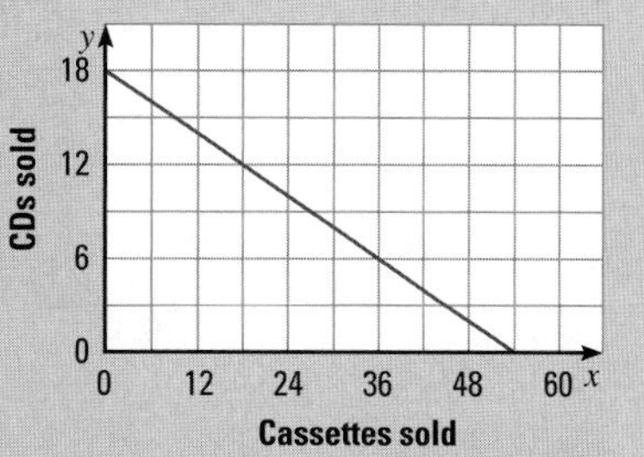

Ⓐ 12 cassettes, 4 CDs Ⓑ 4 cassettes, 12 CDs

Ⓒ 18 cassettes, 12 CDs Ⓓ 28.5 cassettes, 8.5 CDs

Plan

INTERPRET THE INFORMATION Each point on the line represents a solution of the equation. Identify the answer choice that describes a point on the graph shown and that makes sense in the context of the problem.

Solution

STEP 1 Write an ordered pair for each answer choice.

The answer choices correspond to the following ordered pairs.

Ⓐ (12, 4) Ⓑ (4, 12) Ⓒ (18, 12) Ⓓ (28.5, 8.5)

STEP 2 Eliminate points not on the line and points that don't make sense. Check ordered pairs not eliminated to find the solution.

You can eliminate answer choices A and B because the points do not lie on the graph shown. You can also eliminate answer choice D because only whole number solutions make sense in this situation. Check that (18, 12) is a solution of the equation.

$x + 3y = 54$ **Write original equation.**

$\mathbf{18} + 3(\mathbf{12}) = 54$ **Substitute.**

$54 = 54$ ✓ **Solution checks.**

The correct answer is C. Ⓐ Ⓑ Ⓒ Ⓓ

PRACTICE

1. In Problem 2, what is the greatest number of CDs Jack could have sold?

   Ⓐ 3 Ⓑ 18 Ⓒ 36 Ⓓ 54

2. The table shows the total cost for a certain number of people to ice skate at a particular rink. What is the cost per person?

   Ⓐ $.20 Ⓑ $1

   Ⓒ $5 Ⓓ $10

Number of people	Cost (dollars)
2	10
4	20
6	30

Answers

1. B

2. C

Answers

1. B
2. D
3. D
4. C
5. D
6. A
7. C
8. B
9. 1
10. 2
11. 0
12. $\frac{3}{2}$
13. 17 days. *Sample answer:* The two costs are equal when $58 = 1.75n$, or $n = 58 \div 1.75 \approx 33.14$. In this problem situation only whole-number values of n make sense. The graph shows that when $n < 34$, the pay-per-ride cost is lower; when $n \geq 34$, the monthly pass cost is lower. If Patricia rides the bus at least 34 times a month, it will be worth buying the monthly pass. Because she rides the bus to and from work, she rides twice a day, so the number of days is $34 \div 2 = 17$ days.

MULTIPLE CHOICE

In Exercises 1 and 2, use the graph below.

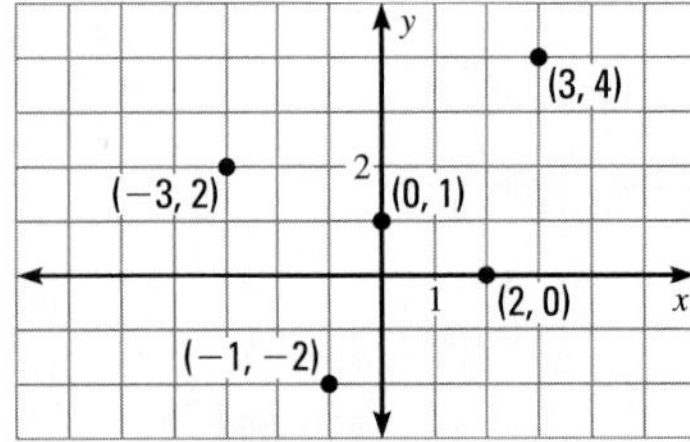

1. The graph represents a function. Which number is in the domain of the function?

Ⓐ −2 Ⓑ −1 Ⓒ 1 Ⓓ 4

2. The graph would no longer represent a function if which point were included?

Ⓐ (−4, −2) Ⓑ (−2, 0) Ⓒ (1, 3) Ⓓ (3, −1)

In Exercises 3 and 4, use the graph below, which shows a traveler's movements through an airport to a terminal. The traveler has to walk and take a shuttle bus to get to the terminal.

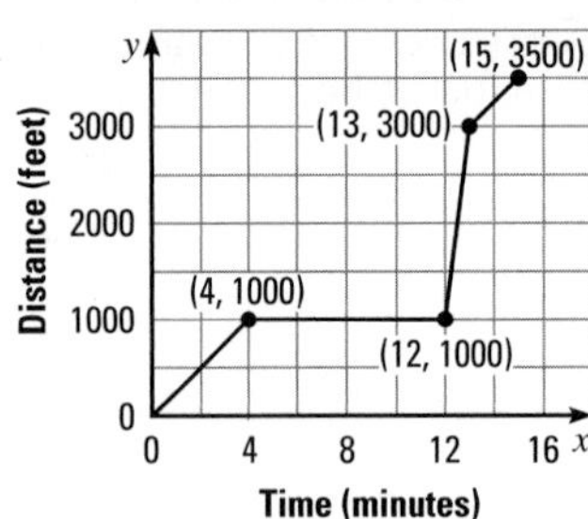

3. For how many minutes does the traveler wait for the shuttle bus?

Ⓐ 1 min Ⓑ 2 min Ⓒ 4 min Ⓓ 8 min

4. For about what distance does the traveler ride on the shuttle bus?

Ⓐ 100 ft Ⓑ 1000 ft Ⓒ 2000 ft Ⓓ 3000 ft

In Exercises 5–7, use the following information.

At a yoga studio, new members pay a sign-up fee of \$50 plus a monthly fee of \$25. The total cost C (in dollars) of a new membership is given by $C = 25m + 50$ where m is the number of months of membership. The owner of the studio is considering changing the cost of a new membership. A graph of four different options for changing the cost is shown.

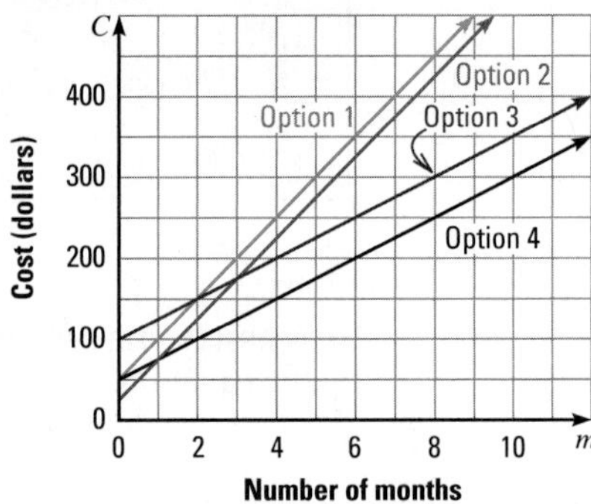

5. For which option are the sign-up fee and monthly fee kept the same?

Ⓐ Option 1 Ⓑ Option 2 Ⓒ Option 3 Ⓓ Option 4

6. For which option is the sign-up fee kept the same and the monthly fee raised?

Ⓐ Option 1 Ⓑ Option 2 Ⓒ Option 3 Ⓓ Option 4

7. For which option is the monthly fee kept the same and the sign-up fee raised?

Ⓐ Option 1 Ⓑ Option 2 Ⓒ Option 3 Ⓓ Option 4

8. The table shows the cost of a therapeutic massage for a given amount of time. What is the cost per minute?

Time (minutes)	30	45	60
Cost (dollars)	42.00	63.00	84.00

Ⓐ \$.71 Ⓑ \$1.40 Ⓒ \$2.80 Ⓓ \$14.00

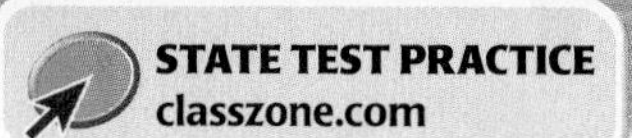

GRIDDED ANSWER

9. What is the slope of the line shown?

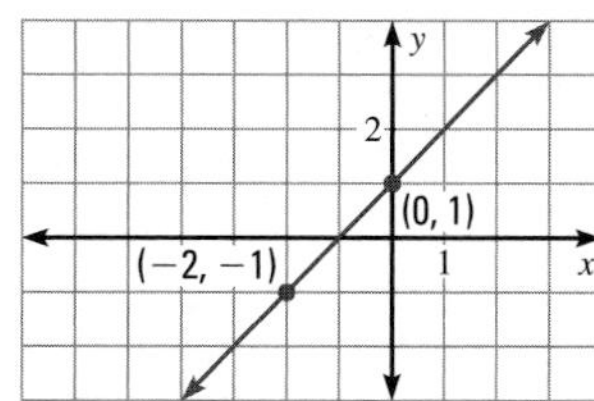

10. What is the y-intercept of the graph of the equation $4x + 8y = 16$?

11. What is the value of $f(x) = -1.8x - 9$ when $x = -5$?

12. The number w of cups of water varies directly with the number u of cups of uncooked rice. Use the table to find the value of the constant of variation a in the direct variation equation $w = au$.

Uncooked rice, u (cups)	$\frac{1}{2}$	1	$1\frac{1}{2}$
Water, w (cups)	$\frac{3}{4}$	$1\frac{1}{2}$	$2\frac{1}{4}$

SHORT RESPONSE

13. Patricia takes a bus to and from her job. She can either pay \$1.75 each way or get a monthly bus pass for \$58 and ride the bus an unlimited number of times. The functions below give the costs C (in dollars) of riding the bus n times in one month. The graphs of the functions are shown.

Monthly pass: $C = 58$

Pay per ride: $C = 1.75n$

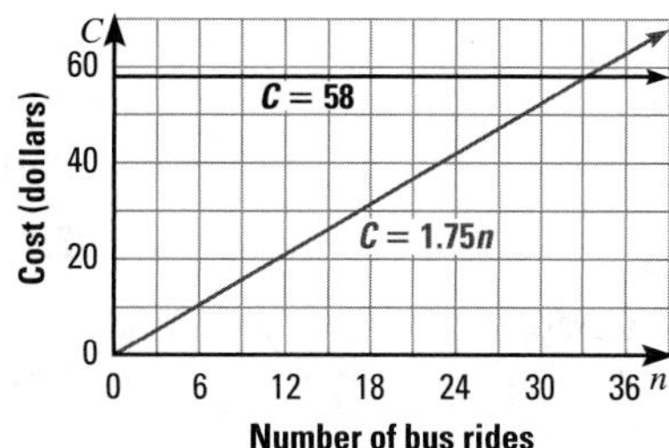

How many days in a month would Patricia need to take the bus to and from work to make buying a monthly pass worth the cost? *Explain.*

EXTENDED RESPONSE

14. A fog machine has a tank that holds 32 fluid ounces of fog fluid and has two settings: low and high. The low setting uses 0.2 fluid ounce of fluid per minute, and the high setting uses 0.25 fluid ounce per minute. The functions below give the amount f (in fluid ounces) of fluid left in the tank after t minutes when the machine starts with a full tank of fluid.

Low setting: $f = -0.2t + 32$ **High setting:** $f = -0.25t + 32$

a. Identify the slope and y-intercept of each function.

b. Graph each function in the same coordinate plane.

c. How much longer can the machine be run on the low setting than on the high setting? *Explain* how you found your answer.

15. At a pizzeria, a cheese pizza costs \$9. Toppings cost \$1.50 each.

a. The cost of a pizza is given by the function $f(x) = 1.5x + 9$ where x is the number of toppings. Graph the function.

b. You have \$14 and buy only a pizza. How many toppings can you get?

c. The pizzeria's owner decides to change the price of toppings to \$2 each. The new cost of a pizza is given by the function $g(x) = 2x + 9$. Graph the function in the same coordinate plane you used in part (a).

d. Can you get the same number of toppings at the new price as you did in part (b)? *Explain.*

14a. low: -0.2, 32; high: -0.25, 32

14b.

Fluid left (fluid ounces); Time (minutes); $f = -0.2t + 32$; $f = -0.25t + 32$

14c. 32 min; the machine can run until the amount of fog fluid is 0, so to find how many minutes the machine can run on each setting, set $f = 0$ in each equation and solve for t. For the low setting, solve $0 = -0.2t + 32$ to get $t = 160$ minutes, and for the high setting solve $0 = -0.25t + 32$ to get $t = 128$ minutes. The difference in time is $160 - 128 = 32$ minutes.

15a, c.

Cost (dollars); Number of toppings; $g(x) = 2x + 9$; $f(x) = 1.5x + 9$

15b. 3 toppings

15d. No; at the new price, a pizza with 3 toppings would cost $g(3) = 2(3) + 9 = \$15$, which is more money than you have.

5 Pacing Guide

Chapter 5: Writing Linear Equations

Chapter Table of Contents

PACING GUIDES

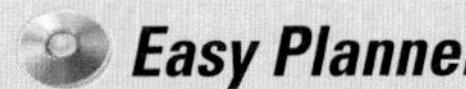

Regular Schedule (50-minute classes)

DAY 1	DAY 2	DAY 3	DAY 4	DAY 5	DAY 6
Inv. Alg. Act. 5.1 Lesson 5.1 Gr. Calc. Act. 5.1	Lesson 5.2	Lesson 5.2 (cont.)	Lesson 5.3	Lesson 5.3 (cont.) Extension 5.3	Lesson 5.4
DAY 7	**DAY 8**	**DAY 9**	**DAY 10**	**DAY 11**	**DAY 12**
Lesson 5.4 (cont.) Mixed Review of Problem Solving	Quiz for Lessons 5.1–5.4 Lesson 5.5	Lesson 5.6 Graphing Calculator Activity 5.6	Inv. Alg. Act. 5.7 Lesson 5.7 Extension 5.7 Internet Activity 5.7 Mixed Review of Problem Solving	Quiz for Lessons 5.5–5.6 Chapter Review	Chapter Test

Block Schedule (90-minute classes)

DAY 1	DAY 2	DAY 3	DAY 4	DAY 5	DAY 6
Investigating Algebra Activity 5.1 Lesson 5.1 Graphing Calculator Activity 5.1 Lesson 5.2	Lesson 5.2 (cont.) Lesson 5.3	Lesson 5.3 (cont.) Extension 5.3 Lesson 5.4	Lesson 5.4 (cont.) Mixed Review of Problem Solving Quiz for Lessons 5.1–5.4 Lesson 5.5	Lesson 5.6 Gr. Calc. Act. 5.6 Extension 5.6 Inv. Alg. Act. 5.7 Lesson 5.7 Internet Activity 5.7 Mixed Review of Problem Solving	Quiz for Lessons 5.5–5.6 Chapter Review Chapter Test

RESOURCE OPTIONS

Chapter/Lesson Resources

Chapter Resource Book
- Parents as Partners
- Teaching Guide/Lesson Plan
- Activity Masters
- Practice (3 levels)
- Study Guide
- Quick Catch-Up for Absent Students
- Problem Solving/Application
- Challenge Practice
- Chapter Review Games and Activities
- Project with Rubric
- Cumulative Review

Notetaking Guide
- Student Workbook and Teacher's Edition

Practice Workbook

Worked-Out Solution Key

Chapter Transparency Book
- Warm-Up Exercises/Daily Homework Quiz
- Notetaking Guide Transparencies
- Homework Answer Transparencies

Teacher Tools Transparencies

Assessment

Assessment Book
- Quizzes
- Chapter Tests (3 levels)
- Standardized and SAT/ACT Chapter Tests
- Alternative Assessments
- Cumulative Tests

Benchmark Tests
- Benchmark Tests, correlated to Remediation Book
- Pre-Course, Mid-Year, and End-of-Year Tests
- Chapter Tests

Spanish Assessment Book

Differentiated Instruction

Differentiated Instruction Resources
- Strategies for Reading Mathematics
- Differentiated Instruction Lesson Notes
- English Learner Lesson Notes
- Inclusion Lesson Notes
- Teaching Strategies with Sample Worksheets
- Tips for New Teachers/Math Background Notes
- Teacher Survival Activities/Bulletin Board Ideas

Student Resources in Spanish

Spanish Study Guide

Remediation Book

Skills Readiness (available on Easy Planner)
- Diagnostic Assessment
- Skill Instruction and Alternative Teaching Strategies
- Skill Practice and Enrichment Masters

Pre-AP Resources
- Pacing and Assignment Guide
- Best Practices
- Copymasters

Technology Resources

Plan	***Easy Planner***
Teach	***Video Tutor*** ***Activity Generator*** ***Power Presentations*** ***Animated Algebra***
Assess	***Test Generator*** ***ML Assessment System***
Reteach	***@HomeTutor***
Online Resources	***Classzone.com*** ***eEdition*** ***eWorkbook***

Video Tutor

Technology Highlights for Each Lesson

Easy Planner

Easy access to the Teacher's Edition and all teaching resources. Includes a search feature to locate the materials you need.

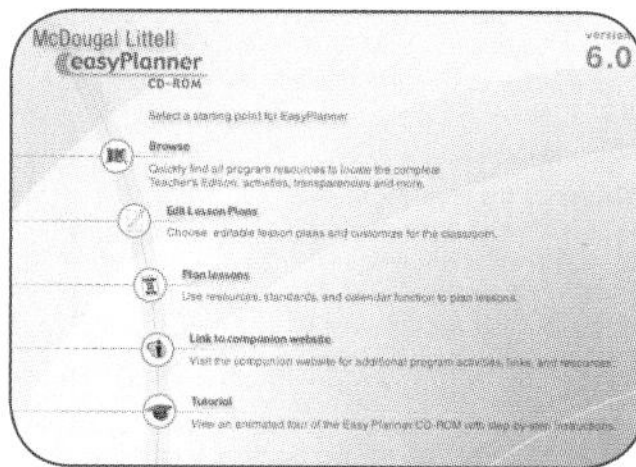

Activity Generator

Leveled, editable activities allow all students to explore a lesson's concepts. Includes teacher notes and closure questions.

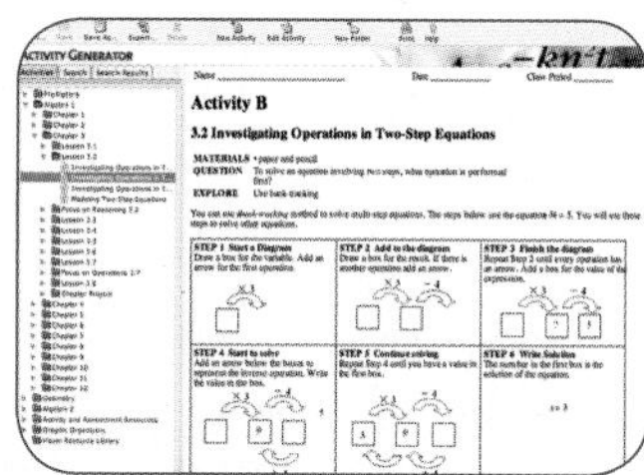

Animated Algebra

Interactive tutorials provide visually engaging alternative opportunities to learn concepts and master skills.

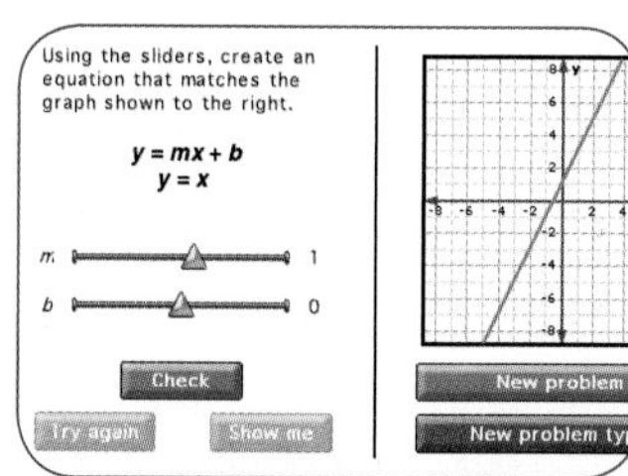

Lesson Practice Level B

LESSON 5.1

Practice B
For use with pages 283–289

Write an equation of the line with the given slope and y-intercept.

1. slope: 7; y-intercept: 4 $y = 7x + 4$
2. slope: −3; y-intercept: 5 $y = -3x + 5$
3. slope: 1; y-intercept: −6 $y = x - 6$

Write an equation of the line shown.

4. 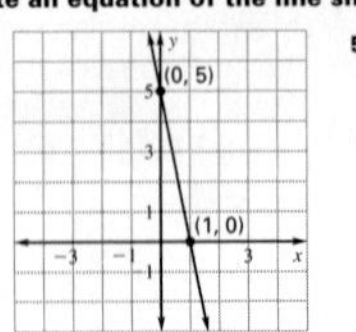 $y = -5x + 5$

5. 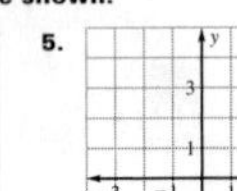 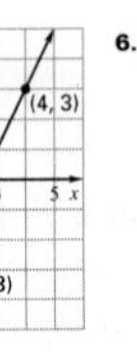 $y = 2x - 5$

6. 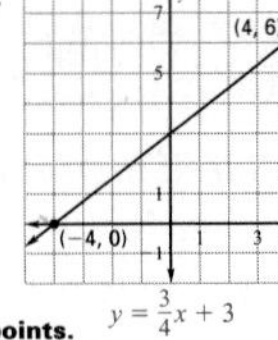 $y = \frac{3}{4}x + 3$

Write an equation of the line that passes through the given points.

7. (−1, 0), (0, −2) $y = -2x - 2$
8. (0, 4), (6, 13) $y = \frac{3}{2}x + 4$
9. (4, 5), (8, 2) $y = -\frac{3}{4}x + 8$
10. (−1, −9), (6, 5) $y = 2x - 7$
11. (2, −13), (−3, 12) $y = -5x - 3$
12. (−4, −21), (1, −1) $y = 4x - 5$

Write an equation for the linear function f with the given values.

13. $f(0) = -1, f(3) = -10$ $f(x) = -3x - 1$
14. $f(-4) = 5, f(2) = 2$ $f(x) = -\frac{1}{2}x + 3$
15. $f(-4) = -2, f(2) = 7$ $f(x) = \frac{3}{2}x + 4$

16. **Landscape Supply** A landscape supply business charges $30 to deliver mulch. The mulch costs $23 per cubic yard.
   a. Write an equation that gives the total cost (in dollars) of having mulch delivered to a site as a function of the number of cubic yards ordered. $y = 23x + 30$
   b. *Identify* the dependent and independent variables in this situation. b. independent: x, number of cubic yards ordered; dependent: y, total cost
   c. Find the cost of having 8 cubic yards of mulch delivered to a site. $214

17. **Cable Television** A cable company charges $44 per month for basic service. Each premium channel costs an additional $16 per month.
   a. Write an equation that gives the total cost (in dollars) of cable each month as a function of the number of premium channels. $y = 16x + 44$
   b. *Identify* the dependent and independent variables in this situation. b. independent: x, number of premium channels; dependent: y, total cost
   c. *Explain* how you can use the equation from part (a) to approximate how many premium channels you can have for $80 a month. Substitute 80 for y in the equation and solve for x.

18. **Laser Printer** A laser printer has a "sleep" mode that is an energy-saving feature. When a job is sent to the printer, it takes 45 seconds for the printer to warm up and then the printer prints pages at a rate of 6 pages per minute.
   a. Write the time it takes the printer to warm up in minutes. 0.75 min
   b. Write an equation that gives the total amount of time (in minutes) it takes the printer to warm up and print a job as a function of the number of pages in the job. $y = \frac{1}{6}x + 0.75$
   c. Find out how long it takes the printer to print a 50-page job if it must first warm up. about 9 min

LESSON 5.1

LESSON 5.2

Practice B
For use with pages 292–299

Write an equation of the line that passes through the given point and has slope m.

1. (−1, 6); m = 5 $y = 5x + 11$
2. (10, 3); m = −2 $y = -2x + 23$
3. (2, −3); m = 7 $y = 7x - 17$
4. (−4, −9); m = 2 $y = 2x - 1$
5. (5, −4); $m = \frac{1}{3}$ $y = \frac{1}{3}x - \frac{17}{3}$
6. (−8, 1); $m = -\frac{3}{4}$ $y = -\frac{3}{4}x - 5$

Write an equation of the line shown.

7. 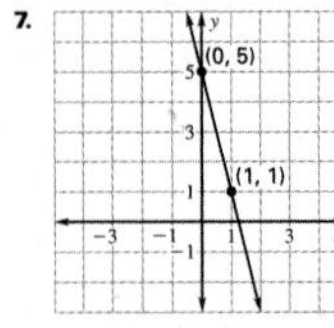 $y = -4x + 5$

8. 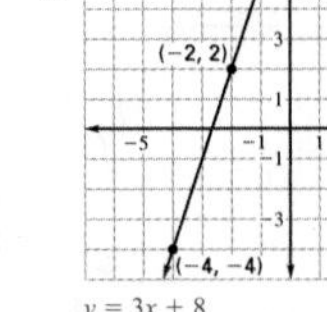 $y = 3x + 8$

9. 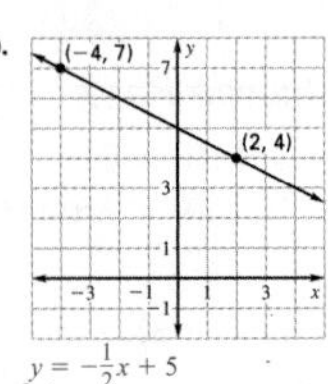 $y = -\frac{1}{2}x + 5$

Write an equation of the line that passes through the given points.

10. (−10, 7), (5, −3) $y = -\frac{2}{3}x + \frac{1}{3}$
11. (−5, −3), (12, 17.4) $y = 1.2x + 3$
12. (−8, 84), (5, −46) $y = -10x + 4$

Write an equation for the linear function f with the given values.

13. $f(4) = -8, f(-3) = 1$ $f(x) = -\frac{9}{7}x - \frac{20}{7}$
14. $f(6) = -4, f(9) = -9$ $f(x) = -\frac{5}{3}x + 6$
15. $f(-1) = -6, f(4) = -14$ $f(x) = -\frac{8}{5}x - \frac{38}{5}$

16. **Oil Changes** You are scheduled to start your job at an oil change shop 2 hours after the shop opens. Two hours after you start, a total of 11 cars have had their oil changed since the shop opened. Three hours later, a total of 14 cars have had their oil changed. At what rate are cars getting their oil changed since you started working? How many cars had their oil changed before you started work? 1 car per hour; 9 cars

17. **Motor Vehicle Licenses** The amount of revenue brought in by states from motor vehicle licenses increased at a relatively constant rate of 499.79 million dollars per year from 1990 to 2000. In 2000, the states brought in 15,099 million dollars in revenue from motor vehicle licenses.
   a. What was the approximate revenue (in million dollars) from licenses in 1990? 10,101.1 million dollars
   b. Write an equation that gives the revenue (in million dollars) as a function of the number of years since 1990. $y = 499.79x + 10{,}101.1$
   c. Find the revenue from licenses in 1999. 14,599.21 million dollars

18. **Imports** The number of metric tons of fruits, nuts, and vegetables imported into the United States increased at a relatively constant rate of 437.5 thousand metric tons per year from 1990 to 2002. In 2002, about 9900.5 thousand metric tons of fruits, nuts, and vegetables were imported. Write an equation that gives the number of thousand metric tons imported as a function of the number of years since 1990. Find the year in which the number of metric tons reached 8000 thousand metric tons. $y = 437.5x + 4650.5$; between 1997 and 1998

LESSON 5.2

LESSON 5.3

Practice B
For use with pages 302–308

Write an equation in point-slope form of the line that passes through the given point and has the given slope m.

1. (1, 9); m = −3 $y - 9 = -3(x - 1)$
2. (4, −10); m = 2 $y + 10 = 2(x - 4)$
3. (−5, 6); m = 4 $y - 6 = 4(x + 5)$
4. (−2, −8); m = 3 $y + 8 = 3(x + 2)$
5. (−4, −7); $m = -\frac{1}{2}$ $y + 7 = -\frac{1}{2}(x + 4)$
6. (−9, 2); m = −5 $y - 2 = -5(x + 9)$
7. (6, −4); $m = \frac{2}{3}$ $y + 4 = \frac{2}{3}(x - 6)$
8. (0, 15); $m = \frac{4}{5}$ $y - 15 = \frac{4}{5}x$
9. (−8, 0); m = 2 $y = 2(x + 8)$

Graph the equation.

10. $y - 6 = 3(x - 4)$ 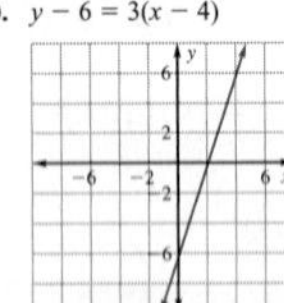 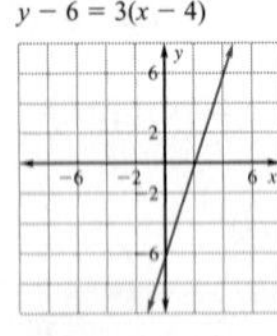

11. $y + 1 = 2(x - 5)$ 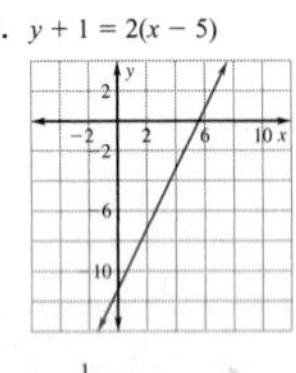 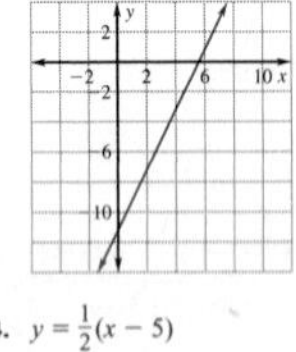

12. $y - 2 = -4(x + 3)$

13. $y + 2 = -(x - 1)$

14. $y = \frac{1}{2}(x - 5)$ 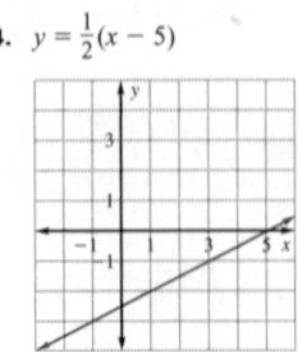 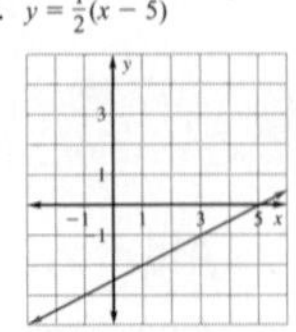

15. $y + 3 = 5x$

16. $y + 1 = \frac{2}{3}(x + 1)$ 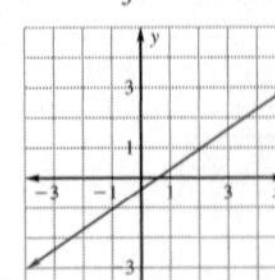

17. $y - 2 = -\frac{1}{2}(x - 3)$ 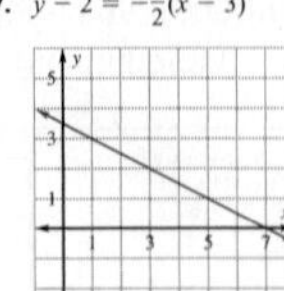

18. $y + \frac{1}{2} = 2(x - 1)$ 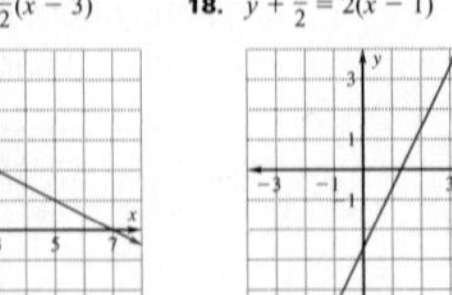

LESSON 5.3

LESSON 5.3

Practice B *continued*
For use with pages 302–308

19. $y - 3 = 2(x + 2)$ 20. $y - 6 = \frac{3}{4}(x - 4)$ 21. $y + 8 = -3(x - 1)$ 22. $y - 3 = \frac{5}{3}(x - 1)$

Write an equation of the line shown. Use the right-hand point to write the equation.

19. 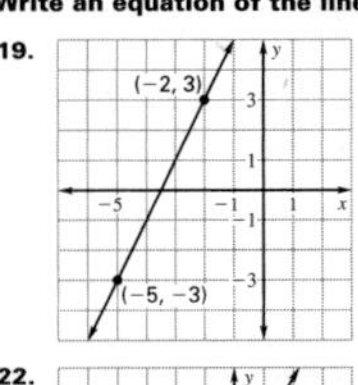

20. 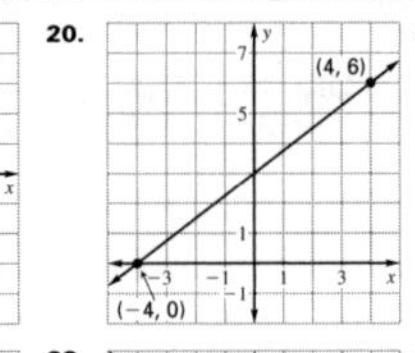

21. 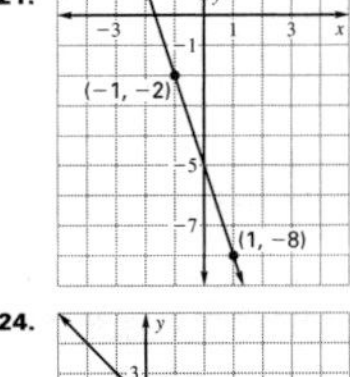

22. 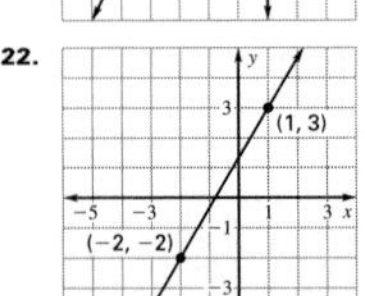

23. 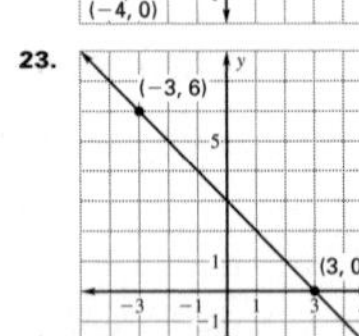

24. 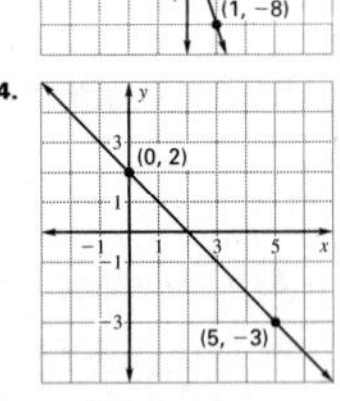

Write an equation of the line that passes through the given points. Use the first point to write the equation.

25. (9, 4), (17, 6) $y - 4 = \frac{1}{4}(x - 9)$
26. (−3, 10), (4, 2) $y - 10 = -\frac{8}{7}(x + 3)$
27. (3, −8), (7, −2) $y + 8 = \frac{3}{2}(x - 3)$
28. (−4, −4), (2, 5) $y + 4 = \frac{3}{2}(x + 4)$

29. **Bryce Canyon National Park** From 1990 to 2000, the number of visits by people to Bryce Canyon National Park increased by about 23.9 thousand visits per year. In 2000, there were about 1102.4 thousand visits to the park.
   a. Write an equation that gives the number of visits (in thousands) as a function of the number of years since 1990. $y - 1102.4 = 23.9(x - 10)$
   b. How many visits were made to the park in 1995? 982.9 thousand visits

30. **Airmail Letter Rates** The table shows the cost of mailing different weights of airmail letters to Canada.

Weight (oz)	2	3	4	8
Cost (dollars)	0.85	1.10	1.35	2.35

   a. *Explain* why the situation can be modeled using a linear equation. The slope between each pair of points is the same.
   b. Write an equation that gives the cost (in dollars) as a function of the weight of an airmail letter (in ounces). $y - 0.85 = 0.25(x - 2)$
   c. How much does it cost to mail a 5-ounce airmail letter to Canada? $1.60

31. **New Mexico** The population density of New Mexico increased at a relatively constant rate from 1980 to 1999. In 1985, the population density was about 11.62 people per square mile. In 1999, the population density was about 14.28 people per square mile. Write an equation that gives the population density (in people per square mile) as a function of the number of years since 1980. What was the population density in 1990? $y - 11.62 = 0.19(x - 5)$; 12.57 people per square mile 23. $y = -1(x - 3)$ 24. $y - 2 = -x$

LESSON 5.3

LESSON 5.4

Practice B
For use with pages 311–316

Write two equations in standard form that are equivalent to the given equation. 1–6. Answers will vary.

1. $6x + 24y = 18$ **2.** $8x - 14y = 2$ **3.** $6x + y = 1$

4. $-4x - 2y = 16$ **5.** $2x + 3y = 11$ **6.** $-9x + 4y = 5$

Write an equation in standard form of the line that passes through the given point and has the given slope *m*.

7. $(4, 3), m = 7$ $7x - y = 25$ **8.** $(5, -1), m = 2$ $2x - y = 11$ **9.** $(-2, 6), m = 1$ $x - y = -8$

10. $(-7, 8), m = -3$ $3x + y = -13$ **11.** $(9, -10), m = -4$ $4x + y = 26$ **12.** $(-15, -4), m = \frac{1}{2}$ $x - 2y = -7$

Write an equation in standard form of the line that passes through the given points.

13. $(2, 6), (3, 8)$ $2x - y = -2$ **14.** $(-1, 2), (5, 4)$ $x - 3y = -7$ **15.** $(7, -3), (4, 1)$ $4x + 3y = 19$

16. $(3, -8), (5, -9)$ $x + 2y = -13$ **17.** $(-5, 6), (2, -3)$ $9x + 7y = -3$ **18.** $(-3, -1), (6, -8)$ $7x + 9y = -30$

Write equations of the horizontal and the vertical lines that pass through the given point.

19. $(8, 3)$ $y = 3, x = 8$ **20.** $(-2, 6)$ $y = 6, x = -2$ **21.** $(5, -5)$ $y = -5, x = 5$

22. Text Messaging Your cell phone plan charges you \$.02 to send a text message and \$.07 to receive a text message. You plan to spend no more than \$5 a month on text messaging.

a. Write an equation in standard form that models the possible combinations of sent text messages and received text messages. $0.02x + 0.07y = 5$

b. Graph the equation from part (a). *Explain* what the intercepts of the graph mean in this situation. b. *x*-intercept: the number of messages you can send when no messages are received; *y*-intercept: the number of messages you can receive when no messages are sent

c. List three other possible combinations of the number of messages you can send and receive. Answers will vary.

23. Potting Soil Mix You are making 24 pounds of your own potting soil mix of sphagnum peat moss and coarse sand. You buy the peat moss in bags that weigh approximately 2 pounds.

a. The last time you made 24 pounds of potting soil, you used 9 bags of sphagnum peat moss and 4 bags of coarse sand. Use this information to find the number of pounds in a bag of coarse sand. 1.5 lb

b. Write an equation in standard form that models the possible combinations of bags of sphagnum peat moss and coarse sand you can use. $2x + 1.5y = 24$

c. List three possible combinations of whole bags of sphagnum peat moss and coarse sand you can use to make the potting soil. Answers will vary.

LESSON 5.5

Practice B
For use with pages 319–324

Write an equation of the line that passes through the given point and is parallel to the given line. See below.

1. $(4, 7), y = 5x - 3$ **2.** $(3, -2), y = \frac{2}{3}x + 1$ **3.** $(-6, 1), 4x + y = 7$

4. $(-5, -5), 6x - y = 1$ **5.** $(0, -8), 8x + 4y = 5$ **6.** $(-9, 11), 5x - 10y = 3$

Write an equation of the line that passes through the given point and is perpendicular to the given line. See below.

7. $(1, -1), y = 3x + 2$ **8.** $(5, 0), y = \frac{2}{3}x - 4$ **9.** $(3, -7), y = -\frac{1}{5}x + 1$

10. $(-9, 2), 10x - 5y = 6$ **11.** $(10, -11), -2x + 5y = 1$ **12.** $(-4, -8), 8x + 3y = 7$

Determine which of the following lines, if any, are parallel or perpendicular.

13. Line *a*: $y = 8x - 5$, Line *b*: $y = \frac{1}{8}x + 1$, Line *c*: $8x + y = 2$

14. Line *a*: $y = -2x + 5$, Line *b*: $2y - x = 3$, Line *c*: $2x + y = 1$

15. Line *a*: $6x + 2y = 5$, Line *b*: $y = \frac{1}{3}x - 4$, Line *c*: $y = -3x + 5$

13. Lines *b* and *c* are perpendicular. **14.** Lines *a* and *b* and lines *b* and *c* are perpendicular. Lines *a* and *c* are parallel. **15.** Lines *a* and *b* and lines *b* and *c* are perpendicular. Lines *a* and *c* are parallel.

16. Kite Design You are beginning to model a kite design on the coordinate plane, as shown.

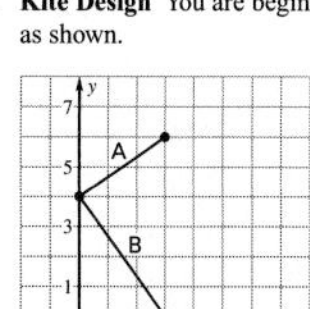

1. $y = 5x - 13$ **2.** $y = \frac{2}{3}x - 4$
3. $y = -4x - 23$ **4.** $y = 6x + 25$
5. $y = -2x - 8$ **6.** $y = \frac{1}{2}x + \frac{31}{2}$
7. $y = -\frac{1}{3}x - \frac{2}{3}$ **8.** $y = -\frac{3}{2}x + \frac{15}{2}$
9. $y = 5x - 22$ **10.** $y = -\frac{1}{2}x - \frac{5}{2}$
11. $y = -\frac{5}{2}x + 14$ **12.** $y = \frac{3}{8}x - \frac{13}{2}$
17. a. you: $y = \frac{1}{2}x$; your friend: $y = \frac{1}{2}x + 5$

a. Write an equation that models part A of the kite. $y = \frac{2}{3}x + 4$

b. Write an equation that models part B of the kite. $y = -\frac{4}{3}x + 4$

c. Do the kite parts form a right angle? *Justify* your answer. No. The lines for part A and part B are not perpendicular.

17. Lunch Duty Everyone at summer camp takes turns being on lunch duty. You and your friend are in charge of making turkey sandwiches. You both can make 1 sandwich in 2 minutes. Your friend arrives 10 minutes earlier and starts making sandwiches.

a. Write equations that model the number of sandwiches made as a function of the number of minutes it takes you and your friend to each make sandwiches. See above.

b. How many sandwiches will each of you make in 20 minutes? you: 10 sandwiches; your friend: 15 sandwiches

c. How are the graphs of the equations from part (a) related? *Justify* your answer. The graphs are parallel; they have the same slope but different *y*-intercepts.

LESSON 5.6

Practice B
For use with pages 325–331

Tell whether *x* and *y* show a *positive correlation*, a *negative correlation*, or *relatively no correlation*.

1. 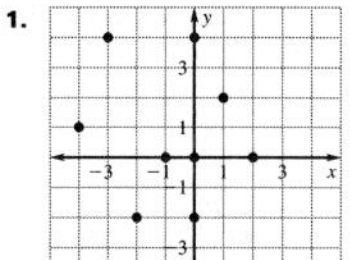
relatively no correlation

2. 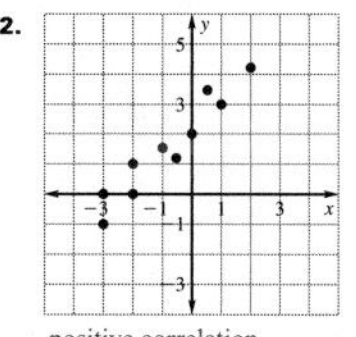
positive correlation

3. 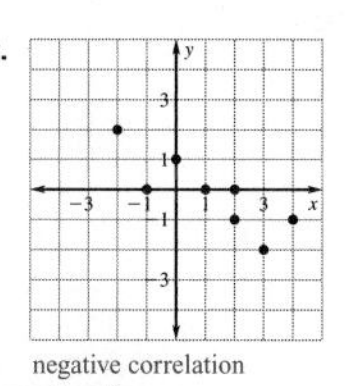
negative correlation

Make a scatter plot of the data. Draw a line of fit. Write an equation for the line.

4. 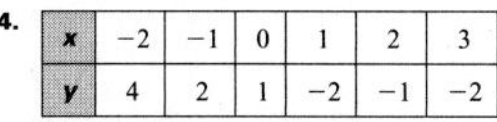

x	−2	−1	0	1	2	3
y	4	2	1	−2	−1	−2

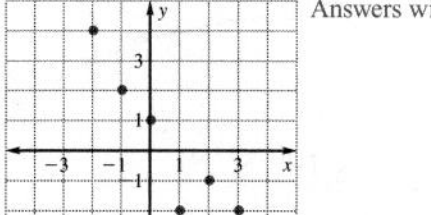
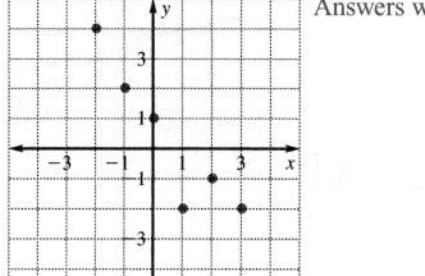
Answers will vary.

5.

x	0	0	0.5	1.5	2	2.5
y	−4	−3	−1.5	1	3	4

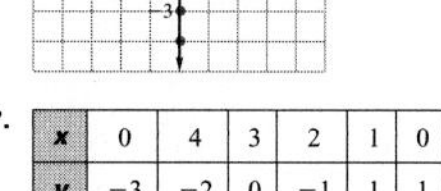
Answers will vary.

6. 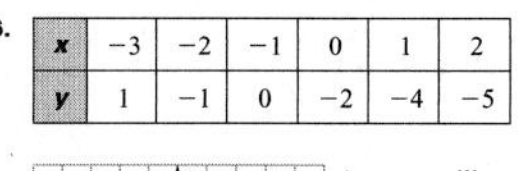

x	−3	−2	−1	0	1	2
y	1	−1	0	−2	−4	−5

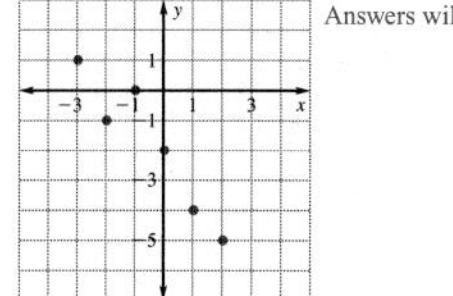
Answers will vary.

7.

x	0	4	3	2	1	0
y	−3	−2	0	−1	1	1

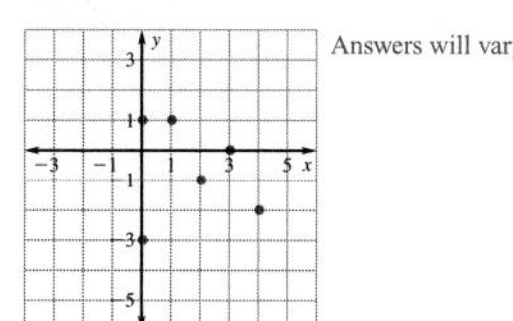
Answers will vary.

LESSON 5.6

Practice B *continued*
For use with pages 325–331

Make a scatter plot of the data. *Describe* the correlation of the data. If possible, fit a line to the data and write an equation of the line.

8.

x	−2	−2	−1	0	1	1	2
y	−4	−3	−2	−1	0	2	1

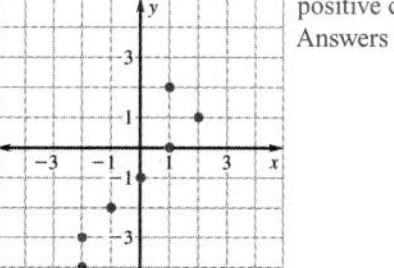
positive correlation
Answers will vary.

9. 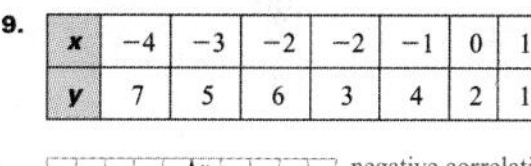

x	−4	−3	−2	−2	−1	0	1
y	7	5	6	3	4	2	1

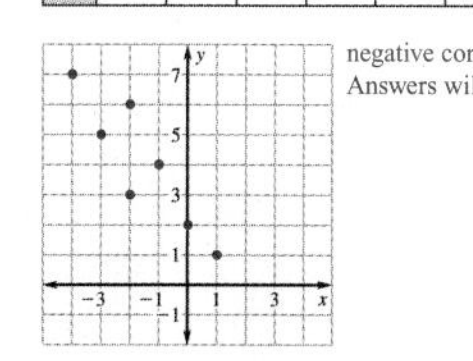
negative correlation
Answers will vary.

10. Thermostat The table shows the thermostat setting (in units called gas marks) on a British gas oven and the corresponding temperature in degrees Celsius.

Setting (gas mark)	2	3	4	5	6	7	8
Temperature (°C)	150	160	180	190	200	220	230

a. Make a scatter plot of the data where *x* represents the thermostat setting (in gas marks) and *y* represents the temperature (in degrees Celsius).

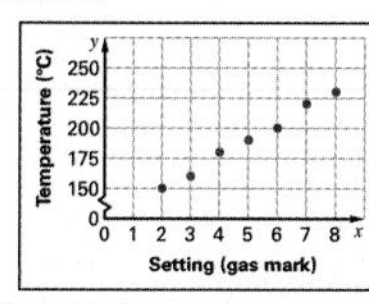

b. *Describe* the correlation of the data. positive correlation

c. An oven set to gas mark 10 heats to a temperature of 260°C. Does this fit the trend shown by your scatter plot? *Explain* your reasoning. Yes; the temperature increases as the setting increases.

11. Fruits The table shows the amount of energy (in kilocalories) and amount of carbohydrates (in grams) in a 100-gram serving of different fruits.

Fruit	Apple	Banana	Blueberries	Kiwi	Pear	Strawberries	Mango
Energy (kcal)	59	92	56	61	59	30	65
Carbohydrates (g)	15.25	23.43	14.13	14.88	15.11	7.02	17

a. Make a scatter plot of the data where *x* represents the energy (in kilocalories) and *y* represents the carbohydrates (in grams).

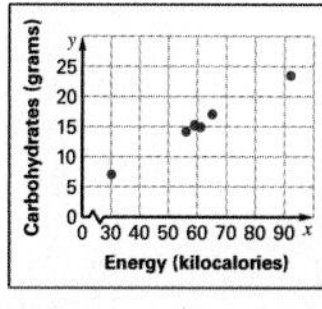

b. *Describe* the correlation of the data. positive correlation

c. A 100-gram serving of an avocado contains 161 kilocalories of energy and 7.39 grams of carbohydrates. Does an avocado fit the trend shown by your scatter plot? *Explain* your reasoning. No; the number of carbohydrates appears to increase as the number of kilocalories increases.

LESSON 5.7

Practice B

For use with pages 335–341

Make a scatter plot of the data. Find the equation of the best-fitting line. Approximate the value of *y* for *x* = 3.

1.

x	−1	0	1	2	4
y	3	3	1	0	−3

Answers will vary.

2.

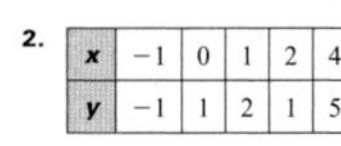

x	−1	0	1	2	4
y	−1	1	2	1	5

Answers will vary.

Make a scatter plot of the data. Find the equation of the best-fitting line. Approximate the value of *y* for *x* = 5.

3.

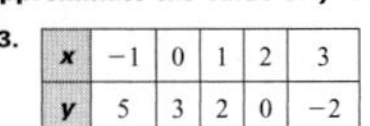

x	−1	0	1	2	3
y	5	3	2	0	−2

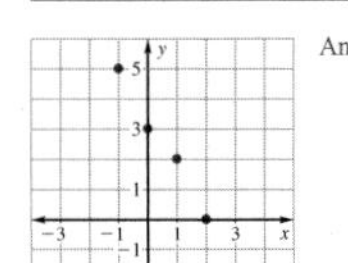

Answers will vary.

4.

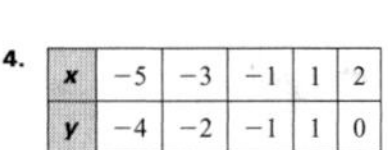

x	−5	−3	−1	1	2
y	−4	−2	−1	1	0

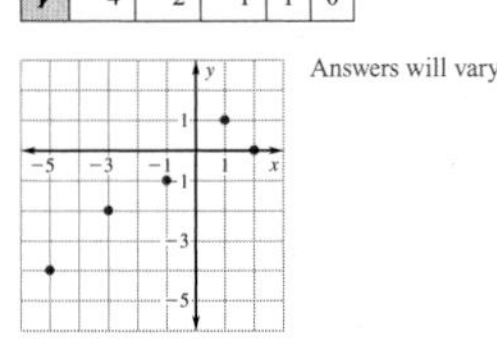

Answers will vary.

5.

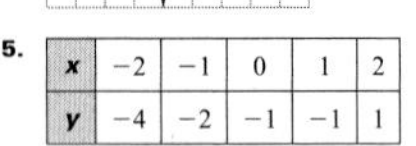

x	−2	−1	0	1	2
y	−4	−2	−1	−1	1

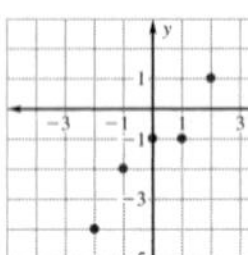

Answers will vary.

6.

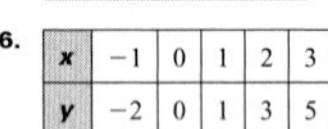

x	−1	0	1	2	3
y	−2	0	1	3	5

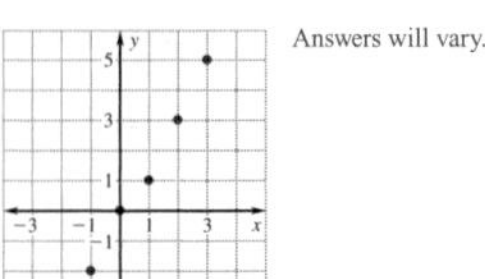

Answers will vary.

LESSON 5.7

LESSON 5.7

Practice B *continued*

For use with pages 335–341

Find the zero of the function.

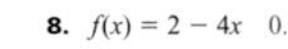

7. $f(x) = 16x - 4$ 0.25

8. $f(x) = 2 - 4x$ 0.5

9. $f(x) = 0.5x + 5$ −10

10. $f(x) = -0.1x - 3$ −30

11. $f(x) = \frac{3}{4}x - 3$ 4

12. $f(x) = -\frac{2}{5}x + 4$ 10

13. $f(x) = 0.25x + 0.5$ −2

14. $f(x) = 9 - 0.7x$ $\frac{90}{7}$

15. $f(x) = 1.2x + 10$ $-\frac{25}{3}$

16. $f(x) = \frac{1}{2}x - 6$ 12

17. $f(x) = -\frac{2}{5}x - 4$ −10

18. $f(x) = -0.8x + 15$ 18.75

19. $f(x) = 1.25x - 5$ 4

20. $f(x) = 6 - 0.2x$ 30

21. $f(x) = 2.5x - 3$ 1.2

22. Profit The table shows the monthly profit of a small company.

Month	January	February	March	April	May
Profit (dollars)	1200	1250	1400	1380	1450

a. Make a scatter plot of the data. Let *x* represent the number of months since January and let *y* represent the profit.

b. Find an equation that models the profit (in dollars) as a function of the number of months since January. Answers will vary.

c. Approximate the profit in August. Answers will vary.

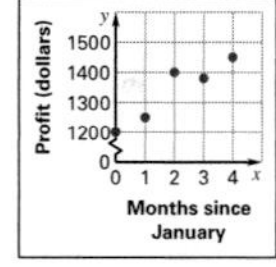

23. Escape Velocity The table shows several planet diameters and escape velocities. The escape velocity is the velocity at which an object has to travel in order to escape the effect of a planet's gravity.

Planet	Mercury	Uranus	Earth	Mars	Venus
Diameter (km)	4879	51,118	12,756	6794	12,104
Escape velocity (km/sec)	4.3	21.3	11.186	5.03	10.36

a. Make a scatter plot of the data. Let *x* represent the diameter of the planet and let *y* represent the escape velocity.

b. Find an equation that models the escape velocity (in kilometers per second) as a function of the diameter (in kilometers). Answers will vary.

c. Approximate the escape velocity of Neptune, which has a diameter of 49,528 kilometers. Answers will vary.

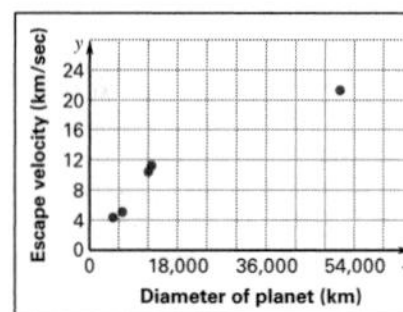

5 Assessment

CHAPTER 5 Quiz 1
For use after Lessons 5.1–5.4

Write an equation in slope-intercept form of the line that passes through the given point and has the given slope m.

1. $(2, 3)$; $m = 2$
2. $(5, -4)$; $m = -1$
3. $(6, 2)$; $m = -\frac{1}{2}$
4. $(-3, -1)$; $m = \frac{4}{5}$

Write an equation in point-slope form of the line that passes through the given points.

5. $(2, -2)$, $(5, 7)$
6. $(6, 4)$, $(2, 1)$

Write an equation in standard form of the line that passes through the given points.

7. $(0, 3)$, $(2, -3)$
8. $(1, -1)$, $(4, 2)$
9. A racquetball club charges \$10 for a one-month trial membership. After the trial month, the regular membership fee is \$12 per month. Write an equation that gives the total cost of a membership C as a function of the length of membership m (in months).
10. Use your equation from Exercise 9 to find the total cost of membership after 8 months.

Answers

1. $y = 2x - 1$
2. $y = -x + 1$
3. $y = -\frac{1}{2}x + 5$
4. $y = \frac{4}{5}x + \frac{7}{5}$
5. $y + 2 = 3(x - 2)$ or $y - 7 = 3(x - 5)$
6. $y - 4 = \frac{3}{4}(x - 6)$ or $y - 1 = \frac{3}{4}(x - 2)$
7. $3x + y = 3$
8. $x - y = 2$
9. $C = 12(m - 1) + 10$
10. \$94

CHAPTER 5 Quiz 2
For use after Lessons 5.5–5.7

Write an equation of the line that passes through the given point and is parallel to the given line.

1. $(1, -2)$, $-5x + y = 9$
2. $(-3, -4)$, $2y = 4 + 3x$

Write an equation of the line that passes through the given point and is perpendicular to the given line.

3. $(5, -8)$, $y = \frac{5}{2}x + 4$
4. $(2, -3)$, $6y = -2x + 1$

Determine which of the following lines, if any, are parallel or perpendicular.

5. Line a: $3y + x = 6$, Line b: $y = 3x + 2$, Line c: $3x + y = 0$
6. Line a: $y = -\frac{4}{5}x - 2$, Line b: $y = -\frac{5}{4}x + 7$, Line c: $5y = -4x + 5$

Tell whether x and y show a *positive correlation*, a *negative correlation*, or *relatively no correlation*.

7.

8.

Find the zero of the function.

9. $f(x) = -13x + 52$
10. $f(x) = \frac{1}{6}x - 3$

Answers

1. $y = 5x - 7$
2. $y = \frac{3}{2}x + \frac{1}{2}$
3. $y = -\frac{2}{5}x - 6$
4. $y = 3x - 9$
5. Lines a and b are perpendicular.
6. Lines a and c are parallel.
7. relatively no correlation
8. negative correlation

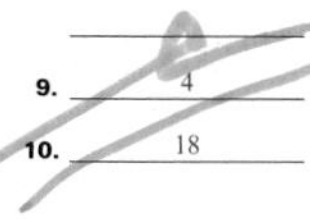

9. 4
10. 18

CHAPTER 5 Chapter Test B
For use after Chapter 5

Write an equation in slope-intercept form of the line shown.

1.

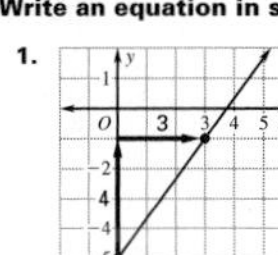

2.

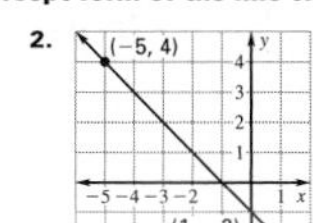

In Exercises 3 and 4, use the following information.

A delivery service charges a base price for an overnight delivery of a package plus an extra charge for each pound the package weighs. A customer is billed \$22.85 for shipping a 3-pound package and \$40 for shipping a 10-pound package.

3. Write an equation that gives the total cost of shipping a package as a function of the weight of the package.
4. Find the cost of shipping a 15-pound package.

Find the missing coefficient in the equation of the line that passes through the given point.

5. $Ax + y = 3$; $(2, -5)$
6. $3x + By = -1$; $(2, 7)$

Graph the equation.

7. $y - 2 = \frac{2}{3}(x - 4)$

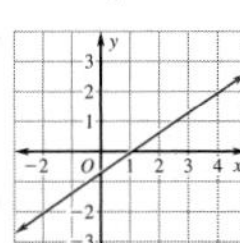

8. $y + 4 = -3(x + 2)$

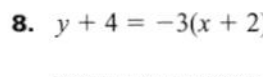

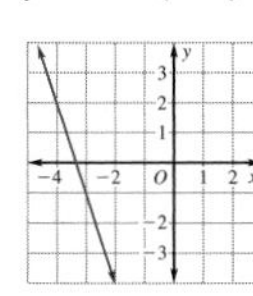

In Exercises 9 and 10, use the table.

x	2	4	6	9	11
y	−3	5	13	25	33

9. Explain why the data can be modeled by a linear equation.
10. Write an equation in point-slope form that relates y to x.

Answers

1. $y = \frac{4}{3}x - 5$
2. $y = -x - 1$
3. $y = 2.45x + 15.50$
4. \$52.25
5. $A = 4$
6. $B = -1$
7. See left.
8. See left.
9. The y-values increase at a constant rate of 4 for each increase of 1 in the x-value.
10. *Sample answer:* $y + 3 = 4(x - 2)$

CHAPTER 5 Chapter Test B *continued*
For use after Chapter 5

Write an equation in standard form of the line that passes through the given point and has the given slope m or that passes through the given points.

11. $(-4, 3)$, $m = \frac{1}{2}$
12. $(2, -3)$, $m = -4$
13. $(-2, -1)$, $(2, -6)$
14. $(-2, 5)$, $(3, 5)$

In Exercises 15 and 16, use the following information.

A piggy bank contains only nickels and quarters. The total value in the bank is \$3.80.

15. Write an equation in standard form that models the possible combinations of nickels and quarters in the piggy bank.
16. List two of these possible combinations.
17. Write an equation of the line that passes through the point $(-4, -1)$ and is (a) parallel to and (b) perpendicular to the line $2x + 7y = 14$.

In Exercises 18–22, use the table.

Fat (g)	31	39	19	34	43	39	35
Calories	580	680	410	590	660	640	570

18. Make a scatter plot of the data.

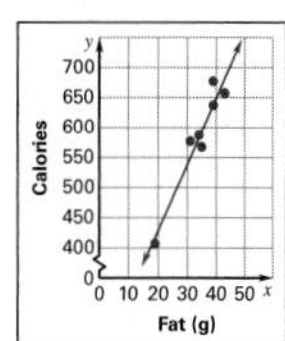

19. Describe the correlation.
20. Use technology to find the equation of the best-fitting line for the data.
21. Graph the best-fitting line for the data on the scatter plot.
22. Predict the number of calories in a hamburger that contains 28 grams of fat.

Answers

11. $-x + 2y = 10$
12. $4x + y = 5$
13. $5x + 4y = -14$
14. $y = 5$
15. $0.05n + 0.25q = 3.80$
16. *Sample answers:* 26 nickels and 10 quarters; 1 nickel and 15 quarters
17. Parallel: $y = -\frac{2}{7}x - \frac{15}{7}$; Perpendicular: $y = \frac{7}{2}x + 13$
18. See left.
19. The scatter plot shows a positive correlation. As the grams of fat increase, the number of calories tends to increase.
20. $y = 11x + 211$
21. See left.
22. 519 calories

CHAPTER 5

Standardized Test

For use after Chapter 5

Multiple Choice

1. Which equation is an equation of the line with a slope of -2 and a y-intercept of 4? D

Ⓐ $y = 4x - 2$ Ⓑ $y = -2x - 4$

Ⓒ $y = 2x - 4$ Ⓓ $y = -2x + 4$

2. Which equation represents the line shown? A

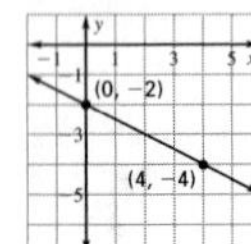

Ⓐ $y = -\frac{1}{2}x - 2$ Ⓑ $y = -2x - 2$

Ⓒ $y = \frac{1}{2}x - 2$ Ⓓ $y = -\frac{1}{2}x + 4$

3. Which function has the values $f(-3) = -11$ and $f(2) = -1$? D

Ⓐ $f(x) = x - 8$ Ⓑ $f(x) = -2x + 3$

Ⓒ $f(x) = \frac{1}{3}x - 10$ Ⓓ $f(x) = 2x - 5$

4. What is the equation of the line that passes through the points $(1, 8)$ and $(-2, -7)$? B

Ⓐ $y = -x + 9$ Ⓑ $y = 5x + 3$

Ⓒ $y = 2x - 3$ Ⓓ $y = \frac{1}{5}x - 5$

5. Which equation is an equation of the line that passes through the point $(2, -1)$ and has a slope of -1? A

Ⓐ $y + 1 = -(x - 2)$

Ⓑ $y - 1 = -(x - 2)$

Ⓒ $y - 1 = -(x + 2)$

Ⓓ $y + 1 = -(x + 2)$

6. Which equation is the point-slope equation of the line that passes through the points $(-2, -1)$ and $(7, -4)$? C

Ⓐ $y + 1 = -3(x + 2)$

Ⓑ $y - 1 = -\frac{1}{3}(x - 2)$

Ⓒ $y + 4 = -\frac{1}{3}(x - 7)$

Ⓓ $y + 4 = \frac{1}{3}(x - 7)$

7. What is the equation of the vertical line that passes through the point $(6, -2)$? C

Ⓐ $y = -2$ Ⓑ $y = 6$

Ⓒ $x = 6$ Ⓓ $x = -2$

8. Which equation is the standard form equation of the line that passes through the point $(-2, 0)$ and has a slope of 4? D

Ⓐ $-4x + y = 2$ Ⓑ $4x - y = 8$

Ⓒ $4x + y = -8$ Ⓓ $-4x + y = 8$

9. The graph of the equation $Ax + 3y = -3$ is a line that passes through $(2, -5)$. What is the value of A? B

Ⓐ 5 Ⓑ 6

Ⓒ 7 Ⓓ 8

10. Which of the following statements is true of the given lines? C

Line a: $2x + y = -4$

Line b: $x + 2y = -10$

Line c: $-2x + 4y = -12$

Ⓐ Lines a and b are parallel.

Ⓑ Lines b and c are parallel.

Ⓒ Lines a and c are perpendicular.

Ⓓ Lines b and c are perpendicular.

CHAPTER 5

Standardized Test *continued*

For use after Chapter 5

11. Which equation represents the line that passes through $(1, 1)$ and is parallel to the line passing through $(2, 3)$ and $(1, 5)$? D

Ⓐ $y = \frac{1}{2}x + 1$ Ⓑ $y = \frac{1}{2}x + 3$

Ⓒ $y = -2x + 1$ Ⓓ $y = -2x + 3$

12. Which equation best models the data in the scatter plot? A

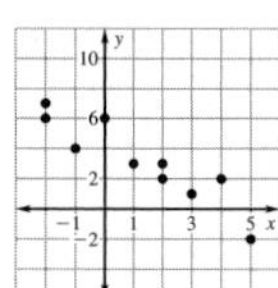

Ⓐ $y = -x + 6$ Ⓑ $y = x + 5$

Ⓒ $y = -5x + 2$ Ⓓ $y = 3x - 2$

13. Given the function $y = -5.2x + 28$, for what value of x does $y = -206$? C

Ⓐ -45 Ⓑ 0

Ⓒ 45 Ⓓ 54

Gridded Answer

14. What is the zero of the function $f(x) = 4x - 5$?

	5	/	4

Short Response

15. You pay an activation fee and a monthly fee for cellular phone service. The table shows the total cost of cellular service over different numbers of months.

Months of Service	2	4	6	8	10
Total Cost (dollars)	137	209	281	353	425

a. *Explain* why the situation can be modeled by a linear equation. See below.

b. What is the activation fee? $65

c. What is the monthly service fee? $36

Extended Response

16. If you sign up for a gym membership during the month of May, you are charged a joining fee of $78. Otherwise, you are charged a joining fee of $155. The monthly membership cost is $33.32.

a. Write an equation that gives the total cost (in dollars) of membership as a function of the number of months of membership if you join in May.

b. Write an equation that gives the total cost (in dollars) of membership as a function of the number of months of membership if you join in a month other than May. $C = 155 + 33.32m$

c. How are the graphs of these functions related? *Explain.*

d. After 6 months, what is the difference in total cost for a person who paid $78 to join and a person who paid $155 to join? After 12 months? *Explain.*

15. a. The situation can be modeled by a linear equation because the monthly fee is constant. **16. a.** $C = 78 + 33.32m$ **c.** The graphs are parallel. The slopes of both lines are equal. **d.** Regardless of the number of months, the difference will always be $77. They both pay the same amount each month. The only difference was in their joining fee.

CHAPTER 5

Alternative Assessment and Math Journal

For use after Chapter 5

Journal **1.** Explain the process that is used to fit a line to data.

Multi-Step Problem **2.** A car wash charges a flat rate for the first 8 minutes of washing time and also charges a certain amount for each additional minute of washing time. Gina took 12 minutes to wash her car and it cost her a total of $5.00. Kris took 17 minutes to wash his truck at a total cost of $6.25.

a. Write an equation that models the total cost of a car wash as a function of the number of minutes spent washing a vehicle.

b. How much is the flat rate for the first 8 minutes?

c. How much is charged for each additional minute of washing time?

d. It took Jermaine 15 minutes to wash his car. How much did he spend?

e. Darci has $10 to spend at the car wash. What is the maximum number of minutes she can take to wash her vehicle?

f. What is the slope of a line parallel to the line in part (a)?

g. What is the slope of a line perpendicular to the line in part (a)?

1. Complete answers should include mention of: making a scatter plot of the data; deciding if the data can be modeled by a line; sketching a line that follows the trend in the data; determining two points on the line drawn in order to determine the equation of the line.

2. a. $C = 0.25x + 2$ **b.** $4.00 **c.** $.25 **d.** $5.75 **e.** 32 minutes **f.** 0.25 **g.** -4

CHAPTER 5

Alternative Assessment Rubric *continued*

For use after Chapter 5

Journal Solution **1.** Complete answers should include mention of:

- making a scatter plot of the data.
- deciding if the data can be modeled by a line.
- sketching a line that follows the trend in the data.
- determining two points on the line drawn in order to determine the equation of the line.

Multi-Step Problem Solution **2.** **a.** $C = 0.25x + 2$

b. $4.00

c. $.25

d. $5.75

e. 32 minutes

f. 0.25

g. -4

Multi-Step Problem Rubric

4 The student answers all parts of the problem correctly and completely. The student shows all work. The student's work is neat.

3 The student answers all parts of the problem. The student's work may contain one or two errors in the calculations or equation. The student shows most work. The student's work is neat.

2 The student answers all parts of the problem, but there are more than two errors in the calculations or equation. The student shows some work. The student's work is sloppy.

1 The student does not complete all parts of the problem. The student's work has several errors in the calculations and equation. The student's work is sloppy, or no work is shown.

PLAN AND PREPARE

Main Ideas

In Chapter 5, students write equations of lines in slope-intercept form given three situations: the slope and y-intercept; the slope and a point; or two points. Also, they write and graph equations using the slope and a point, using a graph of the line, or using real-world data. They write equations of lines in standard form, and use their equations to solve real-world problems. They write and find equations of lines parallel or perpendicular to a given line. They make scatter plots of data, and use lines of fit and the best-fitting line to model data and to make predictions.

Prerequisite Skills

Skills Readiness, available on the *Easy Planner*, provides review and practice for the Skills Check portion of the Prerequisite Skills quiz.

How student answers the exercises	What to assign from *Skills Readiness*
Any of Exs. 4–6 answered incorrectly	**Skill 75** Identify slope and y-intercept
Any of Exs. 7–9 answered incorrectly	**Skill 76** Identify parallel lines
Any of Exs. 10–12 answered incorrectly	**Skill 78** Evaluate functions
All exercises answered correctly	Chapter 5 Enrichment

Additional skills review and practice is available in the Skills Review Handbook, pp. 909–937, and the @HomeTutor.

5 Writing Linear Equations

Making Sense of Chapter 5

Throughout your study of algebra you will use equations to study real-world situations. By the end of this chapter, you will be able to write linear equations, including those that model real-world data.

Before

Previously, you learned the following skills, which you'll use in Chapter 5: evaluating functions and finding the slopes and y-intercepts of lines.

Prerequisite Skills

VOCABULARY CHECK

Copy and complete the statement.

1. For the graph of the equation $y = mx + b$, the value of m is the _?_. **slope**
2. For the graph of the equation $y = mx + b$, the value of b is the _?_. **y-intercept**
3. Two lines are _?_ if their slopes are equal. **parallel**

SKILLS CHECK

Identify the slope and the y-intercept of the line with the equation. *(Prerequisite skill for 5.1–5.6)*

4. $y = x + 1$ **1, 1**
5. $y = \frac{3}{4}x - 6$ **$\frac{3}{4}$, −6**
6. $y = -\frac{2}{5}x - 2$ **$-\frac{2}{5}$, −2**

Tell whether the graphs of the two equations are parallel lines. *(Prerequisite skill for 5.5)*

7. $y = 3x + 5$, $y = 3x - 2$ **parallel**
8. $y = \frac{1}{4}x - 1$, $y = 4x + 3$ **not parallel**
9. $y = \frac{1}{2}x + 4$, $y = \frac{1}{2}x - 4$ **parallel**

Evaluate the function when $x = -2, 0,$ and 4. *(Prerequisite skill for 5.7)*

10. $f(x) = x - 10$ **−12, −10, −6**
11. $f(x) = 2x + 4$ **0, 4, 12**
12. $f(x) = -5x - 7$ **3, −7, −27**

@HomeTutor Prerequisite skills practice at classzone.com

280

Chapter Planning Guide

Chapter Resource Book
- Teaching Guide/Lesson Plan
- Project with Rubric

Assessment and Intervention
- Assessment Book
- Benchmark Tests
- Remediation Book
- Skills Readiness

Interactive Technology
- Easy Planner
- Power Presentations
- Activity Generator
- Animated Algebra
- Test Generator
- Online Quizzes
- eWorkbook
- eEdition
- @HomeTutor

Resources for English Learners
- Spanish Study Guide
- Multi-Language Visual Glossary
- Student Resources in Spanish

Now

In Chapter 5, you will apply the big ideas listed below and reviewed in the Chapter Summary on page 344. You will also use the key vocabulary listed below.

Big Ideas

1. **Writing linear equations in a variety of forms**
2. **Using linear models to solve problems**
3. **Modeling data with a line of fit**

KEY VOCABULARY

- point-slope form, *p. 302*
- converse, *p. 318*
- perpendicular, *p. 319*
- scatter plot, *p. 324*
- correlation, *p. 324*
- line of fit, *p. 325*
- best-fitting line, *p. 335*
- linear regression, *p. 335*
- interpolation, *p. 335*
- extrapolation, *p. 336*
- zero of a function, *p. 337*

Why?

You can use linear equations to solve problems involving a constant rate of change. For example, you can write an equation that models how traffic delays affected excess fuel consumption over time.

Animated Algebra

The animation illustrated below for Exercise 40 on p. 307 helps you to answer the question: In what year was a certain amount of excess fuel consumed?

Find the year in which the given amount of excess fuel was consumed.

Year	Excess Fuel
1992	30
1993	31.4
1992	
	34.2
	35.6
1995	37
	38.4
1997	39.8
	41.2
1999	
	44
2001	

35.6 gallons of annual excess fuel were consumed per person in the year_______?

Continue

Click on the table in order to fill in the missing information.

Animated Algebra at classzone.com

Other animations for Chapter 5: pages 283, 303, 307, 311, 321, 326, and 335

281

Differentiated Instruction Resources

- Reading Strategies for Chapter 5
- Differentiated Instruction Lesson Notes
- English Learners Lesson Notes
- Inclusion Lesson Notes
- Teaching Strategies with Sample Worksheets
- Using Technology in the Classroom
- Tips for New Teachers
- Math Background Notes
- Assessment Strategies
- Teacher Survival Activities
- Bulletin Board Idea

1 PLAN AND PREPARE

Explore the Concept

- Students model a linear relationship using the perimeter formula.
- This activity leads into the study of writing linear equations in slope-intercept form in Example 5 in Lesson 5.1.

Materials

Each student or pair of students will need:

- 8.5 by 11-inch sheet of paper
- inch ruler

Recommended Time

Work activity: 10 min

Discuss results: 5 min

Grouping

Students can work individually or in pairs. If students work in pairs, one can measure and fold the paper and the other can find the paper's perimeter and record the data.

2 TEACH

Key Questions

- What are the independent and dependent variables? **Width of fold; perimeter**
- What is the starting value of the perimeter? **39 in.**
- What happens to the perimeter as the width of the fold increases by one inch? **It decreases by 2 inches.**

Key Discovery

Use a constant rate of change and a starting value to describe a linear relationship.

3 ASSESS AND RETEACH

How do you find the perimeter if the fold is 8 inches? **Multiply 8 by −2 and add 39 to get 23 inches.**

5.1 Modeling Linear Relationships

MATERIALS • 8.5 inch by 11 inch piece of paper • inch ruler

QUESTION How can you model a linear relationship?

You know that the perimeter of a rectangle is given by the formula $P = 2\ell + 2w$. In this activity, you will find a linear relationship using that formula.

EXPLORE Find perimeters of rectangles

Width of fold (inches)	Perimeter of rectangle (inches)
0	39
1	?
2	?
3	?
4	?

STEP 1 ***Find perimeter***

Find the perimeter of a piece of paper that is 8.5 inches wide and 11 inches long. Record the result in a table like the one shown.

STEP 2 ***Change paper size***

Measure 1 inch from a short edge of the paper. Fold over 1 inch of the paper. You now have a rectangle with the same width and a different length than the original piece of paper. Find the perimeter of this new rectangle and record it in your table.

STEP 3 ***Find additional perimeters***

Unfold the paper and repeat Step 2, this time folding the paper 2 inches from a short edge. Find the perimeter of this rectangle and record the result in your table. Repeat with a fold of 3 inches and a fold of 4 inches.

DRAW CONCLUSIONS Use your observations to complete these exercises

1. What were the length and the width of the piece of paper before it was folded? By how much did these dimensions change with each fold? **11 in., 8.5 in.; length: reduced by 1 in., width: did not change**
2. What was the perimeter of the piece of paper before it was folded? By how much did the perimeter change with each fold? **39 in.; reduced by 2 in.**
3. Use the values from your table to predict the perimeter of the piece of paper after a fold of 5 inches. *Explain* your reasoning. **29 in.; with each 1 inch fold, the perimeter is reduced by 2 inches.**
4. Write a rule you could use to find the perimeter of the piece of paper after a fold of n inches. Use the data in the table to show that this rule gives accurate results. **$P = 39 - 2n$; $39 - (2)(1) = 37$; $39 - (2)(2) = 35$; $39 - (2)(3) = 33$; $39 - (2)(4) = 31$**

5.1 Write Linear Equations in Slope-Intercept Form

Before	You graphed equations of lines.
Now	You will write equations of lines.
Why?	So you can model distances in sports, as in Ex. 52.

Key Vocabulary
- **y-intercept,** *p. 225*
- **slope,** *p. 235*
- **slope-intercept form,** *p. 244*

Recall that the graph of an equation in slope-intercept form, $y = mx + b$, is a line with a slope of m and a y-intercept of b. You can use this form to write an equation of a line if you know its slope and y-intercept.

EXAMPLE 1 Use slope and y-intercept to write an equation

Write an equation of the line with a slope of −2 and a y-intercept of 5.

$y = mx + b$ Write slope-intercept form.

$y = -2x + 5$ Substitute −2 for m and 5 for b.

EXAMPLE 2 Standardized Test Practice

Which equation represents the line shown?

Ⓐ $y = -\frac{2}{5}x + 3$ Ⓑ $y = -\frac{5}{2}x + 3$

Ⓒ $y = -\frac{2}{5}x + 1$ Ⓓ $y = 3x + \frac{2}{5}$

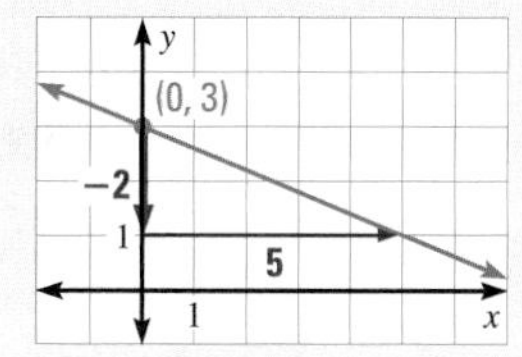

ELIMINATE CHOICES
In Example 2, you can eliminate choices C and D because the y-intercepts of the graphs of these equations are not 3.

The slope of the line is $\frac{\text{rise}}{\text{run}} = \frac{-2}{5} = -\frac{2}{5}$.

The line crosses the y-axis at (0, 3). So, the y-intercept is 3.

$y = mx + b$ Write slope-intercept form.

$y = -\frac{2}{5}x + 3$ Substitute $-\frac{2}{5}$ for m and 3 for b.

▶ The correct answer is A. Ⓐ Ⓑ Ⓒ Ⓓ

Animated Algebra at classzone.com

GUIDED PRACTICE for Examples 1 and 2

Write an equation of the line with the given slope and y-intercept.

1. Slope is 8; y-intercept is −7. $y = 8x - 7$
2. Slope is $\frac{3}{4}$; y-intercept is −3. $y = \frac{3}{4}x - 3$

1 PLAN AND PREPARE

Warm-Up Exercises

Transparency Available

Find the slope of the line that passes through the points.

1. (2, −1), (4, 0) $\frac{1}{2}$

2. (−1, −3), (1, 5) 4

3. A landscape architect charges $75 for a consulting fee and $30 per hour. Write an equation that shows the cost C as a function of time t (in hours). $C = 30t + 75$

Notetaking Guide

Transparency Available

Promotes interactive learning and notetaking skills.

Pacing

Basic: 1 day
Average: 1 day
Advanced: 1 day
Block: 0.5 block with 5.2
- See *Teaching Guide/Lesson Plan.*

2 FOCUS AND MOTIVATE

Essential Question

Big Idea 1, p. 281

How do you write an equation of a line in slope-intercept form? **Tell students they will learn how to answer this question by using the slope and y-intercept or two points to write an equation of the line.**

NCTM STANDARDS

Standard 2: Use models to represent relationships

Standard 4: Understand the units of measurement

Resource Planning Guide

Chapter Resource Book
- Teaching Guide/Lesson Plan
- Activity Master
- Practice levels A, B, C
- Study Guide
- Catch-up for Absent Students
- Application
- Challenge

Workbooks
- Notetaking Guide
- Practice Workbook

Teaching Options
- **Power Presentations** provides dynamic electronic teaching resources for the classroom.
- **Activity Generator** provides editable activities for all ability levels.

Interactive Technology
- Easy Planner
- Power Presentations
- Activity Generator
- Animated Algebra
- Test Generator
- Online Quiz
- eWorkbook
- eEdition
- @HomeTutor

Resources for English Learners
- Spanish Study Guide
- Multi-Language Visual Glossary
- Student Resources in Spanish

See also the *Differentiated Instruction Resources* for more strategies for meeting individual needs.

Motivating the Lesson

Your family has a monthly long distance telephone plan that charges \$3.99 plus \$.05 per minute. If you know how to write an equation that models the plan, and you know the number of minutes you talked on the phone, you can find what you owe on the monthly bill.

3 TEACH

Extra Example 1

Write an equation of the line with a slope of 4 and a y-intercept of -3. $y = 4x - 3$

Extra Example 2

Which equation represents the line shown? **B**

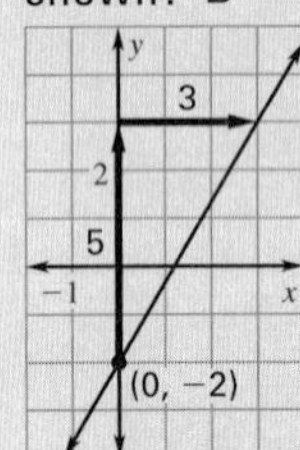

Ⓐ $y = \frac{3}{5}x - 2$

Ⓑ $y = \frac{5}{3}x - 2$

Ⓒ $y = -2x + \frac{3}{5}$

Ⓓ $-2x + \frac{5}{3}$

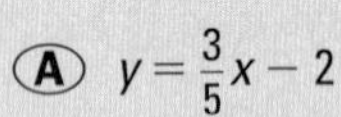

An **Animated Algebra** activity is available online for **Example 2**. This activity is also part of **Power Presentations**.

Extra Example 3

Write an equation of the line shown.

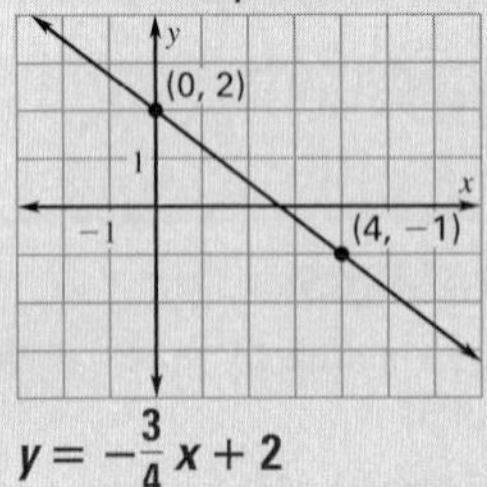

$y = -\frac{3}{4}x + 2$

USING TWO POINTS If you know the point where a line crosses the y-axis and any other point on the line, you can write an equation of the line.

EXAMPLE 3 Write an equation of a line given two points

Write an equation of the line shown.

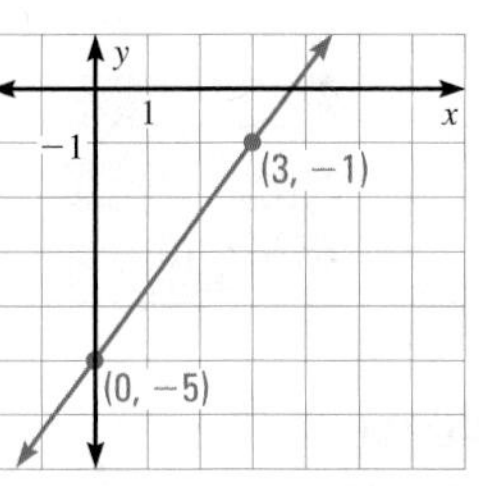

Solution

STEP 1 **Calculate** the slope.

$$m = \frac{y_2 - y_1}{x_2 - x_1} = \frac{-1 - (-5)}{3 - 0} = \frac{4}{3}$$

STEP 2 **Write** an equation of the line. The line crosses the y-axis at $(0, -5)$. So, the y-intercept is -5.

$y = mx + b$ **Write slope-intercept form.**

$y = \frac{4}{3}x - 5$ **Substitute $\frac{4}{3}$ for m and -5 for b.**

WRITING FUNCTIONS Recall that the graphs of linear functions are lines. You can use slope-intercept form to write a linear function.

EXAMPLE 4 Write a linear function

REVIEW FUNCTIONS
For help with using function notation, see p. 262.

Write an equation for the linear function f with the values $f(0) = 5$ and $f(4) = 17$.

Solution

STEP 1 **Write** $f(0) = 5$ as $(0, 5)$ and $f(4) = 17$ as $(4, 17)$.

STEP 2 **Calculate** the slope of the line that passes through $(0, 5)$ and $(4, 17)$.

$$m = \frac{y_2 - y_1}{x_2 - x_1} = \frac{17 - 5}{4 - 0} = \frac{12}{4} = 3$$

STEP 3 **Write** an equation of the line. The line crosses the y-axis at $(0, 5)$. So, the y-intercept is 5.

$y = mx + b$ **Write slope-intercept form.**

$y = 3x + 5$ **Substitute 3 for m and 5 for b.**

▶ The function is $f(x) = 3x + 5$.

✓ GUIDED PRACTICE for Examples 3 and 4

3. Write an equation of the line shown. $y = -\frac{1}{2}x + 1$

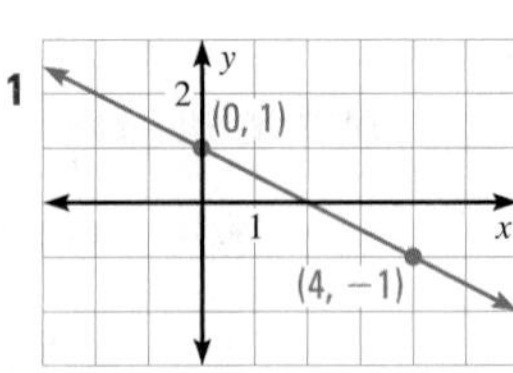

Write an equation for the linear function f with the given values.

4. $f(0) = -2, f(8) = 4$ $y = \frac{3}{4}x - 2$

5. $f(-3) = 6, f(0) = 5$ $y = -\frac{1}{3}x + 5$

READING
The value b is a starting value in a real-world situation modeled by $y = mx + b$, because when $x = 0$, the value of y is b.

MODELING REAL-WORLD SITUATIONS When a quantity y changes at a constant rate with respect to a quantity x, you can use the equation $y = mx + b$ to model the relationship. The value of m is the constant rate of change, and the value of b is an initial, or starting, value for y.

EXAMPLE 5 Solve a multi-step problem

RECORDING STUDIO A recording studio charges musicians an initial fee of $50 to record an album. Studio time costs an additional $35 per hour.

a. Write an equation that gives the total cost of an album as a function of studio time (in hours).

b. Find the total cost of recording an album that takes 10 hours of studio time.

Solution

a. The cost changes at a constant rate, so you can write an equation in slope-intercept form to model the total cost.

STEP 1 **Identify** the rate of change and the starting value.

Rate of change, *m*: cost per hour
Starting value, *b*: initial fee

STEP 2 **Write** a verbal model. Then write the equation.

Total cost (dollars)	=	Cost per hour (dollars per hour)	•	Studio time (hours)	+	Initial fee (dollars)
↓		↓		↓		↓
C	=	35	•	t	+	50

CHECK Use unit analysis to check the equation.

$$\text{dollars} = \frac{\text{dollars}}{\cancel{\text{hour}}} \cdot \cancel{\text{hours}} + \text{dollars} \checkmark$$

▶ The total cost C is given by the function $C = 35t + 50$ where t is the studio time (in hours).

b. Evaluate the function for $t = 10$.

$C = 35(10) + 50 = 400$ **Substitute 10 for t and simplify.**

▶ The total cost for 10 hours of studio time is $400.

✓ **GUIDED PRACTICE** for Example 5

6. **WHAT IF?** In Example 5, suppose the recording studio raises its initial fee to $75 and charges $40 per hour for studio time.

   a. Write an equation that gives the total cost of an album as a function of studio time (in hours). **$C = 40t + 75$**

   b. Find the total cost of recording an album that takes 10 hours of studio time. **$475**

Extra Example 4

Write an equation for the linear function f with the values $f(0) = 3$ and $f(-4) = 11$. **$f(x) = -2x + 3$**

Key Question to Ask for Example 4

- How does $f(4) = 17$ correspond to the ordered pair (x, y)? **Writing the function as $f(x) = y$ and comparing that to $f(4) = 17$, the value of x is 4 and the value of y is 17.**

Extra Example 5

A dance academy charges $20 to use the facility and $25 per hour of instruction.

a. Write an equation that gives the total cost to learn dance at the academy as a function of hours of instruction. **The total cost C is given by $C = 25t + 20$, where t is time in hours.**

b. Find the total cost of 2 hours of dance instruction. **$70**

Closing the Lesson

Have students summarize the major points of the lesson and answer the Essential Question: How do you write an equation of a line in slope-intercept form?

- **An equation in slope-intercept form, $y = mx + b$, has slope m and y-intercept b.**
- **Given two points on a graph, one of which gives the y-intercept, you can find the slope m and the y-intercept b and substitute those values into $y = mx + b$.**
- **You can write a function in slope-intercept form given values of $f(0)$, x, and $f(x)$.**

To write an equation in slope-intercept form, substitute the slope for m and the y-intercept for b in the equation $y = mx + b$. In real-world situations, use the constant rate of change for m and the starting value for b.

Differentiated Instruction

Inclusion Students may have difficulty working with equations when the variables are not x and y. To graph the equation in **Example 5**, have students write the following two equations.

$C = 35t + 50$

$y = 35x + 50$

Because t matches up with x and C matches up with y, it is easy to explain why t is plotted on the x-axis and C is plotted on the y-axis.

See also the *Differentiated Instruction Resources* for more strategies.

4 PRACTICE AND APPLY

Assignment Guide

Answer Transparencies available for all exercises

Basic:
Day 1: EP p. 941 Exs. 33–36
pp. 286–289
Exs. 1–5, 9–12, 16–20, 24–26, 30–32, 39, 40, 45–49, 53–63 odd

Average:
Day 1: pp. 286–289
Exs. 1, 2, 6–9, 13–17, 21–24, 26, 28, 33–35, 39–43, 46–51, 56, 57, 62, 63

Advanced:
Day 1: pp. 286–289
Exs. 1, 7–9, 13–15, 21–23, 27–29, 36–44*, 47–52*, 58, 64

Block:
pp. 286–289
Exs. 1, 2, 6–9, 13–17, 21–24, 26, 28, 33–35, 39–43, 46–51, 56, 57, 62, 63 (with 5.2)

Differentiated Instruction

See *Differentiated Instruction Resources* for suggestions on addressing the needs of a diverse classroom.

Homework Check

For a quick check of student understanding of key concepts, go over the following exercises:

Basic: 4, 10, 20, 32, 45
Average: 6, 13, 26, 34, 46
Advanced: 8, 14, 28, 38, 48

Extra Practice

- Student Edition, p. 942
- Chapter Resource Book: Practice levels A, B, C

Practice Worksheet

An easily-readable reduced practice page (with answers) for this lesson can be found on p. 280C.

5.1 EXERCISES

HOMEWORK KEY
○ = **WORKED-OUT SOLUTIONS** on p. WS10 for Exs. 11, 19, and 47
★ = **STANDARDIZED TEST PRACTICE** Exs. 2, 9, 40, 43, 48, and 50
◆ = **MULTIPLE REPRESENTATIONS** Ex. 49

SKILL PRACTICE

A

1. **VOCABULARY** Copy and complete: The ratio of the rise to the run between any two points on a nonvertical line is called the _?_. **slope**

2. ★ **WRITING** *Explain* how you can use slope-intercept form to write an equation of a line given its slope and y-intercept. **You can substitute the slope for m and the y-intercept for b to get the equation of the line.**

EXAMPLE 1 on p. 283 for Exs. 3–9, 16

WRITING EQUATIONS Write an equation of the line with the given slope and y-intercept.

3. slope: 2, y-intercept: 9 **$y = 2x + 9$**
4. slope: 1, y-intercept: 5 **$y = x + 5$**
5. slope: -3, y-intercept: 0 **$y = -3x$**
6. slope: -7, y-intercept: 1 **$y = -7x + 1$**
7. slope: $\frac{2}{3}$, y-intercept: -9 **$y = \frac{2}{3}x - 9$**
8. slope: $\frac{3}{4}$, y-intercept: -6 **$y = \frac{3}{4}x - 6$**

9. ★ **MULTIPLE CHOICE** Which equation represents the line with a slope of -1 and a y-intercept of 2? **A**

Ⓐ $y = -x + 2$ Ⓑ $y = 2x - 1$ Ⓒ $y = x - 2$ Ⓓ $y = 2x + 1$

EXAMPLE 2 on p. 283 for Exs. 10–15

WRITING EQUATIONS Write an equation of the line shown.

10. 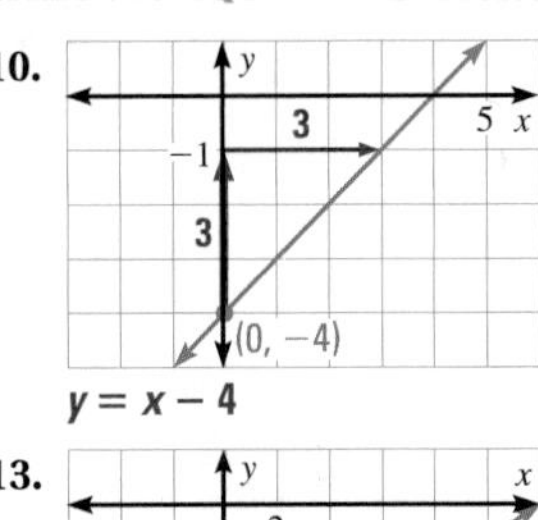

$y = x - 4$

11. 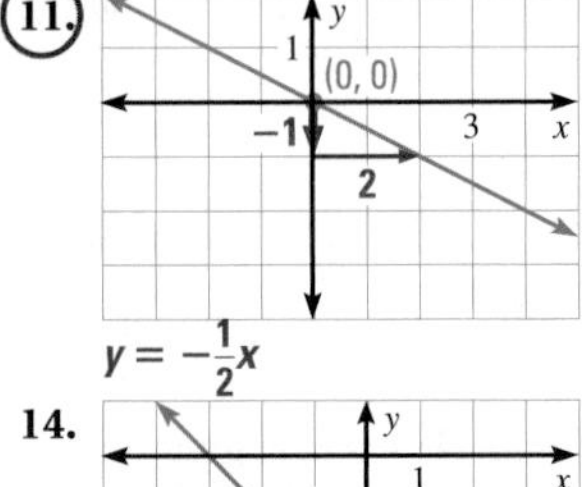

$y = -\frac{1}{2}x$

12. 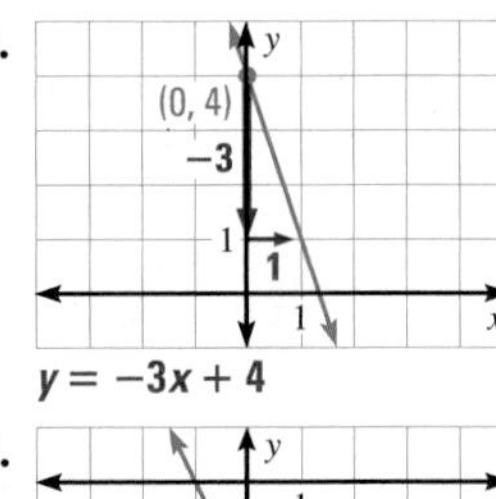

$y = -3x + 4$

13. 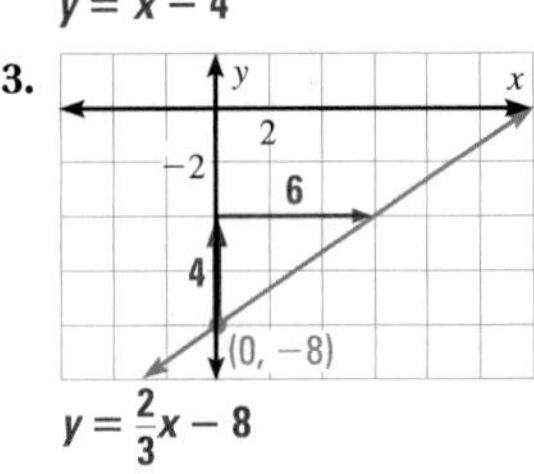

$y = \frac{2}{3}x - 8$

14. 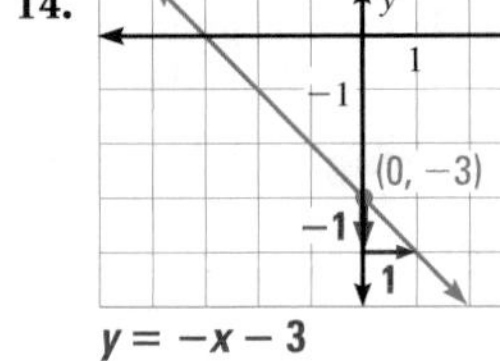

$y = -x - 3$

15. 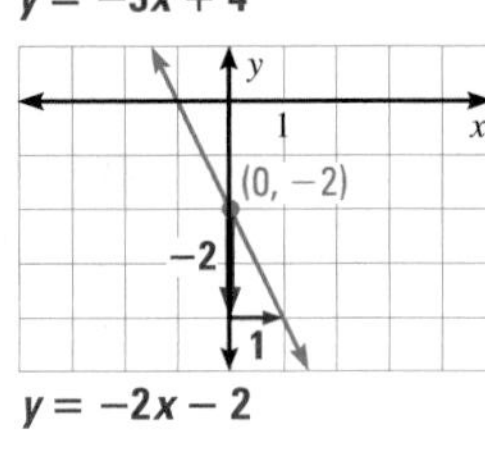

$y = -2x - 2$

16. **ERROR ANALYSIS** *Describe* and correct the error in writing an equation of the line with a slope of 2 and a y-intercept of 7.

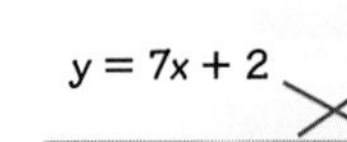

16. The given slope and y-intercept were interchanged in the slope-intercept form of the equation; $y = 2x + 7$.

EXAMPLE 3 on p. 284 for Exs. 17–29

17. **ERROR ANALYSIS** *Describe* and correct the error in writing an equation of the line shown.

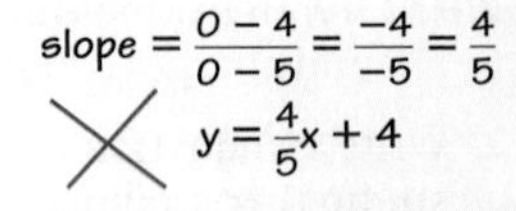

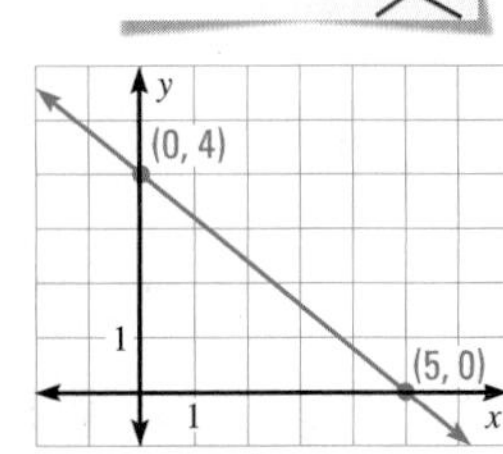

The slope should be $\frac{0-4}{5-0}$, $y = -\frac{4}{5}x + 4$.

USING A GRAPH **Write an equation of the line shown.**

18.
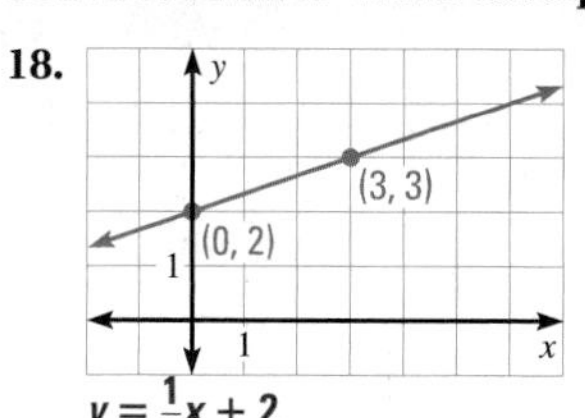

$y = \frac{1}{3}x + 2$

(19.)
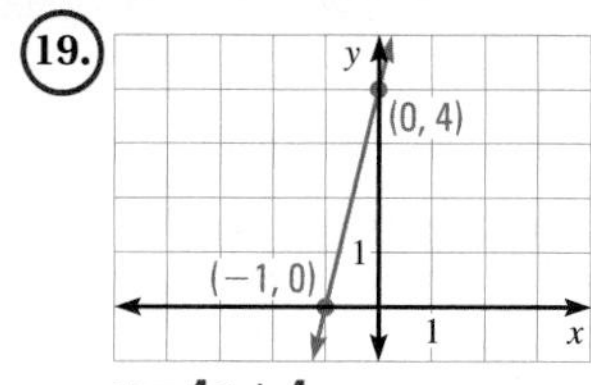

$y = 4x + 4$

20.
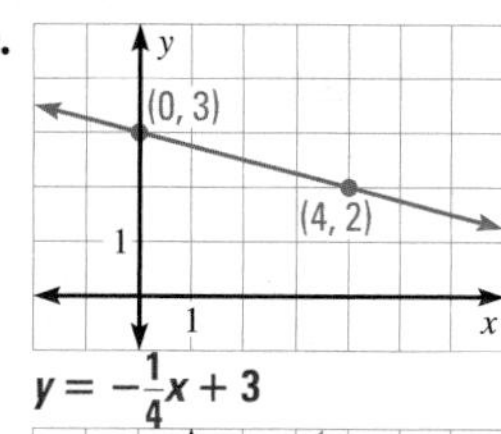

$y = -\frac{1}{4}x + 3$

21.
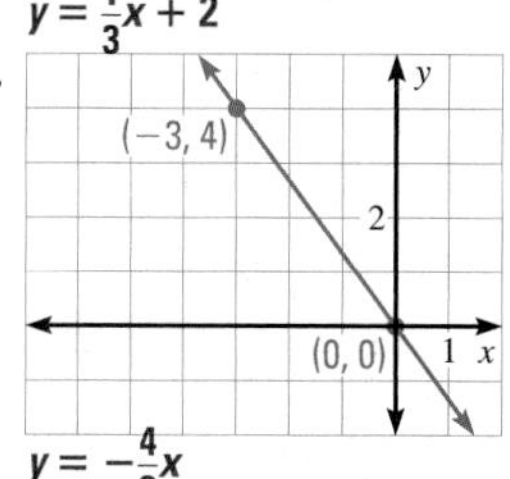

$y = -\frac{4}{3}x$

22.
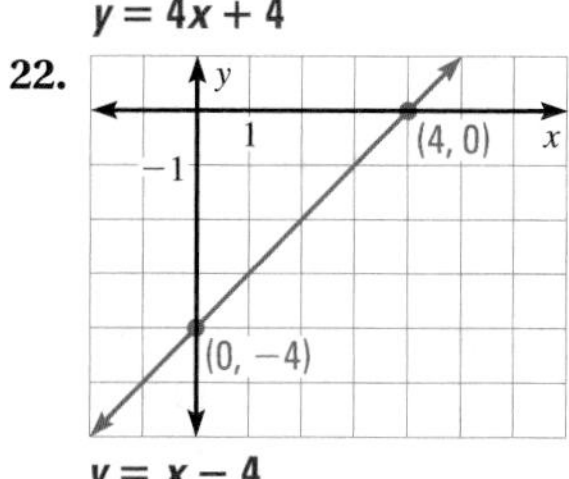

$y = x - 4$

23.
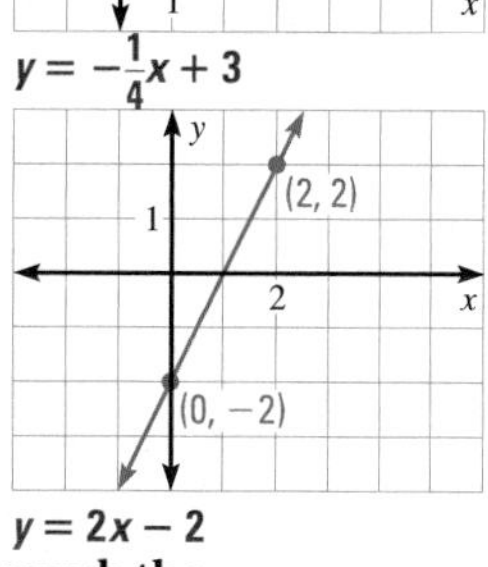

$y = 2x - 2$

USING TWO POINTS **Write an equation of the line that passes through the given points.**

24. $(-3, 1), (0, -8)$ $y = -3x - 8$

25. $(2, -7), (0, -5)$ $y = -x - 5$

26. $(2, -4), (0, -4)$ $y = -4$

27. $(0, 4), (8, 3.5)$ $y = -0.0625x + 4$

28. $(0, 5), (1.5, 1)$ $y = -\frac{8}{3}x + 5$

29. $(-6, 0), (0, -24)$ $y = -4x - 24$

EXAMPLE 4 on p. 284 for Exs. 30–38

WRITING FUNCTIONS **Write an equation for the linear function *f* with the given values.**

30. $f(0) = 2, f(2) = 4$ $y = x + 2$

31. $f(0) = 7, f(3) = 1$ $y = -2x + 7$

32. $f(0) = -2, f(4) = -3$ $y = -\frac{1}{4}x - 2$

33. $f(0) = -1, f(5) = -5$ $y = -\frac{4}{5}x - 1$

34. $f(-2) = 6, f(0) = -4$ $y = -5x - 4$

35. $f(-6) = -1, f(0) = 3$ $y = \frac{2}{3}x + 3$

36. $f(4) = 13, f(0) = 21$ $y = -2x + 21$

37. $f(0) = 9, f(3) = 0$ $y = -3x + 9$

38. $f(0.2) = 1, f(0) = 0.6$ $y = 2x + 0.6$

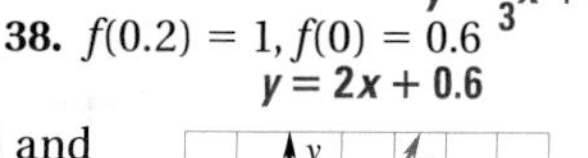

B

39. **VISUAL THINKING** Line ℓ passes through the points (0, 1) and (3, 0). What change(s) in the parameters m and b in the slope-intercept equation of k occurred to produce the slope-intercept equation of ℓ?

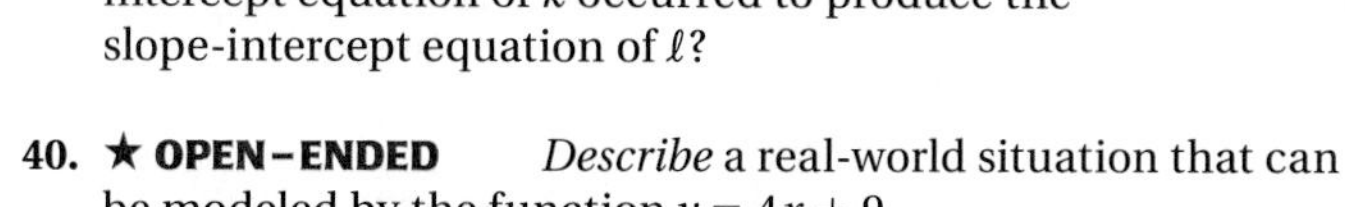

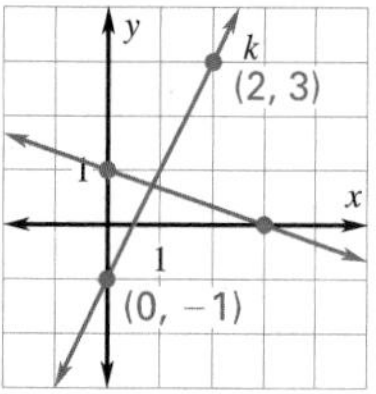

40. ★ **OPEN-ENDED** *Describe* a real-world situation that can be modeled by the function $y = 4x + 9$.

USING A DIAGRAM OR TABLE **Write an equation that represents the linear function shown in the mapping diagram or table.**

41. $y = -2x + 1$

x	$f(x)$
1	−1
0	1
−1	3

42. $y = \frac{1}{2}x$

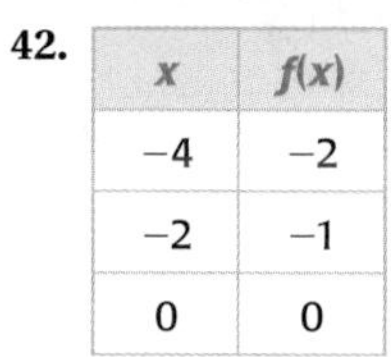

x	$f(x)$
−4	−2
−2	−1
0	0

43. ★ **WRITING** A line passes through the points (3, 5) and (3, −7). Is it possible to write an equation of the line in slope-intercept form? *Justify* your answer. **No; the slope of the line is undefined, the equation is $x = 3$, which is not in slope-intercept form.**

C

44. **CHALLENGE** Show that the equation of the line that passes through the points $(0, b)$ and $(1, b + m)$ is $y = mx + b$. *Explain* how you can be sure that the point $(-1, b - m)$ also lies on the line. **See margin.**

39. The equations in slope-intercept form of the two lines are k: $y = 2x - 1$ and ℓ: $y = -\frac{1}{3}x + 1$. The parameter m changed from 2 to $-\frac{1}{3}$ and the parameter b changed from −1 to 1.

40. *Sample answer:* A health club offers an aerobics membership that charges \$9 plus \$4 per class.

Avoiding Common Errors

Exercises 3–9 Students sometimes interchange the slope and the *y*-intercept when replacing *m* and *b* in the slope-intercept form of an equation of the line. Suggest that students double-check that *m* is the slope and *b* is the *y*-intercept in their equations.

Teaching Strategy

Exercises 10–15 Prior to these exercises, you may want to review how to use the ratio of rise to run to determine slope. In discussing the ratio, you might want to point out that a ratio of 4 to 4, for example, is 1, whereas a ratio of 4 to 1 is 4.

Study Strategy

Exercises 18–23 Tell students they can use the ratio of rise to run to check their slope calculations.

Reading Strategy

Exercises 30–38 Remind students that $f(x)$ is read "the value of *f* at *x*." When *x* in the parentheses is replaced by a number such as 3, it can be read "the value of *f* when *x* is 3."

44. Find the slope by substituting the values: $\frac{b + m - b}{1 - 0} = m$. The *y*-intercept is when $x = 0$, so the *y*-intercept is b. If you substitute $(-1, b - m)$ into the equation $y = mx + b$, you get $b - m = -m + b$ which is a true statement.

Reading Strategy

Exercise 49 Remind students to read instructions carefully. Point out in part a that *x* is the number of years since 1970. Tell them that this affects whether they use 0 or 1 to designate 1970 and, in turn, affects the numbers they use to designate subsequent years.

Exercise 49 For more information about Mt. Kilimanjaro and its glaciers, visit nationalgeographic.com and do a search for "Mt. Kilimanjaro AND glaciers."

Mathematical Reasoning

Exercises 50–51 You may want to discuss with students how an equation of the form $y = mx + b$ can model these situations. Ask them to identify the independent and dependent variables, the values for *m*, and the values for *b*. The starting values of *b* may give students problems in both of these exercises. Point out that, depending on the context, a starting value may require calculation.

49a.

x (years since 1970)	y (km²)
0	5.2
10	4.1
20	3.0
30	1.9

49b.

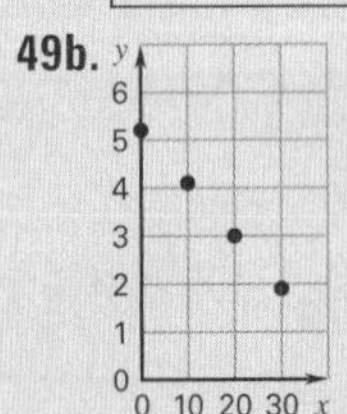

PROBLEM SOLVING

EXAMPLE 5 A on p. 285 for Exs. 45–49

45. WEB SERVER The initial fee to have a website set up using a server is \$48. It costs \$44 per month to maintain the website.

a. Write an equation that gives the total cost of setting up and maintaining a website as a function of the number of months it is maintained. $C = 44m + 48$

b. Find the total cost of setting up and maintaining the website for 6 months. **\$312**

@HomeTutor for problem solving help at classzone.com

46. PHOTOGRAPHS A camera shop charges \$3.99 for an enlargement of a photograph. Enlargements can be delivered for a charge of \$1.49 per order. Write an equation that gives the total cost of an order with delivery as a function of the number of enlargements. Find the total cost of ordering 8 photograph enlargements with delivery. $C = 3.99e + 1.49$; **\$33.41**

@HomeTutor for problem solving help at classzone.com

47. AQUARIUM Your family spends \$30 for tickets to an aquarium and \$3 per hour for parking. Write an equation that gives the total cost of your family's visit to the aquarium as a function of the number of hours that you are there. Find the total cost of 4 hours at the aquarium. $C = 3h + 30$; **\$42**

48. ★ SHORT RESPONSE Scientists found that the number of ant species in Clark Canyon, Nevada, increases at a rate of 0.0037 species per meter of elevation. There are approximately 3 ant species at sea level.

a. Write an equation that gives the number of ant species as a function of the elevation (in meters). $a = 0.0037e + 3$

b. Identify the dependent and independent variables in this situation. **dependent variable: *a*, independent variable: *e***

c. *Explain* how you can use the equation from part (a) to approximate the number of ant species at an elevation of 2 meters. **Substitute 2 for *e* to get approximately 3.**

B **49. MULTIPLE REPRESENTATIONS** The timeline shows the approximate total area of glaciers on Mount Kilimanjaro from 1970 to 2000.

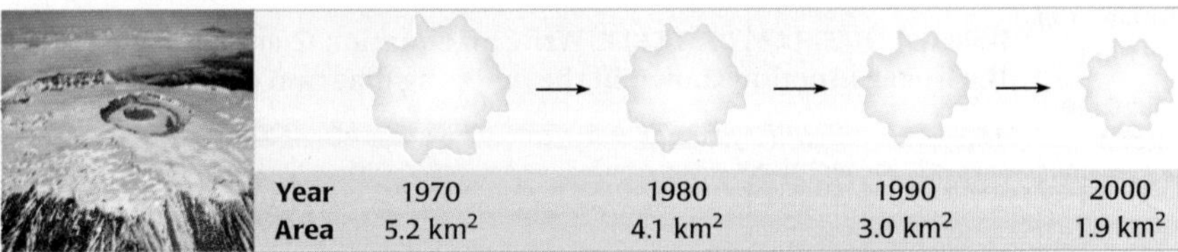

Year 1970 1980 1990 2000
Area 5.2 km² 4.1 km² 3.0 km² 1.9 km²

a. **Making a Table** Make a table that shows the number of years *x* since 1970 and the area of the glaciers *y* (in square kilometers). **See margin.**

b. **Drawing a Graph** Graph the data in the table. *Explain* how you know the area of glaciers changed at a constant rate. **See margin for art; the area of the glaciers changed −1.1 square kilometers between every 10 year interval.**

c. **Writing an Equation** Write an equation that models the area of glaciers as a function of the number of years since 1970. By how much did the area of the glaciers decrease each year from 1970 to 2000? $y = -0.11x + 5.2$; -0.11 km²

○ = WORKED-OUT SOLUTIONS on p. WS1 ★ = STANDARDIZED TEST PRACTICE ◆ = MULTIPLE REPRESENTATIONS

50. ★ **EXTENDED RESPONSE** The Harris Dam in Maine releases water into the Kennebec River. From 10:00 A.M. to 1:00 P.M. during each day of whitewater rafting season, water is released at a greater rate than usual.

Time interval	Release rate (gallons per hour)
12:00 A.M. to 10:00 A.M.	8.1 million
10:00 A.M. to 1:00 P.M.	130 million

a. On a day during rafting season, how much water is released by 10:00 A.M.? **81 million gal**

b. Write an equation that gives, for a day during rafting season, the total amount of water (in gallons) released as a function of the number of hours since 10:00 A.M. $y = 130{,}000{,}000h$

c. What is the domain of the function from part (b)? *Explain.* $0 \le h \le 3$**; water is only released for 3 hours after 10:00 A.M.**

51. **FIREFIGHTING** The diagram shows the time a firefighting aircraft takes to scoop water from a lake, fly to a fire, and drop the water on the fire.

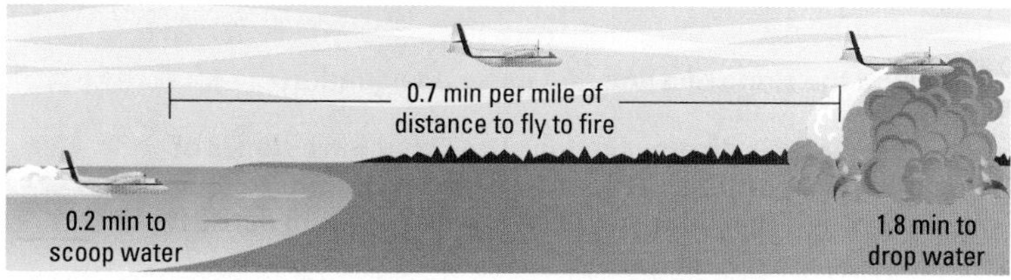

a. **Model** Write an equation that gives the total time (in minutes) that the aircraft takes to scoop, fly, and drop as a function of the distance (in miles) flown from the lake to the fire. $t = 0.7d + 2$

b. **Predict** Find the time the aircraft takes to scoop, fly, and drop if it travels 20 miles from the lake to the fire. **16 min**

C 52. **CHALLENGE** The elevation at which a baseball game is played affects the distance a ball travels when hit. For every increase of 1000 feet in elevation, the ball travels about 7 feet farther. Suppose a baseball travels 400 feet when hit in a ball park at sea level.

a. **Model** Write an equation that gives the distance (in feet) the baseball travels as a function of the elevation of the ball park in which it is hit. $d = \frac{7}{1000}e + 400$

b. **Justify** *Justify* the equation from part (a) using unit analysis. $d \text{ ft} = \frac{7}{1000} \cdot e \text{ ft} + 400 \text{ ft}$

c. **Predict** If the ball were hit in exactly the same way at a park with an elevation of 3500 feet, how far would it travel? **424.5 ft**

MIXED REVIEW

Solve the equation. Check your solution.

53. $x + 11 = 6$ *(p. 134)* **−5**

54. $x - 7 = 13$ *(p. 134)* **20**

55. $0.2x = -1$ *(p. 134)* **−5**

56. $3x + 9 = 21$ *(p. 141)* **4**

57. $2x - 3 = 25$ *(p. 141)* **14**

58. $4x - 8 = -10$ *(p. 141)* **−0.5**

PREVIEW
Prepare for Lesson 5.2 in Exs. 59–64.

Find the slope of the line that passes through the points. *(p. 235)*

59. $(-4, 6), (0, -2)$ **−2**

60. $(-3, -2), (0, 1)$ **1**

61. $(5, 6), (-1, 3)$ $\frac{1}{2}$

62. $(-9, 3), (7, -1)$ $-\frac{1}{4}$

63. $(3, -12), (5, -7)$ $\frac{5}{2}$

64. $(10, 4), (-8, 2)$ $\frac{1}{9}$

5 ASSESS AND RETEACH

Daily Homework Quiz

Transparency Available

1. Write an equation of the line with a slope of −4 and a y-intercept of 1. $y = -4x + 1$

Write an equation of the line that passes through the given points.

2. $(-9, 1), (0, -8)$ $y = -x - 8$

3. $(-4, -6), (0, 6)$ $y = 3x + 6$

4. Write an equation for the linear function f with $f(0) = -4$ and $f(-1) = -9$. $y = 5x - 4$

5. An electronics game store sells used games for $12.99 with a $20 membership fee. Write an equation that gives the total cost to become a member and buy games as a function of the number of games that are purchased. Then find the cost for 6 games. $C = 12.99g + 20$ **where** C **is total cost and** g **is the number of games; $97.94**

 **Online Quiz**

Available at **classzone.com**

Diagnosis/Remediation

- Practice A, B, C in Chapter Resource Book
- Study Guide in Chapter Resource Book
- Practice Workbook
- @HomeTutor

Challenge

Additional challenge is available in the Chapter Resource Book.

1 PLAN AND PREPARE

Learn the Method

- Students will find the slope and the y-intercept of a line using a graphing calculator and then write an equation of the line.
- After the activity, students can use a graphing calculator to check their solutions in Exercises 24–38 in Lesson 5.1.

Keystroke Help

Keystrokes for several models of calculators are available in blackline format in the *Chapter Resource Book*.

2 TEACH

Tips for Success

In Example 1, remind students that a line with a positive slope rises from left to right and a line with a negative slope falls from left to right.

Extra Example 1

In the same viewing window, display the four lines that have slopes of -2, -1, 1, and 2 and a y-intercept of -3. Then use the graphs to determine which line passes through the point $(1, -4)$. Write an equation of the line.

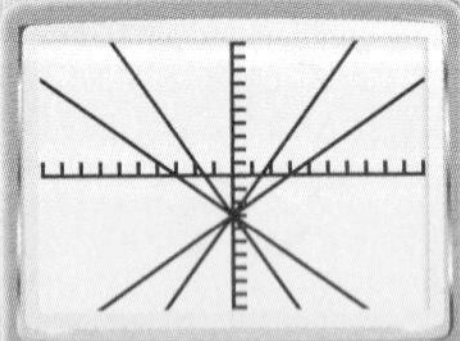

The line that passes through the point $(1, -4)$ is the line with a slope of -1. An equation of the line is $y = -x - 3$.

5.1 Investigate Families of Lines

QUESTION **How can you use a graphing calculator to find equations of lines using slopes and y-intercepts?**

Recall from Chapter 4 that you can create families of lines by varying the value of either m or b in $y = mx + b$. The constants m and b are called *parameters*. Given the value of one parameter, you can determine the value of the other parameter if you also have information that uniquely identifies one member of the family of lines.

EXAMPLE 1 **Find the slope of a line and write an equation**

In the same viewing window, display the four lines that have slopes of -1, -0.5, 0.5, and 1 and a y-intercept of 2. Then use the graphs to determine which line passes through the point (12, 8). Write an equation of the line.

STEP 1 ***Enter equations***

Press Y= and enter the four equations. Because the lines all have the same y-intercept, they constitute a family of lines and can be entered as shown.

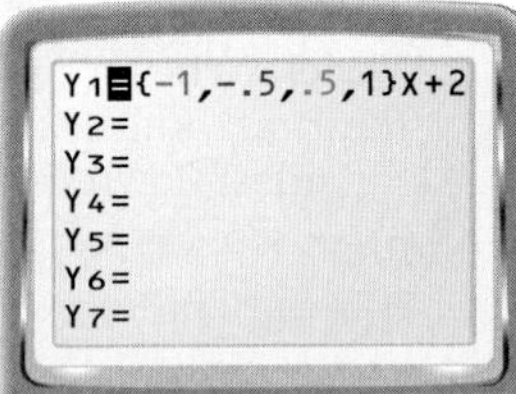

STEP 2 ***Display graphs***

Graph the equations in an appropriate viewing window. Press TRACE and use the left and right arrow keys to move along one of the lines until $x = 12$. Use the up and down arrow keys to see which line passes through (12, 8).

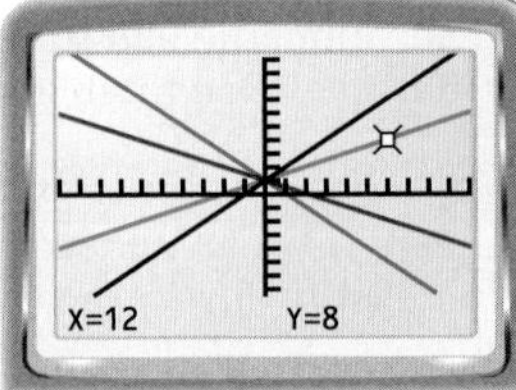

STEP 3 ***Find the line***

The line that passes through (12, 8) is the line with a slope of 0.5. So, an equation of the line is $y = 0.5x + 2$.

PRACTICE

Display the lines that have the same y-intercept but different slopes, as given, in the same viewing window. Determine which line passes through the given point. Write an equation of the line.

1. Slopes: -3, -2, 2, 3; y-intercept: 5; point: $(-3, 11)$ **$y = -2x + 5$**
2. Slopes: 4, -2.5, 2.5, 4; y-intercept: -1; point: $(4, -11)$ **$y = -2.5x - 1$**
3. Slopes: -2, -1, 1, 2; y-intercept: 1.5; point: $(1, 3.5)$ **$y = 2x + 1.5$**

EXAMPLE 2 Find the y-intercept of a line and write an equation

In the same viewing window, display the five lines that have a slope of 0.5 and y-intercepts of −2, −1, 0, 1, and 2. Then use the graphs to determine which line passes through the point (−2, −2). Write an equation of the line.

STEP 1 *Enter equations*
Press [Y=] and enter the five equations. Because the lines all have the same slope, they constitute a family of lines and can be entered as shown below.

STEP 2 *Display graphs*
Graph the equations in an appropriate viewing window. Press [TRACE] and use the left and right arrow keys to move along one of the lines until $x = -2$. Use the up and down arrow keys to see which line passes through (−2, −2).

STEP 3 *Find the line*
The line that passes through (−2, −2) is the line with a y-intercept of −1. So, an equation of the line is $y = 0.5x - 1$.

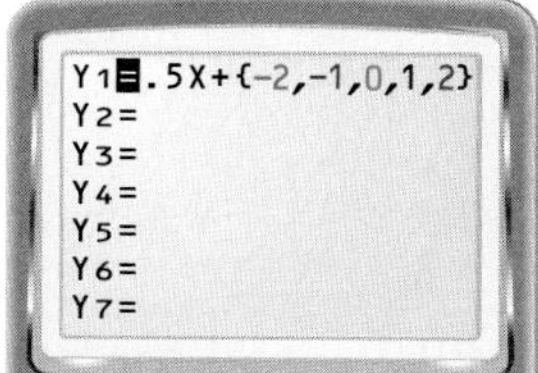

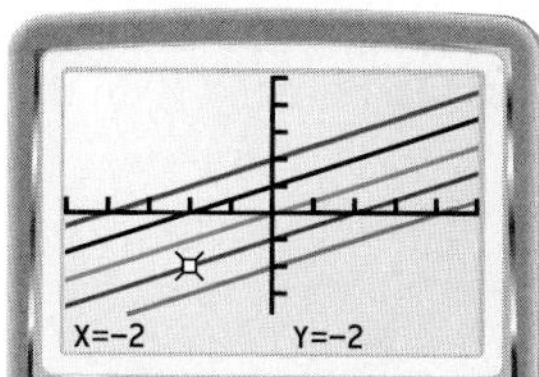

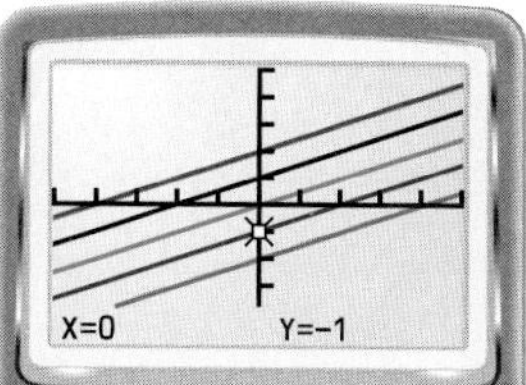

PRACTICE

Display the lines that have the same slope but different y-intercepts, as given, in the same viewing window. Determine which line passes through the given point. Write an equation of the line.

4. Slope: −3; y-intercepts: −2, −1, 0, 1, 2; point: (4, −13) **$y = -3x - 1$**
5. Slope: 1.5; y-intercepts: −2, −1, 0, 1, 2; point: (−2, −1) **$y = 1.5x + 2$**
6. Slope: −0.5; y-intercepts: −3, −1.5, 0, 1.5, 3; point: (−4, 3.5) **$y = -0.5x + 1.5$**
7. Slope: 4; y-intercepts: −3, −1, 0, 1, 3; point: (2, 5) **$y = 4x - 3$**
8. Slope: 2; y-intercepts: −6, −3, 0, 3, 6; point: (−2, −7) **$y = 2x - 3$**

DRAW CONCLUSIONS

9. Of all the lines having equations of the form $y = 0.5x + b$, which one passes through the point (2, 2)? *Explain* how you found your answer. **$y = 0.5x + 1$; substitute 2 for x, 2 for y, and solve for b.**
10. *Describe* a process you could use to find an equation of a line that has a slope of −0.25 and passes through the point (8, −2). ***Sample answer:*** **Substitute −0.25 for m, 8 for x, and −2 for y and solve for b.**

Extra Example 2

In the same viewing window, display the five lines that have a slope of −2 and y-intercepts of −4, −2, 0, 2, and 4. Then use the graphs to determine which line passes through the point (−1, 2). Write an equation of the line.

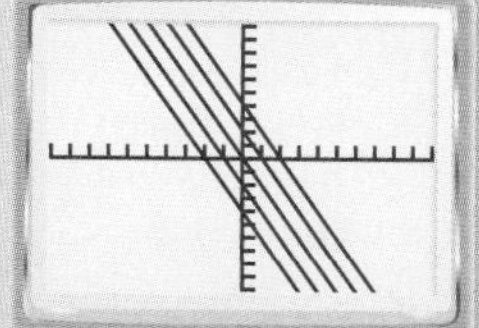

The line that passes through the point (−1, 2) is the line with a y-intercept of 0. An equation of the line is $y = -2x$.

3 ASSESS AND RETEACH

1. Describe a process you could use to find an equation of a line that has a y-intercept of 1 and passes through the point (2, 4). **In the same viewing window, display graphs through (0, 1) with several slopes, such as 0.5, 1, 1.5, and 2. Then use trace to find the line that passes through (2, 4).**
2. Of all the lines having equations of the form $y = mx - 2$, which one passes through the point (3, 4)? Explain how you found your answer. **An equation of the line is $y = 2x - 2$. I first tried $y = x - 2$. That line passes through (3, 1), so in order to pass through (3, 4) I needed a greater slope. I graphed equations of lines through (0, −2) with slopes of 1.5, 2, and 2.5. I used trace to find that a line with a slope of 2 passes through (3, 4).**

5.2 Use Linear Equations in Slope-Intercept Form

Before You wrote an equation of a line using its slope and y-intercept.

Now You will write an equation of a line using points on the line.

Why So you can write a model for total cost, as in Example 5.

1 PLAN AND PREPARE

Warm-Up Exercises

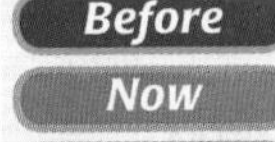

Transparency Available

Find the slope of the line that passes through the points.

1. (0, −2), (1, 3) **5**

2. (3, 2), (5, −2) **−2**

3. Bill borrowed $75 from his parents. He is paying back $5 per week. Write an equation that models this situation. $y = -5x + 75$

Notetaking Guide

Transparency Available

Promotes interactive learning and notetaking skills.

Pacing

Basic: 2 days

Average: 2 days

Advanced: 2 days

Block: 0.5 block with 5.1
0.5 block with 5.3

- See *Teaching Guide/Lesson Plan.*

2 FOCUS AND MOTIVATE

Essential Question

Big Idea 2, p. 281

How do you find the equation of a line given two points? **Tell students they will learn how to answer this question by using the slope formula and finding the y-intercept.**

Key Vocabulary
- ***y*-intercept,** *p. 225*
- **slope,** *p. 235*
- **slope-intercept form,** *p. 244*

KEY CONCEPT — *For Your Notebook*

Writing an Equation of a Line in Slope-Intercept Form

STEP 1 **Identify** the slope m. You can use the slope formula to calculate the slope if you know two points on the line.

STEP 2 **Find** the y-intercept. You can substitute the slope and the coordinates of a point (x, y) on the line in $y = mx + b$. Then solve for b.

STEP 3 **Write** an equation using $y = mx + b$.

EXAMPLE 1 Write an equation given the slope and a point

Write an equation of the line that passes through the point (−1, 3) and has a slope of −4.

Solution

STEP 1 **Identify** the slope. The slope is −4.

STEP 2 **Find** the y-intercept. Substitute the slope and the coordinates of the given point in $y = mx + b$. Solve for b.

$y = mx + b$ — Write slope-intercept form.

$3 = -4(-1) + b$ — Substitute −4 for m, −1 for x, and 3 for y.

$-1 = b$ — Solve for b.

AVOID ERRORS
When you substitute, be careful not to mix up the x- and y-values.

STEP 3 **Write** an equation of the line.

$y = mx + b$ — Write slope-intercept form.

$y = -4x - 1$ — Substitute −4 for m and −1 for b.

GUIDED PRACTICE for Example 1

1. Write an equation of the line that passes through the point (6, 3) and has a slope of 2. $y = 2x - 9$

NCTM STANDARDS

Standard 3: Describe spatial relationships using coordinate geometry

Standard 8: Use the language of math to express ideas

Resource Planning Guide

Chapter Resource Book
- Teaching Guide/Lesson Plan
- Practice levels A, B, C
- Study Guide
- Catch-up for Absent Students
- Application
- Challenge

Workbooks
- Notetaking Guide
- Practice Workbook

Teaching Options
- **Power Presentations** provides dynamic electronic teaching resources for the classroom.
- **Activity Generator** provides editable activities for all ability levels.

Interactive Technology
- Easy Planner
- Power Presentations
- Activity Generator
- Animated Algebra
- Test Generator
- Online Quiz
- eWorkbook
- eEdition
- @HomeTutor

Resources for English Learners
- Spanish Study Guide
- Multi-Language Visual Glossary
- Student Resources in Spanish

See also the *Differentiated Instruction Resources* for more strategies for meeting individual needs.

EXAMPLE 2 Write an equation given two points

Write an equation of the line that passes through (−2, 5) and (2, −1).

Solution

STEP 1 **Calculate** the slope.

$$m = \frac{y_2 - y_1}{x_2 - x_1} = \frac{-1 - 5}{2 - (-2)} = \frac{-6}{4} = -\frac{3}{2}$$

STEP 2 **Find** the y-intercept. Use the slope and the point (−2, 5).

$y = mx + b$ — **Write slope-intercept form.**

$5 = -\frac{3}{2}(-2) + b$ — **Substitute $-\frac{3}{2}$ for m, −2 for x, and 5 for y.**

$2 = b$ — **Solve for b.**

STEP 3 **Write** an equation of the line.

$y = mx + b$ — **Write slope-intercept form.**

$y = -\frac{3}{2}x + 2$ — **Substitute $-\frac{3}{2}$ for m and 2 for b.**

ANOTHER WAY
You can also find the y-intercept using the coordinates of the other given point, (2, −1):
$y = mx + b$
$-1 = -\frac{3}{2}(2) + b$
$2 = b$

★ EXAMPLE 3 Standardized Test Practice

Which function has the values $f(4) = 9$ and $f(-4) = -7$?

Ⓐ $f(x) = 2x + 10$ Ⓑ $f(x) = 2x + 1$

Ⓒ $f(x) = 2x - 13$ Ⓓ $f(x) = 2x - 14$

STEP 1 **Calculate** the slope. Write $f(4) = 9$ as (4, 9) and $f(-4) = -7$ as (−4, −7).

$$m = \frac{y_2 - y_1}{x_2 - x_1} = \frac{-7 - 9}{-4 - 4} = \frac{-16}{-8} = 2$$

STEP 2 **Find** the y-intercept. Use the slope and the point (4, 9).

$y = mx + b$ — **Write slope-intercept form.**

$9 = 2(4) + b$ — **Substitute 2 for m, 4 for x, and 9 for y.**

$1 = b$ — **Solve for b.**

STEP 3 **Write** an equation for the function. Use function notation.

$f(x) = 2x + 1$ — **Substitute 2 for m and 1 for b.**

▶ The answer is B. Ⓐ Ⓑ Ⓒ Ⓓ

ELIMINATE CHOICES
You can also evaluate each function when $x = 4$ and $x = -4$. Eliminate any choices for which $f(4) \neq 9$ or $f(-4) \neq -7$.

GUIDED PRACTICE for Examples 2 and 3

2. Write an equation of the line that passes through (1, −2) and (−5, 4). $y = -x - 1$

3. Write an equation for the linear function with the values $f(-2) = 10$ and $f(4) = -2$. $y = -2x + 6$

Motivating the Lesson

Knowing how to write a linear equation that represents a real-world situation will help you determine information about the situation. For example, if you know that one person paid $135 for a ski club membership and 5 ski lessons and another person paid $183 for membership and 9 lessons, you could determine the membership fee and the cost per ski lesson.

3 TEACH

Extra Example 1

Write an equation of the line that passes through the point (6, 3) and has a slope of −2. $y = -2x + 15$

Extra Example 2

Write an equation of the line that passes through (3, 0) and (2, −4). $y = 4x - 12$

Key Questions to Ask for Example 2

- How is Example 2 different from Example 1? **In Example 1 you are given the slope and in Example 2 you have to use the two points to calculate the slope.**
- What values do you need from the graph of a line to write an equation of the line in slope-intercept form? **You need the coordinates of two points to calculate the slope and to determine the y-intercept.**

Extra Example 3

Which function has the values $f(2) = 8$ and $f(-2) = -4$? **A**

Ⓐ $f(x) = 3x + 2$
Ⓑ $f(x) = 3x + 14$
Ⓒ $f(x) = 3x - 10$
Ⓓ $f(x) = 3x - 12$

Extra Example 4

A carnival charges $2.50 per ride after an entrance fee. You paid a total of $22.50 after 6 rides. Write an equation that gives the total cost as a function of the number of rides. Find the total cost for 15 rides.
$C = 2.5n + 7.5$, where C is the total cost and n is the number of rides. The total cost for 15 rides is $45.

Key Questions to Ask for Example 4

- In a graph of the situation, which values would you graph on the x-and y-axes? **Graph the independent variable, t, time in months, on the x-axis, and the dependent variable, C, total cost, on the y-axis.**
- What would be the coordinates of the y-intercept in a graph of the equation? **(0, 30)**
- Which are two other points that the graph of the equation would pass through? **(1, 63), (9, 327)**
- What do the points (x, y) on the graph represent? **The points represent the total cost y after x months.**

CONCEPT SUMMARY — *For Your Notebook*

How to Write Equations in Slope-Intercept Form

Given slope m and y-intercept b

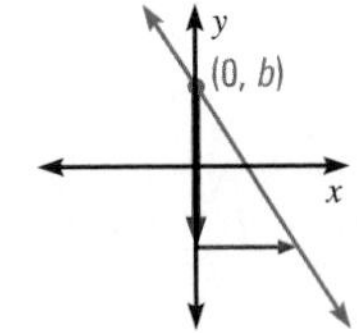

Substitute m and b in the equation $y = mx + b$.

Given slope m and one point

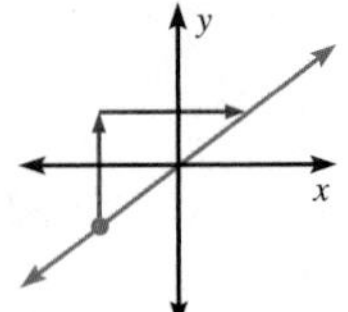

Substitute m and the coordinates of the point in $y = mx + b$. Solve for b. Write the equation.

Given two points

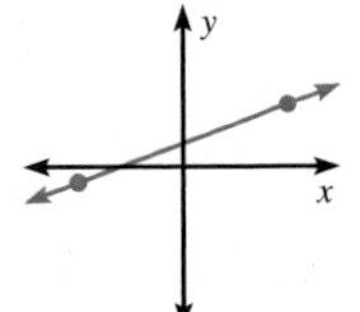

Use the points to find the slope m. Then follow the same steps described at the left.

MODELING REAL-WORLD SITUATIONS You can model a real-world situation that involves a constant rate of change with an equation in slope-intercept form.

EXAMPLE 4 Solve a multi-step problem

GYM MEMBERSHIP Your gym membership costs $33 per month after an initial membership fee. You paid a total of $228 after 6 months. Write an equation that gives the total cost as a function of the length of your gym membership (in months). Find the total cost after 9 months.

Solution

STEP 1 **Identify** the rate of change and starting value.

Rate of change, m: monthly cost, $33 per month
Starting value, b: initial membership fee

STEP 2 **Write** a verbal model. Then write an equation.

Total cost	=	Monthly cost	·	Number of months	+	Membership fee
C	=	33	·	t	+	b

STEP 3 **Find** the starting value. Membership for 6 months costs $228, so you can substitute 6 for t and 228 for C in the equation $C = 33t + b$.

$228 = 33(6) + b$ **Substitute 6 for t and 228 for C.**

$30 = b$ **Solve for b.**

STEP 4 **Write** an equation. Use the function from Step 2.

$C = 33t + 30$ **Substitute 30 for b.**

STEP 5 **Evaluate** the function when $t = 9$.

$C = 33(9) + 30 = 327$ **Substitute 9 for t. Simplify.**

▶ Your total cost after 9 months is $327.

Differentiated Instruction

English Learners The letter t is used for the number of months in **Example 4** because it is a time (and this word begins with the letter t). Tell students that t is commonly used as a variable for most measures of time (seconds, minutes, hours, days, and so on) in algebraic expressions and equations.

See also the *Differentiated Instruction Resources* for more strategies.

EXAMPLE 5 Solve a multi-step problem

BMX RACING In Bicycle Moto Cross (BMX) racing, racers purchase a one year membership to a track. They also pay an entry fee for each race at that track. One racer paid a total of $125 after 5 races. A second racer paid a total of $170 after 8 races. How much does the track membership cost? What is the entry fee per race?

ANOTHER WAY
For alternative methods for solving the problem in Example 5, turn to page 300 for the **Problem Solving Workshop**.

Solution

STEP 1 **Identify** the rate of change and starting value.

Rate of change, *m*: entry fee per race
Starting value, *b*: track membership cost

STEP 2 **Write** a verbal model. Then write an equation.

Total cost	=	Entry fee per race	·	Races entered	+	Membership cost
C	=	m	·	r	+	b

STEP 3 **Calculate** the rate of change. This is the entry fee per race. Use the slope formula. Racer 1 is represented by (5, 125). Racer 2 is represented by (8, 170).

$$m = \frac{y_2 - y_1}{x_2 - x_1} = \frac{170 - 125}{8 - 5} = \frac{45}{3} = 15$$

STEP 4 **Find** the track membership cost b. Use the data pair (5, 125) for racer 1 and the entry fee per race from Step 3.

$C = mr + b$ **Write the equation from Step 2.**

$125 = 15(5) + b$ **Substitute 15 for *m*, 5 for *r*, and 125 for *C*.**

$50 = b$ **Solve for *b*.**

▶ The track membership cost is $50. The entry fee per race is $15.

GUIDED PRACTICE for Examples 4 and 5

4. **GYM MEMBERSHIP** A gym charges $35 per month after an initial membership fee. A member has paid a total of $250 after 6 months. Write an equation that gives the total cost of a gym membership as a function of the length of membership (in months). Find the total cost of membership after 10 months. **$C = 35m + 40$; $390**

5. **BMX RACING** A BMX race track charges a membership fee and an entry fee per race. One racer paid a total of $76 after 3 races. Another racer paid a total of $124 after 7 races.

   a. How much does the track membership cost? **$40**

   b. What is the entry fee per race? **$12**

   c. Write an equation that gives the total cost as a function of the number of races entered. **$C = 12r + 40$**

Extra Example 5

For science class, you need to know the Celsius equivalent of a room temperature of 70°F. To estimate the Celsius equivalent, you use the facts that 32°F is equivalent to 0°C and that 212°F is equivalent to 100°C. Estimate the Celsius equivalent of 70°F. **about 21°C**

Key Questions to Ask for Example 5

- What are the variable quantities? Which variable is dependent on the other? **The variable quantities are the number of races and the amount paid. The amount paid depends on the number of races.**
- How are the values of *m* and *b* related to the racing problem? **The slope *m* is the entry fee per race. The *y*-intercept *b* is the cost of track membership.**

Closing the Lesson

Have students summarize the major points of the lesson and answer the Essential Question: How do you find the equation of a line given two points?

- **You can write an equation of a line given the slope and a point on the line or given two points on the line.**

Use the slope formula to find the slope. Use the slope and the slope-intercept form to find the *y*-intercept. Substitute the slope and *y*-intercept in the slope-intercept form.

Differentiated Instruction

Below Level A graph may help students better understand the relationships in **Example 5**. Have students graph $y = 15x + 50$. Ask how much it would cost if a racer participated in 0 races and what this cost represents. Have students determine the cost to participate in 1, 2, and 3 races. Ask them to find the differences between the costs of consecutive races. Then ask what this difference represents.

Advanced Have students graph the equation $y = 15x + 50$ from **Example 5** and the equation $y = 12x + 40$ they found in **Guided Practice Exercise 5c** on the same coordinate plane. Then ask them to evaluate the savings for various numbers of races under the fees from **Exercise 5** as opposed to the fee from **Example 5**.

See also the *Differentiated Instruction Resources* for more strategies.

4 PRACTICE AND APPLY

Assignment Guide

Answer Transparencies available for all exercises

Basic:
Day 1: EP p. 941 Exs. 27–32
pp. 296–299
Exs. 1–5, 11–13, 17–19, 23–26, 55–58
Day 2: pp. 296–299
Exs. 9, 10, 29–35, 47–52, 59–64

Average:
Day 1: pp. 296–299
Exs. 1, 2, 6–8, 14–16, 20–22, 25–29, 55–58
Day 2: pp. 296–299
Exs. 9, 10, 31–43 odd, 48–53, 59–64

Advanced:
Day 1: pp. 296–299
Exs. 1, 7, 8, 15, 16, 21, 22, 27–37, 57, 58
Day 2: pp. 296–299
Exs. 10, 38–46*, 49–54*, 63, 64

Block:
pp. 296–299
Exs. 1, 2, 6–8, 14–16, 20–22, 25–29, 55–58 (with 5.1)
pp. 296–299
Exs. 9, 10, 31–43 odd, 48–53, 59–64 (with 5.3)

Differentiated Instruction

See *Differentiated Instruction Resources* for suggestions on addressing the needs of a diverse classroom.

Homework Check

For a quick check of student understanding of key concepts, go over the following exercises:

Basic: 4, 12, 25, 47, 48
Average: 7, 20, 31, 48, 49
Advanced: 8, 22, 32, 49, 50

Extra Practice

- Student Edition, p. 942
- Chapter Resource Book: Practice levels A, B, C

Practice Worksheet

An easily-readable reduced practice page (with answers) for this lesson can be found on p. 280C.

5.2 EXERCISES

HOMEWORK KEY
○ = **WORKED-OUT SOLUTIONS** on p. WS11 for Exs. 5, 11, and 49
★ = **STANDARDIZED TEST PRACTICE** Exs. 2, 29, 34–37, 41, and 49
◆ = **MULTIPLE REPRESENTATIONS** Ex. 53

SKILL PRACTICE

A

1. **VOCABULARY** What is the y-coordinate of a point where a graph crosses the y-axis called? **y-intercept**

2. ★ **WRITING** If the equation $y = mx + b$ is used to model a quantity y as a function of the quantity x, why is b considered to be the starting value?
It is the point where x is 0.

EXAMPLE 1 on p. 292 for Exs. 3–9

WRITING EQUATIONS Write an equation of the line that passes through the given point and has the given slope m.

3. $(1, 1)$; $m = 3$ $\quad y = 3x - 2$
4. $(5, 1)$; $m = 2$ $\quad y = 2x - 9$
5. $(-4, 7)$; $m = -5$ $\quad y = -5x - 13$
6. $(5, -5)$; $m = -2$ $\quad y = -2x + 5$
7. $(8, -4)$; $m = -\frac{3}{4}$ $\quad y = -\frac{3}{4}x + 2$
8. $(-3, -11)$; $m = \frac{1}{2}$ $\quad y = \frac{1}{2}x - \frac{19}{2}$

9. **ERROR ANALYSIS** *Describe* and correct the error in finding the y-intercept of the line that passes through the point $(6, -3)$ and has a slope of -2.
-3 was substituted for x instead of y and 6 was substituted for y instead of x, $-3 = -2(6) + b$, $-3 = -12 + b$, $9 = b$.

$y = mx + b$
$6 = -2(-3) + b$
$6 = 6 + b$
$0 = b$
X

EXAMPLE 4 on p. 294 for Ex. 10

10. **ERROR ANALYSIS** An Internet service provider charges \$18 per month plus an initial set-up fee. One customer paid a total of \$81 after 2 months of service. *Describe* and correct the error in finding the set-up fee.
18 should have been substituted for m, not b, $81 = (18)2 + b$, $81 = 36 + b$, $b = \$45$.

$C = mt + b$
$81 = m(2) + 18$
$63 = m(2)$
$31.50 = m$
X

EXAMPLE 2 on p. 293 for Exs. 11–22

USING TWO POINTS Write an equation of the line that passes through the given points.

11. $(1, 4), (2, 7)$ $\quad y = 3x + 1$
12. $(3, 2), (4, 9)$ $\quad y = 7x - 19$
13. $(10, -5), (-5, 1)$ $\quad y = -\frac{2}{5}x - 1$
14. $(-2, 8), (-6, 0)$ $\quad y = 2x + 12$
15. $\left(\frac{9}{2}, 1\right), \left(-\frac{7}{2}, 7\right)$ $\quad y = -\frac{3}{4}x + \frac{35}{8}$
16. $\left(-5, \frac{3}{4}\right), \left(-2, -\frac{3}{4}\right)$ $\quad y = -\frac{1}{2}x - \frac{7}{4}$

USING A GRAPH Write an equation of the line shown.

17. $y = 4x - 15$
18. $y = \frac{2}{5}x + \frac{4}{5}$
19. $y = -\frac{1}{2}x + \frac{1}{2}$
20. $y = -\frac{7}{6}x + \frac{11}{6}$
21. $y = \frac{1}{3}x - \frac{4}{3}$
22. $y = -3x - 7$

17. 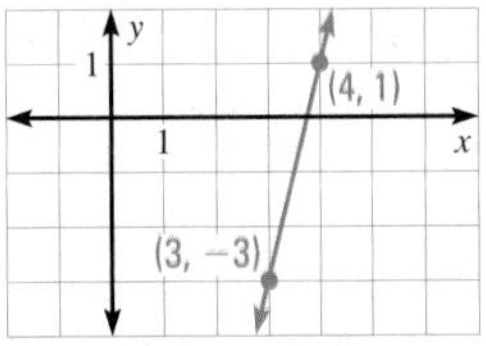

18. 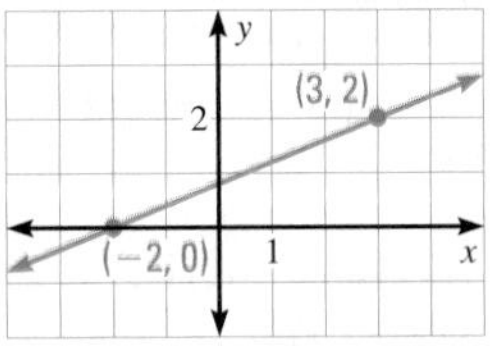

19. 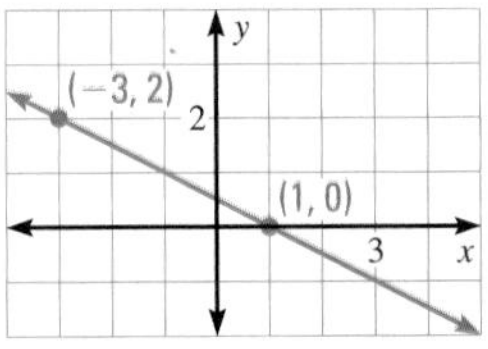

20. 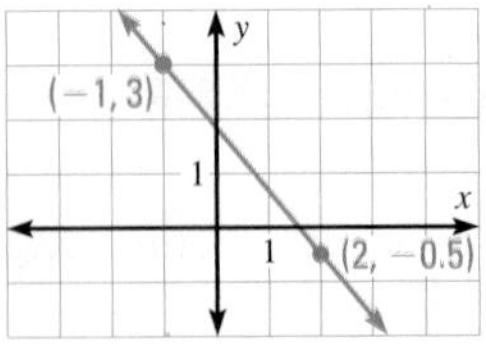

21. 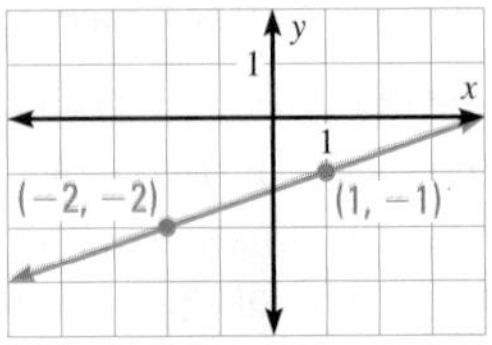

22. 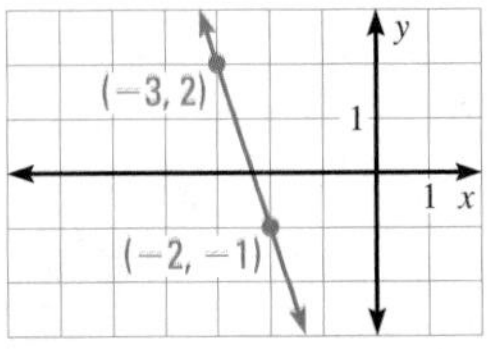

EXAMPLE 3
on p. 293
for Exs. 23–33

WRITING LINEAR FUNCTIONS **Write an equation for a linear function f that has the given values.**

23. $f(-2) = 15, f(1) = 9$ $y = -2x + 11$
24. $f(-2) = -2, f(4) = -8$ $y = -x - 4$
25. $f(2) = 7, f(4) = 6$ $y = -\frac{1}{2}x + 8$
26. $f(-4) = -8, f(-8) = -11$ $y = \frac{3}{4}x - 5$
27. $f(3) = 1, f(6) = 4$ $y = x - 2$
28. $f(-5) = 9, f(11) = -39$ $y = -3x - 6$

29. ★ **MULTIPLE CHOICE** Which function has the values $f(4) = -15$ and $f(7) = 57$? **D**

Ⓐ $f(x) = 14x - 71$ Ⓑ $f(x) = 24x - 1361$

Ⓒ $f(x) = 24x + 360$ Ⓓ $f(x) = 24x - 111$

B **USING A TABLE OR DIAGRAM** **Write an equation that represents the linear function shown in the table or mapping diagram.**

30.

x	$f(x)$
−4	6
4	4
8	3
12	2

$y = -\frac{1}{4}x + 5$

31.

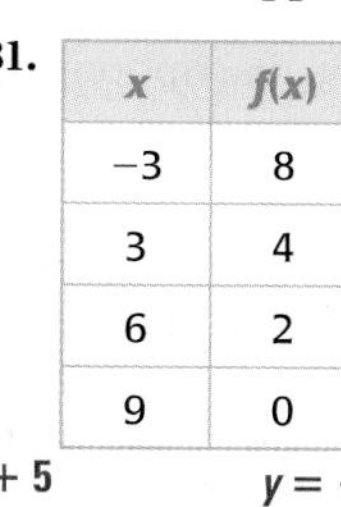

x	$f(x)$
−3	8
3	4
6	2
9	0

$y = -\frac{2}{3}x + 6$

32.

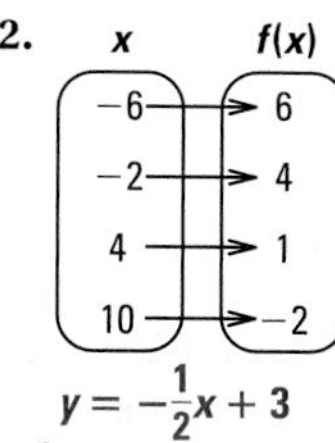

$y = -\frac{1}{2}x + 3$

33.

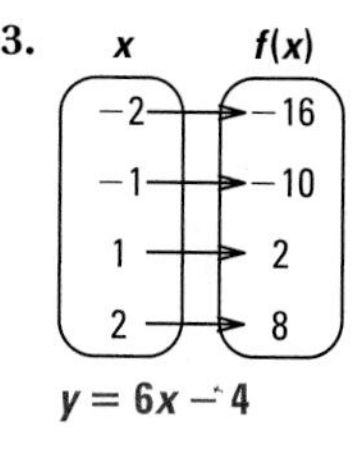

$y = 6x - 4$

★ **SHORT RESPONSE** **Tell whether the given information is enough to write an equation of a line. *Justify* your answer.** **34–37. See margin.**

34. Two points on the line
35. The slope and a point on the line
36. The slope of the line
37. Both intercepts of the line

USING A GRAPH **In Exercises 38–41, use the graph at the right.**

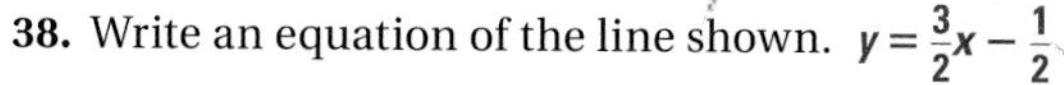

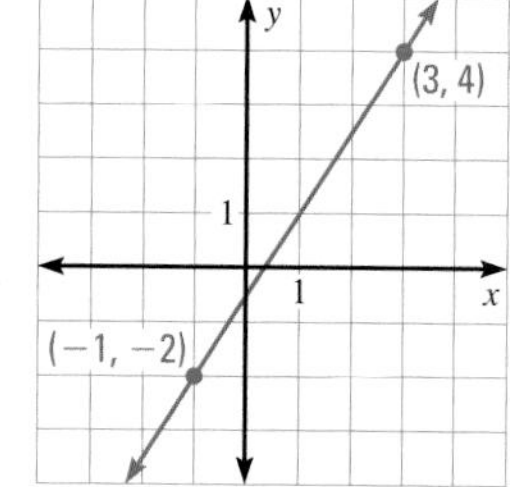

38. Write an equation of the line shown. $y = \frac{3}{2}x - \frac{1}{2}$

39. Write an equation of a line that has the same y-intercept as the line shown but has a slope that is 3 times the slope of the line shown. $y = \frac{9}{2}x - \frac{1}{2}$

40. Write an equation of a line that has the same slope as the line shown but has a y-intercept that is 6 more than the y-intercept of the line shown. $y = \frac{3}{2}x + \frac{11}{2}$

41. ★ **WRITING** Which of the lines from Exercises 38–40 intersect? Which of the lines never intersect? *Justify* your answers.

41. The lines $y = \frac{3}{2}x - \frac{1}{2}$ and $y = \frac{9}{2}x - \frac{1}{2}$ and the lines $y = \frac{9}{2}x - \frac{1}{2}$ and $y = \frac{3}{2}x + \frac{11}{2}$ intersect because they have different slopes; the lines $y = \frac{3}{2}x - \frac{1}{2}$ and $y = \frac{3}{2}x + \frac{11}{2}$ will not intersect, they have the same slope, so they are parallel.

C **REASONING** **Decide whether the three points lie on the same line. *Explain* how you know. If the points do lie on the same line, write an equation of the line that passes through all three points.** **42–45. See margin.**

42. (−4, −2), (2, 2.5), (8, 7)
43. (2, 2), (−4, 5), (6, 1)
44. (−10, 4), (−3, 2.8), (−17, 6.8)
45. (−5.5, 3), (−7.5, 4), (−4, 5)

46. **CHALLENGE** A line passes through the points (−2, 3), (2, 5), and (6, k). Find the value of k. *Explain* your steps.
7; find the equation of the line through (−2, 3) and (2, 5) to be $y = \frac{1}{2}x + 4$, then substitute 6 for x to find k.

Avoiding Common Errors

Exercises 11–22 Students often make errors in computing slope. Remind them that it is helpful to write out the slope formula and then substitute the numbers before simplifying.

Exercises 18, 19 In these exercises, some students may use the x-intercept as the y-intercept. Remind those students that they are being given $(a, 0)$, not $(0, b)$.

Graphing Calculator

Exercises 11–22 Students can check their answers to these exercises by using the *calculate* feature. Students should enter their equation into the calculator, select *value* from the calculate menu, enter the x-values from the exercise, and use the calculator's y-values to check their answers.

42. The three points lie on the same line. If you find the equation of the line between two of the points and then check to see that the third point is a solution, you can see that all three points are on the line $y = \frac{3}{4}x + 1$.

43. The three points do not lie on the same line. If you find the equation of the line between two of the points and then check to see that the third point is a solution, you can see they do not lie on the same line.

44. The three points do not lie on the same line. If you find the equation of the line between two of the points and then check to see that the third point is a solution, you can see they do not lie on the same line.

45. The three points do not lie on the same line. If you find the equation of the line between two of the points and then check to see that the third point is a solution, you can see they do not lie on the same line.

34. Yes; you can find the slope and then substitute m and the coordinates of the point in $y = mx + b$, solve for b, and write the equation.

35. Yes; you can substitute m and the coordinates of the point in $y = mx + b$, solve for b, and write the equation.

36. No; many lines have the same slope but different y-intercepts.

37. Yes; you can find the slope of the line, then substitute the y-intercept for b, and write the equation.

Teaching Strategy

Exercises 47–48 To help students begin these exercises, you may wish to stress that they follow each of the four steps given in Example 5 on page 295. For Exercise 48, point out that part a corresponds to Step 3 and part b corresponds to Step 4. Emphasize that they should perform Steps 1 and 2 before proceeding to Steps 3 and 4.

Exercises 50–52 Similarly, stress that students may want to follow the five steps in Example 4 on page 294 for these exercises. You may want to point out that part a corresponds to Step 3, part b to Step 4, and part c to Step 5. Again, students can use the information given in the problems to perform Step 1 and Step 2.

53b.

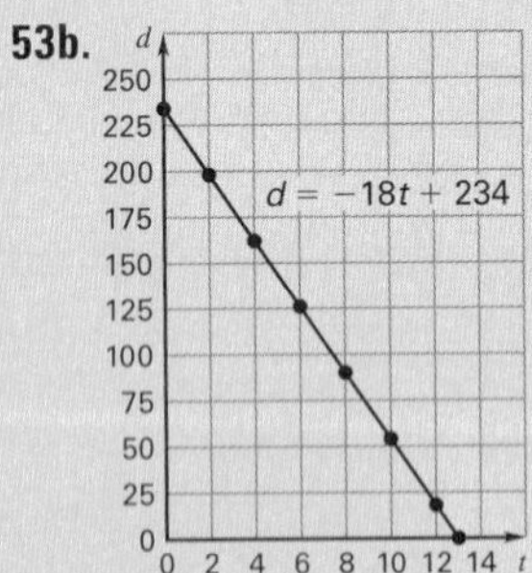

The slope is the rate that the hurricane is traveling, the y-intercept represents the distance from the town at 12 P.M.

53c. 1 A.M.; find the t-intercept to find the value of t when the distance to the town is 0; substitute 0 for d and solve for t; $t = 13$, so you need to add 13 hours to 12 P.M. to get 1 A.M.

54b. The rate of change, 10 meters per second, represents the skater's top racing speed; the initial value, 60, represents the distance the skater traveled from a standstill to where he reached his top racing speed; d meters = $\left(10 \frac{\text{meters}}{\text{second}}\right)$($x$ seconds) + 60 meters.

PROBLEM SOLVING

EXAMPLES A 4 and 5 on pp. 294–295 for Exs. 47–50

47. **BIOLOGY** Four years after a hedge maple tree was planted, its height was 9 feet. Eight years after it was planted, the hedge maple tree's height was 12 feet. What is the growth rate of the hedge maple? What was its height when it was planted? **$\frac{3}{4}$ ft/yr; 6 ft**

@HomeTutor for problem solving help at classzone.com

48. **TECHNOLOGY** You have a subscription to an online magazine that allows you to view 25 articles from the magazine's archives. You are charged an additional fee for each article after the first 25 articles viewed. After viewing 28 archived articles, you paid a total of \$34.80. After viewing 30 archived articles, you paid a total of \$40.70.

   a. What is the cost per archived article after the first 25 articles viewed? **\$2.95**

   b. What is cost of the magazine subscription? **\$25.95**

@HomeTutor for problem solving help at classzone.com

49. 115 min or 1 h 55 min; substitute 30 for m, 2 for x and 85 for y into the equation $y = mx + b$ to find $b = 25$. Then substitute 3 for x into the equation $y = 30x + 25$ to solve for y.

49. ★ **SHORT RESPONSE** You are cooking a roast beef until it is well-done. You must allow 30 minutes of cooking time for every pound of beef, plus some extra time. The last time you cooked a 2 pound roast, it was well-done after 1 hour and 25 minutes. How much time will it take to cook a 3 pound roast? *Explain* how you found your answer. **See margin.**

HINT In part (b), let t represent the number of years since 1981.

50. **TELEPHONE SERVICE** The annual household cost of telephone service in the United States increased at a relatively constant rate of \$27.80 per year from 1981 to 2001. In 2001 the annual household cost of telephone service was \$914.

   a. What was the annual household cost of telephone service in 1981? **\$358**

   b. Write an equation that gives the annual household cost of telephone service as a function of the number of years since 1981. **$y = 27.8t + 358$**

   c. Find the household cost of telephone service in 2000. **\$886.20**

51. **NEWSPAPERS** Use the information in the article about the circulation of Sunday newspapers.

   a. About how many Sunday newspapers were in circulation in 1970? **about 584 newspapers**

   b. Write an equation that gives the number of Sunday newspapers in circulation as a function of the number of years since 1970. **$y = 11.8x + 584$**

   c. About how many Sunday newspapers were in circulation in 2000? **about 938 newspapers**

Sunday Edition C9

SUNDAY PAPERS INCREASE

From 1970 to 2000, the number of Sunday newspapers in circulation increased at a relatively constant rate of 11.8 newspapers per year. In 1997 there were 903 Sunday newspapers in circulation.

B 52. **AIRPORTS** From 1990 to 2001, the number of airports in the United States increased at a relatively constant rate of 175 airports per year. There were 19,306 airports in the United States in 2001.

   a. How many U.S. airports were there in 1990? **17,381 airports**

   b. Write an equation that gives the number of U.S. airports as a function of the number of years since 1990. **$y = 175x + 17,381$**

   c. Find the year in which the number of U.S. airports reached 19,200. **2000**

○ = WORKED-OUT SOLUTIONS on p. WS1 ★ = STANDARDIZED TEST PRACTICE  = MULTIPLE REPRESENTATIONS

53. **MULTIPLE REPRESENTATIONS** A hurricane is traveling at a constant speed on a straight path toward a coastal town, as shown below.

Hurricane position at 1:00 P.M.

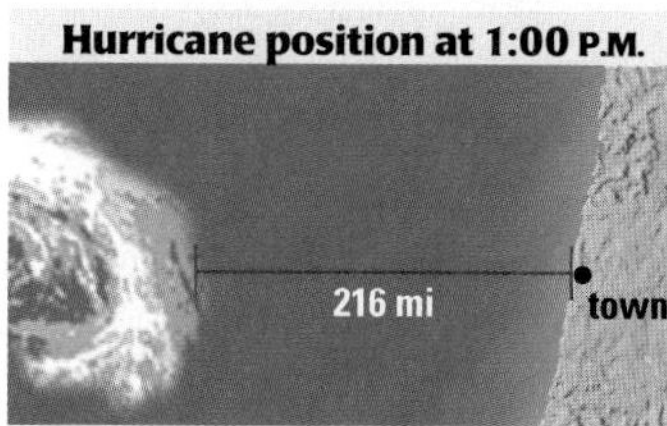

Hurricane position at 5:00 P.M.

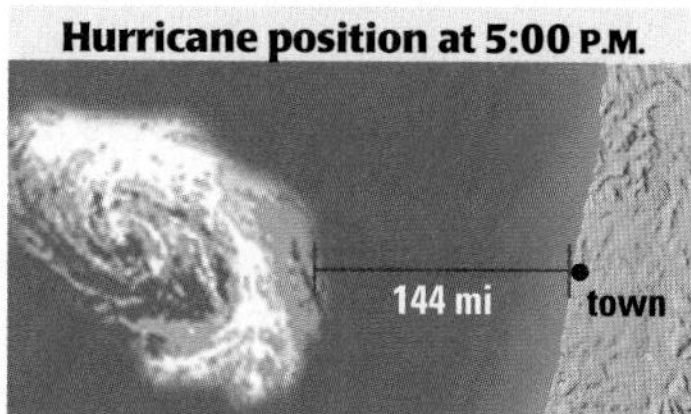

a. **Writing an Equation** Write an equation that gives the distance (in miles) of the hurricane from the town as a function of the number of hours since 12:00 P.M. **$d = -18t + 234$**

b. **Drawing a Graph** Graph the equation from part (a). *Explain* what the slope and the y-intercept of the graph mean in this situation. **b–c. See margin.**

c. **Describing in Words** Predict the time at which the hurricane will reach the town. Your answer should include the following information:

- an explanation of how you used your equation
- a description of the steps you followed to obtain your prediction

C 54. **CHALLENGE** An in-line skater practices at a race track. In two trials, the skater travels the same distance going from a standstill to his top racing speed. He then travels at his top racing speed for different distances.

Trial number	Time at top racing speed (seconds)	Total distance traveled (meters)
1	24	300
2	29	350

a. **Model** Write an equation that gives the total distance traveled (in meters) as a function of the time (in seconds) at top racing speed. **$d = 10t + 60$**

b. **Justify** What do the rate of change and initial value in your equation represent? *Explain* your answer using unit analysis. **See margin.**

c. **Predict** One lap around the race track is 200 meters. The skater starts at a standstill and completes 3 laps. Predict the number of seconds the skater travels at his top racing speed. *Explain* your method.
54 sec; the total distance is the length of the race track times 3 laps, 600 meters. If you substitute 600 for d, $t = 54$.

MIXED REVIEW

Solve the equation. Check your solution.

55. $3x + 2x - 3 = 12$ *(p. 148)* **3**

56. $-2(q + 13) - 8 = 2$ *(p. 148)* **−18**

57. $-3a + 15 = 45 + 7a$ *(p. 154)* **−3**

58. $7c + 25 = -19 + 2c$ *(p. 154)* **−8.8**

PREVIEW
Prepare for Lesson 5.3 in Exs. 59–64.

Write an equation of the line that has the given characteristics. *(p. 283)*

59. Slope: −5; y-intercept: −2 **$y = -5x - 2$**

60. Slope: $\frac{2}{7}$; y-intercept: −3 **$y = \frac{2}{7}x - 3$**

61. Slope: 1; passes through (0, −4) **$y = x - 4$**

62. Slope: 9; passes through (0, 14) **$y = 9x + 14$**

63. Passes through (0, 6), (5, 2) **$y = -\frac{4}{5}x + 6$**

64. Passes through (−12, 3), (0, 2) **$y = -\frac{1}{12}x + 2$**

5 ASSESS AND RETEACH

Daily Homework Quiz

Transparency Available

Write an equation of the line that passes through the given point with the given slope.

1. (4, −1), $m = -1$ **$y = -x + 3$**

2. (2, 0), $m = 4$ **$y = 4x - 8$**

Write an equation of the line that passes through the given points.

3. (2, 3), (4, 7) **$y = 2x - 1$**

4. (−5, 7), (2, −7) **$y = -2x - 3$**

5. A camp charges a registration fee and a daily amount. If the total bill for one camper was \$338 for 12 days and the total bill for another camper was \$506 for 19 days, how much will the bill be for a camper who enrolls for 30 days? **\$770**

Available at **classzone.com**

Diagnosis/Remediation

- Practice A, B, C in Chapter Resource Book
- Study Guide in Chapter Resource Book
- Practice Workbook
- @HomeTutor

Challenge

Additional challenge is available in the Chapter Resource Book.

Alternative Strategy

Students can solve Example 5 on page 295 by using a graph or a table. A graph can help students visualize the racing problem, while a table can help students see the linear pattern. Both methods help students to understand the algebraic solution to the problem.

Mathematical Reasoning

Multiple Representations You may want to discuss the advantages of finding an algebraic solution of the racing problem, and using a graph or table to check the reasonableness of the solution. For example, an algebraic solution allows the student to calculate the total cost for any input value, whereas the graph and the table are limited by scale and by size. The graph readily shows the slope of the line and the table lends itself to calculating the y-intercept, both of which confirm the algebraic solution of the problem.

1. \$5; \$19; Method 1: Use a graph.

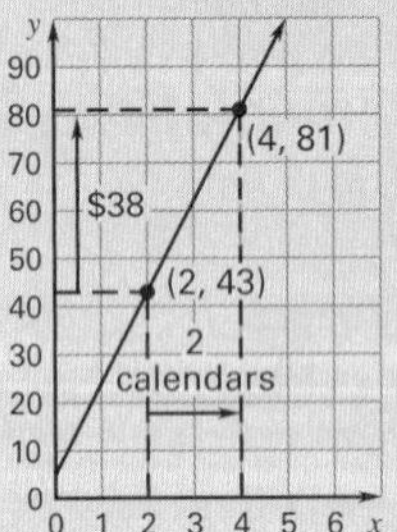

Graph the ordered pairs, (2, 43) and (4, 81), draw a line through the points and find the y-intercept, or the delivery fee, to be \$5. Then find the slope of the line, or the cost per calendar, to be $\frac{38}{2} = \$19$; Method 2: Use a table to calculate the cost of the calendars.

Number of calendars	Cost (dollars)
2	43
3	?
4	81

The number of calendars increased by 2 and the cost increased by \$38, so the cost per calendar is \$38 ÷ 2 = \$19. The delivery fee is the cost when the number of calendars is 0. Use the cost per calendar and work backwards to fill in the table. \$43 − \$19 = \$24; \$24 − \$19 = \$5.

Number of calendars	Cost (dollars)
0	5
1	24
2	43

The delivery fee is \$5.

2. \$119.18; Method 1: Use a graph.

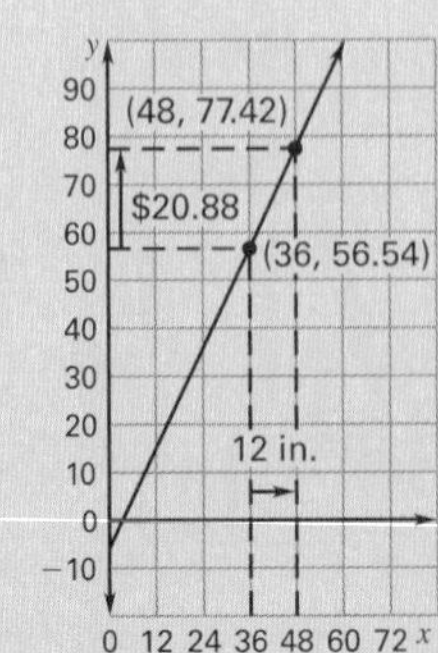

PROBLEM SOLVING WORKSHOP LESSON 5.2

Using ALTERNATIVE METHODS

Another Way to Solve Example 5, page 295

MULTIPLE REPRESENTATIONS In Example 5 on page 295, you saw how to solve a problem about BMX racing using an equation. You can also solve this problem using a graph or a table.

PROBLEM

BMX RACING In Bicycle Moto Cross (BMX) racing, racers purchase a one year membership to a track. They also pay an entry fee for each race at that track. One racer paid a total of \$125 after 5 races. A second racer paid a total of \$170 after 8 races. How much does the track membership cost? What is the entry fee per race?

METHOD 1

Using a Graph One alternative approach is to use a graph.

STEP 1 **Read** the problem. It tells you the number of races and amount paid for each racer. Write this information as ordered pairs.

Racer 1: (5, 125)
Racer 2: (8, 170)

STEP 2 **Graph** the ordered pairs. Draw a line through the points.

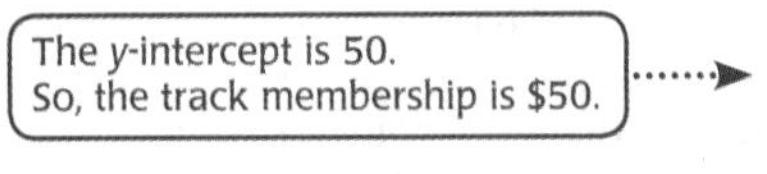

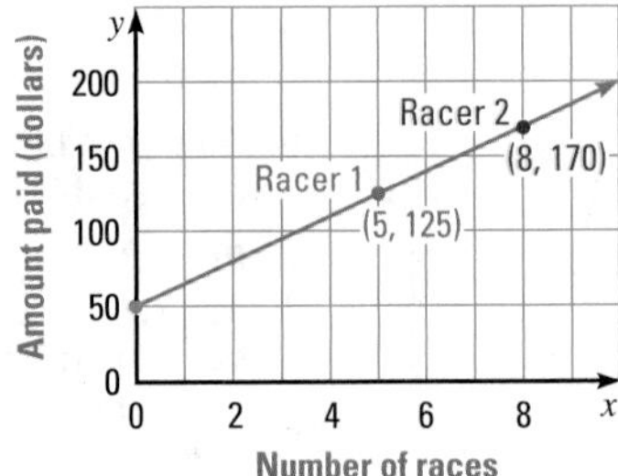

STEP 3 **Find** the slope of the line. This is the entry fee per race.

$$\text{Fee} = \frac{45 \text{ dollars}}{3 \text{ races}} = \$15 \text{ per race}$$

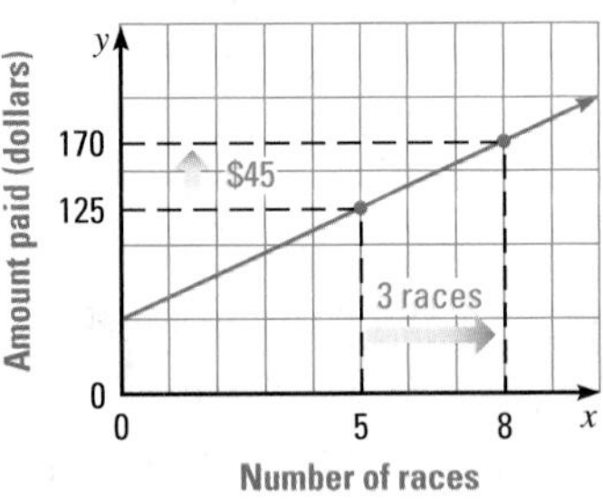

METHOD 2 **Using a Table** Another approach is to use a table showing the amount paid for various numbers of races.

STEP 1 **Calculate** the race entry fee.

Number of races	Amount paid
5	$125
6	?
7	?
8	$170

+ 3   + $45

The number of races increased by 3, and the amount paid increased by $45, so the race entry fee is $\$45 \div 3 = \$15$.

STEP 2 **Find** the membership cost.

Number of races	Amount paid	
0	$50	− $15
1	$65	− $15
2	$80	− $15
3	$95	− $15
4	$110	− $15
5	$125	

The membership cost is the cost with no races. Use the race entry fee and work backwards to fill in the table. The membership cost is $50.

PRACTICE

1. **CALENDARS** A company makes calendars from personal photos. You pay a delivery fee for each order plus a cost per calendar. The cost of 2 calendars plus delivery is $43. The cost of 4 calendars plus delivery is $81. What is the delivery fee? What is the cost per calendar? Solve this problem using two different methods. **See margin.**

2. **BOOKSHELVES** A furniture maker offers bookshelves that have the same width and depth but that differ in height and price, as shown in the table. Find the cost of a bookshelf that is 72 inches high. Solve this problem using two different methods. **See margin.**

Height (inches)	Price (dollars)
36	56.54
48	77.42
60	98.30

3. **WHAT IF?** In Exercise 2, suppose the price of the 60 inch bookshelf was $99.30. Can you still solve the problem? *Explain.* **See margin.**

4. **CONCERT TICKETS** All tickets for a concert are the same price. The ticket agency adds a fixed fee to every order. A person who orders 5 tickets pays $93. A person who orders 3 tickets pays $57. How much will 4 tickets cost? Solve this problem using two different methods. **See margin.**

5. **ERROR ANALYSIS** A student solved the problem in Exercise 4 as shown below. *Describe* and correct the error.

Let p = price paid for 4 tickets

$$\frac{57}{3} = \frac{p}{4}$$

$$228 = 3p$$

$$76 = p$$

✗

The student assumes that there is no fixed fee by using a proportion; $93 - 57 = 36$, $36 \div 2 = 18$, $57 + 18 = 75$.

Avoiding Common Errors

While discussing Method 2, remind students that in Step 1 they need to calculate the increase in both columns to determine the slope.

Study Strategy

Exercises 1–5 Point out to students that if they use a graph, they may not be able to determine an exact y-intercept if the x-coordinates of the ordered pairs fall between the numbers on the scale. Note that Method 1, Step 2 finds the y-intercept by drawing a line through two points. If they plot the points slightly higher or lower on the graph, the line will not pass through (0, 50). Suggest they verify the y-intercept using the slope ratio.

3. No; if the cost of the 60 inch bookshelf changes, the cost no longer increases at a constant rate.

4. $75; Method 1: Use a graph.

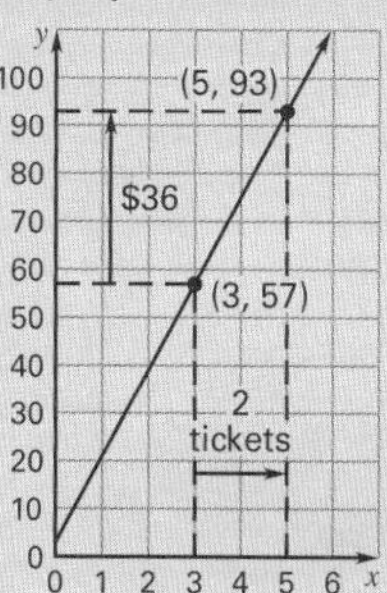

Graph the ordered pairs, (5, 93) and (3, 57), draw a line through the points, and find the y-intercept to be 3, so the fixed fee on every order is $3. Then find the slope of the line to be $\frac{36}{2} = \$18$ per ticket. Write the equation $y = 18x + 3$ and substitute 4 for x to find the total cost of 4 tickets to be $75; Method 2: Use a table to calculate the cost per ticket.

Number of tickets	Total cost (dollars)
3	57
4	?
5	93

The number of tickets increased by 2 and the total cost of tickets increased by $36, so the cost per ticket is $\$36 \div 2 = \$18$; $\$57 + \$18 = \$75$; $\$39 - \$18 = \$21$; $\$21 - \$18 = \$3$; the total cost of 4 tickets is $75.

(Exercise 2 continued)

Graph the ordered pairs, (36, 56.54) and (48, 77.42), draw a line through the points and find the y-intercept to be −6.1. Then find the slope of the line to be $\frac{20.88}{12} = \$1.74$. Write the equation $y = 1.74x - 6.1$ and substitute 72 for x to find the cost to be $119.18; Method 2: Use a table to calculate the cost of the bookshelf.

Height (inches)	Cost (dollars)
36	56.54
48	77.42
60	98.30

The height increased by 12 and the cost increased by $20.88, so the cost per inch is $\$20.88 \div 12 = \$1.74$; $98.30 + 20.88 = 119.18$.

The cost of a bookshelf that is 72 inches is $119.18.

1 PLAN AND PREPARE

Warm-Up Exercises

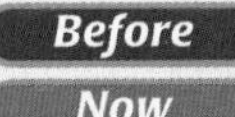
Transparency Available

Write an equation of the line.

1. passes through (3, 4), $m = 3$ **$y = 3x - 5$**
2. passes through (−2, 2) and (1, 8) **$y = 2x + 6$**
3. A carnival charges an entrance fee and a ticket fee. One person paid \$27.50 and bought 5 tickets. Another paid \$45.00 and bought 12 tickets. How much will 22 tickets cost? **\$70**

Notetaking Guide

Transparency Available

Promotes interactive learning and notetaking skills.

Pacing

Basic: 2 days
Average: 2 days
Advanced: 2 days
Block: 0.5 block with 5.2
0.5 block with 5.4

- See *Teaching Guide/Lesson Plan.*

2 FOCUS AND MOTIVATE

Essential Question

Big Idea 1, p. 281

How do you write linear equations in point-slope form? **Tell students they will learn how to answer this question by using two points, or the slope and one point.**

NCTM STANDARDS

Standard 3: Describe spatial relationships using coordinate geometry

Standard 6: Solve problems in math and other contexts

5.3 Write Linear Equations in Point-Slope Form

Before You wrote linear equations in slope-intercept form.
Now You will write linear equations in point-slope form.
Why? So you can model sports statistics, as in Ex. 43.

Key Vocabulary
- point-slope form

Consider the line that passes through the point (2, 3) with a slope of $\frac{1}{2}$.

Let (x, y) where $x \neq 2$ be another point on the line. You can write an equation relating x and y using the slope formula, with $(x_1, y_1) = (2, 3)$ and $(x_2, y_2) = (x, y)$.

$m = \frac{y_2 - y_1}{x_2 - x_1}$ **Write slope formula.**

$\frac{1}{2} = \frac{y - 3}{x - 2}$ **Substitute $\frac{1}{2}$ for m, 3 for y_1, and 2 for x_1.**

$\frac{1}{2}(x - 2) = y - 3$ **Multiply each side by $(x - 2)$.**

USE POINT-SLOPE FORM
When an equation is in point-slope form, you can read the x- and y-coordinates of a point on the line and the slope of the line.

The equation in *point-slope form* is $y - 3 = \frac{1}{2}(x - 2)$.

KEY CONCEPT *For Your Notebook*

Point-Slope Form

The **point-slope form** of the equation of the nonvertical line through a given point (x_1, y_1) with a slope of m is $y - y_1 = m(x - x_1)$.

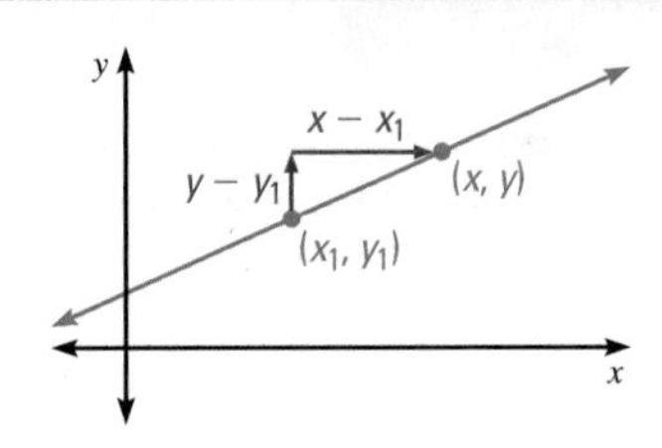

EXAMPLE 1 Write an equation in point-slope form

Write an equation in point-slope form of the line that passes through the point (4, −3) and has a slope of 2.

$y - y_1 = m(x - x_1)$ **Write point-slope form.**

$y + 3 = 2(x - 4)$ **Substitute 2 for m, 4 for x_1, and −3 for y_1.**

GUIDED PRACTICE for Example 1

1. Write an equation in point-slope form of the line that passes through the point (−1, 4) and has a slope of −2. **$y - 4 = -2(x + 1)$**

Resource Planning Guide

Chapter Resource Book
- Teaching Guide/Lesson Plan
- Activity Master
- Practice levels A, B, C
- Study Guide
- Catch-up for Absent Students
- Problem Solving Workshop
- Challenge

Workbooks
- Notetaking Guide
- Practice Workbook

Teaching Options
- **Power Presentations** provides dynamic electronic teaching resources for the classroom.
- **Activity Generator** provides editable activities for all ability levels.

Interactive Technology
- Easy Planner
- Power Presentations
- Activity Generator
- Animated Algebra
- Test Generator
- Online Quiz
- eWorkbook
- eEdition
- @HomeTutor

Resources for English Learners
- Spanish Study Guide
- Multi-Language Visual Glossary
- Student Resources in Spanish

See also the *Differentiated Instruction Resources* for more strategies for meeting individual needs.

EXAMPLE 2 Graph an equation in point-slope form

Graph the equation $y + 2 = \frac{2}{3}(x - 3)$.

Solution

Because the equation is in point-slope form, you know that the line has a slope of $\frac{2}{3}$ and passes through the point (3, −2).

Plot the point (3, −2). Find a second point on the line using the slope. Draw a line through both points.

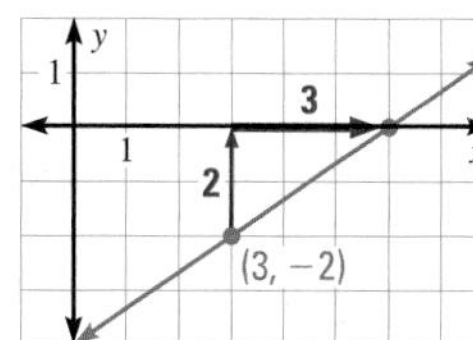

GUIDED PRACTICE for Example 2

2. Graph the equation $y - 1 = -(x - 2)$. **See margin.**

EXAMPLE 3 Use point-slope form to write an equation

Write an equation in point-slope form of the line shown.

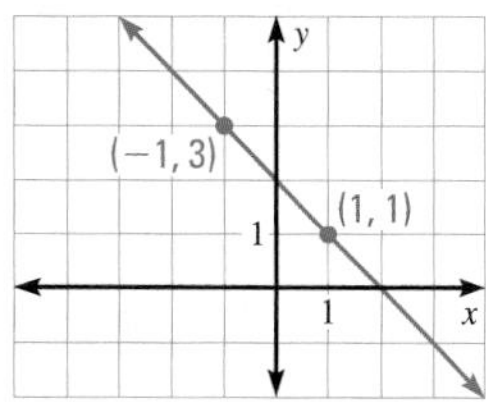

Solution

STEP 1 **Find** the slope of the line.

$$m = \frac{y_2 - y_1}{x_2 - x_1} = \frac{3 - 1}{-1 - 1} = \frac{2}{-2} = -1$$

STEP 2 **Write** the equation in point-slope form. You can use either given point.

Method 1 Use (−1, 3).	**Method 2** Use (1, 1).
$y - y_1 = m(x - x_1)$	$y - y_1 = m(x - x_1)$
$y - 3 = -(x + 1)$	$y - 1 = -(x - 1)$

CHECK Check that the equations are equivalent by writing them in slope-intercept form.

$y - 3 = -x - 1$	$y - 1 = -x + 1$
$y = -x + 2$	$y = -x + 2$

Animated Algebra activity at classzone.com

GUIDED PRACTICE for Example 3

3. Write an equation in point-slope form of the line that passes through the points (2, 3) and (4, 4). $y - 3 = \frac{1}{2}(x - 2)$ **or** $y - 4 = \frac{1}{2}(x - 4)$

Motivating the Lesson

You need to print and bind a report for a project. You have a price list showing a printing company charges \$10.50 for 10 pages, \$11.75 for 15 pages, \$14.25 for 25 pages, and \$18 for 40 pages. You can use this list to determine if the company charges a constant rate to print each page. If so, you can determine the cost to print and bind your report.

3 TEACH

Extra Example 1

Write an equation in point-slope form of the line that passes through the point (−3, 1) and has a slope of 3. $y - 1 = 3(x + 3)$

Extra Example 2

Graph $y - 2 = \frac{1}{2}(x + 2)$.

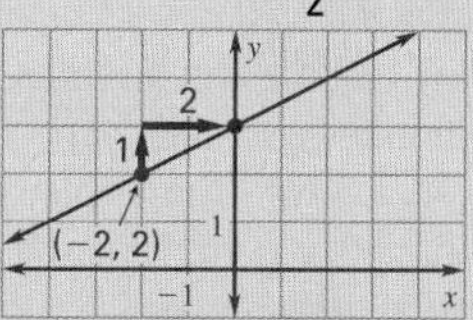

Extra Example 3

Write an equation in point-slope form of the line shown.

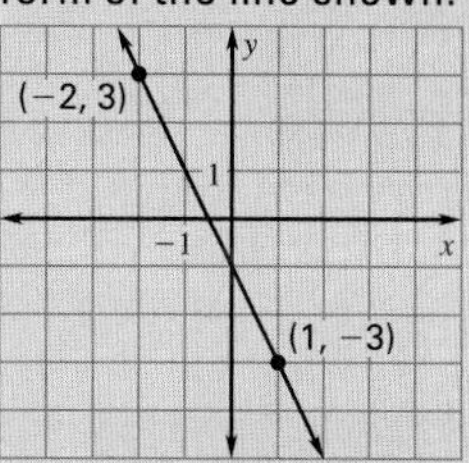

$y - 3 = -2(x + 2)$ or $y + 3 = -2(x - 1)$

2. See Additional Answers beginning on p. AA1.

Differentiated Instruction

Auditory Learners To write the equation of a line in point-slope form, students need to know the slope and a point on the line. Students can state the point-slope form as follows. "For a given *point*, *y* minus the *y*-coordinate equals the *slope* times the quantity *x* minus the *x*-coordinate."

See also the *Differentiated Instruction Resources* for more strategies.

An **Animated Algebra** activity is available online for **Example 3**. This activity is also part of **Power Presentations**.

Extra Example 4

A radio station charges $650 for the first minute of ad time and then $340 for each additional minute. Write an equation that gives the total cost (in dollars) to run an ad as a function of the number of minutes the ad runs. Find the cost of 7 minutes of ad time. **$C = 340t + 310$, where C is total cost (in dollars) and t is time (in minutes). The cost to run the ad for 7 minutes is $2690.**

Extra Example 5

The table shows the cost of renting a canoe for different times (in hours). Can the situation be modeled by a linear equation? *Explain.* If possible, write an equation that gives the cost as a function of time (in hours).

Time (hours)	Cost (dollars)
2	22
4	32
6	42
8	52
10	62

Because the cost increases at a constant rate of $5 per hour, the situation can be modeled by a linear equation. An equation that models the situation is $C = 5t + 12$, where C is the total cost (in dollars) and t is time (in hours).

Key Questions to Ask for Example 5

- When the equation is written in slope-intercept form, what does the y-intercept represent? **a one-time cost of $50**
- If you use the data pair (12, 650), how does it affect the point-slope form and slope-intercept form of the equation? **The point-slope form changes to $C - 650 = 50(p - 12)$, but the slope-intercept form remains the same.**

EXAMPLE 4 Solve a multi-step problem

STICKERS You are designing a sticker to advertise your band. A company charges $225 for the first 1000 stickers and $80 for each additional 1000 stickers. Write an equation that gives the total cost (in dollars) of stickers as a function of the number (in thousands) of stickers ordered. Find the cost of 9000 stickers.

AVOID ERRORS
Remember that s is given in thousands. To find the cost of 9000 stickers, substitute 9 for s.

Solution

STEP 1 **Identify** the rate of change and a data pair. Let C be the cost (in dollars) and s be the number of stickers (in thousands).

Rate of change, m: $80 per 1 thousand stickers
Data pair (s_1, C_1): (1 thousand stickers, $225)

STEP 2 **Write** an equation using point-slope form. Rewrite the equation in slope-intercept form so that cost is a function of the number of stickers.

$C - C_1 = m(s - s_1)$ — **Write point-slope form.**

$C - 225 = 80(s - 1)$ — **Substitute 80 for m, 1 for s_1, and 225 for C_1.**

$C = 80s + 145$ — **Solve for C.**

STEP 3 **Find** the cost of 9000 stickers.

$C = 80(9) + 145 = 865$ — **Substitute 9 for s. Simplify.**

▶ The cost of 9000 stickers is $865.

EXAMPLE 5 Write a real-world linear model from a table

WORKING RANCH The table shows the cost of visiting a working ranch for one day and night for different numbers of people. Can the situation be modeled by a linear equation? *Explain.* If possible, write an equation that gives the cost as a function of the number of people in the group.

Number of people	4	6	8	10	12
Cost (dollars)	250	350	450	550	650

Solution

STEP 1 **Find** the rate of change for consecutive data pairs in the table.

$$\frac{350 - 250}{6 - 4} = 50, \quad \frac{450 - 350}{8 - 6} = 50, \quad \frac{550 - 450}{10 - 8} = 50, \quad \frac{650 - 550}{12 - 10} = 50$$

Because the cost increases at a constant rate of $50 per person, the situation can be modeled by a linear equation.

STEP 2 **Use** point-slope form to write the equation. Let C be the cost (in dollars) and p be the number of people. Use the data pair (4, 250).

$C - C_1 = m(p - p_1)$ — **Write point-slope form.**

$C - 250 = 50(p - 4)$ — **Substitute 50 for m, 4 for p_1, and 250 for C_1.**

$C = 50p + 50$ — **Solve for C.**

GUIDED PRACTICE for Examples 4 and 5

4. **WHAT IF?** In Example 4, suppose a second company charges \$250 for the first 1000 stickers. The cost of each additional 1000 stickers is \$60.

   a. Write an equation that gives the total cost (in dollars)of the stickers as a function of the number (in thousands) of stickers ordered. $C = 60s + 190$

   b. Which company would charge you less for 9000 stickers? **second company**

5. **MAILING COSTS** The table shows the cost (in dollars) of sending a single piece of first class mail for different weights. Can the situation be modeled by a linear equation? *Explain*. If possible, write an equation that gives the cost of sending a piece of mail as a function of its weight (in ounces).

Weight (ounces)	1	4	5	10	12
Cost (dollars)	0.37	1.06	1.29	2.44	2.90

Yes; because the cost increases at a constant rate of \$.23 per ounce, the situation can be modeled by a linear equation; $C = 0.23w + 0.14$.

5.3 EXERCISES

HOMEWORK KEY
○ = **WORKED-OUT SOLUTIONS** on p. WS11 for Exs. 3 and 39
★ = **STANDARDIZED TEST PRACTICE** Exs. 2, 12, 30–34, 38, and 41

SKILL PRACTICE

A

1. **VOCABULARY** Identify the slope of the line given by the equation $y - 5 = -2(x + 5)$. Then identify one point on the line. **−2; (−5, 5)**

2. ★ **WRITING** *Describe* the steps you would take to write an equation in point-slope form of the line that passes through the points (3, −2) and (4, 5). **Find the slope and substitute it for m in the equation $y - y_1 = m(x - x_1)$. Then pick one of the points and substitute the coordinates in for y_1 and x_1.**

EXAMPLE 1 on p. 302 for Exs. 3–13

WRITING EQUATIONS Write an equation in point-slope form of the line that passes through the given point and has the given slope *m*.

3. (2, 1), $m = 2$ — $y - 1 = 2(x - 2)$
4. (3, 5), $m = -1$ — $y - 5 = -(x - 3)$
5. (7, −1), $m = -6$ — $y + 1 = -6(x - 7)$
6. (5, −1), $m = -2$ — $y + 1 = -2(x - 5)$
7. (−8, 2), $m = 5$ — $y - 2 = 5(x + 8)$
8. (−6, 6), $m = \frac{3}{2}$ — $y - 6 = \frac{3}{2}(x + 6)$
9. (−11, −3), $m = -9$ — $y + 3 = -9(x + 11)$
10. (−3, −9), $m = \frac{7}{3}$ — $y + 9 = \frac{7}{3}(x + 3)$
11. (5, −12), $m = -\frac{2}{5}$ — $y + 12 = -\frac{2}{5}(x - 5)$

12. ★ **MULTIPLE CHOICE** Which equation represents the line that passes through the point (−6, 2) and has a slope of −1? **C**

   (A) $y + 2 = -(x + 6)$
   (B) $y + 2 = -(x - 6)$
   (C) $y - 2 = -(x + 6)$
   (D) $y + 1 = -2(x + 6)$

13. **ERROR ANALYSIS** *Describe* and correct the error in writing an equation of the line that passes through the point (1, −5) and has a slope of −2.

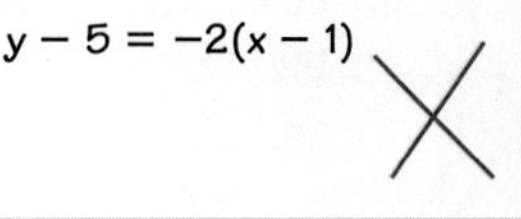

The form is $y - y_1$, so the left side should be $y - (-5)$ or $y + 5$; $y + 5 = -2(x - 1)$.

Mathematical Reasoning

You may want to discuss the relationship between the point-slope form and the slope-intercept form of an equation. Tell students that data as ordered pairs fit well with the point-slope form. The ordered pairs allow them to determine quickly whether there is a constant rate of change, and the pairing allows them to plug the data directly into the point-slope form. Point out that to make calculations and graphing easier, they can rewrite the equation in slope-intercept form. Stress that they can use the form that works best in a situation, and then move from one form to the other as needed to help solve the problem.

Closing the Lesson

Have students summarize the major points of the lesson and answer the Essential Question: How do you write linear equations in point-slope form?

- **The point-slope form of an equation is $y - y_1 = m(x - x_1)$.**
- **The point-slope form uses the x-and y-coordinates of a point and the slope.**

If you are given two points, use the slope formula to find the slope. Substitute the slope and the coordinates of a given point into the point-slope form.

4 PRACTICE AND APPLY

Assignment Guide

Answer Transparencies available for all exercises

Basic:
Day 1: EP p. 939 Exs. 42–45
pp. 305–308
Exs. 1–8, 12–17, 45–53
Day 2: pp. 305–308
Exs. 20–32, 37–42, 54–57

Average:
Day 1: pp. 305–308
Exs. 1, 2, 6–13, 17–19, 45–53
Day 2: pp. 305–308
Exs. 20–28 even, 29–34, 37–43, 54–57

Advanced:
Day 1: pp. 305–308
Exs. 1, 2, 7–12, 17–19, 35*, 36*, 45–53 odd
Day 2: pp. 305–308
Exs. 24–28, 30–34, 37–44*, 55, 57

Block:
pp. 305–308
Exs. 1, 2, 6–13, 17–19, 45–53 (with 5.2)
pp. 305–308
Exs. 20–28 even, 29–34, 37–43, 54–57 (with 5.4)

Differentiated Instruction

See *Differentiated Instruction Resources* for suggestions on addressing the needs of a diverse classroom.

Homework Check

For a quick check of student understanding of key concepts, go over the following exercises:

Basic: 4, 16, 22, 37, 38
Average: 8, 17, 24, 38, 39
Advanced: 10, 18, 27, 38, 40

Extra Practice

- Student Edition, p. 942
- Chapter Resource Book: Practice levels A, B, C

Practice Worksheet

An easily-readable reduced practice page (with answers) for this lesson can be found on p. 280C.

EXAMPLE 2 on p. 303 for Exs. 14–19

GRAPHING EQUATIONS Graph the equation. 14–19. See margin.

14. $y - 5 = 3(x - 1)$ **15.** $y + 3 = -2(x - 2)$ **16.** $y - 1 = 3(x + 6)$

17. $y + 8 = -(x + 4)$ **18.** $y - 1 = \frac{3}{4}(x + 1)$ **19.** $y + 4 = -\frac{5}{2}(x - 3)$

EXAMPLE 3 on p. 303 for Exs. 20–30

USING A GRAPH Write an equation in point-slope form of the line shown.

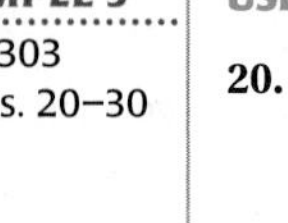

20.

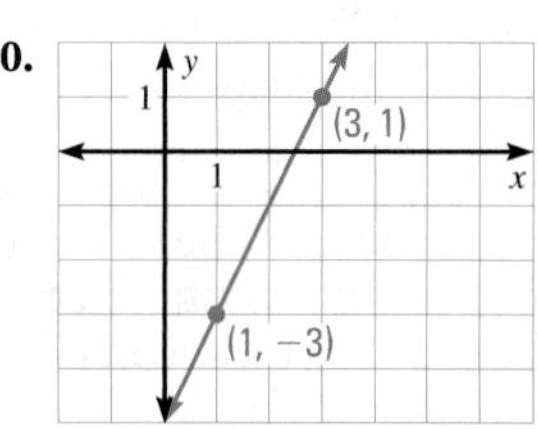

$y - 1 = 2(x - 3)$ or $y + 3 = 2(x - 1)$

21.

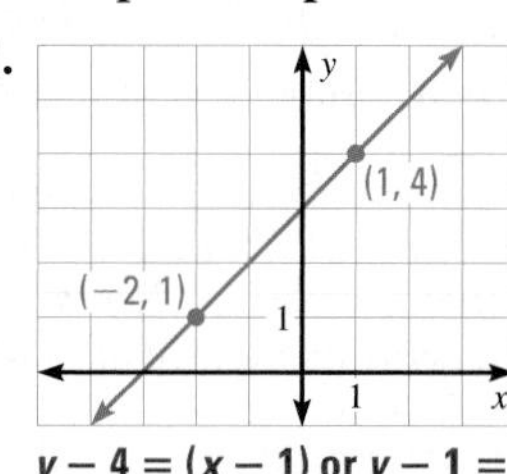

$y - 4 = (x - 1)$ or $y - 1 = (x + 2)$

22.

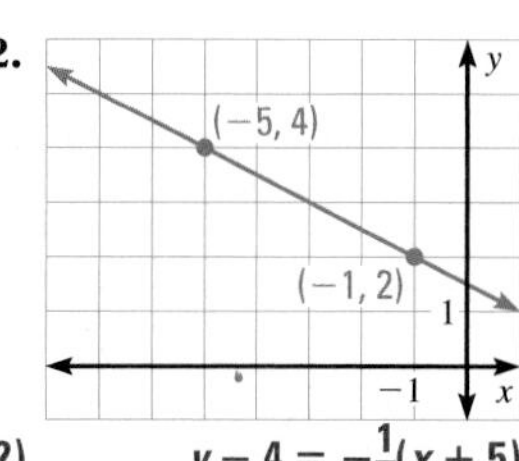

$y - 4 = -\frac{1}{2}(x + 5)$ or $y - 2 = -\frac{1}{2}(x + 1)$

WRITING EQUATIONS Write an equation in point-slope form of the line that passes through the given points. 23–28. See margin.

23. (7, 2), (2, 12) **24.** (6, −2), (12, 1) **25.** (−4, −1), (6, −7)

26. (4, 5), (−4, −5) **27.** (−3, −20), (4, 36) **28.** (−5, −19), (5, 13)

29. **ERROR ANALYSIS** *Describe* and correct the error in writing an equation of the line shown.

$$m = \frac{4 - 2}{4 - 1} = \frac{2}{3} \qquad y - 2 = \frac{2}{3}(x - 4)$$

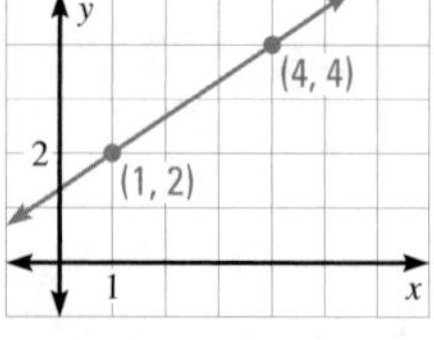

29. A point was not substituted into the equation, the *y*-coordinates of the two points were substituted; $y - 2 = \frac{2}{3}(x - 1)$.

30. ★ **MULTIPLE CHOICE** The graph of which equation is shown? **B**

Ⓐ $y + 4 = -3(x + 2)$ Ⓑ $y - 4 = -3(x - 2)$

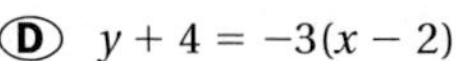

Ⓒ $y - 4 = -3(x + 2)$ Ⓓ $y + 4 = -3(x - 2)$

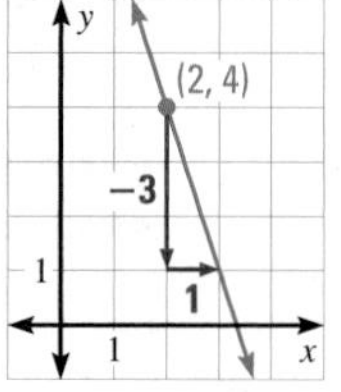

B ★ **SHORT RESPONSE Tell whether the data in the table can be modeled by a linear equation. *Explain*. If possible, write an equation in point-slope form that relates *y* and *x*. 31–34. See margin.**

31.

x	2	4	6	8	10
y	−1	5	15	29	47

32.

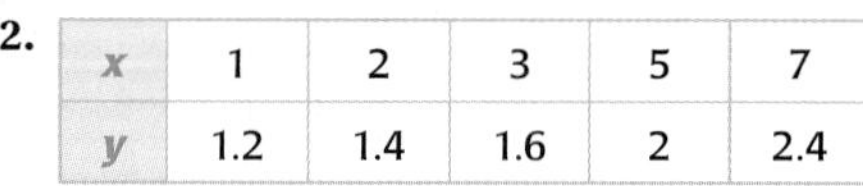

x	1	2	3	5	7
y	1.2	1.4	1.6	2	2.4

33.

x	1	2	3	4	5
y	2	−3	4	−5	6

34.

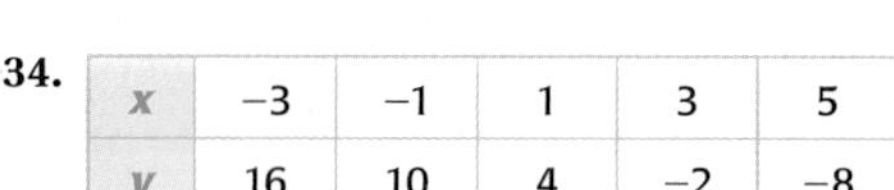

x	−3	−1	1	3	5
y	16	10	4	−2	−8

C **CHALLENGE Find the value of *k* so that the line passing through the given points has slope *m*. Write an equation of the line in point-slope form.**

35. $(k, 4k), (k + 2, 3k), m = -1$
2; $y - 8 = -(x - 2)$ or $y - 6 = -(x - 4)$

36. $(-k + 1, 3), (3, k + 3), m = 3$
−3; $y - 3 = 3(x - 4)$ or $y = 3(x - 3)$

○ = **WORKED-OUT SOLUTIONS on p. WS1** ★ = **STANDARDIZED TEST PRACTICE**

14.

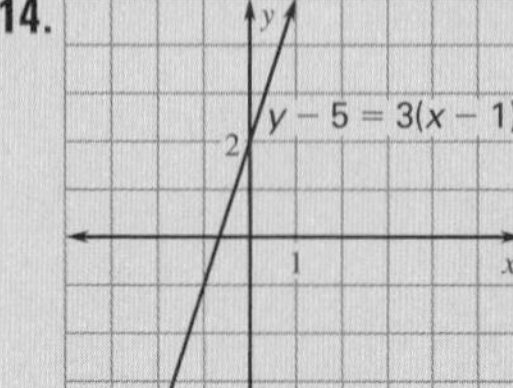

15.

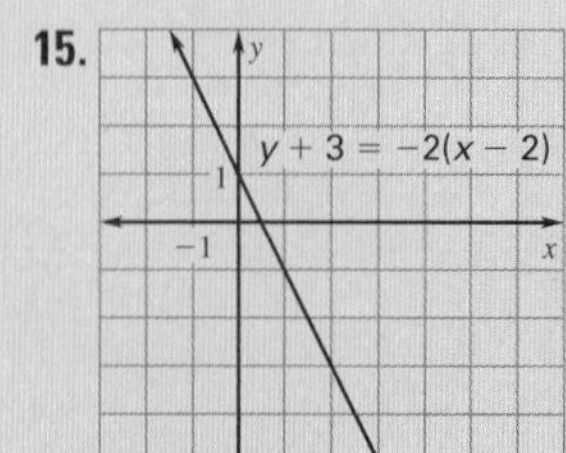

16.

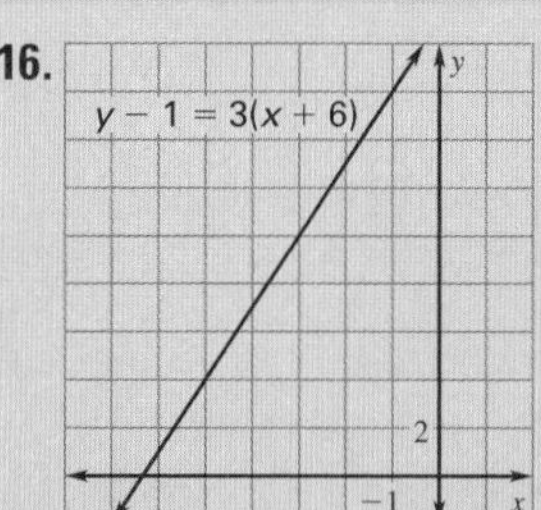

PROBLEM SOLVING

EXAMPLE 4 A on p. 304 for Exs. 37, 39, 40

37. **TELEVISION** In order to use an excerpt from a movie in a new television show, the television producer must pay the director of the movie \$790 for the first 2 minutes of the excerpt and \$130 per minute after that.

   a. Write an equation that gives the total cost (in dollars) of using the excerpt as a function of the length (in minutes) of the excerpt. **$y = 130x + 530$**

   b. Find the total cost of using an excerpt that is 8 minutes long. **\$1570**

   @HomeTutor for problem solving help at classzone.com

EXAMPLE 5 on p. 304 for Exs. 38, 41

38. Since the cost increases at a constant rate of \$1714 per month, the situation can be modeled by a linear equation; \$5950; \$1714.

38. ★ **SHORT RESPONSE** A school district pays an installation fee and a monthly fee for Internet service. The table shows the total cost of Internet service for the school district over different numbers of months. *Explain* why the situation can be modeled by a linear equation. What is the installation fee? What is the monthly service fee?

Months of service	2	4	6	8	10	12
Total cost (dollars)	9,378	12,806	16,234	19,662	23,090	26,518

@HomeTutor for problem solving help at classzone.com

39. **COMPANY SALES** During the period 1994–2004, the annual sales of a small company increased by \$10,000 per year. In 1997 the annual sales were \$97,000. Write an equation that gives the annual sales as a function of the number of years since 1994. Find the sales in 2000. **$y = 10000x + 67000$; \$127,000**

Animated Algebra at classzone.com

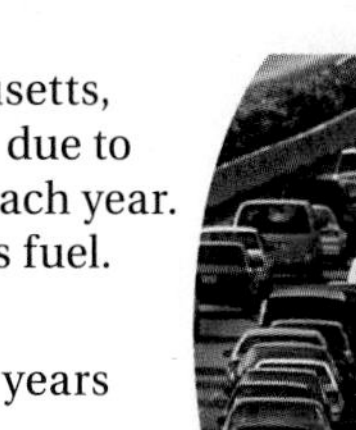

40. **TRAFFIC DELAYS** From 1990 to 2001 in Boston, Massachusetts, the annual excess fuel (in gallons per person) consumed due to traffic delays increased by about 1.4 gallons per person each year. In 1995 each person consumed about 37 gallons of excess fuel.

   a. Write an equation that gives the annual excess fuel (in gallons per person) as a function of the number of years since 1990. **$y = 1.4x + 30$**

   b. How much excess fuel was consumed per person in 2001? **45.4 gal**

   Animated Algebra at classzone.com

41a. Since the cost increases at a constant rate of \$.49 per print, the situation can be modeled by a linear equation.

41. ★ **EXTENDED RESPONSE** The table shows the cost of ordering sets of prints of digital photos from an online service. The cost per print is the same for the first 30 prints. There is also a shipping charge.

Number of prints	1	2	5	8
Total cost (dollars)	1.98	2.47	3.94	5.41

   a. *Explain* why the situation can be modeled by a linear equation.

   b. Write an equation in point-slope form that relates the total cost (in dollars) of a set of prints to the number of prints ordered. ***Sample answer:*** **$y - 1.98 = 0.49(x - 1)$**

   c. Find the shipping charge for up to 10 prints. **\$1.49**

   d. The cost of 15 prints is \$9.14. The shipping charge increases after the first 10 prints. Find the shipping charge for 15 prints. **\$1.79**

Avoiding Common Errors

Exercises 3–11, 23–28 Watch for students who fail to write both the subtraction symbol and negative symbol when they substitute negative values in the point-slope form.

Exercises 31, 32, 38, 41 Caution students that intervals for the data pairs are not always equal. To avoid errors, suggest they model Step 1 in Example 5 on page 304.

Study Strategy

Exercises 23–28 Suggest that students follow Example 3 on page 303 and use both points to write equations in point-slope form. They can then check that the equations are equivalent by writing them in slope-intercept form.

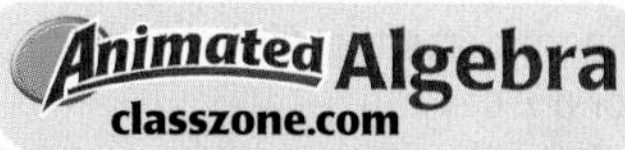

An **Animated Algebra** activity is available online for **Exercise 40.** This activity is also part of **Power Presentations**.

23. $y - 2 = -2(x - 7)$ or $y - 12 = -2(x - 2)$

24. $y + 2 = \frac{1}{2}(x - 6)$ or $y - 1 = \frac{1}{2}(x - 12)$

25. $y + 1 = -\frac{3}{5}(x + 4)$ or $y + 7 = -\frac{3}{5}(x - 6)$

26. $y - 5 = \frac{5}{4}(x - 4)$ or $y + 5 = \frac{5}{4}(x + 4)$

27. $y + 20 = 8(x + 3)$ or $y - 36 = 8(x - 4)$

28. $y + 19 = \frac{16}{5}(x + 5)$ or $y - 13 = \frac{16}{5}(x - 5)$

31–34. See Additional Answers beginning on p. AA1.

17.
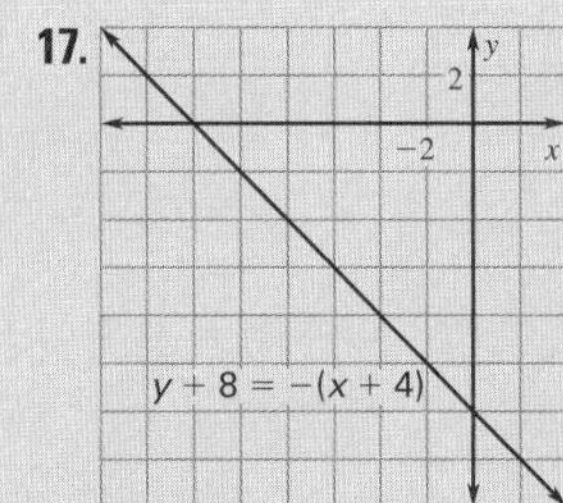

18.
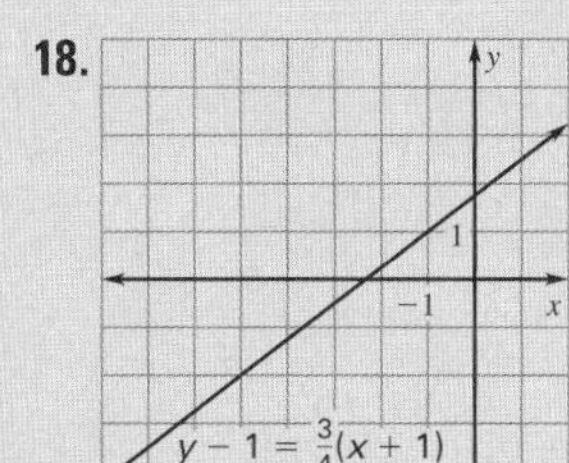

19.
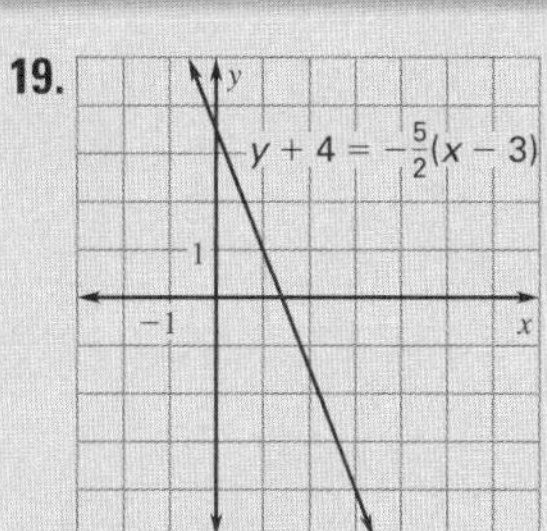

5 ASSESS AND RETEACH

Daily Homework Quiz

Transparency Available

1. Write an equation in point-slope form of the line that passes through (6, −4) and has slope 2. $y + 4 = 2(x - 6)$
2. Write an equation in point-slope form of the line that passes through (−1, −6) and (3, 10). $y + 6 = 4(x + 1)$ or $y - 10 = 4(x - 3)$
3. A travel company offers guided rafting trips for $875 for the first three days and $235 for each additional day. Write an equation that gives the total cost (in dollars) of a rafting trip as a function of the length of the trip. Find the cost for a 7-day trip. **$C = 235t + 170$, where C is total cost and t is time (in days); $1815**

Online Quiz

Available at **classzone.com**

Diagnosis/Remediation

- Practice A, B, C in Chapter Resource Book
- Study Guide in Chapter Resource Book
- Practice Workbook
- @HomeTutor

Challenge

Additional challenge is available in the Chapter Resource Book.

B **42. AQUACULTURE** Aquaculture is the farming of fish and other aquatic animals. World aquaculture increased at a relatively constant rate from 1991 to 2002. In 1994 world aquaculture was about 20.8 million metric tons. In 2000 world aquaculture was about 35.5 million metric tons.

a. Write an equation that gives world aquaculture (in millions of metric tons) as a function of the number of years since 1991. **$y = 2.45x + 13.45$**

b. In 2001 China was responsible for 70.2% of world aquaculture. Approximate China's aquaculture in 2001. **about 26.64 million metric tons**

43. MARATHON The diagram shows a marathon runner's speed at several outdoor temperatures.

a. Write an equation in point-slope form that relates running speed (in feet per second) to temperature (in degrees Fahrenheit). **$y - 17.6 = -0.06(x - 60)$**

b. Estimate the runner's speed when the temperature is 80°F. **16.4 ft/sec**

C **44. CHALLENGE** The number of cans recycled per pound of aluminum recycled in the U.S. increased at a relatively constant rate from 1972 to 2002. In 1977 about 23.5 cans per pound of aluminum were recycled. In 2000, about 33.1 cans per pound of aluminum were recycled.

a. Write an equation that gives the number of cans recycled per pound of aluminum recycled as a function of the number of years since 1972. **$y = 0.417391x + 21.413$**

b. In 2002, there were 53.8 billion aluminum cans collected for recycling. Approximately how many pounds of aluminum were collected? *Explain* how you found your answer.

44b. 1.59 billion lb; find the number of cans recycled per pound of aluminum in 2002 by substituting 30 for x to get about 33.9 cans per pound. Divide 53.8 billion aluminum cans by 33.9 cans per pound to find the number of pounds of aluminum.

MIXED REVIEW

Evaluate the expression.

45. $|-3.2| - 2.8$ *(p. 80)* **0.4**
46. $-6.1 - (-8.4)$ *(p. 80)* **2.3**
47. $\sqrt{196}$ *(p. 110)* **14**

Graph the equation. **48–53. See margin.**

48. $x = 0$ *(p. 215)*
49. $y = 8$ *(p. 215)*
50. $4x - 2y = 7$ *(p. 225)*
51. $-x + 5y = 1$ *(p. 225)*
52. $y = 2x - 7$ *(p. 244)*
53. $y = -\frac{3}{4}x + 2$ *(p. 244)*

PREVIEW Prepare for Lesson 5.4 in Exs. 54–57.

Write an equation of the line that has the given characteristics.

54. Slope: −3; y-intercept: 5 *(p. 283)* **$y = -3x + 5$**
55. Slope: 8; passes through (2, 15) *(p. 292)* **$y = 8x - 1$**
56. Passes through (0, −3), (6, 1) *(p. 283)* **$y = \frac{2}{3}x - 3$**
57. Passes through (3, 3), (6, −1) *(p. 292)* **$y = -\frac{4}{3}x + 7$**

48–53. See Additional Answers beginning on p. AA1.

Relate Arithmetic Sequences to Linear Functions

GOAL Identify, graph, and write the general form of arithmetic sequences.

Key Vocabulary
- sequence
- arithmetic sequence
- common difference

A **sequence** is an ordered list of numbers. The numbers in a sequence are called *terms*. In an **arithmetic sequence**, the difference between consecutive terms is constant. The constant difference is called the **common difference**.

An arithmetic sequence has the form $a_1, a_1 + d, a_1 + 2d, \ldots$ where a_1 is the first term and d is the common difference. For instance, if $a_1 = 2$ and $d = 6$, then the sequence $2, 2 + 6, 2 + 2(6), \ldots$ or $2, 8, 14, \ldots$ is arithmetic.

EXAMPLE 1 Identify an arithmetic sequence

Tell whether the sequence is arithmetic. If it is, find the next two terms.

a. $-4, 1, 6, 11, 16, \ldots$

b. $3, 5, 9, 15, 23, \ldots$

Solution

a. The first term is $a_1 = -4$. Find the differences of consecutive terms.

$a_2 - a_1 = 1 - (-4) = 5$ $\quad a_3 - a_2 = 6 - 1 = 5$

$a_4 - a_3 = 11 - 6 = 5$ $\quad a_5 - a_4 = 16 - 11 = 5$

▶ Because the terms have a common difference ($d = 5$), the sequence is arithmetic. The next two terms are $a_6 = 21$ and $a_7 = 26$.

b. The first term is $a_1 = 3$. Find the differences of consecutive terms.

$a_2 - a_1 = 5 - 3 = 2$ $\quad a_3 - a_2 = 9 - 5 = 4$

$a_4 - a_3 = 15 - 9 = 6$ $\quad a_5 - a_4 = 23 - 15 = 8$

▶ There is no common difference, so the sequence is not arithmetic.

GRAPHING A SEQUENCE To graph a sequence, let a term's position number in the sequence be the x-value. The term is the corresponding y-value.

EXAMPLE 2 Graph a sequence

Graph the sequence $-4, 1, 6, 11, 16, \ldots$.

Make a table pairing each term with its position number.

Position, x	1	2	3	4	5
Term, y	-4	1	6	11	16

Plot the pairs in the table as points in a coordinate plane.

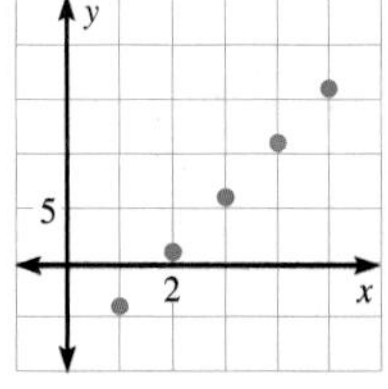

1 PLAN AND PREPARE

Warm-Up Exercises

Find the next two numbers in the pattern.

1. 6, 13, 20, 27, 34, . . . **41, 48**
2. 2, 3, 5, 8, 12, . . . **17, 23**
3. 54, 43, 32, 21, . . . **10, −1**
4. −5, −2, 1, 4, 7, . . . **10, 13**

2 FOCUS AND MOTIVATE

Essential Question

Big Idea 2, p. 281

How do you use a linear model to identify, graph, and write the general form of arithmetic sequences? **Tell students they will learn how to answer this question by using the difference between terms in a sequence to extend the sequence or to find the *n*th term.**

3 TEACH

Extra Example 1

Tell whether the sequence is arithmetic. If it is, find the next two terms.

a. 3, 4, 7, 12, 19, . . . **no**

b. 13, 9, 5, 1, −3, . . . **yes; −7, −11**

NCTM STANDARDS

Standard 9: Understand how mathematical ideas build on one another

Standard 10: Use representations to communicate mathematical ideas

FUNCTIONS Notice that the points plotted in Example 2 appear to lie on a line. In fact, an arithmetic sequence is a linear function. You can think of the common difference d as the slope and $(1, a_1)$ as a point on the graph of the function. An equation in point-slope form for the function is $a_n - a_1 = d(n - 1)$. This equation can be rewritten as $a_n = a_1 + (n - 1)d$.

KEY CONCEPT *For Your Notebook*

Rule for an Arithmetic Sequence

The nth term of an arithmetic sequence with first term a_1 and common difference d is given by $a_n = a_1 + (n - 1)d$.

EXAMPLE 3 Write a rule for the *n*th term of a sequence

Write a rule for the *n*th term of the sequence −4, 1, 6, 11, 16, ... Find a_{100}.

Solution

The first term of the sequence is $a_1 = -4$, and the common difference is $d = 5$.

$a_n = a_1 + (n - 1)d$ — Write general rule for an arithmetic sequence.

$a_n = -4 + (n - 1)5$ — Substitute −4 for a_1 and 5 for d.

Find a_{100} by substituting 100 for n.

$a_n = -4 + (n - 1)5$ — Write the rule for the sequence.

$a_{100} = -4 + (100 - 1)5$ — Substitute 100 for n.

$a_{100} = 491$ — Evaluate.

PRACTICE

EXAMPLE 1 on p. 309 for Exs. 1–3

Tell whether the sequence is arithmetic. If it is, find the next two terms. If it is not, explain why not.

1. 17, 14, 11, 8, 5, . . . **yes; 2, −1**
2. 1, 4, 16, 64, 256, . . . **No; there is no common difference.**
3. −8, −15, −22, −29, −36, . . . **yes; −43, −50**

EXAMPLE 2 on p. 309 for Exs. 4–9

Graph the sequence. **4–9. See margin.**

4. 1, 4, 7, 11, 14, . . .
5. 4, −3, −10, −17, −24, . . .
6. 5, −1, −7, −13, −19, . . .
7. $2, 3\frac{1}{2}, 5, 6\frac{1}{2}, 8, \ldots$
8. 0, 2, 4, 6, 8, . . .
9. −3, −4, −5, −6, −7, . . .

EXAMPLE 3 on p. 310 for Exs. 10–15

Write a rule for the *n*th term of the sequence. Find a_{100}. **10–15. See margin.**

10. −12, −5, 2, 9, 16, . . .
11. 51, 72, 93, 114, 135, . . .
12. 0.25, −0.75, −1.75, −2.75, . . .
13. $\frac{1}{4}, \frac{3}{8}, \frac{1}{2}, \frac{5}{8}, \frac{3}{4}, \ldots$
14. 0, −5, −10, −15, −20, . . .
15. $1, 1\frac{1}{3}, 1\frac{2}{3}, 2, 2\frac{1}{3}, \ldots$
16. **REASONING** For an arithmetic sequence with a first term of a_1 and a common difference of d, show that $a_{n+1} - a_n = d$. **A term after the first term is the sum of the previous term and the common difference, so $a_{n+1} = a_n + d$, subtract a_n from both sides, $a_{n+1} - a_n = d$.**

Extra Example 2

Graph the sequence 13, 9, 5, 1, −3, ...

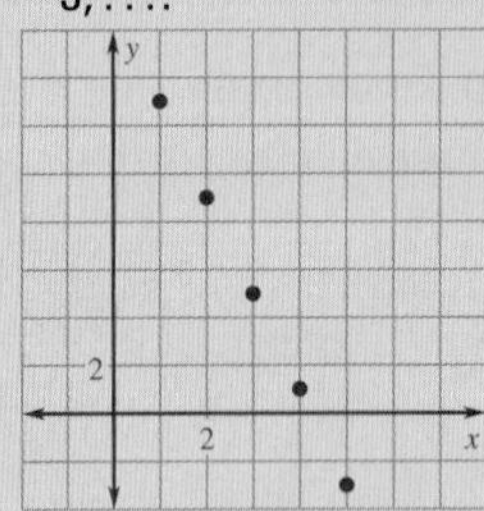

Extra Example 3

Write a rule for the nth term of the sequence 13, 9, 5, 1, −3, ... Find a_{100}. **$a_n = 13 + (n - 1)(-4)$; −383**

Closing the Lesson

Have students summarize the major points of the lesson and answer the Essential Question: How do you use a linear model to identify, graph, and write the general form of arithmetic sequences?

- **A sequence is arithmetic if consecutive terms have a common difference.**
- **The rule for an arithmetic sequence is $a_n = a_1 + (n - 1)d$ where a_n is the nth term, a_1 is the first term, and d is the common difference.**

Use the common difference between consecutive terms to find the next term. Pair a term with its position in the sequence to graph the sequence. Substitute the first term, the value of n, and the common difference into the arithmetic sequence rule to find the nth term.

4 PRACTICE AND APPLY

Avoiding Common Errors

Exercises 1–3 Some students may use a positive number as a common difference when it should be a negative number. Tell students that the common difference between consecutive terms can be a positive or a negative number. Remind them to subtract each term from the one right after it to find the common difference.

4–9. See Additional Answers beginning on p. AA1.

10. $a_n = -12 + (n - 1)7$; 681

11. $a_n = 51 + (n - 1)21$; 2130

12. $a_n = 0.25 + (n - 1)(-1)$; −98.75

13. $a_n = \frac{1}{4} + (n - 1)\frac{1}{8}$; $12\frac{5}{8}$

14. $a_n = (n - 1)(-5)$; −495

15. $a_n = 1 + (n - 1)\frac{1}{3}$; 34

5.4 Write Linear Equations in Standard Form

Before You wrote equations in point-slope form.
Now You will write equations in standard form.
Why? So you can find possible combinations of objects, as in Ex. 41.

Key Vocabulary
- **standard form,** *p. 216*

Recall that the linear equation $Ax + By = C$ is in standard form, where A, B, and C are real numbers and A and B are not both zero. All linear equations can be written in standard form.

EXAMPLE 1 Write equivalent equations in standard form

Write two equations in standard form that are equivalent to $2x - 6y = 4$.

Solution

To write one equivalent equation, multiply each side by 2.

$$4x - 12y = 8$$

To write another equivalent equation, multiply each side by 0.5.

$$x - 3y = 2$$

EXAMPLE 2 Write an equation from a graph

Write an equation in standard form of the line shown.

Solution

STEP 1 **Calculate** the slope.

$$m = \frac{1 - (-2)}{1 - 2} = \frac{3}{-1} = -3$$

STEP 2 **Write** an equation in point-slope form. Use (1, 1).

$y - y_1 = m(x - x_1)$ **Write point-slope form.**

$y - 1 = -3(x - 1)$ **Substitute 1 for y_1, −3 for m, and 1 for x_1.**

STEP 3 **Rewrite** the equation in standard form.

$3x + y = 4$ **Simplify. Collect variable terms on one side, constants on the other.**

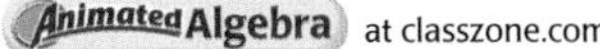
at classzone.com

✓ GUIDED PRACTICE for Examples 1 and 2

1. Write two equations in standard form that are equivalent to $x - y = 3$. ***Sample answer:*** **$2x - 2y = 6$, $3x - 3y = 9$**
2. Write an equation in standard form of the line through $(3, -1)$ and $(2, -3)$. **$-2x + y = -7$**

1 PLAN AND PREPARE

Warm-Up Exercises

Transparency Available

Write an equation in point-slope form of the line that passes through the given points.

1. (1, 4), (6, −1) **$y - 4 = -(x - 1)$ or $y + 1 = -(x - 6)$**
2. (−1, −2), (2, 7) **$y + 2 = 3(x + 1)$ or $y - 7 = 3(x - 2)$**
3. A store rents 3 DVDs for $5, plus $3 for each additional DVD. Find the cost of renting 20 DVDs. **$56**

Notetaking Guide

Transparency Available

Promotes interactive learning and notetaking skills.

Pacing

Basic: 2 days
Average: 2 days
Advanced: 2 days
Block: 0.5 block with 5.3
0.5 block with 5.5

- See *Teaching Guide/Lesson Plan.*

2 FOCUS AND MOTIVATE

Essential Question

Big Idea 1, p. 281

How do you write an equation in standard form? **Tell students they will learn how to answer this question by rewriting equations.**

NCTM STANDARDS

Standard 2: Use models to understand relationships

Standard 6: Apply/adapt strategies to solve problems

Resource Planning Guide

Chapter Resource Book
- Teaching Guide/Lesson Plan
- Activity Master
- Practice levels A, B, C
- Study Guide
- Catch-up for Absent Students
- Problem Solving Workshop
- Challenge

Workbooks
- Notetaking Guide
- Practice Workbook

Teaching Options
- **Power Presentations** provides dynamic electronic teaching resources for the classroom.
- **Activity Generator** provides editable activities for all ability levels.

Interactive Technology
- Easy Planner
- Power Presentations
- Activity Generator
- Animated Algebra
- Test Generator
- Online Quiz
- eWorkbook
- eEdition
- @HomeTutor

Resources for English Learners
- Spanish Study Guide
- Multi-Language Visual Glossary
- Student Resources in Spanish

See also the *Differentiated Instruction Resources* for more strategies for meeting individual needs.

Motivating the Lesson

You want to earn \$1000 teaching children how to swim. You earn \$10 per hour for individual instruction and \$25 per hour for instructing groups. By knowing how to write equations in standard form, you can determine the possible combinations of hours of individual and group instruction that will result in \$1000 in earnings.

3 TEACH

Extra Example 1

Write two equations in standard form that are equivalent to $x + 4y = 3$. $-2x - 8y = -6$; $3x + 12y = 9$

Extra Example 2

Write an equation in standard form of the line shown. $2x + y = 6$

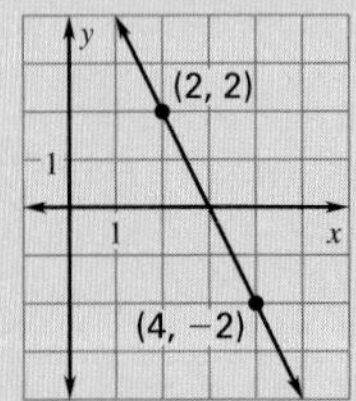

Animated Algebra classzone.com

An **Animated Algebra** activity is available online for **Example 2**. This activity is also part of **Power Presentations**.

Extra Example 3

Write an equation of the line.

a. Line a $x = -3$

b. Line b $y = 2$

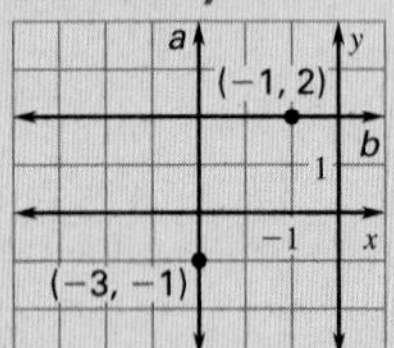

HORIZONTAL AND VERTICAL LINES Recall that equations of horizontal lines have the form $y = a$. Equations of vertical lines have the form $x = b$. You cannot write an equation for a vertical line in slope-intercept form or point-slope form, because a vertical line has no slope. However, you can write an equation for a vertical line in standard form.

EXAMPLE 3 Write an equation of a line

Write an equation of the specified line.

a. Blue line **b.** Red line

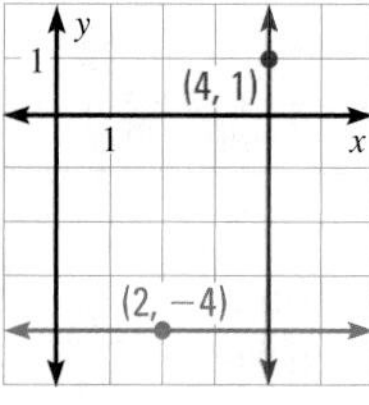

Solution

ANOTHER WAY Using the slope-intercept form to find an equation of the horizontal line gives you $y = 0x - 4$, or $y = -4$.

a. The y-coordinate of the given point on the blue line is -4. This means that all points on the line have a y-coordinate of -4. An equation of the line is $y = -4$.

b. The x-coordinate of the given point on the red line is 4. This means that all points on the line have an x-coordinate of 4. An equation of the line is $x = 4$.

EXAMPLE 4 Complete an equation in standard form

Find the missing coefficient in the equation of the line shown. Write the completed equation.

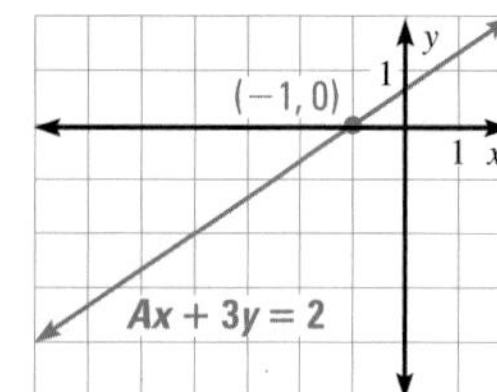

Solution

STEP 1 **Find** the value of A. Substitute the coordinates of the given point for x and y in the equation. Solve for A.

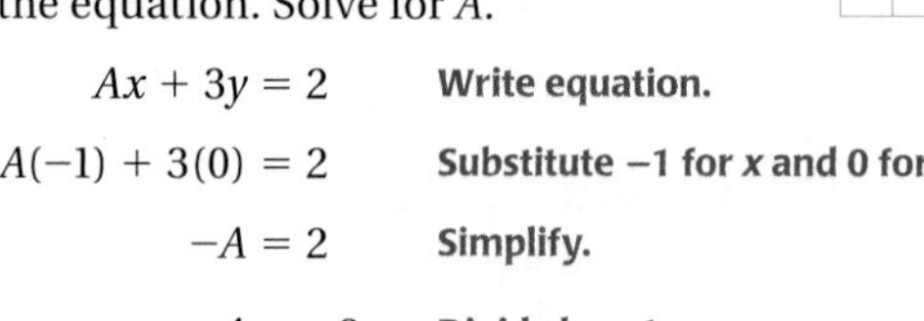

$Ax + 3y = 2$ **Write equation.**

$A(-1) + 3(0) = 2$ **Substitute −1 for x and 0 for y.**

$-A = 2$ **Simplify.**

$A = -2$ **Divide by −1.**

STEP 2 **Complete** the equation.

$-2x + 3y = 2$ **Substitute −2 for A.**

✓ GUIDED PRACTICE for Examples 3 and 4

Write equations of the horizontal and vertical lines that pass through the given point.

3. $(-8, -9)$ $y = -9, x = -8$

4. $(13, -5)$ $y = -5, x = 13$

Find the missing coefficient in the equation of the line that passes through the given point. Write the completed equation.

5. $-4x + By = 7, (-1, 1)$ $3; -4x + 3y = 7$

6. $Ax + y = -3, (2, 11)$ $-7; -7x + y = -3$

Differentiated Instruction

Visual Learners For the equations of vertical lines ($x = a$) and horizontal lines ($y = b$), remind students that the constants a and b are not the same as the A and B in the equation for the standard form of a line. Constants a and b correspond to C in the standard form of a line.

See also the *Differentiated Instruction Resources* for more strategies.

EXAMPLE 5 Solve a multi-step problem

LIBRARY Your class is taking a trip to the public library. You can travel in small and large vans. A small van holds 8 people and a large van holds 12 people. Your class could fill 15 small vans and 2 large vans.

a. **Write** an equation in standard form that models the possible combinations of small vans and large vans that your class could fill.

b. **Graph** the equation from part (a).

c. **List** several possible combinations.

Solution

a. Write a verbal model. Then write an equation.

Capacity of small van	·	Number of small vans	+	Capacity of large van	·	Number of large vans	=	People on trip
8	·	s	+	12	·	ℓ	=	p

Because your class could fill 15 small vans and 2 large vans, use (15, 2) as the s- and ℓ-values to substitute in the equation $8s + 12\ell = p$ to find the value of p.

$8(15) + 12(2) = p$ **Substitute 15 for s and 2 for ℓ.**

$144 = p$ **Simplify.**

Substitute 144 for p in the equation $8s + 12\ell = p$.

▶ The equation $8s + 12\ell = 144$ models the possible combinations.

b. Find the intercepts of the graph.

Substitute 0 for s. Substitute 0 for ℓ.

$8(0) + 12\ell = 144$ $8s + 12(0) = 144$

$\ell = 12$ $s = 18$

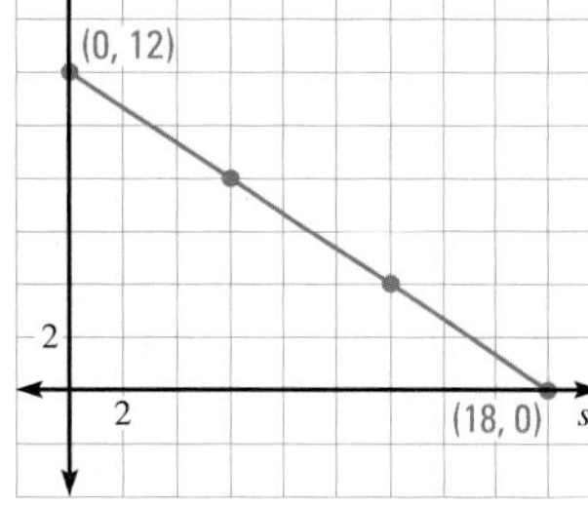

Plot the points (0, 12) and (18, 0). Connect them with a line segment. For this problem only nonnegative whole-number values of s and ℓ make sense.

c. The graph passes through (0, 12), (6, 8),(12, 4), and (18, 0). So, four possible combinations are 0 small and 12 large, 6 small and 8 large, 12 small and 4 large, 18 small and 0 large.

LISTING COMBINATIONS
Other combinations of small and large vans are possible. Another way to find possible combinations is by substituting values for s or ℓ in the equation.

GUIDED PRACTICE for Example 5

7. **WHAT IF?** In Example 5, suppose that 8 students decide not to go on the class trip. Write an equation that models the possible combinations of small and large vans that your class could fill. List several possible combinations. **$8s + 12l = 136$. *Sample answer:* 17 small, 0 large; 14 small, 2 large; 11 small, 4 large; 8 small, 6 large; 5 small, 8 large; 2 small, 10 large**

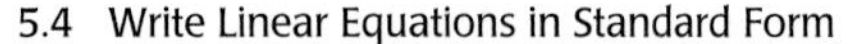

Extra Example 4

Find the missing coefficient in the equation of the line shown. Write the completed equation.

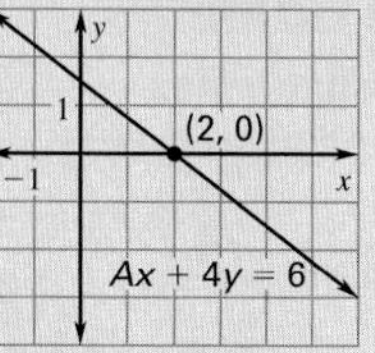

$3x + 4y = 6$

Extra Example 5

T-shirts at a flea market cost $4.50 each and shorts cost $6 each. You have enough money to buy exactly 12 T-shirts and 9 pairs of shorts.

a. Write an equation in standard form that models the possible combinations of T-shirts and shorts you can buy. **$4.5t + 6s = 108$**

b. Graph the equation.

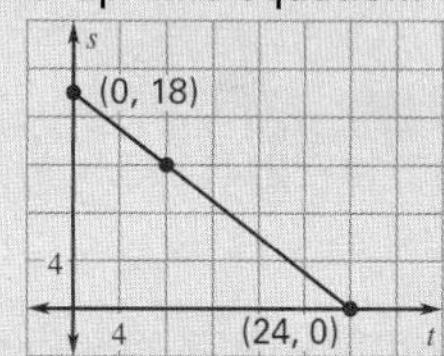

c. List several possible combinations. **0 T-shirts and 18 shorts; 8 T-shirts and 12 shorts; 24 T-shirts and 0 shorts**

Closing the Lesson

Have students summarize the major points of the lesson and answer the Essential Question: How do you write an equation in standard form?

- **$Ax + By = C$ is the standard form of an equation where A, B, and C are real numbers, and A and B are not both 0.**

Use the slope formula to find the slope. Write the equation in point-slope form. Collect variable terms on one side of the equation and constants on the other to rewrite the equation in standard form.

Differentiated Instruction

Below Level Have students find two other combinations in **Example 5** part (c) using the suggestion in the side note to substitute values for s or ℓ in the equation. After the students find the combinations (3, 10) and (9, 6), ask them to describe the combinations in terms of small and large vans and coordinates on a graph. Ask them to compare the methods of using an equation and a graph to obtain possible combinations, leading them to discuss the advantages and disadvantages of both methods.

See also the *Differentiated Instruction Resources* for more strategies.

4 PRACTICE AND APPLY

Assignment Guide

Answer Transparencies available for all exercises

Basic:
Day 1: EP p. 941 Exs. 37–40
pp. 314–316
Exs. 1–8, 11–19, 47–49
Day 2: pp. 314–316
Exs. 23–32, 38–41, 45, 46

Average:
Day 1: pp. 314–316
Exs. 1–4, 8–10, 14–22, 47–49
Day 2: pp. 314–316
Exs. 23–29 odd, 30–36, 38–43, 45, 46

Advanced:
Day 1: pp. 314–316
Exs. 1–4, 8–10, 16–22, 37*, 47–49
Day 2: pp. 314–316
Exs. 26–28, 30–36, 41–46*

Block:
pp. 314–316
Exs. 1–4, 8–10, 14–22, 47–49 (with 5.3)
pp. 314–316
Exs. 23–29 odd, 30–36, 38–43, 45, 46 (with 5.5)

Differentiated Instruction

See *Differentiated Instruction Resources* for suggestions on addressing the needs of a diverse classroom.

Homework Check

For a quick check of student understanding of key concepts, go over the following exercises:

Basic: 6, 12, 24, 29, 38
Average: 9, 16, 27, 32, 39
Advanced: 10, 20, 27, 34, 38

Extra Practice

- Student Edition, p. 942
- Chapter Resource Book: Practice levels A, B, C

Practice Worksheet

An easily-readable reduced practice page (with answers) for this lesson can be found on p. 280D.

5.4 EXERCISES

HOMEWORK KEY
○ = WORKED-OUT SOLUTIONS on p. WS11 for Exs. 17 and 39
★ = STANDARDIZED TEST PRACTICE Exs. 4, 30, 40, and 42
◆ = MULTIPLE REPRESENTATIONS Ex. 41

SKILL PRACTICE

A

VOCABULARY Identify the form of the equation.

1. $2x + 8y = -3$ **standard form**
2. $y = -5x + 8$ **slope-intercept form**
3. $y + 4 = 2(x - 6)$ **point-slope form**

4. ★ **WRITING** *Explain* how to write an equation of a line in standard form when two points on the line are given. **Find the slope of the line then substitute the slope and one of the points into the point-slope form. Collect variables on one side and constants on the other side.**

EXAMPLE 1 on p. 311 for Exs. 5–10

EQUIVALENT EQUATIONS Write two equations in standard form that are equivalent to the given equation. **5–10. See margin.**

5. $x + y = -10$
6. $5x + 10y = 15$
7. $-x + 2y = 9$
8. $-9x - 12y = 6$
9. $9x - 3y = -12$
10. $-2x + 4y = -5$

EXAMPLE 2 on p. 311 for Exs. 11–22

17. $\frac{2}{3}x + y = -\frac{4}{3}$
19. $-\frac{4}{3}x + y = -1$
21. $-\frac{1}{2}x + y = 1$

WRITING EQUATIONS Write an equation in standard form of the line that passes through the given point and has the given slope *m* or that passes through the two given points.

11. $(-3, 2), m = 1$ **$-x + y = 5$**
12. $(4, -1), m = 3$ **$-3x + y = -13$**
13. $(0, 5), m = -2$ **$2x + y = 5$**
14. $(-8, 0), m = -4$ **$4x + y = -32$**
15. $(-4, -4), m = -\frac{3}{2}$ **$\frac{3}{2}x + y = -10$**
16. $(-6, -10), m = \frac{1}{6}$ **$-\frac{1}{6}x + y = -9$**
17. $(-8, 4), (4, -4)$
18. $(-5, 2), (-4, 3)$ **$-x + y = 7$**
19. $(0, -1), (-6, -9)$
20. $(3, 9), (1, 1)$ **$-4x + y = -3$**
21. $(10, 6), (-12, -5)$
22. $(-6, -2), (-1, -2)$ **$y = -2$**

EXAMPLE 3 on p. 312 for Exs. 23–28

HORIZONTAL AND VERTICAL LINES Write equations of the horizontal and vertical lines that pass through the given point.

23. $(3, 2)$ **$y = 2, x = 3$**
24. $(-5, -3)$ **$y = -3, x = -5$**
25. $(-1, 3)$ **$y = 3, x = -1$**
26. $(5, 3)$ **$y = 3, x = 5$**
27. $(-1, 4)$ **$y = 4, x = -1$**
28. $(-6, -2)$ **$y = -2, x = -6$**

EXAMPLE 4 on p. 312 for Exs. 29–36

B

29. (1, −4) was substituted incorrectly, 1 should be substituted for *x* and −4 substituted for *y*, $A(1) - 3(-4) = 5$, $A + 12 = 5$, $A = -7$.

32. $\frac{1}{2}$; $\frac{1}{2}x - 4y = -1$

29. **ERROR ANALYSIS** *Describe* and correct the error in finding the value of A for the equation $Ax - 3y = 5$, if the graph of the equation passes through the point $(1, -4)$.

$A(-4) - 3(1) = 5$
$A = -2$

30. ★ **WRITING** The *intercept form* of the equation of a line with an x-intercept of a and a y-intercept of b is $\frac{x}{a} + \frac{y}{b} = 1$. Write the equation $2x + 3y = 12$ in intercept form. *Describe* your method. **See margin.**

COMPLETING EQUATIONS Find the missing coefficient in the equation of the line that passes through the given point. Write the completed equation.

31. $Ax + 3y = 5, (2, -1)$ **4; $4x + 3y = 5$**
32. $Ax - 4y = -1, (6, 1)$
33. $-x + By = 10, (-2, -2)$ **-4; $-x - 4y = 10$**
34. $8x + By = 4, (-5, 4)$ **11; $8x + 11y = 4$**
35. $Ax - 3y = -5, (1, 0)$ **-5; $-5x - 3y = -5$**
36. $2x + By = -4, (-3, 7)$ **$\frac{2}{7}$; $2x + \frac{2}{7}y = -4$**

C

37. **CHALLENGE** Write an equation in standard form of the line that passes through $(0, a)$ and $(b, 0)$ where $a \neq 0$ and $b \neq 0$. **$\frac{a}{b}x + y = a$**

5–10. Sample answers are given.
5. $2x + 2y = -20$, $3x + 3y = -30$
6. $x + 2y = 3$, $10x + 20y = 30$
7. $x - 2y = -9$, $-2x + 4y = 18$
8. $-3x - 4y = 2$, $-6x - 8y = 4$
9. $3x - y = -4$, $6x - 2y = -8$
10. $2x - 4y = 5$, $-4x + 8y = -10$

30. $\frac{x}{6} + \frac{y}{4} = 1$; *Sample answer:*
I solved the equations $2x + 3(0) = 12$ and $2(0) + 3y = 12$ to find *a*, the *x*-intercept, and *b*, the *y*-intercept, respectively. Then I substituted the values of *a* and *b* into the general intercept form.

PROBLEM SOLVING

EXAMPLE 5 [A] on p. 313 for Exs. 38–41

38. **GARDENING** The diagram shows the prices of two types of ground cover plants. Write an equation in standard form that models the possible combinations of vinca and phlox plants a gardener can buy for $300. List three of these possible combinations. **$2.5p + 1.2v = 300$; *Sample answer:* 120 phlox plants and 0 vinca plants, 0 phlox plants and 250 vinca plants, 60 phlox plants and 125 vinca plants**

@HomeTutor for problem solving help at classzone.com

39. **NUTRITION** A snack mix requires a total of 120 ounces of some corn cereal and some wheat cereal. Corn cereal comes in 12 ounce boxes.

a. The last time you made this mix, you used 5 boxes of corn cereal and 4 boxes of wheat cereal. How many ounces are in a box of wheat cereal? **15 oz**

b. Write an equation in standard form that models the possible combinations of boxes of wheat and corn cereal you can use. **$12c + 15w = 120$**

c. List all possible combinations of whole boxes of wheat and corn cereal you can use to make the snack mix. **10 corn, 0 wheat; 5 corn, 4 wheat; 0 corn, 8 wheat**

@HomeTutor for problem solving help at classzone.com

40. $20n + 5t = 100$; see margin for art. The n-intercept, 5, is the number of nights of boarding the dog at the kennel without any treats. The t-intercept, 20, is the number of treats that can be bought without boarding the dog for any nights.

40. ★ **SHORT RESPONSE** A dog kennel charges $20 per night to board your dog. You can also have a doggie treat delivered to your dog for $5. Write an equation that models the possible combinations of nights at the kennel and doggie treats that you can buy for $100. Graph the equation. *Explain* what the intercepts of the graph mean in this situation.

[B]

41. ◆ **MULTIPLE REPRESENTATIONS** As the student council treasurer, you prepare the budget for your class rafting trip. Each large raft costs $100 to rent, and each small raft costs $40 to rent. You have $1600 to spend.

a. **Writing an Equation** Write an equation in standard form that models the possible combinations of small rafts and large rafts that you can rent. **$100\ell + 40s = 1600$**

b. **Drawing a Graph** Graph the equation from part (a). **See margin.**

c. **Making a Table** Make a table that shows several combinations of small and large rafts that you can rent. **See margin.**

42. ★ **SHORT RESPONSE** One bus ride costs $.75. One subway ride costs $1.00. A monthly pass can be used for unlimited subway and bus rides and costs the same as 36 subway rides plus 36 bus rides.

a. Write an equation in standard form that models the possible combinations of bus and subway rides with the same value as the pass. **$0.75b + s = 63$**

b. You ride the bus 60 times in one month. How many times must you ride the subway in order for the cost of the rides to equal the value of the pass? *Explain* your answer. **18 subway rides; if you ride the bus 60 times, it costs (0.75) ($60) = $45 without the pass. The pass costs $63, you need to spend $18 on subway rides, $18 ÷ $1 = 18.**

Avoiding Common Errors

Exercises 5–10 Watch for students who overlook one of the terms of the equation or one of the sides of the equation when multiplying to write an equivalent equation. Remind these students that they must use every term of the equation as a factor to obtain an equivalent equation.

Teaching Strategy

Exercise 42 You may want to use this exercise to illustrate why it makes sense in some problems to substitute values in an equation to find possible combinations. Point out the side note to Example 5 which mentions the method of substitution as another way to find possible combinations. Point out that either method works well for Example 5. Then draw students' attention to Exercise 42. After they write the equation in part (a), ask them to find the intercepts of the equation. Discuss how the points (0, 63) and (84, 0) would make this a difficult problem to graph. Suggest that students pay attention to practical matters such as very large numbers when solving problems of this type.

41c.

Large rafts	Small rafts
16	0
14	5
12	10
10	15
8	20
6	25
4	30
2	35
0	40

40.

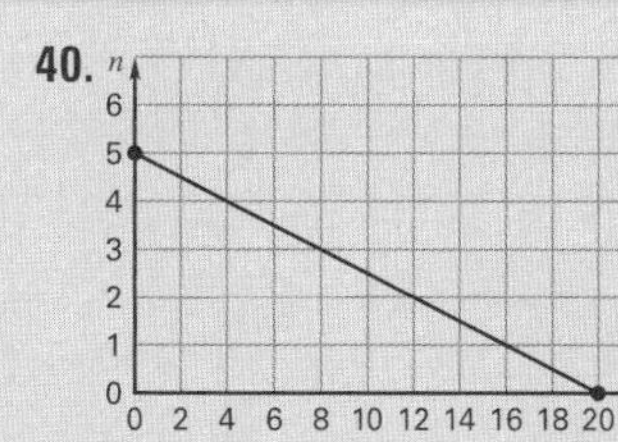

41b.

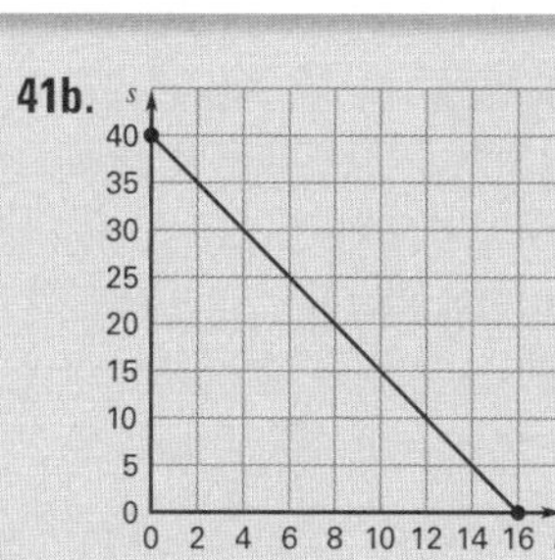

43. GEOMETRY Write an equation in standard form that models the possible lengths and widths (in feet) of a rectangle having the same perimeter as a rectangle that is 10 feet wide and 20 feet long. Make a table that shows five possible lengths and widths of the rectangle.
$2\ell + 2w = 60$; see margin for table.

C 44. CHALLENGE You are working in a chemistry lab. You have 1000 milliliters of pure acid. A dilution of acid is created by adding pure acid to water. A 40% dilution contains 40% acid and 60% water. You have been asked to make a 40% dilution and a 60% dilution of pure acid.

a. Write an equation in standard form that models the possible quantities of each dilution you can prepare using all 1000 milliliters of pure acid. **$0.4x + 0.6y = 1000$**

b. You prepare 700 milliliters of the 40% dilution. How much of the 60% dilution can you prepare? **1200 mL**

c. How much water do you need to prepare 700 milliliters of the 40% dilution? **420 mL**

MIXED REVIEW

PREVIEW
Prepare for Lesson 5.5 in Exs. 45–46.

Tell whether the graphs of the two equations are parallel lines. *Explain* your reasoning. *(p. 244)* **45–46. See margin.**

45. $1 - y = 4x, -6 = -4x - y$

46. $4x = 2y - 6, 4 + y = -2x$

Write an equation in point-slope form of the line that passes through the given point and has the given slope m. *(p. 302)*

47. $(3, -4), m = 1$
$y + 4 = x - 3$

48. $(-6, 6), m = -2$
$y - 6 = -2(x + 6)$

49. $(-8, -1), m = 5$
$y + 1 = 5(x + 8)$

QUIZ for Lessons 5.1–5.4

Write an equation in slope-intercept form of the line that passes through the given point and has the given slope m.

1. $(2, 5), m = 3$ *(p. 292)*
$y = 3x - 1$

2. $(-1, 4), m = -2$ *(p. 292)*
$y = -2x + 2$

3. $(0, -7), m = 5$ *(p. 283)*
$y = 5x - 7$

Write an equation in slope-intercept form of the line that passes through the given points.

4. $(0, 2), (9, 5)$ *(p. 283)*
$y = \frac{1}{3}x + 2$

5. $(5, 7), (19, 14)$ *(p. 292)*
$y = \frac{1}{2}x + \frac{9}{2}$

6. $(4, 24), (-11, 19)$ *(p. 292)*
$y = \frac{1}{3}x + \frac{68}{3}$

Write an equation in (a) point-slope form and (b) standard form of the line that passes through the given points. *(pp. 302, 311)* **7–9. See margin.**

7. $(-5, 2), (-4, 3)$

8. $(0, -1), (-6, -9)$

9. $(3, 9), (1, 1)$

10. **DVDS** The table shows the price per DVD for different quantities of DVDs. Write an equation that models the price per DVD as a function of the number of DVDs purchased. *(p. 302)* **$y = -2x + 22$**

Number of DVDs purchased	1	2	3	4	5	6
Price per DVD (dollars)	20	18	16	14	12	10

EXTRA PRACTICE for Lesson 5.4, p. 942 **ONLINE QUIZ** at classzone.com

5 ASSESS AND RETEACH

Daily Homework Quiz

Transparency Available

Write an equation in standard form of the line that passes through the given point and has the given slope m or that passes through the two given points.

1. $(1, -6), m = -2$ **$2x + y = -4$**
2. $(-4, -3), (2, 9)$ **$-2x + y = 5$**
3. You have \$96 to spend on campground activities. You can rent a paddleboat for \$8 per hour and a kayak for \$6 per hour. Write an equation in standard form that models the possible hourly combinations of activities you can afford. List three possible combinations. **$8p + 6c = 96$; 16 h kayak and 0 h paddleboat; 12 h paddleboat and 0 h kayak; 6 h paddleboat and 8 h kayak**

Online Quiz

Available at **classzone.com**

Diagnosis/Remediation

- Practice A, B, C in Chapter Resource Book
- Study Guide in Chapter Resource Book
- Practice Workbook
- @HomeTutor

Challenge

Additional challenge is available in the Chapter Resource Book.

Quiz

An easily-readable reduced copy of the quiz (with answers) on Lessons 5.1–5.4 from the Assessment Book can be found on p. 280F.

43, Quiz 7–9. See Additional Answers beginning on p. AA1.

45. Parallel; if you write each equation in slope-intercept form, you can see that the slopes are equal.

46. Not parallel; if you write each equation in slope-intercept form, you can see that the slopes are not equal.

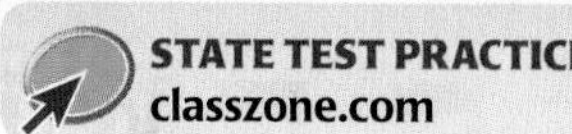

MIXED REVIEW *of Problem Solving*

Lessons 5.1–5.4

1. **MULTI-STEP PROBLEM** A satellite radio company charges a monthly fee of $13 for service. To use the service, you must first buy equipment that costs $100.

   a. Identify the rate of change and starting value in this situation. **$13 per month; $100**

   b. Write an equation that gives the total cost of satellite radio as a function of the number of months of service. $C = 13m + 100$

   c. Find the total cost after 1 year of satellite radio service. **$256**

2. **MULTI-STEP PROBLEM** You hike 5 miles before taking a break. After your break, you continue to hike at an average speed of 3.5 miles per hour.

   a. Write an equation that gives the distance (in miles) that you hike as a function of the time (in hours) since your break. $d = 3.5t + 5$

   b. You hike for 4 hours after your break. Find the total distance you hike for the day. **19 mi**

3. **EXTENDED RESPONSE** The table shows the cost of a catered lunch buffet for different numbers of people.

Number of people	Cost (dollars)
12	192
18	288
24	384
30	480
36	576
42	672

   a. *Explain* why the situation can be modeled by a linear equation. **See margin.**

   b. Write an equation that gives the cost of the lunch buffet as a function of the number of people attending. $C = 16p$

   c. What is the cost of a lunch buffet for 120 people? **$1920**

4. **SHORT RESPONSE** You use a garden hose to fill a swimming pool at a constant rate. The pool is empty when you begin to fill it. The pool contains 15 gallons of water after 5 minutes. After 30 minutes, the pool contains 90 gallons of water. Write an equation that gives the volume (in gallons) of water in the pool as a function of the number of minutes since you began filling it. *Explain* how you can find the time it takes to put 150 gallons of water in the pool. $V = 3t$; **substitute 150 for** V **and solve for** t; $t = 50$ **minutes.**

5. **EXTENDED RESPONSE** A city is paving a bike path. The same length of path is paved each day. After 4 days, there are 8 miles of path remaining to be paved. After 6 more days, there are 5 miles of path remaining to be paved.

   a. *Explain* how you know the situation can be modeled by a linear equation. **See margin.**

   b. Write an equation that gives the distance (in miles) remaining to be paved as a function of the number of days since the project began. $d = -\frac{1}{2}t + 10$

   c. In how many more days will the entire path be paved? **10 days**

6. **OPEN-ENDED** Write an equation in standard form that models the possible combinations of nickels and dimes worth a certain amount of money (in dollars). List several of these possible combinations. **See margin.**

7. **GRIDDED ANSWER** You are saving money to buy a stereo system. You have saved $50 so far. You plan to save $20 each week for the next few months. How much money do you expect to have saved in 7 weeks? **$190**

8. **GRIDDED ANSWER** The cost of renting a moving van for a 26 mile trip is $62.50. The cost of renting the same van for a 38 mile trip is $65.50. The cost changes at a constant rate with respect to the length (in miles) of the trip. Find the total cost of renting the van for a 54 mile trip. **$69.50**

3a. Because the cost increases at a constant rate of $16 per person, the situation can be modeled by a linear equation.

5a. Because the same length of path is paved each day, the situation can be modeled by a linear equation.

6. ***Sample answer:*** $0.05n + 0.1d = 3$;

Nickels	Dimes
60	0
50	5
40	10
30	15
20	20
10	25
0	30

5.5 Write Equations of Parallel and Perpendicular Lines

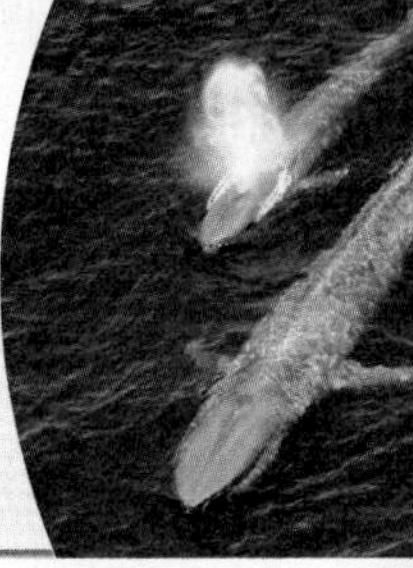

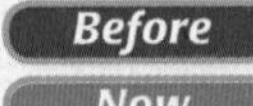

Before You used slope to determine whether lines are parallel.

Now You will write equations of parallel and perpendicular lines.

Why? So you can analyze growth rates, as in Ex. 33.

1 PLAN AND PREPARE

Warm-Up Exercises

Transparency Available

Are the lines parallel? Explain.

1. $y - 2 = 2x$, $2x + y = 7$ **No; one slope is 2 and the other is −2.**
2. $-x = y + 4$, $3x + 3y = 5$ **Yes; both slopes are −1.**
3. You play tennis at two clubs. The total cost C (in dollars) to play for time t (in hours) and rent equipment is given by $C = 15t + 23$ at one club and $C = 15t + 17$ at the other. What is the difference in total cost after 4 hours of play? **$6**

Notetaking Guide

Transparency Available

Promotes interactive learning and notetaking skills.

Pacing

Basic: 1 day

Average: 1 day

Advanced: 1 day

Block: 0.5 block with 5.4

- See *Teaching Guide/Lesson Plan.*

2 FOCUS AND MOTIVATE

Essential Question

Big Idea 1, p. 281

How do you write equations of parallel and perpendicular lines? **Tell students they will learn how to answer this question by comparing slopes.**

NCTM STANDARDS

Standard 3: Describe spatial relationships using coordinate geometry

Standard 9: Use connections among mathematical ideas

Key Vocabulary
- **converse**
- **perpendicular lines**
- **conditional statement,** *p. 66*

The **converse** of a conditional statement interchanges the hypothesis and conclusion. The converse of a true statement is not necessarily true.

In Chapter 4, you learned that the statement "If two nonvertical lines have the same slope, then they are parallel" is true. Its converse is also true.

KEY CONCEPT *For Your Notebook*

Parallel Lines

- If two nonvertical lines in the same plane have the same slope, then they are parallel.
- If two nonvertical lines in the same plane are parallel, then they have the same slope.

EXAMPLE 1 Write an equation of a parallel line

Write an equation of the line that passes through (−3, −5) and is parallel to the line $y = 3x - 1$.

Solution

STEP 1 **Identify** the slope. The graph of the given equation has a slope of 3. So, the parallel line through (−3, −5) has a slope of 3.

STEP 2 **Find** the y-intercept. Use the slope and the given point.

$y = mx + b$	**Write slope-intercept form.**
$-5 = 3(-3) + b$	**Substitute 3 for *m*, −3 for *x*, and −5 for *y*.**
$4 = b$	**Solve for *b*.**

STEP 3 **Write** an equation. Use $y = mx + b$.

$y = 3x + 4$	**Substitute 3 for *m* and 4 for *b*.**

CHECK REASONABLENESS
You can check that your answer is reasonable by graphing both lines.

GUIDED PRACTICE for Example 1

1. Write an equation of the line that passes through (−2, 11) and is parallel to the line $y = -x + 5$. **$y = -x + 9$**

Resource Planning Guide

Chapter Resource Book
- Teaching Guide/Lesson Plan
- Practice levels A, B, C
- Study Guide
- Catch-up for Absent Students
- Problem Solving Workshop
- Challenge

Workbooks
- Notetaking Guide
- Practice Workbook

Teaching Options
- **Power Presentations** provides dynamic electronic teaching resources for the classroom.
- **Activity Generator** provides editable activities for all ability levels.

Interactive Technology
- Easy Planner
- Power Presentations
- Activity Generator
- Animated Algebra
- Test Generator
- Online Quiz
- eWorkbook
- eEdition
- @HomeTutor

Resources for English Learners
- Spanish Study Guide
- Multi-Language Visual Glossary
- Student Resources in Spanish

See also the *Differentiated Instruction Resources* for more strategies for meeting individual needs.

PERPENDICULAR LINES Two lines in the same plane are **perpendicular** if they intersect to form a right angle. Horizontal and vertical lines are perpendicular to each other.

Compare the slopes of the perpendicular lines shown below.

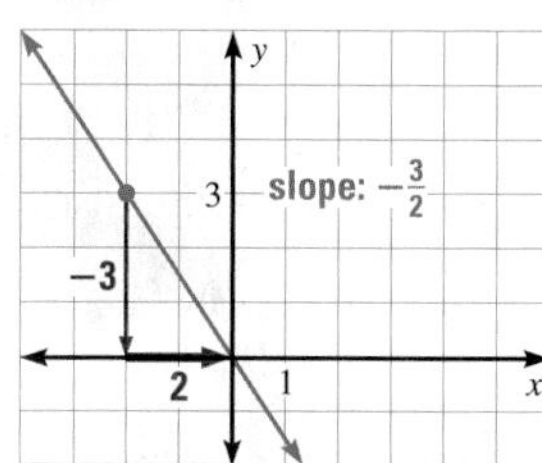

Rotate the line 90° in a clockwise direction about the origin to find a perpendicular line.

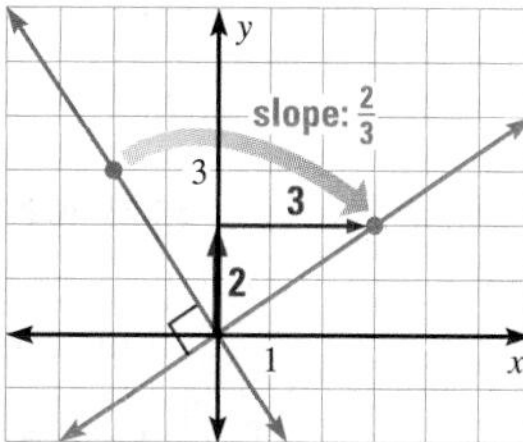

KEY CONCEPT *For Your Notebook*

Perpendicular Lines

- If two nonvertical lines in the same plane have slopes that are negative reciprocals, then the lines are perpendicular.
- If two nonvertical lines in the same plane are perpendicular, then their slopes are negative reciprocals.

USE FRACTIONS
The product of a nonzero number m and its negative reciprocal is −1: $m\left(-\frac{1}{m}\right) = -1$.

EXAMPLE 2 **Determine whether lines are parallel or perpendicular**

Determine which lines, if any, are parallel or perpendicular.

Line *a*: $y = 5x - 3$ **Line *b*:** $x + 5y = 2$ **Line *c*:** $-10y - 2x = 0$

Solution

Find the slopes of the lines.

Line *a*: The equation is in slope-intercept form. The slope is 5.

Write the equations for lines b and c in slope-intercept form.

Line *b*: $x + 5y = 2$

$5y = -x + 2$

$y = -\frac{1}{5}x + \frac{2}{5}$

Line *c*: $-10y - 2x = 0$

$-10y = 2x$

$y = -\frac{1}{5}x$

▶ Lines b and c have slopes of $-\frac{1}{5}$, so they are parallel. Line a has a slope of 5, the negative reciprocal of $-\frac{1}{5}$, so it is perpendicular to lines b and c.

✓ **GUIDED PRACTICE** for Example 2

2. Determine which lines, if any, are parallel or perpendicular.

Line *a*: $2x + 6y = -3$ **Line *b*:** $y = 3x - 8$ **Line *c*:** $-1.5y + 4.5x = 6$

parallel: *b* and *c*; perpendicular: *a* and *b*, *a* and *c*

Motivating the Lesson

Your dad is planning to plant two red oak trees in your backyard. He wants to know how tall they will be in six years. One tree is 56 inches high and the other is 63 inches high. Red oaks grow at an average rate of 24 inches per year. By writing two equations that model the growth of the trees, you can predict the height of each tree in six years.

3 TEACH

Extra Example 1

Write an equation of the line that passes through (−3, 3) and is parallel to the line $y = -2x + 1$.
$y = -2x - 3$

Key Questions to Ask for Example 1

- How are the parallel lines different? **They have different *y*-intercepts.**
- If two lines have different *y*-intercepts, are they parallel? Explain. **No. The line $y = x + 3$ and the line $y = 2x + 1$ have different *y*-intercepts, but they are not parallel since they have different slopes.**

Extra Example 2

Determine which lines, if any, are parallel or perpendicular.

Line a: $-x + 3y = 1$
Line b: $y = -3x + 1$
Line c: $2x - 6y = 4$

Lines *a* and *c* have slopes of $\frac{1}{3}$, so they are parallel. Line *b* has a slope of −3, the negative reciprocal of $\frac{1}{3}$, so it is perpendicular to lines *a* and *c*.

Differentiated Instruction

English Learners Some students may have trouble with the converse. The statements about parallel and perpendicular lines give examples with converses that are true. Give examples to illustrate that the converse of a logical statement is not always true. For example, "If a figure is a square, then it has four sides" is a true statement. The converse, "If a figure has four sides, then it is a square" is false (for example, the figure could be a trapezoid).

See also the *Differentiated Instruction Resources* for more strategies.

Extra Example 3

The path of a golf ball bouncing off a curved wall on a miniature golf course is shown in a coordinate plane. Lines a and b of the path appear to be perpendicular. Are they?

Line a: $3y = 2x - 1$

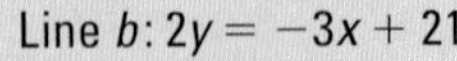

Line b: $2y = -3x + 21$

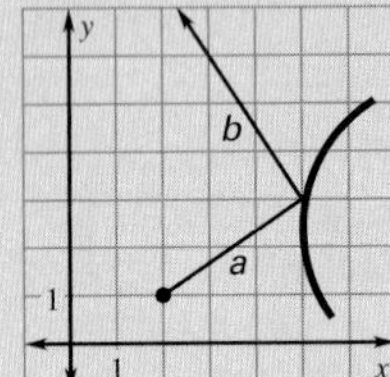

The slope of line a is $\frac{2}{3}$. The slope of line b is $-\frac{3}{2}$. The two slopes are negative reciprocals, so the lines are perpendicular.

Extra Example 4

Write an equation of the line that passes through $(4, -2)$ and is perpendicular to the line $y = 4x + 2$.

$y = -\frac{1}{4}x - 1$

Closing the Lesson

Have students summarize the major points of the lesson and answer the Essential Question: How do you write equations of parallel and perpendicular lines?

- **Two nonvertical lines have the same slope if and only if they are parallel.**
- **The slopes of two nonvertical lines are negative reciprocals if and only if the lines are perpendicular.**

Identify the slope of the line. Use the same slope and a different y-intercept to write an equation of a parallel line. Use the negative reciprocal of the slope to write an equation of a perpendicular line.

EXAMPLE 3 Determine whether lines are perpendicular

STATE FLAG The Arizona state flag is shown in a coordinate plane. Lines a and b appear to be perpendicular. Are they?

Line a: $12y = -7x + 42$

Line b: $11y = 16x - 52$

y
b
a
O
x

Solution

Find the slopes of the lines. Write the equations in slope-intercept form.

Line a: $12y = -7x + 42$ 　　 **Line b:** $11y = 16x - 52$

$$y = -\frac{7}{12}x + \frac{42}{12} \qquad y = \frac{16}{11}x - \frac{52}{11}$$

▶ The slope of line a is $-\frac{7}{12}$. The slope of line b is $\frac{16}{11}$. The two slopes are not negative reciprocals, so lines a and b are not perpendicular.

EXAMPLE 4 Write an equation of a perpendicular line

Write an equation of the line that passes through $(4, -5)$ and is perpendicular to the line $y = 2x + 3$.

Solution

STEP 1 **Identify** the slope. The graph of the given equation has a slope of 2. Because the slopes of perpendicular lines are negative reciprocals, the slope of the perpendicular line through $(4, -5)$ is $-\frac{1}{2}$.

STEP 2 **Find** the y-intercept. Use the slope and the given point.

$y = mx + b$	Write slope-intercept form.
$-5 = -\frac{1}{2}(4) + b$	Substitute $-\frac{1}{2}$ for m, 4 for x, and -5 for y.
$-3 = b$	Solve for b.

STEP 3 **Write** an equation.

$y = mx + b$	Write slope-intercept form.
$y = -\frac{1}{2}x - 3$	Substitute $-\frac{1}{2}$ for m and -3 for b.

3. No; the slope of line a is $-\frac{1}{2}$, the slope of line b is $\frac{3}{2}$. The slopes are not negative reciprocals so the lines are not perpendicular.

GUIDED PRACTICE for Examples 3 and 4

3. Is line a perpendicular to line b? *Justify* your answer using slopes.

   Line a: $2y + x = -12$ 　　 **Line b:** $2y = 3x - 8$

4. Write an equation of the line that passes through $(4, 3)$ and is perpendicular to the line $y = 4x - 7$. $y = -\frac{1}{4}x + 4$

5.5 EXERCISES

HOMEWORK KEY
○ = **WORKED-OUT SOLUTIONS** on p. WS12 for Exs. 19 and 33
★ = **STANDARDIZED TEST PRACTICE** Exs. 2, 16, 17, 28, 30, 34, and 36

SKILL PRACTICE

A

1. **VOCABULARY** Copy and complete: Two lines in a plane are _?_ if they intersect to form a right angle. **perpendicular**

2. ★ **WRITING** *Explain* how you can tell whether two lines are perpendicular, given the equations of the lines. **Identify the slopes of the lines. If the slopes are negative reciprocals, then the lines are perpendicular.**

EXAMPLE 1 on p. 318 for Exs. 3–11

PARALLEL LINES Write an equation of the line that passes through the given point and is parallel to the given line.

3. $(-1, 3), y = 2x + 2$ **$y = 2x + 5$**
4. $(6, 8), y = -\frac{5}{2}x + 10$ **$y = -\frac{5}{2}x + 23$**
5. $(5, -1), y = -\frac{3}{5}x - 3$ **$y = -\frac{3}{5}x + 2$**
6. $(-1, 2), y = 5x + 4$ **$y = 5x + 7$**
7. $(1, 7), -6x + y = -1$ **$y = 6x + 1$**
8. $(18, 2), 3y = x - 12$ **$y = \frac{1}{3}x - 4$**
9. $(-2, 5), 2y = 4x - 6$ **$y = 2x + 9$**
10. $(9, 4), y - x = 3$ **$y = x - 5$**
11. $(-10, 0), -y + 3x = 16$ **$y = 3x + 30$**

EXAMPLE 2 on p. 319 for Exs. 12–16

PARALLEL OR PERPENDICULAR Determine which lines, if any, are parallel or perpendicular.

12. Line a: $y = 4x - 2$, Line b: $y = -\frac{1}{4}x$, Line c: $y = -4x + 1$
parallel: none; perpendicular: *a* and *b*
13. Line a: $y = \frac{3}{5}x + 1$, Line b: $5y = 3x - 2$, Line c: $10x - 6y = -4$
parallel: *a* and *b*; perpendicular: none
14. Line a: $y = 3x + 6$, Line b: $3x + y = 6$, Line c: $3y = 2x + 18$
parallel: none; perpendicular: none
15. Line a: $4x - 3y = 2$, Line b: $3x + 4y = -1$, Line c: $4y - 3x = 20$
parallel: none; perpendicular: *a* and *b*

16. ★ **MULTIPLE CHOICE** Which statement is true of the given lines? **D**

Line a: $-2x + y = 4$ Line b: $2x + 5y = 2$ Line c: $x + 2y = 4$

Ⓐ Lines a and b are parallel. Ⓑ Lines a and c are parallel.
Ⓒ Lines a and b are perpendicular. Ⓓ Lines a and c are perpendicular.

17. ★ **SHORT RESPONSE** Determine which of the lines shown, if any, are parallel or perpendicular. *Justify* your answer using slopes.

17. The line through points (6, 4) and (4, 1) is perpendicular to the line through points (1, 3) and (4, 1); the slope of the line through the points (6, 4) and (4, 1) is $\frac{3}{2}$, the slope of the line through the points (1, 3) and (4, 1) is $-\frac{2}{3}$. The slopes are negative reciprocals, so the lines are perpendicular.

Animated Algebra at classzone.com

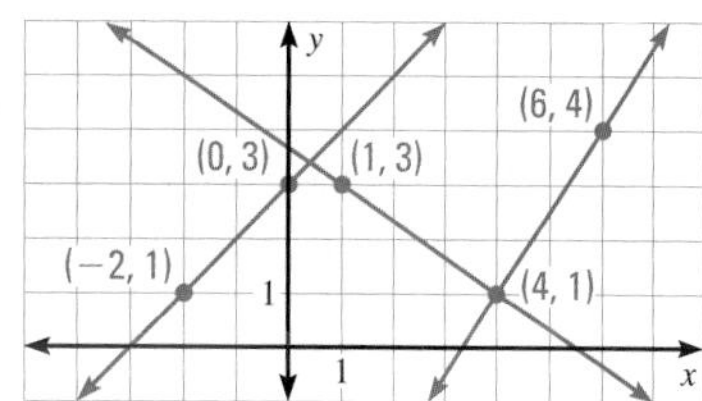

EXAMPLE 4 on p. 320 for Exs. 18–27

PERPENDICULAR LINES Write an equation of the line that passes through the given point and is perpendicular to the given line.

18. $(3, -3), y = x + 5$ **$y = -x$**
19. $(-9, 2), y = 3x - 12$ **$y = -\frac{1}{3}x - 1$**
20. $(5, 1), y = 5x - 2$ **$y = -\frac{1}{5}x + 2$**
21. $(7, 10), y = 0.5x - 9$ **$y = -2x + 24$**
22. $(-2, -4), y = -\frac{2}{7}x + 1$ **$y = \frac{7}{2}x + 3$**
23. $(-4, -1), y = \frac{4}{3}x + 6$ **$y = -\frac{3}{4}x - 4$**
24. $(3, 3), 2y = 3x - 6$ **$y = -\frac{2}{3}x + 5$**
25. $(-5, 2), y + 3 = 2x$ **$y = -\frac{1}{2}x - \frac{1}{2}$**
26. $(8, -1), 4y + 2x = 12$ **$y = 2x - 17$**

4 PRACTICE AND APPLY

Assignment Guide

Answer Transparencies available for all exercises

Basic:
Day 1: pp. 321–323
Exs. 1–8, 12–22, 27, 28, 32–35, 38–42

Average:
Day 1: pp. 321–323
Exs. 1, 2, 7–17, 23–30, 32–37, 39, 41, 42

Advanced:
Day 1: pp. 321–323
Exs. 1, 2, 8–11, 13–17, 24–37*, 40–42

Block:
pp. 321–323
Exs. 1, 2, 7–17, 23–30, 32–37, 39, 41, 42 (with 5.4)

Differentiated Instruction

See *Differentiated Instruction Resources* for suggestions on addressing the needs of a diverse classroom.

Homework Check

For a quick check of student understanding of key concepts, go over the following exercises:

Basic: 6, 12, 16, 20, 32
Average: 8, 14, 24, 32, 34
Advanced: 10, 15, 26, 32, 34

Extra Practice

- Student Edition, p. 942
- Chapter Resource Book: Practice levels A, B, C

Practice Worksheet

An easily-readable reduced practice page (with answers) for this lesson can be found on p. 280D.

Graphing Calculator

Exercises 3–11, 18–26 Students can use their graphing calculators to check that their equations are reasonable. Have them enter both equations on the same viewing screen and then use trace to verify that each equation passes through the point.

Avoiding Common Errors

Exercises 7–11, 13–15, 24, 26 Some students may use the coefficient of x as the slope before rewriting the equation in slope-intercept form. Remind these students that the equation must be in slope-intercept form in order to read the value of m.

Animated Algebra classzone.com

An **Animated Algebra** activity is available online for **Exercise 17**. This activity is also part of **Power Presentations**.

Study Strategy

Exercises 18–26 Remind students that the product of negative reciprocals is −1. They can use this information to check whether or not two numbers are negative reciprocals.

Internet Reference

Exercise 33 More information about blue whales can be found at the American Cetacean Society website, www.acsonline.org/factpack/bluewhl.htm

34. Parallel: 2nd Street and Park Street; the slope of both streets is $\frac{2}{3}$. Since they have the same slope, the streets are parallel. Perpendicular: 2nd Street and Sea Street, Park Street and Sea Street; the slope of Sea Street is $-\frac{3}{2}$, which is the negative reciprocal of $\frac{2}{3}$, the slope of 2nd Street and Park Street. Since the slopes are negative reciprocals, the streets are perpendicular.

27. **ERROR ANALYSIS** *Describe* and correct the error in finding the y-intercept of the line that passes through (2, 1) and is perpendicular to the line $y = -\frac{1}{2}x + 3$.
(2, 1) was substituted incorrectly, 2 should be substituted for x, and 1 should be substituted for y; $1 = 2(2) + b$, $1 = 4 + b$, $-3 = b$.

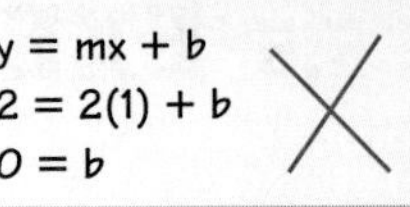

B 28. ★ **MULTIPLE CHOICE** Which equation represents the line that passes through (0, 0) and is parallel to the line passing through (2, 3) and (6, 1)? **B**

Ⓐ $y = \frac{1}{2}x$ Ⓑ $y = -\frac{1}{2}x$ Ⓒ $y = -2x$ Ⓓ $y = 2x$

29. **REASONING** Is the line through (4, 3) and (3, −1) perpendicular to the line through (−3, 3) and (1, 2)? *Justify* your answer using slopes. **See margin.**

30. Sample answer: $y = 2x + 1$ and $y = 2x + 3$; $y = -\frac{1}{2}x + 2$

C 30. ★ **OPEN-ENDED** Write equations of two lines that are parallel. Then write an equation of a line that is perpendicular to those lines.

31. **CHALLENGE** Write a formula for the slope of a line that is perpendicular to the line through the points (x_1, y_1) and (x_2, y_2). $m = \frac{x_1 - x_2}{y_1 - y_2}$

PROBLEM SOLVING

EXAMPLES 3 and 4 on p. 320 for Exs. 32, 34

A 32. **HOCKEY** A hockey puck leaves the blade of a hockey stick, bounces off a wall, and travels in a new direction, as shown.

a. Write an equation that models the path of the puck from the blade of the hockey stick to the wall. $y = 2x + 8$

b. Write an equation that models the path of the puck after it bounces off the wall. $y = -2x + 8$

c. Does the path of the puck form a right angle? *Justify* your answer.

32c. No; the slopes −2 and 2 are not negative reciprocals.

(−4, 16)
(0, 8)
(−4, 0)

@HomeTutor for problem solving help at classzone.com

33. **BIOLOGY** While nursing, blue whale calves can gain weight at a rate of 200 pounds per day. Two particular calves weigh 6000 pounds and 6250 pounds at birth.

a. Write equations that model the weight of each calf as a function of the number of days since birth. $w_1 = 200d + 6000$; $w_2 = 200d + 6250$

b. How much is each calf expected to weigh 30 days after birth? **12,000 lb; 12,250 lb**

c. How are the graphs of the equations from part (a) related? *Justify* your answer.

33c. The graphs of the lines are parallel because they have the same slope, 200. The w-intercept of the second line is 250 more than the w-intercept of the first line.

@HomeTutor for problem solving help at classzone.com

34. ★ **SHORT RESPONSE** The map shows several streets in a city. Determine which of the streets, if any, are parallel or perpendicular. *Justify* your answer using slopes. **See margin.**

Park: $3y - 2x = 12$ Main: $y = -6x + 44$

2nd St.: $3y = 2x - 13$ Sea: $2y = -3x + 37$

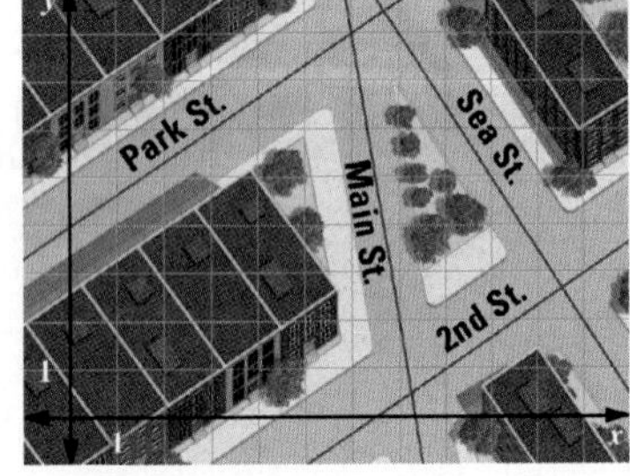

29. Yes; the slope of the line through (4, 3) and (3, −1) is 4 and the slope of the line through (−3, 3) and (1, 2) is $-\frac{1}{4}$. The slopes are negative reciprocals, so the lines are perpendicular.

35. Different registration fees; because the lines are parallel, the rate of change, the monthly fee, for each must be equal. Therefore, the students paid different registration fees.

B 35. **SOFTBALL** A softball training academy charges students a monthly fee plus an initial registration fee. The total amounts paid by two students are given by the functions $f(x)$ and $g(x)$ where x is the numbers of months the students have been members of the academy. The graphs of f and g are parallel lines. Did the students pay different monthly fees or different registration fees? How do you know?

36c. The graphs of the lines are parallel; they have the same slope, 38.75. The C-intercept of the second graph is 100 more than the C-intercept of the first graph.

36. ★ **EXTENDED RESPONSE** If you are one of the first 100 people to join a new health club, you are charged a joining fee of \$49. Otherwise, you are charged a joining fee of \$149. The monthly membership cost is \$38.75.

a. Write an equation that gives the total cost (in dollars) of membership as a function of the number of months of membership if you are one of the first 100 members to join. **$C = 38.75m + 49$**

b. Write an equation that gives the total cost (in dollars) of membership as a function of the number of months of membership if you are *not* one of the first 100 members to join. **$C = 38.75m + 149$**

c. How are the graphs of these functions related? How do you know?

d. After 6 months, what is the difference in total cost for a person who paid \$149 to join and a person who paid \$49 to join? after 12 months? **\$100; \$100**

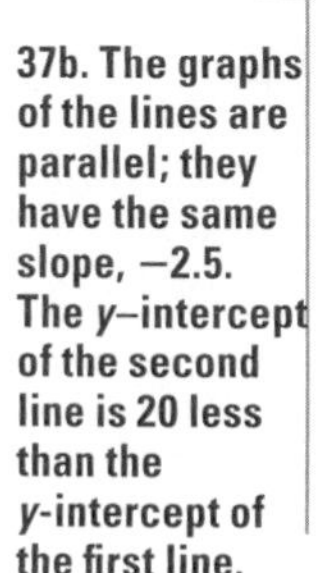

37b. The graphs of the lines are parallel; they have the same slope, −2.5. The y–intercept of the second line is 20 less than the y-intercept of the first line.

C 37. **CHALLENGE** You and your friend have gift cards to a shopping mall. Your card has a value of \$50, and your friend's card has a value of \$30. If neither of you uses the cards, the value begins to decrease at a rate of \$2.50 per month after 6 months.

a. Write two equations, one that gives the value of your card and another that gives the value of your friend's card as functions of the number of months after 6 months of nonuse. **$y = -2.5x + 50$; $y = -2.5x + 30$**

b. How are the graphs of these functions related? How do you know?

c. What are the x-intercepts of the graphs of the functions, and what do they mean in this situation? **20; 12; the x-intercepts show the number of months of nonuse it would take for the value of the gift card to be \$0.**

MIXED REVIEW

Solve the equation or proportion.

38. $5z + 6z = 77$ *(p. 141)* **7**

39. $-8n = 4(3n + 5)$ *(p. 148)* **−1**

40. $\frac{3}{5} = \frac{t}{7}$ *(p. 162)* **4.2**

PREVIEW
Prepare for Lesson 5.6 in Ex. 41.

41. **CAMPING** The table shows the cost C (in dollars) for one person to stay at a campground for n nights. *(p. 253)*

Number of nights, n	1	3	5	9
Cost, C (in dollars)	15	45	75	135

a. *Explain* why C varies directly with n. **See margin.**

b. Write a direct variation equation that relates C and n. **$c = 15n$**

42. Write an equation in standard form of the line that passes through the points (3, −9) and (12, 9). *(p. 311)* **$-2x + y = -15$**

5 ASSESS AND RETEACH

Daily Homework Quiz

Transparency Available

1. Write an equation of the line that passes through the point (−1, 4) and is parallel to the line $y = 5x - 2$. **$y = 5x + 9$**

2. Write an equation of the line that passes through the point (−1, −1) and is perpendicular to the line $y = -\frac{1}{4}x + 2$. **$y = 4x + 3$**

3. Paths a, b, and c are shown in the coordinate grid. Determine which paths, if any, are parallel or perpendicular. Justify your answer using slopes.

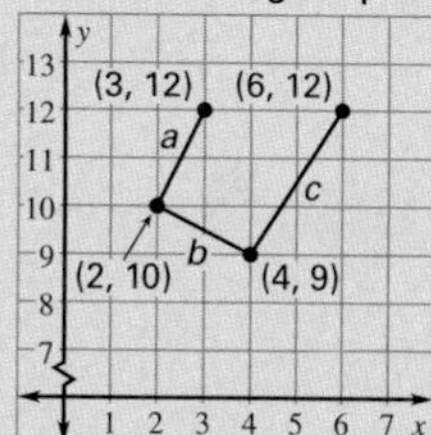

Paths a and b are perpendicular because their slopes, 2 and $-\frac{1}{2}$, are negative reciprocals. No paths are parallel.

Available at **classzone.com**

Diagnosis/Remediation

- Practice A, B, C in Chapter Resource Book
- Study Guide in Chapter Resource Book
- Practice Workbook
- @HomeTutor

Challenge

Additional challenge is available in the Chapter Resource Book.

41a. Compare the ratios, $\frac{c}{n}$, for all data pairs (n, c): $\frac{15}{1} = \frac{45}{3} = \frac{75}{5} = \frac{135}{9} = 15$. Because the ratios all equal 15, c varies directly with n.

5.6 Fit a Line to Data

1 PLAN AND PREPARE

Warm-Up Exercises

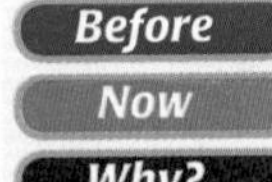 **Transparency Available**

Find the slope of the line that passes through the points.

1. $(-4, 1)$ and $(6, -4)$ $-\frac{1}{2}$

2. $(2, -3)$ and $(-1, 6)$ -3

3. Your commission c varies directly with the number s of pairs of shoes you sell. You made \$180 when you sold 15 pairs of shoes. Write a direct variation equation that relates c to s. $c = 12s$

Notetaking Guide

Transparency Available

Promotes interactive learning and notetaking skills.

Pacing

Basic: 1 day

Average: 1 day

Advanced: 1 day

Block: 0.5 block with 5.7

- See *Teaching Guide/Lesson Plan.*

2 FOCUS AND MOTIVATE

Essential Question

Big Idea 3, p. 281

How do you make scatter plots and write equations to model data?

Tell students they will learn how to answer this question by graphing data pairs and by finding a line of fit for the data pairs.

NCTM STANDARDS

Standard 5: Collect, organize, and display data; Select proper statistical methods to analyze data

---

Before You modeled situations involving a constant rate of change.

Now You will make scatter plots and write equations to model data.

Why? So you can model scientific data, as in Ex. 19.

Key Vocabulary
- **scatter plot**
- **correlation**
- **line of fit**

A **scatter plot** is a graph used to determine whether there is a relationship between paired data. Scatter plots can show trends in the data.

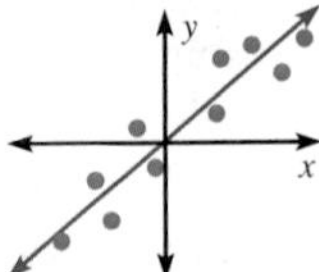

If y tends to increase as x increases, the paired data are said to have a **positive correlation.**

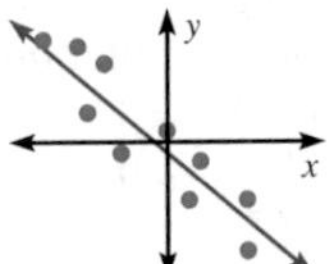

If y tends to decrease as x increases, the paired data are said to have a **negative correlation.**

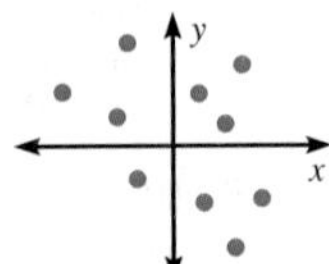

If x and y have no apparent relationship, the paired data are said to have **relatively no correlation.**

EXAMPLE 1 Describe the correlation of data

Describe **the correlation of the data graphed in the scatter plot.**

a.

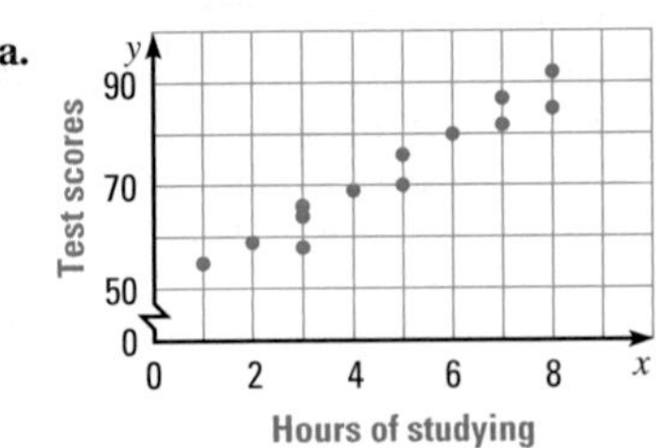

b.

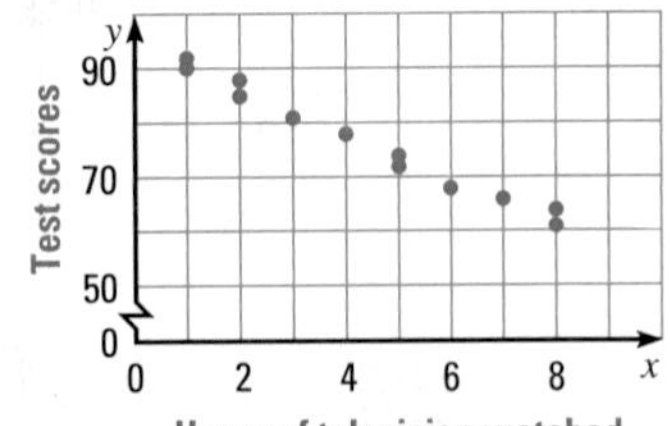

a. The scatter plot shows a positive correlation between hours of studying and test scores. This means that as the hours of studying increased, the test scores tended to increase.

b. The scatter plot shows a negative correlation between hours of television watched and test scores. This means that as the hours of television watched increased, the test scores tended to decrease.

 **GUIDED PRACTICE** for Example 1

1. Using the scatter plots in Example 1, predict a reasonable test score for 4.5 hours of studying and 4.5 hours of television watched. ***Sample answer:* 72, 77**

Resource Planning Guide

Chapter Resource Book
- Teaching Guide/Lesson Plan
- Activity Master
- Practice levels A, B, C
- Study Guide
- Catch-up for Absent Students
- Application
- Challenge

Workbooks
- Notetaking Guide
- Practice Workbook

Teaching Options
- **Power Presentations** provides dynamic electronic teaching resources for the classroom.
- **Activity Generator** provides editable activities for all ability levels.

Interactive Technology
- Easy Planner
- Power Presentations
- Activity Generator
- Animated Algebra
- Test Generator
- Online Quiz
- eWorkbook
- eEdition
- @HomeTutor

Resources for English Learners
- Spanish Study Guide
- Multi-Language Visual Glossary
- Student Resources in Spanish

See also the *Differentiated Instruction Resources* for more strategies for meeting individual needs.

EXAMPLE 2 Make a scatter plot

SWIMMING SPEEDS The table shows the lengths (in centimeters) and swimming speeds (in centimeters per second) of six fish.

Fish	Pike	Red gurnard	Black bass	Gurnard	Norway haddock
Length (cm)	37.8	19.2	21.3	26.2	26.8
Speed (cm/sec)	148	47	88	131	98

a. Make a scatter plot of the data.

b. *Describe* the correlation of the data.

Solution

a. Treat the data as ordered pairs. Let x represent the fish length (in centimeters), and let y represent the speed (in centimeters per second). Plot the ordered pairs as points in a coordinate plane.

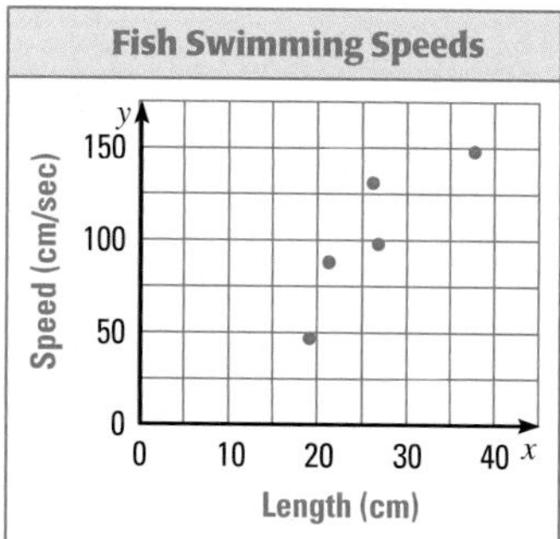

b. The scatter plot shows a positive correlation, which means that longer fish tend to swim faster.

✓ **GUIDED PRACTICE** for Example 2

2. Make a scatter plot of the data in the table. *Describe* the correlation of the data.

x	1	1	2	3	3	4	5	5	6
y	2	3	4	4	5	5	5	7	8

See margin for art; the scatter plot shows a positive correlation.

MODELING DATA When data show a positive or negative correlation, you can model the trend in the data using a **line of fit**.

KEY CONCEPT *For Your Notebook*

Using a Line of Fit to Model Data

STEP 1 **Make** a scatter plot of the data.

STEP 2 **Decide** whether the data can be modeled by a line.

STEP 3 **Draw** a line that appears to fit the data closely. There should be approximately as many points above the line as below it.

STEP 4 **Write** an equation using two points on the line. The points do not have to represent actual data pairs, but they must lie on the line of fit.

Motivating the Lesson

For a science project, you are exploring the relationship between the densities of substances and their melting points. By knowing how to make a scatter plot, you can graph the paired data on a coordinate grid and then determine whether there is a positive relationship, a negative relationship, or relatively no relationship between the densities and the melting points of the substances.

3 TEACH

Extra Example 1

Describe the correlation of the data graphed in the scatter plot.

a.

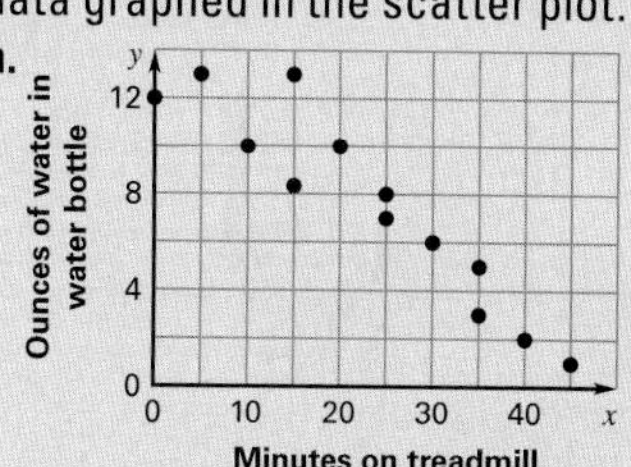

The scatter plot shows a negative correlation between minutes on a treadmill and ounces of water in a water bottle. This means that as the minutes on the treadmill increased, the ounces of water in the water bottle tended to decrease.

b.

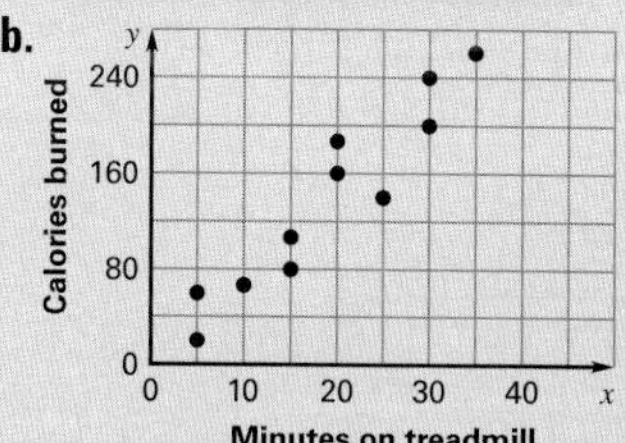

The scatter plot shows a positive correlation between minutes on a treadmill and calories burned. This means that as the minutes on the treadmill increased, the number of calories burned tended to increase.

Differentiated Instruction

Visual Learners After introducing the line of fit, have students go back and draw lines of fit for **Example 1**. Students should observe that a line drawn through positively correlated data has a positive slope and that a line drawn through negatively correlated data has a negative slope. For some students, it may be easier to draw the line of fit before determining the type of correlation. Point out that if a line of fit is not possible, there is no correlation.

See also the *Differentiated Instruction Resources* for more strategies.

EXAMPLE 3 Write an equation to model data

BIRD POPULATIONS The table shows the number of active red-cockaded woodpecker clusters in a part of the De Soto National Forest in Mississippi. Write an equation that models the number of active clusters as a function of the number of years since 1990.

Year	1992	1993	1994	1995	1996	1997	1998	1999	2000
Active clusters	22	24	27	27	34	40	42	45	51

Solution

STEP 1 **Make** a scatter plot of the data. Let x represent the number of years since 1990. Let y represent the number of active clusters.

STEP 2 **Decide** whether the data can be modeled by a line. Because the scatter plot shows a positive correlation, you can fit a line to the data.

STEP 3 **Draw** a line that appears to fit the points in the scatter plot closely.

STEP 4 **Write** an equation using two points on the line. Use (2, 20) and (8, 42).

Find the slope of the line.

$$m = \frac{y_2 - y_1}{x_2 - x_1} = \frac{42 - 20}{8 - 2} = \frac{22}{6} = \frac{11}{3}$$

Find the y-intercept of the line. Use the point (2, 20).

$y = mx + b$ **Write slope-intercept form.**

$20 = \frac{11}{3}(2) + b$ **Substitute $\frac{11}{3}$ for *m*, 2 for *x*, and 20 for *y*.**

$\frac{38}{3} = b$ **Solve for *b*.**

An equation of the line of fit is $y = \frac{11}{3}x + \frac{38}{3}$.

▶ The number y of active woodpecker clusters can be modeled by the function $y = \frac{11}{3}x + \frac{38}{3}$ where x is the number of years since 1990.

 at classzone.com

✓ GUIDED PRACTICE for Example 3

3. Use the data in the table to write an equation that models y as a function of x.

x	1	2	3	4	5	6	8
y	3	5	8	9	11	12	14

***Sample answer:* $y = 1.6x + 2.3$**

Extra Example 2

The table shows the carbohydrates (in grams) and the fiber (in grams) in six types of fruit.

Fruit	Fiber	Carb.
Apple	5	22
Banana	4	29
Blackberries	8	18
Figs	2	12
Guava	5	11
Peach	2	11

a. Make a scatter plot of the data.

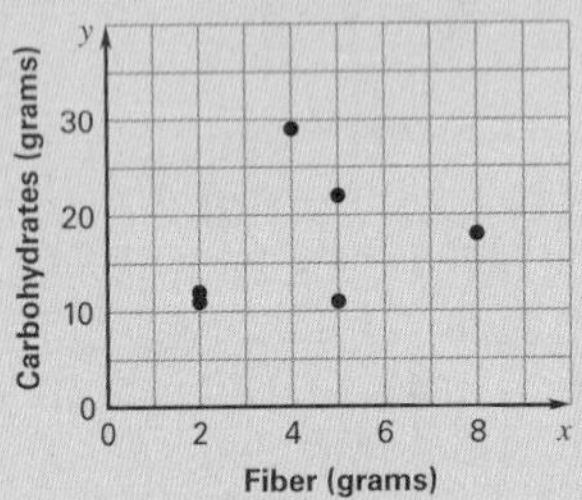

b. Describe the correlation of the data. **The scatter plot shows relatively no correlation, which means there is no general relationship between fiber and carbohydrates in fruit.**

Extra Example 3

The table shows the number of injured birds a person rehabilitated at a veterinary service. Write an equation that models the number of rehabilitated birds as a function of the number of years years since 1995.

Year	Birds
1997	8
1998	11
1999	12
2000	12
2001	15
2002	19
2003	21

The number of rehabilitated birds can be modeled by the function $y = 2.07x + 3.64$ where x is the number of years since 1995.

2.

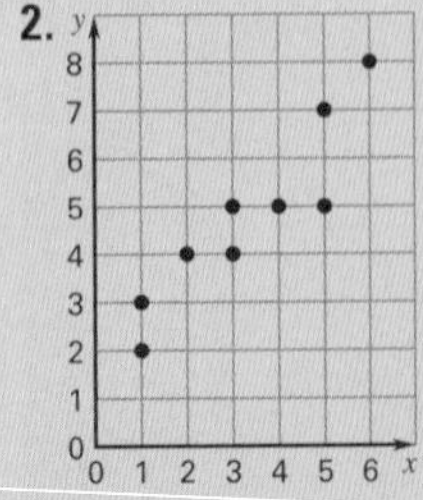

EXAMPLE 4 Interpret a model

Refer to the model for the number of woodpecker clusters in Example 3.

a. *Describe* the domain and range of the function.

b. At about what rate did the number of active woodpecker clusters change during the period 1992–2000?

Solution

a. The domain of the function is the the period from 1992 to 2000, or $2 \le x \le 10$. The range is the the number of active clusters given by the function for $2 \le x \le 10$, or $20 \le y \le 49.3$.

b. The number of active woodpecker clusters increased at a rate of $\frac{11}{3}$ or about 3.7 woodpecker clusters per year.

GUIDED PRACTICE for Example 4

4. In Guided Practice Exercise 2, at about what rate does y change with respect to x? **about 1**

5.6 EXERCISES

HOMEWORK KEY
○ = **WORKED-OUT SOLUTIONS** on p. WS12 for Exs. 7 and 17
★ = **STANDARDIZED TEST PRACTICE** Exs. 2, 8, 11, 12, and 16

SKILL PRACTICE

A

1. **VOCABULARY** Copy and complete: When data have a positive correlation, the dependent variable tends to _?_ as the independent variable increases. **increase**

2. ★ **WRITING** *Describe* how paired data with a positive correlation, a negative correlation, and relatively no correlation differ. **See margin.**

EXAMPLE 1 on p. 324 for Exs. 3–5, 10, 11

DESCRIBING CORRELATIONS **Tell whether x and y show a *positive correlation*, a *negative correlation*, or *relatively no correlation*.**

3. 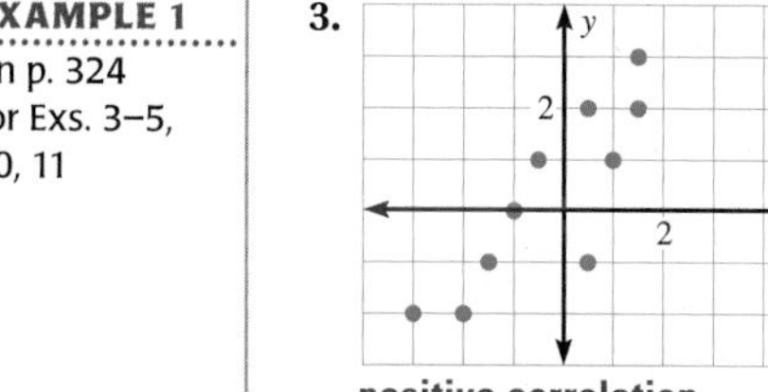
positive correlation

4. **relatively no correlation**

5. 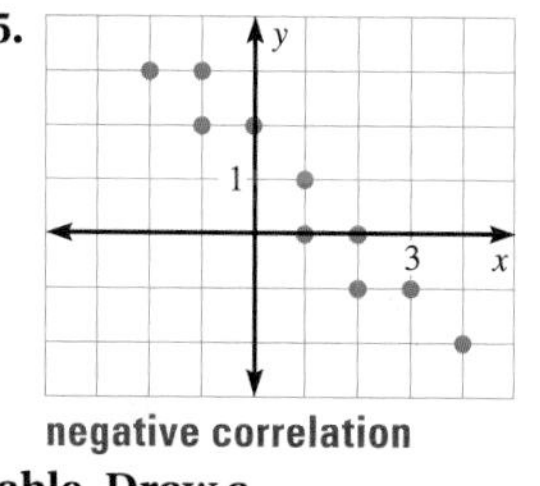
negative correlation

EXAMPLES 2 and 3 on pp. 325–326 for Exs. 6–9

FITTING LINES TO DATA **Make a scatter plot of the data in the table. Draw a line of fit. Write an equation of the line.** 6–7. See margin for art.

6.

x	1	1	3	4	5	6	9
y	10	12	33	46	59	70	102

Sample answer: $y = 11.5x - 0.28$

x	1.2	1.8	2.3	3.0	4.4	5.2
y	10	7	5	−1	−4	−8

Sample answer: $y = -4.5x + 15.4$

6. 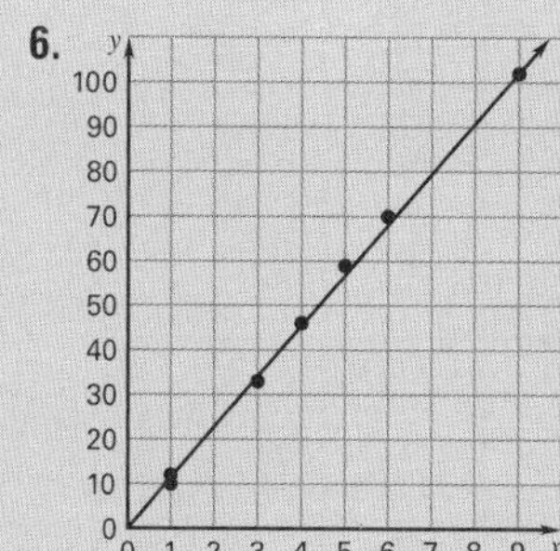

7. 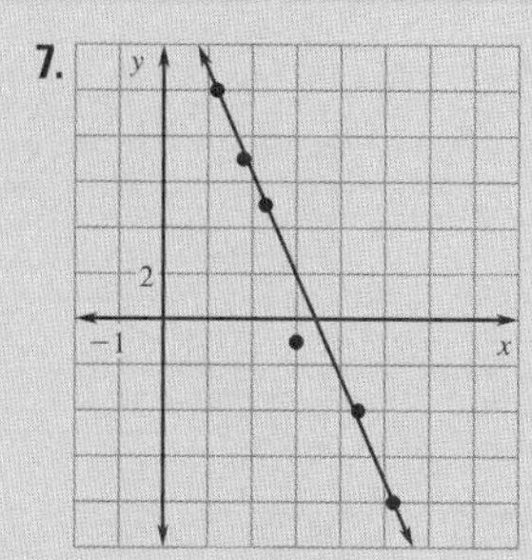

Animated Algebra classzone.com

An **Animated Algebra** activity is available online for **Example 3**. This activity is also part of **Power Presentations**.

Extra Example 4

Refer to the model on the number of birds in Extra Example 3.

a. Describe the domain and range of the function. **The domain is the period 1997 to 2003. Since x is the number of years after 1995, the domain is $2 \le x \le 8$. The range is the number of birds given by the model, so the range is about $8 \le y \le 20$.**

b. At what rate did the number of rehabilitated birds change from 1997 to 2003? **The number of rehabilitated birds increased at a rate of 2 birds per year.**

Closing the Lesson

Have students summarize the major points of the lesson and answer the Essential Question: How do you make scatter plots and write equations to model data?

- **A scatter plot shows whether there is a positive, negative, or no correlation in the data.**
- **A line of fit can model data. The points you use to find the equation must be on the line, but they do not have to be actual data values.**

Plot paired data in a coordinate plane. For a positive or negative correlation, draw a line of fit, with about the same number of points above and below the line. Use two points on the line to find the slope and then use the slope and a point to find the y-intercept. Write an equation of the line.

2. When data has a positive correlation, the dependent variable tends to increase as the independent variable increases. When data has a negative correlation, the dependent variable tends to decrease as the independent variable increases. When data has relatively no correlation there is no apparent relationship between the independent variable and the dependent variable.

4 PRACTICE AND APPLY

Assignment Guide

Answer Transparencies available for all exercises

Basic:
Day 1: EP p. 941 Exs. 1–7 odd
pp. 327–330
Exs. 1–12, 16–18, 22–28

Average:
Day 1: pp. 327–330
Exs. 1, 2, 4–14, 16–20, 22–28

Advanced:
Day 1: pp. 327–330
Exs. 1, 2, 4–8, 11–28*

Block:
pp. 327–330
Exs. 1, 2, 4–14, 16–20, 22–28
(with 5.7)

Differentiated Instruction

See *Differentiated Instruction Resources* for suggestions on addressing the needs of a diverse classroom.

Homework Check

For a quick check of student understanding of key concepts, go over the following exercises:

Basic: 3, 6, 16, 17, 18
Average: 4, 7, 16, 17, 18
Advanced: 5, 7, 16, 17, 18

Extra Practice

- Student Edition, p. 942
- Chapter Resource Book: Practice levels A, B, C

Practice Worksheet

An easily-readable reduced practice page (with answers) for this lesson can be found on p. 280D.

9. 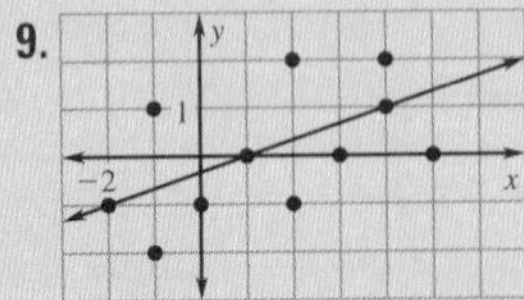

8. ★ MULTIPLE CHOICE Which equation best models the data in the scatter plot? **C**

Ⓐ $y = -x - 6$ Ⓑ $y = x - 6$

Ⓒ $y = -x + 8$ Ⓓ $y = x + 8$

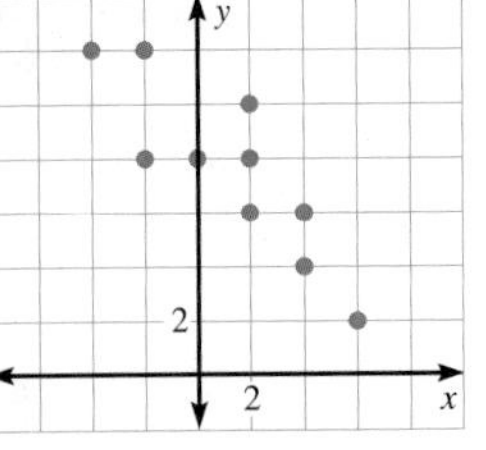

9. The line does not have approximately half the data above it and half below it; see margin for art.

10. The independent variable is *x*, not *y*; the dependent variable decreases as *x* increases.

9. ERROR ANALYSIS *Describe* and correct the error in fitting the line to the data in the scatter plot.

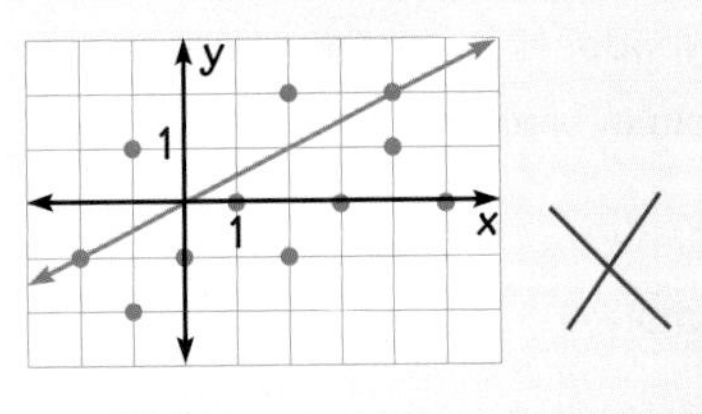

10. ERROR ANALYSIS *Describe* and correct the error in describing the correlation of the data in the scatter plot.

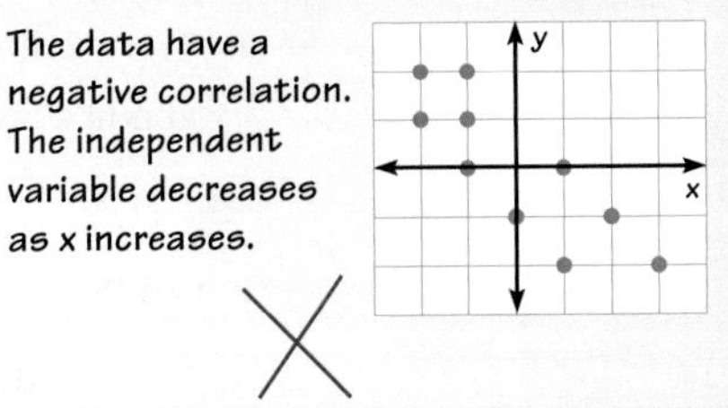

11. ★ OPEN-ENDED Give an example of a data set that shows a negative correlation. ***Sample answer:*** **The amount of time driving a car and the amount of gas left in the gas tank.**

B **12. ★ SHORT RESPONSE** Make a scatter plot of the data. *Describe* the correlation of the data. Is it possible to fit a line to the data? If so, write an equation of the line. If not, explain why.

12. See margin for art; relatively no correlation; no; because there is relatively no correlation in the data you cannot write an equation.

x	−12	−7	−4	−3	−1	2	5	6	7	9	15
y	150	50	15	10	1	5	22	37	52	90	226

MODELING DATA Make a scatter plot of the data. *Describe* the correlation of the data. If possible, fit a line to the data and write an equation of the line.

13–14. See margin for art.

13.

x	10	12	15	20	30	45	60	99
y	−2	4	9	16	32	55	87	128

positive correlation; *Sample answer:* $y = 1.49x - 13$

14.

x	−5	−3	−3	0	1	2	5	6
y	−4	12	10	−6	8	0	3	−9

relatively no correlation

C **15. CHALLENGE** Which line shown is a better line of fit for the scatter plot? *Explain* your reasoning.
Line *b*; line *a* has too many points below the line, but line *b* has about half the points above the line and about half the points below the line.

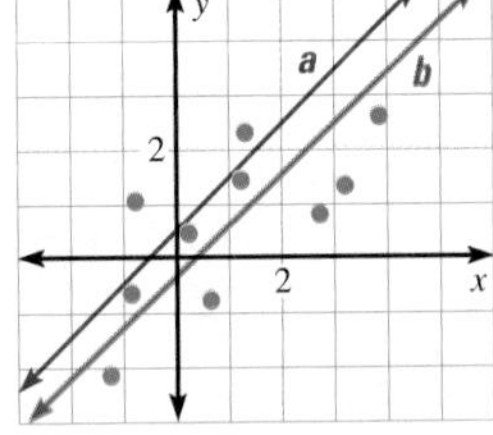

○ = WORKED-OUT SOLUTIONS on p. WS1   ★ = STANDARDIZED TEST PRACTICE

12. 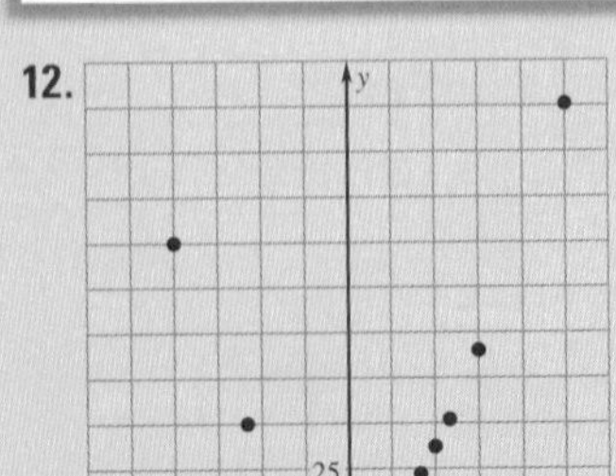

13. 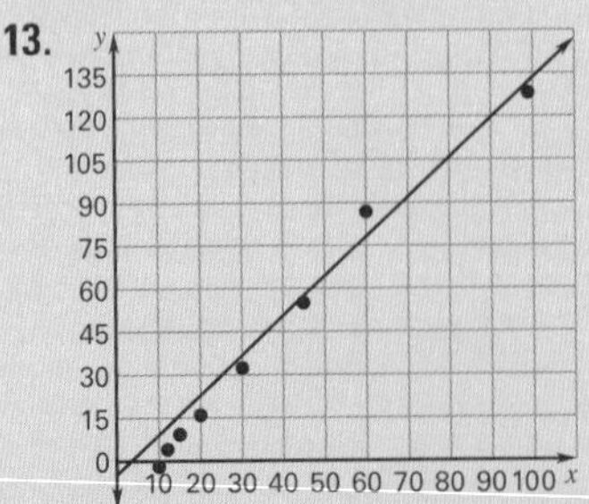

14. 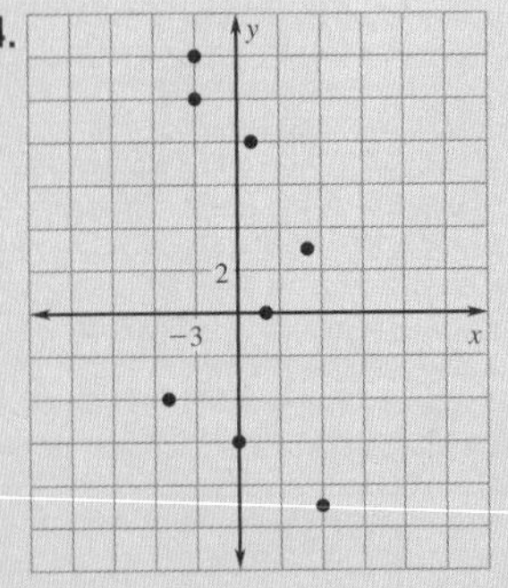

PROBLEM SOLVING

EXAMPLE 2 A on p. 325 for Exs. 16

16. ★ **SHORT RESPONSE** The table shows the approximate home range size of big cats (members of the *Panthera* genus) in their natural habitat and the percent of time that the cats spend pacing in captivity.

Big cat (*Panthera* genus)	Lion	Jaguar	Leopard	Tiger
Home range size (km^2)	148	90	34	48
Pacing (percent of time)	48	21	11	16

16b. Positive correlation; the larger the home range size the larger the percent of pacing time.

a. Make a scatter plot of the data. **See margin.**

b. *Describe* the correlation of the data.

c. The snow leopard's home range size is about 39 square kilometers. It paces about 7% of its time in captivity. Does the snow leopard fit the pacing trend of cats in the *Panthera* genus? *Explain* your reasoning. **No; it is below the expected percent of time spent pacing.**

@HomeTutor for problem solving help at classzone.com

EXAMPLES 3 and 4 on pp. 326–327 for Exs. 17–18

17. **EARTH SCIENCE** The mesosphere is a layer of atmosphere that lies from about 50 kilometers above Earth's surface to about 90 kilometers above Earth's surface. The diagram shows the temperature at certain altitudes in the mesosphere.

100 km, 86 km, 52 km, 0 km

Mesosphere

Altitude (km)	Temperature (°C)
86	−86
80	−65
75	−54
70	−40
65	−26
60	−21
52	−4

17b. *Sample answer:* $y = -2.2x + 111$

a. Make a scatter plot of the data. **See margin.**

b. Write an equation that models the temperature (in degrees Celsius) as a function of the altitude (in kilometers) above 50 kilometers.

c. At about what rate does the temperature change with increasing altitude in the mesosphere? ***Sample answer:* −2.2 degrees per kilometer**

@HomeTutor for problem solving help at classzone.com

B

18. See margin for art; the growth rate of alligator 2 is slightly greater than the growth rate of alligator 1.

18. **ALLIGATORS** The table shows the weights of two alligators at various times during a feeding trial. Make two scatter plots, one for each alligator, where x is the number of weeks and y is the weight of the alligator. Draw lines of fit for both scatter plots. *Compare* the approximate growth rates.

Weeks	0	9	18	27	34	43	49
Alligator 1 weight (pounds)	6	8.6	10	13.6	15	17.2	19.8
Alligator 2 weight (pounds)	6	9.2	12.8	13.6	20.2	21.4	24.3

19. *Sample answer:* $y = 12.6x + 32$

19. **GEOLOGY** The table shows the duration of several eruptions of the geyser Old Faithful and the interval between eruptions. Write an equation that models the interval as a function of an eruption's duration.

Duration (minutes)	1.5	2.0	2.5	3.0	3.5	4.0	4.5	5.0
Interval (minutes)	50	57	65	71	76	82	89	95

Teaching Strategy

Exercise 8 You may want to point out to students that they can immediately eliminate the two choices with positive slope based on the correlation shown on the scatter plot.

Internet Reference

Exercise 17 Additional information about the layers of Earth's atmosphere can be found at www.nasa.gov/audience/forstudents/9–12/features/912_liftoff_atm.html

Avoiding Common Errors

Exercises 17–21 Some students may draw a line through two of the points rather than a line of fit that models the data. Remind them that approximately the same number of points should lie above the line as below it, but that none of the points in the data set actually have to lie on the line.

Exercises 19–21 Some students may attempt to write an equation that models the data without making a scatter plot first. Remind these students that there is not a constant rate of change in the data, and that because of this, they need to plot the data so they can draw a line of fit.

16a.

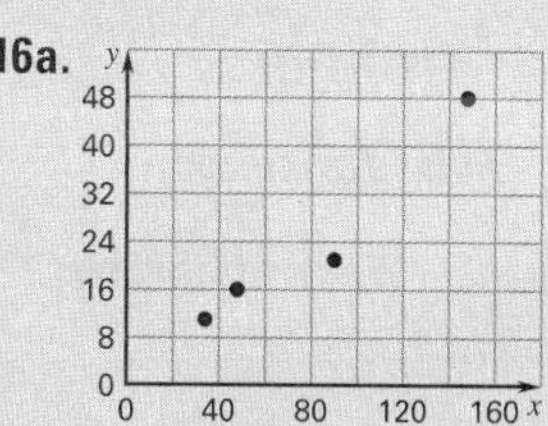

17a.

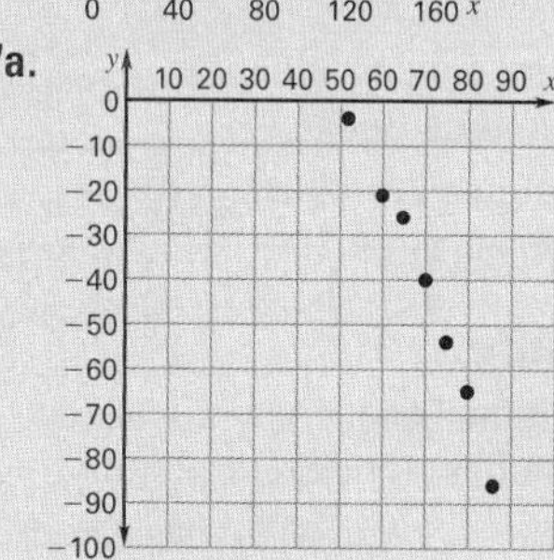

18.

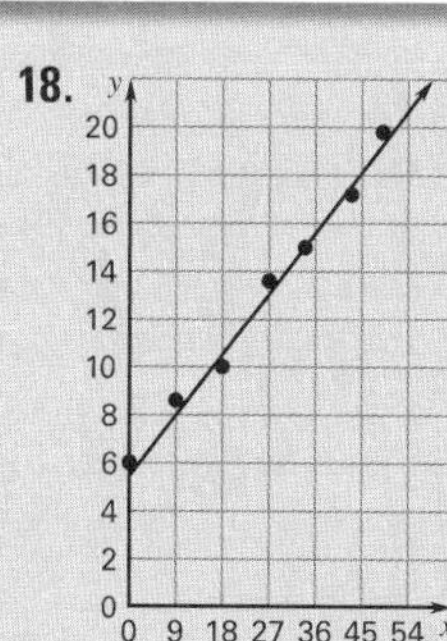

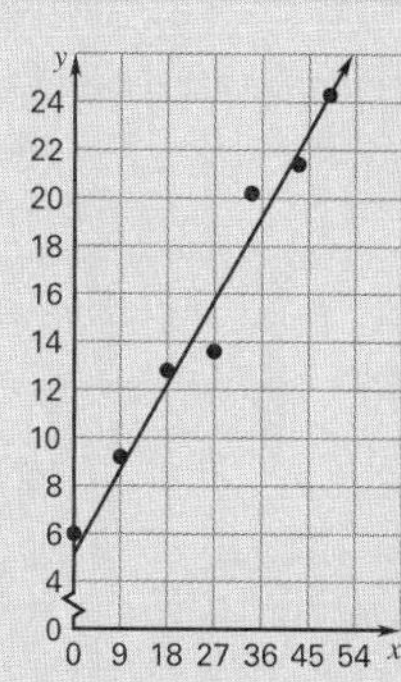

5 ASSESS AND RETEACH

Daily Homework Quiz

Transparency Available

Tell whether x and y show a *positive correlation*, a *negative correlation*, or *relatively no correlation*.

1. 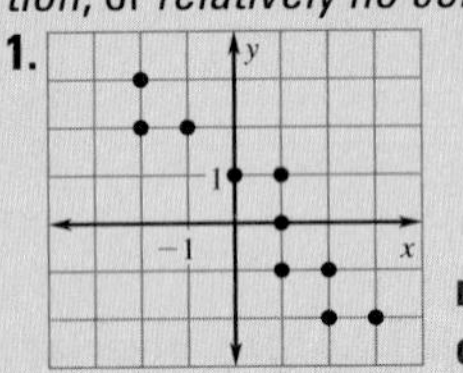

negative correlation

2. The table shows the body length and wingspan (both in inches) of seven birds. Write an equation that models the wingspan as a function of body length.

Bird	Body Length	Wing-span
Cuckoo	12	18
Falcon	16	41
Harrier	18	43
Hawk	19	51
Osprey	23	63
Sandpiper	9	22
Warbler	5	7

$y = 3.1x - 10.3$, where x is body length and y is wingspan

Online Quiz

Available at **classzone.com**

Diagnosis/Remediation

- Practice A, B, C in Chapter Resource Book
- Study Guide in Chapter Resource Book
- Practice Workbook
- @HomeTutor

Challenge

Additional challenge is available in the Chapter Resource Book.

20. DAYLIGHT The table shows the number of hours and minutes of daylight in Baltimore, Maryland, for ten days in January.

Day in January	5	6	7	8	9	10	11	12	13	14
Daylight (hours and minutes)	9:30	9:31	9:32	9:34	9:35	9:36	9:37	9:38	9:40	9:41

a. Write an equation that models the hours of daylight (in minutes in excess of 9 hours) as a function of the number of days since January 5. ***Sample answer:* $y = 1.2x + 30$**

b. At what rate do the hours of daylight change over time in early January? ***Sample answer:* 1.2 min per day**

c. Do you expect the trend described by the equation to continue indefinitely? *Explain.* **No; it will continue through June and then start decreasing.**

21c. *Sample answer:* $m = 13.884y + 39.808$; the function models the amount of money, m, spent on the Internet as a function of the number of years, y, since 1999.

21d. Yes, if you substitute the number of years since 1999 for y, you get about the amount of money, m, given in the data.

21. CHALLENGE The table shows the estimated amount of time and the estimated amount of money the average person in the U.S. spent on the Internet each year from 1999 to 2005. C

Year	1999	2000	2001	2002	2003	2004	2005
Internet time (hours)	88	107	136	154	169	182	193
Internet spending (dollars)	40.55	49.64	68.70	84.73	97.76	110.46	122.67

a. Write an equation that models the amount of time h (in hours) spent on the Internet as a function of the number of years y since 1999. ***Sample answer:* $h = 17.8y + 93.6$**

b. Write an equation that models the amount of money m spent on the Internet as a function of the time h (in hours) spent on the Internet. ***Sample answer:* $m = 0.78h - 33.2$**

c. Substitute the expression that is equal to h from part (a) in the function from part (b). What does the new function tell you? **See margin.**

d. Does the function from part (c) agree with the data given? *Explain.*

MIXED REVIEW

PREVIEW Prepare for Lesson 5.7 in Exs. 22–24.

Evaluate the function when $x = -2, 5,$ and 0. *(p. 262)*

22. $f(x) = 5x - 8$ **$-18, 17, -8$** **23.** $g(x) = -10x$ **$20, -50, 0$** **24.** $v(x) = 14 - 5x$ **$24, -11, 14$**

Write an equation of the line shown. *(p. 283)*

25. 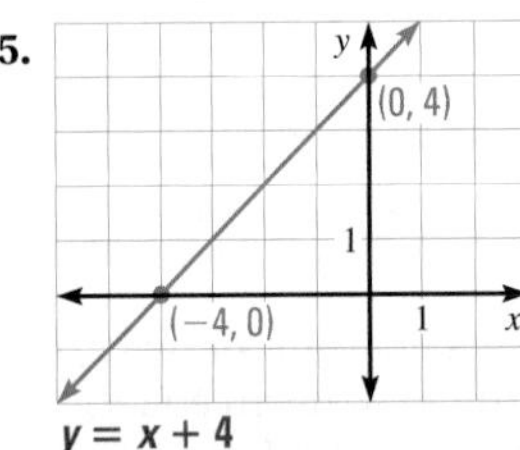

$y = x + 4$

26. (0, −1) (4, −3)

$y = -\frac{1}{2}x - 1$

27. 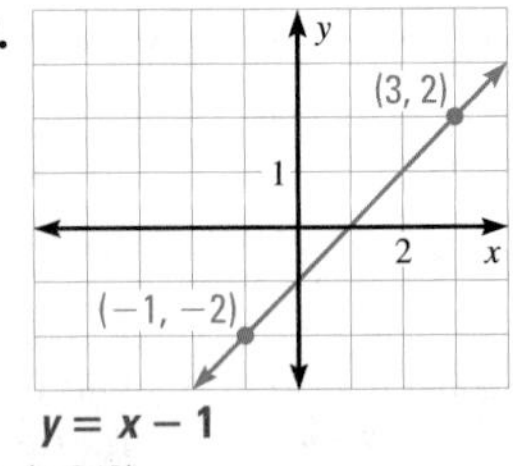

$y = x - 1$

28. Determine which lines, if any, are parallel or perpendicular. *(p. 318)*

Line a: $y = 2x - 5$ Line b: $2x + y = -5$ Line c: $4x - 2y = 3$

parallel: a and c

Graphing Calculator ACTIVITY *Use after Lesson 5.6*

@HomeTutor
classzone.com
Keystrokes

5.6 Perform Linear Regression

QUESTION How can you model data with the best-fitting line?

The line that most closely follows a trend in data is the *best-fitting line.* The process of finding the best-fitting line to model a set of data is called *linear regression*. This process can be tedious to perform by hand, but you can use a graphing calculator to make a scatter plot and perform linear regression on a data set.

EXAMPLE 1 Create a scatter plot

The table shows the total sales from women's clothing stores in the United States from 1997 to 2002. Make a scatter plot of the data. *Describe* the correlation of the data.

Year	1997	1998	1999	2000	2001	2002
Sales (billions of dollars)	27.9	28.7	30.2	32.5	33.1	34.3

STEP 1 ***Enter data***

Press STAT and select Edit. Enter years since 1997 (0, 1, 2, 3, 4, 5) into List 1 (L_1). These will be the x-values. Enter sales (in billions of dollars) into List 2 (L_2). These will be the y-values.

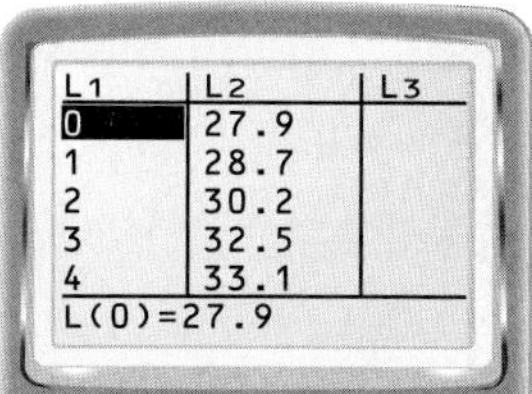

STEP 2 ***Choose plot settings***

Press 2nd Y= and select Plot1. Turn Plot1 On. Select scatter plot as the type of display. Enter L_1 for the Xlist and L_2 for the Ylist.

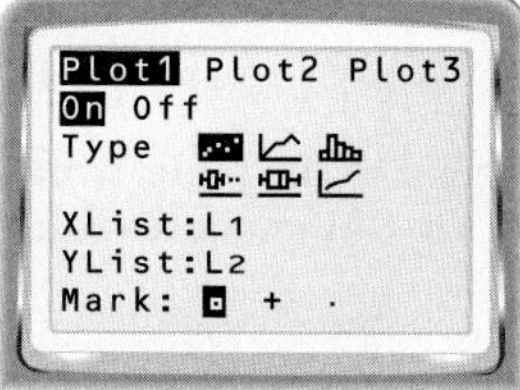

STEP 3 ***Make a scatter plot***

Press ZOOM 9 to display the scatter plot so that the points for all data pairs are visible.

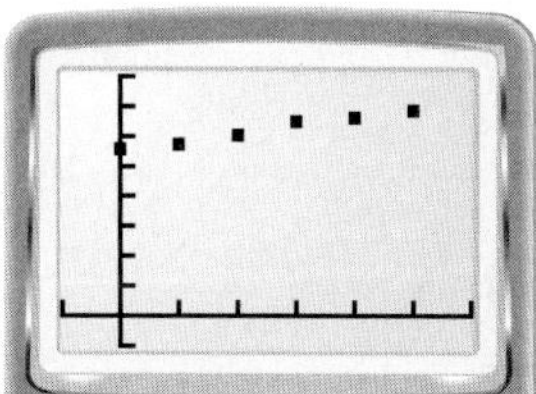

STEP 4 ***Describe the correlation***

Describe the correlation of the data in the scatter plot.

The data have a positive correlation. This means that with each passing year, the sales of women's clothing tended to increase.

1 PLAN AND PREPARE

Learn the Method

- Students will use a graphing calculator to create a scatter plot and perform linear regression on a data set.
- After the activity, students can use a graphing calculator to check their solutions in Exercises 17–21 in Lesson 5.6.

Keystroke Help

Keystrokes for several models of calculators are available in blackline format in the *Chapter Resource Book.*

2 TEACH

Extra Example 1

The table shows the number of endangered plants in the U.S. from 1997 to 2002. Make a scatter plot of the data. *Describe* the correlation of the data.

Year	Endangered Plants
1997	553
1998	567
1999	581
2000	592
2001	595
2002	599

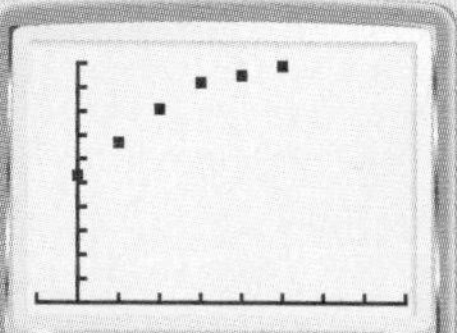

The data have a positive correlation. This means that with each passing year, the number of endangered plants tended to increase.

Extra Example 2

Find an equation of the best-fitting line for the scatter plot from Extra Example 1. Determine the correlation coefficient of the data. Graph the best-fitting line. **Rounding the values from the graphing calculator, the equation of the best-fitting line is $y = 9.29x + 558$. The correlation coefficient is 0.965. Since r is close to 1, the data have a strong positive correlation.**

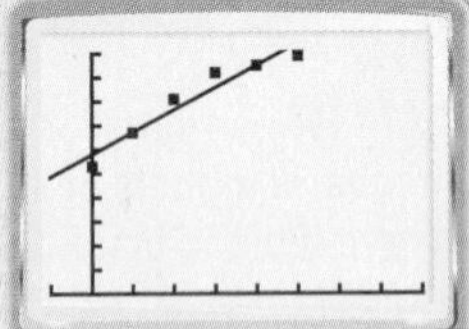

3 ASSESS AND RETEACH

A friend performs linear regression on a data set and tells you that the correlation coefficient is 0.213.

1. What does the value of r tell you about the data set? **Since the value of r is positive but close to zero, there is almost no correlation in the data even though the y values tend to increase as the x values increase.**
2. How reliable is the best-fitting line for predicting future trends in the data? **Since the correlation is low, the best-fitting line would not be accurate in predicting future trends.**

3.

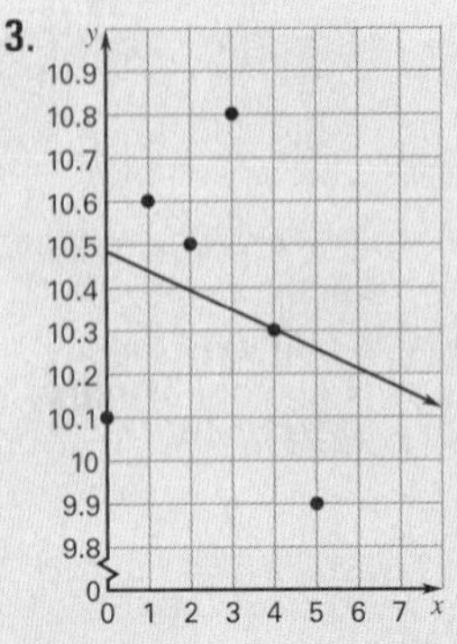

MODELING DATA The *correlation coefficient* r for a set of paired data measures how well the best-fitting line fits the data. You can use a graphing calculator to find a value for r.

For r close to 1, the data have a strong positive correlation. For r close to -1, the data have a strong negative correlation. For r close to 0, the data have relatively no correlation.

EXAMPLE 2 Find the best-fitting line

Find an equation of the best-fitting line for the scatter plot from Example 1. Determine the correlation coefficient of the data. Graph the best-fitting line.

STEP 1 ***Perform regression***

Press STAT. From the CALC menu, choose LinReg(ax+b). The a- and b-values given are for an equation of the form $y = ax + b$. Rounding these values gives the equation $y = 1.36x + 27.7$. Because r is close to 1, the data have a strong positive correlation.

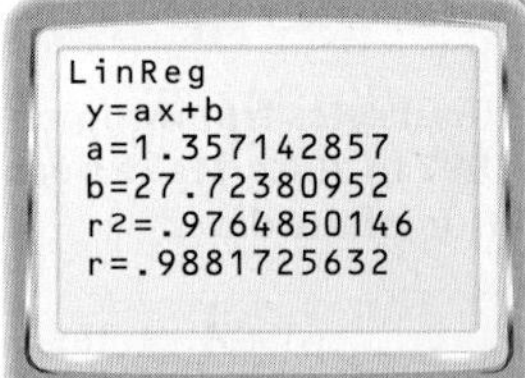

STEP 2 ***Draw the best-fitting line***

Press Y= and enter $1.36x + 27.7$ for y_1.
Press GRAPH.

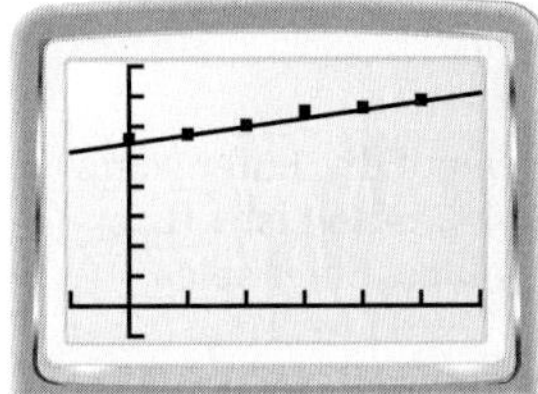

PRACTICE

In Exercises 1–5, refer to the table, which shows the total sales from men's clothing stores in the United States from 1997 to 2002.

Year	1997	1998	1999	2000	2001	2002
Sales (billions of dollars)	10.1	10.6	10.5	10.8	10.3	9.9

1. Make a scatter plot of the data. *Describe* the correlation. **See art in Exercise 3; negative correlation.**
2. Find the equation of the best-fitting line for the data. **$S = -0.046y + 10.5$**
3. Draw the best-fitting line for the data. **See margin.**

DRAW CONCLUSIONS

4. What does the value of r for the equation in Exercise 2 tell you about the correlation of the data? **The data have relatively no correlation.**
5. **PREDICT** How could you use the best-fitting line to predict future sales of men's clothing? *Explain* your answer. ***Sample answer:* You cannot use the best-fitting line to predict future sales because the data do not show a strong correlation.**

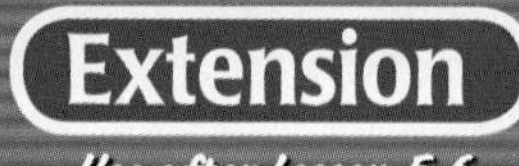

Use after Lesson 5.6

Correlation and Causation

GOAL Understand the difference between causation and correlation.

Key Vocabulary
- **correlation,** *p. 324*

In Graphing Calculator Activity 5.6, you saw that paired data have a strong positive correlation if the correlation coefficient r is close to 1 and a strong negative correlation if r is close to -1. But a strong correlation does not necessarily imply cause and effect, or *causation*, between the paired variables.

EXAMPLE 1 Analyze a set of data

COMPUTERS The table shows the number (in millions) of music album downloads and the number (in millions) of individual federal income tax returns filed electronically each year from 2004 to 2008. Analyze the data in terms of correlation and causation.

Year	2004	2005	2006	2007	2008
Album downloads (millions), x	4.6	13.6	27.6	42.5	56.9
Electronic tax returns (millions), y	61.5	68.5	72.8	78.7	89.5

Solution

First, find the correlation coefficient. Because r is close to 1, there is a strong positive correlation. However, an increase in album downloads does not cause an increase in electronic tax returns. These increases are both a result of other factors, such as advances in technology and increased computer usage.

```
LinReg
 y=ax+b
 a=.4942477768
 b=59.84704456
 r2=.974307673
 r=.9870702472
```

PRACTICE

EXAMPLE 1 for Exs. 1–2

In Exercises 1 and 2, analyze the data in terms of correlation and causation. **1–3. See margin.**

1. **BASKETBALL** The table shows the number of minutes played and the number of points scored by 6 college basketball players.

Minutes, x	30	31	33	30	25	18
Points, y	14	13	13	11	7	5

2. **SALES** The table shows the numbers of cold drinks and hot drinks sold at an outdoor concession stand from June through November.

Hot drinks, x	100	150	200	230	250	275
Cold drinks, y	300	210	175	165	140	125

3. **REASONING** You want to analyze annual data for music downloads and CD sales for the period 2000–2010 in terms of correlation and causation. What would you expect to find? *Explain.*

1 PLAN AND PREPARE

Warm-Up Exercises

1. Find an equation of the best-fitting line for the data.

x	0	1	3	5	6	8
y	2	4	7	13	13	17

$y = 1.9x + 2$

2 FOCUS AND MOTIVATE

Essential Question

Ask this question at the start of the lesson and then have students answer it at the end of the lesson: How do you distinguish between correlation and causation? **If data have a strong correlation, consider whether the correlation implies causation, or whether other factors may explain changes in both data sets.**

3 TEACH

Extra Example 1

The table shows the number x of wolves and the number y of eagles in a park for five consecutive years. Find the correlation coefficient for the data. Then analyze the data in terms of both correlation and causation.

x	10	15	27	36	48
y	80	82	83	85	90

0.965; strong positive correlation; An increase in wolves does not cause an increase in eagles. Other factors such as protective laws may cause both increases.

1. $r \approx 0.927$; there is a strong positive correlation. An increase in the number of minutes played may contribute to an increase in the number of points scored, but there is not causation. Minutes played and the points scored may both be a result of the ability of the player.

2. $r \approx -0.970$; there is a strong negative correlation. An increase in sales of hot drinks does not cause a decrease in sales of cold drinks. The increase in one and the decrease in the other are probably a result of changes in the weather.

3. *Sample answer:* As music downloads increase, sales of CDs decrease, so I would expect a strong negative correlation. The increase in the number of music downloads causes the decline in CD sales as users find downloading a more convenient way to obtain music.

1 PLAN AND PREPARE

Explore the Concept

- Students will make a prediction using a line of fit.
- This activity leads into the study of using the equation of a best-fitting line to make a prediction in Example 1 in Lesson 5.7.

Materials

Each student or group of students will need a metric ruler.

Recommended Time

Work activity: 15 min

Discuss results: 5 min

Grouping

Students can work individually or in groups of four. If students work in groups, they can divide the tasks into collecting (and drawing) the rectangles, measuring the rectangles and recording data, and plotting the data and drawing a line of fit. Two students can share the last task.

2 TEACH

Tips for Success

Remind students to use care in plotting the points on the scatter plot and in drawing the line of fit.

Key Discovery

The closer a line of fit models the data, the better the prediction.

3 ASSESS AND RETEACH

How accurate is your model in predicting the long side of a rectangle if the short side is 2 centimeters? Explain. **Students should give reasons why their model is or is not accurate.**

5.7 Collecting and Organizing Data

MATERIALS • metric ruler

QUESTION **How can you make a prediction using a line of fit?**

EXPLORE **Make a prediction using a line of fit**

A student in your class draws a rectangle with a short side that is 4 centimeters in length. Predict the length of the long side of the rectangle.

STEP 1 ***Collect data***

Ask each of 10 people to draw a rectangle. Do not let anyone drawing a rectangle see a rectangle drawn by someone else.

STEP 2 ***Organize data***

Measure the lengths (in centimeters) of the short and long sides of the rectangles you collected. Create a table like the one shown.

Short side (cm)	2.7	2.7	1.8	2.6	1.4	1.5	1.2	0.8	3.8
Long side (cm)	4.4	6.5	3.4	6	3.4	3	2.8	1.6	6.5

STEP 3 ***Graph data***

Make a scatter plot of the data where each point represents a rectangle that you collected. Let x represent the length of the short side of the rectangle, and let y represent the length of the long side.

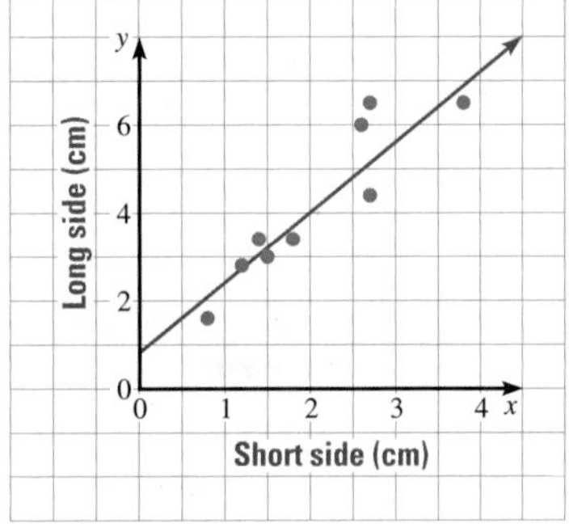

STEP 4 ***Model data***

Draw a line of fit.

STEP 5 ***Predict***

Use the line of fit to find the length of the long side that corresponds to a short side with a length of 4 centimeters. In this case, the long side length predicted by the line of fit has a length of about 7 centimeters.

DRAW CONCLUSIONS **Use your observations to complete these exercises**

1–3. Answers may vary.

1. **COMPARE** What is the slope of your line of fit? How does this slope compare with the slope of the line shown above?
2. **PREDICT** Suppose a student in your class draws a rectangle that has a long side with a length of 5 centimeters. Predict the length of the shorter side. *Explain* how you made your prediction.
3. **EXTEND** The *golden ratio* appears frequently in architectural structures, paintings, sculptures, and even in nature. This ratio of the long side of a rectangle to its short side is approximately 1.618. How does this ratio compare with the slopes of the lines you compared in Exercise 1?

5.7 Predict with Linear Models

Before You made scatter plots and wrote equations of lines of fit.

Now You will make predictions using best-fitting lines.

Why? So you can model trends, as in Ex. 21.

Key Vocabulary
- best-fitting line
- linear regression
- interpolation
- extrapolation
- zero of a function

The line that most closely follows a trend in data is called the **best-fitting line**. The process of finding the best-fitting line to model a set of data is called **linear regression**. You can perform linear regression using technology. Using a line or its equation to approximate a value between two known values is called **linear interpolation**.

EXAMPLE 1 Interpolate using an equation

CD SINGLES The table shows the total number of CD singles shipped (in millions) by manufacturers for several years during the period 1993–1997.

Year	1993	1995	1996	1997
CD singles shipped (millions)	7.8	22	43	67

REVIEW REGRESSION
For help with performing a linear regression to find the best-fitting line, see p. 331.

a. Make a scatter plot of the data.

b. Find an equation that models the number of CD singles shipped (in millions) as a function of the number of years since 1993.

c. Approximate the number of CD singles shipped in 1994.

Solution

a. Enter the data into lists on a graphing calculator. Make a scatter plot, letting the number of years since 1993 be the x-values (0, 2, 3, 4) and the number of CD singles shipped be the y-values.

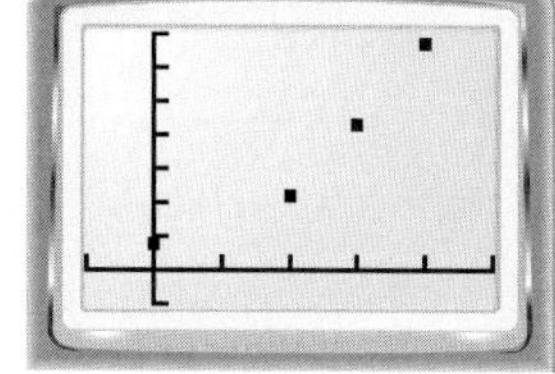

b. Perform linear regression using the paired data. The equation of the best-fitting line is approximately $y = 14x + 2.4$.

ANOTHER WAY
You can also estimate the number of CDs shipped in 1994 by evaluating $y = 14x + 2.4$ when $x = 1$.

c. Graph the best-fitting line. Use the *trace* feature and the arrow keys to find the value of the equation when $x = 1$.

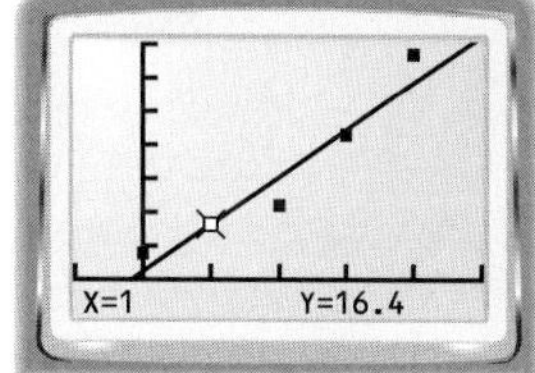

▶ About 16 million CD singles were shipped in 1994.

Animated Algebra at classzone.com

1 PLAN AND PREPARE

Warm-Up Exercises

Transparency Available

1. Evaluate $f(x) = 2.5x + 8$ when x is 3 or 5. **15.5; 20.5**
2. The table shows the profits of a company. Write an equation modeling the profit y as a function of the number of years x since 1998. **$y = 2.8x + 16.4$**

Year	'98	'99	'00	'01	'02
Profit (millions)	15	21	22	25	27

Notetaking Guide

Transparency Available

Promotes interactive learning and notetaking skills.

Pacing

Basic: 1 day
Average: 1 day
Advanced: 1 day
Block: 0.5 block with 5.6
- See *Teaching Guide/Lesson Plan.*

2 FOCUS AND MOTIVATE

Essential Question

Big Idea 3, p. 281

How can you use a best-fitting line to make predictions about data? **Tell students they will learn how to answer this question by performing a linear regression.**

NCTM STANDARDS

Standard 5: Use proper statistical methods to analyze data; Develop inferences that are based on data

Resource Planning Guide

Chapter Resource Book
- Teaching Guide/Lesson Plan)
- Activity Master
- Practice levels A, B, C
- Study Guide
- Catch-up for Absent Students
- Problem Solving Workshop
- Challenge

Workbooks
- Notetaking Guide
- Practice Workbook

Teaching Options
- **Power Presentations** provides dynamic electronic teaching resources for the classroom.
- **Activity Generator** provides editable activities for all ability levels.

Interactive Technology
- Easy Planner
- Power Presentations
- Activity Generator
- Animated Algebra
- Test Generator
- Online Quiz
- eWorkbook
- eEdition
- @HomeTutor

Resources for English Learners
- Spanish Study Guide
- Multi-Language Visual Glossary
- Student Resources in Spanish

See also the *Differentiated Instruction Resources* for more strategies for meeting individual needs.

EXTRAPOLATION Using a line or its equation to approximate a value outside the range of known values is called **linear extrapolation.**

EXAMPLE 2 Extrapolate using an equation

CD SINGLES Look back at Example 1.

a. Use the equation from Example 1 to approximate the number of CD singles shipped in 1998 and in 2000.

b. In 1998 there were actually 56 million CD singles shipped. In 2000 there were actually 34 million CD singles shipped. *Describe* the accuracy of the extrapolations made in part (a).

Solution

a. Evaluate the equation of the best-fitting line from Example 1 for $x = 5$ and $x = 7$.

Y1(5)
72.4
Y1(7)
100.4

The model predicts about 72 million CD singles shipped in 1998 and about 100 million CD singles shipped in 2000.

b. The differences between the predicted number of CD singles shipped and the actual number of CD singles shipped in 1998 and 2000 are 16 million CDs and 66 million CDs, respectively. The difference in the actual and predicted numbers increased from 1998 to 2000. So, the equation of the best-fitting line gives a less accurate prediction for the year that is farther from the given years.

ACCURACY As Example 2 illustrates, the farther removed an x-value is from the known x-values, the less confidence you can have in the accuracy of the predicted y-value. This is true in general but not in every case.

✓ GUIDED PRACTICE for Examples 1 and 2

1. **HOUSE SIZE** The table shows the median floor area of new single-family houses in the United States during the period 1995–1999.

Year	1995	1996	1997	1998	1999
Median floor area (square feet)	1920	1950	1975	2000	2028

a. Find an equation that models the floor area (in square feet) of a new single-family house as a function of the number of years since 1995. $y = 26.6x + 1921.4$

b. Predict the median floor area of a new single-family house in 2000 and in 2001. **about 2054.4 ft^2, about 2081 ft^2**

c. Which of the predictions from part (b) would you expect to be more accurate? *Explain* your reasoning. **The prediction for 2000 because the farther removed an x-value is from the known x-values, the less confidence you can have in the accuracy of the predicted y-value.**

Motivating the Lesson

You have data that gives the yearly sea turtle strandings off North Carolina from 1993 to 2004, with the exception of 1995 and 1998. By using a best-fitting line, you can predict the number of strandings that occurred in 1995 and 1998. You can also predict the number of strandings that are likely in future years.

3 TEACH

Extra Example 1

The table shows the number of hikers who have completed the Appalachian Trail from 1996 to 2000.

Year	Hikers completing trail
1996	405
1998	403
1999	552
2000	623

a. Make a scatter plot of the data.

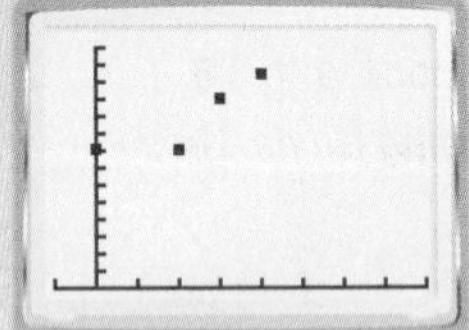

b. Find an equation that models the number of hikers completing the trail as a function of the number of years since 1996. ***Sample answer:*** $y = 56x + 369$

c. Approximate the number of hikers who completed the entire trail in 1997. **about 425 hikers**

An **Animated Algebra** activity is available online for **Example 1**. This activity is also part of **Power Presentations**.

Differentiated Instruction

Auditory Learners Point out that linear *in*terpolation predicts a point *in*side the range of the data points. Linear *ex*trapolation predicts a point *ex*terior to, or outside of, the range of the data points.

See also the *Differentiated Instruction Resources* for more strategies.

EXAMPLE 3 Predict using an equation

SOFTBALL The table shows the number of participants in U.S. youth softball during the period 1997–2001. Predict the year in which the number of youth softball participants reaches 1.2 million.

Year	1997	1998	1999	2000	2001
Participants (millions)	1.44	1.4	1.411	1.37	1.355

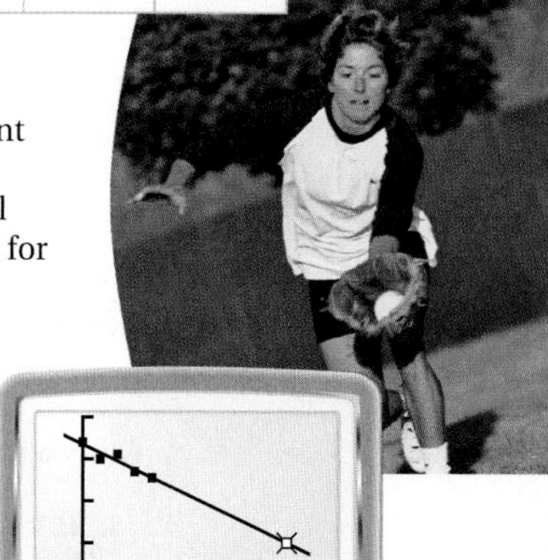

Solution

STEP 1 Perform linear regression. Let x represent the number of years since 1997, and let y represent the number of youth softball participants (in millions). The equation for the best-fitting line is approximately $y = -0.02x + 1.435$.

STEP 2 Graph the equation of the best-fitting line. Trace the line until the cursor reaches $y = 1.2$. The corresponding x-value is shown at the bottom of the calculator screen.

X=11.75 Y=1.2

▶ There will be 1.2 million participants about 12 years after 1997, or in 2009.

ANOTHER WAY

You can also predict the year by substituting 1.2 for y in the equation and solving for x:

$y = -0.02x + 1.435$

$1.2 = -0.02x + 1.435$

$x = 11.75$

✓ GUIDED PRACTICE for Example 3

2. **SOFTBALL** In Example 3, in what year will there be 1.25 million youth softball participants in the U.S.? **2006**

ZERO OF A FUNCTION A **zero of a function** $y = f(x)$ is an x-value for which $f(x) = 0$ (or $y = 0$). Because $y = 0$ along the x-axis of the coordinate plane, a zero of a function is an x-intercept of the function's graph.

KEY CONCEPT *For Your Notebook*

Relating Solutions of Equations, x-Intercepts of Graphs, and Zeros of Functions

In Chapter 3 you learned to solve an equation like $2x - 4 = 0$:

$2x - 4 = 0$

$2x = 4$

$x = 2$

The solution of $2x - 4 = 0$ is 2.

In Chapter 4 you found the x-intercept of the graph of a function like $y = 2x - 4$:

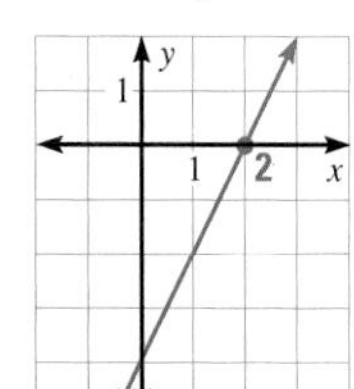

Now you are finding the zero of a function like $f(x) = 2x - 4$:

$f(x) = 0$

$2x - 4 = 0$

$x = 2$

The zero of $f(x) = 2x - 4$ is 2.

Extra Example 2

Look back at Extra Example 1.

a. Use the equation from Extra Example 1 to approximate the number of hikers who completed the entire trail in 2001 and 2003. **about 649 hikers in 2001 and about 761 hikers in 2003**

b. In 2001, 610 hikers actually completed the entire trail. In 2003, 555 hikers completed the entire trail. Describe the accuracy of the extrapolation made in part (a). **The differences between the predicted number of hikers and the actual number in 2001 and 2003 are 39 and 206, respectively. The actual and the predicted numbers are close for 2001, but very different for 2003. So, the equation of the best-fitting line gives a less accurate prediction for the year that is farther from the given years.**

Extra Example 3

The Federal Communications Commission issues licenses for amateur radio stations. The table shows the number of new general class licenses the FCC issued during the period September, 2004, to January, 2005. Predict the month and year in which the number of new general class amateur radio licenses issued reaches 50.

Month/Year	New Licenses
September, 2004	203
October, 2004	185
November, 2004	144
December, 2004	135
January, 2005	138

about 8 months after September, 2004, or about May, 2005

EXAMPLE 4 Find the zero of a function

SOFTBALL Look back at Example 3. Find the zero of the function. *Explain* what the zero means in this situation.

Solution

Substitute 0 for y in the equation of the best-fitting line and solve for x.

$y = -0.02x + 1.435$ Write the equation.

$0 = -0.02x + 1.435$ Substitute 0 for y.

$x \approx 72$ Solve for x.

▶ The zero of the function is about 72. The function has a negative slope, which means that the number of youth softball participants is decreasing. According to the model, there will be no youth softball participants 72 years after 1997, or in 2069.

GUIDED PRACTICE for Example 4

3. **JET BOATS** The number y (in thousands) of jet boats purchased in the U.S. can be modeled by the function $y = -1.23x + 14$ where x is the number of years since 1995. Find the zero of the function. *Explain* what the zero means in this situation. **11.4; the function has a negative slope, which means that the number of jet boats purchased in the U.S. is decreasing. According to the model, there will be no jet boats purchased 11.4 years after 1995, or in 2006.**

5.7 EXERCISES

HOMEWORK KEY

○ = **WORKED-OUT SOLUTIONS** on p. WS13 for Exs. 3 and 19

★ = **STANDARDIZED TEST PRACTICE** Exs. 2, 14, 16, and 21

= **MULTIPLE REPRESENTATIONS** Exs. 22

SKILL PRACTICE

1. **VOCABULARY** Copy and complete: Using a linear function to approximate a value within a range of known data values is called __?__. **linear interpolation**

2. ★ **WRITING** *Explain* how extrapolation differs from interpolation. **See margin.**

EXAMPLE 1 on p. 335 for Exs. 3–4

LINEAR INTERPOLATION Make a scatter plot of the data. Find the equation of the best-fitting line. Approximate the value of y for $x = 5$. **3–4. See margin for art.**

3.

x	0	2	4	6	7
y	2	7	14	17	20

$y = 2.6x + 2.3$; 15.3

4.

x	2	4	6	8	10
y	6.2	22.5	40.2	55.4	72.1

$y = 8.2x - 10.1$; 30.9

EXAMPLE 2 on p. 336 for Exs. 5–6

LINEAR EXTRAPOLATION Make a scatter plot of the data. Find the equation of the best-fitting line. Approximate the value of y for $x = 10$. **5–6. See margin for art.**

5.

x	0	1	2	3	4
y	20	32	39	53	63

$y = 10.7x + 20$; 127

6.

x	1	3	5	7	9
y	0.4	1.4	1.9	2.3	3.2

$y = 0.33x + 0.22$; 3.52

Extra Example 4

Look back at Extra Example 3. Find the zero of the function. *Explain* what the zero means in this situation. **The zero of the function is about 11. The function has a negative slope, which means that the number of new issues of amateur radio licenses in the general class is decreasing. According to the model, there will be no new general licenses issued about 11 months after September, 2004, which will be August, 2005.**

Closing the Lesson

Have students summarize the major points of the lesson and answer the Essential Question: How can you use a best-fitting line to make predictions about data?

- **You can approximate an unknown data value by using the equation of the best-fitting line found by linear regression.**
- **The zero of a function is the x value of the point where the line crosses the x-axis.**

Make a scatter plot of the data and then perform a linear regression to find the equation of the best-fitting line. Use the trace feature of the graphing calculator to trace the line of the equation or evaluate the equation of the best-fitting line to find the predicted values. Substitute 0 for y in the equation to find the zero of the function.

2. Extrapolation is finding an approximate value outside the range of known values. Interpolation is finding an approximate value within the range of known values.

3.

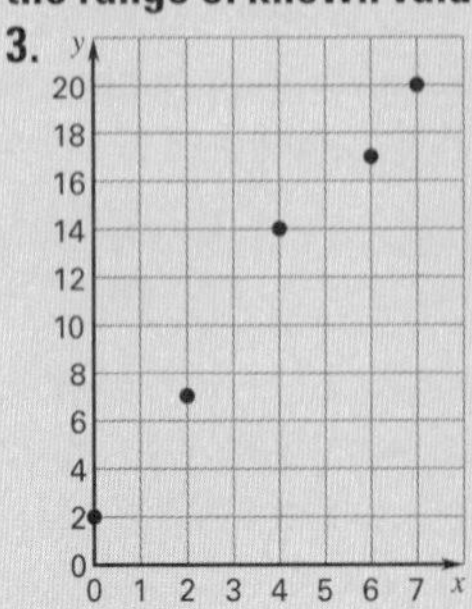

4.

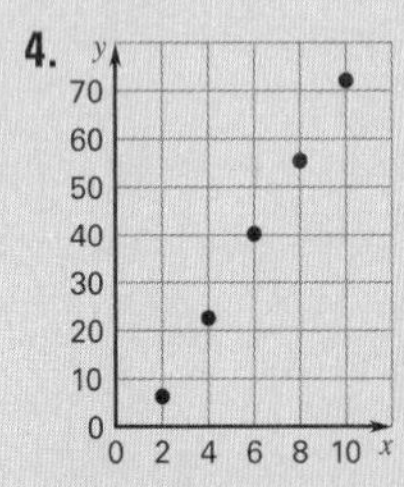

5.

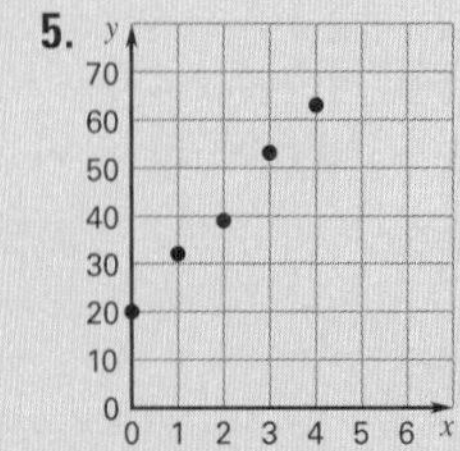

6.

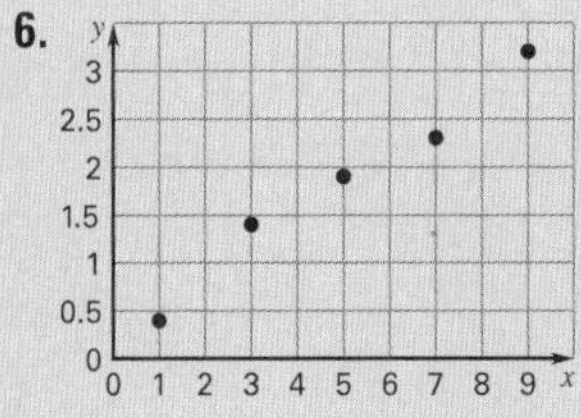

EXAMPLE 4 on p. 338 for Exs. 7–13

ZERO OF A FUNCTION **Find the zero of the function.**

7. $f(x) = 7.5x - 20$ **$2\frac{2}{3}$**
8. $f(x) = -x + 7$ **7**
9. $f(x) = \frac{1}{8}x + 2$ **−16**
10. $f(x) = 17x - 68$ **4**
11. $f(x) = -0.5x + 0.75$ **1.5**
12. $f(x) = 5x - 7$ **1.4**

13. **ERROR ANALYSIS** *Describe* and correct the error made in finding the zero of the function $y = 2.3x - 2$. **To find the zero of a function, substitute 0 for y, not x; $0 = 2.3x - 2$, $2 = 2.3x$, $x = \frac{20}{23}$.**

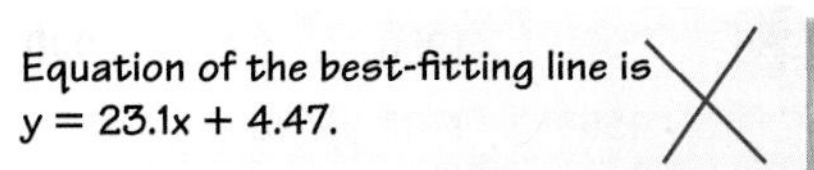

14. ★ **MULTIPLE CHOICE** Given the function $y = 12.6x + 3$, for what x-value does $y = 66$? **B**

Ⓐ 0.2 Ⓑ 5 Ⓒ 5.5 Ⓓ 78.6

B 15. **ERROR ANALYSIS** *Describe* and correct the error in finding an equation of the best-fitting line using a graphing calculator.

```
LinReg
 y=ax+b
 a=4.47
 b=23.1
 r2=.9989451055
 r=.9994724136
```

Equation of the best-fitting line is $y = 23.1x + 4.47$.

a and b were not substituted correctly; $y = 4.47x + 23.1$.

16. ★ **OPEN-ENDED** Give an example of a real-life situation in which you can use linear interpolation to find the zero of a function. *Explain* what the zero means in this situation. ***Sample answer:*** **Temperature on a mountain depends on the elevation. The zero indicates the elevation at which the temperature is 0°F.**

C 17. **CHALLENGE** A quantity increases rapidly for 10 years. During the next 10 years, the quantity decreases rapidly.

a. Can you fit a line to the data? *Explain.* **No; the data would first have a positive slope and then a negative slope.**

b. How could you model the data using more than one line? *Explain* the steps you could take. **You could fit a line to the data for the first 10 years and then fit another line to the data for the following 10 years.**

PROBLEM SOLVING

EXAMPLE 1 A on p. 335 for Ex. 18

18. **SAILBOATS** Your school's sailing club wants to buy a sailboat. The table shows the lengths and costs of sailboats.

Length (feet)	11	12	14	14	16	22	23
Cost (dollars)	600	500	1900	1700	3500	6500	6000

a. Make a scatter plot of the data. Let x represent the length of the sailboat. Let y represent the cost of the sailboat. **See margin.**

b. Find an equation that models the cost (in dollars) of a sailboat as a function of its length (in feet). **$y = 513x - 5258$**

c. Approximate the cost of a sailboat that is 20 feet long. **$5002**

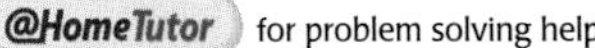

4 PRACTICE AND APPLY

Assignment Guide

Answer Transparencies available for all exercises

Basic:
Day 1: pp. 338–341
Exs. 1–15, 18–21, 24–32

Average:
Day 1: pp. 338–341
Exs. 1–6, 9–16, 18–22, 24–32

Advanced:
Day 1: pp. 338–341
Exs. 1–6, 10–14, 16–32*

Block:
pp. 338–341
Exs. 1–6, 9–16, 18–22, 24–32 (with 5.6)

Differentiated Instruction

See *Differentiated Instruction Resources* for suggestions on addressing the needs of a diverse classroom.

Homework Check

For a quick check of student understanding of key concepts, go over the following exercises:

Basic: 3, 5, 8, 20, 21
Average: 4, 5, 10, 20, 21
Advanced: 6, 12, 18, 20, 22

Extra Practice

- Student Edition, p. 942
- Chapter Resource Book: Practice levels A, B, C

Practice Worksheet

An easily-readable reduced practice page (with answers) for this lesson can be found on p. 280C.

18a.

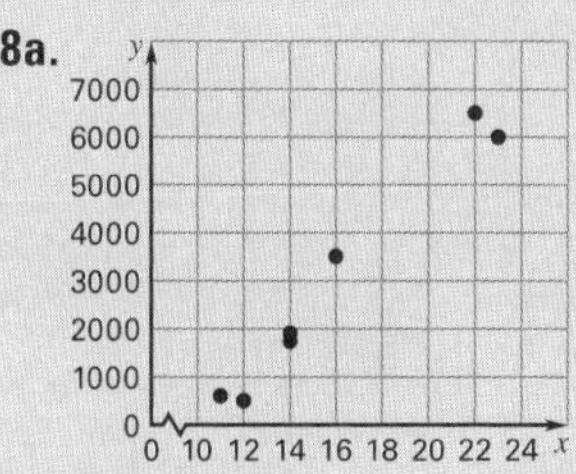

EXAMPLE 2
on p. 336
for Ex. 19

19. **FARMING** The table shows the living space recommended for pigs of certain weights.

Weight (pounds)	40	60	80	100	120	150	230
Area (square feet)	2.5	3	3.5	4	5	6	8

a. Make a scatter plot of the data. **See margin.**

b. Write an equation that models the recommended living space (in square feet) as a function of a pig's weight (in pounds). **$y = 0.03x + 1.23$**

c. About how much living space is recommended for a pig weighing 250 pounds? **about 8.73 ft^2**

@HomeTutor for problem solving help at classzone.com

EXAMPLE 3 B
on p. 338
for Ex. 20

20. **TELEVISION STATIONS** The table shows the number of UHF and VHF broadcast television stations each year from 1996 to 2002.

Year	1996	1997	1998	1999	2000	2001	2002
Television stations	1551	1563	1583	1616	1730	1686	1714

a. Find an equation that models the number of broadcast television stations as a function of the number of years since 1996. **$y = 31.5x + 1540$**

b. Approximate the year in which there were 1790 television stations. **2004**

EXAMPLE 4
on p. 338
for Exs. 21–22

21. ★ **SHORT RESPONSE** The table shows the number of people who lived in high noise areas near U.S. airports for several years during the period 1985–2000.

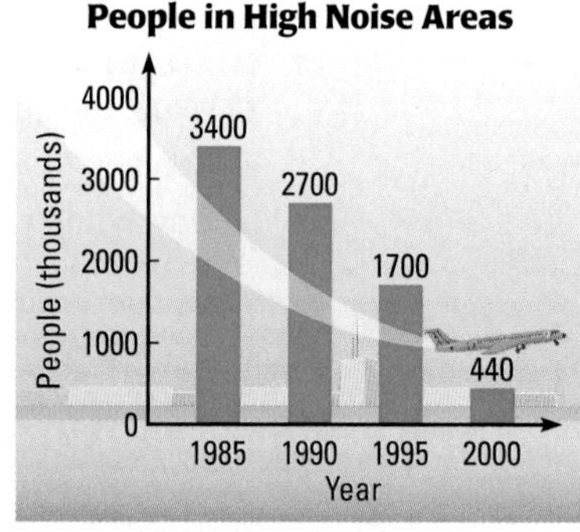

a. Find an equation that models the number of people (in thousands) living in high noise areas as a function of the number of years since 1985. **$y = -197.6x + 3542$**

b. Find the zero of the function from part (a). *Explain* what the zero means in this situation. Is this reasonable?

21b. about 17.9; 17.9 years from 1985, the number of people living in high noise areas will be 0; no.

22. ◆ **MULTIPLE REPRESENTATIONS** An Internet search for used cars of a given make, model, and year in your local area found cars with different mileages and different selling prices, as shown.

Mileage (thousands of miles)	22	14	18	30	8	24
Price (thousands of dollars)	16	17	17	14	18	15

a. **Making a Graph** Draw two scatter plots of the data, one by hand and one using a graphing calculator. **See margin.**

b. **Writing an Equation** Draw a line of fit on your hand-drawn scatter plot. Use the line to write an equation that models the selling price as a function of the mileage. Then use a graphing calculator to find the best-fitting line. *Compare* your models.

Answers may vary; best fitting line: $y = -0.2x + 19.7$; answers may vary.

c. **Describing in Words** Identify the slope and y-intercept of the best-fitting line. *Explain* their meanings in the context of the situation. **See margin.**

○ = WORKED-OUT SOLUTIONS on p. WS1 ★ = STANDARDIZED TEST PRACTICE ◆ = MULTIPLE REPRESENTATIONS

Graphing Calculator

Exercises 3–6, 18–23 If students cannot view the entire scatter plot in the viewing window, remind them that they can press Zoom 9 to display the scatter plot properly. They also can press window to set the bounds of the x-and y-axes and the scale on the axes.

Avoiding Common Errors

Exercises 7–12 Some students, in following Example 4 on page 338, may substitute 0 for x instead of 0 for $f(x)$. Remind these students that $f(x)$ replaces y, so they need to substitute 0 for $f(x)$.

Teaching Strategy

Exercise 21 Prior to students working on this exercise, you may want to discuss the meaning of the zero of a function in real-world situations. Review the meaning when data show a negative correlation. Then ask what occurs on the graph when data show a positive correlation.

Exercise 23 For more information about ducks, visit www.npwrc.usgs.gov/resource/taxa_w.htm

19a.

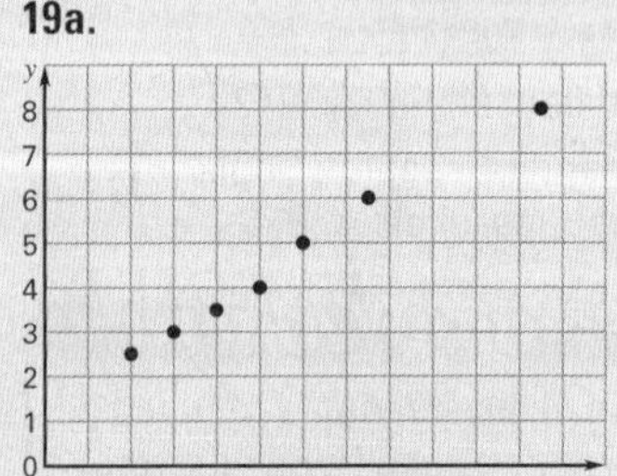

22a. Sample answers:

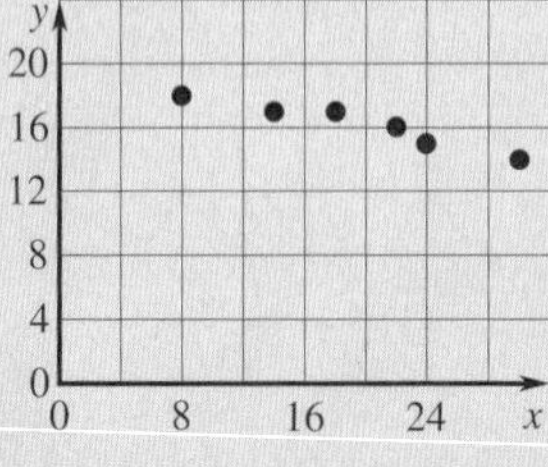

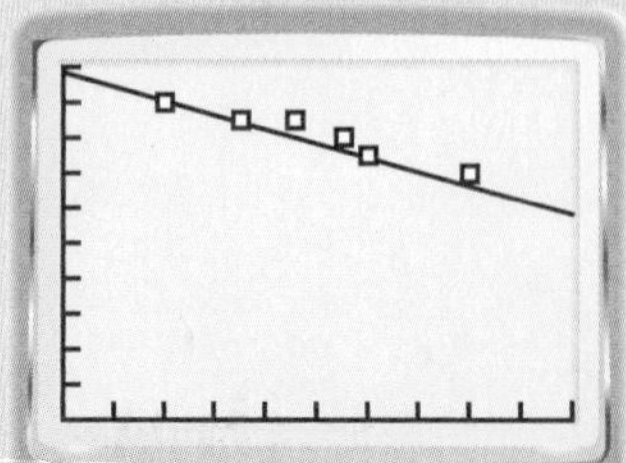

22c. The slope, −0.2, is the change in the cost (in thousands of dollars per thousand miles) of a local car of the same model, make, and year, and the y-intercept, 19.7, is the predicted selling price (in thousands of dollars) for a local car of the same model, make, and year with a mileage of 0.

C **23. CHALLENGE** The table shows the estimated populations of mallard ducks and all ducks in North America for several years during the period 1975–2000.

Year	1975	1980	1985	1990	1995	2000
Mallards (thousands)	7727	7707	4961	5452	8269	9470
All ducks (thousands)	37,790	36,220	25,640	25,080	35,870	41,840

a. Make two scatter plots where x is the number of years since 1975 and y is the number of mallards (in thousands) for one scatter plot, while y is the number of ducks (in thousands) for the other scatter plot. *Describe* the correlation of the data in each scatter plot. **See margin.**

b. Can you use the mallard duck population to predict the total duck population? *Explain.* **No; because you cannot find a line of best fit for either correlation, you cannot use the mallard duck population to predict the total duck population.**

MIXED REVIEW

Find the sum, difference, product, or quotient.

24. $-19 + (-8)$ *(p. 74)* **−27** **25.** $-7.3 + 5$ *(p. 74)* **−2.3** **26.** $-4.03 + (-3.57)$ *(p. 74)* **−7.6**

27. $-2.8 - (-2.3)$ *(p. 80)* **−0.5** **28.** $-4(5)(-5.5)$ *(p. 88)* **110** **29.** $-25 \div (-5)$ *(p. 103)* **5**

PREVIEW Prepare for Lesson 6.1 in Exs. 30–32.

Solve the equation. Check your solution.

30. $x - (-9) = 8$ *(p. 134)* **−1** **31.** $3x - 4 = -4$ *(p. 141)* **0** **32.** $4x + 10x = 98$ *(p. 148)* **7**

QUIZ *for Lessons 5.5–5.7*

1. PARALLEL LINES Write an equation of the line that passes through $(-6, 8)$ and is parallel to the line $y = 3x - 15$. *(p. 318)* $y = 3x + 26$

PERPENDICULAR LINES Write an equation of the line that passes through the given point and is perpendicular to the given line. *(p. 318)*

2. $(5, 5)$, $y = -x + 2$ $y = x$ **3.** $(10, -3)$, $y = 2x + 24$ $y = -\frac{1}{2}x + 2$ **4.** $(2, 3)$, $x + 2y = -7$ $y = 2x - 1$

5. CASSETTE TAPES The table shows the number of audio cassette tapes shipped for several years during the period 1994–2002. *(pp. 324, 335)*

Year	1994	1996	1998	2000	2002
Tapes shipped (millions)	345	225	159	76	31

a. Write an equation that models the number of tapes shipped (in millions) as a function of the number of years since 1994. $y = -38.85x + 322.6$

b. At about what rate did the number of tapes shipped change over time?

5b. about −38.85 million tapes per year

c. Approximate the year in which 125 million tapes were shipped. **1999**

d. Find the zero of the function from part (a). *Explain* what the zero means in this situation.
About 8.3; 8.3 years after 1994, or 2002, there will be no tapes shipped.

23a.

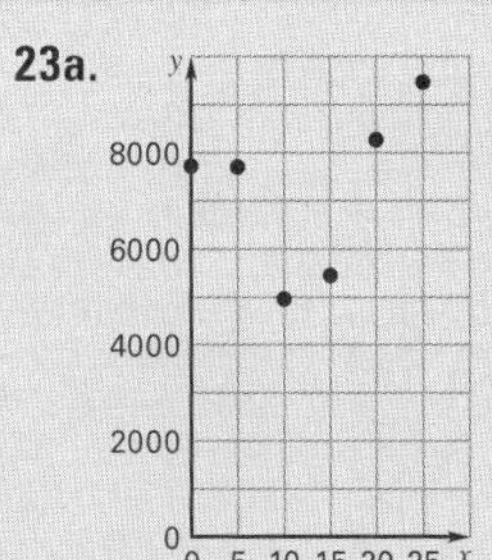

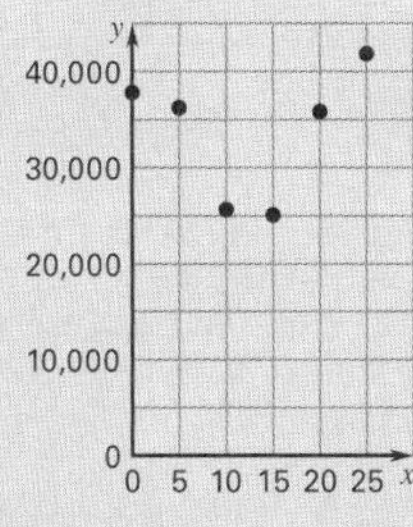

There is relatively no correlation in either scatter plot.

5 ASSESS AND RETEACH

Daily Homework Quiz

Transparency Available

1. Find the zero of the function $f(x) = 2.5x - 6$. **2.4**

2. The table shows the number of video rentals at a store from 1998 to 2002. Find an equation that models the number of video rentals as a function of the number of years since 1998. Predict the number of rentals in 1999 and 2003.

Year	Video Rentals (thousands)
1998	2.3
2000	2.0
2001	1.85
2002	1.45

$y = -0.2x + 2.35$, where x is the number of years after 1998. The model predicts about 2150 video rentals in 1999 and 1350 video rentals in 2003.

Available at **classzone.com**

Diagnosis/Remediation

- Practice A, B, C in Chapter Resource Book
- Study Guide in Chapter Resource Book
- Practice Workbook
- @HomeTutor

Challenge

Additional challenge is available in the Chapter Resource Book.

Quiz

An easily-readable reduced copy of the quiz (with answers) on Lessons 5.5–5.7 from the Assessment Book can be found on p. 280F.

@HomeTutor
classzone.com
Keystrokes

5.7 Model Data from the Internet

QUESTION **How can you find reliable data on the Internet and use it to predict the total U.S voting-age population in 2010?**

EXAMPLE 1 **Collect and analyze data**

Find data for the total U.S. voting-age population over several years. Use an equation that models the data to predict the total U.S. voting-age population in 2010.

STEP 1 ***Find a data source***

Reliable data about the U.S. population can be found in the online *Statistical Abstract*. Go to the address shown below. Click on a link to the most recent version of the *Statistical Abstract*.

Address http://www.census.gov

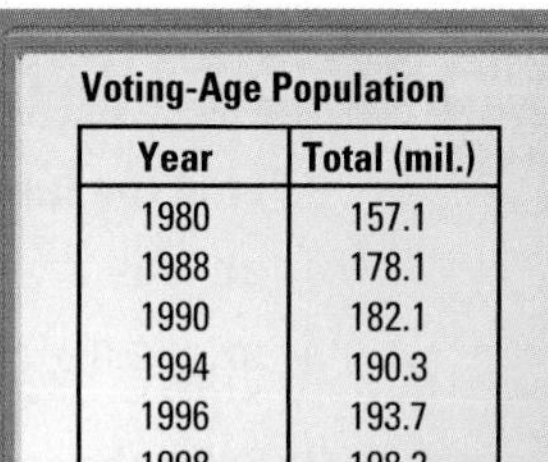

Voting-Age Population

Year	Total (mil.)
1980	157.1
1988	178.1
1990	182.1
1994	190.3
1996	193.7
1998	198.2

STEP 2 ***Find an appropriate data set***

Choose the most recent "Elections" document. In this document, find the table of data entitled "Voting-Age Population."

STEP 3 ***Find a model***

Use a graphing calculator to make a scatter plot. Let x represent the number of years since 1980. Let y represent the total U.S. voting-age population (in millions). Find an equation that models the total U.S. voting-age population (in millions) as a function of the number of years since 1980.

▸ $y = 2.23x + 159$

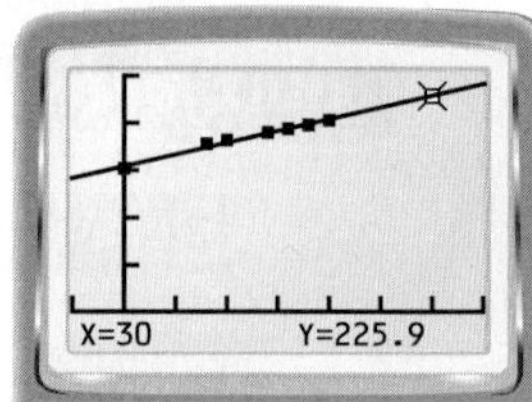

STEP 4 ***Predict***

Use the model to predict the total voting-age population in 2010. You can either evaluate the equation for $x = 30$ or trace the graph of the equation, as shown.

▸ The total U.S. voting-age population will be about 225.9 million in 2010.

DRAW CONCLUSIONS **1–3. Answers may vary.**

1. In the online *Statistical Abstract*, find data for the total value of agricultural imports over several years beginning with 1990.
2. Make a scatter plot of the data you found in Exercise 1. Find an equation that models the total value of agricultural imports (in millions of dollars) as a function of the number of years since 1990.
3. Predict the year in which the total value of agricultural imports will be \$45,000 million. *Describe* the method you used.

1 PLAN AND PREPARE

Learn the Method

- Students will find data on the Internet and use the data to make a prediction about the total U.S. voting-age population in 2010.
- After the activity, students can use the techniques they learned to find data for a real-life situation in Exercise 16 in Lesson 5.7, and then find the zero of the function.

2 TEACH

Tips for Success

Urge students to pay attention to the year of the data as there may be gaps in the years. Remind them that they need to enter the correct year to plot accurate data for the scatter plots.

Extra Example 1

Find data on U.S. postal rates for the first ounce of a letter since 1995. Use an equation that models the data to predict the cost of postage for the first ounce of a letter in 2010. You can find postal rates in the most recent "Transportation" document. **Using the data (1995, 32), (1999, 33), (2001, 34), (2002, 37), an equation is $y = 0.591x + 28.5$, where x is the number of years after 1990. The model predicts that in 2010 the first ounce of postage on a letter will be about 40 cents.**

3 ASSESS AND RETEACH

Looking at the online *Statistical Abstract*, name three different types of data that you can use to explore real-life situations. ***Sample answer:*** **Total energy consumption from 1996 to 2002; the number of oil spills from 1–100 gallons from 1998 to 2001; attendance at major league baseball games from 1985 to 2003.**

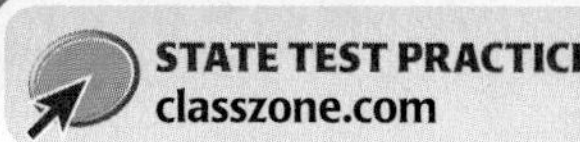

Lessons 5.5–5.7

1. **MULTI-STEP PROBLEM** The table shows the value of primary and secondary schools built in the U.S. each year from 1995 to 2000.

Year	Value (millions of dollars)
1995	1245
1996	1560
1997	2032
1998	2174
1999	2420
2000	2948

a. Make a scatter plot of the data. **See margin.**

b. Write an equation that models the value (in millions of dollars) of the schools built as a function of the number of years since 1995. $y = 321x + 1260$

c. At approximately what rate did the value change from 1995 to 2000? **about $321 million per year**

d. In what year would you predict the value of the schools built in the U.S. to be $3,600,000,000? **2002**

2. **GRIDDED ANSWER** A map of a city shows streets as lines on a coordinate grid. State Street has a slope of $-\frac{1}{2}$. Park Street runs perpendicular to State Street. What is the slope of Park Street on the map? **2**

3. **OPEN-ENDED** The graph represents the cost for one kayak owner for storing a kayak at a marina over time. The total cost includes a standard initial fee and a monthly storage fee. Suppose a different kayak owner pays a lower initial fee during a special promotion. Write an equation that could give the total cost as a function of the number of months of storage for this kayak owner. ***Sample answer:*** $y = 8x + 5$

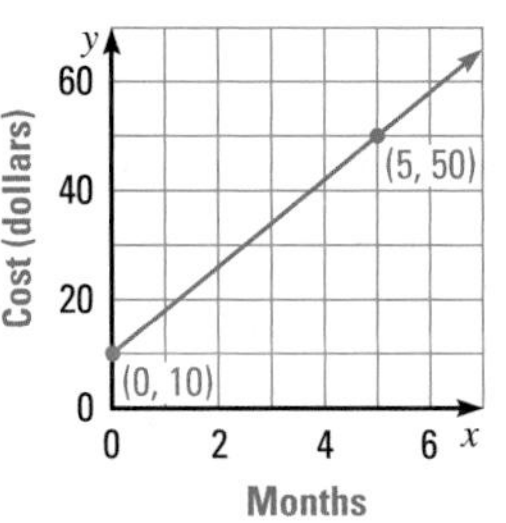

4. **SHORT RESPONSE** The table shows the heights and corresponding lengths of horses in a stable. Make a scatter plot of the data. *Describe* the correlation of the data. **See margin.**

Height (hands)	Length (inches)
17.0	76
16.0	72
16.2	74
15.3	71
15.1	69
16.3	75

5. **EXTENDED RESPONSE** The table shows the percent of revenue from U.S. music sales made through music clubs from 1998 through 2003.

Year	Percent of revenue
1998	9
1999	7.9
2000	7.6
2001	6.1
2002	4
2003	4.1

a. Find an equation that models the percent of revenue from music clubs as a function of the number of years since 1998. $y = -1.1x + 9.1$

b. At approximately what rate did the percent of revenue from music clubs change from 1998 to 2003? **about −1.1 percent per year**

c. Find the zero of the function. *Explain* what the zero means in this situation. **See margin.**

6. **SHORT RESPONSE** The cost of bowling includes a $4.00 fee per game and a shoe rental fee. Shoes for adults cost $2.25. Shoes for children cost $1.75. Write equations that give the total cost of bowling for an adult and for a child as functions of the number of games bowled. How are the graphs of the equations related? *Explain*. **See margin.**

1a.

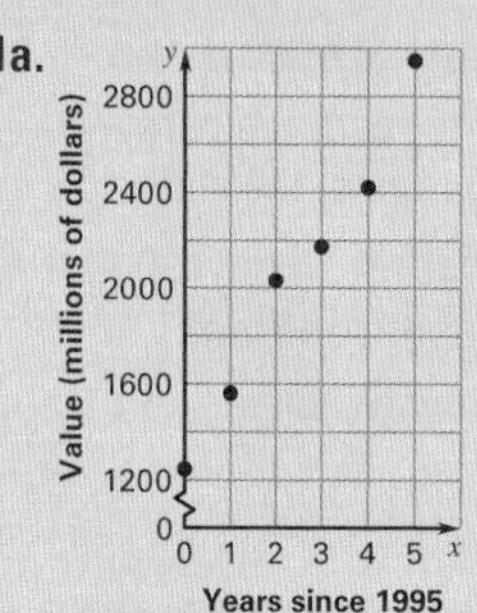

4.

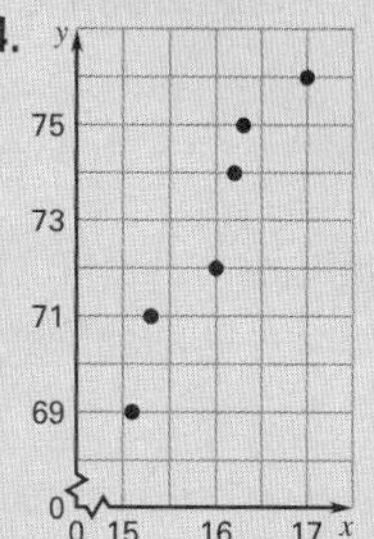

positive correlation

5c. 8.3; 8.3 years after 1998, or 2006 the percent of revenue from U.S. music sales made through music clubs will be 0.

6. $C = 4g + 2.25$, $C = 4g + 1.75$; **the graphs have the same slopes, but different** C**-intercepts.**

5 CHAPTER SUMMARY

Additional Resources

The following resources are available to help review the materials in this chapter.

Chapter Resource Book

- Chapter Review Games and Activities
- Cumulative Practice, Chs. 1–5

Student Resources in Spanish

eWorkbook

@HomeTutor

Vocabulary Practice

Vocabulary practice is available at **classzone.com**

BIG IDEAS *For Your Notebook*

Big Idea 1

Writing Linear Equations in a Variety of Forms

Using given information about a line, you can write an equation of the line in three different forms.

Form	Equation	Important information
Slope-intercept form	$y = mx + b$	• The slope of the line is m. • The y-intercept of the line is b.
Point-slope form	$y - y_1 = m(x - x_1)$	• The slope of the line is m. • The line passes through (x_1, y_1).
Standard form	$Ax + By = C$	• A, B, and C are real numbers. • A and B are not both zero.

Big Idea 2

Using Linear Models to Solve Problems

You can write a linear equation that models a situation involving a constant rate of change. Analyzing given information helps you choose a linear model.

Choosing a Linear Model	
If this is what you know . . .	**. . . then use this equation form**
constant rate of change and initial value	slope-intercept form
constant rate of change and one data pair	slope-intercept form or point-slope form
two data pairs and the fact that the rate of change is constant	slope-intercept form or point-slope form
the sum of two variable quantities is constant	standard form

Big Idea 3

Modeling Data with a Line of Fit

You can use a line of fit to model data that have a positive or negative correlation. The line or an equation of the line can be used to make predictions.

Step 1 Make a scatter plot of the data.

Step 2 Decide whether the data can be modeled by a line.

Step 3 Draw a line that appears to follow the trend in data closely.

Step 4 Write an equation using two points on the line.

Step 5 Interpolate (between known values) or extrapolate (beyond known values) using the line or its equation.

CHAPTER REVIEW

@HomeTutor
classzone.com
- Multi-Language Glossary
- Vocabulary practice

REVIEW KEY VOCABULARY

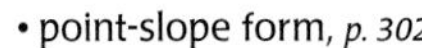

- point-slope form, *p. 302*
- converse, *p. 318*
- perpendicular, *p. 319*
- scatter plot, *p. 324*
- positive correlation, negative correlation, relatively no correlation, *p. 324*
- line of fit, *p. 325*
- causation, *p. 333*
- best-fitting line, *p. 335*
- linear regression, *p. 335*
- interpolation, *p. 335*
- extrapolation, *p. 336*
- zero of a function, *p. 337*

VOCABULARY EXERCISES

1. Copy and complete: If a best-fitting line falls from left to right, then the data have a(n) __?__ correlation. **negative**

2. Copy and complete: Using a linear function to approximate a value beyond a range of known values is called __?__. **extrapolation**

3. **WRITING** What is the zero of a function, and how does it relate to the function's graph? *Explain.* **The zero of a function is the x-value of the function when $y = 0$; it is the x-intercept of the graph.**

REVIEW EXAMPLES AND EXERCISES

Use the review examples and exercises below to check your understanding of the concepts you have learned in each lesson of Chapter 5.

5.1 Write Linear Equations in Slope-Intercept Form

pp. 283–289

EXAMPLE

Write an equation of the line shown.

$y = mx + b$ Write slope-intercept form.

$y = -\frac{2}{3}x + 4$ Substitute $-\frac{2}{3}$ for m and 4 for b.

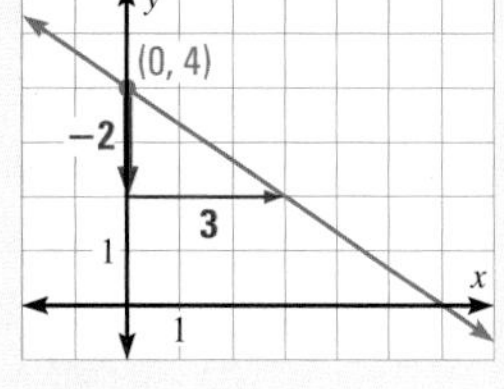

EXERCISES

EXAMPLES 1 and 5 on pp. 283, 285 for Exs. 4–7

Write an equation in slope-intercept form of the line with the given slope and y-intercept.

4. slope: 3
   y-intercept: −10
   $y = 3x - 10$

5. slope: $\frac{4}{9}$
   y-intercept: 5 **$y = \frac{4}{9}x + 5$**

6. slope: $-\frac{2}{11}$
   y-intercept: 7
   $y = -\frac{2}{11}x + 7$

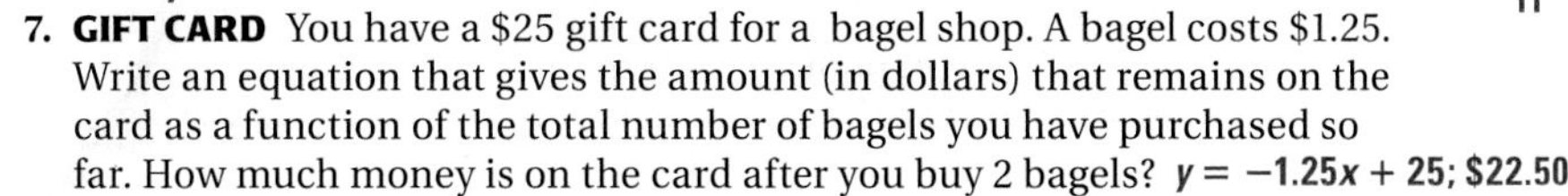

7. **GIFT CARD** You have a \$25 gift card for a bagel shop. A bagel costs \$1.25. Write an equation that gives the amount (in dollars) that remains on the card as a function of the total number of bagels you have purchased so far. How much money is on the card after you buy 2 bagels? **$y = -1.25x + 25$; \$22.50**

Extra Example 5.1

Write an equation of the line shown.

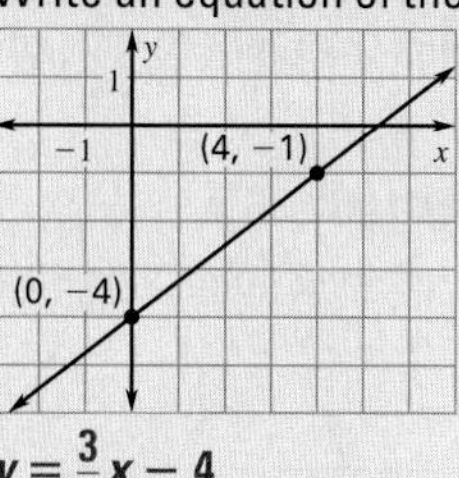

$y = \frac{3}{4}x - 4$

Extra Example 5.2

Write an equation of the line that passes through the point (6, 4) and has a slope of 3. $y = 3x - 14$

Extra Example 5.3

Write an equation in point-slope form of the line shown.

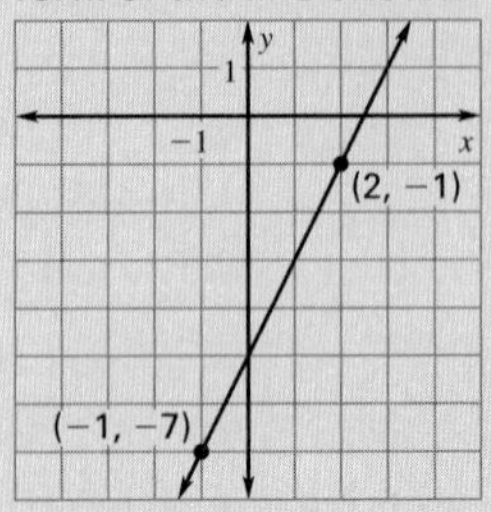

$y + 7 = 2(x + 1)$ or $y + 1 = 2(x - 2)$

11. $y - 7 = -6(x - 4)$ or $y - 1 = -6(x - 5)$

12. $y + 2 = -\frac{1}{3}(x - 9)$ or $y - 2 = -\frac{1}{3}(x + 3)$

13. $y + 2 = -\frac{6}{11}(x + 3)$ or $y + 8 = -\frac{6}{11}(x - 8)$

5.2 Use Linear Equations in Slope-Intercept Form *pp. 292–299*

EXAMPLE

Write an equation of the line that passes through the point (−2, −6) and has a slope of 2.

STEP 1 **Find** the y-intercept.

$y = mx + b$ Write slope-intercept form.

$-6 = 2(-2) + b$ Substitute 2 for m, −2 for x, and −6 for y.

$-2 = b$ Solve for b.

STEP 2 **Write** an equation of the line.

$y = mx + b$ Write slope intercept form.

$y = 2x - 2$ Substitute 2 for m and −2 for b.

EXERCISES

EXAMPLE 1 on p. 292 for Exs. 8–10

Write an equation in slope-intercept form of the line that passes through the given point and has the given slope m.

8. (−3, −1); $m = 4$ $y = 4x + 11$

9. (−2, 1); $m = 1$ $y = x + 3$

10. (8, −4); $m = -3$ $y = -3x + 20$

5.3 Write Linear Equations in Point-Slope Form *pp. 302–308*

EXAMPLE

Write an equation in point-slope form of the line shown.

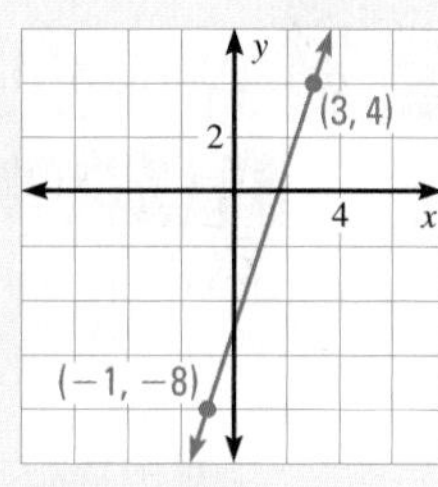

STEP 1 **Find** the slope of the line.

$$m = \frac{y_2 - y_1}{x_2 - x_1} = \frac{-8 - 4}{-1 - 3} = \frac{-12}{-4} = 3$$

STEP 2 **Write** an equation. Use (3, 4).

$y - y_1 = m(x - x_1)$ Write point-slope form.

$y - 4 = 3(x - 3)$ Substitute 3 for m, 3 for x_1, and 4 for y_1.

EXERCISES

EXAMPLES 3 and 5 on pp. 303, 304 for Exs. 11–14

Write an equation in point-slope form of the line that passes through the given points. 11–13. See margin.

11. (4, 7), (5, 1)

12. (9, −2), (−3, 2)

13. (8, −8), (−3, −2)

14. BUS TRIP A bus leaves at 10 A.M. to take students on a field trip to a historic site. At 10:25 A.M., the bus is 100 miles from the site. At 11:15 A.M., the bus is 65 miles from the site. The bus travels at a constant speed. Write an equation in point-slope form that relates the distance (in miles) from the site and the time (in minutes) after 10:00 A.M. How far is the bus from the site at 11:30 A.M.? $y - 100 = -\frac{7}{10}(x - 25)$ or $y - 65 = -\frac{7}{10}(x - 75)$; 54.5 mi

5.4 Write Linear Equations in Standard Form

pp. 311–316

EXAMPLE

Write an equation in standard form of the line shown.

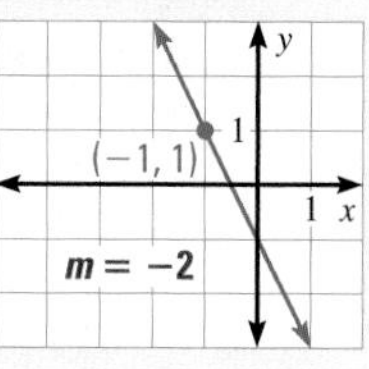

$y - y_1 = m(x - x_1)$	Write point-slope form.
$y - 1 = -2(x - (-1))$	Substitute 1 for y_1, −2 for m, and −1 for x_1.
$y - 1 = -2x - 2$	Distributive property
$2x + y = -1$	Collect variable terms on one side, constants on the other.

EXERCISES

EXAMPLES 2 and 5 on pp. 311, 313 for Exs. 15–17

Write an equation in standard form of the line that has the given characteristics.

15. Slope: −4; passes through (−2, 7) **$4x + y = -1$**

16. Passes through (−1, −5) and (3, 7) **$-3x + y = -2$**

17. COSTUMES You are buying ribbon to make costumes for a school play. Organza ribbon costs \$.07 per yard. Satin ribbon costs \$.04 per yard. Write an equation to model the possible combinations of yards of organza ribbon and yards of satin ribbon you can buy for \$5. List several possible combinations. **$0.07r + 0.04s = 5$. *Sample answer:* 4 organza, 118 satin; 8 organza, 111 satin; 12 organza, 104 satin**

5.5 Write Equations of Parallel and Perpendicular Lines

pp. 318–323

EXAMPLE

Write an equation of the line that passes through (−4, −2) and is perpendicular to the line $y = 4x - 7$.

The slope of the line $y = 4x - 7$ is 4. The slope of the perpendicular line through (−4, −2) is $-\frac{1}{4}$. Find the y-intercept of the perpendicular line.

$y = mx + b$	Write slope-intercept form.
$-2 = -\frac{1}{4}(-4) + b$	Substitute $-\frac{1}{4}$ for m, −4 for x, and −2 for y.
$-3 = b$	Solve for b.

An equation of the perpendicular line through (−4, −2) is $y = -\frac{1}{4}x - 3$.

EXERCISES

EXAMPLES 1 and 4 on pp. 318, 320 for Exs. 18–20

Write an equation of the line that passes through the given point and is (a) parallel to the given line and (b) perpendicular to the given line.

18. (0, 2), $y = -4x + 6$
a. $y = -4x + 2$
b. $y = \frac{1}{4}x + 2$

19. (2, −3), $y = -2x - 3$
a. $y = -2x + 1$
b. $y = \frac{1}{2}x - 4$

20. (6, 0), $y = \frac{3}{4}x - \frac{1}{4}$
a. $y = \frac{3}{4}x - 4\frac{1}{2}$; **b.** $y = -\frac{4}{3}x + 8$

Extra Example 5.4

Write an equation in standard form of the line shown. **$3x + y = 4$**

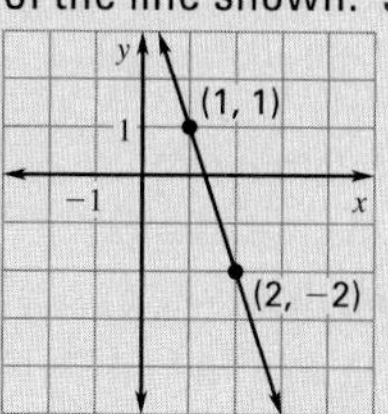

Extra Example 5.5

Write an equation of the line that passes through (−2, −2) and is parallel to the line $y = \frac{3}{2}x - 5$.
$y = \frac{3}{2}x + 1$

5 CHAPTER REVIEW

Extra Example 5.6

The table shows the number of students who joined the astronomy club at a school from 1996 to 2003. Make a scatter plot of the data. *Describe* the correlation of the data.

Year	Students in the Astronomy Club
1996	8
1999	15
2000	18
2001	22
2003	24

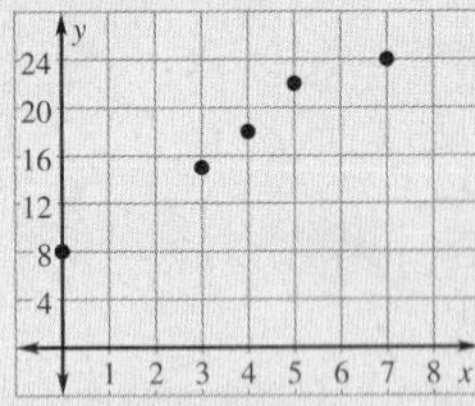

The scatter plot shows a positive correlation, which means that the number of students who joined the astronomy club tended to increase with each passing year.

Extra Example 5.7

Use the scatter plot from Extra Example 5.6 to estimate the number of students who joined the club in 1998. **About 13 students joined the astronomy club in 1998.**

21.

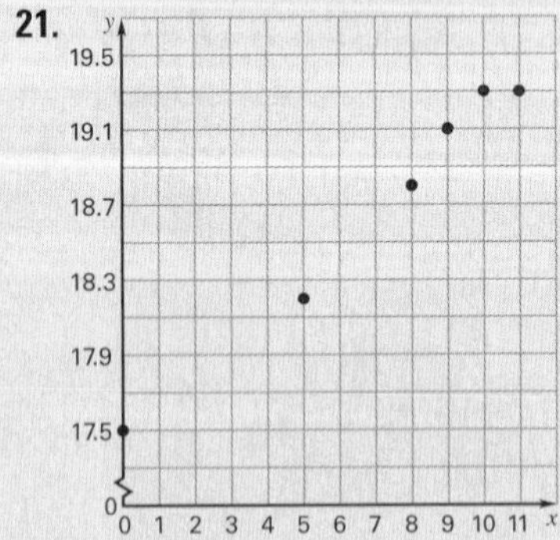

5.6 Fit a Line to Data *pp. 324–330*

EXAMPLE

The table shows the time needed to roast turkeys of different weights. Make a scatter plot of the data. *Describe* the correlation of the data.

Weight (pounds)	6	8	12	14	18	20	24
Roast time (hours)	2.75	3.00	3.50	4.00	4.25	4.75	5.25

Treat the data as ordered pairs. Let x represent the turkey weight (in pounds), and let y represent the time (in hours) it takes to roast the turkey. Plot the ordered pairs as points in a coordinate plane.

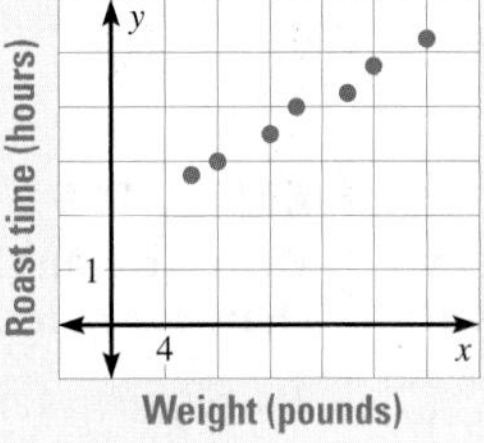

The scatter plot shows a positive correlation, which means that heavier turkeys tend to require more time to roast.

EXERCISES

EXAMPLE 2 on p. 325 for Ex. 21

21. **AIRPORTS** The table shows the number of airports in the Unites States for several years during the period 1990–2001. Make a scatter plot of the data. *Describe* the correlation of the data. **See margin for art; positive correlation.**

Years	1990	1995	1998	1999	2000	2001
Airports (thousands)	17.5	18.2	18.8	19.1	19.3	19.3

5.7 Predict with Linear Models *pp. 335–341*

EXAMPLE

Use the scatter plot from the example for Lesson 5.6 above to estimate the time (in hours) it takes to roast a 10 pound turkey.

Draw a line that appears to fit the points in the scatter plot closely. There should be approximately as many points above the line as below it.

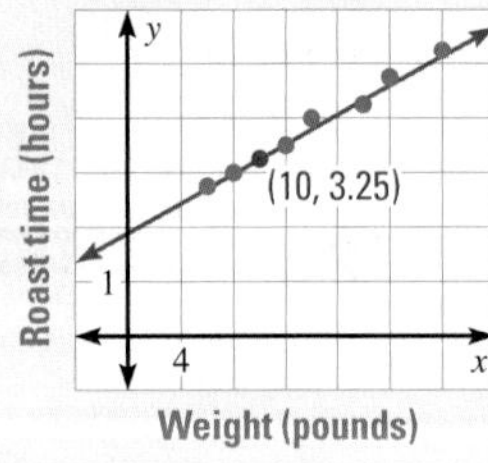

Find the point on the line whose x-coordinate is 10. At that point, you can see that the y-coordinate is about 3.25.

▸ It takes about 3.25 hours to roast a 10 pound turkey.

EXERCISES

EXAMPLE 2 on p. 336 for Ex. 22

22. **COOKING TIMES** Use the graph in the Example above to estimate the time (in hours) it takes to roast a turkey that weighs 30 pounds. *Explain* how you found your answer. **About 5.75 h. *Sample answer:* Use the points (10, 3.25) and (8, 3) to find the slope of the line to be 0.125. Looking at the graph, you can see that the y-intercept is 2, so the equation of the line is $y = 0.125x + 2$. Substitute 30 for x to find $y = 5.75$.**

Write an equation in slope-intercept form of the line with the given slope and y-intercept.

1. slope: 5
   y-intercept: -7 $y = 5x - 7$
2. slope: $\frac{2}{5}$
   y-intercept: -2 $y = \frac{2}{5}x - 2$
3. slope: $-\frac{4}{3}$
   y-intercept: 1 $y = -\frac{4}{3}x + 1$

Write an equation in slope-intercept form of the line that passes through the given point and has the given slope m.

4. $(-2, -8)$; $m = 3$ $y = 3x - 2$
5. $(1, 1)$; $m = -4$ $y = -4x + 5$
6. $(-1, 3)$; $m = -6$ $y = -6x - 3$

Write an equation in point-slope form of the line that passes through the given points. 7–9. See margin.

7. $(4, 5)$, $(2, 9)$
8. $(-2, 2)$, $(8, -3)$
9. $(3, 4)$, $(1, -6)$

Write an equation in standard form of the line with the given characteristics.

10. Slope: 10; passes through $(6, 2)$ $-10x + y = -58$
11. Passes through $(-3, 2)$ and $(6, -1)$ $\frac{1}{3}x + y = 1$

Write an equation of the line that passes through the given point and is (a) parallel to the given line and (b) perpendicular to the given line. 12–14. See margin.

12. $(2, 0)$, $y = -5x + 3$
13. $(-1, 4)$, $y = -x - 4$
14. $(4, -9)$, $y = \frac{1}{4}x + 2$

Make a scatter plot of the data. Draw a line of fit. Write an equation of the line. 15, 16. See margin.

15.

x	0	1	2	3	4
y	15	35	53	74	94

16.

x	0	2	4	8	10
y	-2	6	15	38	50

17. **FIELD TRIP** Your science class is taking a field trip to an observatory. The cost of a presentation and a tour of the telescope is \$60 for the group plus an additional \$3 per person. Write an equation that gives the total cost C as a function of the number of people p in the group. $C = 3p + 60$

18. **GOLF FACILITIES** The table shows the number of golf facilities in the United States during the period 1997–2001.

Year	Golf facilities (thousands)
1997	14.6
1998	14.9
1999	15.2
2000	15.5
2001	15.7

   a. Make a scatter plot of the data where x is the number of years since 1997 and y is the number of golf facilities (in thousands). See margin.
   b. Write an equation that models the number of golf facilities (in thousands) as a function of the number of years since 1997. *Sample answer:* $y = 0.28x + 14.6$
   c. At about what rate did the number of golf facilities change during the period 1997–2001? *Sample answer:* About 280 golf facilities per year
   d. Use the equation from part (b) to predict the number of golf facilities in 2004. *Sample answer:* About 16,560 golf facilities
   e. Predict the year in which the number of golf facilities reached 16,000. *Explain* how you found your answer. *Sample answer:* 2002; substitute 16 for y in the equation $y = 0.28x + 14.6$ and solve for x.

Additional Resources

Assessment Book

- Chapter Test, Levels A, B, C
- Standardized Chapter Test
- SAT/ACT Chapter Test
- Alternative Assessment

Test Generator

Chapter Test

Easily-readable reduced copies (with answers) of Chapter Test B, the Standardized Chapter Test, and the Alternative Assessment from the Assessment Book can be found on pp. 280F–280H.

15.

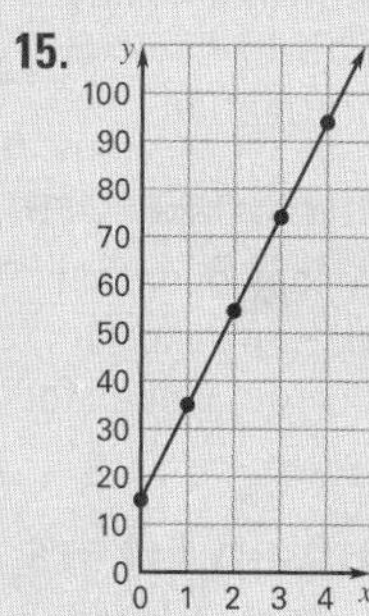

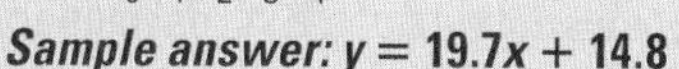
Sample answer: $y = 19.7x + 14.8$

16.

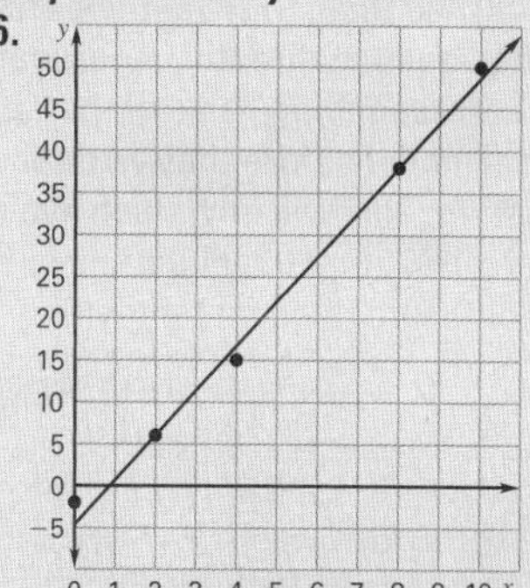

Sample answer: $y = 5.3x - 3.9$

18a.

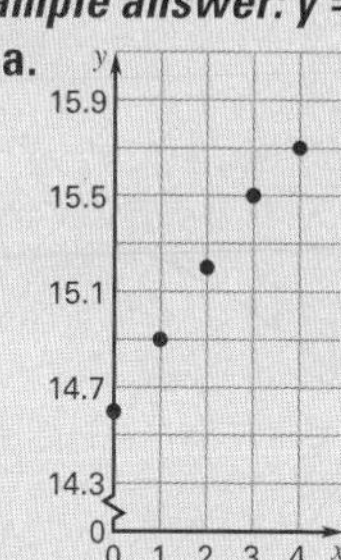

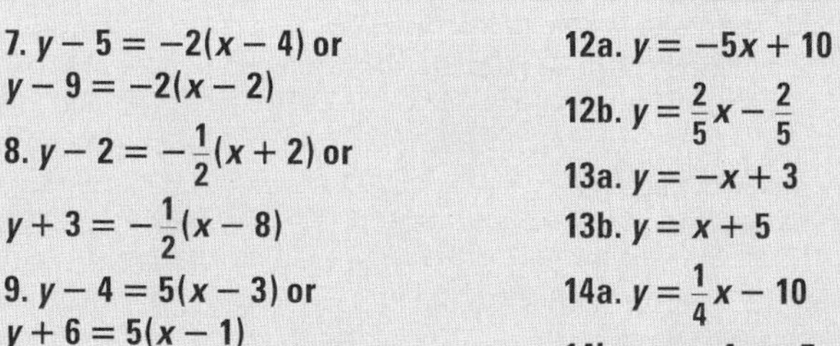
7. $y - 5 = -2(x - 4)$ or $y - 9 = -2(x - 2)$

8. $y - 2 = -\frac{1}{2}(x + 2)$ or $y + 3 = -\frac{1}{2}(x - 8)$

9. $y - 4 = 5(x - 3)$ or $y + 6 = 5(x - 1)$

12a. $y = -5x + 10$

12b. $y = \frac{2}{5}x - \frac{2}{5}$

13a. $y = -x + 3$

13b. $y = x + 5$

14a. $y = \frac{1}{4}x - 10$

14b. $y = -4x + 7$

5 ★ Standardized TEST PREPARATION

Using Rubrics

The rubric given on the pupil page is a sample of a three-level rubric. Other rubrics may contain four, five, or six levels. For more information on rubrics, see the *Differentiated Instruction Resources.*

Test-Taking Strategy

Caution students to show all of the steps they perform when solving a short response question. Some students, especially advanced students, may complete some of the steps mentally and then neglect to write down enough information to receive full credit. Encourage students to "think like a reviewer" who is scoring their work, asking themselves if they have shown all of the important information.

Avoiding Common Errors

Remind students to look over their calculations to make sure they have substituted correct values for the variables.

Avoiding Common Errors

When students use a verbal model, encourage them to write the parts of the equation directly underneath the corresponding parts of the verbal model before they write the equation. This will help them avoid errors in writing the equation, such as confusing the constant with the rate.

Scoring Rubric

Full Credit
- solution is complete and correct

Partial Credit
- solution is complete but has errors,

or
- solution is without error but incomplete

No Credit
- no solution is given,

or
- solution makes no sense

SHORT RESPONSE QUESTIONS

PROBLEM

The average monthly cost of basic cable increased by about \$1.47 each year from 1986 to 2003. In 1986 the average monthly cost of basic cable was \$10.67. Write an equation that gives the monthly cost (in dollars) of basic cable as a function of the number of years since 1986. In what year was the monthly cost of basic cable \$31.25? *Explain* your reasoning.

Below are sample solutions to the problem. Read each solution and the comments on the left to see why the sample represents full credit, partial credit, or no credit.

SAMPLE 1: Full credit solution

A verbal model shows how the equation is obtained.

Let y be the average monthly cost x years since 1986.

Monthly cost	=	Cost in 1986	+	Cost increase per year	·	Years since 1986
y	=	**10.67**	+	**1.47**	·	x

To find the year when the monthly cost was \$31.25, substitute 31.25 for y and solve for x.

Calculations are performed correctly.

$y = 10.67 + 1.47x$

$31.25 = 10.67 + 1.47x$

$14 = x$

The question is answered correctly.

The monthly cost was \$31.25 fourteen years after 1986, or in 2000.

SAMPLE 2: Partial credit solution

The equation is correct, and the student has explained what the variables represent.

Let y be the monthly cost. Let x be the number of years since 1986.

Monthly cost	=	Cost in 1986	+	Cost increase per year	·	Years since 1986
y	=	**10.67**	+	**1.47**	·	x

The answer is incorrect, because the student mistakenly substituted the cost for the variable that represents the years since 1986.

To find the year when the cost was \$31.25, substitute 31.25 for x.

$y = 10.67 + 1.47x$

$= 10.67 + 1.47(31.25) \approx 56.61$

The cost was \$31.25 about 57 years after 1986, or in 2042.

SAMPLE 3: Partial credit solution

The equation and answer are correct. There are no explanations to support the student's work.

$$y = 10.67 + 1.47x$$
$$31.25 = 10.67 + 1.47x$$
$$14 = x$$

The monthly cost was $31.25 fourteen years after 1986, or in 2000.

SAMPLE 4: No credit solution

The student's reasoning is incorrect, and the equation is incorrect. The answer is incorrect.

Year when cost is $31.25 = $31.25 ÷ 1.47

$y = 31.25 \div 1.47 \approx 21.25$

The year is about 21 years after 1986, or in 2007.

PRACTICE Apply the Scoring Rubric

Score the solution to the problem below as *full credit, partial credit,* or *no credit. Explain* your reasoning.

PROBLEM A hot air balloon is flying at an altitude of 870 feet. It descends at a rate of 15 feet per minute. Write an equation that gives the altitude (in feet) of the balloon as a function of the time (in minutes) since it began its descent. Find the time it takes the balloon to reach an altitude of 12 feet. *Explain* your reasoning.

1. Let y be the altitude (in feet) after x minutes.

Final altitude	=	Starting altitude	+	Decrease in altitude per minute	•	Minutes

$y = 870 + (-15)x = 870 - 15(12) = 690$

The balloon will take 690 minutes to reach an altitude of 12 feet.

2. Let y be the altitude (in feet) after x minutes.

Final altitude	=	Starting altitude	+	Decrease in altitude per minute	•	Minutes

$y = 870 + (-15)x$
$12 = 870 - 15x$
$57.2 = x$

The balloon will take about 57 minutes to reach an altitude of 12 feet.

3. $870 \div 15 = 58$

The balloon will take 58 minutes to reach an altitude of 12 feet.

Answers

1. Partial credit; the equation is correct, and the student has explained what the variables represent. The answer is incorrect because the student mistakenly substituted the altitude for the variable that represents the time.

2. Full credit; a verbal model shows how the equation is obtained, and the student has explained what the variables represent. The correct calculations are performed and the question is answered correctly.

3. No credit; the student's reasoning is incorrect, and the equation is incorrect. The answer is incorrect.

5 ★ Standardized TEST PRACTICE

Answers

1. $3.5p + 5j = 50$; 14 boxes of pretzels; if you find the value of p when j is 0, $p = 14.29$. Because you cannot buy part of a box, the greatest number of boxes of pretzels you can buy is 14.

2a. $d = -60t + 180$

2b. The graph of this equation is a line with a negative slope because as the time increases the distance from home decreases.

3. $0.05n + 0.1d = 2.2$; 16 nickels; substitute 14 for d into the equation $0.05n + 0.1d = 2.2$ and solve for n.

4. $-\frac{1}{2}$; 2; write $x + 2y = 4$ in slope-intercept form, $y = -\frac{1}{2}x + 2$ to see that the slope of the line is $-\frac{1}{2}$. If the streets are parallel, the slopes are the same; if the streets are perpendicular then the slopes are negative reciprocals.

5a.

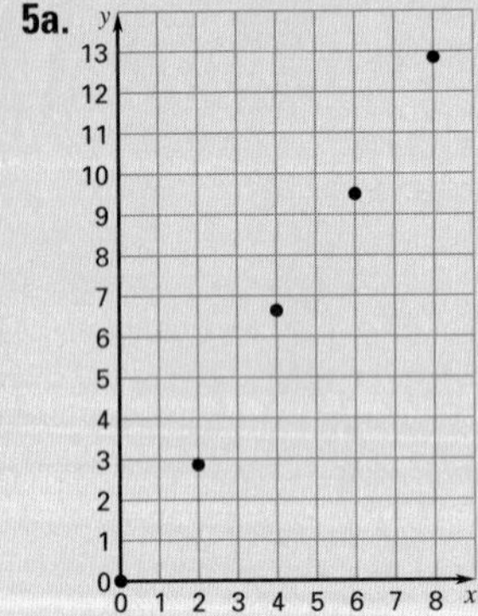

5b. 2010; find the equation of the line of best fit of the data, $y = 1.617x + 0.1$, substitute 20 for y and solve for x. $x = 12.4$, so 12.4 years after 1998 spending per person will reach $20.

6a. $d = 9t + 4$

6b. 40 min; substitute 10 for d and solve for t.

7a. Because there is an initial fee for the first hour and then a constant rate for hours after the first, this situation can be modeled by a linear equation.

7b. $y = 15x + 40$

8a. *Sample answer:* $y = 0.4x + 5.8$

SHORT RESPONSE

1. You have $50 to spend on pretzels and juice drinks for a school dance. A box of pretzels costs $3.50, and a package of juice drinks costs $5.00. Write an equation in standard form that models the possible combinations of boxes of pretzels and packages of juice drinks that you can buy. What is the greatest number of boxes of pretzels you can buy? *Explain.*

2. You and your family are traveling home in a car at an average speed of 60 miles per hour. At noon you are 180 miles from home.
   a. Write an equation that gives your distance from home (in miles) as a function of the number of hours since noon.
   b. *Explain* why the graph of this equation is a line with a negative slope.

3. Robyn needs $2.20 to buy a bag of trail mix. Write an equation in standard form that models the possible combinations of nickels and dimes she could use to pay for the mix. How many nickels would she need if she used 14 dimes? *Explain* your reasoning.

4. On a street map, Main Street and Maple Street can be modeled by the equations $y = ax + 6$ and $x + 2y = 4$. For what value of a are the streets parallel? For what value of a are the streets perpendicular? *Justify* your answers.

5. The table shows the projected dollar amount spent per person in the U.S. on interactive television for several years during the period 1998–2006.

Year	Spending per person (dollars)
1998	0
2000	2.86
2002	6.63
2004	9.50
2006	12.85

   a. Make a scatter plot of the data.
   b. Predict the year in which spending per person in the U.S. on interactive television will reach $20. *Explain* how you found your answer.

6. You are mountain biking on a 10 mile trail. You biked 4 miles before stopping to take a break. After your break, you bike at a rate of 9 miles per hour.
   a. Write an equation that gives the length (in miles) of the trail you have completed as a function of the number of hours since your break ended.
   b. How much time (in minutes) after your break will it take you to complete the entire trail? *Explain.*

7. A guide gives dogsled tours during the winter months. The guide charges one amount for the first hour of a tour and a different amount for each hour after the first. You paid $55 for a 2 hour dogsled tour. Your friend paid $70 for a 3 hour tour.
   a. *Explain* why this situation can be modeled by a linear equation.
   b. Write an equation that gives the cost (in dollars) of a dogsled tour as a function of the number of hours after the first hour of the tour.

8. The scatter plot shows the total carbon dioxide emissions throughout the world for several years during the period 1950–1995.

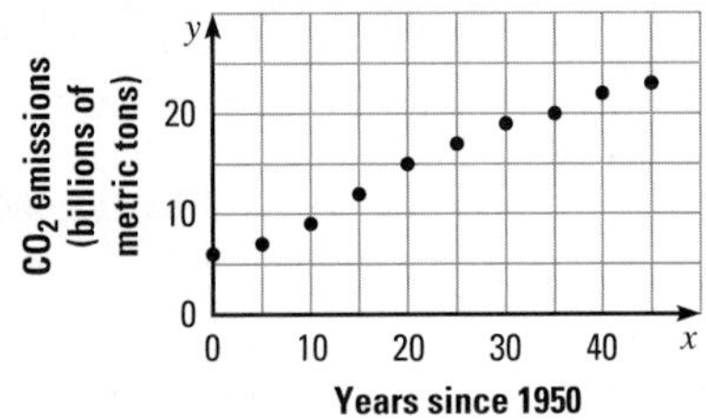

   a. Write an equation that models the carbon dioxide emissions (in billions of metric tons) as a function of the number of years since 1950.
   b. At about what rate did the amount of carbon dioxide emissions increase from 1950 to 1995? *Explain* how you found your answer.

8b. *Sample answer:* 0.4 billion metric tons of carbon dioxide emissions per year; the slope of the line is 0.4, which represents the reate of change.

MULTIPLE CHOICE

9. Which equation represents the line that passes through (0, 8) and (2, 0)?

   Ⓐ $y = 4x + 2$ Ⓑ $y = -4x + 2$

   Ⓒ $y = 4x + 8$ Ⓓ $y = -4x + 8$

10. Which equation represents the line with a slope of 5 and a y-intercept of 2?

   Ⓐ $y = 2x + 5$ Ⓑ $y = 2x - 5$

   Ⓒ $y = 5x + 2$ Ⓓ $y = 5x - 2$

11. Which function has the values $f(1) = 8$ and $f(7) = -10$?

   Ⓐ $f(x) = -3x + 11$ Ⓑ $f(x) = -2x + 10$

   Ⓒ $f(x) = -3x + 25$ Ⓓ $f(x) = 3x - 24$

GRIDDED ANSWER

12. What is the slope of a line that is perpendicular to the line $y = -2x - 7$?

13. What is the y-intercept of the line that has a slope of $\frac{1}{2}$ and passes through (5, 4)?

14. What is the y-intercept of the line that is parallel to the line $y = 2x - 3$ and passes through the point (6, 11)?

15. What is the zero of the function $f(x) = -\frac{4}{5}x + 9$?

16. The graph of the equation $Ax + y = 2$ is a line that passes through $(-2, 8)$. What is the value of A?

EXTENDED RESPONSE

17. The table shows the time several students spent studying for an exam and each student's grade on the exam.

Study time (hours)	1.5	0.5	0.5	1	1	3	2.5	3	0
Grade	90	60	70	72	80	88	89	94	58

   a. Make a scatter plot of the data.

   b. Write an equation that models a student's exam grade as a function of the time (in hours) the student spent studying for the exam.

   c. How many hours would you need to study in order to earn a grade of 93 on the exam? *Justify* your answer using the data above.

18. The scatter plot shows the number of FM radio stations in the United States for several years during the period 1994–2000.

   a. *Describe* the correlation of the data.

   b. Write an equation that models the number of FM radio stations in the United States as a function of the number of years since 1994.

   c. At about what rate did the number of radio stations change during the period 1994–2000?

   d. Find the zero of the function from part (b). *Explain* what the zero means in this situation.

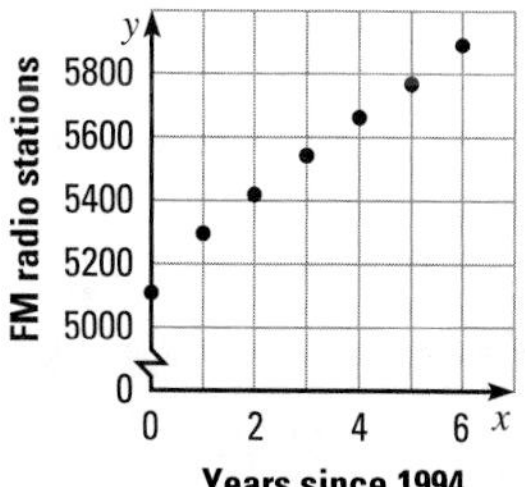

9. D

10. C

11. A

12. $\frac{1}{2}$

13. 1.5

14. −1

15. 11.25

16. 3

17a.

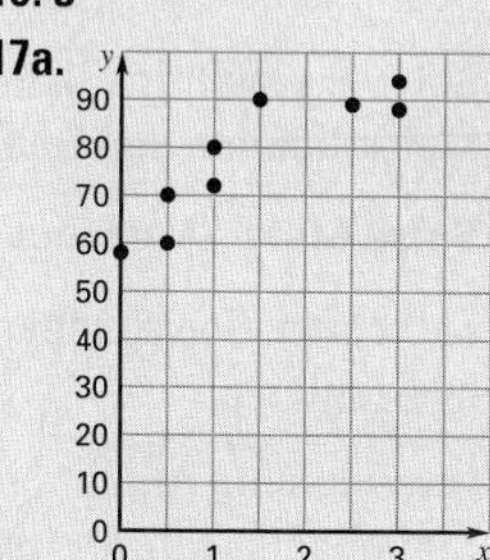

17b. $y = 10.6x + 62.6$

17c. About 2.9 h. *Sample answer:* The data shows that the only student to receive a grade of 93 or above studied for 3 hours and earned a 94. Therefore, to earn a grade of 93, you would need to study almost 3 hours.

18a. positive correlation

18b. *Sample answer:* $y = 128x + 5144$

18c. *Sample answer:* About 128 radio stations per year

18d. Sample answer: About −40; there were 0 radio stations 40 years before 1994.

6 Pacing Guide

Chapter 6: Solving and Graphing Linear Inequalities

Chapter Table of Contents

PACING GUIDES

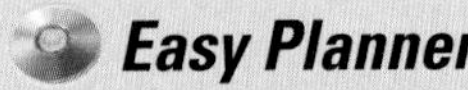 ***Easy Planner***

Regular Schedule (50-minute classes)

DAY 1	DAY 2	DAY 3	DAY 4	DAY 5	DAY 6
Lesson 6.1	Investigating Algebra Activity 6.2 Lesson 6.2	Quiz for Lessons 6.1–6.2 Lesson 6.3 Extension 6.3	Investigating Algebra Activity 6.4 Lesson 6.4	Lesson 6.4 (cont.) Graphing Calculator Activity 6.4 Mixed Review of Problem Solving	Quiz for Lessons 6.3–6.4 Lesson 6.5
DAY 7	**DAY 8**	**DAY 9**	**DAY 10**	**DAY 11**	**DAY 12**
Lesson 6.5 (cont.) Extension 6.5	Lesson 6.6	Investigating Algebra Activity 6.7 Lesson 6.7	Lesson 6.7 (cont.) Mixed Review of Problem Solving	Quiz for Lessons 6.5–6.7 Chapter Review	Chapter Test

Block Schedule (90-minute classes)

DAY 1	DAY 2	DAY 3	DAY 4	DAY 5	DAY 6
Lesson 6.1 Investigating Algebra Activity 6.2 Lesson 6.2	Quiz for Lessons 6.1–6.2 Lesson 6.3 Extension 6.3 Investigating Algebra Activity 6.4 Lesson 6.4	Lesson 6.4 (cont.) Graphing Calculator Activity 6.4 Mixed Review of Problem Solving Quiz for Lessons 6.3–6.4 Lesson 6.5	Lesson 6.5 (cont.) Extension 6.5 Lesson 6.6	Investigating Algebra Activity 6.7 Lesson 6.7 Mixed Review of Problem Solving	Quiz for Lessons 6.5–6.7 Chapter Review Chapter Test

RESOURCE OPTIONS

Chapter/Lesson Resources

Chapter Resource Book
- Parents as Partners
- Teaching Guide/Lesson Plan
- Activity Masters
- Practice (3 levels)
- Study Guide
- Quick Catch-Up for Absent Students
- Problem Solving/Application
- Challenge Practice
- Chapter Review Games and Activities
- Project with Rubric
- Cumulative Review

Notetaking Guide
- Student Workbook and Teacher's Edition

Practice Workbook

Worked-Out Solution Key

Chapter Transparency Book
- Warm-Up Exercises/Daily Homework Quiz
- Notetaking Guide Transparencies
- Homework Answer Transparencies

Teacher Tools Transparencies

Assessment

Assessment Book
- Quizzes
- Chapter Tests (3 levels)
- Standardized and SAT/ACT Chapter Tests
- Alternative Assessments
- Cumulative Tests

Benchmark Tests
- Benchmark Tests, correlated to Remediation Book
- Pre-Course, Mid-Year, and End-of-Year Tests
- Chapter Tests

Spanish Assessment Book

Differentiated Instruction

Differentiated Instruction Resources
- Strategies for Reading Mathematics
- Differentiated Instruction Lesson Notes
- English Learner Lesson Notes
- Inclusion Lesson Notes
- Teaching Strategies with Sample Worksheets
- Tips for New Teachers/Math Background Notes
- Teacher Survival Activities/Bulletin Board Ideas

Student Resources in Spanish

Spanish Study Guide

Remediation Book

Skills Readiness (available on Easy Planner)
- Diagnostic Assessment
- Skill Instruction and Alternative Teaching Strategies
- Skill Practice and Enrichment Masters

Pre-AP Resources
- Pacing and Assignment Guide
- Best Practices
- Copymasters

Technology Resources

Plan	***Easy Planner***
Teach	***Video Tutor*** ***Activity Generator*** ***Power Presentations*** ***Animated Algebra***
Assess	***Test Generator*** ***ML Assessment System***
Reteach	***@HomeTutor***
Online Resources	***Classzone.com*** ***eEdition*** ***eWorkbook***

Video Tutor

Technology Highlights for Each Lesson

Easy Planner

Easy access to the Teacher's Edition and all teaching resources. Includes a search feature to locate the materials you need.

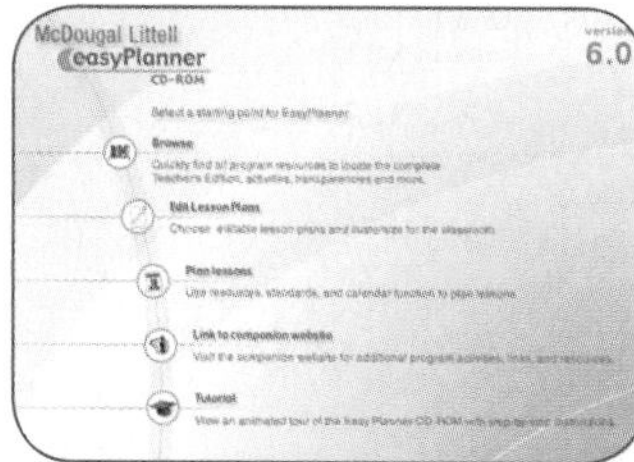

Activity Generator

Leveled, editable activities allow all students to explore a lesson's concepts. Includes teacher notes and closure questions.

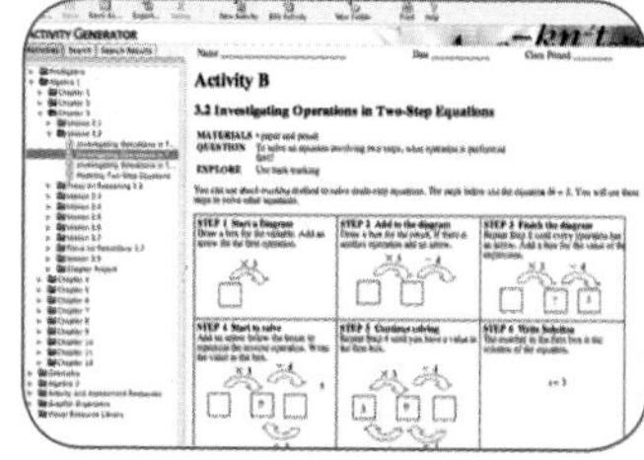

Animated Algebra

Interactive tutorials provide visually engaging alternative opportunities to learn concepts and master skills.

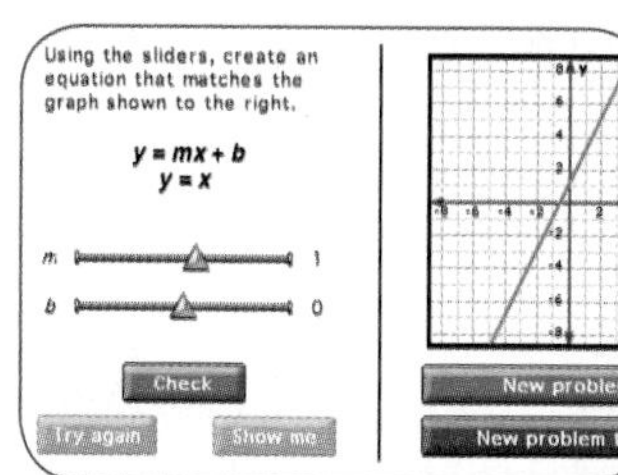

6 Lesson Practice Level B

LESSON 6.1

Practice B

For use with pages 356–361

Write an inequality that is represented by the graph.

1.
2.
3. 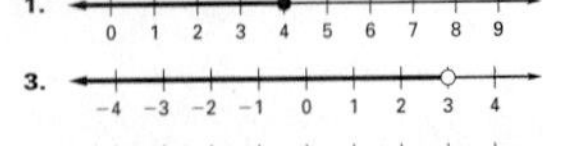
4. 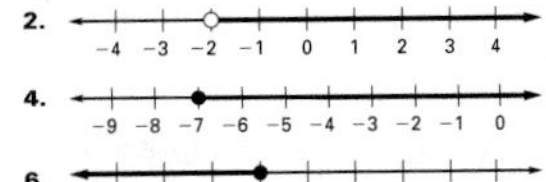
5.
6.

1. $x \le 4$ 2. $x > -2$ 3. $x < 3$ 4. $x \ge -7$ 5. $x < 0$ 6. $x \le -1$

Solve the inequality. Graph your solution.

7. $x + 7 > 1$ $x > -6$

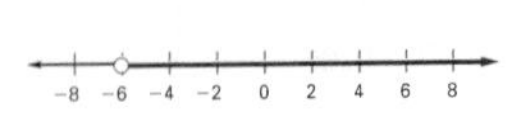

8. $n - 3 \le 9$ $n \le 12$

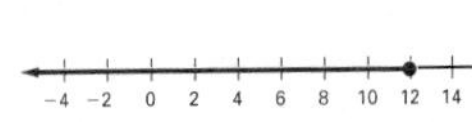

9. $10 \ge a + 7$ $a \le 3$

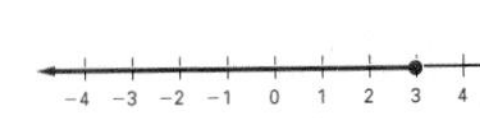

10. $m - 3 < -2$ $m < 1$

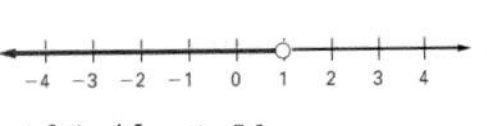

11. $p - 5 > -5$ $p > 0$

12. $x + 3 \le -4.5$ $x \le -7.5$

13. $b + 9.5 \le -6.4$ $b \le -15.9$

14. $y + 2.5 < 7.3$ $y < 4.8$

15. $z - 10.2 > 18.3$ $z > 28.5$

16. $d - 8 > 2.2$ $d > 10.2$

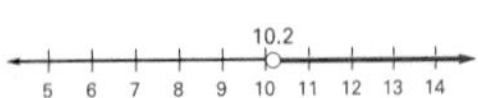

Write the verbal sentence as an inequality. Then solve the inequality and graph your solution.

17. The sum of 15 and n is less than 8. $15 + n < 8$; $n < -7$

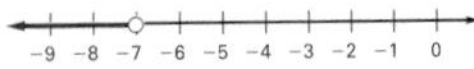

LESSON 6.1

Practice B *continued*

For use with pages 356–361

18. The difference of m and 3 is greater than or equal to 10. $m - 3 \ge 10$; $m \ge 13$

19. Twenty-four is less than or equal to the sum of 35 and x. $24 \le 35 + x$; $x \ge -11$

20. Eighty-five is greater than the difference of x and 63. $85 > x - 63$; $x < 148$

21. **Summer Reading** During the summer you want to read at least 32 books. You have read 21 books so far this summer. What are the possible numbers of books you can read to pass your goal? 11 books or more

22. **Baseball Hats** You are a big baseball fan. You have a goal of attending a baseball game in every major league stadium in the country. Every time you go to a different stadium, you buy a baseball hat. You keep your hats in a display case that holds 25 hats. You have 8 baseball hats so far. What are the possible numbers of hats you can collect without needing another display case? 17 hats or less

23. **Gift Card** You received a \$25 gift card to a sporting goods store for your birthday. You are looking at skateboards and want to spend no more than \$85 of your own money.
    a. Write and solve an inequality to find the prices p in dollars of skateboards you can buy. $p - 25 \le 85$; $p \le 110$
    b. What is the most expensive skateboard you can buy? A \$110 skateboard

24. **Video Games** You and your friend are having a video game competition. The person with the highest score after two games wins. The table shows your friend's first and second scores and your first score.

Game	Friend's score	Your score
1	6532	5034
2	4887	?

a. Write and solve an inequality to find the scores s that you can earn in your second game in order to beat your friend. $6532 + 4887 < 5034 + s$; $s > 6385$

b. Will you win if you earn 6392 points? 6385 points? 6377 points? *Justify* your answers. Yes, because $6392 > 6385$. No, because $6385 \not> 6385$; No, because $6377 \not> 6385$.

LESSON 6.2

Practice B

For use with pages 363–368

Match the verbal sentence with the inequality. Then solve the inequality.

1. The product of 3 and x is less than or equal to 18. C; $x \le 6$ **A.** $\frac{x}{18} \ge 3$
2. The product of 18 and x is greater than or equal to 3. B; $x \ge \frac{1}{6}$ **B.** $18x \ge 3$
3. The quotient of x and 18 is greater than or equal to 3. A; $x \ge 54$ **C.** $3x \le 18$

Solve the inequality. Graph your solution.

4. $3y \ge 4$ $y \ge \frac{4}{3}$
5. $\frac{x}{2} < 6$ $x < 12$
6. $\frac{m}{5} > -5$ $m > -25$
7. $\frac{c}{-10} \le -2$ $c \ge 20$
8. $8n > -1$ $n > -\frac{1}{8}$
9. $42 < 6z$ $z > 7$
10. $-5p \le 2$ $p \ge -\frac{2}{5}$
11. $\frac{w}{-4} < 8$ $w > -32$
12. $-7a \ge -3$ $a \le \frac{3}{7}$
13. $52 \le -13x$ $x \le -4$
14. $0.25x > 18$ $x > 72$
15. $-2d < 3$ $d > -\frac{3}{2}$

LESSON 6.2

Practice B *continued*

For use with pages 363–368

Write the verbal sentence as an inequality. Then solve the inequality and graph your solution.

16. The product of 12 and y is greater than or equal to 60. $12y \ge 60$; $y \ge 5$

17. The product of 7 and b is less than -35. $7b < -35$; $b < -5$

18. The quotient of m and 2 is greater than 23. $\frac{m}{2} > 23$; $m > 46$

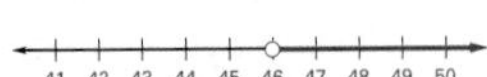

19. The quotient of p and 4.5 is less than or equal to 10. $\frac{p}{4.5} \le 10$; $p \le 45$

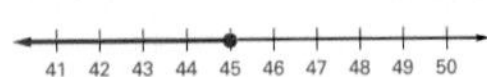

20. **Flower Beds** You are in charge of buying the flowers for the flower beds around your school. You cannot spend over \$80 on flowers. The flowers cost \$10.99 for a flat of flowers. What are the possible numbers of flats of flowers you can buy? 7 flats or less

21. **Pavilion Rental** You and three of your friends decide to rent a pavilion at a local park for an end-of-the-school-year party. The group budget is \$80. The group decides to split the cost equally.
    a. What are the possible amounts of money that each of you can spend? \$20 or less
    b. If two more of your friends decide to pitch in for the party, what are the possible amounts of money that each of you can spend if you all split the cost equally? about \$13.33 or less

22. **Waiting Tables** Restaurants typically pay wait staff an hourly wage that is lower than minimum wage. The wait staff is expected to make up the difference in tips. The minimum wage is \$7.25 per hour and a restaurant pays the wait staff \$6.10 per hour.
    a. If a waitress works an 8-hour shift, write and solve an inequality that gives the total tips t in dollars that the waitress must earn in an 8-hour shift in order to meet or exceed the minimum wage. $\frac{t}{8} \ge 1.15$; $t \ge \$9.20$
    b. If the waitress makes \$10.40 in tips during an 8-hour shift, will she meet or exceed the minimum wage? By how much? yes; by \$1.20
    c. If the waitress makes \$9.20 in tips during an 8-hour shift, will she meet or exceed the minimum wage? By how much? yes; by \$0

LESSON 6.3

Practice B

For use with pages 369–374

Solve the inequality. Graph your solution.

1. $4x - 7 \geq 1$ $x \geq 2$
2. $7p + 3 < -11$ $p < -2$
3. $8 - 2n \geq 26$ $n \leq -9$
4. $3(a - 4) \leq 33$ $a \leq 15$
5. $6(y + 1) > 6$ $y > 0$
6. $-2(c - 1) < -22$ $c > 12$
7. $8m - 7 < 4m + 5$ $m < 3$

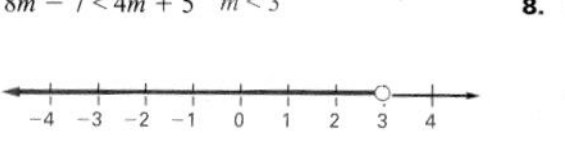

8. $10 - 11d > -5d - 4$ $d < \frac{7}{3}$
9. $9z \leq -7z + 14$ $z \leq \frac{7}{8}$

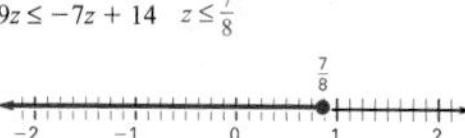

10. $6w + 3 < 2w + 15$ $w < 3$

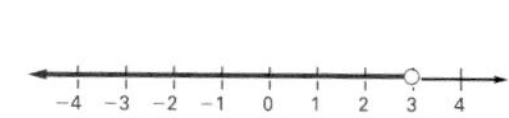

Solve the inequality, if possible.

11. $6y - 9 \leq 4y + 2y - 16$ no solution
12. $7p - 11p + 3 \geq 3 - 4p$ all real numbers
13. $4(c - 5) < 2(c - 10)$ $c < 0$
14. $5(a - 3) \leq 5a - 6$ all real numbers
15. $6(x - 8) > 6x - 48$ no solution
16. $2(3d - 4) < 4 + 6d - 15$ no solution
17. $4m + 14 - 2m \leq 2(m + 7)$ all real numbers
18. $-2(n - 3) \geq 1 - 2n + 5$ all real numbers
19. $4(3 - 2x) > 2(6 - 4x)$ no solution
20. $2(5 - a) > 4a + 13 - 6a$ no solution
21. $-4n + 11 < -4(n + 6)$ no solution
22. $3(5 - 6x) \leq 2(11 - 9x)$ all real numbers
23. $2m + 10 - 7m \leq 5(4 - m)$ all real numbers
24. $6(1-2n) \leq 5 - 12n$ no solution

LESSON 6.3

Practice B *continued*

For use with pages 369–374

Translate the verbal phrase into an inequality. Then solve the inequality and graph your solution.

25. Six more than 5 times a number x is greater than or equal to 31. $6 + 5x \geq 31; x \geq 5$

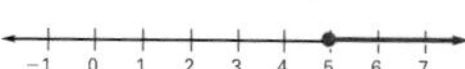

26. Twice the sum of 4 and x is less than -16. $2(4 + x) < -16; x < -12$

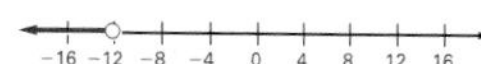

27. The difference of $10x$ and $3x$ is less than or equal to the sum of $4x$ and 21. $10x - 3x \leq 4x + 21; x \leq 7$

28. The sum of $2x$ and $4x$ is greater than or equal to the sum of $2x$ and 36. $2x + 4x \geq 2x + 36; x \geq 9$

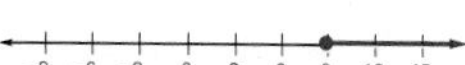

29. The difference of $2x$ and 15 is less than or equal to the sum of $4x$ and 17. $2x - 15 \leq 4x + 17; x \geq -16$

30. **Weaving** A weaver spends \$420 on supplies to make wall hangings and plans to sell the wall hangings for \$80 each.
    a. Write an inequality that gives the possible numbers w of wall hangings the weaver needs to sell in order for the profit to be positive. $80w - 420 > 0$
    b. What are the possible numbers of wall hangings the weaver needs to sell in order for the profit to be positive? 6 wall hangings or more

31. **School Spirit** Your club is in charge of making pins that students can buy to show their school spirit for the upcoming football game. You have made 225 pins so far, and you only have 2 hours left to make the rest of the pins. You need to make at least 400 pins.
    a. Write an inequality that gives the possible numbers p of pins you have to make per minute in order to exceed your goal. $225 + 120p \geq 400$
    b. What are the possible numbers of pins you have to make per minute in order to exceed your goal? 1.5 pins or more

32. **Aquarium** You are getting a larger aquarium for your neon tetra fish and you also want to add more neon tetras to the larger aquarium. The general rule is that each fish needs 2 gallons of water. You currently have 6 neon tetras. If you buy a 20-gallon aquarium, what are the possible numbers of additional fish you can put in your aquarium? *Explain* how you got your answer. At most 4 additional fish; First find the number of gallons needed by the 6 fish by finding the product of 6 and 2, which is 12. Then subtract this amount from 20 to get 8, the number of gallons left for new fish. Then solve the inequality $2f \leq 8$, where f is the number of new fish.

LESSON 6.4

Practice B

For use with pages 380–387

Translate the verbal phrase into an inequality. Then graph the inequality.

1. All real numbers that are less than or equal to -3 *and* greater than or equal to -8 $-8 \leq x \leq -3$

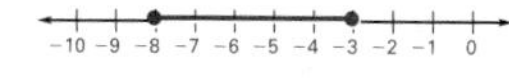

2. All real numbers that are greater than 5 *or* less than or equal to -1 $x \leq -1$ *or* $x > 5$

3. All real numbers that are greater than or equal to -2.5 *and* less than 3.5 $-2.5 \leq x < 3.5$

Solve the inequality. Graph your solution.

4. $-3 < x + 1 \leq 5$ $-4 < x \leq 4$

5. $-7 < x - 8 < 2$ $1 < x < 10$
6. $-5 < -5x \leq 20$ $-4 \leq x < 1$

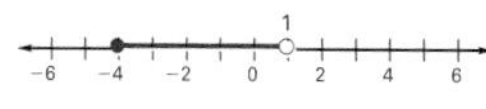

7. $0 \leq 2(x - 3) < 8$ $3 \leq x < 7$
8. $3x + 2 < 8$ *or* $-x + 3 < -2$ $x < 2$ *or* $x > 5$

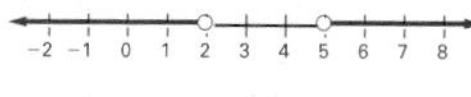

9. $2(x + 4) < 6$ *or* $-x - 3 \leq -7$ $x < -1$ *or* $x \geq 4$
10. $5x < -30$ *or* $x + 10 > 7$ $x < -6$ *or* $x > -3$

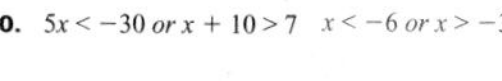

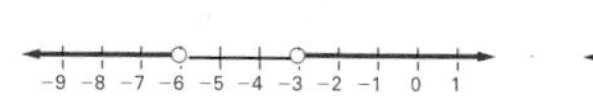

11. $3x + 5 \leq 1$ *or* $8 - x < 5$ $x \leq -\frac{4}{3}$ *or* $x > 3$

LESSON 6.4

Practice B *continued*

For use with pages 380–387

Write the verbal sentence as an inequality. Then solve the inequality and graph your solution.

12. Three times x is less than -6 *and* greater than -21. $-21 < 3x < -6; -7 < x < -2$

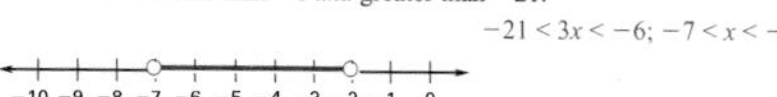

13. One less than x is less than -1 *or* 3 more than x is greater than or equal to 7. $x - 1 < -1$ *or* $3 + x \geq 7; x < 0$ *or* $x \geq 4$
14. The difference of $2x$ and 5 is greater than -3 *and* less than or equal to 11. $-3 < 2x - 5 \leq 11; 1 < x \leq 8$
15. The sum of $3x$ and 1 is greater than -5 *and* less than or equal to 10. $-5 < 3x + 1 \leq 10; -2 < x \leq 3$

16. **Temperature** The high temperature in a city last year was 95°F. The low temperature in this city last year was −5°F. Write and graph a compound inequality that represents the temperatures T throughout the year. $-5 \leq T \leq 95$

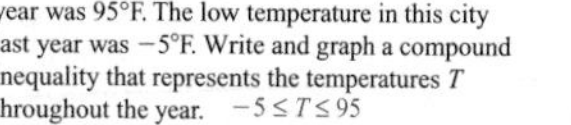

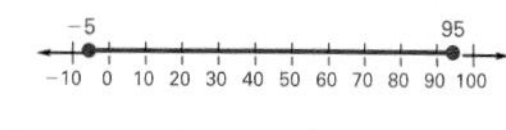

17. **Pollen Count** Weather forecasts will often give reports on the pollen count. For people suffering from allergies, the pollen count indicates the severity of their symptoms. If a pollen count is high, the severity of the symptoms are increased. The table shows ranges for high, medium, and low pollen counts. Write an inequality to find the range at which the pollen count is not medium. $x \leq 4$ *or* $x > 8$

Pollen Count	High	Medium	Low
Range	Greater than 8	Greater than 4 and less than or equal to 8	Less than or equal to 4

18. **Distances** You live 5 miles from work and the gym you go to is 3 miles from work.
    a. Find the minimum distance d between your home and the gym. 2 mi
    b. Find the maximum distance d between your home and the gym. 8 mi
    c. Write an inequality that describes the possible distances d between your home and the gym. $2 \leq d \leq 8$

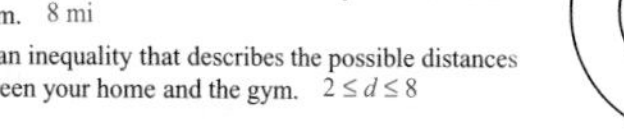

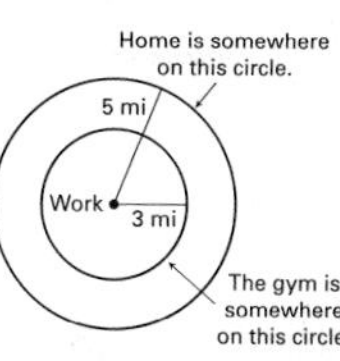

6 Lesson Practice Level B

LESSON 6.5

Practice B

For use with pages 390–397

13. $x = -6, 0$ **14.** $x = 4, 12$ **15.** $x = -\frac{7}{2}, -\frac{5}{2}$
16. no solution **17.** $x = -\frac{3}{2}, 0$ **18.** $x = -\frac{9}{2}, -\frac{1}{2}$
19. no solution **20.** $x = \frac{5}{2}, \frac{17}{6}$ **21.** no solution

Solve the equation.

1. $|x| = 9$ $x = -9, 9$
2. $|x| = 2.25$ $x = -2.25, 2.25$
3. $|x| = \frac{3}{2}$ $x = -\frac{3}{2}, \frac{3}{2}$
4. $|x - 6| = 14$ $x = -8, 20$
5. $|x + 1| = 8$ $x = -9, 7$
6. $|2x - 3| = 15$ $x = -6, 9$
7. $|4x + 1| = 15$ $x = -4, \frac{7}{2}$
8. $|7x + 2| = 23$ $x = -\frac{25}{7}, 3$
9. $|5 - 2x| = 9$ $x = -2, 7$
10. $3|2x - 2| = 18$ $x = -2, 4$
11. $4|5x - 1| = 36$ $x = -\frac{8}{5}, 2$
12. $2|6x + 5| - 1 = 25$ $x = -3, \frac{4}{3}$

Solve the equation, if possible. See above.

13. $|x + 3| - 4 = -1$
14. $|x - 8| - 9 = -5$
15. $|x + 3| + 2.5 = 3$
16. $-6|10 - 2x| = 24$
17. $-3|4x + 3| = -9$
18. $-4|5 + 2x| = -16$
19. $-\frac{1}{3}|1 - 8x| = 2$
20. $|3x - 8| + 0.25 = 0.75$
21. $|6x + 5| - 1.3 = -1.9$

Find the values of x that satisfy the definition of absolute value for the given value and the given absolute deviation.

22. Given value: 3; absolute deviation: 5
23. Given value: 1; absolute deviation: 7
24. Given value: −4; absolute deviation: 2
25. Given value: −2.5; absolute deviation: 8

22. $x = -2, 8$ **23.** $x = -6, 8$ **24.** $x = -6, -2$ **25.** $x = -10.5, 5.5$

26. **Food Scale** Bakers will typically weigh out flour for recipes rather than use a measuring cup because weighing is a more accurate measure. A baker is using a scale that has an absolute error of 0.05 gram.
    a. Find the minimum and maximum possible weights if the scale is used to measure out 225 grams of flour. 224.95 g; 225.05 g
    b. Find the minimum and maximum possible weights if the scale is used to measure out 300 grams of flour. 299.95 g; 300.05 g
    c. Find the minimum and maximum possible weights if the scale is used to measure out 420 grams of flour. 419.95 g; 420.05 g
27. **Toothpaste Prices** The average price of the brand of toothpaste that you buy is \$2.49 for an 8.2-ounce tube. Depending on where you shop, the prices vary by as much as \$.15.
    a. Write an absolute value equation that represents the minimum and maximum prices of the toothpaste. $|x - 2.49| = 0.15$
    b. Find the minimum and maximum prices of the toothpaste. \$2.34; \$2.64
    c. You have a coupon for \$.50 off two tubes of toothpaste. If you go to the store that has the minimum price for the toothpaste, how much will you pay for two tubes? \$4.18

LESSON 6.5

LESSON 6.6

Practice B

For use with pages 398–403

Solve the inequality. Graph your solution.

1. $|x| \geq 5$ $x \leq -5$ *or* $x \geq 5$

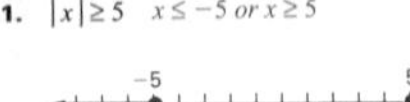

2. $|x| < 6.5$ $-6.5 < x < 6.5$

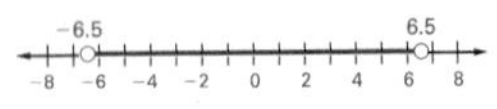

3. $|x| \geq \frac{3}{2}$ $x \leq -\frac{3}{2}$ *or* $x \geq \frac{3}{2}$
4. $|x - 6| \leq 1$ $5 \leq x \leq 7$

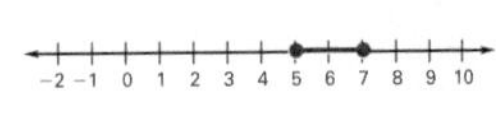

5. $|x + 7| > 11$ $x < -18$ *or* $x > 4$
6. $|10 - x| < 2$ $8 < x < 12$
7. $|-x - 5| < 1$ $-6 < x < -4$
8. $|2x + 1| \geq 5$ $x \leq -3$ *or* $x \geq 2$
9. $|3x - 2| \leq 7$ $-\frac{5}{3} \leq x \leq 3$
10. $|8 - 3x| \geq 7$ $x \leq \frac{1}{3}$ *or* $x \geq 5$
11. $\left|\frac{1}{2}x - 4\right| > 20$ $x < -32$ *or* $x > 48$

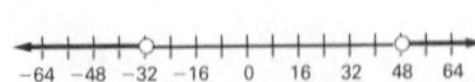

12. $\left|1 - \frac{4}{3}x\right| < 5$ $-3 < x < 4.5$

Write the verbal sentence as an inequality. Then solve the inequality and graph your solution.

13. The distance between x and 8 is less than 14. $|x - 8| < 14$; $-6 < x < 22$

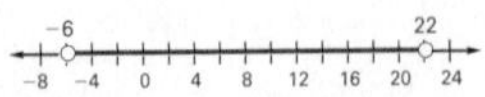

LESSON 6.6

LESSON 6.6

Practice B *continued*

For use with pages 398–403

14. The distance between x and −5 is greater than or equal to 12. $|x + 5| \geq 12$; $x \leq -17$ *or* $x \geq 7$
15. The distance between 9 and x is less than or equal to 8. $|9 - x| \leq 8$; $1 \leq x \leq 17$

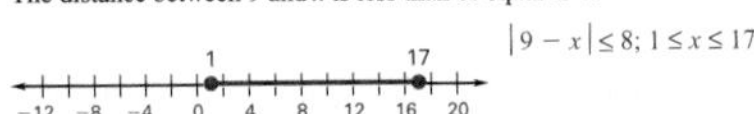

16. The distance between 10 and $2x$ is greater than 34. $|10 - 2x| > 34$; $x < -12$ *or* $x > 22$

Tell whether the statement is *true* or *false*. If it is false, give a counterexample.

17. If a is a solution of $|x + 4| < 7$, then a is also a solution of $x + 4 < 7$. true
18. If a is a solution of $|x - 6| \geq 4$, then a is also a solution of $x - 6 \leq -4$. true
19. **DVDs** The average price of a standard DVD is \$15.99 with a standard deviation of \$4. Write an absolute value inequality that describes this range in prices. $|x - 15.99| \leq 4$
20. **Body Temperature** A canine's body temperature is considered to be normal if it is 101°F with an absolute deviation of 1.5°F. $|x - 101| \leq 1.5$
    a. Write an absolute value inequality that represents the normal temperature range.
    b. Solve the inequality. What is the normal temperature range? At least 99.5°F and at most 102.5°F
21. **Baseball** A baseball should weigh 5.12 ounces with an absolute deviation of 0.035 ounce. The circumference of a baseball should be 9.05 inches with an absolute deviation of 0.05 inch.
    a. Write absolute value inequalities that represent the ranges for the weight and circumference of a baseball. weight: $|x - 5.12| \leq 0.035$; circumference: $|x - 9.05| \leq 0.05$
    b. Is a ball that weighs 5.16 ounces and has a circumference of 9 inches within the ranges that it should be? *Explain* why or why not. No, because the ball weighs too much.
    c. What are the maximum and minimum circumferences of a baseball? 9.1 in.; 9 in.
    d. What are the maximum and minimum weights of a baseball? 5.155 oz; 5.085 oz

LESSON 6.6

LESSON 6.7

Practice B

For use with pages 405–412

Tell whether the ordered pair is a solution of the inequality.

1. $x + y > -9$; $(0, 0)$ yes

2. $x - y \geq 8$; $(14, 9)$ no

3. $2x - y > 4$; $(-6, -15)$ no

4. $2x + y > -5$; $(-5, 12)$ yes

5. $5x + 2y \leq 8$; $(-3, 6)$ yes

6. $4x - 3y \geq -5$; $(6, 8)$ yes

7. $0.5x + 2.5y \geq 2$; $(0, 0)$ no

8. $1.2x - 3.1y < 4$; $(3, -1)$ no

9. $0.2y - 0.5x > -1$; $(-4, -8)$ yes

Graph the inequality.

10. $y - x < 6$

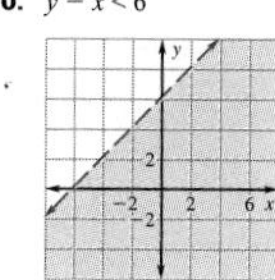

11. $x - y > -4$

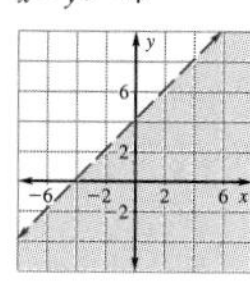

12. $2y - x < 2$

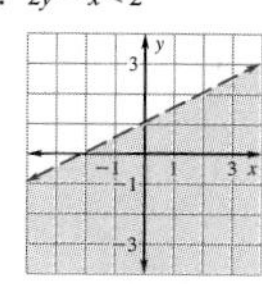

13. $4y \leq 6x - 2$

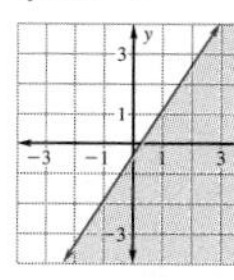

14. $5y \leq 10x + 15$

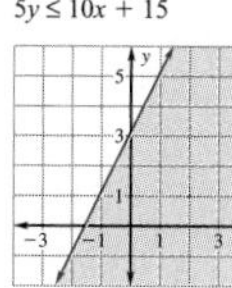

15. $6y + 3 \geq -18x$

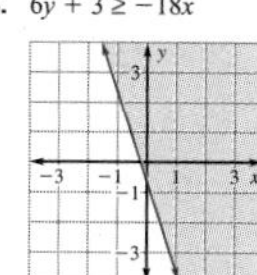

16. $2(y + 3) < 4x$

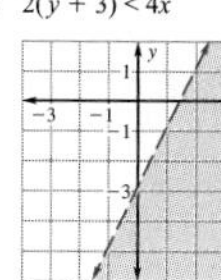

17. $2y - 3x \geq -8$

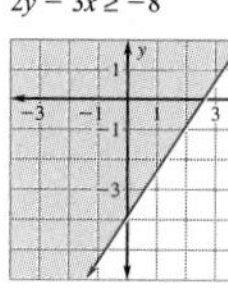

18. $2(x - y) < -5$

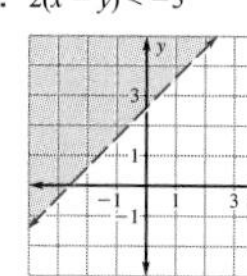

19. $y > 7$

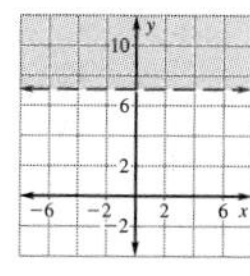

20. $x \leq -5$

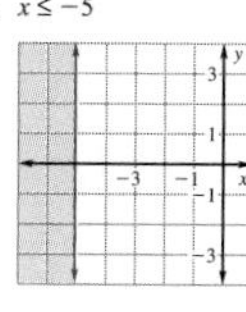

21. $y < -4$

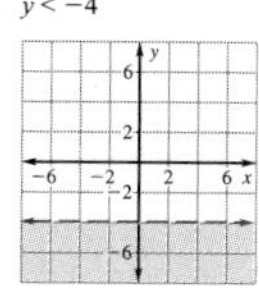

LESSON 6.7

LESSON 6.7

Practice B *continued*

For use with pages 405–412

Write an inequality of the graph shown.

22.

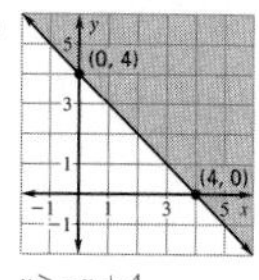

$y \geq -x + 4$

23.

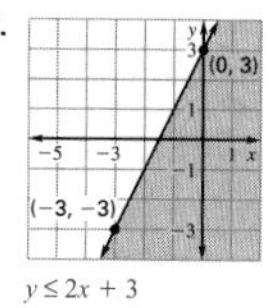

$y \leq 2x + 3$

24.

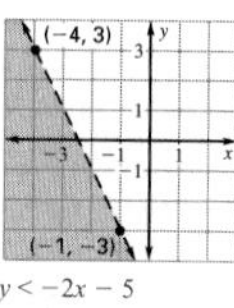

$y < -2x - 5$

25. Clothes You are going clothes shopping and can spend at most $130 on clothes. It costs $30 for a pair of pants and $22 for a shirt. Let x represent the number of pants you can buy. Let y represent the number of shirts you can buy.

a. Write and graph an inequality that describes the different number of shirts and pants you can buy. $30x + 22y \leq 130$

b. Give three possible combinations of pants and shirts that you can buy. Answers will vary.

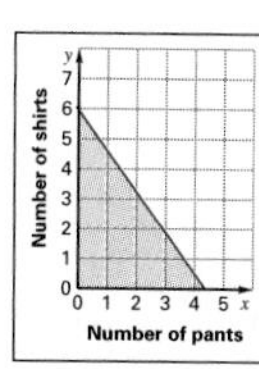

26. Window The area of the window shown is less than 42 square feet. Let x and y represent the heights of the triangular and rectangular portions of the window, respectively.

a. Write and graph an inequality that describes the different dimensions of the window. $4y + 2x < 42$

b. Could the height of the triangular portion be 2 feet and the height of the rectangular portion be 8 feet? yes

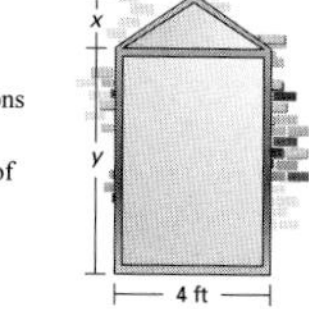

Height of rectangular portion

Height of triangular portion

LESSON 6.7

6 Assessment

CHAPTER 6 Quiz 1
For use after Lessons 6.1–6.2

Solve the inequality. Graph your solution.

1. $y - 9 < -4$

−6 −4 −2 0 2 4 6

2. $4 + m \geq 1$

−6 −4 −2 0 2 4 6

3. $k + 12 \leq 3$

−12 −9 −6 −3 0 3 6

4. $-1 > p - 8$

−2 0 2 4 6 8 10

5. $-15 \leq 3d$

−6 −4 −2 0 2 4 6

6. $-2t > -16$

−2 0 2 4 6 8 10

7. $\frac{b}{3} < 2$

−6 −4 −2 0 2 4 6

8. $48 \geq -4n$

−12 −9 −6 −3 0 3 6

9. $\frac{h}{-5} > 7$

−37 −35 −33 −31

10. You are buying pizzas for a neighborhood party. Each pizza costs \$9. If you have \$72, what are the possible numbers of pizzas that you can buy?

Answers

1. $y < 5$; See left.
2. $m \geq -3$; See left.
3. $k \leq -9$; See left.
4. $p < 7$; See left.
5. $d \geq -5$; See left.
6. $t < 8$; See left.
7. $b < 6$; See left.
8. $n \geq -12$; See left.
9. $h < -35$; See left.
10. 1 to 8 pizzas

CHAPTER 6 Quiz 2
For use after Lessons 6.3–6.4

Solve the inequality, if possible.

1. $5x + 7 \geq 2$
2. $8x - 9 < -2x + 11$
3. $4(3x - 2) > 12(x + 1)$
4. $-3(x - 2) \leq -3x + 7$
5. $x + 3 \leq -2$ *or* $10x - 3 > x + 15$
6. $\frac{1}{2}(x + 10) > -(x + 1)$

Answers

1. $x \geq -1$
2. $x < 2$
3. no solution
4. all real numbers
5. $x \leq -5$ *or* $x > 2$
6. $x > -4$

CHAPTER 6 Quiz 3
For use after Lessons 6.5–6.7

Solve the equation.

1. $|x| = 0.3$
2. $|x + 4| = 2$
3. $2|5x - 1| = 8$

Solve the inequality. Graph your solution.

4. $|x| \geq 5$

−6 −4 −2 0 2 4 6

5. $|3x - 2| < 2$

$\frac{4}{3}$

−3 −2 −1 0 1 2 3

6. $2|x + 3| - 1 \leq 3$

−6 −4 −2 0 2 4 6

Graph the inequality.

7. $y > 3x - 2$

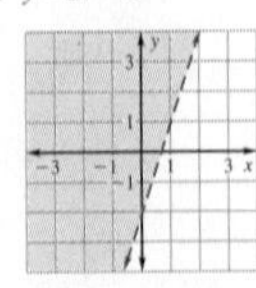

8. $4x + y \leq 0$

9. $x \geq 3$

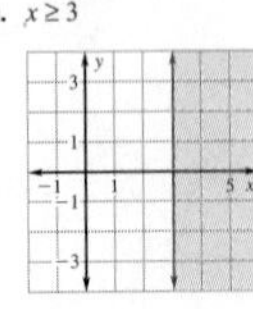

Answers

1. 0.3 and −0.3
2. −2 and −6
3. 1 and $-\frac{3}{5}$
4. $x \leq -5$ *or* $x \geq 5$; See left.
5. $0 < x < \frac{4}{3}$; See left.
6. $-5 \leq x \leq -1$; See left.
7. See left.
8. See left.
9. See left.

CHAPTER 6 Chapter Test B
For use after Chapter 6

Solve the inequality. Graph your solution.

1. $x + 8 > -10$

−20 −16 −12 −8 −4 0

2. $\frac{y}{-4} < -3$

6 8 10 12 14 16 18

3. $7 - 5d < -3$

−4 −2 0 2 4

4. $4a - 8 < 2a$

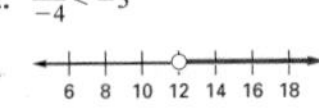

−4 −3 −2 −1 0 1 2 3 4

In Exercises 5 and 6, use the following information.

To be eligible for the playoffs, a baseball team cannot lose more than 40% of its remaining games. The team has 18 games remaining in the regular season.

5. Write and solve an inequality to find the number of games g that the team could lose and still be eligible for the playoffs.
6. If the baseball team loses 8 of its remaining games, will the team advance to the playoffs? Explain your answer.

Solve the inequality, if possible.

7. $2(3x - 1) > 6(x + 1)$
8. $3(2p - 5) \geq 8p - 5$
9. $5(2s + 7) - 4 > 10s - 7$

Translate the verbal statement into an inequality. Then solve the inequality.

10. Five-eighths of a number x is greater than or equal to −10.
11. The difference of 9 and $3x$ is less than or equal to −6.

In Exercises 12 and 13, use the following information.

The photography club at your school decides to publish a calendar to raise money. The initial cost for equipment and software is \$600. In addition to the initial cost, each calendar costs \$2.50 to produce. The club plans to sell the calendars for \$8 each.

12. Write and solve an inequality to find the number n of calendars that the photography club must sell in order to raise at least \$1200.
13. Will the club reach their fundraising goal if they sell 110 calendars? Explain your answer.

Answers

1. $x > -18$; See left.
2. $y > 12$; See left.
3. $d > 2$; See left.
4. $a < 4$; See left.
5. $\frac{g}{18} \leq 0.40$; $g \leq 7.2$
6. No, the team can lose at most 7 games.
7. no solution
8. $p \leq -5$
9. all real numbers
10. $\frac{5}{8}x \geq -10$; $x \geq -16$
11. $9 - 3x \leq -6$; $x \geq 5$
12. $8n - 2.50n - 600 \geq 1200$; $n \geq \frac{3600}{11}$
13. No, they must sell at least 328 calendars.

CHAPTER 6 Chapter Test B
For use after Chapter 6

Solve the compound inequality. Graph your solution.

14. $5 - x > 2$ *or* $5 \le x - 7$

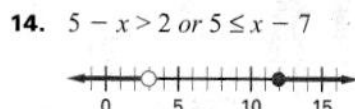

15. $-10 \le 2(x - 1) < 14$

16. The water pressure p (in pounds per square inch) exerted on an object in the ocean can be given by the function $p = 15 + \frac{6}{11}d$ where d is the depth (in feet) below the surface of the water. What are the possible water pressures of an object when the depth ranges from 102 feet to 468 feet?

Solve the equation or inequality, if possible.

17. $|3x - 1| = 2$

18. $2|x| - 7 = 3$

19. $2|x + 8| + 6 = 0$

20. $|x - 2| + 6 > 9$

21. $-2|4 - x| \le -4$

22. $|2x - 8| < 0$

Graph the inequality.

23. $y > -3x - 2$

24. $x - 3y < 6$

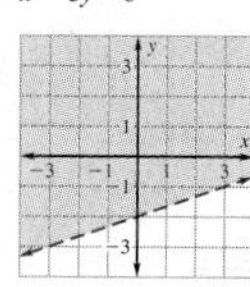

In Exercises 25 and 26, use the following information.

A concert promoter needs to take in at least $380,000 from ticket sales. The promoter charges $30 for floor seats and $20 for bleacher seats.

25. Write and graph an inequality that describes his goal in terms of selling bleacher seat tickets and selling floor seat tickets.

26. Identify and interpret one of the solutions.

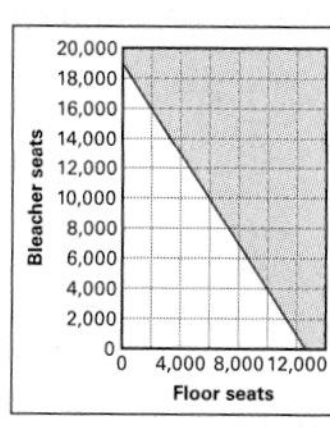

Answers

14. $x < 3$ *or* $x \ge 12$; See left.
15. $-4 \le x < 8$; See left.
16. The pressure is between $70\frac{7}{11}$ lb/in.^{2} and $270\frac{3}{11}$ lb/in.^{2}.
17. $x = -\frac{1}{3}$; $x = 1$
18. $x = \pm 5$
19. no solution
20. $x > 5$ or $x < -1$
21. $x \le 2$ or $x \ge 6$
22. no solution
23. See left.
24. See left.
25. $30x + 20y \ge 380{,}000$; See left.
26. *Sample answer:* (10,000, 12,000); He could sell 10,000 tickets for floor seats and 12,000 tickets for bleacher seats.

CHAPTER 6 Standardized Test
For use after Chapter 6

Multiple Choice

1. Which inequality is represented by the graph? D

Ⓐ $x + 9 > 24$ Ⓑ $x + 7 \ge 22$
Ⓒ $x - 5 < 10$ Ⓓ $x - 7 \le 8$

2. Which inequality is equivalent to $3.4 \ge p - 2.3$? B

Ⓐ $1.1 \ge p$ Ⓑ $p \le 5.7$
Ⓒ $p \ge 1.1$ Ⓓ $5.7 \le p$

3. Which inequality represents the sentence "The difference of r and 12 is less than or equal to 22."? A

Ⓐ $r - 12 \le 22$ Ⓑ $r - 12 > 22$
Ⓒ $r - 12 \ge 22$ Ⓓ $r - 12 < 22$

4. You need to buy 5 notebooks but only have $6 to spend. Which inequality can you use to find the possible number of notebooks that you can afford if n represents the price of one notebook? B

Ⓐ $5n < 6$ Ⓑ $5n \le 6$
Ⓒ $\frac{5}{n} < 6$ Ⓓ $\frac{5}{n} \le 6$

5. Which inequality is equivalent to $\frac{m}{-8} > 7$? D

Ⓐ $m > 56$ Ⓑ $m < 56$
Ⓒ $m > -56$ Ⓓ $m < -56$

6. Which inequality represents the sentence "The product of w and 12 is greater than 54."? C

Ⓐ $\frac{w}{12} > 54$ Ⓑ $\frac{w}{12} < 54$
Ⓒ $12w > 54$ Ⓓ $12w < 54$

7. What is the first step in solving the inequality $5x - 12 < 18$? B

Ⓐ Subtract 12 from each side of the inequality.
Ⓑ Add 12 to each side of the inequality.
Ⓒ Multiply each side of the inequality by 5.
Ⓓ Divide each side of the inequality by 5.

8. Which inequality is equivalent to $\frac{1}{2}f + 5 < 21$? D

Ⓐ $f < 16$ Ⓑ $f < 13$
Ⓒ $f < 8$ Ⓓ $f < 32$

9. Which inequality is equivalent to $5(r - 2) \le -10r + 5$? A

Ⓐ $r \le 1$ Ⓑ $r \ge 1$
Ⓒ $r \le \frac{7}{15}$ Ⓓ $r \ge \frac{7}{15}$

10. For which values of m and n are all the solutions of $mx - n < 0$ negative? C

Ⓐ $m > 0, n > 0$ Ⓑ $m < 0, n < 0$
Ⓒ $m > 0, n < 0$ Ⓓ $m > 0, n = 0$

11. Which inequality is equivalent to $4 \le \frac{2}{3}(9x + 15) < 34$? B

Ⓐ $-\frac{11}{6} \le x < \frac{19}{6}$ Ⓑ $-1 \le x < 4$
Ⓒ $\frac{14}{6} \le x < \frac{44}{6}$ Ⓓ $-36 \le x < 144$

12. Which inequality represents the verbal phrase "All real numbers that are greater than or equal to $-5\frac{1}{3}$ *and* less than $25\frac{2}{3}$"? A

Ⓐ $-5\frac{1}{3} \le x < 25\frac{2}{3}$ Ⓑ $-5\frac{1}{3} \ge x < 25\frac{2}{3}$
Ⓒ $-5\frac{1}{3} \ge x > 25\frac{2}{3}$ Ⓓ $-5\frac{1}{3} \le x > 25\frac{2}{3}$

CHAPTER 6 Standardized Test *continued*
For use after Chapter 6

13. Which of the following are the solutions to the equation $3|x - 8| = 132$? D

Ⓐ $x = 44$ and $x = -44$
Ⓑ $x = 36$ and $x = -36$
Ⓒ $x = 52$ and $x = -52$
Ⓓ $x = 52$ and $x = -36$

14. A toolmaker is making a part that must have a diameter of 2.5 centimeters with an absolute error of 0.0025 centimeter. What is the minimum possible diameter that this part can have? B

Ⓐ 0.00625 cm Ⓑ 2.4975 cm
Ⓒ 2.5025 cm Ⓓ 1000 cm

15. Which inequality is equivalent to $x < -6$ *or* $x > 11$? C

Ⓐ $|x - 7| < -13$ Ⓑ $5|x - 5| > 50$
Ⓒ $4|5 - 2x| > 68$ Ⓓ $2|2 - 4x| > 86$

16. The graph of which inequality is shown? C

Ⓐ $x + y < -2$
Ⓑ $x + y > -2$
Ⓒ $x + y \le -2$
Ⓓ $x + y \ge -2$

Gridded Answer

17. You will be giving a presentation in your Algebra I class. Your teacher gives you a time limit of 12 minutes with an absolute deviation of 1.5 minutes. What is the minimum possible duration (in minutes) of your presentation?

1	0	.	5

18. a. $\frac{98 + 85 + 72 + 78 + x}{5} \ge 85$; $x \ge 92$

b. No, it is not possible to earn an average of 92. A score of 100 on the last test would still only give you an average of 86.6.

Short Response

18. You earned the following scores on four English tests: 98, 85, 72, and 78. You want to have an average of at least 85 after you take the fifth test.

a. Write and solve an inequality to find the possible scores that you can earn on your fifth test in order to meet your goal. See above.

b. The greatest score you can earn on a test is 100. Is it possible for you to have an average score of 92 after the fifth test? *Explain* your reasoning. See above.

Extended Response

19. The math club at your school is selling chances to win a computer in order to help raise funds for a local tournament. Each ticket is $2. The club has 1000 tickets to sell and must sell at least 750 to raise enough money. The table shows the number of tickets sold so far by each member.

Member	1	2	3	4	5
Tickets Sold	98	68	112	75	112

a. Find the possible numbers a of additional tickets that the club can sell in order to meet its goal. $a \ge 285$

b. If the club raises more than $1500, any additional amount will be used to purchase calculators. Find the possible total numbers t of tickets that the club can sell in order to purchase at least $100 worth of calculators. $t \ge 800$

c. Write an inequality that describes the possible amounts c that the club can use toward the purchase of calculators. *Explain* your answer.

$c \le \$500$ or $\$0 \le c \le \$500$; Selling 750 tickets would raise $1500 for the club. Anything over that amount is used to purchase calculators. After selling 750 tickets, there are 250 tickets remaining, which would total $500. So, the maximum amount that can be used towards calculators is $500 and the minimum amount is $0.

CHAPTER 6 Alternative Assessment and Math Journal
For use after Chapter 6

Journal

1. Explain how to solve the absolute value inequality $|ax + b| > 9$ and give a rough sketch of the graph of the resulting solution.

Multi-Step Problem

2. The Math Club has $1500 to spend on a party. The club decides to use a portion of the money to reserve a banquet room and purchase door prizes. The banquet room costs $125 to reserve and the door prizes each cost $8.50.

a. Write and solve an inequality representing the number of door prizes p that can be purchased if the club decides to use no more than $250 to reserve the banquet room and purchase the door prizes.

b. Graph the solution in part (a). What is the maximum number of door prizes that can be purchased?

c. The club decides to purchase the maximum number of door prizes. Determine the amount that remains in the $1500 budget after purchasing door prizes and reserving the banquet room.

d. The remaining money in the budget will be used to pay for the food for the banquet. Vegetarian, beef, and chicken entrée options are available at prices of $7, $11, and $9, respectively. Write an inequality representing the purchase of x beef, y chicken, and 8 vegetarian entrees that stays within the budget.

e. Graph the inequality in part (d).

f. Give 3 possible combinations of numbers of beef and chicken entrees.

g. For each answer given in part (f), determine the amount of money in the budget that was not spent.

1. Complete answers should include: a discussion of the equivalent compound inequality $ax + b > 9$ or $ax + b < -9$; a discussion of how to solve each part of this compound inequality; a rough sketch of a solution consisting of two rays having open circles that point in opposite directions.

2. a. $125 + 8.5p \le 250$; $p \le 14\frac{12}{17}$ **b.** ; 14 door prizes

c. $1256 **d.** $11x + 9y + 56 \le 1256$

e.

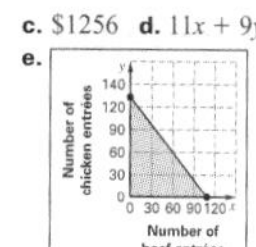

f. *Sample answer:* 100 beef and 10 chicken; 50 beef and 70 chicken; 25 beef and 100 chicken **g.** For sample answer in part (f): $10, $20, and $25, respectively.

PLAN AND PREPARE

Main Ideas

In Chapter 6, students write, solve, and graph one-step and multi-step inequalities using addition, subtraction, multiplication, and division. They learn to reverse an inequality sign when multiplying or dividing by a negative number. Students solve and graph compound inequalities using *and* and *or*. They solve absolute value equations using *or* and they solve and graph absolute value inequalities using *and* and *or*. Finally, students graph linear inequalities in two variables.

Prerequisite Skills

Skills Readiness, available on the *Easy Planner*, provides review and practice for the Skills Check portion of the Prerequisite Skills quiz.

How student answers the exercises	What to assign from *Skills Readiness*
Any of Exs. 4–7 answered incorrectly	**Skill 69** Solve equations
Any of Exs. 8–11 answered incorrectly	**Skill 18** Graph numbers on a number line
Any of Exs. 12–15 answered incorrectly	**Skill 16** Compare decimals
Any of Exs. 16–19 answered incorrectly	**Skill 80** Graph linear equations
All exercises answered correctly	Chapter 6 Enrichment

Additional skill review and practice is available in the Skills Review Handbook, pp. 909–937, and the @HomeTutor.

6 Solving and Graphing Linear Inequalities

Making Sense of Chapter 6

In previous lessons you focused on linear equations. By the end of this chapter, you will be able to write and graph linear inequalities as well as absolute value equations and inequalities.

Before

Previously, you learned the following skills, which you'll use in Chapter 6: solving equations, graphing equations, and comparing rational numbers.

Prerequisite Skills

VOCABULARY CHECK

1. Identify one **ordered pair** that is a solution of $8x - 5y = -2$. ***Sample answer:* (1, 2)**
2. Are $7x - 4 = 10$ and $x = 3$ **equivalent equations**? *Explain.* **See margin.**
3. The **absolute value** of a number a is the distance between a and __?__ on a number line. **0**

SKILLS CHECK

Solve the equation. Check your solution. *(Prerequisite skill for 6.1–6.6)*

4. $m + 8 = -20$ **−28**
5. $7x + 3 = 38$ **5**
6. $-9r - 4 = 25$ $-\frac{29}{9}$
7. $4t - 7t = 9$ **−3**

Graph the number on a number line. *(Prerequisite skill for 6.1–6.4, 6.6)* **8–11. Check graphs.**

8. 6
9. −8
10. −2.1
11. 4.5

Copy and complete the statement using <, >, or =. *(Prerequisite skill for 6.1–6.3, 6.7)*

12. 21.7 __?__ 21 **>**
13. 13.08 __?__ 13.2 **<**
14. 0.1 __?__ 0.04 **>**
15. 0.517 __?__ 0.52 **<**

Graph the equation. *(Prerequisite skill for 6.7)* **16–19. See margin for art.**

16. $y = -7x + 3$
17. $6x + 3y = -5$
18. $x = -8$
19. $y = 4$

@HomeTutor Prerequisite skills practice at classzone.com

Chapter Planning Guide

Chapter 6 Resource Book
- Teaching Guide/Lesson Plan
- Project with Rubric

Assessment and Intervention
- Assessment Book
- Benchmark Tests
- Remediation Book
- Skills Readiness

Interactive Technology
- Easy Planner
- Power Presentations
- Activity Generator
- Animated Algebra
- Test Generator
- Online Quizzes
- eWorkbook
- eEdition
- @HomeTutor

Resources for English Learners
- Spanish Study Guide
- Multi-Language Visual Glossary
- Student Resources in Spanish

Now

In Chapter 6, you will apply the big ideas listed below and reviewed in the Chapter Summary on page 414. You will also use the key vocabulary listed below.

Big Ideas

1. **Applying properties of inequality**
2. **Using statements with *and* or *or***
3. **Graphing inequalities**

KEY VOCABULARY

- graph of an inequality, *p. 356*
- equivalent inequalities, *p. 357*
- compound inequality, *p. 380*
- absolute value equation, *p. 390*
- absolute deviation, *p. 392*
- linear inequality in two variables, *p. 405*
- graph of an inequality in two variables, *p. 405*

Why?

You can use inequalities to solve problems in sound amplification. For example, you can solve an inequality to determine whether an amplifier provides enough amplification for a given number of people in an audience.

Animated Algebra

The animation illustrated below for Exercise 45 on page 387 helps you answer this question: Is a 2900 watt amplifier adequate for an audience of 350 people?

You need to decide whether the amplifier is adequate for 350 people.

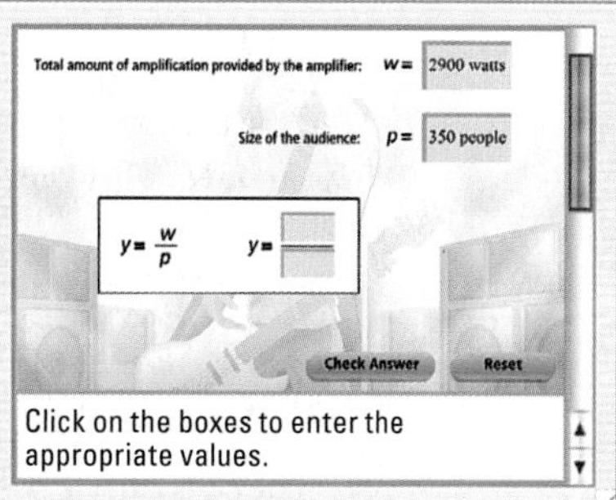

Click on the boxes to enter the appropriate values.

Animated Algebra at classzone.com

Other animations for Chapter 6: pages 358, 364, 382, 390, 391, 399, and 407

Algebra 1 Toolkit

- Reading Strategies for Chapter 6
- Differentiated Instruction Lesson Notes
- English Learners Lesson Notes
- Inclusion Lesson Notes
- Teaching Strategies with Sample Worksheets
- Using Technology in the Classroom
- Tips for New Teachers
- Math Background Notes
- Assessment Strategies
- Teacher Survival Activities
- Bulletin Board Idea

17.
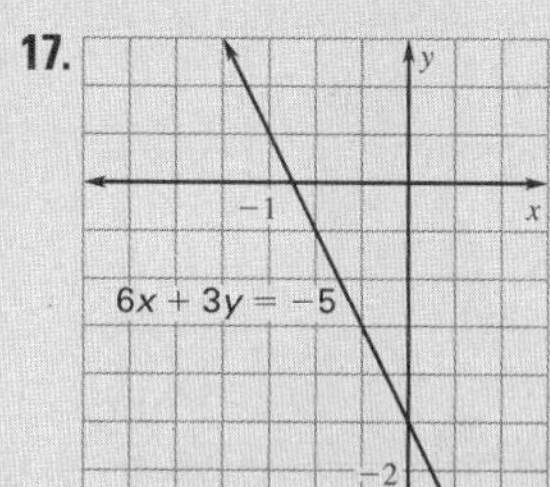

18.
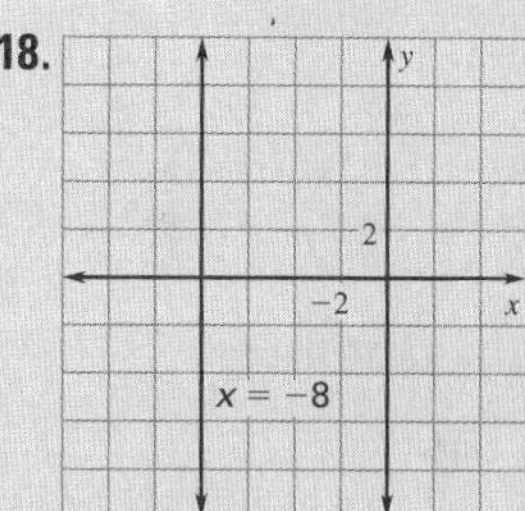

19.
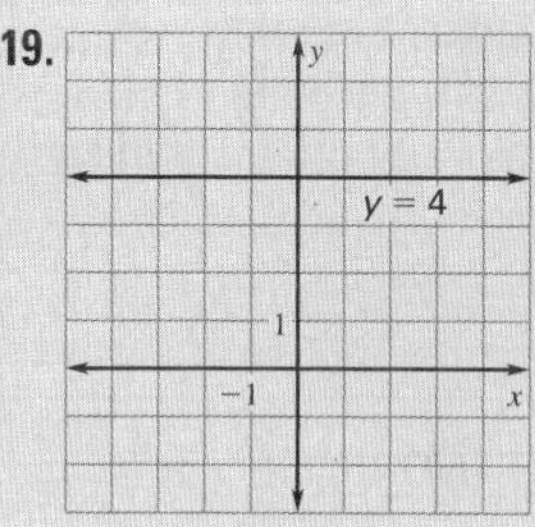

2. No; because the solution of $7x - 4 = 10$ is $x = 2$, the two equations do not have the same solution.

16.
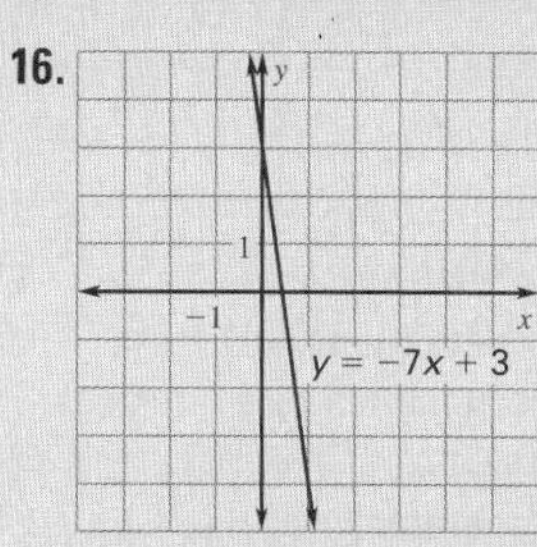

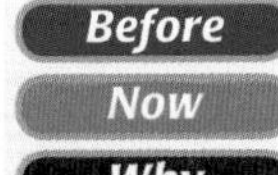

6.1 Solve Inequalities Using Addition and Subtraction

Before You solved equations using addition and subtraction.
Now You will solve inequalities using addition and subtraction.
Why So you can describe desert temperatures, as in Example 1.

Key Vocabulary
- **graph of an inequality**
- **equivalent inequalities**
- **inequality,** *p. 21*
- **solution of an inequality,** *p. 22*

On a number line, the **graph of an inequality** in one variable is the set of points that represent all solutions of the inequality. To graph an inequality in one variable, use an open circle for $<$ or $>$ and a closed circle for $\le$ or $\ge$. The graphs of $x < 3$ and $x \ge -1$ are shown below.

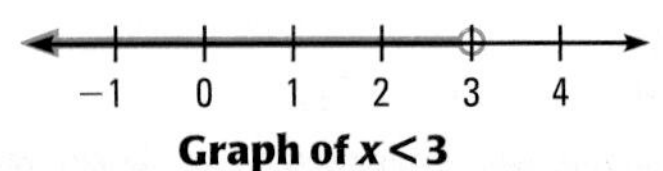

Graph of $x < 3$

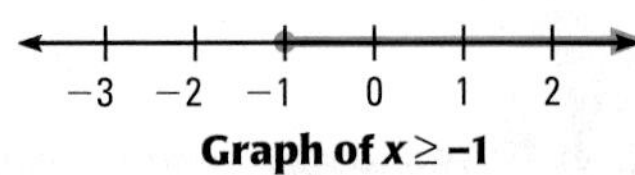

Graph of $x \ge -1$

EXAMPLE 1 Write and graph an inequality

DEATH VALLEY The highest temperature recorded in the United States was 134°F at Death Valley, California, in 1913. Use only this fact to write and graph an inequality that describes the temperatures in the United States.

Solution

Let T represent a temperature (in degrees Fahrenheit) in the United States. The value of T must be less than or equal to 134. So, an inequality is $T \le 134$.

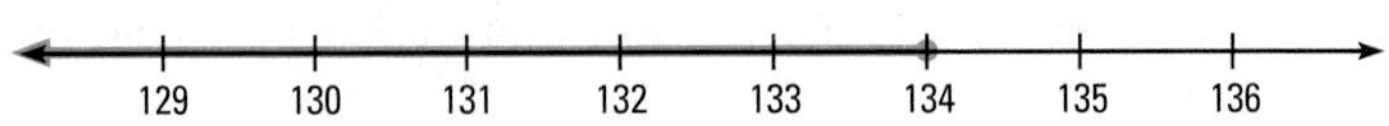

EXAMPLE 2 Write inequalities from graphs

Write an inequality represented by the graph.

a. 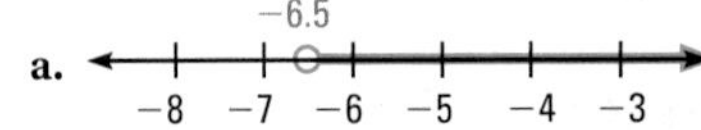

b. 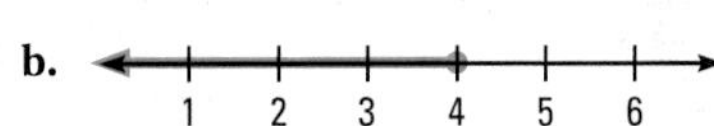

Solution

a. The open circle means that −6.5 is not a solution of the inequality. Because the arrow points to the right, all numbers greater than −6.5 are solutions.

▶ An inequality represented by the graph is $x > -6.5$.

b. The closed circle means that 4 is a solution of the inequality. Because the arrow points to the left, all numbers less than 4 are solutions.

▶ An inequality represented by the graph is $x \le 4$.

1 PLAN AND PREPARE

Warm-Up Exercises

Transparency Available

1. Is −9 a solution of $a + 7 = -2$? **yes**
2. Solve the equation $h + 12 = -8$. **−20**
3. Write an inequality that describes the number of CDs you can buy for $12 each if you have no more than $60 to spend. Can you buy 6 CDs? **$12x \le 60$; no**

Notetaking Guide

Transparency Available

Promotes interactive learning and notetaking skills.

Pacing

Basic: 1 day
Average: 1 day
Advanced: 1 day
Block: 0.5 block with 6.2
- See *Teaching Guide/Lesson Plan.*

2 FOCUS AND MOTIVATE

Essential Question

Big Idea 1, p. 355

How do you solve and graph inequalities using addition and subtraction? **Tell students they will learn how to answer this question by using addition and subtraction properties of inequality.**

NCTM STANDARDS

Standard 2: Represent situations using algebraic symbols; Use models to understand relationships

Resource Planning Guide

Chapter Resource Book
- Teaching Guide/Lesson Plan
- Activity Master
- Practice levels A, B, C
- Study Guide
- Catch-up for Absent Students
- Application
- Challenge

Workbooks
- Notetaking Guide
- Practice Workbook

Teaching Options
- **Power Presentations** provides dynamic electronic teaching resources for the classroom.
- **Activity Generator** provides editable activities for all ability levels.

Interactive Technology
- Easy Planner
- Power Presentations
- Activity Generator
- Animated Algebra
- Test Generator
- Online Quiz
- eWorkbook
- eEdition
- @HomeTutor

Resources for English Learners
- Spanish Study Guide
- Multi-Language Visual Glossary
- Student Resources in Spanish

See also the *Differentiated Instruction Resources* for more strategies for meeting individual needs.

✓ GUIDED PRACTICE for Examples 1 and 2

1. **ANTARCTICA** The lowest temperature recorded in Antarctica was −129°F at the Russian Vostok station in 1983. Use only this fact to write and graph an inequality that describes the temperatures in Antarctica.
$x \geq -129$; see margin for art.

Write an inequality represented by the graph.

2. 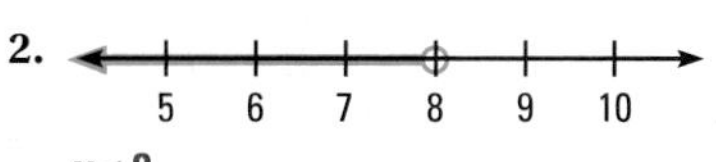

$x < 8$

3. 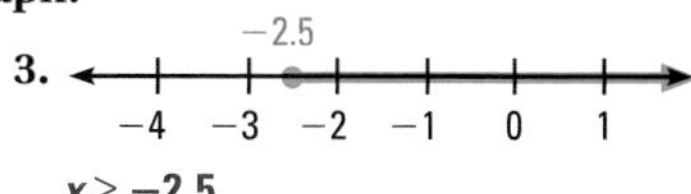

$x \geq -2.5$

EQUIVALENT INEQUALITIES Just as you used properties of equality to produce equivalent equations, you can use properties of inequality to produce *equivalent inequalities.* **Equivalent inequalities** are inequalities that have the same solutions.

KEY CONCEPT *For Your Notebook*

Addition Property of Inequality

Words Adding the same number to each side of an inequality produces an equivalent inequality.

Algebra If $a > b$, then $a + c > b + c$. If $a \geq b$, then $a + c \geq b + c$.

If $a < b$, then $a + c < b + c$. If $a \leq b$, then $a + c \leq b + c$.

EXAMPLE 3 Solve an inequality using addition

Solve $x - 5 > -3.5$. Graph your solution.

$x - 5 > -3.5$	Write original inequality.
$x - 5 + 5 > -3.5 + 5$	Add 5 to each side.
$x > 1.5$	Simplify.

▶ The solutions are all real numbers greater than 1.5. Check by substituting a number greater than 1.5 for x in the original inequality.

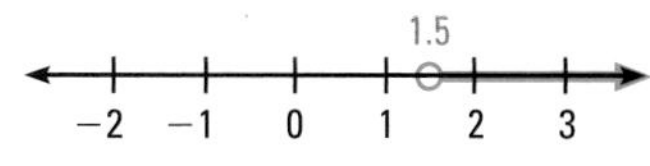

CHECK	$x - 5 > -3.5$	Write original inequality.
	$6 - 5 \overset{?}{>} -3.5$	Substitute 6 for x.
	$1 > -3.5$ ✓	Solution checks.

✓ GUIDED PRACTICE for Example 3

Solve the inequality. Graph your solution. **4–6. See margin for art.**

4. $x - 9 \leq 3$ **$x \leq 12$**
5. $p - 9.2 < -5$ **$p < 4.2$**
6. $-1 \geq m - \frac{1}{2}$ **$m \leq -\frac{1}{2}$**

Motivating the Lesson

You know that you can send no more than 50 text messages on your monthly cell phone plan without incurring additional charges. You sent 18 messages yesterday and 9 today. By knowing how to write and solve inequalities, you can find the maximum number of text messages you can send this month without additional charges.

3 TEACH

Extra Example 1

The lowest elevation recorded in the United States is −282 feet at Death Valley, California. Use this fact to write and graph an inequality that describes the elevations in the United States. **$E \geq -282$, where E is elevation in feet**

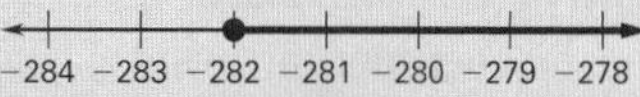

Extra Example 2

Write an inequality represented by the graph. **$x \leq -1.5$**

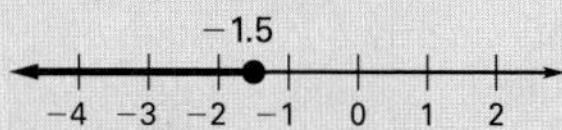

Key Question to Ask for Example 2

- How are the graphs in parts a and b different? **In part a, the graph points to the right and does not include the endpoint. In part b, the graph points to the left and does include the endpoint.**

Extra Example 3

Solve $m - 3.8 < -1$. Graph your solution. **all real numbers less than 2.8**

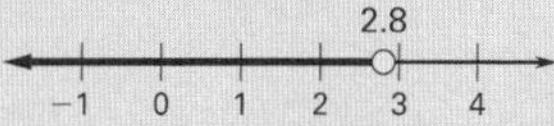

1, 4–6. See Additional Answers beginning on p. AA1.

Extra Example 4

Solve $b + 7 > 3$. Graph your solution. **all real numbers greater than −4**

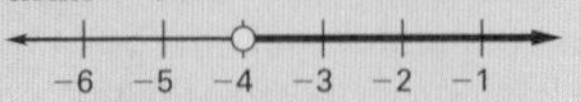

An **Animated Algebra** activity is available online for **Example 4**. This activity is also part of **Power Presentations**.

Extra Example 5

You are shopping for bicycles. The type you want costs at least $185. You have saved $97. Find the possible amounts of money you need to save to buy the bicycle you want. **$88 or more**

Closing the Lesson

Have students summarize the major points of the lesson and answer the Essential Question: How do you solve and graph inequalities using addition and subtraction?

- **The addition property of inequality can be used to produce equivalent inequalities.**
- **On a number line, an open circle on the graph means the number is not a solution of the inequality, while a closed circle means it is a solution.**

Solve the inequality by adding or subtracting the same number from each side of the inequality. To graph the inequality, use an open circle for < or > or use a closed circle for ≤ or ≥. Shade the numbers on the number line in the appropriate direction.

7.

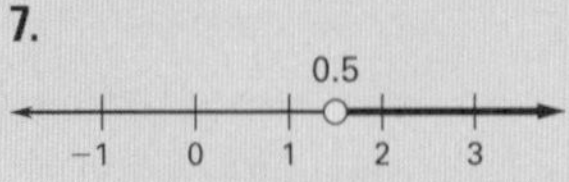

KEY CONCEPT *For Your Notebook*

Subtraction Property of Inequality

Words Subtracting the same number from each side of an inequality produces an equivalent inequality.

Algebra If $a > b$, then $a - c > b - c$. If $a \geq b$, then $a - c \geq b - c$.

If $a < b$, then $a - c < b - c$. If $a \leq b$, then $a - c \leq b - c$.

EXAMPLE 4 Solve an inequality using subtraction

Solve $9 \geq x + 7$. Graph your solution.

$9 \geq x + 7$	**Write original inequality.**
$9 - 7 \geq x + 7 - 7$	**Subtract 7 from each side.**
$2 \geq x$	**Simplify.**

▶ You can rewrite $2 \geq x$ as $x \leq 2$. The solutions are all real numbers less than or equal to 2.

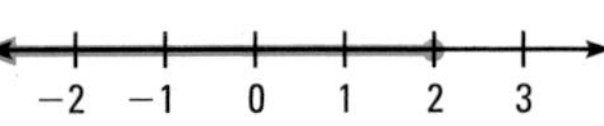

at classzone.com

EXAMPLE 5 Solve a real-world problem

READING The phrase "no more than" indicates that you use the ≤ symbol.

LUGGAGE WEIGHTS You are checking a bag at an airport. Bags can weigh no more than 50 pounds. Your bag weighs 16.8 pounds. Find the possible weights w (in pounds) that you can add to the bag.

Solution

Write a verbal model. Then write and solve an inequality.

Weight of bag	+	Weight you can add	≤	Weight limit
16.8	+	w	≤	**50**

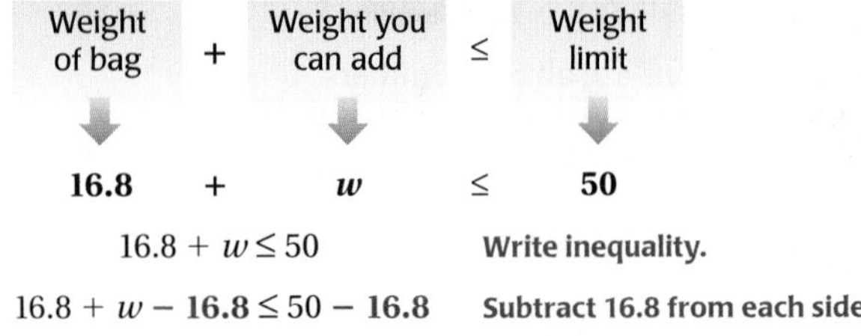

$16.8 + w \leq 50$	**Write inequality.**
$16.8 + w - \mathbf{16.8} \leq 50 - \mathbf{16.8}$	**Subtract 16.8 from each side.**
$w \leq 33.2$	**Simplify.**

▶ You can add no more than 33.2 pounds.

GUIDED PRACTICE for Examples 4 and 5

7. Solve $y + 5.5 > 6$. Graph your solution. **$y > 0.5$; see margin for art.**

8. **WHAT IF?** In Example 5, suppose your bag weighs 29.1 pounds. Find the possible weights (in pounds) that you can add to the bag. **$w \leq 20.9$ lb**

6.1 EXERCISES

HOMEWORK KEY
○ = **WORKED-OUT SOLUTIONS** on p. WS13 for Exs. 7, 15, and 33
★ = **STANDARDIZED TEST PRACTICE** Exs. 2, 29, 34, 35, and 38
◆ = **MULTIPLE REPRESENTATIONS** Ex. 37

SKILL PRACTICE

A

1. **VOCABULARY** Copy and complete: To graph $x < -8$, you draw a(n) _?_ circle at -8, and you draw an arrow to the _?_. **open, left of −8**

2. ★ **WRITING** Are $x + 7 \geq 18$ and $x \geq 25$ equivalent inequalities? *Explain.*
No; because the solution of $x + 7 \geq 18$ is $x \geq 11$, the two inequalities do not have the same solution.

EXAMPLE 1 on p. 356 for Exs. 3–5

WRITING AND GRAPHING INEQUALITIES Write and graph an inequality that describes the situation. **3–5. See margin for art.**

3. The speed limit on a highway is 60 miles per hour. $s \leq 60$
4. You must be at least 16 years old to go on a field trip. $a \geq 16$
5. A child must be taller than 48 inches to get on an amusement park ride. $h > 48$

EXAMPLE 2 on p. 356 for Exs. 6–9

WRITING INEQUALITIES Write an inequality represented by the graph.

6. 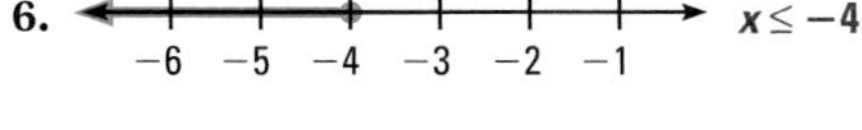
$x \leq -4$

7. 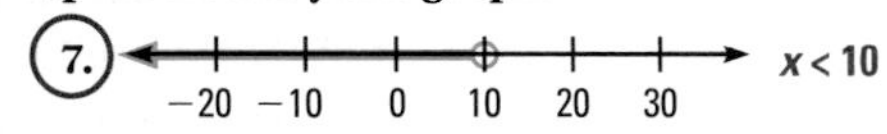
$x < 10$

8. 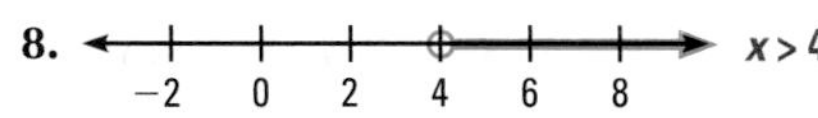
$x > 4$

9. 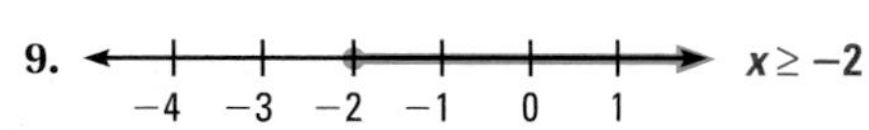
$x \geq -2$

EXAMPLES 3 and 4 on pp. 357–358 for Exs. 10–23

SOLVING INEQUALITIES Solve the inequality. Graph your solution. **10–21. See margin for art.**

10. $x + 4 < 5$ — $x < 1$
11. $-8 \leq 8 + y$ — $y \geq -16$
12. $-1\frac{1}{4} \leq m + 3$ — $m \geq -4\frac{1}{4}$
13. $n + 17 \leq 16\frac{4}{5}$ — $n \leq -\frac{1}{5}$
14. $8.2 + v > -7.6$ — $v > -15.8$
15. $w + 14.9 > -2.7$ — $w > -17.6$
16. $r - 4 < -5$ — $r < -1$
17. $1 \leq s - 8$ — $s \geq 9$
18. $-1\frac{1}{3} \leq p - 8\frac{1}{3}$ — $p \geq 7$
19. $q - 1\frac{1}{3} > -2\frac{1}{2}$ — $q > -1\frac{1}{6}$
20. $2.1 \geq c - 6.7$ — $c \leq 8.8$
21. $d - 1.92 > -8.76$ — $d > -6.84$

ERROR ANALYSIS *Describe* and correct the error in solving the inequality or in graphing the solution. **22, 23. See margin for art.**

22. 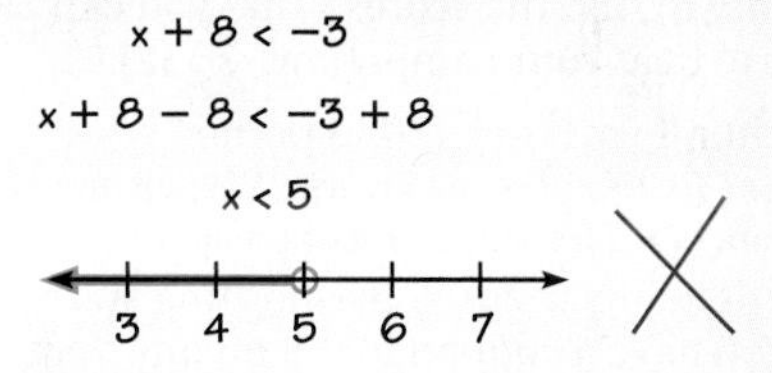

23. 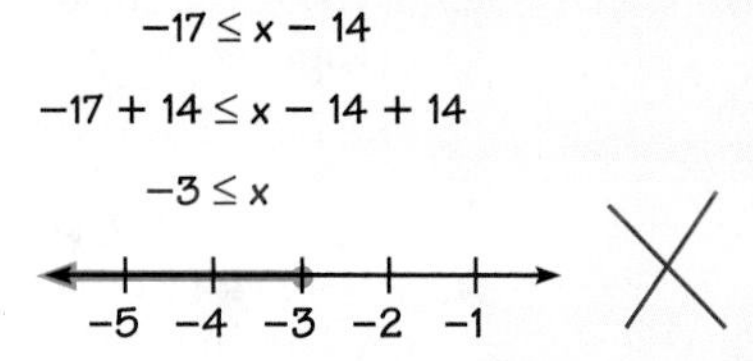

22. 8 must be subtracted from both sides of the equation, not subtracted from one and added to the other; $x + 8 - 8 < -3 - 8$, $x < -11$.

23. The number line should be shaded to the right of −3, not the left.

B

TRANSLATING SENTENCES Write the verbal sentence as an inequality. Then solve the inequality and graph your solution. **24–26. See margin for art.**

24. The sum of 11 and m is greater than -23. $11 + m > -23$; $m > -34$
25. The difference of n and 15 is less than or equal to 37. $n - 15 \leq 37$; $n \leq 52$
26. The difference of c and 13 is less than -19. $c - 13 < -19$; $c < -6$

4 PRACTICE AND APPLY

Assignment Guide

Answer Transparencies available for all exercises

Basic:
Day 1: EP p. 939 Exs. 12–19
pp. 359–361
Exs. 1–17, 22–25, 31–36, 40–50 even

Average:
Day 1: pp. 359–361
Exs. 1–9, 14–28, 31–38, 41, 44, 47, 50

Advanced:
Day 1: pp. 359–361
Exs. 1, 2, 4, 5, 8, 9, 14–21, 24–39*, 42, 45, 48, 51

Block:
pp. 359–361
Exs. 1–9, 14–28, 31–38, 41, 44, 47, 50 (with 6.2)

Differentiated Instruction

See *Differentiated Instruction Resources* for suggestions on addressing the needs of a diverse classroom.

Homework Check

For a quick check of student understanding of key concepts, go over the following exercises:

Basic: 3, 6, 12, 16, 31
Average: 4, 8, 14, 18, 32
Advanced: 5, 9, 15, 20, 33

Extra Practice

- Student Edition, p. 943
- Chapter Resource Book: Practice levels A, B, C

Practice Worksheet

An easily-readable reduced practice page (with answers) for this lesson can be found on p. 354C.

Differentiated Instruction

Inclusion Some students may have difficulty remembering which inequality symbols to use for an open circle and which to use for a closed circle while doing **Exercises 6–9**. Stress that when the circle is open, the symbol (< or >) is an open triangle; when the circle is closed, the inequality sign (≤ or ≥) shows three lines that can be used to form a closed triangle.

See also the *Differentiated Instruction Resources* for more strategies.

3., 4.
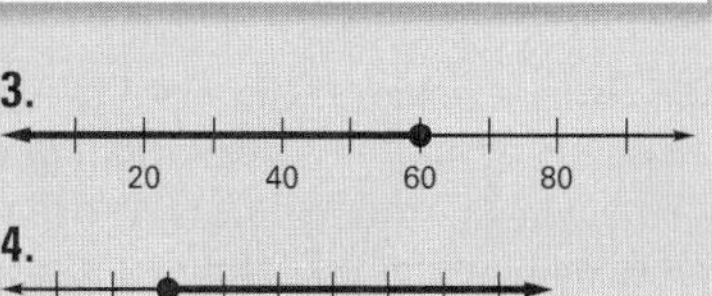

5.
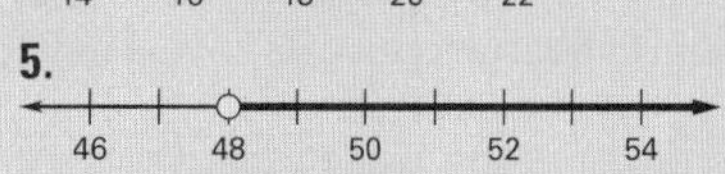

24.
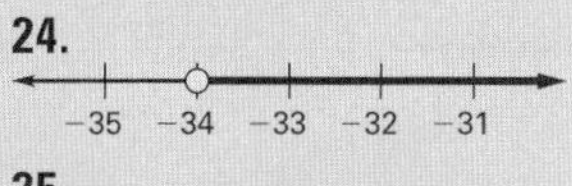

25.
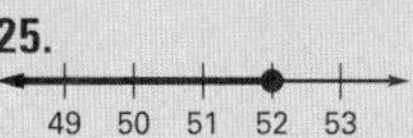

26.
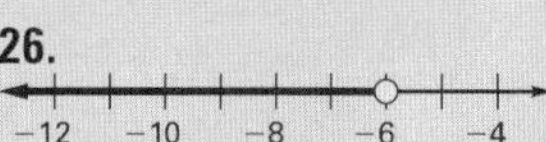

10–23. See Additional Answers beginning on p. AA1.

Avoiding Common Errors

Exercises 10–21 Some students may graph the solution of an inequality correctly, except their "open circle" may look like a closed circle or vice versa. Stress the importance of clearly showing open and closed circles.

Teaching Strategy

Exercises 11, 12, 17, 18, 20 Some students may want to rewrite an inequality such as $-16 \le y$ as $y \ge -16$ with the variable on the left side. Students should realize that is OK, as long as the inequality symbol describes the same relationship between the variable and the constant.

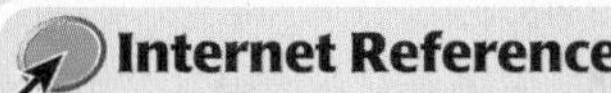

Exercise 32 You can find information about Wayne Gretzky's career and his hockey records at nhl.com/history/gretzky

Vocabulary

Exercises 32–38 These exercises use words such as "at most" and "no more than" and concepts such as "match a record" or "beat a record." Discuss the meanings of these words as they relate to inequality symbols, leading students to see the connections between "at most" and "no more than," and the differences between "match a record" and "beat a record."

29. No; no; there are an infinite number of solutions of an inequality, so it is not possible to check them all. One solution might check in the inequality while another does not. For example, if you incorrectly solve $x + 7 > 10$ as $x > 2$, the solution $x = 4$ checks in the original inequality.

30.

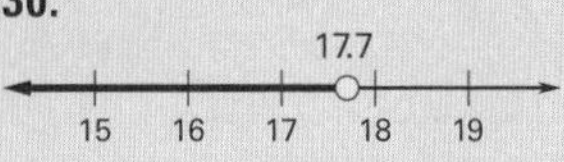

GEOMETRY **Write and solve an inequality to find the possible values of x.**

27. Perimeter < 51.3 inches **$x < 21.6$**

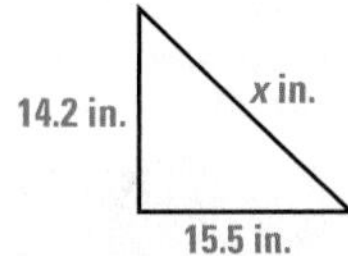

28. Perimeter ≤ 18.7 feet **$x \le 3.3$**

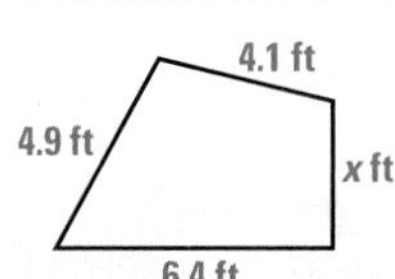

29. ★ **WRITING** Is it possible to check all the numbers that are solutions of an inequality? Does checking one solution guarantee that you have solved an inequality correctly? *Explain* your answers. **See margin.**

C **30.** **CHALLENGE** Write and graph an inequality that represents the numbers that are *not* solutions of $x - 12 \ge 5.7$. **$x < 17.7$; see margin for art.**

PROBLEM SOLVING

EXAMPLE 5 A on p. 358 for Exs. 31–35

31. **INTERNET** You earn points from buying items at an Internet shopping site. You would like to redeem 2350 points to get an item for free, but you want to be sure to have more than 6000 points left over. What are the possible numbers of points you can have before making a redemption? **more than 8350 points**

@HomeTutor for problem solving help at classzone.com

32. **SPORTS RECORDS** In 1982 Wayne Gretsky set a new record for the greatest number of hockey goals in one season with 92 goals. Suppose that a hockey player has 59 goals so far in a season. What are the possible numbers of additional goals that the player can make in order to match or break Wayne Gretsky's record? **at least 33 goals**

@HomeTutor for problem solving help at classzone.com

33. **MULTI-STEP PROBLEM** In aerial ski competitions, athletes perform two acrobatic ski jumps, and the scores on both jumps are added together. The table shows your competitor's first and second scores and your first score.

Ski jump	Competitor's score	Your score
1	127.04	129.49
2	129.98	?

a. Write and solve an inequality to find the scores s that you can earn in your second jump in order to beat your competitor. **$s > 127.53$**

b. Will you beat your competitor if you earn 128.13 points? 126.78 points? 127.53 points? *Justify* your answers. **Yes; no; no; 128.13 > 127.53; 126.78 < 127.53; when your score is 127.53, you and your competitor will tie.**

34. ★ **MULTIPLE CHOICE** You want to buy a jacket at a clothing store, and you can spend at most \$30. You have a coupon for \$3 off any item at the store. Which inequality can you use to find the original prices p of jackets that you can buy? **C**

Ⓐ $3 + p \ge 30$ Ⓑ $30 + p \le 3$ Ⓒ $p - 3 \le 30$ Ⓓ $p - 30 \ge 3$

35. ★ **OPEN-ENDED** *Describe* a real-world situation that can be modeled by the inequality $x + 14 \ge 17$. *Explain* what the solution of the inequality means in this situation. **See margin.**

○ = WORKED-OUT SOLUTIONS on p. WS1 ★ = STANDARDIZED TEST PRACTICE  = MULTIPLE REPRESENTATIONS

35. ***Sample answer:*** **You want to improve on your personal best of 16 points scored in a basketball game. In the first three quarters of the game, you scored 14 points. Write and solve an inequality to find the possible numbers of points that you can score in the fourth quarter to give yourself a new personal best; $x \ge 3$, if you score at least 3 points in the fourth quarter, you will have a new personal best.**

B 36. **VEHICLE WEIGHTS** According to a state law for vehicles traveling on state roads, the maximum total weight of the vehicle and its contents depends on the number of axles the vehicle has.

Maximum Total Weights

2 axles	3 axles	4 axles	5 axles
34,000 lb	54,000 lb	69,000 lb	80,000 lb

For each type of vehicle, write and solve an inequality to find the possible weights w (in pounds) of a vehicle when its contents weigh 14,200 pounds. Can a vehicle that has 2 axles and weighs 20,000 pounds hold 14,200 pounds of contents? *Explain.* **See margin.**

37. **MULTIPLE REPRESENTATIONS** Your friend is willing to spend no more than $17,000 for a new car. The car dealership offers $3000 cash back for the purchase of a new car.

a. **Making a Table** Make a table of values that gives the final price y of a car after the cash back offer is applied to the original price x. Use the following values for x: 19,459, 19,989, 20,549, 22,679, 23,999. **See margin.**

b. **Writing an Inequality** Write and solve an inequality to find the original prices of the cars that your friend will consider buying. **$x - 3000 \le 17{,}000$, $x \le 20{,}000$**

38. ★ **SHORT RESPONSE** A 4-member track team is trying to match or beat last year's winning time of 3 minutes 41.1 seconds for a 1600 meter relay race. The table shows the 400 meter times for the first three athletes.

Athlete	Time (sec)
1	53.34
2	56.38
3	57.46

a. **Calculate** What are the possible times that the last athlete can run 400 meters in order for the team to match or beat last year's time? **at most 53.92 sec**

b. **Decide** So far this season the last athlete's fastest 400 meter time is 53.18 seconds, and his average 400 meter time is 53.92 seconds. In this race the last athlete expects to run faster than his slowest time this season. Is it possible for the team to fail to meet its goal? *Explain.*

38b. Yes; with a fastest time of 53.18 seconds and an average time of 53.92 seconds, his slowest time must be greater than 53.92 seconds. If his time is in between 53.92 seconds and his slowest time, the team will not meet its goal.

C 39. **CHALLENGE** A public television station wants to raise at least $72,000 in a pledge drive. The station raised an average of $5953 per day for the first 3 days and an average of $6153 per day for the next 3 days. What are the possible additional amounts that the station can raise to meet its goal? **at least $35,682**

MIXED REVIEW

Find the sum, difference, product, or quotient.

40. $-18 + (-27)$ *(p. 74)* **−45**
41. $15 - (-23)$ *(p. 80)* **38**
42. $7 \cdot (-9)$ *(p. 88)* **−63**
43. $-11 \cdot (-12)$ *(p. 88)* **132**
44. $-27 \div (-3)$ *(p. 103)* **9**
45. $-30 \div (-5)$ *(p. 103)* **6**

PREVIEW
Prepare for Lesson 6.2 in Exs. 46–51.

Solve the equation. *(p. 134)*

46. $6x = 48$ **8**
47. $-5y = -35$ **7**
48. $400 = -48m$ **$-8\frac{1}{3}$**
49. $\frac{n}{5} = 10$ **50**
50. $\frac{r}{8} = -13$ **−104**
51. $\frac{s}{-2} = -15$ **30**

5 ASSESS AND RETEACH

Daily Homework Quiz

Transparency Available

Solve the inequality. Graph your solution.

1. $s + 0.5 \ge -1.5$ **all real numbers greater than or equal to −2**

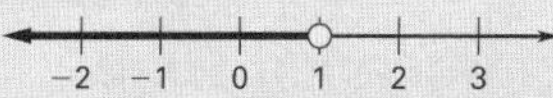

2. $k - 6 < -5$ **all real numbers less than 1**

3. A theater can seat at most 625 people. The box office has sold tickets for 284 seats. Write and solve an inequality to find the possible numbers of remaining tickets t the box office can sell. **$t + 284 \le 625$; $t \le 341$; no more than 341 tickets.**

Online Quiz

Available at **classzone.com**

Diagnosis/Remediation

- Practice A, B, C in Chapter Resource Book
- Study Guide in Chapter Resource Book
- Practice Workbook
- @HomeTutor

Challenge

Additional challenge is available in the Chapter Resource Book.

36, 37a. See Additional Answers beginning on p. AA1.

1 PLAN AND PREPARE

Explore the Concept

- Students will solve an inequality with a negative coefficient.
- This activity leads into the study of solving inequalities in Examples 2 and 3 in Lesson 6.2.

Materials

Each student will need 11 index cards.

Recommended Time

Work activity: 10 min

Discuss results: 5 min

Grouping

Students should work individually.

2 TEACH

Key Question

In Step 3, why is the number -2 a solution of $-4x \geq 8$? **When $x = -2$ the value of $-4x$ is $(-4)(-2) = 8$, and the statement $8 \geq 8$ is true.**

Key Discovery

Change the direction of the inequality symbol when you multiply or divide both sides of the inequality by a negative number.

3 ASSESS AND RETEACH

Explain whether you need to change the direction of the inequality symbol to find the value of x for these inequalities: $3x > -27$, $-3x < 27$, and $-3x \geq -27$. **No for $3x > -27$ because the coefficient of the variable is positive; yes for $-3x < 27$ and for $-3x \geq -27$ because the value of each coefficient is negative.**

Investigating Algebra **ACTIVITY** *Use before Lesson 6.2*

6.2 Inequalities with Negative Coefficients

MATERIALS • index cards

QUESTION **How do you solve an inequality with a negative coefficient?**

EXPLORE **Check solutions of inequalities**

STEP 1 ***Write integers*** Write the integers from -5 to 5 on index cards. Place the cards face up as shown.

−5 −4 −3 −2 −1 0 1 2 3 4 5

STEP 2 ***Check solutions*** Determine whether each integer is a solution of $4x \geq 8$. If the integer is *not* a solution, turn over the card.

STEP 3 ***Check solutions*** Turn all the cards face up. Repeat Step 2 for $-4x \geq 8$.

DRAW CONCLUSIONS **Use your observations to complete these exercises**

1. State an operation that you can perform on both sides of $4x \geq 8$ to obtain the solutions found in Step 2. Then solve the inequality. **divide each side by 4; $x \geq 2$**
2. Copy and complete the steps below for solving $-4x \geq 8$.

$-4x \geq 8$	Write original inequality.
?	Add $4x$ to each side. **$0 \geq 8 + 4x$**
?	Subtract 8 from each side. **$-8 \geq 4x$**
?	Divide each side by 4. **$-2 \geq x$**
?	Rewrite inequality with x on the left side. **$x \leq -2$**

3. Does dividing both sides of $-4x \geq 8$ by -4 give the solution found in Exercise 2? If not, what else must you do to the inequality when you divide by -4? **No; reverse the direction of the inequality symbol.**
4. Do you need to change the direction of the inequality symbol when you divide each side of an inequality by a positive number? by a negative number? **no; yes**

Solve the inequality.

5. $20x \geq 5$ **$x \geq \frac{1}{4}$** **6.** $-9x \leq 45$ **$x \geq -5$** **7.** $-8x > 40$ **$x < -5$** **8.** $7x < 21$ **$x < 3$**

6.2 Solve Inequalities Using Multiplication and Division

Before You solved inequalities using addition and subtraction.

Now You will solve inequalities using multiplication and division.

Why? So you can find possible distances traveled, as in Ex. 40.

Key Vocabulary
- **inequality,** *p. 21*
- **equivalent inequalities,** *p. 357*

Solving an inequality using multiplication is similar to solving an equation using multiplication, but it is different in an important way.

KEY CONCEPT *For Your Notebook*

Multiplication Property of Inequality

Words Multiplying each side of an inequality by a *positive* number produces an equivalent inequality.

Multiplying each side of an inequality by a *negative* number and *reversing the direction of the inequality symbol* produces an equivalent inequality.

Algebra If $a < b$ and $c > 0$, then $ac < bc$. If $a < b$ and $c < 0$, then $ac > bc$.

If $a > b$ and $c > 0$, then $ac > bc$. If $a > b$ and $c < 0$, then $ac < bc$.

This property is also true for inequalities involving ≤ and ≥.

EXAMPLE 1 Solve an inequality using multiplication

Solve $\frac{x}{4} < 5$. Graph your solution.

$\frac{x}{4} < 5$ Write original inequality.

$4 \cdot \frac{x}{4} < 4 \cdot 5$ Multiply each side by 4.

$x < 20$ Simplify.

▶ The solutions are all real numbers less than 20. Check by substituting a number less than 20 in the original inequality.

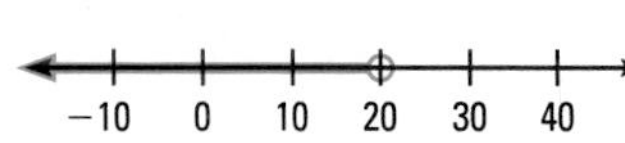

GUIDED PRACTICE for Example 1

Solve the inequality. Graph your solution. **1–3. See margin on p. 364 for art.**

1. $\frac{x}{3} > 8$ **$x > 24$**
2. $\frac{m}{8} \le -2$ **$m \le -16$**
3. $\frac{y}{2.5} \ge -4$ **$y \ge -10$**

1 PLAN AND PREPARE

Warm-Up Exercises

Transparency Available

Check whether the given number is a solution of the inequality.

1. $\frac{x}{3} \le 7$; 20 **yes**
2. $4m > -23$; -6 **no**
3. How long will it take a diver to ascend 36 feet if the average rate of ascent is 30 feet per minute? **1.2 min or 1 min 12 sec**

Notetaking Guide

Transparency Available

Promotes interactive learning and notetaking skills.

Pacing

Basic: 1 day
Average: 1 day
Advanced: 1 day
Block: 0.5 block with 6.1
- See *Teaching Guide/Lesson Plan.*

2 FOCUS AND MOTIVATE

Essential Question

Big Idea 1, p. 355

How do you solve inequalities using multiplication and division? **Tell students they will learn how to answer this question by applying multiplication and division properties of inequality and by learning when to reverse the direction of the inequality symbol.**

NCTM STANDARDS

Standard 2: Understand relations; Analyze situations using algebraic symbols

Resource Planning Guide

Chapter Resource Book
- Teaching Guide/Lesson Plan
- Practice levels A, B, C
- Study Guide
- Catch-up for Absent Students
- Problem Solving Workshop
- Challenge

Workbooks
- Notetaking Guide
- Practice Workbook

Teaching Options
- **Power Presentations** provides dynamic electronic teaching resources for the classroom.
- **Activity Generator** provides editable activities for all ability levels.

Interactive Technology
- Easy Planner
- Power Presentations
- Activity Generator
- Animated Algebra
- Test Generator
- Online Quiz
- eWorkbook
- eEdition
- @HomeTutor

Resources for English Learners
- Spanish Study Guide
- Multi-Language Visual Glossary
- Student Resources in Spanish

See also the *Differentiated Instruction Resources* for more strategies for meeting individual needs.

Motivating the Lesson

Can you think of a time while shopping when you had to decide how many CDs, or shirts, or video games you could possibly buy with the money you had? Answering such a question involves solving an inequality.

3 TEACH

Extra Example 1

Solve $\frac{y}{7} \geq -4$. Graph your solution. **all real numbers greater than or equal to -28**

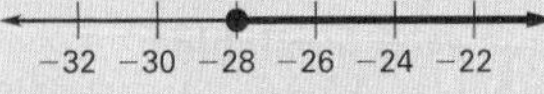

Extra Example 2

Solve $\frac{x}{-3} > -2$. Graph your solution. **all real numbers less than 6**

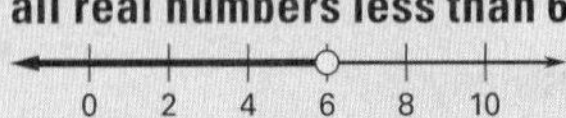

Extra Example 3

Solve $-6x \leq 18$. $x \geq -3$

Key Question to Ask for Example 3

- If you graph $x < -8$, would you use an open or a closed circle? **open**

Animated Algebra classzone.com

An **Animated Algebra** activity is available online for **Example 3**. This activity is also part of **Power Presentations**.

p. 363

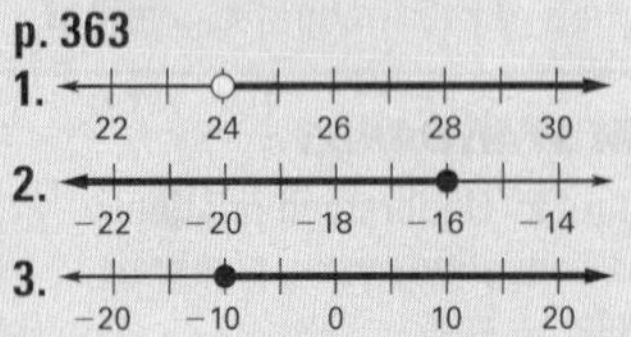

EXAMPLE 2 Solve an inequality using multiplication

Solve $\frac{x}{-6} < 7$. Graph your solution.

$\frac{x}{-6} < 7$	Write original inequality.
$-6 \cdot \frac{x}{-6} > -6 \cdot 7$	Multiply each side by -6. Reverse inequality symbol.
$x > -42$	Simplify.

AVOID ERRORS
Because you are multiplying by a negative number, be sure to reverse the inequality symbol.

▶ The solutions are all real numbers greater than -42. Check by substituting a number greater than -42 in the original inequality.

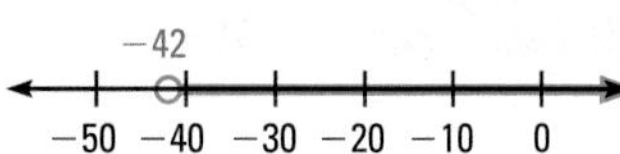

CHECK

$\frac{x}{-6} < 7$	Write original inequality.
$\frac{0}{-6} \overset{?}{<} 7$	Substitute 0 for x.
$0 < 7$ ✓	Solution checks.

USING DIVISION The rules for solving an inequality using division are similar to the rules for solving an inequality using multiplication.

KEY CONCEPT *For Your Notebook*

Division Property of Inequality

Words Dividing each side of an inequality by a *positive* number produces an equivalent inequality.

Dividing each side of an inequality by a *negative* number and *reversing the direction of the inequality symbol* produces an equivalent inequality.

Algebra If $a < b$ and $c > 0$, then $\frac{a}{c} < \frac{b}{c}$. If $a < b$ and $c < 0$, then $\frac{a}{c} > \frac{b}{c}$.

If $a > b$ and $c > 0$, then $\frac{a}{c} > \frac{b}{c}$. If $a > b$ and $c < 0$, then $\frac{a}{c} < \frac{b}{c}$.

This property is also true for inequalities involving $\leq$ and $\geq$.

EXAMPLE 3 Solve an inequality using division

Solve $-3x > 24$.

$-3x > 24$	Write original inequality.
$\frac{-3x}{-3} < \frac{24}{-3}$	Divide each side by -3. Reverse inequality symbol.
$x < -8$	Simplify.

Animated Algebra at classzone.com

Differentiated Instruction

Visual Learners The Division Property of Inequality is equivalent to the Multiplication Property of Inequality. Write both properties on the board. Then replace c with $\frac{1}{c}$ in the Multiplication Property of Inequality to show the equivalence. See also the *Differentiated Instruction Resources* for more strategies.

GUIDED PRACTICE for Examples 2 and 3

Solve the inequality. Graph your solution. **4–7. See margin for art.**

4. $\frac{x}{-4} > 12$ $x < -48$
5. $\frac{m}{-7} < 1.6$ $m > -11.2$
6. $5v \geq 45$ $v \geq 9$
7. $-6n < 24$ $n > -4$

EXAMPLE 4 Standardized Test Practice

A student pilot plans to spend 80 hours on flight training to earn a private license. The student has saved $6000 for training. Which inequality can you use to find the possible hourly rates r that the student can afford to pay for training?

Ⓐ $80r \geq 6000$ Ⓑ $80r \leq 6000$ Ⓒ $6000r \geq 80$ Ⓓ $6000r \leq 80$

Solution

The total cost of training can be at most the amount of money that the student has saved. Write a verbal model for the situation. Then write an inequality.

ELIMINATE CHOICES
You need to multiply the hourly rate and the number of hours, which is 80, not 6000. So, you can eliminate choices C and D.

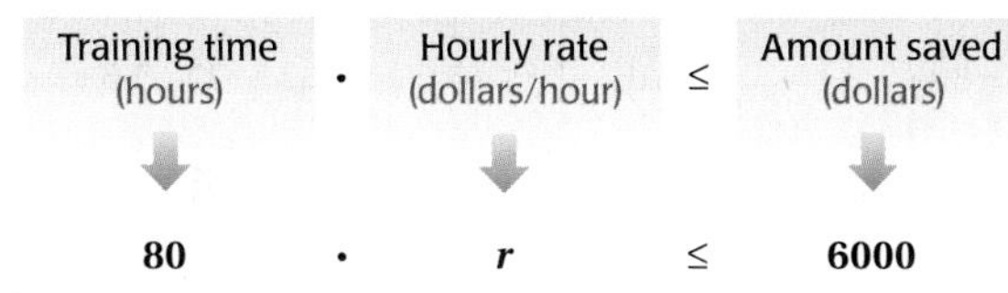

Training time (hours) • Hourly rate (dollars/hour) ≤ Amount saved (dollars)

80 • ***r*** ≤ **6000**

▸ The correct answer is B. Ⓐ Ⓑ Ⓒ Ⓓ

EXAMPLE 5 Solve a real-world problem

PILOTING In Example 4, what are the possible hourly rates that the student can afford to pay for training?

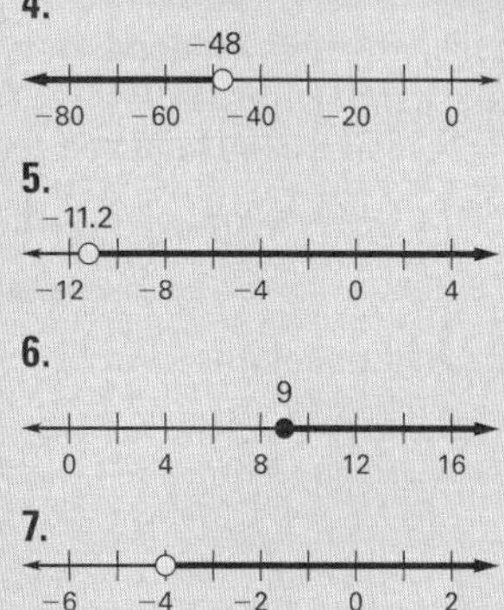

Solution

$80 \cdot r \leq 6000$ **Write inequality.**

$\frac{80r}{80} \leq \frac{6000}{80}$ **Divide each side by 80.**

$r \leq 75$ **Simplify.**

▸ The student can afford to pay at most $75 per hour for training.

GUIDED PRACTICE for Examples 4 and 5

8. **WHAT IF?** In Example 5, suppose the student plans to spend 90 hours on flight training and has saved $6300. Write and solve an inequality to find the possible hourly rates that the student can afford to pay for training. **$90r \leq 6300$, at most $70/h**

Extra Example 4

A restaurant owner plans to place identical bouquets of flowers on 35 tables for opening night. The owner wants to spend no more than $400 for all the bouquets. Which inequality can you use to find the possible amounts of money m that the owner should budget for each bouquet of flowers? **B**

Ⓐ $400 \leq 35m$ Ⓑ $400 \geq 35m$
Ⓒ $400m \geq 35$ Ⓓ $400m \leq 35$

Extra Example 5

In Extra Example 4, what are the possible amounts of money the owner should budget for each bouquet of flowers? **up to $11.42**

Closing the Lesson

Have students summarize the major points of the lesson and answer the Essential Question: How do you solve inequalities using multiplication and division?

- **The multiplication and division properties of inequality can be used to produce equivalent inequalities.**
- **Reverse the direction of the inequality symbol when multiplying or dividing by a negative number.**

Multiply or divide each side of the inequality by the same number to isolate the variable and produce an equivalent inequality. Reverse the direction of the inequality symbol if you multiply or divide by a negative number.

4. Number line: open circle at −48, shaded left; labels −80, −60, −40, −20, 0

5. Number line: open circle at −11.2, shaded right; labels −12, −8, −4, 0, 4

6. Number line: closed circle at 9, shaded right; labels 0, 4, 8, 12, 16

7. Number line: open circle at −4, shaded right; labels −6, −4, −2, 0, 2

6.2 EXERCISES

HOMEWORK KEY

◯ = **WORKED-OUT SOLUTIONS** on p. WS14 for Exs. 5, 9, and 39

★ = **STANDARDIZED TEST PRACTICE** Exs. 2, 27, 34, and 41

◆ = **MULTIPLE REPRESENTATIONS** Ex. 38

4 PRACTICE AND APPLY

Assignment Guide

Answer Transparencies available for all exercises

Basic:
Day 1: pp. 366–368
Exs. 1–18, 27–31, 36–40, 43–53 odd

Average:
Day 1: pp. 366–368
Exs. 1, 2, 15–34, 36–41, 44–52 even

Advanced:
Day 1: pp. 366–368
Exs. 1, 2, 17–27, 30–42*, 44–52 even

Block:
pp. 366–368
Exs. 1, 2, 15–34, 36–41, 44–52 even (with 6.1)

Differentiated Instruction

See *Differentiated Instruction Resources* for suggestions on addressing the needs of a diverse classroom.

Homework Check

For a quick check of student understanding of key concepts, go over the following exercises:

Basic: 4, 6, 10, 36, 37

Average: 16, 18, 21, 37, 38

Advanced: 20, 24, 25, 38, 39

Extra Practice

- Student Edition, p. 943
- Chapter Resource Book: Practice levels A, B, C

Practice Worksheet

An easily-readable reduced practice page (with answers) for this lesson can be found on p. 354C.

3–26. See Additional Answers beginning on p. AA1.

SKILL PRACTICE

A

1. **VOCABULARY** Which property are you using when you solve $5x \geq 30$ by dividing each side by 5? **Division property of inequality**

2. ★ **WRITING** Are $\frac{x}{-4} < -9$ and $x < 36$ equivalent inequalities? *Explain* your answer. **No; when you multiply both sides of $\frac{x}{-4} < -9$ by -4 you must reverse the inequality symbol, producing the inequality $x > 36$.**

EXAMPLES 1, 2, and 3 on pp. 363–364 for Exs. 3–29

SOLVING INEQUALITIES **Solve the inequality. Graph your solution.** **3–26. See margin for art.**

3. $2p \geq 14$ **$p \geq 7$**
4. $\frac{x}{-3} < -10$ **$x > 30$**
5. $-6y < -36$ **$y > 6$**
6. $40 > \frac{w}{5}$ **$w < 200$**
7. $\frac{q}{4} < 7$ **$q < 28$**
8. $72 \leq 9r$ **$r \geq 8$**
9. $\frac{g}{6} > -20$ **$g > -120$**
10. $-11m \leq -22$ **$m \geq 2$**
11. $-90 \geq 4t$ **$t \leq -22.5$**
12. $\frac{n}{3} < -9$ **$n < -27$**
13. $60 \leq -12s$ **$s \leq -5$**
14. $\frac{v}{-4} \geq -8$ **$v \leq 32$**
15. $-8.4f > 2.1$ **$f < -0.25$**
16. $\frac{d}{-2} \leq 18.6$ **$d \geq -37.2$**
17. $9.6 < -16c$ **$c < -0.6$**
18. $0.07 \geq \frac{k}{7}$ **$k \leq 0.49$**
19. $-1.5 \geq 6z$ **$z \leq -0.25$**
20. $\frac{x}{-5} \leq -7.5$ **$x \geq 37.5$**
21. $1.02 < -3j$ **$j < -0.34$**
22. $\frac{y}{-4.5} \geq -10$ **$y \leq 45$**
23. $\frac{r}{-30} < 1.8$ **$r > -54$**
24. $1.9 \leq -5p$ **$p \leq -0.38$**
25. $\frac{m}{0.6} > -40$ **$m > -24$**
26. $-2t > -1.22$ **$t < 0.61$**

27. ★ **WRITING** How is solving $ax > b$ where $a > 0$ similar to solving $ax > b$ where $a < 0$? How is it different? **In both cases, you divide both sides of the inequality by a; when $a > 0$, you do not reverse the inequality symbol, but when $a < 0$, you do.**

ERROR ANALYSIS ***Describe*** **and correct the error in solving the inequality.**

28.

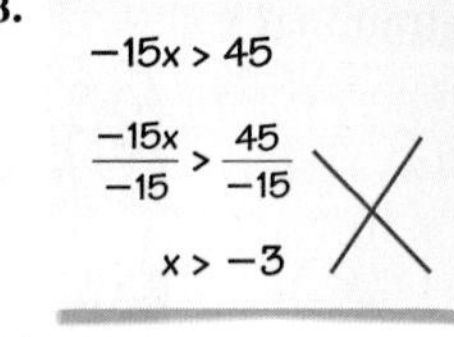

$-15x > 45$

$\frac{-15x}{-15} > \frac{45}{-15}$

$x > -3$

The inequality symbol was not reversed when dividing both sides by -15; $\frac{-15x}{-15} < \frac{45}{-15}$, $x < -3$.

29.

$\frac{x}{9} \leq -7$

$9 \cdot \frac{x}{9} \leq 9 \cdot (-7)$

$x \geq -63$

29. Both sides of the inequality were multiplied by a positive number, so the inequality symbol should not have been reversed; $x \leq -63$.

B

TRANSLATING SENTENCES **In Exercises 30–33, write the verbal sentence as an inequality. Then solve the inequality and graph your solution.** **30–33. See margin for art.**

30. The product of 8 and x is greater than 50. **$8x > 50$; $x > \frac{25}{4}$**

31. The product of -15 and y is less than or equal to 90. **$-15y \leq 90$; $y \geq -6$**

32. The quotient of v and -9 is less than -18. **$\frac{v}{-9} < -18$; $v > 162$**

33. The quotient of w and 24 is greater than or equal to $-\frac{1}{6}$. **$\frac{w}{24} \geq -\frac{1}{6}$; $w \geq -4$**

34. ★ **OPEN-ENDED** Write an inequality in the form $ax < b$ such that the solutions are all real numbers greater than 4. ***Sample answer:*** **$-3x < -12$**

30.

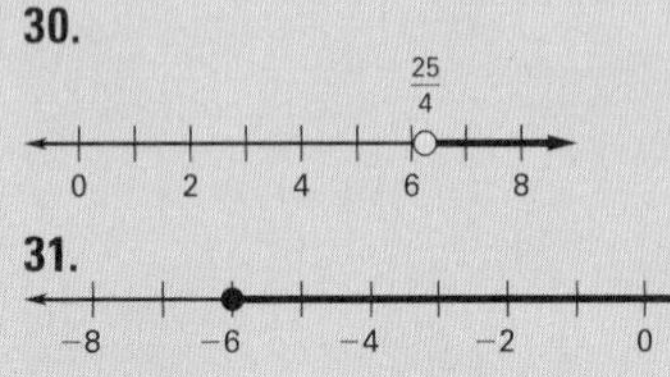

31.

32.

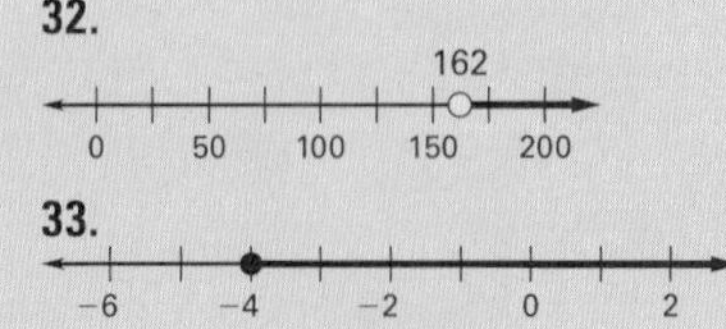

33.

C 35. **CHALLENGE** For the given values of a and b, tell whether the solution of $ax > b$ consists of *positive numbers, negative numbers,* or *both. Explain.* **See margin.**

a. $a < 0, b > 0$ b. $a > 0, b > 0$ c. $a > 0, b < 0$ d. $a < 0, b < 0$

PROBLEM SOLVING

EXAMPLES 4 and 5 on p. 365 for Exs. 36–39

A 36. **MUSIC** You have \$90 to buy CDs for your friend's party. The CDs cost \$18 each. What are the possible numbers of CDs that you can buy? **at most 5 CDs**

@HomeTutor for problem solving help at classzone.com

37. **JOB SKILLS** You apply for a job that requires the ability to type 40 words per minute. You practice typing on a keyboard for 5 minutes. The average number of words you type per minute must at least meet the job requirement. What are the possible numbers of words that you can type in 5 minutes in order to meet or exceed the job requirement? **at least 200 words**

@HomeTutor for problem solving help at classzone.com

38. ◆ **MULTIPLE REPRESENTATIONS** You are stacking books on a shelf that has a height of 66 centimeters. Each book has a thickness of 4 centimeters.

a. **Using a Model** Use a concrete model to find the possible numbers of books that you can stack as follows: Cut strips of paper 4 centimeters wide to represent the books. Then place the strips one above the other until they form a column no taller than 66 centimeters. **at most 16 books**

b. **Writing an Inequality** Write and solve an inequality to find the possible numbers of books that you can stack. **$4x \le 66$, $x \le 16.5$, at most 16 books**

c. **Drawing a Graph** Write and graph an equation that gives the height y of stacked books as a function of the number x of books. Then graph $y = 66$ in the same coordinate plane. To find the possible numbers of books that you can stack, identify the integer x-coordinates of the points on the first graph that lie *on or below* the graph of $y = 66$. **See margin.**

d. **Choosing a Method** Suppose the shelf has a height of 100 centimeters. Which method would you use to find the possible numbers of books, *a concrete model, solving an inequality,* or *drawing a graph*? *Explain.* **Answers may vary.**

39. **MANUFACTURING** A manufacturer of architectural moldings recommends that the length of a piece be no more than 15 times its minimum width w (in inches) in order to prevent cracking. For the piece shown, what could the values of w be? **at least 3.2**

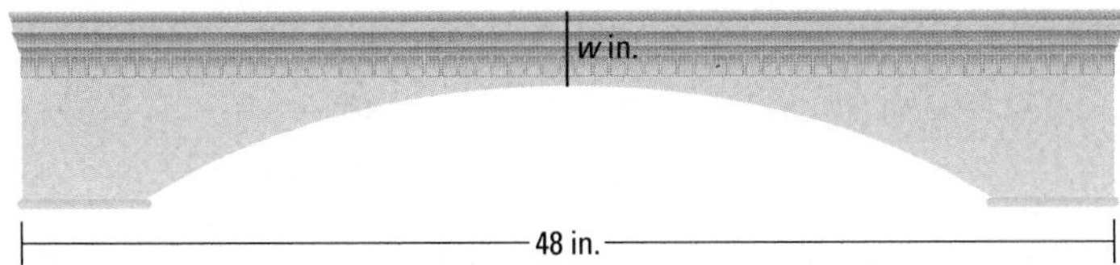

B 40. **RECREATION** A water-skiing instructor recommends that a boat pulling a beginning skier have a speed less than 18 miles per hour. Write and solve an inequality that you can use to find the possible distances d (in miles) that a beginner can travel in 45 minutes of practice time. **$d < 18(0.75)$, $d < 13.5$, less than 13.5 mi**

Avoiding Common Errors

Exercises 3–26 Watch for students who do not reverse the inequality symbol when multiplying by a negative number. Suggest that students write the phrase "reverse the symbol" as soon as they see that an exercise has a negative coefficient.

Reading Strategy

Exercise 34 Suggest to students that they read this exercise carefully. Urge them to pay attention to the inequality symbol and how it is connected to the solutions of the inequality.

Study Strategy

Exercise 35 Remind students that some challenge problems may be more manageable if they substitute numbers for the variables and use their observations to explain their reasoning. Tell them that sometimes they will need to substitute several numbers for the variables before they see a pattern.

35a. Negative; when you divide both sides of the inequality by the negative number a, the inequality symbol becomes < and $\frac{b}{a}$ is negative, because $(+) \div (-) = (-)$. Thus, the answer is in the form $x <$ (a negative number), so x itself must be negative.

35b. Positive; when you divide both sides of the inequality by the positive number a, the inequality symbol stays the same and $\frac{b}{a}$ is positive, because $(+) \div (+) = (+)$. Thus, the answer is in the form $x >$ (a positive number), so x itself must be positive.

35c. Both; when you divide both sides of the inequality by the positive number a, the inequality symbol stays the same and $\frac{b}{a}$ is negative, because $(-) \div (+) = (-)$. Thus, the answer is in the form $x >$ (a negative number), so x itself can be either positive or negative (or 0).

35d. Both; when you divide both sides of the inequality by the negative number a, the inequality symbol becomes < and $\frac{b}{a}$ is positive, because $(-) \div (-) = (+)$. Thus, the answer is in the form $x <$ (a positive number), so x itself can be either positive or negative (or 0).

38c. $y = 4x$;

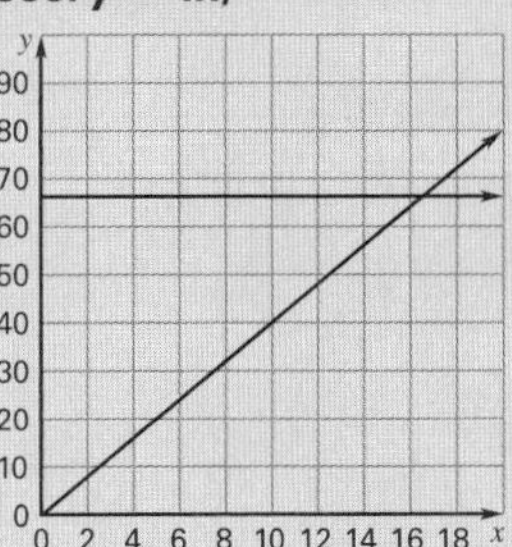

0, 1, 2, 3, 4, 5, 6, 7, 8, 9, 10, 11, 12, 13, 14, 15, 16

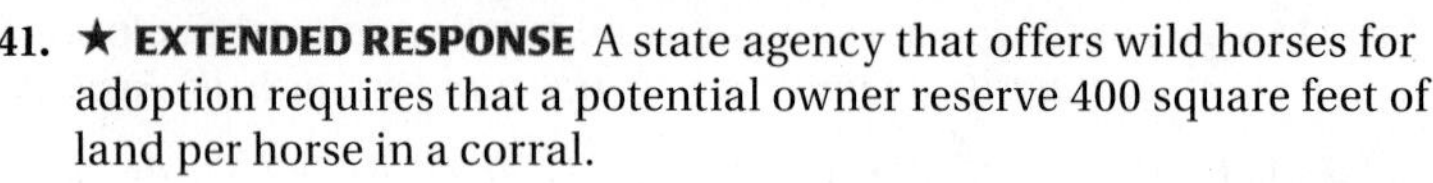

41. ★ **EXTENDED RESPONSE** A state agency that offers wild horses for adoption requires that a potential owner reserve 400 square feet of land per horse in a corral.

a. **Solve** A farmer has a rectangular corral whose length is 80 feet and whose width is 82 feet. Write and solve an inequality to find the possible numbers h of horses that the corral can hold. **$400h \le 6560$, $h \le 16.4$, no more than 16 horses**

b. **Explain** If the farmer increases the length and width of the corral by 20 feet each, will the corral be able to hold only 1 more horse? *Explain* your answer without calculating the new area of the corral. **See margin.**

c. **Calculate** The farmer decides to increase the length and width of the corral by 15 feet each. Find the possible numbers of horses that the corral can hold. Your answer should include the following:

- a calculation of the new area of the corral
- a description of your steps for solving the problem

41c. no more than 23 horses; the area of the new corral is $(80 + 15)(82 + 15) = 9215$ square feet. Find the possible numbers, h, of horses the corral can hold by solving the inequality $9215 \ge 400h$; $h \le 23.04$.

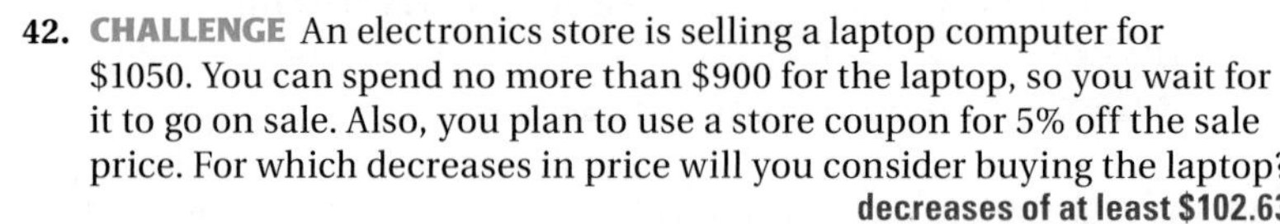

C 42. **CHALLENGE** An electronics store is selling a laptop computer for \$1050. You can spend no more than \$900 for the laptop, so you wait for it to go on sale. Also, you plan to use a store coupon for 5% off the sale price. For which decreases in price will you consider buying the laptop? **decreases of at least \$102.63**

MIXED REVIEW

Write an expression for the situation. *(p. 15)*

43. Total cost of t movie tickets if each ticket costs \$7.50 **$7.5t$**

44. Distance left to travel on a 500 mile trip if you have traveled m miles **$500 - m$**

PREVIEW Prepare for Lesson 6.3 in Exs. 45–50.

Solve the equation or inequality.

45. $9x + 6 = 7$ *(p. 141)* **$\frac{1}{9}$**

46. $3y - 8 = 5y + 2y$ *(p. 154)* **-2**

47. $4(z + 1) = 6z$ *(p. 154)* **2**

48. $p + 8 > 10$ *(p. 356)* **$p > 2$**

49. $q + 6 < -5$ *(p. 356)* **$q < -11$**

50. $r - 2 \ge -9$ *(p. 356)* **$r \ge -7$**

Write an equation in slope-intercept form of the line that has the given slope and y-intercept. *(p. 283)*

51. slope: -3; y-intercept: 4 **$y = -3x + 4$**

52. slope: -8; y-intercept: $\frac{1}{4}$ **$y = -8x + \frac{1}{4}$**

53. slope: $\frac{1}{5}$; y-intercept: $-\frac{2}{3}$ **$y = \frac{1}{5}x - \frac{2}{3}$**

QUIZ *for Lessons 6.1–6.2*

Solve the inequality. Graph your solution. **1–9. See margin for art.**

1. $x + 8 \ge -5$ *(p. 356)* **$x \ge -13$**
2. $y + 6 < 14$ *(p. 356)* **$y < 8$**
3. $-8 \le v - 5$ *(p. 356)* **$v \ge -3$**
4. $w - 11 > 2$ *(p. 356)* **$w > 13$**
5. $-40 < -5r$ *(p. 363)* **$r < 8$**
6. $-93 < 3s$ *(p. 363)* **$s > -31$**
7. $-2m \ge 26$ *(p. 363)* **$m \le -13$**
8. $\frac{n}{-4} > -7$ *(p. 363)* **$n < 28$**
9. $\frac{c}{6} \le -8$ *(p. 363)* **$c \le -48$**

10. **FOOD PREPARATION** You need to make at least 150 sandwiches for a charity event. You can make 3 sandwiches per minute. How long will it take you to make the number of sandwiches you need? *(p. 363)* **at least 50 min**

EXTRA PRACTICE for Lesson 6.2, p. 943

ONLINE QUIZ at classzone.com

5 ASSESS AND RETEACH

Daily Homework Quiz

Transparency Available

Solve each inequality. Graph your solution.

1. $-72 < 8p$ **$p > -9$**

   −11 −10 −9 −8 −7 −6

2. $\frac{w}{-6} \ge -5$ **$w \le 30$**

   0 10 20 30 40 50

3. A fitness walking group walks 4 days each week with a goal of at least 12 miles per week. Write and solve an inequality to find the average number of possible miles m the group should walk each day to meet its goal. **$4m \ge 12$; an average of at least 3 miles per day**

Online Quiz

Available at **classzone.com**

Diagnosis/Remediation

- Practice A, B, C in Chapter Resource Book
- Study Guide in Chapter Resource Book
- Practice Workbook
- @HomeTutor

Challenge

Additional challenge is available in the Chapter 6 Resource Book.

Quiz

An easily-readable reduced copy of the quiz (with answers) on Lessons 6.1–6.2 from the Assessment Book can be found on p. 345G.

41b, Quiz 1–9. See Additional Answers beginning on p. AA1.

6.3 Solve Multi-Step Inequalities

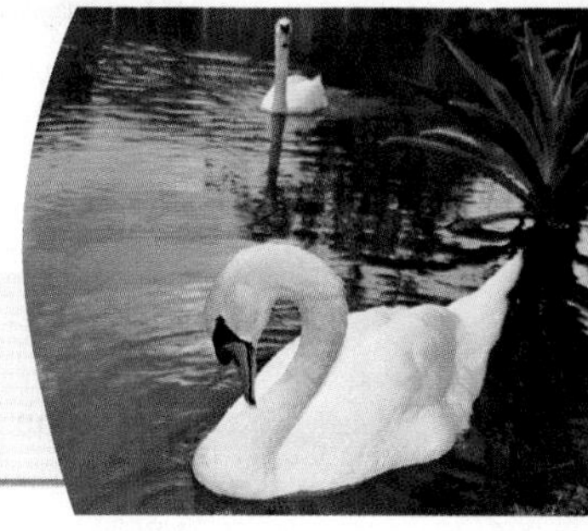

Before You solved one-step inequalities.
Now You will solve multi-step inequalities.
Why? So you can compare animal habitats, as in Ex. 39.

Key Vocabulary
- **inequality,** *p. 21*

The steps for solving two-step and multi-step equations can be applied to linear inequalities. For inequalities, be sure to reverse the inequality symbol when multiplying or dividing by a negative number.

EXAMPLE 1 Solve a two-step inequality

Solve $3x - 7 < 8$. Graph your solution.

$3x - 7 < 8$	Write original inequality.
$3x < 15$	Add 7 to each side.
$x < 5$	Divide each side by 3.

▶ The solutions are all real numbers less than 5. Check by substituting a number less than 5 in the original inequality.

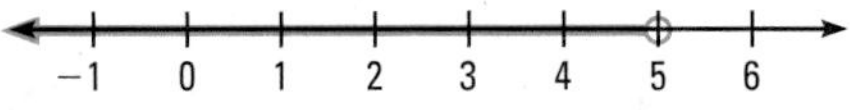

CHECK	
$3x - 7 < 8$	Write original inequality.
$3(0) - 7 \overset{?}{<} 8$	Substitute 0 for *x*.
$-7 < 8$ ✓	Solution checks.

EXAMPLE 2 Solve a multi-step inequality

Solve $-0.6(x - 5) \le 15$.

$-0.6(x - 5) \le 15$	Write original inequality.
$-0.6x + 3 \le 15$	Distributive property
$-0.6x \le 12$	Subtract 3 from each side.
$x \ge -20$	Divide each side by −0.6. Reverse inequality symbol.

GUIDED PRACTICE for Examples 1 and 2

Solve the inequality. Graph your solution. **1–3. See margin on p. 371 for art.**

1. $2x - 5 \le 23$ **$x \le 14$**
2. $-6y + 5 \le -16$ **$y \ge 3.5$**
3. $-\frac{1}{4}(p - 12) > -2$ **$p < 20$**

1 PLAN AND PREPARE

Warm-Up Exercises

Transparency Available

1. Is 4 a solution of the inequality $2a - 1.5 \ge 6$? **yes**
2. Solve the equation $\frac{f}{4} + 8$ 7. **−4**
3. All hats sell for the same price at a swap meet. You buy one pair of sunglasses for \$7 and 2 hats. You spend \$26.50. How much did each hat cost? **\$9.75**

Notetaking Guide

Transparency Available

Promotes interactive learning and notetaking skills.

Pacing

Basic: 1 day
Average: 1 day
Advanced: 1 day
Block: 0.5 block with 6.4
- See *Teaching Guide/Lesson Plan.*

2 FOCUS AND MOTIVATE

Essential Question

Big Idea 1, p. 355

How do you solve multi-step inequalities? **Tell students they will learn how to answer this question by using the distributive property and the properties of inequality.**

NCTM STANDARDS

Standard 2: Analyze situations using algebraic symbols

Standard 6: Solve problems in math and other contexts

Resource Planning Guide

Chapter Resource Book
- Teaching Guide/Lesson Plan
- Practice levels A, B, C
- Study Guide
- Catch-up for Absent Students
- Application
- Challenge

Workbooks
- Notetaking Guide
- Practice Workbook

Teaching Options
- **Power Presentations** provides dynamic electronic teaching resources for the classroom.
- **Activity Generator** provides editable activities for all ability levels.

Interactive Technology
- Easy Planner
- Power Presentations
- Activity Generator
- Animated Algebra
- Test Generator
- Online Quiz
- eWorkbook
- eEdition
- @HomeTutor

Resources for English Learners
- Spanish Study Guide
- Multi-Language Visual Glossary
- Student Resources in Spanish

See also the *Differentiated Instruction Resources* for more strategies for meeting individual needs.

Motivating the Lesson

Ask students if the typical problems they solve in everyday life tend to be one-step or multi-step problems. Invite them to support their views by providing examples. After a short discussion, tell students that many people have trouble solving multi-step problems because they do not know where to begin. Tell them that by learning how to solve a multi-step problem, they will be able to break a problem into its parts, recognize key words, and choose from a variety of methods to solve the problem.

3 TEACH

Extra Example 1

Solve $-7x + 2 < -5$. Graph your solution. **all real numbers greater than 1**

-2 -1 0 1 2 3

Extra Example 2

Solve $\frac{1}{3}(3x + 6) \geq -1$. $\mathbf{x \geq -3}$

Key Question to Ask for Example 2

- Is -21 a solution of the inequality? Explain. **No. The inequality is not true for $x = -21$ because $-21 < -20$ and the solutions are all real numbers greater than -20.**

Extra Example 3

Solve $9x + 6 \leq 6x + 21$. Graph your solution. **all real numbers less than or equal to 5**

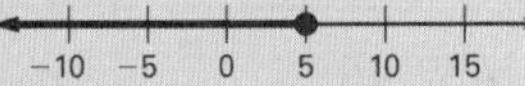

-10 -5 0 5 10 15

EXAMPLE 3 Solve a multi-step inequality

ANOTHER WAY

You can also solve the inequality by subtracting 17 and $6x$ from each side, as follows:

$6x - 7 > 2x + 17$

$6x - 24 > 2x$

$-24 > -4x$

$6 < x$

The inequality $6 < x$ is equivalent to $x > 6$.

Solve $6x - 7 > 2x + 17$. Graph your solution.

$6x - 7 > 2x + 17$	Write original inequality.
$6x > 2x + 24$	Add 7 to each side.
$4x > 24$	Subtract $2x$ from each side.
$x > 6$	Divide each side by 4.

▸ The solutions are all real numbers greater than 6.

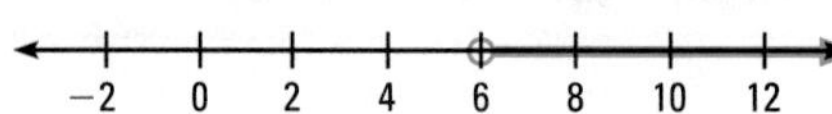

NUMBER OF SOLUTIONS If an inequality is equivalent to an inequality that is true, such as $-3 < 0$, then the solutions of the inequality are *all real numbers.* If an inequality is equivalent to an inequality that is false, such as $4 < -1$, then the inequality has *no solution.*

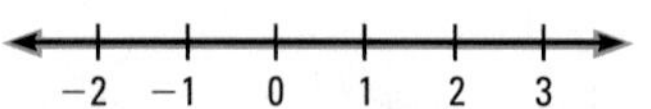

Graph of an inequality whose solutions are all real numbers

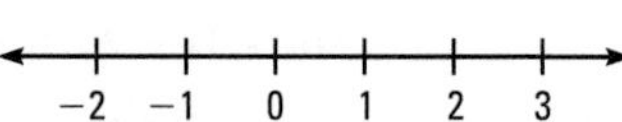

Graph of an inequality that has no solution

EXAMPLE 4 Identify the number of solutions of an inequality

Solve the inequality, if possible.

a. $14x + 5 < 7(2x - 3)$ **b.** $12x - 1 > 6(2x - 1)$

Solution

a. $14x + 5 < 7(2x - 3)$	Write original inequality.
$14x + 5 < 14x - 21$	Distributive property
$5 < -21$	Subtract $14x$ from each side.

▸ There are no solutions because $5 < -21$ is false.

b. $12x - 1 > 6(2x - 1)$	Write original inequality.
$12x - 1 > 12x - 6$	Distributive property
$-1 > -6$	Subtract $12x$ from each side.

▸ All real numbers are solutions because $-1 > -6$ is true.

✓ **GUIDED PRACTICE** for Examples 3 and 4

Solve the inequality, if possible. Graph your solution. **4–6. See margin for art.**

4. $5x - 12 \leq 3x - 4$ $\mathbf{x \leq 4}$

5. $5(m + 5) < 5m + 17$ **no solution**

6. $1 - 8s \leq -4(2s - 1)$ **all real numbers**

Differentiated Instruction

Auditory Learners While discussing **Example 3**, students follow the same steps for solving a multi-step inequality that they would use for solving a multi-step equation. Ask them if there are any differences between solving an inequality and the related equation. Stress that there is an additional step when solving an inequality; they must remember to reverse the symbol when multiplying or dividing by a negative number.

See also the *Differentiated Instruction Resources* for more strategies.

EXAMPLE 5 Solve a multi-step problem

CAR WASH Use the sign shown. A gas station charges \$.10 less per gallon of gasoline if a customer also gets a car wash. What are the possible amounts (in gallons) of gasoline that you can buy if you also get a car wash and can spend at most \$20?

ANOTHER WAY
For an alternative method for solving the problem in Example 5, turn to page 375 for the **Problem Solving Workshop**.

Solution

Because you are getting a car wash, you will pay \$2.09 − \$.10 = \$1.99 per gallon of gasoline. Let g be the amount (in gallons) of gasoline that you buy.

STEP 1 **Write** a verbal model. Then write an inequality.

Price of gasoline (dollars/gallon) · Amount of gasoline (gallons) + Price of car wash (dollars) ≤ Maximum amount (dollars)

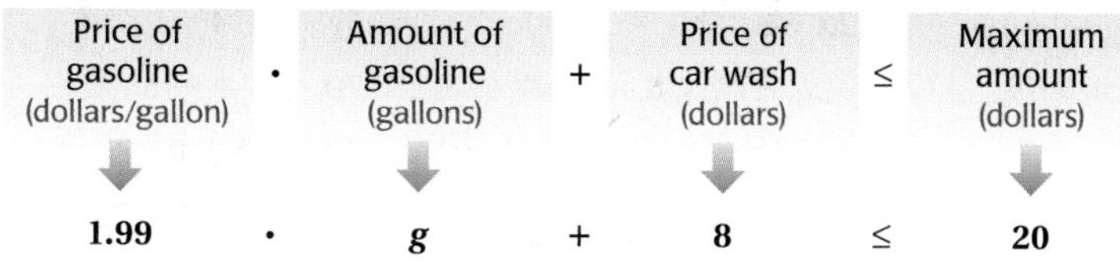

$$1.99 \cdot g + 8 \leq 20$$

STEP 2 **Solve** the inequality.

$1.99g + 8 \leq 20$	**Write inequality.**
$1.99g \leq 12$	**Subtract 8 from each side.**
$g \leq 6.03015...$	**Divide each side by 1.99.**

▶ You can buy up to slightly more than 6 gallons of gasoline.

CHECK You can use a table to check the reasonableness of your answer.

The table shows that you will pay \$19.94 for exactly 6 gallons of gasoline. Because \$19.94 is less than \$20, it is reasonable to conclude that you can buy slightly more than 6 gallons of gasoline.

Gasoline (gal)	Total amount spent (dollars)
0	8.00
1	9.99
2	11.98
3	13.97
4	15.96
5	17.95
6	19.94

GUIDED PRACTICE for Example 5

7. **WHAT IF?** In Example 5, suppose that a car wash costs \$9 and gasoline regularly costs \$2.19 per gallon. What are the possible amounts (in gallons) of gasoline that you can buy? **at most 5.26 gal**

8. **CAMP COSTS** You are saving money for a summer camp that costs \$1800. You have saved \$500 so far, and you have 14 more weeks to save the total amount. What are the possible average amounts of money that you can save per week in order to have a total of at least \$1800 saved? **at least \$92.86/wk**

Extra Example 4

Solve the inequality, if possible.

a. $8x - 4 \geq 4(2x - 1)$ **all real numbers because $-4 \geq -4$ is true**

b. $-2x + 9 < -2(x - 3)$ **no solutions because $9 < 6$ is false**

Extra Example 5

You can work at most 24 hours per week as a nurse's aid. So far this week you have worked 7 hours. If the remaining shifts for the week are each 4 hours long, how many possible full shifts can you work? **You can work up to 4 full shifts.**

Closing the Lesson

Have students summarize the major points of the lesson and answer the Essential Question: How do you solve multi-step inequalities?

- **You can solve multi-step inequalities by applying the same steps used for solving multi-step equations, with the additional step of reversing an inequality symbol if you multiply or divide by a negative number.**

Use the distributive property and the properties of inequality to produce equivalent inequalities. Reverse the direction of the inequality symbol when dividing or multiplying by a negative number. If you reach an inequality that is false, there are no solutions; if you reach an inequality that is always true, then all real numbers are solutions.

pp. 369–370

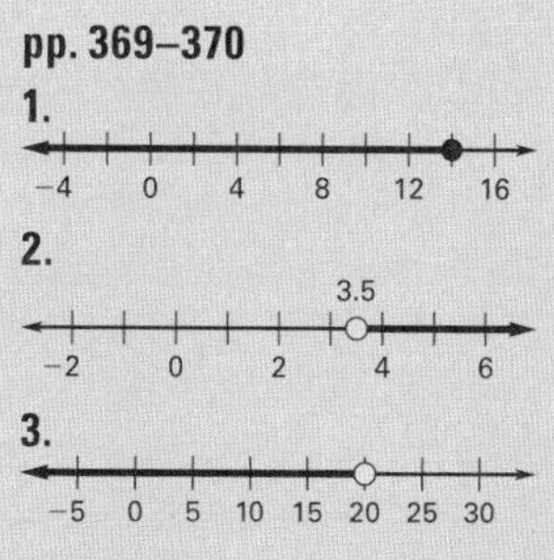

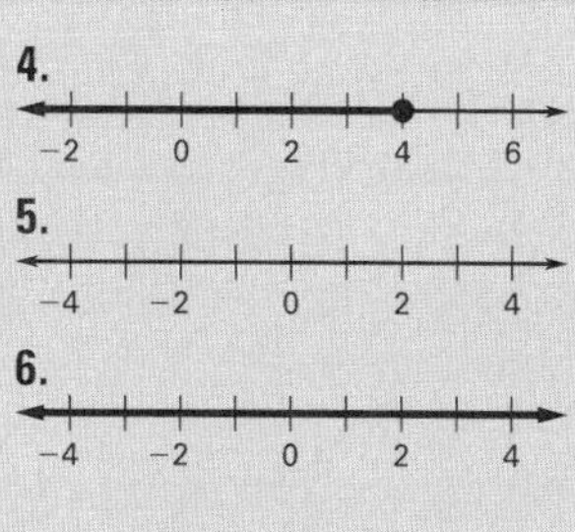

4 PRACTICE AND APPLY

Assignment Guide

Answer Transparencies available for all exercises

Basic:
Day 1: EP p. 940 Exs. 9–14
pp. 372–374
Exs. 1–10, 17–24, 29, 30, 37–41, 44–56 even

Average:
Day 1: pp. 372–374
Exs. 1, 2, 4–14 even, 15, 16, 21–27 odd, 29–34, 37–42, 44, 45–55 odd

Advanced:
Day 1: pp. 372–374
Exs. 1, 2, 4–8 even, 13, 14, 22–28 even, 29–36*, 38–43*, 44–56 even

Block:
pp. 372–374
Exs. 1, 2, 4–14 even, 15, 16, 21–27 odd, 29–34, 37–42, 44, 45–55 odd (with 6.4)

Differentiated Instruction

See *Differentiated Instruction Resources* for suggestions on addressing the needs of a diverse classroom.

Homework Check

For a quick check of student understanding of key concepts, go over the following exercises:

Basic: 3, 6, 9, 20, 37
Average: 4, 6, 12, 25, 38
Advanced: 4, 8, 13, 26, 39

Extra Practice

- Student Edition, p. 943
- Chapter Resource Book: Practice levels A, B, C

Practice Worksheet

An easily-readable reduced practice page (with answers) for this lesson can be found on p. 354D.

2. An inequality has no solutions if it is equivalent to a false inequality such as $0 > 2$. All real numbers are solutions of the inequality if it is equivalent to a true inequality such as $0 < 2$.

6.3 EXERCISES

HOMEWORK KEY
○ = **WORKED-OUT SOLUTIONS** on p. WS14 for Exs. 5, 19, and 39
★ = **STANDARDIZED TEST PRACTICE** Exs. 2, 33, 39, 40, and 42
◆ = **MULTIPLE REPRESENTATIONS** Ex. 41

SKILL PRACTICE

A

1. **VOCABULARY** Copy and complete: The inequalities $3x - 1 < 11$, $3x < 12$, and $x < 4$ are called __?__. **equivalent inequalities**

2. ★ **WRITING** How do you know whether an inequality has no solutions? How do you know whether the solutions are all real numbers? **See margin.**

EXAMPLES 1, 2, and 3 on pp. 369–370 for Exs. 3–16

SOLVING INEQUALITIES Solve the inequality. Graph your solution. **3–14. See margin for art.**

3. $2x - 3 > 7$ $\mathbf{x > 5}$
4. $5y + 9 \le 4$ $\mathbf{y \le -1}$
5. $8v - 3 \ge -11$ $\mathbf{v \ge -1}$
6. $3(w + 12) < 0$ $\mathbf{w < -12}$
7. $7(r - 3) \ge -13$ $\mathbf{r \ge 1\frac{1}{7}}$
8. $2(s + 4) \le 16$ $\mathbf{s \le 4}$
9. $4 - 2m > 7 - 3m$ $\mathbf{m > 3}$
10. $8n - 2 > 17n + 9$ $\mathbf{n < -1\frac{2}{9}}$
11. $-10p > 6p - 8$ $\mathbf{p < \frac{1}{2}}$
12. $4 - \frac{1}{2}q \le 33 - q$ $\mathbf{q \le 58}$
13. $-\frac{2}{3}d - 2 < \frac{1}{3}d + 8$ $\mathbf{d > -10}$
14. $8 - \frac{4}{5}f > -14 - 2f$ $\mathbf{f > -18\frac{1}{3}}$

ERROR ANALYSIS *Describe* and correct the error in solving the inequality. **15, 16. See margin.**

15.
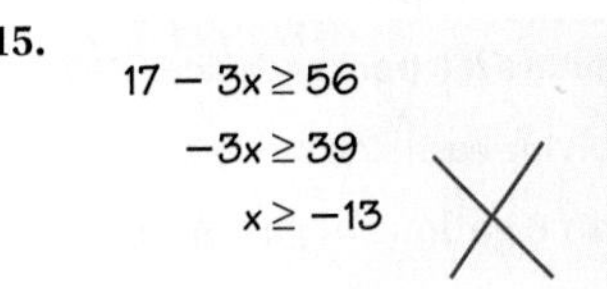
$17 - 3x \ge 56$
$-3x \ge 39$
$x \ge -13$

16.
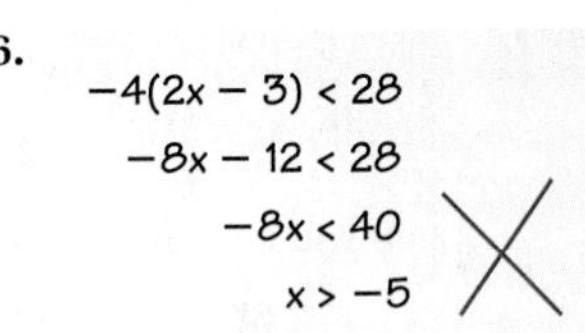
$-4(2x - 3) < 28$
$-8x - 12 < 28$
$-8x < 40$
$x > -5$

EXAMPLE 4 on p. 370 for Exs. 17–28

SOLVING INEQUALITIES Solve the inequality, if possible.

17. $3p - 5 > 2p + p - 7$ **all real numbers**
18. $5d - 8d - 4 \le -4 + 3d$ $\mathbf{d \ge 0}$
19. $3(s - 4) \ge 2(s - 6)$ $\mathbf{s \ge 0}$
20. $2(t - 3) > 2t - 8$ **all real numbers**
21. $5(b + 9) \le 5b + 45$ **all real numbers**
22. $2(4c - 7) \ge 8(c - 3)$ **all real numbers**
23. $6(x + 3) < 5x + 18 + x$ **no solution**
24. $4 + 9y - 3 \ge 3(3y + 2)$ **no solution**
25. $2.2h + 0.4 \le 2(1.1h - 0.1)$ **no solution**
26. $9.5j - 6 + 5.5j \ge 3(5j - 2)$ **all real numbers**
27. $\frac{1}{5}(4m + 10) < \frac{4}{5}m + 2$ **no solution**
28. $\frac{3}{4}(8n - 4) < -3(1 - 2n)$ **no solution**

B

TRANSLATING PHRASES Translate the verbal phrase into an inequality. Then solve the inequality and graph your solution. **29–32. See margin for art.**

29. Four more than the product of 3 and x is less than 40. $\mathbf{3x + 4 < 40; x < 12}$
30. Twice the sum of x and 8 is greater than or equal to -36. $\mathbf{2(x + 8) \ge -36; x \ge -26}$
31. The sum of $5x$ and $2x$ is greater than the difference of $9x$ and 4. $\mathbf{5x + 2x > 9x - 4; x < 2}$
32. The product of 6 and the difference of $6x$ and 3 is less than or equal to the product of -2 and the sum of 4 and $8x$. $\mathbf{6(6x - 3) \le -2(4 + 8x); x \le \frac{5}{26}}$

33. ★ **MULTIPLE CHOICE** For which values of a and b are all the solutions of $ax + b > 0$ positive? **C**

(A) $a > 0, b > 0$ (B) $a < 0, b < 0$ (C) $a > 0, b < 0$ (D) $a < 0, b = 0$

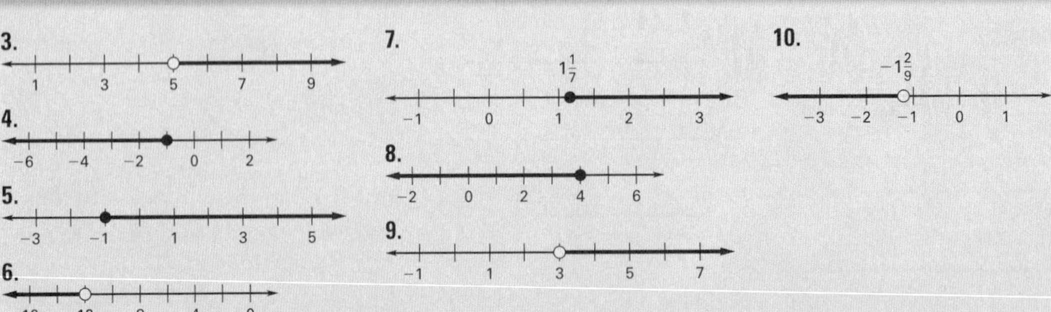

GEOMETRY **Write and solve an inequality to find the possible values of x.**

34. Area > 81 square feet **$9(x + 2) > 81$; $x > 7$**

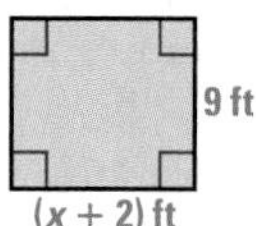

35. Area ≤ 44 square centimeters **$\frac{1}{2} \cdot 8(x + 1) \le 44$; $x \le 10$**

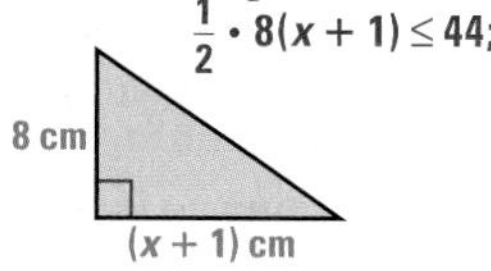

C 36. **CHALLENGE** For which value of a are all the solutions of $2(x - 5) \ge 3x + a$ less than or equal to 5? **−15**

PROBLEM SOLVING

EXAMPLE 5 A on p. 371 for Exs. 37–40

37. **CD BURNING** A blank CD can hold 70 minutes of music. So far you have burned 25 minutes of music onto the CD. You estimate that each song lasts 4 minutes. What are the possible numbers of additional songs that you can burn onto the CD? **at most 11 songs**

@HomeTutor for problem solving help at classzone.com

38. **BUSINESS** You spend $46 on supplies to make wooden ornaments and plan to sell the ornaments for $8.50 each. What are the possible numbers of ornaments that you can sell in order for your profit to be positive? **at least 6 ornaments**

@HomeTutor for problem solving help at classzone.com

39a. Up to 6 swans; the area of the habitat is (20 feet)(50 feet) = 1000 square feet. 500 square feet are needed for the first two swans and the remaining 1000 − 500 = 500 square feet can hold up to 500 ÷ 125 = 4 more swans; so, the maximum number of swans is 2 + 4 = 6 swans.

39. ★ **SHORT RESPONSE** A zookeeper is designing a rectangular habitat for swans, as shown. The zookeeper needs to reserve 500 square feet for the first 2 swans and 125 square feet for each additional swan.

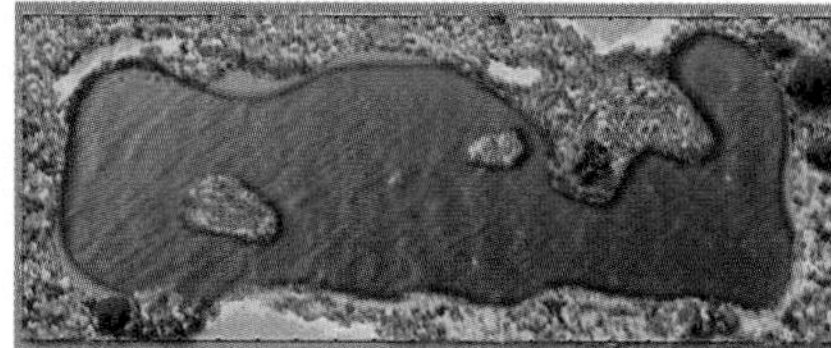

a. **Calculate** What are the possible numbers of swans that the habitat can hold? *Explain* how you got your answer. **See margin.**

b. **Compare** Suppose that the zookeeper increases both the length and width of the habitat by 20 feet. What are the possible numbers of additional swans that the habitat can hold? **at most 14 more swans**

40. ★ **MULTIPLE CHOICE** A gym is offering a trial membership for 3 months by discounting the regular monthly rate by $50. You will consider joining the gym if the total cost of the trial membership is less than $100. Which inequality can you use to find the possible regular monthly rates that you are willing to pay? **C**

Ⓐ $3x - 50 < 100$ Ⓑ $3x - 50 > 100$

Ⓒ $3(x - 50) < 100$ Ⓓ $3(x - 50) > 100$

Avoiding Common Errors

Exercises 3–14 Students should always check that their written solution for an inequality matches the graph of the solution. Specifically, they should check that their inequality uses an open circle for < or > and a closed circle for ≤ or ≥.

Exercises 17–28 When using the distributive property, students who use mental math sometimes fail to distribute the factor to all the numbers inside the parentheses. Encourage all students to get into the habit of checking for this error.

Reading Strategy

Exercises 37–43 As in the previous lessons, students should read the problems carefully in order to determine which inequality symbol to use. Remind them to look for key words and phrases, such as "no more than," "at most," and "at least."

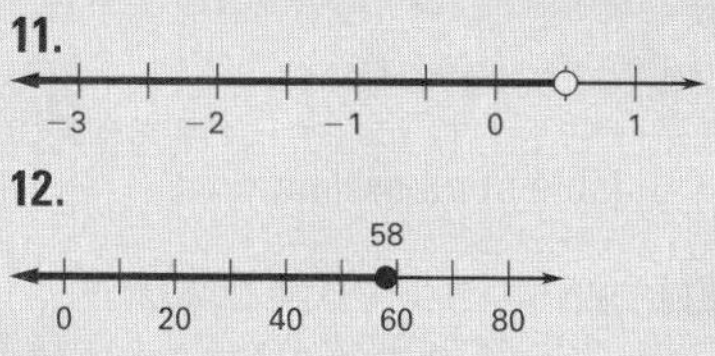

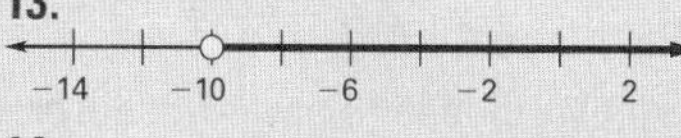

15. The inequality symbol was not reversed when dividing both sides by −3; $x \le -13$.

16. The distributive property was not used correctly, $-8x + 12 < 28$, $-8x < 16$, $x > -2$.

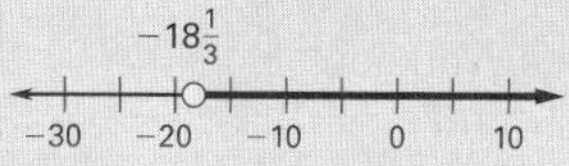

30.

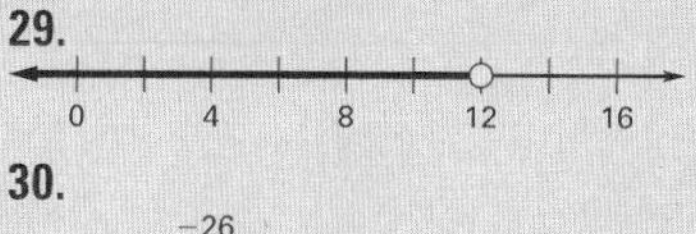

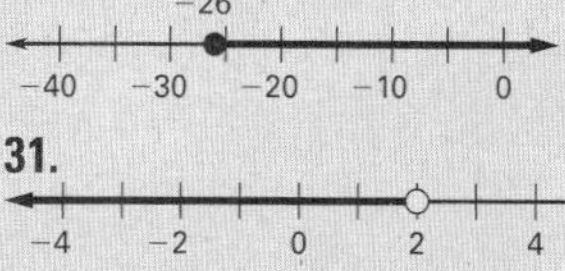

5 ASSESS AND RETEACH

Daily Homework Quiz

Transparency Available

1. Solve $3(x + 8) < 9$. Graph your solution. **all real numbers less than −5**

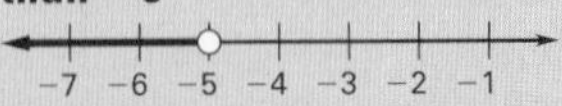

Solve the inequality, if possible.

2. $6k + 1 > 3(2k - 3)$ **all real numbers because $1 > -9$ is true**
3. $5(a - 2) < 5a - 14$ **no solutions because $-10 < -14$ is false**
4. A box of cat treats contains at least 50 treats. So far you have fed your cats 18 treats. If you want the box of treats to last 8 days, what are the possible average numbers of treats you can feed the cats per day? **an average of no more than 4 treats per day**

Available at **classzone.com**

Diagnosis/Remediation

- Practice A, B, C in Chapter Resource Book
- Study Guide in Chapter Resource Book
- Practice Workbook
- @HomeTutor

Challenge

Additional challenge is available in the Chapter Resource Book.

41a, 42c. See Additional Answers beginning on p. AA1.

B

41. ◆ **MULTIPLE REPRESENTATIONS** A baseball pitcher makes 53 pitches in the first four innings of a game and plans to pitch in the next 3 innings.
    a. **Making a Table** Make a table that gives the total number t of pitches made if the pitcher makes an average of p pitches per inning in the next 3 innings. Use the following values for p: 15, 16, 17, 18, 19. **See margin.**
    b. **Writing an Inequality** The baseball coach assigns a maximum of 105 pitches to the pitcher for the game. Write and solve an inequality to find the possible average numbers of pitches that the pitcher can make in each of the next three innings. $53 + 3p \le 105,\ p \le 17\frac{1}{3}$**, at most 17 pitches**

42a. 5%; the amount that was taxed was $300 − $175 = $125. To find the tax rate, solve the proportion $\frac{x}{100} = \frac{6.25}{125}$.

42. ★ **EXTENDED RESPONSE** A state imposes a sales tax on items of clothing that cost more than $175. The tax applies only to the difference of the price of the item and $175.

THE STYLE STORE
Item: Suit — Price: $ 300.00
Tax: $ 6.25
Total: $ 306.25

    a. **Calculate** Use the receipt shown to find the tax rate (as a percent). *Explain* how you got your answer.
    b. **Apply** A shopper has $400 to spend on a winter coat. Write and solve an inequality to find the prices p of coats that the shopper can afford. Assume that $p \ge 175$. $p + 0.05(p - 175) \le 400,\ p \le 389.29$**; up to $389.29**
    c. **Compare** Another state imposes a 4% sales tax on the entire price of an item of clothing. For which prices would paying the 4% tax be cheaper than paying the tax described above? Your answer should include the following:
       - writing and solving an inequality that describes the situation
       - checking the reasonableness of your answer using one of the solutions of the inequality **See margin.**

C

43. **CHALLENGE** Your scores in four bowling league tournaments are 157, 161, 149, and 172. After the next game, you want your average score to be at least 167. What are the possible scores that you can earn in your next tournament in order to meet your goal? **at least 196**

MIXED REVIEW

44. Using the positive integers less than 10, draw a Venn diagram where set A consists of factors of 30 and set B consists of odd numbers. Then tell whether this statement is *true* or *false*: "If a positive integer less than 10 is odd, then it is a factor of 30." *Explain* your reasoning. *(p. 929)*
See margin for art; false; 7 and 9 are odd numbers less than 10 that are not factors of 30.

Simplify the expression.

45. $11(-y)(-y)$ *(p. 88)* $11y^2$
46. $\frac{3}{4} \cdot (-16y)$ *(p. 88)* $-12y$
47. $-2(x + 1) - 7x$ *(p. 96)* $-9x - 2$
48. $5x + 4 - 3x$ *(p. 96)* $2x + 4$
49. $8(x + 6) - 5$ *(p. 96)* $8x + 43$
50. $\frac{-15x + 18}{-6}$ *(p. 103)* $\frac{5}{2}x - 3$

PREVIEW Prepare for Lesson 6.4 in Exs. 51–56.

Solve the inequality. Graph your solution. 51–56. See margin for art.

51. $x + 7 < 8$ *(p. 356)* $x < 1$
52. $y - 4 \ge -2$ *(p. 356)* $y \ge 2$
53. $9 \le z + 13$ *(p. 356)* $z \ge -4$
54. $4.8 > m - 7.4$ *(p. 356)* $m < 12.2$
55. $\frac{n}{4} < -1$ *(p. 363)* $n < -4$
56. $4p \ge 52$ *(p. 363)* $p \ge 13$

EXTRA PRACTICE for Lesson 6.3, p. 943   **ONLINE QUIZ** at classzone.com

44.

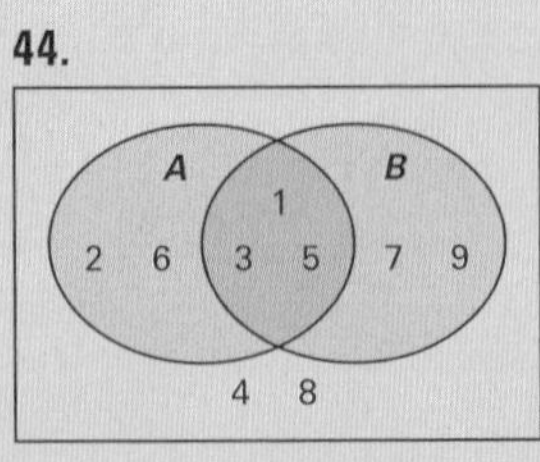

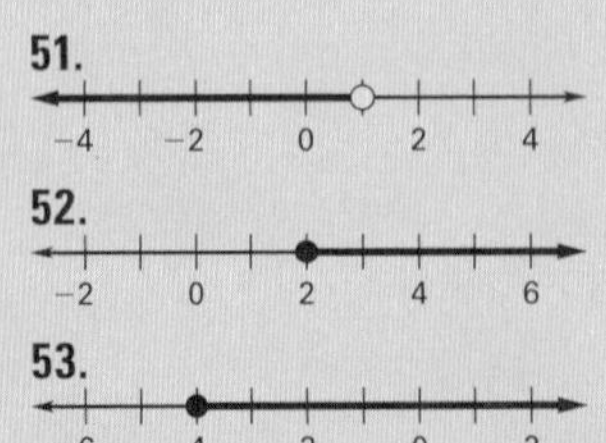

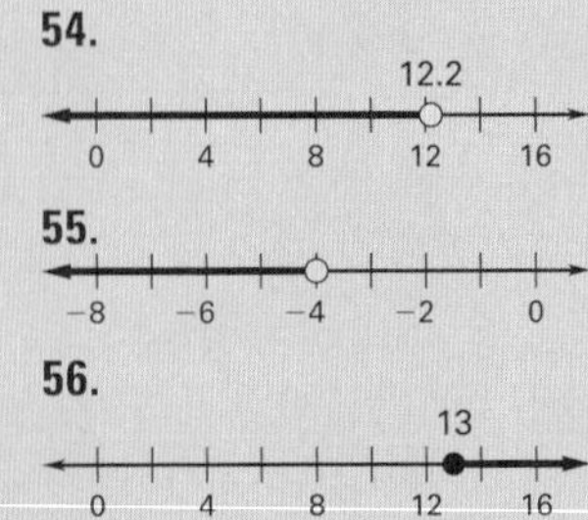

Using ALTERNATIVE METHODS

Another Way to Solve Example 5, page 371

MULTIPLE REPRESENTATIONS In Example 5 on page 371, you saw how to solve a problem about buying gasoline using an inequality. You can also solve the problem by working backward or by using a graph.

PROBLEM

CAR WASH Use the sign shown. A gas station charges $.10 less per gallon of gasoline if a customer also gets a car wash. What are the possible amounts (in gallons) of gasoline that you can buy if you also get a car wash and can spend at most $20?

METHOD 1

Work backward One alternative approach is to work backward.

STEP 1 **Read** the problem. It gives you the following information:

- amount you can spend: up to $20
- price of a car wash: $8
- regular price per gallon of gasoline: $2.09
- discount per gallon of gasoline when you get a car wash: $.10

Because you are getting a car wash, gasoline costs $2.09 − $.10, or $1.99, per gallon.

STEP 2 **Work** backward.

- Start with the amount you have to spend: $20.
- Subtract the cost of a car wash: $20 − $8 = $12.
- Make a table of values showing the amount of money you have left after buying various amounts of gasoline.

Gasoline (gal)	Amount of money left
0	$12.00
1	$10.01
2	$8.02
3	$6.03
4	$4.04
5	$2.05
6	$.06

− $1.99 (between each successive row)

▶ You can buy up to slightly more than 6 gallons of gasoline.

Alternative Strategy

Example 5 on page 371 can be solved by working backward or by using a graph. Working backward is a good strategy because the problem provides a maximum amount and a constant amount, which gives the student an immediate starting point and a quick means to a solution. A graph is a good strategy because it gives an approximate answer, which is all that is needed for this problem.

Avoiding Common Errors

In Method 1, Step 2, you may want to point out a quick way to subtract $1.99 is to subtract $2 and add $.01. This can help students avoid calculation errors and give faster results.

Reading Strategy

Tell students that italicized words usually emphasize important ideas. Draw their attention to the italicized words in Method 2, Step 4. Ask them to explain why they think these words are italicized. Emphasize that they should look for words such as "at most" or "at least" in the Practice exercises so they know whether the solutions are "on-or-below" or "on-or-above" the graph of the line.

1. At least 9 batches; Method 1: Work backward. Begin with 100 cookies and make a table of values showing the number of cookies you have left to make after each batch of 12 cookies.

Number of batches baked	Number of cookies to bake
0	100
1	88
2	76
3	64
4	52
5	40
6	28
7	16
8	4
9	less than 0

After 9 batches you will have at least 100 cookies. Method 2: Use a graph. Write and graph an equation that gives the total number y of cookies baked as a function of the number x of batches baked: $y = 12x$. Graph $y = 100$ on the same coordinate plane.

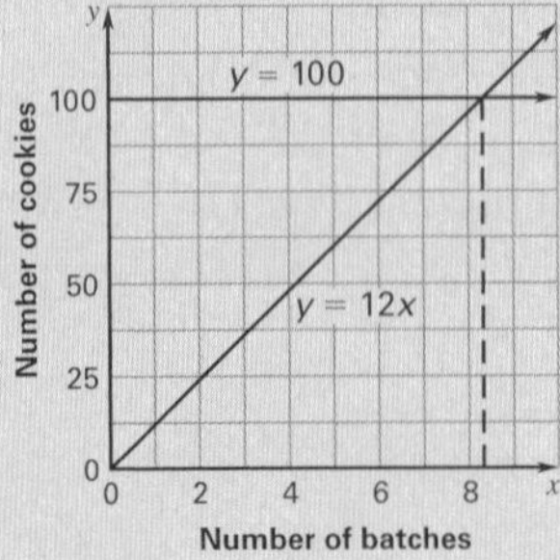

The graphs intersect between $x = 8$ and $x = 9$. Because you must bake at least 100 cookies, the solutions are the x-coordinates of the points on the graph of $y = 12x$ that lie on or above the graph of $y = 100$. Only integer values of x make sense in this situation, so you must bake at least 9 batches.

2, 4. See Additional Answers beginning on p. AA1.

METHOD 2 **Using a graph** Another alternative approach is to use a graph.

STEP 1 **Write** a verbal model. Then write an equation that gives the total amount of money y (in dollars) that you spend as a function of the amount x (in gallons) of gasoline that you buy.

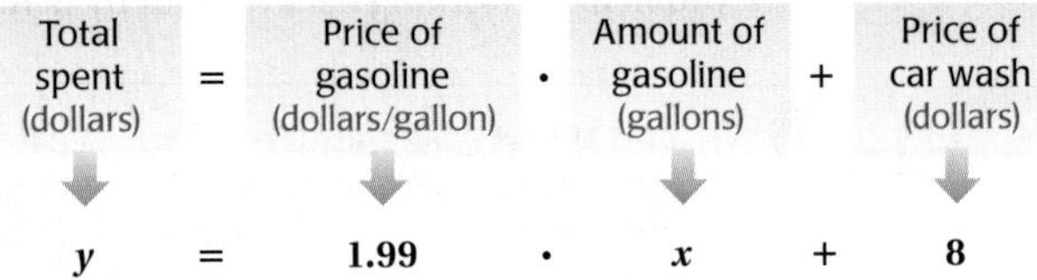

Total spent (dollars)
=
Price of gasoline (dollars/gallon)
·
Amount of gasoline (gallons)
+
Price of car wash (dollars)
y = 1.99 · x + 8

STEP 2 **Graph** $y = 1.99x + 8$.

STEP 3 **Graph** $y = 20$ in the same coordinate plane. This equation gives the maximum amount of money that you can spend for gasoline and a car wash.

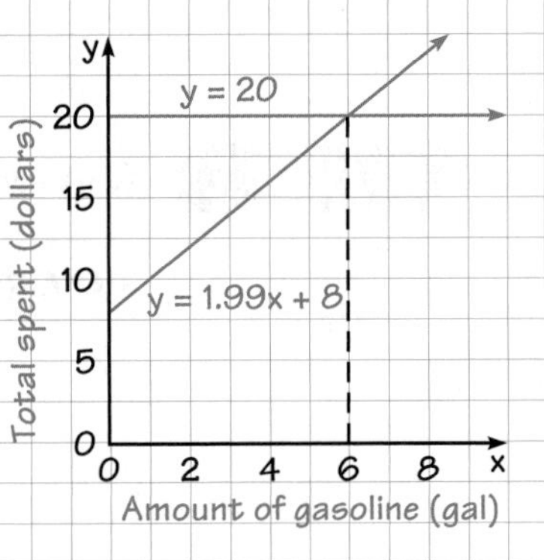

STEP 4 **Analyze** the graphs. The point of intersection shows that you can buy slightly more than 6 gallons of gasoline when you spend $20. Because you can spend *at most* $20, the solutions are the x-coordinates of the points on the graph of $y = 1.99x + 8$ that lie *on or below* the graph of $y = 20$.

▸ You can buy up to slightly more than 6 gallons of gasoline.

PRACTICE

1. **BAKING** You need to bake at least 100 cookies for a bake sale. You can bake 12 cookies per batch of dough. What are the possible numbers of batches that will allow you to bake enough cookies? Solve this problem using two different methods. **See margin.**

2. **VIDEO GAMES** A video game console costs $259, and games cost $29 each. You saved $400 to buy a console and games. What are the possible numbers of games that you can buy? Solve this problem using two different methods. **See margin.**

3. **WHAT IF?** In Exercise 2, suppose that you saved $500 and decide to buy a video game console that costs $299. What are the possible numbers of games that you can buy? **at most 6 games**

4. **MONEY** You need to have at least $100 in your checking account to avoid a low balance fee. You have $247 in your account, and you make withdrawals of $20 per week. What are the possible numbers of weeks that you can withdraw money and avoid paying the fee? Solve this problem using two different methods. **See margin.**

5. **RUNNING TIMES** You are running a 10 mile race. You run the first 3 miles in 24.7 minutes. Your goal is to finish the race in less than 1 hour 20 minutes. What should your average running time (in minutes per mile) be for the remaining miles? **less than 7.9 min/mi**

Solve Linear Inequalities by Graphing

GOAL Use graphs to solve linear inequalities.

So far in Chapter 6 you have seen how to solve linear inequalities algebraically. You can also solve linear inequalities graphically.

KEY CONCEPT *For Your Notebook*

Solving Linear Inequalities Graphically

STEP 1 **Write** the inequality in one of the following forms: $ax + b < 0$, $ax + b \leq 0$, $ax + b > 0$, or $ax + b \geq 0$.

STEP 2 **Write** the related equation $y = ax + b$.

STEP 3 **Graph** the equation $y = ax + b$.

- The solutions of $ax + b > 0$ are the x-coordinates of the points on the graph of $y = ax + b$ that lie above the x-axis.
- The solutions of $ax + b < 0$ are the x-coordinates of the points on the graph of $y = ax + b$ that lie below the x-axis.
- If the inequality symbol is $\leq$ or $\geq$, then the x-intercept of the graph is also a solution.

COMPARE FUNCTION VALUES
If you think of the equation $y = ax + b$ as a function, the solutions of $ax + b > 0$ and $ax + b < 0$ tell you where the values of the function are positive or negative.

EXAMPLE 1 Solve an inequality graphically

Solve $3x + 2 > 8$ graphically.

Solution

STEP 1 **Write** the inequality in the form $ax + b > 0$.

$3x + 2 > 8$ **Write original inequality.**

$3x - 6 > 0$ **Subtract 8 from each side.**

STEP 2 **Write** the related equation $y = 3x - 6$.

STEP 3 **Graph** the equation $y = 3x - 6$.

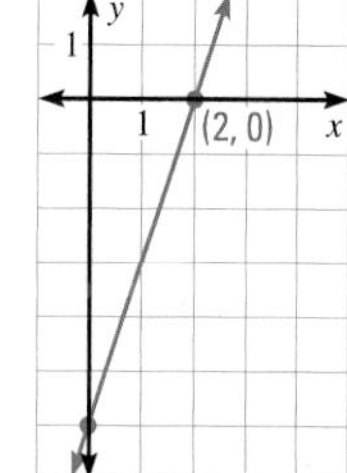

The inequality in Step 1 is in the form $ax + b > 0$, and the x-intercept of the graph in Step 3 is 2. So, $x > 2$.

▶ The solutions are all real numbers greater than 2. Check by substituting a number greater than 2 in the original inequality.

CHECK $3x + 2 > 8$ **Write original inequality.**

$3(4) + 2 \overset{?}{>} 8$ **Substitute 4 for x.**

$14 > 8$ ✓ **Solution checks.**

1 PLAN AND PREPARE

Warm-Up Exercises

1. Write $4x + 2 = 5$ in the form $ax + b = 0$. Then write the related function $y = ax + b$. **$4x - 3 = 0$; $y = 4x - 3$**
2. Solve $2x + 3 = x$ by graphing the related function $y = f(x)$. **−3**

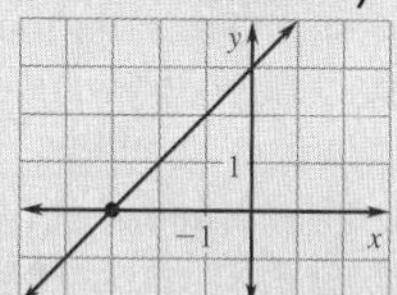

2 FOCUS AND MOTIVATE

Essential Question

Big Idea 3, p. 355

How do you use graphs to solve linear inequalities? **Tell students they will learn how to answer this question by graphing the related function and shading one of the half-planes.**

3 TEACH

Extra Example 1

Solve $2x - 1 < 5$ graphically.

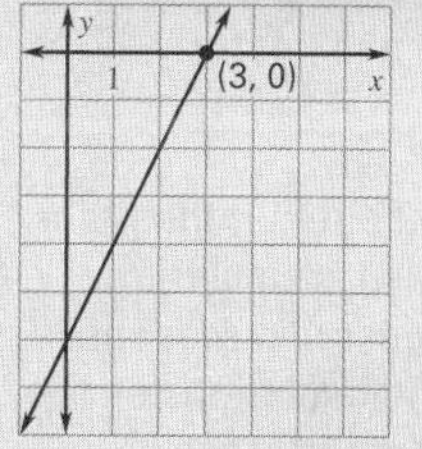

all real numbers less than 3

NCTM STANDARDS

Standard 2: Use models to understand relationships

Standard 6: Solve problems in math and other contexts

Extra Example 2

Your gym membership costs \$18.95 per month. Yoga classes cost \$3.25 each. You budget \$30 per month for gym costs. What are the possible numbers of yoga classes that you can afford each month? **no more than 3 yoga classes per month**

Closing the Lesson

Have students summarize the major points of the lesson and answer the Essential Question: How do you use graphs to solve linear inequalities?

- **You can solve a linear inequality graphically by writing and graphing the related function.**

Write the inequality in a form that sets it to zero. Then write the related function and graph the equation. The inequality symbol specifies whether or not the solutions contain the *x*-intercept and whether the solutions are to the right or to the left of the *x*-intercept.

4 PRACTICE AND APPLY

Avoiding Common Errors

Exercises 1–3 Some students may find the *y*-intercept instead of the *x*-intercept for these exercises. Remind these students that they are solving for *x* and not for *y*.

Study Strategy

Exercise 4 Point out that the problem in the exercise is similar to Example 2. Suggest that students closely model their solutions on the patterns shown in the steps of Example 2.

EXAMPLE 2 Approximate a real-world solution

CELL PHONES Your cell phone plan costs \$49.99 per month for a given number of minutes. Each additional minute or part of a minute costs \$.40. You budgeted \$55 per month for phone costs. What are the possible additional minutes x that you can afford each month?

Solution

STEP 1 **Write** a verbal model. Then write an inequality.

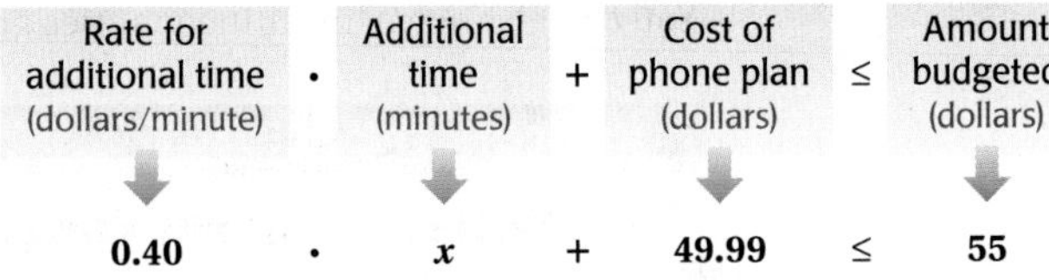

$0.40 \cdot x + 49.99 \leq 55$

Write the inequality in the form $ax + b \leq 0$.

$0.40x + 49.99 \leq 55$ **Write original inequality.**

$0.40x - 5.01 \leq 0$ **Subtract 55 from each side.**

STEP 2 **Write** the related equation $y = 0.40x - 5.01$.

STEP 3 **Graph** the equation $y = 0.40x - 5.01$ on a graphing calculator.

Use the *trace* feature of the graphing calculator to find the *x*-intercept of the graph.

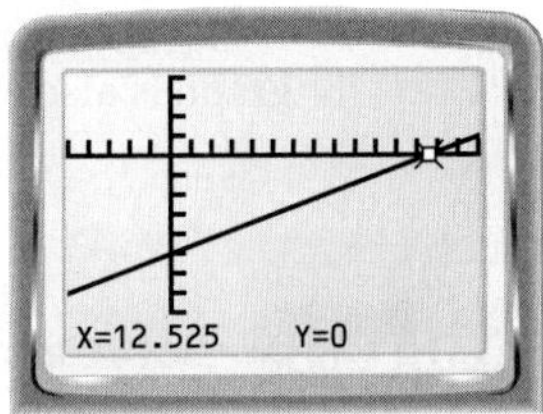

The inequality in Step 1 is in the form $ax + b \leq 0$, and the *x*-intercept is about 12.5. Because a part of a minute costs \$.40, round 12.5 down to 12 to be sure that you stay within your budget.

▸ You can afford up to 12 additional minutes.

PRACTICE

EXAMPLES 1 and 2 on pp. 377–378 for Exs. 1–4

Solve the inequality graphically.

1. $2x + 5 > 11$ **$x > 3$**
2. $\frac{1}{2}x + 6 \leq 13$ **$x \leq 14$**
3. $0.2x - 15.75 < 27$ **$x < 213.75$**
4. **CABLE COSTS** Your family has a cable television package that costs \$40.99 per month. Pay-per-view movies cost \$3.95 each. Your family budgets \$55 per month for cable television costs. What are the possible numbers of pay-per-view movies that your family can afford each month? **up to 3 movies**

Investigating Algebra ACTIVITY *Use before Lesson 6.4*

6.4 Statements with *And* and *Or*

MATERIALS • paper and pencil

QUESTION **What is the difference between a statement with *and* and a statement with *or*?**

EXPLORE **Use a Venn diagram to answer questions about a group**

STEP 1 ***Answer questions*** Copy the questions below and write your answers beside them. **Steps 1, 2. Answers may vary.**

1. Are you taking an art class?
2. Are you taking a foreign language class?

STEP 2 ***Complete a Venn diagram*** Form a group with 3 or 4 classmates. Draw a Venn diagram, like the one shown below, where set *A* consists of students taking an art class, and set *B* consists of students taking a foreign language class. Then write the name of each student in the appropriate section of the diagram.

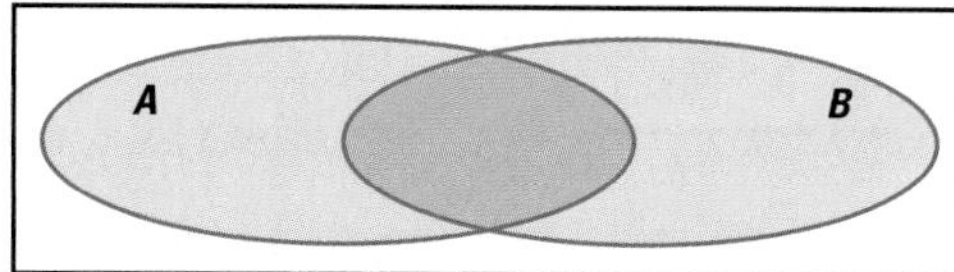

DRAW CONCLUSIONS **Use your observations to complete these exercises**

In Exercises 1–3, use your Venn diagram to list the students who belong in the given set. **1–6. Answers may vary.**

1. Set *A*
2. Set *B*
3. Set *A and* set *B*
4. The students who belong in set *A or* set *B* are all of the students who belong only in set *A*, only in set *B*, or in set *A and* set *B*. List the students in your group who belong in set *A or* set *B*.
5. **OPEN-ENDED** Write a statement with *and* so that the statement is true for all students in your group.
6. **OPEN-ENDED** Write a statement with *or* so that the statement is true for all students in your group.

REASONING **Tell whether the statement is *true* or *false*.**

7. If a student belongs in set *A and* set *B*, then the student belongs in set *A or* set *B*. **true**
8. If a student belongs in set *A or* set *B*, then the student belongs in set *A and* set *B*. **false**

1 PLAN AND PREPARE

Explore the Concept

- Students will use a Venn diagram to explore the difference between statements with *and* and with *or*.
- This activity leads into the study of compound inequalities in Example 1 in Lesson 6.4.

Recommended Time

Work activity: 10 min

Discuss results: 5 min

Grouping

Students can work individually or in groups of 4. If students work in groups, two can ask questions and write answers and two can draw and label the Venn diagram.

2 TEACH

Tips for Success

If students are not taking art or foreign language, then suggest other classes such as science or English.

Key Discovery

Statements with *and* describe the intersection of two sets, while statements with *or* describe the union of two sets.

3 ASSESS AND RETEACH

Which usually contains more students, "Set *A and* Set *B*" or "Set *A or* Set *B*"? Explain. **"Set *A or* Set *B*" includes students in either set, so it usually contains more than "Set *A and* Set *B*," for which students must be in both sets.**

1 PLAN AND PREPARE

Warm-Up Exercises

Transparency Available

Solve the inequality.

1. $8 > x + 10$ **all real numbers less than -2**
2. $6 \le 2x - 4$ **all real numbers greater than or equal to 5**
3. You estimate you can read at least 8 history text pages per day. What are the possible numbers of days it will take you to read at most 118 pages? **at most 15 days**

Notetaking Guide

Transparency Available

Promotes interactive learning and notetaking skills.

Pacing

Basic: 2 days
Average: 2 days
Advanced: 2 days
Block: 0.5 block with 6.3
0.5 block with 6.5

- See *Teaching Guide/Lesson Plan.*

2 FOCUS AND MOTIVATE

Essential Question

Big Idea 2, p. 355

How do you solve compound inequalities? **Tell students they will learn how to answer this question by solving the two parts of the inequality separately.**

NCTM STANDARDS

Standard 6: Solve problems in math and other contexts

Standard 7: Recognize reasoning and proof as fundamental to math

6.4 Solve Compound Inequalities

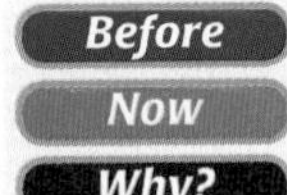

Before You solved one-step and multi-step inequalities.

Now You will solve compound inequalities.

Why? So you can describe possible heights, as in Example 2.

Key Vocabulary
- **compound inequality**

A **compound inequality** consists of two separate inequalities joined by *and* or *or*.

The graph of a compound inequality with *and* is the *intersection* of the graphs of the inequalities.

$x > -2$

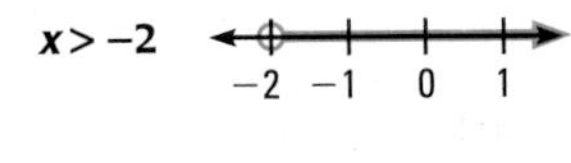

$x \le 1$

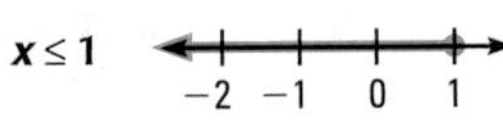

$-2 < x$ *and* $x \le 1$
$-2 < x \le 1$

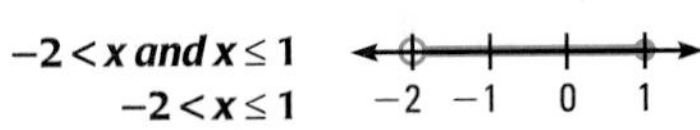

The graph of a compound inequality with *or* is the *union* of the graphs of the inequalities.

$x \ge 0$

$x < -1$

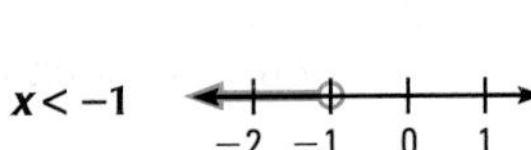

$x < -1$ *or* $x \ge 0$

EXAMPLE 1 Write and graph compound inequalities

Translate the verbal phrase into an inequality. Then graph the inequality.

a. All real numbers that are greater than -2 *and* less than 3

Inequality: $-2 < x < 3$

Graph:

b. All real numbers that are less than 0 *or* greater than or equal to 2

Inequality: $x < 0$ *or* $x \ge 2$

Graph:

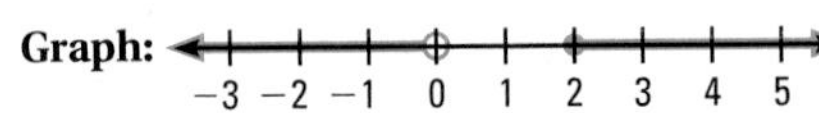

GUIDED PRACTICE for Example 1

Translate the verbal phrase into an inequality. Then graph the inequality. **1–2. See margin for art.**

1. All real numbers that are less than -1 *or* greater than or equal to 4 **$x < -1$ or $x \ge 4$**
2. All real numbers that are greater than or equal to -3 *and* less than 5 **$-3 \le x < 5$**

Resource Planning Guide

Chapter Resource Book
- Teaching Guide/Lesson Plan
- Activity Master
- Practice levels A, B, C
- Study Guide
- Catch-up for Absent Students
- Problem Solving Workshop
- Challenge

Workbooks
- Notetaking Guide
- Practice Workbook

Teaching Options
- **Power Presentations** provides dynamic electronic teaching resources for the classroom.
- **Activity Generator** provides editable activities for all ability levels.

Interactive Technology
- Easy Planner
- Power Presentations
- Activity Generator
- Animated Algebra
- Test Generator
- Online Quiz
- eWorkbook
- eEdition
- @HomeTutor

Resources for English Learners
- Spanish Study Guide
- Multi-Language Visual Glossary
- Student Resources in Spanish

See also the *Differentiated Instruction Resources* for more strategies for meeting individual needs.

EXAMPLE 2 Write and graph a real-world compound inequality

CAMERA CARS A crane sits on top of a camera car and faces toward the front. The crane's maximum height and minimum height above the ground are shown. Write and graph a compound inequality that describes the possible heights of the crane.

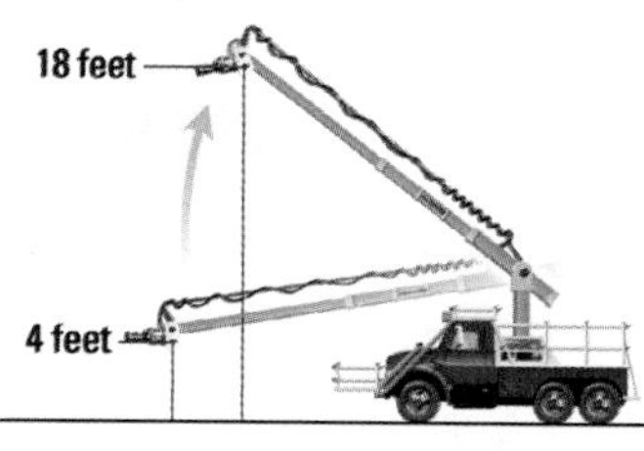

Solution

Let h represent the height (in feet) of the crane. All possible heights are greater than or equal to 4 feet *and* less than or equal to 18 feet. So, the inequality is $4 \le h \le 18$.

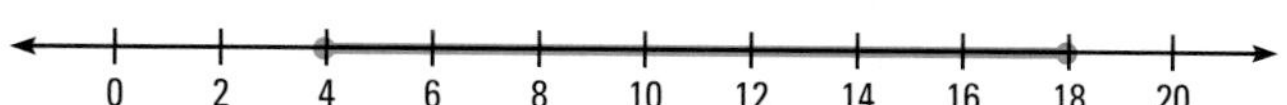

SOLVING COMPOUND INEQUALITIES A number is a solution of a compound inequality with *and* if the number is a solution of *both* inequalities. A number is a solution of a compound inequality with *or* if the number is a solution of *at least one* of the inequalities.

EXAMPLE 3 Solve a compound inequality with *and*

Solve $2 < x + 5 < 9$. Graph your solution.

Solution

Separate the compound inequality into two inequalities. Then solve each inequality separately.

$2 < x + 5$	*and*	$x + 5 < 9$	**Write two inequalities.**
$2 - 5 < x + 5 - 5$	*and*	$x + 5 - 5 < 9 - 5$	**Subtract 5 from each side.**
$-3 < x$	*and*	$x < 4$	**Simplify.**

The compound inequality can be written as $-3 < x < 4$.

▶ The solutions are all real numbers greater than -3 *and* less than 4.

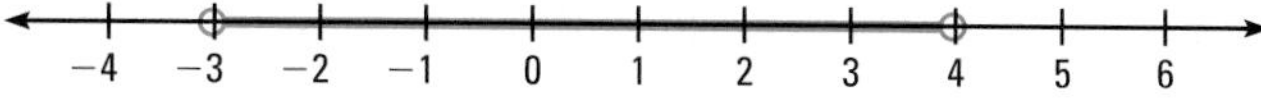

 **GUIDED PRACTICE** for Examples 2 and 3

3. **INVESTING** An investor buys shares of a stock and will sell them if the change c in value from the purchase price of a share is less than $-\$3.00$ or greater than \$4.50. Write and graph a compound inequality that describes the changes in value for which the shares will be sold. **$c < -3$ or $c > 4.5$; see margin for art.**

Solve the inequality. Graph your solution. **4–6. See margin for art.**

4. $-7 < x - 5 < 4$ **$-2 < x < 9$** 5. $10 \le 2y + 4 \le 24$ **$3 \le y \le 10$** 6. $-7 < -z - 1 < 3$ **$-4 < z < 6$**

Motivating the Lesson

Your veterinarian wants you to monitor your dog's weight if it dips 3 pounds below a minimum weight of 8 pounds or increases 5 pounds above a maximum weight of 12 pounds. Knowing how to solve compound inequalities will help you determine the possible weights you need to monitor.

3 TEACH

Extra Example 1

Translate the verbal phrase into an inequality. Then graph the inequality.

a. All real numbers that are greater than or equal to -4 *and* less than 4 **$-4 \le x < 4$**

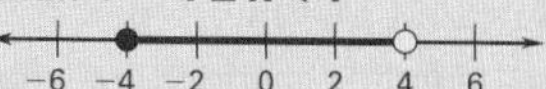

b. All real numbers that are less than -1 or greater than 2 **$x < -1$ *or* $x > 2$**

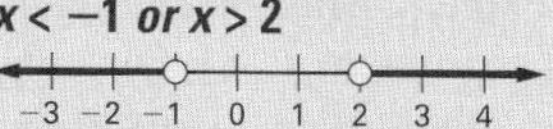

Extra Example 2

At an auction, the lowest bid for an autographed trading card is \$20. The highest bid is \$54. Write and graph a compound inequality that describes the possible bids. **All bids b are greater than or equal to \$20 *and* less than or equal to \$54; $20 \le b \le 54$.**

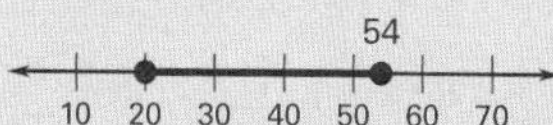

Extra Example 3

Solve $-1 < x + 1 \le 7$. Graph your solution. **all real numbers greater than -2 *and* less than or equal to 6**

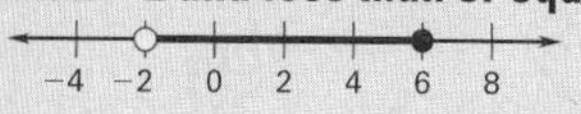

1–6. See Additional Answers beginning on p. AA1.

Extra Example 4

Solve $1 < -2x + 3 < 19$. Graph your solution. **all real numbers greater than -8 *and* less than 1**

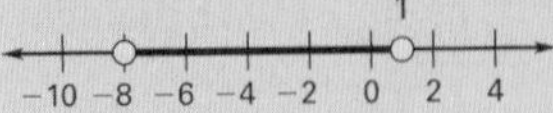

Extra Example 5

Solve $3x - 2 \le -11$ *or* $2x + 8 > 16$. Graph your solution. **all real numbers less than or equal to -3 *or* greater than 4**

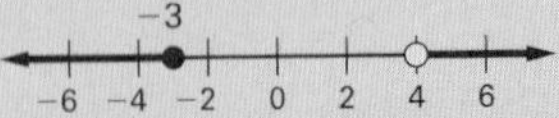

Key Questions to Ask for Example 5

- According to the graph, is 3 a solution of the compound inequality? Explain. **No; the inequality $x < 3$ is not true when x is 3.**
- Does a number have to be a solution of both inequalities to be a solution of the compound inequality? Explain. **No; a number has to be a solution of at least one of the inequalities for an *or* compound inequality.**

An **Animated Algebra** activity is available online for **Example 5**. This activity is also part of **Power Presentations**.

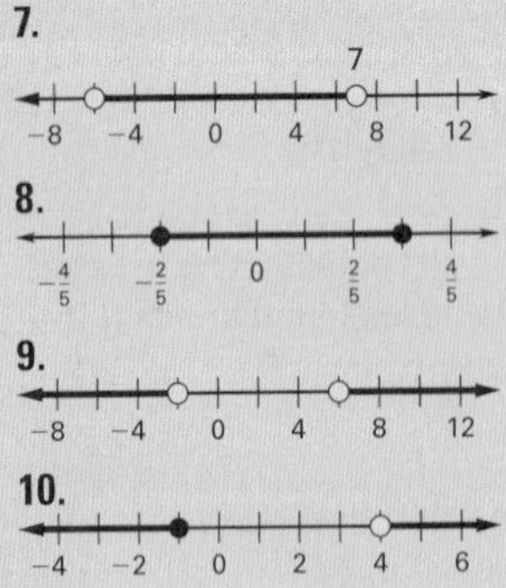

ANOTHER WAY In Example 3, you could solve $2 < x + 5 < 9$ by subtracting 5 from 2, $x + 5$, and 9 without first separating the compound inequality into two separate inequalities. To solve a compound inequality with *and*, you perform the same operation on each expression.

EXAMPLE 4 Solve a compound inequality with *and*

Solve $-5 \le -x - 3 \le 2$. Graph your solution.

$-5 \le -x - 3 \le 2$	Write original inequality.
$-5 + 3 \le -x - 3 + 3 \le 2 + 3$	Add 3 to each expression.
$-2 \le -x \le 5$	Simplify.
$-1(-2) \ge -1(-x) \ge -1(5)$	Multiply each expression by -1 and reverse *both* inequality symbols.
$2 \ge x \ge -5$	Simplify.
$-5 \le x \le 2$	Rewrite in the form $a \le x \le b$.

▸ The solutions are all real numbers greater than or equal to -5 *and* less than or equal to 2.

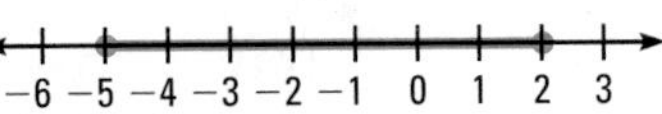

EXAMPLE 5 Solve a compound inequality with *or*

Solve $2x + 3 < 9$ *or* $3x - 6 > 12$. Graph your solution.

Solution

Solve the two inequalities separately.

$2x + 3 < 9$	*or*	$3x - 6 > 12$	Write original inequality.
$2x + 3 - 3 < 9 - 3$	*or*	$3x - 6 + 6 > 12 + 6$	Addition or subtraction property of inequality
$2x < 6$	*or*	$3x > 18$	Simplify.
$\frac{2x}{2} < \frac{6}{2}$	*or*	$\frac{3x}{3} > \frac{18}{3}$	Division property of inequality
$x < 3$	*or*	$x > 6$	Simplify.

▸ The solutions are all real numbers less than 3 *or* greater than 6.

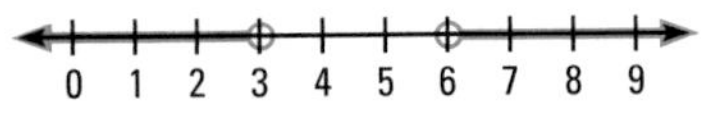

Animated Algebra at classzone.com

GUIDED PRACTICE for Examples 4 and 5

Solve the inequality. Graph your solution. **7–10. See margin for art.**

7. $-14 < x - 8 < -1$ **$-6 < x < 7$**
8. $-1 \le -5t + 2 \le 4$ **$-\frac{2}{5} \le t \le \frac{3}{5}$**
9. $3h + 1 < -5$ *or* $2h - 5 > 7$ **$h < -2$ or $h > 6$**
10. $4c + 1 \le -3$ *or* $5c - 3 > 17$ **$c \le -1$ or $c > 4$**

Differentiated Instruction

Below Level Some students may have difficulty recognizing differences between compound inequalities with *and* and with *or*. Stress that compound inequalities with *and* have solutions that overlap. Have students graph $x \ge -5$ and $x \le 2$ in **Example 4** on separate graphs. This may help them see that the solutions overlap. Point out that graphs of most compound inequalities with *or* have gaps, with arrows heading in opposite directions.

See also the *Differentiated Instruction Resources* for more strategies.

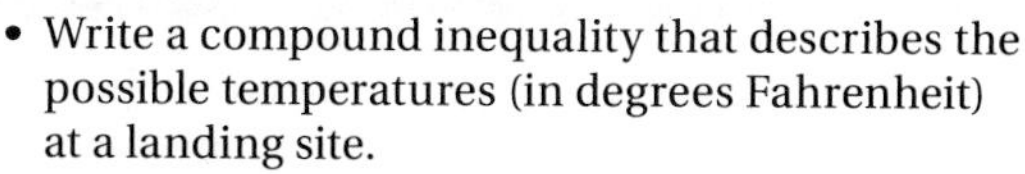

EXAMPLE 6 Solve a multi-step problem

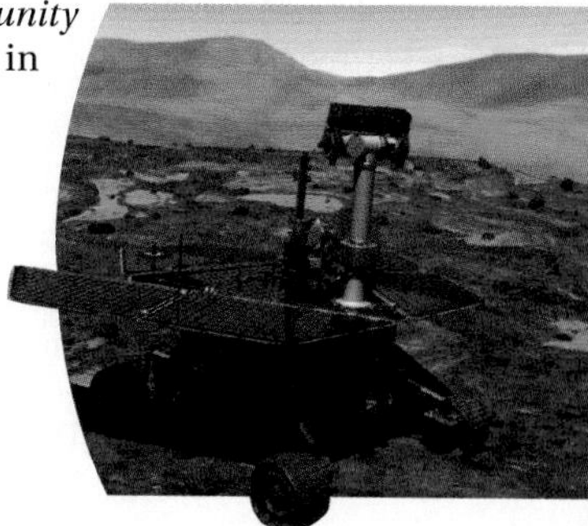

ASTRONOMY The Mars Exploration Rovers *Opportunity* and *Spirit* are robots that were sent to Mars in 2003 in order to gather geological data about the planet. The temperature at the landing sites of the robots can range from −100°C to 0°C.

- Write a compound inequality that describes the possible temperatures (in degrees Fahrenheit) at a landing site.
- Solve the inequality. Then graph your solution.
- Identify three possible temperatures (in degrees Fahrenheit) at a landing site.

Solution

Let F represent the temperature in degrees Fahrenheit, and let C represent the temperature in degrees Celsius. Use the formula $C = \frac{5}{9}(F - 32)$.

STEP 1 **Write** a compound inequality. Because the temperature at a landing site ranges from −100°C to 0°C, the lowest possible temperature is −100°C, and the highest possible temperature is 0°C.

$-100 \le C \le 0$ **Write inequality using C.**

$-100 \le \frac{5}{9}(F - 32) \le 0$ **Substitute $\frac{5}{9}(F - 32)$ for C.**

STEP 2 **Solve** the inequality. Then graph your solution.

$-100 \le \frac{5}{9}(F - 32) \le 0$ **Write inequality from Step 1.**

$-180 \le F - 32 \le 0$ **Multiply each expression by $\frac{9}{5}$.**

$-148 \le F \le 32$ **Add 32 to each expression.**

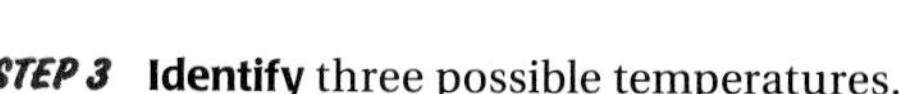

ANOTHER WAY
You can solve the compound inequality by multiplying through by 9:
$-100 \le \frac{5}{9}(F - 32) \le 0$
$-900 \le 5(F - 32) \le 0$
$-900 \le 5F - 160 \le 0$
$-740 \le 5F \le 160$
$-148 \le F \le 32$

STEP 3 **Identify** three possible temperatures.

The temperature at a landing site is greater than or equal to −148°F *and* less than or equal to 32°F. Three possible temperatures are −115°F, 15°F, and 32°F.

✓ **GUIDED PRACTICE** for Example 6

11. MARS Mars has a maximum temperature of 27°C at the equator and a minimum temperature of −133°C at the winter pole.

- Write and solve a compound inequality that describes the possible temperatures (in degrees Fahrenheit) on Mars.
- Graph your solution. Then identify three possible temperatures (in degrees Fahrenheit) on Mars.

$-133 \le \frac{5}{9}(F - 32) \le 27$; $-207.4 \le F \le 80.6$; see margin for art.
Sample answer: **−100°F, 0°F, 25°F**

Extra Example 6

The eggs of a Rocky Mountain Tailed frog can survive in streams where the temperature ranges from 5°C to 18°C. Write a compound inequality that describes the possible stream temperatures (in degrees Fahrenheit) for egg survival. Solve the inequality. Then graph your solution. Identify three possible stream temperatures (in degrees Fahrenheit) for egg survival.

$5 \le \frac{5}{9}(F - 32) \le 18$; $41 \le F \le 64.4$

41 64.4
35 40 45 50 55 60 65 70

examples: 45°F, 53°F, 61°F

Closing the Lesson

Have students summarize the major points of the lesson and answer the Essential Question: How do you solve and graph compound inequalities?

- **Compound inequalities are two inequalities joined by *and* or joined by *or*.**
- **The graph of a compound inequality with *and* is the intersection of the graphs of the inequalities. The graph of an inequality with *or* is the union of the graphs.**

Solve the two inequalities in the compound inequality separately. On the graph of a compound inequality with *and*, shade all the numbers that satisfy both inequalities together. On the graph of a compound inequality with *or*, shade the numbers that satisfy the separate inequalities.

11.

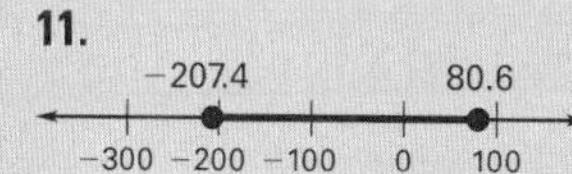

Differentiated Instruction

Advanced Have students search the Internet for astronomical or other scientific data that involve a range and a conversion, as in **Example 6**. Ask them to create a multi-step problem that uses a compound inequality with *and* or *or* and that involves a conversion. Encourage them to share their problems with the class.

See also the *Differentiated Instruction Resources* for more strategies.

4 PRACTICE AND APPLY

Assignment Guide

Answer Transparencies available for all exercises

Basic:
Day 1: pp. 384–387
Exs. 1–8, 23–27, 47–50, 55
Day 2: pp. 384–387
Exs. 9–22, 37–43, 51–54

Average:
Day 1: pp. 384–387
Exs. 1–8, 23–31, 48, 55
Day 2: pp. 384–387
Exs. 12–22, 32, 33, 39–45, 51–54

Advanced:
Day 1: pp. 384–387
Exs. 1, 2, 5–8, 23–32, 50, 55
Day 2: pp. 384–387
Exs. 13–20, 33–36*, 40–46*, 52, 54

Block:
pp. 384–387
Exs. 1–8, 23–31, 48, 55 (with 6.3)
pp. 384–387
Exs. 12–22, 32, 33, 39–45, 51–54 (with 6.5)

Differentiated Instruction

See *Differentiated Instruction Resources* for suggestions on addressing the needs of a diverse classroom.

Homework Check

For a quick check of student understanding of key concepts, go over the following exercises:

Basic: 3, 7, 10, 18, 41
Average: 4, 8, 13, 19, 42
Advanced: 6, 8, 14, 20, 43

Extra Practice

- Student Edition, p. 943
- Chapter Resource Book: Practice levels A, B, C

Practice Worksheet

An easily-readable reduced practice page (with answers) for this lesson can be found on p. 354D.

6.4 EXERCISES

HOMEWORK KEY
○ = **WORKED-OUT SOLUTIONS** on p. WS14 for Exs. 7, 11, and 41
★ = **STANDARDIZED TEST PRACTICE** Exs. 2, 27, 39, and 45
◆ = **MULTIPLE REPRESENTATIONS** Ex. 43

SKILL PRACTICE

A

1. **VOCABULARY** Copy and complete: A(n) _?_ is an inequality that consists of two inequalities joined by *and* or *or*. **compound inequality**

2. ★ **WRITING** *Describe* the difference between the graphs of $-6 \le x \le -4$ and $x \le -6$ *or* $x \ge -4$. **See margin.**

EXAMPLE 1 on p. 380 for Exs. 3–6

TRANSLATING VERBAL PHRASES Translate the verbal phrase into an inequality. Then graph the inequality. 3–6. See margin for art.

3. All real numbers that are less than 6 *and* greater than 2 **$2 < x < 6$**
4. All real numbers that are less than or equal to −8 *or* greater than 12 **$x \le -8$ or $x > 12$**
5. All real numbers that are greater than or equal to −1.5 *and* less than 9.2 **$-1.5 \le x < 9.2$**
6. All real numbers that are greater than or equal to $-7\frac{1}{2}$ *or* less than or equal to −10 **$x \le -10$ or $x \ge -7\frac{1}{2}$**

EXAMPLE 2 on p. 381 for Exs. 7–8

WRITING AND GRAPHING INEQUALITIES Write and graph an inequality that describes the situation. 7, 8. See margin for art.

7. The minimum speed on a highway is 40 miles per hour, and the maximum speed is 60 miles per hour. **$40 \le s \le 60$**
8. The temperature inside a room is uncomfortable if the temperature is lower than 60°F or higher than 75°F. **$t < 60$ or $t > 75$**

EXAMPLES 3, 4, and 5 on pp. 381–382 for Exs. 9–22

SOLVING COMPOUND INEQUALITIES Solve the inequality. Graph your solution. 9–20. See margin for art.

9. $6 < x + 5 \le 11$ **$1 < x \le 6$**
10. $-7 > y - 8 \ge -12$ **$-4 \le y < 1$**
11. $-1 \le -4m \le 16$ **$-4 \le m \le \frac{1}{4}$**
12. $-6 < 3n + 9 < 21$ **$-5 < n < 4$**
13. $-15 \le 5(3p - 2) < 20$ **$-\frac{1}{3} \le p < 2$**
14. $7 > \frac{2}{3}(6q + 18) \ge -9$ **$-5\frac{1}{4} \le q < -1\frac{1}{4}$**
15. $2r + 3 < 7$ *or* $-r + 9 \le 2$ **$r < 2$ or $r \ge 7$**
16. $16 < -s - 6$ *or* $2s + 5 \ge 11$ **$s < -22$ or $s \ge 3$**
17. $v + 13 < 8$ *or* $-8v < -40$ **$v < -5$ or $v > 5$**
18. $-14 > w + 3$ *or* $5w - 13 > w + 7$ **$w < -17$ or $w > 5$**
19. $9g - 6 > 12g + 1$ *or* $4 > -\frac{2}{5}g + 8$ **$g < -2\frac{1}{3}$ or $g > 10$**
20. $-2h - 7 > h + 5$ *or* $\frac{1}{4}(h + 8) \ge 9$ **$h < -4$ or $h \ge 28$**

ERROR ANALYSIS ***Describe* and correct the error in solving the inequality or in graphing the solution. 21, 22. See margin for art.**

21.

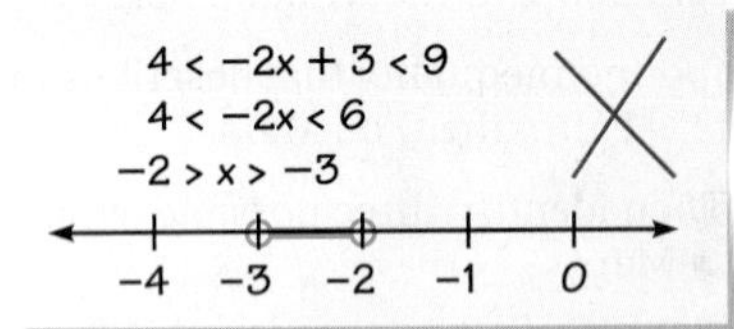

22.

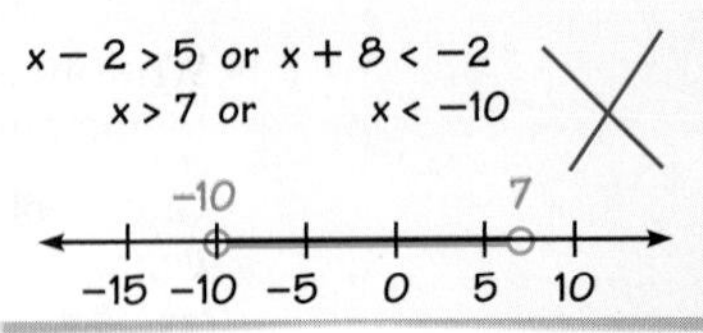

21. 3 was subtracted from only two of the three expressions of the inequality; $1 < -2x < 6$, $-\frac{1}{2} > x > -3$.

22. The graph should include the points of the number line to the left of −10 and to the right of 7, not the points between −10 and 7.

2. The graph of $-6 \le x \le -4$ consists of −6, −4, and all the points on the number line between −6 and −4. The graph of $x \le -6$ *or* $x \ge -4$ consists of −6 and all the points on the number line to the left of −6, along with −4 and all the points on the number line to the right of −4.

3.–5.

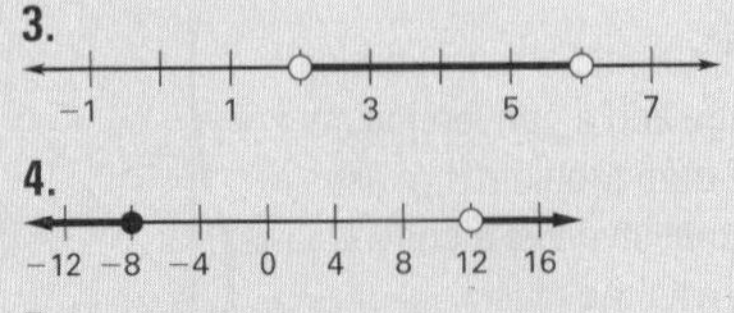

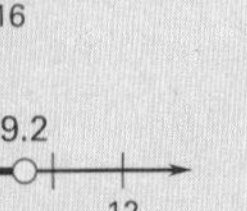

6.

B **TRANSLATING SENTENCES** **Write the verbal sentence as an inequality. Then solve the inequality and graph your solution.** **23–26. See margin for art.**

23. Five more than x is less than 8 *or* 3 less than x is greater than 5. **$x + 5 < 8$ or $x - 3 > 5$; $x < 3$ or $x > 8$**

24. Three less than x is greater than -4 *and* less than -1. **$-4 < x - 3 < -1$; $-1 < x < 2$**

25. Three times the difference of x and 4 is greater than or equal to -8 *and* less than or equal to 10. **$-8 \le 3(x - 4) \le 10$; $1\frac{1}{3} \le x \le 7\frac{1}{3}$**

26. The sum of $-2x$ and 8 is less than or equal to -5 *or* 6 is less than $-2x$. **$-2x + 8 \le -5$ or $6 < -2x$; $x < -3$ or $x \ge 6\frac{1}{2}$**

27. ★ **MULTIPLE CHOICE** Consider the compound inequality $a > 3x + 8$ *or* $a > -4x - 1$. For which value of a does the solution consist of numbers greater than -6 *and* less than 5? **C**

Ⓐ 16   Ⓑ 19   Ⓒ 23   Ⓓ 26

REASONING **In Exercises 28 and 29, tell whether the statement is *true* or *false*. If it is false, give a counterexample.**

28. If a is a solution of $x < 5$, then a is also a solution of $x < 5$ *and* $x \ge -4$. **False. *Sample answer*: $a = -5$**

29. If a is a solution of $x > 5$, then a is also a solution of $x > 5$ *or* $x \le -4$. **true**

30. True; any solution of $x < 5$ *and* $x \ge -4$ lies between -4 and 5 on the number line, so it is to the left of 5 and is therefore a solution of $x < 5$.

30. Is the converse of the statement in Exercise 28 *true* or *false*? *Explain.*

31. Is the converse of the statement in Exercise 29 *true* or *false*? *Explain.* **False. *Sample answer*: $a = -4$ is a solution of $x > 5$ or $x \le -4$, but it is not a solution of $x > 5$.**

32. **GEOMETRY** The sum of the lengths of any two sides of a triangle is greater than the length of the third side.

a. Write and solve three inequalities for the triangle shown. **$x + 5 > 7$, $x > 2$; $5 + 7 > x$, $x < 12$; $x + 7 > 5$, $x > -2$**

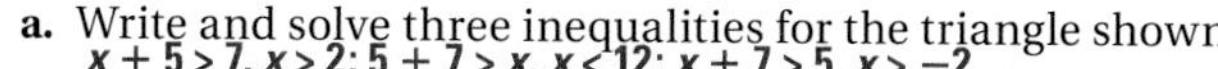

b. Use the inequalities that you wrote in part (a) to write one inequality that describes all the possible values of x. **$2 < x < 12$**

c. Give three possible lengths for the third side of the triangle. ***Sample answer*: 3, 7, 10**

C **CHALLENGE** **Solve the inequality, if possible. Graph your solution.** **33–36. See margin for art.**

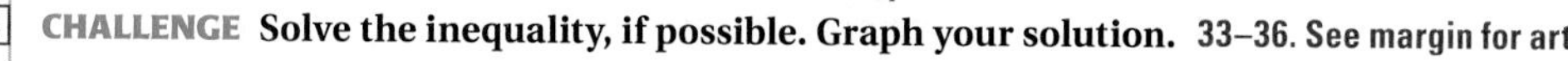

33. $-18 < x - 23$ *and* $x - 16 < -22$ **no solution**

34. $-3y + 7 \le 11$ *and* $y + 4 > 11$ **$y > 7$**

35. $2m - 1 \ge 5$ *or* $5m > -25$ **$m > -5$**

36. $n + 19 \ge 10$ *or* $-5n + 3 > 33$ **all real numbers**

PROBLEM SOLVING

EXAMPLE 2 on p. 381 for Exs. 37, 39, 40

A 37. **SLITSNAILS** Slitsnails are large mollusks that live in deep waters. Slitsnails have been found at elevations from -2600 feet to -100 feet. Write and graph a compound inequality that represents the elevations at which slitsnails have been found.

@HomeTutor for problem solving help at classzone.com

$-2600 \le e \le -100$; see margin for art.

EXAMPLE 6 on p. 383 for Exs. 38, 41–43

38. **ICEBERGS** The temperature inside an iceberg off the coast of Newfoundland, Canada, ranges from $-20°C$ to $-15°C$. Write and graph a compound inequality that describes the possible temperatures (in degrees Fahrenheit) of the iceberg's interior. **$-4 \le t \le 5$; see margin for art.**

@HomeTutor for problem solving help at classzone.com

Avoiding Common Errors

Exercises 9–20 Some students who do not separate compound inequalities with *and* before solving them make calculation errors. Encourage students to break apart the compound inequality and solve the inequalities separately until they are familiar with the solution process.

Internet Reference

Exercise 38 Additional information about icebergs can be found at oceanworld.tamu.edu/students/iceberg/iceberg1.htm

21.

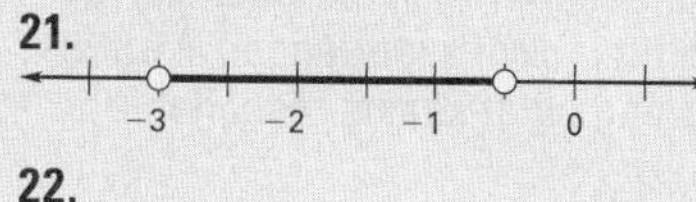

22.

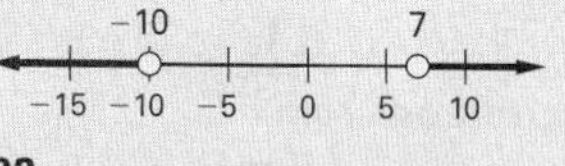

23.

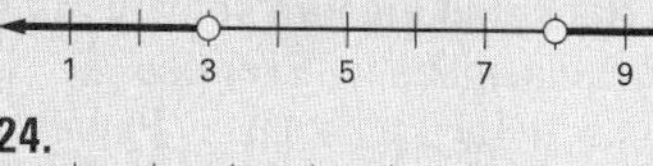

24.

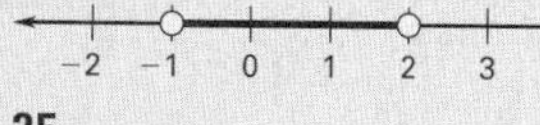

25.

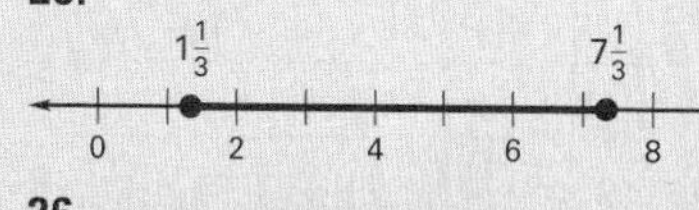

26.

33.

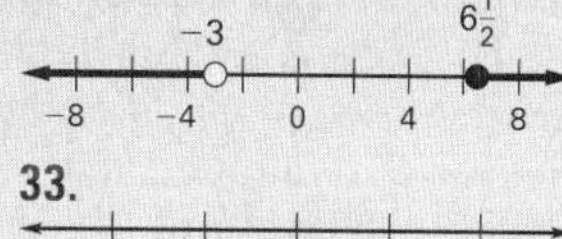

34.

35.

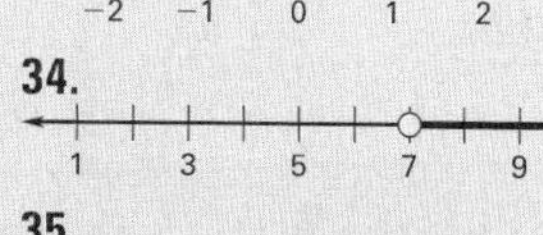

36.

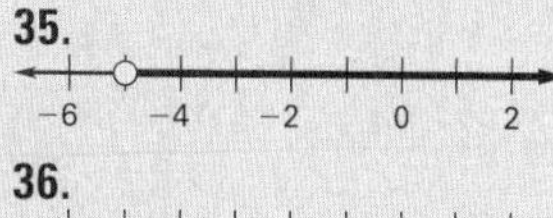

37.

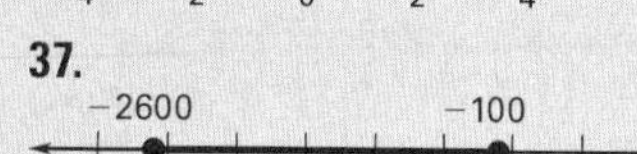

38.

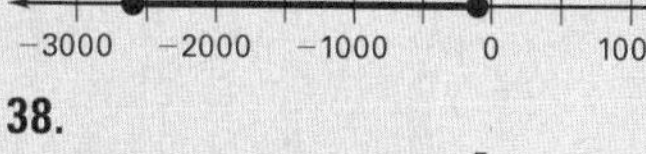

Differentiated Instruction

English Learners Explain the use of the word *or* while discussing **Exercises 35 and 36**. "Left *or* right" means that you can take only one direction, but weather that is "sunny *or* cold" could mean both on a clear winter day. In English, there is no single word to explain if both choices are included. Other languages, including mathematics, are more precise: *or* means to include points from the first inequality, the second, and the intersection (if it exists).

See also the *Differentiated Instruction Resources* for more strategies.

7.

8.

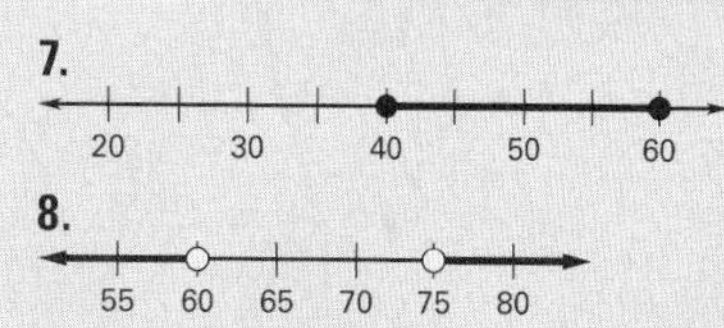

9–20. See Additional Answers beginning on p. AA1.

39. ★ **MULTIPLE CHOICE** The euro is the currency in several countries in Europe. In 2003, the dollar value of one euro ranged from \$1.0361 to \$1.2597. Which inequality represents the dollar values v that the euro was *not* worth during the year? **B**

Ⓐ $1.0361 < v < 1.2597$ Ⓑ $v < 1.0361$ *or* $v > 1.2597$

Ⓒ $1.0361 \le v \le 1.2597$ Ⓓ $v \le 1.0361$ *or* $v \ge 1.2597$

40. **CURRENCY** On October 25, 1865, the steamship *S.S. Republic* sank along with a cargo of gold and silver coins. The list gives the prices of several recovered gold coins. Use the least price and greatest price to write a compound inequality that describes the prices p of the coins. **$5319 \le p \le 73{,}486$**

Prices of Recovered Gold Coins

\$9,098	\$20,995	\$9,798	\$33,592	\$12,597
\$16,796	\$9,798	\$10,498	\$5,319	\$73,486
\$11,897	\$32,895	\$7,349	\$6,578	\$29,395

(41.) **ANIMALS** A deer can eat 2% to 4% of its body weight in food per day. The percent p of the deer's body weight eaten in food is given by the equation $p = \frac{f}{d}$ where f is the amount (in pounds) of food eaten and d is the weight (in pounds) of the deer. Find the possible amounts of food that a 160 pound deer can eat per day. **$3.2 \text{ lb} \le f \le 6.4 \text{ lb}$**

42. **SKIS** A ski shop sells recreational skis with lengths ranging from 150 centimeters to 220 centimeters. The shop recommends that recreational skis be 1.16 times the skier's height (in centimeters). For which heights of skiers does the shop *not* provide recreational skis? **less than 129.31 cm or greater than 189.66 cm**

B 43. ◆ **MULTIPLE REPRESENTATIONS** Water can exist as either a solid, a liquid, or a gas. The table shows the temperatures (in degrees Celsius) at which water can exist in each state.

State of water	Solid	Liquid	Gas
Temperatures (°C)	Less than 0	0 to 100	Greater than 100

a. **Writing an Inequality** Write and solve a compound inequality to find the temperatures (in degrees Fahrenheit) at which water is *not* a liquid. **$\frac{5}{9}(F - 32) < 0$ or $\frac{5}{9}(F - 32) > 100$, $F < 32°F$ or $F > 212°F$**

b. **Making a Table** Make a table that gives the temperature (in degrees Celsius) when the temperature (in degrees Fahrenheit) of water is 23°F, 86°F, 140°F, 194°F, and 239°F. For which temperatures in the table is water *not* a liquid? **23°F, 239°F; see margin for table.**

44. **WEATHER** Wind chill temperature describes how much colder it feels when the speed of the wind is combined with air temperature. At a wind speed of 20 miles per hour, the wind chill temperature w (in degrees Fahrenheit) can be given by the model $w = -22 + 1.3a$ where a is the air temperature (in degrees Fahrenheit). What are the possible air temperatures if the wind chill temperature ranges from −9°F to −2.5°F at a wind speed of 20 miles per hour? **from 10°F to 15°F**

○ = WORKED-OUT SOLUTIONS on p. WS1 ★ = STANDARDIZED TEST PRACTICE ◆ = MULTIPLE REPRESENTATIONS

Study Strategy

Exercises 39–40, 43–45 Recommend to students that they think through whether a compound inequality describing a real-world situation uses *and* or *or*. They can look for clues in the problem, such as the word *range*, which indicates a continuum and an *and* compound inequality. Similarly, there may be clues in the problem that the solution set has two parts, which would indicate an *or* compound inequality. They can also ask themselves whether a compound inequality with *and* or with *or* makes the most sense in the situation. Encourage students to draw on their own experiences in determining what seems reasonable.

An **Animated Algebra** activity is available online for **Exercise 45.** This activity is also part of **Power Presentations**.

43b.

°F	23	86	140	194	239
°C	−5	30	60	90	115

45c. 4800 watts; because each person requires at least 8 watts of amplification, and you want to be sure to provide enough amplification for 600 people, you need at least 8(600) = 4800 watts of amplification.

Quiz

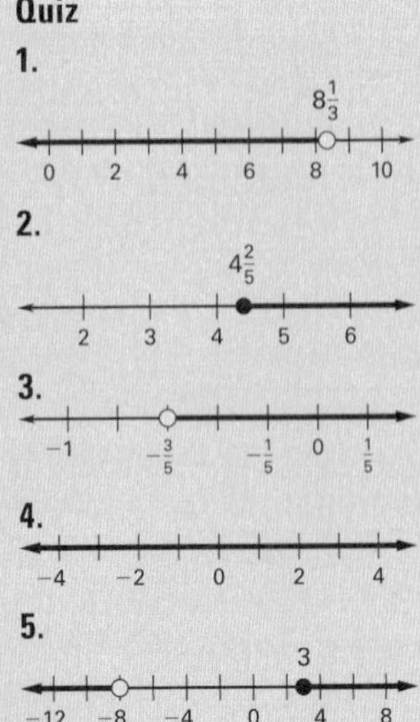

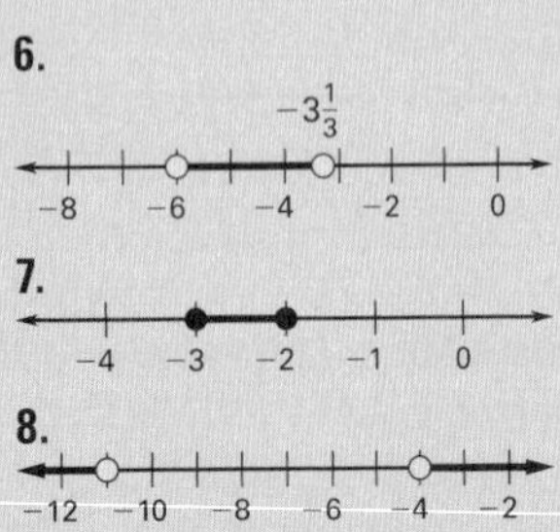

45a. $8 \le \frac{w}{300} \le 10$, $2400 \le w \le 3000$; 2400 watts to 3000 watts

45b. Yes; no; the amplification per person for 350 people is $\frac{2900}{350} \approx 8.3$ watts, which is between 8 watts and 10 watts, the amplification for 400 people is $\frac{2900}{400} = 7.25$ watts, which is not between 8 watts and 10 watts.

45. ★ **EXTENDED RESPONSE** Some musicians use audio amplifiers so that everyone in the audience can hear the performance. The amount y of amplification per person is given by the equation $y = \frac{w}{p}$ where w is the total amount (in watts) of amplification provided by the amplifier and p is the number of people in the audience.

a. **Solve** Each person requires 8 watts to 10 watts of amplification. Write and solve an inequality to find the possible total amounts of amplification that an amplifier would need to provide for 300 people.

b. **Decide** Will an amplifier that provides 2900 watts of amplification be strong enough for an audience of 350 people? 400 people? *Explain.*

c. **Justify** Your band usually performs before an audience of 500 to 600 people. What is the least amount of amplification that your amplifier should provide? *Justify* your answer. **See margin.**

Animated Algebra at classzone.com

C **46.** CHALLENGE You and three friends are planning to eat at a restaurant, and all of you agree to divide the total cost of the meals and the 15% tip equally. Each person agrees to pay at least \$10 but no more than \$20. How much can you spend altogether on meals before the tip is applied? **from \$34.78 up to \$69.57**

MIXED REVIEW

Evaluate the expression.

47. $14x$ when $x = 3$ *(p. 2)* **42**

48. $6d^3$ when $d = 4$ *(p. 8)* **384**

49. $|m|$ when $m = -1$ *(p. 64)* **1**

50. $-8t$ when $t = -5$ *(p. 88)* **40**

PREVIEW
Prepare for Lesson 6.5 in Exs. 51–54.

Solve the equation.

51. $8x - 14 = -16$ *(p. 134)* $-\frac{1}{4}$

52. $2y + 8 + 5y = -1$ *(p. 141)* $-1\frac{2}{7}$

53. $4(f - 3) = -28$ *(p. 148)* **−4**

54. $6r - 2 = 5r - 3$ *(p. 154)* **−1**

55. MUSEUMS You and some friends are taking a trip to a museum. Parking costs \$15, and the price of a ticket is \$14.50. Write an equation that gives the total cost C (in dollars) of the trip as a function of the number p of people who are going. *(p. 283)* $C = 14.5p + 15$

QUIZ for Lessons 6.3–6.4

Solve the inequality, if possible. Graph your solution. **1–8. See margin for art.**

1. $-\frac{1}{5}(x - 5) > x - 9$ *(p. 369)* $x < 8\frac{1}{3}$

2. $\frac{1}{2}y - 8 \ge -2y + 3$ *(p. 369)* $y \ge 4\frac{2}{5}$

3. $-4r + 7 \le r + 10$ *(p. 369)* $r \ge -\frac{3}{5}$

4. $-2(s + 6) \le -2s + 8$ *(p. 369)* **all real numbers**

5. $a - 4 \ge -1$ *or* $3a < -24$ *(p. 380)* $a < -8$ or $a \ge 3$

6. $22 > -3c + 4 > 14$ *(p. 380)* $-6 < c < -3\frac{1}{3}$

7. $-27 \le 9m \le -18$ *(p. 380)* $-3 \le m \le -2$

8. $5n + 2 > -18$ *or* $-3(n + 4) > 21$ *(p. 380)* $n < -11$ or $n > -4$

5 ASSESS AND RETEACH

Daily Homework Quiz

Transparency Available

1. Solve $x + 4 < 7$ *or* $2x - 5 > 3$. Graph your solution. **all real numbers less than 3 *or* greater than 4**

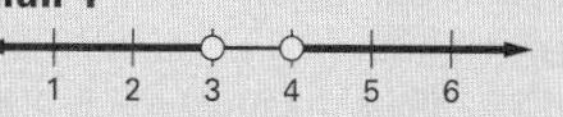

2. Solve $3x + 2 > -7$ *and* $4x - 1 < -5$. Graph your solution. **all real numbers greater than −3 *and* less than −1**

3. The smallest praying mantis is 0.4 inch in length. The largest is 6 inches. Write and graph a compound inequality that describes the possible lengths L of a praying mantis. $0.4 \le L \le 6$

0.4
0 1 2 3 4 5 6 7

Online Quiz

Available at **classzone.com**

Diagnosis/Remediation

- Practice A, B, C in Chapter Resource Book
- Study Guide in Chapter Resource Book
- Practice Workbook
- @HomeTutor

Challenge

Additional challenge is available in the Chapter Resource Book.

Quiz

An easily-readable reduced copy of the quiz (with answers) on Lessons 6.3–6.4 from the Assessment Book can be found on p. 354G.

Graphing Calculator ACTIVITY Use after Lesson 6.4

@HomeTutor classzone.com Keystrokes

1 PLAN AND PREPARE

Learn the Method

- Students will use a graphing calculator to solve compound inequalities.
- After the activity, students can use a graphing calculator to check their solutions in Exercises 9–20 and 33–36 in Lesson 6.4.

Keystroke Help

Keystrokes for several models of calculators are available in blackline format in the *Chapter Resource Book.*

2 TEACH

Tips for Success

Stress to students that the graphing calculator does not draw open or closed circles so they need to pay attention to the inequality symbols in the compound inequality.

Extra Example

Solve $-28 < -4x < 4$ using a graphing calculator. **all real numbers greater than -1 *and* less than 7**

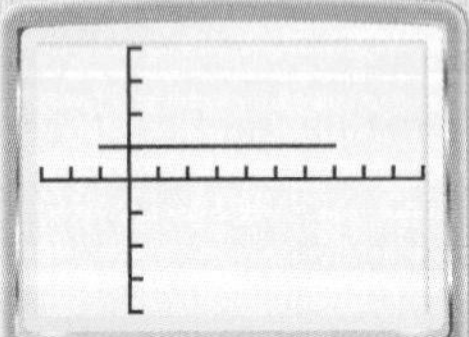

3 ASSESS AND RETEACH

Solve $-5x \le -30$ *or* $-2x > 8$ using a graphing calculator. What inequality symbols should you use in your solution? Explain. **$\ge$ and $<$; you have to reverse both of the original inequality symbols because each solution involves dividing by a negative number.**

6.4 Solve Compound Inequalities

QUESTION How can you use a graphing calculator to display the solutions of a compound inequality?

EXAMPLE Display the solutions of a compound inequality on a graphing calculator

Display the solutions of $12 \le 3x \le 21$ on a graphing calculator.

STEP 1 ***Rewrite inequality***

Rewrite $12 \le 3x \le 21$ as two separate inequalities joined by *and*.

$12 \le 3x \le 21$ Write original inequality.

$12 \le 3x$ *and* $3x \le 21$ Write as two inequalities joined by *and*.

STEP 2 ***Enter inequalities***

Press Y= and enter the two inequalities, as shown. Inequality signs can be found in the TEST menu, and *and* and *or* can be found in the LOGIC menu.

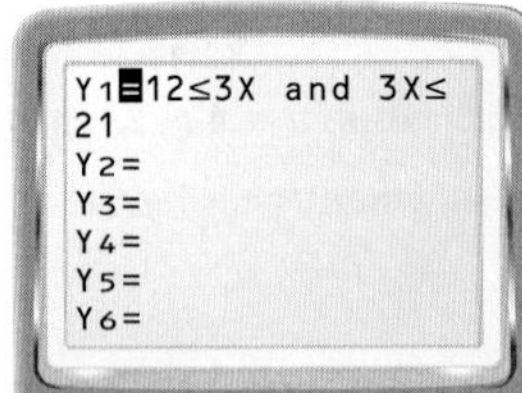

STEP 3 ***Display solutions***

Press GRAPH to display the solutions of $12 \le 3x$ *and* $3x \le 21$. For each value of x that makes the inequality true, the calculator assigns a value of 1 to y and plots the point $(x, 1)$. For each value of x that makes the inequality false, the calculator assigns a value of 0 to y and plots the point $(x, 0)$.

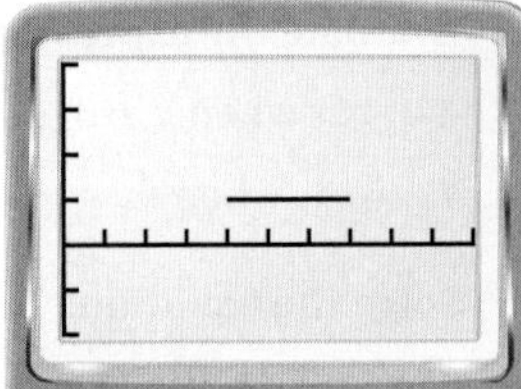

The screen in Step 3 shows the graph of $y = 1$ over the interval $4 \le x \le 7$. This suggests that the solutions are all real numbers greater than or equal to 4 *and* less than or equal to 7.

DRAW CONCLUSIONS

1. Display the solutions of $12 < 3x < 21$ on a graphing calculator. Then compare the graph of $12 < 3x < 21$ with the graph of $12 \le 3x \le 21$. **$4 < x < 7$; the graphs are the same.**
2. When displaying the solutions of an inequality on a graphing calculator, how do you know which inequality symbols you should use in your solution? **Use the inequality symbols from the original inequality.**

Display the solutions of the inequality on a graphing calculator.

3. $9 \le 3x \le 21$ **$3 \le x \le 7$**
4. $4 < 4x < 8$ **$1 < x < 2$**
5. $2 \le \frac{1}{4}x \le 12$ **$8 \le x \le 48$**
6. $-6x > 18$ *or* $9x > 45$ **$x < -3$ or $x > 5$**
7. $4x \le 18$ *or* $5x \ge 25$ **$x \le 4\frac{1}{2}$ or $x \ge 5$**
8. $8x \le 16$ *or* $3x \ge 30$ **$x \le 2$ or $x \ge 10$**

MIXED REVIEW of Problem Solving

STATE TEST PRACTICE
classzone.com

Lessons 6.1–6.4

1. **MULTI-STEP PROBLEM** A nanotube thermometer is so tiny that it is invisible to the human eye. The thermometer can measure temperatures from 50°C to 500°C. **a–c. See margin.**
   a. Write and solve a compound inequality to find the temperatures (in degrees Fahrenheit) that the thermometer can measure.
   b. Graph your solution of the inequality.
   c. Can the thermometer measure a temperature of 1000°F? *Explain.*

2. **SHORT RESPONSE** You earned the following scores on five science tests: 75, 82, 90, 84, and 71. You want to have an average score of at least 80 after you take the sixth test. **a–b. See margin.**
   a. Write and solve an inequality to find the possible scores that you can earn on your sixth test in order to meet your goal.
   b. The greatest score that you can earn on a test is 100. Is it possible for you to have an average score of 90 after the sixth test? *Explain* your reasoning.

3. **GRIDDED ANSWER** You need at least 34 eggs to make enough chiffon cakes for a bake sale. Your grocery store sells cartons of eggs only by the dozen. Of all the possible numbers of cartons that you can buy, which is the least number? **3 cartons**

4. **MULTI-STEP PROBLEM** You have a \$300 gift card to use at a sporting goods store.
   a. You want to use your card to buy 2 pairs of shoes for \$85 each and several pairs of socks. Write and solve an inequality to find the possible amounts of money that you can spend on socks using your card. **up to \$130**
   b. Suppose that socks cost \$4.75 per pair. Write and solve an inequality to find the possible numbers of socks that you can buy using the card. **$4.75s \le 130$; up to 27 pairs of socks**

5. **OPEN-ENDED** *Describe* a real-world situation that can be modeled by the inequality $17x \le 240$. *Explain* what the solution of the inequality means in this situation. **See margin.**

6. **SHORT RESPONSE** A rafting guide plans to take 6 adults on a rafting trip. The raft can hold up to 1520 pounds. The guide weighs 180 pounds and estimates that each adult will bring 10 pounds of baggage.
   a. Write and solve an inequality to find the possible average weights of an adult such that the raft will not exceed its maximum weight capacity. **at most $213\frac{1}{3}$ lb**
   b. Suppose that the weights of the adults range from 105 pounds to 200 pounds. Can the raft accommodate all the people and the baggage at one time? *Justify* your answer. **See margin.**

7. **EXTENDED RESPONSE** In 1862 the United States imposed a tax on annual income in order to pay for the expenses of the Civil War. The table shows the tax rates for different incomes.

Annual income	Tax rate
\$600 to \$10,000	3% of income
Greater than \$10,000	3% of the first \$10,000 plus 5% of income over \$10,000

   a. Write a compound inequality that represents the possible taxes paid by a person whose annual income was at least \$600 but not greater than \$10,000. **$18 \le t \le 300$**
   b. For people whose taxes ranged from \$400 to \$750, tell whether their annual incomes were greater than \$10,000 or less than \$10,000. *Explain* how you know. Then find the possible annual incomes of those people. **See margin.**
   c. Suppose that the tax rate had been 4% of the total income for people whose annual incomes were greater than \$10,000. For which incomes would paying the 4% rate have resulted in less taxes than paying the tax rate described above? *Explain.* **See margin.**

1a. from 122°F to 932°F

1b.

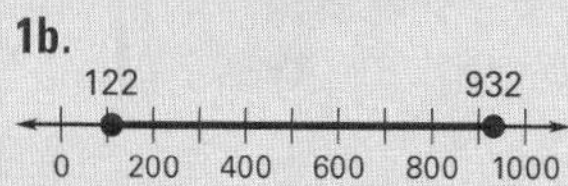

1c. No; the thermometer cannot measure temperatures higher than 932°F.

2a. $x \ge 78$

2b. No; with a score of 100 your average will be $\frac{402 + 100}{6} = \frac{502}{6} \approx 84$.

5. *Sample answer:* The solution $x \le 14.12$ means that the greatest number that will make the inequality true is 14.12.

6b. Yes; since the most the adults weigh is 200 pounds, and that is less than what the average weight needs to be, all the people and baggage can be accommodated on the raft.

7b. Greater than \$10,000; their taxes are higher than \$300, the highest tax paid by people with annual incomes of \$10,000 or less; from \$12,000 up to \$19,000.

7c. Greater than \$20,000; the inequality to describe the situation is $0.04x < 0.03(10,000) + 0.05(x - 10,000)$. Solving the inequality gives $x > \$20,000$.

1 PLAN AND PREPARE

Warm-Up Exercises

Transparency Available

1. For $a = -12$, find $-a$ and $|a|$. **12, 12**
2. Evaluate $|x| - 2$ when $x = -3$. **1**
3. The change in elevation as a diver explored a reef was -0.5 foot, 1.5 feet, -2.5 feet, and 2.25 feet. Which change in elevation had the greatest absolute value? **-2.5 ft**

Notetaking Guide

Transparency Available

Promotes interactive learning and notetaking skills.

Pacing

Basic: 2 days
Average: 2 days
Advanced: 2 days
Block: 0.5 block with 6.4
0.5 block with 6.6

- See *Teaching Guide/Lesson Plan.*

2 FOCUS AND MOTIVATE

Essential Question

Big Idea 2, p. 355

How do you solve absolute value equations? **Tell students they will learn how to answer this question by rewriting absolute value equations as two equations and then solving the equations.**

NCTM STANDARDS

Standard 2: Analyze situations using algebraic symbols

Standard 3: Use geometric modeling

6.5 Solve Absolute Value Equations

Before You solved linear equations.
Now You will solve absolute value equations.
Why? So you can analyze rules of a competition, as in Ex. 43.

Key Vocabulary
- **absolute value equation**
- **absolute deviation**
- **absolute value,** *p. 66*

The absolute value of a number a, written $|a|$, is the distance between a and 0 on a number line. An **absolute value equation**, such as $|x| = 4$, is an equation that contains an absolute value expression. The equation $|x| = 4$ means that the distance between x and 0 is 4. The solutions of the equation are 4 and -4, because they are the only numbers whose distance from 0 is 4.

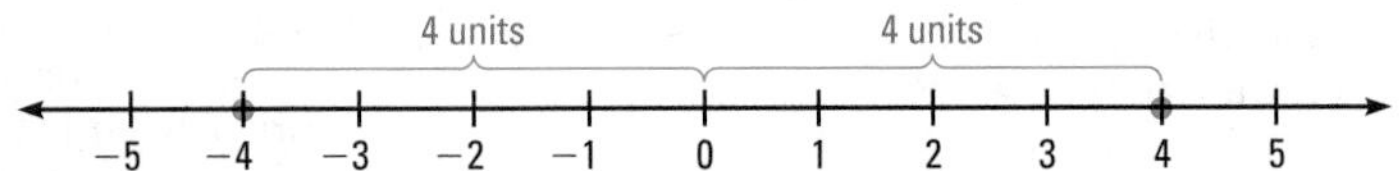

EXAMPLE 1 Solve an absolute value equation

Solve $|x| = 7$.

Solution

The distance between x and 0 is 7. So, $x = 7$ *or* $x = -7$.

▶ The solutions are 7 and -7.

Animated Algebra at classzone.com

✓ GUIDED PRACTICE for Example 1

1. Solve (a) $|x| = 3$ and (b) $|x| = 15$.
   a. 3, −3
   b. 15, −15

SOLVING ABSOLUTE VALUE EQUATIONS In Example 1, notice that the expression inside the absolute value symbols equals 7 or the opposite of 7. This suggests the following rule for solving an absolute value equation.

> **KEY CONCEPT** *For Your Notebook*
>
> **Solving an Absolute Value Equation**
>
> The equation $|ax + b| = c$ where $c \geq 0$ is equivalent to the statement $ax + b = c$ *or* $ax + b = -c$.

Resource Planning Guide

Chapter Resource Book
- Teaching Guide/Lesson Plan
- Practice levels A, B, C
- Study Guide
- Catch-up for Absent Students
- Problem Solving Workshop
- Challenge

Workbooks
- Notetaking Guide
- Practice Workbook

Teaching Options
- **Power Presentations** provides dynamic electronic teaching resources for the classroom.
- **Activity Generator** provides editable activities for all ability levels.

Interactive Technology
- Easy Planner
- Power Presentations
- Activity Generator
- Animated Algebra
- Test Generator
- Online Quiz
- eWorkbook
- eEdition
- @HomeTutor

Resources for English Learners
- Spanish Study Guide
- Multi-Language Visual Glossary
- Student Resources in Spanish

See also the *Differentiated Instruction Resources* for more strategies for meeting individual needs.

EXAMPLE 2 Solve an absolute value equation

Solve $|x - 3| = 8$.

Solution

Rewrite the absolute value equation as two equations. Then solve each equation separately.

> **AVOID ERRORS**
> You cannot solve the equation $|x - 3| = 8$ by adding 3 to each side because $|x - 3| + 3 \neq |x|$.

$\|x - 3\| = 8$		**Write original equation.**
$x - 3 = 8$ *or* $x - 3 = -8$		**Rewrite as two equations.**
$x = 11$ *or* $x = -5$		**Add 3 to each side.**

▶ The solutions are 11 and −5. Check your solutions.

CHECK			
$\|x - 3\| = 8$	$\|x - 3\| = 8$		**Write original inequality.**
$\|11 - 3\| \stackrel{?}{=} 8$	$\|-5 - 3\| \stackrel{?}{=} 8$		**Substitute for *x*.**
$\|8\| \stackrel{?}{=} 8$	$\|-8\| \stackrel{?}{=} 8$		**Subtract.**
$8 = 8$ ✓	$8 = 8$ ✓		**Simplify. The solution checks.**

REWRITING EQUATIONS To solve an absolute value equation, you may first need to rewrite the equation in the form $|ax + b| = c$.

EXAMPLE 3 Rewrite an absolute value equation

Solve $3|2x - 7| - 5 = 4$.

Solution

First, rewrite the equation in the form $|ax + b| = c$.

$3\|2x - 7\| - 5 = 4$	**Write original equation.**
$3\|2x - 7\| = 9$	**Add 5 to each side.**
$\|2x - 7\| = 3$	**Divide each side by 3.**

Next, solve the absolute value equation.

$\|2x - 7\| = 3$	**Write absolute value equation.**
$2x - 7 = 3$ *or* $2x - 7 = -3$	**Rewrite as two equations.**
$2x = 10$ *or* $2x = 4$	**Add 7 to each side.**
$x = 5$ *or* $x = 2$	**Divide each side by 2.**

▶ The solutions are 5 and 2.

at classzone.com

GUIDED PRACTICE for Examples 2 and 3

Solve the equation.

2. $|r - 7| = 9$ **16, −2**

3. $2|s| + 4.1 = 18.9$ **7.4, −7.4**

4. $4|t + 9| - 5 = 19$ **−3, −15**

Motivating the Lesson

Ask students what they think it means when a sports item such as a tennis racquet or a soccer ball is advertised as "official." Invite students to share any specialized knowledge they might have concerning specifications of sports equipment. Point out that some deviations from an official standard generally are permitted. Then tell students that knowing how to solve absolute value equations will help them determine whether a sports item is within the "official" range.

Extra Example 1

Solve $|x| = 9$. **9, −9**

An **Animated Algebra** activity is available online for **Examples 1 and 3**. These activities are also part of **Power Presentations**.

Extra Example 2

Solve $|x + 4| = 3$. **−1, −7**

Key Questions to Ask for Example 2

- When can you perform operations on an absolute value expression? **after you remove the absolute value symbols and rewrite the equation as two equations**
- Why is the expression $x - 3$ inside the absolute value symbol equal to 8 or −8? **because 8 and −8 are 8 units from 0 on a number line**

Extra Example 3

Solve $3|4x + 2| - 7 = 11$. **1, −2**

NO SOLUTIONS The absolute value of a number is never negative. So, when an absolute value expression equals a negative number, there are *no solutions.*

EXAMPLE 4 Decide if an equation has no solutions

Solve $|3x + 5| + 6 = -2$, if possible.

$|3x + 5| + 6 = -2$ **Write original equation.**

$|3x + 5| = -8$ **Subtract 6 from each side.**

▶ The absolute value of a number is never negative. So, there are no solutions.

ABSOLUTE DEVIATION The **absolute deviation** of a number x from a given value is the absolute value of the difference of x and the given value:
absolute deviation $= |x - \text{given value}|$.

EXAMPLE 5 Use absolute deviation

BASKETBALLS Before the start of a professional basketball game, a basketball must be inflated to an air pressure of 8 pounds per square inch (psi) with an absolute error of 0.5 psi. (*Absolute error* is the absolute deviation of a measured value from an accepted value.) Find the minimum and maximum acceptable air pressures for the basketball.

Solution

Let p be the air pressure (in psi) of a basketball. Write a verbal model. Then write and solve an absolute value equation.

Absolute error	=	| Measured air pressure	−	Accepted air pressure |
↓		↓		↓
0.5	=	| p	−	**8** |

$0.5 = |p - 8|$ **Write original equation.**

$0.5 = p - 8$ *or* $-0.5 = p - 8$ **Rewrite as two equations.**

$8.5 = p$ *or* $7.5 = p$ **Add 8 to each side.**

▶ The minimum and maximum acceptable pressures are 7.5 psi and 8.5 psi.

GUIDED PRACTICE for Examples 4 and 5

Solve the equation, if possible.

5. $2|m - 5| + 4 = 2$ **no solution**

6. $-3|n + 2| - 7 = -10$ **−1, −3**

7. The absolute deviation of x from 7.6 is 5.2. What are the values of x that satisfy this requirement? **12.8, 2.4**

Extra Example 4

Solve $3|2x - 8| + 3 = 2$, if possible. **In $|ax + b| = c$ form, the exercise is $|2x - 8| = -\frac{1}{3}$, but the absolute value of a number is never negative. So, there are no solutions.**

Key Question to Ask for Example 4

- Why is the absolute value of a number never negative? **Absolute value is the distance of a number from 0 on the number line. Distance cannot be negative, so absolute value is never negative.**

Extra Example 5

A volleyball league is preparing a two minute radio ad to announce tryouts. The ad has an absolute deviation of 0.05 minute. Find the minimum and maximum acceptable times the radio ad can run. **minimum: 1.95 min; maximum: 2.05 min**

Closing the Lesson

Have students summarize the major points of the lesson and answer the Essential Question: How do you solve absolute value equations?

- **You can rewrite an absolute value equation as two equations and then solve each equation separately to solve the absolute value equation.**
- **Some absolute value equations have no solution.**

Rewrite an absolute value equation in the form $|ax + b| = c$, if necessary, and then rewrite it as two equations $ax + b = c$ and $ax + b = -c$. Solve each equation separately.

Differentiated Instruction

Kinesthetic Learners Students can use a compass to understand the absolute deviation. In **Example 5**, the pressure is centered around 8, so have students plot 8 on a number line with increments of 0.1. Have them set a compass so the radius is equal to 0.5 (the absolute deviation) and draw a circle with center at 8. The points of the circle on the number line give the maximum and minimum values with the desired absolute deviation.

See also the *Differentiated Instruction Resources* for more strategies.

6.5 EXERCISES

HOMEWORK KEY ○ = **WORKED-OUT SOLUTIONS** on p. WS14 for Exs. 11, 23, and 45
★ = **STANDARDIZED TEST PRACTICE** Exs. 2, 32, 44, 48, and 49

SKILL PRACTICE

A

1. **VOCABULARY** Copy and complete: The equation $|x - 7| = 0.15$ is an example of a(n) __?__. **absolute value equation**

2. ★ **WRITING** Given $|x - 9| = 5$, describe the relationship between x, 9, and 5 using absolute deviation. **The absolute deviation of x from 9 is 5.**

EXAMPLES 1, 2, and 3 on pp. 390–391 for Exs. 3–20

SOLVING EQUATIONS Solve the equation.

3. $|x| = 5$ **5, −5**
4. $|y| = 36$ **36, −36**
5. $|v| = 0.7$ **0.7, −0.7**
6. $|w| = 9.2$ **9.2, −9.2**
7. $|r| = \frac{1}{2}$ **$\frac{1}{2}, -\frac{1}{2}$**
8. $|s| = \frac{7}{4}$ **$\frac{7}{4}, -\frac{7}{4}$**
9. $|m + 3| = 7$ **4, −10**
10. $|4n - 5| = 18$ **$5\frac{3}{4}, -3\frac{1}{4}$**
11. $|3p + 7| = 4$ **$-1, -3\frac{2}{3}$**
12. $|q + 8| = 2$ **−6, −10**
13. $|2d + 7| = 11$ **2, −9**
14. $|f - 8| = 14$ **22, −6**
15. $3|13 - 2t| = 15$ **4, 9**
16. $4|b - 1| - 7 = 17$ **7, −5**
17. $\frac{1}{3}|2c - 5| + 3 = 7$ **$8\frac{1}{2}, -3\frac{1}{2}$**
18. $\frac{7}{4}|3j + 5| + 1 = 15$ **$1, -4\frac{1}{3}$**
19. $4|2k + 3| - 2 = 6$ **$-\frac{1}{2}, -2\frac{1}{2}$**
20. $-3|5g + 1| - 6 = -9$ **$0, -\frac{2}{5}$**

21. The absolute value symbol was removed without writing the second equation, $x + 4 = -13$; $x = 9$ or $x = -17$.

22. The absolute value of a number is never negative, so it is incorrect to rewrite this absolute value equation as two equations; there are no solutions.

ERROR ANALYSIS *Describe* and correct the error in solving the absolute value equation.

21.
$|x + 4| = 13$
$x + 4 = 13$
$x = 9$
✗

22.
$|x - 6| = -2$
$x - 6 = -2$ or $x - 6 = 2$
$x = 4$ or $x = 8$
✗

EXAMPLE 4 on p. 392 for Exs. 23–31

SOLVING EQUATIONS Solve the equation, if possible.

23. $|x - 1| + 5 = 2$ **no solution**
24. $|y - 4| + 8 = 6$ **no solution**
25. $|m + 5| + 1.5 = 2$ **−4.5, −5.5**
26. $-4|8 - 5n| = 13$ **no solution**
27. $-3\left|1 - \frac{2}{3}v\right| = -9$ **−3, 6**
28. $-5\left|\frac{4}{5}w + 6\right| = -10$ **−5, −10**
29. $-10|14 - r| - 2 = -7$ **$13\frac{1}{2}, 14\frac{1}{2}$**
30. $-2\left|\frac{1}{3}s - 5\right| + 3 = 8$ **no solution**
31. $-9|4p + 2| - 8 = -35$ **$\frac{1}{4}, -1\frac{1}{4}$**

32. ★ **MULTIPLE CHOICE** Which number is a solution of $|4x - 1| + 2 = 1$? **D**

Ⓐ $-\frac{1}{2}$ Ⓑ 0 Ⓒ 1 Ⓓ There is no solution.

EXAMPLE 5 on p. 392 for Exs. 33–36

USING ABSOLUTE DEVIATION Find the values of x that satisfy the definition of absolute deviation for the given value and the given absolute deviation.

33. Given value: 5; absolute deviation: 8 **13, −3**
34. Given value: 20; absolute deviation: 5 **25, 15**
35. Given value: −9.1; absolute deviation: 1.6 **−7.5, −10.7**
36. Given value: −3.4; absolute deviation: 6.7 **3.3, −10.1**

4 PRACTICE AND APPLY

Assignment Guide

Answer Transparencies available for all exercises

Basic:
Day 1: EP p. 940 Exs. 12–20 pp. 393–395 Exs. 1–22, 51–53
Day 2: pp. 393–395 Exs. 23–37, 42–47, 54–59

Average:
Day 1: pp. 393–395 Exs. 1, 2, 6–17, 37–40, 51–53
Day 2: pp. 393–395 Exs. 21–36, 42–49, 54–59

Advanced:
Day 1: pp. 393–395 Exs. 1, 2, 6–8, 12–20, 37–41*, 54–59
Day 2: pp. 393–395 Exs. 24–36, 43–50*, 54–58 even

Block:
pp. 393–395 Exs. 1, 2, 6–17, 37–40, 51–53 (with 6.4)
pp. 393–395 Exs. 21–36, 42–49, 54–59 (with 6.6)

Differentiated Instruction

See *Differentiated Instruction Resources* for suggestions on addressing the needs of a diverse classroom.

Homework Check

For a quick check of student understanding of key concepts, go over the following exercises:

Basic: 4, 10, 16, 24, 42
Average: 6, 12, 17, 26, 44
Advanced: 8, 14, 20, 30, 45

Extra Practice

- Student Edition, p. 943
- Chapter Resource Book: Practice levels A, B, C

Practice Worksheet

An easily-readable reduced practice page (with answers) for this lesson can be found on p. 354E.

Differentiated Instruction

Below Level Some students may need help in determining whether they can solve **Exercises 23–31**. Demonstrate strategies they can use to determine whether the absolute value equation is equal to a negative number and, thus, has no solution. In **Exercise 24**, point out that the right side becomes $6 - 8$, and in **Exercise 26**, point out that the right side becomes $\frac{13}{-4}$. Have students use these strategies to identify all the exercises that have no solutions.

See also the *Differentiated Instruction Resources* for more strategies.

Avoiding Common Errors

Exercises 15–20 Watch for students who try to solve these equations without rewriting them in the form $|ax + b| = c$. Remind them that the absolute value expression must be equal to a nonnegative number before they can rewrite it as two equations.

Mathematical Reasoning

Exercise 37 Students should know that $|x| = b$ means x is b units from 0 on the number line. You may want to ask them to interpret $|x - 0| = b$ as a middle step in understanding that $|x - a| = b$ means x is b units from a.

B **37. SOLVING AN EQUATION** Interpreted geometrically, the equation $|x - a| = b$ means that the distance between x and a on a number line is b. Solve $|x - 3| = 7$ both geometrically and algebraically. *Compare* your solutions. **The distance between x and 3 is 7, 10, −4; $x - 3 = 7$ or $x - 3 = -7$, 10, −4; the solutions are the same.**

TRANSLATING SENTENCES In Exercises 38 and 39, write the verbal sentence as an absolute value equation. Then solve the equation.

38. Four more than the absolute deviation of x from 3 is 8. **$|x - 3| + 4 = 8$; 7, −1**

39. Five times the absolute deviation of $2x$ from −9 is 15. **$5|2x + 9| = 15$; −3, −6**

40. REASONING Is $a|x|$ equivalent to $|ax|$ when a is positive? when a is negative? when a is 0? Give examples to support your answers. **See margin.**

C **41. CHALLENGE** How many solutions does the equation $a|x + b| + c = d$ have if $a > 0$ and $c = d$? if $a < 0$ and $c > d$? **one, two**

PROBLEM SOLVING

EXAMPLE 5 A on p. 392 for Exs. 42–46

42. GUARDRAILS A safety regulation requires that the height of a guardrail be 42 inches with an absolute deviation of 3 inches. Find the minimum and maximum heights of a guardrail. **39 in., 45 in.**

@HomeTutor for problem solving help at classzone.com

40. Yes; no; yes; when $a = 3$ and $x = -2$, $3|-2| = 3(2) = 6 = |-6| = |3(-2)|$; when $a = -3$ and $x = -2$, $-3|-2| = -3(2) = -6 \neq |6| = |-3(-2)|$; when $a = 0$ and $x = -2$, $0|-2| = 0 = |0| = |0(-2)|$.

43. CHEERLEADING A cheerleading team is preparing a dance program for a competition. The program must last 4 minutes with an absolute deviation of 5 seconds. Find the least and greatest possible times (in seconds) that the program can last. **235 sec, 245 sec**

@HomeTutor for problem solving help at classzone.com

44. ★ MULTIPLE CHOICE The diameter of a billiard ball must be 2.25 inches with an absolute error of 0.005 inch. What is the maximum possible diameter that a billiard ball can have? **C**

Ⓐ 2.2 inches Ⓑ 2.245 inches Ⓒ 2.255 inches Ⓓ 2.3 inches

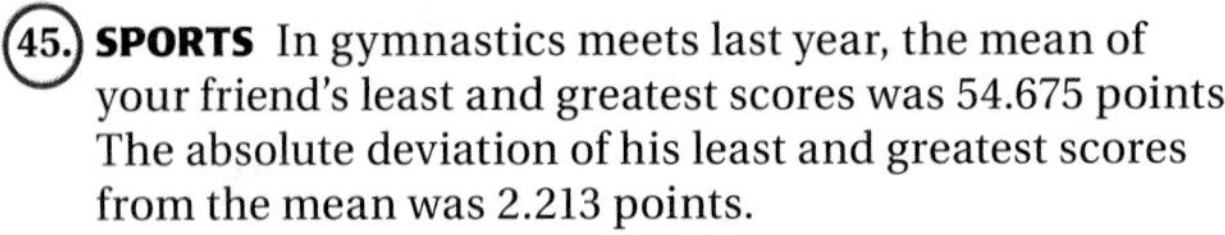

(45.) SPORTS In gymnastics meets last year, the mean of your friend's least and greatest scores was 54.675 points. The absolute deviation of his least and greatest scores from the mean was 2.213 points.

a. What were the least and greatest scores that he earned? **52.462 points, 56.888 points**

b. This year the mean of his least and greatest scores is 56.738 points, and the absolute deviation of the least and greatest scores from the mean is 0.45 point. How many points more than last year's greatest score is this year's greatest score? **0.3 point**

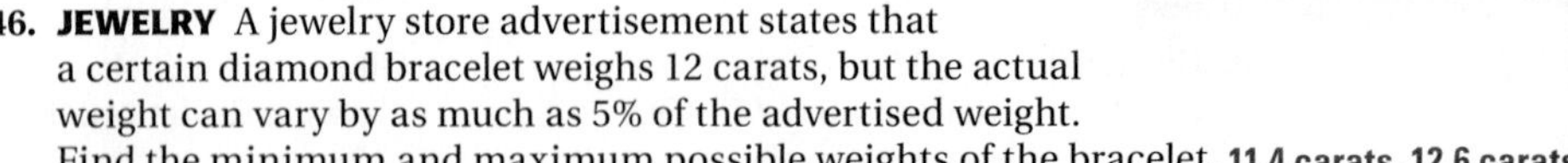

46. JEWELRY A jewelry store advertisement states that a certain diamond bracelet weighs 12 carats, but the actual weight can vary by as much as 5% of the advertised weight. Find the minimum and maximum possible weights of the bracelet. **11.4 carats, 12.6 carats**

394

47. **CONTESTS** You currently have 450 points in an academic contest. You choose the value p of the question you want to answer. The value p represents the absolute deviation of your new score s from 450.
   a. Write an absolute value equation that gives p in terms of s. $p = |s - 450|$
   b. If you choose a question worth 150 points, what are the possible new scores that you can have after answering the question? **300 points, 600 points**

48. ★ **EXTENDED RESPONSE** The percent p of United States residents who were foreign born, or born outside of the United States, during the period 1910–2000 can be modeled by the equation $p = 0.165|t - 60| + 4.8$ where t is the number of years since 1910.
   a. **Approximate** During the period 1910–2000, in approximately what year did foreign-born residents account for 13% of all residents? **1920**
   b. **Predict** If the model holds for years after 2000, predict the year in which foreign-born residents will again account for 13% of all residents. **2020**
   c. **Decide** According to the model, did foreign-born residents account for 4% of all residents at any time during the period 1910–2000? *Explain* your answer. **No; if you substitute 4 for p in the model, the equation has no solution.**

49. ★ **SHORT RESPONSE** A stock's average price p (in dollars) during the period February 2005 to October 2005 can be modeled by the equation $p = 2.3|m - 7| + 9.57$ where m is the number of months since February 2005.
   a. **Approximate** In approximately what month and year was the average price \$16.15? If the model holds for months after October 2005, predict the month and year in which the average price will again be \$16.15. **June 2005; November 2005**
   b. **Justify** Is it possible to use the model to estimate the stock's lowest average price during this period? *Justify* your answer.

49b. Yes; make a table of values for (m, p) using integer values of m from 0 to 8. Look for the lowest value of p in the table.

50. **CHALLENGE** In a recent Olympics, swimmers in a men's 200 meter butterfly event finished with times from 1 minute 54.04 seconds to 1 minute 57.48 seconds. Let t represent the slowest or fastest time (in seconds). Write an absolute value equation that describes the situation. $|t - 115.76| \le 1.72$

MIXED REVIEW

Write an equation of the line shown. *(p. 283)*

51.
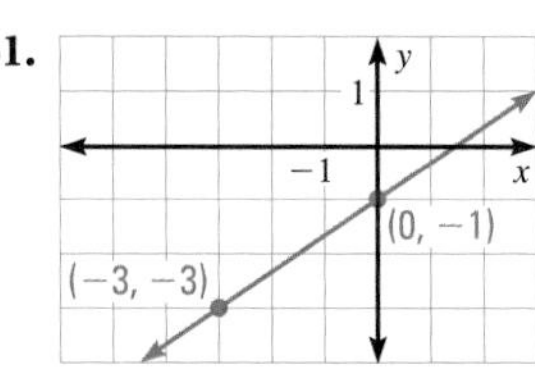

52.
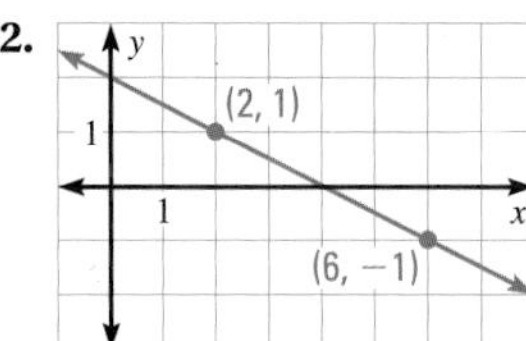

53.
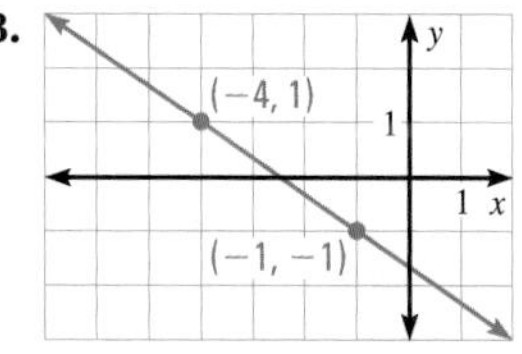

51. $y = \frac{2}{3}x - 1$

52. $y = -\frac{1}{2}x + 2$

53. $y = -\frac{2}{3}x - \frac{5}{3}$

PREVIEW
Prepare for Lesson 6.6 in Exs. 54–59.

Solve the inequality. Graph your solution. **54–59. See margin for art.**

54. $r + 7 \ge 28$ *(p. 356)* $r \ge 21$
55. $-\frac{1}{2}s > -8$ *(p. 363)* $s < 16$
56. $-6t + 7 \le 15$ *(p. 369)* $t \ge -1\frac{1}{3}$
57. $-5(v - 2) < -16$ *(p. 369)* $v > 5\frac{1}{5}$
58. $-14 < 1 - 5w < 12$ *(p. 380)* $-2\frac{1}{5} < w < 3$
59. $-3x > 9$ *or* $4x \ge 8$ *(p. 380)* $x < -3$ or $x \ge 2$

5 ASSESS AND RETEACH

Daily Homework Quiz

Transparency Available

Solve the equation, if possible.

1. $|x - 4| = 13$ **−9, 17**
2. $|x + 2| + 7 = 3$ **no solutions**
3. $|2x - 6| + 4 = 20$ **−5, 11**
4. $-2|x - 5| + 7 = 12$ **no solutions**
5. A pattern for a 26-inch skirt allows for an absolute deviation of 1.5 inches. Find the minimum and maximum skirt lengths that can be made from the pattern. **minimum: 24.5 in.; maximum: 27.5 in.**

Available at **classzone.com**

Diagnosis/Remediation

- Practice A, B, C in Chapter Resource Book
- Study Guide in Chapter Resource Book
- Practice Workbook
- @HomeTutor

Challenge

Additional challenge is available in the Chapter Resource Book.

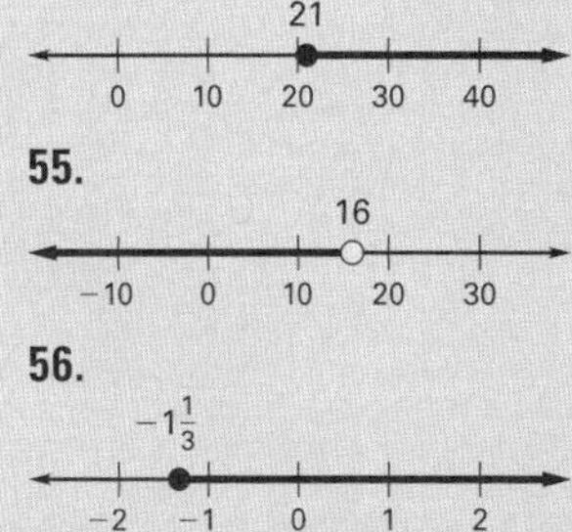

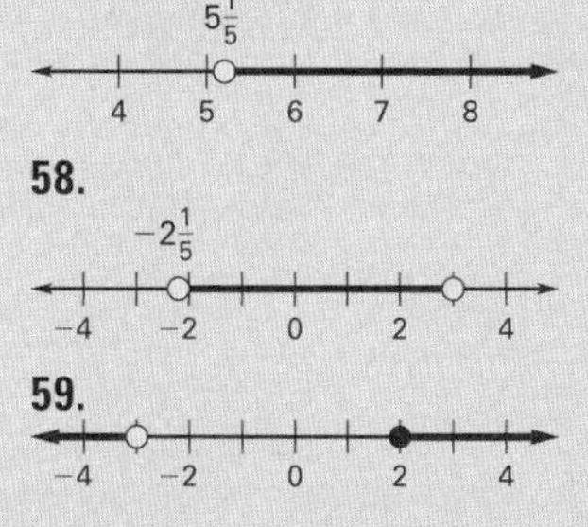

1 PLAN AND PREPARE

Warm-Up Exercises

Evaluate the expression when $x = -2$.

1. $|x - 3|$ 5 2. $-4|x|$ −8

2 FOCUS AND MOTIVATE

Essential Question

Big Idea 2, p. 355

How do you graph absolute value functions? **Tell students they will learn how to answer this question by using a table to plot points.**

3 TEACH

Extra Example 1

Graph each function. Compare the graph with the graph of $f(x) = |x|$.

a. $g(x) = |x + 1|$

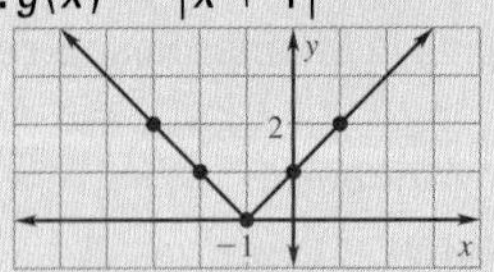

The graph is 1 unit to the left of the graph of $f(x) = |x|$.

b. $g(x) = |x| + 2$

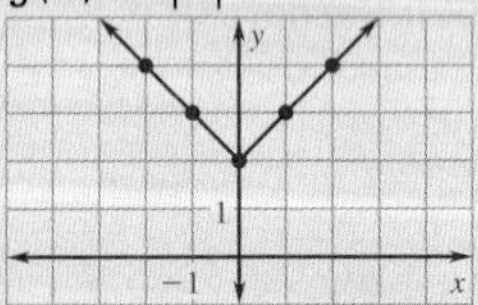

The graph is 2 units above the graph of $f(x) = |x|$.

NCTM STANDARDS

Standard 2: Understand functions

Standard 3: Apply transformations to math situations

Extension Graph Absolute Value Functions

Use after Lesson 6.5

GOAL Graph absolute value functions.

Key Vocabulary
- **absolute value,** *p. 66*

The function $f(x) = |x|$ is an example of an *absolute value function* and is the parent function for all absolute value functions. You can graph absolute value functions by using a table of values, as shown below for $f(x) = |x|$.

KEY CONCEPT *For Your Notebook*

Graph of Parent Function for Absolute Value Functions

The domain of the parent absolute value function is all real numbers. The range is $y \geq 0$.

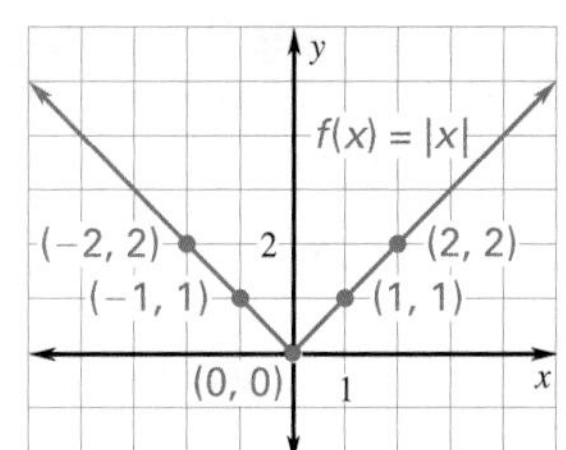

The graph consists of two rays with a common endpoint called the *vertex* of the graph. The minimum value of the function occurs at the vertex.

EXAMPLE 1 Graph $g(x) = |x - h|$ and $g(x) = |x| + k$

Graph each function. Compare the graph with the graph of $f(x) = |x|$.

a. $g(x) = |x - 2|$

STEP 1 **Make** a table of values.

x	0	1	2	3	4
$g(x)$	2	1	0	1	2

STEP 2 **Graph** the function.

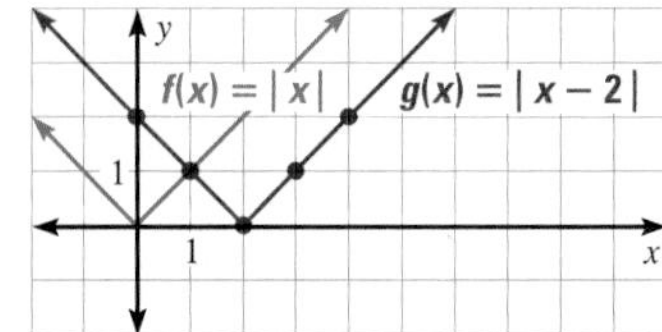

STEP 3 **Compare** the graphs of g and f. The graph of $g(x) = |x - 2|$ is 2 units to the right of the graph of $f(x) = |x|$.

b. $g(x) = |x| - 1$

STEP 1 **Make** a table of values.

x	−2	−1	0	1	2
$g(x)$	1	0	−1	0	1

STEP 2 **Graph** the function.

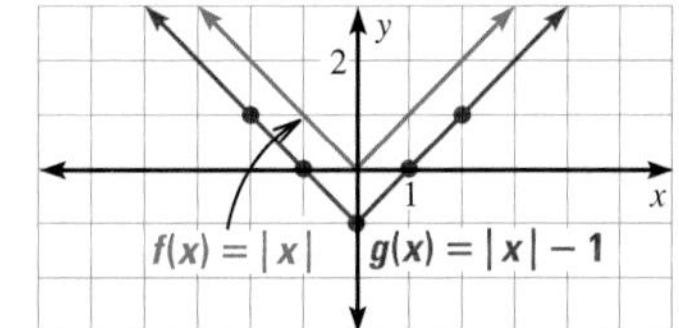

STEP 3 **Compare** the graphs of g and f. The graph of $g(x) = |x| - 1$ is 1 unit below the graph of $f(x) = |x|$.

APPLY TRANSFORMATIONS
The two graphs in Example 1 are translations of the graph of $f(x) = |x|$. The graph in part (a) is a horizontal translation. The graph in part (b) is a vertical translation.

EXAMPLE 2 Graph $g(x) = a|x|$

Graph each function. Compare the graph with the graph of $f(x) = |x|$.

a. $g(x) = 4|x|$

STEP 1 **Make** a table of values.

x	−2	−1	0	1	2
$g(x)$	8	4	0	4	8

STEP 2 **Graph** the function.

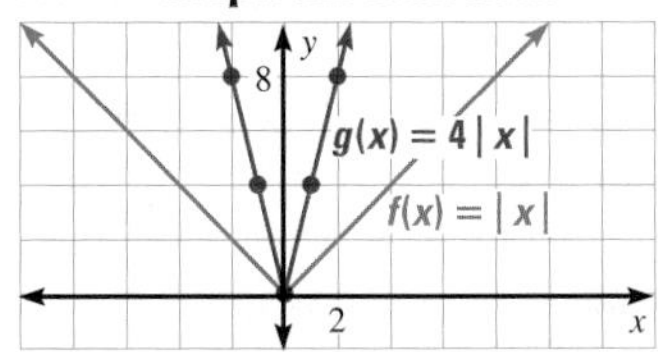

STEP 3 **Compare** the graphs of g and f. The graph of $g(x) = 4|x|$ opens up and is narrower than the graph of $f(x) = |x|$.

b. $g(x) = -0.5|x|$

STEP 1 **Make** a table of values.

x	−4	−2	0	2	4
$g(x)$	−2	−1	0	−1	−2

STEP 2 **Graph** the function.

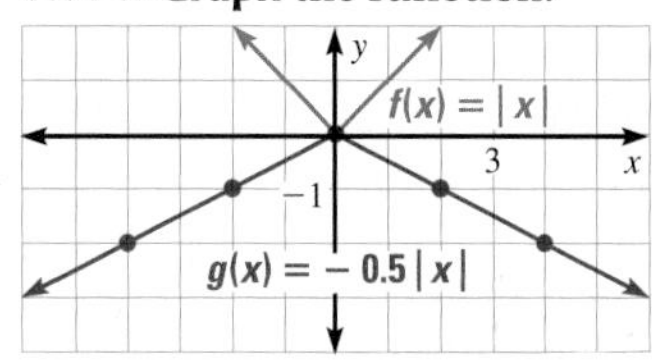

STEP 3 **Compare** the graphs of g and f. The graph of $g(x) = -0.5|x|$ opens down and is wider than the graph of $f(x) = |x|$.

APPLY TRANSFORMATIONS
The graph in part (a) of Example 2 is a vertical stretch of the graph of $f(x) = |x|$. The graph in part (b) is a vertical shrink with a reflection in the x-axis of the graph of $f(x) = |x|$.

KEY CONCEPT *For Your Notebook*

Comparing Graphs of Absolute Value Functions with the Graph of $f(x) = |x|$

$g(x) = |x - h|$

If $h > 0$, the graph of g is $|h|$ units to the right of the graph of $f(x) = |x|$.

If $h < 0$, the graph of g is $|h|$ units to the left of the graph of $f(x) = |x|$.

$g(x) = |x| + k$

If $k > 0$, the graph of g is $|k|$ units above the graph of $f(x) = |x|$.

If $k < 0$, the graph of g is $|k|$ units below the graph of $f(x) = |x|$.

$g(x) = a|x|$

If $|a| > 1$, the graph of g is narrower than the graph of $f(x) = |x|$. If $0 < |a| < 1$, the graph of g is wider.

If $a > 0$, the graph of g opens up. If $a < 0$, the graph opens down.

PRACTICE

EXAMPLES 1 and 2 on pp. 396–397 for Exs. 1–6

Graph the function. ***Compare*** **the graph with the graph of $f(x) = |x|$.** **1–6. See margin.**

1. $g(x) = |x + 3|$
2. $g(x) = |x| + 5$
3. $g(x) = |x| - 7$
4. $g(x) = 2|x|$
5. $g(x) = 0.6|x|$
6. $g(x) = -3|x|$
7. For the absolute value function $g(x) = -|x| + 1$, identify the function's domain and range, the vertex of the function's graph, and the function's minimum or maximum value. **domain: all real numbers, range: $y \leq 1$; vertex of the graph: (0, 1); maximum value: 1**

Extra Example 2

Graph each function. Compare the graph with the graph of $f(x) = |x|$.

a. $g(x) = -2|x|$

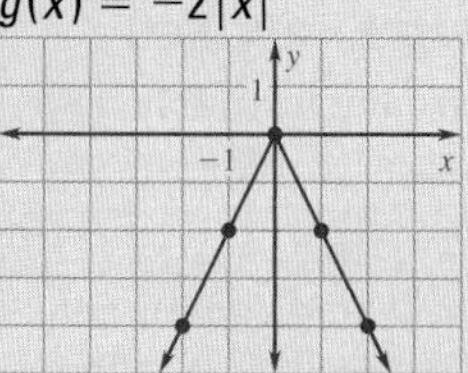

The graph opens down and is narrower than the graph of $f(x) = |x|$.

b. $g(x) = 0.5|x|$

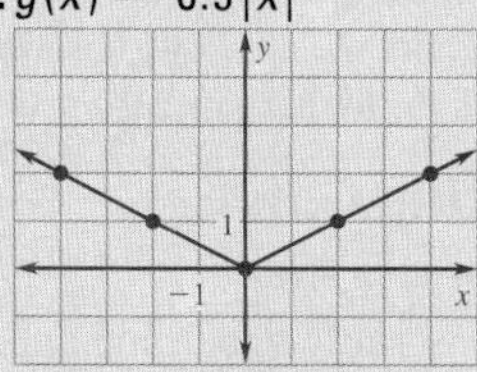

The graph is wider than the graph of $f(x) = |x|$.

Closing the Lesson

Have students summarize the major points of the lesson and answer the Essential Question: How do you graph absolute value functions?

- **Absolute value functions are transformations of the parent function $f(x) = |x|$.**

Make a table of values for the function. Plot points and connect them.

4 PRACTICE AND APPLY

Avoiding Common Errors

Exercises 1–6 Some students may make a table of values for one side of the function only. Have them start in the middle of the table with an x value that gives 0 for the expression inside the absolute value symbols. Then assign x values on each side of that first value.

1–6. See Additional Answers beginning on p. AA1.

1 PLAN AND PREPARE

Warm-Up Exercises

Transparency Available

1. Solve $|x - 6| = 4$. **2, 10**
2. Solve $|x + 5| - 8 = 2$. **−15, 5**
3. A frame will hold photographs that are 5 inches by 8 inches with an absolute deviation of 0.25 inch for length and width. What are the minimum and maximum dimensions for photos? **min: 4.75 in. by 7.75 in.; max: 5.25 in. by 8.25 in.**

Notetaking Guide

Transparency Available

Promotes interactive learning and notetaking skills.

Pacing

Basic: 1 day
Average: 1 day
Advanced: 1 day
Block: 0.5 block with 6.5

- See *Teaching Guide/Lesson Plan.*

2 FOCUS AND MOTIVATE

Essential Question

Big Idea 1, p. 355

How do you solve absolute value inequalities? **Tell students they will learn how to answer this question by rewriting absolute value inequalities as compound inequalities and solving them.**

NCTM STANDARDS

Standard 2: Use models to understand relationships

Standard 3: Use geometric modeling

6.6 Solve Absolute Value Inequalities

Before You solved absolute value equations.

Now You will solve absolute value inequalities.

Why So you can analyze softball compression, as in Ex. 38.

Key Vocabulary
- **absolute value,** *p. 66*
- **equivalent inequalities,** *p. 357*
- **compound inequality,** *p. 380*
- **absolute deviation,** *p. 392*
- **mean,** *p. 918*

Recall that $|x| = 3$ means that the distance between x and 0 is 3. The inequality $|x| < 3$ means that the distance between x and 0 is *less than* 3, and $|x| > 3$ means that the distance between x and 0 is *greater than* 3. The graphs of $|x| < 3$ and $|x| > 3$ are shown below.

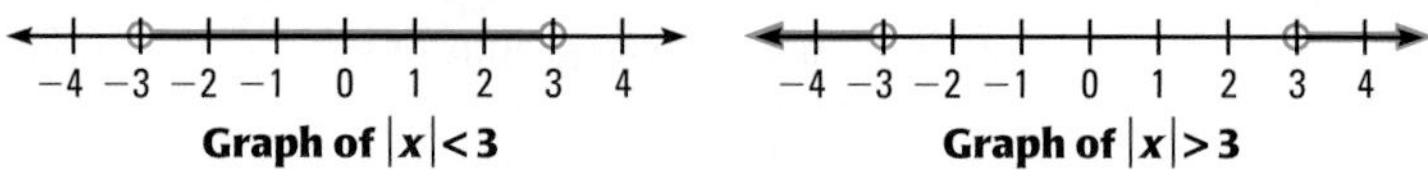

EXAMPLE 1 Solve absolute value inequalities

Solve the inequality. Graph your solution.

a. $|x| \geq 6$ **b.** $|x| \leq 0.5$

Solution

a. The distance between x and 0 is greater than or equal to 6. So, $x \leq -6$ *or* $x \geq 6$.

▶ The solutions are all real numbers less than or equal to −6 *or* greater than or equal to 6.

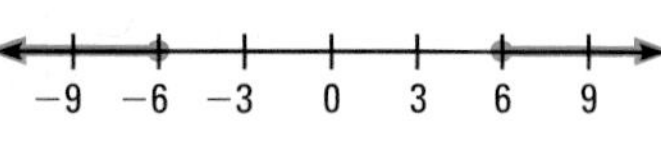

b. The distance between x and 0 is less than or equal to 0.5. So, $-0.5 \leq x \leq 0.5$.

▶ The solutions are all real numbers greater than or equal to −0.5 *and* less than or equal to 0.5.

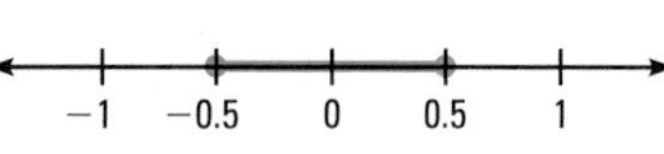

✓ GUIDED PRACTICE for Example 1

Solve the inequality. Graph your solution. **1–3. See margin for art.**

1. $|x| \leq 8$ $\mathbf{-8 \leq x \leq 8}$
2. $|u| < 3.5$ $\mathbf{-3.5 < u < 3.5}$
3. $|v| > \frac{2}{3}$ $\mathbf{v < -\frac{2}{3}}$ **or** $\mathbf{v > \frac{2}{3}}$

SOLVING ABSOLUTE VALUE INEQUALITIES In Example 1, the solutions of $|x| \geq 6$ and $|x| \leq 0.5$ suggest that you can rewrite an absolute value inequality as a compound inequality.

Resource Planning Guide

Chapter Resource Book
- Teaching Guide/Lesson Plan
- Activity Master
- Practice levels A, B, C
- Study Guide
- Catch-up for Absent Students
- Application
- Challenge

Workbooks
- Notetaking Guide
- Practice Workbook

Teaching Options
- **Power Presentations** provides dynamic electronic teaching resources for the classroom.
- **Activity Generator** provides editable activities for all ability levels.

Interactive Technology
- Easy Planner
- Power Presentations
- Activity Generator
- Animated Algebra
- Test Generator
- Online Quiz
- eWorkbook
- eEdition
- @HomeTutor

Resources for English Learners
- Spanish Study Guide
- Multi-Language Visual Glossary
- Student Resources in Spanish

See also the *Differentiated Instruction Resources* for more strategies for meeting individual needs.

READING You can use the words *between* and *beyond* to describe absolute value inequalites. For example, $|x| < 2$ means that x is between -2 *and* 2; $|x| > 2$ means that x is beyond -2 *or* beyond 2.

KEY CONCEPT — *For Your Notebook*

Solving Absolute Value Inequalities

- The inequality $|ax + b| < c$ where $c > 0$ is equivalent to the compound inequality $-c < ax + b < c$.
- The inequality $|ax + b| > c$ where $c > 0$ is equivalent to the compound inequality $ax + b < -c$ *or* $ax + b > c$.

In the inequalities above, $<$ can be replaced by $\le$ and $>$ can be replaced by $\ge$.

EXAMPLE 2 Solve an absolute value inequality

Solve $|x - 5| \ge 7$. Graph your solution.

$|x - 5| \ge 7$	**Write original inequality.**
$x - 5 \le -7$ *or* $x - 5 \ge 7$	**Rewrite as compound inequality.**
$x \le -2$ *or* $x \ge 12$	**Add 5 to each side.**

▶ The solutions are all real numbers less than or equal to -2 *or* greater than or equal to 12. Check several solutions in the original inequality.

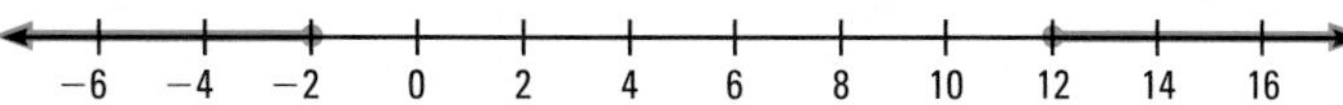

EXAMPLE 3 Solve an absolute value inequality

Solve $|-4x - 5| + 3 < 9$. Graph your solution.

$|-4x - 5| + 3 < 9$	**Write original inequality.**
$|-4x - 5| < 6$	**Subtract 3 from each side.**
$-6 < -4x - 5 < 6$	**Rewrite as compound inequality.**
$-1 < -4x < 11$	**Add 5 to each expression.**
$0.25 > x > -2.75$	**Divide each expression by −4. Reverse inequality symbol.**
$-2.75 < x < 0.25$	**Rewrite in the form $a < x < b$.**

▶ The solutions are all real numbers greater than -2.75 *and* less than 0.25.

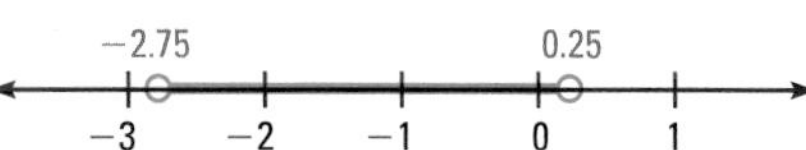

Animated Algebra at classzone.com

✓ GUIDED PRACTICE for Examples 2 and 3

Solve the inequality. Graph your solution. **4–6. See margin for art.**

4. $|x + 3| > 8$ **$x < -11$ or $x > 5$**

5. $|2w - 1| < 11$ **$-5 < w < 6$**

6. $3|5m - 6| - 8 \le 13$ **$-0.2 \le m \le 2.6$**

Motivating the Lesson

Knowing how to solve absolute value inequalities can help you analyze statistical data. For example, if you know that 582 people in a poll voted for a candidate and the poll has a 2% margin of error, you can determine the least and greatest number of people who voted for the candidate.

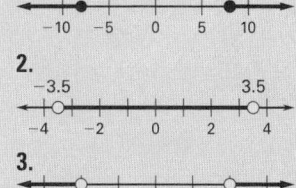

3 TEACH

Extra Example 1

Solve the inequality. Graph your solution.

a. $|x| > 2$ **all real numbers less than −2 *or* greater than 2**

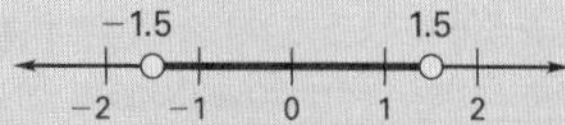

b. $|x| < 1.5$ **all real numbers greater than −1.5 *and* less than 1.5**

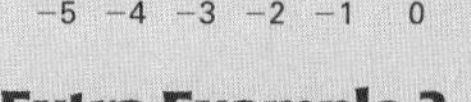

Extra Example 2

Solve $|x + 2| > 1$. Graph your solution. **all real numbers less than −3 *or* greater than −1**

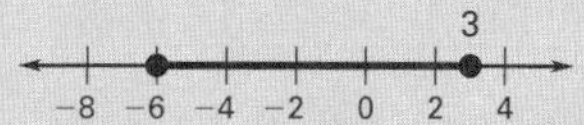

Extra Example 3

Solve $|2x + 3| - 4 \le 5$. Graph your solution. **all real numbers greater than or equal to −6 *and* less than or equal to 3**

Animated Algebra classzone.com

An **Animated Algebra** activity is available online for **Example 3**. This activity is also part of **Power Presentations**.

1.
−8 8
−10 −5 0 5 10

2.

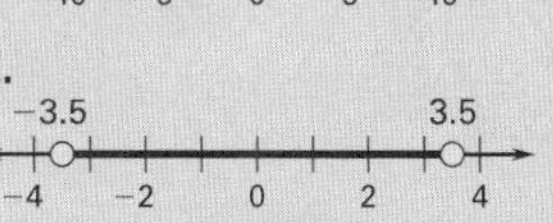

3.

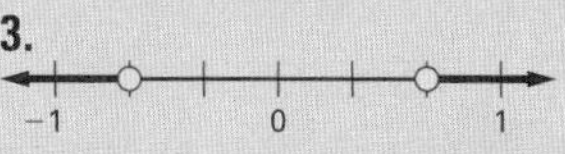

4.

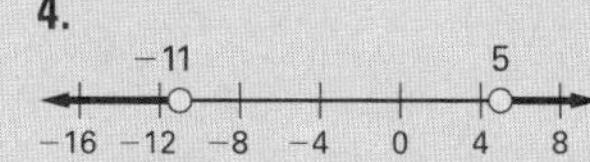

5.

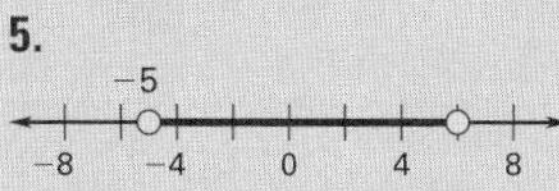

6.

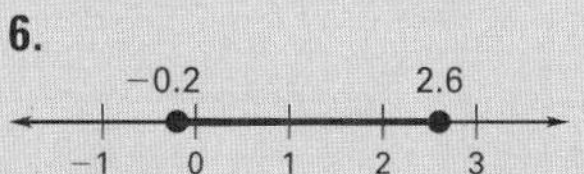

Extra Example 4

You are on the planning committee for a school dance. Ticket sales for the last ten dances are 133, 178, 205, 220, 186, 142, 138, 204, 216, and 198.

- Find the mean number of tickets sold.
- The dance committee estimates they will sell the mean number of tickets with an absolute deviation of at most 40 tickets. How many of the ticket sales to the previous ten dances were within this range?

The mean number of tickets sold is 182. The range of sales within 40 tickets of the mean is 142 to 222 tickets. Eight previous ticket sales fell within this range: 178, 205, 220, 186, 142, 204, 216, and 198.

Closing the Lesson

Have students summarize the major points of the lesson and answer the Essential Question: How do you solve absolute value inequalities?

- **You can rewrite an absolute value inequality as a compound inequality. Inequalities using > or ≥ can be rewritten using *or*. Inequalities using < or ≤ can be rewritten using *and*.**

Rewrite the absolute value inequality so one side is $|ax + b|$. Then write the compound inequality as two inequalities joined by *or* for > and ≥, or by *and* for < and ≤, and solve the inequalities.

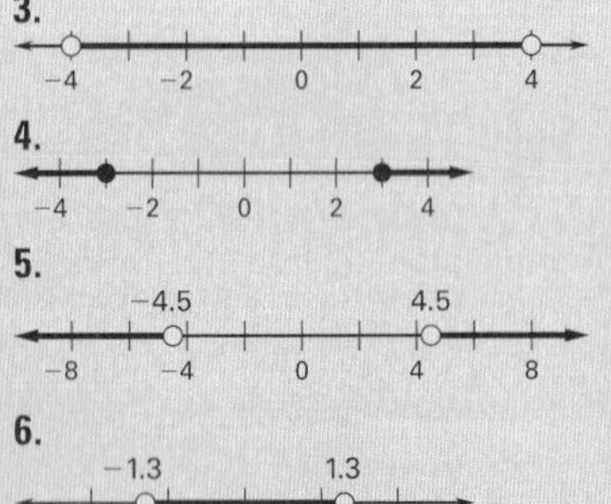

7. See answer at right.

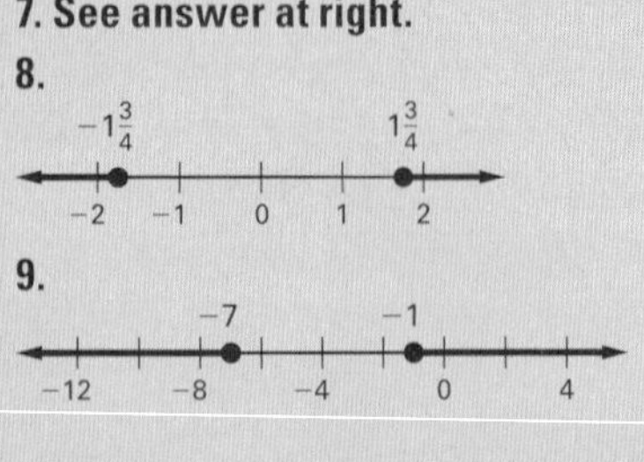

EXAMPLE 4 Solve a multi-step problem

COMPUTERS You are buying a new computer and find 10 models in a store advertisement. The prices are \$890, \$750, \$650, \$370, \$660, \$670, \$450, \$650, \$725, and \$825.

- Find the mean of the computer prices.
- You are willing to pay the mean price with an absolute deviation of at most \$100. How many of the computer prices meet your condition?

Solution

STEP 1 **Find** the mean by dividing the sum of the prices by 10.

REVIEW MEAN
For help with finding a mean, see p. 918.

$$\text{Mean} = \frac{890 + 750 + 650 + 370 + 660 + 670 + 450 + 650 + 725 + 825}{10}$$

$$= \frac{6640}{10} = 664$$

STEP 2 **Write** and solve an inequality. An absolute deviation of at most \$100 from the mean, \$664, is given by the inequality $|x - 664| \le 100$.

$|x - 664| \le 100$ **Write absolute value inequality.**

$-100 \le x - 664 \le 100$ **Write as compound inequality.**

$564 \le x \le 764$ **Add 664 to each expression.**

▶ The prices you will consider must be at least \$564 and at most \$764. Six prices meet your condition: \$750, \$650, \$660, \$670, \$650, and \$725.

✓ GUIDED PRACTICE for Example 4

7. **WHAT IF?** In Example 4, suppose that you are willing to pay the mean price with an absolute deviation of at most \$75. How many of the computer prices meet this condition? **5 computer prices**

CONCEPT SUMMARY *For Your Notebook*

Solving Inequalities

One-Step and Multi-Step Inequalities

- Follow the steps for solving an equation, but reverse the inequality symbol when multiplying or dividing by a negative number.

Compound Inequalities

- If necessary, rewrite the inequality as two separate inequalities. Then solve each inequality separately. Include *and* or *or* in the solution.

Absolute Value Inequalities

- If necessary, isolate the absolute value expression on one side of the inequality. Rewrite the absolute value inequality as a compound inequality. Then solve the compound inequality.

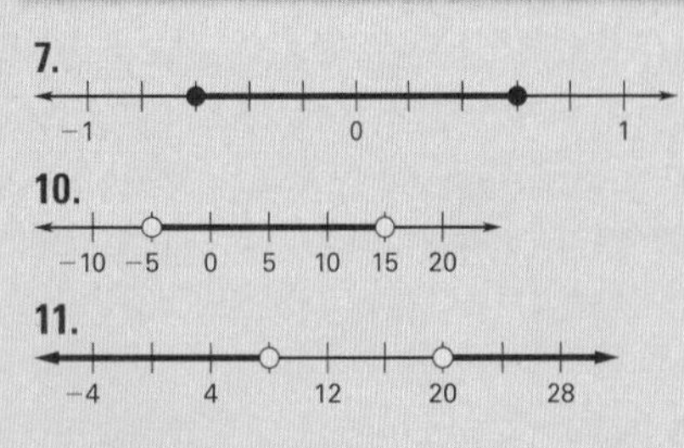

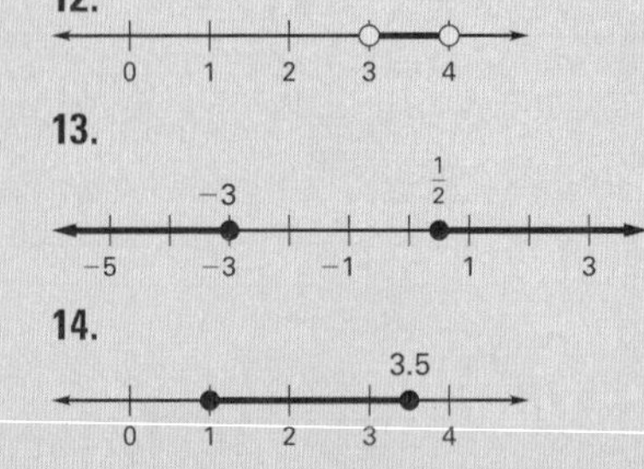

6.6 EXERCISES

HOMEWORK KEY
○ = WORKED-OUT SOLUTIONS on p. WS15 for Exs. 9, 15, and 37
★ = STANDARDIZED TEST PRACTICE Exs. 2, 21, 22, 37, and 40
◆ = MULTIPLE REPRESENTATIONS Ex. 38

SKILL PRACTICE

A

1. **VOCABULARY** Copy and complete: The inequalities $|x| > 8$ and $x > 8$ *or* $x < -8$ are _?_. **equivalent inequalities**

2. ★ **WRITING** *Describe* the difference between solving $|x| \le 5$ and solving $|x| \ge 5$. **Solving $|x| \le 5$ involves solving a compound inequality with *and*, while solving $|x| \ge 5$ involves solving a compound inequality with *or*.**

EXAMPLES 1, 2, and 3 on pp. 398–399 for Exs. 3–24

SOLVING INEQUALITIES **Solve the inequality. Graph your solution.** 3–20. See margin for art.

3. $|x| < 4$ $-4 < x < 4$
4. $|y| \ge 3$ $y \le -3$ or $y \ge 3$
5. $|h| > 4.5$ $h < -4.5$ or $h > 4.5$
6. $|p| < 1.3$ $-1.3 < p < 1.3$
7. $|t| \le \frac{3}{5}$ $-\frac{3}{5} \le t \le \frac{3}{5}$
8. $|j| \ge 1\frac{3}{4}$ $j \le -1\frac{3}{4}$ or $j \ge 1\frac{3}{4}$
9. $|d + 4| \ge 3$ $d \le -7$ or $d \ge -1$
10. $|b - 5| < 10$ $-5 < b < 15$
11. $|14 - m| > 6$ $m < 8$ or $m > 20$
12. $|2s - 7| < 1$ $3 < s < 4$
13. $|4c + 5| \ge 7$ $c \le -3$ or $c \ge \frac{1}{2}$
14. $|9 - 4n| \le 5$ $1 \le n \le 3.5$
15. $5\left|\frac{1}{2}r + 3\right| > 5$ $r < -8$ or $r > -4$
16. $\left|\frac{4}{3}s - 7\right| - 8 > 3$ $s < -3$ or $s > 13\frac{1}{2}$
17. $-3\left|2 - \frac{5}{4}u\right| \le -18$ $u \le -3\frac{1}{5}$ or $u \ge 6\frac{2}{5}$
18. $2|3w + 8| - 13 < -5$ $-4 < w < -1\frac{1}{3}$
19. $2\left|\frac{1}{4}v - 5\right| - 4 > 3$ $v < 6$ or $v > 34$
20. $\frac{2}{7}|4f + 6| - 2 \ge 10$ $f \le -12$ or $f \ge 9$

21. ★ **MULTIPLE CHOICE** Which inequality is equivalent to $x < 1$ *or* $x > 5$? **B**

Ⓐ $|x + 8| - 2 > 10$ Ⓑ $3|6 - 2x| > 12$

Ⓒ $|5x + 9| < 10$ Ⓓ $|7 - 4x| - 9 < 8$

22. ★ **WRITING** How can you tell whether an absolute value inequality is equivalent to a compound inequality with *and* or to a compound inequality with *or*?

22. When the inequality has the absolute value expression isolated on the left side, the equivalent compound inequality will use *and* if the symbol is < *or* ≤, and it will use *or* if the symbol is > or ≥.

ERROR ANALYSIS *Describe* and correct the error in solving the inequality.

23.

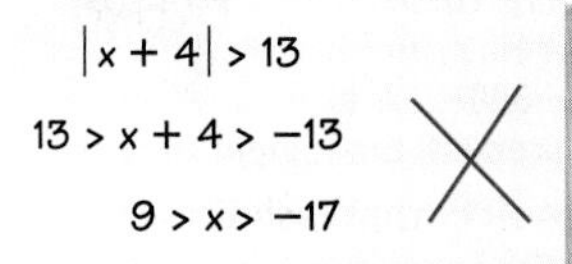

24.

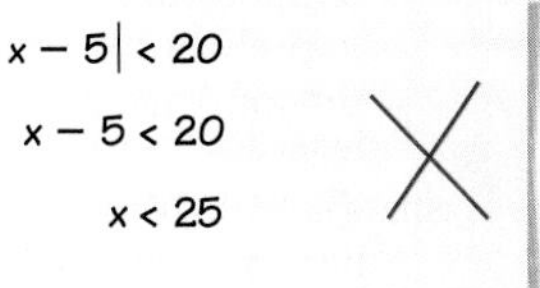

23. The compound inequality should use *or*: $x + 4 > 13$ *or* $x + 4 < -13$; $x > 9$ *or* $x < -17$.

24. Part of the compound inequality is missing; the compound inequality should be $-20 < x - 5 < 20$; $-15 < x < 25$.

B

TRANSLATING SENTENCES **Write the verbal sentence as an inequality. Then solve the inequality and graph your solution.** 25–28. See margin for art.

25. The absolute deviation of x from 6 is less than or equal to 4. $|x - 6| \le 4$; $2 \le x \le 10$
26. The absolute deviation of $2x$ from -7 is greater than or equal to 15. $|2x + 7| \ge 15$; $x \le -11$ *or* $x \ge 4$
27. Three more than the absolute deviation of $-4x$ from 7 is greater than 10. $|-4x - 7| + 3 > 10$; $x < -3.5$ *or* $x > 0$
28. Four times the absolute deviation of x from 9 is less than 8. $4|x - 9| < 8$; $7 < x < 11$

4 PRACTICE AND APPLY

Assignment Guide

Answer Transparencies available for all exercises

Basic:
Day 1: SRH p. 918 Exs. 1–5
pp. 401–403
Exs. 1, 2, 3–21 odd, 22–28, 35–38, 42–52 even

Average:
Day 1: pp. 401–403
Exs. 1, 2, 6–20 even, 21–24, 25–31 odd, 35–40, 45–50

Advanced:
Day 1: pp. 401–403
Exs. 1, 6–20 even, 21, 22, 26–32 even, 33*, 34*, 36–41*, 44, 47, 52

Block:
pp. 401–403
Exs. 1, 2, 6–20 even, 21–24, 25–31 odd, 35–40, 45–50 (with 6.5)

Differentiated Instruction

See *Differentiated Instruction Resources* for suggestions on addressing the needs of a diverse classroom.

Homework Check

For a quick check of student understanding of key concepts, go over the following exercises:

Basic: 5, 11, 17, 25, 35
Average: 6, 10, 18, 25, 36
Advanced: 8, 12, 20, 28, 37

Extra Practice

- Student Edition, p. 943
- Chapter Resource Book: Practice levels A, B, C

Practice Worksheet

An easily-readable reduced practice page (with answers) for this lesson can be found on p. 354E.

15.–17.

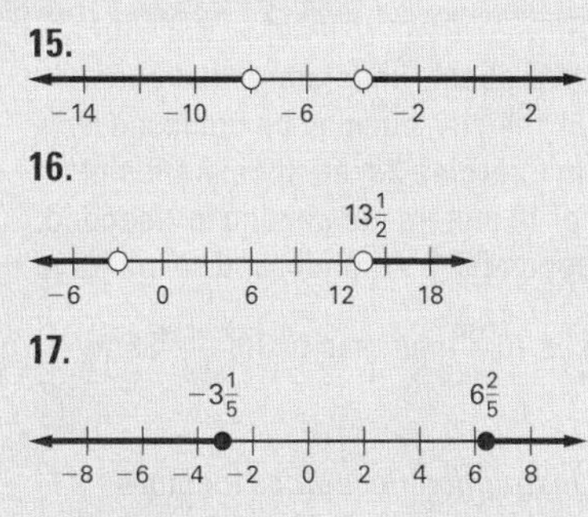

18.

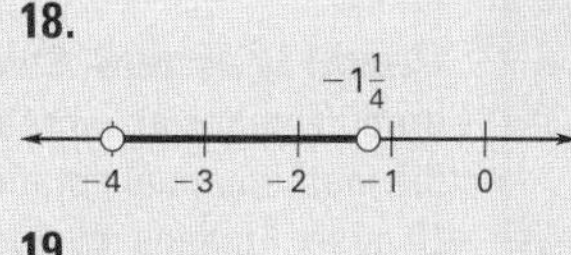

19.

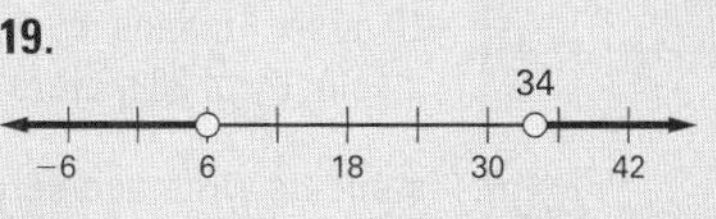

20.

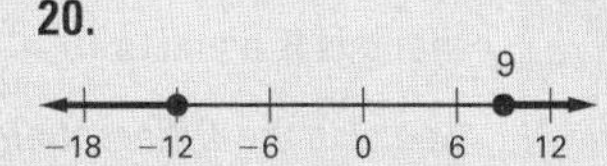

25.

−2 2 6 10 14

26.–28.

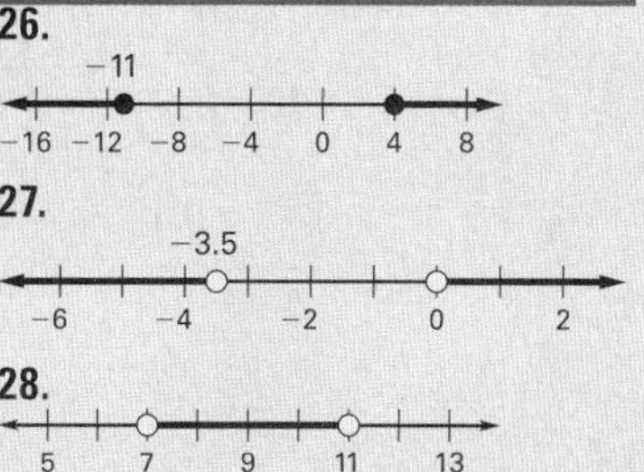

Avoiding Common Errors

Exercises 9–20 Some students may switch *and* and *or* when they rewrite absolute value inequalities. Remind students that $|ax + b| < c$ and $|ax + b| \le c$ are rewritten using *and* and that $|ax + b| > c$ and $|ax + b| \ge c$ are rewritten using *or.*

Mathematical Reasoning

Multiple Representations

Exercise 38 You may want to discuss the advantages of using tables to organize data. Stress that presenting numbers in tables allows students to find the data they need quickly. Suggest they create a table that has three colunns with a title at the top of each, such as minimum, *p*, and maximum. They can also use the top of each column to indicate the calculation they need to perform.

Graphing Calculator

Exercise 39 Students can use a graphing calculator to calculate the mean. They should use the STAT option, then EDIT, and enter the data in the list. After they enter the data, they should go to STAT, then CALC, and then choose 1-VAR stats and the list number, such as L1. This will produce a screen that includes the mean.

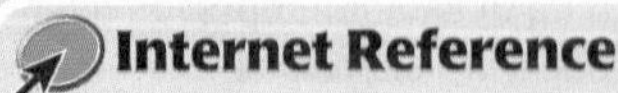

Internet Reference

Exercise 40 For more information about pronghorn antelope, visit www.nps.gov/wica/Pronghorn.htm

38a. See Additional Answers beginning on p. AA1.

REASONING **Tell whether the statement is *true* or *false*. If it is false, give a counterexample.**

29. If a is a solution of $|x + 3| \le 8$, then a is also a solution of $x + 3 \ge -8$. **true**
30. If a is a solution of $|x + 3| > 8$, then a is also a solution of $x + 3 > 8$. **False.** ***Sample answer:*** **−20**
31. If a is a solution of $|x + 3| \ge 8$, then a is also a solution of $x + 3 \le -8$. **False.** ***Sample answer:*** **20**
32. If a is a solution of $x + 3 \le -8$, then a is also a solution of $|x + 3| \ge 8$. **true**

33. $6 < x < 7$; solve each absolute value inequality by rewriting it as a compound inequality. Graph the solutions and find the intersection of the graphs.

33. CHALLENGE Solve $|x - 3| < 4$ *and* $|x + 2| > 8$. *Describe* your steps.
34. CHALLENGE If $|ax + b| < c$ where $c < 0$, what is the solution of the inequality? If $|ax + b| > c$ where $c < 0$, what is the solution of the inequality? *Explain* your answers.
No solution; all real numbers; because an absolute value cannot be negative, for any real number x, $|ax + b|$ is nonnegative, so if c is a negative number, $|ax + b| > c$ for any real number x.

PROBLEM SOLVING

EXAMPLE 4 on p. 400 for Exs. 35–38

35. **ESSAY CONTEST** An essay contest requires that essay entries consist of 500 words with an absolute deviation of at most 30 words. What are the possible numbers of words that the essay can have? **at least 470 words and at most 530 words**

@HomeTutor for problem solving help at classzone.com

36. **SWIMMING POOL** The saturation index for a pool measures the balance between the acid level and the amount of minerals in pool water. Balanced water has an index value of 0. Water is highly corrosive or highly scale forming if the absolute deviation of the index value from 0 is greater than 0.5. Find the index values for which pool water is highly corrosive or highly scale forming. **greater than 0.5 or less than −0.5**

@HomeTutor for problem solving help at classzone.com

37. ★ **SHORT RESPONSE** You are preheating an oven to 350°F before you bake muffins. Several minutes later, the oven thermometer reads 346°F. The measured temperature has an absolute deviation of at most 2°F. Write and solve an inequality to find the possible temperatures in the oven. Should you continue to preheat the oven, or should you start baking the muffins? *Explain* your choice. **$|t - 346| \le 2$, at least 344°F and at most 348°F; continue to preheat; the temperature is still below 350°F.**

38. ◆ **MULTIPLE REPRESENTATIONS** Softball compression measures the hardness of a softball and affects the distance that the softball can travel upon contact with a bat. A softball organization requires that the compression of a softball be 350 pounds but allows an absolute deviation of at most 50 pounds.
    a. **Making a Table** Make a table that shows the absolute deviation from the required compression when the measured compression of a softball is p pounds. Use the following values for p: 275, 325, 375, 425, 475. **See margin.**
    b. **Writing an Inequality** Write and solve an inequality to find the softball compressions that the organization will allow. Which values of p in the table are solutions of the inequality? **$|p - 350| \le 50$, at least 300 lb and at most 400 lb; 325, 375**

○ = WORKED-OUT SOLUTIONS on p. WS1 ★ = STANDARDIZED TEST PRACTICE  = MULTIPLE REPRESENTATIONS

Differentiated Instruction

Visual Learners Students probably understand that acceleration means an increase in velocity, but may be confused by the mathematical notation. In **Exercise 39**, an acceleration of 10 m/sec^2 means a velocity of 10 meters per second in 1 second, a velocity of 20 meters per second in 2 seconds, and so on. Have students write acceleration as $10\,\frac{\text{m}}{\text{sec}}$ per sec or $10\,\frac{\frac{\text{m}}{\text{sec}}}{\text{sec}}$. Show that this is equal to $10\,\frac{\text{m}}{\text{sec}^2}$.

See also the *Differentiated Instruction Resources* for more strategies.

B **39. MULTI-STEP PROBLEM** In a physics class, 7 groups of students experimentally determine the acceleration (in meters per second per second) of an object in free fall. The table below shows the value calculated by each group.

Group	1	2	3	4	5	6	7
Calculated value (m/sec^2)	10.50	9.52	9.73	9.86	9.78	10.90	9.86

a. **Calculate** Find the mean of the measured values given in the table. Round to the nearest hundredth. **10.02 m/sec^2**

b. **Solve** When writing up their lab reports, the students wanted to state that the absolute deviation of each measured value x from the mean was at most d. What is the value of d in this situation? **0.88 m/sec^2**

40b. $|p - 18{,}000| \le 3600$; at least 14,400 antelope and at most 21,600 antelope.

40. ★ EXTENDED RESPONSE *Relative absolute deviation* of a number from a given value is the absolute deviation expressed as a percent of the given value. A wildlife biologist estimates that the number of pronghorn antelope in Nevada is 18,000 with a relative absolute deviation of at most 20%.

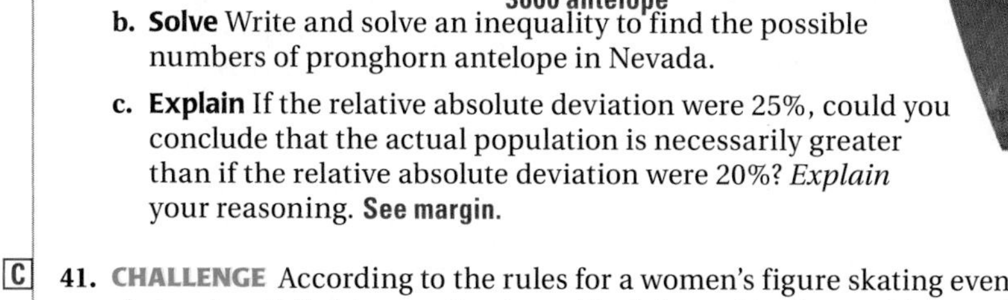

a. **Calculate** Find the absolute deviation from the estimated population of pronghorn antelope by multiplying the estimated population by the relative absolute deviation. **3600 antelope**

b. **Solve** Write and solve an inequality to find the possible numbers of pronghorn antelope in Nevada.

c. **Explain** If the relative absolute deviation were 25%, could you conclude that the actual population is necessarily greater than if the relative absolute deviation were 20%? *Explain* your reasoning. **See margin.**

C **41. CHALLENGE** According to the rules for a women's figure skating event, a skater should finish a routine in an ideal time of 3 minutes 30 seconds. The skater receives a 0.1 point penalty if the absolute deviation of the finishing time from the ideal time is greater than 10 seconds *and* less than or equal to 20 seconds. Write and solve an inequality to find the finishing times for which the skater receives a 0.1 penalty point. **at least 3 minutes 10 seconds and less than 3 minutes 20 seconds, more than 3 minutes 40 seconds and at most 3 minutes 50 seconds**

MIXED REVIEW

PREVIEW Prepare for Lesson 6.7 in Exs. 42–53.

Graph the equation. *(p. 215)* **42–47. See margin.**

42. $y = -5.5$ **43.** $x = 10$ **44.** $3x + y = 3$

45. $y = 2x + 7$ **46.** $y = -5x + 2$ **47.** $5 = -\frac{1}{2}x - y$

Check whether the ordered pair is a solution of the equation. *(p. 215)*

48. $x - y = 1$; (2, 1) **solution** **49.** $-x + 2y = -12$; (3, 0) **not a solution** **50.** $x = -9$; (−9, 3) **solution**

51. $y = -1$; (−1, 10) **not a solution** **52.** $-4y - x = -1$; (−2, −8) **not a solution** **53.** $6y + 5x = 10$; (−4, 8) **not a solution**

42–47. See Additional Answers beginning on p. AA1.

5 ASSESS AND RETEACH

Daily Homework Quiz

Transparency Available

Solve the inequality. Graph your solution.

1. $|x - 5| > 3$ **all real numbers less than 2 *or* greater than 8**

2. $|x + 3| + 6 \le 8$ **all real numbers greater than or equal to −5 *and* less than or equal to −1**

3. The clock in your car has an absolute deviation of at most 4 minutes after 6 months. After 6 months, the clock reads 7:38. Write and solve an inequality to find the possible times. **$|x - 7{:}38| \le 4$; from 7:34 through 7:42**

Online Quiz

Available at **classzone.com**

Diagnosis/Remediation

- Practice A, B, C in Chapter Resource Book
- Study Guide in Chapter Resource Book
- Practice Workbook
- @HomeTutor

Challenge

Additional challenge is available in the Chapter Resource Book.

40c. No; if the relative absolute deviation is 25%, then the actual population is between 13,500 and 22,500 antelope. For the 25% relative absolute deviation the actual population might be 14,000 antelope, which is less than any possible actual population for the 20% relative absolute deviation.

1 PLAN AND PREPARE

Explore the Concept

- Students will use inequalities to describe an overestimate and an underestimate.
- This activity leads into the study of linear inequalities in two variables in Example 2 in Lesson 6.7.

Materials

Each pair of students will need:

- set of tangram pieces
- 4 tangram puzzles
- stopwatch
- Activity Support Master (*Chapter Resource Book*)

Recommended Time

Work activity: 15 min

Discuss results: 5 min

Grouping

Students should work in pairs. Students can take turns conducting the experiment and recording and graphing the results.

2 TEACH

Tips for Success

Test the stopwatch before you begin the experiment.

Key Discovery

You can write inequalities that describe points that are either above or below the graph of a line.

3 ASSESS AND RETEACH

Does the inequality that represents an overestimate or underestimate include the points that lie on the line? Explain. **No; the points that are on the line are neither overestimates nor underestimates.**

6.7 Linear Inequalities in Two Variables

MATERIALS • set of tangram pieces • 4 tangram puzzles • stopwatch

QUESTION **How can you use inequalities to describe an overestimate or an underestimate?**

EXPLORE **Conduct an experiment**

To solve a tangram puzzle, you use seven pieces to create a figure. Each piece must lie flat and touch at least one other piece, and the pieces cannot overlap.

STEP 1 ***Predict a time***

Have your partner give you a tangram puzzle, such as the dog shown below. Predict how long it will take you to create the figure.

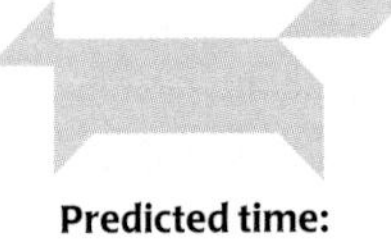

Predicted time: 50 seconds

STEP 2 ***Create figure***

Use the tangrams to create the figure. Your partner will use a stopwatch to record the actual time it takes you to finish.

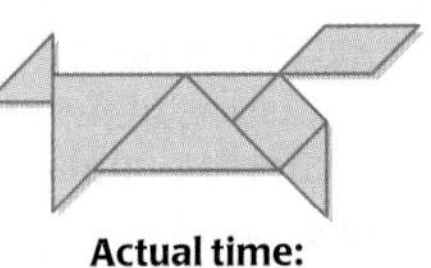

Actual time: 73 seconds

STEP 3 ***Record times***

Record the actual time x and the predicted time y in a table, as below. Repeat Steps 1–3 for three more puzzles. Then switch roles with your partner.

Figure	Actual time x (sec)	Predicted time y (sec)
1	73	50
2	67	67
3	70	88
4	90	74

STEP 4 ***Plot points***

Graph $y = x$ in Quadrant I. Then plot the points (x, y) from the table.

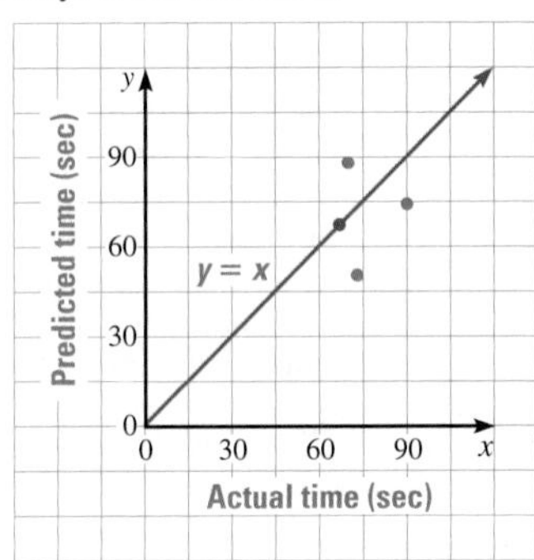

DRAW CONCLUSIONS **Use your observations to complete these exercises**

1. *Describe* the points that represent an *overestimate* of the actual finishing time. Then write an inequality that describes the location of the points in the coordinate plane. **points that lie above the line $y = x$; $y > x$**

2. *Describe* the points that represent an *underestimate* of the actual finishing time. Then write an inequality that describes the location of the points in the coordinate plane. **points that lie below the line $y = x$; $y < x$**

6.7 Graph Linear Inequalities in Two Variables

Before You graphed linear equations in two variables.
Now You will graph linear inequalities in two variables.
Why? So you can analyze a music competition, as in Ex. 56.

Key Vocabulary
- **linear inequality in two variables**
- **graph of an inequality in two variables**

A **linear inequality in two variables**, such as $x - 3y < 6$, is the result of replacing the = sign in a linear equation with $<$, $\leq$, $>$, or $\geq$. A **solution of an inequality in two variables** x and y is an ordered pair (x, y) that produces a true statement when the values of x and y are substituted into the inequality.

EXAMPLE 1 **Standardized Test Practice**

Which ordered pair is *not* a solution of $x - 3y \leq 6$?

Ⓐ (0, 0) Ⓑ (6, −1) Ⓒ (10, 3) Ⓓ (−1, 2)

Solution

Check whether each ordered pair is a solution of the inequality.

Test (0, 0):	$x - 3y \leq 6$	Write inequality.
	$0 - 3(0) \leq 6$	Substitute 0 for x and 0 for y.
	$0 \leq 6$ ✓	Simplify.
Test (6, −1):	$x - 3y \leq 6$	Write inequality.
	$6 - 3(-1) \leq 6$	Substitute 6 for x and −1 for y.
	$9 \leq 6$ ✗	Simplify.

So, (0, 0) is a solution of $x - 3y \leq 6$ but (6, −1) is *not* a solution.

▶ The correct answer is B. Ⓐ Ⓑ Ⓒ Ⓓ

✓ **GUIDED PRACTICE** for Example 1

Tell whether the ordered pair is a solution of $-x + 2y < 8$.

1. (0, 0) **solution**
2. (0, 4) **not a solution**
3. (3, 5) **solution**

GRAPH OF AN INEQUALITY In a coordinate plane, the **graph of an inequality in two variables** is the set of points that represent all solutions of the inequality. The *boundary line* of a linear inequality divides the coordinate plane into two **half-planes**. Only one half-plane contains the points that represent the solutions of the inequality.

1 PLAN AND PREPARE

Warm-Up Exercises

Transparency Available

Tell whether the ordered pair is a solution of the equation.

1. $x + 2y = 4$; (2, −1) **no**
2. $4x + 3y = 22$; (7, −2) **yes**
3. Graph the equation $y - 2x = 4$.

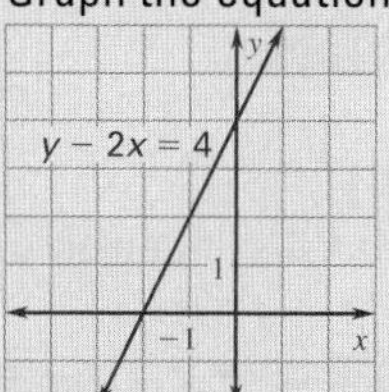

Notetaking Guide

Transparency Available

Promotes interactive learning and notetaking skills.

Pacing

Basic: 2 days
Average: 2 days
Advanced: 2 days
Block: 1 block
- See *Teaching Guide/Lesson Plan.*

2 FOCUS AND MOTIVATE

Essential Question

Big Idea 3, p. 355

How do you graph a linear inequality in two variables? **Tell students they will learn how to answer this question by graphing a boundary line and shading one half-plane.**

NCTM STANDARDS

Standard 9: Use connections among mathematical ideas

Standard 10: Use representations to solve problems

Resource Planning Guide

Chapter Resource Book
- Teaching Guide/Lesson Plan
- Activity Master
- Practice levels A, B, C
- Study Guide
- Catch-up for Absent Students
- Problem Solving Workshop
- Challenge

Workbooks
- Notetaking Guide
- Practice Workbook

Teaching Options
- **Power Presentations** provides dynamic electronic teaching resources for the classroom.
- **Activity Generator** provides editable activities for all ability levels.

Interactive Technology
- Easy Planner
- Power Presentations
- Activity Generator
- Animated Algebra
- Test Generator
- Online Quiz
- eWorkbook
- eEdition
- @HomeTutor

Resources for English Learners
- Spanish Study Guide
- Multi-Language Visual Glossary
- Student Resources in Spanish

See also the *Differentiated Instruction Resources* for more strategies for meeting individual needs.

Motivating the Lesson

Your two favorite rides at the State Fair are the Ferris wheel and the spinner. You need 4 tickets for the Ferris wheel and 6 tickets for the spinner. You have at least 42 tickets. If you know how to write and solve an inequality in two variables, you can determine the possible numbers of times you can go on each ride.

3 TEACH

Extra Example 1

Which point is *not* a solution of $x + 2y \geq 7$? **D**

Ⓐ $(-1, 4)$ Ⓑ $(2, 4)$
Ⓒ $(11, -2)$ Ⓓ $(8, -1)$

Extra Example 2

Graph the inequality $y \geq 3x + 1$.

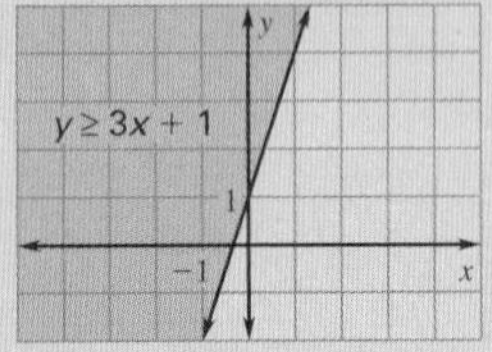

Key Questions to Ask for Example 2

- Why do you test a point that is not on the boundary line? **If the point is on the boundary line, you cannot tell which half-plane should be shaded.**
- What is a point on the graph that is *not* a solution of the inequality? **any point in the unshaded region**

Extra Example 3

Graph the inequality $x + 4y < -8$.

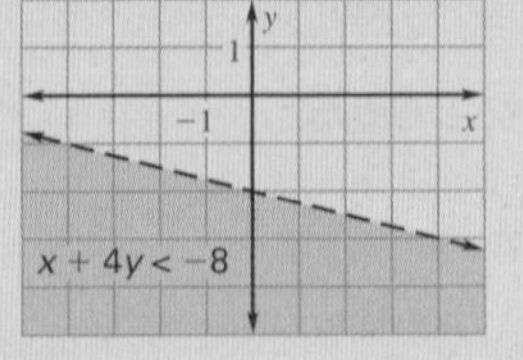

KEY CONCEPT *For Your Notebook*

Graphing a Linear Inequality in Two Variables

STEP 1 **Graph** the boundary line. Use a *dashed line* for < or >, and use a *solid line* for ≤ or ≥.

STEP 2 **Test** a point not on the boundary line by checking whether the ordered pair is a solution of the inequality.

STEP 3 **Shade** the half-plane containing the point if the ordered pair is a solution of the inequality. Shade the other half-plane if the ordered pair is *not* a solution.

EXAMPLE 2 Graph a linear inequality in two variables

Graph the inequality $y > 4x - 3$.

Solution

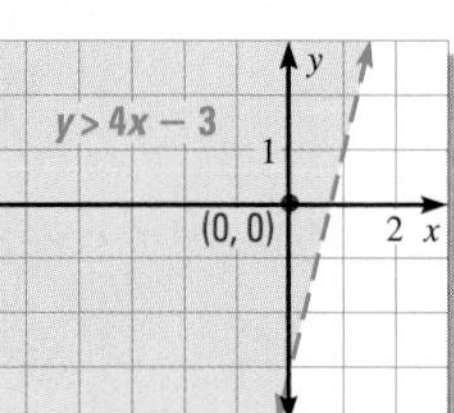

STEP 1 **Graph** the equation $y = 4x - 3$. The inequality is >, so use a dashed line.

STEP 2 **Test** $(0, 0)$ in $y > 4x - 3$.

$$0 \overset{?}{>} 4(0) - 3$$

$$0 > -3 \checkmark$$

STEP 3 **Shade** the half-plane that contains $(0, 0)$, because $(0, 0)$ is a solution of the inequality.

EXAMPLE 3 Graph a linear inequality in two variables

Graph the inequality $x + 2y \leq 0$.

Solution

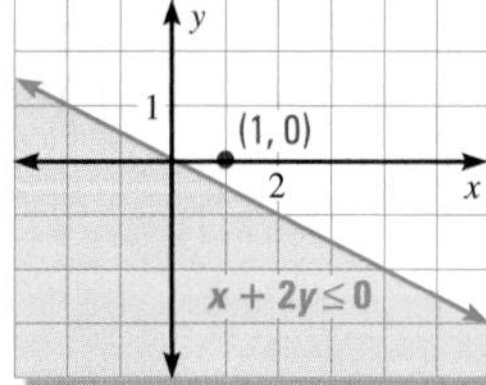

AVOID ERRORS
Be sure to test a point that is not on the boundary line. In Example 3, you can't test (0, 0) because it lies on the boundary line $x + 2y = 0$.

STEP 1 **Graph** the equation $x + 2y = 0$. The inequality is ≤, so use a solid line.

STEP 2 **Test** $(1, 0)$ in $x + 2y \leq 0$.

$$1 + 2(0) \overset{?}{\leq} 0$$

$$1 \leq 0 \times$$

STEP 3 **Shade** the half-plane that does not contain $(1, 0)$, because $(1, 0)$ is *not* a solution of the inequality.

✓ **GUIDED PRACTICE** for Examples 2 and 3

4. Graph the inequality $x + 3y \geq -1$. **See margin.**

Differentiated Instruction

Inclusion Some students may have difficulty remembering which inequality symbol to use when the graph includes a solid line, and which to use when the graph includes a dashed line. Have students make the following connection: when the graph includes a solid line, the inequality symbol has a solid line under it (≤ or ≥), and when the graph includes a dashed line, the symbol does not (< or >).

See also the *Differentiated Instruction Resources* for more strategies.

LINEAR INEQUALITIES IN ONE VARIABLE The steps for graphing a linear inequality in two variables can be used to graph a linear inequality in one variable in a coordinate plane.

The boundary line for an inequality in one variable is either vertical or horizontal. When testing a point to determine which half-plane to shade, do the following:

- If an inequality has only the variable x, substitute the x-coordinate of the test point into the inequality.
- If an inequality has only the variable y, substitute the y-coordinate of the test point into the inequality.

EXAMPLE 4 Graph a linear inequality in one variable

Graph the inequality $y \geq -3$.

Solution

STEP 1 **Graph** the equation $y = -3$. The inequality is $\geq$, so use a solid line.

STEP 2 **Test** $(2, 0)$ in $y \geq -3$. You substitute only the y-coordinate, because the inequality does not have the variable x.

$$0 \geq -3 \checkmark$$

STEP 3 **Shade** the half-plane that contains $(2, 0)$, because $(2, 0)$ is a solution of the inequality.

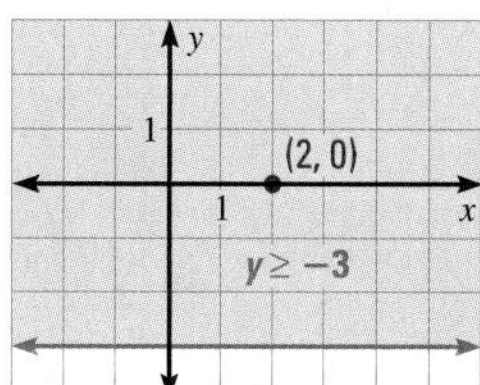

EXAMPLE 5 Graph a linear inequality in one variable

Graph the inequality $x < -1$.

Solution

STEP 1 **Graph** the equation $x = -1$. The inequality is $<$, so use a dashed line.

STEP 2 **Test** $(3, 0)$ in $x < -1$. You substitute only the x-coordinate, because the inequality does not have the variable y.

$$3 < -1 \text{ ✗}$$

STEP 3 **Shade** the half-plane that does *not* contain $(3, 0)$, because $(3, 0)$ is not a solution of the inequality.

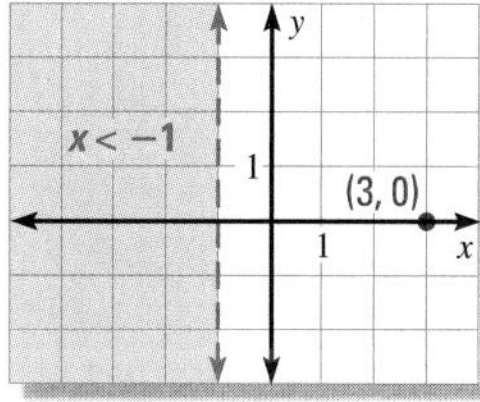

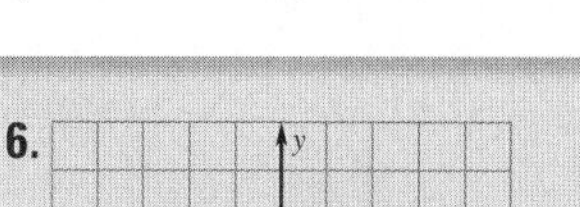

at classzone.com

✓ GUIDED PRACTICE for Examples 4 and 5

Graph the inequality. **5–7. See margin.**

5. $y > 1$ **6.** $y \leq 3$ **7.** $x < -2$

Extra Example 4

Graph the inequality $y < 1$.

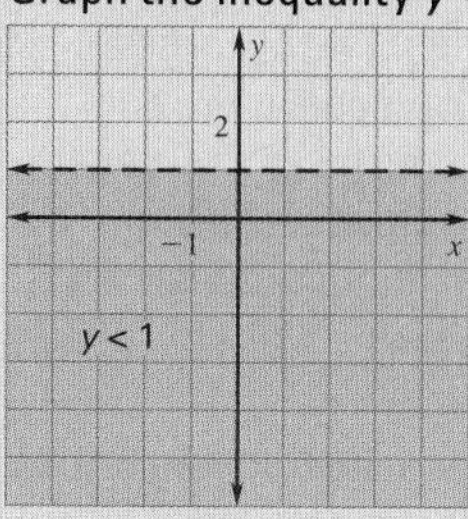

Key Questions to Ask for Example 4

- How is graphing a linear inequality in one variable different from graphing a linear inequality in two variables? **When you test a point for a linear inequality in one variable, you substitute only the variable that appears in the inequality. To test a point for a two-variable inequality, you substitute both coordinates.**
- Does it matter which point you test? **As with linear inequalities in two variables, you should not test a point on the boundary line.**

Extra Example 5

Graph the inequality $x \geq 2$.

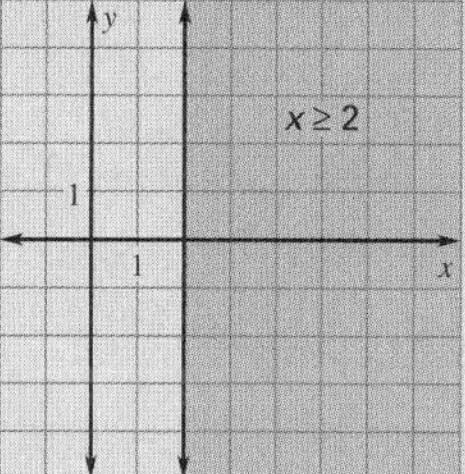

Key Question to Ask for Example 5

- Is the point $(-1, y)$ a solution of the inequality? Explain. **No; the inequality $x < -1$ is not true when x is -1.**

4.

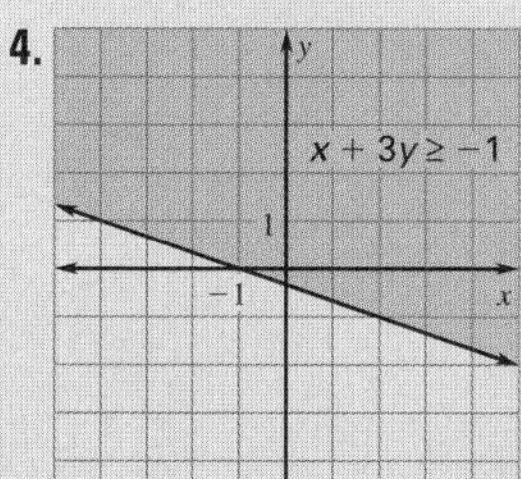

5.

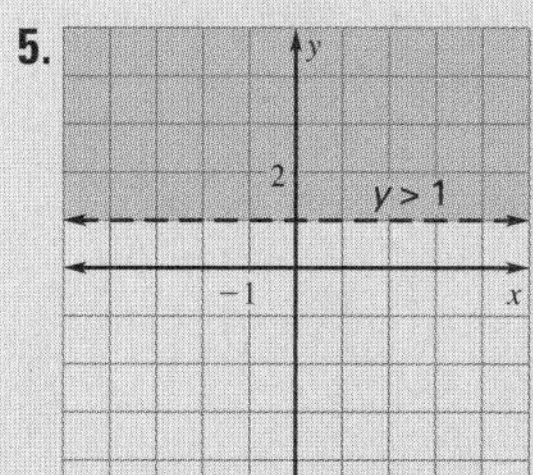

6.

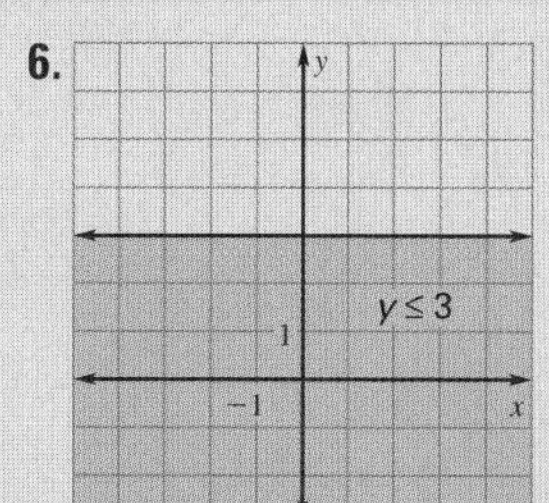

7.

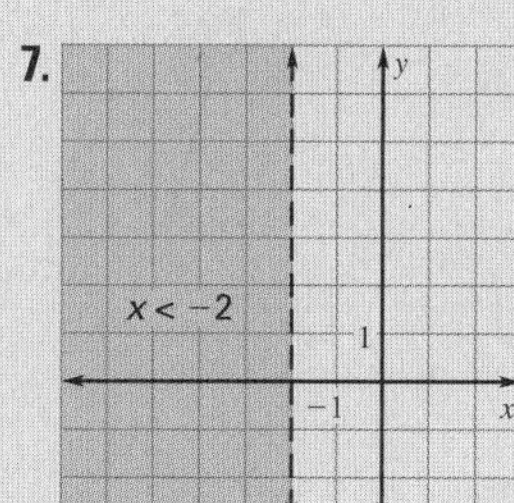

Extra Example 6

A party shop makes gift bags for birthday parties. They charge $4 per glow stick placed in the bag and $10 per T-shirt. Let x represent the number of glow sticks and y represent the number of T-shirts. The goal is to earn at least $500 for the bags.

- Write an inequality that describes the goal in terms of x and y.
- Graph the inequality.
- Give three possible combinations of pairs of items that will allow the shop to meet its goal.

$4x + 10y \geq 500$

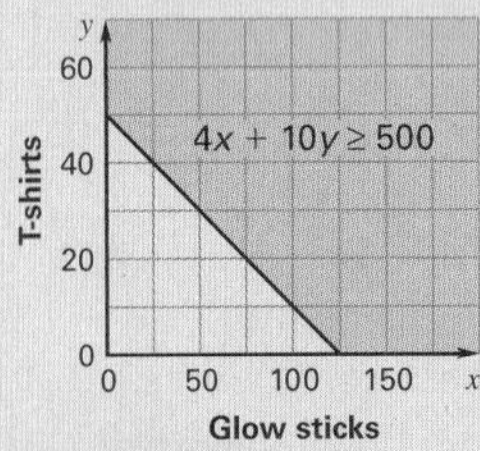

Possible pair combinations: 25 glow sticks, 52 T-shirts; 75 glow sticks, 30 T-shirts; 100 glow sticks, 12 T-shirts

Closing the Lesson

Have students summarize the major points of the lesson and answer the Essential Question: How do you graph linear inequalities in two variables?

- **Graph the boundary line, using a solid or a dashed line.**
- **Use a test point and shade one of the two half-planes.**

Graph the boundary line, using a dashed or solid line. Test a point not on the boundary line. If it is a solution, shade the half-plane that contains the test point. If it is not a solution, shade the half-plane that does not contain the test point.

8.

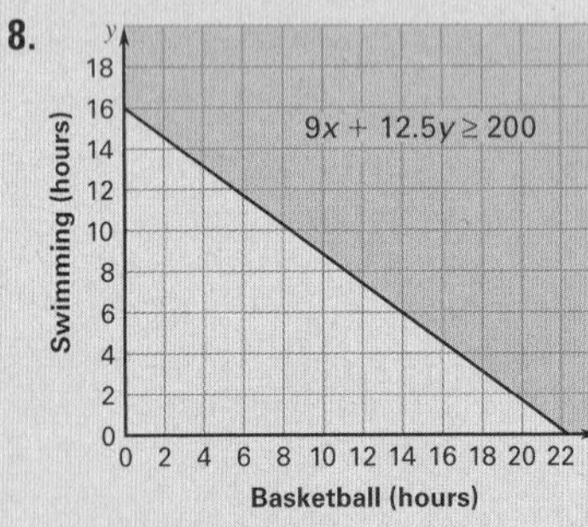

EXAMPLE 6 Solve a multi-step problem

JOB EARNINGS You have two summer jobs at a youth center. You earn $8 per hour teaching basketball and $10 per hour teaching swimming. Let x represent the amount of time (in hours) you teach basketball each week, and let y represent the amount of time (in hours) you teach swimming each week. Your goal is to earn at least $200 per week.

- Write an inequality that describes your goal in terms of x and y.
- Graph the inequality.
- Give three possible combinations of hours that will allow you to meet your goal.

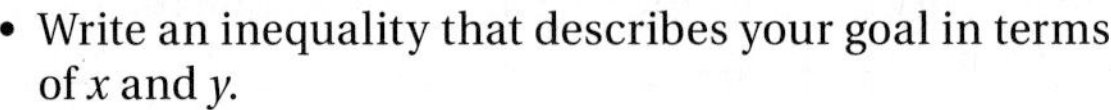

Solution

STEP 1 **Write** a verbal model. Then write an inequality.

Basketball pay rate (dollars/hour)	•	Basketball time (hours)	+	Swimming pay rate (dollars/hour)	•	Swimming time (hours)	≥	Total earnings (dollars)
8	•	x	+	**10**	•	y	≥	**200**

STEP 2 **Graph** the inequality $8x + 10y \geq 200$.

First, graph the equation $8x + 10y = 200$ in Quadrant I. The inequality is $\geq$, so use a solid line.

Next, test (5, 5) in $8x + 10y \geq 200$:

$$8(5) + 10(5) \geq 200$$

$$90 \geq 200 \; ✗$$

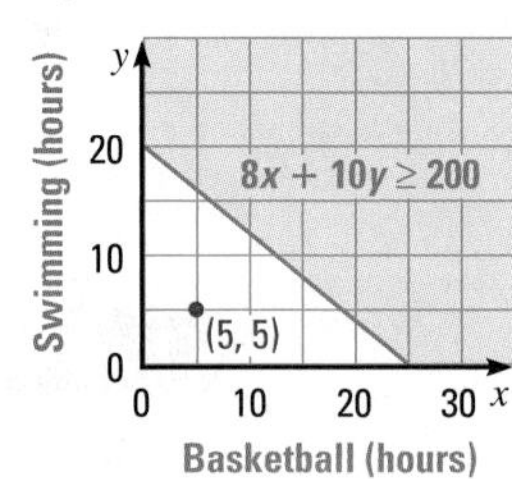

AVOID ERRORS
The variables can't represent negative numbers. So, the graph of the inequality does not include points in Quadrants II, III, or IV.

Finally, shade the part of Quadrant I that does not contain (5, 5), because (5, 5) is not a solution of the inequality.

STEP 3 **Choose** three points on the graph, such as (13, 12), (14, 10), and (16, 9). The table shows the total earnings for each combination of hours.

Basketball time (hours)	13	14	16
Swimming time (hours)	12	10	9
Total earnings (dollars)	224	212	218

✓ GUIDED PRACTICE for Example 6

8. **WHAT IF?** In Example 6, suppose that next summer you earn $9 per hour teaching basketball and $12.50 per hour teaching swimming. Write and graph an inequality that describes your goal. Then give three possible combinations of hours that will help you meet your goal.
$9x + 12.5y \geq 200$; see margin for art. *Sample answer:* (8, 12), (12, 10), (16, 6)

6.7 EXERCISES

HOMEWORK KEY
○ = **WORKED-OUT SOLUTIONS** on p. WS15 for Exs. 5, 19, and 57
★ = **STANDARDIZED TEST PRACTICE** Exs. 2, 15, 16, 39, 56, 59, and 60
◆ = **MULTIPLE REPRESENTATIONS** Ex. 55

SKILL PRACTICE

A

1. **VOCABULARY** Copy and complete: The ordered pair (2, −4) is a(n) _?_ of $3x - y > 7$. **solution**

2. ★ **WRITING** *Describe* the difference between graphing a linear inequality in two variables and graphing a linear equation in two variables. **See margin.**

EXAMPLE 1 on p. 405 for Exs. 3–15

CHECKING SOLUTIONS **Tell whether the ordered pair is a solution of the inequality.**

3. $x + y < -4$; (0, 0) **not a solution**
4. $x - y \le 5$; (8, 3) **solution**
5. $y - x > -2$; (−1, −4) **not a solution**
6. $2x + 3y \ge 14$; (5, 2) **solution**
7. $4x - 7y > 28$; (−2, 4) **not a solution**
8. $-3y - 2x < 12$; (5, −6) **solution**
9. $2.8x + 4.1y \le 1$; (0, 0) **solution**
10. $0.5y - 0.5x > 3.5$; (6, 2) **not a solution**
11. $x \ge -3$; (−4, 0) **not a solution**
12. $y \le 8$; (−9, −7) **solution**
13. $\frac{3}{4}x - \frac{1}{3}y < 6$; (−8, 12) **solution**
14. $\frac{2}{5}x + y \ge 2$; (1, 2) **solution**

15. ★ **MULTIPLE CHOICE** Which ordered pair is *not* a solution of $x + 5y < 15$? **C**

Ⓐ (−1, −3) Ⓑ (−1, 3) Ⓒ (1, 3) Ⓓ (3, 2)

EXAMPLES 2, 3, 4, and 5 on pp. 406–407 for Exs. 16–38

16. ★ **MULTIPLE CHOICE** The graph of which inequality is shown? **A**

Ⓐ $x + y \le -1$ Ⓑ $x + y \ge -1$

Ⓒ $x - y \le -1$ Ⓓ $x - y \ge -1$

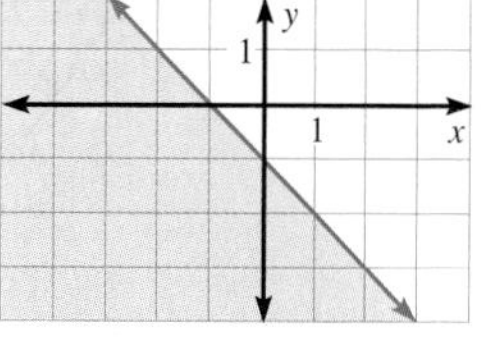

GRAPHING INEQUALITIES **Graph the inequality.** **17–36. See margin.**

17. $y > x + 3$
18. $y \le x - 2$
19. $y < 3x + 5$
20. $y \ge -2x + 8$
21. $x + y < -8$
22. $x - y \le -11$
23. $x + 8y > 16$
24. $5x - y \ge 1$
25. $2(x + 2) > 7y$
26. $y - 4 < x - 6$
27. $-4y \le 16x$
28. $6(2x) \ge -24y$
29. $y < -3$
30. $x \ge 5$
31. $x > -2$
32. $y \le 4$
33. $3(x - 2) > y + 8$
34. $x - 4 \le -2(y + 6)$
35. $\frac{1}{2}(x + 2) + 3y < 8$
36. $2(x + 1) \ge \frac{1}{4}y - 1$

ERROR ANALYSIS ***Describe*** **and correct the error in graphing the inequality.** **37, 38. See margin for art.**

37. $2y - x \ge 2$

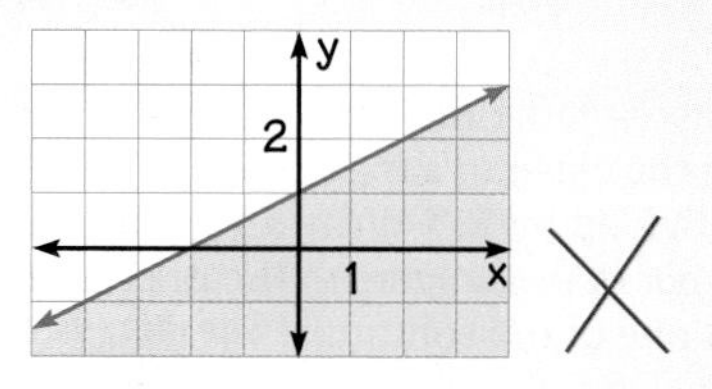

The wrong half-plane is shaded.

38. $x \le -3$

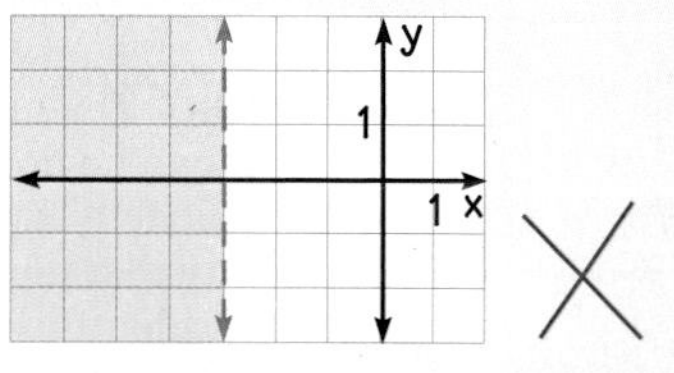

The boundary line should be solid.

2. Graphing a linear inequality in two variables involves graphing the boundary line (as either a solid or dashed line) and then shading the appropriate half-plane. Graphing a linear equation in two variables involves only the graphing of one (solid) line.

17–38. See Additional Answers beginning on p. AA1.

4 PRACTICE AND APPLY

Assignment Guide

Answer Transparencies available for all exercises

Basic:
Day 1: EP p. 941 Exs. 41–44 pp. 409–412 Exs. 1–11, 15–25, 62–70 even
Day 2: pp. 409–412 Exs. 29–41, 53–58, 71–76

Average:
Day 1: pp. 409–412 Exs. 1, 2, 8–16, 20–28, 44–46, 63–69 odd
Day 2: pp. 409–412 Exs. 29–43, 47–50, 54–59, 71–75 odd

Advanced:
Day 1: pp. 409–412 Exs. 1, 10–16, 21–28, 44–46, 51*, 52*, 63–69 odd
Day 2: pp. 409–412 Exs. 29–43, 47–50, 55–61*, 73, 76

Block:
pp. 409–412 Exs. 1, 2, 8–16, 20–50, 54–59, 63–75 odd

Differentiated Instruction

See *Differentiated Instruction Resources* for suggestions on addressing the needs of a diverse classroom.

Homework Check

For a quick check of student understanding of key concepts, go over the following exercises:
Basic: 4, 18, 25, 30, 53
Average: 12, 20, 27, 31, 54
Advanced: 14, 22, 28, 32, 55

Extra Practice

- Student Edition, p. 943
- Chapter Resource Book: Practice levels A, B, C

Practice Worksheet

An easily-readable reduced practice page (with answers) for this lesson can be found on p. 354F.

39. ★ **WRITING** Can you use (0, 0) as a test point when graphing $2x > -5y$? *Explain* your reasoning. **No; (0, 0) is a point on the boundary line $2x = -5y$.**

B **TRANSLATING SENTENCES Write the verbal sentence as an inequality. Then graph the inequality.** **40–43. See margin for art.**

40. Four less than x is greater than or equal to y. $x - 4 \geq y$

41. The product of -2 and y is less than or equal to the sum of x and 6. $-2y \leq x + 6$

42. The quotient of y and 2 is greater than the difference of 7 and x. $\frac{y}{2} > 7 - x$

43. The sum of x and the product of 4 and y is less than -3. $x + 4y < -3$

USING A GRAPH Write an inequality of the graph shown.

44. $y > -\frac{5}{4}x + \frac{7}{4}$

45. $y \leq \frac{5}{7}x - \frac{9}{7}$

46. $y > \frac{1}{2}x + 2$

44. 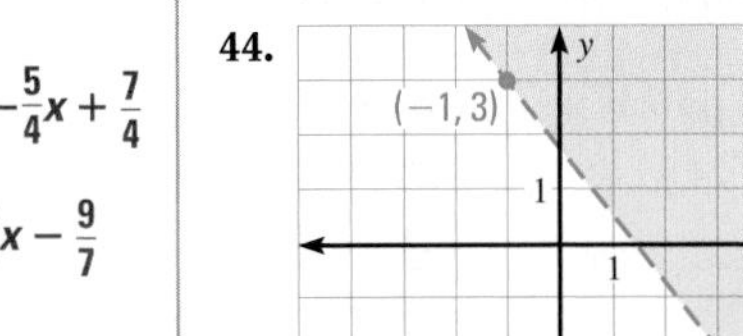

45. 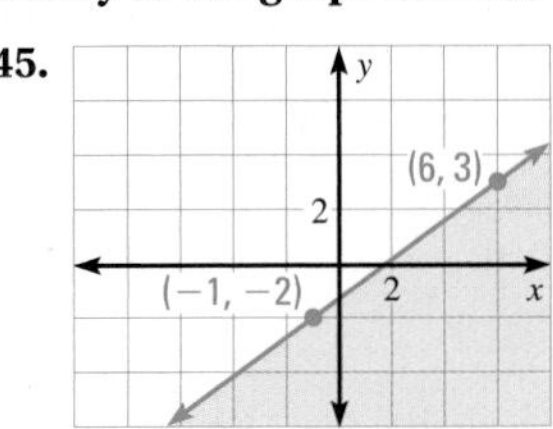

46. 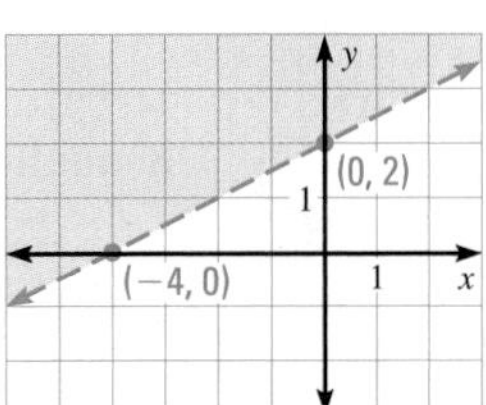

WRITING INEQUALITIES Write an inequality whose graph contains only the points in the given quadrants.

47. Quadrants I and II $y > 0$

48. Quadrants II and III $x < 0$

49. Quadrants III and IV $y < 0$

50. Quadrants I and IV $x > 0$

C **CHALLENGE In Exercises 51 and 52, write and graph an inequality whose graph is described by the given information.** **51, 52. See margin for art.**

51. The points (2, 5) and (−3, −5) lie on the boundary line. The points (6, 5) and (−2, −3) are solutions of the inequality. $y \leq 2x + 1$

52. The points (−7, −16) and (1, 8) lie on the boundary line. The points (−7, 0) and (3, 14) are *not* solutions of the inequality. $y < 3x + 5$

PROBLEM SOLVING

EXAMPLE 6 A on p. 408 for Exs. 53–57

53. **BOBSLEDS** In a two-man bobsled competition, the sum of the weight x (in pounds) of the bobsled and the combined weight y (in pounds) of the athletes must not exceed 860 pounds. Write and graph an inequality that describes the possible weights of the bobsled and the athletes. Identify and interpret one of the solutions.

@HomeTutor for problem solving help at classzone.com

See margin.

54. **ELEVATORS** The number y of passengers riding an elevator can be no greater than the elevator's maximum weight capacity x (in pounds) divided by 150. Write and graph an inequality that relates the number of passengers to the maximum weight capacity. Identify and interpret one of the solutions. **See margin.**

@HomeTutor for problem solving help at classzone.com

○ = WORKED-OUT SOLUTIONS on p. WS1 ★ = STANDARDIZED TEST PRACTICE ◆ = MULTIPLE REPRESENTATIONS

Avoiding Common Errors

Exercises 17–36 Some students may test a point on the boundary line. Remind students that a point on the boundary line cannot be used to determine which half-plane to shade.

Graphing Calculator

Exercises 17–36 Students may want to check the boundary lines using a graphing calculator. They should use the y= key, enter the equation, and then select GRAPH.

Teaching Strategy

Exercises 44–46 Before assigning these exercises, you may want to review how to write a linear equation given two points. Remind students to choose an inequality symbol by looking at whether the boundary line is solid or dashed and by observing which half-plane is shaded.

40. 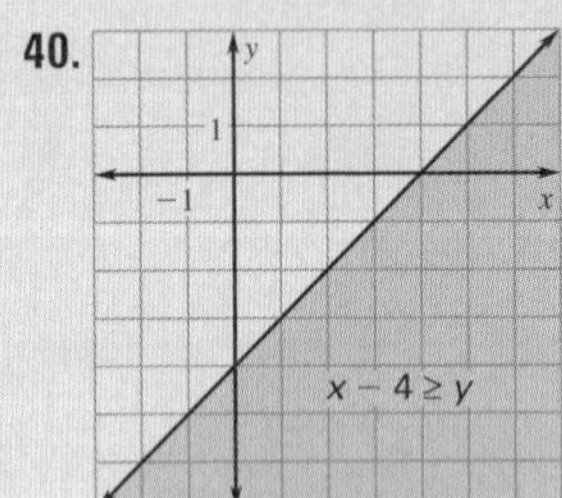

41. 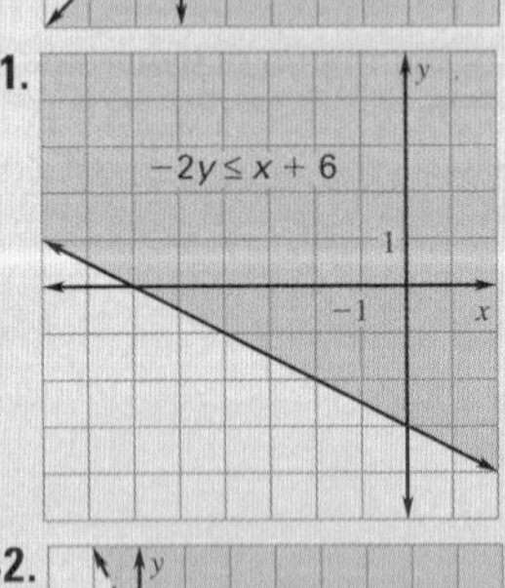

42. 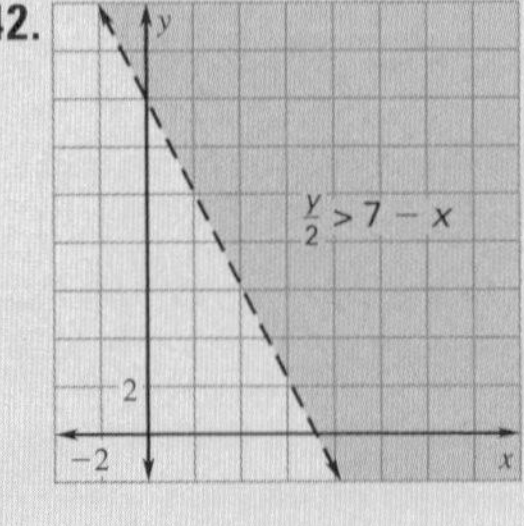

43. 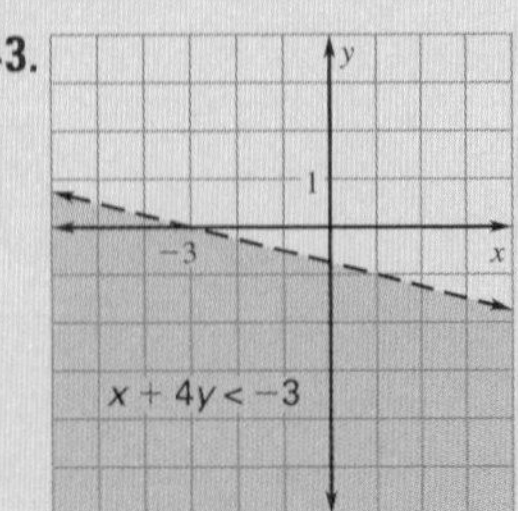

51. 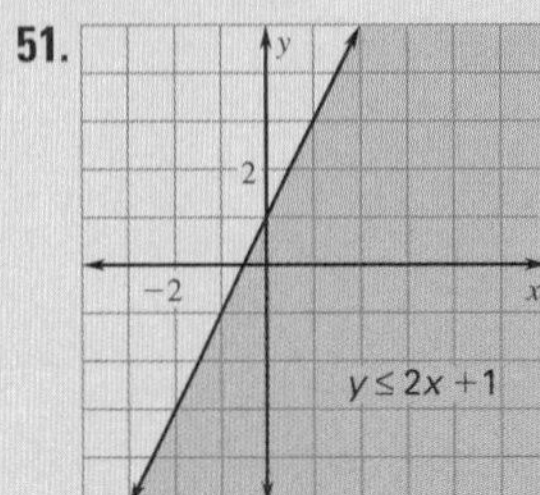

52. 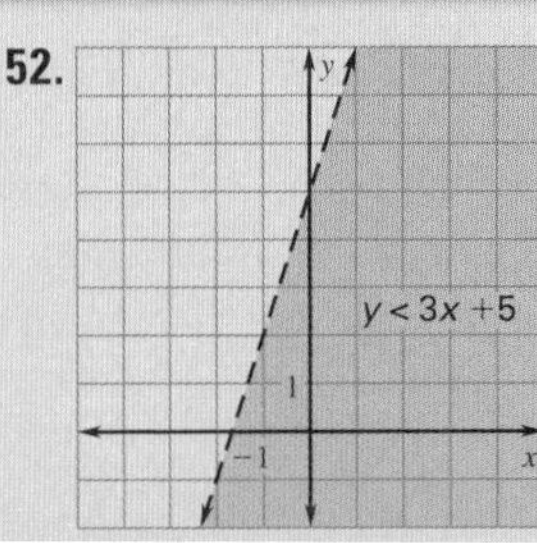

55. ◆ MULTIPLE REPRESENTATIONS You tutor Spanish for $15 per hour and French for $10 per hour. You want to earn at least $100 per week.

a. **Writing an Inequality** Write an inequality that describes your goal in terms of hours spent tutoring Spanish and hours spent tutoring French. **$15x + 10y \geq 100$**

b. **Drawing a Graph** Graph the inequality. Then give three possible combinations of hours that meet your goal. **See margin.**

c. **Making a Table** Make a table that gives the amount of money that you will earn for each combination of hours given in part (b). **See margin.**

56. ★ **MULTIPLE CHOICE** To compete in a piano competition, you need to perform two musical pieces whose combined duration is no greater than 15 minutes. Which inequality describes the possible durations x and y (in minutes) of the pieces? **B**

Ⓐ $x + y < 15$ Ⓑ $x + y \leq 15$ Ⓒ $x + y > 15$ Ⓓ $x + y \geq 15$

57. **MULTI-STEP PROBLEM** You are making muffins and loaves of bread for a bake sale. You need $\frac{1}{6}$ batch of batter per muffin and $\frac{1}{2}$ batch of batter per loaf of bread. You have enough ingredients to make up to 12 batches of batter. **$\frac{1}{6}m + \frac{1}{2}\ell \leq 12$; See margin for art.**

a. Write and graph an inequality that describes the possible combinations of muffins m and loaves ℓ of bread that you can make.

b. You make 4 loaves of bread. What are the possible numbers of muffins that you can make? **$m \leq 60$**

B 58. **NUTRITION** A nutritionist recommends that the fat calories y consumed per day should be at most 30% of the total calories x consumed per day.

a. Write and graph an inequality that relates the number of fat calories consumed to the total calories consumed. **$y \leq 0.3x$; see margin for art.**

b. Use the nutrition labels below. You normally consume 2000 calories per day. So far today you have eaten 6 crackers and 1 container of yogurt. What are the possible additional fat calories that you can consume today? **$y \leq 500$**

59. ★ **SHORT RESPONSE** You need to bring a duffel and a bedroll for a trip in the mountains. The sum of the weight x (in pounds) of the duffel and the weight y (in pounds) of the bedroll cannot exceed 30 pounds.

a. **Graph and Apply** Write and graph a linear inequality that describes the possible weights of the duffel and bedroll. Then give three possible combinations of weights of the duffel and bedroll. **See margin.**

b. **Interpret** Are (0, 30) and (30, 0) solutions of the inequality in part (a)? Do these ordered pairs make sense for this situation? *Explain.*

59a. $x + y \leq 30$, see margin for art. *Sample answer:* (20, 4), (25, 5), (26, 2)

59b. Yes; no; (0, 30) means that you do not take a duffel and have a 30 pound bedroll, while (30, 0) means you take a 30 pound duffel and do not take a bedroll. You need to bring both a duffel and a bedroll.

53, 54. See Additional Answers beginning on p. AA1.

Study Strategy

Exercise 55 Suggest that students review Example 6 before they begin this exercise. This will help them write a verbal model for the problem, graph the inequality, and create a table.

55b.

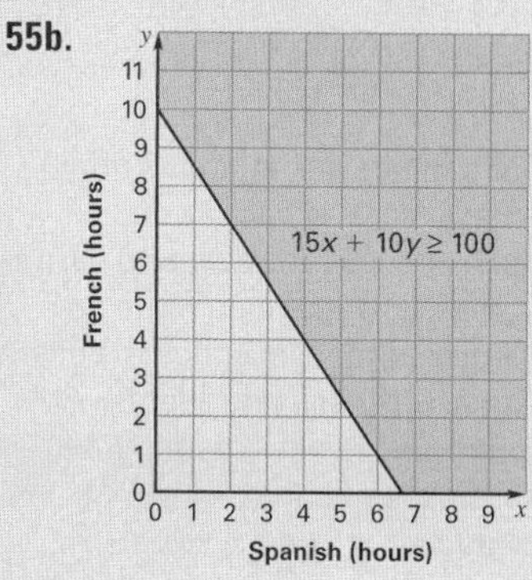

55c. ***Sample answer:***

Spanish time (hours)	4	5	6
French time (hours)	8	3	1
Total earnings (dollars)	140	105	100

57a.

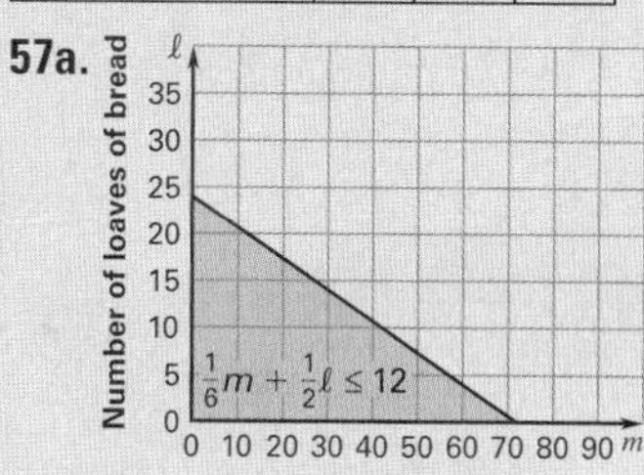

58a.

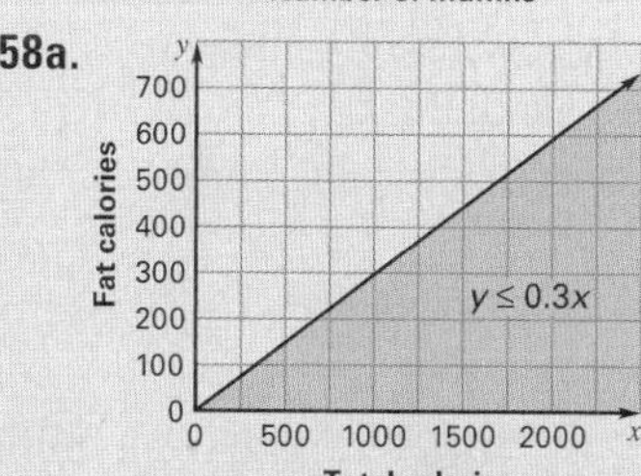

59a.

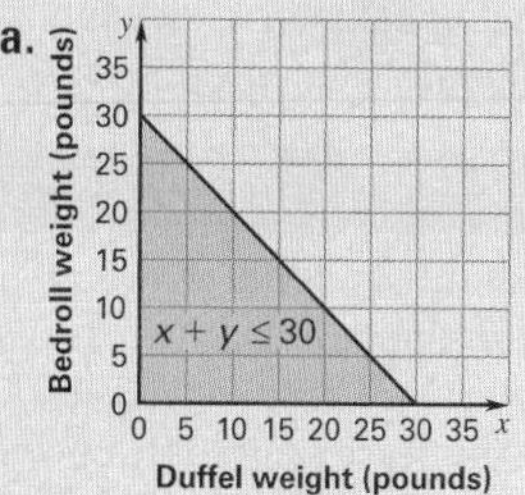

5 ASSESS AND RETEACH

Daily Homework Quiz

Transparency Available

Tell whether the ordered pair is a solution of the inequality.

1. $x + 4y \geq 16$; (3, 3) **no**

2. $3x - 2y < 20$; (5, −2) **yes**

3. For a fundraiser, students offer a basic car wash for \$2 and a deluxe for \$5. They want to earn at least \$100 per day. Write an inequality that describes the goal. Graph the inequality. Identify and interpret one combination that meets the goal. **$2x + 5y \geq 100$, where x represents basic washes and y represents deluxe washes**

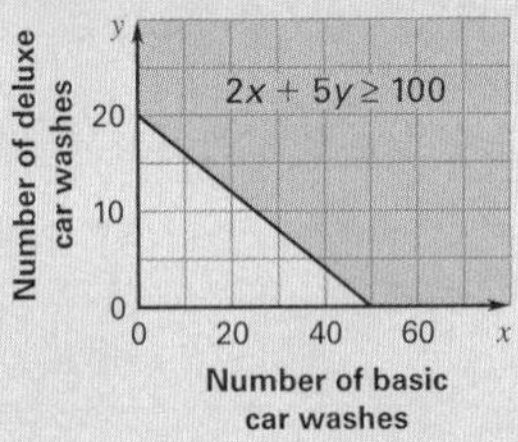

(40, 15); 40 basic washes and 15 deluxe washes

Online Quiz

Available at **classzone.com**

Diagnosis/Remediation

- Practice A, B, C in Chapter Resource Book
- Study Guide in Chapter Resource Book
- Practice Workbook
- @HomeTutor

Challenge

Additional challenge is available in the Chapter Resource Book.

Quiz

An easily-readable reduced copy of the quiz (with answers) on Lessons 6.5–6.7 from the Assessment Book can be found on p. 354G.

60a, 60b, 61a, Quiz 4–9. See Additional Answers beginning on p. AA1.

60c. Less than or equal to 10 years; when x is less than 10 years, y will be greater than 100%. You cannot invest more than 100% of your money.

60. ★ EXTENDED RESPONSE A financial advisor suggests that if a person is an aggressive investor, the percent y of money that the person invests in stocks should be greater than the difference of 110 and the person's age x.

a. Graph Write and graph a linear inequality that relates the percent of money invested in stocks to an aggressive investor's age. **$y > 110 - x$; see margin for art.**

b. Calculate If an aggressive investor is 30 years old, what are the possible percents that the investor can invest in stocks? *Explain* your answer. **See margin.**

c. Justify Are there any ages for which none of the solutions of the inequality makes sense for this situation? *Justify* your answer.

C **61. CHALLENGE** The formula $m = dV$ gives the mass m of an object in terms of the object's density d and its volume V. Water has a density of 1 gram per cubic centimeter. An object immersed in water will sink if its density is greater than the density of water. An object will float in water if its density is less than the density of water.

a. For an object that sinks, write and graph an inequality that relates its mass (in grams) to its volume (in cubic centimeters). For an object that floats, write and graph an inequality that relates its mass (in grams) to its volume (in cubic centimeters). **See margin.**

b. A cylindrical can has a radius of 5 centimeters, a height of 10 centimeters, and a mass of 2119.5 grams. Will the can sink or float in water? *Explain* your answer.
Sink; the volume of the cylindrical can is $\pi r^2 h = \pi(25)(10) \approx 785.40$ cubic centimeters. Since the mass, 2119.5 grams, is greater than the volume, 785.40 cubic centimeters, the can will sink.

MIXED REVIEW

Solve the equation or inequality.

62. $-4a = 20$ *(p. 134)* **−5**

63. $3c + 8 = 17$ *(p. 141)* **3**

64. $6m - 5 = -8m + 2$ *(p. 154)* **$\frac{1}{2}$**

65. $\frac{n}{5} = \frac{n+1}{3}$ *(p. 168)* **$-2\frac{1}{2}$**

66. $p - 9 \geq -15$ *(p. 356)* **$p \geq -6$**

67. $-2s + 3 < -4$ *(p. 369)* **$s > 3\frac{1}{2}$**

68. $2x \geq 8$ *or* $5x < 10$ *(p. 380)* **$x < 2$ or $x \geq 4$**

69. $-2 < 9y - 2 \leq 5$ *(p. 380)* **$0 < y \leq \frac{7}{9}$**

70. $|g - 7| \geq 15$ *(p. 398)* **$g \leq -8$ or $g \geq 22$**

PREVIEW Prepare for Lesson 7.1 in Exs. 71–76.

Graph the equation. *(p. 225)* **71–76. See margin.**

71. $x - y = 8$

72. $-6x + 2y = -12$

73. $12x + 3y = -9$

74. $y = -7x + 1$

75. $y = 5x + 2$

76. $y = 0.5x - 5$

QUIZ for Lessons 6.5–6.7

Solve the equation. *(p. 390)*

1. $|x| = 5$ **5, −5**

2. $|c - 8| = 24$ **32, −16**

3. $-2|r - 5| = -6$ **8, 2**

Solve the inequality. Graph your solution. *(p. 398)* **4–6. See margin for art.**

4. $|y| > 4$ **$y < -4$ or $y > 4$**

5. $|2t - 5| < 3$ **$1 < t < 4$**

6. $4|3s + 7| - 5 \geq 7$ **$s \leq -3\frac{1}{3}$ or $s \geq -1\frac{1}{3}$**

Graph the inequality. *(p. 405)* **7–9. See margin.**

7. $x + y \geq 3$

8. $\frac{5}{7}x < 10$

9. $2y - x \leq 8$

EXTRA PRACTICE for Lesson 6.7, p. 943 **ONLINE QUIZ** at classzone.com

71–76. See Additional Answers beginning on p. AA1.

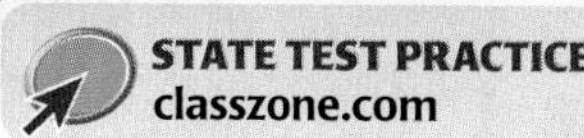

Lessons 6.5–6.7

1. **MULTI-STEP PROBLEM** You gathered 36 apples from your backyard apple tree in order to make apple pies and applesauce. You use 7 apples to make one apple pie and 5 apples to make one pint of applesauce.
   a. Write an inequality that describes the possible numbers of apple pies and pints of applesauce that you can make. **$7p + 5s \le 36$**
   b. Graph the inequality. **See margin.**
   c. Give three possible combinations of apple pies and pints of applesauce that you can make. ***Sample answer:* 1 pie and 5 pints of applesauce, 3 pies and 3 pints of applesauce, 4 pies and 1 pint of applesauce**

2. **SHORT RESPONSE** You are scooping ice cream as part of your training at an ice cream shop. The weight of a scoop must be 4 ounces with an absolute deviation of at most 0.5 ounce.
   a. Write an inequality to find the possible weights (in ounces) of each scoop. **$|x - 4| \le 0.5$**
   b. You make 10 scoops. You can start working at the shop if at least 80% of the scoops meet the weight requirement. The list shows the weights (in ounces) of your scoops.

      3.8, 4.2, 3.9, 4.5, 3.7, 4.6, 4.1, 3.3, 4.3, 4.2

      Can you start working at the shop? *Explain* your reasoning. **See margin.**

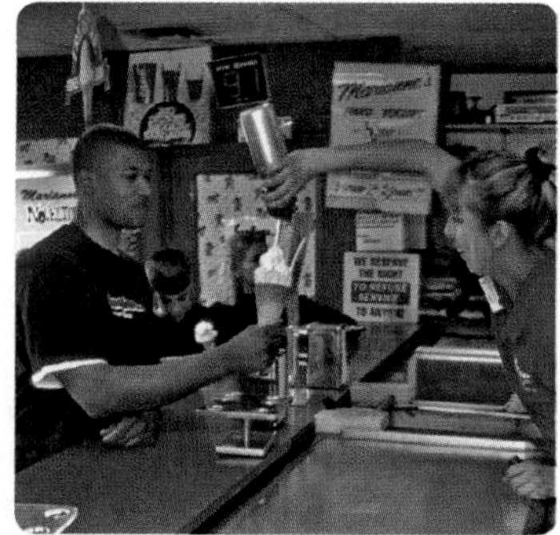

3. **GRIDDED ANSWER** You will be making a presentation in your history class. Your teacher gives you a time limit of 15 minutes with an absolute deviation of 1.5 minutes. What is the maximum possible duration (in minutes) of your presentation? **16.5 min**

4. **OPEN-ENDED** *Describe* a real-world situation that can be modeled by the equation $|x - 50| = 10$. *Explain* what the solution of the equation means in this situation. **See margin.**

5. **EXTENDED RESPONSE** A tour operator recommends that a river rafter wear a protective suit under the temperature conditions described below.

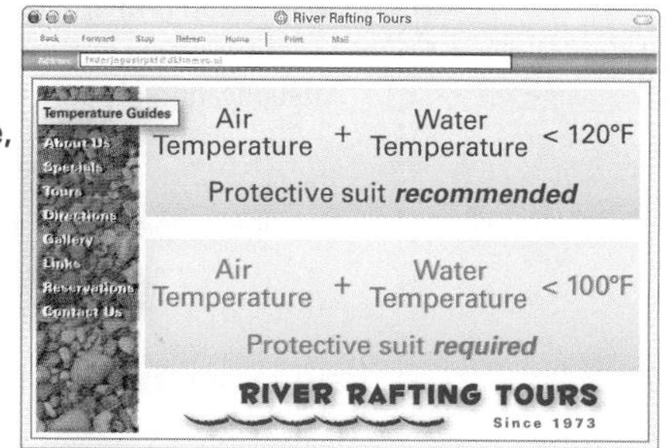

   a. Write and graph an inequality that describes the possible air temperatures and water temperatures for which a protective suit is recommended. **$a + w < 120$; see margin for art.**
   b. If the water temperature is 40°F, for which air temperatures is a protective suit recommended? **$a < 80$°F**
   c. How would you change the graph in part (a) in order to describe the situations in which a protective suit is required? *Explain* your answer. **See margin.**

6. **MULTI-STEP PROBLEM** You are buying a new cell phone and see eight phones listed on a website. The prices of the phones are shown.

   $139, $249, $229, $199, $179, $359, $199, $209

   a. Find the mean price of the phones. **$220.25**
   b. You are willing to purchase a phone that has the mean price with an absolute deviation of at most $50. Write and solve an inequality to find the prices of phones that you will consider. **$|x - 220.25| \le 50$; from $170.25 up to $270.25**
   c. How many of the phones on the website will you consider buying? **6 phones**

1b.

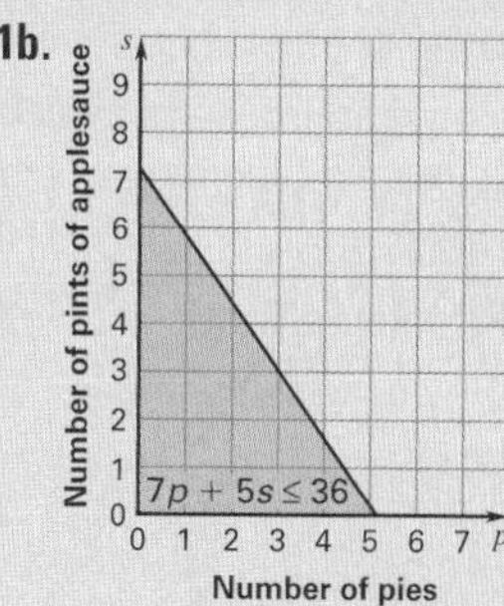

2b. Yes; the solution of the inequality from part (a) is $3.5 \le x \le 4.5$. For at least 80% of your scoops to meet the weight requirement, at least 8 scoops must weigh at least 3.5 ounces and at most 4.5 ounces. Because 8 out of 10 of your scoops are in the required range of weights, you can start working at the shop.

4. *Sample answer:* During a portion of time spent driving on the highway, your average speed is 50 miles per hour with an absolute deviation of your actual speed from your average speed of 10 miles per hour. What are your minimum and maximum speeds during this time? 40, 60; your minimum speed was 40 miles per hour and your maximum speed was 60 miles per hour.

5a.

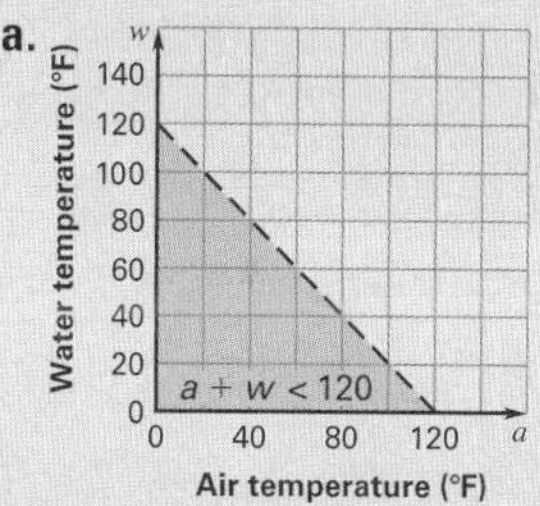

5c. Move the line so that its x- and y-intercepts are 100 instead of 120. The linear inequality that describes the situations in which a protective suit is required is $a + w < 100$.

CHAPTER SUMMARY

Additional Resources

The following resources are available to help review the materials in this chapter.

Chapter Resource Book
- Chapter Review Games and Activities
- Cumulative Practice, Chs. 1–6

Student Resources in Spanish

eWorkbook

@HomeTutor

Vocabulary Practice

Vocabulary practice is available at **classzone.com**

BIG IDEAS

For Your Notebook

Big Idea 1 Applying Properties of Inequality

You can apply the properties of inequality to solve inequalities. The properties listed below are also true for inequalities involving ≤ and ≥.

Property	If $a < b$, then ...	If $a > b$, then ...
Addition property of inequality	$a + c < b + c$.	$a + c > b + c$.
Subtraction property of inequality	$a - c < b - c$.	$a - c > b - c$.
Multiplication property of inequality	$ac < bc$ if $c > 0$. $ac > bc$ if $c < 0$.	$ac > bc$ if $c > 0$. $ac < bc$ if $c < 0$.
Division property of inequality	$\frac{a}{c} < \frac{b}{c}$ if $c > 0$. $\frac{a}{c} > \frac{b}{c}$ if $c < 0$.	$\frac{a}{c} > \frac{b}{c}$ if $c > 0$. $\frac{a}{c} < \frac{b}{c}$ if $c < 0$.

Big Idea 2 Using Statements with *And* or *Or*

An absolute value equation can be rewritten as two equations joined by *or.* An absolute value inequality can be rewritten as a compound inequality with *and* or *or.* In the statements below, < can be replaced by ≤, and > can be replaced by ≥.

Absolute value equation or inequality	Equivalent statement with *and* or *or*
$\lvert ax + b \rvert = c, c \geq 0$	$ax + b = c$ or $ax + b = -c$
$\lvert ax + b \rvert < c, c \geq 0$	$-c < ax + b < c$
$\lvert ax + b \rvert > c, c \geq 0$	$ax + b < -c$ or $ax + b > c$

Big Idea 3 Graphing Inequalities

You use a number line to graph an inequality in one variable. Similarly, you use a coordinate plane to graph a linear inequality in two variables (including cases where one of the variables has a coefficient of 0, such as $0x + y < 1$, or $y < 1$).

Graphing inequalities in one variable	Graphing linear inequalities in two variables
Graph simple inequalities: 1. Solve for the variable. 2. Draw an open circle for < or > and a closed circle for ≤ or ≥. Draw an arrow in the appropriate direction. Graph compound inequalities: 1. Solve the compound inequality. 2. Use the union of graphs of simple inequalities for *or.* Use the intersection for *and.*	1. Graph the boundary line. Use a solid line for ≤ or ≥ and a dashed line for < or >. 2. Test a point that does not lie on the boundary line. 3. Shade the half-plane containing the point if the ordered pair is a solution of the inequality. Shade the other half-plane if the ordered pair is *not* a solution.

CHAPTER REVIEW

@HomeTutor
classzone.com
- Multi-Language Glossary
- Vocabulary practice

REVIEW KEY VOCABULARY

- graph of an inequality, *p. 356*
- equivalent inequalities, *p. 357*
- compound inequality, *p. 380*
- absolute value equation, *p. 390*
- absolute deviation, *p. 392*
- linear inequality in two variables, *p. 405*
- solution of an inequality in two variables, *p. 405*
- graph of an inequality in two variables, half-plane, *p. 405*

VOCABULARY EXERCISES

1. Translate the verbal sentence into an absolute value equation: "The absolute deviation of x from 19 is 8." $|x - 19| = 8$
2. Identify three ordered pairs that are solutions of $2x - 3y \geq -10$. *Sample answer:* (1, 1), (−2, 1), (4, 2)
3. **WRITING** When you graph a linear inequality in two variables, how do you know whether the boundary line is a solid line or a dashed line? How do you know which half-plane to shade? **The boundary line is solid if the inequality symbol is ≤ or ≥, the boundary line is dashed if the inequality symbol is < or >; choose a test point that is not on the boundary line. If the ordered pair is a solution to the inequality, shade the half-plane that contains the test point; if it not a solution, shade the other half-plane.**

REVIEW EXAMPLES AND EXERCISES

Use the review examples and exercises below to check your understanding of the concepts you have learned in each lesson of Chapter 6.

6.1 Solve Inequalities Using Addition and Subtraction *pp. 356–361*

EXAMPLE

Solve $x - 2.1 \leq 1.4$. Graph your solution.

$x - 2.1 \leq 1.4$	Write original inequality.
$x - 2.1 + 2.1 \leq 1.4 + 2.1$	Add 2.1 to each side.
$x \leq 3.5$	Simplify.

▶ The solutions are all real numbers less than or equal to 3.5.

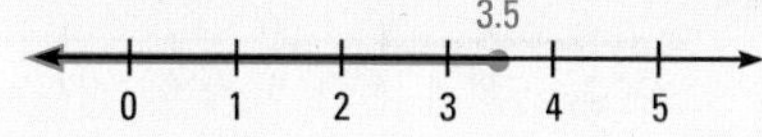

EXERCISES

EXAMPLES 1, 2, 3, and 4 on pp. 356–358 for Exs. 4–7

4. **GEOGRAPHY** The lowest elevation in Mexico is −10 meters at Laguna Salada. Write and graph an inequality that describes all elevations in Mexico that are greater than the lowest elevation. **$x > -10$; see margin for art.**

Solve the inequality. Graph your solution. **5–7. See margin for art.**

5. $x + 5 > -13$ **$x > -18$**
6. $m - 9 \geq -4$ **$m \geq 5$**
7. $s + 3.7 < 1$ **$s < -2.7$**

Extra Example 6.1

Solve $x + 6 > 9$. Graph your solution. **all real numbers greater than 3**

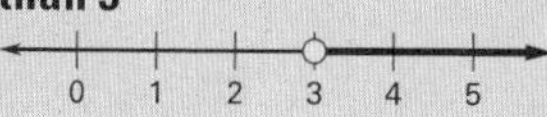

4.

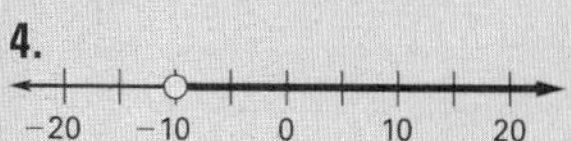

5.

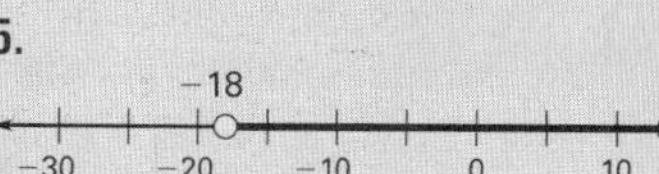

6.

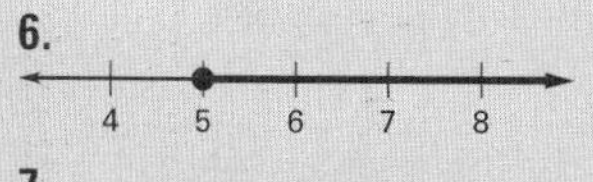

7.

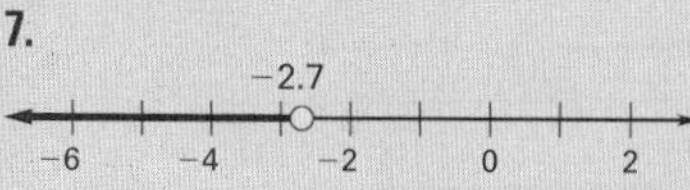

Extra Example 6.2

Solve $\frac{x}{-6} \geq 4$. Graph your solution. **all real numbers less than or equal to −24**

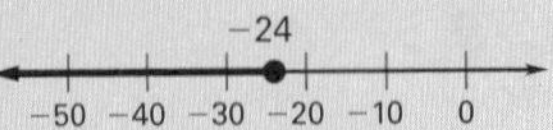

Extra Example 6.3

Solve $-3x - 2 < 10$. Graph your solution. **all real numbers greater than −4**

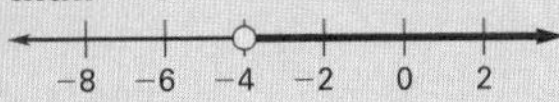

8.

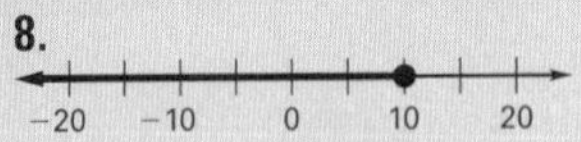

9.

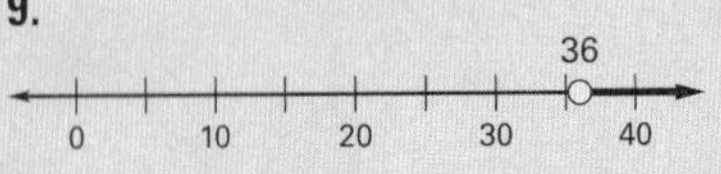

10.

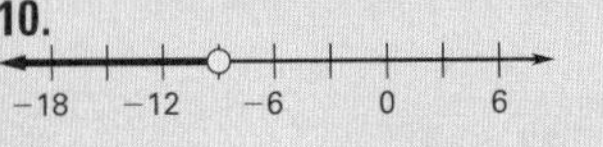

11.

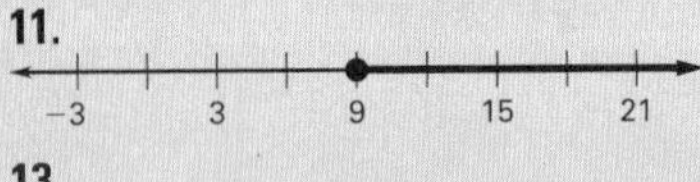

13.

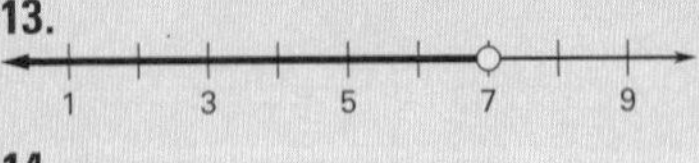

14.

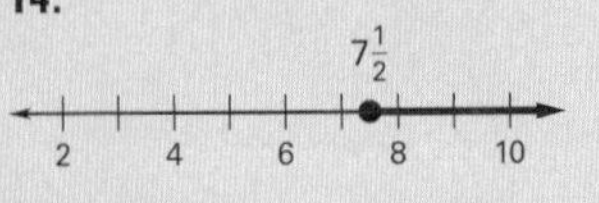

15.

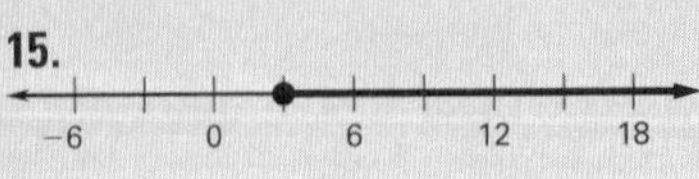

16.

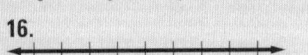

17.

18.

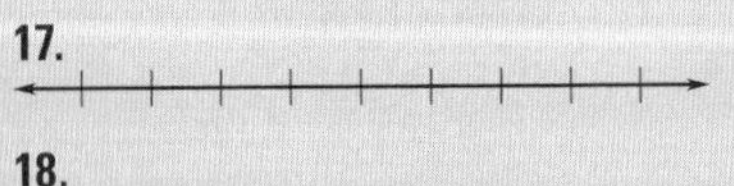

6.2 Solve Inequalities Using Multiplication and Division *pp. 363–368*

EXAMPLE

Solve $\frac{x}{-4} < 9$. Graph your solution.

$\frac{x}{-4} < 9$ **Write original inequality.**

$-4 \cdot \frac{x}{-4} > -4 \cdot 9$ **Multiply each side by −4. Reverse inequality symbol.**

$x > -36$ **Simplify.**

▶ The solutions are all real numbers greater than −36.

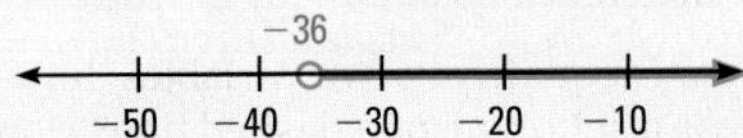

EXERCISES

EXAMPLES 1, 2, 3, 4, and 5 on pp. 363–365 for Exs. 8–12

Solve the inequality. Graph your solution. **8–11. See margin for art.**

8. $\frac{p}{2} \leq 5$ **$p \leq 10$** **9.** $\frac{n}{-4.5} < -8$ **$n > 36$** **10.** $-3x > 27$ **$x < -9$** **11.** $2y \geq 18$ **$y \geq 9$**

12. GYMNASTICS In men's gymnastics, an athlete competes in 6 events. Suppose that an athlete's average score per event is at most 9.7 points. Write and solve an inequality to find the possible total scores for the athlete. **$\frac{x}{6} \leq 9.7$, at most 58.2 points**

6.3 Solve Multi-Step Inequalities *pp. 369–374*

EXAMPLE

Solve $-4x + 7 \geq -13$. Graph your solution.

$-4x + 7 \geq -13$ **Write original inequality.**

$-4x \geq -20$ **Subtract 7 from each side.**

$x \leq 5$ **Divide each side by −4. Reverse inequality symbol.**

▶ The solutions are all real numbers less than or equal to 5.

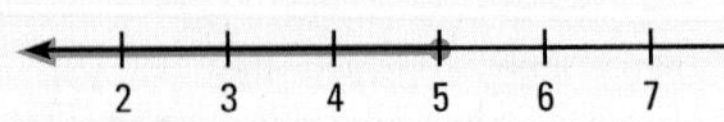

EXERCISES

EXAMPLES 1, 2, 3, and 4 on pp. 369–370 for Exs. 13–19

Solve the inequality, if possible. Graph your solution. **13–18. See margin for art.**

13. $2g + 11 < 25$ **$g < 7$** **14.** $\frac{2}{3}r - 4 \geq 1$ **$r \geq 7\frac{1}{2}$** **15.** $1 - 3x \leq -14 + 2x$ **$x \geq 3$**

16. $3(q + 1) < 3q + 7$ **all real numbers** **17.** $8(t - 1) > -8 + 8t$ **no solution** **18.** $-3(2n - 1) \geq 1 - 8n$ **$n \geq -1$**

19. TICKET PURCHASES You can order discount movie tickets from a website for \$7 each. You must also pay a shipping fee of \$4. You want to spend no more than \$40 on movie tickets. Find the possible numbers of movie tickets that you can order. **at most 5 tickets**

6.4 Solve Compound Inequalities

pp. 380–387

EXAMPLE

Solve $-1 < -2x + 7 < 9$. Graph your solution.

$-1 < -2x + 7 < 9$ **Write original inequality.**

$-8 < -2x < 2$ **Subtract 7 from each expression.**

$4 > x > -1$ **Divide each expression by −2. Reverse both inequality symbols.**

$-1 < x < 4$ **Rewrite in the form $a < x < b$.**

▶ The solutions are all real numbers greater than −1 *and* less than 4.

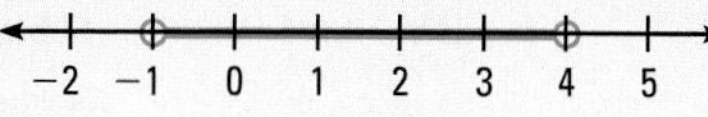

EXERCISES

EXAMPLES 3, 4, and 5 on pp. 381–382 for Exs. 20–23

Solve the inequality. Graph your solution. **20–23. See margin for art.**

20. $-6 \le 2t - 5 \le -3$ **$-\frac{1}{2} \le t \le 1$**
21. $-3 < -3x + 8 < 11$ **$-1 < x < 3\frac{2}{3}$**
22. $9s - 6 < 12$ *or* $3s + 1 > 13$ **$s < 2$ or $s > 4$**
23. $-4w + 12 \ge 10$ *or* $5w - 14 > -4$ **$w \le \frac{1}{2}$ or $w > 2$**

6.5 Solve Absolute Value Equations

pp. 390–395

EXAMPLE

Solve $4|5x - 3| + 6 = 30$.

First, rewrite the equation in the form $|ax + b| = c$.

$4|5x - 3| + 6 = 30$ **Write original equation.**

$4|5x - 3| = 24$ **Subtract 6 from each side.**

$|5x - 3| = 6$ **Divide each side by 4.**

Next, solve the absolute value equation.

$5x - 3 = 6$ *or* $5x - 3 = -6$ **Rewrite as two equations.**

$5x = 9$ *or* $5x = -3$ **Add 3 to each side.**

$x = 1.8$ *or* $x = -0.6$ **Divide each side by 5.**

▶ The solutions are −0.6 and 1.8.

EXERCISES

EXAMPLES 1, 2, 3, 4, and 5 on pp. 390–392 for Exs. 24–30

Solve the equation, if possible.

24. $|r| = 7$ **7, −7**
25. $|a + 6| = 2$ **−4, −8**
26. $|2c + 5| = 21$ **8, −13**
27. $2|x - 3| + 1 = 5$ **5, 1**
28. $3|2q + 1| - 5 = 1$ **0.5, −1.5**
29. $4|3p - 2| + 5 = 11$ **$1\frac{1}{6}, \frac{1}{6}$**
30. **BOWLING** In tenpin bowling, the height of each bowling pin must be 15 inches with an absolute deviation of 0.03125 inch. Find the minimum and maximum possible heights of a bowling pin. **14.96875 in., 15.03125 in.**

Extra Example 6.4

Solve $2x + 3 \le 5$ *or* $5x + 2 > 12$. Graph your solution. **all real numbers less than or equal to 1 *or* greater than 2**

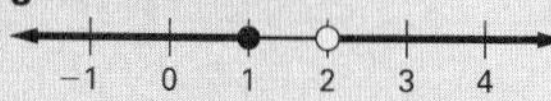

Extra Example 6.5

Solve $3|4x + 2| - 5 = 13$. **1, −2**

20.

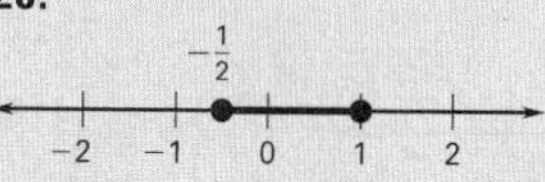

21.

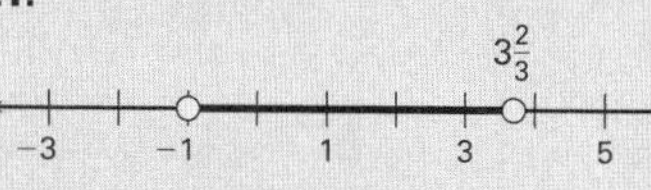

22.

23.

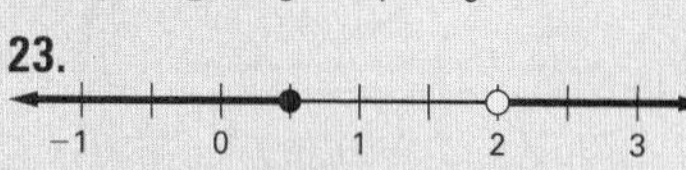

Extra Example 6.6

Solve $|-2x - 3| + 6 < 17$. Graph your solution. **all real numbers greater than -7 and less than 4**

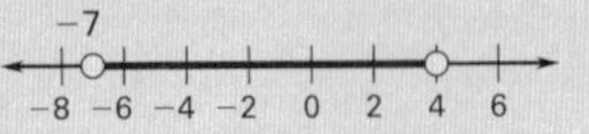

Extra Example 6.7

Graph the inequality $2x + y \geq 4$.

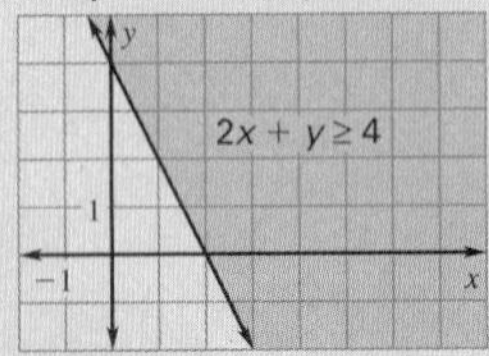

31.

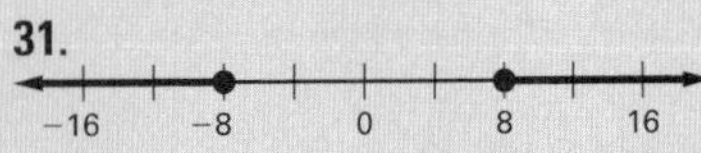

32.

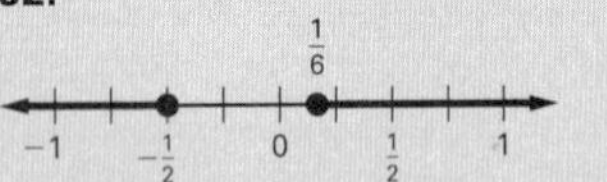

33.

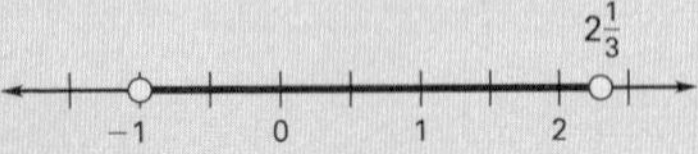

34.

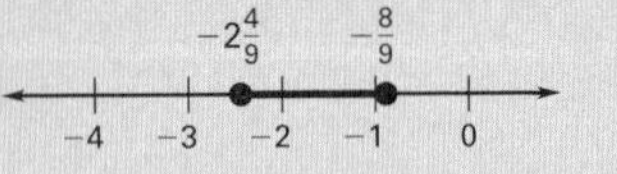

35.

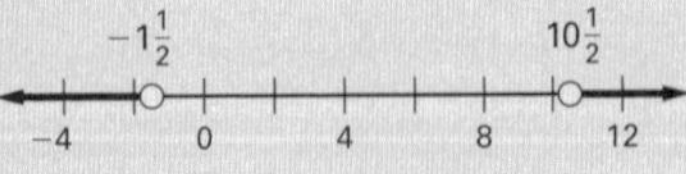

36.

41.

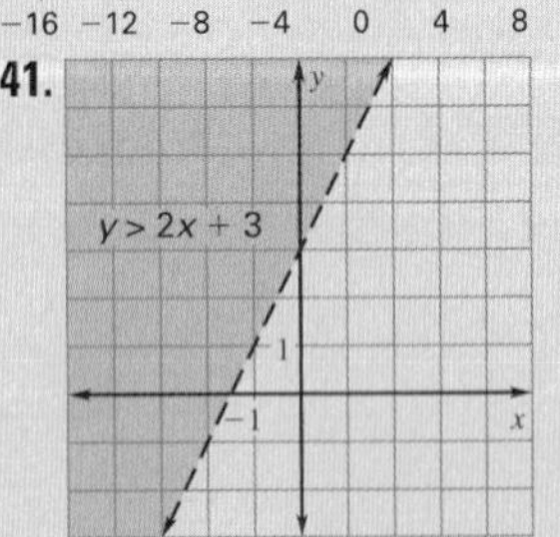

42.

43.

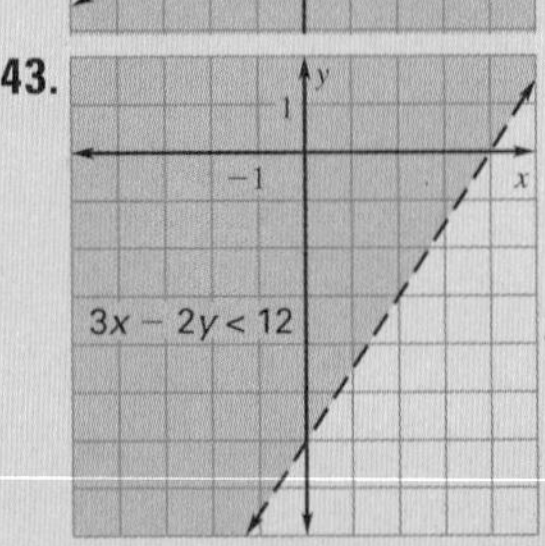

6.6 Solve Absolute Value Inequalities

pp. 398–403

EXAMPLE

Solve $3|2x + 11| + 2 \leq 17$. Graph your solution.

$3\|2x + 11\| + 2 \leq 17$	Write original inequality.
$3\|2x + 11\| \leq 15$	Subtract 2 from each side.
$\|2x + 11\| \leq 5$	Divide each side by 3.
$-5 \leq 2x + 11 \leq 5$	Rewrite as compound inequality.
$-16 \leq 2x \leq -6$	Subtract 11 from each expression.
$-8 \leq x \leq -3$	Divide each expression by 2.

▶ The solutions are all real numbers greater than or equal to -8 *and* less than or equal to -3.

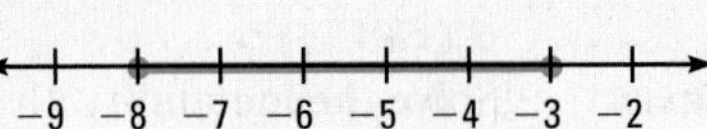

EXERCISES

EXAMPLES 1, 2, and 3 on pp. 398–399 for Exs. 31–36

Solve the inequality. Graph your solution. **31–36. See margin for art.**

31. $|m| \geq 8$ **$m \geq 8$ or $m \leq -8$**

32. $|6k + 1| \geq 2$ **$k \geq \frac{1}{6}$ or $k \leq -\frac{1}{2}$**

33. $|3g - 2| < 5$ **$-1 < g < 2\frac{1}{3}$**

34. $6|3x + 5| \leq 14$ **$-2\frac{4}{9} \leq x \leq -\frac{8}{9}$**

35. $|2j - 9| - 2 > 10$ **$j < -1\frac{1}{2}$ or $j > 10\frac{1}{2}$**

36. $5|d + 8| - 7 > 13$ **$d < -12$ or $d > -4$**

6.7 Graph Linear Inequalities in Two Variables

pp. 405–412

EXAMPLE

Graph the inequality $y < 3x - 1$.

STEP 1 **Graph** the equation $y = 3x - 1$. The inequality is $<$, so use a dashed line.

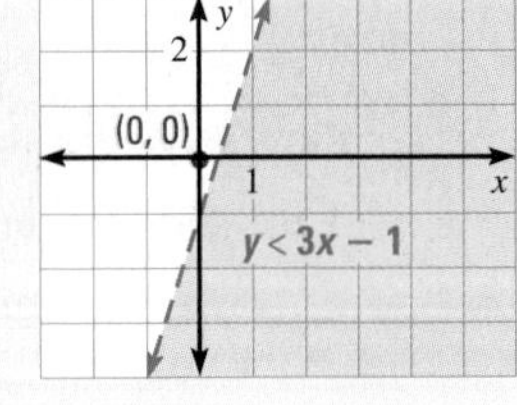

STEP 2 **Test** (0, 0) in $y < 3x - 1$.

$0 \overset{?}{<} 3(0) - 1$

$0 < -1$ ✗

STEP 3 **Shade** the half-plane that does not contain (0, 0), because (0, 0) is *not* a solution of the inequality.

EXERCISES

EXAMPLES 1, 2, 3, 4, and 5 on pp. 405–407 for Exs. 37–44

Tell whether the ordered pair is a solution of $-3x + 2y \geq 16$.

37. $(-2, 8)$ **solution**

38. $(-1, -1)$ **not a solution**

39. $(-2, 10)$ **solution**

40. $(9, -5)$ **not a solution**

Graph the inequality. **41–44. See margin.**

41. $y > 2x + 3$

42. $y \leq \frac{1}{2}x - 1$

43. $3x - 2y < 12$

44. $y \geq 3$

44.

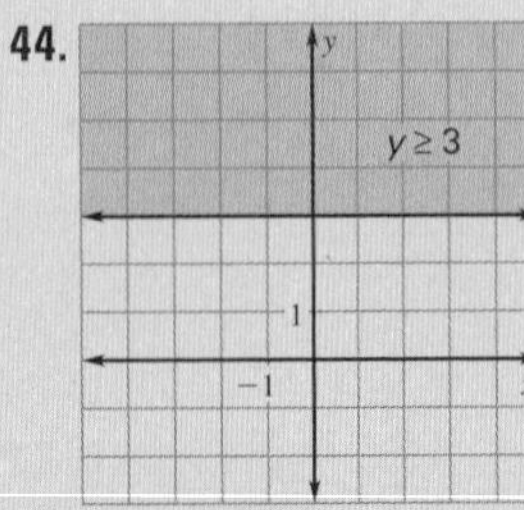

Chapter Test

1.

2.

3.

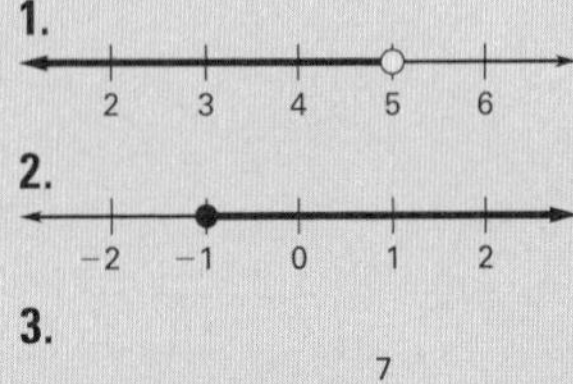

4.

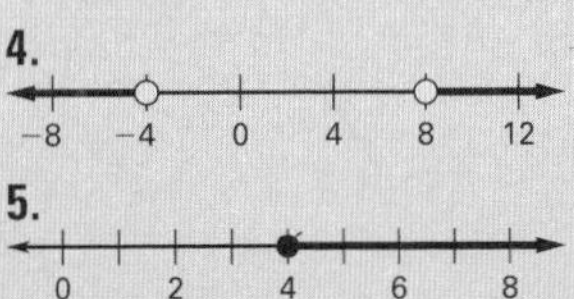

5.

6.

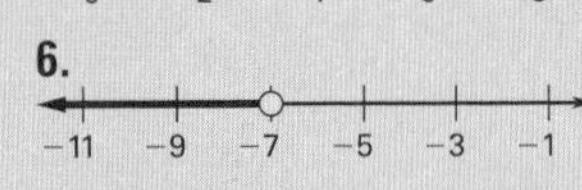

6 CHAPTER TEST

Translate the verbal phrase into an inequality. Then graph the inequality. 1–4. See margin for art.

1. All real numbers that are less than 5 $x < 5$
2. All real numbers that are greater than or equal to -1 $x \geq -1$
3. All real numbers that are greater than -2 *and* less than or equal to 7 $-2 < x \leq 7$
4. All real numbers that are greater than 8 *or* less than -4 $x > 8$ or $x < -4$

Solve the inequality, if possible. Graph your solution. 5–22. See margin for art.

5. $x - 9 \geq -5$ $x \geq 4$
6. $-2 > 5 + y$ $y < -7$
7. $-0.8 \leq z + 7.7$ $z \geq -8.5$
8. $5m \geq 35$ $m \geq 7$
9. $\frac{n}{6} < -1$ $n < -6$
10. $\frac{r}{-3} \leq 4$ $r \geq -12$
11. $-4s < 6s + 1$ $s > -0.1$
12. $4t - 7 \leq 13$ $t \leq 5$
13. $-8 > 5 - v$ $v > 13$
14. $3(5w + 4) < 12w - 11$ $w < -7\frac{2}{3}$
15. $4p - 3 > 2(2p + 1)$ no solution
16. $9q - 12 \geq 3(3q - 4)$ all real numbers
17. $-2 \leq 4 - 3a \leq 13$ $-3 \leq a \leq 2$
18. $-7 < 2c - 1 < 10\frac{1}{2}$ $-3 < c < 5.75$
19. $-5 \leq 2 - h$ *or* $6h + 5 \geq 71$ $h \leq 7$ or $h \geq 11$
20. $|2d + 8| > 3$ $d < -5.5$ or $d > -2.5$
21. $2|3f - 7| + 5 < 11$ $1\frac{1}{3} < f < 3\frac{1}{3}$
22. $|j - 7| - 1 \leq 3\frac{5}{6}$ $2\frac{1}{6} \leq j \leq 11\frac{5}{6}$

Solve the equation, if possible.

23. $-\frac{3}{4}|x - 3| = \frac{1}{4}$ no solution
24. $|3y + 1| - 6 = -2$ $1, -1\frac{2}{3}$
25. $4|2z + 5| + 9 = 5$ no solution

Check whether the ordered pair is a solution of the inequality.

26. $2x - y < 4$; $(2, -1)$ not a solution
27. $y + 3x \geq -5$; $(-3, -4)$ not a solution
28. $y \leq -3$; $(4, -7)$ solution

Graph the inequality. 29–31. See margin.

29. $y < x + 4$
30. $y \geq 2x - 5$
31. $y \geq -6$

32. **BUSINESS** Your friend is starting a small business baking and decorating cakes and wants to make a profit of at least \$250 for the first month. The expenses for the first month are \$155. What are the possible revenues that your friend can earn in order to meet the profit goal? at least \$405

33. **BICYCLES** A manufacturer of bicycle parts requires that a bicycle chain have a width of 0.3 inch with an absolute error of at most 0.0003 inch. Find the possible widths of bicycle chains that the manufacturer will accept. 0.2997 in. up to 0.3003 in.

34. **HORSES** You are planning to ride a horse to a campsite. The sum of your weight x (in pounds) and the combined weight y (in pounds) of your camping supplies can be at most 20% of the weight of the horse.
    a. Suppose that the horse weighs 1000 pounds. Write and graph an inequality that describes the possible combinations of your weight and the combined weight of the camping supplies. $x + y \leq 200$; see margin for art.
    b. Identify and interpret one of the solutions of the inequality in part (a). *Sample answer:* (130, 60); if you weigh 130 pounds and the combined weight of your camping supplies is 60 pounds, the combined weight is 190, so you will be able to ride the horse to the campsite.

Additional Resources

Assessment Book
- Chapter Test, Levels A, B, C
- Standardized Chapter Test
- SAT/ACT Chapter Test
- Alternative Assessment

Test Generator

Chapter Test

Easily-readable reduced copies (with answers) of Chapter Test B, the Standardized Chapter Test, and the Alternative Assessment from the Assessment Book can be found on pp. 354G–354H.

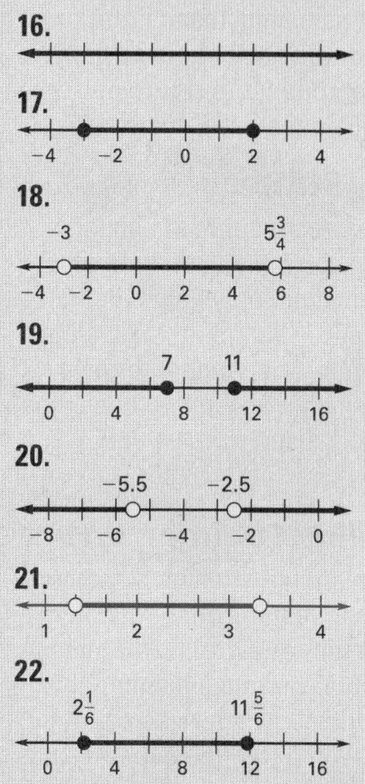

29–31. See Additional Answers beginning on p. AA1.

34a.

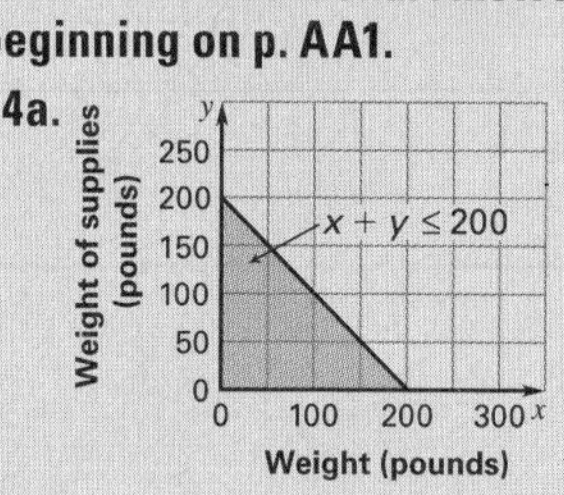

7. −8.5; −10 −8 −6 −4 −2

8. 1 3 5 7 9

9. −8 −6 −4 −2 0

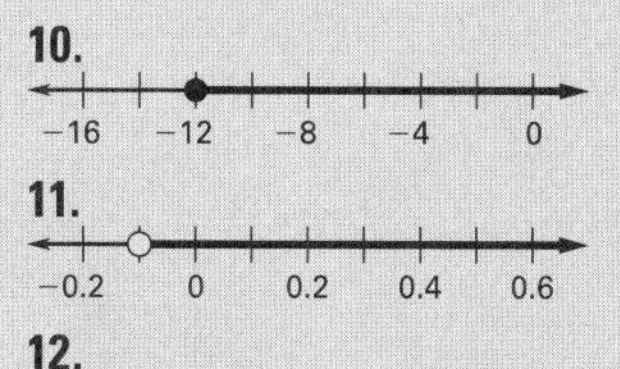

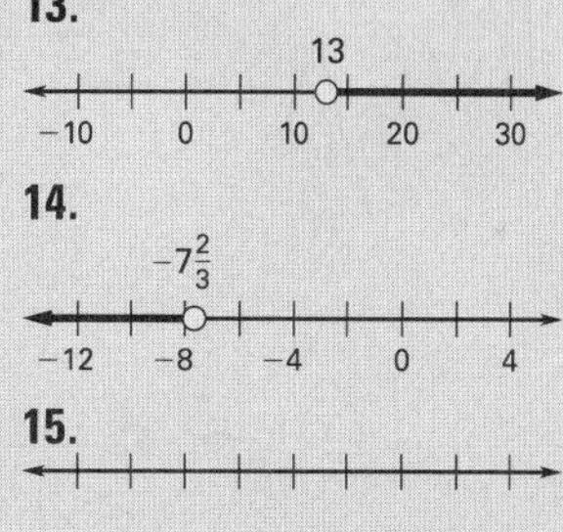

Using Rubrics

The rubric given on the pupil page is a sample of a three-level rubric. Other rubrics may contain four, five, or six levels. For more information on rubrics, see the *Differentiated Instruction Resources.*

Test-Taking Strategy

Encourage students to read all parts of an extended response question before they begin solving each of the parts. Extended response questions are complex and tend to have at least three parts. Parts often build on a previous part and the solution of one part may be required to solve another. Suggest that students use some form of shorthand notation, either words or symbols, to note any interconnections between the parts of a question.

Study Strategy

Point out to students the importance of showing all of their work. Tell them it not only helps the reviewer to see their thinking, but it also helps the student to review their own thinking and to check the steps they used to solve the problem.

Avoiding Common Errors

Caution students to check the context of a question when rounding answers in real-world situations. A student may round a number up or down correctly in terms of method, but the context of the question may require the next or previous integer rather than the rounded value.

Scoring Rubric

Full Credit
- solution is complete and correct

Partial Credit
- solution is complete but errors are made,
or
- solution is without error but incomplete

No Credit
- no solution is given,
or
- solution makes no sense

EXTENDED RESPONSE QUESTIONS

PROBLEM

Your school chess club is selling chess sets for $9 each to raise funds for a regional tournament. The club wants to sell at least 100 of them. The table shows the number of chess sets sold so far by each member of the club.

Member	1	2	3	4	5	6
Chess sets sold	17	16	12	13	16	10

a. Find the possible numbers a of additional chess sets that the club can sell in order to meet its goal.

b. If the club raises more than $1000, it will donate the amount that exceeds $1000 to a charity. Find the possible total numbers t of chess sets that the club can sell in order to donate at least $100 to the charity.

c. Suppose the club has 61 chess sets left to sell. Write an inequality that describes the possible amounts that the club can donate to the charity. *Explain* your answer.

Below are sample solutions to the problem. Read each solution and the comments on the left to see why the sample represents full credit, partial credit, or no credit.

SAMPLE 1: Full credit solution

The correct inequality is given. The solution is correct.

a. $17 + 16 + 12 + 13 + 16 + 10 + a \geq 100$

$$84 + a \geq 100$$

$$a \geq 16$$

The club will meet its goal if it sells at least 16 more chess sets.

The correct inequality is given. The student rounded correctly so that the answer makes sense.

b. $9t - 1000 \geq 100$

$$9t \geq 1100$$

$$t \geq 122.22\ldots$$

The club can donate only $9(122) − $1000 = $98 if it sells 122 sets. So, the club can donate at least $100 if it sells at least 123 sets.

The student's calculation of the least and greatest values is correct. The answer is correct.

c. If the club doesn't sell any more chess sets, it will have raised a total of $9(84) = $756. Because the club will not have raised at least $1000, its donation to the charity would be $0. If the club sells the remaining 61 chess sets, it will have raised a total of $756 + $9(61) = $1305. So, the club's donation to the charity would be $1305 − $1000 = $305. The inequality is $0 \leq d \leq 305$ where d is the donation in dollars.

SAMPLE 2: Partial credit solution

The correct inequality is given. The solution is correct.

a. $84 + a \geq 100$

$a \geq 16$

The club must sell at least 16 chess sets.

The student solved the inequality correctly but gave the wrong answer.

b. $9t - 1000 \geq 100$

$9t \geq 1100$

$t \geq 122.22...$

The club can donate at least $100 if it sells at least 122 sets.

The reasoning doesn't make sense, and the inequality is incorrect.

c. If the club doesn't sell any more chess sets, it will raise $0 more. So, the donation would be $0. If the club sells the remaining 61 sets, it will raise $9(61) = $549 more. So, the donation would be at most $549. The inequality is $0 \leq d \leq 549$ where d is the donation.

SAMPLE 3: No credit solution

The inequalities in parts (a) and (b) are incorrect, and the answers are incorrect.

a. $84 + a \leq 100$

$a \leq 16$

The club will meet its goal if it sells up to 16 chess sets.

b. $9t \geq 1000$

$t \geq 111.11...$

The club can donate at least $100 if it sells at least 112 chess sets.

The student didn't consider the number of chess sets the club can sell.

c. The donation would be $0 if the club raised up to $1000. But the donation would be greater than $0 if the club raised more than $1000. The inequality is $d \geq 0$ where d is the donation.

PRACTICE Apply the Scoring Rubric

1. A student's solution to the problem on the previous page is given below. Score the solution as *full credit, partial credit,* or *no credit. Explain* your reasoning. If you choose *partial credit* or *no credit,* explain how you would change the solution so that it earns a score of full credit.

a. Because $a \geq 100 - 84$, the club must sell at least 16 sets to meet its goal.

b. The total amount raised is 9t. In order to donate at least $100, the club needs to raise a total of at least $1100.

$9t \geq 1100$, so $t \geq 122.22...$

c. If the club sells the remaining 61 sets, then it will have raised $9(61) = $549 more. The inequality is $d \leq 549$ where d is the donation.

Answers

1. Partial credit; in part (a), show how the inequality $a \geq 16$ is arrived at. In part (b), mention that the club can't sell a part of a chess set, so the club has to sell at least 123 sets. In part (c), calculate the total amount raised, not just the additional amount raised, and then subtract $1000 from the total amount to find the largest possible donation. Also consider what the lowest possible donation is.

Answers

1a. from $13\frac{1}{3}$ h up to 20 h

1b. yes; 4 h, $17\frac{1}{3}$ h

1c. Solve $5.5x + 7(20 - x) \geq 150$; the solution is $x \leq -6\frac{2}{3}$. Because x represents a number of hours, x cannot be a negative number, so the solution does not makes sense in this situation.

2a. $3t + 2d \leq 30$;

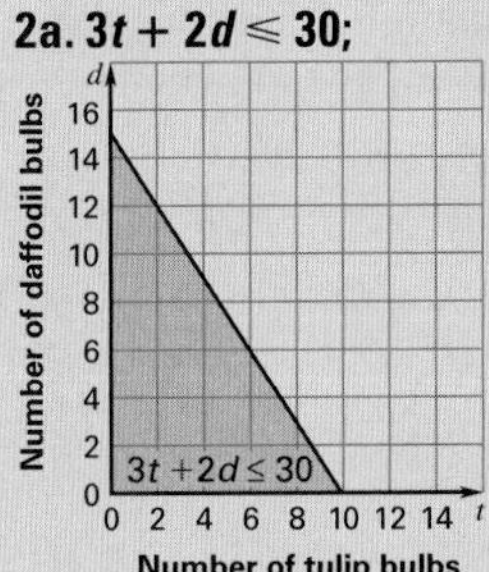

2b. *Sample answer*: 5 tulip bulbs and 5 daffodil bulbs, 0 tulip bulbs and 15 daffodil bulbs, 8 tulip bulbs and 2 daffodil bulbs

2c. Move the line so that the t-intercept is $\frac{40}{3}$ and the d-intercept is 20. The linear inequality that describes the situation in which you can spend up to \$40 is $3t + 2d < 40$.

3a. June 2001; August 2005

3b. No; if you substitute 600 for h in the model, the equation has no solution.

3c. Yes. *Sample answer;* Make a table of values for (m, h) for integer values of m from 0 to 49. Look for the greatest value of h in the table.

EXTENDED RESPONSE

1. You plan to work a total of 20 hours per week at two part-time jobs. The table shows the hourly wage at each job.

Job	Working at a sandwich shop	After-school tutoring
Hourly wage (dollars)	5.50	7.00

   a. You want to earn from \$100 to \$120 per week. What are the possible numbers of hours that you can work at the sandwich shop so that you can meet your earnings goal?

   b. Suppose you need to reduce the total number of hours you work each week to 18 hours. Can you still meet your earnings goal? If so, what are the least and greatest numbers of hours that you can work at the sandwich shop? If not, explain why not.

   c. Show that it is not possible to earn more than \$150 after working 20 hours in one week by writing and solving an inequality that describes the situation and showing that the solutions do not make sense for the situation.

2. You plan to spend up to \$30 on flower bulbs for a garden. The table shows the prices of tulip bulbs and daffodil bulbs.

Flower bulb	Tulip	Daffodil
Price (dollars)	3	2

   a. Write and graph an inequality that describes the possible combinations of tulip bulbs and daffodil bulbs that you can buy.

   b. Give three possible combinations of tulip bulbs and daffodil bulbs that you can buy.

   c. Suppose you plan to spend up to \$40 on flower bulbs. How would you change the graph in part (a) in order to describe this situation? *Explain* your answer.

3. The average number of hits h per day that your website received during the period January 2001 to February 2004 can be modeled by the equation $h = -16|m - 30| + 500$ where m is the number of months since January 2001.

   a. In what month and year did your website receive an average of 100 hits per day? If the model holds for months after February 2004, predict the month and year in which your website will again receive an average of 100 hits per day.

   b. According to the model, did your website receive an average of 600 hits per day at any time during the period January 2001 to February 2004? *Explain* your answer.

   c. Can you use the model to find the month and year in which the average number of hits per day was the greatest? *Justify* your answer.

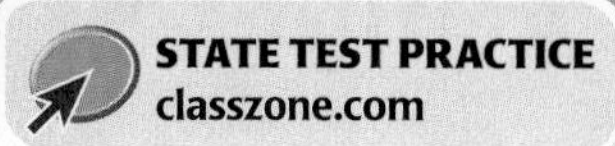

MULTIPLE CHOICE

4. In a piano competition, a pianist must perform a sonata that lasts no less than 8 minutes and no more than 10 minutes. Which inequality represents the durations d (in minutes) of sonatas that can be performed?

Ⓐ $8 < d < 10$ Ⓑ $d \leq 8$ *or* $d \geq 10$

Ⓒ $8 \leq d \leq 10$ Ⓓ $d < 8$ *or* $d > 10$

5. Which ordered pair is a solution of the inequality $4x - y \geq 3$?

Ⓐ (0, 0) Ⓑ (−1, 2)

Ⓒ (1, 1) Ⓓ (0, −2)

6. You are designing an obstacle course for a dog agility event. The course includes a tunnel that must have a height of 24 inches with an absolute deviation of 2 inches. Which equation can you use to find the minimum and maximum heights of the tunnel?

Ⓐ $|x + 24| = 2$ Ⓑ $|x - 24| = 2$

Ⓒ $|x + 2| = 24$ Ⓓ $|x - 2| = 24$

GRIDDED ANSWER

7. You scored the following points in four basketball games: 16, 24, 32, and 22. You want to score an average of more than 25 points per game after your fifth game. Of all the possible points you can score in your fifth game in order to meet your goal, which is the least?

8. In men's weightlifting, the bar that holds the weights must have a length of 2.2 meters with an absolute deviation of 1 millimeter. Of all the possible lengths that the bar can have, which is the greatest length (in millimeters)?

9. Of all the numbers that are solutions of the inequality $\left|-\frac{1}{3}x + 4\right| \leq 2$, which is the least number?

10. The perimeter of the rectangle shown is at least 47 inches and at most 52 inches. Find the greatest value of x that satisfies the condition.

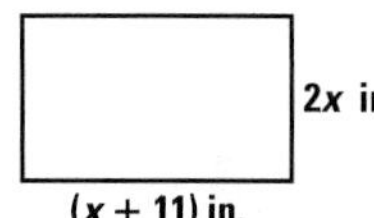

SHORT RESPONSE

11. You and 4 friends each order a three course dinner at a restaurant, and all of you agree to divide the total cost equally. The table shows the range of prices for each of the three courses.

Dinner course	Appetizer	Main course	Dessert
Price range (dollars)	2–4	12–20	3–6

a. Find the least and greatest possible total costs C (in dollars). Then write an inequality that describes the possible total costs.

b. Your share s (in dollars) of the total cost is given by $s = \frac{C}{5}$. You chose a \$3 appetizer, a \$15 main course, and a \$4 dessert. *Explain* why your share could be greater than or less than $\$3 + \$15 + \$4 = \$22$.

12. A family is planning a vacation and is willing to spend no more than \$2000 for 4 airplane tickets and 5 nights at a hotel. Write and graph an inequality that describes the combinations of prices x (in dollars) of an airplane ticket and prices y (in dollars) of a night at a hotel. If the family spends \$275 per airplane ticket, is the family willing to spend \$200 per night at a hotel? *Explain* your answer using the graph.

4. C

5. C

6. B

7. 32 points

8. 2201 mm

9. 6

10. 5

11a. \$85, \$150; $85 \leq C \leq 150$

11b. $C = 5s$, so to find an inequality that describes the possible shares, solve $85 \leq 5s \leq 150$, to get $17 \leq s \leq 30$. Each person's share will be from \$17 to \$30. Your meal cost $\$3 + \$15 + \$4 = \$22$, so your share of the total cost could end up being either more or less than the total price of your meal.

12.

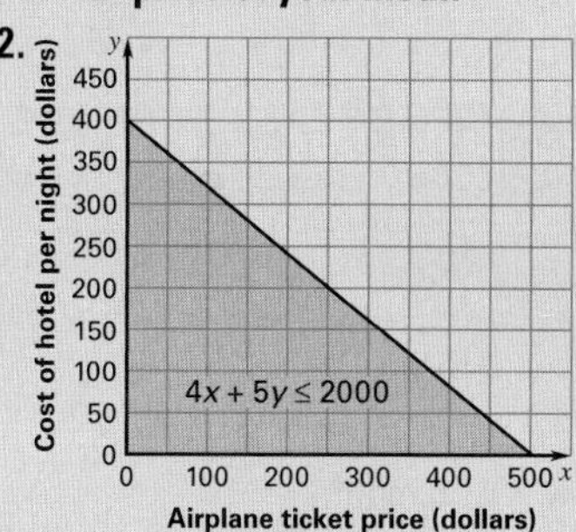

No; spending \$275 on airplane tickets and \$200 per night at a hotel is represented by the ordered pair (275, 200). The point lies above the line of the graph, but the solutions of the graph are all the points below the line, so it is not a solution.

7 Pacing Guide

Chapter 7: Systems of Equations and Inequalities

Chapter Table of Contents

PACING GUIDES

Regular Schedule (50-minute classes)

DAY 1	DAY 2	DAY 3	DAY 4	DAY 5
Investigating Algebra Activity 7.1 Lesson 7.1 Graphing Calculator Activity 7.1	Lesson 7.2	Lesson 7.2 (cont.)	Quiz for Lessons 7.1–7.2 Investigating Algebra Activity 7.3 Lesson 7.3	Lesson 7.4 Mixed Review of Problem Solving
DAY 6	**DAY 7**	**DAY 8**	**DAY 9**	**DAY 10**
Quiz for Lessons 7.3–7.4 Lesson 7.5	Lesson 7.5 (cont.)	Lesson 7.6 Mixed Review of Problem Solving	Quiz for Lessons 7.5–7.6 Chapter Review	Chapter Test

Block Schedule (90-minute classes)

DAY 1	DAY 2	DAY 3	DAY 4	DAY 5
Investigating Algebra Activity 7.1 Lesson 7.1 Graphing Calculator Activity 7.1 Lesson 7.2	Lesson 7.2 (cont.) Quiz for Lessons 7.1–7.2 Investigating Algebra Activity 7.3 Lesson 7.3	Lesson 7.4 Mixed Review of Problem Solving Quiz for Lessons 7.3–7.4 Lesson 7.5	Lesson 7.5 (cont.) Lesson 7.6 Mixed Review of Problem Solving	Quiz for Lessons 7.5–7.6 Chapter Review Chapter Test

RESOURCE OPTIONS

Chapter/Lesson Resources

Chapter Resource Book
- Parents as Partners
- Teaching Guide/Lesson Plan
- Activity Masters
- Practice (3 levels)
- Study Guide
- Quick Catch-Up for Absent Students
- Problem Solving/Application
- Challenge Practice
- Chapter Review Games and Activities
- Project with Rubric
- Cumulative Review

Notetaking Guide
- Student Workbook and Teacher's Edition

Practice Workbook

Worked-Out Solution Key

Chapter Transparency Book
- Warm-Up Exercises/Daily Homework Quiz
- Notetaking Guide Transparencies
- Homework Answer Transparencies

Teacher Tools Transparencies

Assessment

Assessment Book
- Quizzes
- Chapter Tests (3 levels)
- Standardized and SAT/ACT Chapter Tests
- Alternative Assessments
- Cumulative Tests

Benchmark Tests
- Benchmark Tests, correlated to Remediation Book
- Pre-Course, Mid-Year, and End-of-Year Tests
- Chapter Tests

Spanish Assessment Book

Differentiated Instruction

Differentiated Instruction Resources
- Strategies for Reading Mathematics
- Differentiated Instruction Lesson Notes
- English Learner Lesson Notes
- Inclusion Lesson Notes
- Teaching Strategies with Sample Worksheets
- Tips for New Teachers/Math Background Notes
- Teacher Survival Activities/Bulletin Board Ideas

Student Resources in Spanish

Spanish Study Guide

Remediation Book

Skills Readiness (available on Easy Planner)
- Diagnostic Assessment
- Skill Instruction and Alternative Teaching Strategies
- Skill Practice and Enrichment Masters

Pre-AP Resources
- Pacing and Assignment Guide
- Best Practices
- Copymasters

Technology Resources

Plan	***Easy Planner***
Teach	***Video Tutor*** ***Activity Generator*** ***Power Presentations*** ***Animated Algebra***
Assess	***Test Generator*** ***ML Assessment System***
Reteach	***@HomeTutor***
Online Resources	***Classzone.com*** ***eEdition*** ***eWorkbook***

Video Tutor

Technology Highlights for Each Lesson

 **Easy Planner**

Easy access to the Teacher's Edition and all teaching resources. Includes a search feature to locate the materials you need.

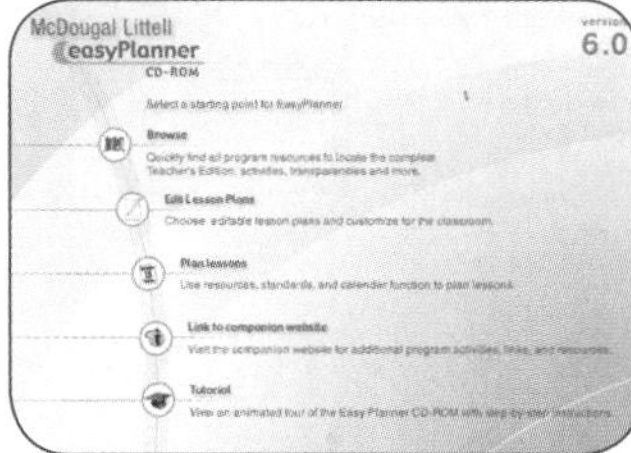

 **Activity Generator**

Leveled, editable activities allow all students to explore a lesson's concepts. Includes teacher notes and closure questions.

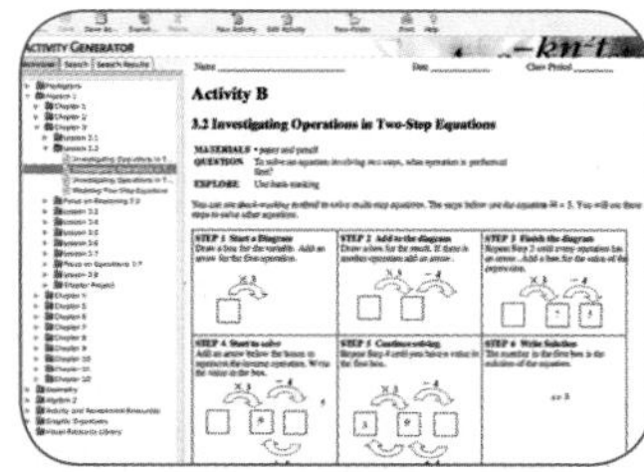

Animated Algebra

Interactive tutorials provide visually engaging alternative opportunities to learn concepts and master skills.

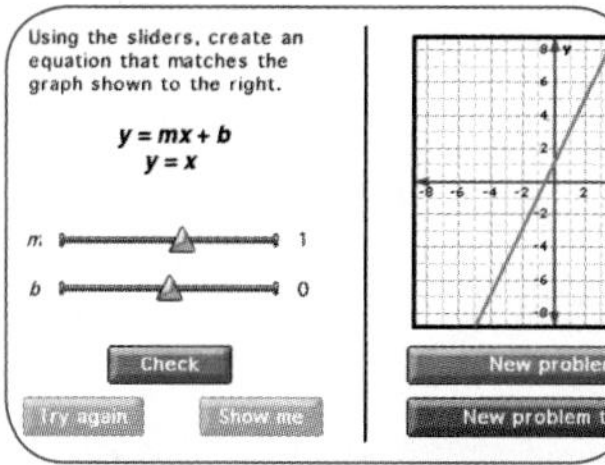

Lesson Practice Level B

LESSON 7.1 Practice B
For use with pages 427–433

Tell whether the ordered pair is a solution of the linear system.

1. $(4, 1)$; no
$x + 2y = 6$
$3x + y = 11$

2. $(-2, 1)$; yes
$5x - 2y = -12$
$x + 3y = 1$

3. $(4, -3)$; yes
$-3x + 2y = -18$
$6x - y = 27$

4. $(-4, -6)$; no
$3x - y = 6$
$-x + 2y = 8$

5. $(-4, 3)$; no
$4x + 3y = -12$
$x + 2y = -6$

6. $(-2, -5)$; yes
$-x + y = -3$
$-x + 3y = -13$

Use the graph to solve the linear system. Check your solution.

7. $x - y = 8$ $(3, -5)$
$x + y = -2$

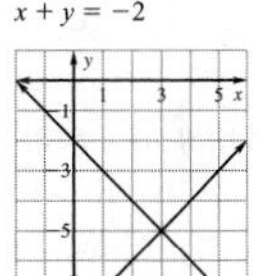

8. $5x - y = -9$ $(-1, 4)$
$y + 2x = 2$

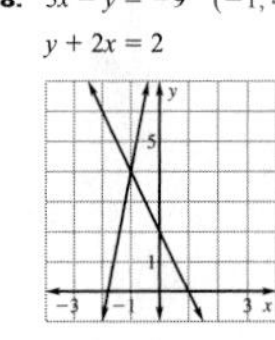

9. $2x + 3y = 2$ $(-2, 2)$
$-2x + y = 6$

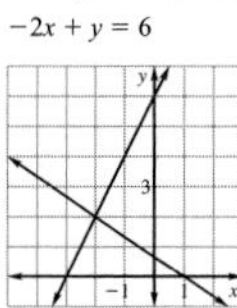

10. $3x - 2y = 16$ $(4, -2)$
$5x + y = 18$

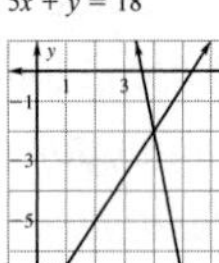

11. $2x - y = -13$ $(-5, 3)$
$y + 3x = -12$

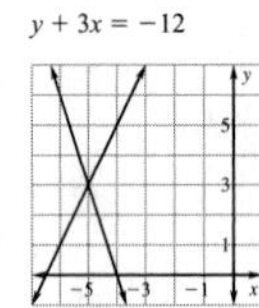

12. $6x + 2y = 8$ $(0, 4)$
$-3x + 4y = 16$

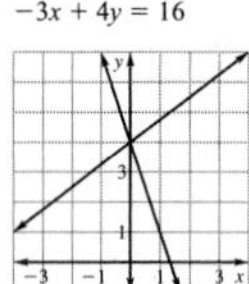

Solve the linear system by graphing. Check your solution.

13. $y = 3x$ $(1, 3)$
$y = 4x - 1$

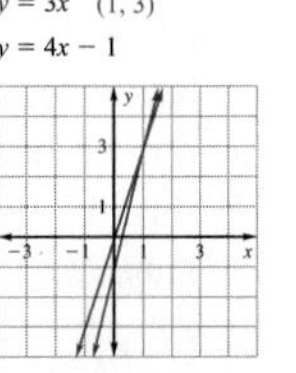

14. $2x + y = -4$ $(-4, 4)$
$x - y = -8$

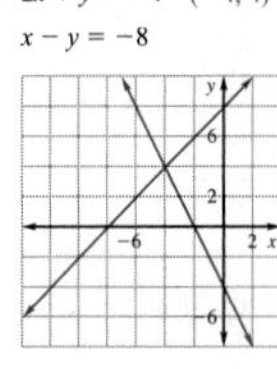

15. $-3x - y = -1$ $(2, -5)$
$2x + 4y = -16$

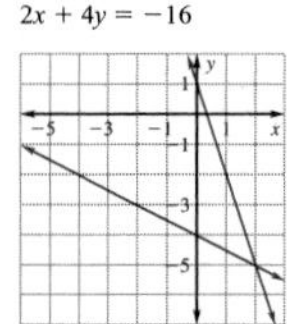

LESSON 7.1

LESSON 7.1 Practice B
For use with pages 427–433

16. $2x + 2y = -6$ $(-3, 0)$
$-5x + y = 15$

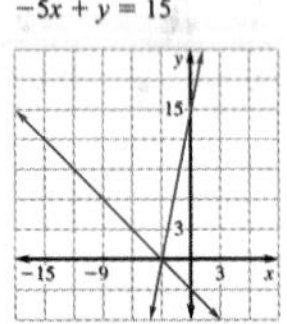

17. $-6x + y = 33$ $(-5, 3)$
$2x - 8y = -34$

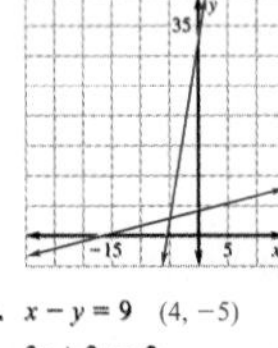

18. $-9x + 6y = -6$ $(-2, -4)$
$2x - 3y = 8$

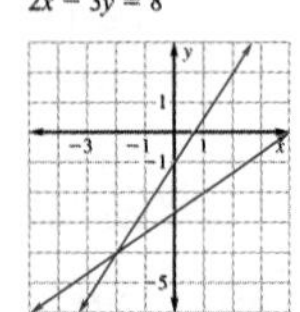

19. $3x + 2y = 3$ $(-3, 6)$
$5x + y = -9$

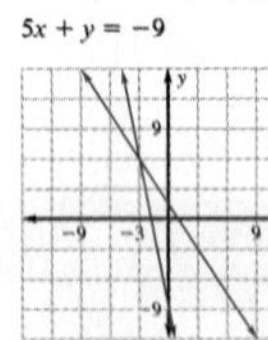

20. $x - y = 9$ $(4, -5)$
$3x + 2y = 2$

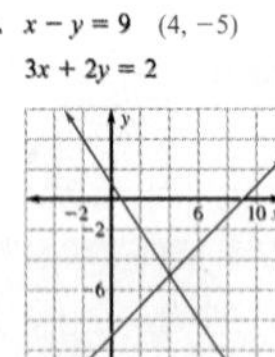

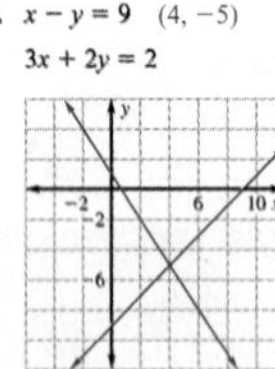

21. $6x + y = 19$ $(2, 7)$
$5x - 2y = -4$

22. Hanging Flower Baskets You will be making hanging flower baskets. The plants you have picked out are blooming annuals and non-blooming annuals. The blooming annuals cost \$3.20 each and the non-blooming annuals cost \$1.50 each. You bought a total of 24 plants for \$49.60. Write a linear system of equations that you can use to find out how many of each type of plant you bought. Then graph the linear system and use the graph to find how many of each type of plant you bought.
8 blooming annuals and 16 non-blooming annuals

$3.2x + 1.5y = 49.6$
$x + y = 24$
Non-blooming annuals
Blooming annuals

23. Baseball Outs In a game, 12 of a baseball team's 27 outs were fly balls. Twenty-five percent of the outs made by infielders and 100% of the outs made by outfielders were fly balls.

a. Write a linear system you can use to find the number of outs made by infielders and the number of outs made by outfielders. (*Hint:* Write one equation for the total number of outs and another equation for the number of fly ball outs.)

b. Graph your linear system. **a.** $x + y = 27$ and $0.25x + y = 12$

c. How many outs were made by infielders? How many outs were made by outfielders? infielders: 20 outs; outfielders: 7 outs

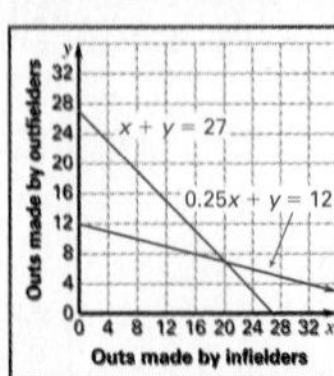

LESSON 7.2 Practice B
For use with pages 435–441

Solve for the indicated variable.

1. $8x + 4y = 12; y$ $y = -2x + 3$ **2.** $3x - 4y = 12; y$ $y = \frac{3}{4}x - 3$ **3.** $6x - 4y = 8; x$ $x = \frac{2}{3}y + \frac{4}{3}$

Tell which equation you would use to isolate a variable. *Explain* your reasoning.

4. $x = 8y - 3$
$3x - 4y = 1$
Equation 1

5. $-4x + 5y = 11$
$y = 4x - 1$
Equation 2

6. $9 - 3x = y$
$3x - y = -2$
Equation 1

Solve the linear system by using substitution.

7. $x = 6 - 4y$ $(2, 1)$
$2x - 3y = 1$

8. $4x + 3y = 0$ $(-3, 4)$
$2x + y = -2$

9. $-x + 2y = -6$ $(4, -1)$
$8x + y = 31$

10. $6x - y = -35$ $(-5, 5)$
$5x - 2y = -35$

11. $-x + 3y = -9$ $(3, -2)$
$8x - 4y = 32$

12. $3x + 3y = -18$ $(-4, -2)$
$4x - y = -14$

13. $2x + 2y = 6$ $(6, -3)$
$-3x + 5y = -33$

14. $5x + 2y = 43$ $(7, 4)$
$-6x + 3y = -30$

15. $4x - 2y = -4$ $(3, 8)$
$7x - 5y = -19$

16. $3x + 2y = 5$ $(1, 1)$
$5x - 9y = -4$

17. $4x - 3y = 28$ $(4, -4)$
$2x + 3y = -4$

18. $8x + 8y = 24$ $(1, 2)$
$x + 5y = 11$

19. Drum Sticks A drummer is stocking up on his drum sticks and brushes. The wood sticks that he buys are \$10.50 a pair and the brushes are \$24 a pair. He ends up spending \$90 on sticks and brushes and buys two times as many pairs of sticks as brushes. How many pairs of sticks and brushes did he buy? 4 pairs of sticks and 2 pairs of brushes

20. Mowing and Shoveling Last year you mowed grass and shoveled snow for 12 households. You earned \$225 for mowing a household's lawn for the entire year and you earned \$200 for shoveling a household's walk and driveway for an entire year. You earned a total of \$2600 last year.

a. Let x be the number of households you mowed for and let y be the number of households you shoveled for. Write an equation in x and y that shows the total number of households you worked for. Then write an equation in x and y that shows the total amount of money you earned. $x + y = 12$; $225x + 200y = 2600$

b. How many households did you mow the lawn for and how many households did you shovel the walk and driveway for? households mowed: 8 households; households shoveled: 4 households

21. Dimensions of a Metal Sheet A rectangular hole 3 centimeters wide and x centimeters long is cut in a rectangular sheet of metal that is 4 centimeters wide and y centimeters long. The length of the hole is 1 centimeter less than the length of the metal sheet. After the hole is cut, the area of the remaining metal sheet is 20 square centimeters. Find the length of the hole and the length of the metal sheet.
length of hole: 16 cm; length of sheet: 17 cm

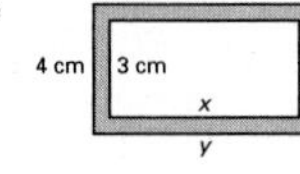

LESSON 7.2

LESSON 7.3 Practice B
For use with pages 444–450

Rewrite the linear system so that the like terms are arranged in columns.

1. $8x - y = 19$; $y + 3x = 7$ — $8x - y = 19$ and $3x + y = 7$
2. $4x = y - 11$; $6y + 4x = -3$ — $4x - y = -11$ and $4x + 6y = -3$
3. $9x - 2y = 5$; $2y = -11x + 8$ — $9x - 2y = 5$ and $11x + 2y = 8$

Describe the first step you would use to solve the linear system.

4. $22x - y = -4$; $y = 6x - 5$ — Arrange the terms.
5. $25 = x - 7y$; $x + 12y = -8$ — Arrange the terms.
6. $3x + 7 = 2y$; $-2y - 1 = 10x$ — Arrange the terms.
7. $x + 9y = 2$; $14x - 9y = -4$ — Add the equations.
8. $4x + 3y = -6$; $3y = -5x + 1$ — Arrange the terms.
9. $4x + y = -10$; $x + y = -14$ — Subtract the equations.

Solve the linear system by using elimination.

10. $x + 5y = 28$; $-x - 2y = -13$ — $(3, 5)$
11. $7x - 4y = -30$; $3x + 4y = 10$ — $(-2, 4)$
12. $6x + y = 39$; $-2x + y = -17$ — $(7, -3)$
13. $3x = y - 20$; $-7x - y = 40$ — $(-6, 2)$
14. $2x - 6y = -10$; $4x = 10 + 6y$ — $(10, 5)$
15. $x - 3y = 6$; $-2x = 3y + 33$ — $(-9, -5)$
16. $-3x = y - 20$; $-y = -5x + 4$ — $(3, 11)$
17. $x - \frac{1}{2}y = \frac{11}{2}$; $-x + 4y = 26$ — $(10, 9)$
18. $-\frac{2}{3}x + 6y = 38$; $x - 6y = -33$ — $(15, 8)$
19. $\frac{3}{2}x + y = -\frac{5}{2}$; $4x + y = -5$ — $(-1, -1)$
20. $7x - \frac{1}{3}y = -29$; $2x - \frac{1}{3}y = -9$ — $(-4, 3)$
21. $\frac{1}{2}x - \frac{3}{2}y = -\frac{29}{2}$; $-\frac{1}{2}x + 3y = 33$ — $\left(8, \frac{37}{3}\right)$

22. **Fishing Barge** A fishing barge leaves from a dock and moves upstream (against the current) at a rate of 3.8 miles per hour until it reaches its destination. After the people on the barge are done fishing, the barge moves the same distance downstream (with the current) at a rate of 8 miles per hour until it returns to the dock. The speed of the current remains constant. Use the models below to write and solve a system of equations to find the average speed of the barge in still water and the speed of the current. Speed of barge in still water: 5.9 mi/h; Speed of current: 2.1 mi/h

    Upstream: Speed of barge in still water − Speed of current = Speed of barge
    Downstream: Speed of barge in still water + Speed of current = Speed of barge

23. **Floor Sander Rental** A rental company charges a flat fee of x dollars for a floor sander rental plus y dollars per hour of the rental. One customer rents a floor sander for 4 hours and pays $63. Another customer rents a floor sander for 6 hours and pays $87.
    a. Find the flat fee and the cost per hour for the rental. Flat fee: $15; Hourly fee: $12
    b. How much would it cost someone to rent a sander for 11 hours? $147

LESSON 7.4 Practice B
For use with pages 451–457

1. *Sample answer:* Multiply the first equation by 2.
2. *Sample answer:* Multiply the second equation by −3.
3. *Sample answer:* Multiply the first equation by −3.

Describe the first step you would use to solve the linear system.

1. $3x - 4y = 7$; $5x + 8y = 10$
2. $9x + 4y = 13$; $3x + 5y = 9$
3. $5x + 7y = -3$; $15x + 4y = -5$
4. $7x - 4y = 6$; $3x - 2y = -15$ — See below.
5. $7x + 9y = -6$; $-5x + 14y = 11$ — See below.
6. $9x - 5y = 14$; $-6x + 8y = 13$ — See below.

Solve the linear system by using elimination.

7. $x + 3y = 1$; $-5x + 4y = -24$ — $(4, -1)$
8. $-3x - y = -15$; $8x + 4y = 48$ — $(3, 6)$
9. $x + 7y = -37$; $2x - 5y = 21$ — $(-2, -5)$
10. $8x - 4y = -76$; $5x + 2y = -16$ — $(-6, 7)$
11. $-3x + 10y = 23$; $5x + 2y = 55$ — $(9, 5)$
12. $9x - 4y = 26$; $18x + 7y = 22$ — $(2, -2)$
13. $4x - 3y = 16$; $16x + 10y = 240$ — $(10, 8)$
14. $20x + 10y = 100$; $-5x + 4y = 53$ — $(-1, 12)$
15. $3x - 10y = -25$; $5x - 20y = -55$ — $(5, 4)$
16. $-3x - 4y = 27$; $5x - 6y = -7$ — $(-5, -3)$
17. $2x + 7y = 2$; $5x - 2y = 83$ — $(15, -4)$
18. $3x - 5y = -16$; $2x - 3y = -8$ — $(8, 8)$

19. **Hockey Game** Two families go to a hockey game. One family purchases two adult tickets and four youth tickets for $28. Another family purchases four adult tickets and five youth tickets for $45.50. Let x represent the cost in dollars of one adult ticket and let y represent the cost in dollars of one youth ticket.
    a. Write a linear system that represents this situation. $2x + 4y = 28$ and $4x + 5y = 45.5$
    b. Solve the linear system to find the cost of one adult and one youth ticket. Adult: $7; Youth: $3.50
    c. How much would it cost two adults and five youths to attend the game? $31.50

20. **Travel Agency** A travel agency offers two Chicago outings. Plan A includes hotel accommodations for three nights and two pairs of baseball tickets worth a total of $557. Plan B includes hotel accommodations for five nights and four pairs of baseball tickets worth a total of $974. Let x represent the cost in dollars of one night's hotel accommodations and let y represent the cost in dollars of one pair of baseball tickets.
    a. Write a linear system you could use to find the cost of one night's hotel accommodations and the cost of one pair of baseball tickets. $3x + 2y = 557$ and $5x + 4y = 974$
    b. Solve the linear system to find the cost of one night's hotel accommodations and the cost of one pair of baseball tickets. Hotel: $140/night; Tickets: $68.50/pair

21. **Highway Project** There are fifteen workers employed on a highway project, some at $180 per day and some at $155 per day. The daily payroll is $2400. Let x represent the number of $180 per day workers and let y represent the number of $155 per day workers. Write and solve a linear system to find the number of workers employed at each wage. $x + y = 15$ and $180x + 155y = 2400$; $180/day: 3 workers; $155/day: 12 workers

4. *Sample answer:* Multiply the second equation by −2.
5. *Sample answer:* Multiply the first equation by −5.
6. *Sample answer:* Multiply the first equation by 2.

LESSON 7.5 Practice B
For use with pages 459–465

Match the linear system with its graph. Then use the graph to tell whether the linear system has *one solution, no solution, or infinitely many solutions.*

1. $y + 3 = 4x$; $3y = 12x - 9$ — C; infinitely many solutions
2. $2x + y = 1$; $2x + y = 5$ — A; no solution
3. $3x + y = 1$; $-2x + y = -3$ — B; one solution

A. B. C.

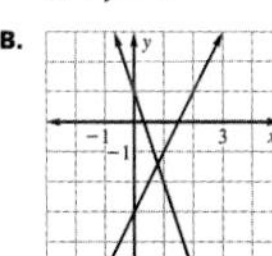

Graph the linear system. Then use the graph to tell whether the linear system has *one solution, no solution, or infinitely many solutions.*

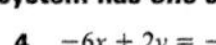

4. $-6x + 2y = -2$; $-3x + y = 2$ — no solution
5. $2y - x = -4$; $2x + y = 3$ — one solution
6. $4x - y = 2$; $-x + 3y = 9$ — one solution

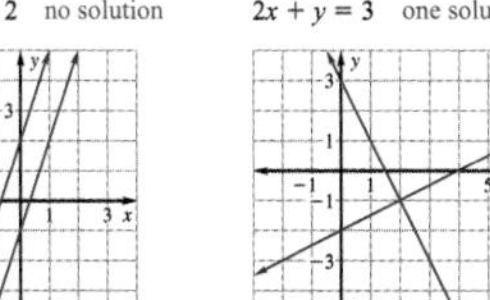

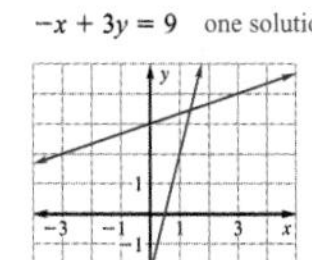

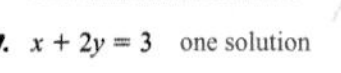

7. $x + 2y = 3$; $-x + 2y = -2$ — one solution
8. $3x + y = 4$; $x + \frac{1}{3}y = 2$ — no solution
9. $2x - y = 4$; $-2x + y = -4$ — infinitely many solutions

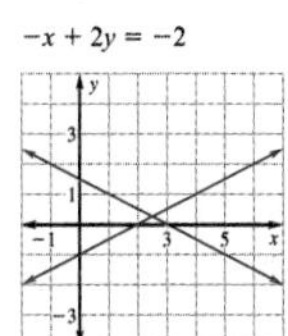

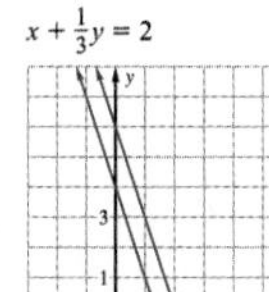

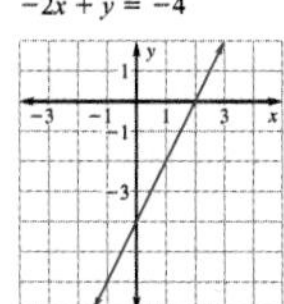

LESSON 7.5 Practice B *continued*
For use with pages 459–465

Solve the linear system by using substitution or elimination.

10. $3x - 2y = 24$; $x + 2y = 8$ — $(8, 0)$
11. $3x + 2y = 4$; $-6x - 4y = -8$ — infinitely many solutions
12. $x + y = 50$; $-3x + 2y = 0$ — $(20, 30)$
13. $-x + 4y = -3$; $-3x + 2y = 1$ — $(-1, -1)$
14. $-x + 3y = 9$; $2x + y = 10$ — $(3, 4)$
15. $2x + y = 6$; $2x + y = -7$ — no solution

Without solving the linear system, tell whether the linear system has *one solution, no solution, or infinitely many solutions.*

16. $-6x + 6y = -4$; $2x - 2y = 5$ — no solution
17. $y + 2x = \frac{8}{3}$; $2x + y = -10$ — no solution
18. $4x + 3y = 9$; $\frac{3}{4}x + y = 3$ — one solution
19. $4x - 6y = -1$; $-\frac{3}{2}x + y = \frac{1}{4}$ — one solution
20. $-\frac{2}{3}x + y = 2$; $-6x + 3y = 6$ — one solution
21. $9x - 15y = 15$; $x + \frac{3}{5}y = 1$ — one solution
22. $-3x + 4y = 2$; $2y = \frac{3}{2}x + 1$ — infinitely many solutions
23. $3x + y = 4$; $x + \frac{1}{3}y = 2$ — no solution
24. $-4x + 3y = 2$; $4 - 6y = -8x$ — infinitely many solutions

25. **Golf Clubs** A sporting goods store stocks a "better" set of golf clubs in both left-handed and right-handed sets. The set of left-handed golf clubs sells for x dollars and the set of right-handed golf clubs sells for y dollars. In one month, the store sells 2 sets of left-handed golf clubs and 12 sets of right-handed golf clubs for a total of $1859.30. The next month, the store sells 2 sets of left-handed golf clubs and 22 sets of right-handed golf clubs for a total of $3158.80. Is there enough information to determine the cost of each kind of set? *Explain.* Yes; The system $2x + 12y = 1859.3$ and $2x + 22y = 3158.8$ can be written to model the situation, and this system has one solution, (about $153, about $130).

26. **Comedy Tickets** The table below shows the tickets sales at an all-ages comedy club on a Friday night and a Saturday night.

Day	Number of adult tickets	Number of student tickets	Total sales (dollars)
Friday	30	20	910
Saturday	45	30	1365

    a. Let x represent the cost (in dollars) of one adult ticket and let y represent the cost (in dollars) of one student ticket. Write a linear system that models the situation.
    b. Solve the linear system. infinitely many solutions
    c. Can you determine how much each kind of ticket costs? Why or why not? No, because one equation in the system is a multiple of the other, no specific values for neither x or y can be found. **26. a.** $30x + 20y = 910$ and $45x + 30y = 1365$

7 Lesson Practice Level B

LESSON 7.6 **Practice B**
For use with pages 466–472

Tell whether the ordered pair is a solution of the system of inequalities.

1. $(3, 0)$ yes

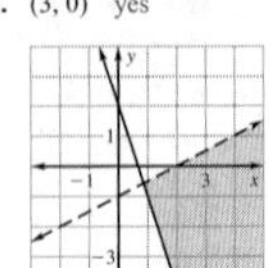

2. $(2, 2)$ yes

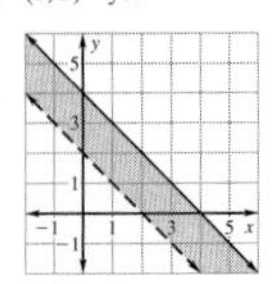

3. $(-2, 2)$ no

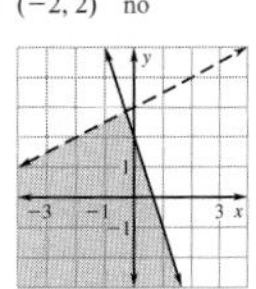

Match the system of inequalities with its graph.

4. $\frac{1}{2}x + y \geq 3$ B
$x > -1$

5. $y - \frac{1}{2}x \leq 3$ A
$x < -1$

6. $y \leq \frac{1}{2}x + 3$ C
$x > -1$

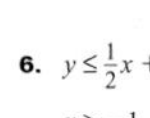

A.

B.

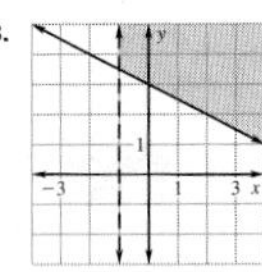

C.

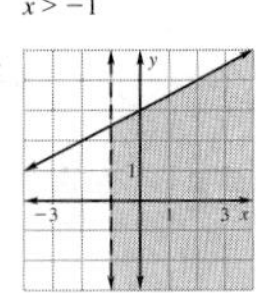

Graph the system of inequalities.

7. $x > -1$
$x < 1$

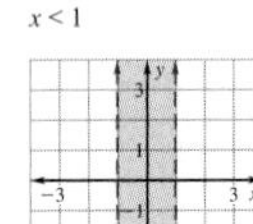

8. $y \geq 2$
$y < 3$

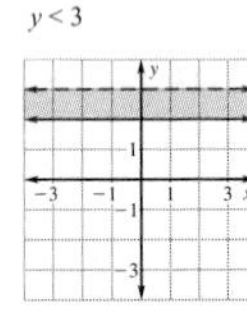

9. $x + y > 1$
$x \leq y$

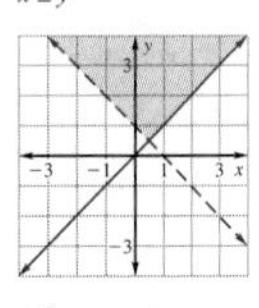

10. $x \geq y + 2$
$2x + y < 4$

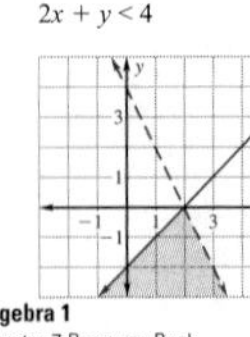

11. $y \geq 2$
$x + y \leq -3$

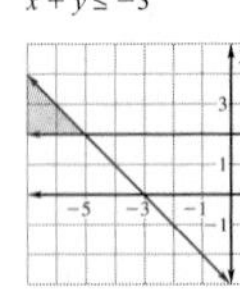

12. $x \leq -y$
$2x - y < 4$

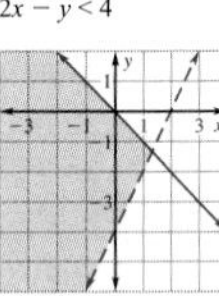

LESSON 7.6 **Practice B** *continued*
For use with pages 466–472

13. $y \geq -4$ and $y < 1$ 14. $x \geq -4$ and $y < -3$
15. $y \geq x + 1$ and $x \leq 0$ 16. $y \leq 4 - x$ and $y > 2$
17. $y \leq x$ and $y \leq 1 - x$ 18. $x \geq 0$, $y \geq 0$, and $y \leq x + 2$

Write a system of inequalities for the shaded region.

13.

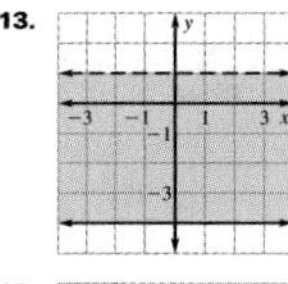

14.

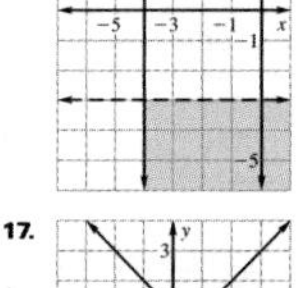

15.

16.

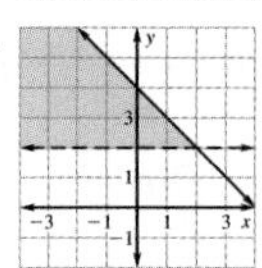

17.

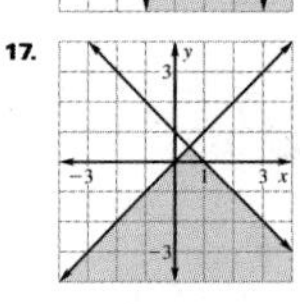

18.

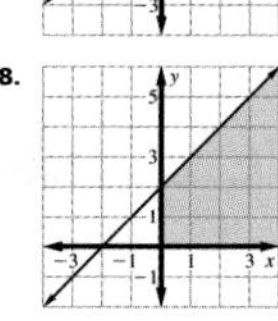

19. Cookout You are planning a cookout. You figure that you will need at least 5 packages of hot dogs and hamburgers. A package of hot dogs costs \$1.90 and a package of hamburgers costs \$5.20. You can spend a maximum of \$20 on the hot dogs and hamburgers.

a. Let x represent the number of packages of hot dogs and let y represent the number of packages of hamburgers. Write a system of linear inequalities for the number of packages of each that can be bought. $x + y \geq 5$ and $1.9x + 5.2y \leq 20$

b. Graph the system of inequalities.

c. Identify two possible combinations of packages of hot dogs and hamburgers you can buy. Answers will vary.

20. Chores You need at least 4 hours to do your chores, which are cleaning out the garage and weeding the flower beds around your house. It is 1:30 P.M. on Sunday and your friend wants you to go to the movies at 7:00 P.M.

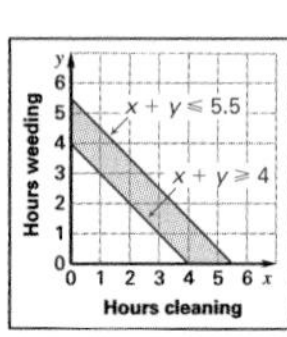

a. How much time do you have between now and 7:00 P.M. to do your chores? 5.5 h

b. Let x represent the number of hours spent cleaning out the garage and let y represent the number of hours spent on weeding the flower beds. Write and graph a system of linear inequalities that shows the number of hours you can work on each chore if you go to the movies.

c. Identify two possible combinations of time you can spend on each chore. Answers will vary.

CHAPTER 7 Quiz 1
For use after Lessons 7.1–7.2

Solve the linear system by graphing. Check your solution.

1. $x - y = 1$
   $x + y = -5$

2. $x - 4y = 10$
   $2x + y = 2$

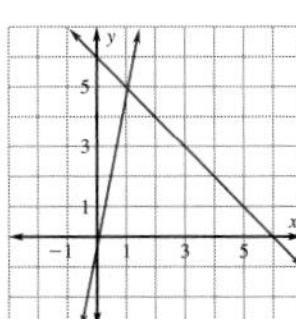

3. $-5x + y = 0$
   $x + y = 6$

Solve the linear system using substitution.

4. $y = 6 - 2x$
   $7x - y = 3$
5. $x = y - 4$
   $3x + y = 12$
6. $y - 5 = x$
   $4x - y = 4$
7. $y - 2x = -6$
   $5x - y = 9$
8. $3y + x = 2$
   $y - x = -6$

Answers

1. $(-2, -3)$
   See left.
2. $(2, -2)$
   See left.
3. $(1, 5)$
   See left.
4. $(1, 4)$
5. $(2, 6)$
6. $(3, 8)$
7. $(1, -4)$
8. $(5, -1)$

CHAPTER 7 Quiz 2
For use after Lessons 7.3–7.4

Solve the linear system using elimination.

1. $5x + y = 4$
   $6x - y = 7$
2. $-3x + 4y = 2$
   $3x + y = 8$
3. $x + 3y = 14$
   $x + 2y = 10$
4. $5x + 3y = 1$
   $5x + y = -3$
5. $6x - y = 8$
   $7x - y = 9$
6. $x - 2y = 8$
   $4x + y = 5$
7. $7x + y = 11$
   $4x + 2y = 12$
8. $3x + y = 10$
   $5x - 2y = 13$

Answers

1. $(1, -1)$
2. $(2, 2)$
3. $(2, 4)$
4. $(-1, 2)$
5. $(1, -2)$
6. $(2, -3)$
7. $(1, 4)$
8. $(3, 1)$

CHAPTER 7 Quiz 3
For use after Lessons 7.5–7.6

Graph the linear system. Then use the graph to tell whether the linear system has *one solution, no solution,* or *infinitely many solutions.*

1. $3y - 7x = -4$
   $3y - 2x = 1$

2. $-8x + 2y = -16$
   $4x - y = 10$

3. $3x + y = 2$
   $-9x - 3y = -6$

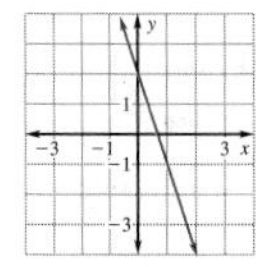

Graph the system of inequalities.

4. $x > 2$
   $y < 3$

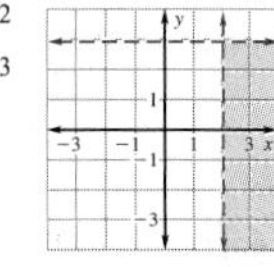

5. $y \leq x + 2$
   $y \geq 1$

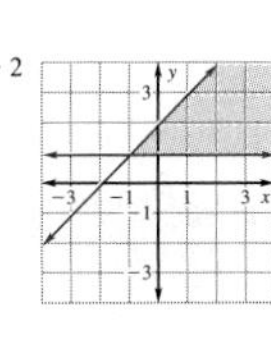

6. $x \geq 0$
   $y > 3x$

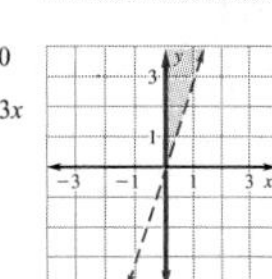

7. $y \leq -x$
   $y > 1$
   $x < -1$

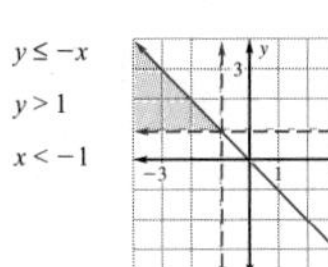

Answers

1. See left.
   one solution
2. See left.
   no solution
3. See left.
   infinitely many solutions
4. See left.
5. See left.
6. See left.
7. See left.

7 Assessment

Chapter Test B

CHAPTER 7 — *For use after Chapter 7*

Tell whether the ordered pair is a solution of the linear system.

1. (4, –1)
$x + 2y = 2$
$x - 2y = 6$

2. (8, 5)
$5x - 4y = 20$
$3y = 2x + 1$

3. (–3, 5)
$9x + 7y = 8$
$8x - 9y = -69$

In Exercises 4–6, use the following information.

Tickets for a school play cost $4 for adults and $2 for students. At the end of the play, the school sold a total of 105 tickets and collected $360.

4. Write a linear system. Let x be the number of adult tickets sold and let y be the number of student tickets sold.

5. Graph the linear system.

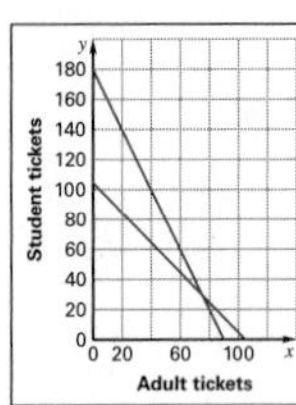

6. Find the number of adult tickets sold and the number of student tickets sold.

Solve the linear system using substitution.

7. $4x + 3y = -5$
$x = y - 3$

8. $x + 3y = -28$
$y = -5x$

9. $x + 4y = -1$
$2x - 5y = 11$

10. $3x + y = -4$
$2x + y = 0$

11. $3x - y = 13$
$2x + 5y = 20$

12. $x - 4y = -3$
$-3x + 5y = 2$

13. A hotel rents a double-occupancy room for $30 more than a single-occupancy room. One night, the hotel took in $3115 after renting 15 double-occupancy rooms and 26 single-occupancy rooms. Write and solve a linear system to find the cost of renting a double-occupancy room and the cost of renting a single-occupancy room.

Answers

1. yes
2. no
3. yes
4. $x + y = 105,$ $4x + 2y = 360$
5. See left.
6. 75 adult tickets and 30 student tickets
7. $(-2, 1)$
8. $(2, -10)$
9. $(3, -1)$
10. $(-4, 8)$
11. $(5, 2)$
12. $(1, 1)$
13. $y = x + 30,$ $26x + 15y = 3115;$ $65 for a single-occupancy room and $95 for a double-occupancy room

Chapter Test B *continued*

CHAPTER 7 — *For use after Chapter 7*

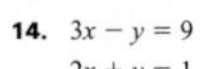

Solve the linear system using elimination.

14. $3x - y = 9$
$2x + y = 1$

15. $5x + 7y = 10$
$3x - 14y = 6$

16. $4x + 3y = 15$
$2x - 5y = 1$

17. $2x + 3y = 1$
$3x - 5y = -8$

18. $2x - 3y = -2$
$-2y + 3x = 12$

19. $2x + 9y = 16$
$5x = 1 - 3y$

Without solving the linear system, tell whether the linear system has *one solution, no solution,* or *infinitely many solutions.*

20. $y = 2 - 3x$
$6x + 2y = 7$

21. $y = x + 2$
$x + y = 6$

22. $2x - y = 1$
$4x - 2y = 2$

23. On Monday, the office staff at your school paid $8.77 for 4 cups of coffee and 7 bagels. On Wednesday, they paid $15.80 for 8 cups of coffee and 14 bagels. Can you determine the cost of a bagel? Explain.

Graph the system of linear inequalities.

24. $y \geq x - 3$
$y \leq -x + 2$

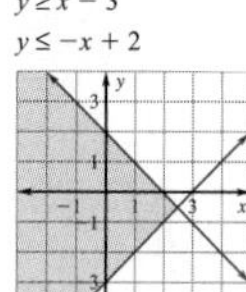

25. $x < 3$
$y > 1$
$y \geq -x$

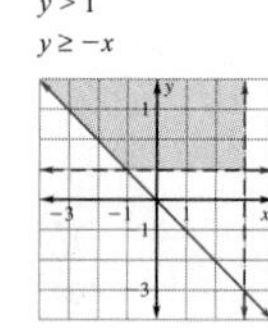

26. In an academic competition, scoring is based on a written examination and an oral presentation. The written examination score cannot exceed 65 points and the oral presentation cannot exceed 35 points. Write and graph a system of inequalities for the scores a school team can receive.

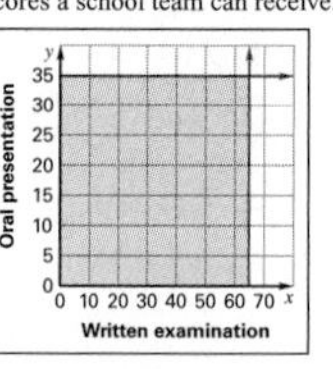

Answers

14. $(2, -3)$
15. $(2, 0)$
16. $(3, 1)$
17. $(-1, 1)$
18. $(8, 6)$
19. $(-1, 2)$
20. no solution
21. one solution
22. infinitely many solutions
23. There is no solution, so you cannot determine the cost of a bagel.
24. See left.
25. See left.
26. $x \geq 0, y \geq 0,$ $x \leq 65, y \leq 35$ See left.

Standardized Test

CHAPTER 7 — *For use after Chapter 7*

Multiple Choice

1. Which ordered pair is a solution of the linear system $x + y = -3$ and $2x - 3y = -16$? D

Ⓐ $(-8, 5)$ Ⓑ $(-2, 4)$
Ⓒ $(-2, -1)$ Ⓓ $(-5, 2)$

2. Which ordered pair is a solution of the linear system $5x + 2y = 29$ and $8x - 8y = 80$? B

Ⓐ $(5, 2)$ Ⓑ $(7, -3)$
Ⓒ $(10, 0)$ Ⓓ $(1, 12)$

3. Which ordered pair is a solution of the linear system shown? A

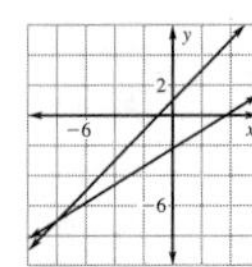

Ⓐ $(-8, -7)$ Ⓑ $(7, 2)$
Ⓒ $(-7, -8)$ Ⓓ $(2, 7)$

4. Which ordered pair is a solution of the linear system $y - x = 2$ and $5x + 4y = 30.5$? B

Ⓐ $(3, 5)$ Ⓑ $(2.5, 4.5)$
Ⓒ $(5.2, 7.2)$ Ⓓ $(2.1, 5)$

5. Which ordered pair is a solution of the linear system $6x - 3y = 2$ and $2x - 9y = -2$? D

Ⓐ $\left(1, \frac{4}{3}\right)$ Ⓑ $(8, 2)$
Ⓒ $\left(\frac{10}{3}, 6\right)$ Ⓓ $\left(\frac{1}{2}, \frac{1}{3}\right)$

6. Which step below contains an error in solving the linear system $2x + y = 10$ and $5y - 6x = 2$? B

Step 1
$2x + y = 10$
$y = 10 - 2x$

Step 2
$5(10 - 2x) - 6x = 2$
$50 - 10x - 6x = 2$
$50 - 4x = 2$
$48 = 4x$
$12 = x$

Step 3
$2(12) + y = 10$
$24 + y = 10$
$y = -14$

Step 4
$(12, -14)$

Ⓐ Step 1 Ⓑ Step 2
Ⓒ Step 3 Ⓓ Step 4

7. Which ordered pair is a solution of the linear system $5x + 3y = 22$ and $4x - 3y = -4$? C

Ⓐ $(5, -1)$ Ⓑ $(-1, 0)$
Ⓒ $(2, 4)$ Ⓓ $(8, -6)$

8. Which of the linear systems has *exactly* one solution? A

Ⓐ $5x + 3y = -22$, $4x - 5y = 12$ Ⓑ $2x + 3y = 45$, $2y + \frac{4}{3}x = 30$
Ⓒ $2x - 3y = -15$, $\frac{2}{3}x - y = 3$ Ⓓ $x + y = 2$, $\frac{1}{2}x + \frac{1}{2}y = 1$

9. Which of the linear systems has no solution? C

Ⓐ $5x + 3y = -22$, $4x - 5y = 12$ Ⓑ $2x + 3y = 45$, $2y + \frac{4}{3}x = 30$
Ⓒ $2x - 3y = -15$, $\frac{2}{3}x - y = 3$ Ⓓ $x + y = 2$, $\frac{1}{2}x + \frac{1}{2}y = 1$

Standardized Test *continued*

CHAPTER 7 — *For use after Chapter 7*

10. Which ordered pair is a solution of the system $x < 5$ and $x + 2y \geq 1$? D

Ⓐ $(4, -2)$ Ⓑ $(8, 2)$
Ⓒ $(1, -1)$ Ⓓ $(4, 5)$

11. The graph of which system of inequalities is shown? C

Ⓐ $y \leq \frac{1}{2}x$, $4x + 2y < 8$ Ⓑ $y \leq \frac{1}{2}x$, $4x + 2y > 8$
Ⓒ $y \geq \frac{1}{2}x$, $4x + 2y < 8$ Ⓓ $y \geq \frac{1}{2}x$, $4x + 2y > 8$

Gridded Answer

12. What is the x-coordinate of the solution of the system whose graph is shown?

1

Short Response

13. Use the linear system below.

$3x + 8y = 32$
$y = -\frac{3}{8}x + m$

$m = 4$

a. Find a value for m so that the linear system has infinitely many solutions.

b. Is it possible to find a value for m so that the linear system has exactly one solution? *Explain.* See below.

Extended Response

14. The owner of a car wash combines x gallons of a 2% liquid soap and 98% water mix with y gallons of a 7% liquid soap and 93% water mix to make 500 gallons of a 5% liquid soap and 95% water mix. See below.

a. Write a system of linear equations that represents the situation.

b. How many fluid ounces of the 2% liquid soap and 98% water mix and the 7% liquid soap and 93% water mix did the car wash owner combine to make 500 gallons of the 5% liquid soap and 95% water mix?

c. Suppose the car wash owner combines pure (100%) water and the 7% liquid soap and 93% water mix to make the 500 gallons of the 5% liquid soap and 95% water mix. Is more of the 7% liquid soap and 93% water mix used in this mix than in the original mix? *Explain.*

13. b. No; because the lines have the same slope, they are parallel. Therefore, there will never be exactly one solution.

14. a. $x + y = 500$ and $0.02x + 0.07y = 25$ **b.** The car wash owner would use 200 gallons of the 2% liquid soap and 98% water solution and 300 gallons of the 7% liquid soap and 93% water solution. **c.** The car wash owner would use more of the 7% liquid soap and 93% water mix than in the original mix because in the original mix the other solution contained soap. In the new mix, there is no soap being added to the 7% liquid soap and 93% water mix.

Alternative Assessment and Math Journal

For use after Chapter 7

Journal

1. There are three different categories for the number of solutions to a system of two linear equations. Name each category and describe the graph of the system for each case.

Multi-Step Problem

2. Last week a football team ran a total of 108 offensive plays. There were twice as many running plays as passing plays.

a. Write a system of equations to represent this information given that x is the number of running plays and y is the number of passing plays.

b. Use the graphing method to solve the system in part (a).

c. Use the method of substitution to solve the system in part (a) and compare this answer to the one that resulted from your work in part (b). Are the solutions the same?

d. How many offensive plays were running plays last week?

e. The team sets some offensive goals for the next game. The first goal is to execute a total of at least 80 offensive plays, and the second goal is to gain at least 360 offensive yards. The team averages 3 yards on each running play and 7 yards on each passing play. The system of inequalities used to model this situation is

$$x + y \geq 80$$
$$3x + 7y \geq 360$$
$$x \geq 0$$
$$y \geq 0$$

Graph this system of inequalities.

f. Give 3 solutions to this system.

g. Suppose the team decided to also set a goal of having more running plays than passing plays. Write an inequality to represent this new goal.

h. Add the graph of the inequality for the new goal to the graph in part (e).

1. Complete answers should include: mention of all three categories for the number of solutions to a system of two linear equations (one solution, no solution, infinitely many solutions); a description of the graph of the system as intersecting, parallel, or coincidental lines.

2. a. $x + y = 108$
$x = 2y$

b. 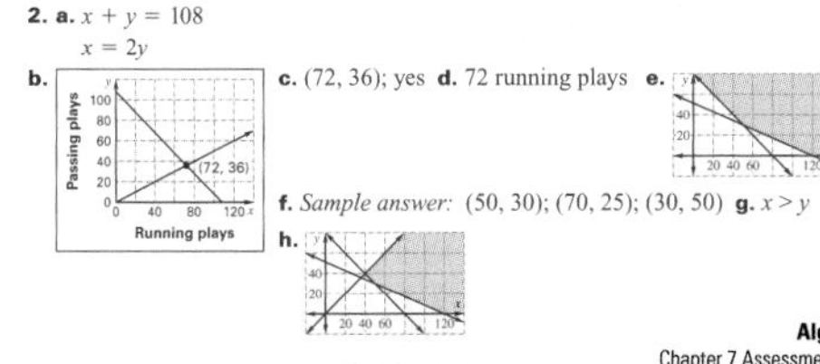
c. (72, 36); yes **d.** 72 running plays **e.**
f. *Sample answer:* (50, 30); (70, 25); (30, 50) **g.** $x > y$
h.

Alternative Assessment Rubric *continued*

For use after Chapter 7

Journal Solution

1. Complete answers should include:

- mention of all three categories for the number of solutions to a system of two linear equations (one solution, no solution, infinitely many solutions).
- a description of the graph of the system as intersecting, parallel, or coincidental lines.

Multi-Step Problem Solution

2. a. $x + y = 108$
$x = 2y$

b.

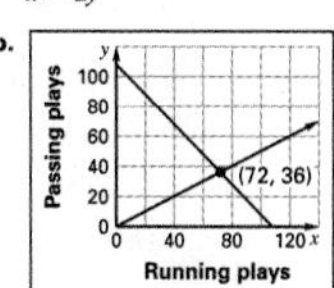

c. (72, 36); yes **d.** 72 running plays

e.

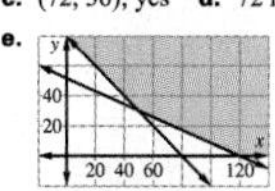

f. *Sample answer:* (50, 30); (70, 25); (30, 50)

g. $x > y$

h.

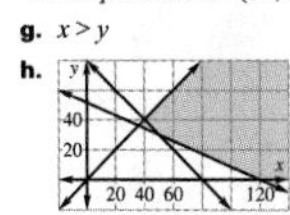

Multi-Step Problem Rubric

4 The student answers all parts of the problem correctly and completely. The student shows all work. The student's work is neat.

3 The student answers all parts of the problem. The student's work may contain one or two errors in the calculations, equations, or graphs. The student shows most work. The student's work is neat.

2 The student answers all parts of the problem, but there are more than two errors in the calculations, equations, or graphs. The student shows some work. The student's work is sloppy.

1 The student does not complete all parts of the problem. The student's work has several errors in the calculations, equations, and graphs. The student's work is sloppy, or no work is shown.

PLAN AND PREPARE

Main Ideas

In Chapter 7, students use graphing, substitution, and elimination to solve systems of linear equations. When solving by the elimination method, they either add or subtract, or they multiply first and then add or subtract. Students identify linear systems as having one solution, no solution, or infinitely many solutions. Students solve systems of linear inequalities.

Prerequisite Skills

Skills Readiness, available on the *Easy Planner*, provides review and practice for the Skills Check portion of the Prerequisite Skills quiz.

How student answers the exercises	What to assign from *Skills Readiness*
Any of Exs. 3–6 answered incorrectly	**Skill 75** Graph linear equations
Any of Exs. 7–8 answered incorrectly	**Skill 69** Solve multi-step equations
Any of Exs. 9–12 answered incorrectly	**Skill 76** Determine whether graphs of lines are parallel
Any of Exs. 13–16 answered incorrectly	**Skill 74** Solve inequalities
All exercises answered correctly	Chapter 3 Enrichment

Additional skill review and practice is available in the Skills Review Handbook, pp. 909–937, and the @HomeTutor.

7 Systems of Equations and Inequalities

Making Sense of Chapter 7

In this chapter, you will put to use what you learned in Chapters 3–6. By the end of this chapter, you will be able to write and solve systems of linear equations and inequalities.

Before

Previously, you learned the following skills, which you'll use in Chapter 7: graphing linear equations, solving equations, and graphing inequalities.

Prerequisite Skills

VOCABULARY CHECK

Copy and complete the statement.

1. The least common multiple of 10 and 15 is _?_. **30**
2. Two lines in the same plane are _?_ if they do not intersect. **parallel**

SKILLS CHECK

Graph the equation. *(Prerequisite skill for 7.1)* **3–6. See margin.**

3. $x - y = 4$ 4. $6x - y = -1$ 5. $4x + 5y = 20$ 6. $3x - 2y = -12$

Solve the equation. *(Prerequisite skill for 7.2–7.4)*

7. $5m + 4 - m = 20$ **4** 8. $10(z + 5) + z = 6$ **–4**

Tell whether the graphs of the two equations are parallel lines. *Explain* your reasoning. *(Prerequisite skill for 7.5)* **9–12. See margin.**

9. $y = 2x - 3, y + 2x = -3$
10. $y - 5x = -1, y - 5x = 1$
11. $y = x + 10, x - y = -9$
12. $6x - y = 4, 4x - y = 6$

Solve the inequality. Graph the solution. *(Prerequisite skill for 7.6)* **13–16. See margin.**

13. $m + 4 > 9$ 14. $-6t \geq 24$ 15. $2x - 5 \leq 13$ 16. $-5y + 1 < -14$

@HomeTutor Prerequisite skills practice at classzone.com

Chapter Planning Guide

Chapter Resource Book
- Teaching Guide/Lesson Plan
- Project with Rubric

Assessment and Intervention
- Assessment Book
- Benchmark Tests
- Remediation Book
- Skills Readiness

Interactive Technology
- Easy Planner
- Power Presentations
- Activity Generator
- Animated Algebra
- Test Generator
- Online Quizzes
- eWorkbook
- eEdition
- @HomeTutor

Resources for English Learners
- Spanish Study Guide
- Multi-Language Visual Glossary
- Student Resources in Spanish

Now

In Chapter 7, you will apply the big ideas listed below and reviewed in the Chapter Summary on page 474. You will also use the key vocabulary listed below.

Big Ideas

1. **Solving linear systems by graphing**
2. **Solving linear systems using algebra**
3. **Solving systems of linear inequalities**

KEY VOCABULARY

- system of linear equations, *p. 427*
- solution of a system of linear equations, *p. 427*
- consistent independent system, *p. 427*
- inconsistent system, *p. 459*
- consistent dependent system, *p. 459*
- system of linear inequalities, *p. 466*
- solution of a system of linear inequalities, *p. 466*
- graph of a system of linear inequalities, *p. 466*

Why?

You can use a system of linear equations to solve problems about traveling with and against a current. For example, you can write and solve a system of linear equations to find the average speed of a kayak in still water.

Animated Algebra

The animation illustrated below for Example 4 on page 446 helps you answer this question: What is the average speed of the kayak in still water?

Start
You have to find the speed of the kayak in still water.

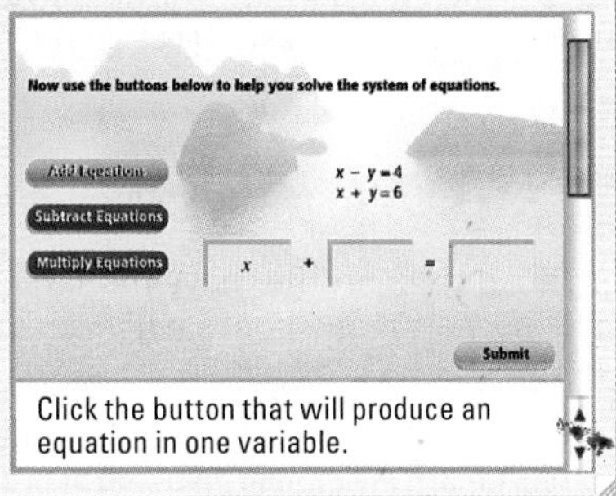

Animated Algebra at classzone.com

Other animations for Chapter 7: pages 428, 435, 441, 446, 452, 459, and 466

Differentiated Instruction Resources

- Reading Strategies for Chapter 7
- Differentiated Instruction Lesson Notes
- English Learners Lesson Notes
- Inclusion Lesson Notes
- Teaching Strategies with Sample Worksheets
- Using Technology in the Classroom
- Tips for New Teachers
- Math Background Notes
- Assessment Strategies
- Teacher Survival Activities
- Bulletin Board Idea

6. 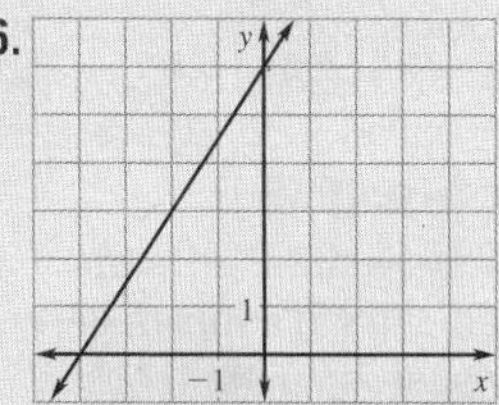

9. Not parallel; the slope of the graph of the first equation is 2, while the slope of the graph of the second equation is −2.

10. Parallel; the 2 lines have a slope of 5, but different *y*-intercepts.

11. Parallel; the 2 lines have a slope of 1, but different *y*-intercepts.

12. Not parallel; the slope of the graph of the first equation is 6, while the slope of the graph of the second equation is 4.

13. $m > 5$

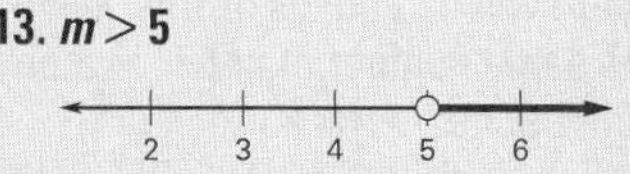

14. $t \le -4$

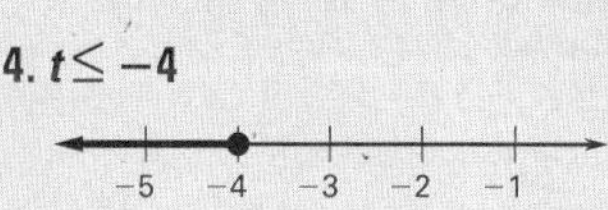

15. $x \le 9$

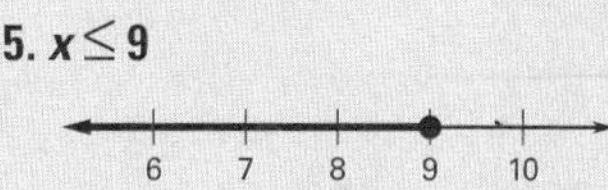

16. $y > 3$

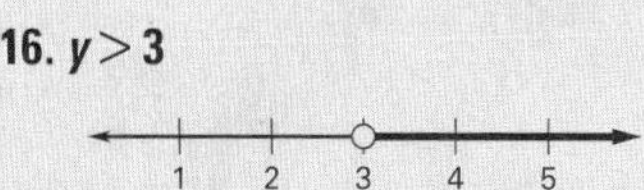

3. 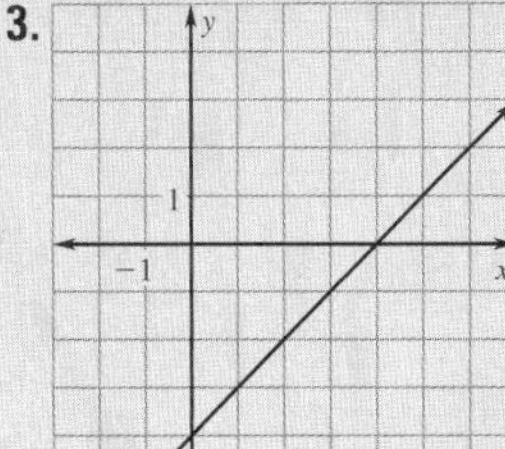

4. 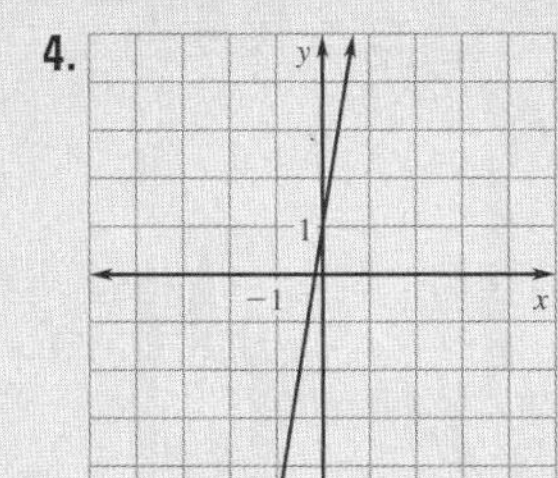

5. 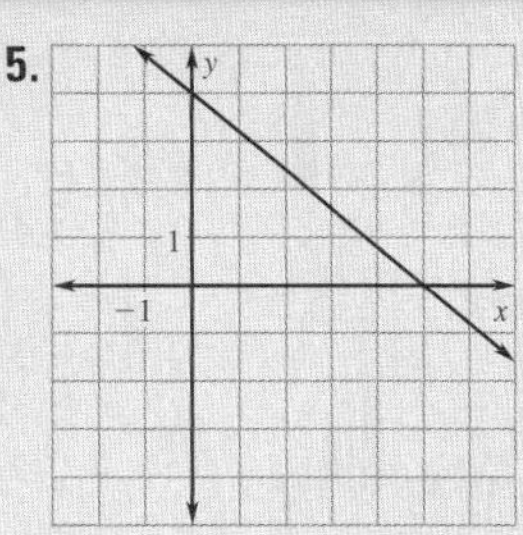

1 PLAN AND PREPARE

Explore the Concept

- Students will use a table to solve a linear system.
- This activity leads into the study of solving linear systems by graphing in Example 1 in Lesson 7.1.

Recommended Time

Work activity: 15 min
Discuss results: 5 min

Grouping

Students should work individually.

2 TEACH

Tips for Success

Students may want to write the two ordered pairs in a fourth column as a visual reminder that the x-value is the same for both y-value columns.

Key Discovery

A solution of a linear system is an ordered pair that must satisfy each equation in the system.

3 ASSESS AND RETEACH

1. If Bill adds 3 books to his collection each month instead of 2, when will he and his brother have the same number of books in their collections? **after 8 mo**
2. Use a table to solve this linear system. **(−4, −16)**
   $y = 5x + 4$
   $y = 2x - 8$

7.1 Solving Linear Systems Using Tables

MATERIALS • pencil and paper

QUESTION **How can you use a table to solve a linear system?**

A *system of linear equations*, or *linear system*, consists of two or more linear equations in the same variables. A *solution of a linear system* is an ordered pair that satisfies each equation in the system. You can use a table to find a solution to a linear system.

EXPLORE **Solve a linear system**

Bill and his brother collect comic books. Bill currently has 15 books and adds 2 books to his collection every month. His brother currently has 7 books and adds 4 books to his collection every month. Use the equations below to find the number x of months after which Bill and his brother will have the same number y of comic books in their collections.

$y = 2x + 15$ Number of comic books in Bill's collection

$y = 4x + 7$ Number of comic books in his brother's collection

STEP 1 ***Make a table***
Copy and complete the table of values shown.

x	$y = 2x + 15$	$y = 4x + 7$
0	15	7
1	? 17	? 11
2	? 19	? 15
3	? 21	? 19
4	? 23	? 23
5	? 25	? 27

STEP 2 ***Find a solution***
Find an x-value that gives the same y-value for both equations. **4**

STEP 3 ***Interpret the solution***
Use your answer to Step 2 to find the number of months after which Bill and his brother have the same number of comic books. **4 mo**

DRAW CONCLUSIONS **Use your observations to complete these exercises**

1. When Bill and his brother have the same number of books in their collections, how many books will each of them have? **23 books**
2. Graph the equations above on the same coordinate plane. What do you notice about the graphs and the solution you found above?
   See margin for art; the graphs intersect at (4, 23), which is a solution of both equations.

Use a table to solve the linear system.

3. $y = 2x + 3$
   $y = -3x + 18$
   (3, 9)
4. $y = -x + 1$
   $y = 2x - 5$
   (2, −1)
5. $y = -3x + 1$
   $y = 5x - 31$
   (4, −11)

2.
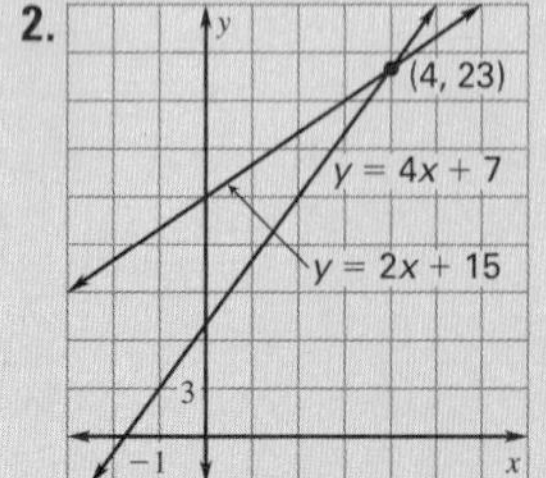

7.1 Solve Linear Systems by Graphing

Before	You graphed linear equations.
Now	You will graph and solve systems of linear equations.
Why?	So you can analyze craft fair sales, as in Ex. 33.

Key Vocabulary
- **system of linear equations**
- **solution of a system of linear equations**
- **consistent independent system**

A **system of linear equations,** or simply a *linear system,* consists of two or more linear equations in the same variables. An example is shown below.

$x + 2y = 7$ **Equation 1**

$3x - 2y = 5$ **Equation 2**

A **solution of a system of linear equations** in two variables is an ordered pair that satisfies each equation in the system.

One way to find the solution of a linear system is by graphing. If the lines intersect in a single point, then the coordinates of the point are the solution of the linear system. A solution found using graphical methods should be checked algebraically.

EXAMPLE 1 Check the intersection point

Use the graph to solve the system. Then check your solution algebraically.

$x + 2y = 7$ **Equation 1**

$3x - 2y = 5$ **Equation 2**

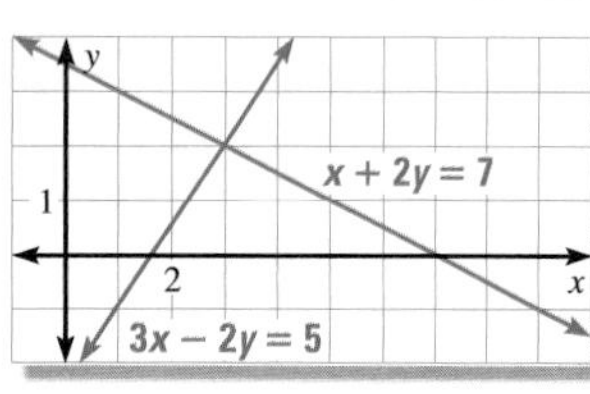

Solution

The lines appear to intersect at the point (3, 2).

CHECK Substitute 3 for x and 2 for y in each equation.

$x + 2y = 7$	$3x - 2y = 5$
$3 + 2(2) \stackrel{?}{=} 7$	$3(3) - 2(2) \stackrel{?}{=} 5$
$7 = 7$ ✓	$5 = 5$ ✓

▶ Because the ordered pair (3, 2) is a solution of each equation, it is a solution of the system.

TYPES OF LINEAR SYSTEMS In Example 1, the linear system has exactly one solution. A linear system that has exactly one solution is called a **consistent independent system** because the lines are distinct (are independent) and intersect (are consistent). You will solve consistent independent systems in Lessons 7.1–7.4. In Lesson 7.5 you will consider other types of systems.

1 PLAN AND PREPARE

Warm-Up Exercises

Transparency Available

1. Graph the equation $-2x + y = 1$.

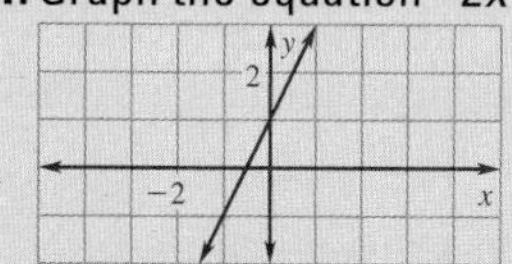

2. It takes 3 hours to mow a lawn and 2 hours to trim hedges. You spend 16 hours doing yard work. What are two possible numbers of lawns you mowed and hedges you trimmed? **2 lawns and 5 hedges, or 4 lawns and 2 hedges**

Notetaking Guide

Transparency Available

Promotes interactive learning and notetaking skills.

Pacing

Basic: 1 day
Average: 1 day
Advanced: 1 day
Block: 0.5 block with 7.2
- See *Teaching Guide/Lesson Plan.*

2 FOCUS AND MOTIVATE

Essential Question

Big Idea 1, p. 425

How do you solve systems of linear equations by graphing? **Tell students they will learn how to answer this question by graphing the equations in the same coordinate plane.**

NCTM STANDARDS

Standard 2: Use models to understand relationships

Standard 9: Use connections among mathematical ideas

Resource Planning Guide

Chapter Resource Book
- Teaching Guide/Lesson Plan
- Activity Master
- Practice levels A, B, C
- Study Guide
- Catch-up for Absent Students
- Problem Solving Workshop
- Challenge

Workbooks
- Notetaking Guide
- Practice Workbook

Teaching Options
- **Power Presentations** provides dynamic electronic teaching resources for the classroom.
- **Activity Generator** provides editable activities for all ability levels.

Interactive Technology
- Easy Planner
- Power Presentations
- Activity Generator
- Animated Algebra
- Test Generator
- Online Quiz
- eWorkbook
- eEdition
- @HomeTutor

Resources for English Learners
- Spanish Study Guide
- Multi-Language Visual Glossary
- Student Resources in Spanish

See also the *Differentiated Instruction Resources* for more strategies for meeting individual needs.

Motivating the Lesson

You raised $260 for the swim team selling calendars and desk planners. You know you sold 22 items and that the calendars are $15 each and the planners are $8 each. By knowing how to solve a system of linear equations, you can determine how many calendars and desk planners you sold.

3 TEACH

Extra Example 1

Use the graph to solve the system. Then check your solution algebraically.

$2x + 5y = 7$
$-x + 2y = -8$ **(6, −1)**

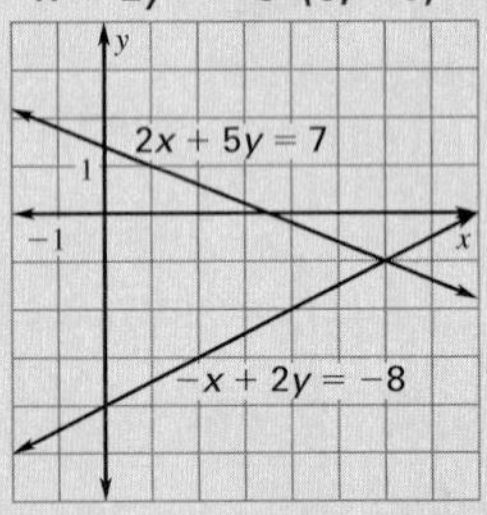

Key Question to Ask for Example 1

- Why is it a good idea to check a solution algebraically? **An algebraic check confirms that you read the point of intersection correctly.**

Extra Example 2

Solve the linear system by graphing.

$-x + y = 5$
$2x + y = 8$ **(1, 6)**

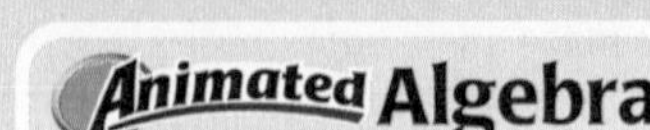

An **Animated Algebra** activity is available online for **Example 2**. This activity is also part of **Power Presentations**.

KEY CONCEPT *For Your Notebook*

Solving a Linear System Using the Graph-and-Check Method

STEP 1 **Graph** both equations in the same coordinate plane. For ease of graphing, you may want to write each equation in slope-intercept form.

STEP 2 **Estimate** the coordinates of the point of intersection.

STEP 3 **Check** the coordinates algebraically by substituting into each equation of the original linear system.

EXAMPLE 2 Use the graph-and-check method

Solve the linear system: $-x + y = -7$ Equation 1
$x + 4y = -8$ Equation 2

Solution

STEP 1 **Graph** both equations.

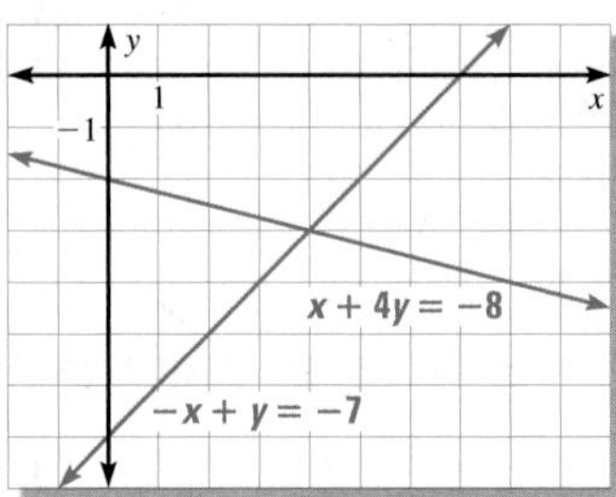

STEP 2 **Estimate** the point of intersection. The two lines appear to intersect at (4, −3).

STEP 3 **Check** whether (4, −3) is a solution by substituting 4 for *x* and −3 for *y* in each of the original equations.

Equation 1	Equation 2
$-x + y = -7$	$x + 4y = -8$
$-(4) + (-3) \stackrel{?}{=} -7$	$4 + 4(-3) \stackrel{?}{=} -8$
$-7 = -7$ ✓	$-8 = -8$ ✓

▶ Because (4, −3) is a solution of each equation, it is a solution of the linear system.

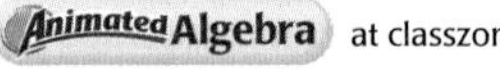 at classzone.com

 **GUIDED PRACTICE** for Examples 1 and 2

Solve the linear system by graphing. Check your solution.

1. $-5x + y = 0$ **(1, 5)**
   $5x + y = 10$
2. $-x + 2y = 3$ **(1, 2)**
   $2x + y = 4$
3. $x - y = 5$ **(2, −3)**
   $3x + y = 3$

Differentiated Instruction

Below Level Some students may need help graphing linear systems. In **Example 2** and **Guided Practice Exercises 1–3**, remind students that they can solve the equation for *y* to give the slope-intercept form of the equation. They can then plot the point for the *y*-intercept, use the slope to find another point, and then draw a line through the points. If they prefer, they can make a table of values for the equations, plot the points, and then draw a line through the points.

See also the *Differentiated Instruction Resources* for more strategies.

 EXAMPLE 3 **Standardized Test Practice**

The parks and recreation department in your town offers a season pass for $90.

- As a season pass holder, you pay $4 per session to use the town's tennis courts.
- Without the season pass, you pay $13 per session to use the tennis courts.

Which system of equations can be used to find the number x of sessions of tennis after which the total cost y with a season pass, including the cost of the pass, is the same as the total cost without a season pass?

ELIMINATE CHOICES
You can eliminate choice A because neither of the equations include the cost of a season pass.

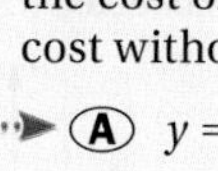

Ⓐ $y = 4x$, $y = 13x$ Ⓑ $y = 4x$, $y = 90 + 13x$

Ⓒ $y = 13x$, $y = 90 + 4x$ Ⓓ $y = 90 + 4x$, $y = 90 + 13x$

Solution

Write a system of equations where y is the total cost (in dollars) for x sessions.

EQUATION 1

Total cost (dollars)	=	Cost per session (dollars/session)	·	Number of sessions (sessions)
y	=	13	·	x

EQUATION 2

Total cost (dollars)	=	Cost for season pass (dollars)	+	Cost per session (dollars/session)	·	Number of sessions (sessions)
y	=	90	+	4	·	x

▶ The correct answer is C. Ⓐ Ⓑ Ⓒ Ⓓ

✓ **GUIDED PRACTICE** for Example 3

4. Solve the linear system in Example 3 to find the number of sessions after which the total cost with a season pass, including the cost of the pass, is the same as the total cost without a season pass. **10 sessions**

5. **WHAT IF?** In Example 3, suppose a season pass costs $135. After how many sessions is the total cost with a season pass, including the cost of the pass, the same as the total cost without a season pass? **15 sessions**

Extra Example 3

The cost to join an art museum is $60. If you are a member, you can take lessons at the museum for $2 each. If you are not a member, lessons cost $6 each. Which system of equations can be used to find the number x of lessons after which the total cost y of lessons with a membership is the same as the total cost of lessons without a membership? **D**

Ⓐ $y = 2x$, $y = 6x$ Ⓑ $y = 60x + 2$, $y = 6x$

Ⓒ $y = 2x + 60$, $y = 6x + 60$ Ⓓ $y = 2x + 60$, $y = 6x$

Key Questions to Ask for Example 3

- Why is it possible to eliminate choice D? Explain. **Both equations include the cost of a season pass.**
- How would a graph of the system of equations in Example 3 be different from the graph of the system of equations in Example 2? **The graph in Example 3 would be restricted to Quadrant I, since the costs would be positive numbers only.**

Differentiated Instruction

English Learners Make mathematical language easier to understand by using more common terms. In **Example 2**, tell students that the coordinates of the intersecting lines "agree" at one point. Mathematicians might say that the two lines are "consistent" at that point. In ordinary language, to be consistent means to be in agreement.

See also the *Differentiated Instruction Resources* for more strategies.

Extra Example 4

Your school is selling football tickets for a home game. The school sold 35 tickets for $86 on the first day of the sale. Student tickets cost $2 each and non-student tickets cost $3 each. Find the number of student tickets and the number of non-student tickets the school sold. **19 student tickets and 16 non-student tickets**

Key Question to Ask for Example 4

- What does the ordered pair (20, 5) represent? **20 pairs of skates and 5 bicycles**

Closing the Lesson

Have students summarize the major points of the lesson and answer the Essential Question: How do you solve systems of linear equations by graphing?

- **You can find the solution of a linear system by graphing both equations in the same coordinate plane.**

Graph the equations in the linear system in the same coordinate plane. The point of intersection is the solution of the system. Check the solution by substituting the coordinates of the point into each equation of the original system.

EXAMPLE 4 Solve a multi-step problem

RENTAL BUSINESS A business rents in-line skates and bicycles. During one day, the business has a total of 25 rentals and collects $450 for the rentals. Find the number of pairs of skates rented and the number of bicycles rented.

Solution

STEP 1 **Write** a linear system. Let x be the number of pairs of skates rented, and let y be the number of bicycles rented.

$x + y = 25$ — Equation for number of rentals

$15x + 30y = 450$ — Equation for money collected from rentals

STEP 2 **Graph** both equations.

STEP 3 **Estimate** the point of intersection. The two lines appear to intersect at (20, 5).

STEP 4 **Check** whether (20, 5) is a solution.

$20 + 5 \stackrel{?}{=} 25$ | $15(20) + 30(5) \stackrel{?}{=} 450$

$25 = 25$ ✓ | $450 = 450$ ✓

▶ The business rented 20 pairs of skates and 5 bicycles.

 **GUIDED PRACTICE** for Example 4

6. **WHAT IF?** In Example 4, suppose the business has a total of 20 rentals and collects $420. Find the number of bicycles rented. **8 bicycles**

7.1 EXERCISES

HOMEWORK KEY

○ = **WORKED-OUT SOLUTIONS** on p. WS16 for Exs. 15 and 31

★ = **STANDARDIZED TEST PRACTICE** Exs. 2, 6, 7, 27, 28, 29, and 32

◆ = **MULTIPLE REPRESENTATIONS** Ex. 35

SKILL PRACTICE

1. **VOCABULARY** Copy and complete: A(n) _?_ of a system of linear equations in two variables is an ordered pair that satisfies each equation in the system. **solution**

2. ★ **WRITING** *Explain* how to use the graph-and-check method to solve a linear system of two equations in two variables. **See margin.**

CHECKING SOLUTIONS Tell whether the ordered pair is a solution of the linear system.

3. (−3, 1); **solution**
$x + y = -2$
$x + 5y = 2$

4. (5, 2); **not a solution**
$2x - 3y = 4$
$2x + 8y = 11$

5. (−2, 1); **not a solution**
$6x + 5y = -7$
$x - 2y = 0$

2. ***Sample answer:*** **Graph both equations and then estimate the point at which the graphs intersect. Then check whether the point is a solution of each equation.**

EXAMPLE 1 on p. 427 for Exs. 6–11

6. ★ **MULTIPLE CHOICE** Which ordered pair is a solution of the linear system $x + y = -2$ and $7x - 4y = 8$? **B**

Ⓐ $(-2, 0)$ Ⓑ $(0, -2)$ Ⓒ $(2, 0)$ Ⓓ $(0, 2)$

7. ★ **MULTIPLE CHOICE** Which ordered pair is a solution of the linear system $2x + 3y = 12$ and $10x + 3y = -12$? **B**

Ⓐ $(-3, 3)$ Ⓑ $(-3, 6)$ Ⓒ $(3, 3)$ Ⓓ $(3, 6)$

SOLVING SYSTEMS GRAPHICALLY Use the graph to solve the linear system. Check your solution.

8. $x - y = 4$ **(1, −3)**
$4x + y = 1$

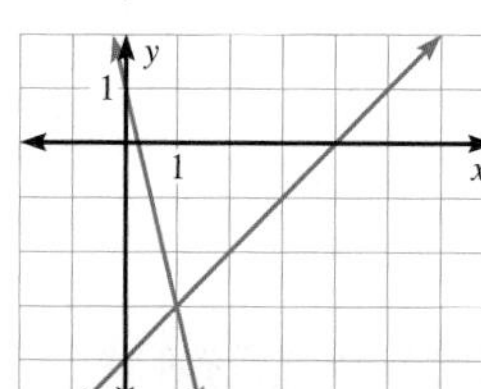

9. $-x + y = -2$ **(4, 2)**
$2x - y = 6$

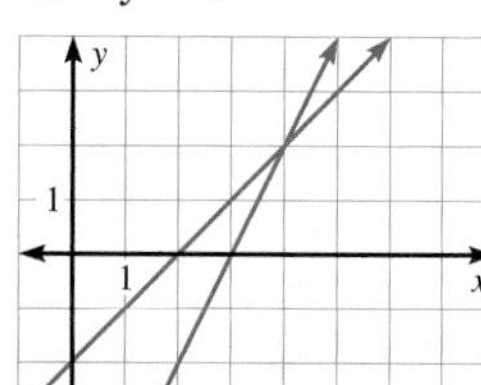

10. $x + y = 5$ **(3, 2)**
$-2x + y = -4$

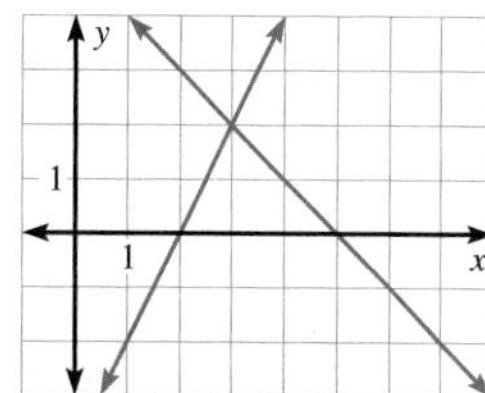

11. **ERROR ANALYSIS** *Describe* and correct the error in solving the linear system below.

$x - 3y = 6$ Equation 1
$2x - 3y = 3$ Equation 2

The solution is (3, −1).

The solution (3, −1) does not satisfy Equation 2. The graph of Equation 2 is incorrect; if properly graphed, the lines would intersect at (−3, −3); see margin for art.

EXAMPLE 2 B on p. 428 for Exs. 12–26

GRAPH-AND-CHECK METHOD Solve the linear system by graphing. Check your solution.

12. $y = -x + 3$ **(1, 2)**
$y = x + 1$

13. $y = -x + 4$ **(4, 0)**
$y = 2x - 8$

14. $y = 2x + 2$ **(−2, −2)**
$y = 4x + 6$

15. $x - y = 2$ **(−3, −5)**
$x + y = -8$

16. $x + 2y = 1$ **(1.8, −0.4)**
$-2x + y = -4$

17. $3x + y = 15$ **(10, −15)**
$y = -15$

18. $2x - 3y = -1$ **(4, 3)**
$5x + 2y = 26$

19. $6x + y = 37$ **(7, −5)**
$4x + 2y = 18$

20. $7x + 5y = -3$ **(1, −2)**
$-9x + y = -11$

21. $6x + 12y = -6$ **(−5, 2)**
$2x + 5y = 0$

22. $2x + y = 9$ **(3, 3)**
$2x + 3y = 15$

23. $-5x + 3y = 3$ **(3, 6)**
$4x + 3y = 30$

24. $\frac{3}{4}x + \frac{1}{4}y = \frac{13}{2}$ **(8, 2)**
$x - \frac{3}{4}y = \frac{13}{2}$

25. $\frac{1}{5}x - \frac{2}{5}y = -\frac{8}{5}$ **(4, 6)**
$-\frac{3}{4}x + y = 3$

26. $-1.6x - 3.2y = -24$ **(5, 5)**
$2.6x + 2.6y = 26$

27. ★ **OPEN-ENDED** Find values for m and b so that the system $y = \frac{3}{5}x - 1$ and $y = mx + b$ has (5, 2) as a solution. ***Sample answer:* m = 0 and b = 2**

28. ★ **WRITING** Solve the linear system shown by graphing. *Explain* why it is important to check your solution.

$y = 4x - 1.5$ Equation 1
$y = -2x + 1.5$ Equation 2

28. (0.5, 0.5). ***Sample answer:*** **It is important to check the solution because the lines do not intersect at integer values.**

4 PRACTICE AND APPLY

Assignment Guide

Answer Transparencies available for all exercises

Basic:
Day 1: EP p. 941 Exs. 19–22
pp. 430–433
Exs. 1–17, 31–34, 38–42 even, 43–48

Average:
Day 1: pp. 430–433
Exs. 1–11, 18–35, 37–41 odd, 43–48

Advanced:
Day 1: pp. 430–433
Exs. 1, 4–7, 9, 10, 21–36*, 38–48 even

Block:
pp. 430–433
Exs. 1–11, 18–35, 37–41 odd, 43–48 (with 7.2)

Differentiated Instruction

See *Differentiated Instruction Resources* for suggestions on addressing the needs of a diverse classroom.

Homework Check

For a quick check of student understanding of key concepts, go over the following exercises:

Basic: 8, 14, 16, 31, 32
Average: 9, 20, 21, 32, 33
Advanced: 10, 22, 24, 32, 33

Extra Practice

- Student Edition, p. 944
- Chapter Resource Book: Practice levels A, B, C

Practice Worksheet

An easily-readable reduced practice page (with answers) for this lesson can be found on p. 424C.

11.

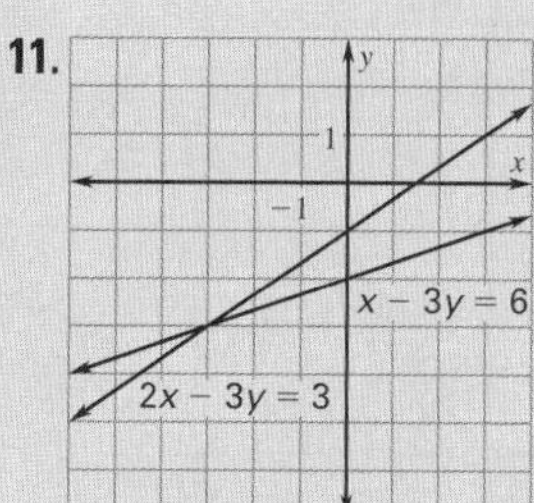

Avoiding Common Errors

Exercises 3–10 Some students may substitute the x- and y-coordinates of a solution into one equation of the linear system only. Remind these students that a solution of a linear system must satisfy both equations of the system.

Exercises 12–26 Some students may reverse the x- and y-coordinates in their solutions. Emphasize that checking their solutions will help correct such errors.

Reading Strategy

Exercises 15, 31 Remind students that there is a worked-out solution for exercises circled in red. Point out the Homework Key at the beginning of the exercises on page 430 and at the bottom of the page on page 432.

Teaching Strategy

Exercise 36 You may want to point out that 20% off of the purchase is the same as paying 80% of the purchase.

29d. ***Sample answer:*** **Set each side of the equation equal to y to create a system of two equations. Then solve the system using the graph-and-check method. The x-coordinate of the system's solution is the solution of the orginal equation.**

29. ★ EXTENDED RESPONSE Consider the equation $-\frac{1}{4}x + 6 = \frac{1}{2}x + 3$.

a. Solve the equation using algebra. **4**

b. Solve the linear system below using a graph. **(4, 5)**

$y = -\frac{1}{4}x + 6$ **Equation 1**

$y = \frac{1}{2}x + 3$ **Equation 2**

c. How is the linear system in part (b) related to the original equation? ***Sample answer:*** **Each side of the equation is set equal to y.**

d. *Explain* how to use a graph to solve the equation $-\frac{2}{5}x + 5 = \frac{1}{5}x + 2$.

C **30. CHALLENGE** The three lines given below form a triangle. Find the coordinates of the vertices of the triangle.

Line 1: $-3x + 2y = 1$ **Line 2:** $2x + y = 11$ **Line 3:** $x + 4y = 9$

(3, 5), (1, 2), and (5, 1)

PROBLEM SOLVING

EXAMPLES 3 and 4 on pp. 429–430 for Exs. 31–33

A **(31.) TELEVISION** The graph shows a projection, from 1990 on, of the percent of eighth graders who watch 1 hour or less of television on a weekday and the percent of eighth graders who watch more than 1 hour of television on a weekday. Use the graph to predict the year when the percent of eighth graders who watch 1 hour or less will equal the percent who watch more than 1 hour. **2040**

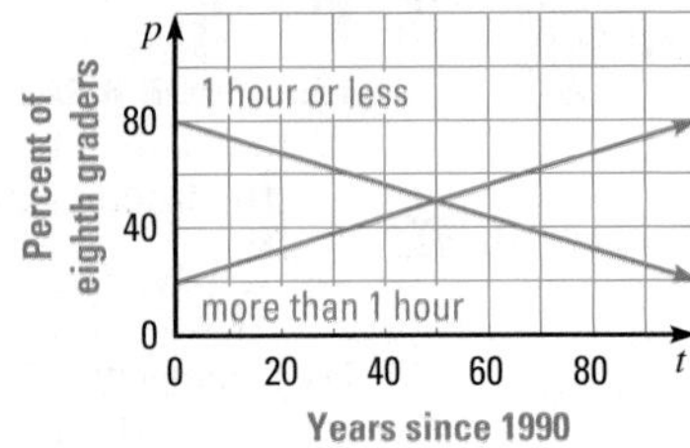

@HomeTutor for problem solving help at classzone.com

32. ★ MULTIPLE CHOICE A car dealership is offering interest-free car loans for one day only. During this day, a salesperson at the dealership sells two cars. One of his clients decides to pay off his \$17,424 car in 36 monthly payments of \$484. His other client decides to pay off his \$15,840 car in 48 monthly payments of \$330. Which system of equations can be used to determine the number x of months after which both clients will have the same loan balance y? **B**

Ⓐ $y = -484x$; $y = -330x$

Ⓑ $y = -484x + 17{,}424$; $y = -330x + 15{,}840$

Ⓒ $y = -484x + 15{,}840$; $y = -330x + 17{,}424$

Ⓓ $y = 484x + 17{,}424$; $y = 330x + 15{,}840$

@HomeTutor for problem solving help at classzone.com

33. CRAFTS Kirigami is the Japanese art of making paper designs by folding and cutting paper. A student sells small and large greeting cards decorated with kirigami at a craft fair. The small cards cost \$3 per card, and the large cards cost \$5 per card. The student collects \$95 for selling a total of 25 cards. How many of each type of card did the student sell?

15 small cards and 10 large cards

○ = WORKED-OUT SOLUTIONS on p. WS1 ★ = STANDARDIZED TEST PRACTICE

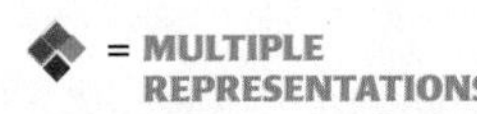

35b.

Tickets	Cost for members	Cost for non-members
1	\$20	\$8
2	\$25	\$16
3	\$30	\$24
4	\$35	\$32
5	\$40	\$40
6	\$45	\$48

35c.

y = 5x + 15

y = 8x

When you view 6 or more movies. ***Sample answer:*** **The graph for a non-member is below the graph for a member up through 4 movies. For 5 movies, the cost is the same. The graph for members is lower than the graph for non-members for 6 or more movies.**

Differentiated Instruction

Advanced When discussing **Exercise 27**, ask students to describe values for b in the equation $y = mx + b$ when the value of m is negative and when the value of m is positive. Have them support their reasoning by graphing several equations in the system $y = \frac{3}{5}x - 1$ and $y = mx + b$ with a solution of (5, 2) and then describing the pattern of graphs in the system as they relate to the values of m and b.

See also the *Differentiated Instruction Resources* for more strategies.

34a. 25 min on the stationary bike and 15 min on the stair machine

34b. 25 min on the elliptical trainer and 5 min on the stair machine

36. You should choose $25 off if your purchase is less than $125, and choose 20% off purchases greater than $125. *Sample answer*: For values less than $125, 20% off is less than $25 off. For values greater than $125, 20% off is greater than $25 off.

B **34. FITNESS** You want to burn 225 calories while exercising at a gym. The number of calories that you burn per minute on different machines at the gym is shown below.

Stair machine	*Elliptical trainer*	*Stationary bike*
You burn 5 Cal/min.	You burn 8 Cal/min.	You burn 6 Cal/min.

a. Suppose you have 40 minutes to exercise at the gym and you want to use the stair machine and stationary bike. How many minutes should you spend on each machine so that you burn 225 calories?

b. Suppose you have 30 minutes to exercise at the gym and you want to use the stair machine and the elliptical trainer. How many minutes should you spend on each machine so that you burn 225 calories?

35. MULTIPLE REPRESENTATIONS It costs $15 for a yearly membership to a movie club at a movie theater. A movie ticket costs $5 for club members and $8 for nonmembers.

a. **Writing a System of Equations** Write a system of equations that you can use to find the number x of movies viewed after which the total cost y for a club member, including the membership fee, is the same as the cost for a nonmember. **$y = 5x + 15$, $y = 8x$**

b. **Making a Table** Make a table of values that shows the total cost for a club member and a nonmember after paying to see 1, 2, 3, 4, 5, and 6 movies. **See margin.**

c. **Drawing a Graph** Use the table to graph the system of equations. Under what circumstances does it make sense to become a movie club member? *Explain* your answer by using the graph. **See margin.**

C **36. CHALLENGE** With a minimum purchase of $25, you can open a credit account with a clothing store. The store is offering either $25 or 20% off of your purchase if you open a credit account. You decide to open a credit account. Should you choose $25 or 20% off of your purchase? *Explain.*

MIXED REVIEW

Solve the equation.

37. $x + 5 = -14$ *(p. 134)* **−19**

38. $-5x + 6 = 21$ *(p. 141)* **−3**

39. $3(x + 2) = -6$ *(p. 148)* **−4**

40. $11x + 9 = 13x - 3$ *(p. 154)* **6**

41. $3x - 8 = 11x + 12$ *(p. 154)* **−2.5**

42. $4(x + 1) = -2x - 18$ *(p. 154)* **$-\frac{11}{3}$**

PREVIEW Prepare for Lesson 7.2 in Exs. 43–48.

Write the equation so that y is a function of x. *(p. 184)*

43. $5y + 25 = 3x$ **$y = \frac{3}{5}x - 5$**

44. $7x = y + 9$ **$y = 7x - 9$**

45. $4y + 11 = 3y + 4x$ **$y = 4x - 11$**

46. $6x + 3y = 2x + 3$ **$y = -\frac{4}{3}x + 1$**

47. $y + 2x + 6 = -1$ **$y = -2x - 7$**

48. $4x - 12 = 5x + 2y$ **$y = -\frac{1}{2}x - 6$**

5 ASSESS AND RETEACH

Daily Homework Quiz

Transparency Available

1. Use the graph to solve the linear system.
$3x - y = 5$
$-x + 3y = 1$ **(2, 1)**

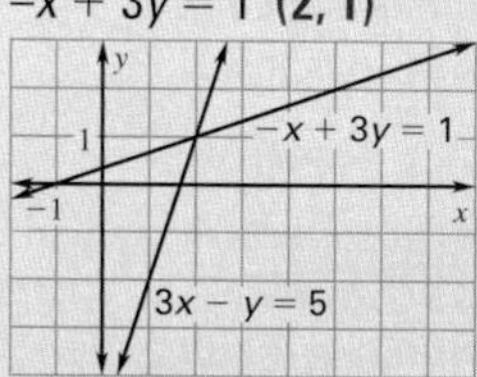

2. Solve the linear system by graphing.
$2x + y = -3$
$-6x + 3y = 3$ **(−1, −1)**

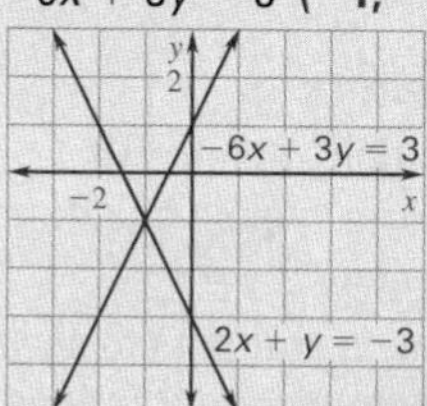

3. A pet store sells angel fish for $6 each and clown loaches for $4 each. If the pet store sold 8 fish for $36, how many of each type of fish did it sell? **2 angel fish and 6 clown loaches**

Online Quiz

Available at **classzone.com**

Diagnosis/Remediation

- Practice A, B, C in Chapter Resource Book
- Study Guide in Chapter Resource Book
- Practice Workbook
- @HomeTutor

Challenge

Additional challenge is available in the Chapter Resource Book.

1 PLAN AND PREPARE

Learn the Method

- Students will use a graphing calculator to solve a linear system.
- After the activity, students can use a graphing calculator to check their solutions in Exercises 3–7 and 12–26 in Lesson 7.1.

Keystroke Help

Keystrokes for several models of calculators are available in blackline format in the *Chapter Resource Book*.

2 TEACH

Tips for Success

In Step 1, caution students to divide each term in each equation by the coefficient of y.

In Step 2, remind students to use parentheses around the fractions.

Extra Example

Solve the linear system using a graphing calculator.

$4x - 3y = 2$

$x + 5y = -6$ **about $(-0.35, -1.13)$**

Key Discovery

The intercept feature of a graphing calculator can be used to approximate a solution to a system of linear equations.

3 ASSESS AND RETEACH

Solve the linear system using a graphing calculator.

$-5x + y = -8$

$x - 4y = 9$ **about $(1.21, -1.95)$**

Graphing Calculator ACTIVITY *Use after Lesson 7.1*

@HomeTutor
classzone.com
Keystrokes

7.1 Solving Linear Systems by Graphing

QUESTION **How can you use a graphing calculator to solve a linear system?**

EXAMPLE **Solve a linear system**

Solve the linear system using a graphing calculator.

$5x + 2y = 6$ Equation 1

$x - 3y = -5$ Equation 2

***STEP 1* Rewrite equations**

Solve each equation for y.

Equation 1	Equation 2
$5x + 2y = 6$	$x - 3y = -5$
$2y = -5x + 6$	$-3y = -x - 5$
$y = -\frac{5}{2}x + 3$	$y = \frac{1}{3}x + \frac{5}{3}$

***STEP 2* Enter equations**

Press Y= and enter the equations.

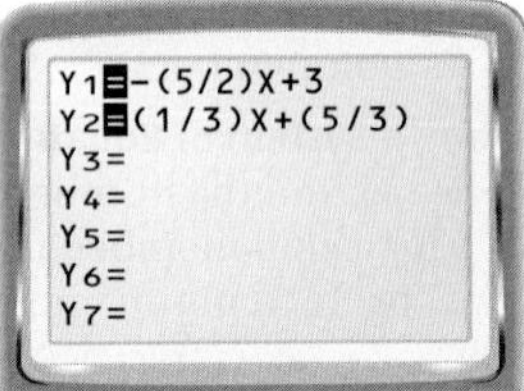

***STEP 3* Display graph**

Graph the equations using a standard viewing window.

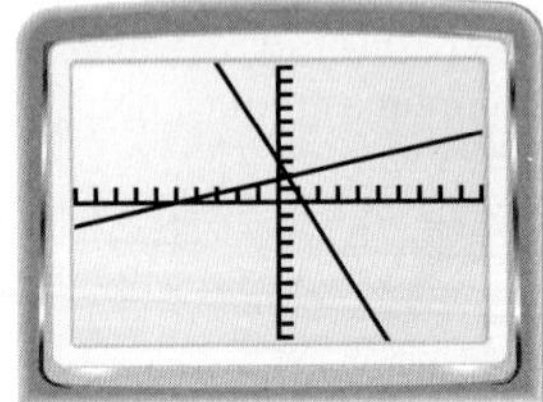

***STEP 4* Find point of intersection**

Use the *intersect* feature to find the point where the graphs intersect.

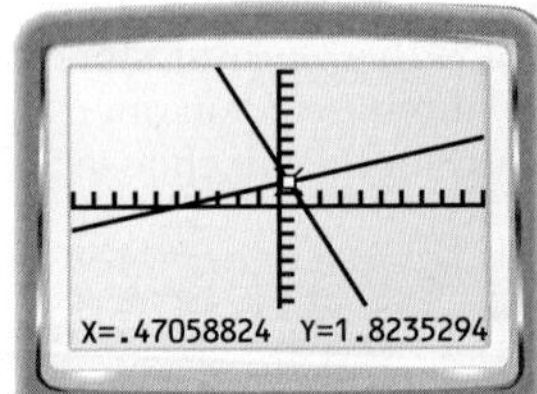

The solution is about (0.47, 1.8).

PRACTICE

Solve the linear system using a graphing calculator.

1. $y = x + 4$
$y = -3x - 2$
$(-1.5, 2.5)$

2. $5x + y = -4$
$x - y = -2$
$(-1, 1)$

3. $-0.45x - y = 1.35$
$-1.8x + y = -1.8$
$(0.2, -1.44)$

4. $-0.4x + 0.8y = -16$
$1.2x + 0.4y = 1$
$(6.43, -16.79)$

7.2 Solve Linear Systems by Substitution

Before You solved systems of linear equations by graphing.

Now You will solve systems of linear equations by substitution.

Why? So you can find tubing costs, as in Ex. 32.

Key Vocabulary
- **system of linear equations,** *p. 427*

KEY CONCEPT *For Your Notebook*

Solving a Linear System Using the Substitution Method

STEP 1 **Solve** one of the equations for one of its variables. When possible, solve for a variable that has a coefficient of 1 or −1.

STEP 2 **Substitute** the expression from Step 1 into the other equation and solve for the other variable.

STEP 3 **Substitute** the value from Step 2 into the revised equation from Step 1 and solve.

EXAMPLE 1 **Use the substitution method**

Solve the linear system: $y = 3x + 2$ Equation 1
$x + 2y = 11$ Equation 2

Solution

STEP 1 **Solve** for y. Equation 1 is already solved for y.

STEP 2 **Substitute** $3x + 2$ for y in Equation 2 and solve for x.

$x + 2y = 11$ Write Equation 2.

$x + 2(3x + 2) = 11$ Substitute $3x + 2$ for y.

$7x + 4 = 11$ Simplify.

$7x = 7$ Subtract 4 from each side.

$x = 1$ Divide each side by 7.

STEP 3 **Substitute** 1 for x in the original Equation 1 to find the value of y.

$y = 3x + 2 = 3(1) + 2 = 3 + 2 = 5$

▶ The solution is (1, 5).

CHECK Substitute 1 for x and 5 for y in each of the original equations.

$y = 3x + 2$	$x + 2y = 11$
$5 \stackrel{?}{=} 3(1) + 2$	$1 + 2(5) \stackrel{?}{=} 11$
$5 = 5$ ✓	$11 = 11$ ✓

Animated Algebra at classzone.com

1 PLAN AND PREPARE

Warm-Up Exercises

Transparency Available

Solve the equation.

1. $6a - 3 + 2a = 13$ **2**
2. $4(n + 2) - n = 11$ **1**
3. You burned 8 calories per minute on a treadmill and 10 calories per minute on an elliptical trainer for a total of 560 calories in 60 minutes. How many minutes did you spend on each machine? **treadmill: 20 min, elliptical trainer: 40 min**

Notetaking Guide

Transparency Available

Promotes interactive learning and notetaking skills.

Pacing

Basic: 2 days
Average: 2 days
Advanced: 2 days
Block: 0.5 block with 7.1
0.5 block with 7.3

- See *Teaching Guide/Lesson Plan.*

2 FOCUS AND MOTIVATE

Essential Question

Big Idea 2, p. 425

How do you solve systems of linear equations by substitution? **Tell students they will learn how to answer this question by substituting an expression for a variable in one equation into the other equation.**

NCTM STANDARDS

Standard 2: Analyze situations using algebraic symbols

Standard 6: Solve problems in math and other contexts

Resource Planning Guide

Chapter Resource Book
- Teaching Guide/Lesson Plan
- Practice levels A, B, C
- Study Guide
- Catch-up for Absent Students
- Application
- Challenge

Workbooks
- Notetaking Guide
- Practice Workbook

Teaching Options
- **Power Presentations** provides dynamic electronic teaching resources for the classroom.
- **Activity Generator** provides editable activities for all ability levels.

Interactive Technology
- Easy Planner
- Power Presentations
- Activity Generator
- Animated Algebra
- Test Generator
- Online Quiz
- eWorkbook
- eEdition
- @HomeTutor

Resources for English Learners
- Spanish Study Guide
- Multi-Language Visual Glossary
- Student Resources in Spanish

See also the *Differentiated Instruction Resources* for more strategies for meeting individual needs.

Motivating the Lesson

In the previous lesson you solved systems of equations by graphing. But what if the point of intersection is not where two grid lines cross? You could approximate the coordinates of the point, but the substitution method provides a means for finding the exact coordinates.

3 TEACH

Extra Example 1

Solve the linear system:
$y = 2x - 3$
$x + 3y = 5$ **(2, 1)**

An **Animated Algebra** activity is available online for **Example 1**. This activity is also part of **Power Presentations**.

Extra Example 2

Solve the linear system:
$-5x - y = 12$
$3x - 5y = 4$ **(−2, −2)**

Key Question to Ask for Example 2

- How is Example 2 different from Example 1? **In Example 2, you first solve one equation in the system for *x* or *y*. In Example 1, an equation is already solved for *y*.**

Avoiding Common Errors

When students solve an equation for *x*, as in Example 2, the first value they find is the *y*-value. Caution them that this number is the *second* coordinate of the ordered pair solution.

EXAMPLE 2 Use the substitution method

Solve the linear system: $x - 2y = -6$ Equation 1
$4x + 6y = 4$ Equation 2

CHOOSE AN EQUATION
Equation 1 was chosen in Step 1 because *x* has a coefficient of 1. So, only one step is needed to solve Equation 1 for *x*.

Solution

STEP 1 **Solve** Equation 1 for *x*.

$x - 2y = -6$ Write original Equation 1.

$x = 2y - 6$ Revised Equation 1

STEP 2 **Substitute** $2y - 6$ for *x* in Equation 2 and solve for *y*.

$4x + 6y = 4$ Write Equation 2.

$4(2y - 6) + 6y = 4$ Substitute $2y - 6$ for *x*.

$8y - 24 + 6y = 4$ Distributive property

$14y - 24 = 4$ Simplify.

$14y = 28$ Add 24 to each side.

$y = 2$ Divide each side by 14.

STEP 3 **Substitute** 2 for *y* in the revised Equation 1 to find the value of *x*.

$x = 2y - 6$ Revised Equation 1

$x = 2(2) - 6$ Substitute 2 for *y*.

$x = -2$ Simplify.

▶ The solution is $(-2, 2)$.

CHECK Substitute −2 for *x* and 2 for *y* in each of the original equations.

Equation 1	Equation 2
$x - 2y = -6$	$4x + 6y = 4$
$-2 - 2(2) \stackrel{?}{=} -6$	$4(-2) + 6(2) \stackrel{?}{=} 4$
$-6 = -6$ ✓	$4 = 4$ ✓

CHECK REASONABLENESS When solving a linear system using the substitution method, you can use a graph to check the reasonableness of your solution. For example, the graph at the right verifies that $(-2, 2)$ is a solution of the linear system in Example 2.

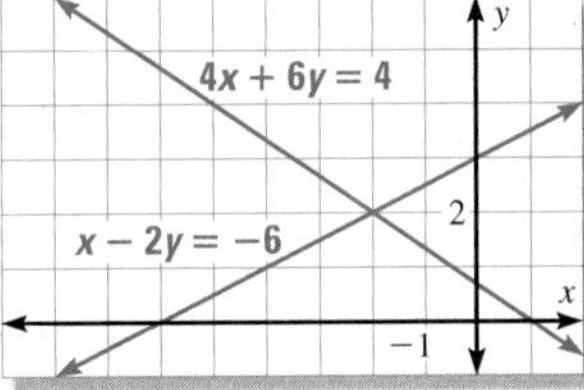

✓ GUIDED PRACTICE for Examples 1 and 2

Solve the linear system using the substitution method.

1. $y = 2x + 5$ **(1, 7)**
$3x + y = 10$

2. $x - y = 3$ **(0, −3)**
$x + 2y = -6$

3. $3x + y = -7$ **(−2, −1)**
$-2x + 4y = 0$

Differentiated Instruction

Visual Learners The substitution method involves many steps when written out verbally. Some students may find it helpful to visualize getting one variable (*x* or *y*) by itself in one equation, and then substituting an expression for that variable into the other equation. Students should look at the equations and highlight any variable with a coefficient of 1 or −1. In **Example 2**, the variable *x* in the first equation would be highlighted.

See also the *Differentiated Instruction Resources* for more strategies.

EXAMPLE 3 Solve a multi-step problem

ANOTHER WAY
For an alternative method for solving the problem in Example 3, turn to page 442 for the **Problem Solving Workshop**.

WEBSITES Many businesses pay website hosting companies to store and maintain the computer files that make up their websites. Internet service providers also offer website hosting. The costs for website hosting offered by a website hosting company and an Internet service provider are shown in the table. Find the number of months after which the total cost for website hosting will be the same for both companies.

Company	Set-up fee (dollars)	Cost per month (dollars)
Internet service provider	10	21.95
Website hosting company	None	22.45

Solution

STEP 1 **Write** a system of equations. Let y be the total cost after x months.

Equation 1: Internet service provider

Total cost = Set-up fee + Cost per month • Number of months

$$y = 10 + 21.95 \cdot x$$

Equation 2: Website hosting company

Total cost = Cost per month • Number of months

$$y = 22.45 \cdot x$$

The system of equations is: $y = 10 + 21.95x$ **Equation 1**
$y = 22.45x$ **Equation 2**

STEP 2 **Substitute** $22.45x$ for y in Equation 1 and solve for x.

$y = 10 + 21.95x$ **Write Equation 1.**

$22.45x = 10 + 21.95x$ **Substitute 22.45*x* for *y*.**

$0.5x = 10$ **Subtract 21.95*x* from each side.**

$x = 20$ **Divide each side by 0.5.**

▶ The total cost will be the same for both companies after 20 months.

✓ GUIDED PRACTICE for Example 3

4. In Example 3, what is the total cost for website hosting for each company after 20 months? **$449**

5. **WHAT IF?** In Example 3, suppose the Internet service provider offers $5 off the set-up fee. After how many months will the total cost for website hosting be the same for both companies? **10 mo**

Extra Example 3

A food cooperative is a business that usually offers special prices on locally grown food and produce. Some cooperatives are clubs and others are retail stores. The weekly costs for seasonal produce offered by a club-based and a store-based food cooperative are shown in the table. Find the number of weeks at which the total cost of weekly produce will be the same.

Type of cooperative	Club fee (dollars)	Cost per week (dollars)
Club	$20	$15
Retail	None	$17.50

The total cost will be the same for both cooperatives at 8 weeks.

Key Question to Ask for Example 3

- Which company will have the greater total cost for 21 months? Explain. **The website hosting company, since its monthly cost is greater than the monthly cost for the Internet service provider.**

Avoiding Common Errors

In Step 2 of Example 3, some students may substitute 22.45 for *y* instead of 22.45*x*. Remind these students that *y* is equivalent to 22.45 • *x* in Equation 2.

Extra Example 4

A chemist needs 15 liters of a 60% alcohol solution. The chemist has a solution that is 50% alcohol. How many liters of the 50% alcohol solution and pure alcohol should the chemist mix together to make 15 liters of a 60% alcohol solution? **3 liters of pure alcohol and 12 liters of the 50% alcohol solution**

Key Question to Ask for Example 4

- In Step 2, why should you solve Equation 1 for x? **The variable x has a coefficient of 1 in Equation 2 and thus the step where you need to multiply by a coefficient is eliminated.**

Closing the Lesson

Have students summarize the major points of the lesson and answer the Essential Question: How do you solve systems of linear equations by substitution?

- **You can solve a linear system by substituting an expression for one variable in an equation into the other equation and then solving for the other variable.**

Solve one of the equations in the system for x or y. Substitute the expression for x or y into the other equation. Solve for the other variable. Substitute the value of this variable into the original equation in the first step. Solve for the other variable.

EXAMPLE 4 Solve a mixture problem

ANTIFREEZE For extremely cold temperatures, an automobile manufacturer recommends that a 70% antifreeze and 30% water mix be used in the cooling system of a car. How many quarts of pure (100%) antifreeze and a 50% antifreeze and 50% water mix should be combined to make 11 quarts of a 70% antifreeze and 30% water mix?

Solution

STEP 1 **Write** an equation for the total number of quarts and an equation for the number of quarts of antifreeze. Let x be the number of quarts of 100% antifreeze, and let y be the number of quarts of a 50% antifreeze and 50% water mix.

Equation 1: Total number of quarts

$x + y = 11$

Equation 2: Number of quarts of antifreeze

DRAW A DIAGRAM
Each bar shows the liquid in each mix. The green portion shows the percent of the mix that is antifreeze.

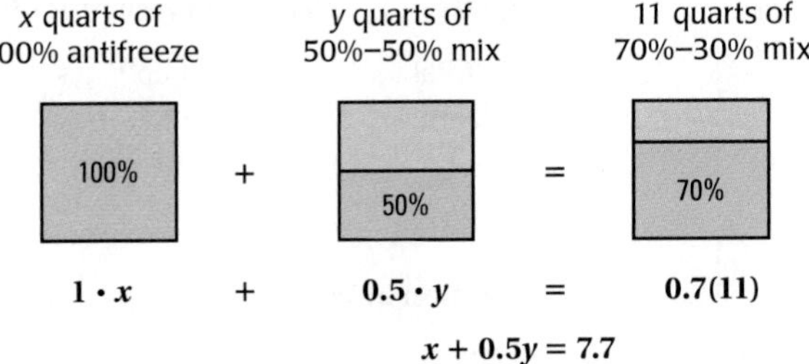

$x + 0.5y = 7.7$

The system of equations is: $x + y = 11$ **Equation 1**

$x + 0.5y = 7.7$ **Equation 2**

STEP 2 **Solve** Equation 1 for x.

$x + y = 11$ **Write Equation 1.**

$x = 11 - y$ **Revised Equation 1**

STEP 3 **Substitute** $11 - y$ for x in Equation 2 and solve for y.

$x + 0.5y = 7.7$ **Write Equation 2.**

$(11 - y) + 0.5y = 7.7$ **Substitute $11 - y$ for x.**

$y = 6.6$ **Solve for y.**

STEP 4 **Substitute** 6.6 for y in the revised Equation 1 to find the value of x.

$x = 11 - y = 11 - 6.6 = 4.4$

▶ Mix 4.4 quarts of 100% antifreeze and 6.6 quarts of a 50% antifreeze and 50% water mix to get 11 quarts of a 70% antifreeze and 30% water mix.

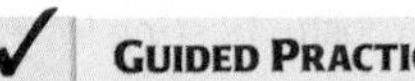

✓ **GUIDED PRACTICE** for Example 4

6. **WHAT IF?** How many quarts of 100% antifreeze and a 50% antifreeze and 50% water mix should be combined to make 16 quarts of a 70% antifreeze and 30% water mix? **6.4 quarts of 100% antifreeze and 9.6 quarts of 50% antifreeze and 50% water mix**

Differentiated Instruction

Below Level Some students avoid mixture problems, such as the one in **Example 4**, because they look complicated. Tell students that following the steps in the example and using diagrams will help them learn how to break mixture problems into parts. Suggest that they solve the problem for 10 quarts of antifreeze instead of 11. This will make the computation more manageable. Break Step 3 into a stepped-out solution so students see how to get a positive value for y. Students can then solve **Guided Practice Exercise 6** for 16 quarts.

See also the *Differentiated Instruction Resources* for more strategies.

7.2 EXERCISES

HOMEWORK KEY ○ = **WORKED-OUT SOLUTIONS** on p. WS16 for Exs. 13 and 33
★ = **STANDARDIZED TEST PRACTICE** Exs. 2, 18, 29, 33, and 37

SKILL PRACTICE

A

1. **VOCABULARY** Give an example of a system of linear equations.
Sample answer: $y = x + 1$, $y = 2x + 1$

2. ★ **WRITING** If you are solving the linear system shown using the substitution method, which equation would you solve for which variable? *Explain.* *Sample answer:* Solve Equation 2 for y; the y term does not have a coefficient.

$2x - 3y = 24$ Equation 1
$2x + y = 8$ Equation 2

EXAMPLE 1 on p. 435 for Exs. 3–8

SOLVING LINEAR SYSTEMS Solve the linear system using substitution.

3. $x = 17 - 4y$, $y = x - 2$ (5, 3)
4. $y = 2x - 1$, $2x + y = 3$ (1, 1)
5. $x = y + 3$, $2x - y = 5$ (2, −1)
6. $4x - 7y = 10$, $y = x - 7$ (13, 6)
7. $x = 16 - 4y$, $3x + 4y = 8$ (−4, 5)
8. $-5x + 3y = 51$, $y = 10x - 8$ (3, 22)

EXAMPLE 2 on p. 436 for Exs. 9–19

9. $2x = 12$, $x - 5y = -29$ (6, 7)
10. $2x - y = 23$, $x - 9 = -1$ (8, −7)
11. $x + y = 0$, $x - 2y = 6$ (2, −2)
12. $2x + y = 9$, $4x - y = -15$ (−1, 11)
13. $5x + 2y = 9$, $x + y = -3$ (5, −8)
14. $5x + 4y = 32$, $9x - y = 33$ (4, 3)
15. $11x - 7y = -14$, $x - 2y = -4$ (0, 2)
16. $20x - 30y = -50$, $x + 2y = 1$ (−1, 1)
17. $6x + y = 4$, $x - 4y = 19$ (1.4, −4.4)

18. ★ **MULTIPLE CHOICE** Which ordered pair is a solution of the linear system $4x - y = 17$ and $-9x + 8y = 2$? **A**

Ⓐ (6, 7) Ⓑ (7, 6) Ⓒ (7, 11) Ⓓ (11, 7)

19. **ERROR ANALYSIS** *Describe* and correct the error in solving the linear system $4x + 2y = 6$ and $3x + y = 9$.

Step 1	Step 2	Step 3	The solution is (6, 1).
$3x + y = 9$ $y = 9 - 3x$	$4x + 2(9 - 3x) = 6$ $4x + 18 - 6x = 6$ $-2x = -12$ $x = 6$	$y = 9 - 3x$ $6 = 9 - 3x$ $-3 = -3x$ $1 = x$	✗

Sample answer: In Step 3, 6 is substituted for y instead of x; $y = 9 - 3(6)$, $y = -9$, the solution is (6, −9).

B

SOLVING LINEAR SYSTEMS Solve the linear system using substitution.

20. $4.5x + 1.5y = 24$, $x - y = 4$ (5, 1)
21. $35x + y = 20$, $1.5x - 0.1y = 18$ (4, −120)
22. $3x - 2y = 8$, $0.5x + y = 17$ (10.5, 11.75)
23. $0.5x + 0.6y = 5.7$, $2x - y = -1$ (3, 7)
24. $x - 9 = 0.5y$, $2.2x - 3.1y = -0.2$ (14, 10)
25. $0.2x + y = -1.8$, $1.8y + 5.5x = 27.6$ (6, −3)
26. $\frac{1}{2}x + \frac{1}{4}y = 5$, $x - \frac{1}{2}y = 1$ $\left(5\frac{1}{2}, 9\right)$
27. $x + \frac{1}{3}y = -2$, $-8x - \frac{2}{3}y = 4$ (0, −6)
28. $\frac{3}{8}x + \frac{3}{4}y = 12$, $\frac{2}{3}x + \frac{1}{2}y = 13$ (12, 10)

4 PRACTICE AND APPLY

Assignment Guide

Answer Transparencies available for all exercises

Basic:
Day 1: EP p. 940 Exs. 21–26
pp. 439–441
Exs. 1–19
Day 2: pp. 439–441
Exs. 20–25, 31–35, 39–50

Average:
Day 1: pp. 439–441
Exs. 1, 2, 4–18 even, 19–29 odd
Day 2: pp. 439–441
Exs. 31–37, 39–50

Advanced:
Day 1: pp. 439–441
Exs. 1, 6–8, 15–18, 20–28
Day 2: pp. 439–441
Exs. 29–38*, 42–44, 48–50

Block:
pp. 439–441
Exs. 1, 2, 4–18 even, 19–29 odd (with 7.1)
pp. 439–441
Exs. 31–37, 39–50 (with 7.3)

Differentiated Instruction

See *Differentiated Instruction Resources* for suggestions on addressing the needs of a diverse classroom.

Homework Check

For a quick check of student understanding of key concepts, go over the following exercises:
Basic: 4, 10, 14, 31, 35
Average: 6, 14, 21, 32, 35
Advanced: 8, 16, 24, 33, 35

Extra Practice

- Student Edition, p. 944
- Chapter Resource Book: Practice levels A, B, C

Practice Worksheet

An easily-readable reduced practice page (with answers) for this lesson can be found on p. 424C.

29. ★ **WRITING** Suppose you solve a linear system using substitution. *Explain* how you can use a graph to check your solution. ***Sample answer:*** **The graphs of the equations should intersect at the solution you found using the substitution method.**

C 30. **CHALLENGE** Find values of a and b so that the linear system shown has a solution of $(-9, 4)$. **$a = 4, b = 5$**

$ax + by = -16$ **Equation 1**

$ax - by = -56$ **Equation 2**

Graphing Calculator

Exercises 3–17, 20–28 Students may want to check their solutions by graphing the equations. They should enter the equations in the graphing calculator using y= key, and then select Graph. They can use the Zoom feature if the standard window does not allow them to view the point of intersection of the graphs. The intersect feature will display the coordinates of the point of intersection.

Avoiding Common Errors

Exercises 35–36 A common error in mixture problems is failing to multiply the percentage of the mixture times the amount of the mixture when writing the equation that represents the contents of the mixture. Suggest that students review Step 1 in Example 4 before writing the equations for the linear system.

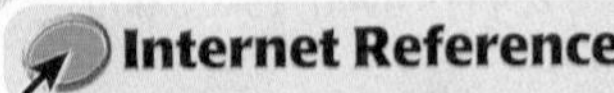

Exercise 37 For more information about gazelles, visit the website http://www.ultimateungulate.com/Artiodactyla/Gazella_dorcas.html

An **Animated Algebra** activity is available online for **Exercise 37**. This activity is also part of **Power Presentations**.

PROBLEM SOLVING

EXAMPLE 3 A on p. 437 for Exs. 31–33

A 31. **FUNDRAISING** During a football game, the parents of the football players sell pretzels and popcorn to raise money for new uniforms. They charge \$2.50 for a bag of popcorn and \$2 for a pretzel. The parents collect \$336 in sales during the game. They sell twice as many bags of popcorn as pretzels. How many bags of popcorn do they sell? How many pretzels do they sell? **96 bags of popcorn; 48 pretzels**

@HomeTutor for problem solving help at classzone.com

32. **TUBING COSTS** A group of friends takes a day-long tubing trip down a river. The company that offers the tubing trip charges \$15 to rent a tube for a person to use and \$7.50 to rent a "cooler" tube, which is used to carry food and water in a cooler. The friends spend \$360 to rent a total of 26 tubes. How many of each type of tube do they rent? **22 tubes for a person and 4 "cooler" tubes**

@HomeTutor for problem solving help at classzone.com

33. ★ **SHORT RESPONSE** In the mobile shown, objects are attached to each end of a dowel. For the dowel to balance, the following must be true:

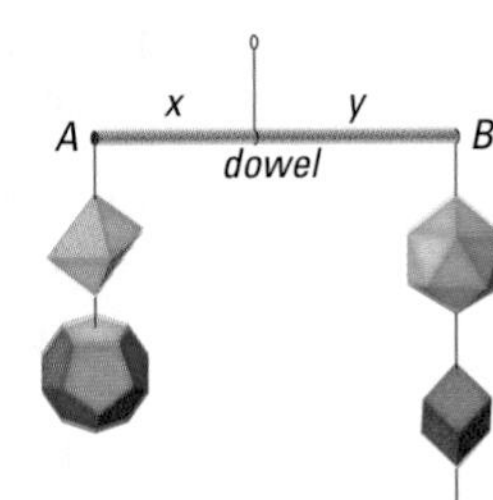

$x \cdot$ Weight hanging from point A $= y \cdot$ Weight hanging from point B

The weight of the objects hanging from point A is 1.5 pounds, and the weight of the objects hanging from point B is 1.2 pounds. The length of the dowel is 9 inches. How far from point A should the string be placed? *Explain.*
4 in. *Sample answer:* (4, 5) is the solution to the appropriate linear system, so x should equal 4.

B 34. **MULTI-STEP PROBLEM** Two swimming teams are competing in a 400 meter medley relay. During the last leg of the race, the swimmer in lane 1 has a 1.2 second head start on the swimmer in lane 2, as shown.

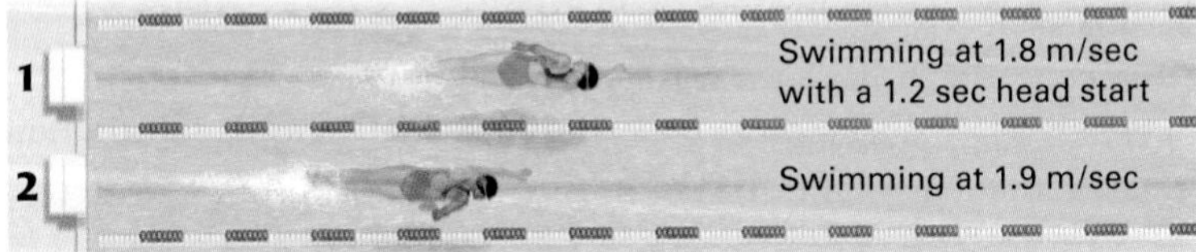

a. Let t be the time since the swimmer in lane 2 started the last leg. After how many seconds into the leg will the swimmer in lane 2 catch up to the swimmer in lane 1? **21.6 sec**

b. Does the swimmer in lane 2 catch up to the swimmer in lane 1 before the race ends? *Explain.*

34b. Yes. *Sample answer:* After 21.6 seconds they have swum 41.04 meters, so the race is not over.

○ = WORKED-OUT SOLUTIONS on p. WS1 ★ = STANDARDIZED TEST PRACTICE

EXAMPLE 4 on p. 438 for Ex. 35

35. CHEMISTRY In your chemistry lab, you have a bottle of 1% hydrochloric acid solution and a bottle of 5% hydrochloric acid solution. You need 100 milliliters of a 3% hydrochloric acid solution for an experiment. How many milliliters of each solution do you need to mix together?
50 milliliters of 1% hydrochloric acid solution and 50 milliliters of 5% hydrochloric acid solution

36. MONEY Laura has $4.50 in dimes and quarters. She has 3 more dimes than quarters. How many quarters does she have? **12 quarters**

37. ★ SHORT RESPONSE A gazelle can run 73 feet per second for several minutes. A cheetah can run 88 feet per second, but it can sustain this speed for only 20 seconds. A gazelle is 350 feet from a cheetah when both animals start running. Can the gazelle stay ahead of the cheetah? *Explain.* **Yes. *Sample answer:* The cheetah would have to run at 88 feet per second for 23.3 seconds to catch the gazelle.**

Animated Algebra at classzone.com

C **38. CHALLENGE** A gardener needs 6 bushels of a potting medium of 40% peat moss and 60% vermiculite. He decides to add 100% vermiculite to his current potting medium that is 50% peat moss and 50% vermiculite. The gardener has 5 bushels of the 50% peat moss and 50% vermiculite mix. Does he have enough of the 50% peat moss and 50% vermiculite mix to make 6 bushels of the 40% peat moss and 60% vermiculite mix? *Explain.*
Yes. *Sample answer:* The gardener needs 4.8 bushels of the 50% peat moss and 50% vermiculite mix, and the gardener had 5 bushels.

MIXED REVIEW

Solve the proportion. Check your solution.

39. $\frac{3}{7} = \frac{x}{21}$ *(p. 162)* **9**

40. $\frac{y}{30} = \frac{9}{10}$ *(p. 162)* **27**

41. $\frac{12}{16} = \frac{3z}{4}$ *(p. 162)* **1**

42. $\frac{35}{q} = \frac{5}{3}$ *(p. 168)* **21**

43. $\frac{3}{2r} = \frac{-6}{16}$ *(p. 168)* **−4**

44. $\frac{4}{3} = \frac{s}{s-2}$ *(p. 168)* **8**

PREVIEW Prepare for Lesson 7.3 in Exs. 45–50.

Write two equations in standard form that are equivalent to the given equation. *(p. 311)* **45–50. Sample answers are given.**

45. $x - 4y = 0$ **$2x - 8y = 0$, $4x - 16y = 0$**

46. $-3x + 9y = 6$ **$x - 3y = -2$, $3x - 9y = -6$**

47. $-7x - y = 1$ **$7x + y = -1$, $-14x - 2y = 2$**

48. $5x - 10y = 5$ **$x - 2y = 1$, $-x + 2y = -1$**

49. $-2x - 12y = 8$ **$-x - 6y = 4$, $x + 6y = -4$**

50. $6x + 15y = -3$ **$2x + 5y = -1$, $12x + 30y = -6$**

QUIZ for Lessons 7.1–7.2

Solve the linear system by graphing. Check your solution. *(p. 427)*

1. $x + y = -2$, $-x + y = 6$ **(−4, 2)**

2. $x - y = 0$, $5x + 2y = -7$ **(−1, −1)**

3. $x - 2y = 12$, $-3x + y = -1$ **(−2, −7)**

Solve the linear system using substitution. *(p. 435)*

4. $y = x - 4$, $-2x + y = 18$ **(−22, −26)**

5. $y = 4 - 3x$, $5x - y = 22$ **(3.25, −5.75)**

6. $x = y + 9$, $5x - 3y = 7$ **(−10, −19)**

7. $2y + x = -4$, $y - x = -5$ **(2, −3)**

8. $5x - 4y = 27$, $-2x + y = 3$ **(−13, −23)**

9. $3x - 5y = 13$, $x + 4y = 10$ **(6, 1)**

5 ASSESS AND RETEACH

Daily Homework Quiz

Transparency Available

Solve the linear system using substitution.

1. $-5x - y = 12$, $3x - 5y = 4$ **(−2, −2)**

2. $2x + 9y = -4$, $x - 2y = 11$ **(7, −2)**

3. You are making 6 quarts of fruit punch for a party. You want the punch to contain 80% fruit juice. You have bottles of 100% fruit juice and 20% fruit juice. How many quarts of 100% fruit juice and how many quarts of 20% fruit juice should you mix to make 6 quarts of 80% fruit juice? **4.5 quarts of 100% fruit juice and 1.5 quarts of 20% fruit juice**

Available at **classzone.com**

Diagnosis/Remediation

- Practice A, B, C in Chapter Resource Book
- Study Guide in Chapter Resource Book
- Practice Workbook
- @HomeTutor

Challenge

Additional challenge is available in the Chapter Resource Book.

Quiz

An easily-readable reduced copy of the quiz (with answers) on Lessons 7.1–7.2 from the Assessment Book can be found on p. 424F.

Alternative Strategy

Example 3 on page 437 can be solved by making a table rather than by writing a system of equations. Making a table is a good alternative for students who have difficulties with algebraic representations. A table in this situation has the added benefit of showing a detailed analysis of the costs of both companies. This allows the student to reason about the benefits of choosing one company over another, which is often the goal in this type of exercise.

Avoiding Common Errors

Calculation errors are the biggest drawback in using this method. One way to avoid these errors is to make tables using a spreadsheet. After students enter the formulas in the appropriate cells, the spreadsheet will enter the correct calculations.

PROBLEM SOLVING WORKSHOP LESSON 7.2

Using ALTERNATIVE METHODS

Another Way to Solve Example 3, page 437

MULTIPLE REPRESENTATIONS In Example 3 on page 437, you saw how to solve the problem about website hosting by solving a linear system algebraically. You can also solve the problem using a table.

PROBLEM

WEBSITES Many businesses pay website hosting companies to store and maintain the computer files that make up their websites. Internet service providers also offer website hosting. The costs for website hosting offered by a website hosting company and an Internet service provider are shown in the table. Find the number of months after which the total cost for website hosting will be the same for both companies.

Company	Set-up fee	Cost per month
Internet service provider	\$10	\$21.95
Website hosting company	None	\$22.45

METHOD

Making a Table An alternative approach is to make a table.

STEP 1 **Make** a table for the total cost of website hosting for both companies.

Include the set-up fee in the cost for the first month.

STEP 2 **Look** for the month in which the total cost of the service from the Internet service provider and the website hosting company is the same. This happens after 20 months.

Months	Internet service provider	Website hosting company
1	\$31.95	\$22.45
2	\$53.90	\$44.90
3	\$75.85	\$67.35
⋮	⋮	⋮
19	\$427.05	\$426.55
20	\$449.00	\$449.00
21	\$470.95	\$471.45

PRACTICE

1. **TAXIS** A taxi company charges \$2.80 for the first mile and \$1.60 for each additional mile. Another taxi company charges \$3.20 for the first mile and \$1.50 for each additional mile. After how many miles will each taxi cost the same? Use a table to solve the problem. **5 mi**

2. **SCHOOL PLAY** An adult ticket to a school play costs \$5 and a student ticket costs \$3. A total of \$460 was collected from the sale of 120 tickets. How many student tickets were purchased? Solve the problem using algebra. Then use a table to check your answer. **70 student tickets**

7.3 Linear Systems and Elimination

MATERIALS • algebra tiles

QUESTION How can you solve a linear system using algebra tiles?

You can use the following algebra tiles to model equations.

1-tiles **x-tiles** **y-tiles**

EXPLORE Solve a linear system using algebra tiles.

Solve the linear system: $3x - y = 5$ Equation 1
$x + y = 3$ Equation 2

STEP 1 ***Model equations***
Model each equation using algebra tiles. Arrange the algebra tiles so that one equation is directly below the other equation.

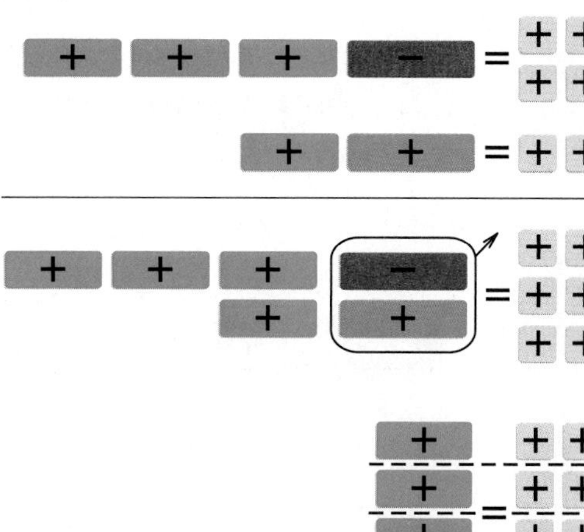

STEP 2 ***Add equations***
Combine the two equations to form one equation. Notice that the new equation has one positive y-tile and one negative y-tile. The y-tiles can be removed because the pair of y-tiles has a value of 0.

STEP 3 ***Solve for x***
Divide the remaining tiles into four equal groups. Each x-tile is equal to two 1-tiles. So, $x = 2$.

STEP 4 ***Solve for y***
To find the value of y, use the model for Equation 2. Because $x = 2$, you can replace the x-tile with two 1-tiles. Solve the new equation for y. So $y = 1$, and the solution of the system is (2, 1).

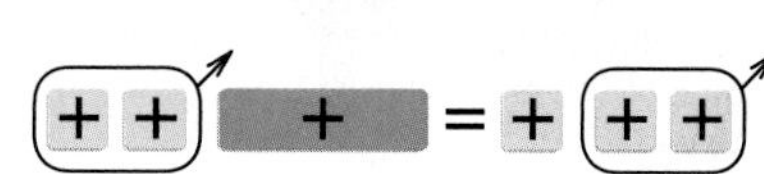

DRAW CONCLUSIONS Use your observations to complete these exercises

Use algebra tiles to model and solve the linear system.

1. $x + 3y = 8$
   $4x - 3y = 2$
   (2, 2)
2. $2x + y = 5$
   $-2x + 3y = 7$
   (1, 3)
3. $5x - 2y = -2$
   $x + 2y = 14$
   (2, 6)
4. $x + 2y = 3$
   $-x + 3y = 2$
   (1, 1)
5. **REASONING** Is it possible to solve the linear system $3x - 2y = 6$ and $2x + y = 11$ using the steps shown above? *Explain* your reasoning. **See margin.**

1 PLAN AND PREPARE

Explore the Concept
- Students will use algebra tiles to solve a linear system.
- This activity leads into the study of solving linear systems by adding, as in Example 1 in Lesson 7.3.

Materials
Each student will need:
- algebra tiles
- Activity Support Master (*Chapter Resource Book*)

Recommended Time
Work activity: 15 min
Discuss results: 5 min

Grouping
Students should work individually.

2 TEACH

Tips for Success
Make sure that the models of the equations are directly beneath each other.

Key Question
- In Step 4, why should you use the model for Equation 2? **Equation 2 is easier to solve for y because the coefficient of y is 1.**

Key Discovery
You can eliminate a variable if the coefficients are opposites.

3 ASSESS AND RETEACH

If you model the linear system $3x - 2y = 1$ and $-3x + y = 4$, which tiles can you remove when you combine the equations? **3 positive x-tiles and 3 negative x-tiles**

5. No. *Sample answer:* When you combine the two equations, the result still has 2 variables.

7.3 Solve Linear Systems by Adding or Subtracting

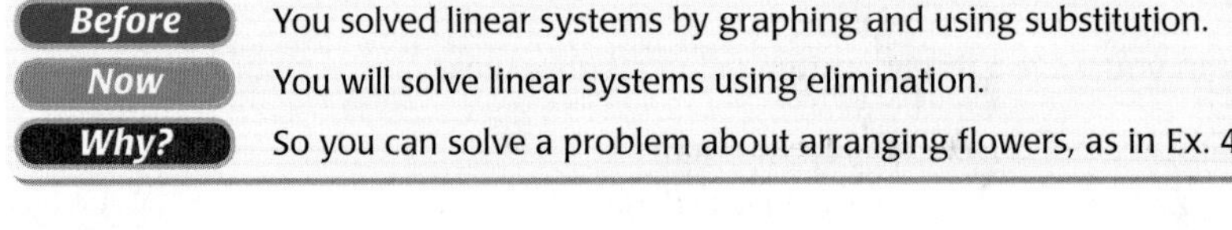
Before You solved linear systems by graphing and using substitution.
Now You will solve linear systems using elimination.
Why? So you can solve a problem about arranging flowers, as in Ex. 42.

Key Vocabulary
- **system of linear equations,** *p. 427*

When solving a linear system, you can sometimes add or subtract the equations to obtain a new equation in one variable. This method is called *elimination.*

KEY CONCEPT *For Your Notebook*

Solving a Linear System Using the Elimination Method

STEP 1 **Add or subtract** the equations to eliminate one variable.

STEP 2 **Solve** the resulting equation for the other variable.

STEP 3 **Substitute** in either original equation to find the value of the eliminated variable.

EXAMPLE 1 Use addition to eliminate a variable

Solve the linear system: $2x + 3y = 11$ **Equation 1**
$-2x + 5y = 13$ **Equation 2**

Solution

ADD EQUATIONS
When the coefficients of one variable are opposites, add the equations to eliminate the variable.

STEP 1 **Add** the equations to eliminate one variable.

$$\begin{array}{r} 2x + 3y = 11 \\ -2x + 5y = 13 \\ \hline 8y = 24 \end{array}$$

STEP 2 **Solve** for y.

$$y = 3$$

STEP 3 **Substitute** 3 for y in either equation and solve for x.

$2x + 3y = 11$ **Write Equation 1.**

$2x + 3(3) = 11$ **Substitute 3 for y.**

$x = 1$ **Solve for x.**

▶ The solution is (1, 3).

CHECK Substitute 1 for x and 3 for y in each of the original equations.

$2x + 3y = 11$	$-2x + 5y = 13$
$2(1) + 3(3) \stackrel{?}{=} 11$	$-2(1) + 5(3) \stackrel{?}{=} 13$
$11 = 11$ ✓	$13 = 13$ ✓

1 PLAN AND PREPARE

Warm-Up Exercises

Transparency Available

1. Solve the linear system using substitution.
$2x + y = 12$
$3x - 2y = 11$ **(5, 2)**
2. One auto repair shop charges \$30 for a diagnosis and \$25 per hour for labor. Another auto repair shop charges \$35 per hour for labor. For how many hours are the total charges for both of the shops the same? **3 h**

Notetaking Guide

Transparency Available

Promotes interactive learning and notetaking skills.

Pacing

Basic: 1 day
Average: 1 day
Advanced: 1 day
Block: 0.5 block with 7.2
- See *Teaching Guide/Lesson Plan.*

2 FOCUS AND MOTIVATE

Essential Question

Big Idea 2, p. 425

How do you solve linear systems by eliminating a variable? **Tell students they will learn how to answer this question by adding or subtracting equations to eliminate one of the variables.**

NCTM STANDARDS

Standard 2: Analyze situations using algebraic symbols

Standard 7: Recognize reasoning and proof as fundamental to math

Resource Planning Guide

Chapter Resource Book
- Teaching Guide/Lesson Plan
- Practice levels A, B, C
- Study Guide
- Catch-up for Absent Students
- Problem Solving Workshop
- Challenge

Workbooks
- Notetaking Guide
- Practice Workbook

Teaching Options
- **Power Presentations** provides dynamic electronic teaching resources for the classroom.
- **Activity Generator** provides editable activities for all ability levels.

Interactive Technology
- Easy Planner
- Power Presentations
- Activity Generator
- Animated Algebra
- Test Generator
- Online Quiz
- eWorkbook
- eEdition
- @HomeTutor

Resources for English Learners
- Spanish Study Guide
- Multi-Language Visual Glossary
- Student Resources in Spanish

See also the *Differentiated Instruction Resources* for more strategies for meeting individual needs.

EXAMPLE 2 Use subtraction to eliminate a variable

Solve the linear system: $4x + 3y = 2$ Equation 1
$5x + 3y = -2$ Equation 2

SUBTRACT EQUATIONS
When the coefficients of one variable are the same, subtract the equations to eliminate the variable.

Solution

STEP 1 **Subtract** the equations to eliminate one variable.

$$\begin{array}{r} 4x + 3y = 2 \\ 5x + 3y = -2 \\ \hline -x \qquad = 4 \end{array}$$

STEP 2 **Solve** for x.

$$x = -4$$

STEP 3 **Substitute** -4 for x in either equation and solve for y.

$4x + 3y = 2$ **Write Equation 1.**

$4(-4) + 3y = 2$ **Substitute −4 for x.**

$y = 6$ **Solve for y.**

▶ The solution is $(-4, 6)$.

EXAMPLE 3 Arrange like terms

Solve the linear system: $8x - 4y = -4$ Equation 1
$4y = 3x + 14$ Equation 2

AVOID ERRORS
Make sure that the equal signs are in the same column, just as the like terms are.

Solution

STEP 1 **Rewrite** Equation 2 so that the like terms are arranged in columns.

$8x - 4y = -4$ → $8x - 4y = -4$
$4y = 3x + 14$ → $-3x + 4y = 14$

STEP 2 **Add** the equations.

$$5x \qquad = 10$$

STEP 3 **Solve** for x.

$$x = 2$$

STEP 4 **Substitute** 2 for x in either equation and solve for y.

$4y = 3x + 14$ **Write Equation 2.**

$4y = 3(2) + 14$ **Substitute 2 for x.**

$y = 5$ **Solve for y.**

▶ The solution is $(2, 5)$.

GUIDED PRACTICE for Examples 1, 2, and 3

Solve the linear system.

1. $4x - 3y = 5$ **(−1, −3)**
$-2x + 3y = -7$
2. $-5x - 6y = 8$ **(2, −3)**
$5x + 2y = 4$
3. $6x - 4y = 14$ **(5, 4)**
$-3x + 4y = 1$
4. $7x - 2y = 5$ **(1, 1)**
$7x - 3y = 4$
5. $3x + 4y = -6$ **(−2, 0)**
$2y = 3x + 6$
6. $2x + 5y = 12$ **(1, 2)**
$5y = 4x + 6$

Motivating the Lesson

You and a friend go to a county fair. Your friend pays an entrance fee and buys 8 tickets for rides, and the total cost is $16.50. You buy 6 tickets for rides and your total cost, with the entrance fee, is $14. By writing and solving a linear system, you can determine the entrance fee for the county fair and the cost per ticket for rides at the fair.

3 TEACH

Extra Example 1

Solve the linear system.
$3x + 4y = 8$
$-3x + 5y = 10$ **(0, 2)**

Extra Example 2

Solve the linear system.
$5x + 6y = 4$
$7x + 6y = 8$ **(2, −1)**

Avoiding Common Errors

When using subtraction to solve, as in Example 2, some students may add terms rather than subtract. One way to avoid this error is to use the definition of subtraction to rewrite Equation 2 with opposite signs and then add the equations.

Extra Example 3

Solve the linear system.
$9x - 3y = 18$
$3y = -7x + 30$ **(3, 3)**

Key Question to Ask for Example 3

- How do you know that you need to add the equations in Example 3? **Since the coefficients of *y* are opposites, you add to solve the system.**

Extra Example 4

A riverboat travels 28 miles upstream in 7 hours. It travels 28 miles downstream in 5 hours. The speed of the current remains the same during the travel upstream and downstream. Find the average speed of the riverboat in still water and the speed of the current. **speed in still water: 4.8 mi/h; speed of current: 0.8 mi/h**

Key Question to Ask for Example 4

- Why is the speed of the current added to the speed of the kayak going downstream? **When the kayak travels downstream, it is moving with the current, which causes its speed to increase.**

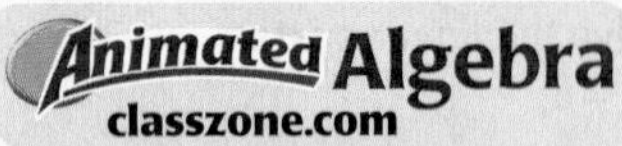

An **Animated Algebra** activity is available online for **Example 4**. This activity is also part of **Power Presentations**.

Closing the Lesson

Have students summarize the major points of the lesson and answer the Essential Question: How do you solve linear systems by eliminating a variable?

- **If the coefficients of one variable are opposites, you add the equations to begin solving the system.**
- **If the coefficients of one variable are the same, you subtract the equations to begin solving the system.**

Add or subtract the equations to eliminate one of the variables. Solve the resulting equation for whichever variable remains, *x* or *y*. Substitute this value of *x* or *y* in either of the original equations to find the value of the eliminated variable.

EXAMPLE 4 Write and solve a linear system

KAYAKING During a kayaking trip, a kayaker travels 12 miles upstream (against the current) and 12 miles downstream (with the current), as shown. The speed of the current remained constant during the trip. Find the average speed of the kayak in still water and the speed of the current.

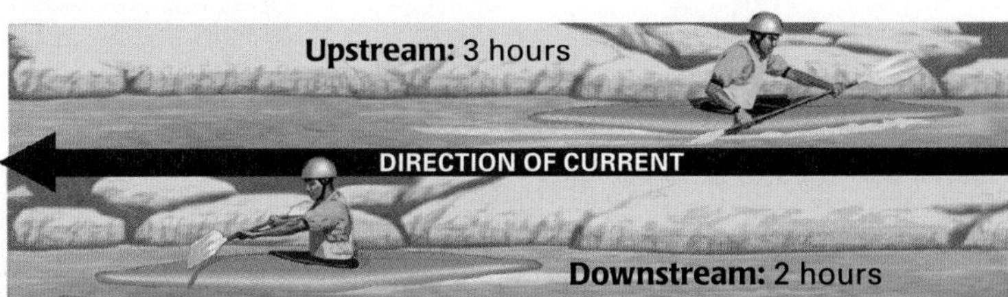

COMBINE SPEEDS
When you go upstream, the speed at which you can travel in still water is decreased by the speed of the current. The opposite is true when you go downstream.

STEP 1 **Write** a system of equations. First find the speed of the kayak going upstream and the speed of the kayak going downstream.

Upstream: $d = rt$	**Downstream:** $d = rt$
$12 = r \cdot 3$	$12 = r \cdot 2$
$4 = r$	$6 = r$

Use the speeds to write a linear system. Let x be the average speed of the kayak in still water, and let y be the speed of the current.

Equation 1: Going upstream

Speed of kayak in still water	−	Speed of current	=	Speed of kayak going upstream
x	−	y	=	**4**

Equation 2: Going downstream

Speed of kayak in still water	+	Speed of current	=	Speed of kayak going downstream
x	+	y	=	**6**

STEP 2 **Solve** the system of equations.

$x - y = 4$ Write Equation 1.
$x + y = 6$ Write Equation 2.
$2x = 10$ Add equations.
$x = 5$ Solve for x.

Substitute 5 for x in Equation 2 and solve for y.

$5 + y = 6$ Substitute 5 for x in Equation 2.
$y = 1$ Subtract 5 from each side.

▶ The average speed of the kayak in still water is 5 miles per hour, and the speed of the current is 1 mile per hour.

Animated Algebra at classzone.com

Differentiated Instruction

English Learners When discussing **Example 4**, students may have difficulty with the meanings of "upstream" and "downstream". When you go up, you move against the force of gravity; so going upstream is going against the force of the river flow. Similarly, going down is moving with the force of gravity; so going downstream is going with the river flow.

See also the *Differentiated Instruction Resources* for more strategies.

✓ **GUIDED PRACTICE** for Example 4

7. **WHAT IF?** In Example 4, suppose it takes the kayaker 5 hours to travel 10 miles upstream and 2 hours to travel 10 miles downstream. The speed of the current remains constant during the trip. Find the average speed of the kayak in still water and the speed of the current.
average speed of the kayak: 3.5 mi/h, speed of the current: 1.5 mi/h

7.3 EXERCISES

HOMEWORK KEY
- ◯ = **WORKED-OUT SOLUTIONS** on p. WS16 for Exs. 17 and 41
- ★ = **STANDARDIZED TEST PRACTICE** Exs. 2, 15, 22, 36, and 44
- ◆ = **MULTIPLE REPRESENTATIONS** Ex. 42

SKILL PRACTICE

1. **VOCABULARY** Give an example of a linear system in two variables that can be solved by first adding the equations to eliminate one variable.
***Sample answer:* $x + y = 10$, $x - y = 5$**

2. ★ **WRITING** *Explain* how to solve the linear system shown using the elimination method.
$2x - y = 2$ Equation 1
$2x + 3y = 22$ Equation 2
***Sample answer:* Subtract Equation 2 from Equation 1 then solve the resulting equation for *y*. Then substitute the value of *y* and solve for *x*.**

EXAMPLE 1 on p. 444 for Exs. 3–8

USING ADDITION Solve the linear system using elimination.

3. $x + 2y = 13$, $-x + y = 5$ **(1, 6)**
4. $9x + y = 2$, $-4x - y = -17$ **(−3, 29)**
5. $-3x - y = 8$, $7x + y = -12$ **(−1, −5)**
6. $3x - y = 30$, $-3x + 7y = 6$ **(12, 6)**
7. $-9x + 4y = -17$, $9x - 6y = 3$ **(5, 7)**
8. $-3x - 5y = -7$, $-4x + 5y = 14$ **(−1, 2)**

EXAMPLE 2 on p. 445 for Exs. 9–15

USING SUBTRACTION Solve the linear system using elimination.

9. $x + y = 1$, $-2x + y = 4$ **(−1, 2)**
10. $x - y = -4$, $x + 3y = 4$ **(−2, 2)**
11. $2x - y = 7$, $2x + 7y = 31$ **(5, 3)**
12. $6x + y = -10$, $5x + y = -10$ **(0, −10)**
13. $5x + 6y = 50$, $-x + 6y = 26$ **(4, 5)**
14. $4x - 9y = -21$, $4x + 3y = -9$ **(−3, 1)**

15. ★ **MULTIPLE CHOICE** Which ordered pair is a solution of the linear system $4x + 9y = -2$ and $11x + 9y = 26$? **C**

Ⓐ $(-2, 4)$ Ⓑ $(2, -4)$ Ⓒ $(4, -2)$ Ⓓ $(4, 2)$

EXAMPLE 3 on p. 445 for Exs. 16–22

ARRANGING LIKE TERMS Solve the linear system using elimination.

16. $2x - y = 32$, $y - 5x = 13$ **(−15, −62)**
17. $-8y + 6x = 36$, $6x - y = 15$ **(2, −3)**
18. $2x - y = -11$, $y = -2x - 13$ **(−6, −1)**
19. $-x - y = 14$, $x = 5y - 38$ **(−18, 4)**
20. $11y - 3x = 18$, $-3x = -16y + 33$ **(5, 3)**
21. $-5x + y = -23$, $-y = 3x - 9$ **(4, −3)**

22. ★ **MULTIPLE CHOICE** Which ordered pair is a solution of the linear system $2x + y = 10$ and $3y = 2x + 6$? **B**

Ⓐ $(-3, -4)$ Ⓑ $(3, 4)$ Ⓒ $(-4, 3)$ Ⓓ $(4, 3)$

4 PRACTICE AND APPLY

Assignment Guide

Answer Transparencies available for all exercises

Basic:
Day 1: pp. 447–450
Exs. 1, 2, 3–21 odd, 22–30, 39–43, 46–54 even

Average:
Day 1: pp. 447–450
Exs. 1, 2, 6–8, 12–15, 19–24, 26–36 even, 39–44, 47–55 odd

Advanced:
Day 1: pp. 447–450
Exs. 1, 2, 7, 8, 13–15, 19–22, 25–33 odd, 34–45*, 49, 52, 54

Block:
pp. 447–450
Exs. 1, 2, 6–8, 12–15, 19–24, 26–36 even, 39–44, 47–55 odd (with 7.2)

Differentiated Instruction

See *Differentiated Instruction Resources* for suggestions on addressing the needs of a diverse classroom.

Homework Check

For a quick check of student understanding of key concepts, go over the following exercises:
Basic: 5, 11, 17, 19, 39
Average: 6, 12, 19, 21, 40
Advanced: 8, 14, 20, 21, 41

Extra Practice

- Student Edition, p. 944
- Chapter Resource Book: Practice levels A, B, C

Practice Worksheet

An easily-readable reduced practice page (with answers) for this lesson can be found on p. 424C.

Mathematical Reasoning

Exercise 15–22, 25–33 Remind students that after the like terms have been arranged in columns, they need to determine whether to add or subtract to solve the system. Refer them to the notes next to Examples 1 and 2 for guidance on whether to add or subtract.

Exercise 36 Point out to students that they should use the same reasoning for eliminating a variable in a system of three equations as they use in a system of two equations.

23. ***Sample answer:*** **The two equations should be subtracted rather than added; $6x = 8$, $x = \frac{4}{3}$.**

24. ***Sample answer:*** **When $-3x$ is moved to the other side, it should become $3x$, the equations should then be subtracted; $3x - 2y = -3$, $3x + 5y = 60$, $-7y = -63$, $y = 9$.**

ERROR ANALYSIS ***Describe*** **and correct the error in finding the value of one of the variables in the given linear system.**

23. $5x - 7y = 16$
$-x - 7y = 8$

24. $3x - 2y = -3$
$5y = 60 - 3x$

5x − 7y = 16
−x − 7y = 8
4x = 24
x = 6

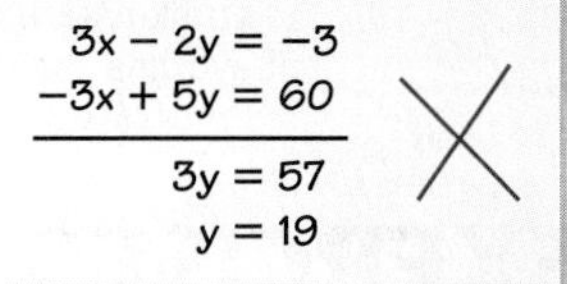

B **SOLVING LINEAR SYSTEMS** **Solve the linear system using elimination.**

25. $-x + \frac{1}{2}y = -19$ **(26, 14)**
$x - y = 12$

26. $\frac{1}{4}x - \frac{2}{3}y = 7$ **(4, −9)**
$\frac{1}{2}x + \frac{2}{3}y = -4$

27. $8x - \frac{1}{2}y = -38$ **(−4, 12)**
$\frac{1}{4}x - \frac{1}{2}y = -7$

28. $5.2x + 3.5y = 54$ **(5, 8)**
$-3.6x + 3.5y = 10$

29. $1.3x - 3y = -17.6$ **(−2, 5)**
$-1.3x + 4.5y = 25.1$

30. $-2.6x - 3.2y = 4.8$
$1.9x - 3.2y = -4.2$ **(−2, 0.125)**

31. $\frac{4}{5}x + \frac{2}{5}y = 14$ **(5, 25)**
$\frac{2}{5}y + \frac{1}{5}x = 11$

32. $2.7x + 1.5y = 36$ **(10, 6)**
$3.5y = 2.7x - 6$

33. $4 - 4.8x = 1.7y$ **(−2, 8)**
$12.8 + 1.7y = -13.2x$

34. WRITING AN EQUATION OF A LINE Use the following steps to write an equation of the line that passes through the points (1, 2) and (−4, 12).

a. Write a system of linear equations by substituting 1 for x and 2 for y in $y = mx + b$ and −4 for x and 12 for y in $y = mx + b$. **$2 = m + b$, $12 = -4m + b$**

b. Solve the system of linear equations from part (a). What is the slope of the line? What is the y-intercept? **slope: −2; y-intercept: 4**

c. Write an equation of the line that passes through (1, 2) and (−4, 12). **$y = -2x + 4$**

35. GEOMETRY The rectangle has a perimeter P of 14 feet, and twice its length ℓ is equal to 1 less than 4 times its width w. Write and solve a system of linear equations to find the length and the width of the rectangle. **$\ell = 4.5$ ft, $w = 2.5$ ft**

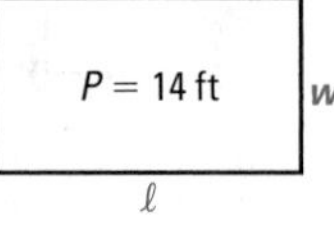

36. ★ SHORT RESPONSE Find the solution of the system of linear equations below. *Explain* your steps. **(−1, 3).** ***Sample answer:*** **First solve the system that consists of Equations 1 and 2 using elimination. Then check the solution for all three equations.**

$x + 3y = 8$ Equation 1
$x - 6y = -19$ Equation 2
$5x - 3y = -14$ Equation 3

C **37. CHALLENGE** For $a \neq 0$, what is the solution of the system $ax + 2y = 4$ and $ax - 3y = -6$? **(0, 2)**

38. CHALLENGE Solve for x, y, and z in the system of equations below. *Explain* your steps. **(−5, 4, 2).** ***Sample answer:*** **Subtract Equation 2 from Equation 1 to solve for y. Then substitute y into Equation 3 to solve for x. Then substitute x and y into Equation 1 or Equation 2 to solve for z. Check solution in all three equations.**

$x + 7y + 3z = 29$ Equation 1
$3z + x - 2y = -7$ Equation 2
$5y = 10 - 2x$ Equation 3

○ = WORKED-OUT SOLUTIONS on p. WS1 ★ = STANDARDIZED TEST PRACTICE

PROBLEM SOLVING

EXAMPLE 4 A on p. 446 for Exs. 39–41

39. **ROWING** During a practice, a 4 person crew team rows a rowing shell upstream (against the current) and then rows the same distance downstream (with the current). The shell moves upstream at a speed of 4.3 meters per second and downstream at a speed of 4.9 meters per second. The speed of the current remains constant. Use the models below to write and solve a system of equations to find the average speed of the shell in still water and the speed of the current. **speed in still water: 4.6 m/sec, speed of current: 0.3 m/sec**

Upstream

Speed of shell in still water − Speed of current = Speed of shell

Downstream

Speed of shell in still water + Speed of current = Speed of shell

@HomeTutor for problem solving help at classzone.com

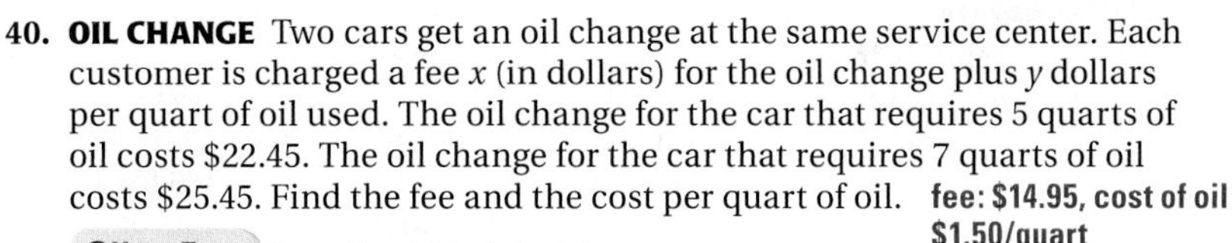

40. **OIL CHANGE** Two cars get an oil change at the same service center. Each customer is charged a fee x (in dollars) for the oil change plus y dollars per quart of oil used. The oil change for the car that requires 5 quarts of oil costs \$22.45. The oil change for the car that requires 7 quarts of oil costs \$25.45. Find the fee and the cost per quart of oil. **fee: \$14.95, cost of oil: \$1.50/quart**

@HomeTutor for problem solving help at classzone.com

41. **PHONES** Cellular phone ring tones can be monophonic or polyphonic. Monophonic ring tones play one tone at a time, and polyphonic ring tones play multiple tones at a time. The table shows the ring tones downloaded from a website by two customers. Use the information to find the cost of a monophonic ring tone and a polyphonic ring tone, assuming that all monophonic ring tones cost the same and all polyphonic ring tones cost the same. **monophonic ring tone: \$1.95, polyphonic ring tone: \$3.50**

Customer	Monophonic ring tones	Polyphonic ring tones	Total cost (dollars)
Julie	3	2	12.85
Tate	1	2	8.95

42. **MULTIPLE REPRESENTATIONS** For a floral arrangement class, Alicia has to create an arrangement of twigs and flowers that has a total of 9 objects. She has to pay for the twigs and flowers that she uses in her arrangement. Each twig costs \$1, and each flower costs \$3.

a. **Writing a System** Alicia spends \$15 on the twigs and flowers. Write and solve a linear system to find the number of twigs and the number of flowers she used.

b. **Making a Table** Make a table showing the number of twigs in the arrangement and the total cost of the arrangement when the number of flowers purchased is 0, 1, 2, 3, 4, or 5. Use the table to check your answer to part (a). **See margin.**

42a. Let x represent the number of twigs and y represent the number of flowers; $x + 3y = 15$, $x + y = 9$, 6 twigs and 3 flowers.

Avoiding Common Errors

Exercise 40 When some students use Example 4 as a model for this exercise, they may believe that they should subtract the x- and y-values for the first equation and add the x- and y-values for the second equation. Remind these students that the context of the problem determines whether they add or subtract the x- and y-values in each equation.

Study Strategy

Exercise 43 Suggest that students use Example 4 as a model for solving this problem. Point out that wind speed is comparable to current speed and that flying into the wind is comparable to going upstream, while flying with the wind is comparable to going downstream.

42b.

Flowers	Twigs	Cost
0	9	\$9
1	8	\$11
2	7	\$13
3	6	\$15
4	5	\$17
5	4	\$19

5 ASSESS AND RETEACH

Daily Homework Quiz

 **Transparency Available**

Solve the linear system using elimination.

1. $-5x + y = 18$
   $3x - y = -10$ **(−4, −2)**
2. $4x + 2y = 14$
   $4x - 3y = -11$ **(1, 5)**
3. $2x - y = -14$
   $y = 3x + 6$ **(8, 30)**
4. $x + 4y = 15$
   $2y = x - 9$ **(11, 1)**
5. A business center charges a flat fee to send faxes plus a fee per page. You send one fax with 4 pages for \$5.36 and another fax with 7 pages for \$7.88. Find the flat fee and the cost per page to send a fax. **flat fee: \$2, price per page: \$.84**

Online Quiz

Available at **classzone.com**

Diagnosis/Remediation

- Practice A, B, C in Chapter Resource Book
- Study Guide in Chapter Resource Book
- Practice Workbook
- @HomeTutor

Challenge

Additional challenge is available in the Chapter Resource Book.

B **43. MULTI-STEP PROBLEM** On a typical day with light winds, the 1800 mile flight from Charlotte, North Carolina, to Phoenix, Arizona, takes longer than the return trip because the plane has to fly into the wind.

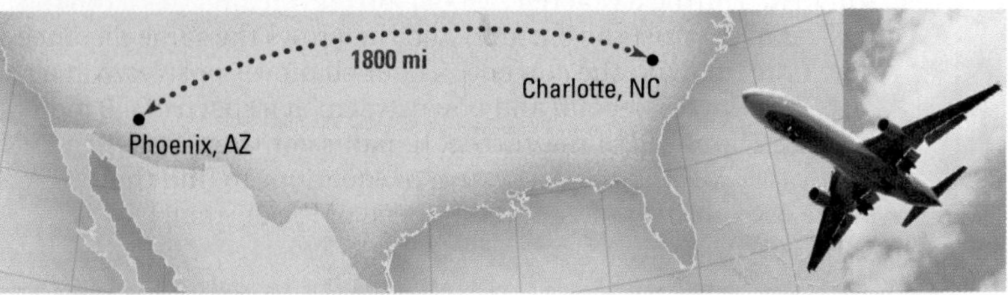

a. The flight from Charlotte to Phoenix is 4 hours 30 minutes long, and the flight from Phoenix to Charlotte is 4 hours long. Find the average speed (in miles per hour) of the airplane on the way to Phoenix and on the return trip to Charlotte. **flight to Phoenix: 400 mi/h, flight to Charlotte: 450 mi/h**

b. Let s be the speed (in miles per hour) of the plane with no wind, and let w be the speed (in miles per hour) of the wind. Use your answer to part (a) to write and solve a system of equations to find the speed of the plane with no wind and the speed of the wind.
$s + w = 450$, $s - w = 400$; plane: 425 mi/h, wind: 25 mi/h

44. ★ SHORT RESPONSE The students in the graduating classes at the three high schools in a school district have to pay for their caps and gowns. A cap-and-gown set costs x dollars, and an extra tassel costs y dollars. At one high school, students pay \$3262 for 215 cap-and-gown sets and 72 extra tassels. At another high school, students pay \$3346 for 221 cap-and-gown sets and 72 extra tassels. How much will students at the third high school pay for 218 cap-and-gown sets and 56 extra tassels? *Explain.*
\$3248. *Sample answer:* Each cap-and-gown costs \$14 and each extra tassel costs \$3.50.

C **45. CHALLENGE** A clothing manufacturer makes men's dress shirts. For the production process, an ideal sleeve length x (in centimeters) for each shirt size and an allowable deviation y (in centimeters) from the ideal length are established. The deviation is expressed as $\pm y$. For a specific shirt size, the minimum allowable sleeve length is 62.2 centimeters and the maximum allowable sleeve length is 64.8 centimeters. Find the ideal sleeve length and the allowable deviation.
ideal sleeve length: 63.5 cm, allowable deviation: 1.3 cm

MIXED REVIEW

Graph the equation. **46–49. See margin.**

46. $x - 5y = -12$ *(p. 225)*

47. $-2x + 3y = -15$ *(p. 225)*

48. $y + 9 = -(x + 2)$ *(p. 302)*

49. $y - 4 = \frac{2}{3}(x + 1)$ *(p. 302)*

Solve the linear system by graphing. Check your solution. *(p. 427)*

50. $y = x - 3$, $y = -x + 1$ **(2, −1)**

51. $y = 2$, $2x - 3y = 6$ **(6, 2)**

52. $2x + y = 6$, $6x - 2y = -12$ **(0, 6)**

PREVIEW
Prepare for Lesson 7.4 in Exs. 53–55.

Find the least common multiple of the pair of numbers. *(p. 910)*

53. 9, 12 **36**

54. 18, 24 **72**

55. 15, 20 **60**

46–49. See Additional Answers beginning on p. AA1.

7.4 Solve Linear Systems by Multiplying First

Before You solved linear systems by adding or subtracting.

Now You will solve linear systems by multiplying first.

Why So you can solve a problem about preparing food, as in Ex. 39.

Key Vocabulary
- **least common multiple,** *p. 910*

In a linear system like the one below, neither variable can be eliminated by adding or subtracting the equations. For systems like these, you can multiply one or both of the equations by a constant so that adding or subtracting the equations will eliminate one variable.

$$\begin{array}{lcl} 5x + 2y = 16 & \xrightarrow{\times 2} & 10x + 4y = 32 \\ 3x - 4y = 20 & \longrightarrow & 3x - 4y = 20 \end{array}$$

The new system is equivalent to the original system.

EXAMPLE 1 Multiply one equation, then add

Solve the linear system: $6x + 5y = 19$ Equation 1; $2x + 3y = 5$ Equation 2

Solution

STEP 1 **Multiply** Equation 2 by -3 so that the coefficients of x are opposites.

$$\begin{array}{lcl} 6x + 5y = 19 & & 6x + 5y = 19 \\ 2x + 3y = 5 & \xrightarrow{\times(-3)} & -6x - 9y = -15 \end{array}$$

STEP 2 **Add** the equations. $\quad -4y = 4$

ANOTHER WAY You can also multiply Equation 2 by 3 and subtract the equations.

STEP 3 **Solve** for y. $\quad y = -1$

STEP 4 **Substitute** -1 for y in either of the original equations and solve for x.

$2x + 3y = 5$ Write Equation 2.

$2x + 3(-1) = 5$ Substitute -1 for y.

$2x + (-3) = 5$ Multiply.

$2x = 8$ Subtract -3 from each side.

$x = 4$ Divide each side by 2.

▶ The solution is $(4, -1)$.

CHECK Substitute 4 for x and -1 for y in each of the original equations.

Equation 1	Equation 2
$6x + 5y = 19$	$2x + 3y = 5$
$6(4) + 5(-1) \stackrel{?}{=} 19$	$2(4) + 3(-1) \stackrel{?}{=} 5$
$19 = 19$ ✓	$5 = 5$ ✓

1 PLAN AND PREPARE

Warm-Up Exercises

Transparency Available

Solve the linear system.

1. $4x - 3y = 15$, $2x - 3y = 9$ **(3, −1)**
2. $-2x + y = -8$, $2x - 2y = 8$ **(4, 0)**
3. You row a canoe 10 miles upstream in 2.5 hours and 10 miles downstream in 2 hours. What is the average speed of the canoe in still water? **4.5 mi/h**

Notetaking Guide

Transparency Available

Promotes interactive learning and notetaking skills.

Pacing

Basic: 1 day

Average: 1 day

Advanced: 1 day

Block: 0.5 block with 7.5

- See *Teaching Guide/Lesson Plan.*

2 FOCUS AND MOTIVATE

Essential Question

Big Idea 2, p. 425

How do you solve linear systems by multiplying first? **Tell students they will learn how to answer this question by multiplying one or both equations by a constant and then adding or subtracting to eliminate a variable.**

NCTM STANDARDS

Standard 2: Analyze situations using algebraic symbols

Standard 10: Use representations to solve problems

Resource Planning Guide

Chapter Resource Book
- Teaching Guide/Lesson Plan
- Activity Master
- Practice levels A, B, C
- Study Guide
- Catch-up for Absent Students
- Problem Solving Workshop
- Challenge

Workbooks
- Notetaking Guide
- Practice Workbook

Teaching Options
- **Power Presentations** provides dynamic electronic teaching resources for the classroom.
- **Activity Generator** provides editable activities for all ability levels.

Interactive Technology
- Easy Planner
- Power Presentations
- Activity Generator
- Animated Algebra
- Test Generator
- Online Quiz
- eWorkbook
- eEdition
- @HomeTutor

Resources for English Learners
- Spanish Study Guide
- Multi-Language Visual Glossary
- Student Resources in Spanish

See also the *Differentiated Instruction Resources* for more strategies for meeting individual needs.

MULTIPLYING BOTH EQUATIONS To eliminate one variable when adding or subtracting equations in a linear system, you may need to multiply both equations by constants. Use the least common multiple of the coefficients of one of the variables to determine the constants.

$2x - 9y = 1$ → ×4 → $8x - 36y = 4$

$7x - 12y = 23$ → ×3 → $21x - 36y = 69$

The least common multiple of −9 and −12 is −36.

EXAMPLE 2 Multiply both equations, then subtract

Solve the linear system: $4x + 5y = 35$ Equation 1
$2y = 3x - 9$ Equation 2

Solution

STEP 1 **Arrange** the equations so that like terms are in columns.

$4x + 5y = 35$ Write Equation 1.

$-3x + 2y = -9$ Rewrite Equation 2.

ANOTHER WAY
You can also multiply Equation 1 by 3 and Equation 2 by 4. Then add the revised equations to eliminate *x*.

STEP 2 **Multiply** Equation 1 by 2 and Equation 2 by 5 so that the coeffcient of *y* in each equation is the least common multiple of 5 and 2, or 10.

$4x + 5y = 35$ → ×2 → $8x + 10y = 70$

$-3x + 2y = -9$ → ×5 → $-15x + 10y = -45$

STEP 3 **Subtract** the equations. $23x = 115$

STEP 4 **Solve** for *x*. → $x = 5$

STEP 5 **Substitute** 5 for *x* in either of the original equations and solve for *y*.

$4x + 5y = 35$ Write Equation 1.

$4(5) + 5y = 35$ Substitute 5 for *x*.

$y = 3$ Solve for *y*.

▶ The solution is (5, 3).

CHECK Substitute 5 for *x* and 3 for *y* in each of the original equations.

Equation 1	Equation 2
$4x + 5y = 35$	$2y = 3x - 9$
$4(5) + 5(3) \stackrel{?}{=} 35$	$2(3) \stackrel{?}{=} 3(5) - 9$
$35 = 35$ ✓	$6 = 6$ ✓

Animated Algebra at classzone.com

✓ **GUIDED PRACTICE** for Examples 1 and 2

Solve the linear system using elimination.

1. $6x - 2y = 1$ **(−0.5, −2)**
   $-2x + 3y = -5$

2. $2x + 5y = 3$ **(9, −3)**
   $3x + 10y = -3$

3. $3x - 7y = 5$ **(−10, −5)**
   $9y = 5x + 5$

Motivating the Lesson

A concession stand offers two different soft drink specials. One special has 3 large drinks and 2 medium drinks for \$15. The other has 2 large drinks and 3 medium drinks for \$13.75. By knowing how to use multiplication with elimination to solve a linear system, you can determine the cost of each drink size.

3 TEACH

Extra Example 1

Solve the linear system.
$2x + y = -9$
$4x + 11y = 9$ **(−6, 3)**

Key Question to Ask for Example 1

- Why do you eliminate *x* rather than *y*? **Since 6 is a multiple of 2, it is easier to eliminate *x*. To eliminate *y*, you would need to multiply by a fraction, either $\frac{5}{3}$ or $\frac{3}{5}$.**

Extra Example 2

Solve the linear system.
$2x - 3y = 6$
$4y = -7x - 8$ **(0, −2)**

Key Question to Ask for Example 2

- Is it possible to eliminate *x* by multiplying each equation by a constant? Explain. **You can eliminate *x* by multiplying Equation 1 by 3 and Equation 2 by 4.**

Animated Algebra
classzone.com

An **Animated Algebra** activity is available online for **Example 2**. This activity is also part of **Power Presentations**.

Differentiated Instruction

English Learners Caution students not to confuse the words "equal" and "equivalent". In **Example 2**, multiplying the first equation by 2 and the second equation by 5 produces "equivalent" equations, because the solution set is not changed. The sides of each equation are "equal".

See also the *Differentiated Instruction Resources* for more strategies.

EXAMPLE 3 Standardized Test Practice

Darlene is making a quilt that has alternating stripes of regular quilting fabric and sateen fabric. She spends \$76 on a total of 16 yards of the two fabrics at a fabric store. Which system of equations can be used to find the amount x (in yards) of regular quilting fabric and the amount y (in yards) of sateen fabric she purchased?

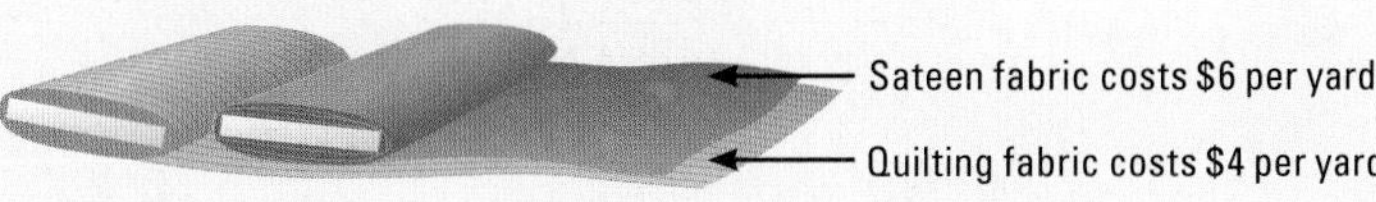
Sateen fabric costs \$6 per yard.
Quilting fabric costs \$4 per yard.

ELIMINATE CHOICES
You can eliminate choice A because $x + y$ cannot equal both 16 and 76.

Ⓐ $x + y = 16$
$x + y = 76$

Ⓑ $x + y = 16$
$4x + 6y = 76$

Ⓒ $x + y = 76$
$4x + 6y = 16$

Ⓓ $x + y = 16$
$6x + 4y = 76$

Solution

Write a system of equations where x is the number of yards of regular quilting fabric purchased and y is the number of yards of sateen fabric purchased.

Equation 1: Amount of fabric

Amount of quilting fabric	+	Amount of sateen fabric	=	Total yards of fabric
x	+	y	=	16

Equation 2: Cost of fabric

Quilting fabric price (dollars/yd)	·	Amount of quilting fabric (yd)	+	Sateen fabric price (dollars/yd)	·	Amount of sateen fabric (yd)	=	Total cost (dollars)
4	·	x	+	6	·	y	=	76

The system of equations is: $x + y = 16$ Equation 1
$4x + 6y = 76$ Equation 2

▸ The correct answer is B. Ⓐ Ⓑ Ⓒ Ⓓ

✓ GUIDED PRACTICE for Example 3

4. **SOCCER** A sports equipment store is having a sale on soccer balls. A soccer coach purchases 10 soccer balls and 2 soccer ball bags for \$155. Another soccer coach purchases 12 soccer balls and 3 soccer ball bags for \$189. Find the cost of a soccer ball and the cost of a soccer ball bag. **soccer ball: \$14.50, soccer ball bag: \$5**

Extra Example 3

Mr. Alvarado bought a total of 20 pounds of grass seed at the nursery for \$168. He paid \$9 per pound for Kentucky bluegrass and \$6 per pound for Tall Fescue. Which system of equations can be used to find the amount x (in pounds) of Kentucky bluegrass and the amount y (in pounds) of Tall Fescue Mr. Alvarado purchased? **D**

Ⓐ $x + y = 168$
$9x + 6y = 20$

Ⓑ $x + y = 20$
$6x + 9y = 168$

Ⓒ $x + y = 168$
$6x + 9y = 20$

Ⓓ $x + y = 20$
$9x + 6y = 168$

Mathematical Reasoning

You may want to point out that choice C does not make sense mathematically because one yard each of quilting fabric and sateen cannot cost \$76 if one costs \$4 per yard and one costs \$6 per yard.

Closing the Lesson

Have students summarize the major points of the lesson and answer the Essential Question: How do you solve linear systems by multiplying first?

- **Multiply one or both equations of a linear system by a constant or constants and then add or subtract to eliminate a variable.**

Determine whether you need to multiply one equation or both equations by constants so you can eliminate one of the variables. After multiplying, use addition or subtraction to eliminate the variable. Solve the equation and then substitute in one of the original equations to find the value of the eliminated variable.

4 PRACTICE AND APPLY

Assignment Guide

Answer Transparencies available for all exercises

Basic:
Day 1: SRH p. 911 Exs. 25, 26, 32, 36
pp. 454–457
Exs. 1, 2, 3–17 odd, 18–25, 37–41, 46–58 even

Average:
Day 1: pp. 454–457
Exs. 1, 2, 6–8, 13–20, 21–33 odd, 34, 37–42, 45–57 odd

Advanced:
Day 1: pp. 454–457
Exs. 1, 7, 8, 15–18, 21–36*, 39–44*, 47, 52, 58

Block:
pp. 454–457
Exs. 1, 2, 6–8, 13–20, 21–33 odd, 34, 37–42, 45–57 odd (with 7.5)

Differentiated Instruction

See *Differentiated Instruction Resources* for suggestions on addressing the needs of a diverse classroom.

Homework Check

For a quick check of student understanding of key concepts, go over the following exercises:

Basic: 5, 11, 13, 37, 38

Average: 7, 14, 21, 38, 39

Advanced: 8, 16, 28, 39, 40

Extra Practice

- Student Edition, p. 944
- Chapter Resource Book: Practice levels A, B, C

Practice Worksheet

An easily-readable reduced practice page (with answers) for this lesson can be found on p. 424C.

CONCEPT SUMMARY — *For Your Notebook*

Methods for Solving Linear Systems

Method	Example	When to Use
Table (p. 426)	see table below	When x-values are integers, so that equal values can be seen in the table
Graphing (p. 427)	graph of $3x - 2y = 2$ and $x + y = 4$	When you want to see the lines that the equations represent
Substitution (p. 435)	$\mathbf{y = 4 - 2x}$ $4x + 2y = 8$	When one equation is already solved for x or y
Addition (p. 444)	$4x + \mathbf{7y} = 15$ $6x - \mathbf{7y} = 5$	When the coefficients of one variable are opposites
Subtraction (p. 445)	$\mathbf{3x} + 5y = -13$ $\mathbf{3x} + y = -5$	When the coefficients of one variable are the same
Multiplication (p. 451)	$9x + 2y = 38$ $3x - 5y = 7$	When no corresponding coefficients are the same or opposites

x	$y = 2x$	$y = 3x - 1$
0	0	−1
1	2	2
2	4	5

7.4 EXERCISES

HOMEWORK KEY
○ = **WORKED-OUT SOLUTIONS** on p. WS17 for Exs. 15 and 39
★ = **STANDARDIZED TEST PRACTICE** Exs. 2, 18, 34, 41, and 42
◆ = **MULTIPLE REPRESENTATIONS** Ex. 40

SKILL PRACTICE

A

1. **VOCABULARY** What is the least common multiple of 12 and 18? **36**

2. ★ **WRITING** *Explain* how to solve the linear system using the elimination method.
$2x - 3y = -4$ **Equation 1**
$7x + 9y = -5$ **Equation 2**
***Sample answer:* Multiply Equation 1 by 3 and add to Equation 2. Then solve for *x* and substitute to find *y*.**

EXAMPLE 1 on p. 451 for Exs. 3–8

SOLVING LINEAR SYSTEMS Solve the linear system using elimination.

3. $x + y = 2$ **(1, 1)**
$2x + 7y = 9$

4. $3x - 2y = 3$ **(5, 6)**
$-x + y = 1$

5. $4x + 3y = 8$ **(5, −4)**
$x - 2y = 13$

6. $10x - 9y = 46$ **(19, 16)**
$-2x + 3y = 10$

7. $8x - 5y = 11$ **(2, 1)**
$4x - 3y = 5$

8. $11x - 20y = 28$ **(8, 3)**
$3x + 4y = 36$

EXAMPLE 2
on p. 452 for Exs. 9–20

19. *Sample answer:* The two equations should be subtracted rather than added; $-x = -9, x = 9$.

20. *Sample answer:* The right side of the equations were not multiplied; $27x + 24y = 33$, $28x + 24y = 36$, $-x = -3, x = 3$.

SOLVING LINEAR SYSTEMS Solve the linear system using elimination.

9. $4x - 3y = 8$ $(-7, -12)$
$5x - 2y = -11$

10. $-2x - 5y = 9$ $(-17, 5)$
$3x + 11y = 4$

11. $7x - 6y = -1$ $(5, 6)$
$5x - 4y = 1$

12. $7x + 3y = -12$ $(-6, 10)$
$2x + 5y = 38$

13. $9x - 8y = 4$ $(4, 4)$
$2x - 3y = -4$

14. $12x - 7y = -2$ $(1, 2)$
$-8x + 11y = 14$

15. $9x + 2y = 39$ $(5, -3)$
$6x + 13y = -9$

16. $-7x + 10y = 11$ $(7, 6)$
$-8x + 15y = 34$

17. $-14x + 15y = 15$ $\left(4\frac{2}{7}, 5\right)$
$21x - 20y = -10$

18. ★ **MULTIPLE CHOICE** Which ordered pair is a solution of the linear system $15x + 8y = 6$ and $25x + 12y = 14$? **D**

Ⓐ $(-3, -2)$ Ⓑ $(-3, 2)$ Ⓒ $(-2, -3)$ Ⓓ $(2, -3)$

ERROR ANALYSIS *Describe* and correct the error when solving the linear system. **19–20. See margin.**

19.

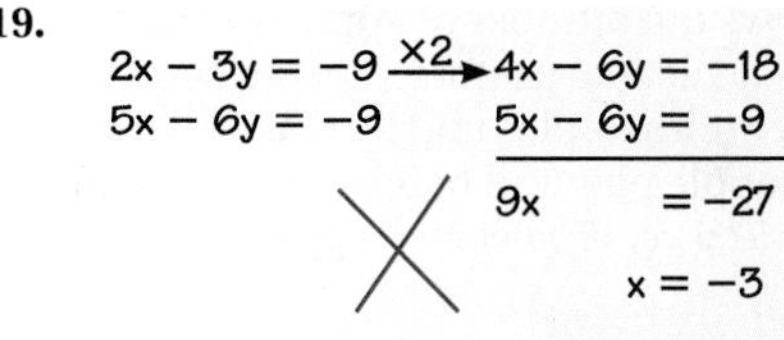

20.

B **SOLVING LINEAR SYSTEMS** Solve the linear system using any algebraic method.

21. $3x + 2y = 4$ $(2, -1)$
$2y = 8 - 5x$

22. $4x - 5y = 18$ $\left(3\frac{4}{11}, -\frac{10}{11}\right)$
$3x = y + 11$

23. $8x - 9y = -15$ $\left(-4\frac{5}{22}, -2\frac{1}{11}\right)$
$-4x = 19 + y$

24. $0.3x + 0.1y = -0.1$ $(-1, 2)$
$-x + y = 3$

25. $4.4x - 3.6y = 7.6$ $(5, 4)$
$x - y = 1$

26. $3x - 2y = -20$ $(-2, 7)$
$x + 1.2y = 6.4$

27. $0.2x - 1.5y = -1$ $(10, 2)$
$x - 4.5y = 1$

28. $1.5x - 3.5y = -5$ $(20, 10)$
$-1.2x + 2.5y = 1$

29. $4.9x + 2.4y = 7.4$ $(2, -1)$
$0.7x + 3.6y = -2.2$

30. $x + y = 0$ $(2, -2)$
$\frac{1}{2}x - \frac{1}{2}y = 2$

31. $3x + y = \frac{1}{3}$ $\left(\frac{1}{3}, -\frac{2}{3}\right)$
$2x - 3y = \frac{8}{3}$

32. $\frac{3}{5}x - \frac{3}{4}y = -3$ $(10, 12)$
$\frac{2}{5}x + \frac{1}{3}y = 8$

33. **GEOMETRY** A rectangle has a perimeter of 18 inches. A new rectangle is formed by doubling the width w and tripling the length ℓ, as shown. The new rectangle has a perimeter P of 46 inches.

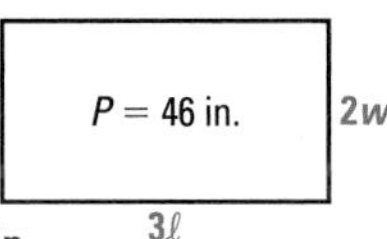

a. Write and solve a system of linear equations to find the length and width of the original rectangle. $2\ell + 2w = 18$, $6\ell + 4w = 46$; **length: 5 in., width: 4 in.**

b. Find the length and width of the new rectangle. **length: 15 in., width: 8 in.**

34. ★ **WRITING** For which values of a can you solve the linear system $ax + 3y = 2$ and $4x + 5y = 6$ without multiplying first? *Explain.*
4 and −4. ***Sample answer:*** **For these values, you can add or subtract to eliminate the x term.**

C **CHALLENGE** Find the values of a and b so that the linear system has the given solution.

$ax - by = 4$ Equation 1
$bx - ay = 10$ Equation 2

35. $(4, 2)$ $a = 3, b = 4$ **36.** $(2, 1)$ $a = 6, b = 8$

Avoiding Common Errors

Exercises 9–17, 21–32 Some students may fail to subtract the equations in a linear system when the coefficients of a variable are the same. Suggest that they give the equations a second look to make sure that the coefficients of the eliminated variable are opposites.

Graphing Calculator

Exercises 24–32 Students may want to graph these linear systems to check their solutions. They should enter the equations using **y=**, and adjust the standard viewing window if necessary. The intersect feature will show the coordinates of the intersection point.

Mathematical Reasoning

Exercises 37–40 Before students begin these exercises, you may want to discuss how a system of linear equations represents a real-world situation. You could point out in Exercise 37 that one equation represents the total number of books and the other equation represents the cost of the books. In contrast, in Exercise 38, one equation represents the number of individual songs and albums and their cost for one person and the other equation represents the same information for a different person.

Internet Reference

Exercise 39 Information about the various apple varieties can be found at http://urbanext.illinois.edu/apples/varieties.html

40b.

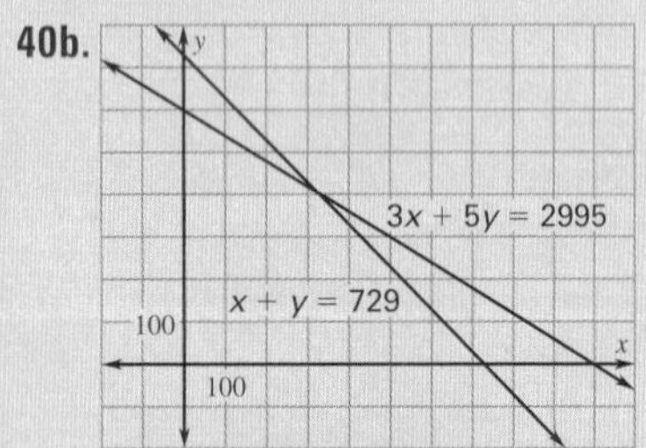

42. ***Sample answer:*** **Two cars are traveling on the same route. One car leaves 30 minutes before the other car and travels at a rate of 40 miles per hour. If the other car travels 45 miles per hour, how many hours will it take for the second car to catch the first car? 4 h, the second car will have to travel 4 hours in order to catch the first car.**

PROBLEM SOLVING

EXAMPLE 3 A on p. 453 for Exs. 37–39

37. BOOK SALE A library is having a book sale to raise money. Hardcover books cost \$4 each and paperback books cost \$2 each. A person spends \$26 for 8 books. How many hardcover books did she purchase? **5 hardcover books**

@HomeTutor for problem solving help at classzone.com

38. MUSIC A website allows users to download individual songs or an entire album. All individual songs cost the same to download, and all albums cost the same to download. Ryan pays \$14.94 to download 5 individual songs and 1 album. Seth pays \$22.95 to download 3 individual songs and 2 albums. How much does the website charge to download a song? an entire album? **\$.99; \$9.99**

@HomeTutor for problem solving help at classzone.com

(39.) FARM PRODUCTS The table shows the number of apples needed to make the apple pies and applesauce sold at a farm store. During a recent apple picking at the farm, 169 Granny Smith apples and 95 Golden Delicious apples were picked. How many apple pies and batches of applesauce can be made if every apple is used? **21 pies, 16 batches of applesauce**

Type of apple	Granny Smith	Golden Delicious
Needed for a pie	5	3
Needed for a batch of applesauce	4	2

B

40. ◆ **MULTIPLE REPRESENTATIONS** Tickets for admission to a high school football game cost \$3 for students and \$5 for adults. During one game, \$2995 was collected from the sale of 729 tickets.

a. Writing a System Write and solve a system of linear equations to find the number of tickets sold to students and the number of tickets sold to adults.

b. Drawing a Graph Graph the system of linear equations. Use the graph to determine whether your answer to part (a) is reasonable. **The answer is reasonable; see margin for art.**

40a. Let x represent the number of student tickets and y represent the number of adult tickets; $3x + 5y = 2995$, $x + y = 729$, 325 student tickets and 404 adult tickets.

41. ★ **SHORT RESPONSE** A dim sum restaurant offers two sizes of dishes: small and large. All small dishes cost the same and all large dishes cost the same. The bills show the cost of the food before the tip is included. What will 3 small and 2 large dishes cost before the tip is included? *Explain.*

41. \$16.50; a small costs \$2.90, and a large costs \$3.90; $3(2.90) + 2(3.90) = 16.50$.

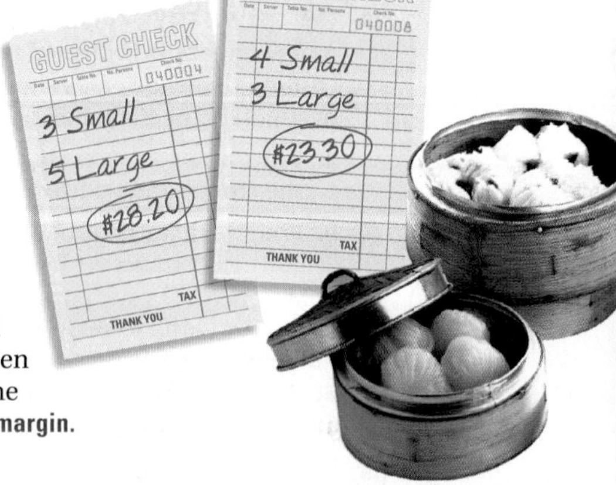

42. ★ **OPEN-ENDED** *Describe* a real-world problem that can be solved using a system of linear equations. Then solve the problem and explain what the solution means in this situation. **See margin.**

○ = WORKED-OUT SOLUTIONS on p. WS1 ★ = STANDARDIZED TEST PRACTICE ◆ = MULTIPLE REPRESENTATIONS

C 43. **INVESTMENTS** Matt invested \$2000 in stocks and bonds. This year the bonds paid 8% interest, and the stocks paid 6% in dividends. Matt received a total of \$144 in interest and dividends. How much money did he invest in stocks? in bonds? **\$800; \$1200**

44. **CHALLENGE** You drive a car 45 miles at an average speed r (in miles per hour) to reach your destination. Due to traffic, your average speed on the return trip is $\frac{3}{4}r$. The round trip took a total of 1 hour 45 minutes. Find the average speed for each leg of your trip. **first leg: 60 mi/h, second leg: 45 mi/h**

MIXED REVIEW

Graph the equation. *(pp. 215, 225, 244)* **45–50. See margin.**

45. $x - 8y = -10$
46. $-2x + 5y = -15$
47. $\frac{1}{4}x + \frac{1}{2}y = 8$
48. $y = \frac{2}{3}x - 1$
49. $y = -9x + 2$
50. $y - 1 = 2x - 7$

PREVIEW Prepare for Lesson 7.5 in Exs. 51–52.

Determine which lines are parallel. *(p. 244)*

51. 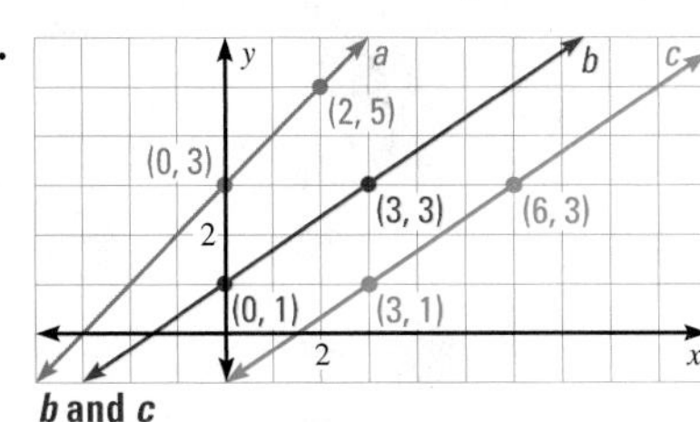

b and c

52. 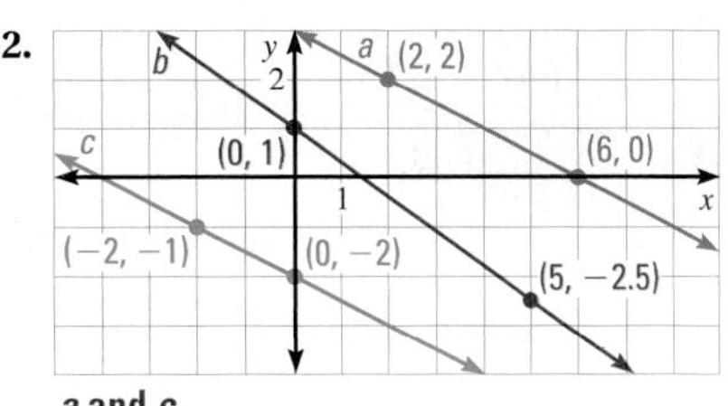

a and c

Solve the linear system using any method. *(pp. 427, 435, 444, 451)*

53. $y = 4x - 9$, $y = -8x + 15$ **(2, −1)**
54. $y = -2x + 20$, $y = -6x + 40$ **(5, 10)**
55. $x + 2y = 0$, $-x = y + 3$ **(−6, 3)**
56. $x + 2y = 2$, $-x + y = -11$ **(8, −3)**
57. $7x - 8y = -15$, $5x + 8y = 3$ **(−1, 1)**
58. $8x + y = 5$, $-2x + y = 0$ **(0.5, 1)**

QUIZ *for Lessons 7.3–7.4*

Solve the linear system using elimination. *(pp. 444, 451)*

1. $x + y = 4$, $-3x + y = -8$ **(3, 1)**
2. $2x - y = 2$, $6x - y = -2$ **(−1, −4)**
3. $x + y = 5$, $-x + y = -3$ **(4, 1)**
4. $x + 3y = -10$, $-x + 5y = -30$ **(5, −5)**
5. $x + 3y = 10$, $3x - y = 13$ **(4.9, 1.7)**
6. $x + 7y = 10$, $x + 2y = -8$ **(−15.2, 3.6)**
7. $4x - y = -2$, $3x + 2y = 7$ $\left(\frac{3}{11}, 3\frac{1}{11}\right)$
8. $x + 3y = 1$, $5x + 6y = 14$ **(4, −1)**
9. $3x + y = 21$, $x + y = 1$ **(10, −9)**
10. $2x - 3y = -5$, $5x + 2y = 16$ **(2, 3)**
11. $7x + 2y = 13$, $4x + 3y = 13$ **(1, 3)**
12. $\frac{1}{3}x + 5y = -3$, $-\frac{2}{3}x + 6y = -10$ **(6, −1)**

5 ASSESS AND RETEACH

Daily Homework Quiz

Transparency Available

Solve the linear system using elimination.

1. $8x + 3y = 12$, $-2x + y = 4$ **(0, 4)**
2. $-3x + 2y = 7$, $5x - 4y = -15$ **(1, 5)**
3. $-7x - 3y = 11$, $4x - 2y = 16$ **(1, −6)**
4. A recreation center charges nonmembers \$3 to use the pool and \$5 to use the basketball courts. A person pays \$42 to use the recreation facilities 12 times. How many times did the person use the pool? **9 times**

 **Online Quiz**

Available at **classzone.com**

Diagnosis/Remediation

- Practice A, B, C in Chapter Resource Book
- Study Guide in Chapter Resource Book
- Practice Workbook
- @HomeTutor

Challenge

Additional challenge is available in the Chapter Resource Book.

Quiz

An easily-readable reduced copy of the quiz (with answers) on Lessons 7.3–7.4 from the Assessment Book can be found on p. 424F.

45–50. See Additional Answers beginning on p. AA1.

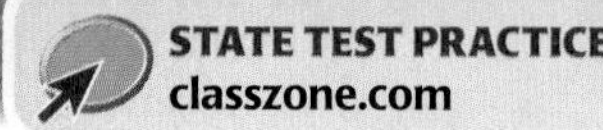

1c. speed in still air: 67.5 km/h, wind speed: 7.5 km/h

2. \$12. *Sample answer:* Potato salad costs \$3.25 per pound, and coleslaw costs \$2.75 per pound. So 2 pounds of each costs \$12.

4. *Sample answer:* You have \$75 to spend on 10 items. Small items cost \$5 each and large items cost \$10 each. How many of each item can you buy? Linear system: $5x + 10y = 75$, $x + y = 10$. Solution: $x = 5$, $y = 5$. You can buy 5 small items and 5 large items for \$75.

5. No. *Sample answer:* After 30 minutes the balloon from Newman Park remains higher than the balloon from Kirby Park.

6b. 250 milliliters of 10% acid and 90% water mix, and 250 milliliters of the 30% acid and 70% water mix

Lessons 7.1–7.4

1. **MULTI-STEP PROBLEM** Flying into the wind, a helicopter takes 15 minutes to travel 15 kilometers. The return flight takes 12 minutes. The wind speed remains constant during the trip.
   a. Find the helicopter's average speed (in kilometers per hour) for each leg of the trip. **first leg: 60 km/h, second leg: 75 km/h**
   b. Write a system of linear equations that represents the situation. $r - w = 60$, $r + w = 75$
   c. What is the helicopter's average speed in still air? What is the speed of the wind? **See margin.**

2. **SHORT RESPONSE** At a grocery store, a customer pays a total of \$9.70 for 1.8 pounds of potato salad and 1.4 pounds of coleslaw. Another customer pays a total of \$6.55 for 1 pound of potato salad and 1.2 pounds of coleslaw. How much do 2 pounds of potato salad and 2 pounds of coleslaw cost? *Explain.* **See margin.**

3. **GRIDDED ANSWER** During one day, two computers are sold at a computer store. The two customers each arrange payment plans with the salesperson. The graph shows the amount y of money (in dollars) paid for the computers after x months. After how many months will each customer have paid the same amount? **4 mo**

4. **OPEN-ENDED** *Describe* a real-world problem that can be modeled by a linear system. Then solve the system and interpret the solution in the context of the problem. **See margin.**

5. **SHORT RESPONSE** A hot air balloon is launched at Kirby Park, and it ascends at a rate of 7200 feet per hour. At the same time, a second hot air balloon is launched at Newman Park, and it ascends at a rate of 4000 feet per hour. Both of the balloons stop ascending after 30 minutes. The diagram shows the altitude of each park. Are the hot air balloons ever at the same height at the same time? *Explain.* **See margin.**

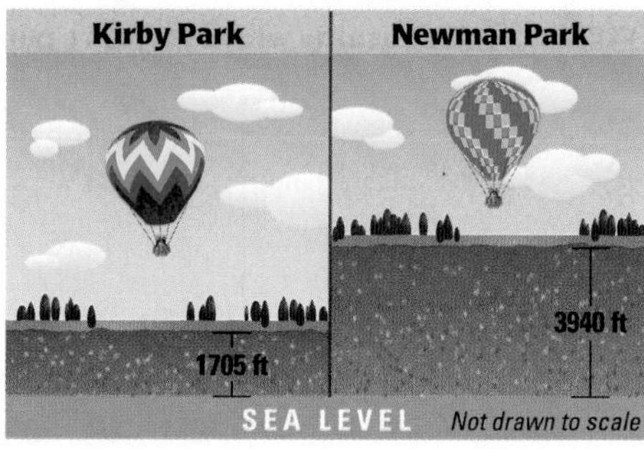

6. **EXTENDED RESPONSE** A chemist needs 500 milliliters of a 20% acid and 80% water mix for a chemistry experiment. The chemist combines x milliliters of a 10% acid and 90% water mix and y milliliters of a 30% acid and 70% water mix to make the 20% acid and 80% water mix.
   a. Write a linear system that represents the situation. $0.1x + 0.3y = 0.2 \cdot 500$, $x + y = 500$
   b. How many milliliters of the 10% acid and 90% water mix and the 30% acid and 70% water mix are combined to make the 20% acid and 80% water mix? **See margin.**
   c. The chemist also needs 500 milliliters of a 15% acid and 85% water mix. Does the chemist need more of the 10% acid and 90% water mix than the 30% acid and 70% water mix to make this new mix? *Explain.* **More of the 10% acid and 90% water mix. *Sample answer:* Adding more of the 30% acid and 70% water mix would raise the percent of acid, not lower it.**

7.5 Solve Special Types of Linear Systems

Before You found the solution of a linear system.
Now You will identify the number of solutions of a linear system.
Why? So you can compare distances traveled, as in Ex. 39.

Key Vocabulary
- **inconsistent system**
- **consistent dependent system**
- **system of linear equations,** *p. 427*
- **parallel,** *p. 244*

A linear system can have no solution or infinitely many solutions. A linear system has no solution when the graphs of the equations are parallel. A linear system with no solution is called an **inconsistent system**.

A linear system has infinitely many solutions when the graphs of the equations are the same line. A linear system with infinitely many solutions is called a **consistent dependent system**.

EXAMPLE 1 A linear system with no solution

Show that the linear system has no solution.

$3x + 2y = 10$ Equation 1
$3x + 2y = 2$ Equation 2

Solution

METHOD 1 Graphing

REVIEW GRAPHING
For help with graphing linear equations, see pp. 215, 225, and 244.

Graph the linear system.

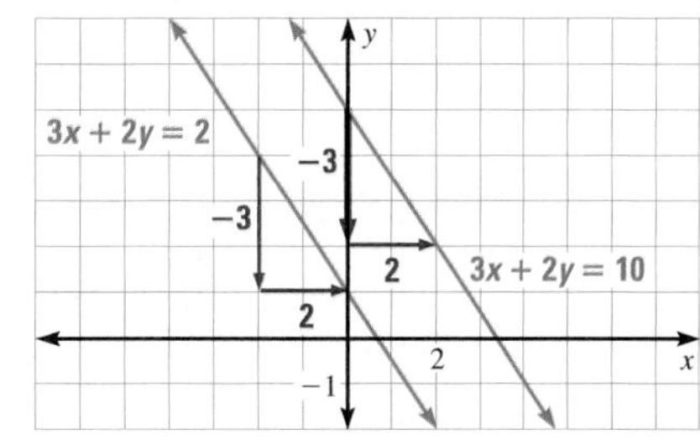

▸ The lines are parallel because they have the same slope but different y-intercepts. Parallel lines do not intersect, so the system has no solution.

METHOD 2 Elimination

Subtract the equations.

$$\begin{array}{r} 3x + 2y = 10 \\ 3x + 2y = 2 \\ \hline 0 = 8 \end{array}$$ ← This is a false statement.

IDENTIFY TYPES OF SYSTEMS
The linear system in Example 1 is called an inconsistent system because the lines do not intersect (are not consistent).

▸ The variables are eliminated and you are left with a false statement regardless of the values of x and y. This tells you that the system has no solution.

Animated Algebra at classzone.com

1 PLAN AND PREPARE

Warm-Up Exercises

Transparency Available

1. Solve the linear system.
$2x + 3y = -9$
$x - 2y = 6$ **(0, −3)**
2. You buy 8 pencils for $8 at the bookstore. Standard pencils cost $.85 and specialty pencils cost $1.25. How many specialty pencils did you buy? **3 specialty pencils**

Notetaking Guide

Transparency Available

Promotes interactive learning and notetaking skills.

Pacing

Basic: 2 days
Average: 2 days
Advanced: 2 days
Block: 0.5 block with 7.4
0.5 block with 7.6
- See *Teaching Guide/Lesson Plan.*

2 FOCUS AND MOTIVATE

Essential Question

Big Idea 1, p. 425

How can you identify the number of solutions of a linear system? **Tell students they will learn how to answer this question by graphing and solving linear systems and by looking at the slopes and the *y*-intercepts of the equations.**

NCTM STANDARDS

Standard 2: Analyze situations using algebraic symbols

Standard 3: Describe spatial relationships using coordinate geometry

Resource Planning Guide

Chapter Resource Book
- Teaching Guide/Lesson Plan
- Activity Master
- Practice levels A, B, C
- Study Guide
- Catch-up for Absent Students
- Application
- Challenge

Workbooks
- Notetaking Guide
- Practice Workbook

Teaching Options
- **Power Presentations** provides dynamic electronic teaching resources for the classroom.
- **Activity Generator** provides editable activities for all ability levels.

Interactive Technology
- Easy Planner
- Power Presentations
- Activity Generator
- Animated Algebra
- Test Generator
- Online Quiz
- eWorkbook
- eEdition
- @HomeTutor

Resources for English Learners
- Spanish Study Guide
- Multi-Language Visual Glossary
- Student Resources in Spanish

See also the *Differentiated Instruction Resources* for more strategies for meeting individual needs.

Motivating the Lesson

A group of people bought 15 bus tickets and 12 transfers for \$63. Another group bought 5 bus tickets and 4 transfers for \$21. You want to know the cost of one bus ticket. By knowing how to identify whether a system has one solution, no solution, or infinitely many solutions, you will be able to determine if you have enough information to find the cost of one ticket.

3 TEACH

Extra Example 1

Show that the linear system has no solution.

$2x - 3y = 6$

$2x - 3y = -4$

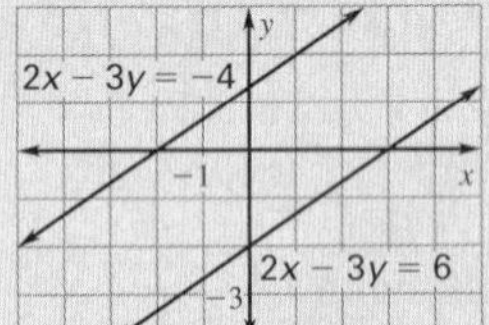

The lines are parallel, so the system has no solution.

Animated Algebra
classzone.com

An **Animated Algebra** activity is available online for **Example 1**. This activity is also part of **Power Presentations**.

Extra Example 2

Show that the linear system has infinitely many solutions.

$4x - 2y = 8$

$y = 2x - 4$

Substitute $2x - 4$ for y in the first equation.

$4x - 2(2x - 4) = 8$

$4x - 4x + 8 = 8$

$8 = 8$

The statement is true; the system has infinitely many solutions.

EXAMPLE 2 A linear system with infinitely many solutions

Show that the linear system has infinitely many solutions.

$x - 2y = -4$ **Equation 1**

$y = \frac{1}{2}x + 2$ **Equation 2**

Solution

METHOD 1 Graphing

Graph the linear system.

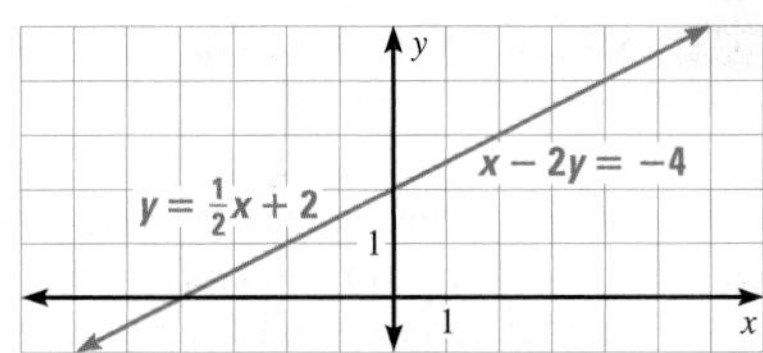

▸ The equations represent the same line, so any point on the line is a solution. So, the linear system has infinitely many solutions.

METHOD 2 Substitution

Substitute $\frac{1}{2}x + 2$ for y in Equation 1 and solve for x.

$x - 2y = -4$ **Write Equation 1.**

$x - 2\left(\frac{1}{2}x + 2\right) = -4$ **Substitute $\frac{1}{2}x + 2$ for y.**

$-4 = -4$ **Simplify.**

▸ The variables are eliminated and you are left with a statement that is true regardless of the values of x and y. This tells you that the system has infinitely many solutions.

IDENTIFY TYPES OF SYSTEMS

The linear system in Example 2 is called a consistent dependent system because the lines intersect (are consistent) and the equations are equivalent (are dependent).

GUIDED PRACTICE for Examples 1 and 2

Tell whether the linear system has *no solution* or *infinitely many solutions*. *Explain.*

1. $5x + 3y = 6$
$-5x - 3y = 3$

2. $y = 2x - 4$
$-6x + 3y = -12$

1. No solution. ***Sample answer:*** **When you solve the system you get $0 = 9$, which is a false statement.**

2. Infinitely many solutions. ***Sample answer:*** **When you solve the system you get $-12 = -12$, which is a true statement.**

IDENTIFYING THE NUMBER OF SOLUTIONS When the equations of a linear system are written in slope-intercept form, you can identify the number of solutions of the system by looking at the slopes and y-intercepts of the lines.

Number of solutions	Slopes and *y*-intercepts
One solution	Different slopes
No solution	Same slope Different *y*-intercepts
Infinitely many solutions	Same slope Same *y*-intercept

Differentiated Instruction

Inclusion Some students may need help understanding the concept of linear dependence. In **Example 2**, have students solve $x - 2y = 24$ for y. By doing so, students will get the second equation. This shows that the two equations are algebraically equivalent.

See also the *Differentiated Instruction Resources* for more strategies.

EXAMPLE 3 Identify the number of solutions

Without solving the linear system, tell whether the linear system has *one solution*, *no solution*, or *infinitely many solutions*.

a. $5x + y = -2$ Equation 1
$-10x - 2y = 4$ Equation 2

b. $6x + 2y = 3$ Equation 1
$6x + 2y = -5$ Equation 2

Solution

a. $y = -5x - 2$ **Write Equation 1 in slope-intercept form.**

$y = -5x - 2$ **Write Equation 2 in slope-intercept form.**

▶ Because the lines have the same slope and the same y-intercept, the system has infinitely many solutions.

b. $y = -3x + \frac{3}{2}$ **Write Equation 1 in slope-intercept form.**

$y = -3x - \frac{5}{2}$ **Write Equation 2 in slope-intercept form.**

▶ Because the lines have the same slope but different y-intercepts, the system has no solution.

EXAMPLE 4 Write and solve a system of linear equations

ART An artist wants to sell prints of her paintings. She orders a set of prints for each of two of her paintings. Each set contains regular prints and glossy prints, as shown in the table. Find the cost of one glossy print.

Regular	Glossy	Cost
45	30	$465
15	10	$155

Solution

STEP 1 **Write** a linear system. Let x be the cost (in dollars) of a regular print, and let y be the cost (in dollars) of a glossy print.

$45x + 30y = 465$ **Cost of prints for one painting**
$15x + 10y = 155$ **Cost of prints for other painting**

STEP 2 **Solve** the linear system using elimination.

$45x + 30y = 465$ → $45x + 30y = 465$
$15x + 10y = 155$ **× (−3)** → $-45x - 30y = -465$

$0 = 0$

▶ There are infinitely many solutions, so you cannot determine the cost of one glossy print. You need more information.

GUIDED PRACTICE for Examples 3 and 4

3. Without solving the linear system, tell whether it has *one solution*, *no solution*, or *infinitely many solutions*. **one solution**

$x - 3y = -15$ Equation 1
$2x - 3y = -18$ Equation 2

4. **WHAT IF?** In Example 4, suppose a glossy print costs $3 more than a regular print. Find the cost of a glossy print. **$8**

Key Question to Ask for Example 2

- What happens if you multiply Equation 2 by 2? **You get $2y = x + 4$, which is the same as Equation 1.**

Extra Example 3

Without solving the linear system, tell whether the linear system has *one solution*, *no solution*, or *infinitely many solutions*.

a. $-3x + 5y = 6$
$6x - 10y = -12$ **infinitely many solutions**

b. $9x - 5y = 12$
$9x - 5y = 8$ **no solution**

Extra Example 4

A pizza parlor fills two pizza orders. Find the cost of one medium pizza.

Medium	Large	Cost
4	12	$168
8	24	$336

You cannot determine the cost of one medium pizza, since there are infinitely many solutions.

Closing the Lesson

Have students summarize the major points of the lesson and answer the Essential Question: How can you identify the number of solutions of a linear system?

- **Linear systems can have one solution, no solution, or infinitely many solutions.**

Systems with one solution have graphs with intersecting lines and equations with different slopes. Systems with no solution have graphs with parallel lines, equations with the same slope but different y-intercepts, and result in false statements when solved algebraically. Systems with infinitely many solutions have graphs with coinciding lines, identical equations, and result in true statements when solved algebraically.

4 PRACTICE AND APPLY

Assignment Guide

Answer Transparencies available for all exercises

Basic:
Day 1: pp. 462–465
Exs. 1–20, 24, 25, 42–45
Day 2: pp. 462–465
Exs. 26–30, 36–39, 46–60

Average:
Day 1: pp. 462–465
Exs. 1–14, 18–25, 42–45
Day 2: pp. 462–465
Exs. 26–34, 36–40, 46–54 even, 56–61

Advanced:
Day 1: pp. 462–465
Exs. 1–4, 11–13, 18–25, 44, 45
Day 2: pp. 462–465
Exs. 26–35*, 37–41*, 51, 52, 55, 59

Block:
pp. 462–465
Exs. 1–14, 18–25, 42–45 (with 7.4)
pp. 462–465
Exs. 26–34, 36–40, 46–54 even, 56–61 (with 7.6)

Differentiated Instruction

See *Differentiated Instruction Resources* for suggestions on addressing the needs of a diverse classroom.

Homework Check

For a quick check of student understanding of key concepts, go over the following exercises:

Basic: 9, 20, 26, 36, 37
Average: 13, 18, 28, 36, 38
Advanced: 12, 21, 30, 37, 38

Extra Practice

- Student Edition, p. 944
- Chapter Resource Book: Practice levels A, B, C

Practice Worksheet

An easily-readable reduced practice page (with answers) for this lesson can be found on p. 424C.

CONCEPT SUMMARY *For Your Notebook*

Number of Solutions of a Linear System

One solution

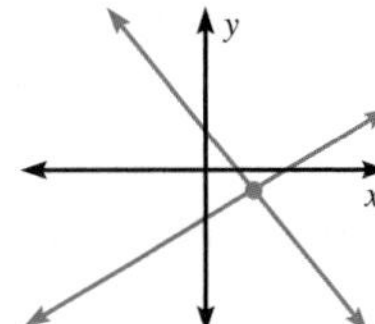

The lines intersect.

The lines have different slopes.

No solution

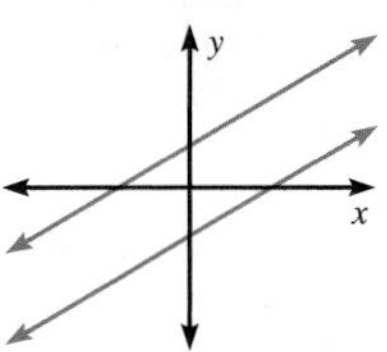

The lines are parallel.

The lines have the same slope and different *y*-intercepts.

Infinitely many solutions

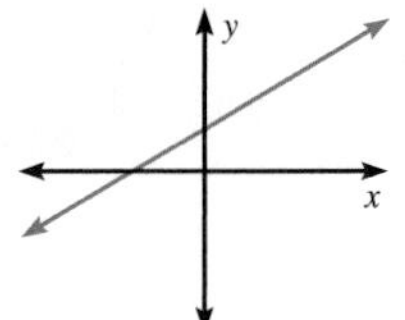

The lines coincide.

The lines have the same slope and the same *y*-intercept.

7.5 EXERCISES

HOMEWORK KEY
○ = **WORKED-OUT SOLUTIONS** on p. WS17 for Exs. 11 and 37
★ = **STANDARDIZED TEST PRACTICE** Exs. 3, 4, 24, 25, 32, 33, and 40

SKILL PRACTICE

A

1. **VOCABULARY** Copy and complete: A linear system with no solution is called a(n) _?_ system. **inconsistent**

2. **VOCABULARY** Copy and complete: A linear system with infinitely many solutions is called a(n) _?_ system. **consistent dependent**

3. ★ **WRITING** *Describe* the graph of a linear system that has no solution. ***Sample answer:*** **The lines have the same slope but different *y*-intercepts.**

4. ★ **WRITING** *Describe* the graph of a linear system that has infinitely many solutions. ***Sample answer:*** **The graph would show only one line.**

INTERPRETING GRAPHS Match the linear system with its graph. Then use the graph to tell whether the linear system has *one solution, no solution,* or *infinitely many solutions.*

5. $x - 3y = -9$
   $x - y = -1$
   B; one solution

6. $x - y = -4$
   $-3x + 3y = 2$
   C; no solution

7. $x + 3y = -1$
   $-2x - 6y = 2$
   A; infinitely many solutions

A.
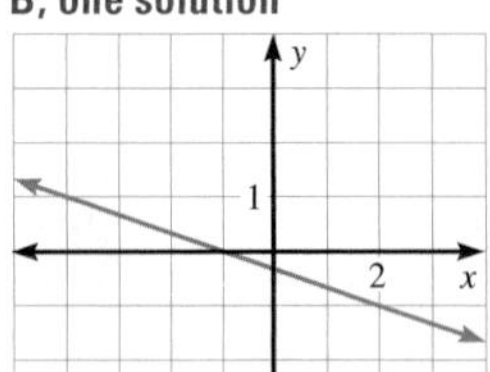

B.
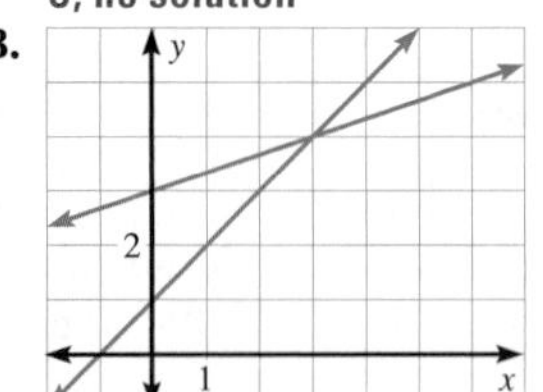

C.
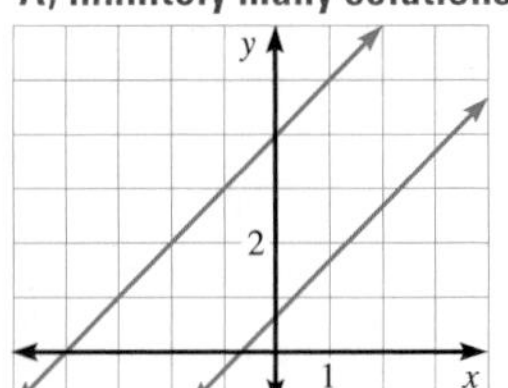

EXAMPLES 1 and 2 on pp. 459–460 for Exs. 8–25

INTERPRETING GRAPHS **Graph the linear system. Then use the graph to tell whether the linear system has *one solution, no solution,* or *infinitely many solutions.*** **8–13. See margin for graphs.**

8. $x + y = -2$
$y = -x + 5$
no solution

9. $3x - 4y = 12$
$y = \frac{3}{4}x - 3$
infinitely many solutions

10. $3x - y = -9$
$3x + 5y = -15$
one solution

11. $-2x + 2y = -16$
$3x - 6y = 30$
one solution

12. $-9x + 6y = 18$
$6x - 4y = -12$
infinitely many solutions

13. $-3x + 4y = 12$
$-3x + 4y = 24$
no solution

14. *Sample answer:* The lines do not have the same slope, so they are not parallel and they do have a solution. If the graph were larger the lines would intersect at (4, 12); see margin for art.

14. ERROR ANALYSIS *Describe* and correct the error in solving the linear system below.

$6x + y = 36$
$5x - y = 8$

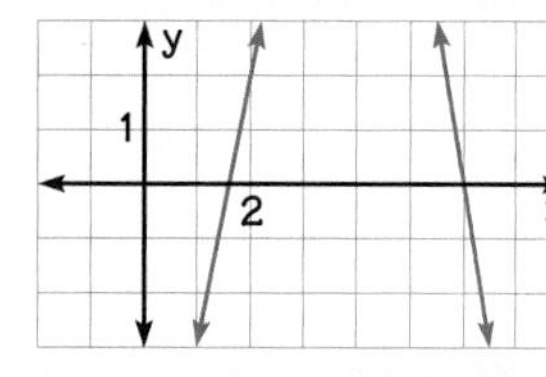

The lines do not intersect, so there is no solution.

SOLVING LINEAR SYSTEMS **Solve the linear system using substitution or elimination.**

15. $2x + 5y = 14$
$6x + 7y = 10$ **(−3, 4)**

16. $-16x + 2y = -2$
$y = 8x - 1$ **infinitely many solutions**

17. $3x - 2y = -5$
$4x + 5y = 47$ **(3, 7)**

18. $5x - 5y = -3$
$y = x + 0.6$ **infinitely many solutions**

19. $x - y = 0$
$5x - 2y = 6$ **(2, 2)**

20. $x - 2y = 7$
$-x + 2y = 7$ **no solution**

21. $-18x + 6y = 24$
$3x - y = -2$ **no solution**

22. $4y + 5x = 15$
$x = 8y + 3$ **(3, 0)**

23. $6x + 3y = 9$
$2x + 9y = 27$ **(0, 3)**

24. ★ MULTIPLE CHOICE Which of the linear systems has *exactly* one solution? **C**

Ⓐ $-x + y = 9$
$x - y = 9$

Ⓑ $-x + y = 9$
$x - y = -9$

Ⓒ $-x + y = 9$
$-x - y = 9$

Ⓓ $x - y = -9$
$-x + y = -9$

25. ★ MULTIPLE CHOICE Which of the linear systems has infinitely many solutions? **D**

Ⓐ $15x + 5y = 20$
$6x - 2y = 8$

Ⓑ $15x - 5y = 20$
$6x - 2y = -8$

Ⓒ $15x - 5y = -20$
$6x - 2y = 8$

Ⓓ $15x - 5y = 20$
$6x - 2y = 8$

EXAMPLE 3 on p. 461 for Exs. 26–31

B **IDENTIFYING THE NUMBER OF SOLUTIONS** **Without solving the linear system, tell whether the linear system has *one solution, no solution,* or *infinitely many solutions.***

26. $y = -6x - 2$
$12x + 2y = -6$
no solution

27. $y = 7x + 13$
$-21x + 3y = 39$
infinitely many solutions

28. $4x + 3y = 27$
$4x - 3y = -27$
one solution

29. $9x - 15y = 24$
$6x - 10y = 16$
infinitely many solutions

30. $0.3x + 0.4y = 2.4$
$0.5x - 0.6y = 0.2$
one solution

31. $0.9x - 2.1y = 12.3$
$1.5x - 3.5y = 20.5$
infinitely many solutions

Avoiding Common Errors

Exercises 15–23 Some students may erroneously correlate true statements with no solution and false statements with infinitely many solutions. Stress that a true statement means that all points on a line are solutions and a false statement means that none of the points on either line are solutions. To reinforce these concepts, suggest that students write the equations of these systems in slope-intercept form and then look at the slopes and *y*-intercepts to determine the number of solutions. This will also help them associate true statements with infinitely many solutions and false statements with no solution.

11.
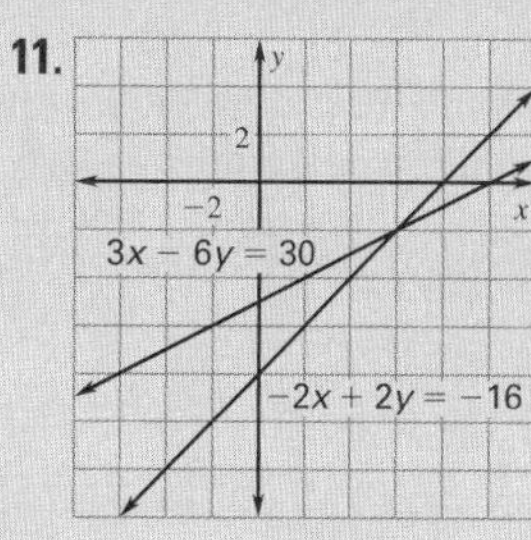

12.
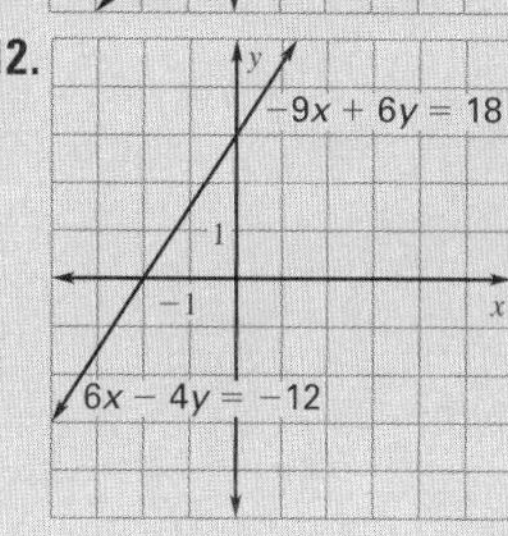

13.
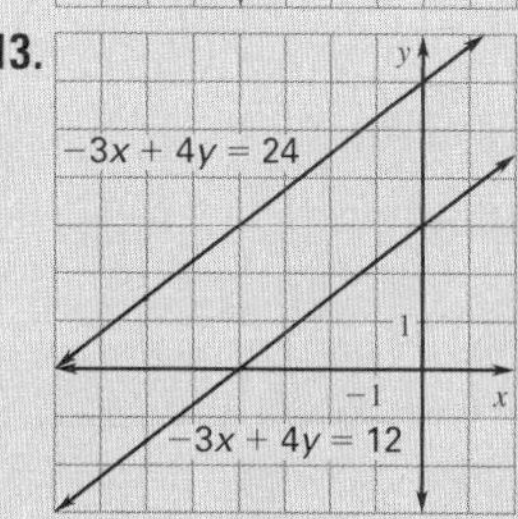

14.
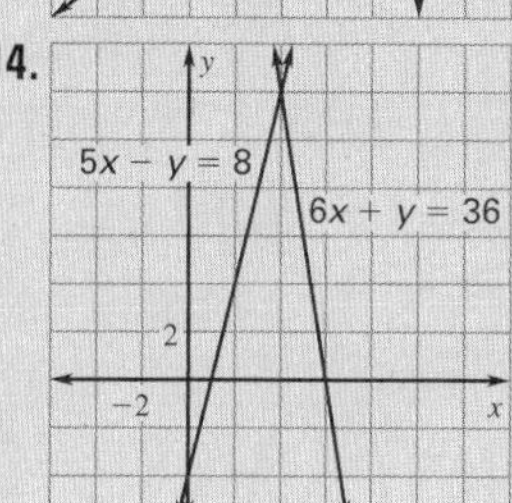

8.
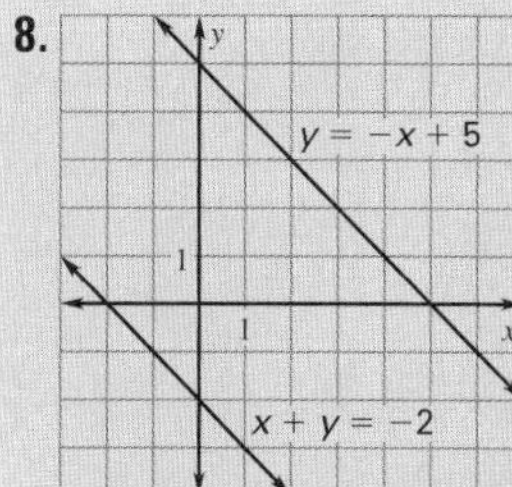

9.
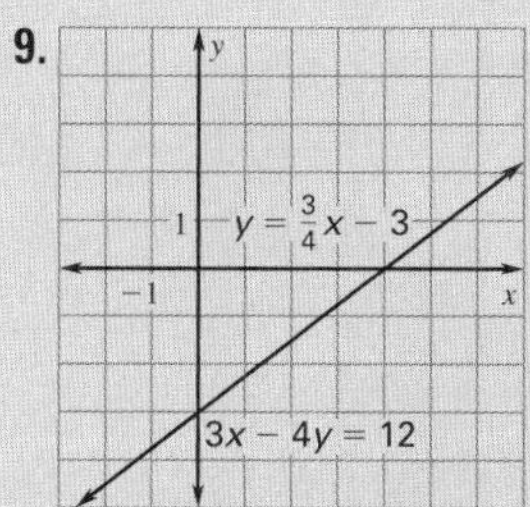

10.
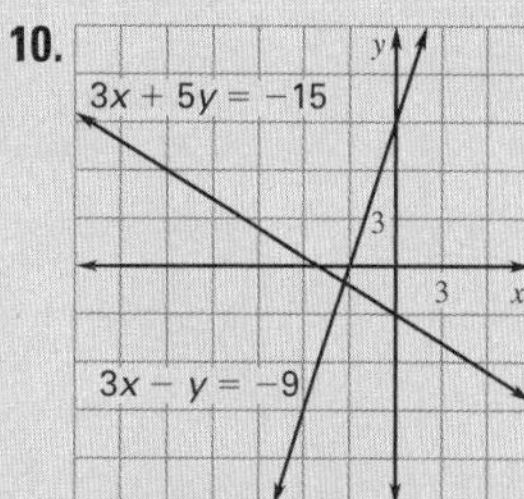

Teaching Strategy

Exercise 37 You may want to point out to students that after they write the equations for this system, they can write the equations in slope-intercept form and then look at the slopes and y-intercepts to determine whether there is enough information to find the cost of one ticket. Note that if the slopes are different, then there is enough information to find the cost of one ticket. If the slopes are the same, then there are either infinitely many solutions or no solution, and in either case, there is not enough information to find the cost of one ticket.

Avoiding Common Errors

Exercise 38 Some students may write the equations in the system, using the first row of the table for x and the second for y. Caution students to read the description in the problem to determine what x and y should represent.

32. ★ **OPEN-ENDED** Write a linear system so that it has infinitely many solutions, and one of the equations is $y = 3x + 2$. ***Sample answer:*** **$y = 3x + 2, 2y = 6x + 4$**

33. ★ **OPEN-ENDED** Write a linear system so that it has no solution and one of the equations is $7x - 8y = -9$.
Sample answer: **$7x - 8y = -9, 7x - 8y = 4$**

C 34. **REASONING** Give a counterexample for the following statement: If the graphs of the equations of a linear system have the same slope, then the linear system has no solution.
Sample answer: **$y = 3x, 2y = 6x$**

35. **CHALLENGE** Find values of p, q, and r that produce the solution(s).

$px + qy = r$ Equation 1
$2x - 3y = 5$ Equation 2

a. No solution ***Sample answer:*** **$p = 2, q = -3, r = 0$**
b. Infinitely many solutions
Sample answer: **$p = 4, q = -6, r = 10$**
c. One solution of (4, 1)
Sample answer: **$p = 1, q = 1, r = 5$**

PROBLEM SOLVING

EXAMPLE 4 on p. 461 for Exs. 36–38

A 36. **RECREATION** One admission to a roller skating rink costs x dollars and renting a pair of skates costs y dollars. A group pays $243 for admission for 36 people and 21 skate rentals. Another group pays $81 for admission for 12 people and 7 skate rentals. Is there enough information to determine the cost of one admission to the roller skating rink? *Explain.*
No. *Sample answer:* There are infinitely many solutions to the resulting linear system.

@HomeTutor for problem solving help at classzone.com

(37.) **TRANSPORTATION** A passenger train travels from New York City to Washington, D.C., then back to New York City. The table shows the number of coach tickets and business class tickets purchased for each leg of the trip. Is there enough information to determine the cost of one coach ticket? *Explain.* **Yes. *Sample answer:* There is one solution to the resulting linear system.**

Destination	Coach tickets	Business class tickets	Money collected (dollars)
Washington, D.C.	150	80	22,860
New York City	170	100	27,280

@HomeTutor for problem solving help at classzone.com

38. **PHOTOGRAPHY** In addition to taking pictures on your digital camera, you can record 30 second movies. All pictures use the same amount of memory, and all 30 second movies use the same amount of memory. The number of pictures and 30 second movies on 2 memory cards is shown.

a. Is there enough information given to determine the amount of memory used by a 30 second movie? *Explain.*

b. Given that a 30 second movie uses 50 times the amount of memory that a digital picture uses, can you determine the amount of memory used by a 30 second movie? *Explain.*

Size of card (megabytes)	64	256
Pictures	450	1800
Movies	7	28

38a. No. *Sample answer:* There are infinitely many solutions to the resulting linear system.

38b. Yes. *Sample answer:* You can write a new equation and create a linear system that has only one solution.

○ = WORKED-OUT SOLUTIONS on p. WS1 ★ = STANDARDIZED TEST PRACTICE

B **39. MULTI-STEP PROBLEM** Two people are training for a speed ice-climbing event. During a practice climb, one climber starts 15 seconds after the first climber. The rates that the climbers ascend are shown.

Climbs 10 feet every 30 seconds

Climbs 5 feet every 15 seconds

a. Let d be the distance (in feet) traveled by a climber t seconds after the first person starts climbing. Write a linear system that models the situation. $d = \frac{t}{3}, d = \frac{t}{3} - 5$

b. Graph the linear system from part (a). Does the second climber catch up to the first climber? *Explain.*

39b. *Sample answer:* No, since the lines are parallel, the two climbers will never be at the same distance at the same time.

40. ★ EXTENDED RESPONSE Two employees at a banquet facility are given the task of folding napkins. One person starts folding napkins at a rate of 5 napkins per minute. The second person starts 10 minutes after the first person and folds napkins at a rate of 4 napkins per minute.

a. **Model** Let y be the number of napkins folded x minutes after the first person starts folding. Write a linear system that models the situation. $y = 5x, y = 4(x - 10)$

b. **Solve** Solve the linear system. $(-40, -200)$

c. **Interpret** Does the solution of the linear system make sense in the context of the problem? *Explain.* **No. *Sample answer:* x and y only make sense for positive values.**

C **41. CHALLENGE** An airplane has an average air speed of 160 miles per hour. The airplane takes 3 hours to travel with the wind from Salem to Lancaster. The airplane has to travel against the wind on the return trip. After 3 hours into the return trip, the airplane is 120 miles from Salem. Find the distance from Salem to Lancaster. If the problem cannot be solved with the information given, *explain* why. **540 mi**

MIXED REVIEW

Solve the equation, if possible. *(p. 154)*

42. $61 + 5c = 7 - 4c$ **−6**

43. $3m - 2 = 7m - 50 + 8m$ **4**

44. $11z + 3 = 10(2z + 3)$ **−3**

45. $-6(1 - w) = 14(w - 5)$ **8**

PREVIEW Prepare for Lesson 7.6 in Exs. 46–61.

Solve the inequality. Then graph your solution. **46–55. See margin for art.**

46. $x + 15 < 23$ *(p. 356)* $x < 8$

47. $x - 1 \geq 10$ *(p. 356)* $x \geq 11$

48. $\frac{x}{4} > -2.5$ *(p. 363)* $x > -10$

49. $-7x \leq 84$ *(p. 363)* $x \geq -12$

50. $2 - 5x \geq 27$ *(p. 369)* $x \leq -5$

51. $3x - 9 > 3(x - 3)$ *(p. 369)* **no solution**

52. $-2 < x + 3 \leq 11$ *(p. 380)* $-5 < x \leq 8$

53. $-7 \leq 5 - 2x \leq 7$ *(p. 380)* $-1 \leq x \leq 6$

54. $|x - 3| \geq 5$ *(p. 398)* $x \leq -2$ or $x \geq 8$

55. $2|2x - 1| - 9 \leq 1$ *(p. 398)* $-2 \leq x \leq 3$

Graph the inequality. *(p. 405)* **56–61. See margin.**

56. $x + y < -3$

57. $x - y \geq 1$

58. $2x - y < 5$

59. $-2x - 3y \leq 9$

60. $y \leq -4$

61. $x > 6.5$

5 ASSESS AND RETEACH

Daily Homework Quiz

Transparency Available

Without solving the linear system, tell whether the linear system has *one solution, no solution,* or *infinitely many solutions.*

1. $4x + 2y = 12$
   $y = -2x + 8$ **no solution**
2. $-2x + 5y = 5$
   $y = \frac{2}{5}x + 1$ **infinitely many solutions**
3. A group of 12 students and 3 teachers pays $57 for admission to a primate research center. Another group of 14 students and 4 teachers pays $69. Find the cost of one student ticket. **$3.50**

Online Quiz

Available at **classzone.com**

Diagnosis/Remediation

- Practice A, B, C in Chapter Resource Book
- Study Guide in Chapter Resource Book
- Practice Workbook
- @HomeTutor

Challenge

Additional challenge is available in the Chapter Resource Book.

39b.

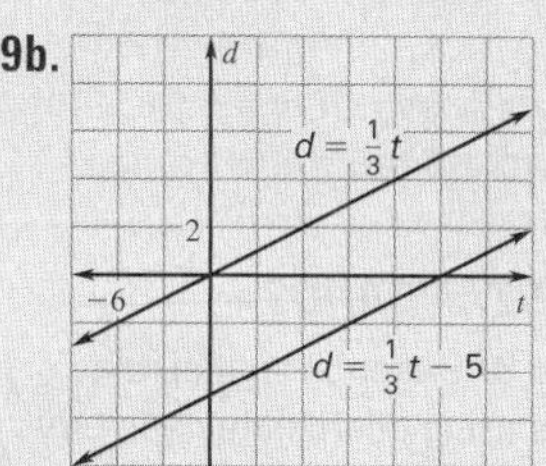

46–61. See Additional Answers beginning on p. AA1.

1 PLAN AND PREPARE

Warm-Up Exercises

Transparency Available

1. Graph $y < \frac{2}{3}x - 1$.

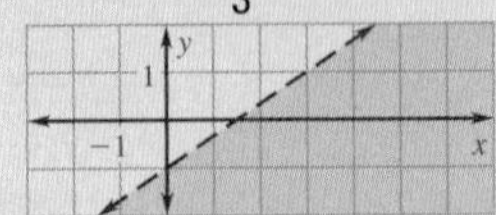

2. You are running one ad that costs \$6 per day and another that costs \$8 per day. You can spend no more than \$120. Name a possible combination of days that you can run the ads. ***Sample:* 16 days of the \$6 ad and 3 days of the \$8 ad**

Notetaking Guide

Transparency Available

Promotes interactive learning and notetaking skills.

Pacing

Basic: 1 day

Average: 1 day

Advanced: 1 day

Block: 0.5 block with 7.5

- See *Teaching Guide/Lesson Plan.*

2 FOCUS AND MOTIVATE

Essential Question

Big Idea 3, p. 425

How do you solve systems of linear inequalities in two variables? **Tell students they will learn how to answer this question by graphing in the same coordinate plane.**

NCTM STANDARDS

Standard 3: Describe spatial relationships using coordinate geometry

Standard 8: Communicate thinking clearly to others

7.6 Solve Systems of Linear Inequalities

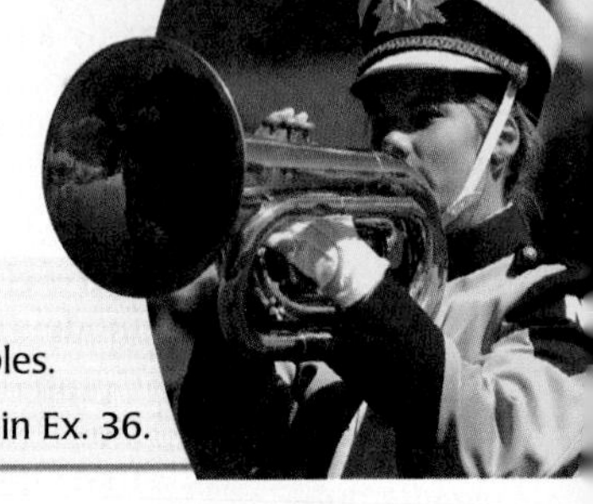

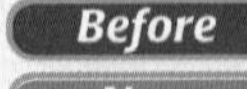

Before You graphed linear inequalities in two variables.

Now You will solve systems of linear inequalities in two variables.

Why So you can find a marching band's competition score, as in Ex. 36.

Key Vocabulary
- **system of linear inequalities**
- **solution of a system of linear inequalities**
- **graph of a system of linear inequalities**

A **system of linear inequalities** in two variables, or simply a *system of inequalities,* consists of two or more linear inequalities in the same variables. An example is shown.

$x - y > 7$ **Inequality 1**

$2x + y < 8$ **Inequality 2**

A **solution of a system of linear inequalities** is an ordered pair that is a solution of each inequality in the system. For example, $(6, -5)$ is a solution of the system above. The **graph of a system of linear inequalities** is the graph of all solutions of the system.

KEY CONCEPT ***For Your Notebook***

Graphing a System of Linear Inequalities

STEP 1 **Graph** each inequality (as you learned to do in Lesson 6.7).

STEP 2 **Find** the intersection of the half-planes. The graph of the system is this intersection.

EXAMPLE 1 Graph a system of two linear inequalities

Graph the system of inequalities. $y > -x - 2$ **Inequality 1**

$y \le 3x + 6$ **Inequality 2**

REVIEW GRAPHING INEQUALITIES
For help with graphing a linear inequality in two variables, see p. 405.

Solution

Graph both inequalities in the same coordinate plane. The graph of the system is the intersection of the two half-planes, which is shown as the darker shade of blue.

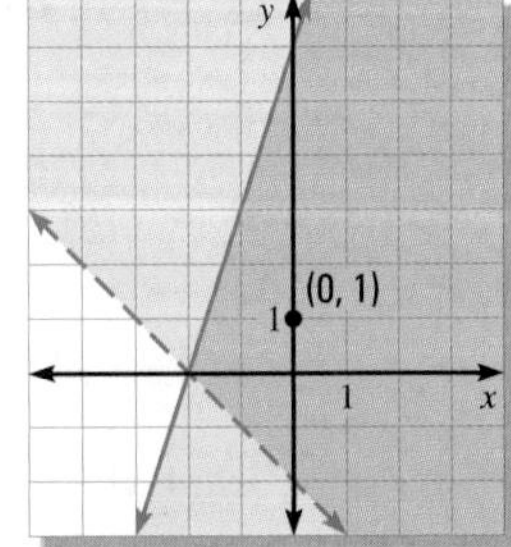

CHECK Choose a point in the dark blue region, such as $(\mathbf{0}, \mathbf{1})$. To check this solution, substitute 0 for x and 1 for y into each inequality.

$1 \overset{?}{>} \mathbf{0} - 2$	$\mathbf{1} \overset{?}{\le} \mathbf{0} + 6$
$1 > -2$ ✓	$1 \le 6$ ✓

Animated Algebra at classzone.com

Resource Planning Guide

Chapter Resource Book
- Teaching Guide/Lesson Plan
- Activity Master
- Practice levels A, B, C
- Study Guide
- Catch-up for Absent Students
- Problem Solving Workshop
- Challenge

Workbooks
- Notetaking Guide
- Practice Workbook

Teaching Options
- **Power Presentations** provides dynamic electronic teaching resources for the classroom.
- **Activity Generator** provides editable activities for all ability levels.

Interactive Technology
- Easy Planner
- Power Presentations
- Activity Generator
- Animated Algebra
- Test Generator
- Online Quiz
- eWorkbook
- eEdition
- @HomeTutor

Resources for English Learners
- Spanish Study Guide
- Multi-Language Visual Glossary
- Student Resources in Spanish

See also the *Differentiated Instruction Resources* for more strategies for meeting individual needs.

THE SOLUTION REGION In Example 1, the half-plane for each inequality is shaded, and the solution region is the intersection of the half-planes. From this point on, only the solution region will be shaded.

EXAMPLE 2 Graph a system of three linear inequalities

Graph the system of inequalities.

$y \geq -1$ Inequality 1
$x > -2$ Inequality 2
$x + 2y \leq 4$ Inequality 3

Solution

Graph all three inequalities in the same coordinate plane. The graph of the system is the triangular region shown.

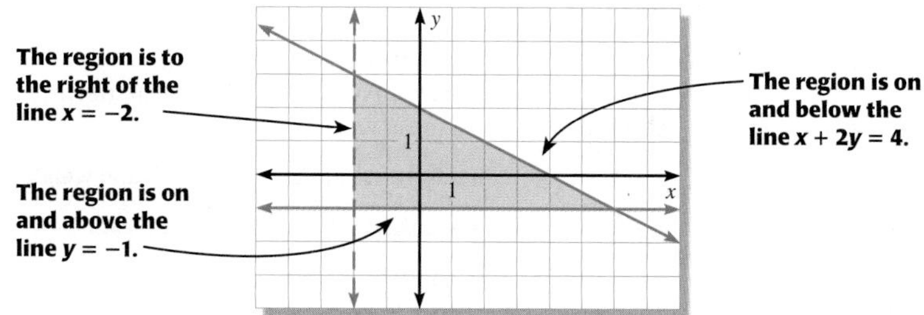

The region is to the right of the line x = −2.
The region is on and above the line y = −1.
The region is on and below the line x + 2y = 4.
y
x
1
1

GUIDED PRACTICE for Examples 1 and 2

Graph the system of linear inequalities. 1–3. See margin.

1. $y < x - 4$
   $y \geq -x + 3$

2. $y \geq -x + 2$
   $y < 4$
   $x < 3$

3. $y > -x$
   $y \geq x - 4$
   $y < 5$

EXAMPLE 3 Write a system of linear inequalities

Write a system of inequalities for the shaded region.

REVIEW EQUATIONS OF LINES
For help with writing an equation of a line, see pp. 283, 302, and 311.

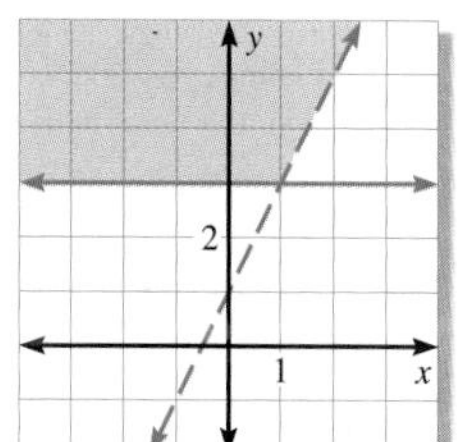

y
x
2
1

Solution

INEQUALITY 1: One boundary line for the shaded region is $y = 3$. Because the shaded region is *above* the *solid* line, the inequality is $y \geq 3$.

INEQUALITY 2: Another boundary line for the shaded region has a slope of 2 and a y-intercept of 1. So, its equation is $y = 2x + 1$. Because the shaded region is *above* the *dashed* line, the inequality is $y > 2x + 1$.

▶ The system of inequalities for the shaded region is:

$y \geq 3$ Inequality 1
$y > 2x + 1$ Inequality 2

Motivating the Lesson

Your science teacher tells you that the written portion of lab reports can be no longer than 4 pages, the illustrated portions can be no longer than 8 pages, and the total number of pages can be no more than 12 pages. By knowing how to write and graph systems of linear inequalities, you can determine whether your lab report fits within the guidelines.

3 TEACH

Extra Example 1

Graph the system of inequalities.
$y < 3x$
$y \geq -2x + 1$

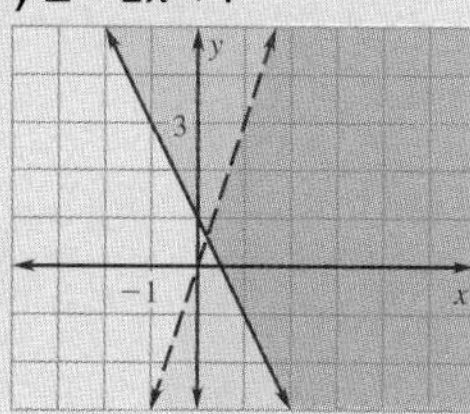

y
3
−1
x

Animated Algebra classzone.com

An **Animated Algebra** activity is available online for **Example 1**. This activity is also part of **Power Presentations**.

Extra Example 2

Graph the system of inequalities.
$y \geq 0$
$x > -3$
$2x + 3y \leq 6$

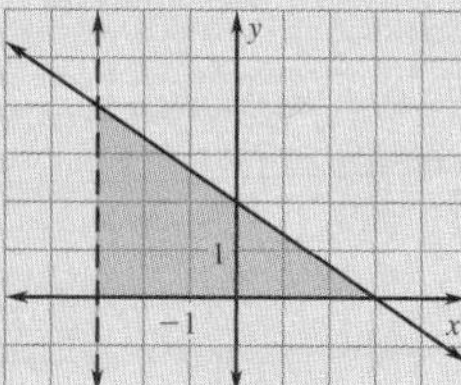

y
1
−1
x

1–3. See Additional Answers beginning on p. AA1.

Differentiated Instruction

Auditory Learners Tell students that the method used in **Example 1** is sometimes called the "graph-and-check" method, because students *graph* the inequalities and then *check* points in each test region. Students should get in the habit of checking their graphs by verifying that points in their solution satisfy each inequality.

See also the *Differentiated Instruction Resources* for more strategies.

Extra Example 3

Write a system of inequalities for the shaded region.

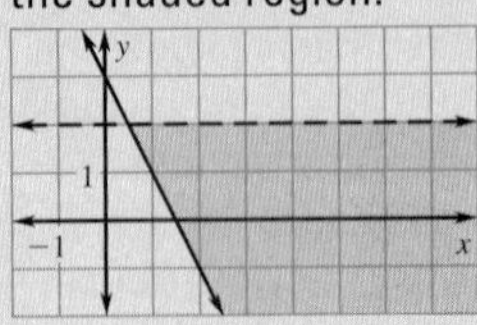

$y < 2$ and $y \geq -2x + 3$

Extra Example 4

A logo contest requires that the logo width be between 3 and 5 inches, the height no less than 2 inches, and the sum of the width and height no more than 9.

a. Write and graph a system of linear inequalities that describes the information given above. **inequalities: $x \geq 3$, $x \leq 5$,**

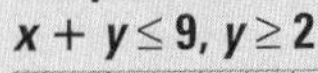

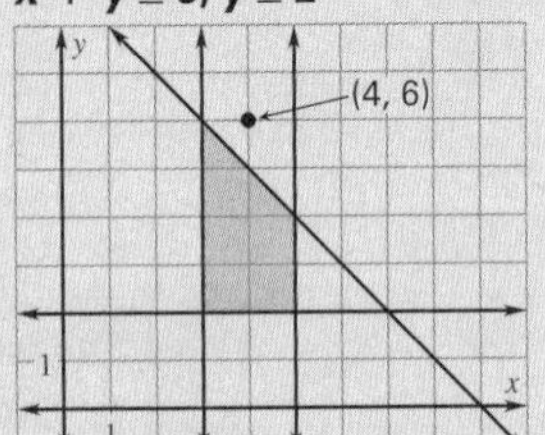

b. You enter a logo 4 inches wide and 6 inches high. Use the graph to determine if it meets contest requirements. **Because the point falls outside the solution region, the logo does not meet requirements.**

Closing the Lesson

Have students summarize the major points of the lesson and answer the Essential Question: How do you solve systems of linear inequalities in two variables?

- **You can use a graph of a system of inequalities to find all the solutions of the system.**

Graph each inequality in the same coordinate plane. The graph of the system is the intersection of all of the graphs.

6.

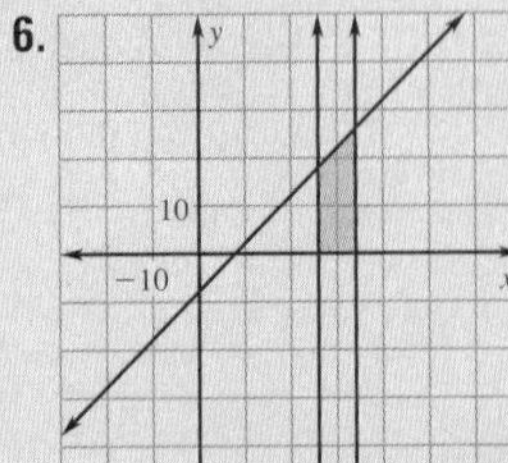

EXAMPLE 4 Write and solve a system of linear inequalities

BASEBALL The National Collegiate Athletic Association (NCAA) regulates the lengths of aluminum baseball bats used by college baseball teams. The NCAA states that the length (in inches) of the bat minus the weight (in ounces) of the bat cannot exceed 3. Bats can be purchased at lengths from 26 to 34 inches.

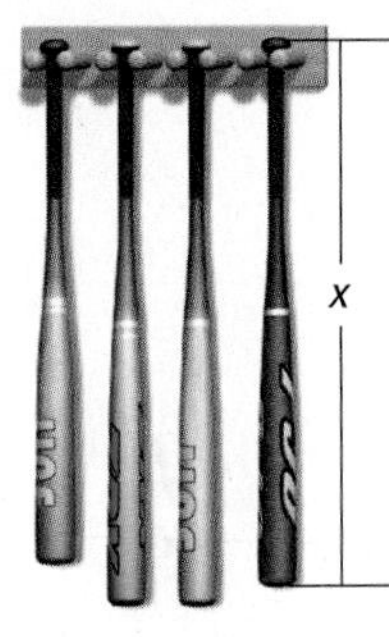

a. Write and graph a system of linear inequalities that describes the information given above.

b. A sporting goods store sells an aluminum bat that is 31 inches long and weighs 25 ounces. Use the graph to determine if this bat can be used by a player on an NCAA team.

Solution

a. Let x be the length (in inches) of the bat, and let y be the weight (in ounces) of the bat. From the given information, you can write the following inequalities:

$x - y \leq 3$	**The difference of the bat's length and weight can be at most 3.**
$x \geq 26$	**The length of the bat must be at least 26 inches.**
$x \leq 34$	**The length of the bat can be at most 34 inches.**
$y \geq 0$	**The weight of the bat cannot be a negative number.**

WRITING SYSTEMS OF INEQUALITIES
Consider the values of the variables when writing a system of inequalities. In many real-world problems, the values cannot be negative.

Graph each inequality in the system. Then identify the region that is common to all of the graphs of the inequalities. This region is shaded in the graph shown.

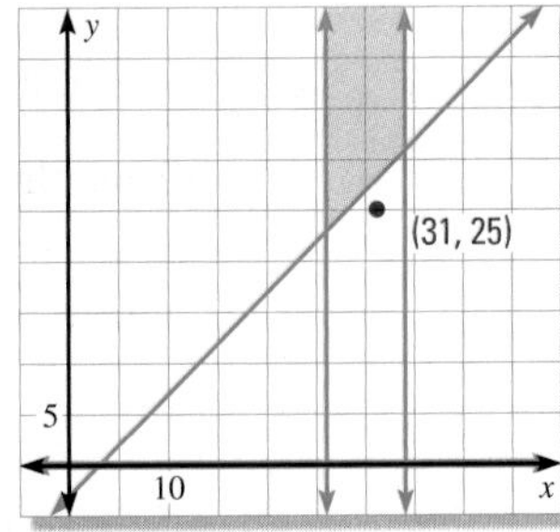

b. Graph the point that represents a bat that is 31 inches long and weighs 25 ounces.

▸ Because the point falls outside the solution region, the bat cannot be used by a player on an NCAA team.

✓ GUIDED PRACTICE for Examples 3 and 4

Write a system of inequalities that defines the shaded region.

4.

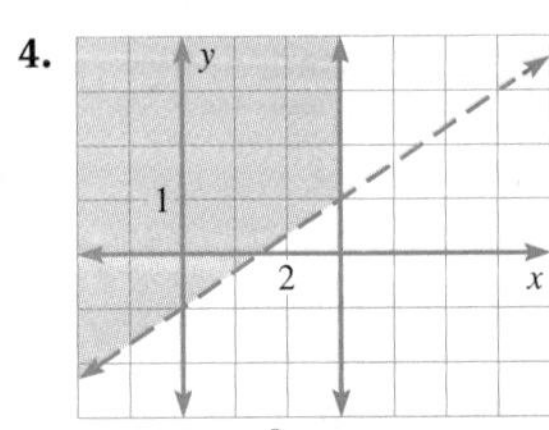

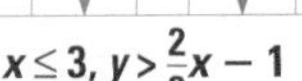

$x \leq 3$, $y > \frac{2}{3}x - 1$

5.

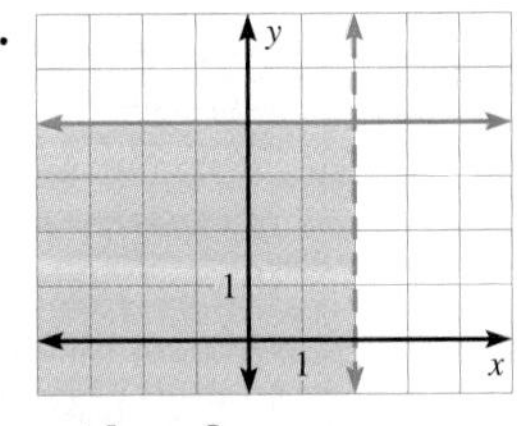

$y \leq 4$, $x < 2$

6. **WHAT IF?** In Example 4, suppose a Senior League (ages 10–14) player wants to buy the bat described in part (b). In Senior League, the length (in inches) of the bat minus the weight (in ounces) of the bat cannot exceed 8. Write and graph a system of inequalities to determine whether the described bat can be used by the Senior League player.
$x - y \leq 8$, $x \geq 26$, $x \leq 34$, $y \geq 0$, see margin for art; the bat can be used.

7.6 EXERCISES

HOMEWORK KEY ○ = **WORKED-OUT SOLUTIONS** on p. WS18 for Exs. 13 and 39
★ = **STANDARDIZED TEST PRACTICE** Exs. 2, 21, 22, 33, and 40

SKILL PRACTICE

A

1. **VOCABULARY** Copy and complete: A(n) __?__ of a system of linear inequalities is an ordered pair that is a solution of each inequality in the system. **solution**

2. ★ **WRITING** *Describe* the steps you would take to graph the system of inequalities shown.

$x - y < 7$ Inequality 1
$y \geq 3$ Inequality 2

2. *Sample answer:* Graph each inequality then shade the region that is the intersection of the solutions to each inequality. Then check the solution with a test point.

CHECKING A SOLUTION **Tell whether the ordered pair is a solution of the system of inequalities.**

3. (1, 1) **not a solution**

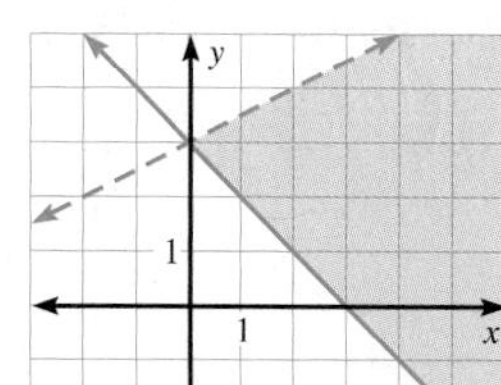

4. (0, 6) **solution**

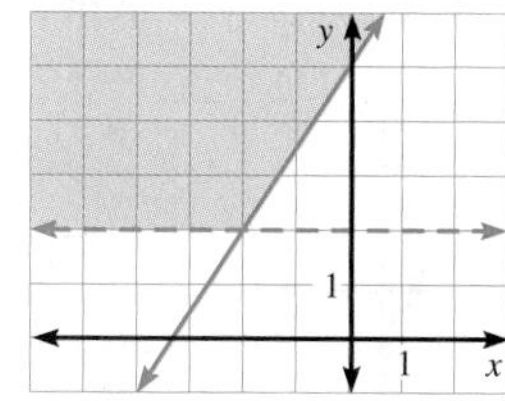

5. (3, −1) **not a solution**

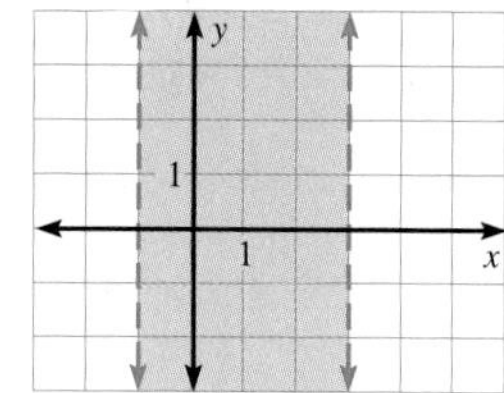

EXAMPLE 1 on p. 466 for Exs. 6–17

MATCHING SYSTEMS AND GRAPHS **Match the system of inequalities with its graph.**

6. $x - 4y > -8$
$x \geq 2$ **C**

7. $x - 4y \geq -8$
$x < 2$ **A**

8. $x - 4y > -8$
$y \geq 2$ **B**

A. 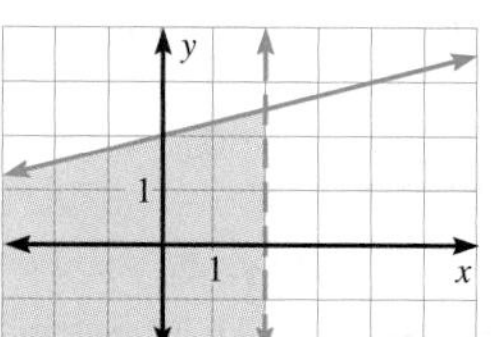

B. 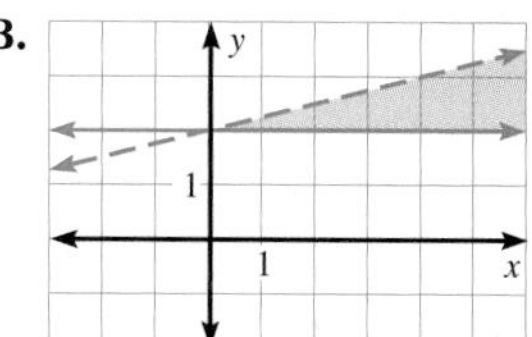

C. 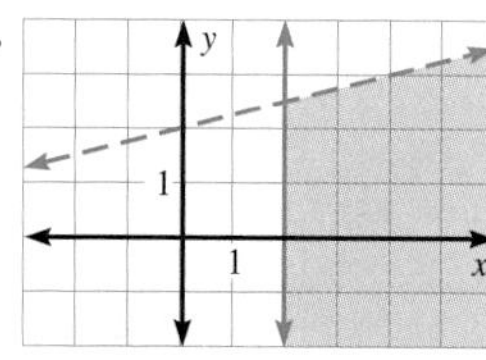

GRAPHING A SYSTEM **Graph the system of inequalities.** **9–20. See margin.**

9. $x > -5$
$x < 2$

10. $y \leq 10$
$y \geq 6$

11. $x > 3$
$y > x$

12. $y < -2x + 3$
$y \geq 4$

(13.) $y \geq 0$
$y < 2.5x - 1$

14. $y \geq 2x + 1$
$y < -x + 4$

15. $x < 8$
$x - 4y \leq -8$

16. $y \geq -2$
$2x + 3y > -6$

17. $y - 2x < 7$
$y + 2x > -1$

EXAMPLE 2 on p. 467 for Exs. 18–21

18. $x < 4$
$y > 1$
$y \geq -x + 1$

19. $x \geq 0$
$y \geq 0$
$6x - y < 12$

20. $x + y \leq 10$
$x - y \geq 2$
$y \geq 2$

21. ★ **MULTIPLE CHOICE** Which ordered pair is a solution of the system $2x - y \leq 5$ and $x + 2y > 2$? **D**

Ⓐ (1, −1) Ⓑ (4, 1) Ⓒ (2, 0) Ⓓ (3, 2)

4 PRACTICE AND APPLY

Assignment Guide

Answer Transparencies available for all exercises

Basic:
Day 1: EP p. 943 Exs. 67–70, 72, 73 pp. 469–472
Exs. 1–8, 9–21 odd, 22–26, 36–39, 43–53 odd

Average:
Day 1: pp. 469–472
Exs. 1–8, 15–23, 25–33 odd, 36–40, 42–52 even

Advanced:
Day 1: pp. 469–472
Exs. 1, 2, 16–22, 24–41*, 47, 52

Block:
pp. 469–472
Exs. 1–8, 15–23, 25–33 odd, 36–40, 42–52 even (with 7.5)

Differentiated Instruction

See *Differentiated Instruction Resources* for suggestions on addressing the needs of a diverse classroom.

Homework Check

For a quick check of student understanding of key concepts, go over the following exercises:
Basic: 11, 19, 21, 24, 36
Average: 16, 18, 22, 27, 37
Advanced: 16, 20, 22, 28, 38

Extra Practice

- Student Edition, p. 944
- Chapter Resource Book: Practice levels A, B, C

Practice Worksheet

An easily-readable reduced practice page (with answers) for this lesson can be found on p. 424C.

9–20. See Additional Answers beginning on p. AA1.

Avoiding Common Errors

Exercise 5 Some students may think the ordered pair is a solution of the system of inequalities since it appears on the boundary. Remind these students that a dashed line is the graph of an inequality containing < or >, so an ordered pair on a dashed line cannot be a solution of the system. You may want to point out that an ordered pair on a solid line is a solution of the system of inequalities.

23.
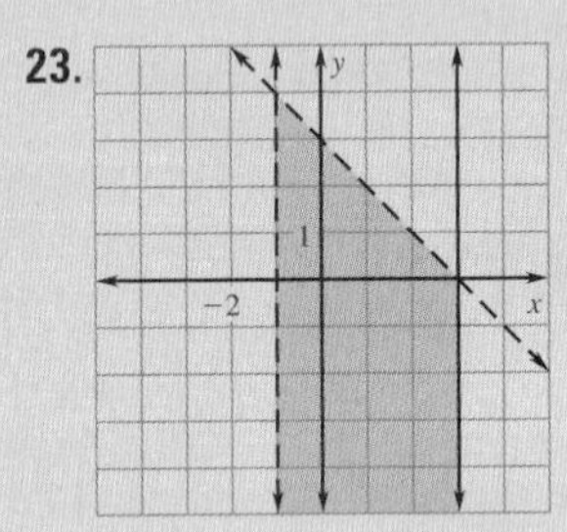

30.
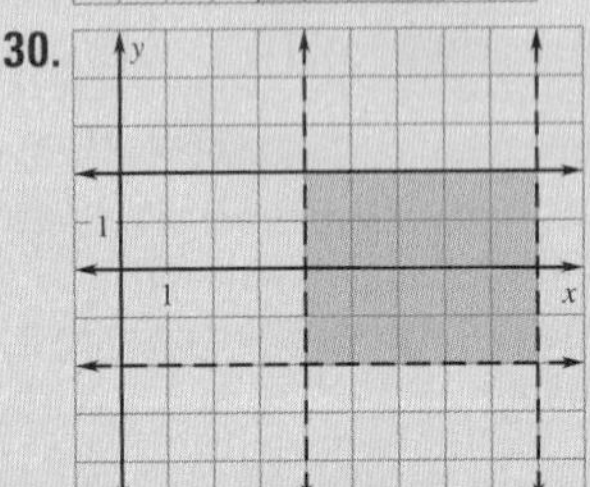

31.
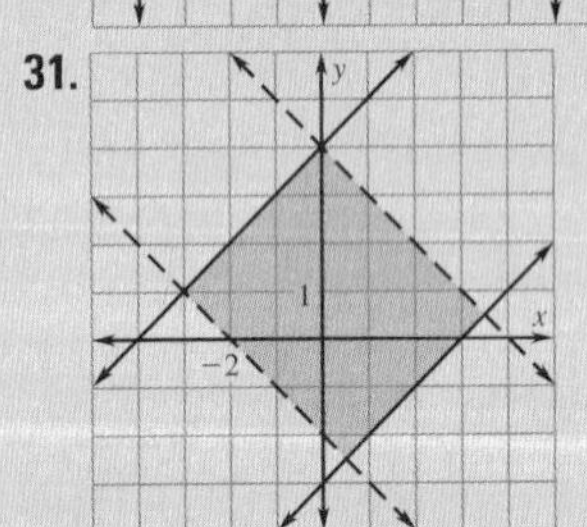

32.
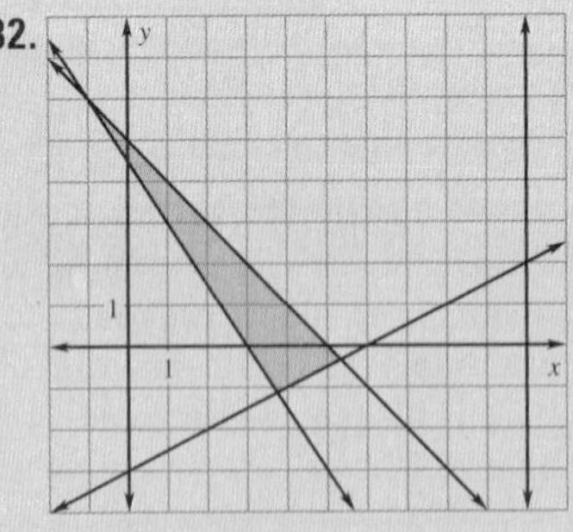

EXAMPLE 2 on p. 467 for Exs. 22–23

22. ★ **MULTIPLE CHOICE** The graph of which system of inequalities is shown? **B**

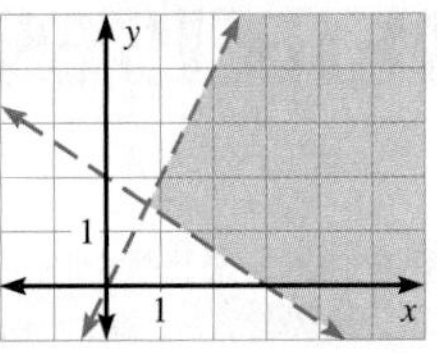

Ⓐ $y < 2x$, $2x + 3y < 6$ Ⓑ $y < 2x$, $2x + 3y > 6$

Ⓒ $y > 2x$, $2x + 3y < 6$ Ⓓ $y > 2x$, $2x + 3y > 6$

23. **ERROR ANALYSIS** *Describe* and correct the error in graphing this system of inequalities:

$x + y < 3$ Inequality 1
$x > -1$ Inequality 2
$x \le 3$ Inequality 3

The graph is shaded to include $x + y > 3$, not $x + y < 3$; see margin for art.

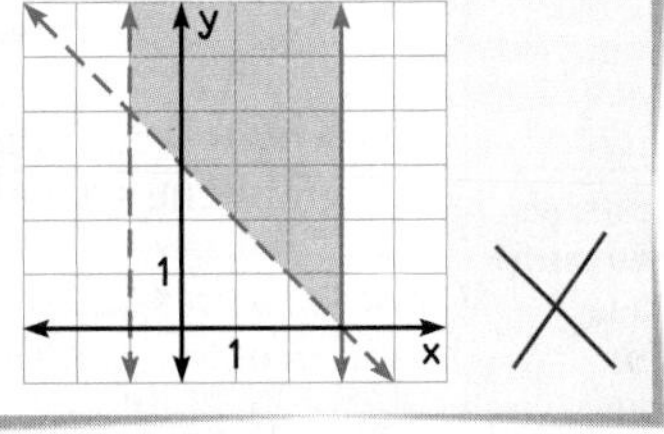

EXAMPLE 3 on p. 467 for Exs. 24–29

WRITING A SYSTEM Write a system of inequalities for the shaded region.

24.
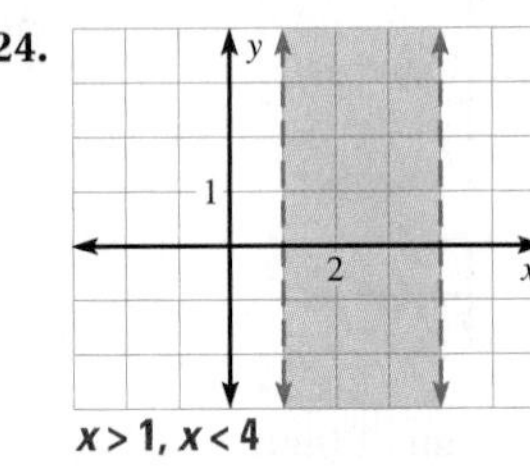
$x > 1$, $x < 4$

25.
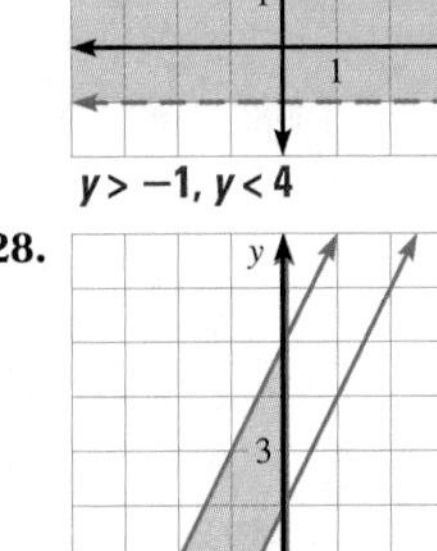
$y > -1$, $y < 4$

26.
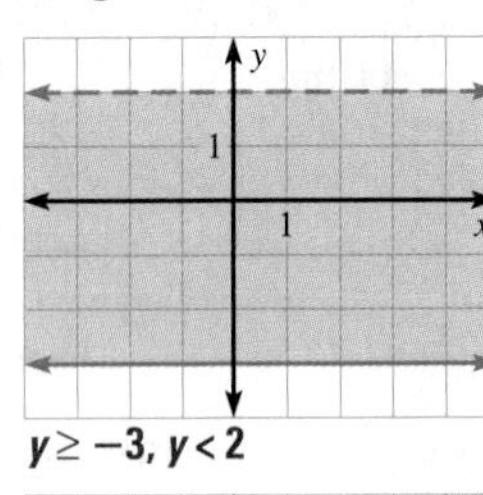
$y \ge -3$, $y < 2$

27.
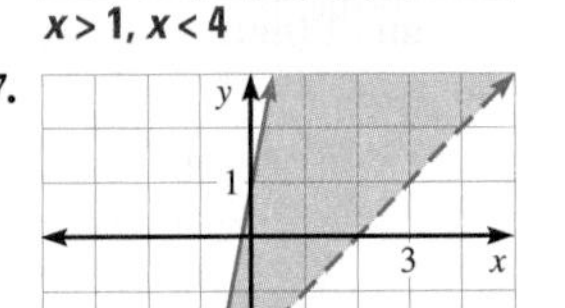
$y \le 5x + 1$, $y > x - 2$

28.
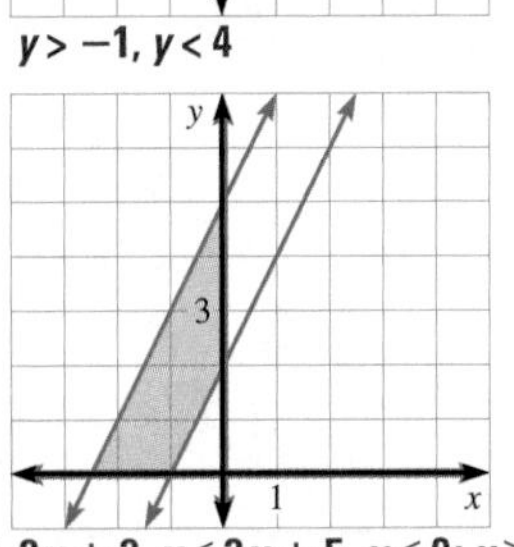
$y \ge 2x + 2$, $y \le 2x + 5$, $x \le 0$; $y \ge 0$

29.
$y \le x - 3$, $y > -2x - 1$, $y > -6$

GRAPHING A SYSTEM Graph the system of inequalities. **30–32. See margin.**

30. $x > 4$
$x < 9$
$y \le 2$
$y > -2$

31. $x + y < 4$
$x + y > -2$
$x - y \le 3$
$x - y \ge -4$

32. $x \le 10$
$3x + 2y \ge 9$
$x - 2y \le 6$
$x + y \le 5$

33. ★ **SHORT RESPONSE** Does the system of inequalities have any solutions? *Explain.* **No; there are no possible values for x and y that satisfy both equations.**

$x - y > 5$ Inequality 1
$x - y < 1$ Inequality 2

CHALLENGE Write a system of inequalities for the shaded region described.

34. The shaded region is a rectangle with vertices at (2, 1), (2, 4), (6, 4), and (6, 1). **$x \ge 2$, $x \le 6$, $y \ge 1$, $y \le 4$**

35. The shaded region is a triangle with vertices at (−3, 0), (3, 2), and (0, −2). **$y \le \frac{1}{3}x + 1$, $y \ge -\frac{2}{3}x - 2$, $y \ge \frac{4}{3}x - 2$**

○ = WORKED-OUT SOLUTIONS on p. WS1 ★ = STANDARDIZED TEST PRACTICE

PROBLEM SOLVING

EXAMPLE 4 A on p. 468 for Exs. 36–38

36. COMPETITION SCORES In a marching band competition, scoring is based on a musical evaluation and a visual evaluation. The musical evaluation score cannot exceed 60 points, the visual evaluation score cannot exceed 40 points. Write and graph a system of inequalities for the scores that a marching band can receive. **Let x represent the musical evaluation score and y represent the visual evaluation score. $x \le 60$, $y \le 40$, $x \ge 0$, $y \ge 0$, see margin for art.**

@HomeTutor for problem solving help at classzone.com

37. NUTRITION For a hiking trip, you are making a mix of x ounces of peanuts and y ounces of chocolate pieces. You want the mix to have less than 70 grams of fat and weigh less than 8 ounces. An ounce of peanuts has 14 grams of fat, and an ounce of chocolate pieces has 7 grams of fat. Write and graph a system of inequalities that models the situation. **$14x + 7y < 70$, $x + y < 8$, $x \ge 0$, $y \ge 0$, see margin for art.**

@HomeTutor for problem solving help at classzone.com

38. FISHING LIMITS You are fishing in a marina for surfperch and rockfish, which are two species of bottomfish. Gaming laws in the marina allow you to catch no more than 15 surfperch per day, no more than 10 rockfish per day, and no more than 15 total bottomfish per day.

a. Write and graph a system of inequalities that models the situation.

b. Use the graph to determine whether you can catch 11 surfperch and 9 rockfish in one day. **no**

39. HEALTH A person's maximum heart rate (in beats per minute) is given by $220 - x$ where x is the person's age in years ($20 \le x \le 65$). When exercising, a person should aim for a heart rate that is at least 70% of the maximum heart rate and at most 85% of the maximum heart rate.

a. Write and graph a system of inequalities that models the situation.

b. A 40-year-old person's heart rate varies from 104 to 120 beats per minute while exercising. Does his heart rate stay in the suggested target range for his age? *Explain.*

B

40. ★ SHORT RESPONSE A photography shop has a self-service photo center that allows you to make prints of pictures. Each sheet of printed pictures costs \$8. The number of pictures that fit on each sheet is shown.

a. You want at least 16 pictures of any size, and you are willing to spend up to \$48. Write and graph a system of inequalities that models the situation.

b. Will you be able to purchase 12 pictures that are 3 inches by 5 inches and 6 pictures that are 4 inches by 6 inches? *Explain.*

Four 3 inch by 5 inch pictures fit on one sheet.

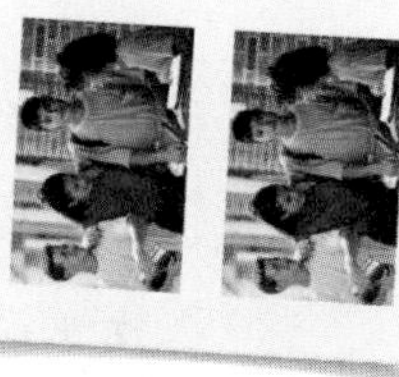

Two 4 inch by 6 inch pictures fit on one sheet.

38a. Let s represent the number of surfperch and r represent the number of rockfish. $s \le 15$, $s + r \le 15$, $r \le 10$, $s \ge 0$, $r \ge 0$, see margin for art.

39a. $20 \le x \le 65$, $y \ge 154 - 0.7x$, $y \le 187 - 0.85x$, see margin for art.

39b. No. *Sample answer:* The heart rate is below 70% of the maximum heart rate.

40a. $8x + 8y \le 48$, $4x + 2y \ge 16$, $x \ge 0$, $y \ge 0$, see margin for art.

40b. Yes. *Sample answer:* It would cost \$48 and give you 18 pictures.

Vocabulary

Exercises 36, 38, 39 Encourage students to pay close attention to the phrases "cannot exceed," "no more than," "at least," and "at most." Point out that all of these phrases share a common meaning of "less than or equal to."

Study Strategy

Exercises 36–40 Remind students that real-world situations often do not include negative solutions. If the situation warrants a restriction to a certain quadrant, students should include that inequality when they write the system of inequalities.

Exercise 39 To learn more about maximum heart rates, visit the American Heart Association's website at www.americanheart.org and do a search for "target heart rates."

39a.

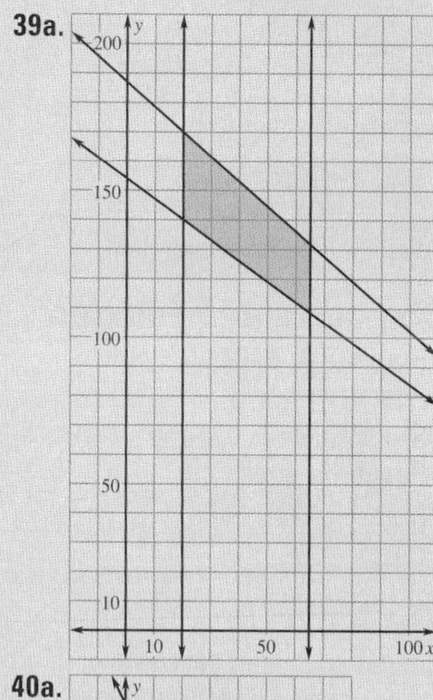

40a.

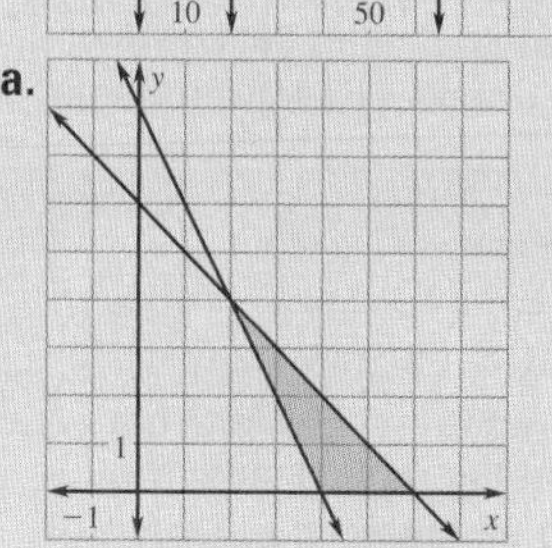

36.

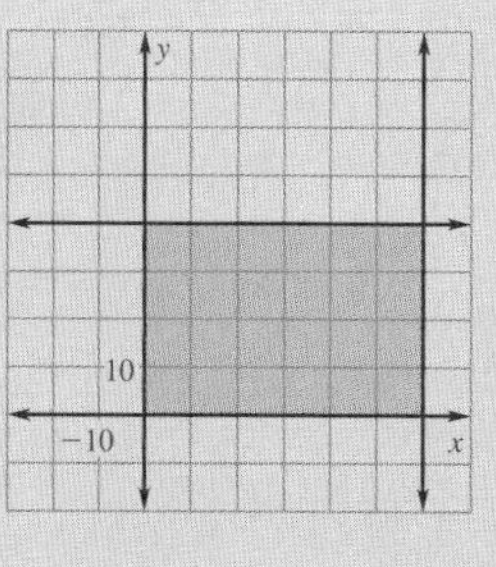

37.

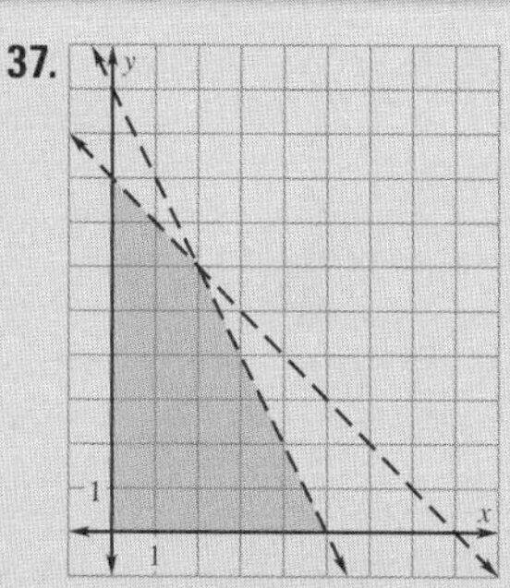

38.

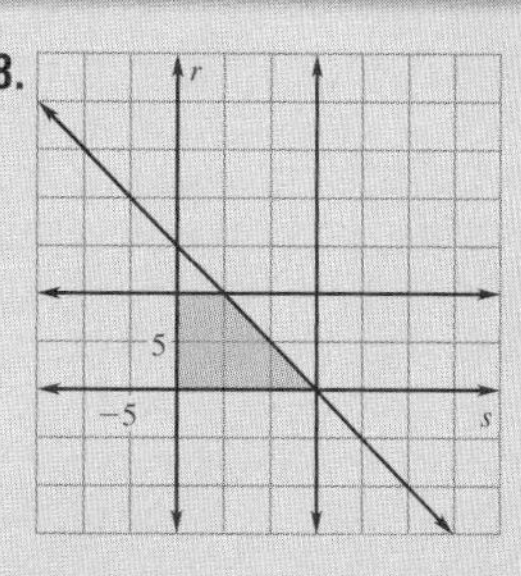

5 ASSESS AND RETEACH

Daily Homework Quiz

Transparency Available

1. Write a system of inequalities for the shaded region.

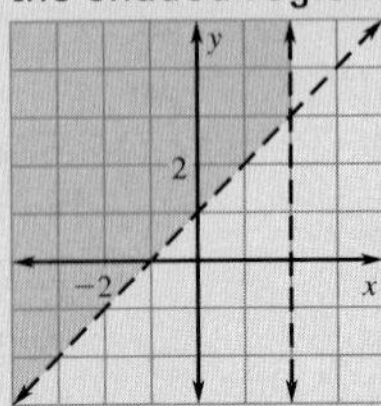

$x < 2$, $y > x + 1$

2. A bibliography can refer to at most 8 articles, at most 4 books, and at most 8 references in all. Write and graph a system of inequalities that models the situation. x = articles, y = books; $x \leq 8$, $y \leq 4$, $x + y \leq 8$, $x \geq 0$, and $y \geq 0$

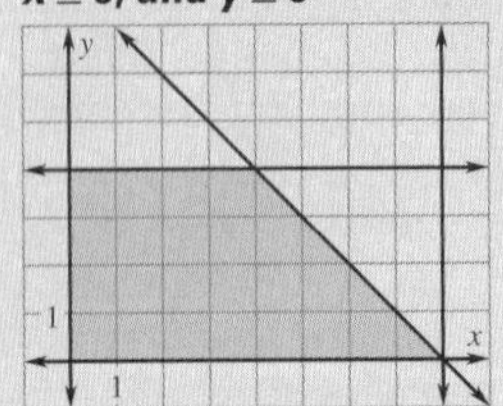

Online Quiz

Available at **classzone.com**

Diagnosis/Remediation

- Practice A, B, C in Chapter Resource Book
- Study Guide in Chapter Resource Book
- Practice Workbook
- @HomeTutor

Challenge

Additional challenge is available in the Chapter Resource Book.

Quiz

An easily-readable reduced copy of the quiz (with answers) on Lessons 7.5–7.6 from the Assessment Book can be found on p. 424F.

41a, Quiz 1–9. See Additional Answers beginning on p. AA1.

C **41. CHALLENGE** You make necklaces and keychains to sell at a craft fair. The table shows the time that it takes to make each necklace and keychain, the cost of materials for each necklace and keychain, and the time and money that you can devote to making necklaces and keychains.

	Necklace	Keychain	Available
Time to make (hours)	0.5	0.25	20
Cost to make (dollars)	2	3	120

a. Write and graph a system of inequalities for the number x of necklaces and the number y of keychains that you can make under the given constraints.

41a. $0.5x + 0.25y \leq 20$, $2x + 3y \leq 120$, $y \geq 0$, $x \geq 0$, see margin for art.

b. Find the vertices (corner points) of the graph. **(0, 0), (40, 0), (0, 40), (30, 20)**

c. You sell each necklace for \$10 and each keychain for \$8. The revenue R is given by the equation $R = 10x + 8y$. Find the revenue for each ordered pair in part (b). Which vertex results in the maximum revenue? **(0, 0): \$0, (40, 0): \$400, (0, 40): \$320, (30, 20): \$460. The maximum revenue is at (30, 20), or 30 necklaces and 20 keychains.**

MIXED REVIEW

PREVIEW Prepare for Lesson 8.1 in Exs. 42–47.

Evaluate the expression.

42. $13x^2$ when $x = 2$ *(p. 8)* **52**

43. $64 \div z^3$ when $z = 2$ *(p. 8)* **8**

44. $-|-c| - 3^2$ when $c = 8$ *(p. 64)* **−17**

45. $-8 + 3y - 16$ when $y = -6$ *(p. 88)* **−42**

46. $\frac{7 - 8w}{11w}$ when $w = 5$ *(p. 103)* $-\frac{3}{5}$

47. $21 + \sqrt{x}$ when $x = 144$ *(p. 110)* **33**

Use any method to solve the linear system. *(pp. 427, 435, 444, 451)*

48. $y = 4x - 1$, $y = -8x + 23$ **(2, 7)**

49. $y = -2x - 6$, $y = -5x - 12$ **(−2, −2)**

50. $x + 2y = -1$, $-x = y - 2$ **(5, −3)**

51. $4x + y = 0$, $-x + y = 5$ **(−1, 4)**

52. $2x - y = -5$, $y = -x - 5$ $\left(-3\frac{1}{3}, -1\frac{2}{3}\right)$

53. $3x + 2y = 2$, $-3x + y = -11$ $\left(2\frac{2}{3}, -3\right)$

QUIZ for Lessons 7.5–7.6

Graph the linear system. Then use the graph to tell whether the linear system has *one solution, no solution,* or *infinitely many solutions.* *(p. 459)* **1–3. See margin for art.**

1. $x - y = 1$, $x - y = 6$ **no solution**

2. $6x + 2y = 16$, $2x - y = 2$ **one solution**

3. $3x - 3y = -2$, $-6x + 6y = 4$ **infinitely many solutions**

Graph the system of linear inequalities. *(p. 466)* **4–9. See margin.**

4. $x > -3$, $x < 7$

5. $y \leq 2$, $y < 6x + 2$

6. $4x \geq y$, $-x + 4y < 4$

7. $x + y < 2$, $2x + y > -3$, $y \geq 0$

8. $y \geq 3x - 4$, $y \leq x$, $y \geq -5x - 15$

9. $x > -5$, $x < 0$, $y \leq 2x + 7$

MIXED REVIEW of Problem Solving

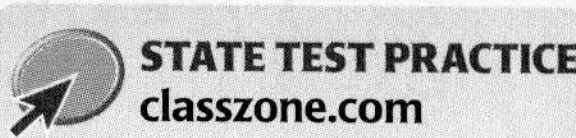

Lessons 7.5–7.6

1. **MULTI-STEP PROBLEM** A minimum of 600 bricks and 12 bags of sand are needed for a construction job. Each brick weighs 2 pounds, and each bag of sand weighs 50 pounds. The maximum weight that a delivery truck can carry is 3000 pounds.
   a. Let x be the number of bricks, and let y be the number of bags of sand. Write a system of linear inequalities that models the situation. **$x \geq 600$, $y \geq 12$, $2x + 50y \leq 3000$**
   b. Graph the system of inequalities. **See margin.**
   c. Use the graph to determine whether 700 bricks and 20 bags of sand can be delivered in one trip. **yes**

2. **MULTI-STEP PROBLEM** Dana decides to paint the ceiling and the walls of a room. She spends \$120 on 2 gallons of paint for the ceiling and 4 gallons of paint for the walls. Then she decides to paint the ceiling and the walls of another room using the same kinds of paint. She spends \$60 for 1 gallon of paint for the ceiling and 2 gallons of paint for the walls.

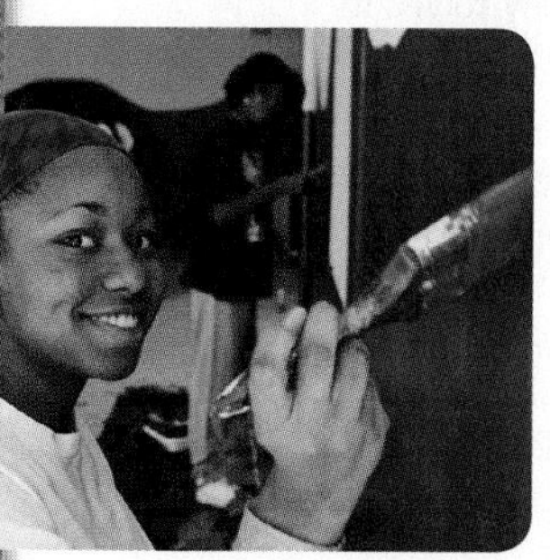

   a. Write a system of linear equations that models the situation. **$2x + 4y = 120$, $x + 2y = 60$**
   b. Is there enough information given to determine the cost of one gallon of each type of paint? *Explain.* **See margin.**
   c. A gallon of ceiling paint costs \$3 more than a gallon of wall paint. What is the cost of one gallon of each type of paint? **ceiling paint: \$22, wall paint: \$19**

3. **SHORT RESPONSE** During a sale at a music and video store, all CDs are priced the same and all DVDs are priced the same. Karen buys 4 CDs and 2 DVDs for \$78. The next day, while the sale is still in progress, Karen goes back and buys 2 CDs and 1 DVD for \$39. Is there enough information to determine the cost of 1 CD? *Explain.* **No. *Sample answer:* The linear system that models the situation has infinitely many solutions.**

4. **SHORT RESPONSE** Two airport shuttles, bus A and bus B, take passengers to the airport from the same bus stop. The graph shows the distance d (in miles) traveled by each bus t hours after bus A leaves the station. The distance from the bus stop to the airport is 25 miles. If bus A and bus B continue at the same rates, will bus B ever catch up to bus A? *Explain.* **See margin.**

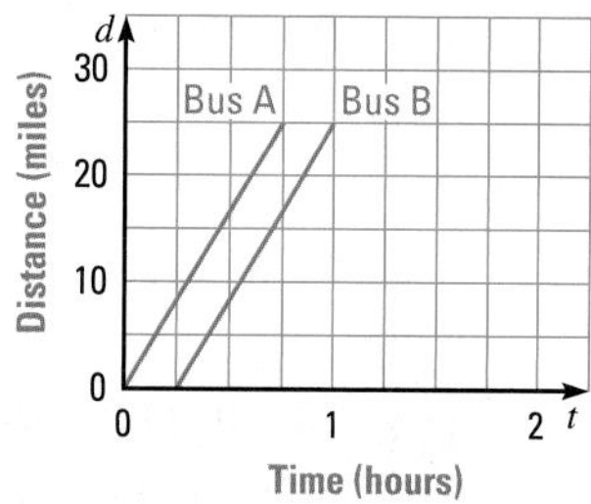

5. **EXTENDED RESPONSE** During the summer, you want to earn at least \$200 per week. You earn \$10 per hour working as a lifeguard, and you earn \$8 per hour working at a retail store. You can work at most 30 hours per week.
   a. Write and graph a system of linear inequalities that models the situation. **See margin.**
   b. If you work 5 hours per week as a lifeguard and 15 hours per week at the retail store, will you earn at least \$200 per week? *Explain.* **No; you will earn \$170.**
   c. You are scheduled to work 20 hours per week at the retail store. What is the range of hours you can work as a lifeguard to earn at least \$200 per week? **$4 \leq x \leq 10$**

6. **OPEN-ENDED** *Describe* a real-world situation that can be modeled by a system of linear inequalities. Then write and graph the system of inequalities. **See margin.**

7. **GRIDDED ANSWER** What is the area (in square feet) of the triangular garden defined by the system of inequalities below? **90 ft²**

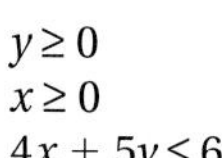

$$y \geq 0$$
$$x \geq 0$$
$$4x + 5y \leq 60$$

1b.

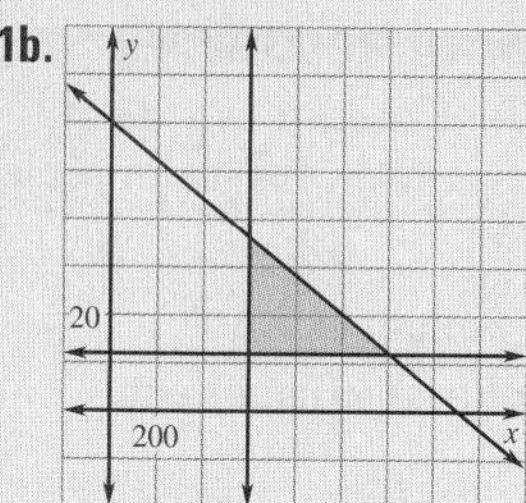

2b. No. *Sample answer:* There are infinitely many solutions to the linear system.

4. No. *Sample answer:* The lines are parallel so there is never a point when the shuttles will have traveled the same distance at the same time.

5a. Let x represent the hours working as a lifeguard, and y represent the hours working at a retail store. $10x + 8y \geq 200$, $x + y \leq 30$, $x \geq 0$, $y \geq 0$

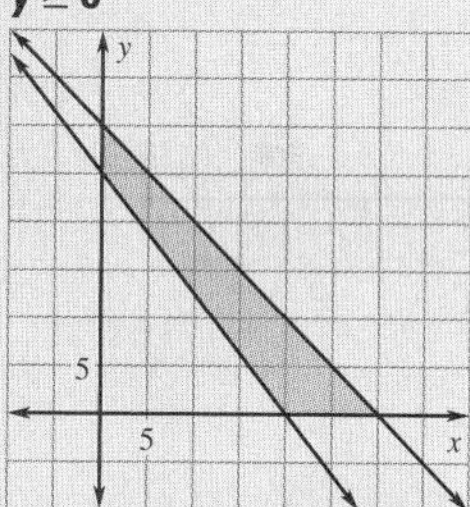

6. *Sample answer:* You have 80 dollars and want to buy cups at a store. Small cups are \$4, and large cups are \$5. The store has 10 small cups and 12 large cups. $x \geq 0$, $y \geq 0$, $x \leq 10$, $y \leq 12$, $4x + 5y \leq 80$

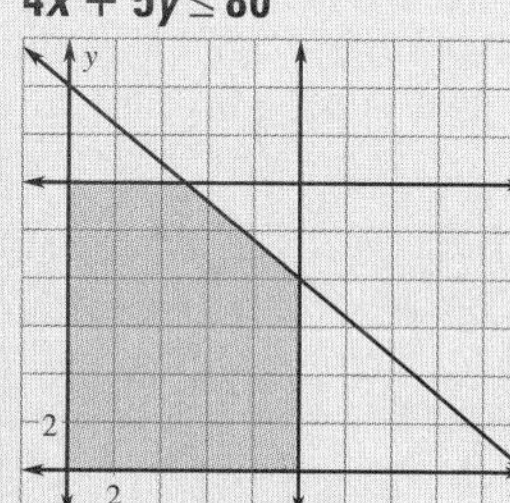

Additional Resources

The following resources are available to help review the materials in this chapter.

Chapter Resource Book

- Chapter Review Games and Activities
- Cumulative Practice, Chs. 1–7

Student Resources in Spanish

eWorkbook

@HomeTutor

Vocabulary Practice

Vocabulary practice is available at **classzone.com**

BIG IDEAS

For Your Notebook

Big Idea 1

Solving Linear Systems by Graphing

The graph of a system of two linear equations tells you how many solutions the system has.

One solution	**No solution**	**Infinitely many solutions**
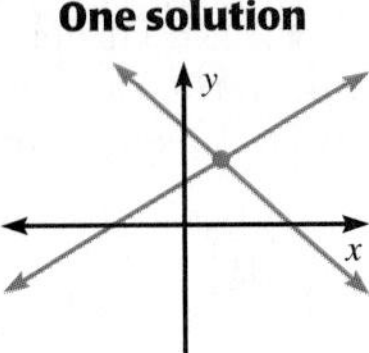		
The lines intersect.	The lines are parallel.	The lines coincide.

Big Idea 2

Solving Linear Systems Using Algebra

You can use any of the following algebraic methods to solve a system of linear equations. Sometimes it is easier to use one method instead of another.

Method	Procedure	When to use
Substitution	Solve one equation for x or y. Substitute the expression for x or y into the other equation.	When one equation is already solved for x or y
Addition	Add the equations to eliminate x or y.	When the coefficients of one variable are opposites
Subtraction	Subtract the equations to eliminate x or y.	When the coefficients of one variable are the same
Multiplication	Multiply one or both equations by a constant so that adding or subtracting the equations will eliminate x or y.	When no corresponding coefficients are the same or opposites

Big Idea 3

Solving Systems of Linear Inequalities

The graph of a system of linear inequalities is the intersection of the half-planes of each inequality in the system. For example, the graph of the system of inequalities below is the shaded region.

$x \le 6$	**Inequality 1**
$y < 2$	**Inequality 2**
$2x + 3y \ge 6$	**Inequality 3**

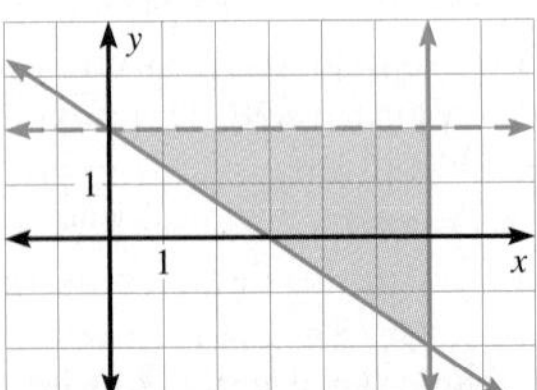

CHAPTER REVIEW

@HomeTutor
classzone.com
- Multi-Language Glossary
- Vocabulary practice

REVIEW KEY VOCABULARY

- system of linear equations, *p. 427*
- solution of a system of linear equations, *p. 427*
- consistent independent system, *p. 427*
- inconsistent system, *p. 459*
- consistent dependent system, *p. 459*
- system of linear inequalities, *p. 466*
- solution of a system of linear inequalities, *p. 466*
- graph of a system of linear inequalities, *p. 466*

VOCABULARY EXERCISES

1. Copy and complete: A(n) _?_ consists of two or more linear inequalities in the same variables. **system of linear inequalities**
2. Copy and complete: A(n) _?_ consists of two or more linear equations in the same variables. **system of linear equations**
3. *Describe* how you would graph a system of two linear inequalities. **See margin.**
4. Give an example of a consistent dependent system. *Explain* why the system is a consistent dependent system. ***Sample answer:* $y = 2x + 3$, $2y = 4x + 6$; the lines intersect (are consistent) and the equations are equivalent (are dependent).**

REVIEW EXAMPLES AND EXERCISES

Use the review examples and exercises below to check your understanding of the concepts you have learned in each lesson of Chapter 7.

7.1 Solve Linear Systems by Graphing *pp. 427–433*

EXAMPLE

Solve the linear system by graphing. Check your solution.

$y = x - 2$ **Equation 1**
$y = -3x + 2$ **Equation 2**

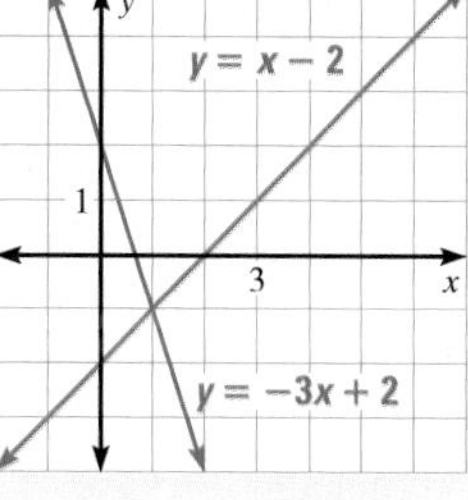

Graph both equations. The lines appear to intersect at (1, −1). Check the solution by substituting 1 for x and −1 for y in each equation.

$y = x - 2$	$y = -3x + 2$
$-1 \stackrel{?}{=} 1 - 2$	$-1 \stackrel{?}{=} -3(1) + 2$
$-1 = -1$ ✓	$-1 = -1$ ✓

EXERCISES

EXAMPLES 1 and 2 on pp. 427–428 for Exs. 5–7

Solve the linear system by graphing. Check your solution.

5. $y = -3x + 1$ **(2, −5)**
   $y = x - 7$
6. $y = 3x + 4$ **(−1, 1)**
   $y = -2x - 1$
7. $x + y = 3$ **(4, −1)**
   $x - y = 5$

Extra Example 7.1
Solve the linear system by graphing. Check your solution.
$y = -x + 4$
$y = 2x - 5$ **(3, 1)**

3. *Sample answer:* Graph each inequality then shade the region that is the intersection of the solutions to each inequality. Then check the solution with a test point.

Extra Example 7.2

Solve the linear system using substitution.

$y + 2x = 13$
$-x + 4y = -2$ **(6, 1)**

Extra Example 7.3

Solve the linear system using elimination.

$-2x + 3y = 6$
$-2x + 5y = -6$ **(−12, −6)**

7 CHAPTER REVIEW

7.2 Solve Linear Systems by Substitution

pp. 435–441

EXAMPLE

Solve the linear system: $3x + y = -9$ **Equation 1**
$y = 5x + 7$ **Equation 2**

STEP 1 **Substitute** $5x + 7$ for y in Equation 1 and solve for x.

$3x + y = -9$ **Write Equation 1.**

$3x + 5x + 7 = -9$ **Substitute $5x + 7$ for y.**

$x = -2$ **Solve for x.**

STEP 2 **Substitute** -2 for x in Equation 2 to find the value of y.

$$y = 5x + 7 = 5(-2) + 7 = -10 + 7 = -3$$

▶ The solution is $(-2, -3)$. Check the solution by substituting -2 for x and -3 for y in each of the original equations.

EXERCISES

EXAMPLES 1, 2, and 3 on pp. 435–437 for Exs. 8–11

Solve the linear system using substitution.

8. $y = 2x - 7$ **(3, −1)**
$x + 2y = 1$

9. $x + 4y = 9$ **(5, 1)**
$x - y = 4$

10. $2x + y = -15$ **(−3, −9)**
$y - 5x = 6$

11. ART Kara spends \$16 on tubes of paint and disposable brushes for an art project. Each tube of paint costs \$3, and each disposable brush costs \$.50. Kara purchases twice as many brushes as tubes of paint. Find the number of brushes and the number of tubes of paint that she purchases. **4 tubes of paint, 8 brushes**

7.3 Solve Linear Systems by Adding or Subtracting

pp. 444–450

EXAMPLE

Solve the linear system: $5x - y = 8$ **Equation 1**
$-5x + 4y = -17$ **Equation 2**

STEP 1 **Add** the equations to eliminate one variable.

$$\begin{array}{r} 5x - y = 8 \\ -5x + 4y = -17 \\ \hline 3y = -9 \end{array}$$

STEP 2 **Solve** for y. $y = -3$

STEP 3 **Substitute** -3 for y in either equation and solve for x.

$5x - y = 8$ **Write Equation 1.**

$5x - (-3) = 8$ **Substitute −3 for y.**

$x = 1$ **Solve for x.**

▶ The solution is $(1, -3)$. Check the solution by substituting 1 for x and -3 for y in each of the original equations.

EXAMPLES 1, 2, and 3 on pp. 444–445 for Exs. 12–17

EXERCISES

Solve the linear system using elimination.

12. $x + 2y = 13$ **(3, 5)**
$x - 2y = -7$

13. $4x - 5y = 14$ **(1, −2)**
$-4x + y = -6$

14. $x + 7y = 12$ **(−2, 2)**
$-2x + 7y = 18$

15. $9x - 2y = 34$ **(6, 10)**
$5x - 2y = 10$

16. $3x = y + 1$ **(−8, −25)**
$2x - y = 9$

17. $4y = 11 - 3x$ **(−7, 8)**
$3x + 2y = -5$

7.4 Solve Linear Systems by Multiplying First

pp. 451–457

EXAMPLE

Solve the linear system: $x - 2y = -7$ **Equation 1**
$3x - y = 4$ **Equation 2**

STEP 1 **Multiply** the first equation by −3.

$x - 2y = -7$ **× (−3)** → $-3x + 6y = 21$
$3x - y = 4$ → $3x - y = 4$

STEP 2 **Add** the equations. $5y = 25$

STEP 3 **Solve** for *y*. $y = 5$

STEP 4 **Substitute** 5 for *y* in either of the original equations and solve for *x*.

$x - 2y = -7$ **Write Equation 1.**

$x - 2(5) = -7$ **Substitute 5 for *y*.**

$x = 3$ **Solve for *x*.**

▶ The solution is (3, 5).

CHECK Substitute 3 for *x* and 5 for *y* in each of the original equations.

Equation 1	Equation 2
$x - 2y = -7$	$3x - y = 4$
$3 - 2(5) \stackrel{?}{=} -7$	$3(3) - 5 \stackrel{?}{=} 4$
$-7 = -7$ ✓	$4 = 4$ ✓

EXAMPLES 1 and 2 on pp. 451–452 for Exs. 18–24

EXERCISES

Solve the linear system using elimination.

18. $-x + y = -4$ **(7, 3)**
$2x - 3y = 5$

19. $x + 6y = 28$ **(−2, 5)**
$2x - 3y = -19$

20. $3x - 5y = -7$ **(−9, −4)**
$-4x + 7y = 8$

21. $8x - 7y = -3$ **(4, 5)**
$6x - 5y = -1$

22. $5x = 3y - 2$ **(2, 4)**
$3x + 2y = 14$

23. $11x = 2y - 1$ **(1, 6)**
$3y = 10 + 8x$

24. CAR MAINTENANCE You pay $24.50 for 10 gallons of gasoline and 1 quart of oil at a gas station. Your friend pays $22 for 8 gallons of the same gasoline and 2 quarts of the same oil. Find the cost of 1 quart of oil. **$2**

Extra Example 7.4

Solve the linear system using elimination.
$3x - 2y = 5$
$2x - 3y = 5$ **(1, −1)**

Extra Example 7.5

Show that the linear system has infinitely many solutions.

$y = -2x - 4$

$6x + 3y = -12$

Substitute $-2x - 4$ for y in the equation $6x + 3y = -12$ and solve for x.

$$6x + 3y = -12$$
$$6x + 3(-2x - 4) = -12$$
$$6x - 6x - 12 = -12$$
$$-12 = -12$$

Since this is a true statement, the system has infinitely many solutions.

Extra Example 7.6

Graph the system of linear inequalities.

$y \geq x - 1$

$y < -2x$

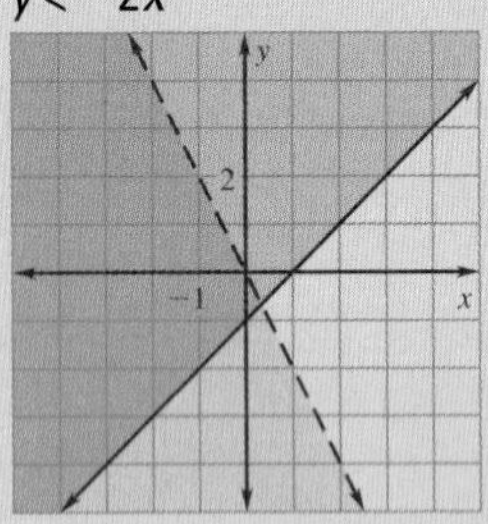

25. No solution. ***Sample answer:*** **When the variables are eliminated, a false statement remains, which means there is no solution.**

26. Infinitely many solutions. ***Sample answer:*** **When the variables are eliminated, a true statement remains, which means there are infinitely many solutions.**

27. One solution. ***Sample answer:*** **The lines have different slopes, so there is only one solution.**

28.

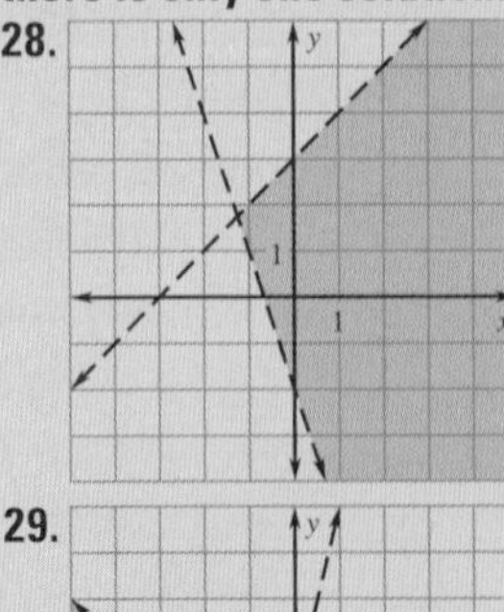

29.

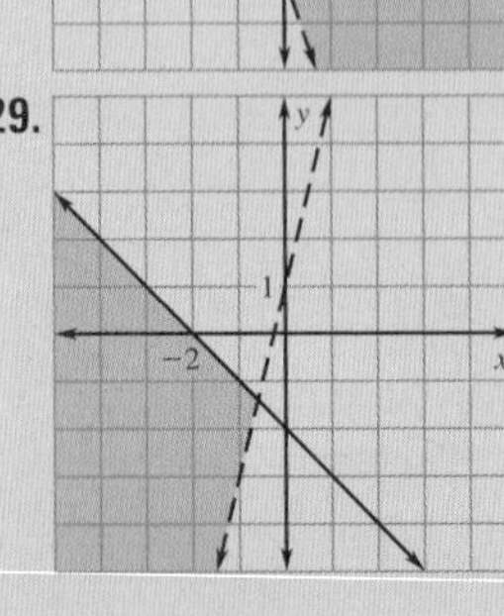

7.5 Solve Special Types of Linear Systems *pp. 459–465*

EXAMPLE

Show that the linear system has no solution. $-2x + y = -3$ **Equation 1**; $y = 2x + 1$ **Equation 2**

Graph the linear system.

The lines are parallel because they have the same slope but different y-intercepts. Parallel lines do not intersect, so the system has no solution.

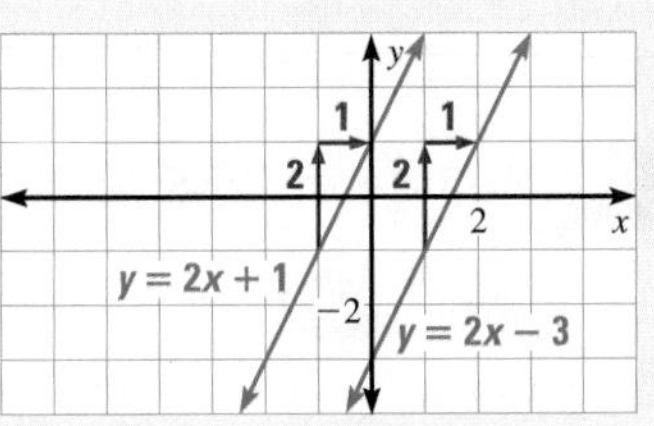

EXERCISES

EXAMPLES 1, 2, and 3 on pp. 459–461 for Exs. 25–27

Tell whether the linear system has *one solution*, *no solution*, or *infinitely many solutions*. Explain. **25–27. See margin.**

25. $x = 2y - 3$, $1.5x - 3y = 0$

26. $-x + y = 8$, $x + 8 = y$

27. $4x = 2y + 6$, $4x + 2y = 10$

7.6 Solve Systems of Linear Inequalities *pp. 466–472*

EXAMPLE

Graph the system of linear inequalities. $y < -2x + 3$ **Inequality 1**; $y \geq x - 3$ **Inequality 2**

The graph of $y < -2x + 3$ is the half-plane *below* the *dashed* line $y = -2x + 3$.

The graph of $y \geq x - 3$ is the half-plane *on and above* the *solid* line $y = x - 3$.

The graph of the system is the intersection of the two half-planes shown as the darker shade of blue.

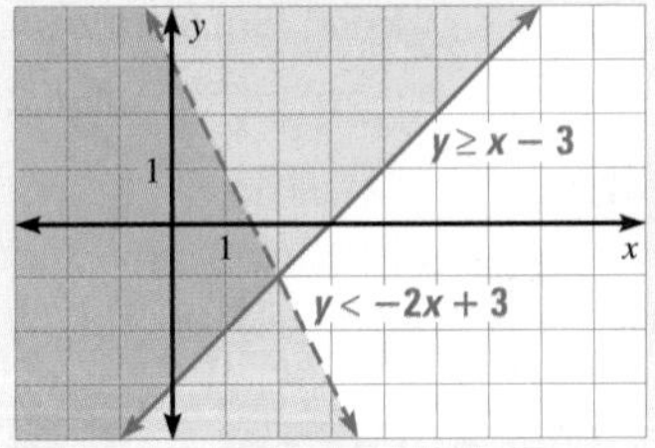

EXERCISES

EXAMPLES 1, 2, 3, and 4 on pp. 466–468 for Exs. 28–31

Graph the system of linear inequalities. **28–30. See margin.**

28. $y < x + 3$, $y > -3x - 2$

29. $y \leq -x - 2$, $y > 4x + 1$

30. $y \geq 0$, $x \leq 2$, $y < x + 4$

31. MOVIE COSTS You receive a \$40 gift card to a movie theater. A ticket to a matinee movie costs \$5, and a ticket to an evening movie costs \$8. Write and graph a system of inequalities for the number of tickets you can purchase using the gift card. **Let m represent the number of matinee movies and n represent the number of evening movies. $5m + 8n \leq 40$, $m \geq 0$, $n \geq 0$, see margin for art.**

30.

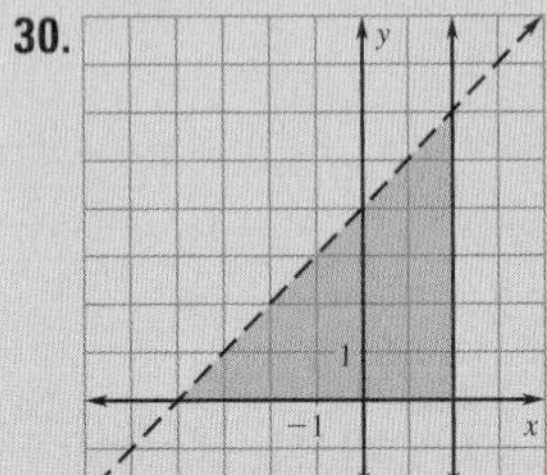

31.

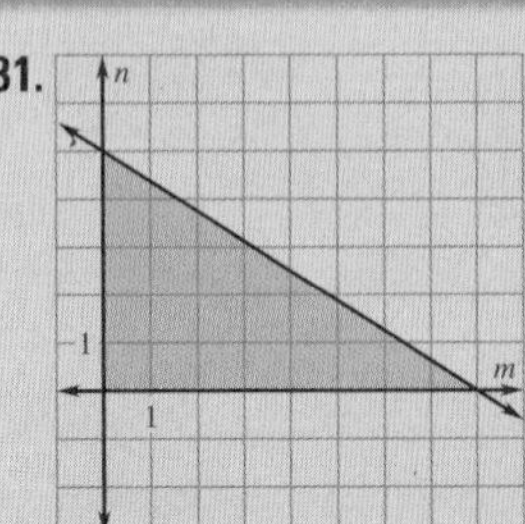

7 CHAPTER TEST

Solve the linear system by graphing. Check your solution.

1. $3x - y = -6$ **(−1, 3)**
   $x + y = 2$
2. $-2x + y = 5$ **(−2, 1)**
   $x + y = -1$
3. $y = 4x + 4$ $\left(\frac{4}{11}, 5\frac{5}{11}\right)$
   $3x + 2y = 12$
4. $5x - 4y = 20$ **(4, 0)**
   $x + 2y = 4$
5. $x + 3y = 9$ **(3, 2)**
   $2x - y = 4$
6. $2x + 7y = 14$ **(−7, 4)**
   $5x + 7y = -7$

Solve the linear system using substitution.

7. $y = 5x - 7$ **(6, 23)**
   $-4x + y = -1$
8. $x = y - 11$ **(−17, −6)**
   $x - 3y = 1$
9. $3x + y = -19$ **(−3, −10)**
   $x - y = 7$
10. $15x + y = 70$ **(4, 10)**
    $3x - 2y = -8$
11. $3y + x = 17$ **(3.5, 4.5)**
    $x + y = 8$
12. $0.5x + y = 9$
    $1.6x + 0.2y = 13$
    $\left(7\frac{7}{15}, 5\frac{4}{15}\right)$

Solve the linear system using elimination.

13. $8x + 3y = -9$ **(−3, 5)**
    $-8x + y = 29$
14. $x - 5y = -3$ **(7, 2)**
    $3x - 5y = 11$
15. $4x + y = 17$ **(4, 1)**
    $7y = 4x - 9$
16. $3x + 2y = -5$ **(3, −7)**
    $x - y = 10$
17. $3y = x + 5$ **(16, 7)**
    $-3x + 8y = 8$
18. $6x - 5y = 9$ **(4, 3)**
    $9x - 7y = 15$

Tell whether the linear system has *one solution*, *no solution*, or *infinitely many solutions*.

19. $15x - 3y = 12$
    $y = 5x - 4$
    infinitely many solutions
20. $4x - y = -4$ **no solution**
    $-8x + 2y = 2$
21. $-12x + 3y = 18$
    $4x + y = -6$
    one solution
22. $6x - 7y = 5$
    $-12x + 14y = 10$ **no solution**
23. $3x - 4y = 24$ **one solution**
    $3x + 4y = 24$
24. $10x - 2y = 14$
    $15x - 3y = 21$
    infinitely many solutions

Graph the system of linear inequalities. **25–27. See margin.**

25. $y < 2x + 2$
    $y \geq -x - 1$
26. $y \leq 3x - 2$
    $y > x + 4$
27. $y \leq 3$
    $x > -1$
    $y > 3x - 3$

28. **TRUCK RENTALS** Carrie and Dave each rent the same size moving truck for one day. They pay a fee of x dollars for the truck and y dollars per mile they drive. Carrie drives 150 miles and pays \$215. Dave drives 120 miles and pays \$176. Find the amount of the fee and the cost per mile.
    fee: \$20, cost per mile: \$1.30

29. **GEOMETRY** The rectangle has a perimeter P of 58 inches. The length ℓ is one more than 3 times the width w. Write and solve a system of linear equations to find the length and width of the rectangle.
    $2\ell + 2w = 58$, $\ell = 3w + 1$, $\ell = 22$ in., $w = 7$ in.

    $P = 58$ in. (w, ℓ)

30. **COMMUNITY SERVICE** A town committee has a budget of \$75 to spend on snacks for the volunteers participating in a clean-up day. The committee chairperson decides to purchase granola bars and at least 50 bottles of water. Granola bars cost \$.50 each, and bottles of water cost \$.75 each. Write and graph a system of linear inequalities for the number of bottles of water and the number of granola bars that can be purchased. **See margin.**

25.
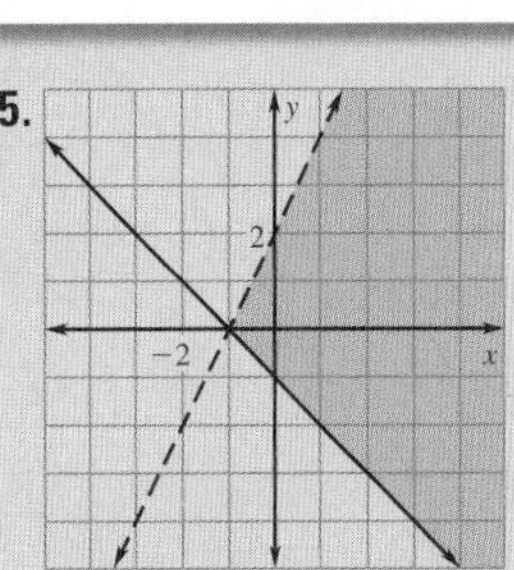

Additional Resources

Assessment Book

- Chapter Test, Levels A, B, C
- Standardized Chapter Test
- SAT/ACT Chapter Test
- Alternative Assessment

Test Generator

Chapter Test

Easily-readable reduced copies (with answers) of Chapter Test B, the Standardized Chapter Test, and the Alternative Assessment from the Assessment Book can be found on pp. 424G–424H.

26.
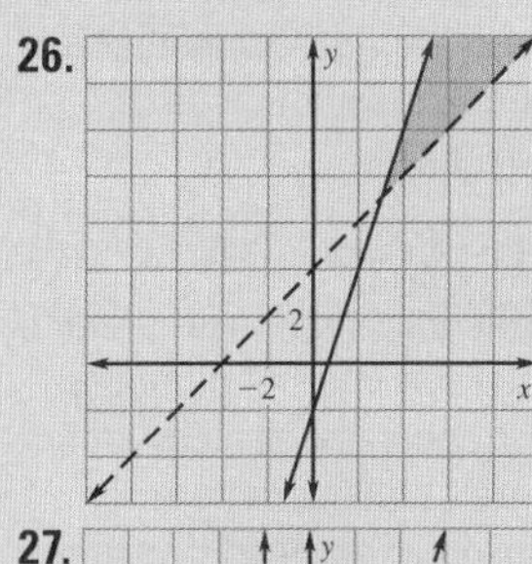

27.
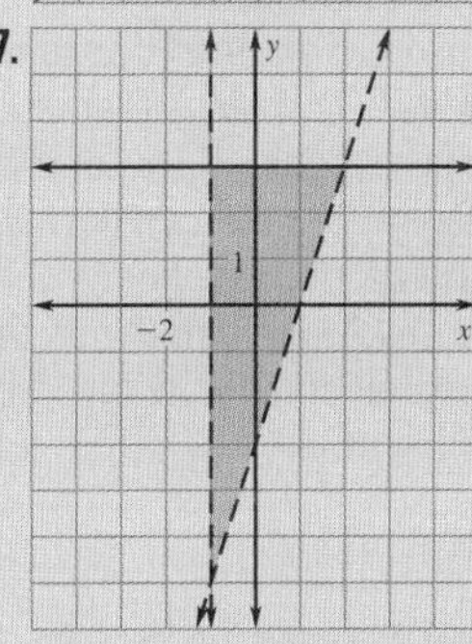

30. Let w represent the number of water bottles and g represent the number of granola bars; $w \geq 50$, $g \geq 0$, $0.5g + 0.75w \leq 75$.

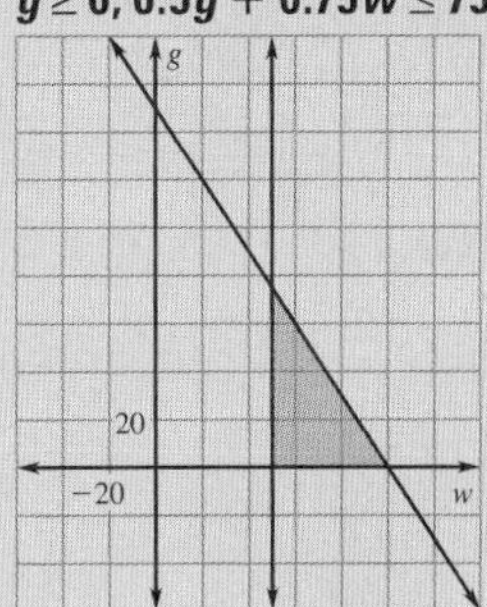

Test-Taking Strategy

When solving multiple-choice questions that have ordered pairs or pairs of numbers for answer choices, eliminate pairs that cannot possibly be the answer based on the conditions of the problem.

For example, the condition $y = \frac{1}{2}x$ in Problem 1 means both x and y must have the same sign. This eliminates choice B. In Problem 2, the condition that the sum has to be −1 means the numbers must have different signs. This eliminates choice B. Once you have eliminated one or two of the answer choices, you can substitute the remaining pairs of numbers in the original question. The fewer numbers you need to substitute in the original question, the fewer chances you have of making a mistake.

Avoiding Common Errors

Multiple choice questions that have ordered pairs or pairs of numbers for answer choices often contain two or more choices that are inverses of one another. For example, in Problem 2, choices C and D fall into this category. If one of the pairs of numbers is the correct answer choice, double check your answer to make sure you chose the correct answer and not its inverse.

MULTIPLE CHOICE QUESTIONS

If you have difficulty solving a multiple choice problem directly, you may be able to use another approach to eliminate incorrect answer choices and obtain the correct answer.

PROBLEM 1

Which ordered pair is the solution of the linear system $y = \frac{1}{2}x$ and $2x + 3y = -7$?

Ⓐ (2, 1) Ⓑ (1, −3) Ⓒ (−2, −1) Ⓓ (4, 2)

Method 1

SOLVE DIRECTLY Use substitution to solve the linear system.

STEP 1 **Substitute** $\frac{1}{2}x$ for y in the equation $2x + 3y = -7$ and solve for x.

$$2x + 3\mathbf{y} = -7$$

$$2x + 3\left(\frac{\mathbf{1}}{\mathbf{2}}\mathbf{x}\right) = -7$$

$$2x + \frac{3}{2}x = -7$$

$$\frac{7}{2}x = -7$$

$$x = -2$$

STEP 2 **Substitute** −2 for x in $y = \frac{1}{2}x$ to find the value of y.

$$y = \frac{1}{2}\mathbf{x}$$

$$= \frac{1}{2}(\mathbf{-2})$$

$$= -1$$

The solution of the system is (−2, −1).

The correct answer is C. Ⓐ Ⓑ Ⓒ Ⓓ

Method 2

ELIMINATE CHOICES Substitute the values given in each answer choice for x and y in both equations.

Choice A: (2, 1)
Substitute 2 for x and 1 for y.

$\mathbf{y} = \frac{1}{2}\mathbf{x}$ $\quad$ $2\mathbf{x} + 3\mathbf{y} = -7$

$\mathbf{1} \stackrel{?}{=} \frac{1}{2}(\mathbf{2})$ $\quad$ $2(\mathbf{2}) + 3(\mathbf{1}) \stackrel{?}{=} -7$

$1 = 1$ ✓ $\quad$ $7 = -7$ ✗

Choice B: (1, −3)
Substitute 1 for x and −3 for y.

$\mathbf{y} = \frac{1}{2}\mathbf{x}$

$\mathbf{-3} \stackrel{?}{=} \frac{1}{2}(\mathbf{1})$

$-3 = \frac{1}{2}$ ✗

Choice C: (−2, −1)
Substitute −2 for x and −1 for y.

$\mathbf{y} = \frac{1}{2}\mathbf{x}$ $\quad$ $2\mathbf{x} + 3\mathbf{y} = -7$

$\mathbf{-1} \stackrel{?}{=} \frac{1}{2}(\mathbf{-2})$ $\quad$ $2(\mathbf{-2}) + 3(\mathbf{-1}) \stackrel{?}{=} -7$

$-1 = -1$ ✓ $\quad$ $-7 = -7$ ✓

The correct answer is C. Ⓐ Ⓑ Ⓒ Ⓓ

PROBLEM 2

The sum of two numbers is −1, and the difference of the two numbers is 5. What are the numbers?

(A) −5 and 4 (B) 1 and 6 (C) 2 and −3 (D) −2 and 3

Method 1

SOLVE DIRECTLY Write and solve a system of equations for the numbers.

STEP 1 **Write** a system of equations. Let x and y be the numbers.

$x + y = -1$ **Equation 1**
$x - y = 5$ **Equation 2**

STEP 2 **Add** the equations to eliminate one variable. Then find the value of the other variable.

$$\begin{array}{l} x + y = -1 \\ \underline{x - y = 5} \\ \quad 2x = 4, \text{ so } x = 2 \end{array}$$

STEP 3 **Substitute** 2 for x in Equation 1 and solve for y.

$2 + y = -1$, so $y = -3$

The correct answer is C. (A) (B) (C) (D)

Method 2

ELIMINATE CHOICES Find the sum and difference of each pair of numbers. Because the difference is positive, be sure to subtract the lesser number from the greater number.

Choice A: −5 and 4

Sum: $-5 + 4 = -1$ ✓

Difference: $-5 - 4 = -9$ ✗

Choice B: 1 and 6

Sum: $1 + 6 = 7$ ✗

Choice C: 2 and −3

Sum: $2 + (-3) = -1$ ✓

Difference: $2 - (-3) = 5$ ✓

The correct answer is C. (A) (B) (C) (D)

PRACTICE

Explain why you can eliminate the highlighted answer choice.

1. The sum of two numbers is –27. One number is twice the other. What are the numbers?

   (A) ✗ 9 and 18 (B) −3 and 24 (C) −18 and −9 (D) −14 and −13

2. Which ordered pair is a solution of the linear system $5x + 2y = -11$ and $x = -\frac{1}{2}y - 4$?

   (A) $\left(-\frac{7}{6}, -\frac{17}{3}\right)$ (B) $\left(-\frac{23}{3}, \frac{1}{3}\right)$ (C) $(-3, 2)$ (D) ✗ $(23, 213)$

3. Long-sleeve and short-sleeve T-shirts can be purchased at a concert. A long-sleeve T-shirt costs \$25 and a short-sleeve T-shirt costs \$15. During a concert, the T-shirt vendor collects \$8415 from the sale of 441 T-shirts. How many short-sleeve T-shirts were sold?

   (A) 100 (B) ✗ 180 (C) 261 (D) 441

Answers

1. The sum of 9 and 18 is not −27.

2. $5(-3) + 2(-13)$ does not equal −11.

3. If 180 short-sleeve T-shirts are sold, then 261 long-sleeve T-shirts would be sold, and 261(\$25) + 180(\$15) does not equal \$8415.

Answers
1. B
2. A
3. D
4. D
5. B
6. B
7. B
8. D
9. A

MULTIPLE CHOICE

1. Which ordered pair is the solution of the linear system $y = \frac{1}{2}x + 1$ and $y = \frac{3}{2}x + 4$?

Ⓐ $\left(3, \frac{5}{2}\right)$ Ⓑ $\left(-3, -\frac{1}{2}\right)$

Ⓒ $\left(\frac{3}{2}, \frac{7}{4}\right)$ Ⓓ $(0, 1)$

2. How many solutions does the linear system $3x + 5y = 8$ and $3x + 5y = 1$ have?

Ⓐ 0 Ⓑ 1

Ⓒ 2 Ⓓ Infinitely many

3. The sum of two numbers is -3, and the difference of the two numbers is 11. What are the numbers?

Ⓐ 4 and 7 Ⓑ -3 and 8

Ⓒ 3 and 14 Ⓓ -7 and 4

4. Which ordered pair is the solution of the system of linear equations whose graph is shown?

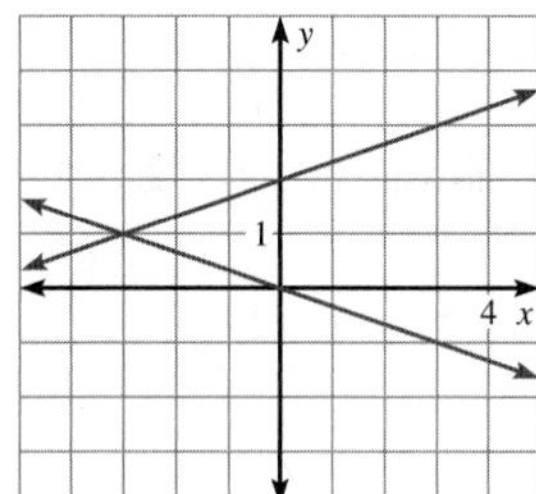

Ⓐ $(3, -1)$ Ⓑ $(0, 0)$

Ⓒ $(0, 2)$ Ⓓ $(-3, 1)$

5. Which ordered pair is the solution of the linear system $3x + y = -1$ and $y = -\frac{1}{2}x - \frac{7}{2}$?

Ⓐ $\left(\frac{5}{2}, -\frac{17}{2}\right)$ Ⓑ $(1, -4)$

Ⓒ $(-1, -3)$ Ⓓ $(0, -1)$

6. Which ordered pair is a solution of the system $x + 2y \leq -2$ and $y \leq -3x + 4$?

Ⓐ $(0, 0)$ Ⓑ $(2, -2)$

Ⓒ $(-2, 2)$ Ⓓ $(5, -4)$

7. How many solutions does the system of linear equations whose graph is shown have?

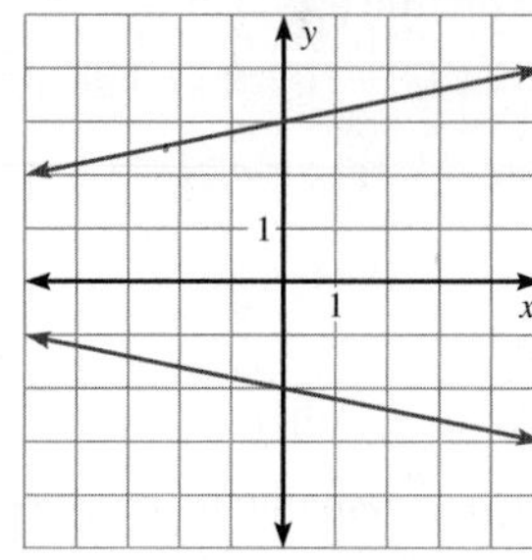

Ⓐ 0 Ⓑ 1

Ⓒ 2 Ⓓ Infinitely many

8. At a bakery, one customer pays \$5.67 for 3 bagels and 4 muffins. Another customer pays \$6.70 for 5 bagels and 3 muffins. Which system of equations can be used to determine the cost x (in dollars) of one bagel and the cost y (in dollars) of one muffin at the bakery?

Ⓐ $x + y = 7$, $x + y = 8$ Ⓑ $y = 3x + 5.67$, $y = 5x + 6.7$

Ⓒ $3x + 4y = 6.7$, $5x + 3y = 5.67$ Ⓓ $3x + 4y = 5.67$, $5x + 3y = 6.7$

9. The perimeter P (in feet) of each of the two rectangles below is given. What are the values of ℓ and w?

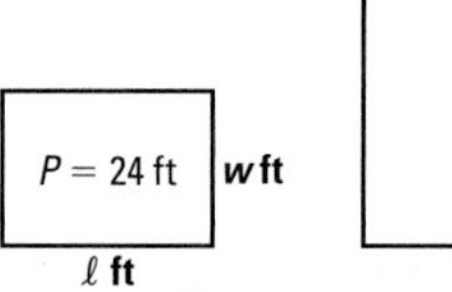

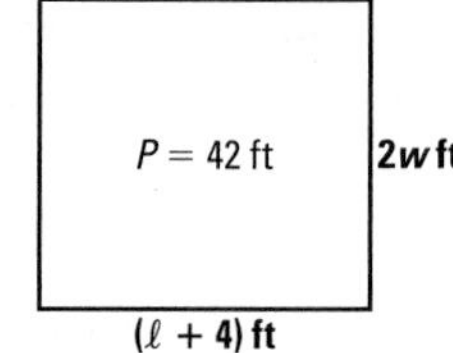

Ⓐ $\ell = 7$ and $w = 5$

Ⓑ $\ell = 8$ and $w = 4$

Ⓒ $\ell = 11$ and $w = 10$

Ⓓ $\ell = 12$ and $w = 9$

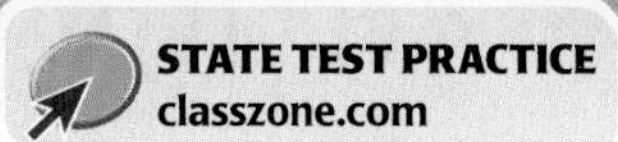

GRIDDED ANSWER

10. What is the x-coordinate of the solution of the system whose graph is shown?

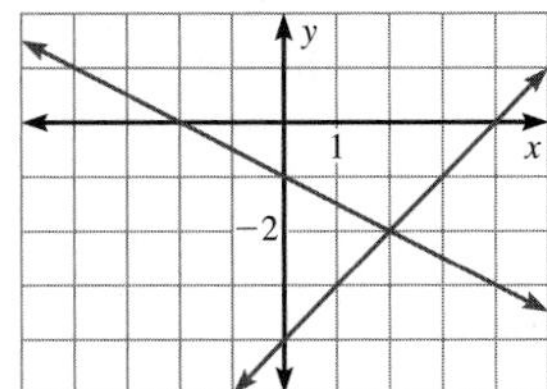

11. What is the x-coordinate of the solution of the system $y = \frac{1}{3}x + 8$ and $2x - y = 2$?

12. A science museum charges one amount for admission for an adult and a lesser amount for admission for a student. Admission to the museum for 28 students and 5 adults costs $284. Admission for 40 students and 10 adults costs $440. What is the admission cost (in dollars) for one student?

SHORT RESPONSE

13. Is it possible to find a value for c so that the linear system below has exactly one solution? *Explain.*

$$5x + 3y = 21 \quad \textbf{Equation 1}$$

$$y = -\frac{5}{3}x + c \quad \textbf{Equation 2}$$

14. A rental car agency charges x dollars per day plus y dollars per mile to rent any of the mid-sized cars at the agency. The total costs for two customers are shown below.

Customer	Time (days)	Distance (miles)	Cost (dollars)
Jackson	3	150	217.50
Bree	2	112	148.00

How much will it cost to rent a mid-sized car for 5 days and drive 250 miles? *Explain.*

EXTENDED RESPONSE

15. A baseball player's batting average is the number of hits the player has divided by the number of at-bats. At the beginning of a game, a player has a batting average of .360. During the game, the player gets 3 hits during 5 at-bats, and his batting average changes to .375.

a. Write a system of linear equations that represents the situation.

b. How many at-bats has the player had so far this season?

c. Another player on the team has a batting average of .240 at the beginning of the same game. During the game, he gets 3 hits during 5 at-bats, and his batting average changes to .300. Has this player had more at-bats so far this season than the other player? *Explain.*

16. A gardener combines x fluid ounces of a 20% liquid fertilizer and 80% water mix with y fluid ounces of a 5% liquid fertilizer and 95% water mix to make 30 fluid ounces of a 10% liquid fertilizer and 90% water mix.

a. Write a system of linear equations that represents the situation.

b. Solve the system from part (a).

c. Suppose the gardener combines pure (100%) water and the 20% liquid fertilizer and 80% water mix to make the 30 fluid ounces of the 10% liquid fertilizer and 90% water mix. Is more of the 20% liquid fertilizer and 80% water mix used in this mix than in the original mix? *Explain.*

10. 2

11. 5

12. $8

13. No. *Sample answer:* Any value of c other than 7 will produce an inconsistent system that has 0 solutions, and $c = 7$ will produce a consistent dependent system.

14. $362.50. *Sample answer:* The company charges $60 per day and $0.25 per mile, so 5 days and 250 miles will cost $362.50.

15a. $\frac{x}{y} = 0.360$, $\frac{(x + 3)}{(y + 5)} = 0.375$

b. 80 at-bats

c. No. *Sample answer:* The player has had 30 at-bats, while the other player has had 80.

16a. $0.2x + 0.05y = 3$, $x + y = 30$

b. 10 fluid ounces of the 20% liquid fertilizer and 80% water mix and 20 fluid ounces of the 5% liquid fertilizer and 95% water mix.

c. Yes. *Sample answer:* The gardener would use 15 fluid ounces of the mix, instead of 10.

Additional Resources

A Cumulative Review for each of Chapters 4–7 is available in the *Chapter Resource Book*. A Cumulative Test for Chapters 1–7 is available in the *Assessment Book*.

28.
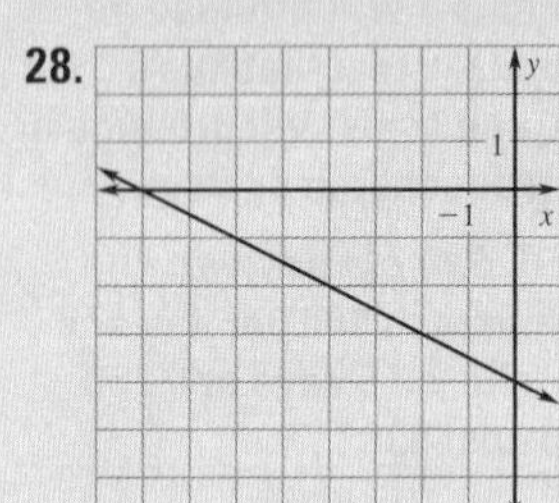

29.
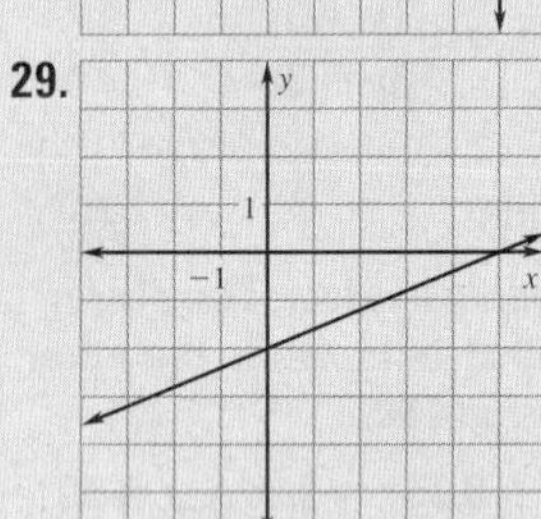

30.
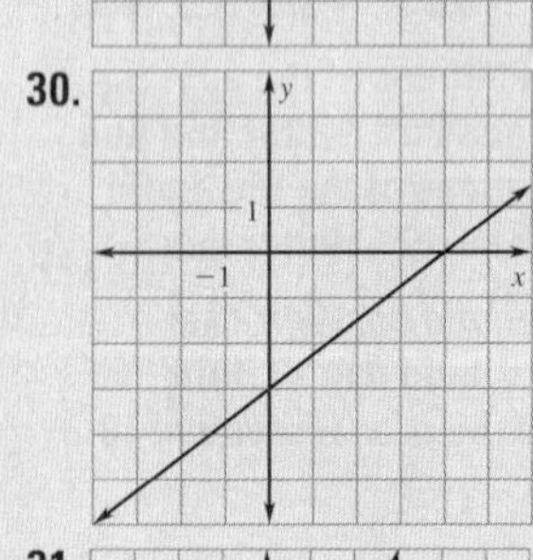

31.

32.
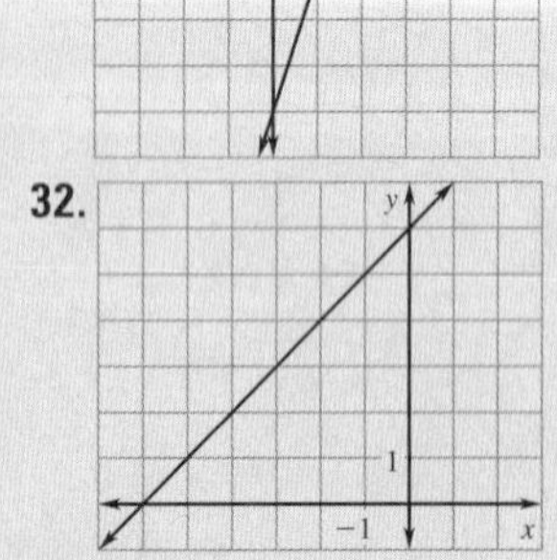

Evaluate the expression.

1. $2^5 \cdot 2 - 4 \div 2$ *(p. 8)* 62
2. $24 \div 6 + (9 - 6)$ *(p. 8)* 7
3. $5[(6 - 2)^2 - 5]$ *(p. 8)* 55
4. $\sqrt{144}$ *(p. 110)* 12
5. $-\sqrt{2500}$ *(p. 110)* −50
6. $\pm\sqrt{400}$ *(p. 110)* ±20

Check whether the given number is a solution of the equation or inequality. *(p. 21)*

7. $7 + 3x = 16; 3$ solution
8. $21y + 1 = 1; 0$ solution
9. $20 - 12h = 12; 1$ not a solution
10. $g - 3 > 2; 5$ not a solution
11. $10 \geq 4 - x; 0$ solution
12. $30 - 4p \geq 5; 6$ solution

Simplify the expression.

13. $5(y - 1) + 4$ *(p. 96)* $5y - 1$
14. $12w + (w - 2)3$ *(p. 96)* $15w - 6$
15. $(g - 1)(-4) + 3g$ *(p. 96)* $-g + 4$
16. $\frac{10h - 25}{5}$ *(p. 103)* $2h - 5$
17. $\frac{21 - 4x}{-7}$ *(p. 103)* $-3 + \frac{4}{7}x$
18. $\frac{32 - 20m}{2}$ *(p. 103)* $16 - 10m$

Solve the equation.

19. $x - 8 = 21$ *(p. 134)* 29
20. $-1 = x + 3$ *(p. 134)* −4
21. $6x = -42$ *(p. 134)* −7
22. $\frac{x}{3} = 8$ *(p. 134)* 24
23. $5 - 2x = 11$ *(p. 141)* −3
24. $\frac{2}{3}x - 3 = 17$ *(p. 141)* 30
25. $3(x - 2) = -15$ *(p. 148)* −3
26. $3(5x - 7) = 5x - 1$ *(p. 154)* 2
27. $-7(2x - 10) = 4x - 10$ *(p. 154)* $4\frac{4}{9}$

Graph the equation. 28–33. See margin.

28. $x + 2y = -8$ *(p. 225)*
29. $-2x + 5y = -10$ *(p. 225)*
30. $3x - 4y = 12$ *(p. 225)*
31. $y = 3x - 7$ *(p. 244)*
32. $y = x + 6$ *(p. 244)*
33. $y = -\frac{1}{3}x$ *(p. 253)*

Write an equation of the line in slope-intercept form with the given slope and *y*-intercept. *(p. 283)*

34. slope: 5
y-intercept: −1 $y = 5x - 1$
35. slope: −1
y-intercept: 3 $y = -x + 3$
36. slope: −7
y-intercept: 0 $y = -7x$

Write an equation in point-slope form of the line that passes through the given points. *(p. 302)* 37–42. See margin.

37. (1, −10), (−5, 2)
38. (4, 7), (−4, 3)
39. (−9, −2), (−6, 8)
40. (−1, 1), (1, −3)
41. (2, 4), (8, 2)
42. (−6, 1), (3, −5)

Solve the inequality. Then graph your solution. 43–54. See margin for art.

43. $x - 9 < -13$ *(p. 356)* $x < -4$
44. $8 \leq x + 7$ *(p. 356)* $x \geq 1$
45. $8x \geq 56$ *(p. 363)* $x \geq 7$
46. $\frac{x}{-4} > 7$ *(p. 363)* $x < -28$
47. $1 - 2x < 11$ *(p. 369)* $x > -5$
48. $8 > -3x - 1$ *(p. 369)* $x > -3$
49. $4x - 10 \leq 7x + 8$ *(p. 369)* $x \geq -6$
50. $7x - 5 < 6x - 4$ *(p. 369)* $x < 1$
51. $-4 < 3x - 1 < 5$ *(p. 380)* $-1 < x < 2$
52. $3 \leq 9 - 2x \leq 15$ *(p. 380)* $-3 \leq x \leq 3$
53. $|3x| < 15$ *(p. 398)* $-5 < x < 5$
54. $|4x - 2| \geq 18$ *(p. 398)* $x \leq -4$ or $x \geq 5$

33.
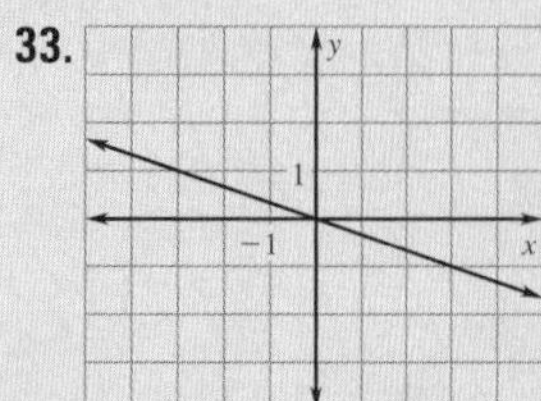

37. $y + 10 = -2(x - 1)$ or $y - 2 = -2(x + 5)$

38. $y - 7 = \frac{1}{2}(x - 4)$ or $y - 3 = \frac{1}{2}(x + 4)$

39. $y + 2 = \frac{10}{3}(x + 9)$ or $y - 8 = \frac{10}{3}(x + 6)$

40. $y - 1 = -2(x + 1)$ or $y + 3 = -2(x - 1)$

41. $y - 4 = -\frac{1}{3}(x - 2)$ or $y - 2 = -\frac{1}{3}(x - 8)$

42. $y - 1 = -\frac{2}{3}(x + 6)$ or $y + 5 = -\frac{2}{3}(x - 3)$

Solve the linear system using elimination. *(p. 451)*

55. $4x + y = 8$
$5x - 2y = -3$ **(1, 4)**

56. $3x - 5y = 5$
$x - 5y = -4$ **(4.5, 1.7)**

57. $12x + 7y = 3$
$8x + 5y = 1$ **(2, −3)**

58. **ART PROJECT** You are making a tile mosaic on the rectangular tabletop shown. A bag of porcelain tiles costs $3.95 and covers 36 square inches. How much will it cost to buy enough tiles to cover the tabletop? *(p. 28)* **$79**

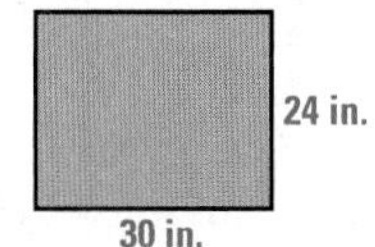

59. **FOOD** The table shows the changes in the price for a dozen grade A, large eggs over 4 years. Find the average yearly change to the nearest cent in the price for a dozen grade A, large eggs during the period 1999–2002. *(p. 103)* **$.02**

Year	1999	2000	2001	2002
Change in price for a dozen grade A, large eggs (dollars)	−0.17	0.04	−0.03	0.25

60. **HONEY PRODUCTION** Honeybees visit about 2,000,000 flowers to make 16 ounces of honey. About how many flowers do honeybees visit to make 6 ounces of honey? *(p. 168)* **750,000 flowers**

61. **MUSIC** The table shows the price p (in dollars) for various lengths of speaker cable. *(p. 253)*

Length, ℓ (feet)	3	5	12	15
Price, p (dollars)	7.50	12.50	30.00	37.50

a. *Explain* why p varies directly with ℓ. **The ratio $\frac{p}{\ell}$ is always the same, so p varies directly with ℓ.**

b. Write a direct variation equation that relates ℓ and p. **$p = 2.5\ell$**

62. **CURRENCY** The table shows the exchange rate between the currency of Bolivia (bolivianos) and U.S. dollars from 1998 to 2003. *(p. 335)*

Year	1998	1999	2000	2001	2002	2003
Bolivianos per U.S. dollar	5.51	5.81	6.18	6.61	7.17	7.66

a. Find an equation that models the bolivianos per U.S. dollar as a function of the number of years since 1998. **See margin.**

b. If the trend continues, predict the number of bolivianos per U.S. dollar in 2010. ***Sample answer:* 10.63 bolivianos**

63. **BATTERIES** A manufacturer of nickel-cadmium batteries recommends storing the batteries at temperatures ranging from −20°C to 45°C. Use an inequality to describe the temperatures (in degrees Fahrenheit) at which the batteries can be stored. *(p. 380)* **$-4 \le F \le 113$**

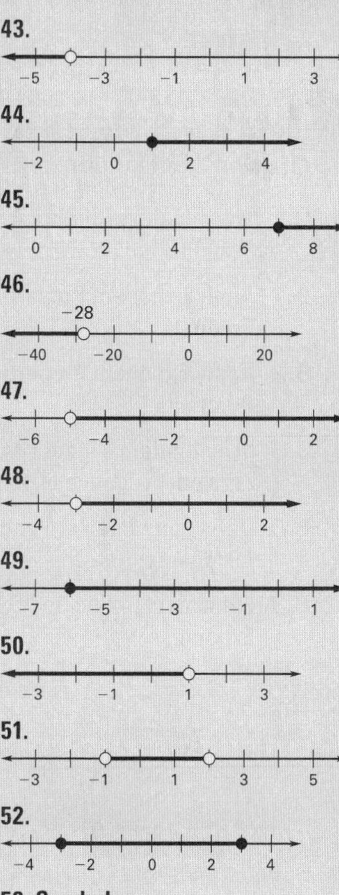

53. See below.

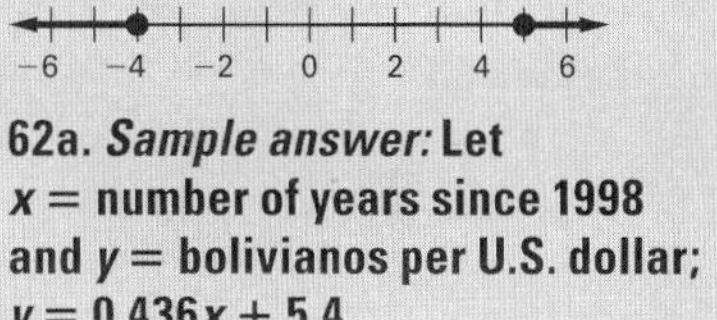

62a. *Sample answer:* Let x = number of years since 1998 and y = bolivianos per U.S. dollar; $y = 0.436x + 5.4$.

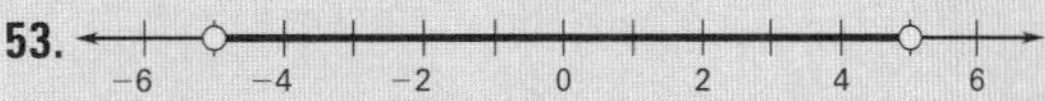

8 Pacing Guide

Chapter 8: Exponents and Exponential Functions

Chapter Table of Contents

PACING GUIDES

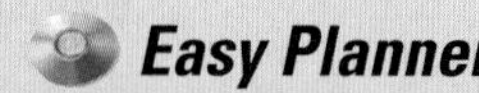

Regular Schedule (50-minute classes)

DAY 1	DAY 2	DAY 3	DAY 4	DAY 5	DAY 6
Investigating Algebra Activity 8.1 Lesson 8.1	Lesson 8.2	Lesson 8.2 (cont.)	Quiz for Lessons 8.1–8.2 Inv. Alg. Act. 8.3 Lesson 8.3 Extension 8.3 Mixed Review of Problem Solving	Lesson 8.4	Lesson 8.4 (cont.) Graphing Calculator Activity 8.4
DAY 7	**DAY 8**	**DAY 9**	**DAY 10**	**DAY 11**	**DAY 12**
Quiz for Lessons 8.3–8.4 Lesson 8.5	Lesson 8.5 (cont.)	Investigating Algebra Activity 8.6 Lesson 8.6	Lesson 8.6 (cont.) Extension 8.6 Mixed Review of Problem Solving	Quiz for Lessons 8.5–8.6 Chapter Review	Chapter Test

Block Schedule (90-minute classes)

DAY 1	DAY 2	DAY 3	DAY 4	DAY 5	DAY 6
Investigating Algebra Activity 8.1 Lesson 8.1 Lesson 8.2	Lesson 8.2 (cont.) Quiz for Lessons 8.1–8.2 Inv. Alg. Act. 8.3 Lesson 8.3 Extension 8.3 Mixed Review of Problem Solving	Lesson 8.4 Graphing Calculator Activity 8.4	Quiz for Lessons 8.3–8.4 Lesson 8.5	Investigating Algebra Activity 8.6 Lesson 8.6 Extension 8.6 Mixed Review of Problem Solving	Quiz for Lessons 8.5–8.6 Chapter Review Chapter Test

RESOURCE OPTIONS

Chapter/Lesson Resources

Chapter Resource Book
- Parents as Partners
- Teaching Guide/Lesson Plan
- Activity Masters
- Practice (3 levels)
- Study Guide
- Quick Catch-Up for Absent Students
- Problem Solving/Application
- Challenge Practice
- Chapter Review Games and Activities
- Project with Rubric
- Cumulative Review

Notetaking Guide
- Student Workbook and Teacher's Edition

Practice Workbook

Worked-Out Solution Key

Chapter Transparency Book
- Warm-Up Exercises/Daily Homework Quiz
- Notetaking Guide Transparencies
- Homework Answer Transparencies

Teacher Tools Transparencies

Assessment

Assessment Book
- Quizzes
- Chapter Tests (3 levels)
- Standardized and SAT/ACT Chapter Tests
- Alternative Assessments
- Cumulative Tests

Benchmark Tests
- Benchmark Tests, correlated to Remediation Book
- Pre-Course, Mid-Year, and End-of-Year Tests
- Chapter Tests

Spanish Assessment Book

Differentiated Instruction

Differentiated Instruction Resources
- Strategies for Reading Mathematics
- Differentiated Instruction Lesson Notes
- English Learner Lesson Notes
- Inclusion Lesson Notes
- Teaching Strategies with Sample Worksheets
- Tips for New Teachers/Math Background Notes
- Teacher Survival Activities/Bulletin Board Ideas

Student Resources in Spanish

Spanish Study Guide

Remediation Book

Skills Readiness (available on Easy Planner)
- Diagnostic Assessment
- Skill Instruction and Alternative Teaching Strategies
- Skill Practice and Enrichment Masters

Pre-AP Resources
- Pacing and Assignment Guide
- Best Practices
- Copymasters

Technology Resources

Plan	***Easy Planner***
Teach	***Video Tutor*** ***Activity Generator*** ***Power Presentations*** ***Animated Algebra***
Assess	***Test Generator*** ***ML Assessment System***
Reteach	***@HomeTutor***
Online Resources	***Classzone.com*** ***eEdition*** ***eWorkbook***

Video Tutor

Technology Highlights for Each Lesson

 **Easy Planner**

Easy access to the Teacher's Edition and all teaching resources. Includes a search feature to locate the materials you need.

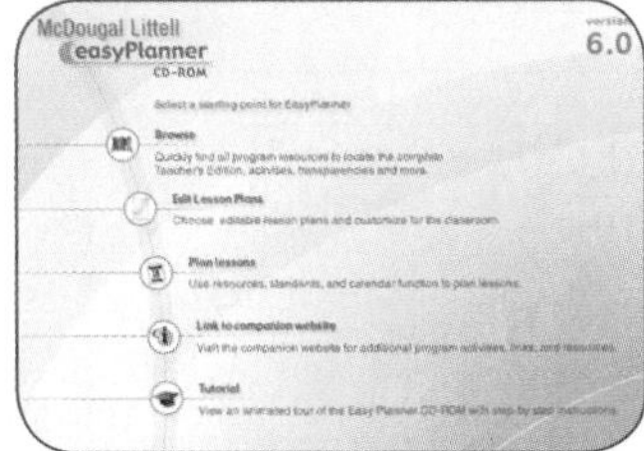

 **Activity Generator**

Leveled, editable activities allow all students to explore a lesson's concepts. Includes teacher notes and closure questions.

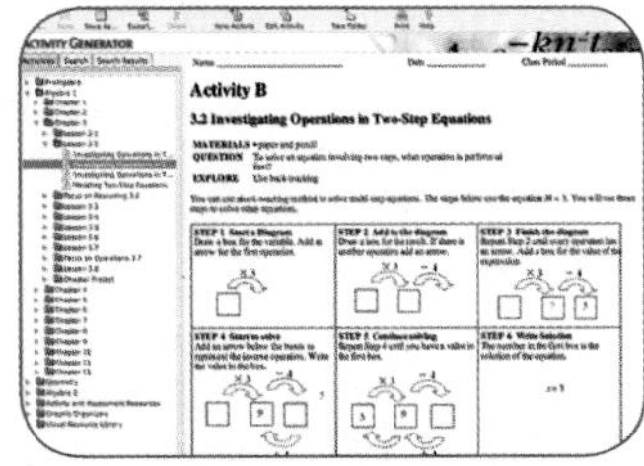

 **Algebra**

Interactive tutorials provide visually engaging alternative opportunities to learn concepts and master skills.

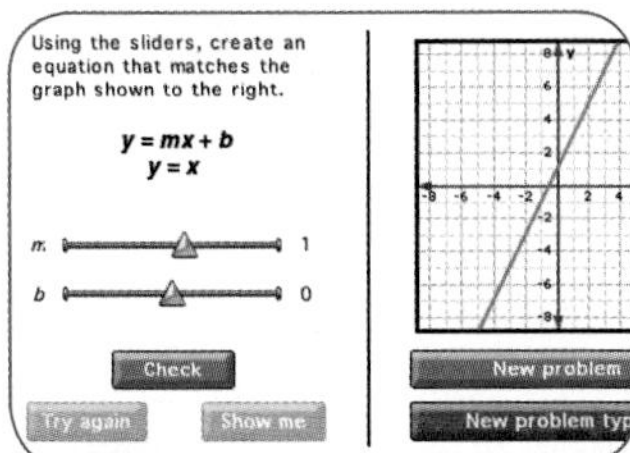

LESSON 8.1 Practice B

For use with pages 489–494

Simplify the expression. Write your answer using exponents.

1. $5^4 \cdot 5^8$ 5^{12}
2. $(-4)^7 \cdot (-4)^3$ $(-4)^{10}$
3. $(-10)^5 \cdot (-10)^2$ $(-10)^7$
4. $8^2 \cdot 8^4 \cdot 8$ 8^7
5. $2^5 \cdot 2 \cdot 2^4$ 2^{10}
6. $(3^5)^2$ 3^{10}
7. $(9^3)^7$ 9^{21}
8. $(15^2)^4$ 15^8
9. $[(-4)^5]^9$ $(-4)^{45}$
10. $(13 \cdot 19)^4$ $13^4 \cdot 19^4$
11. $(48 \cdot 27)^6$ $48^6 \cdot 27^6$
12. $(135 \cdot 8)^5$ $135^5 \cdot 8^5$

Simplify the expression.

13. $x^5 \cdot x^2$ x^7
14. $y^3 \cdot y \cdot y^4$ y^8
15. $a^{10} \cdot a^2 \cdot a^6$ a^{18}
16. $(z^5)^5$ z^{25}
17. $(b^7)^2$ b^{14}
18. $[(b+1)^2]^3$ $(b+1)^6$
19. $(-3x)^4$ $81x^4$
20. $-(3x)^4$ $-81x^4$
21. $(2ab)^5$ $32a^5b^5$
22. $(2x^3y)^6$ $64x^{18}y^6$
23. $(3m^7)^4 \cdot m^3$ $81m^{31}$
24. $4p^2 \cdot (3p^5)^2$ $36p^{12}$

Find the missing exponent.

25. $x^6 \cdot x^? = x^{12}$ 6
26. $(x^4)^? = x^{12}$ 3
27. $(3z^?)^3 = 27z^{18}$ 6

28. **Newspaper Circulation** In 1996, the newspaper circulation in the country of Algeria was approximately 10^3 times the newspaper circulation in the country of Mauritania. The newspaper circulation in Mauritania was 10^3. What was the newspaper circulation in Algeria? 10^6 newspapers

29. **Metric System** The metric system has names for very large weights.
    a. One gigaton is 10^2 times the weight of a hectaton. One hectaton is 10^2 ton. Write one gigaton in tons. 10^4 tons
    b. One teraton is 10^9 times the weight of a kiloton. One kiloton is 10^2 ton. Write one teraton in tons. 10^{11} tons
    c. One exaton is 10^6 times the weight of a teraton. Use your answer to part (b) to write one exaton in tons. 10^{17} tons

30. **Wall Mural** You are designing a wall mural that will be composed of squares of different sizes. One of the requirements of your design is that the side length of each square is itself a perfect square.
    a. If you represent the side length of a square as x^2, write an expression for the area of a mural square. x^4 square units
    b. Find the area of a mural square when $x = 5$. 625 square units
    c. Find the area of a mural square when $x = 10$. 10,000 square units

LESSON 8.2 Practice B

For use with pages 495–501

Simplify the expression. Write your answer using exponents.

1. $\frac{6^{14}}{6^8}$ 6^6
2. $\frac{14^5}{14^4}$ 14^1
3. $\frac{(-5)^7}{(-5)^2}$ $(-5)^5$
4. $\frac{12^5 \cdot 12^3}{12^4}$ 12^4
5. $\frac{8^{17}}{8^3 \cdot 8^7}$ 8^7
6. $\left(\frac{3}{4}\right)^5$ $\frac{3^5}{4^5}$
7. $\left(-\frac{1}{5}\right)^6$ $\frac{(-1)^6}{5^6}$
8. $3^8 \cdot \frac{1}{3^1}$ 3^7
9. $\left(\frac{1}{4}\right)^5 \cdot 4^{13}$ 4^8

Simplify the expression.

10. $\frac{1}{y^9} \cdot y^{15}$ y^6
11. $z^{16} \cdot \frac{1}{z^7}$ z^9
12. $\left(\frac{a}{b}\right)^8$ $\frac{a^8}{b^8}$
13. $\left(-\frac{6}{z}\right)^3$ $-\frac{216}{z^3}$
14. $\left(\frac{a^3}{2b^5}\right)^4$ $\frac{a^{12}}{16b^{20}}$
15. $\left(\frac{3x^4}{y^6}\right)^5$ $\frac{243x^{20}}{y^{30}}$
16. $\left(\frac{m^4}{5n^9}\right)^3$ $\frac{m^{12}}{125n^{27}}$
17. $\left(\frac{3x^7}{2y^{12}}\right)^4$ $\frac{81x^{28}}{16y^{48}}$
18. $\left(\frac{2m^5}{3n^9}\right)^5$ $\frac{32m^{25}}{243n^{45}}$

19. **Area** The area of New Zealand is 104,454 square miles and the area of Saint Kitts and Nevis, islands in the Caribbean Sea, is 104 square miles. Use order of magnitude to estimate how many times greater New Zealand's area is than Saint Kitts and Nevis' area. 10^3

20. **Cell Phone Subscribers** The table below shows the approximate number of cell phone subscribers in selected countries in 2001.

Country	Algeria	Dominican Republic	Poland	Solomon Islands
Number of subscribers	10^5	10^6	10^7	10^3

    a. How many times greater is the number of cell phone subscribers in Poland than in the Solomon Islands? 10^4
    b. How many times greater is the number of cell phone subscribers in the Dominican Republic than in the Solomon Islands? 10^3

21. **Glass Vase** You are taking a glass-blowing class and have created a vase in the shape of a sphere. The vase will have a hole in the top so you can put flowers in it and it will sit on a stand. The radius of your vase is $\frac{21}{2}$ inches. Use the formula $V = \frac{4}{3}\pi r^3$ to write an expression for the volume of your vase. $\frac{3087\pi}{2}$ in.^{3}

LESSON 8.3 Practice B

For use with pages 503–508

Evaluate the expression.

1. 3^{-5} $\frac{1}{243}$
2. 10^{-3} $\frac{1}{1000}$
3. $(-2)^{-6}$ $\frac{1}{64}$
4. 5^0 1
5. $(-6)^0$ 1
6. $\left(\frac{4}{3}\right)^0$ 1
7. $\left(\frac{5}{8}\right)^{-2}$ $\frac{64}{25}$
8. $\left(\frac{7}{4}\right)^3$ $\frac{343}{64}$
9. 0^{-5} undefined
10. $10^{-2} \cdot 10^{-3}$ $\frac{1}{100{,}000}$
11. $4^{-6} \cdot 4^3$ $\frac{1}{64}$
12. $\frac{1}{5^{-4}}$ 625

Simplify the expression. Write your answer using only positive exponents.

13. x^{-7} $\frac{1}{x^7}$
14. $6y^{-4}$ $\frac{6}{y^4}$
15. $(2b)^{-5}$ $\frac{1}{32b^5}$
16. $(-3m)^{-4}$ $\frac{1}{81m^4}$
17. a^2b^{-4} $\frac{a^2}{b^4}$
18. $3x^{-2}y^{-5}$ $\frac{3}{x^2y^5}$
19. $(4x^{-4}y^2)^{-3}$ $\frac{x^{12}}{64y^6}$
20. $(8mn^3)^0$ 1
21. $\frac{c^{-3}}{d^{-5}}$ $\frac{d^5}{c^3}$
22. $\frac{x^2}{y^{-4}}$ x^2y^4
23. $\frac{x^{-6}}{4y^5}$ $\frac{1}{4x^6y^5}$
24. $\frac{1}{3x^{-3}y^{-7}}$ $\frac{x^3y^7}{3}$

25. **Paper** A sheet of 67-pound paper has a thickness of 100^{-1} inch.
    a. Write and evaluate an expression for the total thickness of 5 sheets of 67-pound paper. $\frac{1}{20}$ in.
    b. Write and evaluate an expression for the total thickness of 2^3 sheets of 67-pound paper. $\frac{2}{25}$ in.

26. **Frogs** A frog egg currently has a radius of 5^{-1} centimeter. Write an expression using positive exponents for the volume of the frog egg. Use the formula for the volume of a sphere $V = \frac{4}{3}\pi r^3$. $\frac{4\pi}{375}$ cm^3

27. **Metric System** The metric system has names for very small lengths.
    a. One micrometer is 10^3 times the length of one nanometer. One nanometer is 10^{-9} meter. Write one micrometer in meters. 10^{-6} m
    b. One femtometer is 10^3 times the length of one attometer. One attometer is 10^{-18} meter. Write one femtometer in meters. 10^{-15} m
    c. One centimeter is 10^{10} times the length of one picometer. One picometer is 10^{-12} meter. Write one centimeter in meters. 10^{-2} m

LESSON 8.4 Practice B

For use with pages 512–518

Write the number in scientific notation.

1. 10.4 1.04×10^1
2. 6751 6.751×10^3
3. 0.54 5.4×10^{-1}
4. 0.000103 1.03×10^{-4}
5. 415,620 4.1562×10^5
6. 0.08104 8.104×10^{-2}
7. 3,412,000 3.412×10^6
8. 525.5 5.255×10^2
9. 104.25 1.0425×10^2
10. 0.0000456 4.56×10^{-5}
11. 0.000000207 2.07×10^{-7}
12. 23,551 2.3551×10^4

Write the number in standard form.

13. 15.8×10^4 158,000
14. 3.21×10^8 321,000,000
15. 450.21×10^7 4,502,100,000
16. 8.1045×10^5 810,450
17. 17.22×10^6 17,220,000
18. 1.012×10^2 101.2
19. 8.12×10^{-4} 0.000812
20. 4.014×10^{-7} 0.0000004014
21. 8.1025×10^{-3} 0.0081025
22. 3.12056×10^{-9} 0.00000000312056
23. 1.211×10^{-2} 0.01211
24. 7.00135×10^{-5} 0.0000700135

Order the numbers from least to greatest.

25. 1.3759×10^4; 14,205; 9.287×10^3; 3.0214×10^4 9.287×10^3; 1.3759×10^4; 14,205; 3.0214×10^4
26. 0.16; 2.5×10^{-3}; 1.04×10^{-3}; 0.0985 1.04×10^{-3}; 2.5×10^{-3}; 0.0985; 0.16
27. 8.79×10^2; 1146; 1.0085×10^3; 1023 8.79×10^2; 1.0085×10^3; 1023; 1146
28. 1.2×10^{-5}; 0.001023; 1.045×10^{-3}; 0.01036 1.2×10^{-5}; 0.001023; 1.045×10^{-3}; 0.01036

Evaluate the expression. Write your answer in scientific notation.

29. $(6 \times 10^8)(5 \times 10^{-2})$ 3×10^7
30. $\frac{4.5 \times 10^{-5}}{9 \times 10^{-2}}$ 5×10^{-4}
31. $(2 \times 10^{-5})^5$ 3.2×10^{-24}

32. **Pixels** The images on a computer screen are made up of more than 5000 pixels, or dots, per square inch. How many pixels are on a computer screen that measures 108 square inches? Write your answer in scientific notation. 5.4×10^5 pixels

33. **Oregon** Oregon has an area of approximately 2.52×10^5 square kilometers. In 2000, the population of Oregon was approximately 3.42×10^6 people. How many people were there per square kilometer in Oregon in 2000? about 13.57 people/km^2

34. **Uranus' Moons** The table below shows the masses in kilograms of some of Uranus' moons.

Moon	Miranda	Titania	Ariel	Oberon	Umbriel
Mass (kg)	6.6×10^{19}	3.52×10^{21}	13.5×10^{20}	30.1×10^{20}	11.7×10^{20}

    a. Write the moons in order of largest mass to smallest mass. Titania, Oberon, Ariel, Umbriel, Miranda
    b. How many times larger is the moon of largest mass than the moon of smallest mass? about 53

LESSON 8.5 Practice B

For use with pages 520–527

Write a rule for the function.

1.

x	-2	-1	0	1	2
y	$\frac{1}{121}$	$\frac{1}{11}$	1	11	121

$y = 11^x$

2.

x	-1	0	1	2	3
y	$\frac{1}{8}$	$\frac{1}{4}$	$\frac{1}{2}$	1	2

$y = 0.25(2)^x$

Graph the function and identify its domain and range.

3. $y = 12^x$

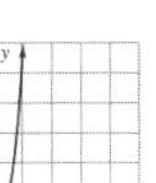

4. $y = (1.75)^x$

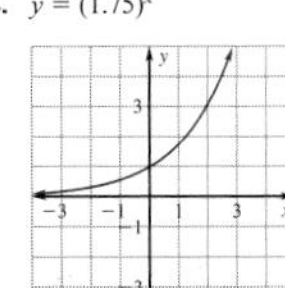

5. $y = (3.1)^x$

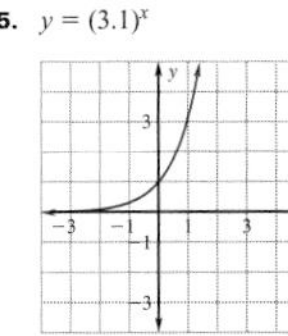

6. $y = \left(\frac{9}{2}\right)^x$ See below.

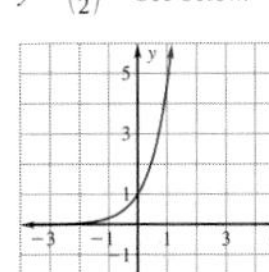

7. $y = -5^x$ See below.

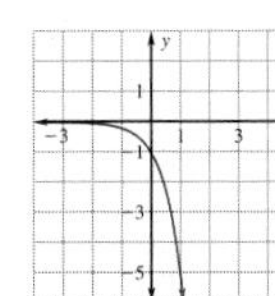

8. $y = -\left(\frac{3}{2}\right)^x$ See below.

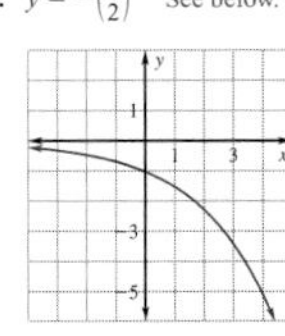

9. $y = 5 \cdot 2^x$ See below.

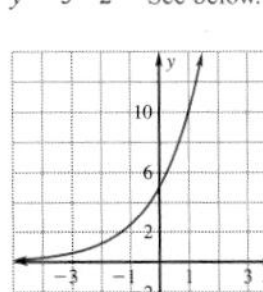

10. $y = 2 \cdot \left(\frac{4}{3}\right)^x$ See below.

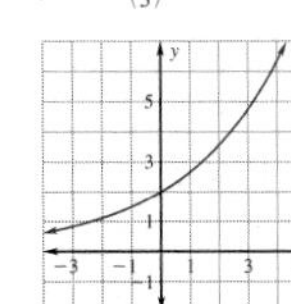

11. $y = -3 \cdot 2^x$ See below.

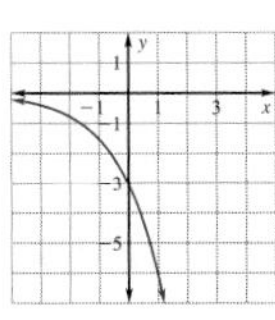

3. domain: all real numbers; range: all positive real numbers
4. domain: all real numbers; range: all positive real numbers
5. domain: all real numbers; range: all positive real numbers
6. domain: all real numbers; range: all positive real numbers
7. domain: all real numbers; range: all negative real numbers
8. domain: all real numbers; range: all negative real numbers
9. domain: all real numbers; range: all positive real numbers
10. domain: all real numbers; range: all positive real numbers
11. domain: all real numbers; range: all negative real numbers

LESSON 8.5

LESSON 8.5 Practice B *continued*

For use with pages 520–527

Graph the function. Compare the graph with the graph of $y = 6^x$.

12. $y = 2 \cdot 6^x$ vertical stretch

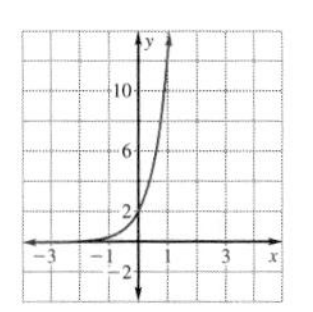

13. $y = -6^x$ reflection in x-axis

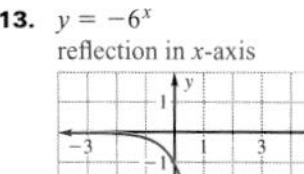

14. $y = \frac{1}{2} \cdot 6^x$ vertical shrink

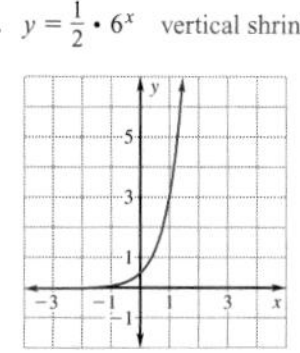

15. $y = -3 \cdot 6^x$ See below.

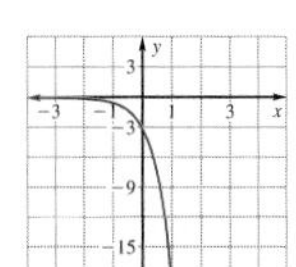

16. $y = -\frac{1}{4} \cdot 6^x$ See below.

17. $y = -\frac{3}{2} \cdot 6^x$ See below.

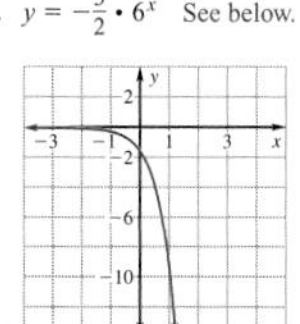

18. **Investments** You deposit \$500 in a savings account that earns 2.5% interest compounded yearly. Find the balance in the account after the given amounts of time.

a. 1 year \$512.50 b. 5 years \$565.70 c. 20 years \$819.31

19. **College Tuition** From 1995 to 2005, the tuition at a college increased by about 7% per year. Use the graph to write an exponential growth function that models the tuition over time. $y = 8000(1.07)^t$

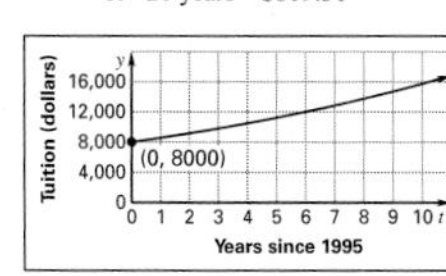

20. **Profit** A business had \$10,000 profit in 2000. Then the profit increased by 8% each year for the next 10 years.

a. Write a function that models the profit in dollars over time. $y = 10{,}000(1.08)^t$

b. Use the function to predict the profit in 2009. \$19,990.05

15. vertical stretch and reflection in x-axis
16. vertical shrink and reflection in x-axis
17. vertical stretch and reflection in x-axis

LESSON 8.5

LESSON 8.6 Practice B

For use with pages 531–538

Tell whether the table represents an exponential function. If so, write a rule for the function.

1.

x	-2	-1	0	1	2
y	25	5	1	$\frac{1}{5}$	$\frac{1}{25}$

yes; $y = \left(\frac{1}{5}\right)^x$

2.

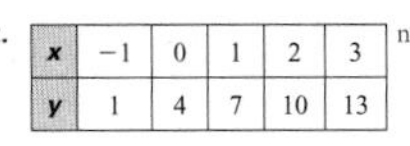

x	-1	0	1	2	3
y	1	4	7	10	13

no

Graph the function and identify its domain and range.

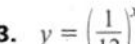

3. $y = \left(\frac{1}{12}\right)^x$

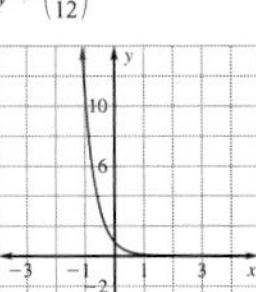

4. $y = \left(\frac{7}{8}\right)^x$

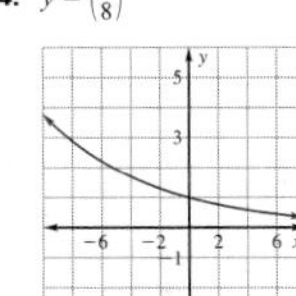

5. $y = \left(\frac{8}{9}\right)^x$

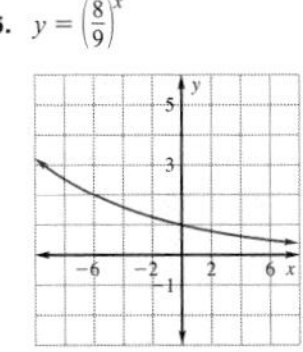

6. $y = -\left(\frac{1}{8}\right)^x$ See below.

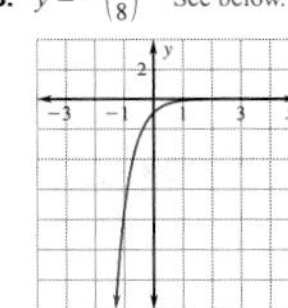

7. $y = 2 \cdot \left(\frac{1}{5}\right)^x$ See below.

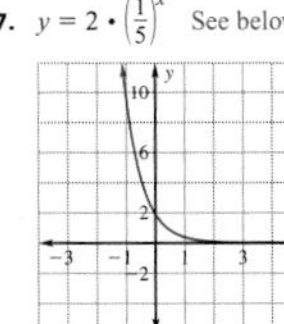

8. $y = -2 \cdot \left(\frac{2}{3}\right)^x$ See below.

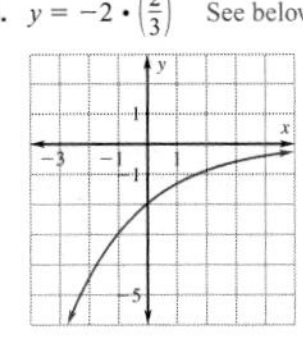

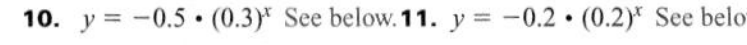

9. $y = 2 \cdot (0.25)^x$ See below. 10. $y = -0.5 \cdot (0.3)^x$ See below. 11. $y = -0.2 \cdot (0.2)^x$ See below.

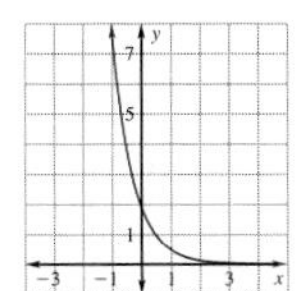

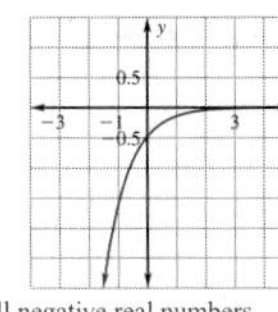

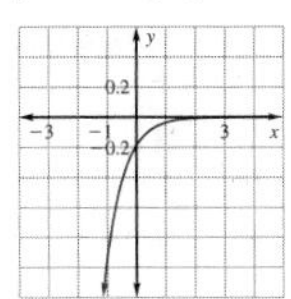

3. domain: all real numbers; range: all positive real numbers
4. domain: all real numbers; range: all positive real numbers
5. domain: all real numbers; range: all positive real numbers
6. domain: all real numbers; range: all negative real numbers
7. domain: all real numbers; range: all positive real numbers
8. domain: all real numbers; range: all negative real numbers
9. domain: all real numbers; range: all positive real numbers
10. domain: all real numbers; range: all negative real numbers
11. domain: all real numbers; range: all negative real numbers

LESSON 8.6

LESSON 8.6 Practice B *continued*

For use with pages 531–538

Graph the function. Compare the graph with the graph of $y = \left(\frac{1}{8}\right)^x$.

12. $y = 2 \cdot \left(\frac{1}{8}\right)^x$ vertical stretch

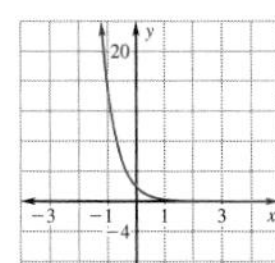

13. $y = -\left(\frac{1}{8}\right)^x$ reflection in x-axis

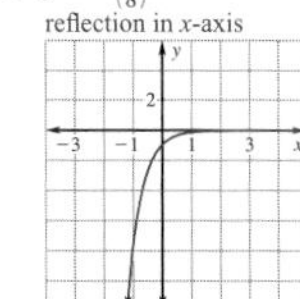

14. $y = \frac{1}{4} \cdot \left(\frac{1}{8}\right)^x$ vertical shrink

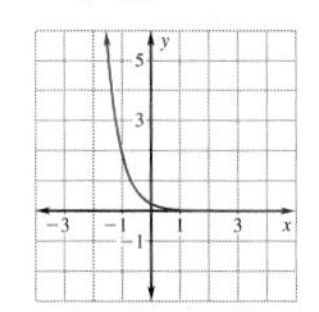

Tell whether the graph represents exponential growth or exponential decay. Then write a rule for the function.

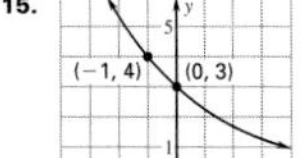

15.

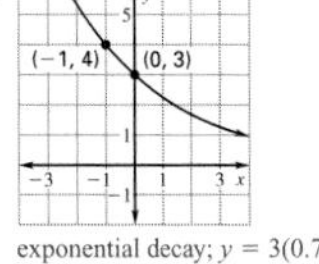

exponential decay; $y = 3(0.75)^x$

16.

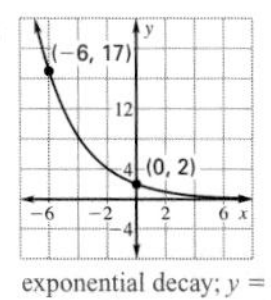

exponential decay; $y = 2(0.7)^x$

17.

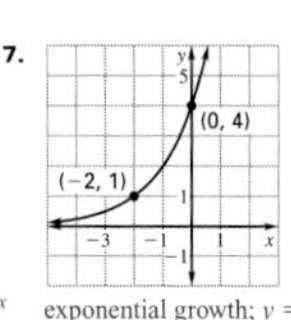

exponential growth; $y = 4(2)^x$

18. **Computer Value** You buy a computer for \$3000. It depreciates at the rate of 20% per year. Find the value of the computer after the given number of years.

a. 1 year \$2400 b. 3 years \$1536 c. 5 years \$983.04

19. **Unemployment Rate** In 2000, the unemployment rate of a city decreased by approximately 2.1% each month. In January, the unemployment rate was 7%.

a. Use the graph at the right to write a function that models the unemployment rate of the city over time.

b. What was the unemployment rate in December? about 5.4% **19. a.** $y = 7(0.979)^t$

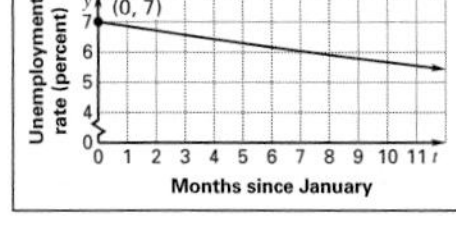

20. **Indoor Water Park** An indoor water park had a declining attendance from 2000 to 2005. The attendance in 2000 was 18,000. Each year for the next 5 years, the attendance decreased by 5.5%.

a. Write a function that models the attendance since 2000. $y = 18{,}000(0.945)^t$

b. What was the attendance in 2005? about 13,565 people

8 Assessment

CHAPTER 8 Quiz 1

For use after Lessons 8.1–8.2

Simplify the expression. Write your answer using exponents.

1. $8^2 \cdot 8^3$
2. $(-3)^4(-3)^2$
3. $(6^3)^5$
4. $[(-2)^2]^5$
5. $(16 \cdot 7)^4$
6. $4^3 \cdot 4 \cdot 4^5$
7. $\frac{9^{12}}{9^5}$
8. $\frac{2^7 \cdot 2^8}{2^3}$

Simplify the expression.

9. $x^3 \cdot x^7$
10. $-(x^7)^2$
11. $(x^2)^4(3x^5)$
12. $(3x^3)^2(2x)^3$
13. $\frac{1}{x^2} \cdot x^{17}$
14. $\left(-\frac{x^5}{2}\right)^4$

Answers

1. 8^5
2. $(-3)^6$
3. 6^{15}
4. $(-2)^{10}$
5. $16^4 \cdot 7^4$
6. 4^9
7. 9^7
8. 2^{12}
9. x^{10}
10. $-x^{14}$
11. $3x^{13}$
12. $72x^9$
13. x^{15}
14. $\frac{x^{20}}{16}$

CHAPTER 8 Quiz 2

For use after Lessons 8.3–8.4

Simplify the expression. Write your answer using only positive exponents.

1. $(8x)^3 \cdot 8^{-4}$
2. $2x^{-5} \cdot y^{-3}$
3. $(4x^4y^{-3})^{-2}$
4. $\frac{1}{(3x)^{-2}}$

Write the number in standard form.

5. 9.3×10^5
6. 7.04×10^4
7. 5.62×10^{-3}
8. 4.209×10^{-6}
9. The distance from Earth to the sun is approximately 93 million miles. Write this distance in scientific notation.

Answers

1. $\frac{x^3}{8}$
2. $\frac{2}{x^5y^3}$
3. $\frac{y^6}{16x^8}$
4. $9x^2$
5. 930,000
6. 70,400
7. 0.00562
8. 0.000004209
9. 9.3×10^7 miles

CHAPTER 8 Quiz 3

For use after Lessons 8.5–8.6

Graph the function.

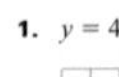

1. $y = 4$

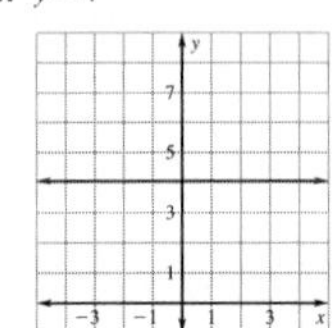

2. $y = \left(\frac{1}{4}\right)^x$

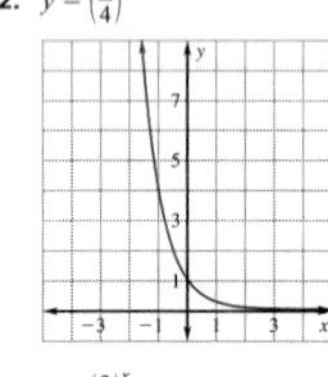

3. $y = 4 \cdot 2^x$

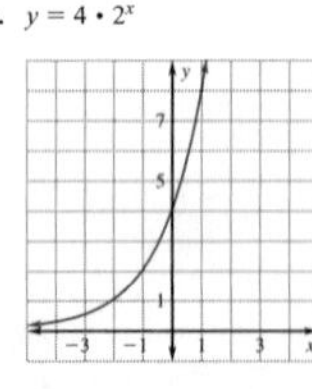

4. $y = \left(\frac{2}{3}\right)^x$

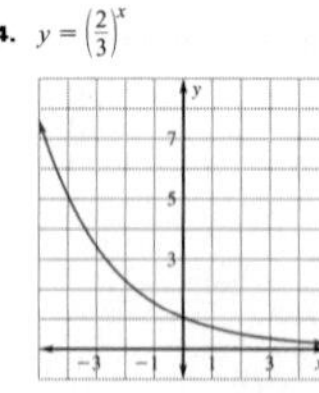

5. $y = 2 \cdot 4^x$

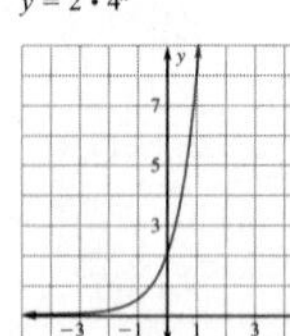

6. $y = 6^x$

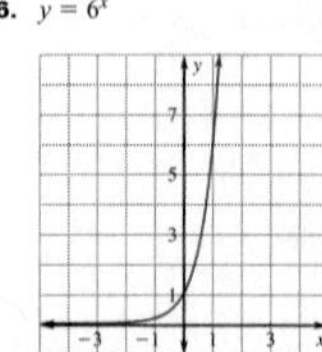

7. A family purchased a house for $80,000. Each year the value of the house increases by 5%. Write a function that models the value of the house over time. Then find the value of the house after 6 years. Round your answer to the nearest dollar.

Answers

1. See left.
2. See left.
3. See left.
4. See left.
5. See left.
6. See left.
7. $y = 80{,}000(1.05)^x$; $107,208

CHAPTER 8 Chapter Test

For use after Chapter 8

Simplify the expression. Write your answer using exponents.

1. $(-7)^9(-7)^2$
2. $(5^3)^8$
3. $\frac{12^2 \cdot 12^4}{12^3}$

In Exercises 4 and 5, use the table.

Unit	tera	giga	mega	kilo	hecto	deka
Meters	10^{12}	10^9	10^6	10^3	10^2	10^1

4. How many hectometers are there in 1 gigameter?
5. How many kilometers are there in 1 terameter?

Simplify the expression.

6. $x^4 \cdot x$
7. $(9pq)^2$
8. $(-5m^6)^2 \cdot m^3$
9. $\frac{1}{y} \cdot y^{11}$
10. $\left(-\frac{1}{t}\right)^5$
11. $\left(\frac{a^8}{2b}\right)^4$
12. Write and simplify an expression for the area of the triangle.

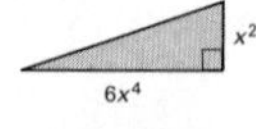

Simplify the expression. Write your answer using only positive exponents.

13. $2w^{-7}$
14. $(5g)^{-3}$
15. $\frac{1}{8c^{10}d^{-6}}$

Complete the statement using <, >, or =.

16. 9.27×10^{-4} ? 0.00927
17. 527,000,000 ? 5.27×10^8

Evaluate the expression. Write your answer in scientific notation.

18. $(4 \times 10^8)^3$
19. $(4 \times 10^{13})(5 \times 10^{-9})$
20. $\frac{9.3 \times 10^{12}}{3.1 \times 10^{-3}}$

Answers

1. $(-7)^{11}$
2. 5^{24}
3. 12^3
4. 10^7
5. 10^9
6. x^5
7. $81p^2q^2$
8. $25m^{15}$
9. y^{10}
10. $-\frac{1}{t^5}$
11. $\frac{a^{32}}{16b^4}$
12. $\frac{1}{2}x^2(6x^4)$; $3x^6$ square units
13. $\frac{2}{w^7}$
14. $\frac{1}{125g^3}$
15. $\frac{d^6}{8c^{10}}$
16. <
17. =
18. 6.4×10^{25}
19. 2×10^5
20. 3×10^{15}

Chapter Test B *continued*

For use after Chapter 8

21. In a recent year, 6.5×10^8 metric tons of wheat were produced in the world. One metric ton is equivalent to 1000 kilograms. A grain of wheat weighs about 0.000008 kilogram. Find the number of grains of wheat that were produced in the world.

Write a rule for the function.

22.

x	−2	−1	0	1	2
y	$\frac{1}{8}$	$\frac{1}{2}$	2	8	32

23.

x	−2	−1	0	1	2
y	24	12	6	3	$\frac{3}{2}$

In Exercises 24–26, use the following information.

A house was bought 20 years ago for $160,000. Due to inflation, its value has increased about 5% each year.

24. Write a function that models the value of the home over time.

25. Identify the initial value, the growth factor, and the growth rate.

26. What is the home worth today?

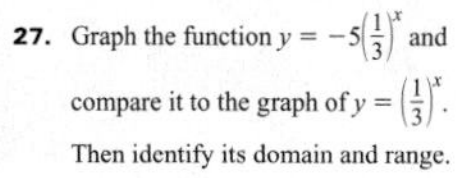

27. Graph the function $y = -5\left(\frac{1}{3}\right)^x$ and compare it to the graph of $y = \left(\frac{1}{3}\right)^x$. Then identify its domain and range.

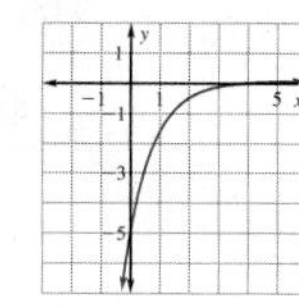

Tell whether the graph represents exponential growth or exponential decay. Then write a rule for the function.

28.

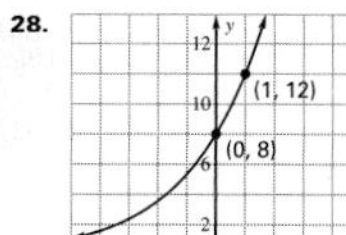

29.

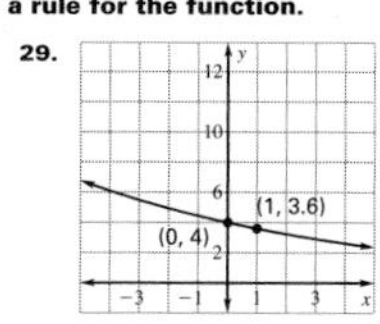

Answers

21. 8.125×10^{16}

22. $y = 2 \cdot 4^x$

23. $y = 6 \cdot \left(\frac{1}{2}\right)^x$

24. $y = 160{,}000(1.05)^t$

25. $160,000; 1.05; 0.05

26. $424,528

27. See left. The graph is a vertical stretch and reflection in the x-axis of the graph of $y = \left(\frac{1}{3}\right)^x$; The domain is all real numbers and the range is all negative real numbers.

28. exponential growth; $y = 8 \cdot (1.5)^x$

29. exponential decay; $y = 4 \cdot (0.9)^x$

Standardized Test

For use after Chapter 8

Multiple Choice

1. Which expression is equivalent to $(-2)^8$? B

Ⓐ $(-2)^2(-2)^4$ Ⓑ $(-2)(-2)^7$

Ⓒ $[(-2)^4]^4$ Ⓓ $[(-2)^5]^3$

2. Which expression is equivalent to $16x^{15}$? A

Ⓐ $(4x^6)^2 \cdot x^3$ Ⓑ $2x^5 \cdot 8x^3$

Ⓒ $2x^5 \cdot (2x)^3$ Ⓓ $(2x^3)^5$

3. Which expression is equivalent to $(-2a)(-4a^2b^3c)^2(-5a^4b^3c^6)^2$? D

Ⓐ $-40a^{13}b^{12}c^{14}$ Ⓑ $800a^{11}b^{10}c^{11}$

Ⓒ $400a^{11}b^{10}c^{10}$ Ⓓ $-800a^{13}b^{12}c^{14}$

4. Which expression is equivalent to 14^6? B

Ⓐ $\frac{14^4}{14^2}$ Ⓑ $\frac{(14^5)^3}{14^9}$

Ⓒ $\frac{14^{12}}{14^2}$ Ⓓ $\left(\frac{14^{11}}{14^5}\right)^3$

5. Which expression is equivalent to $\left(\frac{4x^4}{2x^3}\right)^3$? C

Ⓐ $2x$ Ⓑ $8x$

Ⓒ $8x^3$ Ⓓ $16x^{21}$

6. Which value of x makes the equation $\frac{a^x \cdot a^8}{a^3} = a^6$ true? B

Ⓐ $x = 0$ Ⓑ $x = 1$

Ⓒ $x = 2$ Ⓓ $x = 3$

7. Which expression simplifies to $3x^5$? A

Ⓐ $\frac{3}{x^{-5}}$ Ⓑ $3x^{-5}$

Ⓒ $\frac{1}{3x^{-5}}$ Ⓓ $\left(\frac{1}{3x}\right)^{-5}$

8. Which expression is equivalent to $(-5 \cdot 2^2 \cdot 2^0)^{-2}$? D

Ⓐ -80 Ⓑ -40

Ⓒ $\frac{1}{40}$ Ⓓ $\frac{1}{400}$

9. Which of the following equations is *not* true? C

Ⓐ $\frac{m^{-1}}{p^{-1}} = \frac{p}{m}$

Ⓑ $\frac{2}{(5p)^{-2}} = 50p^2$

Ⓒ $\left(\frac{p^2}{3p}\right)^{-1} = \frac{3p^2}{p}$

Ⓓ $m^{-1} + p^{-1} = \frac{1}{m} + \frac{1}{p}$

10. Which number represents 65,006,000 in scientific notation? B

Ⓐ 6.5006×10^{-7} Ⓑ 6.5006×10^7

Ⓒ 65.006×10^{-6} Ⓓ 65.006×10^6

11. Which number represents 0.00007605 in scientific notation? A

Ⓐ 7.605×10^{-5} Ⓑ 7.605×10^5

Ⓒ 0.7605×10^{-4} Ⓓ 0.7605×10^4

12. Which number represents 8.205×10^{-4} in standard form? B

Ⓐ 0.00008205 Ⓑ 0.0008205

Ⓒ 82,050 Ⓓ 82,050,000

13. Which number represents 5.4289×10^{-3} in standard form? B

Ⓐ 0.00054289 Ⓑ 0.0054289

Ⓒ 54,289 Ⓓ 5428.9

14. Which number is the value of $\frac{1.728 \times 10^6}{5.4 \times 10^8}$? C

Ⓐ 3.2×10^3 Ⓑ 0.32×10^{-1}

Ⓒ 3.2×10^{-3} Ⓓ 3.2×10^{-2}

Standardized Test *continued*

For use after Chapter 8

15. Which expression is written in scientific notation and equivalent to $(7.2 \times 10^{-4})(2.3 \times 10^6)$? D

Ⓐ 16.56×10^2 Ⓑ 16.56×10^{-2}

Ⓒ 1.656×10 Ⓓ 1.656×10^3

16. Which rule applies to the table below? C

x	−2	−1	0	1	2
y	1	2	4	8	16

Ⓐ $y = 2 \cdot 4^x$ Ⓑ $y = 2 \cdot x^4$

Ⓒ $y = 4 \cdot 2^x$ Ⓓ $y = 4 \cdot x^2$

17. The graph of which function is shown? A

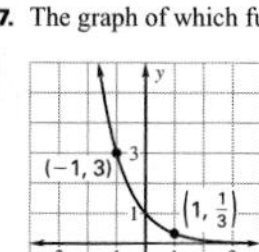

Ⓐ $y = \left(\frac{1}{3}\right)^x$ Ⓑ $y = 3^x$

Ⓒ $y = 2 \cdot \left(\frac{1}{3}\right)^x$ Ⓓ $y = 2 \cdot 3^x$

Gridded Answer

18. The distance from the Sun to Earth is 1.5×10^8 kilometers. Mercury is 5.8×10^7 kilometers from the Sun. What is the difference between these distances in millions of kilometers?

		9	2

Short Response

19. The graph shows the value of a car over time. **a.** $y = 20{,}000 \cdot (0.925)^x$

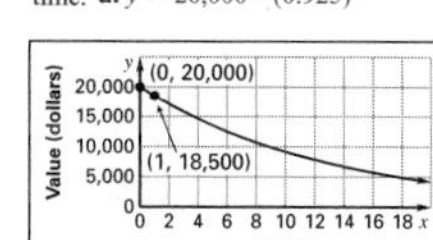

a. Write an equation for the function whose graph is shown. See above.

b. At what rate is the car losing value? *Explain.* The car is losing value at a rate of 7.5% each year.

Extended Response

20. You are saving money to buy a car. You put $2500 in a savings account that pays 4% annual interest compounded yearly.

a. Write a function that models the amount of the money in the account over time. $A = 2500(1 + 0.04)^t$

b. Graph the function. See below.

c. Suppose you want to buy a car for $3,000. Will there be enough money in the account after 5 years? *Explain.* Yes. After 5 years there will be approximately $3041.63 in the account. This is about $41.63 more than what you need to buy the car.

20. b.

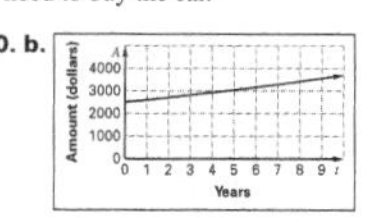

Alternative Assessment and Math Journal

For use after Chapter 8

Journal

1. Describe the difference between numbers that have positive exponents versus negative exponents when written in scientific notation. Give an example of each type of number and include both the scientific notation and the standard form for each.

Multi-Step Problem

2. Let $L = 2^x$ be the function representing the number of layers of paper that has been folded in half x times.

a. Determine the value of L for $x = 0$. Explain the meaning of your answer.

b. Complete the table.

x	0	1	2	3	4
L	?	?	?	?	?

c. What pattern do you notice in the values in part (b)?

d. How many folds are needed to have 128 layers of paper?

e. Consider the function $T = (0.1)2^{x-4}$ where T is the thickness (in centimeters) of a piece of paper folded in half x times. Use properties of exponents to show that an equivalent function is $T = (0.00625)2^x$.

f. Graph the function $T = (0.00625)2^x$.

g. Does this graph represent exponential growth or exponential decay?

h. How thick is a piece of paper that has been folded 10 times?

1. Complete answers should include: an explanation that numbers larger than 10 will have positive exponents when written in scientific notation; an explanation that numbers between 0 and 1 will have negative exponents when written in scientific notation; an example of each case in both scientific notation and standard form.

2. a. $L = 1$; A paper folded 0 times will have 1 layer.

b.

x	0	1	2	3	4
L	1	2	4	8	16

c. Each additional fold results in twice as many layers. **d.** 7 folds

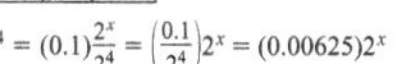

e. $T = (0.1)2^{x-4} = (0.1)\frac{2^x}{2^4} = \left(\frac{0.1}{2^4}\right)2^x = (0.00625)2^x$

f.

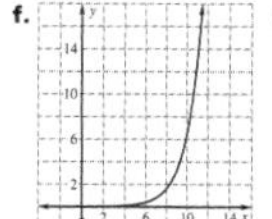

g. exponential growth **h.** 6.4 cm

PLAN AND PREPARE

Main Ideas

In Chapter 8, students learn and use properties of exponents involving products and quotients. They learn how to apply the product of powers property, the power of a power property, the power of a product property, the quotient of powers property, and the power of a quotient property. Students also use zero and negative exponents. Students learn how to read, write, and compute with numbers in scientific notation. Students also learn how to graph and write rules for exponential functions, including exponential growth and exponential decay functions.

Prerequisite Skills

Skills Readiness, available on the *Easy Planner*, provides review and practice for the Skills Check portion of the Prerequisite Skills quiz.

How student answers the exercises	What to assign from *Skills Readiness*
Any of Exs. 3–6 answered incorrectly	**Skill 8** Evaluate powers
Any of Exs. 7–8 answered incorrectly	**Skill 16** Order decimals
Any of Exs. 9–12 answered incorrectly	**Skill 16** Write percents as decimals
Ex. 13 answered incorrectly	**Skill 80** Graph functions
All exercises answered correctly	Chapter 8 Enrichment

Additional skills review and practice is available in the Skills Review Handbook, pp. 909–937, and the @HomeTutor.

8 Exponents and Exponential Functions

Making Sense of Chapter 8

This chapter begins your study of nonlinear relationships. By the end of this chapter, you will be able to use properties of exponents, and write rules for and graph exponential functions.

Before

Previously, you learned the following skills, which you'll use in Chapter 8: using exponents, percents, and decimals, and writing function rules.

Prerequisite Skills

VOCABULARY CHECK

1. Identify the exponent and the base in the expression 13^8. **exponent: 8, base: 13**
2. Copy and complete: An expression that represents repeated multiplication of the same factor is called a(n) _?_. **power**

SKILLS CHECK

Evaluate the expression. ***(Prerequisite skill for 8.1–8.3)***

3. x^2 when $x = 10$ **100**
4. a^3 when $a = 3$ **27**
5. r^2 when $r = \frac{5}{6}$ $\mathbf{\frac{25}{36}}$
6. z^3 when $z = \frac{1}{2}$ $\mathbf{\frac{1}{8}}$

Order the numbers from least to greatest. ***(Prerequisite skill for 8.4)***

7. 6.12, 6.2, 6.01 **6.01, 6.12, 6.2**
8. 0.073, 0.101, 0.0098 **0.0098, 0.073, 0.101**

Write the percent as a decimal. ***(Prerequisite skill for 8.5 and 8.6)***

9. 4% **0.04**
10. 0.5% **0.005**
11. 13.8% **0.138**
12. 145% **1.45**

13. Write a rule for the function. Graph the function *(Prerequisite skill for 8.5 and 8.6)*

Input	0	1	4	6	10
Output	2	3	6	8	12

$f(x) = x + 2$; See margin for art.

@HomeTutor Prerequisite skills practice at classzone.com

486

Chapter Planning Guide

Chapter Resource Book
- Teaching Guide/Lesson Plan
- Project with Rubric

Assessment and Intervention
- Assessment Book
- Benchmark Tests
- Remediation Book
- Skills Readiness

Interactive Technology
- Easy Planner
- Power Presentations
- Activity Generator
- Animated Algebra
- Test Generator
- Online Quizzes
- eWorkbook
- eEdition
- @HomeTutor

Resources for English Learners
- Spanish Study Guide
- Multi-Language Visual Glossary
- Student Resources in Spanish

Now

In Chapter 8, you will apply the big ideas listed below and reviewed in the Chapter Summary on page 542. You will also use the key vocabulary listed below.

Big Ideas

1. **Applying properties of exponents to simplify expressions**
2. **Working with numbers in scientific notation**
3. **Writing and graphing exponential functions**

KEY VOCABULARY

- order of magnitude, *p. 491*
- scientific notation, *p. 512*
- exponential function, *p. 520*
- exponential growth, *p. 522*
- compound interest, *p. 523*
- exponential decay, *p. 533*

You can use exponents to explore exponential growth and decay. For example, you can write an exponential function to find the value of a collector car over time.

Animated Algebra

The animation illustrated below for Example 4 on page 522 helps you answer this question: If you know the growth rate of the value of a collector car over time, can you predict what the car will sell for at an auction?

Find the value of the collector car over time.

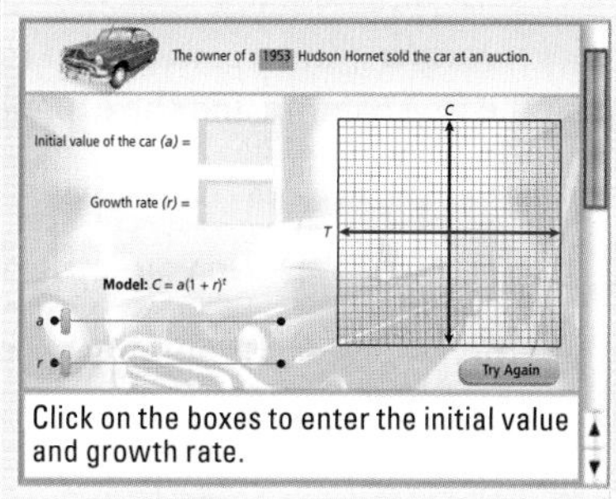

Click on the boxes to enter the initial value and growth rate.

Animated Algebra at classzone.com

Other animations for Chapter 8: pages 491, 505, 512, 534, and 536

487

Differentiated Instruction Resources

- Reading Strategies for Chapter 8
- Differentiated Instruction Lesson Notes
- English Learners Lesson Notes
- Inclusion Lesson Notes
- Teaching Strategies with Sample Worksheets
- Using Technology in the Classroom
- Tips for New Teachers
- Math Background Notes
- Assessment Strategies
- Teacher Survival Activities
- Bulletin Board Idea

13.

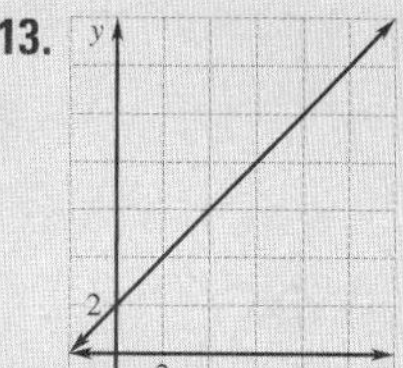

1 PLAN AND PREPARE

Explore the Concept

- Students will find products of powers and powers of powers.
- This activity leads into the study of using the product of powers property in Example 1 and the power of a power property in Example 2 in Lesson 8.1.

Materials

Each student will need:

- Activity Support Master (*Chapter Resource Book*)

Recommended Time

Work activity: 10 min
Discuss results: 5 min

Grouping

Students should work individually.

2 TEACH

Tips for Success

In Explore 2, help students understand how a power of a power is different from a product of powers. For example, contrast the expression $(5^3)^2$, which means $5^3 \cdot 5^3$, with the expression $5^3 \cdot 5^2$.

Key Discovery

When you find a product of powers for powers that have the same base, you add the exponents. When you find a power of a power, you multiply the exponents.

3 ASSESS AND RETEACH

Does $(2x)^3 = 2x^3$? *Explain* your reasoning. **No. The expression $(2x)^3$ means $2x \cdot 2x \cdot 2x$, or $8x^3$.**

Explore 2: Step 1. $[(-6) \cdot (-6)] \cdot [(-6) \cdot (-6)] \cdot [(-6) \cdot (-6)] \cdot [(-6) \cdot (-6)]$

8.1 Products and Powers

MATERIALS • paper and pencil

QUESTION How can you find a product of powers and a power of a power?

EXPLORE 1 Find products of powers

STEP 1 ***Copy and complete*** Copy and complete the table.

Expression	Expression as repeated multiplication	Number of factors	Simplified expression
$7^4 \cdot 7^5$	$(7 \cdot 7 \cdot 7 \cdot 7) \cdot (7 \cdot 7 \cdot 7 \cdot 7 \cdot 7)$	9	7^9
$(-4)^2 \cdot (-4)^3$	$[(-4) \cdot (-4)] \cdot [(-4) \cdot (-4) \cdot (-4)]$	? 5	? $(-4)^5$
$x^1 \cdot x^5$	? $(x) \cdot (x \cdot x \cdot x \cdot x \cdot x)$	? 6	? x^6

STEP 2 ***Analyze results*** Find a pattern that relates the exponents of the factors in the first column and the exponent of the expression in the last column. **See margin.**

EXPLORE 2 Find powers of powers

STEP 1 ***Copy and complete*** Copy and complete the table.

Expression	Expanded expression	Expression as repeated multiplication	Number of factors	Simplified expression
$(5^3)^2$	$(5^3) \cdot (5^3)$	$(5 \cdot 5 \cdot 5) \cdot (5 \cdot 5 \cdot 5)$	6	5^6
$[(-6)^2]^4$	$[(-6)^2] \cdot [(-6)^2] \cdot [(-6)^2] \cdot [(-6)^2]$	? **See margin.**	? 8	? $(-6)^8$
$(a^3)^3$	? $(a^3) \cdot (a^3) \cdot (a^3)$	? $(a \cdot a \cdot a) \cdot (a \cdot a \cdot a) \cdot (a \cdot a \cdot a)$	? 9	? a^9

STEP 2 ***Analyze results*** Find a pattern that relates the exponents of the expression in the first column and the exponent of the expression in the last column. ***Sample answer:*** **The exponent of the simplified expression is equal to the product of the exponents in the first column.**

DRAW CONCLUSIONS Use your observations to complete these exercises

Simplify the expression. Write your answer using exponents.

1. $5^2 \cdot 5^3$ **5^5**
2. $(-6)^1 \cdot (-6)^4$ **$(-6)^5$**
3. $m^6 \cdot m^4$ **m^{10}**
4. $(10^3)^3$ **10^9**
5. $[(-2)^3]^4$ **$(-2)^{12}$**
6. $(c^2)^6$ **c^{12}**

In Exercises 7 and 8, copy and complete the statement.

7. If a is a real number and m and n are positive integers, then $a^m \cdot a^n =$ _?_. **a^{m+n}**
8. If a is a real number and m and n are positive integers, then $(a^m)^n =$ _?_. **a^{mn}**

8.1 Apply Exponent Properties Involving Products

Before You evaluated exponential expressions.

Now You will use properties of exponents involving products.

Why? So you can evaluate agricultural data, as in Example 5.

Key Vocabulary
- **order of magnitude**
- **power,** *p. 3*
- **exponent,** *p. 3*
- **base,** *p. 3*

Notice what happens when you multiply two powers that have the same base.

$$a^2 \cdot a^3 = \underbrace{\overbrace{(a \cdot a)}^{\text{2 factors}} \cdot \overbrace{(a \cdot a \cdot a)}^{\text{3 factors}}}_{\text{5 factors}} = a^5 = a^{2+3}$$

The example above suggests the following property of exponents, known as the product of powers property.

KEY CONCEPT *For Your Notebook*

Product of Powers Property

Let a be a real number, and let m and n be positive integers.

Words To multiply powers having the same base, add the exponents.

Algebra $a^m \cdot a^n = a^{m+n}$ **Example** $5^6 \cdot 5^3 = 5^{6+3} = 5^9$

SIMPLIFY EXPRESSIONS
When simplifying powers with numerical bases only, write your answers using exponents, as in parts (a), (b), and (c).

EXAMPLE 1 **Use the product of powers property**

a. $7^3 \cdot 7^5 = 7^{3+5} = 7^8$

b. $9 \cdot 9^8 \cdot 9^2 = 9^1 \cdot 9^8 \cdot 9^2$
$= 9^{1+8+2}$
$= 9^{11}$

c. $(-5)(-5)^6 = (-5)^1 \cdot (-5)^6$
$= (-5)^{1+6}$
$= (-5)^7$

d. $x^4 \cdot x^3 = x^{4+3} = x^7$

✓ **GUIDED PRACTICE** for Example 1

Simplify the expression.

1. $3^2 \cdot 3^7$ $\mathbf{3^9}$ **2.** $5 \cdot 5^9$ $\mathbf{5^{10}}$ **3.** $(-7)^2(-7)$ $\mathbf{(-7)^3}$ **4.** $x^2 \cdot x^6 \cdot x$ $\mathbf{x^9}$

1 PLAN AND PREPARE

Warm-Up Exercises

Transparency Available

Evaluate the expression.

1. x^4 when $x = 3$ **81**
2. a^2 when $a = -6$ **36**
3. m^3 when $m = -5$ **−125**
4. A food storage container is in the shape of a cube. What is the volume of the container if one side is 4 inches long? Use $V = s^3$. **64 in.³**

Notetaking Guide

Transparency Available

Promotes interactive learning and notetaking skills.

Pacing

Basic: 1 day
Average: 1 day
Advanced: 1 day
Block: 0.5 block with 8.2
- See *Teaching Guide/Lesson Plan.*

2 FOCUS AND MOTIVATE

Essential Question

Big Idea 1, p. 487

How do you use properties of exponents involving products? **Tell students they will learn how to answer this question by applying properties of exponents to simplify expressions.**

NCTM STANDARDS

Standard 1: Understand meanings of operations

Standard 2: Understand patterns

Resource Planning Guide

Chapter Resource Book
- Teaching Guide/Lesson Plan
- Practice levels A, B, C
- Study Guide
- Catch-up for Absent Students
- Application
- Challenge

Workbooks
- Notetaking Guide
- Practice Workbook

Teaching Options
- **Power Presentations** provides dynamic electronic teaching resources for the classroom.
- **Activity Generator** provides editable activities for all ability levels.

Interactive Technology
- Easy Planner
- Power Presentations
- Activity Generator
- Animated Algebra
- Test Generator
- Online Quiz
- eWorkbook
- eEdition
- @HomeTutor

Resources for English Learners
- Spanish Study Guide
- Multi-Language Visual Glossary
- Student Resources in Spanish

See also the *Differentiated Instruction Resources* for more strategies for meeting individual needs.

Motivating the Lesson

By knowing how to use properties of exponents and order of magnitude, you will be able to estimate data using powers of ten. For example, you can estimate and compare the amount of energy released by earthquakes, the brightness and luminosity of stars, and numerous other real-world data.

3 TEACH

Extra Example 1

Use the product of powers property.

a. $4^7 \cdot 4^6$ 4^{13}

b. $8^5 \cdot 8 \cdot 8^2$ 8^8

c. $(-3)^3 \cdot (-3)$ $(-3)^4$

d. $b \cdot b^3 \cdot b^5 \cdot b^2$ b^{11}

Avoiding Common Errors

In parts b and c of Example 1, students often forget that factors like 9 and −5 have an exponent of 1 that must be included in the sum. Suggest that they rewrite the products as shown in the Example to avoid this error.

Extra Example 2

Use the power of a power property.

a. $(7^4)^5$ 7^{20}

b. $[(-3)^4]^2$ $(-3)^8$

c. $(y^3)^3$ y^9

d. $[(n+8)^2]^9$ $(n+8)^{18}$

Key Question to Ask for Example 2

- In part d, why is it not possible to write $(y+2)^{12}$ as $y^{12} + 2^{12}$? **Because $y + 2$ is a quantity, you must add the value of y to 2 before you can raise the base to the power of 12.**

POWER OF A POWER Notice what happens when you raise a power to a power.

$$(a^2)^3 = a^2 \cdot a^2 \cdot a^2 = (a \cdot a) \cdot (a \cdot a) \cdot (a \cdot a) = a^6 = a^{2 \cdot 3}$$

The example above suggests the following property of exponents, known as the power of a power property.

KEY CONCEPT *For Your Notebook*

Power of a Power Property

Let a be a real number, and let m and n be positive integers.

Words To find a power of a power, multiply exponents.

Algebra $(a^m)^n = a^{mn}$

Example $(3^4)^2 = 3^{4 \cdot 2} = 3^8$

EXAMPLE 2 Use the power of a power property

AVOID ERRORS
In part (d), notice that you can write $[(y+2)^6]^2$ as $(y+2)^{12}$, but you cannot write $(y+2)^{12}$ as $y^{12} + 2^{12}$.

a. $(2^5)^3 = 2^{5 \cdot 3}$
$= 2^{15}$

b. $[(-6)^2]^5 = (-6)^{2 \cdot 5}$
$= (-6)^{10}$

c. $(x^2)^4 = x^{2 \cdot 4}$
$= x^8$

d. $[(y+2)^6]^2 = (y+2)^{6 \cdot 2}$
$= (y+2)^{12}$

✓ **GUIDED PRACTICE** for Example 2

Simplify the expression.

5. $(4^2)^7$ 4^{14} **6.** $[(-2)^4]^5$ $(-2)^{20}$ **7.** $(n^3)^6$ n^{18} **8.** $[(m+1)^5]^4$ $(m+1)^{20}$

POWER OF A PRODUCT Notice what happens when you raise a product to a power.

$$(ab)^3 = (ab) \cdot (ab) \cdot (ab) = (a \cdot a \cdot a) \cdot (b \cdot b \cdot b) = a^3b^3$$

The example above suggests the following property of exponents, known as the power of a product property.

KEY CONCEPT *For Your Notebook*

Power of a Product Property

Let a and b be real numbers, and let m be a positive integer.

Words To find a power of a product, find the power of each factor and multiply.

Algebra $(ab)^m = a^m b^m$

Example $(23 \cdot 17)^5 = 23^5 \cdot 17^5$

Differentiated Instruction

Inclusion Students may have difficulty interpreting the symbols used in mathematics (such as exponents), and in memorizing complex rules. At first, it may be more instructive to allow them to write out terms like a^3 as $a \cdot a \cdot a$, rather than memorize rules like the power of a power property. Later, they should have no need of this particular technique.

See also the *Differentiated Instruction Resources* for more strategies.

SIMPLIFY EXPRESSIONS
When simplifying powers with numerical *and* variable bases, be sure to evaluate the numerical power, as in parts (b), (c), and (d).

EXAMPLE 3 Use the power of a product property

a. $(24 \cdot 13)^8 = 24^8 \cdot 13^8$

b. $(9xy)^2 = (9 \cdot x \cdot y)^2 = 9^2 \cdot x^2 \cdot y^2 = 81x^2y^2$

c. $(-4z)^2 = (-4 \cdot z)^2 = (-4)^2 \cdot z^2 = 16z^2$

d. $-(4z)^2 = -(4 \cdot z)^2 = -(4^2 \cdot z^2) = -16z^2$

EXAMPLE 4 Use all three properties

Simplify $(2x^3)^2 \cdot x^4$.

$(2x^3)^2 \cdot x^4 = 2^2 \cdot (x^3)^2 \cdot x^4$ **Power of a product property**

$= 4 \cdot x^6 \cdot x^4$ **Power of a power property**

$= 4x^{10}$ **Product of powers property**

Animated Algebra at classzone.com

ORDER OF MAGNITUDE The **order of magnitude** of a quantity can be defined as the power of 10 nearest the quantity. Order of magnitude can be used to estimate or perform rough calculations. For instance, there are about 91,000 species of insects in the United States. The power of 10 closest to 91,000 is 10^5, or 100,000. So, there are about 10^5 species of insects in the United States.

EXAMPLE 5 Solve a real-world problem

BEES In 2003 the U.S. Department of Agriculture (USDA) collected data on about 10^3 honeybee colonies. There are about 10^4 bees in an average colony during honey production season. About how many bees were in the USDA study?

Solution

To find the total number of bees, find the product of the number of colonies, 10^3, and the number of bees per colony, 10^4.

$10^3 \cdot 10^4 = 10^{3+4} = 10^7$

▶ The USDA studied about 10^7, or 10,000,000, bees.

✓ **GUIDED PRACTICE** for Examples 3, 4, and 5

Simplify the expression.

9. $(42 \cdot 12)^2$ **10.** $(-3n)^2$ $9n^2$ **11.** $(9m^3n)^4$ **12.** $5 \cdot (5x^2)^4$ $3125x^8$

13. WHAT IF? In Example 5, 10^2 honeybee colonies in the study were located in Idaho. About how many bees were studied in Idaho? **about 1,000,000 bees**

9. $42^2 \cdot 12^2$
11. $6561m^{12}n^4$

Extra Example 3

Use the power of a product property.
a. $(34 \cdot 9)^6$ $34^6 \cdot 9^6$
b. $(4mn)^3$ $64m^3n^3$
c. $(-2g)^4$ $16g^4$
d. $-(5x)^2$ $-25x^2$

Key Question to Ask for Example 3

- Why is the simplified expression in part (c) positive and in part (d) negative? **In part (c), −4 is squared, so it simplifies to 16. In part (d), the negative sign represents −1 and since it is outside the parentheses, it is not squared and −1 • 16 = −16.**

Extra Example 4

Simplify $(3d^5)^3 \cdot d$. $27d^{16}$

An **Animated Algebra** activity is available online for **Example 4**. This activity is also part of **Power Presentations**.

Extra Example 5

A box of staples contains 10^4 staples. How many staples do 10^2 boxes contain? **1,000,000 staples**

Closing the Lesson

Have students summarize the major points of the lesson and answer the Essential Question: How do you use properties of exponents involving products?

- **Add exponents when using the product of powers property.**
- **Multiply exponents when using the power of a power or the power of a product property.**

When simplifying expressions, add exponents when multiplying powers and multiply exponents when raising a power to a power or raising a product to a power.

4 PRACTICE AND APPLY

Assignment Guide

Answer Transparencies available for all exercises

Basic:
Day 1: pp. 492–494
Exs. 1, 2, 3–15 odd, 19–39 odd, 40–42, 52–57, 60–74 even

Average:
Day 1: pp. 492–494
Exs. 1, 2, 4–18 even, 29–49, 53–58, 61, 64, 67, 73

Advanced:
Day 1: pp. 492–494
Exs. 1, 2, 8–18 even, 31–38, 40–51*, 54–59*, 62, 65, 68, 74

Block:
pp. 492–494
Exs. 1, 2, 4–18 even, 29–49, 53–58, 61, 64, 67, 73 (with 8.2)

Differentiated Instruction

See *Differentiated Instruction Resources* for suggestions on addressing the needs of a diverse classroom.

Homework Check

For a quick check of student understanding of key concepts, go over the following exercises:

Basic: 7, 11, 15, 27, 52
Average: 8, 12, 16, 33, 53
Advanced: 10, 14, 18, 36, 54

Extra Practice

- Student Edition, p. 945
- Chapter Resource Book: Practice levels A, B, C

Practice Worksheet

An easily-readable reduced practice page (with answers) for this lesson can be found on p. 486C.

8.1 EXERCISES

HOMEWORK KEY
○ = **WORKED-OUT SOLUTIONS** on p. WS18 for Exs. 31 and 55
★ = **STANDARDIZED TEST PRACTICE** Exs. 2, 40, 41, 50, and 58
◆ = **MULTIPLE REPRESENTATIONS** Ex. 55

SKILL PRACTICE

A

1. **VOCABULARY** Copy and complete: The _?_ of the quantity 93,534,004 people is the power of 10 nearest the quantity, or 10^8 people. **order of magnitude**

2. ★ **WRITING** *Explain* when and how to use the product of powers property. **When powers have the same base, their product is the base raised to the sum of the exponents.**

EXAMPLES 1,2,3, and 4 on pp. 489–491 for Exs. 3–41

SIMPLIFYING EXPRESSIONS **Simplify the expression. Write your answer using exponents.**

3. $4^2 \cdot 4^6$ $\mathbf{4^8}$
4. $8^5 \cdot 8^2$ $\mathbf{8^7}$
5. $3^3 \cdot 3$ $\mathbf{3^4}$
6. $9 \cdot 9^5$ $\mathbf{9^6}$
7. $(-7)^4(-7)^5$ $\mathbf{(-7)^9}$
8. $(-6)^6(-6)$ $\mathbf{(-6)^7}$
9. $2^4 \cdot 2^9 \cdot 2$ $\mathbf{2^{14}}$
10. $(-3)^2(-3)^{11}(-3)$ $\mathbf{(-3)^{14}}$
11. $(3^5)^2$ $\mathbf{3^{10}}$
12. $(7^4)^3$ $\mathbf{7^{12}}$
13. $[(-5)^3]^4$ $\mathbf{(-5)^{12}}$
14. $[(-8)^9]^2$ $\mathbf{(-8)^{18}}$
15. $(15 \cdot 29)^3$ $\mathbf{15^3 \cdot 29^3}$
16. $(17 \cdot 16)^4$ $\mathbf{17^4 \cdot 16^4}$
17. $(132 \cdot 9)^6$ $\mathbf{132^6 \cdot 9^6}$
18. $((-14) \cdot 22)^5$ $\mathbf{(-14)^5 \cdot 22^5}$

SIMPLIFYING EXPRESSIONS **Simplify the expression.**

19. $x^4 \cdot x^2$ $\mathbf{x^6}$
20. $y^9 \cdot y$ $\mathbf{y^{10}}$
21. $z^2 \cdot z \cdot z^3$ $\mathbf{z^6}$
22. $a^4 \cdot a^3 \cdot a^{10}$ $\mathbf{a^{17}}$
23. $(x^5)^2$ $\mathbf{x^{10}}$
24. $(y^4)^6$ $\mathbf{y^{24}}$
25. $[(b-2)^2]^6$ $\mathbf{(b-2)^{12}}$
26. $[(d+9)^7]^3$ $\mathbf{(d+9)^{21}}$
27. $(-5x)^2$ $\mathbf{25x^2}$
28. $-(5x)^2$ $\mathbf{-25x^2}$
29. $(7xy)^2$ $\mathbf{49x^2y^2}$
30. $(5pq)^3$ $\mathbf{125p^3q^3}$
31. $(-10x^6)^2 \cdot x^2$ $\mathbf{100x^{14}}$
32. $(-8m^4)^2 \cdot m^3$ $\mathbf{64m^{11}}$
33. $6d^2 \cdot (2d^5)^4$ $\mathbf{96d^{22}}$
34. $(-20x^3)^2(-x^7)$ $\mathbf{-400x^{13}}$
35. $-(2p^4)^3(-1.5p^7)$ $\mathbf{12p^{19}}$
36. $\left(\frac{1}{2}y^5\right)^3(2y^2)^4$ $\mathbf{2y^{23}}$
37. $(3x^5)^3(2x^7)^2$ $\mathbf{108x^{29}}$
38. $(-10n)^2(-4n^3)^3$ $\mathbf{-6400n^{11}}$

39. **ERROR ANALYSIS** *Describe* and correct the error in simplifying $c \cdot c^4 \cdot c^5$. ***Sample answer*: The exponents should be added, not multiplied; $c^1 \cdot c^4 \cdot c^5 = c^{1+4+5} = c^{10}$.**

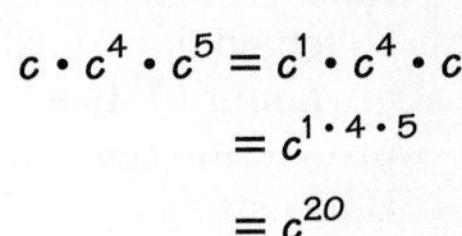

$c \cdot c^4 \cdot c^5 = c^1 \cdot c^4 \cdot c^5$
$= c^{1 \cdot 4 \cdot 5}$
$= c^{20}$

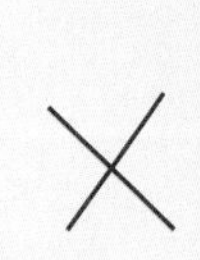

B

40. ★ **MULTIPLE CHOICE** Which expression is equivalent to $(-9)^6$? **B**
   (A) $(-9)^2(-9)^3$ (B) $(-9)(-9)^5$ (C) $[(-9)^4]^2$ (D) $[(-9)^3]^3$

41. ★ **MULTIPLE CHOICE** Which expression is equivalent to $36x^{12}$? **D**
   (A) $(6x^3)^4$ (B) $12x^4 \cdot 3x^3$ (C) $3x^3 \cdot (4x^3)^3$ (D) $(6x^5)^2 \cdot x^2$

SIMPLIFYING EXPRESSIONS **Find the missing exponent.**

42. $x^4 \cdot x^? = x^5$ **1**
43. $(y^8)^? = y^{16}$ **2**
44. $(2z^?)^3 = 8z^{15}$ **5**
45. $(3a^3)^? \cdot 2a^3 = 18a^9$ **2**

46. **POPULATION** The population of New York City in 2000 was 8,008,278. What was the order of magnitude of the population of New York City? **10^7 people**

SIMPLIFYING EXPRESSIONS **Simplify the expression.**

47. $(-3x^2y)^3(11x^3y^5)^2$ $\mathbf{-3267x^{12}y^{13}}$
48. $-(-xy^2z^3)^5(x^4yz)^2$ $\mathbf{x^{13}y^{12}z^{17}}$
49. $(-2s)(-5r^3st)^3(-2r^4st^7)^2$ $\mathbf{1000r^{17}s^6t^{17}}$

C **50.** ★ **OPEN-ENDED** Write three expressions involving products of powers, powers of powers, or powers of products that are equivalent to $12x^8$. ***Sample answer:*** $3x^2 \cdot 4x^6, 12(x^4)^2, 3(2x^4)^2$

51. **CHALLENGE** Show that when a and b are real numbers and n is a positive integer, $(ab)^n = a^n b^n$. **See margin.**

PROBLEM SOLVING

EXAMPLE 5 A on p. 491 for Exs. 52–56

52. ICE CREAM COMPOSITION There are about 954,930 air bubbles in 1 cubic centimeter of ice cream. There are about 946 cubic centimeters in 1 quart. Use order of magnitude to find the approximate number of air bubbles in 1 quart of ice cream. **10^9 air bubbles**

@HomeTutor for problem solving help at classzone.com

53. ASTRONOMY The order of magnitude of the radius of our solar system is 10^{13} meters. The order of magnitude of the radius of the visible universe is 10^{13} times as great. Find the approximate radius of the visible universe. **10^{26} m**

@HomeTutor for problem solving help at classzone.com

54. COASTAL LANDSLIDE There are about 1 billion grains of sand in 1 cubic foot of sand. In 1995 a stretch of beach at Sleeping Bear Dunes National Lakeshore in Michigan slid into Lake Michigan. Scientists believe that around 35 million cubic feet of sand fell into the lake. Use order of magnitude to find about how many grains of sand slid into the lake. **10^{16} grains of sand**

55. ◆ **MULTIPLE REPRESENTATIONS** There are about 10^{23} atoms of gold in 1 ounce of gold.

a. **Making a Table** Copy and complete the table by finding the number of atoms of gold for the given amounts of gold (in ounces).

Gold (ounces)	10	100	1000	10,000	100,000
Number of atoms	?	?	?	?	?
	10^{24}	10^{25}	10^{26}	10^{27}	10^{28}

b. **Writing an Expression** A particular mine in California extracted about 96,000 ounces of gold in 1 year. Use order of magnitude to write an expression you can use to find the approximate number of atoms of gold extracted in the mine that year. Simplify the expression. Verify your answer using the table. **$10^5 \cdot 10^{23}$; 10^{28} atoms**

56. **MULTI-STEP PROBLEM** A microscope has two lenses, the objective lens and the eyepiece, that work together to magnify an object. The total magnification of the microscope is the product of the magnification of the objective lens and the magnification of the eyepiece.

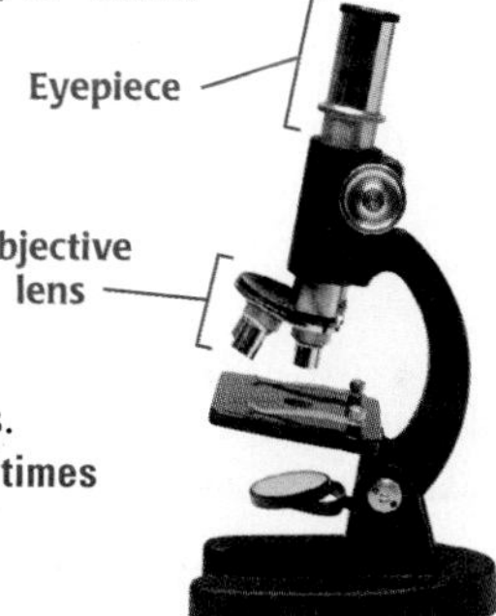

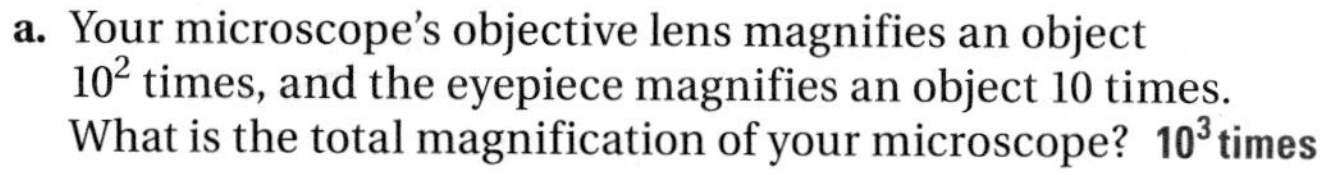

a. Your microscope's objective lens magnifies an object 10^2 times, and the eyepiece magnifies an object 10 times. What is the total magnification of your microscope? **10^3 times**

b. You magnify an object that is 10^2 nanometers long. How long is the magnified image? **10^5 nanometers**

Vocabulary

Exercise 2 Encourage students to write out explanations and give specific examples for all three properties covered in this lesson.

Avoiding Common Errors

Exercises 3–38 Watch for students who fail to account for numerical or variable bases that have an exponent of 1. Remind these students that a base without an exponent is raised to the power of 1 and that they need to add 1 or multiply by 1 when simplifying expressions. Also, some students may overlook the numerical factor when simplifying powers with numerical and variable bases. Remind these students to evaluate the numerical power first.

Study Strategy

Exercise 54 You may want to suggest that students write the standard form of 1 billion and 35 million before they determine the order of magnitude. Students may want to review order of magnitude and estimation on page 491 before they begin this exercise.

51. *Sample answer:* $(ab)^n = (ab) \cdot (ab) \cdot \ldots \cdot (ab)$ so that there are n total factors (ab). By the commutative property, the n a's can be grouped as a repeated multiplication equal to a^n and the n b's can be grouped as a repeated multiplication equal to b^n. $(ab)^n$ is equal to the product of these two groups, or $a^n \cdot b^n$.

5 ASSESS AND RETEACH

Daily Homework Quiz

Transparency Available

Simplify the expression. Write your answer using exponents.

1. $14^5 \cdot 14^2$ **14^7**

2. $[(-8)^4]^3$ **$(-8)^{12}$**

Simplify the expression.

3. $[(m-3)^6]^4$ **$(m-3)^{24}$**

4. $-(2s)^3$ **$-8s^3$**

5. A website had about 102 hits after a week. After a year, it had about 103 times the number of hits of the first week. About how many hits did it have at the end of the year? **about 10,000 hits**

Online Quiz

Available at **classzone.com**

Diagnosis/Remediation

- Practice A, B, C in Chapter Resource Book
- Study Guide in Chapter Resource Book
- Practice Workbook
- @HomeTutor

Challenge

Additional challenge is available in the Chapter Resource Book.

B **57. VOLUME OF THE SUN** The radius of the sun is about 695,000,000 meters. The formula for the volume of a sphere, such as the sun, is $V = \frac{4}{3}\pi r^3$. Because the order of magnitude of $\frac{4}{3}\pi$ is 1, it does not contribute to the formula in a significant way. So, you can find the order of magnitude of the volume of the sun by cubing its radius. Find the order of magnitude of the volume of the sun. **10^{27}**

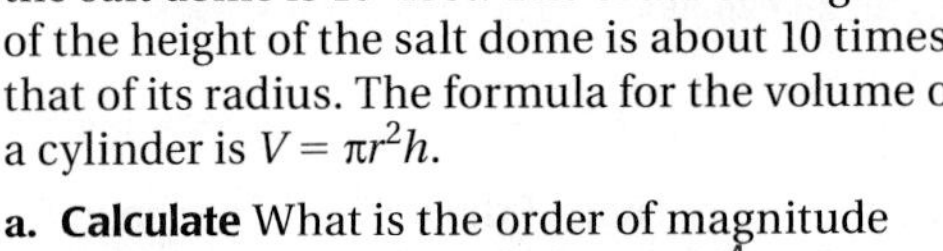

58. ★ EXTENDED RESPONSE Rock salt can be mined from large deposits of salt called salt domes. A particular salt dome is roughly cylindrical in shape. The order of magnitude of the radius of the salt dome is 10^3 feet. The order of magnitude of the height of the salt dome is about 10 times that of its radius. The formula for the volume of a cylinder is $V = \pi r^2 h$.

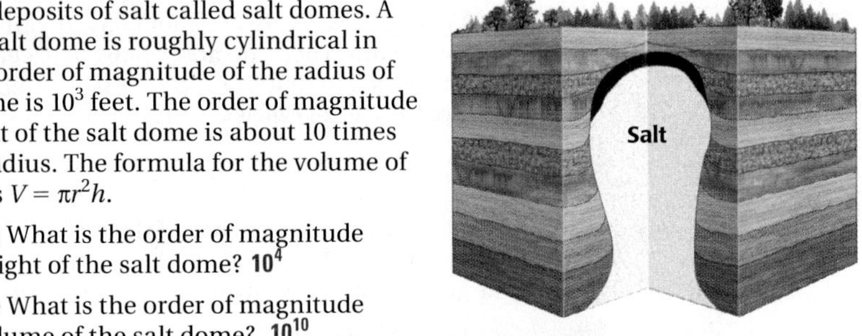

a. **Calculate** What is the order of magnitude of the height of the salt dome? **10^4**

b. **Calculate** What is the order of magnitude of the volume of the salt dome? **10^{10}**

c. **Explain** The order of magnitude of the radius of a salt dome can be 10 times the radius of the salt dome described in this exercise. What effect does multiplying the order of magnitude of the radius of the salt dome by 10 have on the volume of the salt dome? *Explain.*

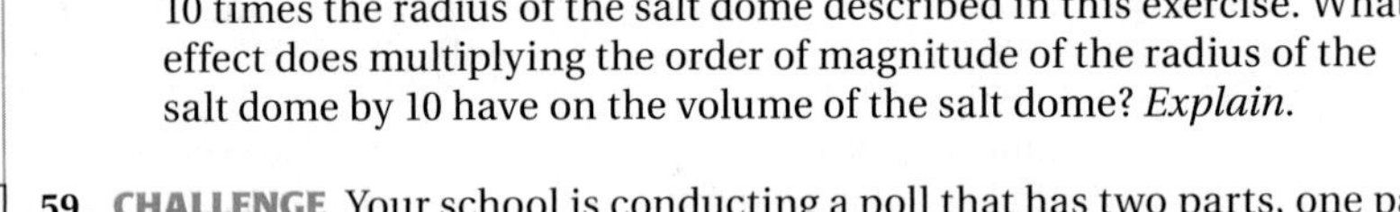

58c. Multiplies the volume by a factor of 10^2. *Sample answer:* Since the radius is squared in the formula for volume, multiplying the radius by 10 would multiply the volume by a factor of $10 \cdot 10$, or 10^2.

C **59. CHALLENGE** Your school is conducting a poll that has two parts, one part that has 13 questions and a second part that has 10 questions. Students can answer the questions in either part with "agree" or "disagree." What power of 2 represents the number of ways there are to answer the questions in the first part of the poll? What power of 2 represents the number of ways there are to answer the questions in the second part of the poll? What power of 2 represents the number of ways there are to answer all of the questions on the poll? **2^{13} ways; 2^{10} ways; 2^{23} ways**

MIXED REVIEW

PREVIEW Prepare for Lesson 8.2 in Exs. 60–65.

Find the product. *(p. 88)*

60. $\left(\frac{1}{2}\right)\left(-\frac{4}{5}\right)$ **$-\frac{2}{5}$**

61. $\left(-\frac{2}{3}\right)\left(\frac{7}{4}\right)$ **$-1\frac{1}{6}$**

62. $\left(-\frac{6}{5}\right)\left(-\frac{3}{8}\right)$ **$\frac{9}{20}$**

Evaluate the expression for the given value of the variable. *(p. 2)*

63. x^4 when $x = 3$ **81**

64. x^2 when $x = -2.2$ **4.84**

65. x^3 when $x = \frac{3}{4}$ **$\frac{27}{64}$**

Graph the equation or inequality. **66–74. See margin.**

66. $y = -4$ *(p. 215)*

67. $3x - y = 15$ *(p. 225)*

68. $7x - 6y = 84$ *(p. 225)*

69. $y = -5x + 3$ *(p. 244)*

70. $y = \frac{1}{2}x - 5$ *(p. 244)*

71. $x \geq -3$ *(p. 405)*

72. $y < 1.5$ *(p. 405)*

73. $x + y \leq 7$ *(p. 405)*

74. $2x - y < 3$ *(p. 405)*

EXTRA PRACTICE for Lesson 8.1, p. 945

ONLINE QUIZ at classzone.com

66–74. See Additional Answers beginning on p. AA1.

8.2 Apply Exponent Properties Involving Quotients

Before You used properties of exponents involving products.
Now You will use properties of exponents involving quotients.
Why? So you can compare magnitudes of earthquakes, as in Ex. 53.

Key Vocabulary
- **power,** *p. 3*
- **exponent,** *p. 3*
- **base,** *p. 3*

Notice what happens when you divide powers with the same base.

$$\frac{a^5}{a^3} = \frac{a \cdot a \cdot \not{a} \cdot \not{a} \cdot \not{a}}{\not{a} \cdot \not{a} \cdot \not{a}} = a \cdot a = a^2 = a^{5-3}$$

The example above suggests the following property of exponents, known as the quotient of powers property.

KEY CONCEPT *For Your Notebook*

Quotient of Powers Property

Let a be a nonzero real number, and let m and n be positive integers such that $m > n$.

Words To divide powers having the same base, subtract exponents.

Algebra $\frac{a^m}{a^n} = a^{m-n}, a \neq 0$ **Example** $\frac{4^7}{4^2} = 4^{7-2} = 4^5$

EXAMPLE 1 Use the quotient of powers property

SIMPLIFY EXPRESSIONS
When simplifying powers with numerical bases only, write your answers using exponents, as in parts (a), (b), and (c).

a. $\frac{8^{10}}{8^4} = 8^{10-4}$
$= 8^6$

b. $\frac{(-3)^9}{(-3)^3} = (-3)^{9-3}$
$= (-3)^6$

c. $\frac{5^4 \cdot 5^8}{5^7} = \frac{5^{12}}{5^7}$
$= 5^{12-7}$
$= 5^5$

d. $\frac{1}{x^4} \cdot x^6 = \frac{x^6}{x^4}$
$= x^{6-4}$
$= x^2$

GUIDED PRACTICE for Example 1

Simplify the expression.

1. $\frac{6^{11}}{6^5}$ **6^6**

2. $\frac{(-4)^9}{(-4)^2}$ **$(-4)^7$**

3. $\frac{9^4 \cdot 9^3}{9^2}$ **9^5**

4. $\frac{1}{y^5} \cdot y^8$ **y^3**

1 PLAN AND PREPARE

Warm-Up Exercises
Transparency Available

1. Evaluate q^3 when $q = \frac{1}{4}$. **$\frac{1}{64}$**

2. Evaluate c^2 when $c = \frac{3}{5}$. **$\frac{9}{25}$**

3. A magazine had a circulation of 9364 in 2001. The circulation was about 125 times greater in 2006. Use order of magnitude to estimate the circulation in 2006. **about 10^6 or 1,000,000**

Notetaking Guide
Transparency Available

Promotes interactive learning and notetaking skills.

Pacing
Basic: 2 days
Average: 2 days
Advanced: 2 days
Block: 0.5 block with 8.1
0.5 block with 8.3

- See *Teaching Guide/Lesson Plan.*

2 FOCUS AND MOTIVATE

Essential Question
Big Idea 1, p. 487

How do you use properties of exponents involving quotients? **Tell students they will learn how to answer this question by simplifying expressions that involve division of powers.**

NCTM STANDARDS
Standard 1: Understand how operations are related
Standard 2: Understand patterns

Resource Planning Guide

Chapter Resource Book
- Teaching Guide/Lesson Plan
- Activity Master
- Practice levels A, B, C
- Study Guide
- Catch-up for Absent Students
- Application
- Challenge

Workbooks
- Notetaking Guide
- Practice Workbook

Teaching Options
- **Power Presentations** provides dynamic electronic teaching resources for the classroom.
- **Activity Generator** provides editable activities for all ability levels.

Interactive Technology
- Easy Planner
- Power Presentations
- Activity Generator
- Animated Algebra
- Test Generator
- Online Quiz
- eWorkbook
- eEdition
- @HomeTutor

Resources for English Learners
- Spanish Study Guide
- Multi-Language Visual Glossary
- Student Resources in Spanish

See also the *Differentiated Instruction Resources* for more strategies for meeting individual needs.

POWER OF A QUOTIENT Notice what happens when you raise a quotient to a power.

$$\left(\frac{a}{b}\right)^4 = \frac{a}{b} \cdot \frac{a}{b} \cdot \frac{a}{b} \cdot \frac{a}{b} = \frac{a \cdot a \cdot a \cdot a}{b \cdot b \cdot b \cdot b} = \frac{a^4}{b^4}$$

The example above suggests the following property of exponents, known as the power of a quotient property.

KEY CONCEPT *For Your Notebook*

Power of a Quotient Property

Let a and b be real numbers with $b \neq 0$, and let m be a positive integer.

Words To find a power of a quotient, find the power of the numerator and the power of the denominator and divide.

Algebra $\left(\frac{a}{b}\right)^m = \frac{a^m}{b^m}, b \neq 0$

Example $\left(\frac{3}{2}\right)^7 = \frac{3^7}{2^7}$

EXAMPLE 2 Use the power of a quotient property

SIMPLIFY EXPRESSIONS
When simplifying powers with numerical *and* variable bases, evaluate the numerical power, as in part (b).

a. $\left(\frac{x}{y}\right)^3 = \frac{x^3}{y^3}$

b. $\left(-\frac{7}{x}\right)^2 = \left(\frac{-7}{x}\right)^2 = \frac{(-7)^2}{x^2} = \frac{49}{x^2}$

EXAMPLE 3 Use properties of exponents

a. $\left(\frac{4x^2}{5y}\right)^3 = \frac{(4x^2)^3}{(5y)^3}$ Power of a quotient property

$= \frac{4^3 \cdot (x^2)^3}{5^3y^3}$ Power of a product property

$= \frac{64x^6}{125y^3}$ Power of a power property

b. $\left(\frac{a^2}{b}\right)^5 \cdot \frac{1}{2a^2} = \frac{(a^2)^5}{b^5} \cdot \frac{1}{2a^2}$ Power of a quotient property

$= \frac{a^{10}}{b^5} \cdot \frac{1}{2a^2}$ Power of a power property

$= \frac{a^{10}}{2a^2b^5}$ Multiply fractions.

$= \frac{a^8}{2b^5}$ Quotient of powers property

Motivating the Lesson

You are preparing a report that compares the radius of Earth at an order of magnitude of 10^7 meters to the radius of the Milky Way galaxy at an order of magnitude of 10^{21} meters. By knowing how to apply properties of exponents that involve quotients, you will be able to approximate how many times as great the radius of the Milky Way galaxy is as the radius of Earth.

3 TEACH

Extra Example 1

Use the quotient of powers property.

a. $\frac{9^{12}}{9^5}$ 9^7

b. $\frac{(-2)^4}{(-2)^3}$ -2

c. $\frac{6^3 \cdot 6^4}{6^2}$ 6^5

d. $\frac{1}{r^5} \cdot r^8$ r^3

Key Question to Ask for Example 1

- How is dividing powers different from multiplying powers? **You subtract exponents when you divide powers and add exponents when you multiply powers.**

Extra Example 2

Use the power of a quotient property.

a. $\left(\frac{c}{d}\right)^6$ $\frac{c^6}{d^6}$

b. $\left(\frac{-2}{y}\right)^4$ $\frac{16}{y^4}$

Differentiated Instruction

Inclusion For smaller exponents, explicitly writing out the factors of each power works for division as well as multiplication. As practice, students can attempt a similar problem with very large exponents. This will allow them to see why the quotient of powers property works, without having to memorize its verbal form.

See also the *Differentiated Instruction Resources* for more strategies.

✓ GUIDED PRACTICE for Examples 2 and 3

Simplify the expression.

5. $\left(\frac{a}{b}\right)^2$ $\frac{a^2}{b^2}$ **6.** $\left(-\frac{5}{y}\right)^3$ $-\frac{125}{y^3}$ **7.** $\left(\frac{x^2}{4y}\right)^2$ $\frac{x^4}{16y^2}$ **8.** $\left(\frac{2s}{3t}\right)^3 \cdot \left(\frac{t^5}{16}\right)$ $\frac{s^3t^2}{54}$

EXAMPLE 4 Solve a multi-step problem

FRACTAL TREE To construct what is known as a *fractal tree*, begin with a single segment (the trunk) that is 1 unit long, as in Step 0. Add three shorter segments that are $\frac{1}{2}$ unit long to form the first set of branches, as in Step 1. Then continue adding sets of successively shorter branches so that each new set of branches is half the length of the previous set, as in Steps 2 and 3.

Step 0 Step 1 Step 2 Step 3

a. Make a table showing the number of new branches at each step for Steps 1–4. Write the number of new branches as a power of 3.

b. How many times greater is the number of new branches added at Step 5 than the number of new branches added at Step 2?

Solution

a.

Step	Number of new branches
1	$3 = 3^1$
2	$9 = 3^2$
3	$27 = 3^3$
4	$81 = 3^4$

b. The number of new branches added at Step 5 is 3^5. The number of new branches added at Step 2 is 3^2. So, the number of new branches added at Step 5 is $\frac{3^5}{3^2} = 3^3 = 27$ times the number of new branches added at Step 2.

GUIDED PRACTICE for Example 4

9. FRACTAL TREE In Example 4, add a column to the table for the length of the new branches at each step. Write the lengths of the new branches as powers of $\frac{1}{2}$. What is the length of a new branch added at Step 9? **See margin.**

Extra Example 3

Use properties of exponents.

a. $\left(\frac{3a^4}{5b}\right)^3$ $\frac{27a^{12}}{125b^3}$

b. $\left(\frac{x^3}{y}\right)^7 \cdot \frac{1}{3x^8}$ $\frac{x^{13}}{3y^7}$

Extra Example 4

Construct a fractal tree that begins with a V-shaped segment, with each side of the V-shape 1 unit long. Then add a V-shaped segment on each end with each side $\frac{1}{2}$ unit long. Continue adding sets of successively shorter branches so that each new set of branches is half the length of the previous set.

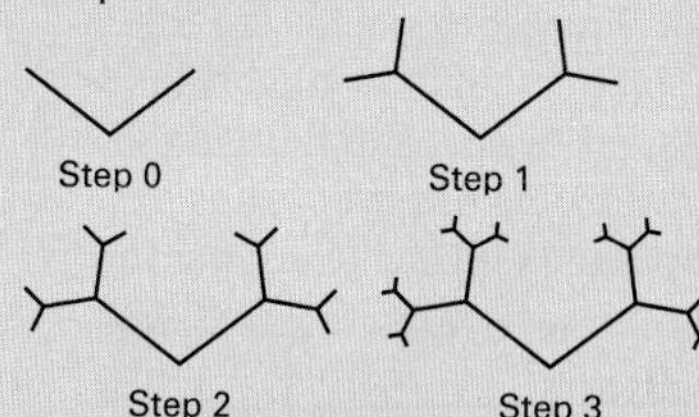

a. Make a table showing the number of new branches at each step for Steps 1–3. Write the number of new branches as a power of 2.

Step	New branches
1	$4 = 2^2$
2	$8 = 2^3$
3	$16 = 2^4$

b. How many times as great is the number of new branches at Step 6 as the number of new branches at Step 2? **16**

Key Question to Ask for Example 4

- Why do you write the number of new branches as a power of 3? **Since you add 3 segments to each set of successive branches, the steps are 3, then 3 × 3, then 3 × 3 × 3, and so on.**

9.

Step	Number of new branches	Length of new branches
1	$3 = 3^1$	$\frac{1}{2} = \left(\frac{1}{2}\right)^1$
2	$9 = 3^2$	$\frac{1}{4} = \left(\frac{1}{2}\right)^2$
3	$27 = 3^3$	$\frac{1}{8} = \left(\frac{1}{2}\right)^3$
4	$81 = 3^4$	$\frac{1}{16} = \left(\frac{1}{2}\right)^4$

$\left(\frac{1}{2}\right)^9 = \frac{1}{512}$ unit

Extra Example 5

The order of magnitude of the luminosity of the Milky Way galaxy is 10^{36} watts. The order of magnitude of the luminosity of a gamma ray burster is 10^{45} watts. How many times as luminous is a gamma ray burster as the Milky Way galaxy? **about 10^9 times as luminous**

Key Question to Ask for Example 5

- How do you know that you need to divide to find the solution to this problem? **The problem asks for a ratio and you divide to find ratios.**

Closing the Lesson

Have students summarize the major points of the lesson and answer the Essential Question: How do you use properties of exponents involving quotients?

- **Subtract exponents to divide powers.**
- **To find the power of a quotient, find the powers of the numerator and the powers of denominator before dividing.**

To simplify an expression involving quotients, subtract the exponent of the denominator from the exponent of the numerator. To raise a quotient to a power, find the power of the numerator and the power of the denominator and divide.

EXAMPLE 5 Solve a real-world problem

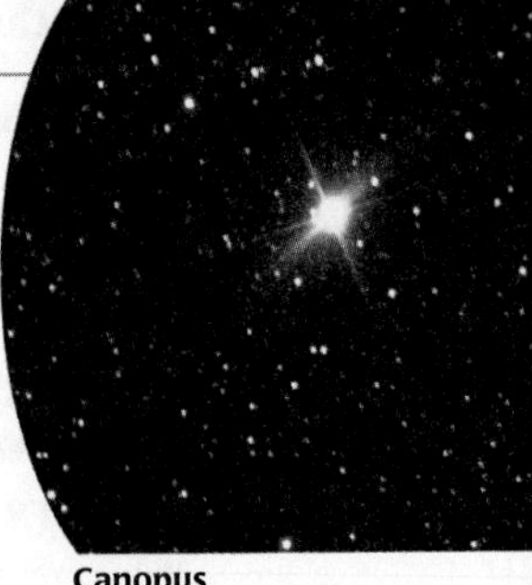
Canopus

ASTRONOMY The luminosity (in watts) of a star is the total amount of energy emitted from the star per unit of time. The order of magnitude of the luminosity of the sun is 10^{26} watts. The star Canopus is one of the brightest stars in the sky. The order of magnitude of the luminosity of Canopus is 10^{30} watts. How many times more luminous is Canopus than the sun?

Solution

$$\frac{\text{Luminosity of Canopus (watts)}}{\text{Luminosity of the sun (watts)}} = \frac{10^{30}}{10^{26}} = 10^{30-26} = 10^4$$

▶ Canopus is about 10^4 times as luminous as the sun.

✓ **GUIDED PRACTICE** for Example 5

10. **WHAT IF?** Sirius is considered the brightest star in the sky. Sirius is less luminous than Canopus, but Sirius appears to be brighter because it is much closer to Earth. The order of magnitude of the luminosity of Sirius is 10^{28} watts. How many times more luminous is Canopus than Sirius? **10^2**

8.2 EXERCISES

HOMEWORK KEY

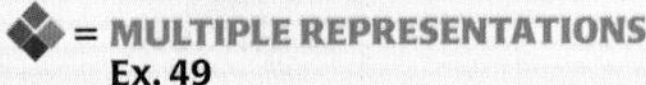

○ = **WORKED-OUT SOLUTIONS** on p. WS18 for Exs. 33 and 51

★ = **STANDARDIZED TEST PRACTICE** Exs. 2, 19, 37, 46, and 54

◆ = **MULTIPLE REPRESENTATIONS** Ex. 49

SKILL PRACTICE

A

1. **VOCABULARY** Copy and complete: In the power 4^3, 4 is the _?_ and 3 is the _?_. **base, exponent**

2. ★ **WRITING** *Explain* when and how to use the quotient of powers property. **When powers have the same base, their quotient is the base raised to the difference of the exponents.**

EXAMPLES 1 and 2 on pp. 495–496 for Exs. 3–20

SIMPLIFYING EXPRESSIONS **Simplify the expression. Write your answer using exponents.**

3. $\frac{5^6}{5^2}$ **5^4**
4. $\frac{2^{11}}{2^6}$ **2^5**
5. $\frac{3^9}{3^5}$ **3^4**
6. $\frac{(-6)^8}{(-6)^5}$ **$(-6)^3$**
7. $\frac{(-4)^7}{(-4)^4}$ **$(-4)^3$**
8. $\frac{(-12)^9}{(-12)^3}$ **$(-12)^6$**
9. $\frac{10^5 \cdot 10^5}{10^4}$ **10^6**
10. $\frac{6^7 \cdot 6^4}{6^6}$ **6^5**
11. $\left(\frac{1}{3}\right)^5$ **$\frac{1}{3^5}$**
12. $\left(\frac{3}{2}\right)^4$ **$\frac{3^4}{2^4}$**
13. $\left(-\frac{5}{4}\right)^4$ **$\frac{5^4}{4^4}$**
14. $\left(-\frac{2}{5}\right)^5$ **$-\frac{2^5}{5^5}$**
15. $7^9 \cdot \frac{1}{7^2}$ **7^7**
16. $\frac{1}{9^5} \cdot 9^{11}$ **9^6**
17. $\left(\frac{1}{3}\right)^4 \cdot 3^{12}$ **3^8**
18. $4^9 \cdot \left(-\frac{1}{4}\right)^5$ **-4^4**

Differentiated Instruction

Advanced In **Example 5**, some students may see that if Canopus is 10,000 times as bright as the sun, then the sun is $\frac{1}{10{,}000}$ as bright as Canopus. Challenge students to use this observation to write a ratio of the luminosity of the sun to the luminosity of Canopus using exponents. Ask them to explain their reasoning by describing the relationship between the two ratios. This prepares students for the definition of negative exponents in Lesson 8.3.

See also the *Differentiated Instruction Resources* for more strategies.

19. ★ **MULTIPLE CHOICE** Which expression is equivalent to 16^6? **C**

Ⓐ $\frac{16^4}{16^2}$ Ⓑ $\frac{16^{12}}{16^2}$ Ⓒ $\left(\frac{16^6}{16^3}\right)^2$ Ⓓ $\left(\frac{16^9}{16^6}\right)^3$

20. **ERROR ANALYSIS** *Describe* and correct the error in simplifying $\frac{9^5 \cdot 9^3}{9^4}$. **See margin.**

$\frac{9^5 \cdot 9^3}{9^4} = \frac{9^8}{9^4} = 9^{12}$ ✗

EXAMPLES 1, 2, and 3 on pp. 495–496 for Exs. 21–37

SIMPLIFYING EXPRESSIONS **Simplify the expression.**

21. $\frac{1}{y^8} \cdot y^{15}$ y^7
22. $z^8 \cdot \frac{1}{z^7}$ z
23. $\left(\frac{a}{y}\right)^9$ $\frac{a^9}{y^9}$
24. $\left(\frac{j}{k}\right)^{11}$ $\frac{j^{11}}{k^{11}}$
25. $\left(\frac{p}{q}\right)^4$ $\frac{p^4}{q^4}$
26. $\left(-\frac{1}{x}\right)^5$ $-\frac{1}{x^5}$
27. $\left(-\frac{4}{x}\right)^3$ $-\frac{64}{x^3}$
28. $\left(-\frac{a}{b}\right)^4$ $\frac{a^4}{b^4}$
29. $\left(\frac{4c}{d^2}\right)^3$ $\frac{64c^3}{d^6}$
30. $\left(\frac{a^7}{2b}\right)^5$ $\frac{a^{35}}{32b^5}$
31. $\left(\frac{x^2}{3y^3}\right)^2$ $\frac{x^4}{9y^6}$
32. $\left(\frac{3x^5}{7y^2}\right)^3$ $\frac{27x^{15}}{343y^6}$
33. $\left(\frac{3x^3}{2y}\right)^2 \cdot \frac{1}{x^2}$ $\frac{9x^4}{4y^2}$
34. $\left(\frac{2x^3}{y}\right)^3 \cdot \frac{1}{6x^3}$ $\frac{4x^6}{3y^3}$
35. $\frac{3}{8m^5} \cdot \left(\frac{m^4}{n^2}\right)^3$ $\frac{3m^7}{8n^6}$
36. $\left(-\frac{5}{x}\right)^2 \cdot \left(\frac{2x^4}{y^3}\right)^2$ $\frac{100x^6}{y^6}$

B

37. ★ **MULTIPLE CHOICE** Which expression is equivalent to $\left(\frac{7x^3}{2y^4}\right)^2$? **D**

Ⓐ $\frac{7x^5}{2y^6}$ Ⓑ $\frac{7x^6}{2y^8}$ Ⓒ $\frac{49x^5}{4y^6}$ Ⓓ $\frac{49x^6}{4y^8}$

SIMPLIFYING EXPRESSIONS **Find the missing exponent.**

38. $\frac{(-8)^7}{(-8)^?} = (-8)^3$ **4**
39. $\frac{7^? \cdot 7^2}{7^4} = 7^6$ **8**
40. $\frac{1}{p^5} \cdot p^? = p^9$ **14**
41. $\left(\frac{2c^3}{d^2}\right)^? = \frac{16c^{12}}{d^8}$ **4**

SIMPLIFYING EXPRESSIONS **Simplify the expression.**

42. $\left(\frac{2f^2g^3}{3fg}\right)^4$ $\frac{16f^4g^8}{81}$
43. $\frac{2s^3t^3}{st^2} \cdot \frac{(3st)^3}{s^2t}$ $54s^3t^3$
44. $\left(\frac{2m^5n}{4m^2}\right)^2 \cdot \left(\frac{mn^4}{5n}\right)^2$ $\frac{m^8n^8}{100}$
45. $\left(\frac{3x^3y}{x^2}\right)^3 \cdot \left(\frac{y^2x^4}{5y}\right)^2$ $\frac{27x^{11}y^5}{25}$

46. ★ **OPEN-ENDED** Write three expressions involving quotients that are equivalent to 14^7. ***Sample answer:*** $\frac{14^8}{14}, \frac{14^{10}}{14^3}, \frac{14^{14}}{14^7}$

C

47. **REASONING** Name the definition or property that justifies each step to show that $\frac{a^m}{a^n} = \frac{1}{a^{n-m}}$ for $m < n$.

Let $m < n$. Given

$\frac{a^m}{a^n} = \frac{a^m}{a^n}\left(\frac{\frac{1}{a^m}}{\frac{1}{a^m}}\right)$ __?__ **Identity property of multiplication**

$= \frac{1}{\frac{a^n}{a^m}}$ __?__ **Multiply fractions.**

$= \frac{1}{a^{n-m}}$ __?__ **Quotient of powers property**

48. **CHALLENGE** Find the values of x and y if you know that $\frac{b^x}{b^y} = b^9$ and $\frac{b^x \cdot b^2}{b^{3y}} = b^{13}$. *Explain* how you found your answer.

48. $x = 8$, $y = -1$. *Sample answer:* Using the quotient of a power property, write two equations for x and y: $x - y = 9$, and $x + 2 - 3y = 13$. Solve the equations.

20. *Sample answer:* When using the quotient of powers property, the base is raised to the difference of the exponents, not the sum; $\frac{9^8}{9^4} = 9^{(8-4)} = 9^4$.

4 PRACTICE AND APPLY

Assignment Guide

Answer Transparencies available for all exercises

Basic:
Day 1: pp. 498–501
Exs. 1–28
Day 2: pp. 498–501
Exs. 29–39, 49–52, 55–66

Average:
Day 1: pp. 498–501
Exs. 1, 2, 7–28, 38–40
Day 2: pp. 498–501
Exs. 31–37, 41–46, 49–53, 55–66

Advanced:
Day 1: pp. 498–501
Exs. 1, 2, 9–19, 21–28, 38–40, 47, 48*
Day 2: pp. 498–501
Exs. 32–37, 41–46, 49–66*

Block:
pp. 498–501
Exs. 1, 2, 7–28, 38–40 (with 8.1)
pp. 498–501
Exs. 31–37, 41–46, 49–53, 55–66 (with 8.3)

Differentiated Instruction

See *Differentiated Instruction Resources* for suggestions on addressing the needs of a diverse classroom.

Homework Check

For a quick check of student understanding of key concepts, go over the following exercises:
Basic: 6, 23, 30, 49, 50
Average: 12, 24, 32, 49, 51
Advanced: 16, 27, 34, 50, 51

Extra Practice

- Student Edition, p. 945
- Chapter Resource Book: Practice levels A, B, C

Practice Worksheet

An easily-readable reduced practice page (with answers) for this lesson can be found on p. 486C.

Avoiding Common Errors

Exercises 3–18, 21–36 Watch for students who add exponents when finding a quotient. Remind these students that you subtract exponents when dividing and add exponents when multiplying.

Study Strategy

Exercises 19, 37 Suggest that students look for ways to eliminate answers. In Exercise 19, point out that they can eliminate two choices quickly by subtracting exponents. In Exercise 37, suggest that students evaluate the numerical bases to eliminate two choices.

Mathematical Reasoning

Exercises 38–40 For students who have difficulty solving these exercises, suggest that they expand numbers and variables into their basic factors and then work backward from what they know. For example, in Exercise 38, tell them that they know there are 7 factors of (-8) in the numerator. They also know that the number of factors in the numerator and denominator cancel so that 3 factors of (-8) remain. So the question they need to ask is how many factors of (-8) are in the denominator so that only 3 factors of (-8) remain in the numerator after canceling.

Internet Reference

Exercise 53 More information about earthquakes can be found at pubs.usgs.gov/gip/earthq1

PROBLEM SOLVING

EXAMPLES A **4 and 5** on pp. 497–498 for Exs. 49–51

49. ◆ **MULTIPLE REPRESENTATIONS** Draw a square with side lengths that are 1 unit long. Divide it into four new squares with side lengths that are one half the side length of the original square, as shown in Step 1. Keep dividing the squares into new squares, as shown in Steps 2 and 3.

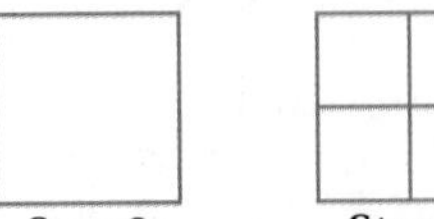

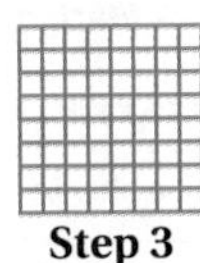

Step 0 Step 1 Step 2 Step 3

a. **Making a Table** Make a table showing the number of new squares and the side length of a new square at each step for Steps 1–4. Write the number of new squares as a power of 4. Write the side length of a new square as a power of $\frac{1}{2}$. **See margin.**

b. **Writing an Expression** Write and simplify an expression to find by how many times the number of new squares increased from Step 2 to Step 4. **$\frac{4^4}{4^2}$; 16 times**

@HomeTutor for problem solving help at classzone.com

50. **GROSS DOMESTIC PRODUCT** In 2003 the gross domestic product (GDP) for the United States was about 11 trillion dollars, and the order of magnitude of the population of the U.S. was 10^8. Use order of magnitude to find the approximate per capita (per person) GDP. **about 10^5 dollars**

@HomeTutor for problem solving help at classzone.com

51. **SPACE TRAVEL** Alpha Centauri is the closest star system to Earth. Alpha Centauri is about 10^{13} kilometers away from Earth. A spacecraft leaves Earth and travels at an average speed of 10^4 meters per second. About how many years would it take the spacecraft to reach Alpha Centauri? **about 31,710 yr**

B

52. **ASTRONOMY** The brightness of one star relative to another star can be measured by comparing the magnitudes of the stars. For every increase in magnitude of 1, the relative brightness is diminished by a factor of 2.512. For instance, a star of magnitude 8 is 2.512 times less bright than a star of magnitude 7.

Ursa Minor

Polaris (magnitude 2)

Eta Ursae Minoris (magnitude 5)

The constellation Ursa Minor (the Little Dipper) is shown. How many times less bright is Eta Ursae Minoris than Polaris? **2.512^3 times**

53. **EARTHQUAKES** The energy released by one earthquake relative to another earthquake can be measured by comparing the magnitudes (as determined by the Richter scale) of the earthquakes. For every increase of 1 in magnitude, the energy released is multiplied by a factor of about 31. How many times greater is the energy released by an earthquake of magnitude 7 than the energy released by an earthquake of magnitude 4? **31^3 times greater**

○ = WORKED-OUT SOLUTIONS on p. WS1 ★ = STANDARDIZED TEST PRACTICE

49a.

Step	Number of new squares	Side length of new square
1	$4 = 4^1$	$\frac{1}{2} = \left(\frac{1}{2}\right)^1$
2	$16 = 4^2$	$\frac{1}{4} = \left(\frac{1}{2}\right)^2$
3	$64 = 4^3$	$\frac{1}{8} = \left(\frac{1}{2}\right)^3$
4	$256 = 4^4$	$\frac{1}{16} = \left(\frac{1}{2}\right)^4$

C 54. ★ **EXTENDED RESPONSE** A byte is a unit used to measure computer memory. Other units are based on the number of bytes they represent. The table shows the number of bytes in certain units. For example, from the table you can calculate that 1 terabyte is equivalent to 2^{10} gigabytes.

Unit	Number of bytes
Kilobyte	2^{10}
Megabyte	2^{20}
Gigabyte	2^{30}
Terabyte	2^{40}
Petabyte	2^{50}

a. **Calculate** How many kilobytes are there in 1 terabyte? **2^{30} kilobytes**

b. **Calculate** How many megabytes are there in 1 petabyte? **2^{30} megabytes**

c. **CHALLENGE** Another unit used to measure computer memory is a bit. There are 8 bits in a byte. *Explain* how you can convert the number of bytes per unit given in the table to the number of bits per unit.
Multiply the number of bytes in each unit by 8, or 2^3.

MIXED REVIEW

PREVIEW Prepare for Lesson 8.3 in Exs. 55–60.

Solve the equation. Check your solution. *(p. 134)*

55. $\frac{3}{4}k = 9$ **12**
56. $\frac{2}{5}t = -4$ **−10**
57. $-\frac{2}{3}v = 14$ **−21**
58. $-\frac{5}{2}y = -35$ **14**
59. $-\frac{7}{5}z = \frac{14}{3}$ **$-3\frac{1}{3}$**
60. $-\frac{3}{2}z = -\frac{3}{4}$ **$\frac{1}{2}$**

Write an equation of the line that passes through the given points. *(p. 292)*

61. (−2, 1), (0, −5) **$y = -3x - 5$**
62. (0, 3), (−4, 1) **$y = \frac{1}{2}x + 3$**
63. (0, −3), (7, −3) **$y = -3$**
64. (4, 3), (5, 6) **$y = 3x - 9$**
65. (4, 1), (−2, 4) **$y = -\frac{1}{2}x + 3$**
66. (−1, −3), (−3, 1) **$y = -2x - 5$**

QUIZ for Lessons 8.1–8.2

Simplify the expression. Write your answer using exponents.

1. $3^2 \cdot 3^6$ *(p. 489)* **3^8**
2. $(5^4)^3$ *(p. 489)* **5^{12}**
3. $(32 \cdot 14)^7$ *(p. 489)* **$32^7 \cdot 14^7$**
4. $7^2 \cdot 7^6 \cdot 7$ *(p. 489)* **7^9**
5. $(-4)(-4)^9$ *(p. 489)* **$(-4)^{10}$**
6. $\frac{7^{12}}{7^4}$ *(p. 495)* **7^8**
7. $\frac{(-9)^9}{(-9)^7}$ *(p. 495)* **$(-9)^2$**
8. $\frac{3^7 \cdot 3^4}{3^6}$ *(p. 495)* **3^5**
9. $\left(\frac{5}{4}\right)^4$ *(p. 495)* **$\frac{5^4}{4^4}$**

Simplify the expression.

10. $x^2 \cdot x^5$ *(p. 489)* **x^7**
11. $(3x^3)^2$ *(p. 489)* **$9x^6$**
12. $-(7x)^2$ *(p. 489)* **$-49x^2$**
13. $(6x^5)^3 \cdot x$ *(p. 489)* **$216x^{16}$**
14. $(2x^5)^3(7x^7)^2$ *(p. 489)* **$392x^{29}$**
15. $\frac{1}{x^9} \cdot x^{21}$ *(p. 495)* **x^{12}**
16. $\left(-\frac{4}{x}\right)^3$ *(p. 495)* **$-\frac{64}{x^3}$**
17. $\left(\frac{w}{v}\right)^6$ *(p. 495)* **$\frac{w^6}{v^6}$**
18. $\left(\frac{x^3}{4}\right)^2$ *(p. 495)* **$\frac{x^6}{16}$**

19. **AGRICULTURE** In 2004 the order of magnitude of the number of pounds of oranges produced in the United States was 10^{10}. The order of magnitude of the number of acres used for growing oranges was 10^6. About how many pounds of oranges per acre were produced in the United States in 2004? *(p. 495)* **about 10^4 pounds**

5 ASSESS AND RETEACH

Daily Homework Quiz

Transparency Available

1. Simplify $\frac{6^3 \cdot 6^5}{6^4}$ **6^4**
2. Simplify $10^7 \cdot \left(\frac{-1}{10}\right)^4$ **10^3**
3. Simplify $\left(\frac{s^8}{3r}\right)^3$ **$\frac{s^{24}}{27r^3}$**
4. The order of magnitude of the power output of a nuclear-powered aircraft carrier is about 10^6 watts. The order of magnitude of peak power at Hoover Dam is about 10^9 watts. How many times as great is the power output of Hoover Dam as the power output of a nuclear-powered aircraft carrier? **10^3**

 **Online Quiz**

Available at **classzone.com**

Diagnosis/Remediation

- Practice A, B, C in Chapter Resource Book
- Study Guide in Chapter Resource Book
- Practice Workbook
- @HomeTutor

Challenge

Additional challenge is available in the Chapter Resource Book.

Quiz

An easily-readable reduced copy of the quiz (with answers) on Lessons 8.1–8.2 from the Assessment Book can be found on p. 486E.

1 PLAN AND PREPARE

Explore the Concept

- Students will simplify expressions with zero or negative exponents.
- This activity leads into the study of using the definitions of zero and negative exponents in Example 1 in Lesson 8.3.

Recommended Time

Work activity: 10 min

Discuss results: 5 min

Grouping

Students should work individually.

2 TEACH

Tips for Success

When students read the table from the bottom up in Step 1, make sure that they look for the pattern in the second column. Point out that the value of 2^n is multiplied by 2, the base of 2^n, and not by the value of the exponent in column 1.

Key Discovery

A number to the zero power is 1. A power with a negative exponent can be written with a positive exponent by taking the reciprocal of the base.

3 ASSESS AND RETEACH

1. What is the value of $(-2xy)^0$? **1**
2. How do you write a^{-n} using a positive exponent if a is a nonzero number and n is a positive integer? $\frac{1}{a^n}$

Investigating Algebra ACTIVITY *Use before Lesson 8.3*

8.3 Zero and Negative Exponents

MATERIALS • paper and pencil

QUESTION **How can you simplify expressions with zero or negative exponents?**

EXPLORE **Evaluate powers with zero and negative exponents**

STEP 1 ***Find a pattern***

Copy and complete the tables for the powers of 2 and 3.

Exponent, n	Value of 2^n
4	16
3	? **8**
2	? **4**
1	? **2**

Exponent, n	Value of 3^n
4	81
3	? **27**
2	? **9**
1	? **3**

As you read the tables from the *bottom up*, you see that each time the exponent is increased by 1, the value of the power is multiplied by the base. What can you say about the exponents and the values of the powers as you read the table from the *top down*?

STEP 2 ***Extend the pattern***

Copy and complete the tables using the pattern you observed in Step 1.

Exponent, n	Power, 2^n
3	8
2	? **4**
1	? **2**
0	? **1**
−1	? $\frac{1}{2}$
−2	? $\frac{1}{4}$

Exponent, n	Power, 3^n
3	27
2	? **9**
1	? **3**
0	? **1**
−1	? $\frac{1}{3}$
−2	? $\frac{1}{9}$

DRAW CONCLUSIONS **Use your observations to complete these exercises**

1. Find 2^n and 3^n for $n = -3, -4,$ and -5. $2^{-3} = \frac{1}{8}, 3^{-3} = \frac{1}{27}; 2^{-4} = \frac{1}{16}, 3^{-4} = \frac{1}{81}; 2^{-5} = \frac{1}{32}, 3^{-5} = \frac{1}{243}$
2. What appears to be the value of a^0 for any nonzero number a? **1**
3. Write each power in the tables above as a power with a positive exponent. For example, you can write 3^{-1} as $\frac{1}{3^1}$. **See margin.**

3.

Power, 2^n	Exponent
8	2^3
4	2^2
2	2^1
1	2^0
$\frac{1}{2}$	$\frac{1}{2^1}$
$\frac{1}{4}$	$\frac{1}{2^2}$

Power, 3^n	Exponent
27	3^3
9	3^2
3	3^1
1	3^0
$\frac{1}{3}$	$\frac{1}{3^1}$
$\frac{1}{9}$	$\frac{1}{3^2}$

8.3 Define and Use Zero and Negative Exponents

Before You used properties of exponents to simplify expressions.

Now You will use zero and negative exponents.

Why? So you can compare masses, as in Ex. 52.

Key Vocabulary
- **reciprocal,** *p. 915*

In the activity, you saw what happens when you raise a number to a zero or negative exponent. The activity suggests the following definitions.

KEY CONCEPT *For Your Notebook*

Definition of Zero and Negative Exponents

Words	Algebra	Example
a to the zero power is 1.	$a^0 = 1, a \neq 0$	$5^0 = 1$
a^{-n} is the reciprocal of a^n.	$a^{-n} = \frac{1}{a^n}, a \neq 0$	$2^{-1} = \frac{1}{2}$
a^n is the reciprocal of a^{-n}.	$a^n = \frac{1}{a^{-n}}, a \neq 0$	$2 = \frac{1}{2^{-1}}$

EXAMPLE 1 Use definition of zero and negative exponents

SIMPLIFY EXPRESSIONS
In this lesson, when simplifying powers with numerical bases, evaluate the numerical power.

a. $3^{-2} = \frac{1}{3^2}$ **Definition of negative exponents**

$= \frac{1}{9}$ **Evaluate power.**

b. $(-7)^0 = 1$ **Definition of zero exponent**

c. $\left(\frac{1}{5}\right)^{-2} = \frac{1}{\left(\frac{1}{5}\right)^2}$ **Definition of negative exponents**

$= \frac{1}{\frac{1}{25}}$ **Evaluate power.**

$= 25$ **Simplify by multiplying numerator and denominator by 25.**

d. $0^{-5} = \frac{1}{0^5}$ (Undefined) **a^{-n} is defined only for a *nonzero* number a.**

✓ **GUIDED PRACTICE** for Example 1

Evaluate the expression.

1. $\left(\frac{2}{3}\right)^0$ **1**
2. $(-8)^{-2}$ $\frac{1}{64}$
3. $\frac{1}{2^{-3}}$ **8**
4. $(-1)^0$ **1**

1 PLAN AND PREPARE

Warm-Up Exercises

Transparency Available

1. Simplify $(-3x)^2$. $9x^2$
2. Simplify $\left(\frac{a^3}{2b}\right)^5$. $\frac{a^{15}}{32b^5}$
3. The order of magnitude of Earth's mass is about 10^{27} grams. The order of magnitude of the sun's mass is about 10^{33} grams. About how many times as great is the sun's mass as Earth's mass? **about 10^6**

Notetaking Guide

Transparency Available

Promotes interactive learning and notetaking skills.

Pacing

Basic: 1 day
Average: 1 day
Advanced: 1 day
Block: 0.5 block with 8.2
- See *Teaching Guide/Lesson Plan.*

2 FOCUS AND MOTIVATE

Essential Question

Big Idea 1, p. 487

How do you use zero and negative exponents? **Tell students they will learn how to answer this question by using properties of exponents to simplify and evaluate expressions.**

NCTM STANDARDS

Standard 1: Understand how operations are related

Standard 8: Use the language of math to express ideas

Resource Planning Guide

Chapter Resource Book
- Teaching Guide/Lesson Plan
- Practice levels A, B, C
- Study Guide
- Catch-up for Absent Students
- Problem Solving Workshop
- Challenge

Workbooks
- Notetaking Guide
- Practice Workbook

Teaching Options
- **Power Presentations** provides dynamic electronic teaching resources for the classroom.
- **Activity Generator** provides editable activities for all ability levels.

Interactive Technology
- Easy Planner
- Power Presentations
- Activity Generator
- Animated Algebra
- Test Generator
- Online Quiz
- eWorkbook
- eEdition
- @HomeTutor

Resources for English Learners
- Spanish Study Guide
- Multi-Language Visual Glossary
- Student Resources in Spanish

See also the *Differentiated Instruction Resources* for more strategies for meeting individual needs.

Motivating the Lesson

The mass of an amoeba is about 10^{-5} gram. The mass of a raindrop is about 1,000 times as great as the mass of an amoeba. By knowing how to evaluate numbers with negative exponents, you can determine the approximate mass of a raindrop.

3 TEACH

Extra Example 1

Use the definition of zero and negative exponents.

a. 6^{-2} **$\frac{1}{36}$**

b. x^0 **1**

c. $\left(\frac{2}{3}\right)^{-2}$ **$\frac{9}{4}$**

d. 0^{-7} **undefined**

Key Questions to Ask for Example 1

- Why is the expression in part d undefined? **Division by zero is not defined.**
- If the base of a power is positive and the exponent is negative, is the power always positive? Explain. **Yes; the reciprocal of a positive number is positive, and the power of a positive number is positive.**

Extra Example 2

Evaluate exponential expressions.

a. $(-2)^5 \cdot (-2)^{-5}$ **1**

b. $(3^3)^{-2}$ **$\frac{1}{729}$**

c. $\frac{1}{8^{-2}}$ **64**

d. $\frac{7^3}{7^5}$ **$\frac{1}{49}$**

Key Question to Ask for Example 2

- In part (c), why is $\frac{1}{3^{-4}}$ equal to 3^4? **3^4 is the reciprocal of 3^{-4}.**

PROPERTIES OF EXPONENTS The properties of exponents you learned in Lessons 8.1 and 8.2 can be used with negative or zero exponents.

KEY CONCEPT *For Your Notebook*

Properties of Exponents

Let a and b be real numbers, and let m and n be integers.

$a^m \cdot a^n = a^{m+n}$	**Product of powers property**
$(a^m)^n = a^{mn}$	**Power of a power property**
$(ab)^m = a^m b^m$	**Power of a product property**
$\frac{a^m}{a^n} = a^{m-n}, a \neq 0$	**Quotient of powers property**
$\left(\frac{a}{b}\right)^m = \frac{a^m}{b^m}, b \neq 0$	**Power of a quotient property**

EXAMPLE 2 Evaluate exponential expressions

a. $6^{-4} \cdot 6^4 = 6^{-4+4}$	**Product of powers property**
$= 6^0$	**Add exponents.**
$= 1$	**Definition of zero exponent**
b. $(4^{-2})^2 = 4^{-2 \cdot 2}$	**Power of a power property**
$= 4^{-4}$	**Multiply exponents.**
$= \frac{1}{4^4}$	**Definition of negative exponents**
$= \frac{1}{256}$	**Evaluate power.**
c. $\frac{1}{3^{-4}} = 3^4$	**Definition of negative exponents**
$= 81$	**Evaluate power.**
d. $\frac{5^{-1}}{5^2} = 5^{-1-2}$	**Quotient of powers property**
$= 5^{-3}$	**Subtract exponents.**
$= \frac{1}{5^3}$	**Definition of negative exponents**
$= \frac{1}{125}$	**Evaluate power.**

✓ **GUIDED PRACTICE** for Example 2

Evaluate the expression.

5. $\frac{1}{4^{-3}}$ **64** **6.** $(5^{-3})^{-1}$ **125** **7.** $(-3)^5 \cdot (-3)^{-5}$ **1** **8.** $\frac{6^{-2}}{6^2}$ **$\frac{1}{1296}$**

Differentiated Instruction

Visual Learners Some of these examples give students a way to visualize zero and negative exponents. In **Example 2a**, 6^0 is simplified from $6^{-4} \cdot 6^4$, which by the quotient of powers property is $\frac{6^4}{6^4}$, or 1. In **Example 2b**, 4^{-4} is 4^{0-4}, which by the quotient of powers property is $\frac{4^0}{4^4}$, or $\frac{1}{256}$.

See also the *Differentiated Instruction Resources* for more strategies.

EXAMPLE 3 Use properties of exponents

Simplify the expression. Write your answer using only positive exponents.

a. $(2xy^{-5})^3 = 2^3 \cdot x^3 \cdot (y^{-5})^3$ — **Power of a product property**

$= 8 \cdot x^3 \cdot y^{-15}$ — **Power of a power property**

$= \frac{8x^3}{y^{15}}$ — **Definition of negative exponents**

b. $\frac{(2x)^{-2}y^5}{-4x^2y^2} = \frac{y^5}{(2x)^2(-4x^2y^2)}$ — **Definition of negative exponents**

$= \frac{y^5}{(4x^2)(-4x^2y^2)}$ — **Power of a product property**

$= \frac{y^5}{-16x^4y^2}$ — **Product of powers property**

$= -\frac{y^3}{16x^4}$ — **Quotient of powers property**

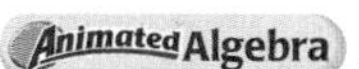 at classzone.com

EXAMPLE 4 Standardized Test Practice

The order of magnitude of the mass of a polyphemus moth larva when it hatches is 10^{-3} gram. During the first 56 days of its life, the moth larva can eat about 10^5 times its own mass in food. About how many grams of food can the moth larva eat during its first 56 days?

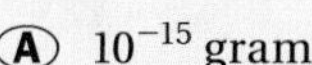

Ⓐ 10^{-15} gram Ⓑ 0.00000001 gram

Ⓒ 100 grams Ⓓ 10,000,000 grams

Not to scale

Solution

To find the amount of food the moth larva can eat in the first 56 days of its life, multiply its original mass, 10^{-3}, by 10^5.

$10^5 \cdot 10^{-3} = 10^{5+(-3)} = 10^2 = 100$

The moth larva can eat about 100 grams of food in the first 56 days of its life.

▶ The correct answer is C. Ⓐ Ⓑ Ⓒ Ⓓ

GUIDED PRACTICE for Examples 3 and 4

9. Simplify the expression $\frac{3xy^{-3}}{9x^3y}$. Write your answer using only positive exponents. $\frac{1}{3x^2y^4}$

10. **SCIENCE** The order of magnitude of the mass of a proton is 10^4 times greater than the order of magnitude of the mass of an electron, which is 10^{-27} gram. Find the order of magnitude of the mass of a proton. 10^{-23} g

Extra Example 3

Simplify the expression. Write your answer using only positive exponents.

a. $(3x^{-2}y^2)^3$ $\frac{27y^6}{x^6}$

b. $\frac{4x^{-2}y^4}{8xy^6}$ $\frac{1}{2x^3y^2}$

Key Question to Ask for Example 3

- In part a, why is the variable y in the denominator after simplifying the expression? **It has a negative exponent.**

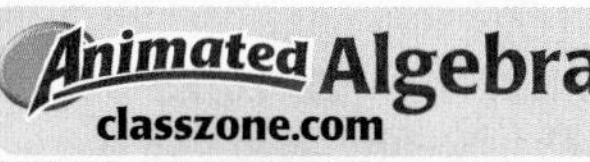

An **Animated Algebra** activity is available online for **Example 3**. This activity is also part of **Power Presentations**.

Extra Example 4

The order of magnitude of the radius of an atom is about 10^5 times as great as the order of magnitude of the radius of a proton, which is about 10^{-15} meter. What is the order of magnitude of the radius of an atom? **about 10^{-10} m**

Closing the Lesson

Have students summarize the major points of the lesson and answer the Essential Question: How do you use zero and negative exponents?

- **A nonzero number raised to the zero power is always 1.**
- **A power with a negative exponent is the reciprocal of the power with a positive exponent.**

To evaluate an expression, write powers with negative exponents as their reciprocals and powers with a zero exponent as 1. Use the properties of exponents to multiply and divide powers and to raise a power or a quotient to a power.

4 PRACTICE AND APPLY

Assignment Guide

Answer Transparencies available for all exercises

Basic:
Day 1: pp. 506–508
Exs. 1, 2, 3–35 odd, 50–55, 60–68 even

Average:
Day 1: pp. 506–508
Exs. 1, 2, 9–14, 21–27, 28–44 even, 45, 51–57, 60–68 even

Advanced:
Day 1: pp. 506–508
Exs. 1, 2, 11–14, 22–26, 29–43 odd, 44–49*, 52–58*, 59, 61, 68

Block:
pp. 506–508
Exs. 1, 2, 9–14, 21–27, 28–44 even, 45, 51–57, 60–68 even (with 8.2)

Differentiated Instruction

See *Differentiated Instruction Resources* for suggestions on addressing the needs of a diverse classroom.

Homework Check

For a quick check of student understanding of key concepts, go over the following exercises:

Basic: 5, 19, 25, 29, 51
Average: 10, 22, 26, 34, 52
Advanced: 12, 24, 33, 43, 53

Extra Practice

- Student Edition, p. 945
- Chapter Resource Book: Practice levels A, B, C

Practice Worksheet

An easily-readable reduced practice page (with answers) for this lesson can be found on p. 486C.

8.3 EXERCISES

HOMEWORK KEY
○ = **WORKED-OUT SOLUTIONS** on p. WS19 for Exs. 11 and 53
★ = **STANDARDIZED TEST PRACTICE** Exs. 2, 44, 45, 54, and 57
◆ = **MULTIPLE REPRESENTATIONS** Ex. 55

SKILL PRACTICE

A

1. **VOCABULARY** Which definitions or properties would you use to simplify the expression $3^5 \cdot 3^{-5}$? *Explain.* **Product of powers property and definition of zero exponent; the expression simplifies using the product of powers property to 3^0, which by definition equals 1**

2. ★ **WRITING** *Explain* why the expression 0^{-4} is undefined.
Sample answer: **The definition of negative exponents is defined only for nonzero bases.**

EXAMPLE 1 on p. 503 for Exs. 3–14

EVALUATING EXPRESSIONS **Evaluate the expression.**

3. 4^{-3} $\frac{1}{64}$
4. 7^{-3} $\frac{1}{343}$
5. $(-3)^{-1}$ $-\frac{1}{3}$
6. $(-2)^{-6}$ $\frac{1}{64}$
7. 2^0 1
8. $(-4)^0$ 1
9. $\left(\frac{3}{4}\right)^0$ 1
10. $\left(\frac{-9}{16}\right)^0$ 1
11. $\left(\frac{2}{7}\right)^{-2}$ $\frac{49}{4}$
12. $\left(\frac{4}{3}\right)^{-3}$ $\frac{27}{64}$
13. 0^{-3} undefined
14. 0^{-2} undefined

EXAMPLE 2 on p. 504 for Exs. 15–27

15. $2^{-2} \cdot 2^{-3}$ $\frac{1}{32}$
16. $7^{-6} \cdot 7^4$ $\frac{1}{49}$
17. $(2^{-1})^5$ $\frac{1}{32}$
18. $(3^{-2})^2$ $\frac{1}{81}$
19. $\frac{1}{3^{-3}}$ 27
20. $\frac{1}{6^{-2}}$ 36
21. $\frac{3^{-3}}{3^2}$ $\frac{1}{243}$
22. $\frac{6^{-3}}{6^{-5}}$ 36
23. $4\left(\frac{3}{2}\right)^{-1}$ $\frac{8}{3}$
24. $16\left(\frac{2^{-3}}{2^2}\right)$ $\frac{1}{2}$
25. $6^0 \cdot \left(\frac{1}{4^{-2}}\right)$ 16
26. $3^{-2} \cdot \left(\frac{5}{7^0}\right)$ $\frac{5}{9}$

27. **ERROR ANALYSIS** *Describe* and correct the error in evaluating the expression $-6 \cdot 3^0$.
3^0 is not equivalent to 0, but to 1; $-6 \cdot 3^0 = -6 \cdot 1 = -6$.

$-6 \cdot 3^0 = -6 \cdot 0$
$= 0$

EXAMPLE 3 B on p. 505 for Exs. 28–43

SIMPLIFYING EXPRESSIONS **Simplify the expression. Write your answer using only positive exponents.**

28. x^{-4} $\frac{1}{x^4}$
29. $2y^{-3}$ $\frac{2}{y^3}$
30. $(4g)^{-3}$ $\frac{1}{64g^3}$
31. $(-11h)^{-2}$ $\frac{1}{121h^2}$
32. x^2y^{-3} $\frac{x^2}{y^3}$
33. $5m^{-3}n^{-4}$ $\frac{5}{m^3n^4}$
34. $(6x^{-2}y^3)^{-3}$ $\frac{x^6}{216y^9}$
35. $(-15fg^2)^0$ 1
36. $\frac{r^{-2}}{s^{-4}}$ $\frac{s^4}{r^2}$
37. $\frac{x^{-5}}{y^2}$ $\frac{1}{x^5y^2}$
38. $\frac{1}{8x^{-2}y^{-6}}$ $\frac{x^2y^6}{8}$
39. $\frac{1}{15x^{10}y^{-8}}$ $\frac{y^8}{15x^{10}}$
40. $\frac{1}{(-2z)^{-2}}$ $4z^2$
41. $\frac{9}{(3d)^{-3}}$ $243d^3$
42. $\frac{(3x)^{-3}y^4}{-x^2y^{-6}}$ $-\frac{y^{10}}{27x^5}$
43. $\frac{12x^8y^{-7}}{(4x^{-2}y^{-6})^2}$ $\frac{3x^{12}y^5}{4}$

44. ★ **MULTIPLE CHOICE** Which expression simplifies to $2x^4$? **D**

Ⓐ $2x^{-4}$ Ⓑ $\frac{32}{(2x)^{-4}}$ Ⓒ $\frac{1}{2x^{-4}}$ Ⓓ $\frac{8}{4x^{-4}}$

45. ★ **MULTIPLE CHOICE** Which expression is equivalent to $(-4 \cdot 2^0 \cdot 3)^{-2}$? **D**

Ⓐ -12 Ⓑ $-\frac{1}{144}$ Ⓒ 0 Ⓓ $\frac{1}{144}$

46. Not true. *Sample answer:* $\frac{2^{-3}}{2^{-4}} = 2$

48. Not true. *Sample answer:* $2^{-1} + 2^{-1} = 1$

C **CHALLENGE In Exercises 46–48, tell whether the statement is true for all nonzero values of *a* and *b*. If it is not true, give a counterexample.**

46. $\frac{a^{-3}}{a^{-4}} = \frac{1}{a}$

47. $\frac{a^{-1}}{b^{-1}} = \frac{b}{a}$ **true**

48. $a^{-1} + b^{-1} = \frac{1}{a+b}$

49. **CHALLENGE** Compare the values of a^n and a^{-n} when $n < 0$, when $n = 0$, and when $n > 0$ for **(a)** $a > 1$ and **(b)** $0 < a < 1$. *Explain* your reasoning. **See margin.**

PROBLEM SOLVING

EXAMPLE 4 A on p. 505 for Exs. 50–54

50. **MASS** The mass of a grain of salt is about 10^{-4} gram. About how many grains of salt are in a box containing 100 grams of salt? **about 10^6 grains of salt**

@HomeTutor for problem solving help at classzone.com

51. **MASS** The mass of a grain of a certain type of rice is about 10^{-2} gram. About how many grains of rice are in a box containing 10^3 grams of rice? **about 10^5 grains of rice**

@HomeTutor for problem solving help at classzone.com

52. **BOTANY** The average mass of the fruit of the wolffia angusta plant is about 10^{-4} gram. The largest pumpkin ever recorded had a mass of about 10^4 kilograms. About how many times greater is the mass of the largest pumpkin than the mass of the fruit of the wolffia angusta plant? **about 10^{11} times greater**

53. **MEDICINE** A doctor collected about 10^{-2} liter of blood from a patient to run some tests. The doctor determined that a drop of the patient's blood, or about 10^{-6} liter, contained about 10^7 red blood cells. How many red blood cells did the entire sample contain? **about 10^{11} red blood cells**

54. ★ **SHORT RESPONSE** One of the smallest plant seeds comes from an orchid, and one of the largest plant seeds comes from a giant fan palm. A seed from an orchid has a mass of 10^{-9} gram and is 10^{13} times less massive than a seed from a giant fan palm. A student says that the seed from the giant fan palm has a mass of about 1 kilogram. Is the student correct? *Explain.* **No. *Sample answer:* The giant fan palm has a mass of about 10^4 grams or 10,000 grams, which equals 10 kilograms.**

Orchid

Giant fan palm

B 55. **MULTIPLE REPRESENTATIONS** Consider folding a piece of paper in half a number of times.

a. **Making a Table** Each time the paper is folded, record the number of folds and the fraction of the original area in a table like the one shown.

Number of folds	0	1	2	3
Fraction of original area	? 1	? $\frac{1}{2}$	? $\frac{1}{4}$	? $\frac{1}{8}$

b. **Writing an Expression** Write an exponential expression for the fraction of the original area of the paper using a base of $\frac{1}{2}$. **$\left(\frac{1}{2}\right)^x$ where x is the number of folds**

Avoiding Common Errors

Exercises 3–26, 28–43 Students often evaluate an expression with an exponent of zero as equal to 0. Remind these students that any nonzero expression with an exponent of 0 is equal to 1.

Exercises 28–43 Caution students to distinguish between a negative number or variable in the base of an expression and a negative exponent. Remind them that they take the reciprocal when the exponent in a power is negative, not when the base is negative.

Study Strategy

Exercises 28–43 Tell students that a variety of strategies and steps can be used to solve these problems and that the best strategy overall is to take their time in simplifying the expressions. Urge them to pay attention to the sign of the exponent, to expressions in parentheses, and to whether an exponent applies to a number or variable. Remind them that they can always expand factors if necessary.

Mathematical Reasoning

Exercises 50, 51 You may want to point out to students that they can determine a reasonable answer to these exercises by asking how many grains of salt are in 1 gram of salt and how many grains of rice are in 1 gram of rice. Suggest that they first write the mass of the grains of salt and rice using positive exponents, then determine how many grains are in a gram, and finally multiply by the number of respective grams in the boxes of salt and rice.

49a. For $a > 1$, when $n < 0$, $-n > 0$, so a^n is between 0 and 1, a^{-n} is greater than 1, and $a^n < a^{-n}$. When $n = 0$, $a^n = a^0 = 1$ and $a^{-n} = a^0 = 1$, so $a^n = a^{-n}$. When $n > 0$, $-n < 0$, so a^n is greater than 1, a^{-n} is between 0 and 1, and $a^n > a^{-n}$.
b. For $0 < a < 1$, when $n < 0$, $-n > 0$, so a^n is a whole number, a^{-n} is a fraction, and $a^n > a^{-n}$. When $n = 0$, $a^n = a^0 = 1$ and $a^{-n} = a^0 = 1$, so $a^n = a^{-n}$. When $n > 0$, $-n < 0$, so a^n is a fraction, a^{-n} is a whole number, and $a^n < a^{-n}$.

5 ASSESS AND RETEACH

Daily Homework Quiz

Transparency Available

1. Evaluate $\left(\frac{5}{2}\right)^{-3}$. $\frac{8}{125}$

2. Evaluate $4^{-7} \cdot 4^3$. $\frac{1}{256}$

3. Simplify $6a^{-4}b^0$. $\frac{6}{a^4}$

4. Simplify $\frac{8x^3y^{-4}}{12x^2y^{-3}}$. $\frac{2x}{3y}$

5. A human cell uses on average about 10^{-12} watt of power. The laser in a CD-R drive uses about 10^9 times as many watts. About how many watts of power does the laser in a CD-R drive use? **about 10^{-3}**

Available at **classzone.com**

Diagnosis/Remediation

- Practice A, B, C in Chapter Resource Book
- Study Guide in Chapter Resource Book
- Practice Workbook
- @HomeTutor

Challenge

Additional challenge is available in the Chapter Resource Book.

56. **SCIENCE** Diffusion is the movement of molecules from one location to another. The time t (in seconds) it takes molecules to diffuse a distance of x centimeters is given by $t = \frac{x^2}{2D}$ where D is the diffusion coefficient.

 a. You can examine a cross section of a drop of ink in water to see how the ink diffuses. The diffusion coefficient for the molecules in the drop of ink is about 10^{-5} square centimeter per second. How long will it take the ink to diffuse 1 micrometer (10^{-4} centimeter)? **0.0005 sec**

 b. Check your answer to part (a) using unit analysis. $\frac{(\text{cm})^2}{\frac{\text{cm}^2}{\text{sec}}} = \text{cm}^2 \cdot \frac{\text{sec}}{\text{cm}^2} = \text{sec}$

57. ★ **EXTENDED RESPONSE** The intensity of sound I (in watts per square meter) can be modeled by $I = 0.08Pd^{-2}$ where P is the power (in watts) of the sound's source and d is the distance (in meters) that you are from the source of the sound.

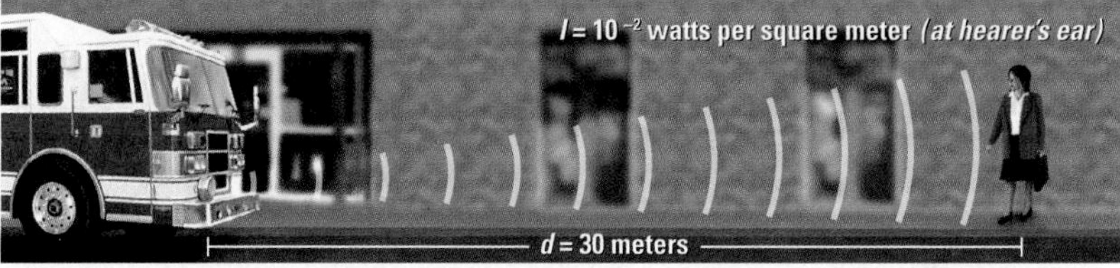

Not to scale

 a. What is the power (in watts) of the siren of the firetruck shown in the diagram? **112.5 watts**

 b. Using the power of the siren you found in part (a), simplify the formula for the intensity of sound from the siren. $I = 9d^{-2}$

 c. *Explain* what happens to the intensity of the siren when you double your distance from it. **The intensity is divided by 4.**

C 58. **CHALLENGE** Coal can be burned to generate energy. The heat energy in 1 pound of coal is about 10^4 BTU (British Thermal Units). Suppose you have a stereo. It takes about 10 pounds of coal to create the energy needed to power the stereo for 1 year.

 a. About how many BTUs does your stereo use in 1 year? **10^5 BTUs**

 b. Suppose the power plant that delivers energy to your home produces 10^{-1} pound of sulfur dioxide for each 10^6 BTU of energy that it creates. How much sulfur dioxide is added to the air by generating the energy needed to power your stereo for 1 year? **0.01 lb**

MIXED REVIEW

PREVIEW
Prepare for Lesson 8.4 in Exs. 59–62.

Evaluate the expression.

59. $10^3 \cdot 10^3$ *(p. 489)* **1,000,000**

60. $10^2 \cdot 10^5$ *(p. 489)* **10,000,000**

61. $\frac{10^9}{10^7}$ *(p. 495)* **100**

62. $\frac{10^6}{10^3}$ *(p. 495)* **1000**

Solve the linear system. Then check your answer. *(pp. 427, 435, 444, 451)*

63. $y = 3x - 6$, $y = -7x - 1$ $\left(\frac{1}{2}, -4\frac{1}{2}\right)$

64. $y = -2x + 12$, $y = -5x + 24$ **(4, 4)**

65. $5x + y = 40$, $-x + y = -8$ **(8, 0)**

66. $-x - 2y = -6.5$, $3x - 6y = 16.5$ $\left(6, \frac{1}{4}\right)$

67. $3x + 4y = -5$, $x - 2y = 5$ **(1, −2)**

68. $2x + 6y = 5$, $-2x - 3y = 2$ $\left(-4\frac{1}{2}, 2\frac{1}{3}\right)$

Use after Lesson 8.3

Define and Use Fractional Exponents

GOAL Use fractional exponents.

Key Vocabulary
- cube root

In Lesson 2.7, you learned to write the square root of a number using a radical sign. You can also write a square root of a number using exponents.

For any $a \geq 0$, suppose you want to write $\sqrt{a}$ as a^k. Recall that a number b (in this case, a^k) is a square root of a number a provided $b^2 = a$. Use this definition to find a value for k as follows.

$b^2 = a$ **Definition of square root**

$(a^k)^2 = a$ **Substitute a^k for b.**

$a^{2k} = a^1$ **Power of a power property**

Because the bases are the same in the equation $a^{2k} = a^1$, the exponents must be equal:

$2k = 1$ **Set exponents equal.**

$k = \frac{1}{2}$ **Solve for k.**

So, for a nonnegative number a, $\sqrt{a} = a^{1/2}$.

You can work with exponents of $\frac{1}{2}$ and multiples of $\frac{1}{2}$ just as you work with integer exponents.

EXAMPLE 1 Evaluate expressions involving square roots

a. $16^{1/2} = \sqrt{16}$
$= 4$

b. $25^{-1/2} = \frac{1}{25^{1/2}}$
$= \frac{1}{\sqrt{25}}$
$= \frac{1}{5}$

c. $9^{5/2} = 9^{(1/2) \cdot 5}$
$= (9^{1/2})^5$
$= (\sqrt{9})^5$
$= 3^5$
$= 243$

d. $4^{-3/2} = 4^{(1/2) \cdot (-3)}$
$= (4^{1/2})^{-3}$
$= (\sqrt{4})^{-3}$
$= 2^{-3}$
$= \frac{1}{2^3}$
$= \frac{1}{8}$

FRACTIONAL EXPONENTS You can work with other fractional exponents just as you did with $\frac{1}{2}$.

1 PLAN AND PREPARE

Warm-Up Exercises

Evaluate the expression.

1. $\sqrt{49}$ **7**
2. $\sqrt{121}$ **11**
3. 2^{-5} **$\frac{1}{32}$**
4. 13^2 **169**

2 FOCUS AND MOTIVATE

Essential Question

Big Idea 1, p. 487

How do you evaluate expressions with fractional exponents? **Tell students they will learn how to answer this question by writing expressions as square roots and cube roots and evaluating them using the properties of exponents.**

3 TEACH

Extra Example 1

Evaluate the expression.

a. $49^{1/2}$ **7**
b. $36^{-1/2}$ **$\frac{1}{6}$**
c. $25^{3/2}$ **125**
d. $4^{-7/2}$ **$\frac{1}{128}$**

Key Questions to Ask for Example 1

- Which part of the fractional exponent is the same for all parts of the example? **denominator**
- Which part of the exponent determines the power to which the base is raised? **numerator**

NCTM STANDARDS

Standard 1: Understand meanings of operations

Standard 9: Understand how mathematical ideas build on one another

Extra Example 2

Evaluate the expression.

a. $216^{1/3}$ **6** b. $64^{-1/3}$ $\frac{1}{4}$

c. $27^{2/3}$ **9** d. $8^{-5/3}$ $\frac{1}{32}$

Key Questions to Ask for Example 2

- How is Example 2 different from Example 1? **The denominators are 3 instead of 2 in Example 2.**
- What does the denominator 3 tell you? **take the cube root**

Extra Example 3

Use properties of exponents.

a. $8^{1/2} \cdot 8^{-5/2}$ $\frac{1}{64}$

b. $\frac{(3^{5/3} \cdot 3^0)}{3^{2/3}}$ **3**

Closing the Lesson

Have students summarize the major points of the lesson and answer the Essential Question: How do you evaluate expressions with fractional exponents?

- **The square root of *a* can be written as $a^{1/2}$, and the cube root of *a* can be written as $a^{1/3}$.**

If an exponent in an expression is $\frac{1}{2}$, take the square root of the base. If an exponent is $\frac{1}{3}$, take the cube root of the base. If the exponent is negative, take the reciprocal. If the exponent is a multiple of $\frac{1}{2}$ or $\frac{1}{3}$, use $\frac{1}{2}$ for the square root, $\frac{1}{3}$ for the cube root, and the other factor as the power. All the properties of integral exponents apply to fractional exponents.

4 PRACTICE AND APPLY

Avoiding Common Errors

Exercises 1–12 Watch for students who multiply the exponent by the base. Remind students that the denominator of the exponent tells them what root to take and the numerator what power to use.

CUBE ROOTS If $b^3 = a$, then b is the **cube root** of a. For example, $2^3 = 8$, so 2 is the cube root of 8. The cube root of a can be written as $\sqrt[3]{a}$ or $a^{1/3}$.

EXAMPLE 2 Evaluate expressions involving cube roots

a. $27^{1/3} = \sqrt[3]{27} = \sqrt[3]{3^3} = 3$

b. $8^{-1/3} = \frac{1}{8^{1/3}} = \frac{1}{\sqrt[3]{8}} = \frac{1}{2}$

c. $64^{4/3} = 64^{(1/3) \cdot 4} = (64^{1/3})^4 = (\sqrt[3]{64})^4 = 4^4 = 256$

d. $125^{-2/3} = 125^{(1/3) \cdot (-2)} = (125^{1/3})^{-2} = (\sqrt[3]{125})^{-2} = 5^{-2} = \frac{1}{5^2} = \frac{1}{25}$

PROPERTIES OF EXPONENTS The properties of exponents for integer exponents also apply to fractional exponents.

EXAMPLE 3 Use properties of exponents

a. $12^{-1/2} \cdot 12^{5/2} = 12^{(-1/2)+(5/2)} = 12^{4/2} = 12^2 = 144$

b. $\frac{6^{4/3} \cdot 6}{6^{1/3}} = \frac{6^{(4/3)+1}}{6^{1/3}} = \frac{6^{7/3}}{6^{1/3}} = 6^{(7/3)-(1/3)} = 6^2 = 36$

PRACTICE

EXAMPLES 1, 2, and 3 on pp. 509–510 for Exs. 1–12

Evaluate the expression.

1. $100^{3/2}$ **1000**
2. $121^{-1/2}$ $\frac{1}{11}$
3. $81^{-3/2}$ $\frac{1}{729}$
4. $216^{2/3}$ **36**
5. $27^{-1/3}$ $\frac{1}{3}$
6. $343^{-2/3}$ $\frac{1}{49}$
7. $9^{7/2} \cdot 9^{-3/2}$ **81**
8. $\left(\frac{1}{16}\right)^{1/2}\left(\frac{1}{16}\right)^{-1/2}$ **1**
9. $36^{5/2} \cdot \frac{36^{-1/2}}{(36^{-1})^{-7/2}}$ $\frac{1}{216}$
10. $(27^{-1/3})^3$ $\frac{1}{27}$
11. $(-64)^{-5/3}(-64)^{4/3}$ $-\frac{1}{4}$
12. $(-8)^{1/3}(-8)^{-2/3}(-8)^{1/3}$ **1**
13. **REASONING** Let $x > 0$. Compare the values of $x^{1/2}$ and $x^{-1/2}$. Give examples to support your thinking. **See margin.**

13. For $0 < x < 1$, $x^{1/2} < x^{-1/2}$; for $x = 1$, $x^{1/2} = x^{-1/2}$; for $x > 1$, $x^{1/2} > x^{-1/2}$.

Samples: $\left(\frac{1}{4}\right)^{1/2} = \frac{1}{2}$ **and** $\left(\frac{1}{4}\right)^{-1/2} = 2$; $4^{1/2} = 2$ **and** $4^{-1/2} = \frac{1}{2}$.

MIXED REVIEW *of Problem Solving*

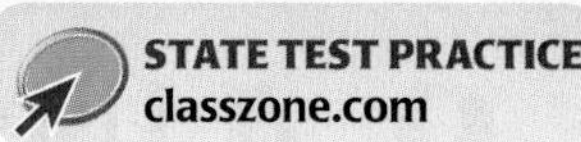

Lessons 8.1–8.3

1. **GRIDDED ANSWER** In 2004 the fastest computers could record about 10^9 bits per second. (A bit is the smallest unit of memory storage for computers.) Scientists believed that the speed limit at the time was about 10^{12} bits per second. About how many times more bits per second was the speed limit than the fastest computers? **1000 times**

2. **MULTI-STEP PROBLEM** An office supply store sells cubical containers that can be used to store paper clips, rubber bands, or other supplies.
   a. One of the containers has a side length of $4\frac{1}{2}$ inches. Find the container's volume by writing the side length as an improper fraction and substituting the length into the formula for the volume of a cube. **$\frac{729}{8}$ in.^{3}**
   b. Identify the property of exponents you used to find the volume in part (a). **Power of a quotient property**

3. **SHORT RESPONSE** Clouds contain millions of tiny spherical water droplets. The radius of one droplet is shown.

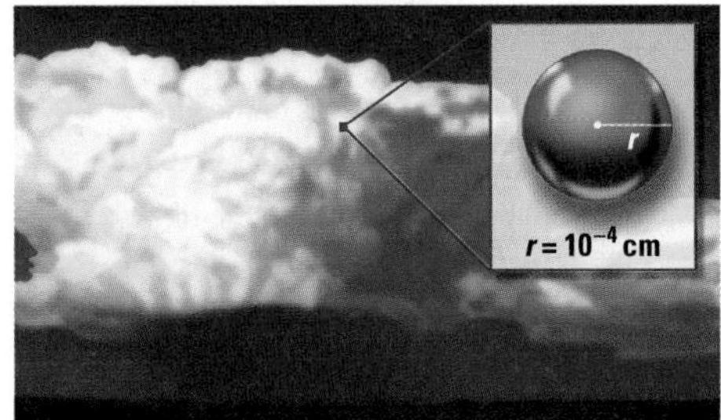

   a. Find the order of magnitude of the volume of the droplet. **10^{-12}**
   b. Droplets combine to form raindrops. The radius of a raindrop is about 10^2 times greater than the droplet's radius. Find the order of magnitude of the volume of the raindrop. **10^{-6}**
   c. *Explain* how you can find the number of droplets that combine to form the raindrop. Then find the number of droplets and identify any properties of exponents you used. **See margin.**

4. **GRIDDED ANSWER** The least intense sound that is audible to the human ear has an intensity of about 10^{-12} watt per square meter. The intensity of sound from a jet engine at a distance of 30 meters is about 10^{15} times greater than the least intense sound. Find the intensity of sound from the jet engine. **1000 watts per square meter**

5. **EXTENDED RESPONSE** For an experiment, a scientist dropped a spoonful, or about 10^{-1} cubic inch, of biodegradable olive oil into a pond to see how the oil would spread out over the surface of the pond. The scientist found that the oil spread until it covered an area of about 10^5 square inches.
   a. About how thick was the layer of oil that spread out across the pond? Check your answer using unit analysis. **10^{-6} in.**
   b. The pond has a surface area of 10^7 square inches. If the oil spreads to the same thickness as in part (a), how many cubic inches of olive oil would be needed to cover the entire surface of the pond? **10 in.^{3}**
   c. *Explain* how you could find the amount of oil needed to cover a pond with a surface area of 10^x square inches. **See margin.**

6. **OPEN-ENDED** The table shows units of measurement of time and the durations of the units in seconds.

Name of unit	Duration (seconds)
Gigasecond	10^9
Megasecond	10^6
Millisecond	10^{-3}
Nanosecond	10^{-9}

   a. Use the table to write a conversion problem that can be solved by applying a property of exponents involving products. **See margin.**
   b. Use the table to write a conversion problem that can be solved by applying a property of exponents involving quotients. ***Sample answer:* How many megaseconds are in 1 gigasecond?**

3c. ***Sample answer:*** **Divide the order of magnitude of the volume of the raindrop by the order of magnitude of the volume of the droplet; 10^2 droplets, Quotient of a power property.**

5c. ***Sample answer:*** **Multiply the surface area 10^x square inches by the thickness of the oil 10^{-6} inch to calculate the volume of oil in cubic inches needed. $10^x \cdot 10^{-6} = 10^{x-6}$ in.^{3}**

6a. ***Sample answer:*** **How many milliseconds are in a gigasecond?**

8.4 Use Scientific Notation

Before	You used properties of exponents.
Now	You will read and write numbers in scientific notation.
Why?	So you can compare lengths of insects, as in Ex. 51.

Key Vocabulary
- scientific notation

Numbers such as 1,000,000, 153,000, and 0.0009 are written in *standard form*. Another way to write a number is to use *scientific notation*.

KEY CONCEPT *For Your Notebook*

Scientific Notation

A number is written in **scientific notation** when it is of the form $c \times 10^n$ where $1 \le c < 10$ and n is an integer.

Number	Standard form	Scientific notation
Two million	2,000,000	2×10^6
Five thousandths	0.005	5×10^{-3}

EXAMPLE 1 Write numbers in scientific notation

a. $42{,}590{,}000 = 4.259 \times 10^7$ — **Move decimal point 7 places to the left. Exponent is 7.**

b. $0.0000574 = 5.74 \times 10^{-5}$ — **Move decimal point 5 places to the right. Exponent is −5.**

EXAMPLE 2 Write numbers in standard form

READING
A positive number in scientific notation is greater than 1 if the exponent is positive. A positive number in scientific notation is between 0 and 1 if the exponent is negative.

a. $2.0075 \times 10^6 = 2{,}007{,}500$ — **Exponent is 6. Move decimal point 6 places to the right.**

b. $1.685 \times 10^{-4} = 0.0001685$ — **Exponent is −4. Move decimal point 4 places to the left.**

 at classzone.com

✓ **GUIDED PRACTICE** for Examples 1 and 2

1. Write the number 539,000 in scientific notation. Then write the number 4.5×10^{-4} in standard form. **5.39×10^5; 0.00045**

1 PLAN AND PREPARE

Warm-Up Exercises

 **Transparency Available**

1. Order the numbers 0.014, 0.1, 0.01 from least to greatest. **0.01, 0.014, 0.1**
2. Find the ratio of the mass of the Milky Way galaxy, which is about 10^{44} grams, to the mass of the universe, which is about 10^{55} grams. **about $\frac{1}{10^{11}}$**

Notetaking Guide

Transparency Available

Promotes interactive learning and notetaking skills.

Pacing

Basic: 2 days
Average: 2 days
Advanced: 2 days
Block: 1 block
- See *Teaching Guide/Lesson Plan.*

2 FOCUS AND MOTIVATE

Essential Question

Big Idea 2, p. 487

How do you write a number in scientific notation? **Tell students they will learn how to answer this question by rewriting a number as the product of a number from 1 up to 10 and a power of 10.**

NCTM STANDARDS

Standard 1: Compute fluently
Standard 2: Analyze situations using algebraic symbols

Resource Planning Guide

Chapter Resource Book
- Teaching Guide/Lesson Plan
- Activity Master
- Practice levels A, B, C
- Study Guide
- Catch-up for Absent Students
- Application
- Challenge

Workbooks
- Notetaking Guide
- Practice Workbook

Teaching Options
- **Power Presentations** provides dynamic electronic teaching resources for the classroom.
- **Activity Generator** provides editable activities for all ability levels.

Interactive Technology
- Easy Planner
- Power Presentations
- Activity Generator
- Animated Algebra
- Test Generator
- Online Quiz
- eWorkbook
- eEdition
- @HomeTutor

Resources for English Learners
- Spanish Study Guide
- Multi-Language Visual Glossary
- Student Resources in Spanish

See also the *Differentiated Instruction Resources* for more strategies for meeting individual needs.

EXAMPLE 3 Order numbers in scientific notation

Order 103,400,000, 7.8×10^8, and 80,760,000 from least to greatest.

Solution

STEP 1 **Write** each number in scientific notation, if necessary.
$103{,}400{,}000 = 1.034 \times 10^8$ $\quad 80{,}760{,}000 = 8.076 \times 10^7$

STEP 2 **Order** the numbers. First order the numbers with different powers of 10. Then order the numbers with the same power of 10.

Because $\mathbf{10^7} < \mathbf{10^8}$, you know that $8.076 \times \mathbf{10^7}$ is less than both $1.034 \times \mathbf{10^8}$ and $7.8 \times \mathbf{10^8}$. Because $\mathbf{1.034} < \mathbf{7.8}$, you know that $\mathbf{1.034} \times 10^8$ is less than $\mathbf{7.8} \times 10^8$.

So, $8.076 \times 10^7 < 1.034 \times 10^8 < 7.8 \times 10^8$.

STEP 3 **Write** the original numbers in order from least to greatest.
80,760,000; 103,400,000; 7.8×10^8

EXAMPLE 4 Compute with numbers in scientific notation

Evaluate the expression. Write your answer in scientific notation.

a. $(8.5 \times 10^2)(1.7 \times 10^6)$

$= (8.5 \cdot 1.7) \times (10^2 \cdot 10^6)$ — Commutative property and associative property

$= 14.45 \times 10^8$ — Product of powers property

$= (1.445 \times 10^1) \times 10^8$ — Write 14.45 in scientific notation.

$= 1.445 \times (10^1 \times 10^8)$ — Associative property

$= 1.445 \times 10^9$ — Product of powers property

b. $(1.5 \times 10^{-3})^2 = 1.5^2 \times (10^{-3})^2$ — Power of a product property

$= 2.25 \times 10^{-6}$ — Power of a power property

c. $\dfrac{1.2 \times 10^4}{1.6 \times 10^{-3}} = \dfrac{1.2}{1.6} \times \dfrac{10^4}{10^{-3}}$ — Product rule for fractions

$= 0.75 \times 10^7$ — Quotient of powers property

$= (7.5 \times 10^{-1}) \times 10^7$ — Write 0.75 in scientific notation.

$= 7.5 \times (10^{-1} \times 10^7)$ — Associative property

$= 7.5 \times 10^6$ — Product of powers property

AVOID ERRORS
Notice that 14.45×10^8 is *not* written in scientific notation because $14.45 > 10$.

REVIEW FRACTIONS
For help with fractions, see p. 915.

GUIDED PRACTICE for Examples 3 and 4

2. Order 2.7×10^5, 3.401×10^4, and 27,500 from least to greatest. **27,500; 3.401×10^4; 2.7×10^5**

Evaluate the expression. Write your answer in scientific notation.

3. $(1.3 \times 10^{-5})^2$ **1.69×10^{-10}**
4. $\dfrac{4.5 \times 10^5}{1.5 \times 10^{-2}}$ **3×10^7**
5. $(1.1 \times 10^7)(4.2 \times 10^2)$ **4.62×10^9**

Motivating the Lesson

Knowing how to write numbers in scientific notation allows you to better manage extremely large or small numbers with lots of zeros. For example, the number of electrons that pass through a 1-amp circuit every second is 625 followed by 16 zeros. It is easier to write the number in scientific notation in order to determine how many electrons pass through the circuit in 60 seconds.

3 TEACH

Extra Example 1

Write in scientific notation.
a. 267,500,000 **2.675×10^8**
b. 0.000486 **4.86×10^{-4}**

Key Question to Ask for Example 1

- How do you know if the exponent of 10 is positive or negative? **If the original number is greater than 1, the exponent is positive. If the original number is between 0 and 1, the exponent is negative.**

Extra Example 2

Write in standard form.
a. 7.0234×10^5 **702,340**
b. 3.096×10^{-6} **0.000003096**

An **Animated Algebra** activity is available online for **Example 2**. This activity is also part of **Power Presentations**.

Extra Example 3

Order 93,000,000, 9.2×10^6, and 9,028,000 from least to greatest. **9,028,000, 9.2×10^6, 93,000,000**

Extra Example 4

Evaluate the expression. Write your answer in scientific notation.

a. $(5.7 \times 10^3)(2.6 \times 10^4)$ **1.482×10^8**

b. $(2.4 \times 10^{-4})^2$ **5.76×10^{-8}**

c. $\frac{2.4 \times 10^5}{2.5 \times 10^{-4}}$ **9.6×10^8**

Extra Example 5

The radius of a red blood cell is about 4.5×10^{-6} meter. The radius of *Mycoplasma* bacteria is about 1.25×10^{-8} meter.

a. Find the ratio of the radius of a red blood cell to the radius of *Mycoplasma* bacteria. What does the ratio tell you? **360; the radius of the red blood cell is about 360 times that of the *Mycoplasma* bacteria.**

b. Find the ratio of the volumes of the red blood cell and the *Mycoplasma* bacteria. What does the ratio tell you? **46,656,000; the volume of the red blood cell is about 46,656,000 times that of the *Mycoplasma* bacteria.**

Closing the Lesson

Have students summarize the major points of the lesson and answer the Essential Question: How do you write numbers in scientific notation?

- **A number written in scientific notation is in the form $c \times 10^n$, where $1 \le c < 10$ and n is an integer.**

Write a positive number as the product of a decimal from 1 up to 10 and a power of 10. If the original number is greater than 1, the power of 10 has a positive exponent. If the number is between 0 and 1, the exponent is negative.

EXAMPLE 5 Solve a multi-step problem

BLOOD VESSELS Blood flow is partially controlled by the cross-sectional area of the blood vessel through which the blood is traveling. Three types of blood vessels are venules, capillaries, and arterioles.

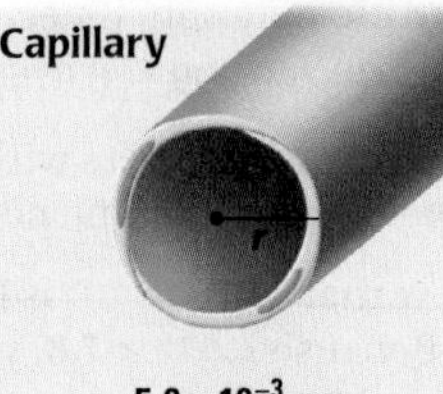

Venule

$r = 1.0 \times 10^{-2}$ mm

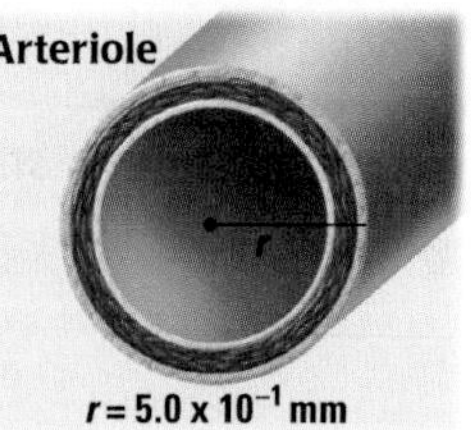

a. Let r_1 be the radius of a venule, and let r_2 be the radius of a capillary. Find the ratio of r_1 to r_2. What does the ratio tell you?

b. Let A_1 be the cross-sectional area of a venule, and let A_2 be the cross-sectional area of a capillary. Find the ratio of A_1 to A_2. What does the ratio tell you?

c. What is the relationship between the ratio of the radii of the blood vessels and the ratio of their cross-sectional areas?

Solution

a. From the diagram, you can see that the radius of the venule r_1 is 1.0×10^{-2} millimeter and the radius of the capillary r_2 is 5.0×10^{-3} millimeter.

$$\frac{r_1}{r_2} = \frac{1.0 \times 10^{-2}}{5.0 \times 10^{-3}} = \frac{1.0}{5.0} \times \frac{10^{-2}}{10^{-3}} = 0.2 \times 10^1 = 2$$

The ratio tells you that the radius of the venule is twice the radius of the capillary.

ANOTHER WAY
You can also find the ratio of the cross-sectional areas by finding the areas using the values for r_1 and r_2, setting up a ratio, and then simplifying.

b. To find the cross-sectional areas, use the formula for the area of a circle.

$$\frac{A_1}{A_2} = \frac{\pi r_1^2}{\pi r_2^2}$$ **Write ratio.**

$$= \frac{r_1^2}{r_2^2}$$ **Divide numerator and denominator by π.**

$$= \left(\frac{r_1}{r_2}\right)^2$$ **Power of a quotient property**

$$= 2^2 = 4$$ **Substitute and simplify.**

The ratio tells you that the cross-sectional area of the venule is four times the cross-sectional area of the capillary.

c. The ratio of the cross-sectional areas of the blood vessels is the square of the ratio of the radii of the blood vessels.

 **GUIDED PRACTICE** for Example 5

6. WHAT IF? *Compare* the radius and cross-sectional area of an arteriole with the radius and cross-sectional area of a capillary.

6. The radius of an arteriole is 10^2 times greater than the radius of a capillary. The cross-sectional area of an arteriole is 10^4 times greater than the cross-sectional area of a capillary.

Differentiated Instruction

Below Level Some students may need extra practice writing numbers in scientific and standard notation. Have students search the Internet for very large and very small numbers. For example, they can search for astronomical data for large numbers and cellular biology data for small numbers. Suggest that they exchange numbers with partners for more practice.

See also the *Differentiated Instruction Resources* for more strategies.

8.4 EXERCISES

HOMEWORK KEY
○ = **WORKED-OUT SOLUTIONS** on p. WS19 for Exs. 3, 17, and 53
★ = **STANDARDIZED TEST PRACTICE** Exs. 2, 15, 48, 49, 54, and 59
◆ = **MULTIPLE REPRESENTATIONS** Ex. 58

SKILL PRACTICE

A

1. **VOCABULARY** Is 0.5×10^6 written in scientific notation? *Explain.*
No; 0.5 is not a number greater than or equal to 1.0 and less than 10.
2. ★ **WRITING** Is 7.89×10^6 between 0 and 1 or greater than 1? *Explain.*
Greater than 1; the exponent is positive.

EXAMPLE 1 on p. 512 for Exs. 3–15

WRITING IN SCIENTIFIC NOTATION **Write the number in scientific notation.**

3. 8.5 **8.5×10^0**
4. 0.72 **7.2×10^{-1}**
5. 82.4 **8.24×10^1**
6. 0.005 **5×10^{-3}**
7. 72,000,000 **7.2×10^7**
8. 0.00406 **4.06×10^{-3}**
9. 1,065,250 **1.06525×10^6**
10. 0.000045 **4.5×10^{-5}**
11. 1,060,000,000 **1.06×10^9**
12. 0.00000526 **5.26×10^{-6}**
13. 900,000,000,000,000 **9×10^{14}**
14. 0.00000007008 **7.008×10^{-8}**
15. ★ **MULTIPLE CHOICE** Which number represents 54,004,000,000 written in scientific notation? **C**

Ⓐ 54004×10^6 Ⓑ 54.004×10^9
Ⓒ 5.4004×10^{10} Ⓓ 0.54004×10^{11}

EXAMPLE 2 on p. 512 for Exs. 16–28

WRITING IN STANDARD FORM **Write the number in standard form.**

16. 2.6×10^3 **2600**
17. 7.5×10^7 **75,000,000**
18. 1.11×10^2 **111**
19. 3.03×10^4 **30,300**
20. 4.709×10^6 **4,709,000**
21. 1.544×10^{10} **15,440,000,000**
22. 6.1×10^{-3} **0.0061**
23. 4.4×10^{-10} **0.00000000044**
24. 2.23×10^{-6} **0.00000223**
25. 8.52×10^{-8} **0.0000000852**
26. 6.4111×10^{-10} **0.00000000064111**
27. 1.2034×10^{-6} **0.0000012034**
28. **ERROR ANALYSIS** *Describe* and correct the error in writing 1.24×10^{-3} in standard form.
The decimal point should be moved to the left, not the right; $1.24 \times 10^{-3} = 0.00124$.

$1.24 \times 10^{-3} = 1240$ 

EXAMPLE 3 on p. 513 for Exs. 29–32

B

ORDERING NUMBERS **Order the numbers from least to greatest.**

29. 45,000; 6.7×10^3; 12,439; 2×10^4 **6.7×10^3; 12,439; 2×10^4; 45,000**
30. 65,000,000; 6.2×10^6; 3.557×10^7; 55,004,000; 6.07×10^6
31. 0.0005; 9.8×10^{-6}; 5×10^{-3}; 0.00008; 0.04065; 8.2×10^{-3}
32. **GRAPHING** Draw a number line labeled with negative powers of 10. Then graph the numbers 0.00008, 5.1×10^{-6}, and 2.4×10^{-5}, and tell which number is greatest. **See margin.**

30. 6.07×10^6; 6.2×10^6; 3.557×10^7; 55,004,000; 65,000,000

31. 9.8×10^{-6}; 0.00008; 0.0005; 5×10^{-3}; 8.2×10^{-3}; 0.04065

COMPARING NUMBERS **Copy and complete the statement using <, >, or =.**

33. 5.6×10^3 __?__ 56,000 **<**
34. 404,000.1 __?__ 4.04001×10^5 **<**
35. 9.86×10^{-3} __?__ 0.00986 **=**
36. 0.003309 __?__ 3.309×10^{-3} **=**
37. 2.203×10^{-4} __?__ 0.0000203 **>**
38. 604,589,000 __?__ 6.04589×10^7 **>**

4 PRACTICE AND APPLY

Assignment Guide

Answer Transparencies available for all exercises

Basic:
Day 1: EP p. 939 Exs. 32–37
pp. 514–518
Exs. 1–28
Day 2: pp. 514–518
Exs. 29–36, 39–41, 51–56, 61–74

Average:
Day 1: pp. 514–518
Exs. 1, 2, 6–15, 19–28, 39–44
Day 2: pp. 514–518
Exs. 29–38, 45–49, 51–59, 62–74 even

Advanced:
Day 1: pp. 514–518
Exs. 1, 2, 8–15, 21–27, 39–47
Day 2: pp. 514–518
Exs. 29–38, 48–60*, 64, 67, 68, 71

Block:
pp. 514–518
Exs. 1, 2, 6–15, 19–49, 51–59, 62–74 even

Differentiated Instruction

See *Differentiated Instruction Resources* for suggestions on addressing the needs of a diverse classroom.

Homework Check

For a quick check of student understanding of key concepts, go over the following exercises:
Basic: 8, 20, 29, 53, 54
Average: 10, 24, 42, 51, 55
Advanced: 12, 26, 45, 52, 55

Extra Practice

- Student Edition, p. 945
- Chapter Resource Book: Practice levels A, B, C

Practice Worksheet

An easily-readable reduced practice page (with answers) for this lesson can be found on p. 486C.

Differentiated Instruction

Kinesthetic Learners In mathematics, a left-shift is associated with negative numbers, and a right-shift is associated with positive numbers. Another way to complete **Exercises 3–14** is as follows. To write 93,000,000 in scientific notation, place the decimal point to the right of 9 and count 7 places right to the last 0 to get 9.3×10^7. Similarly, place the decimal point to the right of 1 in 0.0017 and count 3 places to the left to the original position of the decimal point to get 1.7×10^{-3}.

See also the *Differentiated Instruction Resources* for more strategies.

32. 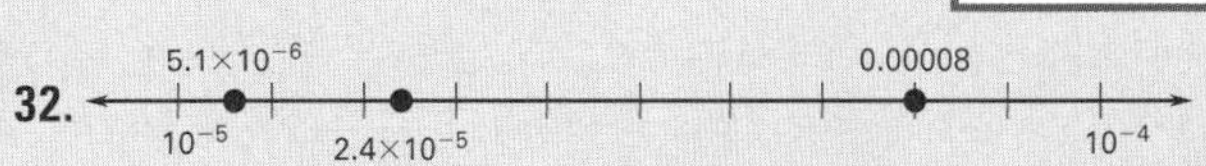

The greatest number is 0.00008.

Avoiding Common Errors

Exercises 3–15 Some students may write scientific notation with two or more digits to the left of the decimal point. Remind them that the decimal must be less than 10 but greater than or equal to 1. Suggest that students check their answers by expanding the scientific notation to make sure they have written the numbers correctly.

Exercises 16–28 Caution students that they need to move the decimal to the right for numbers with positive exponents and to the left for numbers with negative exponents when writing numbers in standard form.

Internet Reference

Exercise 52 For more information about the *Voyager 1* and *Voyager 2* spacecrafts, visit NASA's website voyager.jpl.nasa.gov

Reading Strategy

Exercise 53 Encourage students to read the problem carefully for clues on what operation they should use to solve the problem. Draw their attention to the phrase "per acre."

EXAMPLE 4 on p. 513 for Exs. 39–48

EVALUATING EXPRESSIONS Evaluate the expression. Write your answer in scientific notation.

39. $(4.4 \times 10^3)(1.5 \times 10^{-7})$ **6.6×10^{-4}**

40. $(7.3 \times 10^{-5})(5.8 \times 10^2)$ **4.234×10^{-2}**

41. $(8.1 \times 10^{-4})(9 \times 10^{-6})$ **7.29×10^{-9}**

42. $\dfrac{6 \times 10^{-3}}{8 \times 10^{-6}}$ **7.5×10^2**

43. $\dfrac{5.4 \times 10^{-5}}{1.8 \times 10^{-2}}$ **3×10^{-3}**

44. $\dfrac{4.1 \times 10^4}{8.2 \times 10^8}$ **5×10^{-5}**

45. $(5 \times 10^{-8})^3$ **1.25×10^{-22}**

46. $(7 \times 10^{-5})^4$ **2.401×10^{-17}**

47. $(1.4 \times 10^3)^2$ **1.96×10^6**

48. ★ **MULTIPLE CHOICE** Which number is the value of $\dfrac{1.235 \times 10^4}{9.5 \times 10^7}$? **B**

Ⓐ 0.13×10^{-4} Ⓑ 1.3×10^{-4} Ⓒ 1.3×10^{-3} Ⓓ 0.13×10^3

49. ★ **OPEN-ENDED** Write two numbers in scientific notation whose product is 2.8×10^4. Write two numbers in scientific notation whose quotient is 2.8×10^4. ***Sample answer:* 2.8×10^1 and 1×10^3; 1.12×10^6 and 4.0×10^1**

C **50.** CHALLENGE Add the numbers 3.6×10^5 and 6.7×10^4 *without* writing the numbers in standard form. Write your answer in scientific notation. *Describe* the steps you take. **4.27×10^5. *Sample answer:* Rewrite 6.7×10^4 as 0.67×10^5, then add $3.6 + 0.67 = 4.27$. Since the answer is between 1 and 10, the exponent does not change, so the answer is 4.27×10^5.**

PROBLEM SOLVING

EXAMPLE 3 on p. 513 for Exs. 51–52

51a. 1.4×10^{-4}; 2.5×10^{-1}; 1.67×10^2; 555

A **51. INSECT LENGTHS** The lengths of several insects are shown in the table.

a. List the lengths of the insects in order from least to greatest.

b. Which insects are longer than the fringed ant beetle? **the elephant beetle and the walking stick**

Insect	Length (millimeters)
Fringed ant beetle	2.5×10^{-1}
Walking stick	555
Parasitic wasp	1.4×10^{-4}
Elephant beetle	1.67×10^2

@HomeTutor for problem solving help at classzone.com

52. ASTRONOMY The spacecrafts *Voyager 1* and *Voyager 2* were launched in 1977 to gather data about our solar system. As of March 12, 2004, *Voyager 1* had traveled a total distance of about 9,643,000,000 miles, and *Voyager 2* had traveled a total distance of about 9.065×10^9 miles. Which spacecraft had traveled the greater distance at that time? ***Voyager 1***

@HomeTutor for problem solving help at classzone.com

EXAMPLE 4 on p. 513 for Ex. 53

53. AGRICULTURE In 2002, about 9.7×10^8 pounds of cotton were produced in California. The cotton was planted on 6.9×10^5 acres of land. What was the average number of pounds of cotton produced per acre? Round your answer to the nearest whole number. **1406 pounds per acre**

EXAMPLE 5 on p. 514 for Exs. 54–55

54. 14; the flow rate of the Amazon River is about 14 times faster than the flow rate of the Mississippi River.

54. ★ **SHORT RESPONSE** The average flow rate of the Amazon River is about 7.6×10^6 cubic feet per second. The average flow rate of the Mississippi River is about 5.53×10^5 cubic feet per second. Find the ratio of the flow rate of the Amazon to the flow rate of the Mississippi. Round to the nearest whole number. What does the ratio tell you?

○ = WORKED-OUT SOLUTIONS on p. WS1 ★ = STANDARDIZED TEST PRACTICE ◆ = MULTIPLE REPRESENTATIONS

55. **ASTRONOMY** The radius of Earth and the radius of the moon are shown.

55a. About 3.67; the radius of Earth is about 3.67 times greater than the radius of the moon.

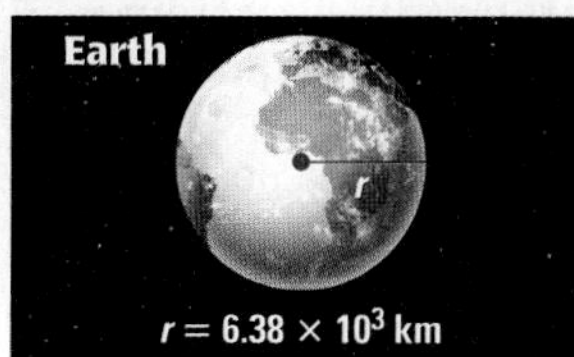

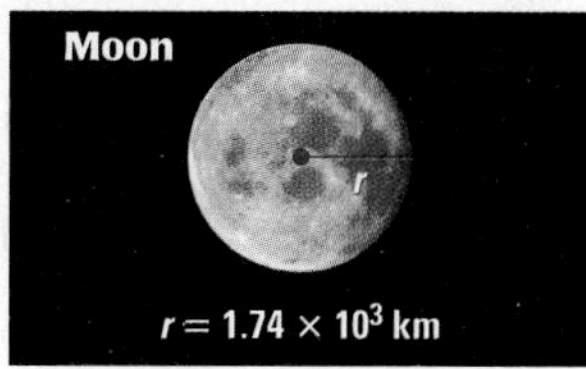

a. Find the ratio of the radius of Earth to the radius of the moon. Round to the nearest hundredth. What does the ratio tell you?

55b. About 49.30; the volume of Earth is about 49.30 times greater than the volume of the moon.

b. Assume Earth and the moon are spheres. Find the ratio of the volume of Earth to the volume of the moon. Round to the nearest hundredth. What does the ratio tell you?

c. What is the relationship between the ratios of the radii and the ratios of the volumes? **The ratio of the volumes is the cube of the ratio of the radii.**

B 56. **MULTI-STEP PROBLEM** In 1954, 50 swarms of locusts were observed in Kenya. The largest swarm covered an area of 200 square kilometers. The average number of locusts in a swarm is about 5×10^7 locusts per square kilometer.

a. About how many locusts were in Kenya's largest swarm? Write your answer in scientific notation. **about 1×10^{10} locusts**

b. The average mass of a desert locust is 2 grams. What was the total mass (in kilograms) of Kenya's largest swarm? Write your answer in scientific notation. **2×10^7 kg**

57. **DIGITAL PHOTOGRAPHY** When a picture is taken with a digital camera, the resulting image is made up of square pixels (the smallest unit that can be displayed on a monitor). For one image, the side length of a pixel is 4×10^{-3} inch. A print of the image measures 1×10^3 pixels by 1.5×10^3 pixels. What are the dimensions of the print in inches? **4 in. by 6 in.**

58. **MULTIPLE REPRESENTATIONS** The speed of light is 1.863×10^5 miles per second.

a. **Writing an Expression** Assume 1 year is 365 days. Write an expression to convert the speed of light from miles per second to miles per year. **See margin.**

59b. about 2.58×10^6 L, about 2.58×10^7 L, about 2.06×10^8 L

b. **Making a Table** Make a table that shows the distance light travels in 1, 10, 100, 1000, 10,000, and 100,000 years. Our galaxy has a diameter of about 5.875×10^{17} miles. Based on the table, about how long would it take for light to travel across our galaxy? **See margin.**

C 59. ★ **EXTENDED RESPONSE** When a person is at rest, approximately 7×10^{-2} liter of blood flows through the heart with each heartbeat. The human heart beats about 70 times per minute.

59c. Underestimates. *Sample answer:* They are calculated when a person is at rest. When a person is not resting, the rate will go up.

a. **Calculate** About how many liters of blood flow through the heart each minute when a person is at rest? **4.9 L**

b. **Estimate** There are approximately 5.265×10^5 minutes in a year. Use your answer from part (a) to estimate the number of liters of blood that flow through the human heart in 1 year, in 10 years, and in 80 years. Write your answers in scientific notation.

c. **Explain** Are your answers to part (b) underestimates or overestimates? *Explain.*

Study Strategy

Exercise 55 Haves students use Example 5 as a model for this exercise. Caution them that part b asks them to find the ratio for volumes, whereas Example 5 has them compare areas.

Exercise 60 Additional information about solar flares can be found at NASA's website hesperia.gsfc.nasa.gov/sftheory

58a. $\frac{1.863 \times 10^5 \text{ mi}}{1 \text{ sec}} \cdot \frac{60 \text{ sec}}{1 \text{ min}} \cdot \frac{60 \text{ min}}{1 \text{ h}} \cdot \frac{24 \text{ h}}{1 \text{ day}} \cdot \frac{365 \text{ days}}{1 \text{ yr}} \approx 5.875 \times 10^{12}$ mi/yr

58b.

Years	1	10	100	1000	10,000	100,000
Miles traveled	5.875×10^{12}	5.875×10^{13}	5.875×10^{14}	5.875×10^{15}	5.875×10^{16}	5.875×10^{17}

100,000 yr

5 ASSESS AND RETEACH

Daily Homework Quiz

Transparency Available

Write the number in scientific notation.

1. 100,500 **1.005×10^5**
2. 0.0203 **2.03×10^{-2}**
3. Write 3.06×10^7 in standard form. **30,600,000**
4. The diameter of Mercury is about 4.9×10^3 kilometers. The diameter of Venus is about 1.2×10^4 kilometers. Find the ratio of the diameter of Venus to that of Mercury. Round to the nearest hundredth. **about 2.45**

Online Quiz

Available at **classzone.com**

Diagnosis/Remediation

- Practice A, B, C in Chapter Resource Book
- Study Guide in Chapter Resource Book
- Practice Workbook
- @HomeTutor

Challenge

Additional challenge is available in the Chapter Resource Book.

Quiz

An easily-readable reduced copy of the quiz (with answers) on Lessons 8.3–8.4 from the Assessment Book can be found on p. 486E.

60. CHALLENGE A solar flare is a sudden eruption of energy in the sun's atmosphere. Solar flares are classified according to their peak X-ray intensity (in watts per meter squared) and are denoted with a capital letter and a number, as shown in the table. For example, a C4 flare has a peak intensity of 4×10^{-6} watt per square meter.

Class	Bn	Cn	Mn	Xn
Peak intensity (w/m^2)	$n \times 10^{-7}$	$n \times 10^{-6}$	$n \times 10^{-5}$	$n \times 10^{-4}$

a. In November 2003, a massive X45 solar flare was observed. In April 2004, a C9 flare was observed. How many times greater was the intensity of the X45 flare than that of the C9 flare? **500 times greater**

b. A solar flare may be accompanied by a coronal mass ejection (CME), a bubble of mass ejected from the sun. A CME related to the X45 flare was estimated to be traveling at 8.2 million kilometers per hour. At that rate, how long would it take the CME to travel from the sun to Earth, a distance of about 1.5×10^{11} meters? **about 18 h**

MIXED REVIEW

PREVIEW Prepare for Lesson 8.5 in Exs. 61–68.

Write the percent as a decimal. *(p. 916)*

61. 33% **0.33**
62. 62.7% **0.627**
63. 0.9% **0.009**
64. 0.04% **0.0004**
65. 3.95% **0.0395**
66. $\frac{1}{4}$% **0.0025**
67. $\frac{5}{2}$% **0.025**
68. 133% **1.33**

Graph the equation. **69–74. See margin.**

69. $x = -5$ *(p. 215)*
70. $y = 4$ *(p. 215)*
71. $3x - 7y = 42$ *(p. 225)*
72. $y - 2x = 12$ *(p. 225)*
73. $y = -2x + 6$ *(p. 244)*
74. $y = 1.5x - 9$ *(p. 244)*

QUIZ for Lessons 8.3–8.4

Simplify the expression. Write your answer using only positive exponents. *(p. 503)*

1. $(-4x)^4 \cdot (-4)^{-6}$ **$\frac{x^4}{16}$**
2. $(-3x^7y^{-2})^{-3}$ **$-\frac{y^6}{27x^{21}}$**
3. $\frac{1}{(5z)^{-3}}$ **$125z^3$**
4. $\frac{(6x)^{-2}y^5}{-x^3y^{-7}}$ **$-\frac{y^{12}}{36x^5}$**

Write the number in standard form. *(p. 512)*

5. 6.02×10^6 **6,020,000**
6. 5.41×10^{11} **541,000,000,000**
7. 8.007×10^{-5} **0.00008007**
8. 9.253×10^{-7} **0.0000009253**

9. **DINOSAURS** The estimated masses of several dinosaurs are shown in the table. *(p. 512)*

a. List the masses of the dinosaurs in order from least to greatest.

b. Which dinosaurs are more massive than Brachiosaurus? **Ultrasaurus**

9a. 1.06×10^4; 29,900; 77,100; 1.36×10^5

Dinosaur	Mass (kilograms)
Brachiosaurus	77,100
Diplodocus	1.06×10^4
Apatosaurus	29,900
Ultrasaurus	1.36×10^5

EXTRA PRACTICE for Lesson 8.4, p. 945

ONLINE QUIZ at classzone.com

69–74. See Additional Answers beginning on p. AA1.

Graphing Calculator ACTIVITY Use after Lesson 8.4

@HomeTutor classzone.com Keystrokes

8.4 Use Scientific Notation

QUESTION How can you use a graphing calculator to solve problems that involve numbers in scientific notation?

EXAMPLE Use numbers in scientific notation

Gold is one of many trace elements dissolved in seawater. There is about 1.1×10^{-8} gram of gold per kilogram of seawater. The mass of the oceans is about 1.4×10^{21} kilograms. About how much gold is present in the oceans?

STEP 1 *Write a verbal model*

Amount of gold present in oceans (grams)	=	Amount of gold in 1 kilogram of seawater (gram/kilogram)	•	Amount of seawater in oceans (kilograms)

STEP 2 *Find product* The product is $(1.1 \times 10^{-8}) \cdot (1.4 \times 10^{21})$.

[( ] 1.1 [×] 10 [^] [(−)] 8 [ )] [( ] 1.4 [×] 10 [^] 21 [ )] [ENTER]

STEP 3 *Read result*

The calculator indicates that a number is in scientific notation by using "E." You can read the calculator's result 1.54E13 as 1.54×10^{13}.

There are about 1.54×10^{13} grams of gold present in the oceans.

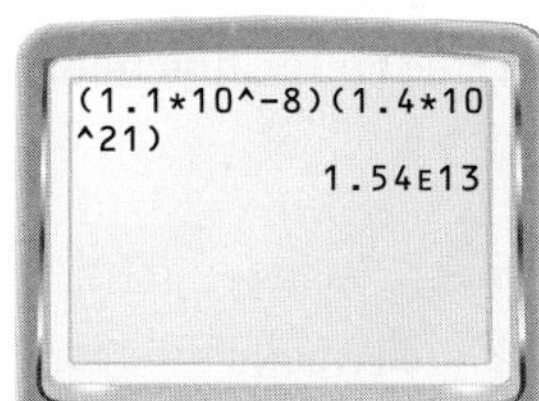

PRACTICE

Evaluate the expression. Write the result in scientific notation.

1. $(1.5 \times 10^4)(1.8 \times 10^9)$ **2.7×10^{13}**
2. $(2.6 \times 10^{-14})(1.4 \times 10^{20})$ **3.64×10^6**
3. $(7.0 \times 10^{25}) \div (2.8 \times 10^6)$ **2.5×10^{19}**
4. $(4.5 \times 10^{15}) \div (9.0 \times 10^{-2})$ **5.0×10^{16}**
5. **GASOLINE** A scientist estimates that it takes about 4.45×10^7 grams of carbon from ancient plant matter to produce 1 gallon of gasoline. In 2002 motor vehicles in the U.S. used about 1.37×10^{11} gallons of gasoline.
   a. If all of the gasoline used in 2002 by motor vehicles in the U.S. came from carbon from ancient plant matter, how many grams of carbon were used to produce the gasoline? **about 6.10×10^{18} g**
   b. There are about 5.0×10^{22} atoms of carbon in 1 gram of carbon. How many atoms of carbon were used? **about 3.05×10^{41} atoms**

1 PLAN AND PREPARE

Learn the Method

- Students will use a graphing calculator to solve a problem involving scientific notation.
- After the activity, students can use a graphing calculator to check their solutions in Exercises 39–48 in Lesson 8.4.

Keystroke Help

Keystrokes for several models of calculators are available in blackline format in the *Chapter Resource Book*.

2 TEACH

Tips for Success

Make sure that students place parentheses around the numbers in scientific notation.

Extra Example

In 2003, about 1.35×10^6 acres of beans were harvested in the United States. The yield per acre was about 1.67×10^3 pounds of beans. About how many pounds of beans were produced in the United States in 2003? **about 2.25×10^9 lb**

3 ASSESS AND RETEACH

Evaluate the expression. Write the result in scientific notation.

1. $(3.6 \times 10^{-16})(1.8 \times 10^5)$ **6.48×10^{-11}**
2. $(2.4 \times 10^{12}) \div (1.5 \times 10^{-3})$ **1.6×10^{15}**

8.5 Write and Graph Exponential Growth Functions

Before You wrote and graphed linear models.

Now You will write and graph exponential growth models.

Why? So you can find the value of a collector car, as in Example 4.

1 PLAN AND PREPARE

Warm-Up Exercises

Transparency Available

Write the percent as a decimal.

1. 2% **0.02**

2. 5.5% **0.055**

3. The table shows the cost of tickets for a matinee. Write a rule for the function. **$c = 2t$**

Tickets, t	2	4	6	8
Cost, c	4	8	12	16

Notetaking Guide

Transparency Available

Promotes interactive learning and notetaking skills.

Pacing

Basic: 2 days

Average: 2 days

Advanced: 2 days

Block: 1 block

- See *Teaching Guide/Lesson Plan.*

2 FOCUS AND MOTIVATE

Essential Question

Big Idea 3, p. 487

How do you write and graph equations for exponential growth functions? **Tell students they will learn how to answer this question by using models to write functions and tables to graph functions.**

NCTM STANDARDS

Standard 2: Understand patterns; Understand functions

Key Vocabulary
- **exponential function**
- **exponential growth**
- **compound interest**

An **exponential function** is a function of the form $y = ab^x$ where $a \neq 0$, $b > 0$, and $b \neq 1$. Exponential functions are *nonlinear* functions. Observe how an exponential function compares with a linear function.

Linear function: $y = 3x + 2$

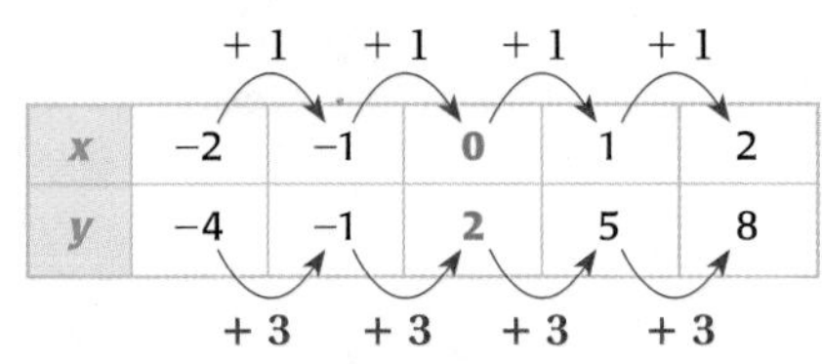

x	−2	−1	0	1	2
y	−4	−1	2	5	8

Exponential function: $y = 2 \cdot 3^x$

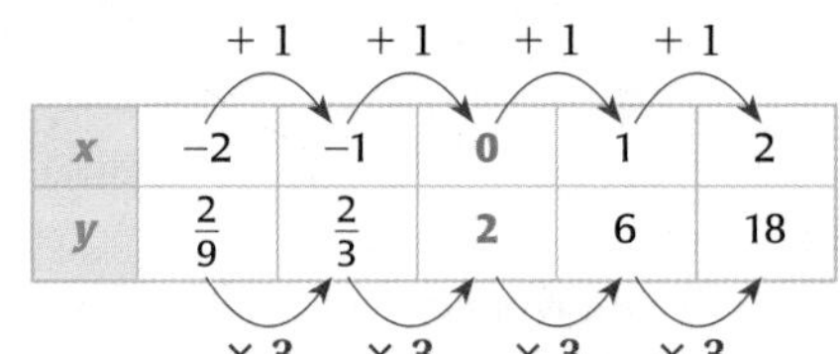

x	−2	−1	0	1	2
y	$\frac{2}{9}$	$\frac{2}{3}$	2	6	18

EXAMPLE 1 Write a function rule

ANALYZE RATE OF CHANGE

Notice that for an exponential function, the rate of change in y with respect to x is not constant as it is for a linear function. For instance, $\frac{4-2}{-1-(-2)} = 2$, while $\frac{8-4}{0-(-1)} = 4$.

Write a rule for the function.

x	−2	−1	0	1	2
y	2	4	8	16	32

Solution

STEP 1 **Tell** whether the function is exponential.

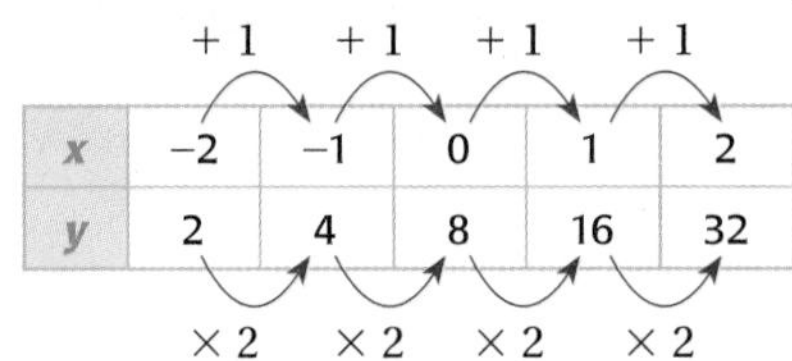

x	−2	−1	0	1	2
y	2	4	8	16	32

Here, the y-values are multiplied by 2 for each increase of 1 in x, so the table represents an exponential function of the form $y = ab^x$ where $b = 2$.

STEP 2 **Find** the value of a by finding the value of y when $x = 0$. When $x = 0$, $y = ab^0 = a \cdot 1 = a$. The value of y when $x = 0$ is 8, so $a = 8$.

STEP 3 **Write** the function rule. A rule for the function is $y = 8 \cdot 2^x$.

✓ **GUIDED PRACTICE** for Example 1

1. Write a rule for the function. **$y = 27 \cdot 3^x$**

x	−2	−1	0	1	2
y	3	9	27	81	243

Resource Planning Guide

Chapter Resource Book
- Teaching Guide/Lesson Plan
- Activity Master
- Practice levels A, B, C
- Study Guide
- Catch-up for Absent Students
- Problem Solving Workshop
- Challenge

Workbooks
- Notetaking Guide
- Practice Workbook

Teaching Options
- **Power Presentations** provides dynamic electronic teaching resources for the classroom.
- **Activity Generator** provides editable activities for all ability levels.

Interactive Technology
- Easy Planner
- Power Presentations
- Activity Generator
- Animated Algebra
- Test Generator
- Online Quiz
- eWorkbook
- eEdition
- @HomeTutor

Resources for English Learners
- Spanish Study Guide
- Multi-Language Visual Glossary
- Student Resources in Spanish

See also the *Differentiated Instruction Resources* for more strategies for meeting individual needs.

EXAMPLE 2 Graph an exponential function

Graph the function $y = 2^x$. Identify its domain and range.

Solution

STEP 1 **Make** a table by choosing a few values for x and finding the values of y. The domain is all real numbers.

x	-2	-1	0	1	2
y	$\frac{1}{4}$	$\frac{1}{2}$	1	2	4

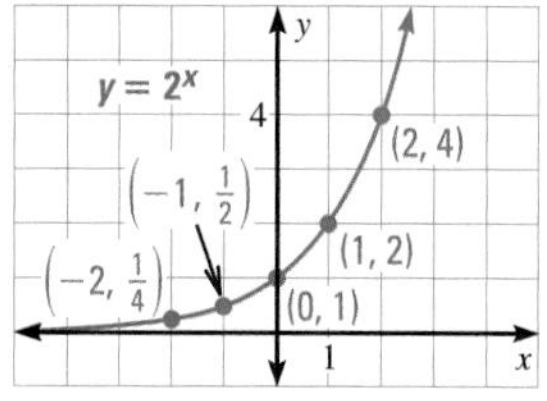

STEP 2 **Plot** the points.

STEP 3 **Draw** a smooth curve through the points. From either the table or the graph, you can see that the range is all positive real numbers.

READ A GRAPH
Notice that the graph has a y-intercept of 1 and that it gets closer to the negative x-axis as the x-values decrease.

EXAMPLE 3 Compare graphs of exponential functions

Graph the functions $y = 3 \cdot 2^x$ and $y = -3 \cdot 2^x$. Compare each graph with the graph of $y = 2^x$.

Solution

To graph each function, make a table of values, plot the points, and draw a smooth curve through the points.

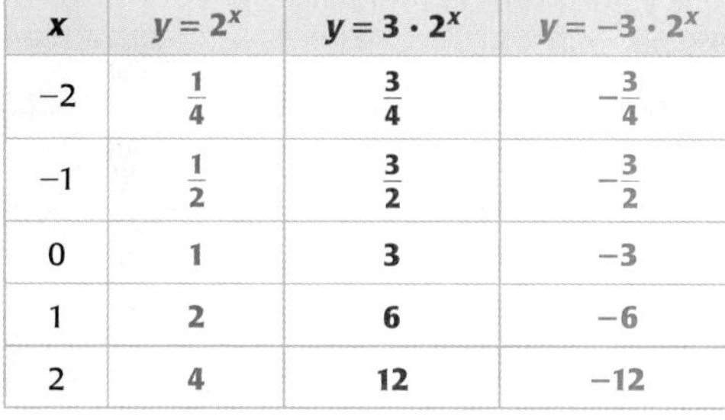

x	$y = 2^x$	$y = 3 \cdot 2^x$	$y = -3 \cdot 2^x$
-2	$\frac{1}{4}$	$\frac{3}{4}$	$-\frac{3}{4}$
-1	$\frac{1}{2}$	$\frac{3}{2}$	$-\frac{3}{2}$
0	1	3	-3
1	2	6	-6
2	4	12	-12

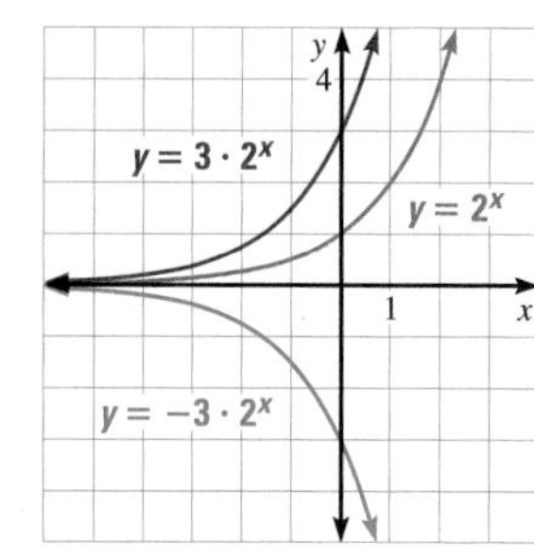

Because the y-values for $y = 3 \cdot 2^x$ are 3 times the corresponding y-values for $y = 2^x$, the graph of $y = 3 \cdot 2^x$ is a vertical stretch of the graph of $y = 2^x$.

Because the y-values for $y = -3 \cdot 2^x$ are -3 times the corresponding y-values for $y = 2^x$, the graph of $y = -3 \cdot 2^x$ is a vertical stretch with a reflection in the x-axis of the graph of $y = 2^x$.

DESCRIBE A FUNCTION
An exponential growth function has an unbroken graph, so the function is continuous, as discussed on p. 223.

✓ GUIDED PRACTICE for Examples 2 and 3

2–4. See margin for art.

2. Graph $y = 5^x$ and identify its domain and range.
domain: all real numbers, range: all positive real numbers
3. Graph $y = \frac{1}{3} \cdot 2^x$. Compare the graph with the graph of $y = 2^x$.
The graph is a vertical shrink of the graph of $y = 2^x$.
4. Graph $y = -\frac{1}{3} \cdot 2^x$. Compare the graph with the graph of $y = 2^x$.
The graph is a vertical shrink with a reflection in the x–axis of the graph of $y = 2^x$.

Motivating the Lesson

You are studying population growth in your city. You know the current population is 128,256 and the annual rate of growth averages 3%. By knowing how to write and evaluate an exponential growth model, you can estimate the population in 2020.

3 TEACH

Extra Example 1

Write a rule for the function.

x	-2	-1	0	1	2
y	1	4	16	64	256

$y = 16 \cdot 4^x$

Extra Example 2

Graph the function $y = 3^x$. Identify its domain and range. **Domain: all real numbers; Range: all positive real numbers**

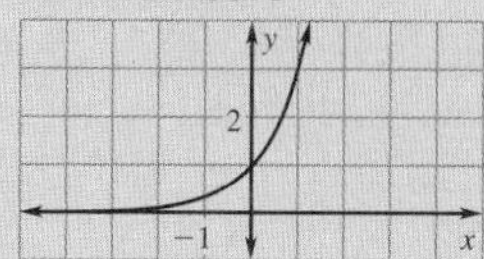

Extra Example 3

Graph $y = \frac{1}{2} \cdot 2^x$ and $y = -\frac{1}{2} \cdot 2^x$.

Compare each graph with the graph of $y = 2^x$.

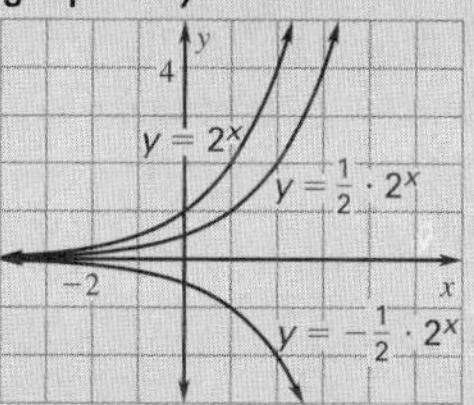

The graph of $y = \frac{1}{2} \cdot 2^x$ is a vertical shrink of the graph of $y = 2^x$. The graph of $y = -\frac{1}{2} \cdot 2^x$ is a vertical shrink and reflection in the x-axis of the graph of $y = 2^x$.

2–4. See Additional Answers beginning on p. AA1.

Differentiated Instruction

Inclusion Students with fine-motor problems may find it difficult to graph exponential functions and thus get frustrated. Have these students understand the general shape of an exponential function and have them graph on a coordinate plane without grid lines. Also show how a spreadsheet program or graphing calculator can be used to generate a graph.

See also the *Differentiated Instruction Resources* for more strategies.

Extra Example 4

The owner of an original copy of a 1938 comic book sold it at an auction in 2005. The owner bought the comic book for $55 in 1980. The value of the comic book increased at a rate of 2.8% per year.

a. Write a function that models the value of the comic book over time. **$C = 55(1.028)^t$**

b. What was the approximate value of the comic book at the time of the auction in 2005? Round your answer to the nearest dollar. **about $110**

Key Questions to Ask for Example 4

- How is an exponential growth model different from a linear model? **The increase in an exponential model is the same percent every year, while the increase in a linear model is the same amount every year.**
- What types of quantities can be represented by an exponential growth model? **quantities that increase by the same percent in equal periods of time**

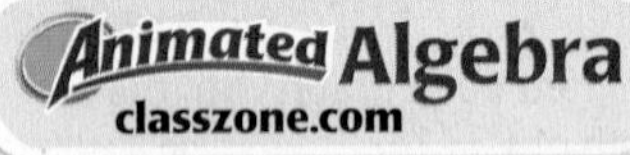

An **Animated Algebra** activity is available online for **Example 4**. This activity is also part of **Power Presentations**.

EXPONENTIAL GROWTH When $a > 0$ and $b > 1$, the function $y = ab^x$ represents **exponential growth**. When a quantity grows exponentially, it increases by the same percent over equal time periods. To find the amount to which the quantity grows after t time periods, use the following model.

REWRITE EQUATIONS
Notice that you can rewrite $y = ab^x$ as $y = a(1 + r)^t$ by replacing b with $1 + r$ and x with t (for time).

KEY CONCEPT *For Your Notebook*

Exponential Growth Model

a is the **initial amount**. r is the **growth rate**.

$$y = a(1 + r)^t$$

$1 + r$ is the **growth factor**. t is the **time period**.

Notice the relationship between the growth rate r and the growth factor $1 + r$. If the initial amount of a quantity is a units and the quantity is growing at a rate of r, then after one time period the new amount is:

$$\text{Initial amount} + \text{amount of increase} = a + r \cdot a = a(1 + r)$$

EXAMPLE 4 Solve a multi-step problem

ANOTHER WAY
For alternative methods for solving Example 4, turn to page 528 for the **Problem Solving Workshop**.

COLLECTOR CAR The owner of a 1953 Hudson Hornet convertible sold the car at an auction. The owner bought it in 1984 when its value was $11,000. The value of the car increased at a rate of 6.9% per year.

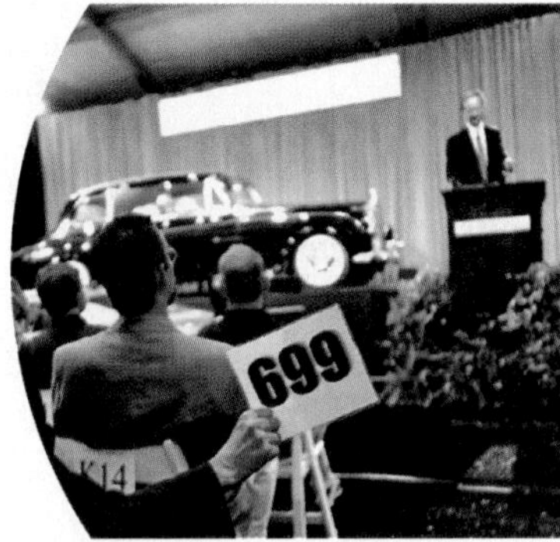

a. Write a function that models the value of the car over time.

b. The auction took place in 2004. What was the approximate value of the car at the time of the auction? Round your answer to the nearest dollar.

Solution

a. Let C be the value of the car (in dollars), and let t be the time (in years) since 1984. The initial value a is $11,000, and the growth rate r is 0.069.

$C = a(1 + r)^t$ **Write exponential growth model.**

$= 11,000(1 + 0.069)^t$ **Substitute 11,000 for a and 0.069 for r.**

$= 11,000(1.069)^t$ **Simplify.**

AVOID ERRORS
The growth rate in this example is 6.9%, or 0.069. So, the growth factor is 1 + 0.069, or 1.069, not 0.069.

b. To find the value of the car in 2004, 20 years after 1984, substitute 20 for t.

$C = 11,000(1.069)^{20}$ **Substitute 20 for t.**

$\approx 41,778$ **Use a calculator.**

▶ In 2004 the value of the car was about $41,778.

Animated Algebra at classzone.com

COMPOUND INTEREST **Compound interest** is interest earned on both an initial investment and on previously earned interest. Compounding of interest can be modeled by exponential growth where a is the initial investment, r is the annual interest rate, and t is the number of years the money is invested.

EXAMPLE 5 Standardized Test Practice

You put \$250 in a savings account that earns 4% annual interest compounded yearly. You do not make any deposits or withdrawals. How much will your investment be worth in 5 years?

Ⓐ \$300 Ⓑ \$304.16 Ⓒ \$1344.56 Ⓓ \$781,250

ESTIMATE
You can use the simple interest formula, $I = prt$, to estimate the amount of interest earned: $(250)(0.04)(5) = 50$. Compounding interest will result in slightly more than \$50.

Solution

$y = a(1 + r)^t$ Write exponential growth model.

$= 250(1 + 0.04)^5$ Substitute 250 for a, 0.04 for r, and 5 for t.

$= 250(1.04)^5$ Simplify.

≈ 304.16 Use a calculator.

You will have \$304.16 in 5 years.

▶ The correct answer is B. Ⓐ Ⓑ Ⓒ Ⓓ

GUIDED PRACTICE for Examples 4 and 5

5. **WHAT IF?** In Example 4, suppose the owner of the car sold it in 1994. Find the value of the car to the nearest dollar. **\$21,437**

6. **WHAT IF?** In Example 5, suppose the annual interest rate is 3.5%. How much will your investment be worth in 5 years? **\$296.92**

8.5 EXERCISES

HOMEWORK KEY

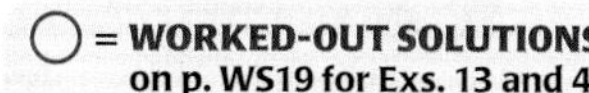

○ = **WORKED-OUT SOLUTIONS** on p. WS19 for Exs. 13 and 41

★ = **STANDARDIZED TEST PRACTICE** Exs. 3, 8, 35, 42, 43, 46, and 50

◆ = **MULTIPLE REPRESENTATIONS** Exs. 34, 41

SKILL PRACTICE

1. **VOCABULARY** In the exponential growth model $y = a(1 + r)^t$, the quantity $1 + r$ is called the __?__. **growth factor**

2. **VOCABULARY** For what values of b does the exponential function $y = ab^x$ (where $a > 0$) represent exponential growth? **$b > 1$**

3. ★ **WRITING** How does the graph of $y = 2 \cdot 5^x$ compare with the graph of $y = 5^x$? *Explain.* **The graph would be a vertical stretch. *Sample answer:* Since the y-values of $y = 2 \cdot 5^x$ are double those of $y = 5^x$.**

Extra Example 5

You put \$125 in a savings account that earns 2% interest compounded yearly. You do not make any deposits or withdrawals. How much will your investment be worth in 5 years? **B**

Ⓐ \$130 Ⓑ \$138.01
Ⓒ \$311.04 Ⓓ \$4000

Key Question to Ask for Example 5

- Why is an estimate using the simple interest formula useful? **Since it shows that simple interest is \$50 and compound interest would be slightly more than \$50, you can eliminate all answer choices except B.**

Closing the Lesson

Have students summarize the major points of the lesson and answer the Essential Question: How do you write and graph equations for exponential growth functions?

- **An exponential function has the form $y = ab^x$, where $a \neq 0$, $b > 0$, and $b \neq 1$.**
- **The exponential growth model is $y = a(1 + r)^t$, where a is the initial amount, r is the growth rate, and t is the time period.**

Use the exponential growth model to write an equation. Substitute the initial amount for a, the rate for r, written as a decimal, and the time period for t. When graphing an exponential function, make a table of negative and positive values, determine the y-intercept, plot the points on a coordinate plane, and connect them with a smooth curve.

Differentiated Instruction

Advanced Suggest that students research several banks, either locally or online, for interest rates on savings accounts, money market accounts, and CDs. Have them develop exponential growth models for each type of account at each bank on an initial deposit of \$500 after 2 years. Ask students to make a chart comparing the rates and potential earnings for the different types of accounts and the different banks.

See also the *Differentiated Instruction Resources* for more strategies.

4 PRACTICE AND APPLY

Assignment Guide

Answer Transparencies available for all exercises

Basic:
Day 1: SRH p. 923 Exs. 9–13
pp. 523–527
Exs. 1–21
Day 2: pp. 523–527
Exs. 22–27, 38–43, 52–61

Average:
Day 1: pp. 523–527
Exs. 1–8, 11–21, 35, 60, 61
Day 2: pp. 523–527
Exs. 22–34, 38–46, 52–58 even

Advanced:
Day 1: pp. 523–527
Exs. 1, 2, 4–8, 13–21, 35–37*, 60
Day 2: pp. 523–527
Exs. 26–34, 39–51*, 54, 58

Block:
pp. 523–527
Exs. 1–8, 11–35, 38–46,
52–58 even, 60, 61

Differentiated Instruction

See *Differentiated Instruction Resources* for suggestions on addressing the needs of a diverse classroom.

Homework Check

For a quick check of student understanding of key concepts, go over the following exercises:

Basic: 4, 12, 24, 38, 39
Average: 5, 16, 28, 38, 40
Advanced: 6, 20, 32, 39, 41

Extra Practice

- Student Edition, p. 945
- Chapter Resource Book: Practice levels A, B, C

Practice Worksheet

An easily-readable reduced practice page (with answers) for this lesson can be found on p. 486C.

EXAMPLE 1 on p. 520 for Exs. 4–8

4. $y = 4 \cdot 2^x$
5. $y = 125 \cdot 5^x$
6. $y = \frac{1}{2} \cdot 2^x$
7. $y = \frac{1}{9} \cdot 3^x$

WRITING FUNCTIONS **Write a rule for the function.**

4.

x	−2	−1	0	1	2
y	1	2	4	8	16

5.

x	−2	−1	0	1	2
y	5	25	125	625	3125

6.

x	−2	−1	0	1	2
y	$\frac{1}{8}$	$\frac{1}{4}$	$\frac{1}{2}$	1	2

7.

x	−2	−1	0	1	2
y	$\frac{1}{81}$	$\frac{1}{27}$	$\frac{1}{9}$	$\frac{1}{3}$	1

8. ★ **WRITING** Given a table of values, describe how can you tell if the table represents a linear function or an exponential function. **See margin.**

EXAMPLE 2 on p. 521 for Exs. 9–21

GRAPHING FUNCTIONS **Graph the function and identify its domain and range.** **9–20. See margin.**

9. $y = 4^x$
10. $y = 7^x$
11. $y = 8^x$
12. $y = 9^x$
13. $y = (1.5)^x$
14. $y = (2.5)^x$
15. $y = (1.2)^x$
16. $y = (4.3)^x$
17. $y = \left(\frac{4}{3}\right)^x$
18. $y = \left(\frac{7}{2}\right)^x$
19. $y = \left(\frac{5}{3}\right)^x$
20. $y = \left(\frac{5}{4}\right)^x$

21. The percent increase was not written as a decimal; $0.27(1 + 0.02)^3 = 0.27(1.02)^3 \approx \$.29$.

21. **ERROR ANALYSIS** The price P (in dollars) of a pound of flour was \$.27 in 1999. The price has increased by about 2% each year. Let t be the number of years since 1999. *Describe and correct the error in finding the price of a pound of flour in 2002.*

$P = a(1 + r)^t$
$= 0.27(1 + 2)^3 = 0.27(3)^3 = 7.29$
In 2002 the price of a pound of flour was \$7.29.

EXAMPLE 3 on p. 521 for Exs. 22–34

B

COMPARING GRAPHS OF FUNCTIONS **Graph the function. Compare the graph with the graph of $y = 3^x$.** **22–33. See margin.**

22. $y = 2 \cdot 3^x$
23. $y = 4 \cdot 3^x$
24. $y = \frac{1}{4} \cdot 3^x$
25. $y = \frac{2}{3} \cdot 3^x$
26. $y = 0.5 \cdot 3^x$
27. $y = 2.5 \cdot 3^x$
28. $y = -2 \cdot 3^x$
29. $y = -4 \cdot 3^x$
30. $y = -\frac{1}{4} \cdot 3^x$
31. $y = -\frac{2}{3} \cdot 3^x$
32. $y = -0.5 \cdot 3^x$
33. $y = -2.5 \cdot 3^x$

34. **MULTIPLE REPRESENTATIONS** Given the function $y = a^x$, you can find x when $y = k$ by solving the *exponential equation* $k = a^x$. Use the following methods to solve $32 = 2^x$. **a, b. See margin.**
   a. **Making a Table** Make a table for the function using $x = 0, 1, 2, \ldots, 6$.
   b. **Graphing Functions** Graph the functions $y = 32$ and $y = 2^x$ on the same coordinate plane. Identify the x-coordinate of the intersection point.
   c. **Using Powers** Write 32 as a power of 2. Then use the fact that powers with the same base are equal provided that their exponents are equal. **$32 = 2 \cdot 2 \cdot 2 \cdot 2 \cdot 2 = 2^5$; because $2^5 = 2^x$, x must equal 5.**

35. 200%. *Sample answer:* A growth rate of 200% would create a growth factor of 1 + 2 = 3, which would represent the tripling of the population every year.

C

35. ★ **WRITING** If a population triples each year, what is the population's growth rate (as a percent)? *Explain.*

36. **CHALLENGE** Write a linear function and an exponential function whose graphs pass through the points (0, 2) and (1, 6). ***Sample answer:*** **$f(x) = 4x + 2$, $f(x) = 2 \cdot 3^x$**

37. *Sample answer:* The graphs are the same. Since by the product of a power property $2^{x+2} = 2^x \cdot 2^2$, and $2^x \cdot 2^2$ simplifies to $4 \cdot 2^x$, $2^{x+2} = 4 \cdot 2^x$.

37. **CHALLENGE** *Compare* the graphs of the functions $f(x) = 2^{x+2}$ and $g(x) = 4 \cdot 2^x$. Use properties of exponents to explain your observations.

○ = WORKED-OUT SOLUTIONS on p. WS1 ★ = STANDARDIZED TEST PRACTICE ◆ = MULTIPLE REPRESENTATIONS

8. *Sample answer:* If the difference between successive terms is constant, the function is linear and if the ratio of successive terms is constant, the function is exponential.

9–20, 22–33. See Additional Answers beginning on p. AA1.

PROBLEM SOLVING

GRAPHING CALCULATOR **You may wish to use a graphing calculator to complete the following Problem Solving exercises.**

EXAMPLES A 4 and 5 on pp. 522–523 for Exs. 38–41

38. **INVESTMENTS** You deposit \$125 in a savings account that earns 5% annual interest compounded yearly. Find the balance in the account after the given amounts of time.

 a. 1 year **\$131.25** b. 2 years **\$137.81** c. 5 years **\$159.54** d. 20 years **\$331.66**

@HomeTutor for problem solving help at classzone.com

39. MULTI-STEP PROBLEM One computer industry expert reported that there were about 600 million computers in use worldwide in 2001 and that the number was increasing at an annual rate of about 10%.

 a. Write a function that models the number of computers in use over time.

 b. Use the function to predict the number of computers that will be in use worldwide in 2009. **about 1,286,153,286 computers**

@HomeTutor for problem solving help at classzone.com

39a. Let x represent the number of years since 2001 and $f(x)$ represent the number of computers (in hundreds of millions); $f(x) = 6 \cdot (1.1)^x$.

40. MULTI-STEP PROBLEM A research association reported that 3,173,000 gas grills were shipped by various manufacturers in the U.S. in 1985. Shipments increased by about 7% per year from 1985 to 2002.

 a. Write a function that models the number of gas grills shipped over time.

 b. About how many gas grills were shipped in 2002? **about 10,022,921 gas grills**

40a. Let x represent the number of years since 1985 and $f(x)$ represent the number of grills shipped; $f(x) = 3,173,000 \cdot (1.07)^x$.

41. MULTIPLE REPRESENTATIONS A tree's cross-sectional area taken at a height of 4.5 feet from the ground is called its basal area and is measured in square inches. Tree growth can be measured by the growth of the tree's basal area. The initial basal area and annual growth rate for two particular trees are shown.

 a. **Writing a Model** Write a function that models the basal area A of each tree over time. **tree 1: $A = 154 \cdot (1.06)^t$, tree 2: $A = 113 \cdot (1.1)^t$**

 b. **Graphing a Function** Use a graphing calculator to graph the functions from part (a) in the same coordinate plane. In about how many years will the trees have the same basal area? **See margin for art; about 8.4 yr.**

Avoiding Common Errors

Exercises 4–6 Some students may fail to find the value of a. Remind students that an exponential function is in the form of $y = ab^x$ and that they can find the value of a by finding the value of y when $x = 0$.

Exercises 38–41 Watch for students who do not write percents as decimals before applying the exponential growth model.

Graphing Calculator

Exercises 9–20, 22–33 Students may want to check their graphs on a graphing calculator. They can enter the function in the Y = menu and then press Graph. They can press Table to check values. They can scroll up or down to see more values.

Reading Strategy

Exercises 38–41 Draw students' attention to the graphing calculator logo at the top of page 525. Point out that the logo appears whenever a graphing calculator is suggested for the exercises.

41b.

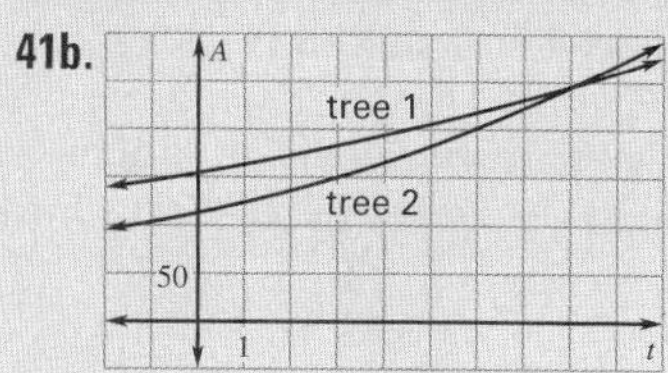

34a.

x	1	2	3	4	5	6
y	2	4	8	16	32	64

34b.

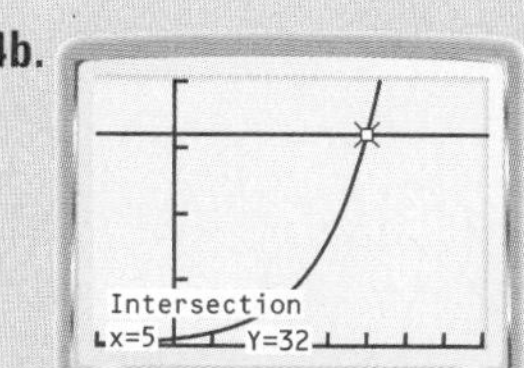

34c. $32 = 2 \cdot 2 \cdot 2 \cdot 2 \cdot 2 = 2^5$; because $2^5 = 2^x$, x must equal 5.

Avoiding Common Errors

Exercises 42–46 Some students may forget to add 1 to the rate of growth in the exponential growth model. Remind students that $1 + r$ is the growth factor in the model.

Study Strategy

Exercises 47–50 Encourage students to study the Example on page 527 in detail. You may wish to present this Example to students to be certain they understand what each variable in the formula represents.

44b.

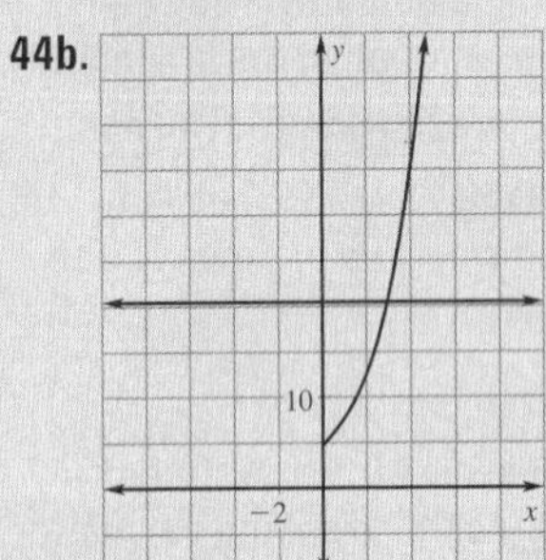

46c. ***Sample answer:*** **The exponential model is more accurate from 1850–1890. The exponential model underestimates the actual totals by less than 2 million in 1850 and 1870, while the linear model overestimates by more than 5 million in each year.**

42. Yes. ***Sample answer:*** **The quotient of each pair of adjacent terms is the same, $\frac{7}{4}$.**

44a. initial amount: 4.67 million, growth factor: 1.65, growth rate: 0.65

44b. See margin for art; domain: $0 \le x \le 10$, range: 4.67 million $\le y \le$ 698.5 million.

45. $y = 25.96(1.059)^x$; about 145 Hz

B

42. ★ SHORT RESPONSE A company sells advertising blimps. The table shows the costs of advertising blimps of different lengths. Does the table represent an exponential function? *Explain.*

Length, ℓ (feet)	10	15	20	25
Cost, c (dollars)	400.00	700.00	1225.00	2143.75

43. ★ MULTIPLE CHOICE A weblog, or blog, refers to a website that contains a personal journal. According to one analyst, over one 18 month period, the number of blogs in existence doubled about every 6 months. The analyst estimated that there were about 600,000 blogs at the beginning of the period. How many blogs were there at the end of the period? **C**

Ⓐ 660,000 Ⓑ 1,200,000 Ⓒ 4,800,000 Ⓓ 16,200,000

44. TELECOMMUNICATIONS For the period 1991–2001, the number y (in millions) of Internet users worldwide can be modeled by the function $y = 4.67(1.65)^x$ where x is the number of years since 1991.

a. Identify the initial amount, the growth factor, and the growth rate.

b. Graph the function. Identify its domain and range.

c. Use your graph from part (b) to graph the line $y = 21$. Estimate the year in which the number of Internet users worldwide was about 21 million. **1994**

45. GRAPHING CALCULATOR The frequency (in hertz) of a note played on a piano is a function of the position of the key that creates the note. The position of some piano keys and the frequencies of the notes created by the keys are shown below. Use the exponential regression feature on a graphing calculator to find an exponential model for the frequency of piano notes. What is the frequency of the note created by the 30th key?

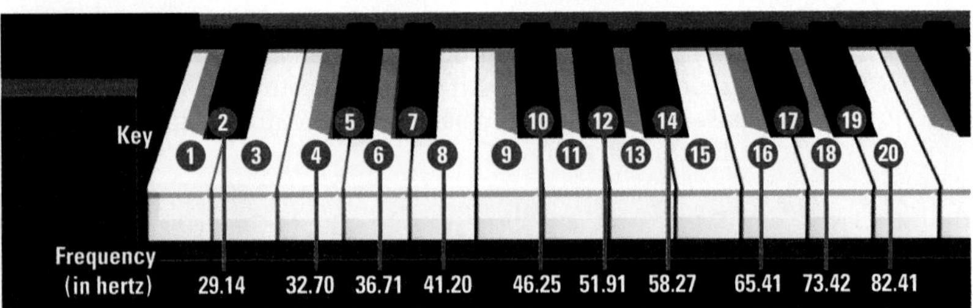

C

46. ★ EXTENDED RESPONSE In 1830, the population of the United States was 12,866,020. By 1890, the population was 62,947,714.

a. **Model** Assume the population growth from 1830 to 1890 was linear. Write a linear model for the U.S. population from 1830 to 1890. By about how much did the population grow per year from 1830 to 1890? **$y = 834694.9x + 12,866,020$; 834694.9 people**

b. **Model** Assume the population growth from 1830 to 1890 was exponential. Write an exponential model for the U.S. population from 1830 to 1890. By approximately what percent did the population grow per year from 1830 to 1890? **$y = 12,866,020(1.0268)^x$; about 2.68%**

c. **Explain** The U.S. population was 23,191,876 in 1850 and 38,558,371 in 1870. Which of the models in parts (a) and (b) is a better approximation of actual U.S. population for the time period 1850–1890? *Explain.* **See margin.**

★ = STANDARDIZED TEST PRACTICE

COMPOUND INTEREST **In Exercises 47–49, use the example below to find the balance of the account compounded with the given frequency.**

EXAMPLE **Use the general compound interest formula**

FINANCE You deposit \$1000 in an account that pays 3% annual interest. Find the balance after 8 years if the interest is compounded monthly.

Solution

The general formula for compound interest is $A = P\left(1 + \frac{r}{n}\right)^{nt}$. In this formula, P is the initial amount, called principal, in an account that pays interest at an annual rate r and that is compounded n times per year. The amount A (in dollars) is the amount in the account after t years.

Here, the interest is compounded monthly. So, $n = 12$.

$A = P\left(1 + \frac{r}{n}\right)^{nt}$ **Write compound interest formula.**

$= 1000\left(1 + \frac{0.03}{12}\right)^{12(8)}$ **Substitute 1000 for *P*, 0.03 for *r*, 12 for *n*, and 8 for *t*.**

$= 1000(1.0025)^{96}$ **Simplify.**

≈ 1270.868467 **Use a calculator.**

▶ The account balance after 8 years will be about \$1270.87.

47. Yearly **\$1266.77** **48.** Quarterly **\$1270.11** **49.** Daily ($n = 365$) **\$1271.24**

50. Daily; in an account compounded daily, each day you earn interest on both the principal and the interest that was accrued on the previous days.

50. ★ **WRITING** Which compounding frequency yields the highest balance in the account in the example above: monthly, yearly, quarterly, or daily? *Explain* why this is so.

51. **CHALLENGE** The value y (in dollars) of an investment of \$1000 is given by $y = 1000(1.05)^t$ where t is the time in years. The *doubling time* is the value of t for which the amount invested doubles, so that $1000(1.05)^t = 2000$, or $(1.05)^t = 2$. Graph the functions $y = (1.05)^t$ and $y = 2$ on a graphing calculator. Estimate the doubling time. **about 14 years**

MIXED REVIEW

PREVIEW
Prepare for Lesson 8.6 in Exs. 52–59.

Evaluate the expression.

52. $\left(\frac{1}{3}\right)^2$ *(p. 495)* $\frac{1}{9}$ **53.** $\left(\frac{1}{8}\right)^2$ *(p. 495)* $\frac{1}{64}$ **54.** $\left(\frac{1}{4}\right)^3$ *(p. 495)* $\frac{1}{64}$ **55.** $\left(\frac{1}{2}\right)^6$ *(p. 495)* $\frac{1}{64}$

56. $\left(\frac{2}{3}\right)^{-2}$ *(p. 503)* $\frac{9}{4}$ **57.** $\left(\frac{7}{5}\right)^{-2}$ *(p. 503)* $\frac{25}{49}$ **58.** $\left(\frac{4}{3}\right)^{-3}$ *(p. 503)* $\frac{27}{64}$ **59.** $\left(\frac{3}{2}\right)^{-4}$ *(p. 503)* $\frac{16}{81}$

Write an equation of the line shown. *(p. 283)*

60.

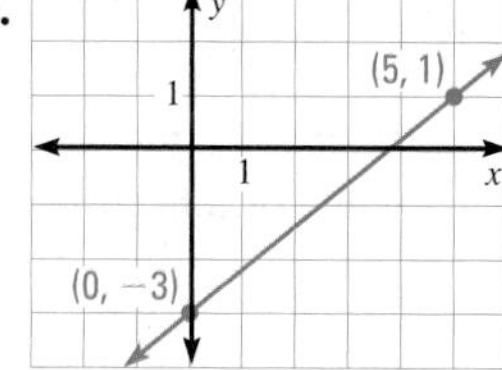

$y = \frac{4}{5}x - 3$

61.

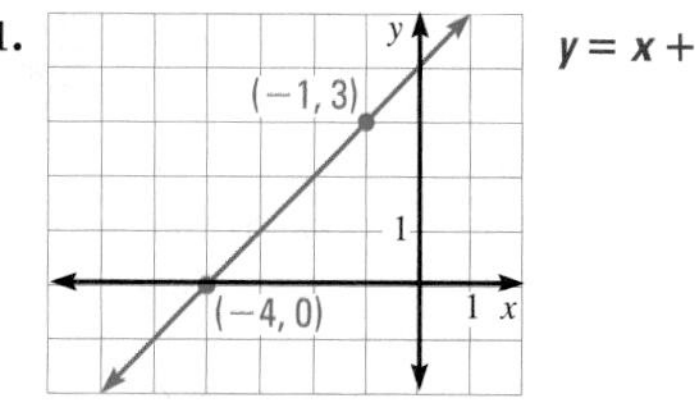

$y = x + 4$

5 ASSESS AND RETEACH

Daily Homework Quiz

Transparency Available

1. Graph $y = 1.4^x$.

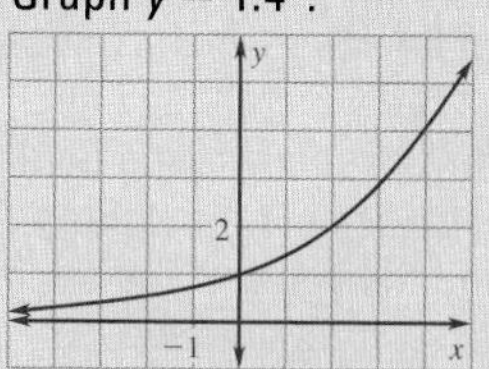

2. Your family bought a house for \$150,000 in 2000. The value of the house increases at an annual rate of 8%. What is the value of the house after 5 years? **about \$220,399**

Online Quiz

Available at **classzone.com**

Diagnosis/Remediation

- Practice A, B, C in Chapter Resource Book
- Study Guide in Chapter Resource Book
- Practice Workbook
- @HomeTutor

Challenge

Additional challenge is available in the Chapter Resource Book.

PROBLEM SOLVING WORKSHOP
LESSON 8.5

Using ALTERNATIVE METHODS

Alternative Strategy

Example 4 on page 522 can be solved by using a spreadsheet. A spreadsheet has the advantage of showing the value of the car each year after1984. If the student wants to find the value for a different year or knows the value of the car but not the year, all the information can be readily found on the spreadsheet. Should the student want to find the value of the car in future years, using the *fill down* feature on the spreadsheet will quickly furnish the value.

Avoiding Common Errors

Watch for students who enter the formula incorrectly. Suggest that they double-check their formulas for accuracy.

Reading Strategy

Point out the note on formatting a spreadsheet. Tell students that the number of decimal places becomes unwieldy if they do not format the cells to round to 2 decimal places.

Another Way to Solve Example 4, page 522

MULTIPLE REPRESENTATIONS In Example 4 on page 522, you saw how to solve a problem about the value of a collector car over time by using an exponential model. You can also solve the problem by using a spreadsheet.

PROBLEM

COLLECTOR CAR The owner of a 1953 Hudson Hornet convertible sold the car at an auction. The owner bought it in 1984 when its value was \$11,000. The value of the car increased at a rate of 6.9% per year.

a. Write a function that models the value of the car over time.

b. The auction took place in 2004. What was the approximate value of the car at the time of the auction? Round your answer to the nearest dollar.

METHOD

Using a Spreadsheet An alternative approach is to use a spreadsheet.

a. The model for the value of the car over time is $C = 11{,}000(1.069)^t$, as shown in Example 4 on page 522.

b. You can find the value of the car in 2004 by creating a spreadsheet.

STEP 1 **Create** a table showing the years since 1984 and the value of the car. Enter the car's value in 1984. To find the value in any year after 1984, multiply the car's value in the preceding year by the growth factor, as shown in cell B3 below.

FORMAT A SPREADSHEET
Format the spreadsheet so that calculations are rounded to 2 decimal places.

	A	B
1	Years since 1984, *t*	Value, *C* (dollars)
2	0	11000
3	1	=B2*1.069

STEP 2 **Find** the value of the car in 2004 by using the *fill down* feature until you get to the desired cell.

	A	B
1	Years since 1984, *t*	Value, *C* (dollars)
2	0	11000
3	1	11759
...	...	...
21	19	39081.31
22	20	41777.92

▸ From the spreadsheet, you can see the value of the car was about \$41,778 in 2004.

PROBLEM WHAT IF? Suppose the owner decided to sell the car when it was worth about \$28,000. In what year did the owner sell the car?

METHOD **Using a Spreadsheet** To solve the equation algebraically, you need to substitute 28,000 for C and solve for t, but you have not yet learned how to solve this type of equation. An alternative to the algebraic approach is using a spreadsheet.

STEP 1 **Use** the same spreadsheet as on the previous page.

STEP 2 **Find** when the value of the car is about \$28,000.

	A	B
1	Years since 1984, t	Value, C (dollars)
2	0	11000
...	...	...
15	13	26188.03
16	14	27995.01

The value of the car is about \$28,000 when $t = 14$.

▸ The owner sold the car in 1998.

PRACTICE

1. **TRANSPORTATION** In 1997 the average intercity bus fare for a particular state was \$20. For the period 1997–2000, the bus fare increased at a rate of about 12% each year.
   a. Write a function that models the intercity bus fare for the period 1997–2000. **See margin.**
   b. Find the intercity bus fare in 1998. Use two different methods to solve the problem. **\$22.40**
   c. In what year was the intercity bus fare \$28.10? *Explain* how you found your answer. **2000. *Sample answer:* Make a table of values.**

2. **ERROR ANALYSIS** *Describe* and correct the error in writing the function for part (a) of Exercise 1.

Let b be the bus fare (in dollars) and t be the number of years since 1997.
$b = 20(0.12)^t$

The growth factor should be 1.12, not 0.12; $b = 20(1.12)^t$.

3. **TECHNOLOGY** A computer's Central Processing Unit (CPU) is made up of transistors. One manufacturer released a CPU in May 1997 that had 7.5 million transistors. The number of transistors in the CPUs sold by the company increased at a rate of 3.9% per month.
   a. Write a function that models the number T (in millions) of transistors in the company's CPUs t months after May 1997. **$T = 7.5(1.039)^t$**
   b. Use a spreadsheet to find the number of transistors in a CPU released by the company in November 2000. **about 37.4 million**

4. **HOUSING** The value of a home in 2002 was \$150,000. The value of the home increased at a rate of about 6.5% per year.
   a. Write a function that models the value of the home over time. **See margin.**
   b. Use a spreadsheet to find the year in which the value of the home was about \$200,000. **2007**

Study Strategy

Suggest that students check their exponential growth models in the Practice problems against the model given at the top of page 522. If they are unsure on how to use the model, suggest that they review Example 4 on page 522.

1a. Let t represent the number of years since 1997 and F represent the bus fare. $F = 20(1.12)^t$

4a. Let V represent the home's value and t represent the number of years since 2002. $V = 150,000(1.065)^t$.

1 PLAN AND PREPARE

Explore the Concept

- Students will model a situation using an exponential function.
- This activity leads into the study of writing function rules in Example 1 in Lesson 8.6.

Materials

Each student or group of students will need:

- yarn
- scissors

Recommended Time

Work activity: 10 min
Discuss results: 5 min

Grouping

Students can work individually or in pairs. If students work in pairs, one student can fold and cut the yarn and the other student can record the data in the chart.

2 TEACH

Tips for Success

Make sure that students fold all the pieces of yarn in half at each stage and then cut all of the pieces.

Key Discovery

Some exponential functions model increases in value, while others model decreases.

3 ASSESS AND RETEACH

How does the function in Exercise 2 differ from the one in Exercise 1?. **The values in Exercise 2 are decreasing rather than increasing as in Exercise 1.**

1a. Yes. *Sample answer:* Each value is twice the value of the previous stage.

2a. Yes. *Sample answer:* Each value is half the value of the previous stage.

8.6 Exponential Models

MATERIALS • yarn • scissors

QUESTION **How can you model a situation using an exponential function?**

EXPLORE **Collect data so that you can write exponential models**

STEP 1 ***Fold and cut*** Take about 1 yard of yarn and consider it to be 1 unit long. Fold it in half and cut, as shown. You are left with two pieces of yarn, each half the length of the original piece of yarn.

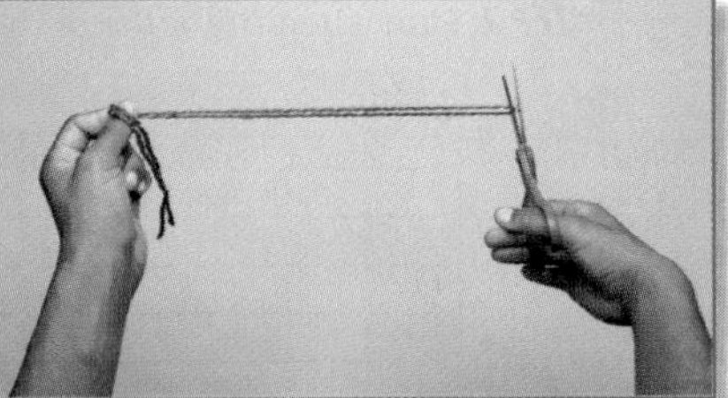

STEP 2 ***Copy and complete*** Copy the table. Notice that the row for stage 1 has the data from Step 1. For each successive stage, fold *all* the pieces of yarn in half and cut. Then record the number of new pieces and the length of each new piece until the table is complete.

Stage	Number of pieces	Length of each new piece
1	2	$\frac{1}{2}$
2	? **4**	? $\frac{1}{4}$
3	? **8**	? $\frac{1}{8}$
4	? **16**	? $\frac{1}{16}$
5	? **32**	? $\frac{1}{32}$

DRAW CONCLUSIONS **Use your observations to complete these exercises**

1. Use the data in the first and second columns of the table.
   a. Do the data represent an exponential function? *Explain* how you know. **See margin.**
   b. Write a function that models the number of pieces of yarn at stage x. $y = 2^x$
   c. Use the function to find the number of pieces of yarn at stage 10. **1024 pieces of yarn**
2. Use the data in the first and third columns of the table.
   a. Do the data represent an exponential function? *Explain* how you know. **See margin.**
   b. Write a function that models the length of each new piece of yarn at stage x. $y = \left(\frac{1}{2}\right)^x$
   c. Use the function to find the length of each new piece of yarn at stage 10. $\frac{1}{1024}$ **units**

8.6 Write and Graph Exponential Decay Functions

Before You wrote and graphed exponential growth functions.

Now You will write and graph exponential decay functions.

Why? So you can use a graph to solve a sports problem, as in Ex. 50.

Key Vocabulary
- **exponential decay**

A table of values represents an exponential function $y = ab^x$ provided successive y-values are multiplied by b each time the x-values increase by 1.

EXAMPLE 1 Write a function rule

Tell whether the table represents an exponential function. If so, write a rule for the function.

a.

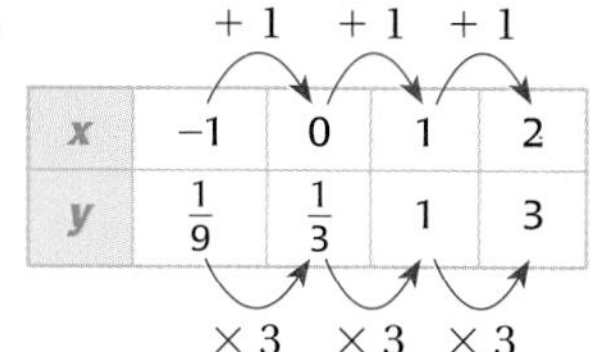

x	-1	0	1	2
y	$\frac{1}{9}$	$\frac{1}{3}$	1	3

The y-values are multiplied by 3 for each increase of 1 in x, so the table represents an exponential function of the form $y = ab^x$ with $b = 3$.

The value of y when $x = 0$ is $\frac{1}{3}$, so $a = \frac{1}{3}$.

The table represents the exponential function $y = \frac{1}{3} \cdot 3^x$.

b.

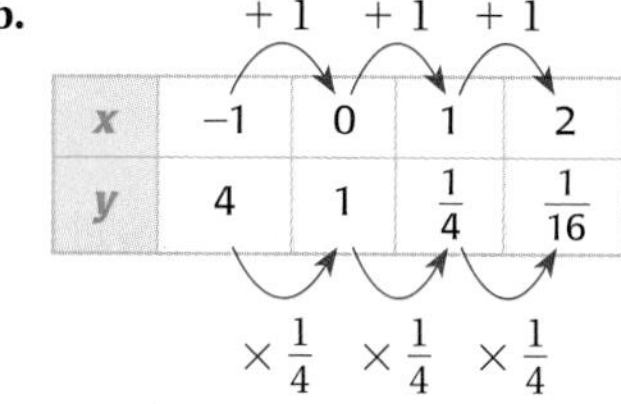

x	-1	0	1	2
y	4	1	$\frac{1}{4}$	$\frac{1}{16}$

The y-values are multiplied by $\frac{1}{4}$ for each increase of 1 in x, so the table represents an exponential function of the form $y = ab^x$ with $b = \frac{1}{4}$.

The value of y when $x = 0$ is 1, so $a = 1$.

The table represents the exponential function $y = \left(\frac{1}{4}\right)^x$.

✓ GUIDED PRACTICE for Example 1

1. Tell whether the table represents an exponential function. If so, write a rule for the function. **yes;** $y = \left(\frac{1}{5}\right)^x$

x	-1	0	1	2
y	5	1	$\frac{1}{5}$	$\frac{1}{25}$

1 PLAN AND PREPARE

Warm-Up Exercises

Transparency Available

1. Evaluate $\left(\frac{1}{2}\right)^3$. $\frac{1}{8}$
2. Evaluate $\left(\frac{1}{4}\right)^{-2}$. **16**
3. The table shows how much money Tess owes after w weeks. Write a rule for the function.

Week, w	0	1	2	3
Owes, m	50	45	40	35

$m = 50 - 5w$

Notetaking Guide

Transparency Available

Promotes interactive learning and notetaking skills.

Pacing

Basic: 2 days
Average: 2 days
Advanced: 2 days
Block: 1 block
- See *Teaching Guide/Lesson Plan.*

2 FOCUS AND MOTIVATE

Essential Question

Big Idea 3, p. 487

How do you write and graph exponential decay functions? **Tell students they will learn how to answer this question by using tables, graphs, and exponential decay models.**

NCTM STANDARDS

Standard 2: Understand patterns; Understand functions

Resource Planning Guide

Chapter Resource Book
- Teaching Guide/Lesson Plan
- Activity Master
- Practice levels A, B, C
- Study Guide
- Catch-up for Absent Students
- Problem Solving Workshop
- Challenge

Workbooks
- Notetaking Guide
- Practice Workbook

Teaching Options
- **Power Presentations** provides dynamic electronic teaching resources for the classroom.
- **Activity Generator** provides editable activities for all ability levels.

Interactive Technology
- Easy Planner
- Power Presentations
- Activity Generator
- Animated Algebra
- Test Generator
- Online Quiz
- eWorkbook
- eEdition
- @HomeTutor

Resources for English Learners
- Spanish Study Guide
- Multi-Language Visual Glossary
- Student Resources in Spanish

See also the *Differentiated Instruction Resources* for more strategies for meeting individual needs.

Motivating the Lesson

Your aunt bought a car two years ago for $12,000 and now she wants to sell it. She knows that the value of similar models has been decreasing at a rate of 17% per year. By knowing how to write and use an exponential decay model, she will be able to determine the value of the car at the time that she sells it.

3 TEACH

Extra Example 1

Tell whether the table represents an exponential function. If so, write a rule for the function.

x	-1	0	1	2
y	$\frac{1}{8}$	$\frac{1}{2}$	2	8

yes; $y = \frac{1}{2} \cdot 4^x$

Extra Example 2

Graph the function $y = \left(\frac{1}{3}\right)^x$ and identify its domain and range.
Domain: all real numbers; Range: all positive real numbers

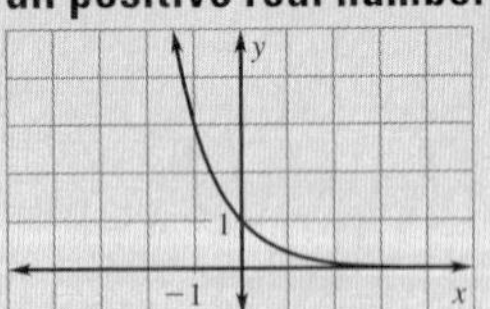

Key Question to Ask for Example 2

- How does the graph in Example 2 differ from a graph that represents exponential growth? **The graph in Example 2 falls from left to right and gets closer to the x-axis as x gets larger. A graph of exponential growth rises from left to right and gets closer to the x-axis as x gets smaller.**

2, 3. See Additional Answers beginning on p. AA1.

EXAMPLE 2 Graph an exponential function

Graph the function $y = \left(\frac{1}{2}\right)^x$ and identify its domain and range.

Solution

READ A GRAPH
Notice that the graph has a y-intercept of 1 and that it gets closer to the positive x-axis as the x-values increase.

STEP 1 **Make** a table of values. The domain is all real numbers.

x	-2	-1	0	1	2
y	4	2	1	$\frac{1}{2}$	$\frac{1}{4}$

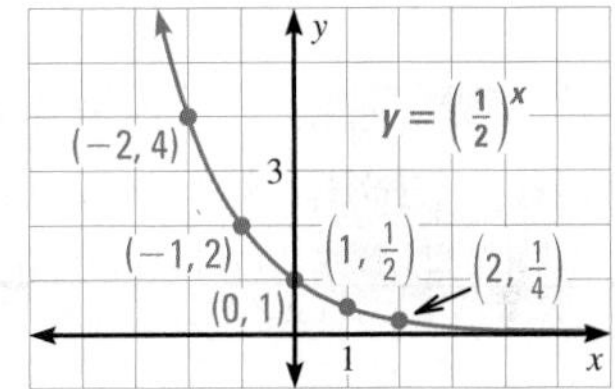

STEP 2 **Plot** the points.

STEP 3 **Draw** a smooth curve through the points. From either the table or the graph, you can see the range is all positive real numbers.

EXAMPLE 3 Compare graphs of exponential functions

Graph the functions $y = 3 \cdot \left(\frac{1}{2}\right)^x$ and $y = -\frac{1}{3} \cdot \left(\frac{1}{2}\right)^x$. Compare each graph with the graph of $y = \left(\frac{1}{2}\right)^x$.

Solution

DESCRIBE A FUNCTION
An exponential decay function has an unbroken graph, so the function is continuous, as discussed on p. 223.

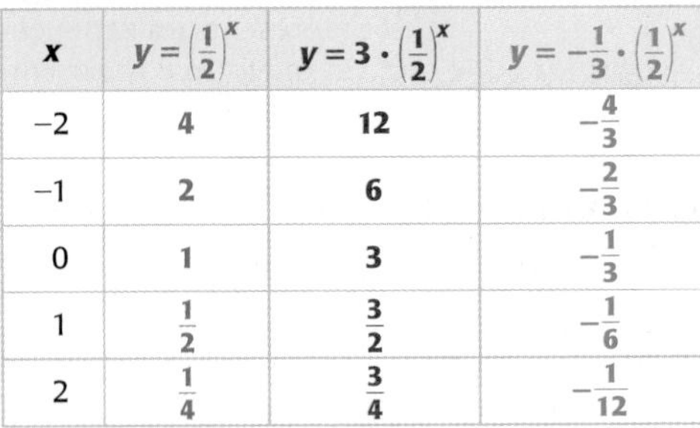

x	$y = \left(\frac{1}{2}\right)^x$	$y = 3 \cdot \left(\frac{1}{2}\right)^x$	$y = -\frac{1}{3} \cdot \left(\frac{1}{2}\right)^x$
-2	4	12	$-\frac{4}{3}$
-1	2	6	$-\frac{2}{3}$
0	1	3	$-\frac{1}{3}$
1	$\frac{1}{2}$	$\frac{3}{2}$	$-\frac{1}{6}$
2	$\frac{1}{4}$	$\frac{3}{4}$	$-\frac{1}{12}$

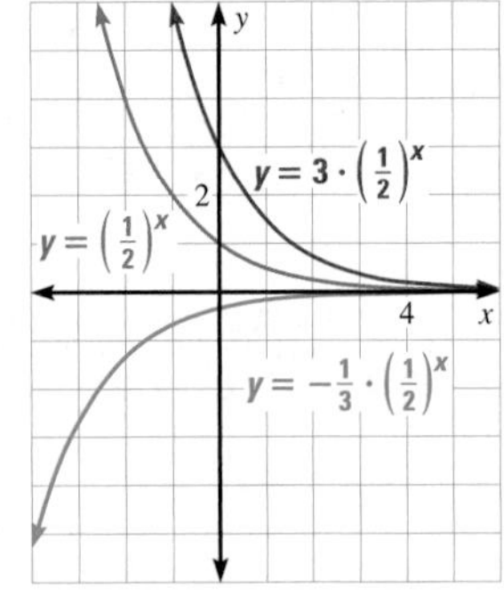

Because the y-values for $y = 3 \cdot \left(\frac{1}{2}\right)^x$ are 3 times the corresponding y-values for $y = \left(\frac{1}{2}\right)^x$, the graph of $y = 3 \cdot \left(\frac{1}{2}\right)^x$ is a vertical stretch of the graph of $y = \left(\frac{1}{2}\right)^x$.

Because the y-values for $y = -\frac{1}{3} \cdot \left(\frac{1}{2}\right)^x$ are $-\frac{1}{3}$ times the corresponding y-values for $y = \left(\frac{1}{2}\right)^x$, the graph of $y = -\frac{1}{3} \cdot \left(\frac{1}{2}\right)^x$ is a vertical shrink with reflection in the x-axis of the graph of $y = \left(\frac{1}{2}\right)^x$.

✓ GUIDED PRACTICE for Examples 2 and 3

2. See margin for art; domain: all real numbers, range: all positive real numbers.

2. Graph $y = (0.4)^x$ and identify its domain and range.
3. Graph $y = 5 \cdot (0.4)^x$. Compare the graph with the graph of $y = (0.4)^x$.
See margin for art; the graph is a vertical stretch of $y = (0.4)^x$.

COMPARE GRAPHS When $a > 0$ and $0 < b < 1$, the function $y = ab^x$ represents **exponential decay**. The graph of an exponential decay function falls from left to right. In comparison, the graph of an exponential growth function $y = ab^x$ where $a > 0$ and $b > 1$ rises from the left.

EXAMPLE 4 Classify and write rules for functions

Tell whether the graph represents *exponential growth* or *exponential decay*. Then write a rule for the function.

a.

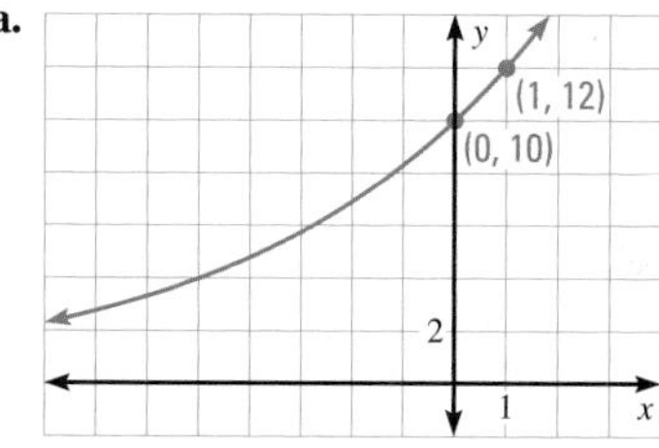

b.

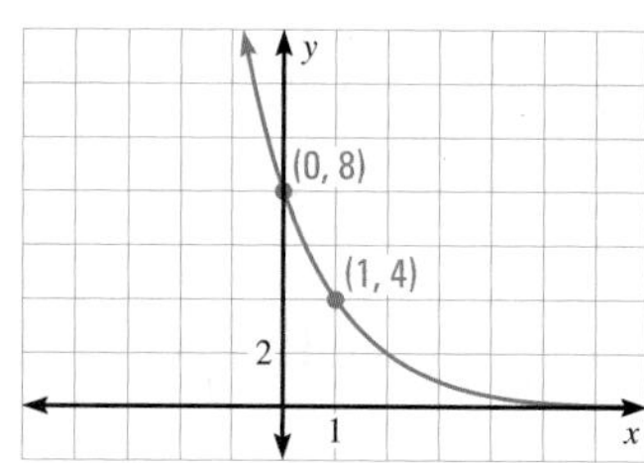

ANALYZE GRAPHS
For the function $y = ab^x$, where $x = 0$, the value of y is $y = ax^0 = a$. This means that the graph of $y = ab^x$ has a y-intercept of a.

Solution

a. The graph represents exponential growth ($y = ab^x$ where $b > 1$). The y-intercept is 10, so $a = 10$. Find the value of b by using the point (1, 12) and $a = 10$.

$y = ab^x$	**Write function.**
$12 = 10 \cdot b^1$	**Substitute.**
$1.2 = b$	**Solve.**

A function rule is $y = 10(1.2)^x$.

b. The graph represents exponential decay ($y = ab^x$ where $0 < b < 1$). The y-intercept is 8, so $a = 8$. Find the value of b by using the point (1, 4) and $a = 8$.

$y = ab^x$	**Write function.**
$4 = 8 \cdot b^1$	**Substitute.**
$0.5 = b$	**Solve.**

A function rule is $y = 8(0.5)^x$.

GUIDED PRACTICE for Example 4

4. The graph of an exponential function passes through the points (0, 10) and (1, 8). Graph the function. Tell whether the graph represents *exponential growth* or *exponential decay*. Write a rule for the function.
See margin for art; exponential decay; $y = 10 \cdot (0.8)^x$.

CONCEPT SUMMARY *For Your Notebook*

Exponential Growth and Decay

Exponential Growth

$y = ab^x$, $a > 0$ and $b > 1$

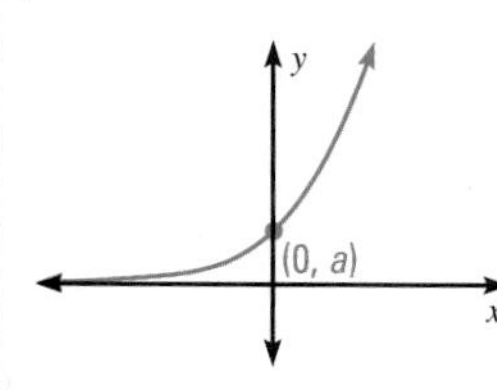

Exponential Decay

$y = ab^x$, $a > 0$ and $0 < b < 1$

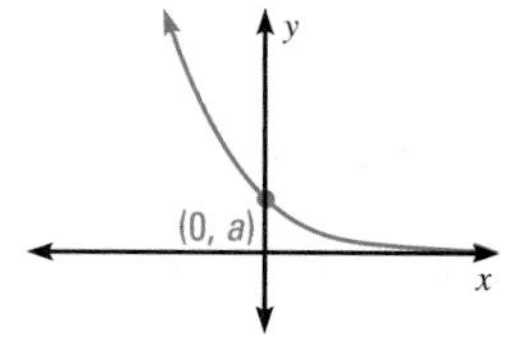

Differentiated Instruction

Visual Learners Have students include in their notebooks general sketches for the graphs of $y = ab^x$ for $a < 0$ and $b > 1$, and $y = ab^x$ for $a < 0$ and $0 < b < 1$. Students should note that even though the first graph is decreasing, it does not model exponential decay. Likewise, even though the second graph is increasing, it does not model exponential growth.

See also the *Differentiated Instruction Resources* for more strategies.

4.

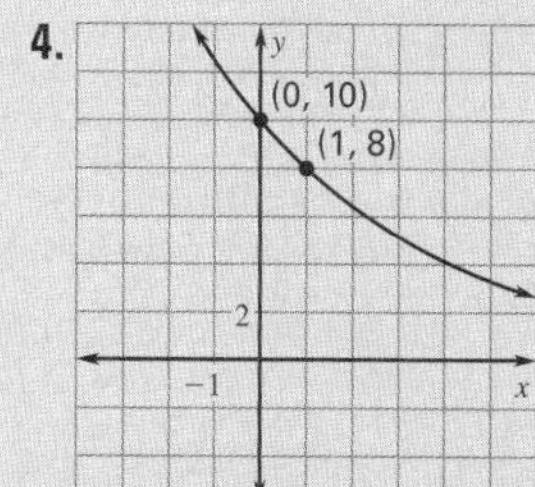

Extra Example 3

Graph the functions $y = 2 \cdot \left(\frac{1}{3}\right)^x$ and $y = -\frac{1}{2} \cdot \left(\frac{1}{3}\right)^x$. Compare each graph with the graph of $y = \left(\frac{1}{3}\right)^x$.

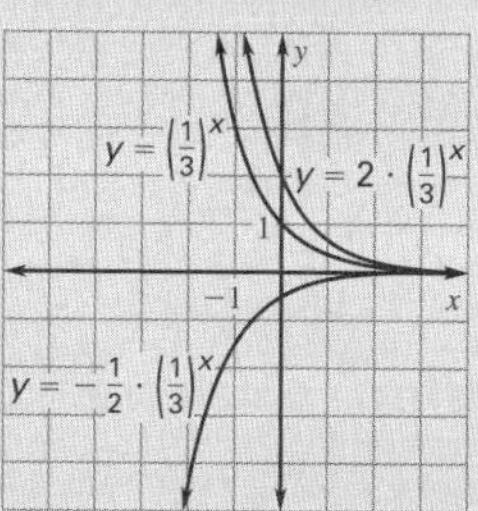

The graph of $y = 2 \cdot \left(\frac{1}{3}\right)^x$ is a vertical stretch of the graph of $y = \left(\frac{1}{3}\right)^x$. The graph of $y = -\frac{1}{2} \cdot \left(\frac{1}{3}\right)^x$ is a vertical shrink and reflection of the graph of $y = \left(\frac{1}{3}\right)^x$.

Key Question to Ask for Example 3

- Why is the graph of $y = 3 \cdot \left(\frac{1}{2}\right)^x$ a vertical stretch of the graph of $y = \left(\frac{1}{2}\right)^x$? **For given x-values, the y-values for $y = 3 \cdot \left(\frac{1}{2}\right)^x$ are 3 times as great as the y-values for $y = \left(\frac{1}{2}\right)^x$.**

Extra Example 4

Tell whether the graph represents exponential growth or exponential decay. Then write a rule for the function.

a.

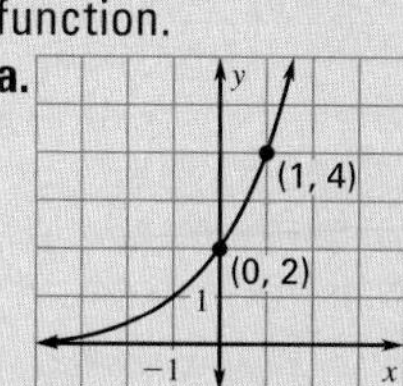

exponential growth; $y = 2(2)^x$

b.

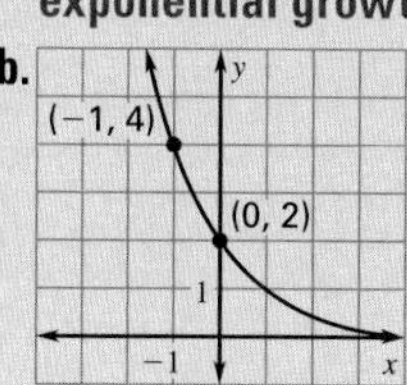

exponential decay; $y = 2(0.5)^x$

Extra Example 5

A farmer bought a tractor in 1999 for \$30,000. The value of the tractor has been decreasing at a rate of 18% per year.

a. Write a function that models the value of the tractor over time. $V = 30{,}000(1 - 0.18)^t$

b. What was the approximate value of the tractor in 2005? **about \$9120**

Key Question to Ask for Example 5

- Why do you subtract the decay rate from 1 in the exponential decay model? **Because the acreage is decreasing, the decay factor is less than 1.**

An **Animated Algebra** activity is available online for **Example 5**. This activity is also part of **Power Presentations**.

Closing the Lesson

Have students summarize the major points of the lesson and answer the Essential Question: How do you write and graph exponential decay functions?

- **The function $y = ab^x$ represents exponential decay when $a > 0$ and $0 < b < 1$.**
- **The exponential decay model is $y = a(1 - r)^t$, where a is the initial amount, $1 - r$ is the decay factor, and t is the time period.**

To write a function rule, use the form $y = ab^x$. Substitute the y-intercept for a and then use another point from the table to solve the equation for b. To graph a function of the form $y = ab^x$, create a table of values, plot the points, and connect the points with a smooth curve.

EXPONENTIAL DECAY When a quantity decays exponentially, it decreases by the same percent over equal time periods. To find the amount of the quantity left after t time periods, use the following model.

REWRITE EQUATIONS
Notice that you can rewrite $y = ab^x$ as $y = a(1 - r)^t$ by replacing b with $1 - r$ and x with t (for time).

KEY CONCEPT — *For Your Notebook*

Exponential Decay Model

$$y = a(1 - r)^t$$

- a is the **initial amount**.
- r is the **decay rate**.
- $1 - r$ is the **decay factor**.
- t is the **time period**.

The relationship between the decay rate r and the decay factor $1 - r$ is similar to the relationship between the growth rate and growth factor in an exponential growth model. You will explore this relationship in Exercise 45.

EXAMPLE 5 Solve a multi-step problem

FORESTRY The number of acres of Ponderosa pine forests decreased in the western United States from 1963 to 2002 by 0.5% annually. In 1963 there were about 41 million acres of Ponderosa pine forests.

a. Write a function that models the number of acres of Ponderosa pine forests in the western United States over time.

b. To the nearest tenth, about how many million acres of Ponderosa pine forests were there in 2002?

Solution

a. Let P be the number of acres (in millions), and let t be the time (in years) since 1963. The initial value is 41, and the decay rate is 0.005.

$P = a(1 - r)^t$ — **Write exponential decay model.**

$= 41(1 - 0.005)^t$ — **Substitute 41 for a and 0.005 for r.**

$= 41(0.995)^t$ — **Simplify.**

AVOID ERRORS
The decay rate in this example is 0.5%, or 0.005. So, the decay factor is $1 - 0.005$, or 0.995, not 0.005.

b. To find the number of acres in 2002, 39 years after 1963, substitute 39 for t.

$P = 41(0.995)^{39} \approx 33.7$ — **Substitute 39 for t. Use a calculator.**

▶ There were about 33.7 million acres of Ponderosa pine forests in 2002.

GUIDED PRACTICE for Example 5

5. **WHAT IF?** In Example 5, suppose the decay rate of the forests remains the same beyond 2002. About how many acres will be left in 2010? **about 32.4 million**

8.6 EXERCISES

HOMEWORK KEY

 = **WORKED-OUT SOLUTIONS** on p. WS19 for Exs. 7 and 49

★ = **STANDARDIZED TEST PRACTICE** Exs. 2, 19, 36, 45, and 49

◆ = **MULTIPLE REPRESENTATIONS** Ex. 50

SKILL PRACTICE

A

1. **VOCABULARY** What is the decay factor in the exponential decay model $y = a(1 - r)^t$? **$1 - r$**

2. ★ **WRITING** *Explain* how you can tell if a graph represents *exponential growth* or *exponential decay.* **See margin.**

EXAMPLE 1 on p. 531 for Exs. 3–6

WRITING FUNCTIONS Tell whether the table represents an exponential function. If so, write a rule for the function.

3.

x	−1	0	1	2
y	2	8	32	128

exponential function; $y = 8 \cdot 4^x$

4.

x	−1	0	1	2
y	50	10	2	0.4

exponential function; $y = 10(0.2)^x$

5.

x	−1	0	1	2
y	6	2	$\frac{2}{3}$	$\frac{2}{9}$

exponential function; $y = 2\left(\frac{1}{3}\right)^x$

6.

x	−1	0	1	2
y	−11	−7	−3	1

not an exponential function

EXAMPLE 2 on p. 532 for Exs. 7–18

GRAPHING FUNCTIONS Graph the function and identify its domain and range. **7–18. See margin.**

7. $y = \left(\frac{1}{5}\right)^x$
8. $y = \left(\frac{1}{6}\right)^x$
9. $y = \left(\frac{2}{3}\right)^x$
10. $y = \left(\frac{3}{4}\right)^x$
11. $y = \left(\frac{4}{5}\right)^x$
12. $y = \left(\frac{3}{5}\right)^x$
13. $y = (0.3)^x$
14. $y = (0.5)^x$
15. $y = (0.1)^x$
16. $y = (0.9)^x$
17. $y = (0.7)^x$
18. $y = (0.25)^x$

EXAMPLE 3 on p. 532 for Exs. 19–31

19. ★ **MULTIPLE CHOICE** The graph of which function is shown? **D**

Ⓐ $y = (0.25)^x$ Ⓑ $y = (0.5)^x$

Ⓒ $y = 0.25 \cdot (0.5)^x$ Ⓓ $y = 4 \cdot (0.5)^x$

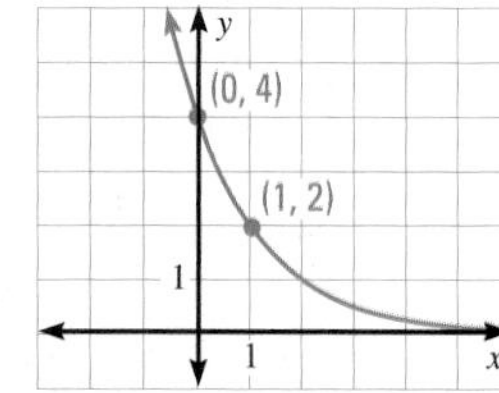

2. *Sample answer:* If the graph increases from left to right, then it represents growth; if it decreases from left to right, then it represents decay.

COMPARING FUNCTIONS Graph the function. Compare the graph with the graph of $y = \left(\frac{1}{4}\right)^x$. **20–31. See margin.**

20. $y = 5 \cdot \left(\frac{1}{4}\right)^x$
21. $y = 3 \cdot \left(\frac{1}{4}\right)^x$
22. $y = \frac{1}{2} \cdot \left(\frac{1}{4}\right)^x$
23. $y = \frac{1}{3} \cdot \left(\frac{1}{4}\right)^x$
24. $y = 0.2 \cdot \left(\frac{1}{4}\right)^x$
25. $y = 1.5 \cdot \left(\frac{1}{4}\right)^x$
26. $y = -5 \cdot \left(\frac{1}{4}\right)^x$
27. $y = -3 \cdot \left(\frac{1}{4}\right)^x$
28. $y = -\frac{1}{2} \cdot \left(\frac{1}{4}\right)^x$
29. $y = -\frac{1}{3} \cdot \left(\frac{1}{4}\right)^x$
30. $y = -0.2 \cdot \left(\frac{1}{4}\right)^x$
31. $y = -1.5 \cdot \left(\frac{1}{4}\right)^x$

4 PRACTICE AND APPLY

Assignment Guide

Answer Transparencies available for all exercises

Basic:
Day 1: pp. 535–538
Exs. 1–18, 63–66
Day 2: pp. 535–538
Exs. 19–35 odd, 36–40, 47–50, 54–62 even

Average:
Day 1: pp. 535–538
Exs. 1–6, 10–18, 32–34, 63–66
Day 2: pp. 535–538
Exs. 19, 20–30 even, 35–44, 47–52, 55, 58, 61

Advanced:
Day 1: pp. 535–538
Exs. 1, 4–6, 12–18, 32–37, 63–66
Day 2: pp. 535–538
Exs. 19, 24–31, 38–53*, 56, 59, 62

Block:
pp. 535–538
Exs. 1–6, 10–19, 20–30 even, 32–44, 47–52, 55, 58, 61, 63–66

Differentiated Instruction

See *Differentiated Instruction Resources* for suggestions on addressing the needs of a diverse classroom.

Homework Check

For a quick check of student understanding of key concepts, go over the following exercises:

Basic: 4, 8, 21, 38, 47
Average: 5, 12, 24, 39, 48
Advanced: 6, 16, 28, 40, 49

Extra Practice

- Student Edition, p. 945
- Chapter Resource Book: Practice levels A, B, C

Practice Worksheet

An easily-readable reduced practice page (with answers) for this lesson can be found on p. 486C.

7–18, 20–31. See Additional Answers beginning on p. AA1.

Avoiding Common Errors

Exercises 7–18 Some students' graphs may cross the x-axis. Remind these students that graphs of exponential functions get closer and closer to the x-axis, but do not cross it.

Graphing Calculator

Exercises 20–31 Students may want to use their graphing calculators to compare the graphs. Remind them to use parentheses around the fractions and carets to indicate the exponent.

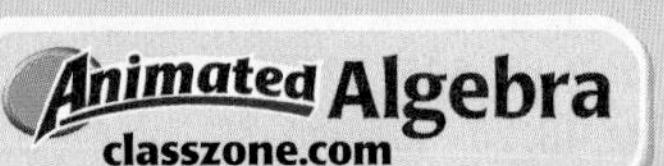

An **Animated Algebra** activity is available online for **Exercise 38.** This activity is also part of **Power Presentations**.

35. initial amount: 90,000 people, decay factor: 0.975, decay rate: 2.5%; Let P represent the population and t represent the number of years. $P = 90{,}000(0.975)^t$

45. To find t, divide the number of days, 40, by the half-life, 10. Then $A = 100(0.5)^4 = 6.25$ grams.

37. The decay rate, r, is 0.14. So the decay factor $(1 - r)$ should be 0.86, not 0.14; $y = 25{,}000(0.86)^t$.

EXAMPLE 4 on p. 533 for Exs. 38–40

38. exponential decay; $y = 6 \cdot 0.8^x$

41b. The graph is a vertical stretch with a reflection in the x-axis.

41c. The graph is a vertical shift up 1 unit.

46. *Sample answer:* The graphs are the same. By the product of powers property, $4^{x-2} = 4^x \cdot 4^{-2}$, or $\frac{1}{16} \cdot 4^x$.

B **MATCHING Match the function with its graph.**

32. $y = (0.2)^x$ **A** **33.** $y = 5(0.2)^x$ **C** **34.** $y = \frac{1}{2}(0.2)^x$ **B**

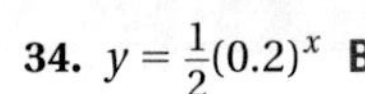

A.

B.

C.

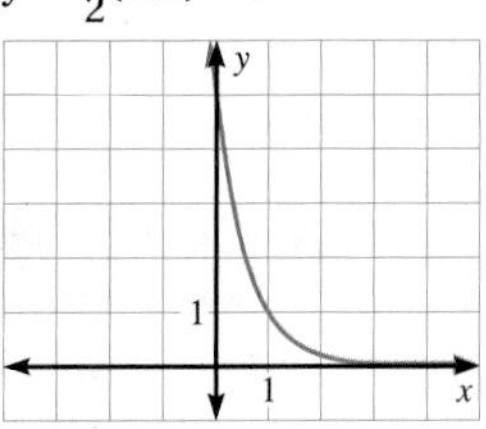

35. POPULATION A population of 90,000 decreases by 2.5% per year. Identify the initial amount, the decay factor, and the decay rate. Then write a function that models the population over time. **See margin.**

36. ★ **MULTIPLE CHOICE** What is the decay rate of the function $y = 4(0.97)^t$? **D**

Ⓐ 4 Ⓑ 0.97 Ⓒ 0.3 Ⓓ 0.03

37. ERROR ANALYSIS In 2004 a person purchased a car for $25,000. The value of the car decreased by 14% annually. *Describe* and correct the error in writing a function that models the value of the car since 2004.

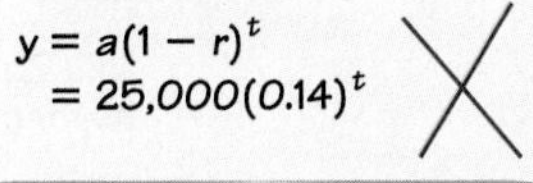
$y = a(1 - r)^t$
$= 25{,}000(0.14)^t$

RECOGNIZING EXPONENTIAL MODELS Tell whether the graph represents *exponential growth* or *exponential decay*. Then write a rule for the function.

38.

39.

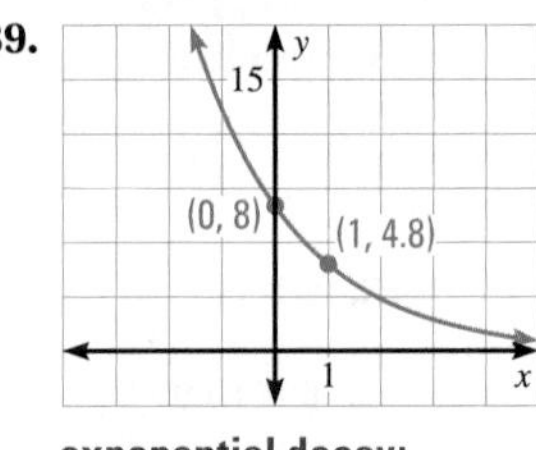

exponential decay; $y = 8 \cdot 0.6^x$

40.

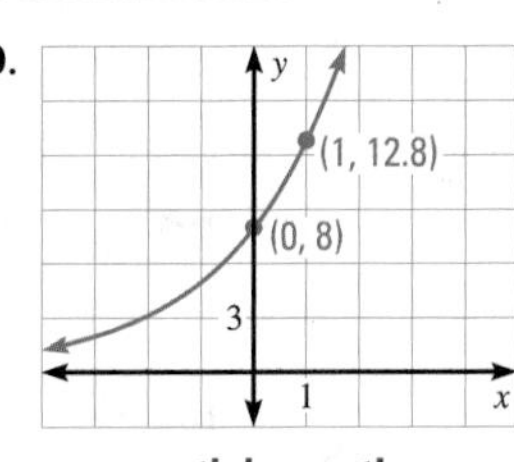

exponential growth; $y = 8 \cdot 1.6^x$

Animated Algebra at classzone.com

41. REASONING Without graphing, explain how the graphs of the given functions are related to the graph of $f(x) = (0.5)^x$.

a. $m(x) = \frac{1}{3} \cdot (0.5)^x$ **b.** $n(x) = -4 \cdot (0.5)^x$ **c.** $p(x) = (0.5)^x + 1$

The graph is a vertical shrink.

C **CHALLENGE Write an exponential function of the form $y = ab^x$ whose graph passes through the given points.**

42. $(0, 1), \left(2, \frac{1}{4}\right)$ $y = \left(\frac{1}{2}\right)^x$ **43.** $(1, 20), (2, 4)$ $y = 100 \cdot \left(\frac{1}{5}\right)^x$ **44.** $\left(1, \frac{3}{2}\right), \left(2, \frac{3}{4}\right)$ $y = 3 \cdot \left(\frac{1}{2}\right)^x$

45. ★ **WRITING** The *half-life* of a radioactive substance is the time required for half the substance to decay. The amount A (in grams) of a 100 gram sample of a radioactive substance remaining after t half-lives is given by $A = 100(0.5)^t$. Suppose the substance has a half-life of 10 days. *Explain* how to find the amount left after 40 days. Then find the amount. **See margin.**

46. CHALLENGE *Compare* the graphs of the functions $f(x) = 4^{x-2}$ and $g(x) = \frac{1}{16} \cdot 4^x$. Use properties of exponents to explain your observation.

○ = WORKED-OUT SOLUTIONS for on p. WS1 ★ = STANDARDIZED TEST PRACTICE

= MULTIPLE REPRESENTATIONS

PROBLEM SOLVING

GRAPHING CALCULATOR **You may wish to use a graphing calculator to complete the following Problem Solving exercises.**

EXAMPLE 5 [A] on p. 534 for Exs. 47–50

47. CELL PHONES You purchase a cell phone for \$125. The value of the cell phone decreases by about 20% annually. Write a function that models the value of the cell phone over time. Then find the value of the cell phone after 3 years. **Let V represent the value of the cell phone and t represent the number of years since purchase, $V = 125(0.8)^t$; \$64.**

@HomeTutor for problem solving help at classzone.com

48. ANIMAL POPULATION Scientists studied the population of a species of bat in some caves in Missouri from 1983 to 2003. In 1983, there were 141,200 bats living in the caves. That number decreased by about 11% annually until 2003.

a. Identify the initial amount, the decay factor, and the decay rate.

b. Write a function that models the number of bats since 1983. Then find the number of bats in 2003.

@HomeTutor for problem solving help at classzone.com

48a. initial amount: 141,200; decay factor: 0.89; decay rate: 11%

48b. Let B represent the number of bats and t represent the number of years since 1983, $B = 141{,}200(0.89)^t$; 13,729 bats.

(49.) ★ **SHORT RESPONSE** In 2003 a family bought a boat for \$4000. The boat depreciates (loses value) at a rate of 7% annually. In 2006 a person offers to buy the boat for \$3000. Should the family sell the boat? *Explain.*
No. *Sample answer:* The boat's value is about \$3217.

50. ◆ **MULTIPLE REPRESENTATIONS** There are a total of 128 teams at the start of a citywide 3-on-3 basketball tournament. Half of the teams are eliminated after each round.

a. Writing a Model Write a function for the number of teams left after x rounds. **$f(x) = 128(0.5)^x$**

b. Making a Table Make a table for the function using $x = 0, 1, 2, \ldots, 7$. **See margin.**

c. Drawing a Graph Use the table in part (b) to graph the function. After which round are there 4 teams left in the tournament?
See margin for art; round 5.

[B] **51. GUITARS** The frets on a guitar are the small metal bars that divide the fingerboard. The distance d (in inches) between the nut and the first fret or any two consecutive frets can be modeled by the function $d = 1.516(0.9439)^f$ where f is the number of the fret farthest from the nut.

a. Identify the decay factor and the decay rate for the model.

b. What is the distance between the nut and the first fret? **about 1.431 in.**

c. The distance between the 12th and 13th frets is about half the distance between the nut and the first fret. Use this fact to find the distance between the 12th and 13th frets. Use the model to verify your answer. **about 0.716 in.**

51a. decay factor: 0.9439, decay rate: 5.61%

Study Strategy

Exercise 48 Suggest that students use the exponential decay model on page 534 to check their solutions to parts (a) and (b).

Vocabulary

Exercise 49 You may want to ask a student to use a dictionary or thesaurus to define the word *depreciate*. Have the student look up the word *appreciate* as an antonym to depreciate. Then ask them to discuss the relationship of these terms to exponential functions.

Internet Reference

Exercise 53 More information about maximal oxygen consumption can be found at www.nismat.org/physcor/max_o2.html

50b.

Rounds completed	Teams remaining
0	128
1	64
2	32
3	16
4	8
5	4
6	2
7	1

50c.

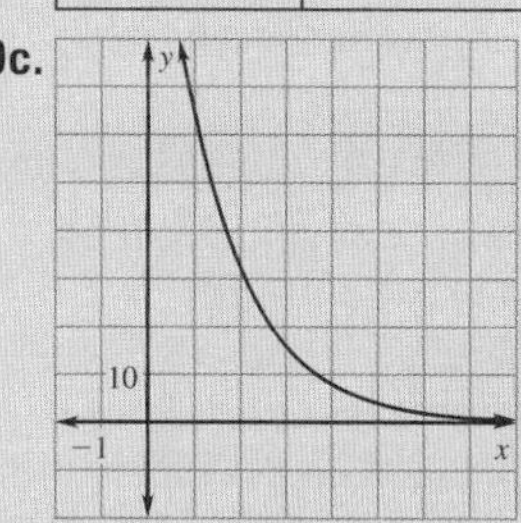

5 ASSESS AND RETEACH

Daily Homework Quiz

Transparency Available

1. Graph $y = \left(\frac{1}{3}\right)^x$.

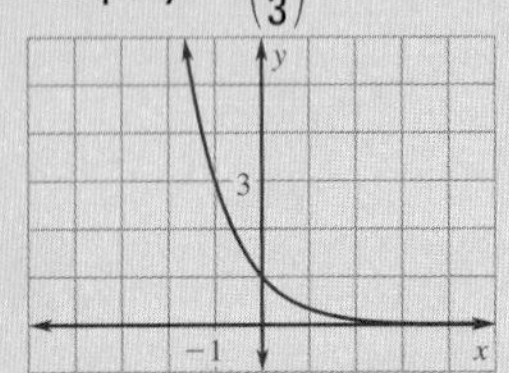

2. The population in a town has been declining at a rate of 2% per year since 2001. The population was 84,223 in 2001. What was the population in 2006? **about 76,130**

Online Quiz

Available at **classzone.com**

Diagnosis/Remediation

- Practice A, B, C in Chapter Resource Book
- Study Guide in Chapter Resource Book
- Practice Workbook
- @HomeTutor

Challenge

Additional challenge is available in the Chapter Resource Book.

Quiz

An easily-readable reduced copy of the quiz (with answers) on Lessons 8.5–8.6 from the Assessment Book can be found on p. 486E.

53b.

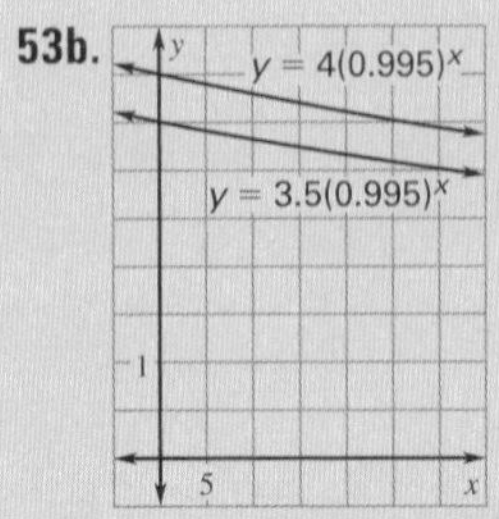

Quiz 1–6. See Additional Answers beginning on p. AA1.

52. CHALLENGE A college student finances a computer that costs \$1850. The financing plan states that as long as a minimum monthly payment of 2.25% of the remaining balance is made, the student does not have to pay interest for 24 months. The student makes only the minimum monthly payments until the last payment. What is the amount of the last payment if the student buys the computer without paying interest? Round your answer to the nearest cent. **\$1096.12**

C **53. MULTI-STEP PROBLEM** Maximal oxygen consumption is the maximum volume of oxygen (in liters per minute) that the body uses during exercise. Maximal oxygen consumption varies from person to person and decreases with age by about 0.5% per year after age 25 for active adults.

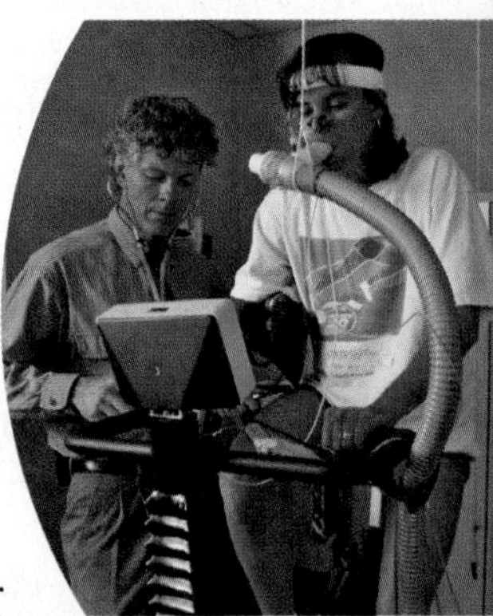

a. **Model** A 25-year-old female athlete has a maximal oxygen consumption of 4 liters per minute. Another 25-year-old female athlete has a maximal oxygen consumption of 3.5 liters per minute. Write a function for each athlete that models the maximal consumption each year after age 25. $y = 4(0.995)^x$, $y = 3.5(0.995)^x$

b. **Graph** Graph the models in the same coordinate plane. **See margin.**

c. **Estimate** About how old will the first athlete be when her maximal oxygen consumption is equal to what the second athlete's maximal oxygen consumption is at age 25? **about 52 yr**

MIXED REVIEW

PREVIEW Prepare for Lesson 9.1 in Exs. 54–62.

Simplify the expression. *(p. 96)*

54. $-12x + (-3x)$ $\mathbf{-15x}$
55. $8x - 3x$ $\mathbf{5x}$
56. $14 + x + 2x$ $\mathbf{14 + 3x}$
57. $7(2x + 1) - 5$ $\mathbf{14x + 2}$
58. $13x + (x - 4)5$ $\mathbf{18x - 20}$
59. $3x + 6(x + 9)$ $\mathbf{9x + 54}$
60. $(5 - x) + x$ **5**
61. $(3x - 4)7 + 21$ $\mathbf{21x - 7}$
62. $-(x - 1) - x^2$ $\mathbf{-x^2 - x + 1}$

Solve the equation.

63. $x + 14 = 8$ *(p. 134)* **−6**
64. $8x - 7 = 17$ *(p. 141)* **3**
65. $4x + 2x - 6 = 18$ *(p. 148)* **4**
66. $2x - 7(x + 5) = 20$ *(p. 148)* **−11**

QUIZ for Lessons 8.5–8.6

Graph the function. 1–6. **See margin.**

1. $y = \left(\frac{5}{2}\right)^x$ *(p. 520)*
2. $y = 3 \cdot \left(\frac{1}{4}\right)^x$ *(p. 531)*
3. $y = \frac{1}{4} \cdot 3^x$ *(p. 520)*
4. $y = (0.1)^x$ *(p. 531)*
5. $y = 10 \cdot 5^x$ *(p. 520)*
6. $y = 7(0.4)^x$ *(p. 531)*

7. **COINS** You purchase a coin from a coin collector for \$25. Each year the value of the coin increases by 8%. Write a function that models the value of the coin over time. Then find the value of the coin after 10 years. Round to the nearest cent. *(p. 520)*

7. Let V represent the value of the coin and t represent the number of years since purchase, $V = 25(1.08)^t$; about \$53.97.

EXTRA PRACTICE for Lesson 8.6, p. 945

ONLINE QUIZ at classzone.com

Relate Geometric Sequences to Exponential Functions

GOAL Identify, graph, and write geometric sequences.

Key Vocabulary
- **geometric sequence**
- **common ratio**

In a **geometric sequence**, the ratio of any term to the previous term is constant. This constant ratio is called the **common ratio** and is denoted by r.

A geometric sequence with first term a_1 and common ratio r has the form a_1, a_1r, a_1r^2, a_1r^3, ... For instance, if $a_1 = 5$ and $r = 2$, the sequence 5, $5 \cdot 2$, $5 \cdot 2^2$, $5 \cdot 2^3$, . . . , or 5, 10, 20, 40, . . . , is geometric.

EXAMPLE 1 Identify a geometric sequence

Tell whether the sequence is *arithmetic* or *geometric*. Then write the next term of the sequence.

a. 3, 6, 9, 12, 15, . . .

b. 128, 64, 32, 16, 8, . . .

Solution

a. The first term is $a_1 = 3$. Find the ratios of consecutive terms:

$\frac{a_2}{a_1} = \frac{6}{3} = 2$ $\quad \frac{a_3}{a_2} = \frac{9}{6} = 1\frac{1}{2}$ $\quad \frac{a_4}{a_3} = \frac{12}{9} = 1\frac{1}{3}$ $\quad \frac{a_5}{a_4} = \frac{15}{12} = 1\frac{1}{4}$

Because the ratios are not constant, the sequence is not geometric. To see if the sequence is arithmetic, find the differences of consecutive terms.

$a_2 - a_1 = 6 - 3 = 3$ $\quad a_3 - a_2 = 9 - 6 = 3$

$a_4 - a_3 = 12 - 9 = 3$ $\quad a_5 - a_4 = 15 - 12 = 3$

The common difference is 3, so the sequence is arithmetic. The next term of the sequence is $a_6 = a_5 + 3 = 18$.

b. The first term is $a_1 = 128$. Find the ratios of consecutive terms:

$\frac{a_2}{a_1} = \frac{64}{128} = \frac{1}{2}$ $\quad \frac{a_3}{a_2} = \frac{32}{64} = \frac{1}{2}$ $\quad \frac{a_4}{a_3} = \frac{16}{32} = \frac{1}{2}$ $\quad \frac{a_5}{a_4} = \frac{8}{16} = \frac{1}{2}$

Because the ratios are constant, the sequence is geometric. The common ratio is $\frac{1}{2}$. The next term of the sequence is $a_6 = a_5 \cdot \frac{1}{2} = 4$.

REVIEW ARITHMETIC SEQUENCES
For help with identifying an arithmetic sequence and finding a common difference, see p. 309.

EXAMPLE 2 Graph a geometric sequence

To graph the sequence from part (b) of Example 1, let each term's position number in the sequence be the x-value. The term is the corresponding y-value. Then make and plot the points.

Position, *x*	1	2	3	4	5
Term, *y*	128	64	32	16	8

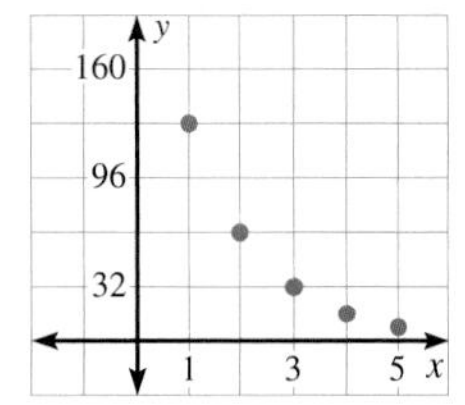

ANALYZE A GRAPH
Notice that the graph in Example 2 appears to be exponential.

1 PLAN AND PREPARE

Warm-Up Exercises

1. Write the next term in the pattern 1, 2, 4, 7, 11, ... **16**
2. Bill earns $16 in 2 hours, $32 in 4 hours, and $48 in 6 hours. What does he earn in 12 hours? **$96**

2 FOCUS AND MOTIVATE

Essential Question

Big Idea 3, p. 487

How do you identify and write geometric sequences? **Tell students they will learn how to answer this question by examining patterns and writing rules.**

3 TEACH

Extra Example 1

Tell whether the sequence is *arithmetic* or *geometric*. Then write the next term of the sequence.

a. 81, 77, 73, 69, 65, . . . **arithmetic; 61**

b. 3, 6, 12, 24, 48, . . . **geometric; 96**

Extra Example 2

Graph the geometric sequence from part b of Extra Example 1.

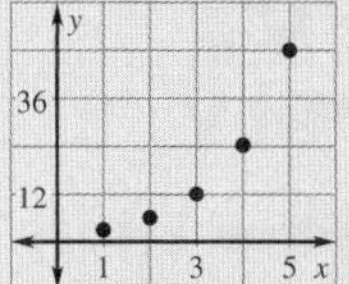

NCTM STANDARDS

Standard 2: Analyze situations using algebraic symbols

Standard 9: Grasp how mathematical ideas interconnect

Extra Example 3

Write a rule for the nth term of the geometric sequence in Extra Example 1. Then find a_{10}.
$a_n = 3 \cdot 2^{n-1}$; $a_{10} = 1536$

Key Question to Ask for Example 3

- Can you substitute any term in the sequence for a_1? Explain. **No; the correct terms would not be generated if a term other than a_1 were substituted.**

Closing the Lesson

Have students summarize the major points of the lesson and answer the Essential Question: How do you identify and write geometric sequences?

- **In a geometric sequence, the ratio of any term to the previous term is constant.**
- **To find the nth term of a geometric sequence, use the general rule $a_n = a_1r^{n-1}$.**

To identify a geometric sequence, find the ratios of consecutive terms. If the ratios are constant, the sequence is geometric. Use the general rule for a geometric sequence to write a specific rule by substituting the first term in the sequence for a_1 and the ratio for r. Substitute the position in the sequence for n to find the nth term.

4 PRACTICE AND APPLY

Avoiding Common Errors

Exercises 1–6 Some students may only look for a common difference between terms of a sequence and fail to see that a sequence is geometric. Remind students to check the ratios of consecutive terms and then determine if the ratios are constant.

1–6. See Additional Answers beginning on p. AA1.

FUNCTIONS The table shows that a rule for finding the nth term of a geometric sequence is $a_n = a_1r^{n-1}$. Notice that the rule is an exponential function.

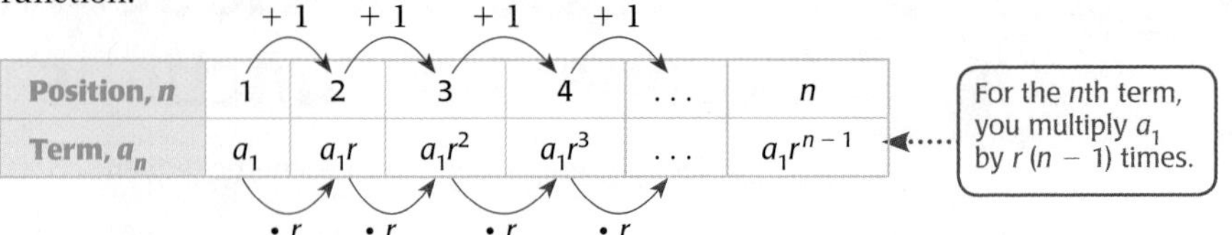

Position, n	1	2	3	4	...	n
Term, a_n	a_1	a_1r	a_1r^2	a_1r^3	...	a_1r^{n-1}

KEY CONCEPT *For Your Notebook*

General Rule for a Geometric Sequence

The nth term of a geometric sequence with first term a_1 and common ratio r is given by: $a_n = a_1r^{n-1}$.

EXAMPLE 3 Write a rule for a geometric sequence

Write a rule for the nth term of the geometric sequence in Example 1. Then find a_{10}.

Solution

To write a rule for the nth term of the sequence, substitute the values for a_1 and r in the general rule $a_n = a_1r^{n-1}$. Because $a_1 = 128$ and $r = \frac{1}{2}$, $a_n = 128 \cdot \left(\frac{1}{2}\right)^{n-1}$. The 10th term of the sequence is $a_{10} = 128 \cdot \left(\frac{1}{2}\right)^{10-1} = \frac{1}{4}$.

PRACTICE

EXAMPLES 1, 2, and 3 on pp. 539–540 for Exs. 1–10

Tell whether the sequence is *arithmetic* or *geometric*. Then graph the sequence. **1–6. See margin for art.**

1. 3, 12, 48, 192, ... **geometric**
2. 7, 16, 25, 34, ... **arithmetic**
3. 34, 28, 22, 16, ... **arithmetic**
4. 1024, 128, 16, 2, ... **geometric**
5. 9, −18, 36, −72, ... **geometric**
6. 29, 43, 57, 71, ... **arithmetic**

Write a rule for the nth term of the geometric sequence. Then find a_7.

7. 1, −5, 25, −125, ... **$a_n = (-5)^{n-1}$; 15,625**
8. 13, 26, 52, 104, ... **$a_n = 13 \cdot 2^{n-1}$; 832**
9. 432, 72, 12, 2, ... **$a_n = 432\left(\frac{1}{6}\right)^{n-1}$; $\frac{1}{108}$**

10. **E-MAIL** A chain e-mail instructs the recipient to forward the e-mail to four more people. The table shows the number of rounds of sending the e-mail and the number of new e-mails generated. Write a rule for the nth term of the sequence. Then graph the first six terms of the sequence. **$a_n = 4^{n-1}$; see margin for art.**

Number of rounds sending e-mail, n	1	2	3	4
Number of new e-mails generated, a_n	1	4	16	64

10.
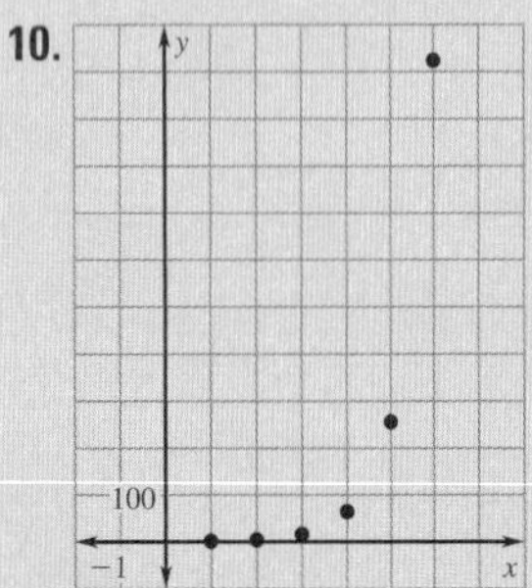

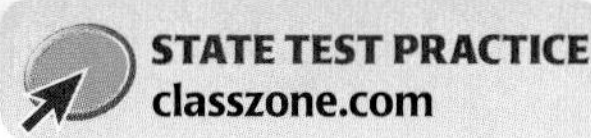

MIXED REVIEW *of Problem Solving*

STATE TEST PRACTICE classzone.com

Lessons 8.4–8.6

1. MULTI-STEP PROBLEM The radius of the sun is about 96,600,000 kilometers. The radius of Earth is about 6370 kilometers. **a–c. See margin.**

a. Write each radius in scientific notation.

b. The surface area S of a sphere with radius r is given by $S = 4\pi r^2$. Assume the sun and Earth are perfect spheres. Find their surface areas. Write your answers in scientific notation.

c. What is the ratio of the surface area of the sun to the surface area of Earth? What does the ratio tell you?

2. SHORT RESPONSE The graph shows the value of a truck over time.

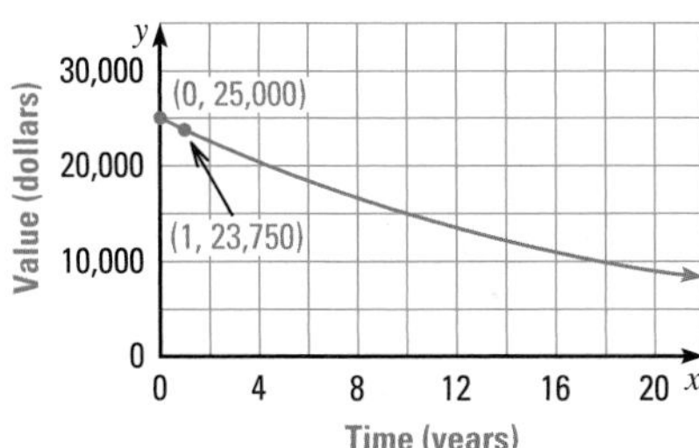

a. Write an equation for the function whose graph is shown. $y = 25{,}000(0.95)^x$

b. At what rate is the truck losing value? *Explain.* **5%; the decay rate for the truck is 0.05, or 5%.**

3. GRIDDED ANSWER A new laptop computer costs \$2000. The value of the computer decreases over time. The value V (in dollars) of the computer after t years is given by the function $V = 2000(0.82)^t$. What is the decay rate, written as a decimal, of the value of the computer? **0.18**

4. OPEN-ENDED The value of a house in Iowa increased, on average, at a rate of about 4% per quarter from the first quarter in 2001 to the last quarter in 2004. Write a function that models the value of the house over time. Choose an initial value of the house and a quarter such that the value of the house is about \$275,000. **See margin.**

5. EXTENDED RESPONSE A musician is saving money to buy a new snare drum. The musician puts \$100 in a savings account that pays 3% annual interest compounded yearly. **a–c. See margin.**

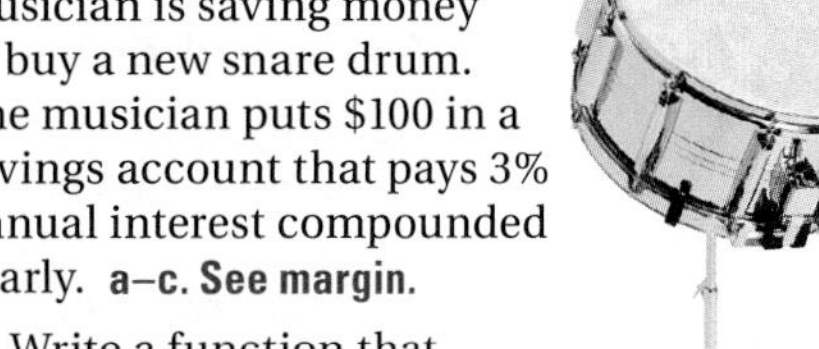

a. Write a function that models the amount of money in the account over time.

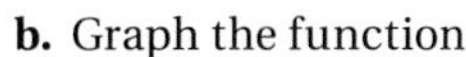

b. Graph the function.

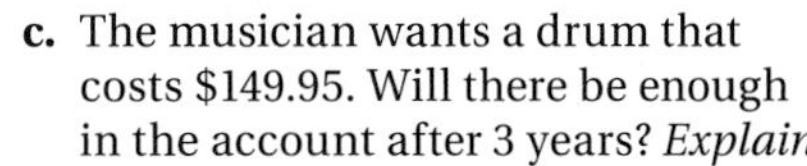

c. The musician wants a drum that costs \$149.95. Will there be enough in the account after 3 years? *Explain.*

6. MULTI-STEP PROBLEM The graph shows the value of a business over time.

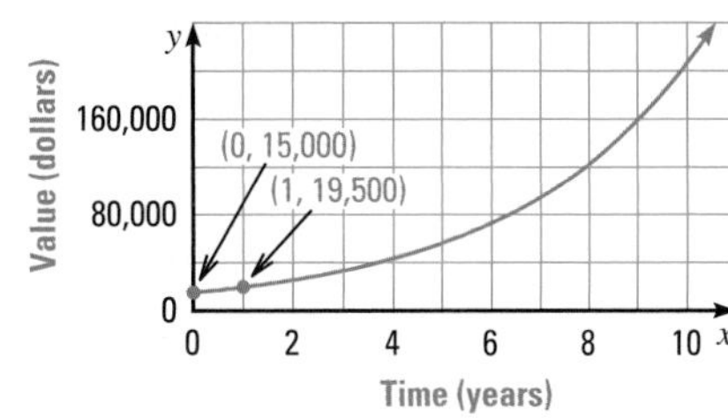

a. Does the graph represent *exponential growth* or *exponential decay*? **exponential growth**

b. Write a function that models the value of the business over time. $y = 15{,}000(1.3)^x$

c. How much is the business worth after 4 years? **\$42,841.50**

7. MULTI-STEP PROBLEM The half-life of a medication is the time it takes for the medication to reduce to half of its original amount in a patient's bloodstream. A certain antibiotic has a half-life of about 8 hours.

a. A patient is administered 500 milligrams of the medication. Write a function that models the amount of the medication in the patient's bloodstream over time. **See margin.**

b. How much of the 500 milligram dose will be in the patient's bloodstream after 24 hours? **62.5 mg**

1a. Sun: 9.66×10^7 km, Earth: 6.37×10^3 km

1b. Sun: about 1.17×10^{17} km, Earth: about 5.10×10^8 km

1c. about 2.23×10^8; *Sample answer:* The Sun's surface area is 223,000,000 times larger than the Earth's.

4. Let V represent the value of the house and t represent the number of quarters since 2001; $V = 200{,}000(1.04)^t$. *Sample answer:* A house with a value of \$200,000 at the end of 2002 would have a value of about \$275,000 at the end of 2004.

5a. Let y represent the amount of money in the account and x represent the number of years since the \$100 was deposited. $y = 100(1.03)^x$.

5b.

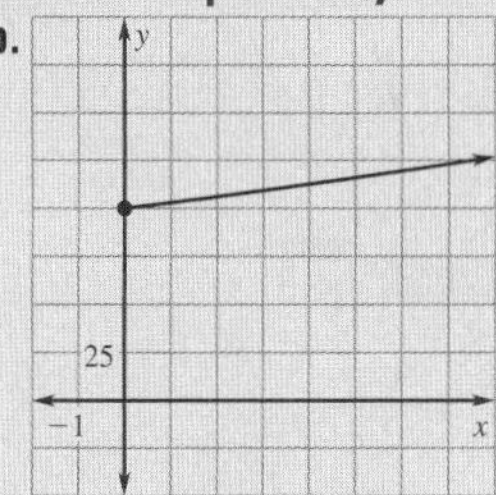

5c. No. *Sample answer:* There will only be \$109.27 in the account in 3 years.

7a. Let M represent the amount of medication in patient's bloodstream (in milligrams) and let t represent the number of 8 hour periods since the medication was taken. $M = 500\left(\frac{1}{2}\right)^t$.

Additional Resources

The following resources are available to help review the materials in this chapter.

Chapter Resource Book
- Chapter Review Games and Activities
- Cumulative Practice, Chs. 1–8

Student Resources in Spanish

eWorkbook

@HomeTutor

Vocabulary Practice

Vocabulary practice is available at **classzone.com**

BIG IDEAS

For Your Notebook

Big Idea 1

Applying Properties of Exponents to Simplify Expressions

You can use the properties of exponents to simplify expressions. For the properties listed below, a and b are real numbers, and m and n are integers.

Expression	Property
$a^m \cdot a^n = a^{m+n}$	**Product of powers property**
$(a^m)^n = a^{mn}$	**Power of a power property**
$(ab)^m = a^m b^m$	**Power of a product property**
$\frac{a^m}{a^n} = a^{m-n}, a \neq 0$	**Quotient of powers property**
$\left(\frac{a}{b}\right)^m = \frac{a^m}{b^m}, b \neq 0$	**Power of a quotient property**

Big Idea 2

Working with Numbers in Scientific Notation

You can write numbers in scientific notation.

Number	Standard form	Scientific notation
Four billion	4,000,000,000	4×10^9
Thirty-two thousandths	0.032	3.2×10^{-2}

You can also compute with numbers in scientific notation. For example:

$$(4 \times 10^9) \times (3.2 \times 10^{-2}) = 12.8 \times 10^7 = 1.28 \times 10^8, \text{ or } 128{,}000{,}000$$

Big Idea 3

Writing and Graphing Exponential Functions

You can write and graph exponential growth and decay functions. You can also model real-world situations involving exponential growth and exponential decay.

Exponential growth	Exponential decay
Function $y = ab^x$, $a > 0$ and $b > 1$	**Function** $y = ab^x$, $a > 0$ and $0 < b < 1$
Graph 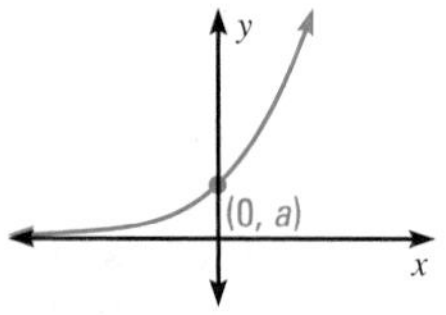	**Graph** 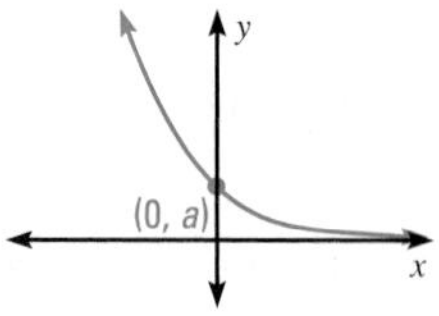
Model $y = a(1 + r)^t$	**Model** $y = a(1 - r)^t$

CHAPTER REVIEW

@HomeTutor
classzone.com
• Multi-Language Glossary
• Vocabulary practice

REVIEW KEY VOCABULARY

- order of magnitude, *p. 491*
- zero exponent, *p. 503*
- negative exponent, *p. 503*
- scientific notation, *p. 512*
- exponential function, *p. 520*
- exponential growth, *p. 522*
- growth factor, growth rate, *p. 522*
- compound interest, *p. 523*
- exponential decay, *p. 533*
- decay factor, decay rate, *p. 534*

VOCABULARY EXERCISES

1. Copy and complete: The function $y = 1200(0.3)^t$ is an exponential _?_ function, and the base 0.3 is called the _?_. **decay, decay factor**

2. **WRITING** *Explain* how you can tell whether a table represents a linear function or an exponential function. **See margin.**

Tell whether the function represents exponential growth or exponential decay. *Explain.* **3–5. See margin.**

3. $y = 3(0.85)^x$ **4.** $y = \frac{1}{2}(1.01)^x$ **5.** $y = 2(2.1)^x$

REVIEW EXAMPLES AND EXERCISES

Use the review examples and exercises below to check your understanding of the concepts you have learned in each lesson of Chapter 8.

8.1 Apply Exponent Properties Involving Products *pp. 489–494*

EXAMPLE

Simplify $(3y^3)^4 \cdot y^5$.

$(3y^3)^4 \cdot y^5 = 3^4 \cdot (y^3)^4 \cdot y^5$ Power of a product property

$= 81 \cdot y^{12} \cdot y^5$ Power of a power property

$= 81y^{17}$ Product of powers property

EXERCISES

EXAMPLES 1, 2, 3, 4, and 5 on pp. 489–491 for Exs. 6–15

Simplify the expression.

6. $4^4 \cdot 4^3$ $\mathbf{4^7}$ **7.** $(-3)^7(-3)$ $\mathbf{(-3)^8}$ **8.** $z^3 \cdot z^5 \cdot z^5$ $\mathbf{z^{13}}$

9. $(y^4)^5$ $\mathbf{y^{20}}$ **10.** $[(-7)^4]^4$ $\mathbf{(-7)^{16}}$ **11.** $[(b + 2)^8]^3$ $\mathbf{(b+2)^{24}}$

12. $(6^4 \cdot 31)^5$ $\mathbf{6^{20} \cdot 31^5}$ **13.** $-(8xy)^2$ $\mathbf{-64x^2y^2}$ **14.** $(2x^2)^4 \cdot x^5$ $\mathbf{16x^{13}}$

15. **EARTH SCIENCE** The order of magnitude of the mass of Earth's atmosphere is 10^{18} kilograms. The order of magnitude of the mass of Earth's oceans is 10^3 times greater. What is the order of magnitude of the mass of Earth's oceans? $\mathbf{10^{21}}$

Extra Example 8.1
Simplify $[(d + 4)^3]^2$. $(d + 4)^6$

2. ***Sample answer:*** **If the difference of each pair of successive terms is constant, the table represents a linear function. If the ratio of each pair of successive terms is constant, the table represents an exponential function.**

3. Exponential decay; $b = 0.85$ which is between 0 and 1, therefore it is exponential decay.

4. Exponential growth; $b = 1.01$ which is greater than 1, therefore it is exponential growth.

5. Exponential growth; $b = 2.1$ which is greater than 1, therefore it is exponential growth.

Extra Example 8.2

Simplify $\left(\frac{2y^3}{z}\right)^5 \cdot \frac{1}{y^2}$. $\frac{32y^{13}}{z^5}$

Extra Example 8.3

Evaluate $(4x^{-4}y^0)^{-2}$. $\frac{x^8}{16}$

8.2 Apply Exponent Properties Involving Quotients

pp. 495–501

EXAMPLE

Simplify $\left(\frac{x^3}{y}\right)^4 \cdot \frac{2}{x^5}$.

$\left(\frac{x^3}{y}\right)^4 \cdot \frac{2}{x^5} = \frac{(x^3)^4}{y^4} \cdot \frac{2}{x^5}$ **Power of a quotient property**

$= \frac{x^{12}}{y^4} \cdot \frac{2}{x^5}$ **Power of a power property**

$= \frac{2x^{12}}{y^4x^5}$ **Multiply fractions.**

$= \frac{2x^7}{y^4}$ **Quotient of powers property**

EXERCISES

EXAMPLES 1, 2, and 3 on pp. 495–496 for Exs. 16–24

Simplify the expression.

16. $\frac{(-3)^7}{(-3)^3}$ $(-3)^4$ **17.** $\frac{5^2 \cdot 5^4}{5^3}$ 5^3 **18.** $\left(\frac{m}{n}\right)^3$ $\frac{m^3}{n^3}$ **19.** $\frac{17^{12}}{17^8}$ 17^4

20. $\left(-\frac{1}{x}\right)^4$ $\frac{1}{x^4}$ **21.** $\left(\frac{7x^5}{y^2}\right)^2$ $\frac{49x^{10}}{y^4}$ **22.** $\frac{1}{p^2} \cdot p^6$ p^4 **23.** $\frac{6}{7r^{10}} \cdot \left(\frac{r^5}{s}\right)^5$ $\frac{6r^{15}}{7s^5}$

24. PER CAPITA INCOME The order of magnitude of the population of Montana in 2003 was 10^6 people. The order of magnitude of the total personal income (in dollars) for Montana in 2003 was 10^{10}. What was the order of magnitude of the mean personal income in Montana in 2003? 10^4

8.3 Define and Use Zero and Negative Exponents

pp. 503–508

EXAMPLE

Evaluate $(2x^0y^{-5})^3$.

$(2x^0y^{-5})^3 = 2^3 \cdot x^0 \cdot y^{-15}$ **Power of a power property**

$= 8 \cdot 1 \cdot y^{-15}$ **Definition of zero exponent**

$= \frac{8}{y^{15}}$ **Definition of negative exponents**

EXERCISES

EXAMPLES 1, 2, and 4 on pp. 503–505 for Exs. 25–29

Evaluate the expression.

25. 14^0 1 **26.** 3^{-4} $\frac{1}{81}$ **27.** $\left(\frac{2}{3}\right)^{-3}$ $\frac{27}{8}$ **28.** $7^{-5} \cdot 7^5$ 1

29. UNITS OF MEASURE Use the fact that 1 femtogram = 10^{-18} kilogram and 1 nanogram = 10^{-12} kilogram to complete the following statement: 1 nanogram = ? femtogram(s). 10^6

8.4 Use Scientific Notation
pp. 512–518

EXAMPLE

Write the number in scientific notation.

a. $2097 = 2.097 \times 10^3$ **Move decimal point left 3 places. Exponent is 3.**

b. $0.00032 = 3.2 \times 10^{-4}$ **Move decimal point right 4 places. Exponent is −4.**

Write the number in standard form.

a. $4.3201 \times 10^2 = 432.01$ **Exponent is 2. Move decimal point right 2 places.**

b. $2.068 \times 10^{-3} = 0.002068$ **Exponent is −3. Move decimal point left 3 places.**

EXERCISES

EXAMPLES 1, 2, 4, and 5 on pp. 512–514 for Exs. 30–34

30. Write 78,120 in scientific notation. **7.812×10^4**

31. Write 7.5×10^{-5} in standard form. **0.000075**

Evaluate the expression. Write your answer in scientific notation.

32. $(6.3 \times 10^3)(1.9 \times 10^{-5})$ **1.197×10^{-1}**

33. $\dfrac{6.5 \times 10^9}{1.6 \times 10^{-4}}$ **4.0625×10^{13}**

34. MASS The mass m_1 of a gate of the Thames Barrier in London is about 1.5×10^6 kilograms. The mass m_2 of the Great Pyramid of Giza is about 6×10^9 kilograms. Find the ratio of m_1 to m_2. What does the ratio tell you? **2.5×10^{-4}; the mass of the gate is 0.00025 or $\frac{1}{4000}$ the mass of the pyramid.**

8.5 Write and Graph Exponential Growth Functions
pp. 520–527

EXAMPLE

Graph the function $y = 4^x$ and identify its domain and range.

STEP 1 **Make** a table. The domain is all real numbers.

x	−1	0	1	2
y	$\frac{1}{4}$	1	4	16

STEP 2 **Plot** the points.

STEP 3 **Draw** a smooth curve through the points.

STEP 4 **Identify** the range. As you can see from the graph, the range is all positive real numbers.

EXERCISES

EXAMPLES 2 and 3 on p. 521 for Exs. 35–39

Graph the function and identify its domain and range. **35–38. See margin.**

35. $y = 6^x$ **36.** $y = (1.1)^x$ **37.** $y = (3.5)^x$ **38.** $y = \left(\frac{5}{2}\right)^x$

39. Graph the function $y = -5 \cdot 2^x$. Compare the graph with the graph of $y = 2^x$. **See margin.**

Extra Example 8.4

Write the number in scientific notation.

a. 463,250 **4.6325×10^5**

b. 0.3457 **3.457×10^{-1}**

Write the number in standard form.

a. 5.23×10^4 **52,300**

b. 9.021×10^{-6} **0.000009021**

Extra Example 8.5

Graph the function $y = \left(\frac{5}{2}\right)^x$ and identify its domain and range.

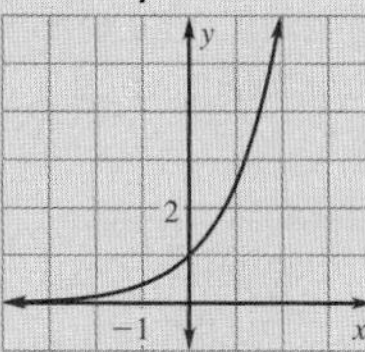

domain: all real numbers; range: all positive real numbers

38.

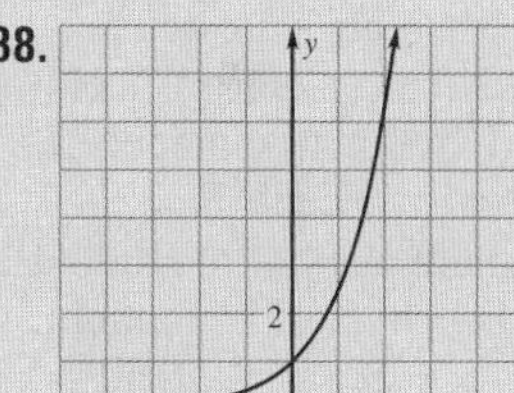

domain: all real numbers, range: all positive real numbers

39.

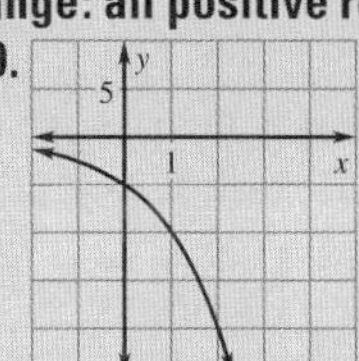

The graph is a vertical stretch with a reflection in the x-axis.

35.

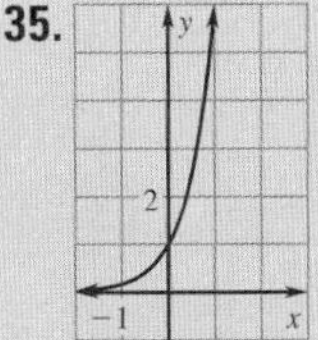

domain: all real numbers, range: all positive real numbers

36.

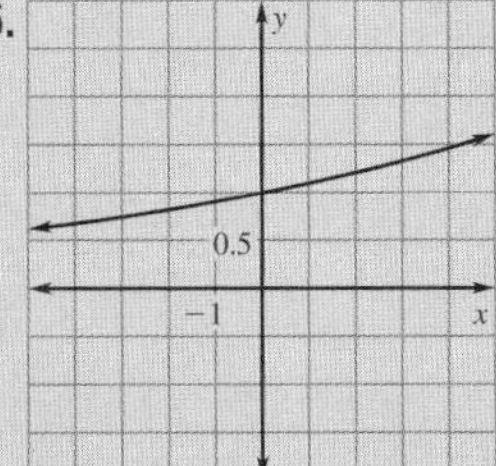

domain: all real numbers, range: all positive real numbers

37.

domain: all real numbers, range: all positive real numbers

Extra Examples 8.6

1. Tell whether the graph represents exponential growth or exponential decay. Then write a rule for the function.

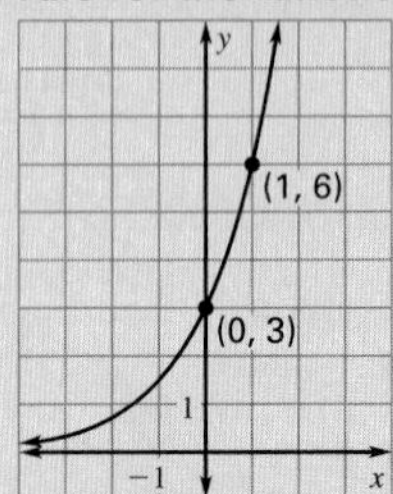

The graph represents exponential growth. A function rule is $y = 3(2)^x$.

2. A high school issued a report that enrollment in physical education classes at their school has been declining at a rate of 6% per year since 1984. For all grades at the high school, enrollment in physical education classes was 2864 in 1984. Write a function that models the enrollment over time. Find the approximate number of students enrolled in physical education in 2006. **$y = 2864(1 - 0.06)^t$; There were about 734 students enrolled in physical education classes at the high school in 2006.**

42. Let V represent the value of the car (in dollars) and x represent the number of years since the initial value. $V = 13{,}000(0.85)^x$; about $6786.

8.6 Write and Graph Exponential Decay Functions *pp. 531–538*

EXAMPLE 1

Tell whether the graph represents *exponential growth* or *exponential decay*. Then write a rule for the function.

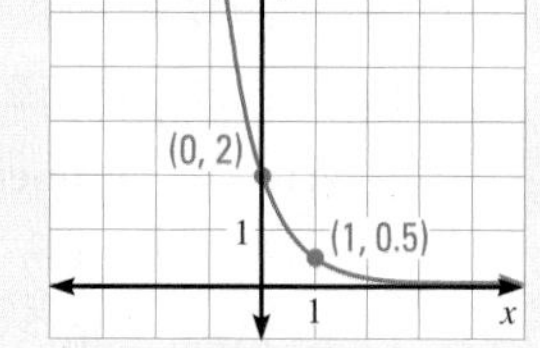

The graph represents exponential decay ($y = ab^x$ where $0 < b < 1$). The y-intercept is 2, so $a = 2$. Find the value of b by using the point (1, 0.5) and $a = 2$.

$y = ab^x$ **Write function.**

$0.5 = 2 \cdot b^1$ **Substitute.**

$0.25 = b$ **Solve for *b*.**

A function rule is $y = 2(0.25)^x$.

EXAMPLE 2

CAR VALUE A family purchases a car for $11,000. The car depreciates (loses value) at a rate of about 16% annually. Write a function that models the value of the car over time. Find the approximate value of the car in 4 years.

Let V represent the value (in dollars) of the car, and let t represent the time (in years since the car was purchased). The initial value is 11,000, and the decay rate is 0.16.

$V = a(1 - r)^t$ **Write exponential decay model.**

$= 11{,}000(1 - 0.16)^t$ **Substitute 11,000 for *a* and 0.16 for *r*.**

$= 11{,}000(0.84)^t$ **Simplify.**

To find the approximate value of the car in 4 years, substitute 4 for t.

$V = 11{,}000(0.84)^t = 11{,}000(0.84)^4 \approx \$5477$

The approximate value of the car in 4 years is $5477.

EXERCISES

EXAMPLES 4 and 5 on pp. 533–534 for Exs. 40–42

Tell whether the graph represents *exponential growth* or *exponential decay*. Then write a rule for the function.

40. 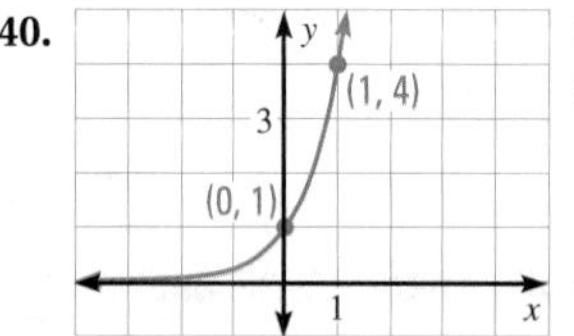

exponential growth; $y = 4^x$

41. 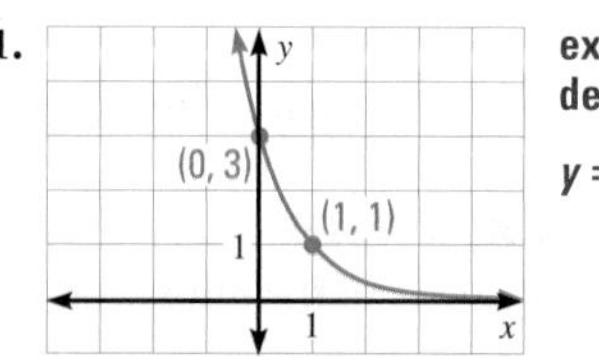

exponential decay; $y = 3 \cdot \left(\frac{1}{3}\right)^x$

42. **CAR VALUE** The value of a car is $13,000. The car depreciates (loses value) at a rate of about 15% annually. Write an exponential decay model for the value of the car. Find the approximate value of the car in 4 years. **See margin.**

8 CHAPTER TEST

Simplify the expression. Write your answer using exponents.

1. $(62 \cdot 17)^4$ **$62^4 \cdot 17^4$**
2. $(-3)(-3)^6$ **$(-3)^7$**
3. $\frac{8^4 \cdot 8^5}{8^3}$ **8^6**
4. $(8^4)^3$ **8^{12}**
5. $\frac{2^{15}}{2^8}$ **2^7**
6. $5^3 \cdot 5^0 \cdot 5^5$ **5^8**
7. $[(-4)^3]^2$ **$(-4)^6$**
8. $\frac{(-5)^{10}}{(-5)^3}$ **$(-5)^7$**

Simplify the expression.

9. $t^2 \cdot t^6$ **t^8**
10. $\left(\frac{s}{t}\right)^6$ **$\frac{s^6}{t^6}$**
11. $\frac{1}{9^{-2}}$ **81**
12. $-(6p)^2$ **$-36p^2$**
13. $(5xy)^2$ **$25x^2y^2$**
14. $\frac{1}{z^7} \cdot z^9$ **z^2**
15. $(x^5)^3$ **x^{15}**
16. $\left(-\frac{4}{c}\right)^2$ **$\frac{16}{c^2}$**

Simplify the expression. Write your answer using only positive exponents.

17. $\left(\frac{a^{-3}}{3b}\right)^4$ **$\frac{1}{81a^{12}b^4}$**
18. $\frac{3}{4d} \cdot \frac{(2d)^4}{c^3}$ **$\frac{12d^3}{c^3}$**
19. $y^0 \cdot (8x^6y^{-3})^{-2}$ **$\frac{y^6}{64x^{12}}$**
20. $(5r^5)^3 \cdot r^{-2}$ **$125r^{13}$**

Write the number in scientific notation.

21. 423.6 **4.236×10^2**
22. 7,194,548 **7.194548×10^6**
23. 500.32 **5.0032×10^2**
24. 71.23884 **7.123884×10^1**
25. 0.562 **5.62×10^{-1}**
26. 0.0348 **3.48×10^{-2}**
27. 0.000123 **1.23×10^{-4}**
28. 0.5603002 **5.603002×10^{-1}**

Write the number in standard form.

29. 4.02×10^5 **402,000**
30. 5.3121×10^4 **53,121**
31. 9.354×10^8 **935,400,000**
32. 1.307×10^{19} **See margin.**
33. 1.3×10^{-3} **0.0013**
34. 3.32×10^{-4} **0.000332**
35. 7.506×10^{-5} **0.00007506**
36. 9.3119×10^{-7} **0.00000093119**

37. Graph the function $y = 4^x$. Identify its domain and range. **See margin.**

38. Graph the function $y = \frac{1}{2} \cdot 4^x$. Compare the graph with the graph of $y = 4^x$. **See margin.**

39. **ANIMATION** About 1.2×10^7 bytes of data make up a single frame of an animated film. There are 24 frames in 1 second of a film. About how many bytes of data are there in 1 hour of an animated film? **about 1.04×10^{12} bytes**

40. **SALARY** A recent college graduate accepts a job at a law firm. The job has a salary of $32,000 per year. The law firm guarantees an annual pay increase of 3% of the employee's salary.
    a. Write a function that models the employee's salary over time. Assume that the employee receives only the guaranteed pay increase. **See margin.**
    b. Use the function to find the employee's salary after 5 years. **$37,096.77**

41. **SCIENCE** At sea level, Earth's atmosphere exerts a pressure of 1 atmosphere. Atmospheric pressure P (in atmospheres) decreases with altitude and can be modeled by $P = (0.99987)^a$ where a is the altitude (in meters).
    a. Identify the initial amount, decay factor, and decay rate. **initial amount: 1, decay factor: 0.99987, decay rate: 0.013%**
    b. Use a graphing calculator to graph the function. **See margin.**
    c. Estimate the altitude at which the atmospheric pressure is about half of what it is at sea level. **about 5332 m**

Additional Resources

Assessment Book

- Chapter Test, Levels A, B, C
- Standardized Chapter Test
- SAT/ACT Chapter Test
- Alternative Assessment

Test Generator

Chapter Test

Easily-readable reduced copies (with answers) of Chapter Test B, the Standardized Chapter Test, and the Alternative Assessment from the Assessment Book can be found on pp. 486E–486F.

37.

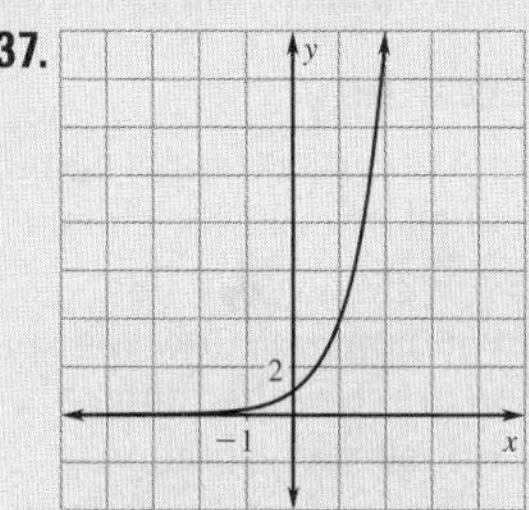

domain: all real numbers, range: all positive real numbers

25.

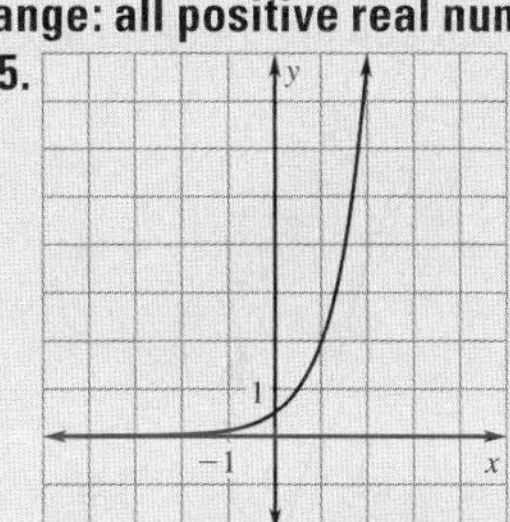

The graph is a vertical shrink of $y = 4^x$.

40a. Let y represent the yearly salary and x represent the number of years since accepting the job. $y = 32{,}000(1.03)^x$.

41b.

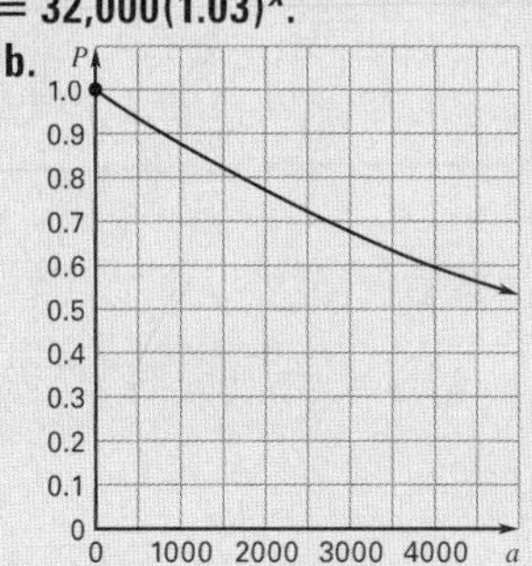

Test-Taking Strategy

When students are developing a plan to solve a problem, encourage them to use what they know to find a solution. Sometimes they will know what is required, such as a formula, but they may not remember the formula. Their plan should therefore focus on alternative methods to solve the problem. For example, if the problem is based on a pattern and they can extend the pattern in a table without using a formula, or they can tell from a diagram how to reach a solution, then they should go ahead without the formula. Sometimes a careful examination of tables and diagrams will trigger the memory of a formula or rule that will help solve the problem.

Study Strategy

Tell students that it is always helpful to look at all the answer choices before they begin to solve the problem. By doing this, they will have a good grasp of the range of solutions. If their own solution is outside the range of answers, then they know they need to rethink their plan for solving the problem.

CONTEXT-BASED MULTIPLE CHOICE QUESTIONS

Some of the information you need to solve a context-based multiple choice question may appear in a table, a diagram, or a graph.

PROBLEM 1

A scientist monitors bacteria cell growth in an experiment. The scientist records the number of bacteria cells in a petri dish every 20 minutes, as shown in the table.

Number of 20 minute time periods, *t*	0	1	2	3	4
Number of bacteria cells, *c*	15	30	60	120	240

How many bacteria cells will there be after 3 hours?

Ⓐ 7.69×10^{10} Ⓑ 7680 Ⓒ 270 Ⓓ 120

Plan

INTERPRET THE TABLE Determine whether the table represents a linear or an exponential function. Use the information in the table to write a function. Then use the function to find the number of bacteria cells after 3 hours.

Solution

STEP 1 Determine whether the function is exponential.

+1 +1 +1 +1

t	0	1	2	3	4
c	15	30	60	120	240

×2 ×2 ×2 ×2

Because the c-values are multiplied by 2 for each increase of 1 in t, the table represents an exponential function of the form $c = ab^t$ where $b = 2$.

STEP 2 Write the function rule.

The value of c when $t = 0$ is 15, as shown in the table, so $a = 15$. Substitute the values of a and b in the function $c = ab^t$.

A function rule is $c = 15 \cdot 2^t$.

STEP 3 Find the number of cells after 3 hours.

There are 180 minutes in 3 hours. So there are nine 20 minute periods in 3 hours. Substitute 9 for t in the function rule you wrote in Step 2.

$$c = 15 \cdot 2^t$$
$$= 15 \cdot 2^9$$
$$= 7680$$

There are 7680 bacteria cells in the petri dish after 3 hours.

The correct answer is B. Ⓐ Ⓑ Ⓒ Ⓓ

Answers

1. C
2. A

PROBLEM 2

A fish tank is a rectangular prism and is partially filled with sand, as shown. The dimensions of the fish tank are given. The order of magnitude of the number of grains of sand in 1 cubic inch is 10^3. Find the order of magnitude of the total number of grains of sand in the fish tank.

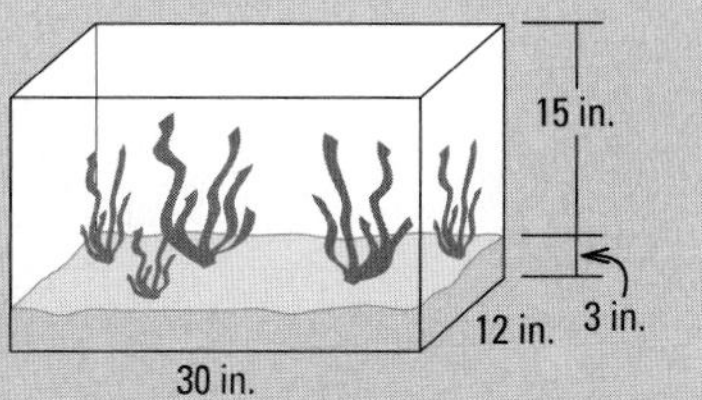

Ⓐ 10^2 grains Ⓑ 10^3 grains Ⓒ 10^5 grains Ⓓ 10^6 grains

Plan

INTERPRET THE DIAGRAM Use the information in the diagram to find the order of magnitude of the volume of sand in the fish tank. Multiply the volume by the order of magnitude of the number of grains of sand in 1 cubic inch.

Solution

STEP 1 Find the order of magnitude of the volume of sand in the fish tank.

Use the formula for the volume of a rectangular prism.

$V = lwh$ **Write formula for volume of rectangular prism.**

$= 30 \cdot 12 \cdot 3$ **Substitute given values.**

$= 1080$ **Multiply.**

The order of magnitude of the volume of sand is 10^3 cubic inches.

STEP 2 Find the order of magnitude of the number of grains of sand in the fish tank.

Multiply the order of magnitude of the volume of sand in the fish tank by the order of magnitude of the grains of sand in 1 cubic inch.

$10^3 \cdot 10^3 = 10^{3+3} = 10^6$

The order of magnitude of the total number of grains of sand in the fish tank is 10^6.

The correct answer is D. Ⓐ Ⓑ Ⓒ Ⓓ

PRACTICE

1. In Problem 2, consider the section of the fish tank occupied by water only. The order of magnitude of the weight of water per cubic inch is 10^{-2} pound. The tank is filled to the top. What is the order of magnitude of the weight of the water in the fish tank?

   Ⓐ 10^{-8} pound Ⓑ 10^{-6} pound Ⓒ 10^2 pounds Ⓓ 10^6 pounds

2. What is the volume of the cylinder shown?

   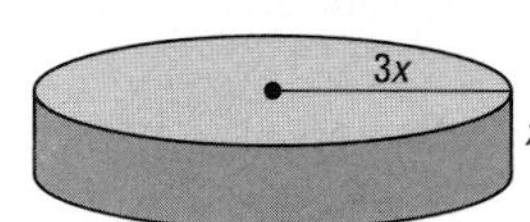

   Ⓐ $9\pi x^3$ Ⓑ $3\pi x^3$

   Ⓒ $9\pi x^2$ Ⓓ $3\pi x^2$

Answers
1. A
2. D
3. D
4. D
5. D
6. C
7. C
8. D
9. A

MULTIPLE CHOICE

1. The table represents which function?

x	-2	-1	0	1	2
y	$\frac{1}{75}$	$\frac{1}{15}$	$\frac{1}{3}$	$\frac{5}{3}$	$\frac{25}{3}$

Ⓐ $y = \frac{1}{3} \cdot 5^x$ Ⓑ $y = -\frac{1}{3} \cdot 5^x$

Ⓒ $y = 3 \cdot 5^x$ Ⓓ $y = -3 \cdot 5^x$

2. What is the volume of the cube?

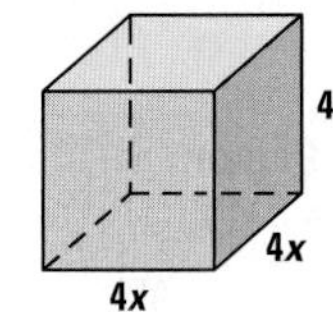

Ⓐ $4x^3$ Ⓑ $12x^3$

Ⓒ $16x^2$ Ⓓ $64x^3$

In Exercises 3 and 4, use the table below.

3. List the elements in order from least concentration to greatest concentration.

Element in Seawater	Concentration (parts per million)
Sulfur	904
Chloride	1.95×10^4
Magnesium	1.29×10^3
Sodium	10,770

Ⓐ Sulfur, sodium, magnesium, chloride

Ⓑ Chloride, sodium, magnesium, sulfur

Ⓒ Sulfur, chloride, magnesium, sodium

Ⓓ Sulfur, magnesium, sodium, chloride

4. About how many times greater is the concentration of chloride than the concentration of magnesium?

Ⓐ 0.066 Ⓑ 0.66

Ⓒ 1.5 Ⓓ 15

In Exercises 5–7, use the table below.

Unit	Number of meters
Kilometer	10^3
Centimeter	10^{-2}
Millimeter	10^{-3}
Nanometer	10^{-9}

5. How many millimeters are in 1 kilometer?

Ⓐ 1 Ⓑ 10

Ⓒ 10^3 Ⓓ 10^6

6. How many nanometers are in a centimeter?

Ⓐ 10^{-11} Ⓑ 10^{-7}

Ⓒ 10^7 Ⓓ 10^{18}

7. A micrometer is 10^3 times greater than a nanometer. How many meters are in a micrometer?

Ⓐ 10^{-27} Ⓑ 10^{-12}

Ⓒ 10^{-6} Ⓓ 10^6

In Exercises 8 and 9, use the graph below.

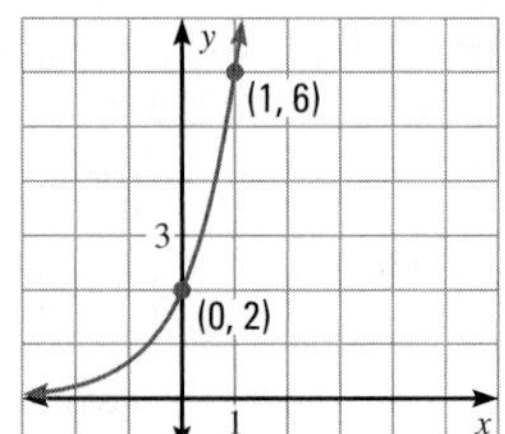

8. The graph of which exponential function is shown?

Ⓐ $y = 3^x$ Ⓑ $y = -3^x$

Ⓒ $y = -2 \cdot 3^x$ Ⓓ $y = 2 \cdot 3^x$

9. How does the graph compare with the graph of $y = 3^x$?

Ⓐ It is a vertical stretch.

Ⓑ It is a vertical shrink.

Ⓒ It is a reflection in the x-axis.

Ⓓ It is the same graph.

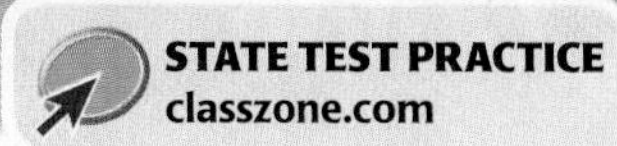

GRIDDED ANSWER

10. If $\left(\frac{x^{-6}}{x^{-5}}\right)^{-3} = x^n$ and $x \neq 0$, what is the value of n?

11. Write the number 7.8×10^{-1} in standard form.

12. What power of 10 is used when you write 12,560,000 in scientific notation?

13. The table shows the values for an exponential function.

x	−2	−1	0	1	2
y	$\frac{3}{25}$	$\frac{3}{5}$	3	15	?

What is the missing value in the table?

14. An initial investment of \$200 is losing value at a rate of 1.5% per year. What is the value of the investment (in dollars) after 3 years? Round your answer to the nearest cent.

15. What is the value of $(2x)^3 \cdot x^2$ when $x = \frac{1}{2}$? Write your answer as a fraction.

SHORT RESPONSE

16. A female sockeye salmon lays about 10^3 eggs in one season.

a. About how many eggs will 10^4 female sockeyes lay?

b. Suppose about 10^6 of the eggs survive to become young salmon. What percent of eggs survive? *Explain* how you found your answer.

17. You deposit \$75 in a bank account that pays 3% annual interest compounded yearly. If you do not make any deposits or withdrawals, how much will your investment be worth in 3 years? *Explain.*

18. Membership in an after-school athletic club declined at a rate of 5% per year for the period 2000–2005. There were 54 members in 2000.

a. Identify the initial amount, the decay rate, and the decay factor.

b. In what year did the club have 44 members? *Explain.*

EXTENDED RESPONSE

19. Europa, one of Jupiter's moons, is roughly spherical. The equatorial radius of Europa is 1.569×10^6 meters.

a. Find the volume of Europa. Write your answer in scientific notation.

b. Find the average density d (in kilograms per cubic meters) of Europa by using the formula $d = \frac{m}{V}$ where m is the mass of Europa (about 4.8×10^{22} kilograms) and V is the volume you calculated in part (a).

c. *Explain* how you could have used order of magnitude to approximate the density of Europa. How would the approximation compare with the density you calculated in part (b)?

20. A gardener is growing a water lily plant. The plant starts out with 4 lily pads and the number of lily pads increases at a rate of about 6.5% per day for the first 20 days.

a. Write a function that models the number of lily pads the plant has over the first 20 days.

b. Graph the model and identify its domain and range.

c. On about what day did the plant have 10 lily pads? *Explain* how you found your answer.

10. 3

11. 0.78

12. 7

13. 75

14. \$191.13

15. $\frac{1}{4}$

16a. 10^7 eggs

16b. 10%. ***Sample answer:*** Divide 10^6 by 10^7: $10^{-1} = 0.1 = 10\%$.

17. \$81.95. ***Sample answer:*** Substitute 3 for t in the formula $75(1.03)^t$ and solve.

18a. initial amount: 54 members, decay rate: 5%, decay factor: 0.95

18b. 2004. ***Sample answer:*** Make a table of values to find that 44 members occurred 4 years after 2000, which is 2004.

19a. about 1.618×10^{19} m^3

19b. about 2.97×10^3 kg/m^3

19c. ***Sample answer:*** Divide 10^{22} by 10^{19}: 10^3. This approximation would underestimate the result by about 2×10^3.

20a. Let ℓ represent the number of lily pads and d represent the number of days since the start; $\ell = 4 \cdot (1.065)^d$, $0 \le d \le 20$.

20b.

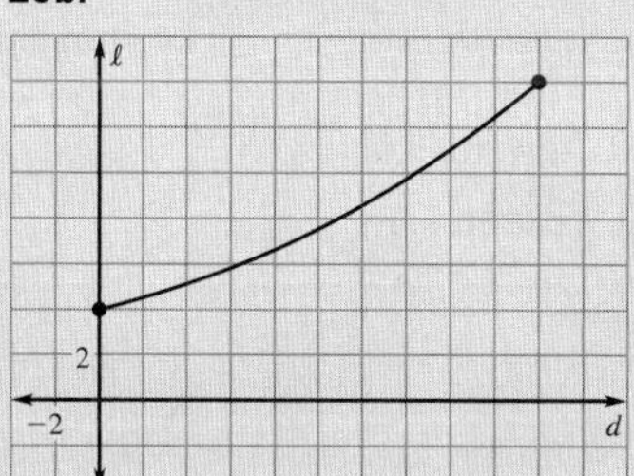

domain: $0 \le d \le 20$, range: $4 \le \ell \le 14$

20c. About 15 days. ***Sample answer:*** By making a table of values and choosing the day with the value closest to 10.

9 Pacing Guide

Chapter 9: Polynomials and Factoring

Chapter Table of Contents

PACING GUIDES

Regular Schedule (50-minute classes)

DAY 1	DAY 2	DAY 3	DAY 4	DAY 5	DAY 6	DAY 7
Lesson 9.1 Graphing Calculator Activity 9.1	Investigating Algebra Activity 9.2 Lesson 9.2	Lesson 9.3	Quiz for Lessons 9.1–9.3 Lesson 9.4	Lesson 9.4 (cont.) Mixed Review of Problem Solving	Investigating Algebra Activity 9.5 Lesson 9.5	Lesson 9.5 (cont.)
DAY 8	**DAY 9**	**DAY 10**	**DAY 11**	**DAY 12**	**DAY 13**	**DAY 14**
Investigating Algebra Activity 9.6 Lesson 9.6	Lesson 9.6 (cont.)	Quiz for Lessons 9.4–9.6 Lesson 9.7	Lesson 9.8	Lesson 9.8 (cont.) Mixed Review of Problem Solving	Quiz for Lessons 9.7–9.8 Chapter Review	Chapter Test

Block Schedule (90-minute classes)

DAY 1	DAY 2	DAY 3	DAY 4	DAY 5	DAY 6	DAY 7
Lesson 9.1 Graphing Calculator Activity 9.1 Investigating Algebra Activity 9.2 Lesson 9.2	Lesson 9.3 Quiz for Lessons 9.1–9.3 Lesson 9.4	Lesson 9.4 (cont.) Mixed Review of Problem Solving Investigating Algebra Activity 9.5 Lesson 9.5	Lesson 9.5 (cont.) Investigating Algebra Activity 9.6 Lesson 9.6	Lesson 9.6 (cont.) Quiz for Lessons 9.4–9.6 Lesson 9.7	Lesson 9.8 Mixed Review of Problem Solving	Quiz for Lessons 9.7–9.8 Chapter Review Chapter Test

RESOURCE OPTIONS

Chapter/Lesson Resources

Chapter Resource Book
- Parents as Partners
- Teaching Guide/Lesson Plan
- Activity Masters
- Practice (3 levels)
- Study Guide
- Quick Catch-Up for Absent Students
- Problem Solving/Application
- Challenge Practice
- Chapter Review Games and Activities
- Project with Rubric
- Cumulative Review

Notetaking Guide
- Student Workbook and Teacher's Edition

Practice Workbook

Worked-Out Solution Key

Chapter Transparency Book
- Warm-Up Exercises/Daily Homework Quiz
- Notetaking Guide Transparencies
- Homework Answer Transparencies

Teacher Tools Transparencies

Assessment

Assessment Book
- Quizzes
- Chapter Tests (3 levels)
- Standardized and SAT/ACT Chapter Tests
- Alternative Assessments
- Cumulative Tests

Benchmark Tests
- Benchmark Tests, correlated to Remediation Book
- Pre-Course, Mid-Year, and End-of-Year Tests
- Chapter Tests

Spanish Assessment Book

Differentiated Instruction

Differentiated Instruction Resources
- Strategies for Reading Mathematics
- Differentiated Instruction Lesson Notes
- English Learner Lesson Notes
- Inclusion Lesson Notes
- Teaching Strategies with Sample Worksheets
- Tips for New Teachers/Math Background Notes
- Teacher Survival Activities/Bulletin Board Ideas

Student Resources in Spanish

Spanish Study Guide

Remediation Book

Skills Readiness (available on Easy Planner)
- Diagnostic Assessment
- Skill Instruction and Alternative Teaching Strategies
- Skill Practice and Enrichment Masters

Pre-AP Resources
- Pacing and Assignment Guide
- Best Practices
- Copymasters

Technology Resources

Plan	***Easy Planner***
Teach	***Video Tutor*** ***Activity Generator*** ***Power Presentations*** ***Animated Algebra***
Assess	***Test Generator*** ***ML Assessment System***
Reteach	***@HomeTutor***
Online Resources	***Classzone.com*** ***eEdition*** ***eWorkbook***

Video Tutor

Technology Highlights for Each Lesson

Easy Planner

Easy access to the Teacher's Edition and all teaching resources. Includes a search feature to locate the materials you need.

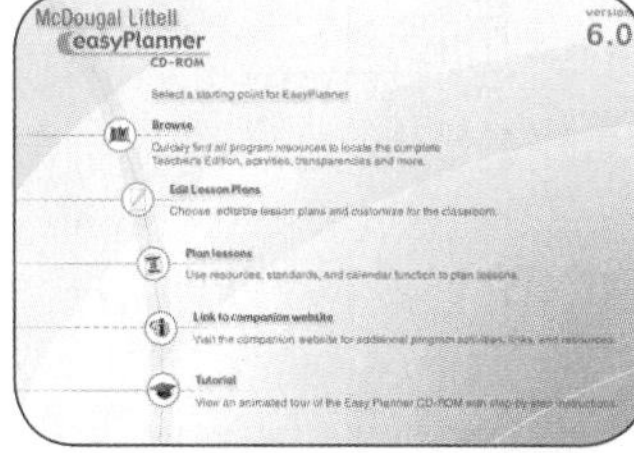

Activity Generator

Leveled, editable activities allow all students to explore a lesson's concepts. Includes teacher notes and closure questions.

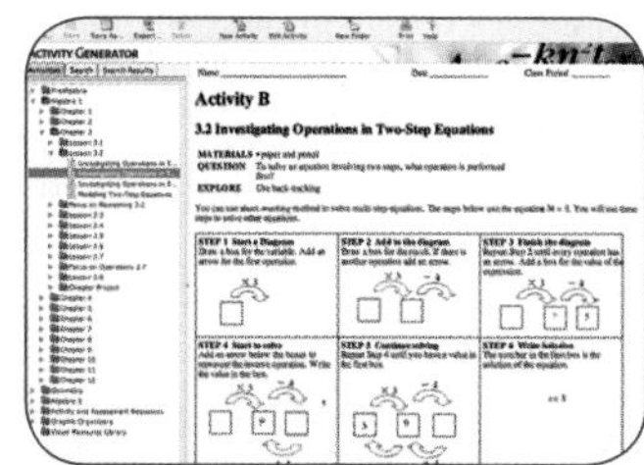

Animated Algebra

Interactive tutorials provide visually engaging alternative opportunities to learn concepts and master skills.

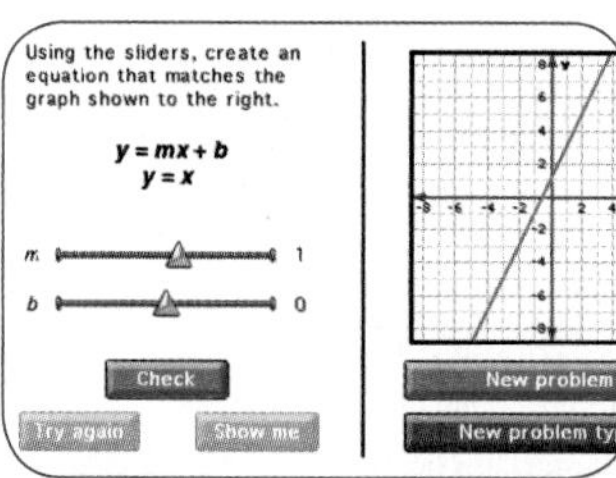

9 Lesson Practice Level B

LESSON 9.1 Practice B
For use with pages 554–559

1. $4n^5$; degree: 5; leading coefficient: 4
2. $-2x^2 + 4x + 3$; degree: 2; leading coefficient: -2
3. $4y^4 + 6y^3 - 2y^2 - 5$; degree: 4; leading coefficient: 4

Write the polynomial so that the exponents decrease from left to right. Identify the degree and leading coefficient of the polynomial.

1. $4n^5$ **2.** $4x - 2x^2 + 3$ **3.** $6y^3 - 2y^2 + 4y^4 - 5$

Tell whether the expression is a polynomial. If it is a polynomial, find its degree and classify it by the number of its terms. Otherwise, tell why it is not a polynomial.

4. 10^x not a polynomial; variable exponent **5.** $-6n^2 - n^3 + 4$ polynomial; degree: 3; trinomial **6.** $w^{-3} + 5$ not a polynomial; negative exponent

Find the sum or difference.

7. $(3z^2 + z - 4) + (2z^2 + 2z - 3)$ $5z^2 + 3z - 7$ **8.** $(8c^2 - 4c + 1) + (-3c^2 + c + 5)$

9. $(2x^2 + 5x - 1) + (x^2 - 5x + 7)$ $3x^2 + 6$ **10.** $(10b^2 - 3b + 2) - (4b^2 + 5b + 1)$

11. $(-4m^2 + 3m - 1) - (m + 2)$ **12.** $(3m + 4) - (2m^2 - 6m + 5)$ $-2m^2 + 9m - 1$

8. $5c^2 - 3c + 6$ 10. $6b^2 - 8b + 1$ 11. $-4m^2 + 2m - 3$

Write a polynomial that represents the perimeter of the figure.

13.

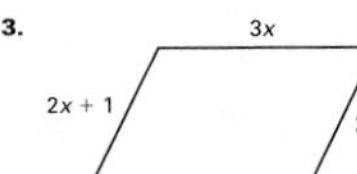
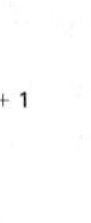

$10x + 2$

14.

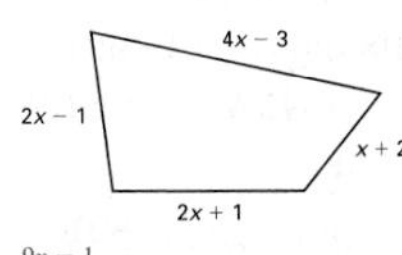

$9x - 1$

15. Floor Plan The first floor of a home has the floor plan shown. Find the area of the first floor.

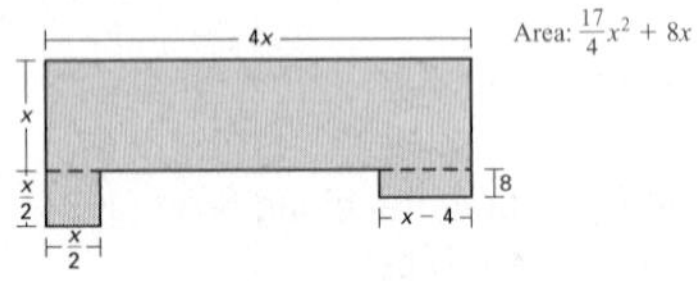

Area: $\frac{17}{4}x^2 + 8x - 32$

16. Profit For 1995 through 2005, the revenue R (in dollars) and the cost C (in dollars) of producing a product can be modeled by

$$R = \frac{1}{4}t^2 + \frac{21}{4}t + 400 \quad \text{and} \quad C = \frac{1}{12}t^2 + \frac{13}{4}t + 200$$

where t is the number of years since 1995. Write an equation for the profit earned from 1995 to 2005. (*Hint:* Profit = Revenue − Cost)

$P = \frac{1}{6}t^2 + 2t + 200$

LESSON 9.2 Practice B
For use with pages 562–568

1. $6x^4 - 3x^3 - x^2$
2. $-20a^7 + 15a^4 - 5a^3$
3. $-8d^5 + 20d^4 - 24d^3 + 8d^2$
4. $6x^2 - 13x - 5$
5. $2y^2 - 7y - 15$
6. $24a^2 - 18a + 3$
7. $5b^2 - 42b + 16$
8. $16m^2 + 38m + 21$

Find the product.

1. $x^2(6x^2 - 3x - 1)$ **2.** $-5a^3(4a^4 - 3a + 1)$ **3.** $4d^2(-2d^3 + 5d^2 - 6d + 2)$

4. $(3x + 1)(2x - 5)$ **5.** $(2y + 3)(y - 5)$ **6.** $(6a - 3)(4a - 1)$

7. $(b - 8)(5b - 2)$ **8.** $(8m + 7)(2m + 3)$ **9.** $(-p + 2)(3p^2 + 1)$

10. $(2z - 7)(-z + 3)$ **11.** $(-3d + 10)(2d - 1)$ **12.** $(n + 1)(n^2 + 4n + 5)$

13. $(w - 3)(w^2 + 8w + 1)$ **14.** $(2s + 5)(s^2 + 3s - 1)$ **15.** $(x^2 - 4xy + y^2)(5xy)$

9. $-3p^3 + 6p^2 - p + 2$
10. $-2z^2 + 13z - 21$
11. $-6d^2 + 23d - 10$
12. $n^3 + 5n^2 + 9n + 5$
13. $w^3 + 5w^2 - 23w - 3$
14. $2s^3 + 11s^2 + 13s - 5$
15. $5x^3y - 20x^2y^2 + 5xy^3$

Simplify the expression.

16. $a(3a + 1) + (a + 1)(a - 1)$ $4a^2 + a - 1$

17. $(x + 2)(x + 5) - x(4x - 1)$ $-3x^2 - 2x - 10$

18. $(m + 7)(m - 3) + (m - 4)(m + 5)$ $2m^2 + 5m - 41$

Write a polynomial for the area of the shaded region.

19. **20.**

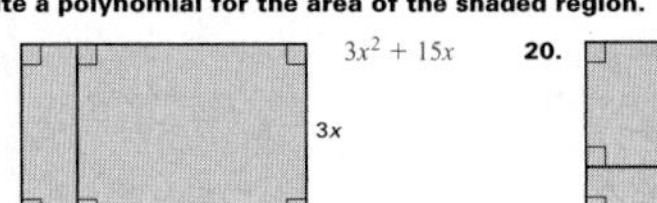

19. $3x^2 + 15x$ 20. $x^2 + 6x + 8$

21. Flower Bed You are designing a rectangular flower bed that you will border using brick pavers. The width of the border around the bed will be the same on every side, as shown.

6 ft, x ft, x ft, 5 ft

a. Write a polynomial that represents the total area of the flower bed and the border. $A = 4x^2 + 22x + 30$

b. Find the total area of the flower bed and border when the width of the border is 1.5 feet. 72 ft^2

22. School Enrollment During the period 1995–2002, the number S of students (in thousands) enrolled in school in the U.S. and the percent P (in decimal form) of this amount that are between 7 and 13 years old can be modeled by

$$S = 32.6t^3 - 376.45t^2 + 1624.2t + 66{,}939$$

and

$$P = 0.000005t^4 - 0.0003t^3 + 0.003t^2 - 0.007t + 0.4$$

where t is the number of years since 1995.

a. Find the values of S and P for $t = 0$. What does the product $S \cdot P$ mean for $t = 0$ in the context of this problem? S: 66,939; P: 0.4; $S \cdot P$ indicates the number of students (in thousands) who were between 7 and 13 in 1995.

b. Write an equation that models the number of students (in thousands) that are between 7 and 13 years old as a function of the number of years since 1995.

c. How many students between 7 and 13 years old were enrolled in 1995? about 26,775,600

22. b. $S \cdot P = 0.000163t^7 - 0.01166225t^6 + 0.218856t^5 - 1.510115t^4 + 0.46605t^3 + 38.8676t^2 + 181.107t + 26{,}775.6$

LESSON 9.3 Practice B
For use with pages 569–574

Find the product of the square of the binomial.

1. $(x - 9)^2$ $x^2 - 18x + 81$ **2.** $(m + 11)^2$ $m^2 + 22m + 121$ **3.** $(5s + 2)^2$ $25s^2 + 20s + 4$

4. $(3m + 7)^2$ $9m^2 + 42m + 49$ **5.** $(4p - 5)^2$ $16p^2 - 40p + 25$ **6.** $(7a - 6)^2$ $49a^2 - 84a + 36$

7. $(10z - 3)^2$ $100z^2 - 60z + 9$ **8.** $(2x + y)^2$ $4x^2 + 4xy + y^2$ **9.** $(3y - x)^2$ $9y^2 - 6xy + x^2$

Find the product of the sum and difference.

10. $(a - 9)(a + 9)$ $a^2 - 81$ **11.** $(z - 20)(z + 20)$ $z^2 - 400$ **12.** $(5r + 1)(5r - 1)$ $25r^2 - 1$

13. $(6m + 10)(6m - 10)$ **14.** $(7p - 2)(7p + 2)$ $49p^2 - 4$ **15.** $(9c - 1)(9c + 1)$ $81c^2 - 1$

16. $(4x + 3)(4x - 3)$ $16x^2 - 9$ **17.** $(4 - w)(4 + w)$ $-w^2 + 16$ **18.** $(5 - 2y)(5 + 2y)$ $-4y^2 + 25$

13. $36m^2 - 100$

Describe **how you can use mental math to find the product.**

19. $15 \cdot 25$ Find the product $(20 - 5)(20 + 5)$. **20.** $43 \cdot 57$ Find the product $(50 - 7)(50 + 7)$. **21.** 18^2 Find the product $(20 - 2)^2$.

Perform the indicated operation using the functions $f(x) = 4x + 0.5$ and $g(x) = 4x - 0.5$.

22. $f(x) \cdot g(x)$ $16x^2 - 0.25$ **23.** $(f(x))^2$ $16x^2 + 4x + 0.25$ **24.** $(g(x))^2$ $16x^2 - 4x + 0.25$

25. Pea Plants In pea plants, the gene S is for spherical seed shape, and the gene s is for wrinkled seed shape. Any gene combination with an S results in a spherical seed shape. Suppose two pea plants have the same gene combination Ss.

a. Make a Punnett square that shows the possible gene combinations of an offspring pea plant and the resulting seed shape. See below.

b. Write a polynomial that models the possible gene combinations of an offspring pea plant. $0.25S^2 + 0.5Ss + 0.25s^2$

c. What percent of the possible gene combinations of the offspring results in a wrinkled seed shape? 25%

26. Basketball Statistics You are on the basketball team and you want to figure out some statistics about foul shots. The area model shows the possible outcomes of two attempted foul shots.

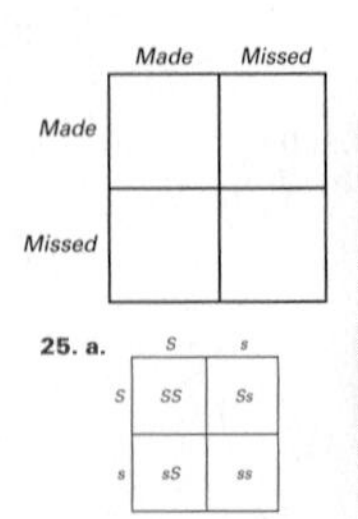

a. What percent of the two possible outcomes of two attempted foul shots results in you making at least one foul shot? *Explain* how you found your answer using the table. 75%; Three of the four squares in the area model represent at least one foul shot being made.

b. Show how you could use a polynomial to model the possible results of two attempted foul shots. The chance of making a foul shot is 50% and the chance of not making a foul shot is 50%. So the polynomial $(0.5C + 0.5I)^2 = 0.25C^2 + 0.5CI + 0.25I^2$ represents this situation where C represents a foul shot made and I represents a foul shot missed.

25. a.

	S	s
S	SS	Ss
s	sS	ss

LESSON 9.4 Practice B
For use with pages 575–580

Solve the equation.

1. $(x + 14)(x - 3) = 0$ $-14, 3$ **2.** $(m - 12)(m + 5) = 0$ $-5, 12$ **3.** $(p + 15)(p + 24) = 0$ $-24, -15$

4. $(n - 8)(n - 9) = 0$ $8, 9$ **5.** $(d + 8)\left(d - \frac{1}{2}\right) = 0$ $-8, \frac{1}{2}$ **6.** $\left(c + \frac{3}{4}\right)(c - 6) = 0$ $-\frac{3}{4}, 6$

7. $(2z - 8)(z + 5) = 0$ $-5, 4$ **8.** $(y - 3)(5y + 10) = 0$ $-2, 3$ **9.** $(6b - 4)(b - 8) = 0$ $\frac{2}{3}, 8$

10. $(8x + 4)(6x - 3) = 0$ $-\frac{1}{2}, \frac{1}{2}$ **11.** $(3x + 9)(6x - 3) = 0$ $-3, \frac{1}{2}$ **12.** $(4x + 5)(4x - 5) = 0$ $-\frac{5}{4}, \frac{5}{4}$

Factor out the greatest common monomial factor.

13. $10x - 10y$ $10(x - y)$ **14.** $8x^2 + 20y$ $4(2x^2 + 5y)$ **15.** $18a^2 - 6b$ $6(3a^2 - b)$

16. $4x^2 - 4x$ $4x(x - 1)$ **17.** $r^2 + 2rs$ $r(r + 2s)$ **18.** $2m^2 + 6mn$ $2m(m + 3n)$

19. $5p^2q + 10q$ $5q(p^2 + 2)$ **20.** $9a^5 + a^3$ $a^3(9a^2 + 1)$ **21.** $6w^3 - 14w^2$ $2w^2(3w - 7)$

Solve the equation.

22. $m^2 - 10m = 0$ $0, 10$ **23.** $b^2 + 14b = 0$ $-14, 0$ **24.** $5w^2 - 5w = 0$ $0, 1$

25. $24k^2 + 24k = 0$ $-1, 0$ **26.** $8r^2 - 24r = 0$ $0, 3$ **27.** $9p^2 + 18p = 0$ $-2, 0$

28. $6n^2 - 15n = 0$ $0, \frac{5}{2}$ **29.** $-8y^2 - 10y = 0$ $-\frac{5}{4}, 0$ **30.** $-10b^2 + 25b = 0$ $0, \frac{5}{2}$

31. $8c^2 = 4c$ $0, \frac{1}{2}$ **32.** $30r^2 = -15r$ $-\frac{1}{2}, 0$ **33.** $-24y^2 = 9y$ $-\frac{3}{8}, 0$

34. Diving Board A diver jumps from a diving board that is 24 feet above the water. The height of the diver is given by

$$h = -16(t - 1.5)(t + 1)$$

where the height h is measured in feet, and the time t is measured in seconds. When will the diver hit the water? Can you see a quick way to find the answer? *Explain.* 1.5 sec; Yes. From the equation, you can see that the factor $t - 1.5$ will be zero when $t = 1.5$.

35. Dog A dog leaps into the air to catch a frisbee with an initial velocity of 14 feet per second.

a. Write a model for the height of the dog above the ground. $h = -16t^2 + 14t$

b. After how many seconds does the dog land on the ground? $\frac{7}{8}$ sec

36. Desktop Areas You have two components to the desktop where you do your homework that fit together into an L shape. The two components have the same area.

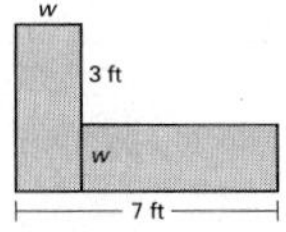

a. Write an equation that relates the areas of the desktop components. $w(w + 3) = w(7 - w)$

b. Find the value of w. 2 ft

c. What is the combined area of the desktop components? 20 ft^2

LESSON 9.5

Practice B
For use with pages 583–589

Factor the trinomial.

1. $x^2 + 8x + 7$ $(x + 7)(x + 1)$ **2.** $b^2 - 7b + 10$ $(b - 5)(b - 2)$ **3.** $w^2 - 12w - 13$

4. $p^2 + 10p + 25$ $(p + 5)^2$ **5.** $m^2 - 10m + 24$ **6.** $y^2 - 5y - 24$ $(y - 8)(y + 3)$

7. $a^2 + 13a + 36$ $(a + 9)(a + 4)$ **8.** $n^2 + 2n - 48$ $(n - 6)(n + 8)$ **9.** $z^2 - 14z + 40$ $(z - 10)(z - 4)$

3. $(w - 13)(w + 1)$ **5.** $(m - 6)(m - 4)$

Solve the equation.

10. $y^2 + 17y + 72 = 0$ $-9, -8$ **11.** $a^2 - 9a - 36 = 0$ $-3, 12$ **12.** $w^2 - 13w + 42 = 0$ $6, 7$

13. $m^2 - 5m - 14 = 0$ $-2, 7$ **14.** $x^2 + 11x + 24 = 0$ **15.** $n^2 - 12n + 27 = 0$ $3, 9$

16. $d^2 + 5d - 50 = 0$ $-10, 5$ **17.** $p^2 + 16p + 48 = 0$ **18.** $z^2 - z - 30 = 0$ $-5, 6$

14. $-8, -3$ **17.** $-12, -4$

Find the zeros of the polynomial function.

19. $f(x) = x^2 - 5x - 36$ **20.** $g(x) = x^2 + 8x - 20$ **21.** $h(x) = x^2 - 11x + 24$ $3, 8$

22. $f(x) = x^2 + 11x + 28$ **23.** $g(x) = x^2 + 11x - 12$ **24.** $h(x) = x^2 + 3x - 18$ $-6, 3$

19. $-4, 9$ **20.** $-10, 2$
22. $-7, -4$ **23.** $-12, 1$

Solve the equation.

25. $x(x + 17) = -60$ $-12, -5$ **26.** $p(p - 4) = 32$ $-4, 8$ **27.** $w(w + 8) = -15$ $-5, -3$

28. $n(n + 6) = 7$ $-7, 1$ **29.** $s^2 - 3(s + 2) = 4$ $-2, 5$ **30.** $d^2 + 18(d + 4) = -9$ -9

31. Patio Area A community center is building a patio area along two sides of its pool. The pool is rectangular with a width of 50 feet and a length of 100 feet. The patio area will have the same width on each side of the pool.

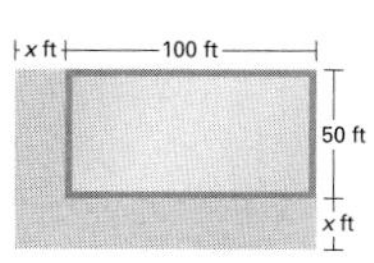

a. Write a polynomial that represents the combined area of the pool and the patio area. $x^2 + 150x + 5000$

b. The combined area of the pool and patio area should be 8400 square feet. How wide should the patio area be? 20 ft

32. Area Rug You are creating your own area rug from a square piece of remnant carpeting. You plan on cutting 4 inches from the length and 3 inches from the width. The area of the resulting area rug is 1056 square inches.

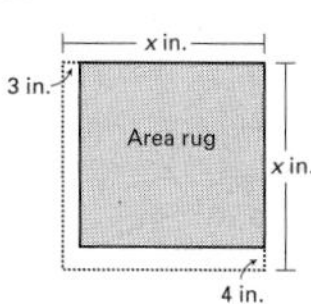

a. Write a polynomial that represents the area of your area rug. $x^2 - 7x + 12$

b. What is the perimeter of the original piece of remnant carpeting? 144 in.

LESSON 9.6

Practice B
For use with pages 593–599

1. $-(x - 4)(x + 7)$ **2.** $-(p - 2)(p - 6)$ **3.** $-(m + 8)(m + 5)$ **4.** $(2y + 1)(y + 7)$ **5.** $(3a - 1)(a - 4)$ **6.** $(5d + 2)(d - 4)$ **7.** $(3c + 2)(2c + 1)$ **8.** $2(5n - 3)(n - 2)$ **9.** $(2w + 3)(6w - 5)$ **10.** $-(b + 4)(2b - 3)$ **11.** $-(r + 5)(3r + 2)$ **12.** $-2(s - 2)(2s + 1)$

Factor the trinomial.

1. $-x^2 - 3x + 28$ **2.** $-p^2 + 8p - 12$ **3.** $-m^2 - 13m - 40$

4. $2y^2 + 15y + 7$ **5.** $3a^2 - 13a + 4$ **6.** $5d^2 - 18d - 8$

7. $6c^2 + 7c + 2$ **8.** $10n^2 - 26n + 12$ **9.** $12w^2 + 8w - 15$

10. $-2b^2 - 5b + 12$ **11.** $-3r^2 - 17r - 10$ **12.** $-4s^2 + 6s + 4$

Solve the equation. See below.

13. $-x^2 + x + 20 = 0$ **14.** $-m^2 - 10m - 16 = 0$ **15.** $-p^2 + 13p - 42 = 0$

16. $2c^2 - 11c + 5 = 0$ **17.** $2y^2 + y - 10 = 0$ **18.** $16r^2 + 18r + 5 = 0$

19. $3w^2 + 19w + 6 = 0$ **20.** $12n^2 - 11n + 2 = 0$ **21.** $15a^2 - 2a - 8 = 0$

22. $-2x^2 - 9x - 4 = 0$ **23.** $-3s^2 - s + 10 = 0$ **24.** $8d^2 - 6d - 5 = 0$

Find the zeros of the polynomial function. See below.

25. $f(x) = -x^2 + 6x + 27$ **26.** $f(x) = 6x^2 + 45x - 24$ **27.** $f(x) = -3x^2 - 14x + 24$

28. $f(x) = -2x^2 + 2x + 4$ **29.** $f(x) = 3x^2 - 17x + 20$ **30.** $f(x) = 8x^2 + 53x - 21$

31. $f(x) = 4x^2 + 29x + 30$ **32.** $f(x) = -2x^2 - 17x + 30$ **33.** $f(x) = 10x^2 + 5x - 5$

34. Summer Business Your weekly revenue R (in dollars) from your tie-dye T-shirt business can be modeled by

$R = -2t^2 + 87t + 90$

where t represents the number of weeks since the first week you started selling T-shirts. How much did you make your first week? $90

35. Cliff Diving A cliff diver jumps from a ledge 96 feet above the ocean with an initial upward velocity of 16 feet per second. How long will it take until the diver enters the water? 3 sec

36. Wall Mirror You plan on making a wall hanging that contains two small mirrors as shown.

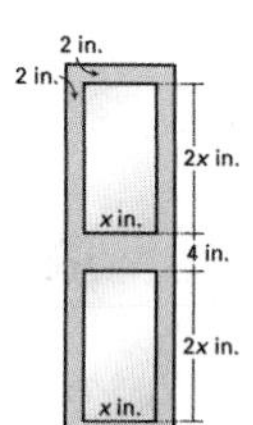

a. Write a polynomial that represents the area of the wall hanging. $4x^2 + 24x + 32$

b. The area of the wall hanging will be 480 square inches. Find the length and width of the mirrors you will use. 8 in. by 16 in.

13. $-4, 5$ **14.** $-8, -2$ **15.** $6, 7$
16. $\frac{1}{2}, 5$ **17.** $-\frac{5}{2}, 2$ **18.** $-\frac{5}{8}, -\frac{1}{2}$
19. $-6, -\frac{1}{3}$ **20.** $\frac{1}{4}, \frac{2}{3}$ **21.** $-\frac{2}{3}, \frac{4}{5}$
22. $-4, -\frac{1}{2}$ **23.** $-2, \frac{5}{3}$ **24.** $-\frac{1}{2}, \frac{5}{4}$
25. $-3, 9$ **26.** $-8, \frac{1}{2}$ **27.** $-6, \frac{4}{3}$
28. $-1, 2$ **29.** $\frac{5}{3}, 4$ **30.** $-7, \frac{3}{8}$
31. $-6, -\frac{5}{4}$ **32.** $-10, \frac{3}{2}$ **33.** $-1, \frac{1}{2}$

LESSON 9.7

Practice B
For use with pages 600–605

2. $(5p - 12)(5p + 12)$ **3.** $4(b - 5)(b + 5)$ **5.** $-2(x - 4)(x + 4)$ **6.** $-4(r - 5s)(r + 5s)$ **7.** $(y + 12)^2$ **8.** $(3c + 4)^2$

Factor the polynomial.

1. $x^2 - 36$ $(x - 6)(x + 6)$ **2.** $25p^2 - 144$ **3.** $4b^2 - 100$

4. $36m^2 - 81$ $9(2m - 3)(2m + 3)$ **5.** $-2x^2 + 32$ **6.** $-4r^2 + 100s^2$

7. $y^2 + 24y + 144$ **8.** $9c^2 + 24c + 16$ **9.** $25w^2 - 20w + 4$ $(5w - 2)^2$

10. $16n^2 - 56n + 49$ $(4n - 7)^2$ **11.** $-18a^2 - 12a - 2$ $-2(3a + 1)^2$ **12.** $20z^2 - 140z + 245$ $5(2z - 7)^2$

Solve the equation.

13. $x^2 + 14x + 49 = 0$ -7 **14.** $8w^2 = 50$ $-\frac{5}{2}, \frac{5}{2}$ **15.** $64p^2 - 16p + 1 = 0$ $\frac{1}{8}$

16. $8a^2 - 72 = 0$ $-3, 3$ **17.** $3m^2 + 30m + 75 = 0$ -5 **18.** $-4y^2 + 32y - 64 = 0$ 4

19. $-5x^2 + 125 = 0$ $-5, 5$ **20.** $-7r^2 + 140r - 700 = 0$ 10 **21.** $24w^2 - 24w + 6 = 0$ $\frac{1}{2}$

22. $18n^2 + 60n + 50 = 0$ $-\frac{5}{3}$ **23.** $\frac{25}{2}x^2 + 15x + \frac{9}{2} = 0$ $-\frac{3}{5}$ **24.** $4x^2 = \frac{9}{16}$ $-\frac{3}{8}, \frac{3}{8}$

Find the value of *x* in the geometric shape.

25. Area = 144π cm^2 8

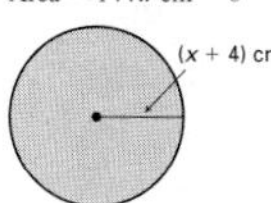

26. Area = 225 in.^{2} 3

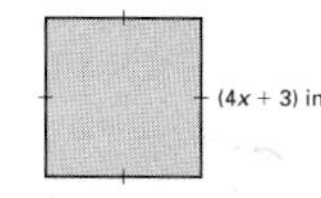

27. Measuring Tape A measuring tape drops from a roof that is 16 feet above the ground. After how many seconds does the measuring tape land on the ground? 1 sec

28. Playground A curved ladder that children can climb on can be modeled by the equation

$y = -\frac{1}{20}x^2 + x$

where x and y are measured in feet.

a. Make a table of values that shows the height of the ladder for $x = 0, 5, 10, 15,$ and 20 feet from the left end. 0; 3.75; 5; 3.75; 0

b. For what additional values of x does the equation make sense? *Explain.*

c. Plot the ordered pairs in the table from part (a) as points in the coordinate plane. Connect the points with a smooth curve.

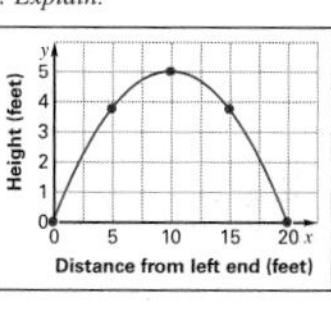

d. At approximately what distance from the left end does the ladder reach a height of 5 feet? Check your answer algebraically. 10 ft

b. Any other values between 0 and 20 because the ladder is on the ground at $x = 0$ and meets the ground again at $x = 20$.

LESSON 9.8

Practice B
For use with pages 606–613

14. $4m(m - 2)(m + 2)$ **19.** $5(m^2 + 4m + 8)$ **20.** $6(x + 5)(x - 4)$ **21.** $4z(z - 2)(z + 1)$ **22.** $9(x^3 + 4x^2 + 4)$ **23.** $(x^2 + 5)(x + 1)$ **24.** $(d^2 + 5)(d + 4)$

Factor the expression.

1. $4x(x + 5) - 3(x + 5)$ $(4x - 3)(x + 5)$ **2.** $12(a - 3) - 2a(a - 3)$ $-2(a - 6)(a - 3)$

3. $w^2(w + 8) - 5(w + 8)$ $(w^2 - 5)(w + 8)$ **4.** $2b^2(b + 6) + 3(b + 6)$ $(2b^2 + 3)(b + 6)$

5. $y(15 + x) - (x + 15)$ $(y - 1)(x + 15)$ **6.** $3x(4 + y) - 6(4 + y)$ $3(x - 2)(y + 4)$

Factor the polynomial by grouping.

7. $x^3 + x^2 + x + 1$ $(x^2 + 1)(x + 1)$ **8.** $y^3 - 14y^2 + y - 14$ $(y^2 + 1)(y - 14)$

9. $m^3 - 6m^2 + 2m - 12$ $(m^2 + 2)(m - 6)$ **10.** $p^3 + 9p^2 + 4p + 36$ $(p^2 + 4)(p + 9)$

11. $t^3 + 12t^2 - 2t - 24$ $(t^2 - 2)(t + 12)$ **12.** $3n^3 - 3n^2 + n - 1$ $(3n^2 + 1)(n - 1)$

Factor the polynomial completely.

13. $7x^3 + 28x^2$ $7x^2(x + 4)$ **14.** $4m^3 - 16m$ See above. **15.** $-16p^3 - 2p$ $-2p(8p^2 + 1)$

16. $48r^3 - 30r^2$ $6r^2(8r - 5)$ **17.** $15y - 60y^2$ $15y(1 - 4y)$ **18.** $18xy - 24x^2$ $6x(3y - 4x)$

19. $5m^2 + 20m + 40$ See above. **20.** $6x^2 + 6x - 120$ See above. **21.** $4z^3 - 4z^2 - 8z$ See above.

22. $9x^3 + 36x^2 + 36$ See above. **23.** $x^3 + x^2 + 5x + 5$ See above. **24.** $d^3 + 4d^2 + 5d + 20$ See above.

Solve the equation.

25. $3x^2 + 18x + 24 = 0$ **26.** $10x^2 = 250$ $-5, 5$ **27.** $4m^2 - 28m + 49 = 0$ $\frac{7}{2}$

28. $12x^2 + 18x + 6 = 0$ **29.** $18x^2 - 48x + 32 = 0$ $\frac{4}{3}$ **30.** $-18x^2 - 60x - 50 = 0$ $-\frac{5}{3}$

25. $-4, -2$ **28.** $-\frac{1}{2}, -1$

31. Countertop A countertop will have a hole drilled in it to hold a cylindrical container that will function as a utensil holder. The area of the entire countertop is given by $5x^2 + 12x + 7$. The area of the hole is given by $x^2 + 2x + 1$. Write an expression for the area in factored form of the countertop that is left after the hole is drilled. $2(2x + 3)(x + 1)$

32. Film Canister A film canister in the shape of a cylinder has a height of 8 centimeters and a volume of 32π cubic centimeters.

a. Write an equation for the volume of the film canister. $8\pi r^2 - 32\pi = 0$

b. What is the radius of the film canister? 2 cm

33. Badminton You hit a badminton birdie upward with a racket from a height of 2 feet with an initial velocity of 4 feet per second.

a. Write an equation that models this situation. $h = -16t^2 + 4t + 2$

b. How high is the birdie at 0.1 second? 2.24 ft

c. How high is the birdie at 0.25 second? 2 ft

d. How long will it take the birdie to reach the ground? about 0.5 sec

9 Assessment

CHAPTER 9 Quiz 1
For use after Lessons 9.1–9.3

Find the sum, difference, or product.

1. $(-3x^2 - 8x + 5) + (x^2 - 6x + 2)$
2. $(q^3 - 7q^2 - 3q) - (q^3 + 10q^2 - 4)$
3. $-5k^2(k^4 - 3k^3)$
4. $(y + 2)(y^2 + y - 1)$
5. $(4z + 9)(z - 2)$
6. $(p - 7)(p + 1)$
7. $(8m + 3)^2$
8. $(5y - 6)^2$
9. A flower garden is 4 feet longer that its width w. Write a polynomial that represents the area of the garden.

Answers

1. $-2x^2 - 14x + 7$
2. $-17q^2 - 3q + 4$
3. $-5k^6 + 15k^5$
4. $y^3 + 3y^2 + y - 2$
5. $4z^2 + z - 18$
6. $p^2 - 6p - 7$
7. $64m^2 + 48m + 9$
8. $25y^2 - 60y + 36$
9. $w^2 + 4w$

CHAPTER 9 Quiz 2
For use after Lessons 9.4–9.6

Factor out the greatest common monomial factor.

1. $12x^2 + 3xy$
2. $21ab^2 + 35ab$
3. $9z^2 - 18z^3$
4. $4p - 8p^2$

Factor the trinomial.

5. $w^2 + 15w + 14$
6. $m^2 - 12m + 20$
7. $2k^2 + 5k - 3$
8. $3b^2 - 20b - 7$
9. $8y^2 + 26y + 15$
10. $-2d^2 - 7d - 5$

Solve the equation.

11. $(h + 6)(h - 4) = 0$
12. $21d^2 - 7d = 0$
13. $s^2 - 7s + 14 = 2$
14. $-5z^2 - 10z = 0$
15. $2g^2 - 14g = -20$
16. $-r^2 - 5r - 6 = 0$

Answers

1. $3x(4x + y)$
2. $7ab(3b + 5)$
3. $9z^2(1 - 2z)$
4. $4p(1 - 2p)$
5. $(w + 1)(w + 14)$
6. $(m - 10)(m - 2)$
7. $(2k - 1)(k + 3)$
8. $(3b + 1)(b - 7)$
9. $(2y + 5)(4y + 3)$
10. $-(2d + 5)(d + 1)$
11. $-6, 4$
12. $0, \frac{1}{3}$
13. $3, 4$
14. $-2, 0$
15. $2, 5$
16. $-3, -2$

CHAPTER 9 Quiz 3
For use after Lessons 9.7–9.8

Factor the polynomial.

1. $x^2 - 81$
2. $9z^2 - 121$
3. $100m^2 - 49n^2$
4. $h^2 + 14h + 49$
5. $64t^2 - 16t + 1$
6. $4a^2 + 4b^2$

Factor the polynomial completely.

7. $6x^2 - 6y^2$
8. $5m^2 - 20n^2$
9. $x^3 - 3x^2 - 10x$
10. $3z^2 + 30z + 75$
11. $2k^3 - 36k^2 + 162k$
12. $x^2 + 2x + xy + 2y$

Solve the equation.

13. $d^2 + 10d + 25 = 0$
14. $20 - 5s^2 = 0$
15. $y^3 - 49y = 0$
16. $6x^3 - 36x^2 + 30x = 0$
17. A box of crackers has a volume of 96 cubic inches. The box has a height of x inches, a width of $(x - 6)$ inches, and a length of $(x - 2)$ inches. Find the dimensions of the box.

Answers

1. $(x + 9)(x - 9)$
2. $(3z + 11)(3z - 11)$
3. $(10m + 7n) \cdot (10m - 7n)$
4. $(h + 7)^2$
5. $(8t - 1)^2$
6. $4(a^2 + b^2)$
7. $6(x + y)(x - y)$
8. $5(m + 2n)(m - 2n)$
9. $x(x - 5)(x + 2)$
10. $3(z + 5)^2$
11. $2k(k - 9)^2$
12. $(x + y)(x + 2)$
13. -5
14. $-2, 2$
15. $-7, 0, 7$
16. $0, 1, 5$
17. 6 in. long by 2 in. wide by 8 in. high

CHAPTER 9 Chapter Test B
For use after Chapter 9

Find the sum or difference.

1. $(4a^3 - 2a + 1) - (a^3 - 2a + 3)$
2. $(3x^3 + 4x + 14) + (-4x^2 + 21)$
3. $(3d - 5d^3 + 2d^2) - (8d^3 + 6d - 1)$
4. $(-3n + 7n) + (4n^3 - 2n^2 + 12)$

In Exercises 5 and 6, use the following information.

During the period 1985–2012, the projected enrollment B (in thousands of students) in public schools and the projected enrollment R (in thousands of students) in private schools can be modeled by

$B = -18.53t^2 + 975.8t + 48{,}140$ and $R = 80.8t + 8049$

where t is the number of years since 1985.

5. Write an equation that models the difference in the projected enrollments for public schools and private schools as a function of the number of years since 1985.
6. Find the difference in projected enrollments for public schools and private schools in 2005.

Find the product.

7. $-4c(-9c^2 + 5c + 8)$
8. $(y + 4)(5y - 3)$
9. $(s^2 + 6s - 5)(5s + 2)$
10. $(4p + 1)(4p - 1)$
11. $(w - 5)^2$
12. $(2b + 3)^2$

In Exercises 13 and 14, use the following information.

You are making an open box from a rectangular sheet of cardboard by cutting squares 2 inches in length from each corner and folding up the sides. The length of the sheet of cardboard is 8 inches more than the width.

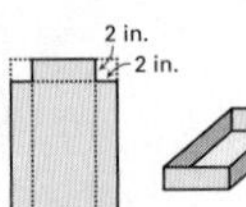

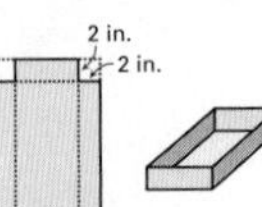

13. Write a polynomial that represents the total volume of the open box.
14. Find the volume of the open box when the width of the sheet of cardboard is 6 inches.

Answers

1. $3a^3 - 2$
2. $3x^3 - 4x^2 + 4x + 35$
3. $-13d^3 + 2d^2 - 3d + 1$
4. $4n^3 - 2n^2 + 4n + 12$
5. $D = -18.53t^2 + 895t + 40{,}091$
6. 50,579,000 students
7. $36c^3 - 20c^2 - 32c$
8. $5y^2 + 17y - 12$
9. $5s^3 + 32s^2 - 13s - 10$
10. $16p^2 - 1$
11. $w^2 - 10w + 25$
12. $4b^2 + 12b + 9$
13. $V = 2(x - 4)(x + 4) = 2x^2 - 32$
14. 40 in.^{3}

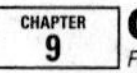

Chapter Test B *continued*

For use after Chapter 9

Solve the equation.

15. $(h - 7)(2h + 1) = 0$

16. $4g^2 - 32g = 0$

17. $3m^2 = -6m$

In Exercises 18 and 19, use the following information.

The room and the hallway shown in the floor plan below have different dimensions but the same area.

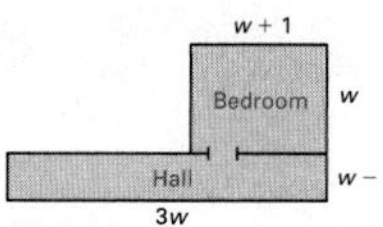

18. Write an equation that relates the areas of the rooms.

19. Find the value of w.

Factor the trinomial.

20. $n^2 - 14n - 72$ **21.** $-x^2 + 14x - 45$ **22.** $6k^2 - k - 12$

In Exercises 23 and 24, use the following information.

A juggler throws a ball from an initial height of 4 feet with an initial vertical velocity of 30 feet per second. The height h (in feet) of the ball can be modeled by $h = -16t^2 + vt + s$ where t is the time (in seconds) the ball has been in the air, v is the initial vertical velocity (in feet per second), and s is the initial height.

23. Write an equation that gives the height (in feet) of the ball as a function of the time (in seconds) since it left the juggler's hand.

24. If the juggler misses the ball, after how many seconds does it hit the ground?

Factor the polynomial completely.

25. $x^5 - x^3$ **26.** $5a(a - 3) - 7(a - 3)$

27. $9t^4 + 30t^3 + 25t^2$ **28.** $b^3 + 5b^2 - 3b - 15$

Solve the equation.

29. $x^2 + 8x + 15 = 0$ **30.** $7y - 2 = 5y^2$

31. $72 = 32q^2$ **32.** $u^3 + 6u^2 = 4u + 24$

Answers

15. $-\frac{1}{2}, 7$
16. $0, 8$
17. $-2, 0$
18. $3w(w - 2) = w(w + 1)$
19. $\frac{7}{2}$
20. $(n - 18)(n + 4)$
21. $-(x - 9)(x - 5)$
22. $(3k + 4)(2k - 3)$
23. $h = -16t^2 + 30t + 4$
24. 2 sec
25. $x^3(x + 1)(x - 1)$
26. $(a - 3)(5a - 7)$
27. $t^2(3t + 5)^2$
28. $(b + 5)(b^2 - 3)$
29. $-5, -3$
30. $1, \frac{2}{5}$
31. $\pm\frac{3}{2}$
32. $-6, \pm 2$

CHAPTER 9

Standardized Test

For use after Chapter 9

Multiple Choice

1. What is the degree of $-5a^2b + 4a^2 - 2b + 5$? C

Ⓐ −5 Ⓑ 2 Ⓒ 3 Ⓓ 4

2. Which expression is *not* a monomial? D

Ⓐ $-2n$ Ⓑ $\frac{m}{2}$ Ⓒ r^2 Ⓓ $3p^{-3}$

3. What is the sum of $6m^2 - 5m + 4$ and $7m^2 + 2m - 5$? B

Ⓐ $13m^2 - 7m - 9$

Ⓑ $13m^2 - 3m - 1$

Ⓒ $13m^2 + 3m - 1$

Ⓓ $13m^2 - 3m + 1$

4. What is $(12s^2 + 8s - 6) - (9s^2 - 2s + 5)$ in simplest form? B

Ⓐ $3s^2 + 6s - 1$ Ⓑ $3s^2 + 10s - 11$

Ⓒ $3s^2 + 10s + 11$ Ⓓ $3s^2 + 6s - 11$

5. What is the product of $x + 5$ and $3x - 2$? A

Ⓐ $3x^2 + 13x - 10$ Ⓑ $3x^2 - 10$

Ⓒ $3x^2 + 17x - 10$ Ⓓ $3x^2 - 13x - 10$

6. Which polynomial represents $f(x) \cdot g(x)$ if $f(x) = -4x^2$ and $g(x) = x^3 + 2x^2 - 5x + 3$? C

Ⓐ $-4x^5 + 8x^4 - 20x^3 - 12x^2$

Ⓑ $-4x^5 - 8x^3 - 20x^3 - 12x^2$

Ⓒ $-4x^5 - 8x^4 + 20x^3 - 12x^2$

Ⓓ $-4x^5 + 8x^4 + 20x^3 - 12x^2$

7. What is the simplest form of $(5x + 2)(5x - 2)$? A

Ⓐ $25x^2 - 4$ Ⓑ $10x^2$

Ⓒ $25x^2 + 10x - 4$ Ⓓ $25x^2 - 20x - 4$

8. What is the simplest form of $(2n + 3)^2$? D

Ⓐ $4n^2 + 12n + 6$ Ⓑ $4n^2 + 6n + 9$

Ⓒ $4n^2 + 9$ Ⓓ $4n^2 + 12n + 9$

9. Which of the following are the roots of the equation $(y - 3)(y + 2) = 0$? B

Ⓐ 2 and 3 Ⓑ −2 and 3

Ⓒ −3 and 2 Ⓓ −3 and −2

10. What is the greatest monomial factor of $32x^5 - 12x^2$? A

Ⓐ $4x^2$ Ⓑ $32x^5$

Ⓒ $12x^2$ Ⓓ $20x^3$

11. What are the roots of the equation $5x^2 = x$? C

Ⓐ −5 and 0 Ⓑ 0 and $-\frac{1}{5}$

Ⓒ 0 and $\frac{1}{5}$ Ⓓ 0 and 5

12. Which of the following is the correct factorization of $x^2 - 15x + 56$? A

Ⓐ $(x - 7)(x - 8)$

Ⓑ $(x + 7)(x - 8)$

Ⓒ $(x - 7)(x + 8)$

Ⓓ $(x + 7)(x + 8)$

13. What are the roots of the equation $x^2 + 30x = 1000$? D

Ⓐ 20 and 50 Ⓑ −50 and −20

Ⓒ −20 and 50 Ⓓ −50 and 20

14. Which of the following is the correct factorization of $6x^2 - 2x - 20$? B

Ⓐ $2(3x - 5)(x + 2)$

Ⓑ $2(3x + 5)(x - 2)$

Ⓒ $2(3x - 5)(x + 2)$

Ⓓ $2(3x + 1)(x - 10)$

CHAPTER 9

Standardized Test *continued*

For use after Chapter 9

15. Which of the following is the correct factorization of $-y^2 + y + 6$? C

Ⓐ $(-y + 3)(y - 2)$

Ⓑ $-(y + 6)(y + 1)$

Ⓒ $-(y + 2)(y - 3)$

Ⓓ $-(y + 2)(y + 3)$

16. What are the roots of the equation $1.5x^2 - 4.5x = -3$? C

Ⓐ −2 and −1 Ⓑ −1 and 1

Ⓒ 1 and 2 Ⓓ 2 and 3

17. Which of the following is the correct factorization of $-60m^2 + 15n^2$? D

Ⓐ $15(2m + n)^2$

Ⓑ $15(2m - n)(2m + n)$

Ⓒ $-15(2m - n)^2$

Ⓓ $-15(2m - n)(2m + n)$

18. Which of the following is the correct factorization of $3x^3 + 24x^2 - 27x$? A

Ⓐ $3x(x + 9)(x - 1)$

Ⓑ $3x(x - 9)(x + 1)$

Ⓒ $3x(x - 9)(x - 1)$

Ⓓ $3x(x + 9)(x + 1)$

19. What is the completely factored form of $4x^5 - 256x^3$? B

Ⓐ $4x^3(x - 8)^2$

Ⓑ $4x^3(x + 8)(x - 8)$

Ⓒ $4x^3(x^2 - 64)$

Ⓓ $4x^3(x + 8)^2$

22. a. h; h + 8; h − 2

22. c. 160 cm²; If you set the polynomial in part (b) equal to 96 and solve for h, you will find that the height is 4 centimeters. From there, you find the area of each side and add to find the total surface area.

Gridded Answer

20. The square of the binomial $x - 4$ has the form $x^2 - ax + 16$. What is the value of a?

8

Short Response

21. You made a square card to send to a friend. The card did not fit in the envelope so you had to trim the card. You trimmed 4 inches from the length and 5 inches from the width. The area of the resulting card is 20 square inches.

a. What were the original dimensions of the card? 9 in. × 9 in.

b. What was the perimeter of the original card? 36 in.

c. What is the difference in the areas of the original and trimmed cards? 61 in.²

Extended Response

22. The length of a box is 2 centimeters less than its height. The width of the box is 8 centimeters more than its height.

a. Draw a diagram of the box and label its dimensions in terms of the height h. See left.

b. Write a polynomial that represents the volume of the box. $h^3 + 6h^2 - 16h$

c. If the box has a volume of 96 cubic centimeters, what is its surface area? *Explain.* See left.

CHAPTER 9

Alternative Assessment and Math Journal

For use after Chapter 9

Journal **1.** Explain the four steps that you should try when factoring a polynomial completely.

Multi-Step Problem **2.** The diagram below represents a picture frame that is being built.

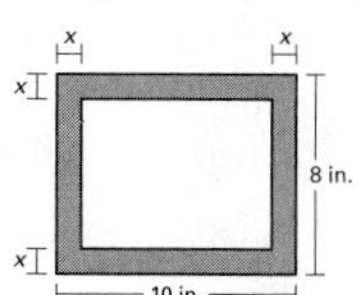

a. Write a polynomial expression to represent each dimension of the inner rectangle.

b. A gold ribbon is to be placed around the outside of each rectangle of the frame. Write a polynomial expression to represent the amount of ribbon needed.

c. How much gold ribbon is needed if the value of x is 1.5 inches?

d. Write a polynomial expression to represent the area of the interior portion of the picture frame.

e. What is the interior area of the picture frame if the value of x is 1.5 inches?

f. Write and solve a polynomial equation to determine the value of x that will make the interior area of the picture frame measure 63 square inches.

g. Write a polynomial expression to represent the area of the shaded portion of the frame.

h. Write and solve a polynomial equation to determine the value of x that will make the shaded area of the picture frame measure 38.75 square inches.

1. Complete answers should include: a brief description of the four steps of factoring a polynomial completely:

1. Factor out the greatest common monomial factor.
2. Look for a difference of two squares or a perfect square trinomial.
3. Factor a trinomial of the form $ax^2 + bx + c$ into a product of binomial factors.
4. Factor a polynomial with four terms by grouping; mention that some of the steps may not work for the polynomial that is being factored.

2. a. $10 - 2x$; $8 - 2x$ **b.** $72 - 8x$ **c.** 60 in. **d.** $4x^2 - 36x + 80$ **e.** 35 in.²
f. $\frac{1}{2}$ in. **g.** $-4x^2 + 36x$ **h.** 1.25 in.

PLAN AND PREPARE

Main Ideas

In Chapter 9 students identify, classify, add, subtract, and multiply polynomials. They use vertical and horizontal formats to find sums and differences. To find products, they use the distributive property, tables of products, and patterns (including the FOIL pattern, the square of a binomial pattern, and the sum and difference patterns). They write polynomials to describe and solve real-world problems and solve polynomial equations. Students factor polynomials and use factoring to solve equations, to find the zeros of functions, and to find the roots of equations. Finally, they factor polynomials completely using a variety of techniques.

Prerequisite Skills

Skills Readiness, available on the *Easy Planner*, provides review and practice for the Skills Check portion of the Prerequisite Skills quiz.

How student answers the exercises	What to assign from *Skills Readiness*
Any of Exs. 3–6 answered incorrectly	**Skill 57** Simplify variable expressions
Any of Exs. 7–10 answered incorrectly	**Skill 59** Apply properties of exponents
Any of Exs. 11–14 answered incorrectly	**Skill 4** Find greatest common factor
All exercises answered correctly	Chapter 9 Enrichment

Additional skills review and practice is available in the Skills Review Handbook, pp. 909–937, and the @HomeTutor.

9 Polynomials and Factoring

Making Sense of Chapter 9

In this chapter you will learn to add, subtract, multiply, and factor polynomials. By the end of this chapter, you will be able to find roots of polynomial equations and zeros of polynomial functions.

Previously, you learned the following skills, which you'll use in Chapter 9: using the distributive property, combining like terms, and using the properties of exponents.

Prerequisite Skills

VOCABULARY CHECK

Copy and complete the statement.

1. Terms that have the same variable part are called __?__. **like terms**
2. For a function $f(x)$, a(n) __?__ is an x-value for which $f(x) = 0$. **zero**

SKILLS CHECK

Simplify the expression. ***(Prerequisite skill for 9.1–9.8)***

3. $3x + (-6x)$ $\mathbf{-3x}$
4. $5 + 4x + 2$ $\mathbf{4x + 7}$
5. $4(2x - 1) + x$ $\mathbf{9x - 4}$
6. $-(x + 4) - 6x$ $\mathbf{-7x - 4}$

Simplify the expression. ***(Prerequisite skill for 9.2–9.8)***

7. $(3xy)^3$ $\mathbf{27x^3y^3}$
8. $xy^2 \cdot xy^3$ $\mathbf{x^2y^5}$
9. $(x^5)^3$ $\mathbf{x^{15}}$
10. $(-x)^3$ $\mathbf{-x^3}$

Find the greatest common factor of the pair of numbers. ***(Prerequisite skill for 9.4)***

11. 121, 77 **11**
12. 96, 32 **32**
13. 81, 42 **3**
14. 12, 56 **4**

@HomeTutor Prerequisite skills practice at classzone.com

Chapter Planning Guide

Chapter Resource Book
- Teaching Guide/Lesson Plan
- Project with Rubric

Assessment and Intervention
- Assessment Book
- Benchmark Tests
- Remediation Book
- Skills Readiness

Interactive Technology
- Easy Planner
- Power Presentations
- Activity Generator
- Animated Algebra
- Test Generator
- Online Quizzes
- eWorkbook
- eEdition
- @HomeTutor

Resources for English Learners
- Spanish Study Guide
- Multi-Language Visual Glossary
- Student Resources in Spanish

Now

In Chapter 9, you will apply the big ideas listed below and reviewed in the Chapter Summary on page 615. You will also use the key vocabulary listed below.

Big Ideas

1. **Adding, subtracting, and multiplying polynomials**
2. **Factoring polynomials**
3. **Writing and solving polynomial equations to solve problems**

KEY VOCABULARY

- monomial, *p. 554*
- degree, *p. 554*
- polynomial, *p. 554*
- leading coefficient, *p. 554*
- binomial, *p. 555*
- trinomial, *p. 555*
- roots, *p. 575*
- vertical motion model, *p. 577*
- perfect square trinomial, *p. 601*
- factor by grouping, *p. 606*
- factor completely, *p. 607*

Why?

You can use a polynomial function to model vertical motion. For example, you can use a polynomial function to model the height of a jumping animal as a function of time.

Animated Algebra

The animation illustrated below for Exercise 62 on page 598 helps you to answer this question: How does changing the initial vertical velocity of a serval, an African cat, affect its jumping height?

Start
Your goal is to find the height of the serval at different times.

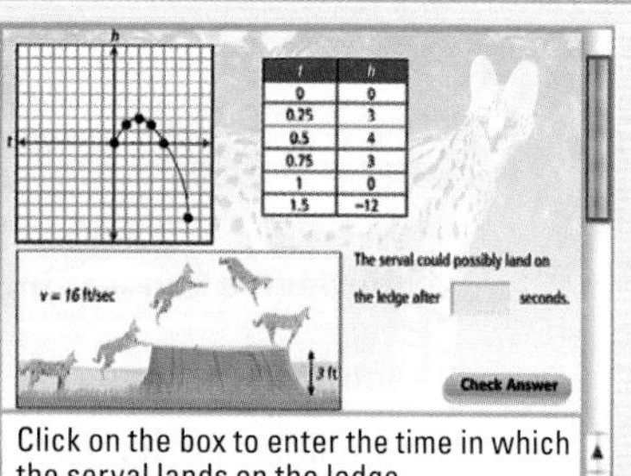

Click on the box to enter the time in which the serval lands on the ledge.

Animated Algebra at classzone.com

Other animations for Chapter 9: pages 555, 582, 592, and 601

Differentiated Instruction Resources

- Reading Strategies for Chapter 9
- Differentiated Instruction Lesson Notes
- English Learners Lesson Notes
- Inclusion Lesson Notes
- Teaching Strategies with Sample Worksheets
- Using Technology in the Classroom
- Tips for New Teachers
- Math Background Notes
- Assessment Strategies
- Teacher Survival Activities
- Bulletin Board Idea

9.1 Add and Subtract Polynomials

Before You added and subtracted integers.
Now You will add and subtract polynomials.
Why? So you can model trends in recreation, as in Ex. 37.

Key Vocabulary
- monomial
- degree
- polynomial
- leading coefficient
- binomial
- trinomial

A **monomial** is a number, a variable, or the product of a number and one or more variables with whole number exponents. The **degree of a monomial** is the sum of the exponents of the variables in the monomial. The degree of a nonzero constant term is 0. The constant 0 does not have a degree.

Monomial	Degree
10	0
$3x$	1
$\frac{1}{2}ab^2$	$1 + 2 = 3$
$-1.8m^5$	5

Not a monomial	Reason
$5 + x$	A sum is not a monomial.
$\frac{2}{n}$	A monomial cannot have a variable in the denominator.
4^a	A monomial cannot have a variable exponent.
x^{-1}	The variable must have a whole number exponent.

A **polynomial** is a monomial or a sum of monomials, each called a *term* of the polynomial. The **degree of a polynomial** is the greatest degree of its terms.

When a polynomial is written so that the exponents of a variable decrease from left to right, the coefficient of the first term is called the **leading coefficient**.

leading coefficient → degree → constant term

$$2x^3 + x^2 - 5x + 12$$

EXAMPLE 1 Rewrite a polynomial

Write $15x - x^3 + 3$ so that the exponents decrease from left to right. Identify the degree and leading coefficient of the polynomial.

Solution

Consider the degree of each of the polynomial's terms.

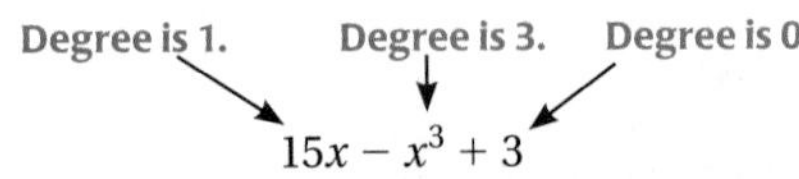

Degree is 1.
Degree is 3.
Degree is 0.

$$15x - x^3 + 3$$

The polynomial can be written as $-x^3 + 15x + 3$. The greatest degree is 3, so the degree of the polynomial is 3, and the leading coefficient is -1.

1 PLAN AND PREPARE

Warm-Up Exercises

Transparency Available

Simplify the expression.

1. $5x + 4(2x + 7)$ **$13x + 28$**
2. $9x - 6(x + 2) + 3$ **$3x - 9$**
3. Imported square tiles used for a kitchen floor measure 18 centimeters on one side. What is the area of a floor composed of 50 tiles? Use $A = s^2$ for the area of a tile. **16,200 cm^2**

Notetaking Guide

Transparency Available

Promotes interactive learning and notetaking skills.

Pacing

Basic: 1 day
Average: 1 day
Advanced: 1 day
Block: 0.5 block with 9.2
- See *Teaching Guide/Lesson Plan.*

2 FOCUS AND MOTIVATE

Essential Question

Big Idea 1, p. 553

How do you add and subtract polynomials? **Tell students they will learn how to answer this question by using vertical and horizontal formats to find sums and differences of polynomials.**

NCTM STANDARDS

Standard 2: Represent situations using algebraic symbols

Standard 10: Use representations to communicate mathematical ideas

Resource Planning Guide

Chapter Resource Book
- Teaching Guide/Lesson Plan
- Activity Master
- Practice levels A, B, C
- Study Guide
- Catch-up for Absent Students
- Problem Solving Workshop
- Challenge

Workbooks
- Notetaking Guide
- Practice Workbook

Teaching Options
- **Power Presentations** provides dynamic electronic teaching resources for the classroom.
- **Activity Generator** provides editable activities for all ability levels.

Interactive Technology
- Easy Planner
- Power Presentations
- Activity Generator
- Animated Algebra
- Test Generator
- Online Quiz
- eWorkbook
- eEdition
- @HomeTutor

Resources for English Learners
- Spanish Study Guide
- Multi-Language Visual Glossary
- Student Resources in Spanish

See also the *Differentiated Instruction Resources* for more strategies for meeting individual needs.

BINOMIALS AND TRINOMIALS A polynomial with two terms is called a **binomial**. A polynomial with three terms is called a **trinomial**.

EXAMPLE 2 Identify and classify polynomials

Tell whether the expression is a polynomial. If it is a polynomial, find its degree and classify it by the number of its terms. Otherwise, tell why it is not a polynomial.

	Expression	Is it a polynomial?	Classify by degree and number of terms
a.	9	Yes	0 degree monomial
b.	$2x^2 + x - 5$	Yes	2nd degree trinomial
c.	$6n^4 - 8^n$	No; variable exponent	
d.	$n^{-2} - 3$	No; negative exponent	
e.	$7bc^3 + 4b^4c$	Yes	5th degree binomial

ADDING POLYNOMIALS To add polynomials, add like terms. You can use a vertical or a horizontal format.

EXAMPLE 3 Add polynomials

Find the sum.

a. $(2x^3 - 5x^2 + x) + (2x^2 + x^3 - 1)$ **b.** $(3x^2 + x - 6) + (x^2 + 4x + 10)$

Solution

ALIGN TERMS
If a particular power of the variable appears in one polynomial but not the other, leave a space in that column, or write the term with a coefficient of 0.

a. Vertical format: Align like terms in vertical columns.

$$\begin{array}{r} 2x^3 - 5x^2 + x \\ + \quad x^3 + 2x^2 - 1 \\ \hline 3x^3 - 3x^2 + x - 1 \end{array}$$

b. Horizontal format: Group like terms and simplify.

$$(3x^2 + x - 6) + (x^2 + 4x + 10) = (3x^2 + x^2) + (x + 4x) + (-6 + 10)$$
$$= 4x^2 + 5x + 4$$

 at classzone.com

✓ GUIDED PRACTICE for Examples 1, 2, and 3

1. Write $5y - 2y^2 + 9$ so that the exponents decrease from left to right. Identify the degree and leading coefficient of the polynomial. **$-2y^2 + 5y + 9$; 2, −2**
2. Tell whether $y^3 - 4y + 3$ is a polynomial. If it is a polynomial, find its degree and classify it by the number of its terms. Otherwise, tell why it is not a polynomial. **polynomial; 3, trinomial**
3. Find the sum $(5x^3 + 4x - 2x) + (4x^2 + 3x^3 - 6)$. **$8x^3 + 4x^2 + 2x - 6$**

Motivating the Lesson

Tell students that they can add or subtract polynomials to model a real-world situation. For example, if one polynomial models ticket sales for boys' sports and another models ticket sales for girls' sports, they can add the polynomials and evaluate the sum to find total ticket sales.

3 TEACH

Extra Example 1

Write $3b^3 - 4b^4 + b^2$ so that the exponents decrease from left to right. Identify the degree and leading coefficient of the polynomial. **$-4b^4 + 3b^3 + b^2$; degree: 4; leading coefficient: −4**

Extra Example 2

Tell whether the expression is a polynomial. If it is a polynomial, find its degree and classify it by the number of its terms. Otherwise, tell why it is not a polynomial.

a. $5xy^2$ **yes, 3rd degree monomial**
b. $3a^{-5}$ **no, negative exponent**
c. $x^4 + 3x^3 - x$ **yes, 4th degree trinomial**
d. $\frac{9}{m}$ **no, variable in denominator**
e. $6a^2c + 5ac^5$ **yes, 6th degree binomial**

Extra Example 3

Find the sum.

a. $(-2x^2 + 3x - x^3) + (3x^2 + x^3 - 12)$ **$x^2 + 3x - 12$**
b. $(4x^3 + 2x^2 - 4) + (x^3 - 3x^2 + x)$ **$5x^3 - x^2 + x - 4$**

An **Animated Algebra** activity is available online for **Example 3**. This activity is also part of **Power Presentations**.

Differentiated Instruction

Below Level To help students gain confidence in recognizing polynomials, have them work with partners to write examples of 1st degree through 6th degree monomials, binomials, and trinomials. Suggest that they create a table to organize their work. Encourage students to write some polynomials with more than one variable per term. Have partners exchange their polynomials so that other partners can check that the polynomials fit the descriptions.

See also the *Differentiated Instruction Resources* for more strategies.

Extra Example 4

Find the difference.

a. $(2c^2 - 8) - (3c^2 - 4c + 1)$ $-c^2 + 4c - 9$

b. $(5y^2 + 2y - 4) - (-y^2 + 4y - 3)$ $6y^2 - 2y - 1$

Key Question to Ask for Example 4

- How do you group terms in the horizontal format for part (a)? $(4n^2 - (-2n^2)) + (-2n) + (5 - (-4))$

Extra Example 5

During the period 1999–2005, the number of hours an individual person watched broadcast television B and cable and satellite television C can be modeled by $B = 2.8t^2 - 35t + 879$ and $C = -5t^2 + 80t + 712$ where t is the number of years since 1999. About how many hours did people watch television in 2002? **about 1706 h**

Closing the Lesson

Have students summarize the major points of the lesson and answer the Essential Question: How do you add and subtract polynomials?

- **A polynomial is a monomial or the sum of monomials. The degree of a polynomial is the greatest degree of its terms.**
- **Use a vertical or horizontal format to add and subtract polynomials.**

To use a vertical format, align like terms in columns. To use a horizontal format, group like terms and simplify. To add, add the terms. To subtract, add the opposite of each term of the subtracted polynomial.

SUBTRACTING POLYNOMIALS To subtract a polynomial, add its opposite. To find the opposite of a polynomial, multiply each of its terms by −1.

EXAMPLE 4 Subtract polynomials

Find the difference.

a. $(4n^2 + 5) - (-2n^2 + 2n - 4)$ **b.** $(4x^2 - 3x + 5) - (3x^2 - x - 8)$

Solution

AVOID ERRORS
Remember to multiply *each* term in the polynomial by −1 when you write the subtraction as addition.

a.

$$\begin{array}{r} (4n^2 \quad\quad + 5) \\ -(-2n^2 + 2n - 4) \\ \hline \end{array} \quad\longrightarrow\quad \begin{array}{r} 4n^2 \quad\quad + 5 \\ + 2n^2 - 2n + 4 \\ \hline 6n^2 - 2n + 9 \end{array}$$

b. $(4x^2 - 3x + 5) - (3x^2 - x - 8) = 4x^2 - 3x + 5 - 3x^2 + x + 8$

$= (4x^2 - 3x^2) + (-3x + x) + (5 + 8)$

$= x^2 - 2x + 13$

EXAMPLE 5 Solve a multi-step problem

BASEBALL ATTENDANCE Major League Baseball teams are divided into two leagues. During the period 1995–2001, the attendance N and A (in thousands) at National and American League baseball games, respectively, can be modeled by

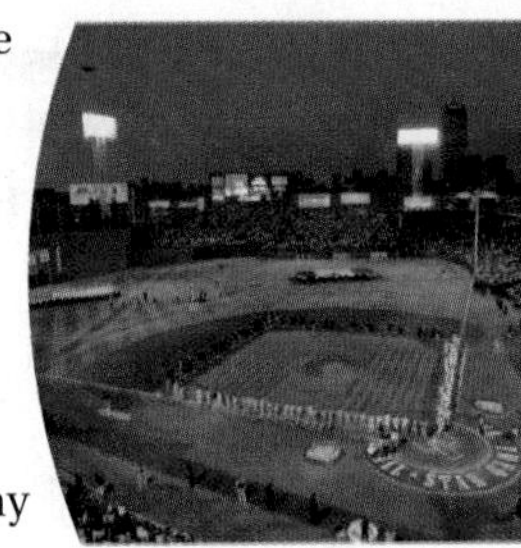

$N = -488t^2 + 5430t + 24{,}700$ and

$A = -318t^2 + 3040t + 25{,}600$

where t is the number of years since 1995. About how many people attended Major League Baseball games in 2001?

Solution

STEP 1 **Add** the models for the attendance in each league to find a model for M, the total attendance (in thousands).

$M = (-488t^2 + 5430t + 24{,}700) + (-318t^2 + 3040t + 25{,}600)$

$= (-488t^2 - 318t^2) + (5430t + 3040t) + (24{,}700 + 25{,}600)$

$= -806t^2 + 8470t + 50{,}300$

AVOID ERRORS
Because a value of M represents *thousands* of people, $M \approx 72{,}100$ represents 72,100,000 people.

STEP 2 **Substitute** 6 for t in the model, because 2001 is 6 years after 1995.

$M = -806(6)^2 + 8470(6) + 50{,}300 \approx 72{,}100$

▶ About 72,100,000 people attended Major League Baseball games in 2001.

✓ **GUIDED PRACTICE** for Examples 4 and 5

4. Find the difference $(4x^2 - 7x) - (5x^2 + 4x - 9)$. $-x^2 - 11x + 9$

5. **BASEBALL ATTENDANCE** Look back at Example 5. Find the difference in attendance at National and American League baseball games in 2001.

5. about 7,320,000 people

Differentiated Instruction

Advanced Have students use the online U.S. Statistical Abstract to research a favorite sport or activity. Have them create a problem similar to **Example 5** using data that appear nonlinear. If necessary, they can review the Activity on page 342 on using the Abstract. They can enter data on a graphing calculator and use the quadratic and cubic regression option to find a best-fit equation. Students can discuss which equations best fit the data and exchange and solve each other's problems.

See also the *Differentiated Instruction Resources* for more strategies.

9.1 EXERCISES

HOMEWORK KEY

○ = **WORKED-OUT SOLUTIONS** on p. WS20 for Exs. 21 and 39

★ = **STANDARDIZED TEST PRACTICE** Exs. 2, 9, 10, 39, and 41

SKILL PRACTICE

A

1. **VOCABULARY** Copy and complete: A number, a variable, or the product of one or more variables is called a(n) __?__. **monomial**

2. ★ **WRITING** Is 6 a polynomial? *Explain* why or why not. **Yes; a polynomial is a monomial or a sum of monomials. Since 6 is a monomial, it is also a polynomial.**

EXAMPLE 1 on p. 554 for Exs. 3–9

REWRITING POLYNOMIALS Write the polynomial so that the exponents decrease from left to right. Identify the degree and leading coefficient of the polynomial.

3. $9m^5$ **$9m^5$; 5, 9**
4. $2 - 6y$ **$-6y + 2$; 1, −6**
5. $2x^2y^2 - 8xy$ **$2x^2y^2 - 8xy$; 4, 2**
6. $5n^3 + 2n - 7$ **$5n^3 + 2n - 7$; 3, 5**
7. $5z + 2z^3 - z^2 + 3z^4$ **$3z^4 + 2z^3 - z^2 + 5z$; 4, 3**
8. $-2h^2 + 2h^4 - h^6$ **$-h^6 + 2h^4 - 2h^2$; 6, −1**

9. ★ **MULTIPLE CHOICE** What is the degree of $-4x^3 + 6x^4 - 1$? **C**

Ⓐ −4 Ⓑ 3 Ⓒ 4 Ⓓ 6

EXAMPLE 2 on p. 555 for Exs. 10–16

10. ★ **MULTIPLE CHOICE** Which expression is *not* a monomial? **D**

Ⓐ $-5x^2$ Ⓑ $0.2y^4$ Ⓒ $3mn$ Ⓓ $3s^{-2}$

IDENTIFYING AND CLASSIFYING POLYNOMIALS Tell whether the expression is a polynomial. If it is a polynomial, find its degree and classify it by the number of its terms. Otherwise, tell why it is not a polynomial.

11. -4^x **not a polynomial; variable exponent**
12. $w^{-3} + 1$ **not a polynomial; negative exponent**
13. $3x - 5$ **polynomial; 1, binomial**
14. $\frac{4}{5}f^2 - \frac{1}{2}f + \frac{2}{3}$ **polynomial; 2, trinomial**
15. $6 - n^2 + 5n^3$ **polynomial; 3, trinomial**
16. $10y^4 - 3y^2 + 11$ **polynomial; 4, trinomial**

EXAMPLES 3 and 4 on pp. 555–556 for Exs. 17–28

ADDING AND SUBTRACTING POLYNOMIALS Find the sum or difference.

17. $(5a^2 - 3) + (8a^2 - 1)$ **$13a^2 - 4$**
18. $(h^2 + 4h - 4) + (5h^2 - 8h + 2)$ **$6h^2 - 4h - 2$**
19. $(4m^2 - m + 2) + (-3m^2 + 10m + 7)$ **$m^2 + 9m + 9$**
20. $(7k^2 + 2k - 6) + (3k^2 - 11k - 8)$ **$10k^2 - 9k - 14$**
21. $(6c^2 + 3c + 9) - (3c - 5)$ **$6c^2 + 14$**
22. $(3x^2 - 8) - (4x^3 + x^2 - 15x + 1)$ **$-4x^3 + 2x^2 + 15x - 9$**
23. $(-n^2 + 2n) - (2n^3 - n^2 + n + 12)$ **$-2n^3 + n - 12$**
24. $(9b^3 - 13b^2 + b) - (-13b^2 - 5b + 14)$ **$9b^3 + 6b - 14$**
25. $(4d - 6d^3 + 3d^2) - (9d^3 + 7d - 2)$ **$-15d^3 + 3d^2 - 3d + 2$**
26. $(9p^2 - 6p^3 + 3 - 11p) + (7p^3 - 3p^2 + 4)$ **$p^3 + 6p^2 - 11p + 7$**

ERROR ANALYSIS ***Describe*** **and correct the error in finding the sum or difference of the polynomials.**

27.

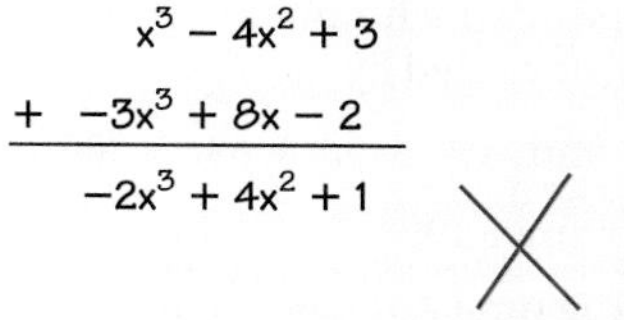

27. Two unlike terms, $-4x^2$ and $8x$, were combined; $-2x^3 - 4x^2 + 8x + 1$.

28.

$(6x^2 - 5x) - (2x^2 + 3x - 2)$
$= (6x^2 - 2x^2) + (-5x + 3x) - 2$
$= 4x^2 - 2x - 2$

28. When the subtraction was rewritten as addition, the last two terms of the second polynomial were not multiplied by −1; $(6x^2 - 2x^2) + (-5x - 3x) + 2$, $4x^2 - 8x + 2$.

B

29. **ORDERING POLYNOMIALS BY DEGREE** Write the polynomials in decreasing order of *degree*: $1 - 3x + 5x^2$, $3x^5$, $x + 2x^3 + x^2$, $12x + 1$. **$3x^5$, $x + 2x^3 + x^2$, $1 - 3x + 5x^2$, $12x + 1$**

4 PRACTICE AND APPLY

Assignment Guide

Answer Transparencies available for all exercises

Basic:
Day 1: pp. 557–559
Exs. 1, 2, 3–7 odd, 9, 10, 11–25 odd, 27–31, 37–40, 43–53 odd

Average:
Day 1: pp. 557–559
Exs. 1, 2, 6–10, 12–26 even, 27–34, 37–41, 44, 47, 50, 53

Advanced:
Day 1: pp. 557–559
Exs. 1, 2, 7–10, 14–16, 18–26 even, 29–42*, 48, 51, 54

Block:
pp. 557–559
Exs. 1, 2, 6–10, 12–26 even, 27–34, 37–41, 44, 47, 50, 53 (with 9.2)

Differentiated Instruction

See *Differentiated Instruction Resources* for suggestions on addressing the needs of a diverse classroom.

Homework Check

For a quick check of student understanding of key concepts, go over the following exercises:

Basic: 3, 13, 17, 23, 37
Average: 6, 14, 18, 24, 38
Advanced: 8, 16, 20, 24, 39

Extra Practice

- Student Edition, p. 946
- Chapter Resource Book: Practice levels A, B, C

Practice Worksheet

An easily-readable reduced practice page (with answers) for this lesson can be found on p. 552C.

Differentiated Instruction

English Learners Prefixes such as *mono-*, *bi-*, *tri-*, and *poly-* occur often in English. For example, the word *monotonous* means "one tone" and the word *bisect* means "cut into two." For some English learners, these prefixes do not occur in their native language, so the meanings of the terms *monomial*, *binomial*, *trinomial*, and *polynomial* may not be familiar. Try using more common language such as saying "one term" instead of monomial in classifying various polynomials.

See also the *Differentiated Instruction Resources* for more strategies.

Mathematical Reasoning

Exercise 2 Some students may ask why a monomial such as 6 has degree 0. Remind them that a variable to the zero power, such as x^0, is equal to 1. So, $6 \cdot x^0 = 6 \cdot 1$ or 6. Since 6 can be written as $6x^0$, the degree of 6 or any constant term is 0. After discussing this concept, you may want to ask if it is possible to have a 0 degree binomial. Have students use examples such as $6x^0 + 5y^0 = 6 + 5 = 11$ to support their reasoning.

Vocabulary

Exercises 11–16 Some students may confuse monomials, binomials, and trinomials. Point out that the prefixes mono, bi, and tri, mean one, two, and three, respectively. Suggest that they pair each term with a more familiar term, such as monorail, bicycle, and tricycle, to help them distinguish between the three types of polynomials.

Avoiding Common Errors

Exercises 21–25, 34–35 Caution students to pay attention to signs when subtracting polynomials. To avoid errors, urge them to first multiply each term of the subtrahend by −1 and then add like terms.

Reading Strategy

Exercise 41 Point out to students that the key at the bottom of page 558 indicates that problem 41 is an example of an extended response question on a standardized test. Tell them that a good reading strategy for this type of question is to read all of the parts of the question to see if one part is dependent upon an answer to a previous part, as part (b) is on part (a).

Internet Reference

Exercise 41 To find more information about Cy Young, go to www.baseballhalloffame.org and do a search for "Cy Young."

GEOMETRY **Write a polynomial that represents the perimeter of the figure.**

30. $x + 8$, $2x + 6$, $9x - 6$ **$12x + 8$**

31. 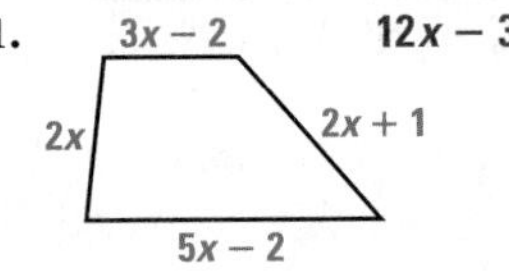

$12x - 3$

ADDING AND SUBTRACTING POLYNOMIALS **Find the sum or difference.**

32. $(3r^2s + 5rs + 3) + (-8rs^2 - 9rs - 12)$ **$3r^2s - 8rs^2 - 4rs - 9$**

33. $(x^2 + 11xy - 3y^2) + (-2x^2 - xy + 4y^2)$ **$-x^2 + 10xy + y^2$**

34. $(5mn + 3m - 9n) - (13mn + 2m)$ **$-8mn + m - 9n$**

35. $(8a^2b - 6a) - (2a^2b - 4b + 19)$ **$6a^2b - 6a + 4b - 19$**

C **36. CHALLENGE** Consider any integer x. The next consecutive integer can be represented by the binomial $(x + 1)$.

a. Write a polynomial for the sum of any two consecutive integers. **$2x + 1$**

b. *Explain* how you can be sure that the sum of two consecutive integers is always odd. Use the polynomial from part (a) in your explanation. **The sum of any two consecutive integers can be written in the form $2x + 1$ where x is an integer. Since x is an integer, $2x$ is an integer with a factor of 2, so $2x$ must be even. Then $2x + 1$ must be odd.**

PROBLEM SOLVING

EXAMPLE 5 A on p. 556 for Exs. 37–39

37. BACKPACKING AND CAMPING During the period 1992–2002, the participation B (in millions of people) in backpacking and the participation C (in millions of people) in camping can be modeled by

$B = -0.0262t^3 + 0.376t^2 - 0.574t + 9.67$ and

$C = -0.0182t^3 + 0.522t^2 - 2.59t + 47$

where t is the number of years since 1992. About how many more people camped than backpacked in 2002? **about 39,800,000 people**

@HomeTutor for problem solving help at classzone.com

38. CAR COSTS During the period 1990–2002, the average costs D (in dollars) for a new domestic car and the average costs I (in dollars) for a new imported car can be modeled by

$D = 442.14t + 14,433$ and $I = -137.63t^2 + 2705.2t + 15,111$

where t is the number of years since 1990. Find the difference in average costs (in dollars) for a new imported car and a new domestic car in 2002. **$8016**

@HomeTutor for problem solving help at classzone.com

39. ★ **SHORT RESPONSE** During the period 1998–2002, the number A (in millions) of books for adults and the number J (in millions) of books for juveniles sold can be modeled by

$A = 9.5t^3 - 58t^2 + 66t + 500$ and $J = -15t^2 + 64t + 360$

where t is the number of years since 1998.

a. Write an equation that gives the total number (in millions) of books for adults and for juveniles sold as a function of the number of years since 1998. **$T = 9.5t^3 - 73t^2 + 130t + 860$**

b. Were more books sold in 1998 or in 2002? *Explain* your answer.

39b. 1998; substitute $t = 0$ into the equation for T to find the number of books sold in 1998 to get 860 million books. Substitute 4 into the equation for T to find the number of books sold in 2002 to get 820 million books. More books were sold in 1998.

○ = WORKED-OUT SOLUTIONS on p. WS1 ★ = STANDARDIZED TEST PRACTICE

B **40. SCHOOL ENROLLMENT** During the period 1985–2012, the projected enrollment B (in thousands of students) in public schools and the projected enrollment R (in thousands of students) in private schools can be modeled by

$$B = -18.53t^2 + 975.8t + 48{,}140 \quad \text{and} \quad R = 80.8t + 8049$$

where t is the number of years since 1985. Write an equation that models the total school enrollment (in thousands of students) as a function of the number of years since 1985. What percent of all students is expected to be enrolled in public schools in 2012? **$T = -18.53t^2 + 1056.6t + 56{,}189$; about 86%**

41c. about 61%; Cy Young's career lasted 1911 − 1890 = 21 years. To find the number of wins in his career, find the value of W when $t = 21$; about 525 wins. From part (b), we know that the total number of decisions in his career is about 855, so to find the percent of the decisions that were wins, find 525 ÷ 855 ≈ 0.614, or about 61%.

41. ★ **EXTENDED RESPONSE** The award for the best pitchers in baseball is named after the pitcher Cy Young. During the period 1890–1911, the total number of Cy Young's wins W and losses L can be modeled by

$$W = -0.44t^2 + 34t + 4.7 \quad \text{and} \quad L = 15t + 15$$

where t is the number of years since 1890.

a. A game credited to a pitcher as a win or a loss is called a decision. Write an equation that models the number of decisions for Cy Young as a function of the number of years since 1890. **$D = -0.44t^2 + 49t + 19.7$**

b. Cy Young's career in Major League Baseball lasted from 1890 to 1911. Approximately how many total decisions did Cy Young have during his career? **about 855 decisions**

c. About what percent of the decisions in Cy Young's career were wins? *Explain* how you found your answer.

Cy Young Award

C **42. CHALLENGE** In 1970 the United States produced 63.5 quadrillion BTU (British Thermal Units) of energy and consumed 67.86 quadrillion BTU. From 1970 through 2001, the total U.S. energy production increased by about 0.2813 quadrillion BTU per year, and the total U.S. energy consumption increased by about 0.912 quadrillion BTU per year.

a. Write two equations that model the total U.S. energy production and consumption (in quadrillion BTU) as functions of the number of years since 1970. **$P = 0.2813t + 63.5$, $C = 0.912t + 67.86$**

b. How much more energy was consumed than produced in the U.S. in 1970 and in 2001? What was the change in the amount of energy consumed from 1970 to 2001? **4.36 quadrillion BTU, about 23.91 quadrillion BTU; 28.272 quadrillion BTU**

MIXED REVIEW

PREVIEW Prepare for Lesson 9.2 in Exs. 43–48.

Simplify the expression.

43. $0.6(3 - x)$ *(p. 96)* **$1.8 - 0.6x$**
44. $4(y + 6)$ *(p. 96)* **$4y + 24$**
45. $4(1 - b) - 5b$ *(p. 96)* **$4 - 9b$**
46. $-4(16c - 8)$ *(p. 96)* **$-64c + 32$**
47. $(6t^7)^2$ *(p. 489)* **$36t^{14}$**
48. $n(2m^2n)$ *(p. 489)* **$2m^2n^2$**

Graph the equation or inequality. **49–54. See margin.**

49. $y = -8$ *(p. 215)*
50. $x - 3y = 15$ *(p. 215)*
51. $y = -5x - 14$ *(p. 215)*
52. $x \geq -3$ *(p. 405)*
53. $x + y \leq 9$ *(p. 405)*
54. $2x - y < 7$ *(p. 405)*

EXTRA PRACTICE for Lesson 9.1, p. 946

ONLINE QUIZ at classzone.com

5 ASSESS AND RETEACH

Daily Homework Quiz

Transparency Available

If the expression is a polynomial, find its degree and classify it by the number of terms. Otherwise, tell why it is not a polynomial.

1. $m^3 + n^4m^2 + m^{-2}$ **No; one exponent is not a whole number.**

2. $-3b^3c^4 - 4b^2c + c^8$ **8th degree trinomial**

Find the sum or difference.

3. $(3m^2 - 2m + 9) + (m^2 + 2m - 4)$ **$4m^2 + 5$**

4. $(-4a^2 + 3a - 1) - (a^2 + 2a - 6)$ **$-5a^2 + a + 5$**

5. The number of dog adoptions D and cat adoptions C can be modeled by $D = 1.35t^2 - 9.8t + 131$ and $C = 0.1t^2 - 3t + 79$ where t represents the years since 1998. About how many dogs and cats were adopted in 2004? **about 185 dogs and cats**

Available at **classzone.com**

Diagnosis/Remediation

- Practice A, B, C in Chapter Resource Book
- Study Guide in Chapter Resource Book
- Practice Workbook
- @HomeTutor

Challenge

Additional challenge is available in the Chapter Resource Book.

49–54. See Additional Answers beginning on p. AA1.

1 PLAN AND PREPARE

Learn the Method

- Students will graph polynomial functions to check whether a sum or difference of polynomials is correct.
- After the activity, students can use a graphing calculator to check their solutions for Exercises 17–26 and 32–35 in Lesson 9.1.

Keystroke Help

Keystrokes for several models of calculators are available in blackline format in the *Chapter Resource Book*.

2 TEACH

Tips for Success

Remind students to use the caret key to indicate powers. If students cannot see a graph in the viewing window, suggest that they use the zoom feature on their graphing calculator.

Extra Example

Tell whether the sum or difference is correct.

a. $(2x^2 + x + 2) + (3x^2 - x - 4) \stackrel{?}{=} 5x^2 + 2$ **The thick curve deviates from the thin curve, so the sum is incorrect.**

b. $(4x^3 + 2x^2 - 3) - (2x^3 + x^2 + 2) \stackrel{?}{=} 2x^3 + x^2 - 5$ **The thick curve coincides with the thin curve, so the difference is correct.**

3 ASSESS AND RETEACH

Is $(-x^3 + 2x^2 + 3x) - (2x^3 + x^2 - x) \stackrel{?}{=} -3x^3 + x^2 + 2x$ correct? Explain. **The two curves do not coincide, so the difference is incorrect. The correct difference is $-3x^3 + x^2 + 4x$.**

Graphing Calculator ACTIVITY Use after Lesson 9.1

@HomeTutor classzone.com Keystrokes

9.1 Graph Polynomial Functions

QUESTION How can you use a graph to check your work with polynomials?

EXAMPLE Check a sum or difference of polynomials

Tell whether the sum or difference is correct.

a. $(x^2 - 2x + 3) + (2x^2 + 4x - 5) \stackrel{?}{=} 3x^2 + 2x - 2$

b. $(x^3 + x + 1) - (5x^3 - 2x + 7) \stackrel{?}{=} -4x^3 - x - 6$

STEP 1 ***Enter expressions***

Let y_1 equal the original expression. Let y_2 equal the sum.

a.

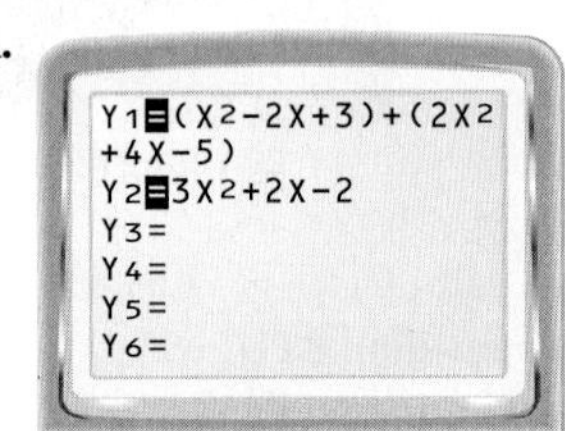

b.

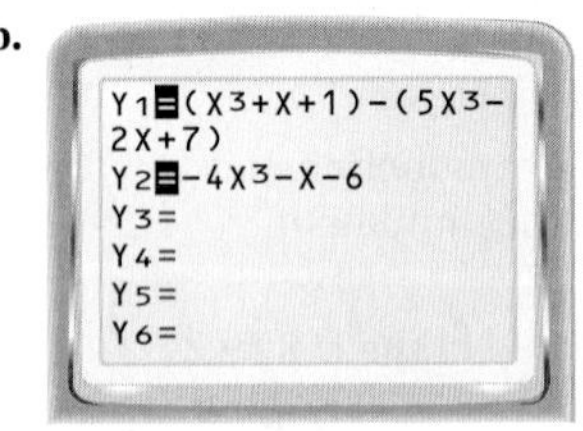

STEP 2 ***Graph expressions***

For y_1, choose a normal graph style. For y_2, choose a thicker graph style.

a.

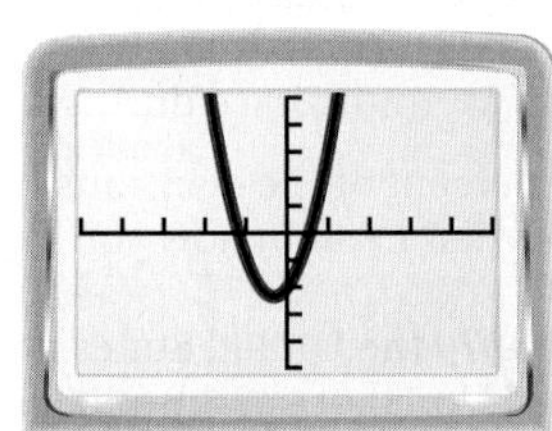

b.

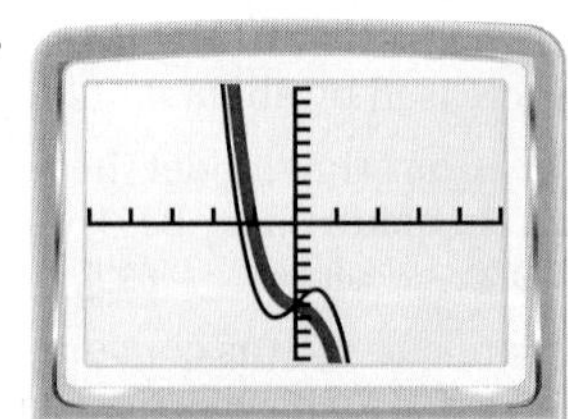

STEP 3 ***Analyze graphs***

a. The thick curve coincides with the thin curve, so the sum is correct.

b. The thick curve deviates from the thin curve, so the difference is incorrect.

PRACTICE

Find the sum or difference. Use a graphing calculator to check your answer.

1. $(6x^2 + 4x - 1) + (x^2 - 2x + 2)$ $\mathbf{7x^2 + 2x + 1}$

2. $(3x^2 - 2x + 1) - (4x^2 - 5x + 1)$ $\mathbf{-x^2 + 3x}$

Tell whether the sum or difference is correct. Correct any incorrect answers.

3. $(3x^2 - 2x + 4) + (-x^2 + 3x + 2) \stackrel{?}{=} 2x^2 + x + 6$ **correct**

4. $(-4x^2 - 5x - 1) - (-5x^2 + 6x + 3) \stackrel{?}{=} -9x^2 + x + 2$ **not correct; $x^2 - 11x - 4$**

9.2 Multiplication with Algebra Tiles

MATERIALS • algebra tiles

QUESTION How can you multiply binomials using algebra tiles?

You can use the following algebra tiles to model polynomials. Notice that the value of each tile is the same as its area.

1-tile

***x*-tile**

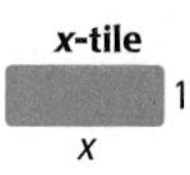

x^2-tile

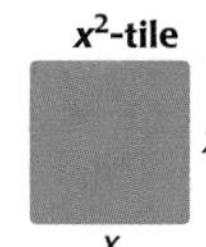

EXPLORE Multiply binomials

Find the product $(x + 3)(2x + 1)$.

STEP 1 ***Model the rectangle's dimensions***

Model each binomial with algebra tiles. Arrange the first binomial vertically and the second horizontally, as shown. These polynomials model the length and width of a rectangle.

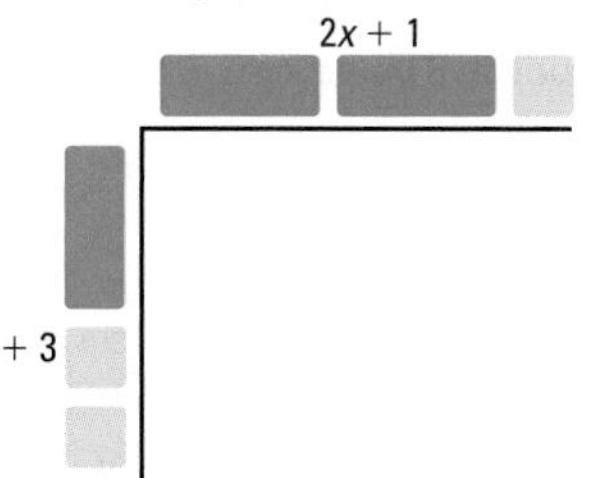

STEP 2 ***Fill in the area***

Fill in the rectangle with the appropriate algebra tiles.

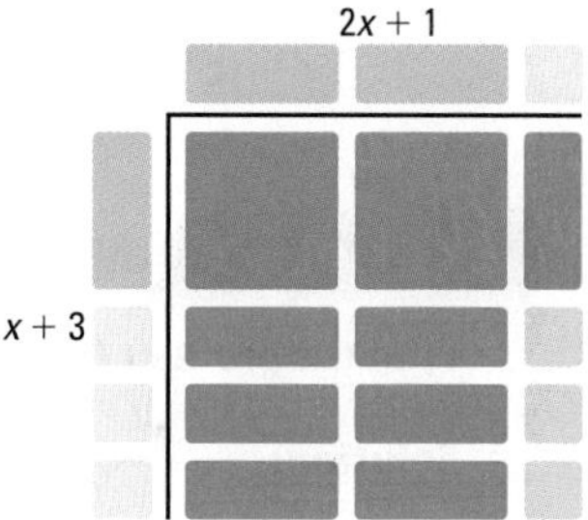

STEP 3 ***Find the product***

The rectangle you created represents the polynomial $2x^2 + 7x + 3$.
So, $(x + 3)(2x + 1) = 2x^2 + 7x + 3$.

DRAW CONCLUSIONS Use your observations to complete these exercises

Use algebra tiles to find the product. Include a drawing of your model. **1–6. See margin for art.**

1. $(x + 1)(x + 3)$ $\mathbf{x^2 + 4x + 3}$
2. $(x + 5)(x + 4)$ $\mathbf{x^2 + 9x + 20}$
3. $(2x + 1)(x + 2)$ $\mathbf{2x^2 + 5x + 2}$
4. $(3x + 2)(x + 1)$ $\mathbf{3x^2 + 5x + 2}$
5. $(3x + 2)(2x + 1)$ $\mathbf{6x^2 + 7x + 2}$
6. $(4x + 1)(2x + 3)$ $\mathbf{8x^2 + 14x + 3}$
7. **REASONING** Find the product $x(2x + 1)$ and the product $3(2x + 1)$. What is the sum of these two products? What do your answers suggest you can do to find the product $(x + 3)(2x + 1)$? **See margin.**

1 PLAN AND PREPARE

Explore the Concept

- Students will use algebra tiles to multiply binomials.
- This activity leads into the study of multiplying polynomials using a table of products in Example 2 of Lesson 9.2.

Materials

Each student will need:

- algebra tiles
- Activity Support Master (*Chapter Resource Book*)

Recommended Time

Work activity: 10 min

Discuss results: 5 min

Grouping

Students should work individually.

2 TEACH

Key Question

- How do you know which are appropriate algebra tiles to fill in the rectangle? **The length and width of each tile matches the tiles at the left of and above the rectangle.**

Key Discovery

Multiplying binomials is based on the distributive property.

3 ASSESS AND RETEACH

If you use algebra tiles to multiply $(3x + 1)(3x + 4)$, how many x^2-tiles will you need to fill in the rectangle? Explain. **9, since you need to fill in 3 columns and 3 rows of tiles where both dimensions are determined by *x*-tiles.**

1–6. See Additional Answers beginning on p. AA1.

7. $2x^2 + x$, $6x + 3$; $2x^2 + 7x + 3$; multiply $(2x + 1)$ by each term of $(x + 3)$ and then add the products.

1 PLAN AND PREPARE

Warm-Up Exercises

Transparency Available

1. Simplify $-2(9a - b)$. $\mathbf{-18a + 2b}$
2. Simplify $r^2s \cdot rs^3$. $\mathbf{r^3s^4}$
3. The number of hardback h and paperback p books (in hundreds) sold from 1999–2005 can be modeled by
$h = 0.2t^2 - 1.7t + 14$ and
$p = 0.17t^3 - 2.7t^2 + 11.7t + 27$
where t is the number of years since 1999. About how many books sold in 2003? **5200**

Notetaking Guide

Transparency Available

Promotes interactive learning and notetaking skills.

Pacing

Basic: 1 day

Average: 1 day

Advanced: 1 day

Block: 0.5 block with 9.1

- See *Teaching Guide/Lesson Plan.*

2 FOCUS AND MOTIVATE

Essential Question

Big Idea 1, p. 553

How do you multiply polynomials? **Tell students they will learn how to answer this question by using the distributive property to find the product of two polynomials.**

NCTM STANDARDS

Standard 8: Use the language of math to express ideas

Standard 10: Use representations to communicate mathematical ideas

9.2 Multiply Polynomials

Before	You added and subtracted polynomials.
Now	You will multiply polynomials.
Why?	So you can determine areas, as in Example 7.

Key Vocabulary
- **polynomial,** *p. 554*
- **binomial,** *p. 555*

The diagram shows that a rectangle with width x and length $2x + 3$ has an area of $2x^2 + 3x$. You can also find this product by using the distributive property.

$$x(2x + 3) = x(2x) + x(3) = 2x^2 + 3x$$

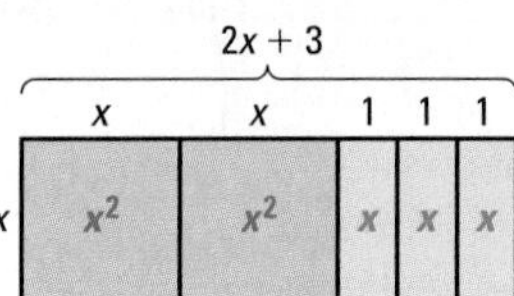

In this lesson, you will learn several methods for multiplying polynomials. Each method is based on the distributive property.

EXAMPLE 1 Multiply a monomial and a polynomial

REVIEW PROPERTIES OF EXPONENTS
For help with using the properties of exponents, see p. 489.

Find the product $2x^3(x^3 + 3x^2 - 2x + 5)$.

$2x^3(x^3 + 3x^2 - 2x + 5)$	**Write product.**
$= 2x^3(x^3) + 2x^3(3x^2) - 2x^3(2x) + 2x^3(5)$	**Distributive property**
$= 2x^6 + 6x^5 - 4x^4 + 10x^3$	**Product of powers property**

EXAMPLE 2 Multiply polynomials using a table

Find the product $(x - 4)(3x + 2)$.

Solution

STEP 1 **Write** subtraction as addition in each polynomial.

$$(x - 4)(3x + 2) = [x + (-4)](3x + 2)$$

STEP 2 **Make** a table of products.

	$3x$	2
x	$3x^2$	
-4		

→

	$3x$	2
x	$3x^2$	$2x$
-4	$-12x$	-8

▶ The product is $3x^2 + 2x - 12x - 8$, or $3x^2 - 10x - 8$.

GUIDED PRACTICE for Examples 1 and 2

Find the product.

1. $x(7x^2 + 4)$ $\mathbf{7x^3 + 4x}$
2. $(a + 3)(2a + 1)$ $\mathbf{2a^2 + 7a + 3}$
3. $(4n - 1)(n + 5)$ $\mathbf{4n^2 + 19n - 5}$

Resource Planning Guide

Chapter Resource Book
- Teaching Guide/Lesson Plan
- Practice levels A, B, C
- Study Guide
- Catch-up for Absent Students
- Application
- Challenge

Workbooks
- Notetaking Guide
- Practice Workbook

Teaching Options
- **Power Presentations** provides dynamic electronic teaching resources for the classroom.
- **Activity Generator** provides editable activities for all ability levels.

Interactive Technology
- Easy Planner
- Power Presentations
- Activity Generator
- Animated Algebra
- Test Generator
- Online Quiz
- eWorkbook
- eEdition
- @HomeTutor

Resources for English Learners
- Spanish Study Guide
- Multi-Language Visual Glossary
- Student Resources in Spanish

See also the *Differentiated Instruction Resources* for more strategies for meeting individual needs.

EXAMPLE 3 Multiply polynomials vertically

Find the product $(b^2 + 6b - 7)(3b - 4)$.

Solution

AVOID ERRORS
Remember that the terms of $(3b - 4)$ are $3b$ and -4. They are *not* $3b$ and 4.

STEP 1 **Multiply** by -4.

$$\begin{array}{r} b^2 + 6b - 7 \\ \times \quad 3b - 4 \\ \hline -4b^2 - 24b + 28 \end{array}$$

STEP 2 **Multiply** by $3b$.

$$\begin{array}{r} b^2 + 6b - 7 \\ \times \quad 3b - 4 \\ \hline -4b^2 - 24b + 28 \\ 3b^3 + 18b^2 - 21b \quad \end{array}$$

STEP 3 **Add** products.

$$\begin{array}{r} b^2 + 6b - 7 \\ \times \quad 3b - 4 \\ \hline -4b^2 - 24b + 28 \\ 3b^3 + 18b^2 - 21b \quad \\ \hline 3b^3 + 14b^2 - 45b + 28 \end{array}$$

EXAMPLE 4 Multiply polynomials horizontally

Find the product $(2x^2 + 5x - 1)(4x - 3)$.

$(2x^2 + 5x - 1)(4x - 3)$	Write product.
$= 2x^2(4x - 3) + 5x(4x - 3) - 1(4x - 3)$	Distributive property
$= 8x^3 - 6x^2 + 20x^2 - 15x - 4x + 3$	Distributive property
$= 8x^3 + 14x^2 - 19x + 3$	Combine like terms.

FOIL PATTERN The letters of the word FOIL can help you to remember how to use the distributive property to multiply binomials. The letters should remind you of the words **F**irst, **O**uter, **I**nner, and **L**ast.

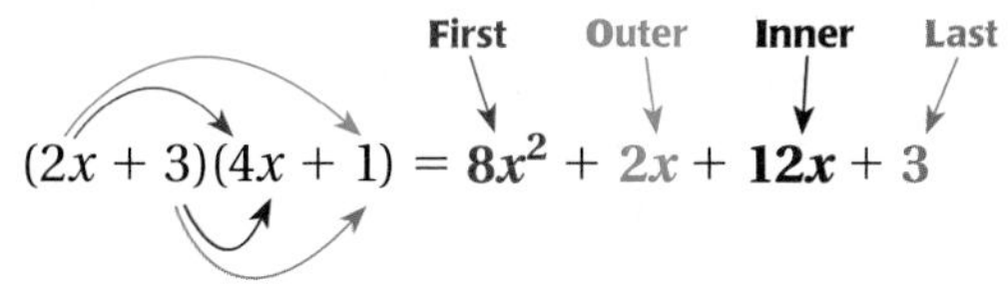

EXAMPLE 5 Multiply binomials using the FOIL pattern

Find the product $(3a + 4)(a - 2)$.

$(3a + 4)(a - 2)$	
$= (3a)(a) + (3a)(-2) + (4)(a) + (4)(-2)$	Write products of terms.
$= 3a^2 + (-6a) + 4a + (-8)$	Multiply.
$= 3a^2 - 2a - 8$	Combine like terms.

GUIDED PRACTICE for Examples 3, 4, and 5

Find the product.

4. $(x^2 + 2x + 1)(x + 2)$ **$x^3 + 4x^2 + 5x + 2$**
5. $(3y^2 - y + 5)(2y - 3)$ **$6y^3 - 11y^2 + 13y - 15$**
6. $(4b - 5)(b - 2)$ **$4b^2 - 13b + 10$**

Motivating the Lesson

You want to know how much wall space you need for a poster surrounded by different borders. If you know the length and width of the poster, you can write an expression that models the total area of the poster and its border. You can then evaluate the expression to determine how much wall space you need.

3 TEACH

Extra Example 1

Find the product $3x^2(2x^3 - x^2 + 4x - 3)$.
$6x^5 - 3x^4 + 12x^3 - 9x^2$

Key Question to Ask for Example 1

- How do you multiply powers that have the same base? **Write the base, add the exponents.**

Extra Example 2

Find the product $(x + 4)(2x - 1)$.
$2x^2 + 7x - 4$

Extra Example 3

Find the product $(a^2 + 3a - 4)(2a + 3)$.
$2a^3 + 9a^2 + a - 12$

Extra Example 4

Find the product $(2x^2 - x - 2)(3x - 1)$.
$6x^3 - 5x^2 - 5x + 2$

Extra Example 5

Find the product $(4a + 3)(a + 2)$.
$4a^2 + 11a + 6$

Differentiated Instruction

Below Level Some students may find the FOIL pattern confusing. To help these students, you may want to use algebra tiles to show how the filled-in rectangle corresponds to each letter of the FOIL pattern. After they have a better understanding of the pattern, encourage them to use notecards to write out each step of the pattern. Suggest that they write an example at the top of the card, such as $(4x + 2)(3x - 1)$, and then First, Outer, Inner, and Last, each on one line of the card. They should show the step next to each word and explain the step in words.

See also the *Differentiated Instruction Resources* for more strategies.

Extra Example 6

A rectangle has dimensions $x + 3$ and $x + 5$. Which expression shows the area of the rectangle? **C**

Ⓐ $x^2 + 15$

Ⓑ $x^2 + 3x + 15$

Ⓒ $x^2 + 8x + 15$

Ⓓ $x^2 + 8x$

Extra Example 7

A rectangular trivet has a ceramic center and a wooden border. The dimensions of the center and border are shown in the diagram.

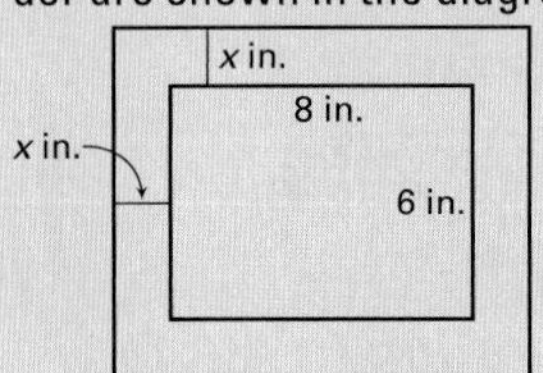

- Write a polynomial that represents the total area of the trivet. **$48 + 28x + 4x^2$**
- What is the total area of the trivet if the width of the border is 2 inches? **120 in.^{2}**

Closing the Lesson

Have students summarize the major points of the lesson and answer the Essential Question: How do you multiply polynomials?

- **Use the distributive property to multiply polynomials.**
- **Use the FOIL pattern to multiply binomials.**

To use the distributive property, multiply each term of one polynomial by each term of the other, using properties of exponents if necessary. Then combine like terms. To use the FOIL pattern, multiply the two First terms of each binomial, the two Outer terms, the two Inner terms, the two Last terms, and then combine like terms.

EXAMPLE 6 Standardized Test Practice

The dimensions of a rectangle are $x + 3$ and $x + 2$. Which expression represents the area of the rectangle?

Ⓐ $x^2 + 6$ Ⓑ $x^2 + 5x + 6$ Ⓒ $x^2 + 6x + 6$ Ⓓ $x^2 + 6x$

ELIMINATE CHOICES
When you multiply $x + 3$ and $x + 2$, the product will have a constant term of $3 \cdot 2 = 6$. So, you can eliminate choice D.

Solution

Area = length • width	**Formula for area of a rectangle**
$= (x + 3)(x + 2)$	**Substitute for length and width.**
$= x^2 + 2x + 3x + 6$	**Multiply binomials.**
$= x^2 + 5x + 6$	**Combine like terms.**

▶ The correct answer is B. Ⓐ Ⓑ Ⓒ Ⓓ

CHECK You can use a graph to check your answer. Use a graphing calculator to display the graphs of $y_1 = (x + 3)(x + 2)$ and $y_2 = x^2 + 5x + 6$ in the same viewing window. Because the graphs coincide, you know that the product of $x + 3$ and $x + 2$ is $x^2 + 5x + 6$.

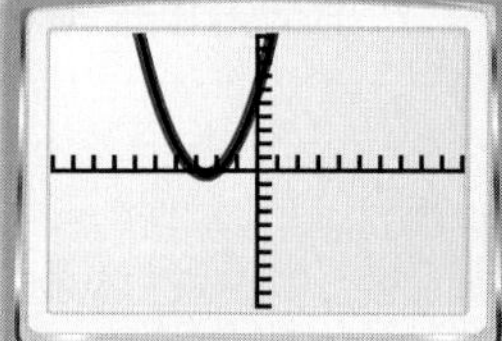

EXAMPLE 7 Solve a multi-step problem

SKATEBOARDING You are designing a rectangular skateboard park on a lot that is on the corner of a city block. The park will have a walkway along two sides. The dimensions of the lot and the walkway are shown in the diagram.

- Write a polynomial that represents the area of the skateboard park.
- What is the area of the park if the walkway is 3 feet wide?

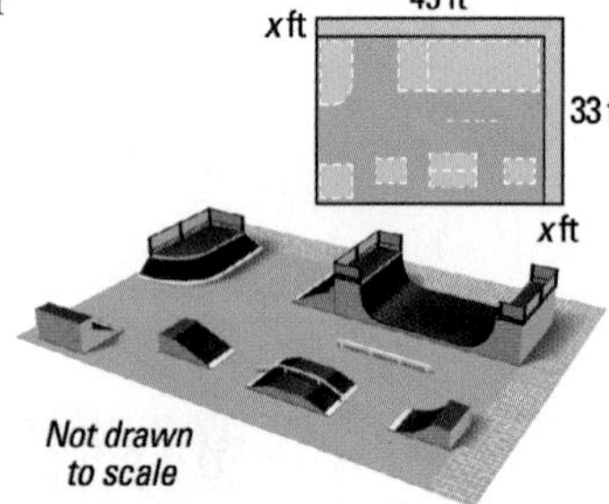

Not drawn to scale

Solution

STEP 1 **Write** a polynomial using the formula for the area of a rectangle. The length is $45 - x$. The width is $33 - x$.

Area = length • width	**Formula for area of a rectangle**
$= (45 - x)(33 - x)$	**Substitute for length and width.**
$= 1485 - 45x - 33x + x^2$	**Multiply binomials.**
$= 1485 - 78x + x^2$	**Combine like terms.**

STEP 2 **Substitute** 3 for x and evaluate.

Area $= 1485 - 78(3) + (3)^2 = 1260$

▶ The area of the park is 1260 square feet.

 **GUIDED PRACTICE** for Examples 6 and 7

7. The dimensions of a rectangle are $x + 5$ and $x + 9$. Which expression represents the area of the rectangle? **C**

Ⓐ $x^2 + 45x$ Ⓑ $x^2 + 45$

Ⓒ $x^2 + 14x + 45$ Ⓓ $x^2 + 45x + 45$

8. **GARDEN DESIGN** You are planning to build a walkway that surrounds a rectangular garden, as shown. The width of the walkway around the garden is the same on every side.

a. Write a polynomial that represents the combined area of the garden and the walkway. **$4x^2 + 38x + 90$**

b. Find the combined area when the width of the walkway is 4 feet. **306 ft^2**

9.2 EXERCISES

HOMEWORK KEY
○ = **WORKED-OUT SOLUTIONS** on p. WS20 for Exs. 23 and 51
★ = **STANDARDIZED TEST PRACTICE** Exs. 2, 26, 44, 52, and 53

SKILL PRACTICE

1. **VOCABULARY** Copy and complete: The FOIL pattern can be used to multiply any two _?_. **binomials**

2. ★ **WRITING** *Explain* how the letters of the word FOIL can help you multiply polynomials. **See margin.**

EXAMPLE 1 on p. 562 for Exs. 3–8

MULTIPLYING POLYNOMIALS **Find the product.**

3. $x(2x^2 - 3x + 9)$ **$2x^3 - 3x^2 + 9x$**
4. $4y(-y^3 - 2y - 1)$ **$-4y^4 - 8y^2 - 4y$**
5. $z^2(4z^4 + z^3 - 11z^2 - 6)$ **$4z^6 + z^5 - 11z^4 - 6z^2$**
6. $3c^3(8c^4 - c^2 - 3c + 5)$ **$24c^7 - 3c^5 - 9c^4 + 15c^3$**
7. $-a^5(-9a^2 + 5a + 13)$ **$9a^7 - 5a^6 - 13a^5$**
8. $-5b^3(4b^5 - 2b^3 + b - 11)$ **$-20b^8 + 10b^6 - 5b^4 + 55b^3$**

EXAMPLE 2 on p. 562 for Exs. 9–15

USING TABLES **Use a table to find the product.**

9. $(x + 2)(x - 3)$ **$x^2 - x - 6$**
10. $(y - 5)(2y + 3)$ **$2y^2 - 7y - 15$**
11. $(4b - 3)(b - 7)$ **$4b^2 - 31b + 21$**
12. $(5s + 2)(s + 8)$ **$5s^2 + 42s + 16$**
13. $(3k - 1)(4k + 9)$ **$12k^2 + 23k - 9$**
14. $(8n - 5)(3n - 6)$ **$24n^2 - 63n + 30$**

EXAMPLES 3 and 4 on p. 563 for Exs. 16–26

ERROR ANALYSIS *Describe* and correct the error in finding the product of the polynomials.

15.

$(x - 5)(3x + 1)$

	3x	1
x	$3x^2$	x
5	15x	5

$(x - 5)(3x + 1) = 3x^2 + 16x + 5$

15. The second term of the first binomial is −5, not 5, so the entries in the second row of the diagram should be −15x and −5; $3x^2 - 14x - 5$.

16.

$$\begin{array}{r} 2x^2 - 3x - 4 \\ \times \quad x + 7 \\ \hline 14x^2 - 21x - 28 \\ 2x^3 - 3x^2 - 4x \\ \hline 2x^3 + 11x^4 - 25x^2 - 28 \end{array}$$

When combining like terms, the exponents on the variables should stay the same, rather than being added together; $2x^3 + 11x^2 - 25x - 28$.

4 PRACTICE AND APPLY

Assignment Guide

Answer Transparencies available for all exercises

Basic:
Day 1: pp. 565–568
Exs. 1, 2, 4–14 even, 15, 16, 17–39 odd, 49–52, 56–66 even

Average:
Day 1: pp. 565–568
Exs. 1, 2, 3–43 odd, 45, 46, 49–53, 56, 59, 62, 65

Advanced:
Day 1: pp. 565–568
Exs. 1, 2, 7, 8, 14, 21–26, 30–32, 33–41 odd, 43–54*, 60, 63, 66

Block:
pp. 565–568
Exs. 1, 2, 3–43 odd, 45, 46, 49–53, 56, 59, 62, 65 (with 9.1)

Differentiated Instruction

See *Differentiated Instruction Resources* for suggestions on addressing the needs of a diverse classroom.

Homework Check

For a quick check of student understanding of key concepts, go over the following exercises:
Basic: 6, 19, 27, 39, 49
Average: 11, 22, 29, 41, 50
Advanced: 14, 24, 31, 41, 50

Extra Practice

- Student Edition, p. 946
- Chapter Resource Book: Practice levels A, B, C

Practice Worksheet

An easily-readable reduced practice page (with answers) for this lesson can be found on p. 552C.

2. The letters of the word FOIL remind you to find the sum of the products of these terms: First terms of each binomial, Outer terms of each binomial, Inner terms of each binomial, Last terms of each binomial.

Graphing Calculator

Exercises 9–14, 17–32 Encourage students to use a graphing calculator to check their answers. They should display two graphs in the same viewing window, using a thin line and a thick line. If the two graphs for an exercise do not coincide, students should review the method they used to find the product.

Avoiding Common Errors

Exercises 17–25 Caution students to align like terms in columns when they are using the vertical format. This will help them avoid errors such as combining unlike terms.

Study Strategy

Exercises 27–32 Refer students who are having trouble using FOIL to the diagram on page 563. Tell them to draw arrows as in the diagram to help them see and use the pattern. Reinforce the idea that the more they use the pattern, the more familiar it will become.

MULTIPLYING POLYNOMIALS **Use a vertical or a horizontal format to find the product.**

17. $(y + 6)(y - 5)$ $\mathbf{y^2 + y - 30}$
18. $(5x - 8)(2x - 5)$ $\mathbf{10x^2 - 41x + 40}$
19. $(7w + 5)(11w - 3)$ $\mathbf{77w^2 + 34w - 15}$
20. $(b - 2)(b^2 - b + 1)$ $\mathbf{b^3 - 3b^2 + 3b - 2}$
21. $(s + 4)(s^2 + 6s - 5)$ $\mathbf{s^3 + 10s^2 + 19s - 20}$
22. $(-r + 7)(2r^2 - r - 9)$ $\mathbf{-2r^3 + 15r^2 + 2r - 63}$
23. $(5x + 2)(-3x^2 + 4x - 1)$ $\mathbf{-15x^3 + 14x^2 + 3x - 2}$
24. $(y^2 + 8y - 6)(4y - 3)$ $\mathbf{4y^3 + 29y^2 - 48y + 18}$
25. $(6z^2 + z - 1)(9z - 5)$ $\mathbf{54z^3 - 21z^2 - 14z + 5}$
26. ★ **MULTIPLE CHOICE** What is the product of $2x - 9$ and $4x + 1$? **B**

   (A) $8x^2 - 38x - 9$ (B) $8x^2 - 34x - 9$
   (C) $8x^2 + 34x - 9$ (D) $8x^2 + 38x - 9$

EXAMPLE 5 on p. 563 for Exs. 27–32

USING THE FOIL PATTERN **Use the FOIL pattern to find the product.**

27. $(2r - 1)(5r + 3)$ $\mathbf{10r^2 + r - 3}$
28. $(7a - 2)(3a - 4)$ $\mathbf{21a^2 - 34a + 8}$
29. $(4m + 9)(2m + 7)$ $\mathbf{8m^2 + 46m + 63}$
30. $(8t + 11)(6t - 1)$ $\mathbf{48t^2 + 58t - 11}$
31. $(4x - 5)(12x - 7)$ $\mathbf{48x^2 - 88x + 35}$
32. $(8z + 3)(5z + 4)$ $\mathbf{40z^2 + 47z + 12}$

B **SIMPLIFYING EXPRESSIONS** **Simplify the expression.**

33. $p(2p - 3) + (p - 3)(p + 3)$ $\mathbf{3p^2 - 3p - 9}$
34. $x^2(7x + 5) - (2x + 6)(x - 1)$ $\mathbf{7x^3 + 3x^2 - 4x + 6}$
35. $-3c^2(c + 11) - (4c - 5)(3c - 2)$ $\mathbf{-3c^3 - 45c^2 + 23c - 10}$
36. $2w^3(2w^3 - 7w - 1) + w(5w^2 + 2w)$ $\mathbf{4w^6 - 14w^4 + 3w^3 + 2w^2}$

EXAMPLES 6 and 7 on p. 564 for Exs. 37–42

GEOMETRY **Write a polynomial that represents the area of the shaded region.**

37.
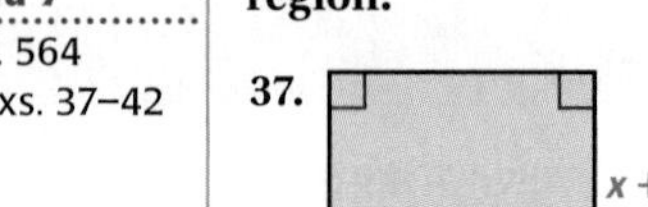
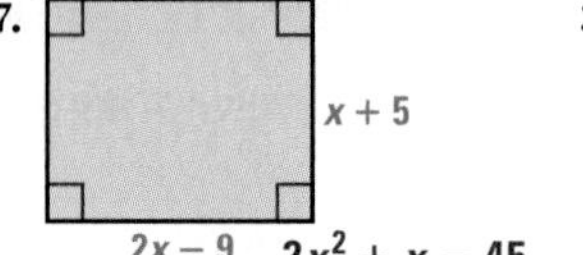

$\mathbf{2x^2 + x - 45}$

38.
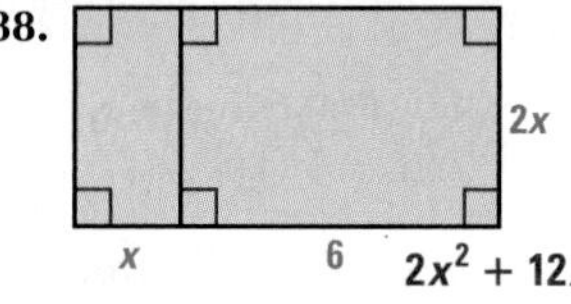

$\mathbf{2x^2 + 12x}$

39.
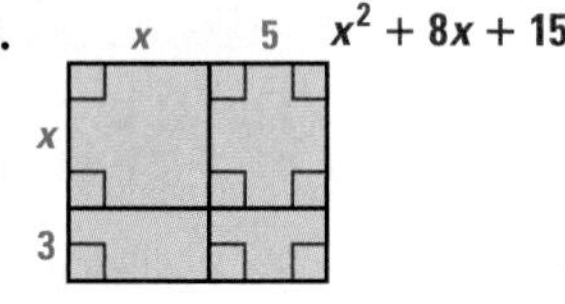

$\mathbf{x^2 + 8x + 15}$

40.
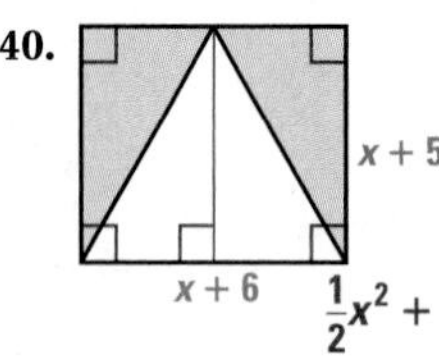

$\mathbf{\frac{1}{2}x^2 + \frac{11}{2}x + 15}$

41.
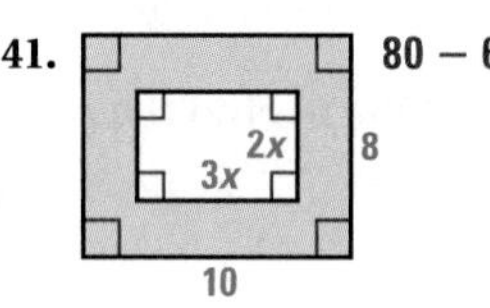

$\mathbf{80 - 6x^2}$

42.
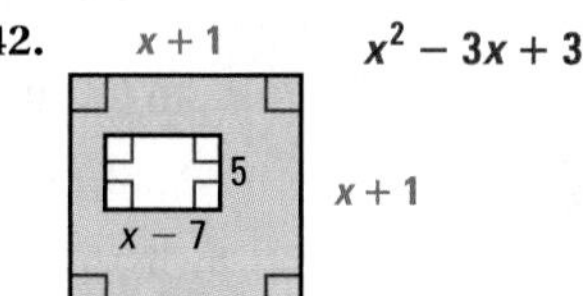

$\mathbf{x^2 - 3x + 36}$

43. **POLYNOMIAL FUNCTIONS** Find the product $f(x) \cdot g(x)$ for the functions $f(x) = x - 11$ and $g(x) = 2x + 12$. $\mathbf{2x^2 - 10x - 132}$
44. ★ **MULTIPLE CHOICE** Which polynomial represents $f(x) \cdot g(x)$ if $f(x) = -2x^2$ and $g(x) = x^3 - 5x^2 + 2x - 1$? **C**

   (A) $-2x^5 - 10x^4 + 4x^3 - 2x^2$ (B) $-2x^5 + 10x^4 - 4x^3 - 2x^2$
   (C) $-2x^5 + 10x^4 - 4x^3 + 2x^2$ (D) $2x^5 - 10x^4 + 4x^3 - 2x^2$

45. **REASONING** Find the product $(x^2 - 7x)(2x^2 + 3x + 1)$. Show that the product is correct by using a graphing calculator. *Explain* your reasoning.

45. $\mathbf{2x^4 - 11x^3 - 20x^2 - 7x}$**; graph** $\mathbf{Y_1 = (x^2 - 7x)(2x^2 + 3x + 1)}$ **and** $\mathbf{Y_2 = 2x^4 - 11x^3 - 20x^2 - 7x}$ **in the same viewing window. Because the graphs coincide, the expressions for** $\mathbf{Y_1}$ **and** $\mathbf{Y_2}$ **must be equivalent.**

C **CHALLENGE** **Find the product.**

46. $(x - y)(3x + 4y)$ $\mathbf{3x^2 + xy - 4y^2}$
47. $(x^2y + 9y)(2x + 3y)$ $\mathbf{2x^3y + 3x^2y^2 + 18xy + 27y^2}$
48. $(x^2 - 5xy + y^2)(4xy)$ $\mathbf{4x^3y - 20x^2y^2 + 4xy^3}$

PROBLEM SOLVING

EXAMPLE 7 A on p. 564 for Exs. 49–50

49. PICTURE FRAME You are designing a frame to surround a rectangular picture. The width of the frame around the picture is the same on every side, as shown.

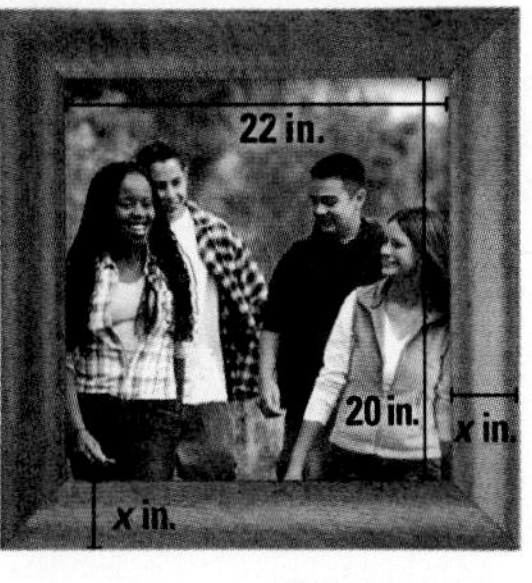

a. Write a polynomial that represents the total area of the picture and the frame. $4x^2 + 84x + 440$

b. Find the combined area of the picture and the frame when the width of the frame is 4 inches. 840 in.^2

@HomeTutor for problem solving help at classzone.com

50. SWIMMING POOL A rectangular swimming pool is bordered on one side by a deck. A contractor is hired to build a walkway along the remaining three sides of the pool. The width of the walkway is the same on every side, as shown.

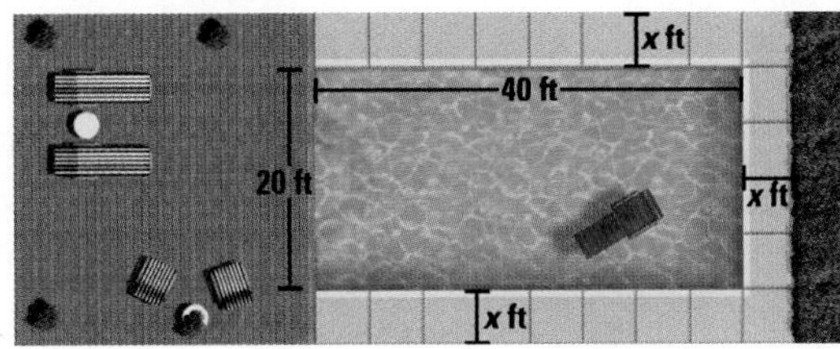

a. Write a polynomial that represents the total area of the pool and the walkway. $2x^2 + 100x + 800$

b. Find the combined area of the pool and the walkway when the width of the walkway is 5 feet. 1350 ft^2

@HomeTutor for problem solving help at classzone.com

51a. \$12,300 million, 0.171; for $t = 0$, the amount of money (in millions of dollars) people between 15 and 19 years old spent on sound recordings in the U.S. in 1997.

51. SOUND RECORDINGS During the period 1997–2002, the amount of money R (in millions of dollars) spent on sound recordings in the U.S. and the percent P (in decimal form) of this amount spent by people who are between 15 and 19 years old can be modeled by

$$R = -336t^2 + 1730t + 12{,}300 \text{ and } P = 0.00351t^2 - 0.0249t + 0.171$$

where t is the number of years since 1997.

a. Find the values of R and P for $t = 0$. What does the product $R \cdot P$ mean for $t = 0$ in this situation?

b. Write an equation that models the amount spent on sound recordings by people who are between 15 and 19 years old as a function of the number of years since 1997. $R \cdot P \approx -1.18t^4 + 14.4t^3 - 57.4t^2 - 10.4t + 2100$

c. How much money did people between 15 and 19 years old spend on sound recordings in 2002? about \$1680 million

52a. $H \cdot P \approx 2t^2 + 263t + 8366$; find the product $H \cdot P$, because the number of housing units times the percent of housing units that were vacant will give the number of vacant housing units.

52. ★ SHORT RESPONSE During the period 1980–2002, the number H (in thousands) of housing units in the U.S. and the percent P (in decimal form) of housing units that were vacant can be modeled by

$$H = 1570t + 89{,}000 \quad \text{and} \quad P = 0.0013t + 0.094$$

where t is the number of years since 1980.

a. Write an equation that models the number (in thousands) of vacant housing units as a function of the number of years since 1980. *Explain* how you found this equation.

b. How many housing units were vacant in 2002? about 15,120 housing units

Mathematical Reasoning

Exercise 49 You may want to discuss the usefulness of using a variable to represent the width of the frame. Lead students to see that the ease of manipulating a variable at the design stage allows them to consider the impact of various widths.

Reading Strategy

Exercises 51–52 You may want to point out that Exercise 51 has a worked-out solution and that Exercise 52 uses the same concepts. Exercise 52 is also an example of a short response question, so the worked-out solution for Exercise 51 can provide useful strategies for this type of test question. Suggest that students carefully read Exercise 51 so they understand the problem before they attempt a solution.

5 ASSESS AND RETEACH

Daily Homework Quiz

 **Transparency Available**

Find the product.

1. $3x(x^3 - 3x^2 + 2x - 4)$ $\mathbf{3x^4 - 9x^3 + 6x^2 - 12x}$
2. $(y - 4)(2y + 5)$ $\mathbf{2y^2 - 3y - 20}$
3. $(4x + 3)(3x - 2)$ $\mathbf{12x^2 + x - 6}$
4. $(b^2 - 2b - 1)(3b - 5)$ $\mathbf{3b^3 - 11b^2 + 7b + 5}$
5. The dimensions of a rectangle are $x + 4$ and $3x - 1$. Write an expression to represent the area of the rectangle. $\mathbf{3x^2 + 11x - 4}$

Online Quiz

Available at **classzone.com**

Diagnosis/Remediation

- Practice A, B, C in Chapter Resource Book
- Study Guide in Chapter Resource Book
- Practice Workbook
- @HomeTutor

Challenge

Additional challenge is available in the Chapter Resource Book.

53a. ***Sample answer:*** **$T = t + 90$; use the data points from 1995–1999: (5, 95), (6, 96), (7, 97), (8, 98), (9, 99). All these points lie on a line with slope $m = 1$; use any one of the points to find the y-intercept $b = 90$. The other data points, (0, 92), (10, 101), and (11, 102), lie close to the line $T = t + 90$.**

B **53.** ★ **EXTENDED RESPONSE** The bar graph shows the number of households with a television for various years during the period 1990–2001.

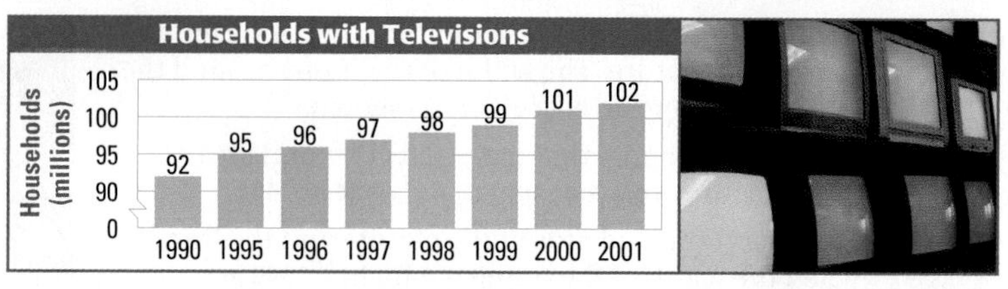

a. Find a linear equation that models the number of households T (in millions) with a television as a function of the number of years since 1990. *Explain* how you found your model.

b. During the period 1990–2001, the percent P (in decimal form) of television households that also have a VCR can be modeled by

$$P = -0.0015t^2 + 0.032t + 0.069$$

where t is the number of years since 1990. Write an equation that models the number of households V (in millions) with a VCR and a television as a function of the number of years since 1990. $\mathbf{V = -0.0015t^3 - 0.103t^2 + 2.949t + 6.21}$

c. Use the equation from part (b) to predict the number of households that had a VCR and a television in 2002 and in 2005. **about 24.2 million households, about 22.2 million households**

C **54.** **CHALLENGE** For the period 1990–2001, the total United States energy consumption C (in quadrillion British Thermal Units, or BTU) and the percent P of the total energy that was consumed in the United States for industrial purposes can be modeled by

$$C = 1.5t + 84$$
$$P = -0.05t^2 + 0.25t + 38$$

where t is the number of years since 1990.

a. Find the percent of total energy that was consumed in the United States for industrial purposes in 2000. **35.5%**

b. Write an equation that gives the total energy (in quadrillion BTU) consumed in the United States for industrial purposes as a function of the number of years since 1990. To write the equation, you may need to rewrite one of the given equations.
$\mathbf{C \cdot 0.01P = -0.00075t^3 - 0.03825t^2 + 0.78t + 31.92}$

MIXED REVIEW

PREVIEW Prepare for Lesson 9.3 in Exs. 55–60.

Simplify the expression. *(p. 96)*

55. $5(2x - 7) + 5x$ $\mathbf{15x - 35}$ **56.** $2x + 3(4x - 1)$ $\mathbf{14x - 3}$ **57.** $15x - 7(x + 3)$ $\mathbf{8x - 21}$

58. $-2x(x + 1) + 2x$ $\mathbf{-2x^2}$ **59.** $x(x - 4) - 9x$ $\mathbf{x^2 - 13x}$ **60.** $11x + (x - 1)(8x)$ $\mathbf{8x^2 + 3x}$

Solve the system.

61. $2x + y = -5$, $y = -3x + 2$ *(p. 435)* **(7, −19)**

62. $x - 2y = -7$, $x + 2y = 13$ *(p. 444)* **(3, 5)**

63. $-2x + 4y = -2$, $x - 2y = -1$ *(p. 451)* **no solution**

64. $-6x + 4y = 40$, $-3x + 2y = 20$ *(p. 451)* **all real numbers**

65. $x \geq -3$, $y < 5$ *(p. 466)* **See margin.**

66. $y \leq 2x - 5$, $y > -3x + 1$ *(p. 466)* **See margin.**

65.

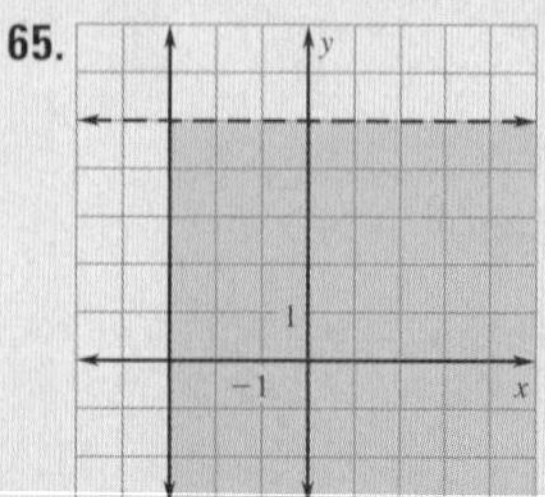

66.

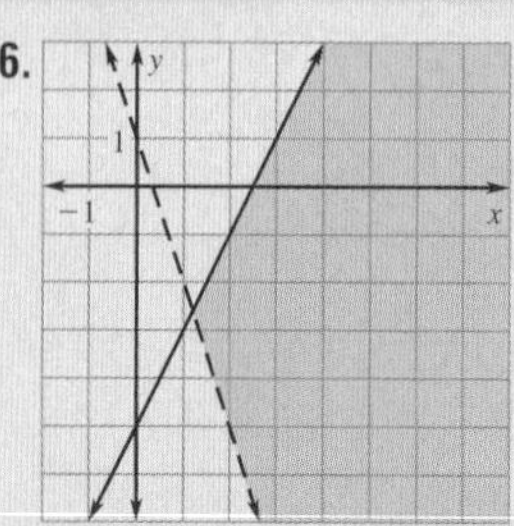

9.3 Find Special Products of Polynomials

Before You multiplied polynomials.
Now You will use special product patterns to multiply polynomials.
Why? So you can make a scientific prediction, as in Example 4.

Key Vocabulary
- **binomial,** *p. 555*
- **trinomial,** *p. 555*

The diagram shows a square with a side length of $(a + b)$ units. You can see that the area of the square is

$(a + b)^2 = a^2 + 2ab + b^2$.

	a	b
a	a^2	ab
b	ab	b^2

This is one version of a pattern called the square of a binomial. To find another version of this pattern, use algebra: replace b with $-b$.

$(a + (-b))^2 = a^2 + 2a(-b) + (-b)^2$ **Replace b with $-b$ in the pattern above.**

$(a - b)^2 = a^2 - 2ab + b^2$ **Simplify.**

KEY CONCEPT *For Your Notebook*

Square of a Binomial Pattern

Algebra	Example
$(a + b)^2 = a^2 + 2ab + b^2$	$(x + 5)^2 = x^2 + 10x + 25$
$(a - b)^2 = a^2 - 2ab + b^2$	$(2x - 3)^2 = 4x^2 - 12x + 9$

EXAMPLE 1 Use the square of a binomial pattern

USE PATTERNS
When you use special product patterns, remember that a and b can be numbers, variables, or variable expressions.

Find the product.

a. $(3x + 4)^2 = (3x)^2 + 2(3x)(4) + 4^2$ **Square of a binomial pattern**

$= 9x^2 + 24x + 16$ **Simplify.**

b. $(5x - 2y)^2 = (5x)^2 - 2(5x)(2y) + (2y)^2$ **Square of a binomial pattern**

$= 25x^2 - 20xy + 4y^2$ **Simplify.**

 **GUIDED PRACTICE** for Example 1

Find the product.

1. $(x + 3)^2$ **$x^2 + 6x + 9$**
2. $(2x + 1)^2$ **$4x^2 + 4x + 1$**
3. $(4x - y)^2$ **$16x^2 - 8xy + y^2$**
4. $(3m + n)^2$ **$9m^2 + 6mn + n^2$**

1 PLAN AND PREPARE

Warm-Up Exercises
Transparency Available
Find the product.
1. $(x + 7)(x + 2)$ **$x^2 + 9x + 14$**
2. $(3x - 1)(3x + 2)$ **$9x^2 + 3x - 2$**
3. The dimensions of a rectangular playground can be represented by $3x + 8$ and $5x + 2$. Write a polynomial that represents the area of the playground. What is the area of the playground if x is 8 meters? **$15x^2 + 46x + 16$; 1344 m^2**

Notetaking Guide
Transparency Available
Promotes interactive learning and notetaking skills.

Pacing
Basic: 1 day
Average: 1 day
Advanced: 1 day
Block: 0.5 block with 9.4
- See *Teaching Guide/Lesson Plan.*

2 FOCUS AND MOTIVATE

Essential Question
Big Idea 1, p. 553
How do you use special product patterns to multiply binomials? **Tell students they will learn how to answer this question by using patterns to write products of binomials.**

NCTM STANDARDS
Standard 2: Understand patterns; Use models to understand relationships

Resource Planning Guide

Chapter Resource Book
- Teaching Guide/Lesson Plan
- Practice levels A, B, C
- Study Guide
- Catch-up for Absent Students
- Application
- Challenge

Workbooks
- Notetaking Guide
- Practice Workbook

Teaching Options
- **Power Presentations** provides dynamic electronic teaching resources for the classroom.
- **Activity Generator** provides editable activities for all ability levels.

Interactive Technology
- Easy Planner
- Power Presentations
- Activity Generator
- Animated Algebra
- Test Generator
- Online Quiz
- eWorkbook
- eEdition
- @HomeTutor

Resources for English Learners
- Spanish Study Guide
- Multi-Language Visual Glossary
- Student Resources in Spanish

See also the *Differentiated Instruction Resources* for more strategies for meeting individual needs.

SUM AND DIFFERENCE PATTERN To find the product $(x + 2)(x - 2)$, you can multiply the two binomials using the FOIL pattern.

$(x + 2)(x - 2) = x^2 - 2x + 2x - 4$ Use FOIL pattern.

$= x^2 - 4$ Combine like terms.

This suggests a pattern for the product of the sum and difference of two terms.

KEY CONCEPT *For Your Notebook*

Sum and Difference Pattern

Algebra	**Example**
$(a + b)(a - b) = a^2 - b^2$	$(x + 3)(x - 3) = x^2 - 9$

EXAMPLE 2 Use the sum and difference pattern

Find the product.

a. $(t + 5)(t - 5) = t^2 - 5^2$ Sum and difference pattern

$= t^2 - 25$ Simplify.

b. $(3x + y)(3x - y) = (3x)^2 - y^2$ Sum and difference pattern

$= 9x^2 - y^2$ Simplify.

✓ **GUIDED PRACTICE** for Example 2

Find the product.

5. $(x + 10)(x - 10)$ $x^2 - 100$

6. $(2x + 1)(2x - 1)$ $4x^2 - 1$

7. $(x + 3y)(x - 3y)$ $x^2 - 9y^2$

SPECIAL PRODUCTS AND MENTAL MATH The special product patterns can help you use mental math to find certain products of numbers.

EXAMPLE 3 Use special products and mental math

Use special products to find the product 26 • 34.

Solution

Notice that 26 is 4 less than 30 while 34 is 4 more than 30.

$26 \cdot 34 = (30 - 4)(30 + 4)$ Write as product of difference and sum.

$= 30^2 - 4^2$ Sum and difference pattern

$= 900 - 16$ Evaluate powers.

$= 884$ Simplify.

Motivating the Lesson

If both parents have brown eyes, it is possible for one child to have brown eyes while another child has blue eyes. By using a special pattern to multiply binomials, you can calculate the likelihood of such an occurrence.

3 TEACH

Extra Example 1

Find the product.

a. $(2x + 5)^2$ **$4x^2 + 20x + 25$**

b. $(3x - y)^2$ **$9x^2 - 6xy + y^2$**

Key Question to Ask for Example 1

- How would the product $(3x - 4)^2$ be different from the product in part (a)? **The middle term would be negative rather than positive.**

Extra Example 2

Find the product.

a. $(r + 3)(r - 3)$ **$r^2 - 9$**

b. $(4x + y)(4x - y)$ **$16x^2 - y^2$**

Key Question to Ask for Example 2

- What happens to the middle terms when you find the product using the sum and difference pattern? **The sum of the two middle terms is zero.**

Extra Example 3

Use special products to find the product 18 • 22. **396**

Differentiated Instruction

Visual Learners Students sometimes forget the coefficient of the linear term *ab* in the square of a binomial, or they misplace the minus sign. In addition to the colored tiles shown on page 569, another way to remember the formulas is to apply the FOIL method to the product of two binomials using mental math.

See also the *Differentiated Instruction Resources* for more strategies.

EXAMPLE 4 Solve a multi-step problem

BORDER COLLIES The color of the dark patches of a border collie's coat is determined by a combination of two genes. An offspring inherits one patch color gene from each parent. Each parent has two color genes, and the offspring has an equal chance of inheriting either one.

The gene B is for black patches, and the gene r is for red patches. Any gene combination with a B results in black patches. Suppose each parent has the same gene combination Br. The Punnett square shows the possible gene combinations of the offspring and the resulting patch color.

- What percent of the possible gene combinations of the offspring result in black patches?
- Show how you could use a polynomial to model the possible gene combinations of the offspring.

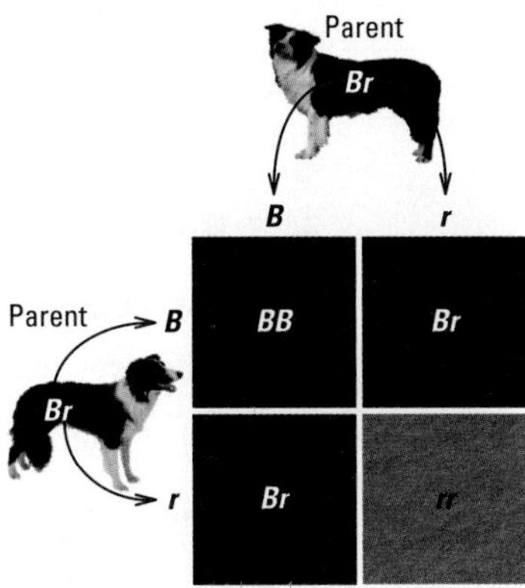

Solution

STEP 1 **Notice** that the Punnett square shows 4 possible gene combinations of the offspring. Of these combinations, 3 result in black patches.

▶ 75% of the possible gene combinations result in black patches.

STEP 2 **Model** the gene from each parent with $0.5B + 0.5r$. There is an equal chance that the collie inherits a black or red gene from each parent.

The possible genes of the offspring can be modeled by $(0.5B + 0.5r)^2$. Notice that this product also represents the area of the Punnett square.

Expand the product to find the possible patch colors of the offspring.

$$(0.5B + 0.5r)^2 = (0.5B)^2 + 2(0.5B)(0.5r) + (0.5r)^2$$

$$= 0.25B^2 + 0.5Br + 0.25r^2$$

Consider the coefficients in the polynomial.

The coefficients show that 25% + 50% = 75% of the possible gene combinations will result in black patches.

✓ **GUIDED PRACTICE** for Examples 3 and 4

8. *Describe* how you can use special products to find 21^2.
Use the square of a binomial pattern to find the product $(20 + 1)^2$.
9. **BORDER COLLIES** Look back at Example 4. What percent of the possible gene combinations of the offspring result in red patches? **25%**

Extra Example 4

In dogs, the gene E is for erect ears and the gene e is for droopy ears. Any gene combination with an E results in erect ears. The Punnett square shows the possible gene combinations of the offspring and the resulting type of ear.

	E	e
E	EE erect	Ee erect
e	Ee erect	ee droopy

- What percent of the possible gene combinations of the offspring result in droopy ears? **25%**
- Show how you could use a polynomial to model the possible gene combinations of the offspring. **Use $(0.5E + 0.5e)^2$ to model the possible genes of the offspring. Expand the product to find the possible gene combinations: $0.25E^2 + 0.5Ee + 0.25e^2$. The coefficient of e^2 shows that 25% of the possible gene combinations will result in droopy ears.**

Closing the Lesson

Have students summarize the major points of the lesson and answer the Essential Question: How do you use special product patterns to multiply binomials?

- **The square of a binomial pattern is for $(a + b)^2$ or $(a - b)^2$.**
- **The sum and difference pattern is for $(a + b)(a - b)$.**

To find $(a + b)^2$ or $(a - b)^2$, square a, add (or subtract) twice the product ab, and add the square of b. The product $(a + b)(a - b)$ is $a^2 - b^2$.

9.3 EXERCISES

HOMEWORK KEY
- ○ = WORKED-OUT SOLUTIONS on p. WS21 for Exs. 11 and 41
- ★ = STANDARDIZED TEST PRACTICE Exs. 2, 17, 18, 42, and 44
- ◆ = MULTIPLE REPRESENTATIONS Ex. 41

4 PRACTICE AND APPLY

Assignment Guide

Answer Transparencies available for all exercises

Basic:
Day 1: SRH p. 917 Exs. 1–9 odd
pp. 572–574
Exs. 1, 2, 4–8 even, 9–13, 17–22, 24–34 even, 40–43, 46–56 even

Average:
Day 1: pp. 572–574
Exs. 1, 2, 4–22, 24–34 even, 35–37, 40–44, 48, 52, 54, 56

Advanced:
Day 1: pp. 572–574
Exs. 1, 2, 6–8, 14–18, 19–33 odd, 35–45*, 53, 57

Block:
pp. 572–574
Exs. 1, 2, 4–22, 24–34 even, 35–37, 40–44, 48, 52, 54, 56 (with 9.4)

Differentiated Instruction

See *Differentiated Instruction Resources* for suggestions on addressing the needs of a diverse classroom.

Homework Check

For a quick check of student understanding of key concepts, go over the following exercises:

Basic: 4, 12, 19, 26, 40
Average: 6, 15, 20, 28, 41
Advanced: 8, 16, 21, 31, 42

Extra Practice

- Student Edition, p. 946
- Chapter Resource Book: Practice levels A, B, C

Practice Worksheet

An easily-readable reduced practice page (with answers) for this lesson can be found on p. 552C.

2. See Additional Answers beginning on p. AA1.

SKILL PRACTICE

A

1. **VOCABULARY** Give an example of two binomials whose product you can find using the sum and difference pattern. ***Sample answer:*** $x - 5, x + 5$

2. ★ **WRITING** *Explain* how to use the square of a binomial pattern. **See margin.**

EXAMPLE 1 on p. 569 for Exs. 3–10, 18

SQUARE OF A BINOMIAL Find the product.

3. $(x + 8)^2$ $\mathbf{x^2 + 16x + 64}$
4. $(a + 6)^2$ $\mathbf{a^2 + 12a + 36}$
5. $(2y + 5)^2$ $\mathbf{4y^2 + 20y + 25}$
6. $(t - 7)^2$ $\mathbf{t^2 - 14t + 49}$
7. $(n - 11)^2$ $\mathbf{n^2 - 22n + 121}$
8. $(6b - 1)^2$ $\mathbf{36b^2 - 12b + 1}$

ERROR ANALYSIS ***Describe* and correct the error in multiplying. 9, 10. See margin.**

9. $(s - 3)^2 = s^2 + 9$ ✗

10. $(2d - 10)^2 = 4d^2 - 20d + 100$ ✗

9. The middle term of the product, $2s(-3)$, was left out; $s^2 - 6s + 9$.

10. The middle term of the products should be twice the product of the terms of the binomial; $4d^2 - 40d + 100$.

EXAMPLE 2 on p. 570 for Exs. 11–17

SUM AND DIFFERENCE PATTERN Find the product.

11. $(t + 4)(t - 4)$ $\mathbf{t^2 - 16}$
12. $(m - 6)(m + 6)$ $\mathbf{m^2 - 36}$
13. $(2x + 1)(2x - 1)$ $\mathbf{4x^2 - 1}$
14. $(3x - 1)(3x + 1)$ $\mathbf{9x^2 - 1}$
15. $(7 + w)(7 - w)$ $\mathbf{49 - w^2}$
16. $(3s - 8)(3s + 8)$ $\mathbf{9s^2 - 64}$

17. ★ **MULTIPLE CHOICE** Find the product $(7x + 3)(7x - 3)$. **B**

Ⓐ $7x^2 - 9$ Ⓑ $49x^2 - 9$ Ⓒ $49x^2 - 21x - 9$ Ⓓ $49x^2 - 42x - 9$

18. ★ **MULTIPLE CHOICE** Find the product $(5n - 3)^2$. **D**

Ⓐ $5n^2 - 9$ Ⓑ $25n^2 - 9$ Ⓒ $25n^2 - 15n + 9$ Ⓓ $25n^2 - 30n + 9$

EXAMPLE 3 on p. 570 for Exs. 19–22

MENTAL MATH ***Describe* how you can use mental math to find the product. 19–22. See margin.**

19. $16 \cdot 24$
20. $28 \cdot 32$
21. 17^2
22. 44^2

SPECIAL PRODUCT PATTERNS Find the product.

23. $(r + 9s)^2$ $\mathbf{r^2 + 18rs + 81s^2}$
24. $(6x + 5)^2$ $\mathbf{36x^2 + 60x + 25}$
25. $(3m + 11n)(3m - 11n)$ $\mathbf{9m^2 - 121n^2}$
26. $(7a + 8b)(7a - 8b)$ $\mathbf{49a^2 - 64b^2}$
27. $(3m - 7n)^2$ $\mathbf{9m^2 - 42mn + 49n^2}$
28. $(13 - 2x)^2$ $\mathbf{169 - 52x + 4x^2}$
29. $(3f - 9)(3f + 9)$ $\mathbf{9f^2 - 81}$
30. $(9 - 4t)(9 + 4t)$ $\mathbf{81 - 16t^2}$
31. $(3x + 8y)^2$ $\mathbf{9x^2 + 48xy + 64y^2}$
32. $(-x - 2y)^2$ $\mathbf{x^2 + 4xy + 4y^2}$
33. $(2a - 5b)(2a + 5b)$ $\mathbf{4a^2 - 25b^2}$
34. $(6x + y)(6x - y)$ $\mathbf{36x^2 - y^2}$

B

MULTIPLYING FUNCTIONS Perform the indicated operation using the functions $f(x) = 3x + 0.5$ and $g(x) = 3x - 0.5$.

35. $f(x) \cdot g(x)$ $\mathbf{9x^2 - 0.25}$
36. $(f(x))^2$ $\mathbf{9x^2 + 3x + 0.25}$
37. $(g(x))^2$ $\mathbf{9x^2 - 3x + 0.25}$

C

38. **CHALLENGE** Write two binomials that have the product $x^2 - 121$. *Explain.* **See margin.**

39. **CHALLENGE** Write a pattern for the cube of a binomial $(a + b)^3$. $\mathbf{a^3 + 3a^2b + 3ab^2 + b^3}$

19. Use the sum and difference pattern to find the product $(20 - 4)(20 + 4)$.

20. Use the sum and difference pattern to find the product $(30 - 2)(30 + 2)$.

21. Use the square of a binomial pattern to find the product $(20 - 3)^2$.

22. Use the square of a binomial pattern to find the product $(40 + 4)^2$.

38. $x - 11, x + 11$; since $x^2 - 121 = x^2 - 11^2$ is in the form $a^2 - b^2$, you can use the sum and difference pattern in reverse to find the binomials $a - b = x - 11$ and $a + b = x + 11$.

PROBLEM SOLVING

EXAMPLE 4 A on p. 571 for Exs. 40–42

40. **PEA PLANTS** In pea plants, the gene G is for green pods, and the gene y is for yellow pods. Any gene combination with a G results in a green pod. Suppose two pea plants have the same gene combination Gy. The Punnett square shows the possible gene combinations of an offspring pea plant and the resulting pod color.

	G	y
G	GG	Gy
y	Gy	yy

a. What percent of possible gene combinations of the offspring plant result in a yellow pod? **25%**

b. Show how you could use a polynomial to model the possible gene combinations of the offspring. **See margin.**

@HomeTutor for problem solving help at classzone.com

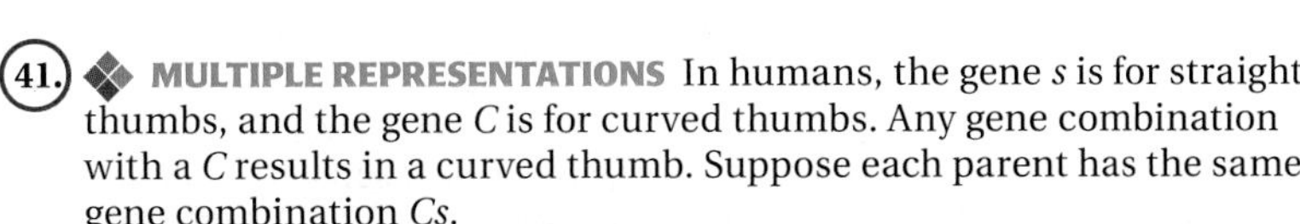

41. ◆ **MULTIPLE REPRESENTATIONS** In humans, the gene s is for straight thumbs, and the gene C is for curved thumbs. Any gene combination with a C results in a curved thumb. Suppose each parent has the same gene combination Cs.

a. **Making a Diagram** Make a Punnett square that shows the possible gene combinations inherited by a child. **See margin.**

b. **Writing a Model** Write a polynomial that models the possible gene combinations of the child. $\mathbf{0.25C^2 + 0.5Cs + 0.25s^2}$

c. **Interpreting a Model** What percent of the possible gene combinations of the child result in a curved thumb? **75%**

@HomeTutor for problem solving help at classzone.com

42. ★ **SHORT RESPONSE** In ball pythons, the gene N is for normal coloring, and the gene a is for no coloring, or albino. Any gene combination with an N results in normal coloring. Suppose one parent python has the gene combination Na and the other parent python has the gene combination aa. What percent of the possible gene combinations of the offspring result in an albino python? *Explain* how you found your answer. **See margin.**

B 43. **FOOTBALL STATISTICS** During the 2004 regular season, the San Diego Chargers' quarterback Drew Brees completed 65.5% of the passes he attempted. The area model shows the possible outcomes of two attempted passes. **a, b. See margin.**

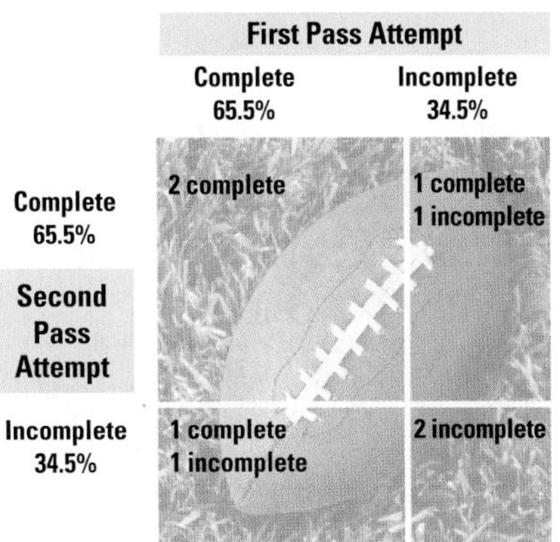

a. What percent of the possible outcomes of two attempted passes results in Drew Brees's throwing at least one complete pass? *Explain* how you found your answer using the area model.

b. Show how you could use a polynomial to model the possible results of two attempted passes.

40b. The gene from each parent is modeled by $0.5G + 0.5y$. The possible genes of the offspring are modeled by $(0.5G + 0.5y)^2 = 0.25G^2 + 0.5Gy + 0.25y^2$. Because any gene combination with a G results in a green pod, the coefficients of the first two terms show that 25% + 50% = 75% of the offspring will have green pods, and the coefficient of the last term shows that 25% of the offspring will have yellow pods.

41a.

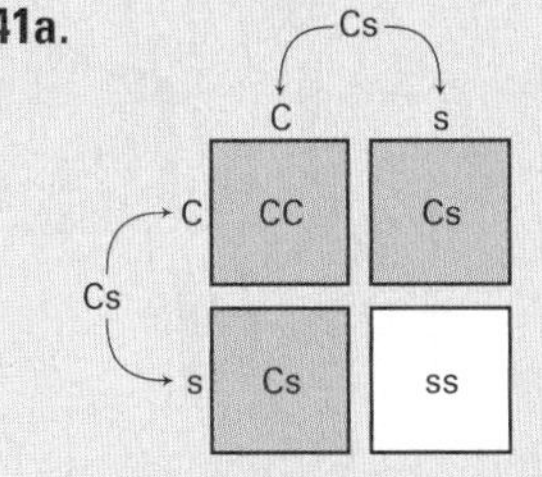

Avoiding Common Errors

Exercises 23–34 Students often use an incorrect pattern when finding products of binomials. Suggest that students go through all of the exercises before finding the products to determine which pattern they should use for each exercise. If the square of a binomial pattern is appropriate, encourage them to indicate whether the middle term is positive or negative.

Teaching Strategy

Exercise 42 It may be useful to have students make Punnet squares for several other possible combinations of genes, such as NN and aa or NN and Na, so they can see the range of possible combinations. They may find it interesting to compare the Punnett squares. Ask students to determine the percent of each of the possible gene combinations for each of the Punnett squares. You may want to challenge students to write offspring polynomials for each of the possible parent combinations.

Internet Reference

Exercises 40–42 To learn more about Mendel and his pea plant experiment, visit anthro.palomar.edu/mendel/mendel_1.htm

42. 50%; the gene from one parent is modeled by $0.5N + 0.5a$ and the gene from the other parent in modeled by $0.5a + 0.5a = a$, so the possible gene combinations of the offspring are modeled by $a(0.5N + 0.5a) = 0.5Na + 0.5a^2$. Because any gene combination with an N results in normal coloring, only the second term, $0.5a^2$, represents albino offspring. The coefficient of a^2, 0.5, shows that 50% of the offspring will be albino.

43a–b. See Additional Answers beginning on p. AA1.

44. ★ **EXTENDED RESPONSE** The iris of an eye surrounds the pupil. It regulates the amount of light entering the eye by opening and closing the pupil. For parts (a)–(c) below, leave your answers in terms of π.

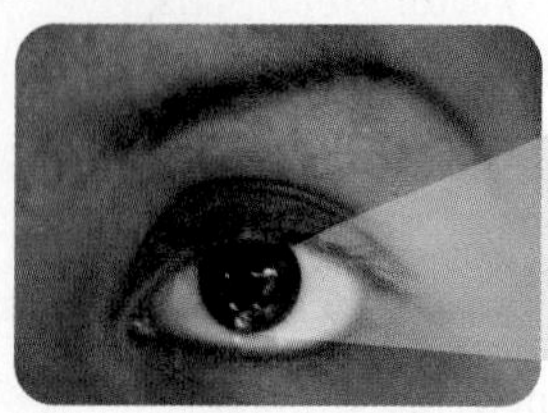

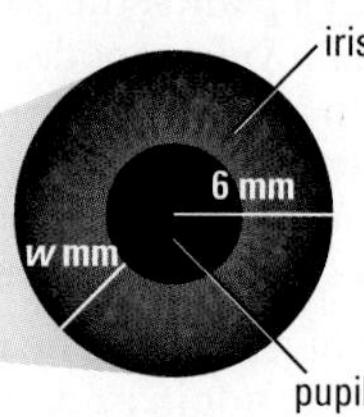

The iris of a human eye has a width w that varies from 0.5 millimeter to 4 millimeters.

a. Write a polynomial that represents the pupil's radius. **$6 - w$**

b. Write a polynomial that represents the pupil's area. **$\pi w^2 - 12\pi w + 36\pi$**

c. What is the least possible area and the greatest possible area of the pupil? *Explain* how you found your answers. **See margin.**

C 45. **CHALLENGE** You use 100 feet of fencing to form a square with a side length of 25 feet. You want to change the dimensions of the enclosed region. For every 1 foot you increase the width, you must decrease the length by 1 foot. Write a polynomial that gives the area of the rectangle after you increase the width by x feet and decrease the length by x feet. *Explain* why *any* change in dimensions results in an area less than that of the original square. **$625 - x^2$; the area of the original square is $25^2 = 625$ square feet, and the area of a square when the dimensions are changed is $(25 - x)(25 + x) = 625 - x^2$ square feet; since x^2 is always positive, the area of the new square will be less than 625 square feet.**

MIXED REVIEW

PREVIEW Prepare for Lesson 9.4 in Exs. 46–53.

Find the greatest common factor of the pair of numbers. *(p. 910)*

46. 25, 30 **5**
47. 36, 54 **18**
48. 14, 21 **7**
49. 36, 50 **2**
50. 65, 39 **13**
51. 13, 20 **1**
52. 77, 143 **11**
53. 24, 162 **6**

Solve the equation. Check your solution.

54. $x + 11 = 6$ *(p. 134)* **-5**
55. $11x + 8 = -14$ *(p. 141)* **-2**
56. $2x - 5(x - 13) = 35$ *(p. 148)* **10**
57. $9x + 4 - 4x = 6x + 7$ *(p. 154)* **-3**

QUIZ *for Lessons 9.1–9.3*

Find the sum, difference, or product.

1. $(x^2 - 3x + 5) + (-2x^2 + 11x + 1)$ *(p. 554)* **$-x^2 + 8x + 6$**
2. $(8y^3 - 7y^2 + y) - (9y^2 - 5y + 7)$ *(p. 554)* **$8y^3 - 16y^2 + 6y - 7$**
3. $(2r + 11)(r - 6)$ *(p. 562)* **$2r^2 - r - 66$**
4. $(m + 3)(-2m^2 + 5m - 1)$ *(p. 562)* **$-2m^3 - m^2 + 14m - 3$**
5. $(2 + 8p)(2 - 10p)$ *(p. 562)* **$4 - 4p - 80p^2$**
6. $(15 - 2s)^2$ *(p. 569)* **$225 - 60s + 4s^2$**
7. $(5w + 9z)^2$ *(p. 569)* **$25w^2 + 90wz + 81z^2$**
8. $(5x - 4y)(5x + 4y)$ *(p. 569)* **$25x^2 - 16y^2$**
9. **AREA** The length of a rectangular rug is 2 times its width. The rug is centered in a rectangular room. Each edge is 3 feet from the nearest wall. Write a polynomial that represents the area of the room. *(p. 564)* **$2w^2 + 18w + 36$**

EXTRA PRACTICE for Lesson 9.3, p. 946

 **ONLINE QUIZ** at classzone.com

5 ASSESS AND RETEACH

Daily Homework Quiz

 **Transparency Available**

Find the product.

1. $(y + 8)(y - 8)$ **$y^2 - 64$**
2. $(3m - 2n)^2$ **$9m^2 - 12mn + 4n^2$**
3. $(2m + 5)^2$ **$4m^2 + 20m + 25$**
4. In humans, the genes for being able to roll and not roll the tongue are R and r, respectively. Offspring with R can roll the tongue. If one parent is Rr and the other is rr, what percent of the offspring will not be able to roll the tongue? **50%**

Online Quiz

Available at **classzone.com**

Diagnosis/Remediation

- Practice A, B, C in Chapter Resource Book
- Study Guide in Chapter Resource Book
- Practice Workbook
- @HomeTutor

Challenge

Additional challenge is available in the Chapter Resource Book.

Quiz

An easily-readable reduced copy of the quiz (with answers) on Lessons 9.1–9.3 from the Assessment Book can be found on p. 552E.

44c. 4π, 30.25π; substitute the greatest width $w = 4$ millimeters into the polynomial from part (b) to find the least possible area: $\pi(4)^2 - 12\pi(4) + 36\pi = 16\pi - 48\pi + 36\pi = 4\pi$ square millimeters. Substitute the least width $w = 0.5$ millimeters into the polynomial from part (b) to find the greatest possible area: $\pi(0.5)^2 - 12\pi(0.5) + 36\pi = 0.25\pi - 6\pi + 36\pi = 30.25\pi$ square millimeters.

9.4 Solve Polynomial Equations in Factored Form

Before You solved linear equations.

Now You will solve polynomial equations.

Why So you can analyze vertical motion, as in Ex. 55.

Key Vocabulary
- **roots**
- **vertical motion model**

In Lesson 2.4, you learned the property of zero: For any real number a, $a \cdot 0 = 0$. This is equivalent to saying:

For real numbers a and b, if $a = 0$ or $b = 0$, then $ab = 0$.

The converse of this statement is also true (as shown in Exercise 49), and it is called the zero-product property.

KEY CONCEPT *For Your Notebook*

Zero-Product Property

Let a and b be real numbers. If $ab = 0$, then $a = 0$ or $b = 0$.

The zero-product property is used to solve an equation when one side is zero and the other side is a product of polynomial factors. The solutions of such an equation are also called **roots**.

EXAMPLE 1 Use the zero-product property

Solve $(x - 4)(x + 2) = 0$.

$(x - 4)(x + 2) = 0$	**Write original equation.**
$x - 4 = 0$ *or* $x + 2 = 0$	**Zero-product property**
$x = 4$ *or* $x = -2$	**Solve for *x*.**

▶ The solutions of the equation are 4 and −2.

CHECK Substitute each solution into the original equation to check.

$(4 - 4)(4 + 2) \stackrel{?}{=} 0$ $\quad$ $(-2 - 4)(-2 + 2) \stackrel{?}{=} 0$

$0 \cdot 6 \stackrel{?}{=} 0$ $\quad$ $-6 \cdot 0 \stackrel{?}{=} 0$

$0 = 0$ ✓ $\quad$ $0 = 0$ ✓

GUIDED PRACTICE for Example 1

1. Solve the equation $(x - 5)(x - 1) = 0$. **5, 1**

1 PLAN AND PREPARE

Warm-Up Exercises

Transparency Available

1. Find the GCF of 12 and 28. **4**
2. Find the GCF of 18 and 42. **6**
3. The number (in hundreds) of sunscreen and sun tanning products sold at a pharmacy from 1999–2005 can be modeled by $-0.8t^2 + 0.3t + 107$, where t is the number of years since 1999. About how many products were sold in 2002? **about 10,070**

Notetaking Guide

Transparency Available

Promotes interactive learning and notetaking skills.

Pacing

Basic: 2 days
Average: 2 days
Advanced: 2 days
Block: 0.5 block with 9.3
0.5 block with 9.5

- See *Teaching Guide/Lesson Plan.*

2 FOCUS AND MOTIVATE

Essential Question

Big Idea 3, p. 553

How do you solve polynomial equations in factored form? **Tell students they will learn how to answer this question by using the zero-product property.**

NCTM STANDARDS

Standard 2: Analyze situations using algebraic symbols

Standard 6: Solve problems in math and other contexts

Resource Planning Guide

Chapter Resource Book
- Teaching Guide/Lesson Plan
- Activity Master
- Practice levels A, B, C
- Study Guide
- Catch-up for Absent Students
- Problem Solving Workshop
- Challenge

Workbooks
- Notetaking Guide
- Practice Workbook

Teaching Options
- **Power Presentations** provides dynamic electronic teaching resources for the classroom.
- **Activity Generator** provides editable activities for all ability levels.

Interactive Technology
- Easy Planner
- Power Presentations
- Activity Generator
- Animated Algebra
- Test Generator
- Online Quiz
- eWorkbook
- eEdition
- @HomeTutor

Resources for English Learners
- Spanish Study Guide
- Multi-Language Visual Glossary
- Student Resources in Spanish

See also the *Differentiated Instruction Resources* for more strategies for meeting individual needs.

Motivating the Lesson

Ask students to recount events in which they experienced or witnessed a person or animal jumping in an upward motion. After they share some of their experiences, tell them that this lesson offers a way to calculate how long the person or animal will be in the air.

3 TEACH

Extra Example 1

Solve $(x + 3)(x - 5) = 0$. **−3, 5**

Key Question to Ask for Example 1

- Why does this type of equation have two solutions? **The left side of the equation is the product of two quantities. By the zero-product property, either of them could be zero. This allows for the equation to have two solutions.**

Extra Example 2

Factor out the greatest common monomial factor.

a. $8x + 12y$ **$4(2x + 3y)$**

b. $14y^2 + 21y$ **$7y(2y + 3)$**

Key Question to Ask for Example 2

- In part (b), how do you know x^3 is a factor of x^3 and x^4? **$\frac{x^4}{x^3} = x^{4-3}$ or x and $\frac{x^3}{x^3} = x^{3-3} = x^0$ or 1**

Extra Example 3

Solve $3x^2 + 18x = 0$ **−6, 0**

Extra Example 4

Solve $4s^2 = 14s$. **$0, \frac{7}{2}$**

REVIEW GCF
For help with finding the GCF, see p. 910.

FACTORING To solve a polynomial equation using the zero-product property, you may need to *factor* the polynomial, or write it as a product of other polynomials. Look for the *greatest common factor* (GCF) of the polynomial's terms. This is a monomial with an integer coefficient that divides evenly into each term.

EXAMPLE 2 Find the greatest common monomial factor

Factor out the greatest common monomial factor.

a. $12x + 42y$ **b.** $4x^4 + 24x^3$

Solution

a. The GCF of 12 and 42 is 6. The variables x and y have no common factor. So, the greatest common monomial factor of the terms is 6.

▸ $12x + 42y = 6(2x + 7y)$

b. The GCF of 4 and 24 is 4. The GCF of x^4 and x^3 is x^3. So, the greatest common monomial factor of the terms is $4x^3$.

▸ $4x^4 + 24x^3 = 4x^3(x + 6)$

✓ **GUIDED PRACTICE** for Example 2

2. Factor out the greatest common monomial factor from $14m + 35n$. **$7(2m + 5n)$**

EXAMPLE 3 Solve an equation by factoring

Solve $2x^2 + 8x = 0$.

$2x^2 + 8x = 0$	Write original equation.
$2x(x + 4) = 0$	Factor left side.
$2x = 0$ *or* $x + 4 = 0$	Zero-product property
$x = 0$ *or* $x = -4$	Solve for x.

▸ The solutions of the equation are 0 and −4.

EXAMPLE 4 Solve an equation by factoring

Solve $6n^2 = 15n$.

AVOID ERRORS
To use the zero-product property, you must write the equation so that one side is 0. For this reason, $15n$ must be subtracted from each side.

$6n^2 - 15n = 0$	Subtract $15n$ from each side.
$3n(2n - 5) = 0$	Factor left side.
$3n = 0$ *or* $2n - 5 = 0$	Zero-product property
$n = 0$ *or* $n = \frac{5}{2}$	Solve for n.

▸ The solutions of the equation are 0 and $\frac{5}{2}$.

✓ GUIDED PRACTICE for Examples 3 and 4

Solve the equation.

3. $a^2 + 5a = 0$ **0, −5**

4. $3s^2 - 9s = 0$ **0, 3**

5. $4x^2 = 2x$ **0, $\frac{1}{2}$**

VERTICAL MOTION A *projectile* is an object that is propelled into the air but has no power to keep itself in the air. A thrown ball is a projectile, but an airplane is not. The height of a projectile can be described by the **vertical motion model**.

UNDERSTAND THE MODEL
The vertical motion model takes into account the effect of gravity but ignores other, less significant, factors such as air resistance.

KEY CONCEPT — *For Your Notebook*

Vertical Motion Model

The height h (in feet) of a projectile can be modeled by

$$h = -16t^2 + vt + s$$

where t is the time (in seconds) the object has been in the air, v is the initial vertical velocity (in feet per second), and s is the initial height (in feet).

EXAMPLE 5 Solve a multi-step problem

ARMADILLO A startled armadillo jumps straight into the air with an initial vertical velocity of 14 feet per second. After how many seconds does it land on the ground?

Solution

STEP 1 **Write** a model for the armadillo's height above the ground.

$h = -16t^2 + vt + s$	Vertical motion model
$h = -16t^2 + 14t + 0$	Substitute 14 for v and 0 for s.
$h = -16t^2 + 14t$	Simplify.

STEP 2 **Substitute** 0 for h. When the armadillo lands, its height above the ground is 0 feet. Solve for t.

$0 = -16t^2 + 14t$	Substitute 0 for h.
$0 = 2t(-8t + 7)$	Factor right side.
$2t = 0$ *or* $-8t + 7 = 0$	Zero-product property
$t = 0$ *or* $t = 0.875$	Solve for t.

▶ The armadillo lands on the ground 0.875 second after the armadillo jumps.

AVOID ERRORS
The solution $t = 0$ means that before the armadillo jumps, its height above the ground is 0 feet.

✓ GUIDED PRACTICE for Example 5

6. **WHAT IF?** In Example 5, suppose the initial vertical velocity is 12 feet per second. After how many seconds does the armadillo land on the ground? **0.75 sec**

Extra Example 5

A dolphin jumped out of the water with an initial vertical velocity of 32 feet per second. After how many seconds did the dolphin enter the water?
2 sec

Key Questions to Ask for Example 5

- Can you use the vertical motion model to calculate when a hot air balloon will return to the ground? Explain. **No, a hot air balloon is not a projectile.**
- What steps can you use to solve $-8t + 7 = 0$? **Subtract 7 from both sides of the equation and then divide both sides of the equation by −8.**

Closing the Lesson

Have students summarize the major points of the lesson and answer the Essential Question: How do you solve polynomial equations in factored form?

- **The zero-product property can be used to solve a polynomial equation in factored form.**
- **If a polynomial expression can be factored, rewrite it in factored form before solving the equation.**

If necessary, rewrite the equation so one side is 0 and factor out any monomial factor. Then use the zero-product property to set each factor equal to 0 and find the solutions.

4 PRACTICE AND APPLY

Assignment Guide

Answer Transparencies available for all exercises

Basic:
Day 1: SRH p. 911 Exs. 13–23 odd
pp. 578–580
Exs. 2, 3–15 odd, 16–26, 72–74
Day 2: pp. 578–580
Exs. 1, 27–42, 51–56, 60–70 even

Average:
Day 1: pp. 578–580
Exs. 2, 9–16, 18–26 even, 40–45, 72–74
Day 2: pp. 578–580
Exs. 1, 31–39, 46–49, 51–58, 61–71 odd

Advanced:
Day 1: pp. 578–580
Exs. 2, 10–15, 22–26, 40–45, 72–74
Day 2: pp. 578–580
Exs. 1, 32–39, 46–50*, 52–59*, 60–70 even

Block:
pp. 578–580
Exs. 2, 9–16, 18–26 even, 40–45, 72–74 (with 9.3)
pp. 578–580
Exs. 1, 31–39, 46–49, 51–58, 61–71 odd (with 9.5)

Differentiated Instruction

See *Differentiated Instruction Resources* for suggestions on addressing the needs of a diverse classroom.

Homework Check

For a quick check of student understanding of key concepts, go over the following exercises:

Basic: 5, 18, 28, 34, 51
Average: 10, 22, 31, 36, 52
Advanced: 12, 24, 32, 38, 53

Extra Practice

- Student Edition, p. 946
- Chapter Resource Book: Practice levels A, B, C

Practice Worksheet

An easily-readable reduced practice page (with answers) for this lesson can be found on p. 552C.

9.4 EXERCISES

HOMEWORK KEY
○ = **WORKED-OUT SOLUTIONS** on p. WS21 for Exs. 3 and 55
★ = **STANDARDIZED TEST PRACTICE** Exs. 2, 15, 39, 53, and 56
◆ = **MULTIPLE REPRESENTATIONS** Ex. 58

SKILL PRACTICE

A

1. **VOCABULARY** What is the vertical motion model and what does each variable in the model represent? **See margin.**

2. ★ **WRITING** *Explain* how to use the zero-product property to find the solutions of the equation $3x(x - 7) = 0$. **Set each of the two polynomial factors, $3x$ and $x - 7$, equal to zero and then solve each equation for x.**

EXAMPLE 1 on p. 575 for Exs. 3–16

ZERO-PRODUCT PROPERTY **Solve the equation.**

(3.) $(x - 5)(x + 3) = 0$ **5, −3**
4. $(y + 9)(y - 1) = 0$ **−9, 1**
5. $(z - 13)(z - 14) = 0$ **13, 14**
6. $(c + 6)(c + 8) = 0$ **−6, −8**
7. $(d - 7)\left(d + \frac{4}{3}\right) = 0$ **$7, -\frac{4}{3}$**
8. $\left(g - \frac{1}{8}\right)(g + 18) = 0$ **$\frac{1}{8}, -18$**
9. $(m - 3)(4m + 12) = 0$ **±3**
10. $(2n - 14)(3n + 9) = 0$ **7, −3**
11. $(3n + 11)(n + 1) = 0$ **$-\frac{11}{3}, -1$**
12. $(3x + 1)(x + 6) = 0$ **$-\frac{1}{3}, -6$**
13. $(2y + 5)(7y - 5) = 0$ **$-\frac{5}{2}, \frac{5}{7}$**
14. $(8z - 6)(12z + 14) = 0$ **$\frac{3}{4}, -\frac{7}{6}$**

15. ★ **MULTIPLE CHOICE** What are the roots of the equation $(y - 12)(y + 6) = 0$? **C**

Ⓐ −12 and −6 Ⓑ −12 and 6 Ⓒ −6 and 12 Ⓓ 6 and 12

16. **ERROR ANALYSIS** *Describe* and correct the error in solving $(z - 15)(z + 21) = 0$. **The step of setting each factor equal to zero was left out; $z - 15 = 0$ or $z + 21 = 0$, $z = 15$ or $z = -21$.**

$(z - 15)(z + 21) = 0$
$z = -15$ or $z = 21$

26. A common monomial factor, $3x$, was factored out, but not the greatest common factor, which is $3x^3$; $3x^3(6x^5 - 3x - 2)$.

EXAMPLE 2 on p. 576 for Exs. 17–26

FACTORING EXPRESSIONS **Factor out the greatest common monomial factor.**

17. $2x + 2y$ **$2(x + y)$**
18. $6x^2 - 15y$ **$3(2x^2 - 5y)$**
19. $3s^4 + 16s$ **$s(3s^3 + 16)$**
20. $5d^6 + 2d^5$ **$d^5(5d + 2)$**
21. $7w^5 - 35w^2$ **$7w^2(w^3 - 5)$**
22. $9m^7 - 3m^2$ **$3m^2(3m^5 - 1)$**
23. $15n^3 + 25n$ **$5n(3n^2 + 5)$**
24. $12a^5 + 8a$ **$4a(3a^4 + 2)$**
25. $\frac{5}{2}x^6 - \frac{1}{2}x^4$ **$\frac{1}{2}x^4(5x^2 - 1)$**

26. **ERROR ANALYSIS** *Describe* and correct the error in factoring out the greatest common monomial factor of $18x^8 - 9x^4 - 6x^3$. **See margin.**

$18x^8 - 9x^4 - 6x^3 = 3x(6x^7 - 3x^3 - 2x^2)$ ✗

EXAMPLES 3 and 4 on p. 576 for Exs. 27–39

SOLVING EQUATIONS **Solve the equation.**

27. $b^2 + 6b = 0$ **0, −6**
28. $5w^2 - 5w = 0$ **0, 1**
29. $-10n^2 + 35n = 0$ **$0, \frac{7}{2}$**
30. $2x^2 + 15x = 0$ **$0, -\frac{15}{2}$**
31. $18c^2 + 6c = 0$ **$0, -\frac{1}{3}$**
32. $-32y^2 - 24y = 0$ **$0, -\frac{3}{4}$**
33. $3k^2 = 6k$ **0, 2**
34. $6h^2 = 3h$ **$0, \frac{1}{2}$**
35. $4s^2 = 10s$ **$0, \frac{5}{2}$**
36. $-42z^2 = 14z$ **$0, -\frac{1}{3}$**
37. $28m^2 = -8m$ **$0, -\frac{2}{7}$**
38. $-12p^2 = -30p$ **$0, \frac{5}{2}$**

39. ★ **MULTIPLE CHOICE** What are the solutions of $4x^2 = x$? **C**

Ⓐ −4 and 0 Ⓑ $-\frac{1}{4}$ and 0 Ⓒ 0 and $\frac{1}{4}$ Ⓓ 0 and 4

1. The vertical motion model is the equation $h = -16t^2 + vt + s$, where h is the height (in feet) of a projectile after t seconds in the air, given an initial vertical velocity of v feet per second and an initial height of s feet.

B **FACTORING EXPRESSIONS** **Factor out the greatest common monomial factor.**

40. $20x^2y^2 - 4xy$ **$4xy(5xy - 1)$** 41. $8a^2b - 6ab^2$ **$2ab(4a - 3b)$** 42. $18s^2t^5 - 2s^3t$ **$2s^2t(9t^4 - s)$**

43. $v^3 - 5v^2 + 9v$ **$v(v^2 - 5v + 9)$** 44. $-2g^4 + 14g^2 + 6g$ **$-2g(g^3 - 7g - 3)$** 45. $6q^5 - 21q^4 - 15q^2$ **$3q^2(2q^3 - 7q^2 - 5)$**

HINT
For help with finding zeros of functions, see p. 335.

FINDING ZEROS OF FUNCTIONS **Find the zeros of the function.**

46. $f(x) = x^2 - 15x$ **0, 15** 47. $f(x) = -2x^2 + x$ **$0, \frac{1}{2}$** 48. $f(x) = 3x^2 - 27x$ **0, 9**

C 49. **CHALLENGE** Consider the equation $ab = 0$. Assume that $a \neq 0$ and solve the equation for b. Then assume that $b \neq 0$ and solve the equation for a. What conclusion can you draw about the values of a and b? **0; 0; at least one of them must be 0.**

50. **CHALLENGE** Consider the equation $z = x^2 - xy$. For what values of x and y does $z = 0$? **for $x = 0$ and y any real number, or for all real numbers x and y where $x = y$**

PROBLEM SOLVING

EXAMPLE 5 **A** on p. 577 for Exs. 51–53

51. **MOTION** A cat leaps from the ground into the air with an initial vertical velocity of 11 feet per second. After how many seconds does the cat land on the ground? **about 0.69 sec**

@HomeTutor for problem solving help at classzone.com

52. **SPITTLEBUG** A spittlebug jumps into the air with an initial vertical velocity of 10 feet per second.

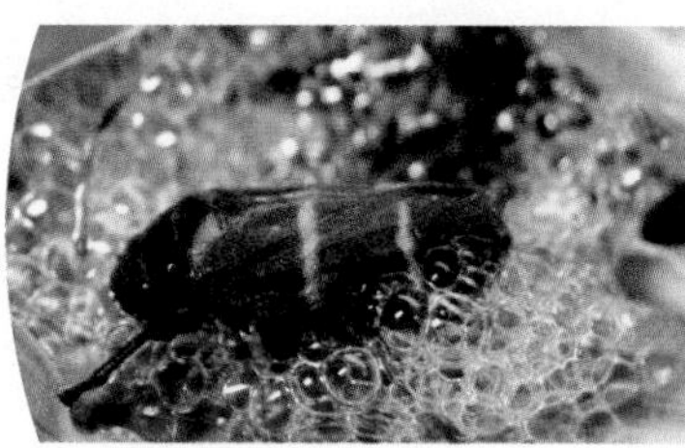

a. Write an equation that gives the height of the spittlebug as a function of the time (in seconds) since it left the ground. **$h = -16t^2 + 10t$**

b. The spittlebug reaches its maximum height after 0.3125 second. How high can it jump?

52b. about 1.563 ft

@HomeTutor for problem solving help at classzone.com

53. ★ **SHORT RESPONSE** A penguin jumps out of the water while swimming. This action is called porpoising. The height h (in feet) of the porpoising penguin can be modeled by $h = -16t^2 + 4.5t$ where t is the time (in seconds) since the penguin jumped out of the water. Find the zeros of the function. *Explain* what the zeros mean in this situation. **See margin.**

VERTICAL MOTION **In Exercises 54 and 55, use the information below.**

The height h (in meters) of a projectile can be modeled by $h = -4.9t^2 + vt + s$ where t is the time (in seconds) the object has been in the air, v is the initial vertical velocity (in meters per second), and s is the initial height (in meters).

54. **SOCCER** A soccer ball is kicked upward from the ground with an initial vertical velocity of 3.6 meters per second. After how many seconds does it land? **about 0.73 sec**

55. **RABBIT HIGH JUMP** A rabbit in a high jump competition leaves the ground with an initial vertical velocity of 4.9 meters per second.

a. Write an equation that gives the height of the rabbit as a function of the time (in seconds) since it left the ground. **$h = -4.9t^2 + 4.9t$**

b. What is a reasonable domain for the function? *Explain* your answer. **See margin.**

Avoiding Common Errors

Exercises 3–14, 27–38 Urge students to pay attention to the sign of each solution. Remind them that they must use properties of equality to solve an equation.

Exercises 17–25 Watch for students who factor a common factor that is not the greatest common monomial factor. Suggest to all students that they check each non-monomial factor to see if the terms still have a common factor.

Graphing Calculator

Exercise 58 Students can check their graphs by graphing $y = -2x^2 + 8x$ on a graphing calculator using the y= key. They can use the trace feature to check the value of y for the given x-values.

53. 0, about 0.28; the zero $t =$ 0 seconds means that the penguin begins at a height of 0 feet in the air as it leaves the water; the zero $t \approx 0.28$ second means that the penguin lands back in the water (at a height of 0 feet in the air) after about 0.28 second.

55b. $0 \leq t \leq 1$; a reasonable domain for the function will cover the time from when the rabbit leaves the ground until the rabbit lands back on the ground; these times t are the zeros of the function, 0 seconds and 1 second.

5 ASSESS AND RETEACH

Daily Homework Quiz

Transparency Available

Solve the equation.

1. $(y + 5)(y - 9) = 0$ **$-5, 9$**

2. $(2n + 3)(n - 4) = 0$ **$-\frac{3}{2}, 4$**

3. $6x^2 = 20x$ **$0, \frac{10}{3}$**

4. $12x^2 = 18x$ **$0, \frac{3}{2}$**

5. A dog jumps in the air with an initial vertical velocity of 18 feet per second to catch a flying disc. How long does the dog remain in the air? **1.125 sec**

Online Quiz

Available at **classzone.com**

Diagnosis/Remediation

- Practice A, B, C in Chapter Resource Book
- Study Guide in Chapter Resource Book
- Practice Workbook
- @HomeTutor

Challenge

Additional challenge is available in the Chapter Resource Book.

58a.

x (feet)	y (feet)
0	0
1	6
2	8
3	6
4	0

58b.

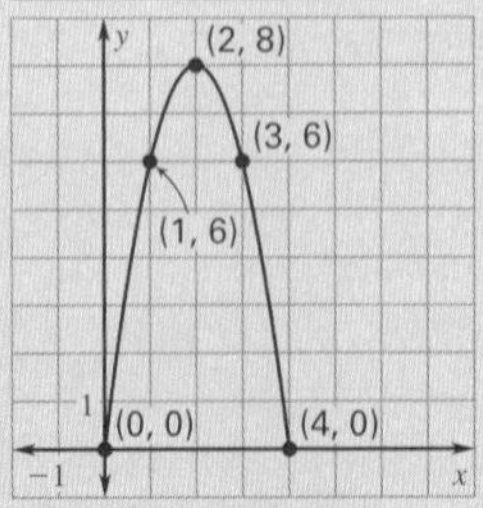

59a–b. See Additional Answers beginning on p. AA1.

B **56.** ★ **MULTIPLE CHOICE** Two rectangular rooms in a building's floor plan have different dimensions but the same area. The dimensions (in meters) are shown. What is the value of w? **B**

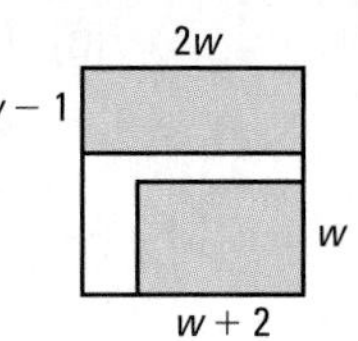

Ⓐ 3 m Ⓑ 4 m Ⓒ 6 m Ⓓ 8 m

57. TABLETOP AREAS A display in your school library sits on top of two rectangular tables arranged in an L shape, as shown. The tabletops have the same area.

a. Write an equation that relates the areas of the tabletops. **$w(w + 2) = w(10 - w)$**

b. Find the value of w. **4 ft**

c. What is the combined area of the tabletops? **48 ft^2**

58. ◆ **MULTIPLE REPRESENTATIONS** An arch frames the entrance to a garden. The shape of the arch is modeled by the graph of the equation $y = -2x^2 + 8x$ where x and y are measured in feet. On a coordinate plane, the ground is represented by the x-axis.

a. **Making a Table** Make a table of values that shows the height of the arch for $x = 0, 1, 2, 3,$ and 4 feet. **See margin.**

b. **Drawing a Graph** Plot the ordered pairs in the table as points in a coordinate plane. Connect the points with a smooth curve that represents the arch. **See margin.**

c. **Interpreting a Graph** How wide is the base of the arch? **4 ft**

C **59. CHALLENGE** The shape of an arched doorway is modeled by the graph of the function $y = -0.5x(x - 8)$ where x and y are measured in feet. On a coordinate plane, the floor is represented by the x-axis. **a, b. See margin.**

a. How wide is the doorway at its base? *Justify* your answer using the zeros of the function.

b. The doorway's highest point occurs above the center of its base. How high is the highest point of the arched doorway? *Explain* how you found your answer.

MIXED REVIEW

PREVIEW Prepare for Lesson 9.5 in Exs. 60–71.

Find the product.

60. $45(-x)(-x)$ *(p. 88)* **$45x^2$**

61. $-9a(-6a)(-a)$ *(p. 88)* **$-54a^3$**

62. $-7(8n)(-4)$ *(p. 88)* **$224n$**

63. $(y - 1)(y + 7)$ *(p. 562)* **$y^2 + 6y - 7$**

64. $(m - 5)(m - 13)$ *(p. 562)* **$m^2 - 18m + 65$**

65. $(2b + 5)(b + 3)$ *(p. 562)* **$2b^2 + 11b + 15$**

66. $(3p + 8)(4p - 1)$ *(p. 562)* **$12p^2 + 29p - 8$**

67. $(5z - 2)(5z - 4)$ *(p. 562)* **$25z^2 - 30z + 8$**

68. $(9t + 7)(4t + 5)$ *(p. 562)* **$36t^2 + 73t + 35$**

69. $(2c + 7)^2$ *(p. 569)* **$4c^2 + 28c + 49$**

70. $(9 - 5w)^2$ *(p. 569)* **$81 - 90w + 25w^2$**

71. $(3g - 4h)^2$ *(p. 569)* **$9g^2 - 24gh + 16h^2$**

Graph the system of linear inequalities. *(p. 466)* **72–74. See margin.**

72. $x > -3$
$x \le 3$

73. $x \ge 0$
$-3x + y < -1$
$y \ge 0$

74. $x < 6$
$y > -4$
$y < 2$
$y \le x$

EXTRA PRACTICE for Lesson 9.4, p. 946 **ONLINE QUIZ** at classzone.com

72.

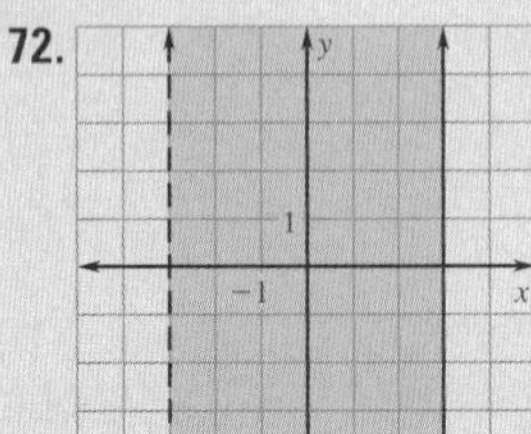

73.

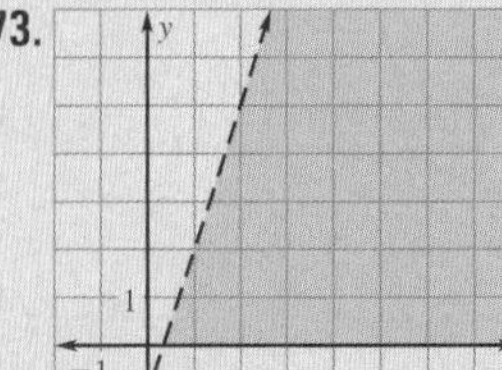

74.

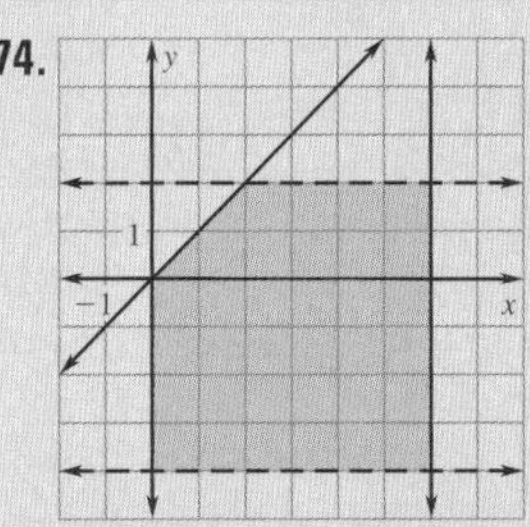

MIXED REVIEW *of Problem Solving*

STATE TEST PRACTICE classzone.com

Lessons 9.1–9.4

1. **MULTI-STEP PROBLEM** You are making a blanket with a fringe border of equal width on each edge, as shown.

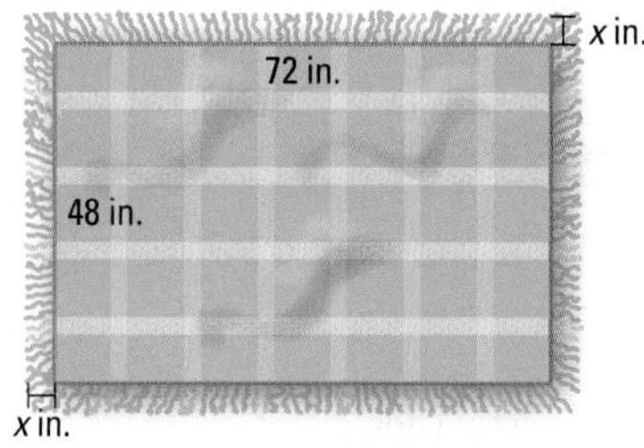

   a. Write a polynomial that represents the total area of the blanket with the fringe. $4x^2 + 240x + 3456$

   b. Find the total area of the blanket with fringe when the width of the fringe is 4 inches. **4480 in.^{2}**

2. **OPEN-ENDED** A horse with pinto coloring has white fur with patches of color. The gene *P* is for pinto coloring, and the gene *s* is for solid coloring. Any gene combination with a *P* results in pinto coloring.

   a. Suppose a male horse has the gene combination *Ps*. Choose a color gene combination for a female horse. Create a Punnett square to show the possible gene combinations of the two horses' offspring. **See margin.**

   b. What percent of the possible gene combinations of the offspring result in pinto coloring? ***Sample answer:* 100%**

   c. Show how you could use a polynomial to model the possible color gene combinations of the offspring. **See margin.**

3. **SHORT RESPONSE** One football is kicked into the air with an initial vertical velocity of 44 feet per second. Another football is kicked into the air with an initial vertical velocity of 40 feet per second. **a, b. See margin.**

   a. Which football is in the air for more time?

   b. *Justify* your answer to part (a).

4. **GRIDDED ANSWER** During the period 1996–2000, the total value *T* (in millions of dollars) of toys imported to the United States can be modeled by

$$T = 82.9t^3 - 848t^2 + 3030t + 9610$$

where *t* is the number of years since 1996. What is the degree of the polynomial that represents *T*? **3**

5. **EXTENDED RESPONSE** During the period 1992–2000, the number *C* (in millions) of people participating in cross-country skiing and the number *S* (in millions) of people participating in snowboarding can be modeled by

$$C = 0.067t^3 - 0.107t^2 + 0.27t + 3.5$$

$$S = 0.416t + 1.24$$

where *t* is the number of years since 1992.

   a. Write an equation that models the total number of people *T* (in millions) participating in cross-country skiing and snowboarding as a function of the number of years since 1992. $T = 0.067t^3 - 0.107t^2 + 0.686t + 4.74$

   b. Find the total participation in these activities in 1992 and 2000. **about 4.74 million people, about 37.7 million people**

   c. What was the average rate of change in total participation from 1992 to 2000? *Explain* how you found this rate. **See margin.**

6. **SHORT RESPONSE** A circular rug has an interior circle and two rings around the circle, as shown.

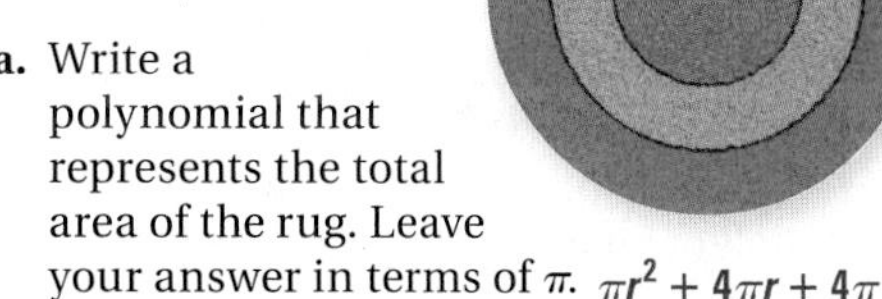

   a. Write a polynomial that represents the total area of the rug. Leave your answer in terms of π. $\pi r^2 + 4\pi r + 4\pi$

   b. The interior circle of the rug has a diameter of 3 feet. What is the area of the rug? Leave your answer in terms of π. *Explain* how you found your answer. **See margin.**

2a. *Sample:*

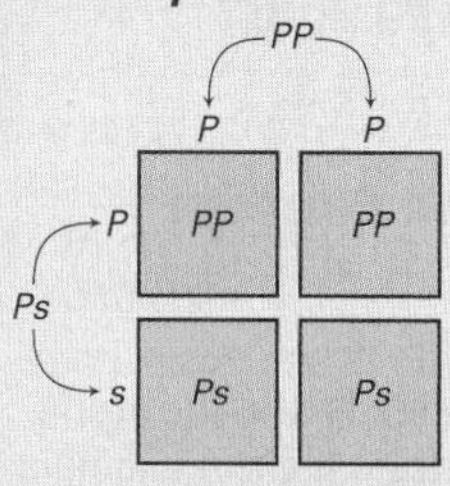

2c. The gene from the father is modeled by $0.5P + 0.5s$ and the gene from the mother is modeled by $0.5P + 0.5P = P$, so the possible gene combinations of the offspring are modeled by $P(0.5P + 0.5s) = 0.5P^2 + 0.5Ps$. Because any gene combination with a *P* results in pinto coloring, both terms represent pinto offspring. The sum of the coefficients, $0.5 + 0.5 = 1$, shows that 100% of the offspring will be pinto.

3a. The football with the initial vertical velocity of 44 ft/sec

3b. The height of the football with the initial vertical velocity of 44 feet per second is modeled by the equation $h = -16t^2 + 44t$, which has zeros $t = 0$ seconds and $t = 2.75$ seconds. The height of the football with the initial vertical velocity of 40 feet per second is modeled by the equation $h = -16t^2 + 40t$, which has zeros $t = 0$ seconds and $t = 2.5$ seconds. The first football stays in the air $2.75 - 2.5 = 0.25$ second longer than the second football.

5c. About 4.12 million people per year; to find the average rate of change, divide the total change in participation from 1992 to 2000 by the number of years from 1992 to 2000: $\frac{(37.7 - 4.74) \text{ million people}}{(2000 - 1992) \text{ years}} = \frac{32.96 \text{ million people}}{8 \text{ years}} \approx 4.12$ million people per year.

6b. 12.25π ft^2; evaluate the polynomial from part (a) when $r = 1.5$: $\pi(1.5^2) + 4\pi(1.5) + 4\pi = 2.25\pi + 6\pi + 4\pi = 12.25\pi$ square feet.

Animated Algebra classzone.com

1 PLAN AND PREPARE

Explore the Concept

- Students will factor a trinomial using algebra tiles.
- This activity leads into the study of factoring trinomials in Example 1 of Lesson 9.5.

Materials

Each student will need:

- algebra tiles
- Activity Support Master (*Chapter Resource Book*)

Recommended Time

Work activity: 10 min

Discuss results: 5 min

Grouping

Students should work individually.

2 TEACH

Tips for Success

If students cannot see that $x + 4$ and $x + 2$ are factors of the trinomial, have them arrange algebra tiles above and to the left of the rectangle to model the factors.

An **Animated Algebra** activity is available online. This activity is also part of **Power Presentations**.

Key Discovery

If 1 is the coefficient of the x^2-term of a factorable trinomial, then the coefficient of the x-term is the sum of the constant terms of the factors.

3 ASSESS AND RETEACH

What factors should you use to factor $x^2 + 7x + 12$? Explain. **4 and 3, because $4 + 3 = 7$ and $4 \cdot 3 = 12$.**

9.5 Factorization with Algebra Tiles

MATERIALS • algebra tiles

QUESTION **How can you factor a trinomial using algebra tiles?**

You have seen that algebra tiles can be used to model polynomials and to multiply binomials. Now, you will use algebra tiles to factor trinomials.

EXPLORE **Factor the trinomial $x^2 + 6x + 8$**

STEP 1 ***Make a rectangle***

Model the trinomial with algebra tiles. You will need one x^2-tile, six x-tiles, and eight 1-tiles. Arrange all of the tiles to form a rectangle. There can be no gaps or leftover tiles. The area of the rectangle represents the trinomial.

STEP 2 ***Find the side lengths***

The side lengths of the rectangle represent the polynomials $x + 2$ and $x + 4$. So, $x^2 + 6x + 8 = (x + 2)(x + 4)$.

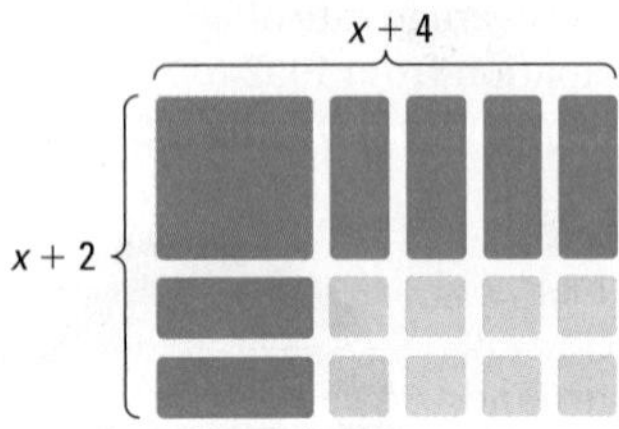

DRAW CONCLUSIONS **Use your observations to complete these exercises**

1. Use multiplication to show that $x + 4$ and $x + 2$ are factors of the polynomial $x^2 + 6x + 8$. $\mathbf{(x + 4)(x + 2) = x^2 + 2x + 4x + 8 = x^2 + 6x + 8}$

Use algebra tiles to factor the trinomial. Include a drawing of your model. **2–7. See margin for art.**

2. $x^2 + 6x + 5$ $\mathbf{(x + 5)(x + 1)}$
3. $x^2 + 9x + 14$ $\mathbf{(x + 7)(x + 2)}$
4. $x^2 + 5x + 6$ $\mathbf{(x + 3)(x + 2)}$
5. $x^2 + 8x + 16$ $\mathbf{(x + 4)^2}$
6. $x^2 + 5x + 4$ $\mathbf{(x + 4)(x + 1)}$
7. $x^2 + 8x + 12$ $\mathbf{(x + 6)(x + 2)}$
8. **REASONING** The factors of the trinomial $x^2 + 6x + 8$ have the form $x + p$ and $x + q$, as shown above. How are p and q related to 6 and 8? $\mathbf{p + q = 6, pq = 8}$

2–7. See Additional Answers beginning on p. AA1.

9.5 Factor $x^2 + bx + c$

Before You factored out the greatest common monomial factor.
Now You will factor trinomials of the form $x^2 + bx + c$.
Why So you can find the dimensions of figures, as in Ex. 61.

Key Vocabulary
- **zero of a function,** *p. 337*

From Lesson 9.2, you know that

$$(x + 3)(x + 4) = x^2 + (4 + 3)x + 4 \cdot 3 = x^2 + 7x + 12.$$

You will reverse this process to factor trinomials of the form $x^2 + bx + c$.

KEY CONCEPT *For Your Notebook*

Factoring $x^2 + bx + c$

Algebra $x^2 + bx + c = (x + p)(x + q)$ provided $p + q = b$ and $pq = c$.

Example $x^2 + 5x + 6 = (x + 3)(x + 2)$ because $3 + 2 = 5$ and $3 \cdot 2 = 6$.

EXAMPLE 1 Factor when *b* and *c* are positive

Factor $x^2 + 11x + 18$.

Solution

Find two positive factors of 18 whose sum is 11. Make an organized list.

Factors of 18	Sum of factors	
18, 1	18 + 1 = 19	✗
9, 2	9 + 2 = **11**	← Correct sum
6, 3	6 + 3 = 9	✗

The factors 9 and 2 have a sum of 11, so they are the correct values of p and q.

▶ $x^2 + 11x + 18 = (x + 9)(x + 2)$

CHECK $(x + 9)(x + 2) = x^2 + 2x + 9x + 18$ **Multiply binomials.**

$= x^2 + 11x + 18$ ✓ **Simplify.**

GUIDED PRACTICE for Example 1

Factor the trinomial.

1. $x^2 + 3x + 2$ **$(x + 2)(x + 1)$**
2. $a^2 + 7a + 10$ **$(a + 5)(a + 2)$**
3. $t^2 + 9t + 14$ **$(t + 7)(t + 2)$**

1 PLAN AND PREPARE

Warm-Up Exercises

Transparency Available

Find the product.

1. $(x + 6)(x - 4)$ **$x^2 + 2x - 24$**
2. $(2y + 3)(y + 5)$ **$2y^2 + 13y + 15$**
3. The dimensions of a rectangular print can be represented by $x - 2$ and $2x + 1$. Write an expression that models the area of the print. What is its area if x is 4 inches? **$2x^2 - 3x - 2$; 18 in.^{2}**

Notetaking Guide

Transparency Available

Promotes interactive learning and notetaking skills.

Pacing

Basic: 2 days
Average: 2 days
Advanced: 2 days
Block: 0.5 block with 9.4
0.5 block with 9.6
- See *Teaching Guide/Lesson Plan.*

2 FOCUS AND MOTIVATE

Essential Question

Big Idea 2, p. 553

How do you factor trinomials of the form $x^2 + bx + c$? **Tell students they will learn how to answer this question by making lists of the possible factors.**

NCTM STANDARDS

Standard 2: Analyze situations using algebraic symbols

Standard 6: Solve problems in math and other contexts

Resource Planning Guide

Chapter Resource Book
- Teaching Guide/Lesson Plan
- Practice levels A, B, C
- Study Guide
- Catch-up for Absent Students
- Application
- Challenge

Workbooks
- Notetaking Guide
- Practice Workbook

Teaching Options
- **Power Presentations** provides dynamic electronic teaching resources for the classroom.
- **Activity Generator** provides editable activities for all ability levels.

Interactive Technology
- Easy Planner
- Power Presentations
- Activity Generator
- Animated Algebra
- Test Generator
- Online Quiz
- eWorkbook
- eEdition
- @HomeTutor

Resources for English Learners
- Spanish Study Guide
- Multi-Language Visual Glossary
- Student Resources in Spanish

See also the *Differentiated Instruction Resources* for more strategies for meeting individual needs.

Motivating the Lesson

Ask students to give examples of situations in which they wanted to find one of the dimensions of an object. After students give some examples, tell them that this lesson teaches them how to find the length or the width of a rectangular figure if they know the other dimension and the area of the figure.

3 TEACH

Extra Example 1

Factor $x^2 + 8x + 12$. $(x + 6)(x + 2)$

Key Questions to Ask for Example 1

- In the Key Concept, what do b and c represent? **b represents the coefficient of the x-term and c represents the constant; in Example 1, b and c are 11 and 18, respectively.**
- What do p and q represent? **p and q represent the constant terms in the binomial factors of the trinomial; $p + q$ is equal to b and $p \cdot q$ is equal to c. In Example 1, p is 9 and q is 2.**

Extra Example 2

Factor $n^2 - 5n + 6$. $(n - 3)(n - 2)$

Key Question to Ask for Example 2

- Why must p and q both be negative when b is negative and c is positive? **Since $c = p \cdot q$, c is positive when p and q are either both positive or both negative. Since b is negative and c is positive, p and q must be negative.**

Extra Example 3

Factor $y^2 + 3y - 10$. $(y + 5)(y - 2)$

FACTORING When factoring a trinomial, first consider the signs of p and q.

$(x + p)(x + q)$	$x^2 + bx + c$	Signs of b and c
$(x + 2)(x + 3)$	$x^2 + 5x + 6$	b is positive; c is positive.
$(x + 2)(x + (-3))$	$x^2 - x - 6$	b is negative; c is negative.
$(x + (-2))(x + 3)$	$x^2 + x - 6$	b is positive; c is negative.
$(x + (-2))(x + (-3))$	$x^2 - 5x + 6$	b is negative; c is positive.

By observing the signs of b and c in the table, you can see that:

- b and c are positive when both p and q are positive.
- b is negative and c is positive when both p and q are negative.
- c is negative when p and q have different signs.

EXAMPLE 2 Factor when b is negative and c is positive

Factor $n^2 - 6n + 8$.

Because b is negative and c is positive, p and q must both be negative.

Factors of 8	Sum of factors	
−8, −1	$-8 + (-1) = -9$	✗
−4, −2	$-4 + (-2) = -6$	← Correct sum

▶ $n^2 - 6n + 8 = (n - 4)(n - 2)$

EXAMPLE 3 Factor when b is positive and c is negative

Factor $y^2 + 2y - 15$.

Because c is negative, p and q must have different signs.

Factors of −15	Sum of factors	
−15, 1	$-15 + 1 = -14$	✗
15, −1	$15 + (-1) = 14$	✗
−5, 3	$-5 + 3 = -2$	✗
5, −3	$5 + (-3) = 2$	← Correct sum

▶ $y^2 + 2y - 15 = (y + 5)(y - 3)$

✓ GUIDED PRACTICE for Examples 2 and 3

Factor the trinomial.

4. $x^2 - 4x + 3$ **$(x - 3)(x - 1)$**
5. $t^2 - 8t + 12$ **$(t - 6)(t - 2)$**
6. $m^2 + m - 20$ **$(m + 5)(m - 4)$**
7. $w^2 + 6w - 16$ **$(w + 8)(w - 2)$**

Differentiated Instruction

Inclusion Some students may have difficulty using and organizing a table. Instead, they can begin by partially writing out the answer, and then fill in the blanks. When discussing **Example 2**, begin by writing $(n - \quad)(n - \quad)$, since p and q are both negative. Then, ask students to try various factors of 8, and add the Outer and Inner terms generated by the FOIL method. Point out that the product $(n - 4)(n - 2)$ is correct because the sum of the Outer and Inner terms is $-2n + (-4n) = -6n$.

See also the *Differentiated Instruction Resources* for more strategies.

EXAMPLE 4 Solve a polynomial equation

Solve the equation $x^2 + 3x = 18$.

$x^2 + 3x = 18$	Write original equation.
$x^2 + 3x - 18 = 0$	Subtract 18 from each side.
$(x + 6)(x - 3) = 0$	Factor left side.
$x + 6 = 0$ *or* $x - 3 = 0$	Zero-product property
$x = -6$ *or* $x = 3$	Solve for *x*.

▶ The solutions of the equation are −6 and 3.

GUIDED PRACTICE for Example 4

8. Solve the equation $s^2 - 2s = 24$. **−4, 6**

EXAMPLE 5 Solve a multi-step problem

BANNER DIMENSIONS You are making banners to hang during school spirit week. Each banner requires 16.5 square feet of felt and will be cut as shown. Find the width of one banner.

ANOTHER WAY
For alternative methods for solving Example 5, turn to page 590 for the **Problem Solving Workshop**.

Solution

STEP 1 **Draw** a diagram of two banners together.

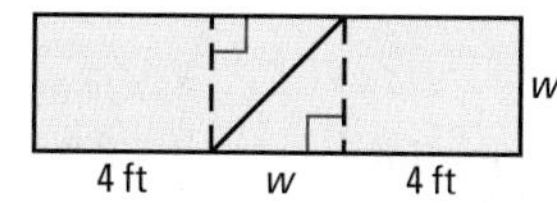

STEP 2 **Write** an equation using the fact that the area of 2 banners is $2(16.5) = 33$ square feet. Solve the equation for *w*.

$A = \ell \cdot w$	Formula for area of a rectangle
$33 = (4 + w + 4) \cdot w$	Substitute 33 for *A* and $(4 + w + 4)$ for ℓ.
$0 = w^2 + 8w - 33$	Simplify and subtract 33 from each side.
$0 = (w + 11)(w - 3)$	Factor right side.
$w + 11 = 0$ *or* $w - 3 = 0$	Zero-product property
$w = -11$ *or* $w = 3$	Solve for *w*.

▶ The banner cannot have a negative width, so the width is 3 feet.

GUIDED PRACTICE for Example 5

9. **WHAT IF?** In Example 5, suppose the area of a banner is to be 10 square feet. What is the width of one banner? **2 ft**

Extra Example 4

Solve the equation $x^2 - 3x = 28$. **−4, 7**

Extra Example 5

You are designing a flag for the school football team with the dimensions shown in the diagram. The shaded region will show the team name. The flag requires 117 square inches of fabric. Find the width *w* of the flag. **9 in.**

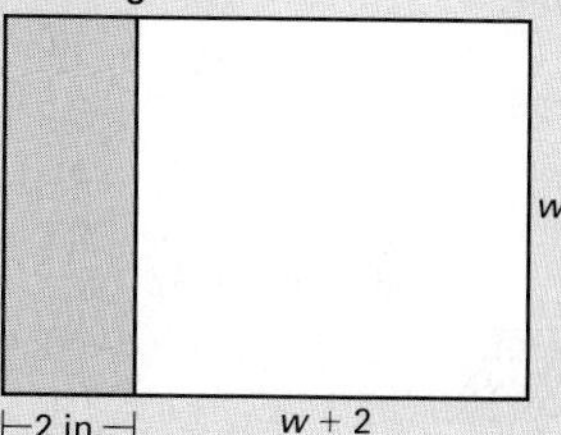

Key Question to Ask for Example 5

- In Step 2, why do you subtract 33 from both sides of the equation? **One side of the equation must be 0 to use the zero-product property.**

Closing the Lesson

Have students summarize the major points of the lesson and answer the Essential Question: How do you factor trinomials of the form $x^2 + bx + c$?

- **To factor $x^2 + bx + c$, find factors of the form $(x + p)(x + q)$ where $p + q = b$ and $pq = c$.**

Find factors of *c* whose sum $p + q$ is *b*. When *b* and *c* are positive, *p* and *q* are positive. When *b* is negative and *c* is positive, *p* and *q* are negative. When *c* is negative, *p* and *q* have different signs.

Differentiated Instruction

Advanced Some students may be interested in learning about Descartes' Rule of Signs. Tell them they can use this rule to determine the maximum number of positive and negative real roots of a polynomial. Suggest that students research the rule and then test it on polynomials in the lesson or on ones they create for their classmates.

See also the *Differentiated Instruction Resources* for more strategies.

9.5 EXERCISES

HOMEWORK KEY
○ = **WORKED-OUT SOLUTIONS** on p. WS21 for Exs. 7 and 61
★ = **STANDARDIZED TEST PRACTICE** Exs. 2, 29, 42, 61, 62, and 63
◆ = **MULTIPLE REPRESENTATIONS** Ex. 64

4 PRACTICE AND APPLY

Assignment Guide

Answer Transparencies available for all exercises

Basic:
Day 1: SRH p. 911 Exs. 1–11 odd
pp. 586–589
Exs. 1–19, 66–73
Day 2: pp. 586–589
Exs. 20–28 even, 29, 30–43, 59–62, 74–80 even

Average:
Day 1: pp. 586–589
Exs. 1, 2, 3–17 odd, 18, 19, 47–55, 66–72 even
Day 2: pp. 586–589
Exs. 21–29 odd, 33–46, 59–64, 74, 78

Advanced:
Day 1: pp. 586–589
Exs. 1, 2, 12–17, 47–58*, 66–72 even
Day 2: pp. 586–589
Exs. 24–29, 34–46, 60–65*, 76, 80

Block:
pp. 586–589
Exs. 1, 2, 3–17 odd, 18, 19, 47–55, 66–72 even (with 9.4)
pp. 586–589
Exs. 21–29 odd, 33–46, 59–64, 74, 78 (with 9.6)

Differentiated Instruction

See *Differentiated Instruction Resources* for suggestions on addressing the needs of a diverse classroom.

Homework Check

For a quick check of student understanding of key concepts, go over the following exercises:
Basic: 4, 10, 13, 22, 59
Average: 5, 11, 15, 25, 60
Advanced: 13, 14, 17, 27, 61

Extra Practice

- Student Edition, p. 946
- Chapter Resource Book: Practice levels A, B, C

Practice Worksheet

An easily-readable reduced practice page (with answers) for this lesson can be found on p. 552C.

SKILL PRACTICE

A

1. **VOCABULARY** Copy and complete: The _?_ of $t^2 + 3t + 2$ are $t + 2$ and $t + 1$. **factors**

2. ★ **WRITING** If $x^2 - 8x + 12 = (x + p)(x + q)$, what are the signs of p and q? *Justify* your answer. **See margin.**

EXAMPLES 1, 2, and 3 on pp. 583–584 for Exs. 3–19

FACTORING TRINOMIALS Factor the trinomial.

3. $x^2 + 4x + 3$ **$(x + 3)(x + 1)$**
4. $a^2 + 6a + 8$ **$(a + 4)(a + 2)$**
5. $b^2 - 17b + 72$ **$(b - 9)(b - 8)$**
6. $s^2 - 10s + 16$ **$(s - 8)(s - 2)$**
7. $z^2 + 8z - 48$ **$(z + 12)(z - 4)$**
8. $w^2 + 18w + 56$ **$(w + 14)(w + 4)$**
9. $y^2 - 7y - 18$ **$(y - 9)(y + 2)$**
10. $n^2 - 9n + 14$ **$(n - 7)(n - 2)$**
11. $x^2 + 3x - 70$ **$(x + 10)(x - 7)$**
12. $f^2 + 4f - 32$ **$(f + 8)(f - 4)$**
13. $m^2 - 7m - 120$ **$(m - 15)(m + 8)$**
14. $d^2 - 20d + 99$ **$(d - 11)(d - 9)$**
15. $p^2 + 20p + 64$ **$(p + 16)(p + 4)$**
16. $x^2 + 6x - 72$ **$(x + 12)(x - 6)$**
17. $c^2 + 15c + 44$ **$(c + 11)(c + 4)$**

ERROR ANALYSIS *Describe* and correct the error in factoring the trinomial.

18. $s^2 - 17s - 60 = (s - 5)(s - 12)$

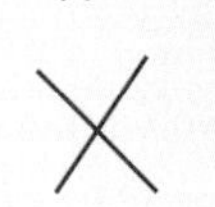

18. In order to have a product of −60, p and q cannot both be negative; $(s - 20)(s + 3)$.

19. $m^2 - 10m + 24 = (m - 12)(m + 2)$

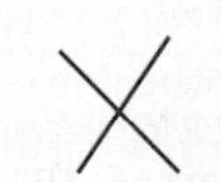

In order to have a product of +24, p and q must have the same sign; $(m - 6)(m - 4)$.

EXAMPLE 4 on p. 585 for Exs. 20–29

SOLVING EQUATIONS Solve the equation.

20. $x^2 - 10x + 21 = 0$ **7, 3**
21. $n^2 - 7n - 30 = 0$ **10, −3**
22. $w^2 - 15w + 44 = 0$ **11, 4**
23. $a^2 + 5a = 50$ **−10, 5**
24. $r^2 + 2r = 24$ **−6, 4**
25. $t^2 + 9t = -20$ **−5, −4**
26. $y^2 - 2y - 8 = 7$ **5, −3**
27. $m^2 + 22 = -23m$ **−22, −1**
28. $b^2 + 5 = 8b - 10$ **5, 3**

29. ★ **MULTIPLE CHOICE** What are the solutions of the equation $x^2 - 8x = 240$? **C**

Ⓐ −20 and −12
Ⓑ −20 and 12
Ⓒ 20 and −12
Ⓓ 12 and 20

B

FINDING ZEROS OF FUNCTIONS Find the zeros of the polynomial function.

30. $f(x) = x^2 + 11x + 18$ **−9, −2**
31. $g(x) = x^2 + 5x + 6$ **−3, −2**
32. $h(x) = x^2 - 18x + 32$ **16, 2**
33. $f(x) = x^2 - 14x + 45$ **9, 5**
34. $h(x) = x^2 - 5x - 24$ **8, −3**
35. $g(x) = x^2 - 14x - 51$ **17, −3**
36. $g(x) = x^2 + 10x - 39$ **−13, 3**
37. $f(x) = -x^2 + 16x - 28$ **14, 2**
38. $f(x) = -x^2 + 24x + 180$ **30, −6**

SOLVING EQUATIONS Solve the equation.

39. $s(s + 1) = 72$ **−9, 8**
40. $x^2 - 10(x - 1) = -11$ **7, 3**
41. $q(q + 19) = -34$ **−17, −2**

2. p and q are both negative; $pq = 12$, so the product pq is positive, which means p and q are either both positive or both negative. Also, $p + q = -8$. In order for p and q to have the same sign and have a negative sum, both p and q must be negative.

42. ★ **SHORT RESPONSE** Write an equation of the form $x^2 + bx + c = 0$ that has the solutions -4 and 6. *Explain* how you found your answer. **See margin.**

GEOMETRY Find the dimensions of the rectangle or triangle that has the given area.

43. Area: 100 square inches **20 in., 5 in.**

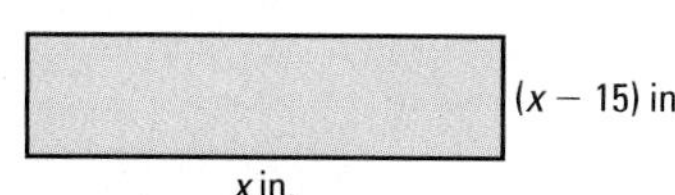

44. Area: 34 square meters **17 m, 2 m**

(x − 4) m

(x + 11) m

HINT In Ex. 45, convert the given area to square yards. Use the conversion factor $\frac{1\text{ yd}^2}{9\text{ ft}^2}$.

45. Area: 702 square feet **26 yd, 6 yd**

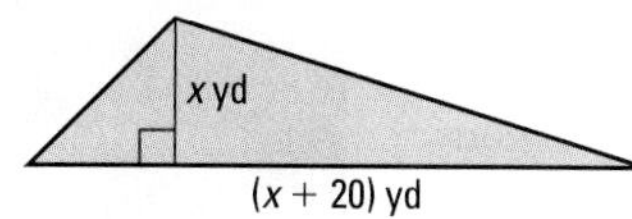

46. Area: 119 square feet **17 ft, 14 ft**

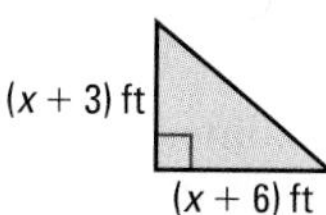

FACTORING TRINOMIALS In Exercises 47–55, use the example below to factor the trinomial.

EXAMPLE Factor a trinomial in two variables

Factor $x^2 + 9xy + 14y^2$.

Solution

To factor the trinomial, you must find factors of the form $x + py$ and $x + qy$.

First, consider the signs of the factors needed. In this example, b is 9, and c is 14. Because both b and c are positive, you must find two positive factors of 14 that have a sum of 9.

Factors of 14	Sum of factors	
14, 1	14 + 1 = 15	✗
7, 2	7 + 2 = 9	← Correct sum

The factors 7 and 2 have a sum of 9, so 7 and 2 are the correct values of p and q.

▶ $x^2 + 9xy + 14y^2 = (x + 7y)(x + 2y)$

47. $x^2 - 4xy + 4y^2$ **$(x - 2y)^2$**
48. $y^2 - 6yz + 5z^2$ **$(y - 5z)(y - z)$**
49. $c^2 + 13cd + 36d^2$ **$(c + 9d)(c + 4d)$**
50. $r^2 + 15rs + 50s^2$ **$(r + 10s)(r + 5s)$**
51. $a^2 + 2ab - 15b^2$ **$(a + 5b)(a - 3b)$**
52. $x^2 + 8xy - 65y^2$ **$(x + 13y)(x - 5y)$**
53. $m^2 - mn - 42n^2$ **$(m - 7n)(m + 6n)$**
54. $u^2 - 3uv - 108v^2$ **$(u - 12v)(u + 9v)$**
55. $g^2 + 4gh - 60h^2$ **$(g + 10h)(g - 6h)$**

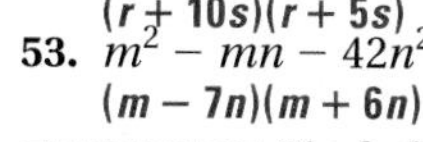

C **CHALLENGE Find all integer values of b for which the trinomial has factors of the form $x + p$ and $x + q$ where p and q are integers.**

56. $x^2 + bx + 15$ **±8, ±16**
57. $x^2 - bx + 21$ **±10, ±22**
58. $x^2 + bx - 42$ **±1, ±11, ±19, ±41**

Avoiding Common Errors

Exercises 3–17 Warn students that it is easy to use the wrong signs when factoring trinomials. After they complete the exercises, suggest that they use FOIL to check the binomial factors against the original trinomials.

Study Strategy

Exercises 20–28 Remind students that they may need to combine like terms or write the equation so that one side is equal to 0.

Teaching Strategy

Exercises 47–55 For each exercise, students can begin by identifying the variable parts of the two factors and confirming that those variables will give the variable part of the middle term of the original trinomial.

42. $x^2 - 2x - 24$; any root $x = r$ of $x^2 + bx + c = 0$ comes from setting the factor $x - r$ equal to zero after $x^2 + bx + c$ is written in factored form; so, the roots -4 and 6 come from the factors $x - (-4)$, or $x + 4$, and $x - 6$. The product of these factors is $(x + 4)(x - 6) = x^2 - 6x + 4x - 24 = x^2 - 2x - 24$.

Teaching Strategy

Exercise 59 If students do not see how to start a solution, tell them that they can use Step 2 in Example 5 as a model for finding the dimensions of the white part of the card.

61. 40 in.; the side lengths of the trimmed photo can be represented by $x - 5$ and $x - 6$; the area of the trimmed photo is 20 square inches, so to find the side length x of the original square photo, solve the equation $(x - 5)(x - 6) = 20$. The equation has two solutions, 10 and 1, but when $x = 1$ inch, both $x - 5$ and $x - 6$ are negative, which does not make sense in this situation. So, $x = 10$ inches, and the perimeter of the original square photo was $4(10) = 40$ inches.

PROBLEM SOLVING

EXAMPLE 5 A on p. 585 for Exs. 59–61

62c. 625 feet does not make sense as a path width in this problem situation because it is wider than the length of either path. In the diagram w is also the side length of the overlapping square. If $w = 625$ feet, the square is larger than either part of the path. Only the solution $w = 5$ feet makes sense as a path width.

59. CARD DESIGN You are designing a gift card that has a border along one side, as shown. The area of the white part of the card is 30 square centimeters. What is the area of the border? **10 cm^2**

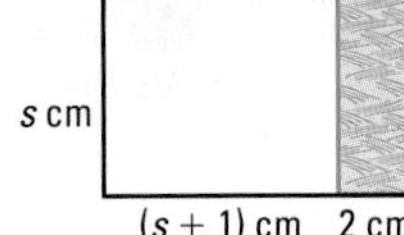

@HomeTutor for problem solving help at classzone.com

60. CONSTRUCTION A contractor is building a porch along two sides of a house. The house is rectangular with a width of 32 feet and a length of 50 feet. The porch will have the same width on each side of the house.

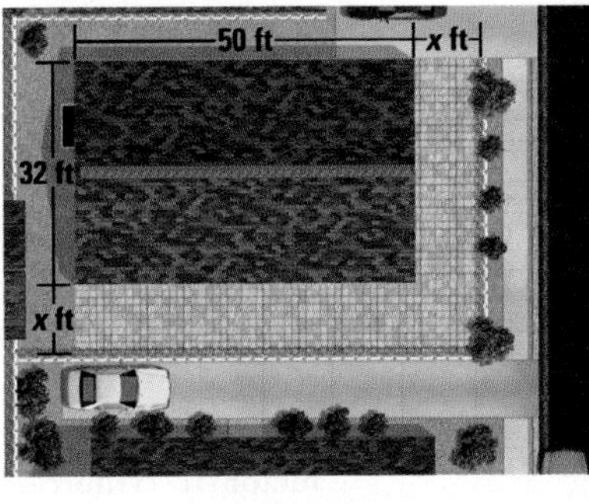

a. Write a polynomial that represents the combined area of the first floor of the house and the porch. **$x^2 + 82x + 1600$**

b. The owners want the combined area of the first floor and the porch to be 2320 square feet. How wide should the contractor build the porch? **8 ft**

@HomeTutor for problem solving help at classzone.com

61. ★ **SHORT RESPONSE** You trimmed a large square picture so that you could fit it into a frame. You trimmed 6 inches from the length and 5 inches from the width. The area of the resulting picture is 20 square inches. What was the perimeter of the original large square picture? *Explain* how you found your answer. **See margin.**

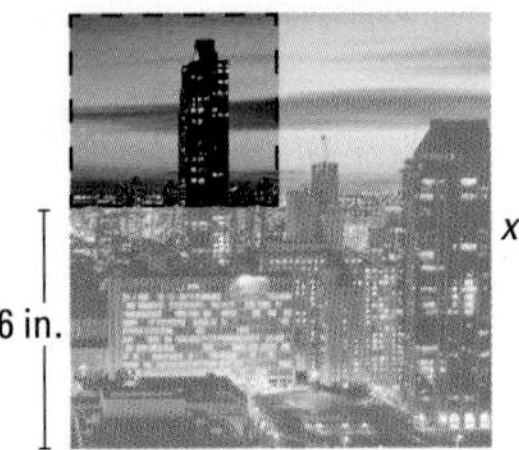

B **62.** ★ **EXTENDED RESPONSE** A town has a rectangular park. The parks department is planning to install two brick paths that will intersect at right angles. One path will be 130 feet long, and the other path will be 500 feet long. The paths will have the same width.

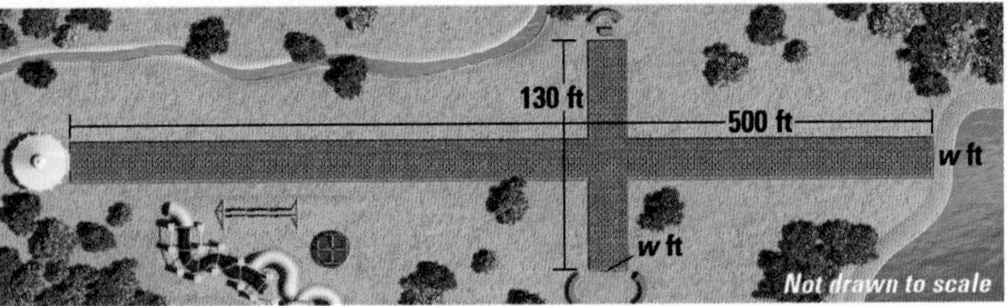

HINT Add the path areas, but subtract the overlap, so that it is not counted twice.

a. Write a polynomial that represents the combined area of the two paths. **$630w - w^2$**

b. The parks department can afford brick for 3125 square feet of path. Write and solve an equation to find the width of the paths. **$630w - w^2 = 3125$; 625, 5; 5 ft**

c. In part (b) you used one solution of the equation to find your answer. *Explain* how you chose which solution to use. **See margin.**

○ = WORKED-OUT SOLUTIONS on p. WS1 ★ = STANDARDIZED TEST PRACTICE ◆ = MULTIPLE REPRESENTATIONS

64a.

x (feet)	y (feet)
2	17
4	21
6	17
8	0

64b.

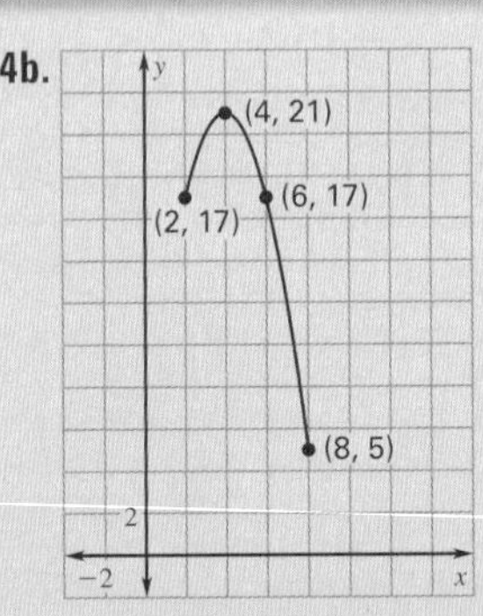

63. ★ **MULTIPLE CHOICE** A square quilt has a border that is 1 foot wide on each side. The quilt has an area of 25 square feet. What is the side length of the quilt without the border? **B**

Ⓐ 2 feet　　Ⓑ 3 feet　　Ⓒ 4 feet　　Ⓓ 5 feet

64. **MULTIPLE REPRESENTATIONS** You toss a set of keys to a friend who is standing at a window 20 feet above the ground in a building that is 5 feet away from where you are standing. The path of the keys can be modeled by the graph of the equation $y = -x^2 + 8x + 5$ where x and y are measured in feet. On a coordinate plane, the ground is represented by the x-axis, and you are standing at the origin. **a–d. See margin.**

a. **Making a Table** Make a table of values that shows the height of the keys for $x = 2, 4, 6,$ and 8 feet.

b. **Drawing a Graph** Plot the ordered pairs in the table as points in a coordinate plane. Connect the points with a smooth curve.

c. **Interpreting a Graph** Based on your graph, do you expect the keys to reach your friend? *Explain* your answer.

d. **Using an Equation** Find the value of x when $y = 20$. (You may need to factor out a -1 in order to factor the trinomial.) What do you notice? *Explain* how the x-value justifies your answer from part (c).

C 65. **CHALLENGE** A rectangular stage is positioned in the center of a rectangular room, as shown. The area of the stage is 120 square feet.

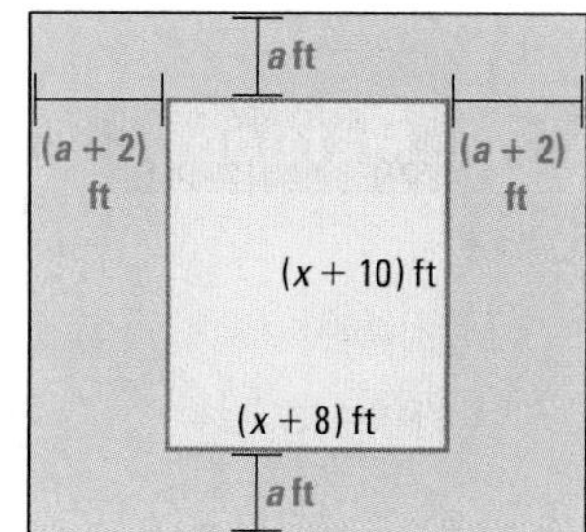

a. Use the dimensions given in the diagram to find the length and width of the stage. **10 ft, 12 ft**

b. The combined area of the stage and the surrounding floor is 360 square feet. Find the length and width of the room. **20 ft, 18 ft**

MIXED REVIEW

Solve the equation.

66. $x + 12 = 4$ *(p. 134)* **−8**

67. $5y - 2 = 13$ *(p. 141)* **3**

68. $6n + 4 = -14$ *(p. 141)* **−3**

69. $3a - 5a + 12 = -6$ *(p. 148)* **9**

70. $3 - 2(w + 7) = -1$ *(p. 148)* **−5**

71. $-6 + 2(d - 9) = 8d$ *(p. 154)* **−4**

72. $(x - 8)(x + 3) = 0$ *(p. 575)* **8, −3**

73. $(3t + 5)(t + 2) = 0$ *(p. 575)* $-\frac{5}{3}, -2$

PREVIEW
Prepare for Lesson 9.6 in Exs. 74–81.

Find the product.

74. $(3x + 7)(x - 5)$ *(p. 562)* $3x^2 - 8x - 35$

75. $(3a - 4)(2a - 9)$ *(p. 562)* $6a^2 - 35a + 36$

76. $(c + 2)(c^2 + c - 4)$ *(p. 562)* $c^3 + 3c^2 - 2c - 8$

77. $(7 + 3y)(7 - 5y)$ *(p. 562)* $49 - 14y - 15y^2$

78. $(2k - 8)(2k + 8)$ *(p. 569)* $4k^2 - 64$

79. $(14 - 2n)^2$ *(p. 569)* $196 - 56n + 4n^2$

80. $(5x + 16y)^2$ *(p. 569)* $25x^2 + 160xy + 256y^2$

81. $(3x - 6y)(3x + 6y)$ *(p. 569)* $9x^2 - 36y^2$

5 ASSESS AND RETEACH

Daily Homework Quiz

Transparency Available

Factor the trinomial.

1. $x^2 - 6x - 16$ $(x + 2)(x - 8)$
2. $y^2 + 11y + 24$ $(y + 3)(y + 8)$
3. $x^2 + x - 12$ $(x + 4)(x - 3)$
4. Solve $a^2 - a = 20$. **−4, 5**
5. Each wooden slat on a set of blinds has width w and length $w + 17$. The area of one slat is 38 square inches. What are the dimensions of a slat? **2 in. by 19 in.**

Online Quiz

Available at **classzone.com**

Diagnosis/Remediation

- Practice A, B, C in Chapter Resource Book
- Study Guide in Chapter Resource Book
- Practice Workbook
- @HomeTutor

Challenge

Additional challenge is available in the Chapter Resource Book.

64c. Yes. *Sample answer:* From the graph it appears that the keys reach a height of 21 feet when they are still 1 foot from the edge of the building (when $x = 4$ feet); when the keys are at the edge of the building ($x = 5$ feet), they have started to fall back down and appear to be at a height of about 20 feet, the height of the window.

64d. 3, 5; there are two points at which the keys reach a height of 20 feet; because you are standing 5 feet from the building, the x-value of 5 feet means that when the keys reach the edge of the building they are at a height of 20 feet.

PROBLEM SOLVING WORKSHOP
LESSON 9.5

Using ALTERNATIVE METHODS

Another Way to Solve Example 5, page 585

MULTIPLE REPRESENTATIONS In Example 5 on page 585, you saw how to solve the problem about a school banner by solving an equation. You can also solve the problem using a table or a graph.

PROBLEM

BANNER DIMENSIONS You are making banners to hang during school spirit week. Each banner requires 16.5 square feet of felt and will be cut as shown. Find the width of one banner.

METHOD 1

Using a Table Consider the separate geometric figures that form one banner and find their areas in terms of w. Then find the total area of the banner for different values of w until you find a value that gives a total area of 16.5 square feet. Use a table to organize your work.

STEP 1 **Write** equations for the area of the pieces and the total area.

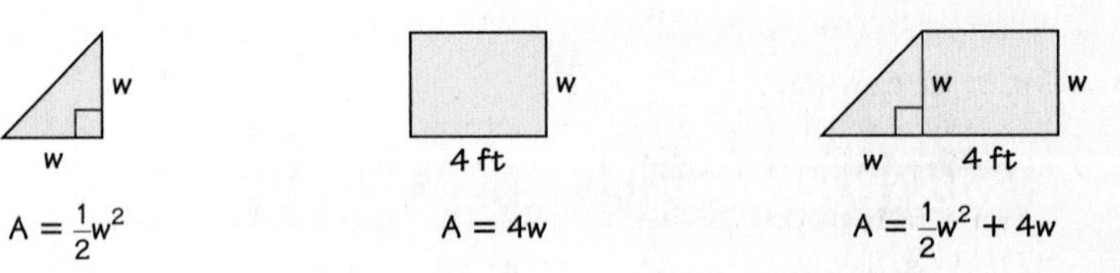

STEP 2 **Organize** your work in a table.

w	Triangle's area $\left(\frac{1}{2}w^2\right)$	Rectangle's area $(4w)$	Total area $\left(\frac{1}{2}w^2 + 4w\right)$	
1	0.5	4	4.5	← $4.5 < 16.5$, so try a greater value of w.
2	2	8	10	← $10 < 16.5$, so try a greater value of w.
3	4.5	12	16.5	← Correct area

▶ The width of the banner is 3 feet.

Alternative Strategy

Example 5 on page 585 can be solved using a table or a graph. Both methods work well for students who prefer to use one of the figures to determine the width of the banner rather than combining the two complex figures. Though both alternative methods require a few more steps to determine an area formula for the figure, many students find it easier to break a figure into its component parts, determine an appropriate formula for each, and then combine the formulas. The table method aids students by using the familiar guess and check strategy in an organized way. The graphing method aids students who prefer visual solutions to problems.

Avoiding Common Errors

Because both the base and height of the triangle are w, some students may write the formula for the area of a triangle as $A = 2\left(\frac{1}{2}w\right)^2 + 4w$. Remind these students to substitute into the area formula $A = \frac{1}{2}bh$ to get $A = \frac{1}{2} \cdot w \cdot w$ or $A = \frac{1}{2}w^2$.

1. 2 ft; Method 1: Use a table. Write the area of the countertop as the sum of the areas of the two triangles and the rectangle: $A = 2\left(\frac{1}{2}w^2\right) + 4w = w^2 + 4w$. Make a table showing the total area A for various values of w and look for the value of w that gives a total area of 12 square feet.

w	Total area ($A = w^2 + 4w$)
1	5
2	12

The total area is 12 square feet when $w = 2$ feet. Method 2: Use a graph. Write the area of the countertop as the sum of the areas of the two triangles and the rectangle: $A = 2\left(\frac{1}{2}w^2\right) + 4w = w^2 + 4w$. Graph the equations $A = w^2 + 4w$ and $A = 12$ on the same coordinate plane.

To use a graphing calculator, enter the equations as $y = x^2 + 4x$ and $y = 12$ in the same viewing window. To find the w-value for which $A = 12$ square feet, use the calculator's *intersect* feature to find that the graphs intersect at (2, 12).

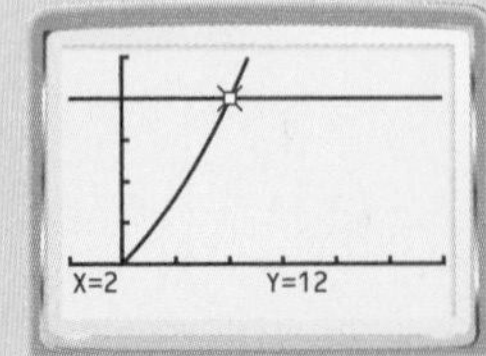

The total area is 12 square feet when the width is 2 feet.

2. The signs are reversed in the factorization of $w^2 + 4w - 12$; $(w + 2)(w - 6)$ gives a middle term of $-4w$ instead of $+4w$. The correct factorization is $(w - 2)(w + 6)$, which leads to solutions of 2 and -6. The width cannot be negative, so the width is 2 feet.

METHOD 2 **Using a Graph** Another approach is to use a graph.

STEP 1 **Write** an equation for the area of the banner. The area of the banner can be thought of as the area of a triangle plus the area of a rectangle.

Area of banner = Area of triangle + Area of rectangle

$$A = \frac{1}{2}w^2 + 4w$$

STEP 2 **Graph** the equation for the area of the banner using a graphing calculator. Graph $y_1 = 0.5x^2 + 4x$. Because you are looking for the value of x that gives an area of 16.5 square feet, you should display the graph of $y_2 = 16.5$ in the same viewing window.

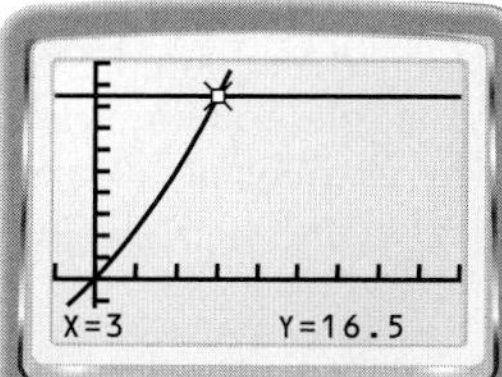

STEP 3 **Find** the intersection of the graphs by using the *intersect* feature on your calculator. The graphs intersect at (3, 16.5).

▶ The width of the banner is 3 feet.

PRACTICE

1–4. See margin.

1. **COUNTER DESIGN** A contractor is building a counter in a kitchen using the diagram shown. The countertop will have an area of 12 square feet. How wide should it be? Solve this problem using two different methods.

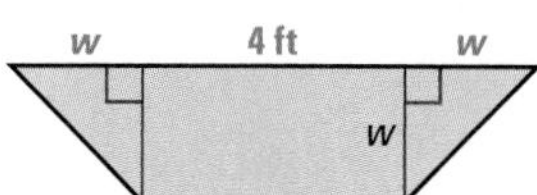

2. **ERROR ANALYSIS** *Describe* and correct the error in using an equation to solve the problem in Exercise 1.

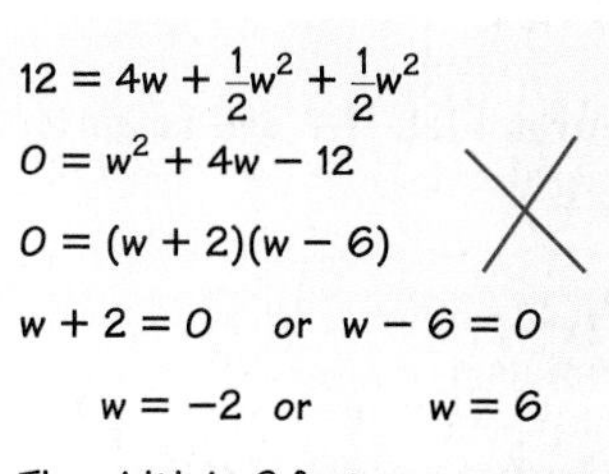

$12 = 4w + \frac{1}{2}w^2 + \frac{1}{2}w^2$

$0 = w^2 + 4w - 12$

$0 = (w + 2)(w - 6)$

$w + 2 = 0$ or $w - 6 = 0$

$w = -2$ or $w = 6$

The width is 6 feet.

3. **FOUNTAIN DESIGN** A square fountain in a city plaza is surrounded by brick patios as shown. The combined area of the fountain and brick patios is 205 square feet. What is the side length of the fountain? Solve this problem using two different methods.

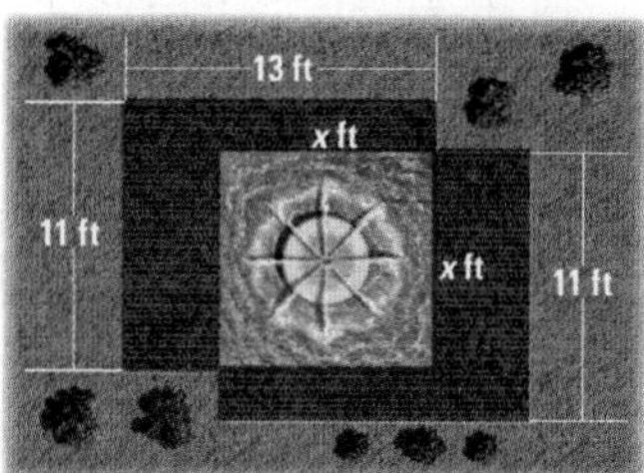

4. **WHAT IF?** You want to make a larger banner using the same pattern shown in the problem on page 585. The new banner will have an area of 24 square feet. Find the width of the new banner. *Describe* the method you used to find your answer.

(Exercise 3 continued)

The combined area is 205 square feet when $x = 9$ feet. Method 2: Use a graph. Write the combined area of the fountain and the brick patios as the sum of the areas of the rectangles minus the area of the fountain (so that the fountain's area is not counted twice): $A = 2(13)(11) - x^2$, or $A = 286 - x^2$. Graph the equations $A = 286 - x^2$ and $A = 205$ on the same coordinate plane. To use a graphing calculator, enter the equations as $y = 286 - x^2$ and $y = 205$ in the same viewing window. To find the x-value for which $A = 205$ square feet, use the calculator's *intersect* feature to find that the graphs intersect at (9, 205).

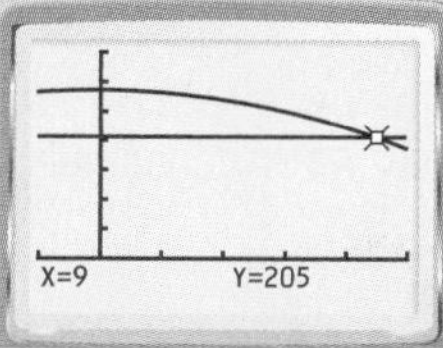

The combined area is 205 square feet when the side length of the fountain is 9 feet.

4. 4 ft. *Sample answer:* Use a graph. Write the area of the banner as the sum of the area of the triangle and the rectangle: $A = \frac{1}{2}w^2 + 4w$. Graph the equations $A = \frac{1}{2}w^2 + 4w$ and $A = 24$ on the same coordinate plane. To use a graphing calculator, enter the equations as $y = 0.5x^2 + 4x$ and $y = 24$ in the same viewing window. To find the w-value for which $A = 24$ square feet, use the calculator's *intersect* feature to find the x-value of the intersection point of the graphs.

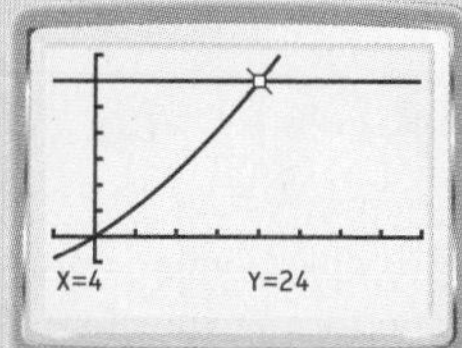

3. 9 ft; Method 1: Use a table. To write a polynomial that represents the combined area of the fountain and the brick patios, find the sum of the areas of the rectangles and subtract the area of the fountain (so that the fountain's area is not counted twice): $A = 2(13)(11) - x^2$, or $A = 286 - x^2$. Make a table showing the combined area A for various values of x and look for the value of x that gives a combined area of 205 square feet.

x	Combined area ($A = 286 - x^2$)
5	261
6	250
7	237
8	222
9	205

Animated Algebra classzone.com

1 PLAN AND PREPARE

Explore the Concept

- Students will use algebra tiles to factor a trinomial.
- This activity leads into the study of factoring a trinomial in Example 1 of Lesson 9.6.

Materials

Each student will need:

- algebra tiles
- Activity Support Master (*Chapter Resource Book*)

Recommended Time

Work activity: 10 min

Discuss results: 5 min

Grouping

Students should work individually.

2 TEACH

Tips for Success

Tell students to begin forming the rectangle by placing all the x^2-tiles at the upper left corner of the rectangle.

Animated Algebra classzone.com

An **Animated Algebra** activity is available online. This activity is also part of **Power Presentations**.

Key Discovery

The leading coefficient of the original trinomial is the product of the leading coefficients of the factors.

3 ASSESS AND RETEACH

Without factoring $4x^2 - 4x - 3$, what are the possible leading coefficients of the factors? Explain. **4 and 1, 2 and 2; their product must be 4, the coefficient of the x^2-term.**

9.6 More Factorization with Algebra Tiles

MATERIALS • algebra tiles

QUESTION How can you factor a trinomial using algebra tiles?

EXPLORE Factor the trinomial $2x^2 + 7x + 3$

STEP 1 *Make a rectangle*

Model the trinomial with algebra tiles. Arrange all of the tiles to form a rectangle. You may have to try a few arrangements to make the rectangle. There can be no gaps or leftover tiles.

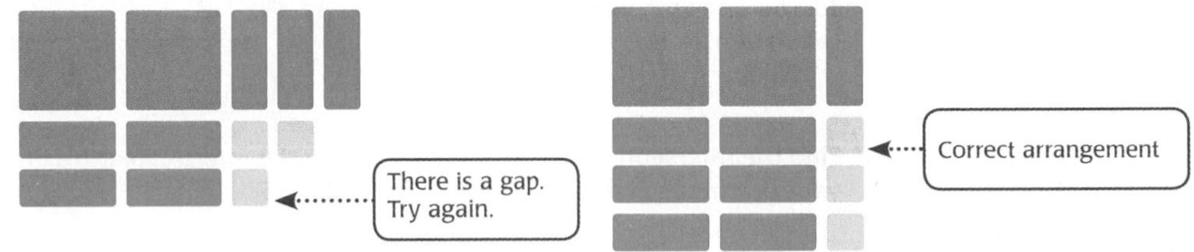
There is a gap.
Try again.
Correct arrangement

STEP 2 *Find the side lengths*

The side lengths of the rectangle represent the polynomials $x + 3$ and $2x + 1$. So $2x^2 + 7x + 3 = (x + 3)(2x + 1)$.

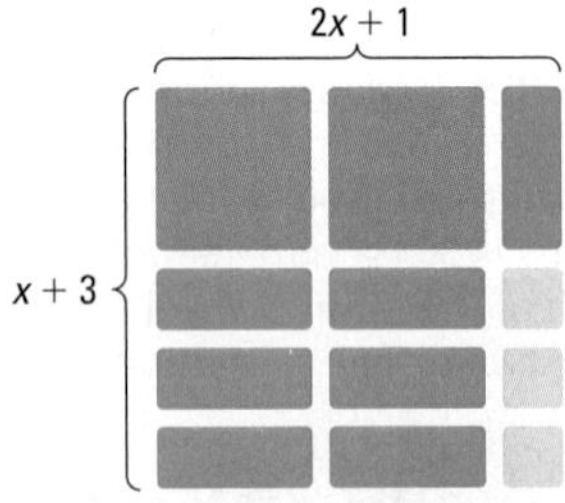
2x + 1
x + 3

DRAW CONCLUSIONS Use your observations to complete these exercises

1. Use multiplication to show that $x + 3$ and $2x + 1$ are factors of the polynomial $2x^2 + 7x + 3$. **$(x + 3)(2x + 1) = 2x^2 + x + 6x + 3 = 2x^2 + 7x + 3$**

Use algebra tiles to factor the trinomial. Include a drawing of your model. **2–7. See margin for art.**

2. $2x^2 + 5x + 3$ **$(x + 1)(2x + 3)$**
3. $3x^2 + 5x + 2$ **$(x + 1)(3x + 2)$**
4. $4x^2 + 9x + 2$ **$(x + 2)(4x + 1)$**
5. $3x^2 + 13x + 4$ **$(x + 4)(3x + 1)$**
6. $4x^2 + 11x + 6$ **$(x + 2)(4x + 3)$**
7. $4x^2 + 8x + 3$ **$(2x + 1)(2x + 3)$**
8. **REASONING** Factor the trinomial $2x^2 + 11x + 5$ into two binomials. How is the leading coefficient of the trinomial related to the leading coefficients of its binomial factors? **$(x + 5)(2x + 1)$; the leading coefficient of the trinomial is the product of the leading coefficients of its binomial factors.**

2–7. See Additional Answers beginning on p. AA1.

9.6 Factor $ax^2 + bx + c$

Before	You factored trinomials of the form $x^2 + bx + c$.
Now	You will factor trinomials of the form $ax^2 + bx + c$.
Why?	So you can find the dimensions of a building, as in Ex. 61.

Key Vocabulary
- **trinomial,** *p. 555*

When factoring a trinomial of the form $ax^2 + bx + c$, first consider the signs of b and c, as in Lesson 9.5. This approach works when a is positive.

EXAMPLE 1 Factor when b is negative and c is positive

Factor $2x^2 - 7x + 3$.

Solution

REVIEW FACTORING
For help with determining the signs of the factors of a trinomial, see p. 584.

Because b is negative and c is positive, both factors of c must be negative. Make a table to organize your work.

You must consider the order of the factors of 3, because the x-terms of the possible factorizations are different.

Factors of 2	Factors of 3	Possible factorization	Middle term when multiplied	
1, 2	−1, −3	$(x - 1)(2x - 3)$	$-3x - 2x = -5x$	✗
1, 2	−3, −1	$(x - 3)(2x - 1)$	$-x - 6x = -7x$	← Correct

▶ $2x^2 - 7x + 3 = (x - 3)(2x - 1)$

EXAMPLE 2 Factor when b is positive and c is negative

Factor $3n^2 + 14n - 5$.

Solution

Because b is positive and c is negative, the factors of c have different signs.

Factors of 3	Factors of −5	Possible factorization	Middle term when multiplied	
1, 3	1, −5	$(n + 1)(3n - 5)$	$-5n + 3n = -2n$	✗
1, 3	−1, 5	$(n - 1)(3n + 5)$	$5n - 3n = 2n$	✗
1, 3	5, −1	$(n + 5)(3n - 1)$	$-n + 15n = 14n$	← Correct
1, 3	−5, 1	$(n - 5)(3n + 1)$	$n - 15n = -14n$	✗

▶ $3n^2 + 14n - 5 = (n + 5)(3n - 1)$

1 PLAN AND PREPARE

Warm-Up Exercises

Transparency Available

Find the product.

1. $(3c + 3)(2c - 3)$ $6c^2 - 3c - 9$
2. $(2y + 3)(2y + 1)$ $4y^2 + 8y + 3$
3. A cat leaps into the air with an initial vertical velocity of 12 feet per second to catch a speck of dust, and then falls back to the floor. How long does the cat remain in the air? **0.75 sec**

Notetaking Guide

Transparency Available

Promotes interactive learning and notetaking skills.

Pacing

Basic: 2 days
Average: 2 days
Advanced: 2 days
Block: 0.5 block with 9.5
0.5 block with 9.7

- See *Teaching Guide/Lesson Plan.*

2 FOCUS AND MOTIVATE

Essential Question

Big Idea 2, p. 553

How do you factor trinomials of the form $ax^2 + bx + c$? **Tell students they will learn how to answer this question by factoring polynomials with positive and negative leading coefficients other than 1 or −1.**

NCTM STANDARDS

Standard 6: Solve problems in math and other contexts

Standard 10: Use representations to communicate mathematical ideas

Resource Planning Guide

Chapter Resource Book
- Teaching Guide/Lesson Plan
- Practice levels A, B, C
- Study Guide
- Catch-up for Absent Students
- Problem Solving Workshop
- Challenge

Workbooks
- Notetaking Guide
- Practice Workbook

Teaching Options
- **Power Presentations** provides dynamic electronic teaching resources for the classroom.
- **Activity Generator** provides editable activities for all ability levels.

Interactive Technology
- Easy Planner
- Power Presentations
- Activity Generator
- Animated Algebra
- Test Generator
- Online Quiz
- eWorkbook
- eEdition
- @HomeTutor

Resources for English Learners
- Spanish Study Guide
- Multi-Language Visual Glossary
- Student Resources in Spanish

See also the *Differentiated Instruction Resources* for more strategies for meeting individual needs.

Motivating the Lesson

Engage students in a discussion about football, baseball, or soccer. Remark that when a ball is kicked, thrown, or hit in the air, sometimes the ball's starting position is some distance above the ground. Tell students that if they know the initial vertical velocity of the ball and the height at which it was kicked or thrown, they can calculate when it will hit the ground.

3 TEACH

Extra Example 1

Factor $2x^2 - 13x + 6$.
$(x - 6)(2x - 1)$

Key Question to Ask for Example 1

- Which terms of the binomial factors do you multiply to find the middle term? **the two outer terms, the two inner terms**

Extra Example 2

Factor $4n^2 + 11n - 3$.
$(n + 3)(4n - 1)$

Extra Example 3

Factor $-3x^2 - 13x - 4$.
$-(3x + 1)(x + 4)$

Key Question to Ask for Example 3

- What are the possible first terms for the binomial factors? What are the possible second terms? **4 and −1, −4 and 1, 2 and −2; 1 and 7; −1 and −7**

GUIDED PRACTICE for Examples 1 and 2

Factor the trinomial.

1. $3t^2 + 8t + 4$ **$(t + 2)(3t + 2)$**
2. $4s^2 - 9s + 5$ **$(s - 1)(4s - 5)$**
3. $2h^2 + 13h - 7$ **$(h + 7)(2h - 1)$**

FACTORING WHEN *a* IS NEGATIVE To factor a trinomial of the form $ax^2 + bx + c$ when a is negative, first factor −1 from each term of the trinomial. Then factor the resulting trinomial as in the previous examples.

EXAMPLE 3 Factor when *a* is negative

Factor $-4x^2 + 12x + 7$.

Solution

STEP 1 **Factor** −1 from each term of the trinomial.

$$-4x^2 + 12x + 7 = -(4x^2 - 12x - 7)$$

STEP 2 **Factor** the trinomial $4x^2 - 12x - 7$. Because b and c are both negative, the factors of c must have different signs. As in the previous examples, use a table to organize information about the factors of a and c.

Factors of 4	Factors of −7	Possible factorization	Middle term when multiplied	
1, 4	1, −7	$(x + 1)(4x - 7)$	$-7x + 4x = -3x$	✗
1, 4	7, −1	$(x + 7)(4x - 1)$	$-x + 28x = 27x$	✗
1, 4	−1, 7	$(x - 1)(4x + 7)$	$7x - 4x = 3x$	✗
1, 4	−7, 1	$(x - 7)(4x + 1)$	$x - 28x = -27x$	✗
2, 2	1, −7	$(2x + 1)(2x - 7)$	$-14x + 2x = -12x$	← Correct
2, 2	−1, 7	$(2x - 1)(2x + 7)$	$14x - 2x = 12x$	✗

AVOID ERRORS
Remember to include the −1 that you factored out in Step 1.

▶ $-4x^2 + 12x + 7 = -(2x + 1)(2x - 7)$

CHECK You can check your factorization using a graphing calculator. Graph $y_1 = -4x^2 + 12x + 7$ and $y_2 = -(2x + 1)(2x - 7)$. Because the graphs coincide, you know that your factorization is correct.

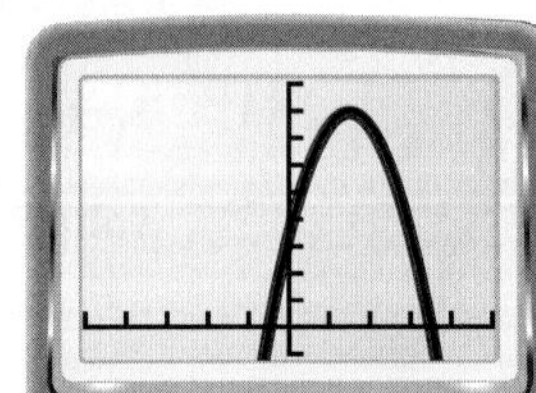

GUIDED PRACTICE for Example 3

Factor the trinomial.

4. $-2y^2 - 5y - 3$ **$-(y + 1)(2y + 3)$**
5. $-5m^2 + 6m - 1$ **$-(m - 1)(5m - 1)$**
6. $-3x^2 - x + 2$ **$-(x + 1)(3x - 2)$**

Differentiated Instruction

Inclusion Organizing a table may be difficult for some students. When discussing **Example 3**, consider adding an additional column for the factors of a and c. Start the table as follows.

Factors of 4		Factors of −7		Possible factorization	Middle term when multiplied
1	4	1	−7	$(x + 1)(4x - 7)$	$-7x + 4x = -3x$

See also the *Differentiated Instruction Resources* for more strategies.

FINDING A COMMON FACTOR In Lesson 9.4, you learned to factor out the greatest common monomial factor from the terms of a polynomial. Sometimes you may need to do this before finding two binomial factors of a trinomial.

EXAMPLE 4 Write and solve a polynomial equation

DISCUS An athlete throws a discus from an initial height of 6 feet and with an initial vertical velocity of 46 feet per second.

a. Write an equation that gives the height (in feet) of the discus as a function of the time (in seconds) since it left the athlete's hand.

b. After how many seconds does the discus hit the ground?

Solution

a. Use the vertical motion model to write an equation for the height h (in feet) of the discus. In this case, $v = 46$ and $s = 6$.

USE VERTICAL MOTION MODEL
For help with using the vertical motion model, see p. 577.

$h = -16t^2 + vt + s$ Vertical motion model

$h = -16t^2 + 46t + 6$ Substitute 46 for v and 6 for s.

b. To find the number of seconds that pass before the discus lands, find the value of t for which the height of the discus is 0. Substitute 0 for h and solve the equation for t.

$0 = -16t^2 + 46t + 6$ Substitute 0 for h.

$0 = -2(8t^2 - 23t - 3)$ Factor out -2.

$0 = -2(8t + 1)(t - 3)$ Factor the trinomial. Find factors of 8 and -3 that produce a middle term with a coefficient of -23.

$8t + 1 = 0$ *or* $t - 3 = 0$ Zero-product property

$t = -\frac{1}{8}$ *or* $t = 3$ Solve for t.

The solutions of the equation are $-\frac{1}{8}$ and 3. A negative solution does not make sense in this situation, so disregard $-\frac{1}{8}$.

▶ The discus hits the ground after 3 seconds.

✓ GUIDED PRACTICE for Example 4

7. **WHAT IF?** In Example 4, suppose another athlete throws the discus with an initial vertical velocity of 38 feet per second and releases it from a height of 5 feet. After how many seconds does the discus hit the ground? **2.5 sec**

8. **SHOT PUT** In a shot put event, an athlete throws the shot put from an initial height of 6 feet and with an initial vertical velocity of 29 feet per second. After how many seconds does the shot put hit the ground? **2 sec**

Extra Example 4

A soccer goalie throws a ball into the air at an initial height of 8 feet and an initial vertical velocity of 28 feet per second.

a. Write an equation that gives the height (in feet) of the soccer ball as a function of the time (in seconds) since it left the goalie's hand. **$h = -16t^2 + 28t + 8$**

b. After how many seconds does it hit the ground? **2 sec**

Key Questions to Ask for Example 4

- Why do you substitute 0 for h in the vertical motion model? **$h = 0$ means that the discus is at 0 height or ground level. You use 0 because you want to find the number of seconds it takes the discus to reach the ground.**
- How could you use the model if you want to know how long it takes the discus to reach a height of 6 feet on the way down? **Substitute 6 for h, get 0 on one side of the equation, and solve.**
- Can you use the model if the vertical motion is given in miles per hour or meters per second? Explain. **No, for this model the motion must be measured in feet per second. You can convert miles per hour to feet per second and then use the model. A different model is used for metric units.**

Extra Example 5

A rectangle's length is 5 feet more than 4 times its width. The area is 6 square feet. What is the width? **B**

Ⓐ $\frac{1}{2}$ ft Ⓑ $\frac{3}{4}$ ft

Ⓒ 2 ft Ⓓ $\frac{4}{3}$ ft

Key Question to Ask for Example 5

- Is there a way to eliminate any of the answer choices? **Since the length of the rectangle is greater than 13 meters and the area is 10 square meters, the width has to be less than 1 meter. You can eliminate all answer choices except A.**

Closing the Lesson

Have students summarize the major points of the lesson and answer the Essential Question: How do you factor trinomials of the form $ax^2 + bx + c$?

- **You can use the factors of *a* and *c* to determine possible terms of the factors.**
- **If the leading coefficient is negative, first factor out −1 from each term of the trinomial.**

The leading coefficient of the trinomial should be positive before you factor. If it is negative, factor out −1 from each term of the trinomial. Then use the signs of *b* and *c* to determine the signs of the second terms. After you determine possible factors of *a* and *c*, find out which of the possible factors gives the middle term of the original trinomial.

2. Enter the polynomial as Y_1 and enter the polynomial in factored form as Y_2. Graph Y_1 and Y_2 in the same viewing window. If the graphs coincide then the factorization is correct.

3. To factor the polynomial that has a leading coefficient of 1, $x^2 - x - 2$, you only need to find factors of the constant term, −2, that add to the coefficient of the middle term, −1. To factor the polynomial that has a leading coefficient that is not 1, $6x^2 - x - 2$, you must also take into account how the factors of the leading coefficient, 6, affect the coefficient of the middle term.

★ EXAMPLE 5 Standardized Test Practice

A rectangle's length is 13 meters more than 3 times its width. The area is 10 square meters. What is the width?

Ⓐ $\frac{2}{3}$ m Ⓑ 3 m Ⓒ 5 m Ⓓ 10 m

$w(3w + 13) = 10$	Write an equation to model area.
$3w^2 + 13w - 10 = 0$	Simplify and subtract 10 from each side.
$(w + 5)(3w - 2) = 0$	Factor left side.
$w + 5 = 0$ *or* $3w - 2 = 0$	Zero-product property
$w = -5$ *or* $w = \frac{2}{3}$	Solve for *w*.

Reject the negative width.

▶ The correct answer is A. Ⓐ Ⓑ Ⓒ Ⓓ

✓ GUIDED PRACTICE for Example 5

9. A rectangle's length is 1 inch more than twice its width. The area is 6 square inches. What is the width? **B**

Ⓐ $\frac{1}{2}$ in. Ⓑ $\frac{3}{2}$ in. Ⓒ 2 in. Ⓓ $\frac{5}{2}$ in.

9.6 EXERCISES

HOMEWORK KEY

○ = **WORKED-OUT SOLUTIONS** on p. WS22 for Exs. 5, 25, and 61

★ = **STANDARDIZED TEST PRACTICE** Exs. 2, 3, 22, 41, 51, and 60

◆ = **MULTIPLE REPRESENTATIONS** Ex. 62

SKILL PRACTICE

A

1. **VOCABULARY** What is another word for the solutions of $x^2 + 2x + 1 = 0$? **roots**

2. ★ **WRITING** *Explain* how you can use a graph to check a factorization. **See margin.**

3. ★ **WRITING** *Compare* factoring $6x^2 - x - 2$ with factoring $x^2 - x - 2$. **See margin.**

EXAMPLES 1, 2, and 3 on pp. 593–594 for Exs. 4–22

FACTORING TRINOMIALS Factor the trinomial.

4. $-x^2 + x + 20$ **$-(x - 5)(x + 4)$**
5. $-y^2 + 2y + 8$ **$-(y - 4)(y + 2)$**
6. $-a^2 + 12a - 27$ **$-(a - 3)(a - 9)$**
7. $5w^2 - 6w + 1$ **$(5w - 1)(w - 1)$**
8. $-3p^2 - 10p - 3$ **$-(3p + 1)(p + 3)$**
9. $6s^2 - s - 5$ **$(6s + 5)(s - 1)$**
10. $2t^2 + 5t - 63$ **$(2t - 9)(t + 7)$**
11. $2c^2 - 7c + 3$ **$(2c - 1)(c - 3)$**
12. $3n^2 - 17n + 10$ **$(3n - 2)(n - 5)$**
13. $-2h^2 + 5h + 3$ **$-(2h + 1)(h - 3)$**
14. $-6k^2 - 13k - 6$ **$-(2k + 3)(3k + 2)$**
15. $10x^2 - 3x - 27$ **$(2x + 3)(5x - 9)$**
16. $4m^2 + 9m + 5$ **$(4m + 5)(m + 1)$**
17. $3z^2 + z - 14$ **$(3z + 7)(z - 2)$**
18. $4a^2 + 9a - 9$ **$(4a - 3)(a + 3)$**
19. $4n^2 + 16n + 15$ **$(2n + 3)(2n + 5)$**
20. $-5b^2 + 7b - 2$ **$-(5b - 2)(b - 1)$**
21. $6y^2 - 5y - 4$ **$(3y - 4)(2y + 1)$**

38. In order to solve an equation by factoring and using the zero-product property, the equation must first be put in the form $ax^2 + bx + c = 0$. The left side of the equation should not be factored until 4 is subtracted from each side, making the right side of the equation zero; $5x^2 + x - 4 = 0$, $(5x - 4)(x + 1) = 0$, $5x - 4 = 0$ or $x + 1 = 0$, $x = \frac{4}{5}$ or $x = -1$; $\frac{4}{5}$, −1.

22. ★ **MULTIPLE CHOICE** What is the correct factorization of $8x^2 - 10x + 3$? **B**

Ⓐ $(2x - 3)(4x - 1)$ Ⓑ $(2x - 1)(4x - 3)$

Ⓒ $(4x + 1)(2x - 3)$ Ⓓ $(8x - 3)(x - 1)$

EXAMPLES 4 and 5 on pp. 595–596 for Exs. 23–39

SOLVING EQUATIONS **Solve the equation.**

23. $2x^2 - 3x - 35 = 0$ $-\frac{7}{2}, 5$
24. $3w^2 + 22w + 7 = 0$ $-\frac{1}{3}, -7$
25. $4s^2 + 11s - 3 = 0$ $\frac{1}{4}, -3$
26. $7a^2 + 2a = 5$ $\frac{5}{7}, -1$
27. $8t^2 - 2t = 3$ $\frac{3}{4}, -\frac{1}{2}$
28. $6m^2 - 5m = 14$ $-\frac{7}{6}, 2$
29. $b(20b - 3) - 2 = 0$ $-\frac{1}{4}, \frac{2}{5}$
30. $4(3y^2 - 7y + 4) = 1$ $\frac{5}{6}, \frac{3}{2}$
31. $p(3p + 14) = 5$ $\frac{1}{3}, -5$
32. $4n^2 - 2n - 90 = 0$ $-\frac{9}{2}, 5$
33. $10c^2 - 14c + 4 = 0$ $\frac{2}{5}, 1$
34. $-16k^2 + 8k + 24 = 0$ $\frac{3}{2}, -1$
35. $6r^2 - 15r = 99$ $\frac{11}{2}, -3$
36. $56z^2 + 2 = 22z$ $\frac{1}{7}, \frac{1}{4}$
37. $30x^2 + 25x = 20$ $-\frac{4}{3}, \frac{1}{2}$

ERROR ANALYSIS ***Describe*** **and correct the error in solving the equation.**

38.
$5x^2 + x = 4$
$x(5x + 1) = 4$
$x = 4$ or $5x + 1 = 4$
$x = 4$ or $x = \frac{3}{5}$

See margin.

39.
$12x^2 + 5x - 2 = 0$
$(3x - 1)(4x + 2) = 0$
$3x - 1 = 0$ or $4x + 2 = 0$
$x = \frac{1}{3}$ or $x = -\frac{1}{2}$

39. The factorization of the polynomial should be $(3x + 2)(4x - 1)$ instead of $(3x - 1)(4x + 2)$; $-\frac{2}{3}, \frac{1}{4}$.

40. **GEOMETRY** The length of a rectangle is 7 inches more than 5 times its width. The area of the rectangle is 6 square inches. What is the width? $\frac{3}{5}$ **in.**

41. ★ **SHORT RESPONSE** The length of a rectangle is 1 inch more than 4 times its width. The area of the rectangle is 3 square inches. What is the perimeter of the rectangle? *Explain* how you found your answer. **See margin.**

B **FINDING ZEROS OF FUNCTIONS** **Find the zeros of the polynomial function.**

42. $g(x) = 2x^2 + x - 1$ $\frac{1}{2}, -1$
43. $f(x) = -x^2 + 12x - 35$ **5, 7**
44. $h(x) = -3x^2 + 2x + 5$ $\frac{5}{3}, -1$
45. $f(x) = 3x^2 + x - 14$ $-\frac{7}{3}, 2$
46. $g(x) = 8x^2 - 6x - 14$ $\frac{7}{4}, -1$
47. $f(x) = 12x^2 - 24x - 63$ $\frac{7}{2}, -\frac{3}{2}$

SOLVING EQUATIONS **Multiply each side of the equation by an appropriate power of 10 to obtain integer coefficients. Then solve the equation.**

48. $0.3x^2 - 0.7x - 4.0 = 0$ $-\frac{8}{3}, 5$
49. $0.8x^2 - 1.8x - 0.5 = 0$ $-\frac{1}{4}, \frac{5}{2}$
50. $0.4x^2 - 0.4x = 9.9$ $-\frac{9}{2}, \frac{11}{2}$

51. ★ **MULTIPLE CHOICE** What are the solutions of the equation $0.4x^2 - 1.1x = 2$? **C**

Ⓐ -12.5 and 40 Ⓑ -4 and 1.25 Ⓒ -1.25 and 4 Ⓓ -0.125 and 0.4

WRITING EQUATIONS **Write a polynomial equation that has the given solutions. The equation must have integer coefficients.** ***Explain*** **your reasoning.** **52–54. See margin.**

52. -3 and 2
53. $-\frac{1}{2}$ and 5
54. $-\frac{3}{4}$ and $-\frac{1}{3}$

C **CHALLENGE** **Factor the trinomial.**

55. $2x^2 - 11xy + 5y^2$ $(2x - y)(x - 5y)$
56. $3x^2 + 2xy - 8y^2$ $(3x - 4y)(x + 2y)$
57. $6x^3 - 10x^2y - 56xy^2$ $2x(3x + 7y)(x - 4y)$

41. $9\frac{1}{2}$ **in.; to find the width, solve the equation $w(4w + 1) = 3$ to get $w = \frac{3}{4}$ or $w = -1$. The width cannot be negative, so the width is $\frac{3}{4}$ inch. Then the length is $4\left(\frac{3}{4}\right) + 1 = 4$ inches, and the perimeter is $2\left(\frac{3}{4}\right) + 2(4) = 9\frac{1}{2}$ inches.**

52–54. See Additional Answers beginning on p. AA1.

4 PRACTICE AND APPLY

Assignment Guide

Answer Transparencies available for all exercises

Basic:
Day 1: pp. 596–599
Exs. 1–22, 64–72 even
Day 2: pp. 596–599
Exs. 23–37 odd, 38–45, 58–62, 73–81 odd

Average:
Day 1: pp. 596–599
Exs. 1–3, 8–21, 52–55, 65–71 odd
Day 2: pp. 596–599
Exs. 26–38 even, 39–51, 58–62, 74, 77, 80

Advanced:
Day 1: pp. 596–599
Exs. 1–3, 12–21, 52–57*, 65–71 odd
Day 2: pp. 596–599
Exs. 30–37, 40–51, 58–63*, 75, 78, 81

Block:
pp. 596–599
Exs. 1–3, 8–21, 52–55, 65–71 odd (with 9.5)
pp. 596–599
Exs. 26–38 even, 39–51, 58–62, 74, 77, 80 (with 9.7)

Differentiated Instruction

See *Differentiated Instruction Resources* for suggestions on addressing the needs of a diverse classroom.

Homework Check

For a quick check of student understanding of key concepts, go over the following exercises:
Basic: 7, 10, 13, 27, 59
Average: 12, 14, 18, 30, 60
Advanced: 17, 20, 21, 58, 61

Extra Practice

- Student Edition, p. 946
- Chapter Resource Book: Practice levels A, B, C

Practice Worksheet

An easily-readable reduced practice page (with answers) for this lesson can be found on p. 552C.

Avoiding Common Errors

Exercises 4–21 Remind students to factor out −1 before they factor trinomials with a negative leading coefficient. Remind them to include it after they have factored the trinomial.

Graphing Calculator

Exercises 4–21 Have students use a graphing calculator to check their factorizations. They can graph the trinomial and the factorization in the same viewing window using a thin line and a thick line. If the graphs do not coincide, they can try different factors.

Vocabulary

Exercise 58 Some students may not know what "center of gravity" means. Explain that *center of gravity* generally means the point on which a person or object will balance.

An **Animated Algebra** activity is available online for **Exercise 62**. This activity is also part of **Power Presentations**.

Exercise 62 For more information about serval cats, visit the African Wildlife Foundation's website www.awf.org/wildlives/185

60. 2 sec; the ball's height (in feet) is modeled by the equation $h = -16t^2 + 31t + 6$, where t is the time (in seconds) since you threw it. To find when the height is 4 feet, substitute 4 for h. Solve the equation $4 = -16t^2 + 31t + 6$, or $16t^2 - 31t - 2 = 0$. The roots of this equation are $-\frac{1}{16}$ and 2. The time t cannot be negative, so disregard the root $-\frac{1}{16}$; the ball reaches a height of 4 feet after 2 seconds.

PROBLEM SOLVING

EXAMPLE 4 on p. 595 for Exs. 58, 60

[A]

58. DIVING A diver dives from a cliff when her center of gravity is 46 feet above the surface of the water. Her initial vertical velocity leaving the cliff is 9 feet per second. After how many seconds does her center of gravity enter the water? **2 sec**

@HomeTutor for problem solving help at classzone.com

EXAMPLE 5 on p. 596 for Exs. 59, 61

59. SCRAPBOOK DESIGN You plan to make a scrapbook. On the cover, you want to show three pictures with space between them, as shown. Each of the pictures is twice as long as it is wide.

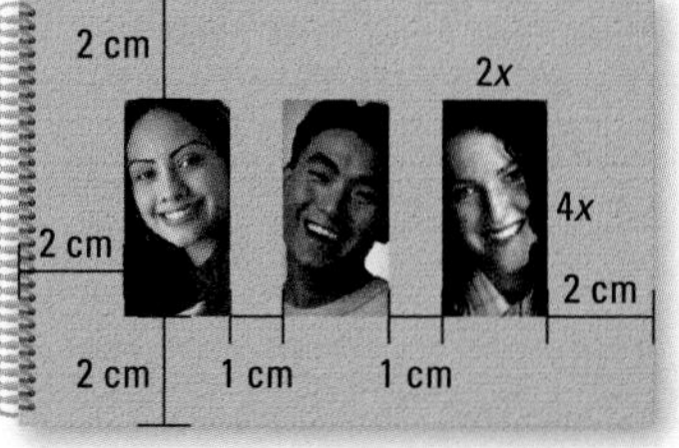

a. Write a polynomial that represents the area of the scrapbook cover. **$24x^2 + 48x + 24$**

b. The area of the cover will be 96 square centimeters. Find the length and width of the pictures you will use. **4 cm, 2 cm**

@HomeTutor for problem solving help at classzone.com

60. ★ SHORT RESPONSE You throw a ball into the air with an initial vertical velocity of 31 feet per second. The ball leaves your hand when it is 6 feet above the ground. You catch the ball when it reaches a height of 4 feet. After how many seconds do you catch the ball? *Explain* how you can use the solutions of an equation to find your answer. **See margin.**

(61.) PARTHENON The Parthenon in Athens, Greece, is an ancient structure that has a rectangular base. The length of the Parthenon's base is 8 meters more than twice its width. The area of the base is about 2170 square meters. Find the length and width of the Parthenon's base. **70 m, 31 m**

[B]

62. ◆ MULTIPLE REPRESENTATIONS An African cat called a serval leaps from the ground in an attempt to catch a bird. The serval's initial vertical velocity is 24 feet per second.

a. **Writing an Equation** Write an equation that gives the serval's height (in feet) as a function of the time (in seconds) since it left the ground. **$h = -16t^2 + 24t$**

b. **Making a Table** Use the equation from part (a) to make a table that shows the height of the serval for $t = 0, 0.3, 0.6, 0.9, 1.2,$ and 1.5 seconds. **See margin.**

c. **Drawing a Graph** Plot the ordered pairs in the table as points in a coordinate plane. Connect the points with a smooth curve. After how many seconds does the serval reach a height of 9 feet? *Justify* your answer using the equation from part (a).

Animated Algebra at classzone.com

See margin for art; 0.75 sec; substitute $h = 9$ feet into the equation $h = -16t^2 + 24t$ and solve for t, $t = 0.75$ second.

○ = WORKED-OUT SOLUTIONS on p. WS1 ★ = STANDARDIZED TEST PRACTICE ◆ = MULTIPLE REPRESENTATIONS

62b.

x (feet)	y (feet)
0	0
0.3	5.76
0.6	8.64
0.9	8.64
1.2	5.76
1.5	0

62c.

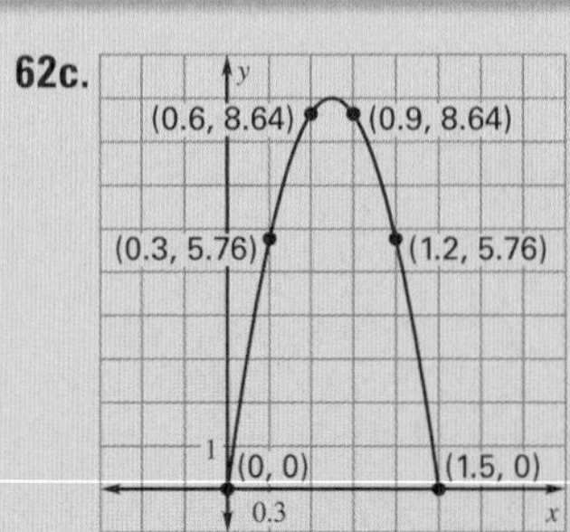

 **63. CHALLENGE** A bush cricket jumps from the ground into the air with an initial vertical velocity of 4 feet per second.

a. Write an equation that gives the cricket's height (in feet) as a function of the time (in seconds) since it left the ground. **$h = -16t^2 + 4t$**

b. After how many seconds is the cricket 3 inches off the ground? **0.125 sec**

c. Does the cricket jump higher than 3 inches? *Explain* your reasoning using your answer from part (b). **See margin.**

MIXED REVIEW

Check whether the given number is a solution of the equation or inequality.

64. $b - 9 = 18;\ 3$ *(p. 21)* **not a solution**
65. $8 - 3h = 2;\ 2$ *(p. 21)* **solution**
66. $\frac{28 - 2x}{x} < 5;\ 4$ *(p. 21)* **not a solution**
67. $6t + 18 = 0;\ -3$ *(p. 21)* **solution**
68. $6c = 3c;\ 2$ *(p. 21)* **not a solution**
69. $|x + 3| = 2;\ -5$ *(p. 64)* **solution**
70. $|y - 2| + 6 = 5;\ 1$ *(p. 64)* **not a solution**
71. $|3n - 11| < 1;\ 2$ *(p. 64)* **not a solution**
72. $4|3a - 8| > 2;\ 3$ *(p. 64)* **solution**

PREVIEW Prepare for Lesson 9.7 in Exs. 73–81.

Find the product. *(p. 569)*

73. $(a - 9)^2$ **$a^2 - 18a + 81$**
74. $(k + 12)^2$ **$k^2 + 24k + 144$**
75. $(3x - 2)^2$ **$9x^2 - 12x + 4$**
76. $(m + 4)(m - 4)$ **$m^2 - 16$**
77. $(2c + 1)(2c - 1)$ **$4c^2 - 1$**
78. $(5n - 3)(5n + 3)$ **$25n^2 - 9$**
79. $(8 - 3y)^2$ **$64 - 48y + 9y^2$**
80. $(2s - 5t)^2$ **$4s^2 - 20st + 25t^2$**
81. $(x + 2y)(x - 2y)$ **$x^2 - 4y^2$**

QUIZ *for Lessons 9.4–9.6*

Factor out the greatest common monomial factor. *(p. 575)*

1. $16a^2 - 40b$ **$8(2a^2 - 5b)$**
2. $9xy^2 + 6x^2y$ **$3xy(3y + 2x)$**
3. $4n^4 - 22n^3 - 8n^2$ **$2n^2(2n^2 - 11n - 4)$**
4. $3x^2 + 6xy - 3y^2$ **$3(x^2 + 2xy - y^2)$**
5. $12abc^2 - 6a^2c$ **$6ac(2bc - a)$**
6. $-36s^3 + 18s^2 - 54s$ **$-18s(2s^2 - s + 3)$**

Factor the trinomial.

7. $r^2 + 15r + 56$ *(p. 583)* **$(r + 7)(r + 8)$**
8. $s^2 - 6s + 5$ *(p. 583)* **$(s - 5)(s - 1)$**
9. $w^2 + 6w - 40$ *(p. 583)* **$(w + 10)(w - 4)$**
10. $-a^2 + 9a + 22$ *(p. 593)* **$-(a - 11)(a + 2)$**
11. $2x^2 - 9x + 4$ *(p. 593)* **$(2x - 1)(x - 4)$**
12. $5m^2 + m - 6$ *(p. 593)* **$(5m + 6)(m - 1)$**
13. $6h^2 - 19h + 3$ *(p. 593)* **$(6h - 1)(h - 3)$**
14. $-7y^2 - 23y - 6$ *(p. 593)* **$-(7y + 2)(y + 3)$**
15. $18c^2 + 12c - 6$ *(p. 593)* **$6(3c - 1)(c + 1)$**

Solve the equation.

16. $(4p - 7)(p + 5) = 0$ *(p. 575)* **$\frac{7}{4}, -5$**
17. $-8u^2 + 28u = 0$ *(p. 575)* **$0, \frac{7}{2}$**
18. $51x^2 = -17x$ *(p. 575)* **$0, -\frac{1}{3}$**
19. $b^2 - 11b = -24$ *(p. 583)* **3, 8**
20. $m^2 + 12m = -35$ *(p. 583)* **−7, −5**
21. $q^2 + 19 = -20q$ *(p. 583)* **−19, −1**
22. $3t^2 - 11t + 10 = 0$ *(p. 593)* **$\frac{5}{3}, 2$**
23. $4y^2 + 31y = 8$ *(p. 593)* **$\frac{1}{4}, -8$**
24. $14s^2 + 12s = 2$ *(p. 593)* **$\frac{1}{7}, -1$**

25. **BASEBALL** A baseball player hits a baseball into the air with an initial vertical velocity of 72 feet per second. The player hits the ball from a height of 3 feet. *(p. 593)*

a. Write an equation that gives the baseball's height as a function of the time (in seconds) after it is hit. **$h = -16t^2 + 72t + 3$**

b. After how many seconds is the baseball 84 feet above the ground? **2.25 sec**

5 ASSESS AND RETEACH

Daily Homework Quiz

Transparency Available

Factor the trinomial.

1. $-x^2 + x + 30$ **$-(x + 5)(x - 6)$**
2. $5b^2 + 3b - 14$ **$(b + 2)(5b - 7)$**
3. $6y^2 - 13y - 5$ **$(3y + 1)(2y - 5)$**
4. Solve $2x^2 + 7x = -3$. **$-\frac{1}{2}, -3$**
5. A baseball is hit into the air at an initial height of 4 feet and an initial vertical velocity of 30 feet per second. For how many seconds is it in the air? **2 sec**

 **Online Quiz**

Available at **classzone.com**

Diagnosis/Remediation

- Practice A, B, C in Chapter Resource Book
- Study Guide in Chapter Resource Book
- Practice Workbook
- @HomeTutor

Challenge

Additional challenge is available in the Chapter Resource Book.

Quiz

An easily-readable reduced copy of the quiz (with answers) on Lessons 9.4–9.6 from the Assessment Book can be found on p. 552E.

63c. No; $t = 0.125$ is the only solution of the equation $\frac{1}{4} = -16t^2 + 4t$, so the cricket is 3 inches off the ground only once. This happens only at the highest point of the cricket's jump; all other heights are reached twice, once on the way up and once on the way down.

9.7 Factor Special Products

Before You factored polynomials of the form $ax^2 + bx + c$.

Now You will factor special products.

Why? So you can use a scientific model, as in Ex. 48.

1 PLAN AND PREPARE

Warm-Up Exercises

Transparency Available

Find the product.

1. $(m + 2)(m - 2)$ **$m^2 - 4$**
2. $(2y - 3)^2$ **$4y^2 - 12y + 9$**
3. $(s + 2t)(s - 2t)$ **$s^2 - 4t^2$**
4. A football is thrown in the air at an initial height of 5 feet and an initial vertical velocity of 16 feet per second. After how many seconds does it hit the ground? **1.25 sec**

Notetaking Guide

Transparency Available

Promotes interactive learning and notetaking skills.

Pacing

Basic: 1 day
Average: 1 day
Advanced: 1 day
Block: 0.5 block with 9.6
- See *Teaching Guide/Lesson Plan.*

2 FOCUS AND MOTIVATE

Essential Question

Big Idea 2, p. 553

How do you factor special products? **Tell students they will learn how to answer this question by using the difference of two squares pattern and the perfect square trinomial patterns.**

NCTM STANDARDS

Standard 2: Understand patterns; Analyze situations using algebraic symbols

Key Vocabulary
- **perfect square trinomial**

You can use the special product patterns you studied in Lesson 9.3 to factor polynomials, such as the difference of two squares.

KEY CONCEPT *For Your Notebook*

Difference of Two Squares Pattern

Algebra	Example
$a^2 - b^2 = (a + b)(a - b)$	$4x^2 - 9 = (2x)^2 - 3^2 = (2x + 3)(2x - 3)$

EXAMPLE 1 Factor the difference of two squares

Factor the polynomial.

a. $y^2 - 16 = y^2 - 4^2$ — **Write as $a^2 - b^2$.**

$= (y + 4)(y - 4)$ — **Difference of two squares pattern**

b. $25m^2 - 36 = (5m)^2 - 6^2$ — **Write as $a^2 - b^2$.**

$= (5m + 6)(5m - 6)$ — **Difference of two squares pattern**

c. $x^2 - 49y^2 = x^2 - (7y)^2$ — **Write as $a^2 - b^2$.**

$= (x + 7y)(x - 7y)$ — **Difference of two squares pattern**

EXAMPLE 2 Factor the difference of two squares

Factor the polynomial $8 - 18n^2$.

$8 - 18n^2 = 2(4 - 9n^2)$ — **Factor out common factor.**

$= 2[2^2 - (3n)^2]$ — **Write $4 - 9n^2$ as $a^2 - b^2$.**

$= 2(2 + 3n)(2 - 3n)$ — **Difference of two squares pattern**

GUIDED PRACTICE for Examples 1 and 2

1. Factor the polynomial $4y^2 - 64$. **$4(y - 4)(y + 4)$**

Resource Planning Guide

Chapter Resource Book
- Teaching Guide/Lesson Plan
- Practice levels A, B, C
- Study Guide
- Catch-up for Absent Students
- Application
- Challenge

Workbooks
- Notetaking Guide
- Practice Workbook

Teaching Options
- **Power Presentations** provides dynamic electronic teaching resources for the classroom.
- **Activity Generator** provides editable activities for all ability levels.

Interactive Technology
- Easy Planner
- Power Presentations
- Activity Generator
- Animated Algebra
- Test Generator
- Online Quiz
- eWorkbook
- eEdition
- @HomeTutor

Resources for English Learners
- Spanish Study Guide
- Multi-Language Visual Glossary
- Student Resources in Spanish

See also the *Differentiated Instruction Resources* for more strategies for meeting individual needs.

PERFECT SQUARE TRINOMIALS The pattern for finding the square of a binomial gives you the pattern for factoring trinomials of the form $a^2 + 2ab + b^2$ and $a^2 - 2ab + b^2$. These are called **perfect square trinomials**.

KEY CONCEPT *For Your Notebook*

Perfect Square Trinomial Pattern

Algebra	Example
$a^2 + 2ab + b^2 = (a + b)^2$	$x^2 + 6x + 9 = x^2 + 2(x \cdot 3) + 3^2 = (x + 3)^2$
$a^2 - 2ab + b^2 = (a - b)^2$	$x^2 - 10x + 25 = x^2 - 2(x \cdot 5) + 5^2 = (x - 5)^2$

EXAMPLE 3 Factor perfect square trinomials

Factor the polynomial.

a. $n^2 - 12n + 36 = n^2 - 2(n \cdot 6) + 6^2$ Write as $a^2 - 2ab + b^2$.

$= (n - 6)^2$ Perfect square trinomial pattern

b. $9x^2 - 12x + 4 = (3x)^2 - 2(3x \cdot 2) + 2^2$ Write as $a^2 - 2ab + b^2$.

$= (3x - 2)^2$ Perfect square trinomial pattern

c. $4s^2 + 4st + t^2 = (2s)^2 + 2(2s \cdot t) + t^2$ Write as $a^2 + 2ab + b^2$.

$= (2s + t)^2$ Perfect square trinomial pattern

Animated Algebra at classzone.com

EXAMPLE 4 Factor a perfect square trinomial

Factor the polynomial $-3y^2 + 36y - 108$.

$-3y^2 + 36y - 108 = -3(y^2 - 12y + 36)$ Factor out -3.

$= -3[y^2 - 2(y \cdot 6) + 6^2]$ Write $y^2 - 12y + 36$ as $a^2 - 2ab + b^2$.

$= -3(y - 6)^2$ Perfect square trinomial pattern

CHECK Check your factorization using a graphing calculator. Graph $y_1 = -3x^2 + 36x - 108$ and $y_2 = -3(x - 6)^2$. Because the graphs coincide, you know that your factorization is correct.

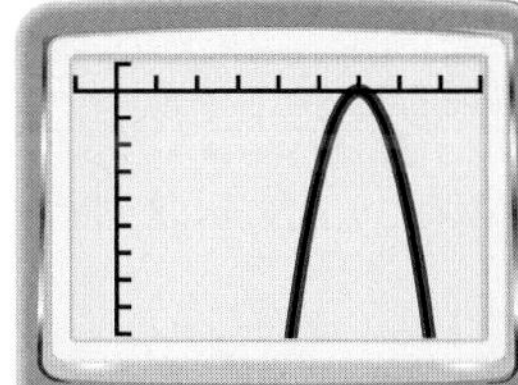

✓ **GUIDED PRACTICE** for Examples 3 and 4

Factor the polynomial.

2. $h^2 + 4h + 4$ $(h + 2)^2$ **3.** $2y^2 - 20y + 50$ $2(y - 5)^2$ **4.** $3x^2 + 6xy + 3y^2$ $3(x + y)^2$

Motivating the Lesson

Ask students to discuss how long it takes objects to fall from different heights. Tell them that if they know the height from which an object is dropped, they can calculate the time it takes the object to reach the ground.

3 TEACH

Extra Example 1

Factor the polynomial.

a. $y^2 - 9$ $(y + 3)(y - 3)$

b. $64c^2 - 16$ $(8c + 4)(8c - 4)$

c. $x^2 - 81y^2$ $(x + 9y)(x - 9y)$

Extra Example 2

Factor the polynomial $12 - 48m^2$. $12(1 + 2m)(1 - 2m)$

Extra Example 3

Factor the polynomial.

a. $a^2 + 6a + 9$ $(a + 3)^2$

b. $4n^2 + 20n + 25$ $(2n + 5)^2$

c. $9c^2 - 6cd + d^2$ $(3c - d)^2$

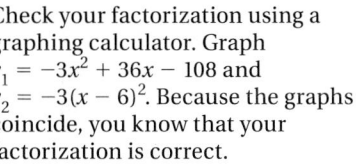

Animated Algebra classzone.com

An **Animated Algebra** activity is available online for **Example 3**. This activity is also part of **Power Presentations**.

Extra Example 4

Factor the polynomial $-2x^2 - 16x - 32$. $-2(x + 4)^2$

Key Question to Ask for Example 4

- How can you check the factorization other than by graphing? **Use FOIL and then multiply each term by −3.**

Differentiated Instruction

Inclusion The number of formulas in this section may overwhelm students. Instead of asking students to memorize the formulas, have them apply the FOIL method to the products $(a + b)(a + b)$, $(a + b)(a - b)$, and $(a - b)(a - b)$ to learn the patterns of the special products.

See also the *Differentiated Instruction Resources* for more strategies.

Extra Example 5

Solve the equation $x^2 - 5x + \frac{25}{4} = 0$. $\frac{5}{2}$

Key Question to Ask for Example 5

- Why does the equation have only one solution? **The factored form is $(3x + 1)^2 = 0$ or $(3x + 1)(3x + 1) = 0$. Since the two factors are the same, the equation has only one solution.**

Extra Example 6

A rock is dropped from a riverbank that is 4 feet above the surface of the river. After how many seconds does the rock hit the surface of the water? **0.5 sec**

Key Question to Ask for Example 6

- How is the vertical motion model in Example 6 different from the model for an object launched from ground level? **For the vertical motion model in Example 6, the initial vertical velocity is 0.**

Closing the Lesson

Have students summarize the major points of the lesson and answer the Essential Question: How do you factor special products?

- **You can use patterns to factor the difference of two squares, $a^2 - b^2$, and perfect square trinomials, $a^2 + 2ab + b^2$ and $a^2 - 2ab + b^2$.**

Use the pattern $a^2 - b^2 = (a + b)(a - b)$ to factor a polynomial that is the difference of two squares. Use the patterns $a^2 + 2ab + b^2 = (a + b)^2$ and $a^2 - 2ab + b^2 = (a - b)^2$ to factor perfect square trinomials.

EXAMPLE 5 Solve a polynomial equation

Solve the equation $x^2 + \frac{2}{3}x + \frac{1}{9} = 0$.

$x^2 + \frac{2}{3}x + \frac{1}{9} = 0$	**Write original equation.**
$9x^2 + 6x + 1 = 0$	**Multiply each side by 9.**
$(3x)^2 + 2(3x \cdot 1) + (1)^2 = 0$	**Write left side as $a^2 + 2ab + b^2$.**
$(3x + 1)^2 = 0$	**Perfect square trinomial pattern**
$3x + 1 = 0$	**Zero-product property**
$x = -\frac{1}{3}$	**Solve for x.**

FIND SOLUTIONS
This equation has two identical solutions, because it has two identical factors.

▶ The solution of the equation is $-\frac{1}{3}$.

EXAMPLE 6 Solve a vertical motion problem

FALLING OBJECT A window washer drops a wet sponge from a height of 64 feet. After how many seconds does the sponge land on the ground?

Solution

Use the vertical motion model to write an equation for the height h (in feet) of the sponge as a function of the time t (in seconds) after it is dropped.

The sponge was dropped, so it has no initial vertical velocity. Find the value of t for which the height is 0.

$h = -16t^2 + vt + s$	**Vertical motion model**
$0 = -16t^2 + (0)t + 64$	**Substitute 0 for h, 0 for v, and 64 for s.**
$0 = -16(t^2 - 4)$	**Factor out −16.**
$0 = -16(t - 2)(t + 2)$	**Difference of two squares pattern**
$t - 2 = 0$ *or* $t + 2 = 0$	**Zero-product property**
$t = 2$ *or* $t = -2$	**Solve for t.**

Disregard the negative solution of the equation.

▶ The sponge lands on the ground 2 seconds after it is dropped.

GUIDED PRACTICE for Examples 5 and 6

Solve the equation.

5. $a^2 + 6a + 9 = 0$ **−3**

6. $w^2 - 14w + 49 = 0$ **7**

7. $n^2 - 81 = 0$ **±9**

8. **WHAT IF?** In Example 6, suppose the sponge is dropped from a height of 16 feet. After how many seconds does it land on the ground? **1 sec**

9.7 EXERCISES

HOMEWORK KEY
○ = **WORKED-OUT SOLUTIONS** on p. WS22 for Exs. 11 and 49
★ = **STANDARDIZED TEST PRACTICE** Exs. 2, 23, 24, 49, and 50

SKILL PRACTICE

A

1. **VOCABULARY** Copy and complete: The polynomial $9n^2 + 6n + 1$ is called a(n) _?_ trinomial. **perfect square**

2. ★ **WRITING** *Explain* how to factor the difference of two squares. **Write the binomial in the form $a^2 - b^2$ and then factor it as $(a + b)(a - b)$, the sum and difference of a and b.**

EXAMPLES 1 and 2 on p. 600 for Exs. 3–8

DIFFERENCE OF TWO SQUARES Factor the polynomial.

3. $x^2 - 25$ $(x + 5)(x - 5)$
4. $n^2 - 64$ $(n + 8)(n - 8)$
5. $81c^2 - 4$ $(9c + 2)(9c - 2)$
6. $49 - 121p^2$ $(7 + 11p)(7 - 11p)$
7. $-3m^2 + 48n^2$ $-3(m + 4n)(m - 4n)$
8. $225x^2 - 144y^2$ $9(5x + 4y)(5x - 4y)$

EXAMPLES 3 and 4 on p. 601 for Exs. 9–14

PERFECT SQUARE TRINOMIALS Factor the polynomial.

9. $x^2 - 4x + 4$ $(x - 2)^2$
10. $y^2 - 10y + 25$ $(y - 5)^2$
11. $49a^2 + 14a + 1$ $(7a + 1)^2$
12. $9t^2 - 12t + 4$ $(3t - 2)^2$
13. $m^2 + m + \frac{1}{4}$ $\left(m + \frac{1}{2}\right)^2$
14. $2x^2 + 12xy + 18y^2$ $2(x + 3y)^2$

EXAMPLES 1, 2, 3, and 4 on pp. 600–601 for Exs. 15–24

FACTORING POLYNOMIALS Factor the polynomial.

15. $4c^2 - 400$ $4(c + 10)(c - 10)$
16. $4f^2 - 36f + 81$ $(2f - 9)^2$
17. $-9r^2 + 4s^2$ $(2s + 3r)(2s - 3r)$
18. $z^2 + 12z + 36$ $(z + 6)^2$
19. $72 - 32y^2$ $8(3 + 2y)(3 - 2y)$
20. $45r^2 - 120rs + 80s^2$ $5(3r - 4s)^2$

ERROR ANALYSIS *Describe* and correct the error in factoring. **21, 22. See margin.**

21.
$$36x^2 - 81 = 9(4x^2 - 9)$$
$$= 9((2x)^2 - 3^2)$$
$$= 9(2x - 3)^2$$

22.
$$y^2 - 6y + 9 = y^2 - 2(y \cdot 3) + 3^2$$
$$= (y - 3)(y + 3)$$

23. ★ **MULTIPLE CHOICE** Which is the correct factorization of $-45x^2 + 20y^2$? **C**

(A) $-5(3x + 2y)^2$ (B) $5(3x - 2y)^2$
(C) $-5(3x + 2y)(3x - 2y)$ (D) $5(3x + 2y)(3x - 2y)$

24. ★ **MULTIPLE CHOICE** Which is the correct factorization of $16m^2 - 8mn + n^2$? **A**

(A) $(4m - n)^2$ (B) $(4m + n)^2$
(C) $(8m - n)^2$ (D) $(4m - n)(4m + n)$

EXAMPLE 5 on p. 602 for Exs. 25–39

B

SOLVING EQUATIONS Solve the equation.

25. $x^2 + 8x + 16 = 0$ -4
26. $16a^2 - 8a + 1 = 0$ $\frac{1}{4}$
27. $4w^2 - 36 = 0$ ± 3
28. $32 - 18m^2 = 0$ $\pm\frac{4}{3}$
29. $27c^2 + 108c + 108 = 0$ -2
30. $-2h^2 - 28h - 98 = 0$ -7
31. $6p^2 = 864$ ± 12
32. $-3t^2 = -108$ ± 6
33. $8k^2 = 98$ $\pm\frac{7}{2}$
34. $-\frac{4}{3}x + \frac{4}{9} = -x^2$ $\frac{2}{3}$
35. $y^2 - \frac{5}{3}y = -\frac{25}{36}$ $\frac{5}{6}$
36. $\frac{2}{9} = 8n^2$ $\pm\frac{1}{6}$
37. $-9c^2 = -16$ $\pm\frac{4}{3}$
38. $-20s - 3 = 25s^2 + 1$ $-\frac{2}{5}$
39. $y^4 - 2y^3 + y^2 = 0$ $0, 1$

4 PRACTICE AND APPLY

Assignment Guide

Answer Transparencies available for all exercises

Basic:
Day 1: pp. 603–605
Exs. 1, 2, 3–21 odd, 22–30, 46–50, 53–75 odd

Average:
Day 1: pp. 603–605
Exs. 1, 2, 6–8, 12–24, 25–39 odd, 46–51, 54–76 even

Advanced:
Day 1: pp. 603–605
Exs. 1, 2, 6–9, 12–20, 23, 24, 26–38 even, 40–52*, 61, 70, 76

Block:
pp. 603–605
Exs. 1, 2, 6–8, 12–24, 25–39 odd, 46–51, 54–76 even (with 9.6)

Differentiated Instruction

See *Differentiated Instruction Resources* for suggestions on addressing the needs of a diverse classroom.

Homework Check

For a quick check of student understanding of key concepts, go over the following exercises:

Basic: 5, 9, 17, 26, 46
Average: 6, 12, 19, 29, 47
Advanced: 8, 14, 20, 38, 48

Extra Practice

- Student Edition, p. 946
- Chapter Resource Book: Practice levels A, B, C

Practice Worksheet

An easily-readable reduced practice page (with answers) for this lesson can be found on p. 552C.

21. $(2x)^2 - 3^2$ is in the form $a^2 - b^2$, so it must be factored using the difference of two squares pattern, not the perfect square trinomial pattern; $9(2x + 3)(2x - 3)$.

22. $y^2 - 2(y \cdot 3) + 3^2$ is in the form $a^2 - 2ab + b^2$, so it must be factored using the perfect square trinomial pattern, not the difference of two squares pattern; $(y - 3)^2$.

Avoiding Common Errors

Exercises 15–20 Some students confuse the patterns associated with $a^2 - b^2$ and $(a - b)^2$. Remind students to watch for this error. Sometimes it helps students to say the pattern aloud, listening for the difference between "the difference of two squares" and "the square of a difference."

Study Strategy

Exercises 23–24 Recommend that students eliminate answer choices before factoring the polynomials. Tell them that using elimination not only helps them in choosing the correct answer choice, but also helps them become better at recognizing patterns.

Teaching Strategy

Exercise 49 It may help some students to graph the equation so they can better explain the number of times the ball reaches a height of 54 feet. You may also want to ask students the number of times the ball reaches a height of 53 feet.

49. Once; the ball's height (in feet) is modeled by the equation $h = -16t^2 + 56t + 5$, where t is the time (in seconds) since it was thrown. To find when the height is 54 feet, substitute 54 for h and solve the equation $54 = -16t^2 + 56t + 5$, or $16t^2 - 56t + 49 = 0$. Because the left side of the equation factors as a perfect square trinomial, $(4t - 7)^2$, the equation has only one solution, $\frac{7}{4}$ or 1.75; so, the ball reaches a height of 54 feet only once, 1.75 seconds after being thrown.

50a.

x (feet)	y (feet)
0	0
2	5
5	8.75
8	8
11	2.75

C **CHALLENGE Determine the value(s) of k for which the expression is a perfect square trinomial.**

40. $x^2 + kx + 36$ **±12**

41. $4x^2 + kx + 9$ **±12**

42. $16x^2 + kx + 4$ **±16**

43. $25x^2 + 10x + k$ **1**

44. $49x^2 - 84x + k$ **36**

45. $4x^2 - 48x + k$ **144**

PROBLEM SOLVING

EXAMPLE 6 A on p. 602 for Exs. 46–48

46. FALLING BRUSH While standing on a ladder, you drop a paintbrush from a height of 25 feet. After how many seconds does the paintbrush land on the ground? **1.25 sec**

@HomeTutor for problem solving help at classzone.com

47. FALLING OBJECT A hickory nut falls from a branch that is 100 feet above the ground. After how many seconds does the hickory nut land on the ground? **2.5 sec**

@HomeTutor for problem solving help at classzone.com

48. GRASSHOPPER A grasshopper jumps straight up from the ground with an initial vertical velocity of 8 feet per second.

a. Write an equation that gives the height (in feet) of the grasshopper as a function of the time (in seconds) since it leaves the ground. $h = -16t^2 + 8t$

b. After how many seconds is the grasshopper 1 foot off the ground? **0.25 sec**

(49.) ★ **SHORT RESPONSE** A ball is thrown up into the air from a height of 5 feet with an initial vertical velocity of 56 feet per second. How many times does the ball reach a height of 54 feet? *Explain* your answer. **See margin.**

B **50.** ★ **EXTENDED RESPONSE** An arch of balloons decorates the stage at a high school graduation. The balloons are tied to a frame. The shape of the frame can be modeled by the graph of the equation $y = -\frac{1}{4}x^2 + 3x$ where x and y are measured in feet.

a. Make a table of values that shows the height of the balloon arch for $x = 0, 2, 5, 8,$ and 11 feet. **See margin.**

b. For what additional values of x does the equation make sense? *Explain.* **See margin.**

c. At approximately what distance from the left end does the arch reach a height of 9 feet? Check your answer algebraically. **6 ft**

○ = WORKED-OUT SOLUTIONS on p. WS1

★ = STANDARDIZED TEST PRACTICE

50b. $0 \le x \le 12$; the table in part (a) shows the heights of the arch for various values of x from 0 to 11; to find the greatest x-value for which the equation gives a height that makes sense, find the other value of x for which the height is 0. Solve the equation $0 = -\frac{1}{4}x^2 + 3x$; the roots are 0 and 12, so the equation makes sense for $0 \le x \le 12$.

51. **FRAMING** A square mirror is framed with stained glass as shown. Each corner of the frame began as a square with a side length of d inches before it was cut to fit the mirror. The mirror has a side length of 3 inches. The area of the stained glass frame is 91 square inches.

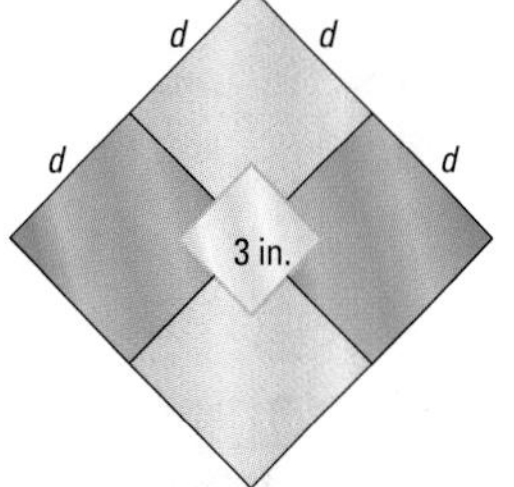

a. Write a polynomial that represents the area of the stained glass frame. **$4d^2 - 9$**

b. What is the side length of the frame? **10 in.**

C 52. **CHALLENGE** You have 120 folding chairs to set up in a park for an outdoor play. You want each row to have an odd number of chairs. You also want each row after the first to have 2 more chairs than the row in front of it. The first row will have 15 chairs.

a. Copy and complete the table below.

n	nth odd integer	Sum of first n odd integers	Sum as a power
1	1	1	1^2
2	3	$1 + 3 = 4$	2^2
3	5	$1 + 3 + 5 = 9$	? **3^2**
4	7	? **$1 + 3 + 5 + 7 = 16$**	? **4^2**
5	9	?	? **5^2**

$1 + 3 + 5 + 7 + 9 = 25$

b. *Describe* the relationship between n and the sum of the first n odd integers. Then find the sum of the first 10 odd integers. **The sum of the first n odd integers is n^2; 100.**

c. *Explain* how to find the sum of the odd integers from 11 to 21. **See margin.**

d. How many rows of chairs will you need for the outdoor play? *Explain* your thinking. **See margin.**

MIXED REVIEW

PREVIEW Prepare for Lesson 9.8 in Exs. 53–61.

Solve the equation.

53. $a + 6 = 3$ (p. 134) **−3**

54. $5y - 2 = -32$ (p. 141) **−6**

55. $8m + 4 = 20$ (p. 141) **2**

56. $5b - 3b + 6 = 4$ (p. 148) **−1**

57. $(x - 9)(x + 1) = 0$ (p. 575) **−1, 9**

58. $x^2 + 17x = -66$ (p. 583) **−11, −6**

59. $x^2 = -12x + 45$ (p. 583) **−15, 3**

60. $2y^2 + y = 15$ (p. 593) **$-3, \frac{5}{2}$**

61. $22z - 35 = 3z^2$ (p. 593) **$\frac{7}{3}, 5$**

Graph the linear equation. **62–70. See margin.**

62. $y = -6$ (p. 215)

63. $x = 14$ (p. 215)

64. $2x + y = 8$ (p. 225)

65. $-4x + 5y = -20$ (p. 225)

66. $0.6x + 0.2y = 3.6$ (p. 225)

67. $y = -\frac{3}{2}x - 9$ (p. 225)

68. $y = \frac{5}{2}x$ (p. 244)

69. $y = -12x + 3$ (p. 244)

70. $y = \frac{4}{3}x + 2$ (p. 244)

Find the product.

71. $(2a - 3)(5a - 2)$ (p. 562) **$10a^2 - 19a + 6$**

72. $(2x^2 + x + 3)(x - 1)$ (p. 562) **$2x^3 - x^2 + 2x - 3$**

73. $(c + 3)(c + 5)$ (p. 562) **$c^2 + 8c + 15$**

74. $(3x - 4)(2x - 7)$ (p. 562) **$6x^2 - 29x + 28$**

75. $(2k - 11)(2k + 11)$ (p. 569) **$4k^2 - 121$**

76. $(y - 7)^2$ (p. 569) **$y^2 - 14y + 49$**

5 ASSESS AND RETEACH

Daily Homework Quiz

Transparency Available

Factor the polynomial.

1. $4m^2 - n^2$ **$(2m - n)(2m + n)$**
2. $x^2 + 6x + 9$ **$(x + 3)^2$**
3. $4y^2 - 16y + 16$ **$(2y - 4)^2$**
4. Solve the equation $x^2 + x + \frac{1}{4} = 0.$ **$-\frac{1}{2}$**
5. An apple falls from a branch 9 feet above the ground. After how many seconds does the apple hit the ground? **0.75 sec**

Online Quiz

Available at **classzone.com**

Diagnosis/Remediation

- Practice A, B, C in Chapter Resource Book
- Study Guide in Chapter Resource Book
- Practice Workbook
- @HomeTutor

Challenge

Additional challenge is available in the Chapter Resource Book.

52c. The nth odd integer is in the form $2n - 1$, so 11 is the sixth odd integer and 21 is the eleventh odd integer. To find the sum of the odd integers from 11 to 21, find the sum of the first 11 odd integers ($11^2 = 121$) and subtract the sum of the first 5 odd integers ($5^2 = 25$) to get $121 - 25 = 96$.

52d. See Additional Answers beginning on p. AA1.

62–70. See Additional Answers beginning on p. AA1.

1 PLAN AND PREPARE

Warm-Up Exercises

Transparency Available

1. Solve $2x^2 + 11x = 21$. $\frac{3}{2}, -7$
2. Factor $4x^2 + 10x + 4$. $2(x + 2)(2x + 1)$
3. A replacement piece of sod for a lawn has an area of 112 square inches. The width is w and the length is $2w - 2$. What are the dimensions of the sod? **width: 8 in., length: 14 in.**

Notetaking Guide

Transparency Available

Promotes interactive learning and notetaking skills.

Pacing

Basic: 2 days
Average: 2 days
Advanced: 2 days
Block: 1 block
- See *Teaching Guide/Lesson Plan.*

2 FOCUS AND MOTIVATE

Essential Question

Big Idea 3, p. 553

How do you factor polynomials completely? **Tell students they will learn how to answer this question by grouping terms and factoring out binomials.**

NCTM STANDARDS

Standard 2: Analyze situations using algebraic symbols

Standard 6: Solve problems in math and other contexts

9.8 Factor Polynomials Completely

Before	You factored polynomials.
Now	You will factor polynomials completely.
Why?	So you can model the height of a projectile, as in Ex. 71.

Key Vocabulary
- **factor by grouping**
- **factor completely**

You have used the distributive property to factor a greatest common monomial from a polynomial. Sometimes, you can factor out a common binomial.

EXAMPLE 1 Factor out a common binomial

Factor the expression.

a. $2x(x + 4) - 3(x + 4)$ **b.** $3y^2(y - 2) + 5(2 - y)$

Solution

a. $2x(x + 4) - 3(x + 4) = (x + 4)(2x - 3)$

b. The binomials $y - 2$ and $2 - y$ are opposites. Factor -1 from $2 - y$ to obtain a common binomial factor.

$3y^2(y - 2) + 5(2 - y) = 3y^2(y - 2) - 5(y - 2)$ **Factor −1 from (2 − y).**

$= (y - 2)(3y^2 - 5)$ **Distributive property**

GROUPING You may be able to use the distributive property to factor polynomials with four terms. Factor a common monomial from pairs of terms, then look for a common binomial factor. This is called **factor by grouping**.

EXAMPLE 2 Factor by grouping

Factor the polynomial.

a. $x^3 + 3x^2 + 5x + 15$ **b.** $y^2 + y + yx + x$

Solution

a. $x^3 + 3x^2 + 5x + 15 = (x^3 + 3x^2) + (5x + 15)$ **Group terms.**

$= x^2(x + 3) + 5(x + 3)$ **Factor each group.**

$= (x + 3)(x^2 + 5)$ **Distributive property**

b. $y^2 + y + yx + x = (y^2 + y) + (yx + x)$ **Group terms.**

$= y(y + 1) + x(y + 1)$ **Factor each group.**

$= (y + 1)(y + x)$ **Distributive property**

CHECK WORK
Remember that you can check a factorization by multiplying the factors.

Resource Planning Guide

Chapter Resource Book
- Teaching Guide/Lesson Plan
- Practice levels A, B, C
- Study Guide
- Catch-up for Absent Students
- Problem Solving Workshop
- Challenge

Workbooks
- Notetaking Guide
- Practice Workbook

Teaching Options
- **Power Presentations** provides dynamic electronic teaching resources for the classroom.
- **Activity Generator** provides editable activities for all ability levels.

Interactive Technology
- Easy Planner
- Power Presentations
- Activity Generator
- Animated Algebra
- Test Generator
- Online Quiz
- eWorkbook
- eEdition
- @HomeTutor

Resources for English Learners
- Spanish Study Guide
- Multi-Language Visual Glossary
- Student Resources in Spanish

See also the *Differentiated Instruction Resources* for more strategies for meeting individual needs.

EXAMPLE 3 Factor by grouping

Factor $x^3 - 6 + 2x - 3x^2$.

Solution

The terms x^3 and -6 have no common factor. Use the commutative property to rearrange the terms so that you can group terms with a common factor.

$$\begin{aligned} x^3 - 6 + 2x - 3x^2 &= x^3 - 3x^2 + 2x - 6 && \textbf{Rearrange terms.} \\ &= (x^3 - 3x^2) + (2x - 6) && \textbf{Group terms.} \\ &= x^2(x - 3) + 2(x - 3) && \textbf{Factor each group.} \\ &= (x - 3)(x^2 + 2) && \textbf{Distributive property} \end{aligned}$$

CHECK Check your factorization using a graphing calculator. Graph $y_1 = x^3 - 6 + 2x - 3x^2$ and $y_2 = (x - 3)(x^2 + 2)$. Because the graphs coincide, you know that your factorization is correct.

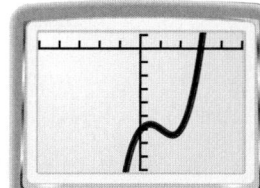

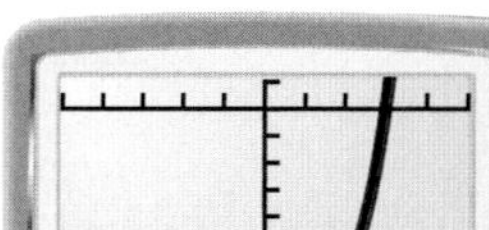

✓ GUIDED PRACTICE for Examples 1, 2, and 3

Factor the expression.

1. $x(x - 2) + (x - 2)$ **$(x - 2)(x + 1)$**
2. $a^3 + 3a^2 + a + 3$ **$(a + 3)(a^2 + 1)$**
3. $y^2 + 2x + yx + 2y$ **$(y + 2)(y + x)$**

READING If a polynomial has two or more terms and is unfactorable, it is called a *prime polynomial.*

FACTORING COMPLETELY You have seen that the polynomial $x^2 - 1$ can be factored as $(x + 1)(x - 1)$. This polynomial is factorable. Notice that the polynomial $x^2 + 1$ cannot be written as the product of polynomials with integer coefficients. This polynomial is unfactorable. A factorable polynomial with integer coefficients is **factored completely** if it is written as a product of unfactorable polynomials with integer coefficients.

CONCEPT SUMMARY *For Your Notebook*

Guidelines for Factoring Polynomials Completely

To factor a polynomial completely, you should try each of these steps.

Step	Example
1. Factor out the greatest common monomial factor. *(Lesson 9.4)*	$3x^2 + 6x = 3x(x + 2)$
2. Look for a difference of two squares or a perfect square trinomial. *(Lesson 9.7)*	$x^2 + 4x + 4 = (x + 2)^2$
3. Factor a trinomial of the form $ax^2 + bx + c$ into a product of binomial factors. *(Lessons 9.5 and 9.6)*	$3x^2 - 5x - 2 = (3x + 1)(x - 2)$
4. Factor a polynomial with four terms by grouping. *(Lesson 9.8)*	$x^3 + x - 4x^2 - 4 = (x^2 + 1)(x - 4)$

Differentiated Instruction

Visual Learners Some students may see that the grouping method is not unique. Show the following for **Example 3**.

$$\begin{aligned} x^3 - 6 + 2x - 3x^2 &= x^3 + 2x - 6 - 3x^2 \\ &= (x^3 + 2x) - (6 + 3x^2) \\ &= x(x^2 + 2) - 3(2 + x^2) \\ &= x(x^2 + 2) - 3(x^2 + 2) \\ &= (x - 3)(x^2 + 2) \end{aligned}$$

See also the *Differentiated Instruction Resources* for more strategies.

Motivating the Lesson

Food packagers often know what the volume of a package must be and have to decide what the package's dimensions can be. If they know how the dimensions are related, they can use factoring to find the dimensions.

3 TEACH

Extra Example 1

Factor the expression.

a. $4x(x - 3) + 5(x - 3)$
$(x - 3)(4x + 5)$

b. $2y^2(y - 5) - 3(5 - y)$
$(y - 5)(2y^2 + 3)$

Key Questions to Ask for Example 1

- In part (b), why is one of the factors $3y^2 - 5$ instead of $3y^2 + 5$? **When you factor out −1 to obtain the common binomial factor $y - 2$, you are left with the factor $-1 \cdot 5$, or −5.**
- In part (b), if the binomials were $(y + 2)(2 + y)$, how would you obtain a common binomial? **Use the commutative property to change $2 + y$ to $y + 2$.**

Extra Example 2

Factor the polynomial.

a. $x^3 + 2x^2 + 8x + 16$
$(x + 2)(x^2 + 8)$

b. $r^2 + 4r + rs + 4s$ **$(r + 4)(r + s)$**

Extra Example 3

Factor $x^3 - 10 - 5x + 2x^2$.
$(x + 2)(x^2 - 5)$

Extra Example 4

Factor the polynomial completely.

a. $x^2 - 4x - 3$ **cannot be factored**

b. $3x^3 - 21x^2 - 54x$ **$3x(x + 2)(x - 9)$**

c. $8d^3 + 24d$ **$8d(d^2 + 3)$**

Key Question to Ask for Example 4

- How do you determine if a polynomial is not factorable? **If the terms have no common factors, if it does not follow one of the factor patterns, and if none of the possible factors gives the middle term of the original trinomial, then it is not factorable.**

Extra Example 5

Solve $2x^3 - 18x^2 = -36x$. **0, 3, 6**

Key Question to Ask for Example 5

- Could the equation have more than 3 solutions? Explain. **No; a 3rd degree equation can have at most 3 factors and thus at most 3 solutions.**

EXAMPLE 4 Factor completely

Factor the polynomial completely.

a. $n^2 + 2n - 1$ **b.** $4x^3 - 44x^2 + 96x$ **c.** $50h^4 - 2h^2$

Solution

a. The terms of the polynomial have no common monomial factor. Also, there are no factors of -1 that have a sum of 2. This polynomial cannot be factored.

b. $4x^3 - 44x^2 + 96x = 4x(x^2 - 11x + 24)$ **Factor out $4x$.**

$= 4x(x - 3)(x - 8)$ **Find two negative factors of 24 that have a sum of -11.**

c. $50h^4 - 2h^2 = 2h^2(25h^2 - 1)$ **Factor out $2h^2$.**

$= 2h^2(5h - 1)(5h + 1)$ **Difference of two squares pattern**

✓ **GUIDED PRACTICE for Example 4**

Factor the polynomial completely.

4. $3x^3 - 12x$ **$3x(x - 2)(x + 2)$**

5. $2y^3 - 12y^2 + 18y$ **$2y(y - 3)^2$**

6. $m^3 - 2m^2 - 8m$ **$m(m - 4)(m + 2)$**

EXAMPLE 5 Solve a polynomial equation

Solve $3x^3 + 18x^2 = -24x$.

$3x^3 + 18x^2 = -24x$	**Write original equation.**
$3x^3 + 18x^2 + 24x = 0$	**Add $24x$ to each side.**
$3x(x^2 + 6x + 8) = 0$	**Factor out $3x$.**
$3x(x + 2)(x + 4) = 0$	**Factor trinomial.**
$3x = 0$ *or* $x + 2 = 0$ *or* $x + 4 = 0$	**Zero-product property**
$x = 0$ $\quad x = -2$ $\quad x = -4$	**Solve for x.**

▶ The solutions of the equation are 0, -2, and -4.

CHECK Check each solution by substituting it for x in the equation. One check is shown here.

$$3(-2)^3 + 18(-2)^2 \stackrel{?}{=} -24(-2)$$

$$-24 + 72 \stackrel{?}{=} 48$$

$$48 = 48 \checkmark$$

 **GUIDED PRACTICE for Example 5**

Solve the equation.

7. $w^3 - 8w^2 + 16w = 0$ **0, 4**

8. $x^3 - 25x = 0$ **0, ±5**

9. $c^3 - 7c^2 + 12c = 0$ **0, 3, 4**

EXAMPLE 6 Solve a multi-step problem

TERRARIUM A terrarium in the shape of a rectangular prism has a volume of 4608 cubic inches. Its length is more than 10 inches. The dimensions of the terrarium are shown. Find the length, width, and height of the terrarium.

Solution

STEP 1 **Write** a verbal model. Then write an equation.

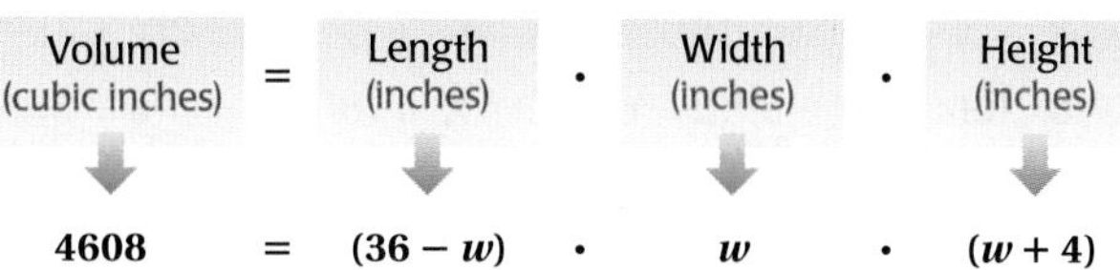

$$4608 = (36 - w) \cdot w \cdot (w + 4)$$

STEP 2 **Solve** the equation for w.

$4608 = (36 - w)(w)(w + 4)$	Write equation.
$0 = 32w^2 + 144w - w^3 - 4608$	Multiply. Subtract 4608 from each side.
$0 = (-w^3 + 32w^2) + (144w - 4608)$	Group terms.
$0 = -w^2(w - 32) + 144(w - 32)$	Factor each group.
$0 = (w - 32)(-w^2 + 144)$	Distributive property
$0 = -1(w - 32)(w^2 - 144)$	Factor −1 from $-w^2 + 144$.
$0 = -1(w - 32)(w - 12)(w + 12)$	Difference of two squares pattern
$w - 32 = 0$ *or* $w - 12 = 0$ *or* $w + 12 = 0$	Zero-product property
$w = 32$ $w = 12$ $w = -12$	Solve for w.

STEP 3 **Choose** the solution of the equation that is the correct value of w. Disregard $w = -12$, because the width cannot be negative.

You know that the length is more than 10 inches. Test the solutions 12 and 32 in the expression for the length.

Length $= 36 - 12 = 24$ ✓ *or* Length $= 36 - 32 = 4$ ✗

The solution 12 gives a length of 24 inches, so 12 is the correct value of w.

STEP 4 **Find** the height.

Height $= w + 4 = 12 + 4 = 16$

▸ The width is 12 inches, the length is 24 inches, and the height is 16 inches.

GUIDED PRACTICE for Example 6

10. 3 ft long by 2 ft wide by 12 ft high

10. **DIMENSIONS OF A BOX** A box in the shape of a rectangular prism has a volume of 72 cubic feet. The box has a length of x feet, a width of $(x - 1)$ feet, and a height of $(x + 9)$ feet. Find the dimensions of the box.

Extra Example 6

A kitchen drawer has a volume of 768 cubic inches. The dimensions of the drawer are shown. Find the length, width, and height of the drawer if none of the dimensions are the same. **width: 12 in., length: 16 in., height: 4 in.**

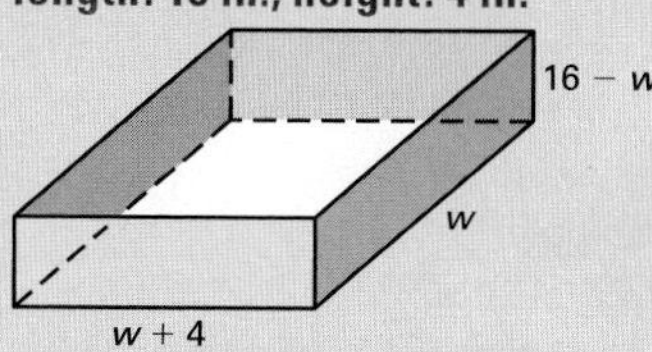

Key Question to Ask for Example 6

- How do you get $32w^2 + 144w - w^3 - 4608$ in Step 2? **Multiply $(36 - w)$, w, and $(w + 4)$, and subtract 4608.**

Closing the Lesson

Have students summarize the major points of the lesson and answer the Essential Question: How do you factor polynomials completely?

- **Factor a polynomial completely by writing it as a monomial or the product of a monomial and one or more prime polynomials.**
- **A polynomial is unfactorable if you cannot write it as the product of polynomials of lesser degrees.**

Before trying to factor a polynomial, look for a greatest common monomial and common binomials and factor them out. If a trinomial is in the form of $ax^2 + bx + c$, look for binomial factors. If a polynomial has four terms, factor by grouping the terms. Look for a difference of two squares pattern or a perfect square trinomial pattern.

4 PRACTICE AND APPLY

Assignment Guide

Answer Transparencies available for all exercises

Basic:
Day 1: SRH p. 926 Exs. 1, 2, 4, 6, 10
pp. 610–613
Exs. 1–22, 87–89
Day 2: pp. 610–613
Exs. 23–41 odd, 42–50, 68–72, 76–86 even

Average:
Day 1: pp. 610–613
Exs. 1–12, 14–22 even, 61–66, 87–89
Day 2: pp. 610–613
Exs. 32–60, 68–73, 76, 80, 84

Advanced:
Day 1: pp. 610–613
Exs. 1, 6–12, 16–21, 61–67*, 87–89
Day 2: pp. 610–613
Exs. 34–42, 48–60, 68–74*, 78, 82, 86

Block:
pp. 610–613
Exs. 1–12, 14–22 even, 32–66, 68–73, 76, 80, 84, 87–89

Differentiated Instruction

See *Differentiated Instruction Resources* for suggestions on addressing the needs of a diverse classroom.

Homework Check

For a quick check of student understanding of key concepts, go over the following exercises:

Basic: 6, 15, 29, 44, 68
Average: 8, 18, 34, 50, 69
Advanced: 10, 20, 37, 53, 70

Extra Practice

- Student Edition, p. 946
- Chapter Resource Book: Practice levels A, B, C

Practice Worksheet

An easily-readable reduced practice page (with answers) for this lesson can be found on p. 552C.

9.8 EXERCISES

HOMEWORK KEY
○ = **WORKED-OUT SOLUTIONS on p. WS23 for Exs. 13, 23, and 71**
★ = **STANDARDIZED TEST PRACTICE Exs. 2, 12, 41, 55, 71, and 73**

SKILL PRACTICE

A

1. **VOCABULARY** What does it mean for a polynomial to be factored completely? **The polynomial is written as a monomial or as a product of a monomial and one or more prime polynomials.**

2. ★ **WRITING** *Explain* how you know if a polynomial is unfactorable. **See margin.**

EXAMPLE 1 on p. 606 for Exs. 3–12

BINOMIAL FACTORS Factor the expression.

3. $x(x-8)+(x-8)$ $\mathbf{(x-8)(x+1)}$
4. $5y(y+3)-2(y+3)$ $\mathbf{(y+3)(5y-2)}$
5. $6z(z-4)-7(z-4)$ $\mathbf{(z-4)(6z-7)}$
6. $10(a-6)-3a(a-6)$ $\mathbf{(a-6)(10-3a)}$
7. $b^2(b+5)-3(b+5)$ $\mathbf{(b+5)(b^2-3)}$
8. $7c^2(c+9)+2(c+9)$ $\mathbf{(c+9)(7c^2+2)}$
9. $x(13+x)-(x+13)$ $\mathbf{(x+13)(x-1)}$
10. $y^2(y-4)+5(4-y)$ $\mathbf{(y-4)(y^2-5)}$
11. $12(z-1)-5z^2(1-z)$ $\mathbf{(z-1)(12+5z^2)}$

12. ★ **MULTIPLE CHOICE** Which is the correct factorization of $x^2(x-8)+5(8-x)$? **C**

Ⓐ $(x^2+5)(x-8)$ Ⓑ $(x^2+5)(8-x)$
Ⓒ $(x^2-5)(x-8)$ Ⓓ $(x^2-5)(8-x)$

EXAMPLES 2 and 3 on pp. 606–607 for Exs. 13–22

FACTORING BY GROUPING Factor the polynomial. **13–21. See margin.**

13. x^3+x^2+2x+2
14. y^3-9y^2+y-9
15. $z^3-4z^2+3z-12$
16. $c^3+7c^2+5c+35$
17. $a^3+13a^2-5a-65$
18. $2s^3-3s^2+18s-27$
19. $5n^3-4n^2+25n-20$
20. $x^2+8x-xy-8y$
21. $y^2+y+5xy+5x$

22. **ERROR ANALYSIS** *Describe* and correct the error in factoring. **See margin.**

$$a^3+8a^2-6a-48 = a^2(a+8)+6(a+8)$$
$$= (a+8)(a^2+6)$$

EXAMPLE 4 on p. 608 for Exs. 23–42

FACTORING COMPLETELY Factor the polynomial completely.

23. x^4-x^2 $\mathbf{x^2(x-1)(x+1)}$
24. $36a^4-4a^2$ $\mathbf{4a^2(3a-1)(3a+1)}$
25. $3n^5-48n^3$ $\mathbf{3n^3(n-4)(n+4)}$
26. $4y^6-16y^4$ $\mathbf{4y^4(y-2)(y+2)}$
27. $75c^9-3c^7$ $\mathbf{3c^7(5c-1)(5c+1)}$
28. $72p-2p^3$ $\mathbf{2p(6-p)(6+p)}$
29. $32s^4-8s^2$ $\mathbf{8s^2(2s-1)(2s+1)}$
30. $80z^8-45z^6$ $\mathbf{5z^6(4z-3)(4z+3)}$
31. $m^2-5m-35$ **cannot be factored**
32. $6g^3-24g^2+24g$ $\mathbf{6g(g-2)^2}$
33. $3w^4+24w^3+48w^2$ $\mathbf{3w^2(w+4)^2}$
34. $3r^5+3r^4-90r^3$ $\mathbf{3r^3(r+6)(r-5)}$
35. $b^3-5b^2-4b+20$ $\mathbf{(b-5)(b-2)(b+2)}$
36. $h^3+4h^2-25h-100$ $\mathbf{(h+4)(h-5)(h+5)}$
37. $9t^3+18t-t^2-2$ $\mathbf{(9t-1)(t^2+2)}$
38. $2x^5y-162x^3y$ $\mathbf{2x^3y(x-9)(x+9)}$
39. $7a^3b^3-63ab^3$ $\mathbf{7ab^3(a-3)(a+3)}$
40. $-4s^3t^3+24s^2t^2-36st$ $\mathbf{-4st(st-3)^2}$

41. ★ **MULTIPLE CHOICE** What is the completely factored form of $3x^6-75x^4$? **D**

Ⓐ $3x^4(x^2-25)$ Ⓑ $3x^4(x-5)^2$ Ⓒ $3x^4(x+5)^2$ Ⓓ $3x^4(x-5)(x+5)$

B

42. **ERROR ANALYSIS** *Describe* and correct the error in factoring the polynomial completely.

$$x^3-6x^2-9x+54 = x^2(x-6)-9(x-6)$$
$$= (x-6)(x^2-9)$$

42. The factorization is correct, but the polynomial has not been factored completely. The binomial factor (x^2-9) can be factored using the difference of two squares pattern; $(x-6)(x-3)(x+3)$.

2. A polynomial with integer coefficients is not factorable if it cannot be written as the product of polynomials of lesser degree using only integer coefficients and constants, and if the only common factors of its terms are 1 and −1.

13. $(x+1)(x^2+2)$
14. $(y-9)(y^2+1)$
15. $(z-4)(z^2+3)$
16. $(c+7)(c^2+5)$
17. $(a+13)(a^2-5)$
18. $(2s-3)(s^2+9)$
19. $(5n-4)(n^2+5)$
20. $(x+8)(x-y)$
21. $(y+1)(y+5x)$

22. −6, not +6, was the common monomial factored out of the third and fourth terms of the polynomial, so the sign between the two groups of factors should be − not +; $(a+8)(a^2-6)$.

EXAMPLE 5 on p. 608 for Exs. 43–54

45. $\frac{7}{4}$, ±2

SOLVING EQUATIONS **Solve the equation.**

43. $x^3 + x^2 - 4x - 4 = 0$ **−1, ±2**

44. $a^3 - 11a^2 - 9a + 99 = 0$ **11, ±3**

45. $4y^3 - 7y^2 - 16y + 28 = 0$

46. $5n^3 - 30n^2 + 40n = 0$ **0, 2, 4**

47. $3b^3 + 24b^2 + 45b = 0$ **0, −5, −3**

48. $2t^5 + 2t^4 - 144t^3 = 0$ **0, −9, 8**

49. $z^3 - 81z = 0$ **0, ±9**

50. $c^4 - 100c^2 = 0$ **0, ±10**

51. $12s - 3s^3 = 0$ **0, ±2**

52. $2x^3 - 10x^2 + 40 = 8x$ **5, ±2**

53. $3p + 1 = p^2 + 3p^3$ **$-\frac{1}{3}$, ±1**

54. $m^3 - 3m^2 = 4m - 12$ **3, ±2**

55. ★ **WRITING** Is it possible to find three solutions of the equation $x^3 + 2x^2 + 3x + 6 = 0$? *Explain* why or why not. **See margin.**

GEOMETRY **Find the length, width, and height of the rectangular prism with the given volume.**

HINT
In Ex. 57, convert the given volume to cubic yards. Use the conversion factor $\frac{1 \text{ yd}^3}{27 \text{ ft}^3}$.

56. Volume = 12 cubic inches **6 in., 1 in., 2 in.**

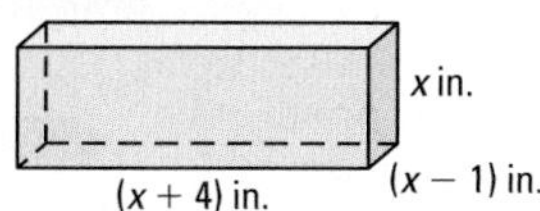

57. Volume: 2592 cubic feet **12 yd, 4 yd, 2 yd**

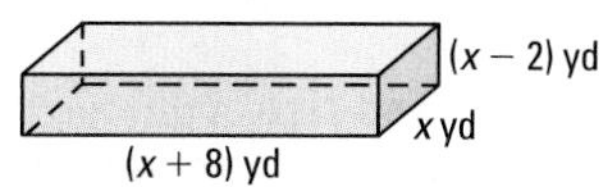

FACTORING COMPLETELY **Factor the polynomial completely.**

58. $x^3 + 2x^2y - x - 2y$ **(x + 2y)(x − 1)(x + 1)**

59. $8b^3 - 4b^2a - 18b + 9a$ **(2b − a)(2b − 3)(2b + 3)**

60. $4s^2 - s + 12st - 3t$ **(4s − 1)(s + 3t)**

FACTOR BY GROUPING **In Exercises 61–66, use the example below to factor the trinomial by grouping.**

EXAMPLE **Factor a trinomial by grouping**

Factor $8x^2 + 10x - 3$ by grouping.

Solution

Notice that the polynomial is in the form $ax^2 + bx + c$.

STEP 1 **Write** the product ac as the product of two factors that have a sum of b. In this case, the product ac is $8(-3) = -24$. Find two factors of −24 that have a sum of 10.

$-24 = 12 \cdot (-2)$ and $12 + (-2) = 10$

STEP 2 **Rewrite** the middle term as two terms with coefficients 12 and −2.

$8x^2 + \mathbf{10x} - 3 = 8x^2 + \mathbf{12x - 2x} - 3$

STEP 3 **Factor** by grouping.

$8x^2 + 12x - 2x - 3 = (8x^2 + 12x) + (-2x - 3)$	Group terms.
$= 4x(2x + 3) - (2x + 3)$	Factor each group.
$= (2x + 3)(4x - 1)$	Distributive property

61. $6x^2 + 5x - 4$ **(3x + 4)(2x − 1)**

62. $10s^2 + 19s + 6$ **(2s + 3)(5s + 2)**

63. $12n^2 - 13n + 3$ **(4n − 3)(3n − 1)**

64. $16a^2 + 14a + 3$ **(8a + 3)(2a + 1)**

65. $21w^2 + 8w - 4$ **(3w + 2)(7w − 2)**

66. $15y^2 - 31y + 10$ **(3y − 5)(5y − 2)**

C **67.** **CHALLENGE** Use factoring by grouping to show that a trinomial of the form $a^2 + 2ab + b^2$ can be factored as $(a + b)^2$. *Justify* your steps. **See margin.**

Avoiding Common Errors

Exercises 10–11 Watch for students who identify and rewrite opposite binomial factors but who do not multiply the rest of the term by −1.

Exercises 43–54 Remind students that 3rd degree or higher degree polynomials may have 3 or more roots. Encourage students to examine their solutions to make sure they have not missed one of the solutions.

Study Strategy

Exercises 23–40 Students may find it easier to factor completely if they follow a systematic plan for factoring. Suggest that they develop a set of steps in which they look for common monomial factors, grouping, and so on. Suggest that they write the steps on notecards for reference.

55. No; when the polynomial is factored completely, the equation becomes $(x + 2)(x^2 + 3) = 0$. When the factor $x^2 + 3$ is set equal to zero, the resulting equation, $x^2 + 3 = 0$, or $x^2 = -3$, has no real number solutions because x^2 cannot be negative.

67. First, rewrite the middle term as $ab + ab$ and group the terms: $a^2 + 2ab + b^2 = (a^2 + ab) + (ab + b^2)$. Factor each group and then use the distributive property to factor out the common binomial: $(a^2 + ab) + (ab + b^2) = a(a + b) + b(a + b) = (a + b)(a + b) = (a + b)^2$.

Study Strategy

Exercises 69–70 You may want to point out that in Exercise 69, part (a) corresponds to Step 1 in Example 6 and that part (b) corresponds to Steps 2–4. Suggest that students write a stepped-out solution to Exercise 70 using Example 6 as a model.

Internet Reference

Exercise 71 Additional information about the game of bocce can be found on the Bocce Standards Association's website at www.boccestandardsassociation.org

72b. 3 ft; to find how far the robot has traveled horizontally when it lands back on the ground, find the non-zero x-value that makes the height y equal to zero. Solve $0 = -10x^2 + 30x$; the roots are $x = 0$ feet (which is the starting point of the jump) and $x = 3$ feet (which is the ending point of the jump).

PROBLEM SOLVING

EXAMPLE 6 on p. 609 for Exs. 68–70

68. **CYLINDRICAL VASE** A vase in the shape of a cylinder has a height of 6 inches and a volume of 24π cubic inches. What is the radius of the vase? **2 in.**

@HomeTutor for problem solving help at classzone.com

69b. 4 in. long by 4 in. wide by 8 in. high

69. **CARPENTRY** You are building a birdhouse that will have a volume of 128 cubic inches. The birdhouse will have the dimensions shown.

a. Write a polynomial that represents the volume of the birdhouse. $4w^2 + 16w$

b. What are the dimensions of the birdhouse?

@HomeTutor for problem solving help at classzone.com

70. **BAG SIZE** A gift bag is shaped like a rectangular prism and has a volume of 1152 cubic inches. The dimensions of the gift bag are shown. The height is greater than the width. What are the dimensions of the gift bag?
16 in. long by 6 in. wide by 12 in. high

(18 − w) in.
w in.
(2w + 4) in.

71b. The zero $t \approx -0.2$ has no meaning because t, which represents time in seconds, cannot be negative in this situation. The zero $t = 1$ means that the ball hits the ground 1 second after you throw it. B

71. ★ **SHORT RESPONSE** A pallino is the small target ball that is tossed in the air at the beginning of a game of bocce. The height h (in meters) of the pallino after you throw it can be modeled by $h = -4.9t^2 + 3.9t + 1$ where t is the time (in seconds) since you released it.

a. Find the zeros of the function. **1, about −0.2**

b. Do the zeros of the function have any meaning in this situation? *Explain* your reasoning.

72. **JUMPING ROBOT** The path of a jumping robot can be modeled by the graph of the equation $y = -10x^2 + 30x$ where x and y are both measured in feet. On a coordinate plane, the ground is represented by the x-axis, and the robot's starting position is the origin.

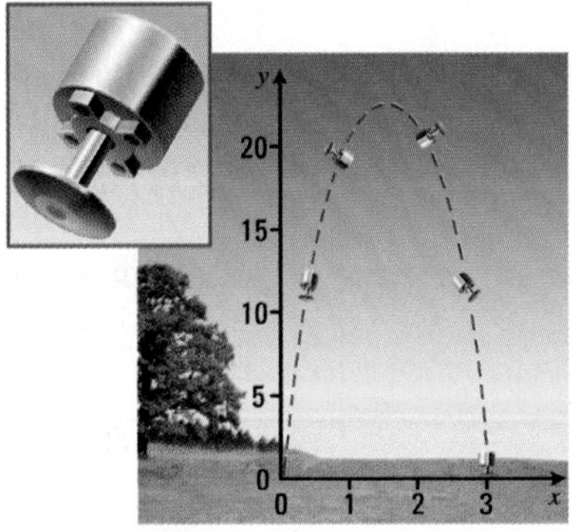

a. The robot's maximum height is 22.5 feet. What is the robot's horizontal distance from its starting point when its height is 22.5 feet? **1.5 ft**

b. How far has the robot traveled horizontally when it lands on the ground? *Explain* your answer. **See margin.**

73. ★ **EXTENDED RESPONSE** The width of a box is 4 inches more than the height h. The length is the difference of 9 inches and the height.

a. Write a polynomial that represents the volume of the box. $-h^3 + 5h^2 + 36h$

b. The volume of the box is 180 cubic inches. What are all the possible dimensions of the box? **4 in. long by 9 in. wide by 5 in. high, 3 in. long by 10 in. wide by 6 in. high**

c. Which dimensions result in a box with the smallest possible surface area? *Explain* your reasoning.
4 in. long by 9 in. wide by 5 in. high; the 4-inch long box has a surface area of 202 square inches and the 3-inch long box has a surface area of 216 square inches.

○ = WORKED-OUT SOLUTIONS on p. WS1 ★ = STANDARDIZED TEST PRACTICE

74. CHALLENGE A plastic cube is used to display an autographed baseball. The cube has an outer surface area of 54 square inches.

a. What is the length of an outer edge of the cube? **3 in.**

b. What is the greatest volume the cube can possibly have? *Explain* why the actual volume inside of the cube may be less than the greatest possible volume. **27 in.^{3}; the thickness of the plastic used to make the sides of the box will make the edge length of the interior of the cube be less than 3 inches, so the volume of the interior will be less than 27 cubic inches.**

MIXED REVIEW

PREVIEW Prepare for Lesson 10.1 in Exs. 75–86.

Graph the equation. *(p. 244)* **75–86. See margin.**

75. $y - 2x = 0$
76. $y + 2x = 3$
77. $y + 5x = 2$
78. $2y - 6x = 6$
79. $-3y + 4x = 12$
80. $-4x + 2y = 8$
81. $x - 4y = 2$
82. $x - 2y = -10$
83. $y = 5$
84. $y = 0$
85. $x = -4$
86. $x = 2$

Write an equation of the line shown.

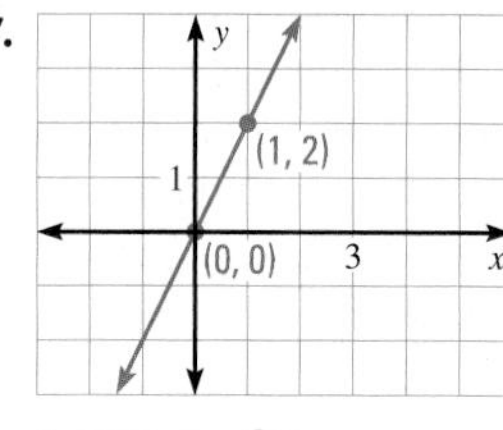

(p. 283) **$y = 2x$**

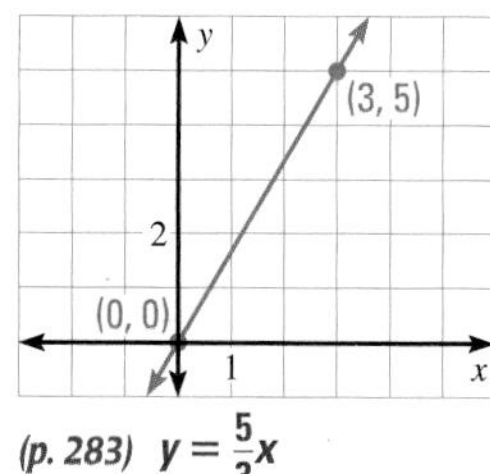

(p. 283) **$y = \frac{5}{3}x$**

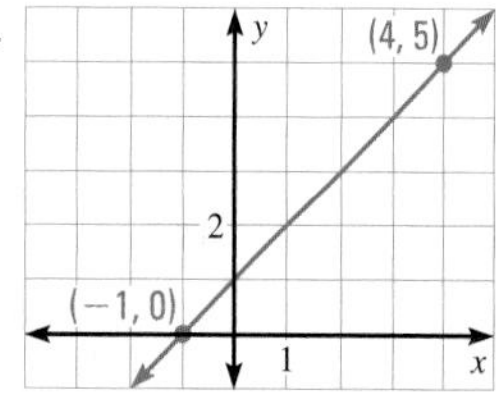

(p. 283) **$y = x + 1$**

QUIZ for Lessons 9.7–9.8

Factor the polynomial. *(p. 600)*

1. $x^2 - 400$ **$(x - 20)(x + 20)$**
2. $18 - 32z^2$ **$2(3 - 4z)(3 + 4z)$**
3. $169x^2 - 25y^2$ **$(13x - 5y)(13x + 5y)$**
4. $n^2 - 6n + 9$ **$(n - 3)^2$**
5. $100a^2 + 20a + 1$ **$(10a + 1)^2$**
6. $8r^2 - 40rs + 50s^2$ **$2(2r - 5s)^2$**

Factor the polynomial completely. *(p. 606)*

7. $3x^5 - 75x^3$ **$3x^3(x - 5)(x + 5)$**
8. $72s^4 - 8s^2$ **$8s^2(3s - 1)(3s + 1)$**
9. $3x^4y - 300x^2y$ **$3x^2y(x - 10)(x + 10)$**
10. $a^3 - 4a^2 - 21a$ **$a(a - 7)(a + 3)$**
11. $2h^4 + 28h^3 + 98h^2$ **$2h^2(h + 7)^2$**
12. $z^3 - 4z^2 - 16z + 64$ **$(z + 4)(z - 4)^2$**

Solve the equation.

13. $x^2 + 10x + 25 = 0$ *(p. 600)* **-5**
14. $48 - 27m^2 = 0$ *(p. 600)* **$\pm\frac{4}{3}$**
15. $w^3 - w^2 - 4w + 4 = 0$ *(p. 606)* **1, ±2**
16. $4x^3 - 28x^2 + 40x = 0$ *(p. 606)* **0, 2, 5**
17. $3x^5 - 6x^4 - 45x^3 = 0$ *(p. 606)* **0, −3, 5**
18. $x^3 - 121x = 0$ *(p. 606)* **0, ±11**

19. **VOLUME** The cylinder shown has a volume of 72π cubic inches. *(p. 600)*

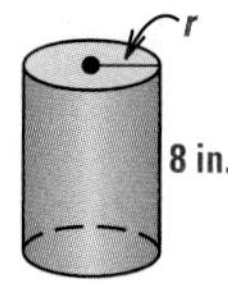

a. Write a polynomial that represents the volume of the cylinder. Leave your answer in terms of π. **$8\pi r^2$**

b. Find the radius of the cylinder. **3 in.**

75–86. See Additional Answers beginning on p. AA1.

5 ASSESS AND RETEACH

Daily Homework Quiz

Transparency Available

Factor the polynomial completely.

1. $40b^5 - 5b^3$ **$5b^3(8b^2 - 1)$**
2. $x^3 + 6x^2 - 7x$ **$x(x - 1)(x + 7)$**
3. $y^3 + 6y^2 - y - 6$ **$(y + 6)(y + 1)(y - 1)$**
4. Solve $2x^3 + 18x^2 = -40x$. **−5, −4, 0**
5. A sewing kit has a volume of 72 cubic inches. Its dimensions are width w, length $w + 1$, and height $9 - w$ inches. The height is less than 5 inches. Find the dimensions of the kit. **8 in. by 9 in. by 1 in.**

Online Quiz

Available at **classzone.com**

Diagnosis/Remediation

- Practice A, B, C in Chapter Resource Book
- Study Guide in Chapter Resource Book
- Practice Workbook
- @HomeTutor

Challenge

Additional challenge is available in the Chapter Resource Book.

Quiz

An easily-readable reduced copy of the quiz (with answers) on Lessons 9.7–9.8 from the Assessment Book can be found on p. 552E.

Lessons 9.5–9.8

1. **MULTI-STEP PROBLEM** A rectangular room has the dimensions shown.

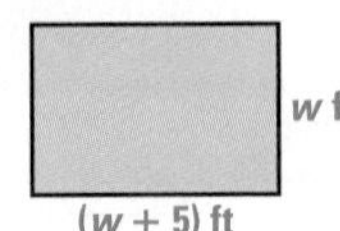

   a. Write a polynomial that represents the area of the room. $w^2 + 5w$

   b. The room has an area of 150 square feet. What are the length and width of the room? **15 ft, 10 ft**

2. **MULTI-STEP PROBLEM** A block of clay has the dimensions shown.

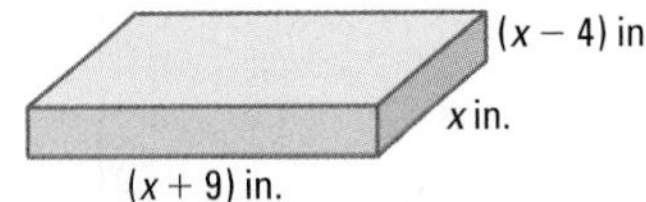

   a. Write a polynomial that represents the volume of the clay. $x^3 + 5x^2 - 36x$

   b. The clay has a volume of 180 cubic inches. What are the length, width, and height of the block? **15 in., 6 in., 2 in.**

3. **MULTI-STEP PROBLEM** You are making a wooden game board. You cut a square piece of wood, as shown.

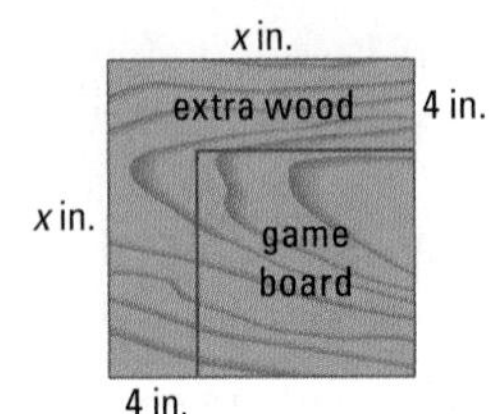

   a. Write a polynomial that represents the area of the game board. $x^2 - 8x + 16$

   b. The area of the game board is 100 square inches. What was the area of the original piece of wood? *Explain* how you found your answer. **See margin.**

4. **OPEN-ENDED** *Describe* a situation that can be modeled using the vertical motion model $h = -16t^2 + 48t$. Then find the value of t when $h = 0$. *Explain* what this value of t means in this situation. **See margin.**

5. **EXTENDED RESPONSE** You hit a baseball straight up into the air. The baseball is hit with an initial vertical velocity of 80 feet per second when it is 3 feet off the ground.

   a. Write an equation that gives the height (in feet) of the baseball as a function of the time (in seconds) since it was hit. $h = -16t^2 + 80t + 3$

   b. After how many seconds does the ball reach a height of 99 feet? **2 sec**

   c. Does the ball reach a height of 99 feet more than once? *Justify* your answer. **See margin.**

6. **EXTENDED RESPONSE** The length of a box is 25 inches more than its height. The width of the box is 1 inch less than its height.

   a. Draw a diagram of the box. Label its dimensions in terms of the height h. **See margin.**

   b. Write a polynomial that represents the volume of the box. $h^3 + 24h^2 - 25h$

   c. The box has a volume of 600 cubic inches. What is the area of its top? *Explain*. **See margin.**

7. **SHORT RESPONSE** A tennis player hits a ball with an initial vertical velocity of 63 feet per second. Can you find the number of seconds the tennis ball is in the air? *Explain* why not or find the number of seconds. **See margin.**

8. **GRIDDED ANSWER** During an experiment in physics class, you drop a ball from a height of 144 feet. After how many seconds does the ball hit the ground? **3 sec**

9. **SHORT RESPONSE** A football is kicked toward a goal post that is 10 feet high. The path of the football is modeled by the graph of $y = -0.005x^2 + 0.6x$ where x and y are measured in feet. On a coordinate plane, the x-axis represents the ground, and the ball leaves the ground at the origin. The ball hits the goal post on the way down. How far from the goal post is the kicker? *Explain*. **See margin.**

3b. 196 in.^{2}; set the area polynomial from part (a) equal to 100 and solve for x. There are two solutions, $x = 14$ and $x = -6$. Because x represents a length in this situation, x cannot be negative, so disregard the solution $x = -6$. The length of a side of the original piece of wood is 14 inches, so its area is $14^2 = 196$ square inches.

4. *Sample answer:* A ball is kicked from the ground with an initial vertical velocity of 48 feet per second; 0, 3; the starting time is 0, the ball lands back on the ground after 3 seconds.

5c. Yes; to find the values of t for which the height is 99 feet, solve the equation $99 = -16t^2 + 80t + 3$. The equation has two solutions, $t = 2$ and $t = 3$, so the ball reaches the height of 99 feet twice, after 2 seconds and after 3 seconds.

6a.

h in.
(h − 1) in.
(h + 25) in.

6c. 120 in.^{2}; to find the height h of the box, set the volume polynomial from part (b) equal to 600 and solve for h; the only positive solution is $h = 5$ inches, so the length and width of the top of the box are $h + 25 = 5 + 25 = 30$ inches and $h - 1 = 5 - 1 = 4$ inches. So the area of the top of the box is $30(4) = 120$ square inches.

7. No; we are not given the initial height from which the ball is hit. We do not know the value of s in the vertical motion model $h = -16t^2 + vt + s$.

9. 100 ft. *Sample answer:* Replacing y in the equation $y = -0.005x^2 + 0.6x$ with 10 and solving for x gives $x = 20$ and $x = 100$. The lesser value is the distance from the kicker while the ball is on its way up and the greater value is the distance while the ball is on its way down. So the kicker is 100 feet from the goal post.

BIG IDEAS *For Your Notebook*

Big Idea 1 Adding, Subtracting, and Multiplying Polynomials

You can perform operations with polynomials using the steps below.

Operation	Steps
Add	Group like terms and add.
Subtract	First, rewrite subtraction as addition. Second, group like terms and add.
Multiply	First, multiply terms using the distributive property. Second, combine like terms.

Big Idea 2 Factoring Polynomials

When factoring a polynomial, you should use the following checklist so that you can be sure you have factored the polynomial completely.

STEP 1 **Factor** out the greatest common monomial factor.

STEP 2 **Look** for special products to factor.

STEP 3 **Factor** a trinomial into a pair of binomials, if possible.

STEP 4 **Factor** a polynomial with four terms by grouping, if possible.

Big Idea 3 Writing and Solving Polynomial Equations to Solve Problems

You can write polynomials that model real-world situations in order to solve problems. For example, you can use the vertical motion model.

Height (in feet) of a projectile: $h = -16t^2 + vt + s$ where t is the time (in seconds) the object has been in the air, v is the initial vertical velocity (in feet per second), and s is the initial height (in feet).

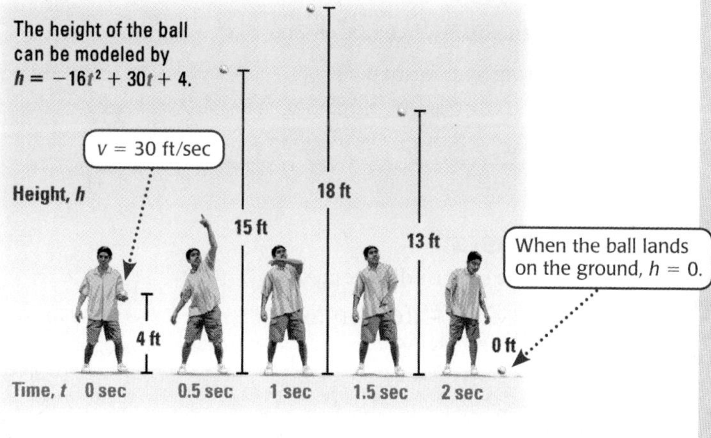

Additional Resources

The following resources are available to help review the materials in this chapter.

Chapter Resource Book

- Chapter Review Games and Activities
- Cumulative Practice, Chs. 1–9

Student Resources in Spanish

eWorkbook

@HomeTutor

Vocabulary Practice

Vocabulary practice is available at **classzone.com**

9 CHAPTER REVIEW

@HomeTutor
classzone.com
- Multi-Language Glossary
- Vocabulary practice

Extra Example 9.1
Find the sum
$(3x^3 - x^2 + 6) + (-x^3 + 3x^2 + x)$.
$2x^3 + 2x^2 + x + 6$

3. A factorable polynomial with integer coefficients is factored completely if it is written as a product of unfactorable polynomials with integer coefficients.
Sample answer: $3x(x - 4)(2x + 1)$

REVIEW KEY VOCABULARY

- monomial, *p. 554*
- degree of a monomial, *p. 554*
- polynomial, *p. 554*
- degree of a polynomial, *p. 554*
- leading coefficient, *p. 554*
- binomial, *p. 555*
- trinomial, *p. 555*
- roots, *p. 575*
- vertical motion model, *p. 577*
- perfect square trinomial, *p. 601*
- factor by grouping, *p. 606*
- factor completely, *p. 607*

VOCABULARY EXERCISES

1. Copy and complete: The greatest degree of the terms in a polynomial is called the __?__. **degree of the polynomial**
2. **WRITING** Is $2x^{-1}$ a monomial? *Explain* why or why not.
   No; a monomial cannot have a negative exponent.
3. **WRITING** What does it mean for a polynomial to be factored completely? Give an example of a polynomial that has been factored completely. **See margin.**

In Exercises 4–6, match the polynomial with its classification.

4. $5x - 22$ **B**
5. $-11x^3$ **A**
6. $x^2 + x + 1$ **C**

A. Monomial
B. Binomial
C. Trinomial

REVIEW EXAMPLES AND EXERCISES

Use the review examples and exercises below to check your understanding of the concepts you have learned in each lesson of Chapter 9.

9.1 Add and Subtract Polynomials *pp. 554–559*

EXAMPLE

Find the difference $(3x^2 + 2) - (4x^2 - x - 9)$.

Use a vertical format.

$$\begin{array}{rr} & 3x^2 \quad\quad + 2 \\ - & (4x^2 - x - 9) \\ \hline \end{array} \quad\longrightarrow\quad \begin{array}{rr} & 3x^2 \quad\quad + 2 \\ + & -4x^2 + x + 9 \\ \hline & -x^2 + x + 11 \end{array}$$

EXERCISES

EXAMPLES 3 and 4 on pp. 555–556 for Exs. 7–12

Find the sum or difference.

7. $(9x + 6x^3 - 8x^2) + (-5x^3 + 6x)$
   $x^3 - 8x^2 + 15x$
8. $(7a^3 - 4a^2 - 2a + 1) + (a^3 - 1)$
   $8a^3 - 4a^2 - 2a$
9. $(11y^5 + 3y^2 - 4) + (y^2 - y + 1)$
   $11y^5 + 4y^2 - y - 3$
10. $(3n^2 - 4n + 1) - (8n^2 - 4n + 17)$
    $-5n^2 - 16$
11. $(2s^3 + 8) - (-3s^3 + 7s - 5)$
    $5s^3 - 7s + 13$
12. $(-k^2 + 7k + 5) - (2k^4 - 3k^3 - 6)$
    $-2k^4 + 3k^3 - k^2 + 7k + 11$

9.2 Multiply Polynomials

pp. 562–568

EXAMPLE

Find the product.

a. $(x^2 + 4x - 5)(2x - 1)$ **b.** $(5y + 6)(y - 3)$

Solution

a. Use a horizontal format.

$(x^2 + 4x - 5)(2x - 1)$ **Write product.**

$= x^2(2x - 1) + 4x(2x - 1) - 5(2x - 1)$ **Distributive property**

$= 2x^3 - x^2 + 8x^2 - 4x - 10x + 5$ **Distributive property**

$= 2x^3 + 7x^2 - 14x + 5$ **Combine like terms.**

b. Use a vertical format.

STEP 1 **Multiply** by −3.

$$\begin{array}{r} 5y + 6 \\ \times \quad y - 3 \\ \hline -15y - 18 \end{array}$$

STEP 2 **Multiply** by y.

$$\begin{array}{r} 5y + 6 \\ \times \quad y - 3 \\ \hline -15y - 18 \\ 5y^2 + 6y \quad\quad \end{array}$$

STEP 3 **Add** products.

$$\begin{array}{r} 5y + 6 \\ \times \quad y - 3 \\ \hline -15y - 18 \\ 5y^2 + 6y \quad\quad \\ \hline 5y^2 - 9y - 18 \end{array}$$

EXERCISES

EXAMPLES 1, 2, 3, and 4 on pp. 562–563 for Exs. 13–21

Find the product.

13. $(x^2 - 2x + 1)(x - 3)$ $\mathbf{x^3 - 5x^2 + 7x - 3}$

14. $(y^2 + 5y + 4)(3y + 2)$ $\mathbf{3y^3 + 17y^2 + 22y + 8}$

15. $(x - 4)(x + 2)$ $\mathbf{x^2 - 2x - 8}$

16. $(5b^2 - b - 7)(b + 6)$ $\mathbf{5b^3 + 29b^2 - 13b - 42}$

17. $(z + 8)(z - 11)$ $\mathbf{z^2 - 3z - 88}$

18. $(2a - 1)(a - 3)$ $\mathbf{2a^2 - 7a + 3}$

19. $(6n + 7)(3n + 1)$ $\mathbf{18n^2 + 27n + 7}$

20. $(4n - 5)(7n - 3)$ $\mathbf{28n^2 - 47n + 15}$

21. $(3x - 2)(x + 4)$ $\mathbf{3x^2 + 10x - 8}$

9.3 Find Special Products of Polynomials

pp. 569–574

EXAMPLE

Find the product $(3x + 2)(3x - 2)$.

$(3x + 2)(3x - 2) = (3x)^2 - 2^2$ **Sum and difference pattern**

$= 9x^2 - 4$ **Simplify.**

EXERCISES

EXAMPLES 1 and 2 on pp. 569–570 for Exs. 22–27

Find the product.

22. $(x + 11)^2$ $\mathbf{x^2 + 22x + 121}$

23. $(6y + 1)^2$ $\mathbf{36y^2 + 12y + 1}$

24. $(2x - y)^2$ $\mathbf{4x^2 - 4xy + y^2}$

25. $(4a - 3)^2$ $\mathbf{16a^2 - 24a + 9}$

26. $(k + 7)(k - 7)$ $\mathbf{k^2 - 49}$

27. $(3s + 5)(3s - 5)$ $\mathbf{9s^2 - 25}$

Extra Example 9.2

Find the product.

a. $(5y + 4)(y - 2)$ $\mathbf{5y^2 - 6y - 8}$

b. $(s^2 + 3s - 6)(4s - 2)$ $\mathbf{4s^3 + 10s^2 - 30s + 12}$

Extra Example 9.3

Find the product $(4x + 3)^2$.

$\mathbf{16x^2 + 24x + 9}$

Extra Example 9.4

Solve $4x^2 = 18x$. $0, \frac{9}{2}$

Extra Example 9.5

Factor $x^2 - 3x - 54$.
$(x + 6)(x - 9)$

9.4 Solve Polynomial Equations in Factored Form

pp. 575–580

EXAMPLE

Solve $6x^2 + 42x = 0$.

$6x^2 + 42x = 0$	**Write original equation.**
$6x(x + 7) = 0$	**Factor left side.**
$6x = 0$ *or* $x + 7 = 0$	**Zero-product property**
$x = 0$ *or* $x = -7$	**Solve for x.**

▸ The solutions of the equation are 0 and −7.

EXERCISES

EXAMPLES 3 and 4 on p. 576 for Exs. 28–33

Solve the equation.

28. $2a^2 + 26a = 0$ **0, −13**
29. $3t^2 - 33t = 0$ **0, 11**
30. $8x^2 - 4x = 0$ **$0, \frac{1}{2}$**
31. $m^2 = 9m$ **0, 9**
32. $5y^2 = -50y$ **0, −10**
33. $21h^2 = 7h$ **$0, \frac{1}{3}$**

9.5 Factor $x^2 + bx + c$

pp. 583–589

EXAMPLE

Factor $x^2 + 2x - 63$.

Find two factors of −63 whose sum is 2. One factor will be positive, and the other will be negative. Make an organized list of factors.

Factors of −63	Sum of factors	
1, −63	1 + (−63) = −62	✗
−1, 63	−1 + 63 = 62	✗
3, −21	3 + (−21) = −18	✗
−3, 21	−3 + 21 = 18	✗
9, −7	9 + (−7) = 2	← Correct sum
−9, 7	−9 + 7 = −2	✗

▸ $x^2 + 2x - 63 = (x + 9)(x - 7)$

EXERCISES

EXAMPLES 1,2 and 3 on pp. 583–584 for Exs. 34–42

Factor the trinomial.

34. $n^2 + 15n + 26$ **$(n + 13)(n + 2)$**
35. $s^2 + 10s - 11$ **$(s + 11)(s - 1)$**
36. $b^2 - 5b - 14$ **$(b - 7)(b + 2)$**
37. $a^2 + 5a - 84$ **$(a + 12)(a - 7)$**
38. $t^2 - 24t + 135$ **$(t - 9)(t - 15)$**
39. $x^2 + 4x - 32$ **$(x + 8)(x - 4)$**
40. $p^2 + 9p + 14$ **$(p + 7)(p + 2)$**
41. $c^2 + 8c + 15$ **$(c + 5)(c + 3)$**
42. $y^2 - 10y + 21$ **$(y - 7)(y - 3)$**

9.6 Factor $ax^2 + bx + c$ *pp. 593–599*

EXAMPLE

THROWN BALL You throw a ball up into the air. At 4 feet above the ground, the ball leaves your hand with an initial vertical velocity of 30 feet per second.

a. Write an equation that gives the height (in feet) of the ball as a function of the time (in seconds) since it left your hand.

b. After how many seconds does the ball land on the ground?

Solution

a. Use the vertical motion model $h = -16t^2 + vt + s$ to write an equation for the height h (in feet) of the ball as a function of the time t (in seconds). In this case, $v = 30$ and $s = 4$.

$h = -16t^2 + vt + s$ **Vertical motion model**

$h = -16t^2 + 30t + 4$ **Substitute 30 for *v* and 4 for *s*.**

b. When the ball lands on the ground, its height is 0 feet. Substitute 0 for h and solve the equation for t.

$0 = -16t^2 + 30t + 4$ **Substitute 0 for *h*.**

$0 = -2(8t^2 - 15t - 2)$ **Factor out −2.**

$0 = -2(8t + 1)(t - 2)$ **Factor the trinomial. Find factors of 8 and −2 that produce a middle term with a coefficient of −15.**

$8t + 1 = 0$ *or* $t - 2 = 0$ **Zero-product property**

$t = -\frac{1}{8}$ *or* $t = 2$ **Solve for *t*.**

The solutions of the equation are $-\frac{1}{8}$ and 2. A negative solution does not make sense in this situation, so disregard $-\frac{1}{8}$.

▶ The ball lands on the ground after 2 seconds.

EXERCISES

EXAMPLES 1, 2, 3, and 4 on pp. 593–595 for Exs. 43–50

Solve the equation.

43. $7x^2 - 8x = -1$ **$\frac{1}{7}$, 1**

44. $4n^2 + 3 = 7n$ **$\frac{3}{4}$, 1**

45. $3s^2 + 4s + 4 = 8$ **$\frac{2}{3}$, −2**

46. $6z^2 + 13z = 5$ **$\frac{1}{3}$, $-\frac{5}{2}$**

47. $-4r^2 = 18r + 18$ **$-\frac{3}{2}$, −3**

48. $9a^2 = 6a + 24$ **$-\frac{4}{3}$, 2**

49. THROWN BALL You throw a ball up into the air with an initial vertical velocity of 46 feet per second. The ball leaves your hand when it is 6 feet above the ground. After how many seconds does the ball land on the ground? **3 sec**

50. GEOMETRY The length of a rectangle is 1 inch less than twice the width. The area of the rectangle is 21 square inches. What is the length of the rectangle? **6 in.**

Extra Example 9.6

You throw a ball up into the air with an initial vertical velocity of 38 feet per second. The ball leaves your hand at 5 feet above the ground.

a. Write an equation that gives the height (in feet) of the ball as a function of the time (in seconds) since it left your hand. **$h = -16t^2 + 38t + 5$**

b. After how many seconds does the ball land on the ground? **2.5 sec**

Extra Example 9.7

Factor the polynomial.

a. $a^2 - 36y^2$ $(a - 6y)(a + 6y)$

b. $9x^2 + 12x + 4$ $(3x + 2)^2$

Extra Example 9.8

Factor the polynomial completely.

a. $c^3 - 7c^2 + 3c - 21$ $(c - 7)(c^2 + 3)$

b. $4y^3 + 24y^2 + 36y$ $4y(y + 3)^2$

9.7 Factor Special Products

pp. 600–605

EXAMPLE

Factor the polynomial.

a. $100x^2 - y^2$

b. $4x^2 - 36x + 81$

Solution

a. $100x^2 - y^2 = (10x)^2 - y^2$ — Write as $a^2 - b^2$.

$= (10x + y)(10x - y)$ — Difference of two squares pattern

b. $4x^2 - 36x + 81 = (2x)^2 - 2(2x \cdot 9) + 9^2$ — Write as $a^2 - 2ab + b^2$.

$= (2x - 9)^2$ — Perfect square trinomial pattern

EXERCISES

EXAMPLES 1, 2, 3, 4, and 6 on pp. 600–602 for Exs. 51–57

Factor the polynomial.

51. $z^2 - 225$ $(z - 15)(z + 15)$

52. $a^2 - 16y^2$ $(a - 4y)(a + 4y)$

53. $12 - 48n^2$ $12(1 - 2n)(1 + 2n)$

54. $x^2 + 20x + 100$ $(x + 10)^2$

55. $16p^2 - 8p + 1$ $(4p - 1)^2$

56. $-2y^2 + 32y - 128$ $-2(y - 8)^2$

57. **DROPPED OBJECT** You drop a penny from a height of 16 feet. After how many seconds does the penny land on the ground? **1 sec**

9.8 Factor Polynomials Completely

pp. 606–613

EXAMPLE

Factor the polynomial completely.

a. $y^3 - 4y^2 + 8y - 32$

b. $5x^3 - 40x^2 + 80x$

Solution

a. $y^3 - 4y^2 + 8y - 32 = (y^3 - 4y^2) + (8y - 32)$ — Group terms.

$= y^2(y - 4) + 8(y - 4)$ — Factor each group.

$= (y - 4)(y^2 + 8)$ — Distributive property

b. $5x^3 - 40x^2 + 80x = 5x(x^2 - 8x + 16)$ — Factor out 5x.

$= 5x(x - 4)^2$ — Perfect square trinomial pattern

EXERCISES

EXAMPLE 4 on p. 608 for Exs. 58–66

Factor the polynomial completely.

58. $a^3 + 6a - 5a^2 - 30$ $(a^2 + 6)(a - 5)$

59. $y^2 + 3y + yx + 3x$ $(y + 3)(y + x)$

60. $x^3 - 11x^2 - x + 11$ $(x - 11)(x - 1)(x + 1)$

61. $5s^4 - 125s^2$ $5s^2(s - 5)(s + 5)$

62. $147n^5 - 3n^3$ $3n^3(7n - 1)(7n + 1)$

63. $2z^3 + 2z^2 - 60z$ $2z(z + 6)(z - 5)$

64. $x^3 + 5x^2 - x - 5$ $(x + 5)(x + 1)(x - 1)$

65. $2b^3 + 3b^2 - 8b - 12$ $(2b + 3)(b - 2)(b + 2)$

66. $x^3 + x^2 - 6x - 6$ $(x + 1)(x^2 - 6)$

Find the sum or difference.

1. $(a^2 - 4a + 6) + (-3a^2 + 13a + 1)$ **$-2a^2 + 9a + 7$**
2. $(5x^2 - 2) + (8x^3 + 2x^2 - x + 9)$ **$8x^3 + 7x^2 - x + 7$**
3. $(15n^2 + 7n - 1) - (4n^2 - 3n - 8)$ **$11n^2 + 10n + 7$**
4. $(9c^3 - 11c^2 + 2c) - (-6c^2 - 3c + 11)$ **$9c^3 - 5c^2 + 5c - 11$**

Find the product.

5. $(2z + 9)(z - 7)$ **$2z^2 - 5z - 63$**
6. $(5m - 8)(5m - 7)$ **$25m^2 - 75m + 56$**
7. $(b + 2)(-b^2 + 4b - 3)$ **$-b^3 + 2b^2 + 5b - 6$**
8. $(5 + 7y)(1 - 9y)$ **$5 - 38y - 63y^2$**
9. $(2x^2 - 3x + 5)(x - 4)$ **$2x^3 - 11x^2 + 17x - 20$**
10. $(5p - 6)(5p + 6)$ **$25p^2 - 36$**
11. $(12 - 3g)^2$ **$144 - 72g + 9g^2$**
12. $(2s + 9t)^2$ **$4s^2 + 36st + 81t^2$**
13. $(11a - 4b)(11a + 4b)$ **$121a^2 - 16b^2$**

Factor the polynomial.

14. $x^2 + 8x + 7$ **$(x + 7)(x + 1)$**
15. $2n^2 - 11n + 15$ **$(2n - 5)(n - 3)$**
16. $-12r^2 + 5r + 3$ **$-(3r + 1)(4r - 3)$**
17. $t^2 - 10t + 25$ **$(t - 5)^2$**
18. $-3n^2 + 75$ **$-3(n - 5)(n + 5)$**
19. $3x^2 + 29x - 44$ **$(3x - 4)(x + 11)$**
20. $x^2 - 49$ **$(x - 7)(x + 7)$**
21. $2a^4 + 21a^3 + 49a^2$ **$a^2(2a + 7)(a + 7)$**
22. $y^3 + 2y^2 - 81y - 162$ **$(y + 2)(y - 9)(y + 9)$**

Solve the equation.

23. $25a = 10a^2$ **$0, \frac{5}{2}$**
24. $21z^2 + 85z - 26 = 0$ **$-\frac{13}{3}, \frac{2}{7}$**
25. $x^2 - 22x = -121$ **11**
26. $a^2 - 11a + 24 = 0$ **3, 8**
27. $t^2 + 7t = 60$ **$-12, 5$**
28. $4x^2 = 22x + 42$ **$-\frac{3}{2}, 7$**
29. $56b^2 + b = 1$ **$\frac{1}{8}, -\frac{1}{7}$**
30. $n^3 - 121n = 0$ **$0, \pm 11$**
31. $a^3 + a^2 = 64a + 64$ **$-1, \pm 8$**

32. **VERTICAL MOTION** A cricket jumps off the ground with an initial vertical velocity of 4 feet per second.
    a. Write an equation that gives the height (in feet) of the cricket as a function of the time (in seconds) since it jumps. **$h = -16t^2 + 4t$**
    b. After how many seconds does the cricket land on the ground? **0.25 sec**

33. **POSTER AREA** Two posters have the lengths and widths shown. The posters have the same area.
    a. Write an equation that relates the areas of the two posters. **$3w^2 = 2w(w + 2)$**
    b. Find the length and width of each poster. **12 ft, 4 ft; 8 ft, 6 ft**

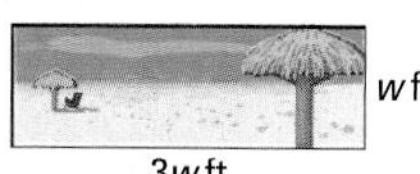

34. **CONSTRUCTION** A construction worker is working on the roof of a building. A drop of paint falls from a rafter that is 225 feet above the ground. After how many seconds does the paint hit the ground? **3.75 sec**

35. **BOX DIMENSIONS** A cardboard box that is a rectangular prism has the dimensions shown.
    a. Write a polynomial that represents the volume of the box. **$x^3 + 3x^2 - 16x + 12$**
    b. The volume of the box is 60 cubic inches. What are the length, width, and height of the box? **10 in., 2 in., 3 in.**

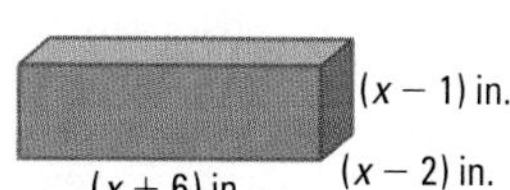

Additional Resources

Assessment Book

- Chapter Test, Levels A, B, C
- Standardized Chapter Test
- SAT/ACT Chapter Test
- Alternative Assessment

Test Generator

Chapter Test

Easily-readable reduced copies (with answers) of Chapter Test B, the Standardized Chapter Test, and the Alternative Assessment from the Assessment Book can be found on pp. 552E–552F.

Using Rubrics

The rubric given on the pupil page is a sample of a three-level rubric. Other rubrics may contain four, five, or six levels. For more information on rubrics, see the *Differentiated Instruction Resources*.

Test-Taking Strategy

Encourage students to draw diagrams or models to help them visualize and solve problems. This is a useful strategy for a range of problems, including problems that involve area, perimeter, volume, patterns, and counting techniques. Diagrams often support an answer, so stress to students that a diagram should be understandable, it should have labels, and it should clearly show what its relationship is to the test question.

Avoiding Common Errors

Remind students that as equations become more complex, it becomes more important to write legibly to avoid calculation errors and loss of credit because the calculations appear incorrect. Caution students to write powers in superscript and to distinguish between the multiplication symbol × and the variable *x*.

Avoiding Common Errors

Students often perform calculations correctly and include appropriate explanations for short response questions, but fail to answer the right question. Remind students to re-read the original problem to make sure that they have answered the question posed in the problem.

Scoring Rubric

Full Credit
- solution is complete and correct

Partial Credit
- solution is complete but errors are made,

or
- solution is without error but incomplete

No Credit
- no solution is given,

or
- solution makes no sense

SHORT RESPONSE QUESTIONS

PROBLEM

A rectangular photo has an area of 24 square inches. You trim the photo so that it fits into a square frame. You trim 3 inches from the length and 1 inch from the width of the photo. Write and solve an equation to find the side length of the resulting square photo. *Explain* how you chose one solution of the equation to find the side length.

Below are sample solutions to the problem. Read each solution and the comments on the left to see why the sample represents full credit, partial credit, or no credit.

SAMPLE 1: Full credit solution

A diagram shows how the equation is obtained.

Draw a diagram. Use the formula for the area of a rectangle.

$A = \ell \cdot w$

$= (x + 3)(x + 1)$

$= x^2 + 4x + 3$

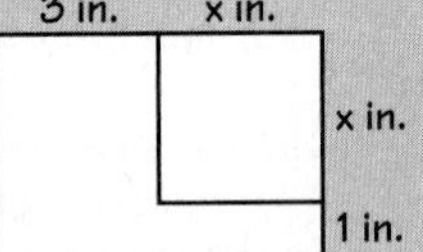

The correct calculations are performed.

Substitute 24 for A and solve.

$24 = x^2 + 4x + 3$

$0 = x^2 + 4x - 21$

$0 = (x - 3)(x + 7)$

$0 = x - 3$ *or* $0 = x + 7$

$x = 3$ *or* $x = -7$

The question is answered correctly and includes an explanation.

A solution represents the side length of the square photo. A negative side length does not make sense, so choose $x = 3$. The side length is 3 inches.

SAMPLE 2: Partial credit solution

The length of the rectangular photo is $x + 3$. The width is $x + 1$.

The equation is correct, and the student has explained how it was obtained.

$A = (x + 3)(x + 1)$

$24 = x^2 + 4x + 3$

$0 = x^2 + 4x - 21$

$0 = (x - 3)(x + 7)$

$x = 3$ *or* $x = -7$

The question is answered correctly but does not include an explanation.

The side length of the square photo is 3 inches.

SAMPLE 3: Partial credit solution

The equation and its solutions are correct, but the student found the length and width of the original photo instead of the trimmed photo.

$24 = (x + 3)(x + 1)$
$0 = x^2 + 4x - 21$
$0 = (x - 3)(x + 7)$
$x = 3 \quad or \quad x = -7$

A negative solution does not make sense in the situation. The length is $3 + 3 = 6$ inches, and the width is $3 + 1 = 4$ inches.

SAMPLE 4: No credit solution

The student's reasoning is incorrect, and the equation is incorrect. The answer is incorrect.

$(x - 3)(x - 1) = 24$
$x^2 - 4x - 21 = 0$
$(x - 3)(x + 7) = 0$

$x = -3$ or 7, so the side length of the square is 7 inches.

PRACTICE Apply the Scoring Rubric

Score the solution to the problem below as *full credit, partial credit,* or *no credit. Explain* your reasoning.

PROBLEM You are making a banner for a surprise birthday party. The banner will have the dimensions shown in the diagram. Its area will be 6 square feet. Write and solve an equation to find the length and width of the banner. *Explain* your reasoning.

Happy Birthday $(x - 7)$ ft
$(x - 2)$ ft

1.

$6 = (x - 2)(x - 7)$
$6 = x^2 - 9x + 14$
$0 = x^2 - 9x + 8$
$0 = (x - 8)(x - 1)$
$x = 8$ or $x = 1$

In this problem, the solutions of the equation are 8 and 1. If $x = 1$, then the width of the banner is $x - 7 = -6$. A width cannot be negative, so disregard the solution $x = 1$.

The length of the banner is $8 - 2 = 6$ feet, and the width is $8 - 7 = 1$ foot.

2.

$6 = (x - 2)(x - 7)$
$6 = x^2 - 2x - 7x + 14$
$0 = x^2 - 9x + 20$
$0 = (x - 5)(x - 4)$
$x = 5$ or $x = 4$

The equation has two solutions. They are 5 and 4. So, the width of the banner is 5 feet, and the length of the banner is 4 feet.

Answers

1. Partial credit; the equation and its solution are correct, but the student did not explain how the equation was obtained. The question is answered correctly and includes an explanation.

2. No credit; although the equation is correct, the student did not explain how the equation was obtained and made an error in solving the equation. The student's reasoning about how to interpret the solutions of the equation is incorrect and the answer is incorrect.

Answers

1a. $h = -16t^2 + 10t$

1b. $0, \frac{5}{8}$; the zero $t = 0$ seconds means that the cat is on the ground at the start of its jump, and the zero $t = \frac{5}{8}$ second means that the cat lands back on the ground after $\frac{5}{8}$ second.

2a. $-w^3 + 16w^2 + 36w$

2b. 12 in., 6 in., 8 in.; to find the width of the tank, set the volume polynomial from part (a) equal to 576 (the given volume of the tank) and solve for w. The solutions are $w = 16$, $w = 6$, and $w = -6$. The length and width cannot be negative, so disregard the solution $w = -6$ because it makes the width negative, and disregard the solution $w = 16$ because it makes the length $18 - w$ less than 10. The width is 6 inches, so the length is $18 - 6 = 12$ inches and the height is $6 + 2 = 8$ inches.

3a. $h = -16t^2 + 36t + 5$

3b. Twice; to find the times(s) at which the ball reaches a height of 25 feet, substitute 25 for h in the equation from part (a) and solve for t; the solutions are $t = 1$ and $t = \frac{5}{4}$. The ball reaches the height of 25 feet two times, after 1 second and after $\frac{5}{4}$ seconds.

4a. 0 ft/sec; the pencil has no initial vertical velocity because it falls from a position of rest.

4b. 0.5 sec

5a. $S \cdot P = 0.22x^3 + 6.55x^2 - 13.7x + 4166.4$; the number of public school students in the United States enrolled in a foreign language class is the number of students multiplied by the percent of those students who are enrolled in a foreign language class.

5b. about 6,178,000 students

6a. $24 - x^2 = 80$; 4, 20, 4 ft

6b. The solution $x = 20$ feet does not make sense in this situation because if the path was 20 feet wide, it would be wider than the whole garden. Only a path width of 4 feet makes sense for a garden that is 16 feet long and 8 feet wide.

SHORT RESPONSE

1. A cat jumps straight up from the ground with an initial vertical velocity of 10 feet per second.
   a. Write an equation that gives the height of the cat (in feet) as a function of the time (in seconds) since it left the ground.
   b. Find the zeros of the function from part (a). *Explain* what the zeros mean in this situation.

2. A fish tank is shaped like a rectangular prism with a volume of 576 cubic inches. Its length is greater than 10 inches. The dimensions of the tank are shown in the diagram.

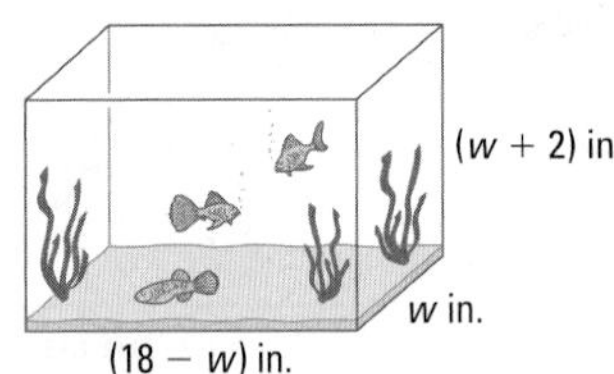

   a. Write a polynomial that represents the volume of the fish tank.
   b. Find the length, width, and height of the fish tank. *Explain* your reasoning using the solutions of the equation from part (a).

3. You throw a ball from an initial height of 5 feet and with an initial vertical velocity of 36 feet per second.
   a. Write an equation that gives the height of the ball (in feet) as a function of the time (in seconds) since it left your hand.
   b. How many times does the ball reach a height of 25 feet? *Explain* your reasoning using the function from part (a).

4. A pencil falls off a shelf with a height of 4 feet.
   a. What is the initial vertical velocity of the pencil? *Explain* your answer.
   b. After how many seconds does the pencil hit the ground?

5. During the period 1985–2000, the number S (in thousands) of students enrolled in public school in the United States and the percent p (in decimal form) of the students enrolled in public school who are also enrolled in a foreign language class can be modeled by

$$S = 27.5x^2 - 336x + 12{,}400 \text{ and}$$
$$p = 0.008x + 0.336$$

where x is the number of years since 1985.

   a. Write an equation that models the number (in thousands) of public school students in the United States enrolled in a foreign language class as a function of the number of years since 1985. *Explain* how you found this equation.
   b. How many public school students in the United States were enrolled in a foreign language class in 2000?

6. Students in an environmental club are planning a garden with four rectangular plots of land separated by stone paths, as shown. The stone paths will have the same width.

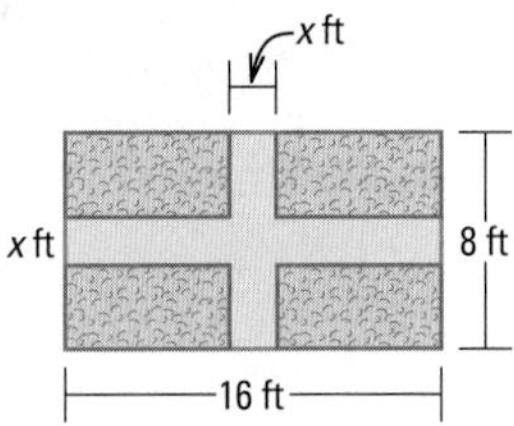

   a. The students plan to cover 80 square feet of path with stone. Write and solve an equation to find the width of the paths.
   b. In part (a) you used one solution of an equation to find your answer. *Explain* how you chose which solution to use.

7. The shape of an entrance to a tunnel can be modeled by the graph of the equation $y = -0.2x(x - 20)$ where x and y are measured in feet. On a coordinate plane, the ground is represented by the x-axis. How wide is the tunnel at its base? *Explain* how you found your answer.

7. 20 ft; substitute 0 for y in the equation $y = -0.2x(x - 20)$ and solve for x: $0 = -0.2x(x - 20)$, $x = 0$ and $x = 20$, which are the points where the tunnel touches the ground. The distance between 0 and 20 feet is 20 feet.

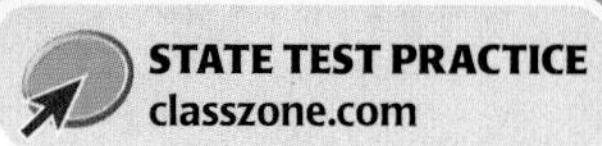

MULTIPLE CHOICE

8. Which is the correct factorization of $25x^2 - 144$?

   Ⓐ $(5x + 9)(5x - 16)$

   Ⓑ $(5x - 12)^2$

   Ⓒ $(5x + 18)(5x - 8)$

   Ⓓ $(5x - 12)(5x + 12)$

9. What are the solutions of the equation $(x + 4)(x - 12) = 0$?

   Ⓐ 4 and −12 Ⓑ 4 and 12

   Ⓒ −4 and −12 Ⓓ −4 and 12

10. What are the solutions of the equation $x^2 - 26 = 11x$?

   Ⓐ −2 and 13 Ⓑ 2 and 13

   Ⓒ −2 and −13 Ⓓ 2 and −13

GRIDDED ANSWER

11. The equation $x^2 - 20x + 100 = 0$ has two identical solutions. What is the solution of the equation?

12. The square of the binomial $x + 3$ has the form $x^2 + bx + 9$. What is the value of b?

13. What is the degree of the polynomial $6x^4 - 3x^2 + 10x$?

14. The function $f(x) = 4x^2 - 36$ has two zeros. What is the greater of the two zeros?

15. The area of a rectangle is 28 square inches. The length of the rectangle is 3 inches more than its width. What is the width (in inches) of the rectangle?

16. A pine cone falls from a tree branch that is 144 feet above the ground. After how many seconds does the pine cone land on the ground?

EXTENDED RESPONSE

17. The shape of a stone arch in a park can be modeled by the graph of the equation $y = -x^2 + 6x$ where x and y are measured in feet. On a coordinate plane, the ground is represented by the x-axis.
   a. Make a table of values that shows the height of the stone arch for $x = 0, 1, 2, 3, 4,$ and 5 feet.
   b. Plot the ordered pairs in the table from part (a) as points in a coordinate plane. Connect the points with a smooth curve.
   c. How wide is the base of the arch? *Justify* your answer using the zeros of the given function.
   d. At how many points does the arch reach a height of 9 feet? *Justify* your answer algebraically.

18. A box is a rectangular prism with a volume of 768 cubic inches. The length of the box is 4 inches more than its height. Its width is the difference of 16 and its height.
   a. Draw a diagram of the box and label its dimensions in terms of its height.
   b. Write a polynomial that represents the volume of the box.
   c. Use the polynomial from part (b) to find two sets of possible dimensions of the box.
   d. Which set of dimensions results in a box with the least possible surface area? *Explain* your reasoning.

8. D

9. D

10. A

11. 10

12. 6

13. 4

14. 3

15. 4 in.

16. 3 sec

17a.

x (feet)	y (feet)
0	0
1	5
2	8
3	9
4	8
5	5

17b.

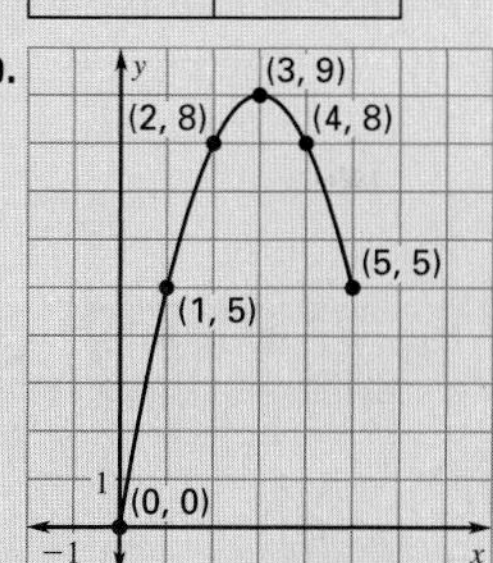

17c. 6 ft; the zeros of the function $y = -x^2 + 6x$ are the solutions of the equation $0 = -x^2 + 6x$, $x = 0$ and $x = 6$. These two x-values are the ends of the base of the arch, because at these x-values, the height y of the arch is 0. So, the arch is $6 - 0 = 6$ feet wide at the base.

17d. One; to find any points at which the arch reaches a height of 9 feet, substitute 9 for y in the equation $y = -x^2 + 6x$ and solve for x; the equation $9 = -x^2 + 6x$ becomes the equation $x^2 - 6x + 9 = 0$, or $(x - 3)^2 = 0$, an equation with one (double) root. So there is only one point at which the arch reaches a height of 9 feet.

18a.

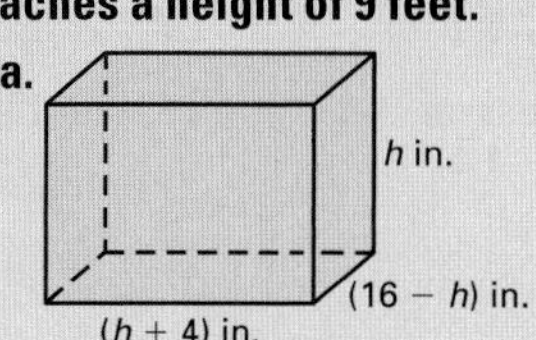

18b. $-h^3 + 14h^2 + 64h$

18c. 8 in. by 8 in. by 12 in., 4 in. by 12 in. by 16 in.

18d. 8 in. by 8 in. by 12 in. *Sample answer:* The surface area of the 8 by 8 by 12 prism is 512 in.^{2}, while the surface area of the 4 by 12 by 16 prism is 608 in.^{2}.

10 Pacing Guide

Chapter 10: Quadratic Equations and Functions

Chapter Table of Contents

PACING GUIDES

Easy Planner

Regular Schedule (50-minute classes)

DAY 1	DAY 2	DAY 3	DAY 4	DAY 5	DAY 6	DAY 7	DAY 8
Lesson 10.1	Lesson 10.1 (cont.)	Lesson 10.2 Extension 10.2	Lesson 10.3	Lesson 10.3 (cont.) Graphing Calc. Act. 10.3	Quiz for Less. 10.1–10.3 Lesson 10.4	Lesson 10.4 (cont.) Mixed Rev. of Prob. Solv.	Investigating Algebra Activity 10.5 Lesson 10.5

DAY 9	DAY 10	DAY 11	DAY 12	DAY 13	DAY 14	DAY 15	DAY 16
Lesson 10.5 (cont.) Extension 10.5	Lesson 10.6	Lesson 10.6 (cont.)	Quiz for Less. 10.4–10.6 Inv. Alg. Act. 10.7 Lesson 10.7	Lesson 10.8	Lesson 10.8 (cont.) Graphing Calc. Act. 10.8 Mixed Rev. of Prob. Solv.	Quiz for Less. 10.7–10.8 Chapter Review	Chapter Test

Block Schedule (90-minute classes)

DAY 1	DAY 2	DAY 3	DAY 4	DAY 5	DAY 6	DAY 7	DAY 8
Lesson 10.1	Lesson 10.2 Extension 10.2 Lesson 10.3	Lesson 10.3 (cont.) Graphing Calc. Act. 10.3 Quiz for Less. 10.1–10.3 Lesson 10.4	Lesson 10.4 (cont.) Mixed Rev. of Prob. Solv. Inv. Algebra Act. 10.5 Lesson 10.5	Lesson 10.5 (cont.) Extension 10.5 Lesson 10.6	Lesson 10.6 (cont.) Quiz for Less. 10.4–10.6 Inv. Algebra Activity 10.7 Lesson 10.7	Lesson 10.8 Graphing Calculator Activity 10.8 Mixed Review of Problem Solving	Quiz for Less. 10.7–10.8 Chapter Review Chapter Test

RESOURCE OPTIONS

Chapter/Lesson Resources

Chapter Resource Book
- Parents as Partners
- Teaching Guide/Lesson Plan
- Activity Masters
- Practice (3 levels)
- Study Guide
- Quick Catch-Up for Absent Students
- Problem Solving/Application
- Challenge Practice
- Chapter Review Games and Activities
- Project with Rubric
- Cumulative Review

Notetaking Guide
- Student Workbook and Teacher's Edition

Practice Workbook

Worked-Out Solution Key

Chapter Transparency Book
- Warm-Up Exercises/Daily Homework Quiz
- Notetaking Guide Transparencies
- Homework Answer Transparencies

Teacher Tools Transparencies

Assessment

Assessment Book
- Quizzes
- Chapter Tests (3 levels)
- Standardized and SAT/ACT Chapter Tests
- Alternative Assessments
- Cumulative Tests

Benchmark Tests
- Benchmark Tests, correlated to Remediation Book
- Pre-Course, Mid-Year, and End-of-Year Tests
- Chapter Tests

Spanish Assessment Book

Differentiated Instruction

Differentiated Instruction Resources
- Strategies for Reading Mathematics
- Differentiated Instruction Lesson Notes
- English Learner Lesson Notes
- Inclusion Lesson Notes
- Teaching Strategies with Sample Worksheets
- Tips for New Teachers/Math Background Notes
- Teacher Survival Activities/Bulletin Board Ideas

Student Resources in Spanish

Spanish Study Guide

Remediation Book

Skills Readiness (available on Easy Planner)
- Diagnostic Assessment
- Skill Instruction and Alternative Teaching Strategies
- Skill Practice and Enrichment Masters

Pre-AP Resources
- Pacing and Assignment Guide
- Best Practices
- Copymasters

Technology Resources

Plan	***Easy Planner***
Teach	***Video Tutor*** ***Activity Generator*** ***Power Presentations*** ***Animated Algebra***
Assess	***Test Generator*** ***ML Assessment System***
Reteach	***@HomeTutor***
Online Resources	***Classzone.com*** ***eEdition*** ***eWorkbook***

Video Tutor

Technology Highlights for Each Lesson

Easy Planner

Easy access to the Teacher's Edition and all teaching resources. Includes a search feature to locate the materials you need.

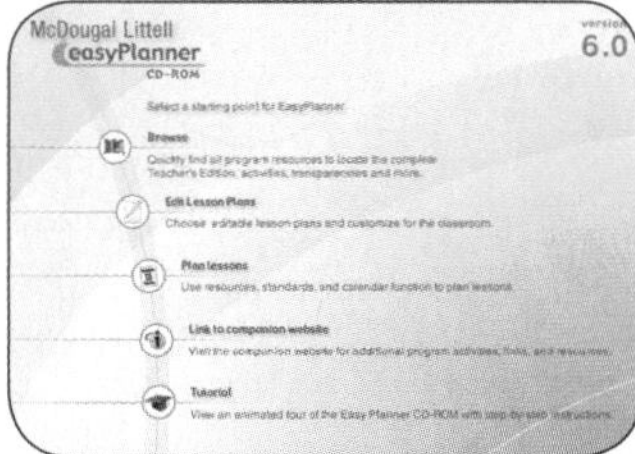

Activity Generator

Leveled, editable activities allow all students to explore a lesson's concepts. Includes teacher notes and closure questions.

Animated Algebra

Interactive tutorials provide visually engaging alternative opportunities to learn concepts and master skills.

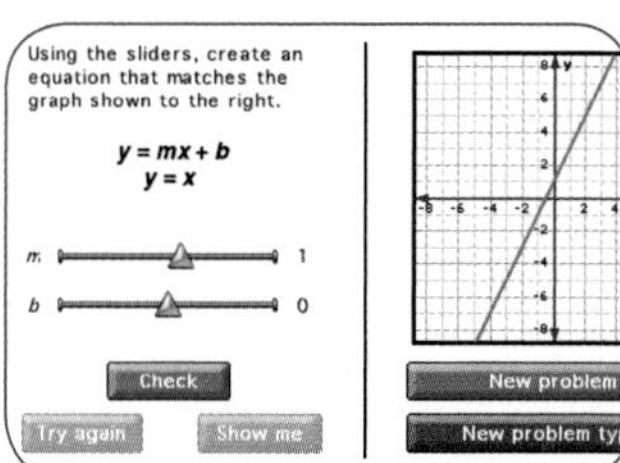

LESSON 10.1 **Practice B** For use with pages 628–634

Use the quadratic function to complete the table of values.

1. $y = 9x^2$

x	−2	−1	0	1	2
y	36	9	0	9	36

2. $y = -5x^2$

x	−2	−1	0	1	2
y	−20	−5	0	−5	−20

3. $y = \frac{5}{2}x^2 + 1$

x	−4	−2	0	2	4
y	41	11	1	11	41

4. $y = -\frac{1}{8}x^2 - 2$

x	−16	−8	0	8	16
y	−34	−10	−2	−10	−34

5. $y = -4x^2 + 3$

x	−2	−1	0	1	2
y	−13	−1	3	−1	−13

6. $y = 6x^2 - 5$

x	−2	−1	0	1	2
y	19	1	−5	1	19

Match the function with its graph.

7. $y = -4x^2 + 3$ F
8. $y = 3x^2 + 4$ A
9. $y = \frac{1}{3}x^2 - 4$ D
10. $y = \frac{1}{4}x^2 - 3$ B
11. $y = -3x^2 + 4$ C
12. $y = 4x^2 + 3$ E

A. 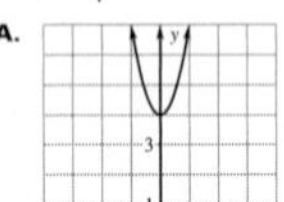

B.  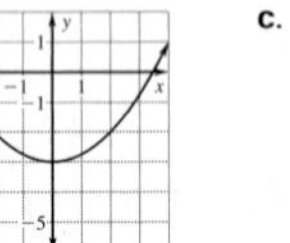

C. 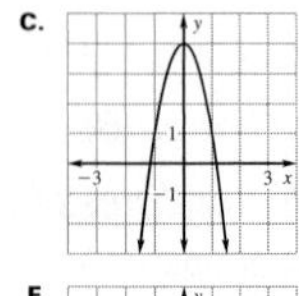

D. 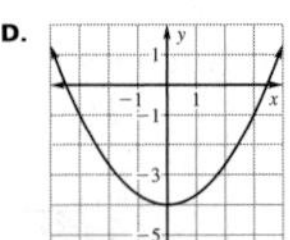

E. 

F. 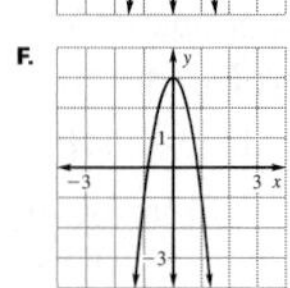

Describe how you can use the graph of $y = x^2$ to graph the given function.

13. $y = x^2 - 8$ See above.
14. $y = -x^2 + 4$ See above.
15. $y = 2x^2 + 3$ See above.
16. $y = -5x^2 + 1$ See above.
17. $y = \frac{1}{2}x^2 - 2$
18. $y = -\frac{3}{4}x^2 - 5$

13. shift the graph 8 units down
14. shift the graph 4 units up and reflect over x-axis
15. stretch vertically by a factor of 2 and shift 3 units up
16. stretch vertically by a factor of 5, reflect in x-axis, and shift 1 unit up
17. shrink vertically by a factor of $\frac{1}{2}$ and shift 2 units down
18. shrink vertically by a factor of $\frac{3}{4}$, reflect over x-axis, and shift 5 units up

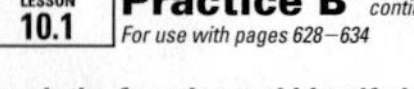

LESSON 10.1 **Practice B** *continued* For use with pages 628–634

Graph the function and identify its domain and range. Compare the graph with the graph of $y = x^2$.

19. $y = x^2 + 9$ See above.
20. $y = -\frac{1}{5}x^2$ See above.
21. $y = -\frac{3}{2}x^2$ See below.

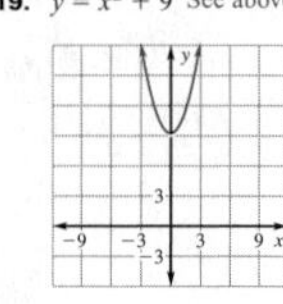 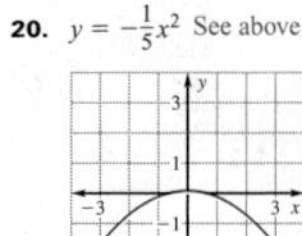 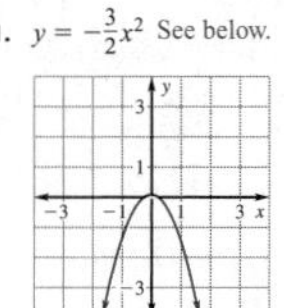

22. $y = x^2 - 3.5$ See below.
23. $y = 2x^2 - 9$ See below.
24. $y = -5x^2 + 2$ See below.

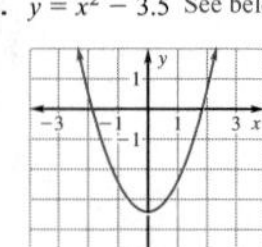 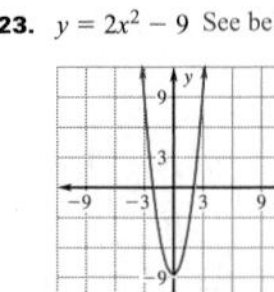 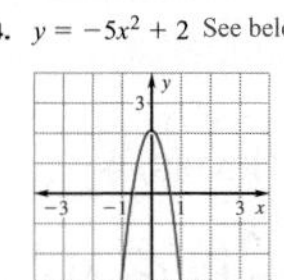

19. domain: all reals; range: $y \geq 9$; vertical shift 9 units up
20. domain: all reals; range: $y \leq 0$; vertical shrink by a factor of $\frac{1}{5}$ and reflection in x-axis

25. **Serving Plate** The top view of a freeform serving plate you made in a ceramics class is shown in the graph. One edge of the plate can be modeled by the graph of the function $y = -\frac{5}{81}x^2 + 20$ where x and y are measured in inches.
   a. Find the domain of the function in this situation. $-18 \leq x \leq 18$
   b. Find the range of the function in this situation. $0 \leq y \leq 20$

26. **Roof Shingle** A roof shingle is dropped from a rooftop that is 100 feet above the ground. The height y (in feet) of the dropped roof shingle is given by the function $y = -16t^2 + 100$ where t is the time (in seconds) since the shingle is dropped.
   a. Graph the function.
   b. Identify the domain and range of the function in this situation.
   c. Use the graph to estimate the shingle's height at 1 second. 84 ft
   d. Use the graph to estimate when the shingle is at a height of 50 feet.
   e. Use the graph to estimate when the shingle is at a height of 0 feet. 2.5 sec

26. b. $0 \leq t \leq 2.5$; $0 \leq y \leq 100$
d. about 1.8 sec

21. domain: all reals; range: $y \leq 0$; vertical stretch by a factor of $\frac{3}{2}$ and reflection in x-axis
22. domain: all reals; range: $y \geq -3.5$; vertical shift 3.5 units down
23. domain: all reals; range: $y \geq -9$; vertical stretch by a factor of 2 and shift 9 units down
24. domain: all reals; range: $y \leq 2$; vertical stretch by a factor of 5, reflection in x-axis, and vertical shift 2 units up

LESSON 10.2 **Practice B** For use with pages 635–640

Identify the values of a, b, and c in the quadratic function.

1. $y = 6x^2 + 3x + 5$
2. $y = \frac{3}{2}x^2 - x + 8$
3. $y = 7x^2 - 3x - 1$
4. $y = -2x^2 + 9x$
5. $y = \frac{3}{4}x^2 - 10$
6. $y = -8x^2 + 3x - 7$

1. $a = 6, b = 3, c = 5$ 2. $a = \frac{3}{2}, b = -1, c = 8$
3. $a = 7, b = -3, c = -1$ 4. $a = -2, b = 9, c = 0$
5. $a = \frac{3}{4}, b = 0, c = -10$ 6. $a = -8, b = 3, c = -7$

Tell whether the graph opens upward or downward. Then find the axis of symmetry and vertex of the graph of the function. See below.

7. $y = x^2 - 5$
8. $y = -x^2 + 9$
9. $y = -2x^2 + 6x + 7$
10. $y = 3x^2 - 12x + 1$
11. $y = 3x^2 + 6x - 2$
12. $y = -2x^2 + 7x - 21$
13. $y = \frac{1}{2}x^2 + 5x - 4$
14. $y = -\frac{1}{4}x^2 - 24$
15. $y = -3x^2 + 9x - 8$
16. $y = 3x^2 - 2x + 3$
17. $y = -2x^2 + 7x + 1$
18. $y = 3x^2 + 2x - 5$

Find the vertex of the graph of the function. Make a table of values using x-values to the left and right of the vertex.

19. $y = x^2 - 10x + 3$ vertex: $(5, -22)$

x	3	4	5	6	7
y	−18	−21	−22	−21	−18

20. $y = -x^2 + 6x - 2$ vertex: $(3, 7)$

x	1	2	3	4	5
y	3	6	7	6	3

21. $y = \frac{1}{2}x^2 - x + 7$ vertex: $(1, \frac{13}{2})$

x	−1	0	1	2	3
y	$\frac{17}{2}$	7	$\frac{13}{2}$	7	$\frac{17}{2}$

22. $y = \frac{1}{3}x^2 - 2x + 3$ vertex: $(3, 0)$

x	1	2	3	4	5
y	$\frac{4}{3}$	$\frac{1}{3}$	0	$\frac{1}{3}$	$\frac{4}{3}$

Graph the function. Label the vertex and axis of symmetry.

23. $y = -x^2 - 10$
24. $y = 2x^2 + 3$
25. $y = -2x^2 + 2x + 1$

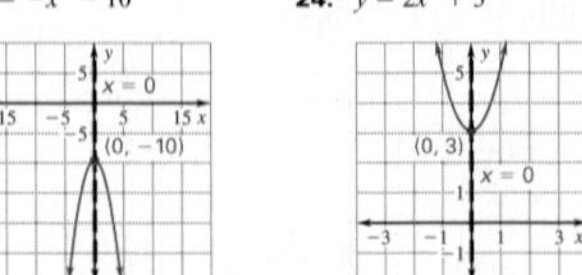 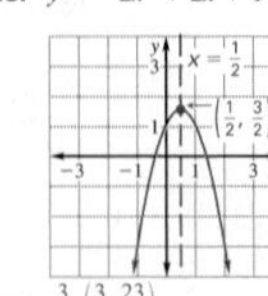

7. upward; $x = 0$; $(0, -5)$ 8. downward; $x = 0$; $(0, 9)$ 9. downward; $x = \frac{3}{2}$; $\left(\frac{3}{2}, \frac{23}{2}\right)$

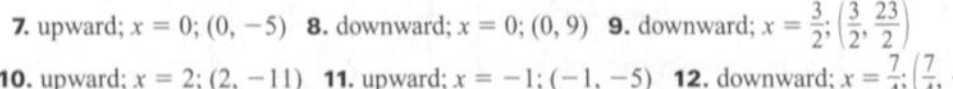

10. upward; $x = 2$; $(2, -11)$ 11. upward; $x = -1$; $(-1, -5)$ 12. downward; $x = \frac{7}{4}$; $\left(\frac{7}{4}, -\frac{119}{8}\right)$
13. upward; $x = -5$; $\left(-5, -\frac{33}{2}\right)$ 14. downward; $x = 0$; $(0, -24)$ 15. downward; $x = \frac{3}{2}$; $\left(\frac{3}{2}, -\frac{5}{4}\right)$
16. upward; $x = \frac{1}{3}$; $\left(\frac{1}{3}, \frac{8}{3}\right)$ 17. downward; $x = \frac{7}{4}$; $\left(\frac{7}{4}, \frac{57}{8}\right)$ 18. upward; $x = -\frac{1}{3}$; $\left(-\frac{1}{3}, -\frac{16}{3}\right)$

LESSON 10.2 **Practice B** *continued* For use with pages 635–640

26. $y = 5x^2 + 2x$
27. $y = -2x^2 + x - 4$
28. $y = x^2 - 8x + 5$

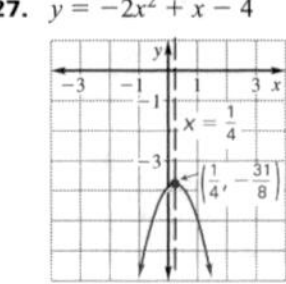 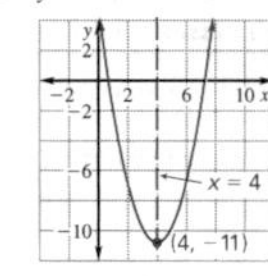

29. $y = -\frac{1}{2}x^2 - 8x + 3$
30. $y = \frac{1}{4}x^2 + 3x - 1$
31. $y = -\frac{3}{4}x^2 - 2x + 2$

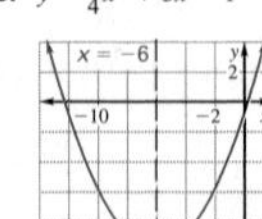 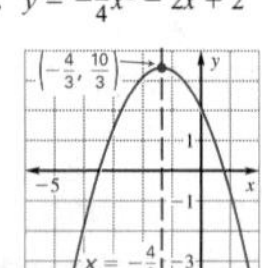

Tell whether the function has a *minimum value* or a *maximum value*. Then find the minimum or maximum value.

32. $f(x) = 8x^2 - 40$ minimum; −40
33. $f(x) = -5x^2 + 10x - 2$ maximum; 3
34. $f(x) = 8x^2 - 4x + 4$ minimum; $\frac{7}{2}$

35. **Storage Building** The storage building shown can be modeled by the graph of the function $y = -0.12x^2 + 2.4x$ where x and y are measured in feet. What is the height h at the highest point of the building as shown in the diagram? 12 ft

 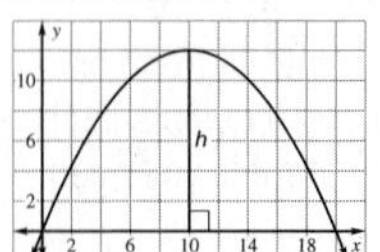

36. **Velvet Rope** A parabola is formed by a piece of velvet rope found around a museum display as shown. This parabola can be modeled by the graph of the function $y = \frac{4}{225}x^2 - \frac{16}{15}x + 40$ where x and y are measured in inches and y represents the number of inches the parabola is above the ground. How far above the ground is the lowest point on the rope? 24 in.

LESSON 10.3 Practice B
For use with pages 643–649

Determine whether the given value is a solution of the equation.

1. $x^2 - 2x + 15 = 0; 3$ 2. $x^2 - 4x - 12 = 0; 2$ 3. $-x^2 - 5x - 6 = 0; 3$
4. $x^2 + 3x - 4 = 0; 1$ 5. $2x^2 + 9x - 5 = 0; -2$ 6. $3x^2 - 5x - 2 = 0; 2$

1. not a solution 2. not a solution 3. not a solution 4. solution 5. not a solution 6. solution

Use the graph to find the solutions of the given equation.

7. $x^2 + 8x + 16 = 0$ -4 8. $-x^2 + 36 = 0$ $-6, 6$ 9. $x^2 + 5x - 24 = 0$ $-8, 3$

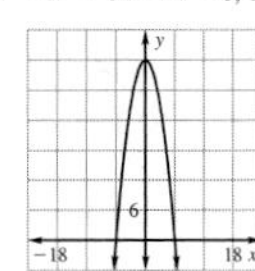

10. $x^2 + 11x + 30 = 0$ $-6, -5$ 11. $x^2 - 25 = 0$ $-5, 5$ 12. $x^2 + 7 = 0$ no solution

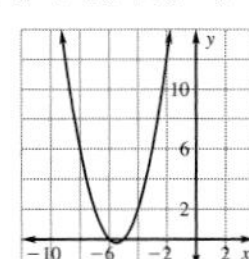

Solve the equation by graphing.

13. $-x^2 - 6x = 0$ $-6, 0$ 14. $2x^2 = 2$ $-1, 1$ 15. $x^2 - 7x + 10 = 0$ $2, 5$

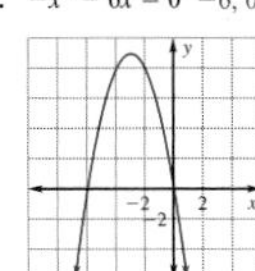

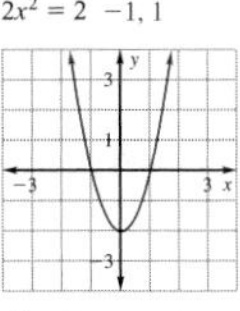

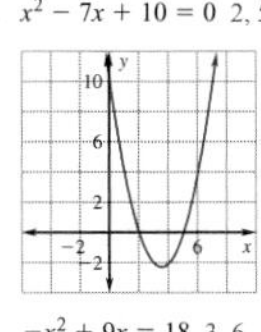

16. $x^2 = 10x$ $0, 10$ 17. $x^2 - 6x + 9 = 0$ 3 18. $-x^2 + 9x = 18$ $3, 6$

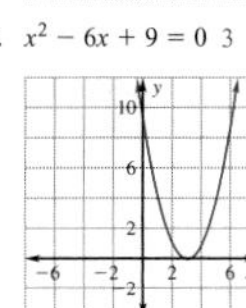

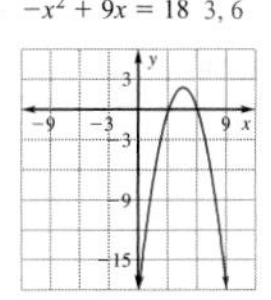

LESSON 10.3

LESSON 10.3 Practice B
For use with pages 643–649

Find the zeros of the function by graphing.

19. $f(x) = -x^2 - 5x - 10$ no zeros 20. $f(x) = x^2 + 12x + 36$ -6 21. $f(x) = 2x^2 + 24x$ $-12, 0$

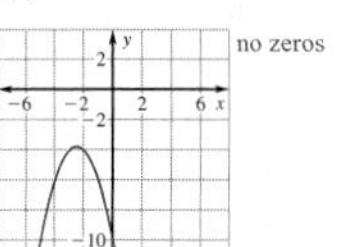

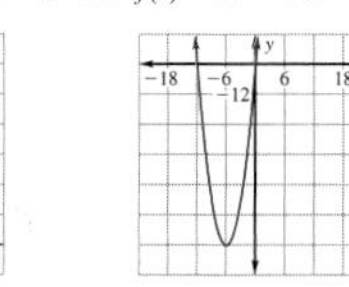

22. $f(x) = x^2 - 49$ $-7, 7$ 23. $f(x) = -x^2 + 1$ $-1, 1$ 24. $f(x) = 3x^2 + 12x$ $-4, 0$

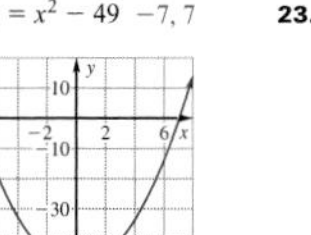

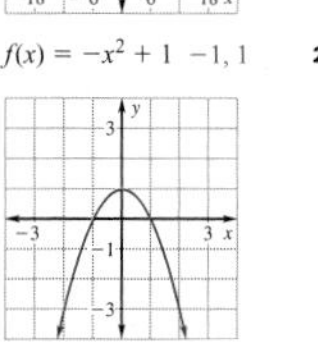

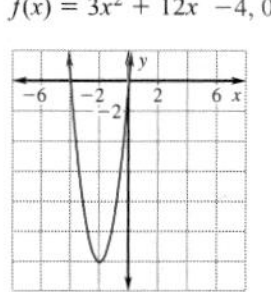

25. **Stunt Double** A movie stunt double jumps from the top of a building 50 feet above the ground onto a pad on the ground below. The stunt double jumps with an initial vertical velocity of 10 feet per second.
    a. Write and graph a function that models the height h (in feet) of the stunt double t seconds after she jumps.
    b. How long does it take the stunt double to reach the ground? about 2.1 sec

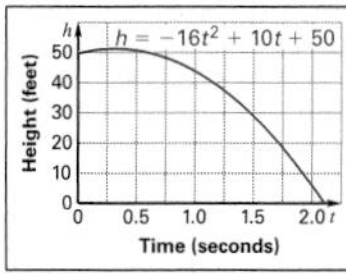

26. **Wastebasket** You throw a wad of used paper towards a wastebasket from a height of about 1.3 feet above the floor with an initial vertical velocity of 3 feet per second.
    a. Write and graph a function that models the height h (in feet) of the paper t seconds after it is thrown.
    b. If you miss the wastebasket and the paper hits the floor, how long does it take for the ball of paper to reach the floor? about 0.39 sec
    c. If the ball of paper hits the rim of the wastebasket one-half foot above the ground, how long was the ball in the air? about 0.34 sec

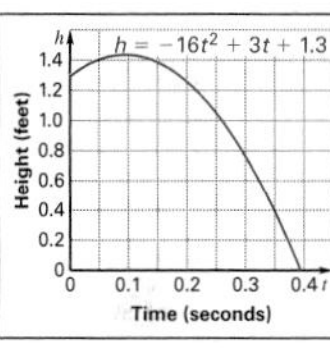

LESSON 10.3

LESSON 10.4 Practice B
For use with pages 652–658

LESSON 10.4

Solve the equation.

1. $6x^2 - 24 = 0$ $-2, 2$ 2. $8x^2 - 128 = 0$ $-4, 4$ 3. $x^2 - 13 = 23$ $-6, 6$
4. $3x^2 - 60 = 87$ $-7, 7$ 5. $2x^2 - 33 = 17$ $-5, 5$ 6. $5x^2 - 200 = 205$ $-9, 9$
7. $4x^2 - 125 = -25$ $-5, 5$ 8. $7x^2 - 50 = 13$ $-3, 3$ 9. $\frac{1}{2}x^2 - \frac{1}{2} = 0$ $-1, 1$

Solve the equation. Round the solutions to the nearest hundredth.

10. $x^2 + 15 = 23$ $-2.83, 2.83$ 11. $x^2 - 16 = -13$ $-1.73, 1.73$ 12. $12 - x^2 = 17$ no solution
13. $3x^2 - 8 = 7$ $-2.24, 2.24$ 14. $9 - x^2 = 9$ 0 15. $4 + 5x^2 = 34$ $-2.45, 2.45$
16. $48 = 14 + 2x^2$ $-4.12, 4.12$ 17. $8x^2 = 50$ $-2.5, 2.5$ 18. $3x^2 + 23 = 18$ no solution
19. $(x - 3)^2 = 5$ $0.76, 5.24$ 20. $(x + 2)^2 = 10$ $-5.16, 1.16$ 21. $3(x - 4)^2 = 18$ $1.55, 6.45$

Use the given area A of the circle to find the radius r or the diameter d of the circle. Round the answer to the nearest hundredth, if necessary.

22. $A = 169\pi\ \text{m}^2$ 13 m 23. $A = 38\pi\ \text{in.}^2$ about 6.16 in. 24. $A = 45\pi\ \text{cm}^2$ about 13.42 cm

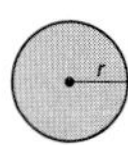

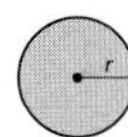

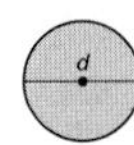

25. **Flower Seed** A manufacturer is making a cylindrical can that will hold and dispense flower seeds through small holes in the top of the can. The manufacturer wants the can to have a volume of 42 cubic inches and be 6 inches tall. What should the diameter of the can be? (*Hint:* Use the formula for volume, $V = \pi r^2 h$, where V is the volume, r is the radius, and h is the height.) Round your answer to the nearest inch. about 3 in.

6 in.

26. **Stockpile** You can find the diameter D (in feet) of a conical pile of sand, dirt, etc. by using the formula $V = 0.2618hD^2$ where h is the height of the pile (in feet) and V is the volume of the pile (in cubic feet). Find the diameter of each stockpile in the table. Round your answers to the nearest foot. 5 ft, 8 ft, 10 ft

Stockpile	Height (ft)	Diameter (ft)	Volume (ft³)
A	10	?	68
B	15	?	230
C	20	?	545

LESSON 10.5 Practice B
For use with pages 663–668

Find the value of c that makes the expression a perfect square trinomial. Then write the expression as a square of a binomial.

1. $x^2 + 12x + c$ $36; (x + 6)^2$ 2. $x^2 + 50x + c$ $625; (x + 25)^2$ 3. $x^2 - 26x + c$ $169; (x - 13)^2$
4. $x^2 - 18x + c$ $81; (x - 9)^2$ 5. $x^2 + 13x + c$ $\frac{169}{4}; \left(x + \frac{13}{2}\right)^2$ 6. $x^2 - 9x + c$ $\frac{81}{4}; \left(x - \frac{9}{2}\right)^2$
7. $x^2 - 11x + c$ $\frac{121}{4}; \left(x - \frac{11}{2}\right)^2$ 8. $x^2 + \frac{1}{2}x + c$ $\frac{1}{16}; \left(x + \frac{1}{4}\right)^2$ 9. $x^2 - \frac{6}{5}x + c$ $\frac{9}{25}; \left(x - \frac{3}{5}\right)^2$

Solve the equation by completing the square. Round your solutions to the nearest hundredth, if necessary.

10. $x^2 + 6x = 1$ $-6.16, 0.16$ 11. $x^2 + 4x = 13$ $-6.12, 2.12$ 12. $x^2 - 10x = 15$ $-1.32, 11.32$
13. $x^2 + 8x = 10$ $-9.10, 1.10$ 14. $x^2 - 2x - 7 = 0$ 15. $x^2 - 12x - 21 = 0$
16. $x^2 + 3x - 2 = 0$ 17. $x^2 + 5x - 3 = 0$ 18. $x^2 - x = 1$ $-0.62, 1.62$

14. $-1.83, 3.83$ 15. $-1.55, 13.55$ 16. $-3.56, 0.56$ 17. $-5.54, 0.54$

LESSON 10.5

Find the value of x. Round your answer to the nearest hundredth, if necessary.

19. Area of triangle = 30 ft² 6 20. Area of rectangle = 140 in.² 5

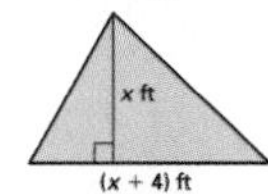

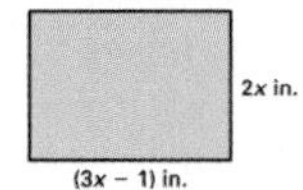

21. **Colorado** The state of Colorado is almost perfectly rectangular, with its north border is 111 miles longer than its west border. If the state encompasses 104,000 square miles, estimate the dimensions of Colorado. Round your answer to the nearest mile. about 272 mi by about 383 mi

22. **Baseball** After a baseball is hit, the height h (in feet) of the ball above the ground t seconds after it is hit can be approximated by the equation $h = -16t^2 + 64t + 3$. Determine how long it will take for the ball to hit the ground. Round your answer to the nearest hundredth. about 4.05 sec

23. **Fenced-In Yard** You have 60 feet of fencing to fence in part of your backyard for your dog. You want to make sure that your dog has 400 square feet of space to run around in. The back of your house will be used as one side of the enclosure as shown.
    a. Write equations in terms of ℓ and w for the amount of fencing and the area of the enclosure.
    b. Use substitution to solve the system of equations from part (a). What are the possible lengths and widths of the enclosure? 20 ft by 20 ft, 40 ft by 10 ft

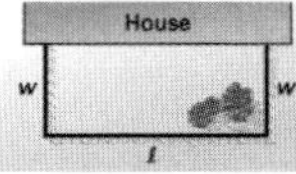

23. a. $\ell + 2w = 60$; $\ell w = 400$

Lesson Practice Level B

LESSON 10.6 Practice B

For use with pages 671–676

Use the quadratic formula to solve the equation. Round your solutions to the nearest hundredth, if necessary.

1. $x^2 + 7x - 80 = 0$ $-13.10, 6.10$
2. $3x^2 - x - 16 = 0$ $-2.15, 2.48$
3. $8x^2 - 2x - 30 = 0$ $-1.82, 2.07$
4. $x^2 + 4x + 1 = 0$ $-3.73, -0.27$
5. $-x^2 + x + 12 = 0$ $-3, 4$
6. $-3x^2 - 4x + 10 = 0$ N$-2.61, 1.28$
7. $5x^2 + 30x + 32 = 0$ $-4.61, -1.39$
8. $x^2 + 6x - 100 = 0$ $-13.44, 7.44$
9. $4x^2 - x - 20 = 0$ $-2.11, 2.36$
10. $5x^2 + x - 9 = 0$ $-1.45, 1.25$
11. $6x^2 + 7x - 3 = 0$ $-\frac{3}{2}, \frac{1}{3}$
12. $10x^2 - 7x + 5 = 0$ no solution

Tell which method(s) you would use to solve the quadratic equation. *Explain* your choice(s).

13. $6x^2 - 216 = 0$ See above.
14. $8x^2 = 56$ See above.
15. $5x^2 - 10x = 0$ See below.
16. $x^2 + 8x + 7 = 0$ See below.
17. $x^2 - 6x + 1 = 0$ See below.
18. $-9x^2 + 10x = 5$ See below.

13. *Sample answer:* Use finding square roots because the equation can be written in the form $x^2 = d$.
14. *Sample answer:* Use finding square roots because the equation can be written in the form $x^2 = d$.

Solve the quadratic equation using any method. Round your solutions to the nearest hundredth, if necessary.

19. $-10x^2 = -50$ $-2.24, 2.24$
20. $x^2 - 16x = -64$ 8
21. $x^2 + 3x - 8 = 0$ $-4.70, 1.70$
22. $x^2 = 14x - 49$ 7
23. $x^2 + 6x = 14$ $-7.80, 1.80$
24. $-5x^2 + x = 13$ no solution

15. *Sample answer:* Use factoring because the equation is easily factored.
16. *Sample answer:* Use factoring because the equation is easily factored.

25. **Pasta** For the period 1990–2003, the amount of biscuits, pasta, and noodles y (in thousands of metric tons) imported into the United States can be modeled by the function $y = 1.36x^2 + 27.8x + 304$ where x is the number of years since 1990.
   a. Write and solve an equation that you can use to approximate the year in which 500 thousand metric tons of biscuits, pasta, and noodles were imported. See below.
   b. Write and solve an equation that you can use to approximate the year in which 575 thousand metric tons of biscuits, pasta, and noodles were imported. See below.

26. **Eggs** For the period 1997–2003, the number of eggs y (in billions) produced in the United States can be modeled by the function $y = -0.27x^2 + 3.3x + 77$ where x is the number of years since 1997.
   a. Write and solve an equation that you can use to approximate the year(s) in which 80 billion eggs were produced. $80 = -0.27x^2 + 3.3x + 77$; 1998
   b. Graph the function on a graphing calculator. Use the *trace* feature to find the year when 80 billion eggs were produced. Use the graph to check your answer from part (a).

Number of eggs (billions): 65, 70, 75, 80, 85, 90, 95; Years since 1997: 0 1 2 3 4 5 6 7

17. *Sample answer:* Use the quadratic formula because it cannot be factored easily.
18. *Sample answer:* Use the quadratic formula because it cannot be factored easily.
25. a. $500 = 1.36x^2 + 27.8x + 304$; 1995
b. $575 = 1.36x^2 + 27.8x + 304$; 1997

LESSON 10.7 Practice B

For use with pages 678–683

2. two solutions **3.** two solutions **4.** no solution **5.** two solutions

Tell whether the equation has *two solutions, one solution,* or *no solution.*

1. $x^2 + x + 3 = 0$ no solution
2. $2x^2 - 4x - 5 = 0$
3. $-2x^2 + 10x - 5 = 0$
4. $3x^2 - 9x + 8 = 0$
5. $10x^2 - 8x + 1 = 0$
6. $-4x^2 + 9 = 0$ two solutions
7. $36x^2 - 9x = 0$ two solutions
8. $3x^2 + 2 = 4x$ no solution
9. $12 = x^2 - 6x$ two solutions
10. $\frac{1}{6}x^2 + 3 = x$ no solution
11. $-8x^2 - 9x = \frac{2}{3}$ two solutions
12. $8x^2 + 12x + 2 = 4x$ one solution

Find the number of *x*-intercepts that the graph of the function has.

13. $y = x^2 - 6x - 3$ two
14. $y = 5x^2 - x - 1$ two
15. $y = 6x^2 - 6x + 1$ two
16. $y = x^2 + x + 6$ none
17. $y = -4x^2 + x + 1$ two
18. $y = 4x^2 + 5x - 1$ two
19. $y = 2x^2 - 4x + 2$ one
20. $y = 10x^2 - 5x + 1$ none
21. $y = 8x^2 + x + 4$ none
22. $y = -15x^2 + 3x + 5$ two
23. $y = \frac{1}{2}x^2 - 4x + 8$ one
24. $y = \frac{2}{3}x^2 - 5x + 2$ two

Give a value of *c* for which the equation has (a) two solutions, (b) one solution, and (c) no solution.

25. $x^2 + 10x + c = 0$
26. $x^2 - 4x + c = 0$
27. $25x^2 + 10x + c = 0$
28. $49x^2 - 14x + c = 0$
29. $2x^2 + 4x + c = 0$
30. $3x^2 - 18x + c = 0$

25–30. Answers will vary.

31. **Playhouse** You want to build a playhouse for your sister in your backyard. You have blueprints which show that the playhouse is 12 feet long and 13 feet wide. You want to change the dimensions as shown. The new area can be modeled by the function $y = -x^2 + x + 156$.

12 ft, x, 13 ft, $13 - x$

   a. Write an equation that you can use to determine if there is a value of x that gives an area of 150 square feet.
   b. Use the discriminant of your equation from part (a) to show that it is possible to find a value of x for which the area is 150 square feet. discriminant: $25 > 0$
   c. Find the value(s) of x for which the area is 150 square feet. 3 ft

31. a. $150 = -x^2 + x + 156$

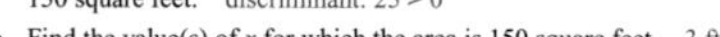

32. **Tennis** You and your friend are walking around the exterior of a tennis court that has a 12-foot high fence around it. You pick up a ball and try to throw it from a height of 5 feet over the fence. You throw it with an initial vertical velocity of 20 feet per second. Did the ball make it over the fence? no

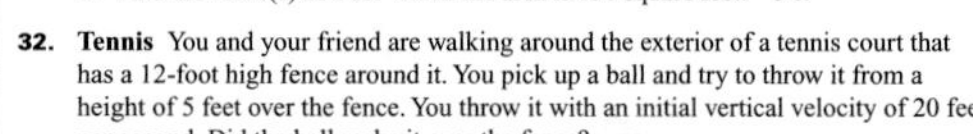

LESSON 10.8 Practice B

For use with pages 684–691

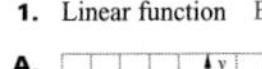

Match the function with the graph it represents.

1. Linear function B **2.** Exponential function C **3.** Quadratic function A

A. **B.** **C.**

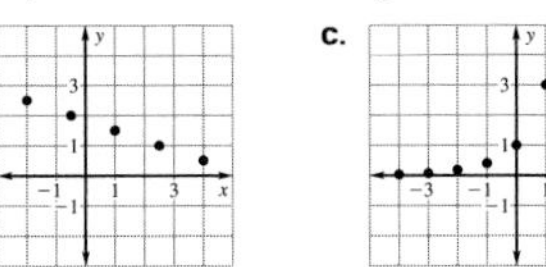

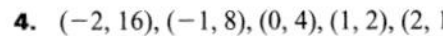

Use a graph to tell whether the ordered pairs represent a *linear function*, an *exponential function*, or a *quadratic function*.

4. (−2, 16), (−1, 8), (0, 4), (1, 2), (2, 1) exponential

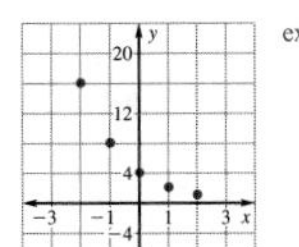

5. (−3, 4), (−2, 0), (−1, −2), (0, −2), (1, 0) quadratic

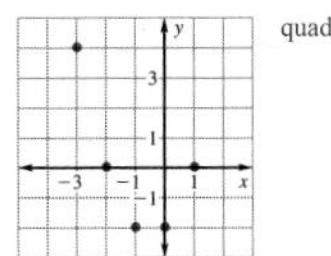

6. (−4, 17), (−2, 11), (0, 5), (2, −1), (4, −7) linear

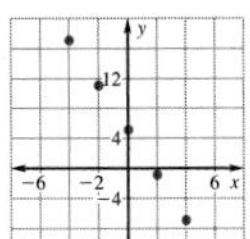

7. (−9, −1), (−6, −2), (−3, −3), (0, −4), (3, −5) linear

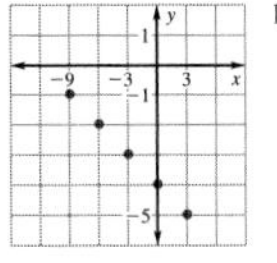

8. $\left(-2, \frac{1}{9}\right), \left(-1, \frac{1}{3}\right)$, (0, 1), (1, 3), (2, 9) exponential

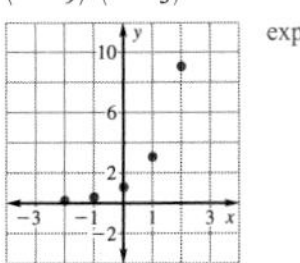

9. (2, 5), (3, 2), (4, 1), (5, 2), (6, 5) quadratic

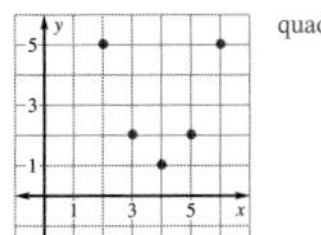

LESSON 10.8 Practice B *continued*

For use with pages 684–691

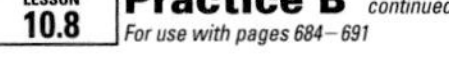

Tell whether the table of values represents a *linear function*, an *exponential function*, or a *quadratic function*.

10. exponential

x	0	1	2	3	4
y	1	5	25	125	625

11. linear

x	−2	−1	0	1	2
y	−10	−7	−4	−1	2

12. quadratic

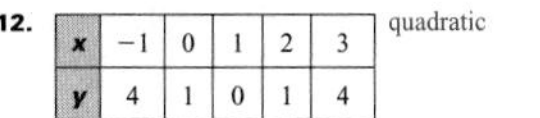

x	−1	0	1	2	3
y	4	1	0	1	4

13. linear

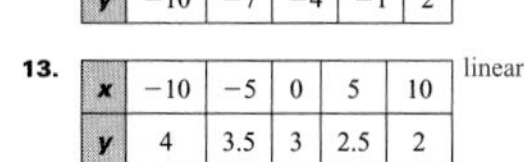

x	−10	−5	0	5	10
y	4	3.5	3	2.5	2

14. exponential

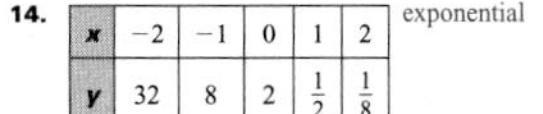

x	−2	−1	0	1	2
y	32	8	2	$\frac{1}{2}$	$\frac{1}{8}$

15. quadratic

x	−4	−3	−2	−1	0
y	−3	0	1	0	−3

16. linear

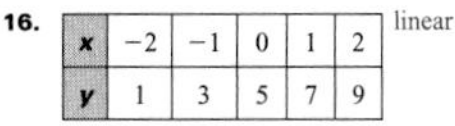

x	−2	−1	0	1	2
y	1	3	5	7	9

17. exponential

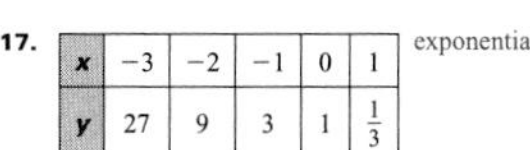

x	−3	−2	−1	0	1
y	27	9	3	1	$\frac{1}{3}$

18. Use the graph shown.

a. Which function does the graph represent, an *exponential function* or a *quadratic function*? *Explain* your reasoning. exponential; The graph rises quickly.

b. Make a table of values for the points on the graph. Then use differences or ratios to check your answer in part (a).

c. Write an equation for the function that the table of values from part (b) represents. $y = 4^x$

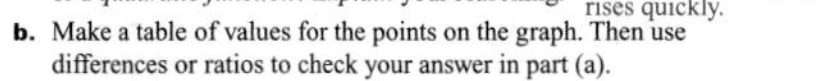

b.

x	0	1	2	3	4
y	1	4	16	64	256

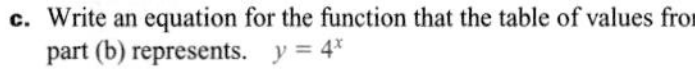

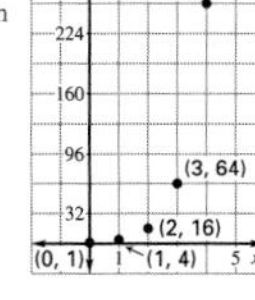

19. Pleasure Boats The graph shows total amount of sales (in millions of dollars) of pleasure boats in the United States for the period 1990–2002. Tell whether the data should be modeled by a *linear function*, an *exponential function*, or a *quadratic function*. *Explain* your reasoning. Answers will vary.

Pleasure Boats

Sales (millions of dollars): 6,000; 8,000; 10,000; 12,000; 14,000; 16,000

Years since 1990: 0 2 4 6 8 10 12

20. Computer Value The value V of a computer between 1999 and 2003 is given in the table. Tell whether the data should be modeled by a *linear function*, an *exponential function*, or a *quadratic function*. Then write an equation for the function.

Years since 1999, *t*	0	1	2	3	4
Value, *V* (dollars)	800	725	650	575	500

linear; $V = -75t + 800$

10 Assessment

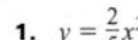

CHAPTER 10 Quiz 1

For use after Lessons 10.1–10.3

Graph the function. Compare the graph with the graph of $y = x^2$.

1. $y = \frac{2}{5}x^2$

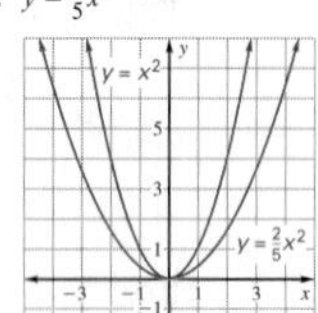

2. $y = -3x^2 + 2$

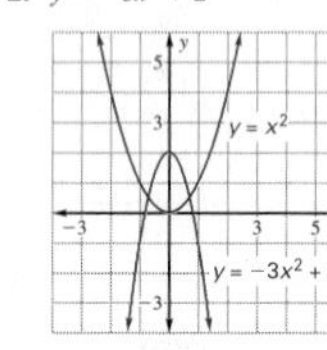

Graph the function. Label the vertex and axis of symmetry.

3. $y = x^2 + 2x + 3$

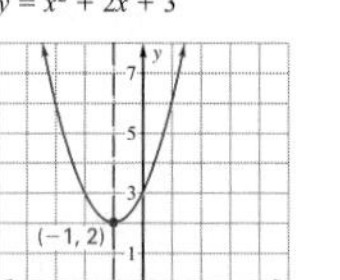

4. $y = -2x^2 + 8x - 5$

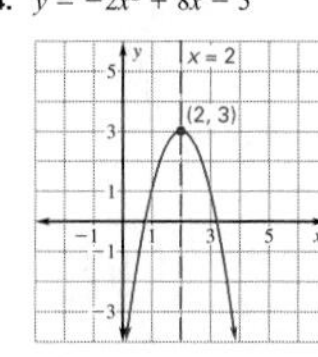

Solve the equation by graphing.

5. $x^2 - 5x + 6 = 0$

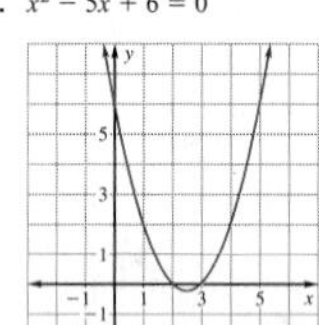

6. $x^2 - 8x = -12$

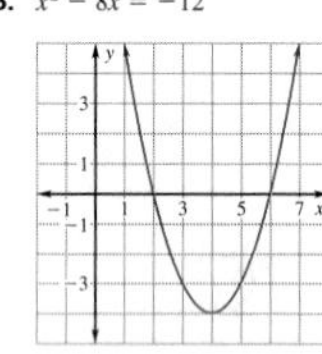

Find the zeros of the function.

7. $y = x^2 - 7x + 12$
8. $y = -x^2 - 6x - 5$

Answers

1. See left. The graph of $y = \frac{2}{5}x^2$ is a vertical shrink (by a factor of $\frac{2}{5}$) of the graph of $y = x^2$.
2. See left. The graph of $y = -3x^2 + 2$ is a reflection in the x-axis, a vertical stretch (by a factor of 3), and a vertical translation (of 2 units up) of the graph of $y = x^2$.
3. See left.
4. See left.
5. See left. 2, 3
6. See left. 2, 6
7. 3, 4
8. −5, −1

CHAPTER 10 Quiz 2

For use after Lessons 10.4–10.6

Solve the equation using square roots.

1. $5x^2 = 45$
2. $x^2 - 3 = 4$

Solve the equation by completing the square.

3. $x^2 + 4x - 5 = 0$
4. $x^2 - 10x + 24 = 0$
5. $x^2 - 8x + 12 = 0$
6. $x^2 - 2x = 10$
7. $x^2 + 6x + 2 = 0$
8. $x^2 + 8x = -4$

Solve the equation by using the quadratic formula.

9. $3x^2 - 5x - 2 = 0$
10. $x^2 - 2x - 15 = 0$
11. $x^2 + 6x + 9 = 0$
12. $2x^2 - 7x = -3$

Answers

1. −3, 3
2. $-\sqrt{7}, \sqrt{7}$
3. −5, 1
4. 4, 6
5. 2, 6
6. $1 - \sqrt{11}, 1 + \sqrt{11}$
7. $-3 - \sqrt{7}, -3 + \sqrt{7}$
8. $-4 - 2\sqrt{3}, -4 + 2\sqrt{3}$
9. $-\frac{1}{3}, 2$
10. −3, 5
11. −3
12. $\frac{1}{2}, 3$

CHAPTER 10 Quiz 3

For use after Lessons 10.7–10.8

Tell whether the equation has *two solutions*, *one solution*, or *no solution*.

1. $2x^2 + x + 2 = 0$
2. $3x^2 - 4x + 1 = 0$

Find the number of x-intercepts of the graph of the function.

3. $y = 4x^2 - 12x + 9$
4. $y = x^2 + x - 20$

Tell whether the table of values represents a *linear function*, an *exponential function*, or a *quadratic function*. Then write an equation for the function.

5.

x	−2	−1	0	1	2
y	−5	−3	−1	1	3

6.

x	−2	−1	0	1	2
y	−3	0	1	0	−3

Answers

1. no solution
2. two solutions
3. one x-intercept
4. two x-intercepts
5. linear function; $y = 2x - 1$
6. quadratic function; $y = -x^2 + 1$

CHAPTER 10 Chapter Test B

For use after Chapter 10

Graph the function. Compare the graph with the graph of $y = x^2$.

1. $y = \frac{1}{4}x^2 - 1$

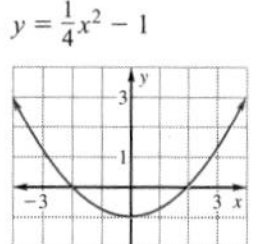

2. $y = -x^2 + 5$

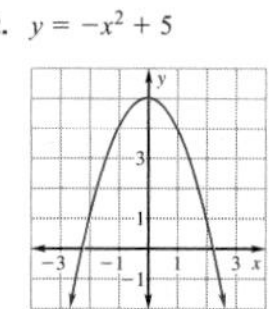

3. A cross section of the parabolic glass mirror of the Hubble space telescope shown can be modeled by the graph of the function $y = 0.0043x^2$ where x and y are measured in meters. Find the domain and range of the function in this situation.

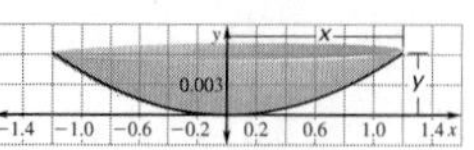

Find the axis of symmetry and the vertex of the graph of the function. Then tell whether the function has a *maximum value* or a *minimum value*.

4. $y = -2x^2 + 8x + 3$
5. $y = \frac{1}{2}x^2 - 2x + 5$
6. $y = 6x^2 + 7$
7. An arch of balloons decorates the entrance to a high school prom. The balloons are tied to a frame. The shape of the frame can be modeled by the graph of the equation $y = -\frac{1}{4}x^2 + 3x$ where x and y are measured in feet. What is the maximum height of the arch of balloons?

Solve the equation by graphing.

8. $x^2 + 5x - 14 = 0$

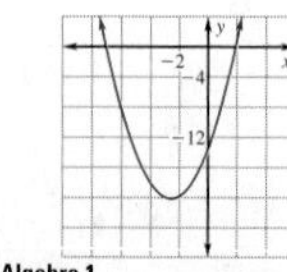

9. $-x^2 + 3x + 4 = 0$

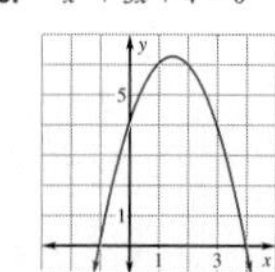

Answers

1. See left. The graph is a vertical shrink (by a factor of $\frac{1}{4}$) and a vertical translation (of 1 unit down) of the graph of $y = x^2$.
2. See left. The graph is a reflection in the x-axis and a vertical translation (of 5 units up) of the graph of $y = x^2$.
3. $-1.2 \le x \le 1.2$; $0 \le y \le 0.006$
4. $x = 2$; (2, 11); maximum value
5. $x = 2$; (2, 3); minimum value
6. $x = 0$; (0, 7); minimum value
7. 9 ft
8. See left. −7, 2
9. See left. −1, 4

CHAPTER 10 Chapter Test B *continued*
For use after Chapter 10

Solve the equation. Round the solutions to the nearest hundredth, if necessary.

10. $16t^2 - 9 = 0$ **11.** $2(x - 6)^2 = 24$ **12.** $4n^2 - 13 = -20$

13. Sailors need to consider the speed of the wind when adjusting the sails on their boat. The force F (in pounds per square foot) on a sail when the wind is blowing perpendicular to the sail can be modeled by the function $F = 0.004v^2$ where v is the wind speed (in knots). Find the wind speed that will produce a force of 2.5 pounds per square foot on a sail.

14. Complete the steps to solve the equation $x^2 - 8x - 3 = 0$ by completing the square.

$x^2 - 8x = \underline{?}$

$x^2 - 8x + \underline{?} = 19$

$(x - \underline{?})^2 = 19$

$x - \underline{?} = \underline{?}$

$x = \underline{?}$

Use the quadratic formula to solve the equation. Round the solutions to the nearest hundredth, if necessary.

15. $p^2 + 8p - 15 = 0$ **16.** $2y^2 - 7y = 10$ **17.** $9z^2 + 12z + 4 = 0$

18. During the period 1998–2002, the number y (in millions) of juvenile books shipped to bookstores can be modeled by the equation $y = -15x^2 + 64x + 360$ where x is the number of years since 1998. In what years were there 400 million juvenile books shipped to bookstores?

Find the number of x-intercepts that the graph of the function has.

19. $f(x) = 3x^2 - 3x + 4$

20. $f(x) = 4x^2 - 2x - 1$

21. $f(x) = 4x^2 + 12x + 9$

Tell whether the ordered pairs represent a *linear function*, an *exponential function*, or a *quadratic function*.

22. $(-2, -13), (-1, -8), (0, -3), (1, 2), (2, 7)$

23. $(-2, 0), (-1, -3), (0, -4), (1, -3), (2, 0)$

24. $\left(-2, \frac{1}{9}\right), \left(-1, \frac{1}{3}\right), (0, 1), (1, 3), (2, 9)$

Answers

10. ± 0.75

11. 2.54, 9.46

12. no solution

13. 25 knots

14. 3; 16; 4; 4; $\pm\sqrt{19}$

$4 \pm \sqrt{19}$

15. -9.57, 1.57

16. -1.09, 4.59

17. $-\frac{2}{3}$

18. 1999 and 2001

19. none

20. two

21. one

22. linear function

23. quadratic function

24. exponential function

CHAPTER 10 Standardized Test
For use after Chapter 10

Multiple Choice

1. What is the vertex of the graph of the function $y = -\frac{2}{3}x^2 + 5$? A

Ⓐ $(0, 5)$ Ⓑ $(5, 0)$
Ⓒ $(0, -5)$ Ⓓ $(-5, 0)$

2. How would the graph of the function $y = x^2 - 3$ be affected if the function were changed to $y = x^2 + 2$? B

Ⓐ The graph would shift 2 units up.
Ⓑ The graph would shift 5 units up.
Ⓒ The graph would shift 2 units to the right.
Ⓓ The graph would shift 5 unit down.

3. What is the vertex of the graph of the function $y = -2x^2 + 16x - 15$? D

Ⓐ $(-4, -111)$ Ⓑ $(-4, -81)$
Ⓒ $(4, -47)$ Ⓓ $(4, 17)$

4. What is the axis of symmetry of the function $y = -x^2 + 6x - 8$? B

Ⓐ $x = -3$ Ⓑ $x = 3$
Ⓒ $x = -8$ Ⓓ $x = 8$

5. What are the solutions of the equation whose graph is shown? C

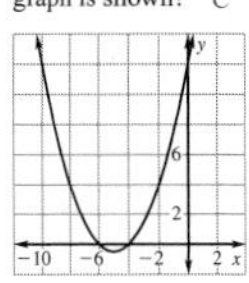

Ⓐ 4 and 6 Ⓑ 4 and -6
Ⓒ -4 and -6 Ⓓ -4 and 6

6. Which function has a zero between 7 and 8? C

Ⓐ $f(x) = \frac{1}{2}x^2 + 5x + 12$
Ⓑ $f(x) = -4x^2 + 6x + 5$
Ⓒ $f(x) = 3x^2 - 24x + 12$
Ⓓ $f(x) = \frac{1}{2}x^2 + 12$

7. What are the approximate zeros of the function $y = -x^2 - 5x + 5$ to the nearest tenth? D

Ⓐ 1.4 and 3.6 Ⓑ -0.9 and 5.9
Ⓒ -3.6 and -1.4 Ⓓ -5.9 and 0.9

8. Which of the following is a solution of the equation $107 - 5x^2 = -18$? B

Ⓐ -25 Ⓑ -5 Ⓒ 15 Ⓓ 25

9. Which of the following is a solution of the equation $2x^2 - 5 = -4\frac{1}{2}$? A

Ⓐ $-\frac{1}{2}$ Ⓑ $-\frac{1}{4}$ Ⓒ 1 Ⓓ $\frac{3}{4}$

10. What are the solutions of $4x^2 + 40x = -91$? A

Ⓐ $-\frac{13}{2}, -\frac{7}{2}$ Ⓑ $-\frac{13}{2}, \frac{7}{2}$
Ⓒ $\frac{13}{2}, -\frac{7}{2}$ Ⓓ $\frac{13}{2}, \frac{7}{2}$

11. What are the solutions of $4x^2 + 48x + 20 = 0$? D

Ⓐ $6 \pm \sqrt{41}$ Ⓑ $6 \pm \sqrt{31}$
Ⓒ $-6 \pm \sqrt{41}$ Ⓓ $-6 \pm \sqrt{31}$

12. What are the solutions of $4x^2 - 16x = 16x - 39$? D

Ⓐ $-\frac{13}{2}, -\frac{3}{2}$ Ⓑ $-\frac{13}{2}, \frac{3}{2}$
Ⓒ $\frac{13}{2}, -\frac{3}{2}$ Ⓓ $\frac{13}{2}, \frac{3}{2}$

CHAPTER 10 Standardized Test *continued*
For use after Chapter 10

13. What is the value of the discriminant of the equation $6x^2 - 5x - 3 = 0$? C

Ⓐ -47 Ⓑ 24 Ⓒ 97 Ⓓ 115

14. How many solutions does $5x^2 - 2x + 3 = 0$ have? A

Ⓐ None Ⓑ One
Ⓒ Two Ⓓ Three

15. Which function is represented by the following ordered pairs: $(-5, 50), (-2, 8), (0, 0), (1, 2), (3, 18)$? C

Ⓐ $y = 2^x$ Ⓑ $y = 2x$
Ⓒ $y = 2x^2$ Ⓓ $y = 0.5x^2$

16. The graph represents what kind of function? B

Ⓐ absolute value function
Ⓑ exponential function
Ⓒ linear function
Ⓓ quadratic function

Gridded Answer

17. The value of the discriminant of the equation $2x^2 - x - c = 2$ is 49. What is the value of c?

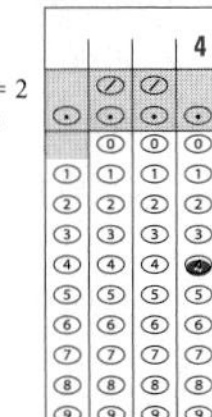

Short Response

18. The science club wants to have fliers made to advertise their upcoming science fair. The table shows the cost y (in dollars) for x fliers.

Fliers, x	75	125	175	225
Cost (dollars), y	17	23	29	35

a. Tell whether the data can be modeled by a *linear function*, an *exponential function*, or a *quadratic function*. Then write an equation for the function.

b. If the number of fliers printed is tripled, does the price triple? *Explain.* See below.

Extended Response

19. The Art Club is selling scrapbooks to raise money for supplies. Last year, when the students charged \$10 per scrapbook, they sold 250 scrapbooks. The students want to increase the cost per scrapbook. They estimate that they will lose 5 sales for each \$1 increase in the cost per package. The revenue R (in dollars) generated by selling the scrapbooks is given by the function $R = (10 + n)(250 - 5n)$ where n is the number of \$1 increases.

a. Write the function in standard form.

b. Find the maximum value of the function. 4500 See below.

c. At what price should the scrapbooks be sold to generate the most revenue? *Explain* your reasoning. \$30; According to the function, the maximum amount of revenue is \$4500. The maximum amount of revenue is made when n is 20. This means they can increase their price by \$20 to make their maximum amount of revenue. So, the new selling price would be \$30.

18. a. Linear function; $y = \frac{3}{25}x + 8$ **b.** No; *Sample answer:* 225 fliers is three times 75 fliers, but \$35 is not three times \$17.

19. a. $R = -5n^2 + 200n + 2500$

CHAPTER 10 Alternative Assessment and Math Journal
For use after Chapter 10

Journal **1.** Discuss the behavior of successive y-values for linear, exponential, and quadratic functions given that the increments between successive x-values are all equal. Give an example of an equation for each type of function.

Multi-Step Problem **2.** During a halftime show, a baton twirler releases her baton from a point 4 feet above the ground with an initial vertical velocity of 25 feet per second.

a. Use the vertical motion model to write a function for the height h (in feet) of the baton after t seconds.

b. Graph the function in part (a). Label the vertex of the graph.

c. How high does the baton go? Round your answer to the nearest tenth.

d. How long after the baton is released does it reach its maximum height?

e. At what moments is the baton at a height of 10 feet? Round your answer to the nearest hundredth.

f. How much time does the twirler have if she plans to catch the baton on its way down at a height of 5 feet? Round your answer to the nearest hundredth.

1. Complete answers should include: an explanation that the differences in successive y-values will be equal for linear functions; an explanation that the ratios in successive y-values will be equal for exponential functions; an explanation that the differences in successive first differences in y-values will be equal for quadratic functions; an example of an equation for each type of function.

2. a. $h = -16t^2 + 25t + 4$

b.

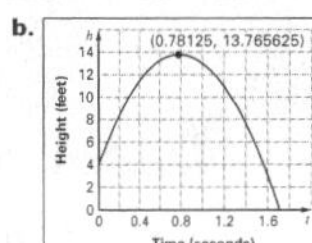

c. 13.8 ft **d.** 0.78125 sec **e.** 0.30 sec and 1.27 sec after release **f.** 1.52 sec

PLAN AND PREPARE

Main Ideas

In Chapter 10, students graph quadratic functions and compare them to the parent graph. They find the axis of symmetry, the vertex, and minimum or maximum values. They solve quadratic equations by factoring, graphing, using square roots, completing the square, and using the quadratic formula. Students use the discriminant to determine the number and type of solutions of a quadratic equation. Finally, students determine whether a linear, exponential, or quadratic function best models a set of data.

Prerequisite Skills

Skills Readiness, available on the *Easy Planner*, provides review and practice for the Skills Check portion of the Prerequisite Skills quiz.

How student answers the exercises	What to assign from *Skills Readiness*
Any of Exs. 3–5 answered incorrectly	**Skill 40** Reflections in the coordinate plane
Any of Exs. 6–9 answered incorrectly	**Skill 6** Evaluate square roots
All exercises answered correctly	Chapter 10 Enrichment

Additional skills review and practice is available in the Skills Review Handbook, pp. 909–937, and the @HomeTutor.

10 Quadratic Equations and Functions

Making Sense of Chapter 10

In this chapter you will graph, write, and solve quadratic equations. By the end of the chapter, you will be able to write quadratic models for data and compare them with linear and exponential models.

Before

Previously, you learned the following skills, which you'll use in Chapter 10: reflecting points in a line and finding square roots.

Prerequisite Skills

VOCABULARY CHECK

Copy and complete the statement.

1. The x-coordinate of a point where a graph crosses the x-axis is a(n) __?__. **x-intercept**
2. A(n) __?__ is a function of the form $y = a \cdot b^x$ where $a \neq 0$, $b > 0$, and $b \neq 1$. **exponential function**

SKILLS CHECK

Draw the blue figure. Then draw its image after a reflection in the red line. *(Prerequisite skill for 10.1–10.3)* **3–5. See margin.**

3. 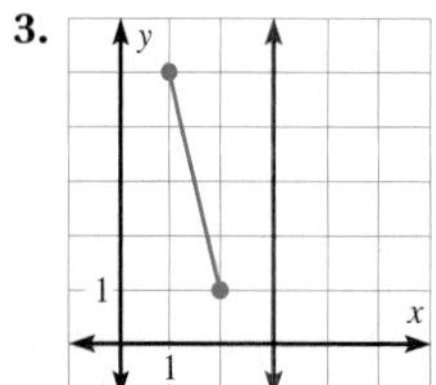
4. 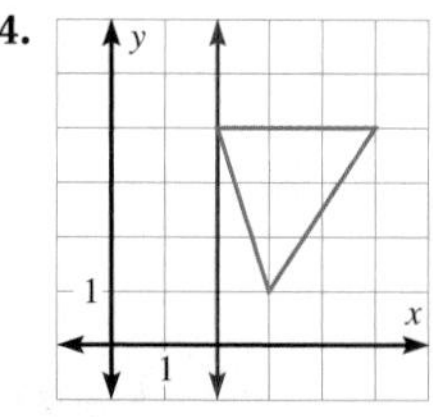
5. 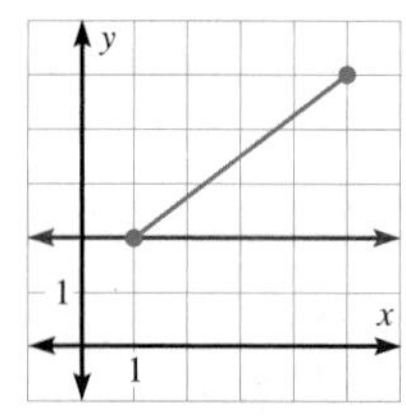

Evaluate the expression. *(Prerequisite skill for 10.4–10.6)*

6. $\sqrt{81}$ **9**
7. $-\sqrt{25}$ **−5**
8. $\sqrt{1}$ **1**
9. $\pm\sqrt{64}$ **±8**

@HomeTutor Prerequisite skills practice at classzone.com

Chapter Planning Guide

Chapter Resource Book
- Teaching Guide/Lesson Plan
- Project with Rubric

Assessment and Intervention
- Assessment Book
- Benchmark Tests
- Remediation Book
- Skills Readiness

Interactive Technology
- Easy Planner
- Power Presentations
- Activity Generator
- Animated Algebra
- Test Generator
- Online Quizzes
- eWorkbook
- eEdition
- @HomeTutor

Resources for English Learners
- Spanish Study Guide
- Multi-Language Visual Glossary
- Student Resources in Spanish

In Chapter 10, you will apply the big ideas listed below and reviewed in the Chapter Summary on page 695. You will also use the key vocabulary listed below.

Big Ideas

1. **Graphing quadratic functions**
2. **Solving quadratic equations**
3. **Comparing linear, exponential, and quadratic models**

KEY VOCABULARY

- quadratic function, *p. 628*
- parabola, *p. 628*
- parent quadratic function, *p. 628*
- vertex, *p. 628*
- axis of symmetry, *p. 628*
- minimum value, *p. 636*
- maximum value, *p. 636*
- quadratic equation, *p. 643*
- completing the square, *p. 663*
- quadratic formula, *p. 671*
- discriminant, *p. 678*

Why?

You can use a quadratic model for real-world situations involving vertical motion. For example, you can write and solve a quadratic equation to find the time a snowboarder is in the air during a jump.

Animated Algebra

The animation illustrated below for Exercise 50 on page 668 helps you answer this question: How many seconds is the snowboarder in the air during a jump?

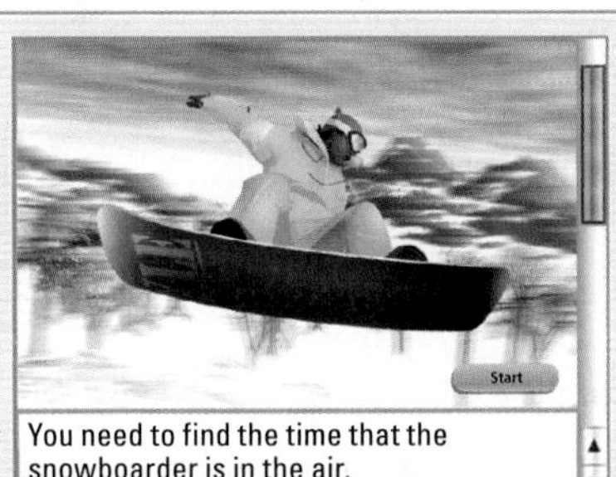

You need to find the time that the snowboarder is in the air.

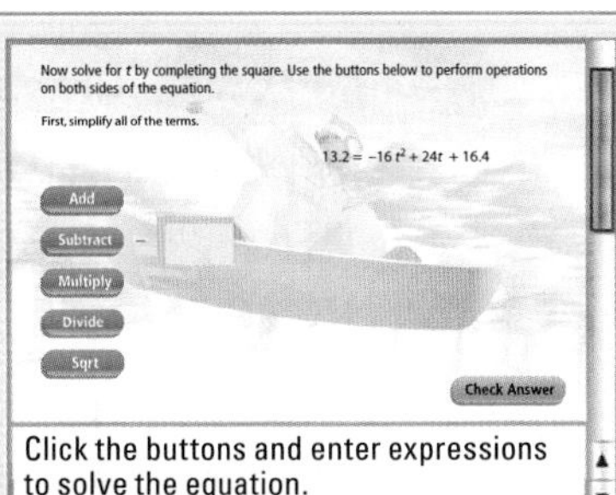

Now solve for t by completing the square. Use the buttons below to perform operations on both sides of the equation.
First, simplify all of the terms.
13.2 = −16t² + 24t + 16.4
Add
Subtract
Multiply
Divide
Sqrt
Check Answer

Click the buttons and enter expressions to solve the equation.

Animated Algebra at classzone.com

Other animations for Chapter 10: pages 634, 636, 642, 662, 668, 672, 684, and 695

Differentiated Instruction Resources

- Reading Strategies for Chapter 10
- Differentiated Instruction Lesson Notes
- English Learners Lesson Notes
- Inclusion Lesson Notes
- Teaching Strategies with Sample Worksheets
- Using Technology in the Classroom
- Tips for New Teachers
- Math Background Notes
- Assessment Strategies
- Teacher Survival Activities
- Bulletin Board Idea

3. 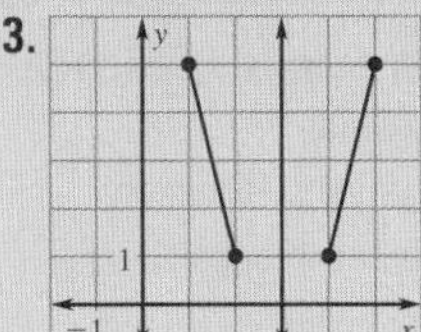

4. 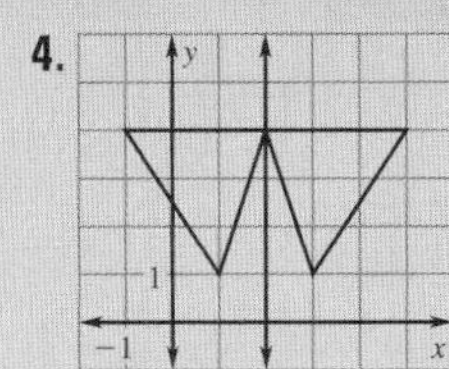

5. 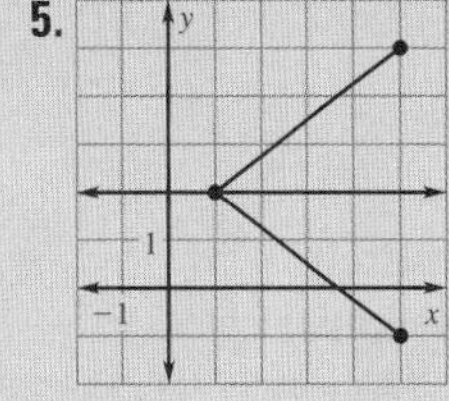

10.1 Graph $y = ax^2 + c$

1 PLAN AND PREPARE

Warm-Up Exercises

Transparency Available

1. Graph the function $y = 2^x$.

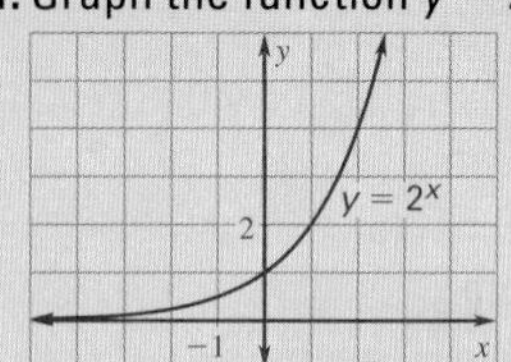

2. Identify the domain and range of your graph in Exercise 1. **domain: all real numbers; range: all positive real numbers**

Notetaking Guide

Transparency Available

Promotes interactive learning and notetaking skills.

Pacing

Basic: 2 days
Average: 2 days
Advanced: 2 days
Block: 1 block
- See *Teaching Guide/Lesson Plan.*

2 FOCUS AND MOTIVATE

Essential Question

Big Idea 1, p. 627

How do you graph a quadratic function? **Tell students they will learn how to answer this question by drawing a smooth curve through points from a table of values.**

NCTM STANDARDS

Standard 2: Understand functions

Standard 3: Apply transformations to math situations

Before	You graphed linear and exponential functions.
Now	You will graph simple quadratic functions.
Why?	So you can solve a problem involving an antenna, as in Ex. 40.

Key Vocabulary
- **quadratic function**
- **parabola**
- **parent quadratic function**
- **vertex**
- **axis of symmetry**

A **quadratic function** is a nonlinear function that can be written in the **standard form** $y = ax^2 + bx + c$ where $a \neq 0$. Every quadratic function has a U-shaped graph called a **parabola**. In this lesson, you will graph quadratic functions where $b = 0$.

KEY CONCEPT *For Your Notebook*

Parent Quadratic Function

The most basic quadratic function in the family of quadratic functions, called the **parent quadratic function**, is $y = x^2$. The graph of $y = x^2$ is shown below.

The lowest or highest point on a parabola is the **vertex**. The vertex of the graph of $y = x^2$ is (0, 0).

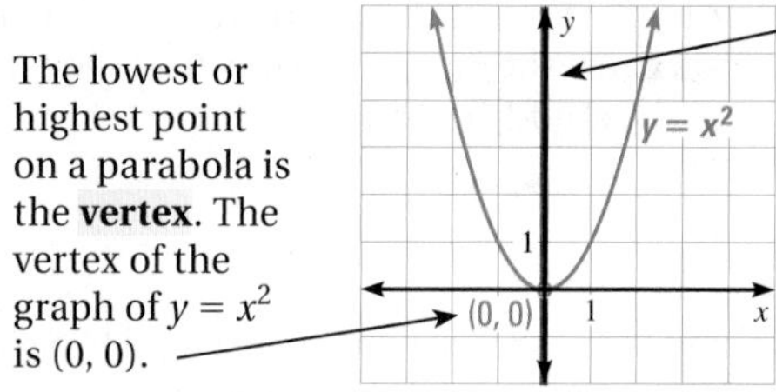

The line that passes through the vertex and divides the parabola into two symmetric parts is called the **axis of symmetry**. The axis of symmetry for the graph of $y = x^2$ is the y-axis, $x = 0$.

EXAMPLE 1 Graph $y = ax^2$ where $|a| > 1$

STEP 1 **Make** a table of values for $y = 3x^2$.

x	−2	−1	0	1	2
y	12	3	0	3	12

STEP 2 **Plot** the points from the table.

STEP 3 **Draw** a smooth curve through the points.

STEP 4 **Compare** the graphs of $y = 3x^2$ and $y = x^2$. Both graphs open up and have the same vertex, (0, 0), and axis of symmetry, $x = 0$. The graph of $y = 3x^2$ is narrower than the graph of $y = x^2$ because the graph of $y = 3x^2$ is a vertical stretch (by a factor of 3) of the graph of $y = x^2$.

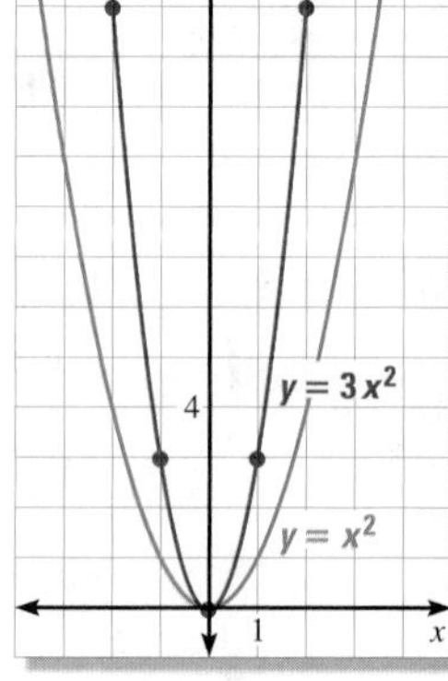

DESCRIBE A FUNCTION
A quadratic function has an unbroken graph, so the function is continuous, as discussed on p. 223.

Resource Planning Guide

Chapter Resource Book
- Teaching Guide/Lesson Plan
- Activity Master
- Practice levels A, B, C
- Study Guide
- Catch-up for Absent Students
- Application
- Challenge

Workbooks
- Notetaking Guide
- Practice Workbook

Teaching Options
- **Power Presentations** provides dynamic electronic teaching resources for the classroom.
- **Activity Generator** provides editable activities for all ability levels.

Interactive Technology
- Easy Planner
- Power Presentations
- Activity Generator
- Animated Algebra
- Test Generator
- Online Quiz
- eWorkbook
- eEdition
- @HomeTutor

Resources for English Learners
- Spanish Study Guide
- Multi-Language Visual Glossary
- Student Resources in Spanish

See also the *Differentiated Instruction Resources* for more strategies for meeting individual needs.

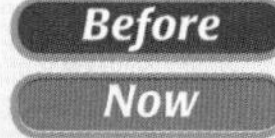

EXAMPLE 2 Graph $y = ax^2$ where $|a| < 1$

Graph $y = -\frac{1}{4}x^2$. Compare the graph with the graph of $y = x^2$.

MAKE A TABLE
To make the calculations easier, choose values of x that are multiples of 2.

STEP 1 **Make** a table of values for $y = -\frac{1}{4}x^2$.

x	−4	−2	0	2	4
y	−4	−1	0	−1	−4

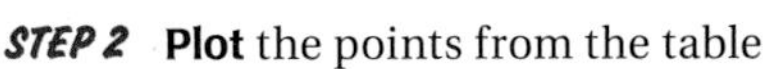

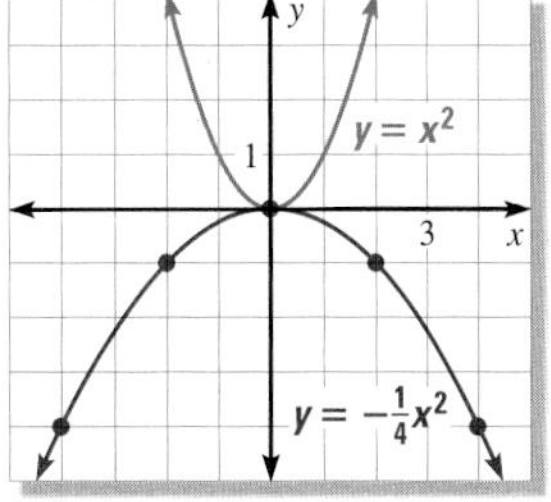

STEP 2 **Plot** the points from the table.

STEP 3 **Draw** a smooth curve through the points.

STEP 4 **Compare** the graphs of $y = -\frac{1}{4}x^2$ and $y = x^2$. Both graphs have the same vertex $(0, 0)$, and the same axis of symmetry, $x = 0$. However, the graph of $y = -\frac{1}{4}x^2$ is wider than the graph of $y = x^2$ and it opens down. This is because the graph of $y = -\frac{1}{4}x^2$ is a vertical shrink $\left(\text{by a factor of } \frac{1}{4}\right)$ with a reflection in the x-axis of the graph of $y = x^2$.

GRAPHING QUADRATIC FUNCTIONS Examples 1 and 2 suggest the following general result: a parabola opens up when the coefficient of x^2 is positive and opens down when the coefficient of x^2 is negative.

EXAMPLE 3 Graph $y = x^2 + c$

Graph $y = x^2 + 5$. Compare the graph with the graph of $y = x^2$.

ANALYZE RATE OF CHANGE
Notice that for a quadratic function, the rate of change in y with respect to x is *not* constant as it is for a linear function. For instance, $\frac{6 - 9}{-1 - (-2)} = -3$, while $\frac{5 - 6}{0 - (-1)} = -1$.

STEP 1 **Make** a table of values for $y = x^2 + 5$.

x	−2	−1	0	1	2
y	9	6	5	6	9

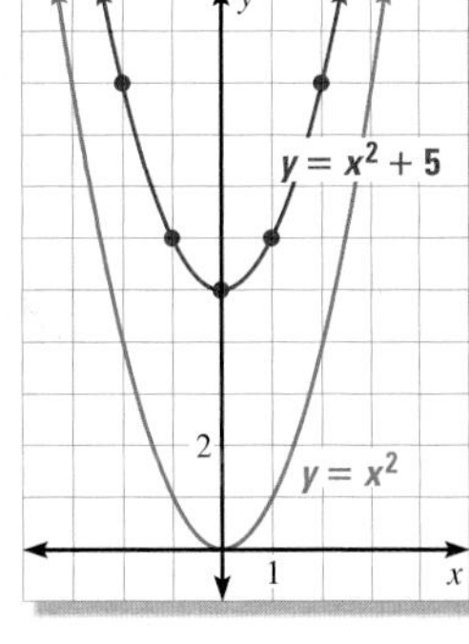

STEP 2 **Plot** the points from the table.

STEP 3 **Draw** a smooth curve through the points.

STEP 4 **Compare** the graphs of $y = x^2 + 5$ and $y = x^2$. Both graphs open up and have the same axis of symmetry, $x = 0$. However, the vertex of the graph of $y = x^2 + 5$, $(0, 5)$, is different than the vertex of the graph of $y = x^2$, $(0, 0)$, because the graph of $y = x^2 + 5$ is a vertical translation (of 5 units up) of the graph of $y = x^2$.

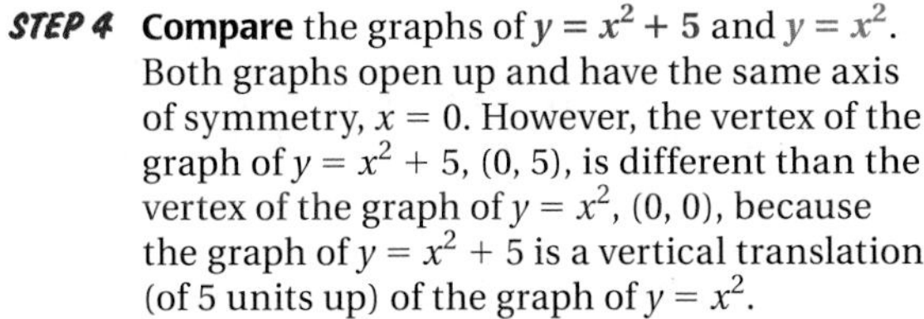

✓ **GUIDED PRACTICE** for Examples 1, 2, and 3

Graph the function. Compare the graph with the graph of $y = x^2$. 1–3. See margin.

1. $y = -4x^2$ **2.** $y = \frac{1}{3}x^2$ **3.** $y = x^2 + 2$

Differentiated Instruction

English Learners The parent quadratic function $y = x^2$ produces the family of quadratic functions $y = ax^2 + bx + c$. Students may notice the analogy with a parent linear function producing a family of linear functions (Section 4.7).

See also the *Differentiated Instruction Resources* for more strategies.

Motivating the Lesson

You see that your neighbors have a satellite dish on the roof of their house. You notice that the face of the dish is curved. In this lesson you will learn about that curve, called a parabola, and learn how to solve problems involving parabolas.

3 TEACH

Extra Example 1

Graph $y = 2x^2$. Compare the graph with the graph of $y = x^2$.

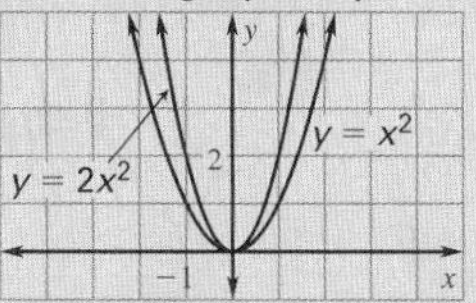

Both graphs open up and have the same vertex, (0, 0), and the same axis of symmetry, $x = 0$. The graph of $y = 2x^2$ is narrower than the graph of $y = x^2$ because it is a vertical stretch (by a factor of 2) of the parent graph.

Extra Example 2

Graph $y = -\frac{1}{2}x^2$. Compare the graph with the graph of $y = x^2$.

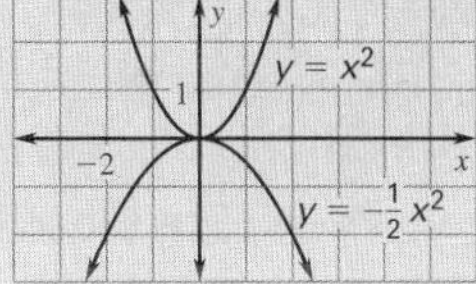

Both graphs have the same vertex, (0, 0), and the same axis of symmetry, $x = 0$. The graph of $y = -\frac{1}{2}x^2$ opens down. Also, the graph of $y = -\frac{1}{2}x^2$ is a reflection in the x-axis of $y = x^2$ after a vertical shrink $\left(\text{by a factor of } \frac{1}{2}\right)$.

1–3. See Additional Answers beginning on p. AA1.

Extra Example 3

Graph $y = x^2 + 1$. Compare the graph with the graph of $y = x^2$.

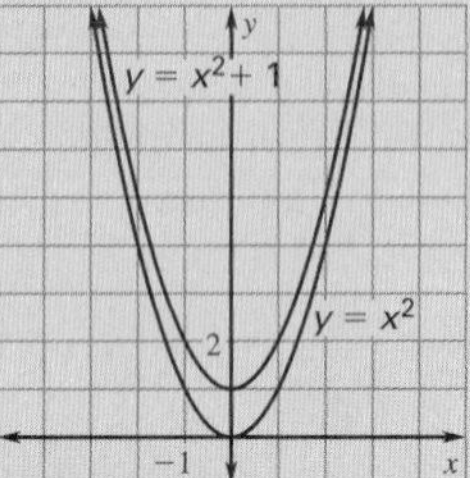

Both graphs open up and have the same axis of symmetry, $x = 0$. The vertex of the graph of $y = x^2 + 1$, which is (0, 1), is different that the vertex of the graph of $y = x^2$, which is (0, 0), because the graph of $y = x^2 + 1$ is a vertical translation (of 1 unit up) of the graph of $y = x^2$.

Key Questions to Ask for Example 3

- Why does the parabola open up? **The coefficient of x^2 is positive.**
- How can you tell that the parabola is shifted a positive number of units? **The value of c in $y = x^2 + c$ is positive.**

Extra Example 4

Graph $y = \frac{3}{2}x^2 - 2$. Compare the graph with the graph of $y = x^2$.

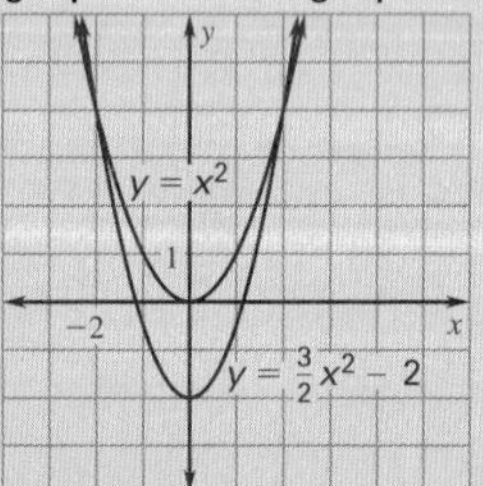

Both graphs open up and have the same axis of symmetry, $x = 0$. The graph of $y = \frac{3}{2}x^2 - 2$ is narrower and has a lower vertex than the graph of $y = x^2$ because it is a vertical stretch and a vertical translation of the graph of $y = x^2$.

EXAMPLE 4 Graph $y = ax^2 + c$

Graph $y = \frac{1}{2}x^2 - 4$. Compare the graph with the graph of $y = x^2$.

STEP 1 **Make** a table of values for $y = \frac{1}{2}x^2 - 4$.

x	−4	−2	0	2	4
y	4	−2	−4	−2	4

STEP 2 **Plot** the points from the table.

STEP 3 **Draw** a smooth curve through the points.

STEP 4 **Compare** the graphs of $y = \frac{1}{2}x^2 - 4$ and $y = x^2$. Both graphs open up and have the same axis of symmetry, $x = 0$. However, the graph of $y = \frac{1}{2}x^2 - 4$ is wider and has a lower vertex than the graph of $y = x^2$ because the graph of $y = \frac{1}{2}x^2 - 4$ is a vertical shrink and a vertical translation of the graph of $y = x^2$.

✓ GUIDED PRACTICE for Example 4

Graph the function. Compare the graph with the graph of $y = x^2$. **4–6. See margin.**

4. $y = 3x^2 - 6$ **5.** $y = -5x^2 + 1$ **6.** $y = \frac{3}{4}x^2 - 2$

KEY CONCEPT *For Your Notebook*

$y = ax^2, a > 0$

a > 1
a = 1
0 < a < 1

Compared with the graph of $y = x^2$, the graph of $y = ax^2$ is:

- a vertical stretch if $a > 1$,
- a vertical shrink if $0 < a < 1$.

$y = ax^2, a < 0$

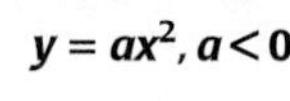

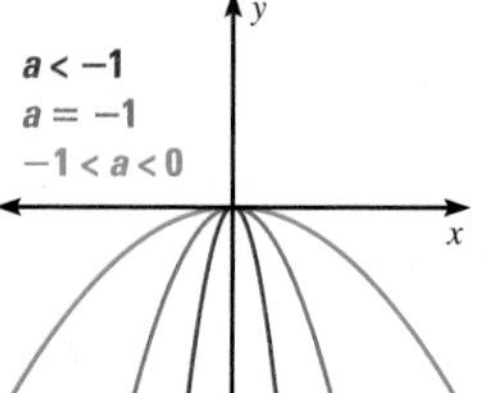

Compared with the graph of $y = x^2$, the graph of $y = ax^2$ is:

- a vertical stretch with a reflection in the x-axis if $a < -1$,
- a vertical shrink with a reflection in the x-axis if $-1 < a < 0$.

$y = x^2 + c$

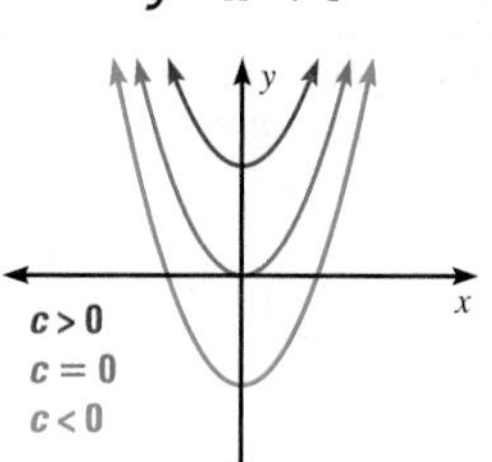

Compared with the graph of $y = x^2$, the graph of $y = x^2 + c$ is:

- an upward vertical translation if $c > 0$,
- a downward vertical translation if $c < 0$.

4.

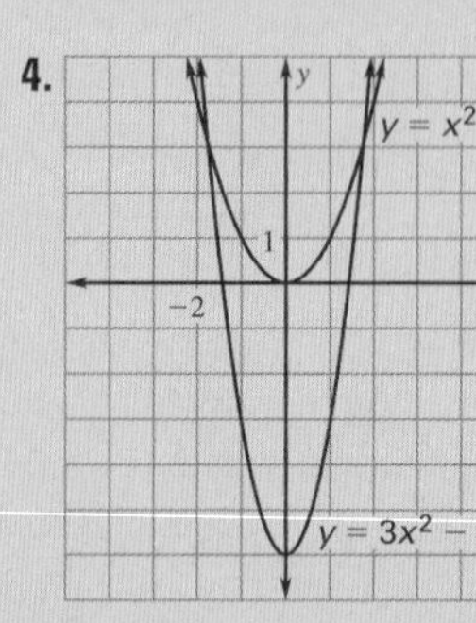

The graph is a vertical stretch (by a factor of 3) with a vertical translation (of 6 units down) of the graph of $y = x^2$.

5.

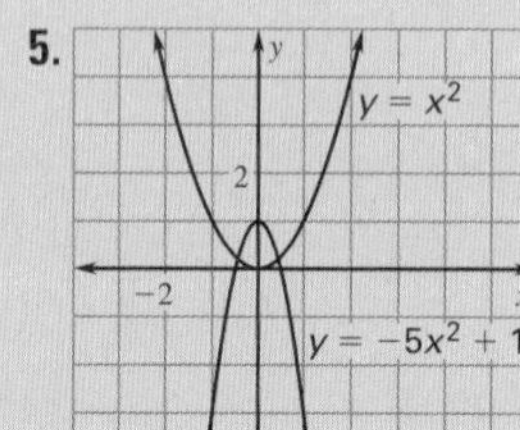

The graph is a vertical stretch (by a factor of 5) with a vertical translation (of 1 unit up) and a reflection in the x-axis of the graph of $y = x^2$.

EXAMPLE 5 Standardized Test Practice

How would the graph of the function $y = x^2 + 6$ be affected if the function were changed to $y = x^2 + 2$?

Ⓐ The graph would shift 2 units up.

Ⓑ The graph would shift 4 units up.

Ⓒ The graph would shift 4 units down.

Ⓓ The graph would shift 4 units to the left.

ELIMINATE CHOICES
You can eliminate choice D because changing the value of c in a function of the form $y = x^2 + c$ translates the graph up or down.

Solution

The vertex of the graph of $y = x^2 + 6$ is 6 units above the origin, or (0, 6). The vertex of the graph of $y = x^2 + 2$ is 2 units above the origin, or (0, 2). Moving the vertex from (0, 6) to (0, 2) translates the graph 4 units down.

▶ The correct answer is C. Ⓐ Ⓑ Ⓒ Ⓓ

EXAMPLE 6 Use a graph

SOLAR ENERGY A solar trough has a reflective parabolic surface that is used to collect solar energy. The sun's rays are reflected from the surface toward a pipe that carries water. The heated water produces steam that is used to produce electricity.

ANALYZE A GRAPH
You can use the graph to estimate the range of the function. The lowest point is at the origin. The two highest points are just above the line $y = 2$. So, an estimate of the range is $0 \leq y \leq 2$.

The graph of the function $y = 0.09x^2$ models the cross section of the reflective surface where x and y are measured in meters. Use the graph to find the domain and range of the function in this situation.

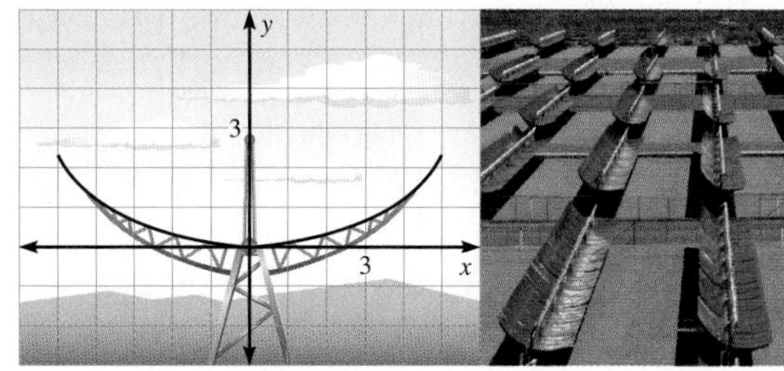

Solution

STEP 1 **Find** the domain. In the graph, the reflective surface extends 5 meters on either side of the origin. So, the domain is $-5 \leq x \leq 5$.

STEP 2 **Find** the range using the fact that the lowest point on the reflective surface is (0, 0) and the highest point occurs at $x = 5$ or $x = -5$.

$$y = 0.09(5)^2 = 2.25 \quad \text{Substitute 5 for } x\text{. Then simplify.}$$

The range is $0 \leq y \leq 2.25$.

✓ GUIDED PRACTICE for Examples 5 and 6

7. *Describe* how the graph of the function $y = x^2 + 2$ would be affected if the function were changed to $y = x^2 - 2$.
The graph would be translated 4 units down.

8. **WHAT IF?** In Example 6, suppose the reflective surface extends just 4 meters on either side of the origin. Find the domain and range of the function in this situation. **$-4 \leq x \leq 4$, $0 \leq y \leq 1.44$**

Extra Example 5

How would the graph of the function $y = x^2 - 3$ be affected if the function were changed to $y = x^2 - 2$? **B**

Ⓐ The graph would shift 2 units up.

Ⓑ The graph would shift 1 unit up.

Ⓒ The graph would shift 1 unit down.

Ⓓ The graph would shift 2 units down.

Extra Example 6

This graph shows a large parabolic umbrella. The graph of the function $y = -0.25x^2$ models the cross section of the surface, where x and y are measured in meters. Use the graph to find the domain and range of the function.

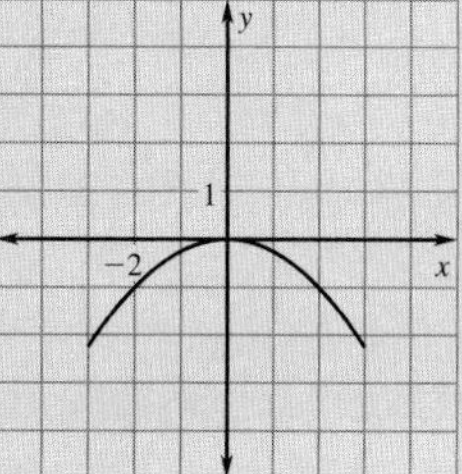

domain: $-3 \leq x \leq 3$
range: $-2.25 \leq y \leq 0$

Closing the Lesson

Have students summarize the major points of the lesson and answer the Essential Question: How do you graph a quadratic function?

- **The parent quadratic function is $y = x^2$.**
- **The vertex is the lowest or highest point on a parabola. The axis of symmetry passes through the vertex.**

Make a table of values for the function. Since a parabola is U-shaped, include values to the left and right of the vertex. Plot the points from the table and then draw a smooth curve through the points.

6. 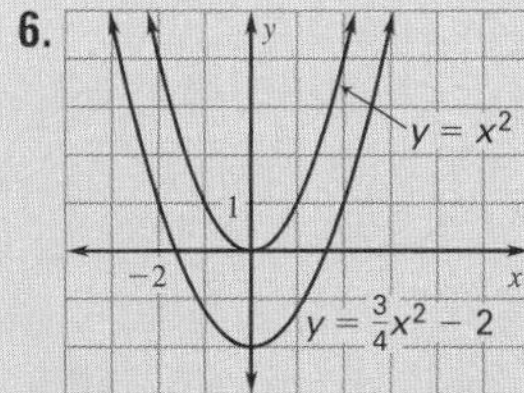

The graph is a vertical shrink $\left(\text{by a factor of } \frac{3}{4}\right)$ with a vertical translation (of 2 units down) of the graph of $y = x^2$.

10.1 EXERCISES

HOMEWORK KEY
○ = **WORKED-OUT SOLUTIONS** on p. WS23 for Exs. 7 and 41
★ = **STANDARDIZED TEST PRACTICE** Exs. 2, 22, 33, 43, and 44

SKILL PRACTICE

A

1. **VOCABULARY** Copy and complete: Every quadratic function has a U-shaped graph called a(n) __?__. **parabola**

2. ★ **WRITING** *Explain* how you can tell whether the graph of a quadratic function opens up or down. **The graph of the quadratic function $y = ax^2 + bx + c$ opens up if $a > 0$ and opens down if $a < 0$.**

MATCHING Match the quadratic function with its graph.

3. $y = \frac{1}{2}x^2 - 4$ **C**
4. $y = \frac{1}{2}x^2 - 2$ **A**
5. $y = -\frac{1}{2}x^2 + 2$ **B**

A. 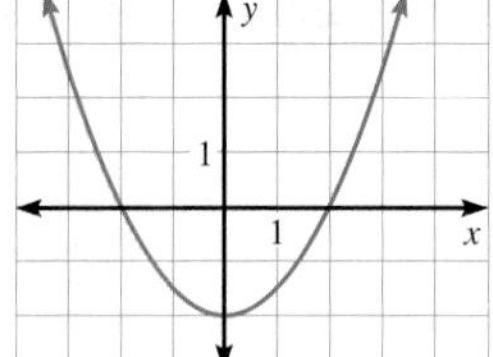

B. 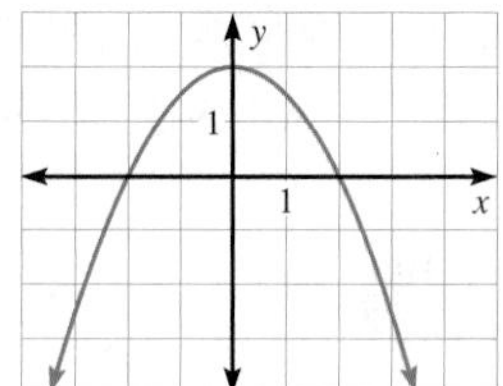

C. 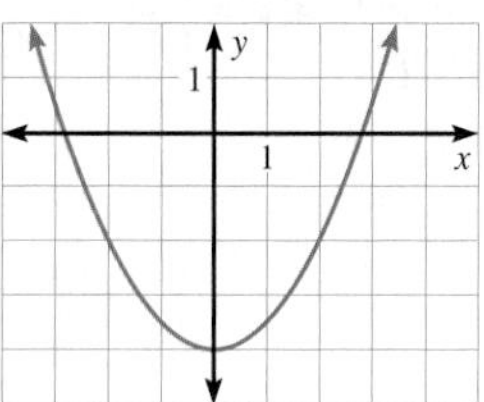

EXAMPLES 1, 2, and 3 on pp. 628–629 for Exs. 6–23

GRAPHING QUADRATIC FUNCTIONS Graph the function. Compare the graph with the graph of $y = x^2$. **6–21. See margin.**

6. $y = 8x^2$
7. $y = -2x^2$
8. $y = -3x^2$
9. $y = 5x^2$
10. $y = \frac{11}{2}x^2$
11. $y = \frac{2}{3}x^2$
12. $y = -\frac{3}{4}x^2$
13. $y = -\frac{1}{9}x^2$
14. $y = \frac{3}{8}x^2$
15. $y = -\frac{1}{5}x^2$
16. $y = x^2 - 7$
17. $y = x^2 + 9$
18. $y = x^2 + 6$
19. $y = x^2 - 4$
20. $y = x^2 - 1$
21. $y = x^2 + \frac{7}{4}$

22. ★ **MULTIPLE CHOICE** What is the vertex of the graph of the function $y = -\frac{3}{4}x^2 + 7$? **C**

Ⓐ (−7, 0) Ⓑ (0, −7) Ⓒ (0, 7) Ⓓ (7, 0)

23. **ERROR ANALYSIS** *Describe* and correct the error in drawing and comparing the graphs of $y = x^2$ and $y = x^2 - 2$.

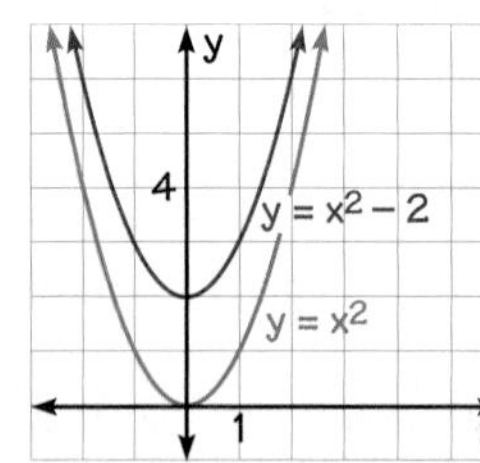

Both graphs open up and have the same axis of symmetry. However, the vertex of the graph of $y = x^2 - 2$, (0, 2), is 2 units above the vertex of the graph of $y = x^2$, (0, 0).

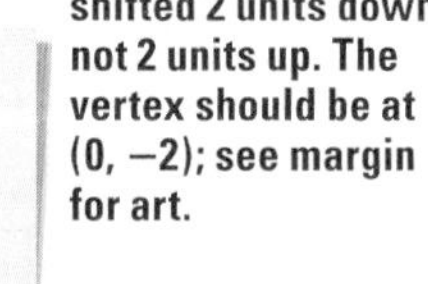
The graph of $y = x^2 - 2$ should be shifted 2 units down, not 2 units up. The vertex should be at (0, −2); see margin for art.

4 PRACTICE AND APPLY

Assignment Guide

Answer Transparencies available for all exercises

Basic:
Day 1: EP p. 941 Exs. 56–59 pp. 632–634 Exs. 1–23
Day 2: pp. 632–634 Exs. 24–35, 40–42, 46–57

Average:
Day 1: pp. 632–634 Exs. 1–5, 10–23, 52–57
Day 2: pp. 632–634 Exs. 26–36, 40–44, 46–51

Advanced:
Day 1: pp. 632–634 Exs. 1–5, 12–23, 45*, 52–57
Day 2: pp. 632–634 Exs. 28–44*, 46–51

Block:
pp. 632–634 Exs. 1–5, 10–23, 26–37, 40–44, 46–57

Differentiated Instruction

See *Differentiated Instruction Resources* for suggestions on addressing the needs of a diverse classroom.

Homework Check

For a quick check of student understanding of key concepts, go over the following exercises:
Basic: 8, 16, 26, 34, 40
Average: 12, 18, 28, 35, 40
Advanced: 15, 20, 31, 36, 41

Extra Practice

- Student Edition, p. 947
- Chapter Resource Book: Practice levels A, B, C

Practice Worksheet

An easily-readable reduced practice page (with answers) for this lesson can be found on p. 626C.

6–21. See Additional Answers beginning on p. AA1.

23.
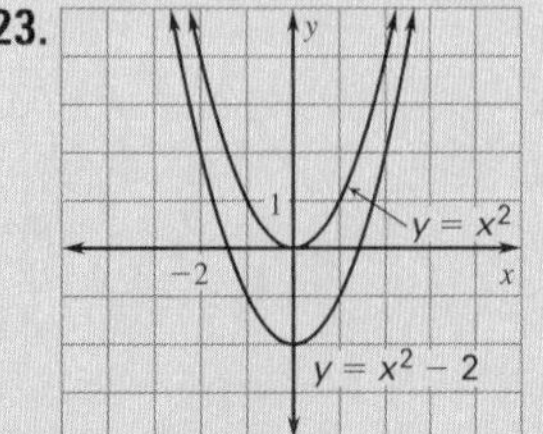

EXAMPLE 4 on p. 630 for Exs. 24–32

GRAPHING QUADRATIC FUNCTIONS Graph the function. Compare the graph with the graph of $y = x^2$. **24–32. See margin.**

24. $y = 7x^2 + 7$
25. $y = -x^2 + 5$
26. $y = 2x^2 - 12$
27. $y = -2x^2 - 1$
28. $y = -3x^2 - 2$
29. $y = \frac{3}{4}x^2 - 3$
30. $y = \frac{1}{5}x^2 + 10$
31. $y = \frac{1}{2}x^2 - 5$
32. $y = -\frac{2}{3}x^2 + 9$

EXAMPLE 5 on p. 631 for Exs. 33–36

33. ★ **MULTIPLE CHOICE** How would the graph of the function $y = x^2 + 3$ be affected if the function were changed to $y = x^2 + 9$? **B**

(A) The graph would shift 9 units to the right.

(B) The graph would shift 6 units up.

(C) The graph would shift 9 units up.

(D) The graph would shift 6 units down.

B **COMPARING GRAPHS Tell how you can obtain the graph of g from the graph of f using transformations.** **34–36. See margin.**

34. $f(x) = x^2 - 5$, $g(x) = x^2 + 8$
35. $f(x) = 3x^2 - 11$, $g(x) = 3x^2 - 16$
36. $f(x) = 4x^2$, $g(x) = 2x^2$

C **CHALLENGE Write a function of the form $y = ax^2 + c$ whose graph passes through the two given points.**

37. (−1, 9), (0, 3) **$y = 6x^2 + 3$**
38. (2, 1), (5, −20) **$y = -x^2 + 5$**
39. (−2, −16.5), (1, 4.5) **$y = -7x^2 + 11.5$**

PROBLEM SOLVING

GRAPHING CALCULATOR You may wish to use a graphing calculator to complete the following Problem Solving exercises.

EXAMPLE 6 on p. 631 for Exs. 40–41

A 40. **ASTRONOMY** A cross section of the parabolic surface of the antenna shown can be modeled by the graph of the function $y = 0.012x^2$ where x and y are measured in meters.

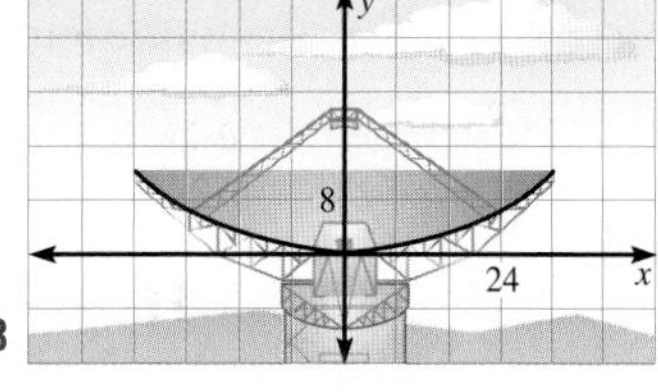

a. Find the domain of the function in this situation. **$-32 \le x \le 32$**

b. Find the range of the function in this situation. **$0 \le y \le 12.288$**

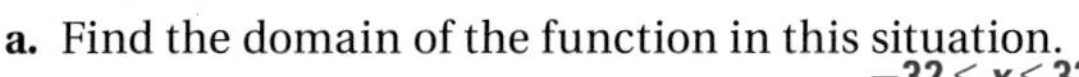

41. **SAILING** Sailors need to consider the speed of the wind when adjusting the sails on their boat. The force F (in pounds per square foot) on a sail when the wind is blowing perpendicular to the sail can be modeled by the function $F = 0.004v^2$ where v is the wind speed (in knots).

a. Graph the function for wind speeds from 0 knots to 50 knots. **See margin for art.**

b. Use the graph to estimate the wind speed that will produce a force of 1 pound per square foot on a sail. **about 16 knots**

c. Estimate the wind speed that will produce a force of 5 pounds per square foot on a sail. **about 35 knots**

@HomeTutor for problem solving help at classzone.com

Avoiding Common Errors

Exercises 6–21, 24–32 Watch for students who do not graph points on both side of the vertex of the parabola. Remind these students that a parabola is U-shaped and symmetric, and they can use that symmetry to locate points on both sides of the vertex.

Graphing Calculator

Exercises 40–45 A graphing calculator will help students find approximate values for these exercises. Tell students to use the same steps to graph quadratic functions as they use to graph any other function.

Animated Algebra classzone.com

An **Animated Algebra** activity is available online for **Exercise 44.** This activity is also part of **Power Presentations**.

24–32. See Additional Answers beginning on p. AA1.

34. Translate the graph of f 13 units up.

35. Translate the graph of f 5 units down.

36. Shrink the graph of f by a factor of $\frac{1}{2}$.

41a.

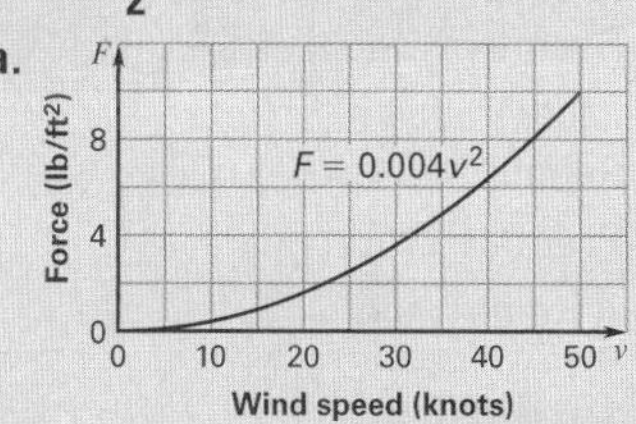

5 ASSESS AND RETEACH

Daily Homework Quiz

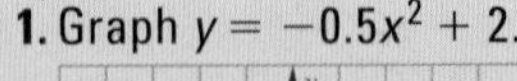

1. Graph $y = -0.5x^2 + 2$.

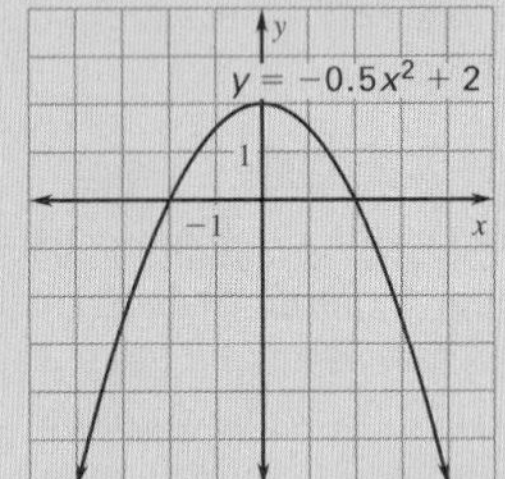

2. How would the graph of the function $y = -2x^2 + 3$ be affected if the function were changed to $y = -2x^2 - 3$? **It would be shifted down 6 units.**
3. A pinecone falls about 50 feet from the branch of a pine tree. Its height (in feet) can be modeled by the function $h(t) = -16t^2 + 50$, where t is the time in seconds. How long does it take to land on the ground? **about 1.8 sec**

Available at **classzone.com**

Diagnosis/Remediation

- Practice A, B, C in Chapter Resource Book
- Study Guide in Chapter Resource Book
- Practice Workbook
- @HomeTutor

Challenge

Additional challenge is available in the Chapter Resource Book.

43a–b, 44a–c. See Additional Answers beginning on p. AA1.

45.

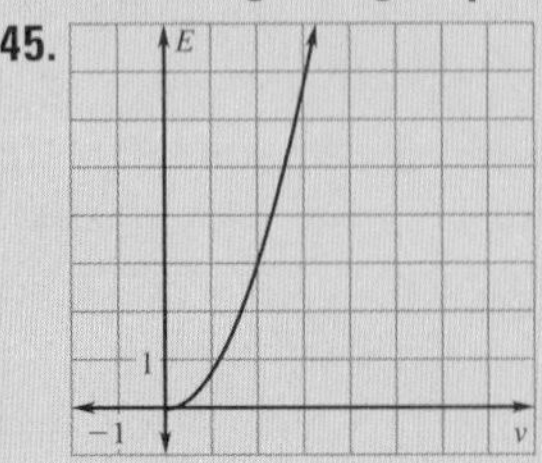

REVIEW VERTICAL MOTION
For help with the vertical motion model, see p. 575.

42b. ***Sample answer:*** **The graph of $h = -16t^2 + 45$ is a vertical translation (of 13 units up) of the graph of $h = -16t^2 + 32$.**

B

42. FALLING OBJECTS Two acorns drop from an oak tree. One falls 45 feet, while the other falls 32 feet.

a. For each acorn, write an equation that gives the height h (in feet) of the acorn as a function of the time t (in seconds) it has fallen. **$h = -16t^2 + 45$, $h = -16t^2 + 32$**

b. *Describe* how the graphs of the two equations are related.

43. ★ SHORT RESPONSE The breaking strength w (in pounds) of a manila rope can be modeled by the function $w = 8900d^2$ where d is the diameter (in inches) of the rope.

a. Graph the function. **a–b. See margin.**

b. If a manila rope has 4 times the breaking strength of another manila rope, does the rope have 4 times the diameter of the other rope? *Explain.*

44. ★ EXTENDED RESPONSE For an engineering contest, you have to create a container for an egg so that the container can be dropped from a height of 30 feet without breaking the egg.

a. The distance y (in feet) that the container falls is given by the function $y = 16t^2$ where t is the time (in seconds) the container has fallen. Graph the function. **a–c. See margin.**

b. The height y (in feet) of the dropped container is given by the function $y = -16t^2 + 30$ where t is the time (in seconds) since the container is dropped. Graph the function.

c. How are the graphs from part (a) and part (b) related? *Explain* how you can use each graph to find the number of seconds after which the container has fallen 10 feet.

 at classzone.com

C

45. CHALLENGE The kinetic energy E (in joules) of an object in motion is given by $E = \frac{1}{2}mv^2$ where m is the object's mass (in kilograms) and v is the object's velocity (in meters per second). Suppose a baseball has 918.75 joules of energy when traveling 35 meters per second. Use this information to write and graph an equation that gives the energy E of the baseball as a function of its velocity v. **$E = 0.75v^2$; see margin for art.**

MIXED REVIEW

PREVIEW
Prepare for Lesson 10.2 in Exs. 46–51.

Evaluate the expression. *(p. 8)*

46. $x^2 + 5$ when $x = 2$ **9**
47. $4y^2 + 1$ when $y = 0$ **1**
48. $16 + 3m^2$ when $m = 5$ **91**
49. $5b^2 + 11$ when $b = 10$ **511**
50. $20 - 8w^2$ when $w = 1$ **12**
51. $7z^2 - 22$ when $z = 3$ **41**

Solve the linear system using substitution. *(p. 435)*

52. $x = 20 - 3y$; $2x - y = -4$ **$\left(1\frac{1}{7}, 6\frac{2}{7}\right)$**
53. $y = 2x - 10$; $11 = 3x - 2y$ **(9, 8)**
54. $x = 11y + 4$; $2x - 17y = 13$ **(15, 1)**

Use the FOIL pattern to find the product. *(p. 562)*

55. $(2p + 3)(p + 2)$ **$2p^2 + 7p + 6$**
56. $(7x + 5)(3x - 1)$ **$21x^2 + 8x - 5$**
57. $(5n - 10)(5n - 9)$ **$25n^2 - 95n + 90$**

EXTRA PRACTICE for Lesson 10.1, p. 947 | **ONLINE QUIZ** at classzone.com

10.2 Graph $y = ax^2 + bx + c$

Before You graphed simple quadratic functions.

Now You will graph general quadratic functions.

Why? So you can investigate a cable's height, as in Example 4.

Key Vocabulary
- **minimum value**
- **maximum value**

You can use the properties below to graph any quadratic function. You will justify the formula for the axis of symmetry in Exercise 38 on page 639.

KEY CONCEPT *For Your Notebook*

Properties of the Graph of a Quadratic Function

The graph of $y = ax^2 + bx + c$ is a parabola that:

- opens up if $a > 0$ and opens down if $a < 0$.
- is narrower than the graph of $y = x^2$ if $|a| > 1$ and wider if $|a| < 1$.
- has an axis of symmetry of $x = -\frac{b}{2a}$.
- has a vertex with an x-coordinate of $-\frac{b}{2a}$.
- has a y-intercept of c. So, the point $(0, c)$ is on the parabola.

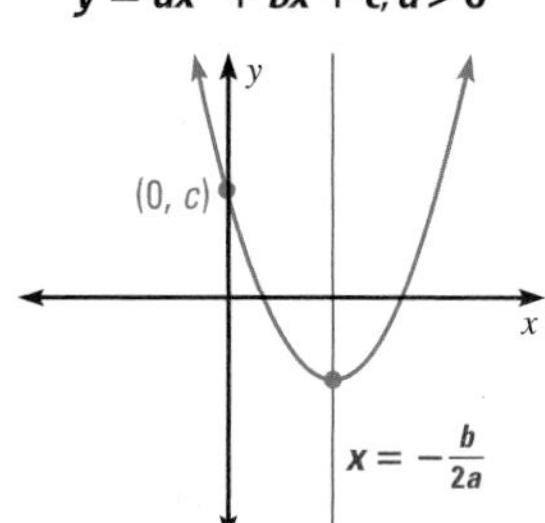

EXAMPLE 1 Find the axis of symmetry and the vertex

Consider the function $y = -2x^2 + 12x - 7$.

a. Find the axis of symmetry of the graph of the function.

b. Find the vertex of the graph of the function.

Solution

a. For the function $y = -2x^2 + 12x - 7$, $a = -2$ and $b = 12$.

$$x = -\frac{b}{2a} = -\frac{12}{2(-2)} = 3$$ **Substitute −2 for *a* and 12 for *b*. Then simplify.**

IDENTIFY THE VERTEX
Because the vertex lies on the axis of symmetry, $x = 3$, the x-coordinate of the vertex is 3.

b. The x-coordinate of the vertex is $-\frac{b}{2a}$, or 3.

To find the y-coordinate, substitute 3 for x in the function and find y.

$$y = -2(3)^2 + 12(3) - 7 = 11$$ **Substitute 3 for *x*. Then simplify.**

▶ The vertex is (3, 11).

1 PLAN AND PREPARE

Warm-Up Exercises
Transparency Available

Evaluate the expression.

1. $x^2 - 2$ when $x = 3$ **7**

2. $2x^2 + 9$ when $x = 2$ **17**

3. Martin is replacing a square patch of counter top. The area of the patch is represented by $A = s^2$. What is the area of the patch if the side length is 2.5 inches? **6.25 in.²**

Notetaking Guide
Transparency Available

Promotes interactive learning and notetaking skills.

Pacing
Basic: 1 day
Average: 1 day
Advanced: 1 day
Block: 0.5 block with 10.3
- See *Teaching Guide/Lesson Plan.*

2 FOCUS AND MOTIVATE

Essential Question
Big Idea 1, p. 627

How do you graph a quadratic function of the form $y = ax^2 + bx + c$? **Tell students they will learn how to answer this question by finding the axis of symmetry, finding the vertex, and using symmetry to plot several points.**

NCTM STANDARDS

Standard 3: Describe spatial relationships using coordinate geometry

Standard 10: Use representations to communicate mathematical ideas

Resource Planning Guide

Chapter Resource Book
- Teaching Guide/Lesson Plan
- Activity Master
- Practice levels A, B, C
- Study Guide
- Catch-up for Absent Students
- Problem Solving Workshop
- Challenge

Workbooks
- Notetaking Guide
- Practice Workbook

Teaching Options
- **Power Presentations** provides dynamic electronic teaching resources for the classroom.
- **Activity Generator** provides editable activities for all ability levels.

Interactive Technology
- Easy Planner
- Power Presentations
- Activity Generator
- Animated Algebra
- Test Generator
- Online Quiz
- eWorkbook
- eEdition
- @HomeTutor

Resources for English Learners
- Spanish Study Guide
- Multi-Language Visual Glossary
- Student Resources in Spanish

See also the *Differentiated Instruction Resources* for more strategies for meeting individual needs.

EXAMPLE 2 Graph $y = ax^2 + bx + c$

Graph $y = 3x^2 - 6x + 2$.

STEP 1 **Determine** whether the parabola opens up or down. Because $a > 0$, the parabola opens up.

AVOID ERRORS
Be sure to include the negative sign before the fraction when calculating the axis of symmetry.

STEP 2 **Find** and draw the axis of symmetry: $x = -\frac{b}{2a} = -\frac{-6}{2(3)} = 1$.

STEP 3 **Find** and plot the vertex.

The x-coordinate of the vertex is $-\frac{b}{2a}$, or 1.

To find the y-coordinate, substitute 1 for x in the function and simplify.

$y = 3(1)^2 - 6(1) + 2 = -1$

So, the vertex is $(1, -1)$.

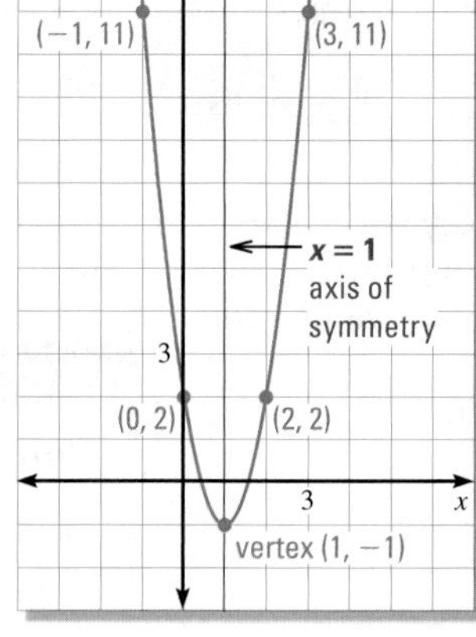

STEP 4 **Plot** two points. Choose two x-values less than the x-coordinate of the vertex. Then find the corresponding y-values.

x	0	−1
y	2	11

REVIEW REFLECTIONS
For help with reflections, see p. 922.

STEP 5 **Reflect** the points plotted in Step 4 in the axis of symmetry.

STEP 6 **Draw** a parabola through the plotted points.

Animated **Algebra** at classzone.com

✓ GUIDED PRACTICE for Examples 1 and 2

1. Find the axis of symmetry and the vertex of the graph of the function $y = x^2 - 2x - 3$. **$x = 1$, $(1, -4)$**
2. Graph the function $y = 3x^2 + 12x - 1$. Label the vertex and axis of symmetry. **See margin.**

KEY CONCEPT — *For Your Notebook*

Minimum and Maximum Values

For $y = ax^2 + bx + c$, the y-coordinate of the vertex is the **minimum value** of the function if $a > 0$ or the **maximum value** of the function if $a < 0$.

$y = ax^2 + bx + c$, $a > 0$

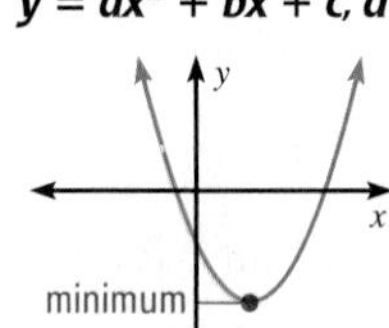

$y = ax^2 + bx + c$, $a < 0$

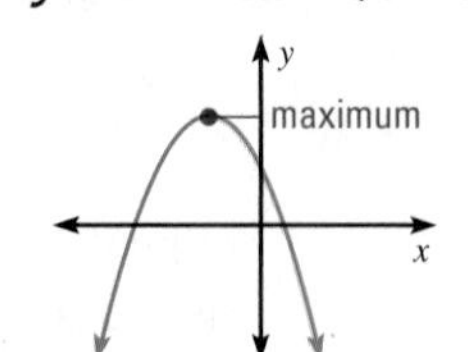

Motivating the Lesson

As you pass over a suspension bridge, you notice that the cables form a parabola. You also notice, as you pass beneath a bridge, that arches in the shape of a parabola support the bridge. In this lesson you will learn how to find maximum and minimum points on a parabola and how to use that information to find the highest and lowest points of suspension cables and support arches.

Extra Example 1

Consider the function $y = 3x^2 + 12x - 8$.

a. Find the axis of symmetry of the graph of the function. **$x = -2$**

b. Find the vertex of the graph of the function. **$(-2, -20)$**

Extra Example 2

Graph $y = 2x^2 - 8x + 7$.

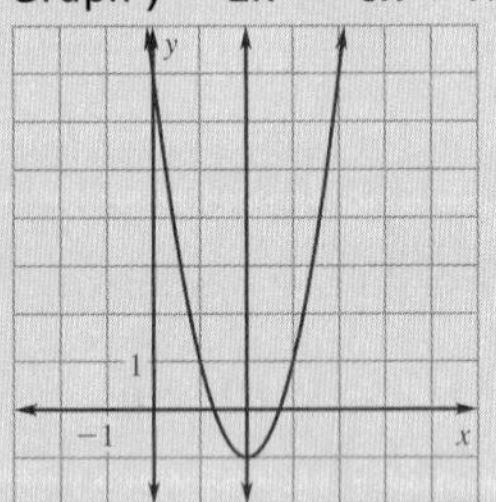

Key Question to Ask for Example 2

- In Step 4, why do you find two x-values less than the x-coordinate of the vertex? **The parabola is U-shaped, so after you find two points to the left of the vertex you can use symmetry to locate corresponding points to the right of the vertex.**

Differentiated Instruction

Visual Learners Show students that the Key Concept in Lesson 10.1 on p. 630 shows the special cases of the function $y = ax^2 + bx + c$ when $b = 0$ and when $b = c = 0$.

See also the *Differentiated Instruction Resources* for more strategies.

EXAMPLE 3 Find the minimum or maximum value

Tell whether the function $f(x) = -3x^2 - 12x + 10$ has a *minimum value* or a *maximum value*. Then find the minimum or maximum value.

Solution

Because $a = -3$ and $-3 < 0$, the parabola opens down and the function has a maximum value. To find the maximum value, find the vertex.

$x = -\frac{b}{2a} = -\frac{-12}{2(-3)} = -2$ **The x-coordinate is $-\frac{b}{2a}$.**

$f(-2) = -3(-2)^2 - 12(-2) + 10 = 22$ **Substitute −2 for x. Then simplify.**

▶ The maximum value of the function is $f(-2) = 22$.

EXAMPLE 4 Find the minimum value of a function

SUSPENSION BRIDGES The suspension cables between the two towers of the Mackinac Bridge in Michigan form a parabola that can be modeled by the graph of $y = 0.000097x^2 - 0.37x + 549$ where x and y are measured in feet. What is the height of the cable above the water at its lowest point?

Solution

The lowest point of the cable is at the vertex of the parabola. Find the x-coordinate of the vertex. Use $a = 0.000097$ and $b = -0.37$.

$x = -\frac{b}{2a} = -\frac{-0.37}{2(0.000097)} \approx 1910$ **Use a calculator.**

Substitute 1910 for x in the equation to find the y-coordinate of the vertex.

$y \approx 0.000097(1910)^2 - 0.37(1910) + 549 \approx 196$

▶ The cable is about 196 feet above the water at its lowest point.

✓ **GUIDED PRACTICE** for Examples 3 and 4

3. minimum value; $-\frac{1}{2}$ 

3. Tell whether the function $f(x) = 6x^2 + 18x + 13$ has a *minimum value* or a *maximum value*. Then find the minimum or maximum value.

4. **SUSPENSION BRIDGES** The cables between the two towers of the Takoma Narrows Bridge form a parabola that can be modeled by the graph of the equation $y = 0.00014x^2 - 0.4x + 507$ where x and y are measured in feet. What is the height of the cable above the water at its lowest point? Round your answer to the nearest foot. **221 ft**

2. 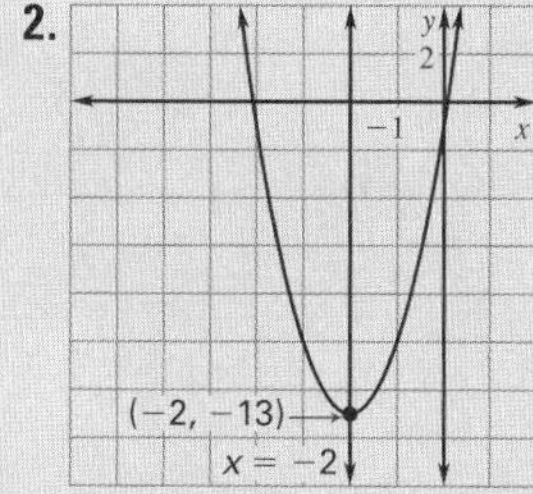

Animated Algebra classzone.com

An **Animated Algebra** activity is available online for **Example 2.** This activity is also part of **Power Presentations.**

Extra Example 3

Tell whether the function $f(x) = 2x^2 - 16x + 4$ has a *minimum value* or a *maximum value*. Then find the minimum or maximum value. **The graph opens up, so it has a minimum value. The minimum value is $f(4) = -28$.**

Extra Example 4

The cables between two telephone poles can be modeled by the equation $y = 0.0024x^2 - 0.1x + 24$, where x and y are measured in feet. To the nearest foot, what is the height of the cable above the ground at its lowest point? **23 ft**

Closing the Lesson

Have students summarize the major points of the lesson and answer the Essential Question: How do you graph a quadratic function of the form $y = ax^2 + bx + c$?

- **The graph of a quadratic function is a parabola that opens up if $a > 0$ and opens down if $a < 0$.**
- **An equation for the axis of symmetry of a quadratic function is $x = -\frac{b}{2a}$.**
- **The x-coordinate of the vertex is $-\frac{b}{2a}$.**

Determine whether the graph opens up or opens down. Then find and draw the axis of symmetry by substituting values for a and b in the equation $x = -\frac{b}{2a}$. Substitute that x-value into the function and simplify to find the y-coordinate of the vertex. Choose two x-values less than the x-coordinate of the vertex and plot the points. Reflect the points in the axis of symmetry. Draw a parabola through the points.

10.2 EXERCISES

HOMEWORK KEY ◯ = WORKED-OUT SOLUTIONS on p. WS23 for Exs. 9 and 41

★ = STANDARDIZED TEST PRACTICE Exs. 2, 12, 27, 37, 42, and 44

SKILL PRACTICE

A

1. **VOCABULARY** *Explain* how you can tell whether a quadratic function has a maximum value or minimum value without graphing the function. **See margin.**

2. ★ **WRITING** *Describe* the steps you would take to graph a quadratic function in standard form. **See margin.**

EXAMPLE 1 on p. 635 for Exs. 3–14

FINDING AXIS OF SYMMETRY AND VERTEX **Find the axis of symmetry and the vertex of the graph of the function.**

3. $y = 2x^2 - 8x + 6$
4. $y = x^2 - 6x + 11$
5. $y = -3x^2 + 24x - 22$
6. $y = -x^2 - 10x$
7. $y = 6x^2 + 6x$
8. $y = 4x^2 + 7$
9. $y = -\frac{2}{3}x^2 - 1$
10. $y = \frac{1}{2}x^2 + 8x - 9$
11. $y = -\frac{1}{4}x^2 + 3x - 2$

12. ★ **MULTIPLE CHOICE** What is the vertex of the graph of the function $y = -3x^2 + 18x - 13$? **D**

Ⓐ $(-3, -94)$ Ⓑ $(-3, -14)$ Ⓒ $(3, -13)$ Ⓓ $(3, 14)$

ERROR ANALYSIS ***Describe*** **and correct the error in finding the axis of symmetry of the graph of the given function.** **13, 14. See margin.**

13. $y = 2x^2 + 16x - 1$

$x = \frac{b}{2a} = \frac{16}{2(2)} = 4$ ✗

The axis of symmetry is x = 4.

14. $y = -\frac{3}{2}x^2 + 18x - 5$

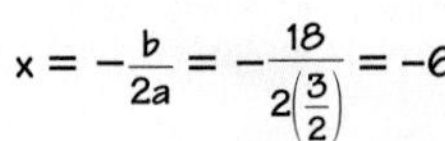

$x = -\frac{b}{2a} = -\frac{18}{2\left(\frac{3}{2}\right)} = -6$ ✗

The axis of symmetry is x = −6.

EXAMPLE 2 on p. 636 for Exs. 15–27

GRAPHING QUADRATIC FUNCTIONS **Graph the function. Label the vertex and axis of symmetry.** **15–26. See margin for art.**

15. $y = x^2 + 6x + 2$
16. $y = x^2 + 4x + 8$
17. $y = 2x^2 + 7x + 21$
18. $y = 5x^2 + 10x - 3$
19. $y = 4x^2 + x - 32$
20. $y = -4x^2 + 4x + 8$
21. $y = -3x^2 - 2x - 5$
22. $y = -8x^2 - 12x + 1$
23. $y = -x^2 + \frac{1}{4}x + \frac{1}{2}$
24. $y = \frac{1}{3}x^2 + 6x - 9$
25. $y = -\frac{1}{2}x^2 + 6x + 3$
26. $y = -\frac{1}{4}x^2 - x + 1$

27. ★ **MULTIPLE CHOICE** Which function has the graph shown? **B**

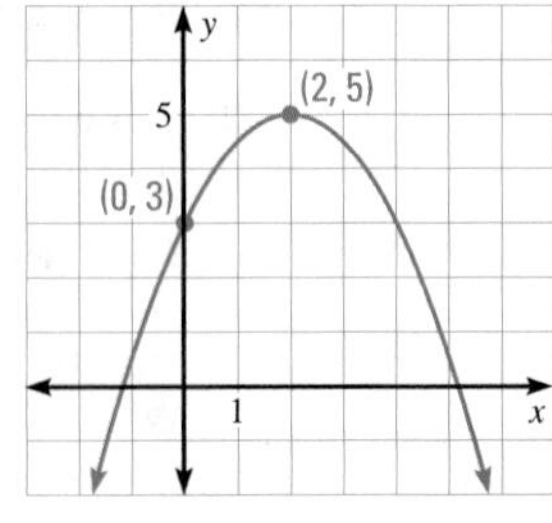

Ⓐ $y = -2x^2 + 8x + 3$

Ⓑ $y = -\frac{1}{2}x^2 + 2x + 3$

Ⓒ $y = \frac{1}{2}x^2 + 2x + 3$

Ⓓ $y = 2x^2 + 8x + 3$

Answers (margin):

3. $x = 2, (2, -2)$
4. $x = 3, (3, 2)$
5. $x = 4, (4, 26)$
6. $x = -5, (-5, 25)$
7. $x = -\frac{1}{2}, \left(-\frac{1}{2}, -\frac{3}{2}\right)$
8. $x = 0, (0, 7)$
9. $x = 0, (0, -1)$
10. $x = -8, (-8, -41)$
11. $x = 6, (6, 7)$

13. The equation of the axis of symmetry is $x = -\frac{b}{2a}$, not $x = \frac{b}{2a}$; $x = -\frac{b}{2a} = -\frac{16}{2(2)}$, $x = -4$.

14. $-\frac{3}{2}$ should be substituted for a; $x = -\frac{18}{2\left(-\frac{3}{2}\right)}$, $x = 6$.

4 PRACTICE AND APPLY

Assignment Guide

Answer Transparencies available for all exercises

Basic:
Day 1: pp. 638–640
Exs. 1, 2, 3–11 odd, 12–20, 27–32, 37, 40–43, 46, 49, 51, 55

Average:
Day 1: pp. 638–640
Exs. 1, 2, 6–14 even, 20–27, 31–38, 40–44, 47, 52, 56

Advanced:
Day 1: pp. 638–640
Exs. 1, 8–12, 20–27, 32–45*, 48, 53, 54, 58

Block:
pp. 638–640
Exs. 1, 2, 6–14 even, 20–27, 31–38, 40–44, 47, 52, 56 (with 10.3)

Differentiated Instruction

See *Differentiated Instruction Resources* for suggestions on addressing the needs of a diverse classroom.

Homework Check

For a quick check of student understanding of key concepts, go over the following exercises:

Basic: 5, 17, 20, 30, 40
Average: 8, 22, 24, 33, 41
Advanced: 10, 24, 25, 35, 42

Extra Practice

- Student Edition, p. 947
- Chapter Resource Book: Practice levels A, B, C

Practice Worksheet

An easily-readable reduced practice page (with answers) for this lesson can be found on p. 626C.

1. When the function is in standard form, $y = ax^2 + bx + c$, it will have a minimum value if $a > 0$ and a maximum value if $a < 0$.

2. Use the sign of a to tell if the parabola opens up or down. Find the axis of symmetry, $x = -\frac{b}{2a}$, which also gives the x-coordinate of the vertex. Substitute $-\frac{b}{2a}$ for x in the function to find the y-coordinate of the vertex. Calculate y-values for two x-values on one side of the vertex. Plot the vertex and the two points; then reflect the two points through the axis of symmetry to locate two more points. Draw a parabola through the plotted points.

15–26. See Additional Answers beginning on p. AA1.

EXAMPLE 3 on p. 637 for Exs. 28–36

28. minimum value; -6
29. maximum value; 7
30. minimum value; -64
31. maximum value; -8
32. minimum value; $-\frac{17}{4}$
33. maximum value; $\frac{81}{8}$
34. minimum value; 3
35. maximum value; 54
36. minimum value; -38

MAXIMUM AND MINIMUM VALUES Tell whether the function has a *minimum value* or a *maximum value*. Then find the minimum or maximum value.

28. $f(x) = x^2 - 6$ **29.** $f(x) = -5x^2 + 7$ **30.** $f(x) = 4x^2 + 32x$

31. $f(x) = -3x^2 + 12x - 20$ **32.** $f(x) = x^2 + 7x + 8$ **33.** $f(x) = -2x^2 - x + 10$

34. $f(x) = \frac{1}{2}x^2 - 2x + 5$ **35.** $f(x) = -\frac{3}{8}x^2 + 9x$ **36.** $f(x) = \frac{1}{4}x^2 + 7x + 11$

B **37.** ★ **WRITING** Compare the graph of $y = x^2 + 4x + 1$ with the graph of $y = x^2 - 4x + 1$. **The graph of $y = x^2 + 4x + 1$ is a horizontal translation (of 4 units left) of the graph $y = x^2 - 4x + 1$.**

38. REASONING Follow the steps below to justify the equation for the axis of symmetry for the graph of $y = ax^2 + bx + c$. Because the graph of $y = ax^2 + bx + c$ is a vertical translation of the graph of $y = ax^2 + bx$, the two graphs have the same axis of symmetry. Use the function $y = ax^2 + bx$ in place of $y = ax^2 + bx + c$.

a. Find the x-intercepts of the graph of $y = ax^2 + bx$. (You can do this by finding the zeros of the function $y = ax^2 + bx$ using factoring.) **$0, -\frac{b}{a}$**

b. Because a parabola is symmetric about its axis of symmetry, the axis of symmetry passes through a point halfway between the x-intercepts of the parabola. Find the x-coordinate of this point. What is an equation of the vertical line through this point? **$-\frac{b}{2a}$; $x = -\frac{b}{2a}$**

C **39. CHALLENGE** Write a function of the form $y = ax^2 + bx$ whose graph contains the points (1, 6) and (3, 6). ***Sample answer:* $y = -2x^2 + 8x$**

PROBLEM SOLVING

GRAPHING CALCULATOR You may wish to use a graphing calculator to complete the following Problem Solving exercises.

EXAMPLE 4 on p. 637 for Exs. 40–42

A **40. SPIDERS** Fishing spiders can propel themselves across water and leap vertically from the surface of the water. During a vertical jump, the height of the body of the spider can be modeled by the function $y = -4500x^2 + 820x + 43$ where x is the duration (in seconds) of the jump and y is the height (in millimeters) of the spider above the surface of the water. After how many seconds does the spider's body reach its maximum height? What is the maximum height? **about 0.091 sec; about 80 mm**

@HomeTutor for problem solving help at classzone.com

(41.) ARCHITECTURE The parabolic arches that support the roof of the Dallas Convention Center can be modeled by the graph of the equation $y = -0.0019x^2 + 0.71x$ where x and y are measured in feet. What is the height h at the highest point of the arch as shown in the diagram? **about 66 ft**

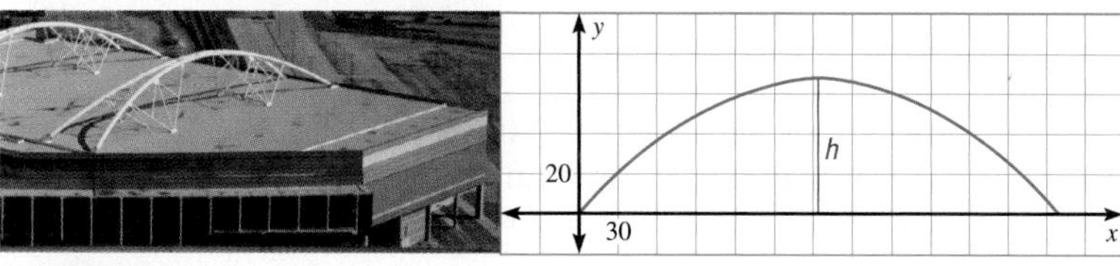

@HomeTutor for problem solving help at classzone.com

Avoiding Common Errors

Exercises 3–11, 15–26 Some students may overlook the negative sign in $-\frac{b}{2a}$ when calculating the axis of symmetry. Suggest that students double check that they included the negative sign before finding the vertex of the graph.

Teaching Strategy

Exercises 27, 28–36 Before students begin these exercises, have a class discussion about whether each has a minimum or maximum value. This will help students focus on the sign of a in the quadratic function. Point out that, in Exercise 27, students can use this method to eliminate two of the answer choices.

Study Strategy

Exercise 40 Suggest to students that they make a note on what the values of x and y represent before they work the problem. This can help them identify the values for height and time.

5 ASSESS AND RETEACH

Daily Homework Quiz

Transparency Available

1. Find the axis of symmetry and the vertex of the graph of the function $y = -4x^2 + 8x - 9$. $x = 1$; $(1, -5)$
2. Graph $y = -2x^2 + 4x + 1$.

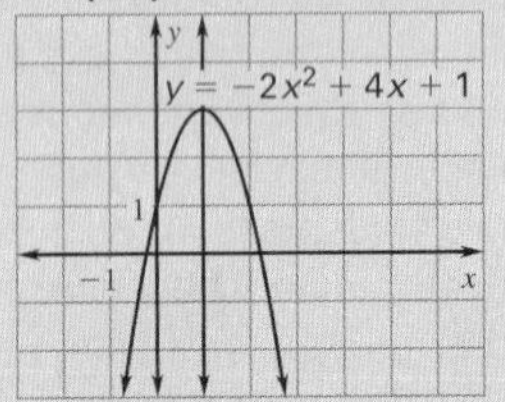

3. An arch to the entrance of the library can be modeled by $y = -0.13x^2 + 2.5x$, where x and y are measured in feet. To the nearest foot, what is the height of the highest point of the arch? **12 ft**

Available at **classzone.com**

Diagnosis/Remediation

- Practice A, B, C in Chapter Resource Book
- Study Guide in Chapter Resource Book
- Practice Workbook
- @HomeTutor

Challenge

Additional challenge is available in the Chapter Resource Book.

43. See Additional Answers beginning on p. AA1.

44. No; the maximum value of the function $S = 332 + 132t - 10.4t^2$ occurs when $t = -\frac{132}{2(-10.4)} \approx 6.35$. Because the function S makes sense only for integer values of t, the maximum value of S occurs at either $t = 6$ or $t = 7$. These t-values correspond to 1996 and 1997, so the greatest number of tickets for Broadway tours was sold after 1995.

42c. \$10; the maximum value of \$1000 occurs when $n = 5$, so the students should charge 5 \$1 increases, or \$5 + \$5 = \$10 in order to generate the most sales revenue.

42. ★ **EXTENDED RESPONSE** Students are selling packages of flower bulbs to raise money for a class trip. Last year, when the students charged \$5 per package, they sold 150 packages. The students want to increase the cost per package. They estimate that they will lose 10 sales for each \$1 increase in the cost per package. The sales revenue R (in dollars) generated by selling the packages is given by the function $R = (5 + n)(150 - 10n)$ where n is the number of \$1 increases.
   a. Write the function in standard form. $R = -10n^2 + 100n + 750$
   b. Find the maximum value of the function. **\$1000**
   c. At what price should the packages be sold to generate the most sales revenue? *Explain* your reasoning.

B

43. **AIRCRAFT** An aircraft hangar is a large building where planes are stored. The opening of one airport hangar is a parabolic arch that can be modeled by the graph of the equation $y = -0.007x^2 + 1.7x$ where x and y are measured in feet. Graph the function. Use the graph to determine how wide the hangar is at its base. **See margin for art; about 243 ft.**

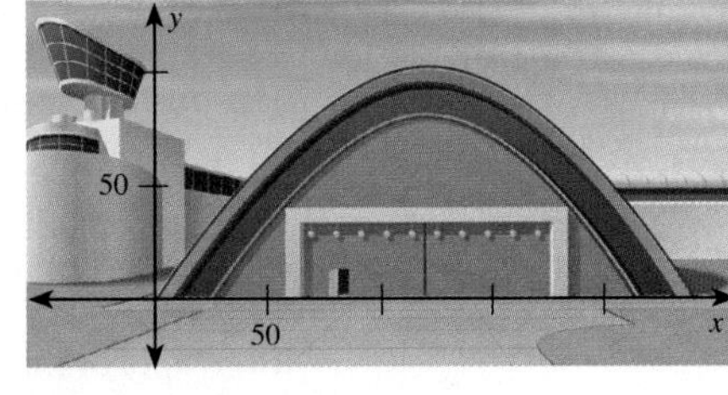

44. ★ **SHORT RESPONSE** The casts of some Broadway shows go on tour, performing their shows in cities across the United States. For the period 1990–2001, the number of tickets sold S (in millions) for Broadway road tours can be modeled by the function $S = 332 + 132t - 10.4t^2$ where t is the number of years since 1990. Was the greatest number of tickets for Broadway road tours sold in 1995? *Explain*. **See margin.**

C

45. **CHALLENGE** During an archery competition, an archer shoots an arrow from 1.5 meters off of the ground. The arrow follows the parabolic path shown and hits the ground in front of the target 90 meters away. Use the y-intercept and the points on the graph to write an equation for the graph that models the path of the arrow. $y = -0.00031x^2 + 0.011x + 1.5$

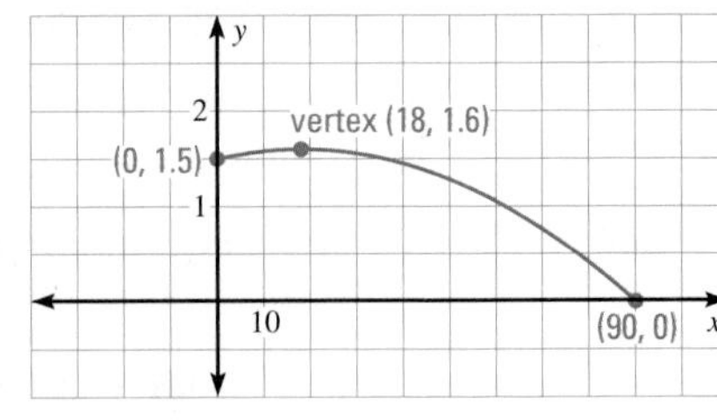

MIXED REVIEW

Graph the equation. *(pp. 215, 225, 244)* **46–48. See margin for art.**

46. $y = 3$
47. $x - 5y = 15$
48. $y = -\frac{2}{3}x - 6$

Simplify.

49. $-3(4 - 2x) - 9$ *(p. 96)* $6x - 21$
50. $2(1 - a) - 5a$ *(p. 96)* $2 - 7a$
51. $\frac{12y - 4}{-4}$ *(p. 103)* $-3y + 1$
52. $(-2mn)^4$ *(p. 489)* $16m^4n^4$
53. $5 \cdot (7w^7)^2$ *(p. 489)* $245w^{14}$
54. $\frac{6u^3}{v} \cdot \frac{uv^2}{36}$ *(p. 495)* $\frac{u^4v}{6}$

PREVIEW
Prepare for Lesson 10.3 in Exs. 55–58.

Find the zeros of the polynomial function.

55. $f(x) = x^2 - 4x - 21$ *(p. 583)* $-3, 7$
56. $f(x) = x^2 + 10x + 24$ *(p. 583)* $-6, -4$
57. $f(x) = 5x^2 + 18x + 9$ *(p. 593)* $-3, -\frac{3}{5}$
58. $f(x) = 2x^2 + 4x - 6$ *(p. 593)* $-3, 1$

46.

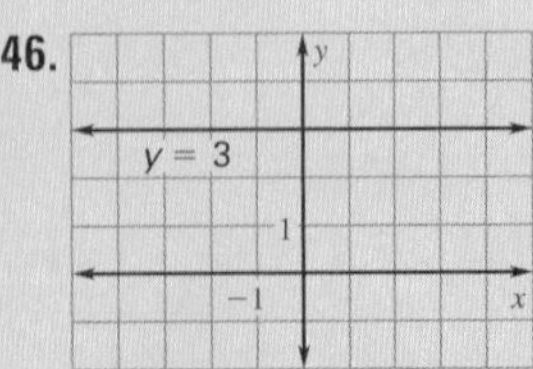

47.

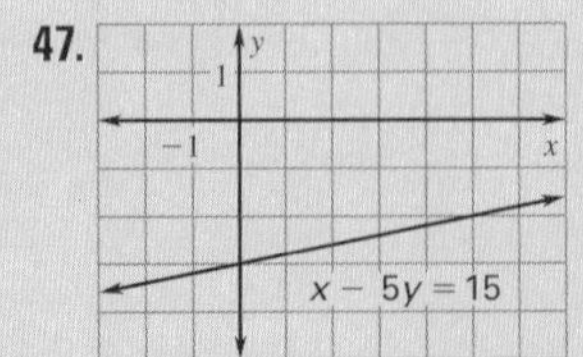

48.

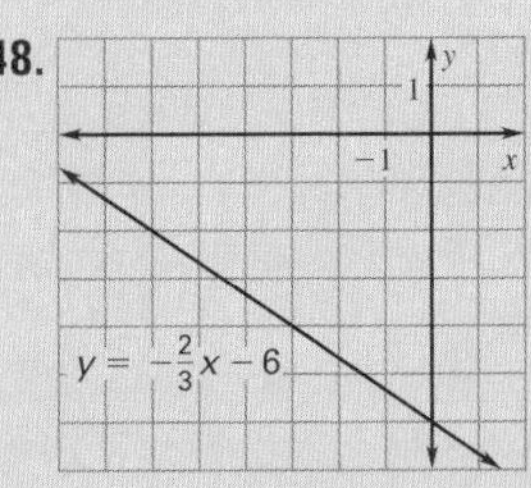

Extension
Use after Lesson 10.2

Graph Quadratic Functions in Intercept Form

GOAL Graph quadratic functions in intercept form.

Key Vocabulary
- **intercept form**

In Lesson 10.2 you graphed quadratic functions written in standard form. Quadratic functions can also be written in **intercept form**, $y = a(x - p)(x - q)$ where $a \neq 0$. In this form, the x-intercepts of the graph can easily be determined.

KEY CONCEPT *For Your Notebook*

Graph of Intercept Form $y = a(x - p)(x - q)$

Characteristics of the graph of $y = a(x - p)(x - q)$:

- The x-intercepts are p and q.
- The axis of symmetry is halfway between $(p, 0)$ and $(q, 0)$. So, the axis of symmetry is $x = \frac{p+q}{2}$.
- The parabola opens up if $a > 0$ and opens down if $a < 0$.

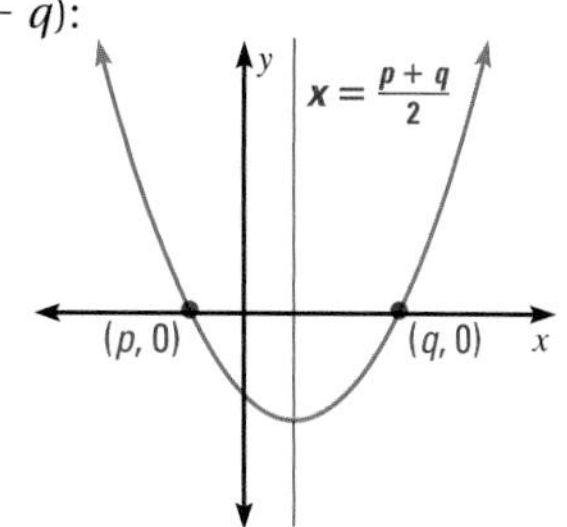

EXAMPLE 1 Graph a quadratic function in intercept form

Graph $y = -(x + 1)(x - 5)$.

Solution

FIND ZEROS OF A FUNCTION
Notice that the x-intercepts of the graph are also the zeros of the function:
$0 = -(x + 1)(x - 5)$
$x + 1 = 0$ *or* $x - 5 = 0$
$x = -1$ *or* $x = 5$

STEP 1 **Identify** and plot the x-intercepts. Because $p = -1$ and $q = 5$, the x-intercepts occur at the points $(-1, 0)$ and $(5, 0)$.

STEP 2 **Find** and draw the axis of symmetry.

$$x = \frac{p+q}{2} = \frac{-1+5}{2} = 2$$

STEP 3 **Find** and plot the vertex.

The x-coordinate of the vertex is 2.

To find the y-coordinate of the vertex, substitute 2 for x and simplify.

$$y = -(2 + 1)(2 - 5) = 9$$

So, the vertex is $(2, 9)$.

STEP 4 **Draw** a parabola through the vertex and the points where the x-intercepts occur.

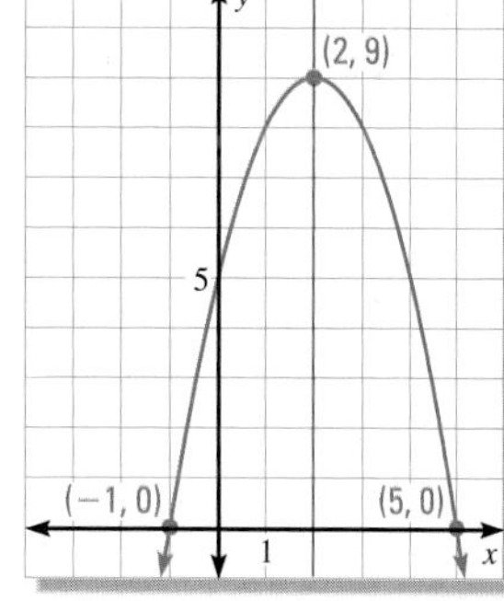

1 PLAN AND PREPARE

Warm-Up Exercises

1. Find the axis of symmetry and the vertex of the graph of the function $y = x^2 + 2x - 15$. **$x = -1$; $(-1, -16)$**
2. Graph $y = 3x^2 - 6x + 1$.

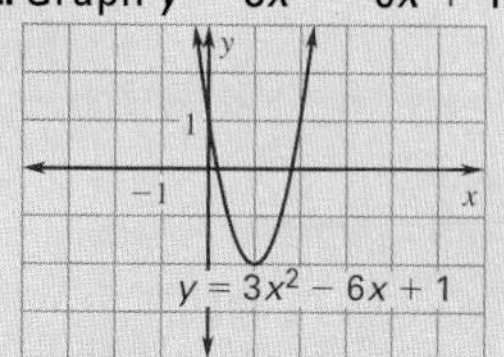

2 FOCUS AND MOTIVATE

Essential Question

Big Idea 1, p. 627

How do you graph a quadratic function in intercept form? **Tell students they will learn how to answer this question by identifying and plotting the x-intercepts, the axis of symmetry, and the vertex of the function.**

3 TEACH

Extra Example 1

Graph $y = (x + 1)(x - 3)$.

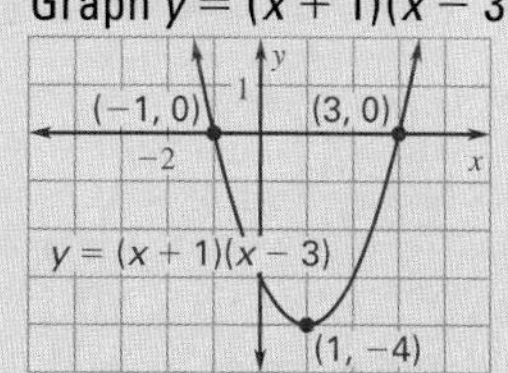

NCTM STANDARDS

Standard 2: Analyze situations using algebraic symbols

Standard 3: Use symmetry to analyze math situations

Extra Example 2

Graph $y = 2x^2 - 2$.

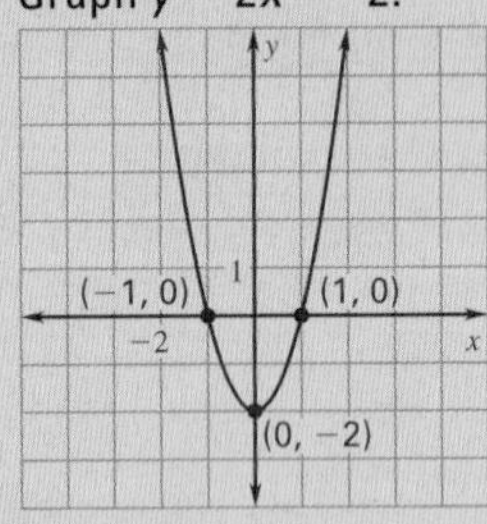

Key Question to Ask for Example 2

- What is the relationship between the x-intercepts of the graph and the zeros of the function? **The x-intercepts of the graph are the zeros of the function.**

An **Animated Algebra** activity is available online for **Example 2**. This activity is also part of **Power Presentations**.

Closing the Lesson

Have students summarize the major points of the lesson and answer the Essential Question: How do you graph a quadratic function in intercept form?

- **The intercept form of a quadratic function is $y = a(x - p)(x - q)$. The x-intercepts are p and q.**
- **The axis of symmetry is $x = \frac{p + q}{2}$.**

Identify and plot the x-intercepts. Find and plot the axis of symmetry. Find and plot the vertex and another point on each side of the vertex. Draw a parabola through those points.

4 PRACTICE AND APPLY

Avoiding Common Errors

Exercises 4–9 When finding the y-coordinate of the vertex, some students may forget to multiply by the coefficient of the factored terms. Tell students they can avoid this error by using *all* the terms of the function when calculating the value of the y-coordinate of the vertex.

EXAMPLE 2 Graph a quadratic function

Graph $y = 2x^2 - 8$.

Solution

STEP 1 **Rewrite** the quadratic function in intercept form.

$y = 2x^2 - 8$ — **Write original function.**

$= 2(x^2 - 4)$ — **Factor out common factor.**

$= 2(x + 2)(x - 2)$ — **Difference of two squares pattern**

STEP 2 **Identify** and plot the x-intercepts. Because $p = -2$ and $q = 2$, the x-intercepts occur at the points $(-2, 0)$ and $(2, 0)$.

STEP 3 **Find** and draw the axis of symmetry.

$$x = \frac{p + q}{2} = \frac{-2 + 2}{2} = 0$$

STEP 4 **Find** and plot the vertex.

The x-coordinate of the vertex is 0.

The y-coordinate of the vertex is:

$y = 2(0)^2 - 8 = -8$

So, the vertex is $(0, -8)$.

STEP 5 **Draw** a parabola through the vertex and the points where the x-intercepts occur.

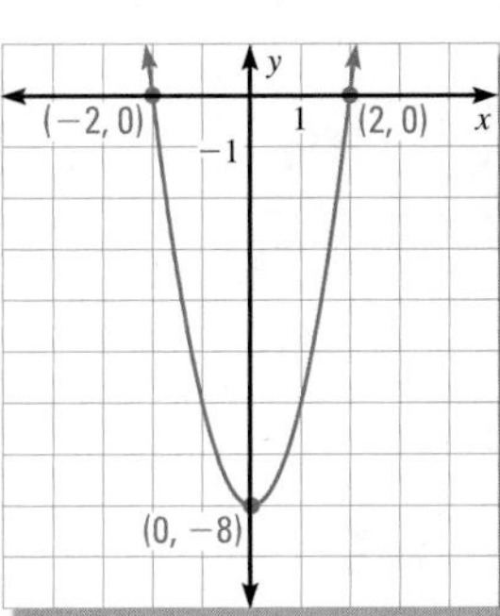

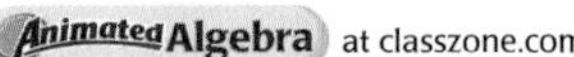

PRACTICE

EXAMPLE 1 on p. 641 for Exs. 1–9

Graph the quadratic function. Label the vertex, axis of symmetry, and x-intercepts. **1–15. See margin for art.**

1. $y = (x + 2)(x - 3)$
2. $y = (x + 5)(x + 2)$
3. $y = (x + 9)^2$
4. $y = -2(x - 5)(x + 1)$
5. $y = -5(x + 7)(x + 2)$
6. $y = 3(x - 6)(x - 3)$
7. $y = -\frac{1}{2}(x + 4)(x - 2)$
8. $y = (x - 7)(2x - 3)$
9. $y = 2(x + 10)(x - 3)$

EXAMPLE 2 on p. 642 for Exs. 10–12

10. $y = -x^2 + 8x - 16$
11. $y = -x^2 - 9x - 18$
12. $y = 12x^2 - 48$
13. Use factoring to determine how many x-intercepts the graph of the function $y = 3x^2 - 12x + 12$ has. **See margin.**
14. Follow the steps below to write an equation of the parabola shown.
    a. Find the x-intercepts. **−3, 5**
    b. Use the values of p and q and the coordinates of the vertex to find the value of a in the equation $y = a(x - p)(x - q)$. $-\frac{3}{8}$
    c. Write a quadratic equation in intercept form. $y = -\frac{3}{8}(x + 3)(x - 5)$

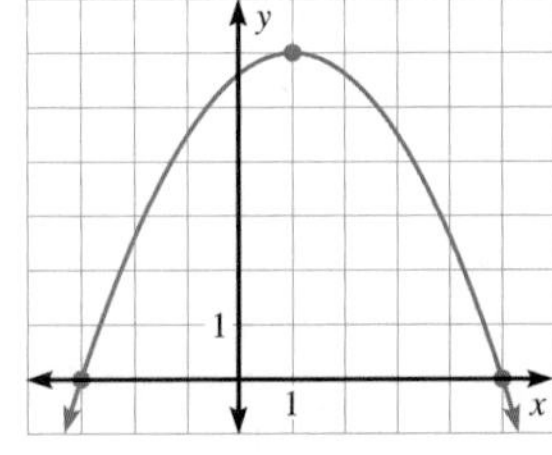

1–12. See Additional Answers beginning on p. AA1.

13. $3x^2 - 12x + 12 = 3(x - 2)(x - 2)$, so the intercept form of the function is $y = 3(x - 2)(x - 2)$, and the graph has one intercept, 2.

10.3 Solve Quadratic Equations by Graphing

Before You solved quadratic equations by factoring.
Now You will solve quadratic equations by graphing.
Why? So you can solve a problem about sports, as in Example 6.

Key Vocabulary
- **quadratic equation**
- **x-intercept,** *p. 225*
- **roots,** *p. 575*
- **zero of a function,** *p. 337*

A **quadratic equation** is an equation that can be written in the **standard form** $ax^2 + bx + c = 0$ where $a \neq 0$.

In Chapter 9, you used factoring to solve a quadratic equation. You can also use graphing to solve a quadratic equation. Notice that the solutions of the equation $ax^2 + bx + c = 0$ are the x-intercepts of the graph of the related function $y = ax^2 + bx + c$.

Solve by Factoring

$x^2 - 6x + 5 = 0$

$(x - 1)(x - 5) = 0$

$x = 1$ *or* $x = 5$

Solve by Graphing

To solve $x^2 - 6x + 5 = 0$, graph $y = x^2 - 6x + 5$. From the graph you can see that the x-intercepts are 1 and 5.

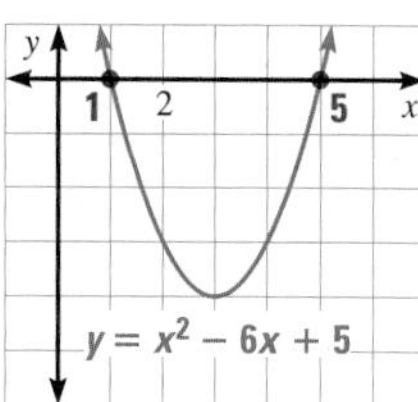

READING
In this course, *solutions* refers to real-number solutions.

To solve a quadratic equation by graphing, first write the equation in standard form, $ax^2 + bx + c = 0$. Then graph the related function $y = ax^2 + bx + c$. The x-intercepts of the graph are the solutions, or roots, of $ax^2 + bx + c = 0$.

EXAMPLE 1 Solve a quadratic equation having two solutions

Solve $x^2 - 2x = 3$ by graphing.

Solution

STEP 1 **Write** the equation in standard form.

$x^2 - 2x = 3$ **Write original equation.**

$x^2 - 2x - 3 = 0$ **Subtract 3 from each side.**

STEP 2 **Graph** the function $y = x^2 - 2x - 3$. The x-intercepts are -1 and 3.

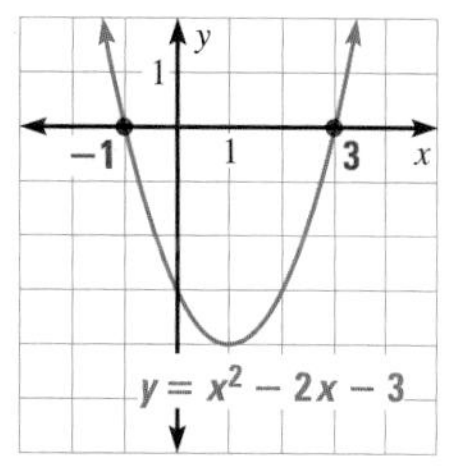

▶ The solutions of the equation $x^2 - 2x = 3$ are -1 and 3.

CHECK You can check -1 and 3 in the original equation.

$x^2 - 2x = 3$	$x^2 - 2x = 3$	**Write original equation.**
$(-1)^2 - 2(-1) \stackrel{?}{=} 3$	$(3)^2 - 2(3) \stackrel{?}{=} 3$	**Substitute for x.**
$3 = 3$ ✓	$3 = 3$ ✓	**Simplify. Each solution checks.**

1 PLAN AND PREPARE

Warm-Up Exercises

Transparency Available

Find the zeros of the polynomial function.

1. $f(x) = x^2 + 5x - 36$ **−9, 4**

2. $f(x) = x^2 - 9x + 20$ **4, 5**

3. You are making a rectangular flag for your school team. The number of square inches in the area of the flag is $9x + 108$. The number of inches in the length of the flag is $x + 12$. What is the width of the flag? **9 in.**

Notetaking Guide

Transparency Available

Promotes interactive learning and notetaking skills.

Pacing

Basic: 2 days
Average: 2 days
Advanced: 2 days
Block: 0.5 block with 10.2
0.5 block with 10.4
- See *Teaching Guide/Lesson Plan.*

2 FOCUS AND MOTIVATE

Essential Question

Big Idea 2, p. 627

How do you solve a quadratic equation by graphing? **Tell students they will learn how to answer this question by finding the *x*-intercepts of the related function.**

NCTM STANDARDS

Standard 6: Solve problems in math and other contexts

Standard 10: Use representations to solve problems

Resource Planning Guide

Chapter Resource Book
- Teaching Guide/Lesson Plan
- Practice levels A, B, C
- Study Guide
- Catch-up for Absent Students
- Application
- Challenge

Workbooks
- Notetaking Guide
- Practice Workbook

Teaching Options
- **Power Presentations** provides dynamic electronic teaching resources for the classroom.
- **Activity Generator** provides editable activities for all ability levels.

Interactive Technology
- Easy Planner
- Power Presentations
- Activity Generator
- Animated Algebra
- Test Generator
- Online Quiz
- eWorkbook
- eEdition
- @HomeTutor

Resources for English Learners
- Spanish Study Guide
- Multi-Language Visual Glossary
- Student Resources in Spanish

See also the *Differentiated Instruction Resources* for more strategies for meeting individual needs.

Motivating the Lesson

In soccer, the path of the ball depends on the velocity of the kick and the height of the ball when it is kicked. In this lesson, you will learn how to use the vertical motion model to determine how high and how far a kicked soccer ball will go.

3 TEACH

Extra Example 1

Solve $x^2 + 4x = 5$ by graphing. **−5, 1**

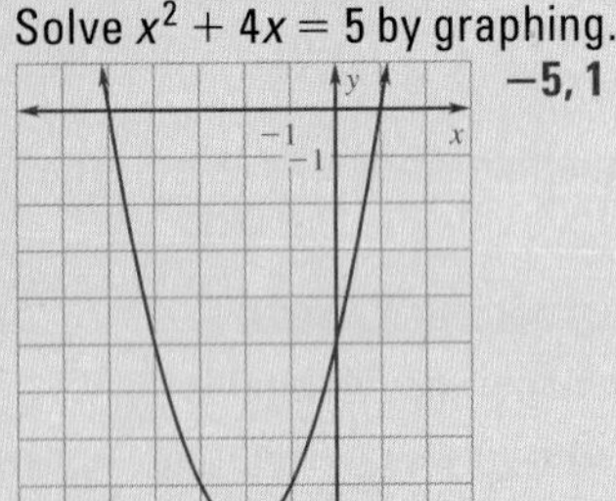

Extra Example 2

Solve $-x^2 - 6x = 9$ by graphing. **−3**

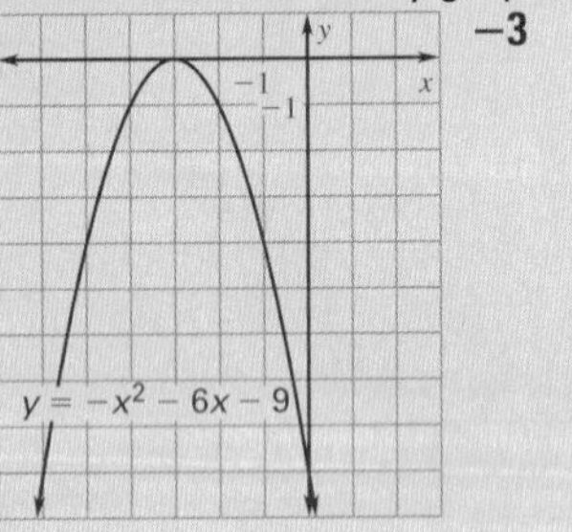

Extra Example 3

Solve $x^2 + 4x = -6$ by graphing. **no solutions**

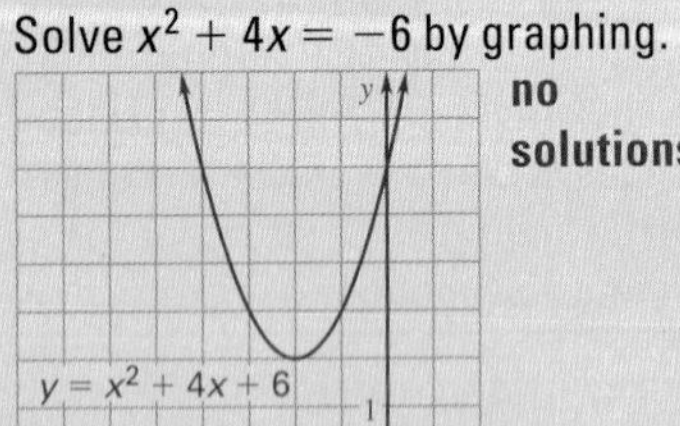

EXAMPLE 2 Solve a quadratic equation having one solution

Solve $-x^2 + 2x = 1$ by graphing.

Solution

STEP 1 **Write** the equation in standard form.

$-x^2 + 2x = 1$ **Write original equation.**

$-x^2 + 2x - 1 = 0$ **Subtract 1 from each side.**

STEP 2 **Graph** the function $y = -x^2 + 2x - 1$. The x-intercept is 1.

▸ The solution of the equation $-x^2 + 2x = 1$ is 1.

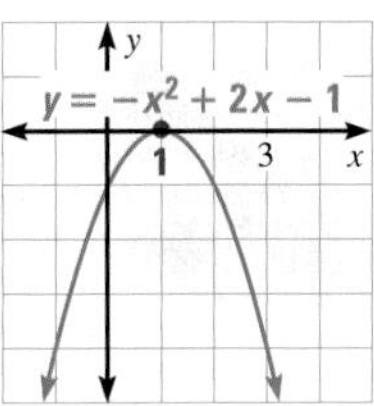

EXAMPLE 3 Solve a quadratic equation having no solution

Solve $x^2 + 7 = 4x$ by graphing.

Solution

STEP 1 **Write** the equation in standard form.

$x^2 + 7 = 4x$ **Write original equation.**

$x^2 - 4x + 7 = 0$ **Subtract $4x$ from each side.**

STEP 2 **Graph** the function $y = x^2 - 4x + 7$. The graph has no x-intercepts.

▸ The equation $x^2 + 7 = 4x$ has no solution.

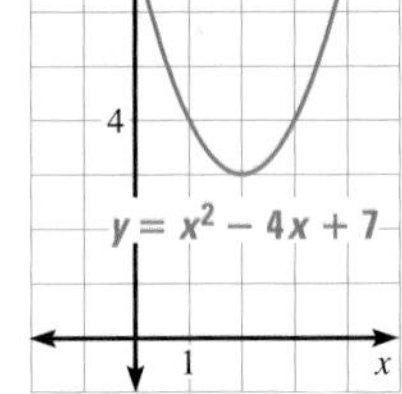

AVOID ERRORS

Do not confuse y-intercepts and x-intercepts. Although the graph has a y-intercept, it does not have any x-intercepts.

GUIDED PRACTICE for Examples 1, 2, and 3

Solve the equation by graphing.

1. $x^2 - 6x + 8 = 0$ **2, 4** **2.** $x^2 + x = -1$ **no solution** **3.** $-x^2 + 6x = 9$ **3**

KEY CONCEPT *For Your Notebook*

Number of Solutions of a Quadratic Equation

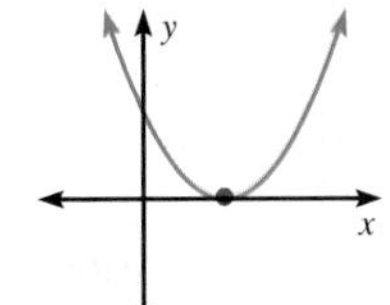

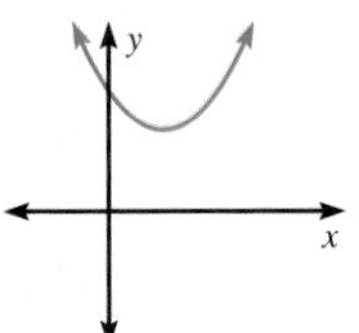

A quadratic equation has **two solutions** if the graph of its related function has **two x-intercepts**.

A quadratic equation has **one solution** if the graph of its related function has **one x-intercept**.

A quadratic equation has **no real solution** if the graph of its related function has **no x-intercepts**.

FINDING ZEROS Because a zero of a function is an x-intercept of the function's graph, you can use the function's graph to find the zeros of a function.

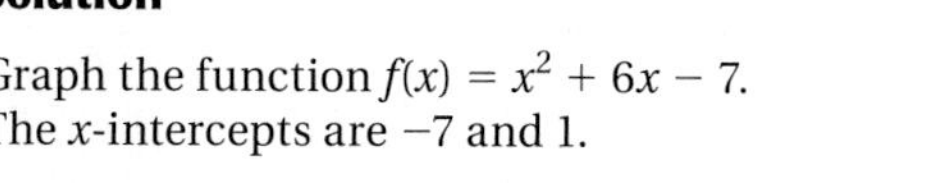

EXAMPLE 4 Find the zeros of a quadratic function

Find the zeros of $f(x) = x^2 + 6x - 7$.

ANOTHER WAY
You can find the zeros of a function by factoring:
$f(x) = x^2 + 6x - 7$
$0 = x^2 + 6x - 7$
$0 = (x + 7)(x - 1)$
$x = -7$ *or* $x = 1$

Solution

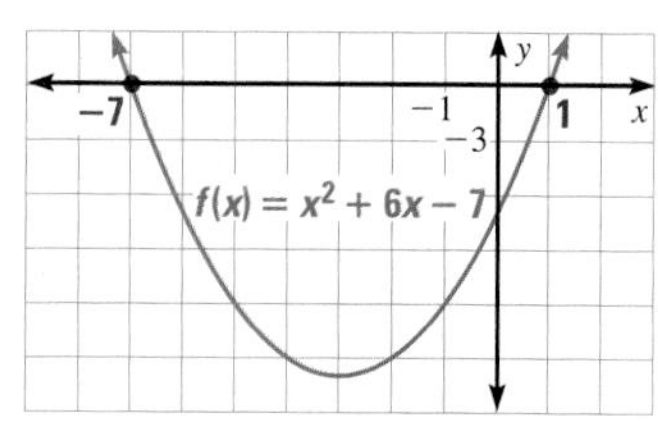

Graph the function $f(x) = x^2 + 6x - 7$. The x-intercepts are -7 and 1.

▶ The zeros of the function are -7 and 1.

CHECK Substitute -7 and 1 in the original function.

$f(-7) = (-7)^2 + 6(-7) - 7 = 0$ ✓

$f(1) = (1)^2 + 6(1) - 7 = 0$ ✓

APPROXIMATING ZEROS The zeros of a function are not necessarily integers. To approximate zeros, look at the signs of the function values. If two function values have opposite signs, then a zero falls between the x-values that correspond to the function values.

EXAMPLE 5 Approximate the zeros of a quadratic function

Approximate the zeros of $f(x) = x^2 + 4x + 1$ to the nearest tenth.

Solution

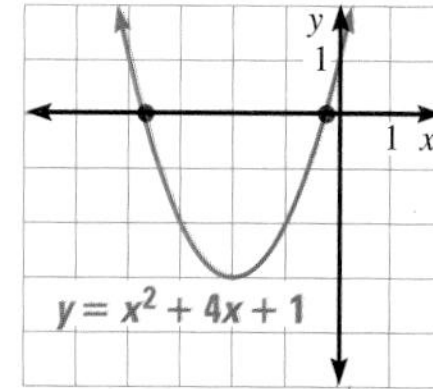

STEP 1 **Graph** the function $f(x) = x^2 + 4x + 1$. There are two x-intercepts: one between -4 and -3 and another between -1 and 0.

STEP 2 **Make** a table of values for x-values between -4 and -3 and between -1 and 0 using an increment of 0.1. Look for a change in the signs of the function values.

INTERPRET FUNCTION VALUES
The function value that is closest to 0 indicates the x-value that best approximates a zero of the function.

x	−3.9	−3.8	**−3.7**	−3.6	−3.5	−3.4	−3.3	−3.2	−3.1
$f(x)$	0.61	0.24	**−0.11**	−0.44	−0.75	−1.04	−1.31	−1.56	−1.79

x	−0.9	−0.8	−0.7	−0.6	−0.5	−0.4	**−0.3**	−0.2	−0.1
$f(x)$	−1.79	−1.56	−1.31	−1.04	−0.75	−0.44	**−0.11**	0.24	0.61

▶ In each table, the function value closest to 0 is -0.11. So, the zeros of $f(x) = x^2 + 4x + 1$ are about -3.7 and about -0.3.

GUIDED PRACTICE for Examples 4 and 5

4. Find the zeros of $f(x) = x^2 + x - 6$. **−3, 2**

5. Approximate the zeros of $f(x) = -x^2 + 2x + 2$ to the nearest tenth. **−0.7, 2.7**

Extra Example 4

Use a graph to find the zeros of $f(x) = x^2 + 7x + 6$. **−6, −1**

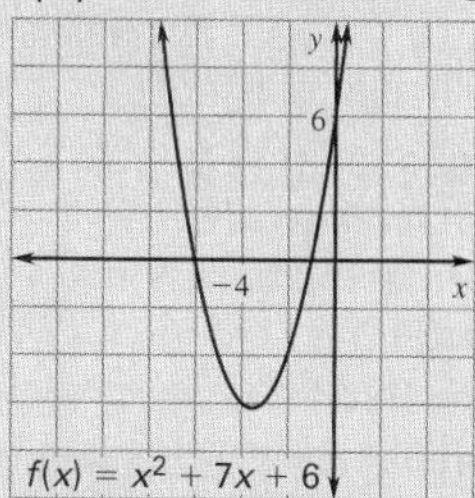

Key Question to Ask for Example 4

- Does every quadratic function have two zeros? Explain. **The zeros of a function occur when the graph of the function crosses or touches the x-axis. The graph of a quadratic function can touch the x-axis once, which indicates two solutions that are the same; it can cross the x-axis twice, which indicates two distinct solutions; or it can lie completely above or completely below the x-axis, which indicates no real-number solutions.**

Extra Example 5

Approximate the zeros of $f(x) = x^2 + 2x - 4$ to the nearest tenth. **−3.2, 1.2**

Key Question to Ask for Example 5

- Can $x^2 + 4x + 1$ be factored? Explain. **No; the c-value, 1, can only be factored as $1 \bullet 1$ or $(-1)(-1)$, and neither $(x+1)(x+1) = x^2 + 2x + 1$ nor $(x-1)(x-1) = x^2 - 2x + 1$ results in $4x$ as the middle term.**

Differentiated Instruction

Below Level Have students work in pairs to approximate the zeros of the function in **Guided Practice Exercise 5**. Suggest that they use a step-by-step process and have you confirm that they have completed each step correctly. Check that their graphs are correct, that the calculations in their tables are correct, and that they have chosen the values in the tables for which $f(x)$ is closest to 0. After they have successfully worked through the example, have them write a summary of the steps they used.

See also the *Differentiated Instruction Resources* for more strategies.

Extra Example 6

A baseball player throws a ball into the air with an initial vertical velocity of 32 feet per second. The ball is released at a height of 5 feet.

a. Write an equation that models the height h (in feet) of the ball as a function of the time t (in seconds) after it is thrown. $h = -16t^2 + 32t + 5$

b. Use the equation to find the time that the ball is in the air if the player lets the ball drop to the ground. **about 2.1 sec**

Key Question to Ask for Example 6

- What do the x- and y-axes on the graphing calculator display represent? **The x-axis represents time in seconds and the y-axis represents height in feet.**

Closing the Lesson

Have students summarize the major points of the lesson and answer the Essential Question: How do you solve a quadratic equation by graphing?

- **The standard form of a quadratic equation is $ax^2 + bx + c = 0$.**
- **A quadratic equation can have one real solution, two real solutions, or no real solutions.**

To solve a quadratic equation by graphing, write it in standard form and graph the related function. The x-intercepts are the solutions of the equation. Check the solutions in the original equation.

EXAMPLE 6 Solve a multi-step problem

SPORTS An athlete throws a shot put with an initial vertical velocity of 40 feet per second as shown.

a. Write an equation that models the height h (in feet) of the shot put as a function of the time t (in seconds) after it is thrown.

b. Use the equation to find the time that the shot put is in the air.

Solution

a. Use the initial vertical velocity and the release height to write a vertical motion model.

$h = -16t^2 + vt + s$ **Vertical motion model**

$h = -16t^2 + 40t + 6.5$ **Substitute 40 for v and 6.5 for s.**

b. The shot put lands when $h = 0$. To find the time t when $h = 0$, solve $0 = -16t^2 + 40t + 6.5$ for t.

USE A GRAPHING CALCULATOR
When entering $h = -16t^2 + 40t + 6.5$ in a graphing calculator, use y instead of h and x instead of t.

To solve the equation, graph the related function $h = -16t^2 + 40t + 6.5$ on a graphing calculator. Use the *trace* feature to find the t-intercepts.

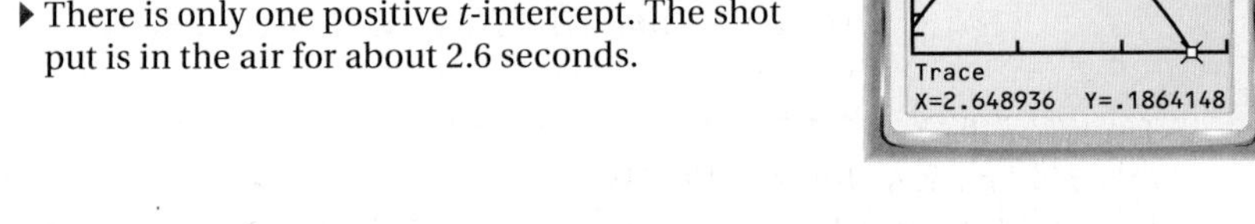

▶ There is only one positive t-intercept. The shot put is in the air for about 2.6 seconds.

✓ **GUIDED PRACTICE** for Example 6

6. WHAT IF? In Example 6, suppose the initial vertical velocity is 30 feet per second. Find the time that the shot put is in the air. **about 2.1 sec**

CONCEPT SUMMARY *For Your Notebook*

Relating Solutions of Equations, x-Intercepts of Graphs, and Zeros of Functions

Solutions of an Equation
The solutions of the equation $-x^2 + 8x - 12 = 0$ are 2 and 6.

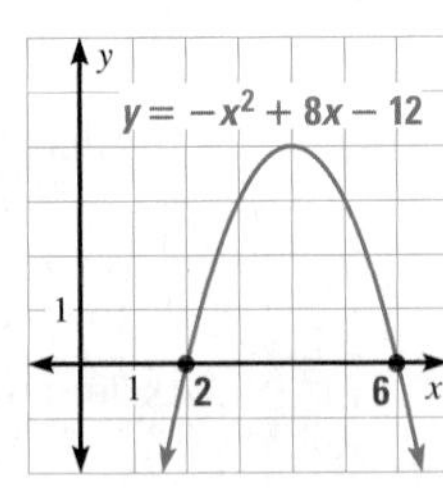

x-Intercepts of a Graph
The x-intercepts of the graph of $y = -x^2 + 8x - 12$ occur where $y = 0$, so the x-intercepts are 2 and 6, as shown.

Zeros of a Function
The zeros of the function $f(x) = -x^2 + 8x - 12$ are the values of x for which $f(x) = 0$, so the zeros are 2 and 6.

Differentiated Instruction

Auditory Learners When discussing **Example 6**, ask students how the time the shot put is in air changes as the velocity increases and decreases. Engage in discussion first. Students should propose that as velocity increases, the time in the air increases, and as velocity decreases, the time in the air decreases. Then work out examples using different values of v near 40.

See also the *Differentiated Instruction Resources* for more strategies.

10.3 EXERCISES

HOMEWORK KEY ○ = **WORKED-OUT SOLUTIONS** on p. WS24 for Exs. 5 and 51
★ = **STANDARDIZED TEST PRACTICE** Exs. 2, 46, 53, and 54

SKILL PRACTICE

A

1. **VOCABULARY** Write $2x^2 + 11 = 9x$ in standard form. **$2x^2 - 9x + 11 = 0$**

2. ★ **WRITING** Is $3x^2 - 2 = 0$ a quadratic equation? *Explain.*

EXAMPLES 1, 2, and 3 on pp. 643–644 for Exs. 3–21

2. Yes; $3x^2 - 2 = 0$ is a quadratic equation in the standard form $ax^2 + bx + c = 0$, where $a = 3$, $b = 0$, and $c = -2$: $3x^2 + 0x + (-2) = 0$ or $3x^2 - 2 = 0$.

SOLVING EQUATIONS Solve the equation by graphing.

3. $x^2 - 5x + 4 = 0$ **4, 1**
4. $x^2 + 5x + 6 = 0$ **−3, −2**
5. $x^2 + 6x = -8$ **−4, −2**
6. $x^2 - 4x = 5$ **5, −1**
7. $x^2 - 16 = 6x$ **8, −2**
8. $x^2 - 12x = -35$ **7, 5**
9. $x^2 - 6x + 9 = 0$ **3**
10. $x^2 + 8x + 16 = 0$ **−4**
11. $x^2 + 10x = -25$ **−5**
12. $x^2 + 81 = 18x$ **9**
13. $-x^2 - 14x = 49$ **−7**
14. $-x^2 + 16x = 64$ **8**
15. $x^2 - 5x + 7 = 0$ **no solution**
16. $x^2 - 2x + 3 = 0$ **no solution**
17. $x^2 + x = -2$ **no solution**
18. $\frac{1}{5}x^2 - 5 = 0$ **±5**
19. $\frac{1}{2}x^2 + 2x = 6$ **−6, 2**
20. $-\frac{1}{4}x^2 - 8 = x$ **no solution**

21. **ERROR ANALYSIS** The graph of the function related to the equation $0 = x^2 - 4x + 4$ is shown. *Describe* and correct the error in solving the equation. **See margin.**

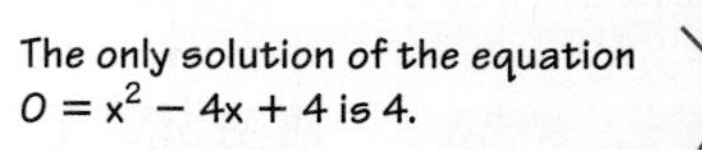

The only solution of the equation
$0 = x^2 - 4x + 4$ is 4.

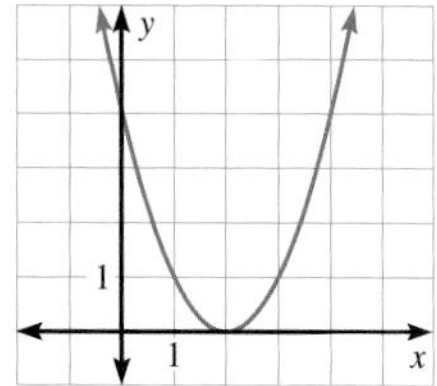

y
1
1
x

EXAMPLE 4 on p. 645 for Exs. 22–30

FINDING ZEROS Find the zeros of the function.

22. $f(x) = x^2 + 4x - 5$ **−5, 1**
23. $f(x) = x^2 - x - 12$ **−3, 4**
24. $f(x) = x^2 - 5x - 6$ **−1, 6**
25. $f(x) = x^2 + 3x - 10$ **−5, 2**
26. $f(x) = -x^2 + 8x + 9$ **−1, 9**
27. $f(x) = x^2 + x - 20$ **−5, 4**
28. $f(x) = -x^2 - 7x + 8$ **−8, 1**
29. $f(x) = x^2 - 12x + 11$ **1, 11**
30. $f(x) = -x^2 + 4x + 12$ **−2, 6**

B

SOLVING EQUATIONS Solve the equation by graphing.

31. $2x^2 + x = 3$ **$-1\frac{1}{2}, 1$**
32. $4x^2 - 5 = 8x$ **$-\frac{1}{2}, 2\frac{1}{2}$**
33. $4x^2 - 4x + 1 = 0$ **$\frac{1}{2}$**
34. $x^2 + x = -\frac{1}{4}$ **$-\frac{1}{2}$**
35. $3x^2 + 1 = 2x$ **no solution**
36. $5x^2 + x + 3 = 0$ **no solution**

EXAMPLE 5 on p. 645 for Exs. 37–46

40. −3.8, 0.8
41. 0.8, 6.2
42. −4.6, −0.4

APPROXIMATING ZEROS Approximate the zeros of the function to the nearest tenth.

37. $f(x) = x^2 + 4x + 2$ **−3.4, −0.6**
38. $f(x) = x^2 - 5x + 3$ **0.7, 4.3**
39. $f(x) = x^2 - 2x - 5$ **−1.4, 3.4**
40. $f(x) = -x^2 - 3x + 3$
41. $f(x) = -x^2 + 7x - 5$
42. $f(x) = -x^2 - 5x - 2$
43. $f(x) = 2x^2 + x - 2$ **−1.3, 0.8**
44. $f(x) = -3x^2 + 8x - 2$ **0.3, 2.4**
45. $f(x) = 5x^2 + 30x + 30$ **−4.7, −1.3**

46. ★ **MULTIPLE CHOICE** Which function has a zero between −3 and −2? **C**

Ⓐ $f(x) = -3x^2 + 4x + 11$
Ⓑ $f(x) = 4x^2 - 3x - 11$
Ⓒ $f(x) = 3x^2 + 4x - 11$
Ⓓ $f(x) = 3x^2 + 11$

21. Any solution of a quadratic equation is an x-intercept of the graph of the related quadratic function. The x-intercept of the function shown in the graph is 2, not 4; the only solution of the equation is 2.

4 PRACTICE AND APPLY

Assignment Guide

Answer Transparencies available for all exercises

Basic:
Day 1: EP p. 944 Exs. 1–4
pp. 647–649
Exs. 1–21
Day 2: pp. 647–649
Exs. 22–36 even, 37–41, 50–53, 56–64

Average:
Day 1: pp. 647–649
Exs. 1, 2, 5–21, 47, 48, 59–63 odd
Day 2: pp. 647–649
Exs. 24–46, 50–54, 56–58

Advanced:
Day 1: pp. 647–649
Exs. 1, 2, 6–20, 47–49*, 60–64 even
Day 2: pp. 647–649
Exs. 25–46, 50–56*, 58

Block:
pp. 647–649
Exs. 1, 2, 5–21, 47, 48, 59–63 odd (with 10.2)
pp. 647–649
Exs. 24–46, 50–54, 56–58 (with 10.4)

Differentiated Instruction

See *Differentiated Instruction Resources* for suggestions on addressing the needs of a diverse classroom.

Homework Check

For a quick check of student understanding of key concepts, go over the following exercises:
Basic: 6, 9, 24, 38, 50
Average: 10, 16, 26, 41, 51
Advanced: 12, 17, 29, 44, 52

Extra Practice

- Student Edition, p. 947
- Chapter Resource Book: Practice levels A, B, C

Practice Worksheet

An easily-readable reduced practice page (with answers) for this lesson can be found on p. 626C.

Avoiding Common Errors

Exercises 5–20 Some students may attempt to graph an equation without first writing it in standard form. Suggest that students go through the exercises and write each of the equations in standard form before they solve the equations by graphing.

Mathematical Reasoning

Exercises 50–52 To help students make a connection between the real life situations in these problems and visual and algebraic representations of them, you may want to discuss how the values of x and y in these exercises are similar to the variable values in Example 6, and how they are different.

Study Strategy

Exercise 54 Point out to students that they must solve part (a) of the problem before they can solve parts (b) or (c). If students are confused by part (c), ask how many times the ball reaches a height of 5.5 feet. Then suggest that they examine the graph in terms of x and y to determine which point they should use to solve part (c).

53. 16 ft; the distance from the nozzle to the circle is the distance between the x-intercepts of $y = -0.75x^2 + 6x$. Substitute 0 for y and solve for x: $0 = -0.75x^2 + 6x$ has solutions 0 and 8. The radius of the display circle is 8 feet, so the diameter is 16 feet.

54c. 2.5 sec; the two points on the graph of $h = -16t^2 + 40t + 5.5$ that correspond to a height of 5.5 feet are the two points with h-coordinate 5.5. These points are reflections of each other in the parabola's axis of symmetry, $t = 1.25$. Because one point with h-coordinate 5.5 is (0, 5.5), the t-coordinate of the other point with h-coordinate 5.5 is 2(1.25) = 2.5. So, after 2.5 seconds, the ball is again at a height of 5.5 feet.

C **CHALLENGE Use the given surface area S of the cylinder to find the radius r to the nearest tenth. (Use 3.14 for π.)**

47. $S = 251\text{ ft}^2$ **4.0 ft**

48. $S = 716\text{ m}^2$ **6.0 m**

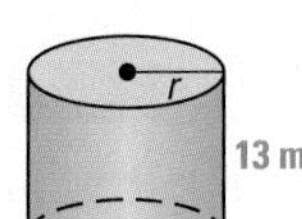

49. $S = 1074\text{ cm}^2$ **9.0 cm**

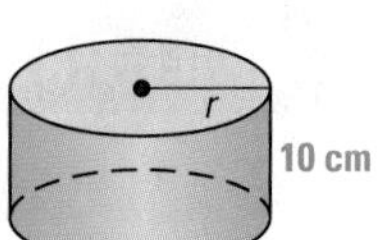

PROBLEM SOLVING

GRAPHING CALCULATOR You may wish to use a graphing calculator to complete the following Problem Solving exercises.

EXAMPLE 6 A on p. 646 for Exs. 50–52

50. SOCCER The height y (in feet) of a soccer ball after it is kicked can be modeled by the graph of the equation $y = -0.04x^2 + 1.2x$ where x is the horizontal distance (in feet) that the ball travels. The ball is not touched, and it lands on the ground. Find the distance that the ball was kicked. **30 ft**

@HomeTutor for problem solving help at classzone.com

51. SURVEYING To keep water off a road, the road's surface is shaped like a parabola as in the cross section below. The surface of the road can be modeled by the graph of $y = -0.0017x^2 + 0.041x$ where x and y are measured in feet. Find the width of the road to the nearest tenth of a foot. **24.1 ft**

@HomeTutor for problem solving help at classzone.com

52. DIVING During a cliff diving competition, a diver begins a dive with his center of gravity 70 feet above the water. The initial vertical velocity of his dive is 8 feet per second.

a. Write an equation that models the height h (in feet) of the diver's center of gravity as a function of time t (in seconds). $h = -16t^2 + 8t + 70$

b. How long after the diver begins his dive does his center of gravity reach the water? **about 2.4 sec**

B **53. ★ SHORT RESPONSE** An arc of water sprayed from the nozzle of a fountain can be modeled by the graph of $y = -0.75x^2 + 6x$ where x is the horizontal distance (in feet) from the nozzle and y is the vertical distance (in feet). The diameter of the circle formed by the arcs on the surface of the water is called the display diameter. Find the display diameter of the fountain. *Explain* your reasoning. **See margin.**

○ = WORKED-OUT SOLUTIONS on p. WS1 ★ = STANDARDIZED TEST PRACTICE

54. ★ **EXTENDED RESPONSE** Two softball players are practicing catching fly balls. One player throws a ball to the other. She throws the ball upward from a height of 5.5 feet with an initial vertical velocity of 40 feet per second for her teammate to catch.

a. Write an equation that models the height h (in feet) of the ball as a function of time t (in seconds) after it is thrown. **$h = -16t^2 + 40t + 5.5$**

b. If her teammate misses the ball and it lands on the ground, how long was the ball in the air? **about 2.6 sec**

c. If her teammate catches the ball at a height of 5.5 feet, how long was the ball in the air? *Explain* your reasoning. **See margin.**

C 55. **CHALLENGE** A stream of water from a fire hose can be modeled by the graph of $y = -0.003x^2 + 0.58x + 3$ where x and y are measured in feet. A firefighter is holding the hose 3 feet above the ground, 137 feet from a building. Will the stream of water pass through a window if the top of the window is 26 feet above the ground? *Explain.* **No; the height of the water at the point 137 feet from the firefighter is $-0.003(137)^2 + 0.58(137) + 3 \approx 26.2$ feet. The water will hit the building just above the window.**

MIXED REVIEW

PREVIEW
Prepare for Lesson 10.4 in Exs. 56–58.

Evaluate the expression. *(p. 110)*

56. $-\sqrt{25}$ **−5**
57. $\sqrt{400}$ **20**
58. $\pm\sqrt{625}$ **±25**

Simplify the expression. *(p. 495)*

59. $\frac{(-8)^{10}}{(-8)^7}$ **−512**
60. $\frac{9^2 \cdot 9^6}{9^4}$ **6561**
61. $\left(-\frac{1}{2}\right)^3$ **$-\frac{1}{8}$**

Write the number in standard form. *(p. 512)*

62. 4.4×10^{-6} **0.0000044**
63. 1.7×10^5 **170,000**
64. 6.804×10^8 **680,400,000**

QUIZ *for Lessons 10.1–10.3*

Graph the function. Compare the graph with the graph of $y = x^2$. *(p. 628)* **1–3. See margin.**

1. $y = -\frac{1}{2}x^2$
2. $y = 2x^2 - 5$
3. $y = -x^2 + 3$

Graph the function. Label the vertex and axis of symmetry. **4–9. See margin.**

4. $y = x^2 + 5$ *(p. 628)*
5. $y = -5x^2 + 1$ *(p. 628)*
6. $y = x^2 + 4x - 2$ *(p. 635)*
7. $y = 2x^2 - 12x + 5$ *(p. 635)*
8. $y = -\frac{1}{2}x^2 + 2x - 5$ *(p. 635)*
9. $y = -4x^2 - 10x + 2$ *(p. 635)*

Solve the equation by graphing. *(p. 643)*

10. $x^2 - 7x = 8$ **−1, 8**
11. $x^2 + 6x + 9 = 0$ **−3**
12. $x^2 + 10x = 11$ **−11, 1**
13. $x^2 - 7 = -6x$ **−7, 1**
14. $-x^2 + x - 1 = 0$ **no solution**
15. $x^2 - 4x + 9 = 0$ **no solution**

Find the zeros of the function. *(p. 643)*

16. $f(x) = x^2 + 3x - 10$ **−5, 2**
17. $f(x) = x^2 - 8x + 12$ **2, 6**
18. $f(x) = -x^2 + 5x + 14$ **−2, 7**

5 ASSESS AND RETEACH

Daily Homework Quiz

Transparency Available

1. Solve $x^2 + 6x + 8 = 0$ by graphing.

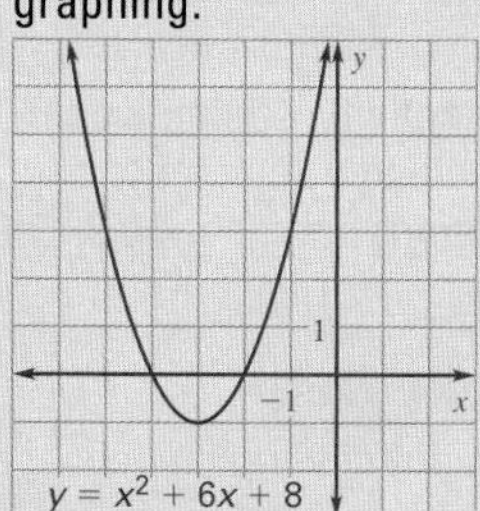

−4, −2

Find the number of solutions for each equation.

2. $x^2 + 6x = -10$ **none**
3. $x^2 + 6x = -9$ **one**
4. Find the zeros of $f(x) = -x^2 + 2x + 3$. **−1, 3**
5. Approximate the zeros of $f(x) = x^2 + x - 3$ to the nearest tenth. **−2.3, 1.3**
6. Maria throws a shot put with an initial vertical velocity of 25 feet per second. She releases it at a height of 5 feet. Find the time the shot put is in the air. **about 1.7 sec**

 **Online Quiz**

Available at **classzone.com**

Diagnosis/Remediation

- Practice A, B, C in Chapter Resource Book
- Study Guide in Chapter Resource Book
- Practice Workbook
- @HomeTutor

Challenge

Additional challenge is available in the Chapter Resource Book.

Quiz

An easily-readable reduced copy of the quiz (with answers) on Lessons 10.1–10.3 from the Assessment Book can be found on p. 626G.

Quiz 1–9. See Additional Answers beginning on p. AA1.

1 PLAN AND PREPARE

Learn the Method

- Students will find the maximum or minimum value and approximate the zeros of a quadratic function using their graphing calculators.
- After the activity, students can use a graphing calculator to check their solutions in Lesson 10.3, Exercises 3–46.

Keystroke Help

Keystrokes for several models of calculators are available in blackline format in the *Chapter Resource Book.*

2 TEACH

Tips for Success

In Example 1, point out to students that the lower right calculator screen indicates the maximum value of the function: Y = 11.5. In Example 2, make sure that students understand that they will need to give lower and upper bounds on one of the zeros at a time, not both. For the lower bound they need a number to the left of the *x*-intercept, and for the upper bound they need a number to the right of the *x*-intercept.

Extra Example 1

Find the minimum value of $y = 3x^2 + 9x - 2$. **−8.75**

10.3 Find Minimum and Maximum Values and Zeros

QUESTION **How can you find the minumum or maximum value and the zeros of a quadratic function using a graphing calculator?**

EXAMPLE 1 **Find the maximum value of a function**

Find the maximum value of the function $y = -2x^2 - 6x + 7$.

STEP 1 ***Enter the function***

Press Y= and enter the function $y = -2x^2 - 6x + 7$.

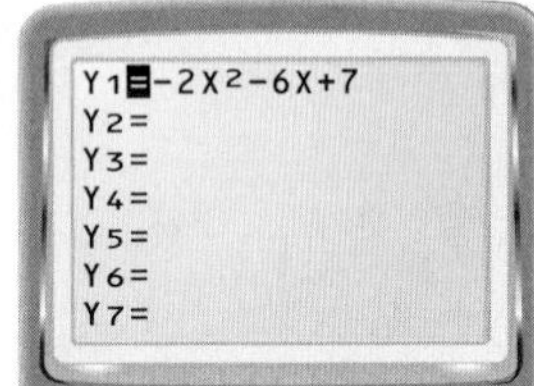

STEP 2 ***Adjust the window***

Display the graph. Adjust the viewing window as needed so that the vertex of the parabola is visible.

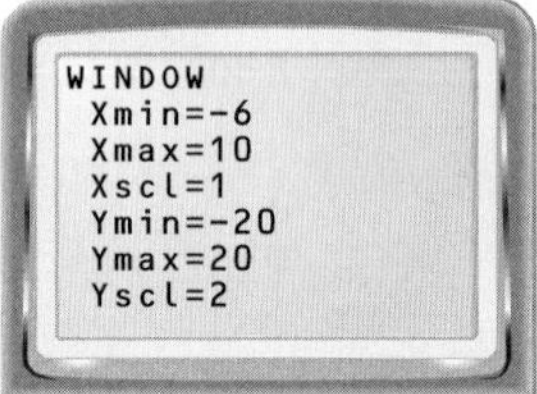

STEP 3 ***Use the maximum feature***

The *maximum* feature is located under the CALCULATE menu.

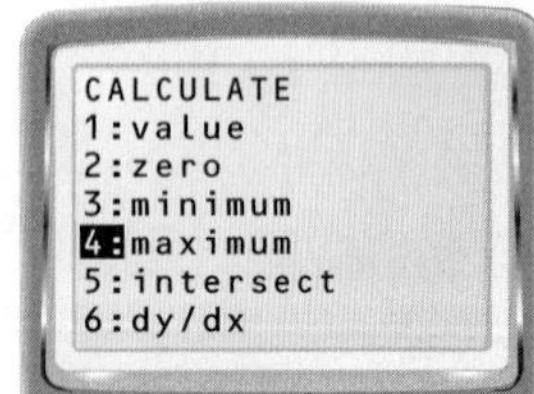

STEP 4 ***Find the maximum value***

Follow the graphing calculator's procedure to find the maximum of the function.

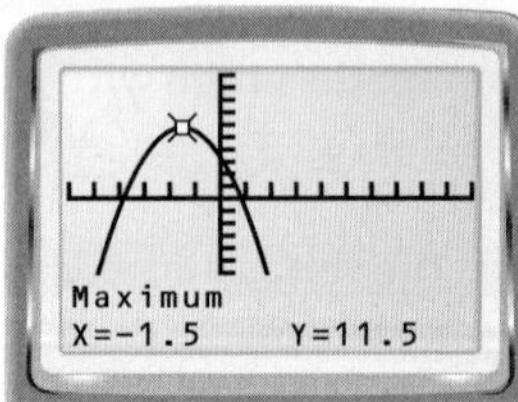

▸ The maximum value of the function $y = -2x^2 - 6x + 7$ is 11.5.

PRACTICE

Find the maximum or minimum value of the function.

1. $y = 3x^2 - 8x + 7$ **$1\frac{2}{3}$**
2. $y = -x^2 + 3x + 10$ **12.25**
3. $y = -4x^2 - 6x - 6$ **−3.75**
4. $y = 5x^2 + 10x - 8$ **−13**
5. $y = -1.4x^2 + 3.8x - 6.1$ **about −3.5**
6. $y = 2.57x^2 - 8.45x - 5.04$ **about −12**

@HomeTutor
classzone.com
Keystrokes

EXAMPLE 2 Approximate the zeros of a function

Approximate the zeros of the function $y = 3x^2 + 2x - 4$.

STEP 1 *Enter the function*

Press [Y=] and enter the function $y = 3x^2 + 2x - 4$.

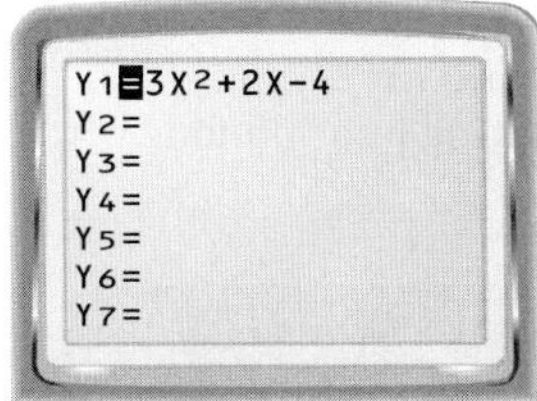

STEP 2 *Adjust the window*

Display the graph. Adjust the viewing window as needed so that the x-intercepts of the parabola are visible.

STEP 3 *Use the zero feature*

The *zero* feature is under the CALCULATE menu.

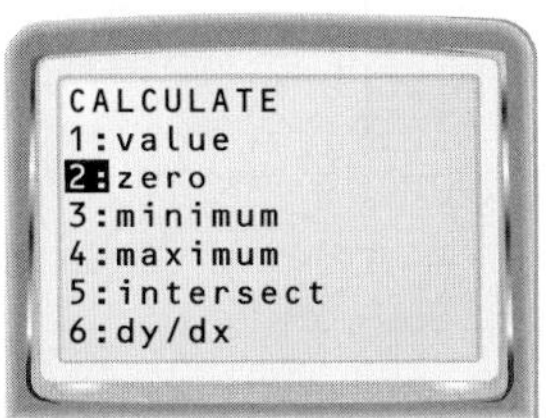

STEP 4 *Find the zeros*

Follow the graphing calculator's procedure to find a zero of the function. Then repeat the process to find the other zero.

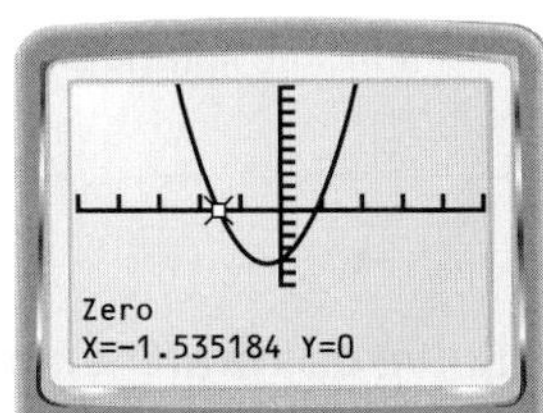

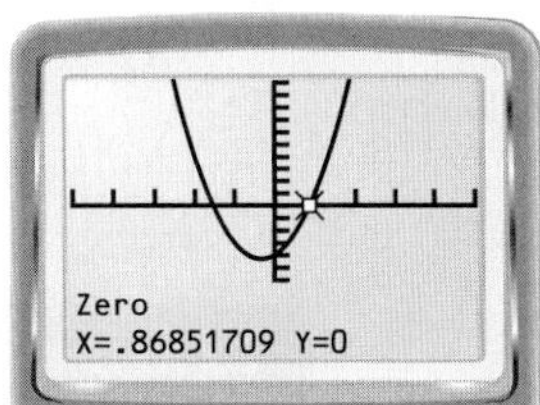

▶ The zeros are about −1.54 and about 0.87.

PRACTICE

Approximate the zeros of the quadratic function to the nearest hundredth.

7. $y = 2x^2 - 5x - 8$ **−1.11, 3.61**
8. $y = -3x^2 + 6x - 2$ **0.42, 1.58**
9. $y = -x^2 + 4x + 9$ **−1.61, 5.61**
10. $y = 4x^2 - 7x + 1$ **0.16, 1.59**
11. $y = -2.5x^2 + 7.7x - 4.9$ **0.90, 2.18**
12. $y = 1.56x^2 - 5.19x - 2.25$ **−0.39, 3.72**
13. $y = -0.82x^2 - 4x + 12.4$ **−7.03, 2.15**
14. $y = 5.36x^2 + 17x + 2.67$ **−3.01, −0.17**

DRAW CONCLUSIONS

15. If a quadratic function has only one zero, what is the maximum or minimum value of the function? *Explain.* **See margin.**
16. If a quadratic function has a maximum value that is greater than 0, how many zeros does the function have? *Explain.* **See margin.**

Extra Example 2

Approximate the zeros of the function $y = -2x^2 + 5x + 6$. **−0.89, 3.39**

3 ASSESS AND RETEACH

1. If a quadratic function has a minimum value less than 0, how many zeros does the function have? Explain. **Two zeros; a minimum value means the parabola opens upward, and if it opens upward from a negative y-value, it must cross the x-axis in two points.**
2. If a quadratic function has a minimum value greater than 0, how many zeros does the function have? Explain. **No zeros; a minimum value means the parabola opens upward, and if it opens upward from a positive y-value, it does not cross the x-axis.**

15. 0; the maximum or minimum value of a quadratic function occurs at the vertex of the parabola that is the graph of the function. When a quadratic function has only one zero, its graph has only one x-intercept, which must also be the x-coordinate of the vertex of the parabola. Then the y-coordinate of the vertex is 0, so the maximum or minimum value of the function is 0.

16. 2; the graph of a quadratic function with a maximum value must open down. Because the maximum is greater than 0, the vertex of the parabola is above the x-axis; then, because the parabola opens down, it must cross the x-axis in two points. The two x-intercepts are the two zeros of the function.

Warm-Up Exercises

Transparency Available

Evaluate the expression.

1. $-\sqrt{49}$ **−7**
2. $\sqrt{200}$ **about 14.1**
3. $\pm\sqrt{121}$ **±11**
4. A ball is dropped from a height 9 feet above the ground. How long does it take the ball to hit the ground? **0.75 sec**

Notetaking Guide

Transparency Available

Promotes interactive learning and notetaking skills.

Pacing

Basic: 2 days

Average: 2 days

Advanced: 2 days

Block: 0.5 block with 10.3
0.5 block with 10.5

- See *Teaching Guide/Lesson Plan.*

2 FOCUS AND MOTIVATE

Essential Question

Big Idea 2, p. 627

How do you solve a quadratic equation by finding square roots? **Tell students they will learn how to answer this question for equations that can be written in the form $ax^2 + c = 0$.**

NCTM STANDARDS

Standard 2: Analyze situations using algebraic symbols

Standard 6: Apply/adapt strategies to solve problems

10.4 Use Square Roots to Solve Quadratic Equations

Before You solved a quadratic equation by graphing.

Now You will solve a quadratic equation by finding square roots.

Why? So you can solve a problem about a falling object, as in Example 5.

Key Vocabulary
- **square root,** *p. 110*
- **perfect square,** *p. 111*

To use square roots to solve a quadratic equation of the form $ax^2 + c = 0$, first isolate x^2 on one side to obtain $x^2 = d$. Then use the following information about the solutions of $x^2 = d$ to solve the equation.

KEY CONCEPT *For Your Notebook*

Solving $x^2 = d$ by Taking Square Roots

- If $d > 0$, then $x^2 = d$ has two solutions: $x = \pm\sqrt{d}$.
- If $d = 0$, then $x^2 = d$ has one solution: $x = 0$.
- If $d < 0$, then $x^2 = d$ has no solution.

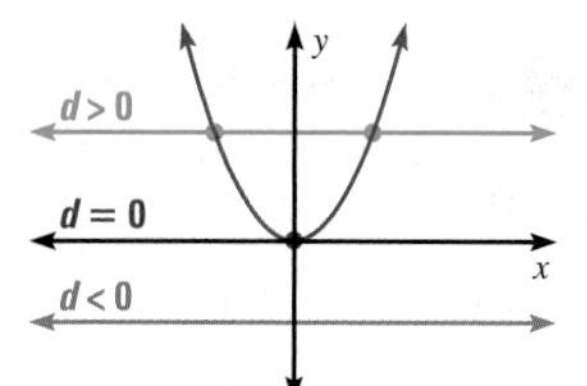

READING Recall that in this course, *solutions* refers to real-number solutions.

EXAMPLE 1 Solve quadratic equations

Solve the equation.

a. $2x^2 = 8$ **b.** $m^2 - 18 = -18$ **c.** $b^2 + 12 = 5$

Solution

a. $2x^2 = 8$ **Write original equation.**

$x^2 = 4$ **Divide each side by 2.**

$x = \pm\sqrt{4} = \pm 2$ **Take square roots of each side. Simplify.**

▶ The solutions are −2 and 2.

b. $m^2 - 18 = -18$ **Write original equation.**

$m^2 = 0$ **Add 18 to each side.**

$m = 0$ **The square root of 0 is 0.**

▶ The solution is 0.

c. $b^2 + 12 = 5$ **Write original equation.**

$b^2 = -7$ **Subtract 12 from each side.**

▶ Negative real numbers do not have real square roots. So, there is no solution.

ANOTHER WAY You can also use factoring to solve $2x^2 - 8 = 0$:

$2x^2 - 8 = 0$
$2(x^2 - 4) = 0$
$2(x - 2)(x + 2) = 0$
$x = 2$ or $x = -2$

Resource Planning Guide

Chapter Resource Book
- Teaching Guide/Lesson Plan
- Activity Master
- Practice levels A, B, C
- Study Guide
- Catch-up for Absent Students
- Problem Solving Workshop
- Challenge

Workbooks
- Notetaking Guide
- Practice Workbook

Teaching Options
- **Power Presentations** provides dynamic electronic teaching resources for the classroom.
- **Activity Generator** provides editable activities for all ability levels.

Interactive Technology
- Easy Planner
- Power Presentations
- Activity Generator
- Animated Algebra
- Test Generator
- Online Quiz
- eWorkbook
- eEdition
- @HomeTutor

Resources for English Learners
- Spanish Study Guide
- Multi-Language Visual Glossary
- Student Resources in Spanish

See also the *Differentiated Instruction Resources* for more strategies for meeting individual needs.

SIMPLIFYING SQUARE ROOTS In cases where you need to take the square root of a fraction whose numerator and denominator are perfect squares, the radical can be written as a fraction. For example, $\sqrt{\frac{16}{25}}$ can be written as $\frac{4}{5}$ because $\left(\frac{4}{5}\right)^2 = \frac{16}{25}$.

EXAMPLE 2 Take square roots of a fraction

Solve $4z^2 = 9$.

Solution

$4z^2 = 9$ — Write original equation.

$z^2 = \frac{9}{4}$ — Divide each side by 4.

$z = \pm\sqrt{\frac{9}{4}}$ — Take square roots of each side.

$z = \pm\frac{3}{2}$ — Simplify.

▶ The solutions are $-\frac{3}{2}$ and $\frac{3}{2}$.

APPROXIMATING SQUARE ROOTS In cases where d in the equation $x^2 = d$ is not a perfect square or a fraction whose numerator and denominator are not perfect squares, you need to approximate the square root. A calculator can be used to find an approximation.

EXAMPLE 3 Approximate solutions of a quadratic equation

Solve $3x^2 - 11 = 7$. Round the solutions to the nearest hundredth.

Solution

$3x^2 - 11 = 7$ — Write original equation.

$3x^2 = 18$ — Add 11 to each side.

$x^2 = 6$ — Divide each side by 3.

$x = \pm\sqrt{6}$ — Take square roots of each side.

$x \approx \pm 2.45$ — Use a calculator. Round to the nearest hundredth.

▶ The solutions are about −2.45 and about 2.45.

✓ GUIDED PRACTICE for Examples 1, 2, and 3

Solve the equation.

1. $c^2 - 25 = 0$ **±5**
2. $5w^2 + 12 = -8$ **no solution**
3. $2x^2 + 11 = 11$ **0**
4. $25x^2 = 16$ **$\pm\frac{4}{5}$**
5. $9m^2 = 100$ **$\pm\frac{10}{3}$**
6. $49b^2 + 64 = 0$ **no solution**

Solve the equation. Round the solutions to the nearest hundredth.

7. $x^2 + 4 = 14$ **±3.16**
8. $3k^2 - 1 = 0$ **±0.58**
9. $2p^2 - 7 = 2$ **±2.12**

Motivating the Lesson

Tell students that if an object is dropped from a known height, they can calculate how long the object is in the air. For example, if you are standing on a balcony 12 feet above the ground and you drop a key to a friend who catches it at a height of 4 feet, you can use the vertical motion model to find how long the key is in the air.

3 TEACH

Extra Example 1

Solve the equation.

a. $3x^2 = 27$ **−3, 3**

b. $p^2 + 12 = 12$ **0**

c. $a^2 - 3 = -4$ **no solution**

Extra Example 2

Solve $25s^2 = 49$. **$-\frac{7}{5}, \frac{7}{5}$**

Key Question to Ask for Example 2

- Why do you get two solutions when you take the square root of each side of the equation? **The square root of a positive number has two values, one positive and one negative.**

Extra Example 3

Solve $2x^2 - 10 = 6$. Round the solutions to the nearest hundredth. **−2.83, 2.83**

Differentiated Instruction

Visual Learners Use **Example 3** to provide students with another way to see square roots. First graph $y = x^2$ and then graph $y = 6$. The intersections of the two graphs occur when $x = \pm\sqrt{6}$. This gives a concrete example of the sketch in the Key Concept on p. 652 and illustrates one way to visualize the square roots of 6.

See also the *Differentiated Instruction Resources* for more strategies.

Extra Example 4

Solve $4(x + 6)^2 = 32$. Round the solutions to the nearest hundredth.
$-6 + \sqrt{8} \approx -3.17$, $-6 - \sqrt{8} \approx -8.83$

Extra Example 5

You drop a towel from a balcony 18 feet above your den onto a table that is 3 feet above the ground. How long is the towel in the air?
about 0.97 sec

Closing the Lesson

Have students summarize the major points of the lesson and answer the Essential Question: How do you solve a quadratic equation by finding square roots?

- **If a quadratic equation is in the form $ax^2 + c = 0$, rewrite it in the form $x^2 = d$.**
- **If $d > 0$, then $x^2 = d$ has two solutions. If $d = 0$, there is one solution, 0. If $d < 0$, there is no real-number solution.**

You can use square roots to solve a quadratic equation if you can write it as $x^2 = d$. If $d > 0$ and d is not a perfect square, approximate the values of d using a calculator.

EXAMPLE 4 Solve a quadratic equation

Solve $6(x - 4)^2 = 42$. Round the solutions to the nearest hundredth.

$6(x - 4)^2 = 42$	**Write original equation.**
$(x - 4)^2 = 7$	**Divide each side by 6.**
$x - 4 = \pm\sqrt{7}$	**Take square roots of each side.**
$x = 4 \pm \sqrt{7}$	**Add 4 to each side.**

▶ The solutions are $4 + \sqrt{7} \approx 6.65$ and $4 - \sqrt{7} \approx 1.35$.

CHECK To check the solutions, first write the equation so that 0 is on one side as follows: $6(x - 4)^2 - 42 = 0$. Then graph the related function $y = 6(x - 4)^2 - 42$. The x-intercepts appear to be about 6.6 and about 1.3. So, each solution checks.

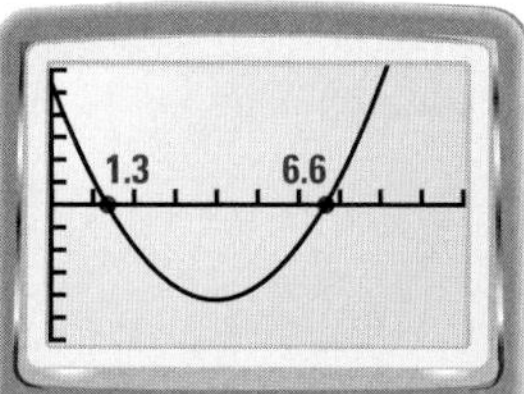

EXAMPLE 5 Solve a multi-step problem

ANOTHER WAY
For alternative methods for solving the problem in Example 5, turn to page 659 for the **Problem Solving Workshop**.

SPORTS EVENT During an ice hockey game, a remote-controlled blimp flies above the crowd and drops a numbered table-tennis ball. The number on the ball corresponds to a prize. Use the information in the diagram to find the amount of time that the ball is in the air.

WILDCATS
45 ft
17 ft
Not drawn to scale

Solution

STEP 1 **Use** the vertical motion model to write an equation for the height h (in feet) of the ball as a function of time t (in seconds).

$h = -16t^2 + vt + s$	**Vertical motion model**
$h = -16t^2 + 0t + 45$	**Substitute for v and s.**

DETERMINE VELOCITY
When an object is dropped, it has an initial vertical velocity of 0 feet per second.

STEP 2 **Find** the amount of time the ball is in the air by substituting 17 for h and solving for t.

$h = -16t^2 + 45$	**Write model.**
$17 = -16t^2 + 45$	**Substitute 17 for h.**
$-28 = -16t^2$	**Subtract 45 from each side.**
$\frac{28}{16} = t^2$	**Divide each side by −16.**
$\sqrt{\frac{28}{16}} = t$	**Take positive square root.**
$1.32 \approx t$	**Use a calculator.**

INTERPRET SOLUTION
Because the time cannot be a negative number, ignore the negative square root.

▶ The ball is in the air for about 1.32 seconds.

Differentiated Instruction

Below Level Real world situations often motivate students to learn mathematical concepts, so have students work with a partner to create and solve a real world situation based on **Example 5**. Explain that they want a situation in which a dropped object is caught or interrupted in its fall before it hits the ground. Have students develop stepped-out solutions for their problems, which they can use as a guide for future work.

See also the *Differentiated Instruction Resources* for more strategies.

✓ GUIDED PRACTICE for Examples 4 and 5

Solve the equation. Round the solutions to the nearest hundredth, if necessary.

10. $2(x-2)^2 = 18$ **−1, 5** **11.** $4(q-3)^2 = 28$ **0.35, 5.65** **12.** $3(t+5)^2 = 24$ **−7.83, −2.17**

13. **WHAT IF?** In Example 5, suppose the table-tennis ball is released 58 feet above the ground and is caught 12 feet above the ground. Find the amount of time that the ball is in the air. Round your answer to the nearest hundredth of a second. **1.70 sec**

10.4 EXERCISES

HOMEWORK KEY

○ = **WORKED-OUT SOLUTIONS** on p. WS24 for Exs. 25 and 59

★ = **STANDARDIZED TEST PRACTICE** Exs. 2, 15, 16, 29, 51, 52, 57, and 60

 = **MULTIPLE REPRESENTATIONS** Ex. 62

SKILL PRACTICE

A

1. **VOCABULARY** Copy and complete: If $b^2 = a$, then b is a(n) _?_ of a. **square root**

2. ★ **WRITING** *Describe* two methods for solving a quadratic equation of the form $ax^2 + c = 0$. **(1) Graph the parabola $y = ax^2 + c$ and find its x-intercepts. (2) Write the equation in the form $x^2 = -\frac{c}{a}$ and take the square roots of each side.**

EXAMPLES 1 and 2 on pp. 652–653 for Exs. 3–16

SOLVING EQUATIONS **Solve the equation.**

3. $3x^2 - 3 = 0$ **±1** **4.** $2x^2 - 32 = 0$ **±4** **5.** $4x^2 - 400 = 0$ **±10**

6. $2m^2 - 42 = 8$ **±5** **7.** $15d^2 = 0$ **0** **8.** $a^2 + 8 = 3$ **no solution**

9. $4g^2 + 10 = 11$ $\pm\frac{1}{2}$ **10.** $2w^2 + 13 = 11$ **no solution** **11.** $9q^2 - 35 = 14$ $\pm\frac{7}{3}$

12. $25b^2 + 11 = 15$ $\pm\frac{2}{5}$ **13.** $3z^2 - 18 = -18$ **0** **14.** $5n^2 - 17 = -19$ **no solution**

15. ★ **MULTIPLE CHOICE** Which of the following is a solution of the equation $61 - 3n^2 = -14$? **A**

Ⓐ 5 Ⓑ 10 Ⓒ 25 Ⓓ 625

16. ★ **MULTIPLE CHOICE** Which of the following is a solution of the equation $13 - 36x^2 = -12$? **C**

Ⓐ $-\frac{6}{5}$ Ⓑ $\frac{1}{6}$ Ⓒ $\frac{5}{6}$ Ⓓ 5

EXAMPLE 3 on p. 653 for Exs. 17–29

APPROXIMATING SQUARE ROOTS **Solve the equation. Round the solutions to the nearest hundredth.**

17. $x^2 + 6 = 13$ **±2.65** **18.** $x^2 + 11 = 24$ **±3.61** **19.** $14 - x^2 = 17$ **no solution**

20. $2a^2 - 9 = 11$ **±3.16** **21.** $4 - k^2 = 4$ **0** **22.** $5 + 3p^2 = 38$ **±3.32**

23. $53 = 8 + 9m^2$ **±2.24** **24.** $-21 = 15 - 2z^2$ **±4.24** **(25.)** $7c^2 = 100$ **±3.78**

26. $5d^2 + 2 = 6$ **±0.89** **27.** $4b^2 - 5 = 2$ **±1.32** **28.** $9n^2 - 14 = -3$ **±1.11**

29. ★ **MULTIPLE CHOICE** The equation $17 - \frac{1}{4}x^2 = 12$ has a solution between which two integers? **D**

Ⓐ 1 and 2 Ⓑ 2 and 3 Ⓒ 3 and 4 Ⓓ 4 and 5

4 PRACTICE AND APPLY

Assignment Guide

Answer Transparencies available for all exercises

Basic:
Day 1: pp. 655–658
Exs. 1–11, 15–25, 29
Day 2: pp. 655–658
Exs. 30–46, 56–60, 64–73

Average:
Day 1: pp. 655–658
Exs. 1, 2, 7–16, 21–29, 47–49
Day 2: pp. 655–658
Exs. 30–46, 50–52, 56–62, 64–72 even

Advanced:
Day 1: pp. 655–658
Exs. 1, 2, 8–16, 23–29, 47–52
Day 2: pp. 655–658
Exs. 32–46, 53–63*, 66, 70, 73

Block:
pp. 655–658
Exs. 1, 2, 7–16, 21–29, 47–49 (with 10.3)
pp. 655–658
Exs. 30–46, 50–52, 56–62, 64–72 even (with 10.5)

Differentiated Instruction

See *Differentiated Instruction Resources* for suggestions on addressing the needs of a diverse classroom.

Homework Check

For a quick check of student understanding of key concepts, go over the following exercises:

Basic: 6, 11, 20, 33, 56
Average: 7, 12, 24, 36, 56
Advanced: 8, 13, 27, 38, 57

Extra Practice

- Student Edition, p. 947
- Chapter Resource Book: Practice levels A, B, C

Practice Worksheet

An easily-readable reduced practice page (with answers) for this lesson can be found on p. 626C.

Avoiding Common Errors

Exercises 3–14, 17–28, 32–46 Students often indicate only one solution to a quadratic equation. Remind students that there may be zero, one, or two real-number solutions to a quadratic equation.

Graphing Calculator

Exercises 17–28, 32–40 Encourage students to use their graphing calculators to check their solutions. To do so, they need to write the equation so that 0 is on one side. Tell students they can also use the CALCULATE menu to find the zeros of a function. Encourage students to get familiar with all the methods and decide which one is quickest and easiest for them.

51. $\pm\frac{6}{5}$, or ± 1.2. ***Sample answer:*** **Rewrite the decimal as a fraction and then take square roots of each side of the equation:** $x^2 = \frac{100}{144}$, **so** $x = \pm\sqrt{\frac{144}{100}} = \pm\frac{12}{10} = \pm\frac{6}{5}$, **or** ± 1.2.

30. 36 has two square roots, 6 and −6, so both numbers should be given as solutions of the equation; $x = \pm\sqrt{36}$, $x = \pm 6$; **the solutions are −6 and 6.**

31. Negative numbers do not have real number square roots, so $\pm\sqrt{-\frac{11}{7}}$ **are not real numbers; there is no solution.**

ERROR ANALYSIS ***Describe*** **and correct the error in solving the equation.**

30. $2x^2 - 54 = 18$

$2x^2 - 54 = 18$
$2x^2 = 72$
$x^2 = 36$
$x = \sqrt{36}$
$x = 6$
The solution is 6.

31. $7d^2 - 6 = -17$

$7d^2 - 6 = -17$
$7d^2 = -11$
$d^2 = -\frac{11}{7}$
$d \approx \pm 1.25$
The solutions are about −1.25 and about 1.25.

EXAMPLE 4 on p. 654 for Exs. 32–40

SOLVING EQUATIONS **Solve the equation. Round the solutions to the nearest hundredth.**

32. $(x - 7)^2 = 6$ **4.55, 9.45**
33. $7(x - 3)^2 = 35$ **0.76, 5.24**
34. $6(x + 4)^2 = 18$ **−5.73, −2.27**
35. $20 = 2(m + 5)^2$ **−8.16, −1.84**
36. $5(a - 2)^2 = 70$ **−1.74, 5.74**
37. $21 = 3(z + 14)^2$ **−16.65, −11.**
38. $\frac{1}{2}(c - 8)^2 = 3$ **5.55, 10.45**
39. $\frac{3}{2}(n + 1)^2 = 33$ **−5.69, 3.69**
40. $\frac{4}{3}(k - 6)^2 = 20$ **2.13, 9.87**

B **SOLVING EQUATIONS** **Solve the equation. Round the solutions to the nearest hundredth, if necessary.**

41. $3x^2 - 35 = 45 - 2x^2$ **±4**
42. $42 = 3(x^2 + 5)$ **±3**
43. $11x^2 + 3 = 5(4x^2 - 3)$ **±1.41**
44. $\left(\frac{t - 5}{3}\right)^2 = 49$ **−16, 26**
45. $11\left(\frac{w - 7}{2}\right)^2 - 20 = 101$ **0.37, 13.63**
46. $(4m^2 - 6)^2 = 81$ **±1.94**

GEOMETRY **Use the given area** ***A*** **of the circle to find the radius** ***r*** **or the diameter** ***d*** **to the nearest hundredth.**

47. $A = 144\pi$ in.^{2} **12 in.**

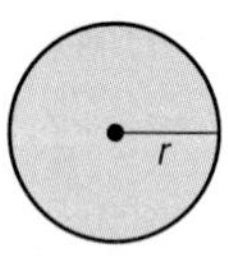

48. $A = 21\pi$ m^2 **4.58 m**

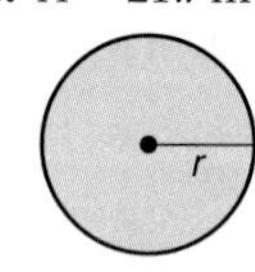

49. $A = 34\pi$ ft^2 **11.66 ft**

50. REASONING An equation of the graph shown is $y = \frac{1}{2}(x - 2)^2 + 1$. Two points on the parabola have y-coordinates of 9. Find the x-coordinates of these points. **−2, 6**

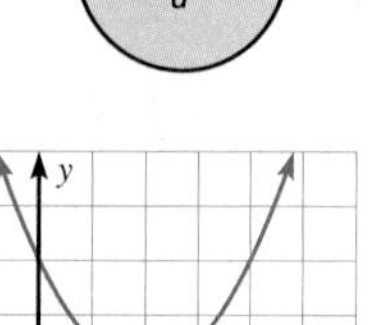

51. ★ SHORT RESPONSE Solve $x^2 = 1.44$ without using a calculator. *Explain* your reasoning. **See margin.**

52. ★ OPEN-ENDED Give values for a and c so that $ax^2 + c = 0$ has (a) two solutions, (b) one solution, and (c) no solution.
Sample answers are given. (a) 5, −1; (b) 3, 0; (c) 2, 4

C **CHALLENGE** **Solve the equation without graphing.**

53. $x^2 - 12x + 36 = 64$ **−2, 14**
54. $x^2 + 14x + 49 = 16$ **−11, −3**
55. $x^2 + 18x + 81 = 25$ **−4, −14**

○ = WORKED-OUT SOLUTIONS on p. WS1 ★ = STANDARDIZED TEST PRACTICE

PROBLEM SOLVING

EXAMPLE 5 A on p. 654 for Exs. 56–57

56. FALLING OBJECT Fenway Park is a Major League Baseball park in Boston, Massachusetts. The park offers seats on top of the left field wall. A person sitting in one of these seats accidentally drops his sunglasses on the field. The height h (in feet) of the sunglasses can be modeled by the function $h = -16t^2 + 38$ where t is the time (in seconds) since the sunglasses were dropped. Find the time it takes for the sunglasses to reach the field. Round your answer to the nearest hundredth of a second. **1.54 sec**

@HomeTutor for problem solving help at classzone.com

57. ★ MULTIPLE CHOICE Which equation can be used to find the time it takes for an object to hit the ground after it was dropped from a height of 68 feet? **C**

Ⓐ $-16t^2 = 0$ Ⓑ $-16t^2 - 68 = 0$ Ⓒ $-16t^2 + 68 = 0$ Ⓓ $-16t^2 = 68$

@HomeTutor for problem solving help at classzone.com

58. INTERNET USAGE For the period 1995–2001, the number y (in thousands) of Internet users worldwide can be modeled by the function $y = 12{,}697x^2 + 55{,}722$ where x is the number of years since 1995. Between which two years did the number of Internet users worldwide reach 100,000,000? **1996 and 1997**

59. GEMOLOGY To find the weight w (in carats) of round faceted gems, gemologists use the formula $w = 0.0018D^2ds$ where D is the diameter (in millimeters) of the gem, d is the depth (in millimeters) of the gem, and s is the specific gravity of the gem. Find the diameter to the nearest tenth of a millimeter of each round faceted gem in the table.

	Gem	Weight (carats)	Depth (mm)	Specific gravity	Diameter (mm)	
a.	Amethyst	1	4.5	2.65	?	**6.8 mm**
b.	Diamond	1	4.5	3.52	?	**5.9 mm**
c.	Ruby	1	4.5	4.00	?	**5.6 mm**

B **60. ★ SHORT RESPONSE** In deep water, the speed s (in meters per second) of a series of waves and the wavelength L (in meters) of the waves are related by the equation $2\pi s^2 = 9.8L$.

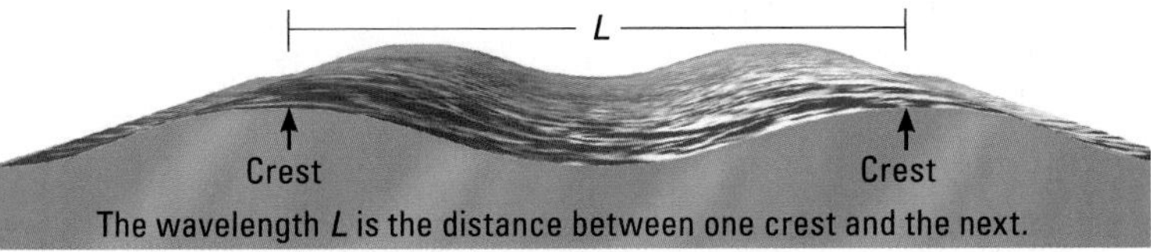

The wavelength L is the distance between one crest and the next.

a. Find the speed to the nearest hundredth of a meter per second of a series of waves with the following wavelengths: 6 meters, 10 meters, and 25 meters. (Use 3.14 for π.) **3.06 m/sec, 3.95 m/sec, 6.25 m/sec**

b. Does the speed of a series of waves increase or decrease as the wavelength of the waves increases? *Explain.* **Increase; as the wavelength in part (a) increased, respective speeds increased.**

Internet Reference

Exercise 56 Additional information about Fenway Park can be found at mlb.com/bos/ballpark/history.jsp

Teaching Strategy

Exercises 56–57 Before assigning these exercises, you may want to discuss how they are similar. Ask students to identify the value of h in Exercise 56 and explain what "+ 38" represents in the function. Then have them identify similar values in Exercise 57. Ask students how they can use these similarities to identify the correct solution to Exercise 57.

5 ASSESS AND RETEACH

Daily Homework Quiz

Transparency Available

Solve the equation. Round solutions to the nearest hundredth, if necessary.

1. $4b^2 - 13 = 3$ **$-2, 2$**

2. $9x^2 = 25$ **$-\frac{5}{3}, \frac{5}{3}$**

3. $3n^2 - 18 = 12$ **$-3.16, 3.16$**

4. At a football game you are sitting 32 feet above the ground. If your hat comes off and falls to the ground, how long will it be in the air? **about 1.41 sec**

Available at **classzone.com**

Diagnosis/Remediation

- Practice A, B, C in Chapter Resource Book
- Study Guide in Chapter Resource Book
- Practice Workbook
- @HomeTutor

Challenge

Additional challenge is available in the Chapter Resource Book.

62b.

Time of free fall, t (sec)	Height, h (ft)
0	250
1	234
2	186
3	106
4	−6

61. MULTI-STEP PROBLEM The Doyle log rule is a formula used to estimate the amount of lumber that can be sawn from logs of various sizes. The amount of lumber V (in board feet) is given by $V = \frac{L(D-4)^2}{16}$ where L is the length (in feet) of a log and D is the small-end diameter (in inches) of the log.

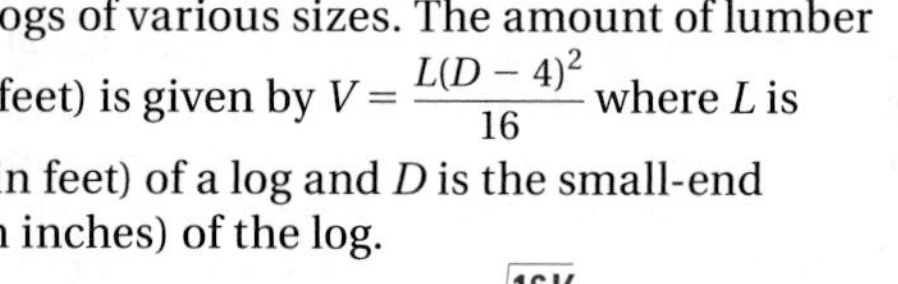

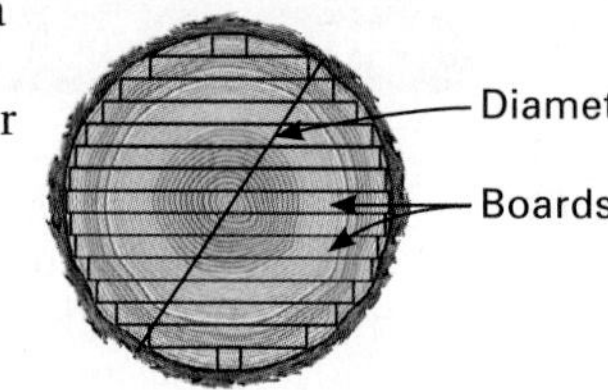

a. Solve the formula for D. **$D = 4 \pm \sqrt{\frac{16V}{L}}$**

b. Use the rewritten formula to find the diameters, to the nearest tenth of an inch, of logs that will yield 50 board feet and have the following lengths: 16 feet, 18 feet, 20 feet, and 22 feet. **11.1 in., 10.7 in., 10.3 in., 10.0 in.**

62. MULTIPLE REPRESENTATIONS A ride at an amusement park lifts seated riders 250 feet above the ground. Then the riders are dropped. They experience free fall until the brakes are activated at 105 feet above the ground.

a. Writing an Equation Use the vertical motion model to write an equation for the height h (in feet) of the riders as a function of the time t (in seconds) into the free fall. **$h = -16t^2 + 250$**

b. Making a Table Make a table that shows the height of the riders after 0, 1, 2, 3, and 4 seconds according to the model. Use the table to estimate the amount of time the riders experience free fall. **See margin for table; about 3 sec.**

c. Solving an Equation Use the equation to find the amount of time, to the nearest tenth of a second, that the riders experience free fall. **3.0 sec**

C **63. CHALLENGE** The height h (in feet) of a dropped object on any planet can be modeled by $h = -\frac{g}{2}t^2 + s$ where g is the acceleration (in feet per second per second) due to the planet's gravity, t is the time (in seconds) after the object is dropped, and s is the initial height (in feet) of the object. Suppose the same object is dropped from the same height on Earth and Mars. Given that g is 32 feet per second per second on Earth and 12 feet per second per second on Mars, on which planet will the object hit the ground first? *Explain.* **See margin.**

MIXED REVIEW

PREVIEW
Prepare for Lesson 10.5 in Exs. 64–67.

Evaluate the power. *(p. 2)*

64. $\left(\frac{5}{2}\right)^2$ **$\frac{25}{4}$** **65.** $\left(\frac{9}{5}\right)^2$ **$\frac{81}{25}$** **66.** $\left(\frac{3}{4}\right)^2$ **$\frac{9}{16}$** **67.** $\left(\frac{7}{2}\right)^2$ **$\frac{49}{4}$**

Write an equation of the line with the given slope and y-intercept. *(p. 283)*

68. slope: −9, y-intercept: 11 **$y = -9x + 11$**

69. slope: 7, y-intercept: −7 **$y = 7x - 7$**

70. slope: 3, y-intercept: −2 **$y = 3x - 2$**

Write an equation of the line that passes through the given point and is perpendicular to the given line. *(p. 318)*

71. $(1, -1), y = 2x$ **$y = -\frac{1}{2}x - \frac{1}{2}$**

72. $(0, 8), y = 4x + 1$ **$y = -\frac{1}{4}x + 8$**

73. $(-9, -4), y = -3x + 6$ **$y = \frac{1}{3}x - 1$**

Using ALTERNATIVE METHODS

Another Way to Solve Example 5, page 654

MULTIPLE REPRESENTATIONS In Example 5 on page 654, you saw how to solve a problem about a dropped table-tennis ball by using a square root. You can also solve the problem by using factoring or by using a table.

PROBLEM

SPORTS EVENT During an ice hockey game, a remote-controlled blimp flies above the crowd and drops a numbered table-tennis ball. The number on the ball corresponds to a prize. Use the information in the diagram to find the amount of time that the ball is in the air.

METHOD 1

Using Factoring One alternative approach is to use factoring.

STEP 1 **Write** an equation for the height h (in feet) of the ball as a function of time t (in seconds) after it is dropped using the vertical motion model.

$h = -16t^2 + vt + s$ — Vertical motion model

$h = -16t^2 + 0t + 45$ — Substitute 0 for v and 45 for s.

STEP 2 **Substitute** 17 for h to find the time it takes the ball to reach a height of 17 feet. Then write the equation so that 0 is on one side.

$17 = -16t^2 + 45$ — Substitute 17 for h.

$0 = -16t^2 + 28$ — Subtract 17 from each side.

STEP 3 **Solve** the equation by factoring. Replace 28 with the closest perfect square, 25, so that the right side of the equation is factorable as a difference of two squares.

USE AN APPROXIMATION
By replacing 28 with 25, you will obtain an answer that is an approximation of the amount of time that the ball is in the air.

$0 = -16t^2 + 25$ — Use 25 as an approximation for 28.

$0 = -(16t^2 - 25)$ — Factor out −1.

$0 = -(4t - 5)(4t + 5)$ — Difference of two squares pattern

$4t - 5 = 0$ *or* $4t + 5 = 0$ — Zero-product property

$t = \frac{5}{4}$ *or* $t = -\frac{5}{4}$ — Solve for t.

▸ The ball is in the air about $\frac{5}{4}$, or 1.25, seconds.

Alternative Strategy

Example 5 on page 654 can be solved by using factoring or by using a table. You may want to point out that these alternative strategies do not give the same exact result as the vertical motion model, though the results are close for all three methods. Stress that all three methods give an approximation, and that they all round to 1.3 seconds. Point out that each strategy can be used to check a solution found by using a different strategy.

Avoiding Common Errors

In Method 1, watch for students who use a perfect square that is not closest to 28. Suggest that students list the perfect squares on each side of 28 to make sure they choose the closest one.

p. 658

63. Earth; on Earth the fraction $-\frac{g}{2}$ is $-\frac{32}{2} = -16$, and on Mars the fraction $-\frac{g}{2}$ is $-\frac{12}{2} = -6$; so, on Earth the height of the object is modeled by $h = -16t^2 + s$ and on Mars the height of the object is modeled by $h = -6t^2 + s$. To compare how long it takes the same object dropped from the same height s to hit the ground on each planet, substitute 0 for h in each equation and solve for t in terms of s (disregard any negative solutions). Earth's equation: $0 = -16t^2 + s$; $16t^2 = s$; $t^2 = \frac{s}{16}$, $t = \sqrt{\frac{s}{16}} = \frac{\sqrt{s}}{\sqrt{16}}$, or $t = \frac{\sqrt{s}}{4}$. Mars's equation: $0 = -6t^2 + s$; $6t^2 = s$; $t^2 = \frac{s}{6}$; $t = \sqrt{\frac{s}{6}} = \frac{\sqrt{s}}{\sqrt{6}}$, or $t \approx \frac{\sqrt{s}}{2.45}$. Because $4 > 2.45$, $\frac{1}{4} < \frac{1}{2.45}$, and $\frac{\sqrt{s}}{4} < \frac{\sqrt{s}}{2.45}$; thus, it takes less time for the object to hit the ground on Earth than on Mars.

Teaching Strategy

Emphasize to students the usefulness of using two tables. Point out that the first table gives the time in increments of 1 second, which is fairly easy to calculate, and narrows the focus to a time between 1 and 2 seconds. Then they can calculate in tenths of a second beginning with 1.0 second.

1. See Additional Answers beginning on p. AA1.

2. *Sample answer:* A bird flying 50 feet above the ground drops a twig it was carrying in its beak. How many seconds does it take the twig to reach a height of 15 feet off the ground? The height (in feet) of the twig t seconds after it falls is modeled by $h = -16t^2 + 50$. To find the time it takes the twig to reach a height of 15 feet, substitute 15 for h and solve for t: $15 = -16t^2 + 50$, or $0 = -16t^2 + 35$. Replace 35 with the closest perfect square and factor: $0 = -16t^2 + 36$; $0 = -(4t + 6)(4t - 6)$; $4t + 6 = 0$ *or* $4t - 6 = 0$; $t = -\frac{3}{2}$ *or* $t = \frac{3}{2}$. The time cannot be negative, so disregard the negative solution; the twig is at a height of 15 feet after about $\frac{3}{2}$, or 1.5 seconds.

3b, 3c. See Additional Answers beginning on p. AA1.

4. About 1.73 sec. *Sample answer:* Use factoring. The height h (in feet) of the shoe t seconds after it falls is modeled by $h = -16t^2 + 54$. To find the time it takes the shoe to reach a height of 6 feet, substitute 6 for h and solve for t: $6 = -16t^2 + 54$, or $0 = -16t^2 + 48$. Replace 48 with the closest perfect square and factor: $0 = -16t^2 + 49$; $0 = -(16t^2 - 49)$; $0 = -(4t + 7)(4t - 7)$; $4t + 7 = 0$ *or* $4t - 7 = 0$; $t = -\frac{7}{4}$ *or* $t = \frac{7}{4}$. The time cannot be negative, so disregard the negative solution; the shoe hits the net in about $\frac{7}{4}$, or 1.75 seconds.

METHOD 2 **Using a Table** Another approach is to make and use a table.

STEP 1 **Make** a table that shows the height h (in feet) of the ball by substituting values for time t (in seconds) in the function $h = -16t^2 + 45$. Use increments of 1 second.

Time t (seconds)	Height h (feet)
0	45
1	29
2	−19

STEP 2 **Identify** the time interval in which the height of the ball is 17 feet. This happens between 1 and 2 seconds.

STEP 3 **Make** a second table using increments of 0.1 second to get a closer approximation.

Time t (seconds)	Height h (feet)
1.0	29.00
1.1	25.64
1.2	21.96
1.3	**17.96**
1.4	13.64

▶ The ball is in the air about 1.3 seconds.

PRACTICE

1. **WHAT IF?** In the problem on page 659, suppose the ball is caught at a height of 10 feet. For how many seconds is the ball in the air? Solve this problem using two different methods. **See margin.**

2. **OPEN-ENDED** *Describe* a problem about a dropped object. Then solve the problem and explain what your solution means in this situation. **See margin.**

3. **GEOMETRY** The box below is a rectangular prism with the dimensions shown.

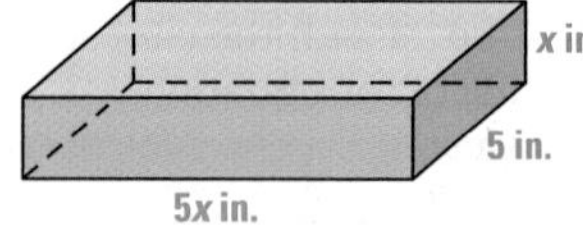

   a. Write an equation that gives the volume V (in cubic inches) of the box as a function of x. $V = 25x^2$

   b. The volume of the box is 83 cubic inches. Find the dimensions of the box. Use factoring to solve the problem. **b–c. See margin.**

   c. Make a table to check your answer from part (b).

4. **TRAPEZE** You are learning how to perform on a trapeze. While hanging from a still trapeze bar, your shoe comes loose and falls to a safety net that is 6 feet off the ground. If your shoe falls from a height of 54 feet, how long does it take your shoe to hit the net? Choose any method for solving the problem. Show your steps. **See margin.**

5. **ERROR ANALYSIS** A student solved the problem in Exercise 4 as shown below. *Describe* and correct the error. **See margin.**

   Let t be the time (in seconds) that the shoe is in the air.

   $6 = -16t^2 + 54$

   $0 = -16t^2 + 60$

   Replace 60 with the closest perfect square, 64.

   $0 = -16t^2 + 64$

   $0 = -16(t - 2)(t + 2)$

   $t = 2$ or $t = -2$

   It takes about 2 seconds.

5. To rewrite the equation $6 = -16t^2 + 54$ so that one side is 0, you must subtract 6 from each side; $0 = -16t^2 + 48$, replace 48 with the closest perfect square, 49. $0 = -16t^2 + 49 = -(16t^2 - 49) = -(4t + 7)(4t - 7)$, so the approximate solutions of this equation are $\pm\frac{7}{4}$. Disregard the negative solution because time cannot be negative; so, it takes about $\frac{7}{4}$, or 1.75, seconds for the shoe to hit the net.

MIXED REVIEW of Problem Solving

STATE TEST PRACTICE classzone.com

Lessons 10.1–10.4

1. **MULTI-STEP PROBLEM** A company's yearly profits from 1996 to 2006 can be modeled by the function $y = x^2 - 8x + 80$ where y is the profit (in thousands of dollars) and x is the number of years since 1996.
   a. In what year did the company experience its lowest yearly profit? **2000**
   b. What was the lowest yearly profit? **\$64,000**

2. **MULTI-STEP PROBLEM** Use the rectangle below.

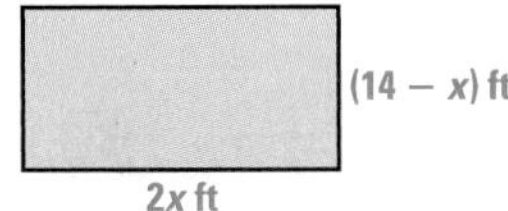

   a. Find the value of x that gives the greatest possible area of the rectangle. **7**
   b. What is the greatest possible area of the rectangle? **98 ft²**

3. **EXTENDED RESPONSE** You throw a lacrosse ball twice using a lacrosse stick. **a–c. See margin.**

   a. For your first throw, the ball is released 8 feet above the ground with an initial vertical velocity of 35 feet per second. Use the vertical motion model to write an equation for the height h (in feet) of the ball as a function of time t (in seconds).
   b. For your second throw, the ball is released 7 feet above the ground with an initial vertical velocity of 45 feet per second. Use the vertical motion model to write an equation for the height h (in feet) of the ball as a function of time t (in seconds).
   c. If no one catches either throw, for which throw is the ball in the air longer? *Explain.*

4. **OPEN-ENDED** Describe a real-world situation of an object being dropped. Then write an equation that models the height of the object as a function of time. Use the equation to determine the time it takes the object to hit the ground. **See margin.**

5. **SHORT RESPONSE** A football player is attempting a field goal. The path of the kicked football can be modeled by the graph of $y = -0.03x^2 + 1.8x$ where x is the horizontal distance (in yards) traveled by the football and y is the corresponding height (in feet) of the football. Will the football pass over the goal post that is 10 feet above the ground and 45 yards away? *Explain.* **See margin.**

6. **GRIDDED ANSWER** The force F (in newtons) a rider feels while a train goes around a curve is given by $F = \frac{mv^2}{r}$ where m is the mass (in kilograms) of the rider, v is the velocity (in meters per second) of the train, and r is the radius (in meters) of the curve. A rider with a mass of 75 kilograms experiences a force of 18,150 newtons, while going around a curve that has a radius of 8 meters. Find the velocity (in meters per second) the train travels around the curve. **44 m/sec**

7. **SHORT RESPONSE** The opening of the tunnel shown can be modeled by the graph of the equation $y = -0.18x^2 + 4.4x - 12$ where x and y are measured in feet. **a, b. See margin.**

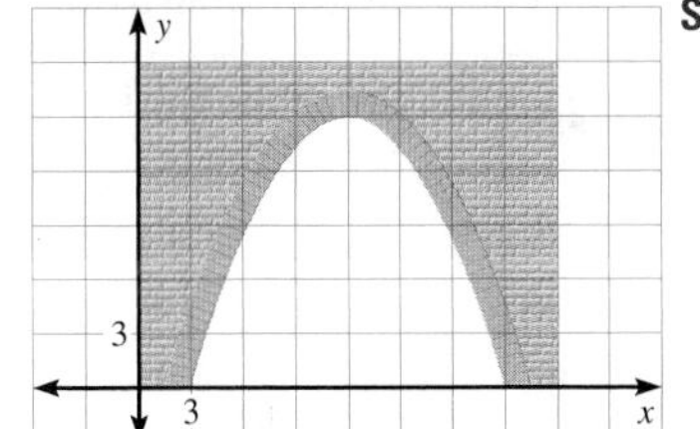

   a. Find the maximum height of the tunnel.
   b. A semi trailer is 7.5 feet wide, and the top of the trailer is 10.5 feet above the ground. Given that traffic travels one way on one lane through the center of the tunnel, will the semi trailer fit through the opening of the tunnel? *Explain.*

3a. $h = -16t^2 + 35t + 8$

3b. $h = -16t^2 + 45t + 7$

3c. The second throw; when the ball lands back on the ground, $h = 0$. To find the time t when $h = 0$ for the first throw, solve $0 = -16t^2 + 35t + 8$; $t \approx 2.40$ seconds (disregard the negative solution). To find the time t when $h = 0$ for the second throw, solve $0 = -16t^2 + 45t + 7$; $t \approx 2.96$ seconds (disregard the negative solution). The second throw is in the air longer.

4. *Sample answer:* A pine cone hanging on a branch 20 feet above the ground drops off the branch; $h = -16t^2 + 20$; $t =$ about 1.1 seconds.

5. Yes; to find the height of the football 45 yards from where it was kicked, find the value of y when $x = 45$: $y = -0.03(45^2) + 1.8(45) = 20.25$ feet. The ball will be above the 10-foot high goal post.

7a. about 15 ft

7b. Yes; since the trailer is 7.5 feet wide, the height of the tunnel must be at least 10.5 feet high 3.75 units to the left and right of the axis of symmetry, $x = 12\frac{2}{9}$. Find the height of the tunnel at these points to be about 12.4 feet, which is higher than the height of the truck, so the truck will fit.

1 PLAN AND PREPARE

Explore the Concept

- Students will use algebra tiles to complete the square.
- This activity leads into the study of completing the square in Lesson 10.5, Example 1.

Materials

Each student will need:

- algebra tiles
- Activity Support Master (*Chapter Resource Book*)

Recommended Time

Work activity: 10 min

Discuss results: 5 min

Grouping

Students should work individually.

2 TEACH

Tips for Success

Make sure that the tiles in Step 2 are arranged to form a square.

Animated Algebra
classzone.com

An **Animated Algebra** activity is available online. This activity is also part of **Power Presentations**.

Key Discovery

You can complete the square for an expression in the form of $x^2 + bx$ by adding the square of one-half the value of b.

3 ASSESS AND RETEACH

Predict the number of 1-tiles needed to complete the square for each expression.

1. $x^2 + 2x$ **1**

2. $x^2 + 12x$ **36**

10.5 Completing the Square Using Algebra Tiles

MATERIALS • algebra tiles

QUESTION How can you use algebra tiles to complete the square?

For an expression of the form $x^2 + bx$, you can add a constant c to the expression so that the expression $x^2 + bx + c$ is a perfect square trinomial. This process is called *completing the square.*

EXPLORE Complete the square

Find the value of c that makes $x^2 + 4x + c$ a perfect square trinomial.

STEP 1 *Model expression*
Use algebra tiles to model the expression $x^2 + 4x$. You will need one x^2-tile and four x-tiles for this expression.

STEP 2 *Rearrange tiles*
Arrange the tiles to form a square. The arrangement will be incomplete in one of the corners.

STEP 3 *Complete the square*
Determine the number of 1-tiles needed to complete the square. The number of 1-tiles is the value of c. So, the perfect square trinomial is $x^2 + 4x + 4$ or $(x + 2)^2$.

DRAW CONCLUSIONS Use your observations to complete these exercises

1. Copy and complete the table using algebra tiles.

Expression	Number of 1-tiles needed to complete the square	Expression written as a square
$x^2 + 4x$	4	$x^2 + 4x + 4 = (x + 2)^2$
$x^2 + 6x$	? **9**	?
$x^2 + 8x$	? **16**	?
$x^2 + 10x$	? **25**	?

$x^2 + 6x + 9 = (x + 3)^2$

$x^2 + 8x + 16 = (x + 4)^2$

$x^2 + 10x + 25 = (x + 5)^2$

2. In the statement $x^2 + bx + c = (x + d)^2$, how are b and d related? How are c and d related? $b = 2d$; $c = d^2$

3. Use your answer to Exercise 2 to predict the number of 1-tiles you would need to add to complete the square for the expression $x^2 + 18x$. **81 1–tiles**

10.5 Solve Quadratic Equations by Completing the Square

Before You solved quadratic equations by finding square roots.
Now You will solve quadratic equations by completing the square.
Why? So you can solve a problem about snowboarding, as in Ex. 50.

Key Vocabulary
- **completing the square**
- **perfect square trinomial,** *p. 601*

For an expression of the form $x^2 + bx$, you can add a constant c to the expression so that the expression $x^2 + bx + c$ is a perfect square trinomial. This process is called **completing the square**.

KEY CONCEPT *For Your Notebook*

Completing the Square

Words To complete the square for the expression $x^2 + bx$, add the square of half the coefficient of the term bx.

Algebra $x^2 + bx + \left(\frac{b}{2}\right)^2 = \left(x + \frac{b}{2}\right)^2$

EXAMPLE 1 Complete the square

Find the value of c that makes the expression $x^2 + 5x + c$ a perfect square trinomial. Then write the expression as the square of a binomial.

STEP 1 **Find** the value of c. For the expression to be a perfect square trinomial, c needs to be the square of half the coefficient of bx.

$c = \left(\frac{5}{2}\right)^2 = \frac{25}{4}$ Find the square of half the coefficient of bx.

STEP 2 **Write** the expression as a perfect square trinomial. Then write the expression as the square of a binomial.

$x^2 + 5x + c = x^2 + 5x + \frac{25}{4}$ Substitute $\frac{25}{4}$ for c.

$= \left(x + \frac{5}{2}\right)^2$ Square of a binomial

GUIDED PRACTICE for Example 1

Find the value of c that makes the expression a perfect square trinomial. Then write the expression as the square of a binomial.

1. $x^2 + 8x + c$ **16; $(x + 4)^2$**
2. $x^2 - 12x + c$ **36; $(x - 6)^2$**
3. $x^2 + 3x + c$ **$\frac{9}{4}$; $\left(x + \frac{3}{2}\right)^2$**

1 PLAN AND PREPARE

Warm-Up Exercises

Transparency Available

Evaluate the expression.

1. $\left(\frac{2}{3}\right)^2$ **$\frac{4}{9}$**
2. $\left(\frac{7}{5}\right)^2$ **$\frac{49}{25}$**
3. An acorn falls to the ground from a height of 25 feet. How long was the acorn in the air? **1.25 sec**

Notetaking Guide

Transparency Available

Promotes interactive learning and notetaking skills.

Pacing

Basic: 2 days
Average: 2 days
Advanced: 2 days
Block: 0.5 block with 10.4
0.5 block with 10.6
- See *Teaching Guide/Lesson Plan*.

2 FOCUS AND MOTIVATE

Essential Question

Big Idea 2, p. 627

How do you solve a quadratic equation by completing the square?
Tell students they will learn how to answer this question by adding a value to each side of the equation so one side is a perfect square trinomial.

NCTM STANDARDS

Standard 2: Understand patterns; Analyze situations using algebraic symbols

Resource Planning Guide

Chapter Resource Book
- Teaching Guide/Lesson Plan
- Practice levels A, B, C
- Study Guide
- Catch-up for Absent Students
- Application
- Challenge

Workbooks
- Notetaking Guide
- Practice Workbook

Teaching Options
- **Power Presentations** provides dynamic electronic teaching resources for the classroom.
- **Activity Generator** provides editable activities for all ability levels.

Interactive Technology
- Easy Planner
- Power Presentations
- Activity Generator
- Animated Algebra
- Test Generator
- Online Quiz
- eWorkbook
- eEdition
- @HomeTutor

Resources for English Learners
- Spanish Study Guide
- Multi-Language Visual Glossary
- Student Resources in Spanish

See also the *Differentiated Instruction Resources* for more strategies for meeting individual needs.

Motivating the Lesson

You want to put a mat frame around a photograph. You know the outside dimensions of the mat and you know the area of the photograph. You can write an equation to model this situation, and solve it to find the width of the mat frame.

3 TEACH

Extra Example 1

Find the value of c that makes the expression $x^2 + 7x + c$ a perfect square trinomial. Then write the expression as the square of a binomial. $\frac{49}{4}$; $\left(x + \frac{7}{2}\right)^2$

Key Question to Ask for Example 1

- What is a perfect square trinomial? **A perfect square trinomial can be written in the form of $(a + b)^2$ or $(a - b)^2$.**

Extra Example 2

Solve $x^2 + 6x = 7$ by completing the square. **$(x + 3)^2 = 16$; $-7, 1$**

Key Question to Ask for Example 2

- What is the value of $\left(\frac{b}{2}\right)^2$? **64**

Extra Example 3

Solve $3x^2 + 12x - 18 = 0$ by completing the square. **$(x + 2)^2 = 10$; $-2 + \sqrt{10} \approx 1.16$, $-2 - \sqrt{10} \approx -5.16$**

SOLVING EQUATIONS The method of completing the square can be used to solve any quadratic equation. To use completing the square to solve a quadratic equation, you must write the equation in the form $x^2 + bx = d$.

EXAMPLE 2 Solve a quadratic equation

Solve $x^2 - 16x = -15$ by completing the square.

Solution

$x^2 - 16x = -15$	**Write original equation.**
$x^2 - 16x + (-8)^2 = -15 + (-8)^2$	**Add $\left(\frac{-16}{2}\right)^2$, or $(-8)^2$, to each side.**
$(x - 8)^2 = -15 + (-8)^2$	**Write left side as the square of a binomial.**
$(x - 8)^2 = 49$	**Simplify the right side.**
$x - 8 = \pm 7$	**Take square roots of each side.**
$x = 8 \pm 7$	**Add 8 to each side.**

▶ The solutions of the equation are $8 + 7 = 15$ and $8 - 7 = 1$.

AVOID ERRORS
When completing the square to solve an equation, be sure you add the term $\left(\frac{b}{2}\right)^2$ to both sides of the equation.

CHECK You can check the solutions in the original equation.

If $x = 15$:	**If $x = 1$:**
$(15)^2 - 16(15) \stackrel{?}{=} -15$	$(1)^2 - 16(1) \stackrel{?}{=} -15$
$-15 = -15$ ✓	$-15 = -15$ ✓

EXAMPLE 3 Solve a quadratic equation in standard form

Solve $2x^2 + 20x - 8 = 0$ by completing the square.

Solution

$2x^2 + 20x - 8 = 0$	**Write original equation.**
$2x^2 + 20x = 8$	**Add 8 to each side.**
$x^2 + 10x = 4$	**Divide each side by 2.**
$x^2 + 10x + 5^2 = 4 + 5^2$	**Add $\left(\frac{10}{2}\right)^2$, or 5^2, to each side.**
$(x + 5)^2 = 29$	**Write left side as the square of a binomial.**
$x + 5 = \pm\sqrt{29}$	**Take square roots of each side.**
$x = -5 \pm \sqrt{29}$	**Subtract 5 from each side.**

▶ The solutions are $-5 + \sqrt{29} \approx 0.39$ and $-5 - \sqrt{29} \approx -10.39$.

AVOID ERRORS
Be sure that the coefficient of x^2 is 1 before you complete the square.

GUIDED PRACTICE for Examples 2 and 3

Solve the equation by completing the square. Round your solutions to the nearest hundredth, if necessary.

4. $x^2 - 2x = 3$ **$-1, 3$**

5. $m^2 + 10m = -8$ **$-9.12, -0.88$**

6. $3g^2 - 24g + 27 = 0$ **$1.35, 6.65$**

Differentiated Instruction

Below Level The exercises in this lesson provides numerous places where students can make calculation errors, so encourage them to use their graphing calculators to check their solutions. After they enter and graph an equation, have them check the x-intercepts or the zeros of the function. If the solutions do not check, have them go over their calculations to discover and correct the error. Encourage students to think of their graphing calculators as a way to check their answers and to find and correct errors.

See also the *Differentiated Instruction Resources* for more strategies.

EXAMPLE 4 Solve a multi-step problem

CRAFTS You decide to use chalkboard paint to create a chalkboard on a door. You want the chalkboard to have a uniform border as shown. You have enough chalkboard paint to cover 6 square feet. Find the width of the border to the nearest inch.

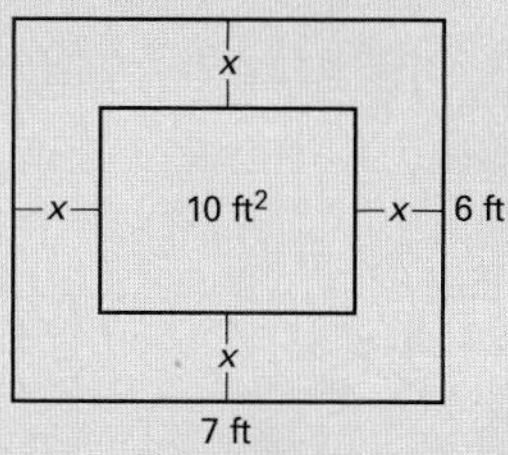

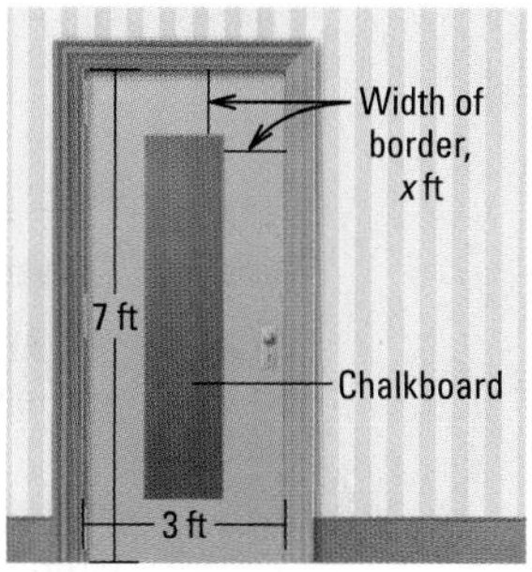

Solution

STEP 1 **Write** a verbal model. Then write an equation. Let x be the width (in feet) of the border.

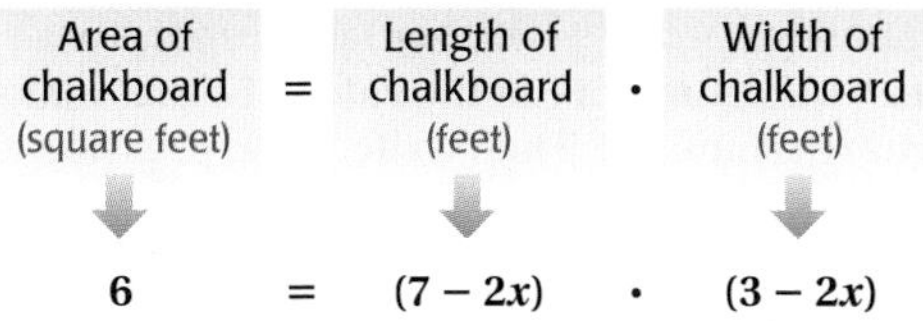

$$6 = (7 - 2x) \cdot (3 - 2x)$$

WRITE EQUATION
The width of the border is subtracted twice because it is at the top and the bottom of the door, as well as at the left and the right.

STEP 2 **Solve** the equation.

$6 = (7 - 2x)(3 - 2x)$ **Write equation.**

$6 = 21 - 20x + 4x^2$ **Multiply binomials.**

$-15 = 4x^2 - 20x$ **Subtract 21 from each side.**

$-\frac{15}{4} = x^2 - 5x$ **Divide each side by 4.**

$-\frac{15}{4} + \frac{25}{4} = x^2 - 5x + \frac{25}{4}$ **Add $\left(-\frac{5}{2}\right)^2$, or $\frac{25}{4}$, to each side.**

$-\frac{15}{4} + \frac{25}{4} = \left(x - \frac{5}{2}\right)^2$ **Write right side as the square of a binomial.**

$\frac{5}{2} = \left(x - \frac{5}{2}\right)^2$ **Simplify left side.**

$\pm\sqrt{\frac{5}{2}} = x - \frac{5}{2}$ **Take square roots of each side.**

$\frac{5}{2} \pm \sqrt{\frac{5}{2}} = x$ **Add $\frac{5}{2}$ to each side.**

The solutions of the equation are $\frac{5}{2} + \sqrt{\frac{5}{2}} \approx 4.08$ and $\frac{5}{2} - \sqrt{\frac{5}{2}} \approx 0.92$.

It is not possible for the width of the border to be 4.08 feet because the width of the door is 3 feet. So, the width of the border is 0.92 foot. Convert 0.92 foot to inches.

$0.92 \text{ ft} \cdot \frac{12 \text{ in.}}{1 \text{ ft}} = 11.04$ in. **Multiply by conversion factor.**

▶ The width of the border should be about 11 inches.

✓ GUIDED PRACTICE for Example 4

7. **WHAT IF?** In Example 4, suppose you have enough chalkboard paint to cover 4 square feet. Find the width of the border to the nearest inch. **13 in.**

Extra Example 4

You are designing an herb garden with a uniform border of ornamental grass around it as shown. Your design includes 10 square feet for the herb garden. Find the width of the grass border to the nearest inch. **20 in.**

(Figure: outer rectangle 7 ft by 6 ft; inner rectangle 10 ft^2; border width x on each side.)

Key Questions to Ask for Example 4

- Why do you divide each side of the equation by 4? **You want the leading coefficient to be 1.**
- How can you check that your solution is correct? **You can substitute the solution for x in the original equation.**

Closing the Lesson

Have students summarize the major points of the lesson and answer the Essential Question: How do you solve a quadratic equation by completing the square?

- **Starting with an expression in the form $x^2 + bx$, you can add a constant $c = \left(\frac{b}{2}\right)^2$ to the expression so that $x^2 + bx + c$ is a perfect square trinomial.**

To complete the square, write the equation in the form $x^2 + bx = d$. Add $\left(\frac{b}{2}\right)^2$ to each side so that one side is $x^2 + bx + \left(\frac{b}{2}\right)^2$ or $\left(x + \frac{b}{2}\right)^2$. Then take the square root of each side and solve for x.

Differentiated Instruction

Kinesthetic Learners As you begin **Example 4**, have students sketch scale models of the chalkboard using 1 inch equal to 1 foot. Then have them vary the width of the border and calculate the corresponding areas. This will help students get an idea of what the width of the border should be.

See also the *Differentiated Instruction Resources* for more strategies.

4 PRACTICE AND APPLY

Assignment Guide

Answer Transparencies available for all exercises

Basic:
Day 1: EP p. 946 Exs. 13–18
pp. 666–668
Exs. 1–23
Day 2: pp. 666–668
Exs. 24–33, 45–48, 52–64 even

Average:
Day 1: pp. 666–668
Exs. 1, 2, 5–11, 15–23, 28–33
Day 2: pp. 666–668
Exs. 24–27, 34–42, 45–50, 55–58, 62

Advanced:
Day 1: pp. 666–668
Exs. 1, 7–11, 18–25, 28–36
Day 2: pp. 666–668
Exs. 37–51*, 56, 57, 60, 63, 64

Block:
pp. 666–668
Exs. 1, 2, 5–11, 15–23, 28–33 (with 10.4)
pp. 666–668
Exs. 24–27, 34–42, 45–50, 55–58, 62 (with 10.6)

Differentiated Instruction

See *Differentiated Instruction Resources* for suggestions on addressing the needs of a diverse classroom.

Homework Check

For a quick check of student understanding of key concepts, go over the following exercises:

Basic: 6, 14, 17, 28, 45
Average: 8, 18, 21, 34, 46
Advanced: 10, 20, 22, 38, 46

Extra Practice

- Student Edition, p. 947
- Chapter Resource Book: Practice levels A, B, C

Practice Worksheet

An easily-readable reduced practice page (with answers) for this lesson can be found on p. 626C.

10.5 EXERCISES

HOMEWORK KEY
○ = **WORKED-OUT SOLUTIONS** on p. WS24 for Exs. 19 and 47
★ = **STANDARDIZED TEST PRACTICE** Exs. 2, 24, 25, 42, and 49
◆ = **MULTIPLE REPRESENTATIONS** Ex. 47

SKILL PRACTICE

A

1. **VOCABULARY** Copy and complete: The process of writing an expression of the form $x^2 + bx$ as a perfect square trinomial is called __?__. **completing the square**

2. ★ **WRITING** Give an example of an expression that is a perfect square trinomial. *Explain* why the expression is a perfect square trinomial.
Sample answer: $x^2 + 14x + 49$**; when factored, it is the square of a binomial:** $(x + 7)^2$.

EXAMPLE 1 on p. 663 for Exs. 3–11

COMPLETING THE SQUARE Find the value of c that makes the expression a perfect square trinomial. Then write the expression as the square of a binomial.

3. $x^2 + 6x + c$ **9;** $(x + 3)^2$
4. $x^2 + 12x + c$ **36;** $(x + 6)^2$
5. $x^2 - 4x + c$ **4;** $(x - 2)^2$
6. $x^2 - 8x + c$ **16;** $(x - 4)^2$
7. $x^2 - 3x + c$ $\frac{9}{4}$; $\left(x - \frac{3}{2}\right)^2$
8. $x^2 + 5x + c$ $\frac{25}{4}$; $\left(x + \frac{5}{2}\right)^2$
9. $x^2 + 2.4x + c$ **1.44;** $(x + 1.2)^2$
10. $x^2 - \frac{1}{2}x + c$ $\frac{1}{16}$; $\left(x - \frac{1}{4}\right)^2$
11. $x^2 - \frac{4}{3}x + c$ $\frac{4}{9}$; $\left(x - \frac{2}{3}\right)^2$

EXAMPLES 2 and 3 on p. 664 for Exs. 12–27

SOLVING EQUATIONS Solve the equation by completing the square. Round your solutions to the nearest hundredth, if necessary.

12. $x^2 + 2x = 3$ **−3, 1**
13. $x^2 + 10x = 24$ **−12, 2**
14. $c^2 - 14c = 15$ **−1, 15**
15. $n^2 - 6n = 72$ **−6, 12**
16. $a^2 - 8a + 15 = 0$ **3, 5**
17. $y^2 + 4y - 21 = 0$ **−7, 3**
18. $w^2 - 5w = \frac{11}{4}$ **−0.5, 5.5**
19. $z^2 + 11z = -\frac{21}{4}$ **−10.5, −0.5**
20. $g^2 - \frac{2}{3}g = 7$ **−2.33, 3**
21. $k^2 - 8k - 7 = 0$ **−0.80, 8.80**
22. $v^2 - 7v + 1 = 0$ **0.15, 6.85**
23. $m^2 + 3m + \frac{5}{4} = 0$ **−2.5, −0.5**

24. ★ **MULTIPLE CHOICE** What are the solutions of $4x^2 + 16x = 9$? **C**

Ⓐ $-\frac{1}{2}, -\frac{9}{2}$ Ⓑ $-\frac{1}{2}, \frac{9}{2}$ Ⓒ $\frac{1}{2}, -\frac{9}{2}$ Ⓓ $\frac{1}{2}, \frac{9}{2}$

25. ★ **MULTIPLE CHOICE** What are the solutions of $x^2 + 12x + 10 = 0$? **B**

Ⓐ $-6 \pm \sqrt{46}$ Ⓑ $-6 \pm \sqrt{26}$ Ⓒ $6 \pm \sqrt{26}$ Ⓓ $6 \pm \sqrt{46}$

ERROR ANALYSIS ***Describe*** **and correct the error in solving the given equation.** **26, 27. See margin.**

26. $x^2 - 14x = 11$

$$x^2 - 14x = 11$$
$$x^2 - 14x + 49 = 11$$
$$(x - 7)^2 = 11$$
$$x - 7 = \pm\sqrt{11}$$
$$x = 7 \pm \sqrt{11}$$

27. $x^2 - 2x - 4 = 0$

$$x^2 - 2x - 4 = 0$$
$$x^2 - 2x = 4$$
$$x^2 - 2x + 1 = 4 + 1$$
$$(x + 1)^2 = 5$$
$$x + 1 = \pm\sqrt{5}$$
$$x = 1 \pm \sqrt{5}$$

26. When completing the square, you must add the same number to each side of the equation, not just to the side of the equation for which you complete the square; $x^2 - 14x + 49 = 11 + 49$, $(x - 7)^2 = 60$, $x - 7 = \pm\sqrt{60}$, $x = 7 \pm \sqrt{60}$.

27. The perfect square trinomial $x^2 - 2x + 1$ **factors as** $(x - 1)^2$ **not** $(x + 1)^2$; $(x - 1)^2 = 5$, $x - 1 = \pm\sqrt{5}$, $x = 1 \pm \sqrt{5}$.

31. −1.91, 0.91
32. −3.67, −0.33
33. −0.96, 6.96
34. −0.30, 12.30
35. 0.79, 2.21
36. −0.65, 4.65

B **SOLVING EQUATIONS** **Solve the equation by completing the square. Round your solutions to the nearest hundredth, if necessary.**

28. $2x^2 - 8x - 14 = 0$ **−1.32, 5.32**
29. $2x^2 + 24x + 10 = 0$ **−11.57, −0.43**
30. $3x^2 - 48x + 39 = 0$ **0.86, 15.14**

31. $4y^2 + 4y - 7 = 0$
32. $9n^2 + 36n + 11 = 0$
33. $3w^2 - 18w - 20 = 0$

34. $3p^2 - 30p - 11 = 6p$
35. $3a^2 - 12a + 3 = -a^2 - 4$
36. $15c^2 - 51c - 30 = 9c + 15$

37. $7m^2 + 24m - 2 = m^2 - 9$ **−3.68, −0.32**
38. $g^2 + 2g + 0.4 = 0.9g^2 + g$ **−9.58, −0.42**
39. $11z^2 - 10z - 3 = -9z^2 + \frac{3}{4}$ **−0.25, 0.75**

GEOMETRY **Find the value of x. Round your answer to the nearest hundredth, if necessary.**

40. Area of triangle = 108 m^2 **12**

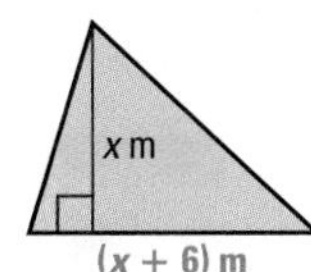

41. Area of rectangle = 288 $in.^2$ **4.87**

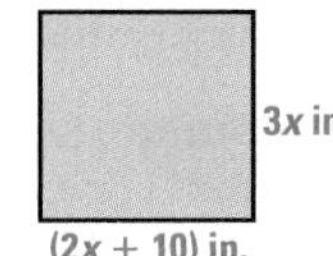

42. ★ **WRITING** How many solutions does $x^2 + bx = c$ have if $c < -\left(\frac{b}{2}\right)^2$? *Explain.* **See margin.**

C **43. CHALLENGE** The product of two consecutive negative integers is 210. Find the integers. **−15, −14**

44. CHALLENGE The product of two consecutive positive even integers is 288. Find the integers. **16, 18**

PROBLEM SOLVING

EXAMPLE 4 on p. 665 for Exs. 45–46

A **45. LANDSCAPING** You are building a rectangular brick patio surrounded by crushed stone in a rectangular courtyard as shown. The crushed stone border has a uniform width x (in feet). You have enough money in your budget to purchase patio bricks to cover 140 square feet. Solve the equation $140 = (20 - 2x)(16 - 2x)$ to find the width of the border. **3 ft**

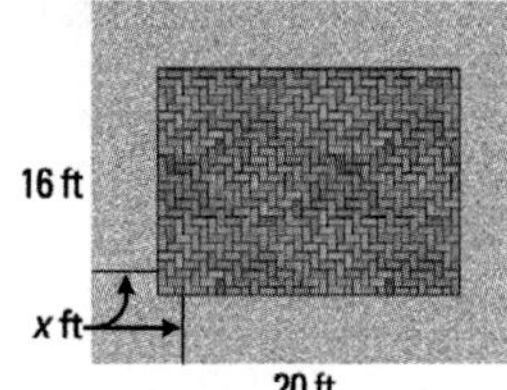

@HomeTutor for problem solving help at classzone.com

46. TRAFFIC ENGINEERING The distance d (in feet) that it takes a car to come to a complete stop on dry asphalt can be modeled by $d = 0.05s^2 + 1.1s$ where s is the speed of the car (in miles per hour). A car has 78 feet to come to a complete stop. Find the maximum speed at which the car can travel. **30 mi/h**

@HomeTutor for problem solving help at classzone.com

47. ◆ **MULTIPLE REPRESENTATIONS** For the period 1985–2001, the average salary y (in thousands of dollars) per season of a Major League Baseball player can be modeled by $y = 7x^2 - 4x + 392$ where x is the number of years since 1985.

a. **Solving an Equation** Write and solve an equation to find the year when the average salary was \$1,904,000. $\mathbf{1904 = 7x^2 - 4x + 392}$**, 2000**

b. **Drawing a Graph** Use a graph to check your solution to part (a). **See margin.**

Avoiding Common Errors

Exercises 12–25, 28–39 Watch for students who add the term $\left(\frac{b}{2}\right)^2$ to one side of the equation only. Stress to students that they must add the term to each side in order to write an equivalent equation.

An **Animated Algebra** activity is available online for **Exercise 50.** This activity is also part of **Power Presentations**.

Study Strategy

Exercise 51 Suggest to students that they draw a diagram to help them visualize the solution to this problem.

42. Zero; $\left(\frac{b}{2}\right)^2$ is always positive, so if $c < -\left(\frac{b}{2}\right)^2$, c must be a negative number whose absolute value is greater than $\left(\frac{b}{2}\right)^2$. Then $c + \left(\frac{b}{2}\right)^2$ will simplify to a negative number, implying that $\left(x + \frac{b}{2}\right)^2 = c + \left(\frac{b}{2}\right)^2$ has no solution.

47b.

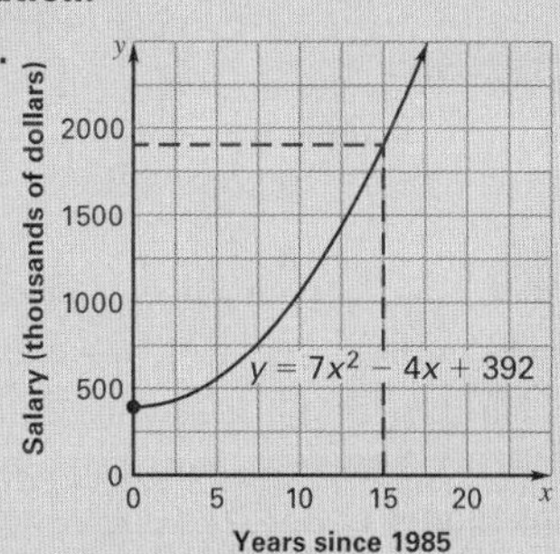

When $y \approx 1904$, the value of x is about 15. So, the year 2000 (1985 + 15) found in part (a) is correct.

5 ASSESS AND RETEACH

Daily Homework Quiz

Transparency Available

Solve the equation by completing the square. Round to the nearest hundredth, if necessary.

1. $x^2 + 12x = 28$ **−14, 2**
2. $m^2 - 8m = 12$ **−1.29, 9.29**
3. What is the width of the border that surrounds this poster? **1 in.**

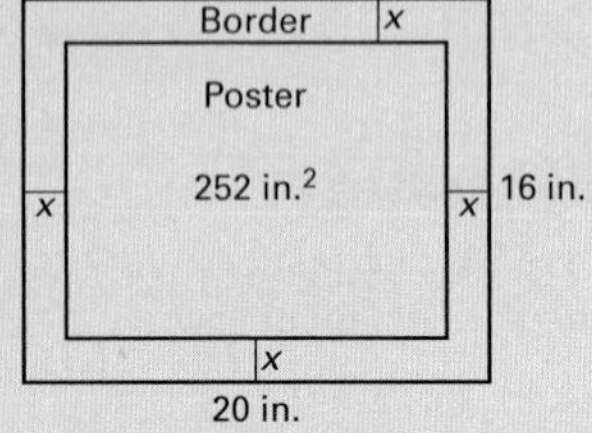

Available at **classzone.com**

Diagnosis/Remediation

- Practice A, B, C in Chapter Resource Book
- Study Guide in Chapter Resource Book
- Practice Workbook
- @HomeTutor

Challenge

Additional challenge is available in the Chapter Resource Book.

49. Yes; to find the number of days *x* after which the stock price was \$23.50 per share, substitute 23.5 for *y* and solve for *x* by completing the square to find that the solutions are 10 and 30. You could have sold the stock for \$23.50 per share 10 days after you purchased it.

B **48. MULTI-STEP PROBLEM** You have 80 feet of fencing to make a rectangular horse pasture that covers 750 square feet. A barn will be used as one side of the pasture as shown.

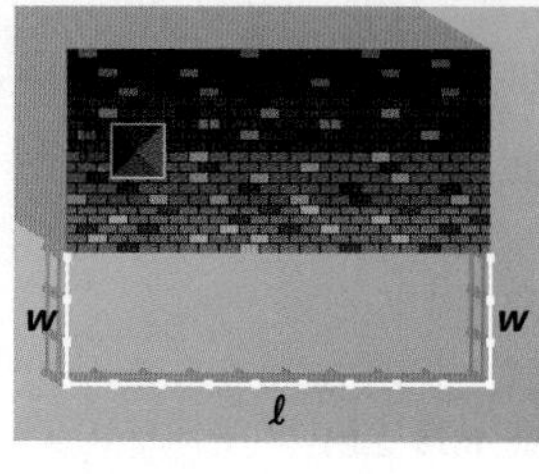

a. Write equations for the perimeter and area of the pasture. **$\ell + 2w = 80$, $\ell w = 750$**

b. Use substitution to solve the system of equations from part (a). What are the possible dimensions of the pasture? **length: 50 ft, width: 15 ft; length: 30 ft, width: 25 ft**

49. ★ SHORT RESPONSE You purchase stock for \$16 per share, and you sell the stock 30 days later for \$23.50 per share. The price y (in dollars) of a share during the 30 day period can be modeled by $y = -0.025x^2 + x + 16$ where x is the number of days after the stock is purchased. Could you have sold the stock earlier for \$23.50 per share? *Explain.* **See margin.**

50. SNOWBOARDING During a "big air" competition, snowboarders launch themselves from a half pipe, perform tricks in the air, and land back in the half pipe.

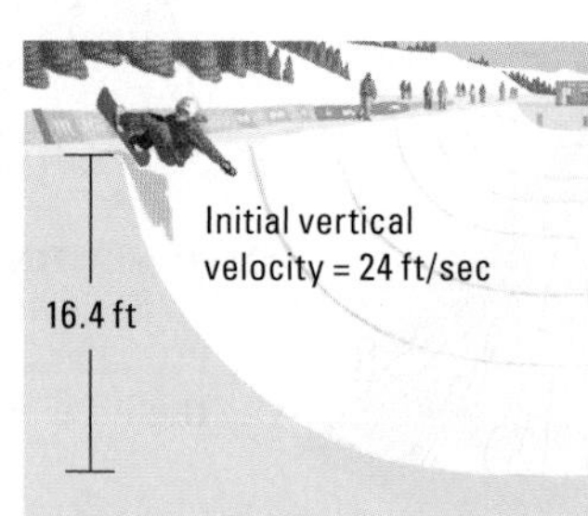

Cross section of a half pipe

a. **Model** Use the vertical motion model to write an equation that models the height h (in feet) of a snowboarder as a function of the time t (in seconds) she is in the air. **$h = -16t^2 + 24t + 16.4$**

b. **Apply** How long is the snowboarder in the air if she lands 13.2 feet above the base of the half pipe? Round your answer to the nearest tenth of a second. **about 1.6 sec**

Algebra at classzone.com

C **51. CHALLENGE** You are knitting a rectangular scarf. The pattern you have created will result in a scarf that has a length of 60 inches and a width of 4 inches. However, you happen to have enough yarn to cover an area of 480 square inches. You decide to increase the dimensions of the scarf so that all of your yarn will be used. If the increase in the length is 10 times the increase in the width, what will the dimensions of the scarf be? **length: 80 in., width: 6 in.**

MIXED REVIEW

PREVIEW Prepare for Lesson 10.6 in Exs. 52–57.

Evaluate the expression for the given value of *x*. *(p. 74)*

52. $3 + x - 6$; $x = 8$ **5**
53. $11 - (-x) + 15$; $x = -1$ **25**
54. $-x + 18 - 20$; $x = -10$ **8**
55. $32 - x - 5$; $x = 5$ **22**
56. $x + 14.7 - 16.2$; $x = 2.3$ **0.8**
57. $-9.2 - (-11.4) - x$; $x = -4.5$ **6.7**

Solve the proportion. *(p. 168)*

58. $\frac{8}{m-3} = \frac{4}{3}$ **9**
59. $\frac{3}{a} = \frac{5}{a+5}$ **$\frac{15}{2}$**
60. $\frac{c+2}{6} = \frac{2c-3}{5}$ **4**

Solve the equation.

61. $(x-4)(x+9) = 0$ *(p. 575)* **−9, 4**
62. $x^2 - 15x + 26 = 0$ *(p. 583)* **2, 13**
63. $3x^2 + 10x + 7 = 0$ *(p. 593)* **$-2\frac{1}{3}$, −1**
64. $4x^2 - 20x + 25 = 0$ *(p. 600)* **$2\frac{1}{2}$**

EXTRA PRACTICE for Lesson 10.5, p. 947 **ONLINE QUIZ** at classzone.com

Graph Quadratic Functions in Vertex Form

GOAL Graph quadratic functions in vertex form.

Key Vocabulary
- vertex form

In Lesson 10.2, you graphed quadratic functions in standard form. Quadratic functions can also be written in **vertex form**, $y = a(x - h)^2 + k$ where $a \neq 0$. In this form, the vertex of the graph can be easily determined.

KEY CONCEPT *For Your Notebook*

Graph of Vertex Form $y = a(x - h)^2 + k$

The graph of $y = a(x - h)^2 + k$ is the graph of $y = ax^2$ translated h units horizontally and k units vertically.

Characteristics of the graph of $y = a(x - h)^2 + k$:

- The vertex is (h, k).
- The axis of symmetry is $x = h$.
- The graph opens up if $a > 0$, and the graph opens down if $a < 0$.

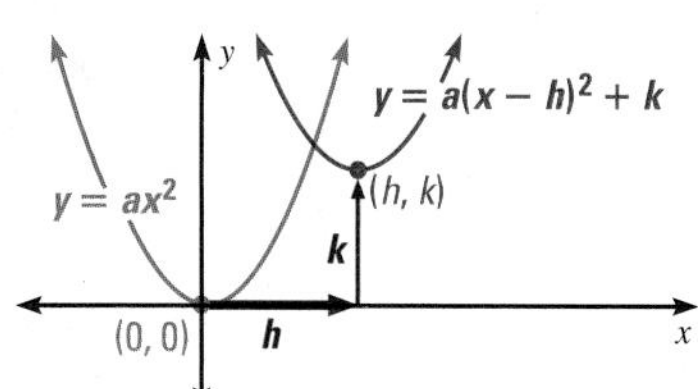

EXAMPLE 1 Graph a quadratic function in vertex form

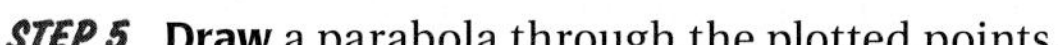

Graph $y = -(x + 2)^2 + 3$.

Solution

STEP 1 **Identify** the values of a, h, and k: $a = -1$, $h = -2$, and $k = 3$. Because $a < 0$, the parabola opens down.

STEP 2 **Draw** the axis of symmetry, $x = -2$.

STEP 3 **Plot** the vertex $(h, k) = (-2, 3)$.

STEP 4 **Plot** four points. Evaluate the function for two x-values less than the x-coordinate of the vertex.

$x = -3$: $y = -(-3 + 2)^2 + 3 = 2$

$x = -5$: $y = -(-5 + 2)^2 + 3 = -6$

Plot the points $(-3, 2)$ and $(-5, -6)$ and their reflections, $(-1, 2)$ and $(1, -6)$, in the axis of symmetry.

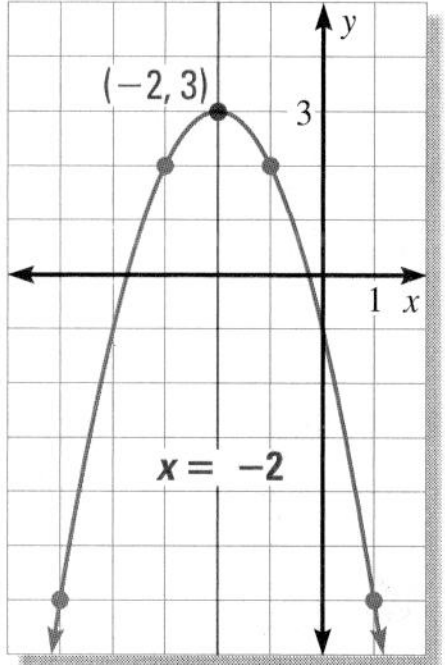

STEP 5 **Draw** a parabola through the plotted points.

1 PLAN AND PREPARE

Warm-Up Exercises

1. Find the axis of symmetry and vertex of the graph of $y = -x^2 + 2x + 1$. $x = 1$; $(1, 2)$
2. Graph $y = -2x^2 + 4x + 1$.

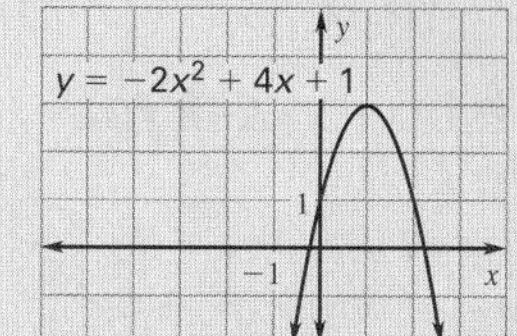

2 FOCUS AND MOTIVATE

Essential Question

Big Idea 1, p. 627

How do you graph a quadratic function in vertex form? **Tell students they will learn how to answer this question by using the vertex form of a quadratic to identify the axis of symmetry, the vertex, and other points.**

3 TEACH

Extra Example 1

Graph $y = (x + 1)^2 - 1$.

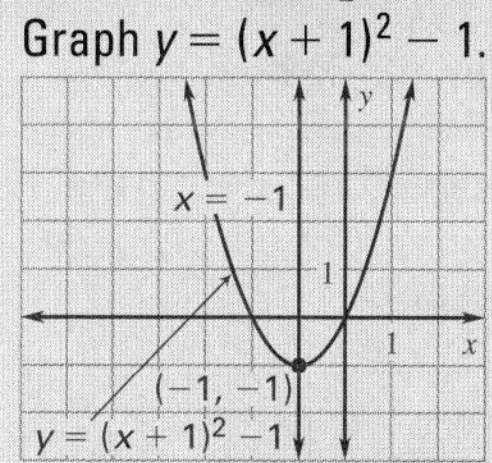

NCTM STANDARDS

Standard 2: Analyze situations using algebraic symbols

Standard 3: Use symmetry to analyze math situations

Extra Example 2

Graph $y = x^2 - 6x + 5$ by writing it in vertex form. $y = (x - 3)^2 - 4$

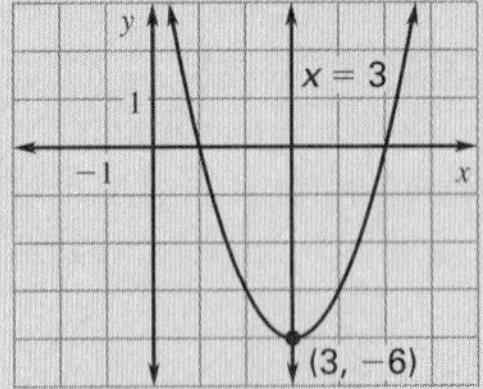

Key Question to Ask for Example 2

- Why is $h = 4$? Why is $k = 5$? **Comparing $y = (x - h)^2 + k$ and $y = (x - 4)^2 - 5$, you get $h = 4$ and $k = -5$.**

Closing the Lesson

Have students summarize the major points of the lesson and answer the Essential Question: How do you graph a quadratic function in intercept form?

- **The vertex form of a quadratic function is $y = a(x - h)^2 + k$. The vertex is (h, k). The axis of symmetry is $x = h$.**

If necessary, use the method of completing the square to write the function in vertex form. Determine whether the parabola opens up or down. Use the value of h to draw the axis of symmetry, and use the values of h and k to plot the vertex. Evaluate the function for two x-values to the left of the vertex, and use symmetry to find corresponding points to the right of the vertex. Draw a parabola through the points.

4 PRACTICE AND APPLY

Avoiding Common Errors

Exercises 1–12 Some students forget to use the sign of the leading coefficient. Remind students that if $a < 0$ the parabola opens down, and if $a > 0$ the parabola opens up.

1–12. See Additional Answers beginning on p. AA1.

EXAMPLE 2 Graph a quadratic function

Graph $y = x^2 - 8x + 11$.

Solution

STEP 1 **Write** the function in vertex form by completing the square.

$y = x^2 - 8x + 11$	**Write original function.**
$y + \square = (x^2 - 8x + \square) + 11$	**Prepare to complete the square.**
$y + 16 = (x^2 - 8x + 16) + 11$	**Add $\left(\frac{-8}{2}\right)^2 = (-4)^2 = 16$ to each side.**
$y + 16 = (x - 4)^2 + 11$	**Write $x^2 - 8x + 16$ as a square of a binomial.**
$y = (x - 4)^2 - 5$	**Subtract 16 from each side.**

STEP 2 **Identify** the values of a, h, and k: $a = 1$, $h = 4$, and $k = -5$. Because $a > 0$, the parabola opens up.

STEP 3 **Draw** the axis of symmetry, $x = 4$.

STEP 4 **Plot** the vertex $(h, k) = (4, -5)$.

STEP 5 **Plot** four more points. Evaluate the function for two x-values less than the x-coordinate of the vertex.

$x = 3$: $y = (3 - 4)^2 - 5 = -4$
$x = 1$: $y = (1 - 4)^2 - 5 = 4$

Plot the points $(3, -4)$ and $(1, 4)$ and their reflections, $(5, -4)$ and $(7, 4)$, in the axis of symmetry.

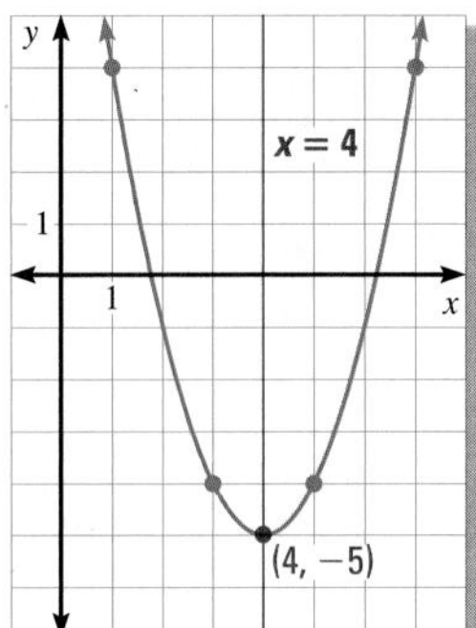

STEP 6 **Draw** a parabola through the plotted points.

PRACTICE

EXAMPLE 1 on p. 669 for Exs. 1–6

Graph the quadratic function. Label the vertex and axis of symmetry. **1–6. See margin.**

1. $y = (x + 2)^2 - 5$
2. $y = -(x - 4)^2 + 1$
3. $y = x^2 + 3$
4. $y = 3(x - 1)^2 - 2$
5. $y = -2(x + 5)^2 - 2$
6. $y = -\frac{1}{2}(x + 4)^2 + 4$

EXAMPLE 2 on p. 670 for Exs. 7–12

Write the function in vertex form, then graph the function. Label the vertex and axis of symmetry. **7–12. See margin.**

7. $y = x^2 - 12x + 36$
8. $y = x^2 + 8x + 15$
9. $y = -x^2 + 10x - 21$
10. $y = 2x^2 - 12x + 19$
11. $y = -3x^2 - 6x - 1$
12. $y = -\frac{1}{2}x^2 - 6x - 21$

13. Write an equation in vertex form of the parabola shown. Use the coordinates of the vertex and the coordinates of a point on the graph to write the equation. $y = \frac{1}{4}(x + 6)^2 + 1$

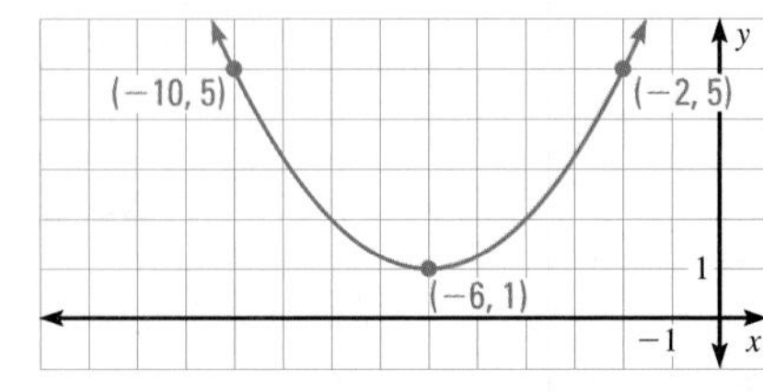

10.6 Solve Quadratic Equations by the Quadratic Formula

Before You solved quadratic equations by completing the square.

Now You will solve quadratic equations using the quadratic formula.

Why? So you can solve a problem about film production, as in Example 3.

Key Vocabulary
- **quadratic formula**

By completing the square for the quadratic equation $ax^2 + bx + c = 0$, you can develop a formula that gives the solutions of any quadratic equation in standard form. This formula is called the **quadratic formula**. (The quadratic formula is developed on page 727.)

KEY CONCEPT *For Your Notebook*

The Quadratic Formula

The solutions of the quadratic equation $ax^2 + bx + c = 0$ are

$x = \frac{-b \pm \sqrt{b^2 - 4ac}}{2a}$ where $a \neq 0$ and $b^2 - 4ac \geq 0$.

EXAMPLE 1 **Standardized Test Practice**

What are the solutions of $3x^2 + 5x = 8$?

Ⓐ -1 and $-\frac{8}{3}$ Ⓑ -1 and $\frac{8}{3}$ Ⓒ 1 and $-\frac{8}{3}$ Ⓓ 1 and $\frac{8}{3}$

ANOTHER WAY
Instead of solving the equation, you can check the answer choices in the equation.

Solution

$3x^2 + 5x = 8$ **Write original equation.**

$3x^2 + 5x - 8 = 0$ **Write in standard form.**

$x = \frac{-b \pm \sqrt{b^2 - 4ac}}{2a}$ **Quadratic formula**

$x = \frac{-5 \pm \sqrt{5^2 - 4(3)(-8)}}{2(3)}$ **Substitute values in the quadratic formula: $a = 3$, $b = 5$, and $c = -8$.**

$= \frac{-5 \pm \sqrt{121}}{6}$ **Simplify.**

$= \frac{-5 \pm 11}{6}$ **Simplify the square root.**

The solutions of the equation are $\frac{-5 + 11}{6} = 1$ and $\frac{-5 - 11}{6} = -\frac{8}{3}$.

▶ The correct answer is C. Ⓐ Ⓑ Ⓒ Ⓓ

1 PLAN AND PREPARE

Warm-Up Exercises

Transparency Available

Evaluate the expression for the given value of x.

1. $15 - (-x) + 9$; $x = -2$ **22**

2. $14 - x + 3$; $x = 8$ **9**

3. A basketball is thrown in the air from a height of 6 feet with an initial vertical velocity of 40 feet per second. What is the height (in feet) of the ball after 2 seconds? **22 ft**

Notetaking Guide

Transparency Available

Promotes interactive learning and notetaking skills.

Pacing

Basic: 2 days
Average: 2 days
Advanced: 2 days
Block: 0.5 block with 10.5
0.5 block with 10.7

- See *Teaching Guide/Lesson Plan.*

2 FOCUS AND MOTIVATE

Essential Question

Big Idea 2, p. 627

How do you solve a quadratic equation using the quadratic formula? **Tell students they will learn how to answer this question by substituting values in the quadratic formula and then simplifying.**

NCTM STANDARDS

Standard 2: Analyze situations using algebraic symbols

Standard 8: Use the language of math to express ideas

Resource Planning Guide

Chapter Resource Book
- Teaching Guide/Lesson Plan
- Practice levels A, B, C
- Study Guide
- Catch-up for Absent Students
- Problem Solving Workshop
- Challenge

Workbooks
- Notetaking Guide
- Practice Workbook

Teaching Options
- **Power Presentations** provides dynamic electronic teaching resources for the classroom.
- **Activity Generator** provides editable activities for all ability levels.

Interactive Technology
- Easy Planner
- Power Presentations
- Activity Generator
- Animated Algebra
- Test Generator
- Online Quiz
- eWorkbook
- eEdition
- @HomeTutor

Resources for English Learners
- Spanish Study Guide
- Multi-Language Visual Glossary
- Student Resources in Spanish

See also the *Differentiated Instruction Resources* for more strategies for meeting individual needs.

Motivating the Lesson

Ask students how they would solve a quadratic equation such as $0.5x^2 - 1.25x - 7.5 = 0$. Tell them that in this lesson they will learn how to use a formula to solve *any* quadratic equation.

3 TEACH

Extra Example 1

What are the solutions of $2x^2 + 7x = 9$? **B**

(A) -1 and $-\frac{9}{2}$ (B) 1 and $-\frac{9}{2}$

(C) -1 and $\frac{9}{2}$ (D) 1 and $\frac{9}{2}$

Extra Example 2

Use the quadratic formula to solve $3x^2 - 1 = x$. **$a = 3, b = -1, c = -1$; $\frac{1 + \sqrt{13}}{6} \approx 0.77, \frac{1 - \sqrt{13}}{6} \approx -0.43$**

An **Animated Algebra** activity is available online for **Example 2**. This activity is also part of **Power Presentations**.

Extra Example 3

For the period 1990–2003, the number of book titles published by a small publishing company can be modeled by the function $y = 0.5x^2 + 4x + 19$, where x is the number of years since 1990. In what year did the company publish 80 books? **almost 8 years after 1990, or during 1997**

EXAMPLE 2 Solve a quadratic equation

Solve $2x^2 - 7 = x$.

$2x^2 - 7 = x$ — **Write original equation.**

$2x^2 - x - 7 = 0$ — **Write in standard form.**

$x = \frac{-b \pm \sqrt{b^2 - 4ac}}{2a}$ — **Quadratic formula**

$= \frac{-(-1) \pm \sqrt{(-1)^2 - 4(2)(-7)}}{2(2)}$ — **Substitute values in the quadratic formula: $a = 2$, $b = -1$, and $c = -7$.**

$= \frac{1 \pm \sqrt{57}}{4}$ — **Simplify.**

▶ The solutions are $\frac{1 + \sqrt{57}}{4} \approx 2.14$ and $\frac{1 - \sqrt{57}}{4} \approx -1.64$.

Animated Algebra at classzone.com

CHECK Write the equation in standard form, $2x^2 - x - 7 = 0$. Then graph the related function $y = 2x^2 - x - 7$. The x-intercepts are about -1.6 and 2.1. So, each solution checks.

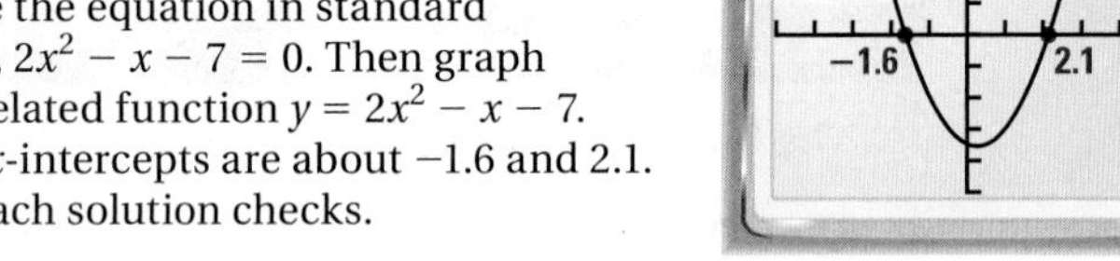

✓ GUIDED PRACTICE for Examples 1 and 2

Use the quadratic formula to solve the equation. Round your solutions to the nearest hundredth, if necessary.

1. $x^2 - 8x + 16 = 0$ **4**
2. $3n^2 - 5n = -1$ **0.23, 1.43**
3. $4z^2 = 7z + 2$ **−0.25, 2**

EXAMPLE 3 Use the quadratic formula

FILM PRODUCTION For the period 1971–2001, the number y of films produced in the world can be modeled by the function $y = 10x^2 - 94x + 3900$ where x is the number of years since 1971. In what year were 4200 films produced?

Solution

$y = 10x^2 - 94x + 3900$ — **Write function.**

$4200 = 10x^2 - 94x + 3900$ — **Substitute 4200 for y.**

$0 = 10x^2 - 94x - 300$ — **Write in standard form.**

$x = \frac{-(-94) \pm \sqrt{(-94)^2 - 4(10)(-300)}}{2(10)}$ — **Substitute values in the quadratic formula: $a = 10$, $b = -94$, and $c = -300$.**

$= \frac{94 \pm \sqrt{20,836}}{20}$ — **Simplify.**

The solutions of the equation are $\frac{94 + \sqrt{20,836}}{20} \approx 12$ and $\frac{94 - \sqrt{20,836}}{20} \approx -3$.

▶ There were 4200 films produced about 12 years after 1971, or in 1983.

INTERPRET SOLUTIONS The solution −3 can be ignored because −3 represents the year 1968, which is not in the given time period.

Differentiated Instruction

Visual Learners Students may find the quadratic formula easier to memorize by visualizing the graph of the quadratic function $y = ax^2 + bx + c$. Write the quadratic formula as $x = -\frac{b}{2a} \pm \frac{\sqrt{b^2 - 4ac}}{2a}$. Point out that $x = -\frac{b}{2a}$ is the axis of symmetry for the function $y = ax^2 + bx + c$ and the x-intercepts of the function are $\frac{\sqrt{b^2 - 4ac}}{2a}$ units to the left and right of the axis of symmetry.

See also the *Differentiated Instruction Resources* for more strategies.

GUIDED PRACTICE for Example 3

4. **WHAT IF?** In Example 3, find the year when 4750 films were produced. **1986**

CONCEPT SUMMARY *For Your Notebook*

Methods for Solving Quadratic Equations

Method	Lesson(s)	When to Use
Factoring	9.4–9.8	Use when a quadratic equation can be factored easily.
Graphing	10.3	Use when approximate solutions are adequate.
Finding square roots	10.4	Use when solving an equation that can be written in the form $x^2 = d$.
Completing the square	10.5	Can be used for *any* quadratic equation $ax^2 + bx + c = 0$ but is simplest to apply when $a = 1$ and b is an even number.
Quadratic formula	10.6	Can be used for *any* quadratic equation.

EXAMPLE 4 Choose a solution method

Tell what method you would use to solve the quadratic equation. ***Explain*** **your choice(s).**

a. $10x^2 - 7 = 0$ **b.** $x^2 + 4x = 0$ **c.** $5x^2 + 9x - 4 = 0$

Solution

a. The quadratic equation can be solved using square roots because the equation can be written in the form $x^2 = d$.

b. The equation can be solved by factoring because the expression $x^2 + 4x$ can be factored easily. Also, the equation can be solved by completing the square because the equation is of the form $ax^2 + bx + c = 0$ where $a = 1$ and b is an even number.

c. The quadratic equation cannot be factored easily, and completing the square will result in many fractions. So, the equation can be solved using the quadratic formula.

GUIDED PRACTICE for Example 4

Tell what method you would use to solve the quadratic equation. ***Explain*** **your choice(s).** **5–7. See margin.**

5. $x^2 + x - 6 = 0$ 6. $x^2 - 9 = 0$ 7. $x^2 + 6x = 5$

Key Question to Ask for Example 3

- Can you use the model to approximate the number of films for any particular year? Explain. **The model is based on data from 1971 through 2001. It may not be accurate for years prior to 1971 or after 2001.**

Extra Example 4

Tell what method you would use to solve the quadratic equation. *Explain* your choice(s).

a. $3x^2 + 14x + 13 = 0$
b. $9x^2 - 3 = 0$
c. $x^2 + 8x = 0$

a. The quadratic formula is best since the equation cannot be factored easily and completing the square would result in too many fractions.

b. The equation can be written in the form $x^2 = d$, so the easiest method is finding square roots.

c. You could use factoring because it can be factored easily, or you can use completing the square since a is 1 and b is even.

Closing the Lesson

Have students summarize the major points of the lesson and answer the Essential Question: How do you solve a quadratic equation using the quadratic formula?

- **For the general quadratic equation $ax^2 + bx + c = 0$, the quadratic formula is $x = \frac{-b \pm \sqrt{b^2 - 4ac}}{2a}$. Substitute values for a, b, and c into the quadratic formula, and then simplify.**

5. ***Sample answer:*** **Factoring, the expression $x^2 + x - 6$ factors easily.**

6. ***Sample answer:*** **Factoring, the expression $x^2 - 9$ factors easily; or using square roots, the equation can be written in the form $x^2 = d$.**

7. ***Sample answer:*** **Completing the square, the equation is of the form $ax^2 + bx = c$ where $a = 1$ and b is an even number; or quadratic formula, the equation does not factor easily.**

10.6 EXERCISES

HOMEWORK KEY
○ = **WORKED-OUT SOLUTIONS** on p. WS25 for Exs. 19 and 47
★ = **STANDARDIZED TEST PRACTICE** Exs. 2, 12, 25, and 50
◆ = **MULTIPLE REPRESENTATIONS** Ex. 49

SKILL PRACTICE

A

1. **VOCABULARY** What formula can be used to solve any quadratic equation? **quadratic formula**

2. ★ **WRITING** What method(s) would you use to solve $-x^2 + 8x = 1$? *Explain* your choice(s). **See margin.**

EXAMPLES 1 and 2 on pp. 671–672 for Exs. 3–27

SOLVING QUADRATIC EQUATIONS **Use the quadratic formula to find the roots of the equation. Round your solutions to the nearest hundredth, if necessary.**

3. $x^2 + 5x - 104 = 0$ **−13, 8**
4. $4x^2 - x - 18 = 0$ **−2, 2.25**
5. $6x^2 - 2x - 28 = 0$ **−2, 2.33**
6. $m^2 + 3m + 1 = 0$ **−2.62, −0.38**
7. $-z^2 + z + 14 = 0$ **−3.27, 4.27**
8. $-2n^2 - 5n + 16 = 0$ **−4.34, 1.84**
9. $4w^2 + 20w + 25 = 0$ **−2.5**
10. $2t^2 + 3t - 11 = 0$ **−3.21, 1.71**
11. $-6g^2 + 9g + 8 = 0$ **−0.63, 2.13**

12. ★ **MULTIPLE CHOICE** What are the solutions of $10x^2 - 3x - 1 = 0$? **B**

Ⓐ $-\frac{1}{5}$ and $-\frac{1}{2}$ Ⓑ $-\frac{1}{5}$ and $\frac{1}{2}$ Ⓒ $\frac{1}{5}$ and $-\frac{1}{2}$ Ⓓ $\frac{1}{5}$ and $\frac{1}{2}$

SOLVING QUADRATIC EQUATIONS **Use the quadratic formula to solve the equation. Round your solutions to the nearest hundredth, if necessary.**

13. $x^2 - 5x = 14$ **−2, 7**
14. $3x^2 - 4 = 11x$ **−0.33, 4**
15. $9 = 7x^2 - 2x$ **−1, 1.29**
16. $2m^2 + 9m + 7 = 3$ **−4, −0.5**
17. $-10 = r^2 - 10r + 12$ **3.27, 6.73**
18. $3g^2 - 6g - 14 = 3g$ **−1.13, 4.13**
19. $6z^2 = 2z^2 + 7z + 5$ **−0.54, 2.29**
20. $8h^2 + 8 = 6 - 9h$ **−0.82, −0.30**
21. $4t^2 - 3t = 5 - 3t^2$ **−0.66, 1.09**
22. $-4y^2 - 3y + 3 = 2y + 4$ **−1, −0.25**
23. $7n + 5 = -3n^2 + 2$ **−1.77, −0.57**
24. $5w^2 + 4 = w + 6$ **−0.54, 0.74**

25. ★ **MULTIPLE CHOICE** What are the solutions of $x^2 + 14x = 2x - 11$? **B**

Ⓐ −2 and −22 Ⓑ −1 and −11 Ⓒ 1 and 11 Ⓓ 2 and 22

ERROR ANALYSIS ***Describe*** **and correct the error in solving the equation.** **26–27. See margin.**

26. $7x^2 - 5x - 1 = 0$

$$x = \frac{-5 \pm \sqrt{(-5)^2 - 4(7)(-1)}}{2(7)}$$
$$= \frac{-5 \pm \sqrt{53}}{14}$$
$x \approx -0.88$ and $x \approx 0.16$ ✗

27. $-2x^2 + 3x = 1$

$$x = \frac{-3 \pm \sqrt{3^2 - 4(-2)(1)}}{2(-2)}$$
$$= \frac{-3 \pm \sqrt{17}}{-4}$$
$x \approx -0.28$ and $x \approx 1.78$ ✗

EXAMPLE 4 on p. 673 for Exs. 28–33

CHOOSING A METHOD **Tell what method(s) you would use to solve the quadratic equation.** ***Explain*** **your choice(s).** **28–33. See margin.**

28. $3x^2 - 27 = 0$
29. $5x^2 = 25$
30. $2x^2 - 12x = 0$
31. $m^2 + 5m + 6 = 0$
32. $z^2 - 4z + 1 = 0$
33. $-10g^2 + 13g = 4$

4 PRACTICE AND APPLY

Assignment Guide

Answer Transparencies available for all exercises

Basic:
Day 1: pp. 674–676
Exs. 1–8, 12–21, 25–27
Day 2: pp. 674–676
Exs. 28–38, 46–49, 52–61

Average:
Day 1: pp. 674–676
Exs. 1, 2, 6–12, 16–27
Day 2: pp. 674–676
Exs. 28–44, 46–50, 52–60 even

Advanced:
Day 1: pp. 674–676
Exs. 1, 2, 6–12, 16–25
Day 2: pp. 674–676
Exs. 28–51*, 53–61 odd

Block:
pp. 674–676
Exs. 1, 2, 6–12, 16–27 (with 10.5)
pp. 674–676
Exs. 28–44, 46–50, 52–60 even (with 10.7)

Differentiated Instruction

See *Differentiated Instruction Resources* for suggestions on addressing the needs of a diverse classroom.

Homework Check

For a quick check of student understanding of key concepts, go over the following exercises:

Basic: 8, 12, 28, 32, 46
Average: 12, 16, 31, 36, 46
Advanced: 20, 25, 33, 40, 47

Extra Practice

- Student Edition, p. 947
- Chapter Resource Book: Practice levels A, B, C

Practice Worksheet

An easily-readable reduced practice page (with answers) for this lesson can be found on p. 626C.

2. *Sample answer:* **Completing the square, the equation can be put in the form $ax^2 + bx = c$ where $a = 1$ and b is an even number; or quadratic formula, the equation does not factor easily.**

26. The first term of the numerator of the quadratic formula is $-b$, so the first term of the numerator of the answer should be $-(-5) = 5$; $x = \frac{5 \pm \sqrt{(-5)^2 - 4(7)(-1)}}{2(7)}$, $x = \frac{5 \pm \sqrt{53}}{14}$, $x \approx -0.16$ and $x \approx 0.88$.

27. Before identifying the values of a, b, and c, the equation must be written in standard form $ax^2 + bx + c = 0$; $-2x^2 + 3x - 1 = 0$, so $c = -1$, not 1; $x = \frac{-3 \pm \sqrt{3^2 - 4(-2)(-1)}}{2(-2)}$, $x = \frac{-3 \pm \sqrt{1}}{-4}$, $x = \frac{1}{2}$ and $x = 1$.

B **SOLVING QUADRATIC EQUATIONS Solve the quadratic equation using any method. Round your solutions to the nearest hundredth, if necessary.**

34. $-2x^2 = -32$ **±4**

35. $x^2 - 8x = -16$ **4**

36. $x^2 + 2x - 6 = 0$ **−3.65, 1.65**

37. $x^2 = 12x - 36$ **6**

38. $x^2 + 4x = 9$ **−5.61, 1.61**

39. $-4x^2 + x = -17$ **−1.94, 2.19**

40. $11x^2 - 1 = 6x^2 + 2$ **±0.77**

41. $-2x^2 + 5 = 3x^2 - 10x$ **−0.41, 2.41**

42. $(x + 13)^2 = 25$ **−18, −8**

GEOMETRY Use the given area *A* of the rectangle to find the value of *x*. Then give the dimensions of the rectangle.

43. $A = 91 \text{ m}^2$ **5; 13 m by 7 m**

(x + 2) m

(2x + 3) m

44. $A = 209 \text{ ft}^2$ **4; 19 ft by 11 ft**

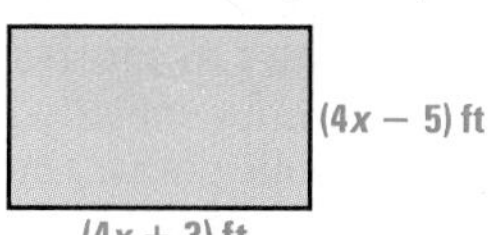

C **45. CHALLENGE** The solutions of the quadratic equation $ax^2 + bx + c = 0$ are $x = \frac{-b + \sqrt{b^2 - 4ac}}{2a}$ and $x = \frac{-b - \sqrt{b^2 - 4ac}}{2a}$. Find the mean of the solutions. How is the mean of the solutions related to the graph of $y = ax^2 + bx + c$? *Explain.* **See margin.**

PROBLEM SOLVING

EXAMPLE 3 on p. 672 for Exs. 46–47

A **46. ADVERTISING** For the period 1990–2000, the amount of money *y* (in billions of dollars) spent on advertising in the U.S. can be modeled by the function $y = 0.93x^2 + 2.2x + 130$ where *x* is the number of years since 1990. In what year was 164 billion dollars spent on advertising? **1995**

@HomeTutor for problem solving help at classzone.com

47. CELL PHONES For the period 1985–2001, the number *y* (in millions) of cell phone service subscribers in the U.S. can be modeled by the function $y = 0.7x^2 - 4.3x + 5.5$ where *x* is the number of years since 1985. In what year were there 16,000,000 cell phone service subscribers? **1993**

@HomeTutor for problem solving help at classzone.com

48. MULTI-STEP PROBLEM A football is punted from a height of 2.5 feet above the ground and with an initial vertical velocity of 45 feet per second.

a. Use the vertical motion model to write an equation that gives the height *h* (in feet) of the football as a function of the time *t* (in seconds) after it has been punted. $h = -16t^2 + 45t + 2.5$

b. The football is caught 5.5 feet above the ground as shown in the diagram. Find the amount of time that the football is in the air. **about 2.7 sec**

Avoiding Common Errors

Exercises 3–25 Students often make calculation errors when using the quadratic formula, especially when substituting values with negative signs. For each exercise, prior to doing any calculations they should write the values of *a*, *b*, and *c* and then rewrite the formula using those values.

Graphing Calculator

Exercises 3–25 Suggest that students use their graphing calculators to check their solutions.

Study Strategy

Exercise 47 Point out to students that this exercise has a worked-out solution. Recommend that they attempt a solution first. Then they can use the worked-out solution to check their results and compare solution methods.

32. Completing the square, the equation is in the form $ax^2 + bx + c = 0$ where $a = 1$ and b is an even number; or quadratic formula, the equation does not factor easily.

33. Quadratic formula, the equation does not factor easily.

45. $-\frac{b}{2a}$; $x = -\frac{b}{2a}$ is the equation of the axis of symmetry of the parabola $y = ax^2 + bx + c$, and $-\frac{b}{2a}$ is the x-coordinate of the vertex of the parabola; the axis of symmetry of $y = ax^2 + bx + c$ is located half-way between the x-intercepts, and the x-intercepts are the solutions of $ax^2 + bx + c = 0$, so the mean of the solutions is the equation of the axis of symmetry; the equation of the axis of symmetry gives the x-coordinate of the vertex of the parabola.

28–33. Sample answers are given.

28. Factoring, the expression $3x^2 - 27$ factors easily; or using square roots, the equation can be written in the form $x^2 = d$.

29. Using square roots, the equation can be written in the form $x^2 = d$.

30. Factoring, the expression $2x^2 - 12x$ factors easily; or completing the square, the equation is of the form $ax^2 + bx = c$ where $a = 1$ and b is an even number.

31. Factoring, the expression $m^2 + 5m + 6$ factors easily.

5 ASSESS AND RETEACH

Daily Homework Quiz

Transparency Available

Use the quadratic formula to solve the equation. Round your solutions to the nearest hundredth, if necessary.

1. $6x^2 - 6 = -5x$ $-\frac{3}{2}, \frac{2}{3}$
2. $2x^2 + 3x - 8 = 0$ **−2.87, 1.39**
3. $3m^2 - m + 9 = 12$ **−0.85, 1.18**
4. You have seen that the function $y = 10x^2 - 94x + 3900$ models the number y of films produced in the world, where x is the number of years since 1971. In what year were 10,000 films produced? **about 29.8 years after 1971, or during the year 2000**

Available at **classzone.com**

Diagnosis/Remediation

- Practice A, B, C in Chapter Resource Book
- Study Guide in Chapter Resource Book
- Practice Workbook
- @HomeTutor

Challenge

Additional challenge is available in the Chapter Resource Book.

Quiz

An easily-readable reduced copy of the quiz (with answers) on Lessons 10.4–10.6 from the Assessment Book can be found on p. 626G.

49b.

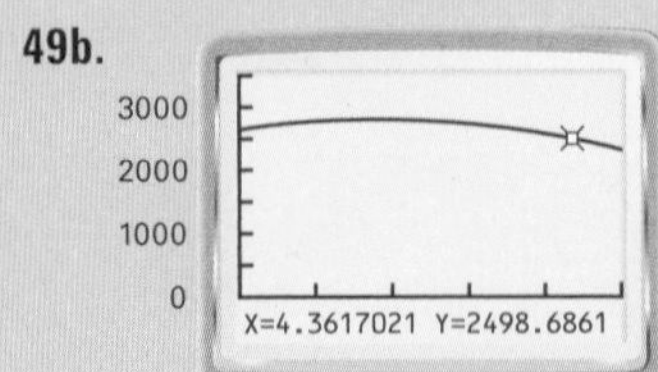

B

49. **MULTIPLE REPRESENTATIONS** For the period 1997–2002, the number y (in thousands) of 16- and 17-year-olds employed in the United States can be modeled by the function $y = -46.7x^2 + 169x + 2650$ where x is the number of years since 1997.

a. Solving an Equation Write and solve an equation to find the year during which 2,500,000 16- and 17-year-olds were employed. **2001**

b. Drawing a Graph Graph the function on a graphing calculator. Use the *trace* feature to find the year when 2,500,000 16- and 17-year-olds were employed. Use the graph to check your answer from part (a). **See margin.**

50. ★ **SHORT RESPONSE** NASA creates a weightless environment by flying a plane in a series of parabolic paths. The height h (in feet) of a plane after t seconds in a parabolic flight path can be modeled by the graph of $h = -11t^2 + 700t + 21{,}000$. The passengers experience a weightless environment when the height of the plane is greater than or equal to 30,800 feet. Find the period of weightlessness on such a flight. *Explain.* **about 22 sec**

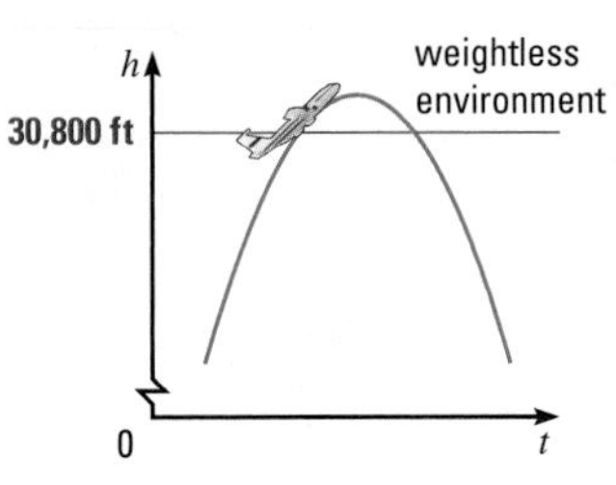

C

51. **CHALLENGE** Mineral deposits have formed a uniform coating that is 4 millimeters thick on the inside of a water pipe. The cross-sectional area of the pipe has decreased by 10%. What was the original diameter of the pipe (to the nearest tenth of a millimeter)? **about 156.0 mm**

MIXED REVIEW

PREVIEW Prepare for Lesson 10.7 in Exs. 52–55.

Evaluate the expression.

52. $9x^2$ when $x = 2$ *(p. 8)* **36**

53. $\frac{6 - 5w}{2w}$ when $w = 10$ *(p. 103)* $-2\frac{1}{5}$

54. $2 + \sqrt{x}$ when $x = 121$ *(p. 110)* **13**

55. $8 - \sqrt{x}$ when $x = 49$ *(p. 110)* **1**

Graph the equation. **56–61. See margin.**

56. $x = 8$ *(p. 215)*

57. $3x - y = 2$ *(p. 225)*

58. $y = -\frac{2}{5}x - 6$ *(p. 244)*

59. $y = -7x^2$ *(p. 628)*

60. $y = 8x^2 - 2$ *(p. 628)*

61. $y = -x^2 - 6x + 5$ *(p. 635)*

QUIZ *for Lessons 10.4–10.6*

Solve the equation using square roots. *(p. 652)*

1. $3x^2 - 48 = 0$ **±4**

2. $-6x^2 = -24$ **±2**

3. $x^2 + 5 = 16$ **about ±3.32**

Solve the equation by completing the square. *(p. 663)*

4. $x^2 + 2x + 6 = 0$ **no solution**

5. $x^2 + 10x - 12 = 0$ **−11.08, 1.08**

6. $x^2 - 8x = -6$ **0.84, 7.16**

7. $x^2 - 12x = 30$ **−2.12, 14.12**

8. $x^2 - 5x = -\frac{9}{4}$ **0.5, 4.5**

9. $x^2 + x = -7.75$ **no solution**

Solve the equation using the quadratic formula. *(p. 671)*

10. $x^2 + 4x + 1 = 0$ **−3.73, −0.27**

11. $-3x^2 + 3x = -1$ **−0.26, 1.26**

12. $4x^2 - 11x = 3$ **−0.25, 3**

EXTRA PRACTICE for Lesson 10.6, p. 947 **ONLINE QUIZ** at classzone.com

56–61. See Additional Answers beginning on p. AA1.

10.7 The Discriminant

QUESTION **How can you determine the number of solutions of a quadratic equation?**

In the quadratic formula, $x = \frac{-b \pm \sqrt{b^2 - 4ac}}{2a}$, the expression $b^2 - 4ac$ is called the *discriminant*.

EXPLORE **Determine how the discriminant is related to the number of solutions of a quadratic equation**

STEP 1 ***Find the number of solutions*** **See Step 3.**

Find the number of solutions of the equations below by finding the number of x-intercepts of the graphs of the related functions.

$0 = x^2 - 6x - 7$

$0 = x^2 - 6x + 9$

$0 = x^2 - 6x + 12$

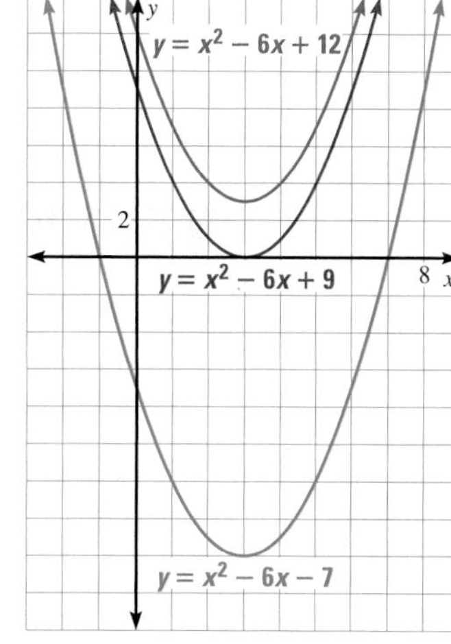

STEP 2 ***Find the value of $b^2 - 4ac$*** **See Step 3.**

For each equation in Step 1, determine whether the value of $b^2 - 4ac$ is positive, negative, or zero.

STEP 3 ***Make a table***

Organize your results from Steps 1 and 2 in a table as shown.

Equation	Number of solutions	Value of $b^2 - 4ac$
$0 = x^2 - 6x - 7$	? 2	? 64
$0 = x^2 - 6x + 9$	? 1	? 0
$0 = x^2 - 6x + 12$	? 0	? −12

STEP 4 ***Make a conjecture***

Make a generalization about the value of the discriminant and the number of solutions of a quadratic equation.
The number of solutions of a quadratic equation $ax^2 + bx + c = 0$ is 2 if $b^2 - 4ac > 0$, is 1 if $b^2 - 4ac = 0$, and is 0 if $b^2 - 4ac < 0$.

DRAW CONCLUSIONS **Use your observations to complete these exercises**
1, 2. See margin.

1. Repeat Steps 1–3 using the following equations: $x^2 + 4x - 5 = 0$, $x^2 + 4x + 4 = 0$, and $x^2 + 4x + 6 = 0$. Is your conjecture still true?
2. Notice that the expression $b^2 - 4ac$ is under the radical sign in the quadratic formula. Use this observation to explain why the value of $b^2 - 4ac$ determines the number of solutions of a quadratic equation.

1 PLAN AND PREPARE

Explore the Concept

- Students will determine how the discriminant is related to the number of solutions of a quadratic formula.
- This activity leads into the study of using the discriminant in Lesson 10.7, Example 1.

Recommended Time

Work activity: 10 min
Discuss results: 5 min

Grouping

Students should work individually.

2 TEACH

Tips for Success

Caution students to make sure that they are using the correct graphs to find the number of x-intercepts and record the number of solutions. Remind students that the number of solutions is the same as the number of x-intercepts.

Key Discovery

If the value of the discriminant is positive, there are two solutions. If the value is 0, there is one solution. If the value is negative, there is no real-number solution.

3 ASSESS AND RETEACH

Use the discriminant to find the number of x-intercepts of the graph of $5x^2 + 14x = 7$.
$b^2 - 4ac = 14^2 - 4(5)(-7) = 336$; $336 > 0$, so there are 2 x-intercepts.

1.

Equation	Number of solutions	Value of $b^2 - 4ac$
$x^2 + 4x - 5 = 0$	2	36
$x^2 + 4x + 4 = 0$	1	0
$x^2 + 4x + 6 = 0$	0	−8

yes

2. See Additional Answers beginning on p. AA1.

10.7 Interpret the Discriminant

Before	You used the quadratic formula.
Now	You will use the value of the discriminant.
Why?	So you can solve a problem about gymnastics, as in Ex. 49.

1 PLAN AND PREPARE

Warm-Up Exercises

Transparency Available

Evaluate the expression.

1. $8x^2$ when $x = 4$ **128**
2. $-4 + \sqrt{x}$ when $x = 9$ **−1**
3. A ball is kicked into the air from a height of 4.5 feet with an initial vertical velocity of 30 feet per second. What is the height of the ball after 1 second? **18.5 ft**

Notetaking Guide

Transparency Available

Promotes interactive learning and notetaking skills.

Pacing

Basic: 1 day

Average: 1 day

Advanced: 1 day

Block: 0.5 block with 10.6

- See *Teaching Guide/Lesson Plan.*

2 FOCUS AND MOTIVATE

Essential Question

Big Idea 2, p. 627

How do you use the value of the discriminant? **Tell students they will learn how to answer this question by using the discriminant to find the number of solutions of a quadratic equation.**

NCTM STANDARDS

Standard 2: Analyze situations using algebraic symbols

Standard 8: Communicate thinking clearly to others

Key Vocabulary
- **discriminant**

In the quadratic formula, the expression $b^2 - 4ac$ is called the **discriminant** of the associated equation $ax^2 + bx + c = 0$.

$$x = \frac{-b \pm \sqrt{b^2 - 4ac}}{2a} \quad \longleftarrow \text{discriminant}$$

Because the discriminant is under the radical symbol, the value of the discriminant can be used to determine the number of solutions of a quadratic equation and the number of x-intercepts of the graph of the related function.

READING
Recall that in this course, *solutions* refers to real-number solutions.

KEY CONCEPT *For Your Notebook*

Using the Discriminant of $ax^2 + bx + c = 0$

Value of the discriminant	$b^2 - 4ac > 0$	$b^2 - 4ac = 0$	$b^2 - 4ac < 0$
Number of solutions	Two solutions	One solution	No solution
Graph of $y = ax^2 + bx + c$	Two x-intercepts	One x-intercept	No x-intercept

EXAMPLE 1 Use the discriminant

THE NUMBER *i*
The equation $x^2 + 1 = 0$ has no *real* solutions. In a future course, you will learn that the *imaginary* number i, defined as $\sqrt{-1}$, and its opposite are solutions.

	Equation $ax^2 + bx + c = 0$	**Discriminant** $b^2 - 4ac$	**Number of solutions**
a.	$x^2 + 1 = 0$	$0^2 - 4(1)(1) = -4$	No solution
b.	$x^2 - 7 = 0$	$0^2 - 4(1)(-7) = 28$	Two solutions
c.	$4x^2 - 12x + 9 = 0$	$(-12)^2 - 4(4)(9) = 0$	One solution

Resource Planning Guide

Chapter Resource Book
- Teaching Guide/Lesson Plan
- Practice levels A, B, C
- Study Guide
- Catch-up for Absent Students
- Application
- Challenge

Workbooks
- Notetaking Guide
- Practice Workbook

Teaching Options
- **Power Presentations** provides dynamic electronic teaching resources for the classroom.
- **Activity Generator** provides editable activities for all ability levels.

Interactive Technology
- Easy Planner
- Power Presentations
- Activity Generator
- Animated Algebra
- Test Generator
- Online Quiz
- eWorkbook
- eEdition
- @HomeTutor

Resources for English Learners
- Spanish Study Guide
- Multi-Language Visual Glossary
- Student Resources in Spanish

See also the *Differentiated Instruction Resources* for more strategies for meeting individual needs.

EXAMPLE 2 Find the number of solutions

Tell whether the equation $3x^2 - 7 = 2x$ has *two solutions, one solution,* or *no solution.*

Solution

STEP 1 **Write** the equation in standard form.

$3x^2 - 7 = 2x$ Write equation.

$3x^2 - 2x - 7 = 0$ Subtract $2x$ from each side.

STEP 2 **Find** the value of the discriminant.

$b^2 - 4ac = (-2)^2 - 4(3)(-7)$ Substitute 3 for a, −2 for b, and −7 for c.

$= 88$ Simplify.

▶ The discriminant is positive, so the equation has two solutions.

GUIDED PRACTICE for Examples 1 and 2

Tell whether the equation has *two solutions, one solution,* or *no solution.*

1. $x^2 + 4x + 3 = 0$ **two solutions**
2. $2x^2 - 5x + 6 = 0$ **no solution**
3. $-x^2 + 2x = 1$ **one solution**

EXAMPLE 3 Find the number of *x*-intercepts

Find the number of *x*-intercepts of the graph of $y = x^2 + 5x + 8$.

Solution

Find the number of solutions of the equation $0 = x^2 + 5x + 8$.

$b^2 - 4ac = (5)^2 - 4(1)(8)$ Substitute 1 for a, 5 for b, and 8 for c.

$= -7$ Simplify.

▶ The discriminant is negative, so the equation has no solution. This means that the graph of $y = x^2 + 5x + 8$ has no x-intercepts.

CHECK You can use a graphing calculator to check the answer. Notice that the graph of $y = x^2 + 5x + 8$ has no x-intercepts.

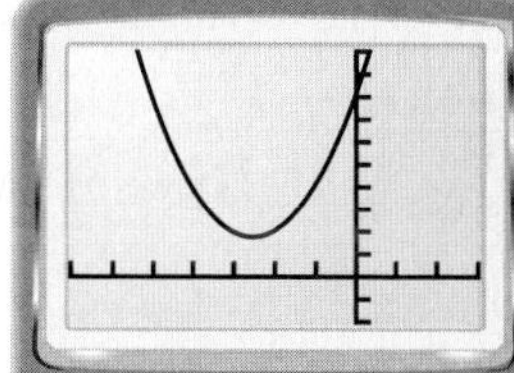

GUIDED PRACTICE for Example 3

Find the number of *x*-intercepts of the graph of the function.

4. $y = x^2 + 10x + 25$ **1**
5. $y = x^2 - 9x$ **2**
6. $y = -x^2 + 2x - 4$ **0**

Motivating the Lesson

You are helping a friend's family move to a new house. On the drive to the new house, the truck has to pass under an overpass that has an arch in the shape of a parabola. You can model the situation with a quadratic equation and then use the discriminant to determine whether the truck will fit under the overpass.

3 TEACH

Extra Example 1

Use the discriminant to find the number of solutions of each equation.

a. $3x^2 + 8x + 7 = 0$ **Discriminant is −20; no solution**

b. $x^2 + 2x - 3 = 0$ **Discriminant is 16; two solutions**

c. $4x^2 + 20x + 25 = 0$ **Discriminant is 0; one solution**

Key Question to Ask for Example 1

- Can you tell how many x-intercepts each of the equations has? Explain. **Each x-intercept of the graph of the equation represents a solution of the equation, so the number of x-intercepts of the graph is the same as the number of solutions of the equation.**

Extra Example 2

Use the discriminant to tell whether the equation $4x^2 + 1 = -4x$ has *two solutions, one solution,* or *no solution.* **Discriminant is 0; one solution**

Extra Example 3

Use the discriminant to find the number of x-intercepts of the graph of $y = x^2 + 7x - 2$. **Discriminant is 57; that is positive, so the graph has two x-intercepts.**

Differentiated Instruction

Inclusion Students who have difficulty memorizing the rules for the discriminant should think of how the square root of the discriminant is used in the quadratic formula. For a positive discriminant, the square root has two real values; for a zero discriminant, the square root has one real value; and for a negative discriminant, the square root has no real values.

See also the *Differentiated Instruction Resources* for more strategies.

Extra Example 4

The arc of a baseball hit into the outfield can be modeled by the function $y = -0.005x^2 + 1.2x + 3$, where x is the horizontal distance (in feet) that the baseball travels and y is the height of the baseball. Does the baseball reach a height of 50 feet? If it does, about how far has it traveled horizontally from the hitter? **The ball reaches a height of 50 feet twice. The first time it reaches a height of 50 feet (on its way up), it is at a horizontal distance of 49 feet from the hitter. The second time (on its way down), it is at a horizontal distance of 191 feet from the hitter.**

Closing the Lesson

Have students summarize the major points of the lesson and answer the Essential Question: How do you use the value of the discriminant?

- **The discriminant is $b^2 - 4ac$, where a, b, and c are the values when the equation is written in the form $ax^2 + bx + c = 0$.**

If the value of the discriminant is positive, there are two solutions. If the value is negative, there are no real-number solutions. If the value is 0, there is one solution.

EXAMPLE 4 Solve a multi-step problem

FOUNTAINS The Centennial Fountain in Chicago shoots a water arc that can be modeled by the graph of the equation $y = -0.006x^2 + 1.2x + 10$ where x is the horizontal distance (in feet) from the river's north shore and y is the height (in feet) above the river. Does the water arc reach a height of 50 feet? If so, about how far from the north shore is the water arc 50 feet above the water?

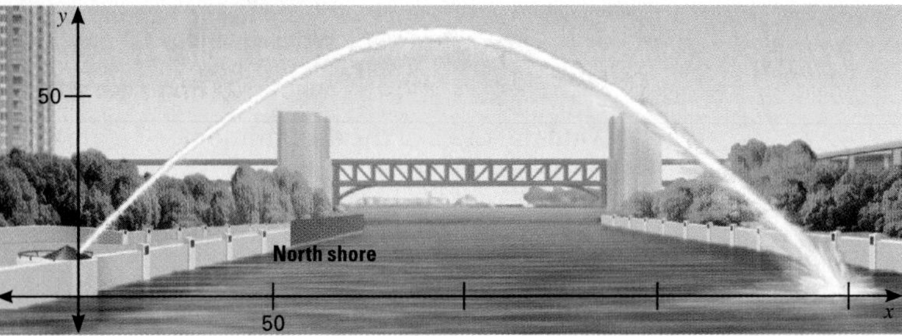

Solution

STEP 1 **Write** a quadratic equation. You want to know whether the water arc reaches a height of 50 feet, so let $y = 50$. Then write the quadratic equation in standard form.

$y = -0.006x^2 + 1.2x + 10$ — **Write given equation.**

$50 = -0.006x^2 + 1.2x + 10$ — **Substitute 50 for y.**

$0 = -0.006x^2 + 1.2x - 40$ — **Subtract 50 from each side.**

STEP 2 **Find** the value of the discriminant of $0 = -0.006x^2 + 1.2x - 40$.

$b^2 - 4ac = (1.2)^2 - 4(-0.006)(-40)$ — **$a = -0.006$, $b = 1.2$, $c = -40$**

$= 0.48$ — **Simplify.**

STEP 3 **Interpret** the discriminant. Because the discriminant is positive, the equation has two solutions. So, the water arc reaches a height of 50 feet at two points on the water arc.

STEP 4 **Solve** the equation $0 = -0.006x^2 + 1.2x - 40$ to find the distance from the north shore where the water arc is 50 feet above the water.

$x = \frac{-b \pm \sqrt{b^2 - 4ac}}{2a}$ — **Quadratic formula**

$= \frac{-1.2 \pm \sqrt{0.48}}{2(-0.006)}$ — **Substitute values in the quadratic formula.**

$x \approx 42$ *or* $x \approx 158$ — **Use a calculator.**

▶ The water arc is 50 feet above the water about 42 feet from the north shore and about 158 feet from the north shore.

USE A SHORTCUT
Because the value of $b^2 - 4ac$ was calculated in Step 2, you can substitute 0.48 for $b^2 - 4ac$.

✓ **GUIDED PRACTICE** for Example 4

7. **WHAT IF?** In Example 4, does the water arc reach a height of 70 feet? If so, about how far from the north shore is the water arc 70 feet above the water? **yes; 100 ft**

Differentiated Instruction

Below Level Have students, working with partners, look at Example 4 and determine whether the water arc reaches a height of 100 feet. (It does not.) Then challenge the students to determine the greatest height of the arc. (It is 70 feet.) Have them check their results by graphing the function on their graphing calculators. Then have them write a brief summary of what they discovered.

See also the *Differentiated Instruction Resources* for more strategies.

10.7 EXERCISES

HOMEWORK KEY
○ = **WORKED-OUT SOLUTIONS** on p. WS25 for Exs. 9 and 47
★ = **STANDARDIZED TEST PRACTICE** Exs. 2, 18, 19, 40, 41, and 47

SKILL PRACTICE

A

1. **VOCABULARY** Write the quadratic formula and circle the expression that represents the discriminant. $x = \frac{-b \pm \sqrt{b^2 - 4ac}}{2a}$, $b^2 - 4ac$ **should be circled.**

2. ★ **WRITING** *Explain* how the discriminant of $ax^2 + bx + c = 0$ is related to the graph of $y = ax^2 + bx + c$. **See margin.**

EXAMPLES 1 and 2 on pp. 678–679 for Exs. 3–21

USING THE DISCRIMINANT **Tell whether the equation has *two solutions, one solution,* or *no solution.***

3. $x^2 + x + 1 = 0$ **no solution**
4. $2x^2 - 5x - 6 = 0$ **two solutions**
5. $-2x^2 + 8x - 4 = 0$ **two solutions**
6. $3m^2 - 6m + 7 = 0$ **no solution**
7. $9v^2 - 6v + 1 = 0$ **one solution**
8. $-3q^2 + 8 = 0$ **two solutions**
9. $25p^2 - 16p = 0$ **two solutions**
10. $2h^2 + 3 = 4h$ **no solution**
11. $10 = x^2 - 5x$ **two solutions**
12. $\frac{1}{4}z^2 + 2 = z$ **no solution**
13. $-3g^2 - 4g = \frac{4}{3}$ **one solution**
14. $8r^2 + 10r - 1 = 4r$ **two solutions**
15. $3n^2 + 3 = 10n - 3n^2$ **two solutions**
16. $8x^2 + 9 = 4x^2 - 4x + 8$ **one solution**
17. $w^2 - 7w + 29 = 4 - 7w$ **no solution**

18. ★ **MULTIPLE CHOICE** What is the value of the discriminant of the equation $5x^2 - 7x - 2 = 0$? **D**

Ⓐ -9 Ⓑ 9 Ⓒ 59 Ⓓ 89

19. ★ **MULTIPLE CHOICE** How many solutions does $-x^2 + 4x = 8$ have? **A**

Ⓐ None Ⓑ One Ⓒ Two Ⓓ Three

ERROR ANALYSIS ***Describe*** **and correct the error in finding the number of solutions of the equation.** **20–21. See margin.**

20. $4x^2 + 12x + 9 = 0$

$$b^2 - 4ac = 12^2 - 4(4)(9)$$
$$= 144 - 144$$
$$= 0$$

The equation has two solutions. ✗

21. $3x^2 - 7x - 4 = -9$

$$b^2 - 4ac = (-7)^2 - 4(3)(-4)$$
$$= 49 - (-48)$$
$$= 97$$

The equation has two solutions. ✗

EXAMPLE 3 on p. 679 for Exs. 22–30

FINDING THE NUMBER OF *x*-INTERCEPTS **Find the number of *x*-intercepts of the graph of the function.**

22. $y = x^2 - 2x - 4$ **2**
23. $y = 2x^2 - x - 1$ **2**
24. $y = 4x^2 + 4x + 1$ **1**
25. $y = 2x^2 - 5x + 5$ **0**
26. $y = x^2 - 6x + 9$ **1**
27. $y = 6x^2 + x + 2$ **0**
28. $y = -13x^2 + 2x + 6$ **2**
29. $y = \frac{1}{4}x^2 - 3x + 9$ **1**
30. $y = \frac{2}{3}x^2 - 5x + 12$ **0**

B

REASONING **Give a value of *c* for which the equation has (a) two solutions, (b) one solution, and (c) no solution.** **31–33. Sample answers are given for parts (a) and (c).**

31. $x^2 - 2x + c = 0$ **(a) 0, (b) 1, (c) 2**
32. $x^2 - 8x + c = 0$ **(a) 15, (b) 16, (c) 17**
33. $4x^2 + 12x + c = 0$ **(a) 8, (b) 9, (c) 10**

4 PRACTICE AND APPLY

Assignment Guide

Answer Transparencies available for all exercises

Basic:
Day 1: pp. 681–683
Exs. 1–11, 18–26, 31–35, 45–48, 51, 54, 57, 60, 63

Average:
Day 1: pp. 681–683
Exs. 1, 2, 11–21, 27–41, 45–49, 52, 58, 64

Advanced:
Day 1: pp. 681–683
Exs. 1, 2, 13–19, 28–50*, 56, 62, 65

Block:
pp. 681–683
Exs. 1, 2, 11–21, 27–41, 45–49, 52, 58, 64 (with 10.6)

Differentiated Instruction

See *Differentiated Instruction Resources* for suggestions on addressing the needs of a diverse classroom.

Homework Check

For a quick check of student understanding of key concepts, go over the following exercises:
Basic: 6, 10, 23, 26, 45
Average: 12, 14, 28, 31, 45
Advanced: 15, 17, 30, 32, 46

Extra Practice

- Student Edition, p. 947
- Chapter Resource Book: Practice levels A, B, C

Practice Worksheet

An easily-readable reduced practice page (with answers) for this lesson can be found on p. 626C.

2. The value of the discriminant (positive, zero, or negative) determines the number of solutions of the equation $ax^2 + bx + c = 0$, which is the same as the number of x-intercepts of the graph of $y = ax^2 + bx + c$.

20. The discriminant, 0, was interpreted incorrectly; the equation has one solution.

21. Before calculating the discriminant, the equation must be written in standard form: $3x^2 - 7x + 5 = 0$. Thus, c is 5, not -4, so $b^2 - 4ac = (-7)^2 - 4(3)(5) = 49 - 60 = -11$, the equation has no solution.

Avoiding Common Errors

Exercises 3–19, 22–30 A common error students make is equating a discriminant of 0 with no solution. Remind these students that when the discriminant is zero, then the quadratic formula simplifies to $x = \frac{-b \pm \sqrt{0}}{2a} = -\frac{b}{2a}$, so there is one solution to the quadratic equation.

Mathematical Reasoning

Exercises 34–39 Before students attempt these exercises, you may want to ask them to describe when the graph of an opening-upward parabola has and does not have solutions, and when the graph of an opening-downward parabola has and does not have solutions.

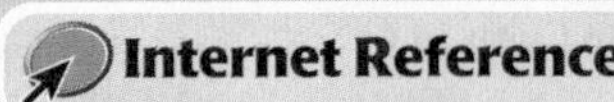

Internet Reference

Exercise 49 For more information about trampoline competitions, visit the USA Gymnastics site at www.usa-gymnastics.org and click on the "t&t" icon.

34. Below; $a > 0$, so the graph opens up. The value of the discriminant is $(-3)^2 - 4(1)(2) = 1 > 0$, so the graph has two x-intercepts; a parabola that opens up and has two x-intercepts must have its vertex below the x-axis.

35. On; the value of the discriminant is $(-6)^2 - 4(3)(3) = 0$, so the graph has exactly one x-intercept. A parabola that has exactly one x-intercept must have its vertex on the x-axis.

36. Above; $a > 0$, so the graph opens up. The value of the discriminant is $(-2)^2 - 4(6)(4) = -60 < 0$, so the graph has no x-intercepts; a parabola that opens up and has no x-intercepts must have its vertex above the x-axis.

37. Below; $a < 0$, so the graph opens down. The value of the discriminant is $(10)^2 - 4(-15)(-25) = -1400 < 0$, so the graph has no x-intercepts; a parabola that opens down and has no x-intercepts must have its vertex below the x-axis.

USING THE DISCRIMINANT **Tell whether the vertex of the graph of the function lies above, below, or on the x-axis. *Explain* your reasoning.** **34–39. See margin.**

34. $y = x^2 - 3x + 2$ **35.** $y = 3x^2 - 6x + 3$ **36.** $y = 6x^2 - 2x + 4$

37. $y = -15x^2 + 10x - 25$ **38.** $y = -3x^2 - 4x + 8$ **39.** $y = 9x^2 - 24x + 16$

40. ★ **OPEN-ENDED** Write a function of the form $y = ax^2 + bx + c$ whose graph has one x-intercept. ***Sample answer:*** $y = x^2 + 14x + 49$

41. ★ **EXTENDED RESPONSE** Use the rectangular prism shown.

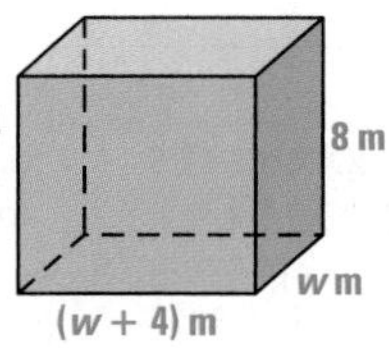

a. The surface area of the prism is 314 square meters. Write an equation that you can solve to find the value of w. $314 = 2w^2 + 40w + 64$

b. Use the discriminant to determine the number of values of w in the equation from part (a). **2**

c. Solve the equation. Do the value(s) of w make sense in the context of the problem? *Explain.* **See margin.**

C CHALLENGE **Find all values of k for which the equation has (a) two solutions, (b) one solution, and (c) no solution.** **See margin.**

42. $2x^2 + x + 3k = 0$ **43.** $x^2 - 4kx + 36 = 0$ **44.** $kx^2 + 5x - 16 = 0$

PROBLEM SOLVING

EXAMPLE 4 A on p. 680 for Exs. 45–46

45. BIOLOGY The amount y (in milliliters per gram of body mass per hour) of oxygen consumed by a parakeet during flight can be modeled by the function $y = 0.06x^2 - 4x + 87$ where x is the speed (in kilometers per hour) of the parakeet.

a. Use the discriminant to show that it is possible for a parakeet to consume 25 milliliters of oxygen per gram of body mass per hour. **See margin.**

b. Find the speed(s) at which the parakeet consumes 25 milliliters of oxygen per gram of body mass per hour. Round your solution(s) to the nearest tenth. **24.5 km/h and 42.2 km/h**

@HomeTutor for problem solving help at classzone.com

46. FOOD For the period 1950–1999, the average amount y (in pounds per person per year) of butter consumed in the United States can be modeled by $y = 0.0051x^2 - 0.37x + 11$ where x is the number of years since 1950. According to the model, did the butter consumption in the United States ever reach 5 pounds per person per year? If so, in what year(s)? **yes; 1974 and 1998**

@HomeTutor for problem solving help at classzone.com

(47.) ★ **SHORT RESPONSE** The frame of the tent shown is defined by a rectangular base and two parabolic arches that connect the opposite corners of the base. The graph of $y = -0.18x^2 + 1.6x$ models the height y (in feet) of one of the arches x feet along the diagonal of the base. Can a child that is 4 feet tall walk under one of the arches without having to bend over? *Explain.* **See margin.**

○ = WORKED-OUT SOLUTIONS on p. WS1 ★ = STANDARDIZED TEST PRACTICE

38. Above; $a < 0$, so the graph opens down. The value of the discriminant is $(-4)^2 - 4(-3)(8) = 112 > 0$, so the graph has two x-intercepts; a parabola that opens down and has two x-intercepts must have its vertex above the x-axis.

39. On; the value of the discriminant is $(-24)^2 - 4(9)(16) = 0$, so the graph has exactly one x-intercept; a parabola that has exactly one x-intercept must have its vertex on the x-axis.

41c, 42–44, 45a, 47. See Additional Answers beginning on p. AA1.

B 48. **SCIENCE** Between the months of April and September, the number y of hours of daylight per day in Seattle, Washington, can be modeled by $y = -0.00046x^2 + 0.076x + 13$ where x is the number of days since April 1.

a. Do any of the days between April and September in Seattle have 17 hours of daylight? If so, how many? **no**

b. Do any of the days between April and September in Seattle have 14 hours of daylight? If so, how many? **yes; 2**

49. **MULTI-STEP PROBLEM** During a trampoline competition, a trampolinist leaves the mat when her center of gravity is 6 feet above the ground. She has an initial vertical velocity of 32 feet per second.

a. Use the vertical motion model to write an equation that models the height h (in feet) of the center of gravity of the trampolinist as a function of the time t (in seconds) into her jump. $h = -16t^2 + 32t + 6$

b. Does her center of gravity reach a height of 24 feet during the jump? If so, at what time(s)? **no**

c. On another jump, the trampolinist leaves the mat when her center of gravity is 6 feet above the ground and with an initial vertical velocity of 35 feet per second. Does her center of gravity reach a height of 24 feet on this jump? If so, at what time(s)? **yes; about 0.8 sec and about 1.4 sec**

C 50. **CHALLENGE** Last year, a manufacturer sold backpacks for \$24 each. At this price, the manufacturer sold about 1000 backpacks per week. A marketing analyst predicts that for every \$1 reduction in the price of the backpack, the manufacturer will sell 100 more backpacks per week.

a. Write a function that models the weekly revenue R (in dollars) that the manufacturer will receive for x reductions of \$1 in the price of the backpack. $R = -100x^2 + 1400x + 24{,}000$

b. Is it possible for the manufacturer to receive a weekly revenue of \$28,000? \$30,000? What is the maximum weekly revenue that the manufacturer can receive? *Explain* your answers using the discriminants of quadratic equations. **See margin.**

MIXED REVIEW

PREVIEW
Prepare for Lesson 10.8 in Exs. 51–56.

Graph the function. **51–56. See margin.**

51. $y = 5x - 10$ *(p. 225)*
52. $y = \frac{1}{4}x$ *(p. 244)*
53. $y = \frac{3}{4}x - 5$ *(p. 244)*
54. $y = 5^x$ *(p. 520)*
55. $y = (0.2)^x$ *(p. 531)*
56. $y = 6x^2 - 3$ *(p. 628)*

Solve the equation.

57. $a + 5 = 2$ *(p. 134)* **−3**
58. $f - 6 = 13$ *(p. 134)* **19**
59. $4z - 3 = -7$ *(p. 141)* **−1**
60. $9w + 4 = -41$ *(p. 141)* **−5**
61. $2b - b - 6 = 8$ *(p. 148)* **14**
62. $5 + 2(x - 4) = 9$ *(p. 148)* **6**

Solve the equation by factoring. *(p. 593)*

63. $2x^2 - 3x - 5 = 0$ $-1, 2\frac{1}{2}$
64. $4n^2 + 2n - 6 = 0$ $-1\frac{1}{2}, 1$
65. $5a^2 + 21a + 4 = 0$ $-4, -\frac{1}{5}$

51–56. See Additional Answers beginning on p. AA1.

5 ASSESS AND RETEACH

Daily Homework Quiz

Transparency Available

Tell whether the equation has *two solutions, one solution,* or *no solutions.*

1. $4b^2 + 2b - 5 = 0$ **two solutions**
2. $2g^2 + 8g = -11$ **no solution**

Find the number of x-intercepts of the graph of the equation.

3. $y = x^2 + 14x + 49$ **one**
4. $y = x^2 + 14x + 50$ **none**
5. The graph of $y = -0.2x^2 + 3.5x$ models the height of one of the arches at the entrance to a parking structure. Can a truck that is 20 feet high fit under the arch? **The value of the discriminant of $0 = -0.2x^2 + 3.5x - 20$ is negative, so there is no solution. The truck will not fit under the arch.**

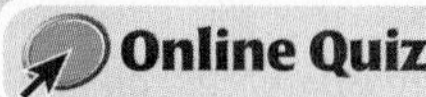

Online Quiz

Available at **classzone.com**

Diagnosis/Remediation

- Practice A, B, C in Chapter Resource Book
- Study Guide in Chapter Resource Book
- Practice Workbook
- @HomeTutor

Challenge

Additional challenge is available in the Chapter Resource Book.

50b. See Additional Answers beginning on p. AA1.

10.8 Compare Linear, Exponential, and Quadratic Models

Before	You graphed linear, exponential, and quadratic functions.
Now	You will compare linear, exponential, and quadratic models.
Why?	So you can solve a problem about biology, as in Ex. 23.

1 PLAN AND PREPARE

Warm-Up Exercises

Transparency Available

1. Graph $y = 3^x$.

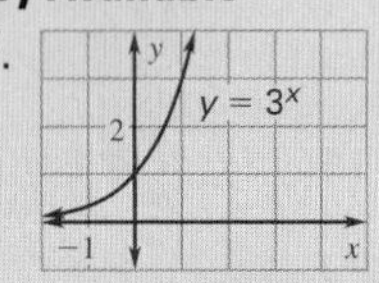

2. Tell whether the ordered pairs (0, 0), (1, 2), (2, 4), and (3, 6) represent a linear function. **yes**
3. For $y = x^2 - 3x - 5$, find corresponding y-values for the x-values -2, 1, and 3. **5, −7, −5**

Notetaking Guide

Transparency Available

Promotes interactive learning and notetaking skills.

Pacing

Basic: 2 days
Average: 2 days
Advanced: 2 days
Block: 1 block
- See *Teaching Guide/Lesson Plan.*

2 FOCUS AND MOTIVATE

Essential Question

Big Idea 3, p. 627

How do you decide whether a linear, exponential, or quadratic model best represents data? **Tell students they will learn how to answer this question by making comparisons between the models.**

NCTM STANDARDS

Standard 2: Understand patterns; Understand functions

Key Vocabulary
- **linear function,** *p. 217*
- **exponential function,** *p. 520*
- **quadratic function,** *p. 628*

So far you have studied linear functions, exponential functions, and quadratic functions. You can use these functions to model data.

KEY CONCEPT — *For Your Notebook*

Linear, Exponential, and Quadratic Functions

Linear Function	Exponential Function	Quadratic Function
$y = mx + b$	$y = ab^x$	$y = ax^2 + bx + c$

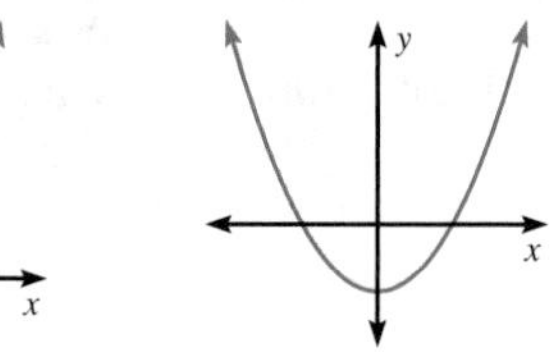

EXAMPLE 1 Choose functions using sets of ordered pairs

Use a graph to tell whether the ordered pairs represent a *linear function*, an *exponential function*, or a *quadratic function*.

a. $\left(-4, \frac{1}{32}\right), \left(-2, \frac{1}{8}\right), \left(0, \frac{1}{2}\right), (2, 2), (4, 8)$

b. $(-4, 1), (-2, 2), (0, 3), (2, 4), (4, 5)$

c. $(-4, 5), (-2, 2), (0, 1), (2, 2), (4, 5)$

Solution

a. Exponential function

b. Linear function

c. Quadratic function

Animated Algebra at classzone.com

Resource Planning Guide

Chapter Resource Book
- Teaching Guide/Lesson Plan
- Practice levels A, B, C
- Study Guide
- Catch-up for Absent Students
- Problem Solving Workshop
- Challenge

Workbooks
- Notetaking Guide
- Practice Workbook

Teaching Options
- **Power Presentations** provides dynamic electronic teaching resources for the classroom.
- **Activity Generator** provides editable activities for all ability levels.

Interactive Technology
- Easy Planner
- Power Presentations
- Activity Generator
- Animated Algebra
- Test Generator
- Online Quiz
- eWorkbook
- eEdition
- @HomeTutor

Resources for English Learners
- Spanish Study Guide
- Multi-Language Visual Glossary
- Student Resources in Spanish

See also the *Differentiated Instruction Resources* for more strategies for meeting individual needs.

DIFFERENCES AND RATIOS A table of values represents a linear function if the *differences* of successive *y*-values are all equal. A table of values represents an exponential function if the *ratios* of successive *y*-values are all equal. In both cases, the increments between successive *x*-values need to be equal.

Linear function: $y = 3x + 5$

x	−1	0	1	2
y	2	5	8	11

Differences: $5 - 2 = 3$ 3 3

Exponential function: $y = 0.5(2)^x$

x	−1	0	1	2
y	0.25	0.5	1	2

Ratios: $\frac{0.5}{0.25} = 2$ 2 2

ANALYZE FIRST DIFFERENCES
The first differences of a linear function are constant, which is not the case for quadratic functions or exponential functions. For instance, the first differences for the *y*-values shown for $y = 0.5(2)^x$ are $0.5 - 0.25 = 0.25$, $1 - 0.5 = 0.5$, and $2 - 1 = 1$.

You can use differences to tell whether a table of values represents a quadratic function, as shown.

Quadratic function: $y = x^2 - 2x + 2$

x	−1	0	1	2	3
y	5	2	1	2	5

First differences: −3 −1 1 3 ← First find the differences of successive *y*-values, or *first differences*.

Second differences: 2 2 2 ← Then find the differences of successive first differences, or *second differences*.

The table of values represents a quadratic function if the second differences are all equal.

EXAMPLE 2 Identify functions using differences or ratios

Use differences or ratios to tell whether the table of values represents a *linear function*, an *exponential function*, or a *quadratic function*. Extend the table to find the *y*-value for the next *x*-value.

a.

x	−2	−1	0	1	2
y	−6	−6	−4	0	6

First differences: 0 2 4 6

Second differences: 2 2 2

▶ The table of values represents a quadratic function. When $x = 3$, $y = 6 + 8 = 14$.

b.

x	−2	−1	0	1	2
y	−2	1	4	7	10

Differences: 3 3 3 3

▶ The table of values represents a linear function. When $x = 3$, $y = 10 + 3 = 13$.

✓ **GUIDED PRACTICE** for Examples 1 and 2

1. Tell whether the ordered pairs represent a *linear function*, an *exponential function*, or a *quadratic function*: (0, −1.5), (1, −0.5), (2, 2.5), (3, 7.5). **quadratic function**

2. Tell whether the table of values represents a *linear function*, an *exponential function*, or a *quadratic function*. **exponential function**

x	−2	−1	0	1
y	0.08	0.4	2	10

Motivating the Lesson

You create T-shirts with designs and slogans. You want to examine your sales for the past year to determine whether you should increase the price of the T-shirts, decrease the price, or keep the price the same. By knowing how to choose a linear, exponential, or quadratic model that fits the data, you can model the situation and determine the best price for your T-shirts.

3 TEACH

Extra Example 1

Use a graph to tell whether the ordered pairs represent a *linear function*, an *exponential function*, or a *quadratic function.*

a. $\left(-2, \frac{1}{4}\right)$, $\left(-1, \frac{1}{2}\right)$, (0, 1), (1, 2), (2, 4)

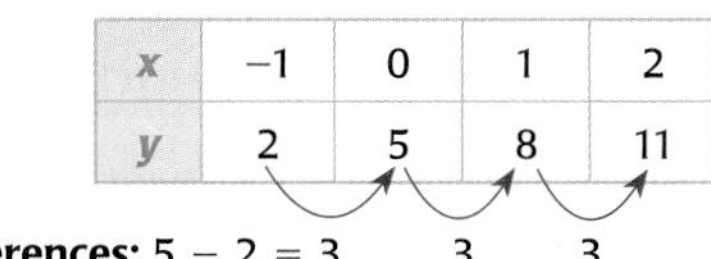
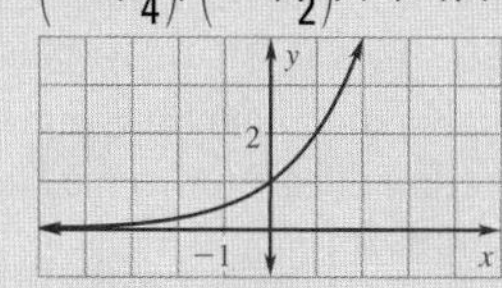

exponential function

b. (−2, −1), (−1, 0), (0, 1), (1, 2), (2, 3)

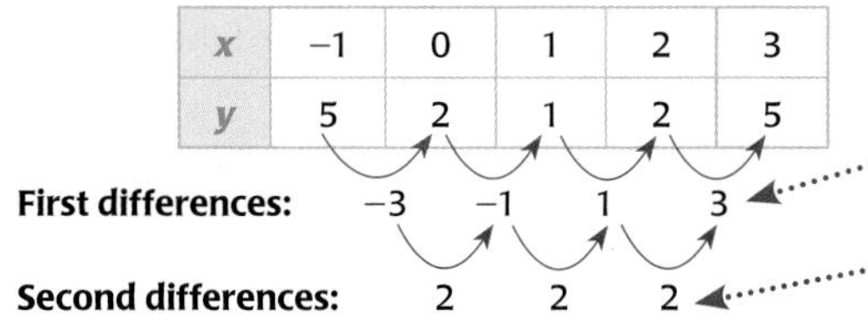
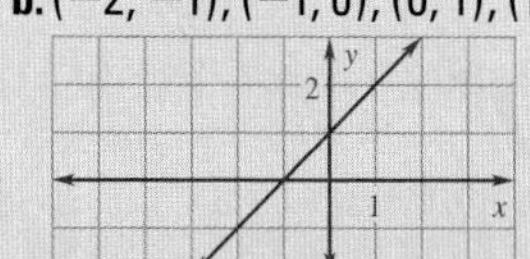

linear function

c. (−2, 5), (−1, 2), (0, 1), (1, 2), (2, 5)

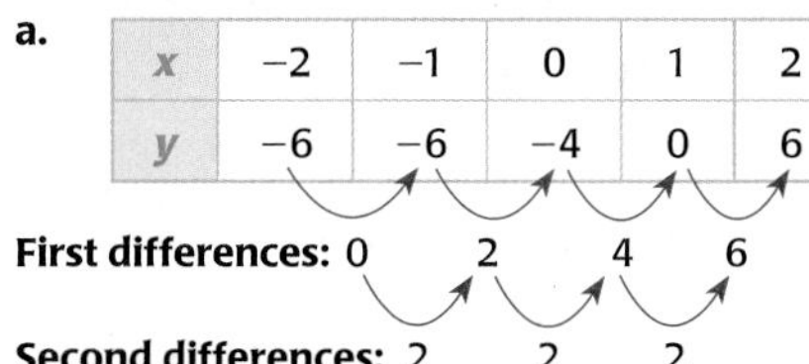
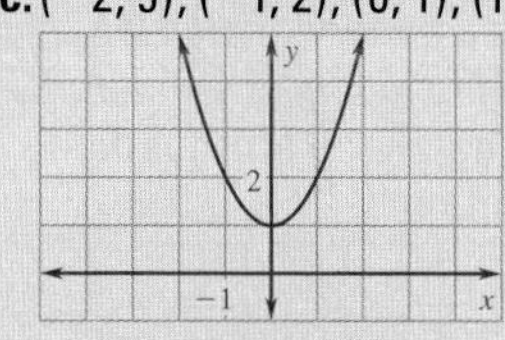

quadratic function

Animated Algebra classzone.com

An **Animated Algebra** activity is available online for **Example 1**. This activity is also part of **Power Presentations**.

Differentiated Instruction

Inclusion Some students may find a table of differences difficult to write because the alignment of the columns must be precise. One method is to align a page of ruled notebook paper so that the lines are vertical. Each ordered pair (x, y) occupies one column.

See also the *Differentiated Instruction Resources* for more strategies.

WRITING AN EQUATION When you decide that a set of ordered pairs represents a linear, an exponential, or a quadratic function, you can write an equation for the function. In this lesson, when you write an equation for a quadratic function, the equation will have the form $y = ax^2$.

EXAMPLE 3 Write an equation for a function

Tell whether the table of values represents a *linear function*, an *exponential function*, or a *quadratic function*. Then write an equation for the function.

x	−2	−1	0	1	2
y	2	0.5	0	0.5	2

Solution

STEP 1 **Determine** which type of function the table of values represents.

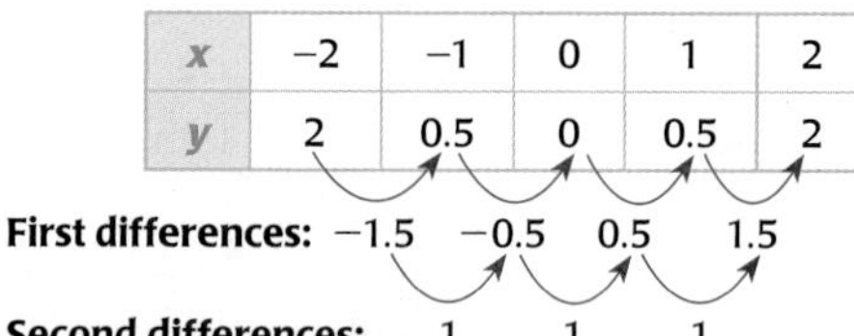

x	−2	−1	0	1	2
y	2	0.5	0	0.5	2

First differences: −1.5 −0.5 0.5 1.5

Second differences: 1 1 1

The table of values represents a quadratic function because the second differences are equal.

STEP 2 **Write** an equation for the quadratic function. The equation has the form $y = ax^2$. Find the value of a by using the coordinates of a point that lies on the graph, such as (1, 0.5).

$y = ax^2$ **Write equation for quadratic function.**

$0.5 = a(1)^2$ **Substitute 1 for x and 0.5 for y.**

$0.5 = a$ **Solve for a.**

AVOID ERRORS
In Example 3, do not use (0, 0) to find the value of a, even though (0, 0) lies on the graph of $y = ax^2$. If you do, you will obtain an undefined value for a.

▸ The equation is $y = 0.5x^2$.

CHECK Plot the ordered pairs from the table. Then graph $y = 0.5x^2$ to see that the graph passes through the plotted points.

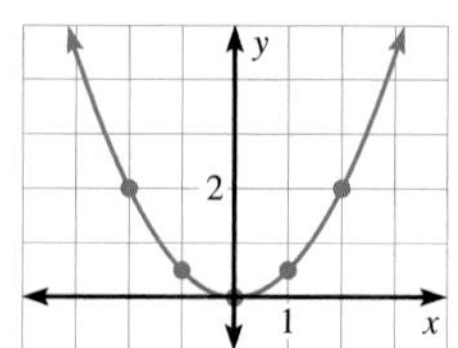

✓ **GUIDED PRACTICE** for Example 3

Tell whether the table of values represents a *linear function*, an *exponential function*, or a *quadratic function*. Then write an equation for the function.

3.

x	−3	−2	−1	0	1
y	−7	−5	−3	−1	1

4.

x	−2	−1	0	1	2
y	8	2	0	2	8

3, 4. See margin.

Extra Example 2

Use differences or ratios to tell whether the table of values represents a *linear function*, an *exponential function*, or a *quadratic function*.

a.

x	−2	−1	0	1	2
y	9	4	1	0	1

The second differences are constant, so the table represents a quadratic function.

b.

x	−2	−1	0	1	2
y	4	2	1	0.5	0.25

The ratio of successive y-values are equal, so the table represents an exponential function.

Key Questions to Ask for Example 2

- How do you know that the table of values in part (b) represents a linear function? **The differences of successive y-values are equal.**
- How is a table of values for a quadratic function different from a table of values for a linear function? **In a table for a linear function, the first differences are constant; in a table for a quadratic function, the first differences are not constant but the second differences are.**

Extra Example 3

Tell whether the table of values represents a *linear function*, an *exponential function*, or a *quadratic function*. Then write an equation for the function.

x	−2	−1	0	1	2
y	8	4	2	1	0.5

Ratios of successive y-values are equal, so the table represents an exponential function; $y = 2(0.5)^x$.

3. linear function; $y = 2x - 1$
4. quadratic function; $y = 2x^2$

EXAMPLE 4 Solve a multi-step problem

CYCLING The table shows the breathing rates y (in liters of air per minute) of a cyclist traveling at different speeds x (in miles per hour). Tell whether the data can be modeled by a *linear function*, an *exponential function*, or a *quadratic function*. Then write an equation for the function.

Speed of cyclist, x (mi/h)	20	21	22	23	24	25
Breathing rate, y (L/min)	51.4	57.1	63.3	70.3	78.0	86.6

Solution

STEP 1 **Graph** the data. The graph has a slight curve. So, a linear function does not appear to model the data.

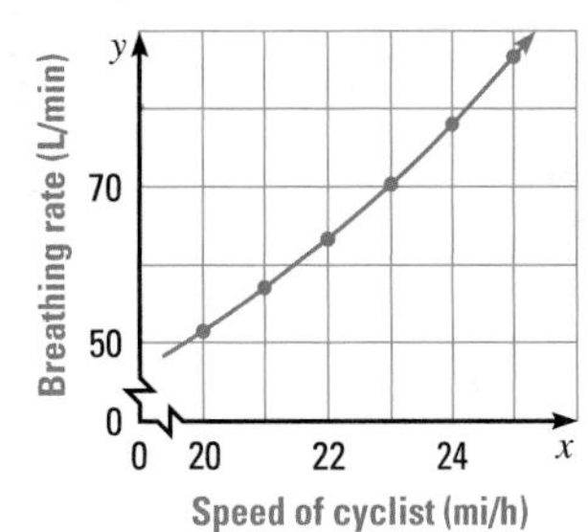

STEP 2 **Decide** which function models the data.

In the table below, notice that $\frac{57.1}{51.4} \approx 1.11$, $\frac{63.3}{57.1} \approx 1.11$, $\frac{70.3}{63.3} \approx 1.11$, $\frac{78.0}{70.3} \approx 1.11$, and $\frac{86.6}{78.0} \approx 1.11$. So, the ratios are all approximately equal. An exponential function models the data.

Speed of cyclist, x (mi/h)	20	21	22	23	24	25
Breathing rate, y (L/min)	51.4	57.1	63.3	70.3	78.0	86.6

Ratios: 1.11 1.11 1.11 1.11 1.11

STEP 3 **Write** an equation for the exponential function. The breathing rate increases by a factor of 1.11 liters per minute, so $b = 1.11$. Find the value of a by using one of the data pairs, such as (20, 51.4).

$y = ab^x$ **Write equation for exponential function.**

$51.4 = a(1.11)^{20}$ **Substitute 1.11 for *b*, 20 for *x*, and 51.4 for *y*.**

$\frac{51.4}{(1.11)^{20}} = a$ **Solve for *a*.**

$6.38 \approx a$ **Use a calculator.**

▶ The equation is $y = 6.38(1.11)^x$.

REVIEW EXPONENTIAL FUNCTIONS

For help with writing an equation for an exponential function, see p. 520.

✓ **GUIDED PRACTICE** for Example 4

5. In Example 4, suppose the cyclist is traveling at 15 miles per hour. Find the breathing rate of the cyclist at this speed. **about 30.5 liters of air per minute**

Extra Example 4

The table shows the cost to run an ad in a magazine. Tell whether the data can be modeled by a *linear function*, an *exponential function*, or a *quadratic function*. Then write an equation for the function.

Number of lines, x	Total cost, y
4	\$10.40
5	\$12.25
6	\$14.10
7	\$15.95
8	\$17.80
9	\$19.65

The equation can be modeled by a linear function; $y = 1.85x + 3$

Closing the Lesson

Have students summarize the major points of the lesson and answer the Essential Question: How do you decide whether a linear, exponential, or quadratic model best describes data?

- **A table of values represents a linear function if the differences of successive *y*-values are equal.**
- **A table of values represents an exponential function if the ratios of successive *y*-values are equal.**
- **A table of values represents a quadratic function if the second differences of successive *y*-values are equal.**

To identify whether a function is linear, exponential, or quadratic, plot points, draw the graph, and then identify the function from the graph. If given a table of values, use differences and ratios to identify the type of function.

HOMEWORK KEY

○ = **WORKED-OUT SOLUTIONS** on p. WS25 for Exs. 7, 13, and 25

★ = **STANDARDIZED TEST PRACTICE** Exs. 2, 18, 26, and 27

◆ = **MULTIPLE REPRESENTATIONS** Ex. 25

4 PRACTICE AND APPLY

Assignment Guide

Answer Transparencies available for all exercises

Basic:
Day 1: pp. 688–691
Exs. 1–11, 35–43
Day 2: pp. 688–691
Exs. 12–20, 23–26, 29–34

Average:
Day 1: pp. 688–691
Exs. 1–11, 35–43
Day 2: pp. 688–691
Exs. 14–21, 23–27, 29–34

Advanced:
Day 1: pp. 688–691
Exs. 1–11, 35–43
Day 2: pp. 688–691
Exs. 15–18, 20–34*

Block:
pp. 688–691
Exs. 1–11, 14–21, 23–27, 29–43

Differentiated Instruction

See *Differentiated Instruction Resources* for suggestions on addressing the needs of a diverse classroom.

Homework Check

For a quick check of student understanding of key concepts, go over the following exercises:

Basic: 4, 6, 12, 15, 23
Average: 3, 8, 15, 20, 24
Advanced: 10, 16, 20, 25, 26

Extra Practice

- Student Edition, p. 947
- Chapter Resource Book: Practice levels A, B, C

Practice Worksheet

An easily-readable reduced practice page (with answers) for this lesson can be found on p. 626C.

SKILL PRACTICE

A

1. **VOCABULARY** Copy and complete: A function that is of the form $y = ab^x$ is a(n) _?_. **exponential function**

2. ★ **WRITING** *Describe* how you can tell whether a table of values represents a quadratic function. **See margin.**

EXAMPLE 1 on p. 684 for Exs. 3–11

MATCHING **Match the function with the graph that the function represents.**

3. Linear function **B**
4. Exponential function **C**
5. Quadratic function **A**

A.
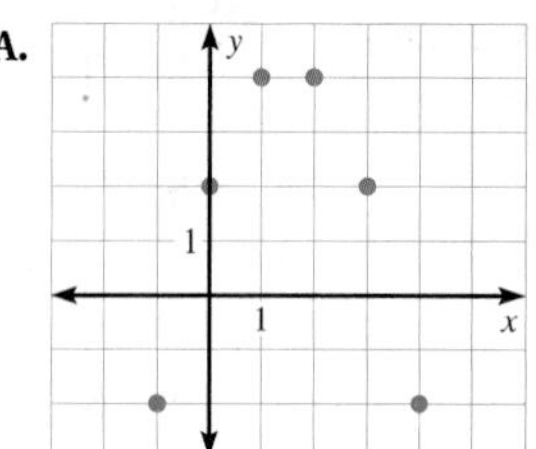

B.

C.

USING A GRAPH **Use a graph to tell whether the ordered pairs represent a *linear function*, an *exponential function*, or a *quadratic function*.**

6. (−4, −7), (−2, −1), (0, 1), (2, −1), (4, −7) **quadratic function**
7. (−5, −1), (−3, 0), (−1, 1), (1, 2), (3, 3) **linear function**
8. $\left(-1, \frac{1}{16}\right), \left(0, \frac{1}{4}\right)$, (1, 1), (2, 4), (3, 16) **exponential function**
9. (−1, 8), (1, 2), $\left(3, \frac{1}{2}\right), \left(5, \frac{1}{8}\right), \left(7, \frac{1}{32}\right)$ **exponential function**
10. (−4, −4), (−2, −3.5), (0, −3), (2, −2.5) **linear function**
11. (−1, 0.5), (0, −0.5), (1, 0.5), (2, 3.5) **quadratic function**

EXAMPLES 2 and 3 on p. 685–686 for Exs. 12–19

USING DIFFERENCES AND RATIOS **Tell whether the table of values represents a *linear function*, an *exponential function*, or a *quadratic function*. Then write an equation for the function.**

12.
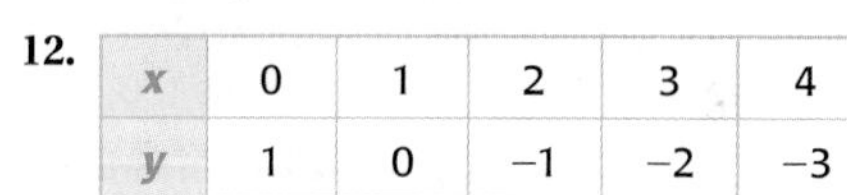

x	0	1	2	3	4
y	1	0	−1	−2	−3

linear function; $y = -x + 1$

13.
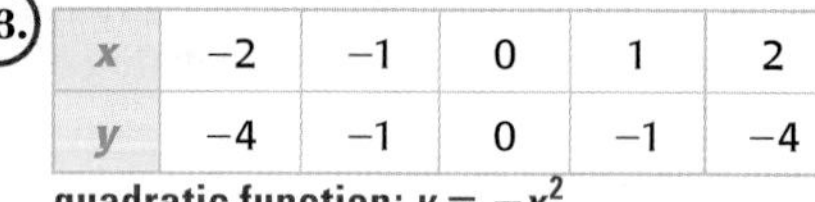

x	−2	−1	0	1	2
y	−4	−1	0	−1	−4

quadratic function; $y = -x^2$

14.

x	−3	−2	−1	0	1
y	13.5	6	1.5	0	1.5

quadratic function; $y = 1.5x^2$

15.

x	−2	−1	0	1	2
y	−5	−2	1	4	7

linear function; $y = 3x + 1$

16.
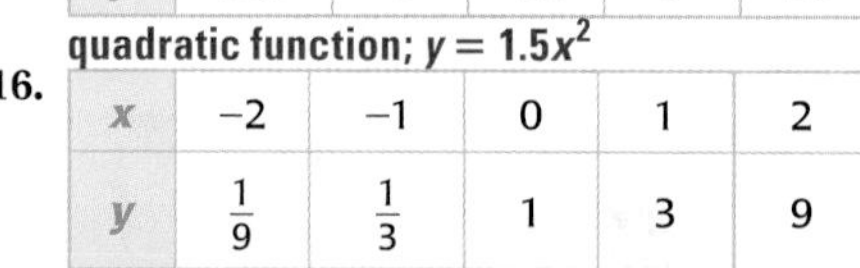

x	−2	−1	0	1	2
y	$\frac{1}{9}$	$\frac{1}{3}$	1	3	9

exponential function; $y = 3^x$

17.

x	−1	0	1	2	3
y	16	4	1	$\frac{1}{4}$	$\frac{1}{16}$

exponential function; $y = 4\left(\frac{1}{4}\right)^x$

18. ★ **MULTIPLE CHOICE** Which function is represented by the following ordered pairs: (−1, 4), (0, 0), (1, 4), (2, 16), (3, 36)? **C**

Ⓐ $y = 0.25x^2$ Ⓑ $y = 4^x$ Ⓒ $y = 4x^2$ Ⓓ $y = 4x$

2. Find the differences of successive *y*-values, called the first differences. If they are not equal, then find the differences of successive first differences, called second differences. If the second differences are equal, then the table of values represents a quadratic function.

19. **ERROR ANALYSIS** *Describe* and correct the error in writing an equation for the function represented by the ordered pairs. **See margin.**

(0, 0), (1, 2.5), (2, 10), (3, 22.5), (4, 40)

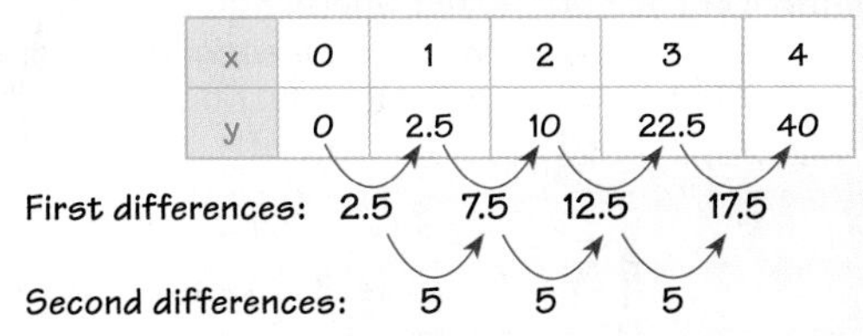

x 0 1 2 3 4
y 0 2.5 10 22.5 40
First differences: 2.5 7.5 12.5 17.5
Second differences: 5 5 5

The ordered pairs represent a quadratic function.

$y = ax^2$

$2 = a(10)^2$

$0.02 = a$

So, the equation is $y = 0.02x^2$.

B 20. **REASONING** Use the graph shown.

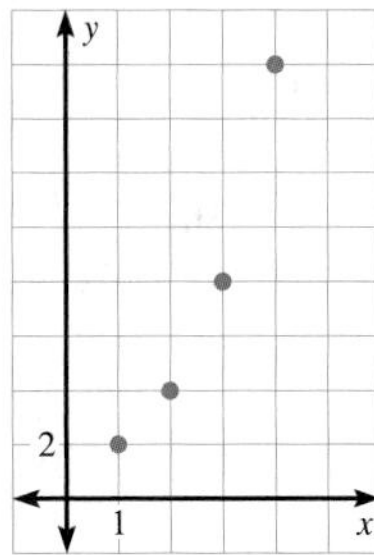

a. Tell whether the graph represents an *exponential function* or a *quadratic function* by looking at the graph. **exponential function**

b. Make a table of values for the points on the graph. Then use differences or ratios to check your answer in part (a). **See margin.**

c. Write an equation for the function that the table of values from part (b) represents. **$y = 2^x$**

21. **GEOMETRY** The table shows the area A (in square centimeters) of an equilateral triangle for various side lengths s (in centimeters). Write an equation for the function that the table of values represents. Then find the area of an equilateral triangle that has a side length of 10 centimeters.

Side length, s (cm)	1	2	3	4	5
Area, A (cm²)	$0.25\sqrt{3}$	$\sqrt{3}$	$2.25\sqrt{3}$	$4\sqrt{3}$	$6.25\sqrt{3}$

$A = \left(\frac{\sqrt{3}}{4}\right)s^2$; $25\sqrt{3}$ cm²

C 22. **CHALLENGE** In the ordered pairs below, the y-values are given in terms of m. Tell whether the ordered pairs represent a *linear function*, an *exponential function*, or a *quadratic function*.

$(1, 3m - 1), (2, 10m + 2), (3, 26m), (4, 51m - 7), (5, 85m - 19)$ **quadratic function**

PROBLEM SOLVING

EXAMPLE 4 on p. 687 for Exs. 23–25

A 23. **LIZARDS** The table shows the body temperature B (in degrees Celsius) of a desert spiny lizard at various air temperatures A (in degrees Celsius). Tell whether the data can be modeled by a *linear function*, an *exponential function*, or a *quadratic function*. Then write an equation for the function.

Air temperature, A (°C)	26	27	28	29	30
Body temperature, B (°C)	33.44	33.78	34.12	34.46	34.80

@HomeTutor for problem solving help at classzone.com

linear function; $y = 0.34x + 24.6$

Avoiding Common Errors

Exercises 6–11, 12–17 A common error arises out of trying to identify a function by looking at a table of values or ordered pairs without graphing the ordered pairs or checking for differences or ratios in the table of values. Encourage students to plot points and calculate differences and ratios.

Graphing Calculator

Exercises 12–17 Encourage students to use their graphing calculators to check their equations.

Internet Reference

Exercise 23 More information about desert spiny lizards can be found at www.werc.usgs.gov/fieldguide/scma.htm

19. The x- and y-values were reversed when substituting the coordinates of the ordered pair (2, 10) into the equation $y = ax^2$. Substituting 2 for x and 10 for y gives $10 = a(2)^2$, $a = 2.5$; so, the equation is $y = 2.5x^2$.

20b.

x	1	2	3	4
y	2	4	8	16
Ratios of successive y-values		$\frac{4}{2} = 2$	$\frac{8}{4} = 2$	$\frac{16}{8} = 2$

The ratios are the same, so the table of values and the graph represent an exponential function.

Study Strategy

Exercises 24–27 Remind students that for data modeled by exponential functions, the ratios may be approximately equal, not exact. Students should also keep in mind that for quadratic functions, second difference are equal and first differences are not.

25a. Troy: Population doubled every decade; data can be modeled by an exponential function. Union: Population increased by a fixed amount every decade; data can be modeled by a linear function.

25b.

Decades since 1970	Troy's pop.
0	3000
1	6000
2	12,000
3	24,000
4	48,000

Decades since 1970	Union's pop.
0	3000
1	6000
2	9000
3	12,000
4	15,000

Troy: Ratios of successive y-values are equal. Union: First differences are constant.

c. Let P = population and n = number of decades since 1970. Troy: $P = 3000 \cdot 2^n$, 192,000; Union: $P = 3000n + 3000$; 21,000

24. **NAUTILUS** A chambered nautilus is a marine animal that lives in the outermost chamber of its shell. When the nautilus outgrows a chamber, it adds a new, larger chamber to its shell. The table shows the volumes (in cubic centimeters) of consecutive chambers of a nautilus. Tell whether the data can be modeled by a *linear function*, an *exponential function*, or a *quadratic function*. Then write an equation for the function. **exponential function; $y = 0.789(1.06)^x$**

Chamber	1	2	3	4	5	6
Volume (cm^3)	0.836	0.889	0.945	1.005	1.068	1.135

@HomeTutor for problem solving help at classzone.com

B (25) ◆ **MULTIPLE REPRESENTATIONS** In 1970, the populations of Troy and Union were each 3000. From 1970 to 2010, the population of Troy doubled every decade. The population of Union increased by 3000 every decade. For each town, consider the set of data pairs (n, P) where n is the number of decades since 1970 and P is the population. **a–c. See margin.**

a. **Describing in Words** Tell whether the data for each town can be modeled by a *linear function*, an *exponential function*, or a *quadratic function*. *Explain* your reasoning.

b. **Making a Table** Make a table for each town. Use the tables to justify your answers in part (a).

c. **Writing a Model** For each town, do the following: Write an equation for the function that models the data. Suppose that the growth pattern continues. *Predict* the population in 2030.

26. ★ **MULTIPLE CHOICE** The table shows the cost of a custom circular rug for various diameters (in feet). What is the approximate cost of a custom circular rug that has a diameter of 8 feet? **C**

Diameter (ft)	2	3	4	5	6
Cost (dollars)	28.40	63.90	113.60	177.50	255.60

(A) \$333.70 (B) \$411.80 (C) \$454.40 (D) \$908.80

27. ★ **EXTENDED RESPONSE** The time it takes for a clock's pendulum to swing from one side to the other and back again, as shown in the back view of the clock, is called the pendulum's period. The table shows the period t (in seconds) of a pendulum of length ℓ (in feet).

Period, t (sec)	1	2	3	4	5
Length, ℓ (ft)	0.82	3.28	7.38	13.12	20.5

a. **Model** Tell whether the data can be modeled by a *linear function*, an *exponential function*, or a *quadratic function*. Then write an equation for the function. **quadratic function; $\ell = 0.82t^2$**

b. **Apply** Find the length of a pendulum that has a period of 0.5 second. **0.205 ft**

c. **Analyze** How does decreasing the length of the pendulum by 50% change the period? *Justify* your answer using several examples. **See margin.**

○ = WORKED-OUT SOLUTIONS on p. WS1 ★ = STANDARDIZED TEST PRACTICE ◆ = MULTIPLE REPRESENTATIONS

27c. The period decreases by about 71%. For example, consider $t = 4$ for $\ell = 13.12$. To find t for 50% of ℓ, solve $0.5(13.12) = 0.82t^2$; $t \approx 2.83$, and $\frac{2.83}{4} = 0.708$, so the period decreased by about 71%. Consider $t = 2$ for $\ell = 3.28$. To find t for 50% of ℓ, solve $0.5(3.28) = 0.82t^2$; $t \approx 1.41$, and $\frac{1.41}{2} = 0.705$, so the period decreased by about 71%. Consider $t = 1$ for $\ell = 0.82$. To find t for 50% of ℓ, solve $0.5(0.82) = 0.82t^2$; $t \approx 0.707$, and $\frac{0.707}{1} = 0.707$, so the period decreased by about 71%.

C **28. CHALLENGE** The table shows the height h (in feet) that a pole vaulter's center of gravity reaches for various running speeds s (in feet per second) at the moment the pole vaulter launches himself into the air.

Running speed, s (ft/sec)	30	31	32	33	34
Height of center of gravity, h (ft)	$14\frac{1}{16}$	$15\frac{1}{64}$	16	$17\frac{1}{64}$	$18\frac{1}{16}$

a. A pole vaulter is running at $31\frac{1}{2}$ feet per second when he launches himself into the air. Find the height that the pole vaulter's center of gravity reaches. **about 15.5 ft**

b. Find the speed at which the pole vaulter needs to be running when he launches himself into the air in order for his center of gravity to reach a height of 19 feet. Round your answer to the nearest foot per second. **about 35 ft/sec**

MIXED REVIEW

PREVIEW Prepare for Lesson 11.1 in Exs. 29–43.

Approximate the square root to the nearest integer. *(p. 110)*

29. $\sqrt{32}$ **6**
30. $\sqrt{45}$ **7**
31. $-\sqrt{10}$ **−3**
32. $-\sqrt{60}$ **−8**
33. $-\sqrt{79}$ **−9**
34. $\sqrt{57}$ **8**

Graph the function. Compare the graph with the graph of $f(x) = x$. *(p. 262)* **35–40. See margin.**

35. $g(x) = x - 4$
36. $g(x) = x + 1$
37. $g(x) = 8x$
38. $g(x) = -x$
39. $g(x) = \frac{1}{4}x$
40. $g(x) = -\frac{1}{2}x$

Graph the function. Compare the graph with the graph of $y = x^2$. *(p. 628)* **41–43. See margin.**

41. $y = 7x^2$
42. $y = -\frac{1}{5}x^2$
43. $y = 2x^2 + 3$

QUIZ *for Lessons 10.7–10.8*

Tell whether the equation has *two solutions, one solution,* or *no solution*. *(p. 678)*

1. $x^2 + x + 5 = 0$ **no solution**
2. $5x^2 + 4x - 1 = 0$ **two solutions**

Find the number of x-intercepts of the graph of the function. *(p. 678)*

3. $y = -3x^2 + 4x - 2$ **0**
4. $y = \frac{4}{9}x^2 + 4x + 9$ **1**

Tell whether the table of values represents a *linear function*, an *exponential function*, or a *quadratic function*. Then write an equation for the function. *(p. 684)*

5. **quadratic function; $y = -0.25x^2$**

x	−6	−3	0	3	6
y	−9	−2.25	0	−2.25	−9

6. **exponential function; $y = 25\left(\frac{1}{5}\right)^x$**

x	1	2	3	4	5
y	5	1	$\frac{1}{5}$	$\frac{1}{25}$	$\frac{1}{125}$

35–43. See Additional Answers beginning on p. AA1.

5 ASSESS AND RETEACH

Daily Homework Quiz

Transparency Available

1. Tell whether the data can be modeled by a *linear function*, an *exponential function*, or a *quadratic function*. **quadratic**

x	−2	−1	0	1	2
y	7	1	−1	1	7

2. Tell whether the data can be modeled by a *linear function*, an *exponential function*, or a *quadratic function*. Then write an equation for the function.

x	1	2	3	4	5
y	0.05	0.1	0.2	0.4	0.8

exponential; $y = 0.025(2)^x$

Online Quiz

Available at **classzone.com**

Diagnosis/Remediation

- Practice A, B, C in Chapter Resource Book
- Study Guide in Chapter Resource Book
- Practice Workbook
- @HomeTutor

Challenge

Additional challenge is available in the Chapter Resource Book.

Quiz

An easily-readable reduced copy of the quiz (with answers) on Lessons 10.7–10.8 from the Assessment Book can be found on p. 626G.

10.8 Perform Regressions

QUESTION How can you use a graphing calculator to find models for data?

On page 335, you used a graphing calculator to perform linear regression on data to find a linear model for the data. A graphing calculator can also be used to perform exponential regression and quadratic regression.

EXAMPLE 1 Use exponential regression to find a model

The table shows the sales (in millions of dollars) of organic milk, organic half and half, and organic cream in the U.S. each year for the period 1996–2000. Find an exponential model for the data.

Year	1996	1997	1998	1999	2000
Sales (millions of dollars)	15.8	30.7	46	75.7	104

***STEP 1* Enter data**

Enter the data into two lists. Let $x = 0$ represent 1996.

L1	L2	L3
0	15.8	
1	30.7	
2	46	
3	75.7	
4	104	

L2(4)=104

***STEP 2* Make scatter plot**

Make a scatter plot of the data. Notice that the points show an exponential trend.

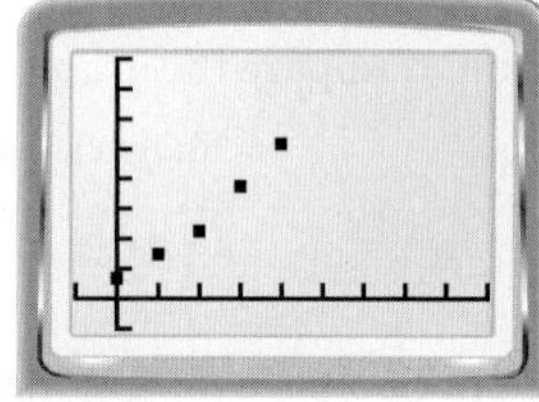

***STEP 3* Perform regression**

Use the exponential regression feature to obtain the model $y = 17.5(1.6)^x$.

***STEP 4* Check model**

Check how well the model fits the data by graphing the model and the data.

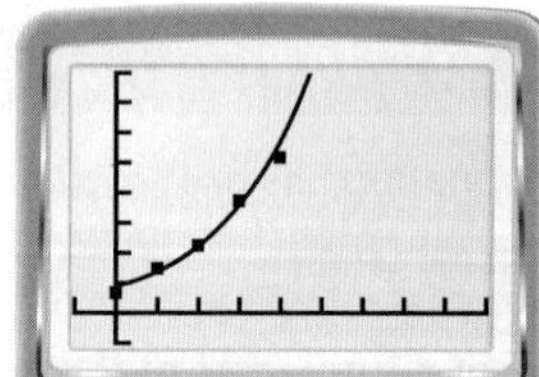

PRACTICE

1. The table shows the value of a car over time. Find an exponential model for the data. Use the model to estimate the value of the car after 7 years. **$y = 15{,}600(0.866)^x$; about $5698**

Age of car (years)	0	1	2	3	4	5
Value (dollars)	15,600	13,510	11,700	10,132	8774	7598

1 PLAN AND PREPARE

Learn the Method

- Students will use a graphing calculator to find models for data.
- After the activity, students can use a graphing calculator to check their solutions in Lesson 10.8, Exercises 23–27.

Keystroke Help

Keystrokes for several models of calculators are available in blackline format in the *Chapter Resource Book*.

2 TEACH

Tips for Success

For both examples, encourage students to check that they entered the data correctly.

Extra Example 1

The table shows the shipment (in millions of units) of DVD videos in the U.S. each year for the period 1998–2003. Find an exponential model for the data.

Year	Shipments (millions of units)
1998	0.5
1999	2.5
2000	3.3
2001	7.9
2002	10.7
2003	17.5

$y = 0.83(1.9)^x$

@HomeTutor
classzone.com
Keystrokes

EXAMPLE 2 Use quadratic regression to find a model

The table shows the number of subscribers to the first U.S. digital satellite radio service for various months after its launch. Find a quadratic model for the data.

Months after launch	0	3	6	9	12	15
Subscribers	500	31,000	76,000	135,500	201,500	360,000

STEP 1 *Make scatter plot*
Enter the data into two lists and make a scatter plot. Notice the quadratic trend in the data.

STEP 2 *Perform regression*
Use the quadratic regression feature to obtain the model $y = 1440x^2 + 1010x + 8000$.

STEP 3 *Check model*
Check how well the model fits the data by graphing the model and the data.

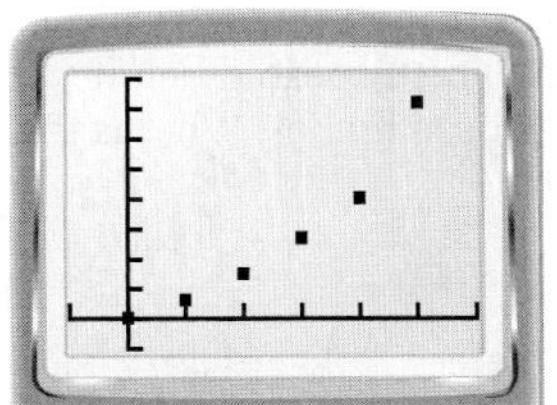

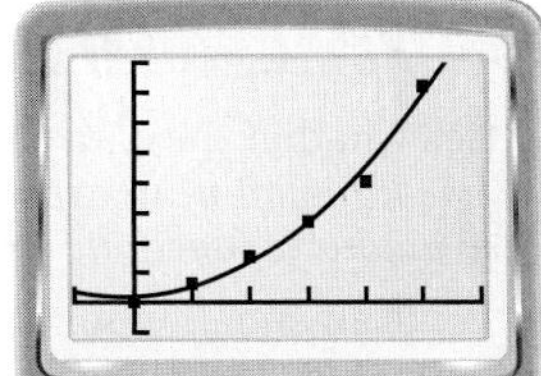

PRACTICE

2. The table shows the maximum weight that can be supported by a 16 foot floor beam of different depths. Find a quadratic model for the data. **$y = 10.2x^2 - 96.8x + 285.4$**

Depth (inches)	6	7.5	9	10.5	12	13.5
Weight (pounds)	68	137	242	389	586	838

DRAW CONCLUSIONS

3. The table shows the temperature (in degrees Fahrenheit) of a cup of hot chocolate over time. Find an exponential model and a quadratic model for the data. Make a scatter plot of the data and graph both models. Which model fits the data better? *Explain.* **See margin.**

Time (minutes)	0	10	20	30	40	50	60
Temperature (°F)	200	157	128	109	99	92	90

4. **DATA COLLECTION** For this exercise, you will need a collection of pennies. Use a compass to draw 7 or 8 circles with diameters d ranging in size from 8 centimeters to 20 centimeters. Count the number n of pennies you need to (**a**) surround each circle completely and (**b**) cover each circle completely. For each set of ordered pairs (d, n), find a linear model, an exponential model, and a quadratic model, and tell which model fits the data best. **See margin.**

Extra Example 2

The table shows the number (in thousands) of basic cable television subscribers in the U.S. from 1997–2002. Find a quadratic model for the data.

Year	Number of Subscribers (in hundred thousands)
1997	636
1998	646.5
1999	855
2000	862.5
2001	667.32
2002	664.72

$y = -30x^2 + 156x + 607$

3 ASSESS AND RETEACH

The table shows the time it takes Nikki to keyboard 200 words each week with practice. Find an exponential and a quadratic model for the data. Does the exponential or the quadratic model fit the data better? *Explain.*

Week	Number of Minutes to Keyboard 200 Words
1	6
2	5.7
3	4.7
4	4.5
5	3.9
6	3.7

The quadratic model is $y = 0.038x^2 - 0.75x + 6.8$ and the exponential model is $y = 6.70(0.9)^x$. Both models fit the data, so one model is not better than the other.

3. $y = 179(0.987)^x$, $y = 0.040x^2 - 4.13x + 197$

The exponential model; although the quadratic model appears to fit the given data points more closely than the exponential model does, the graph shows that after the last data point, (60, 90), the quadratic model implies increasing temperatures as time goes on, while the exponential model shows gradually decreasing temperatures as time goes on; the exponential model is a more accurate model of what will happen as the hot chocolate continues to cool.

4. Models may vary, but a linear model should fit the data in part (a) best, and a quadratic model should fit the data in part (b) best.

3. No; substitute 20 for h in the equation from part (a) to find the time at which the flyer's center of gravity reaches a height of 20 feet: $20 = -16t^2 + 30t + 4.5$, or $16t^2 - 30t + 15.5 = 0$. The discriminant is -92. Since the discriminant is negative, the equation has no solution, and the flyer's center of gravity never reaches a height of 20 feet.

4. *Sample answer:* 37 ft/sec; to show that $25 = -16t^2 + 37t + 4.5$ has at least one solution, first write the equation in standard form, $16t^2 - 37t + 20.5 = 0$; find the discriminant to be 57. Since the discriminant is positive, the equation has two solutions.

5b. Yes; using the value of the discriminant, 1.44, evaluate the quadratic formula for the equation $-0.05x^2 + 2.2x - 17 = 0$;
$x = \frac{-2.2 \pm \sqrt{1.44}}{(2)(-0.05)}$; $x = 10$ *or* $x = 34$.
$x = 10$ corresponds to the year $1990 + 10 = 2000$, which is in the given period of 1990–2000.
$x = 34$ corresponds to the year $1990 + 34 = 2024$, which is not in the given period of 1990–2000.

7. No; let x be the length of the rectangular dog pen of perimeter 24 feet. Then $12 - x$ is the width of the dog pen and its area is represented by the expression $x(12 - x)$. To find the value of x for which the area will be 150 square feet, solve the equation $150 = x(12 - x)$. Write the equation in standard form, $x^2 - 12x + 150 = 0$; find the value of the discriminant, -456. Since the discriminant is negative, the equation has no solution, and the 24 feet of fencing cannot enclose an area of 150 square feet.

8c. Because x represents a length, x cannot be a negative number.

MIXED REVIEW *of Problem Solving*

STATE TEST PRACTICE
classzone.com

Lessons 10.5–10.8

1. **MULTI-STEP PROBLEM** Different masses (in kilograms) are hung from a spring. The distances (in centimeters) that the spring stretches are shown in the table.

Mass (kilograms)	Distance (centimeters)
1	2.6
2	5.2
3	7.8
4	10.4
5	13.0

   a. Tell whether the data can be modeled by a *linear function*, an *exponential function*, or a *quadratic function*. **linear function**

   b. Write an equation for the function. **$y = 2.6x$**

2. **MULTI-STEP PROBLEM** In slow-pitch softball, the ball is pitched in an underhand motion. A batter in a softball game is pitched a ball that has an initial height of 2 feet above the ground and an initial vertical velocity of 35 feet per second.

   a. Write an equation for the height h (in feet) of the ball as a function of the time t (in seconds) after it is pitched. **$h = -16t^2 + 35t + 2$**

   b. The batter hits the ball when it is 2.5 feet above the ground. How long after the ball is pitched is the ball hit? Round your answer to the nearest tenth of a second. **2.2 sec**

3. **SHORT RESPONSE** Part of a cheerleading routine involves throwing a flyer straight up into the air and catching her on the way down. The flyer begins this stunt with her center of gravity 4.5 feet above the ground, and she is thrown with an initial vertical velocity of 30 feet per second. Will her center of gravity reach a height of 20 feet? *Explain.* **See margin.**

4. **OPEN-ENDED** In Exercise 3, suppose the flyer wants to have her center of gravity reach a height of at least 25 feet above the ground. Give an initial vertical velocity that will accomplish this. Use the discriminant to show that your answer is correct. **See margin.**

5. **SHORT RESPONSE** For the period 1990–2000, the sales y (in billions of dollars) of computers, computer accessories, and computer software can be modeled by the function $y = -0.05x^2 + 2.2x + 7$ where x is the number of years since 1990.

   a. Use the discriminant to determine the number of values of x that correspond to $y = 24$. **2**

   b. Were there any years during the period 1990–2000 in which the sales reached 24 billion dollars? *Explain.* **See margin.**

6. **GRIDDED ANSWER** The trapezoid below has an area of 54 square inches. What is the value of x? **5**

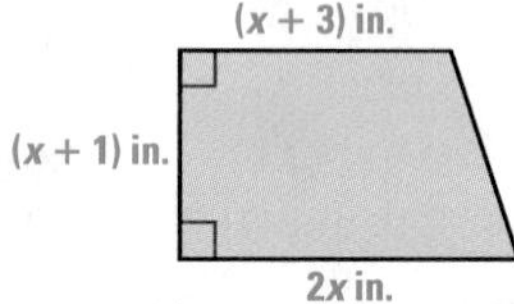

7. **SHORT RESPONSE** You have 24 feet of fencing that you are using to make a rectangular dog pen. You want the dog pen to enclose 150 square feet. Is it possible for the 24 feet of fencing to enclose a rectangular area of 150 square feet? *Explain.* **See margin.**

8. **EXTENDED RESPONSE** You are making a tiled tabletop with a uniform mosaic tile border as shown.

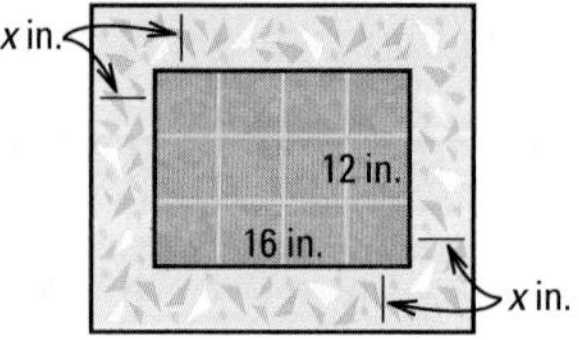

   a. Write an equation for the area A (in square inches) of the border. **$A = 4x^2 + 56x$**

   b. You have enough mosaic tiles to cover 130 square inches. What should the width of the border be? Round your answer to the nearest inch. **about 2 in.**

   c. *Explain* why you could ignore one of the values of x in part (b). **See margin.**

Animated Algebra
classzone.com
Electronic Function Library

BIG IDEAS

For Your Notebook

Big Idea 1

Graphing Quadratic Functions

You can use the properties below to graph any quadratic function.

The graph of $y = ax^2 + bx + c$ is a parabola that:

- opens up if $a > 0$ and opens down if $a < 0$.
- is narrower than the graph of $y = x^2$ if $|a| > 1$ and wider if $|a| < 1$.
- has an axis of symmetry of $x = -\frac{b}{2a}$.
- has a vertex with an x-coordinate of $-\frac{b}{2a}$.
- has a y-intercept of c. So, the point $(0, c)$ is on the parabola.

$y = ax^2 + bx + c, a > 0$

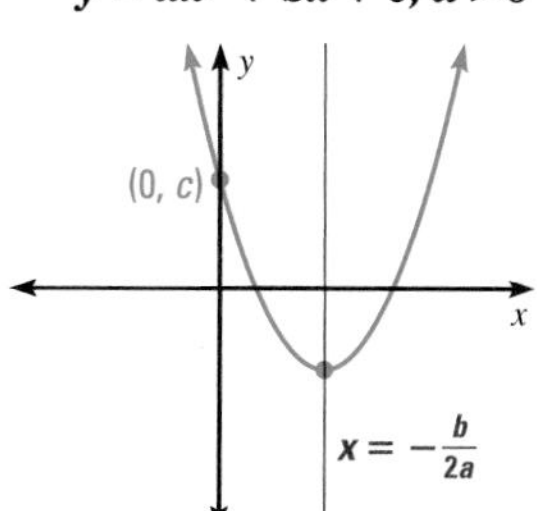

Big Idea 2

Solving Quadratic Equations

You can use the following methods to solve a quadratic equation. Sometimes it is easier to use one method instead of another.

Method	Lesson	When to use
Graphing	10.3	Use when approximate solutions are adequate.
Finding square roots	10.4	Use when solving an equation that can be written in the form $x^2 = d$.
Completing the square	10.5	Can be used for *any* quadratic equation $y = ax^2 + bx + c$ but is simplest to apply when $a = 1$ and b is an even number.
Quadratic formula	10.6	Can be used for *any* quadratic equation

Big Idea 3

Comparing Linear, Exponential, and Quadratic Models

You can use linear, exponential, and quadratic functions to model data.

Function	Example	x- and y-values
Linear	$y = 5x + 1$	If the increments between successive x-values are equal, the differences of successive y-values are all equal.
Exponential	$y = 3(2)^x$	If the increments between successive x-values are equal, the ratios of successive y-values are all equal.
Quadratic	$y = x^2 - 4x + 6$	If the increments between successive x-values are equal, the differences of successive first differences of y-values are all equal.

Additional Resources

The following resources are available to help review the materials in this chapter.

Chapter Resource Book
- Chapter Review Games and Activities
- Cumulative Practice, Chs. 1–10

Student Resources in Spanish

eWorkbook

@HomeTutor

Vocabulary Practice

Vocabulary practice is available at **classzone.com**

10 CHAPTER REVIEW

@HomeTutor
classzone.com
- Multi-Language Glossary
- Vocabulary practice

Extra Example 10.1

Graph $y = -x^2 + 1$. Compare the graph with the graph of $y = x^2$.

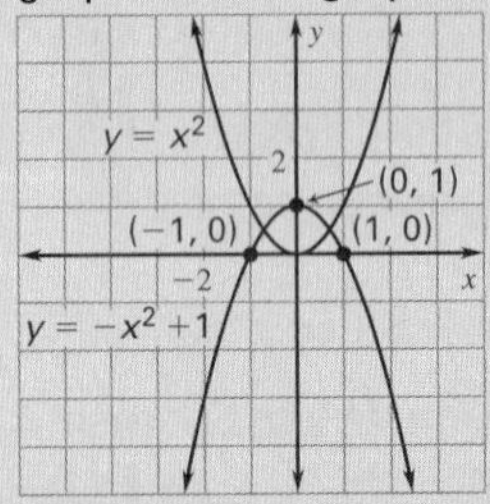

Both graphs have the same line of symmetry, $x = 0$. The graph of $y = -x^2 + 1$ is a reflection in the x-axis of $y = x^2$ and then a vertical translation (of 1 unit up).

5.

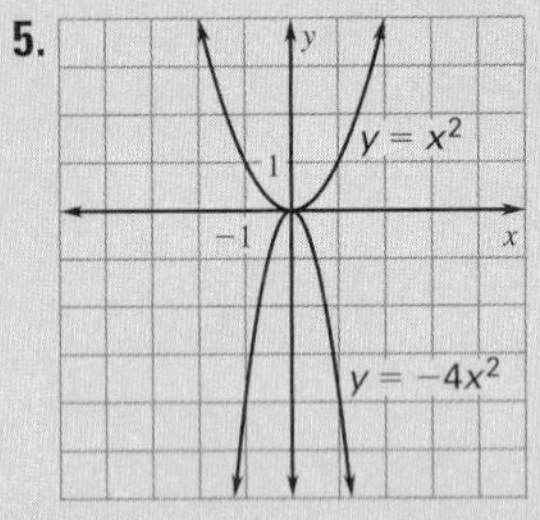

The graph is a vertical stretch (by a factor of 4) with a reflection in the x-axis of the graph of $y = x^2$.

6.

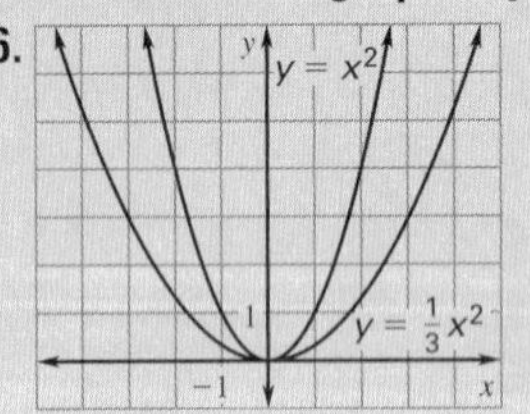

The graph is a vertical shrink $\left(\text{by a factor of } \frac{1}{3}\right)$ of the graph of $y = x^2$.

7.

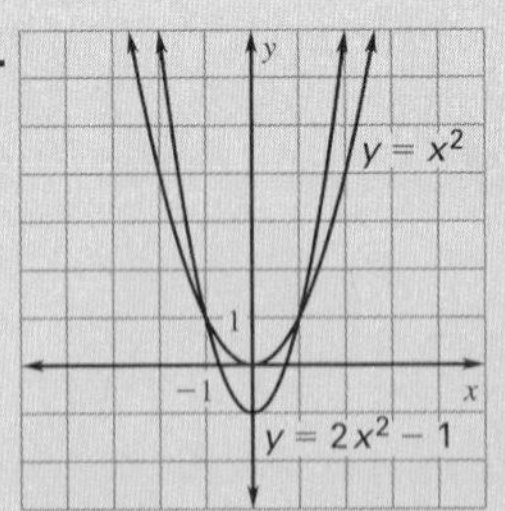

The graph is a vertical stretch (by a factor of 2) with a vertical translation (of 1 unit down) of the graph of $y = x^2$.

REVIEW KEY VOCABULARY

- quadratic function, *p. 628*
- standard form of a quadratic function, *p. 628*
- parabola, *p. 628*
- parent quadratic function, *p. 628*
- vertex of a parabola, *p. 628*
- axis of symmetry, *p. 628*
- minimum value, *p. 636*
- maximum value, *p. 636*
- intercept form of a quadratic function, *p. 641*
- quadratic equation, *p. 643*
- standard form of a quadratic equation, *p. 643*
- completing the square, *p. 663*
- vertex form of a quadratic function, *p. 669*
- quadratic formula, *p. 671*
- discriminant, *p. 678*

VOCABULARY EXERCISES

1. Copy and complete: The line that passes through the vertex and divides a parabola into two symmetric parts is called the __?__. **axis of symmetry**

Tell whether the function has a *minimum value* or a *maximum value*.

2. $f(x) = 5x^2 - 4x$ **minimum**
3. $f(x) = -x^2 + 6x + 2$ **maximum**
4. $f(x) = 0.3x^2 - 7.7x + 1.8$ **minimum**

REVIEW EXAMPLES AND EXERCISES

Use the review examples and exercises below to check your understanding of the concepts you have learned in each lesson of Chapter 10.

10.1 Graph $y = ax^2 + c$ *pp. 628–634*

EXAMPLE

Graph $y = -x^2 + 3$. Compare the graph with the graph of $y = x^2$.

Make a table of values for $y = -x^2 + 3$. Then plot the points from the table and draw a smooth curve through the points.

x	−2	−1	0	1	2
y	−1	2	3	2	−1

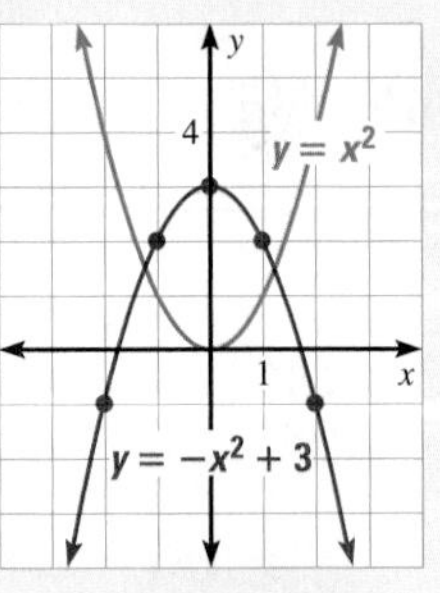

Both graphs have the same axis of symmetry, $x = 0$. However, the graph of $y = -x^2 + 3$ has a different vertex than the graph of $y = x^2$, and it opens down. This is because the graph of $y = -x^2 + 3$ is a vertical translation (of 3 units up) and a reflection in the x-axis of the graph of $y = x^2$.

EXAMPLES 1, 2, and 4 on pp. 628–630 for Exs. 5–7

EXERCISES

Graph the function. Compare the graph with the graph of $y = x^2$. **5–7. See margin.**

5. $y = -4x^2$
6. $y = \frac{1}{3}x^2$
7. $y = 2x^2 - 1$

10.2 Graph $y = ax^2 + bx + c$

pp. 635–640

EXAMPLE

Graph $y = -x^2 + 2x + 1$.

STEP 1 **Determine** whether the parabola opens up or down. Because $a < 0$, the parabola opens down.

STEP 2 **Find** and draw the axis of symmetry:

$$x = -\frac{b}{2a} = -\frac{2}{2(-1)} = 1$$

STEP 3 **Find** and plot the vertex. The x-coordinate of the vertex is $-\frac{b}{2a}$, or 1. The y-coordinate of the vertex is $y = -(1)^2 + 2(1) + 1 = 2$.

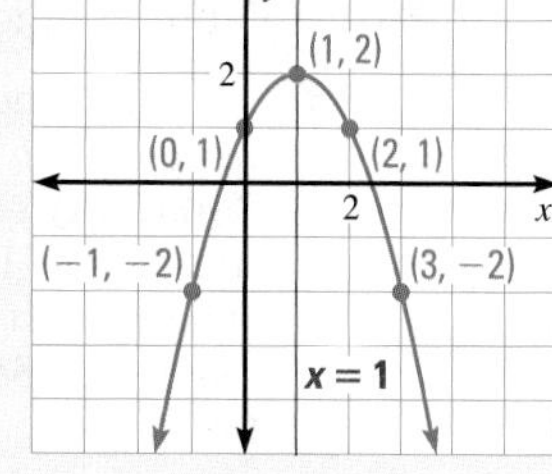

STEP 4 **Plot** four more points. Evaluating the function for $x = 0$ and $x = -1$ gives the points $(0, 1)$ and $(-1, -2)$. Plot these points and their reflections in the axis of symmetry.

STEP 5 **Draw** a parabola through the plotted points.

EXAMPLE 2 on p. 636 for Exs. 8–10

EXERCISES

Graph the function. Label the vertex and axis of symmetry. **8–10. See margin.**

8. $y = x^2 + 4x + 1$ **9.** $y = 2x^2 - 4x - 3$ **10.** $y = -2x^2 + 8x + 5$

10.3 Solve Quadratic Equations by Graphing

pp. 643–649

EXAMPLE

Solve $x^2 - 7x = -12$ by graphing.

STEP 1 **Write** the equation in standard form.

$x^2 - 7x = -12$ **Write original equation.**

$x^2 - 7x + 12 = 0$ **Add 12 to each side.**

STEP 2 **Graph** the related function $y = x^2 - 7x + 12$. The x-intercepts of the graph are 3 and 4.

▶ The solutions of the equation $x^2 - 7x + 12 = 0$ are 3 and 4.

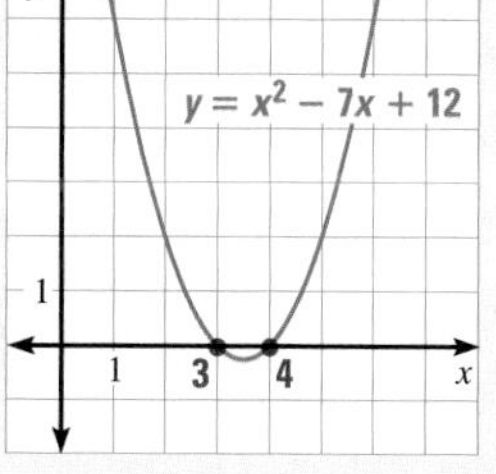

EXAMPLES 1, 2, and 3 on pp. 643–644 for Exs. 11–13

EXERCISES

Solve the equation by graphing.

11. $4x^2 + x + 3 = 0$ **no solution** **12.** $x^2 + 2x = -1$ **−1** **13.** $-x^2 + 8 = 7x$ **−8, 1**

Extra Example 10.2

Graph $y = x^2 + 4x + 4$.

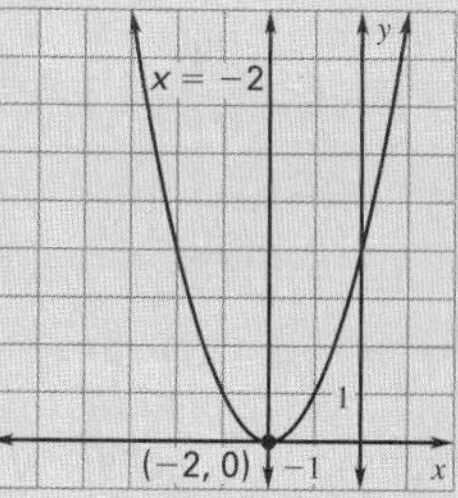

Extra Example 10.3

Solve $x^2 - 5x = -4$ by graphing. **1, 4**

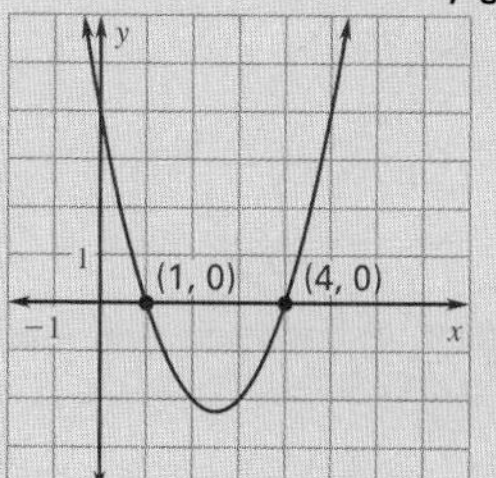

8.

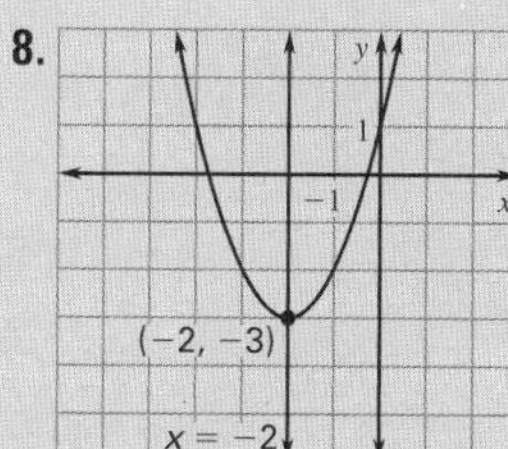

9.

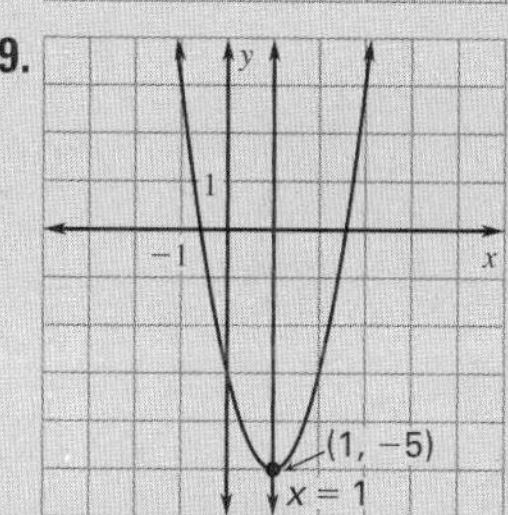

10.

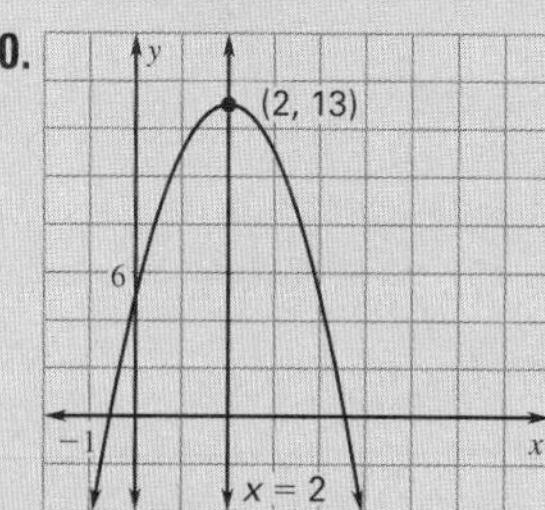

Extra Example 10.4

Solve $2(x-1)^2 = 10$. Round your solutions to the nearest hundredth. $(x-1)^2 = 5$; $1 + \sqrt{5} \approx 3.24$, $1 - \sqrt{5} \approx -1.24$

Extra Example 10.5

Solve $2x^2 + 8x = 6$ by completing the square. Round your solutions to the nearest hundredth, if necessary. $(x+2)^2 = 7$; $-2 + \sqrt{7} \approx 0.65$, $-2 - \sqrt{7} \approx -4.65$

10.4 Use Square Roots to Solve Quadratic Equations

pp. 652–658

EXAMPLE

Solve $5(x-6)^2 = 30$. Round the solutions to the nearest hundredth.

$5(x-6)^2 = 30$	Write original equation.
$(x-6)^2 = 6$	Divide each side by 5.
$x - 6 = \pm\sqrt{6}$	Take square roots of each side.
$x = 6 \pm \sqrt{6}$	Add 6 to each side.

▶ The solutions of the equation are $6 + \sqrt{6} \approx 8.45$ and $6 - \sqrt{6} \approx 3.55$.

CHECK To check the solutions, first rewrite the equation so that 0 is on the one side as follows: $5(x-6)^2 - 30 = 0$. Then graph the related function $y = 5(x-6)^2 - 30$. The x-intercepts are about 8.4 and about 3.5. So, each solution checks.

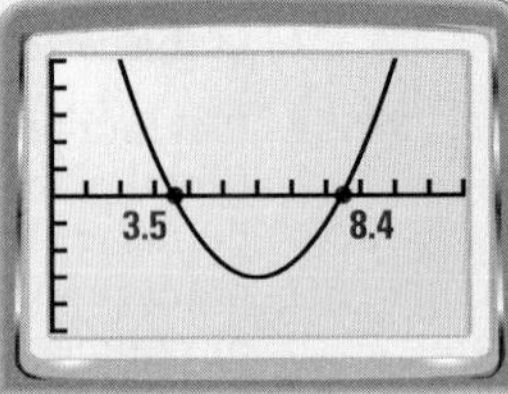

EXERCISES

Solve the equation. Round your solutions to the nearest hundredth, if necessary.

EXAMPLES 1–4 on p. 652–654 for Exs. 14–19

14. $6x^2 - 54 = 0$ **±3**
15. $3x^2 + 7 = 4$ **no solution**
16. $g^2 + 11 = 24$ **±3.61**
17. $7n^2 + 5 = 9$ **±0.76**
18. $2(a+7)^2 = 34$ **−11.12, −2.88**
19. $3(w-4)^2 = 5$ **2.71, 5.29**

10.5 Solve Quadratic Equations by Completing the Square

pp. 663–668

EXAMPLE

Solve $3x^2 + 12x = 18$ by completing the square.

$3x^2 + 12x = 18$	Write original equation.
$x^2 + 4x = 6$	Divide each side by 3.
$x^2 + 4x + 2^2 = 6 + 2^2$	Add $\left(\frac{4}{2}\right)^2$, or 2^2, to each side.
$(x+2)^2 = 10$	Write left side as the square of a binomial.
$x + 2 = \pm\sqrt{10}$	Take square roots of each side.
$x = -2 \pm \sqrt{10}$	Subtract 2 from each side.

▶ The solutions of the equation are $-2 + \sqrt{10} \approx 1.16$ and $-2 - \sqrt{10} \approx -5.16$.

EXERCISES

EXAMPLES 2 and 3 on p. 664 for Exs. 20–23

Solve the equation by completing the square. Round your solutions to the nearest hundredth, if necessary.

20. $x^2 - 14x = 51$ **−3, 17**

21. $2a^2 + 12a - 4 = 0$ **0.32, −6.32**

22. $2n^2 + 4n + 1 = 10n + 9$ **−1, 4**

23. $5g^2 - 3g + 6 = 2g^2 + 9$ **−0.62, 1.62**

10.6 Solve Quadratic Equations by the Quadratic Formula *pp. 671–676*

EXAMPLE

Solve $4x^2 + 3x = 1$.

$4x^2 + 3x = 1$ — **Write original equation.**

$4x^2 + 3x - 1 = 0$ — **Write in standard form.**

$x = \frac{-b \pm \sqrt{b^2 - 4ac}}{2a}$ — **Quadratic formula**

$= \frac{-3 \pm \sqrt{3^2 - 4(4)(-1)}}{2(4)}$ — **Substitute values in the quadratic formula: $a = 4$, $b = 3$, and $c = -1$.**

$= \frac{-3 \pm \sqrt{25}}{8}$ — **Simplify.**

$= \frac{-3 \pm 5}{8}$ — **Simplify the square root.**

▶ The solutions of the equation are $\frac{-3+5}{8} = \frac{1}{4}$ and $\frac{-3-5}{8} = -1$.

CHECK You can check the solutions in the original equation.

If $x = \frac{1}{4}$:

$4x^2 + 3x = 1$

$4\left(\frac{1}{4}\right)^2 + 3\left(\frac{1}{4}\right) \stackrel{?}{=} 1$

$1 = 1$ ✓

If $x = -1$:

$4x^2 + 3x = 1$

$4(-1)^2 + 3(-1) \stackrel{?}{=} 1$

$1 = 1$ ✓

EXERCISES

EXAMPLES 1, 2, and 3 on p. 671–672 for Exs. 24–30

Use the quadratic formula to solve the equation. Round your solutions to the nearest hundredth, if necessary.

24. $x^2 - 2x - 15 = 0$ **−3, 5**

25. $2m^2 + 7m - 3 = 0$ **−3.89, 0.39**

26. $-w^2 + 5w = 3$ **0.70, 4.30**

27. $5n^2 - 7n = -1$ **0.16, 1.24**

28. $t^2 - 4 = 6t + 8$ **−1.58, 7.58**

29. $2h - 1 = 10 - 9h^2$ **−1.22, 1**

30. The area A of the rectangle shown is 500 square meters. Find the value of x. Then give the dimensions of the rectangle. **7; 25 m by 20 m**

(2x + 6) m

(4x − 3) m

Extra Example 10.6

Use the quadratic formula to solve $x^2 + 11x = -30$. $a = 1$, $b = 11$, $c = 30$; $\frac{-11+1}{2} = -5$, $\frac{-11-1}{2} = -6$

Extra Example 10.7

Use the discriminant to find the number of solutions for each equation.

a. $4x^2 + 12x + 9 = 0$ **one solution**

b. $8x^2 + 2x + 2 = 0$ **no solution**

c. $x^2 + 5x = 0$ **two solutions**

Extra Example 10.8

Use differences or ratios to tell whether the table of values represents a *linear function*, an *exponential function*, or a *quadratic function*.

a.

x	−1	0	1	2	3
y	2	6	12	20	30

Second differences are constant; quadratic function.

b.

x	−1	0	1	2	3
y	8	4	2	1	0.5

Ratios of successive y-values are equal; exponential function.

10.7 Interpret the Discriminant

pp. 678–683

EXAMPLE

	Equation $ax^2 + bx + c = 0$	Discriminant $b^2 - 4ac$	Number of solutions
a.	$-16x^2 + 8x - 1 = 0$	$8^2 - 4(-16)(-1) = 0$	One solution
b.	$4x^2 - 5x + 2 = 0$	$(-5)^2 - 4(4)(2) = -7$	No solution
c.	$x^2 + 3x = 0$	$3^2 - 4(1)(0) = 9$	Two solutions

EXAMPLES 1 and 2 on pp. 678–679 for Exs. 31–36

EXERCISES

Tell whether the equation has *two solutions, one solution,* or *no solution.*

31. $x^2 - 2x + 2 = 0$ **no solution**

32. $4g^2 + 12g + 9 = 0$ **one solution**

33. $5w^2 - 4w - 1 = 0$ **two solutions**

34. $\frac{1}{8}v^2 - 6 = 0$ **two solutions**

35. $n^2 - 3n = 4 - 2n^2$ **two solutions**

36. $2q^2 + 1 = 3q - 5$ **no solution**

10.8 Compare Linear, Exponential, and Quadratic Models

pp. 684–691

EXAMPLE

Use differences or ratios to tell whether the table of values represents a *linear function*, an *exponential function*, or a *quadratic function*.

a.

x	−1	0	1	2
y	5	3	1	−1

Differences: −2 −2 −2

▸ The table of values represents a linear function.

b.

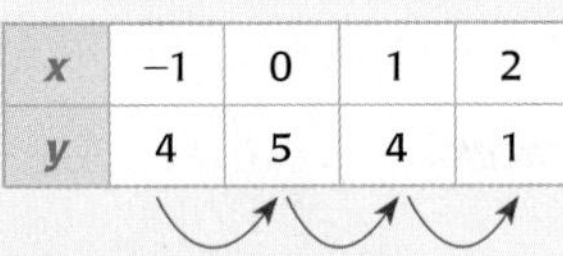

x	−1	0	1	2
y	4	5	4	1

First differences: 1 −1 −3

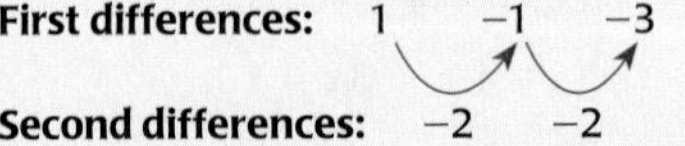

Second differences: −2 −2

▸ The table of values represents a quadratic function.

EXAMPLE 2 on pp. 685 for Exs. 37–38

EXERCISES

Tell whether the table of values represents a *linear function*, an *exponential function*, or a *quadratic function*.

37.

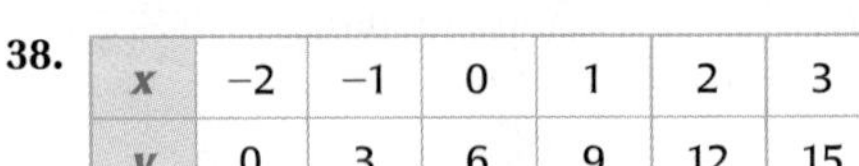

x	1	2	3	4	5	6
y	1	2	4	8	16	32

exponential function

38.

x	−2	−1	0	1	2	3
y	0	3	6	9	12	15

linear function

Match the quadratic function with its graph.

1. $y = x^2 - 2$ **C**
2. $y = x^2 + 2$ **A**
3. $y = -2x^2$ **B**

A. 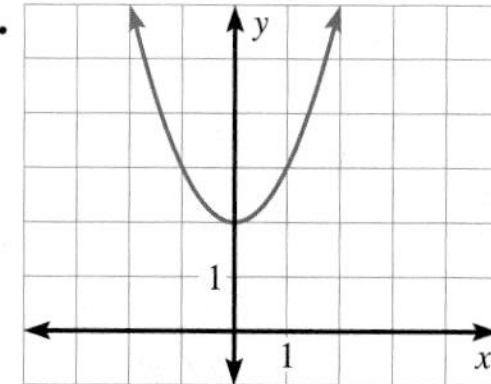

B. 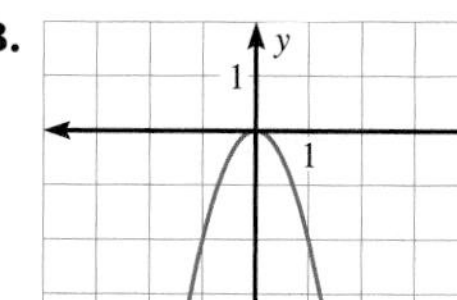

C. 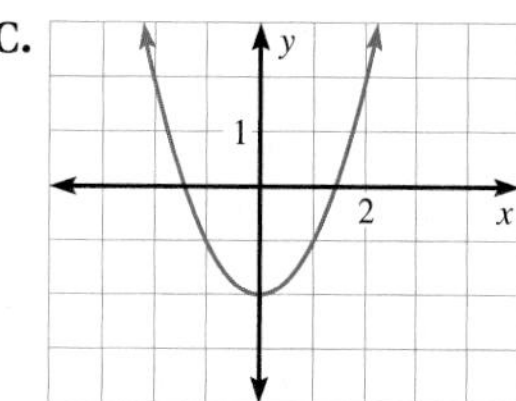

Graph the function. Label the vertex and axis of symmetry. **4–6. See margin.**

4. $y = 2x^2 + 6x - 5$
5. $y = -4x^2 - 8x + 25$
6. $y = \frac{1}{4}x^2 - x - 7$

Approximate the zeros of the function to the nearest tenth.

7. $f(x) = x^2 + 5x + 1$ **−4.8, −0.2**
8. $f(x) = x^2 - 8x + 3$ **0.4, 7.6**
9. $f(x) = -3x^2 - 2x + 5$ **−1.7, 1**

Solve the equation. Round your solutions to the nearest hundredth, if necessary.

10. $3x^2 = 108$ **±6**
11. $-5w^2 + 51 = 6$ **±3**
12. $-p^2 + 2p + 3 = 0$ **−1, 3**
13. $-2t^2 + 6t + 9 = 0$ **−1.10, 4.10**
14. $5m^2 - m = 5$ **−0.90, 1.10**
15. $2x^2 - 12x - 1 = -7x + 6$ **−1, 3.5**

Tell whether the equation has *two solutions*, *one solution*, or *no solution*.

16. $3x^2 - 4x + 9 = 0$ **no solution**
17. $4g^2 - 12g + 11 = 0$ **no solution**
18. $-2n^2 + 7n - 1 = 0$ **two solutions**
19. $-m^2 - 17m = 0$ **two solutions**
20. $-6x^2 - x - 5 = 0$ **no solution**
21. $10x^2 - 13 = 0$ **two solutions**

Tell whether the table of values represents a *linear function*, an *exponential function*, or a *quadratic function*. Then write an equation for the function.

22.

x	−3	−2	−1	0	1	2
y	18	8	2	0	2	8

quadratic function; $y = 2x^2$

23.

x	−4	0	4	8	12	16
y	1	2	3	4	5	6

linear function; $y = \frac{1}{4}x + 2$

24. **TENNIS** You are playing tennis with a friend. The path of the tennis ball after you hit the ball can be modeled by the graph of the equation $y = -0.005x^2 + 0.17x + 3$ where x is the horizontal distance (in feet) from where you hit the ball and y is the height of the ball (in feet) above the court.

   a. What is the maximum height reached by the tennis ball? Round your answer to the nearest tenth of a foot. **4.4 ft**

   b. Suppose you are standing 30 feet from the net, which has a height of 3 feet. Will the ball clear the net? *Explain* your reasoning. **See margin.**

   c. If your friend does not hit the ball back to you, how far from you does the ball strike the ground? **about 47 ft**

Additional Resources

Assessment Book

- Chapter Test, Levels A, B, C
- Standardized Chapter Test
- SAT/ACT Chapter Test
- Alternative Assessment

Test Generator

Chapter Test

Easily-readable reduced copies (with answers) of Chapter Test B, the Standardized Chapter Test, and the Alternative Assessment from the Assessment Book can be found on pp. 626G–626H.

4. 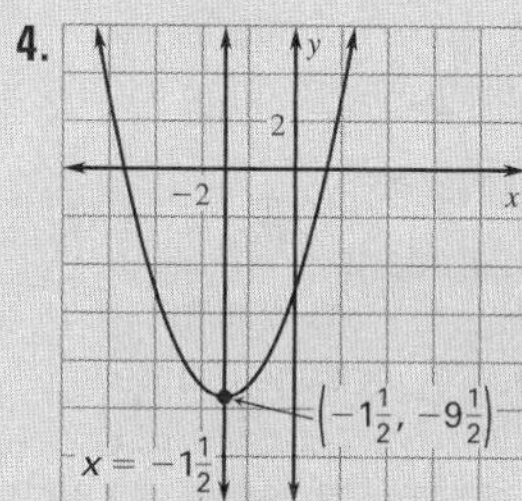

5. 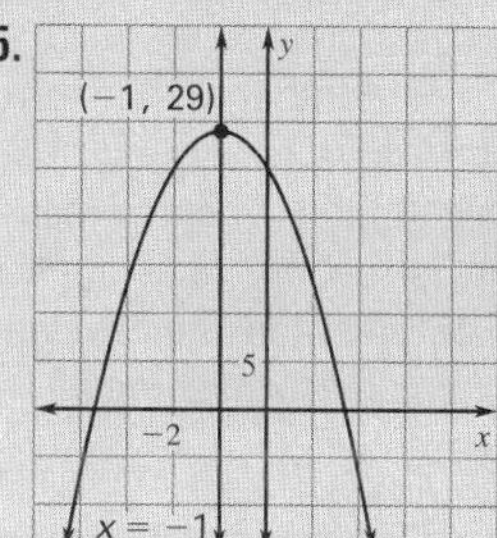

6. 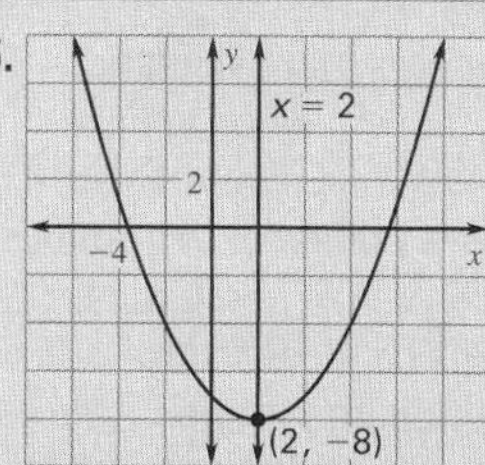

24b. Yes; to find the height of the ball 30 feet from where you hit it, evaluate y when x is 30: $y = -0.005(30)^2 + 0.17(30) + 3 = 3.6$ feet. The height of the ball is greater than the height of the net, so the ball will go over the net.

Using Rubrics

The rubric given on the pupil page is a sample of a three-level rubric. Other rubrics may contain four, five, or six levels. For more information on rubrics, see the *Differentiated Instruction Resources.*

Test-Taking Strategy

Encourage students to give a detailed, clear explanation when an extended response question asks them to explain their reasoning. Tell them that a reviewer wants to see that they grasp the basic concepts in the problem and that they see how their calculations and conclusions are connected. Emphasize that the explanations can be brief, but should include one or two details that relate calculations, graphs, or diagrams to conclusions.

Study Strategy

Point out to students that it is a good idea to get into the habit of labeling each part of the problem, as in Sample 1. Labeling the parts makes it easier for reviewers to find the answers, and it also serves as a check to the students that they have answered all the parts of the problem. Note also that it is a good idea in test-taking situations for students to show all of the steps of a problem even if they can perform some of the steps mentally.

Avoiding Common Errors

Remind students that calculation errors are frequent when calculations are complex. Encourage students to write values for *a*, *b*, and *c*, and then rewrite the quadratic formula in full using those values. Also encourage students to check their answers by using substitution in the original equation, a different method, or even the same method again.

Scoring Rubric

Full Credit
- solution is complete and correct

Partial Credit
- solution is complete but errors are made,

or
- solution is without error but incomplete

No Credit
- no solution is given,

or
- solution makes no sense

EXTENDED RESPONSE QUESTIONS

PROBLEM

A skateboarder in a half pipe launches himself from the half pipe, performs a trick in the air, and lands back in the half pipe. The top of the half pipe is 12 feet above the base of the half pipe as shown.

a. During his first run, the skateboarder leaves the half pipe with an initial vertical velocity of 17 feet per second. Write an equation that models the height h (in feet) of a skateboarder as a function of the time t (in seconds) after leaving the half pipe.

b. How long is the skateboarder in the air if he lands 5 feet above the base of the half pipe? Round your answer to the nearest hundredth of a second.

c. During his second run, the skateboarder leaves the half pipe with an initial vertical velocity that is greater than his initial vertical velocity during his first run. He again lands 5 feet above the base of the half pipe. During which run is his time spent in the air greater? *Explain.*

Below are sample solutions to the problem. Read each solution and the comments on the left to see why the sample represents full credit, partial credit, or no credit.

SAMPLE 1: Full credit solution

The correct equation is given.

a. $h = -16t^2 + 17t + 12$

b. $5 = -16t^2 + 17t + 12$

$0 = -16t^2 + 17t + 7$

$t = \frac{-17 \pm \sqrt{17^2 - 4(-16)(7)}}{2(-16)} \approx -0.32 \text{ or } 1.38$

The correct equation is given, and the answer that makes sense is given.

The skateboarder is in the air for about 1.38 seconds.

c. $5 = -16t^2 + 18t + 12$ $\qquad$ $5 = -16t^2 + 20t + 12$

$0 = -16t^2 + 18t + 7$ $\qquad$ $0 = -16t^2 + 20t + 7$

$t = \frac{-18 \pm \sqrt{18^2 - 4(-16)(7)}}{2(-16)}$ $\qquad$ $t = \frac{-20 \pm \sqrt{20^2 - 4(-16)(7)}}{2(-16)}$

$t \approx -0.31$ (crossed out) or $t \approx 1.43$ $\qquad$ $t \approx -0.29$ (crossed out) or $t \approx 1.54$

The answer is correct, and it includes an explanation.

The examples above show that the time the skateboarder spends in the air increases as the initial vertical velocity increases and the landing height remains constant. So, the skateboarder spends more time in the air during his second run.

SAMPLE 2: Partial credit solution

The correct equation is given.

In parts (b) and (c), the reasoning is correct but errors are made in calculating the values of t. So, the answers are incorrect.

a. $h = -16t^2 + 17t + 12$

b. $0 = -16t^2 + 17t + 7$

$$t = \frac{-17 \pm \sqrt{17^2 - 4(-16)(7)}}{2(-16)} \approx -1.38 \text{ or } 0.32$$

The skateboarder is in the air for about 0.32 second.

c. $0 = -16t^2 + 19t + 7$

$$t = \frac{-19 \pm \sqrt{19^2 - 4(-16)(7)}}{2(-16)} \approx -1.48 \text{ or } 0.3$$

With an initial vertical velocity of 19 feet per second, the skateboarder is in the air for about 0.3 second, which is less than 0.32 second. So, the skateboarder spends more time in the air during his first run.

SAMPLE 3: No credit solution

The equation is incorrect.

In parts (b) and (c), the incorrect equations are solved, and no answers are given.

a. $h = -16t^2 + 12t + 17$

b. $0 = -16t^2 + 12t + 17$

$$t = \frac{-12 \pm \sqrt{12^2 - 4(-16)(17)}}{2(-16)} \approx -0.72 \text{ or } 1.47$$

c. $0 = -16t^2 + 15t + 17$

$$t = \frac{-15 \pm \sqrt{15^2 - 4(-16)(17)}}{2(-16)} \approx -0.66 \text{ or } 1.6$$

PRACTICE Apply Scoring Rubric

1. A student's solution to the problem on the previous page is given below. Score the solution as *full credit*, *partial credit*, or *no credit*. *Explain* your reasoning. If you choose *partial credit* or *no credit*, explain how you would change the solution so that it earns a score of full credit.

a. $h = -16t^2 + 17t + 12$

b. $0 = -16t^2 + 17t + 7$

$$t = \frac{-17 \pm \sqrt{17^2 - 4(-16)(7)}}{2(-16)} \approx 0.32$$

The skateboarder is in the air for about 0.32 second.

c. A greater initial vertical velocity means that the skateboarder will go higher. This means that he will be in the air longer. So, the skateboarder will be in the air longer during his second run.

Answers

1. Partial credit; the correct equations are given in parts (a) and (b). The student substituted correctly into the quadratic formula in part (b), but did not evaluate the expression correctly. The correct values of *t* are −0.32 and 1.38. Disregard the negative solution, so the skateboarder is in the air about 1.38 seconds. The student's reasoning in part (c) is not valid. Even though the skateboarder goes higher, we cannot necessarily conclude that he is in the air longer; he is also moving faster, so perhaps his air time will decrease. We must check by finding landing times for one or more initial vertical velocities that are greater than 17 feet per second.

Answers

1a. $A = 20x^2 + 200x$

1b. 10 plots; to find the maximum number of plots, substitute 4000 for A in the equation from part (a) and solve for x: $4000 = 20x^2 + 200x$, or $0 = 20x^2 + 200x - 4000$; $x = -20$ *or* $x = 10$. Only the positive solution makes sense in this situation, so the maximum number of plots is 10.

1c. 1.5 ft; Since there are 10 plots, each plot is 20 feet wide, so the area of each plot is $20(20) = 400$ square feet. If w is the width of the wildflower border, then the area of the resident's plot without the border is $(20 - 2w)(20 - 2w)$. To find the value of w that gives a border area of 111 square feet, solve the equation $400 - 111 = (20 - 2w)(20 - 2w)$, or $289 = (20 - 2w)^2$; $w = 1.5$ feet.

2a. 1.6 ft

2b. *Sample answer:* 10 ft; when the ball is 10 feet from the player, its height is $y = -0.018(10^2) + 0.25(10) + 0.7 = 1.4$ feet. The ball is lower than the crossbar, so it will go into the goal if the player is 10 feet from the goal.

2c. Distances of 16 ft or less; from part (a), the maximum height of the ball is about 1.6 feet, so the ball is always lower than the crossbar. The ball will land back in the water when $y = 0$, so solve the equation $0 = -0.018x^2 + 0.25x + 0.7$ for x to determine the distance of the ball from the player when the ball hits the water; $x \approx 16$ feet. As long as the player is within 16 feet of the goal, the ball will go into the goal.

3a. 8 row planter

3b. 12 row planter

3c. Yes; if the farmer drives the trailer, the cost of each planter for each field would be reduced by the same amount, \$.82 per acre, so the 12 row planter will still cost the least per acre to operate.

EXTENDED RESPONSE

1. A community garden is being planned in the town-owned field behind the housing development where you live. The rectangular garden will border the development and extend into the field. Each household that joins the project will have a rectangular plot that is 20 feet wide. The town has already permitted the plots to extend 10 feet into the field, and promised another foot for every household that reserves a plot.

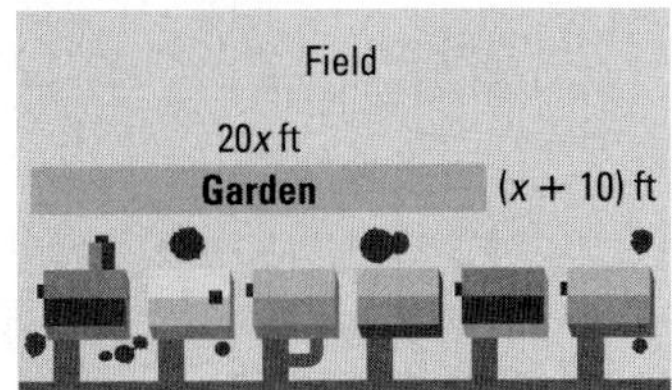

   a. Write an equation that gives the area A (in square feet) of the community garden as a function of the number x of households that reserve a plot.

   b. The housing association decides that the entire area of the garden cannot exceed 4000 square feet. What is the maximum number of plots there can be? *Explain.*

   c. The maximum number of plots is used. One of the residents decides to plant a uniform border of wildflowers around all four sides of her plot. She has enough wildflower seeds to cover 111 square feet. How wide should the border be? *Explain.*

2. During a water-polo practice, a player positioned directly in front of the goal throws the ball at the goal. The ball follows a parabolic path that can be modeled by the graph of the equation $y = -0.018x^2 + 0.25x + 0.7$ where y is the height (in feet) of the ball above the surface of the water x feet from the player.

   a. What is the maximum height of the ball to the nearest tenth of a foot?

   b. The ball goes into the goal. The goal is bounded by the surface of the water and a crossbar that is 3 feet high above the surface of the water. Give a possible distance that the player is from the goal. *Explain.*

   c. Describe all possible distances that the player can be from the goal in order for the ball to go into the goal. *Explain.*

3. A farm machine called a planter plants multiple rows of seeds while being pulled by a tractor. Planters can be purchased in various sizes. The operation costs of a 6 row, 8 row, 12 row, 16 row, and 24 row planter are analyzed. The operation cost y (in dollars per acre) for a planter that plants x rows at once for two different sizes of fields is shown in the table.

   a. Which planter costs the least per acre to operate for planting 400 acres?

   b. Which planter costs the least per acre to operate for planting 800 acres?

Acres planted	Operation cost (dollars per acre), y
400	$y = 0.071x^2 - 1.1x + 17$
800	$y = 0.062x^2 - 1.6x + 20$

   c. A farmer who is planting 800 acres uses the planter that costs the least per acre to operate. The operation cost function takes into account that a tractor operator is paid \$.82 per acre to drive the tractor pulling the planter. The farmer drives the tractor, so he doesn't have to pay for labor. Does his planter still cost the least per acre to operate? *Explain.*

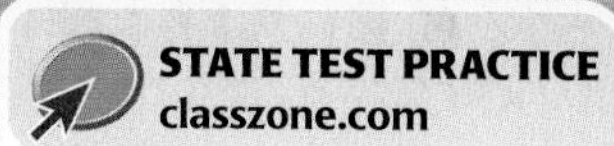

MULTIPLE CHOICE

4. How would the graph of the function $y = -3x^2 + 6$ be affected if the function were changed to $y = -3x^2 - 1$?

   (A) The graph would shift 5 units up.

   (B) The graph would shift 5 units down.

   (C) The graph would shift 7 units up.

   (D) The graph would shift 7 units down.

5. A volleyball player serves the ball from a height of 6.5 feet above the ground with an initial vertical velocity of 21 feet per second. Which function models the height h (in feet) of the ball t seconds after it is served?

   (A) $h = 21t - t^2 + 6.5$

   (B) $h = -16t^2 + 6.5$

   (C) $h = 16t^2 + 21t + 6.5$

   (D) $h = 6.5 + 21t - 16t^2$

GRIDDED ANSWER

6. The value of the discriminant of the equation $7x^2 - 8x + c = 6$ is -20. What is the value of c?

7. The area of the rectangle below is 170 square meters. What is the value of x?

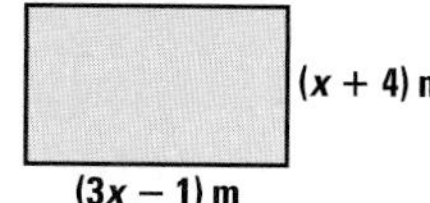

8. A cross section of the glass lamp shade below can be modeled by the graph of the equation $y = -0.625x^2 + 5x$ where x and y are measured in inches. How tall (in inches) is the shade?

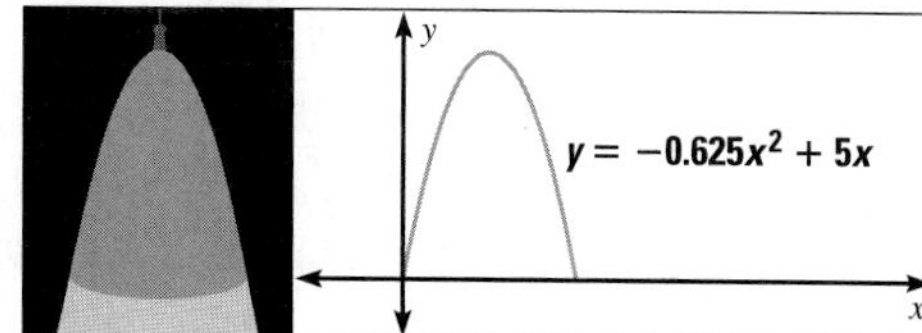

SHORT RESPONSE

9. From January to May in 2003, the monthly snowfall y (in inches) recorded at the observatory at Mount Washington in New Hampshire can be modeled by the function $y = -5.34x^2 + 17.4x + 21.2$ where x is the number of months since January. Did the greatest monthly snowfall during the given time period occur in January? *Explain.*

10. You throw a tennis ball upward from a height of 4 feet with an initial vertical velocity of 36 feet per second.

    a. Write an equation that models the height h (in feet) of the tennis ball as a function of the time t (in seconds) after it is thrown.

    b. Does the ball reach a height of 30 feet? *Explain.*

11. A band wants to have customized stickers printed. The table shows the cost y (in dollars) for x customized stickers.

Stickers, x	1000	2000	3000	4000
Cost (dollars), y	199	239	279	319

    a. Tell whether the data can be modeled by a *linear function*, an *exponential function*, or a *quadratic function*. Then write an equation for the function.

    b. If the number of stickers printed is doubled, does the price double? *Explain.*

4. D

5. D

6. 9

7. 6

8. 10in.

9. *Sample answer:* A table of values for the function shows that the greatest monthly snowfall, 34.6 inches, occurred in March.

10a. $h = -16t^2 + 36t + 4$

10b. No; substitute 30 for h in the equation from part (a): $30 = -16t^2 + 36t + 4$. Write the equation in standard form $0 = -16t^2 + 36t - 26$; find the discriminant to be -368. The discriminant is negative, so the equation has no solution and the ball cannot reach a height of 30 feet.

11a. linear function; $y = 0.04x + 159$

11b. No; the cost for n stickers is $0.04n + 159$ dollars, and the cost for $2n$ stickers is $0.04(2n) + 159 = 0.08n + 159$ dollars, which is not the same as twice the cost of n stickers. Twice the cost of n stickers would be $2(0.04n + 159) = 0.08n + 318$ dollars, or \$159 more than the cost of $2n$ stickers.

Additional Resources

A Cumulative Review for each of Chapters 8–10 is available in the *Chapter Resource Book*.

7.
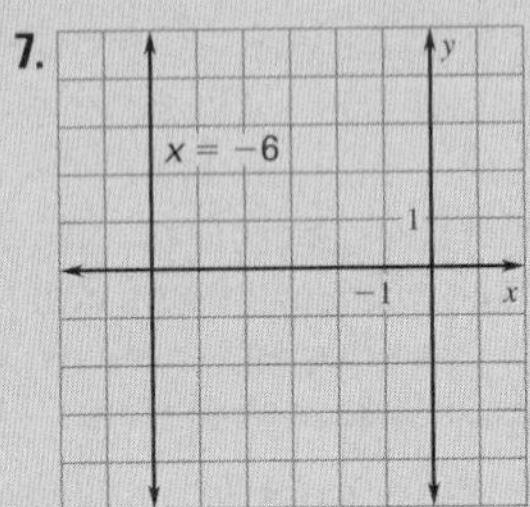

8.
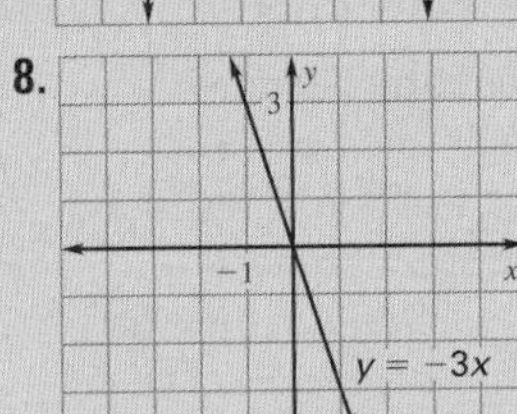

9.
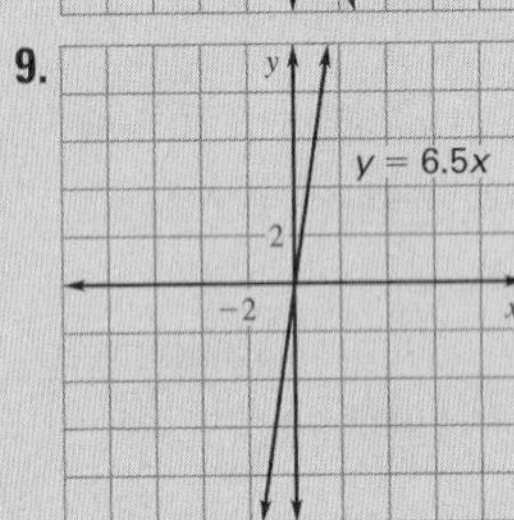

10.
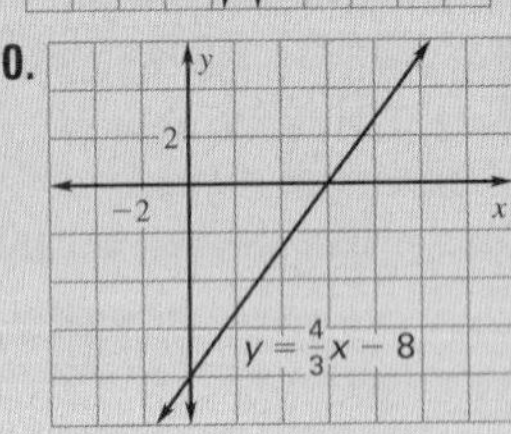

11.
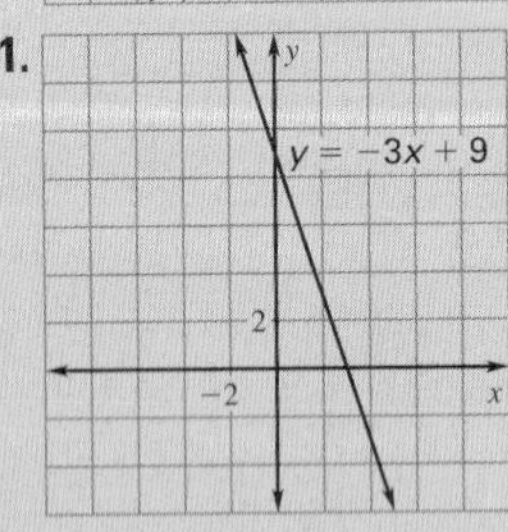

12.
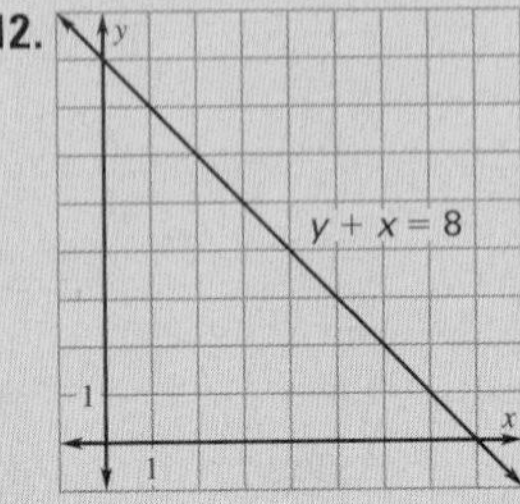

Evaluate the expression for the given value of *x*. *(p. 64)*

1. $-|x| + 9$ when $x = -6$ **3** **2.** $|-x| + 2.6$ when $x = 2$ **4.6** **3.** $0.7 - |x|$ when $x = -0.5$ **0.2**

Solve the equation.

4. $5 - 2a = 13$ *(p. 141)* **−4** **5.** $13y + 16 - y = 4$ *(p. 148)* **−1** **6.** $-(w + 1) = w + 3$ *(p. 154)* **−2**

Graph the equation. *(pp. 215, 225, 244, 253)* **7–14. See margin.**

7. $x = -6$ **8.** $y = -3x$ **9.** $y = 6.5x$ **10.** $y = \frac{4}{3}x - 8$

11. $y = -3x + 9$ **12.** $y + x = 8$ **13.** $2y - x = 2$ **14.** $2x + 5y = -40$

Write an equation of the line that passes through the given point and is perpendicular to the given line. *(p. 319)*

15. $(0, 3)$, $y = -5x + 2$ $\mathbf{y = \frac{1}{5}x + 3}$ **16.** $(2, 2)$, $y = -x - 7$ $\mathbf{y = x}$ **17.** $(8, 3)$, $y = \frac{1}{2}x + 2$ $\mathbf{y = -2x + 19}$

Solve the inequality. Then graph the solution.
18–23. See margin for art.

18. $m - 8 < -15$ *(p. 356)* $\mathbf{m < -7}$ **19.** $\frac{x}{-3} > 12$ *(p. 363)* $\mathbf{x < -36}$ **20.** $1 - 4n < -11$ *(p. 369)* $\mathbf{n > 3}$

21. $5b - 7 \le 7b - 5$ *(p. 369)* $\mathbf{b \ge -1}$ **22.** $12 < z + 9 \le 16$ *(p. 380)* $\mathbf{3 < z \le 7}$ **23.** $4 \le 2c + 7 \le 21$ *(p. 380)* $\mathbf{-\frac{3}{2} \le c \le 7}$

Solve the linear system. *(pp. 427, 435, 444, 451, 459)*

24. $y = 5x - 4$; $-4x + y = -2$ **(2, 6)** **25.** $x - 4y = -44$; $-3x + 12y = 132$ **all real numbers** **26.** $-4x + 7y = -33$; $-3x + 2y = -15$ **(3, −3)**

Simplify the expression.

27. $(-9r)^3$ *(p. 489)* $\mathbf{-729r^3}$ **28.** $(2p^4)^3 \cdot p^7$ *(p. 489)* $\mathbf{8p^{19}}$ **29.** $\frac{(3x)^4y}{xy^3}$ *(p. 495)* $\mathbf{\frac{81x^3}{y^2}}$

Graph the function. **30–32. See margin.**

30. $y = (2.5)^x$ *(p. 520)* **31.** $y = (0.8)^x$ *(p. 531)* **32.** $y = \frac{1}{2} \cdot \left(\frac{1}{4}\right)^x$ *(p. 531)*

Find the sum or difference. *(p. 554)*

33. $(x^2 - 3x + 8) + (-2x^2 + 15x + 4)$ $\mathbf{-x^2 + 12x + 12}$ **34.** $(5m^2 - 6) - (8m^3 + m^2 - 2m + 11)$ $\mathbf{-8m^3 + 4m^2 + 2m - 17}$

Find the product.

35. $(z + 9)(2z - 7)$ *(p. 562)* $\mathbf{2z^2 + 11z - 63}$ **36.** $(5b - 2)(8b - 7)$ *(p. 562)* $\mathbf{40b^2 - 51b + 14}$

37. $(q + 2)(-3q^2 + 6q - 1)$ *(p. 562)* $\mathbf{-3q^3 + 11q - 2}$ **38.** $(7 + y)^2$ *(p. 569)* $\mathbf{49 + 14y + y^2}$

39. $(2k - 11)^2$ *(p. 569)* $\mathbf{4k^2 - 44k + 121}$ **40.** $(12w - 5)(12w + 5)$ *(p. 569)* $\mathbf{144w^2 - 25}$

Factor the expression.

41. $x^2 + 6x - 72$ *(p. 583)* $\mathbf{(x + 12)(x - 6)}$ **42.** $2m^2 - 5mn - 3n^2$ *(p. 593)* $\mathbf{(2m + n)(m - 3n)}$

43. $25d^2 + 60d + 36$ *(p. 600)* $\mathbf{(5d + 6)^2}$ **44.** $-2a^2 + 50b^2$ *(p. 600)* $\mathbf{-2(a + 5b)(a - 5b)}$

45. $z^2(z - 6) + 4(6 - z)$ *(p. 606)* $\mathbf{(z - 6)(z + 2)(z - 2)}$ **46.** $y^3 + 8y^2 - 9y - 72$ *(p. 606)* $\mathbf{(y + 8)(y + 3)(y - 3)}$

13.
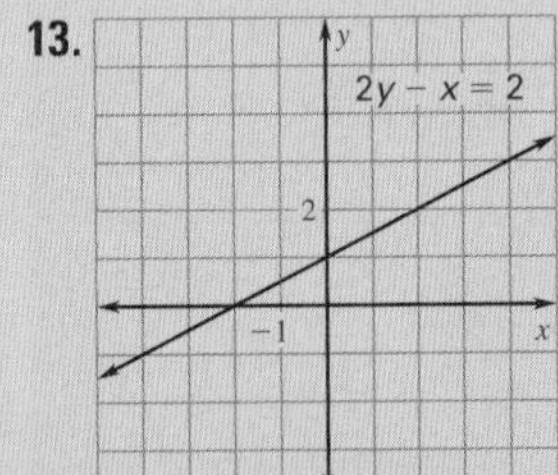

14.
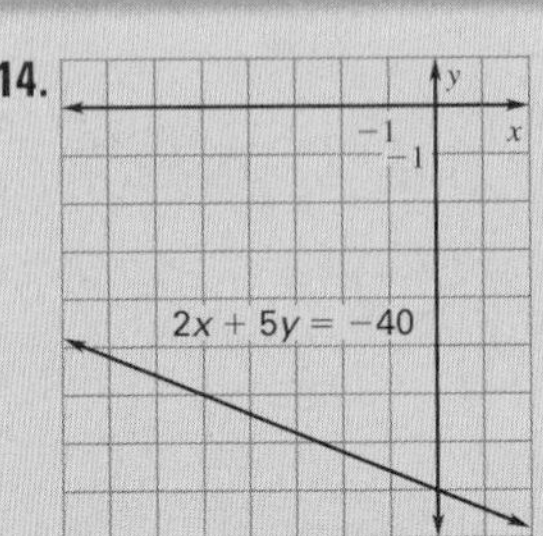

18–23. See Additional Answers beginning on p. AA1.

Graph the function. Label the vertex and axis of symmetry. ***(p. 635)*** **47–49. See margin.**

47. $y = x^2 - 4x + 1$ **48.** $y = 3x^2 + 6x + 4$ **49.** $y = -x^2 - 4x + 10$

Solve the equation. Round your solutions to the nearest hundredth, if necessary. ***(pp. 643, 652, 663, 671)***

50. $5x^2 = 720$ **±12**

51. $-x^2 + 12 = 1$ **±3.32**

52. $x^2 + 6x - 13 = 0$ **−7.69, 1.69**

53. $-2x^2 + 7x - 3 = 0$ **0.5, 3**

54. $4x^2 - 9x = 9$ **−0.75, 3**

55. $-7x^2 + 7x + 3 = 4x - 1$ **−0.57, 1**

56. SPORTS The Pan American Games is a sports event that is held every four years. Athletes from countries in North America, Central America, and South America compete in the games. The table shows the number c of countries that participated in each Pan American Games as a function of the time t (in years) since 1951. Graph the function. ***(p. 43)*** **See margin.**

Years since 1951, t	0	4	8	12	16	20	24	28	32
Countries, c	21	22	25	22	29	32	33	34	36

57. INCOME A salesperson earns a 5% commission on the sales of computers. If the salesperson's computer sales total $9500, how much is the commission? ***(p. 176)*** **$475**

58. CUSTOM PRINTING You create a design for a T-shirt. The table shows the cost for printing your design on T-shirts at a printing company. The printing company requires that your design be printed on a minimum of 6 T-shirts. ***(p. 302)***

T-shirts	6	7	8	9	10
Cost (dollars)	78	81	84	87	90

a. *Explain* why the situation can be modeled by a linear equation. **See margin.**

b. Write an equation in point-slope form that gives the cost of the T-shirts as a function of the number of T-shirts printed. ***Sample answer:*** $y - 78 = 3(x - 6)$

59. GEOMETRY A rectangle has a perimeter of 54 inches. Its length is 3 more than twice its width. Find the dimensions of the rectangle. ***(p. 435)*** **length 19 in., width: 8 in.**

60. SCHOOL ENROLLMENT In 1990, 5000 students were enrolled at a school. The number of students enrolled at the school increased by about 2% per year from 1990 to 2005. Write a model for the number of students enrolled at the school over time. According to the model, how many students were enrolled at the school in 2005? ***(p. 520)*** $y = 5000(1.02)^x$**; about 6730 students**

61. LANDSCAPING An arc of water sprayed from a lawn sprinkler can be modeled by the graph of the equation $y = -0.05x^2 + 0.9x$ where x is the distance (in feet) from the sprinkler and y is the height (in feet) of the arc.

a. Graph the function. Label the vertex and axis of symmetry. ***(p. 635)*** **See margin.**

b. How far from the sprinkler does the water hit the ground? ***(p. 643)*** **18 ft**

47.

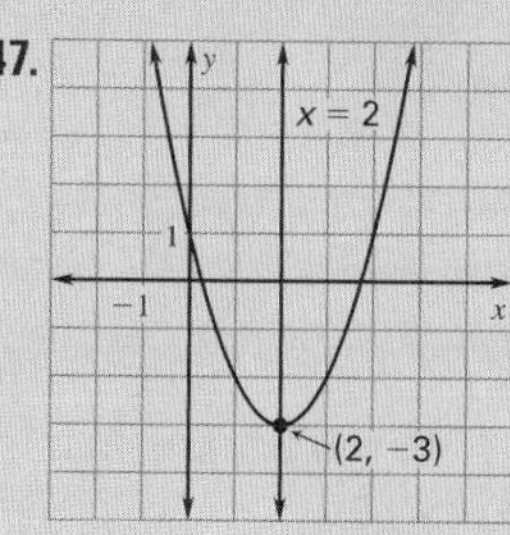

48.

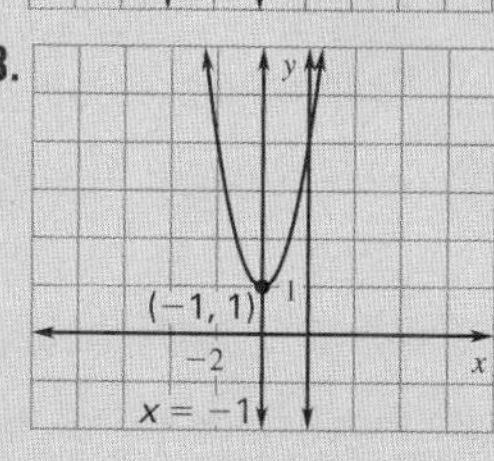

49.

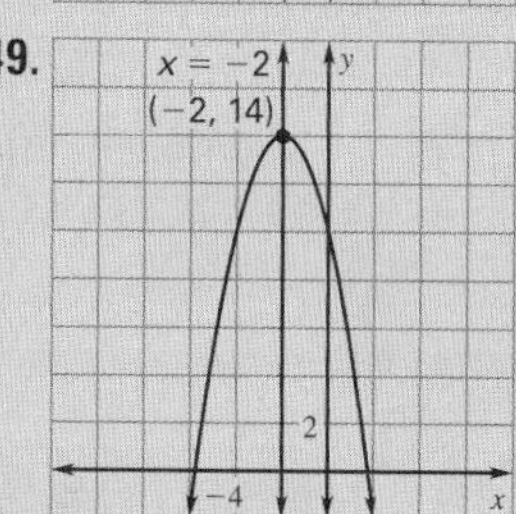

56.

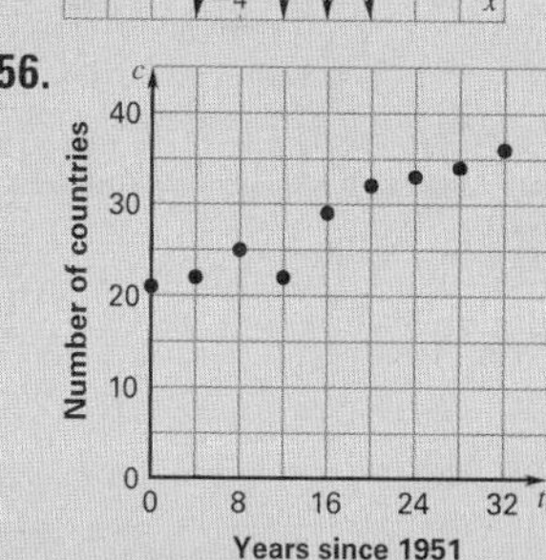

58a. Each time the number of T-shirts increases by 1, the cost increases by $3, so the rate of change is $3 per T-shirt.

61a.

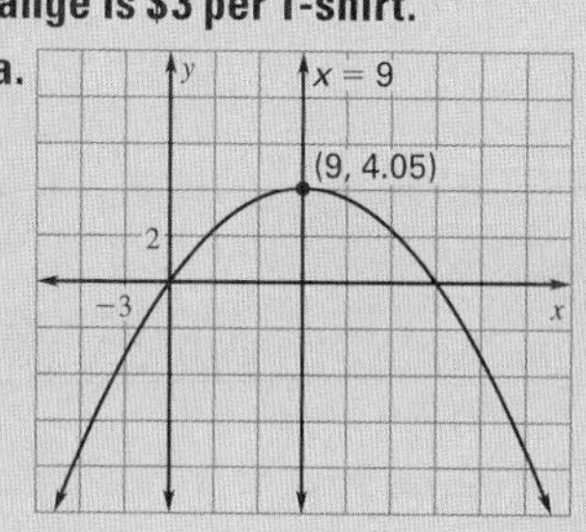

30.

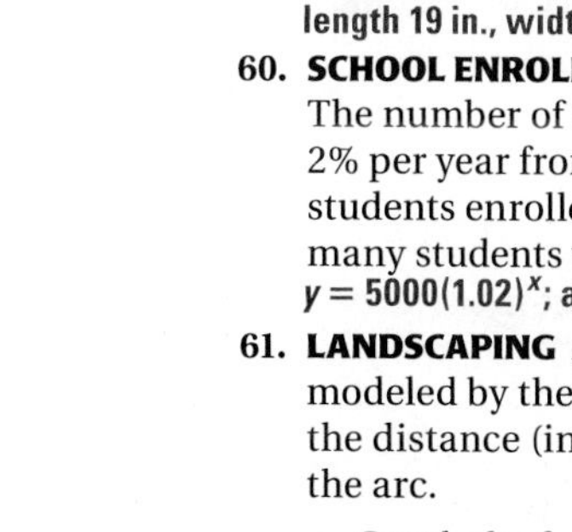

31.

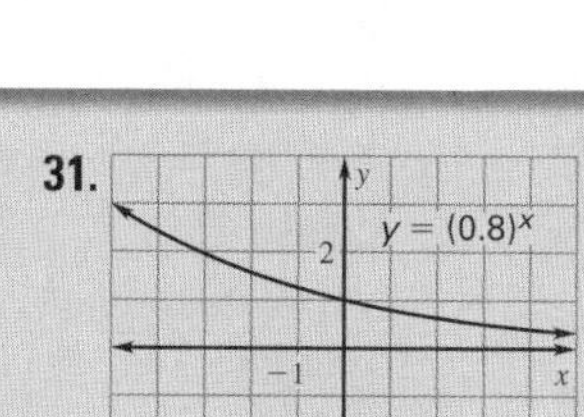

32.

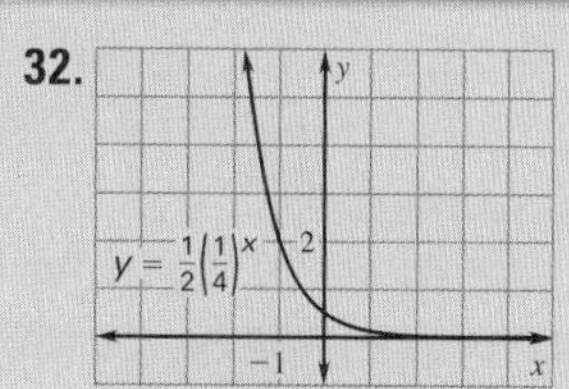

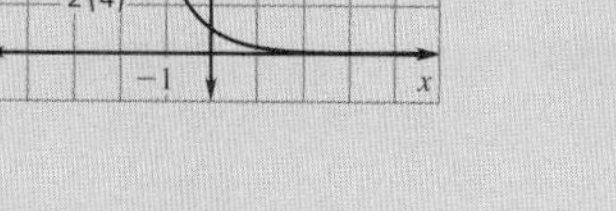

11 Pacing Guide

Chapter 11: Radicals and Geometry Connections

Chapter Table of Contents

PACING GUIDES

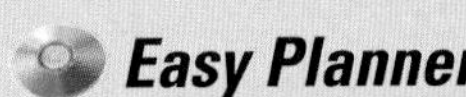

Regular Schedule **(50-minute classes)**

DAY 1	DAY 2	DAY 3	DAY 4	DAY 5
Lesson 11.1	Lesson 11.1 (cont.) Graphing Calculator Activity 11.1	Investigating Algebra Activity 11.2 Lesson 11.2	Lesson 11.2 (cont.) Extension 11.2	Lesson 11.3
DAY 6	**DAY 7**	**DAY 8**	**DAY 9**	**DAY 10**
Lesson 11.3 (cont.) Mixed Review of Problem Solving	Quiz for Lessons 11.1–11.3 Investigating Algebra Activity 11.4 Lesson 11.4	Investigating Algebra Activity 11.5 Lesson 11.5 Mixed Review of Problem Solving	Quiz for Lessons 11.4–11.5 Chapter Review	Chapter Test

Block Schedule **(90-minute classes)**

DAY 1	DAY 2	DAY 3	DAY 4	DAY 5
Lesson 11.1 Graphing Calculator Activity 11.1	Investigating Algebra Activity 11.2 Lesson 11.2 Extension 11.2	Lesson 11.3 Mixed Review of Problem Solving	Quiz for Lessons 11.1–11.3 Investigating Algebra Activity 11.4 Lesson 11.4 Investigating Algebra Activity 11.5 Lesson 11.5 Mixed Review of Problem Solving	Quiz for Lessons 11.4–11.5 Chapter Review Chapter Test

RESOURCE OPTIONS

Chapter/Lesson Resources

Chapter Resource Book
- Parents as Partners
- Teaching Guide/Lesson Plan
- Activity Masters
- Practice (3 levels)
- Study Guide
- Quick Catch-Up for Absent Students
- Problem Solving/Application
- Challenge Practice
- Chapter Review Games and Activities
- Project with Rubric
- Cumulative Review

Notetaking Guide
- Student Workbook and Teacher's Edition

Practice Workbook

Worked-Out Solution Key

Chapter Transparency Book
- Warm-Up Exercises/Daily Homework Quiz
- Notetaking Guide Transparencies
- Homework Answer Transparencies

Teacher Tools Transparencies

Assessment

Assessment Book
- Quizzes
- Chapter Tests (3 levels)
- Standardized and SAT/ACT Chapter Tests
- Alternative Assessments
- Cumulative Tests

Benchmark Tests
- Benchmark Tests, correlated to Remediation Book
- Pre-Course, Mid-Year, and End-of-Year Tests
- Chapter Tests

Spanish Assessment Book

Differentiated Instruction

Differentiated Instruction Resources
- Strategies for Reading Mathematics
- Differentiated Instruction Lesson Notes
- English Learner Lesson Notes
- Inclusion Lesson Notes
- Teaching Strategies with Sample Worksheets
- Tips for New Teachers/Math Background Notes
- Teacher Survival Activities/Bulletin Board Ideas

Student Resources in Spanish

Spanish Study Guide

Remediation Book

Skills Readiness (available on Easy Planner)
- Diagnostic Assessment
- Skill Instruction and Alternative Teaching Strategies
- Skill Practice and Enrichment Masters

Pre-AP Resources
- Pacing and Assignment Guide
- Best Practices
- Copymasters

Technology Resources

Plan	*Easy Planner*
Teach	*Video Tutor* *Activity Generator* *Power Presentations* *Animated Algebra*
Assess	*Test Generator* *ML Assessment System*
Reteach	*@HomeTutor*
Online Resources	*Classzone.com* *eEdition* *eWorkbook*

Video Tutor

Technology Highlights for Each Lesson

Easy Planner

Easy access to the Teacher's Edition and all teaching resources. Includes a search feature to locate the materials you need.

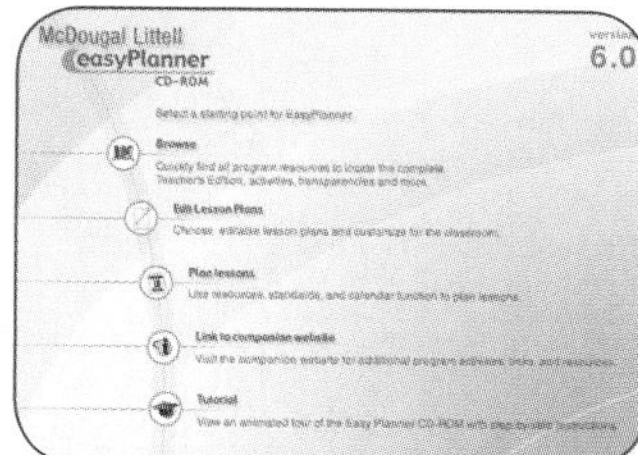

Activity Generator

Leveled, editable activities allow all students to explore a lesson's concepts. Includes teacher notes and closure questions.

Animated Algebra

Interactive tutorials provide visually engaging alternative opportunities to learn concepts and master skills.

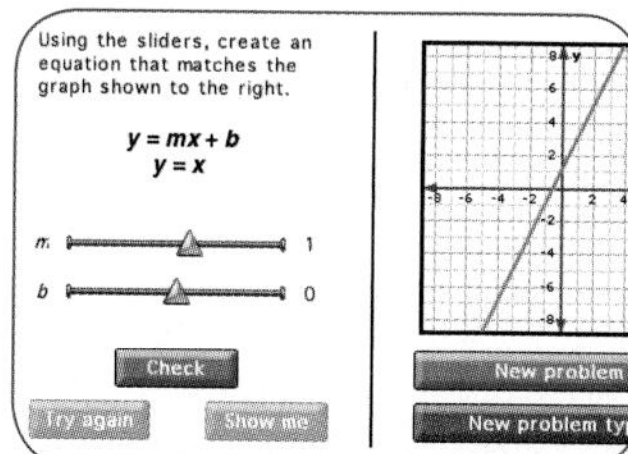

11 Lesson Practice Level B

LESSON 11.1 Practice B
For use with pages 710–716

1. domain: $x \ge 0$; range: $y \ge 0$; vertical stretch by a factor of 7
2. domain: $x \ge 0$; range: $y \ge 0$; vertical shrink by a factor of $\frac{1}{5}$
3. domain: $x \ge 0$; range: $y \le 0$; vertical stretch by a factor of 4 and reflection in x-axis

Graph the function and identify its domain and range. Compare the graph with the graph of $y = \sqrt{x}$.

1. $y = 7\sqrt{x}$
2. $y = \frac{1}{5}\sqrt{x}$
3. $y = -4\sqrt{x}$

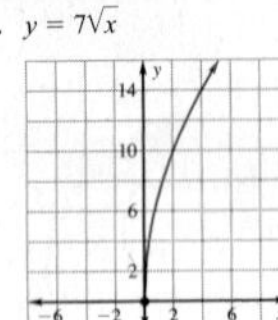
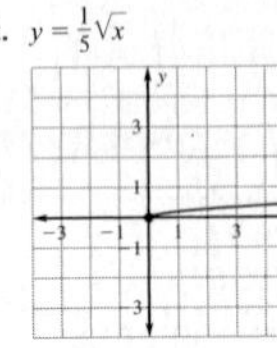
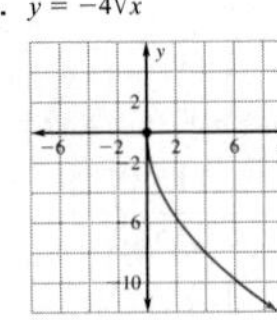

Describe how you would graph the function by using the graph of $y = \sqrt{x}$.

4. $y = \sqrt{x - 8}$
5. $y = \sqrt{x} + 3$
6. $y = \sqrt{x + 7}$
7. $y = \sqrt{x} - 5$
8. $y = \sqrt{x} + 3.5$
9. $y = \sqrt{x - \frac{1}{2}}$

4. translate graph of $y = \sqrt{x}$ horizontally 8 units right 5. translate graph of $y = \sqrt{x}$ vertically 3 units up

Match the function with its graph.

10. $y = \sqrt{x + 4} - 3$ E
11. $y = \sqrt{x - 3} + 4$ C
12. $y = \sqrt{x - 4} + 3$ A
13. $y = \sqrt{x - 4} - 3$ F
14. $y = \sqrt{x + 3} - 4$ B
15. $y = \sqrt{x + 3} + 3$ D

A. 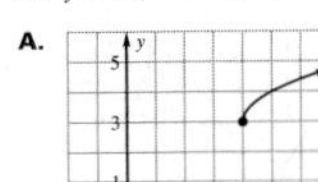
B. 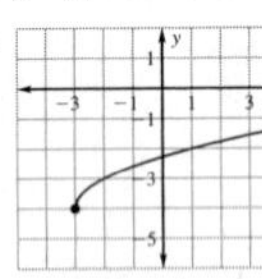
C. 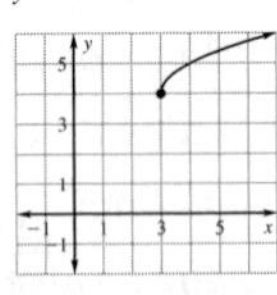
D. 
E. 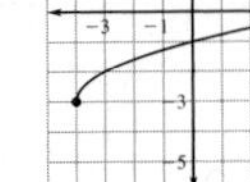
F. 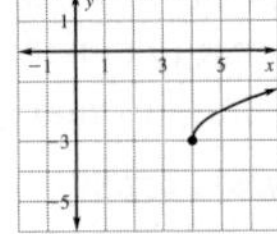

6. translate graph of $y = \sqrt{x}$ horizontally 7 units left
7. translate graph of $y = \sqrt{x}$ vertically 5 units down
8. translate graph of $y = \sqrt{x}$ vertically 3.5 units up
9. translate graph of $y = \sqrt{x}$ horizontally $\frac{1}{2}$ unit right

LESSON 11.1 Practice B *continued*
For use with pages 710–716

16. domain: $x \ge -4$; range: $y \ge -4$; vertical translation 4 units down and horizontal translation 4 units left
17. domain: $x \ge -5$; range: $y \ge 1$; vertical translation 1 unit up and horizontal translation 5 units left

Graph the function and identify its domain and range. Compare the graph with the graph of $y = \sqrt{x}$.

16. $y = \sqrt{x + 4} - 4$
17. $y = \sqrt{x + 5} + 1$
18. $y = \sqrt{x - 6} + 4$ See below.

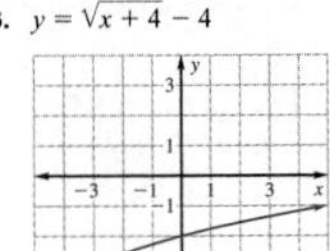
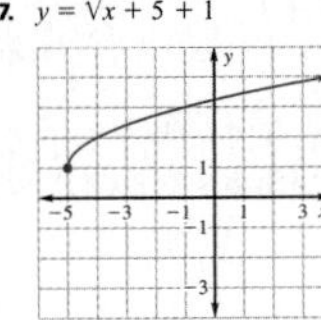
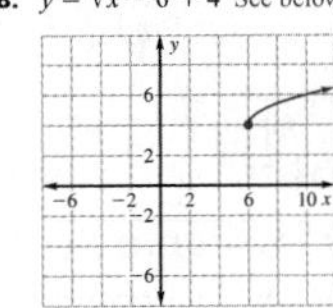

19. $y = \sqrt{x - 5} - 7$ See below.
20. $y = \sqrt{x - 1} + 2$ See below.
21. $y = \sqrt{x + 5} - 4$ See below.

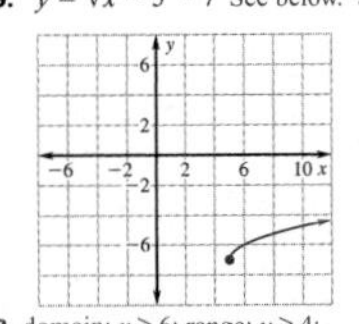
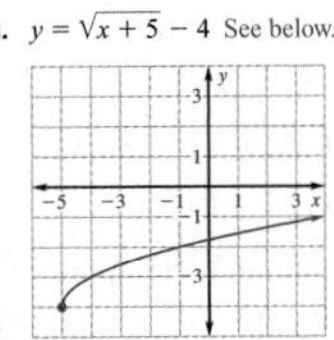

18. domain: $x \ge 6$; range: $y \ge 4$; vertical translation 4 units up and horizontal translation 6 units right

22. **Box Design** You are designing a box with a square base that will hold popcorn. The box must be 9 inches tall. The side length x (in inches) of the box is given by the function $x = \frac{1}{3}\sqrt{V}$ where V is the volume (in cubic inches) of the box. domain: $V > 0$; range: $x > 0$
   a. Graph the function and identify its domain and range.
   b. What is the volume of a box with a side length of 5 inches? 225 in.³
   c. What is the volume of a box with a side length of 8 inches? 576 in.³

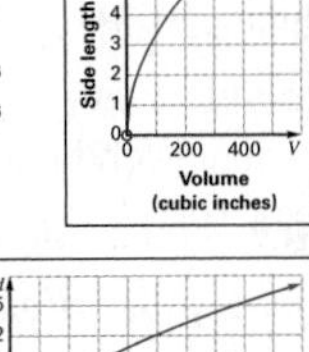

19. domain: $x \ge 5$; range: $y \ge -7$; vertical translation 7 units down and horizontal translation 5 units right
20. domain: $x \ge 1$; range: $y \ge 2$; vertical translation 2 units up and horizontal translation 1 unit right

23. **Steel Pipe** The inside diameter d of a steel pipe (in inches) and the weight w of water in the pipe (in pounds) are related by the function $d = 1.71\sqrt{w}$. domain: $w \ge 0$; range: $d \ge 0$
   a. Graph the function and identify its domain and range.
   b. What does the water weigh in a pipe with an inside diameter of 17 inches? Round your answer to the nearest pound. about 99 lb
   c. What does the water weigh in a pipe with an inside diameter of 3.5 inches? Round your answer to the nearest pound. about 4 lb

21. domain: $x \ge -5$; range: $y \ge -4$; vertical translation 4 units down and horizontal translation 5 units left

LESSON 11.2 Practice B
For use with pages 719–726

Simplify the expression.

1. $\sqrt{200}$ $10\sqrt{2}$
2. $\sqrt{45}$ $3\sqrt{5}$
3. $\sqrt{112}$ $4\sqrt{7}$
4. $\sqrt{400d}$ $20\sqrt{d}$
5. $\sqrt{9y^2}$ $3y$
6. $\sqrt{25n^3}$ $5n\sqrt{n}$
7. $\sqrt{3} \cdot \sqrt{21}$ $3\sqrt{7}$
8. $\sqrt{20} \cdot \sqrt{15}$ $10\sqrt{3}$
9. $\sqrt{10x} \cdot \sqrt{2x}$ $2x\sqrt{5}$
10. $\sqrt{\frac{16}{81}}$ $\frac{4}{9}$
11. $\sqrt{\frac{5}{49}}$ $\frac{\sqrt{5}}{7}$
12. $\sqrt{\frac{x^2}{144}}$ $\frac{x}{12}$

Simplify the expression by rationalizing the denominator.

13. $\frac{4}{\sqrt{5}}$ $\frac{4\sqrt{5}}{5}$
14. $\sqrt{\frac{3}{50}}$ $\frac{\sqrt{6}}{10}$
15. $\sqrt{\frac{9}{75}}$ $\frac{\sqrt{3}}{5}$
16. $\frac{2}{\sqrt{p}}$ $\frac{2\sqrt{p}}{p}$
17. $\frac{1}{\sqrt{3y}}$ $\frac{\sqrt{3y}}{3y}$
18. $\frac{9}{\sqrt{2x}}$ $\frac{9\sqrt{2x}}{2x}$

Simplify the expression.

19. $10\sqrt{7} + 3\sqrt{7}$ $13\sqrt{7}$
20. $4\sqrt{5} - 7\sqrt{5}$ $-3\sqrt{5}$
21. $\sqrt{7}(4 - \sqrt{7})$ $-7 + 4\sqrt{7}$
22. $\sqrt{5}(8\sqrt{10} + 1)$ $40\sqrt{2} + \sqrt{5}$
23. $(2\sqrt{3} + 5)^2$ $37 + 20\sqrt{3}$
24. $(6 + \sqrt{3})(6 - \sqrt{3})$ 33

25. **Water Flow** You can measure the speed of water by using an L-shaped tube. The speed V of the water (in miles per hour) is given by the function $V = \sqrt{\frac{5}{2}h}$ where h is the height of the column of water above the surface (in inches).

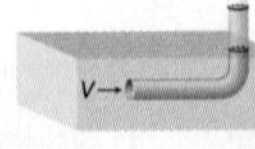

   a. If you use the tube in a river and find that h is 6 inches, what is the speed of the water? Round your answer to the nearest hundredth. about 3.87 mi/h
   b. If you use the tube in a river and find that h is 8.5 inches, what is the speed of the water? Round your answer to the nearest hundredth. about 4.61 mi/h

26. **Walking Speed** The maximum walking speed S (in feet per second) of an animal is given by the function $S = \sqrt{gL}$ where g is 32 feet per second squared and L is the length of the animal's leg (in feet).
   a. How fast can an animal whose legs are 9 inches long walk? Round your answer to the nearest hundredth. about 4.90 ft/sec
   b. How fast can an animal whose legs are 3 feet long walk? Round your answer to the nearest hundredth. about 9.80 ft/sec

LESSON 11.3 Practice B
For use with pages 729–734

7. Add 5 to each side, then square each side, subtract 3 from each side, and divide each side by 7.
8. Add 3 to each side, divide each side by 6, square each side and solve the linear equation for x.

Determine whether the given value is a solution of the equation.

1. $4\sqrt{2x - 3} = 12$; 2 not a solution
2. $2\sqrt{9x - 1} = 20$; 7 not a solution
3. $\sqrt{4x + 8} = \sqrt{6 + 2x}$; -1 solution
4. $\sqrt{7x - 2} = \sqrt{8 - 3x}$; -1 not a solution
5. $x = \sqrt{4x - 3}$; 3 solution
6. $\sqrt{4x - 3} = x - 2$; 7 solution

Describe the steps you would use to solve the equation. Do not solve the equation.

9. Square each side and solve the resulting linear equation for x.
10. Divide each side by 2, square each side, and solve the resulting linear equation for x.

7. $\sqrt{7x + 3} - 5 = 2$
8. $6\sqrt{4 - x} - 3 = 1$
9. $\sqrt{12x - 7} = \sqrt{9x + 3}$
10. $10\sqrt{6 - x} = 2\sqrt{x + 4}$
11. $\sqrt{5x - 3} - \sqrt{10 - 4x} = 0$ See below.
12. $\sqrt{9x + 1} - 2 = x$ See below.

Solve the equation. Check for extraneous solutions.

13. $8\sqrt{x} - 32 = 0$ 16
14. $\sqrt{5x} - 4 = 16$ 80
15. $\sqrt{x + 3} + 8 = 15$ 46
16. $\sqrt{x - 6} - 2 = 4$ 42
17. $\sqrt{x + 9} - 5 = 2$ 40
18. $\sqrt{8 - 3x} + 5 = 6$ $\frac{7}{3}$
19. $\sqrt{5x + 4} - 12 = -6$ $\frac{32}{5}$
20. $3\sqrt{x + 5} - 3 = 6$ 4
21. $4\sqrt{2x + 1} - 7 = 1$ $\frac{3}{2}$
22. $\sqrt{x} = \sqrt{5x - 1}$ $\frac{1}{4}$
23. $\sqrt{7x - 6} = \sqrt{x}$ 1
24. $\sqrt{6x - 8} = \sqrt{4x - 10}$
25. $\sqrt{7x - 5} = \sqrt{3x + 19}$ 6
26. $\sqrt{x - 15} - \sqrt{x - 7} = 0$
27. $\sqrt{10x - 3} - \sqrt{8x - 11} = 0$
28. $\sqrt{5x - 6} = x$ 2, 3
29. $x = \sqrt{2x + 24}$ 6
30. $\sqrt{2x - 15} = x$ no solution

24. no solution 26. no solution 27. no solution

31. **Market Research** A marketing department determines that the price of a magazine subscription and the demand to subscribe are related by the function $P = 40 - \sqrt{0.0004x + 1}$ where P is the price per subscription and x is the number of subscriptions sold.
   a. If the subscription price is set at \$25, how many subscriptions would be sold? about 560,000 subscriptions
   b. If the subscription price is set at \$30, how many more subscriptions are sold in part (a) than when the price is \$30? 312,500 subscriptions

32. **Awning** The area A of a portion of a circle bounded by two radii r and angle t of a sector of a circle are related by the function $r = \sqrt{\frac{2A}{t}}$.
The length of a side (radius) of the top view of the awning shown at the right is 6 feet and the angle that is formed by the awning is $\frac{5\pi}{3}$. Find the area of the awning. Round your answer to the nearest hundredth. about 94.25 ft²

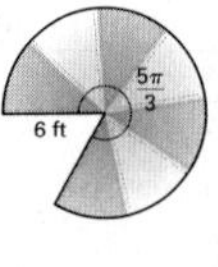

11. Add the second radical expression to each side, square each side, and solve the resulting linear equation for x.
12. Add 2 to each side, square each side, and then solve the resulting quadratic equation for x.

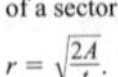

LESSON 11.4

Practice B

For use with pages 737–742

Let *a* and *b* represent the lengths of the legs of a right triangle, and let *c* represent the length of the hypotenuse. Find the unknown length.

1. $a = 1, b = 5$ $\sqrt{26}$ **2.** $b = 4, c = 9$ $\sqrt{65}$ **3.** $a = 6, b = 6$ $6\sqrt{2}$

4. $b = 7, c = 12$ $\sqrt{95}$ **5.** $a = 2, b = 8$ $2\sqrt{17}$ **6.** $a = 6, b = 30$ $6\sqrt{26}$

7. $a = 4, b = 15$ $\sqrt{241}$ **8.** $b = 7, c = 11$ $6\sqrt{2}$ **9.** $a = 10, b = 20$ $10\sqrt{5}$

10. $a = 30, b = 40$ 50 **11.** $a = 15, c = 25$ 20 **12.** $a = 11, b = 22$ $11\sqrt{5}$

Find the unknown lengths.

13. 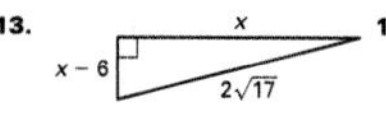

2, 8

14. 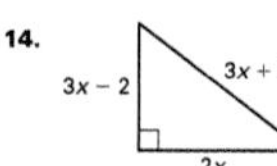 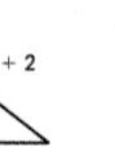

12, 16, 20

15. 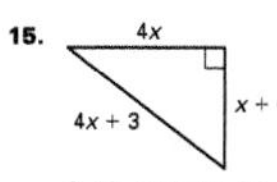

9, 12, 15 or 15, 36, 39

16. A right triangle has one leg that is 3 inches longer than the other leg. The hypotenuse is $\sqrt{65}$ inches. Find the lengths of the legs. 4 in., 7 in.

Tell whether the triangle with the given side lengths is a right triangle.

17. 4, 5, 6 not a right triangle **18.** 15, 20, 25 right triangle **19.** 9, 15, 20 not a right triangle

20. Shuffleboard The playing bed of a shuffleboard table is in the shape of a rectangle. If the playing bed measures 154 inches by 20 inches, what is the length of the diagonal from one corner of the playing bed to the opposite corner? Round your answer to the nearest inch. about 155 in.

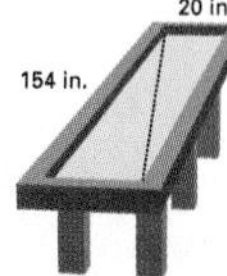

21. Indirect Measurement You are trying to determine the distance across a pond. You put posts into the ground at *A*, *B*, and *C* so that angle *B* is a right angle. You measure and find that *AB* is 18 feet and *CB* is 28 feet. How wide is the pond from *A* to *C*? Round your answer to the nearest foot. about 33 ft

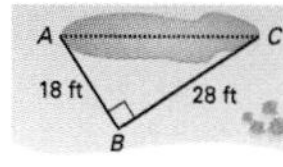

22. Badminton You are setting up a badminton net. To keep each pole standing straight, you use two ropes and two stakes as shown. How long is each piece of rope? Round your answer to the nearest tenth. about 9.2 ft

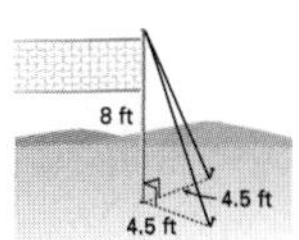

LESSON 11.5

Practice B

For use with pages 744–750

Find the distance between the two points.

1. (8, 3), (10, 4) $\sqrt{5}$ **2.** (2, 7), (5, 6) $\sqrt{10}$ **3.** (9, 6), (4, 1) $5\sqrt{2}$

4. (0, 4), (8, −2) 10 **5.** (−5, 3), (1, 2) $\sqrt{37}$ **6.** (1, −6), (−2, 4) $\sqrt{109}$

7. (8, −7), (4, −3) $4\sqrt{2}$ **8.** (−10, −2), (6, 5) $\sqrt{305}$ **9.** (−1, −8), (−5, −2) $2\sqrt{13}$

The distance *d* between two points is given. Find the value of *b*.

10. $(b, 4), (2, -1); d = 5$ 2 **11.** $(-3, 2), (7, b); d = 10$ 2 **12.** $(3, 2), (b, -9); d = 11$ 3

13. $(4, 1), (5, b); d = \sqrt{17}$ −3, 5 **14.** $(b, 2), (3, -1); d = \sqrt{58}$ −4, 10 **15.** $(-4, b), (5, -2); d = \sqrt{106}$ −7, 3

Find the midpoint of the line segment with the given endpoints.

16. (2, 5), (4, 12) $\left(3, \frac{17}{2}\right)$ **17.** (−7, 2), (−10, 14) $\left(-\frac{17}{2}, 8\right)$ **18.** (−9, −5), (7, −14) $\left(-1, -\frac{19}{2}\right)$

19. (8, −8), (3, 5) $\left(\frac{11}{2}, -\frac{3}{2}\right)$ **20.** (20, 5), (30, −5) (25, 0) **21.** (−11, 7), (8, −3) $\left(-\frac{3}{2}, 2\right)$

Use the distance formula and the converse of the Pythagorean theorem to determine whether the points are vertices of a right triangle. See below.

22. (1, 1), (4, 4), (1, 4) **23.** (6, 0), (6, 4), (2, 4) **24.** (−2, 1), (3, 5), (6, −2)

25. (6, 4), (−1, −2), (−4, 3) **26.** (5, 3), (4, −2), (10, 2) **27.** (2, −4), (2, −3), (6, 1)

28. Walking Trail A walking trail follows the path shown on the map. The distance between consecutive grid lines is 1 mile. Find the total distance of the trail from start to finish. Round your answer to the nearest mile. 15 mi

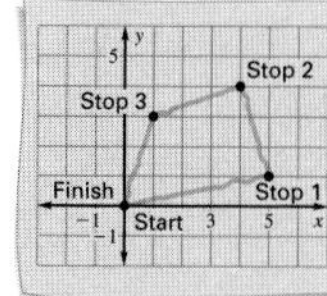

22. right triangle **23.** right triangle **24.** not a right triangle
25. not a right triangle **26.** right triangle **27.** not a right triangle

29. Amusement Park An amusement park designer wants to place a Ferris wheel midway between the two largest coasters. The distance between consecutive grid lines is 500 feet. (1750, 2000)

a. Determine the coordinates of where the Ferris wheel should be.

b. How far will the Ferris wheel be from each of the coasters? Round your answer to the nearest foot. 1953 ft

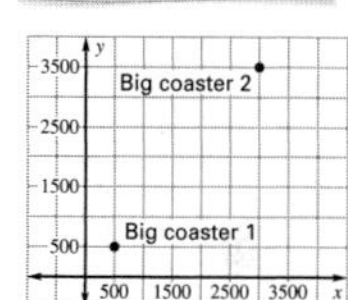

30. Reading You have 30 days left to read the books on your summer reading list. As of today, you have read 5 books. By the end of the 30 days, you have to have read 12 books. Assume that the books are all approximately the same length and you read at a relatively constant pace. After 15 days, how many books should you have read? 8.5 books

CHAPTER 11 Quiz 1
For use after Lessons 11.1–11.3

1. Graph the function $y = \sqrt{x - 2}$ and identify its domain and range. Compare the graph with the graph of $y = \sqrt{x}$.

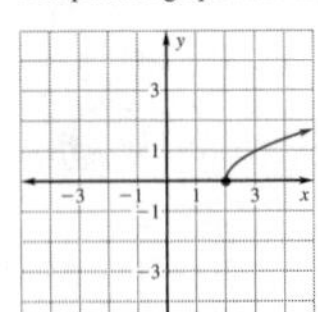

Simplify the expression.

2. $\sqrt{90}$
3. $\sqrt{12} \cdot \sqrt{3y^2}$
4. $(\sqrt{3} + 4)(\sqrt{3} - 1)$
5. $\frac{10}{\sqrt{5}}$
6. $\sqrt{\frac{125}{x^4}}$
7. $\sqrt{\frac{72k^6}{6g^2}}$

Solve the equation. Check for extraneous solutions.

8. $\sqrt{x} - 9 = 0$
9. $\sqrt{4x + 3} = \sqrt{3x + 4}$
10. $\sqrt{4x - 3} = x$
11. $\sqrt{x - 6} + 4 = 9$

Answers

1. See left. The domain is $x \geq 2$. The range is $y \geq 0$. The graph of $y = \sqrt{x - 2}$ is a horizontal translation (of 2 units to the right) of the graph of $y = \sqrt{x}$.
2. $3\sqrt{10}$
3. $6y$
4. $3\sqrt{3} - 1$
5. $2\sqrt{5}$
6. $\frac{5\sqrt{5}}{x^2}$
7. $\frac{2\sqrt{3}k^3}{g}$
8. 81
9. 1
10. 1, 3
11. 31

CHAPTER 11 Quiz 2
For use after Lessons 11.4–11.5

Let *a* and *b* represent the lengths of the legs of a right triangle, and let *c* represent the length of the hypotenuse. Find the unknown length.

1. $a = 8, b = 15$
2. $b = 3, c = 7$
3. $a = 5, c = 10$
4. $a = 6, b = 6$

Find the unknown lengths.

5. $3\sqrt{10}$, x, $3x$

6. 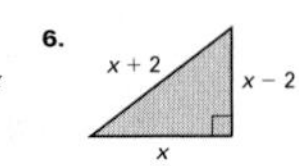

Find the distance between the two points.

7. $(4, -5), (0, -5)$
8. $(3, 2), (3, -4)$

Find the midpoint of the line segment with the given endpoints.

9. $(0, 4), (14, 2)$
10. $(6, -2), (4, -8)$

Answers

1. $c = 17$
2. $a = 2\sqrt{10}$
3. $b = 5\sqrt{3}$
4. $c = 6\sqrt{2}$
5. $x = 3, 3x = 9$
6. $x = 8, x - 2 = 6, x + 2 = 10$
7. 4
8. 6
9. $(7, 3)$
10. $(5, -5)$

CHAPTER 11 Chapter Test B
For use after Chapter 11

Graph the function and identify the domain and range. Then compare the graph with the graph of $y = \sqrt{x}$.

1. $y = \frac{1}{2}\sqrt{x} - 3$
2. $y = -\sqrt{x + 2}$

Simplify the expression.

3. $\sqrt{72a^5}$
4. $5\sqrt{2} - 3\sqrt{2} + 12\sqrt{2}$
5. $3\sqrt{12} - 5\sqrt{27}$
6. $\frac{6}{\sqrt{3b}}$
7. $\sqrt{\frac{4p^2}{q^6}}$
8. $(2\sqrt{7} + 4)^2$

In Exercises 9 and 10, use the following information.

The time t (in seconds) it takes an object dropped from a height h (in feet) to reach the ground is given by the equation $t = \sqrt{\frac{h}{16}}$.

9. Write the equation in simplified form.
10. Find the exact time it takes a stone to reach the ground if it is dropped from a bridge that is 200 feet high.

Solve the equation. Check for extraneous solutions.

11. $\sqrt{4x} + 5 = 2$
12. $\sqrt{3x + 4} = \sqrt{12x - 14}$
13. $\sqrt{6x + 7} + 3 = x + 5$

Answers

1. See left. domain: $x \geq 0$; range: $y \geq -3$; The graph is a vertical shrink and a shift 3 units down from the graph of $y = \sqrt{x}$.
2. See left. domain: $x \geq -2$; range: $y \leq 0$; The graph is a reflection in the x-axis and a shift 2 units to the left of the graph of $y = \sqrt{x}$.
3. $6a^2\sqrt{2a}$
4. $14\sqrt{2}$
5. $-9\sqrt{3}$
6. $\frac{2\sqrt{3b}}{b}$
7. $\frac{2p}{q^3}$
8. $44 + 16\sqrt{7}$
9. $t = \frac{\sqrt{h}}{4}$
10. $\frac{5\sqrt{2}}{2}$ sec
11. no solution
12. 2
13. $-1, 3$

CHAPTER 11 Chapter Test B *continued*

14. A person's maximum running speed s (in meters per second) can be approximated by the function $s = \pi\sqrt{\frac{9.8\ell}{6}}$ where ℓ is the person's leg length (in meters). To the nearest tenth of a meter, what is the leg length of a person whose maximum running speed is about 3.4 meters per second?

Find the unknown lengths.

15. A right triangle has one leg that is twice as long as the other leg. The hypotenuse is $2\sqrt{5}$ inches.
16. A right triangle has a hypotenuse that is 3 feet longer than one leg. The other leg is 4 feet.

Find the midpoint of the line segment with the given endpoints.

17. $(5, 4), (1, 1)$
18. $(-1, 1), (-4, -3)$
19. $(9, -2), (3, -2)$

In Exercises 20 and 21, use the following graph.

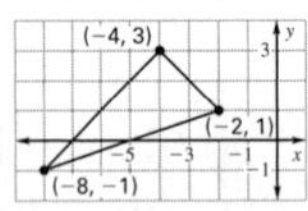

20. Find the length of each line segment.
21. Use the converse of the Pythagorean theorem to determine whether the points are the vertices of a right triangle.

The distance *d* between two points is given. Find the value of *b*.

22. $(b, -2), (6, 1); d = 5$
23. $(5, 1), (0, b); d = \sqrt{29}$

24. A fire is sighted in the forest from a helicopter. The forest ranger can send a crew from one of the two towers, as shown on the map. The distance between consecutive grid lines represents 0.5 mile. Which tower is closer to the fire?

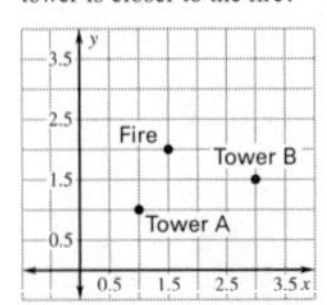

Answers

14. 0.7 m
15. 4 in., 2 in.
16. $\frac{7}{6}$ ft, $\frac{25}{6}$ ft
17. $\left(3, \frac{5}{2}\right)$
18. $\left(-\frac{5}{2}, -1\right)$
19. $(6, -2)$
20. $2\sqrt{2}, 2\sqrt{10}, 4\sqrt{2}$
21. yes
22. 2 or 10
23. 3 or -1
24. Tower A

CHAPTER 11 Standardized Test

For use after Chapter 11

Multiple Choice

1. The graph of which function is a vertical stretch of the graph $y = \sqrt{x}$? C

Ⓐ $y = \frac{1}{2}\sqrt{x}$ Ⓑ $y = 5 + \sqrt{x}$

Ⓒ $y = 4\sqrt{x}$ Ⓓ $y = \sqrt{x + 3}$

2. The graph of which function is a horizontal translation of 2 units to the left of the graph $y = \sqrt{x}$? D

Ⓐ $y = \sqrt{x} - 2$ Ⓑ $y = \sqrt{x} + 2$

Ⓒ $y = \sqrt{x - 2}$ Ⓓ $y = \sqrt{x + 2}$

3. The graph of which function is shown? A

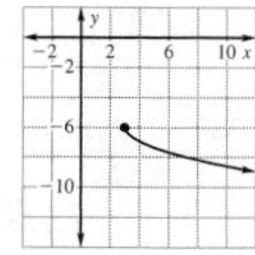

Ⓐ $y = -\sqrt{x - 3} - 6$

Ⓑ $y = -\sqrt{x + 3} + 6$

Ⓒ $y = -\sqrt{x - 3} + 6$

Ⓓ $y = -\sqrt{x + 3} - 6$

4. How is the graph of $f(x) = \sqrt{x} + 5$ related to the graph of $g(x) = \sqrt{x} - 5$. B

Ⓐ It is a vertical translation of 5 units up of the graph of g.

Ⓑ It is a vertical translation of 10 units up of the graph of g.

Ⓒ It is a horizontal translation of 5 units to the right of the graph of g.

Ⓓ It is a horizontal translation of 10 units to the right of the graph of g.

5. Which expression is equivalent to $\sqrt{72}$? B

Ⓐ $\sqrt{70} + \sqrt{2}$ Ⓑ $6\sqrt{2}$

Ⓒ 12 Ⓓ 36

6. Which expression is equivalent to $\sqrt{24} \cdot \sqrt{2}$ in its simplest form? A

Ⓐ $4\sqrt{3}$ Ⓑ $16\sqrt{3}$

Ⓒ $2\sqrt{12}$ Ⓓ $12\sqrt{2}$

7. Which expression is equivalent to $\sqrt{\frac{16x}{49}}$? C

Ⓐ $\frac{4x}{7}$ Ⓑ $\frac{4\sqrt{x}}{49}$

Ⓒ $\frac{4\sqrt{x}}{7}$ Ⓓ $\frac{\sqrt{4x}}{7}$

8. Which expression is equivalent to $\sqrt{\frac{9}{32}}$ in its simplest form? D

Ⓐ $\frac{3}{\sqrt{32}}$ Ⓑ $\frac{3}{4\sqrt{2}}$

Ⓒ $\frac{3\sqrt{2}}{4}$ Ⓓ $\frac{3\sqrt{2}}{8}$

9. Which expression is equivalent to $\sqrt{\frac{5x^2}{6}}$ in its simplest form? D

Ⓐ $\frac{x\sqrt{5}}{\sqrt{6}}$ Ⓑ $\frac{30\sqrt{x}}{6}$

Ⓒ $\frac{x\sqrt{5}}{6}$ Ⓓ $\frac{x\sqrt{30}}{6}$

10. Which expression is equivalent to $\sqrt{24} + 5\sqrt{6} - \sqrt{54}$? B

Ⓐ $10\sqrt{2}$ Ⓑ $4\sqrt{6}$

Ⓒ $5 - \sqrt{24}$ Ⓓ $10\sqrt{6}$

11. Which expression is equivalent to $(3\sqrt{5} - 2)^2$? A

Ⓐ $49 - 12\sqrt{5}$ Ⓑ $4 - 3\sqrt{5}$

Ⓒ $30 - 12\sqrt{5}$ Ⓓ $-4 - 3\sqrt{5}$

12. Which expression is equivalent to $\frac{5}{\sqrt{r}} - \frac{2}{\sqrt{r}}$ in its simplest form? C

Ⓐ $\frac{3r}{r}$ Ⓑ $\frac{5r - 2}{r^2}$

Ⓒ $\frac{3\sqrt{r}}{r}$ Ⓓ $\frac{3}{\sqrt{r}}$

13. Which expression is equivalent to $\frac{15}{\sqrt{6} - \sqrt{3}}$ in its simplest form? B

Ⓐ $-\frac{15\sqrt{9}}{3}$ Ⓑ $5\sqrt{6} + 5\sqrt{3}$

Ⓒ $-\frac{15\sqrt{6} + 15\sqrt{3}}{3}$ Ⓓ $15\sqrt{3}$

14. What is the solution of the equation $6\sqrt{x + 2} + 5 = 35$? C

Ⓐ $\sqrt{3}$ Ⓑ 3 Ⓒ 23 Ⓓ 25

15. Given a right triangle with side lengths 7 and 24, what is the length of the hypotenuse? A

Ⓐ 25 Ⓑ 31 Ⓒ 62 Ⓓ 625

16. Which of the triangles with the given side lengths is *not* a right triangle? D

Ⓐ 3, 4, 5 Ⓑ 11, 60, 61

Ⓒ 15, 20, 25 Ⓓ 9, 39, 41

17. What is the midpoint of the line segment with endpoints $(-3, -2)$ and $(5, -4)$? A

Ⓐ $(1, -3)$ Ⓑ $(-4, -1)$

Ⓒ $(-1, 3)$ Ⓓ $(4, 1)$

18. What is the distance between $(5, 3.5)$ and $(-2, -2.5)$? C

Ⓐ 2 Ⓑ $\sqrt{13}$

Ⓒ $\sqrt{85}$ Ⓓ 13

21. a. Twenty-four steps are needed. The height from floor to ceiling is 12 feet or 144 inches. If the riser of each step is 6 inches, you would need 24 steps to reach the second floor. **b.** 24 ft; Each step has a tread of 12 inches and there are 24 steps, so the linear distance would be 288 inches or 24 feet. **c.** A 322 inch rail is needed.

Gridded Answer

19. What is the value of x in the equation $4\sqrt{x + 5} + 2 = 18$?

(Grid answer: 11)

20. You would meet at the fountain. The midpoint between the two locations is the point (4, 3). The two locations closest to this point are the school and the fountain. You can use either the distance formula or your knowledge of right triangles to determine that the fountain is closest.

Short Response

20. A map of your town is shown. See above.

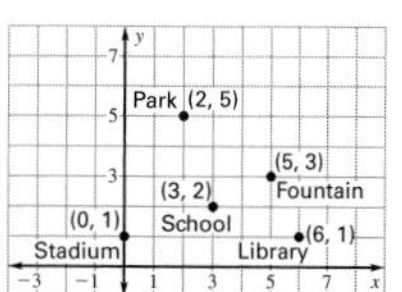

You are at the library. Your friend is at the park. You want to meet at the place that is closest to the midpoint of your locations. At which location should you meet? *Explain.*

Extended Response

21. The vertical distance from the first floor of a house to the second floor is 12 feet. The tread of each step is 12 inches and the riser is 6 inches. See left.

a. How many steps are needed? *Explain.*

b. What is the linear distance (in feet) needed for the staircase? *Explain.*

c. If a railing is installed from the edge of the bottom step to the edge of the top step, how long of a rail is needed? Round your answer to the nearest inch.

CHAPTER 11 Alternative Assessment and Math Journal

For use after Chapter 11

Journal **1.** State and explain the product and quotient properties of radicals for $a \geq 0$ and $b \geq 0$. Use examples to illustrate why there are not sum or difference properties of radicals.

Multi-Step Problem **2.** The function $t = \frac{1}{4}\sqrt{36 - h}$ represents the time t (in seconds) it takes an object to fall to a height h (in feet) after being dropped from an initial height of 36 feet.

a. Graph the function and state the domain.

b. Identify the intercepts of this function and explain what each conveys about the position of the object.

c. Determine the distance between the intercepts. Round your answer to the nearest hundredth.

d. What is the height of the object after $\frac{1}{2}$ second?

e. What is the height of the object after 1 second?

f. How long does it take for the object to travel halfway to the ground? Round your answer to the nearest hundredth.

g. Does the second half of the object's fall take more or less time than the first half? Explain your reasoning.

1. Complete answers should include: an explanation of each property of radicals; an example illustrating why there is no sum property of radicals; an example illustrating why there is no difference property of radicals.

2. a.

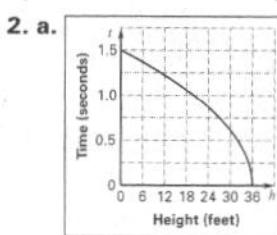

Domain: $0 \leq h \leq 36$

b. (0, 1.5), (36, 0); 1.5 seconds after the object is dropped it has a height of 0 feet; the object is at a height of 36 feet right before it is released.
c. 36.03 units **d.** 32 ft **e.** 20 ft **f.** 1.06 sec
g. Less time; The object is in the air for a total of 1.5 seconds, and it takes just over 1 second to fall the first 18 feet, which means it takes less than 0.5 second to fall the second 18 feet.

CHAPTER 11 Alternative Assessment Rubric *continued*

For use after Chapter 11

Journal Solution **1.** Complete answers should include:

- an explanation of each property of radicals.
- an example illustrating why there is no sum property of radicals.
- an example illustrating why there is no difference property of radicals.

Multi-Step Problem Solution **2. a.**

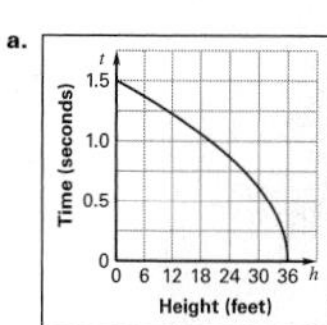

Domain: $0 \leq h \leq 36$

b. t-intercept: (0, 1.5), h-intercept: (36, 0); 1.5 seconds after the object is dropped it has a height of 0 feet; the object is at a height of 36 feet right before it is released.

c. 36.03 units

d. 32 feet

e. 20 feet

f. 1.06 seconds

g. Less time; The object is in the air for a total of 1.5 seconds, and it takes just over 1 second to fall the first 18 feet, which means it takes less than 0.5 second to fall the second 18 feet.

Multi-Step Problem Rubric

4 The student answers all parts of the problem correctly and completely. The student shows all work. The student's work is neat.

3 The student answers all parts of the problem. The student's work may contain one or two errors in the calculations, graph, or equations. The student shows most work. The student's work is neat.

2 The student answers all parts of the problem, but there are more than two errors in the calculations, graph, or equations. The student shows some work. The student's work is sloppy.

1 The student does not complete all parts of the problem. The student's work has several errors in the calculations, graph, and equations. The student's work is sloppy, or no work is shown.

PLAN AND PREPARE

Main Ideas

In Chapter 11, students graph square root functions. They simplify radical expressions, including rationalizing the denominator. They add, subtract, and multiply radicals. They solve radical equations, including equations with extraneous solutions. They apply the Pythagorean theorem and its converse as well as the distance and midpoint formulas to solve problems.

Prerequisite Skills

Skills Readiness, available on the *Easy Planner*, provides review and practice for the Skills Check portion of the Prerequisite Skills quiz.

How student answers the exercises	What to assign from *Skills Readiness*
Ex. 3 answered incorrectly	**Skill 80** Graph a function
Any of Exs. 4–7 answered incorrectly	**Skill 6** Evaluate square roots
Any of Exs. 8–11 answered incorrectly	**Skill 56** Use the distributive property
Any of Exs. 12–15 answered incorrectly	**Skill 67** Factor trinomials
Ex. 16 answered incorrectly	**Skill 8** Evaluate powers
All exercises answered correctly	Chapter 11 Enrichment

Additional skills review and practice is available in the Skills Review Handbook, pp. 909–937, and the @HomeTutor.

11 Radicals and Geometry Connections

Making Sense of Chapter 11

In Chapter 11 you will work with radical functions, expressions, and equations. By the end of this chapter, you will be able to apply the Pythagorean theorem and the midpoint and distance formulas.

Before

Previously, you learned the following skills, which you'll use in Chapter 11: graphing functions, evaluating square roots, and factoring trinomials.

Prerequisite Skills

VOCABULARY CHECK

Copy and complete the statement.

1. The number or expression inside a radical symbol is called the _?_. **radicand**
2. If $b^2 = a$, then b is a(n) _?_ of a. **square root**

SKILLS CHECK

3. Graph $y = 3 \cdot 2^x$. *(Prerequisite skill for 11.1)* **See margin.**

Evaluate the expression. *(Prerequisite skill for 11.2)*

4. $\sqrt{81}$ **9**
5. $-\sqrt{64}$ **−8**
6. $\pm\sqrt{100}$ **±10**
7. $-\sqrt{121}$ **−11**

Use the distributive property to write an equivalent expression. *(Prerequisite skill for 11.2)*

8. $4(y - 3)$ **$4y - 12$**
9. $2(x - 2)$ **$2x - 4$**
10. $-x(x + 11)$ **$-x^2 - 11x$**
11. $4x(x - 9)$ **$4x^2 - 36x$**

Factor the trinomial. *(Prerequisite skill for 11.3)*

12. $x^2 + 4x + 4$ **$(x + 2)^2$**
13. $m^2 + 9m + 8$ **$(m + 8)(m + 1)$**
14. $r^2 + 8r + 7$ **$(r + 7)(r + 1)$**
15. $b^2 + 10b + 16$ **$(b + 8)(b + 2)$**
16. Evaluate a^2 when $a = 7$. *(Prerequisite skill for 11.4–11.5)* **49**

@HomeTutor Prerequisite skills practice at classzone.com

Chapter Planning Guide

Chapter Resource Book
- Teaching Guide/Lesson Plan
- Project with Rubric

Assessment and Intervention
- Assessment Book
- Benchmark Tests
- Remediation Book
- Skills Readiness

Interactive Technology
- Easy Planner
- Power Presentations
- Activity Generator
- Animated Algebra
- Test Generator
- Online Quizzes
- eWorkbook
- eEdition
- @HomeTutor

Resources for English Learners
- Spanish Study Guide
- Multi-Language Visual Glossary
- Student Resources in Spanish

In Chapter 11, you will apply the big ideas listed below and reviewed in the Chapter Summary on page 753. You will also use the key vocabulary listed below.

Big Ideas

1. **Graphing square root functions**
2. **Using properties of radicals in expressions and equations**
3. **Working with radicals in geometry**

KEY VOCABULARY

- radical expression, *p. 710*
- radical function, *p. 710*
- square root function, *p. 710*
- parent square root function, *p. 710*
- simplest form of a radical expression, *p. 719*
- rationalizing the denominator, *p. 721*
- radical equation, *p. 729*
- extraneous solution, *p. 730*
- hypotenuse, *p. 737*
- legs of a right triangle, *p. 737*
- Pythagorean theorem, *p. 737*
- distance formula, *p. 744*
- midpoint, *p. 745*
- midpoint formula, *p. 745*

Why?

You can use radical equations to solve real-world problems. For example, you can find the length of a sailboat's waterline given the hull speed of the sailboat.

Animated Algebra

The animation illustrated below for Example 5 on page 731 helps you answer this question: What is the length of a sailboat's waterline if the sailboat has a hull speed of 8 nautical miles per hour?

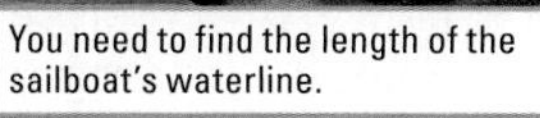
You need to find the length of the sailboat's waterline.

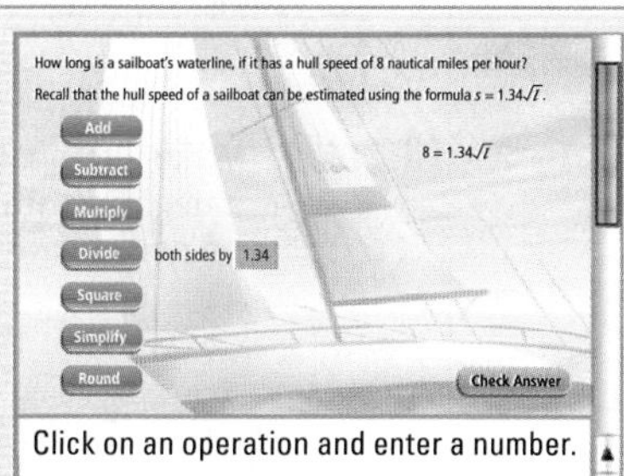

How long is a sailboat's waterline, if it has a hull speed of 8 nautical miles per hour?
Recall that the hull speed of a sailboat can be estimated using the formula $s = 1.34\sqrt{\ell}$.
$8 = 1.34\sqrt{\ell}$
Add
Subtract
Multiply
Divide
both sides by 1.34
Square
Simplify
Round
Check Answer

Click on an operation and enter a number.

Animated Algebra at classzone.com

Other animations for Chapter 11: pages 711, 719, 722, 737, 746, and 753

709

Differentiated Instruction Resources

- Reading Strategies for Chapter 11
- Differentiated Instruction Lesson Notes
- English Learners Lesson Notes
- Inclusion Lesson Notes
- Teaching Strategies with Sample Worksheets
- Using Technology in the Classroom
- Tips for New Teachers
- Math Background Notes
- Assessment Strategies
- Teacher Survival Activities
- Bulletin Board Idea

3.

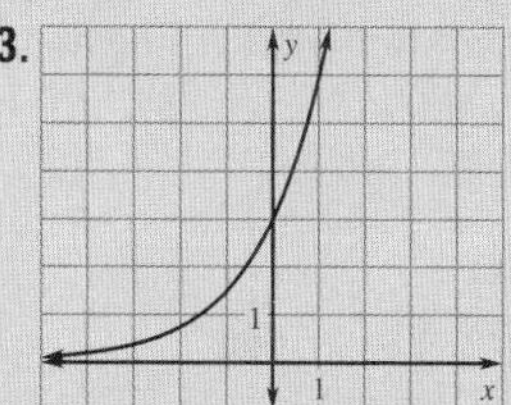

1 PLAN AND PREPARE

Warm-Up Exercises

Transparency Available

1. Graph the function $y = 2^x$.

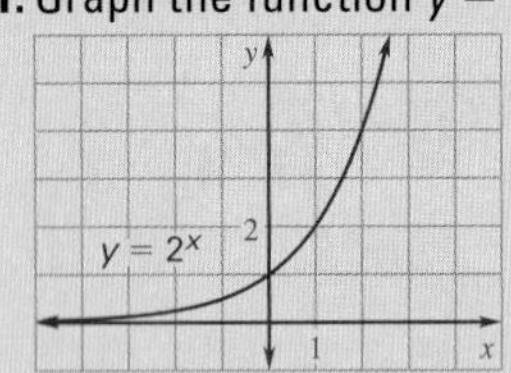

2. Evaluate $3\sqrt{x}$ when $x = 4$. 6
3. Evaluate $\sqrt{x + 5}$ when $x = 11$. 4

Notetaking Guide

Transparency Available

Promotes interactive learning and notetaking skills.

Pacing

Basic: 2 days
Average: 2 days
Advanced: 2 days
Block: 1 block

- See *Teaching Guide/Lesson Plan.*

2 FOCUS AND MOTIVATE

Essential Question

Big Idea 1, p. 709

How do you graph square root functions? **Tell students they will learn how to answer this question by making tables, plotting points, and then connecting the points.**

NCTM STANDARDS

Standard 2: Understand functions

Standard 3: Apply transformations to math situations

11.1 Graph Square Root Functions

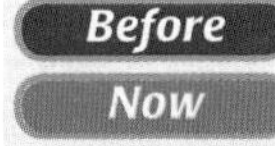

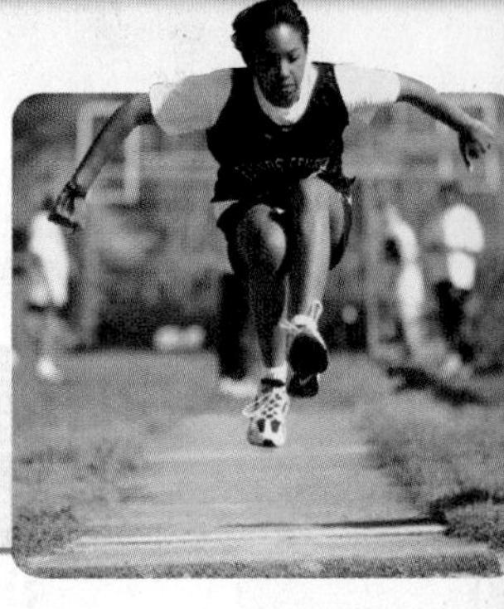

Before You graphed linear, exponential, and quadratic functions.

Now You will graph square root functions.

Why? So you can analyze the speed of an athlete, as in Ex. 45.

Key Vocabulary
- **radical expression**
- **radical function**
- **square root function**
- **parent square root function**

A **radical expression** is an expression that contains a radical, such as a square root, cube root, or other root. A **radical function** contains a radical expression with the independent variable in the radicand. For example, $y = \sqrt[3]{2x}$ and $y = \sqrt{x + 2}$ are radical functions. If the radical is a square root, then the function is called a **square root function**.

KEY CONCEPT *For Your Notebook*

Parent Function for Square Root Functions

The most basic square root function in the family of all square root functions, called the **parent square root function**, is:

$$y = \sqrt{x}$$

The graph of the parent square root function is shown.

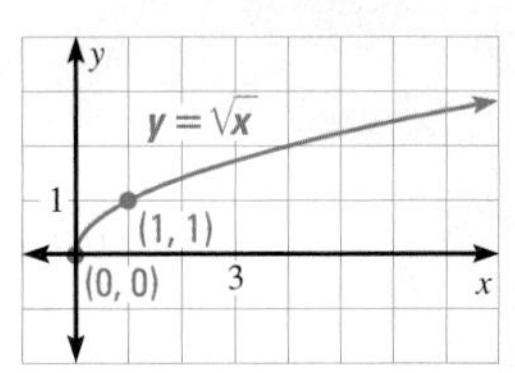

EXAMPLE 1 **Graph a function of the form $y = a\sqrt{x}$**

Graph the function $y = 3\sqrt{x}$ and identify its domain and range. Compare the graph with the graph of $y = \sqrt{x}$.

Solution

STEP 1 **Make** a table. Because the square root of a negative number is undefined, x must be nonnegative. So, the domain is $x \geq 0$.

x	0	1	2	3	4
y	0	3	4.2	5.2	6

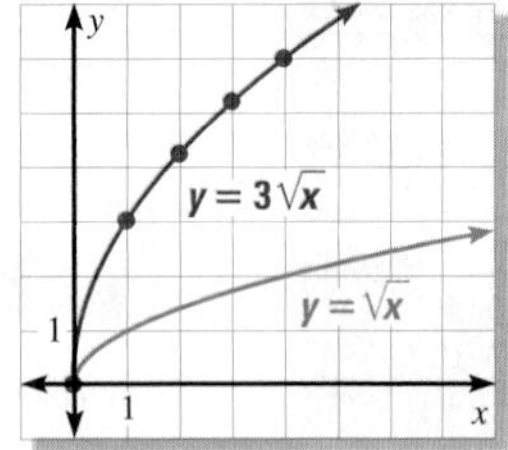

STEP 2 **Plot** the points.

STEP 3 **Draw** a smooth curve through the points. From either the table or the graph, you can see the range of the function is $y \geq 0$.

STEP 4 **Compare** the graph with the graph of $y = \sqrt{x}$. The graph of $y = 3\sqrt{x}$ is a vertical stretch (by a factor of 3) of the graph of $y = \sqrt{x}$.

DESCRIBE A FUNCTION

A radical function has an unbroken graph, so the function is continuous, as discussed on p. 223.

Resource Planning Guide

Chapter Resource Book
- Teaching Guide/Lesson Plan
- Activity Master
- Practice levels A, B, C
- Study Guide
- Catch-up for Absent Students
- Problem Solving Workshop
- Challenge

Workbooks
- Notetaking Guide
- Practice Workbook

Teaching Options
- **Power Presentations** provides dynamic electronic teaching resources for the classroom.
- **Activity Generator** provides editable activities for all ability levels.

Interactive Technology
- Easy Planner
- Power Presentations
- Activity Generator
- Animated Algebra
- Test Generator
- Online Quiz
- eWorkbook
- eEdition
- @HomeTutor

Resources for English Learners
- Spanish Study Guide
- Multi-Language Visual Glossary
- Student Resources in Spanish

See also the *Differentiated Instruction Resources* for more strategies for meeting individual needs.

EXAMPLE 2 Graph a function of the form $y = a\sqrt{x}$

Graph the function $y = -0.5\sqrt{x}$ and identify its domain and range. Compare the graph with the graph of $y = \sqrt{x}$.

Solution

To graph the function, make a table, plot the points, and draw a smooth curve through the points. The domain is $x \geq 0$.

x	0	1	2	3	4
y	0	−0.5	−0.7	−0.9	−1

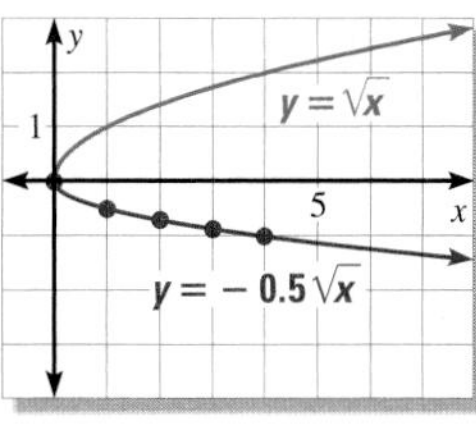

The range is $y \leq 0$. The graph of $y = -0.5\sqrt{x}$ is a vertical shrink (by a factor of 0.5) with a reflection in the x-axis of the graph of $y = \sqrt{x}$.

GRAPHS OF SQUARE ROOT FUNCTIONS Examples 1 and 2 illustrate the following:

- When $|a| > 1$, the graph of $y = a\sqrt{x}$ is a vertical stretch of the graph of $y = \sqrt{x}$. When $0 < |a| < 1$, the graph of $y = a\sqrt{x}$ is a vertical shrink of the graph of $y = \sqrt{x}$.
- When $a < 0$, the graph of $y = a\sqrt{x}$ is the reflection in the x-axis of the graph of $y = |a|\sqrt{x}$.

EXAMPLE 3 Graph a function of the form $y = \sqrt{x} + k$

Graph the function $y = \sqrt{x} + 2$ and identify its domain and range. Compare the graph with the graph of $y = \sqrt{x}$.

Solution

To graph the function, make a table, then plot and connect the points. The domain is $x \geq 0$.

x	0	1	2	3	4
y	2	3	3.4	3.7	4

The range is $y \geq 2$. The graph of $y = \sqrt{x} + 2$ is a vertical translation (of 2 units up) of the graph of $y = \sqrt{x}$.

Animated Algebra at classzone.com

ANALYZE RATE OF CHANGE

Notice that for a radical function, the rate of change in y with respect to x is *not* constant as it is for a linear function. For instance, $\frac{3-2}{1-0} = 1$, while $\frac{3.4-3}{2-1} = 0.4$.

✓ **GUIDED PRACTICE** for Examples 1, 2, and 3

Graph the function and identify its domain and range. Compare the graph with the graph of $y = \sqrt{x}$. **1–4. See margin.**

1. $y = 2\sqrt{x}$ **2.** $y = -2\sqrt{x}$ **3.** $y = \sqrt{x} - 1$ **4.** $y = \sqrt{x} + 3$

Motivating the Lesson

Tell students that if they know how long two skydivers are in freefall and they know how to use a square root function, they can determine how far the skydivers fall before they open their parachutes.

3 TEACH

Extra Example 1

Graph the function $y = 0.5\sqrt{x}$ and identify its domain and range. Compare the graph with the graph of $y = \sqrt{x}$.

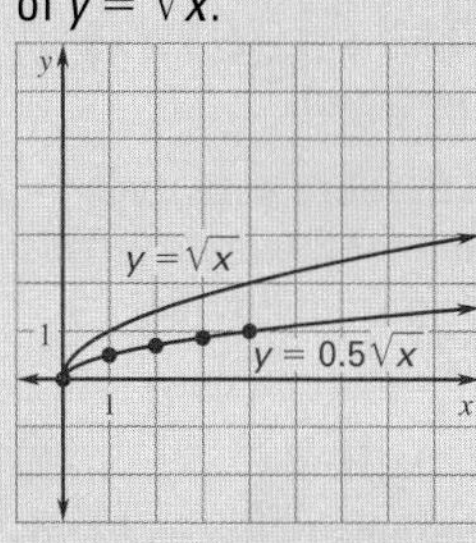

Domain: $x \geq 0$; range: $y \geq 0$; the graph is a vertical shrink (by a factor of 0.5) of the graph of $y = \sqrt{x}$.

Extra Example 2

Graph the function $y = -1.5\sqrt{x}$ and identify its domain and range. Compare the graph with the graph of $y = \sqrt{x}$.

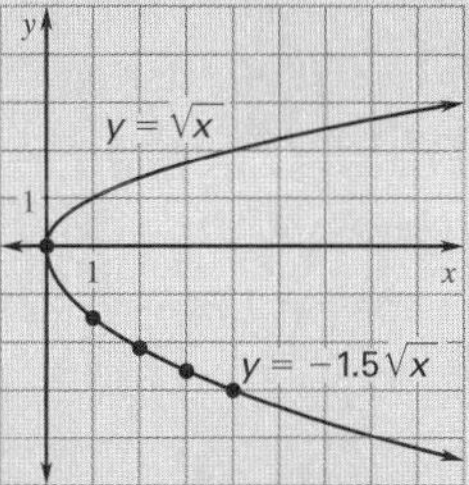

Domain: $x \geq 0$; range: $y \leq 0$; the graph is a vertical stretch (by a factor of 1.5) and a reflection in the x-axis of the graph of $y = \sqrt{x}$.

1–4. See Additional Answers beginning on p. AA1.

Differentiated Instruction

Below Level Some students may find it easier to graph the parent function and to compare graphs if they first make a table for $y = \sqrt{x}$. Suggest that they use five x-values to help them draw a smooth curve. Show students they can check the factor of the vertical stretch or shrink in Examples 1 and 2 by multiplying the y-value of the parent graph by the factor of the stretch or shrink. Compare this to Example 3 where they check that the translation is 2 units up by adding 2 to the y-value of the parent graph, rather than multiplying.

See also the *Differentiated Instruction Resources* for more strategies.

EXAMPLE 4 Graph a function of the form $y = \sqrt{x - h}$

Graph the function $y = \sqrt{x - 4}$ and identify its domain and range. Compare the graph with the graph of $y = \sqrt{x}$.

Solution

To graph the function, make a table, then plot and connect the points. To find the domain, find the values of x for which the radicand, $x - 4$, is nonnegative. The domain is $x \geq 4$.

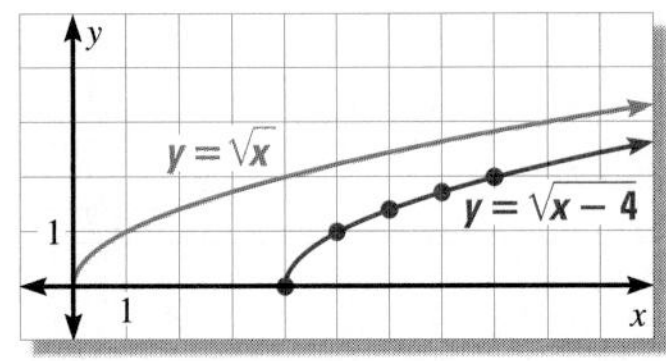

x	4	5	6	7	8
y	0	1	1.4	1.7	2

The range is $y \geq 0$. The graph of $y = \sqrt{x - 4}$ is a horizontal translation (of 4 units to the right) of the graph of $y = \sqrt{x}$.

KEY CONCEPT *For Your Notebook*

Graphs of Square Root Functions

To graph a function of the form $y = a\sqrt{x - h} + k$, you can follow these steps.

STEP 1 **Sketch** the graph of $y = a\sqrt{x}$. The graph of $y = a\sqrt{x}$ starts at the origin and passes through the point $(1, a)$.

STEP 2 **Shift** the graph $|h|$ units horizontally (to the right if h is positive and to the left if h is negative) and $|k|$ units vertically (up if k is positive and down if k is negative).

EXAMPLE 5 Graph a function of the form $y = a\sqrt{x - h} + k$

Graph the function $y = 2\sqrt{x + 4} - 1$.

STEP 1 **Sketch** the graph of $y = 2\sqrt{x}$.

STEP 2 **Shift** the graph $|h|$ units horizontally and $|k|$ units vertically. Notice that

$$y = 2\sqrt{x + 4} - 1 = 2\sqrt{x - (-4)} + (-1).$$

So, $h = -4$ and $k = -1$. Shift the graph left 4 units and down 1 unit.

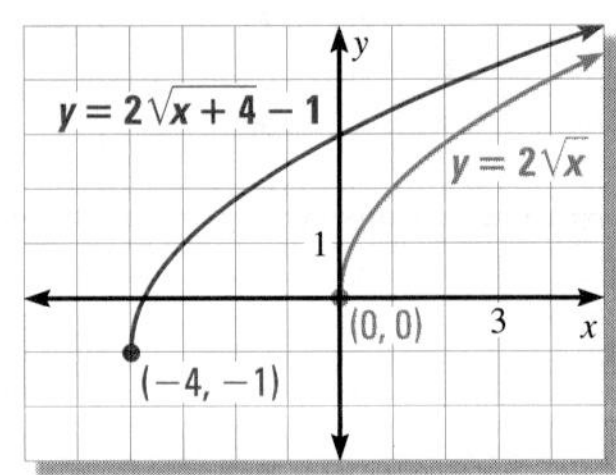

✓ GUIDED PRACTICE for Examples 4 and 5

5. Graph the function $y = \sqrt{x + 3}$ and identify its domain and range. Compare the graph with the graph of $y = \sqrt{x}$.
See margin for art; domain: $x \geq -3$, range: $y \geq 0$; horizontal translation 3 units to the left.

6. Identify the domain and range of the function in Example 5.
domain: $x \geq -4$, range: $y \geq -1$

Extra Example 3

Graph the function $y = \sqrt{x} - 2$ and identify its domain and range. Compare the graph with the graph of $y = \sqrt{x}$.

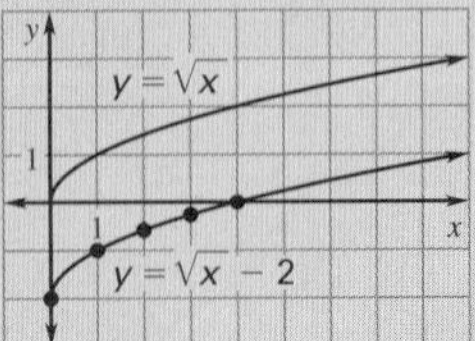

Domain: $x \geq 0$; range: $y \geq -2$; the graph is a translation 2 units down of the graph of $y = \sqrt{x}$.

An **Animated Algebra** activity is available online for **Example 3**. This activity is also part of **Power Presentations**.

Extra Example 4

Graph the function $y = \sqrt{x + 2}$ and identify its domain and range. Compare the graph with the graph of $y = \sqrt{x}$.

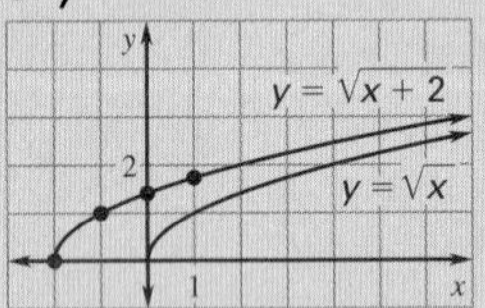

Domain: $x \geq -2$; range: $y \geq 0$; the graph is a horizontal translation 2 units to the left of $y = \sqrt{x}$.

Extra Example 5

Graph the function $y = 2\sqrt{x - 1} + 2$.

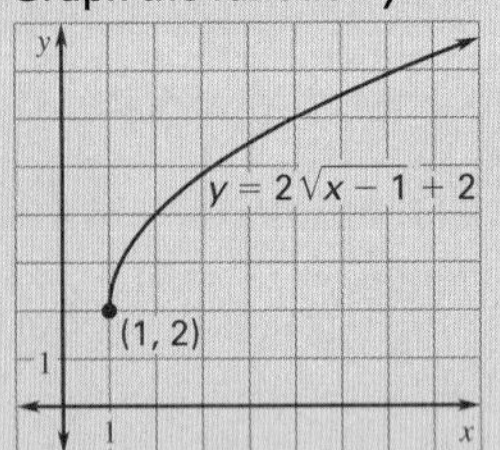

Key Question to Ask for Example 5

- What are the domain and range of $y = 2\sqrt{x + 4} - 1$? **The domain is $x \geq -4$ and the range is $y \geq -1$.**

5.

Differentiated Instruction

Visual Learners Some students may notice that the graph of the parent function $y = \sqrt{x}$ is the right half of the graph of $y = x^2$ flipped onto its side. Explain that such a transformation of a graph is a result of switching the variables x and y. That is, switching x and y in $y = x^2$ gives $x = y^2$. Taking the square root of both sides gives $\sqrt{x} = y$, or $y = \sqrt{x}$.

See also the *Differentiated Instruction Resources* for more strategies.

EXAMPLE 6 Solve a real-world problem

MICROPHONE SALES For the period 1988–2002, the amount of sales y (in millions of dollars) of microphones in the United States can be modeled by the function $y = 93\sqrt{x + 2.2}$ where x is the number of years since 1988. Graph the function on a graphing calculator. In what year were microphone sales about \$325 million?

ANOTHER WAY
You can graph $y = 93\sqrt{x + 2.2}$ and $y = 325$. The x-coordinate of the point where the graphs intersect represents the year in which sales were about \$325 million.

Solution

The graph of the function is shown.

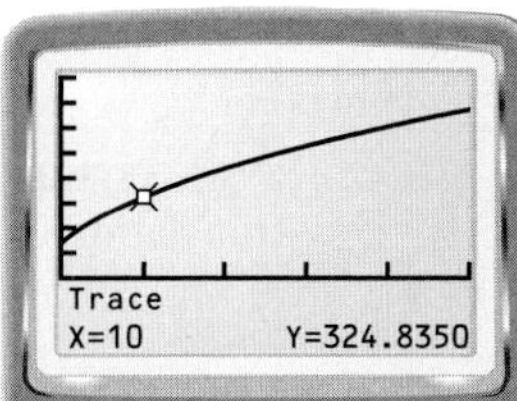

Using the *trace* feature, you can see that $y \approx 325$ when $x = 10$. So, microphone sales were about \$325 million 10 years after 1988, or in 1998.

✓ GUIDED PRACTICE for Example 6

7. **MICROPHONE SALES** Use the function in Example 6 to find the year in which microphone sales were about \$250 million. **1993**

11.1 EXERCISES

HOMEWORK KEY
○ = **WORKED-OUT SOLUTIONS** on p. WS26 for Exs. 7, 23, and 45
★ = **STANDARDIZED TEST PRACTICE** Exs. 2, 15, 16, 29, 39, 41, and 48

SKILL PRACTICE

A

1. **VOCABULARY** Copy and complete: A function containing a radical expression with the independent variable in the radicand is called a(n) __?__. **radical function**

2. ★ **WRITING** Is the graph of $y = 1.25\sqrt{x}$ a vertical stretch or a vertical shrink of the graph of $y = \sqrt{x}$? *Explain* your answer.
Vertical stretch. *Sample answer*: Since $|1.25| > 1$, the graph is a vertical stretch.

EXAMPLES 1 and 2 on pp. 710–711 for Exs. 3–16

GRAPHING FUNCTIONS Graph the function and identify its domain and range. Compare the graph with the graph of $y = \sqrt{x}$. **3–14. See margin.**

3. $y = 4\sqrt{x}$
4. $y = 5\sqrt{x}$
5. $y = 0.5\sqrt{x}$
6. $y = 0.25\sqrt{x}$
7. $y = \frac{3}{2}\sqrt{x}$
8. $y = \frac{1}{3}\sqrt{x}$
9. $y = -3\sqrt{x}$
10. $y = -6\sqrt{x}$
11. $y = -0.8\sqrt{x}$
12. $y = -0.75\sqrt{x}$
13. $y = -\frac{1}{4}\sqrt{x}$
14. $y = -\frac{5}{2}\sqrt{x}$

15. ★ **MULTIPLE CHOICE** The graph of which function is a vertical shrink of the graph of $y = \sqrt{x}$? **C**

Ⓐ $y = -5\sqrt{x}$ Ⓑ $y = -\sqrt{x}$ Ⓒ $y = \frac{1}{2}\sqrt{x}$ Ⓓ $y = 8\sqrt{x}$

16. ★ **WRITING** The range of the function $y = a\sqrt{x}$ is $y \le 0$. What can you conclude about the value of a? How do you know? **See margin.**

Extra Example 6

For the period 1990–2004, the amount of sales y (in thousands of dollars) of bicycles at a shop can be modeled by the function $y = 24\sqrt{x + 4.6}$, where x is the number of years since 1990. Graph the function on a graphing calculator. In what year were bicycle sales about \$95 thousand? **2001**

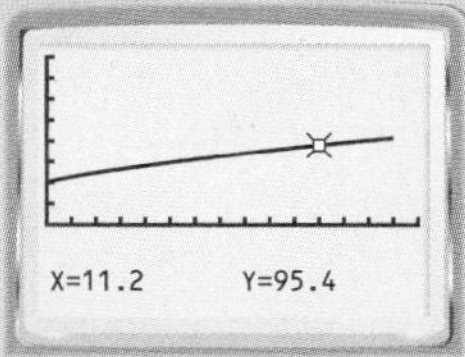

Closing the Lesson

Have students summarize the major points of the lesson and answer the Essential Question: How do you graph square root functions?

- **The parent square root function is $y = \sqrt{x}$. A vertical stretch of the parent function results when $|a|$ in the equation $y = a\sqrt{x}$ is greater than 1. If $|a|$ is between 0 and 1, a vertical shrink results. A reflection in the x-axis results when $a < 0$.**
- **Vertical and horizontal translations of $y = a\sqrt{x}$ result when h and k in the equation $y = a\sqrt{x - h} + k$ are replaced by real numbers.**

To graph square root functions, make a table of values, plot the points, and then draw a smooth curve through the points. The radicand must be nonnegative, so values of x in the radicand must result in nonnegative numbers.

3–14. See Additional Answers beginning on p. AA1.

16. $a < 0$; *Sample answer:* If $a > 0$, the range of the function would include positive numbers, so a cannot be greater than 0. If a were 0, y would always be 0.

4 PRACTICE AND APPLY

Assignment Guide

Answer Transparencies available for all exercises

Basic:
Day 1: EP p. 947 Exs. 1–7 odd
pp. 713–716
Exs. 1–22
Day 2: pp. 713–716
Exs. 23–34, 43–46, 50–66 even

Average:
Day 1: pp. 713–716
Exs. 1, 2, 5–22, 41
Day 2: pp. 713–716
Exs. 25–40, 43–47, 51–67 odd

Advanced:
Day 1: pp. 713–716
Exs. 1, 2, 6–22, 41, 42*
Day 2: pp. 713–716
Exs. 26–40, 43–49*, 50–66 even

Block:
pp. 713–716
Exs. 1, 2, 5–22, 25–41, 43–47, 51–67 odd

Differentiated Instruction

See *Differentiated Instruction Resources* for suggestions on addressing the needs of a diverse classroom.

Homework Check

For a quick check of student understanding of key concepts, go over the following exercises:

Basic: 6, 18, 24, 31, 43
Average: 10, 20, 25, 34, 44
Advanced: 13, 21, 26, 36, 45

Extra Practice

- Student Edition, p. 948
- Chapter Resource Book: Practice levels A, B, C

Practice Worksheet

An easily-readable reduced practice page (with answers) for this lesson can be found on p.708C.

17–28, 30–38. See Additional Answers beginning on p. AA1.

EXAMPLES 3 and 4 on pp. 711–712 for Exs. 17–29

GRAPHING FUNCTIONS **Graph the function and identify its domain and range. Compare the graph with the graph of $y = \sqrt{x}$.** **17–28. See margin.**

17. $y = \sqrt{x} + 1$ **18.** $y = \sqrt{x} + 5$ **19.** $y = \sqrt{x} - 3$

20. $y = \sqrt{x} - 4$ **21.** $y = \sqrt{x} + \frac{3}{4}$ **22.** $y = \sqrt{x} - 4.5$

23. $y = \sqrt{x - 1}$ **24.** $y = \sqrt{x - 6}$ **25.** $y = \sqrt{x + 2}$

26. $y = \sqrt{x + 4}$ **27.** $y = \sqrt{x + 1.5}$ **28.** $y = \sqrt{x - \frac{1}{2}}$

29. ★ **MULTIPLE CHOICE** The graph of which function is a horizontal translation of 3 units to the right of the graph of $y = \sqrt{x}$? **D**

Ⓐ $y = \sqrt{x} + 3$ Ⓑ $y = \sqrt{x} - 3$

Ⓒ $y = \sqrt{x + 3}$ Ⓓ $y = \sqrt{x - 3}$

EXAMPLE 5 B on p. 712 for Exs. 30–39

GRAPHING FUNCTIONS **Graph the function.** **30–38. See margin.**

30. $y = \sqrt{x + 3} - 2$ **31.** $y = \sqrt{x - 2} + 5$ **32.** $y = 2\sqrt{x} + 1$

33. $y = -\sqrt{x + 1} + 2$ **34.** $y = -3\sqrt{x + 2} - 6$ **35.** $y = 4\sqrt{x + 4} - 4$

36. $y = \frac{1}{2}\sqrt{x - 5} - 3$ **37.** $y = -\frac{3}{2}\sqrt{x - 1} - 5$ **38.** $y = -\frac{3}{4}\sqrt{x + 8} - 3$

39. ★ **MULTIPLE CHOICE** The graph of which function is shown? **A**

Ⓐ $y = \sqrt{x + 1} + 2$
Ⓑ $y = \sqrt{x - 1} + 2$
Ⓒ $y = \sqrt{x + 1} - 2$
Ⓓ $y = \sqrt{x - 1} - 2$

40. **ERROR ANALYSIS** *Describe* and correct the error in explaining how to graph the function $y = -5\sqrt{x - 9} - 10$.
The discussion about shifting the graph is incorrect. It should say "Then shift the graph 9 units to the right and 10 units down."

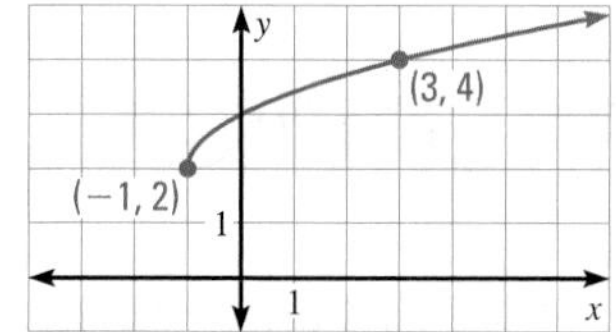

To graph y = −5√x − 9 − 10,
sketch the graph of
y = −5√x. Then shift the
graph 9 units to the left
and 10 units down.

C **41.** ★ **MULTIPLE CHOICE** How is the graph of $g(x) = 4\sqrt{x} - 3$ related to the graph of $h(x) = 4\sqrt{x} + 3$? **C**

Ⓐ It is a vertical stretch by a factor of 3 of the graph of h.
Ⓑ It is a vertical translation of 3 units down of the graph of h.
Ⓒ It is a vertical translation of 6 units down of the graph of h.
Ⓓ It is a horizontal translation of 6 units to the left of the graph of h.

42. **CHALLENGE** Write a rule for a radical function that has a domain of all real numbers greater than or equal to −5 and a range of all real numbers less than or equal to 3. $y = -\sqrt{x + 5} + 3$

○ = WORKED-OUT SOLUTIONS on p. WS1 ★ = STANDARDIZED TEST PRACTICE

PROBLEM SOLVING

EXAMPLE 6 A on p. 713 for Exs. 43–45

GRAPHING CALCULATOR **You may wish to use a graphing calculator to complete the following Problem Solving exercises.**

43. **SUSPENSION BRIDGE** The time t (in seconds) it takes an object dropped from a height h (in feet) to reach the ground is given by the function $t = \frac{1}{4}\sqrt{h}$.

 a. Graph the function and identify its domain and range. **See margin for art; domain: $h \ge 0$, range: $t \ge 0$.**

 b. The Royal Gorge Bridge in Colorado is the world's highest suspension bridge. It takes about 8 seconds for a stone dropped from the bridge to reach the gorge below. About how high is the bridge?

43b. about 1024 ft

@HomeTutor for problem solving help at classzone.com

44. **OCEANOGRAPHY** Ocean waves can be shallow water, intermediate depth, or deep water waves. The speed s (in meters per second) of a shallow water wave can be modeled by the function $s = 3.13\sqrt{d}$ where d is the depth (in meters) of the water over which the wave is traveling.

 a. Graph the function and identify its domain and range. **See margin for art; domain: $d \ge 0$, range: $s \ge 0$.**

 b. A tsunami is a type of shallow water wave. Suppose a tsunami has a speed of 200 meters per second. Over approximately what depth of water is the tsunami traveling? **about 4083 m**

@HomeTutor for problem solving help at classzone.com

45. **LONG JUMP** A function for the speed at which a long jumper is running before jumping is $s = 10.9\sqrt{h}$ where s and h are defined in the diagram. Graph the function and identify its domain and range. To the nearest tenth, approximate the maximum height reached when the long jumper's speed before jumping is 10.25 meters per second.
See margin for art; domain: $h \ge 0$, range: $s \ge 0$; about 0.9 m.

46. **MULTI-STEP PROBLEM** The reading age of written materials is the age at which an average person can read and understand the materials. A function that is sometimes used to identify the reading age r (in years) of written materials is $r = \sqrt{w} + 8$ where w is the average number of words with 3 or more syllables in samples taken from the written materials.

 a. Graph the function and identify its domain and range. **See margin for art; domain: $w \ge 0$, range: $r \ge 8$.**

 b. What is the average number of words with 3 or more syllables in samples taken from material that can be read and understood by a 10-year-old? **4 words**

Avoiding Common Errors

Exercises 17–22 Watch for students who treat a number added to the radical expression as part of the radicand. You may want to remind these students that the graphs in these exercises are vertical translations.

Study Strategy

Exercises 30–38 Tell students that it may be helpful to go through each of the functions before they begin to graph them to determine the general form of the graph of the function. This will help them to start focusing on whether the graph is a vertical stretch or shrink, a reflection, or a translation of the parent function. Suggest that they make short notes next to the exercises and then check their graphs against these notes to see whether they have a good grasp of the concepts.

Mathematical Reasoning

Exercises 23–28, 30–31, 33–38 Some students may wonder why the radicand must be a nonnegative number. You may want to ask what would be the square root of −9, leading students to see that square root functions are limited to real numbers and therefore the radicand cannot be a negative number.

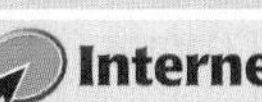

Internet Reference

Exercise 44 For more information about tsunamis, visit the National Oceanic and Atmospheric Administration website at www.tsunami.noaa.gov/tsunami_story.html

43a.
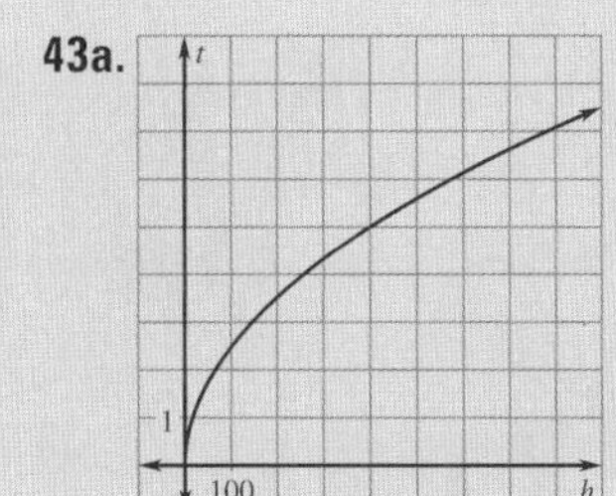

44a.
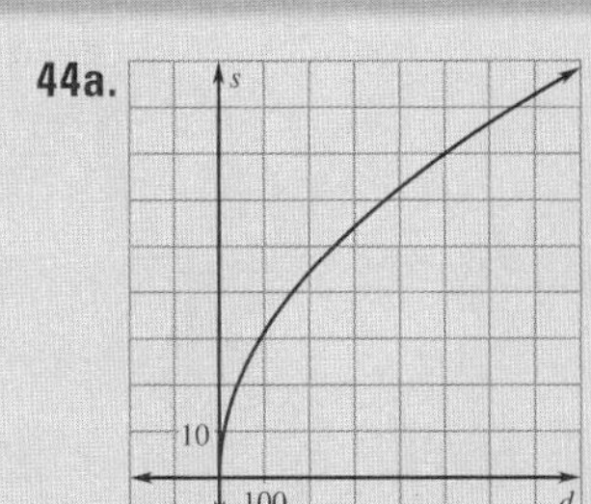

45.
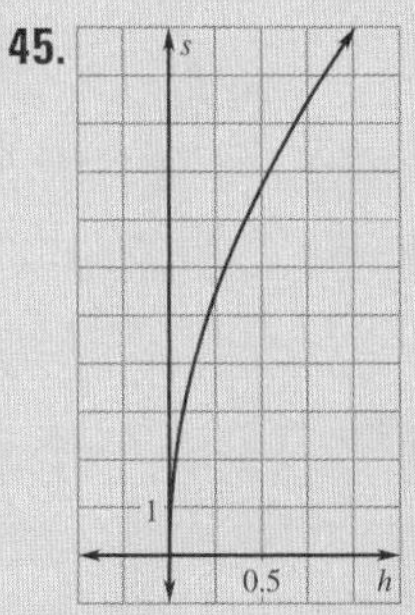

46a.
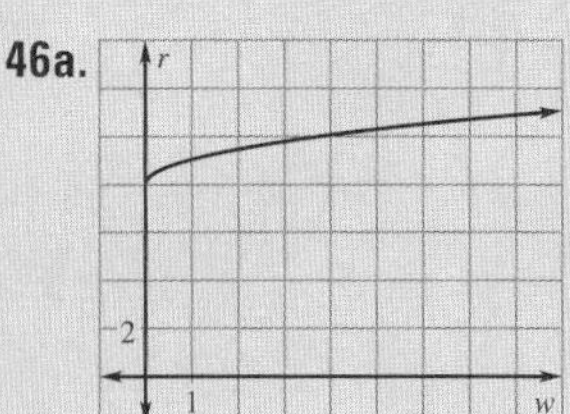

5 ASSESS AND RETEACH

Daily Homework Quiz

Transparency Available

1. Graph the function $y = 2\sqrt{x} + 1$.

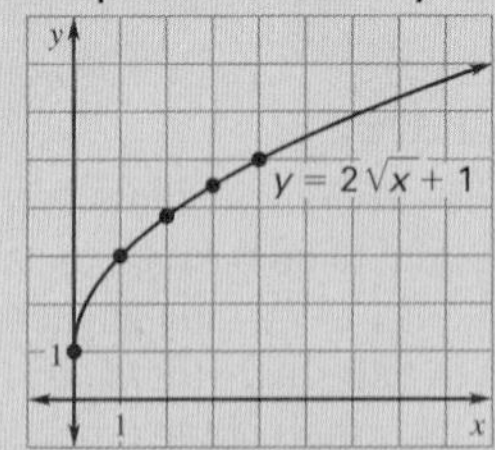

2. Graph the function $y = \frac{1}{2}\sqrt{x-2} + 1$.

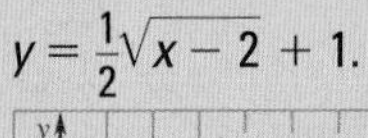

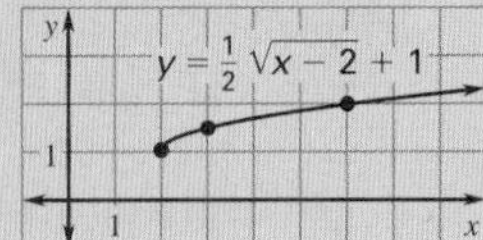

3. Use the function $t = \frac{1}{4}\sqrt{h}$, where t is time (in seconds) and h is distance (in feet) to model a sky diver's freefall. How many feet did a sky diver freefall if the freefall lasted 9 seconds? **1296 ft**

Available at **classzone.com**

Diagnosis/Remediation

- Practice A, B, C in Chapter Resource Book
- Study Guide in Chapter Resource Book
- Practice Workbook
- @HomeTutor

Challenge

Additional challenge is available in the Chapter Resource Book.

47a, 48a, 48c. See Additional Answers beginning on p. AA1.

B **47. BIOLOGY** Biologists studied two types of duck in the northern Great Plains of the United States from 1987 to 1990. The biologists found functions, given below, that model the number y of breeding pairs of each type of duck in wetlands with area x (in hectares).

Blue-winged teal: $y = 0.7\sqrt{x}$

Northern pintail: $y = 0.2\sqrt{x}$

a. Graph the functions in the same coordinate plane. Identify the domain and range of each function. **See margin.**

b. Find the area (to the nearest hectare) for 1 breeding pair of each type of duck. **blue-winged teal: about 2 hectares, northern pintail: 25 hectares**

C **48. ★ EXTENDED RESPONSE** The amount of mozzarella cheese y (in pounds per person) consumed in the United States for the period 1980–2001 can be modeled by $y = 2\sqrt{x+1}$ where x is the number of years since 1980.

a. **Graph** Graph the function and identify its domain and range. **See margin for art; domain: $x \geq -1$, range: $y \geq 0$.**

b. **Apply** In what year was the amount of mozzarella cheese consumed equal to 2 pounds per person? **1980**

c. **Explain** In what year was the amount of mozzarella cheese consumed per person double the amount consumed per person in 1980? *Explain.* **See margin.**

49. CHALLENGE The flow rate r (in gallons per minute) of water through a high-pressure water hose is given by $r = 29.7d^2\sqrt{p}$ where d is the nozzle diameter (in inches) and p is the nozzle pressure (in pounds per square inch). For what value of d would the graph of the function be identical to the graph of the parent square root function? For what values of d would the graph be a vertical stretch? a vertical shrink?

$\frac{1}{\sqrt{29.7}}$; $d > \frac{1}{\sqrt{29.7}}$; $0 < d < \frac{1}{\sqrt{29.7}}$

MIXED REVIEW

Write the prime factorization of the number if it is not a prime number. If the number is prime, write *prime*. *(p. 910)*

50. 7 **prime**	**51.** 14 $2 \cdot 7$	**52.** 18 $3^2 \cdot 2$	**53.** 9 3^2
54. 24 $2^3 \cdot 3$	**55.** 13 **prime**	**56.** 53 **prime**	**57.** 72 $2^3 \cdot 3^2$

PREVIEW Prepare for Lesson 11.2 in Exs. 58–61.

Evaluate the expression. *(p. 110)*

58. $\sqrt{16}$ **4**	**59.** $\sqrt{64}$ **8**	**60.** $\sqrt{144}$ **12**	**61.** $\sqrt{900}$ **30**

Factor the expression.

62. $x^2 - 31x + 58$ *(p. 583)* $(x - 29)(x - 2)$

63. $2x^2 - 7x + 6$ *(p. 593)* $(2x - 3)(x - 2)$

64. $7x^2 + 9x + 2$ *(p. 593)* $(7x + 2)(x + 1)$

65. $6x^2 - 11x - 35$ *(p. 593)* $(2x - 7)(3x + 5)$

66. $400x^2 - 9y^2$ *(p. 600)* $(20x - 3y)(20x + 3y)$

67. $25x^2 + 20xy + 4y^2$ *(p. 600)* $(5x + 2y)^2$

Graphing Calculator ACTIVITY Use after Lesson 11.1

@HomeTutor
classzone.com
Keystrokes

11.1 Graph Square Root Functions

QUESTION **How can you use a graphing calculator to graph square root functions?**

EXAMPLE **Graph the function $y = \sqrt{2x + 3}$ and describe its domain and range**

STEP 1 ***Enter the function***
Enter the function into a graphing calculator. Use parentheses around the radicand.

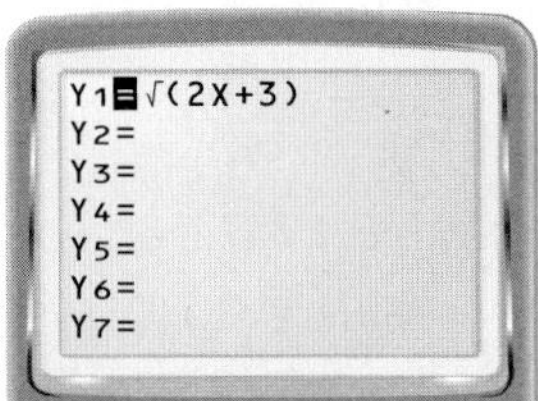

STEP 2 ***Graph the function***
Graph the function. Adjust the viewing window if necessary.

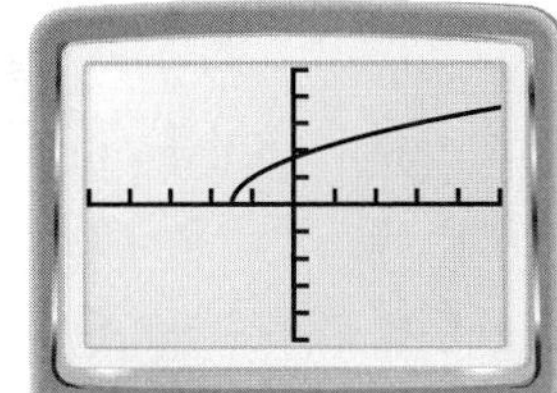

STEP 3 ***Describe the domain and range***
From the graph, you can see that the domain is all real numbers greater than or equal to -1.5, or $x \geq -1.5$. The range is all nonnegative numbers, or $y \geq 0$.

PRACTICE

Graph the function using a graphing calculator. Then describe the domain and range of the function. **1–12. See margin.**

1. $y = \sqrt{4x}$
2. $y = \sqrt{9x}$
3. $y = \sqrt{7x}$
4. $y = -\sqrt{10x}$
5. $y = -3\sqrt{x}$
6. $y = 1.5\sqrt{3x}$
7. $y = 4.4\sqrt{8x}$
8. $y = \sqrt{2x + 8}$
9. $y = \sqrt{3x + 4}$
10. $y = -\sqrt{2x - 5}$
11. $y = -\sqrt{4x - 6}$
12. $y = \frac{1}{2}\sqrt{6 - 5x}$

13. **ROLLER COASTER** If friction is ignored, the velocity v (in meters per second) of a roller coaster when it reaches the bottom of a hill can be calculated using the formula $v = \sqrt{19.6h}$ where h (in meters) is the height of the hill.
    a. Graph the function and describe its domain and range. **See margin for art; domain: $h \geq 0$, range: $v \geq 0$.**
    b. Use the graph to find the height of a hill if the velocity of the roller coaster at the bottom of the hill is 55 meters per second. **about 154.3 m**

1 PLAN AND PREPARE

Learn the Method
- Students will graph square root functions.
- After the activity, students can use a graphing calculator to check their solutions in Exercises 3–14, 17–28, and 30–38 in Lesson 11.1.

Keystroke Help
Keystrokes for several models of calculators are available in blackline format in the *Chapter Resource Book*.

2 TEACH

Tips for Success
In Step 3, students can use the *trace* feature if they are unsure of the domain.

Extra Example
Graph the function $y = \sqrt{2x - 5}$ and describe its domain and range.
Domain: $x \geq 2.5$, Range: $y \geq 0$.

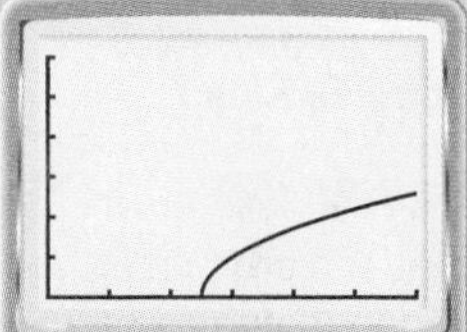

3 ASSESS AND RETEACH

The velocity v (in feet per second) of an object dropped from a height can be found using the formula $v = \sqrt{64d}$, where d is the distance (in feet) the object is dropped. Explain how to use your graphing calculator to find the velocity of an object that has fallen 80 feet. **Graph the function using x for distance and y for velocity. Use the trace feature to find the value of y when $x = 80$.**

1–12. See Additional Answers beginning on p. AA1.

13a.

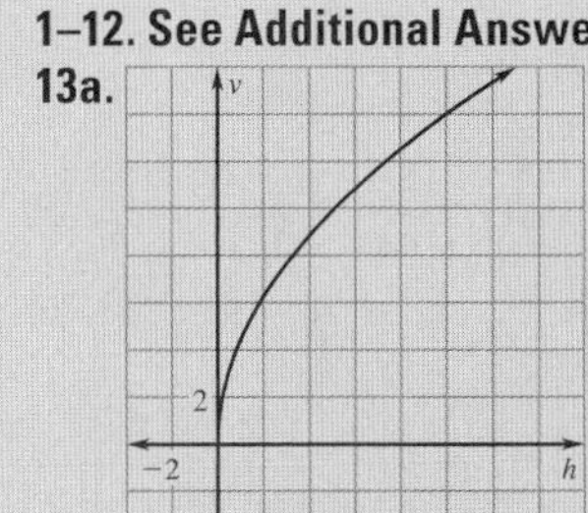

Investigating Algebra ACTIVITY Use before Lesson 11.2

1 PLAN AND PREPARE

Explore the Concept

- Students will simplify products and quotients of square roots.
- This activity leads into the study of using the product property of radicals in Example 1 in Lesson 11.2.

Materials

Each student will need:

- calculator
- Activity Support Master (*Chapter Resource Book*)

Recommended Time

Work activity: 10 min

Discuss results: 5 min

Grouping

Students should work individually.

2 TEACH

Key Question

- How are the examples in Step 1 different from those in Step 2? **The factors are perfect squares in Step 1 but not in Step 2.**

Key Discovery

The square root of a product is equal to the product of the square roots of the factors. The square root of a quotient is equal to the quotient of the square roots of the numerator and denominator.

3 ASSESS AND RETEACH

1. Write an equivalent expression for $\sqrt{6b}$. $\sqrt{6} \cdot \sqrt{b}$
2. Write an equivalent expression for $\sqrt{\frac{7}{a}}$. $\frac{\sqrt{7}}{\sqrt{a}}$

11.2 Properties of Radicals

MATERIALS • calculator

QUESTION How can you simplify products and quotients of square roots?

EXPLORE Simplify products and quotients of square roots

STEP 1 ***Find products of square roots***

Copy and complete the table without using a calculator. Compare the values in the second and third columns.

Values of a and b	Value of $\sqrt{a} \cdot \sqrt{b}$	Value of $\sqrt{ab}$
$a = 4, b = 9$	? 6	? 6
$a = 9, b = 16$	? 12	? 12
$a = 25, b = 4$	? 10	? 10
$a = 16, b = 36$	? 24	? 24

STEP 2 ***Find products of square roots***

Use a calculator to copy and complete the table. Compare the values in the second and third columns.

Values of a and b	Value of $\sqrt{a} \cdot \sqrt{b}$	Value of $\sqrt{ab}$
$a = 2, b = 3$	? 2.45	? 2.45
$a = 10, b = 5$	? 7.07	? 7.07
$a = 7, b = 11$	? 8.77	? 8.77
$a = 13, b = 6$	? 8.83	? 8.83

STEP 3 ***Find quotients of square roots***

Copy and complete the table without using a calculator. Compare the values in the second and third columns.

Values of a and b	Value of $\frac{\sqrt{a}}{\sqrt{b}}$	Value of $\sqrt{\frac{a}{b}}$
$a = 4, b = 16$	? $\frac{1}{2}$	? $\frac{1}{2}$
$a = 9, b = 25$	? $\frac{3}{5}$	? $\frac{3}{5}$
$a = 36, b = 4$	? 3	? 3
$a = 4, b = 49$	? $\frac{2}{7}$	? $\frac{2}{7}$

STEP 4 ***Find quotients of square roots***

Use a calculator to copy and complete the table. Compare the values in the second and third columns.

Values of a and b	Value of $\frac{\sqrt{a}}{\sqrt{b}}$	Value of $\sqrt{\frac{a}{b}}$
$a = 1, b = 2$	? 0.71	? 0.71
$a = 3, b = 8$	? 0.61	? 0.61
$a = 12, b = 7$	? 1.31	? 1.31
$a = 6, b = 11$	? 0.74	? 0.74

DRAW CONCLUSIONS Use your observations to complete these exercises

In Exercises 1 and 2, copy and complete the statement.

1. The product of two square roots is equal to __?__. **the square root of the product of the radicands**
2. The quotient of a square root and a nonzero square root is equal to __?__. **the square root of the quotient of the radicands**
3. **REASONING** Do you think that $\sqrt{a} + \sqrt{b} = \sqrt{a + b}$ for any $a \geq 0$ and any $b \geq 0$? *Justify* your answer. **No. *Sample answer*: If $a = 1$ and $b = 4$, then $\sqrt{a} + \sqrt{b} = 1 + 2 = 3$, which does not equal $\sqrt{a + b} = \sqrt{1 + 2} = \sqrt{3}$.**

11.2 Simplify Radical Expressions

Before You found square roots.

Now You will simplify radical expressions.

Why? So you can find the distance to the horizon, as in Ex. 68.

Key Vocabulary
- **simplest form of a radical expression**
- **rationalizing the denominator**

A radical expression is in **simplest form** if the following conditions are true:

- No perfect square factors other than 1 are in the radicand.
- No fractions are in the radicand.
- No radicals appear in the denominator of a fraction.

You can use the following property to simplify radical expressions.

KEY CONCEPT *For Your Notebook*

Product Property of Radicals

Words The square root of a product equals the product of the square roots of the factors.

Algebra $\sqrt{ab} = \sqrt{a} \cdot \sqrt{b}$ where $a \geq 0$ and $b \geq 0$

Example $\sqrt{4x} = \sqrt{4} \cdot \sqrt{x} = 2\sqrt{x}$

You can also use the fact that $\sqrt{a^2} = a$, where $a \geq 0$, to simplify radical expressions. In this lesson, whenever a variable appears in the radicand *assume that it has only nonnegative values.*

REVIEW SQUARE ROOTS
For help finding square roots of perfect squares, see p. 110.

EXAMPLE 1 Use the product property of radicals

a. $\sqrt{32} = \sqrt{16 \cdot 2}$ **Factor using perfect square factor.**

$= \sqrt{16} \cdot \sqrt{2}$ **Product property of radicals**

$= 4\sqrt{2}$ **Simplify.**

b. $\sqrt{9x^3} = \sqrt{9 \cdot x^2 \cdot x}$ **Factor using perfect square factors.**

$= \sqrt{9} \cdot \sqrt{x^2} \cdot \sqrt{x}$ **Product property of radicals**

$= 3x\sqrt{x}$ **Simplify.**

Animated Algebra at classzone.com

GUIDED PRACTICE for Example 1

1. Simplify (a) $\sqrt{24}$ and (b) $\sqrt{25x^2}$. **(a) $2\sqrt{6}$; (b) $5x$**

1 PLAN AND PREPARE

Warm-Up Exercises

Transparency Available

Use the distributive property to write an equivalent expression.

1. $2(x + 6)$ **$2x + 12$**
2. $x(x^2 + 2)$ **$x^3 + 2x$**
3. $(x + x^2)(-3)$ **$-3x - 3x^2$**
4. $0.1(6 + 10x)$ **$0.6 + x$**
5. The area of a square field is 148 square meters. What is the side length of the field? **about 12.2 m**

Notetaking Guide

Transparency Available

Promotes interactive learning and notetaking skills.

Pacing

Basic: 2 days
Average: 2 days
Advanced: 2 days
Block: 1 block
- See *Teaching Guide/Lesson Plan.*

2 FOCUS AND MOTIVATE

Essential Question

Big Idea 2, p. 709

How do you simplify radical expressions? **Tell students they will learn how to answer this question by using properties of radicals.**

NCTM STANDARDS

Standard 2: Analyze situations using algebraic symbols

Standard 1: Understand operations; compute fluently

Resource Planning Guide

Chapter Resource Book
- Teaching Guide/Lesson Plan
- Practice levels A, B, C
- Study Guide
- Catch-up for Absent Students
- Application
- Challenge

Workbooks
- Notetaking Guide
- Practice Workbook

Teaching Options
- **Power Presentations** provides dynamic electronic teaching resources for the classroom.
- **Activity Generator** provides editable activities for all ability levels.

Interactive Technology
- Easy Planner
- Power Presentations
- Activity Generator
- Animated Algebra
- Test Generator
- Online Quiz
- eWorkbook
- eEdition
- @HomeTutor

Resources for English Learners
- Spanish Study Guide
- Multi-Language Visual Glossary
- Student Resources in Spanish

See also the *Differentiated Instruction Resources* for more strategies for meeting individual needs.

Motivating the Lesson

Ask students if they have ever wondered how far away the horizon is from a height of 32,000 feet in an airplane. Tell them that a formula containing a radical expression can help them estimate the distance.

3 TEACH

Extra Example 1

Simplify.

a. $\sqrt{48}$ **$4\sqrt{3}$**

b. $\sqrt{25x^5}$ **$5x^2\sqrt{x}$**

An **Animated Algebra** activity is available online for **Example 1**. This activity is also part of **Power Presentations**.

Extra Example 2

Simplify.

a. $\sqrt{7} \cdot \sqrt{7}$ **7**

b. $3\sqrt{b} \cdot \sqrt{2b^3}$ **$3b^2\sqrt{2}$**

c. $2\sqrt{mn^2} \cdot \sqrt{5m^2}$ **$2mn\sqrt{5m}$**

Extra Example 3

Simplify.

a. $\sqrt{\frac{5}{49}}$ **$\frac{\sqrt{5}}{7}$**

b. $\sqrt{\frac{11}{d^4}}$ **$\frac{\sqrt{11}}{d^2}$**

Key Question to Ask for Example 3

- In part b, why does the numerator remain the same but the denominator simplifies? **The radicand in the numerator has no perfect squares other than 1, but the radicand in the denominator can be simplified since x^2 is the product of $x \cdot x$.**

EXAMPLE 2 Multiply radicals

a. $\sqrt{6} \cdot \sqrt{6} = \sqrt{6 \cdot 6}$ Product property of radicals

$= \sqrt{36}$ Multiply.

$= 6$ Simplify.

b. $\sqrt{3x} \cdot 4\sqrt{x} = 4\sqrt{3x \cdot x}$ Product property of radicals

$= 4\sqrt{3x^2}$ Multiply.

$= 4 \cdot \sqrt{3} \cdot \sqrt{x^2}$ Product property of radicals

$= 4x\sqrt{3}$ Simplify.

WRITE RADICALS
When writing a product involving a radical, write the radical last to avoid confusion. For instance, if you write the product of x and $\sqrt{2}$ as $\sqrt{2}x$, it might be read as $\sqrt{2x}$.

c. $\sqrt{7xy^2} \cdot 3\sqrt{x} = 3\sqrt{7xy^2 \cdot x}$ Product property of radicals

$= 3\sqrt{7x^2y^2}$ Multiply.

$= 3 \cdot \sqrt{7} \cdot \sqrt{x^2} \cdot \sqrt{y^2}$ Product property of radicals

$= 3xy\sqrt{7}$ Simplify.

KEY CONCEPT *For Your Notebook*

Quotient Property of Radicals

Words The square root of a quotient equals the quotient of the square roots of the numerator and denominator.

Algebra $\sqrt{\frac{a}{b}} = \frac{\sqrt{a}}{\sqrt{b}}$ where $a \geq 0$ and $b > 0$

Example $\sqrt{\frac{16}{25}} = \frac{\sqrt{16}}{\sqrt{25}} = \frac{4}{5}$

EXAMPLE 3 Use the quotient property of radicals

a. $\sqrt{\frac{13}{100}} = \frac{\sqrt{13}}{\sqrt{100}}$ Quotient property of radicals

$= \frac{\sqrt{13}}{10}$ Simplify.

b. $\sqrt{\frac{7}{x^2}} = \frac{\sqrt{7}}{\sqrt{x^2}}$ Quotient property of radicals

$= \frac{\sqrt{7}}{x}$ Simplify.

✓ **GUIDED PRACTICE** for Examples 2 and 3

2. Simplify (a) $\sqrt{2x^3} \cdot \sqrt{x}$ and (b) $\sqrt{\frac{1}{y^2}}$. **(a) $x^2\sqrt{2}$; (b) $\frac{1}{y}$**

Differentiated Instruction

Below Level Until students develop facility in simplifying square roots, it may help if they write out notecards or make charts listing some of the multiples of perfect squares such as $16 \cdot 2 = 32$, $25 \cdot 2 = 50$, $36 \cdot 2 = 72$ and so on up to 100. Encourage students to make organized lists so it is easy to find the factors of a product.

See also the *Differentiated Instruction Resources* for more strategies.

RATIONALIZING THE DENOMINATOR Example 4 shows how to eliminate a radical from the denominator of a radical expression by multiplying the expression by an appropriate form of 1. The process of eliminating a radical from an expression's denominator is called **rationalizing the denominator.**

EXAMPLE 4 Rationalize the denominator

MULTIPLY BY 1
In part (a), notice that $\frac{\sqrt{7}}{\sqrt{7}}$ is equal to 1, so multiplying by it does not change the value of the expression.

a. $\frac{5}{\sqrt{7}} = \frac{5}{\sqrt{7}} \cdot \frac{\sqrt{7}}{\sqrt{7}}$ — Multiply by $\frac{\sqrt{7}}{\sqrt{7}}$.

$= \frac{5\sqrt{7}}{\sqrt{49}}$ — Product property of radicals

$= \frac{5\sqrt{7}}{7}$ — Simplify.

b. $\frac{\sqrt{2}}{\sqrt{3b}} = \frac{\sqrt{2}}{\sqrt{3b}} \cdot \frac{\sqrt{3b}}{\sqrt{3b}}$ — Multiply by $\frac{\sqrt{3b}}{\sqrt{3b}}$.

$= \frac{\sqrt{6b}}{\sqrt{9b^2}}$ — Product property of radicals

$= \frac{\sqrt{6b}}{\sqrt{9} \cdot \sqrt{b^2}}$ — Product property of radicals

$= \frac{\sqrt{6b}}{3b}$ — Simplify.

SUMS AND DIFFERENCES You can use the distributive property to simplify sums and differences of radical expressions when the expressions have the same radicand.

EXAMPLE 5 Add and subtract radicals

a. $4\sqrt{10} + \sqrt{13} - 9\sqrt{10} = 4\sqrt{10} - 9\sqrt{10} + \sqrt{13}$ — Commutative property

$= (4 - 9)\sqrt{10} + \sqrt{13}$ — Distributive property

$= -5\sqrt{10} + \sqrt{13}$ — Simplify.

b. $5\sqrt{3} + \sqrt{48} = 5\sqrt{3} + \sqrt{16 \cdot 3}$ — Factor using perfect square factor.

$= 5\sqrt{3} + \sqrt{16} \cdot \sqrt{3}$ — Product property of radicals

$= 5\sqrt{3} + 4\sqrt{3}$ — Simplify.

$= (5 + 4)\sqrt{3}$ — Distributive property

$= 9\sqrt{3}$ — Simplify.

✓ GUIDED PRACTICE for Examples 4 and 5

Simplify the expression.

3. $\frac{1}{\sqrt{3}}$ **$\frac{\sqrt{3}}{3}$**

4. $\frac{1}{\sqrt{x}}$ **$\frac{\sqrt{x}}{x}$**

5. $\frac{3}{\sqrt{2x}}$ **$\frac{3\sqrt{2x}}{2x}$**

6. $2\sqrt{7} + 3\sqrt{63}$ **$11\sqrt{7}$**

Extra Example 4

Rationalize the denominator.

a. $\frac{7}{\sqrt{6}}$ **$\frac{7\sqrt{6}}{6}$**

b. $\frac{\sqrt{3}}{\sqrt{5a}}$ **$\frac{\sqrt{15a}}{5a}$**

Key Question to Ask for Example 4

- Could you multiply the expression in part a by $\frac{5}{\sqrt{7}}$ to rationalize the denominator? Explain. **No; it would change the value of the expression.**

Extra Example 5

Add and subtract radicals.

a. $7\sqrt{14} + \sqrt{21} - 4\sqrt{14}$ **$3\sqrt{14} + \sqrt{21}$**

b. $2\sqrt{7} + \sqrt{28}$ **$4\sqrt{7}$**

Key Question to Ask for Example 5

- Why do you use the commutative property in part a? **You want to arrange the terms so that you can combine like terms.**

Differentiated Instruction

Auditory Learners Phrases which have parallel structure are easier to learn for some students. The product property of radicals, when abridged slightly to read, "The square root of a product is the product of the square roots", has a parallel structure which is easy for students to remember. Show students that the quotient property of radicals follows from the product property by changing b to $\frac{1}{b}$.

See also the *Differentiated Instruction Resources* for more strategies.

Extra Example 6

Multiply radical expressions.

a. $\sqrt{3}(2+\sqrt{12})$ **$2\sqrt{3}+6$**

b. $(\sqrt{2}+\sqrt{5})(\sqrt{2}-3\sqrt{5})$ **$-13-2\sqrt{10}$**

An **Animated Algebra** activity is available online for **Example 6**. This activity is also part of **Power Presentations**.

Extra Example 7

An investigator can determine the speed S (in miles per hour) of a car by using the formula $S=\sqrt{27\ell}$, where ℓ is the length (in feet) of the car's skid mark.

a. Simplify the formula. **$S=3\sqrt{3\ell}$**

b. A skid mark is 96 feet long. What was the speed of the car? **about 51 mi/h**

Closing the Lesson

Have students summarize the major points of the lesson and answer the Essential Question: How do you simplify radical expressions?

- **When simplifying radical expressions, look for perfect square factors in the radicand, eliminate radicals in the denominator of a fraction, and eliminate fractions in the radicand.**

Simplify after you factor out perfect squares and eliminate fractions in the radicand. If the denominator of a fraction contains a radical, eliminate the radical by rationalizing the denominator.

8. No. *Sample answer:* Neptune's orbital period is $(6\cdot5.2)(\sqrt{6\cdot5.2})=6\cdot(5.2)\cdot\sqrt{6}\cdot\sqrt{5.2}=(6\sqrt{6})\cdot(5.2\sqrt{5.2})$. Thus, Neptune's orbital period is $6\sqrt{6}$ times the orbital period of Jupiter.

EXAMPLE 6 Multiply radical expressions

a. $\sqrt{5}(4-\sqrt{20})=4\sqrt{5}-\sqrt{5}\cdot\sqrt{20}$ **Distributive property**

$=4\sqrt{5}-\sqrt{100}$ **Product property of radicals**

$=4\sqrt{5}-10$ **Simplify.**

REVIEW FOIL METHOD
For help with the FOIL method, see p. 562.

b. $(\sqrt{7}+\sqrt{2})(\sqrt{7}-3\sqrt{2})$

$=(\sqrt{7})^2+\sqrt{7}(-3\sqrt{2})+\sqrt{2}\cdot\sqrt{7}+\sqrt{2}(-3\sqrt{2})$ **Multiply.**

$=7-3\sqrt{7\cdot2}+\sqrt{7\cdot2}-3(\sqrt{2})^2$ **Product property of radicals**

$=7-3\sqrt{14}+\sqrt{14}-6$ **Simplify.**

$=1-2\sqrt{14}$ **Simplify.**

Animated Algebra at classzone.com

EXAMPLE 7 Solve a real-world problem

ASTRONOMY The orbital period of a planet is the time that it takes the planet to travel around the sun. You can find the orbital period P (in Earth years) using the formula $P=\sqrt{d^3}$ where d is the average distance (in astronomical units, abbreviated AU) of the planet from the sun.

a. Simplify the formula.

b. Jupiter's average distance from the sun is shown in the diagram. What is Jupiter's orbital period?

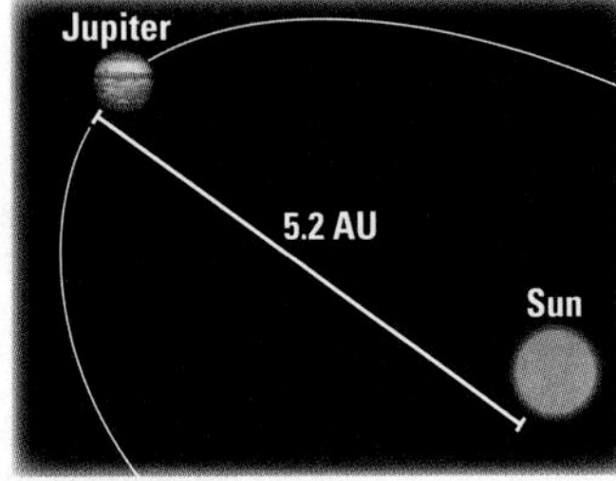

Not drawn to scale

Solution

a. $P=\sqrt{d^3}$ **Write formula.**

$=\sqrt{d^2\cdot d}$ **Factor using perfect square factor.**

$=\sqrt{d^2}\cdot\sqrt{d}$ **Product property of radicals**

$=d\sqrt{d}$ **Simplify.**

b. Substitute 5.2 for d in the simplified formula.

$P=d\sqrt{d}=5.2\sqrt{5.2}$

▸ The orbital period of Jupiter is $5.2\sqrt{5.2}$, or about 11.9, Earth years.

✓ **GUIDED PRACTICE** for Examples 6 and 7

7. Simplify the expression $(4-\sqrt{5})(1-\sqrt{5})$. **$9-5\sqrt{5}$**

8. ASTRONOMY Neptune's average distance from the sun is about 6 times Jupiter's average distance from the sun. Is the orbital period of Neptune 6 times the orbital period of Jupiter? *Explain.* **See margin.**

11.2 EXERCISES

HOMEWORK KEY

○ = **WORKED-OUT SOLUTIONS** on p. WS26 for Exs. 9, 37, and 69

★ = **STANDARDIZED TEST PRACTICE** Exs. 2, 23, 25, 64, and 71

◆ = **MULTIPLE REPRESENTATIONS** Ex. 70

SKILL PRACTICE

A

1. **VOCABULARY** Copy and complete: The process of eliminating a radical from the denominator of a radical expression is called _?_. **rationalizing the denominator**

2. ★ **WRITING** Is the expression $\sqrt{\frac{2x}{9}}$ written in simplest form? *Explain* why or why not.
No. *Sample answer*: An expression is not in simplest form if there is a fraction in the radicand.

EXAMPLES 1, 2, and 3 on pp. 719–720 for Exs. 3–25

USING PRODUCT AND QUOTIENT PROPERTIES Simplify the expression.

3. $\sqrt{20}$ $2\sqrt{5}$
4. $\sqrt{48}$ $4\sqrt{3}$
5. $\sqrt{96}$ $4\sqrt{6}$
6. $\sqrt{72}$ $6\sqrt{2}$
7. $\sqrt{125b}$ $5\sqrt{5b}$
8. $\sqrt{4x^2}$ $2x$
9. $\sqrt{81m^3}$ $9m\sqrt{m}$
10. $\sqrt{32m^5}$ $4m^2\sqrt{2m}$
11. $\sqrt{5} \cdot \sqrt{30}$ $5\sqrt{6}$
12. $\sqrt{50} \cdot \sqrt{18}$ 30
13. $\sqrt{14x} \cdot \sqrt{2x}$ $2x\sqrt{7}$
14. $\sqrt{3b^3} \cdot \sqrt{18b}$ $3b^2\sqrt{6}$
15. $2\sqrt{a^4b^5}$ $2a^2b^2\sqrt{b}$
16. $\sqrt{64s^4t^3}$ $8s^2t\sqrt{t}$
17. $\sqrt{m^2n} \cdot \sqrt{n}$ mn
18. $\sqrt{75xy} \cdot \sqrt{2x^3}$ $5x^2\sqrt{6y}$
19. $\sqrt{\frac{4}{49}}$ $\frac{2}{7}$
20. $\sqrt{\frac{7}{81}}$ $\frac{\sqrt{7}}{9}$
21. $\sqrt{\frac{a^3}{121}}$ $\frac{a\sqrt{a}}{11}$
22. $\sqrt{\frac{100}{4x^2}}$ $\frac{5}{x}$

23. ★ **MULTIPLE CHOICE** Which expression is equivalent to $\sqrt{\frac{9x}{16}}$? **B**

Ⓐ $\frac{\sqrt{3x}}{4}$ Ⓑ $\frac{3\sqrt{x}}{4}$ Ⓒ $\frac{3\sqrt{x}}{16}$ Ⓓ $\frac{3x}{4}$

24. **ERROR ANALYSIS** *Describe* and correct the error in simplifying the expression $\sqrt{72}$.
***Sample answer*: The answer is not simplified completely. $2\sqrt{18}$ can be written as $2\sqrt{2} \cdot \sqrt{9} = 6\sqrt{2}$.**

$\sqrt{72} = \sqrt{4} \cdot \sqrt{18}$
$= 2\sqrt{18}$ ✗

25. ★ **WRITING** *Describe* two different sequences of steps you could take to simplify the expression $\sqrt{45} \cdot \sqrt{5}$. ***Sample answer*: Simplify $\sqrt{45}$ to $\sqrt{9} \cdot \sqrt{5} = 3\sqrt{5}$. Then multiply $3\sqrt{5} \cdot \sqrt{5} = 3 \cdot 5 = 15$. Or, combine the expressions to create $\sqrt{45 \cdot 5} = \sqrt{225} = 15$.**

EXAMPLE 4 on p. 721 for Exs. 26–33

RATIONALIZING THE DENOMINATOR Simplify the expression.

26. $\frac{2}{\sqrt{2}}$ $\sqrt{2}$
27. $\frac{4}{\sqrt{3}}$ $\frac{4\sqrt{3}}{3}$
28. $\sqrt{\frac{5}{48}}$ $\frac{\sqrt{15}}{12}$
29. $\sqrt{\frac{4}{52}}$ $\frac{\sqrt{13}}{13}$
30. $\frac{3}{\sqrt{a}}$ $\frac{3\sqrt{a}}{a}$
31. $\frac{1}{\sqrt{2x}}$ $\frac{\sqrt{2x}}{2x}$
32. $\sqrt{\frac{2x^2}{5}}$ $\frac{x\sqrt{10}}{5}$
33. $\sqrt{\frac{8}{3n^3}}$ $\frac{2\sqrt{6n}}{3n^2}$

EXAMPLES 5 and 6 on pp. 721–722 for Exs. 34–45

38. $8\sqrt{3} + 2\sqrt{6}$
39. $7\sqrt{7} - 5\sqrt{14}$

PERFORMING OPERATIONS ON RADICALS Simplify the expression.

34. $2\sqrt{2} + 6\sqrt{2}$ $8\sqrt{2}$
35. $\sqrt{5} - 6\sqrt{5}$ $-5\sqrt{5}$
36. $2\sqrt{6} - 5\sqrt{54}$ $-13\sqrt{6}$
37. $9\sqrt{32} + \sqrt{2}$ $37\sqrt{2}$
38. $\sqrt{12} + 6\sqrt{3} + 2\sqrt{6}$
39. $3\sqrt{7} - 5\sqrt{14} + 2\sqrt{28}$
40. $\sqrt{5}(5 - \sqrt{5})$ $5\sqrt{5} - 5$
41. $\sqrt{6}(7\sqrt{3} + 6)$ $21\sqrt{2} + 6\sqrt{6}$
42. $\sqrt{3}(6\sqrt{2} - 4\sqrt{3})$ $6\sqrt{6} - 12$
43. $(4 - \sqrt{2})(5 + \sqrt{2})$ $18 - \sqrt{2}$
44. $(2\sqrt{5} + 7)^2$ $69 + 28\sqrt{5}$
45. $(\sqrt{7} + \sqrt{3})(6 + \sqrt{8})$ $6\sqrt{7} + 6\sqrt{3} + 2\sqrt{14} + 2\sqrt{6}$

4 PRACTICE AND APPLY

Assignment Guide

Answer Transparencies available for all exercises

Basic:
Day 1: EP p. 946 Exs. 7–12
pp. 723–726
Exs. 1–25
Day 2: pp. 723–726
Exs. 26–50 even, 67–70, 73–93 odd

Average:
Day 1: pp. 723–726
Exs. 1, 2, 4–22 even, 23–32, 55–58
Day 2: pp. 723–726
Exs. 35–53 odd, 59–63, 67–71, 74, 77, 80, 82, 84, 87, 90, 93

Advanced:
Day 1: pp. 723–726
Exs. 1, 15–23, 25–33, 55–62
Day 2: pp. 723–726
Exs. 34–54 even, 59–72*, 78, 81, 88, 94

Block:
pp. 723–726
Exs. 1, 2, 4–22 even, 23–32, 35–53 odd, 55–63, 67–71, 74, 77, 80, 82, 84, 87, 90, 93

Differentiated Instruction

See *Differentiated Instruction Resources* for suggestions on addressing the needs of a diverse classroom.

Homework Check

For a quick check of student understanding of key concepts, go over the following exercises:

Basic: 14, 28, 36, 42, 67
Average: 18, 30, 35, 43, 67
Advanced: 21, 32, 38, 44, 68

Extra Practice

- Student Edition, p. 948
- Chapter Resource Book: Practice levels A, B, C

Practice Worksheet

An easily-readable reduced practice page (with answers) for this lesson can be found on p. 708C.

Avoiding Common Errors

Exercises 3–22 Some students may factor a perfect square in a radicand and then simplify without checking to see if there is more than one perfect square factor. It may help some students to use prime factorization or a factor tree to avoid missing perfect square factors.

Teaching Strategy

Exercises 43–45 Recommend that students use the FOIL pattern to multiply the expressions. Some students may find it easier to multiply each term on a separate line. If they use this method, remind them to combine like terms after they have multiplied.

Exercises 55–58 You may want to offer students an additional example before they begin these exercises. One example is $\frac{2}{3+\sqrt{5}}$. Ask students to identify the conjugate $3-\sqrt{5}$ and then continue asking them to describe the next step as you work the example on the board.

63. Because $a > 0$, $a \cdot a < a \cdot b$. Similarly, $a \cdot b < b \cdot b$. Then $a^2 < ab < b^2$, so $\sqrt{a^2} < \sqrt{ab} < \sqrt{b^2}$, or $a < \sqrt{ab} < b$. That is, $\sqrt{ab}$ is between a and b on a number line.

64. If $a > 0$, then the positive square root of a^2 is a. If $a < 0$, then the positive square root of a^2 is $-a$. If $a = 0$, then the square root of a^2 is 0; in other words, $\sqrt{a^2} = |a|$; $4|x|$, $2|x|\cdot|y|$, $7n^2|m|\cdot|p^3|$.

66. Odd values of m; even values of m. *Sample answer:* If m is even, then $m = 2n$ for some integer n, so $\sqrt{2^m} = \sqrt{2^{2n}} = \sqrt{(2^n)^2} = 2^n$. If m is odd, then $m = 2n + 1$ for some integer n, so $\sqrt{2^m} = \sqrt{2^{2n+1}} = \sqrt{2^{2n} \cdot 2} = 2^n \cdot \sqrt{2}$.

B **SIMPLIFYING RADICAL EXPRESSIONS** Simplify the expression.

46. $\sqrt{75m^2np^4}$ **$5mp^2\sqrt{3n}$**
47. $\sqrt{512rs^6} \cdot \sqrt{t^3}$ **$16s^3t\sqrt{2rt}$**
48. $\sqrt{\frac{600a}{4b^3}}$ **$\frac{5\sqrt{6ab}}{b^2}$**
49. $\sqrt{\frac{50gh^2}{125f^3}}$ **$\frac{h\sqrt{10gf}}{5f^2}$**
50. $\frac{4}{\sqrt{3}} + \frac{7}{\sqrt{12}}$ **$\frac{5\sqrt{3}}{2}$**
51. $\frac{2\sqrt{6}}{\sqrt{30}} - \frac{3}{\sqrt{20}}$ **$\frac{\sqrt{5}}{10}$**
52. $\frac{7}{\sqrt{x}} + \frac{3}{2\sqrt{x}}$ **$\frac{17\sqrt{x}}{2x}$**
53. $\frac{3}{\sqrt{x^3}} + \frac{4}{\sqrt{x}}$ **$\frac{3\sqrt{x} + 4x\sqrt{x}}{x^2}$**
54. $\frac{6m}{\sqrt{m^3}} - \frac{8}{\sqrt{m}}$ **$\frac{-2\sqrt{m}}{m}$**

CONJUGATES In Exercises 55–58, use the example to simplify the expression.

EXAMPLE **Rationalize the denominator using conjugates**

Simplify $\frac{9}{2-\sqrt{3}}$.

The binomials $a\sqrt{b} + c\sqrt{d}$ and $a\sqrt{b} - c\sqrt{d}$ are called *conjugates*. They differ only by the sign of one term. The product of two conjugates $a\sqrt{b} + c\sqrt{d}$ and $a\sqrt{b} - c\sqrt{d}$ does not contain a radical: $(2+\sqrt{3})(2-\sqrt{3}) = 2^2 - (\sqrt{3})^2 = 4 - 3 = 1$. You can use conjugates to simplify the expression.

$$\frac{9}{2-\sqrt{3}} = \frac{9}{2-\sqrt{3}} \cdot \frac{2+\sqrt{3}}{2+\sqrt{3}}$$ **Multiply the numerator and denominator by the conjugate of the denominator.**

$$= \frac{9(2+\sqrt{3})}{(2-\sqrt{3})(2+\sqrt{3})}$$ **Multiply fractions.**

$$= \frac{18+9\sqrt{3}}{4-3}$$ **Simplify numerator and denominator.**

$$= 18 + 9\sqrt{3}$$ **Simplify.**

55. $\frac{1}{\sqrt{7}+1}$ **$\frac{\sqrt{7}-1}{6}$**
56. $\frac{2}{5-\sqrt{3}}$ **$\frac{5+\sqrt{3}}{11}$**
57. $\frac{\sqrt{10}}{7-\sqrt{2}}$ **$\frac{7\sqrt{10}+2\sqrt{5}}{47}$**
58. $\frac{\sqrt{5}}{6+\sqrt{5}}$ **$\frac{6\sqrt{5}-5}{31}$**

REVIEW SOLVING EQUATIONS
For help with using square roots to solve equations, see p. 652.

Solve for the variable in red. Assume the variables have positive values.

59. $S = 4\pi r^2$ **$\frac{\sqrt{\pi S}}{2\pi}$**
60. $V = \pi r^2 h$ **$\frac{\sqrt{\pi h V}}{\pi h}$**
61. $W = \frac{CV^2}{2}$ **$\frac{\sqrt{2WC}}{C}$**
62. $F = \frac{mv^2}{r}$ **$\frac{\sqrt{Frm}}{m}$**

C 63. **REASONING** Let a and b be positive numbers. *Explain* why $\sqrt{ab}$ lies between a and b on a number line. (*Hint:* Let $a < b$ and multiply both sides of $a < b$ by a. Then let $a < b$ and multiply both sides by b.) **See margin.**

64. ★ **WRITING** For any number a, a^2 has a and $-a$ as square roots. *Explain* why for any number a, $\sqrt{a^2} = |a|$. Then, assuming no restrictions on the variables, simplify the expressions $\sqrt{16x^2}$, $\sqrt{4x^2y^2}$, and $\sqrt{49m^2n^4p^6}$. **See margin.**

65. **MULTIPLYING FUNCTIONS** Let $f(x) = \sqrt{x} - \sqrt{4x}$, and let $g(x) = \sqrt{x}$. Find $h(x) = f(x) \cdot g(x)$. **$-x$**

66. **CHALLENGE** Let m be a positive integer. Consider the simplified form of the expression $\sqrt{2^m}$. For what values of m will the simplified form contain a radical? For what values will it *not* contain a radical? *Explain.* **See margin.**

○ = WORKED-OUT SOLUTIONS on p. WS1 ★ = STANDARDIZED TEST PRACTICE  = MULTIPLE REPRESENTATIONS

724

PROBLEM SOLVING

EXAMPLE 7 A on p. 722 for Exs. 67, 68

67. FINANCE You invest \$225 in a savings account for two years. The account has an annual interest rate that changes from year to year. You can find the average annual interest rate r that the account earned over two years using the formula $r = \sqrt{\frac{V_2}{V_0}} - 1$ where V_0 is the initial investment and V_2 is the amount in the account after two years. At the end of two years, you have \$270 in the account. What was the average annual interest rate (written as a percent) the account earned over two years? **about 9.54%**

@HomeTutor for problem solving help at classzone.com

68. DISTANCE TO THE HORIZON The distance d (in miles) that a person can see to the horizon is given by the formula $d = \sqrt{\frac{3h}{2}}$ where h is the person's eye level (in feet) above the water. To the nearest mile, find the distance that the person shown can see to the horizon. **12 mi**

@HomeTutor for problem solving help at classzone.com

69. MULTI-STEP PROBLEM You are making a cube-shaped footrest. You want to cover the footrest with fabric. At a fabric store, you choose fabric that costs \$6 per square yard.

a. You have \$30 to spend on fabric. How much fabric can you buy? **5 yd²**

b. The edge length s (in yards) of the largest footrest you can cover can be found using the formula $s = \sqrt{\frac{S}{6}}$ where S is the surface area of the footrest (in square yards). Use unit analysis to check the units in the formula. **The side length s is in yd, and $\sqrt{\frac{S}{6}}$ is $\sqrt{yd^2} = yd$.**

c. Find the edge length of the largest footrest you can cover to the nearest tenth of a yard. **0.9 yd**

B **70. MULTIPLE REPRESENTATIONS** The velocity v (in feet per second) of an object that has been dropped can be found using the equation $v = \sqrt{64d}$ where d is the distance the object falls (in feet) before hitting the ground.

a. **Writing an Equation** Write the equation in simplified form. $v = 8\sqrt{d}$

b. **Drawing a Graph** Graph the equation. For what value of d is the velocity about 16 feet per second? **See margin for art; 4 ft.**

c. **Solving an Equation** Use the equation from part (a) to find the exact value of d when the velocity is 16 feet per second. **4 ft**

Study Strategy

Exercises 67–69 Point out to students that these exercises contain fractions in the radicand and that they will need to rationalize the denominator after they use the quotient property of radicals. Suggest that they simplify the formulas before substituting values for the variables.

Vocabulary

Exercise 72 Tell students that the *coefficient of friction* is a ratio of resistive forces that apply when two objects come in contact.

70b.

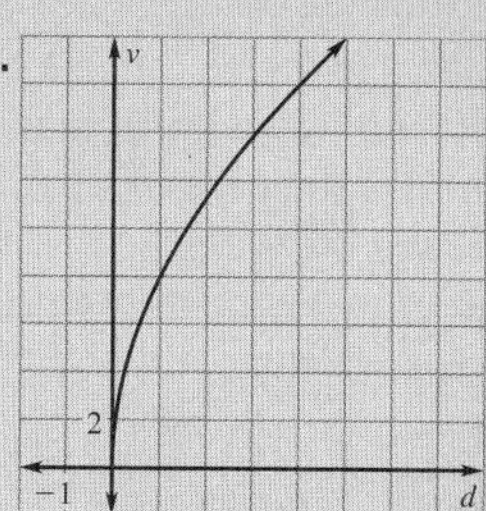

5 ASSESS AND RETEACH

Daily Homework Quiz

Transparency Available

Simplify the expression.

1. $\sqrt{56a^2}$ **$2a\sqrt{14}$**

2. $\sqrt{\frac{b}{64}}$ **$\frac{\sqrt{b}}{8}$**

3. $5\sqrt{2} - 2\sqrt{8} + \sqrt{6}$ **$\sqrt{2} + \sqrt{6}$**

4. A person is standing on a cliff, with an eye level at 60 feet, looking out across the ocean. Use the formula $d = \sqrt{\frac{3h}{2}}$ where d (in miles) is the distance a person can see to the horizon and h (in feet) is the person's eye level above the water to find the number of miles the person can see to the horizon. **about 9.5 mi**

Available at **classzone.com**

Diagnosis/Remediation

- Practice A, B, C in Chapter Resource Book
- Study Guide in Chapter Resource Book
- Practice Workbook
- @HomeTutor

Challenge

Additional challenge is available in the Chapter Resource Book.

71. ★ **SHORT RESPONSE** Physicians can calculate the body surface area S (in square meters) of an adult using the formula $S = \sqrt{\frac{hw}{3600}}$ where h is the adult's height (in centimeters) and w is the adult's mass (in kilograms).
    a. Simplify the formula. **$S = \frac{\sqrt{hw}}{60}$**
    b. Does an adult who is 1.7 meters tall and has a mass of 70 kilograms have a greater body surface area than an adult who is 1.5 meters tall and has a mass of 70 kilograms? *Explain* what effect height has on surface area if two people have the same mass. **Yes. *Sample answer*: If the mass stays the same, then the greater the height the greater the body surface area will be.**

C 72. **CHALLENGE** The speed s (in miles per hour) at which a vehicle is traveling before an accident is given by $s = \sqrt{30df}$ where d is the length of the skid mark (in feet) and f is the coefficient of friction. The coefficient of friction varies depending on the type of road surface and on the road conditions.

a. A driver is traveling on a newly paved road with a coefficient of friction of 0.80. The driver sees a hazard in the road and is forced to brake. The car skids to a halt leaving a skid mark that is 100 feet long. At what speed was the car traveling when the driver applied the brakes? **about 49.0 mi/h**
b. A perception-reaction time is the amount of time it takes for a person to react to a situation after perceiving it, such as applying the brakes after seeing a hazard in the road. The driver in part (a) has a perception-reaction time of 1.5 seconds. How many feet does the car travel before the driver applies the brakes? *Explain* how you found your answer.
c. What is the total distance (in feet) traveled from the time the driver in part (a) sees the hazard until the time the car skids to a halt? **207.8 ft**

72b. about 107.8 ft. *Sample answer*: First, convert 49 miles per hour from part (a) to feet per second $\frac{49 \cdot 5280}{60 \cdot 60} =$ 71.0867 feet per second. Then multiply by 1.5 seconds.

MIXED REVIEW

Graph the function and identify its domain and range. **73–81. See margin.**

73. $y = -6$ for $x \geq 0$ *(p. 215)*
74. $y = -\frac{1}{3}x$ *(p. 215)*
75. $5x + y = 3$ *(p. 244)*
76. $y = 0.4x - 7$ *(p. 244)*
77. $y = 4^x$ *(p. 520)*
78. $y = (0.4)^x$ *(p. 531)*
79. $y = -7x^2$ *(p. 628)*
80. $y = 5x^2 + 2$ *(p. 628)*
81. $y = 3x^2 - 10x - 8$ *(p. 635)*
82. Write the equation of the line that passes through (1, 2) and is perpendicular to the line $y = \frac{1}{2}x + 3$. *(p. 318)* **$y = -2x + 4$**

PREVIEW
Prepare for Lesson 11.3 in Exs. 83–94.

Solve the equation. *(pp. 575, 583, 593, and 600)*

83. $(a - 3)(a + 8) = 0$ **$-8, 3$**
84. $(2y + 3)(2y + 5) = 0$ **$-\frac{5}{2}, -\frac{3}{2}$**
85. $-12m^2 + 48 = 0$ **$-2, 2$**
86. $x^2 - 8x + 16 = 0$ **4**
87. $d^2 + 8d = -2$ **$-4 \pm \sqrt{14}$**
88. $x^2 - 2x = 24$ **$-4, 6$**
89. $10z - 21 = -2z^2$ **$\frac{-5 \pm \sqrt{67}}{2}$**
90. $5x^2 + 13x + 6 = 0$ **$-2, -\frac{3}{5}$**
91. $4x^2 - 11x - 3 = 0$ **$-\frac{1}{4}, 3$**
92. $8x^2 - 64 = 0$ **$\pm 2\sqrt{2}$**
93. $4z^2 = 36$ **$-3, 3$**
94. $b^2 + 12b + 36 = 0$ **-6**

73–81. See Additional Answers beginning on p. AA1.

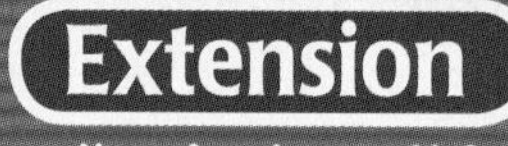

Derive the Quadratic Formula

GOAL Solve quadratic equations and check solutions.

In Lesson 10.6, you learned how to find solutions of quadratic equations using the quadratic formula. You can use the method of completing the square and the quotient property of radicals to derive the quadratic formula.

$ax^2 + bx + c = 0$ **Write standard form of a quadratic equation.**

$ax^2 + bx = -c$ **Subtract c from each side.**

$x^2 + \frac{b}{a}x = -\frac{c}{a}$ **Divide each side by a, $a \neq 0$.**

$x^2 + \frac{b}{a}x + \left(\frac{b}{2a}\right)^2 = -\frac{c}{a} + \left(\frac{b}{2a}\right)^2$ **Add $\left(\frac{b}{2a}\right)^2$ to each side to complete the square.**

$\left(x + \frac{b}{2a}\right)^2 = -\frac{c}{a} + \frac{b^2}{4a^2}$ **Write left side as the square of a binomial.**

$\left(x + \frac{b}{2a}\right)^2 = \frac{b^2 - 4ac}{4a^2}$ **Simplify right side.**

$x + \frac{b}{2a} = \pm\sqrt{\frac{b^2 - 4ac}{4a^2}}$ **Take square roots of each side.**

$x + \frac{b}{2a} = \frac{\pm\sqrt{b^2 - 4ac}}{2a}$ **Quotient property of radicals**

$x = \frac{-b \pm \sqrt{b^2 - 4ac}}{2a}$ **Subtract $\frac{b}{2a}$ from each side.**

SOLVING QUADRATIC EQUATIONS You can use the quadratic formula and properties of radicals to solve quadratic equations.

EXAMPLE 1 Solve an equation

Solve $x^2 - 6x + 3 = 0$.

Solution

$x^2 - 6x + 3 = 0$ **Identify $a = 1$, $b = -6$, and $c = 3$.**

$x = \frac{-(-6) \pm \sqrt{(-6)^2 - 4(1)(3)}}{2(1)}$ **Substitute values in the quadratic formula.**

$= \frac{6 \pm \sqrt{24}}{2}$ **Simplify.**

$= \frac{6 \pm \sqrt{4 \cdot 6}}{2}$ **Product property of radicals**

$= \frac{6 \pm 2\sqrt{6}}{2} = 3 \pm \sqrt{6}$ **Simplify.**

▸ The solutions of the equation are $3 + \sqrt{6}$ and $3 - \sqrt{6}$.

1 PLAN AND PREPARE

Warm-Up Exercises

Solve the equation.

1. $x^2 + 3x - 4 = 0$ **1, −4**
2. $x^2 - 6x + 2 = 0$ **$3 \pm \sqrt{7}$**
3. $2x^2 + 3x - 5 = 0$ **1, −2.5**
4. A ball is thrown upward in the air from a height of 5 feet and with an initial vertical velocity of 15 feet per second. After how many seconds does the ball hit the ground? **about 1.2 sec**

2 FOCUS AND MOTIVATE

Essential Question

Big Idea 2, p. 709

How do you solve quadratic equations? **Tell students they will learn how to answer this question by using the quadratic formula.**

3 TEACH

Extra Example 1

Solve $x^2 + 8x + 1 = 0$. **$-4 \pm \sqrt{15}$**

Key Question to Ask for Example 1

- Why are there two solutions of the equation? **The discriminant is positive, so the equation has two real solutions.**

NCTM STANDARDS

Standard 2: Analyze situations using algebraic symbols

Standard 7: Develop mathematical arguments and proofs

Extra Example 2

Check the solutions of the equation from Extra Example 1. **The solutions check when you substitute them into the original equation.**

Closing the Lesson

Have students summarize the major points of the lesson and answer the Essential Question: How do you solve quadratic equations?

- **The quadratic formula is** $x = \frac{-b \pm \sqrt{b^2 - 4ac}}{2a}$. **When using the quadratic formula, first identify the values of *a*, *b*, and *c*. Then substitute the values into the formula and simplify. Check the solutions by substituting each into the original equation.**

4 PRACTICE AND APPLY

Avoiding Common Errors

Exercises 1–18 Urge students to use caution when substituting values into the quadratic formula to avoid calculation errors. Places to be especially careful include replacing *b* with a negative number and remembering that the denominator is 2 • *a*, not 2 or *a*.

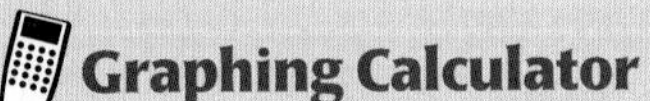

Graphing Calculator

Exercises 1–18 Students may want to check their solutions by graphing the equations. They can use the *zero* feature to check the solutions.

EXAMPLE 2 Check the solutions of an equation

Check the solutions of the equation from Example 1.

Solution

The solutions of $x^2 - 6x + 3 = 0$ are $3 + \sqrt{6}$ and $3 - \sqrt{6}$. You can check each solution by substituting it into the original equation.

Check $x = 3 + \sqrt{6}$:

$x^2 - 6x + 3 = 0$	Write original equation.
$(3 + \sqrt{6})^2 - 6(3 + \sqrt{6}) + 3 \stackrel{?}{=} 0$	Substitute $3 + \sqrt{6}$ for *x*.
$9 + 6\sqrt{6} + 6 - 18 - 6\sqrt{6} + 3 \stackrel{?}{=} 0$	Multiply.
$0 = 0$ ✓	Solution checks.

Check $x = 3 - \sqrt{6}$:

$x^2 - 6x + 3 = 0$	Write original equation.
$(3 - \sqrt{6})^2 - 6(3 - \sqrt{6}) + 3 \stackrel{?}{=} 0$	Substitute $3 - \sqrt{6}$ for *x*.
$9 - 6\sqrt{6} + 6 - 18 + 6\sqrt{6} + 3 \stackrel{?}{=} 0$	Multiply.
$0 = 0$ ✓	Solution checks.

PRACTICE

EXAMPLES 1 and 2 on pp. 727–728 for Exs. 1–18

Solve the equation using the quadratic formula. Check the solution. **1–18. See margin.**

1. $x^2 + 4x + 2 = 0$
2. $x^2 + 6x - 1 = 0$
3. $x^2 + 8x + 8 = 0$
4. $x^2 - 7x + 1 = 0$
5. $3x^2 + 6x - 1 = 0$
6. $2x^2 - 4x - 3 = 0$
7. $5x^2 - 2x - 2 = 0$
8. $4x^2 + 10x + 3 = 0$
9. $x^2 - x - 3 = 0$
10. $x^2 - 2x - 8 = 0$
11. $-x^2 + 7x + 3 = 0$
12. $x^2 + 3x - 9 = 0$
13. $-\frac{5}{2}x^2 + 10x - 5 = 0$
14. $\frac{1}{2}x^2 + 3x - 9 = 0$
15. $3x^2 - 2 = 0$
16. $-2x^2 - 7x = 0$
17. $3x^2 + x = 6$
18. $x^2 - 4x = -2$
19. Show that $\frac{-b + \sqrt{b^2 - 4ac}}{2a}$ and $\frac{-b - \sqrt{b^2 - 4ac}}{2a}$ are solutions of $ax^2 + bx + c = 0$ by substituting. **See margin.**
20. Derive a formula to find solutions of equations that have the form $ax^2 + x + c = 0$. Use your formula to find solutions of $-2x^2 + x + 8 = 0$. **See margin.**
21. Find the sum and product of $\frac{-b + \sqrt{b^2 - 4ac}}{2a}$ and $\frac{-b - \sqrt{b^2 - 4ac}}{2a}$. Write a quadratic expression whose solutions have a sum of 2 and a product of $\frac{1}{2}$. **See margin.**
22. What values can *a* have in the equation $ax^2 + 12x + 3 = 0$ in order for the equation to have one or two real solutions? *Explain.* **See margin.**

1. $-2 - \sqrt{2}, -2 + \sqrt{2}$
2. $-3 - \sqrt{10}, -3 + \sqrt{10}$
3. $-4 - 2\sqrt{2}, -4 + 2\sqrt{2}$
4. $\frac{7}{2} - \frac{5\sqrt{5}}{2}, \frac{7}{2} + \frac{5\sqrt{5}}{2}$
5. $-1 - \frac{2\sqrt{3}}{3}, -1 + \frac{2\sqrt{3}}{3}$
6. $1 - \frac{\sqrt{10}}{2}, 1 + \frac{\sqrt{10}}{2}$
7. $\frac{1}{5} - \frac{\sqrt{11}}{5}, \frac{1}{5} + \frac{\sqrt{11}}{5}$
8. $-\frac{5}{4} - \frac{\sqrt{13}}{4}, -\frac{5}{4} + \frac{\sqrt{13}}{4}$
9. $\frac{1}{2} - \frac{\sqrt{13}}{2}, \frac{1}{2} + \frac{\sqrt{13}}{2}$
10. 4, −2
11. $\frac{7}{2} - \frac{\sqrt{61}}{2}, \frac{7}{2} + \frac{\sqrt{61}}{2}$
12. $-\frac{3}{2} - \frac{3\sqrt{5}}{2}, -\frac{3}{2} + \frac{3\sqrt{5}}{2}$
13. $2 - \sqrt{2}, 2 + \sqrt{2}$
14. $-3 - 3\sqrt{3}, -3 + 3\sqrt{3}$
15. $-\frac{\sqrt{6}}{3}, \frac{\sqrt{6}}{3}$
16. $-\frac{7}{4} - \sqrt{57}, -\frac{7}{4} + \sqrt{57}$
17. $-\frac{1}{6} - \frac{\sqrt{73}}{6}, -\frac{1}{6} + \frac{\sqrt{73}}{6}$,
18. $2 - \sqrt{2}, 2 + \sqrt{2}$
19. See Additional Answers beginning on p. AA1.
20. $\frac{-1 \pm \sqrt{1 - 4ac}}{2a}, \frac{1}{4} \pm \frac{\sqrt{65}}{4}$
21. Sum: $-\frac{b}{a}$, product: $\frac{c}{a}$. *Sample answer:* $y = 2x^2 - 4x + 1$
22. See Additional Answers beginning on p. AA1.

11.3 Solve Radical Equations

Before You solved linear, quadratic, and exponential equations.

Now You will solve radical equations.

Why? So you can use scientific formulas to study animals, as in Ex. 39.

Key Vocabulary
- **radical equation**
- **extraneous solution**

An equation that contains a radical expression with a variable in the radicand is a **radical equation.** To solve a radical equation, you need to isolate the radical on one side and then square both sides of the equation.

KEY CONCEPT *For Your Notebook*

Squaring Both Sides of an Equation

Words If two expressions are equal, then their squares are equal.

Algebra If $a = b$, then $a^2 = b^2$. **Example** If $\sqrt{x} = 3$, then $(\sqrt{x})^2 = 3^2$.

EXAMPLE 1 **Solve a radical equation**

Solve $2\sqrt{x} - 8 = 0$.

Solution

$2\sqrt{x} - 8 = 0$ Write original equation.

$2\sqrt{x} = 8$ Add 8 to each side.

$\sqrt{x} = 4$ Divide each side by 2.

$(\sqrt{x})^2 = 4^2$ Square each side.

$x = 16$ Simplify.

▶ The solution is 16.

CHECK Check the solution by substituting it in the original equation.

$2\sqrt{x} - 8 = 0$ Write original equation.

$2\sqrt{16} - 8 \stackrel{?}{=} 0$ Substitute 16 for *x*.

$2 \cdot 4 - 8 \stackrel{?}{=} 0$ Simplify.

$0 = 0$ ✓ Solution checks.

✓ **GUIDED PRACTICE** for Example 1

1. Solve (**a**) $\sqrt{x} - 7 = 0$ and (**b**) $12\sqrt{x} - 3 = 0$. **a. 49 b. $\frac{1}{16}$**

1 PLAN AND PREPARE

Warm-Up Exercises

Transparency Available

Solve the equation.

1. $2x + 3 = 13$ **$x = 5$**

2. $3x - 8 = 16$ **$x = 8$**

3. $4x^2 - 16 = 0$ **$x = -2, x = 2$**

4. $x^2 - x = 12$ **$x = -3, x = 4$**

5. You put $250 in a savings account that earns 3% interest compounded yearly. If you make no deposits and no withdrawals, how much will your savings be worth in 5 years? **about $290**

Notetaking Guide

Transparency Available

Promotes interactive learning and notetaking skills.

Pacing

Basic: 2 days

Average: 2 days

Advanced: 2 days

Block: 1 block

- See *Teaching Guide/Lesson Plan.*

2 FOCUS AND MOTIVATE

Essential Question

Big Idea 2, p. 709

How do you solve radical equations? **Tell students they will learn how to answer this question by squaring both sides of the equation and checking for extraneous solutions.**

NCTM STANDARDS

Standard 2: Represent situations using algebraic symbols; Analyze situations using algebraic symbols

Resource Planning Guide

Chapter Resource Book
- Teaching Guide/Lesson Plan
- Activity Master
- Practice levels A, B, C
- Study Guide
- Catch-up for Absent Students
- Problem Solving Workshop
- Challenge

Workbooks
- Notetaking Guide
- Practice Workbook

Teaching Options
- **Power Presentations** provides dynamic electronic teaching resources for the classroom.
- **Activity Generator** provides editable activities for all ability levels.

Interactive Technology
- Easy Planner
- Power Presentations
- Activity Generator
- Animated Algebra
- Test Generator
- Online Quiz
- eWorkbook
- eEdition
- @HomeTutor

Resources for English Learners
- Spanish Study Guide
- Multi-Language Visual Glossary
- Student Resources in Spanish

See also the *Differentiated Instruction Resources* for more strategies for meeting individual needs.

Motivating the Lesson

Ask students to describe some of their favorite rides at recreational parks. Tell them that solving radical equations will give them information about rides, such as the speeds of roller coasters or the forces acting on rides that spin.

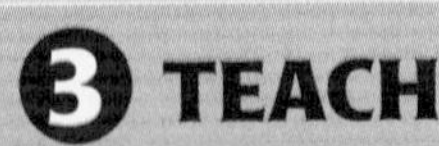

3 TEACH

Extra Example 1

Solve $3\sqrt{x} - 6 = 0$. **$x = 4$**

Key Question to Ask for Example 1

- What is the first step in solving a radical equation? **Isolate the radical.**
- What is the next step? **Square each side of the equation.**

Extra Example 2

Solve $2\sqrt{x+6} + 9 = 21$. **$x = 30$**

Extra Example 3

Solve $\sqrt{4x - 12} = \sqrt{x + 3}$. **$x = 5$**

Key Question to Ask for Example 3

- How is Example 3 different from Examples 1 and 2? **In the previous examples, you isolate the radical and then square each side. In this example, you square each side first since each side contains a radical, and then you isolate the variable.**

EXAMPLE 2 Solve a radical equation

Solve $4\sqrt{x-7} + 12 = 28$.

Solution

$4\sqrt{x-7} + 12 = 28$	**Write original equation.**
$4\sqrt{x-7} = 16$	**Subtract 12 from each side.**
$\sqrt{x-7} = 4$	**Divide each side by 4.**
$(\sqrt{x-7})^2 = 4^2$	**Square each side.**
$x - 7 = 16$	**Simplify.**
$x = 23$	**Add 7 to each side.**

▶ The solution is 23.

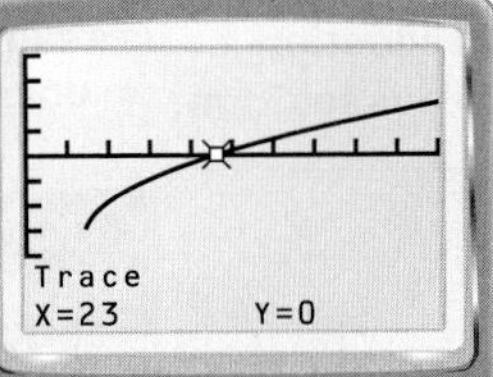

CHECK To check the solution using a graphing calculator, first rewrite the equation so that one side is 0: $4\sqrt{x-7} - 16 = 0$. Then graph the related equation $y = 4\sqrt{x-7} - 16$. You can see that the graph crosses the x-axis at $x = 23$.

EXAMPLE 3 Solve an equation with radicals on both sides

Solve $\sqrt{3x - 17} = \sqrt{x + 21}$.

Solution

SOLVE EQUATIONS
To solve a radical equation that contains two radical expressions, be sure that each side of the equation has only one radical expression before squaring each side.

$\sqrt{3x - 17} = \sqrt{x + 21}$	**Write original equation.**
$(\sqrt{3x - 17})^2 = (\sqrt{x + 21})^2$	**Square each side.**
$3x - 17 = x + 21$	**Simplify.**
$2x - 17 = 21$	**Subtract x from each side.**
$2x = 38$	**Add 17 to each side.**
$x = 19$	**Divide each side by 2.**

▶ The solution is 19. Check the solution.

GUIDED PRACTICE for Examples 2 and 3

Solve the equation.

2. $\sqrt{x-5} + 7 = 12$ **30** **3.** $\sqrt{x+4} = \sqrt{2x-1}$ **5** **4.** $\sqrt{4x-3} - \sqrt{x} = 0$ **1**

EXTRANEOUS SOLUTIONS Squaring both sides of the equation $a = b$ can result in a solution of $a^2 = b^2$ that is *not* a solution of the original equation. Such a solution is called an **extraneous solution.** When you square both sides of an equation, check each solution in the original equation to be sure there are no extraneous solutions.

Differentiated Instruction

English Learners The vocabulary of mathematics can sometimes be more difficult than the mathematics itself. Explain that an extraneous solution is an *extra* solution which is to be discarded. Point out that in words such as *extracurricular* or *extraordinary*, the prefix "extra-" means *outside*. Suggest that students remember the term extraneous solution as meaning outside of the set of solutions.

See also the *Differentiated Instruction Resources* for more strategies.

EXAMPLE 4 Solve an equation with an extraneous solution

Solve $\sqrt{6 - x} = x$.

$\sqrt{6 - x} = x$	**Write original equation.**
$(\sqrt{6 - x})^2 = x^2$	**Square each side.**
$6 - x = x^2$	**Simplify.**
$0 = x^2 + x - 6$	**Write in standard form.**
$0 = (x - 2)(x + 3)$	**Factor.**
$x - 2 = 0$ *or* $x + 3 = 0$	**Zero-product property**
$x = 2$ *or* $x = -3$	**Solve for *x*.**

REVIEW FACTORING

For help with factoring, see pp. 583, 593, 600, and 606.

CHECK Check 2 and −3 in the original equation.

If $x = 2$: $\sqrt{6 - 2} \stackrel{?}{=} 2$ **If $x = -3$:** $\sqrt{6 - (-3)} \stackrel{?}{=} -3$

$2 = 2$ ✓ $3 = -3$ ✗

▶ Because −3 does not check in the original equation, it is an extraneous solution. The only solution of the equation is 2.

 at classzone.com

EXAMPLE 5 Solve a real-world problem

SAILING The hull speed *s* (in nautical miles per hour) of a sailboat can be estimated using the formula $s = 1.34\sqrt{\ell}$ where ℓ is the length (in feet) of the sailboat's waterline, as shown. Find the length (to the nearest foot) of the sailboat's waterline if it has a hull speed of 8 nautical miles per hour.

Solution

$s = 1.34\sqrt{\ell}$	**Write original equation.**
$8 = 1.34\sqrt{\ell}$	**Substitute 8 for *s*.**
$\frac{8}{1.34} = \sqrt{\ell}$	**Divide each side by 1.34.**
$\left(\frac{8}{1.34}\right)^2 = (\sqrt{\ell})^2$	**Square each side.**
$35.6 \approx \ell$	**Simplify.**

▶ The sailboat has a waterline length of about 36 feet.

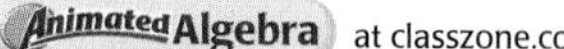 at classzone.com

GUIDED PRACTICE for Examples 4 and 5

5. Solve $\sqrt{3x + 4} = x$. **4**

6. **WHAT IF?** In Example 5, suppose the sailboat's hull speed is 6.5 nautical miles per hour. Find the sailboat's waterline length to the nearest foot. **24 ft**

Extra Example 4

Solve $\sqrt{20 - x} = x$. **$x = 4$**

An **Animated Algebra** activity is available online for **Example 4**. This activity is also part of **Power Presentations**.

Extra Example 5

If friction is ignored, the velocity *v* (in feet per second) of a roller coaster when it reaches the bottom of a hill, can be found by using the formula $v = \sqrt{64h}$, where *h* is the height (in feet) of the hill. The approximate velocity of one of the fastest roller coasters in the world is 176 feet per second. Find the height of the hill. **about 484 ft**

An **Animated Algebra** activity is available online for **Example 5**. This activity is also part of **Power Presentations**.

Closing the Lesson

Have students summarize the major points of the lesson and answer the Essential Question: How do you solve radical equations?

- **If two expressions are equal, their squares are equal.**
- **Squaring both sides of an equation can result in an extraneous solution.**

Isolate the radical on one side of the equation, square both sides, and then solve for the variable. If there are radicals on both sides of the equation, square both sides, isolate the variable, and then solve. Always check both solutions in the original equation to rule out an extraneous solution.

11.3 EXERCISES

HOMEWORK KEY
○ = **WORKED-OUT SOLUTIONS** on p. WS27 for Exs. 11 and 37
★ = **STANDARDIZED TEST PRACTICE** Exs. 2, 21, 34, and 40

4 PRACTICE AND APPLY

Assignment Guide

Answer Transparencies available for all exercises

Basic:
Day 1: EP p. 946 Exs. 19–24
pp. 732–734
Exs. 1–21
Day 2: pp. 732–734
Exs. 22–26, 36–39, 42–49

Average:
Day 1: pp. 732–734
Exs. 1, 2, 5–21, 31, 32
Day 2: pp. 732–734
Exs. 22–30, 36–40, 42–48 even

Advanced:
Day 1: pp. 732–734
Exs. 1, 6–21, 31–34
Day 2: pp. 732–734
Exs. 22–30, 35–41*, 43–47 odd

Block:
pp. 732–734
Exs. 1, 2, 5–32, 36–40, 42–48 even

Differentiated Instruction

See *Differentiated Instruction Resources* for suggestions on addressing the needs of a diverse classroom.

Homework Check

For a quick check of student understanding of key concepts, go over the following exercises:

Basic: 4, 10, 14, 22, 36
Average: 5, 12, 16, 24, 37
Advanced: 6, 13, 18, 26, 38

Extra Practice

- Student Edition, p. 948
- Chapter Resource Book: Practice levels A, B, C

Practice Worksheet

An easily-readable reduced practice page (with answers) for this lesson can be found on p.708C.

SKILL PRACTICE

A

1. **VOCABULARY** Copy and complete: To find the solution of $\sqrt{12 - x} = x$, you square both sides of the equation and solve. The solutions of $(\sqrt{12 - x})^2 = x^2$ are -4 and 3, but -4 is a(n) _?_ of $\sqrt{12 - x} = x$. **extraneous solution**

2. ★ **WRITING** Is $x + x\sqrt{2} = 4$ a radical equation? *Explain* why or why not.
No. ***Sample answer*: It does not contain a variable in a radicand.**

EXAMPLES 1, 2, and 3 on pp. 729–730 for Exs. 3–21, 28

SOLVING EQUATIONS Solve the equation. Check for extraneous solutions.

3. $3\sqrt{x} - 6 = 0$ **4**
4. $2\sqrt{x} - 9 = 0$ $\mathbf{\frac{81}{4}}$
5. $\sqrt{3x} + 4 = 16$ **48**
6. $\sqrt{5x} + 5 = 0$ **no real solutions**
7. $\sqrt{x + 7} + 5 = 11$ **29**
8. $\sqrt{x - 8} - 4 = -2$ **12**
9. $2\sqrt{x - 4} - 2 = 2$ **8**
10. $3\sqrt{x - 1} - 5 = 5$ $\mathbf{\frac{109}{9}}$
11. $\sqrt{6 - 2x} + 12 = 21$ $\mathbf{-\frac{75}{2}}$
12. $5\sqrt{x - 3} + 4 = 14$ **7**
13. $2\sqrt{x - 11} - 8 = 4$ **47**
14. $\sqrt{3x - 2} = \sqrt{x}$ **1**
15. $\sqrt{7 - 2x} = \sqrt{9 - x}$ **−2**
16. $\sqrt{3x + 8} = \sqrt{x + 4}$ **−2**
17. $\sqrt{9x - 30} = \sqrt{4x + 5}$ **7**
18. $\sqrt{21 - x} - \sqrt{1 - x} = 0$ **no real solutions**
19. $\sqrt{x - 12} - \sqrt{x - 8} = 0$ **no real solutions**
20. $\sqrt{\frac{1}{2}x - 2} - \sqrt{x - 8} = 0$ **12**

21. ★ **MULTIPLE CHOICE** Which is the solution of the equation $10\sqrt{x + 3} + 3 = 18$? **B**

Ⓐ $-\frac{3}{2}$ Ⓑ $-\frac{3}{4}$ Ⓒ $\frac{3}{4}$ Ⓓ $\frac{3}{2}$

EXAMPLE 4 B on p. 731 for Exs. 22–27, 29

SOLVING EQUATIONS Solve the equation. Check for extraneous solutions.

22. $x = \sqrt{42 - x}$ **6**
23. $\sqrt{4 - 3x} = x$ **1**
24. $\sqrt{11x - 24} = x$ **3, 8**
25. $\sqrt{14x - 3} = 4x$ $\mathbf{\frac{3}{8}, \frac{1}{2}}$
26. $2x = \sqrt{1 - 3x}$ $\mathbf{\frac{1}{4}}$
27. $\sqrt{2 - x} = x + 4$ **−2**

ERROR ANALYSIS *Describe* and correct the error in solving the equation.

28.

$\sqrt{3x} + 9 = 0$
$\sqrt{3x} = -9$
$3x = 81$
$x = 27$ ✗

***Sample answer*: The solution $x = 27$ does not check in the original equation, so it is an extraneous solution. There are no real solutions to this equation.**

29.

$x = \sqrt{18 - 7x}$
$x^2 = 18 - 7x$
$x^2 + 7x - 18 = 0$
$(x - 2)(x + 9) = 0$
$x - 2 = 0$ or $x + 9 = 0$
$x = 2$ or $x = -9$ ✗

29. *Sample answer*: The solution $x = -9$ does not check in the original equation, so it is an extraneous solution. The only real solution is $x = 2$.

30. **GEOMETRY** The formula for the slant height s (in inches) of a cone is $s = \sqrt{h^2 + r^2}$ where h is the height of the cone (in inches) and r is the radius of its base (in inches), as shown. Find the height of the cone if you know the slant height is 4 inches and the radius is 2 inches. **$2\sqrt{3}$ in. or about 3.5 in.**

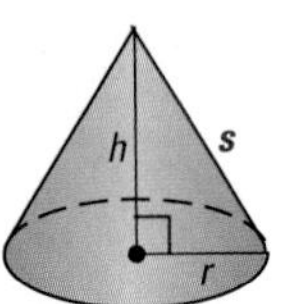

C **SOLVING EQUATIONS** **Solve the equation. Check for extraneous solutions.**

31. $\sqrt{x} + 2 = \sqrt{x - 1}$ **no real solutions**

32. $2 - \sqrt{x + 1} = \sqrt{x + 3}$ **$-\frac{3}{4}$**

33. $\sqrt{5x + 9} + \sqrt{5x} = 9$ **$\frac{16}{5}$**

34. ★ **WRITING** A student solves the equation $\sqrt{x + 2} = x$ and finds that $x = 2$ or $x = -1$. Without checking by substituting into the equation, which is the extraneous solution, 2 or -1? How do you know? **-1; since in the equation x is equal to a radical expression, x cannot be a negative number.**

35. **CHALLENGE** Write a radical equation that has 3 and 4 as solutions. ***Sample answer:*** $\sqrt{7x - 12} = x$

PROBLEM SOLVING

EXAMPLE 5 A on p. 731 for Exs. 36–38

36. **FORESTS** The dark green areas on the image shown represent regions with heavy foliage. In Texas, the area of land y (in millions of acres) that was covered by forest during the period 1907–2002 can be modeled by the function $y = 2.5\sqrt{143 - x}$ where x is the number of years since 1907. In what year were about 20 million acres of land covered by forest in Texas? **1986**

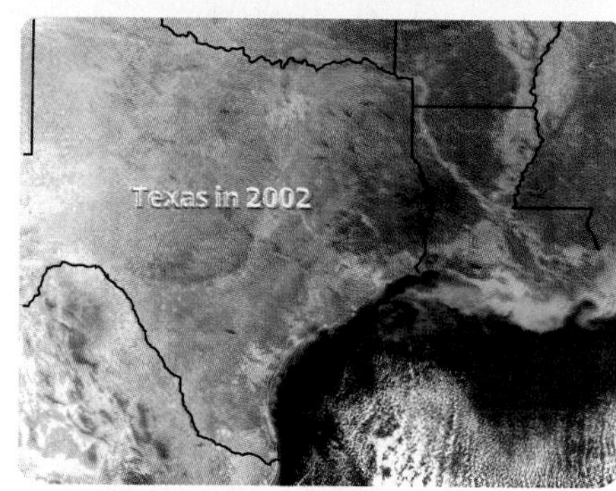
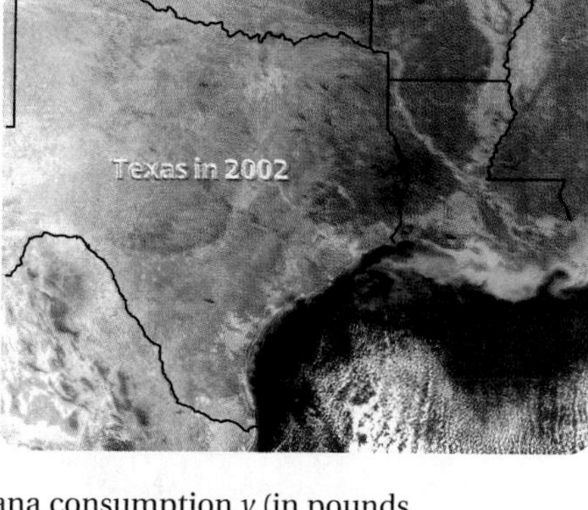

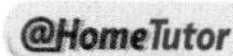 for problem solving help at classzone.com

37. **PER CAPITA CONSUMPTION** The annual banana consumption y (in pounds per person) in the United States for the period 1970–2000 can be modeled by the function $y = \sqrt{18x + 272}$ where x is the number of years since 1970. In what year were about 20 pounds of bananas consumed per person? **1977**

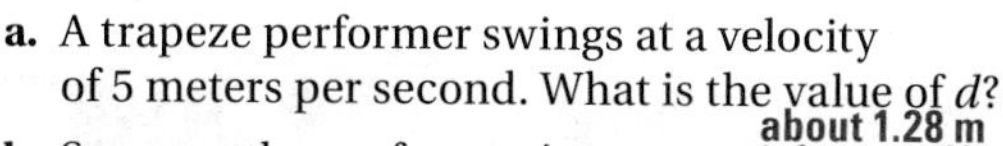 for problem solving help at classzone.com

38. **MULTI-STEP PROBLEM** The velocity v (in meters per second) at which a trapeze performer swings can be modeled by the function $v = \sqrt{19.6d}$ where d is the difference (in meters) between the highest and lowest position of the performer's center of gravity during the swing.

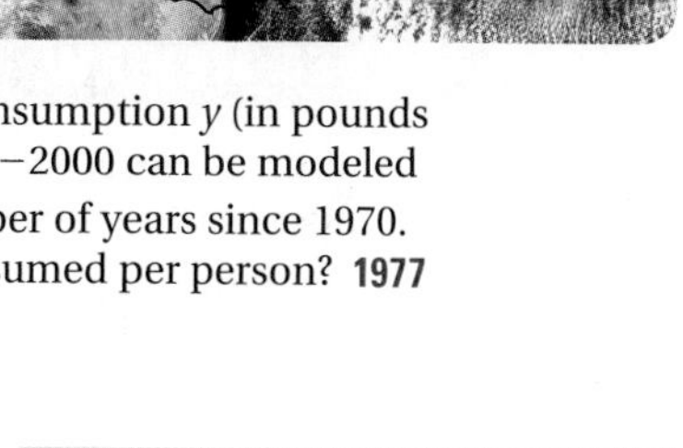
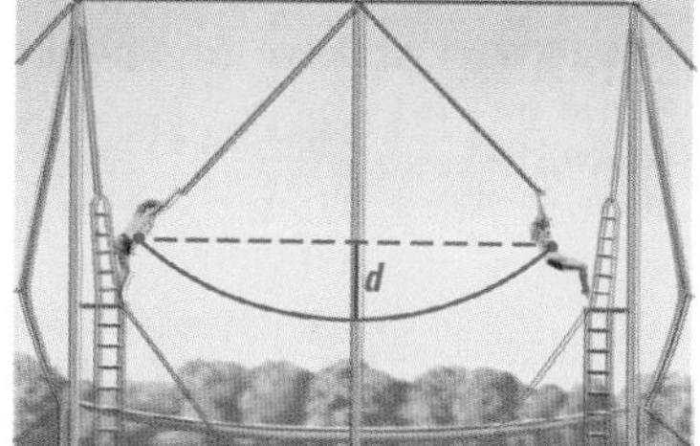

a. A trapeze performer swings at a velocity of 5 meters per second. What is the value of d? **about 1.28 m**

b. Suppose the performer jumps straight up off the starting board, increasing the velocity of the swing by 0.4 meter per second. By how many meters does the value of d increase? **about 0.21 m**

B **39.** **BIOLOGY** A bushbaby is a small animal that can perform standing jumps of over 2 meters. Scientists found that the time t (in seconds) in which a bushbaby must extend its legs in order to jump to a height h (in meters) is given by the function $t = 0.45\ell\sqrt{\frac{1}{h}}$ where ℓ is the length of the bushbaby's legs (in meters). A particular bushbaby has a leg length of 0.16 meter. The bushbaby can extend its legs in 0.05 second. About how high does the bushbaby jump? Round your answer to the nearest tenth of a meter. **2.1 m**

Avoiding Common Errors

Exercises 3–13 Students often fail to isolate the radical before they square both sides. Remind students that they first use properties of equality to isolate the radical on one side of the equation in the same way that they isolate the variable on one side of a linear equation.

Study Strategy

Exercise 35 Suggest to students that they use a strategy of working backward to solve this challenge. They could start by asking what two binomials they would need to multiply to get solutions of 3 and 4.

Graphing Calculator

Exercises 36–41 Students may want to use their calculators for these problems so they can concentrate on problem-solving strategies rather than calculations.

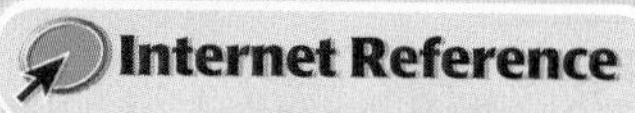

Internet Reference

Exercise 39 Additional information about bushbabies can be found at the African Wildlife Foundation website at www.awf.org/wildlives/7

5 ASSESS AND RETEACH

Daily Homework Quiz

Transparency Available

Solve the equation. Check for extraneous solutions.

1. $2\sqrt{x+11} - 4 = 10$ **$x = 38$**
2. $\sqrt{2x-29} = \sqrt{x-11}$ **$x = 18$**
3. $\sqrt{3+2x} = x$ **$x = 3$**
4. Find the length (to the nearest foot) of a sailboat's waterline if it has a hull speed of 10 nautical miles per hour. Use the formula $s = 1.34\sqrt{\ell}$ where s is hull speed (in nautical miles per hour) and ℓ is the length (in feet) of the sailboat's waterline. **about 56 feet**

Online Quiz

Available at **classzone.com**

Diagnosis/Remediation

- Practice A, B, C in Chapter Resource Book
- Study Guide in Chapter Resource Book
- Practice Workbook
- @HomeTutor

Challenge

Additional challenge is available in the Chapter Resource Book.

Quiz

An easily-readable reduced copy of the quiz (with answers) on Lessons 11.1–11.3 from the Assessment Book can be found on p. 708E.

Quiz

1.

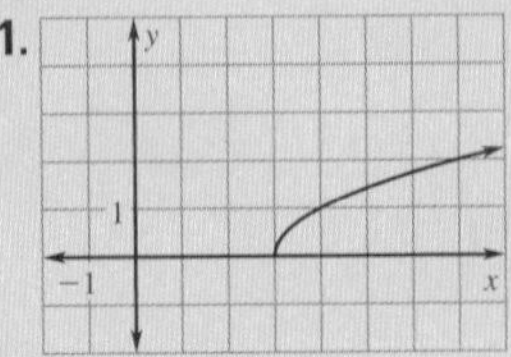

40b. Increase. *Sample answer*: The greater the value of ℓ, the greater the value of the radicand, and the greater the value of t.

40. ★ **SHORT RESPONSE** The amount of time t (in seconds) it takes a simple pendulum to complete one full swing is called the period of the pendulum and is given by $t = 2\pi\sqrt{\frac{\ell}{32}}$ where ℓ is the length of the pendulum (in feet).

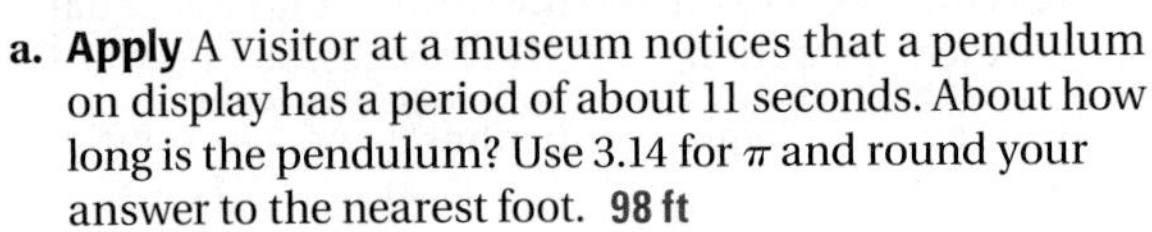

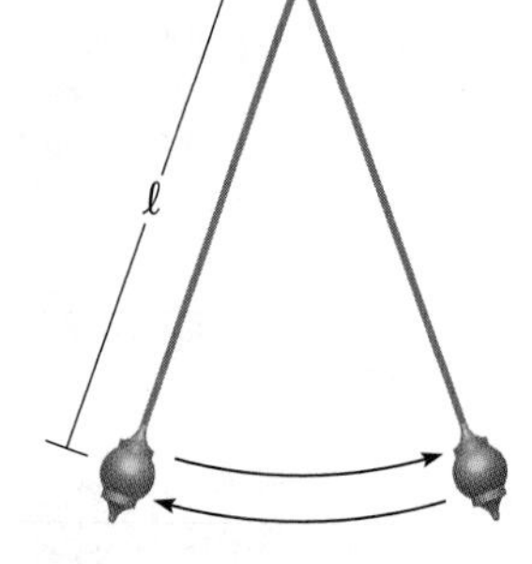

   a. **Apply** A visitor at a museum notices that a pendulum on display has a period of about 11 seconds. About how long is the pendulum? Use 3.14 for π and round your answer to the nearest foot. **98 ft**

   b. **Explain** Does increasing the length of a pendulum increase or decrease its period? *Explain.*

C 41. **CHALLENGE** The frequency f (in cycles per second) of a string of an electric guitar is given by the equation $f = \frac{1}{2\ell}\sqrt{\frac{T}{m}}$ where ℓ is the length of the string (in meters), T is the string's tension (in newtons), and m is the string's mass per unit length (in kilograms per meter). The high E string of a particular electric guitar is 0.64 meter long with a mass per unit length of 0.000401 kilogram per meter. How much tension is required to produce a frequency of about 330 cycles per second? Would you need more or less tension if you want to create the same frequency on a string with greater mass per unit length? *Explain.* **About 71.5 N; more. *Sample answer*: If the mass increased then the tension would have to increase to create the same value in the radicand. If the radicand has the same value and the length is constant, the frequency will stay the same.**

MIXED REVIEW

Make a scatter plot of the data. *Describe* the correlation of the data. If possible, fit a line to the data and write an equation for the line. *(p. 324)* **42, 43. See margin for art.**

42.

x	0	1	2	3	4
y	−5	−2	2	4	7

positive; $y = 3x - 4.8$

43.

x	2	4	6	8	10
y	0	11	24	31	44

positive; $y = 5.4x - 10.4$

PREVIEW Prepare for Lesson 11.4 in Exs. 44–49.

Solve the equation.

44. $x^2 + 21x + 20 = 0$ *(p. 583)* **−20, −1**
45. $x^2 - 21x + 38 = 0$ *(p. 583)* **2, 19**
46. $x^2 - 8x - 9 = 0$ *(p. 583)* **−1, 9**
47. $11x^2 - 11 = 0$ *(p. 600)* **−1, 1**
48. $5x^2 - 125 = 0$ *(p. 600)* **−5, 5**
49. $8x^2 - 32 = 0$ *(p. 600)* **−2, 2**

QUIZ for Lessons 11.1–11.3

1. Graph the function $y = \sqrt{x-3}$ and identify its domain and range. Compare the graph with the graph of $y = \sqrt{x}$. *(p. 710)* **See margin for art; domain: $x \ge 3$, range: $y \ge 0$; the graph is a horizontal translation 3 units to the right.**

Simplify the expression. *(p. 719)*

2. $\sqrt{150}$ **$5\sqrt{6}$**
3. $\sqrt{2c^2} \cdot \sqrt{8c}$ **$4c\sqrt{c}$**
4. $(7+\sqrt{5})(2-\sqrt{5})$ **$9 - 5\sqrt{5}$**
5. $\frac{14}{\sqrt{2}}$ **$7\sqrt{2}$**
6. $\sqrt{\frac{98}{x^6}}$ **$\frac{7\sqrt{2}}{x^3}$**
7. $\sqrt{\frac{80x^3}{5y}}$ **$\frac{4x\sqrt{xy}}{y}$**

Solve the equation. Check for extraneous solutions. *(p. 729)*

8. $\sqrt{x} - 15 = 0$ **225**
9. $\sqrt{4x-7} = \sqrt{2x+19}$ **13**
10. $\sqrt{6x-5} = x$ **1, 5**

EXTRA PRACTICE for Lesson 11.3, p. 948 **ONLINE QUIZ** at classzone.com

42.

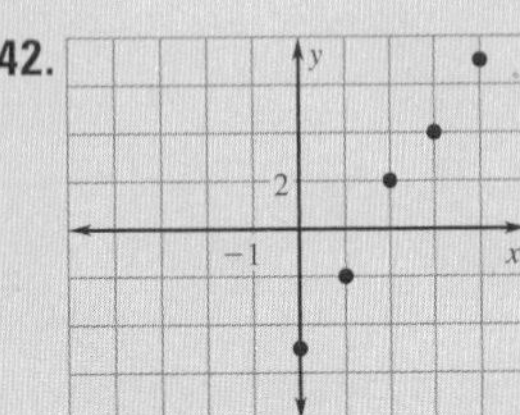

43.

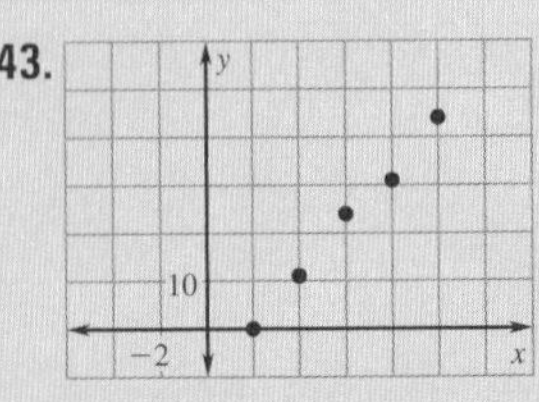

MIXED REVIEW of Problem Solving

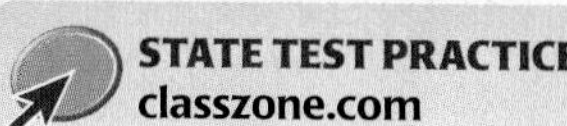

Lessons 11.1–11.3

1. **OPEN-ENDED** The velocity v (in meters per second) of a car moving in a circular path that has radius r (in meters) is given by $v = \sqrt{\frac{Fr}{m}}$ where F is the force (in newtons) pulling the car toward the center of the circular path and m is the mass of the car (in kilograms).

A 1200 kilogram car is traveling at a constant velocity of 20 meters per second in a circular path of radius r meters where $r \geq 100$. Choose two different values of r to show how the force, F, acting on the car changes as the radius increases. **See margin.**

2. **MULTI-STEP PROBLEM** The number y of companies listed on the New York Stock Exchange for the period 1999–2002 can be modeled by the function $y = 3018 - 146\sqrt{x}$ where x is the number of years since 1999.
   a. Graph the function. **See margin.**
   b. How many companies were listed on the New York Stock Exchange in 1999? **3018 companies**
   c. In what year were there about 220 companies fewer than the number of companies listed on the New York Stock Exchange in 1999? **2001**

3. **GRIDDED ANSWER** The voltage V (in volts) of an amplifier is given by the function $V = \sqrt{PR}$ where P is the power (in watts) and R is the resistance (in ohms). A particular amplifier produces 10 volts and has a resistance of 4 ohms. How many watts are produced by the amplifier? **25 watts**

4. **MULTI-STEP PROBLEM** For the period 1994–2001, the annual consumption of corn products y (in pounds per person) in the United States can be modeled by the function $y = 6.1\sqrt{x + 15.8}$ where x is the number of years since 1994.
   a. Graph the function. **See margin.**
   b. In what year were about 25 pounds of corn products consumed per person? **1995**

5. **EXTENDED RESPONSE** Competitors in a ski mountaineering race must climb a mountain and ski down it as quickly as possible. The race begins with the firing of a starting gun. Near Earth's surface, the speed of sound s (in meters per second) through air is given by $s = 20\sqrt{T + 273}$ where T is the air temperature (in degrees Celsius). **a–c. See margin.**

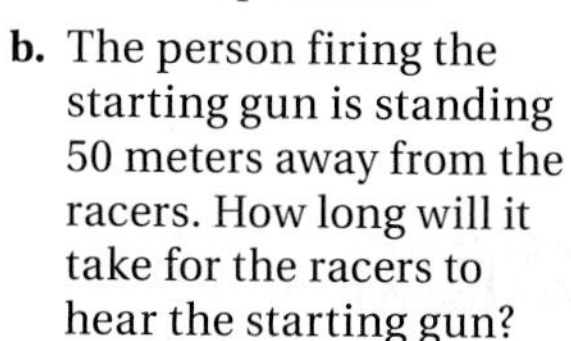

   a. A typical temperature at the start of a race is −5°C. What is the speed of sound at this temperature?
   b. The person firing the starting gun is standing 50 meters away from the racers. How long will it take for the racers to hear the starting gun?
   c. What happens to the time it takes for the racers to hear the starting gun if the temperature at the start of the race is lower? *Explain.*

6. **SHORT RESPONSE** A person's maximum running speed s (in meters per second) can be approximated by the function $s = \pi\sqrt{\frac{9.8\ell}{6}}$ where ℓ is the person's leg length (in meters).

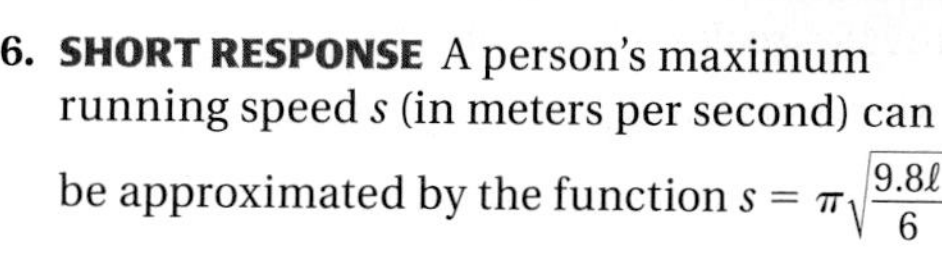

   a. To the nearest tenth of a meter, what is the leg length of a person whose maximum running speed is about 3.8 meters per second? **about 0.9 m**
   b. What happens to running speed as leg length increases? *Explain.*
   It increases. ***Sample answer*: As ℓ increases, the radicand increases as does the radical.**

1. ***Sample answer:*** **If $r = 100$, $F = 4800$. If $r = 400$, $F = 1200$. As r increases, F decreases, so that the product $Fr = 480{,}000$.**

2a.

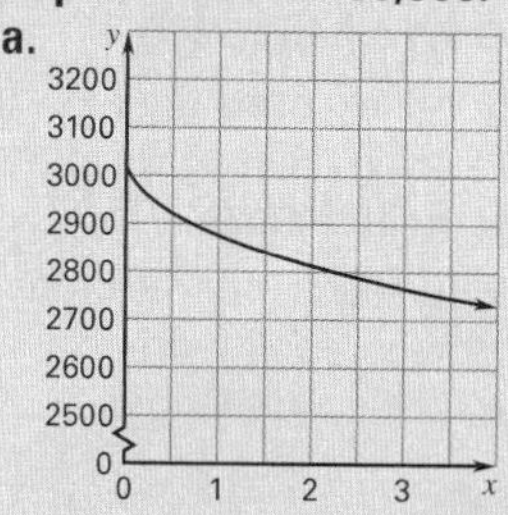

4a.

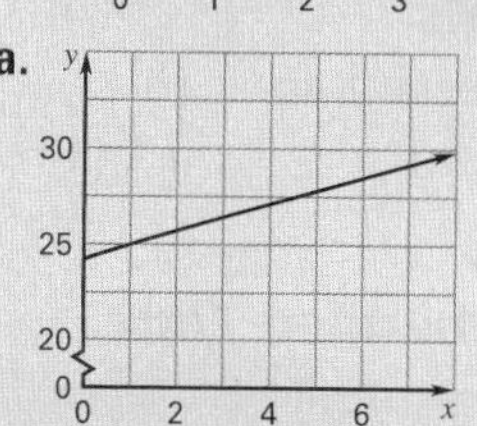

5a. about 327.4 m/sec

5b. about 0.15 sec

5c. It increases. ***Sample answer:*** **As the temperature gets colder, the speed decreases and the time needed to cover the distance increases.**

11.4 The Pythagorean Theorem

MATERIALS • graph paper • scissors

QUESTION **How are the lengths of the sides of a right triangle related to each other?**

EXPLORE **Examine the relationship among the lengths of the sides of a right triangle**

STEP 1 ***Make right triangles***

Cut a right triangle out of graph paper. Make three copies of it.

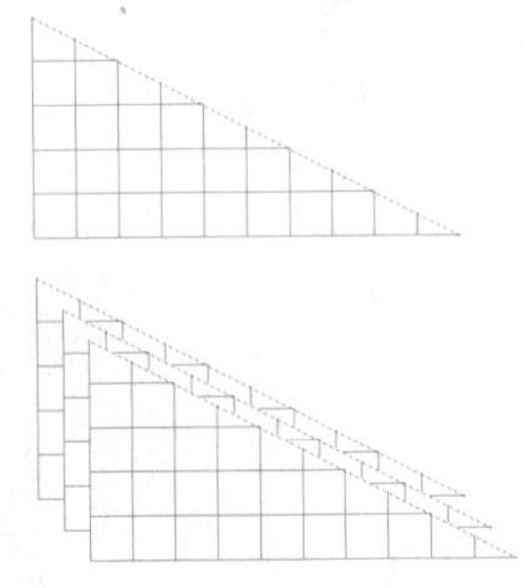

STEP 2 ***Arrange as a square***

Arrange the right triangles to form a square within a square, as shown.

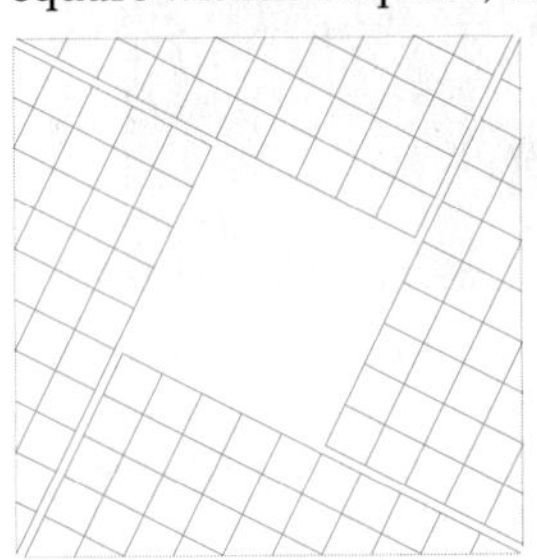

DRAW CONCLUSIONS **Use your observations to complete these exercises**

1. How are the areas of the triangles and inner square related to the area of the outer square? **The sum of the areas of the triangles and the inner square is equal to the area of the outer square.**

In Exercises 2–4, let a, b, and c be the lengths of the sides of a right triangle with $a < b < c$, as shown. Write an expression for the area of the figure described below.

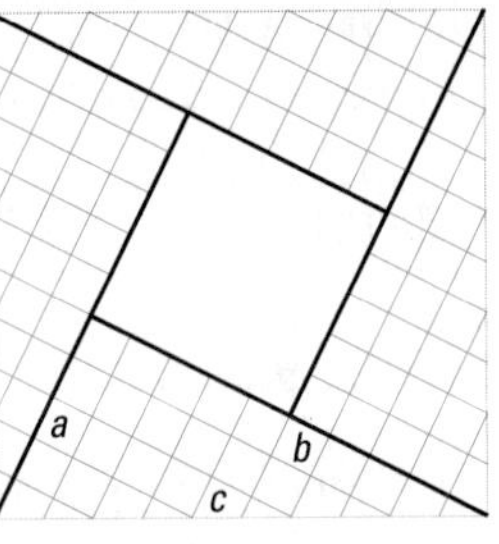

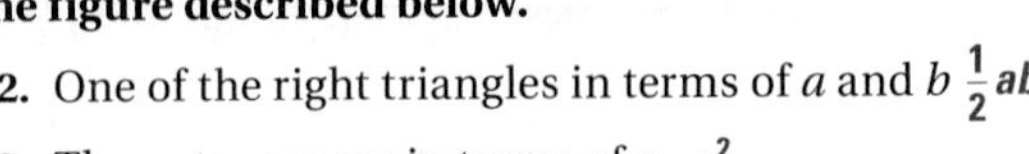

2. One of the right triangles in terms of a and b $\frac{1}{2}ab$
3. The outer square in terms of c c^2
4. The inner square in terms of a and b $(b - a)^2$
5. Use the relationship you determined in Exercise 1 and your results from Exercises 2–4 to write an equation that relates a, b, and c. Simplify the equation. $c^2 = 4 \cdot \frac{1}{2} \cdot ab + (b - a)^2 = 2ab + b^2 - 2ab + a^2 = b^2 + a^2$
6. **REASONING** The triangle shown is a right triangle. Find the value of x. *Explain* how you found your answer. **26. *Sample answer*: Use the equation found in Exercise 5, and let $a = 10$, $b = 24$, and $c = x$. Solve for x.**

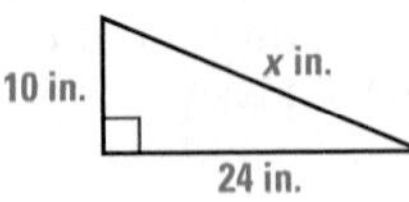

1 PLAN AND PREPARE

Explore the Concept

- Students will examine the relationship among the lengths of the sides of a right triangle.
- This activity leads into the study of the Pythagorean theorem in Example 1 in Lesson 11.4.

Materials

Each student will need:

- graph paper
- scissors

Recommended Time

Work activity: 10 min

Discuss results: 5 min

Grouping

Students should work individually.

2 TEACH

Tips for Success

Make sure students relate the total areas of the four triangles and the inner square to the area of the outer square.

Key Discovery

The relationship between side lengths of a right triangle with side lengths a, b, and c is $a^2 + b^2 = c^2$, where c is the longest side length.

3 ASSESS AND RETEACH

The longest side length of a right triangle is 15 inches. One of the other side lengths is 9 inches. What is the unknown side length? Justify your answer. **12 inches; Using $a^2 + b^2 = c^2$ results in $9^2 + x^2 = 15^2$ or $81 + x^2 = 225$. Solving for x gives $x = 12$.**

11.4 Apply the Pythagorean Theorem and Its Converse

Before You solved radical equations.

Now You will use the Pythagorean theorem and its converse.

Why? So you can examine angles in architecture, as in Ex. 35.

Key Vocabulary
- **hypotenuse**
- **legs of a right triangle**
- **Pythagorean theorem**

The **hypotenuse** of a right triangle is the side opposite the right angle. It is the longest side of a right triangle. The **legs** are the two sides that form the right angle.

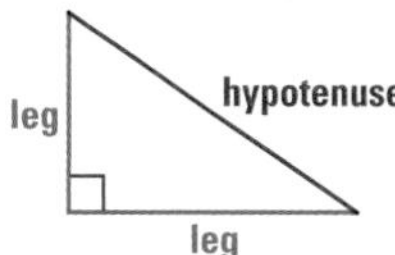

A *theorem* is a statement that can be proved true. The **Pythagorean theorem** states the relationship among the lengths of the sides of a right triangle.

KEY CONCEPT *For Your Notebook*

The Pythagorean Theorem

Words If a triangle is a right triangle, then the sum of the squares of the lengths of the legs equals the square of the length of the hypotenuse.

Algebra $a^2 + b^2 = c^2$

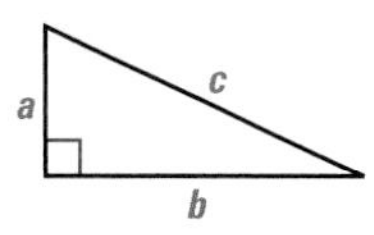

EXAMPLE 1 Use the Pythagorean theorem

Find the unknown length for the triangle shown.

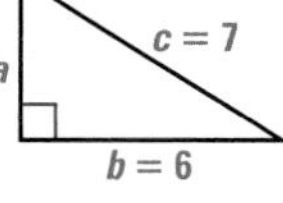

Solution

$a^2 + b^2 = c^2$	Pythagorean theorem
$a^2 + 6^2 = 7^2$	Substitute 6 for *b* and 7 for *c*.
$a^2 + 36 = 49$	Simplify.
$a^2 = 13$	Subtract 36 from each side.
$a = \sqrt{13}$	Take positive square root of each side.

▶ The side length a is $\sqrt{13}$.

Animated Algebra at classzone.com

REVIEW QUADRATIC EQUATIONS
For help with solving quadratic equations by using square roots, see p. 652.

✓ **GUIDED PRACTICE** for Example 1

1. The lengths of the legs of a right triangle are $a = 5$ and $b = 12$. Find c. **13**

1 PLAN AND PREPARE

Warm-Up Exercises

Transparency Available

Solve the equation.

1. $\sqrt{x-5} + 2 = 7$ **$x = 30$**
2. $2\sqrt{x} + 9 = 9$ **$x = 0$**
3. $\sqrt{x+11} - 3 = 5$ **$x = 53$**
4. Use the equation $v = \sqrt{64d}$, where v is velocity (in feet per second) and d is the distance (in feet) an object falls to find how far an object has dropped when its velocity is about 24 feet per second. **9 ft**

Notetaking Guide

Transparency Available

Promotes interactive learning and notetaking skills.

Pacing

Basic: 1 day
Average: 1 day
Advanced: 1 day
Block: 0.5 block with 11.5
- See *Teaching Guide/Lesson Plan.*

2 FOCUS AND MOTIVATE

Essential Question

Big Idea 3, p. 709

How do you use the Pythagorean theorem and its converse? **Tell students they will learn how to answer this question by using known side lengths of right triangles to find unknown lengths.**

NCTM STANDARDS

Standard 3: Analyze properties of 2-D shapes

Standard 6: Solve problems in math and other contexts

Resource Planning Guide

Chapter Resource Book
- Teaching Guide/Lesson Plan
- Practice levels A, B, C
- Study Guide
- Catch-up for Absent Students
- Application
- Challenge

Workbooks
- Notetaking Guide
- Practice Workbook

Teaching Options
- **Power Presentations** provides dynamic electronic teaching resources for the classroom.
- **Activity Generator** provides editable activities for all ability levels.

Interactive Technology
- Easy Planner
- Power Presentations
- Activity Generator
- Animated Algebra
- Test Generator
- Online Quiz
- eWorkbook
- eEdition
- @HomeTutor

Resources for English Learners
- Spanish Study Guide
- Multi-Language Visual Glossary
- Student Resources in Spanish

See also the *Differentiated Instruction Resources* for more strategies for meeting individual needs.

Motivating the Lesson

You are shopping for an entertainment center and you find one that you like. If you know the dimensions of the entertainment center and the dimensions of your television screen, you can use the Pythagorean theorem to determine whether your television set will fit in the entertainment center.

3 TEACH

Extra Example 1

Find the unknown length for the triangle shown. $\sqrt{65}$

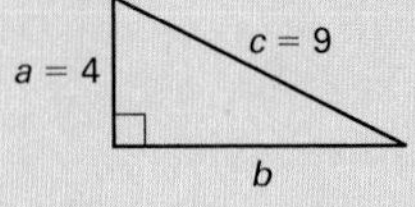

Animated Algebra classzone.com

An **Animated Algebra** activity is available online for **Example 1**. This activity is also part of **Power Presentations**.

Extra Example 2

A right triangle has one leg that is 1 foot longer than the other leg. The hypotenuse is $\sqrt{13}$ feet. Find the unknown lengths. **2 ft and 3 ft**

Extra Example 3

A person at *A* in the diagram throws a flying disc to a person at *C*. To the nearest foot, how far does the person throw the flying disc? **D**

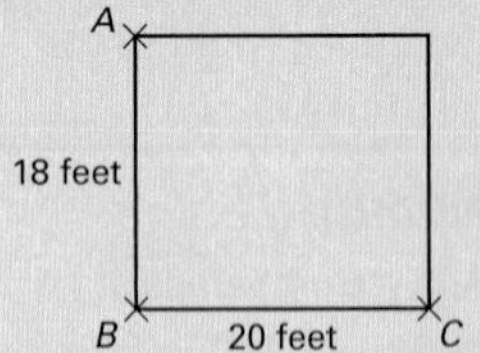

Ⓐ 6 feet Ⓑ 19 feet
Ⓒ 22 feet Ⓓ 27 feet

EXAMPLE 2 Use the Pythagorean theorem

A right triangle has one leg that is 2 inches longer than the other leg. The length of the hypotenuse is $\sqrt{10}$ inches. Find the unknown lengths.

Solution

Sketch a right triangle and label the sides with their lengths. Let x be the length of the shorter leg.

$a^2 + b^2 = c^2$	**Pythagorean theorem**
$x^2 + (x + 2)^2 = (\sqrt{10})^2$	**Substitute.**
$x^2 + x^2 + 4x + 4 = 10$	**Simplify.**
$2x^2 + 4x - 6 = 0$	**Write in standard form.**
$2(x - 1)(x + 3) = 0$	**Factor.**
$x - 1 = 0$ *or* $x + 3 = 0$	**Zero-product property**
$x = 1$ *or* $x = -3$	**Solve for *x*.**

▶ Because length is nonnegative, the solution $x = -3$ does not make sense. The legs have lengths of 1 inch and $1 + 2 = 3$ inches.

EXAMPLE 3 Standardized Test Practice

A soccer player makes a corner kick to another player, as shown. To the nearest yard, how far does the player kick the ball?

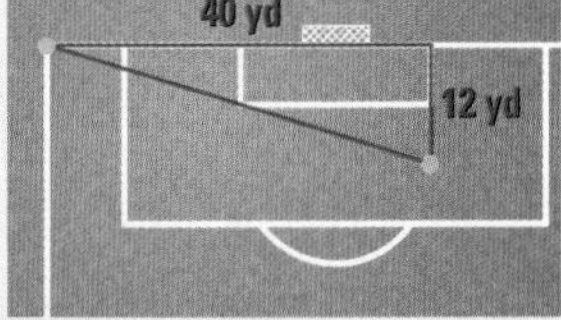

Ⓐ 7 yards Ⓑ 38 yards
Ⓒ 42 yards Ⓓ 52 yards

ELIMINATE CHOICES
The hypotenuse is the longest side of the triangle, so the length must be greater than 40 yards. Eliminate choices A and B.

Solution

The path of the kicked ball is the hypotenuse of a right triangle. The length of one leg is 12 yards, and the length of the other leg is 40 yards.

$c^2 = a^2 + b^2$	**Pythagorean theorem**
$c^2 = 12^2 + 40^2$	**Substitute 12 for *a* and 40 for *b*.**
$c^2 = 1744$	**Simplify.**
$c = \sqrt{1744} \approx 42$	**Take positive square root of each side.**

▶ The correct answer is C. Ⓐ Ⓑ Ⓒ Ⓓ

GUIDED PRACTICE for Examples 2 and 3

2. A right triangle has one leg that is 3 inches longer than the other leg. The length of the hypotenuse is 15 inches. Find the unknown lengths. **9 in. and 12 in.**

3. **SWIMMING** A rectangular pool is 30 feet wide and 60 feet long. You swim diagonally across the pool. To the nearest foot, how far do you swim? **67 ft**

Differentiated Instruction

English Learners The word *hypotenuse* comes from the Greek *hypo* meaning under and *teinein* meaning tension. Thus, the word could be translated as "under tension." Looking at a triangle such as the one in **Example 2**, the hypotenuse can be envisioned as a wire stretched from one side of the triangle to the other, with the wire being under tension.

See also the *Differentiated Instruction Resources* for more strategies.

REVIEW REASONING
For help with if-then statements and converses, see pp. 64, 110, and 319.

CONVERSE OF THE PYTHAGOREAN THEOREM Recall that when you reverse the hypothesis and conclusion of an if-then statement, the new statement is called the converse. Although not all converses of true statements are true, the converse of the Pythagorean theorem is true.

KEY CONCEPT *For Your Notebook*

Converse of the Pythagorean Theorem

If a triangle has side lengths a, b, and c such that $a^2 + b^2 = c^2$, then the triangle is a right triangle.

EXAMPLE 4 Determine right triangles

Tell whether the triangle with the given side lengths is a right triangle.

a. 8, 15, 17

$8^2 + 15^2 \stackrel{?}{=} 17^2$

$64 + 225 \stackrel{?}{=} 289$

$289 = 289$ ✓

▶ The triangle is a right triangle.

b. 5, 8, 9

$5^2 + 8^2 \stackrel{?}{=} 9^2$

$25 + 64 \stackrel{?}{=} 81$

$89 = 81$ ✗

▶ The triangle is *not* a right triangle.

EXAMPLE 5 Use the converse of the Pythagorean theorem

CONSTRUCTION A construction worker is making sure one corner of the foundation of a house is a right angle. To do this, the worker makes a mark 8 feet from the corner along one wall and another mark 6 feet from the same corner along the other wall. The worker then measures the distance between the two marks and finds the distance to be 10 feet. Is the corner a right angle?

Solution

$8^2 + 6^2 \stackrel{?}{=} 10^2$ — Check to see if $a^2 + b^2 = c^2$ when $a = 8$, $b = 6$, and $c = 10$.

$64 + 36 \stackrel{?}{=} 100$ — Simplify.

$100 = 100$ ✓ — Add.

▶ Because the sides that the construction worker measured form a right triangle, the corner of the foundation is a right angle.

GUIDED PRACTICE for Examples 4 and 5

Tell whether the triangle with the given side lengths is a right triangle.

4. 7, 11, 13 **not a right triangle** **5.** 15, 36, 39 **right triangle** **6.** 15, 112, 113 **right triangle**

7. WINDOW DESIGN A window has the shape of a triangle with side lengths of 120 centimeters, 120 centimeters, and 180 centimeters. Is the window a right triangle? *Explain.*

7. No. ***Sample answer:*** **$120^2 + 120^2 \neq 180^2$, so it cannot be a right triangle.**

Extra Example 4

Tell whether the triangle with the given side lengths is a right triangle.

a. 7, 23, 24 **no**

b. 5, 12, 13 **yes**

Key Question to Ask for Example 4

- Which side length in part a is the length of the hypotenuse of the triangle? **17**

Extra Example 5

A real estate lot is in the shape of a triangle. The side lengths are 48 feet, 55 feet, and 73 feet. The real estate agent told a potential buyer that one of the corners forms a right angle. Is the real estate agent correct? **yes**

Closing the Lesson

Have students summarize the major points of the lesson and answer the Essential Question: How do you use the Pythagorean theorem and its converse?

- **The Pythagorean theorem is $a^2 + b^2 = c^2$, where a and b are leg lengths of a right triangle and c is the length of the hypotenuse.**

To find an unknown length in a right triangle, use the Pythagorean theorem and substitute values for either the hypotenuse and one leg or both legs, and solve by isolating the variable and then taking the positive square root of each side. The hypotenuse is always the side with length c. Use the converse of the Pythagorean theorem to determine whether a triangle is a right triangle by checking to see if the sum of the squares of the shorter lengths is equal to the square of the longest length.

4 PRACTICE AND APPLY

Assignment Guide

Answer Transparencies available for all exercises

Basic:
Day 1: pp. 740–742
Exs. 1, 2, 3–15 odd, 16–30, 33–36, 39–49 odd

Average:
Day 1: pp. 740–742
Exs. 1, 2, 9–22, 26–31, 33–37, 40–50 even

Advanced:
Day 1: pp. 740–742
Exs. 1, 10–15, 17–22, 26–32*, 34–38*, 44–46, 48, 50

Block:
pp. 740–742
Exs. 1, 2, 9–22, 26–31, 33–37, 40–50 even (with 11.5)

Differentiated Instruction

See *Differentiated Instruction Resources* for suggestions on addressing the needs of a diverse classroom.

Homework Check

For a quick check of student understanding of key concepts, go over the following exercises:

Basic: 7, 18, 24, 33, 34
Average: 11, 20, 26, 33, 35
Advanced: 14, 22, 28, 34, 35

Extra Practice

- Student Edition, p. 948
- Chapter Resource Book: Practice levels A, B, C

Practice Worksheet

An easily-readable reduced practice page (with answers) for this lesson can be found on p.708C.

11.4 EXERCISES

HOMEWORK KEY
○ = **WORKED-OUT SOLUTIONS** on p. WS27 for Exs. 9, 23, and 35
★ = **STANDARDIZED TEST PRACTICE** Exs. 2, 15, 29, 30, and 37

SKILL PRACTICE

A

1. **VOCABULARY** Copy and complete: In a right triangle, the side opposite the right angle is called the __?__. **hypotenuse**

2. ★ **WRITING** *Explain* how you can tell whether a triangle with side lengths of 9, 12, and 15 is a right triangle. **If the sum of 9 squared and 12 squared is 15 squared, then it is a right triangle. If they are not equal, then it is not a right triangle.**

EXAMPLE 1 on p. 737 for Exs. 3–16

USING THE PYTHAGOREAN THEOREM **Let a and b represent the lengths of the legs of a right triangle, and let c represent the length of the hypotenuse. Find the unknown length.**

3. $a = 3, c = 5$ **$b = 4$**
4. $b = 3, c = 7$ **$a = 2\sqrt{10}$**
5. $a = 5, b = 6$ **$c = \sqrt{61}$**
6. $b = 5, c = 10$ **$a = 5\sqrt{3}$**
7. $a = 8, b = 8$ **$c = 8\sqrt{2}$**
8. $a = 5, b = 12$ **$c = 13$**
9. $a = 8, b = 12$ **$c = 4\sqrt{13}$**
10. $a = 7, c = 25$ **$b = 24$**
11. $b = 15, c = 17$ **$a = 8$**
12. $a = 9, c = 41$ **$b = 40$**
13. $b = 3, c = 3.4$ **$a = 1.6$**
14. $a = 1.2, c = 3.7$ **$b = 3.5$**

15. ★ **MULTIPLE CHOICE** A tennis court is 36 feet by 78 feet. What is the length of a diagonal? Round your answer to the nearest tenth of a foot. **C**

Ⓐ 42.0 feet Ⓑ 69.2 feet Ⓒ 85.9 feet Ⓓ 114.0 feet

16. **ERROR ANALYSIS** *Describe* and correct the error in finding the unknown length.

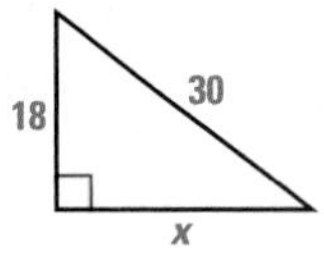

$18^2 + 30^2 = x^2$
$1224 = x^2$
$6\sqrt{34} = x$

The side with length 30 is the hypotenuse, and should be substituted for c in the Pythagorean theorem, not b; $18^2 + x^2 = 30^2$, $324 + x^2 = 900$, $x^2 = 576$, $x = 24$.

EXAMPLE 2 on p. 738 for Exs. 17–22

USING THE PYTHAGOREAN THEOREM **Find the unknown lengths.**

17.
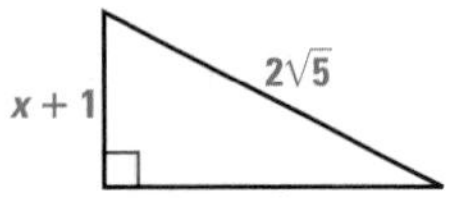

2, 4

18.
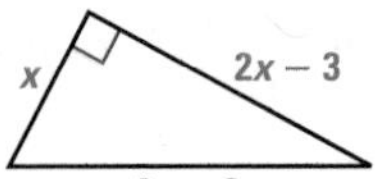

24, 45, 51

19.
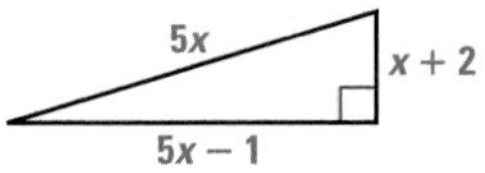

3, 4, 5, or 7, 24, 25

20. A right triangle has one leg that is 2 inches longer than the other leg. The length of the hypotenuse is $\sqrt{130}$ inches. Find the lengths of the legs. **7 in., 9 in.**

21. A right triangle has one leg that is 3 times as long as the other leg. The length of the hypotenuse is $\sqrt{40}$ inches. Find the lengths of the legs. **2 in., 6 in.**

22. A right triangle has one leg that is $\frac{1}{2}$ of the length of the other leg. The length of the hypotenuse is $6\sqrt{5}$ inches. Find the lengths of the legs. **6 in., 12 in.**

EXAMPLE 4 on p. 739 for Exs. 23–28

DETERMINING RIGHT TRIANGLES **Tell whether the triangle with the given side lengths is a right triangle.**

23. 2, 3, 4 **not a right triangle**
24. 9, 12, 15 **right triangle**
25. 8, 16, 18 **not a right triangle**
26. 9, 21, 24 **not a right triangle**
27. 11, 60, 61 **right triangle**
28. 24, 143, 145 **right triangle**

29. ★ **MULTIPLE CHOICE** What is the area of the largest square in the coordinate plane shown? **A**

Ⓐ 100 square units

Ⓑ 64 square units

Ⓒ 36 square units

Ⓓ 25 square units

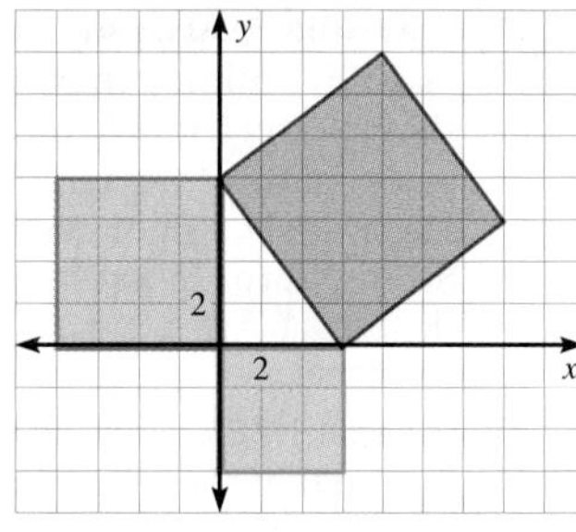

30. No. *Sample answer:* The unknown side might be the hypotenuse, or it might be a leg of the triangle. Each case would give a different answer.

B 30. ★ **WRITING** Given that two side lengths of a right triangle are 11 inches and 6 inches, is it possible to find the length of the third side? *Explain.*

31. **REASONING** A *Pythagorean triple* is a group of integers a, b, and c that represent the side lengths of a right triangle. For example, the integers 3, 4, and 5 form a Pythagorean triple. Choose any two positive integers m and n such that $m < n$. Then find a, b, and c as follows: $a = n^2 - m^2$, $b = 2mn$, and $c = n^2 + m^2$. Show that the numbers you generated form a Pythagorean triple. Then use the converse of the Pythagorean theorem to show that the equations for a, b, and c always generate Pythagorean triples. **See margin.**

C 32. **CHALLENGE** The edge length of the cube is 7 inches.

a. Find the value of x. $7\sqrt{2}$

b. Find the value of y. $7\sqrt{3}$

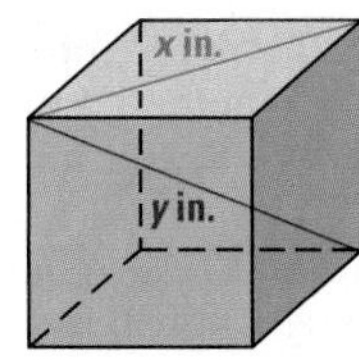

Problem Solving

EXAMPLES 3 and 5 on pp. 738–739 for Exs. 33–35

A 33. **ARCHITECTURE** An earthquake-resistant building has dampers built into its structure to help minimize damage caused by an earthquake. A section of the structural frame of such a building is shown. What is the length of the damper? Round your answer to the nearest foot. **16 ft**

@HomeTutor for problem solving help at classzone.com

34. No; the sum of the squares of the two shorter sides is not equal to the square of the longer side.

34. **SAILS** A sail has the shape of a triangle. The side lengths are 146 inches, 131 inches, and 84 inches. Is the sail a right triangle? *Explain.*

@HomeTutor for problem solving help at classzone.com

Avoiding Common Errors

Exercises 3–14 Some students may forget to take the square of both sides when finding a leg or hypotenuse length. Suggest that students substitute the side lengths into the Pythagorean theorem to make sure that their answers make sense.

Mathematical Reasoning

Exercises 17–22 Point out to students that if they find that one or both of the legs of the triangle are longer than the hypotenuse, given that the hypotenuse is the longest side of the triangle, then they know that they need to recalculate the side lengths of the triangle.

Reading Strategy

Exercise 29 Draw students' attention to the diagram and note that the 2 on the grid indicates the length of one unit on the grid, not the length of the sides of the squares.

Exercise 33 For more information about earthquake-resistant structures, visit the United States Geological Survey website at quake.wr.usgs.gov/prepare/factsheets/SaferStructures

31. ***Sample answer:*** **Let $m = 3$ and $n = 6$. Then $a = 6^2 - 3^2 = 27$, $b = 2(3)(6) = 36$, $c = 6^2 + 3^2 = 45$; substitute the values from the equation for a, b, and c in the Pythagorean theorem: $(n^2 - m^2)^2 + (2mn)^2 = (n^2 + m^2)^2$. Simplify to $n^4 - 2m^2n^2 + m^4 + 4m^2n^2 = n^4 + 2m^2n^2 + m^4$; $-2m^2n^2 + 4m^2n^2 = 2m^2n^2$; $2 = 2$. The equations are equal, so by the converse of the Pythagorean theorem, the lengths a, b, and c are a Pythagorean triple.**

5 ASSESS AND RETEACH

Daily Homework Quiz

Transparency Available

Let a and b represent the lengths of the legs of a right triangle, and let c represent the length of the hypotenuse. Find the unknown length.

1. $a = 4$, $c = 8$ **$b = \sqrt{48}$ or $4\sqrt{3}$**

2. $a = 5$, $b = 7$ **$c = \sqrt{74}$**

3. $b = 15$, $c = 21$ **$a = \sqrt{216}$ or $6\sqrt{6}$**

4. $a = 3$, $c = 11$ **$b = \sqrt{112}$ or $4\sqrt{7}$**

5. A triangular garden has side lengths of 5 feet, 12 feet, and 14 feet. Is the garden in the shape of a right triangle? **no**

Online Quiz

Available at **classzone.com**

Diagnosis/Remediation

- Practice A, B, C in Chapter Resource Book
- Study Guide in Chapter Resource Book
- Practice Workbook
- @HomeTutor

Challenge

Additional challenge is available in the Chapter Resource Book.

35. **FLATIRON BUILDING** A top view of the Flatiron Building in New York City is shown. The triangle indicates the basic shape of the building's roof. Is the triangle a right triangle? *Explain.* **No; the sum of the squares of the two shorter sides is not equal to the square of the longer side.**

B **36.** **SCREEN SIZES** The size of a television is indicated by the length of a diagonal of the television screen. The aspect ratio of a television screen is the ratio of the length of the screen to the width of the screen. The size of a particular television is 30 inches, and its aspect ratio is 4 : 3. What are the width and the length of the television screen? **18 in., 24 in.**

37. ★ **EXTENDED RESPONSE** The *Wheel of Theodorus* is a figure formed by a chain of right triangles with consecutive triangles sharing a common side. The hypotenuse of one triangle becomes a leg of the next, as shown.

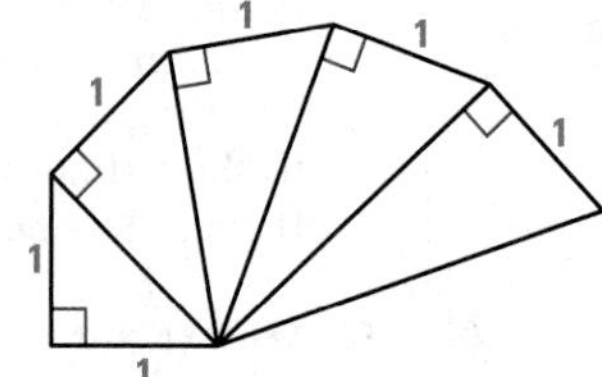

a. Calculate What is the length of the longest hypotenuse in the diagram? **$\sqrt{6}$**

b. Extend Extend the diagram to include two more triangles. What is the length of the longest hypotenuse in the new diagram? **$\sqrt{8}$**

c. Analyze Find a formula for the length of the hypotenuse of the nth triangle. *Explain* how you found your answer. **$c_n = \sqrt{n+1}$; *Sample answer*: A list of the hypotenuses for the first few triangles is $\sqrt{2}, \sqrt{3}, \sqrt{4}, \sqrt{5}, \ldots$. A general formula for this series is $c_n = \sqrt{n+1}$.**

C **38.** **CHALLENGE** A baseball diamond has the shape of a square with side lengths of 90 feet. A catcher wants to get a player running from first base to second base out, so the catcher must throw the ball to second base before the runner reaches second base.

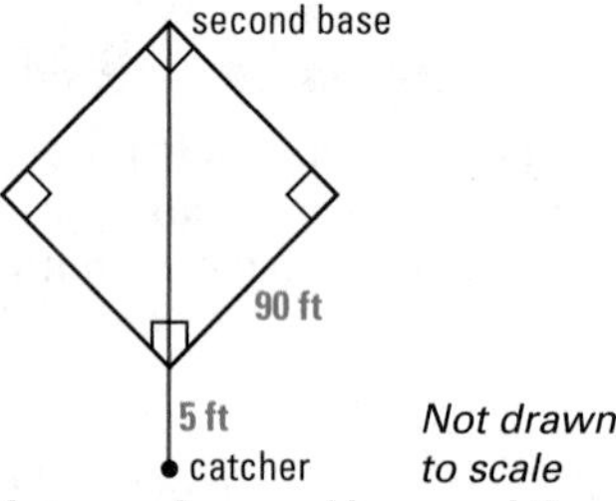

a. The catcher is 5 feet behind home plate. How far does the catcher have to throw the ball to reach second base? Round your answer to the nearest foot. **132 ft**

b. The catcher throws the ball at a rate of 90 feet per second when the player is 30 feet away from second base. Will the catcher get the player out if the player is running at a rate of 22 feet per second? *Explain.*
No. *Sample answer*: The ball will take about 1.47 seconds to reach second base, and the player will reach the base in about 1.36 seconds.

MIXED REVIEW

PREVIEW
Prepare for Lesson 11.5 in Exs. 39–46.

Plot the point in a coordinate plane. *Describe* the location of the point. (p. 206)
39–46. See margin for art.

39. (5, 4) **Quadrant I** **40.** (−2, 6) **Quadrant II** **41.** (−1, −3) **Quadrant III** **42.** (0, 5) ***y*-axis**

43. (0, 0) **origin** **44.** (−8, −2) **Quadrant III** **45.** (−1.5, 0) ***x*-axis** **46.** (3.25, −2.5) **Quadrant IV**

Evaluate the expression.

47. $5x^2$ when $x = 3$ (p. 8) **45** **48.** $-|x| - 8$ when $x = -2$ (p. 64) **−10**

49. $\sqrt{x-y}$ when $x = 9$, $y = -7$ (p. 110) **4** **50.** $\sqrt{xy}$ when $x = 27$, $y = 3$ (p. 110) **9**

39–46. See Additional Answers beginning on p. AA1.

11.5 Distance in The Coordinate Plane

MATERIALS • graph paper

QUESTION How can you find the distance between two points?

EXPLORE Find the distance between points $A(-3, -2)$ and $B(4, -2)$

STEP 1 *Plot points*

Plot the points $A(-3, -2)$ and $B(4, -2)$ in the same coordinate plane.

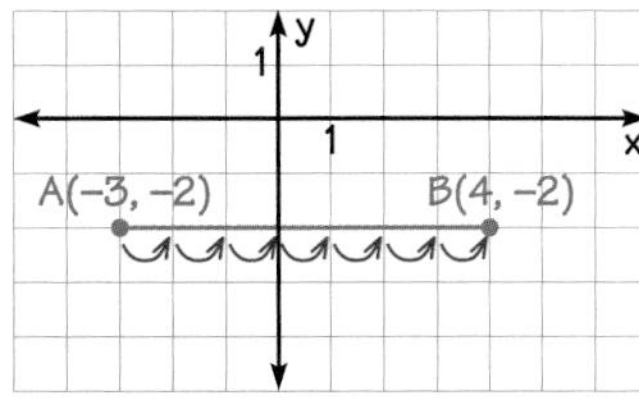

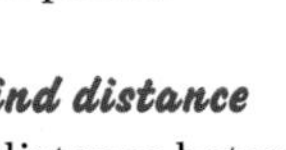

STEP 2 *Find distance*

Find the distance between the points by counting the grid spaces between them. **7 units**

STEP 3 *Find distance*

Find the distance by subtracting the x-coordinate of point A from the x-coordinate of point B. **7 units**

STEP 4 *Compare results*

How does your result from Step 2 compare with your result from Step 3? **They are the same.**

DRAW CONCLUSIONS Use your observations to complete these exercises

1. Subtract the x-coordinate of point B from the x-coordinate of point A. How is the value different from the values found in Steps 2 and 3 above? How could you make them the same? **−7; it is the opposite of the value in Step 2 and 3; take the absolute value.**
2. Assume points $C(x_1, y_1)$ and $D(x_2, y_2)$ lie on the same horizontal line. Write an expression that can be used to find the distance between the points. $|x_2 - x_1|$ **or** $|x_1 - x_2|$
3. Assume points $C(x_1, y_1)$ and $D(x_2, y_2)$ lie on the same vertical line. Write an expression that can be used to find the distance between the points. Check your expression using $(-2, 4)$ and $(-2, -3)$. $|y_2 - y_1|$ **or** $|y_1 - y_2|$**; 7**

In Exercises 4–12, find the distance between the two points.

4. $(2, 3), (-5, 3)$ **7**
5. $(0, -4), (7, -4)$ **7**
6. $(-1, 5), (2, 5)$ **3**
7. $(4, -6), (6, -6)$ **2**
8. $(-5, -4), (-2, -4)$ **3**
9. $(2, 8), (2, 3)$ **5**
10. $(5, -6), (5, -2)$ **4**
11. $(0, -4), (0, 2)$ **6**
12. $(-3, 0), (-3, 6)$ **6**

13. **REASONING** Plot the points $A(6, 5)$, $B(2, 5)$, and $C(6, 2)$. Find the distance between points A and B. Find the distance between points A and C. Use the distances and the Pythagorean theorem to find the distance between points B and C. **See margin for art; 4; 3; 5.**

1 PLAN AND PREPARE

Explore the Concept

- Students will find the distance between two points on a coordinate plane.
- This activity leads into the study of the distance formula in Example 1 in Lesson 11.5.

Materials

Each student will need graph paper.

Recommended Time

Work activity: 10 min

Discuss results: 5 min

Grouping

Students should work individually.

2 TEACH

Tips for Success

In Step 3, watch for students who subtract the y-coordinate of point A from the x-coordinate of point B. Point out that the red arrows on the diagram refer to the number of grid lines between the points, not to the coordinates of the points.

Key Discovery

On a coordinate plane, find the horizontal distance between two points by subtracting the x-coordinates and find the vertical distance by subtracting the y-coordinates.

3 ASSESS AND RETEACH

Show how to find the vertical distance between points (x_1, y_1) and (x_2, y_2) for $(6, 4)$ and $(8, 9)$. **Use $y_2 - y_1$, or $9 - 4$, to find a vertical distance of 5 units.**

13.

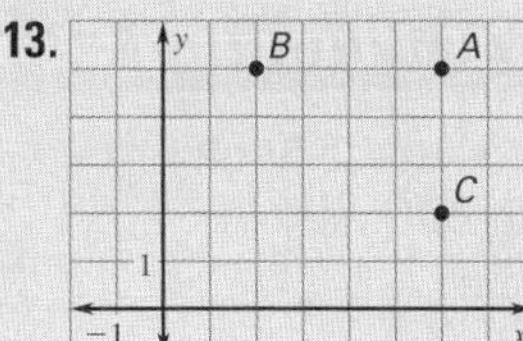

11.5 Apply the Distance and Midpoint Formulas

Before You used the Pythagorean theorem and its converse.

Now You will use the distance and midpoint formulas.

Why? So you can calculate distances traveled, as in Ex. 47.

1 PLAN AND PREPARE

Warm-Up Exercises

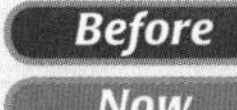

Transparency Available

1. Is a triangle with side lengths 9, 40, 41 a right triangle? **yes**
2. A triangular window is 14 inches wide and 18 inches high. The height and width of the window meet at a right angle. What is the length of the other side to the nearest whole number? **23 in.**

Notetaking Guide

Transparency Available

Promotes interactive learning and notetaking skills.

Pacing

Basic: 1 day
Average: 1 day
Advanced: 1 day
Block: 0.5 block with 11.4
• See *Teaching Guide/Lesson Plan.*

2 FOCUS AND MOTIVATE

Essential Question

Big Idea 3, p. 709

How do you use the distance and midpoint formulas? **Tell students they will learn how to answer this question by using coordinates to find the distance between two points and the midpoint of two points.**

NCTM STANDARDS

Standard 3: Analyze properties of 2-D shapes; Describe spatial relationships using coordinate geometry

Key Vocabulary
- **distance formula**
- **midpoint**
- **midpoint formula**

To find the distance between the points $A(-2, -1)$ and $B(3, 2)$, draw a right triangle, as shown. The lengths of the legs of the right triangle are as follows.

$$AC = |3 - (-2)| = 5$$

$$BC = |-1 - 2| = 3$$

You can use the Pythagorean theorem to find AB, the length of the hypotenuse of the right triangle.

$(AB)^2 = (AC)^2 + (BC)^2$ **Pythagorean theorem**

$AB = \sqrt{(AC)^2 + (BC)^2}$ **Take positive square root of each side.**

$AB = \sqrt{5^2 + 3^2} = \sqrt{34}$ **Substitute 5 for *AC* and 3 for *BC* and simplify.**

This example suggests that you can find the distance between two points in a coordinate plane using the following formula, called the **distance formula**.

KEY CONCEPT *For Your Notebook*

The Distance Formula

The distance d between any two points (x_1, y_1) and (x_2, y_2) is

$$d = \sqrt{(x_2 - x_1)^2 + (y_2 - y_1)^2}.$$

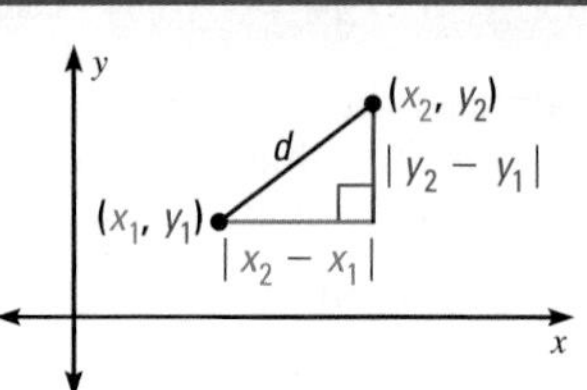

EXAMPLE 1 Find the distance between two points

Find the distance between (−1, 3) and (5, 2).

Let $(x_1, y_1) = (-1, 3)$ and $(x_2, y_2) = (5, 2)$.

$d = \sqrt{(x_2 - x_1)^2 + (y_2 - y_1)^2}$ **Distance formula**

$= \sqrt{(5 - (-1))^2 + (2 - 3)^2}$ **Substitute.**

$= \sqrt{6^2 + (-1)^2} = \sqrt{37}$ **Simplify.**

▶ The distance between the points is $\sqrt{37}$ units.

Resource Planning Guide

Chapter Resource Book
- Teaching Guide/Lesson Plan
- Practice levels A, B, C
- Study Guide
- Catch-up for Absent Students
- Problem Solving Workshop
- Challenge

Workbooks
- Notetaking Guide
- Practice Workbook

Teaching Options
- **Power Presentations** provides dynamic electronic teaching resources for the classroom.
- **Activity Generator** provides editable activities for all ability levels.

Interactive Technology
- Easy Planner
- Power Presentations
- Activity Generator
- Animated Algebra
- Test Generator
- Online Quiz
- eWorkbook
- eEdition
- @HomeTutor

Resources for English Learners
- Spanish Study Guide
- Multi-Language Visual Glossary
- Student Resources in Spanish

See also the *Differentiated Instruction Resources* for more strategies for meeting individual needs.

EXAMPLE 2 Find a missing coordinate

The distance between (3, −5) and (7, *b*) is 5 units. Find the value of *b*.

Solution

Use the distance formula with $d = 5$. Let $(x_1, y_1) = (3, -5)$ and $(x_2, y_2) = (7, b)$. Then solve for b.

$d = \sqrt{(x_2 - x_1)^2 + (y_2 - y_1)^2}$	Distance formula
$5 = \sqrt{(7-3)^2 + (b - (-5))^2}$	Substitute.
$5 = \sqrt{16 + b^2 + 10b + 25}$	Multiply.
$5 = \sqrt{b^2 + 10b + 41}$	Simplify.
$25 = b^2 + 10b + 41$	Square each side.
$0 = b^2 + 10b + 16$	Write in standard form.
$0 = (b+2)(b+8)$	Factor.
$b + 2 = 0$ *or* $b + 8 = 0$	Zero-product property
$b = -2$ *or* $b = -8$	Solve for *b*.

▶ The value of b is −2 or −8.

INTERPRET GEOMETRICALLY
The point (7, *b*) lies on the line $x = 7$. If you let the point (3, −5) be the center of a circle with radius 5, you will see that the circle crosses the line at (7, −2) and (7, −8).

✓ **GUIDED PRACTICE** for Examples 1 and 2

Find the distance between the points.

1. (3, 0), (3, 6) **6**
2. (−2, 1), (2, 5) $4\sqrt{2}$
3. (6, −2), (−4, 7) $\sqrt{181}$
4. The distance between (1, *a*) and (4, 2) is 3 units. Find the value of *a*. **2**

MIDPOINT The **midpoint** of a line segment is the point on the segment that is equidistant from the endpoints. You can find the coordinates of the midpoint of a line segment using the following formula, called the **midpoint formula**.

KEY CONCEPT *For Your Notebook*

The Midpoint Formula

The midpoint M of the line segment with endpoints $A(x_1, y_1)$ and $B(x_2, y_2)$ is

$$M\left(\frac{x_1 + x_2}{2}, \frac{y_1 + y_2}{2}\right).$$

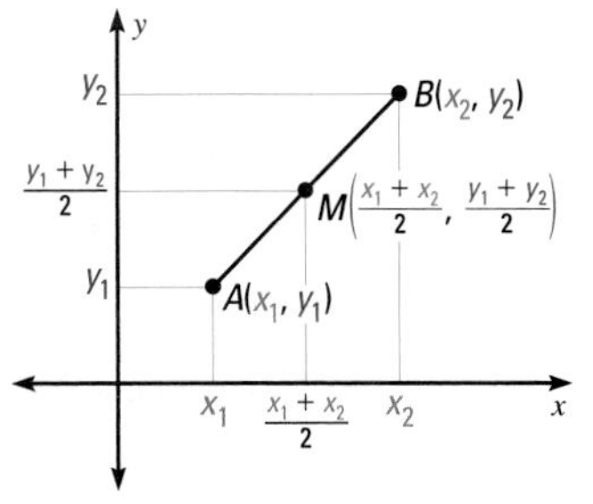

Motivating the Lesson

You are trying to find a place to meet a friend who lives in a different part of the city. By superimposing a coordinate grid over a map, you can use coordinates and the midpoint formula to find a meeting place that is about halfway for both of you.

3 TEACH

Extra Example 1

Find the distance between (−3, 1) and (2, 3). **$\sqrt{29}$ units**

Key Questions to Ask for Example 1

- Can either addend in the radicand be negative? Explain. **No; even if you obtain a negative value by subtracting two coordinates, the value is squared and a squared value is always positive.**
- Does it matter which ordered pair is first when using the distance formula? Explain. **No, either ordered pair can be first since the distance between the two points is the same no matter the order.**
- Is the distance between the two points one of the legs of the right triangle or the hypotenuse? **The distance between the points represents the hypotenuse of the triangle.**

Extra Example 2

The distance between (4, *a*) and (1, 6) is 5 units. Find the value of *a*. **The value of *a* is 2 or 10.**

Differentiated Instruction

Kinesthetic Learners Students may learn the distance formula more easily by first doing a few examples involving plotting two points, drawing a related right triangle, and applying the properties of a right triangle. For **Example 1**, students would construct a triangle with side lengths 6 and 1 and then apply the Pythagorean theorem. This should help students see the relationship between the horizontal and vertical distances between the two points and the side lengths of the right triangle.

See also the *Differentiated Instruction Resources* for more strategies.

Extra Example 3

What is the midpoint of the line segment with endpoints $(-3, -1)$ and $(7, -5)$? **B**

Ⓐ $(-3, 2)$ Ⓑ $(2, -3)$
Ⓒ $(-3, 5)$ Ⓓ $(5, -3)$

Animated Algebra classzone.com

An **Animated Algebra** activity is available online for **Example 3**. This activity is also part of **Power Presentations**.

Extra Example 4

The grid shows the locations of several buildings in a town. Which building is closest to the midpoint of the library and fire station? **the bank**

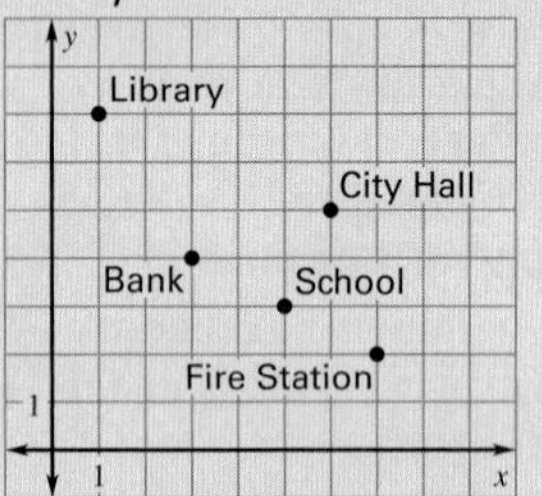

Closing the Lesson

Have students summarize the major points of the lesson and answer the Essential Question: How do you use the distance and midpoint formulas?

- **The distance formula is** $d = \sqrt{(x_2 - x_1)^2 + (y_2 - y_1)^2}$.
- **The midpoint formula is** $M\left(\frac{x_1 + x_2}{2}, \frac{y_1 + y_2}{2}\right)$.

To find the distance between two points, substitute coordinates in the distance formula and simplify. To find the coordinates of the midpoint of two points, substitute the endpoint coordinates in the midpoint formula and simplify.

★ EXAMPLE 3 Standardized Test Practice

What is the midpoint of the line segment with endpoints $(-1, -2)$ and $(3, -4)$?

Ⓐ $(2, -1)$ Ⓑ $(1, -3)$ Ⓒ $(-2, 1)$ Ⓓ $(-3, 1)$

ELIMINATE CHOICES
The y-coordinate of the midpoint has to be negative because it is an average of the y-coordinates of the endpoints of the line segment. Eliminate choices C and D.

Solution

Let $(x_1, y_1) = (-1, -2)$ and $(x_2, y_2) = (3, -4)$.

$$\left(\frac{x_1 + x_2}{2}, \frac{y_1 + y_2}{2}\right) = \left(\frac{-1 + 3}{2}, \frac{-2 + (-4)}{2}\right) \quad \textbf{Substitute.}$$

$$= (1, -3) \quad \textbf{Simplify.}$$

▶ The correct answer is B. Ⓐ Ⓑ Ⓒ Ⓓ

Animated Algebra at classzone.com

EXAMPLE 4 Solve a real-world problem

ANOTHER WAY
For alternative methods for solving Example 4, turn to page 751 for the **Problem Solving Workshop**.

SIGHTSEEING You and a friend are sightseeing in Washington, D.C. You are at the National Gallery of Art, and your friend is at the Washington Monument, as shown on the map. You want to meet at the landmark that is closest to the midpoint of your locations. At which landmark should you meet?

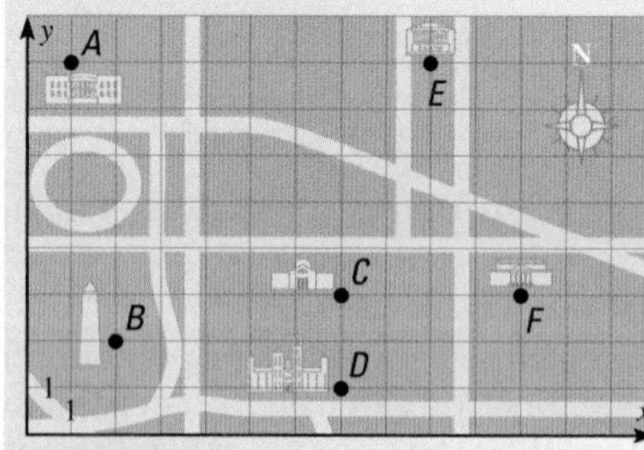

SIGHTS IN WASHINGTON, D.C.
A) White House
B) Washington Monument
C) Natural History Museum
D) Smithsonian Institution
E) National Portrait Gallery
F) National Gallery of Art

Solution

Your coordinates are $(11, 3)$, and your friend's coordinates are $(2, 2)$. First, find the midpoint of your locations, which is

$$\left(\frac{x_1 + x_2}{2}, \frac{y_1 + y_2}{2}\right) = \left(\frac{11 + 2}{2}, \frac{3 + 2}{2}\right) = (6.5, 2.5).$$

Next, find the distance from the midpoint to the Smithsonian Institution, located at $(7, 1)$, and to the Natural History Museum, located at $(7, 3)$.

Distance to Smithsonian Institution: $d = \sqrt{(6.5 - 7)^2 + (2.5 - 1)^2} \approx 1.58$ units

Distance to Natural History Museum: $d = \sqrt{(6.5 - 7)^2 + (2.5 - 3)^2} \approx 0.71$ unit

▶ You should meet at the Natural History Museum.

2. No. *Sample answer*: Since the differences are squared, any negative differences would be eliminated, so the points can be interchanged without affecting the distance.

✓ **GUIDED PRACTICE** for Examples 3 and 4

5. Find the midpoint of the line segment with endpoints (4, 3) and (2, 5). **(3, 4)**

6. **WHAT IF?** In Example 4, suppose you are at the Smithsonian and your friend is at the National Portrait Gallery. Which landmark on the map is closest to the midpoint of your locations? **Natural History Museum**

11.5 EXERCISES

HOMEWORK KEY
○ = **WORKED-OUT SOLUTIONS** on p. WS27 for Exs. 7, 23, and 49
★ = **STANDARDIZED TEST PRACTICE** Exs. 2, 15, 34, 37, 45, and 50

SKILL PRACTICE

1. **VOCABULARY** Copy and complete: The point on a line segment that is equidistant from its endpoints is called the _?_ of the line segment. **midpoint**

2. ★ **WRITING** You want to know the distance between the points (3, 2) and (6, 8). Does it matter which point represents (x_1, y_1) and which point represents (x_2, y_2)? *Explain.*

EXAMPLE 1 on p. 744 for Exs. 3–15

FINDING DISTANCE **Find the distance between the two points.**

3. (4, 8), (4, 7) **1**
4. (5, −9), (8, −9) **3**
5. (2, −2), (6, 1) **5**
6. (5, 1), (0, 3) $\sqrt{29}$
7. (−4, 1), (3, −1) $\sqrt{53}$
8. (2, 4), (−5, 0) $\sqrt{65}$
9. (−6, 7), (2, 9) $2\sqrt{17}$
10. (−10, 8), (2, −3) $\sqrt{265}$
11. (7, 5), (−12, −1) $\sqrt{397}$
12. (4, 2.5), (2.5, −3) $\frac{\sqrt{130}}{2}$
13. $\left(5, -\frac{1}{2}\right), \left(-3, \frac{5}{2}\right)$ $\sqrt{73}$
14. $\left(-\frac{3}{4}, \frac{7}{2}\right), \left(\frac{5}{4}, \frac{1}{4}\right)$ $\frac{\sqrt{233}}{4}$

15. ★ **MULTIPLE CHOICE** What is the distance between (4.5, 1) and (−2.5, −5)? **D**

Ⓐ $\sqrt{13}$ Ⓑ $\sqrt{24}$ Ⓒ $\sqrt{68.5}$ Ⓓ $\sqrt{85}$

EXAMPLE 2 on p. 745 for Exs. 16–21

FINDING MISSING COORDINATES **The distance d between two points is given. Find the value of b.**

16. (0, b), (3, 1); $d = 5$ **−3, 5**
17. (13, −3), (b, 2); $d = 13$ **1, 25**
18. (−9, −2), (b, 5); $d = 7$ **−9**
19. (b, −6), (−5, 2); $d = 10$ **−11, 1**
20. (−6, 8), (−1, b); $d = \sqrt{29}$ **6, 10**
21. (b, −4), (4, 7); $d = 11\sqrt{2}$ **−7, 15**

EXAMPLE 3 on p. 746 for Exs. 22–34

FINDING THE MIDPOINT **Find the midpoint of the line segment with the given endpoints.**

22. (0, 1), (8, 3) **(4, 2)**
23. (6, −3), (4, −7) **(5, −5)**
24. (−5, 0), (1, 14) **(−2, 7)**
25. (11, −4), (−9, −4) **(1, −4)**
26. (−6, 6), (4, −4) **(−1, 1)**
27. (−17, −8), (−5, −4)
28. (2, 7), (5, 3) **(3.5, 5)**
29. (−2, 3), (−2, −3) **(−2, 0)**
30. (12, −5), (−12, 4) **(0, −0.5)**
31. (−15, −8), (−1, −1) **(−8, −4.5)**
32. (18, −17), (12, −7) **(15, −12)**
33. (−50, −75), (8, 9) **(−21, −33)**

27. **(−11, −6)**

34. ★ **MULTIPLE CHOICE** What is the midpoint of the line segment with endpoints (2, 1) and (4, 7)? **C**

Ⓐ (1, 3) Ⓑ (1.5, 5.5) Ⓒ (3, 4) Ⓓ (4, 3)

4 PRACTICE AND APPLY

Assignment Guide

Answer Transparencies available for all exercises

Basic:
Day 1: pp. 747–750
Exs. 1, 2, 3–33 odd, 34–38, 47–50, 53–63 odd

Average:
Day 1: pp. 747–750
Exs. 1, 2, 10–15, 19–21, 30–44, 48–51, 54–64 even

Advanced:
Day 1: pp. 747–750
Exs. 1, 11–15, 20, 21, 31–46*, 49–52*, 56, 58, 62, 64

Block:
pp. 747–750
Exs. 1, 2, 10–15, 19–21, 30–44, 48–51, 54–64 even (with 11.4)

Differentiated Instruction

See *Differentiated Instruction Resources* for suggestions on addressing the needs of a diverse classroom.

Homework Check

For a quick check of student understanding of key concepts, go over the following exercises:
Basic: 9, 17, 27, 47, 48
Average: 12, 20, 32, 48, 49
Advanced: 14, 21, 32, 49, 50

Extra Practice

- Student Edition, p. 948
- Chapter Resource Book: Practice levels A, B, C

Practice Worksheet

An easily-readable reduced practice page (with answers) for this lesson can be found on p. 708C.

Avoiding Common Errors

Exercises 16–21 Remind students that there are often two values for the missing coordinate. Encourage them to check both values against the distance formula to confirm that both result in the same distance.

Study Strategy

Exercises 38–40 Suggest that students plot the points in the coordinate plane. This will help them visualize the solution.

35. ***Sample answer:*** **The square of the difference in the *x* values and the square of the difference in the *y* values should be added, not subtracted;** $d = \sqrt{(3-(-17))^2 + (8-(-2))^2} = \sqrt{400 + 100} = \sqrt{500} = 10\sqrt{5}$.

36. ***Sample answer:*** **The *x* terms should be added, not subtracted, as should the *y* terms;** $\left(\frac{3+(-17)}{2}, \frac{8+(-2)}{2}\right) = \left(\frac{-14}{2}, \frac{6}{3}\right) = (-7, 3)$.

46. ***Sample answer:*** **(0, 1) and (0, −1), (1, 0) and (−1, 0),** $\left(\frac{\sqrt{2}}{2}, \frac{\sqrt{2}}{2}\right)$, **and** $\left(-\frac{\sqrt{2}}{2}, -\frac{\sqrt{2}}{2}\right)$**; since (0, 0) is the midpoint, the *x*-coordinates must be opposites as well as the *y*-coordinates. Choose 3 lines that go through the origin; $x = 0$, $y = 0$, and $y = x$. For $x = 0$, start at the origin and move 1 unit up and 1 unit down to find the points (0, 1) and (0, −1). For $y = 0$, start at the origin and move 1 unit right and 1 unit left to find the points (1, 0) and (−1, 0). For $y = x$, the points must be in the forms (a, a) and $(-a, -a)$. Use the distance formula to find a.** $2 = \sqrt{(2a)^2 + (2a)^2}$, $2 = \sqrt{8a^2}$, $4 = 8a^2$, $\frac{1}{2} = a^2$, $a = \frac{\sqrt{2}}{2}$; **so** $-a = -\frac{\sqrt{2}}{2}$, **giving the points** $\left(\frac{\sqrt{2}}{2}, \frac{\sqrt{2}}{2}\right)$ **and** $\left(-\frac{\sqrt{2}}{2}, -\frac{\sqrt{2}}{2}\right)$.

B **ERROR ANALYSIS** ***Describe*** **and correct the error in finding the distance between (−17, −2) and (3, 8), and the midpoint of the line segment with endpoints (−17, −2) and (3, 8).** **35, 36. See margin.**

35.
Distance:
$d = \sqrt{(3-(-17))^2 - (8-(-2))^2}$
$= \sqrt{400 - 100}$
$= \sqrt{300} = 10\sqrt{3}$

36.
Midpoint:
$\left(\frac{3-(-17)}{2}, \frac{8-(-2)}{2}\right) = \left(\frac{20}{2}, \frac{10}{2}\right)$
$= (10, 5)$

37. ★ **MULTIPLE CHOICE** What is the distance between point *A* and the midpoint of the line segment that joins points *A* and *B*? **A**

Ⓐ $\sqrt{17}$ units Ⓑ $3\sqrt{5}$ units

Ⓒ $2\sqrt{17}$ units Ⓓ $\sqrt{117}$ units

FINDING ENDPOINTS **The midpoint and an endpoint of a line segment are given. Find the other endpoint.**

38. endpoint: (1, 2)
midpoint: (−6, 4)
(−13, 6)

39. endpoint: (−2, −4)
midpoint: (3, −3)
(8, −2)

40. endpoint: (7, 5)
midpoint: (1, 0.5)
(−5, −4)

RIGHT TRIANGLES **Use the distance formula and the converse of the Pythagorean theorem to determine whether the points are vertices of a right triangle.**

41. (3, 5), (3, −1), (−2, −1) **right triangle**

42. (3, −1), (1, 4), (−3, 0) **not a right triangle**

43. (−5, −2), (0, −4), (−2, 3) **not a right triangle**

44. (−2, 1), (−4, 3), (−8, −1) **right triangle**

45. ***Sample answer:*** **Use the distance formula to find the distance between the midpoint and each of the endpoints. If they are equal, the midpoint is equidistant from each endpoint.**

C **45.** ★ **WRITING** *Explain* how you can use the distance formula to verify that the midpoint of a line segment is equidistant from its endpoints.

46. **CHALLENGE** The midpoint of a line segment is (0, 0). The line segment has a length of 2 units. Give three possible sets of endpoints for the line segment. *Explain* how you found your answer. **See margin.**

PROBLEM SOLVING

EXAMPLE 4 A on p. 746 for Exs. 47–50

47. **MULTI-STEP PROBLEM** A rescue helicopter and an ambulance are both traveling from the dispatch center to the scene of an accident. The distance between consecutive grid lines represents 1 mile.

a. Find the distance that the ambulance traveled (red route). **10 mi**

b. How many times greater is the distance that the ambulance traveled than the distance that the helicopter traveled (blue route)?

47b. $\sqrt{2}$ **times greater**

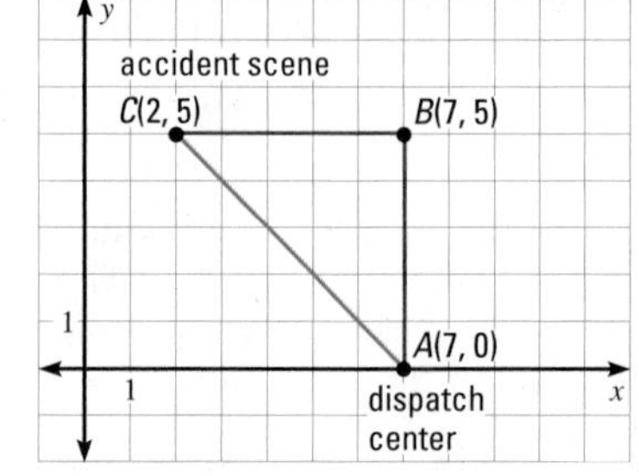

@HomeTutor for problem solving help at classzone.com

○ = WORKED-OUT SOLUTIONS on p. WS1 ★ = STANDARDIZED TEST PRACTICE

48. SUBWAY A student is taking the subway to the public library. The student can get off the subway at one of two stops, as shown in the map. The distance between consecutive grid lines represents 0.25 mile. Which stop is closer to the library? **stop 2**

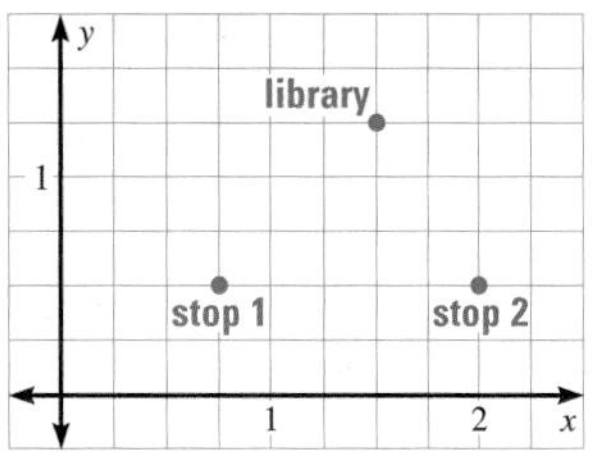

@HomeTutor for problem solving help at classzone.com

49. ARCHAEOLOGY Underwater archaeologists sometimes lay survey grids of the site they are studying. A sample survey grid is shown. The distance between consecutive grid lines represents 50 feet.

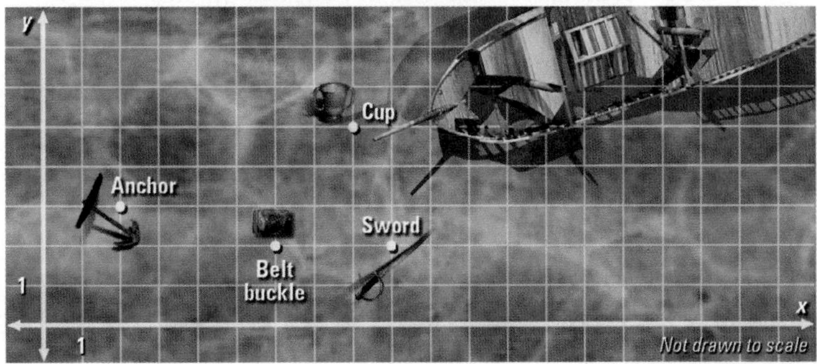

a. Which is shorter, the distance between the anchor and the sword or the distance between the anchor and the cup? **the anchor and the cup**

b. Which two objects are closest together? Which two objects are farthest apart? **the belt buckle and the sword; the anchor and the sword**

B **50. ★ SHORT RESPONSE** The point of no return in aviation is the farthest point to which a plane can fly and still have enough fuel to return to its starting place or to fly to an alternative landing destination. After a plane passes the point of no return, it must fly to its planned destination. The distance between consecutive grid lines represents 50 nautical miles.

y
airport B
(4, 7)
airport A
(1, 1)
1
1
x

a. The flight path of a plane is from airport A to airport B. The plane is currently at the midpoint of the flight path. How far away is the plane from airport A? Round your answer to the nearest nautical mile. **168 mi**

b. The plane's point of no return is calculated to be 200 nautical miles. Has the plane reached its point of no return? *Explain.*
No. *Sample answer*: The plane has only traveled about 168 miles.

REVIEW PARALLEL LINES
For help with using slope to determine whether lines are parallel, see p. 246.

51. ROAD SIGN Describe the quadrilateral formed by the sides of the road sign shown by answering the following questions.

- Are opposite sides parallel? **yes**
- Do the sides form right angles? **yes**
- Which sides, if any, are congruent? **all of them**

The quadrilateral is a square.

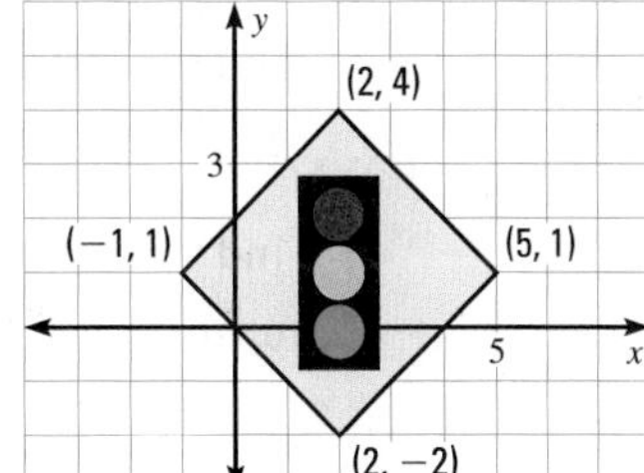

Avoiding Common Errors

Exercises 48–50 Remind students that they need to multiply the total units by the appropriate value.

Exercises 50–51 Caution students to use care when using the midpoint formula. They often confuse the midpoint formula with the distance formula and subtract the coordinates rather than add them. Tell students to think of the coordinates of the midpoint as the "average" of the coordinates of the endpoints.

5 ASSESS AND RETEACH

Daily Homework Quiz

Transparency Available

1. Find the distance between $(-4, 3)$ and $(5, 4)$. **$\sqrt{82}$ units**
2. The distance between $(4, -1)$ and $(a, 5)$ is 10 units. Find the value of a. **-4 or 12**
3. Find the coordinates of the midpoint of the line segment with endpoints $(6, -1)$ and $(-4, -5)$. **$(1, -3)$**
4. Each unit of distance on the map represents 1.5 miles. What is the distance between High Point and Big Rock? **about 6.7 mi**

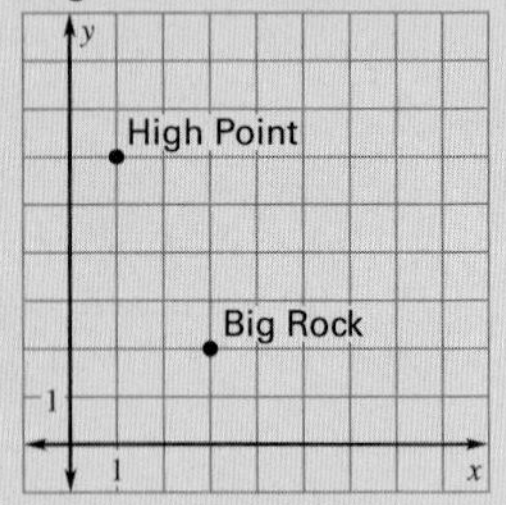

Online Quiz

Available at **classzone.com**

Diagnosis/Remediation

- Practice A, B, C in Chapter Resource Book
- Study Guide in Chapter Resource Book
- Practice Workbook
- @HomeTutor

Challenge

Additional challenge is available in the Chapter Resource Book.

Quiz

An easily-readable reduced copy of the quiz (with answers) on Lessons 11.4–11.5 from the Assessment Book can be found on p. 708E.

C **52. CHALLENGE** A computer programmer is creating a baseball player's strike zone for a video game, as shown. The strike zone is a rectangular region over home plate through which a ball must pass to be called a strike. In the animation, $\overline{AB}$ is the top of the strike zone and lies on a horizontal line that passes through the midpoint of $\overline{XY}$. The distance between grid lines represents 1 foot.

a. If the coordinates of X are $(4, 5.5)$ and the coordinates of Y are $(4, 3.5)$, what is the midpoint of $\overline{XY}$? **(4, 4.5)**

b. The coordinates of C are $(7, 2)$ and the coordinates of D are $(8.5, 2)$. Find the coordinates of point A and point B. **A: (7, 4.5), B: (8.5, 4.5)**

c. What is the area of the strike zone in the animation? **3.75 ft^2**

MIXED REVIEW

PREVIEW Prepare for Lesson 12.1 in Exs. 53–58.

Given that y varies directly with x, use the specified values to write a direct variation equation that relates x and y. *(p. 253)*

53. $x = 10, y = 30$ **$y = 3x$**
54. $x = 81, y = 27$ **$y = \frac{x}{3}$**
55. $x = -6, y = -9$ **$y = \frac{3x}{2}$**
56. $x = 12, y = -1.5$ **$y = -\frac{x}{8}$**
57. $x = -11, y = -11$ **$y = x$**
58. $x = \frac{2}{3}, y = 6$ **$y = 9x$**

Graph the function. **59–64. See margin.**

59. $y = 4^x$ *(p. 520)*
60. $y = 3 \cdot 4^x$ *(p. 520)*
61. $y = (0.5)^x$ *(p. 531)*
62. $y = 2 \cdot (0.5)^x$ *(p. 531)*
63. $y = x^2 - 6$ *(p. 628)*
64. $y = 2x^2 - x + 8$ *(p. 635)*

QUIZ for Lessons 11.4–11.5

Let a and b represent the lengths of the legs of a right triangle, and let c represent the length of the hypotenuse. Find the unknown length. *(p. 737)*

1. $a = 6, c = 10$ **$b = 8$**
2. $b = 2, c = 6$ **$a = 4\sqrt{2}$**
3. $a = 4, b = 7$ **$c = \sqrt{65}$**

Find the unknown lengths. *(p. 737)*

4.

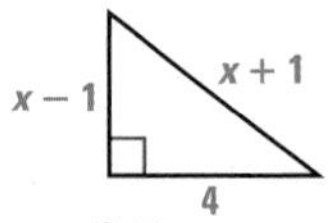

3, 5

5.

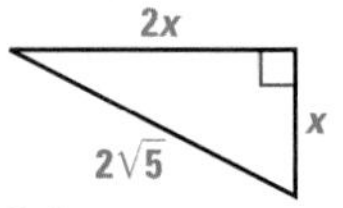

2, 4

6.

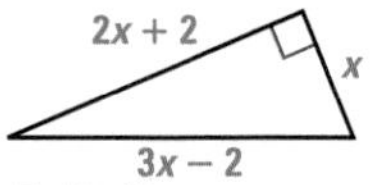

5, 12, 13

Find the distance between the two points. *(p. 744)*

7. $(7, 2), (7, 5)$ **3**
8. $(-1, -3), (4, -3)$ **5**
9. $(0, 0), (-6, 9)$ **$3\sqrt{13}$**

Find the midpoint of the line segment with the given endpoints. *(p. 744)*

10. $(0, 5), (-6, 3)$ **$(-3, 4)$**
11. $(8, -1), (2, -7)$ **$(5, -4)$**
12. $(-5, -3), (5, -3)$ **$(0, -3)$**
13. $(0, 6), (1.5, 4)$ **$(0.75, 5)$**
14. $(2.5, -3), (0.5, 6)$ **$(1.5, 1.5)$**
15. $\left(-\frac{1}{4}, \frac{3}{4}\right), \left(\frac{1}{4}, \frac{5}{4}\right)$ **$(0, 1)$**

EXTRA PRACTICE for Lesson 11.5, p. 948 **ONLINE QUIZ** at classzone.com

59–64. See Additional Answers beginning on p. AA1.

PROBLEM SOLVING WORKSHOP
LESSON 11.5

Using ALTERNATIVE METHODS

Another Way to Solve Example 4, page 746

MULTIPLE REPRESENTATIONS In Example 4 on page 746, you saw how to solve a problem about finding a meeting place by using the midpoint and distance formulas. You can also solve the problem by folding a map and using a compass.

PROBLEM

SIGHTSEEING You and a friend are sightseeing in Washington, D.C. You are at the National Gallery of Art, and your friend is at the Washington Monument, as shown on the map. You want to meet at the landmark that is closest to the midpoint of your locations. At which landmark should you meet?

METHOD 1

Folding a map and using a compass An alternative approach is to fold a map and use a compass. First, draw a line connecting your location to your friend's location. Then fold the map so that your locations coincide. The point where the line connecting your locations is folded represents the midpoint. Place the point of your compass at the midpoint. Adjust the opening of the compass to match the distance between the midpoint and the apparent closest landmark. Swing the compass to see if the other landmark is closer.

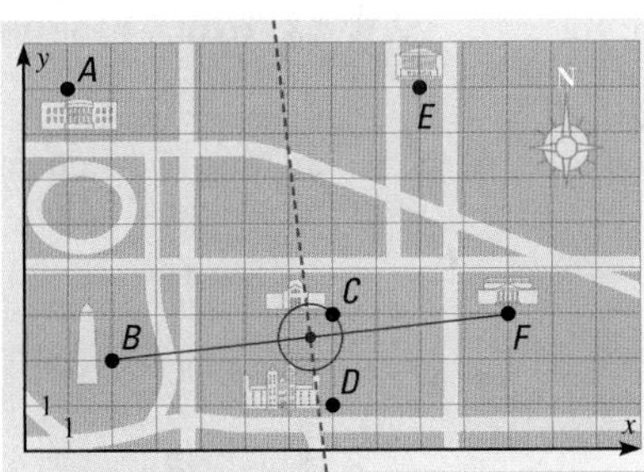

SIGHTS IN WASHINGTON, D.C.
A) White House
B) Washington Monument
C) Natural History Museum
D) Smithsonian Institution
E) National Portrait Gallery
F) National Gallery of Art

▶ Because the Smithsonian lies outside the circle, the Natural History Museum is closer to the midpoint of your locations.

PRACTICE

1. **WHAT IF?** In the problem above, suppose your friend is at the White House.
   a. At which landmark should you meet? **Natural History Museum**
   b. Suppose you can walk directly to the landmark in part (a). If the distance between consecutive grid lines represents 0.06 mile, how far do you have to walk? **0.24 mi**

2. **MAPS** A student makes a map of a town in which the student's house is located at (1, 2) and a friend's house is located at (8, 5). A grocery store is located at (5, 3), and a shoe store is located at (3, 4). The student and the friend want to meet at the store that is closer to the midpoint between their houses. At which store should they meet? Solve this problem using two methods. **grocery store**

Alternative Strategy

Example 4 on page 746 can be solved by folding a map and using a compass. This strategy will appeal to students who prefer a hands-on approach to solving problems. It is also a good method to use in the field when coordinate grids are scarce. Even if students do not have a compass handy when using a map, they can still fold the map to find a midpoint.

Avoiding Common Errors

Students should make sure that the locations coincide when they fold their maps or the midpoint will be off. Students should also make sure that their compasses are stable so that when they swing the compass, it does not change calibration.

4. The library. *Sample answer:* The midpoint between the school and the stadium is at (3, 3.5). Using the distance formula, you can find that the midpoint is closer to the library than any other point.

6c. 1 h 30 min after the ferries first leave. *Sample answer:* The red ferry takes 15 + 10 + 15 = 40 minutes to return to Shore City, remains in the city for 10 minutes, and then is back in the city again 40 minutes later, or 90 minutes after it first leaves. The blue ferry takes 15 + 10 + 11.25 + 10 + 11.25 + 10 + 15 = 82.5 minutes to return to Shore City, and then remains in the city for 10 minutes, or until 92.5 minutes after its first departure. While the blue ferry is waiting, the red ferry will arrive at exactly 90 minutes after its first departure. So the ferries will be in the city together until the blue ferry leaves again 2.5 minutes later.

MIXED REVIEW *of Problem Solving*

STATE TEST PRACTICE classzone.com

Lessons 11.4–11.5

1. **SHORT RESPONSE** Construction workers are building a staircase for a house. Use the drawing of the staircase to answer the following questions. Round each answer to the nearest inch.

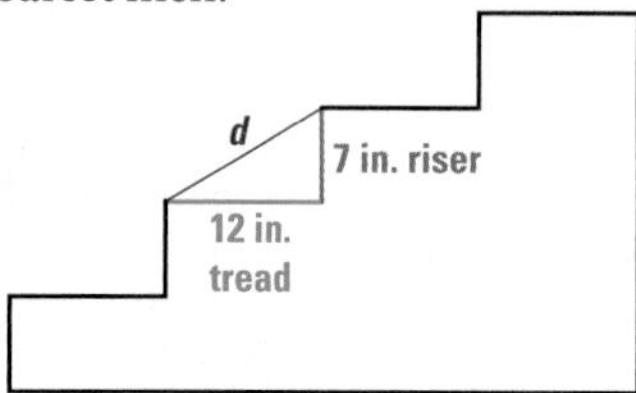

   a. Find the distance d between the edges of two consecutive steps. **14 in.**

   b. Suppose the workers install a handrail that is as long as the distance between the front edge of the bottom step and the front edge of the top step. How long is the handrail? *Explain.* **42 in.; there are 3 steps, so you can multiply the distance from part (a) by 3.**

2. **MULTI-STEP PROBLEM** At the start of a football game, the kicker on one team must kick the ball to the opposing team. To position himself for the starting kick, the kicker places a football on a tee, walks 8 yards behind the tee, then 6 yards to his left.

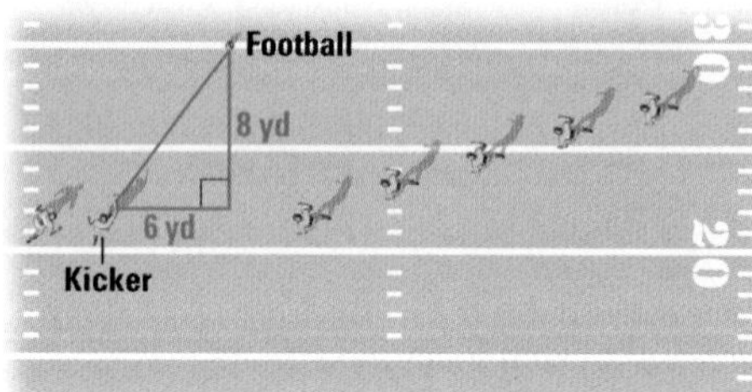

   a. What is the kicker's distance (in yards) from the football? **10 yd**

   b. The kicker takes 11 strides to kick the ball. What is his average stride length? Round your answer to the nearest tenth of a foot. **2.7 ft**

3. **GRIDDED ANSWER** You go on a hiking trip. You walk 2 miles directly east and then 4 miles directly north. If you could walk in a straight path back to your starting point, how far would you have to walk? Round your answer to the nearest tenth of a mile. **4.5 mi**

4. **SHORT RESPONSE** A map of a town is shown. A student is at the school. The student's friend is at the stadium. They want to meet at the place that is closest to the midpoint of their locations. At which location should they meet? *Explain* how you found your answer. **See margin.**

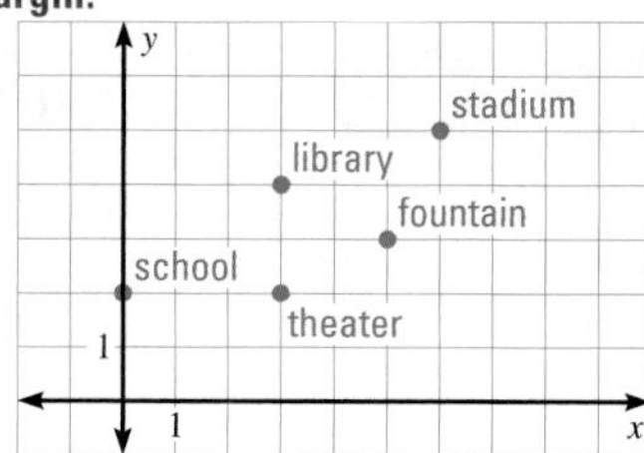

5. **OPEN-ENDED** City planners want to build a rectangular park. They want the park to have a straight path that is 2500 feet long and connects opposite corners of the park. What are three possibilities for the length and width of the park? ***Sample answer:*** **2000 ft by 1500 ft, $500\sqrt{21}$ ft by 1000 ft, 2400 ft by 700 ft**

6. **EXTENDED RESPONSE** One ferry makes round trips shown in red. A second ferry makes round trips shown in blue. The distance between consecutive grid lines represents 1 mile.

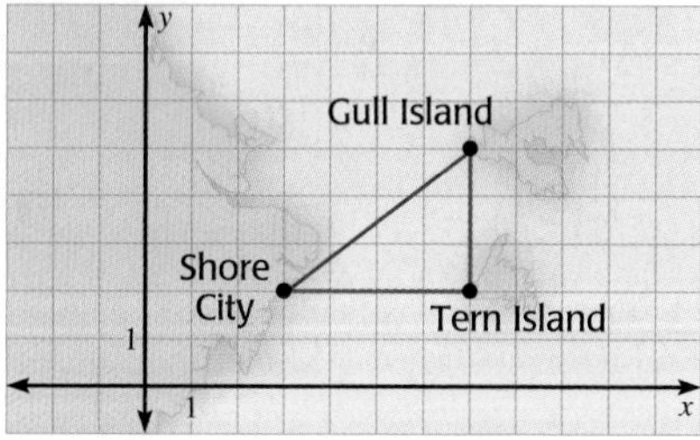

   a. Find the distance (in miles) of a round trip for the first ferry. **10 mi**

   b. Find the distance (in miles) of a round trip for the second ferry. **14 mi**

   c. Each stop the ferries make takes 10 minutes. The first ferry travels at 20 miles per hour, and the second ferry travels at 16 miles per hour. The ferries leave Shore City at the same time each day. When will they be back at the city at the same time? *Explain.* **See margin.**

Animated Algebra
classzone.com
Electronic Function Library

BIG IDEAS

For Your Notebook

Big Idea 1

Graphing Square Root Functions

You can graph a square root function $y = a\sqrt{x - h} + k$ and compare its graph with the graph of the parent function, $y = \sqrt{x}$, based on the constants a, h, and k.

Constant	Comparison of graphs
a	• When $a > 0$, the graph is a vertical stretch or shrink of the parent graph. • When $a < 0$, the graph is a vertical stretch or shrink with a reflection in the x-axis of the parent graph.
h	The graph is a horizontal translation of the parent graph.
k	The graph is a vertical translation of the parent graph.

Big Idea 2

Using Properties of Radicals in Expressions and Equations

You can use the properties of radicals to simplify radical expressions and to solve radical equations.

Product property of radicals	$\sqrt{ab} = \sqrt{a} \cdot \sqrt{b}$ where $a \geq 0$ and $b \geq 0$
Quotient property of radicals	$\sqrt{\frac{a}{b}} = \frac{\sqrt{a}}{\sqrt{b}}$ where $a \geq 0$ and $b > 0$

Big Idea 3

Working with Radicals in Geometry

You can use radicals to solve problems involving the following geometric theorems and formulas.

Pythagorean theorem	If a triangle is a right triangle, then the sum of the squares of the lengths of the legs, a and b, equals the square of the length of the hypotenuse c. $a^2 + b^2 = c^2$
Converse of Pythagorean theorem	If a triangle has side lengths a, b, and c such that $a^2 + b^2 = c^2$, then the triangle is a right triangle.
Distance formula	$d = \sqrt{(x_2 - x_1)^2 + (y_2 - y_1)^2}$
Midpoint formula	$M\left(\frac{x_1 + x_2}{2}, \frac{y_1 + y_2}{2}\right)$

Additional Resources

The following resources are available to help review the materials in this chapter.

Chapter Resource Book

- Chapter Review Games and Activities
- Cumulative Practice, Chs. 1–11

Student Resources in Spanish

eWorkbook

@HomeTutor

Vocabulary Practice

Vocabulary practice is available at **classzone.com**

Extra Example 11.1

Graph the function $3\sqrt{x} + 1$ and identify its domain and range. Compare the graph with the graph of $y = \sqrt{x}$.

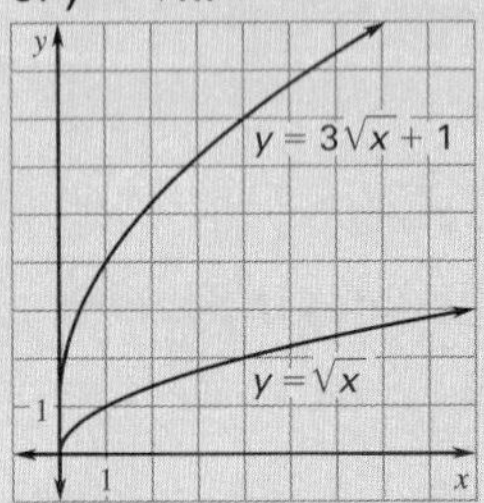

Domain: $x \geq 0$, range: $y \geq 1$; the graph of $y = 3\sqrt{x} + 1$ is a vertical stretch (by a factor of 3) and a translation 1 unit up of the graph of $y = \sqrt{x}$.

2. *Sample answer:* To rationalize the denominator of a radical expression, multiply the fraction by the denominator over itself. This will not change the value of the expression and will remove the radical from the denominator. If the denominator is a binomial that contains a radical, multiply by the conjugate of the binomial over itself.

5.

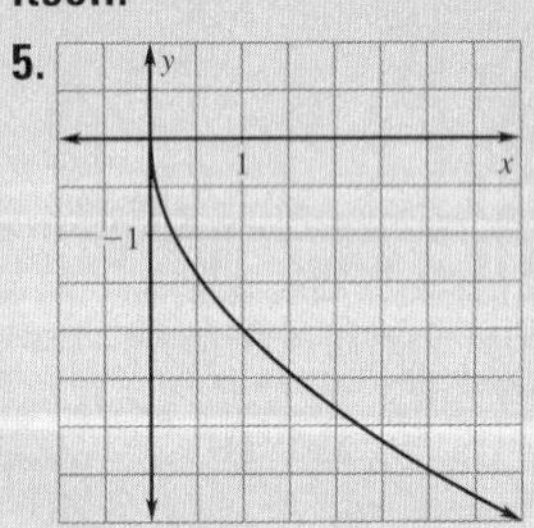

domain: $x \geq 0$, range: $y \leq 0$; vertical stretch by a factor of 2 with a reflection in the x-axis

6.

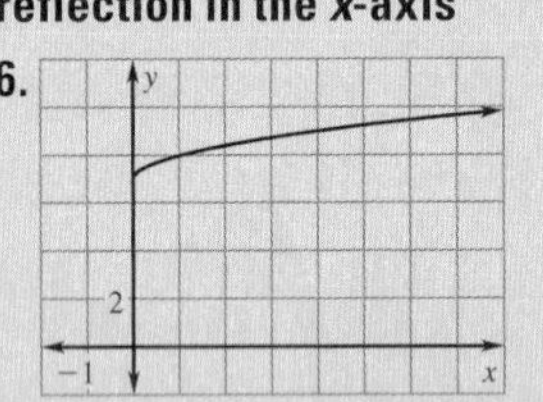

domain: $x \geq 0$, range: $y \geq 7$; vertical translation of 7 units up

REVIEW KEY VOCABULARY

- radical expression, *p. 710*
- radical function, *p. 710*
- square root function, *p. 710*
- parent square root function, *p. 710*
- simplest form of a radical expression, *p. 719*
- rationalizing the denominator, *p. 721*
- radical equation, *p. 729*
- extraneous solution, *p. 730*
- hypotenuse, legs of a right triangle, *p. 737*
- Pythagorean theorem, *p. 737*
- distance formula, *p. 744*
- midpoint, midpoint formula, *p. 745*

VOCABULARY EXERCISES

1. *Describe* how the graph of the function $y = 3\sqrt{x}$ compares with the graph of the parent square root function. **It is a vertical stretch by a factor of 3.**
2. *Describe* the steps you would take to rationalize the denominator of a radical expression. **See margin.**

Tell which theorem or formula you would use to complete the exercise.

3. Tell whether a triangle with side lengths 2, 4, and 6 is a right triangle. **converse of the Pythagorean theorem**
4. The point $(b, 4)$ is 10 units away from the point $(5, 10)$. Find b. **distance formula**

REVIEW EXAMPLES AND EXERCISES

Use the review examples and exercises below to check your understanding of the concepts you have learned in each lesson of Chapter 11.

11.1 Graph Square Root Functions *pp. 710–716*

EXAMPLE

Graph the function $y = \sqrt{x - 3}$ and identify its domain and range. Compare the graph with the graph of $y = \sqrt{x}$.

To graph the function, make a table, plot the points, and draw a smooth curve through the points. The domain is $x \geq 3$.

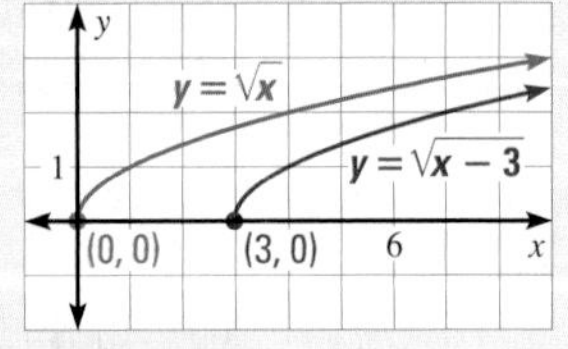

x	3	4	5	6
y	0	1	1.4	1.7

The range is $y \geq 0$. The graph of $y = \sqrt{x - 3}$ is a horizontal translation (of 3 units to the right) of the graph of $y = \sqrt{x}$.

EXERCISES

EXAMPLES 2, 3, and 4 on pp. 711–712 for Exs. 5–7

Graph the function and identify its domain and range. Compare the graph with the graph of $y = \sqrt{x}$. **5–7. See margin.**

5. $y = -2\sqrt{x}$
6. $y = \sqrt{x} + 7$
7. $y = \sqrt{x + 7}$

7.

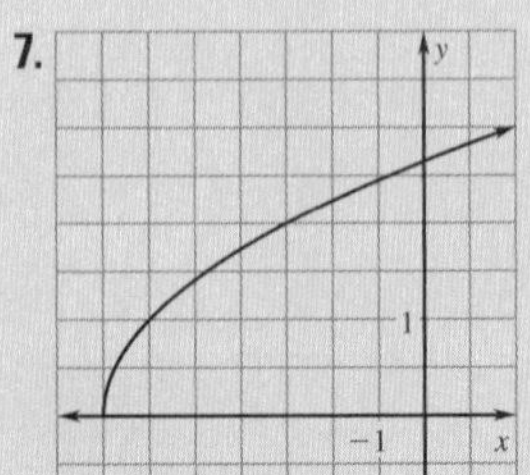

domain: $x \geq -7$, range: $y \geq 0$; horizontal translation of 7 units to the left

@HomeTutor
classzone.com
Chapter Review Practice

11.2 Simplify Radical Expressions

pp. 719–726

EXAMPLE

Simplify $7\sqrt{5} - \sqrt{45}$.

$7\sqrt{5} - \sqrt{45} = 7\sqrt{5} - \sqrt{9 \cdot 5}$ Factor using perfect square factor.

$= 7\sqrt{5} - \sqrt{9} \cdot \sqrt{5}$ Product property of radicals

$= 7\sqrt{5} - 3\sqrt{5}$ Simplify.

$= (7 - 3)\sqrt{5}$ Distributive property

$= 4\sqrt{5}$ Simplify.

EXERCISES

EXAMPLES 1–7 on pp. 719–722 for Exs. 8–16

Simplify the expression.

8. $\sqrt{98}$ $7\sqrt{2}$
9. $\sqrt{121x^3}$ $11x\sqrt{x}$
10. $\sqrt{7} \cdot \sqrt{21}$ $7\sqrt{3}$
11. $\sqrt{7x} \cdot 7\sqrt{x}$ $7x\sqrt{7}$
12. $\sqrt{\frac{5}{x^2}}$ $\frac{\sqrt{5}}{x}$
13. $\frac{2}{\sqrt{5}}$ $\frac{2\sqrt{5}}{5}$
14. $3\sqrt{2} - \sqrt{128}$ $-5\sqrt{2}$
15. $\sqrt{2}(7 - \sqrt{6})$ $7\sqrt{2} - 2\sqrt{3}$
16. **GEOMETRY** The lateral surface area L of a square pyramid with height h and base length ℓ is given by $L = 2\ell\sqrt{0.25\ell^2 + h^2}$. Find L (in square feet) for a square pyramid that has a height of 4 feet and a base length of 4 feet. $16\sqrt{5}$ ft^2

11.3 Solve Radical Equations

pp. 729–734

EXAMPLE

Solve $\sqrt{x + 90} = x$.

$\sqrt{x + 90} = x$ Write original equation.

$(\sqrt{x + 90})^2 = x^2$ Square each side.

$x + 90 = x^2$ Simplify.

$0 = x^2 - x - 90$ Write in standard form.

$0 = (x - 10)(x + 9)$ Factor.

$x - 10 = 0$ *or* $x + 9 = 0$ Zero-product property

$x = 10$ *or* $x = -9$ Solve for x.

▶ Checking 10 and −9 in the original equation shows that −9 is an extraneous solution. The only solution of the equation is 10.

EXERCISES

EXAMPLES 1, 2, 3, and 4 on pp. 729–731 for Exs. 17–22

Solve the equation. Check for extraneous solutions.

17. $\sqrt{x} - 28 = 0$ 784
18. $8\sqrt{x - 5} + 34 = 58$ 14
19. $\sqrt{5x - 3} = \sqrt{x + 17}$ 5
20. $\sqrt{5x} + 6 = 5$ no real solutions
21. $\sqrt{x} + 36 = 0$ no real solutions
22. $x = \sqrt{2 - x}$ 1

Extra Example 11.2

Simplify $6\sqrt{7} + \sqrt{28}$. $8\sqrt{7}$

Extra Example 11.3

Solve $\sqrt{6x} + 5 = 11$. 6

Extra Example 11.4

Find the unknown length.

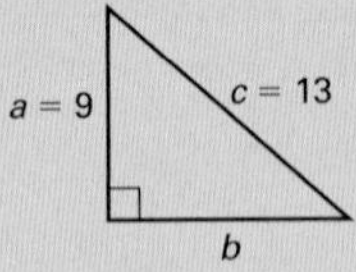

$\sqrt{88}$ **or** $2\sqrt{22}$

Extra Example 11.5

Find the midpoint of the line segment with endpoints (−2, 7) and (4, −5).
(1, 1)

11.4 Apply the Pythagorean Theorem and Its Converse

pp. 737–742

EXAMPLE

Find the unknown length for the triangle shown.

a = 6, c = 11, b

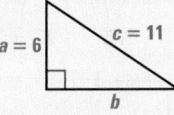

$a^2 + b^2 = c^2$	**Pythagorean theorem**
$6^2 + b^2 = 11^2$	**Substitute 6 for *a* and 11 for *c*.**
$36 + b^2 = 121$	**Simplify.**
$b^2 = 85$	**Subtract 36 from each side.**
$b = \sqrt{85}$	**Take positive square root of each side.**

EXERCISES

EXAMPLES 1 and 4 on pp. 737, 739 for Exs. 23–29

Let *a* and *b* represent the lengths of the legs of a right triangle, and let *c* represent the length of the hypotenuse. Find the unknown length.

23. $a = 7, b = 13$ **$c = \sqrt{218}$** **24.** $a = 10, c = 21$ **$b = \sqrt{341}$** **25.** $a = 8, c = 11$ **$b = \sqrt{57}$**

26. $a = 9, b = 17$ **$c = \sqrt{370}$** **27.** $b = 4, c = 15$ **$a = \sqrt{209}$** **28.** $b = 6, c = 6.5$ **$a = 2.5$**

29. REFLECTING POOL The Reflecting Pool in front of the Lincoln Memorial in Washington, D.C., is rectangular with a length of 2029 feet and a width of 167 feet. To the nearest foot, what is the length of a diagonal of the Reflecting Pool? **2036 ft**

11.5 Apply the Distance and Midpoint Formulas

pp. 744–750

EXAMPLE

Find the distance between (−3, 8) and (5, −12).

Let $(x_1, y_1) = (-3, 8)$ and $(x_2, y_2) = (5, -12)$.

$d = \sqrt{(x_2 - x_1)^2 + (y_2 - y_1)^2}$	**Distance formula**
$= \sqrt{(5 - (-3))^2 + (-12 - 8)^2}$	**Substitute.**
$= \sqrt{464} = 4\sqrt{29}$	**Simplify.**

EXERCISES

EXAMPLES 1, 3, and 4 on pp. 744, 746 for Exs. 30–36

Find the distance between the two points.

30. (−1, −3), (9, −13) **$10\sqrt{2}$** **31.** (−8, −4), (0, 2) **10** **32.** (7, 1), (4, −0.25) **3.25**

Find the midpoint of the line segment with the given endpoints.

33. (−2, −4), (9, −4) **(3.5, −4)** **34.** (−8, 0), (−8, 2) **(−8, 1)** **35.** (6, 1), (4, −5) **(5, −2)**

36. ISLANDS On a coordinate grid, an island is located at (1, 6). Another island is located at (4, 9). What is the distance between the islands if the distance between consecutive grid lines represents 2 miles? **$6\sqrt{2}$ mi**

Graph the function and identify its domain and range. Compare the graph with the graph of $y = \sqrt{x}$. **1–4. See margin.**

1. $y = 3\sqrt{x}$ 2. $y = -\sqrt{x}$ 3. $y = \sqrt{x - 5}$ 4. $y = -\sqrt{x - 1} + 4$

Simplify the expression.

5. $\sqrt{72m^6}$ **$6m^3\sqrt{2}$** 6. $\sqrt{8z^3} \cdot \sqrt{6z^3}$ **$4z^3\sqrt{3}$** 7. $\sqrt{\dfrac{20}{3n^3}}$ **$\dfrac{2\sqrt{15n}}{3n^2}$**

8. $7\sqrt{6} - 2\sqrt{12} + \sqrt{24}$ **$9\sqrt{6} - 4\sqrt{3}$** 9. $\sqrt{3}(7 - \sqrt{15})$ **$7\sqrt{3} - 3\sqrt{5}$** 10. $(8 - \sqrt{7})(1 + \sqrt{7})$ **$1 + 7\sqrt{7}$**

Solve the equation. Check for extraneous solutions.

11. $\sqrt{x} = 8$ **64** 12. $\sqrt{x + 5} - 6 = -2$ **11** 13. $-4\sqrt{3x} - 6 = 30$ **no real solutions**

14. $\sqrt{5x - 11} = \sqrt{x}$ **$\frac{11}{4}$** 15. $\sqrt{x + 7} = \sqrt{2x - 3}$ **10** 16. $x = \sqrt{12 - x}$ **3**

Find the unknown lengths.

17. 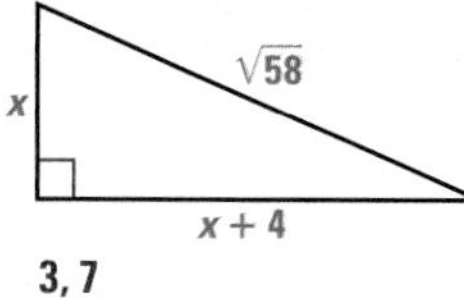

3, 7

18. 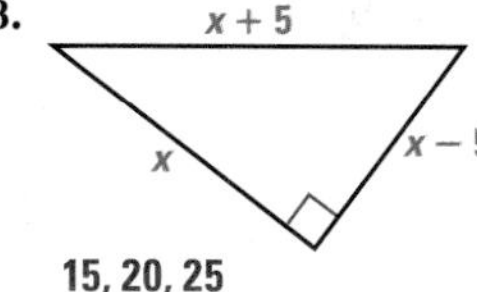

15, 20, 25

19. 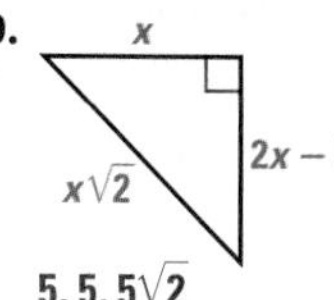

5, 5, $5\sqrt{2}$

Tell whether the triangle with the given side lengths is a right triangle.

20. 8, 16, 20 **not a right triangle** 21. 11, 60, 61 **right triangle** 22. 7.5, 10, 12.5 **right triangle**

Find the distance between the given points. Then find the midpoint of the line segment whose endpoints are the given points.

23. (6, 6), (9, 10) **5; (7.5, 8)** 24. (−8, 7), (4, 3) **$4\sqrt{10}$; (−2, 5)** 25. $\left(5, -\frac{3}{2}\right), \left(-2, \frac{9}{2}\right)$ **$\sqrt{85}$; $\left(1\frac{1}{2}, 1\frac{1}{2}\right)$**

26. **LADDERS** A ladder that is 25 feet long is placed against a house. The bottom of the ladder is 10 feet from the base of the house. How far up the house does the ladder reach? Round your answer to the nearest tenth of a foot. **22.9 ft**

27. **BIRD HOUSES** The front view of a bird house is shown. Find the height of the house to the nearest tenth of a foot. **1.9 ft**

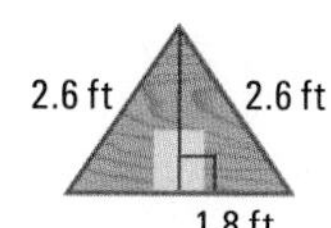

28. **LACROSSE** Two lacrosse players are playing on a field, as shown. The distance between consecutive grid lines represents 2 meters. **player A: 8.2 m; player B: 10.8 m**
   a. How far is each player from the ball? Round your answer to the nearest tenth of a meter.
   b. Both players start running toward the ball. Player A can run at a rate of 6 meters per second. Player B can run at a rate of 7 meters per second. Who will reach the ball first? **player A**

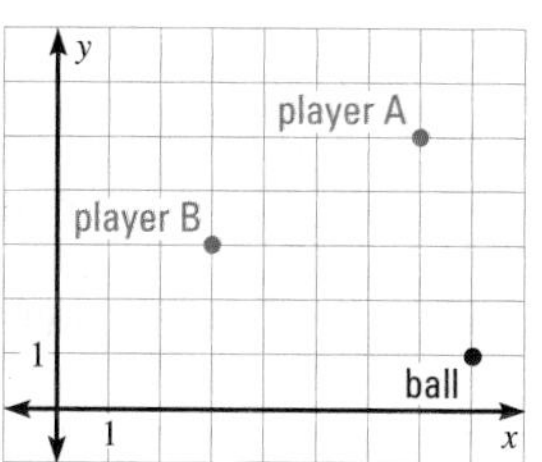

Additional Resources

Assessment Book
- Chapter Test, Levels A, B, C
- Standardized Chapter Test
- SAT/ACT Chapter Test
- Alternative Assessment

Test Generator

Chapter Test

Easily-readable reduced copies (with answers) of Chapter Test B, the Standardized Chapter Test, and the Alternative Assessment from the Assessment Book can be found on pp. 708E–708F.

2. 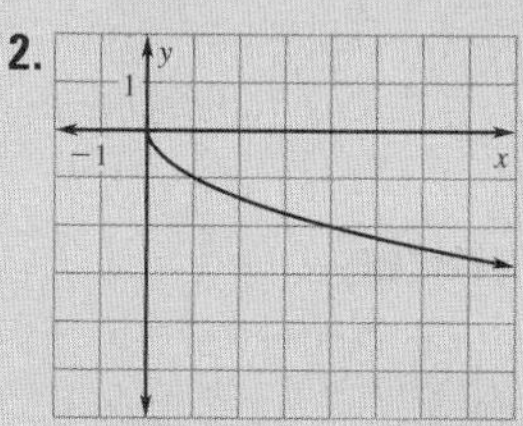

domain: $x \ge 0$, range: $y \le 0$; reflection in the x-axis

3. 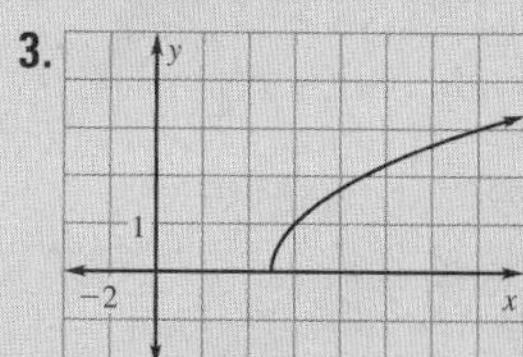

domain: $x \ge 5$, range: $y \ge 0$; horizontal translation of 5 units to the right

4. 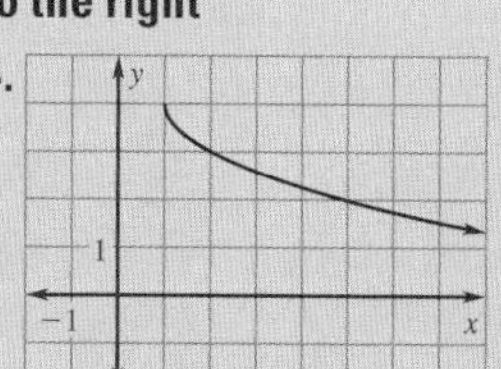

domain: $x \ge 1$, range: $y \le 4$; horizontal translation of 1 unit to the right with a reflection in the x-axis and a translation vertically 4 units up

1. 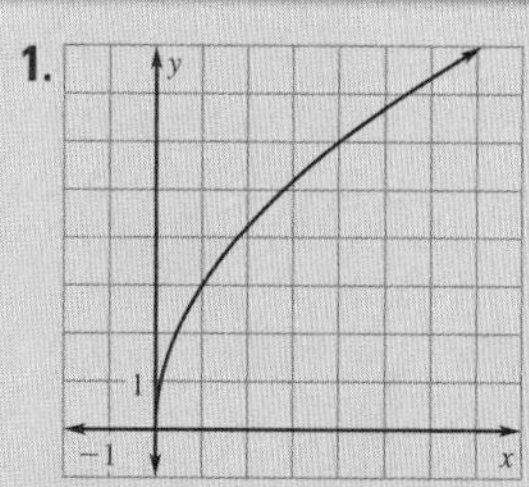

domain: $x \ge 0$, range: $y \ge 0$; vertical stretch by a factor of 3

Test-Taking Strategy

Tell students that some equations and formulas on tests will have two solutions and some will appear to have two solutions, but actually have only one. For this reason, they need to check all solutions in the original equation to make sure the solutions check, and they need to be aware that some equations have more than one solution. Quadratic equations often have two solutions. Radical equations often have extraneous solutions. When using the distance formula to find a missing coordinate, more than one value for the missing coordinate often results in the same distance.

Avoiding Common Errors

Remind students that they must square both sides of a radical equation so that the sides remain equal.

Study Strategy

Stress to students that the Pythagorean theorem and its converse are used so extensively that they should commit the theorem to memory. Suggest that they use notecards until they are familiar with the theorem and its converse. The notecards should include a diagram that shows that the hypotenuse is opposite the right angle of the triangle and is the longest side.

MULTIPLE CHOICE QUESTIONS

If you have difficulty solving a multiple choice problem directly, you may be able to use another approach to eliminate incorrect answer choices and obtain the correct answer.

PROBLEM 1

What is the solution of the equation $\sqrt{3-x} = 2x$?

Ⓐ $1, -\frac{3}{4}$ Ⓑ $-1, \frac{3}{4}$ Ⓒ -1 Ⓓ $\frac{3}{4}$

METHOD 1

SOLVE DIRECTLY Solve the radical equation and check for extraneous solutions.

STEP 1 **Solve** the radical equation.

$$\sqrt{3-x} = 2x$$
$$3 - x = 4x^2$$
$$0 = 4x^2 + x - 3$$
$$0 = (4x - 3)(x + 1)$$
$$4x - 3 = 0 \quad or \quad x + 1 = 0$$
$$x = \frac{3}{4} \quad or \quad x = -1$$

STEP 2 **Check** $\frac{3}{4}$ and -1 in the original equation.

Check $\frac{3}{4}$: $\sqrt{3 - \frac{3}{4}} \stackrel{?}{=} 2\left(\frac{3}{4}\right)$

$$\frac{3}{2} = \frac{3}{2} \checkmark$$

Solution checks.

Check -1: $\sqrt{3-(-1)} \stackrel{?}{=} 2(-1)$

$$2 = -2 \text{ ✗}$$

Solution does not check.

The only solution is $\frac{3}{4}$.

The correct answer is D. Ⓐ Ⓑ Ⓒ Ⓓ

METHOD 2

ELIMINATE CHOICES Substitute the values given in each answer choice for x in the equation.

Choice A: $1, -\frac{3}{4}$

$\sqrt{3-1} \stackrel{?}{=} 2(1)$ | $\sqrt{3-\left(-\frac{3}{4}\right)} \stackrel{?}{=} -\frac{3}{4}$

$\sqrt{2} = 2$ ✗ | $\frac{\sqrt{15}}{2} = -\frac{3}{4}$ ✗

The values do not check, so choice A can be eliminated.

Choice B: $-1, \frac{3}{4}$

$\sqrt{3-(-1)} \stackrel{?}{=} 2(-1)$ | $\sqrt{3 - \frac{3}{4}} \stackrel{?}{=} 2\left(\frac{3}{4}\right)$

$2 = -2$ ✗ | $\frac{3}{2} = \frac{3}{2}$ ✓

Because -1 does not check, both choice B and choice C can be eliminated.

Choice D: $\frac{3}{4}$

You know that $\frac{3}{4}$ is a solution from checking the values in choice B.

The only solution is $\frac{3}{4}$.

The correct answer is D. Ⓐ Ⓑ Ⓒ Ⓓ

PROBLEM 2

A carpenter is building a wooden bench and wants to be sure that the back and the seat make a right angle. The back is 24 inches tall, and the seat is 18 inches deep. What should the distance from the front of the seat to the top of the back be?

(A) 6 inches (B) 15.9 inches (C) 30 inches (D) 42 inches

METHOD 1

SOLVE DIRECTLY Use the Pythagorean theorem to find the unknown distance.

STEP 1 **Identify** the known values by drawing a diagram.

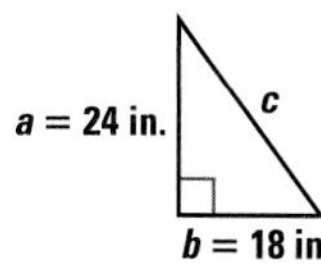

STEP 2 **Substitute** the values of a and b and solve for c.

$$a^2 + b^2 = c^2$$
$$18^2 + 24^2 = c^2$$
$$900 = c^2$$
$$\sqrt{900} = c$$
$$30 = c$$

The distance from the front of the seat to the top of the back should be 30 inches.

The correct answer is C. (A) (B) (C) (D)

METHOD 2

ELIMINATE CHOICES You can eliminate choices either by using the fact that the hypotenuse is the longest side of a right triangle or by using the converse of the Pythagorean theorem. Check to see if the value given in each answer choice could represent the length of the hypotenuse of a right triangle with leg lengths of 18 and 24 inches.

Choice A: 6 inches

$6 < 18$ ✗

Choice B: 15.9 inches

$15.9 < 18$ ✗

Choice C: 30 inches

$30 > 24$, so use the converse of the Pythagorean theorem.

$$18^2 + 24^2 \stackrel{?}{=} 30^2$$
$$900 = 900 \checkmark$$

The correct answer is C. (A) (B) (C) (D)

PRACTICE

Explain why you can eliminate the highlighted answer choice.

1. What is the solution of the equation $\sqrt{20 - x} = x$?

   (A) 4, −5 (B) −4, 5 (C) ✗ −5 (D) 4

2. Which of the following represents the side lengths of a right triangle?

   (A) 1, 2, 3 (B) ✗ 6, 8, 14 (C) 12, 13, 15 (D) 8, 15, 17

3. A side view of a wheelchair ramp can be represented by the hypotenuse of a right triangle. The triangle has a length of 24 feet and a height of 2 feet. To the nearest tenth, how long is the ramp?

    (A) ✗ 22 feet (B) 23.9 feet (C) 24.1 feet (D) 26 feet

Answers

1. ***Sample answer:*** **The answer $x = -5$ does not check in the original equation, so you can eliminate both A and C as answer choices.**

2. ***Sample answer:*** **$6^2 + 8^2 \neq 14^2$, so you can eliminate choice B.**

3. ***Sample answer:*** **The square of the length of the ramp should equal the sum of the squares of 24 and 2; $24^2 + 2^2 = 580$. Since $22^2 \neq 580$, you can eliminate choice A.**

Answers
1. D
2. B
3. B
4. B
5. C
6. C
7. A
8. C
9. B

11 ★ *Standardized* TEST PRACTICE

MULTIPLE CHOICE

1. What is the solution of the equation $\sqrt{2x + 8} = x$?

   Ⓐ $-2, 4$ Ⓑ $24, 2$
   Ⓒ -2 Ⓓ 4

2. Which expression is equivalent to $\sqrt{4x^2 y} \cdot \sqrt{y}$?

   Ⓐ $4xy$ Ⓑ $2xy$
   Ⓒ $2x\sqrt{y}$ Ⓓ $4x\sqrt{y}$

3. The graph of which function is shown?

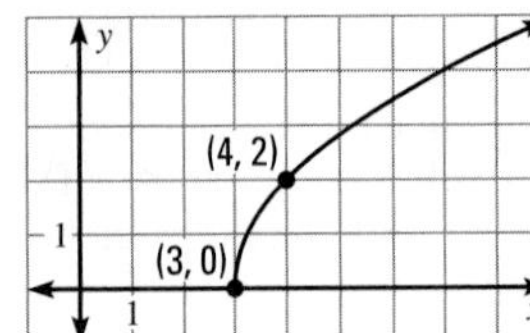

   Ⓐ $y = \sqrt{x - 3}$ Ⓑ $y = 2\sqrt{x - 3}$
   Ⓒ $y = 2\sqrt{x + 3}$ Ⓓ $y = 2\sqrt{x} - 3$

4. How does the graph of $y = \sqrt{x} + 3$ compare with the graph of $y = \sqrt{x}$?

   Ⓐ It is a vertical stretch by a factor of 3 of the graph of $y = \sqrt{x}$.
   Ⓑ It is a vertical translation of 3 units up of the graph of $y = \sqrt{x}$.
   Ⓒ It is a vertical translation of 3 units down of the graph of $y = \sqrt{x}$.
   Ⓓ It is a horizontal translation of 3 units to the right of the graph of $y = \sqrt{x}$.

5. Which expression represents the length of a diagonal of the rectangle?

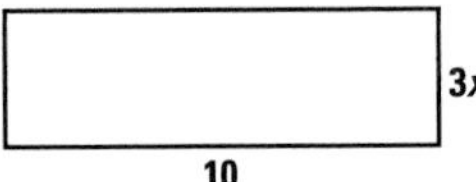

   Ⓐ $3x^2 + 100$
   Ⓑ $9x^2 + 100$
   Ⓒ $\sqrt{9x^2 + 100}$
   Ⓓ $\sqrt{3x^2 + 100}$

6. What is the solution of the equation $\sqrt{x + 3} = x - 9$?

   Ⓐ $-13, -6$ Ⓑ $13, 6$
   Ⓒ 13 Ⓓ 6

7. The table below represents which function?

x	4	5	8	13
y	5	8	11	14

   Ⓐ $y = 3\sqrt{x - 4} + 5$
   Ⓑ $y = 3\sqrt{x - 3} + 8$
   Ⓒ $y = 3\sqrt{x - 4} + 8$
   Ⓓ $y = 3\sqrt{x - 3} + 5$

In Exercises 8 and 9, use the map of the college campus shown.

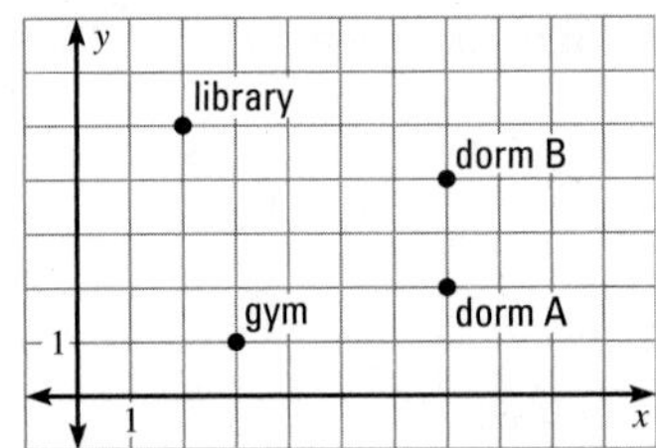

8. Which of the following pairs of buildings are closest together?

   Ⓐ Dorm A and the library
   Ⓑ Dorm B and the gym
   Ⓒ The gym and the library
   Ⓓ Dorm B and the library

9. A student who lives in dorm A forgets a book at the library. The student jogs at a rate of 6 miles per hour from the dorm straight to the library and back. The distance between consecutive grid lines represents 0.1 mile. To the nearest tenth of an hour, how long does it take the student to jog to the library and back?

   Ⓐ 0.1 hour Ⓑ 0.2 hour
   Ⓒ 0.3 hour Ⓓ 0.4 hour

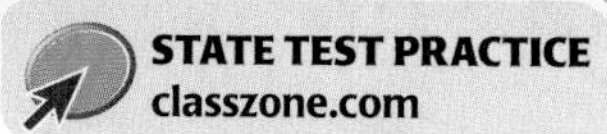

GRIDDED ANSWER

10. A line segment has endpoints (8, 0) and (14, 8). What is the distance from either endpoint to the midpoint?

11. A right triangle has a hypotenuse of 18 centimeters. The length of one leg is 8 centimeters. To the nearest tenth of a centimeter, how long is the other leg?

12. The leg lengths of a triangle are shown.

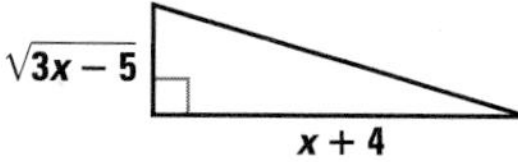

To the nearest tenth, what is the length of the hypotenuse when $x = 3$?

13. A rectangular table is 7 feet long and 3.5 feet wide. To the nearest tenth of a foot, what is the length of a diagonal of the table?

14. What is the solution of the equation $2\sqrt{x} = 3\sqrt{8} - \sqrt{2}$? Write your answer as a decimal.

SHORT RESPONSE

15. A person lives in Glenville. The person's friend lives in Newport.

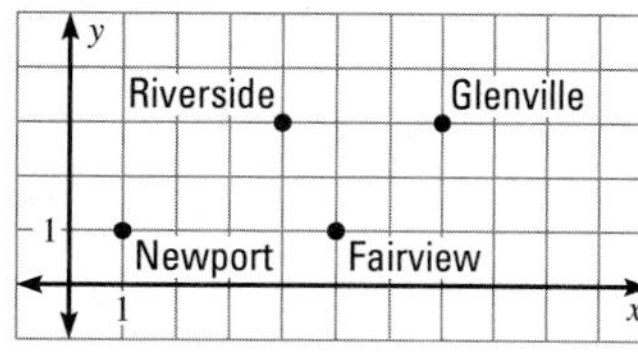

The friends decide to meet at the city that is closer to the midpoint of their locations. In which city should they meet? *Explain.*

16. The front view of a shed is shown. Roofers are going to replace the tin roof of the shed.

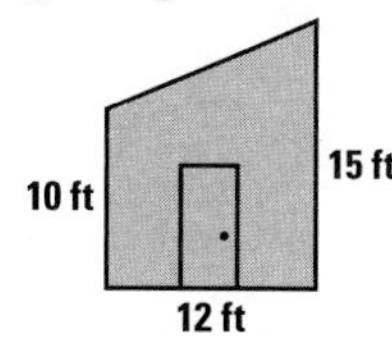

If the depth of the shed is 20 feet, how many square feet of tin will the roofers need? *Explain.*

EXTENDED RESPONSE

17. For the period 1900–2000, the life expectancy at birth e (in years) for people born in the United States can be modeled by the function $e = 3.66\sqrt{t} + 40.6$ where t is the number of years since 1900.

a. Graph the function and identify its domain and range.

b. In what year was the life expectancy at birth about 75 years? *Explain.*

c. During which decade (1900–1909, 1910–1919, and so on) did life expectancy increase the most? *Explain.*

18. A planet's mean radius r (in meters) is given by $r = \sqrt{\frac{(6.67 \times 10^{-11})M}{a}}$ where a is the planet's acceleration due to gravity (in meters per second squared) and M is the planet's mass (in kilograms).

a. For Earth, the value of a is about 9.8 meters per second squared, and the value of M is about 5.98×10^{24} kilograms. Find the value of r.

b. For Jupiter, the value of a is about 24.8 meters per second squared, and the value of M is about 1.9×10^{27} kilograms. Find the value of r.

c. Jupiter's mass is abouut 300 times Earth's mass, and Jupiter's acceleration due to gravity is about 2.5 times that of Earth's. If you multiply M by 300 and a by 2.5, what happens to the value of r? *Compare* your answer with your results from parts (a) and (b).

10. 5

11. 16.1 cm

12. 7.3

13. 7.8 ft

14. 12.5

15. Riverside. *Sample answer:* The midpoint between Newport and Glenville is at (4, 2). Riverside is only 1 unit away, while Fairview is $\sqrt{2}$ units away.

16. 260 ft^2. *Sample answer:* Subtract 10 from 15 to find the height the roof rises, then use the Pythagorean theorem to find the length of the hypotenuse, which is one side of the roof: $12^2 + 5^2 = 169$. The length of the roof is 13, which is multiplied by a depth of 20 to give the area of the roof, 260 square feet.

17a.

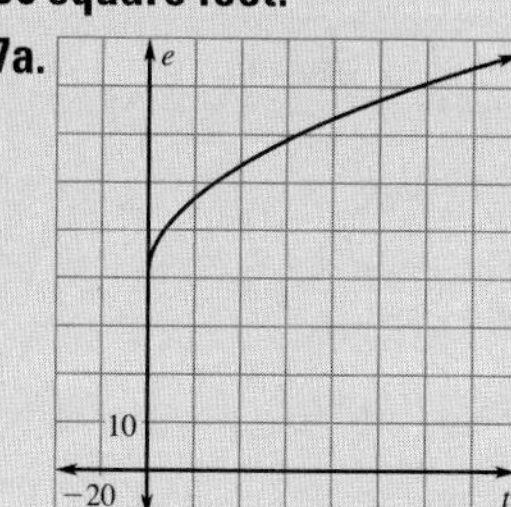

domain: $x \geq 0$, range: $y \geq 40.6$

17b. In 1988. *Sample answer:* Substituting 75 for e into the equation gives a value of about 88.3, or 1988.

17c. During 1900–1910. *Sample answer:* The graph of life expectancy is modeled on the parent graph $y = \sqrt{x}$, which increases less steeply as x increases. So, in the first decade the graph increased the most.

18a. about 6.38×10^6 m

18b. about 7.15×10^7 m

18c. r will increase by a factor of $\sqrt{\frac{300}{2.5}} = \sqrt{120} \approx 10.95$. *Sample answer:* The r value for Jupiter is close to 10.95 times the r value of Earth.

12 Pacing Guide

Chapter 12: Rational Equations and Functions

Chapter Table of Contents

PACING GUIDES

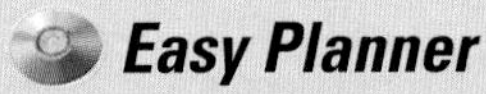

Regular Schedule (50-minute classes)

DAY 1	DAY 2	DAY 3	DAY 4	DAY 5	DAY 6	DAY 7
Investigating Algebra Activity 12.1 Lesson 12.1	Lesson 12.1 (cont.)	Investigating Algebra Activity 12.2 Lesson 12.2	Lesson 12.2 (cont.)	Quiz for Lessons 12.1–12.2 Investigating Algebra Activity 12.3 Lesson 12.3	Lesson 12.3 (cont.) Graphing Calculator Activity 12.3	Lesson 12.4 Mixed Review of Problem Solving
DAY 8	**DAY 9**	**DAY 10**	**DAY 11**	**DAY 12**	**DAY 13**	**DAY 14**
Quiz for Lessons 12.3–12.4 Lesson 12.5	Lesson 12.5 (cont.) Extension 12.5	Lesson 12.6	Lesson 12.6 (cont.)	Lesson 12.7 Mixed Review of Problem Solving	Quiz for Lessons 12.5–12.6 Chapter Review	Chapter Test

Block Schedule (90-minute classes)

DAY 1	DAY 2	DAY 3	DAY 4	DAY 5	DAY 6	DAY 7
Investigating Algebra Activity 12.1 Lesson 12.1	Investigating Algebra Activity 12.2 Lesson 12.2	Quiz for Lessons 12.1–12.2 Investigating Algebra Activity 12.3 Lesson 12.3 Graphing Calculator Activity 12.3	Lesson 12.4 Mixed Review of Problem Solving Quiz for Lessons 12.3–12.4 Lesson 12.5	Lesson 12.5 (cont.) Extension 12.5 Lesson 12.6	Lesson 12.6 (cont.) Lesson 12.7 Mixed Review of Problem Solving	Quiz for Lessons 12.5–12.6 Chapter Review Chapter Test

RESOURCE OPTIONS

Chapter/Lesson Resources

Chapter Resource Book
- Parents as Partners
- Teaching Guide/Lesson Plan
- Activity Masters
- Practice (3 levels)
- Study Guide
- Quick Catch-Up for Absent Students
- Problem Solving/Application
- Challenge Practice
- Chapter Review Games and Activities
- Project with Rubric
- Cumulative Review

Notetaking Guide
- Student Workbook and Teacher's Edition

Practice Workbook

Worked-Out Solution Key

Chapter Transparency Book
- Warm-Up Exercises/Daily Homework Quiz
- Notetaking Guide Transparencies
- Homework Answer Transparencies

Teacher Tools Transparencies

Assessment

Assessment Book
- Quizzes
- Chapter Tests (3 levels)
- Standardized and SAT/ACT Chapter Tests
- Alternative Assessments
- Cumulative Tests

Benchmark Tests
- Benchmark Tests, correlated to Remediation Book
- Pre-Course, Mid-Year, and End-of-Year Tests
- Chapter Tests

Spanish Assessment Book

Differentiated Instruction

Differentiated Instruction Resources
- Strategies for Reading Mathematics
- Differentiated Instruction Lesson Notes
- English Learner Lesson Notes
- Inclusion Lesson Notes
- Teaching Strategies with Sample Worksheets
- Tips for New Teachers/Math Background Notes
- Teacher Survival Activities/Bulletin Board Ideas

Student Resources in Spanish

Spanish Study Guide

Remediation Book

Skills Readiness (available on Easy Planner)
- Diagnostic Assessment
- Skill Instruction and Alternative Teaching Strategies
- Skill Practice and Enrichment Masters

Pre-AP Resources
- Pacing and Assignment Guide
- Best Practices
- Copymasters

Technology Resources

Plan	***Easy Planner***
Teach	***Video Tutor*** ***Activity Generator*** ***Power Presentations*** ***Animated Algebra***
Assess	***Test Generator*** ***ML Assessment System***
Reteach	***@HomeTutor***
Online Resources	***Classzone.com*** ***eEdition*** ***eWorkbook***

Video Tutor

Technology Highlights for Each Lesson

Easy Planner

Easy access to the Teacher's Edition and all teaching resources. Includes a search feature to locate the materials you need.

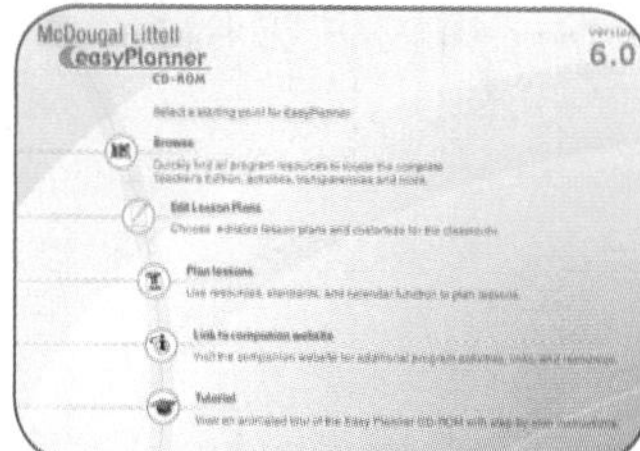

Activity Generator

Leveled, editable activities allow all students to explore a lesson's concepts. Includes teacher notes and closure questions.

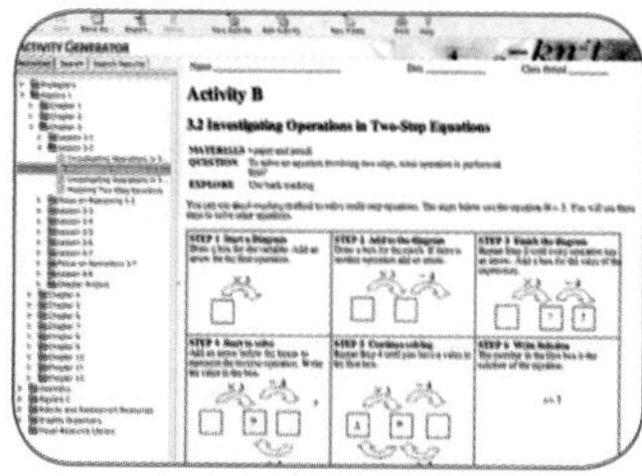

Animated Algebra

Interactive tutorials provide visually engaging alternative opportunities to learn concepts and master skills.

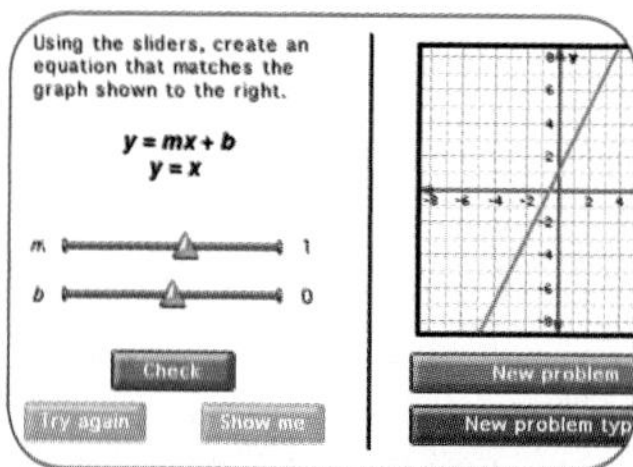

12 Lesson Practice Level B

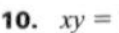

LESSON 12.1 Practice B

For use with pages 765–772

Tell whether the equation represents *direct variation, inverse variation,* or *neither.*

1. $y = -11x$ direct variation
2. $xy = -5$ inverse variation
3. $y = x - 4$ neither
4. $x = \frac{-8}{y}$ inverse variation
5. $xy = 14$ inverse variation
6. $\frac{y}{x} = 13$ direct variation
7. $2x + y = 8$ neither
8. $3y = \frac{9}{x}$ inverse variation
9. $4x - 4y = 0$ direct variation

Graph the inverse variation equation.

10. $xy = 12$

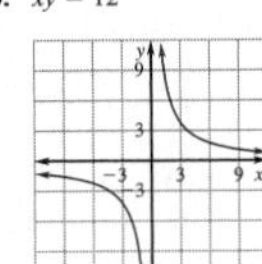

11. $xy = -6$

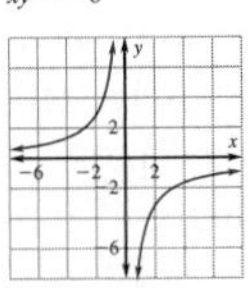

12. $xy = 7$

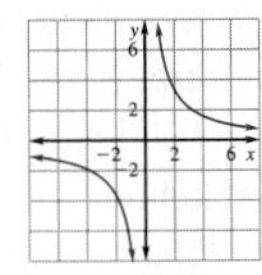

13. $y = \frac{-8}{x}$

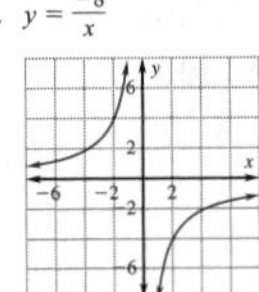

14. $y = \frac{15}{x}$

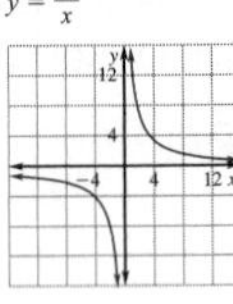

15. $y = \frac{14}{x}$

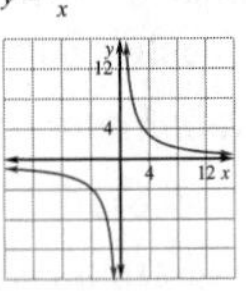

16. $y = \frac{-9}{x}$

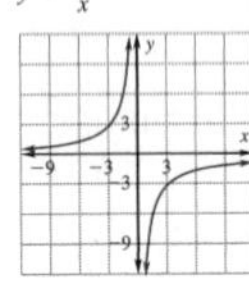

17. $y = \frac{-12}{x}$

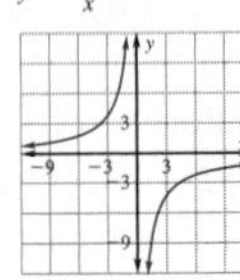

18. $y = \frac{5}{x}$

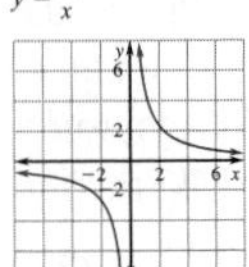

LESSON 12.1

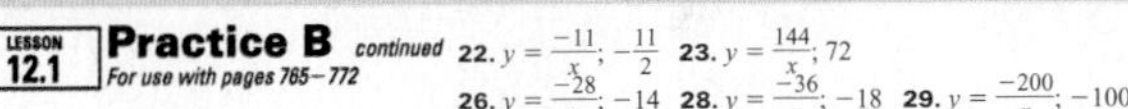

LESSON 12.1 Practice B *continued*

For use with pages 765–772

22. $y = \frac{-11}{x}; -\frac{11}{2}$ 23. $y = \frac{144}{x}; 72$ 26. $y = \frac{-28}{x}; -14$ 28. $y = \frac{-36}{x}; -18$ 29. $y = \frac{-200}{x}; -100$

Given that *y* varies inversely with *x*, use the specified values to write an inverse variation equation that relates *x* and *y*. Then find the value of *y* when $x = 2$.

19. $x = 7, y = 2$ $y = \frac{14}{x}; 7$
20. $x = 3, y = 9$ $y = \frac{27}{x}; \frac{27}{2}$
21. $x = -3, y = 1$ $y = \frac{-3}{x}; -\frac{3}{2}$
22. $x = 11, y = -1$
23. $x = -12, y = -12$
24. $x = -18, y = -4$ $y = \frac{72}{x}; 36$
25. $x = 10, y = 5$ $y = \frac{50}{x}; 25$
26. $x = 7, y = -4$
27. $x = 6, y = 6$ $y = \frac{36}{x}; 18$
28. $x = -3, y = 12$
29. $x = -5, y = 40$
30. $x = -5, y = -11$ $y = \frac{55}{x}; \frac{55}{2}$

Tell whether the table represents inverse variation. If so, write the inverse variation equation.

31. 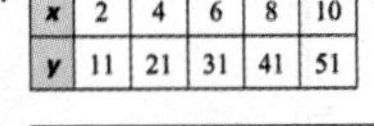

x	2	4	6	8	10
y	11	21	31	41	51

no

32. 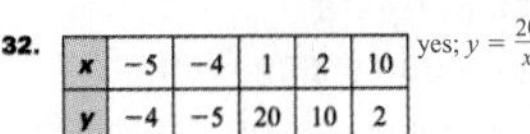

x	−5	−4	1	2	10
y	−4	−5	20	10	2

yes; $y = \frac{20}{x}$

33. 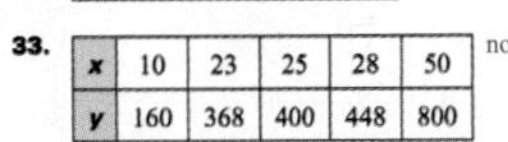

x	10	23	25	28	50
y	160	368	400	448	800

no

34. 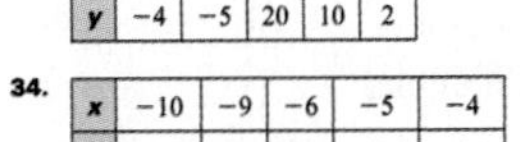

x	−10	−9	−6	−5	−4
y	−1.8	−2	−3	−3.6	−4.5

yes; $y = \frac{18}{x}$

35. **Catalog Orders** A clothing company allows customers to place orders on the Internet or by phone. The orders must be entered into the computer inventory system. The amount of time t needed to enter 1000 orders varies inversely with the number p of people working. The company estimates that 10 people can enter 1000 orders in 240 minutes.
    a. Write an inverse variation equation that relates t and p. $t = \frac{2400}{p}$
    b. Find the time needed to enter 1000 orders if 20 people are working. 120 minutes
    c. Find the time needed to enter 1000 orders if 8 people are working. 300 minutes

36. **Volume and Pressure** The volume V of a gas at a constant temperature varies inversely with the pressure P. When the volume is 125 cubic inches, the pressure is 20 pounds per cubic inch.
    a. Write the inverse variation equation that relates P and V. $V = \frac{2500}{P}$
    b. Find the pressure of a gas with a volume of 250 cubic inches. 10 pounds per in.^{3}

37. **Running** Every other day, weather permitting, you run 5 miles. Write and graph an equation that relates your average running speed s (in miles per hour) and the time t (in hours) that it takes for you to complete the run. Is the equation an inverse variation equation? *Explain.* yes; Answers will vary.

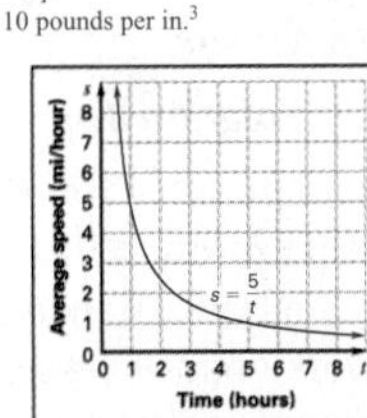

LESSON 12.1

LESSON 12.2 Practice B

For use with pages 775–782

1. domain: all reals except 3; range: all reals except 1
2. domain: all reals except 4; range: all reals except 3
3. domain: all reals except −6; range: all reals except −4
4. domain: all reals except −6; range: all reals except −8

Identify the domain and range of the function from its graph.

1. 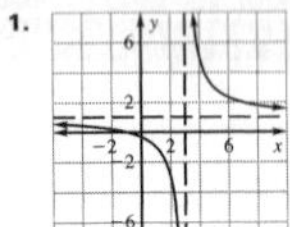

2. 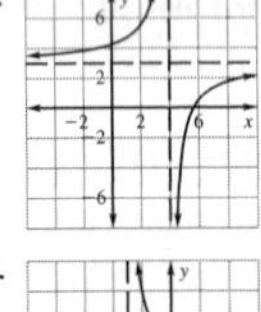

3. 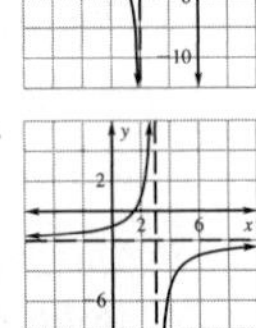

4. 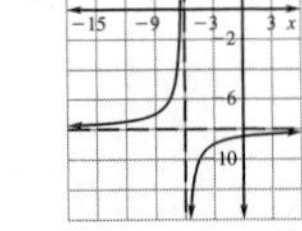

5.

6.

Graph the function and identify its domain and range. Then compare the graph with the graph of $y = \frac{1}{x}$.

5. domain: all reals except −3; range: all reals except 3
6. domain: all reals except 3; range: all reals except −2

7. $y = \frac{8}{x}$

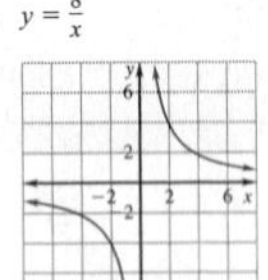

8. $y = \frac{1}{6x}$

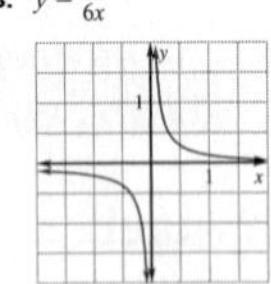

9. $y = \frac{-3}{2x}$

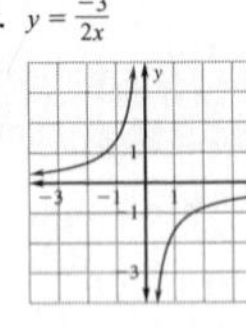

10. $y = \frac{1}{x} - 7$

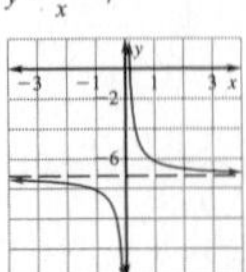

11. $y = \frac{1}{x} + 10$

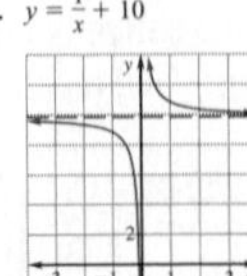

12. $y = \frac{1}{x - 4}$

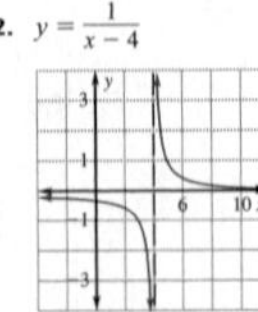

7. domain: all reals except 0; range: all reals except 0; vertical stretch
8. domain: all reals except 0; range: all reals except 0; vertical shrink
9. domain: all reals except 0; range: all reals except 0; vertical stretch and reflection in x-axis
10. domain: all reals except 0; range: all reals except −7; vertical translation 7 units down
11. domain: all reals except 0; range: all reals except 10; vertical translation 10 units up
12. domain: all reals except 4; range: all reals except 0; horizontal translation 4 units right

LESSON 12.2

LESSON 12.2 Practice B *continued*

For use with pages 775–782

13. $x = 6, y = 4$ 14. $x = -5, y = -6$
15. $x = 3, y = -8$ 16. $x = -7, y = 7$
17. $x = 8, y = 12$ 18. $x = -5, y = 10$

Determine the asymptotes of the graph of the function.

13. $y = \frac{10}{x - 6} + 4$
14. $y = \frac{-8}{x + 5} - 6$
15. $y = \frac{14}{x - 3} - 8$
16. $y = \frac{12}{x + 7} + 7$
17. $y = \frac{-4}{x - 8} + 12$
18. $y = \frac{9}{x + 5} + 10$
19. $y = \frac{14}{x - 14} + 1$ $x = 14, y = 1$
20. $y = \frac{-12}{x + 12} - 3$ $x = -12, y = -3$
21. $y = \frac{7}{x - 5} - 14$ $x = 5, y = -14$

Graph the function.

22. $y = \frac{2}{x} + 5$

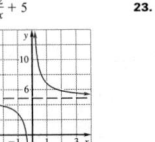

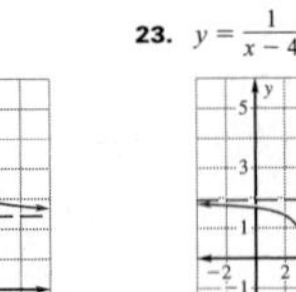

23. $y = \frac{1}{x - 4} + 2$

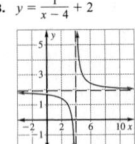

24. $y = \frac{-3}{x + 6} - 1$

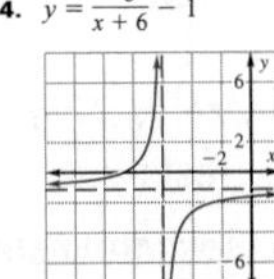

25. **Baseball Hall of Fame** Your baseball team is planning a bus trip to the National Baseball Hall of Fame. The cost for renting a bus is \$515, and the cost will be divided equally among the people who are going on the trip. One admission costs \$14.50.
    a. Write an equation that gives the cost C (in dollars per person) of the trip as a function of the number p of people going on the trip. $C = \frac{515}{p} + 14.5$
    b. Graph the equation.
    c. What would the cost per person be if 20 people go on the trip? \$40.25

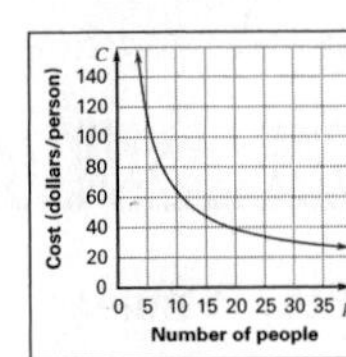

26. **Fundraiser** A pizza shop makes pizzas that organizations sell for fundraisers. One organization has placed an order for 450 pizzas. Currently, 4 people are scheduled to put together the pizzas. The owner of the shop hopes to call in some extra workers to complete all of the pizzas.
    a. Write an equation that gives the average number n of pizzas made per person as a function of the number p of extra workers that can come in and help complete the work. $n = \frac{450}{4 + p}$
    b. Graph the equation.
    c. If 2 people come in to help out, what is the average number of pizzas made per person? 75 pizzas

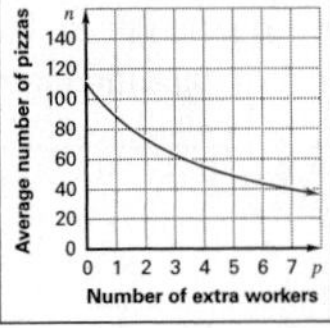

LESSON 12.3

Practice B

For use with pages 784–791

Divide.

1. $(18x^3 - 24x^2 + 12x) \div 6x$ $3x^2 - 4x + 2$
2. $(-5x^3 + 15x^2 - 30x) \div (-5x)$ $x^2 - 3x + 6$
3. $(22x^4 - 18x^2 + 6x) \div (-2x)$ $-11x^3 + 9x - 3$
4. $(x^2 + 6x + 5) \div (x + 5)$ $x + 1$
5. $(5x^2 + 7x - 6) \div (x + 2)$ $5x - 3$
6. $(4x^2 + x - 5) \div (x - 1)$ $4x + 5$
7. $(6x^2 + 22x - 8) \div (x + 4)$ $6x - 2$
8. $(4x^2 + x - 8) \div (x - 2)$ $4x + 9 + \frac{10}{x - 2}$
9. $(9x^2 + 5x - 6) \div (x + 1)$ $9x - 4 - \frac{2}{x + 1}$
10. $(3x^2 - 7x + 14) \div (3x + 2)$ $x - 3 + \frac{20}{3x + 2}$

Graph the function.

11. $y = \frac{x + 8}{x}$

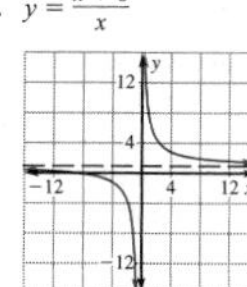

12. $y = \frac{3x - 5}{x}$

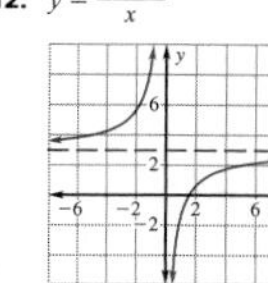

13. $y = \frac{x + 5}{x - 2}$

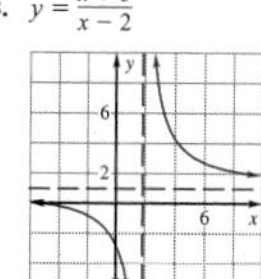

14. **Scootcar Rental** A resort area offers rentals of scootcars (a cross between a scooter and a small car) for \$40 per hour plus a \$4.50 gasoline fill-up fee.

    a. Write an equation that gives the average cost C per hour as a function of the number h of hours the scootcar is rented. $C = \frac{40h + 4.5}{h}$

    b. Graph the equation.

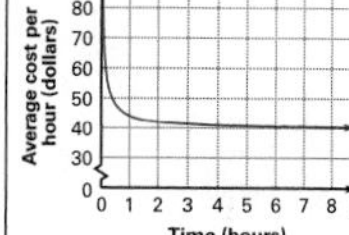

15. **Juice Bar** Between 1995 and 2004, the number D of drinks (in thousands) sold at a juice bar can be modeled by $D = 4t + 18$ where t is the number of years since 1995. The number F of drinks (in thousands) made from fruit juice rather than vegetable juice can be modeled by $F = 2t + 32$.

    a. Use long division to find a model for the ratio R of the number of fruit drinks sold to the total number of drinks sold. $R = \frac{1}{2} + \frac{23}{2(2t + 9)}$

    b. Graph the model.

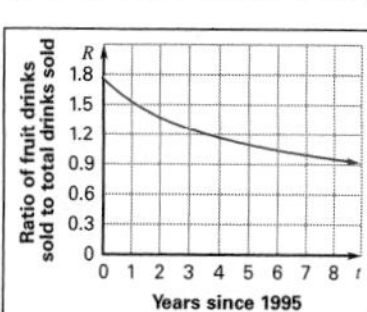

LESSON 12.3

LESSON 12.4

Practice B

For use with pages 794–800

Find the excluded values, if any, of the expression.

1. $\frac{14}{3x}$ $x = 0$
2. $\frac{-8}{x - 5}$ $x = 5$
3. $\frac{5x}{x + 10}$ $x = -10$
4. $\frac{-x}{4x - 8}$ $x = 2$
5. $\frac{3x}{7x + 21}$ $x = -3$
6. $\frac{x + 1}{3x + 7}$ $x = -\frac{7}{3}$
7. $\frac{x + 6}{x^2 - 2x + 1}$ $x = 1$
8. $\frac{8}{x^2 + 4x - 12}$ $x = -6, 2$
9. $\frac{7x}{x^2 - 25}$ $x = -5, 5$

Simplify the rational expression, if possible. Find the excluded values.

10. $\frac{-36x^2}{18x}$ $-2x; x = 0$
11. $\frac{6x - 24}{x - 4}$ $6; x = 4$
12. $\frac{4x - 12}{3 - x}$ $-4; x = 3$
13. $\frac{x + 11}{x^2 - 121}$ $\frac{1}{x - 11}; x = -11, 11$
14. $\frac{x + 3}{x^2 + 10x + 21}$ $\frac{1}{x + 7}; x = -3, -7$
15. $\frac{x - 4}{x^2 + 11x + 24}$ in simplest form; $x = -3, -8$

Write and simplify a rational expression for the ratio of the perimeter to the area of the given figure.

16. Square $\frac{1}{2x}$

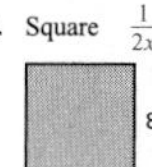

17. Rectangle $\frac{3x + 5}{x(x + 5)}$

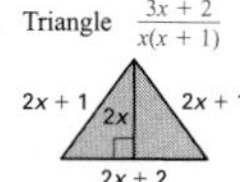

18. Triangle $\frac{3x + 2}{x(x + 1)}$

19. **Zoo Exhibit** The directors of a zoo have drawn up preliminary plans for a rectangular exhibit. They have decided on dimensions that are related as shown.

    a. Write a rational expression for the ratio of the perimeter to the area of the exhibit.

    b. Simplify your expression from part (a).

19. a. $\frac{2(4x + 3) + 2(4x - 2)}{(4x + 3)(4x - 2)}$ b. $\frac{8x + 1}{(4x + 3)(2x - 1)}$

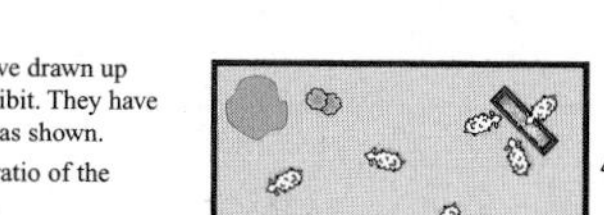
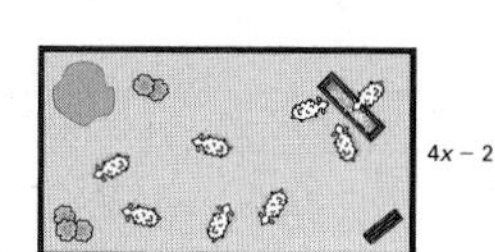

20. **Materials Used** The material consumed M (in thousands of pounds) by a plastic injection molding machine per year between 1995 and 2004 can be modeled by

$$M = \frac{8t^2 + 66t + 70}{(3 - 0.2t + 0.1t^2)(t + 7)}$$

where t is the number of years since 1995. Simplify the model and approximate the number of pounds consumed in 2000.

$\frac{2(4t + 5)}{0.1t^2 - 0.2t + 3}$; about 11 thousand pounds

LESSON 12.5

Practice B

For use with pages 802–809

5. $\frac{1}{2(x + 5)}$ 7. $\frac{x(x + 3)}{3(2x - 1)}$ 9. $3(x + 5)$

Find the product.

1. $\frac{4x^2}{15} \cdot \frac{5}{8x^5}$ $\frac{1}{6x^3}$
2. $\frac{24}{7x^2} \cdot \frac{14x^6}{40}$ $\frac{6x^4}{5}$
3. $\frac{21}{2x + 12} \cdot \frac{4x + 24}{15}$ $\frac{14}{5}$
4. $\frac{5x + 10}{2x - 6} \cdot \frac{x - 3}{10x + 20}$ $\frac{1}{4}$
5. $\frac{x - 3}{2x + 8} \cdot \frac{x + 4}{x^2 + 2x - 15}$
6. $\frac{x^2 + 4x - 12}{x^2 + 7x + 10} \cdot \frac{x + 5}{2x - 4}$ $\frac{x + 6}{2(x + 2)}$
7. $\frac{6x}{4x^2 - 1} \cdot \frac{2x^2 + 7x + 3}{18}$
8. $\frac{x^4}{x^4 + 5x^3} \cdot (x + 5)$ x
9. $\frac{3x - 6}{x^2 - x - 2} \cdot (x^2 + 6x + 5)$

Find the quotient.

10. $\frac{24}{5x^3} \div \frac{6}{25x^2}$ $\frac{20}{x}$
11. $\frac{11x^4}{18} \div \frac{22}{9x^2}$ $\frac{x^6}{4}$
12. $\frac{7x + 21}{30} \div \frac{21x + 63}{20}$ $\frac{2}{9}$
13. $\frac{4x - 24}{3x + 15} \div \frac{12x - 72}{x + 5}$ $\frac{1}{9}$
14. $\frac{x + 2}{3x - 3} \div \frac{x^2 + 11x + 18}{x - 1}$ $\frac{1}{3(x + 9)}$
15. $\frac{x^2 + 4x}{4x} \div \frac{x^2 + x - 12}{x - 3}$ $\frac{1}{4}$
16. $\frac{2x + 10}{x^2 - 25} \div \frac{4x^2}{2x^2 - 10x}$ $\frac{1}{x}$
17. $\frac{2x - 14}{x^2 - 4x - 21} \div (x + 3)$ $\frac{2}{(x + 3)^2}$

18. **Wall Art** You want to create a rectangular picture from 2-inch by 3-inch tiles. You want the picture's dimensions to be related as shown.

    a. Write and simplify an expression that you can use to determine the number of 2-inch by 3-inch tiles that will be needed for the picture. $4x^2$

    b. If $x = 5$, how many tiles will you need? 100 tiles

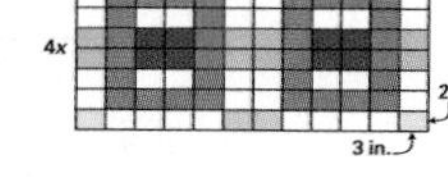

19. **Profit** The total profit P (in millions of dollars) earned by a company from 1995 to 2004 can be modeled by

$$P = \frac{3500 + 500t}{98 - t}$$

where t is the number of years since 1995. The number N (in hundreds of thousands) of units sold can be modeled by

$$N = \frac{(t + 7)(3000 - 20t)}{490 - 5t}$$

where t is the number of years since 1995. Write a model that gives the profit earned per unit per year. Then approximate the profit per unit in 2002.

$\frac{1250}{150 - t}$; about \$8.74 per unit

LESSON 12.5

12 Lesson Practice Level B

LESSON 12.6 Practice B

For use with pages 812–819

Find the sum or difference.

1. $\frac{8}{x+5} + \frac{x}{x+5}$ $\frac{x+8}{x+5}$

2. $\frac{10x}{x-4} - \frac{6x}{x-4}$ $\frac{4x}{x-4}$

3. $\frac{x+3}{x-9} + \frac{5x}{x-9}$ $\frac{3(2x+1)}{x-9}$

4. $\frac{x-5}{x+2} - \frac{x+6}{x+2}$ $\frac{-11}{x+2}$

5. $\frac{3x-4}{x^2-9} + \frac{7x-3}{x^2-9}$ $\frac{10x-7}{x^2-9}$

6. $\frac{2x+4}{3x^2} - \frac{x-1}{3x^2}$ $\frac{x+5}{3x^2}$

Find the LCD of the rational expressions.

7. $\frac{6}{5x^3}, \frac{7}{15x}$ $15x^3$

8. $\frac{10}{x}, \frac{9x}{x+7}$ $x(x+7)$

9. $\frac{3x+1}{x-4}, \frac{x-4}{x+6}$ $(x-4)(x+6)$

10. $\frac{x+5}{2x-4}, \frac{4x}{x-2}$ $2(x-2)$

11. $\frac{1}{x^2-5x}, \frac{8}{x^2-3x-10}$ $x(x-5)(x+2)$

12. $\frac{3}{x^2+5x+4}, \frac{4x}{x^2+2x+1}$ $(x+1)^2(x+4)$

Find the sum or difference.

13. $\frac{11}{2x} + \frac{4}{7x}$ $\frac{85}{14x}$

14. $\frac{8}{3x^3} - \frac{5}{12x}$ $\frac{32-5x^2}{12x^3}$

15. $\frac{8x}{x-5} - \frac{3x}{x+2}$ $\frac{x(5x+31)}{(x-5)(x+2)}$

16. $\frac{x}{6x-5} + \frac{1}{5x-3}$

17. $\frac{4}{x^2-7x} - \frac{3}{x}$ $\frac{25-3x}{x(x-7)}$

18. $\frac{5}{x^2} + \frac{x+3}{x-1}$ $\frac{x^3+3x^2+5x-5}{x^2(x-1)}$

19. $\frac{x+3}{x-1} + \frac{x+2}{x+1}$ $\frac{2x^2+5x+1}{(x-1)(x+1)}$

20. $\frac{2x}{x^2-3x} + \frac{x+4}{x-3}$ $\frac{(x+6)}{(x-3)}$

21. $\frac{1}{x^2+5x+4} - \frac{1}{x^2-16}$ $\frac{-5}{(x+1)(x+4)(x-4)}$

16. $\frac{5x^2+3x-5}{(6x-5)(5x-3)}$

22. **Paddle Boat** You paddle boat 8 miles upstream (against the current) and 8 miles downstream (with the current). The speed of the current is 1 mile per hour.
   a. Write an equation that gives the total travel time t (in hours) as a function of your average speed r (in miles per hour) in still water. $t = \frac{16r}{(r-1)(r+1)}$
   b. Find your total travel time if your average speed in still water is 3 miles per hour. 6 h
   c. How much faster is your total travel time if you increased your average speed in still water to 3.5 miles per hour? Round your answer to the nearest tenth. about 1.0 h

23. **Bike Ride** You bike 50 miles from home. On your way back home, your average speed increases by 3 miles per hour.
   a. Write an equation that gives the total biking time t (in hours) as a function of your average speed r (in miles per hour) when you are biking away from home. $t = \frac{100r+150}{r(r+3)}$
   b. Find the total biking time if you bike away from your home at an average speed of 15 miles per hour. Round your answer to the nearest tenth. about 6.1 h
   c. How much longer is your total biking time if you bike away from your home at an average speed of 12 miles per hour? about 1.4 h

LESSON 12.6

LESSON 12.7 Practice B

For use with pages 820–826

Solve the equation. Check your solution.

1. $\frac{x}{27} = \frac{3}{x}$ $-9, 9$

2. $\frac{3}{x} = \frac{2}{x+4}$ -12

3. $\frac{4}{x-7} = \frac{2}{x}$ -7

4. $\frac{10}{x+2} = \frac{7}{x-4}$ 18

5. $\frac{-5}{x+4} = \frac{x}{x+4}$ -5

6. $\frac{8}{x+8} = \frac{x}{x+2}$ $-4, 4$

7. $\frac{-1}{x+2} = \frac{x}{x+2}$ -1

8. $\frac{2}{3x} = \frac{x+3}{2x-5}$ no solution

9. $\frac{6x}{x+2} = \frac{-2}{x+2}$ $-\frac{1}{3}$

Find the LCD of the rational expressions in the equation.

10. $\frac{7x}{x-3} + 4 = \frac{x+1}{x-3}$ $x-3$

11. $\frac{3}{2x-2} + 4 = \frac{7x}{x-1}$ $2(x-1)$

12. $\frac{7}{x-2} + 1 = \frac{4}{x-3}$ $(x-2)(x-3)$

Solve the equation. Check your solution.

13. $\frac{3x}{x+4} - 2 = \frac{-12}{x+4}$ no solution

14. $\frac{3}{x+2} + 5 = \frac{4}{x+2}$ $-\frac{9}{5}$

15. $\frac{2x}{x-1} + 2 = \frac{10}{x+2}$ no solution

16. $\frac{x-1}{x+5} + 6 = \frac{-2}{x+2}$ $-4, -\frac{17}{7}$

17. $\frac{4x}{x-5} + 1 = \frac{9}{x-1}$ no solution

18. $\frac{x}{x-4} - \frac{5x}{x-2} = \frac{-18}{x-2}$ 3, 6

19. **Stain Mixing** You are staining a coffee table you just made. After testing some sample pieces of wood, you decide that you want a mix of a yellow stain and a red stain. You estimate that you want a mix that contains 75% of the yellow stain. You only have 1-pint that is made up of equal parts of the stain. How many pints of the yellow stain do you have to add to the current mixture? 1 pt

20. **Wallpaper** Working together an expert wallpaper hanger and an assistant can hang the wallpaper in a room in 3 hours. The assistant can hang the wallpaper in one and one-half times the time it takes the expert wallpaper hanger to hang the wallpaper alone. Let x represent the time (in hours) that the assistant can hang the wallpaper alone.
   a. Copy and complete the table.

Person	Fraction of room papered each hour	Time (hours)	Fraction of room papered
Assistant	$\frac{1}{x}$	3	$\frac{3}{x}$
Expert	$\frac{3}{2x}$	3	$\frac{9}{2x}$

   b. *Explain* why the sum of the expressions in the last column must be 1. Answers will vary.
   c. Write a rational equation that you can use to find the amount of time it takes the assistant to wallpaper the room alone. Then solve the equation. $\frac{3}{x} + \frac{9}{2x} = 1$; 7.5 h

LESSON 12.7

CHAPTER 12
Quiz 1
For use after Lessons 12.1–12.2

Tell whether the equation represents *direct variation, inverse variation,* or *neither*.

1. $y = 3x$

2. $xy = -2$

3. $2x + y = 7$

Given that *y* varies inversely with *x*, use the specified values to write an inverse equation that relates *x* and *y*. Then find the value of *y* when *x* = 2.

4. $x = 7, y = 5$

5. $x = 3, y = -8$

6. $x = \frac{1}{2}, y = 14$

Graph the function and identify its domain and range.

7. $y = \frac{7}{x}$

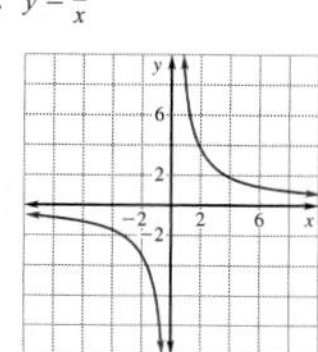

8. $y = \frac{-1}{x}$

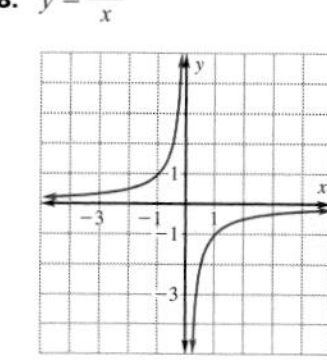

9. $y = \frac{-2}{x + 1}$

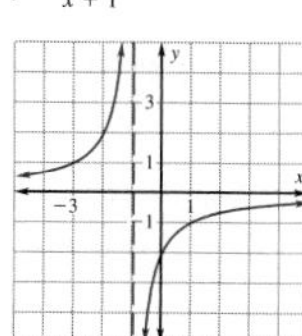

Answers

1. direct variation

2. inverse variation

3. neither

4. $y = \frac{35}{x}; \frac{35}{2}$

5. $y = \frac{-24}{x}; -12$

6. $y = \frac{7}{x}; \frac{7}{2}$

7. See left. The domain and range are all nonzero real numbers.

8. See left. The domain and range are all nonzero real numbers.

9. See left. The domain is all real numbers except $x = -1$. The range is all real numbers except $y = 0$.

CHAPTER 12
Quiz 2
For use after Lessons 12.3–12.4

Divide.

1. $(x^2 - 8x + 15) \div (x - 5)$

2. $(x^2 + 7x - 18) \div (x - 2)$

Graph the function.

3. $y = \frac{x + 5}{x - 6}$

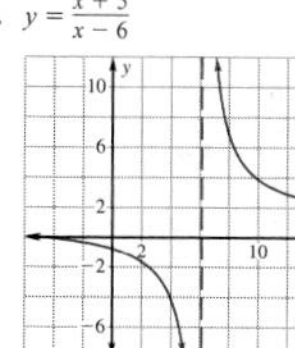

4. $y = \frac{3x + 4}{x + 3}$

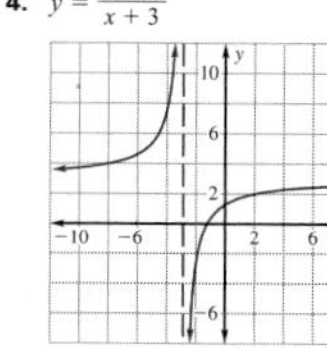

Simplify the rational expression, if possible. Find the excluded values.

5. $\frac{x - 1}{x^2 - 1}$

6. $\frac{4x^3 - 12x^2}{8x^2}$

7. $\frac{132x^4}{55x}$

8. $\frac{x^2 - 2x - 15}{x^2 - 9}$

Answers

1. $x - 3$

2. $x + 9$

3. See left.

4. See left.

5. $\frac{1}{x + 1}$; The excluded values are -1 and 1.

6. $\frac{x - 3}{2}$; The excluded value is 0.

7. $\frac{12x^3}{5}$; The excluded value is 0.

8. $\frac{x - 5}{x - 3}$; The excluded values are -3 and 3.

CHAPTER 12
Quiz 3
For use after Lessons 12.5–12.7

Find the product or quotient.

1. $\frac{6x^3}{5} \cdot \frac{7}{18x^4}$

2. $\frac{20 - 4x}{25 - x^2} \div \frac{x}{5 + x}$

Find the sum or difference.

3. $\frac{3x + 5}{x - 6} - \frac{x - 4}{x - 6}$

4. $\frac{x}{x^2 + 9x + 8} + \frac{7}{x + 8}$

Solve the equation. Check your solution.

5. $\frac{3x}{x + 4} = \frac{x}{x - 2}$

6. $\frac{3}{x + 1} + \frac{1}{x - 1} = 2$

7. Jeremy and Paul can plant a garden in 4 hours if they work together. If each worked alone, it would take Jeremy 6 hours longer than Paul to plant the garden. How long would it take Jeremy to plant the garden if he worked alone?

Answers

1. $\frac{7}{15x}$

2. $\frac{4}{x}$

3. $\frac{2x + 9}{x - 6}$

4. $\frac{8x + 7}{(x + 8)(x + 1)}$

5. 0 and 5

6. 0 and 2

7. 12 h

12 Assessment

CHAPTER 12 Chapter Test B
For use after Chapter 12

Tell whether the table represents inverse variation. If so, write the inverse variation equation.

1.

x	−10	−5	5	10	15
y	−40	−20	20	40	60

2.

x	−8	−1	12	32	64
y	−6	−48	4	1.5	0.5

In Exercises 3 and 4, use the following information.

In chemistry, Boyle's law states that at a constant temperature, the volume V of a gas varies inversely with the pressure P. For a certain gas, the pressure is 5 when the volume is 20.

3. Write the inverse variation equation that relates V and P.
4. Find the volume of the gas when the pressure is 10.

Graph the function and identify its domain and range. Then compare the graph with the graph of $y = \frac{1}{x}$.

5. $y = \frac{2}{x+3}$

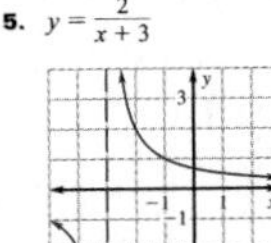

6. $y = \frac{-1}{x} + 2$

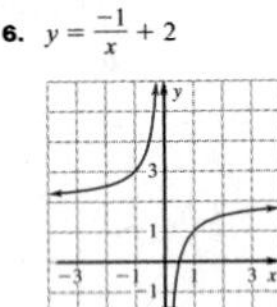

Write a function whose graph is a hyperbola that has the asymptotes and passes through the point.

7. $x = 5, y = 6; (4, 2)$
8. $x = -1, y = -3; (1, -2)$

Divide.

9. $(x^2 + 3x - 6) \div (x + 1)$
10. $(6x^2 - 3x + 5) \div (2x - 3)$

Simplify the expression, if possible. Find the excluded values.

11. $\frac{-35x^6}{25x^2}$
12. $\frac{2x - 18}{9 - x}$
13. $\frac{2x^2 - x - 15}{x^2 + x - 12}$

14. Write and simplify a rational expression for the ratio of the surface area to the volume of the rectangular solid.

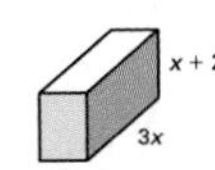

Answers

1. no
2. yes; $y = \frac{48}{x}$
3. $V = \frac{100}{P}$
4. 10
5. See left. domain: all real numbers except −3; range: all real numbers except 0; The graph is a vertical stretch and horizontal shift (of 3 units to the left) of the graph of $y = \frac{1}{x}$.
6. See left. domain: all real numbers except 0; range: all real numbers except 2; The graph is a reflection in the x-axis and a vertical shift (of 2 units up) of the graph of $y = \frac{1}{x}$.
7. $y = \frac{4}{x-5} + 6$
8. $y = \frac{2}{x+1} - 3$
9. $x + 2 + \frac{-8}{x+1}$
10. $3x + 3 + \frac{14}{2x-3}$
11. $\frac{-7x^4}{5}$; 0
12. −2; 9
13. $\frac{2x+5}{x+4}$; −4, 3
14. $\frac{2(7x+8)}{3x(x+2)}$

CHAPTER 12 Chapter Test B *continued*
For use after Chapter 12

15. The percent p of salt in a saltwater solution can be modeled by $p = \frac{100x + 100}{x + 10}$ where x is the number of grams of salt that are added to the solution. Write the model in the form $y = \frac{a}{x-h} + k$. Then graph the equation.

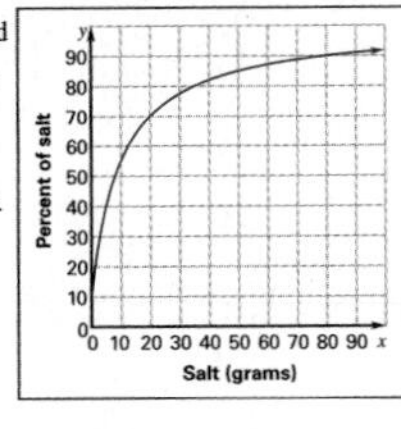

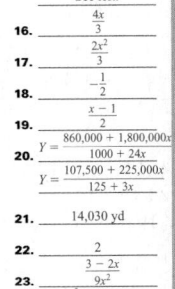

Find the product or quotient.

16. $\frac{18x^4}{25x^2} \cdot \frac{50x^5}{27x^6}$
17. $\frac{20}{x^3} \div \frac{30}{x^5}$
18. $\frac{x^2 - 9}{x + 3} \cdot \frac{1}{6 - 2x}$
19. $\frac{x^2 - 25}{x^2 - 4x - 5} \div \frac{2x + 10}{x^2 - 1}$

In Exercises 20 and 21, use the following information.

For the period of 1990-2002, the number Y of rushing yards gained by Emmitt Smith can be modeled by $Y = \frac{860 + 1800x}{1 + 0.024x}$ where x is the number of years since 1990.

20. Rewrite the model so that it has only whole number coefficients. Then simplify the model.
21. Approximate the number of rushing yards Smith gained in 1999.

Find the sum or difference.

22. $\frac{x-2}{x+3} + \frac{x+8}{x+3}$
23. $\frac{1}{3x^2} - \frac{2}{9x}$
24. $\frac{x}{x-1} + \frac{2x+3}{x^2-1}$

Solve the equation. Check your solutions.

25. $\frac{8}{x+3} = \frac{4}{x}$
26. $\frac{3x}{x-4} = 5 + \frac{12}{x-4}$

27. The body mass index expresses the relationship between a person's height and weight by the equation $B = \frac{705W}{H^2}$ where H is the height (in inches) and W is the weight (in pounds). A woman weighs 160 pounds and is 5 feet 4 inches tall. How many pounds must the woman lose to lower her BMI to 25?

Answers

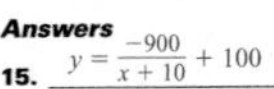

15. $y = \frac{-900}{x+10} + 100$; See left.

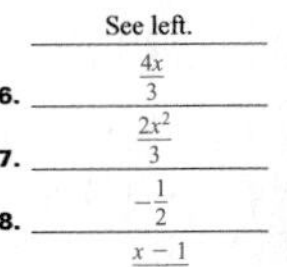

16. $\frac{4x}{3}$
17. $\frac{2x^2}{3}$
18. $-\frac{1}{2}$
19. $\frac{x-1}{2}$
20. $Y = \frac{860{,}000 + 1{,}800{,}000x}{1000 + 24x}$; $Y = \frac{107{,}500 + 225{,}000x}{125 + 3x}$
21. 14,030 yd
22. 2
23. $\frac{3 - 2x}{9x^2}$
24. $\frac{x^2 + 3x + 3}{(x-1)(x+1)}$
25. 3
26. no solution
27. about 15 pounds

CHAPTER 12 Standardized Test
For use after Chapter 12

Multiple Choice

1. Suppose that y varies inversely with x, and $y = 8$ when $x = 9$. What is the constant of variation? D

   Ⓐ $\frac{9}{8}$ Ⓑ 8 Ⓒ 9 Ⓓ 72

2. Which equation represents the given graph? D

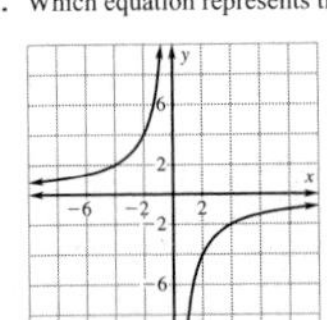

   Ⓐ $y = \frac{2}{x}$ Ⓑ $y = -\frac{2}{x}$
   Ⓒ $y = \frac{8}{x}$ Ⓓ $y = -\frac{8}{x}$

3. What are the vertical and horizontal asymptotes of the graph shown? B

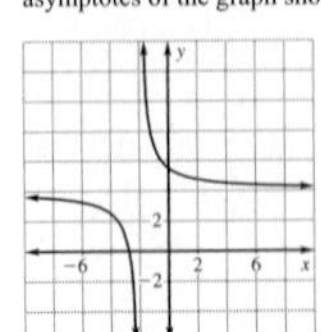

   Ⓐ $x = 4, y = -2$ Ⓑ $x = -2, y = 4$
   Ⓒ $x = -4, y = 2$ Ⓓ $x = 2, y = -4$

4. What is the range of the equation $y = \frac{a}{x-2} - 5$? B

   Ⓐ All real numbers except $y = 5$
   Ⓑ All real numbers except $y = -5$
   Ⓒ All real numbers except $x = 2$
   Ⓓ All real numbers except $x = -2$

5. Which equation represents the given graph? C

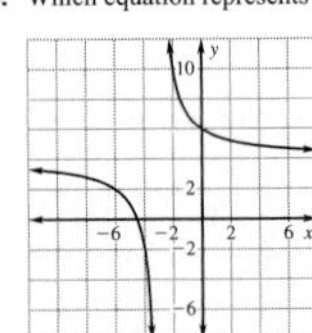

   Ⓐ $y = \frac{6}{x+3} - 4$ Ⓑ $y = \frac{6}{x-3} - 4$
   Ⓒ $y = \frac{6}{x+3} + 4$ Ⓓ $y = \frac{6}{x-3} + 4$

6. What is the remainder when you divide $5x^2 + 4x - 40$ by $x - 4$? D

   Ⓐ −15 Ⓑ −24
   Ⓒ 24 Ⓓ 56

7. What is the horizontal asymptote of the graph of $y = \frac{bx + c}{x} + k$? A

   Ⓐ $y = b$ Ⓑ $y = c$
   Ⓒ $y = k$ Ⓓ $y = 0$

CHAPTER 12 Standardized Test *continued*
For use after Chapter 12

8. The expression $\frac{a}{x^2 - 9x + 20}$ simplifies to $\frac{x+2}{x-4}$. What is the value of a? C

   Ⓐ $x^2 + 5x - 6$ Ⓑ $x^2 - 8x + 15$
   Ⓒ $x^2 - 3x - 10$ Ⓓ $x^2 + 7x + 12$

9. What is the quotient $\frac{x^2 - 9}{-(x+3)} \div (x - 3)$? A

   Ⓐ −1 Ⓑ 0
   Ⓒ 1 Ⓓ $-(x^2 - 9)$

10. Which is a factor of the LCD of $\frac{x-5}{x^2 + 8x + 15}$ and $\frac{x-2}{x^2 - 4x - 21}$? D

   Ⓐ $x - 5$ Ⓑ $x - 2$
   Ⓒ $x + 7$ Ⓓ $x - 7$

11. What is the solution of $\frac{4}{x-5} = \frac{2}{x+5} + \frac{10}{x^2 - 25}$? A

   Ⓐ −10 Ⓑ −5 Ⓒ 0 Ⓓ 5

12. If the solution to the equation $\frac{6}{x-n} = \frac{10}{x+n} - \frac{4}{x^2 - n^2}$ is 9, what is the value of n? C

   Ⓐ −2 Ⓑ 0 Ⓒ 2 Ⓓ 4

Gridded Answer

13. What value of x makes the expression $\frac{6}{x-5} - 8$ undefined?

(Grid: 5)

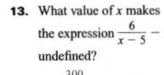

14. a. $t = \frac{300}{r} + 0.75$;

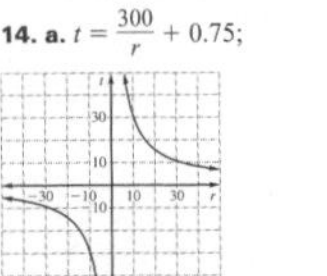

b. The graph shifts 5 units to the right and 0.25 unit down.

Short Response

14. Your aunt is driving 300 miles to your house. On her way, she takes a 45 minute lunch break. See below.

   a. Write and graph an equation that gives the total time t (in hours) of your aunt's trip as a function of her average driving speed r (in miles per hour).

   b. Your aunt drives to your house again. This time her average speed is 5 miles per hour less than her average driving speed in part (a), and she takes a 30 minute lunch break. *Explain* how the graph would change.

Extended Response

15. A gift wrap company offers you the opportunity to sell its gift wrap packages, but you must pay the company a one-time fee of $350 plus $3 for each package that you plan to sell.

   a. Write an equation that gives the average cost C per package (including the fee) as a function of the number of packages p that you plan to sell.

   b. You want to sell enough gift wrap packages so that the average cost C per package (including the fee) decreases to $4. Write and solve an equation to find the number of packages you need to sell.

   c. Is it possible for you to sell enough packages so that the average cost per package drops to $2.25? *Explain* your answer. No; If you were to substitute $2.25 for C in the equation, you would get a negative answer for p. It is not possible to sell a negative number of packages.

15. a. $C = \frac{350 + 3p}{p}$ b. $\frac{350 + 3p}{p} = 4$; You would need to sell 350 packages to reduce the cost of each package to $4.

Alternative Assessment and Math Journal

For use after Chapter 12

Journal

1. Explain and show how to add, subtract, multiply, and divide the rational expressions $\frac{5 + x}{x^2 + 1}$ and $\frac{4}{x - 3}$.

Multi-Step Problem

2. Your family is planning a big reunion picnic at a local park. The cost to reserve a pavilion for a day is \$400. It is a potluck-style picnic, but your family has agreed to purchase all of the beverages and accessories (i.e., plates, napkins, cups) for the entire group. It has been determined that the cost for these items is \$4.75 per person.
   a. Write a function C for the average cost (including pavilion) per person attending the picnic.
   b. Graph the function in part (a).
   c. If 50 people attend the picnic, what is the average cost per person?
   d. How many people need to attend to get the average cost per person below \$6?
   e. What is the domain of this function? What is the range?
   f. Describe the values for the average cost per person as the number of people increases.
   g. Will the average cost per person ever go below \$4.75? Explain.

1. Complete answers should include: work showing each operation being carried out; explanations of the steps being used to carry out each operation.

2. a. $C = \frac{400}{x} + 4.75$ or $C = \frac{400 + 4.75x}{x}$

b.

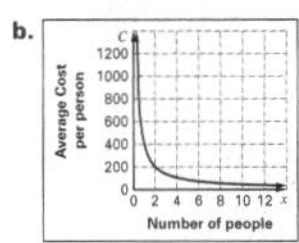

c. \$12.75 **d.** over 320 people **e.** $x > 0$; $C > 4.75$ **f.** The average cost per person decreases toward \$4.75 as the number of people increases. The decreases are rapid at first, but become more gradual. **g.** No, the average cost per person cannot go below \$4.75. This value is a horizontal asymptote for the function. Because the accessories cost \$4.75 per person and a portion of the pavilion cost will be added to this amount, the average cost per person will never drop below this amount.

CHAPTER 12

Alternative Assessment Rubric *continued*

For use after Chapter 12

Journal Solution

1. Complete answers should include:
   - work showing each operation being carried out.
   - explanations of the steps being used to carry out each operation.

Multi-Step Problem Solution

2. **a.** $C = \frac{400 + 4.75x}{x}$
   b.

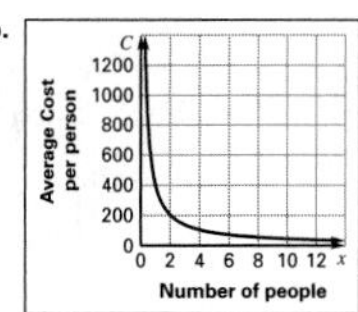

   c. \$12.75
   d. over 320 people
   e. $x > 0$; $C > 4.75$
   f. The average cost per person decreases toward 4.75 as the number of people increases. The decreases are rapid at first, but become more gradual.
   g. No, the average cost per person cannot go below \$4.75. This value is a horizontal asymptote for the function. Because the extra items cost \$4.75 per person and a portion of the pavilion cost will be added to this amount, the average cost per person will never drop below this amount.

Multi-Step Problem Rubric

4 The student answers all parts of the problem correctly and completely. The student shows all work. The student's work is neat.

3 The student answers all parts of the problem. The student's work may contain one or two errors in the calculations, graph, or equation. The student shows most work. The student's work is neat.

2 The student answers all parts of the problem, but there are more than two errors in the calculations, graph, or equation. The student shows some work. The student's work is sloppy.

1 The student does not complete all parts of the problem. The student's work has several errors in the calculations, graph, and equation. The student's work is sloppy, or no work is shown.

PLAN AND PREPARE

Main Ideas

In Chapter 12, students model inverse variation by writing and graphing inverse equations. Students graph rational equations and compare them to the parent function. They divide polynomials and then use this skill to graph rational functions. Students simplify rational expressions, stating any excluded values. They multiply, divide, add, and subtract rational expressions and then use these operations to solve rational equations.

Prerequisite Skills

Skills Readiness, available on the *Easy Planner*, provides review and practice for the Skills Check portion of the Prerequisite Skills quiz.

How student answers the exercises	What to assign from *Skills Readiness*
Any of Exs. 5–8 answered incorrectly	**Skill 67** Factor polynomials
Any of Exs. 9–12 answered incorrectly	**Skill 47** Multiply and divide fractions
Any of Exs. 13–16 answered incorrectly	**Skill 77** Solve proportions
All exercises answered correctly	Chapter 12 Enrichment

Additional skills review and practice is available in the Skills Review Handbook, pp. 909–937, and the @HomeTutor.

12 Rational Equations and Functions

Making Sense of Chapter 12
Rational functions are nonlinear functions. By the end of this chapter, you will be able to graph rational functions, perform operations with rational expressions, and solve rational equations.

Before

Previously, you learned the following skills, which you'll use in Chapter 12: performing operations on numerical fractions, solving proportions, and factoring polynomials.

Prerequisite Skills

VOCABULARY CHECK

1. What is the **least common denominator** of $\frac{3}{8}$ and $\frac{7}{10}$? **40**
2. Which equation is a **direct variation** equation, $\frac{y}{5} = x$ or $\frac{5}{y} = x$? $\mathbf{\frac{y}{5} = x}$
3. What is the **degree** of the polynomial $4x - 2 + 5x^2$? **2**
4. Identify the **extraneous solution** when solving $\sqrt{x + 2} = x$. **−1**

SKILLS CHECK

Factor the polynomial. ***(Prerequisite skill for 12.4–12.6)***

5. $x^2 - 2x - 15$ **$(x - 5)(x + 3)$**
6. $2x^2 - 8x + 6$ **$2(x - 3)(x - 1)$**
7. $9x^2 - 25$ **$(3x + 5)(3x - 5)$**
8. $3x^3 - 48x$ **$3x(x + 4)(x - 4)$**

Multiply or divide. ***(Prerequisite skill for 12.5–12.6)***

9. $\frac{5}{9} \times \frac{3}{5}$ **$\frac{1}{3}$**
10. $\frac{3}{10} \div \frac{6}{25}$ **$\frac{5}{4}$**
11. $\frac{7}{9} \times \frac{6}{11}$ **$\frac{14}{33}$**
12. $\frac{4}{15} \div \frac{16}{45}$ **$\frac{3}{4}$**

Solve the proportion. ***(Prerequisite skill for 12.7)***

13. $\frac{x}{10} = \frac{3}{5}$ **6**
14. $\frac{12}{x} = \frac{3}{2}$ **8**
15. $\frac{7}{4} = \frac{x}{24}$ **42**
16. $\frac{5}{6} = \frac{60}{x}$ **72**

@HomeTutor Prerequisite skills practice at classzone.com

Chapter Planning Guide

Chapter 12 Resource Book
- Teaching Guide/Lesson Plan
- Project with Rubric

Assessment and Intervention
- Assessment Book
- Benchmark Tests
- Remediation Book
- Skills Readiness

Interactive Technology
- Easy Planner
- Power Presentations
- Activity Generator
- Animated Algebra
- Test Generator
- Online Quizzes
- eWorkbook
- eEdition
- @HomeTutor

Resources for English Learners
- Spanish Study Guide
- Multi-Language Visual Glossary
- Student Resources in Spanish

Now

In Chapter 12, you will apply the big ideas listed below and reviewed in the Chapter Summary on page 830. You will also use the key vocabulary listed below.

Big Ideas

1. **Graphing rational functions**
2. **Performing operations on rational expressions**
3. **Solving rational equations**

KEY VOCABULARY

- inverse variation, *p. 765*
- constant of variation, *p. 765*
- hyperbola, *p. 767*
- branches, asymptotes of a hyperbola, *p. 767*
- rational function, *p. 775*
- rational expression, *p. 794*
- excluded value, *p. 794*
- simplest form of a rational expression, *p. 795*
- least common denominator (LCD) of rational expressions, *p. 813*
- rational equation, *p. 820*

Why?

You can use rational functions to solve problems in biology. For example, you can graph a rational function to describe how a microorganism's efficiency at performing metabolic tasks changes as its dimensions change.

Animated Algebra

The animation illustrated below for Exercise 49 on page 791 helps you answer this question: How does changing one dimension of a cylindrical microorganism change the ratio of the cylinder's surface area to its volume?

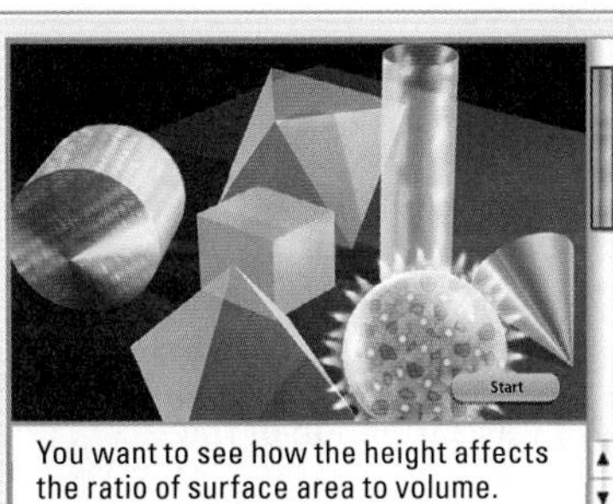

You want to see how the height affects the ratio of surface area to volume.

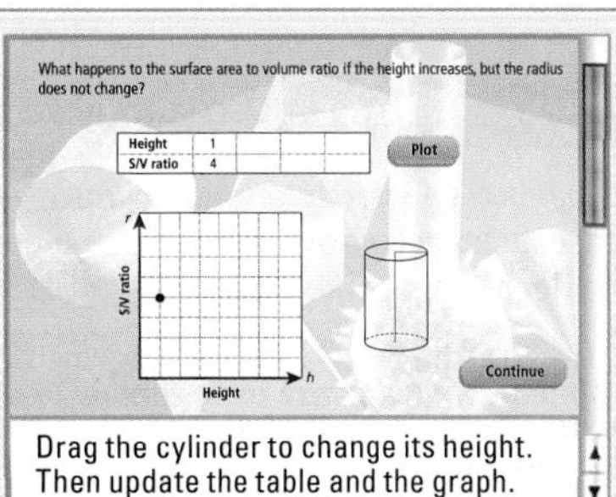

Drag the cylinder to change its height. Then update the table and the graph.

Animated Algebra at classzone.com

Other animations for Chapter 12: pages 766, 777, 783, 804, 814, and 830

Differentiated Instruction Resources

- Reading Strategies for Chapter 12
- Differentiated Instruction Lesson Notes
- English Learners Lesson Notes
- Inclusion Lesson Notes
- Teaching Strategies with Sample Worksheets
- Using Technology in the Classroom
- Tips for New Teachers
- Math Background Notes
- Assessment Strategies
- Teacher Survival Activities
- Bulletin Board Idea

1 PLAN AND PREPARE

Explore the Concept

- Students will graph the relationship between the dimensions of a rectangle.
- This activity leads into the study of inverse variation in Lesson 12.1, Example 1.

Materials

Each student will need:

- 12 square tiles
- Activity Support Master (*Chapter Resource Book*)

Recommended Time

Work activity: 10 min
Discuss results: 5 min

Grouping

Students should work individually.

2 TEACH

Tips for Success

You may want to recommend that students form rectangles in sequence beginning with 1 column of 12 tiles, then 2 columns of 6 tiles, and so on so that they form all possible rectangles.

Key Discovery

If the product of two variables is constant, then as one variable increases the other variable decreases. Such variables are inversely related.

3 ASSESS AND RETEACH

Let A = the area of a rectangle. For $A = 48$, write an equation that gives y as a function of x. If the horizontal length x is 12, what is the vertical length y? $y = \frac{48}{x}$; 4

12.1 Relationships Between Dimensions of a Rectangle

MATERIALS • 12 square tiles

QUESTION **Given a rectangle with a fixed area, how is one dimension related to the other?**

EXPLORE **Graph the relationship between the dimensions of a rectangle**

STEP 1 ***Form rectangle***
Draw the x- and y-axes on a sheet of paper as shown. Use all of the tiles to form a rectangle in Quadrant I with the lower left vertex on the origin. Then label the upper right vertex with the coordinates (x, y) where x is the horizontal length of the rectangle and y is the vertical length.

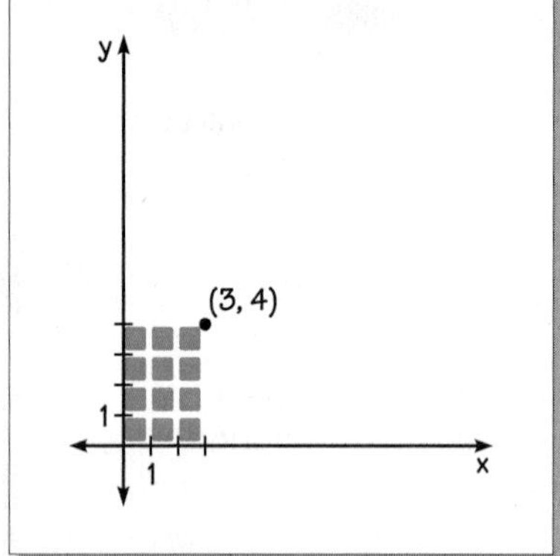

STEP 2 ***Draw curve***
Repeat Step 1 for all possible rectangles that can be formed with the tiles. Then connect the points by drawing a smooth curve through them.

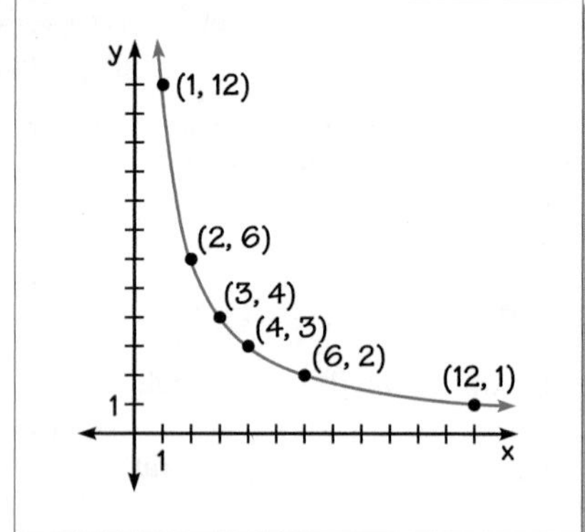

DRAW CONCLUSIONS **Use your observations to complete these exercises**

1. *Describe* how the vertical length changes as the horizontal length increases. *Describe* how the vertical length changes as the horizontal length decreases. **The vertical length decreases; the vertical length increases.**
2. Does the graph cross the axes? *Explain* your reasoning. **No; for the graph to cross an axis, one coordinate would have to be zero, but neither x nor y can be zero if their product is 12.**
3. Write an equation that gives the vertical length y as a function of the horizontal length x. $y = \frac{12}{x}$
4. Let A represent the area of a rectangle. For $A = 40$, write an equation that gives y as a function of x. Then graph the equation. $y = \frac{40}{x}$**; see margin for art.**
5. *Compare* the graph of the equation that you wrote in Exercise 4 with the graph of the equation that you wrote in Exercise 3. **See margin.**

4. 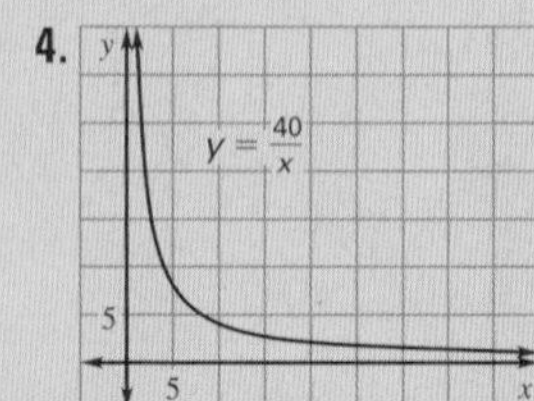

5. The two graphs have the same general shape: a wide curve in the first quadrant; the curve approaches both axes, but does not cross them.

12.1 Model Inverse Variation

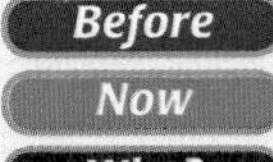

Before You wrote and graphed direct variation equations.

Now You will write and graph inverse variation equations.

Why? So you can find a person's work time, as in Example 6.

Key Vocabulary
- **inverse variation**
- **constant of variation**
- **hyperbola**
- **branches of a hyperbola**
- **asymptotes of a hyperbola**

Recall that two variables x and y show direct variation if $y = ax$ and $a \neq 0$. The variables x and y show **inverse variation** if $y = \frac{a}{x}$ and $a \neq 0$. The nonzero number a is the **constant of variation**, and y is said to *vary inversely* with x.

EXAMPLE 1 Identify direct and inverse variation

Tell whether the equation represents *direct variation, inverse variation,* or *neither.*

a. $xy = 4$ **b.** $\frac{y}{2} = x$ **c.** $y = 2x + 3$

Solution

a. $xy = 4$ **Write original equation.**

$y = \frac{4}{x}$ **Divide each side by x.**

Because $xy = 4$ can be written in the form $y = \frac{a}{x}$, $xy = 4$ represents inverse variation. The constant of variation is 4.

b. $\frac{y}{2} = x$ **Write original equation.**

$y = 2x$ **Multiply each side by 2.**

Because $\frac{y}{2} = x$ can be written in the form $y = ax$, $\frac{y}{2} = x$ represents direct variation.

c. Because $y = 2x + 3$ cannot be written in the form $y = \frac{a}{x}$ or $y = ax$, $y = 2x + 3$ does not represent either direct variation or inverse variation.

GUIDED PRACTICE for Example 1

Tell whether the equation represents *direct variation, inverse variation,* or *neither.*

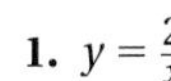

1. $y = \frac{2}{x}$ **inverse variation**
2. $4y = 3x$ **direct variation**
3. $5x - y = 3$ **neither**
4. $xy = \frac{1}{2}$ **inverse variation**

1 PLAN AND PREPARE

Warm-Up Exercises

Transparency Available

1. Rewrite $2x - 5y = 0$ as a direct variation equation. $y = \frac{2}{5}x$
2. The number of words w you type on a keyboard varies directly with the number of minutes m that you type. You can type 360 words in 8 minutes. How many words can you type in 12 minutes? **540 words**

Notetaking Guide

Transparency Available

Promotes interactive learning and notetaking skills.

Pacing

Basic: 2 days
Average: 2 days
Advanced: 2 days
Block: 1 block
- See *Teaching Guide/Lesson Plan.*

2 FOCUS AND MOTIVATE

Essential Question

Big Idea 1, p. 763

How do you graph and solve inverse variation equations? **Tell students they will learn how to answer this question by using tables to graph equations and by using x- and y-values to write equations.**

NCTM STANDARDS

Standard 2: Use models to represent relationships

Standard 5: Collect, organize, and display data

Resource Planning Guide

Chapter Resource Book
- Teaching Guide/Lesson Plan
- Practice levels A, B, C
- Study Guide
- Catch-up for Absent Students
- Application
- Challenge

Workbooks
- Notetaking Guide
- Practice Workbook

Teaching Options
- **Power Presentations** provides dynamic electronic teaching resources for the classroom.
- **Activity Generator** provides editable activities for all ability levels.

Interactive Technology
- Easy Planner
- Power Presentations
- Activity Generator
- Animated Algebra
- Test Generator
- Online Quiz
- eWorkbook
- eEdition
- @HomeTutor

Resources for English Learners
- Spanish Study Guide
- Multi-Language Visual Glossary
- Student Resources in Spanish

See also the *Differentiated Instruction Resources* for more strategies for meeting individual needs.

Motivating the Lesson

You are part of a crew that is cleaning up after a football game. By knowing how to write and solve an inverse variation equation, you can determine how long it will take to clean the grounds depending on whether there are 2, 3, 4 or more students in the cleaning crew.

3 TEACH

Extra Example 1

Tell whether the equation represents *direct variation, inverse variation*, or *neither*.

a. $xy = 7$ **inverse variation**

b. $\frac{x}{y} = 2$ **direct variation**

c. $3x - y = 5$ **neither**

Extra Example 2

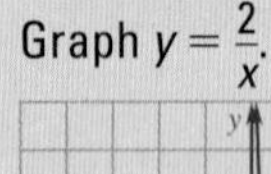

Graph $y = \frac{2}{x}$.

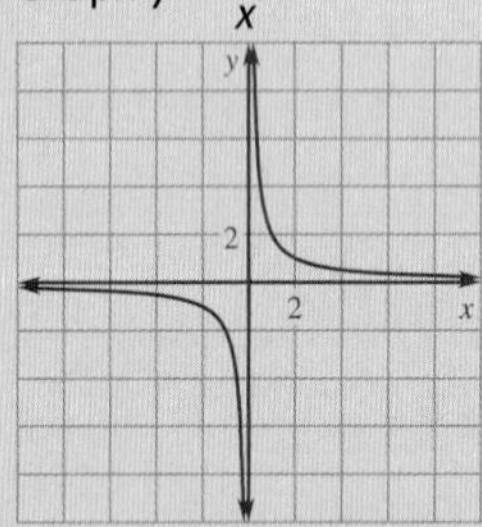

Key Question to Ask for Example 2

- How is the graph of an inverse variation equation different from the graph of a direct variation equation? **The graph of an inverse variation equation is a two-part curve and it does not cross the x- or y-axis. The graph of a direct variation equation is a line and it passes through the origin.**

EXAMPLE 2 Graph an inverse variation equation

Graph $y = \frac{4}{x}$.

Solution

STEP 1 **Make** a table by choosing several integer values of x and finding the values of y. Then plot the points. To see how the function behaves for values of x very close to 0 and very far from 0, make a second table for such values and plot the points.

DESCRIBE A FUNCTION
Note that y is undefined when $x = 0$. There is no point $(0, y)$ on the graph of $y = \frac{4}{x}$. The function is said to be *discontinuous* at $x = 0$.

x	y
−4	−1
−2	−2
−1	−4
0	undefined
1	4
2	2
4	1

x	y
−10	−0.4
−5	−0.8
−0.5	−8
−0.4	−10
0.4	10
0.5	8
5	0.8
10	0.4

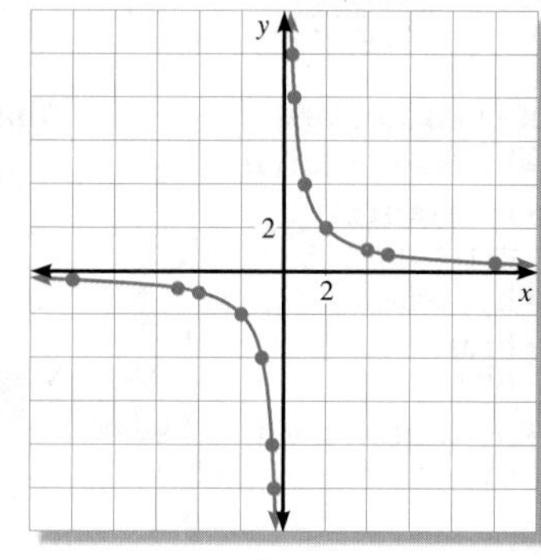

STEP 2 **Connect** the points in Quadrant I by drawing a smooth curve through them. Repeat for the points in Quadrant III.

GRAPHS OF INVERSE VARIATION As shown in Example 2, as you move away from the origin along the x-axis, the graph of an inverse variation equation approaches the x-axis without crossing it. As you move away from the origin along the y-axis, the graph approaches the y-axis without crossing it.

EXAMPLE 3 Graph an inverse variation equation

Graph $y = \frac{-4}{x}$.

Solution

COMPARE GRAPHS
The graph of an inverse variation equation lies in Quadrants I and III if $a > 0$, and the graph lies in Quadrants II and IV if $a < 0$.

Notice that $y = \frac{-4}{x} = -1 \cdot \frac{4}{x}$. So, for every nonzero value of x, the value of y in $y = \frac{-4}{x}$ is the opposite of the value of y in $y = \frac{4}{x}$. You can graph $y = \frac{-4}{x}$ by reflecting the graph of $y = \frac{4}{x}$ (see Example 2) in the x-axis.

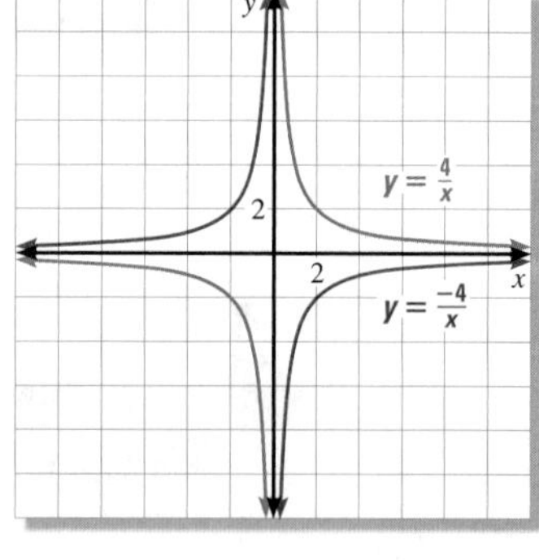

Animated **Algebra** at classzone.com

CONCEPT SUMMARY — *For Your Notebook*

Graphs of Direct Variation and Inverse Variation Equations

Direct variation		Inverse variation	
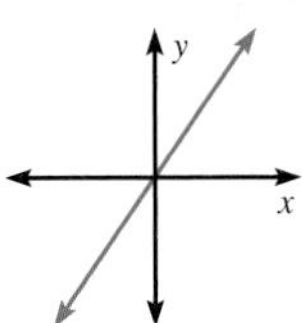	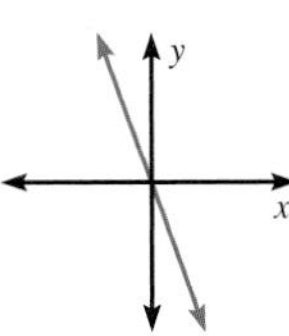	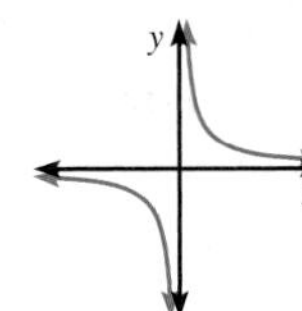	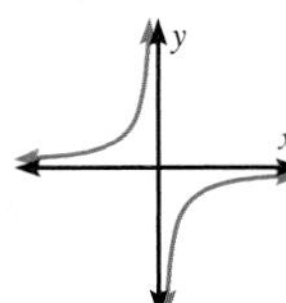
$y = ax, a > 0$	$y = ax, a < 0$	$y = \frac{a}{x}, a > 0$	$y = \frac{a}{x}, a < 0$

HYPERBOLAS The graph of the inverse variation equation $y = \frac{a}{x}$ $(a \neq 0)$ is a **hyperbola**. The two symmetrical parts of a hyperbola are called the **branches of the hyperbola**. The lines that the hyperbola approaches but doesn't intersect are called the **asymptotes of the hyperbola**. The asymptotes of the graph of $y = \frac{a}{x}$ are the x-axis and the y-axis.

EXAMPLE 4 Use an inverse variation equation

The variables x and y vary inversely, and $y = 6$ when $x = -3$.

a. Write an inverse variation equation that relates x and y.

b. Find the value of y when $x = 4$.

Solution

a. Because y varies inversely with x, the equation has the form $y = \frac{a}{x}$.

Use the fact that $x = -3$ and $y = 6$ to find the value of a.

$y = \frac{a}{x}$	**Write inverse variation equation.**
$6 = \frac{a}{-3}$	**Substitute −3 for x and 6 for y.**
$-18 = a$	**Multiply each side by −3.**

An equation that relates x and y is $y = \frac{-18}{x}$.

b. When $x = 4$, $y = \frac{-18}{4} = -\frac{9}{2}$.

✓ GUIDED PRACTICE for Examples 2, 3, and 4

5. Graph **(a)** $y = \frac{3}{x}$ and **(b)** $y = \frac{-3}{x}$. **See margin.**

6. The variables x and y vary inversely, and $y = -2$ when $x = 12$. Write an inverse variation equation that relates x and y. Then find the value of y when $x = -3$. $y = \frac{-24}{x}$; **8**

Differentiated Instruction

Inclusion Some students may confuse direct and inverse variation. For problems similar to **Example 4**, give additional practice by having students find the direct variation equation under the same conditions. Then have students graph both the inverse variation and direct variation equations on the same graph.

See also the *Differentiated Instruction Resources* for more strategies.

5a.

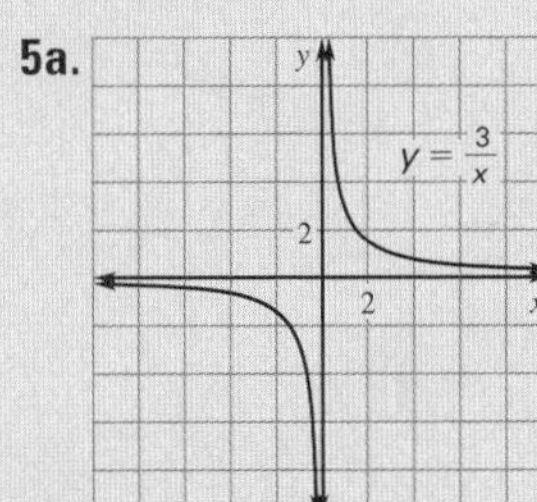

5b.

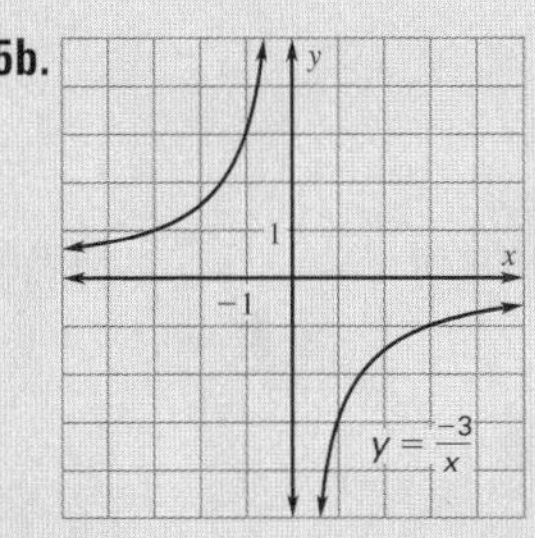

Extra Example 3

Graph $y = \frac{-2}{x}$.

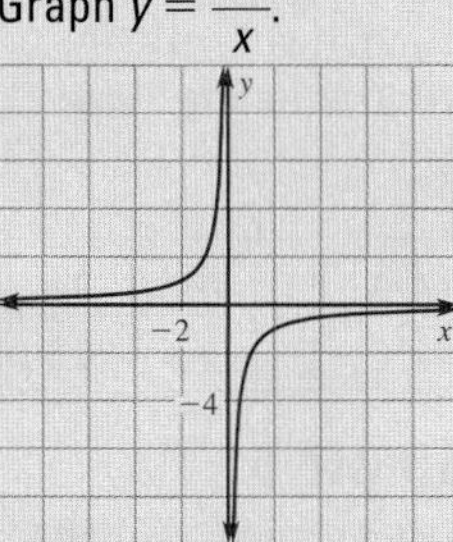

Key Questions to Ask for Example 3

- In which quadrants is the graph of the equation $y = \frac{-4}{x}$? **II and IV**
- What would happen if you reflected the graph of $y = \frac{-4}{x}$ in the x-axis? **The new graph represents $y = \frac{4}{x}$ and lies in quadrants I and III.**

An **Animated Algebra** activity is available online for **Example 3**. This activity is also part of **Power Presentations**.

Extra Example 4

The variables x and y vary inversely, and $y = 2$ when $x = -6$.

a. Write an inverse variation equation that relates x and y. $y = \frac{-12}{x}$

b. Find the value of y when $x = 8$. $-\frac{3}{2}$

Key Questions to Ask for Example 4

- What is the constant of the inverse variation equation in part (a)? **−18**
- If you graph the equation in part (a), in which quadrants is it? **II and IV**

Extra Example 5

Tell whether the table represents inverse variation. If so, write the inverse variation equation. **yes; $xy = 8$ or $y = \frac{8}{x}$**

x	−5	−2	4	10	16
y	−1.6	−4	2	0.8	0.5

Extra Example 6

The coaches of a youth baseball league estimate that 15 adults working for 25 hours each can repaint all of the bleachers in time for the baseball season. The work time t (in hours) varies inversely with the number of adults a who volunteer to repaint the bleachers. Find the total work time per person if there are 75 adult volunteers. **5 h**

Closing the Lesson

Have students summarize the major points of the lesson and answer the Essential Question: How do you graph and solve inverse variation equations?

- **Write an inverse variation equation in the form $y = \frac{a}{x}$, where a is the constant of variation.**
- **The graph of an inverse variation equation is a hyperbola. The hyperbola approaches the x- and y-axes, but does not intersect the axes.**

To graph an inverse variation equation, make a table of positive and negative values of x, some close to 0 and some far away from 0. Plot and connect the points. The resulting curve is a hyperbola. Write an inverse variation equation by substituting values for y and x in the form $y = \frac{a}{x}$ and then solving for a.

PRODUCTS By multiplying both sides of $y = \frac{a}{x}$ by x, you can write the equation as $xy = a$. This means that a set of ordered pairs (x, y) shows inverse variation if all the products xy are constant.

EXAMPLE 5 Write an inverse variation equation

ANALYZE RATE OF CHANGE
From the table, you can see that the rate of change in y with respect to x is not constant as it would be for a direct variation.

Tell whether the table represents inverse variation. If so, write the inverse variation equation.

x	−5	−3	4	8	24
y	2.4	4	−3	−1.5	−0.5

Solution

Find the products xy for all pairs (x, y):

$-5(2.4) = -12 \quad -3(4) = -12 \quad 4(-3) = -12 \quad 8(-1.5) = -12 \quad 24(-0.5) = -12$

The products are equal to the same number, −12. So, y varies inversely with x.

▶ The inverse variation equation is $xy = -12$, or $y = \frac{-12}{x}$.

EXAMPLE 6 Solve a multi-step problem

THEATER A theater company plans to hire people to build a stage set. The work time t (in hours per person) varies inversely with the number p of people hired. The company estimates that 25 people working for 300 hours each can complete the job. Find the work time per person if the company hires 30 people.

Solution

STEP 1 **Write** the inverse variation equation that relates p and t.

$t = \frac{a}{p}$ Write inverse variation equation.

$300 = \frac{a}{25}$ Substitute 25 for p and 300 for t.

$7500 = a$ Multiply each side by 25.

The inverse variation equation is $t = \frac{7500}{p}$.

ANALYZE UNITS
The constant of variation is measured in person-hours. Unit analysis shows that the inverse variation equation checks: person-hours ÷ number of people = hours.

STEP 2 **Find** t when $p = 30$: $t = \frac{7500}{p} = \frac{7500}{30} = 250$.

▶ If 30 people are hired, the work time per person is 250 hours.

GUIDED PRACTICE for Examples 5 and 6

7. Tell whether the ordered pairs (−5, 2), (−4, 2.5), (8, −1.25), and (20, −0.5) represent inverse variation. If so, write the inverse variation equation. **inverse variation; $y = \frac{-10}{x}$**

8. **WHAT IF?** In Example 6, suppose the theater company estimates that 20 people working for 270 hours each can complete the job. Find the work time per person if the company hires 30 people. **180 hours per person**

15–26. See Additional Answers beginning on p. AA1.

28. $y = \frac{10}{x}$; 5

29. $y = \frac{21}{x}$; 10.5

30. $y = \frac{-20}{x}$; −10

12.1 EXERCISES

HOMEWORK KEY
○ = **WORKED-OUT SOLUTIONS** on p. WS28 for Exs. 17, 33, and 57
★ = **STANDARDIZED TEST PRACTICE** Exs. 2, 43, 59, and 60
◆ = **MULTIPLE REPRESENTATIONS** Ex. 58

SKILL PRACTICE

A

1. **VOCABULARY** Identify the constant of variation in the equation $y = \frac{-3}{x}$. **−3**

2. ★ **WRITING** *Describe* the difference between a direct variation equation and an inverse variation equation. **In direct variation, y is the product of x and the constant of variation; in inverse variation, y is the quotient of the constant of variation and x.**

EXAMPLE 1 on p. 765 for Exs. 3–14, 43

DESCRIBING EQUATIONS **Tell whether the equation represents *direct variation, inverse variation,* or *neither.***

3. $y = -2x$ **direct variation**
4. $xy = 1$ **inverse variation**
5. $y = x + 5$ **neither**
6. $x = \frac{-1}{y}$ **inverse variation**
7. $xy = 5$ **inverse variation**
8. $\frac{y}{x} = 4$ **direct variation**
9. $x = 7y$ **direct variation**
10. $2x + y = 6$ **neither**
11. $2x = \frac{8}{y}$ **inverse variation**
12. $x = -7$ **neither**
13. $3x - 3y = 0$ **direct variation**
14. $3xy = 20$ **inverse variation**

EXAMPLES 2 and 3 on p. 766 for Exs. 15–26

GRAPHING EQUATIONS **Graph the inverse variation equation.** **15–26. See margin.**

15. $y = \frac{2}{x}$
16. $y = \frac{-1}{x}$
17. $y = \frac{-7}{x}$
18. $y = \frac{10}{x}$
19. $y = \frac{-5}{x}$
20. $y = \frac{18}{x}$
21. $y = \frac{9}{x}$
22. $y = \frac{-2}{x}$
23. $y = \frac{15}{x}$
24. $y = \frac{6}{x}$
25. $y = \frac{-12}{x}$
26. $y = \frac{-8}{x}$

EXAMPLE 4 on p. 767 for Exs. 27–42

27. An inverse variation equation has the form $y = \frac{a}{x}$, not $y = ax$; $8 = \frac{a}{2}$, $16 = a$, so $y = \frac{16}{x}$.

27. **ERROR ANALYSIS** The variables x and y vary inversely, and $y = 8$ when $x = 2$. *Describe* and correct the error in writing an inverse variation equation that relates x and y.

$y = ax$
$8 = a(2)$
$4 = a$
So, $y = 4x$.

USE INVERSE VARIATION **Given that y varies inversely with x, use the specified values to write an inverse variation equation that relates x and y. Then find the value of y when $x = 2$.** **28–42. See margin.**

28. $x = 5, y = 2$
29. $x = 3, y = 7$
30. $x = -5, y = 4$
31. $x = 13, y = -1$
32. $x = -15, y = -15$
33. $x = -22, y = -6$
34. $x = 8, y = 3$
35. $x = 9, y = -2$
36. $x = 3, y = 3$
37. $x = -2, y = -10$
38. $x = -3, y = 40$
39. $x = -7, y = -10$
40. $x = -17, y = 8$
41. $x = 6, y = 11$
42. $x = -12, y = -13$

43. ★ **MULTIPLE CHOICE** The variables x and y vary inversely, and $y = 6$ when $x = 4$. What is the constant of variation? **D**

Ⓐ 1.5 Ⓑ 4 Ⓒ 6 Ⓓ 24

31. $y = \frac{-13}{x}$; −6.5
32. $y = \frac{225}{x}$; 112.5
33. $y = \frac{132}{x}$; 66
34. $y = \frac{27}{x}$; 12
35. $y = \frac{-18}{x}$; −9
36. $y = \frac{9}{x}$; 4.5
37. $y = \frac{20}{x}$; 10
38. $y = \frac{-120}{x}$; −60
39. $y = \frac{70}{x}$; 35
40. $y = \frac{-136}{x}$; −68
41. $y = \frac{66}{x}$; 33
42. $y = \frac{156}{x}$; 78

4 PRACTICE AND APPLY

Assignment Guide

Answer Transparencies available for all exercises

Basic:
Day 1: pp. 769–772
Exs. 1–26
Day 2: pp. 769–772
Exs. 27–43 odd, 44–49, 54–59, 62–74 even

Average:
Day 1: pp. 769–772
Exs. 1, 2, 6–26, 49–51
Day 2: pp. 769–772
Exs. 27, 35–48, 54–60, 63–73 odd

Advanced:
Day 1: pp. 769–772
Exs. 1, 2, 7–26, 49–51
Day 2: pp. 769–772
Exs. 37–48, 52–61*, 62–74 even

Block:
pp. 769–772
Exs. 1, 2, 6–27, 35–51, 54–60, 63–73 odd

Differentiated Instruction

See *Differentiated Instruction Resources* for suggestions on addressing the needs of a diverse classroom.

Homework Check

For a quick check of student understanding of key concepts, go over the following exercises:
Basic: 8, 18, 31, 44, 55
Average: 11, 22, 38, 54, 55
Advanced: 13, 23, 40, 56, 57

Extra Practice

- Student Edition, p. 946
- Chapter Resource Book: Practice levels A, B, C

Practice Worksheet

An easily-readable reduced practice page (with answers) for this lesson can be found on p. 762C.

Avoiding Common Errors

Exercises 28–42, 43 Watch for students who use the direct variation form of an equation rather than the inverse variation form. Suggest that students examine the values of x and y to make sure that the value of one variable increases as the value of the other variable decreases.

Study Strategy

Exercise 55 Encourage students to use two steps to solve this problem, using Example 6 as a model.

48. Divided by 2; divided by 3. ***Sample answer:*** **Let $x = 2$ in the inverse variation equation $y = \frac{12}{x}$, then $y = \frac{12}{2} = 6$. If x is doubled, then $x = 2(2) = 4$ and $y = \frac{12}{4} = 3 = \frac{6}{2}$, so y is divided by 2. If x is tripled, then $x = 3(2) = 6$ and $y = \frac{12}{6} = 2 = \frac{6}{3}$, so y is divided by 3.**

52. *Sample answer:*

x	y
1	12
2	6
3	4
4	3
6	2
12	1

The rate of change in y with respect to x for the function $y = \frac{12}{x}$ is not constant. For instance, $\frac{6-12}{2-1} = -6$, while $\frac{4-6}{3-2} = -2$. The direct variation $y = 12x$ is a linear function. The rate of change of y with respect to x is the slope of the function's graph, the constant 12.

EXAMPLE 5 on p. 768 for Exs. 44–47

WRITING EQUATIONS Tell whether the table represents inverse variation. If so, write the inverse variation equation.

44.

x	4	8	12	16	20
y	1	2	3	4	5

not inverse variation

45.

x	−20	−5	14	32	50
y	−80	−20	56	128	200

not inverse variation

46.

x	−10	−5	15	20	40
y	−30	−60	20	15	7.5

inverse variation; $y = \frac{300}{x}$

47.

x	−12	−10	−8	−5	−4
y	2	2.4	3	4.8	6

inverse variation; $y = \frac{-24}{x}$

B **48. REASONING** The variables x and y vary inversely. How does the value of y change if the value of x is doubled? tripled? Give examples. **See margin.**

REVIEW FORMULAS For help with geometric formulas, see pp. 922–926.

GEOMETRY Translate the verbal sentence into an equation. Then tell whether the equation represents *direct variation, inverse variation,* or *neither.*

49. The circumference of a circle with radius r units is C units. **$2\pi r = C$; direct variation**

50. The perimeter of a rectangle with length ℓ units and width w units is 27 units. **$2\ell + 2w = 27$; neither**

51. The volume of a rectangular prism with base B square units and height h units is 400 cubic units. **$Bh = 400$; inverse variation**

C **52. REASONING** Make a table of positive x-values for the inverse variation function $y = \frac{12}{x}$. Compare the rate of change in y with respect to x with that of the direct variation function $y = 12x$. **See margin.**

53. CHALLENGE The variables x and y vary inversely with constant of variation a. The variables y and z vary inversely with constant of variation b. Write an equation that gives z as a function of x. Then tell whether x and z vary *directly* or *inversely*. **$z = \frac{b}{a} \cdot x$; directly**

PROBLEM SOLVING

EXAMPLE 5 on p. 768 for Exs. 54, 57

54. inverse variation; $s = \frac{3600}{p}$

A **54. BICYCLES** Does the table, which shows the bicycle speed s for various pedaling speeds p, represent inverse variation? If so, write the inverse variation equation that relates p and s.

Pedaling speed, p (pedal rotations/mi)	831	612	420	305
Bicycle speed, s (mi/h)	4.33	5.88	8.57	11.8

@HomeTutor for problem solving help at classzone.com

EXAMPLE 6 on p. 768 for Exs. 55–56, 58

55. ECONOMICS The owner of an electronics store determines that the monthly demand d (in units) for a computer varies inversely with the price p (in dollars) of the computer. When the price is \$700, the monthly demand is 250 units. Write the inverse variation equation that relates p and d. Then find the monthly demand when the price is \$500. **$d = \frac{175,000}{p}$; 350 units**

@HomeTutor for problem solving help at classzone.com

○ = WORKED-OUT SOLUTIONS on p. WS1 ★ = STANDARDIZED TEST PRACTICE

56. $t = \frac{200}{r}$; Yes; the equation is in the form $y = \frac{a}{x}$.

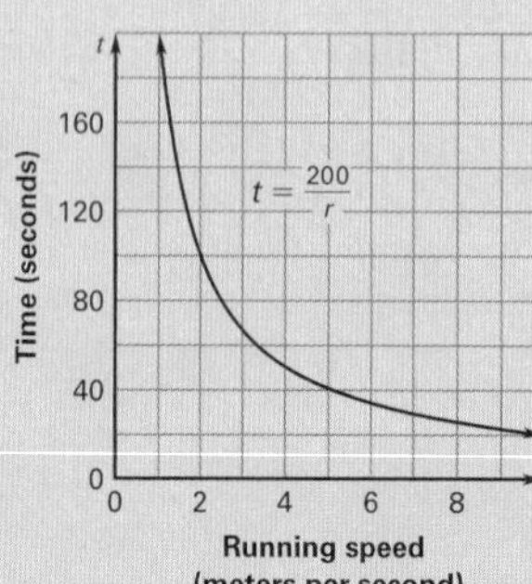

57a.

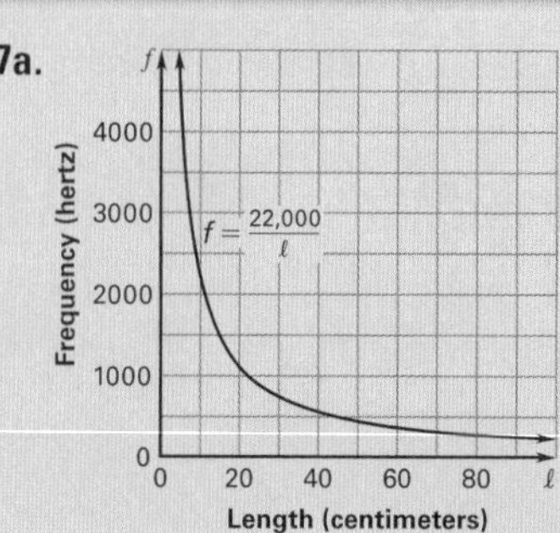

56. **SPORTS** An athlete is running a 200 meter dash. Write and graph an equation that relates the athlete's average running speed r (in meters per second) and the time t (in seconds) that the athlete will take to finish the race. Is the equation an inverse variation equation? *Explain.* **See margin.**

57. **MULTI-STEP PROBLEM** The table shows the vibration frequencies f (in hertz) for various lengths ℓ (in centimeters) of strings on a stringed instrument.

Length of string, ℓ (cm)	42.1	37.5	33.4	31.5
Frequency, f (Hz)	523	587	659	698

57a. Yes; $f = \frac{22,000}{\ell}$; see margin for art.

a. **Decide** Tell whether an inverse variation equation can be used to model the data. If so, write and graph the inverse variation equation.

b. **Calculate** Find the frequency of a string with a length of 29.4 centimeters. **about 748 Hz**

c. **Describe** *Describe* the change in the frequency as the length of the string decreases. Does your answer in part (b) support your description? **The frequency increases; yes.**

58. **MULTIPLE REPRESENTATIONS** You plan to save the same amount of money each month to pay for a summer sports camp that costs \$1200.

a. **Making a Table** Let a represent the amount (in dollars) that you plan to save each month. Make a table that shows the number m of months that you need to save money for the following values of a: 75, 100, 120, 150, 200, and 240. *Describe* how the number of months changes as the amount of money that you save each month increases. **a, b. See margin.**

b. **Drawing a Graph** Use the values in the table to draw a graph of the situation. Does the graph suggest a situation that represents *direct variation* or *inverse variation*? *Explain* your choice.

c. **Writing an Equation** Write the equation that relates a and m. $m = \frac{1200}{a}$

B 59. ★ **SHORT RESPONSE** As shown in the diagram, the focal length of a camera lens is the distance between the lens and the point at which light rays meet after passing through the aperture, or opening, in the lens. The f-stop s is the ratio of the focal length f (in millimeters) to the diameter a (in millimeters) of the aperture.

59a. $s = \frac{35}{a}$, see margin for art, inverse variation.

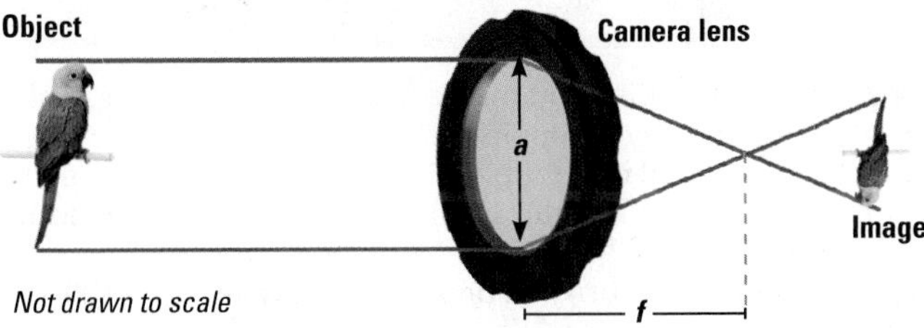

59b. 4; when $s = 4$, the diameter of the aperture is $a = \frac{35}{4} =$ 8.75 millimeters, and when $s = 8$, the diameter of the aperture is $a = \frac{35}{8} =$ 4.375 millimeters.

a. **Model** A photographer has a camera with a focal length of 35 millimeters. Write and graph an equation that relates a and s. Tell whether the equation represents inverse variation.

b. **Compare** The greater the diameter of the aperture, the more light that passes through the aperture. For the camera in part (a), does more light pass through the aperture when the f-stop is 4 or when the f-stop is 8? *Explain.*

Avoiding Common Errors

Exercise 56 Some students may think that 200 meters represents a variable in the inverse variation equation. Ask them if 200 meters is constant or if it varies, leading them to the idea that, for this exercise, d is constant and r and t are the variables.

Mathematical Reasoning

Exercise 58 In part (b), have students use 5 to 7 values, with increments of 10 or 20, so that their graphs clearly show the Quadrant-I branch of a hyperbola.

Exercise 60 More information about the aspect ratio of a wing can be found at www.grc.nasa.gov/WWW/K-12/airplane/geom.html

58b.

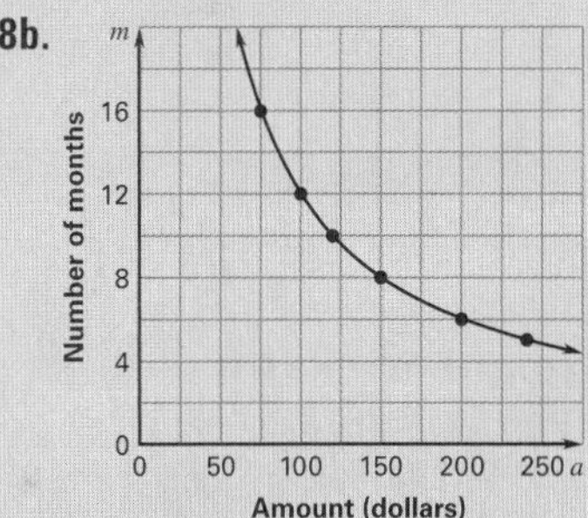

Inverse variation; the points (a, m) appear to lie on a hyperbola.

59a.

s
16
12
8
4
0
0 4 8 12 16 a
$s = \frac{35}{a}$
f-stop
Diameter of aperture (mm)

58a.

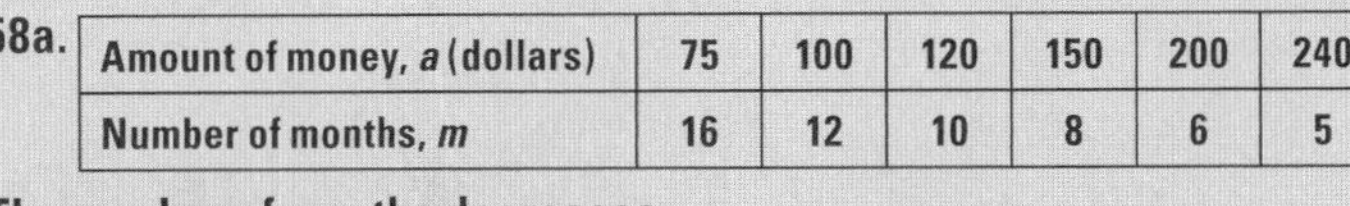

Amount of money, a (dollars)	75	100	120	150	200	240
Number of months, m	16	12	10	8	6	5

The number of months decreases.

5 ASSESS AND RETEACH

Daily Homework Quiz

Transparency Available

1. Graph $y = \frac{-6}{x}$.

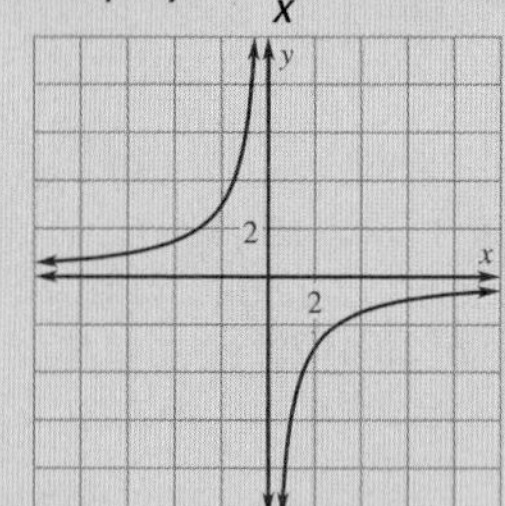

Given that y varies inversely with x, use the specified values to write an inverse variation equation that relates x and y. Then find the value of y when $x = 3$.

2. $x = -6, y = 5$ **$y = -\frac{30}{x}$; −10**

3. $x = 12, y = 7$ **$y = \frac{84}{x}$; 28**

Online Quiz

Available at **classzone.com**

Diagnosis/Remediation

- Practice A, B, C in Chapter Resource Book
- Study Guide in Chapter Resource Book
- Practice Workbook
- @HomeTutor

Challenge

Additional challenge is available in the Chapter Resource Book.

60c. $0 < c < 6$; substituting $\frac{20}{3}$ for r and 40 for s in the formula $r = \frac{s}{c}$ gives a value of $c = 6$ feet for the chord of a wing of the Wright brothers' airplane. The aspect ratio $r = \frac{40}{c}$ gets larger when the denominator c gets smaller; so, $0 < c < 6$ are the values of c for which the plane would have glided more easily.

60. ★ **EXTENDED RESPONSE** The photo below shows a replica of an airplane designed by Orville and Wilbur Wright, who were aviation pioneers in the early 20th century. The aspect ratio r of a wing from similar airplanes is given by the formula $r = \frac{s^2}{A}$ where s is the span, or the distance (in feet) between the wing tips, and A is the area (in square feet) of the wing.

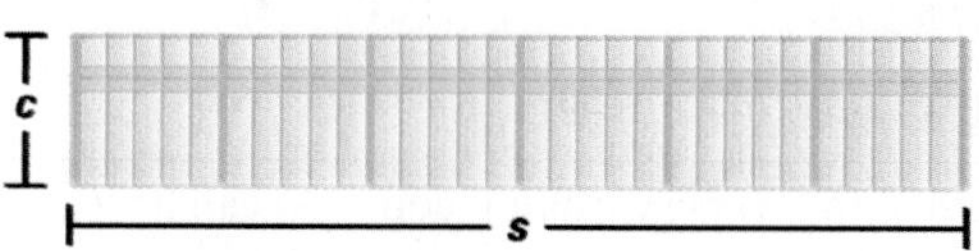

a. **Model** The length c of the chord of a wing is the distance (in feet) between the front and the back of the wing. For the rectangular wing shown, rewrite the formula for r in terms of c and s. **$r = \frac{s}{c}$**

b. **Analyze** How does the value of r change when s is constant and c increases? when c is constant and s increases? **r decreases; r increases.**

c. **Interpret** The greater the aspect ratio, the easier it is for an airplane to glide. Orville and Wilbur Wright designed an airplane with two rectangular wings that each had an aspect ratio of $\frac{20}{3}$ and a span of 40 feet. For what values of c would the airplane have glided more easily? *Explain.* **See margin.**

C 61. **CHALLENGE** A fulcrum is placed under the center of a board. In order for two objects to balance on the board, the distance (in feet) of each object from the center of the board must vary inversely with its weight (in pounds). In the diagram shown, what is the distance of each animal from the center of the board? **The dog is 1.875 feet from the fulcrum and the cat is 3.125 feet from the fulcrum.**

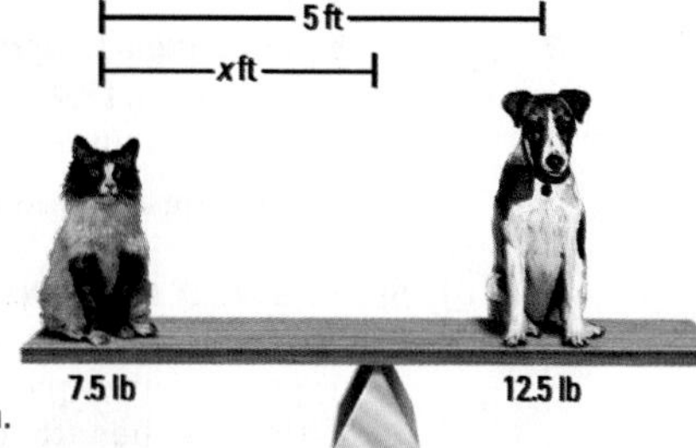

MIXED REVIEW

62. **MOVIES** You buy discount movie tickets from a website. Tickets cost \$3.60 each. You pay a shipping fee of \$3 per order. Write an equation that gives the total cost C (in dollars) of the tickets as a function of the number t of tickets bought. Then find the total cost of 8 tickets. *(p. 283)* **$C = 3.6t + 3$; \$31.80**

PREVIEW
Prepare for Lesson 12.2 in Exs. 63–68.

Graph the function. Identify its domain and range. **63–68. See margin.**

63. $y = 5^x$ *(p. 520)* 64. $y = 0.4^x$ *(p. 531)* 65. $y = x^2 + 5$ *(p. 628)*

66. $y = x^2 + 6x - 20$ *(p. 635)* 67. $y = -\sqrt{x}$ *(p. 710)* 68. $y = 2\sqrt{x-1} + 1$ *(p. 710)*

Solve the equation. Check for extraneous solutions. *(p. 729)*

69. $\sqrt{x} = 10$ **100** 70. $\sqrt{x+6} - 4 = 8$ **138** 71. $\sqrt{x-2} = -10$ **no solution**

72. $2\sqrt{x} - 5 = 23$ **196** 73. $\sqrt{4x-3} = \sqrt{2x+7}$ **5** 74. $x = \sqrt{x+30}$ **6**

 EXTRA PRACTICE for Lesson 12.1, p. 949 

63–68. See Additional Answers beginning on p. AA1.

12.2 Graphing $y = \dfrac{a}{x - h} + k$

MATERIALS • graph paper • graphing calculator

QUESTION What characteristics does the graph of $y = \frac{a}{x - h} + k$ have?

EXPLORE 1 Use tables to graph a function

Graph $y = \frac{2}{x - 3} + 4$ using a table.

STEP 1 *Use a table*

Make a table of values for $y = \frac{2}{x - 3} + 4$ by choosing several integer values of x. Round the values of y, if necessary. Then plot the points.

x	0	1	2	3	4	5	6
y	3.3	3	2	undefined	6	5	4.7

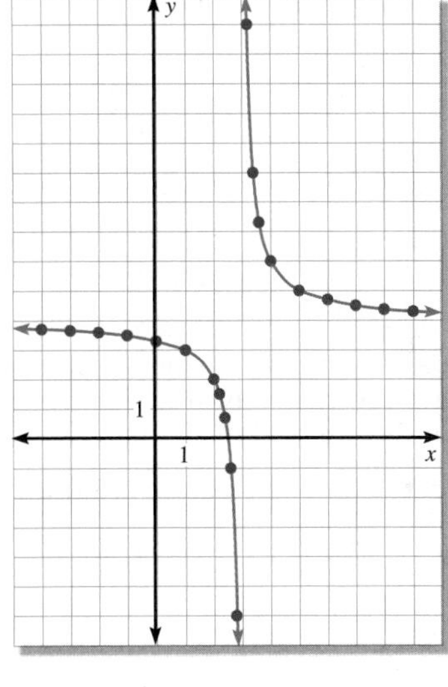

STEP 2 *Check close to and far from 3*

To see how the function behaves for values of x closer to 3 and farther from 3, make tables for such values and plot the points.

x	2.2	2.4	2.6	2.8	3.2	3.4	3.6
y	1.5	0.7	−1	−6	14	9	7.3

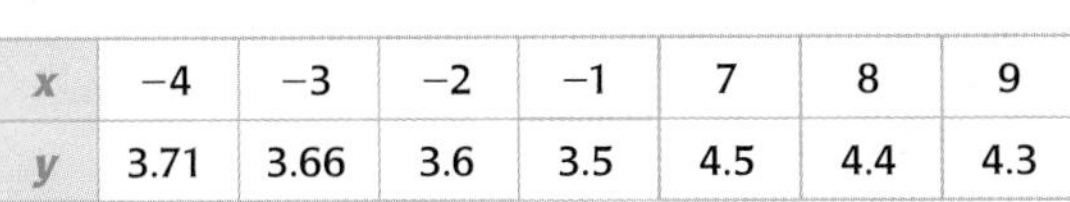

x	−4	−3	−2	−1	7	8	9
y	3.71	3.66	3.6	3.5	4.5	4.4	4.3

STEP 3 *Draw a graph*

Draw a smooth curve through the points (x, y) where $x > 3$. Repeat for the points (x, y) where $x < 3$.

PRACTICE

1. *Describe* how the values of y change as the values of x get close to 3. What is the equation of the vertical asymptote? **See margin.**
2. *Describe* how the values of y change as the values of x get far from 3. What is the equation of the horizontal asymptote? **As the absolute value of x becomes greater and greater, the value of y approaches 4; $y = 4$.**

Graph the function using a table.
3–5. See margin.

3. $y = \frac{5}{x - 4} - 6$
4. $y = \frac{-10}{x + 3} - 1$
5. $y = \frac{-11}{x + 13} + 9$

1 PLAN AND PREPARE

Explore the Concept

- Students will use tables and a graphing calculator to graph functions.
- This activity leads into the discussion in Lesson 12.2, Example 4, of how to transform the graph of $y = \frac{1}{x}$ into the graph of $y = \frac{a}{x - h} + k$.

Materials

Each student will need:

- graph paper
- graphing calculator

Recommended Time

Work activity: 15 min
Discuss results: 5 min

Grouping

Students should work individually.

2 TEACH

Key Questions

- In Explore 1, why is the value of y undefined when $x = 3$? **The expression $x - 3$ appears in a denominator of the equation. If $x = 3$ the denominator is zero, and division by zero is undefined.**
- In Explore 2, why do you think that the vertical line connecting the two branches of the hyperbola is $x = -1.7$? **The expression $x + 1.7$ appears in a denominator, so the line at $x = -1.7$, which would make the denominator equal zero, is the vertical asymptote.**

Key Discovery

In the graph of $y = \frac{a}{x - h} + k$, the horizontal asymptote is $y = k$ and the vertical asymptote is $x = h$.

1. As the value of x approaches 3 through numbers less than 3, the value of y becomes a smaller and smaller negative number (larger and larger in absolute value); as the value of x approaches 3 through numbers greater than 3, the value of y becomes a larger and larger positive number; $x = 3$.

3.
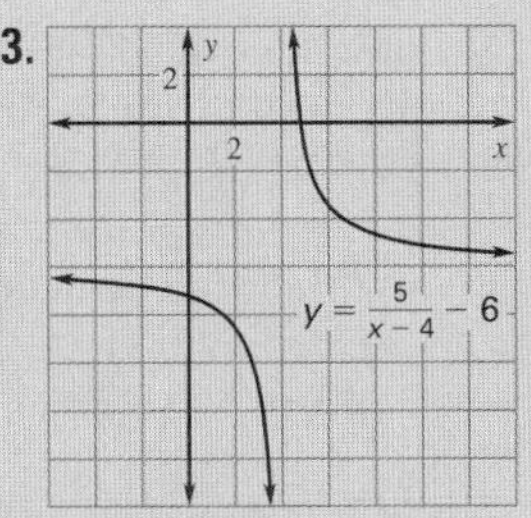

4.
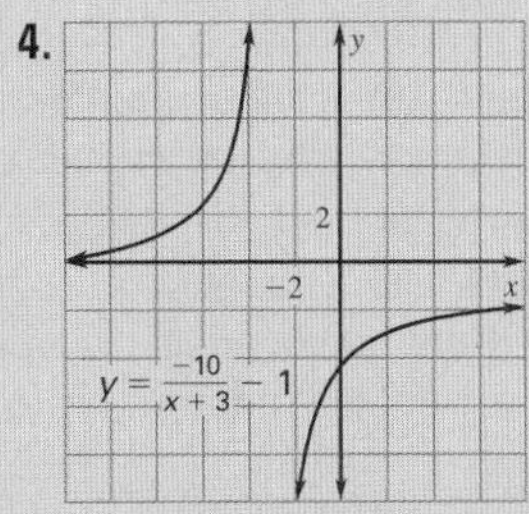

5.
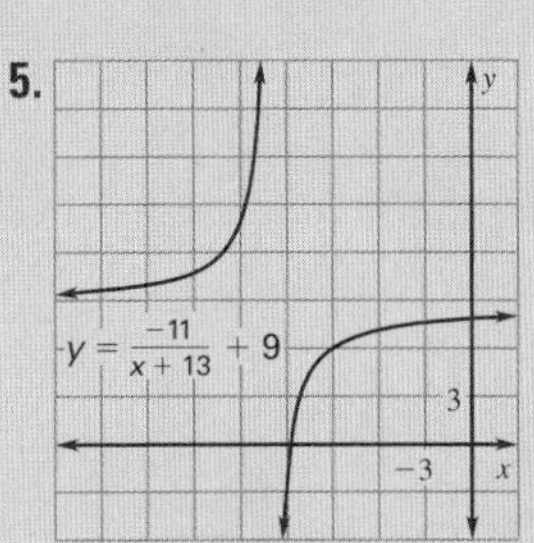

EXPLORE 2 Use a graphing calculator to graph a function

Graph $y = \frac{-3.4}{x + 1.7} - 2.8$ using a graphing calculator.

Enter $y_1 = \frac{-3.4}{x + 1.7} - 2.8$ into your graphing calculator. Press MODE and select either connected mode or dot mode. Then graph the function.

Connected mode

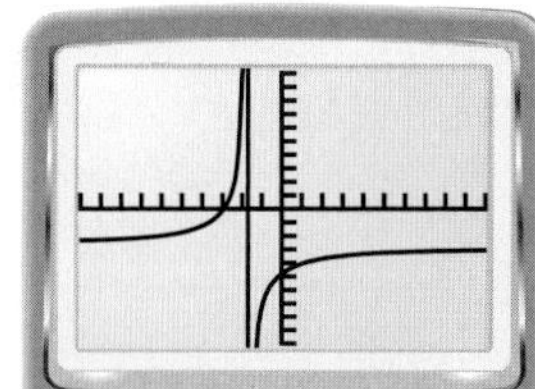

Dot mode

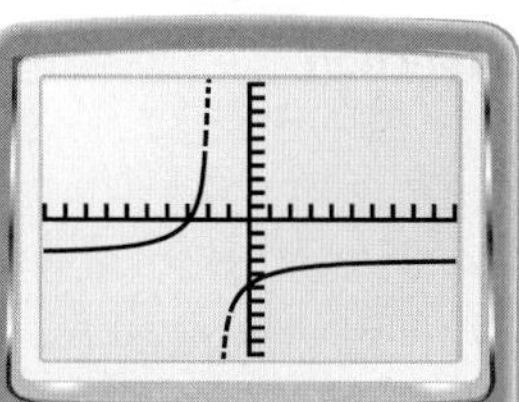

In connected mode, the screen appears to show the line $x = -1.7$. This line is *not* part of the graph. The calculator is instead connecting the two branches of the hyperbola. In dot mode, the screen does not show the line, but the points that are plotted are not connected by a smooth curve.

PRACTICE

6. *Describe* how the value of y changes as the value of x gets closer to -1.7. Use the *trace* feature of the graphing calculator to find the equation of the vertical asymptote. **See margin.**

7. *Describe* how the value of y changes as the value of x gets farther from -1.7. Use the *trace* feature of the graphing calculator to find the equation of the horizontal asymptote. **As the absolute value of x becomes greater and greater, the value of y approaches -2.8; $y = -2.8$.**

Graph the function using a graphing calculator.
8–10. See margin.

8. $y = \frac{5.3}{x - 4.6} - 1.2$
9. $y = \frac{-7.1}{x - 3.2} + 4.5$
10. $y = \frac{-10.2}{x + 12.4} + 9.8$

DRAW CONCLUSIONS Use your observations to complete these exercises

11. How are the constants in the equations of the asymptotes in Exercises 1 and 2 related to the constants in the function $y = \frac{2}{x - 3} + 4$? **See margin.**

12. How are the constants in the equations of the asymptotes in Exercises 6 and 7 related to the constants in the function $y = \frac{-3.4}{x + 1.7} - 2.8$? **See margin.**

13. **CONJECTURE** Copy and complete: The graph of $y = \frac{a}{x - h} + k$ has a vertical asymptote of $x = \underline{\ ?\ }$ and a horizontal asymptote of $y = \underline{\ ?\ }$. ***h, k***

3 ASSESS AND RETEACH

1. Identify the horizontal and vertical asymptotes of the graph of $y = \frac{-8}{x + 5} - 3$. **The horizontal asymptote is $y = -3$ and the vertical asymptote is $x = -5$.**

2. Using the form of $y = \frac{a}{x - h} + k$, write an equation of a graph that has a horizontal asymptote of $y = 3$ and a vertical asymptote of $x = 2$. ***Sample answer:*** $y = \frac{2}{x - 2} + 3$

6. As the value of x approaches -1.7 through numbers less than -1.7, the value of y becomes a smaller and smaller negative number (larger and larger in absolute value); as the value of x approaches -1.7 through numbers greater than -1.7, the value of y becomes a larger and larger positive number; $x = -1.7$.

8.

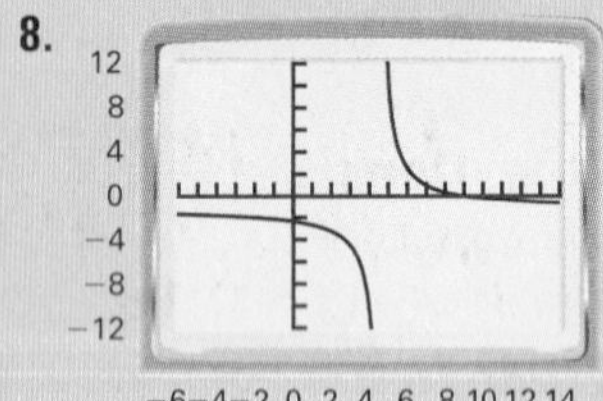

9.

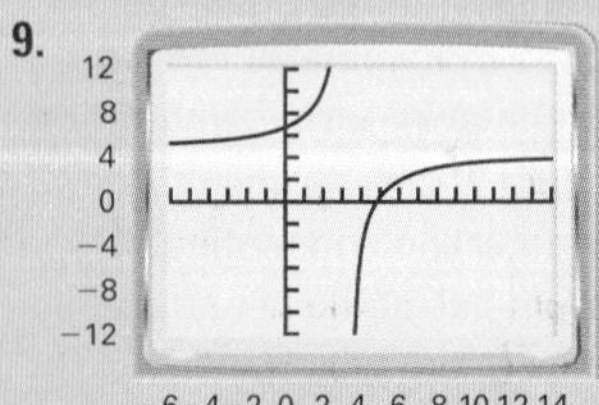

10.

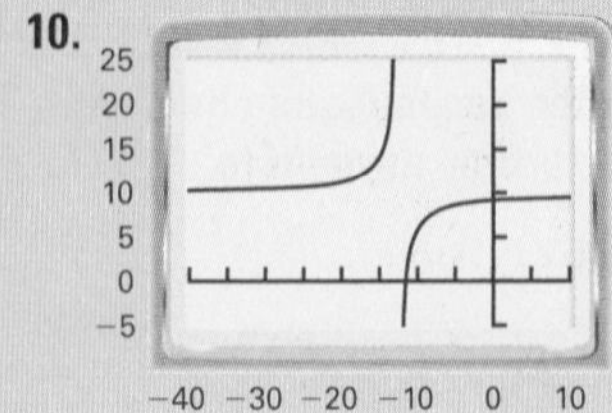

11. The constant in the equation of the vertical asymptote is the same as the constant that is subtracted from x in the function. The constant in the equation of the horizontal asymptote is the same as the constant term of the function.

12. The constant in the equation of the vertical asymptote is the opposite of the constant that is added to x in the function. The constant in the equation of the horizontal asymptote is the same as the constant term of the function.

12.2 Graph Rational Functions

Before You graphed inverse variation equations.

Now You will graph rational functions.

Why? So you can find the cost of a group trip, as in Ex. 39.

Key Vocabulary
- **rational function**
- **hyperbola,** *p. 767*
- **branches of a hyperbola,** *p. 767*
- **asymptotes of a hyperbola,** *p. 767*

p. 767

The inverse variation equation $y = \frac{a}{x}$ $(a \neq 0)$ is a type of *rational function*.

A **rational function** has a rule given by a fraction whose numerator and denominator are polynomials and whose denominator is not 0.

KEY CONCEPT — *For Your Notebook*

Parent Rational Function

The function $y = \frac{1}{x}$ is the parent function for any rational function whose numerator has degree 0 or 1 and whose denominator has degree 1. The function and its graph have the following characteristics:

- The domain and range are all nonzero real numbers.
- The horizontal asymptote is the x-axis. The vertical asymptote is the y-axis.

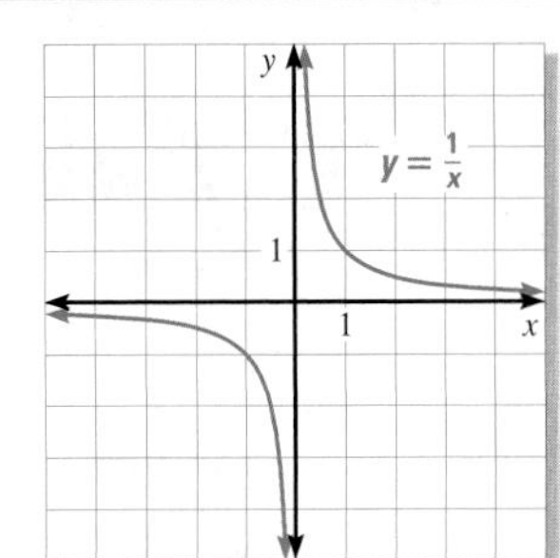

EXAMPLE 1 Compare graph of $y = \frac{a}{x}$ with graph of $y = \frac{1}{x}$

REWRITE FUNCTION

In the function $y = \frac{1}{3x}$, the value of a is $\frac{1}{3}$ as shown:

$$y = \frac{1}{3x} = \frac{1}{3} \cdot \frac{1}{x} = \frac{\frac{1}{3}}{x}$$

a. The graph of $y = \frac{-2}{x}$ is a vertical stretch with a reflection in the x-axis of the graph of $y = \frac{1}{x}$.

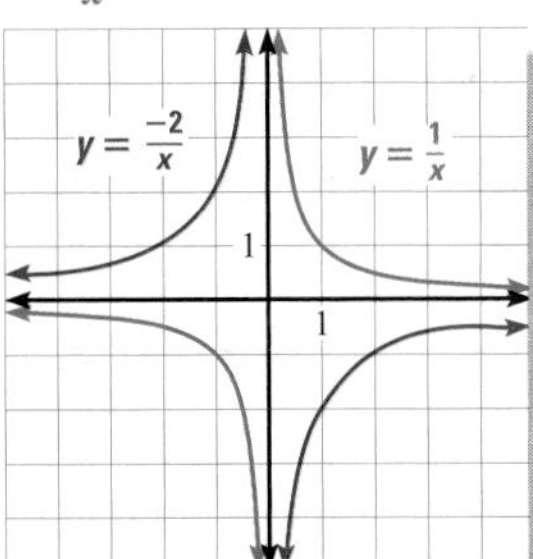

b. The graph of $y = \frac{1}{3x}$ is a vertical shrink of the graph of $y = \frac{1}{x}$.

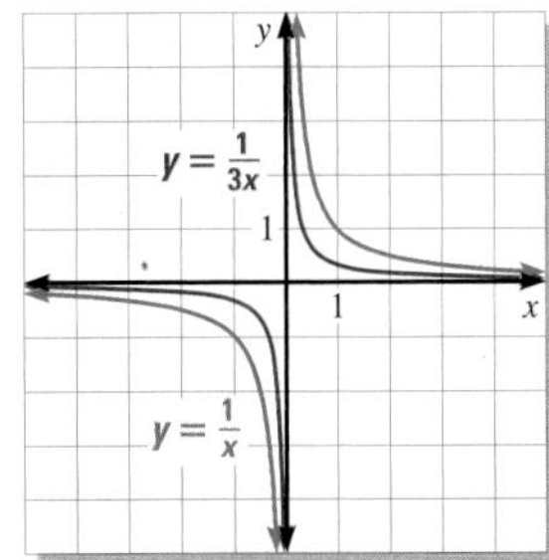

1 PLAN AND PREPARE

Warm-Up Exercises

Transparency Available

1. Graph $y = \frac{5}{x}$.

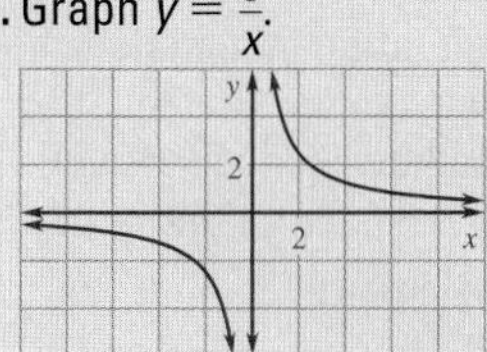

2. It takes a crew of 8 construction workers 150 hours to frame a house. How long will it take a crew of 12 workers? **100 h**

Notetaking Guide

Transparency Available

Promotes interactive learning and notetaking skills.

Pacing

Basic: 2 days
Average: 2 days
Advanced: 2 days
Block: 1 block
- See *Teaching Guide/Lesson Plan.*

2 FOCUS AND MOTIVATE

Essential Question

Big Idea 1, p. 763

How do you graph a rational function? **Tell students they will learn how to answer this question by using the parent function $y = \frac{1}{x}$ and the values of the constants to graph a rational function.**

NCTM STANDARDS

Standard 3: Apply transformations to math situations

Standard 6: Solve problems in math and other contexts

Resource Planning Guide

Chapter Resource Book
- Teaching Guide/Lesson Plan
- Practice levels A, B, C
- Study Guide
- Catch-up for Absent Students
- Application
- Challenge

Workbooks
- Notetaking Guide
- Practice Workbook

Teaching Options
- **Power Presentations** provides dynamic electronic teaching resources for the classroom.
- **Activity Generator** provides editable activities for all ability levels.

Interactive Technology
- Easy Planner
- Power Presentations
- Activity Generator
- Animated Algebra
- Test Generator
- Online Quiz
- eWorkbook
- eEdition
- @HomeTutor

Resources for English Learners
- Spanish Study Guide
- Multi-Language Visual Glossary
- Student Resources in Spanish

See also the *Differentiated Instruction Resources* for more strategies for meeting individual needs.

Motivating the Lesson

You purchase a swimming pass at a community pool for the summer. The pass allows you to use the pool as many times as you want during the season. You would like the average cost per use to be $3 or less. By writing an equation that models the situation, you can use the equation to determine how many times you need to use the pass so that the average cost is $3 or less.

3 TEACH

Extra Example 1

a. Compare the graph of $y = \frac{4}{x}$ with the graph of $y = \frac{1}{x}$.

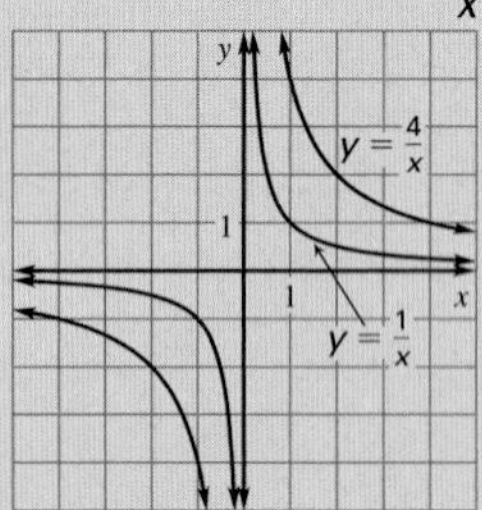

vertical stretch of the graph of $y = \frac{1}{x}$

b. Compare the graph of $y = \frac{-1}{2x}$ with the graph of $y = \frac{1}{x}$.

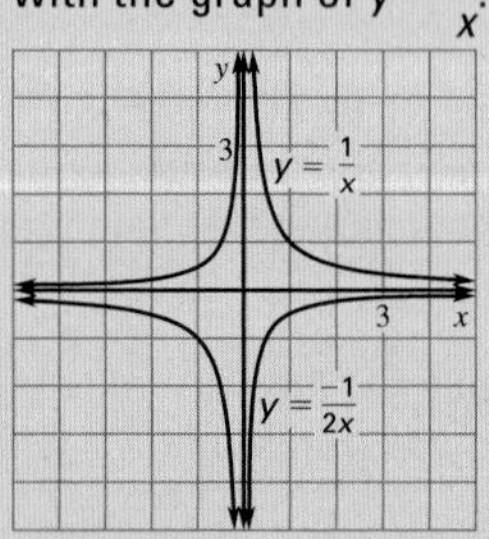

vertical shrink of $y = \frac{1}{x}$, and reflection in the x-axis

1–4. See Additional Answers beginning on p. AA1.

EXAMPLE 2 Graph $y = \frac{1}{x} + k$

Graph $y = \frac{1}{x} + 3$ and identify its domain and range. Compare the graph with the graph of $y = \frac{1}{x}$.

Solution

Graph the function using a table of values.

The domain is all real numbers except 0. The range is all real numbers except 3.

The graph of $y = \frac{1}{x} + 3$ is a vertical translation (of 3 units up) of the graph of $y = \frac{1}{x}$.

x	y
−2	2.5
−1	2
−0.5	1
0	undefined
0.5	5
1	4
2	3.5

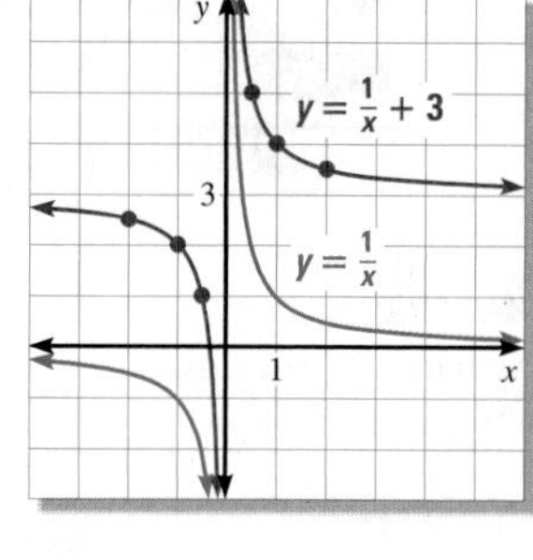

EXAMPLE 3 Graph $y = \frac{1}{x - h}$

Graph $y = \frac{1}{x - 2}$ and identify its domain and range. Compare the graph with the graph of $y = \frac{1}{x}$.

Solution

Graph the function using a table of values.

The domain is all real numbers except 2. The range is all real numbers except 0.

The graph of $y = \frac{1}{x - 2}$ is a horizontal translation (of 2 units to the right) of the graph of $y = \frac{1}{x}$.

x	y
0	−0.5
1	−1
1.5	−2
2	undefined
2.5	2
3	1
4	0.5

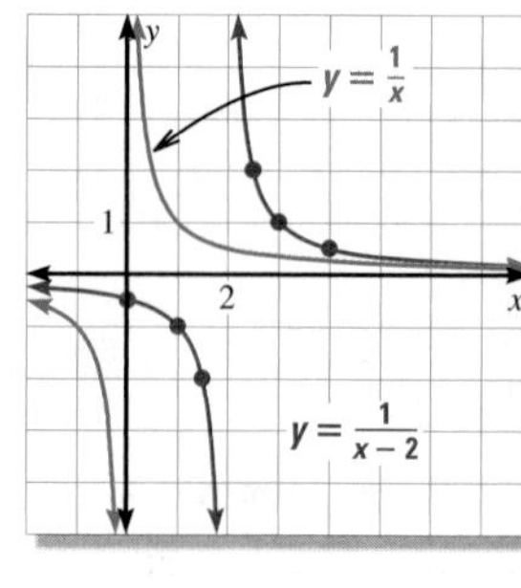

✓ **GUIDED PRACTICE** for Examples 1, 2, and 3

Graph the function and identify its domain and range. *Compare* the graph with the graph of $y = \frac{1}{x}$. **1–3. See margin.**

1. $y = \frac{-4}{x}$ **2.** $y = \frac{1}{x} - 4$ **3.** $y = \frac{1}{x + 5}$

4. *Describe* how the graph of $y = \frac{1}{x + 3}$ is related to the graph of $y = \frac{1}{x}$. **See margin.**

Differentiated Instruction

English Learners When reading mathematics, students should learn to always see the word *ratio* as part of *rational*. This will help them to remember that a rational number is a ratio of two integers (as in Lesson 3.5), and a rational function is a ratio of two polynomials.

See also the *Differentiated Instruction Resources* for more strategies.

GRAPHING RATIONAL FUNCTIONS You can graph a rational function of the form $y = \frac{a}{x-h} + k$ $(a \neq 0)$ by using the values of a, k, and h.

KEY CONCEPT — *For Your Notebook*

Graph of $y = \frac{a}{x-h} + k$

The graph of $y = \frac{a}{x-h} + k$ is a hyperbola that has the following characteristics:

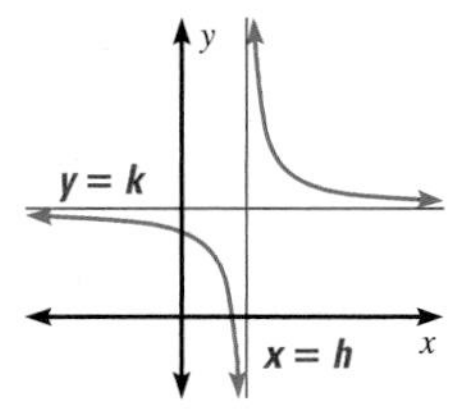

- If $|a| > 1$, the graph is a vertical stretch of the graph of $y = \frac{1}{x}$. If $0 < |a| < 1$, the graph is a vertical shrink of the graph of $y = \frac{1}{x}$. If $a < 0$, the graph is a reflection in the x-axis of the graph of $y = \frac{1}{x}$.
- The horizontal asymptote is $y = k$. The vertical asymptote is $x = h$.

The domain of the function is all real numbers except $x = h$. The range is all real numbers except $y = k$.

EXAMPLE 4 Graph $y = \frac{a}{x-h} + k$

Graph $y = \frac{2}{x+1} - 3$.

Solution

AVOID ERRORS
The asymptotes are used to help you draw a hyperbola. They are *not* part of the hyperbola.

STEP 1 **Identify** the asymptotes of the graph. The vertical asymptote is $x = -1$. The horizontal asymptote is $y = -3$.

STEP 2 **Plot** several points on each side of the vertical asymptote.

STEP 3 **Graph** two branches that pass through the plotted points and approach the asymptotes.

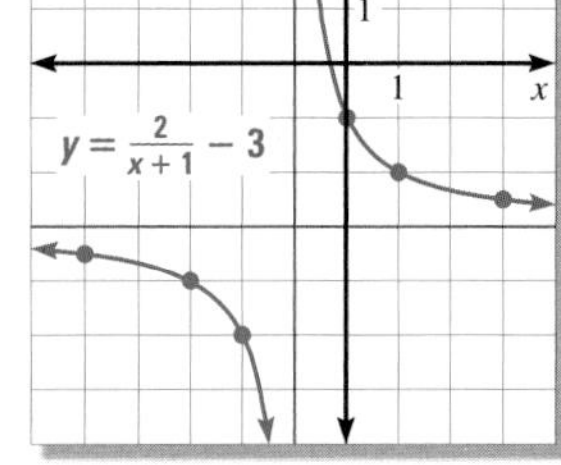

Animated Algebra at classzone.com

✓ GUIDED PRACTICE for Example 4

5. Graph $y = \frac{4}{x-5} + 6$. **See margin.**

6. For which function is the domain all real numbers except -3 and the range all real numbers except 7? **C**

 (A) $y = \frac{2}{x-3} + 7$ (B) $y = \frac{2}{x-3} - 7$ (C) $y = \frac{2}{x+3} + 7$ (D) $y = \frac{2}{x+3} - 7$

5.

Extra Example 2

Graph $y = \frac{1}{x} - 1$ and identify its domain and range. Compare the graph with the graph of $y = \frac{1}{x}$.

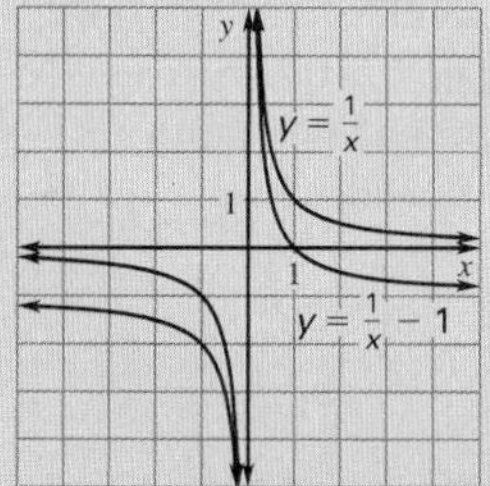

Domain: all real numbers except 0; range: all real numbers except −1; vertical translation of $y = \frac{1}{x}$, 1 unit down

Extra Example 3

Graph $y = \frac{1}{x+2}$ and identify its domain and range. Compare the graph with the graph of $y = \frac{1}{x}$.

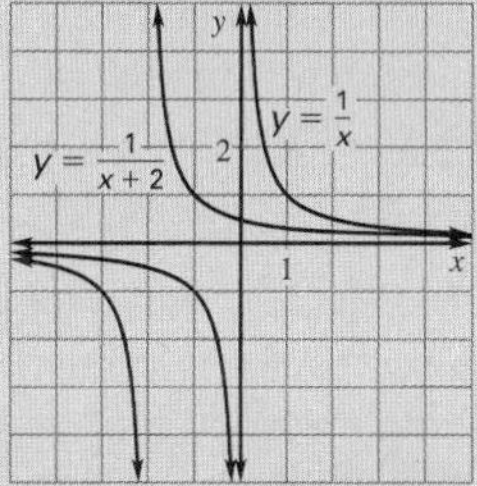

Domain: all real numbers except −2; range: all real numbers except 0; the graph of $y = \frac{1}{x+2}$ is a horizontal translation of $y = \frac{1}{x}$, 2 units left.

Extra Example 4

Graph $y = \frac{3}{x+2} + 1$.

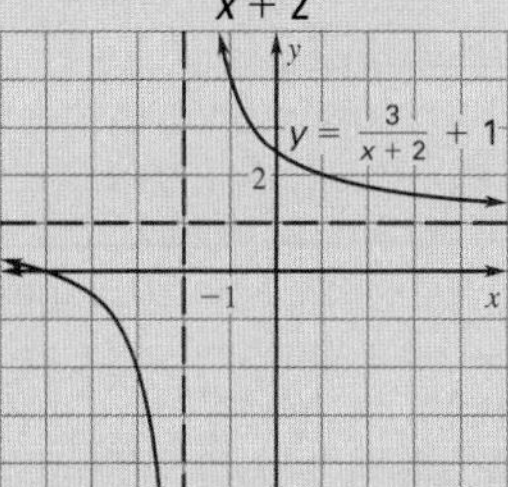

Animated Algebra classzone.com

An **Animated Algebra** activity is available online for **Example 4**. This activity is also part of **Power Presentations**.

Extra Example 5

A ski club rented a cabin for \$750. The club also purchased ski lift tickets for \$22.50 each. The cost will be divided equally among all who use the cabin.

- Write an equation that gives the cost C for each person as a function of the number p of people renting the cabin.
  $C = \frac{750}{p} + 22.50$
- Graph the equation. *Describe* the change in the cost as the number of people increases.

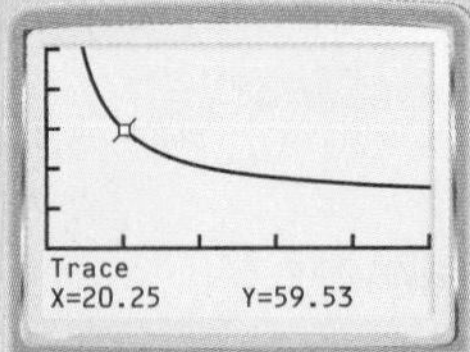

As the number of people increases, the cost decreases.

- Use the graph to approximate the number of people who need to rent the cabin so that the cost is \$60 per person. **20 people**

Closing the Lesson

Have students summarize the major points of the lesson and answer the Essential Question: How do you graph a rational function?

- **The parent function for a rational function is $y = \frac{1}{x}$.**
- **For the graph of $y = \frac{a}{x-h} + k$, the horizontal asymptote is $y = k$ and the vertical asymptote is $x = h$.**

Use the value of a to determine whether the graph of a rational function is a vertical stretch, vertical shrink, and/or reflection in the x-axis of the parent graph. Use the value of k to determine the value of the vertical translation, and use the value of h to determine the value of the horizontal translation. You can also use the asymptotes $y = k$ and $x = h$ to graph the function.

EXAMPLE 5 Solve a multi-step problem

TRIP EXPENSES Your art club is planning a bus trip to an art museum. The cost for renting a bus is \$495, and the cost will be divided equally among the people who are going on the trip. A museum ticket costs \$12.50 per person.

- Write an equation that gives the cost C (in dollars per person) of the trip as a function of the number p of people going on the trip.
- Graph the equation. *Describe* the change in the cost as the number of people increases.
- Use the graph to approximate the number of people who need to go on the trip so that the cost is about \$25 per person.

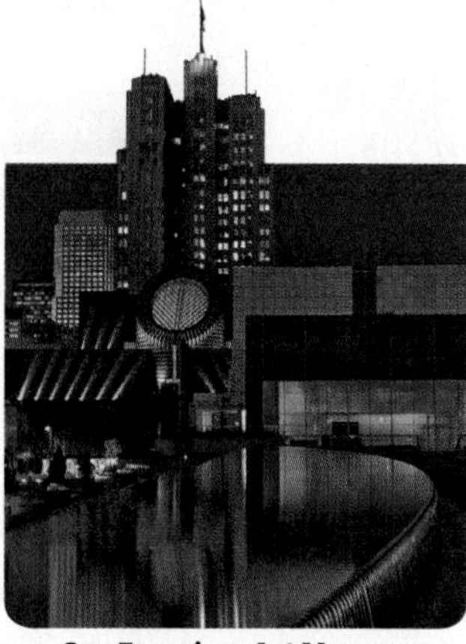
San Francisco Art Museum

Solution

STEP 1 **Write** a verbal model. Then write an equation.

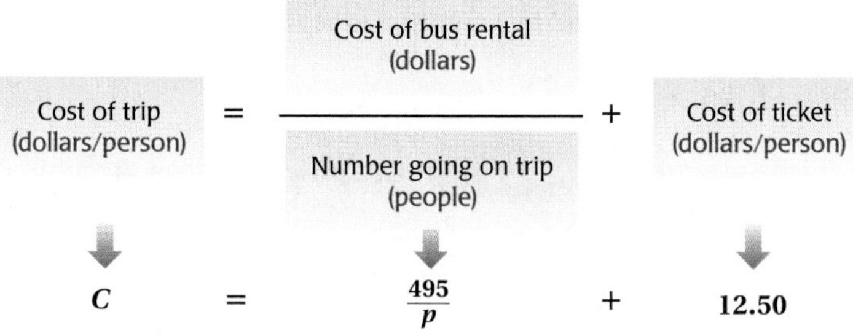

$$C = \frac{495}{p} + 12.50$$

STEP 2 **Graph** $C = \frac{495}{p} + 12.50$ on a graphing calculator. The vertical asymptote is $p = 0$. The horizontal asymptote is $C = 12.5$. As the number of people increases, the cost decreases.

STEP 3 **Approximate** the number of people needed in order for the cost to be about \$25. When $C \approx 25$, the value of p is about 40. So, if about 40 people go on the trip, each person will pay about \$25.

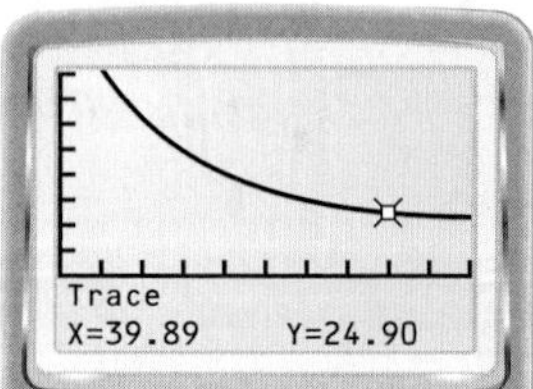

✓ GUIDED PRACTICE for Example 5

7. **WHAT IF?** In Example 5, suppose the club rents a larger bus for \$610. Write and graph an equation that gives the cost C (in dollars per person) of the trip as a function of the number p of people going on the trip. Then approximate the number of people who need to go on the trip so that the cost is about \$25 per person. **$C = \frac{610}{p} + 12.50$; see margin for art; 49 people.**

7.

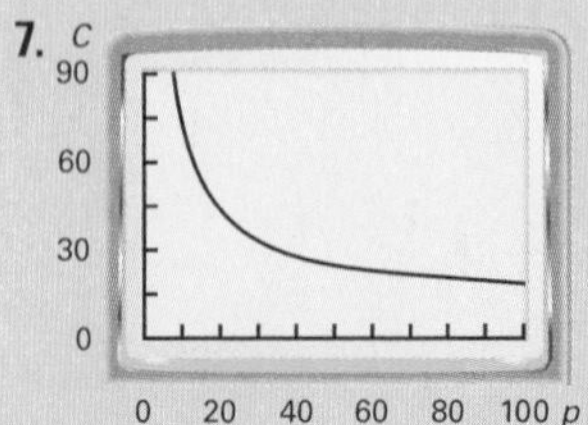

12.2 EXERCISES

HOMEWORK KEY

○ = **WORKED-OUT SOLUTIONS** on p. WS28 for Exs. 7, 21, and 41

★ = **STANDARDIZED TEST PRACTICE** Exs. 2, 18, 28, 29, 36, 42, and 44

◆ = **MULTIPLE REPRESENTATIONS** Ex. 41

SKILL PRACTICE

A

1. **VOCABULARY** Identify the vertical asymptote and horizontal asymptote of the graph of $y = \frac{1}{x-3} - 6$. **$x = 3$, $y = -6$**

2. ★ **WRITING** *Describe* the difference between the graph of $y = \frac{1}{x+2}$ and the graph of $y = \frac{1}{x}$. **The graph of $y = \frac{1}{x+2}$ is the graph of $y = \frac{1}{x}$ translated 2 units to the left.**

EXAMPLES 1, 2, and 3 on pp. 775–776 for Exs. 3–17

GRAPHING FUNCTIONS **Graph the function and identify its domain and range. *Compare* the graph with the graph of $y = \frac{1}{x}$.** **3–17. See margin.**

3. $y = \frac{3}{x}$
4. $y = \frac{1}{2x}$
5. $y = \frac{-3}{x}$
6. $y = \frac{-2}{3x}$
7. $y = \frac{-1}{4x}$
8. $y = \frac{1}{x} + 7$
9. $y = \frac{1}{x} - 5$
10. $y = \frac{1}{x} + 4$
11. $y = \frac{1}{x} + 8$
12. $y = \frac{1}{x} - 6$
13. $y = \frac{1}{x+3}$
14. $y = \frac{1}{x-7}$
15. $y = \frac{1}{x+8}$
16. $y = \frac{1}{x-1}$
17. $y = \frac{1}{x-6}$

EXAMPLE 4 on p. 777 for Exs. 18–31

18. ★ **MULTIPLE CHOICE** For which function is the domain all real numbers except -5 and the range all real numbers except 0? **C**

Ⓐ $y = \frac{5}{x}$ Ⓑ $y = \frac{5}{x-5}$ Ⓒ $y = \frac{5}{x+5}$ Ⓓ $y = \frac{-5}{x-5}$

GRAPHING FUNCTIONS **Graph the function.** **19–27. See margin.**

19. $y = \frac{1}{x-2} - 8$
20. $y = \frac{2}{x-6} + 3$
21. $y = \frac{4}{x+7} + 5$
22. $y = \frac{-3}{x+3} - 4$
23. $y = \frac{-1}{x+5} + 6$
24. $y = \frac{2}{x-1} + 2$
25. $y = \frac{1}{x-4} + 2$
26. $y = \frac{4}{x-3} - 1$
27. $y = \frac{-5}{x-1} - 4$

28. ★ **MULTIPLE CHOICE** The graph of which function has the same horizontal asymptote as the graph of $y = \frac{1}{x}$? **C**

Ⓐ $y = \frac{2}{x} + 3$ Ⓑ $y = \frac{1}{x} - 1$ Ⓒ $y = \frac{-10}{x}$ Ⓓ $y = \frac{-10}{x-1} + 1$

29. ★ **OPEN-ENDED** Write an equation whose graph is a hyperbola that has the following characteristics: ***Sample answer:*** **$y = \frac{1}{x+1} + 2$**
   - The vertical asymptote is $x = -1$.
   - The horizontal asymptote is $y = 2$.

4 PRACTICE AND APPLY

Assignment Guide

Answer Transparencies available for all exercises

Basic:
Day 1: EP p. 948 Exs. 1–9 odd
pp. 779–782
Exs. 1–17, 52–60
Day 2: pp. 779–782
Exs. 18–33, 39–43, 46–51

Average:
Day 1: pp. 779–782
Exs. 1, 2, 6–17, 37, 52–60
Day 2: pp. 779–782
Exs. 18–28 even, 29–36, 39–44, 46–51

Advanced:
Day 1: pp. 779–782
Exs. 1, 6–17, 37, 52–60
Day 2: pp. 779–782
Exs. 18, 24–36, 38–45*, 46–50 even

Block:
pp. 779–782
Exs. 1, 2, 6–17, 18–28 even, 29–37, 39–44, 46–60

Differentiated Instruction

See *Differentiated Instruction Resources* for suggestions on addressing the needs of a diverse classroom.

Homework Check

For a quick check of student understanding of key concepts, go over the following exercises:

Basic: 4, 10, 14, 22, 39

Average: 6, 11, 15, 24, 40

Advanced: 7, 12, 16, 26, 41

Extra Practice

- Student Edition, p. 946
- Chapter Resource Book: Practice levels A, B, C

Practice Worksheet

An easily-readable reduced practice page (with answers) for this lesson can be found on p. 762C.

3–17, 19–27. See Additional Answers beginning on p. AA1.

ERROR ANALYSIS *Describe* **and correct the error in identifying the asymptotes of the graph of the given rational function. 30–31. See margin.**

30. $y = \frac{3}{x+1} - 4$

Vertical asymptote: $x = 1$
Horizontal asymptote: $y = -4$

31. $y = \frac{-2}{x-6} + 7$

Vertical asymptote: $x = 6$
Horizontal asymptote: $y = -7$

B **WRITING EQUATIONS** **Write an equation whose graph is a hyperbola that has the given asymptotes and passes through the given point.**

32. $x = 7, y = 8; (-6, 0)$ $y = \frac{104}{x-7} + 8$

33. $x = -2, y = 5; (0, -9)$ $y = \frac{-28}{x+2} + 5$

34. $x = 3, y = -2; (5, -1)$ $y = \frac{2}{x-3} - 2$

35. $x = -4, y = -4; (-8, 3)$ $y = \frac{-28}{x+4} - 4$

36. ★ **WRITING** Let f be a function of the form $f(x) = \frac{a}{x-h} + k$. Can you graph f if you know only two points on the graph? *Explain.* **No; two points do not provide enough information to determine the three unknown values, a, h, and k.**

37. **GEOMETRY** The height h of a trapezoid is given by the formula

$$h = \frac{2A}{b_1 + b_2}$$

where A is the area and b_1 and b_2 are the bases.

a. Let $A = 50$ and $b_1 = 4$. Write h as a function of b_2. Then graph the function and identify its domain and range. **See margin.**

b. Use the graph to approximate the value of b_2 when $h = 6$. **about 13**

C **38. CHALLENGE** *Describe* how to find the asymptotes of the graph of $g(x) = \frac{3}{2x-4} + 8$. Then graph the function. **See margin.**

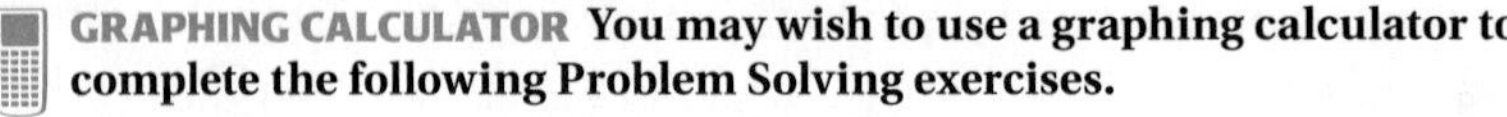

GRAPHING CALCULATOR **You may wish to use a graphing calculator to complete the following Problem Solving exercises.**

EXAMPLE 5 A
on p. 778
for Exs. 39–42

39. TEAM SPORTS A figure skating troupe is planning an out-of-town trip. The expenses for the trip are shown in the flyer. Write an equation that gives the cost C (in dollars per person) as a function of the number p of people going on the trip. Then graph the equation.

@HomeTutor for problem solving help at classzone.com

Trip Expenses

Bus rental.................................... \$900
Food and lodging (per person) \$400

39. $C = \frac{900}{p} +$ **400; see margin for art.**

40. CHARITY EVENTS A committee of 5 people is responsible for making 500 sandwiches for a charity picnic. The committee hopes to recruit extra people for the task. Write an equation that gives the average number s of sandwiches made per person as a function of the number p of extra people recruited for the task. Then graph the equation.

@HomeTutor for problem solving help at classzone.com

40. $s = \frac{500}{5+p}$; **see margin for art.**

○ = **WORKED-OUT SOLUTIONS** on p. WS1 ★ = **STANDARDIZED TEST PRACTICE**

Avoiding Common Errors

Exercises 3–17 Watch for students who confuse vertical and horizontal translations. Remind students that in the equation $y = \frac{a}{x-h} + k$, the value of h determines the horizontal translation and the value of k determines the vertical translation.

Study Strategy

Exercises 3–17 Suggest that students draw the graph of $y = \frac{1}{x}$ and then use it as a guide to make comparisons with the graph for each exercise.

Teaching Strategy

Exercises 19–27 Before students begin these exercises, you may want to ask them to identify the horizontal and vertical asymptote of each function. This will serve as a quick check that they understand the concept, and they can use the asymptotes to graph the functions.

30. To identify the asymptotes $x = h$ and $y = k$ of the hyperbola, write its equation in the form $y = \frac{a}{x-h} + k$: $y = \frac{3}{x-(-1)} + (-4)$; thus the vertical asymptote is $x = -1$, not $x = 1$.

31. To identify the asymptotes of the hyperbola, write its equation in the form $y = \frac{a}{x-h} + k$: $y = \frac{-2}{x-6} + 7$; thus the horizontal asymptote is $y = 7$, not $y = -7$.

37a. $h = \frac{100}{b_2 + 4}$;

Height; $h = \frac{100}{b_2+4}$; Base length; 0, 10, 20, 30; 0, 4, 8, 12, 16, b_2

domain: $b_2 > 0$, range: $0 < h < 25$

38. To write the equation in the form $y = \frac{a}{x-h} + k$, divide the numerator and denominator of $\frac{3}{2x-4}$ by 2: $y = \frac{\frac{3}{2}}{x-2} + 8$; so, the asymptotes are $x = 2$ and $y = 8$.

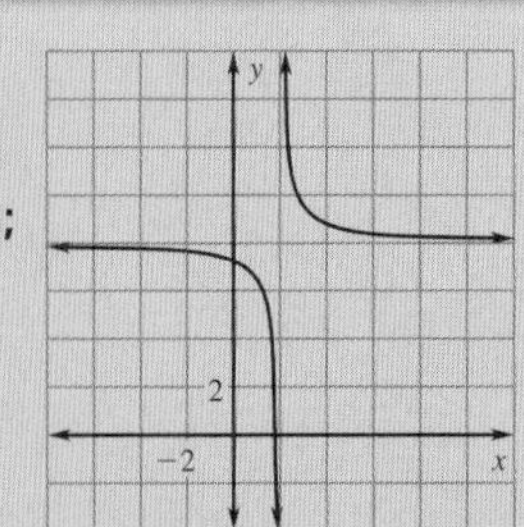

(41.) ◆ **MULTIPLE REPRESENTATIONS** Your movie rental membership lets you rent any number of movies for \$22 per month. You rent at least 2 movies per month.

a. **Writing an Equation** Write an equation that gives the average cost C (in dollars per rental) as a function of the number r of additional rentals beyond 2 rentals. $C = \frac{22}{r+2}$

b. **Drawing a Graph** Graph the equation from part (a). Then use the graph to approximate the number of additional rentals needed per month so that the average cost is \$1.50 per rental.
See margin for art; 13 additional rentals.

42. ★ **SHORT RESPONSE** The Mount Washington Auto Road in New Hampshire is a 7.6 mile uphill road that leads to the mountain's 6288 foot peak. The year's fastest time t (in seconds) for driving up the road during the period 1904–1998 can be modeled by

$$t = \frac{56{,}000}{x + 40}$$

where x is the number of years since 1904. Graph the function. *Describe* how the fastest times changed during the period. Was the *change* in the fastest time from year to year *increasing* or *decreasing*? *Explain.* **See margin.**

B

43. **DIVING DEPTHS** The percent p (in decimal form) of time that an elephant seal spends gliding through the water while diving can be modeled by

$$p = \frac{-28.2}{d} + 0.859$$

where d is the depth (in meters) of the dive. Graph the equation and identify its domain and range. *Describe* how the percent of time gliding changes as the depth increases.

43. See margin for art; domain: $d \geq 32.8$, range: $0 \leq p < 0.859$; the percent of time gliding increases.

44. ★ **EXTENDED RESPONSE** Oxygen cost is a measure of a person's walking efficiency. The models below give the oxygen cost c (in millimeters per kilogram of body mass per meter) as a function of the walking speed v (in meters per minute) for various age groups.

Ages 6–12	Ages 13–19	Ages 20–59

$c = \frac{2.61}{v} + 0.188$	$c = \frac{1.68}{v} + 0.147$	$c = \frac{2.60}{v} + 0.129$

a. **Graph** Normal walking speeds range from 40 meters per minute to 100 meters per minute. Graph the models in the same coordinate plane. Use the domain $40 \leq v \leq 100$. **See margin.**

b. **Interpret** The greater the oxygen cost, the less efficient the person is while walking. Use the graphs to tell whether a person is *more efficient* or *less efficient* while walking as the person's speed increases. **more efficient**

c. **Compare** Which age group has the least efficient walkers at the speeds given in part (a)? *Justify* your choice.

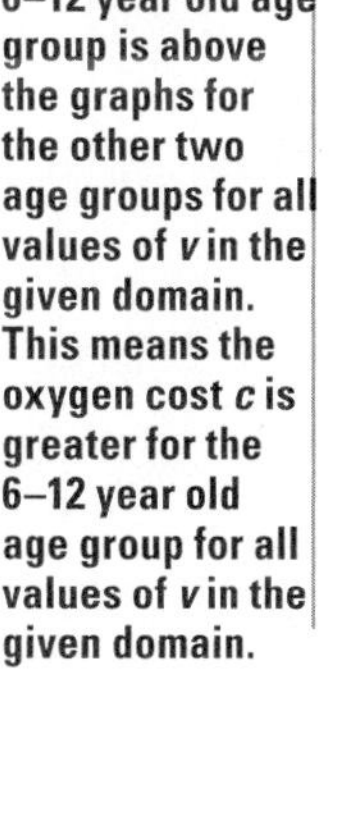

44c. Ages 6–12; the graph for the 6–12 year old age group is above the graphs for the other two age groups for all values of v in the given domain. This means the oxygen cost c is greater for the 6–12 year old age group for all values of v in the given domain.

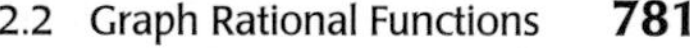

39.

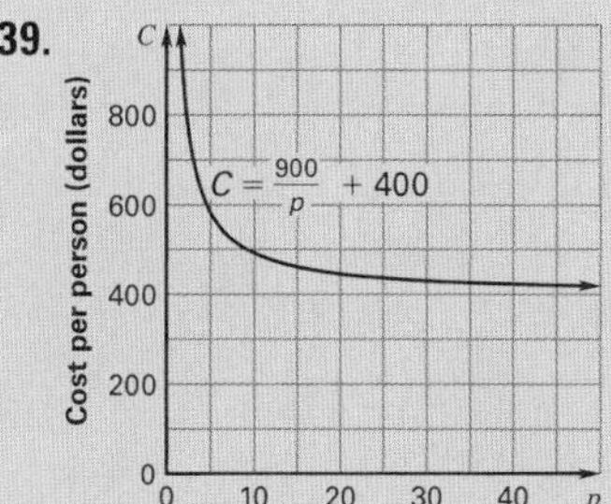

40.

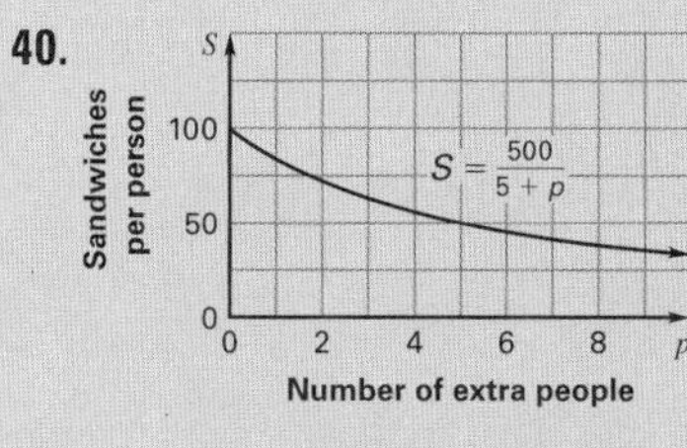

41b.

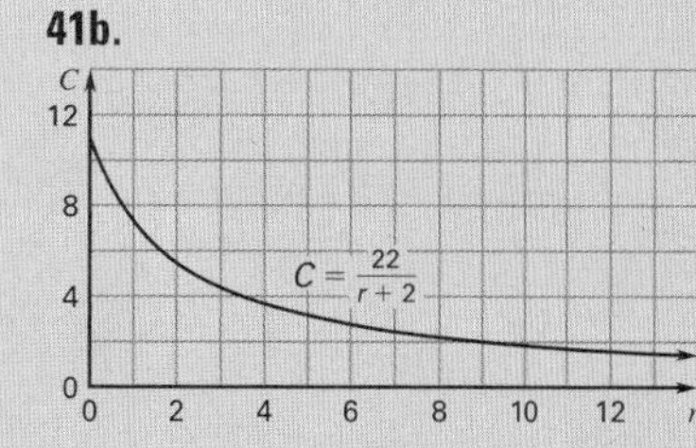

Avoiding Common Errors

Exercises 42–44 Some students confuse variables when discussing inverse relations. Caution students to make sure that their descriptions, explanations, and justifications refer to the correct relationship between specific variables.

Internet Reference

Exercise 43 Additional information about elephant seals can be found at www.marinemammalcenter.org/learning/education/pinnipeds/noelephseal.asp

42.

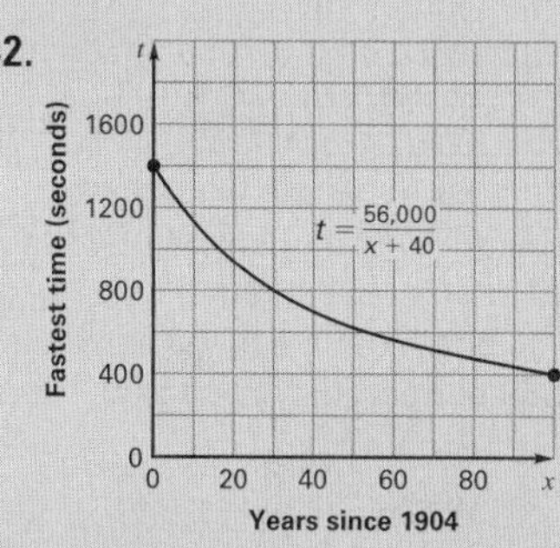

The fastest time decreased. The change in the fastest time was decreasing; the graph is steeper for the years near the beginning of the time period and then gradually becomes less steep, implying that the p-value changed more between two successive years near the beginning of the time period than it changed between two successive years near the end of the time period.

43.

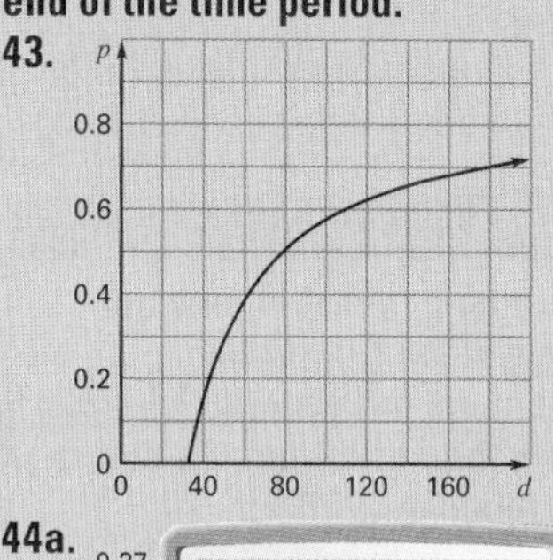

44a.

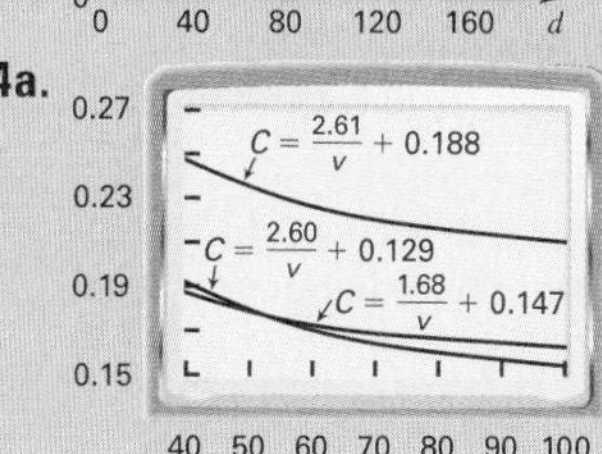

5 ASSESS AND RETEACH

Daily Homework Quiz

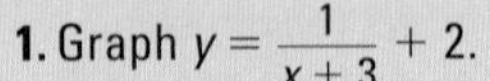

1. Graph $y = \frac{1}{x+3} + 2$.

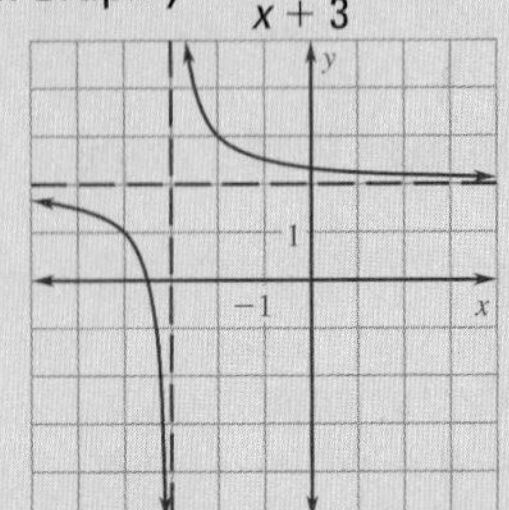

2. The cost per person C for a chartered boat can be modeled by $C = \frac{850}{p} + 12$, where p is the number of people who charter the boat. Find the least number of people who need to charter the boat so the cost is less than \$80 per person. **13 people**

Available at **classzone.com**

Diagnosis/Remediation

- Practice A, B, C in Chapter Resource Book
- Study Guide in Chapter Resource Book
- Practice Workbook
- @HomeTutor

Challenge

Additional challenge is available in the Chapter Resource Book.

Quiz

An easily-readable reduced copy of the quiz (with answers) on Lessons 12.1–12.2 from the Assessment Book can be found on p. 762F.

45a, Quiz 7–9. See Additional Answers beginning on p. AA1.

C **45. CHALLENGE** To decide whether a person qualifies for a loan to buy a house, a lender uses the ratio r of the person's expected monthly housing expenses to monthly income. Suppose the person has a monthly income of \$4150 and expects to pay \$1200 per month in housing expenses. The person also expects to receive a raise of x dollars this month.

a. Write and graph an equation that gives r as a function of x. $r = \frac{1200}{4150 + x}$; **see margin for art.**

b. The person will qualify for a loan if the ratio is 0.28. What must the amount of the raise be in order for the person to qualify for a loan? **about \$136**

MIXED REVIEW

PREVIEW Prepare for Lesson 12.3 in Exs. 46–51.

Write the mixed number as an improper fraction, or write the improper fraction as a mixed number. *(p. 913)*

46. $1\frac{4}{7}$ $\frac{11}{7}$ **47.** $2\frac{3}{8}$ $\frac{19}{8}$ **48.** $5\frac{1}{9}$ $\frac{46}{9}$

49. $\frac{8}{5}$ $1\frac{3}{5}$ **50.** $\frac{13}{6}$ $2\frac{1}{6}$ **51.** $\frac{15}{4}$ $3\frac{3}{4}$

Find the surface area and volume of the solid. For spheres and cylinders, give your answers in terms of π and as decimals rounded to the nearest tenth. *(p. 925)*

52. surface area: 230π cm², 722.2 cm², volume: 450π cm³, 1413 cm³

53. surface area: 64π in.², 201.0 in.², volume: $\frac{256\pi}{3}$ in.³, 267.9 in.³

52.

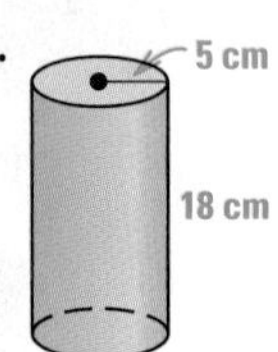

53.

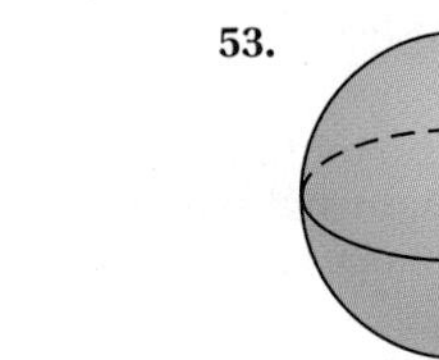

54. 108 ft²; 72 ft³

6 ft
4 ft
3 ft

Simplify the expression.

55. $5x + 7 - 14x - 8$ *(p. 96)* $-9x - 1$

56. $15x - (7 - 2x)$ *(p. 96)* $17x - 7$

57. $\frac{12x - 4}{2}$ *(p. 103)* $6x - 2$

58. $\frac{-32x + 4}{-8}$ *(p. 103)* $4x - \frac{1}{2}$

59. $\sqrt{81x^2}$ *(p. 719)* $9x$

60. $\sqrt{100x^3y^2}$ *(p. 719)* $10xy\sqrt{x}$

QUIZ for Lessons 12.1–12.2

Tell whether the equation represents *direct variation*, *inverse variation*, or *neither*. *(p. 765)*

1. $\frac{1}{5}xy = 1$ **inverse variation** **2.** $y = -9x$ **direct variation** **3.** $5x + y = 3$ **neither**

Given that y varies inversely with x, use the specified values to write an inverse variation equation that relates x and y. Then find the value of y when $x = 3$. *(p. 765)*

4. $x = 6, y = 4$ $y = \frac{24}{x}$; 8 **5.** $x = -3, y = 7$ $y = \frac{-21}{x}$; -7 **6.** $x = \frac{5}{2}, y = 2$ $y = \frac{5}{x}$; $\frac{5}{3}$

Graph the function. Identify its domain and range. *(p. 775)* **7–9. See margin.**

7. $y = \frac{4}{x}$ **8.** $y = \frac{-2}{x - 6}$ **9.** $y = \frac{3}{x + 2} - 5$

 **ONLINE QUIZ** at classzone.com

Animated Algebra classzone.com

12.3 Dividing Polynomials Using Algebra Tiles

MATERIALS • algebra tiles

QUESTION How can you divide polynomials using algebra tiles?

In the equation $36 \div 5 = 7\frac{1}{5}$, the dividend is 36, the divisor is 5, the quotient is 7, and the remainder is 1. This equation illustrates the following rule:

$$\text{Dividend} \div \text{Divisor} = \text{Quotient} + \frac{\text{Remainder}}{\text{Divisor}}$$

This rule can also be applied when dividing polynomials.

EXPLORE Divide polynomials

Divide $2x^2 + 3x + 5$ by $x + 1$.

STEP 1 *Model using algebra tiles*

Think of $2x^2 + 3x + 5$ as the area of a figure. Try to arrange the tiles to form a rectangle with $x + 1$ as one of the side lengths.

Notice that the other side length is $2x + 1$, but there are four 1-tiles remaining.

STEP 2 *Write equation*

The divisor is $x + 1$, the quotient is $2x + 1$, and the remainder is 4.

So, $(2x^2 + 3x + 5) \div (x + 1) = 2x + 1 + \frac{4}{x + 1}$.

DRAW CONCLUSIONS Use your observations to complete these exercises

1. To check that $36 \div 5 = 7\frac{1}{5}$, you can evaluate $5 \cdot 7 + 1$ to obtain 36. Use this method to check the division equation in Step 2 above. **$(x + 1)(2x + 1) + 4 = 2x^2 + 3x + 1 + 4 = 2x^2 + 3x + 5$**

Use algebra tiles to divide the polynomials. Include a drawing of your model. **2–7. See margin.**

2. $(2x^2 + 7x + 6) \div (x + 2)$
3. $(2x^2 + 9x + 10) \div (x + 3)$
4. $(4x^2 + 4x + 5) \div (2x + 1)$
5. $(2x^2 + 5x + 7) \div (2x + 3)$
6. $(3x^2 + 7x + 3) \div (x + 2)$
7. $(4x^2 + 6x + 5) \div (x + 1)$
8. **REASONING** For which of the division problems in Exercises 2–7 is the divisor a factor of the dividend? How do you know? **Exercise 2; the remainder is zero so it is a factor.**

2–7. See Additional Answers beginning on p. AA1.

1 PLAN AND PREPARE

Explore the Concept

- Students will divide polynomials using algebra tiles.
- This activity leads into the study of dividing a polynomial by a binomial in Lesson 12.3, Example 2.

Materials

Each student will need:

- algebra tiles
- Activity Support Master (*Chapter Resource Book*)

Recommended Time

Work activity: 10 min

Discuss results: 5 min

Grouping

Students should work individually.

2 TEACH

Tips for Success

Encourage students to use the divisor as the length of one side of the rectangle.

Animated Algebra classzone.com

An **Animated Algebra** activity is available online. This activity is also part of **Power Presentations**.

Key Discovery

When dividing polynomials, represent the remainder as a fraction, using the divisor as the denominator of the fraction.

3 ASSESS AND RETEACH

Explain how to check the division equation $(2x^2 + 10x + 12) \div (x + 4) = 2x + 2 + \frac{4}{x + 2}$. **Find the product of the divisor and the quotient. Add the numerator of the fraction to the product, and compare the result with the original dividend.**

12.3 Divide Polynomials

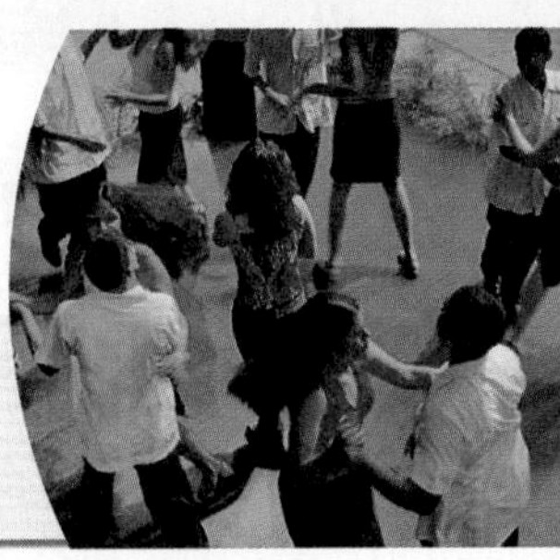

Before You multiplied polynomials.
Now You will divide polynomials.
Why? So you can describe an average cost, as in Ex. 43.

Key Vocabulary
- **monomial,** *p. 554*
- **polynomial,** *p. 554*
- **binomial,** *p. 555*
- **rational function,** *p. 775*

Just as you can find the product of two polynomials, you can divide the product by one of the polynomials to obtain the other polynomial. For example, $x^2 + 5x + 6 = (x + 2)(x + 3)$ is equivalent to $\frac{x^2 + 5x + 6}{x + 2} = x + 3$.

EXAMPLE 1 Divide a polynomial by a monomial

Divide $4x^3 + 8x^2 + 10x$ by $2x$.

Solution

Method 1: Write the division as a fraction.

$$(4x^3 + 8x^2 + 10x) \div 2x = \frac{4x^3 + 8x^2 + 10x}{2x}$$ **Write as fraction.**

$$= \frac{4x^3}{2x} + \frac{8x^2}{2x} + \frac{10x}{2x}$$ **Divide each term by $2x$.**

$$= 2x^2 + 4x + 5$$ **Simplify.**

Method 2: Use long division.

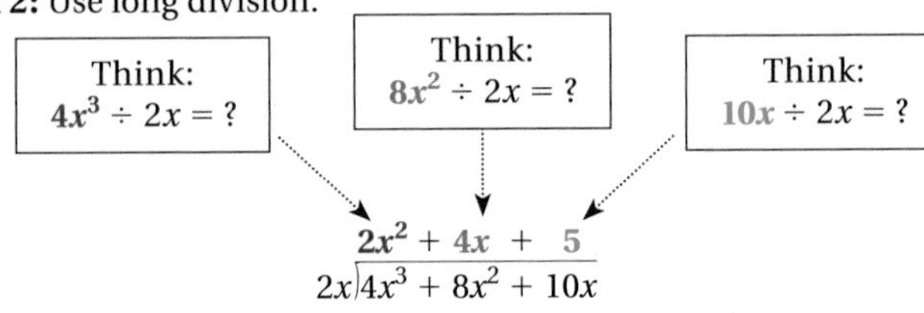

Think:
$4x^3 \div 2x = ?$
Think:
$8x^2 \div 2x = ?$
Think:
$10x \div 2x = ?$
$2x^2 + 4x + 5$
$2x\overline{)4x^3 + 8x^2 + 10x}$

▶ $(4x^3 + 8x^2 + 10x) \div 2x = 2x^2 + 4x + 5$

CHECK
$$2x(2x^2 + 4x + 5) \stackrel{?}{=} 4x^3 + 8x^2 + 10x$$
$$2x(2x^2) + 2x(4x) + 2x(5) \stackrel{?}{=} 4x^3 + 8x^2 + 10x$$
$$4x^3 + 8x^2 + 10x = 4x^3 + 8x^2 + 10x \checkmark$$

✓ GUIDED PRACTICE for Example 1

Divide.

1. $(6x^3 + 3x^2 - 12x) \div 3x$ $\mathbf{2x^2 + x - 4}$
2. $(12y^4 - 16y^3 + 20y^2) \div 4y$ $\mathbf{3y^3 - 4y^2 + 5y}$

1 PLAN AND PREPARE

Warm-Up Exercises
Transparency Available
Find the product.
1. $2x(x^2 + 3x + 5)$ $\mathbf{2x^3 + 6x^2 + 10x}$
2. $(x + 4)(x - 5)$ $\mathbf{x^2 - x - 20}$
3. $(x - 3)(2x + 1)$ $\mathbf{2x^2 - 5x - 3}$
4. $(3x + 1)(2x + 3)$ $\mathbf{6x^2 + 11x + 3}$
5. The dimensions of a rectangle are $x + 3$ and $2x - 5$. Write an expression to represent the number of units for the area of the rectangle. $\mathbf{2x^2 + x - 15}$

Notetaking Guide
Transparency Available
Promotes interactive learning and notetaking skills.

Pacing
Basic: 2 days
Average: 2 days
Advanced: 2 days
Block: 1 block
- See *Teaching Guide/Lesson Plan.*

2 FOCUS AND MOTIVATE

Essential Question
Big Idea 2, p. 763
How do you divide polynomials? **Tell students they will learn how to answer this question by using a method similar to long division.**

NCTM STANDARDS
Standard 2: Analyze situations using algebraic symbols
Standard 6: Solve problems in math and other contexts

Resource Planning Guide

Chapter Resource Book
- Teaching Guide/Lesson Plan
- Activity Master
- Practice levels A, B, C
- Study Guide
- Catch-up for Absent Students
- Application
- Challenge

Workbooks
- Notetaking Guide
- Practice Workbook

Teaching Options
- **Power Presentations** provides dynamic electronic teaching resources for the classroom.
- **Activity Generator** provides editable activities for all ability levels.

Interactive Technology
- Easy Planner
- Power Presentations
- Activity Generator
- Animated Algebra
- Test Generator
- Online Quiz
- eWorkbook
- eEdition
- @HomeTutor

Resources for English Learners
- Spanish Study Guide
- Multi-Language Visual Glossary
- Student Resources in Spanish

See also the *Differentiated Instruction Resources* for more strategies for meeting individual needs.

DIVIDING BY A BINOMIAL As shown in Example 1, you can use two methods when dividing a polynomial by a monomial. To divide a polynomial by a binomial, use long division.

EXAMPLE 2 Divide a polynomial by a binomial

Divide $x^2 + 2x - 3$ by $x - 1$.

Solution

STEP 1 **Divide** the first term of $x^2 + 2x - 3$ by the first term of $x - 1$.

$$\begin{array}{r l} x & \\ x-1\overline{)x^2+2x-3} & \text{Think: } x^2 \div x = ? \\ x^2 - x & \text{Multiply } x \text{ and } x-1. \\ \hline 3x & \text{Subtract } x^2 - x \text{ from } x^2+2x. \end{array}$$

STEP 2 **Bring** down -3. Then divide the first term of $3x - 3$ by the first term of $x - 1$.

$$\begin{array}{r l} x+3 & \\ x-1\overline{)x^2+2x-3} & \\ x^2 - x & \\ \hline 3x-3 & \text{Think: } 3x \div x = ? \\ 3x-3 & \text{Multiply 3 and } x-1. \\ \hline 0 & \text{Subtract } 3x-3 \text{ from } 3x-3. \end{array}$$

▶ $(x^2 + 2x - 3) \div (x - 1) = x + 3$

AVOID ERRORS
Be sure to *subtract* $x^2 - x$ from $x^2 + 2x$ in order to obtain $3x$. Do *not* add the expressions.

NONZERO REMAINDERS In Example 2, if the dividend had been $x^2 + 2x - 2$, the remainder would have been 1. When you obtain a nonzero remainder, you can apply the following rule: Dividend ÷ Divisor = Quotient + $\frac{\text{Remainder}}{\text{Divisor}}$.

EXAMPLE 3 Divide a polynomial by a binomial

Divide $2x^2 + 11x - 9$ by $2x - 3$.

$$\begin{array}{r l} x+7 & \\ 2x-3\overline{)2x^2+11x-9} & \\ 2x^2 - 3x & \text{Multiply } x \text{ and } 2x-3. \\ \hline 14x-9 & \text{Subtract } 2x^2-3x. \text{ Bring down } -9. \\ 14x-21 & \text{Multiply 7 and } 2x-3. \\ \hline 12 & \text{Subtract } 14x-21. \end{array}$$

▶ $(2x^2 + 11x - 9) \div (2x - 3) = x + 7 + \frac{12}{2x - 3}$

CHECK DIVISION
To check your answer, multiply the quotient by the divisor, then add the remainder to the product.

✓ GUIDED PRACTICE for Examples 2 and 3

3. Divide: $(a^2 + 3a - 4) \div (a + 1)$ **$a + 2 + \frac{-6}{a+1}$**

4. Divide: $(9b^2 + 6b + 8) \div (3b - 4)$ **$3b + 6 + \frac{32}{3b-4}$**

Motivating the Lesson

Before you join a teen bowling league, you want to know what your costs will be. If you know the cost to join the league and the cost per game, you can write an equation that models the situation and gives your total cost as a function of the number of games that you bowl.

3 TEACH

Extra Example 1

Divide $6x^3 - 12x^2 + 9x$ by $3x$. **$2x^2 - 4x + 3$**

Key Question to Ask for Example 1

- In Method 2, how can you check each step as you solve the problem? **Multiply each term in the quotient by the divisor to see if you get each term in the dividend.**

Extra Example 2

Divide $x^2 + x - 6$ by $x + 3$. **$x - 2$**

Key Questions to Ask for Example 2

- In Step 1, why do you place the quotient term x over the dividend term $2x$? **When you multiply x and $x - 1$, each term in the product will be aligned under the like term in the dividend.**
- How do you subtract $x^2 - x$ from $x^2 + 2x$? **For each term in $x^2 - x$, add its opposite by multiplying that term by -1.**

Extra Example 3

Divide $3x^2 + 17x + 13$ by $3x + 2$.
$x + 5 + \frac{3}{3x+2}$

Extra Example 4

Divide $-3n + n^2 - 21$ by $3 + n$.
$n - 6 + \frac{-3}{n + 3}$

Key Questions to Ask for Example 4

- How can you check your answer? **Find the product of the divisor and the quotient. Then add the numerator of the fraction. The result should be the original dividend.**
- What is the remainder? What is the entire quotient? **-2, $y + 3 + \frac{-2}{y + 2}$**

Extra Example 5

Divide $-12 + 4y^2$ by $-1 + 2y$.
$2y + 1 + \frac{-11}{2y - 1}$

Key Questions to Ask for Example 5

- Why do you insert missing terms using zero coefficients? **The dividend has no *m*-term, and the long-division process requires a place for *m*-terms.**
- What is the purpose of inserting missing terms? **Missing terms, with 0 coefficients, serve as placeholders in the long-division process.**

Extra Example 6

Graph $y = \frac{2x + 1}{x - 1}$.

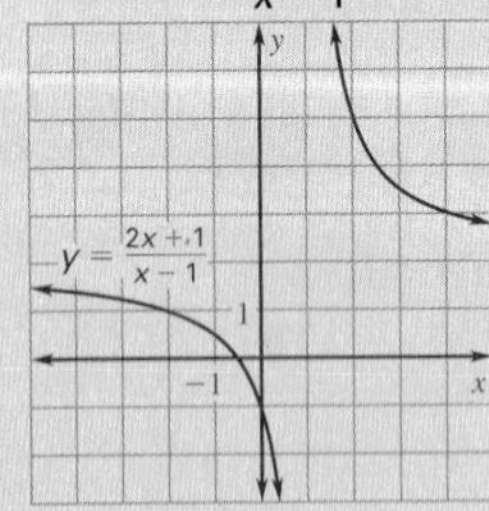

REWRITING POLYNOMIALS When dividing polynomials, you may first need to rewrite the polynomials so that the exponents decrease from left to right. When rewriting polynomials, insert any missing terms using zero coefficients. For example, $8 + 3x^2$ should be rewritten as $3x^2 + 0x + 8$.

EXAMPLE 4 Rewrite polynomials

Divide $5y + y^2 + 4$ by $2 + y$.

REVIEW POLYNOMIALS
For help with rewriting a polynomial, see p. 554.

$$\begin{array}{rl} y + 3 & \\ y + 2\overline{)y^2 + 5y + 4} & \text{Rewrite polynomials.} \\ \underline{y^2 + 2y} & \text{Multiply } y \text{ and } y + 2. \\ 3y + 4 & \text{Subtract } y^2 + 2y. \text{ Bring down 4.} \\ \underline{3y + 6} & \text{Multiply 3 and } y + 2. \\ -2 & \text{Subtract } 3y + 6. \end{array}$$

▶ $(5y + y^2 + 4) \div (2 + y) = y + 3 + \frac{-2}{y + 2}$

EXAMPLE 5 Insert missing terms

Divide $13 + 4m^2$ by $-1 + 2m$.

$$\begin{array}{rl} 2m + 1 & \\ 2m - 1\overline{)4m^2 + 0m + 13} & \text{Rewrite polynomials. Insert missing term.} \\ \underline{4m^2 - 2m} & \text{Multiply } 2m \text{ and } 2m - 1. \\ 2m + 13 & \text{Subtract } 4m^2 - 2m. \text{ Bring down 13.} \\ \underline{2m - 1} & \text{Multiply 1 and } 2m - 1. \\ 14 & \text{Subtract } 2m - 1. \end{array}$$

▶ $(13 + 4m^2) \div (-1 + 2m) = 2m + 1 + \frac{14}{2m - 1}$

EXAMPLE 6 Rewrite and graph a rational function

Graph $y = \frac{2x - 1}{x - 2}$.

Solution

USE ASYMPTOTES
Use the graphing technique in Lesson 12.2 to graph the function. For instance, the lines $x = 2$ and $y = 2$ are asymptotes of the graph.

STEP 1 **Rewrite** the rational function in the form $y = \frac{a}{x - h} + k$.

$$\begin{array}{r} 2 \\ x - 2\overline{)2x - 1} \\ \underline{2x - 4} \\ 3 \end{array}$$

So, $y = \frac{3}{x - 2} + 2$.

STEP 2 **Graph** the function.

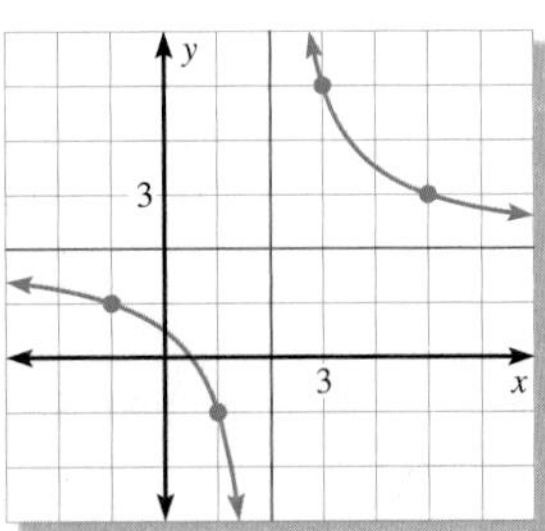

7.

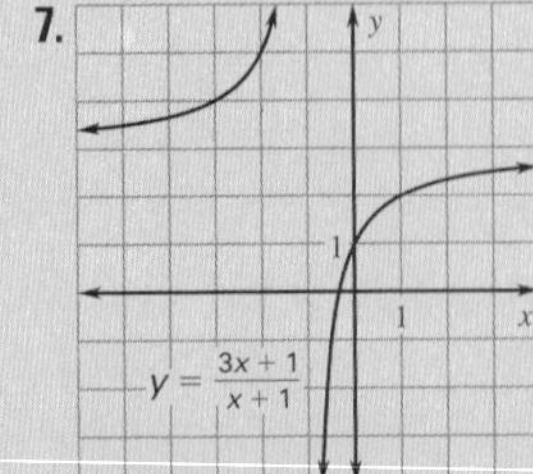

8.

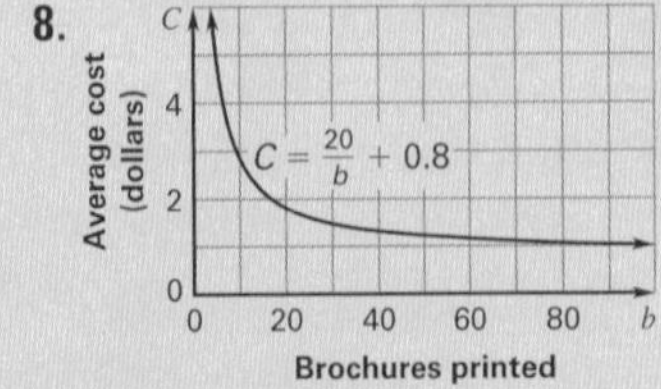

Differentiated Instruction

Inclusion Students may forget to organize the exponents in descending order before performing the long division as shown in **Examples 4 and 5**. It may help to show them the similarity to long division done in arithmetic. When they divide $23\overline{)648}$ for example, the highest powers (of 10) also appear first.

$$2.3 \times 10^1 + 3 \times 10^0\overline{)6 \times 10^2 + 4 \times 10^1 + 8 \times 10^0}$$

See also the *Differentiated Instruction Resources* for more strategies.

GUIDED PRACTICE for Examples 4, 5, and 6

5. Divide: $(8m - 7 + 4m^2) \div (5 + 2m)$ $\quad 2m - 1 + \frac{-2}{2m+5}$

6. Divide: $(n^2 - 6) \div (-3 + n)$ $\quad n + 3 + \frac{3}{n-3}$

7. Graph $y = \frac{3x+1}{x+1}$. See margin.

EXAMPLE 7 Solve a multi-step problem

PRINTING COSTS You are creating brochures that promote your school's sports events. You pay \$20 for computer time. The cost of printing a brochure is \$.60. Write and graph an equation that gives the average cost C (in dollars per brochure) as a function of the number b of brochures printed.

Solution

STEP 1 **Write** a verbal model. Then write an equation.

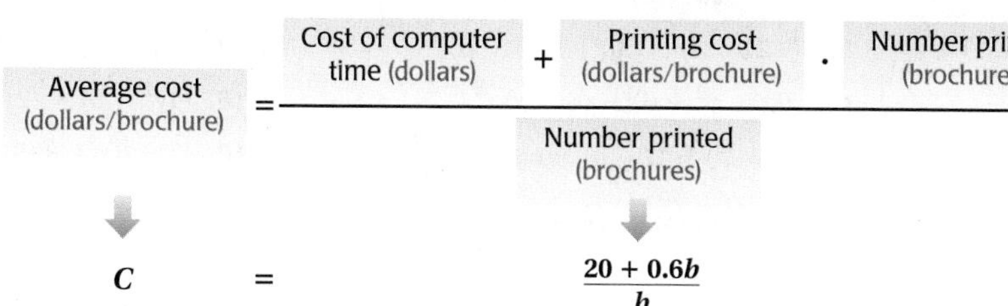

$$C = \frac{20 + 0.6b}{b}$$

STEP 2 **Rewrite** the rational function.

$$C = \frac{20 + 0.6b}{b}$$

$$= \frac{20}{b} + \frac{0.6b}{b}$$

$$= \frac{20}{b} + 0.6$$

STEP 3 **Graph** the function.

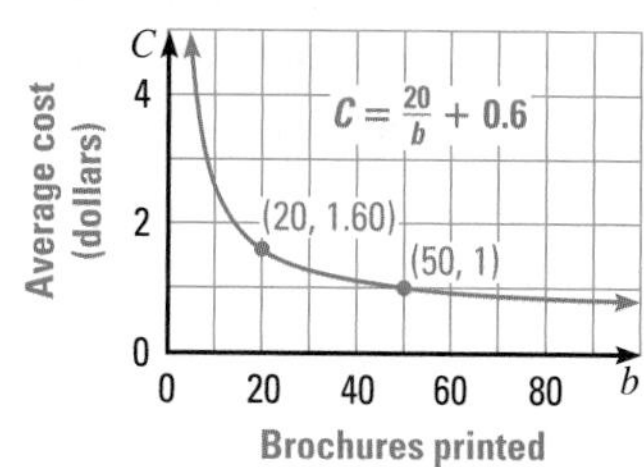

GUIDED PRACTICE for Example 7

8. **WHAT IF?** In Example 7, suppose the cost of printing a brochure is \$.80. Write and graph an equation that gives the average cost C (in dollars per brochure) as a function of the number b of brochures printed.

9. **INTERNET COSTS** A cable Internet service provider charges an installation fee of \$100 and a monthly service charge of \$45. Write and graph an equation that gives the average cost C (in dollars per month) as a function of the number m of months of Internet service.

8. $C = \frac{20}{b} + 0.8$, see margin for art.

9. $C = \frac{100}{m} + 45$, see margin for art.

Extra Example 7

You pay \$50 for an annual park permit and \$5 per day for camping fees. Write and graph an equation that gives the average cost per day C of camping as a function of the number of d days that you camp.

$C = \frac{50}{d} + 5$

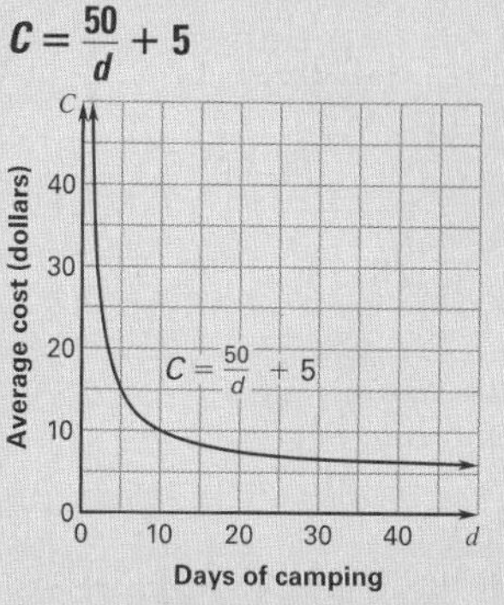

Closing the Lesson

Have students summarize the major points of the lesson and answer the Essential Question: How do you divide polynomials?

- **Write the problem as long division, using placeholders with a zero coefficient for missing terms.**
- **Write the result of dividing as: Dividend ÷ Divisor = Quotient + $\frac{\text{Remainder}}{\text{Divisor}}$.**
- **To check, find the product of the quotient and the divisor. Then add the numerator of the fraction. The result should be the original dividend.**

When dividing a polynomial by a monomial, write the division as a fraction and simplify, or use long division. Use long division when dividing a polynomial by a binomial. Write the polynomials so that the exponents decrease from left to right.

9.

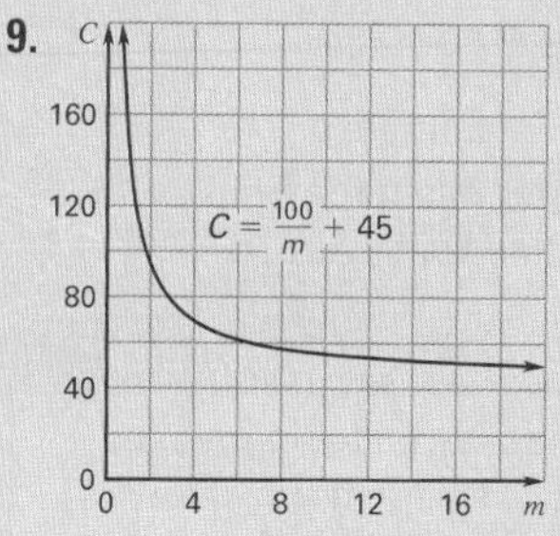

Differentiated Instruction

Below Level For **Example 7**, have students find the cost to print 5, 15, 25, 70, and 80 brochures. Ask them to find those costs two ways: by substituting values for b in the equation, and by using the graph. Then ask them to compare and contrast the two methods.

Advanced For **Example 7**, have students research several local printing stores to find what they charge for computer time and for printing brochures. Ask them to do a comparison analysis of the costs by writing equations for all of the stores and then graphing them in the same coordinate plane.

See also the *Differentiated Instruction Resources* for more strategies.

12.3 EXERCISES

HOMEWORK KEY
○ = **WORKED-OUT SOLUTIONS** on p. WS29 for Exs. 7, 25, and 45
★ = **STANDARDIZED TEST PRACTICE** Exs. 2, 19, 33, 34, 38, 47, 48, and 49
◆ = **MULTIPLE REPRESENTATIONS** Ex. 46

SKILL PRACTICE

A

1. **VOCABULARY** Copy and complete: To divide a polynomial by a(n) __?__, you can either write the division as a fraction or use long division. **monomial**

2. ★ **WRITING** *Describe* the steps you would take in graphing the rational function $f(x) = \frac{3x - 2}{x + 6}$. **See margin.**

EXAMPLES 1, 2, 3, 4, and 5 on pp. 784–786 for Exs. 3–21

DIVIDING POLYNOMIALS Divide.

3. $(8x^3 - 12x^2 + 16x) \div 4x$ $\mathbf{2x^2 - 3x + 4}$
4. $(10y^3 + 20y^2 + 55y) \div 5y$ $\mathbf{2y^2 + 4y + 11}$
5. $(12r^4 - 30r^2 - 72r) \div (-6r)$ $\mathbf{-2r^3 + 5r + 12}$
6. $(21s^4 + 49s^3 - 35s^2) \div (-7s)$ $\mathbf{-3s^3 - 7s^2 + 5s}$
7. $(3v^2 - v - 10) \div (v - 2)$ $\mathbf{3v + 5}$
8. $(7w^2 + 3w - 4) \div (w + 1)$ $\mathbf{7w - 4}$
9. $(2m^2 - 5m - 12) \div (2m + 3)$ $\mathbf{m - 4}$
10. $(6n^2 + 7n - 3) \div (3n - 1)$ $\mathbf{2n + 3}$
11. $(a^2 - 5a + 3) \div (a - 1)$ $\mathbf{a - 4 + \frac{-1}{a - 1}}$
12. $(c^2 - 2c - 4) \div (c + 4)$ $\mathbf{c - 6 + \frac{20}{c + 4}}$
13. $(-21 - 4p + 3p^2) \div (3 + p)$ $\mathbf{3p - 13 + \frac{18}{3 + p}}$
14. $(8q + q^2 + 7) \div (7 + q)$ $\mathbf{q + 1}$
15. $(9x + x^2 + 6) \div (6 + x)$ $\mathbf{x + 3 + \frac{-12}{6 + x}}$
16. $(4y^2 - 5) \div (2y + 5)$ $\mathbf{2y - 5 + \frac{20}{2y + 5}}$
17. $(5 - t^2) \div (t - 3)$ $\mathbf{-t - 3 + \frac{-4}{t - 3}}$
18. $(7 - 8x^2) \div (3 + 2x)$ $\mathbf{-4x + 6 + \frac{-11}{3 + 2x}}$

19. ★ **MULTIPLE CHOICE** What is the remainder when you divide $x^2 + 4x + 9$ by $x - 4$? **B**

(A) $x - 4$ (B) 41 (C) $x + 8$ (D) $\frac{41}{x - 4}$

ERROR ANALYSIS *Describe* and correct the error in dividing the polynomials. **20, 21. See margin.**

20. $(5x + 6) \div (x + 2)$

$$\begin{array}{r} 5 \\ x + 2\overline{)5x + 6} \\ 5x + 10 \\ \hline -4 \end{array}$$

$$(5x + 6) \div (x + 2) = 5 + \frac{-4}{5x + 6}$$

21. $(8x - 9) \div (x - 3)$

$$\begin{array}{r} 8 \\ x - 3\overline{)8x - 9} \\ 8x - 24 \\ \hline -33 \end{array}$$

$$(8x - 9) \div (x - 3) = 8 + \frac{-33}{x - 3}$$

EXAMPLE 6 on p. 786 for Exs. 22–30

GRAPHING FUNCTIONS Graph the function. **22–30. See margin.**

22. $y = \frac{x + 10}{x}$
23. $y = \frac{2x - 7}{x}$
24. $y = \frac{x + 4}{x - 3}$
25. $y = \frac{2x - 4}{x - 1}$
26. $y = \frac{5x + 2}{x + 3}$
27. $y = \frac{6x - 4}{x + 5}$
28. $y = \frac{2 - x}{x + 9}$
29. $y = \frac{2 + 4x}{x - 3}$
30. $y = \frac{7 - 10x}{x + 7}$

4 PRACTICE AND APPLY

Assignment Guide

Answer Transparencies available for all exercises

Basic:
Day 1: EP p. 946 Exs. 3–6
pp. 788–791
Exs. 1–12, 19–21, 51–59
Day 2: pp. 788–791
Exs. 13–18, 23–29 odd, 31–34, 42–47, 60–65

Average:
Day 1: pp. 788–791
Exs. 1, 2, 5–12, 19–21, 35–37, 51–59
Day 2: pp. 788–791
Exs. 13–18, 22–30 even, 31–34, 38, 42–49, 60–64 even

Advanced:
Day 1: pp. 788–791
Exs. 1, 2, 4–12 even, 19, 35–41*, 51–59
Day 2: pp. 788–791
Exs. 13–18, 22–30 even, 31–34, 42–50*, 60–64 even

Block:
pp. 788–791
Exs. 1, 2, 5–21, 22–30 even, 31–38, 42–49, 51–59, 60–64 even

Differentiated Instruction

See *Differentiated Instruction Resources* for suggestions on addressing the needs of a diverse classroom.

Homework Check

For a quick check of student understanding of key concepts, go over the following exercises:
Basic: 6, 9, 17, 24, 42
Average: 8, 10, 18, 26, 43
Advanced: 12, 16, 18, 28, 44

Extra Practice

- Student Edition, p. 946
- Chapter Resource Book: Practice levels A, B, C

Practice Worksheet

An easily-readable reduced practice page (with answers) for this lesson can be found on p. 762C.

2. *Sample answer:* Use long division to divide $3x - 2$ by $x + 6$, thus rewriting the function in the form $f(x) = \frac{a}{x - h} + k$. Then identify the asymptotes of the function, plot several points on each side of the vertical asymptote, and sketch the hyperbola.

20. The remainder, -4, should be placed over the divisor, $x + 2$, not the dividend, $5x + 6$; $(5x + 6) \div (x + 2) = 5 + \frac{-4}{x + 2}$.

 GEOMETRY **Divide the surface area of the rectangular prism by its volume.**

31. 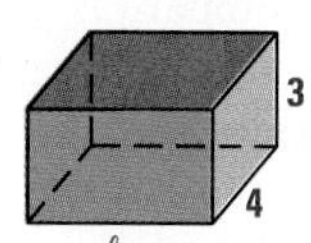 $\frac{7}{6} + \frac{2}{\ell}$

32. 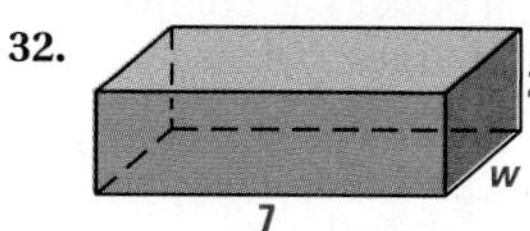 $\frac{9}{7} + \frac{2}{w}$

33. ★ **MULTIPLE CHOICE** What is the horizontal asymptote of the graph of $y = \frac{bx + c}{x - d}$? **A**

Ⓐ $y = b$ Ⓑ $y = c$ Ⓒ $y = d$ Ⓓ $y = 0$

34. ★ **MULTIPLE CHOICE** The graph of which function is shown? **C**

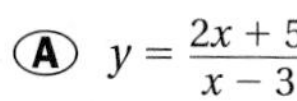

Ⓐ $y = \frac{2x + 5}{x - 3}$ Ⓑ $y = \frac{2x + 5}{x + 3}$

Ⓒ $y = \frac{2x - 5}{x - 3}$ Ⓓ $y = \frac{2x - 5}{x + 3}$

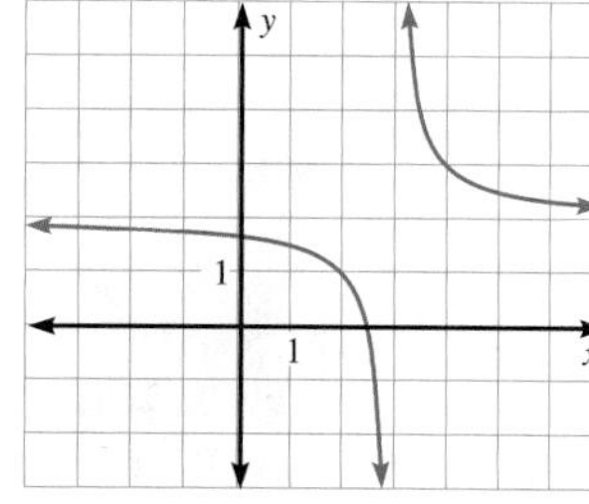

REASONING In Exercises 35–37, find the value of k using the given information.

35. When $8x^2 + 26x + k$ is divided by $x + 3$, the remainder is 4. **10**

36. When $100x^2 + k$ is divided by $5x + 2$, the remainder is 0. **−16**

37. The graph of $y = \frac{kx + 4}{x - 6}$ has $y = -5$ as its horizontal asymptote. **−5**

38. ★ **OPEN-ENDED** Write a function of the form $f(x) = \frac{bx + c}{x - h}$ such that the graph of the function has $x = 4$ and $y = 6$ as its asymptotes. ***Sample answer:*** $\frac{6x + 1}{x - 4}$

C **CHALLENGE Graph the function. 39–41. See margin.**

39. $y = \frac{6x + 10}{3x + 6}$ **40.** $y = \frac{12x - 7}{4x - 8}$ **41.** $y = \frac{10x + 3}{2x - 6}$

PROBLEM SOLVING

EXAMPLE 7 on p. 787 for Exs. 42–45

A **42. MOVIE RENTALS** You order movie rental coupons from a website for \$3 each. The total cost of your order includes a \$4 shipping fee. Write an equation that gives the average cost C (in dollars per coupon) as a function of the number r of coupons ordered. Then graph the function. $C = \frac{4 + 3r}{r}$; **see margin for art.**

@HomeTutor for problem solving help at classzone.com

43. MEMBERSHIP FEES You pay \$80 for an annual membership to a dance club and pay \$3 per dance class. Write an equation that gives the average cost C (in dollars per class) as a function of the number d of dance classes that you take. Then graph the function. $C = \frac{80 + 3d}{d}$; **see margin for art.**

@HomeTutor for problem solving help at classzone.com

Avoiding Common Errors

Exercises 3–18 Some students may write the remainder fraction using the dividend as the fraction's denominator, rather than the divisor. Suggest that students write the following rule on a notecard and use it to check the form of their answers: Dividend ÷ Divisor = Quotient + $\frac{\text{Remainder}}{\text{Divisor}}$.

Teaching Strategy

Exercises 22–30 Before students graph the functions, ask for one or two volunteers to rewrite each function in the form $y = \frac{a}{x - h} + k$ on the chalkboard. Ask students to identify the asymptotes for each example and to explain how the asymptotes are related to the graph of the function.

41. 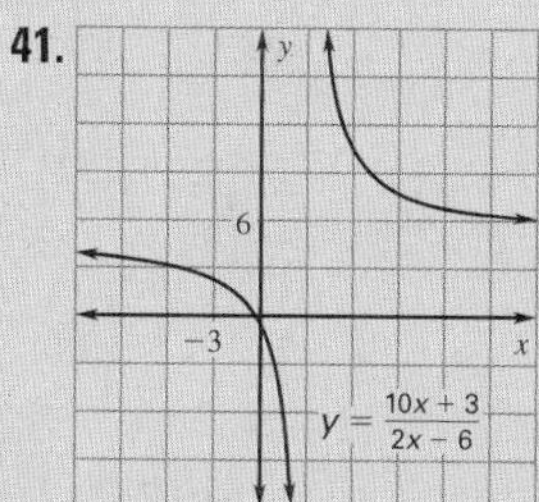

42. 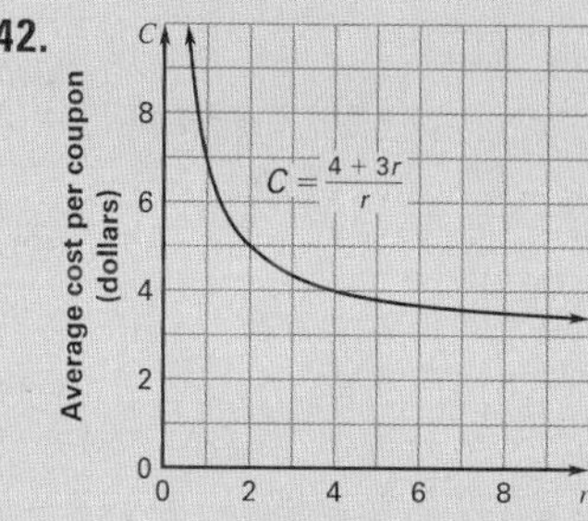

43. 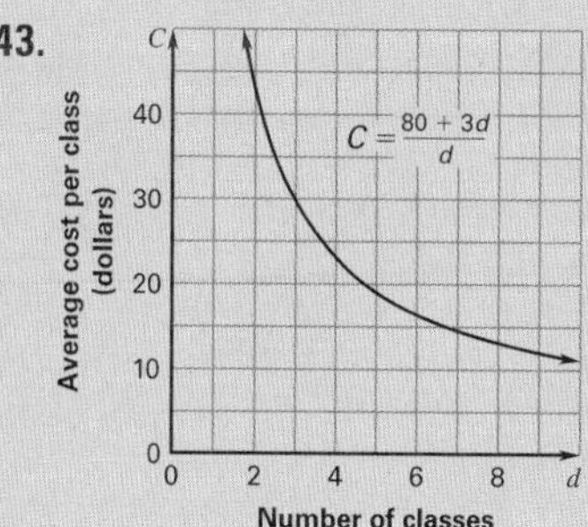

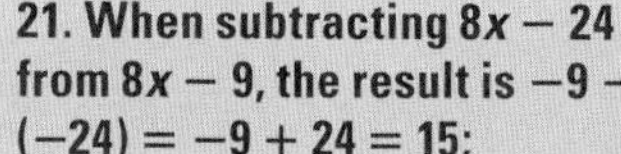

21. When subtracting $8x - 24$ from $8x - 9$, the result is $-9 - (-24) = -9 + 24 = 15$; $(8x - 9) \div (x - 3) = 8 + \frac{15}{x - 3}$.

22–30. See Additional Answers beginning on p. AA1.

39. 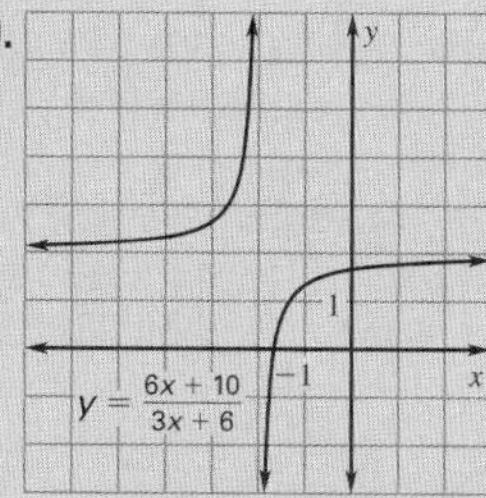

40. 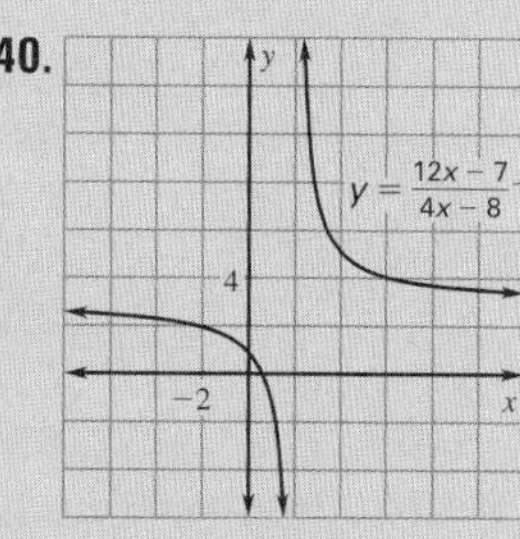

Mathematical Reasoning

Exercise 46 For part (a), review scatter plots and lines of fit before students attempt this exercise. For part (b), make sure students understand how to calculate what percent is represented by a specific tip.

An **Animated Algebra** activity is available online for **Exercise 49**. This activity is also part of **Power Presentations**.

44a.

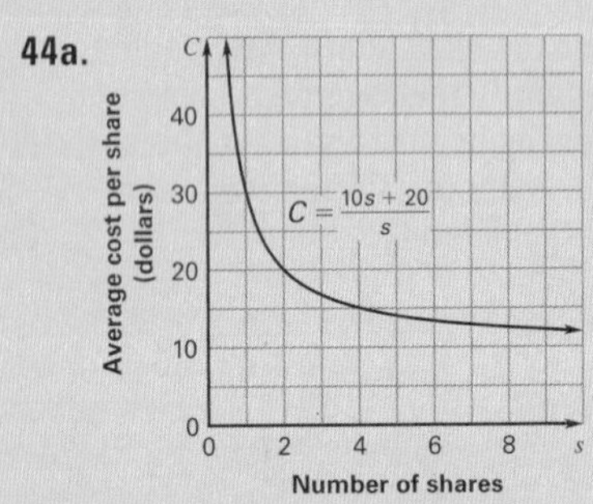

45b.

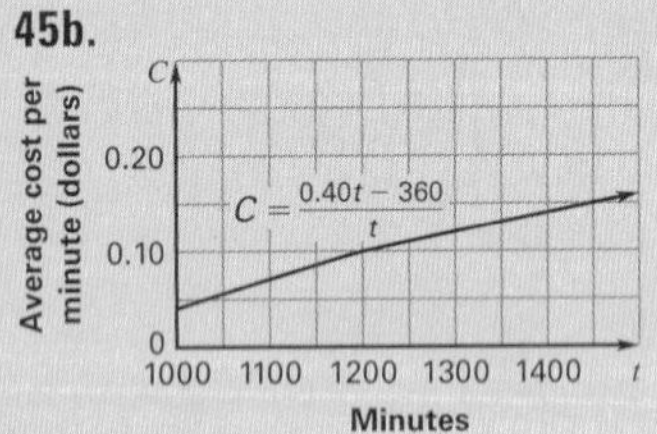

46a.

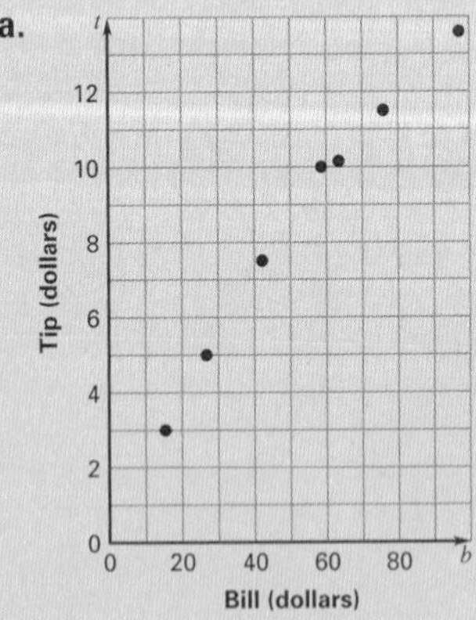

46c.

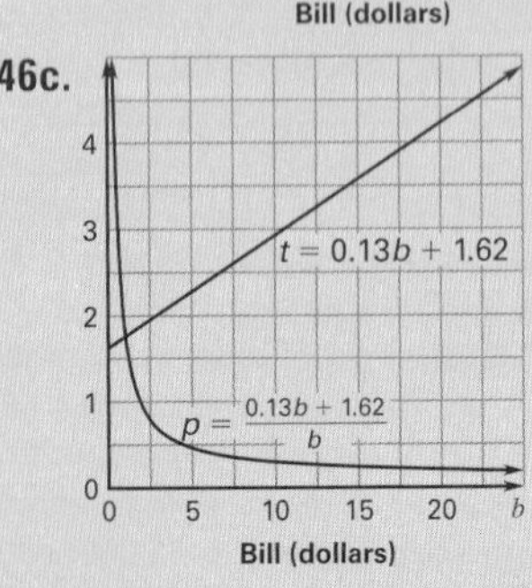

44. **INVESTING** An investor plans to purchase shares of a stock through a brokerage company. Each share costs \$10, and the company charges a transaction fee of \$20.

    a. **Model** Write and graph an equation that gives the average cost C (in dollars per share) as a function of the number s of shares that the investor purchases. **$C = \frac{10s + 20}{s}$; see margin for art.**

    b. **Approximate** Use the graph to approximate the number of shares purchased if the average cost is \$12 per share. **10 shares**

45. **CELL PHONE PLAN** You are thinking about subscribing to the cell phone plan described in the advertisement below.

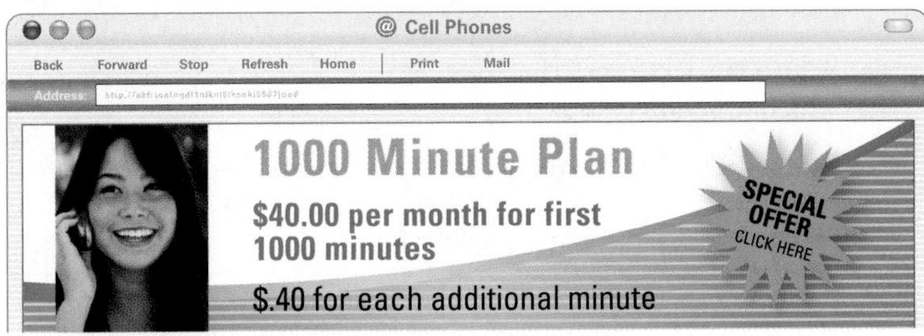

   a. **Model** Write an equation that gives the average cost C (in dollars per minute) as a function of the time t (in minutes) of cell phone use for 1000 or more minutes. **$C = \frac{0.4t - 360}{t}$**

   b. **Describe** Graph the function. *Describe* how the average cost per minute changes as time increases.

   45b. See margin for art; the average cost increases.

   c. **Approximate** Use the graph to approximate the number of minutes used if the average cost is \$.05 per minute. **about 1030 min**

B

46. **MULTIPLE REPRESENTATIONS** The table shows several restaurant bills and their corresponding tips.

Bill, b (dollars)	15.42	26.75	42.18	58.66	63.48	75.89	97.14
Tip, t (dollars)	3.00	5.00	7.50	10.00	10.15	11.50	13.60

   a. **Writing an Equation** Make a scatter plot of the data. Then write a linear equation that models the tip t as a function of the bill b. **$t = 0.13b + 1.62$; see margin for art.**

   b. **Writing an Equation** Write an equation that gives the percent tip p (in decimal form) as a function of the bill b. **$p = \frac{0.13b + 1.62}{b}$**

   c. **Drawing Graphs** Draw the graphs of both equations in the same coordinate plane. *Compare* how the tip changes with how the percent tip changes as the bill increases. **See margin for art; the tip increases, but the percent tip decreases.**

47. ★ **SHORT RESPONSE** The number y (in millions) of households that owned VCRs during the period 1984–2000 can be modeled by

$$y = \frac{60 + 120x}{7 + x}$$

   where x is the number of years since 1984.

   a. **Describe** Graph the model. *Describe* how the number of households that owned VCRs changed during this period.

   47a. See margin for art; the number of households with VCRs increased.

   b. **Justify** Do you expect that the number of households that own VCRs will ever exceed 150 million? *Justify* your answer. **See margin.**

○ = **WORKED-OUT SOLUTIONS** on p. WS1   ★ = **STANDARDIZED TEST PRACTICE**    = **MULTIPLE REPRESENTATIONS**

47a.

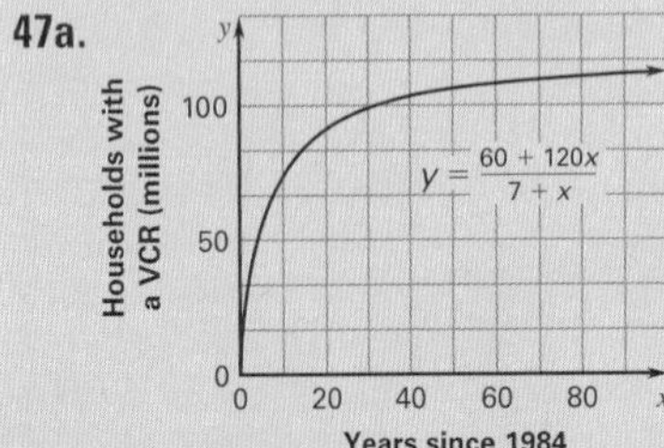

47b. No; as x increases, the graph of the function approaches its horizontal asymptote $y = 120$ from below, so the value of y will never exceed 120 million if this model applies to years beyond 2000.

48. ★ **MULTIPLE CHOICE** A building's ratio y of surface area to volume is a measure of how well the building minimizes heat loss. A company plans to build a store in the shape of a rectangular prism. The store will have a length of 500 feet and a width of 300 feet, but the company hasn't decided on a height h (in feet). Which equation gives the ratio y as a function of the height h? **A**

Ⓐ $y = \frac{4}{375} + \frac{2}{h}$ Ⓑ $y = 1600 + \frac{1}{150{,}000h}$

Ⓒ $y = 1600 + \frac{2}{h}$ Ⓓ $y = 300 + \frac{500}{h}$

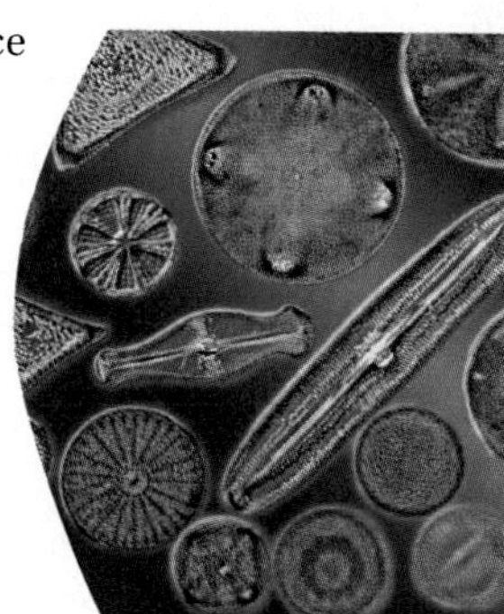

49. ★ **EXTENDED RESPONSE** The ratio of a microorganism's surface area to its volume is a measure of how efficiently the microorganism can perform certain metabolic tasks. Suppose a microorganism is shaped approximately like a cylinder and grows by increasing its length but not its radius. **a–c. See margin.**

a. **Model and Graph** Write an equation that gives the ratio y of surface area to volume in terms of the length ℓ (in micrometers) and the radius r (in micrometers). Then graph the equation for a microorganism whose radius is 50 micrometers.

b. **Interpret** The greater the ratio, the less efficiently a microorganism performs metabolic tasks. As the microorganism's length increases, is the microorganism *more efficient* or *less efficient* at performing metabolic tasks? *Explain* your choice.

c. **Explain** How would the microorganism's efficiency change if the length remained constant but the radius increased? *Explain.*

Animated Algebra at classzone.com

50. No; the effective tax rate e for total income I is given by the function $e(I) = \frac{-600}{I} + 0.06$. As seen in the graph, the value of $e(I)$ approaches 0.06 from below but never actually takes on the value 0.06; see margin for art.

C 50. **CHALLENGE** The effective tax rate is the percent of total income that a worker pays in taxes. Suppose that a worker doesn't pay taxes on income up to \$10,000 and pays taxes of 6% on total income that exceeds \$10,000. Will the effective tax rate be 6% for any amount of total income? *Justify* your answer graphically.

MIXED REVIEW

Write the fraction in simplest form. *(p. 912)*

51. $\frac{8}{12}$ $\frac{2}{3}$ 52. $\frac{9}{45}$ $\frac{1}{5}$ 53. $\frac{18}{30}$ $\frac{3}{5}$

Simplify the expression.

54. $4x^4 \cdot (2x^3)^4$ *(p. 489)* $64x^{16}$ 55. $z^6 \cdot \frac{1}{z^2}$ *(p. 495)* z^4 56. $\frac{4a^3}{b^4} \cdot \left(\frac{b}{a^2}\right)^{-3}$ *(p. 495)* $\frac{4a^9}{b^7}$

57. $\sqrt{150}$ *(p. 719)* $5\sqrt{6}$ 58. $\frac{4}{\sqrt{3}}$ *(p. 719)* $\frac{4\sqrt{3}}{3}$ 59. $\frac{3}{\sqrt{15}}$ *(p. 719)* $\frac{\sqrt{15}}{5}$

PREVIEW Prepare for Lesson 12.4 in Exs. 60–65.

Factor the polynomial.

60. $14x - 8x^2$ *(p. 575)* $2x(7 - 4x)$ 61. $x^2 - 13x + 40$ *(p. 583)* $(x - 5)(x - 8)$ 62. $-x^2 + 11x - 28$ *(p. 593)* $-(x - 7)(x - 4)$

63. $12x^2 - 13x + 1$ *(p. 593)* $(12x - 1)(x - 1)$ 64. $-2x^2 - 3x + 20$ *(p. 593)* $-(2x - 5)(x + 4)$ 65. $5x^4 - 5x^2$ *(p. 600)* $5x^2(x - 1)(x + 1)$

5 ASSESS AND RETEACH

Daily Homework Quiz

Transparency Available

Divide.

1. $(6x^3 - 4x^2 + 18x) \div 2x$ $3x^2 - 2x + 9$
2. $(3x^2 - x - 2) \div (x - 1)$ $3x + 2$
3. $(-20 + 4x^2) \div (5 + 2x)$ $2x - 5 + \frac{5}{2x + 5}$
4. A print shop charges \$15 plus \$.12 per page to copy and bind reports. Write an equation that gives the average cost C per page as a function of the number of pages p that are copied. $C = \frac{15}{p} + 0.12$

Online Quiz

Available at **classzone.com**

Diagnosis/Remediation

- Practice A, B, C in Chapter Resource Book
- Study Guide in Chapter Resource Book
- Practice Workbook
- @HomeTutor

Challenge

Additional challenge is available in the Chapter Resource Book.

49a–c. See Additional Answers beginning on p. AA1.

50.

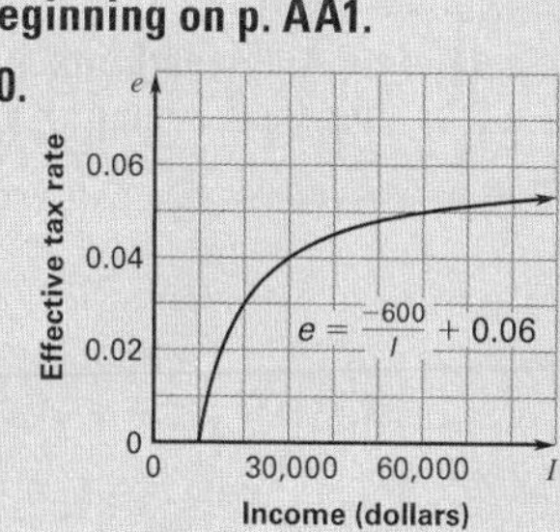

1 PLAN AND PREPARE

Learn the Method

- Students will use graphing calculators to find the asymptotes of the graph of a rational function.
- After the activity, students can use a graphing calculator to check their solutions in Lesson 12.3, Exercises 22–30, 33–34, and 39–41.

Keystroke Help

Keystrokes for several models of calculators are available in blackline format in the *Chapter Resource Book.*

2 TEACH

Tips for Success

When students enter a rational function into a graphing calculator, make sure they use parentheses around the numerator and around the denominator.

Extra Example 1

Graph $y = \frac{x+1}{x^2 - 6x + 9}$ using a graphing calculator. Identify any vertical or horizontal asymptotes.

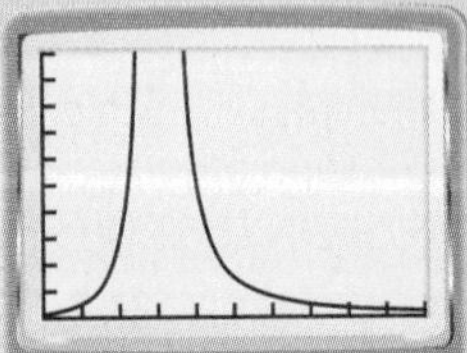

$y = 0$ is a horizontal asymptote and $x = 3$ is a vertical asymptote.

12.3 Find Asymptotes of Graphs

QUESTION **How can you find the asymptotes of the graph of a rational function?**

EXAMPLE 1 **Graph a rational function**

Graph $y = \frac{2x+1}{3x^2 - 4x + 5}$ using a graphing calculator. Identify any vertical or horizontal asymptotes.

STEP 1 ***Enter function***

Press Y= and enter the function as shown.

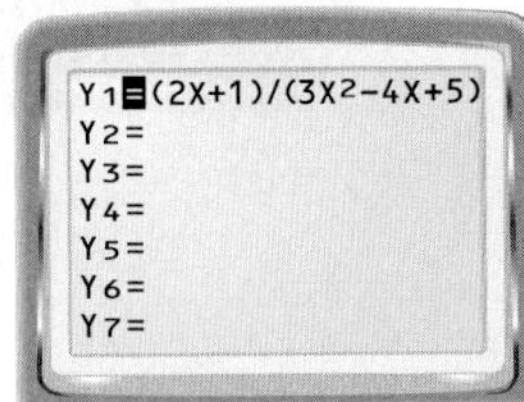

STEP 2 ***Identify asymptotes***

Graph the function. Use the *trace* feature to identify the asymptotes.

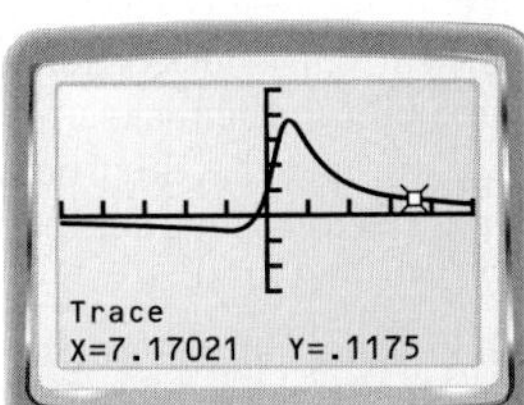

The graph doesn't approach a vertical line. So, the graph doesn't have a vertical asymptote. The graph approaches the x-axis. So, $y = 0$ is a horizontal asymptote.

PRACTICE

Graph the function using a graphing calculator. Identify any vertical or horizontal asymptotes. **1–6. See margin.**

1. $y = \frac{8}{x-2}$ **2.** $y = \frac{4}{6x-7}$ **3.** $y = \frac{x-9}{x^2+1}$

4. $y = \frac{x+5}{x^2+4x+4}$ **5.** $y = \frac{x+1}{4x^2-36}$ **6.** $y = \frac{5}{10x^2+9}$

7. Make a table that shows the following information for each function in Exercises 1–6: **See margin.**
- vertical asymptotes, if any
- values, if any, of x that make the function undefined
- horizontal asymptotes, if any
- degree of numerator
- degree of denominator

1.

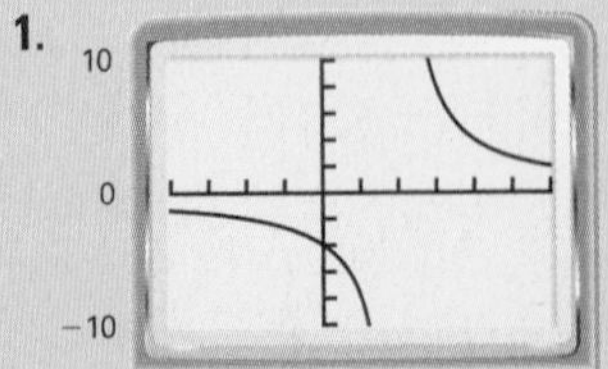

vertical: $x = 2$, horizontal: $y = 0$

2.

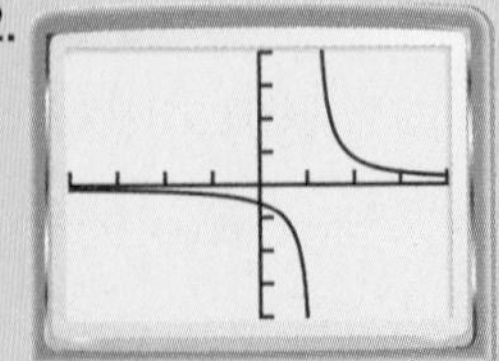

vertical: $x = \frac{7}{6}$, horizontal: $y = 0$

3.

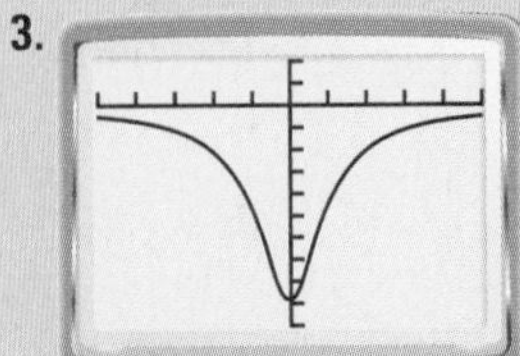

vertical: none, horizontal: $y = 0$

4.

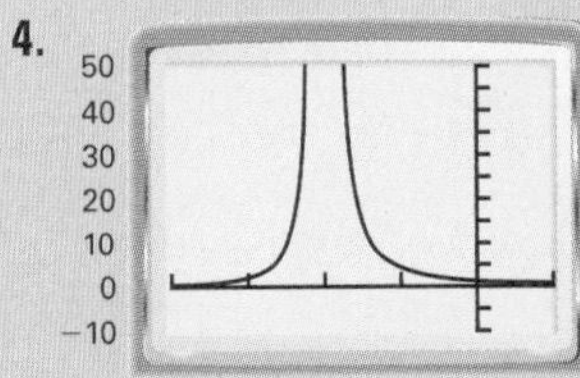

vertical: $x = -2$, horizontal: $y = 0$

@HomeTutor
classzone.com
Keystrokes

EXAMPLE 2 Graph a rational function

Graph $y = \dfrac{2x^2 + 1}{x^2 - 9}$ using a graphing calculator. Identify any vertical or horizontal asymptotes.

STEP 1 *Enter function*

Press Y= and enter the function as shown.

STEP 2 *Identify asymptotes*

Graph the function. Use the *trace* feature to identify the asymptotes.

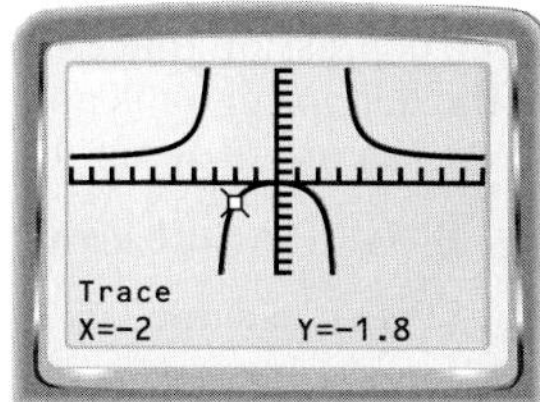

The graph approaches one of two vertical lines, $x = -3$ and $x = 3$. So, $x = -3$ and $x = 3$ are vertical asymptotes. The graph also approaches the line $y = 2$. So, $y = 2$ is a horizontal asymptote.

PRACTICE

Graph the function using a graphing calculator. Identify any vertical or horizontal asymptotes. 8–13. See margin.

8. $y = \dfrac{-6x}{x + 9}$
9. $y = \dfrac{5x - 12}{x - 1}$
10. $y = \dfrac{10x}{2x - 9}$
11. $y = \dfrac{12x^2 - 7}{4x^2 + 2}$
12. $y = \dfrac{27x^2 - x}{9x^2 - 16}$
13. $y = \dfrac{18x^2 - 1}{6x^2 - 6}$
14. Repeat Exercise 7 for the functions in Exercises 8–13. For each function, include in your table the quotient of the leading coefficient of the numerator and the leading coefficient of the denominator. See margin.

DRAW CONCLUSIONS

15. What vertical asymptotes, if any, does the graph of a rational function whose numerator and denominator do not have any common factors have? Vertical lines $x = a$, where a is an x-value that makes the denominator of the rational function equal to 0.
16. If the degree of the numerator of a rational function is less than the degree of the denominator, what is a horizontal asymptote of the graph? $y = 0$
17. If the degree of the numerator of a rational function equals the degree of the denominator, what is a horizontal asymptote of the graph? $y = a$, where a is the quotient of the leading coefficient of the numerator and the leading coefficient of the denominator.
18. **CONJECTURE** Suppose the degree of the numerator of a rational function is greater than the degree of the denominator. Does the graph of the function have a horizontal asymptote? Give examples. See margin.

5. vertical: $x = -3$, $x = 3$, horizontal: $y = 0$

6. vertical: none, horizontal: $y = 0$

1.0
0.8
0.6
0.4
0.2
0
−0.2

7–14. See Additional Answers beginning on p. AA1.

Extra Example 2

Graph $y = \dfrac{x^2 + 4}{x^2 - 1}$ using a graphing calculator. Identify any vertical or horizontal asymptotes.

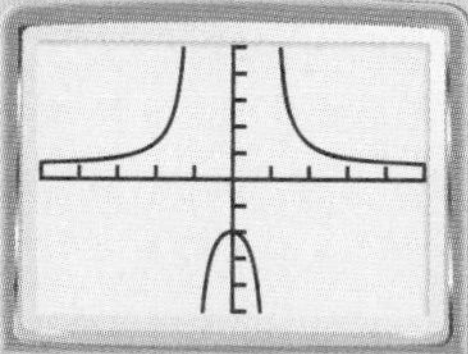

$y = 1$ is a horizontal asymptote and $x = 1$ and $x = -1$ are vertical asymptotes.

3 ASSESS AND RETEACH

Without graphing the following functions, explain whether they have a horizontal asymptote.

1. $y = \dfrac{x + 2}{x^2 + 6x + 8}$ **There is a horizontal asymptote (it is $y = 0$) since the degree of the denominator is greater than the degree of the numerator.**
2. $y = \dfrac{x + 4}{2x + 1}$ **There is a horizontal asymptote $\left(\text{it is } y = \frac{1}{2}\right)$ since the degree of the denominator and the degree of the numerator are the same.**

18. No. *Sample answer:* For example, a linear equation, such as $y = 2x$, can be written as a rational equation, $y = \frac{2x}{1}$, where the degree of the numerator is 1 and the degree of the denominator is 0. The graph of a linear equation is a straight line, which has no horizontal asymptote. A quadratic equation, such as $y = x^2$, can also be written as a rational equation, $y = \frac{x^2}{1}$, where the degree of the numerator is 2 and the degree of the denominator is 0. The graph of a quadratic equation is a parabola, which has no horizontal asymptote.

12.4 Simplify Rational Expressions

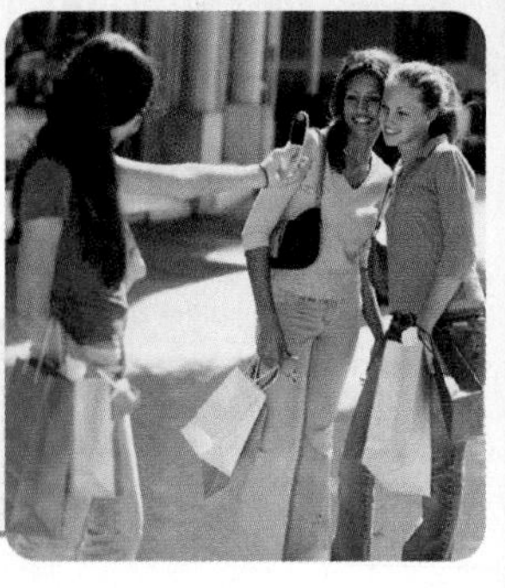

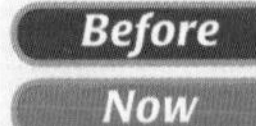

Before You simplified polynomials.

Now You will simplify rational expressions.

Why So you can model a cost over time, as in Example 5.

Key Vocabulary
- **rational expression**
- **excluded value**
- **simplest form of a rational expression**

A **rational expression** is an expression that can be written as a ratio of two polynomials where the denominator is not 0. A rational expression is undefined when the denominator is 0. A number that makes a rational expression undefined is called an **excluded value**. For example, $\frac{2}{x-3}$ is undefined when $x = 3$. So, 3 is an excluded value.

EXAMPLE 1 Find excluded values

Find the excluded values, if any, of the expression.

a. $\frac{x+8}{10x}$ **b.** $\frac{5}{2y+14}$ **c.** $\frac{4v}{v^2-9}$ **d.** $\frac{7w+2}{8w^2+w+5}$

Solution

a. The expression $\frac{x+8}{10x}$ is undefined when $10x = 0$, or $x = 0$.

▶ The excluded value is 0.

b. The expression $\frac{5}{2y+14}$ is undefined when $2y + 14 = 0$, or $x = -7$.

▶ The excluded value is −7.

c. The expression $\frac{4v}{v^2-9}$ is undefined when $v^2 - 9 = 0$, or $(v + 3)(v - 3) = 0$. The solutions of the equation are −3 and 3.

▶ The excluded values are −3 and 3.

d. The expression $\frac{7w+2}{8w^2+w+5}$ is undefined when $8w^2 + w + 5 = 0$. The discriminant is $b^2 - 4ac = 1^2 - 4(8)(5) < 0$. So, the quadratic equation has no real roots.

▶ There are no excluded values.

REVIEW DISCRIMINANT
For help with finding the discriminant of a quadratic equation, see p. 678.

GUIDED PRACTICE for Example 1

Find the excluded values, if any, of the expression.

1. $\frac{x+2}{3x-5}$ $\frac{5}{3}$ **2.** $\frac{2}{5y^2+2y+3}$ none **3.** $\frac{n-6}{2n^2-5n-12}$ $-\frac{3}{2}, 4$ **4.** $\frac{2m}{m^2-4}$ −2, 2

1 PLAN AND PREPARE

Warm-Up Exercises

Transparency Available

Factor the polynomial.

1. $x^2 + 8x + 15$ $(x + 3)(x + 5)$

2. $2x^2 + 15x - 8$ $(x + 8)(2x - 1)$

3. You pay \$20 to join an aerobics center and pay \$4 per class session. Write an equation that gives the average cost C per session as a function of the number a of aerobics sessions that you take. $C = \frac{20}{a} + 4$

Notetaking Guide

Transparency Available

Promotes interactive learning and notetaking skills.

Pacing

Basic: 1 day

Average: 1 day

Advanced: 1 day

Block: 0.5 block with 12.5

- See *Teaching Guide/Lesson Plan.*

2 FOCUS AND MOTIVATE

Essential Question

Big Idea 2, p. 763

How do you simplify a rational expression? **Tell students they will learn how to answer this question by factoring, dividing, and finding excluded values.**

NCTM STANDARDS

Standard 2: Use models to represent relationships

Standard 10: Use representations to solve problems

Resource Planning Guide

Chapter Resource Book
- Teaching Guide/Lesson Plan
- Activity Master
- Practice levels A, B, C
- Study Guide
- Catch-up for Absent Students
- Problem Solving Workshop
- Challenge

Workbooks
- Notetaking Guide
- Practice Workbook

Teaching Options
- **Power Presentations** provides dynamic electronic teaching resources for the classroom.
- **Activity Generator** provides editable activities for all ability levels.

Interactive Technology
- Easy Planner
- Power Presentations
- Activity Generator
- Animated Algebra
- Test Generator
- Online Quiz
- eWorkbook
- eEdition
- @HomeTutor

Resources for English Learners
- Spanish Study Guide
- Multi-Language Visual Glossary
- Student Resources in Spanish

See also the *Differentiated Instruction Resources* for more strategies for meeting individual needs.

SIMPLIFYING A RATIONAL EXPRESSION To simplify a rational expression, you factor the numerator and denominator and then divide out any common factors. A rational expression is in **simplest form** if the numerator and denominator have no factors in common other than 1.

KEY CONCEPT *For Your Notebook*

Simplifying Rational Expressions

Let a, b, and c be polynomials where $b \neq 0$ and $c \neq 0$.

Algebra $\frac{ac}{bc} = \frac{a \cdot \cancel{c}}{b \cdot \cancel{c}} = \frac{a}{b}$ **Example** $\frac{2x + 4}{3x + 6} = \frac{2\cancel{(x+2)}}{3\cancel{(x+2)}} = \frac{2}{3}$

EXAMPLE 2 **Simplify expressions by dividing out monomials**

Simplify the rational expression, if possible. State the excluded values.

a. $\frac{r}{2r}$ b. $\frac{5x}{5(x + 2)}$ c. $\frac{6m^3 - 12m^2}{18m^2}$ d. $\frac{y}{7 - y}$

Solution

AVOID ERRORS
When finding excluded values, be sure to use the original expression, not the simplified expression.

a. $\frac{r}{2r} = \frac{\cancel{r}}{2\cancel{r}}$ **Divide out common factor.**

$= \frac{1}{2}$ **Simplify.**

▶ The excluded value is 0.

b. $\frac{5x}{5(x + 2)} = \frac{\cancel{5} \cdot x}{\cancel{5} \cdot (x + 2)}$ **Divide out common factor.**

$= \frac{x}{x + 2}$ **Simplify.**

▶ The excluded value is −2.

c. $\frac{6m^3 - 12m^2}{18m^2} = \frac{6m^2(m - 2)}{6 \cdot 3 \cdot m^2}$ **Factor numerator and denominator.**

$= \frac{\cancel{6m^2}(m - 2)}{\cancel{6} \cdot 3 \cdot \cancel{m^2}}$ **Divide out common factors.**

$= \frac{m - 2}{3}$ **Simplify.**

▶ The excluded value is 0.

d. The expression $\frac{y}{7 - y}$ is already in simplest form.

▶ The excluded value is 7.

GUIDED PRACTICE for Example 2

Simplify the rational expression, if possible. State the excluded values.

5. $\frac{4a^3}{22a^6}$ $\frac{2}{11a^3}$; 0 6. $\frac{2c}{c + 5}$ $\frac{2c}{c + 5}$; −5 7. $\frac{2s^2 + 8s}{3s + 12}$ $\frac{2s}{3}$; −4 8. $\frac{8x}{8x^3 + 16x^2}$ $\frac{1}{x^2 + 2x}$; 0, −2

Motivating the Lesson

You are thinking about switching to a different Internet Service Provider and you would like to analyze the average monthly costs of several providers over the past 10 years. By knowing how to use and simplify models of real world situations, you can analyze and compare costs to help make a decision.

3 TEACH

Extra Example 1

Find the excluded values, if any, of the expression.

a. $\frac{x + 6}{4x}$ 0

b. $\frac{7}{3x - 9}$ 3

c. $\frac{2x}{x^2 - 16}$ −4, 4

d. $\frac{5x + 3}{x^2 + 4x + 5}$ no excluded values

Key Question to Ask for Example 1

- In part (b), why is −7 the excluded value? **The value $x = -7$ would give a zero denominator.**

Extra Example 2

Simplify the rational expression, if possible. State the excluded values.

a. $\frac{2x}{3x}$ $\frac{2}{3}$; 0

b. $\frac{6x}{6(x + 5)}$ $\frac{x}{x + 5}$; −5

c. $\frac{8b^2 + 16b}{32b}$ $\frac{b + 2}{4}$; 0

d. $\frac{a}{1 - a}$ simplest form; 1

Key Question to Ask for Example 2

- How do you determine the excluded value in part (b)? **The denominator is $5(x + 2)$, and the value $x = -2$ would give a zero denominator.**

Extra Example 3

Simplify $\frac{x^2 + x - 12}{x^2 - x - 6}$. State the excluded values. $\frac{x + 4}{x + 2}$; $-2, 3$

Key Questions to Ask for Example 3

- What step makes it easier to determine excluded values? **If you factor the denominator, you can more easily tell what values would give a zero denominator.**
- Why is -2 an excluded value if the expression simplifies to $\frac{x - 5}{x - 4}$? **You use the original expression to find excluded values. In the original expression, -2 is an excluded value.**

Extra Example 4

Simplify $\frac{x^2 - 7x + 10}{25 - x^2}$. State the excluded values. $-\frac{x - 2}{x + 5}$; $-5, 5$

Key Question to Ask for Example 4

- Why can't you rewrite $(4 - x)$ as $(x - 4)$? **$(4 - x)$ is the opposite of $(x - 4)$.**

EXAMPLE 3 Simplify an expression by dividing out binomials

Simplify $\frac{x^2 - 3x - 10}{x^2 + 6x + 8}$. State the excluded values.

$$\frac{x^2 - 3x - 10}{x^2 + 6x + 8} = \frac{(x - 5)(x + 2)}{(x + 4)(x + 2)} \quad \text{Factor numerator and denominator.}$$

$$= \frac{(x - 5)\cancel{(x + 2)}}{(x + 4)\cancel{(x + 2)}} \quad \text{Divide out common factor.}$$

$$= \frac{x - 5}{x + 4} \quad \text{Simplify.}$$

▶ The excluded values are -4 and -2.

CHECK In the graphing calculator activity on page 560, you saw how to use a graph to check a sum or difference of polynomials.

Check your simplification using a graphing calculator.

Graph $y_1 = \frac{x^2 - 3x - 10}{x^2 + 6x + 8}$ and $y_2 = \frac{x - 5}{x + 4}$.

The graphs coincide. So, the expressions are equivalent for all values of x other than the excluded values (-4 and -2).

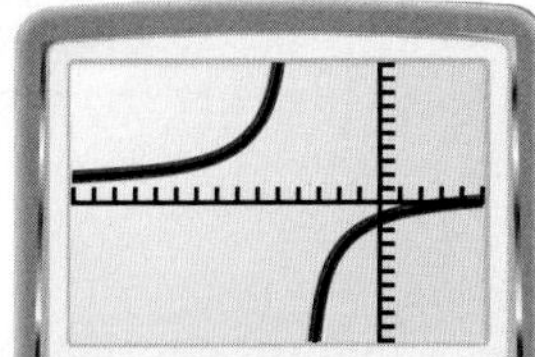

INTERPRET THE GRAPH

Although the graphs of y_1 and y_2 appear to pass through $(-2, -3.5)$, the point is not on either graph because -2 is an excluded value of both y_1 and y_2.

OPPOSITES When simplifying a rational expression, look for factors that are opposites of each other. For example, $x - 1$ and $1 - x$ are opposites, because $x - 1 = -(1 - x)$.

EXAMPLE 4 Recognize opposites

Simplify $\frac{x^2 - 7x + 12}{16 - x^2}$. State the excluded values.

$$\frac{x^2 - 7x + 12}{16 - x^2} = \frac{(x - 3)(x - 4)}{(4 - x)(4 + x)} \quad \text{Factor numerator and denominator.}$$

$$= \frac{(x - 3)(x - 4)}{-(x - 4)(4 + x)} \quad \text{Rewrite } 4 - x \text{ as } -(x - 4).$$

$$= \frac{(x - 3)\cancel{(x - 4)}}{-\cancel{(x - 4)}(4 + x)} \quad \text{Divide out common factor.}$$

$$= \frac{x - 3}{-(4 + x)} = -\frac{x - 3}{x + 4} \quad \text{Simplify.}$$

▶ The excluded values are -4 and 4.

✓ GUIDED PRACTICE for Examples 3 and 4

Simplify the rational expression. State the excluded values.

9. $\frac{x^2 + 3x + 2}{x^2 + 7x + 10}$ $\frac{x + 1}{x + 5}$; $-2, -5$ **10.** $\frac{y^2 - 64}{y^2 - 16y + 64}$ $\frac{y + 8}{y - 8}$; 8 **11.** $\frac{5 + 4z - z^2}{z^2 - 3z - 10}$ $-\frac{z + 1}{z + 2}$; $5, -2$

EXAMPLE 5 Simplify a rational model

CELL PHONE COSTS The average cost C (in dollars per minute) for cell phone service in the United States during the period 1991–2000 can be modeled by

$$C = \frac{46 - 2.2x}{100 - 18x + 2.2x^2}$$

where x is the number of years since 1991. Rewrite the model so that it has only whole number coefficients. Then simplify the model.

1991 cell phone

Solution

$C = \dfrac{46 - 2.2x}{100 - 18x + 2.2x^2}$	**Write model.**
$= \dfrac{460 - 22x}{1000 - 180x + 22x^2}$	**Multiply numerator and denominator by 10.**
$= \dfrac{2(230 - 11x)}{2(500 - 90x + 11x^2)}$	**Factor numerator and denominator.**
$= \dfrac{\cancel{2}(230 - 11x)}{\cancel{2}(500 - 90x + 11x^2)}$	**Divide out common factor.**
$= \dfrac{230 - 11x}{500 - 90x + 11x^2}$	**Simplify.**

GUIDED PRACTICE for Example 5

12. In Example 5, approximate the average cost per minute in 2000. **about $.23/min**

12.4 EXERCISES

HOMEWORK KEY ○ = **WORKED-OUT SOLUTIONS** on p. WS29 for Exs. 9, 23, and 43
★ = **STANDARDIZED TEST PRACTICE** Exs. 2, 33, 34, 35, and 45

SKILL PRACTICE

A

1. **VOCABULARY** Copy and complete: A value that makes a rational expression undefined is called a(n) _?_. **excluded value**

2. ★ **WRITING** Is $\dfrac{(x+3)(x-6)}{(x-3)(6-x)}$ in simplest form? *Explain.* **See margin.**

EXAMPLE 1 on p. 794 for Exs. 3–10

FINDING EXCLUDED VALUES **Find the excluded values, if any, of the expression.**

3. $\dfrac{4x}{20}$ **none**
4. $\dfrac{13}{2y}$ **0**
5. $\dfrac{5}{r+1}$ **−1**
6. $\dfrac{-s}{3s+4}$ $-\dfrac{4}{3}$
7. $\dfrac{-m}{4m^2 - 3m + 9}$ **none**
8. $\dfrac{n+2}{n^2 - 64}$ **−8, 8**
9. $\dfrac{-3}{2p^2 - p}$ **0, $\frac{1}{2}$**
10. $\dfrac{5q}{q^2 - 6q + 9}$ **3**

Extra Example 5

The average amount of a customer's purchase P applied to a credit card account at a toy store during the period 1998–2004 can be modeled by $P = \dfrac{24 + 0.8x^2}{0.5 + 0.02x^2}$, where x is the number of years since 1998. Rewrite the model so that it has only whole number coefficients. Then simplify the model. **$P = \dfrac{2400 + 80x^2}{50 + 2x^2}$; $\dfrac{1200 + 40x^2}{25 + x^2}$**

Key Questions to Ask for Example 5

- How do you approximate the average cost for cell phone service in 2000? **Since 2000 is 9 years since 1991, evaluate the model for $x = 9$.**
- Do you have to use the simplified model to approximate the cost for a particular year? Explain. **Either model will give the same value, but it may be easier to calculate with the simplified model.**

Closing the Lesson

Have students summarize the major points of the lesson and answer the Essential Question: How do you simplify a rational expression?

- **Exclude values that would result in a zero denominator.**
- **Some rational expressions can be simplified by factoring and dividing.**

To simplify a rational expression, factor the numerator and denominator, divide out the common factors, and note excluded values. When factoring, watch for expressions that are opposites.

2. No, after rewriting $6 - x$ in the denominator as $-1(x - 6)$, you can divide out the common factor of $x - 6$ from the numerator and denominator.

Differentiated Instruction

Visual Learners Show students that an excluded value can be represented on a graph by an open circle or dashed vertical line. For **Example 3**, plot the graph of $y = \dfrac{x-5}{x+4}$ and place an open circle at the point $(-2, -3.5)$. The other excluded value can be illustrated by a dashed vertical line at $x = -4$.

See also the *Differentiated Instruction Resources* for more strategies.

4 PRACTICE AND APPLY

Assignment Guide

Answer Transparencies available for all exercises

Basic:
Day 1: EP p. 946 Exs. 25–30
pp. 797–800
Exs. 1–12, 13–33 odd, 34–36, 40–44, 48, 52, 55, 58

Average:
Day 1: pp. 797–800
Exs. 1, 2, 7–12, 14–32 even, 33–38, 40–45, 49, 53, 56, 59

Advanced:
Day 1: pp. 797–800
Exs. 1, 8–11, 14–32 even, 33–46*, 50, 54, 57, 60

Block:
pp. 797–800
Exs. 1, 2, 7–12, 14–32 even, 33–38, 40–45, 49, 53, 56, 59 (with 12.5)

Differentiated Instruction

See *Differentiated Instruction Resources* for suggestions on addressing the needs of a diverse classroom.

Homework Check

For a quick check of student understanding of key concepts, go over the following exercises:
Basic: 4, 15, 19, 28, 40
Average: 10, 16, 24, 30, 41
Advanced: 8, 16, 26, 32, 42

Extra Practice

- Student Edition, p. 946
- Chapter Resource Book: Practice levels A, B, C

Practice Worksheet

An easily-readable reduced practice page (with answers) for this lesson can be found on p. 762C.

EXAMPLES 2, 3, and 4 on pp. 795–796 for Exs. 11–33

23. $\frac{1}{h-4}$; −3, 4
24. $\frac{1}{j-4}$; 2, 4
25. $\frac{-6}{2w-5}$; 0, $\frac{5}{2}$
26. $\frac{2y^3}{2y+3}$; 0, $-\frac{3}{2}$
27. 3; 0, 4
28. $\frac{7x}{x-1}$; 1, $-\frac{3}{2}$
29. $\frac{s+8}{s-1}$; 1, −8
30. $\frac{t+5}{2t-3}$; 9, $\frac{3}{2}$
31. $\frac{1}{m^2+5m}$; 0, −5
32. $-\frac{1}{3n}$; −7, 0, 4

ERROR ANALYSIS *Describe* and correct the error in simplifying the rational expression or in stating the excluded values. **11, 12. See margin.**

11. $\frac{2x^2-x-3}{2x^2-11x+12}$

$$\frac{2x^2-x-3}{2x^2-11x+12} = \frac{(x+1)(2x-3)}{(2x-3)(x-4)} = \frac{(x+1)\cancel{(2x-3)}}{\cancel{(2x-3)}(x-4)} = \frac{x+1}{x-4}$$

The excluded value is 4. ✗

12. $\frac{2(x-5)}{(x-5)(x+2)}$

$$\frac{2(x-5)}{(x-5)(x+2)} = \frac{2\cancel{(x-5)}}{\cancel{(x-5)}(x+2)} = \frac{2}{x+2} = \frac{\cancel{2}}{x+\cancel{2}} = \frac{1}{x+1}$$

The excluded values are −2 and 5. ✗

SIMPLIFYING EXPRESSIONS Simplify the rational expression, if possible. State the excluded values.

13. $\frac{10x}{25}$ **$\frac{2x}{5}$; none**
14. $\frac{63}{18y}$ **$\frac{7}{2y}$; 0**
15. $\frac{-48a^2}{16a}$ **$-3a$; 0**
16. $\frac{27b^2}{30b^5}$ **$\frac{9}{10b^3}$; 0**
17. $\frac{3c+33}{c+11}$ **3; −11**
18. $\frac{d+8}{d-8}$ **$\frac{d+8}{d-8}$; 8**
19. $\frac{2u-6}{3-u}$ **−2; 3**
20. $\frac{v+2}{v^2-4}$ **$\frac{1}{v-2}$; ±2**
21. $\frac{2}{f^2-9}$ **$\frac{2}{f^2-9}$; ±3**
22. $\frac{g+4}{g^2-16}$ **$\frac{1}{g-4}$; ±4**
(23.) $\frac{h+3}{h^2-h-12}$
24. $\frac{j-2}{j^2-6j+8}$
25. $\frac{-48w}{16w^2-40w}$
26. $\frac{12y^4}{12y^2+18y}$
27. $\frac{6z^2-24z}{2z^2-8z}$
28. $\frac{14x^2+21x}{2x^2+x-3}$
29. $\frac{s^2+16s+64}{s^2+7s-8}$
30. $\frac{t^2-4t-45}{2t^2-21t+27}$
31. $\frac{m+5}{m^3+10m^2+25m}$
32. $\frac{-n^2-3n+28}{3n^3+9n^2-84n}$

33. ★ **WRITING** Are the rational expressions $\frac{x^2+x}{x^2-1}$ and $\frac{x^2}{x^2-x}$ equivalent? *Explain* how you know. What are the excluded values, if any, of the rational expressions? **See margin.**

B

34. ★ **OPEN-ENDED** Write a rational expression whose excluded values are −3 and −5. ***Sample answer:*** **$\frac{1}{x^2+8x+15}$**

35. ★ **MULTIPLE CHOICE** The expression $\frac{a}{x^2+5x-6}$ simplifies to $\frac{2x+5}{x+6}$. What is a? **C**

Ⓐ $2x^2+7x+5$ Ⓑ $2x^2+5x-1$ Ⓒ $2x^2+3x-5$ Ⓓ $2x^2+7x-5$

GEOMETRY Write and simplify a rational expression for the ratio of the perimeter of the given figure to its area.

36. Square **$\frac{4}{5x}$**

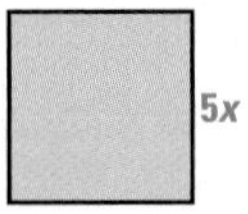

37. Rectangle **$\frac{3(x+2)}{x(x+6)}$**

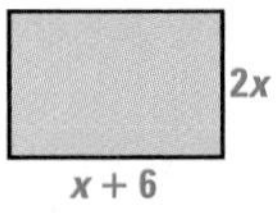

38. Triangle **$\frac{3}{x}$**

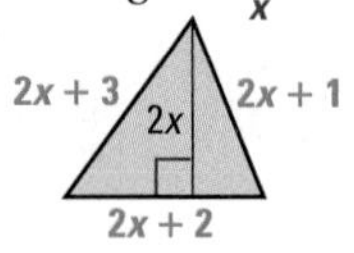

C

39. **CHALLENGE** Find two polynomials whose ratio simplifies to $\frac{3x-1}{2x+1}$ and whose sum is $5x^2+20x$. *Describe* your steps. **See margin.**

○ = WORKED-OUT SOLUTIONS on p. WS1 ★ = STANDARDIZED TEST PRACTICE

11. When finding the excluded values you must find the values for which the denominator of the original expression, $2x^2-11x+12$, is 0; the excluded values are $\frac{3}{2}$ and 4.

12. 2 cannot be divided out of the numerator and denominator of $\frac{2}{x+2}$ because 2 is not a factor of the denominator, $x+2$; $\frac{2}{x+2}$.

33. No; the two expressions do not have the same excluded values; the excluded values for $\frac{x^2+x}{x^2-1}$ are ±1, while the excluded values for $\frac{x^2}{x^2-x}$ are 0 and 1. The expressions are not equivalent for $x = 0$ and for $x = -1$.

PROBLEM SOLVING

EXAMPLE 5 [A] on p. 797 for Exs. 40–43

40. CREDIT CARD FEES The average late payment fee F (in dollars) on a credit card account during the period 1994–2003 can be modeled by

$$F = \frac{12 + 1.6x^2}{1 + 0.04x^2}$$

where x is the number of years since 1994. Rewrite the model so that it has only whole number coefficients. Then simplify the model and approximate the average late payment fee in 2003.

@HomeTutor for problem solving help at classzone.com

$F = \frac{300 + 40x^2}{25 + x^2}$; \$33.40

41. TELEVISION For the period 1980–2003, the percent p (in decimal form) of non-network television commercials in the United States that lasted 15 seconds can be modeled by

$$p = \frac{0.12x^2 - 0.48}{0.88x^2 + 100}$$

where x is the number of years since 1980. Rewrite the model so that it has only whole number coefficients. Then simplify the model and approximate the percent of non-network television commercials in 2003 that lasted 15 seconds.

@HomeTutor for problem solving help at classzone.com

$p = \frac{3x^2 - 12}{22x^2 + 2500}$; about 11%

42. CAR RADIOS A company forecasts that the number R (in thousands) of digital car radios sold annually and the sales S (in millions of dollars) of digital car radios during the period 2004–2007 can be modeled by

$$R = 190x^2 + 55x + 140 \qquad \text{and} \qquad S = 170x + 60$$

where x is the number of years since 2004. Write and simplify a model that gives the average price P (in thousands of dollars) of a digital car radio as a function of x. Then predict the average price in 2007.

$P = \frac{34x + 12}{38x^2 + 11x + 28}$; about \$280

43. HOUSES The total number H of new single-family houses and the number W of new single-family wood houses in the United States during the period 1990–2002 can be modeled by

$$H = 34{,}500x + 913{,}000$$
$$\text{and } W = -20{,}200x + 366{,}000$$

where x is the number of years since 1990. Write and simplify a model that gives the percent p (in decimal form) of the houses that were wood houses as a function of x. *Describe* how the percent that were wood houses changed during the period 1990–2002.

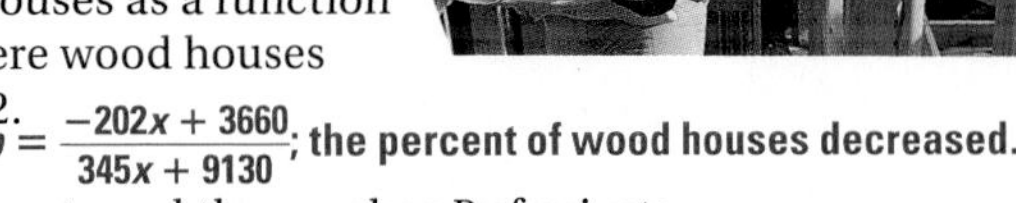

$p = \frac{-202x + 3660}{345x + 9130}$; the percent of wood houses decreased.

[B] **44. AIRPORTS** The total number A of airports and the number P of private airports in the United States during the period 1989–2002 can be modeled by

$$A = 0.18x^3 + 140x + 17{,}000 \qquad \text{and} \qquad P = 0.16x^3 + 120x + 12{,}000$$

where x is the number of years since 1989. Using only whole number coefficients, write a model that gives the percent p (in decimal form) of all airports that were private airports. Simplify the model and approximate the percent of airports in 2002 that were private airports.

$p = \frac{8x^3 + 6000x + 600{,}000}{9x^3 + 7000x + 850{,}000}$; about 72%

Avoiding Common Errors

Exercises 13–32 Some students start to identify excluded values after expressions are simplified. Remind them to use the original expression. If they are in doubt about the excluded values, suggest they check whether the values would give a zero denominator.

Graphing Calculator

Exercises 13–32 Suggest that students use their graphing calculators to check their simplified expressions. They can use the check in Example 3, page 796, as a guide.

Reading Strategy

Exercises 40–41, 44–45 Encourage students to look carefully at each of the models in these exercises. Suggest that when they rewrite the models using only whole number coefficients, they pay close attention to place value.

39. $3x^2 + 11x - 4$, $2x^2 + 9x + 4$; if the ratio of the polynomials simplifies to $\frac{3x - 1}{2x + 1}$, then find a value a such that the ratio of the polynomials can be written in the form $\frac{(x + a)(3x - 1)}{(x + a)(2x + 1)}$. To solve for a, multiply out the factored polynomials, find their sum, and set the sum equal to $5x^2 + 20x$. Then solve for a. Substitute the value of a into the expressions for the polynomials and simplify.

5 ASSESS AND RETEACH

Daily Homework Quiz

Transparency Available

Simplify the rational expression, if possible. Find the excluded values.

1. $\frac{12x^3}{18x^5}$ $\frac{2}{3x^2}$; 0

2. $\frac{2x-14}{x^2-9x+14}$ $\frac{2}{x-2}$; 2, 7

3. The average cost C (in dollars per hour) for a cleaning service during the period 1994–2003 can be modeled by $C = \frac{52-1.4x}{10-14x+2.1x^2}$, where x is the number of years since 1994. Rewrite the model so that it has only whole number coefficients. Then simplify the model, if possible. $C = \frac{520-14x}{100-140x+21x^2}$

Online Quiz

Available at **classzone.com**

Diagnosis/Remediation

- Practice A, B, C in Chapter Resource Book
- Study Guide in Chapter Resource Book
- Practice Workbook
- @HomeTutor

Challenge

Additional challenge is available in the Chapter Resource Book.

Quiz

An easily-readable reduced copy of the quiz (with answers) on Lessons 12.3–12.4 from the Assessment Book can be found on p. 762F.

45b, Quiz 3, 4. See Additional Answers beginning on p. AA1.

45a. $R = \frac{37{,}500 + 2500x}{125 + x}$; about \$522 million

45c. No; if the price per copy of printed music went up during the period 1988–2002, then the revenue may have increased without the number of copies sold increasing.

45. ★ **EXTENDED RESPONSE** The revenue R (in millions of dollars) from sales of printed music in the United States during the period 1988–2002 can be modeled by

$$R = \frac{300 + 20x}{1 + 0.008x}$$

where x is the number of years since 1988.

a. **Model and Calculate** Rewrite the model so that it has only whole number coefficients. Then simplify the model and approximate the revenue from sales of printed music in 2002.

b. **Graph** Graph the model. *Describe* how revenue changed during the period. **See margin for art; revenue increased.**

c. **Decide** Can you use the model to conclude that the number of copies of printed music sold increased over time? *Explain.*

C 46. **CHALLENGE** The average annual expenses E (in dollars) of a middle income family and the average annual amount T (in dollars) spent on telephone service during the period 1992–2001 can be modeled by

$$E = 1240x + 24{,}800 \quad \text{and} \quad T = 31x + 620$$

where x is the number of years since 1992. Write and simplify a model to show that the average annual amount spent on telephone service was 2.5% of the average annual expenses during the period. $\frac{T}{E} = \frac{31x+620}{1240x+24{,}800} = \frac{31(x+20)}{1240(x+20)} = \frac{31}{1240} = 0.025$. **Thus, $T = 0.025E$, so T is 2.5% of E.**

MIXED REVIEW

PREVIEW Prepare for Lesson 12.5 in Exs. 47–54.

Multiply or divide. *(p. 915)*

47. $\frac{1}{3} \times \frac{1}{3}$ $\frac{1}{9}$
48. $\frac{2}{7} \times \frac{4}{5}$ $\frac{8}{35}$
49. $\frac{8}{5} \times \frac{1}{4}$ $\frac{2}{5}$
50. $\frac{5}{9} \times \frac{9}{10}$ $\frac{1}{2}$
51. $\frac{1}{4} \div \frac{1}{4}$ 1
52. $\frac{2}{5} \div \frac{4}{11}$ $\frac{11}{10}$
53. $\frac{4}{9} \div \frac{4}{3}$ $\frac{1}{3}$
54. $\frac{14}{27} \div \frac{7}{4}$ $\frac{8}{27}$

Simplify the expression.

55. $5x - (-4x + 3)$ *(p. 96)* **55. $9x - 3$**
56. $(-2x^2)^4$ *(p. 489)* $16x^8$
57. $8x^3 \cdot (3x^4)^3$ *(p. 489)* $216x^{15}$
58. $\frac{y^6}{8} \cdot \frac{2}{y^2}$ *(p. 495)* $\frac{y^4}{4}$
59. $\frac{12m^4}{n^4} \cdot \left(\frac{n}{m^0}\right)^6$ *(p. 495)* $12m^4n^2$
60. $\frac{x^2}{y^4} \cdot \left(\frac{y^6}{x^{-5}}\right)^{-1}$ *(p. 495)* $\frac{1}{x^3y^{10}}$

QUIZ for Lessons 12.3–12.4

Divide. *(p. 784)*

1. $(y^2 - 5y + 6) \div (y - 3)$ $y - 2$
2. $(x^2 + 3x - 28) \div (x - 6)$ $x + 9 + \frac{26}{x-6}$

Graph the function. *(p. 784)* **3–4. See margin.**

3. $y = \frac{x+3}{x-4}$
4. $y = \frac{2x-1}{x+3}$

Simplify the rational expression, if possible. State the excluded values. *(p. 794)*

5. $\frac{w+10}{w^2-100}$ $\frac{1}{w-10}$; ±10
6. $\frac{250x^3}{14x}$ $\frac{125x^2}{7}$; 0
7. $\frac{y+7}{y-7}$ $\frac{y+7}{y-7}$; 7
8. $\frac{z^2-4z-45}{3z^2+25z+50}$ $\frac{z-9}{3z+10}$; $-\frac{10}{3}$, −5

EXTRA PRACTICE for Lesson 12.4, p. 949

ONLINE QUIZ at classzone.com

MIXED REVIEW *of Problem Solving*

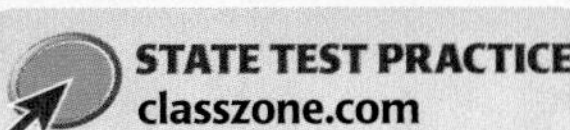

Lessons 12.1–12.4

1. **MULTI-STEP PROBLEM** A bookseller uses shipping cartons in the shape of rectangular prisms. The cartons have the same size base but vary in height.

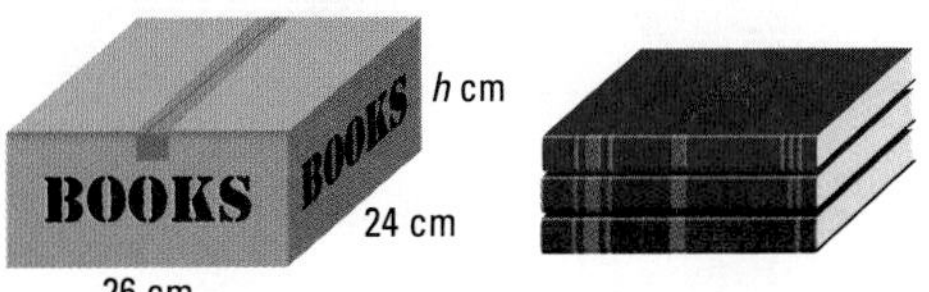

   a. Write an equation that gives the ratio r of surface area to volume as a function of the height h. Then graph the equation. **See margin.**

   b. The lesser the ratio, the more efficient the carton is. *Describe* how the efficiency of the carton changes as the height increases. **The efficiency increases.**

2. **GRIDDED ANSWER** You and some friends are taking a car trip to an amusement park. Admission costs \$50 per person, and everyone will share the combined cost of gas and parking, which is \$30. How much more (in dollars) will one person pay if 4 people go on the trip than if 5 people go? **\$1.50**

3. **OPEN-ENDED** A city's population density (in people per square mile) is the ratio of the population of the city to the area (in square miles) of the city. Suppose that a city has a population of 150,000 people and an area of 40 square miles. *Describe* two ways that the population density can decrease to 3125 people per square mile. **See margin.**

4. **MULTI-STEP PROBLEM** The average amount A (in pounds per person) of fish and shellfish consumed in the United States during the period 1992–2001 can be modeled by

$$A = \frac{52x + 3800}{3.2x + 260}$$

   where x is the number of years since 1992.

   a. Rewrite the model so that it has only whole number coefficients. Then simplify the model. $A = \frac{65x + 4750}{4x + 325}$

   b. Approximate the average amount of fish and shellfish consumed per person in 2001. **about 15 pounds per person**

5. **EXTENDED RESPONSE** A professional baseball team may pay a luxury tax if the team's combined annual salary exceeds a certain amount. In 2003, a team whose combined annual salary exceeded \$117 million paid a luxury tax of 17.5% on the amount over \$117 million. **a–c. See margin.**

   a. Write an equation that gives the percent p (in decimal form) of the salary paid in luxury tax as a function of the salary s (in millions of dollars) for $s > 117$.

   b. Graph the function. *Describe* how the percent changed as the salary increased.

   c. Was it possible for a team to pay 17.5% of its salary in luxury tax? *Explain.*

6. **SHORT RESPONSE** You plan to hike a mountain trail that is 15 miles long and stop halfway to camp overnight for 10 hours.

   a. Write an equation that gives the combined time t (in hours) for hiking and camping as a function of the average rate r (in miles per hour) at which you hike. Then graph the equation. $t = \frac{15}{r} + 10$; **see margin for art.**

   b. *Explain* how the graph would change if you camped for 12 hours instead of 10 hours. **See margin.**

7. **SHORT RESPONSE** The table shows the relationship between the volume V (in liters) and the pressure P (in kilopascals) of a gas in a cylindrical container.

Volume, V (L)	Pressure, P (kPa)
20	1
5	4
2.5	8
1.6	12.5
0.4	50

   a, b. See margin.

   a. *Explain* why the volume and pressure are inversely related. Then write an equation that relates the volume and the pressure.

   b. Suppose that only the height of the container can be changed. *Describe* how the pressure changes as the height increases.

1a. $r = \frac{2}{h} + \frac{25}{156}$;

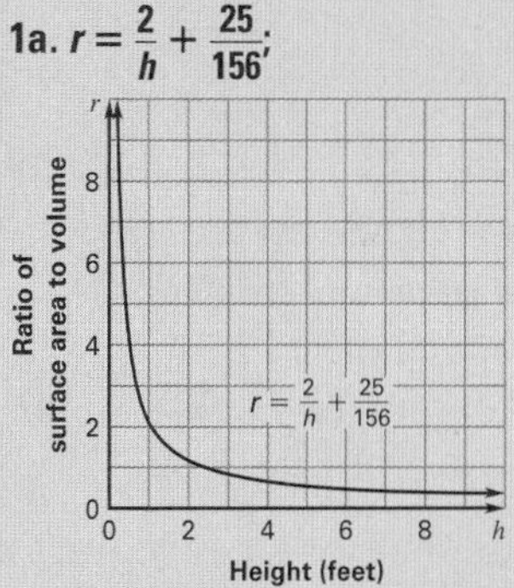

3. ***Sample answer:*** **The city's population decreases to 125,000 people while its area remains the same; the city's population increases to 156,250 people when 10 square miles of surrounding land are added to its area.**

5a. $p = \frac{0.175s - 20.475}{s}$

5b.

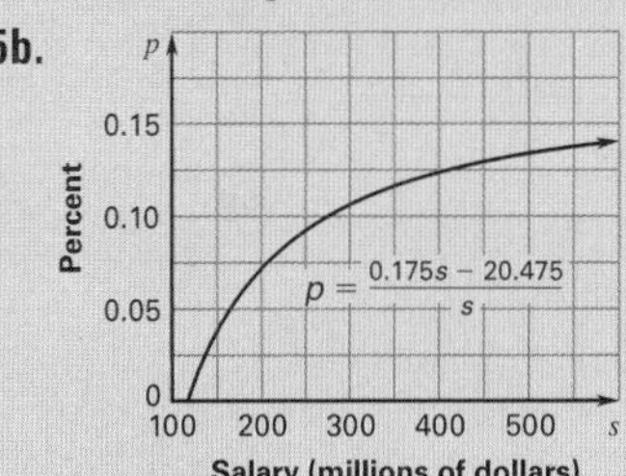

The percent increases.

5c. No; the graph in part (b) approaches its horizontal asymptote $p = 0.175$ from below, so the percent of the salary paid in luxury tax is always less than 17.5%.

6a.

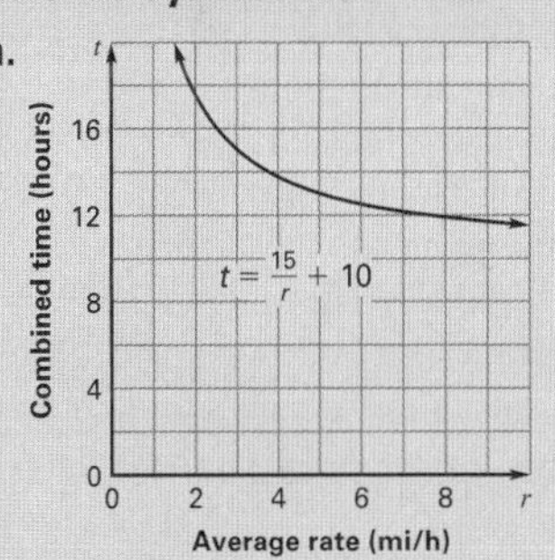

6b. The horizontal asymptote would change from $t = 10$ to $t = 12$.

7a. For each pair of values (V, P), the product VP is the same number, 20; $P = \frac{20}{V}$.

7b. The pressure decreases.

12.5 Multiply and Divide Rational Expressions

Before You multiplied and divided polynomials.
Now You will multiply and divide rational expressions.
Why? So you can describe football data, as in Ex. 35.

1 PLAN AND PREPARE

Warm-Up Exercises

Transparency Available

Factor the polynomial.

1. $x^2 + 3x - 18$ $(x - 3)(x + 6)$
2. $2x^2 - 4x - 16$ $2(x - 4)(x + 2)$
3. $2x^2 + 8x - 10$ $2(x + 5)(x - 1)$
4. A golf clinic charges a \$30 enrollment fee and \$5 per session. What is the average cost per session if you attend 8 sessions? **\$8.75**

Notetaking Guide

Transparency Available

Promotes interactive learning and notetaking skills.

Pacing

Basic: 2 days
Average: 2 days
Advanced: 2 days
Block: 0.5 block with 12.4
0.5 block with 12.6

- See *Teaching Guide/Lesson Plan.*

2 FOCUS AND MOTIVATE

Essential Question

Big Idea 2, p. 763

How do you multiply and divide rational expressions? **Tell students they will learn how to answer this question by using processes that are similar to multiplying and dividing fractions.**

NCTM STANDARDS

Standard 2: Analyze situations using algebraic symbols

Standard 9: Understand how mathematical ideas build on one another

---

Key Vocabulary
- **multiplicative inverse,** *p. 103*
- **polynomial,** *p. 554*
- **rational expression,** *p. 794*

Multiplying and dividing rational expressions is similar to multiplying and dividing numerical fractions.

KEY CONCEPT *For Your Notebook*

Multiplying and Dividing Rational Expressions

Let a, b, c, and d be polynomials.

Algebra $\frac{a}{b} \cdot \frac{c}{d} = \frac{ac}{bd}$ where $b \neq 0$ and $d \neq 0$

$\frac{a}{b} \div \frac{c}{d} = \frac{a}{b} \cdot \frac{d}{c} = \frac{ad}{bc}$ where $b \neq 0$, $c \neq 0$, and $d \neq 0$

Examples $\frac{x+2}{x} \cdot \frac{3}{x^2} = \frac{3(x+2)}{x^3}$ $\quad \frac{x}{x-1} \div \frac{4}{x} = \frac{x}{x-1} \cdot \frac{x}{4} = \frac{x^2}{4(x-1)}$

EXAMPLE 1 Multiply rational expressions involving monomials

Find the product $\frac{2x^2}{3x} \cdot \frac{6x^2}{12x^3}$.

$\frac{2x^2}{3x} \cdot \frac{6x^2}{12x^3} = \frac{(2x^2)(6x^2)}{(3x)(12x^3)}$ **Multiply numerators and denominators.**

$= \frac{12x^4}{36x^4}$ **Product of powers property**

$= \frac{\cancel{12} \cdot \cancel{x^4}}{3 \cdot \cancel{12} \cdot \cancel{x^4}}$ **Factor and divide out common factors.**

$= \frac{1}{3}$ **Simplify.**

APPLY EXCLUDED VALUES
When performing operations with rational expressions, remember that the answer may have excluded values. In Example 1, the excluded value is 0.

GUIDED PRACTICE for Example 1

Find the product.

1. $\frac{2y^3}{5y} \cdot \frac{15y^3}{8y^5}$ $\frac{3}{4}$
2. $\frac{7z^2}{4z^3} \cdot \frac{z^3}{14z}$ $\frac{z}{8}$

Resource Planning Guide

Chapter Resource Book
- Teaching Guide/Lesson Plan
- Activity Master
- Practice levels A, B, C
- Study Guide
- Catch-up for Absent Students
- Application
- Challenge

Workbooks
- Notetaking Guide
- Practice Workbook

Teaching Options
- **Power Presentations** provides dynamic electronic teaching resources for the classroom.
- **Activity Generator** provides editable activities for all ability levels.

Interactive Technology
- Easy Planner
- Power Presentations
- Activity Generator
- Animated Algebra
- Test Generator
- Online Quiz
- eWorkbook
- eEdition
- @HomeTutor

Resources for English Learners
- Spanish Study Guide
- Multi-Language Visual Glossary
- Student Resources in Spanish

See also the *Differentiated Instruction Resources* for more strategies for meeting individual needs.

EXAMPLE 2 Multiply rational expressions involving polynomials

Find the product $\frac{3x^2+3x}{4x^2-24x+36} \cdot \frac{x^2-4x+3}{x^2-x}$.

$$\frac{3x^2+3x}{4x^2-24x+36} \cdot \frac{x^2-4x+3}{x^2-x}$$

$$= \frac{(3x^2+3x)(x^2-4x+3)}{(4x^2-24x+36)(x^2-x)}$$ **Multiply numerators and denominators.**

$$= \frac{3x(x+1)(x-3)(x-1)}{4x(x-3)(x-3)(x-1)}$$ **Factor and divide out common factors.**

$$= \frac{3(x+1)}{4(x-3)}$$ **Simplify.**

CHECK Check your simplification using a graphing calculator.

Graph $y_1 = \frac{3x^2+3x}{4x^2-24x+36} \cdot \frac{x^2-4x+3}{x^2-x}$

and $y_2 = \frac{3(x+1)}{4(x-3)}$.

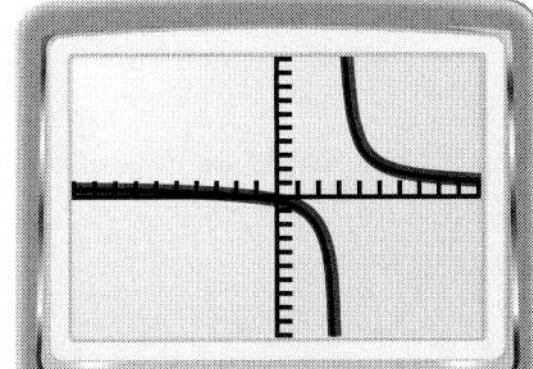

The graphs coincide. So, the expressions are equivalent for all values of x other than the excluded values (0, 1, and 3).

MULTIPLYING BY A POLYNOMIAL When you multiply a rational expression by a polynomial, first write the polynomial as a fraction with a denominator of 1.

EXAMPLE 3 Multiply a rational expression by a polynomial

Find the product $\frac{5x}{x^2+5x+6} \cdot (x+3)$.

$$\frac{5x}{x^2+5x+6} \cdot (x+3)$$

$$= \frac{5x}{x^2+5x+6} \cdot \frac{x+3}{1}$$ **Rewrite polynomial as a fraction.**

$$= \frac{5x(x+3)}{x^2+5x+6}$$ **Multiply numerators and denominators.**

$$= \frac{5x(x+3)}{(x+2)(x+3)}$$ **Factor and divide out common factor.**

$$= \frac{5x}{x+2}$$ **Simplify.**

✓ **GUIDED PRACTICE** for Examples 2 and 3

Find the product.

3. $\frac{x^2+x-2}{x^2+2x} \cdot \frac{2x^2+2x}{5x^2-15x+10}$ $\frac{2(x+1)}{5(x-2)}$

4. $\frac{2w^2}{w^2-7w+12} \cdot (w-4)$ $\frac{2w^2}{w-3}$

Motivating the Lesson

A local basketball association wants to report some statistics for a brochure. They have expressions that model the total number of points per game and the total number of free throw points per game for the past 6 years. By learning how to divide rational expressions, you can determine what percent of the total points scored were free throws.

3 TEACH

Extra Example 1

Find the product $\frac{3x^2}{2x} \cdot \frac{8x^3}{15x}$. $\frac{4x^3}{5}$

Key Question to Ask for Example 1

- What is the product of powers property? $a^m \cdot a^n = a^{m+n}$

Extra Example 2

Find the product $\frac{3x+6}{3x^2+18x+27} \cdot \frac{x^2-x-12}{x^2-4}$. $\frac{x-4}{(x+3)(x-2)}$

Extra Example 3

Find the product $\frac{4x^2}{x^2+3x-10} \cdot (x-2)$. $\frac{4x^2}{x+5}$

Key Question to Ask for Example 3

- Are there any excluded values in the expression? Explain. **The two excluded values are −3 and −2, even though −3 is not an excluded value for the simplified product.**

Differentiated Instruction

Below Level It may help students to see that the original expressions and the simplified expressions in **Examples 1–3** are equivalent if they substitute values for the variables. Have students substitute 2 for *x* in the original expression in Example 1 and then compare it to the simplified expression. Have them do the same for Examples 2 and 3. To make sure that they understand the concept, have them substitute 3 for *x* in Example 2 and ask them to explain the results.

See also the *Differentiated Instruction Resources* for more strategies.

Extra Example 4

Find the quotient

$\frac{x^2 - 9}{x^2 + 5x + 6} \div \frac{4x^2 - 12x}{x^2 - 2x - 8}$. $\frac{x - 4}{4x}$

Key Questions to Ask for Example 4

- How do you find the multiplicative inverse of an expression? **Switch the numerator and denominator.**
- How do you check whether two expressions are multiplicative inverses? **Their product is 1.**

Extra Example 5

Find the quotient

$\frac{3x^2 + 24x + 36}{6x + 9} \div (x + 2)$. $\frac{x + 6}{2x + 3}$

Key Questions to Ask for Example 5

- What are the excluded values? **0, −6**
- What can you tell about the graph of $y = \frac{2x^2 + 16x + 24}{3x^2} \div (x + 6)$ by looking at the expression? **A vertical asymptote is $x = 0$.**

An **Animated Algebra** activity is available online for **Example 5**. This activity is also part of **Power Presentations**.

DIVIDING RATIONAL EXPRESSIONS To divide by a rational expression, multiply by its multiplicative inverse.

EXAMPLE 4 Divide rational expressions involving polynomials

Find the quotient $\frac{7x^2 - 7x}{x^2 + 2x - 3} \div \frac{x + 1}{x^2 - 7x - 8}$.

$\frac{7x^2 - 7x}{x^2 + 2x - 3} \div \frac{x + 1}{x^2 - 7x - 8}$

$= \frac{7x^2 - 7x}{x^2 + 2x - 3} \cdot \frac{x^2 - 7x - 8}{x + 1}$ **Multiply by multiplicative inverse.**

$= \frac{(7x^2 - 7x)(x^2 - 7x - 8)}{(x^2 + 2x - 3)(x + 1)}$ **Multiply numerators and denominators.**

$= \frac{7x\cancel{(x - 1)}(x - 8)\cancel{(x + 1)}}{(x + 3)\cancel{(x - 1)}\cancel{(x + 1)}}$ **Factor and divide out common factors.**

$= \frac{7x(x - 8)}{x + 3}$ **Simplify.**

REVIEW INVERSES
For help with finding the multiplicative inverse of a number, see p. 103.

DIVIDING BY A POLYNOMIAL When you divide a rational expression by a polynomial, first write the polynomial as a fraction with a denominator of 1. Then multiply by the multiplicative inverse of the polynomial.

EXAMPLE 5 Divide a rational expression by a polynomial

Find the quotient $\frac{2x^2 + 16x + 24}{3x^2} \div (x + 6)$.

$\frac{2x^2 + 16x + 24}{3x^2} \div (x + 6)$

$= \frac{2x^2 + 16x + 24}{3x^2} \div \frac{x + 6}{1}$ **Rewrite polynomial as fraction.**

$= \frac{2x^2 + 16x + 24}{3x^2} \cdot \frac{1}{x + 6}$ **Multiply by multiplicative inverse.**

$= \frac{2x^2 + 16x + 24}{3x^2(x + 6)}$ **Multiply numerators and denominators.**

$= \frac{2(x + 2)\cancel{(x + 6)}}{3x^2\cancel{(x + 6)}}$ **Factor and divide out common factor.**

$= \frac{2(x + 2)}{3x^2}$ **Simplify.**

Animated Algebra at classzone.com

✓ **GUIDED PRACTICE** for Examples 4 and 5

Find the quotient.

5. $\frac{m^2 - 4}{2m^2 + 4m} \div \frac{6m - 3m^2}{4m + 44}$ $\frac{-2(m + 11)}{3m^2}$

6. $\frac{n^2 - 6n + 9}{12n} \div (n - 3)$ $\frac{n - 3}{12n}$

Differentiated Instruction

Kinesthetic Learners The excluded values of the quotient are the x-values that make the value of any denominator equal to zero. In **Example 4**, the excluded values include not only $x = -3$, but also $x = -1$, 1, and 8. Students can find the excluded values by using the TABLE feature of a calculator. Because the quotient is complicated, let $Y_1 = \frac{7x^2 - 7x}{x^2 + 2x - 3}$, $Y_2 = \frac{x + 1}{x^2 - 7x - 8}$, and $Y_3 = \frac{Y_1}{Y_2}$. Make a TABLE of values for Y_3.

See also the *Differentiated Instruction Resources* for more strategies.

EXAMPLE 6 Solve a multi-step problem

ADVERTISING The amount A (in millions of dollars) spent on all advertising and the amount T (in millions of dollars) spent on television advertising in the United States during the period 1970–2003 can be modeled by

$$A = \frac{13{,}000 + 3700x}{1 - 0.015x} \quad \text{and} \quad T = \frac{1800 + 860x}{1 - 0.016x}$$

where x is the number of years since 1970. Write a model that gives the percent p (in decimal form) of the amount spent on all advertising that was spent on television advertising. Then approximate the percent spent on television advertising in 2003.

Solution

STEP 1 **Write** a verbal model. Then write an equation.

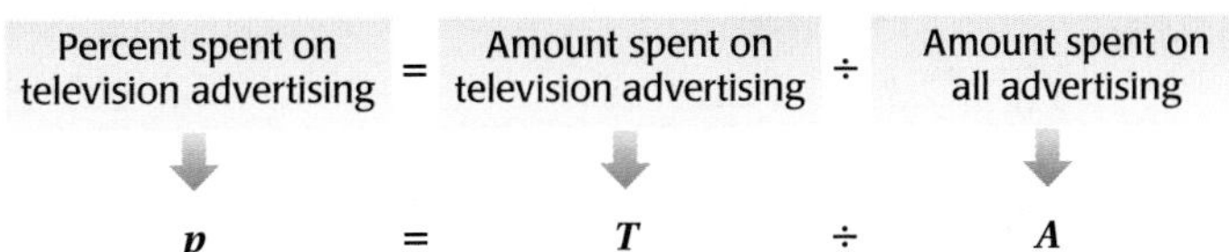

$$p = T \div A$$

STEP 2 **Find** the quotient.

$p = T \div A$ — **Write equation.**

$= \frac{1800 + 860x}{1 - 0.016x} \div \frac{13{,}000 + 3700x}{1 - 0.015x}$ — **Substitute for T and for A.**

$= \frac{1800 + 860x}{1 - 0.016x} \cdot \frac{1 - 0.015x}{13{,}000 + 3700x}$ — **Multiply by multiplicative inverse.**

$= \frac{(1800 + 860x)(1 - 0.015x)}{(1 - 0.016x)(13{,}000 + 3700x)}$ — **Multiply numerators and denominators.**

$= \frac{\cancel{20}(90 + 43x)(1 - 0.015x)}{(1 - 0.016x)(\cancel{20})(650 + 185x)}$ — **Factor and divide out common factor.**

$= \frac{(90 + 43x)(1 - 0.015x)}{(1 - 0.016x)(650 + 185x)}$ — **Simplify.**

STEP 3 **Approximate** the percent spent on television advertising in 2003. Because $2003 - 1970 = 33$, $x = 33$. Substitute 33 for x in the model and use a calculator to evaluate.

$$p = \frac{(90 + 43 \cdot 33)(1 - 0.015 \cdot 33)}{(1 - 0.016 \cdot 33)(650 + 185 \cdot 33)} \approx 0.239$$

▶ About 24% of the amount spent on all advertising was spent on television advertising in 2003.

GUIDED PRACTICE for Example 6

7. About $63,941 million, about $267,525 million; about 0.239; the answers are the same.

7. In Example 6, find the values of T and of A separately when $x = 33$. Then divide the value of T by the value of A. *Compare* your answer with the answer in Step 3 above.

Extra Example 6

The average amount T of gross revenue (in thousands of dollars) from toys sold at a toy store and the average amount G (in thousands of dollars) of gross revenue from games sold at the toy store during the period 1995–2003 can be modeled by $T = \frac{1950 - 30x}{1 - 0.03x}$ and $G = \frac{1010 + 70x}{1 - 0.007x}$ where x is the number of years since 1995. Write a model that gives the percent p (in decimal form) of the amount of gross revenue from toys that was gross revenue from games. Then approximate the percent of gross revenue from games in 2003.
$p = \frac{(101 + 7x) \cdot (1 - 0.03x)}{(1 - 0.007x) \cdot (195 - 3x)}$; in 2003, about 74% of the gross revenue of toys was games.

Closing the Lesson

Have students summarize the major points of the lesson and answer the Essential Question: How do you multiply and divide rational expressions?

- **Rational expressions can be multiplied and divided using the rules for multiplying and dividing rational numbers.**
- **Check for excluded values when performing operations with rational expressions.**

When multiplying rational expressions, factor and divide out common factors, multiply numerators and multiply denominators, then simplify. When multiplying by a polynomial, write the polynomial as a fraction with a denominator of 1. When dividing polynomials, multiply by the multiplicative inverse.

4 PRACTICE AND APPLY

Assignment Guide

Answer Transparencies available for all exercises

Basic:
Day 1: EP p. 946 Exs. 49–57 odd
pp. 806–809
Exs. 1–10, 12, 22, 23, 47–52
Day 2: pp. 806–809
Exs. 11, 13–21, 24–26, 33–36, 39–46

Average:
Day 1: pp. 806–809
Exs. 1, 2, 4–10, 12, 22, 23, 29, 47–52
Day 2: pp. 806–809
Exs. 11, 13–21, 24–28, 30, 33–37, 39–45 odd

Advanced:
Day 1: pp. 806–809
Exs. 1, 4–10, 22, 23, 29–31*, 47–52
Day 2: pp. 806–809
Exs. 13–21, 24–28, 32–38*, 40–46 even

Block:
pp. 806–809
Exs. 1, 2, 4–10, 12, 22, 23, 29, 47–52 (with 12.4)
pp. 806–809
Exs. 11, 13–21, 24–28, 30, 33–37, 39–45 odd (with 12.6)

Differentiated Instruction

See *Differentiated Instruction Resources* for suggestions on addressing the needs of a diverse classroom.

Homework Check

For a quick check of student understanding of key concepts, go over the following exercises:
Basic: 4, 8, 14, 16, 33
Average: 6, 9, 17, 19, 34
Advanced: 7, 10, 18, 20, 35

Extra Practice

- Student Edition, p. 946
- Chapter Resource Book: Practice levels A, B, C

Practice Worksheet

An easily-readable reduced practice page (with answers) for this lesson can be found on p. 762C.

12.5 EXERCISES

HOMEWORK KEY
○ = **WORKED-OUT SOLUTIONS** on p. WS30 for Exs. 5, 15, and 35
★ = **STANDARDIZED TEST PRACTICE** Exs. 2, 21, 26, 27, 28, 36, and 37
◆ = **MULTIPLE REPRESENTATIONS** Ex. 35

SKILL PRACTICE

A

1. **VOCABULARY** Copy and complete: To divide by a rational expression, multiply by its _?_. **multiplicative inverse**

2. ★ **WRITING** *Describe* how to multiply a rational expression by a polynomial. **See margin.**

EXAMPLES 1, 2, and 3 on pp. 802–803 for Exs. 3–10, 12

MULTIPLYING EXPRESSIONS Find the product.

3. $\frac{9p^2}{7} \cdot \frac{5}{6p^4}$ $\mathbf{\frac{15}{14p^2}}$

4. $\frac{5}{8q^6} \cdot \frac{4q^5}{3}$ $\mathbf{\frac{5}{6q}}$

5. $\frac{v^2+v-12}{5v+10} \cdot \frac{-v-2}{v^2+5v+4}$ $\mathbf{\frac{-(v-3)}{5(v+1)}}$

6. $\frac{y-2}{-2y^2-10y} \cdot \frac{4y^2+20y}{y^2-4}$ $\mathbf{\frac{-2}{y+2}}$

7. $\frac{5x}{2x^3-17x^2-9x} \cdot \frac{4x^2-20x-144}{20}$ $\mathbf{\frac{x+4}{2x+1}}$

8. $\frac{r^5}{7r^3+56r} \cdot (r^2+8)$ $\mathbf{\frac{r^4}{7}}$

9. $\frac{-3m}{m^2-7m+10} \cdot (m-5)$ $\mathbf{\frac{-3m}{m-2}}$

10. $\frac{2n-6}{3n^2-7n-6} \cdot (3n^2+14n+8)$ $\mathbf{2(n+4)}$

EXAMPLES 4 and 5 on p. 804 for Exs. 11, 13–21

ERROR ANALYSIS ***Describe* and correct the error in finding the product or quotient.** **11–12. See margin.**

11. $\frac{x^3}{5} \div \frac{15x^3}{2}$

$\frac{x^3}{5} \div \frac{15x^3}{2} = \frac{5}{x^3} \cdot \frac{15x^3}{2}$

$= \frac{75x^3}{2x^3}$

$= \frac{75}{2}$

12. $\frac{x-2}{x+5} \cdot \frac{x}{2-x}$

$\frac{x-2}{x+5} \cdot \frac{x}{2-x} = \frac{(x-2)x}{(x+5)(2-x)}$

$= \frac{(x-2)x}{(x+5)(2-x)}$

$= \frac{x}{x+5}$

DIVIDING EXPRESSIONS Find the quotient.

13. $\frac{16r^2}{3} \div \frac{12}{5r}$ $\mathbf{\frac{20r^3}{9}}$

14. $\frac{25s^{12}}{18} \div \frac{5s^6}{2}$ $\mathbf{\frac{5s^6}{9}}$

15. $\frac{2w^2+5w}{w^2-81} \div \frac{w^2}{w+9}$ $\mathbf{\frac{2w+5}{w(w-9)}}$

16. $\frac{c^2+c}{c^2+c-30} \div \frac{c-6}{c^2-11c+30}$ $\mathbf{\frac{c(c+1)}{c+6}}$

17. $\frac{a^2+3a-10}{a^2+6a-7} \div \frac{9a^3-18a^2}{3a^2+18a-21}$ $\mathbf{\frac{a+5}{3a^2}}$

18. $\frac{2x^2-9x+9}{35x+14} \div \frac{-3x^2+13x-12}{15x^2-14x-8}$ $\mathbf{\frac{3-2x}{7}}$

19. $\frac{4k^2+4k-15}{2k-3} \div (2k+5)$ **1**

20. $\frac{t^2-9t-22}{5t-1} \div (5t^2+9t-2)$ $\mathbf{\frac{t-11}{(5t-1)^2}}$

21. ★ **MULTIPLE CHOICE** What common factor do you divide out when finding the quotient $\frac{x^2-3x+2}{x^2-2x-3} \div \frac{x^2+4x+3}{x^2-7x+12}$? **B**

Ⓐ $x-1$ Ⓑ $x-3$ Ⓒ $x+1$ Ⓓ $x+3$

2. First write the polynomial as a fraction with a denominator of 1. Then write the product of the numerators over the product of the denominators, leaving the products in factored form. Factor the numerator and denominator completely and divide out any common factors.

11. To divide by the rational expression $\frac{15x^3}{2}$, you must multiply by its multiplicative inverse, $\frac{2}{15x^3}$; $\frac{x^3}{5} \cdot \frac{2}{15x^3} = \frac{2x^3}{75x^3} = \frac{2}{75}$.

B TRANSLATING PHRASES **Translate the verbal phrase into a product or quotient of rational expressions. Then find the product or quotient.**

22. The product of $x + 3$ and the ratio of $x + 5$ to $x^2 - 9$ $(x + 3) \cdot \frac{x+5}{x^2-9}; \frac{x+5}{x-3}$

23. The product of $8x^2$ and the multiplicative inverse of $2x^3$ $8x^2 \cdot \frac{1}{2x^3}; \frac{4}{x}$

24. $(x^2 + 3x - 18) \div \frac{x+6}{2}; 2(x - 3)$

24. The quotient of $x^2 + 3x - 18$ and the ratio of $x + 6$ to 2

25. The quotient of the multiplicative inverse of $x^2 - 3x - 4$ and twice the multiplicative inverse of $x^2 - 1$ $\frac{1}{x^2-3x-4} \div \frac{2}{x^2-1}; \frac{x-1}{2(x-4)}$

26. ★ **MULTIPLE CHOICE** What is the quotient $\frac{x^2-1}{-(x+1)} \div (x - 1)$? **A**

Ⓐ -1 Ⓑ 0 Ⓒ 1 Ⓓ $x^2 - 1$

★ **OPEN-ENDED** **Let a, b, c, and d be different polynomials. Find two rational expressions $\frac{a}{b}$ and $\frac{c}{d}$ that satisfy the given conditions.**

27. The product of the rational expressions is $\frac{x-3}{x+2}$, and the excluded values are $-2, -1, 4$, and 5. *Sample answer:* $\frac{x^2-2x-3}{x^2-2x-8}, \frac{x^2-9x+20}{x^2-4x-5}$

28. The quotient of the rational expressions is $\frac{x-6}{x+4}$, and the excluded values are $-4, -2, 3$, and 6. *Sample answer:* $\frac{x^2-4x-12}{x^2-2x-24}, \frac{x^2-x-6}{x^2-9x+18}$

GEOMETRY **Write an expression for the area of the figure. Find a value of x less than 5 for which the given dimensions and the area are positive.**

29. Rectangle

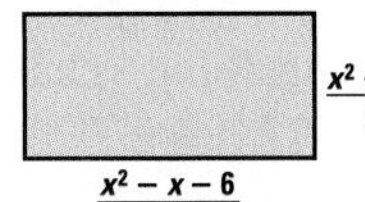

$\frac{x^2-x-6}{x-5}$

$(x - 1)(x - 3)$. *Sample answer:* 0

30. Triangle

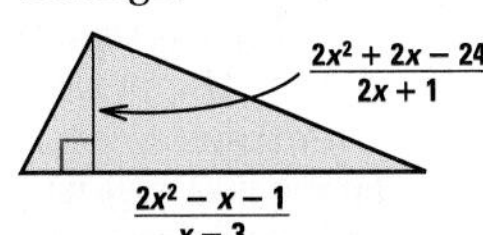

$\frac{2x^2-x-1}{x-3}$

$(x - 1)(x + 4)$. *Sample answer:* 4

C CHALLENGE **Let a be a polynomial in the given equation. Find a.**

31. $\frac{a}{x+2} \cdot \frac{3x^2+5x-2}{x-4} = 6x^2 + 7x - 3$
$2x^2 - 5x - 12$

32. $\frac{8x^2-2x-3}{x-5} \div \frac{2x+1}{a} = 12x^2 - x - 6$
$3x^2 - 13x - 10$

PROBLEM SOLVING

EXAMPLE 6 **A** on p. 805 for Exs. 33–35

33. **VEHICLES** The total distance M (in billions of miles) traveled by all motor vehicles and the distance T (in billions of miles) traveled by trucks in the United States during the period 1980–2002 can be modeled by

$$M = 1500 + 63x \quad \text{and} \quad T = \frac{100 + 2.2x}{1 - 0.014x}$$

where x is the number of years since 1980. Write a model that gives the percent p (in decimal form) of the total motor vehicle distance that was traveled by trucks as a function of x. Then approximate the percent traveled by trucks in 2002. **See margin.**

@HomeTutor for problem solving help at classzone.com

Avoiding Common Errors

Exercises 13–21 Watch for students who do not rewrite division as multiplication. Remind students that when they see a division symbol, they should multiply by the reciprocal.

Reading Strategy

Exercises 5, 15, 35 Point out to students that each of these exercises is circled in red, which means that there is a worked-out solution. Encourage them to solve the problem first and then check their solutions against the worked-out solutions.

12. Before dividing out the common factor $(x - 2)$, you must first rewrite the factor $(2 - x)$ in the denominator as $-1(x - 2)$, leaving a factor of -1 in the denominator; $\frac{(x-2)x}{-1(x+5)(x-2)} = \frac{-x}{x+5}$.

33. $p = \frac{100 + 2.2x}{(1 - 0.014x)(1500 + 63x)}$; about 7%

Study Strategy

Exercise 34 Suggest that students write a stepped-out solution to this problem using the model from Example 6, page 805. Encourage them to model each step of Example 6, including Step 1.

Avoiding Common Errors

Exercises 35–38 Tell students that writing a verbal model of an equation can help them avoid confusion between which expression is the dividend and which is the divisor.

Internet Reference

Exercise 36 For more information about Hank Aaron, go to www.baseballhalloffame.org and do a search for "Hank Aaron."

35b. See below.

36a. $A = \dfrac{(31 + 120x)(1 + 0.01x)}{(1 + 0.017x)(150 + 350x)}$

37a. $T = \dfrac{4700 - 74x}{(1 - 0.053x)(0.015x^2 + 4.1)}$

37b.

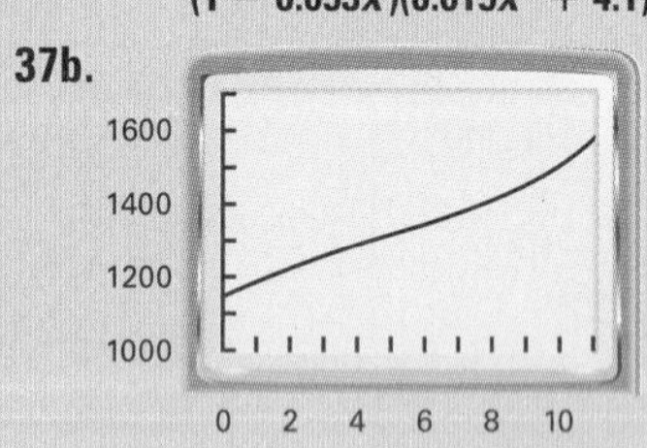

The number of tickets increased. No; the graph only shows how the *ratio* of the gross revenue and the ticket prices changed. *R* and *P* could go up and/or down while their ratio increases.

37c.

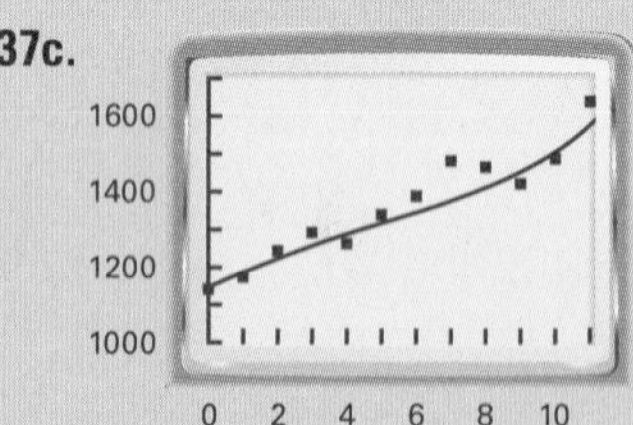

The points of the scatter plot are very close to the graph of the model for all years except 1998, 1999, and 2002.

34. CONSUMER SPENDING The average annual amount T (in dollars) spent on reading and entertainment and the average annual amount E (in dollars) spent on entertainment by consumers in the United States during the period 1985–2002 can be modeled by

$$T = \frac{1300 + 84x}{1 + 0.015x} \quad \text{and} \quad E = \frac{1100 + 64x}{1 + 0.0062x}$$

where x is the number of years since 1985. Write a model that gives the percent p (in decimal form) of the amount spent on reading and entertainment that was spent on entertainment as a function of x. Then approximate the percent spent on entertainment in 2000.

@HomeTutor for problem solving help at classzone.com

$p = \dfrac{(275 + 16x)(1 + 0.015x)}{(1 + 0.0062x)(325 + 21x)}$; **about 90%**

35. ◆ **MULTIPLE REPRESENTATIONS** Football player Emmitt Smith's career number Y of rushing yards gained and his career number A of rushing attempts from 1990 (when he started playing professional football) through the 2002 football season can be modeled by

$$Y = \frac{860 + 1800x}{1 + 0.024x} \quad \text{and} \quad A = \frac{230 + 380x}{1 + 0.014x}$$

where x is the number of years since 1990.

a. **Writing an Equation** A football player's rushing average is the number of rushing yards gained divided by the number of rushing attempts. Write a model that gives Smith's career rushing average R as a function of x for the period 1990–2002. $R = \dfrac{(86 + 180x)(1 + 0.014x)}{(1 + 0.024x)(23 + 38x)}$

b. **Making a Table** Make a table that shows Smith's approximate career rushing average (rounded to the nearest hundredth) for each year during the period. *Describe* how the career rushing average changed over time. **See margin for table; Smith's career rushing average increased for the first several years and then began to decrease.**

B

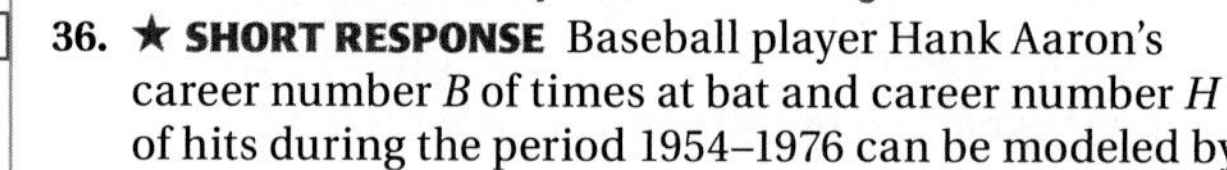

36. ★ **SHORT RESPONSE** Baseball player Hank Aaron's career number B of times at bat and career number H of hits during the period 1954–1976 can be modeled by

$$B = \frac{300 + 700x}{1 + 0.01x} \quad \text{and} \quad H = \frac{62 + 240x}{1 + 0.017x}$$

where x is the number of years since 1954.

a. **Model** A baseball player's batting average is the number of hits divided by the number of times at bat. Write a model that gives Hank Aaron's career batting average A as a function of x. **See margin.**

b. **Decide** The table shows Aaron's actual career number of times at bat and actual career number of hits for three different years. For which year does the model give the best approximation of A? *Explain* your choice.

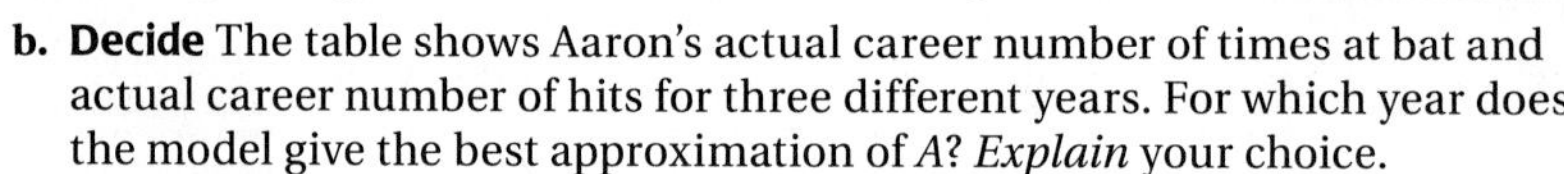

Year	1954	1959	1976
Career times at bat	468	3524	12,364
Career hits	131	1137	3771

1959; using the values in the table to calculate the ratio $\frac{H}{B}$ for the three given years gives batting averages A of 0.280 in 1954, 0.323 in 1959, and 0.305 in 1976. Calculating A using the model from part (a) for $x = 0$, 5, and 22 gives batting averages of 0.207 in 1954, 0.321 in 1959, and 0.302 in 1976.

○ = WORKED-OUT SOLUTIONS on p. WS1 ★ = STANDARDIZED TEST PRACTICE

= MULTIPLE REPRESENTATIONS

35b.

Year	1990	1991	1992	1993	1994	1995	1996
R	3.74	4.32	4.42	4.44	4.44	4.42	4.40

Year	1997	1998	1999	2000	2001	2002
R	4.38	4.35	4.33	4.30	4.28	4.25

37. ★ **EXTENDED RESPONSE** The gross revenue R (in millions of dollars) from movie tickets sold and the average movie ticket price P (in dollars) in the United States during the period 1991–2002 can be modeled by

$$R = \frac{4700 - 74x}{1 - 0.053x} \quad \text{and} \quad P = 0.015x^2 + 4.1$$

where x is the number of years since 1991. **a–c. See margin.**

a. **Model** Write a model that gives the number T of movie tickets sold (in millions) as a function of x.

b. **Describe** Graph the model on a graphing calculator and describe how the number of tickets sold changed over time. Can you use the graph to describe how the gross revenue and ticket prices changed over time? *Explain* your reasoning.

c. **Compare** The table shows the actual number of tickets sold for each year during the period. Make a scatter plot of the data on the same screen as the graph of the model in part (b). *Compare* the scatter plot with the graph of the model.

Year	1991	1992	1993	1994	1995	1996
Tickets (millions)	1141	1173	1244	1292	1263	1339

Year	1997	1998	1999	2000	2001	2002
Tickets (millions)	1388	1481	1465	1421	1487	1639

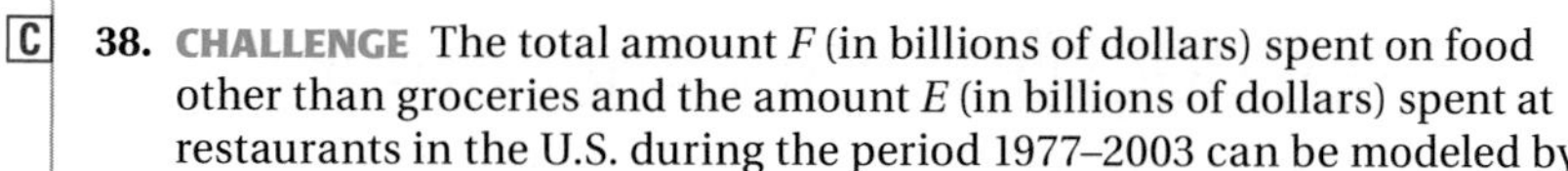

C 38. **CHALLENGE** The total amount F (in billions of dollars) spent on food other than groceries and the amount E (in billions of dollars) spent at restaurants in the U.S. during the period 1977–2003 can be modeled by

$$F = \frac{88 + 9.2x}{1 - 0.0097x} \quad \text{and} \quad E = \frac{54 + 6.5x}{1 - 0.012x}$$

where x is the number of years since 1977. Write a model that gives the percent p (in decimal form) of the amount spent on food other than groceries that was spent at restaurants as a function of x. Approximate the percent that was spent at locations other than restaurants in 2002.

$p = \frac{(54 + 6.5x)(1 - 0.0097x)}{(1 - 0.012x)(88 + 9.2x)}$; **about 26%**

MIXED REVIEW

PREVIEW
Prepare for Lesson 12.6 in Exs. 39–52.

Add or subtract. *(p. 914)*

39. $\frac{2}{5} + \frac{2}{3}$ **$1\frac{1}{15}$**
40. $\frac{3}{8} + \frac{5}{12}$ **$\frac{19}{24}$**
41. $\frac{1}{4} + \frac{5}{6}$ **$1\frac{1}{12}$**
42. $\frac{7}{9} + \frac{8}{21}$ **$1\frac{10}{63}$**
43. $\frac{7}{8} - \frac{7}{10}$ **$\frac{7}{40}$**
44. $\frac{7}{15} - \frac{1}{4}$ **$\frac{13}{60}$**
45. $\frac{9}{14} - \frac{5}{21}$ **$\frac{17}{42}$**
46. $\frac{5}{17} - \frac{2}{51}$ **$\frac{13}{51}$**

Find the sum, difference, or product. **47–52. See margin.**

47. $(25x^2 - 6x) + (4x^2 - 5)$ *(p. 554)*
48. $(7x^2 + 5x + 1) + (-6x^2 + 13x)$ *(p. 554)*
49. $(2x^2 - x + 12) - (3x + 8)$ *(p. 554)*
50. $(7x^2 + 16) - (8x^3 + 3x^2 - 7)$ *(p. 554)*
51. $(5x - 6)(4x - 5)$ *(p. 562)*
52. $(2x + 9)(3x - 7)$ *(p. 562)*

47. $29x^2 - 6x - 5$
48. $x^2 + 18x + 1$
49. $2x^2 - 4x + 4$
50. $-8x^3 + 4x^2 + 23$
51. $20x^2 - 49x + 30$
52. $6x^2 + 13x - 63$

5 ASSESS AND RETEACH

Daily Homework Quiz

Transparency Available

1. Find the product $\frac{3x}{x^2 - 3x - 10} \cdot (x + 2)$. $\frac{3x}{x - 5}$
2. Find the quotient $(2x^3 + 11x^2 + 11x - 4) \div (x + 4)$. **$2x^2 + 3x - 1$**
3. The average total revenue (in thousands of dollars) of books B sold at a used bookstore and the average revenue of paperback books P sold at the store during 1990–2004 can be represented by $B = \frac{824 + 12x}{1 - 0.02x}$ and $P = \frac{720 - 36x}{1 - 0.017x}$ where x is the number of years since 1990. Approximate the percent of the total revenue of books from paperback sales in 2004. **about 21%**

Online Quiz

Available at **classzone.com**

Diagnosis/Remediation

- Practice A, B, C in Chapter Resource Book
- Study Guide in Chapter Resource Book
- Practice Workbook
- @HomeTutor

Challenge

Additional challenge is available in the Chapter Resource Book.

1 PLAN AND PREPARE

Warm-Up Exercises

Find the quotient.

1. $\frac{5x}{3} \div 5x^2$ $\frac{1}{3x}$

2. $\frac{x^2 - 10x + 16}{2x} \div (x - 2)$ $\frac{x - 8}{2x}$

2 FOCUS AND MOTIVATE

Essential Question

Big Idea 2, p. 736

How do you simplify a complex fraction? **Tell students they will learn how to answer this question by treating a complex fraction as division of two rational expressions.**

3 TEACH

Extra Example 1

Simplify the complex fraction.

a. $\frac{\frac{8x^2}{5}}{-2x}$ $-\frac{4x}{5}$

b. $\frac{\frac{x - 4}{x + 4}}{x^2 - 16}$ $\frac{1}{(x + 4)^2}$

Key Question to Ask for Example 1

- In part (b), how can you tell which expression represents the complex fraction's numerator? **The longest fraction bar separates the numerator and denominator of the complex fraction.**

NCTM STANDARDS

Standard 1: Understand how operations are related

Standard 2: Analyze situations using algebraic symbols

Extension Simplify Complex Fractions

Use after Lesson 12.5

GOAL Simplify complex fractions.

Key Vocabulary
- **complex fraction**

A **complex fraction** is a fraction that contains a fraction in its numerator, denominator, or both. To simplify a complex fraction, divide its numerator by its denominator.

KEY CONCEPT *For Your Notebook*

Simplifying a Complex Fraction

Let a, b, c, and d be polynomials where $b \neq 0$, $c \neq 0$, and $d \neq 0$.

Algebra $\frac{\frac{a}{b}}{\frac{c}{d}} = \frac{a}{b} \div \frac{c}{d} = \frac{a}{b} \cdot \frac{d}{c}$

Example $\frac{\frac{x}{2}}{\frac{x}{3}} = \frac{x}{2} \div \frac{x}{3} = \frac{x}{2} \cdot \frac{3}{x} = \frac{3x}{2x} = \frac{3}{2}$

READING
The widest fraction bar separates the numerator of a complex fraction from the denominator.

EXAMPLE 1 Simplify a complex fraction

Simplify the complex fraction.

a. $\frac{\frac{3x}{2}}{-6x^3} = \frac{3x}{2} \div (-6x^3)$ **Write fraction as quotient.**

$= \frac{3x}{2} \cdot \frac{1}{-6x^3}$ **Multiply by multiplicative inverse.**

$= \frac{3x}{-12x^3}$ **Multiply numerators and denominators.**

$= -\frac{1}{4x^2}$ **Simplify.**

b. $\frac{x^2 - 1}{\frac{x + 1}{x - 1}} = (x^2 - 1) \div \frac{x + 1}{x - 1}$ **Write fraction as quotient.**

$= (x^2 - 1) \cdot \frac{x - 1}{x + 1}$ **Multiply by multiplicative inverse.**

$= \frac{(x^2 - 1)(x - 1)}{x + 1}$ **Multiply numerators and denominators.**

$= \frac{\cancel{(x + 1)}(x - 1)(x - 1)}{\cancel{x + 1}}$ **Factor and divide out common factor.**

$= (x - 1)^2$ **Simplify.**

EXAMPLE 2 Simplify a complex fraction

Simplify $\dfrac{\dfrac{2x^2 - 8x}{x^2 + 4x + 4}}{\dfrac{x^3 - 16x}{x + 2}}$.

$\dfrac{\dfrac{2x^2 - 8x}{x^2 + 4x + 4}}{\dfrac{x^3 - 16x}{x + 2}} = \dfrac{2x^2 - 8x}{x^2 + 4x + 4} \div \dfrac{x^3 - 16x}{x + 2}$ Write fraction as quotient.

$= \dfrac{2x^2 - 8x}{x^2 + 4x + 4} \cdot \dfrac{x + 2}{x^3 - 16x}$ Multiply by multiplicative inverse.

$= \dfrac{(2x^2 - 8x)(x + 2)}{(x^2 + 4x + 4)(x^3 - 16x)}$ Multiply numerators and denominators.

$= \dfrac{2\cancel{x}\cancel{(x - 4)}\cancel{(x + 2)}}{\cancel{(x + 2)}(x + 2)\cancel{x}(x + 4)\cancel{(x - 4)}}$ Factor and divide out common factors.

$= \dfrac{2}{(x + 2)(x + 4)}$ Simplify.

PRACTICE

EXAMPLES 1 and 2 on pp. 810–811 for Exs. 1–9

Simplify the complex fraction.

1. $\dfrac{\dfrac{-9x^5}{7}}{-12x^2}$ $\dfrac{3x^3}{28}$

2. $\dfrac{\dfrac{-2}{11x^4}}{18x^4}$ $\dfrac{-1}{99x^8}$

3. $\dfrac{\dfrac{x^2 + 7x}{2x - 6}}{x^2 - 49}$ $\dfrac{x}{2(x - 3)(x - 7)}$

4. $\dfrac{-24x^4}{\dfrac{8x^2}{-4x^3}}$ $12x^5$

5. $\dfrac{\dfrac{x^2 + 4x}{x + 4}}{x^2 - x}$ $x^2(x - 1)$

6. $\dfrac{\dfrac{2x^2 + 5x - 3}{x^2 + 4x + 3}}{15x}$ $\dfrac{15x(2x - 1)}{x + 1}$

7. $\dfrac{\dfrac{x^2 - x - 20}{4}}{\dfrac{x - 5}{10}}$ $\dfrac{5(x + 4)}{2}$

8. $\dfrac{\dfrac{x^2 - 2x - 8}{6x - 3x^2}}{\dfrac{x^3 + 4x^2}{x^2 - 4}}$ $-\dfrac{(x - 4)(x + 2)^2}{3x^3(x + 4)}$

9. $\dfrac{\dfrac{2x^2 + 5x - 3}{3x^2 + 4x + 1}}{\dfrac{10x^2 - 5x}{2x^3 - 2x}}$ $\dfrac{2(x + 3)(x - 1)}{5(3x + 1)}$

GEOMETRY Write a rational expression for the ratio of the surface area S of the given solid to its volume V.

10. Sphere $\dfrac{3}{r}$

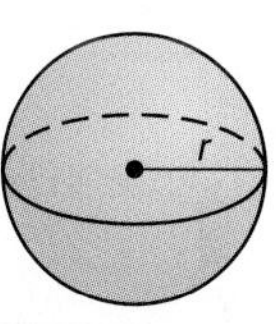

$S = 4\pi r^2$

$V = \dfrac{4\pi r^3}{3}$

11. Cone $\dfrac{3(r + \ell)}{rh}$

$S = \pi r^2 + \pi r\ell$

$V = \dfrac{\pi r^2 h}{3}$

12. Pyramid with a square base $\dfrac{3(s + 2\ell)}{sh}$

$S = s^2 + 2s\ell$

$V = \dfrac{s^2 h}{3}$

13. Are the complex fractions $\dfrac{\dfrac{a}{b}}{c}$ and $\dfrac{a}{\dfrac{b}{c}}$ equivalent? *Explain* your answer. **See margin.**

Extra Example 2

Simplify $\dfrac{\dfrac{3x - 18}{2x^2 + 16x + 30}}{\dfrac{x - 6}{x^2 + 2x - 15}}$. $\dfrac{3(x - 3)}{2(x + 3)}$

Key Questions to Ask for Example 2

- How many fractions make up the complex fraction? **two; one in the numerator and one in the denominator**
- For which fraction do you find the multiplicative inverse? **the one in the denominator**

Closing the Lesson

Have students summarize the major points of the lesson and answer the Essential Question: How do you simplify a complex fraction?

- **A complex fraction contains a fraction in its numerator, denominator, or both.**

To simplify a complex fraction, first write the fraction as a quotient. Then use the reciprocal of the divisor to rewrite the expression as a product. Factor numerators and/or denominators, divide out common factors, and simplify.

4 PRACTICE AND APPLY

Avoiding Common Errors

Exercises 1–9 Watch for students who separate the complex fraction incorrectly, using part of the numerator as the denominator or vice versa. Remind these students that the longest fraction bar indicates how to rewrite the complex fraction as the division of two rational expressions.

13. No; $\dfrac{\frac{a}{b}}{c} = \dfrac{a}{b} \div c = \dfrac{a}{b} \cdot \dfrac{1}{c} = \dfrac{a}{bc}$ **and** $\dfrac{a}{\frac{b}{c}} = a \div \dfrac{b}{c} = \dfrac{a}{1} \cdot \dfrac{c}{b} = \dfrac{ac}{b}$. **Thus,** $\dfrac{\frac{a}{b}}{c} \neq \dfrac{a}{\frac{b}{c}}$.

12.6 Add and Subtract Rational Expressions

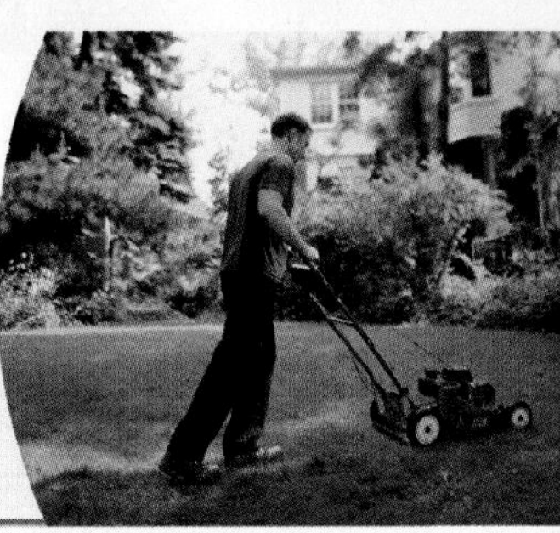

Before You multiplied and divided rational expressions.
Now You will add and subtract rational expressions.
Why? So you can solve work problems, as in Ex. 49.

Key Vocabulary
- **least common denominator (LCD) of rational expressions**

Adding and subtracting rational expressions with the same denominator is similar to adding and subtracting numerical fractions with the same denominator.

KEY CONCEPT *For Your Notebook*

Adding and Subtracting Rational Expressions with the Same Denominator

Let a, b, and c be polynomials where $c \neq 0$.

Algebra $\frac{a}{c} + \frac{b}{c} = \frac{a+b}{c}$ $\qquad \frac{a}{c} - \frac{b}{c} = \frac{a-b}{c}$

Examples $\frac{2}{x} + \frac{3}{x} = \frac{2+3}{x} = \frac{5}{x}$ $\qquad \frac{5}{4x} - \frac{2}{4x} = \frac{5-2}{4x} = \frac{3}{4x}$

EXAMPLE 1 **Add and subtract with the same denominator**

a. $\frac{5}{3x} + \frac{7}{3x} = \frac{12}{3x}$ — **Add numerators.**

$= \frac{\cancel{3} \cdot 4}{\cancel{3} \cdot x}$ — **Factor and divide out common factor.**

$= \frac{4}{x}$ — **Simplify.**

b. $\frac{3x}{x-1} - \frac{x+5}{x-1} = \frac{3x-(x+5)}{x-1}$ — **Subtract numerators.**

$= \frac{2x-5}{x-1}$ — **Simplify.**

CHECK Check your simplification using a graphing calculator. For part (b), graph $y_1 = \frac{3x}{x-1} - \frac{x+5}{x-1}$ and $y_2 = \frac{2x-5}{x-1}$. The graphs coincide. So, the expressions are equivalent for all values of x other than the excluded value of 1.

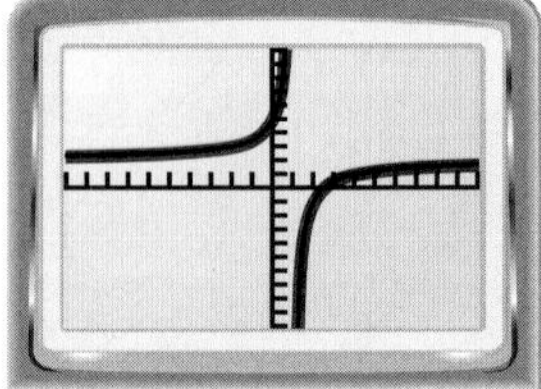

1 PLAN AND PREPARE

Warm-Up Exercises

Transparency Available

1. Find $\frac{1}{4} + \frac{2}{3}$. $\frac{11}{12}$
2. Find $\frac{7}{8} - \frac{5}{6}$. $\frac{1}{24}$
3. A boat travels 8 miles upstream (against the current) in 4 hours, and 8 miles downstream (with the current) in 3.2 hours. What is the average speed of the boat in still water? **2.25 mi/h**

Notetaking Guide

Transparency Available

Promotes interactive learning and notetaking skills.

Pacing

Basic: 2 days
Average: 2 days
Advanced: 2 days
Block: 0.5 block with 12.5
0.5 block with 12.7

- See *Teaching Guide/Lesson Plan.*

2 FOCUS AND MOTIVATE

Essential Question

Big Idea 2, p. 736

How do you add or subtract rational expressions? **Tell students they will learn how to answer this question by using processes similar to adding or subtracting fractions.**

NCTM STANDARDS

Standard 2: Analyze situations using algebraic symbols

Standard 6: Solve problems in math and other contexts

Resource Planning Guide

Chapter Resource Book
- Teaching Guide/Lesson Plan
- Activity Master
- Practice levels A, B, C
- Study Guide
- Catch-up for Absent Students
- Problem Solving Workshop
- Challenge

Workbooks
- Notetaking Guide
- Practice Workbook

Teaching Options
- **Power Presentations** provides dynamic electronic teaching resources for the classroom.
- **Activity Generator** provides editable activities for all ability levels.

Interactive Technology
- Easy Planner
- Power Presentations
- Activity Generator
- Animated Algebra
- Test Generator
- Online Quiz
- eWorkbook
- eEdition
- @HomeTutor

Resources for English Learners
- Spanish Study Guide
- Multi-Language Visual Glossary
- Student Resources in Spanish

See also the *Differentiated Instruction Resources* for more strategies for meeting individual needs.

GUIDED PRACTICE for Example 1

Find the sum or difference.

1. $\frac{2}{y} + \frac{y+1}{y}$ $\frac{y+3}{y}$

2. $\frac{4x+1}{2x-1} - \frac{2x-3}{2x-1}$ $\frac{2x+4}{2x-1}$

LEAST COMMON DENOMINATOR The **least common denominator (LCD)** of two or more rational expressions is the product of the factors of the denominators of the rational expressions with each common factor used only once.

EXAMPLE 2 Find the LCD of rational expressions

Find the LCD of the rational expressions.

a. $\frac{1}{4r}, \frac{r+3}{10r^2}$ **b.** $\frac{5}{(x-3)^2}, \frac{3x+4}{x^2-x-6}$ **c.** $\frac{3}{c-2}, \frac{c+8}{2c+7}$

Solution

a. Find the least common multiple (LCM) of $4r$ and $10r^2$.

$4r = \boxed{2} \cdot 2 \cdot \boxed{r}$ ← **The common factors are circled.**

$10r^2 = \boxed{2} \cdot 5 \cdot \boxed{r} \cdot r$

AVOID ERRORS
When finding the LCD, be sure to use the common factors only once.

LCM $= 2 \cdot r \cdot 2 \cdot 5 \cdot r = 20r^2$

▶ The LCD of $\frac{1}{4r}$ and $\frac{r+3}{10r^2}$ is $20r^2$.

b. Find the least common multiple (LCM) of $(x-3)^2$ and $x^2 - x - 6$.

$(x-3)^2 = \boxed{(x-3)} \cdot (x-3)$

$x^2 - x - 6 = \boxed{(x-3)} \cdot (x+2)$

LCM $= (x-3) \cdot (x-3) \cdot (x+2) = (x-3)^2(x+2)$

▶ The LCD of $\frac{5}{(x-3)^2}$ and $\frac{3x+4}{x^2-x-6}$ is $(x-3)^2(x+2)$.

c. Find the least common multiple of $c - 2$ and $2c + 7$.

Because $c - 2$ and $2c + 7$ cannot be factored, they don't have any factors in common. The least common multiple is their product, $(c-2)(2c+7)$.

▶ The LCD of $\frac{3}{c-2}$ and $\frac{c+8}{2c+7}$ is $(c-2)(2c+7)$.

GUIDED PRACTICE for Example 2

Find the LCD of the rational expressions.

3. $\frac{1}{28m}, \frac{m+1}{7m^3}$ $28m^3$

4. $\frac{2}{x^2+4x-5}, \frac{x^2+2}{x^2+7x+10}$ $(x+5)(x-1)(x+2)$

5. $\frac{5a}{a+3}, \frac{a+6}{a-4}$ $(a+3)(a-4)$

DIFFERENT DENOMINATORS To add or subtract rational expressions that have different denominators, use the LCD to write equivalent rational expressions that have the same denominator just as you would for numerical fractions.

Motivating the Lesson

You are planning a 500-mile trip to the Grand Canyon. You estimate that your average speed driving to the Canyon will be greater than your average speed returning home. In this lesson you will learn how to write an equation to model this situation and how to use the model to determine your average speed for the entire trip to and from the Grand Canyon.

3 TEACH

Extra Example 1

Add or subtract.

a. $\frac{2x}{x+2} + \frac{x+1}{x+2}$ $\frac{3x+1}{x+2}$

b. $\frac{4x+1}{5x} - \frac{x+3}{5x}$ $\frac{3x-2}{5x}$

Extra Example 2

Find the LCD of the rational expressions.

a. $\frac{1}{12x}, \frac{x+7}{4x^2}$ $12x^2$

b. $\frac{4}{x^2-x-6}, \frac{3x^2}{(x+2)^2}$ $(x+2)^2(x-3)$

c. $\frac{2x}{x-8}, \frac{3x+15}{x+1}$ $(x-8)(x+1)$

Key Question to Ask for Example 2

- If two denominators have repeated factors, such as $2 \cdot 2 \cdot 2 \cdot x$ and $2 \cdot 2 \cdot x \cdot x$, how many times does each factor appear in the LCD? **In the LCD, use the greater number of times it occurs. For these denominators, the LCD is $2 \cdot 2 \cdot 2 \cdot x \cdot x$ or $8x^2$.**

Extra Example 3

Find the sum $\frac{6}{18x} + \frac{4}{6x^2}$. $\frac{x+2}{3x^2}$

Key Question to Ask for Example 3

- How did you determine the LCD? **The denominators are $2 \cdot 2 \cdot 2 \cdot x \cdot x$ and $2 \cdot 2 \cdot 3 \cdot x \cdot x \cdot x$. Taking each factor the greater number of times, the LCD is $2 \cdot 2 \cdot 2 \cdot 3 \cdot x \cdot x \cdot x$, or $24x^3$.**

Extra Example 4

Find the difference $\frac{5}{2x} - \frac{3x}{x-1}$.
$\frac{-6x^2+5x-5}{2x(x-1)}$

Key Question to Ask for Example 4

- In the second step of the example, can you divide out the common factor of $(x + 2)$ on the right side of the equation? Explain. **No; $(x + 2)$ does not appear in the numerator of one of the terms.**

Extra Example 5

Find the difference $\frac{x+3}{x^2-8x+15} - \frac{x+6}{x^2-x-20}$.
$\frac{4x+30}{(x-3)(x-5)(x+4)}$

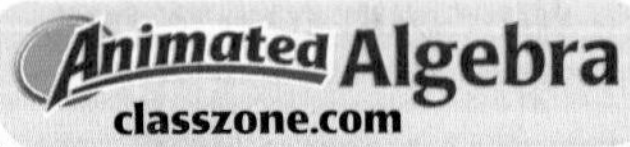

An **Animated Algebra** activity is available online for **Example 5**. This activity is also part of **Power Presentations**.

EXAMPLE 3 Add expressions with different denominators

Find the sum $\frac{9}{8x^2} + \frac{5}{12x^3}$.

$\frac{9}{8x^2} + \frac{5}{12x^3} = \frac{9 \cdot 3x}{8x^2 \cdot 3x} + \frac{5 \cdot 2}{12x^3 \cdot 2}$ **Rewrite fractions using LCD, $24x^3$.**

$= \frac{27x}{24x^3} + \frac{10}{24x^3}$ **Simplify numerators and denominators.**

$= \frac{27x+10}{24x^3}$ **Add fractions.**

EXAMPLE 4 Subtract expressions with different denominators

Find the difference $\frac{10}{3x} - \frac{7x}{x+2}$.

$\frac{10}{3x} - \frac{7x}{x+2} = \frac{10(x+2)}{3x(x+2)} - \frac{7x(3x)}{(x+2)(3x)}$ **Rewrite fractions using LCD, $3x(x + 2)$.**

$= \frac{10(x+2) - 7x(3x)}{3x(x+2)}$ **Subtract fractions.**

$= \frac{-21x^2+10x+20}{3x(x+2)}$ **Simplify numerator.**

EXAMPLE 5 Subtract expressions with different denominators

Find the difference $\frac{x+4}{x^2+3x-10} - \frac{x-1}{x^2+2x-8}$.

$\frac{x+4}{x^2+3x-10} - \frac{x-1}{x^2+2x-8}$

$= \frac{x+4}{(x-2)(x+5)} - \frac{x-1}{(x+4)(x-2)}$ **Factor denominators.**

$= \frac{(x+4)(x+4)}{(x-2)(x+5)(x+4)} - \frac{(x-1)(x+5)}{(x+4)(x-2)(x+5)}$ **Rewrite fractions using LCD, $(x-2)(x+5)(x+4)$.**

$= \frac{(x+4)(x+4) - (x-1)(x+5)}{(x-2)(x+5)(x+4)}$ **Subtract fractions.**

$= \frac{x^2+8x+16-(x^2+4x-5)}{(x-2)(x+5)(x+4)}$ **Find products in numerator.**

$= \frac{4x+21}{(x-2)(x+5)(x+4)}$ **Simplify.**

AVOID ERRORS
Because you are subtracting $x^2 + 4x - 5$ in the numerator, you need to add the opposite of *every* term in $x^2 + 4x - 5$.

 at classzone.com

✓ GUIDED PRACTICE for Examples 3, 4, and 5

Find the sum or difference.

6. $\frac{3}{2x} + \frac{7}{5x^4}$ $\frac{15x^3+14}{10x^4}$

7. $\frac{y}{y+1} + \frac{3}{y+2}$ $\frac{y^2+5y+3}{(y+1)(y+2)}$

8. $\frac{2z-1}{z^2+2z-8} - \frac{z+1}{z^2-4}$ $\frac{z^2-2z-6}{(z+4)(z-2)(z+2)}$

Differentiated Instruction

Auditory Learners Students may find other methods of adding and subtracting fractions easier to recall. In **Example 3**, students can "cross-multiply" to get a numerator of $9 \cdot 12x^3 + 5 \cdot 8x^2$ and then multiply the denominators to get $96x^5$. Students can conclude by simplifying the resulting rational expression, $\frac{9 \cdot 12x^3 + 5 \cdot 8x^2}{96x^5}$, as $\frac{27x+10}{24x^3}$.

See also the *Differentiated Instruction Resources* for more strategies.

EXAMPLE 6 Solve a multi-step problem

BOAT TRAVEL A boat travels 24 kilometers upstream (against the current) and 24 kilometers downstream (with the current) as shown in the diagram. Write an equation that gives the total travel time t (in hours) as a function of the boat's average speed r (in kilometers per hour) in still water. Find the total travel time if the boat's average speed in still water is 10 kilometers per hour.

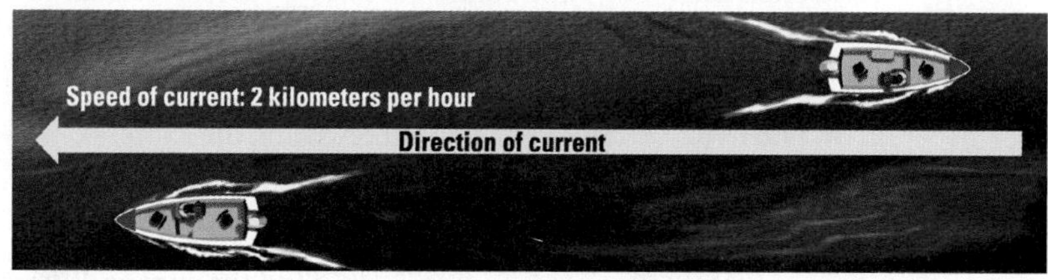

Solution

STEP 1 **Write** a verbal model. Then write an equation.

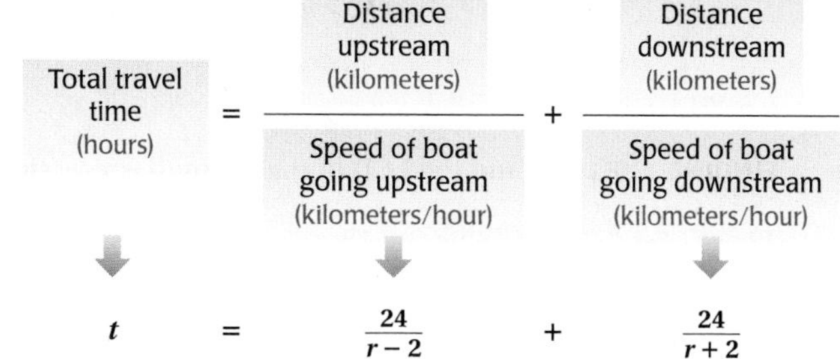

$$\frac{\text{Total travel time (hours)}}{} = \frac{\text{Distance upstream (kilometers)}}{\text{Speed of boat going upstream (kilometers/hour)}} + \frac{\text{Distance downstream (kilometers)}}{\text{Speed of boat going downstream (kilometers/hour)}}$$

$$t = \frac{24}{r-2} + \frac{24}{r+2}$$

COMBINE SPEEDS
When you go upstream, you subtract the speed of the current from the speed at which you travel in still water. When you go downstream, you add the speeds.

STEP 2 **Find** the sum of the expressions on the right side of the equation.

$t = \frac{24}{r-2} + \frac{24}{r+2}$ **Write equation.**

$= \frac{24(r+2)}{(r-2)(r+2)} + \frac{24(r-2)}{(r+2)(r-2)}$ **Rewrite fractions using LCD, $(r-2)(r+2)$.**

$= \frac{24(r+2) + 24(r-2)}{(r-2)(r+2)}$ **Add fractions.**

$= \frac{48r}{(r-2)(r+2)}$ **Simplify.**

STEP 3 **Calculate** the value of t when $r = 10$.

$$t = \frac{48(10)}{(10-2)(10+2)} = \frac{480}{(8)(12)} = \frac{480}{96} = 5$$

▶ The total travel time is 5 hours.

✓ **GUIDED PRACTICE** for Example 6

9. **WHAT IF?** In Example 6, suppose the speed of the current is 3 kilometers per hour. Find the total travel time. **about 5.3 h**

Extra Example 6

A rowing crew rows a boat 18 miles upstream (against the current) and 18 miles downstream (with the current). The speed of the current is 3 miles per hour. Write an equation that gives the boat's total travel time t (in hours) as a function of the boat's average speed r (in miles per hour) in still water. Find the total travel time if the boat's average speed in still water is 5 miles per hour. $t = \frac{36r}{(r-3)(r+3)}$; **11.25 h**

Closing the Lesson

Have students summarize the major points of the lesson and answer the Essential Question: How do you add or subtract rational expressions?

- **Rational expressions can be added or subtracted by using the rules for adding and subtracting rational numbers.**
- **To find the least common denominator (LCD) of two rational expressions, find the product of the factors of each denominator. If the denominators have a common factor, use it just once. If either denominator has repeated factors, the LCD also will have repeated factors.**

When adding or subtracting rational expressions with the same denominator, write the sum or difference of the numerators over the common denominator and simplify. When adding or subtracting rational expressions with different denominators, start by using the LCD to write equivalent rational expressions.

12.6 EXERCISES

HOMEWORK KEY

○ = **WORKED-OUT SOLUTIONS** on p. WS30 for Exs. 7, 29, and 45

★ = **STANDARDIZED TEST PRACTICE** Exs. 2, 32, 44, and 48

SKILL PRACTICE

A

1. **VOCABULARY** Copy and complete: The _?_ of two rational expressions is the product of the factors of their denominators with each common factor used only once. **least common denominator**

2. ★ **WRITING** *Describe* your steps in rewriting the expressions $\frac{1}{x+2}$ and $\frac{2x}{x^2-4}$ so that they have the same denominator. **See margin.**

EXAMPLE 1 on p. 812 for Exs. 3–11

ADDING AND SUBTRACTING EXPRESSIONS Find the sum or difference.

3. $\frac{2}{5x}+\frac{3}{5x}$ $\mathbf{\frac{1}{x}}$

4. $\frac{y+1}{2y}+\frac{5}{2y}$ $\mathbf{\frac{y+6}{2y}}$

5. $\frac{6z}{z^2}-\frac{2z}{z^2}$ $\mathbf{\frac{4}{z}}$

6. $\frac{7}{a+2}-\frac{3a}{a+2}$ $\mathbf{\frac{7-3a}{a+2}}$

7. $\frac{b}{b-3}+\frac{b+1}{b-3}$ $\mathbf{\frac{2b+1}{b-3}}$

8. $\frac{c+2}{c-9}+\frac{c+5}{c-9}$ $\mathbf{\frac{2c+7}{c-9}}$

9. $\frac{7}{m^2+1}-\frac{8}{m^2+1}$ $\mathbf{\frac{-1}{m^2+1}}$

10. $\frac{2n+1}{n^2-16}-\frac{n}{n^2-16}$ $\mathbf{\frac{n+1}{n^2-16}}$

11. $\frac{3r}{r^2+r-7}+\frac{1}{r^2+r-7}$ $\mathbf{\frac{3r+1}{r^2+r-7}}$

EXAMPLE 2 on p. 813 for Exs. 12–17, 32

FINDING THE LCD Find the LCD of the rational expressions.

12. $\frac{1}{24x}, \frac{x+2}{6x^3}$ $\mathbf{24x^3}$

13. $\frac{3}{15v^2}, \frac{v^2-4}{20v^3}$ $\mathbf{60v^3}$

14. $\frac{4w}{w+5}, \frac{w+3}{w-2}$ $\mathbf{(w+5)(w-2)}$

15. $\frac{s-1}{s+2}, \frac{s+2}{s-1}$ $\mathbf{(s+2)(s-1)}$

16. $\frac{1}{t^2-4t}, \frac{6}{t^2-2t-8}$ $\mathbf{t(t+2)(t-4)}$

17. $\frac{u+9}{u^2+8u+7}, \frac{-3}{u^2-2u-3}$ $\mathbf{(u+7)(u+1)(u-3)}$

EXAMPLES 3, 4, and 5 on p. 814 for Exs. 18–31

ERROR ANALYSIS ***Describe*** **and correct the error in finding the sum or difference. 18, 19. See margin.**

18. $\frac{8}{2x+3}-\frac{4x}{x+2}$

$$\frac{8}{2x+3}-\frac{4x}{x+2}=\frac{8-4x}{2x+3-(x+2)}=\frac{8-4x}{2x+3-x-2}=\frac{8-4x}{x+1}$$

19. $\frac{5x}{x-4}+\frac{2}{x+3}$

$$\frac{5x}{x-4}+\frac{2}{x+3}=\frac{5x(x-4)+2(x+3)}{(x-4)(x+3)}=\frac{5x^2-20x+2x+6}{(x-4)(x+3)}=\frac{5x^2-18x+6}{(x-4)(x+3)}$$

ADDING AND SUBTRACTING EXPRESSIONS Find the sum or difference. 20–31. See margin.

20. $\frac{5x}{4}+\frac{2}{5x}$

21. $\frac{13}{3y}+\frac{2}{11y}$

22. $\frac{7}{2z}-\frac{2}{3z^2}$

23. $\frac{7r}{r-2}-\frac{2r}{r-3}$

24. $\frac{s}{5s-2}-\frac{1}{4s+1}$

25. $\frac{c+3}{c-6}+\frac{c}{3c+10}$

26. $\frac{d-5}{d+7}+\frac{d-5}{4d}$

27. $\frac{f+3}{7f}-\frac{3f}{f+4}$

28. $\frac{1}{g^2+5g+6}-\frac{1}{g^2-4}$

29. $\frac{2j}{j^2-1}+\frac{j-1}{j^2-7j+6}$

30. $\frac{k+7}{k^2+6k+9}+\frac{k-5}{k^2-5k-24}$

31. $\frac{v+2}{2v^2-v-15}-\frac{v-2}{v^2+2v-15}$

4 PRACTICE AND APPLY

Assignment Guide

Answer Transparencies available for all exercises

Basic:
Day 1: pp. 816–819
Exs. 1–17, 19–21, 25, 26, 58–62
Day 2: pp. 816–819
Exs. 18, 22–24, 27–35, 42–47, 50–57

Average:
Day 1: pp. 816–819
Exs. 1, 2, 7–17, 19–21, 25, 26, 29, 30, 35, 36, 58–62
Day 2: pp. 816–819
Exs. 18, 22–24, 27–34, 37–40, 42–48, 50–56 even

Advanced:
Day 1: pp. 816–819
Exs. 1, 2, 7–17, 19–21, 25, 26, 35, 36, 58–62
Day 2: pp. 816–819
Exs. 22–24, 27, 28, 31–34, 37, 41–49*, 51–57 odd

Block:
pp. 816–819
Exs. 1, 2, 7–17, 19–21, 25, 26, 29, 30, 35, 36, 58–62 (with 12.5)
pp. 816–819
Exs. 18, 22–24, 27–34, 37–40, 42–48, 50–56 even (with 12.7)

Differentiated Instruction

See *Differentiated Instruction Resources* for suggestions on addressing the needs of a diverse classroom.

Homework Check

For a quick check of student understanding of key concepts, go over the following exercises:

Basic: 8, 20, 23, 25, 42
Average: 10, 21, 24, 26, 44
Advanced: 11, 22, 26, 31, 46

Extra Practice

- Student Edition, p. 946
- Chapter Resource Book: Practice levels A, B, C

Practice Worksheet

An easily-readable reduced practice page (with answers) for this lesson can be found on p. 762C.

2. Write each denominator in factored form: $(x+2)$ and $(x+2)(x-2)$. The least common denominator (LCD) will have all the factors of both denominators, using any common factor only once: the denominator of the second fraction, $(x+2)(x-2)$, is the LCD. Write the first fraction with the LCD by multiplying its numerator and its denominator by $(x-2)$: $\frac{x-2}{(x+2)(x-2)}$.

32. ★ **MULTIPLE CHOICE** Which is a factor of the LCD of $\frac{3}{x^2 - 4x}$ and $\frac{4x}{x + 2}$? **B**

Ⓐ 3 Ⓑ $x - 4$ Ⓒ $4x$ Ⓓ $x - 2$

B 33. **GEOMETRY** The height h of a rectangular prism is given by

$$h = \frac{S}{2(\ell + w)} - \frac{\ell w}{\ell + w}$$

where S is the surface area, ℓ is the length, and w is the width. Find the difference of the expressions on the right side of the equation. $\frac{S - 2\ell w}{2(\ell + w)}$

USING ORDER OF OPERATIONS **Use the order of operations to write the expression as a single rational expression.**

34. $2\left(\frac{x}{x + 1}\right) - 3\left(\frac{x - 4}{x + 2}\right)$ $\frac{-x^2 + 13x + 12}{(x + 1)(x + 2)}$

35. $5\left(\frac{3x}{x - 2} + \frac{4}{x^2 + 6x - 16}\right)$ $\frac{15x^2 + 120x + 20}{(x - 2)(x + 8)}$

36. $\frac{x - 3}{x^2 + 9x + 20} + \frac{5x}{x + 2} \cdot \frac{12}{x + 4}$ $\frac{61x^2 + 299x - 6}{(x + 5)(x + 4)(x + 2)}$

37. $\frac{x + 5}{x - 9} - \frac{3x^2 + 2x - 1}{x + 4} \div \frac{x^2 - 3x - 4}{x^2 - 16}$ $\frac{-3x^2 + 29x - 4}{x - 9}$

WRITING EQUATIONS **For the given hyperbola, write an equation of the form $y = \frac{a}{b}$ where a and b are first-degree polynomials.**

38. $y = \frac{2x + 4}{x - 1}$

39. $y = \frac{-4x - 16}{x + 2}$

40. $y = \frac{-3x - 8}{x + 6}$

38. 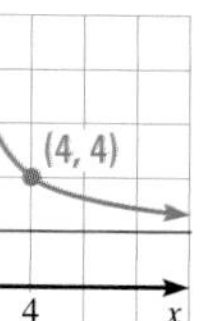

39. 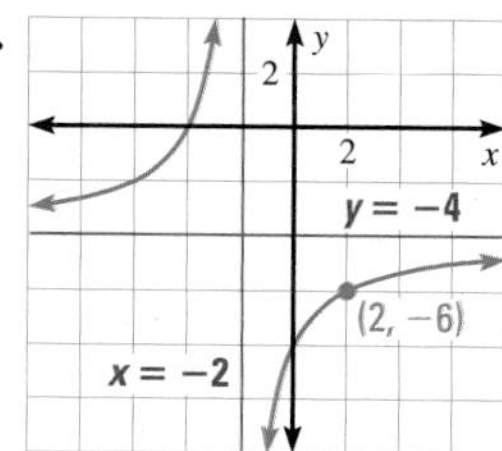

40. 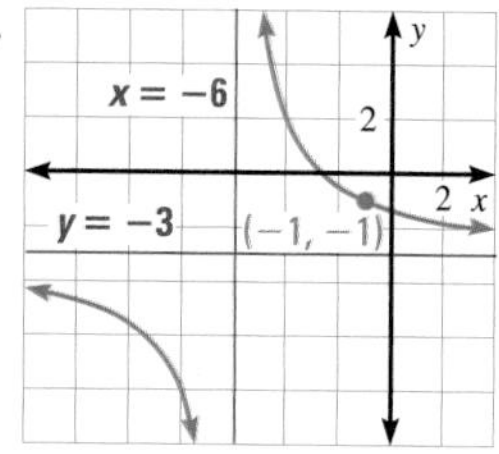

41. **CHALLENGE** Let a, b, c, and d be first-degree polynomials. Find two rational expressions $\frac{a}{b}$ and $\frac{c}{d}$ such that $\frac{a}{b} - \frac{c}{d} = \frac{5x + 7}{(x + 2)(x + 3)}$.

Sample answer: $\frac{-3}{x + 2}, \frac{-8}{x + 3}$

PROBLEM SOLVING

EXAMPLE 6 A on p. 815 for Exs. 42–46

42. **CANOEING** A canoeist travels 16 miles upstream (against the current) and 16 miles downstream (with the current). The speed of the current is 1 mile per hour. Write an equation that gives the total travel time t (in hours) as a function of the canoeist's average speed r (in miles per hour) in still water. Then find the total travel time if the canoeist's average speed in still water is 6 miles per hour. $t = \frac{32r}{(r - 1)(r + 1)}$; about 5.5 h

@HomeTutor for problem solving help at classzone.com

43. **DRIVING** Matt drives 200 miles to another city. On the drive back home, his average speed decreases by 5 miles per hour. Write an equation that gives the total driving time t (in hours) as a function of his average speed r (in miles per hour) when driving to the city. Then find the total driving time if he drives to the city at an average speed of 50 miles per hour. $t = \frac{400r - 1000}{r(r - 5)}$; about 8.4 h

@HomeTutor for problem solving help at classzone.com

Avoiding Common Errors

Exercises 3–11, 20–31 Watch for students who divide out common factors before adding or subtracting. Remind students that they must combine the expressions before they look for common factors in the numerator and denominator.

Exercises 20–31 Students sometimes find the correct LCD but calculate an incorrect numerator for the equivalent rational expression. Suggest that students check their calculations for this type of error.

Teaching Strategy

Exercises 34–37 Before students begin these exercises, you may want to ask them to describe the steps they will take to rewrite each of the exercises. Make sure students know that they must distribute the factor outside the parentheses to each term inside the parentheses.

20. $\frac{25x^2 + 8}{20x}$

21. $\frac{149}{33y}$

22. $\frac{21z - 4}{6z^2}$

23. $\frac{5r^2 - 17r}{(r - 2)(r - 3)}$

24. $\frac{4s^2 - 4s + 2}{(5s - 2)(4s + 1)}$

25. $\frac{4c^2 + 13c + 30}{(c - 6)(3c + 10)}$

26. $\frac{5d^2 - 18d - 35}{4d(d + 7)}$

27. $\frac{-20f^2 + 7f + 12}{7f(f + 4)}$

28. $\frac{-5}{(g + 2)(g + 3)(g - 2)}$

29. $\frac{3j^2 - 12j - 1}{(j - 1)(j + 1)(j - 6)}$

30. $\frac{2k^2 - 3k - 71}{(k - 8)(k + 3)^2}$

31. $\frac{-v^2 + 6v + 20}{(2v + 5)(v - 3)(v + 5)}$

18. Rational expressions are not subtracted by subtracting their numerators and subtracting their denominators. Instead, you must write the expressions with a common denominator and then subtract the numerators over the common denominator; $\frac{8}{2x + 3} - \frac{4x}{x + 2} = \frac{8(x + 2)}{(2x + 3)(x + 2)} - \frac{4x(2x + 3)}{(2x + 3)(x + 2)} = \frac{8x + 16 - 8x^2 - 12x}{(2x + 3)(x + 2)} = \frac{-8x^2 - 4x + 16}{(2x + 3)(x + 2)}$.

19. See Additional Answers beginning on p. AA1.

Study Strategy

Exercises 44, 48 Point out to students that these exercises mimic a type of question often found on standardized tests. Tell them that a useful strategy for these questions is to read all of the parts before starting to answer. For each part, they may want to write a note about how to answer it.

Vocabulary

Exercises 46, 47 You may want to ask students who are familiar with the concepts of resistance and ohms in parallel circuits and with amplitude modulation and frequency modulation in radio broadcasting to explain these concepts in class.

44a. $t = \frac{420{,}000}{(300 - w)(300 + w)}$; 4.7 h

44b. 0; the flying time one way will be half the total flying time only when the flying time against the wind, which is $\frac{700}{300 + w}$, and the flying time with the wind, which is $\frac{700}{300 - w}$, are equal. Because these two rational expressions have equal numerators, they can only be equal if they also have equal denominators: $300 + w = 300 - w$, so $2w = 0$, and $w = 0$.

45a. $\frac{2A^2 + 200A}{3}$; $\frac{7A^2 + 18{,}750A - 205{,}050}{150}$

44. ★ **SHORT RESPONSE** An airplane makes a round trip between two destinations as shown in the diagram. The airplane flies against the wind when traveling west and flies with the wind when traveling east. Assume that the speed of the wind remains constant during each flight.

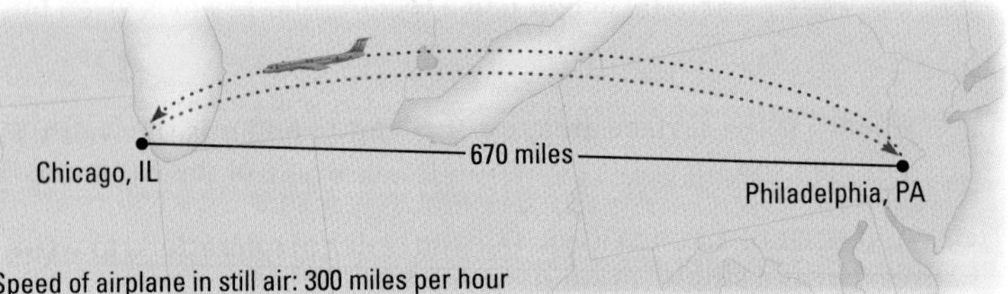

a. **Model** Write an equation that gives the total flying time t (in hours) as a function of the speed w (in miles per hour) of the wind. Then find the total flying time if the speed of the wind is 15 miles per hour. **a, b. See margin.**

b. **Decide** For what value of w does the flying time one way take half as long as the total flying time? *Explain* your reasoning.

(45.) **ELEVATORS** According to the law in one state, the minimum weight W (in pounds) that a passenger elevator must hold is given by

$$W = \frac{2A^2}{3} + \frac{200A}{3} \text{ if } A \le 50 \qquad \text{and} \qquad W = \frac{7A^2}{150} + (125A - 1367) \text{ if } A > 50$$

where A represents the area (in square feet) of the elevator platform.

a. Write the right side of each equation as a single rational expression. **See margin.**

b. What is the minimum weight that an elevator must hold if the area of the platform is 30 square feet? 60 square feet? **2600 lb; 6301 lb**

46. **MULTI-STEP PROBLEM** A parallel electric circuit consists of a power source and several parallel resistors through which electricity can flow. For a parallel circuit with two resistors, let r_1 represent the resistance (in ohms) of one resistor, and let r_2 represent the resistance (in ohms) of the other resistor.

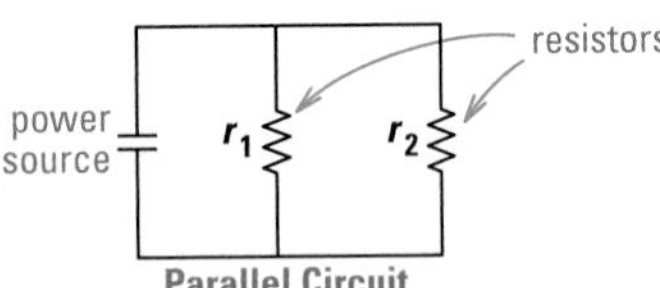

Parallel Circuit

a. **Model** The total resistance r_T is equal to the multiplicative inverse of $\frac{1}{r_1} + \frac{1}{r_2}$. Write $\frac{1}{r_1} + \frac{1}{r_2}$ as a single rational expression. Then write an equation that gives r_T in terms of r_1 and r_2. $\frac{r_2 + r_1}{r_1 r_2}$; $r_T = \frac{r_1 r_2}{r_2 + r_1}$

b. **Calculate** Find the total resistance when one resistor has a resistance of 2 ohms and the other resistor has a resistance of 6 ohms. **1.5 ohms**

B 47. **RADIO STATIONS** Radio stations use either amplitude modulation (AM) broadcasting or frequency modulation (FM) broadcasting. The percent a (in decimal form) of commercial radio stations that used AM broadcasting during the period 1990–2003 can be modeled by

$$a = \frac{2.8 + 0.085x}{5.3 + 0.30x}$$

where x is the number of years since 1990. Write a model that gives the percent f (in decimal form) of commercial radio stations that used FM broadcasting as a function of x. Then approximate the value of f in 2003. $f = \frac{2.5 + 0.215x}{5.3 + 0.30x}$; **about 58%**

○ = **WORKED-OUT SOLUTIONS** on p. WS1 ★ = **STANDARDIZED TEST PRACTICE**

48. ★ **EXTENDED RESPONSE** The axle load for a tow vehicle is the weight (in pounds) that an axle on the vehicle supports. The rear axle load R and the front axle load F are given by the formulas

$$R = \frac{t(w+h)}{w} \quad \text{and} \quad F = \frac{th}{w}$$

where t represents the weight (in pounds) that presses down on the hitch by a trailer and w and h represent the distances (in feet) shown.

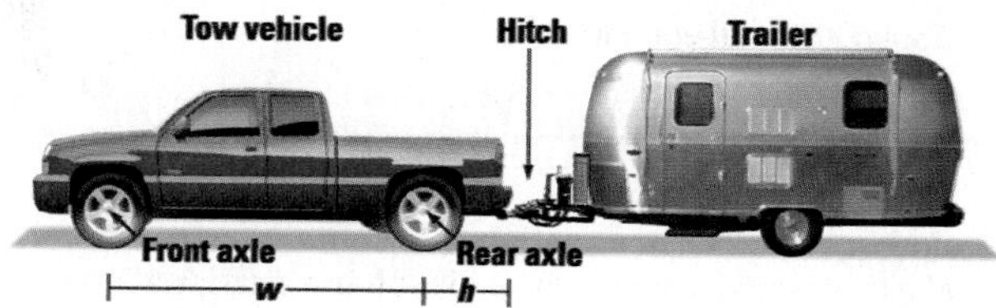

a. **Calculate** For a certain tow vehicle, $t = 300$, $w = 9$, and $h = 3.5$. Find the rear axle load and the front axle load. **$416\frac{2}{3}$ lb, $116\frac{2}{3}$ lb**

b. **Compare** Find the difference of the rear axle load and the front axle load found in part (a). *Compare* your answer with the given value of t. **300 lb; the answers are the same.**

c. **Model** Write an equation that gives t in terms of R and F. *Justify* your answer algebraically. $t = R - F$; $R - F = \frac{t(w+h)}{w} - \frac{th}{w} = \frac{tw + th - th}{w} = \frac{tw}{w} = t$

C 49. **CHALLENGE** You and your friend plan to spend 10 minutes mowing your family's lawn together. You can mow the entire lawn alone in 30 minutes.

a. Write an equation that gives the fraction y of the lawn that you and your friend can mow in 10 minutes as a function of the time t (in minutes) in which your friend can mow the entire lawn alone. $y = \frac{t+30}{3t}$

b. Suppose your friend can mow the entire lawn alone in 20 minutes. Can the entire lawn be mowed if you and your friend work together for 10 minutes? *Explain.* **No; to find the fraction of the lawn that you and your friend can mow in 10 minutes, find the value of y when $t = 20$ in the equation in part (a): $y = \frac{20+30}{3(20)} = \frac{50}{60} = \frac{5}{6}$. You and your friend can mow only $\frac{5}{6}$ of the lawn in 10 minutes.**

MIXED REVIEW

PREVIEW
Prepare for Lesson 12.7 in Exs. 50–57.

Solve the equation or proportion.

50. $-4(f - 5) = -16$ *(p. 148)* **9**

51. $2x + 11 + 3x = 21$ *(p. 148)* **2**

52. $5g - 18 = 4g - 3$ *(p. 154)* **15**

53. $7.5k = 5(2k + 1)$ *(p. 154)* **−2**

54. $\frac{7}{3} = \frac{m}{6}$ *(p. 168)* **14**

55. $\frac{14}{10} = \frac{v}{15}$ *(p. 168)* **21**

56. $x^2 - 9x + 14 = 0$ *(p. 583)* **7, 2**

57. $-7m^2 + 56 = 0$ *(p. 653)* **$\pm 2\sqrt{2}$**

58. **SPORTS** An athlete kicks a football upward from the ground with an initial vertical velocity of 64 feet per second. After how many seconds does the football land on the ground? *(p. 575)* **4 sec**

Factor the expression.

59. $12x^2 - 24x$ *(p. 575)* **$12x(x - 2)$**

60. $x^2 - 9x - 22$ *(p. 583)* **$(x - 11)(x + 2)$**

61. $x^2 + 15x + 56$ *(p. 583)* **$(x + 8)(x + 7)$**

62. $100 - 9x^2$ *(p. 600)* **$(10 - 3x)(10 + 3x)$**

5 ASSESS AND RETEACH

Daily Homework Quiz

Transparency Available

Find the sum or difference.

1. $\frac{4}{2x} + \frac{x+1}{3}$ $\frac{x^2+x+6}{3x}$

2. $\frac{x-6}{x-1} - \frac{x-1}{3x}$ $\frac{2x^2-16x-1}{(x-1)(3x)}$

3. $\frac{2x}{x^2+6x-16} + \frac{x+3}{x^2-3x+2}$ $\frac{3x^2+9x+24}{(x+8)(x-2)(x-1)}$

4. You hike 4 miles up a hill and then 4 miles back down the hill. Your speed hiking up the hill is 1.5 miles per hour less than your speed hiking back down. Find the total time of your hike if you hiked 2.5 miles per hour up the hill. **2.6 h**

Available at **classzone.com**

Diagnosis/Remediation

- Practice A, B, C in Chapter Resource Book
- Study Guide in Chapter Resource Book
- Practice Workbook
- @HomeTutor

Challenge

Additional challenge is available in the Chapter Resource Book.

12.7 Solve Rational Equations

1 PLAN AND PREPARE

Warm-Up Exercises

Transparency Available

Solve the equation or proportion.

1. $3x + 7 = 22$ **5**
2. $\frac{6}{m} = \frac{3}{7}$ **14**
3. Daniel mixes 5 measures of Kenyan beans to every 7 measures of Jamaican beans to make a blend. If he uses 21 measures of Jamaican beans, how many measures of Kenyan beans should he use? **15 measures**

Notetaking Guide

Transparency Available

Promotes interactive learning and notetaking skills.

Pacing

Basic: 1 day

Average: 1 day

Advanced: 1 day

Block: 0.5 block with 12.6

- See *Teaching Guide/Lesson Plan.*

2 FOCUS AND MOTIVATE

Essential Question

Big Idea 3, p. 763

How do you solve a rational equation? **Tell students they will learn how to answer this question by using cross products and the LCD.**

NCTM STANDARDS

Standard 2: Analyze situations using algebraic symbols

Standard 6: Solve problems in math and other contexts

Before	You simplified rational expressions.
Now	You will solve rational equations.
Why?	So you can calculate a hockey statistic, as in Ex. 31.

Key Vocabulary
- **rational equation**
- **cross product,** *p. 168*
- **extraneous solution,** *p. 730*
- **least common denominator (LCD) of rational expressions,** *p. 813*

A **rational equation** is an equation that contains one or more rational expressions. One method for solving a rational equation is to use the cross products property. You can use this method when both sides of the equation are single rational expressions.

REVIEW CROSS PRODUCTS

For help with using the cross products property, see p. 168.

EXAMPLE 1 Use the cross products property

Solve $\frac{6}{x+4} = \frac{x}{2}$. Check your solution.

$\frac{6}{x+4} = \frac{x}{2}$	Write original equation.
$12 = x^2 + 4x$	Cross products property
$0 = x^2 + 4x - 12$	Subtract 12 from each side.
$0 = (x + 6)(x - 2)$	Factor polynomial.
$x + 6 = 0$ *or* $x - 2 = 0$	Zero-product property
$x = -6$ *or* $x = 2$	Solve for x.

▶ The solutions are −6 and 2.

CHECK **If $x = -6$:** $\frac{6}{-6+4} \stackrel{?}{=} \frac{-6}{2}$, $-3 = -3$ ✓ **If $x = 2$:** $\frac{6}{2+4} \stackrel{?}{=} \frac{2}{2}$, $1 = 1$ ✓

GUIDED PRACTICE for Example 1

Solve the equation. Check your solution.

1. $\frac{5}{y-2} = \frac{y}{3}$ **−3, 5**
2. $\frac{2}{z+5} = \frac{z}{7}$ **−7, 2**

USING THE LCD Given an equation with fractional coefficients such as $\frac{2}{3}x + \frac{1}{6} = \frac{3}{4}$, you can multiply each side by the least common denominator (LCD), 12. The equation becomes $8x + 2 = 9$, which you may find easier to solve than the original equation. You can use this method to solve a rational equation.

Resource Planning Guide

Chapter Resource Book
- Teaching Guide/Lesson Plan
- Practice levels A, B, C
- Study Guide
- Catch-up for Absent Students
- Problem Solving Workshop
- Challenge

Workbooks
- Notetaking Guide
- Practice Workbook

Teaching Options
- **Power Presentations** provides dynamic electronic teaching resources for the classroom.
- **Activity Generator** provides editable activities for all ability levels.

Interactive Technology
- Easy Planner
- Power Presentations
- Activity Generator
- Animated Algebra
- Test Generator
- Online Quiz
- eWorkbook
- eEdition
- @HomeTutor

Resources for English Learners
- Spanish Study Guide
- Multi-Language Visual Glossary
- Student Resources in Spanish

See also the *Differentiated Instruction Resources* for more strategies for meeting individual needs.

EXAMPLE 2 Multiply by the LCD

Solve $\frac{x}{x-2} + \frac{1}{5} = \frac{2}{x-2}$. Check your solution.

$$\frac{x}{x-2} + \frac{1}{5} = \frac{2}{x-2}$$ **Write original equation.**

$$\frac{x}{x-2} \cdot 5(x-2) + \frac{1}{5} \cdot 5(x-2) = \frac{2}{x-2} \cdot 5(x-2)$$ **Multiply by LCD, $5(x - 2)$.**

$$\frac{x \cdot 5\cancel{(x-2)}}{\cancel{x-2}} + \frac{\cancel{5}(x-2)}{\cancel{5}} = \frac{2 \cdot 5\cancel{(x-2)}}{\cancel{x-2}}$$ **Multiply and divide out common factors.**

$$5x + x - 2 = 10$$ **Simplify.**

$$6x - 2 = 10$$ **Combine like terms.**

$$6x = 12$$ **Add 2 to each side.**

$$x = 2$$ **Divide each side by 6.**

AVOID ERRORS
Be sure to identify the excluded values for the rational expressions in the original equation.

The solution appears to be 2, but the expressions $\frac{x}{x-2}$ and $\frac{2}{x-2}$ are undefined when $x = 2$. So, 2 is an extraneous solution.

▶ There is no solution.

EXAMPLE 3 Factor to find the LCD

Solve $\frac{3}{x-7} + 1 = \frac{8}{x^2 - 9x + 14}$. Check your solution.

Solution

Write each denominator in factored form. The LCD is $(x - 2)(x - 7)$.

$$\frac{3}{x-7} + 1 = \frac{8}{(x-2)(x-7)}$$

$$\frac{3}{x-7} \cdot (x-2)(x-7) + 1 \cdot (x-2)(x-7) = \frac{8}{(x-2)(x-7)} \cdot (x-2)(x-7)$$

$$\frac{3(x-2)\cancel{(x-7)}}{\cancel{x-7}} + (x-2)(x-7) = \frac{8\cancel{(x-2)}\cancel{(x-7)}}{\cancel{(x-2)}\cancel{(x-7)}}$$

$$3(x-2) + (x^2 - 9x + 14) = 8$$

$$x^2 - 6x + 8 = 8$$

$$x^2 - 6x = 0$$

$$x(x-6) = 0$$

$$x = 0 \text{ or } x - 6 = 0$$

$$x = 0 \text{ or } \quad x = 6$$

▶ The solutions are 0 and 6.

CHECK If $x = 0$:

$$\frac{3}{0-7} + 1 \stackrel{?}{=} \frac{8}{0^2 - 9 \cdot 0 + 14}$$

$$\frac{4}{7} = \frac{4}{7} \checkmark$$

If $x = 6$:

$$\frac{3}{6-7} + 1 \stackrel{?}{=} \frac{8}{6^2 - 9 \cdot 6 + 14}$$

$$-2 = -2 \checkmark$$

Motivating the Lesson

You and a friend work together during the summer to mow and trim lawns. You know that you can finish the work alone twice as fast as when your friend works alone. If you know the time it takes the two of you to complete a job together, you can write an equation to find the amount of time it would take you to do the job alone.

3 TEACH

Extra Example 1

Solve $\frac{8}{x+6} = \frac{x}{2}$. Check your solution. **−8 and 2; both solutions check.**

Key Question to Ask for Example 1

- When is it appropriate to use cross products to solve a rational equation? **Use cross products if both sides of the equation are single rational expressions.**

Extra Example 2

Solve $\frac{2x}{x+3} + \frac{1}{3} = \frac{-6}{x+3}$. Check your solution. **There is no solution. The solution appears to be −3, but the expressions $\frac{2x}{x+3}$ and $\frac{-6}{x+3}$ are undefined when $x = -3$.**

Extra Example 3

Solve $\frac{4}{x-1} + 1 = \frac{-10}{x^2 - 9x + 8}$. Check your solution. **−2 and 7; both solutions check.**

Differentiated Instruction

Visual Learners Teach students to use the factored form as a way to visualize the solution. In **Example 3**, first visualize $x^2 - 9x + 14$ in the factored form $(x - 2)(x - 7)$. Next visualize $\frac{3}{x-7}$ as $\frac{3}{x-7} \cdot 1$, or $\frac{3}{x-7} \cdot \frac{x-2}{x-2}$. Finally, the constant 1 is the fraction $\frac{(x-2)(x-7)}{(x-2)(x-7)}$. Now that all of the fractions have the same denominator, the numerators can be used to write the equation $3(x - 2) + (x - 2)(x - 7) = 8$ which can be solved for x.

See also the *Differentiated Instruction Resources* for more strategies.

Extra Example 4

You are mixing a bug repellent solution for your plants. Your mixture contains 12 units of jojoba oil and water in equal parts. You want to make a solution that is 70% jojoba oil. How many units of jojoba oil do you need to add to the solution? **8 units**

Key Questions to Ask for Example 4

- Why do you write the verbal model with the number of pints of yellow paint in the mixture as the numerator of the expression and the number of total pints in the paint mixture as the denominator of the expression? **You need to compare the amount of yellow paint in the mixture to the total amount of paint in the mixture since you want the total mixture to be 80% yellow.**

Closing the Lesson

Have students summarize the major points of the lesson and answer the Essential Question: How do you solve a rational equation?

- **Use cross products and the LCD to solve rational equations.**
- **Check for excluded values.**

If both sides of an equation are single rational expressions, use cross products and then solve for the variable. If an equation has fractional coefficients, multiply each term on each side of the equation by the LCD. Then solve the resulting equation for the variable. If the result is an excluded value, it is extraneous and not a solution.

EXAMPLE 4 Solve a multi-step problem

PAINT MIXING You have an 8 pint mixture of paint that is made up of equal amounts of yellow paint and blue paint. To create a certain shade of green, you need a paint mixture that is 80% yellow. How many pints of yellow paint do you need to add to the mixture?

ANOTHER WAY
For an alternative method for solving the problem in Example 4, turn to page 827 for the **Problem Solving Workshop**.

Solution

Because the amount of yellow paint equals the amount of blue paint, the mixture has 4 pints of yellow paint. Let p represent the number of pints of yellow paint that you need to add.

STEP 1 **Write** a verbal model. Then write an equation.

$$\frac{\text{Pints of yellow paint in mixture} + \text{Pints of yellow paint needed}}{\text{Pints of paint in mixture} + \text{Pints of yellow paint needed}} = \text{Desired percent yellow in mixture}$$

$$\frac{4+p}{8+p} = 0.8$$

STEP 2 **Solve** the equation.

$\frac{4+p}{8+p} = 0.8$	Write equation.
$4 + p = 0.8(8 + p)$	Cross products property
$4 + p = 6.4 + 0.8p$	Distributive property
$0.2p = 2.4$	Rewrite equation.
$p = 12$	Solve for p.

▶ You need to add 12 pints of yellow paint.

CHECK	
$\frac{4+p}{8+p} = 0.8$	Write original equation.
$\frac{4+12}{8+12} \stackrel{?}{=} 0.8$	Substitute 12 for p.
$\frac{16}{20} \stackrel{?}{=} 0.8$	Simplify numerator and denominator.
$0.8 = 0.8$ ✓	Write fraction as decimal. Solution checks.

✓ **GUIDED PRACTICE** for Examples 2, 3, and 4

Solve the equation. Check your solution.

3. $\frac{a}{a+4} + \frac{1}{3} = \frac{-12}{a+4}$ **−10**

4. $\frac{n}{n-11} - 1 = \frac{22}{n^2 - 5n - 66}$ **−4**

5. **WHAT IF?** In Example 4, suppose you need a paint mixture that is 75% yellow. How many pints of yellow paint do you need to add to the mixture? **8 pints**

12.7 EXERCISES

HOMEWORK KEY ○ = **WORKED-OUT SOLUTIONS** on p. WS31 for Exs. 7, 15, and 33
★ = **STANDARDIZED TEST PRACTICE** Exs. 2, 24, 28, and 35

SKILL PRACTICE

A

1. **VOCABULARY** The equation $\frac{3}{x-1} = \frac{7}{x} + 4$ is an example of a(n) __?__ . **rational equation**

2. ★ **WRITING** *Describe* two methods for solving a rational equation. Which method can you use to solve any kind of rational equation? *Explain.* **See margin.**

EXAMPLE 1 on p. 820 for Exs. 3–13, 24

SOLVING EQUATIONS Solve the equation. Check your solution.

3. $\frac{5}{r} = \frac{r}{20}$ **±10**
4. $\frac{3}{s-13} = \frac{s}{10}$ **−2, 15**
5. $\frac{2}{t} = \frac{10}{t-6}$ $-1\frac{1}{2}$
6. $\frac{2}{c+3} = \frac{-5}{c-1}$ $-1\frac{6}{7}$
7. $\frac{2m}{m+4} = \frac{3}{m-1}$ $-1\frac{1}{2}$, **4**
8. $\frac{n-3}{n-6} = \frac{n+1}{n+5}$ $1\frac{2}{7}$
9. $\frac{w}{2} = \frac{15}{w+1}$ **−6, 5**
10. $\frac{2x}{4-x} = \frac{x}{x-4}$ **0**
11. $\frac{2y}{y-3} = \frac{24}{y}$ **6**

ERROR ANALYSIS *Describe* and correct the error in solving the equation. **12, 13. See margin.**

12. $\frac{x+1}{2x+2} = \frac{3}{2x}$

$\frac{x+1}{2x+2} = \frac{3}{2x}$

$(x+1)2x = 3(2x+2)$

$2x^2 + 2x = 6x + 6$

$2x^2 - 4x - 6 = 0$

$2(x-3)(x+1) = 0$

$x - 3 = 0$ or $x + 1 = 0$

$x = 3$ or $x = -1$

The solutions are 3 and −1.

13. $\frac{4x+1}{8x-1} = \frac{3}{5}$

$\frac{4x+1}{8x-1} = \frac{3}{5}$

$5(4x+1) = 3(8x-1)$

$20x + 1 = 24x - 3$

$1 = 4x - 3$

$4 = 4x$

$1 = x$

The solution is 1.

EXAMPLES 2 and 3 on p. 821 for Exs. 14–23

SOLVING EQUATIONS Solve the equation. Check your solution.

14. $\frac{6x}{x-11} + 1 = \frac{3}{x-11}$ **2**
15. $\frac{z}{z+7} - 3 = \frac{-1}{z+7}$ **−10**
16. $\frac{a+7}{a+4} - 1 = \frac{a+10}{2a+8}$ **no solution**
17. $\frac{1}{b+3} + 2 = \frac{b^2-3}{b^2+12b+27}$ **−22**
18. $\frac{m}{m-2} - \frac{3m}{m-4} = \frac{-2m+2}{m^2-6m+8}$ **1**
19. $\frac{3n}{n+1} = \frac{12}{n^2-1} + \frac{n+4}{n-1}$ $2 \pm 2\sqrt{3}$
20. $\frac{3}{p-1} - \frac{2}{p-1} = \frac{-6}{p^2-3p+2}$ **−4**
21. $\frac{5}{q+4} = \frac{q}{q-3} + \frac{2q-27}{q^2+q-12}$ **no solution**
22. $\frac{r+2}{r^2+6r-7} = \frac{8}{r^2+3r-4}$ **−6, 8**
23. $\frac{9}{s^2-4} = \frac{4-5s}{s-2}$ $-\frac{1}{5}$, **−1**

24. ★ **OPEN-ENDED** Write a rational equation that can be solved using the cross products property. Then solve the equation. ***Sample answer:*** $\frac{x}{x+1} = \frac{2}{x+3}$; **−2, 1**

4 PRACTICE AND APPLY

Assignment Guide

Answer Transparencies available for all exercises

Basic:
Day 1: EP p. 946 Exs. 43–48
pp. 823–826
Exs. 1–8, 12–19, 24–26, 31–35, 39–53 odd

Average:
Day 1: pp. 823–826
Exs. 1, 2, 7–13, 19–29, 31–37, 40–52 even

Advanced:
Day 1: pp. 823–826
Exs. 1, 2, 8–11, 20–38*, 40–52 even

Block:
pp. 823–826
Exs. 1, 2, 7–13, 19–29, 31–37, 40–52 even (with 12.6)

Differentiated Instruction

See *Differentiated Instruction Resources* for suggestions on addressing the needs of a diverse classroom.

Homework Check

For a quick check of student understanding of key concepts, go over the following exercises:

Basic: 6, 14, 18, 31, 32
Average: 8, 20, 22, 32, 33
Advanced: 10, 21, 23, 33, 34

Extra Practice

- Student Edition, p. 946
- Chapter Resource Book: Practice levels A, B, C

Practice Worksheet

An easily-readable reduced practice page (with answers) for this lesson can be found on p. 762C.

2. Method 1: Use the cross products property, Method 2: Multiply each side of the equation by the LCD of all the rational expressions in the equation. Method 2 can be used for any rational equation, but Method 1 can be used only for rational equations for which both sides are single rational expressions.

12. The solutions must be checked in the original equation. The solution $x = -1$ is extraneous because it is an excluded value for the original equation. The correct solution is 3.

13. The distributive property must be used to find the product of 5 and $(4x + 1)$; $5(4x + 1) = 3(8x - 1)$, $20x + 5 = 24x - 3$, $8 = 4x$, $2 = x$. The solution is 2.

Avoiding Common Errors

Exercises 3–11 Some students may multiply the numerators and multiply the denominators of the two expressions rather than find the cross products. Discuss with students when they multiply pairs of numerators and pairs of denominators and when they find cross products.

Exercises 14–21 Remind students that they must multiply the LCD by each term on both sides of an equation.

Teaching Strategy

Exercise 26 To get students started on this exercise, ask them how they can write the left side of the equation as a single rational expression.

25. All real numbers except 2; 2; two fractions with equal denominators must also have equal numerators, so $x = 2$, and the denominator of both fractions is $2 - a$. The equation has this one solution as long as the denominator $2 - a$ is not 0; so, the equation has no solution when $a = 2$.

27b.

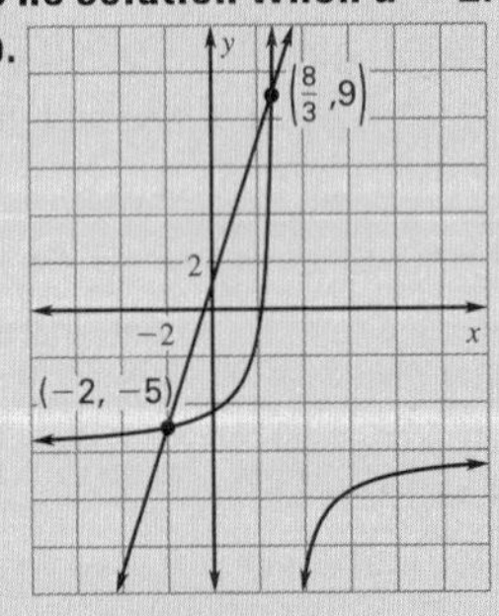

29. No; suppose that $\frac{x+a}{x+1+a} = \frac{x}{x+1}$. Then, using the cross products property, $(x+1)(x+a) = x(x+1+a)$; $x^2 + xa + x + a = x^2 + x + xa$; $x^2 + x(a+1) + a = x^2 + x(1+a)$. Then, subtracting $x^2 + x(1+a)$ from both sides gives the result $a = 0$; so, the only value of a for which the equation is true is 0.

B

25. **REASONING** Consider the equation $\frac{2}{x-a} = \frac{x}{x-a}$ where a is a real number. For what value(s) of a does the equation have exactly one solution? no solution? *Explain* your answers. **See margin.**

26. **USING ANOTHER METHOD** Another way to solve a rational equation is to write each side of the equation as a single rational expression and then use the cross products property. Use this method to solve the equation $\frac{x}{x+1} + \frac{x-2}{2} = \frac{2x-1}{4}$. **3**

27. **SOLVING SYSTEMS OF EQUATIONS** Consider the following system:

$$y = 3x + 1$$

$$y = \frac{-5}{x-3} - 6$$

 a. Solve the system algebraically. $\left(\frac{8}{3}, 9\right), (-2, -5)$

 b. Check your solution by graphing the equations. **See margin.**

28. ★ **MULTIPLE CHOICE** Let a be a real number. How many solutions does the equation $\frac{2}{x-a} = \frac{1}{x+a} + \frac{2a}{x^2-a^2}$ have? **A**

 (A) Zero (B) One (C) Two (D) Infinitely many

29. **REASONING** Is the expression $\frac{x+a}{x+1+a}$ ever equivalent to $\frac{x}{x+1}$ for some nonzero value of a? *Justify* your answer algebraically. **See margin.**

C

30. **CHALLENGE** Let a and b be real numbers. The solutions of the equation $ax + b = \frac{30}{x+2} - 1$ are -8 and 8. What are the values of a and b? *Explain* your answer.
$a = \frac{1}{2}$, $b = -2$. *Sample answer:* Replacing x in the equation with -8 and then again with 8 gives two equations in two variables, a and b. Solving this system of two equations yields $a = \frac{1}{2}$ and $b = -2$.

PROBLEM SOLVING

EXAMPLE 4 A
on p. 822
for Exs. 31–34

31. **ICE HOCKEY** In ice hockey, a goalie's save percentage (in decimal form) is the number of shots blocked by a goalie divided by the number of shots made by an opposing team. Suppose a goalie has blocked 160 out of 200 shots. How many consecutive shots does the goalie need to block in order to raise the save percentage to 0.840? **50 consecutive shots**

@HomeTutor for problem solving help at classzone.com

32. **RUNNING TIMES** You are running a 6000 meter charity race. Your average speed in the first half of the race is 50 meters per minute faster than your average speed in the second half. You finish the race in 27 minutes. What is your average speed in the second half of the race? **200 m/min**

@HomeTutor for problem solving help at classzone.com

○ = WORKED-OUT SOLUTIONS on p. WS1 ★ = STANDARDIZED TEST PRACTICE

33. **CLEANING SOLUTIONS** You have a cleaning solution that consists of 2 cups of vinegar and 7 cups of water. You need a cleaning solution that consists of 5 parts water and 1 part vinegar in order to clean windows. How many cups of water do you need to add to your cleaning solution so that you can use it to clean windows? **3 c**

34. **MULTI-STEP PROBLEM** Working together, a painter and an assistant can paint a certain room in 2 hours. The painter can paint the room alone in half the time it takes the assistant to paint the room alone. Let t represent the time (in hours) that the painter can paint the room alone.

a. Copy and complete the table.

Person	Fraction of room painted each hour	Time (hours)	Fraction of room painted
Painter	$\frac{1}{t}$	2	? $\frac{2}{3}$
Assistant	? $\frac{1}{2t}$	2	? $\frac{1}{3}$

b. *Explain* why the sum of the expressions in the fourth column of the table must be 1. **See margin.**

c. Write a rational equation that you can use to find the time that the painter takes to paint the room alone. Then solve the equation. $\frac{2}{t} + \frac{1}{t} = 1$; **3 h**

d. How long does the assistant take to paint the room alone? **6 h**

B **35.** ★ **EXTENDED RESPONSE** You and your sister can rake a neighbor's front lawn together in 30 minutes. Your sister takes 1.5 times as long as you to rake the lawn by herself.

a. Solve Write an equation that you can use to find the time t (in minutes) you take to rake the lawn by yourself. Then solve the equation. $\frac{30}{t} + \frac{30}{1.5t} = 1$; **50 min**

b. Compare With more experience, both of you can now rake the lawn together in 20 minutes, and your sister can rake the lawn alone in the same amount of time as you. Tell how you would change the equation in part (a) in order to describe this situation. Then solve the equation. **Change each 30 to 20, and change 1.5 to 1; 40 min.**

c. Explain *Explain* why your solution of the equation in part (b) makes sense. Then justify your explanation algebraically for any given amount of time that both of you rake the lawn together. **See margin.**

36. **TELEVISION** The average time t (in minutes) that a person in the United States watched television per day during the period 1950–2000 can be modeled by

$$t = \frac{265 + 8.85x}{1 + 0.0114x}$$

where x is the number of years since 1950.

a. Approximate the year in which a person watched television for an average of 6 hours per day. **1970**

b. About how many years had passed when the average time a person spent watching television per day increased from 5 hours to 7 hours? **about 32 yr**

Study Strategy

Exercise 33 Some students may prefer one of the alternative methods, shown on pages 827–828, for solving this problem. Suggest that students make themselves familiar with the three methods (Example 4 on page 822 and the two alternative methods), and identify which method they prefer.

34b. The expressions in the fourth column represent the fractions of the room painted by each person in 2 hours. Because the painter and assistant can paint the whole room in 2 hours, the sum of the fractions must be 1 (one whole room).

35c. Because you now both rake at the same rate, whenever you work together, the time it takes to rake a portion of the lawn will be half the time it takes either of you to rake that portion alone. Suppose you rake together for m minutes. Then you each rake $\frac{m}{40}$ of the lawn, and together you rake $\frac{m}{40} + \frac{m}{40} = \frac{2m}{40} = \frac{m}{20}$ of the lawn. To rake $\frac{m}{20}$ of the lawn alone would take you $2m$ minutes.

5 ASSESS AND RETEACH

Daily Homework Quiz

Transparency Available

Solve the equation.

1. $\frac{7}{x-4} = \frac{x}{3}$ **−3 and 7**
2. $\frac{x+9}{x+6} - 2 = \frac{x+12}{2x+12}$ **no solution**
3. $\frac{3}{x-2} + 1 = \frac{8}{x^2+x-6}$ **−5 and 1**
4. You have a 6-ounce spice blend that is made up of equal parts of basil and oregano. A recipe calls for a blend that is 60% basil. How many ounces of basil do you need to add to the blend? **1.5 oz**

Online Quiz

Available at **classzone.com**

Diagnosis/Remediation

- Practice A, B, C in Chapter Resource Book
- Study Guide in Chapter Resource Book
- Practice Workbook
- @HomeTutor

Challenge

Additional challenge is available in the Chapter Resource Book.

Quiz

An easily-readable reduced copy of the quiz (with answers) on Lessons 12.5–12.7 from the Assessment Book can be found on p. 762F.

37. From 8 psi to 7 psi; substitute the given psi values for *p* in the given equation and then solve for *a*: for $p = 10$, $a \approx 10{,}722$; for $p = 9$, $a \approx 13{,}536$; for $p = 8$, $a \approx 16{,}600$; for $p = 7$, $a \approx 19{,}948$. The change in altitude when the atmospheric pressure changes from 10 psi to 9 psi is about $13{,}536 - 10{,}722 = 2814$, and the change in altitude when the atmospheric pressure changes from 8 psi to 7 psi is about $19{,}948 - 16{,}600 = 3348$.

37. **SCIENCE** Atmospheric pressure, measured in pounds per square inch (psi), is the pressure exerted on an object by the weight of the atmosphere above the object. The atmospheric pressure p (in psi) can be modeled by

$$p = \frac{14.55(56{,}267 - a)}{55{,}545 + a}$$

where a is the altitude (in feet). Is the change in altitude greater when the atmospheric pressure changes from 10 psi to 9 psi or from 8 psi to 7 psi? *Explain* your answer. **See margin.**

C 38. **CHALLENGE** Butterfat makes up about 1% of the volume of milk in 1% milk. Butterfat can make up no more than 0.2% of the volume of milk in skim milk. A container holds 15 fluid ounces of 1% milk. How many fluid ounces of butterfat must be removed in order for the milk to be considered skim milk? Round your answer to the nearest hundredth. **0.12 fl oz**

MIXED REVIEW

PREVIEW Prepare for Lesson 13.1 in Exs. 39–44.

Write the fraction as a decimal and as a percent. Round decimals to the nearest thousandth. Round percents to the nearest tenth of a percent. *(p. 916)*

39. $\frac{1}{4}$ **0.25, 25%**
40. $\frac{1}{8}$ **0.125, 12.5%**
41. $\frac{7}{10}$ **0.7, 70%**
42. $\frac{24}{25}$ **0.96, 96%**
43. $\frac{25}{30}$ **0.833, 83.3%**
44. $\frac{7}{2}$ **3.5, 350%**

Evaluate the expression.

45. $(9^2 - 7) \div 2$ *(p. 8)* **37**
46. $6[4 - (16 - 14)^2]$ *(p. 8)* **0**
47. $\sqrt{289}$ *(p. 110)* **17**
48. $\pm\sqrt{1600}$ *(p. 110)* **±40**
49. $\frac{3^2}{3^{-7}}$ *(p. 495)* **19,683**
50. $\frac{4^2}{4^5}$ *(p. 495)* $\frac{1}{64}$
51. $\left(-\frac{1}{8}\right)^3$ *(p. 495)* $-\frac{1}{512}$
52. $\frac{1.61 \times 10^{-7}}{2.3 \times 10^{-3}}$ *(p. 512)* 7×10^{-5}
53. $(1.2 \times 10^6)^2$ *(p. 512)* 1.44×10^{12}

QUIZ for Lessons 12.5–12.7

Find the product or quotient. *(p. 802)*

1. $\frac{5}{8x^2} \cdot \frac{4x^3}{15}$ $\frac{x}{6}$
2. $\frac{3y^2 + 6y}{y^2 - 16} \div \frac{y^2}{y-4}$ $\frac{3(y+2)}{y(y+4)}$

Find the sum or difference. *(p. 812)*

3. $\frac{8a}{a+11} - \frac{5a-1}{a+11}$ $\frac{3a+1}{a+11}$
4. $\frac{6n}{n+3} + \frac{n-1}{n^2+5n+6}$ $\frac{6n^2+13n-1}{(n+3)(n+2)}$

Solve the equation. Check your solution. *(p. 820)*

5. $\frac{2z}{z+5} = \frac{z}{z-3}$ **0, 11**
6. $\frac{2x}{x} + \frac{3-x}{x+1} = \frac{-4}{x^2+x}$ **−4**
7. **BATTING AVERAGES** A softball player's batting average is the number of hits divided by the number of times at bat. A softball player has a batting average of .200 after 90 times at bat. How many consecutive hits does the player need in order to raise the batting average to .250? *(p. 820)* **6 hits**

EXTRA PRACTICE for Lesson 12.7, p. 949

ONLINE QUIZ at classzone.com

Using ALTERNATIVE METHODS

Another Way to Solve Example 4, page 822

MULTIPLE REPRESENTATIONS In Example 4 on page 822, you saw how to solve a problem about mixing paint by using a rational equation. You can also solve the problem by using a table or by reinterpreting the problem.

PROBLEM

PAINT MIXING You have an 8 pint mixture of paint that is made up of equal amounts of yellow paint and blue paint. To create a certain shade of green, you need a paint mixture that is 80% yellow. How many pints of yellow paint do you need to add to the mixture?

METHOD 1

Use a Table One alternative approach is to use a table.

The mixture has 8 pints of paint. Because the mixture has an equal amount of yellow paint and blue paint, the mixture has $8 \div 2 = 4$ pints of yellow paint.

STEP 1 **Make** a table that shows the percent of the mixture that is yellow paint after you add various amounts of yellow paint.

Yellow paint (pints)	Paint in mixture (pints)	Percent of mixture that is yellow paint
4	8	$\frac{4}{8} = 50\%$
6	10	$\frac{6}{10} = 60\%$
8	12	$\frac{8}{12} \approx 67\%$
10	14	$\frac{10}{14} \approx 71\%$
12	16	$\frac{12}{16} = 75\%$
14	18	$\frac{14}{18} \approx 78\%$
15	19	$\frac{15}{19} \approx 79\%$
16	20	$\frac{16}{20} = 80\%$

A mixture with 6 pints of yellow paint is the result of adding 2 pints of yellow paint to the mixture.

This amount of yellow paint gives you the percent yellow you want.

STEP 2 **Find** the number of pints of yellow paint needed. Subtract the number of pints of yellow paint already in the mixture from the total number of pints of yellow paint you have: $16 - 4 = 12$.

▸ You need to add 12 pints of yellow paint.

Alternative Strategy

Example 4 on page 822 can be solved by using a table or by reinterpreting the problem. When using a table, students should be careful to organize the table to include all existing data and to show all of the data they need to solve the problem. Reinterpreting the problem as a ratio allows students to write an equation whose solution has fewer steps than solving a rational equation.

Avoiding Common Errors

In Method 1, some students may forget to perform Step 2 after they have found the percent of the mixture that is yellow paint. Remind students that the original mixture already contains some yellow paint, and that they need to subtract this amount from the total amount needed.

Avoiding Common Errors

In Step 1, some students may think that $\frac{4}{5}$ to $\frac{1}{5}$ means the ratio is 4 : 5. It may help these students to ask how many pints of yellow paint would be in a mixture that contains 5 pints of yellow and blue paint, given the ratio of 4 pints of yellow paint to 1 pint of blue paint.

1. See Additional Answers beginning on p. AA1.

2. Because Jill already has \$1000 in the mutual fund she only needs to add \$2250 − \$1000 = \$1250 to the account.

3, 5. See Additional Answers beginning on p. AA1.

METHOD 2 **Reinterpret Problem** Another alternative approach is to reinterpret the problem.

STEP 1 **Reinterpret** the problem. A mixture with 80% yellow paint means that $\frac{4}{5}$ of the mixture is yellow and $\frac{1}{5}$ of the mixture is blue. So, the ratio of yellow paint to blue paint needs to be 4 : 1. You need 4 times as many pints of yellow paint as pints of blue paint.

STEP 2 **Write** a verbal model. Then write an equation. Let p represent the number of pints of yellow paint that you need to add.

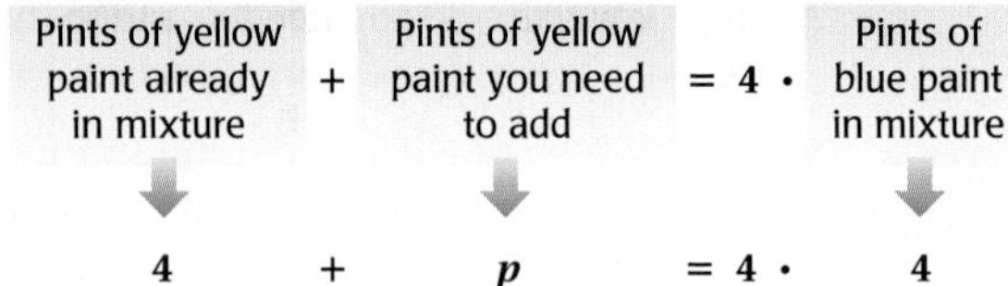

$$4 + p = 4 \cdot 4$$

STEP 3 **Solve** the equation.

$4 + p = 4 \cdot 4$ Write equation.

$4 + p = 16$ Multiply.

$p = 12$ Subtract 4 from each side.

▶ You need to add 12 pints of yellow paint to the mixture.

PRACTICE

1. **INVESTING** Jill has \$10,000 in various investments, including \$1000 in a mutual fund. Jill wants the amount in the mutual fund to make up 20% of the amount in all of her investments. How much money should she add to the mutual fund? Solve this problem using two different methods. **See margin.**

2. **ERROR ANALYSIS** *Describe* and correct the error in solving Exercise 1. **See margin.**

Amount in mutual fund	Amount in all investments	Percent in mutual fund
1000	10,000	10%
1400	10,400	About 13%
1800	10,800	About 17%
2250	11,250	20%

Jill needs to add \$2250 to her mutual fund. ✗

3. **BASKETBALL** A basketball player has made 40% of 30 free throw attempts so far. How many consecutive free throws must the player make in order to increase the percent of free throw attempts made to 50%? Solve this problem using two different methods. **See margin.**

4. **WHAT IF?** In Exercise 3, suppose the basketball player instead wants to increase the percent of free throw attempts made to 60%. How many consecutive free throws must the player make? **15 free throws**

5. **SNOW SHOVELING** You and your friend are shoveling snow out of a driveway. You can shovel the snow alone in 50 minutes. Both of you can shovel the snow in 30 minutes when working together. How many minutes will your friend take to shovel the snow alone? Solve this problem using two different methods. **See margin.**

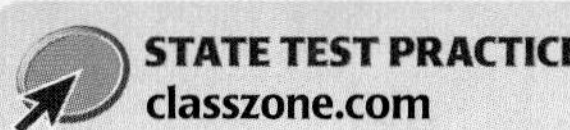

Lessons 12.5–12.7

1. **MULTI-STEP PROBLEM** For the period 1991–2002, the average total revenue T (in dollars per admission) that a movie theater earned and the average revenue C (in dollars per admission) from concessions in the United States can be modeled by

$$T = \frac{0.018x^2 + 5.4}{1 - 0.0011x^2} \text{ and } C = \frac{0.013x^2 + 1.1}{0.0011x^2 + 1}$$

where x is the number of years since 1991.

 a. Write a model that gives the percent p (in decimal form) of the average total revenue per admission that came from concessions as a function of x. **See margin.**

 b. About what percent of the average total revenue came from concessions in 2001? **about 27%**

2. **SHORT RESPONSE** The diagram of the truck shows the distance between the first axle and the last axle for each of two groups of consecutive axles.

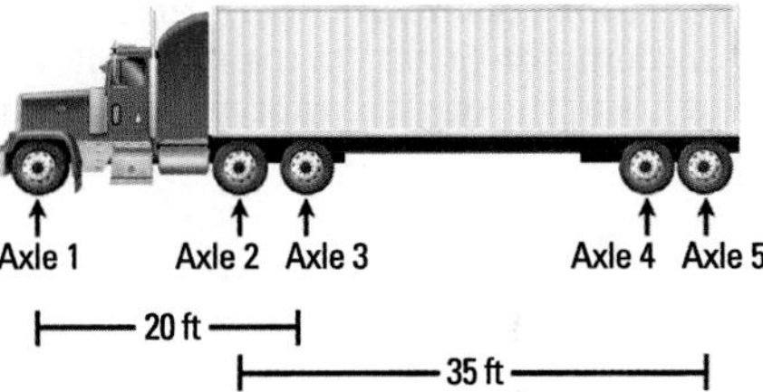

The maximum weight W (to the nearest 500 pounds) that a truck on a highway can carry on a group of consecutive axles is given by the formula

$$W = 500\left(\frac{d}{n-1} + 12n + 36\right)$$

where d is the distance (in feet) between the first axle and the last axle of the group and n is the number of axles in the group.

 a. Rewrite the expression on the right side of the equation as a single rational expression. Then find the maximum weight that the truck shown can carry on axles 1–3. $\frac{500(12n^2 + 24n + d - 36)}{n-1}$**; 41,000 lb**

 b. Can the truck carry 65,500 pounds on axles 2–5? *Explain* your answer. **See margin.**

3. **MULTI-STEP PROBLEM** A rower travels 5 miles upstream (against the current) and 5 miles downstream (with the current). The speed of the current is 1 mile per hour.

 a. Write an equation that gives the total travel time t (in hours) as a function of the rower's average speed r (in miles per hour) in still water. $\frac{10r}{(r-1)(r+1)}$

 b. Find the total travel time if the rower's average speed in still water is 7 miles per hour. **about 1.5 h**

4. **GRIDDED ANSWER** You take 7 minutes to fill your washing machine tub using only the cold water valve. You take 4 minutes to fill the tub using both the cold water valve and the hot water valve. How many minutes will you take to fill the tub using only the hot water valve? $\frac{28}{3}$ **min**

5. **OPEN-ENDED** *Describe* a real-world situation that can be modeled by the equation $\frac{115 + x}{170 + x} = 0.75$. *Explain* what the solution of the equation means in this situation. **See margin.**

6. **EXTENDED RESPONSE** The number D (in thousands) of all college degrees earned and the number M (in thousands) of master's degrees earned in the United States during the period 1984–2001 can be modeled by

$$D = \frac{1800 + 17x^2}{1 + 0.0062x^2} \text{ and } M = \frac{280 + 2.5x^2}{1 + 0.0040x^2}$$

where x is the number of years since 1984.

 a. Write a model that gives the percent p (in decimal form) of all college degrees earned that were master's degrees. **See margin.**

 b. Approximate the percent of all college degrees earned that were master's degrees in 2000. **about 19.1%**

 c. Graph the equation in part (a) on a graphing calculator. *Describe* how the percent of college degrees that were master's degrees changed during the period. Can you use the graph to describe how the *number* of master's degrees changed during the period? *Explain*. **See margin.**

1a. $p = \frac{(0.013x^2 + 1.1)(1 - 0.0011x^2)}{(0.0011x^2 + 1)(0.018x^2 + 5.4)}$

2b. No; for the group of axles from axle 2 to axle 5, $d = 35$ feet and $n = 4$. Substitute these values into the expression for W to find the maximum weight this group of axles can carry: $\frac{500[12(4)^2 + 24(4) + 35 - 36]}{4 - 1} \approx$ 48,000 pounds. 65,500 pounds is greater than 48,000 pounds, so the truck cannot carry a weight of 65,500 pounds between axle 2 and axle 5.

5. *Sample answer:* A basketball player who has made 115 free throws out of 170 attempts wants to raise his free throw shooting percentage to 75%; the solution $x = 50$ means that the basketball player would have to make 50 consecutive free throws in order to raise his free throw shooting percentage to 75%.

6a. $p = \frac{(280 + 2.5x^2)(1 + 0.0062x^2)}{(1 + 0.0040x^2)(1800 + 17x^2)}$

6c. The percent of college degrees that were master's degrees increased from 1984–2001; no. *Sample answer:* The graph only shows what percent of college degrees are master's degrees, it does not show the number of college degrees that are master's degrees so you cannot describe how the number of master's degrees changed during the period.

12 CHAPTER SUMMARY

Animated Algebra
classzone.com
Electronic Function Library

Additional Resources

The following resources are available to help review the materials in this chapter.

Chapter Resource Book

- Chapter Review Games and Activities
- Cumulative Practice, Chs. 1–12

Student Resources in Spanish

eWorkbook

@HomeTutor

Vocabulary Practice

Vocabulary practice is available at **classzone.com**

BIG IDEAS

For Your Notebook

Big Idea 1

Graphing Rational Functions

The graphs of $y = \frac{a}{x}$ $(a \neq 0)$ and $y = \frac{a}{x-h} + k$ $(a \neq 0)$ are hyperbolas that have two symmetrical branches. The characteristics of the functions and their graphs are given below. To graph a rational function whose numerator and denominator are first-degree polynomials, you can first use long division to rewrite the function so that it has the form $y = \frac{a}{x-h} + k$.

Function	Vertical asymptote	Horizontal asymptote	Domain	Range
$y = \frac{a}{x}$	$x = 0$	$y = 0$	All real numbers except $x = 0$	All real numbers except $y = 0$
$y = \frac{a}{x-h} + k$	$x = h$	$y = k$	All real numbers except $x = h$	All real numbers except $y = k$

Big Idea 2

Performing Operations on Rational Expressions

Performing operations on rational expressions is similar to performing operations on numerical fractions. Any common factors in the numerator and denominator should be divided out, and the original expression should be used when finding excluded values.

Operation	Rule
Multiplication	$\frac{a}{b} \cdot \frac{c}{d} = \frac{ac}{bd}$ where $b \neq 0$ and $d \neq 0$
Division	$\frac{a}{b} \div \frac{c}{d} = \frac{a}{b} \cdot \frac{d}{c}$ where $b \neq 0$, $c \neq 0$, and $d \neq 0$
Addition	Same denominator: $\frac{a}{c} + \frac{b}{c} = \frac{a+b}{c}$ where $c \neq 0$ Different denominators: Use LCD of rational expressions.
Subtraction	Same denominator: $\frac{a}{c} - \frac{b}{c} = \frac{a-b}{c}$ where $c \neq 0$ Different denominators: Use LCD of rational expressions.

Big Idea 3

Solving Rational Equations

You can use the following steps to solve a rational equation.

1. Rewrite the rational equation by using the cross products property or by multiplying each side by the least common denominator (LCD) of the rational expressions in the equation.
2. Solve the rewritten equation.
3. Check for extraneous solutions.

12 CHAPTER REVIEW

@HomeTutor
classzone.com
- Multi-Language Glossary
- Vocabulary practice

REVIEW KEY VOCABULARY

- inverse variation, *p. 765*
- constant of variation, *p. 765*
- hyperbola, branches of a hyperbola, asymptotes of a hyperbola, *p. 767*
- rational function, *p. 775*
- rational expression, *p. 794*
- excluded value, *p. 794*
- simplest form of a rational expression, *p. 795*
- least common denominator (LCD) of rational expressions, *p. 813*
- rational equation, *p. 820*

VOCABULARY EXERCISES

1. Copy and complete: A(n) _?_ of a hyperbola is a line that the hyperbola approaches but doesn't intersect. **asymptote**
2. **WRITING** *Explain* how you can use an LCD to solve a rational equation. **See margin.**
3. Identify the vertical asymptote and horizontal asymptote of the graph of $y = \frac{-5}{x+2} - 4$. **$x = -2, y = -4$**

REVIEW EXAMPLES AND EXERCISES

Use the review examples and exercises below to check your understanding of the concepts you have learned in each lesson of Chapter 12.

12.1 Model Inverse Variation *pp. 765–772*

EXAMPLE

The variables x and y vary inversely, and $y = 14$ when $x = 4$. Write the inverse variation equation that relates x and y. Then find the value of y when $x = 7$.

$y = \frac{a}{x}$ Write inverse variation equation.

$14 = \frac{a}{4}$ Substitute 4 for x and 14 for y.

$56 = a$ Simplify.

▶ The inverse variation equation is $y = \frac{56}{x}$. When $x = 7$, $y = \frac{56}{7} = 8$.

EXERCISES

EXAMPLES 4 and 5 on pp. 767–768 for Exs. 4–7

Given that y varies inversely with x, use the specified values to write an inverse variation equation that relates x and y. Then find y when $x = 5$.

4. $x = 9, y = 2$ **$y = \frac{18}{x}$, 3.6**
5. $x = 3, y = 21$ **$y = \frac{63}{x}$, 12.6**
6. $x = -6, y = 6$ **$y = \frac{-36}{x}$, −7.2**
7. Tell whether the ordered pairs (−10, 0.8), (−4, 2), (5, −1.6), and (16, −0.5) represent inverse variation. If so, write the inverse variation equation. **See margin.**

Extra Example 12.1

The variables x and y vary inversely, and $y = 8$ when $x = 3$. Write the inverse variation equation that relates x and y. Then find the value of y when $x = 12$. **$y = \frac{24}{x}$; 2**

2. Multiply each side of the equation by the least common denominator of all the rational expressions in the equation. This will make all the denominators in the equation equal to 1 and allow you to identify the equation as linear or quadratic in form.

7. inverse variation; $y = \frac{-8}{x}$

Extra Example 12.2

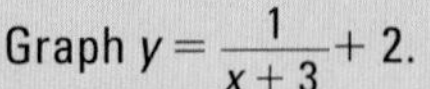

Graph $y = \frac{1}{x+3} + 2$.

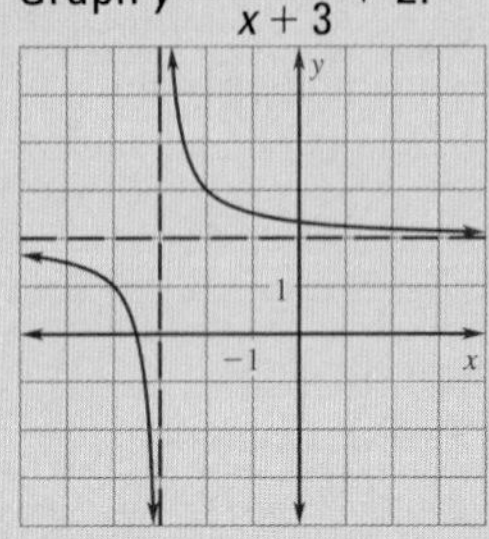

Extra Example 12.3

Divide $x^2 + 4x + 8$ by $x + 2$.

$x + 2 + \frac{4}{x+2}$

8.

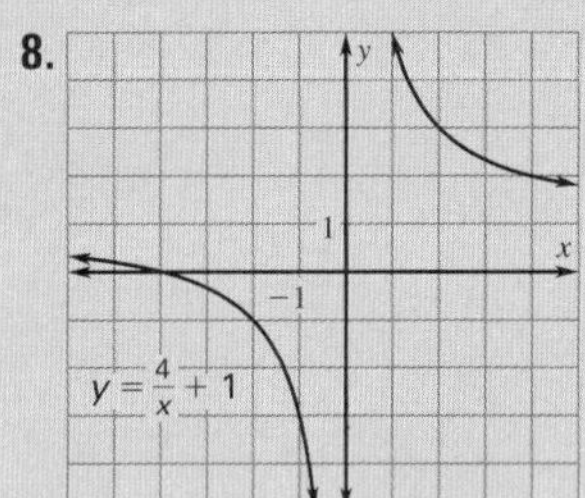

9.

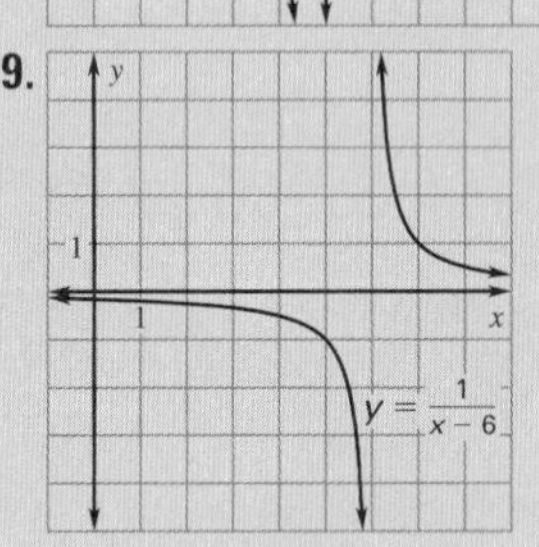

10.

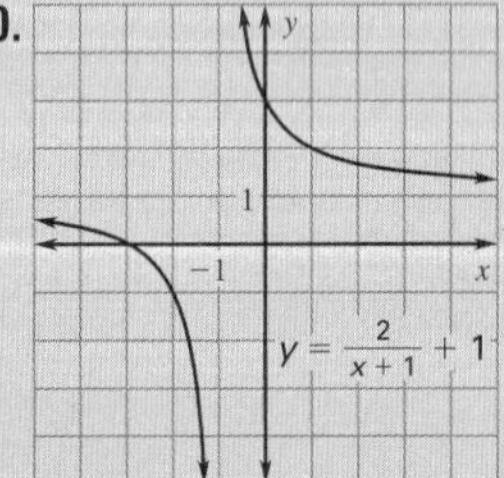

15.

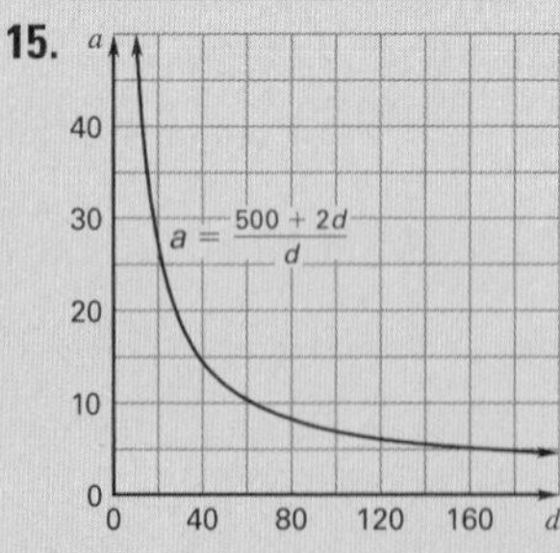

12.2 Graph Rational Functions

pp. 775–782

EXAMPLE

Graph $y = \frac{-1}{x-2} - 3$.

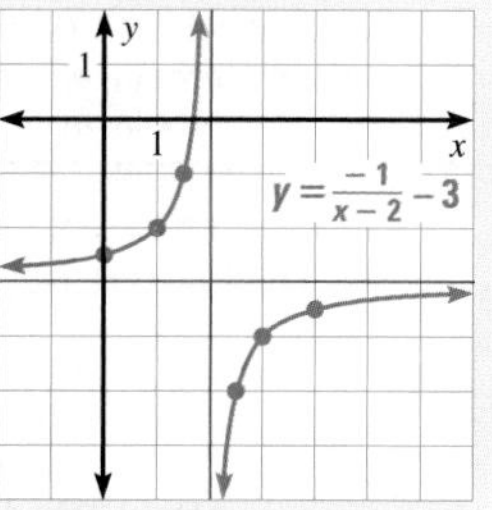

STEP 1 **Identify** the asymptotes of the graph. The vertical asymptote is $x = 2$, and the horizontal asymptote is $y = -3$.

STEP 2 **Plot** several points on each side of the vertical asymptote.

STEP 3 **Graph** two branches that pass through the plotted points and approach the asymptotes.

EXERCISES

EXAMPLES 2, 3, and 4 on pp. 776–777 for Exs. 8–10

Graph the function. **8–10. See margin.**

8. $y = \frac{4}{x} + 1$ **9.** $y = \frac{1}{x-6}$ **10.** $y = \frac{2}{x+1} + 1$

12.3 Divide Polynomials

pp. 784–791

EXAMPLE

Divide $x^2 + 7x - 2$ by $x - 2$.

$$\begin{array}{r l} x + 9 & \\ x - 2\overline{)x^2 + 7x - 2} & \\ \underline{x^2 - 2x} & \text{Multiply } x \text{ and } x - 2. \\ 9x - 2 & \text{Subtract } x^2 - 2x. \text{ Bring down } -2. \\ \underline{9x - 18} & \text{Multiply 9 and } x - 2. \\ 16 & \text{Subtract } 9x - 18. \end{array}$$

▶ $(x^2 + 7x - 2) \div (x - 2) = x + 9 + \frac{16}{x-2}$

EXERCISES

EXAMPLES 2, 3, 4, 5, and 7 on pp. 785–787 for Exs. 11–15

Divide.

11. $(x^2 + 12x + 35) \div (x + 7)$ $\mathbf{x + 5}$

12. $(y^2 - 5y - 8) \div (y - 3)$ $\mathbf{y - 2 + \frac{-14}{y-3}}$

13. $(4z + z^2 - 1) \div (5 + z)$ $\mathbf{z - 1 + \frac{4}{z+5}}$

14. $(3a^2 - 2) \div (3 + 3a)$ $\mathbf{a - 1 + \frac{1}{3+3a}}$

15. CHARITY DONATIONS Sean intends to collect \$500 in individual donations for a charity. His company will contribute \$2 for every donation collected. Write and graph an equation that gives the average amount a (including the company contribution) that the charity will receive per individual donation as a function of the number d of donations. $\mathbf{a = \frac{500 + 2d}{d}}$**; see margin for art.**

12.4 Simplify Rational Expressions

pp. 794–800

EXAMPLE

Simplify $\frac{x^2 - 3x - 18}{x^2 + 11x + 24}$. State the excluded values.

$\frac{x^2 - 3x - 18}{x^2 + 11x + 24} = \frac{(x + 3)(x - 6)}{(x + 3)(x + 8)}$ **Factor numerator and denominator.**

$= \frac{\cancel{(x + 3)}(x - 6)}{\cancel{(x + 3)}(x + 8)}$ **Divide out common factor.**

$= \frac{x - 6}{x + 8}$ **Simplify.**

▶ The excluded values are −8 and −3.

EXERCISES

EXAMPLES 1, 2, 3, and 4 on pp. 794–796 for Exs. 16–21

Find the excluded values, if any, of the expression.

16. $\frac{x + 3}{2x - 4}$ **2**

17. $\frac{3}{y^2 - 4y - 12}$ **−2, 6**

18. $\frac{8z}{9z^2 - 1}$ $\pm\frac{1}{3}$

Simplify the expression, if possible. State the excluded values.

19. $\frac{5m^3 - 15m^2}{20m^2}$ $\frac{m-3}{4}$; 0

20. $\frac{3n^2 - n - 2}{2n^2 - 3n + 1}$ $\frac{3n+2}{2n-1}$; $\frac{1}{2}$, 1

21. $\frac{4 - r^2}{r^2 - r - 2}$ $\frac{-(r+2)}{r+1}$; −1, 2

12.5 Multiply and Divide Rational Expressions

pp. 802–809

EXAMPLE

Find the quotient $\frac{5x^2 + 3x - 2}{4x} \div (5x - 2)$.

$\frac{5x^2 + 3x - 2}{4x} \div (5x - 2) = \frac{5x^2 + 3x - 2}{4x} \div \frac{5x - 2}{1}$ **Rewrite polynomial as fraction.**

$= \frac{5x^2 + 3x - 2}{4x} \cdot \frac{1}{5x - 2}$ **Multiply by multiplicative inverse.**

$= \frac{5x^2 + 3x - 2}{4x(5x - 2)}$ **Multiply numerators and denominators.**

$= \frac{\cancel{(5x - 2)}(x + 1)}{4x\cancel{(5x - 2)}}$ **Factor and divide out common factor.**

$= \frac{x + 1}{4x}$ **Simplify.**

EXERCISES

EXAMPLES 3 and 4 on pp. 803–804 for Exs. 22–24

Find the product or quotient.

22. $\frac{-x^3}{x^2 + 5x - 14} \cdot (2 - x)$ $\frac{x^3}{x+7}$

23. $\frac{6v^8}{2v^5} \div \frac{8v}{14v^5}$ $\frac{21v^7}{4}$

24. $\frac{w^2 - 9}{2w + 1} \div \frac{w + 3}{4w^2 - 1}$ $(w-3)(2w-1)$

Extra Example 12.4

Simplify $\frac{x^2 - 6x - 16}{x^2 + 8x + 12}$. State the excluded values. $\frac{x-8}{x+6}$; −6, −2

Extra Example 12.5

Find the product $\frac{2x}{x^2 + 3x - 4} \cdot (x + 4)$. $\frac{2x}{x-1}$

Extra Example 12.6

Find the sum $\frac{5x}{x+2} + \frac{4}{x-3}$. $\frac{5x^2 - 11x + 8}{(x+2)(x-3)}$

Extra Example 12.7

Solve $\frac{8}{x+5} + \frac{3}{4} = \frac{2}{x+5}$. **−13**

12 CHAPTER REVIEW

12.6 Add and Subtract Rational Expressions

pp. 812–819

EXAMPLE

Find the difference $\frac{x}{x-4} - \frac{5}{x+3}$.

$$\frac{x}{x-4} - \frac{5}{x+3} = \frac{x(x+3)}{(x-4)(x+3)} - \frac{5(x-4)}{(x+3)(x-4)}$$ Rewrite fractions using LCD, $(x-4)(x+3)$.

$$= \frac{x(x+3) - 5(x-4)}{(x-4)(x+3)}$$ Subtract fractions.

$$= \frac{x^2 - 2x + 20}{(x-4)(x+3)}$$ Simplify numerator.

EXERCISES

EXAMPLES 1, 3, 5, and 6 on pp. 812–815 for Exs. 25–28

Find the sum or difference.

25. $\frac{x+13}{5x-3} - \frac{9x-20}{5x-3}$ $\frac{-8x+33}{5x-3}$

26. $\frac{5}{6a} + \frac{1}{9a^3}$ $\frac{15a^2+2}{18a^3}$

27. $\frac{6}{c+1} - \frac{c}{c^2-2c-8}$ $\frac{5c^2-13c-48}{(c+1)(c-4)(c+2)}$

28. **BICYCLING** You ride your bike to a beach that is 15 miles away. Your average speed on the way home is 5 miles per hour less than your average speed on the way to the beach. Write an equation that gives the total travel time t (in hours) as a function of your average speed r (in miles per hour) on the way to the beach. Then find the total travel time if you biked to the beach at an average speed of 15 miles per hour. $t = \frac{30r - 75}{r(r-5)}$; 2.5 h

12.7 Solve Rational Equations

pp. 820–826

EXAMPLE

Solve $\frac{2x}{x-1} + \frac{2}{3} = \frac{10}{x-1}$.

$$\frac{2x}{x-1} + \frac{2}{3} = \frac{10}{x-1}$$ Write original equation.

$$\frac{2x}{x-1} \cdot 3(x-1) + \frac{2}{3} \cdot 3(x-1) = \frac{10}{x-1} \cdot 3(x-1)$$ Multiply each expression by LCD, $3(x-1)$.

$$\frac{2x \cdot 3\cancel{(x-1)}}{\cancel{(x-1)}} + \frac{2 \cdot \cancel{3}(x-1)}{\cancel{3}} = \frac{10 \cdot 3\cancel{(x-1)}}{\cancel{(x-1)}}$$ Divide out common factors.

$$6x + 2x - 2 = 30$$ Simplify.

$$8x - 2 = 30$$ Combine like terms.

$$x = 4$$ Solve for x.

EXERCISES

EXAMPLES 1, 2, and 3 on pp. 820–821 for Exs. 29–31

Solve the equation. Check your solution.

29. $\frac{18}{x-3} = \frac{x}{3}$ **−6, 9**

30. $\frac{4}{y+6} - 2 = \frac{20}{y^2+3y-18}$ **−2, 1**

31. $\frac{1}{z+3} - \frac{5}{6} = \frac{2}{z+3}$ $-\frac{21}{5}$

12 CHAPTER TEST

Given that y varies inversely with x, use the specified values to write an inverse variation equation that relates x and y. Then find y when $x = 3$.

1. $x = 2, y = 5$ **$y = \frac{10}{x}, \frac{10}{3}$**
2. $x = 9, y = 9$ **$y = \frac{81}{x}, 27$**
3. $x = \frac{9}{2}, y = 4$ **$y = \frac{18}{x}, 6$**
4. Tell whether the table represents inverse variation. If so, write the inverse variation equation. **inverse variation; $y = \frac{-5}{x}$**

x	−10	−2	4	5	20
y	0.5	2.5	−1.25	−1	−0.25

Graph the function.
5–7. See margin.

5. $y = \frac{-6}{x}$
6. $y = \frac{2}{x-5} + 2$
7. $y = \frac{3x-1}{x+4}$

Divide.

8. $(v^2 - 16v + 49) \div (v - 8)$ **$v - 8 + \frac{-15}{v-8}$**
9. $(8w - 2w^2 - 6) \div (w - 1)$ **$-2w + 6$**
10. $(6x^2 + x) \div (2x + 1)$ **$3x - 1 + \frac{1}{2x+1}$**

Simplify the expression, if possible. State the excluded values.

11. $\frac{42x^4}{3x^2}$ **$14x^2; 0$**
12. $\frac{2y-8}{4-y}$ **$-2; 4$**
13. $\frac{z^2 - 4z - 77}{z^2 - 13z + 22}$ **$\frac{z+7}{z-2}; 2, 11$**

Find the sum, difference, product, or quotient. **14–19. See margin.**

14. $\frac{r^2 - 9r + 18}{r^2 + 11r + 30} \cdot \frac{r+5}{r^2 - 36}$
15. $\frac{s^2 + 3s - 10}{s^2 - 9} \div \frac{s-2}{s+3}$
16. $\frac{x^2 - 9x}{x+3} \div (x^2 - 6x - 27)$
17. $\frac{4}{m+2} - \frac{3m}{m-3}$
18. $\frac{2n+7}{n-1} - \frac{8n}{n+5}$
19. $\frac{p+1}{p^2 - 49} + \frac{p-1}{p^2 + 10p + 21}$

Solve the equation. Check your solution.

20. $\frac{7}{u+1} = \frac{4}{u+4}$ **-8**
21. $\frac{t+11}{t-11} = \frac{11t+121}{t^2 - 6t - 55}$ **$6, -11$**
22. $\frac{8}{x+4} = \frac{5x}{x^2 - 2x - 24} - 1$ **$-9, 8$**

23. **GOLF** Your local golf club offers two payment options to anyone who wants to use its course. For the first option, you pay a one-time fee of \$750 to join for the season plus \$25 each time you use the golf course. For the second option, you instead pay \$45 each time you use the golf course.
   a. Using the first option, write an equation that gives your average cost C (in dollars) per use of the golf course as a function of the number g of times you use the golf course. Then graph the equation. **See margin.**
   b. Use the graph to approximate the number of times you need to use the golf course before the average cost is less than \$45. **38 times**

24. **CLEANING** You and your brother start a house cleaning business for the summer. Your brother needs twice the time you need to clean a certain room. Working together, the two of you need 60 minutes to clean the room.
   a. Write an equation that you can use to find the time t (in minutes) you need to clean the room by yourself. Then solve the equation. **$\frac{60}{t} + \frac{60}{2t} = 1; 90$**
   b. How long will each of you need to clean the room individually? **You need 90 minutes and your brother needs 180 minutes.**

Additional Resources

Assessment Book

- Chapter Test, Levels A, B, C
- Standardized Chapter Test
- SAT/ACT Chapter Test
- Alternative Assessment

Test Generator

Chapter Test

Easily-readable reduced copies (with answers) of Chapter Test B, the Standardized Chapter Test, and the Alternative Assessment from the Assessment Book can be found on pp. 762G–762H.

14. $\frac{r-3}{(r+6)^2}$

15. $\frac{s+5}{s-3}$

16. $\frac{x}{(x+3)^2}$

17. $\frac{-3m^2 - 2m - 12}{(m+2)(m-3)}$

18. $\frac{-6n^2 + 25n + 35}{(n-1)(n+5)}$

19. $\frac{2p^2 - 4p + 10}{(p-7)(p+7)(p+3)}$

23a. $C = \frac{750 + 25g}{g}$;

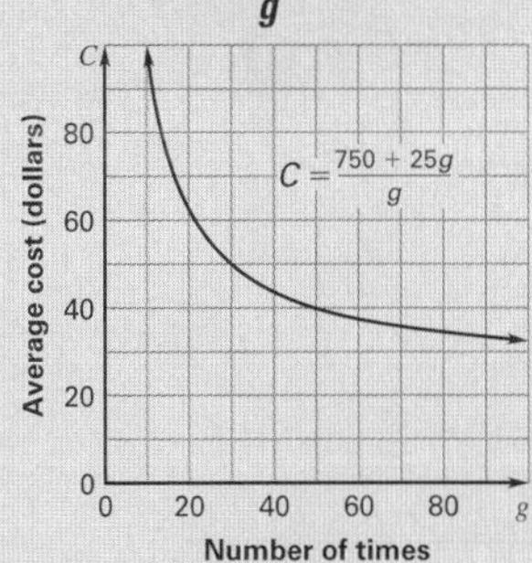

5.

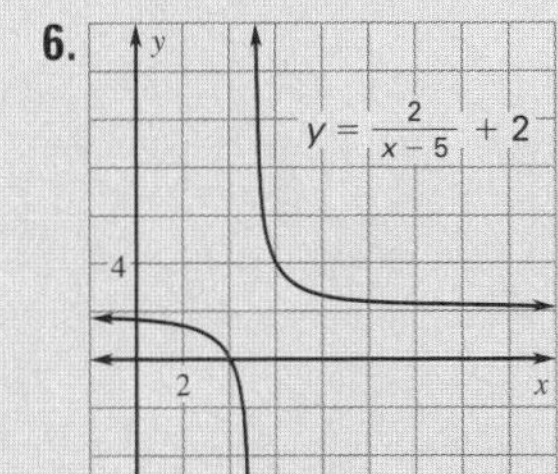

6.

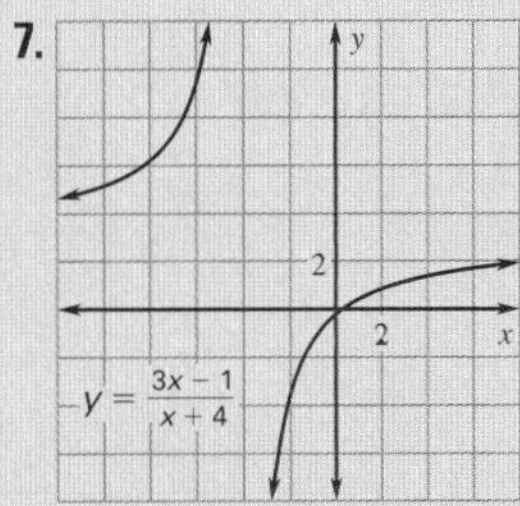

7.

$y = \frac{3x-1}{x+4}$

Test-Taking Strategy

Encourage students to check their answers against the context of the question, including any diagrams, tables, or graphs, to make sure that they have answered the right question and that their answer makes sense in the context of the question. This strategy is also useful when calculations are complex and the likelihood of error is high.

Avoiding Common Errors

It is easy to misread diagrams or other graphics if students are in a hurry to finish a question. Urge students to take enough time to check that their answers match diagrams and graphs.

Teaching Strategy

Suggest that students mark diagrams and graphs to help solve problems. For example, they could circle the important information in the diagram in Problem 1 and draw the asymptotes in the graph for Problem 2.

CONTEXT-BASED MULTIPLE CHOICE QUESTIONS

Some of the information you need to solve a context-based multiple choice question may appear in a table, a diagram, or a graph.

PROBLEM 1

Gary competes in the triathlon described in the flyer. His average biking speed is 8 times his average swimming speed. His average running speed is 4 times his average swimming speed. He takes 0.75 minute to transition from swimming to biking and 0.25 minute to transition from biking to running. He finishes the triathlon in 2 hours 25 minutes. What is his average swimming speed?

OAK CITY TRIATHLON
July 29, 8 A.M.
Swim: 1.5 kilometers
Bike: 40 kilometers
Run: 10 kilometers

Ⓐ 0.0625 kilometer per minute
Ⓑ 0.125 kilometer per minute
Ⓒ 0.25 kilometer per minute
Ⓓ 0.5 kilometer per minute

Plan

INTERPRET THE INFORMATION Use the distance for each stage of the triathlon and Gary's average speed for each stage to write a rational equation that describes the situation. Then solve the equation to find his average swimming speed.

Solution

STEP 1 Use the information in the problem to write an equation that describes the situation.

The time that Gary takes to complete each stage of the triathlon is the distance of the stage divided by the average speed for that stage. The sum of the times of each stage and the transition times equals 2 hours 25 minutes, or 145 minutes. Let x represent Gary's average swimming speed (in kilometers per minute).

$$\frac{1.5}{x} + \frac{40}{8x} + \frac{10}{4x} + 0.75 + 0.25 = 145$$

STEP 2 Solve the equation to find Gary's average swimming speed.

$$\frac{1.5}{x} \cdot \mathbf{8x} + \frac{40}{8x} \cdot \mathbf{8x} + \frac{10}{4x} \cdot \mathbf{8x} + 0.75 \cdot \mathbf{8x} + 0.25 \cdot \mathbf{8x} = 145 \cdot \mathbf{8x}$$

$$\frac{1.5 \cdot 8\cancel{x}}{\cancel{x}} + \frac{40 \cdot \cancel{8x}}{\cancel{8x}} + \frac{10 \cdot 8\cancel{x}}{4\cancel{x}} + 0.75 \cdot 8x + 0.25 \cdot 8x = 145 \cdot 8x$$

$$12 + 40 + 20 + 6x + 2x = 1160x$$

$$72 + 8x = 1160x$$

$$0.0625 = x$$

Gary's average swimming speed is 0.0625 kilometer per minute.

The correct answer is A. Ⓐ Ⓑ Ⓒ Ⓓ

PROBLEM 2

The graph of which function is shown?

Ⓐ $y = \frac{2}{x - 3} + 4$ Ⓑ $y = \frac{2}{x + 3} + 4$

Ⓒ $y = \frac{1}{x + 3} + 4$ Ⓓ $y = \frac{1}{x + 4} - 3$

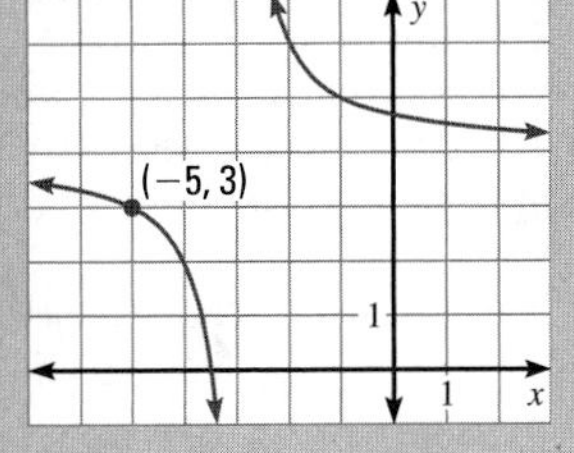

Plan

INTERPRET THE GRAPH The graph is a hyperbola that represents a rational function of the form $y = \frac{a}{x - h} + k$. Use the asymptotes and the fact that (−5, 3) lies on the graph to find the function.

Solution

STEP 1 Find the values of h and k.

The hyperbola has a vertical asymptote of $x = -3$ and a horizontal asymptote of $y = 4$. So, the function has the form $y = \frac{a}{x - (-3)} + 4$, or $y = \frac{a}{x + 3} + 4$.

STEP 2 Find the value of a.

To find the value of a, substitute the coordinates of (−5, 3) into the function.

$3 = \frac{a}{-5 + 3} + 4$ **Substitute −5 for *x* and 3 for *y*.**

$2 = a$ **Solve for *a*.**

The function is $y = \frac{2}{x + 3} + 4$. The correct answer is B. Ⓐ Ⓑ Ⓒ Ⓓ

PRACTICE

1. A community service club is recruiting volunteers to work at a charity event. The table shows the number of hours that each volunteer needs to work for various numbers of volunteers that the club recruits. If the club recruits 50 volunteers, how many hours does each volunteer need to work?

Volunteers	Work time (hours/person)
20	4
25	3.2
32	2.5

Ⓐ 1 hour Ⓑ 1.6 hours Ⓒ 2 hours Ⓓ 2.8 hours

2. What is the area of the right triangle shown?

Ⓐ $\frac{x^2 - 12x + 35}{2}$ Ⓑ $\frac{x^2 + 12x - 35}{2}$

Ⓒ $\frac{x^2 + 12x - 35}{4}$ Ⓓ $x^2 - 12x + 35$

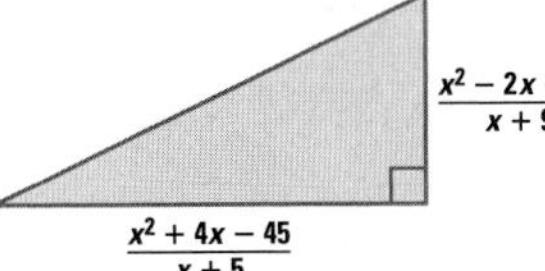

Answers

1. B

2. A

Answers
1. D
2. B
3. C
4. A
5. D
6. B
7. B
8. B

MULTIPLE CHOICE

In Exercises 1–3, use the following information. The length of a string on a stringed instrument varies inversely with the frequency of vibration. The table gives several notes and their approximate frequencies (in hertz).

Note	Frequency (Hz)
C	65.4
D	73.4
E	82.4
F	87.3
G	98.0

1. The string corresponding to which note has the shortest length?
   Ⓐ C note Ⓑ D note
   Ⓒ E note Ⓓ G note

2. If the string that produces the C note has a length of 42 centimeters, what is the approximate length of the string that produces the F note?
   Ⓐ 28 cm Ⓑ 31 cm
   Ⓒ 35 cm Ⓓ 46 cm

3. If the string that produces the D note has a length of 56 centimeters, what is the approximate length of the string that produces the G note?
   Ⓐ 31 cm Ⓑ 35 cm
   Ⓒ 42 cm Ⓓ 65 cm

4. Which equation gives the ratio r of the surface area of the rectangular prism to its volume as a function of the height h?

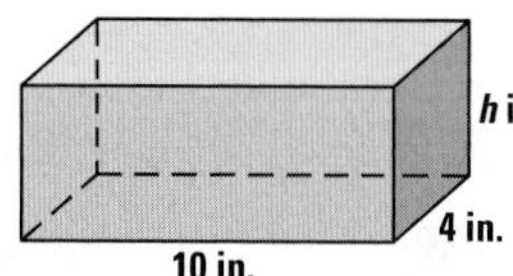

   Ⓐ $r = \frac{2}{h} + 0.7$ Ⓑ $r = \frac{1}{20h} + 0.7$
   Ⓒ $r = \frac{1}{20h} + 28$ Ⓓ $r = \frac{2}{h} + 0.05$

5. Which point lies on the hyperbola shown?
   Ⓐ $(-7, 2.5)$ Ⓑ $(-9, 2.6)$
   Ⓒ $(9, 3.4)$ Ⓓ $(11, 3.2)$

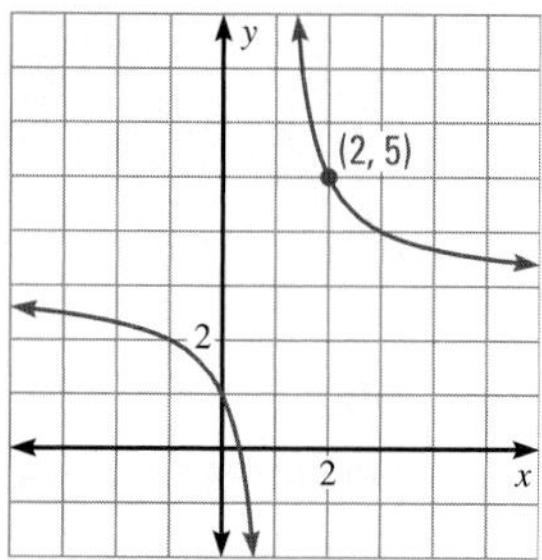

In Exercises 6–8, use the following information.

Jan is hiking a trail and plans to rest for 2 hours along the way. The hyperbola shown is the graph of her combined time t (in hours) for hiking and resting as a function of her average hiking speed r (in miles per hour).

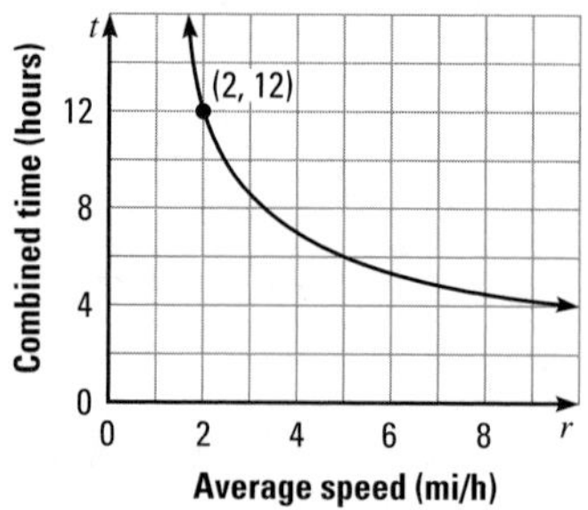

6. If $r = 5$, what is the value of t?
   Ⓐ 5 Ⓑ 6
   Ⓒ 7 Ⓓ 10

7. What is the length of the trail?
   Ⓐ 10 miles Ⓑ 20 miles
   Ⓒ 30 miles Ⓓ 40 miles

8. Suppose Jan's combined time for hiking and resting is 8 hours 15 minutes. What is her average hiking speed?
   Ⓐ 3 mi/h Ⓑ 3.2 mi/h
   Ⓒ 3.4 mi/h Ⓓ 3.6 mi/h

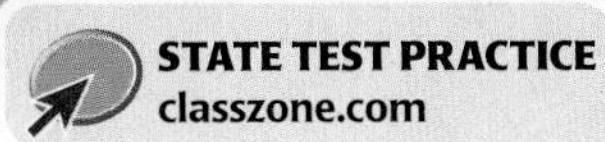

GRIDDED ANSWER

9. The variables x and y vary inversely, and $y = 15$ when $x = 2$. What is the value of y when $x = 5$?

10. You and your friend wash cars to raise money for your school club. Both of you can wash a certain car in 10 minutes when working together. Your friend can wash the car alone in twice the time that you can wash the car alone. How many minutes do you take to wash the car alone?

11. What is the remainder when you divide $2x^2 - 5x + 10$ by $2x + 1$?

12. What is the excluded value of the rational expression $\frac{6x^2 + 19x - 7}{x^2 - 8x + 16}$?

13. You and several friends are planning a ski trip. Your plane ticket costs \$180. A ski lodge costs \$2000 to rent. Everyone will share the cost of renting the ski lodge equally. How much more money (in dollars) would you spend if 8 people go on the trip than if 10 people go?

SHORT RESPONSE

14. A town's two street sweepers can clean the streets together in 20 hours. The older sweeper takes 4 times as long as the newer sweeper to clean the streets by itself.
    a. Write an equation that you can use to find the time t (in hours) that the newer sweeper takes to clean the streets by itself. Then solve the equation.
    b. Suppose that the older sweeper takes only twice as long as the newer sweeper to clean the streets by itself. Will the two sweepers take 10 hours to clean the streets together? *Explain.*

15. Your cousin is driving 500 miles to your house. On her way, she takes a 45 minute lunch break. Write and graph an equation that gives the total time t (in hours) of your cousin's trip as a function of her average driving speed r (in miles per hour). How would the graph change if she took a 60 minute lunch break? *Explain* your answer.

EXTENDED RESPONSE

16. The table shows the taxes paid for various incomes.
    a. Write a linear equation that gives the taxes paid t (in dollars) as a function of the income i (in dollars).
    b. Write a rational equation that gives the percent p (in decimal form) of income that is paid in taxes as a function of the income i (in dollars). Use the equation to find the income of a person who pays 4.5% of income in taxes.
    c. Does the function in part (b) make sense for incomes less than \$3000? *Justify* your answer algebraically.

Income (dollars)	Taxes paid (dollars)
10,000	420
15,000	720
20,000	1020
25,000	1320

17. A greeting card company offers you the opportunity to sell its cards, but you must first pay the company a one-time fee of \$300 plus \$2 for each card that you sell.
    a. Write and graph an equation that gives the average cost C per card (including the fee) as a function of the number of cards s that you sell.
    b. You want to sell enough cards so that the average cost per card (including the fee) drops to \$3. Write and solve an equation to find the number of cards that you need to sell.
    c. Is it possible for you to sell enough cards so that the average cost per card drops to \$1.75? *Explain* your answer.

15.

The horizontal asymptote will move from $t = 0.75$ to $t = 1$. *Sample answer:* The equation would change from $t = \frac{500}{t} + 0.75$ to $t = \frac{500}{t} + 1$, which changes the horizontal asymptote to 1 instead of 0.75.

16a. $t = 0.06i - 180$

16b. $p = \frac{0.06i - 180}{i}$; \$12,000

16c. No; a person cannot pay a negative amount of tax, so the equation in part (b) only makes sense for incomes i for which $t \ge 0$. Solve the inequality $0.06i - 180 \ge 0$ to get $i \ge 3000$.

17a. $C = \frac{300 + 2s}{s}$;

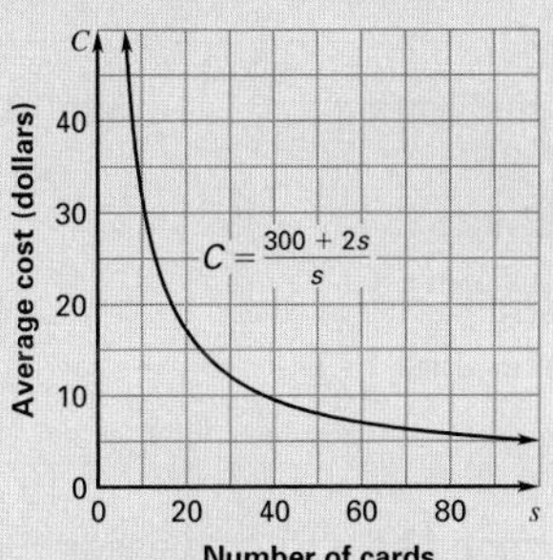

17b. $\frac{300 + 2s}{s} = 3$; 300 cards

17c. No; as the graph in part (a) shows, the average cost decreases as the number of cards sold increases, but the average cost C never gets as low as \$2.00 (or \$1.75) because $C = 2$ is the horizontal asymptote of the graph.

9. 6

10. 15 min

11. 13

12. 4

13. \$50

14a. $\frac{20}{t} + \frac{20}{4t} = 1$; 25 h

14b. No; from part (a) we know that the new sweeper takes 25 hours to clean the streets by itself, so the old sweeper takes 2(25) = 50 hours to clean the streets by itself. In 1 hour the new sweeper cleans $\frac{1}{25}$ of the streets and the old sweeper cleans $\frac{1}{50}$ of the streets. To find the number of hours t it takes them to clean the streets together, solve the equation $\frac{t}{25} + \frac{t}{50} = 1$. The solution is $t = 16\frac{2}{3}$ hours.

Chapter 13: Probability and Data Analysis

Chapter Table of Contents

PACING GUIDES

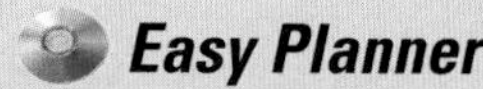

Easy Planner

Regular Schedule (50-minute classes)

DAY 1	DAY 2	DAY 3	DAY 4	DAY 5	DAY 6	DAY 7
Investigating Algebra Activity 13.1 Lesson 13.1 Extension 13.1	Lesson 13.2	Lesson 13.2 (cont.)	Lesson 13.3 Graphing Calculator Activity 13.3	Lesson 13.4	Lesson 13.4 (cont.) Mixed Review of Problem Solving	Quiz for Lessons 13.1–13.4 Lesson 13.5
DAY 8	**DAY 9**	**DAY 10**	**DAY 11**	**DAY 12**	**DAY 13**	**DAY 14**
Lesson 13.6 Extension 13.6	Lesson 13.7	Lesson 13.7 (cont.) Graphing Calculator Activity 13.7	Lesson 13.8	Lesson 13.8 (cont.) Graphing Calculator Activity 13.8 Mixed Review of Problem Solving	Quiz for Lessons 13.5–13.8 Chapter Review	Chapter Test

Block Schedule (90-minute classes)

DAY 1	DAY 2	DAY 3	DAY 4	DAY 5	DAY 6	DAY 7
Investigating Algebra Activity 13.1 Lesson 13.1 Extension 13.1 Lesson 13.2	Lesson 13.2 (cont.) Lesson 13.3 Graphing Calculator Activity 13.3	Lesson 13.4 Mixed Review of Problem Solving	Quiz for Lessons 13.1–13.4 Lesson 13.5 Lesson 13.6 Extension 13.6	Lesson 13.7 Graphing Calculator Activity 13.7	Lesson 13.8 Graphing Calculator Activity 13.8 Mixed Review of Problem Solving	Quiz for Lessons 13.5–13.8 Chapter Review Chapter Test

RESOURCE OPTIONS

Chapter/Lesson Resources

Chapter Resource Book
- Parents as Partners
- Teaching Guide/Lesson Plan
- Activity Masters
- Practice (3 levels)
- Study Guide
- Quick Catch-Up for Absent Students
- Problem Solving/Application
- Challenge Practice
- Chapter Review Games and Activities
- Project with Rubric
- Cumulative Review

Notetaking Guide
- Student Workbook and Teacher's Edition

Practice Workbook

Worked-Out Solution Key

Chapter Transparency Book
- Warm-Up Exercises/Daily Homework Quiz
- Notetaking Guide Transparencies
- Homework Answer Transparencies

Teacher Tools Transparencies

Assessment

Assessment Book
- Quizzes
- Chapter Tests (3 levels)
- Standardized and SAT/ACT Chapter Tests
- Alternative Assessments
- Cumulative Tests

Benchmark Tests
- Benchmark Tests, correlated to Remediation Book
- Pre-Course, Mid-Year, and End-of-Year Tests
- Chapter Tests

Spanish Assessment Book

Differentiated Instruction

Differentiated Instruction Resources
- Strategies for Reading Mathematics
- Differentiated Instruction Lesson Notes
- English Learner Lesson Notes
- Inclusion Lesson Notes
- Teaching Strategies with Sample Worksheets
- Tips for New Teachers/Math Background Notes
- Teacher Survival Activities/Bulletin Board Ideas

Student Resources in Spanish

Spanish Study Guide

Remediation Book

Skills Readiness (available on Easy Planner)
- Diagnostic Assessment
- Skill Instruction and Alternative Teaching Strategies
- Skill Practice and Enrichment Masters

Pre-AP Resources
- Pacing and Assignment Guide
- Best Practices
- Copymasters

Technology Resources

Plan	***Easy Planner***
Teach	***Video Tutor*** ***Activity Generator*** ***Power Presentations*** ***Animated Algebra***
Assess	***Test Generator*** ***ML Assessment System***
Reteach	***@HomeTutor***
Online Resources	***Classzone.com*** ***eEdition*** ***eWorkbook***

Video Tutor

Technology Highlights for Each Lesson

 **Easy Planner**

Easy access to the Teacher's Edition and all teaching resources. Includes a search feature to locate the materials you need.

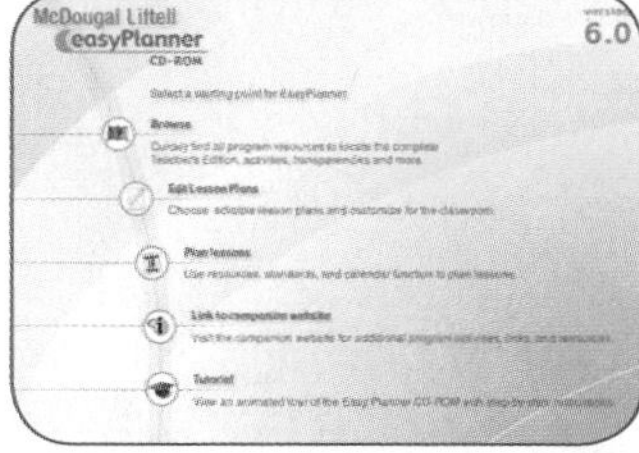

 **Activity Generator**

Leveled, editable activities allow all students to explore a lesson's concepts. Includes teacher notes and closure questions.

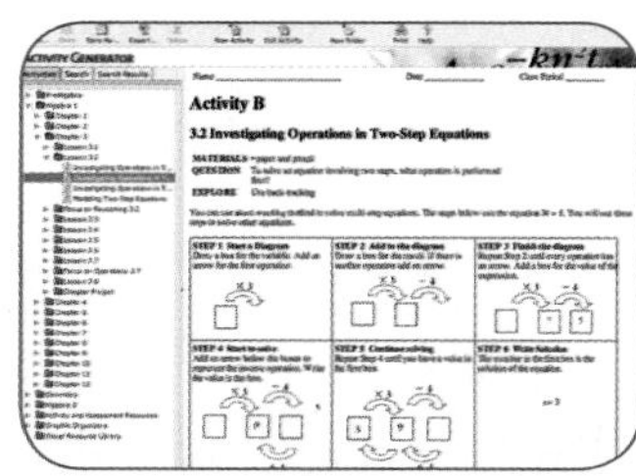

Animated Algebra

Interactive tutorials provide visually engaging alternative opportunities to learn concepts and master skills.

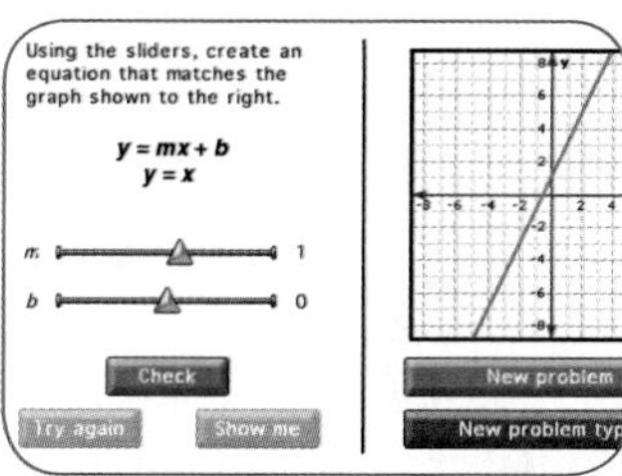

13 Lesson Practice Level B

LESSON 13.1 Practice B
For use with pages 843–848

3. 36; 1, 1; 1, 2; 1, 3; 1, 4; 1, 5; 1, 6; 2, 1; 2, 2; 2, 3; 2, 4; 2, 5; 2, 6; 3, 1; 3, 2; 3, 3; 3, 4; 3, 5; 3, 6; 4, 1; 4, 2; 4, 3; 4, 4; 4, 5; 4, 6; 5, 1; 5, 2; 5, 3; 5, 4; 5, 5; 5, 6; 6, 1; 6, 2; 6, 3; 6, 4; 6, 5; 6, 6

Find the number of possible outcomes in the sample space. Then list the possible outcomes.

1. A bag contains 6 blue cards numbered 1–6 and 8 red cards numbered 1–8. You choose a card at random. 14; blue 1; blue 2; blue 3; blue 4; blue 5; blue 6; red 1; red 2; red 3; red 4; red 5; red 6; red 7; red 8
2. You roll one 3-sided number cube and toss two coins.
3. You roll two number cubes. See above.

2. 12; 1, H, H; 1, H, T; 1, T, H; 1, T, T; 2, H, H; 2, H, T; 2, T, H; 2, T, T; 3, H, H; 3, H, T; 3, T, H; 3, T, T

In Exercises 4–9, refer to the spinner shown. The spinner is divided into sections with the same area.

4. What is the probability that the spinner stops on an even number? $\frac{4}{9}$
5. What is the probability that the spinner stops on an odd number? $\frac{5}{9}$
6. You spin the spinner 24 times. It stops on 27 twice. What is the experimental probability of stopping on 27? $\frac{1}{12}$
7. You spin the spinner 30 times. It stops on a multiple of 3 five times. What is the experimental probability of stopping on a multiple of 3? $\frac{1}{6}$
8. What are the odds in favor of stopping on a multiple of 4? $\frac{1}{2}$
9. What are the odds against stopping on a multiple of 6? $\frac{7}{2}$

LESSON 13.1

10. **Favorite Spectator Sport** A survey asked a total of 180 students in your school about their favorite spectator sports. The table shows the results of the survey.

Sport	Basketball	Soccer	Football	Baseball	Volleyball	Wrestling	Hockey
Number of students	40	20	45	20	16	18	21

a. What is the probability that a randomly selected student who participated in this survey chose football as his or her favorite spectator sport? $\frac{1}{4}$
b. What is the probability that a randomly selected student who participated in this survey chose wrestling or hockey as his or her favorite spectator sport? $\frac{13}{60}$
c. What are the odds in favor of a randomly selected student who participated in this survey choosing basketball as his or her favorite spectator sport? $\frac{2}{7}$

11. **Movies** A local movie theater did a survey of students to determine their favorite types of movies. The circle graph shows the results of the survey.
a. What is the probability that a randomly selected student chose science fiction as his or her favorite type of movie?
b. What is the probability that a randomly selected student chose drama or comedy as his or her favorite type of movie? **11. a.** $\frac{9}{100}$ **b.** $\frac{37}{50}$

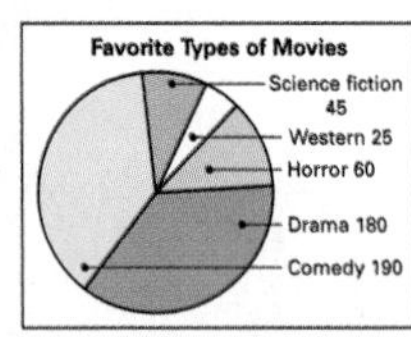

LESSON 13.2 Practice B
For use with pages 851–855

4. the number of permutations of 14 objects taken 3 at a time
5. the number of permutations of 24 objects taken 10 at a time
6. the number of permutations of 30 objects taken 20 at a time

Find the number of ways you can arrange (a) all of the letters in the given word and (b) 2 of the letters in the word.

1. TACK **a.** 24 **b.** 12
2. MAR **a.** 6 **b.** 6
3. GAMER **a.** 120 **b.** 20

Write the meaning of the notation in words. See above.

4. $_{14}P_3$
5. $_{24}P_{10}$
6. $_{30}P_{20}$

Evaluate the expression.

7. 6! 720
8. 9! 362,880
9. 11! 39,916,800
10. $\frac{8!}{3!}$ 6720
11. $\frac{12!}{9!}$ 1320
12. $\frac{15!}{14!}$ 15
13. $_6P_3$ 120
14. $_4P_4$ 24
15. $_{15}P_3$ 2730
16. $_8P_7$ 40,320
17. $_{10}P_6$ 151,200
18. $_5P_0$ 1

Complete the statement using >, <, or =.

19. $_6P_4$? $_4P_1$ >
20. $_8P_6$? $_{10}P_8$ <
21. $_3P_0$? $_6P_5$ <
22. $_6P_3$? $_4P_1$ >
23. $_{24}P_1$? $_4P_4$ =
24. $_7P_5$? $_{12}P_3$ >

25. **Summer Reading List** At the beginning of the summer, you have 6 books to read. In how many orders can you read the books? 720
26. **Air Conditioning Repair** An air conditioner repair person has repairs to make at 7 different homes. The destinations are all so close, it doesn't matter the order in which the repairs are made. In how many orders can the repairs be made? 5040
27. **Boat Racing** You are in a boat racing competition. In each heat, 4 boats race and the positions of the boats are randomly assigned.
a. In how many ways can a position be assigned? 24
b. What is the probability that you are chosen to be in the last position? *Explain* how you found your answer.
c. What is the probability that you are chosen to be in the first or second position of the heat that you are racing in? *Explain* how you found your answer.
d. What is the probability that you are chosen to be in the second or third position of the heat that you are racing in? *Compare* your answer with that in part (c).
28. **Math Exam** On an exam, you are asked to list the 6 steps to solving a particular kind of problem in order. You guess the order of the steps at random. What is the probability that you choose the correct order? $\frac{1}{720}$

27. b. $\frac{1}{4}$; The number of ways to be chosen to be in last position is given by 3!. The total number of ways a position is chosen is 4! = 24. So, the probability is $\frac{3!}{4!} = \frac{1}{4}$. **c.** $\frac{1}{2}$; You can be chosen to be in the first position 6 out of 24 ways and you can be chosen to be in the second position 6 out of 24 ways, so you can be chosen to be in the first or second position 12 out of 24 ways. **d.** $\frac{1}{2}$; You can be chosen to be in the second position 6 out of 24 ways and you can be chosen to be in the third position 6 out of 24 ways, so you can be chosen to be in the second or third position 12 out of 24 ways. The answers are the same.

LESSON 13.2

LESSON 13.3 Practice B
For use with pages 856–859

Evaluate the expression.

1. $_8C_4$ 70
2. $_5C_5$ 1
3. $_{12}C_0$ 1
4. $_7C_1$ 7
5. $_{15}C_{11}$ 1365
6. $_{10}C_3$ 120
7. $_6C_5$ 6
8. $_4C_2$ 6
9. $_{16}C_8$ 12,870

Complete the statement using >, <, or =.

10. $_{10}C_6$? $_8C_5$ >
11. $_{22}C_3$? $_{18}C_4$ <
12. $_9C_6$? $_9C_3$ =
13. $_8C_2$? $_{15}C_{14}$ >
14. $_7C_7$? $_{14}C_{14}$ =
15. $_5C_3$? $_8C_3$ <

In Exercises 16–18, tell whether the question can be answered using *combinations* or *permutations*. *Explain* your choice, then answer the question.

16. Five students from the 90 students in your class not running for class president will be selected to count the ballots for the vote for class president. In how many ways can the 5 students be selected? combinations; Answers will vary. 43,949,268
17. Twenty students are running for 3 different positions on student council. In how many ways can the 3 positions be filled? permutations; Answers will vary. 6840
18. To complete a quiz, you must answer 3 questions from a list of 6 questions. In how many ways can you complete the quiz? combinations; Answers will vary. 20
19. **Sweaters** The buyer for a retail store must decide which sweaters to stock for the upcoming fall season. A sweater from one manufacturer comes in 5 different colors and 3 different textures. The buyer decides that the store will stock the sweater in 3 different colors and 2 different textures. How many different sweaters are possible? 30
20. **Greeting Cards** A greeting card company packages 4 different cards together that are randomly selected from 10 different cards with a different animal on each card. What is the probability that one of the cards in a package is the card that has a dog on it? $\frac{2}{5}$
21. **Open-Mike Night** A coffee shop offers an open-mike night for poetry. Tonight, 15 people would like to read, but there is only enough time to have 7 people read.
a. Seven of the 15 people that would like to read are randomly chosen. How many combinations of 7 readers from the group of people that would like to read are possible? 6435
b. You and your friend are part of the group that would like to read. What is the probability that you and your friend are chosen? What is the probability that you are chosen first and your friend is chosen second? Which event is more likely to occur? $\frac{1}{5}$; $\frac{1}{210}$; The event that you and your friend are chosen (no particular order) is more likely.

LESSON 13.3

LESSON 13.4

LESSON 13.4 Practice B

For use with pages 861–867

1. overlapping; $\frac{4}{9}$

In Exercises 1–4, you draw a card from a bag that contains 4 yellow cards numbered 1–4 and 5 blue cards numbered 1–5. Tell whether the events A *and* B are *mutually exclusive* or *overlapping*. Then find *P*(A *or* B).

1. **Event A:** You choose a card with an even number.
Event B: You choose a number 4 card.

2. **Event A:** You choose a yellow card.
Event B: You choose a number 5 card.
mutually exclusive; $\frac{5}{9}$

3. **Event A:** You choose a blue number 3 card.
Event B: You choose a blue card.
overlapping; $\frac{5}{9}$

4. **Event A:** You choose a card with an odd number.
Event B: You choose a blue card.
overlapping; $\frac{7}{9}$

In Exercises 5 and 6, tell whether the events A *and* B are *dependent* or *independent*. Then find *P*(A *and* B).

5. A bag contains 6 red balls and 5 green balls. You randomly draw one ball, replace it, and randomly draw a second ball.
Event A: The first ball is green.
Event B: The second ball is green. independent; $\frac{25}{121}$

6. You write each of the letters of the word BRILLIANT on pieces of paper and place them in a bag. You randomly draw one letter, do not replace it, then randomly draw a second letter.
Event A: The first letter is an L.
Event B: The second letter is a T. dependent; $\frac{1}{36}$

7. **Eating Habits** A survey of 500 students in a school found that about 100 households consist of only vegetarians, 240 consist of vegetarians and non-vegetarians, and 160 consist of non-vegetarians.

a. What is the probability that one of the households surveyed, chosen at random, consists of vegetarians or non-vegetarians? $\frac{13}{25}$

b. What is the probability that one of the households surveyed, chosen at random, consists of vegetarians and non-vegetarians? $\frac{12}{25}$

c. *Explain* how your answers to parts (a) and (b) are related. The sum of the probabilities is 1.

8. **Coordinating Time** You study with a group for an upcoming math competition on Mondays, Tuesdays, and Thursdays. You volunteer at a hospital on Mondays, Wednesdays, and Thursdays.

a. Make a Venn diagram that shows the days of the week that you participate in each activity.

b. Your class is taking a field trip that could be scheduled for any day of the week (Monday through Friday). Find the probability that it is scheduled for a day when you are studying with your group or are volunteering. $\frac{4}{5}$

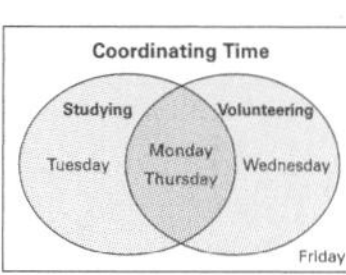

LESSON 13.5 Practice B

For use with pages 871–874

1. music store customers; self-selected sample
3. likely to result in a biased sample
4. not likely to result in a biased sample

In Exercises 1 and 2, identify the population and classify the sampling method.

1. The manager of a music store wants to evaluate how customers rate the selection of music the store has in stock. Customers are given comment cards with their receipts.

2. Your school's administrators want to know if students are satisfied with the choices of activities for activity period. In each grade, every seventh student in alphabetical order is surveyed. all students in school; systematic sample

Tell whether the survey method used is likely to result in a biased sample.

3. A bicycling club wants to gather information about biking conditions throughout a city. A survey for bicycle riders is posted on the club's website.

4. A management company that owns several apartment buildings wants to gather information about tenant satisfaction with the condition of the apartments. They send a survey to 30 random tenants in each of the buildings.

In Exercises 5 and 6, tell whether the question is potentially biased. *Explain* your answer.

5. Don't you think that the lunch menu should include grilled chicken rather than pizza because grilled chicken is healthier for you? See below.

6. Do you think that the city's excess revenue should be spent on road repairs or building a new sports stadium? See below.

In Exercises 7–9, explain why the question is biased. Then rewrite it so that it is not.

7. Don't you agree that it is better to offer an accounting class as an elective rather than a computer programming class? See below.

8. Don't you agree that a science center would be more fun to go to than a planetarium? See below.

9. Would you pay even higher taxes to fund a new highway? biased because it suggests that taxes are already high; Would you use your taxes to fund a new highway?

10. **Bus Stop Conditions** A newspaper does a report on the condition of the bus stops in a large city. Part of the report includes a survey of people living in the area. The survey is done by asking people at a mall what they think of local bus stops. Is the sample likely to be biased? *Explain.* Answers will vary.

11. **After-School Activities** You plan a report on the participation of students at your school in after-school activities for your school's website. *Describe* how you could choose a representative sample. *Justify* your sampling method. Answers will vary.

5. biased because it suggests that grilled chicken is healthier than pizza
6. not biased because a particular response is not encouraged
7. biased because it suggests that accounting class is better than a computer programming class; Which class should your school offer as an elective, an accounting class or a computer programming class?
8. biased because it suggests that going to a science center is more fun than going to a planetarium; Where would you like to go, to a science center or to a planetarium?

LESSON 13.5

LESSON 13.6 Practice B

For use with pages 875–878

1. mean: 5; median: 5; modes: 1, 5
2. mean: 68; median: 67.5; mode: 81
3. mean: 19; median: 22; mode: 25
4. mean: 16; median: 13.5; modes: 8, 28

Find the mean, median, and mode(s) of the data.

1. 6, 1, 3, 8, 5, 11, 1, 5

2. 60, 81, 52, 75, 59, 81

3. 15, 27, 10, 25, 9, 22, 25

4. 23, 6, 8, 14, 28, 8, 13, 28

5. 16, 11, 14, 30, 22, 9, 19, 15
mean: 17; median: 15.5; mode: none

6. 4.2, 2.2, 3.7, 2.8, 1.1
mean: 2.8; median: 2.8; mode: none

For the set of data, determine which measure of central tendency best represents the data.

7. 89, 86, 96, 87, 100, 86 median

8. 38, 35, 40, 36, 36, 33, 42, 37, 39, 34 median

9. 50, 47, 48, 49, 72, 47, 54, 50 median

10. 115, 112, 127, 116, 123, 113 median

11. 87, 77, 151, 105, 65, 141, 104, 166 mean

12. 100, 106, 180, 41, 161, 292, 116, 213 mean

Find the range and mean absolute deviation of the data. Round to the nearest hundredth, if necessary.

13. range: 6; mean absolute deviation: 1.68
14. range: 10; mean absolute deviation: 2.88
15. range: 13; mean absolute deviation: 4.67
16. range: 8; mean absolute deviation: 2.25

13. 10, 7, 13, 10, 8

14. 110, 114, 104, 108, 106

15. 87, 75, 85, 77, 74, 82

16. 15, 17, 15, 17, 21, 17, 15, 23

17. 40, 46, 41, 46, 49, 49, 46, 44, 44
range: 9; mean absolute deviation: 2.44

18. 50.8, 51.6, 51.9, 52, 52.5, 52.8, 53.1
range: 2.3; mean absolute deviation: 0.6

19. **Bean Plants** The heights (in inches) of eight bean plants are 28, 36, 41, 50, 35, 42, 46, and 52.

a. What is the range of the bean plant heights? 24

b. Find the mean, median, and mode(s) of the bean plant heights. mean: 41.25; median: 41.5; mode: none

c. Which measure of central tendency best represents the data? *Explain.* either the mean or the median because they are about the same

20. **Hotel Stay** You are planning a trip to Washington, D.C. and are looking up hotel room rates. On the Internet, you find the following rates for a one-night stay in a hotel in Washington, D.C.
\$109, \$126.50, \$175.95, \$139, \$77.50, \$145, \$162.35, \$173, \$181.50, \$105

a. Find the mean, median, and mode(s) of the rates. mean: 139.48; median: 142; mode: none

b. Which measure of central tendency best represents the data? *Explain.* either the mean or the median because they are about the same

21. **Temperature** The high and low temperatures for the last seven days are given.
High temperatures: 81°F, 78°F, 83°F, 89°F, 90°F, 87°F, 89°F
Low temperatures: 64°F, 53°F, 62°F, 66°F, 68°F, 69°F, 67°F

a. Find the mean, median, and mode of each data set. Round your answers to the nearest tenth. highs: mean: 85.3; median: 87; mode: 89; lows: mean: 64.1; median: 66; mode: none

b. For each data set, determine which measure of central tendency best represents the data. *Explain.* either the mean or the median for each set because they are about the same

c. *Compare* the spreads of data by using the range. The range of the lows is greater than the range of the highs, so the lows cover a wider interval than the highs.

d. *Compare* the spreads of data by using the mean absolute deviation. Round your answers to the nearest hundredth. The mean absolute deviation of the highs is greater, so the average variation from the mean is greater for the highs than the lows.

LESSON 13.6

13 Lesson Practice Level B

LESSON 13.7

Practice B

For use with pages 881–885

Give two possible keys for the stem-and-leaf plot.

1.

4	1 1 5
5	0 2 7 8
6	3 9
7	4 5 6 9
8	0 1 3

4 | 1 = 41; 4 | 1 = 4.1

2.

0	0 2 3 8 9
1	0 2 5 5 8
2	4 6 8
3	3 3 4 5
4	6 7

1 | 0 = 10; 1 | 0 = 1.0

Make a stem-and-leaf plot of the data.

3. 21, 10, 14, 26, 8, 30, 17, 15, 34, 27, 36, 20, 7, 19, 25, 33, 19, 32, 12, 25

0	7 8
1	0 2 4 5 7 9 9
2	0 1 5 5 6 7
3	0 2 3 4 6

Key: 1 | 0 = 10

4. 52, 66, 61, 82, 51, 60, 62, 54, 73, 70, 89, 85, 74, 53, 61, 75, 89, 85, 77, 55

5	1 2 3 4 5
6	0 1 1 2 6
7	0 3 4 5 7
8	2 5 5 9 9

Key: 5 | 1 = 51

5. 3, 5, 11, 34, 28, 19, 4, 6, 14, 17, 22, 30, 1, 1, 9, 10, 24, 27, 33, 20, 9, 4

0	1 1 3 4 4 5 6 9 9
1	0 1 4 7 9
2	0 2 4 7 8
3	0 3 4

Key: 1 | 0 = 10

6. 0.1, 3.6, 2.2, 1.0, 2.1, 1.1, 0.2, 3.5, 3.1, 2.4, 0.3, 1.5, 2.3, 0.5, 1.2

0	1 2 3 5
1	0 1 2 5
2	1 2 3 4
3	1 5 6

Key: 0 | 1 = 0.1

Make a histogram of the data.

7. 78, 96, 72, 108, 82, 108, 99, 118, 94, 100, 86, 74

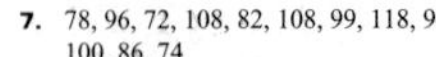

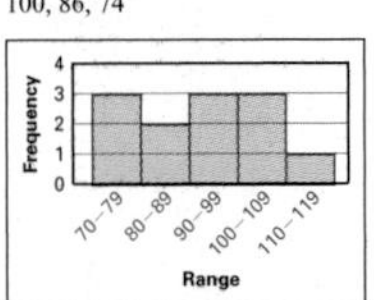

8. 58, 55, 65, 69, 66, 53, 60, 68, 61, 52, 66, 51

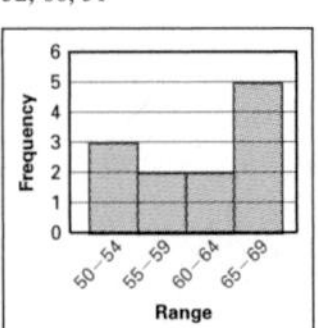

LESSON 13.7

Practice B *continued*

For use with pages 881–885

9. 4, 2.7, 3.2, 3, 3.7, 2.9, 3.1, 2.6, 3.4, 3, 3.6, 2.9

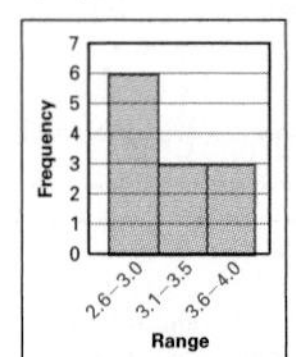

10. 18, 17.1, 15.5, 16.3, 15.2, 17.4, 16.6, 17.2, 15.1

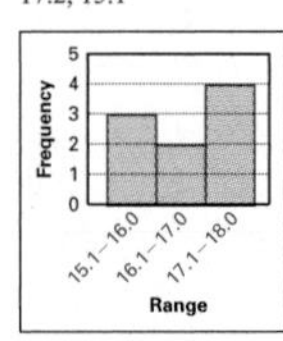

11. Mountains The table shows the heights of the world's 14 tallest mountains (in thousands of meters). Make a stem-and-leaf plot of the data.

Mountain	Height	Mountain	Height
Aconagua	7.0	Mt. Damavand	5.8
Annapurna	8.1	Mt. Everest	8.8
Cotopoxi	5.9	Mt. Godwin Austen (K-2)	8.6
Illampu	6.6	Mt. Logan	6.1
Kanchenjuga	8.6	Mt. Makalu	8.5
Kilimanjaro	5.9	Mt. McKinley	6.2
Lenin	7.1	Orizaba	5.7

5	7 8 9 9
6	1 2 6
7	0 1
8	1 5 6 6 8

Key: 5 | 7 = 5.7

12. Books A survey asked people how many books they have read in the last month. The results are shown in the table.

Books	0–5	6–11	12–17	18–23
Frequency	12	4	3	1

a. Make a histogram of the data.

b. What is the probability that a person surveyed, chosen at random, has read 0–5 books in the last month? $\frac{3}{5}$

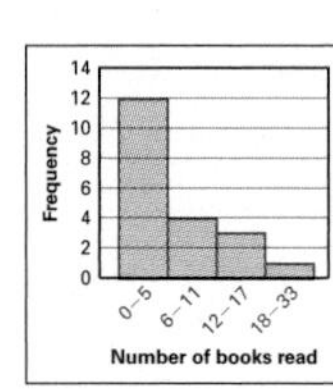

LESSON 13.8

Practice B

For use with pages 887–892

Identify the median, quartiles, and interquartile range of the data from the box-and-whisker plot. See below.

1.

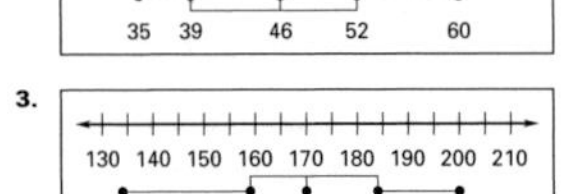

2.

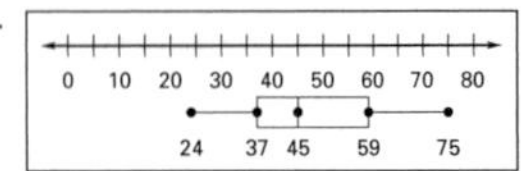

3.

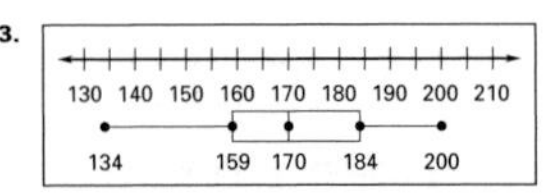

4.

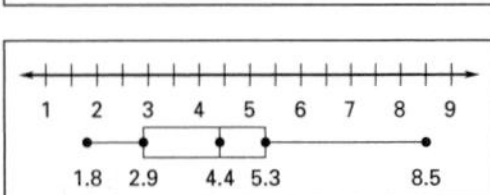

Make a box-and-whisker plot of the data.

5. 11, 33, 39, 27, 25, 31, 28, 33, 31, 49

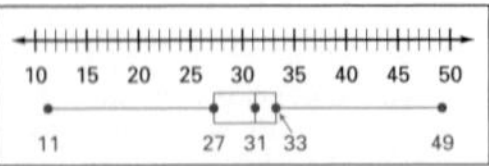

6. 10, 16, 18, 10, 13, 7, 10, 13, 2, 48

0 5 10 15 20 25 30 35 40 45 50

2 10 11.5 16 48

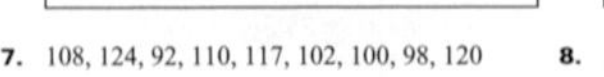

7. 108, 124, 92, 110, 117, 102, 100, 98, 120

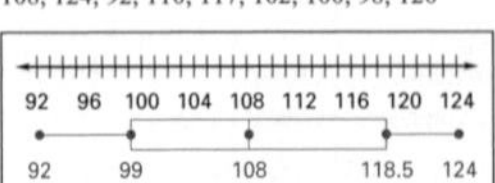

8. 350, 225, 300, 314, 210, 321, 275, 290, 310

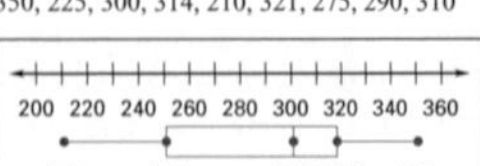

In Exercises 9 and 10, use the box-and-whisker plot.

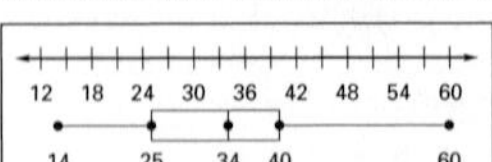

9. About what percent of the data are greater than 25? 75%

10. About what percent of the data are less than 34? 50%

1. median: 46; lower quartile: 39; upper quartile: 52; interquartile range: 13
2. median: 45; lower quartile: 37; upper quartile: 59; interquartile range: 22
3. median: 170; lower quartile: 159; upper quartile: 184; interquartile range: 25
4. median: 4.4; lower quartile: 2.9; upper quartile: 5.3; interquartile range: 2.4

LESSON 13.8

Practice B *continued*

For use with pages 887–892

Make a box-and-whisker plot of the data. Identify any outliers.

11. 17, 38, 22, 15, 13, 24, 18, 10, 20, 13, 17, 12

10 15 20 25 30 35 40

10 13 17 21 38

38 is an outlier

12. 134, 115, 105, 100, 115, 134, 200, 310, 124

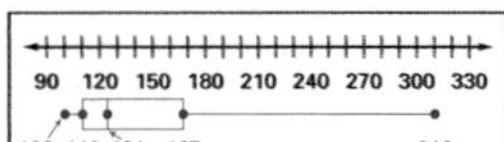

310 is an outlier

13. 45, 30, 30, 17, 15, 27, 23, 25, 26, 30, 33, 30

10 15 20 25 30 35 40 45 50

15 24 28.5 30 45

45 is an outlier

14. 730, 640, 500, 719, 620, 645, 740, 703, 690

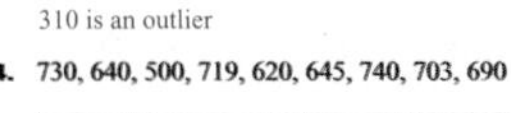

no outliers

15. Gas Prices The prices of a gallon of gasoline (in dollars) for selected countries in 2003 are listed below.

Australia: $2.20 Canada: $2.02
Germany: $4.58 Japan: $3.47
Mexico: $2.09 Taiwan: $2.16
United States: $1.59

a. Make a box-and-whisker plot of the gasoline prices.

b. Which countries, if any, had gasoline prices that can be considered outliers? no outliers

2003 Gas Prices (dollars)

1.00 1.50 2.00 2.50 3.00 3.50 4.00 4.50 5.00

1.59 2.02 2.16 3.47 4.58

16. Supreme Court Justices The stem-and-leaf plot shows the lengths of the terms (in years) of Supreme Court justices appointed from 1902 until 1986.

Stems	Leaves
0	1 3 3 4 4 5 5 5 5 5 6 6 7 7 7 8 9
1	0 0 1 2 3 5 5 5 6 6 6 6 6 7 8 9 9
2	2 3 3 4 4 6 6 9
3	1 3 4 6

Key: 1 | 5 = 15

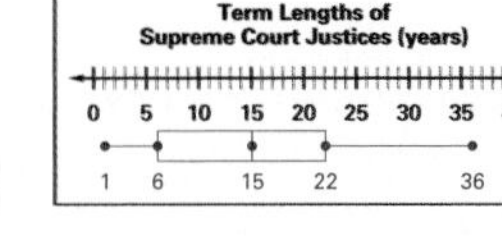

a. Make a box-and-whisker plot of the lengths of the terms.

b. William Douglas has served the longest so far with a term of 36 years. Can his term be considered an outlier? *Explain* why or why not. no, because 36 < 22 + 1.5(16)

13 Assessment

CHAPTER 13 Quiz 1
For use after Lessons 13.1–13.4

In Exercises 1 and 2, use the following information.

A box contains 10 green balls and 6 red balls. You choose a ball at random.

1. What is the probability that you select a green ball?
2. What is the probability that you select a red ball?

In Exercises 3 and 4, use the following information.

A bucket contains 10 balls numbered as follows: 1, 2, 2, 3, 3, 3, 3, 4, 4, 5. A single ball is randomly chosen from the bucket.

3. What is the probability of drawing a ball numbered 3?
4. What is the probability of drawing a ball with a number greater than 3?
5. Consider the number of permutations of the letters in the word BOATS. In how many ways can you arrange all of the letters?

Evaluate the expression.

6. ${}_4P_2$
7. ${}_5P_3$
8. ${}_5C_2$
9. ${}_6C_3$

Answers

1. $\frac{5}{8}$
2. $\frac{3}{8}$
3. $\frac{2}{5}$
4. $\frac{3}{10}$
5. 120
6. 12
7. 60
8. 10
9. 20

CHAPTER 13 Quiz 2
For use after Lessons 13.5–13.8

In Exercises 1 and 2, use the following information.

A community hospital conducts a survey to determine patient satisfaction. One hundred patients are randomly selected to complete the survey.

1. Identify the population.
2. Classify the sampling method.

In Exercises 3 and 4, find the range and mean absolute deviation of the data. Round to the nearest hundredth, if necessary.

3. 13, 21, 17, 8, 19, 18
4. 83, 90, 49, 57, 74, 63, 32
5. Make a histogram of the data: 1.4, 2.5, 1.7, 2.0, 1.6, 2.2, 2.7, 1.5, 2.3.

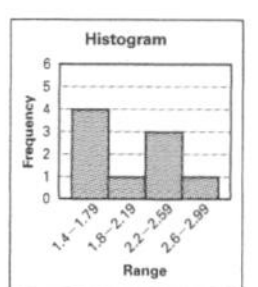

6. Make a stem-and-leaf plot of the data: 24, 12, 6, 31, 8, 17, 35, 15.

0	6 8
1	2 5 7
2	4
3	1 5

Key: 1|2 = 12

In Exercises 7 and 8, use the following information.

The ages of senior citizens who play on a chess team are given in years: 77, 65, 78, 70, 71, 86, 73, 65, 75, 69, 68.

7. Make a box-and-whisker plot of the data.

Age of Senior Citizens (years)
60 64 68 72 76 80 84 88 92
65 68 71 77 86

8. Identify any outliers.

Answers

1. all selected patients
2. random sample
3. 13; 3.67
4. 58; 15.71
5. See left.
6. See left.
7. See left.
8. none

CHAPTER 13 Chapter Test B
For use after Chapter 13

In Exercises 1–3, use the following information.

Cystic fibrosis is an inherited disease that effects the functioning of the glands. F is the normal gene and f is the mutant gene. Any gene combination with an F results in healthy offspring. Suppose each parent has the same gene combination Ff.

1. Use a Punnett square to list the possible outcomes for their offspring.
2. What is the probability that a child will have cystic fibrosis?
3. What are the odds against a child being a carrier of cystic fibrosis?
4. The table shows the data collected from a citizen's group concerned about the safety of three intersections in their community. Find the probability that a randomly chosen vehicle will be involved in an accident at each intersection. Which intersection is the most dangerous? Explain.

Intersection	1	2	3
Number of vehicles (per day)	8330	25,250	3640
Number of accidents (per year)	110	175	45

Evaluate the expression.

5. 0!
6. ${}_{10}P_4$
7. ${}_7C_3$

Tell whether the question can be answered using *combinations* or *permutations*. Explain your choice, then answer the question.

8. On a sailboat there are 6 signal flags. The order the flags are strung on the mast determines the signal being sent. How many 3-flag signals can the captain send?
9. You are taking an online algebra quiz in which 6 questions are randomly selected from a test bank containing 50 questions. How many versions of the quiz are possible?

In Exercises 10 and 11, refer to a bag containing 13 red balls numbered 1–13 and 5 green balls numbered 14–18.

10. You choose a ball at random. What is the probability that you choose a red or an even numbered ball?
11. You randomly choose 2 balls from the bag at the same time. What is the probability that you choose a red ball and a green ball?

Answers

1. FF, Ff, Ff, ff
2. $\frac{1}{4}$
3. 1 : 1
4. $\frac{11}{833}$, $\frac{7}{1010}$, $\frac{9}{728}$; Intersection #1 because the probability is the highest.
5. 1
6. 5040
7. 35
8. permutations; the order of the flags is important; 120
9. combinations; the order of the questions is not important; 15,890,700
10. $\frac{8}{9}$
11. $\frac{65}{306}$

CHAPTER 13 Chapter Test B *continued*
For use after Chapter13

In Exercises 12–14, use the following information.

A manager of a buffet-style restaurant wants to gather information about his customers' perceptions of the cleanliness of the restaurant. The first 25 people leaving the restaurant are briefly interviewed.

12. Identify the population.
13. Classify the sampling method.
14. Tell whether the survey method used is likely to result in a biased sample.

Find the mean, median, and mode(s) of the data.

15. 1, 2, 5, 7, 8, 18, 22
16. 14, 12, 17, 15, 11, 12, 11, 13

Find the range and mean absolute deviation of the data. Round to the nearest hundredth, if necessary.

17. 48, 93, 87, 93, 59, 70
18. 1, 3, 6, 7, 5

In Exercises 19–21, use the following information.

A survey asked people how many minutes they talked during a long-distance phone call. The results are: 15, 7, 25, 10, 18, 10, 10, 23, 4, 12, 8, 6.

19. Make a stem-and-leaf plot of the data.

0	4 6 7 8
1	0 0 0 2 5 8
2	3 5

Key: 2 | 3 = 23

20. Make a histogram of the data.

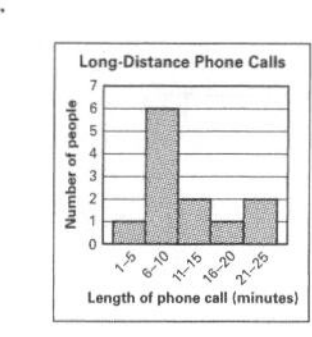

21. What is the probability that a randomly chosen long-distance phone call was more than 15 minutes?

In Exercises 22–24, use the box-and-whisker plot.

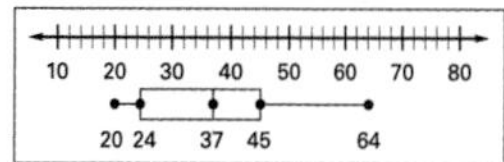

22. About what percent of the data are less than 45?
23. About what percent of the data are greater than 37?
24. Which value, if any, is an outlier?

Answers

12. all patrons of the restaurant
13. convenience sample
14. The restaurant may lack cleanliness later in the day or during other shifts, so the method may result in a biased sample.
15. 9; 7; none
16. 13; 13.125; 12 and 11
17. 45; 16
18. 6; 1.92
19. See left.
20. See left.
21. $\frac{1}{4}$
22. 75%
23. 50%
24. none

13 Assessment

CHAPTER 13 Standardized Test

For use after Chapter 13

Multiple Choice

1. How many possible outcomes are there when you roll two number cubes and toss one coin? C

Ⓐ 13 Ⓑ 36 Ⓒ 72 Ⓓ 144

2. The probability of an event occurring is 7 : 10. What are the odds against the event? C

Ⓐ 3 : 10 Ⓑ 10 : 3
Ⓒ 3 : 7 Ⓓ 10 : 7

3. According to a meteorologist, there is a 60% chance of thunderstorms today. What are the odds that it will *not* storm? B

Ⓐ 3 : 5 Ⓑ 2 : 3
Ⓒ 2 : 5 Ⓓ 1 : 25

4. How many ways can you arrange all the letters in the word MATH? D

Ⓐ 4 Ⓑ 6 Ⓒ 12 Ⓓ 24

5. The judges of the science fair will be awarding ribbons for first, second, and third place, plus a ribbon for honorable mention out of 15 entries. Which expression gives the number of ways the judges can award first place, second place, third place, and honorable mention? B

Ⓐ $\frac{4!}{11!}$ Ⓑ $\frac{15!}{11!}$ Ⓒ $\frac{11!}{15!}$ Ⓓ $\frac{11!}{4!}$

6. You need to go to the library, grocery store, and pharmacy. In how many orders can you visit these places? B

Ⓐ 3 Ⓑ 6 Ⓒ 9 Ⓓ 12

7. What is the value of ${}_8P_5$? C

Ⓐ 56 Ⓑ 120
Ⓒ 6720 Ⓓ 40,320

8. What is the value of ${}_6C_3$? A

Ⓐ 20 Ⓑ 120 Ⓒ 240 Ⓓ 1200

9. How many combinations of 3 letters can you make from the list A, B, C, D, and E? A

Ⓐ 10 Ⓑ 20 Ⓒ 30 Ⓓ 60

10. You are ordering a 3-topping pizza from a pizzeria. You have 10 topping choices. How many different pizzas are possible? B

Ⓐ 60 Ⓑ 120 Ⓒ 720 Ⓓ 5040

11. You roll a number cube. What is the probability that you will roll an even number *or* a number greater than 4? C

Ⓐ $0.1\overline{6}$ Ⓑ 0.5 Ⓒ $0.\overline{6}$ Ⓓ $0.8\overline{3}$

12. You flip a coin and roll a number cube. What is the probability that the coin shows tails and the number cube shows a 3? D

Ⓐ $\frac{2}{3}$ Ⓑ $\frac{1}{2}$ Ⓒ $\frac{1}{6}$ Ⓓ $\frac{1}{12}$

13. A jar contains 6 red marbles, 5 blue marbles, and 9 green marbles. What is the probability of randomly choosing a blue marble and then another blue marble if the first marble is not replaced? B

Ⓐ $\frac{1}{20}$ Ⓑ $\frac{1}{19}$ Ⓒ $\frac{1}{18}$ Ⓓ $\frac{1}{16}$

14. Which of the following statements is *not* potentially biased? C

Ⓐ Do you prefer creamy macaroni and cheese or bland rice?

Ⓑ Don't you feel the city is wasting money by building that new stadium?

Ⓒ Do you prefer shopping online or in the stores?

Ⓓ Don't you agree that the driving age should be raised to 18 so as to decrease the number of accidents?

CHAPTER 13 Standardized Test *continued*

For use after Chapter 13

15. What is the mean absolute deviation of the data? Round your answer to the nearest hundredth if necessary. D

36.2, 3.4, 76.4, 5.5, 2.8, 84.8

Ⓐ 22.54 Ⓑ 28.72
Ⓒ 32.6 Ⓓ 30.95

In Exercises 16 and 17, use the stem-and-leaf plot.

Set A		Set B
2 0	1	2 5 7 8 8
8 7 4 1	2	1 3 4 6
9 5 3 1 0	3	
8 7 4 1 1	4	2 5 8 9 9

Key: 2 | 1 | 5 = 12, 15

16. What is the range of data set A? C

Ⓐ 36 Ⓑ 37 Ⓒ 38 Ⓓ 48

17. What is the mean of data set B? Round your answer to the nearest hundredth if necessary. D

Ⓐ 24.89 Ⓑ 25.48
Ⓒ 27.32 Ⓓ 29.07

18. In a box-and-whisker plot, each whisker represents about what percent of the data? A

Ⓐ 25% Ⓑ 50% Ⓒ 75% Ⓓ 100%

Gridded Answer

19. What is the median of the following data set?

0.2, 0.5, 0.2, 1.2, 0.8, 1.4, 0.6, 1.8

Answer grid: 0 . 7

21. a. $\frac{6}{11}$ **b.** $\frac{2}{3}$; $\frac{3}{7}$; $\frac{1}{3}$

c. The star player is most likely to make attempted 3-point shots during games with a point difference of 0–7 points at the end of the game because the probability of the player making them is $\frac{2}{3}$, rather than $\frac{3}{7}$ and $\frac{1}{3}$.

20. a. Number of Years Spent Teaching: box-and-whisker plot on a number line from −5 to 40, with values 0, 8, 12, 20, 36.

Short Response

20. The stem-and-leaf plot shows the number of years spent teaching by teachers in your school.

0	0 3 5 5 8 8 9
1	0 1 2 2 4 5 7
2	0 1 7 9
3	6

Key: 1 | 0 = 10 years

20. b. Yes, 36 would be considered an outlier because it is more than 1.5 times the upper quartile.

a. Make a box-and-whisker plot of the data. See above.

b. Mrs. Smith has been teaching for 36 years. Can the number of years she has spent teaching be considered an outlier? *Explain* your reasoning.

Extended Response

21. The table shows last season's 3-point shot statistics for your school's star basketball player.

	Point Difference at end of game		
	0–7 points	**8–14 points**	**≥ 15 points**
3-point shots attempted	12	7	3
3-point shots made	8	3	1

a. During last season, what was the probability that your school's star basketball player would make an attempted 3-point shot, regardless of the point difference? Write your answer in fraction form. See left.

b. Find the probabilities that the star player made an attempted 3-point shot when the point difference at the end of the game was 0–7 points, 8–14 points, and at least 15 points. Write your answers in fraction form. See left.

c. During what kind of games is the star player most likely to make attempted 3-point shots. *Justify* your conclusion. See left.

CHAPTER 13 Alternative Assessment and Math Journal

For use after Chapter 13

Journal

1. Write a survey question that is biased in some way and explain the reason. Rewrite the question so that it is no longer biased.

Multi-Step Problem

2. The data given represent the heights (in inches) of a class of ninth grade students. The first row are the heights of the girls in the class and the second row are the heights of the boys.

Girls: 60, 58, 63, 54, 65, 66, 65, 67, 64, 59

Boys: 62, 65, 60, 69, 70, 68, 61, 65, 71, 67

a. A student is randomly selected from the class, what is the probability that the student is over 60 inches tall?

b. A student is randomly selected from the class, what is the probability that the student is a girl and over 60 inches tall?

c. A student is randomly selected from the class, what is the probability that the student is a boy or over 60 inches tall?

d. Determine the mean, median, and mode(s) of the students' heights.

e. Compare the spread of the data for the girls and boys heights using the range and the mean absolute deviation.

f. Make a stem-and-leaf plot of the entire set of data.

g. Make a box-and-whisker plot of the data for each group.

1. Complete answers should include: a survey question that is biased; an explanation of the reason for the bias; an edited survey question that is no longer biased.

2. a. $\frac{3}{4} = 0.75$ **b.** $\frac{3}{10} = 0.3$ **c.** $\frac{4}{5} = 0.8$ **d.** 63.95; 65; 65

e. Girls: range = 13, mean absolute deviation = 3.48; Boys: range = 11, mean absolute deviation = 3.2

f. Students' Heights

Girls		Boys
9 8 4	5	
7 6 5 5 4 3 0	6	0 1 2 5 5 7 8 9
	7	0 1

Key: 3 | 6 | 1 = 63 in., 61 in.

g.

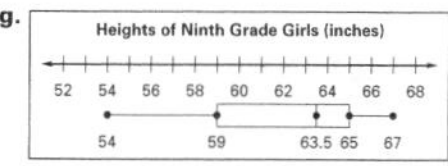

Heights of Ninth Grade Boys (inches)

58 60 62 64 66 68 70 72 74

60 62 66 69 71

CHAPTER 13 Alternative Assessment Rubric *continued*

For use after Chapter 13

Journal Solution

1. Complete answers should include:

- a survey question that is biased.
- an explanation of the reason for the bias.
- an edited survey question that is no longer biased.

Multi-Step Problem Solution

2. a. $\frac{3}{4} = 0.75$ **b.** $\frac{3}{10} = 0.3$ **c.** $\frac{4}{5} = 0.8$ **d.** 63.95; 65; 65

e. Girls: range = 13, mean absolute deviation = 3.48; Boys: range = 11, mean absolute deviation = 3.2

f. Students' Heights

Girls		Boys
9 8 4	5	
7 6 5 5 4 3 0	6	0 1 2 5 5 7 8 9
	7	0 1

Key: 3 | 6 | 1 = 63 in., 61 in.

g.

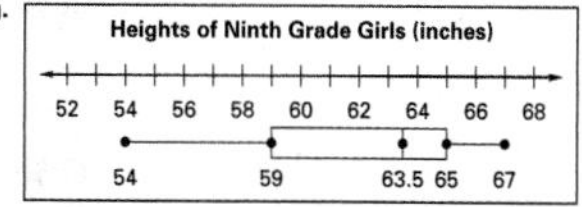

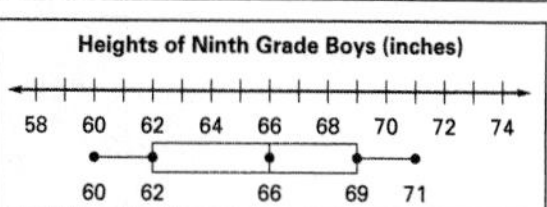

Multi-Step Problem Rubric

4 The student answers all parts of the problem correctly and completely. The student shows all work. The student's work is neat.

3 The student answers all parts of the problem. The student's work may contain one or two errors in the calculations or plots. The student shows most work. The student's work is neat.

2 The student answers all parts of the problem, but there are more than two errors in the calculations or plots. The student shows some work. The student's work is sloppy.

1 The student does not complete all parts of the problem. The student's work has several errors in the calculations and plots. The student's work is sloppy, or no work is shown.

PLAN AND PREPARE

Main Ideas

In Chapter 13, students calculate probabilities and odds of simple events. They calculate probabilities of compound events, identifying whether events are mutually exclusive or overlapping, or whether they are dependent or independent. Students identify potentially biased samples and questions. They compare measures of central tendency and measures of dispersion, and analyze and display data.

Prerequisite Skills

Skills Readiness, available on the *Easy Planner*, provides review and practice for the Skills Check portion of the Prerequisite Skills quiz.

How student answers the exercises	What to assign from *Skills Readiness*
Any of Exs. 2–3 answered incorrectly	**Skill 84** Mean, median, and mode
Any of Exs. 4–7 answered incorrectly	**Skill 10** Simplify fractions
Any of Exs. 8–11 answered incorrectly	**Skill 48** Add and subtract fractions
Any of Exs. 12–15 answered incorrectly	**Skill 47** Multiply fractions
All exercises answered correctly	Chapter 13 Enrichment

Additional skills review and practice is available in the Skills Review Handbook, pp. 909–937, and the @HomeTutor.

13 Probability and Data Analysis

Making Sense of Chapter 13

Chapter 13 focuses on data. By the end of this chapter, you will be able to compute probabilities and odds, and to analyze data using measures of central tendency and dispersion.

Before

In previous courses, you learned the following skills, which you'll use in Chapter 13: finding the mean, median, and mode(s) of data, simplifying fractions, and performing operations with fractions.

Prerequisite Skills

VOCABULARY CHECK

1. Copy and complete: The _?_ of a numerical data set is the middle number when the values are written in numerical order. **median**

SKILLS CHECK

Find the mean, median, and mode(s) of the data. *(Prerequisite skill for 13.6)*

2. 0.2, 1.3, 0.9, 1.5, 2.1, 1.8, 0.6 **1.2, 1.3, no mode**
3. 103, 121, 111, 194, 99, 160, 134, 160 **135.25, 127.5, 160**

Write the fraction in simplest form. *(Prerequisite skill for 13.1–13.4)*

4. $\frac{16}{24}$ $\frac{2}{3}$
5. $\frac{12}{40}$ $\frac{3}{10}$
6. $\frac{16}{36}$ $\frac{4}{9}$
7. $\frac{12}{50}$ $\frac{6}{25}$

Perform the indicated operation. *(Prerequisite skill for 13.4)*

8. $\frac{4}{15} + \frac{8}{15}$ $\frac{4}{5}$
9. $\frac{7}{27} + \frac{11}{27}$ $\frac{2}{3}$
10. $\frac{15}{32} - \frac{7}{32}$ $\frac{1}{4}$
11. $\frac{19}{28} - \frac{5}{28}$ $\frac{1}{2}$
12. $\frac{2}{3} \cdot \frac{3}{4}$ $\frac{1}{2}$
13. $\frac{3}{8} \cdot \frac{4}{5}$ $\frac{3}{10}$
14. $\frac{9}{20} \cdot \frac{5}{12}$ $\frac{3}{16}$
15. $\frac{14}{26} \cdot \frac{13}{25}$ $\frac{7}{25}$

@HomeTutor Prerequisite skills practice at classzone.com

840

Chapter Planning Guide

Chapter Resource Book
- Teaching Guide/Lesson Plan
- Project with Rubric

Assessment and Intervention
- Assessment Book
- Benchmark Tests
- Remediation Book
- Skills Readiness

Interactive Technology
- Easy Planner
- Power Presentations
- Activity Generator
- Animated Algebra
- Test Generator
- Online Quizzes
- eWorkbook
- eEdition
- @HomeTutor

Resources for English Learners
- Spanish Study Guide
- Multi-Language Visual Glossary
- Student Resources in Spanish

See also the *Differentiated Instruction Resources* for more strategies for meeting individual needs.

Now

In Chapter 13, you will apply the big ideas listed below and reviewed in the Chapter Summary on page 895. You will also use the key vocabulary listed below.

Big Ideas

1. **Finding probabilities of simple and compound events**
2. **Analyzing sets of data**
3. **Making and interpreting data displays**

KEY VOCABULARY

- outcome, *p. 843*
- event, *p. 843*
- probability, *p. 843*
- odds, *p. 845*
- permutation, *p. 851*
- combination, *p. 856*
- compound event, *p. 861*
- survey, *p. 871*
- sample, *p. 871*
- measure of dispersion, *p. 876*
- range, *p. 876*
- stem-and-leaf plot, *p. 881*
- frequency, *p. 882*
- histogram, *p. 882*
- box-and-whisker plot, *p. 887*
- interquartile range, *p. 888*
- outlier, *p. 889*

Why?

You can use probability and data analysis to make predictions. For example, you can use data about a kicker's past successes in football games to find the chance of his success in the future.

Animated Algebra

The animation illustrated below for Exercise 22 on page 848 helps you to answer this question: What is the probability that the kicker makes an attempted field goal?

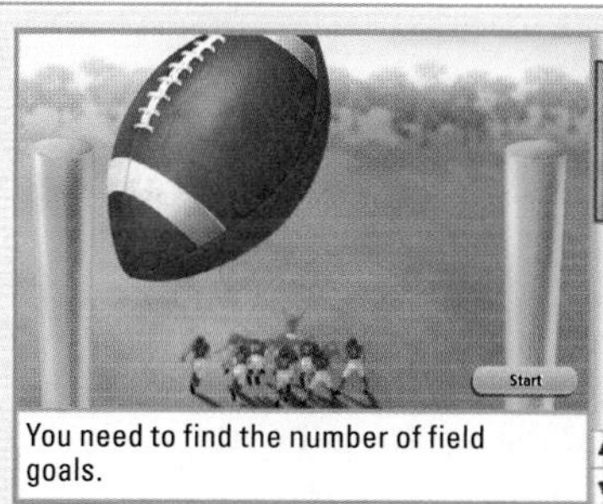

Start
You need to find the number of field goals.

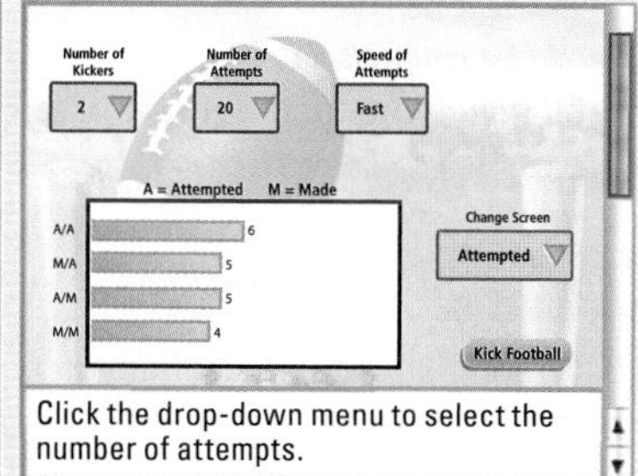

Animated Algebra at classzone.com

Other animations for Chapter 13: pages 845, 856, 875, and 887

Differentiated Instruction Resources

- Reading Strategies for Chapter 13
- Differentiated Instruction Lesson Notes
- English Learners Lesson Notes
- Inclusion Lesson Notes
- Teaching Strategies with Sample Worksheets
- Using Technology in the Classroom
- Tips for New Teachers
- Math Background Notes
- Assessment Strategies
- Teacher Survival Activities
- Bulletin Board Idea

1 PLAN AND PREPARE

Explore the Concept

- Students will perform an experiment and record the results to find the likelihood of selecting the first initial, the last initial, or both first and last initials of students in the class.
- This activity leads into the study of experimental probability in Example 3 in Lesson 13.1.

Materials

Each student or group of students will need a paper bag.

Recommended Time

Work activity: 10 min
Discuss results: 5 min

Grouping

Students can work individually or in pairs. If students work in pairs, one student can draw a letter at random and the other student can record the result.

2 TEACH

Tips for Success

Tell students to make both selections before they put any tally marks in their table so that they do not end up with too many tally marks.

Key Discovery

You can use the outcomes of an experiment to predict the likelihood of an event.

3 ASSESS AND RETEACH

How many times would you expect to select the first initial of a student after 60 experiments? **Answers will vary.**

13.1 Find a Probability

MATERIALS • paper bag

QUESTION **What is the chance that you would select the initials of a student in your class from a bag of letters?**

You can perform an experiment and record the results to approximate the likelihood of selecting the initials of a student in your class.

EXPLORE **Perform an experiment**

STEP 1 ***Select letters***

Write each of the 26 letters of the alphabet on separate pieces of paper. Put all of the letters into a bag. Select a letter at random (without looking into the bag). Replace the letter and select a second letter at random.

STEP 2 ***Record the results***

Record the results of the selections in a table like the one shown.

- If the first letter is the first initial of any student in your class, put a tally mark in the "first initial" column.
- If the second letter is the last initial of any student in your class, put a tally mark in the "last initial" column.
- If the two letters are the first and last initials of any student in your class, put a tally mark in the "both initials" column, but do not put a tally mark in the other columns.

Perform this experiment 30 times.

	First initial	Last initial	Both initials
Tally	𝍸	𝍸 II	I
Frequency	?	?	?

STEP 3 ***Record the frequencies***

Record the *frequency*, the total number of tally marks, of each possible result.

DRAW CONCLUSIONS **Use your observations to complete these excercises**
1–3. Answers may vary.

1. For what fraction of the times that you performed the experiment did you select the first initial of a student in your class? the last initial? both?
2. Which of these results do you think is least likely to happen if you repeat the experiment 30 more times? *Explain* your choice.
3. **REASONING** You perform the experiment 90 times. How many times do you expect to select both the first and last initials of a student in your class? *Explain* how you made your prediction.

13.1 Find Probabilities and Odds

Before You made organized lists and tree diagrams.
Now You will find sample spaces and probabilities.
Why? So you can find the likelihood of an event, as in Example 2.

Key Vocabulary
- outcome
- event
- sample space
- probability
- odds

A possible result of an experiment is an **outcome**. For instance, when you roll a number cube there are 6 possible outcomes: a 1, 2, 3, 4, 5, or 6. An **event** is an outcome or a collection of outcomes, such as rolling an odd number. The set of all possible outcomes is called a **sample space**.

EXAMPLE 1 **Find a sample space**

You flip a coin and roll a number cube. How many possible outcomes are in the sample space? List the possible outcomes.

REVIEW TREE DIAGRAMS
For help with tree diagrams, see p. 930.

Solution

Use a tree diagram to find the outcomes in the sample space.

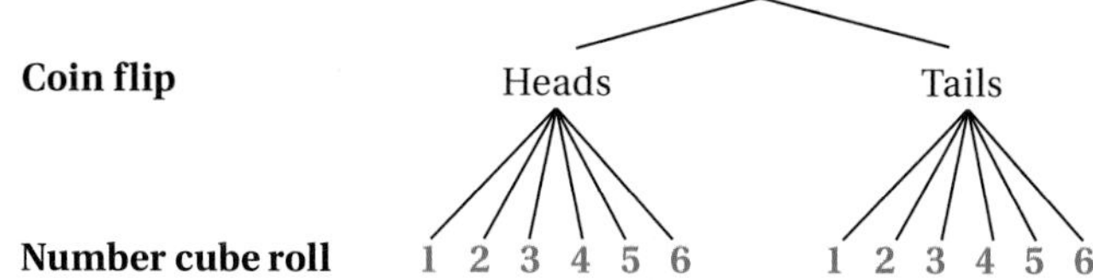

The sample space has 12 possible outcomes. They are listed below.

Heads, 1 Heads, 2 Heads, 3 Heads, 4 Heads, 5 Heads, 6
Tails, 1 Tails, 2 Tails, 3 Tails, 4 Tails, 5 Tails, 6

✓ **GUIDED PRACTICE** for Example 1

1. You flip 2 coins and roll a number cube. How many possible outcomes are in the sample space? List the possible outcomes.
24 outcomes; HH1, HH2, HH3, HH4, HH5, HH6, HT1, HT2, HT3, HT4, HT5, HT6, TH1, TH2, TH3, TH4, TH5, TH6, TT1, TT2, TT3, TT4, TT5, TT6

PROBABILITY The **probability of an event** is a measure of the likelihood, or chance, that the event will occur. Probability is a number from 0 to 1 and can be expressed as a decimal, fraction, or percent.

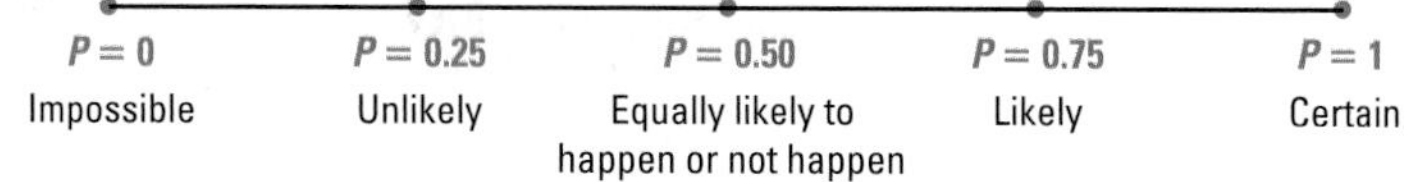

1 PLAN AND PREPARE

Warm-Up Exercises

Transparency Available

1. Use a tree diagram to find the number of possible outfits you can make using one shirt and one pair of shorts if you have 3 shirts and 4 pairs of shorts. **12 outfits**
2. Use an organized list to find the number of possible ways to travel to and from Chicago if you can travel by car, bus, train, or airplane. **16 ways**

Notetaking Guide

Transparency Available

Promotes interactive learning and notetaking skills.

Pacing

Basic: 1 day
Average: 1 day
Advanced: 1 day
Block: 0.5 block with 13.2
- See *Teaching Guide/Lesson Plan.*

2 FOCUS AND MOTIVATE

Essential Question

Big Idea 1, p. 841

How do you find the probability an event? **Tell students they will learn how to answer this question by comparing favorable and possible outcomes in a theoretical situation and successes and trials in an experimental situation.**

NCTM STANDARDS

Standard 5: Understand basic concepts of probability; Apply basic concepts of probability

Resource Planning Guide

Chapter Resource Book
- Teaching Guide/Lesson Plan
- Activity Master
- Practice levels A, B, C
- Study Guide
- Catch-up for Absent Students
- Application
- Challenge

Workbooks
- Notetaking Guide
- Practice Workbook

Teaching Options
- **Power Presentations** provides dynamic electronic teaching resources for the classroom.
- **Activity Generator** provides editable activities for all ability levels.

Interactive Technology
- Easy Planner
- Power Presentations
- Activity Generator
- Animated Algebra
- Test Generator
- Online Quiz
- eWorkbook
- eEdition
- @HomeTutor

Resources for English Learners
- Spanish Study Guide
- Multi-Language Visual Glossary
- Student Resources in Spanish

See also the *Differentiated Instruction Resources* for more strategies for meeting individual needs.

THEORETICAL PROBABILITY The outcomes for a specified event are called *favorable outcomes*. When all outcomes are equally likely, the **theoretical probability** of the event can be found using the following:

$$\textbf{Theoretical probability} = \frac{\textbf{Number of favorable outcomes}}{\textbf{Total number of outcomes}}$$

The probability of event A is written as $P(A)$.

EXAMPLE 2 Find a theoretical probability

T-SHIRTS You and your friends designed T-shirts with silk screened emblems, and you are selling the T-shirts to raise money. The table below shows the number of T-shirts you have in each design. A student chooses a T-shirt at random. What is the probability that the student chooses a red T-shirt?

	Gold emblem	Silver emblem
Green T-shirt	10	8
Red T-shirt	6	6

Solution

You and your friends have a total of $10 + 6 + 8 + 6 = 30$ T-shirts. So, there are 30 possible outcomes. Of all the T-shirts, 12 T-shirts are red. There are 12 favorable outcomes.

$$P(\text{red T-shirt}) = \frac{\text{Number of favorable outcomes}}{\text{Total number of outcomes}}$$

$$= \frac{\text{Number of red T-shirts}}{\text{Total number of T-shirts}}$$

$$= \frac{12}{30}$$

$$= \frac{2}{5}$$

GUIDED PRACTICE for Example 2

2. **T-SHIRTS** In Example 2, what is the probability that the student chooses a T-shirt with a gold emblem? $\frac{8}{15}$
3. You toss a coin and roll a number cube. What is the probability that the coin shows tails and the number cube shows 4? $\frac{1}{12}$

EXPERIMENTAL PROBABILITY An **experimental probability** is based on repeated *trials* of an experiment. The number of trials is the number of times the experiment is performed. Each trial in which a favorable outcome occurs is called a *success*.

$$\textbf{Experimental probability} = \frac{\textbf{Number of successes}}{\textbf{Number of trials}}$$

Motivating the Lesson

In a contest on a local radio station, one female and one male teen will be chosen at random to be on the air for an hour with a disc jockey. If you enter the contest and you know the number of other teens of your gender who entered the contest, you can determine the likelihood that you will be chosen as one of the teen disc jockeys.

3 TEACH

Extra Example 1

You flip a coin twice. How many possible outcomes are in the sample space? List the possible outcomes. **The sample space has 4 outcomes.**

heads, heads **heads, tails**
tails, heads **tails, tails**

Key Question to Ask for Example 1

- Does the sample space change if you flip the coin first and then roll the number cube? Explain. **No; each number on the number cube will still be paired with heads and also with tails.**

Extra Example 2

A department store is offering a discount on sunglasses. The table shows the number of each type of discounted sunglasses. You choose a pair at random. What is the probability that the pair you choose is polarized? $\frac{3}{7}$

	Green Lens	Brown Lens
Polarized	8	4
Mirrored	7	9

Differentiated Instruction

Below Level Ask students to find the probability of choosing a T-shirt for each of the four designs. Then ask which design is most likely to be chosen at random and which design is least likely to be chosen. Have them support their answers using the probabilities they found for each of the designs. Then have them reproduce the probability line on page 843 and insert the probabilities for each T-shirt design on the line. Suggest that they include the probability of choosing a T-shirt that is red, that is green, that has a gold emblem, and that has a silver emblem.

See also the *Differentiated Instruction Resources* for more strategies.

EXAMPLE 3 Standardized Test Practice

Each section of the spinner shown has the same area. The spinner was spun 20 times. The table shows the results. For which color is the experimental probability of stopping on the color the same as the theoretical probability?

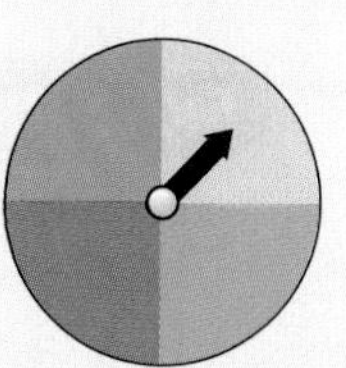

Spinner Results			
Red	Green	Blue	Yellow
5	9	3	3

Ⓐ Red Ⓑ Green Ⓒ Blue Ⓓ Yellow

Solution

The theoretical probability of stopping on each of the four colors is $\frac{1}{4}$. Use the outcomes in the table to find the experimental probabilities.

$P(\text{red}) = \frac{5}{20} = \frac{1}{4}$ $P(\text{green}) = \frac{9}{20}$ $P(\text{blue}) = \frac{3}{20}$ $P(\text{yellow}) = \frac{3}{20}$

▶ The correct answer is A. Ⓐ Ⓑ Ⓒ Ⓓ

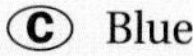

at classzone.com

ODDS The odds of an event compare the number of favorable and unfavorable outcomes when all outcomes are equally likely.

$$\textbf{Odds in favor} = \frac{\textbf{Number of favorable outcomes}}{\textbf{Number of unfavorable outcomes}}$$

$$\textbf{Odds against} = \frac{\textbf{Number of unfavorable outcomes}}{\textbf{Number of favorable outcomes}}$$

EXAMPLE 4 Find the odds

READING
Odds are read as the ratio of one number to another. For instance, the odds $\frac{3}{1}$ are read as "three to one." Odds are usually written as $a : b$.

SPINNER In Example 3, find the odds against stopping on green.

Solution

The 4 possible outcomes are all equally likely. Green is the 1 favorable outcome. The other 3 colors are unfavorable outcomes.

$$\text{Odds against green} = \frac{\text{Number of unfavorable outcomes}}{\text{Number of favorable outcomes}} = \frac{3}{1} \text{ or } 3 : 1.$$

GUIDED PRACTICE for Examples 3 and 4

4. In Example 3, for which color is the experimental probability of stopping on the color greater than the theoretical probability? **green**
5. In Example 3, what are the odds in favor of stopping on blue? $\frac{1}{3}$ **or 1 : 3**

Extra Example 3

A bag contains one blue, one green, one yellow, and one red ball. A ball is drawn at random from the bag and then replaced. The table shows the results for 24 drawings. For which color of ball is the experimental probability of drawing the color the same as the theoretical probability?

Random Drawing Results			
Blue	Green	Yellow	Red
4	6	9	5

Ⓐ Blue Ⓑ Green
Ⓒ Red Ⓓ Yellow

The correct answer is B.

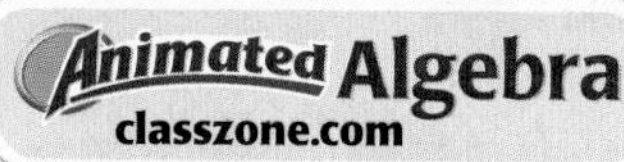

An **Animated Algebra** activity is available online for **Example 3**. This activity is also part of **Power Presentations**.

Extra Example 4

In Extra Example 3, find the odds in favor of drawing a yellow ball. **1:3**

Closing the Lesson

Have students summarize the major points of the lesson and answer the Essential Question: How do you find the probability of an event?

- **Theoretical probability is based on all possible outcomes being equally likely.**
- **Experimental probability is based on repeated trials, which is the number of times the experiment is performed.**

The theoretical probability of an event is the ratio of the number of favorable outcomes to the total number of outcomes. The experimental probability of an event is the ratio of the number of successes of the experiment to the number of trials.

13.1 EXERCISES

HOMEWORK KEY
○ = **WORKED-OUT SOLUTIONS** on p. WS31 for Exs. 3 and 21
★ = **STANDARDIZED TEST PRACTICE** Exs. 2, 14–16, 21, and 22

4 PRACTICE AND APPLY

Assignment Guide

Answer Transparencies available for all exercises

Basic:
Day 1: SRH p. 931 Exs. 4–8
pp. 846–848
Exs. 1–15, 19–21, 24–26

Average:
Day 1: pp. 846–848
Exs. 1, 2–12 even, 13–17, 19–22, 24–26

Advanced:
Day 1: pp. 846–848
Exs. 1, 2–6 even, 10, 12, 13–26*

Block:
pp. 846–848
Exs. 1, 2–12 even, 13–17, 19–22, 24–26 (with 13.2)

Differentiated Instruction

See *Differentiated Instruction Resources* for suggestions on addressing the needs of a diverse classroom.

Homework Check

For a quick check of student understanding of key concepts, go over the following exercises:

Basic: 4, 7, 9, 11, 21
Average: 4, 10, 12, 19, 21
Advanced: 6, 10, 14, 20, 21

Extra Practice

- Student Edition, p. 950
- Chapter Resource Book: Practice levels A, B, C

Practice Worksheet

An easily-readable reduced practice page (with answers) for this lesson can be found on p. 840C.

SKILL PRACTICE

A

1. **VOCABULARY** Copy and complete: A number that describes the likelihood of an event is the __?__ of the event. **probability**

2. ★ **WRITING** *Explain* how the probability of an event differs from the odds in favor of the event when all outcomes are equally likely. **See margin.**

EXAMPLE 1 on p. 843 for Exs. 3–6

SAMPLE SPACE In Exercises 3–6, find the number of possible outcomes in the sample space. Then list the possible outcomes.

3. A bag contains 4 red cards numbered 1–4, 4 white cards numbered 1–4, and 4 black cards numbered 1–4. You choose a card at random. **12 outcomes; R1, R2, R3, R4, W1, W2, W3, W4, B1, B2, B3, B4**

4. You toss two coins. **4 outcomes; HH, TT, HT, TH**

5. You roll a number cube and toss three coins. **See margin.**

6. You roll two number cubes. **See margin.**

EXAMPLE 2 on p. 844 for Exs. 7–8

PROBABILITY AND ODDS In Exercises 7–13, refer to the spinner shown. The spinner is divided into sections with the same area.

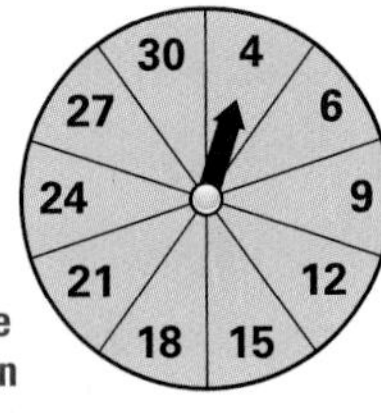

7. What is the probability that the spinner stops on a multiple of 3? $\frac{9}{10}$

8. **ERROR ANALYSIS** *Describe* and correct the error in finding the probability of stopping on a multiple of 9.

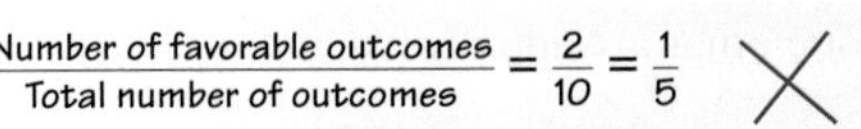

$$\frac{\text{Number of favorable outcomes}}{\text{Total number of outcomes}} = \frac{2}{10} = \frac{1}{5}$$

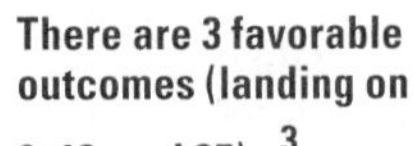

There are 3 favorable outcomes (landing on 9, 18, and 27); $\frac{3}{10}$.

EXAMPLE 3 on p. 845 for Exs. 9–10

9. You spin the spinner 30 times. It stops on 12 three times. What is the experimental probability of stopping on 12? $\frac{1}{10}$

10. You spin the spinner 10 times. It stops on an even number 6 times. What is the experimental probability of stopping on an even number? $\frac{3}{5}$

EXAMPLE 4 on p. 845 for Exs. 11–14

11. What are the odds in favor of stopping on a multiple of 4? $\frac{3}{7}$ **or 3 : 7**

12. What are the odds against stopping on a number less than 12? $\frac{7}{3}$ **or 7 : 3**

13. **ERROR ANALYSIS** *Describe* and correct the error in finding the odds in favor of stopping on a multiple of 3. **See margin.**

$$\text{Odds in favor of a multiple of 3} = \frac{\text{Number of favorable outcomes}}{\text{Total number of outcomes}} = \frac{9}{10} \text{ or } 9:10$$

B

14. ★ **MULTIPLE CHOICE** The odds in favor of an event are 5 : 8. What are the odds against the event? **D**

Ⓐ 3 : 8 Ⓑ 8 : 3 Ⓒ 5 : 8 Ⓓ 8 : 5

15. ★ **WRITING** A manufacturer tests 1200 computers and finds that 1191 of them have no defects. Find the probability that a computer chosen at random has no defects. *Predict* the number of computers without defects in a shipment of 15,000 computers. *Explain* your reasoning.

15. 99.25%; about 14,888 computers; *Sample answer:* I would expect that about 99.25% of the computers or about 14,888 would have no defects.

2. *Sample answer:* The probability of an event is the number of favorable outcomes divided by the number of possible outcomes, while the odds in favor of an event is the number of favorable outcomes divided by the number of unfavorable outcomes.

5. 48; HHH1, HHH2, HHH3, HHH4, HHH5, HHH6, HHT1, HHT2, HHT3, HHT4, HHT5, HHT6, HTH1, HTH2, HTH3, HTH4, HTH5, HTH6, HTT1, HTT2, HTT3, HTT4, HTT5, HTT6, THH1, THH2, THH3, THH4, THH5, THH6, THT1, THT2, THT3, THT4, THT5, THT6, TTH1, TTH2, TTH3, TTH4, TTH5, TTH6, TTT1, TTT2, TTT3, TTT4, TTT5, TTT6

6. 36 outcomes; 1-1, 1-2, 1-3, 1-4, 1-5, 1-6, 2-1, 2-2, 2-3, 2-4, 2-5, 2-6, 3-1, 3-2, 3-3, 3-4, 3-5, 3-6, 4-1, 4-2, 4-3, 4-4, 4-5, 4-6, 5-1, 5-2, 5-3, 5-4, 5-5, 5-6, 6-1, 6-2, 6-3, 6-4, 6-5, 6-6

13. See Additional Answers beginning on p. AA1.

16. ★ **MULTIPLE CHOICE** According to a meteorologist, there is a 40% chance that it will rain today. What are the odds in favor of rain? **B**

Ⓐ 2 : 5 Ⓑ 2 : 3 Ⓒ 3 : 2 Ⓓ 4 : 1

17. **DECISION MAKING** A driver wants to determine which of two possible routes to work he should choose. For 60 work days he recorded which route he took and whether or not he encountered heavy traffic. On 28 days he took route A, and on 7 of those days he encountered heavy traffic. On 32 days he took route B, and on 12 of those days he encountered heavy traffic. Which route would you suggest he choose? *Explain* your answer using experimental probabilities. **See margin.**

C 18. **CHALLENGE** You randomly draw a marble from a bag containing white, red, and blue marbles. The odds against drawing a white marble are 47 : 3.

a. There are fewer than 100 marbles in the bag. How many marbles are in the bag? *Justify* your answer. **See margin.**

b. The probability of drawing a red marble is 0.5. What is the probability of drawing a blue marble? *Explain* how you found your answer. **See margin.**

PROBLEM SOLVING

EXAMPLE 2 on p. 844 for Exs. 19–20

A 19. **MUSIC PROGRAM** You have created a playlist of 7 songs on your MP3 player. You play these songs in a random shuffle, where each song has an equally likely chance of being played. What is the probability that the second song on the list will be played first? $\frac{1}{7}$

@HomeTutor for problem solving help at classzone.com

20. **SURVEY** A survey asked a total of 600 students (100 male students and 100 female students who were 11, 13, and 15 years old) about their exercise habits. The table shows the numbers of students who said they exercise 2 hours or more each week.

	11 years	13 years	15 years
Female	53	57	51
Male	65	68	67

a. What is the probability that a randomly selected female student who participated in this survey exercises 2 hours or more each week? $\frac{161}{300}$

b. What is the probability that a randomly selected 15-year-old student who participated in this survey exercises 2 hours or more each week? $\frac{59}{100}$

c. What is the probability that a randomly selected student who participated in this survey exercises 2 hours or more each week? $\frac{361}{600}$

@HomeTutor for problem solving help at classzone.com

EXAMPLES 2 and 4 on pp. 844–845 for Ex. 21

21. ★ **SHORT RESPONSE** Suppose there are 15 girls and 12 boys in your homeroom. The teacher chooses one student representative at random. What is the probability that a boy is chosen? What are the odds in favor of choosing a boy? *Explain* how the probablity and odds are related. **See margin.**

Avoiding Common Errors

Exercises 7, 9–14 Students often confuse probabilities and odds and experimental and theoretical probability. Remind students that experimental probabilities are based on the number of trials or experiments, and that theoretical probability and odds are based on equally likely outcomes. Suggest that students check each of their answers against the respective formulas for probabilities and odds.

Study Strategy

Exercise 16 Suggest that students ask themselves what the chances are that it will not rain and then compare favorable chances to unfavorable chances to find the odds.

An **Animated Algebra** activity is available online for **Exercise 22.** This activity is also part of **Power Presentations.**

18a. 50 marbles. *Sample answer:* The odds against picking a white marble says that the number of non-white marbles to white marbles must be 47:3. The only pair of numbers that simplifies to this ratio and whose sum is less than 100 total marbles is 47 and 3. There are 47 non-white marbles and 3 white marbles, for a total of 50 marbles.

18b. 0.44. *Sample answer:* There are 50 marbles in the bag, and half of them are blue. So there are 25 blue marbles and 3 white marbles. The rest are red, so there are 22 red marbles. The probability that a red marble is drawn is $\frac{22}{50}$ = 0.44.

21. See Additional Answers beginning on p. AA1.

17. *Sample answer:* route A; The experimental probability that he will encounter heavy traffic on route A is 0.25, and the experimental probability that he will encounter heavy traffic on route B is 0.375.

5 ASSESS AND RETEACH

Daily Homework Quiz

Transparency Available

1. The table shows the number of students in your history class. Your teacher chooses one student at random to give an oral report. What is the probability the student is female? $\frac{7}{15}$

	9th Grade	10th Grade
Male	12	4
Female	8	6

2. A bag contains 8 white marbles, 6 red marbles, and 12 blue marbles. Find the odds against choosing a white marble. **9:4**

Available at **classzone.com**

Diagnosis/Remediation

- Practice A, B, C in Chapter Resource Book
- Study Guide in Chapter Resource Book
- Practice Workbook
- @HomeTutor

Challenge

Additional challenge is available in the Chapter Resource Book.

B 22. ★ **EXTENDED RESPONSE** The table shows the 2003 regular season field goal statistics for kicker Adam Vinatieri.

	Point difference at end of game		
	0–7 points	8–14 points	≥ 15 points
Field goals attempted	20	11	3
Field goals made	16	7	2

a. During the 2003 regular season, what was the probability that Adam Vinatieri would make an attempted field goal, regardless of the point difference? $\frac{25}{34}$

b. Find the probabilities that Vinatieri made an attempted field goal when the point difference at the end of the game was 0–7 points, 8–14 points, and at least 15 points.

c. During what kinds of games was Adam Vinatieri most likely to make attempted field goals? *Justify* your answer.

Animated Algebra classzone.com

22b. $0–7: \frac{4}{5}$, $8–14: \frac{7}{11}$, $\geq 15: \frac{2}{3}$

22c. Games where the point difference is 0–7. *Sample answer:* In these games he mades 80% of his field goals, while during his other games he made about 64%.

C 23. **CHALLENGE** The table shows the results of Congressional elections that involved incumbent candidates (representatives or senators who ran for re-election) during the period 1980–2000.

	Incumbent representatives		Incumbent senators	
	Ran	Re-elected	Ran	Re-elected
Presidential election year	2373	2235	163	130
Midterm election year	1984	1873	145	130

a. Did a representative or a senator have a better chance of being re-elected? *Justify* your answer using the data in the table.

b. Did a member of Congress have a better chance of being re-elected during a presidential election year than during a midterm election year? *Justify* your answer.

23b. No. *Sample answer:* Members of Congress have about a 94% chance of being re-elected during midterm election years, and about a 93% chance in presidential election years.

23a. A representative. *Sample answer:* The data in the table show that about 94% of representatives that ran for re-election were re-elected, while only about 84% of senators running for re-election were re-elected.

MIXED REVIEW

PREVIEW
Prepare for Lesson 13.2 in Exs. 24–26.

Use the indicated counting method to answer the question. *(p. 931)*

24. You have 3 posters to hang beside each other on a wall. In how many different ways can you hang the posters? (Make a list.) **6 ways**

25. Members of a credit union choose a personal identification number (PIN) for their debit card. The PIN consists of 4 digits from 0 to 9. Digits cannot be repeated. How many PINs are possible? (Use the counting principle.) **5040 PINs**

26. Weekly pottery classes are offered on Monday, Wednesday, and Thursday. On each of those days there is a class at 5:00 and a class at 7:00. How many classes are offered? (Make a tree diagram.) **6 classes**

EXTRA PRACTICE for Lesson 13.1, p. 950

ONLINE QUIZ at classzone.com

Perform Simulations

Extension — *Use after Lesson 13.1*

GOAL Perform simulations to make predictions.

Key Vocabulary
• **simulation**

A **simulation** is an experiment that you can perform to make predictions about real-world situations.

EXAMPLE 1 Perform a simulation

CONCESSION PRIZES Each time you buy an item from the concession stand at a baseball stadium, you receive a prize coupon, chosen at random. There is an equal chance of winning each prize from the following list: hot dog, popcorn, peanuts, pretzel, ice cream, and small drink. About how many times must you buy an item from the concession stand before you win each prize at least once?

Solution

You can perform a simulation to answer the question.

STEP 1 **Write** each prize on a separate piece of paper. Put the pieces of paper in a container.

STEP 2 **Draw** a piece of paper from the container at random. Record the result in a table like the one shown. Put the piece of paper back in the container. Repeat until you put a tally mark in the last empty cell of the table.

Prize	Hot dog	Popcorn	Peanuts	Pretzel	Ice cream	Small drink
Tally	I	IIII	II	~~IIII~~	~~IIII~~ I	II

The sum of all of the tally marks is the number of times you must buy an item from the concession stand before you win each prize at least once.

▶ In this simulation, you must buy an item from the concession stand 20 times.

USING A GRAPHING CALCULATOR You can also use the random integer generator on a graphing calculator to perform simulations.

The random integer generator is found by pressing the MATH key and selecting the PRB menu. It is the fifth item on the list and is displayed as randInt(.

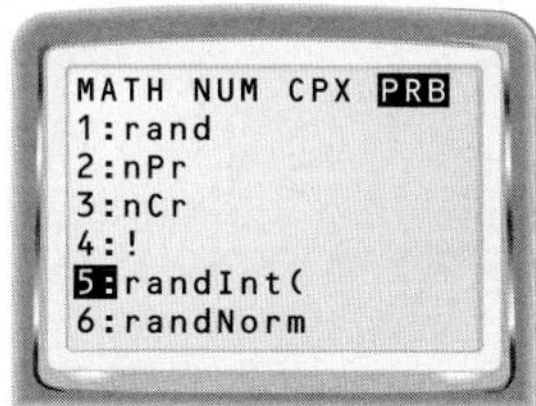

1 PLAN AND PREPARE

Warm-Up Exercises

1. You bought 4 raffle tickets for a weekend trip for two in New York City. If 120 tickets were sold, what is the probability you will win the raffle? $\frac{1}{30}$
2. A sports store is giving away 4 basketballs, 6 footballs, and 8 soccer balls in a random drawing. If you are the first to draw a winning ticket, what is the probability you will win a football? $\frac{1}{3}$

2 FOCUS AND MOTIVATE

Essential Question

Big Idea 1, p.841

How do you perform simulations to make predictions? **Tell students they will learn how to answer this question by using the results of experiments to make predictions.**

3 TEACH

Extra Example 1

Each time you buy an item at a movie store, you receive one of eight prize coupons chosen at random. There is an equal chance of winning each prize. Perform a simulation to predict the number of items you must buy before you win each prize at least once. **Answers will vary.**

NCTM STANDARDS

Standard 5: Understand basic concepts of probability

Standard 10: Use representations to solve problems

Extra Example 2

An electronics store offers a game card for each purchase of $100 or more. Each card has one circle to scratch. There is a $\frac{1}{2}$ chance that the scratched circle will show "Try Again," a $\frac{1}{12}$ chance that it will show a digital camera, a $\frac{1}{6}$ chance that it will show a DVD, and a $\frac{1}{4}$ chance that it will show a computer mouse. Use a calculator simulation to predict the number of game cards you must scratch before you win a digital camera. **Answers will vary.**

Closing the Lesson

Have students summarize the major points of the lesson and answer the Essential Question: How do you perform simulations to make predictions?

- **A simulation is an experiment that you can perform to make a prediction about a real-world situation.**
- **Two simulations of the same event can have different results.**

One way to perform a simulation is to write each possible outcome on a slip of paper, place the slips of paper in a container, and then randomly draw a slip and record the results until you have satisfied the goal of the experiment. Another way to perform a simulation is to use the random integer generator on a graphing calculator.

4 PRACTICE AND APPLY

Avoiding Common Errors

Exercise 1 Students may think that the number of drawings increases by one because the number of items increases by one. Remind students that the probability of selecting each item is equal, so each item must be present at the start of the simulation.

EXAMPLE 2 Perform a simulation using technology

GAME CARDS You receive a game card with every purchase at a sandwich shop. Each card has two circles to scratch. One circle reveals a prize, and the other says "Not a Winner." You cannot claim a prize if you scratch both circles. There is a $\frac{1}{6}$ chance that a card is for a CD, a $\frac{1}{2}$ chance that it is for a drink, and a $\frac{1}{3}$ chance that it is for a sandwich. About how many game cards must you scratch before you win a CD?

Solution

STEP 1 **Use** List 1 to show whether you scratch the circle with the prize. Generate a list of 50 random 1s and 0s. Each 1 means that you scratch the circle with the prize, and each 0 means that you scratch "Not a Winner."

L1	L2	L3
1		
1		
0		
1		
0		

L1=randInt(0,1,50)

Press STAT and select Edit. Highlight L_1. Enter randInt(0,1,50).

STEP 2 **Use** List 2 to show whether your game card contains the CD as the prize. Generate a list of 50 random integers from 1 to 6. Each 1 represents a prize card with a CD.

Highlight L_2. Enter randInt(1,6,50).

STEP 3 **Compare** the results of your two lists using List 3. Multiply the numbers from List 1 and List 2. Each 0 in List 3 means that you chose the wrong circle, so the prize does not matter. Because $1 \cdot 1 = 1$, you chose the correct circle *and* your card contains the CD prize when you see a 1 in L_3.

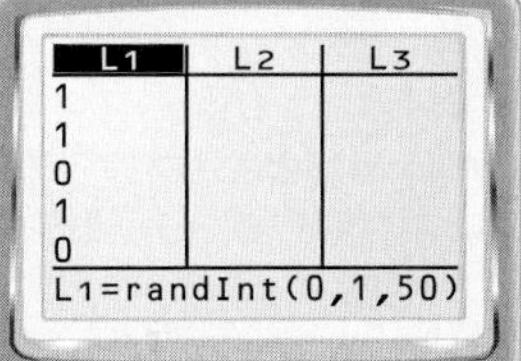

L1	L2	L3
1	3	3
1	2	2
0	1	0
1	1	1
0	2	0

L3=L1*L2

Highlight L_3. Enter $L_1 {*} L_2$.

STEP 4 **Find** the first occurrence of a 1 in List 3. In this simulation, you can see that the first occurrence of a 1 in List 3 happens after 4 trials.

▶ For this simulation, you must scratch 4 game cards before you win a CD.

PRACTICE

EXAMPLE 1 on p. 849 for Exs. 1–3

1. In Example 1, suppose you can receive a prize coupon for nachos in addition to the items listed in the example. About how many times must you buy an item from the concession stand before you win each prize at least once? *Explain* how you found your answer. **Answers will vary.**

EXAMPLE 2 on p. 850 for Exs. 2–3

2. In Example 2, about how many game cards must you scratch before you win one of each prize? *Explain* how you found your answer. **Answers will vary.**

3. In Example 2, there are 3 prizes. *Explain* why the results of the simulation would be inaccurate if you generated random integers from 1 to 3. **See margin.**

3. ***Sample answer:*** **There are 3 prizes to win, but since the prizes do not have an equal likelihood of being won, generating a list of random integers from 1 to 3 wouldn't represent the situation. The probability of winning a CD is $\frac{1}{6}$, so if there were only 3 possible outcomes in the simulation you couldn't represent winning a CD properly.**

13.2 Find Probabilities Using Permutations

Before You used the counting principle.
Now You will use the formula for the number of permutations.
Why? So you can find the number of possible arrangements, as in Ex. 38.

Key Vocabulary
- **permutation**
- ***n* factorial**

A **permutation** is an arrangement of objects in which order is important. For instance, the 6 possible permutations of the letters A, B, and C are shown.

ABC ACB BAC BCA CAB CBA

EXAMPLE 1 Count permutations

Consider the number of permutations of the letters in the word JULY.

a. In how many ways can you arrange all of the letters?

b. In how many ways can you arrange 2 of the letters?

Solution

REVIEW COUNTING PRINCIPLE
For help with using the counting principle, see p. 930.

a. Use the counting principle to find the number of permutations of the letters in the word JULY.

Number of permutations = Choices for 1st letter • Choices for 2nd letter • Choices for 3rd letter • Choices for 4th letter

= 4 • 3 • 2 • 1

= 24

▸ There are 24 ways you can arrange all of the letters in the word JULY.

b. When arranging 2 letters of the word JULY, you have 4 choices for the first letter and 3 choices for the second letter.

Number of permutations = Choices for 1st letter • Choices for 2nd letter

= 4 • 3

= 12

▸ There are 12 ways you can arrange 2 of the letters in the word JULY.

✓ **GUIDED PRACTICE** for Example 1

1. In how many ways can you arrange the letters in the word MOUSE? **120 ways**
2. In how many ways can you arrange 3 of the letters in the word ORANGE? **120 ways**

1 PLAN AND PREPARE

Warm-Up Exercises

Transparency Available

1. There are 8 football teams in your district and 7 teams in a neighboring district. How many teams can you match up for games? **56**
2. A padlock has 9 numbers and uses 3 of them in sequence to open the lock. If you randomly choose 3 numbers, what is the probability that you choose the correct sequence? $\frac{1}{729}$

Notetaking Guide

Transparency Available

Promotes interactive learning and notetaking skills.

Pacing

Basic: 2 days
Average: 2 days
Advanced: 2 days
Block: 0.5 block with 13.1
0.5 block with 13.3
- See *Teaching Guide/Lesson Plan.*

2 FOCUS AND MOTIVATE

Essential Question

Big Idea 1, p. 841

How do you use the formula for permutations? **Tell students they will learn how to answer this question by finding the number of arrangements of *n* objects.**

NCTM STANDARDS

Standard 5: Apply basic concepts of probability

Standard 6: Build knowledge through problem solving

Resource Planning Guide

Chapter Resource Book
- Teaching Guide/Lesson Plan
- Activity Master
- Practice levels A, B, C
- Study Guide
- Catch-up for Absent Students
- Problem Solving Workshop
- Challenge

Workbooks
- Notetaking Guide
- Practice Workbook

Teaching Options
- **Power Presentations** provides dynamic electronic teaching resources for the classroom.
- **Activity Generator** provides editable activities for all ability levels.

Interactive Technology
- Easy Planner
- Power Presentations
- Activity Generator
- Animated Geometry
- Test Generator
- Online Quiz
- eWorkbook
- eEdition
- @HomeTutor

Resources for English Learners
- Spanish Study Guide
- Multi-Language Visual Glossary
- Student Resources in Spanish

See also the *Differentiated Instruction Resources* for more strategies for meeting individual needs.

Motivating the Lesson

You want to photograph five of your friends. If you know how to calculate permutations, you can find the number of ways you can arrange them in a row for a photograph.

TEACH

Extra Example 1

Consider the number of permutations of the letters in the word BRIGHTEN.

a. In how many ways can you arrange all of the letters? **40,320 ways**

b. In how many ways can you arrange 2 of the letters? **56 ways**

Key Questions to Ask for Example 1

- How can you tell that order is important for this exercise? **The word "arrange" means to put in order, so order is important.**
- Why are there 3 choices for the second letter? **There are 4 letters in the word *July*. Once one has been chosen for the first letter, there are 3 letters left from which to choose the second letter.**

Extra Example 2

You have 14 CDs. You can arrange 12 of the 14 in a CD wallet. In how many ways can you arrange the CDs in the CD wallet? **43,589,145,600 ways**

Key Questions to Ask for Example 2

- What permutations formula would you use to find the number of ways the band might arrange 10 of the 12 songs? $_{12}P_{10} = \frac{12!}{2!}$

FACTORIAL In Example 1, you evaluated the expression $4 \cdot 3 \cdot 2 \cdot 1$. This expression can be written as 4! and is read "4 *factorial*." For any positive integer n, the product of the integers from 1 to n is called ***n* factorial** and is written as $n!$. The value of 0! is defined to be 1.

$$n! = n \cdot (n-1) \cdot (n-2) \cdot \ldots \cdot 3 \cdot 2 \cdot 1 \text{ and } 0! = 1$$

In Example 1, you also found the permutations of four objects taken two at a time. You can find the number of permutations using the formulas below.

KEY CONCEPT *For Your Notebook*

Permutations

Formulas	Examples
The number of permutations of n objects is given by: $_nP_n = n!$	The number of permutations of 4 objects is: $_4P_4 = 4! = 4 \cdot 3 \cdot 2 \cdot 1 = 24$
The number of permutations of n objects taken r at a time, where $r \le n$, is given by: $_nP_r = \frac{n!}{(n-r)!}$	The number of permutations of 4 objects taken 2 at a time is: $_4P_2 = \frac{4!}{(4-2)!} = \frac{4 \cdot 3 \cdot \cancel{2!}}{\cancel{2!}} = 12$

EXAMPLE 2 Use a permutations formula

CD RECORDING Your band has written 12 songs and plans to record 9 of them for a CD. In how many ways can you arrange the songs on the CD?

Solution

To find the number of permutations of 9 songs chosen from 12, find $_{12}P_9$.

DIVIDE COMMON FACTORS
When you divide out common factors, remember that 3! is a factor of 12!.

$_{12}P_9 = \frac{12!}{(12-9)!}$ — **Permutations formula**

$= \frac{12!}{3!}$ — **Subtract.**

$= \frac{12 \cdot 11 \cdot 10 \cdot 9 \cdot 8 \cdot 7 \cdot 6 \cdot 5 \cdot 4 \cdot \cancel{3!}}{\cancel{3!}}$ — **Expand factorials. Divide out common factor, 3!.**

$= 79{,}833{,}600$ — **Multiply.**

▶ There are 79,833,600 ways to arrange 9 songs out of 12.

✓ **GUIDED PRACTICE** for Example 2

3. **WHAT IF?** In Example 2, suppose your band has written 15 songs. You will record 9 of them for a CD. In how many ways can you arrange the songs on the CD? **1,816,214,400 ways**

Differentiated Instruction

Below Level Have students work in pairs to confirm that the permutations formula works. Suggest that they make a list of the number of ways the letters in the word SAID can be arranged and then find the arrangements using the permutations formula. Ask them to make a similar list for two of the letters in the word. Then lead students to see the usefulness of the permutations formula by having them examine what happens to the number of permutations as the number of letters in a word increases.

See also the *Differentiated Instruction Resources* for more strategies.

EXAMPLE 3 Find a probability using permutations

PARADE For a town parade, you will ride on a float with your soccer team. There are 12 floats in the parade, and their order is chosen at random. Find the probability that your float is first and the float with the school chorus is second.

Solution

STEP 1 **Write** the number of possible outcomes as the number of permutations of the 12 floats in the parade. This is ${}_{12}P_{12} = 12!$.

STEP 2 **Write** the number of favorable outcomes as the number of permutations of the other floats, given that the soccer team is first and the chorus is second. This is ${}_{10}P_{10} = 10!$.

STEP 3 **Calculate** the probability.

$$P\left(\begin{array}{c}\text{soccer team is first}\\ \text{chorus is second}\end{array}\right) = \frac{10!}{12!}$$ **Form a ratio of favorable to possible outcomes.**

$$= \frac{\cancel{10!}}{12 \cdot 11 \cdot \cancel{10!}}$$ **Expand factorials. Divide out common factor, 10!.**

$$= \frac{1}{132}$$ **Simplify.**

 **GUIDED PRACTICE** for Example 3

4. **WHAT IF?** In Example 3, suppose there are 14 floats in the parade. Find the probability that the soccer team is first and the chorus is second. $\frac{1}{182}$

13.2 EXERCISES

HOMEWORK KEY
○ = **WORKED-OUT SOLUTIONS** on p. WS32 for Exs. 21 and 35
★ = **STANDARDIZED TEST PRACTICE** Exs. 2, 11, 30, 33, and 35
◆ = **MULTIPLE REPRESENTATIONS** Ex. 34

SKILL PRACTICE

A

1. **VOCABULARY** Copy and complete: An arrangement of objects in which order is important is called a(n) _?_. **permutation**

2. ★ **WRITING** *Explain* what the notation ${}_9P_2$ means. What is the value of this expression? **The number of permutations containing 2 items chosen from a group of 9 possible items; 72**

EXAMPLES 1 and 2 on pp. 851–852 for Exs. 3–11

COUNTING PERMUTATIONS Find the number of ways you can arrange (a) all of the letters in the given word and (b) 2 of the letters in the word.

3. AT **a. 2 ways; b. 2 ways**
4. TRY **a. 6 ways; b. 6 ways**
5. GAME **a. 24 ways; b. 12 ways**
6. CAT **a. 6 ways; b. 6 ways**
7. WATER **a. 120 ways; b. 20 ways**
8. ROCK **a. 24 ways; b. 12 ways**
9. APRIL **a. 120 ways; b. 20 ways**
10. FAMILY **a. 720 ways; b. 30 ways**

11. ★ **OPEN-ENDED** *Describe* a real-world situation where the number of possibilities is given by ${}_5P_2$. ***Sample answer:*** **5 people are running in a race. How many different results can there be for first and second place?**

Extra Example 3

Ten students in your science class are giving reports on endangered animals. The order of the reports is chosen at random. Find the probability that your report on the humpback whale is first and your friend's report on the American crocodile is second. $\frac{1}{90}$

Closing the Lesson

Have students summarize the major points of the lesson and answer the Essential Question: How do you use the formula for permutations?

- **A permutation is an arrangement of objects in which order is important.**
- **The product of positive integers from 1 to n is called n factorial ($n!$). 4! is $4 \cdot 3 \cdot 2 \cdot 1$ or 24.**

Use the formula ${}_nP_n = n!$ to find the arrangement of n objects. You can arrange 5 objects in ${}_5P_5 = 5!$ ways, or $5 \cdot 4 \cdot 3 \cdot 2 \cdot 1 = 120$ ways.
Use the permutations formula ${}_nP_r = \frac{n!}{(n-r)!}$ to find the number of permutations of n objects taken r at a time. You can arrange 2 of 5 objects in $\frac{5!}{(5-2)!} = \frac{5!}{3!}$, or 20 ways.

To find a probability using permutations, use formulas to write a ratio of favorable to possible outcomes.

Differentiated Instruction

Visual Learners For Step 2 in **Example 3**, draw a simple diagram to show why the number of outcomes is 10!.

1st	2nd	
soccer team	chorus	remaining 10 floats

The number of permutations of the remaining 10 floats is given by ${}_{10}P_{10} = 10!$.

See also the *Differentiated Instruction Resources* for more strategies.

4 PRACTICE AND APPLY

Assignment Guide

Answer Transparencies available for all exercises

Basic:
Day 1: pp. 853–855
Exs. 1–19
Day 2: pp. 853–855
Exs. 20–29, 32–36, 40–43

Average:
Day 1: pp. 853–855
Exs. 1–19
Day 2: pp. 853–855
Exs. 22–30, 32–38, 40–43

Advanced:
Day 1: pp. 853–855
Exs. 1–19
Day 2: pp. 853–855
Exs. 24–43*

Block:
pp. 853–855
Exs. 1–19 (with 13.1)
pp. 853–855
Exs. 22–30, 32–38, 40–43
(with 13.3)

Differentiated Instruction

See *Differentiated Instruction Resources* for suggestions on addressing the needs of a diverse classroom.

Homework Check

For a quick check of student understanding of key concepts, go over the following exercises:

Basic: 6, 13, 22, 32, 34
Average: 8, 15, 24, 33, 35
Advanced: 10, 17, 26, 36, 37

Extra Practice

- Student Edition, p. 950
- Chapter Resource Book: Practice levels A, B, C

Practice Worksheet

An easily-readable reduced practice page (with answers) for this lesson can be found on p. 840C.

EXAMPLE 2 on p. 852 for Exs. 12–30

FACTORIALS AND PERMUTATIONS **Evaluate the expression.**

12. 1! **1** **13.** 3! **6** **14.** 0! **1** **15.** 5! **120**

16. 8! **40,320** **17.** 10! **3,628,800** **18.** 12! **479,001,600** **19.** 13! **6,227,020,800**

20. ${}_5P_2$ **20** **(21.)** ${}_7P_3$ **210** **22.** ${}_9P_1$ **9** **23.** ${}_6P_5$ **720**

24. ${}_8P_8$ **40,320** **25.** ${}_{12}P_0$ **1** **26.** ${}_{30}P_2$ **870** **27.** ${}_{25}P_5$ **6,375,600**

B **ERROR ANALYSIS** ***Describe*** **and correct the error in evaluating the expression.**

28. ${}_{11}P_7 = \frac{11!}{(11-7)} = \frac{11!}{4} = 9{,}979{,}200$ ✗

29. ${}_5P_3 = \frac{5!}{3!} = \frac{5 \cdot 4 \cdot \cancel{3!}}{\cancel{3!}} = 20$ ✗

28. The denominator of the fraction should be (11 − 7)!, not (11 − 7); $\frac{11!}{(11-7)!} = \frac{11!}{4!} =$ 1,663,200.

29. The denominator of the fraction should be (5 − 3)!, not 3!; $\frac{5!}{(5-3)!} = \frac{5!}{2!} =$ 60.

30. ★ **MULTIPLE CHOICE** The judges in an art contest award prizes for first, second, and third place out of 11 entries. Which expression gives the number of ways the judges can award first, second, and third place? **C**

Ⓐ $\frac{3!}{11!}$ Ⓑ $\frac{8!}{11!}$ Ⓒ $\frac{11!}{8!}$ Ⓓ $\frac{11!}{3!}$

C **31.** **CHALLENGE** Consider a set of 4 objects and a set of n objects.

a. Are there more permutations of all 4 of the objects or of 3 of the 4 objects? *Justify* your answer using an organized list. **a–b. See margin.**

b. In general, are there more permutations of n objects taken n at a time or of n objects taken $n - 1$ at a time? *Justify* your answer using the formula for the number of permutations.

PROBLEM SOLVING

EXAMPLE 2 on p. 852 for Exs. 32–33

A **32.** **MOVIES** Six friends go to a movie theater. In how many different ways can they sit together in a row of 6 empty seats? **720 ways**

@HomeTutor for problem solving help at classzone.com

33. ★ **MULTIPLE CHOICE** You plan to visit 4 stores during a shopping trip. In how many orders can you visit these stores? **C**

Ⓐ 4 Ⓑ 16 Ⓒ 24 Ⓓ 256

@HomeTutor for problem solving help at classzone.com

EXAMPLE 3 on p. 853 for Exs. 34–38

34. ◆ **MULTIPLE REPRESENTATIONS** You and your friend are two of 4 servers working a shift in a restaurant. The host assigns tables of new diners to the servers in a particular order. This order remains the same, so that all servers are likely to wait on the same number of tables by the end of the shift.

a. **Making a List** List all the possible orders in which the host can assign tables to the servers. **See margin.**

b. **Using a Formula** Use the formula for permutations to find the number of ways in which the host can assign tables to the servers. **24 ways**

c. **Describe in Words** What is the likelihood that you and your friend are assigned the first 2 tables? *Explain* your answer using probability. **See margin.**

○ = WORKED-OUT SOLUTIONS on p. WS1 ★ = STANDARDIZED TEST PRACTICE ◆ = MULTIPLE REPRESENTATIONS

31a. They are the same; 4 of 4 items: ABCD, ABDC, ACBD, ACDB, ADBC, ADCB, BACD, BADC, BCDA, BCAD, BDAC, BDCA, CABD, CADB, CBAD, CBDA, CDAB, CDBA, DABC, DACB, DBAC, DBCA, DCAB, DCBA; 3 of 4 items: ABC, ABD, ACB, ACD, ADB, ADC, BAC, BAD, BCD, BCA, BDA, BDC, CAB, CAD, CBA, CBD, CDA, CDB, DAB, DAC, DBA, DBC, DCA, DCB.

31b. See Additional Answers beginning on p. AA1.

35a. $\frac{1}{2}$. *Sample answer:* Make a list of possible permutations and count the number in which you are first or second and divide it by the total number of outcomes.

35. ★ **SHORT RESPONSE** Every student in your history class is required to present a project in front of the class. Each day, 4 students make their presentations in an order chosen at random by the teacher. You make your presentation on the first day.
   a. What is the probability that you are chosen to be the first or second presenter on the first day? *Explain* how you found your answer.
   b. What is the probability that you are chosen to be the second or third presenter on the first day? *Compare* your answer with that in part (a). **$\frac{1}{2}$; the answers are the same.**

B

36. **HISTORY EXAM** On an exam, you are asked to list 5 historical events in the order in which they occurred. You guess the order of the events at random. What is the probability that you choose the correct order? $\frac{1}{120}$

37. **SPIRIT** You make 6 posters to hold up at a basketball game. Each poster has a letter of the word TIGERS. You and 5 friends sit next to each other in a row. The posters are distributed at random. What is the probability that TIGERS is spelled correctly when you hold up the posters? $\frac{1}{720}$

38. **BAND COMPETITION** Seven marching bands will perform at a competition. The order of the performances is determined at random. What is the probability that your school band will perform first, followed by the band from the one other high school in your town? $\frac{1}{42}$

C

39. **CHALLENGE** You are one of 10 students performing in a school talent show. The order of the performances is determined at random. The first five performers go on stage before the intermission, while the remaining five performers go on stage after the intermission.
   a. What is the probability that you are the last performer before the intermission and your rival performs immediately before you? $\frac{1}{90}$
   b. What is the probability that you are *not* the first performer? $\frac{9}{10}$

MIXED REVIEW

PREVIEW
Prepare for Lesson 13.3 in Exs. 40–43.

40. You are randomly assigned a day of the week to work an extra shift at your part-time job. Find the probability that you are assigned to work on Saturday. *(p. 843)* $\frac{1}{7}$

41. You choose a letter at random out of a bag that contains one of each letter of the alphabet. Find the probability that you choose the letter K. *(p. 843)* $\frac{1}{26}$

42. You roll a number cube. Find the probability that you roll an even number. *(p. 843)* $\frac{1}{2}$

43. You toss a coin twice. Find the probability that the coin shows tails twice. *(p. 843)* $\frac{1}{4}$

5 ASSESS AND RETEACH

Daily Homework Quiz

Transparency Available

1. Find the number of ways you can arrange all of the letters of the word BOUNDARY and then 3 of the letters of the word. **40,320 ways; 336 ways**
2. Evaluate ${}_6P_3$. **120**
3. Evaluate ${}_{14}P_9$. **726,485,760**
4. There are 8 students auditioning for the main role in a school play. The order of the student auditions is chosen at random. Find the probability that you are chosen first to audition and your friend Petra is chosen second. $\frac{1}{56}$

Available at **classzone.com**

Diagnosis/Remediation

- Practice A, B, C in Chapter Resource Book
- Study Guide in Chapter Resource Book
- Practice Workbook
- @HomeTutor

Challenge

Additional challenge is available in the Chapter Resource Book.

34a. ABCD, ABDC, ACBD, ACDB, ADBC, ADCB, BACD, BADC, BCDA, BCAD, BDAC, BDCA, CABD, CADB, CBAD, CBDA, CDAB, CDBA, DABC, DACB, DBAC, DBCA, DCAB, DCBA

34c. $\frac{1}{6}$. *Sample answer:* Say A and B represent you and your friend. There are 4 permutations in the list from part (a) in which A and B are given the first 2 tables. There are 24 total permutations, so the probability that you and your friend are given the first two tables is $\frac{4}{24} = \frac{1}{6}$.

1 PLAN AND PREPARE

Warm-Up Exercises

Transparency Available

1. Evaluate ${}_6P_2$. **30**
2. Evaluate ${}_{15}P_8$. **259,459,200**
3. You are given the 6 letter tiles, E, K, M, N, O, and Y, face down in no particular order. Find the probability that the letter tiles spell MONKEY as each tile is turned over from left to right. $\frac{1}{720}$

Notetaking Guide

Transparency Available

Promotes interactive learning and notetaking skills.

Pacing

Basic: 1 day

Average: 1 day

Advanced: 1 day

Block: 0.5 block with 13.2

• See *Teaching Guide/Lesson Plan.*

2 FOCUS AND MOTIVATE

Essential Question

Big Idea 1, p. 841

How do you use combinations to count possibilities? **Tell students they will learn how to answer this question by using a formula to find the number of combinations of selected objects.**

NCTM STANDARDS

Standard 5: Apply basic concepts of probability

Standard 6: Solve problems in math and other contexts

13.3 Find Probabilities Using Combinations

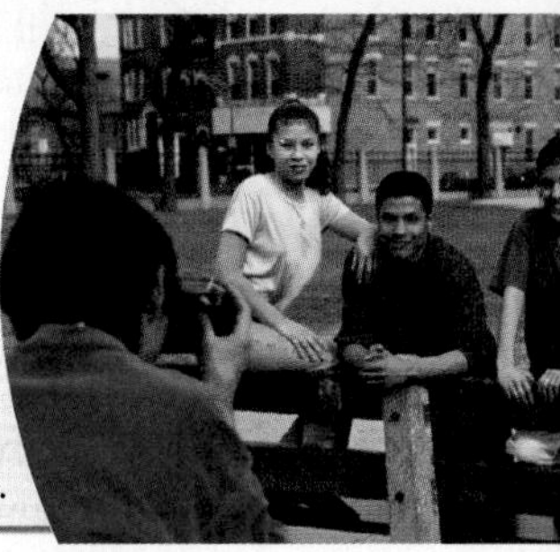

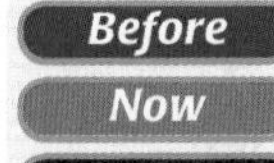

Before You used permutations to count possibilities.

Now You will use combinations to count possibilities.

Why? So you can find the probability of an event, as in Example 3.

Key Vocabulary
• **combination**

A **combination** is a selection of objects in which order is *not* important. For instance, in a drawing for 3 identical prizes, you would use combinations, because the order of the winners would not matter. If the prizes were different, you would use permutations, because the order would matter.

EXAMPLE 1 Count combinations

Count the combinations of two letters from the list A, B, C, D.

Solution

List all of the permutations of two letters in the list A, B, C, D. Because order is not important in a combination, cross out any duplicate pairs.

AB	AC	AD	~~BA~~	BC	BD
~~CA~~	~~CB~~	CD	~~DA~~	~~DB~~	~~DC~~

BD and DB are the same pair.

▶ There are 6 possible combinations of 2 letters from the list A, B, C, D.

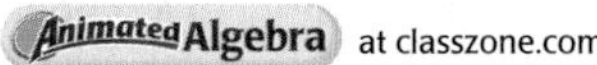

Animated Algebra at classzone.com

GUIDED PRACTICE for Example 1

1. Count the combinations of 3 letters from the list A, B, C, D, E. **10 combinations**

COMBINATIONS In Example 1, you found the number of combinations of objects by making an organized list. You can also find the number of combinations using the following formula.

KEY CONCEPT *For Your Notebook*

Combinations

Formula

The number of combinations of n objects taken r at a time, where $r \le n$, is given by:

$${}_nC_r = \frac{n!}{(n-r)! \cdot r!}$$

Example

The number of combinations of 4 objects taken 2 at a time is:

$${}_4C_2 = \frac{4!}{(4-2)! \cdot 2!} = \frac{4 \cdot 3 \cdot \cancel{2!}}{\cancel{2!} \cdot (2 \cdot 1)} = 6$$

Resource Planning Guide

Chapter Resource Book
• Teaching Guide/Lesson Plan
• Activity Master
• Practice levels A, B, C
• Study Guide
• Catch-up for Absent Students
• Application
• Challenge

Workbooks
• Notetaking Guide
• Practice Workbook

Teaching Options
• **Power Presentations** provides dynamic electronic teaching resources for the classroom.
• **Activity Generator** provides editable activities for all ability levels.

Interactive Technology
• Easy Planner
• Power Presentations
• Activity Generator
• Animated Algebra
• Test Generator
• Online Quiz
• eWorkbook
• eEdition
• @HomeTutor

Resources for English Learners
• Spanish Study Guide
• Multi-Language Visual Glossary
• Student Resources in Spanish

See also the *Differentiated Instruction Resources* for more strategies for meeting individual needs.

EXAMPLE 2 Use the combinations formula

LUNCH MENU You order a sandwich at a restaurant. You can choose 2 side dishes from a list of 8. How many combinations of side dishes are possible?

Solution

The order in which you choose the side dishes is not important. So, to find the number of combinations of 8 side dishes taken 2 at a time, find ${}_8C_2$.

$${}_8C_2 = \frac{8!}{(8-2)! \cdot 2!} \quad \text{Combinations formula}$$

$$= \frac{8!}{6! \cdot 2!} \quad \text{Subtract.}$$

$$= \frac{8 \cdot 7 \cdot \cancel{6!}}{\cancel{6!} \cdot (2 \cdot 1)} \quad \text{Expand factorials. Divide out common factor, 6!.}$$

$$= 28 \quad \text{Simplify.}$$

▶ There are 28 different combinations of side dishes you can order.

EXAMPLE 3 Find a probability using combinations

PHOTOGRAPHY A yearbook editor has selected 14 photos, including one of you and one of your friend, to use in a collage for the yearbook. The photos are placed at random. There is room for 2 photos at the top of the page. What is the probability that your photo and your friend's photo are the two placed at the top of the page?

Solution

STEP 1 **Write** the number of possible outcomes as the number of combinations of 14 photos taken 2 at a time, or ${}_{14}C_2$, because the order in which the photos are chosen is not important.

$${}_{14}C_2 = \frac{14!}{(14-2)! \cdot 2!} = \frac{14!}{12! \cdot 2!} = \frac{14 \cdot 13 \cdot \cancel{12!}}{\cancel{12!} \cdot (2 \cdot 1)} = 91$$

STEP 2 **Find** the number of favorable outcomes. Only one of the possible combinations includes your photo and your friend's photo.

STEP 3 **Calculate** the probability.

$P(\text{your photo and your friend's photos are chosen}) = \frac{1}{91}$

 **GUIDED PRACTICE** for Examples 2 and 3

2. **WHAT IF?** In Example 2, suppose you can choose 3 side dishes out of the list of 8 side dishes. How many combinations are possible? **56 combinations**

3. **WHAT IF?** In Example 3, suppose there are 20 photos in the collage. Find the probability that your photo and your friend's photo are the two placed at the top of the page. $\frac{1}{190}$

Motivating the Lesson

You sing in a chorus after school. The director will choose at random 2 songs out of 5 for the chorus to learn to sing. You can use combinations to help find the probability that the director will choose your two favorite songs.

3 TEACH

Extra Example 1

Count the combinations of 2 letters from the list A, B, C, D, E. **10**

An **Animated Algebra** activity is available online for **Example 1**. This activity is also part of **Power Presentations**.

Extra Example 2

You can choose 2 courses out of a list of 6. How many combinations of electives are possible? **15**

Extra Example 3

Your teacher randomly chooses 2 out of 18 students to give an impromptu debate on freedom of the press in high school newspapers. What is the probability that your teacher chooses you and your best friend? $\frac{1}{153}$

Closing the Lesson

Have students summarize the major points of the lesson and answer the Essential Question: How do you use combinations to count possibilities?

- **A combination is a selection of objects in which order is not important.**

Use the formula ${}_nC_r = \frac{n!}{(n-r) \cdot r!}$ **to find the number of combinations of** n **objects taken** r **at a time.**

Differentiated Instruction

Advanced Have students create two situations in which 2 out of 16 objects are selected, with order important in one of the situations and not important in the other. Ask students to use the situations to compare and contrast permutations and combinations, explaining why the number of selections is greater in one than the other, and describing the relationship between the two. Tell students it may be necessary to create several situations in which order is and is not important to be able to describe the relationship between permutations and combinations.

See also the *Differentiated Instruction Resources* for more strategies.

4 PRACTICE AND APPLY

Assignment Guide

Answer Transparencies available for all exercises

Basic:
Day 1: pp. 858–859
Exs. 1–17, 23–25, 28–33

Average:
Day 1: pp. 858–859
Exs. 1–5, 6–14 even, 15–20, 23–26, 28–33

Advanced:
Day 1: pp. 858–859
Exs. 1–3, 10–33*

Block:
pp. 858–859
Exs. 1–5, 6–14 even, 15–20, 23–26, 28–33 (with 13.2)

Differentiated Instruction

See *Differentiated Instruction Resources* for suggestions on addressing the needs of a diverse classroom.

Homework Check

For a quick check of student understanding of key concepts, go over the following exercises:

Basic: 3, 8, 16, 23, 24
Average: 4, 10, 17, 24, 25
Advanced: 3, 12, 18, 25, 26

Extra Practice

- Student Edition, p. 950
- Chapter Resource Book: Practice levels A, B, C

Practice Worksheet

An easily-readable reduced practice page (with answers) for this lesson can be found on p. 840C.

13.3 EXERCISES

HOMEWORK KEY
○ = **WORKED-OUT SOLUTIONS** on p. WS32 for Exs. 7 and 25
★ = **STANDARDIZED TEST PRACTICE** Exs. 2, 14–20, and 25

SKILL PRACTICE

A

1. **VOCABULARY** Copy and complete: A(n) _?_ is a selection of objects in which order is not important. **combination**

2. ★ **WRITING** *Explain* how a combination differs from a permutation. **See margin.**

EXAMPLE 1 on p. 856 for Exs. 3, 4

3. **COMBINATIONS** How many combinations of 3 letters from the list A, B, C, D, E, F are possible? **20 combinations**

4. **ERROR ANALYSIS** *Describe* and correct the error in listing all of the possible combinations of 2 letters from the list A, B, C. **See margin.**

AB	BA	CA
AC	BC	CB

EXAMPLE 2 on p. 857 for Exs. 5–15

5. **ERROR ANALYSIS** *Describe* and correct the error in evaluating ${}_9C_4$. **See margin.**

$${}_9C_4 = \frac{9!}{(9-4)!} = \frac{9!}{5!} = 3024$$

COMBINATIONS Evaluate the expression.

6. ${}_5C_1$ **5**
7. ${}_8C_5$ **56**
8. ${}_9C_9$ **1**
9. ${}_8C_6$ **28**
10. ${}_{12}C_3$ **220**
11. ${}_{11}C_4$ **330**
12. ${}_{15}C_8$ **6435**
13. ${}_{20}C_5$ **15,504**

14. ★ **MULTIPLE CHOICE** What is the value of ${}_{10}C_6$? **C**
(A) 7 (B) 60 (C) 210 (D) 151,200

B

15. ★ **MULTIPLE CHOICE** You have the first season of your favorite television show on a set of DVDs. The set contains 13 episodes. You have time to watch 3 episodes. How many combinations of 3 episodes can you watch? **A**
(A) 286 (B) 572 (C) 1716 (D) 589,680

★ **SHORT RESPONSE In Exercises 16–19, tell whether the question can be answered using *combinations* or *permutations*. *Explain* your choice, then answer the question.** **16–19. See margin.**

16. Four students from your class of 120 students will be selected to organize a fundraiser. How many groups of 4 students are possible?

17. Ten students are auditioning for 3 different roles in a play. In how many ways can the 3 roles be filled?

18. To complete an exam, you must answer 8 questions from a list of 10 questions. In how many ways can you complete the exam?

19. In how many ways can 5 people sit in a car that holds 5 passengers?

20. ★ **WRITING** Which is greater, ${}_6P_r$ or ${}_6C_r$? *Justify* your answer. **See margin.**

C

21. **REASONING** Write an equation that relates ${}_nP_r$ and ${}_nC_r$. *Explain* your reasoning. **See margin.**

22. **CHALLENGE** Prove that ${}_nC_r = {}_nC_{n-r}$. *Explain* why this makes sense. **See margin.**

2. In a combination, the order in which the objects are arranged is not important. In a permutation, the order is important.

4. Each combination is duplicated, since the order of the letters does not matter. AB and BA are the same, as are CA and AC and BC and CB; list: AB, AC, BC.

5. *Sample answer:* The answer given was ${}_9P_4$ not ${}_9C_4$; $\frac{9!}{(9-4)!\cdot 4!} = \frac{9!}{5!\cdot 4!} = 126$.

16. Combinations; the order in which the students are picked for the group does not matter, 8,214,570 groups.

17. Permutations; since the roles are different, the order in which students are selected for the roles matters, 720 ways.

18. Combinations; the order in which you answer the questions does not matter, 45 ways.

19. Permutations; the arrangement of people in the car matters, 120 ways.

20–22. See Additional Answers beginning on p. AA1.

Differentiated Instruction

Kinesthetic Learners Some students may have trouble distinguishing between combinations and permutations. For **Exercises 3 and 4**, have students write single letters on index cards and use the cards to compute combinations and permutations by sorting them. Provide additional exercises to be solved using the cards, such as distinguishing ${}_3C_2 = 3$ from ${}_3P_2 = 6$, and distinguishing ${}_5C_2 = 10$ from ${}_5P_2 = 20$.

See also the *Differentiated Instruction Resources* for more strategies.

PROBLEM SOLVING

EXAMPLE 2 A on p. 857 for Ex. 23

23. **RESTAURANT** You are ordering a burrito with 2 main ingredients and 3 toppings. The menu below shows the possible choices. How many different burritos are possible? **840 burritos**

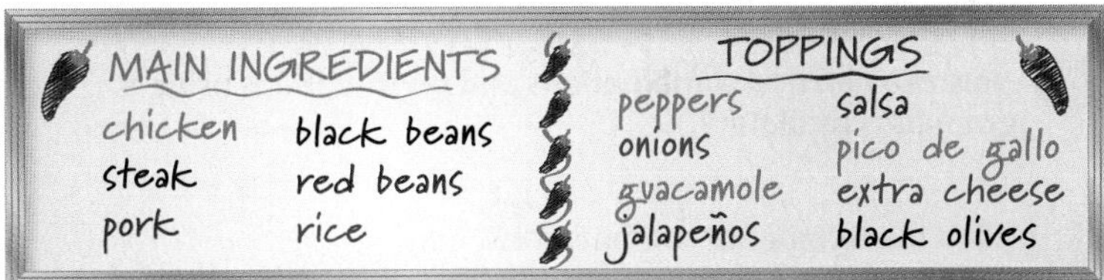

MAIN INGREDIENTS
chicken
black beans
steak
red beans
pork
rice
TOPPINGS
peppers
salsa
onions
pico de gallo
guacamole
extra cheese
jalapeños
black olives

@HomeTutor for problem solving help at classzone.com

EXAMPLE 3 on p. 857 for Exs. 24–26

24. **WORK SCHEDULE** You work 3 evenings each week at a bookstore. Your supervisor assigns you 3 evenings at random from the 7 possibilities. What is the probability that your schedule this week includes working on Friday? $\frac{3}{7}$

@HomeTutor for problem solving help at classzone.com

25. ★ **SHORT RESPONSE** On a television game show, 9 members of the studio audience are randomly selected to be eligible contestants.

a. Six of the 9 eligible contestants are randomly chosen to play a game on the stage. How many combinations of 6 players from the group of eligible contestants are possible? **84 combinations**

b. You and your two friends are part of the group of 9 eligible contestants. What is the probability that all three of you are chosen to play the game on stage? *Explain* how you found your answer. **See margin.**

26. $\frac{1}{435}$; $\frac{1}{870}$; **my best friend and I are chosen, regardless of order.**

B 26. **REPRESENTATIVES** Your teacher chooses 2 students at random to represent your homeroom. The homeroom has a total of 30 students, including your best friend. What is the probability that you and your best friend are chosen? What is the probability that you are chosen first and your best friend is chosen second? Which event is more likely to occur?

C 27. **CHALLENGE** There are 30 students in your class. Your science teacher will choose 5 students at random to complete a group project. Find the probability that you and your 2 best friends in the science class are chosen to work in the group. *Explain* how you found your answer. **See margin.**

MIXED REVIEW

PREVIEW Prepare for Lesson 13.4 in Exs. 28–32.

Find the product. *(p. 915)*

28. $\frac{1}{6} \cdot \frac{4}{5}$ $\frac{2}{15}$

29. $\frac{4}{25} \cdot \frac{7}{24}$ $\frac{7}{150}$

30. $\frac{13}{30} \cdot \frac{5}{26}$ $\frac{1}{12}$

31. $\frac{7}{24} \cdot \frac{4}{51}$ $\frac{7}{306}$

32. You roll a number cube. What is the probability that you roll a multiple of 3? *(p. 843)* $\frac{1}{3}$

33. In how many ways can you arrange 3 letters from the list P, Q, R, S, T, L? *Explain* how you found your answer. *(p. 851)* **120 ways.** ***Sample answer:*** **Calculate** $_6P_3$.

5 ASSESS AND RETEACH

Daily Homework Quiz

Transparency Available

1. You can choose 3 toppings for a pizza out of 14 for no extra charge. How many combinations of pizza toppings are possible? **364 combinations**
2. Evaluate $_9C_4$. **126**
3. Evaluate $_{11}C_6$. **462**
4. Two out of 10 flag twirlers are randomly chosen to lead the flag twirlers in a school parade. What is the probability that the two flag twirlers are you and your sister? $\frac{1}{45}$

Online Quiz

Available at **classzone.com**

Diagnosis/Remediation

- Practice A, B, C in Chapter Resource Book
- Study Guide in Chapter Resource Book
- Practice Workbook
- @HomeTutor

Challenge

Additional challenge is available in the Chapter Resource Book.

25b. $\frac{5}{21}$. ***Sample answer:*** **There are 84 possible outcomes of the choice. Find the number of combinations that include you and your 2 friends. After you and your friends are chosen, 3 other contestants from a pool of 6 can be chosen in any combination, so the number of favorable combinations is** $_6C_3 = 20$. **The probability that you and your friends are chosen is** $\frac{20}{84} = \frac{5}{21}$.

27. See Additional Answers beginning on p. AA1.

1 PLAN AND PREPARE

Learn the Method

- Students will find combinations and permutations using a graphing calculator.
- After the activity, students can use a graphing calculator to check their solutions in Exercises 6–19 in Lesson 13.3.

Keystroke Help

Keystrokes for several models of calculators are available in blackline format in the *Chapter Resource Book.*

2 TEACH

Tips for Success

Make sure that students use the correct sequence of keystrokes, the correct numbers for n and r, and select the correct item from the PRB menu.

Extra Example 1

Your supervisor at the tutoring center chooses 4 students out of 20 to tutor after school. How many combinations of student tutors are possible? **4845 combinations**

Extra Example 2

One student each will tutor reading, algebra, history, and writing. In how many ways can the tutoring roles be assigned using all 20 students? **116,280 ways**

3 ASSESS AND RETEACH

For given values of n and r, which number is greater, ${}_nC_r$ or ${}_nP_r$? **${}_nP_r$, unless $r = 0$ or $r = 1$, in which case ${}_nC_r = {}_nP_r$**

Graphing Calculator ACTIVITY *Use after Lesson 13.3*

@HomeTutor classzone.com Keystrokes

13.3 Find Permutations and Combinations

QUESTION **How can you find combinations and permutations using a graphing calculator?**

EXAMPLE 1 Find the number of combinations

STARTERS There are 15 players on your softball team, but only 9 of them can be the starting players in one game. How many combinations of starting players are possible?

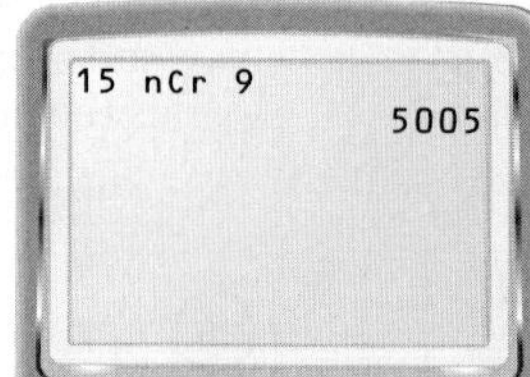

Solution

You are finding ${}_nC_r$ where $n = 15$ and $r = 9$. Enter 15 for n. Press MATH. Go to the PRB menu and select ${}_nC_r$. Then enter 9 for r.

▶ There are 5005 possible combinations of starting players.

EXAMPLE 2 Find the number of permutations

BATTING ORDER Before each softball game, your coach announces the batting order of the 9 starting players. This is the order in which the starting players will bat. How many batting orders can be formed using 9 players on your team of 15 players?

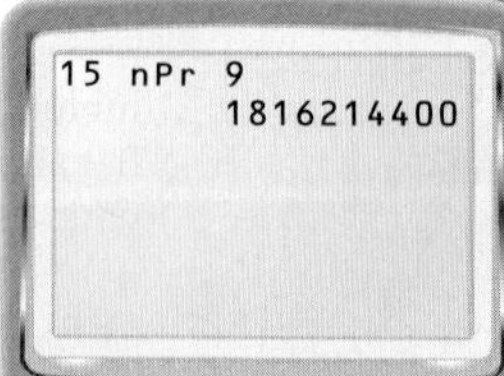

Solution

You are finding ${}_nP_r$ where $n = 15$ and $r = 9$. Enter 15 for n. Press MATH. Go to the PRB menu and select ${}_nP_r$. Then enter 9 for r.

▶ There are 1,816,214,400 possible batting orders.

PRACTICE

Evaluate the expression.

1. ${}_7C_4$ **35**
2. ${}_6C_6$ **1**
3. ${}_{10}C_3$ **120**
4. ${}_{16}C_8$ **12,870**
5. ${}_9P_5$ **15,120**
6. ${}_7P_6$ **5040**
7. ${}_{11}P_8$ **6,652,800**
8. ${}_{12}P_5$ **95,040**
9. **GROUP PROJECT** Your teacher selects 3 students from a class of 28 students to work on a project in a group. Within the group, one member must be the writer, one must be the researcher, and one must be the presenter.
   a. How many different groups of 3 can your teacher select? **3276 groups**
   b. After the group is formed, in how many ways can the roles in the group be assigned? **6 ways**

13.4 Find Probabilities of Compound Events

Before You found the probability of a simple event.
Now You will find the probability of a compound event.
Why? So you can analyze scientific data, as in Ex. 23.

Key Vocabulary
- **compound event**
- **mutually exclusive events**
- **overlapping events**
- **independent events**
- **dependent events**

A **compound event** combines two or more events, using the word *and* or the word *or*. To find the probability that either event A or event B occurs, determine how the events are related. **Mutually exclusive events** have no common outcomes. **Overlapping events** have at least one common outcome.

For instance, suppose you roll a number cube.

REVIEW VENN DIAGRAMS
For help with using Venn diagrams, see p. 929.

Mutually Exclusive Events

Event *A*: Roll a 3.

Event *B*: Roll an even number.

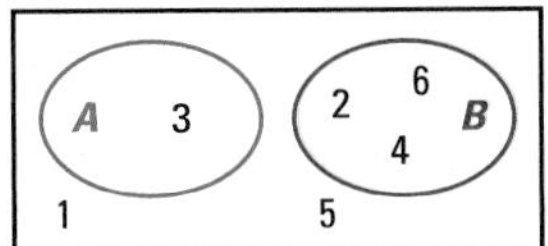

Set A has 1 number, and set B has 3 numbers.

$P(3 \text{ or even}) = \frac{1}{6} + \frac{3}{6}$

$\mathbf{P(A \text{ or } B) = P(A) + P(B)}$

Overlapping Events

Event *A*: Roll an odd number.

Event *B*: Roll a prime number.

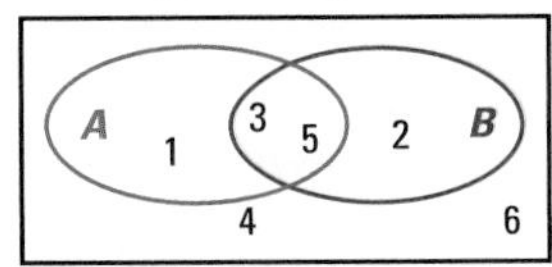

Set A has 3 numbers, and set B has 3 numbers. There are 2 numbers in both sets.

$P(\text{odd or prime}) = \frac{3}{6} + \frac{3}{6} - \frac{2}{6}$

$\mathbf{P(A \text{ or } B) = P(A) + P(B) - P(A \text{ and } B)}$

EXAMPLE 1 Find the probability of *A* or *B*

You roll a number cube. Find the probability that you roll a 2 or an odd number.

Solution

Because 2 is an even number, rolling a 2 and rolling an odd number are mutually exclusive events.

$$P(2 \text{ or odd}) = P(2) + P(\text{odd})$$
$$= \frac{1}{6} + \frac{3}{6}$$
$$= \frac{4}{6}$$
$$= \frac{2}{3}$$

1 PLAN AND PREPARE

Warm-Up Exercises

Transparency Available

Find the product.

1. $\frac{2}{5} \cdot \frac{3}{4}$ $\frac{3}{10}$
2. $\frac{7}{8} \cdot \frac{2}{7}$ $\frac{1}{4}$
3. $\frac{12}{15} \cdot \frac{8}{14}$ $\frac{16}{35}$
4. $\frac{18}{52} \cdot \frac{17}{51}$ $\frac{3}{26}$
5. A bag contains 3 green, 5 blue, and 6 yellow marbles. What is the probability of selecting a yellow marble at random? $\frac{3}{7}$

Notetaking Guide

Transparency Available

Promotes interactive learning and notetaking skills.

Pacing

Basic: 2 days
Average: 2 days
Advanced: 2 days
Block: 1 block
- See *Teaching Guide/Lesson Plan.*

2 FOCUS AND MOTIVATE

Essential Question

Big Idea 1, p. 841

How do you find the probability of compound events? **Tell students they will learn how to answer this question by finding probabilities of mutually exclusive events or overlapping events and independent or dependent events.**

NCTM STANDARDS

Standard 9: Grasp connections among mathematical ideas

Standard 10: Create representations to communicate mathematical ideas

Resource Planning Guide

Chapter Resource Book
- Teaching Guide/Lesson Plan
- Activity Master
- Practice levels A, B, C
- Study Guide
- Catch-up for Absent Students
- Problem Solving Workshop
- Challenge

Workbooks
- Notetaking Guide
- Practice Workbook

Teaching Options
- **Power Presentations** provides dynamic electronic teaching resources for the classroom.
- **Activity Generator** provides editable activities for all ability levels.

Interactive Technology
- Easy Planner
- Power Presentations
- Activity Generator
- Animated Algebra
- Test Generator
- Online Quiz
- eWorkbook
- eEdition
- @HomeTutor

Resources for English Learners
- Spanish Study Guide
- Multi-Language Visual Glossary
- Student Resources in Spanish

See also the *Differentiated Instruction Resources* for more strategies for meeting individual needs.

EXAMPLE 2 Find the probability of *A* or *B*

You roll a number cube. Find the probability that you roll an even number or a prime number.

Solution

Because 2 is both an even number and a prime number, rolling an even number and rolling a prime number are overlapping events. There are 3 even numbers, 3 prime numbers, and 1 number that is both.

$$P(\text{even or prime}) = P(\text{even}) + P(\text{prime}) - P(\text{even and prime})$$

$$= \frac{3}{6} + \frac{3}{6} - \frac{1}{6}$$

$$= \frac{5}{6}$$

✓ **GUIDED PRACTICE** for Examples 1 and 2

1. You roll a number cube. Find the probability that you roll a 2 or a 5. $\frac{1}{3}$
2. You roll a number cube. Find the probability that you roll a number less than 4 or an odd number. $\frac{2}{3}$

INDEPENDENT AND DEPENDENT EVENTS To find the probability that event *A* and event *B* both occur, determine how the events are related. Two events are **independent events** if the occurrence of one event has no effect on the occurrence of the other. Two events are **dependent events** if the occurrence of one event affects the occurrence of the other.

For instance, consider the probability of choosing a green marble and then a blue marble from the bag shown. If you choose one marble and replace it before choosing the second, then the events are independent. If you do not replace the first marble, then the sample space has changed, and the events are dependent.

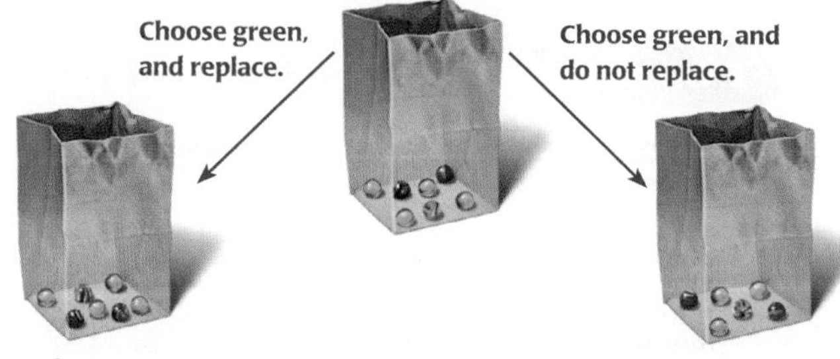
Choose green, and replace.
Choose green, and do not replace.

Independent Events

With replacement:

$P(\text{green and blue}) = \frac{4}{7} \cdot \frac{1}{7} = \frac{4}{49}$

$P(A \text{ and } B) = P(A) \cdot P(B)$

Dependent Events

Without replacement:

$P(\text{green and blue}) = \frac{4}{7} \cdot \frac{1}{6} = \frac{2}{21}$

$P(A \text{ and } B) = P(A) \cdot P(B \text{ given } A)$

Motivating the Lesson

You are one out of 50 students who will be selected at random to recite a poem or play a song. If you know how to find the probability of compound events, you can determine your chances of being selected for one or the other of these performances.

3 TEACH

Extra Example 1

You roll a number cube. Find the probability of rolling a 1 or a number greater than 4. $\frac{1}{2}$

Key Question to Ask for Example 1

- How is a mutually exclusive compound probability similar to a simple probability? **Each of the probabilities in a mutually exclusive compound event is represented as the ratio of the number of favorable outcomes to the number of possible outcomes, just as in a simple probability.**

Extra Example 2

You roll a number cube. Find the probability of rolling an odd number or a number less than 5. $\frac{5}{6}$

Key Question to Ask for Example 2

- Why do you subtract the probability of the overlapping event in a compound probability? **The overlapping event is a subset of both events. You need to subtract its probability so that it is not included twice.**

Differentiated Instruction

Inclusion To help students associate *or* with addition, and *and* with multiplication, students can use a simple example. The sample space {H, T} for one toss of a coin gives *P*(heads *or* tails) = 1. Using addition, *P*(heads *or* tails) $= \frac{1}{2} + \frac{1}{2} = 1$. So, *or* means addition. Similarly, the sample space {HH, HT, TH, TT} for two tosses of a coin gives *P*(heads *and* then tails) $= \frac{1}{4}$. By multiplication, *P*(heads *and* then tails) $= \frac{1}{2} \cdot \frac{1}{2} = \frac{1}{4}$. So, *and* means multiplication.

See also the *Differentiated Instruction Resources* for more strategies.

EXAMPLE 3 Find the probability of *A* and *B*

BUS SCHEDULE You take a city bus from your neighborhood to a location within walking distance of your school. The express bus arrives at your neighborhood between 7:30 and 7:36. The local bus arrives at your neighborhood between 7:30 and 7:40. You arrive at the bus stop at 7:33. Find the probability that you have missed both the express bus and the local bus.

ANOTHER WAY
For alternative methods for solving the problem in Example 3, turn to page 868 for the **Problem Solving Workshop**.

Solution

The events are independent. The arrival of one bus does not affect the arrival of the other bus.

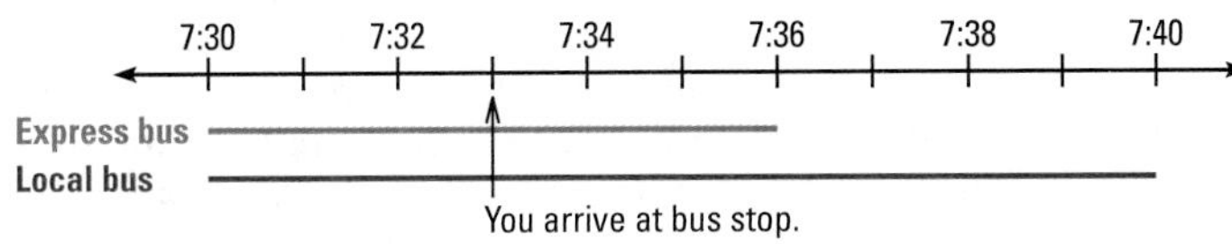

There are 6 minutes when the express bus can arrive. You are not at the bus stop for 3 of those minutes.

$P(\text{you miss express bus}) = \frac{3}{6} = \frac{1}{2}$

There are 10 minutes when the local bus can arrive. You are not at the bus stop for 3 of those minutes.

$P(\text{you miss local bus}) = \frac{3}{10}$

Multiply the probabilities of the two events:

$$P(\text{you miss both buses}) = \frac{1}{2} \cdot \frac{3}{10} = \frac{3}{20}$$

▶ The probability that you miss the express bus and the local bus is $\frac{3}{20}$.

EXAMPLE 4 Find the probability of *A* and *B*

PEN COLORS A box contains 3 blue pens and 5 black pens. You choose one pen at random, do not replace it, then choose a second pen at random. What is the probability that both pens are blue?

USE A TREE DIAGRAM
You can show the probabilities in a tree diagram. Let **Bl** = **Blue** and **Bk** = **Black**.

Solution

Because you do not replace the first pen, the events are dependent. Before you choose a pen, there are 8 pens, and 3 of them are blue. After you choose a blue pen, there are 7 pens left and 2 of them are blue.

$$P(\text{blue and then blue}) = P(\text{blue}) \cdot P(\text{blue given blue})$$

$$= \frac{3}{8} \cdot \frac{2}{7} = \frac{6}{56} = \frac{3}{28}$$

✓ **GUIDED PRACTICE** for Examples 3 and 4

3. **MARBLES** A bag contains 4 red, 5 green, and 2 blue marbles. You randomly draw 2 marbles, one at a time. Find the probabililty that both are red if:

   a. you replace the first marble. $\frac{16}{121}$

   b. you do not replace the first marble. $\frac{6}{55}$

Extra Example 3

An acceptable two-digit code, made from the digits 1 through 9, consists of an even number followed by an odd number. You choose two numbers at random. Find the probability that you have chosen an acceptable code. $\frac{20}{81}$

Extra Example 4

A bag contains 4 blue marbles and 8 yellow marbles. You choose one marble at random, do not replace it, and then choose a second marble at random. What is the probability that both marbles are blue? $\frac{1}{11}$

Closing the Lesson

Have students summarize the major points of the lesson and answer the Essential Question: How do you find the probability of compound events?

- **A compound event combines two or more events using the word *and* or the word *or*.**
- **Mutually exclusive events have no common outcomes, while overlapping events have at least one common outcome.**
- **Independent events are ones in which the occurrence of one event has no effect on the occurrence of the other. Two events are dependent if the occurrence of one event affects the occurrence of the other.**

To find the probability that event A *or* event B occurs, determine if the events are mutually exclusive or overlapping. If mutually exclusive, add the probabilities. If overlapping, add the probabilities and subtract the probability of the overlapping event. To find the probability of events A *and* B occurring, multiply the probabilities of the events.

4 PRACTICE AND APPLY

Assignment Guide

Answer Transparencies available for all exercises

Basic:
Day 1: SRH p. 915 Exs. 1, 2, 6, 7
pp. 864–867
Exs. 1–8, 30–34
Day 2: pp. 864–867
Exs. 9–17, 22–25, 28, 29

Average:
Day 1: pp. 864–867
Exs. 1, 2, 5–8, 18, 19, 30–34
Day 2: pp. 864–867
Exs. 11–17, 20, 22–26, 28, 29

Advanced:
Day 1: pp. 864–867
Exs. 1, 2, 6–8, 18, 19, 21*, 30–34
Day 2: pp. 864–867
Exs. 11–17, 20, 22–29*

Block:
pp. 864–867
Exs. 1, 2, 5–8, 11–20, 22–26, 28–34

Differentiated Instruction

See *Differentiated Instruction Resources* for suggestions on addressing the needs of a diverse classroom.

Homework Check

For a quick check of student understanding of key concepts, go over the following exercises:

Basic: 4, 8, 10, 22, 24

Average: 5, 11, 23, 24, 25

Advanced: 6, 12, 23, 24, 25

Extra Practice

- Student Edition, p. 950
- Chapter Resource Book: Practice levels A, B, C

Practice Worksheet

An easily-readable reduced practice page (with answers) for this lesson can be found on p. 840C.

13.4 EXERCISES

HOMEWORK KEY
○ = **WORKED-OUT SOLUTIONS** on p. WS32 for Exs. 5 and 23
★ = **STANDARDIZED TEST PRACTICE** Exs. 2, 8, 13, 20, and 24
◆ = **MULTIPLE REPRESENTATIONS** Ex. 25

SKILL PRACTICE

A

1. **VOCABULARY** Copy and complete: The probability of _?_ events is found using the formula $P(A \text{ and } B) = P(A) \cdot P(B \text{ given } A)$. **dependent**

2. ★ **WRITING** *Explain* how overlapping events differ from mutually exclusive events. **Overlapping events have one or more outcomes in common, mutually exclusive events do not.**

EXAMPLES 1 and 2 on pp. 861–862 for Exs. 3–8

PROBABILITY OF A OR B In Exercises 3–6, you roll a number cube. Tell whether the events *A* and *B* are *mutually exclusive* or *overlapping*. Then find *P*(*A* or *B*).

3. **Event *A*:** Roll a 6. **Event *B*:** Roll a prime number. **mutually exclusive; $\frac{2}{3}$**

4. **Event *A*:** Roll an even number. **Event *B*:** Roll a 5. **mutually exclusive; $\frac{2}{3}$**

5. **Event *A*:** Roll an odd number. **Event *B*:** Roll a number less than 5. **overlapping; $\frac{5}{6}$**

6. **Event *A*:** Roll a multiple of 3. **Event *B*:** Roll an even number. **overlapping; $\frac{2}{3}$**

7. **ERROR ANALYSIS** A bag contains 7 yellow marbles, 4 red marbles, and 5 blue marbles. *Describe* and correct the error in finding the probability that you randomly draw a yellow or blue marble. **See margin.**

$$P(\text{yellow or blue}) = P(\text{yellow}) \cdot P(\text{blue}) = \frac{7}{16} \cdot \frac{5}{16} = \frac{35}{256}$$

7. To find the probability that you draw a yellow *or* a blue marble, the individual probabilities should be added, not multiplied; $\frac{7}{16} + \frac{5}{16} = \frac{12}{16} = \frac{3}{4}$.

8. ★ **MULTIPLE CHOICE** A bag contains tiles with the numbers 1–10 on them. You randomly choose a tile from the bag. What is the probability that you choose an even number or a number less than 5? **A**

Ⓐ 0.7 Ⓑ 0.8 Ⓒ 0.9 Ⓓ 1

EXAMPLES 3 and 4 on p. 863 for Exs. 9–12

PROBABILITY OF A AND B In Exercises 9–12, tell whether the events *A* and *B* are *dependent* or *independent*. Then find *P*(*A* and *B*).

9. You roll two number cubes.
Event *A*: You roll a 2 first.
Event *B*: You roll a 5 second. **independent; $\frac{1}{36}$**

10. You write each of the letters of the word BIOLOGY on pieces of paper and place them in a bag. You randomly draw one letter, do not replace it, then randomly draw a second letter.
Event *A*: The first letter is O.
Event *B*: The second letter is B. **dependent; $\frac{1}{21}$**

11. You flip a coin and roll a number cube.
Event *A*: The coin shows heads.
Event *B*: The number cube shows 2. **independent; $\frac{1}{12}$**

12. A box contains 3 milk chocolates, 3 white chocolates, and 4 dark chocolates. You choose a chocolate at random, eat it, then choose a second chocolate at random.
Event *A*: You choose a dark chocolate.
Event *B*: You choose a dark chocolate. **dependent; $\frac{2}{15}$**

13. ★ **MULTIPLE CHOICE** A vase holds 7 red roses and 5 pink roses. You randomly choose a rose, remove it, then randomly choose another. What is the approximate probability that both roses are red? **B**

Ⓐ 0.29 Ⓑ 0.32 Ⓒ 0.34 Ⓓ 0.37

B **CHESS PIECES In Exercises 14–17, consider a bag that contains all of the chess pieces in a set, as shown in the diagram.**

	King	Queen	Bishop	Rook	Knight	Pawn
Black	1	1	2	2	2	8
White	1	1	2	2	2	8

14. You choose one piece at random. Find the probability that you choose a black piece or a queen. $\frac{17}{32}$

15. You choose one piece at random, replace it, then choose a second piece at random. Find the probability that you choose a rook, then a bishop. $\frac{1}{64}$

16. You choose one piece at random, do not replace it, then choose a second piece at random. Find the probability that you choose a king, then a pawn. $\frac{1}{31}$

17. **ERROR ANALYSIS** *Describe* and correct the error made in making a tree diagram to determine the probability that you randomly choose a king and a second king, without replacement. **See margin.**

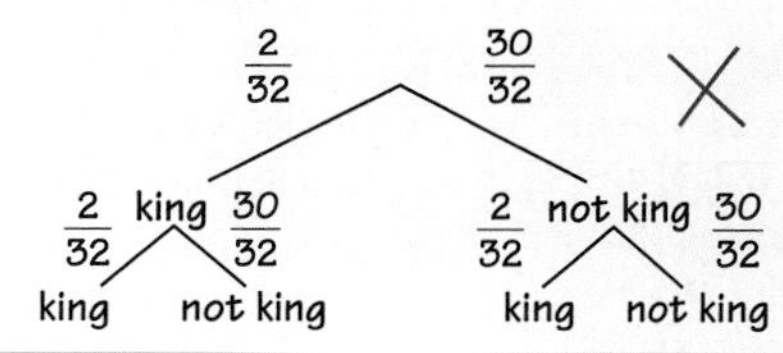

In Exercises 18 and 19, use the following information. Two mutually exclusive events for which one or the other must occur are called *complementary* events. If events A and B are complementary events, then $P(A) + P(B) = 1$.

18. **WEATHER** A local meteorologist reports that there is a 70% chance of rain tomorrow. What is the probability that it will *not* rain tomorrow? **30%**

19. **BASKETBALL** You make 31% of your attempted 3-point shots. What is the probability that you miss your next attempted 3-point shot? **69%**

20. ★ **WRITING** You write the letters of the word WISDOM on pieces of paper and place them in a bag. You randomly choose 2 letters from the bag at the same time. *Explain* whether these events are independent or dependent. What is the probability that you choose the letters S and D?

20. Dependent. *Sample answer*: Even though two pieces of paper are selected at the same time, the selection of one piece of paper affects the selection of the other, so the events are dependent; $\frac{1}{15}$.

C 21. **CHALLENGE** The sections of the spinner shown all have the same area. You spin the spinner.

a. Find the probability that the spinner stops on red *or* a prime number *or* a multiple of 3. $\frac{7}{8}$

b. Write a general formula for $P(A \text{ or } B \text{ or } C)$ where A, B, and C are overlapping events. *Explain* your reasoning. **See margin.**

HINT
In part (a), you may want to draw a Venn diagram.

Avoiding Common Errors

Exercises 3–12 Some students may add probabilities when finding $P(A \text{ and } B)$ and multiply probabilities when finding $P(A \text{ or } B)$. Remind these students that they add when the conjunction is *or* and multiply when the conjunction is *and.*

Study Strategy

Exercises 3–8, 9–16 Suggest that students ask themselves key questions when trying to determine whether events are mutually exclusive or overlapping or whether the events are dependent or independent. For example, when finding $P(A \text{ or } B)$, students could ask: *If I choose A, could I also be choosing B?* When finding $P(A \text{ and } B)$, students can ask: *After I find the probability of A, do I then want to find the probability of B or the probability of B given A?*

21b. $P(A) + P(B) + P(C) - P(A \text{ and } B) - P(A \text{ and } C) - P(B \text{ and } C) + P(A \text{ and } B \text{ and } C)$; when $P(A) + P(B) + P(C)$ is added, the overlap of each set is counted twice so it must be subtracted. When you subtract the overlap of each set the overlap of all three sets gets subtracted 3 times, so it must be added one time.

17. The second-draw probabilities are incorrect. There are 31 pieces left.

$P(\text{king given king}) = \frac{1}{31}$, $P(\text{not king given king}) = \frac{30}{31}$, $P(\text{king given not king}) = \frac{2}{31}$, $P(\text{not king given not king}) = \frac{29}{31}$.

Reading Strategy

Exercises 22–25 Point out to students that these exercises are referenced to examples in the lesson. Encourage students to read through the examples when working on the exercises and to choose the appropriate example as a model for solving the problem.

Exercise 23 More information about walruses can be found at www.walruses.com/didyouknow.php

Teaching Strategy

Exercises 24, 25 You may want to read these exercises with the class and then discuss the type of compound probability exemplified in each exercise or in each part of the exercise. After the discussion, have students solve the exercises individually and then discuss the solutions as a class. This will help students focus on the processes they should use in learning how to recognize and solve compound probabilities.

25a. See below.

25b.

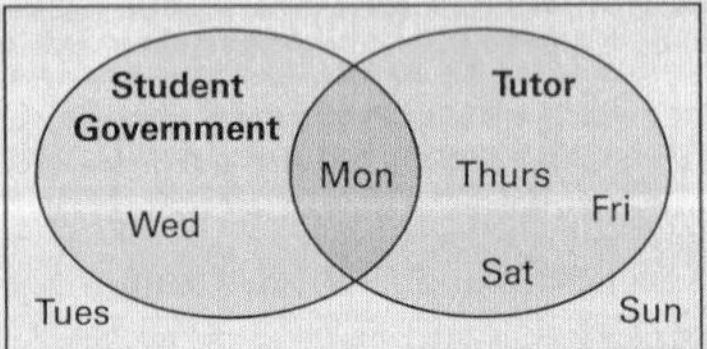

27c. *Sample answer:* You can calculate both the number of favorable outcomes and the number of total outcomes using permutations. There are $_5P_5$ arrangements of the 5 tickets. If you have the aisle seat and your best friend is next to you, there are $_3P_3$ permutations for the remaining seats, which represents the number of favorable outcomes; $\frac{_3P_3}{_5P_5} = \frac{6}{120} = \frac{1}{20}$.

PROBLEM SOLVING

EXAMPLES A **3 and 4** on p. 863 for Exs. 22–23

22. **CONTEST** You can win concert tickets from a radio station if you are the first person to call when the song of the day is played, or if you are the first person to correctly answer the trivia question. The song of the day is played between 5:00 and 5:30 P.M. The trivia question is asked between 5:15 and 5:45 P.M. You begin listening to the radio station at 5:20. Find the probability that you miss the song of the day and the trivia question. $\frac{1}{9}$

@HomeTutor for problem solving help at classzone.com

23. **WALRUS** When a walrus forages for food, it waves its flipper to move sediment 70% of the time. When using the flipper wave technique, a walrus uses its right flipper 89% of the time. Find the probability that a walrus foraging for food uses a flipper and it is the right flipper. **62.3%**

@HomeTutor for problem solving help at classzone.com

EXAMPLES **1, 2, 3, and 4** on pp. 861–863 for Ex. 24

24. ★ **SHORT RESPONSE** A survey of 887,403 households found that 270,658 households have a dog, 326,591 have a cat, and 81,641 have both.

    a. What is the probability that one of the households surveyed, chosen at random, has a dog and a cat? **about 0.092**

    b. What is the probability that one of the households surveyed, chosen at random, has a dog or a cat? **0.58**

    c. *Explain* how your answers to parts (a) and (b) are related. **See margin.**

24c. *Sample answer:* The answer to part b is equal to the sum of the probability of households with dogs and the probability of households with cats, minus the answer to part a.

EXAMPLES B **1 and 2** on pp. 861–862 for Ex. 25

25. ◆ **MULTIPLE REPRESENTATIONS** You have student government meetings on Monday and Wednesday. You tutor in the morning on Monday, Thursday, Friday, and Saturday.

    a. **Making a Table** Make a table that shows your schedule for the week. **See margin.**

    b. **Drawing a Diagram** Make a Venn diagram that shows the days of the week that you participate in each activity. **See margin.**

    c. **Using a Formula** Your class is taking a field trip that could be scheduled for any day of the week. Find the probability that it is scheduled for a day when you tutor or have a student government meeting. $\frac{5}{7}$

26. **EARTH SCIENCE** The table shows the ranges of annual mean temperature and precipitation for 57 cities in the U.S. Find the probability that a city in this study has an annual mean temperature in the range 39°F–52°F or an annual precipitation in the range 0–24 inches. $\frac{35}{57}$

Precipitation (inches)	Temperature (degrees Fahrenheit)	
	39–52	**53–66**
0–24	7	7
25–49	21	22

○ = **WORKED-OUT SOLUTIONS** on p. WS1 ★ = **STANDARDIZED TEST PRACTICE** ◆ = **MULTIPLE REPRESENTATIONS**

25a.

Mon	Tues	Wed	Thurs	Fri	Sat	Sun
st. gov.		st. gov.				
tutor			tutor	tutor	tutor	

C 27. **CHALLENGE** You have 5 tickets to a play. You invite 4 friends to see the play. You hand out the tickets at random. One ticket is for an aisle seat, and the other tickets are for the next 4 seats in the row.

a. What is the probability that you will get the aisle seat? $\frac{1}{5}$

b. What is the probability that you will get the aisle seat and your best friend will get the ticket for the seat next to you? $\frac{1}{20}$

c. *Explain* how you could solve the problem in part (b) using permutations. **See margin.**

MIXED REVIEW

PREVIEW Prepare for Lesson 13.5 in Exs. 28–29.

In Exercises 28 and 29, the spinner shown has sections with equal area. *(p. 843)*

28. You flip a coin and spin the spinner. How many possible outcomes are in the sample space? List the possible outcomes. **16 outcomes; H1, H2, H3, H4, H5, H6, H7, H8, T1, T2, T3, T4, T5, T6, T7, T8**

29. You roll a number cube and spin the spinner. How many possible outcomes are in the sample space? List the possible outcomes. **See margin.**

Evaluate the expression.

30. ${}_5P_3$ *(p. 851)* **60** 31. ${}_{15}P_0$ *(p. 851)* **1** 32. ${}_{15}C_0$ *(p. 856)* **1** 33. ${}_5C_3$ *(p. 856)* **10**

34. **ELECTIVES** Your school offers 10 elective courses each semester. You have time in your schedule for 2 of these courses. How many combinations of 2 elective courses can you choose? *(p. 856)* **45 combinations**

QUIZ *for Lessons 13.1–13.4*

1. **MARBLES** A bag contains 16 red marbles and 8 white marbles. You select a marble at random. *(p. 843)*

a. What is the probability that you select a red marble? $\frac{2}{3}$

b. What are the odds in favor of selecting a red marble? **2 : 1**

2. **PASSWORD** The password for an e-mail account is the word FISH followed by a 3-digit number. The 3-digit number contains the digits 1, 2, and 3. How many different passwords are possible? *(p. 851)* **6**

3. **SHUFFLE** A CD plays on random shuffle. The CD has 12 songs on it. Your CD player selects a song at random, plays it, then selects a second song at random. No song is repeated until every song has been played. What is the probability that song 3 is played first and song 1 is played second? *(p. 851)* $\frac{1}{132}$

Evaluate the expression.

4. ${}_5P_4$ *(p. 851)* **120** 5. ${}_8P_5$ *(p. 851)* **6720** 6. ${}_5C_2$ *(p. 856)* **10** 7. ${}_8C_5$ *(p. 856)* **56**

8. **NUMBER TILES** Tiles numbered 1–30 are placed in a bag. You select a tile at random. Find the probability that you select an odd number or a prime number. Are the events mutually exclusive or overlapping? *Explain.* *(p. 861)*

8. $\frac{8}{15}$; overlapping. *Sample answer:* The events are overlapping because numbers like 3 and 11 are both odd and prime.

EXTRA PRACTICE for Lesson 13.4, p. 950  **ONLINE QUIZ** at classzone.com

5 ASSESS AND RETEACH

Daily Homework Quiz

Transparency Available

1. A bag contains 4 yellow marbles, 3 blue marbles, and 5 red marbles. You randomly draw a marble, replace it, and draw another marble. What is the probability that you draw a red marble and then a yellow marble? $\frac{5}{36}$

2. A survey of 100 students at your school found that 58 students ride the bus, 22 drive to school, 14 walk, and 6 get a ride from a relative. If one of the students surveyed is chosen at random, what is the probability the student either drives to school or walks? $\frac{9}{25}$

Available at **classzone.com**

Diagnosis/Remediation

- Practice A, B, C in Chapter Resource Book
- Study Guide in Chapter Resource Book
- Practice Workbook
- @HomeTutor

Challenge

Additional challenge is available in the Chapter Resource Book.

Quiz

An easily-readable reduced copy of the quiz (with answers) on Lessons 13.1–13.4 from the Assessment Book can be found on p. 840F.

29. 48 outcomes; 1-1, 1-2, 1-3, 1-4, 1-5, 1-6, 1-7, 1-8, 2-1, 2-2, 2-3, 2-4, 2-5, 2-6, 2-7, 2-8, 3-1, 3-2, 3-3, 3-4, 3-5, 3-6, 3-7, 3-8, 4-1, 4-2, 4-3, 4-4, 4-5, 4-6, 4-7, 4-8, 5-1, 5-2, 5-3, 5-4, 5-5, 5-6, 5-7, 5-8, 6-1, 6-2, 6-3, 6-4, 6-5, 6-6, 6-7, 6-8

Alternative Strategy

Example 3 on page 863 can be solved by performing a simulation or by using geometry. Point out to students that the simulation in Method 1 gives a probability close to Example 3 on page 863, but not the same as the example. Be sure students realize that different simulations will give different probabilities. Method 2 can help students visualize the relationship between possible and favorable outcomes.

Graphing Calculator

If students need help generating random numbers to perform a simulation, refer them to the directions for the simulations they performed in the extension on page 849.

Teaching Strategy

You may want students to compare their simulations to see how closely they approximate the probability calculated by using the formula in Example 3 in Lesson 13.4 and by using geometry in alternative method 2.

PROBLEM SOLVING WORKSHOP
LESSON 13.4

Using ALTERNATIVE METHODS

Another Way to Solve Example 3, page 863

MULTIPLE REPRESENTATIONS In Example 3 on page 863, you saw how to solve the problem about a bus schedule by using a number line and a formula. You can also solve the problem by performing a simulation or using geometry.

PROBLEM

BUS SCHEDULE You take a city bus from your neighborhood to a location within walking distance of your school. The express bus arrives at your neighborhood between 7:30 and 7:36. The local bus arrives at your neighborhood between 7:30 and 7:40. You arrive at the bus stop at 7:33. Find the probability that you have missed both the express bus and the local bus.

METHOD 1

Performing a Simulation One alternative approach is to perform a simulation.

STEP 1 **Read** the problem. Notice that there is a 6 minute interval when the express bus could arrive and a 10 minute interval when the local bus could arrive. Let 1 represent the first minute, from 7:30 to 7:31, that a bus could arrive. Let 2 represent the second minute, from 7:31 to 7:32, that a bus could arrive. Continue to number the minutes when a bus could arrive.

STEP 2 **Generate** random integers. Use a graphing calculator to generate a random integer from 1 to 6. This number represents the minute that the express bus arrives. Then generate a random integer from 1 to 10. This number represents the minute that the local bus arrives. Perform this simulation 10 times.

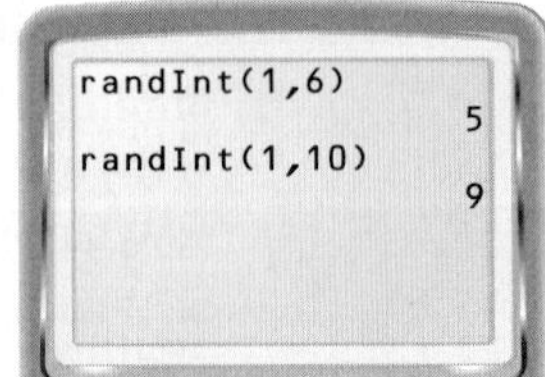

You are not at the bus stop until the fourth minute, so if both numbers that you generate are less than 4, then you miss both buses.

First number	5	4	2	5	2	1	2	3	3	1
Second number	9	1	1	8	4	7	9	10	6	2
Miss both buses?	No	No	Yes	No	No	No	No	No	No	Yes

STEP 3 **Find** the experimental probability that you miss both buses.

$P(\text{miss both buses}) = \frac{2}{10} = \frac{1}{5}$

METHOD 2 **Using Geometry** Another approach is to use geometry. Use the formula for the area of a rectangle to find the number of possible outcomes and the number of favorable outcomes.

STEP 1 **Draw** a rectangle whose side lengths represent the number of minutes that each bus could arrive.

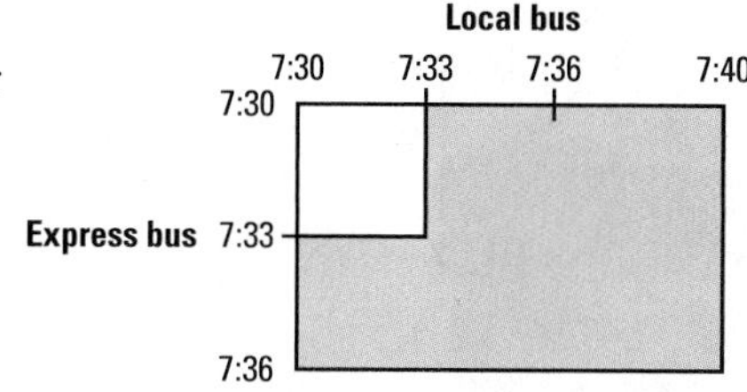

STEP 2 **Draw** a square within the rectangle to represent the number of minutes that you are *not* at the bus stop.

STEP 3 **Calculate** the area of the rectangle that represents the time a bus could arrive. Also calculate the area of the square that represents the time that you are *not* at the bus stop.

Time a bus could arrive: $A = 6 \cdot 10 = 60$

Time you are *not* at bus stop: $A = 3 \cdot 3 = 9$

STEP 4 **Find** the probability that you miss both buses by forming the ratio of the areas from step 2.

$P(\text{miss both buses}) = \frac{9}{60} = \frac{3}{20}$

PRACTICE

1. **WHAT IF?** In the problem on page 868, suppose you arrive at 7:34. What is the probability that you miss both buses? **$\frac{4}{15}$**

2. **VISITING FRIENDS** Two friends are planning to visit you this evening. You expect one friend to arrive at your house between 7:00 and 7:30 P.M. You expect the other friend to arrive between 7:10 and 7:20 P.M. You have to run an errand from 7:00 until 7:15 P.M. What is the probability that you are home when both friends arrive? Solve this problem using two different methods. **$\frac{1}{4}$**

3. **WHAT IF?** In Exercise 2, suppose a third friend plans to visit you this evening. This friend plans to arrive at your house between 7:00 and 7:20 P.M. What is the probability that you are home when all three of your friends arrive? *Explain* how you found your answer. **See margin.**

4. **RAFFLE** You enter two different raffles during your neighborhood's street fair. The winner of the first raffle will be announced between 6:00 and 6:30 P.M. The winner of the second raffle will be announced between 6:15 and 6:45 P.M. You leave the fair at 5:00 P.M. and return at 6:20 P.M. What is the probability that you hear the winner of each raffle announced? Solve this problem using two different methods. **$\frac{5}{18}$**

5. **ERROR ANALYSIS** A student solved the problem in Exercise 4 as shown. *Describe* and correct the error. **See margin.**

$$P(\text{hear both winners}) = \frac{\text{Favorable time}}{\text{Total time}} = \frac{10 \text{ minutes}}{30 \text{ minutes}} = \frac{1}{3}$$

Avoiding Common Errors

When using simulations in the practice exercises, caution students to generate random numbers that match the minutes which represent the *possible* outcomes of the events.

Study Strategy

Encourage students to rotate the three methods they have learned in solving the problems in the exercises. Tell them that they will gain experience with all three methods and that by trying each method, they will be able to ascertain which method works best for them.

3. $\frac{1}{16}$. *Sample answer:* The third friend can arrive any time in a 20 minute span, and I will be away from the house for 15 of those minutes. The probability is $\frac{1}{4}$ that I will be home when the third friend arrives. Since the three friends arrive independently of each other, you can multiply the probability that you are home when the other two friends arrive by $\frac{1}{4}$ to calculate the probability that you are home when all three friends arrive; $\frac{1}{4} \cdot \frac{1}{4} = \frac{1}{16}$.

5. *Sample answer:* The times at which each raffle is announced are independent, so the two probabilities should be calculated separately and then multiplied; $\frac{10}{30} \cdot \frac{25}{30} = \frac{1}{3} \cdot \frac{5}{6} = \frac{5}{18}$.

2a. cheese, mushrooms; cheese, onions; cheese, tomatoes; cheese, peppers; cheese, sausage; cheese, ham; cheese, steak; mushrooms, onions; mushrooms, tomatoes; mushrooms, peppers; mushrooms, sausage; mushrooms, ham; mushrooms, steak; onions, tomatoes; onions, peppers; onions, sausage; onions, ham; onions, steak; tomatoes, peppers; tomatoes, sausage; tomatoes, ham; tomatoes, steak; peppers, sausage; peppers, ham; peppers, steak; sausage, ham; sausage, steak; ham, steak

4. 3 : 17. *Sample answer:* 15% is equivalent to $\frac{3}{20}$. There is a $\frac{17}{20}$ chance that it will not snow. So, the odds in favor of snow are $\frac{3}{20}:\frac{17}{20} = 3:17$.

5. *Sample answer:* A club of 10 students is choosing a president and vice-president. How many choices could the club make?

6b. How many states have a team in both the National Basketball Association and in Major League Baseball. *Sample answer:* The probability that the state has a team in the National Basketball Association or a Major League Baseball team is the sum of the probability that the state has a team in the National Basketball Association and the probability that the state has a Major League Baseball team minus the probability that the state has a team in both the National Basketball Association and in Major League Baseball.

7c. 21 : 29. *Sample answer:* The total number of students from the survey who eat fruit every day is 232. The total number of students surveyed is 400, so 168 students surveyed do not eat fruit every day. Therefore, the odds against a random student from the survey eating fruit every day is 168 : 232, or 21 : 29.

MIXED REVIEW of Problem Solving

STATE TEST PRACTICE
classzone.com

Lessons 13.1–13.4

1. **MULTI-STEP PROBLEM** There are 5743 known amphibian species in the world. Of these, 1856 species are judged to be at risk of extinction, and another 113 species may already be extinct.

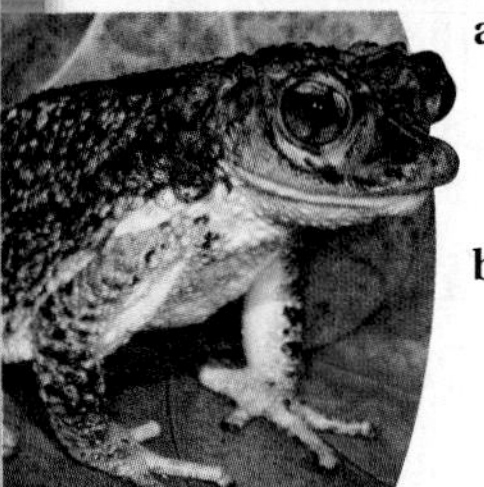

The Puerto Rican crested toad is at risk of extinction.

   a. Find the probability that an amphibian species chosen at random is at risk of extinction or may already be extinct. **about 0.343**

   b. Find the probability that two different amphibian species, each chosen at random, are at risk of extinction. **about 0.104**

2. **MULTI-STEP PROBLEM** You are ordering an omelet with two ingredients. You can choose from the following list: cheese, mushrooms, onions, tomatoes, peppers, sausage, ham, and steak.

   a. Make an organized list of all the possible omelets that you can order. **See margin.**

   b. Use a permutation or combination formula to find the number of possible omelets. **28 omelets**

3. **MULTI-STEP PROBLEM** In NCAA women's basketball tournaments from 1982 to 2003, teams seeded, or ranked, number one have won 283 games and lost 71 games in the tournament. Suppose a team is chosen at random from all those that have been seeded number one.

   a. What is the probability that the team won a game in the tournament? $\frac{283}{354}$

   b. What are the odds in favor of the team's having won a game in the tournament? **283 : 71**

4. **SHORT RESPONSE** A meteorologist reports that there is a 15% chance of snow tomorrow. What are the odds in favor of snow tomorrow? *Explain* how you found your answer. **See margin.**

5. **OPEN-ENDED** *Describe* a real-world situation in which the number of possible arrangements is given by ${}_{10}P_2$. **See margin.**

6. **SHORT RESPONSE** In the United States there are 21 states (not including Washington, D.C.) with teams in the National Football League and 17 states with Major League Baseball teams. There are 15 states that have both types of teams. Suppose a state is chosen at random.

   a. Find the probability that the state has either a National Football League team or a Major League Baseball team. $\frac{23}{50}$

   b. There are 21 states that have a team in the National Basketball Association. What additional information would you need in order to find the probability that the state chosen at random has either a team in the National Basketball Association or a Major League Baseball team? *Explain* your reasoning. **See margin.**

7. **EXTENDED RESPONSE** A survey asked a total of 400 students, 100 male students and 100 female students who were 13 and 15 years old, about their eating habits. The table shows the numbers of students who said that they eat fruit every day.

	13 years old	15 years old
Male	60	53
Female	61	58

   a. Find the probability that a female student, chosen at random from the students surveyed, eats fruit every day. **0.595**

   b. Find the probability that a 15-year-old student, chosen at random from the students surveyed, eats fruit every day. **0.555**

   c. You select a student at random from the students surveyed. Find the odds against the student's eating fruit every day. *Explain* your reasoning. **See margin.**

8. **GRIDDED ANSWER** A music club gives you 6 free CDs for joining. You would like to own 11 of the free CDs that are offered. How many combinations of 6 CDs from the 11 CDs can you choose? **462 combinations**

13.5 Analyze Surveys and Samples

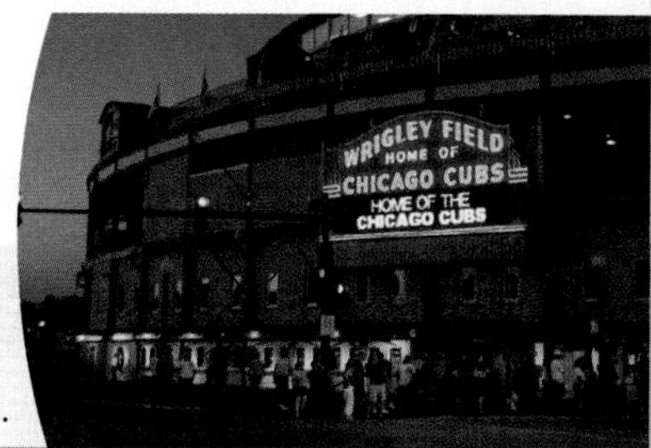

Before You found experimental probabilities.

Now You will identify populations and sampling methods.

Why? So you can analyze surveys of sports fans, as in Ex. 15.

Key Vocabulary
- survey
- population
- sample
- biased sample
- biased question

A **survey** is a study of one or more characteristics of a group. The entire group you want information about is called a **population** . A survey of an entire population is called a *census*. When it is difficult to perform a census, you can survey a **sample** , which is a part of the population.

KEY CONCEPT *For Your Notebook*

Sampling Methods

In a **random sample**, every member of the population has an equal chance of being selected.

In a **stratified random sample**, the population is divided into distinct groups. Members are selected at random from each group.

In a **systematic sample**, a rule is used to select members of the population.

In a **convenience sample**, only members of the population who are easily accessible are selected.

In a **self-selected sample**, members of the population select themselves by volunteering.

EXAMPLE 1 **Classify a sampling method**

EMPLOYEE SAFETY The owners of a company with several factories conduct a survey to determine whether employees are informed about safety regulations. At each factory, 50 employees are chosen at random to complete the survey. Identify the population and classify the sampling method.

Solution

The population is all company employees. Because the population is divided into distinct groups (individual factories), with employees chosen at random from each group, the sample is a stratified random sample.

GUIDED PRACTICE for Example 1

1. **WHAT IF?** In Example 1, suppose the owners survey each employee whose last name begins with M. Classify the sampling method. **systematic**

1 PLAN AND PREPARE

Warm-Up Exercises

Transparency Available

A spinner has 5 sections of equal area, with sections numbered 1–5.

1. You toss a coin and spin the spinner. How many outcomes are in the sample space? **10**
2. You spin the spinner twice. How many outcomes are in the sample space? **25**

Notetaking Guide

Transparency Available

Promotes interactive learning and notetaking skills.

Pacing

Basic: 1 day
Average: 1 day
Advanced: 1 day
Block: 0.5 block with 13.6
- See *Teaching Guide/Lesson Plan.*

2 FOCUS AND MOTIVATE

Essential Question

Big Idea 2, p. 841

How do you identify populations and sampling methods? **Tell students they will learn how to answer this question by analyzing surveys and samples.**

NCTM STANDARDS

Standard 5: Devise questions that can be addressed with data

Standard 8: Communicate thinking clearly to others

Resource Planning Guide

Chapter Resource Book
- Teaching Guide/Lesson Plan
- Activity Master
- Practice levels A, B, C
- Study Guide
- Catch-up for Absent Students
- Application
- Challenge

Workbooks
- Notetaking Guide
- Practice Workbook

Teaching Options
- **Power Presentations** provides dynamic electronic teaching resources for the classroom.
- **Activity Generator** provides editable activities for all ability levels.

Interactive Technology
- Easy Planner
- Power Presentations
- Activity Generator
- Animated Algebra
- Test Generator
- Online Quiz
- eWorkbook
- eEdition
- @HomeTutor

Resources for English Learners
- Spanish Study Guide
- Multi-Language Visual Glossary
- Student Resources in Spanish

See also the *Differentiated Instruction Resources* for more strategies for meeting individual needs.

Motivating the Lesson

You want to know how many students participate in Internet chat rooms. By learning how to identify populations and sampling methods, you can design an unbiased survey.

3 TEACH

Extra Example 1

Owners of a computer store survey customers to see whether they should expand their game selection. They survey customers in the game aisle. Identify the population and classify the sampling method. **Population: store customers; Method: convenience sampling**

Extra Example 2

In Extra Example 1, suppose owners randomly survey all customers at the store on a Saturday. Is the method likely to result in a biased sample? **Saturday customers may reflect different buying attitudes than weekday customers, so the method may result in a biased sample.**

Extra Example 3

Tell whether the question is potentially biased. Explain your answer. *Do you think the city should renovate the library*? **It does not encourage a particular response, so the question is not biased.**

Closing the Lesson

Have students summarize the major points of the lesson and answer the Essential Question: How do you identify populations and sampling methods?

- **A population is the entire group you want information about.**

Identify populations by looking for all members of a group affected by a survey. Identify sampling methods by deciding if they represent the selected population.

BIASED SAMPLES A sample chosen for a survey should be representative of the population. A **biased sample** is a sample that is not representative. In a biased sample, parts of the population may be over-represented or under-represented.

Random samples and stratified random samples (as in Example 1) are the most likely types of samples to be representative. A systematic sample may be representative if the rule used to choose individuals is not biased.

EXAMPLE 2 Identify a potentially biased sample

In Example 1, suppose the owners question 50 workers chosen at random from one factory. Is the method likely to result in a biased sample?

Solution

Workers at other factories may hold significantly different opinions, so the method may result in a biased sample.

BIASED QUESTIONS A question that encourages a particular response is a **biased question**. Survey questions should be worded to avoid bias.

EXAMPLE 3 Identify potentially biased questions

Tell whether the question is potentially biased. Explain your answer. If the question is potentially biased, rewrite it so that it is not.

a. Don't you agree that the voting age should be lowered to 16 because many 16-year-olds are responsible and informed?

b. Do you think the city should risk an increase in pollution by allowing expansion of the Northern Industrial Park?

Solution

a. This question is biased because it suggests that lowering the voting age is a good thing to do. An unbiased question is "Do you think the voting age should be lowered to 16?"

b. This question is biased because it suggests that the proposed expansion will be bad for the environment. An unbiased question is "Do you think the city should allow expansion of the Northern Industrial Park?"

✓ GUIDED PRACTICE for Examples 2 and 3

2. **SOCCER** In a survey about Americans' interest in soccer, the first 25 people admitted to a high school soccer game were asked, "How interested are you in the world's most popular sport, soccer?" **a, b. See margin.**
   a. Is the sampling method likely to result in a biased sample? *Explain.*
   b. Is the question potentially biased? *Explain* your answer. If the question is potentially biased, rewrite it so that it is not.

Differentiated Instruction

English Learners Students should be aware that there can be more than one way to rewrite a biased question as an unbiased one. In **Example 3b**, the basic question is biased because it asks if you agree to increasing pollution. An equally valid, unbiased question, would be "Do you think the city will have an increase in pollution by allowing the expansion of the Northern Industrial Park?"

See also the *Differentiated Instruction Resources* for more strategies.

13.5 EXERCISES

HOMEWORK KEY ○ = **WORKED-OUT SOLUTIONS** on p. WS33 for Exs. 3 and 15
★ = **STANDARDIZED TEST PRACTICE** Exs. 2, 6, and 17

SKILL PRACTICE

A

1. **VOCABULARY** Copy and complete: In a(n) _?_ sample, participants are chosen using a rule. **systematic**

2. ★ **WRITING** *Describe* the difference between a census and a sample. **A census involves an entire population, while a sample is just part of the population.**

POPULATIONS AND SAMPLES In Exercises 3–5, identify the population and classify the sampling method.

EXAMPLE 1 on p. 871 for Exs. 3–6

3. **RESTAURANT SERVICE** A restaurant manager wants to evaluate the restaurant's quality of service. Diners are given mail-in comment cards. **people who have eaten at the restaurant, self-selected**
4. **EXTRACURRICULAR ACTIVITIES** Your school wants to know if students are satisfied with the school's extracurricular activities. In each grade, every tenth student on an alphabetized list is surveyed. **students at your school, systematic**
5. **CUSTOMER SATISFACTION** An airline wants to gather information on passenger satisfaction during a flight. A computer randomly selects 30 passengers to complete a survey. **passengers of the airline, random**

6. ★ **MULTIPLE CHOICE** Scientists wanted to gather information about the birds in a particular region. They chose observation sites and asked bird watchers at those sites to record the number and types of birds they saw in 3 minutes. What population was being studied? **A**

   (A) Birds (B) Sites (C) Scientists (D) Bird watchers

EXAMPLE 2 on p. 872 for Exs. 7–8

BIASED SAMPLES Tell whether the sampling method used is likely to result in a biased sample. *Explain*.

7. **NEIGHBORHOOD WATCH** A family wants to gather information from other residents on their street about forming a neighborhood watch. They survey every third house on both sides of the street. **Not likely. *Sample answer:* The sample should represent the neighborhood.**
8. **NURSE SURVEY** The American Nurses Association wanted to gather information about the working environment for nurses in hospitals. A survey for nurses was posted on the association's website. **See margin.**

EXAMPLE 3 on p. 872 for Exs. 9–11

B

BIASED QUESTIONS In Exercises 9 and 10, tell whether the question is potentially biased. *Explain* your answer. 9, 10. See margin.

9. Do you support the incumbent's tax plan or the challenger's tax plan?
10. Do you prefer the ease of shopping online or the fun of going to a mall?

11. **ERROR ANALYSIS** *Describe* and correct the error in revising the survey question "Don't you think the minimum driving age should be lower?" so that it is not biased. **See margin.**

    Not biased:
    Is the minimum driving age too high or too low? ✗

C

12. **CHALLENGE** Two toothpaste manufacturers each claim that 4 out of every 5 dentists use their brand exclusively. Both manufacturers can support their claims with survey results. *Explain* how this is possible.

12. *Sample answer:* Both manufacturers can make this claim if they used biased survey questions, techniques, or samples.

4 PRACTICE AND APPLY

Assignment Guide

Answer Transparencies available for all exercises

Basic:
Day 1: pp. 873–874
Exs. 1–10, 13–16, 19–27

Average:
Day 1: pp. 873–874
Exs. 1, 2, 4–11, 13–17, 19–27

Advanced:
Day 1: pp. 873–874
Exs. 1, 2, 5–27*

Block:
pp. 873–874
Exs. 1, 2, 4–11, 13–17, 19–27 (with 13.6)

Differentiated Instruction

See *Differentiated Instruction Resources* for suggestions on addressing the needs of a diverse classroom.

Homework Check

For a quick check of student understanding of key concepts, go over the following exercises:

Basic: 4, 7, 9, 13, 14
Average: 5, 8, 10, 14, 15
Advanced: 6, 8, 11, 15, 16

Extra Practice

- Student Edition, p. 950
- Chapter Resource Book: Practice levels A, B, C

Practice Worksheet

An easily-readable reduced practice page (with answers) for this lesson can be found on p. 840C.

p. 872

2a–b. See Additional Answers beginning on p. AA1.

p. 873

8. Likely. *Sample answer:* Since it is a self-selected sample, only the nurses with extreme views are likely to take the time to respond, and the results of the survey will be swayed toward either extreme negative or positive views.

9. Not potentially biased. *Sample answer:* This question simply presents the two choices.

10. Potentially biased. *Sample answer:* Even though it presents both choices in a favorable light, the question is not neutral and is likely to affect the survey's results.

11. *Sample answer:* The new question presumes that the driving age should be changed, and does not present the option that it should remain the same; "What do you think about the current driving age?"

PROBLEM SOLVING

EXAMPLES 2 and 3 on p. 872 for Exs. 13–16

A **Explain** why the question is biased. Then rewrite it so that it is not.

13. Don't you agree that the school needs a new athletic field more than a new science lab? **13, 14. See margin.**

@HomeTutor for problem solving help at classzone.com

14. Would you pay even higher concert ticket prices to finance a new arena?

@HomeTutor for problem solving help at classzone.com

15. **BASEBALL** Each baseball season, Major League Baseball (MLB) fans cast ballots to choose players for the MLB All-Star Game. Do the ballots cast necessarily represent the opinions of all baseball fans? *Explain.* **No. *Sample answer:* The sample is self-selected.**

16. **WATER SAMPLING** Scientists designed a project in which students performed tests on local water sources each day. Students from 18 countries participated in the project. The results of the survey were used to assess the quality of the world's fresh water. Is the sample likely to be biased? *Explain.* **See margin.**

B 17. ★ **SHORT RESPONSE** You plan to report on the academic performance of students in your school for your school newspaper. *Describe* how you could choose a representative sample. Then write an unbiased question you could use to collect information on how many hours each day a student studies. *Explain* why your question is unbiased. **See margin.**

C 18. **CHALLENGE** The results of two five-year studies of a possible link between exercise and decreased risk of heart attack in men appear in a newspaper. The studies involve two different groups of 1000 men over the age of 40 who have never had a heart attack. In the *randomized experiment*, half of the 1000 men are chosen at random to take part in a supervised exercise program, while the other half continue their usual routines. In the *observational study*, the men are divided into two groups, those who exercise regularly and those who do not, and their health status is observed. Which study's results would you expect to be more reliable? *Explain.* **See margin.**

MIXED REVIEW

PREVIEW Prepare for Lesson 13.6 in Exs. 19–23.

Order the numbers from least to greatest. *(p. 909)*

19. 0.02, 0.015, 0.021, 0.012 **0.012, 0.015, 0.02, 0.021**
20. 6.51, 6.15, 6.02, 6.23 **6.02, 6.15, 6.23, 6.51**
21. 12.3, 11.9, 11.09, 12.08 **11.09, 11.9, 12.08, 12.3**

Find the mean, median, and mode(s) of the data. *(p. 918)*

22. Cost (in dollars) of computer monitors: 296, 215, 426, 390, 351, 215, 289 **about $311.71, $296, $215**
23. Size (in megabytes) of files to be downloaded: 10.9, 12.1, 6.4, 2.8, 5.1, 7.6 **about 7.483 MB, 7 MB, no mode**

Evaluate the expression.

24. ${}_5P_3$ *(p. 851)* **60**
25. ${}_{10}P_4$ *(p. 851)* **5040**
26. ${}_8C_4$ *(p. 856)* **70**
27. ${}_7C_2$ *(p. 856)* **21**

 EXTRA PRACTICE for Lesson 13.5, p. 950 **ONLINE QUIZ** at classzone.com

5 ASSESS AND RETEACH

Daily Homework Quiz

Transparency Available

Identify the population and classify the sampling method.

1. You want to know if students would like year-round schools. You survey every fifth student entering first period classes. **Population: all students at a school; systematic sample**
2. A theater owner asks people in line to see a horror movie if they think the theater should show more comedies. Explain whether the survey method is likely to result in a biased survey. **People who go to horror movies may prefer horror to comedy, so the survey may be biased.**

Available at **classzone.com**

Diagnosis/Remediation

- Practice A, B, C in Chapter Resource Book
- Study Guide in Chapter Resource Book
- Practice Workbook
- @HomeTutor

Challenge

Additional challenge is available in the Chapter Resource Book.

13. *Sample answer:* This question is phrased to prompt people into agreeing that the athletic field is more important than the science lab; "Which do you think the school needs more: a new athletic field or a new science lab?"

14. *Sample answer:* This question suggests that prices are already too high, and is likely to make respondents more likely to say no; "Would you pay higher concert ticket prices to finance a new arena?"

16. Yes. *Sample answer:* The sample is not likely to be truly representative of the world's fresh water since it was such a small sample of the population.

17. *Sample answer:* Obtain a list of all students. Select names randomly using a random number generator. "How many hours per day do you study?" This question is unbiased because it does not prompt respondents to give any particular answer.

18. *Sample answer:* The randomized experiment; the men are similar in age and health status. Other issues such as diet or family history should be distributed between the groups randomly. In the observational study, any occurrences of heart attack within either group might be the result of factors such as diet or family history.

13.6 Use Measures of Central Tendency and Dispersion

Before You analyzed surveys and samples.
Now You will compare measures of central tendency and dispersion.
Why? So you can analyze and compare data, as in Example 1.

Key Vocabulary
- **measure of dispersion**
- **range**
- **mean absolute deviation**

KEY CONCEPT *For Your Notebook*

Measures of Central Tendency

The **mean**, or *average*, of a numerical data set is denoted by $\overline{x}$, which is read as "x-bar." For the data set $x_1, x_2, \ldots, x_n$, the mean is $\overline{x} = \frac{x_1 + x_2 + \ldots + x_n}{n}$.

The **median** of a numerical data set is the middle number when the values are written in numerical order. If the data set has an even number of values, the median is the mean of the two middle values.

The **mode** of a data set is the value that occurs most frequently. There may be one mode, no mode, or more than one mode.

EXAMPLE 1 Compare measures of central tendency

The heights (in feet) of 8 waterfalls in the state of Washington are listed below. Which measure of central tendency best represents the data?

1000, 1000, 1181, 1191, 1200, 1268, 1328, 2584

Solution

$$\overline{x} = \frac{1000 + 1000 + 1181 + 1191 + 1200 + 1268 + 1328 + 2584}{8} = \frac{10{,}752}{8} = 1344$$

The median is the mean of the two middle values, 1191 and 1200, or 1195.5.

The mode is 1000.

▶ The median best represents the data. The mode is significantly less than most of the data, and the mean is significantly greater than most of the data.

Animated Algebra at classzone.com

✓ **GUIDED PRACTICE** for Example 1

1. **WHAT IF?** In Example 1, suppose you eliminate the greatest data value, 2584. Which measure of central tendency best represents the remaining data? *Explain* your reasoning. ***Sample answer:* Median; the median, 1191, is close to the data points.**

1 PLAN AND PREPARE

Warm-Up Exercises

Transparency Available

1. Order from least to greatest: 10.14, 11.2, 10.1, 10.08, 11.21 **10.08, 10.1, 10.14, 11.2, 11.21**
2. Jenna scored the following points in her last five basketball games: 28, 18, 24, 22, and 18. What is Jenna's average score for the 5 games? **22 points**

Notetaking Guide

Transparency Available

Promotes interactive learning and notetaking skills.

Pacing

Basic: 1 day
Average: 1 day
Advanced: 1 day
Block: 0.5 block with 13.5
- See *Teaching Guide/Lesson Plan.*

2 FOCUS AND MOTIVATE

Essential Question

Big Idea 2, p. 841

How do you compare measures of central tendency and dispersion? **Tell students they will learn how to answer this question by using the mean, median, mode, range, and mean absolute deviation to analyze data.**

NCTM STANDARDS

Standard 1: Compute fluently

Standard 5: Use proper statistical methods to analyze data

Resource Planning Guide

Chapter Resource Book
- Teaching Guide/Lesson Plan
- Activity Master
- Practice levels A, B, C
- Study Guide
- Catch-up for Absent Students
- Problem Solving Workshop
- Challenge

Workbooks
- Notetaking Guide
- Practice Workbook

Teaching Options
- **Power Presentations** provides dynamic electronic teaching resources for the classroom.
- **Activity Generator** provides editable activities for all ability levels.

Interactive Technology
- Easy Planner
- Power Presentations
- Activity Generator
- Animated Algebra
- Test Generator
- Online Quiz
- eWorkbook
- eEdition
- @HomeTutor

Resources for English Learners
- Spanish Study Guide
- Multi-Language Visual Glossary
- Student Resources in Spanish

See also the *Differentiated Instruction Resources* for more strategies for meeting individual needs.

MEASURES OF DISPERSION A **measure of dispersion** describes the dispersion, or spread, of data. Two such measures are the *range*, which gives the length of the interval containing the data, and the *mean absolute deviation*, which gives the average variation of the data from the mean.

REVIEW ABSOLUTE VALUE
For help with absolute value, see p. 66.

KEY CONCEPT *For Your Notebook*

Measures of Dispersion

The **range** of a numerical data set is the difference of the greatest value and the least value.

The **mean absolute deviation** of the data set $x_1, x_2, \ldots, x_n$ is given by:

$$\text{Mean absolute deviation} = \frac{|x_1 - \bar{x}| + |x_2 - \bar{x}| + \ldots + |x_n - \bar{x}|}{n}$$

EXAMPLE 2 Compare measures of dispersion

RUNNING The top 10 finishing times (in seconds) for runners in two men's races are given. The times in a 100 meter dash are in set *A*, and the times in a 200 meter dash are in set *B*. Compare the spread of the data for the two sets using (**a**) the range and (**b**) the mean absolute deviation.

A: 10.62, 10.94, 10.94, 10.98, 11.05, 11.13, 11.15, 11.28, 11.29, 11.32

B: 21.37, 21.40, 22.23, 22.23, 22.34, 22.34, 22.36, 22.60, 22.66, 22.73

Solution

a. *A*: 11.32 − 10.62 = 0.7 *B*: 22.73 − 21.37 = 1.36

▶ The range of set *B* is greater than the range of set *A*. So, the data in *B* cover a wider interval than the data in *A*.

b. The mean of set *A* is 11.07, so the mean absolute deviation is:

$$\frac{|10.62 - 11.07| + |10.94 - 11.07| + \ldots + |11.32 - 11.07|}{10} = 0.164$$

The mean of set *B* is 22.226, so the mean absolute deviation is:

$$\frac{|21.37 - 22.226| + |21.40 - 22.226| + \ldots + |22.73 - 22.226|}{10} = 0.3364$$

▶ The mean absolute deviation of set *B* is greater, so the average variation from the mean is greater for the data in *B* than for the data in *A*.

REVIEW NEGATIVE NUMBERS
When using the formula for mean absolute deviation, you will encounter negative numbers. For help with negative numbers, see p. 64.

✓ **GUIDED PRACTICE** for Example 2

2. **RUNNING** The top 10 finishing times (in seconds) for runners in a men's 400 meter dash are 46.89, 47.65, 48.15, 49.05, 49.19, 49.50, 49.68, 51.09, 53.31, and 53.68. *Compare* the spread of the data with that of set *A* in Example 2 using (**a**) the range and (**b**) the mean absolute deviation.

2a. The range of finishing times for the men's 400 m dash (6.79) is greater than the range for set *A* (0.7).
2b. The mean absolute deviation is greater for the men's 400 m dash (1.7246) than it is for set *A* (0.164).

Motivating the Lesson

You follow the career of a baseball player. You can use measures of central tendency and dispersion to analyze and compare statistical data gathered on the player.

Extra Example 1

The lengths (in miles) of the 10 longest rivers in the U.S. are listed below. Which measure of central tendency best represents the data?

1290, 1310, 1420, 1450, 1460, 1900, 1900, 1980, 2340, 2540

the mean or the median, since both are close to the middle of the data

An **Animated Algebra** activity is available online for **Example 1**. This activity is also part of **Power Presentations**.

Extra Example 2

The top 5 finishing times (in seconds) for swimmers in two women's races are given. Times for the 50-yard free are in set *A* and for the 100-yard free in set *B*. Compare the spread of the data for the two sets using (a) the range and (b) the mean absolute deviation.

A: 24.32, 24.34, 24.48, 24.82, 25.02
B: 52.90, 52.96, 52.98, 53.02, 53.24

Data in set *A* cover a wider interval than data in set *B*. The average variation from the mean is greater for set *A* than for set *B*.

Closing the Lesson

Have students summarize the major points of the lesson and answer the Essential Question: How do you compare measures of central tendency and dispersion?

- **Measures of central tendency are the mean, median, and mode.**
- **Measures of dispersion are range and mean absolute deviation.**

Compare mean, median, and mode to find which measure best represent most of the data. Compare measures of dispersion to find which data set covers a wider interval.

Differentiated Instruction

Auditory Learners Students may have difficulty with relating the mathematical notation in a formula to its meaning. The mean absolute deviation can be verbalized as *the average of all of the distances of the data points from the mean.*

See also the *Differentiated Instruction Resources* for more strategies.

13.6 EXERCISES

HOMEWORK KEY ○ = **WORKED-OUT SOLUTIONS** on p. WS33 for Exs. 7 and 19
★ = **STANDARDIZED TEST PRACTICE** Exs. 2, 9, 17, 19, and 22

SKILL PRACTICE

A

1. **VOCABULARY** Copy and complete: The value that occurs most frequently in a data set is called the _?_ of the data. **mode**

2. ★ **WRITING** How are measures of central tendency and measures of dispersion used to compare data? **See margin.**

EXAMPLE 1 on p. 875 for Exs. 3–10

MEASURES OF CENTRAL TENDENCY Find the mean, median, and mode(s) of the data.

3. 1, 1, 1, 2, 3, 3, 5, 5, 6 **3, 3, 1**
4. 9, 10, 12, 15, 16 **12.4, 12, no mode**
5. 13, 16, 19, 20, 22, 25, 30, 31 **22, 21, no mode**
6. 14, 15, 15, 14, 14, 16, 18, 15 **15.125, 15, 14 and 15**
7. 5.52, 5.44, 3.60, 5.76, 3.80, 7.22 **$5.22\overline{3}$, 5.48, no mode**
8. 300, 320, 341, 348, 360, 333 **$333.\overline{6}$, 337, no mode**

9. ★ **MULTIPLE CHOICE** What is the median of the data set? **B**

0.7, 0.3, 0.7, 0.8, 0.9, 0.4, 1.0, 1.6, 1.2

Ⓐ 0.7 Ⓑ 0.8 Ⓒ 0.9 Ⓓ 1.0

10. **ERROR ANALYSIS** *Describe* and correct the error in finding the median of the data set. **The list needs to be ordered before you can find the median; 2, 3, 4, 4, 6, 6, 7, 8, 8, the median is 6.**

7 4 6 2 4 6 8 8 3
The median is 4.

B

EXAMPLE 2 on p. 876 for Exs. 11–16

MEASURES OF DISPERSION Find the range and mean absolute deviation of the data. Round to the nearest hundredth, if necessary.

11. 30, 35, 20, 85, 60 **65, 21.2**
12. 111, 135, 115, 120, 145, 130 **34, 10.67**
13. 30, 45, 52, 48, 100, 45, 42, 45 **70, 12.56**
14. 505, 510, 480, 550, 495, 500 **70, 15.56**
15. 1.25, 1.50, 1.70, 0.85, 1.00, 1.25 **0.85, 0.23**
16. 38.2, 80.1, 2.6, 84.2, 2.5, 5.5 **81.7, 31.98**

17. ★ **WRITING** *Explain* why the mean absolute deviation of a data set is generally a better measure of dispersion than the range.

17. *Sample answer:* The range only considers the two extreme values, while the mean absolute deviation is affected by all of the values.

C

18. **CHALLENGE** Suppose you **(a)** add the same constant to each value in a data set or **(b)** multiply each value by the same nonzero constant. *Describe* the effect on the mean, median, mode, range, and mean absolute deviation. **a. The mean, median, modes (if any) and range are each increased by the same constant. The mean absolute deviation is unchanged. b. All five measures are multiplied by the same nonzero constant.**

PROBLEM SOLVING

A

EXAMPLE 1 on p. 875 for Exs. 19–20

19. ★ **SHORT RESPONSE** The weights (in pounds) of ten pumpkins are 22, 21, 24, 24, 5, 24, 5, 23, 24, and 24.
   a. What is the range of the pumpkin weights? **19 lb**
   b. Find the mean, median, and mode(s) of the pumpkin weights. **19.6 lb, 23.5 lb, 24 lb**
   c. Which measure of central tendency best represents the data? *Explain.* **See margin.**

@HomeTutor for problem solving help at classzone.com

4 PRACTICE AND APPLY

Assignment Guide

Answer Transparencies available for all exercises

Basic:
Day 1: pp. 877–878
Exs. 1–14, 19–21, 24

Average:
Day 1: pp. 877–878
Exs. 1, 2, 4–10, 13–17, 19–22, 24

Advanced:
Day 1: pp. 877–878
Exs. 1, 5–9, 13–24*

Block:
pp. 877–878
Exs. 1, 2, 4–10, 13–17, 19–22, 24 (with 13.5)

Differentiated Instruction

See *Differentiated Instruction Resources* for suggestions on addressing the needs of a diverse classroom.

Homework Check

For a quick check of student understanding of key concepts, go over the following exercises:

Basic: 4, 10, 12, 19, 21
Average: 6, 14, 16, 20, 21
Advanced: 8, 16, 17, 20, 21

Extra Practice

- Student Edition, p. 950
- Chapter Resource Book: Practice levels A, B, C

Practice Worksheet

An easily-readable reduced practice page (with answers) for this lesson can be found on p. 840C.

2. *Sample answer:* Measures of central tendency and measures of dispersion are useful in comparing data by providing numbers that represent how spread apart the data are and where the center of the data is. These numbers can be compared for different data sets, providing a picture of the relative position and spread of the data sets.

19c. Median. *Sample answer:* The mode is the greatest data value and the mean is less than 8 of the 10 data values.

5 ASSESS AND RETEACH

Daily Homework Quiz

Transparency Available

1. The list shows the number of e-mails Brennan sent in 8 days. Find the mean, median, and mode(s) of the data. Which measure of central tendency best represents the data?

   45, 25, 38, 42, 51, 52, 24, 51

   Mean: 41, Median: 43.5, Mode: 51; the median best represents the data since the mean is toward the lower end of the data and the mode is toward the upper end.

2. Find the range and mean absolute deviation of the data. Round to the nearest hundredth, if necessary.

   38, 43, 56, 84, 98, 99, 102, 103

   Range: 65; mean absolute deviation: 24.16

Available at **classzone.com**

Diagnosis/Remediation

- Practice A, B, C in Chapter Resource Book
- Study Guide in Chapter Resource Book
- Practice Workbook
- @HomeTutor

Challenge

Additional challenge is available in the Chapter Resource Book.

22a. Mean: about 67, median: 40. *Sample answer:* The median better represents the data because the mean is highly affected by the Mississippi River, which is substantially higher than the other rivers.

22b. 39.33; yes. *Sample answer:* It is a better representation because the extremely high relative value of the Mississippi river greatly inflated the mean in part (a).

22c. See Additional Answers beginning on p. AA1.

20. POPULATION The population densities (in people per square mile) for each of the 10 most densely populated states in 2003 were 719.0, 418.5, 315.6, 563.6, 820.6, 1164.6, 406.5, 279.3, 275.9, and 1029.9.

a. Find the mean, median, and mode(s) of the data set. **599.35, 491.05, no mode**

b. Which measure of central tendency best represents the data? *Explain.*

@HomeTutor for problem solving help at classzone.com

EXAMPLE 2 B on p. 876 for Ex. 21

20b. Mean and median. *Sample answer:* The mean and median are both close to the center of the data. There is no mode.

21a. The range for Team 2 is 56 and the range for Team 1 is 52, so the scores for Team 2 cover a slightly greater range.

21b. The mean absolute deviation for Team 1 is 15.75 and the mean deviation for Team 2 is 22.5, so the scores for Team 2 are more dispersed.

21. BOWLING The average scores of the bowlers on two different bowling teams are given. *Compare* the spreads of the data sets using (**a**) the range and (**b**) the mean absolute deviation.

Team 1: 162, 150, 173, 202 **Team 2:** 140, 153, 187, 196

22. ★ EXTENDED RESPONSE Use the information in the article about the sediment discharges of U.S. rivers. For parts (a)–(c), round your answers to the nearest whole number, if necessary. **a–c. See margin.**

a. Find the mean and the median of the data for all seven rivers. Which measure represents the data better? *Explain.*

b. Find the mean of the data for the other six rivers, excluding the Mississippi River. Does this mean represent the data better than the mean you found in part (a)? *Explain.*

c. Find the range and mean absolute deviation of the data for all seven rivers. *Describe* what the measures tell you about the dispersion of the data.

> **Sunday Edition**
>
> **MISSISSIPPI RIVER DOMINATES AS SEDIMENT MOVER**
>
> **The Mississippi River** discharges an average of 230 million tons of sediment per year. Other U.S. rivers with the greatest average sediment discharges (in millions of tons per year) are the Copper (80), Yukon (65), Columbia (40), Susitna (25), Eel (15), and Brazos (11) rivers.

C

23. CHALLENGE A student asked 12 friends how many sisters and brothers they have. The line plot shows the results. **a, b. See margin.**

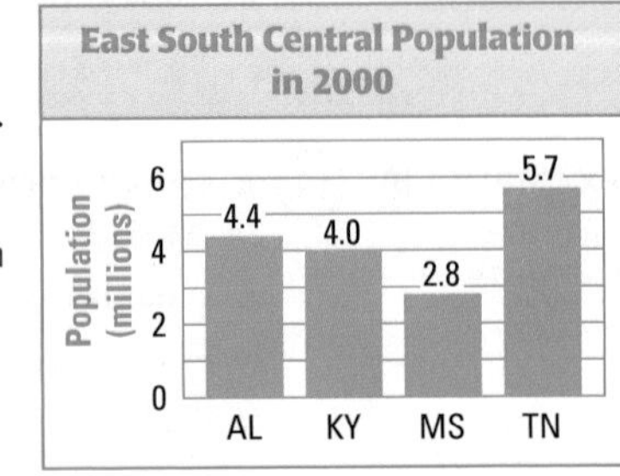

a. *Describe* how you would find the mean, median, and mode of the data. Then calculate each value.

b. The *weight* of a distinct data value is the quotient of its frequency and the total number of data values. Compute the *weighted average* of the data by taking the sum of the products of the distinct values and their weights. *Explain* why the weighted average of the data is simply the mean.

MIXED REVIEW

PREVIEW Prepare for Lesson 13.7 in Ex. 24.

24. POPULATION The bar graph shows the populations of Alabama, Kentucky, Mississippi, and Tennessee (the East South Central states) according to the U.S. Census of 2000. *(p. 932)*

a. What was the total population of the four states? **16.9 million**

b. How much greater was the population of Tennessee than the population of Kentucky? **1.7 million**

East South Central Population in 2000

State	Population (millions)
AL	4.4
KY	4.0
MS	2.8
TN	5.7

 EXTRA PRACTICE for Lesson 13.6, p. 950 **ONLINE QUIZ** at classzone.com

23a. *Sample answer:* Mean: add the data values and divide by the number of data values. Median: count from left to right or from right to left to locate the middle data values. Mode(s): find the data value(s) with the greatest number of Xs; 2, 2, 1 and 3.

23b. 2; whether you find the sum of the data values by simply adding them, or by first multiplying each distinct value by its weight and finding that sum, the result is the same.

That is $\frac{0+0+1+1+1+2+2+3+3+3+4+4}{12} = \frac{2\cdot 0 + 3\cdot 1 + 2\cdot 2 + 3\cdot 3 + 2\cdot 4}{12}$

$= \frac{2}{12}\cdot 0 + \frac{3}{12}\cdot 1 + \frac{2}{12}\cdot 2 + \frac{3}{12}\cdot 3 + \frac{2}{12}\cdot 4.$

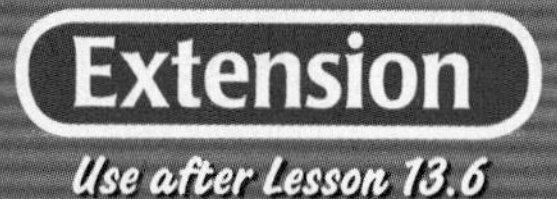

Extension

Use after Lesson 13.6

Calculate Variance and Standard Deviation

GOAL Find the variance and standard deviation of a data set.

Key Vocabulary
- **variance**
- **standard deviation**

In addition to range and mean absolute deviation, *variance* and *standard deviation* are also measures of dispersion that can be used to describe the spread of a set of data.

KEY CONCEPT *For Your Notebook*

Variance and Standard Deviation

The **variance** of a numerical data set is denoted by σ^2, which is read as "sigma squared." For the data set $x_1, x_2, \dots, x_n$, the variance is given by:

$$\sigma^2 = \frac{(x_1 - \overline{x})^2 + (x_2 - \overline{x})^2 + \dots + (x_n - \overline{x})^2}{n}$$

The **standard deviation** of a numerical data set is denoted by σ, which is read as "sigma." For the data set $x_1, x_2, \dots, x_n$, the standard deviation is the square root of the variance and is given by:

$$\sigma = \sqrt{\frac{(x_1 - \overline{x})^2 + (x_2 - \overline{x})^2 + \dots + (x_n - \overline{x})^2}{n}}$$

EXAMPLE 1 **Find variance and standard deviation**

E-MAIL SIZES The sizes of e-mails (in kilobytes) in your inbox are 1, 2, 2, 7, 4, 1, 10, 3, and 6. Find the variance and standard deviation of the data.

Solution

STEP 1 **Find** the mean.

$$\overline{x} = \frac{1 + 2 + 2 + 7 + 4 + 1 + 10 + 3 + 6}{9} = \frac{36}{9} = 4$$

STEP 2 **Find** the variance.

$$\sigma^2 = \frac{(1 - 4)^2 + (2 - 4)^2 + \dots + (6 - 4)^2}{9} = \frac{76}{9} = 8.444\dots$$

STEP 3 **Find** the standard deviation.

$$\sigma = \sqrt{\sigma^2} = \sqrt{8.444\dots} \approx 2.9$$

▶ The variance is about 8.4, and the standard deviation is about 2.9.

IMPROVE ACCURACY
The more accurate the value of σ^2 you use to calculate σ, the more accurate the value of σ you obtain. In the final answer, both results are rounded.

1 PLAN AND PREPARE

Warm-Up Exercises

1. Find the mean of the data. 12, 18, 17, 6, 10, 15 **13**
2. Find the range and the mean absolute deviation of the data. 19, 24, 22, 27, 54, 52, 32 **35; about 11.51**
3. The scores on your English test are 82, 86, 87, 94, and 88. Find the range and the mean absolute deviation of the data. **12; 2.88**

2 FOCUS AND MOTIVATE

Essential Question

Big Idea 2, p. 841

How do you find the variance and standard deviation of a data set? **Tell students they will learn how to answer this question by using formulas based on the mean to find the variance and the standard deviation.**

3 TEACH

Extra Example 1

The distances (in miles) that you walked last week are 4, 3, 3, 5, 2, 2, and 4. Find the variance and the standard deviation of the data. **The variance is about 1.06 and the standard deviation is about 1.03.**

NCTM STANDARDS

Standard 1: Compute fluently

Standard 5: Use proper statistical methods to analyze data

Extra Example 2

The numbers of visitors (in thousands, rounded to the nearest thousand) to Yellowstone National Park for 10 years are given. Find the standard deviation of the data.

3047, 3125, 3012, 2890, 2496, 3131, 2838, 2759, 2943, 3019 **about 183**

Closing the Lesson

Have students summarize the major points of the lesson and answer the Essential Question: How do you find the variance and standard deviation of a data set?

- **Variance and standard deviation are measures of dispersion that can be used to describe the spread of data.**

Find the mean of the data and then substitute the values of the mean and the data in the formula for variance and solve. Find the square root of the variance to find the standard deviation.

4 PRACTICE AND APPLY

Avoiding Common Errors

Exercises 1–7 When using graphing calculators, students should make sure that they use the numbers for standard deviation and not for some other statistic.

Teaching Strategy

Exercises 2, 3, 5, 6 Have students compare the data sets in Exercises 2 and 3 for variance and standard deviation and for standard deviation in Exercises 5 and 6. Have students explain what these measures mean in terms of spread.

USING A CALCULATOR You can use a graphing calculator to find the standard deviation of a data set.

EXAMPLE 2 Find standard deviation

HOUSEHOLDS In 2000 the numbers (in thousands) of households in the 13 states with Atlantic Ocean coastline are given. Find the standard deviation of the data.

299 6338 3006 518 1981 2444 475 3065
7057 3132 408 1534 2699

Solution

STEP 1 **Enter** the data into a graphing calculator. Press STAT and select Edit. Enter the data into List 1 (L_1).

STEP 2 **Calculate** the standard deviation. Press STAT. From the CALC menu select 1-Var Stats.

On this screen, σ_x stands for standard deviation.

▶ The standard deviation of the data is about 2056.

PRACTICE

EXAMPLE 1 on p. 879 for Exs. 1–3

Use the formulas for variance and standard deviation to find the variance and standard deviation of the data. Round to the nearest tenth, if necessary.

1. 4, 5, 3, 2, 4, 7, 8, 9, 4, 6, 7, 8, 9, 1 **6.3, 2.5**
2. 14, 16, 19, 20, 28, 7, 24, 15, 16, 30, 33, 24 **52.1, 7.2**
3. 110, 205, 322, 608, 1100, 240, 185, 552, 418, 300 **76,656.6, 276.9**

EXAMPLE 2 on p. 880 for Exs. 4–7

In Exercises 4–6, use a graphing calculator to find the standard deviation of the data. Round to the nearest tenth, if necessary.

4. 3.5, 3.8, 4.1, 3.0, 3.8, 3.6, 3.3, 4.0, 3.8, 3.9, 3.2, 3.0, 3.3, 4.2, 3.0 **0.4**
5. 66, 43, 9, 28, 7, 5, 90, 9, 78, 6, 69, 55, 28, 43, 10, 54, 13, 88, 21, 4 **29.1**
6. 1002, 1540, 480, 290, 2663, 3800, 690, 1301, 1750, 2222, 4040, 800 **1192.5**
7. **REASONING** The heights (in feet) of 9 pecan trees are 72, 84, 81, 78, 80, 86, 70, 80, and 88. For parts (a)–(c) below, round your answers to the nearest tenth.
   a. Find the standard deviation of the data. **5.6**
   b. Suppose you include a pecan tree with a height of 136 feet. *Predict* the effect of the additional data on the standard deviation of the data set.
   c. Find the standard deviation of the new data set in part (b). *Compare* the results to your prediction in part (b).

7b. *Sample answer:* Since 136 is much greater than the mean, the standard deviation will increase.
7c. 17.7. *Sample answer:* The standard deviation more than tripled, so the prediction was correct.

13.7 Interpret Stem-and-Leaf Plots and Histograms

Before You found measures of central tendency and dispersion.
Now You will make stem-and-leaf plots and histograms.
Why? So you can analyze historical data, as in Ex. 20.

Key Vocabulary
- stem-and-leaf plot
- frequency
- frequency table
- histogram

A **stem-and-leaf plot** is a data display that organizes data based on their digits. Each value is separated into a *stem* (the leading digit(s)) and a *leaf* (the last digit). A stem-and-leaf plot has a key that tells you how to read the data. A stem-and-leaf plot shows how the data are distributed.

EXAMPLE 1 Make a stem-and-leaf plot

BASEBALL The number of home runs hit by the 20 baseball players with the best single-season batting averages in Major League Baseball since 1900 are listed below. Make a stem-and-leaf plot of the data.

14, 25, 8, 8, 7, 7, 19, 37, 39, 18, 42, 23, 4, 32, 14, 21, 3, 12, 19, 41

Solution

STEP 1 **Separate** the data into stems and leaves.

Home Runs

Stem	Leaves
0	8 8 7 7 4 3
1	4 9 8 4 2 9
2	5 3 1
3	7 9 2
4	2 1

Key: 1 | 4 = 14 home runs

STEP 2 **Write** the leaves in increasing order.

Home Runs

Stem	Leaves
0	3 4 7 7 8 8
1	2 4 4 8 9 9
2	1 3 5
3	2 7 9
4	1 2

Key: 1 | 4 = 14 home runs

INTERPRET INTERVALS
Each stem in a stem-and-leaf plot defines an interval. For instance, the stem 2 represents the interval 20–29. The data values in this interval are 21, 23, and 25.

GUIDED PRACTICE for Example 1

1. **U.S. HISTORY** The years in which each of the first 20 states were admitted to the Union are listed below. Make a stem-and-leaf plot of the years. **See margin on p. 883.**

   1788, 1787, 1788, 1816, 1792, 1812, 1788, 1788, 1817, 1788, 1787, 1788, 1789, 1803, 1787, 1790, 1788, 1796, 1791, 1788

2. **REASONING** In Example 1, describe the distribution of the data on the intervals represented by the stems. Are the data clustered together in a noticeable way? *Explain.*

2. ***Sample answer:*** **The data are clustered from 3–19. Over half of the values are from 3–19.**

1 PLAN AND PREPARE

Warm-Up Exercises

Transparency Available

1. The data give the ages of people in an art class. Find the mean, median, and mode of the data.
   38, 15, 13, 32, 13, 17, 29, 43 **mean: 25, median: 23, mode: 13**
2. Find the range and the mean absolute deviation of the data.
   8, 3, 3, 8, 9, 2, 3 **7, about 2.73**

Notetaking Guide

Transparency Available

Promotes interactive learning and notetaking skills.

Pacing

Basic: 2 days
Average: 2 days
Advanced: 2 days
Block: 1 block
- See *Teaching Guide/Lesson Plan.*

2 FOCUS AND MOTIVATE

Essential Question

Big Idea 3, p. 841

How do you make stem-and-leaf plots and histograms? **Tell students they will learn how to answer this question by organizing the data and then displaying the results in a graph.**

NCTM STANDARDS

Standard 5: Collect, organize, and display data; Develop inferences that are based on data

Resource Planning Guide

Chapter Resource Book
- Teaching Guide/Lesson Plan
- Activity Master
- Practice levels A, B, C
- Study Guide
- Catch-up for Absent Students
- Application
- Challenge

Workbooks
- Notetaking Guide
- Practice Workbook

Teaching Options
- **Power Presentations** provides dynamic electronic teaching resources for the classroom.
- **Activity Generator** provides editable activities for all ability levels.

Interactive Technology
- Easy Planner
- Power Presentations
- Activity Generator
- Animated Algebra
- Test Generator
- Online Quiz
- eWorkbook
- eEdition
- @HomeTutor

Resources for English Learners
- Spanish Study Guide
- Multi-Language Visual Glossary
- Student Resources in Spanish

See also the *Differentiated Instruction Resources* for more strategies for meeting individual needs.

Motivating the Lesson

You volunteer at an animal shelter on the weekends. The director of the shelter wants you to analyze the number of hours volunteers work. By knowing how to organize data in stem-and-leaf plots and histograms, you can display the data in an appropriate graph.

3 TEACH

Extra Example 1

A software developer advertised a position at its home office. The list below shows the number of applications the office received per day. Make a stem-and-leaf plot of the data.

9, 8, 24, 18, 27, 25, 24, 38, 32, 29, 41, 56, 42, 38, 40, 47, 32, 52, 39, 41

Software Applications

Stem	Leaves
0	8 9
1	8
2	4 4 5 7 9
3	2 2 8 8 9
4	0 1 1 2 7
5	2 6

Key: 3 | 2 = 32 applications

Extra Example 2

The back-to-back stem-and-leaf plot shows the ages of participants in two yoga classes. Compare the ages of the participants in the two yoga classes.

Yoga Class Ages

Class 1		Class 2
9	1	8 8 9 9
6 5 4 4 2	2	0 0 1 3
7 4 2 2	3	0 0

Key: 2 | 2 | 0 = 22, 20

Participants in Class 2 are generally younger than participants in Class 1.

EXAMPLE 2 Interpret a stem-and-leaf plot

GYMNASTICS The back-to-back stem-and-leaf plot shows the ages of members of the U.S men's and women's 2004 Olympic gymnastics teams. Compare the ages of the gymnasts on the two teams.

2004 Olympic Gymnast Ages

Men		Women
	1	6 6 8 8
7 4 3 1 1	2	5 6
0	3	

Key: 1 | 2 | 5 = 21, 25

Solution

Consider the distribution of the data. The interval for 10–19 years old contains more than half of the female gymnasts. The interval for 20–29 years old contains more than half of the male gymnasts. The clustering of the data shows that the men's team was generally older than the women's team.

FREQUENCY The **frequency** of an interval is the number of data values in that interval. A stem-and-leaf plot shows the frequencies of intervals determined by the stems. A **frequency table** is also used to group data values into equal intervals, with no gaps between intervals and no intervals overlapping.

A **histogram** is a bar graph that displays data from a frequency table. Each bar represents an interval. Because intervals have equal size, the bars have equal width. A bar's length indicates the frequency. There is no space between bars.

EXAMPLE 3 Make a histogram

SANDWICH PRICES The prices (in dollars) of sandwiches at a restaurant are listed below. Make a histogram of the data.

4.00, 4.00, 4.25, 4.50, 4.75, 4.25, 5.95, 5.50, 5.50, 5.75

Solution

CHOOSE AN INTERVAL SIZE
To choose the interval size for a frequency table, divide the range of the data by the number of intervals you want the table to have. Use the quotient as an approximate interval size.

STEP 1 **Choose** intervals of equal size that cover all of the data values. Organize the data using a frequency table.

Prices	Sandwiches
$4.00–4.49	||||
$4.50–4.99	||
$5.00–5.49	
$5.50–5.99	||||

STEP 2 **Draw** the bars of the histogram using the intervals from the frequency table.

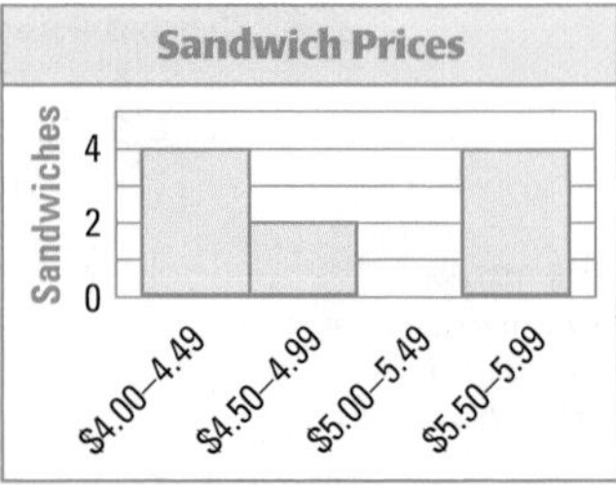

Differentiated Instruction

Kinesthetic Learners Stem-and-leaf plots and histograms place statistical data in equally spaced groups, or "bins." It may be helpful to write numerical data on slips of paper for students to sort and place in small boxes. Then they can construct the appropriate histogram or stem-and-leaf plot, and see how it corresponds to the sorted data.

See also the *Differentiated Instruction Resources* for more strategies.

✓ GUIDED PRACTICE for Examples 2 and 3

3. *Sample answer:* Most of the data for the females is between 10% and 30%, while most of the data for males is between 20% and 40%. There is considerable overlap, but in general the male students watch more television than do the female students.

3. TELEVISION The back-to-back stem-and-leaf plot shows the percents of students in 24 countries who report watching television for 4 or more hours each day. *Compare* the data for female and male students.

Female		Male
9 9 9 8 8 8 6 6 5 4	1	7 8 9
6 6 5 4 3 3 0 0	2	0 1 2 2 4 5 5 6 6 7 7 8
8 3 2 2 1	3	4 6 6 8 8 9
1	4	0 6 6

Key: 4 | 1 | 7 = 14%, 17%

4. PRECIPITATION The average number of days each month with precipitation of 0.01 inch or more in Buffalo, New York, are 20, 17, 16, 14, 13, 11, 10, 10, 11, 12, 16, and 19. Make a histogram of the data. **See margin.**

Extra Example 3

The number of song requests per day for a two week period at a radio station are shown below. Make a histogram of the data.

12, 22, 18, 26, 31, 34, 17, 26, 28, 10, 20, 14, 15, 32

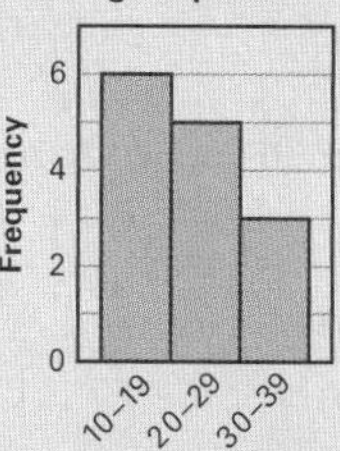

13.7 EXERCISES

HOMEWORK KEY
○ = **WORKED-OUT SOLUTIONS** on p. WS33 for Exs. 3 and 19
★ = **STANDARDIZED TEST PRACTICE** Exs. 2, 8, 9, 15, and 20

SKILL PRACTICE

A

1. **VOCABULARY** Copy and complete: The number of data values in an interval is the __?__ of that interval. **frequency**

2. ★ **WRITING** *Explain* how a histogram differs from a bar graph. ***Sample answer:*** **A histogram displays the frequency of numerical data. A bar graph displays categorical data.**

EXAMPLE 1 on p. 881 for Exs. 3–7

STEM-AND-LEAF PLOTS **Make a stem-and-leaf plot of the data.** **3–6. See margin.**

3. 17, 31, 42, 33, 38, 20, 24, 30, 39, 38, 35, 20, 55

4. 2, 8, 17, 7, 14, 20, 32, 5, 33, 6, 6, 8, 11, 9

5. 121, 124, 133, 111, 109, 182, 105, 127, 156, 179, 142

6. 1.23, 1.05, 1.11, 1.29, 1.31, 1.19, 1.45, 1.22, 1.19, 1.35

7. **ERROR ANALYSIS** *Describe* and correct the error in making a stem-and-leaf plot of the following data: 18, 19, 18, 19, 20, 20, 21, 22, 18, 19, 20, 21, 23, 21.
There is no key given for the stem-and-leaf plot; Key: 1|8 = 18.

1	888999
2	00011123

STEM-AND-LEAF PLOT **In Exercises 8 and 9, consider the back-to-back stem-and-leaf plot that shows data sets *A* and *B*.**

8. ★ **MULTIPLE CHOICE** What is the median of data set *A*? **C**
Ⓐ 21 Ⓑ 32 Ⓒ 33 Ⓓ 34

9. ★ **MULTIPLE CHOICE** What is the range of data set *B*? **C**
Ⓐ 18 Ⓑ 19 Ⓒ 20 Ⓓ 21

Set *A*		Set *B*
1 1 1	2	
4 3 3 2	3	1 2 2
2 0	4	1 1 3 4
	5	0 1

Key: 2 | 3 | 1 = 32, 31

Closing the Lesson

Have students summarize the major points of the lesson and answer the Essential Question: How do you make stem-and-leaf plots and histograms?

- **A stem-and-leaf plot organizes data based on their digits, with the leading digit(s) in stems and the last digit in leaves.**
- **A histogram is a bar graph that displays data from a frequency table, with no space between bars and bars of equal width.**

To make a stem-and-leaf plot, separate the data into stems and leaves. Each stem represents an interval, such as 0 represents 0–9. Write the leaves in increasing order and make a key that tells how to read the data. To make a histogram, choose equal intervals that cover all of the data, organize the data using a frequency table, and then use the intervals from the frequency table to draw the bars of the histogram.

p. 881

1.

Stem	Leaves
178	7 7 7 8 8 8 8 8 8 8 8 9
179	0 1 2 6
180	3
181	2 6 7

Key: 178 | 7 = 1787

p. 883

3.

Stem	Leaves
1	7
2	0 0 4
3	0 1 3 5 8 8 9
4	2
5	5

Key: 1 | 7 = 17

4.

Stem	Leaves
0	2 5 6 6 7 8 8 9
1	1 4 7
2	0
3	2 3

Key: 0 | 2 = 2

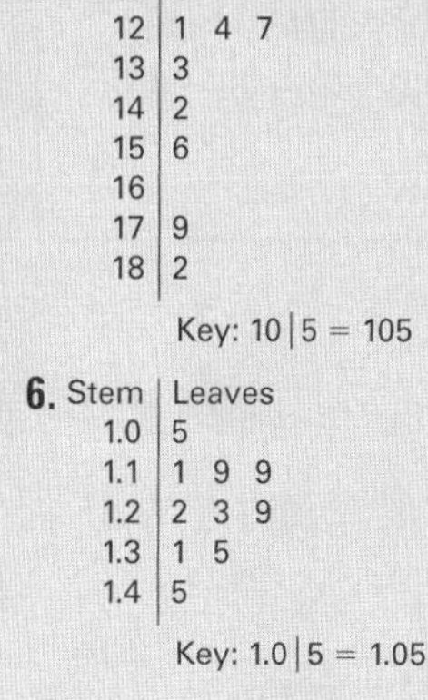

5.

Stem	Leaves
10	5 9
11	1
12	1 4 7
13	3
14	2
15	6
16	
17	9
18	2

Key: 10 | 5 = 105

6.

Stem	Leaves
1.0	5
1.1	1 9 9
1.2	2 3 9
1.3	1 5
1.4	5

Key: 1.0 | 5 = 1.05

p. 883

Guided Practice Ex. 4. See Additional Answers beginning on p. AA1.

4 PRACTICE AND APPLY

Assignment Guide

Answer Transparencies available for all exercises

Basic:
Day 1: pp. 883–885
Exs. 1–9, 17, 20
Day 2: pp. 883–885
Exs. 10–13, 18, 19, 23–27

Average:
Day 1: pp. 883–885
Exs. 1, 2, 4–9, 17, 20, 21
Day 2: pp. 883–885
Exs. 10–15, 18, 19, 23–27

Advanced:
Day 1: pp. 883–885
Exs. 1, 4–9, 17, 20, 21
Day 2: pp. 883–885
Exs. 11–16*, 18, 19, 22–27*

Block:
pp. 883–885
Exs. 1, 2, 4–15, 17–21, 23–27

Differentiated Instruction

See *Differentiated Instruction Resources* for suggestions on addressing the needs of a diverse classroom.

Homework Check

For a quick check of student understanding of key concepts, go over the following exercises:

Basic: 4, 10, 17, 18, 20

Average: 5, 12, 17, 18, 20

Advanced: 6, 14, 17, 19, 20

Extra Practice

- Student Edition, p. 950
- Chapter Resource Book: Practice levels A, B, C

Practice Worksheet

An easily-readable reduced practice page (with answers) for this lesson can be found on p. 840C.

10–14. See Additional Answers beginning on p. AA1.

EXAMPLE 3 on p. 882 for Exs. 10–14

10. ERROR ANALYSIS *Describe* and correct the error in creating a histogram using the frequency table below. **See margin.**

Ages	0–9	10–19	20–29	30–39
Frequency	III	𝍸I		IIII

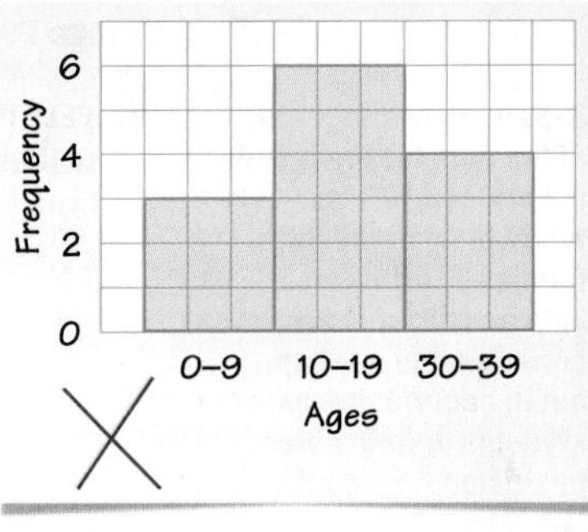

B **HISTOGRAMS** Make a histogram of the data.
11–14. See margin.

11. 55, 82, 94, 75, 61, 69, 77, 98, 81, 83, 75, 90, 51

12. 12, 0, 22, 31, 14, 7, 7, 45, 31, 28, 21, 25, 25, 18

13. 0.01, 0.13, 0.09, 1.10, 1.33, 0.99, 0.50, 0.95, 1.05, 1.50, 0.75, 1.01

14. 111, 109, 224, 657, 284, 120, 119, 415, 180, 105, 208, 108

15. ★ **WRITING** *Explain* why a histogram can show the distribution of the data below better than a stem-and-leaf plot. **See margin.**

15, 21, 18, 10, 12, 11, 17, 18, 16, 12, 20, 12, 17, 16

C **16. CHALLENGE** Create a stem-and-leaf plot that has the same distribution of data as the histogram shown. *Explain* the steps you took to create the stem-and-leaf plot.
See margin for art. *Sample answer:* I created values for each interval of the histogram that would have generated the frequencies shown in the histogram, then plotted the values on a stem-and-leaf plot.

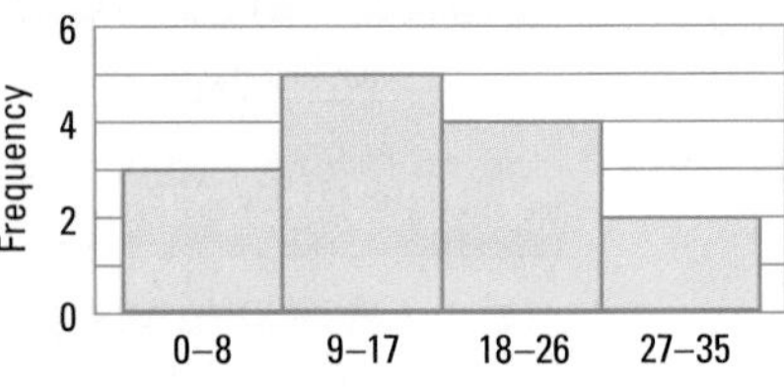

PROBLEM SOLVING

EXAMPLE 1 on p. 881 for Ex. 17

A **17. HEIGHTS** The heights (in inches) of players on a boys' basketball team are as follows: 80, 76, 81, 69, 81, 78, 74, 68, 78, 74, 81, 72, 69, 81, 70. Make a stem-and-leaf plot of the heights. **See margin.**

@HomeTutor for problem solving help at classzone.com

EXAMPLE 3 on p. 882 for Exs. 18–19

18. SURVEY A survey asked people how many 8 ounce glasses of water they drink in one day. The results are below. Make a histogram of the data.

3, 0, 9, 1, 4, 2, 11, 5, 3, 6, 0, 5, 7, 8, 5, 2, 9, 6, 10, 2, 4 **See margin.**

@HomeTutor for problem solving help at classzone.com

(19.) MEMORY A survey asked people how many phone numbers they have memorized. The results are shown in the table.

Phone numbers	1–5	6–10	11–15	16–20	21–25
Frequency	88	85	50	28	14

a. Make a histogram of the data. **See margin.**

b. What is the probability that a person surveyed, chosen at random, has 11–25 phone numbers memorized? $\frac{92}{265}$

◯ = WORKED-OUT SOLUTIONS on p. WS1 ★ = STANDARDIZED TEST PRACTICE

---

15. ***Sample answer:*** **A histogram can show a variety of intervals, but a stem-and-leaf plot can only show intervals that are powers of 10. The given data range from 10 to 20, so a stem-and-leaf plot would place all the data into only two intervals, making it difficult to see trends within the data. The histogram could use an interval of 3 or 4.**

16. ***Sample:***

Stem	Leaves
0	5 6 7
1	0 1 2 3 4
2	0 1 2 3
3	0 1

Key: 0|5 = 5

17, 18, 19a. See Additional Answers beginning on p. AA1.

EXAMPLE 2
on p. 882
for Ex. 20

20c. *Sample answer:* The Senate generally spends more time in session than the House of Representatives and has more variation in the number of days they spend in session.

21c. $\frac{1}{3}$. *Sample answer:* Since 13 of the 39 passengers, or $\frac{1}{3}$ of them, were ages 18–29, we can predict that another passenger about whom we have no information has a $\frac{1}{3}$ probability of being in that age group.

20. ★ **EXTENDED RESPONSE** The back-to-back stem-and-leaf plot shows the numbers of days the House of Representatives and the Senate spent in session each year from 1996 to 2004.

Days in Session

House		Senate
9 0	11	
3 2	12	
7 5 3 2	13	2 3
2	14	1 3 9
	15	3
	16	2 7
	17	3

Key: 2 | 14 | 1 = 142, 141

a. What was the median number of days the House of Representatives spent in session? the Senate? **132 days; 149 days**

b. What is the range of the number of days the House of Representatives spent in session? the Senate? **32 days; 41 days**

c. *Compare* the data for the House of Representatives and the Senate. What does the distribution of the data tell you?

B

21. MAYFLOWER The known ages (in years) of adult male passengers on the *Mayflower* at the time of its departure are listed below.

21, 34, 29, 38, 30, 54, 39, 20, 35, 64, 37, 45, 21, 25, 55, 45, 40, 38, 38, 21, 21, 20, 34, 38, 50, 41, 48, 18, 32, 21, 32, 49, 30, 42, 30, 25, 38, 25, 20

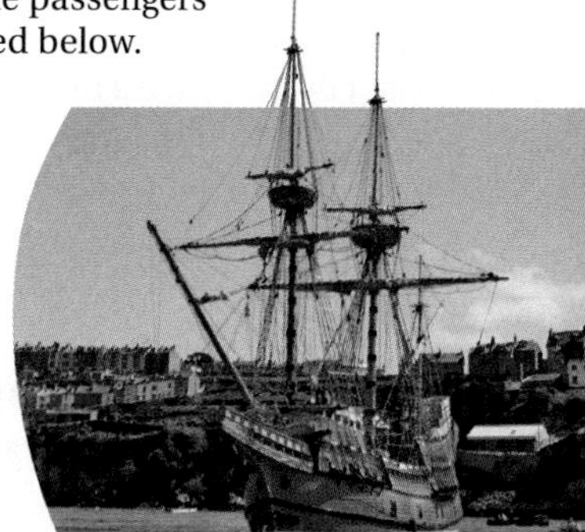
Replica of the *Mayflower*

a. Make a stem-and-leaf plot of the ages. **See margin.**

b. Find the median age and range of the ages. **median: 34 yr, range: 46 yr**

c. According to one source, the age of passenger Thomas English was unknown at the time of the *Mayflower's* departure. What is the probability that he was 18–29 years old? *Explain* your reasoning.

C

22. CHALLENGE The first two rows of a *cumulative frequency table* for the data in Exercise 21 are shown. The *cumulative frequency* for a given interval is the sum of the current frequency and all preceding frequencies. A histogram constructed from a cumulative frequency table is called a *cumulative frequency histogram.* Copy and complete the table. Then make a cumulative frequency histogram for the data. **See margin.**

Ages	Frequency	Cumulative frequency
15–24	9	9
25–34	11	9 + 11 = 20
?	?	?

MIXED REVIEW

PREVIEW
Prepare for Lesson 13.8 in Exs. 23–25.

Find the mean, median, and mode(s) of the data. *(p. 918)*

23. Ages of family members (in years): 62, 35, 51, 28, 22, 25, 16, 58, 30, 14 **34.1 yr, 29 yr, no mode**

24. Minutes of exercise each day: 35, 20, 25, 20, 0, 30, 45, 40, 20, 30, 35, 0 **25 min, 27.5 min, 20 min**

25. Hours worked per week: 10, 9, 11, 12, 8, 15, 20, 9, 16, 14, 15, 12 **about 12.6 h; 12 h; 9 h; 12 h, and 15 h**

Tell whether the question is potentially biased. *Explain* your answer. If the question is biased, rewrite it so that it is not. *(p. 871)* **26, 27. See margin.**

26. Don't you agree that science fiction movies are boring?

27. Is your ideal vacation a trip to Florida or a trip to Alaska?

26. *Sample answer:* This question is potentially biased because it encourages the respondent to agree. A better question would be "What do you think of science fiction movies?"

27. *Sample answer:* This question is potentially biased because it assumes that the respondent's ideal vacation is one of the two choices. A less biased question would be "Would you rather take a trip to Florida or Alaska?" or "Tell me about your ideal vacation."

5 ASSESS AND RETEACH

Daily Homework Quiz

Transparency Available

The data show the hours Henry worked at a photo shop over a 10-week period.

21, 2, 10, 4, 12, 4, 10, 9, 8, 9

1. Make a stem-and-leaf plot of the data.

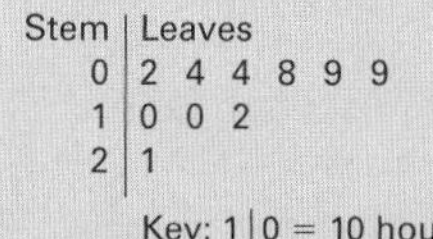
Hours at the Photo Shop

Stem	Leaves
0	2 4 4 8 9 9
1	0 0 2
2	1

Key: 1 | 0 = 10 hours

2. Describe the data in the stem-and-leaf plot in Exercise 1. **Henry generally works fewer than 10 hours per week.**

3. Make a histogram of the data.

Hours Worked

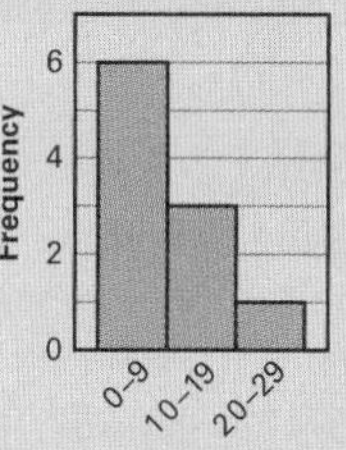

Online Quiz

Available at **classzone.com**

Diagnosis/Remediation

- Practice A, B, C in Chapter Resource Book
- Study Guide in Chapter Resource Book
- Practice Workbook
- @HomeTutor

Challenge

Additional challenge is available in the Chapter Resource Book.

21a, 22. See Additional Answers beginning on p. AA1.

1 PLAN AND PREPARE

Learn the Method

- Students will use a graphing calculator to make a histogram.
- After the activity, students can use a graphing calculator to check their solutions in Exercises 11–14 in Lesson 13.7.

Keystroke Help

Keystrokes for several models of calculators are available in blackline format in the *Chapter Resource Book*.

2 TEACH

Tips for Success

In Step 3, have students analyze the data to see how the settings correlate to intervals and frequencies in the graph.

Extra Example

Turtle strandings in North Carolina from 1993–2002 are listed below. Make a histogram of the data.

197, 287, 347, 505, 403, 358, 600, 832, 366, 479

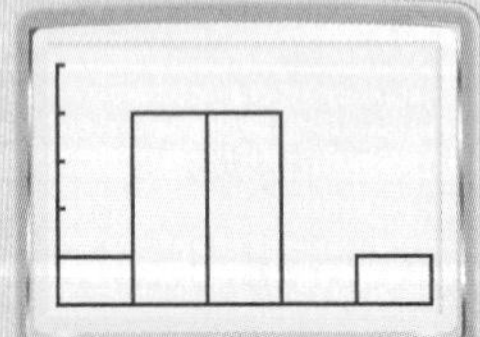

3 ASSESS AND RETEACH

What does each gap in a histogram represent? **The gaps represent intervals in which the frequency of the data is 0.**

1. *Sample answer:* The majority of the data are at the lower end of the scale, between 3000 and 12,000, with the highest frequency between 3000 and 6000.

@HomeTutor classzone.com Keystrokes

13.7 Draw Histograms

QUESTION How can you use a graphing calculator to make a histogram?

EXAMPLE Make a histogram

POPULATION The populations (in thousands) of metropolitan areas in the states with the greatest metropolitan populations in the United States in 2000 are listed below. Make a histogram of the data.

4527 32,750 14,837 5667 10,542 4390 4911 6101 8169 3795 8414
17,473 5437 9214 10,392 3862 17,692 5528 4899 3640

STEP 1 *Enter the data*

Go to the STAT menu and choose Edit. Enter the data into List 1.

STEP 2 *Select histogram*

Go to the STAT PLOT screen. Select Plot 1. Use the settings shown below.

STEP 3 *Set the viewing window*

Go to the WINDOW screen. Use the settings shown below.

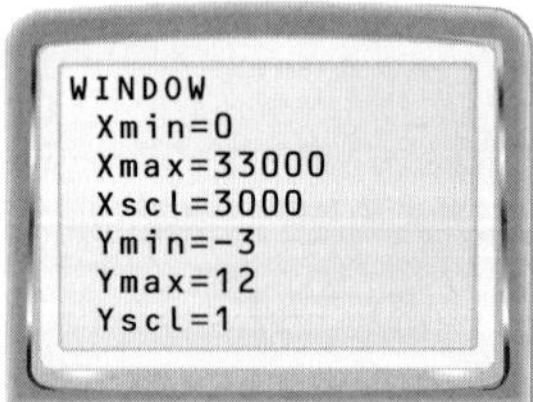

STEP 4 *Graph*

Press GRAPH. Use the *trace* feature to move from bar to bar.

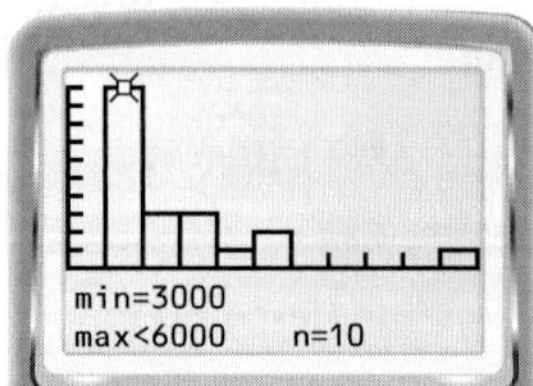

DRAW CONCLUSIONS

1. *Describe* the distribution of the population data in the example above. **See margin.**
2. **BOWLING** Use a graphing calculator to make a histogram of the following bowling scores: 200, 210, 105, 300, 180, 175, 162, 110, 140, 300, 152, 165, 175, 115, 250, 270, 145, 182, 164, 122, 141, 135, 189, 170, 151, 158. **See margin.**

2.

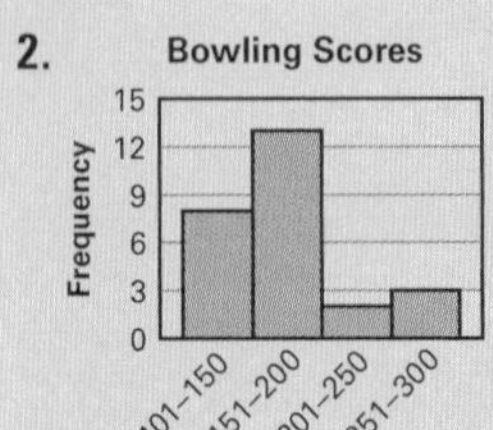

13.8 Interpret Box-and-Whisker Plots

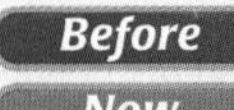

Before	You made stem-and-leaf plots and histograms.
Now	You will make and interpret box-and-whisker plots.
Why?	So you can compare sets of scientific data, as in Ex. 19.

Key Vocabulary
- **box-and-whisker plot**
- **quartile**
- **interquartile range**
- **outlier**

A **box-and-whisker plot** organizes data values into four groups. Ordered data are divided into lower and upper halves by the median. The median of the lower half is the **lower quartile**. The median of the upper half is the **upper quartile**.

EXAMPLE 1 Make a box-and-whisker plot

SONG LENGTHS The lengths of songs (in seconds) on a CD are listed below. Make a box-and-whisker plot of the song lengths.

173, 206, 179, 257, 198, 251, 239, 246, 295, 181, 261

Solution

STEP 1 **Order** the data. Then find the median and the quartiles.

Lower half | Median | Upper half

173, 179, 181, 198, 206, 239, 246, 251, 257, 261, 295

Lower quartile: 181 | Upper quartile: 257

STEP 2 **Plot** the median, the quartiles, the maximum value, and the minimum value below a number line.

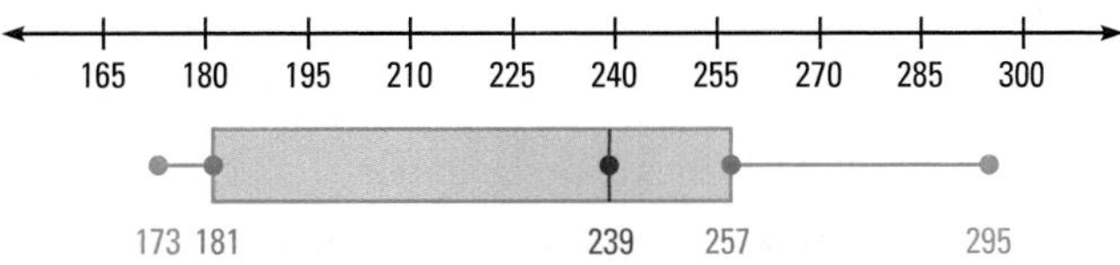

STEP 3 **Draw** a box from the lower quartile to the upper quartile. Draw a vertical line through the median. Draw a line segment (a "whisker") from the box to the maximum and another from the box to the minimum.

Animated Algebra at classzone.com

✓ **GUIDED PRACTICE** for Example 1

1. Make a box-and-whisker plot of the ages of eight family members: 60, 15, 25, 20, 55, 70, 40, 30. **See margin on p. 889.**

1 PLAN AND PREPARE

Warm-Up Exercises

Transparency Available

Find the mean, median, and mode(s) of the data.

1. 8, 12, 15, 17, 18, 26 **16, 16, no mode**
2. 186, 144, 201, 164, 182, 164 **173.5, 173, 164**
3. The monthly charge for seven dial-up internet service providers are listed. What is the mean price? $10, $22, $17, $11, $16, $23, $25 **about $17.71**

Notetaking Guide

Transparency Available

Promotes interactive learning and notetaking skills.

Pacing

Basic: 2 days
Average: 2 days
Advanced: 2 days
Block: 1 block
- See *Teaching Guide/Lesson Plan*.

2 FOCUS AND MOTIVATE

Essential Question

Big Idea 3, p. 841

How do you make and interpret box-and-whisker plots? **Tell students they will learn how to answer this question by organizing data values into four groups, each containing 25% of the data.**

NCTM STANDARDS

Standard 5: Collect, organize, and display data; Develop inferences that are based on data

Resource Planning Guide

Chapter Resource Book
- Teaching Guide/Lesson Plan
- Activity Master
- Practice levels A, B, C
- Study Guide
- Catch-up for Absent Students
- Problem Solving Workshop
- Challenge

Workbooks
- Notetaking Guide
- Practice Workbook

Teaching Options
- **Power Presentations** provides dynamic electronic teaching resources for the classroom.
- **Activity Generator** provides editable activities for all ability levels.

Interactive Technology
- Easy Planner
- Power Presentations
- Activity Generator
- Animated Algebra
- Test Generator
- Online Quiz
- eWorkbook
- eEdition
- @HomeTutor

Resources for English Learners
- Spanish Study Guide
- Multi-Language Visual Glossary
- Student Resources in Spanish

See also the *Differentiated Instruction Resources* for more strategies for meeting individual needs.

Motivating the Lesson

You want to compare the weather in two cities before your family takes a vacation in one of them. You can easily compare the two places by making box-and-whisker plots to display the weather data from past years.

3 TEACH

Extra Example 1

The prices (in dollars) of 27-inch television sets at an electronics store are given below. Make a box-and-whisker plot of the television prices.

188, 225, 192, 239, 271, 286, 224, 334, 316, 275

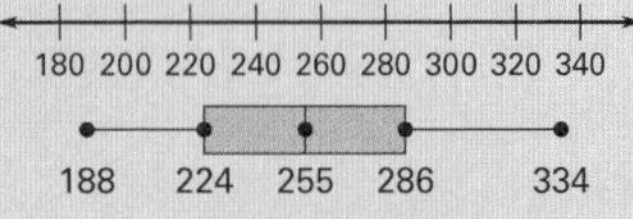

An **Animated Algebra** activity is available online for **Example 1**. This activity is also part of **Power Presentations**.

Extra Example 2

The box-and-whisker plots below show the normal monthly wind speeds (in miles per hour) in Athens and Savannah, Georgia.

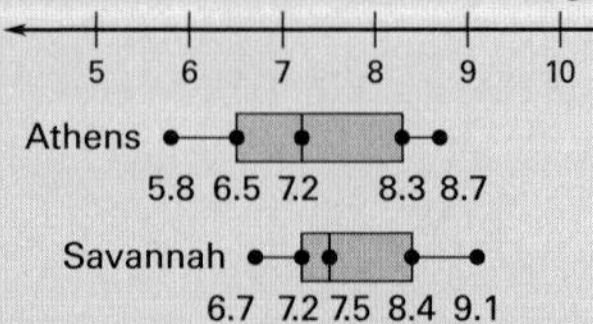

a. For how many months is Athens' wind speed more than 8.3 miles per hour? **3 months**

b. Compare the wind speeds in the two cities. **Wind speed is more variable in Athens, but in general is stronger in Savannah.**

INTERPRET A BOX-AND-WHISKER PLOT A box-and-whisker plot separates data into four groups: the two parts of the box and the two whiskers. Each part contains approximately the same number of data values.

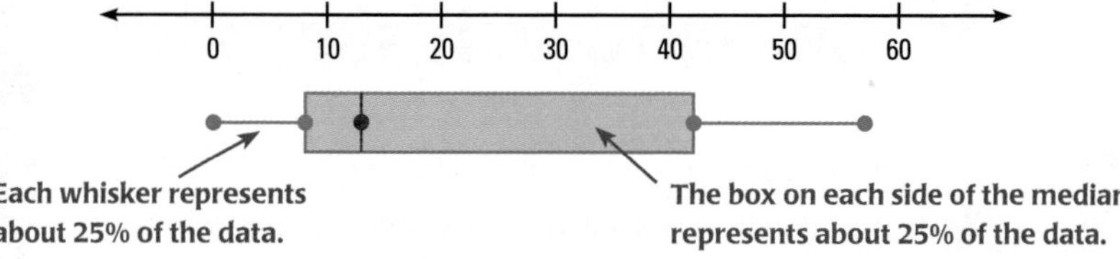

INTERPRET VARIATION
The interquartile range measures the variation in the middle half of the data and ignores the extreme values, whose variation may not be representative of the data.

You know that the range of a data set is the difference of the maximum value and the minimum value. The **interquartile range** of a data set is the difference of the upper quartile and the lower quartile.

EXAMPLE 2 Interpret a box-and-whisker plot

PRECIPITATION The box-and-whisker plots below show the normal precipitation (in inches) each month in Dallas and in Houston, Texas.

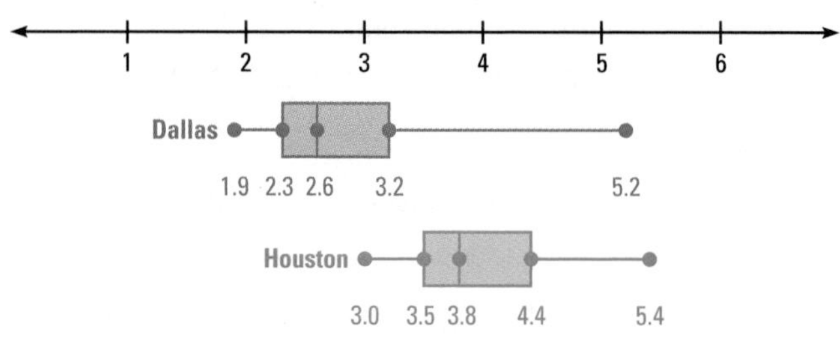

a. For how many months is Houston's precipitation less than 3.5 inches?

b. Compare the precipitation in Dallas with the precipitation in Houston.

Solution

INTERPRET QUARTILES
When the number of data values is a multiple of 4, the median and quartiles will divide the data into four groups of *exactly* the same size.

a. For Houston, the lower quartile is 3.5. A whisker represents 25% of the data, so for 25% of 12 months, or 3 months, Houston has less than 3.5 inches of precipitation.

b. The median precipitation for a month in Dallas is 2.6 inches. The median for Houston is 3.8 inches. In general, Houston has more precipitation.

For Dallas, the interquartile range is $3.2 - 2.3$, or 0.9 inch. For Houston, the interquartile range is $4.4 - 3.5 = 0.9$ inch. So, the cities have the same variation in the middle 50% of the data. The range for Dallas is greater than the range for Houson. When all the data are considered, Dallas has more variation in precipitation.

GUIDED PRACTICE for Example 2

2. PRECIPITATION In Example 2, for how many months was the precipitation in Dallas more than 2.6 inches? **6 mo**

Differentiated Instruction

Below Level Have students work with values that are easier to manipulate so that they can concentrate on dividing the data into groups and learning the vocabulary. For example, they could make a box-and-whisker plot that displays the number of e-mail messages a friend receives. The number of messages could be 6, 9, 12, 8, 6, 4, 5, 10, 8, 9, and 11, with median 8, lower quartile 6, upper quartile 10, minimum value 4, and maximum value 12.

See also the *Differentiated Instruction Resources* for more strategies.

OUTLIERS A value that is widely separated from the rest of the data in a data set is called an **outlier**. Typically, a data value is considered to be an outlier if it is greater than the upper quartile by more than 1.5 times the interquartile range or if it is less than the lower quartile by more than 1.5 times the interquartile range.

EXAMPLE 3 Standardized Test Practice

The normal monthly amounts of precipitation (in inches) in Dallas are: 1.9, 2.4, 3.1, 3.2, 5.2, 3.2, 2.1, 2.0, 2.4, 4.1, 2.6, 2.6. These data were used to create the box-and-whisker plot in Example 2. Which value, if any, is an outlier?

Ⓐ 1.9 Ⓑ 5.2 Ⓒ 1.9 and 5.2 Ⓓ No outlier

Solution

From Example 2, you know the interquartile range of the data is 0.9 inch. Find 1.5 times the interquartile range: $1.5(0.9) = 1.35$.

From Example 2, you also know that the lower quartile is 2.3 and the upper quartile is 3.2. A value less than $2.3 - 1.35 = 0.95$ is an outlier. A value greater than $3.2 + 1.35 = 4.55$, is an outlier. Notice that $5.2 > 4.55$.

▶ The correct answer is B. Ⓐ Ⓑ Ⓒ Ⓓ

✓ GUIDED PRACTICE for Example 3

3. Which value, if any, is an outlier in the data set? D

3.7, 3.0, 3.4, 3.6, 5.2, 5.4, 3.2, 3.8, 4.3, 4.5, 4.2, 3.7

Ⓐ 3.0 Ⓑ 5.4 Ⓒ 3.0 and 5.4 Ⓓ No outlier

13.8 EXERCISES

HOMEWORK KEY
◯ = **WORKED-OUT SOLUTIONS** on p. WS33 for Exs. 3 and 17
★ = **STANDARDIZED TEST PRACTICE** Exs. 2, 8, 9, 18, and 19

SKILL PRACTICE

A

1. **VOCABULARY** What is the interquartile range of a data set?
the difference of the upper quartile and the lower quartile

2. ★ **WRITING** *Explain* how you can identify an outlier in a data set. **See margin.**

EXAMPLE 1 on p. 887 for Exs. 3–7

BOX-AND-WHISKER PLOTS Make a box-and-whisker plot of the data. **3–6. See margin.**

3. 1, 7, 0, 7, 2, 6, 3, 6, 0, 7, 8
4. 10, 1, 7, 5, 1, 8, 5, 4, 6, 5, 9, 12
5. 52, 20, 24, 45, 35, 32, 39, 42, 23, 64
6. 0.8, 0.4, 0.3, 0.6, 0.7, 0.2, 0.7, 0.9

Extra Example 3

The normal wind speeds (in miles per hour) each month in Savannah are: 8.2, 8.6, 9.1, 8.6, 7.6, 7.4, 6.9, 6.7, 7.2, 7.3, 7.2, 7.6. These data were used to create the box-and-whisker plot in Extra Example 2. Which value, if any, is an outlier? **D**

Ⓐ 6.7 Ⓑ 9.1
Ⓒ 6.7 and 9.1 Ⓓ No outlier

Closing the Lesson

Have students summarize the major points of the lesson and answer the Essential Question: How do you make and interpret box-and-whisker plots?

- **Each whisker in a box-and-whisker plot represents about 25% of the data.**
- **Each box on each side of the median represents about 25% of the data.**

To make a box-and-whisker plot, order the data from least to greatest, then find the median and the quartiles. The lower quartile is the median of the lower half of the data and the upper quartile is the median of the upper half. Plot the median, the quartiles, and the minimum and maximum values below a number line. Draw a box from the lower to the upper quartile. Draw a vertical line through the median. Draw a horizontal segment from the box to the minimum and another from the box to the maximum. Use median, quartiles, minimum, maximum, and the interquartile range to interpret and compare data.

2. See Additional Answers beginning on p. AA1.

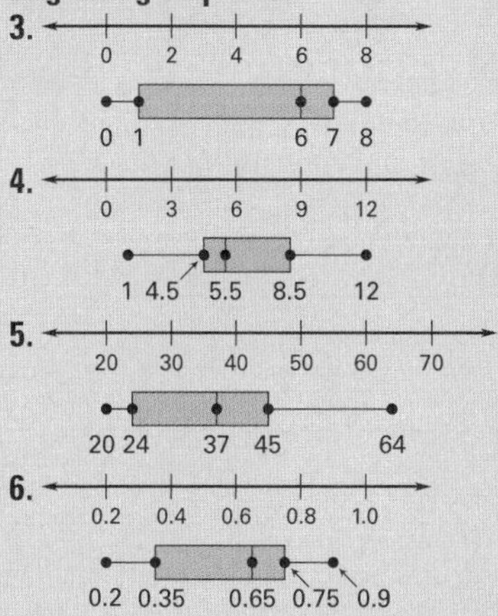

Differentiated Instruction

Kinesthetic Learners Ordering data can be difficult to do on paper. For problems similar to **Example 3**, have students write each data value on a small self-stick note so they can sort the data by moving the self-stick notes on their desk or on a sheet of paper.

See also the *Differentiated Instruction Resources* for more strategies.

p. 887 Guided Practice Ex. 1

15 30 45 60 75
15 22.5 35 57.5 70

4 PRACTICE AND APPLY

Assignment Guide

Answer Transparencies available for all exercises

Basic:
Day 1: pp. 889–892
Exs. 1–7, 15, 16
Day 2: pp. 889–892
Exs. 8–12, 17–19, 21–24

Average:
Day 1: pp. 889–892
Exs. 1, 2, 4–7, 15, 16, 21, 22
Day 2: pp. 889–892
Exs. 8–13, 17–19, 23, 24

Advanced:
Day 1: pp. 889–892
Exs. 1, 2, 4–6, 15, 16, 21, 22
Day 2: pp. 889–892
Exs. 8–14*, 17–20*, 23, 24

Block:
pp. 889–892
Exs. 1, 2, 4–13, 15–19, 21–24

Differentiated Instruction

See *Differentiated Instruction Resources* for suggestions on addressing the needs of a diverse classroom.

Homework Check

For a quick check of student understanding of key concepts, go over the following exercises:

Basic: 4, 8, 11, 15, 17
Average: 5, 9, 12, 16, 18
Advanced: 6, 10, 13, 17, 19

Extra Practice

- Student Edition, p. 950
- Chapter Resource Book: Practice levels A, B, C

Practice Worksheet

An easily-readable reduced practice page (with answers) for this lesson can be found on p. 840C.

---

7. **ERROR ANALYSIS** *Describe* and correct the error in creating a box-and-whisker plot of the data 0, 2, 4, 0, 6, 10, 8, 12, 5.
Sample answer: The upper quartile is incorrect. The upper quartile should be the median of 8 and 10, or 9; see margin for art.

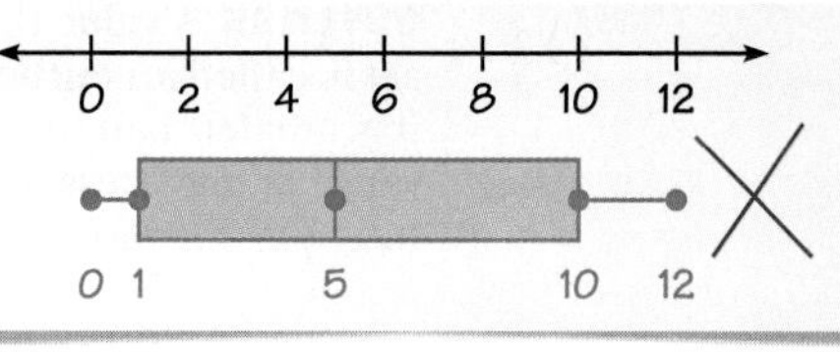

BOX-AND-WHISKER PLOT **In Exercises 8–10, use the box-and-whisker plot.**

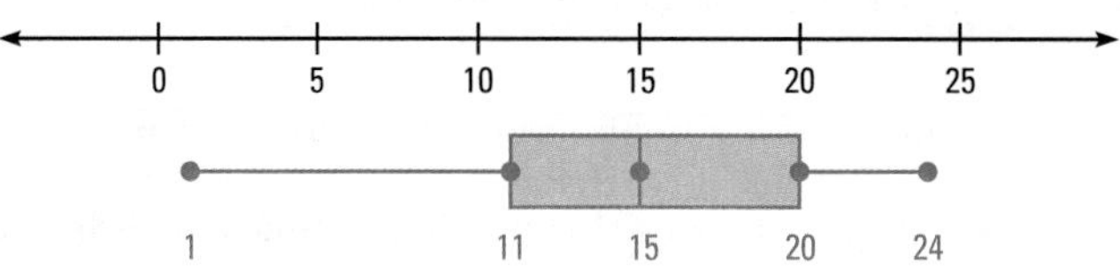

EXAMPLE 2 on p. 888 for Exs. 8–10

8. ★ **MULTIPLE CHOICE** About what percent of the data are greater than 20? **A**

Ⓐ 25% Ⓑ 50% Ⓒ 75% Ⓓ 100%

9. ★ **MULTIPLE CHOICE** About what percent of the data are less than 15? **B**

Ⓐ 25% Ⓑ 50% Ⓒ 75% Ⓓ 100%

10. **ERROR ANALYSIS** *Describe* and correct the error in interpreting the box-and-whisker plot.
Sample answer: The box represents 50% of the data values; about 50% of the data values lie between 11 and 20.

About 25% of the data values lie between 11 and 20.

EXAMPLES 1 and 3 on pp. 887, 889 for Exs. 11–13

B **OUTLIERS** **Make a box-and-whisker plot of the data. Identify any outliers.** **11–13. See margin.**

11. Hours worked per week: 15, 15, 10, 12, 22, 10, 8, 14, 18, 22, 18, 15, 12, 11, 10
12. Prices of MP3 players: $124, $95, $105, $110, $95, $124, $300, $190, $114
13. Annual salaries: $30,000, $35,000, $48,000, $68,500, $32,000, $38,000

C

14. **CHALLENGE** Two data sets have the same mean, the same interquartile range, and the same range. Is it possible for the box-and-whisker plots of such data sets to be different? *Justify* your answer by creating data sets that fit the situation. **Yes. _Sample answer:_ A: 0, 2, 4, 6, 8; B: –1, 3, 4, 7, 7**

PROBLEM SOLVING

EXAMPLE 1 on p. 887 for Exs. 15–16

A

15. **SEAWAY** The average sailing times to the Atlantic Ocean from several ports on the St. Lawrence Seaway are shown on the map. Make a box-and-whisker plot of the sailing times. **See margin.**

@HomeTutor for problem solving help at classzone.com

○ = WORKED-OUT SOLUTIONS on p. WS1 ★ = STANDARDIZED TEST PRACTICE

7.

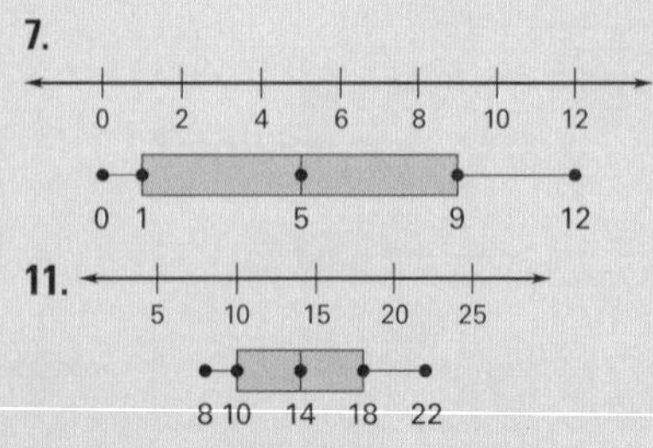

There are no outliers.

12.

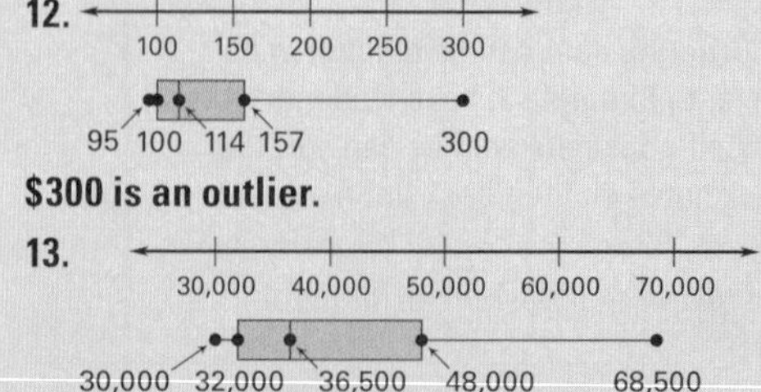

$300 is an outlier.

13.

There are no outliers.

16. **BASEBALL STATISTICS** In 2004, Ichiro Suzuki scored 101 runs. The numbers of runs he scored against different opposing teams are listed below. Make a box-and-whisker plot of the numbers of runs scored. **See margin.**

Runs scored: 18, 8, 4, 8, 2, 8, 0, 9, 0, 4, 2, 5, 9, 1, 2, 1, 2, 11, 7

@HomeTutor for problem solving help at classzone.com

EXAMPLES 1 and 3 on pp. 887, 889 for Exs. 17–18

17. **RETAIL SALES** The retail sales (in billions of dollars) of the nine U.S. states with the highest retail sales in 2002 are listed below.

California: $153.1	Florida: $118.2	Georgia: $38.4
Illinois: $52.4	New Jersey: $35.8	New York: $54.7
Ohio: $50.7	Pennsylvania: $49.9	Texas: $107.0

a. Make a box-and-whisker plot of the retail sales. **See margin.**

b. Which states, if any, had retail sales in 2002 that can be considered outliers? **none**

18b. Yes. ***Sample answer:*** **Ronald Reagan's age is more than 1.5 times the interquartile range of 7 away from the upper quartile.**

18. ★ **SHORT RESPONSE** The stem-and-leaf plot shows the ages of the first 43 presidents of the United States when they first took the oath of office.

Stem	Leaves
4	2 3 6 6 7 8 9 9
5	0 0 1 1 1 1 2 2 4 4 4 4 4 5 5 5 5 6 6 6 7 7 7 7 8
6	0 1 1 1 2 4 4 5 8 9

Key: 4 | 2 = 42 years

a. Make a box-and-whisker plot of the ages. **See margin.**

b. Ronald Reagan was the oldest United States president, and Theodore Roosevelt was the youngest. Can either of these presidents' ages be considered outliers? *Explain* why or why not.

EXAMPLE 2 B on p. 888 for Ex. 19

19. ★ **EXTENDED RESPONSE** The box-and-whisker plots show the diameters (in kilometers) of craters on Jupiter's moons Callisto and Ganymede.

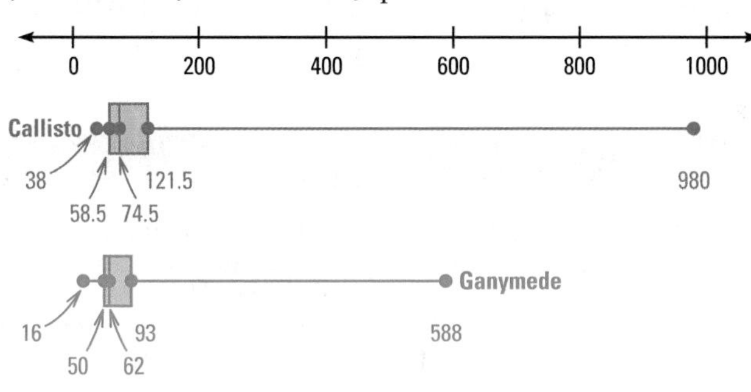

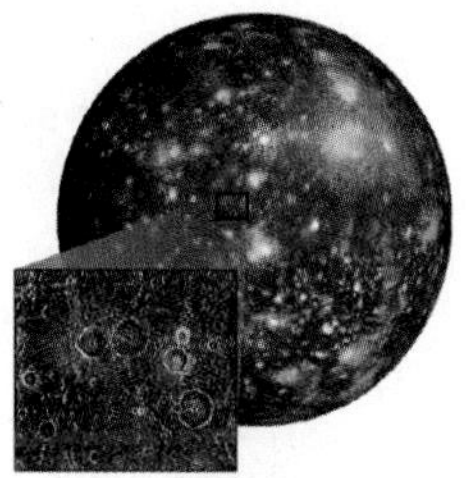

Callisto

a. *Compare* the diameters of craters on Callisto with the diameters of craters on Ganymede. **See margin.**

b. The largest crater in the United States is the Chesapeake Bay in Virginia, with a diameter of 90 kilometers. *Compare* the diameter of the Chesapeake Bay with diameters of craters on Callisto and Ganymede.

c. The largest crater on Earth is Vredefort in South Africa, with a diameter of 300 kilometers. *Compare* the diameter of Vredefort with the diameter of craters on Callisto and Ganymede.

19b. ***Sample answer:*** **Chesapeake Bay is larger than between 50% and 75% of the craters on both Callisto and Ganymede.**

19c. ***Sample answer:*** **Vredefort is larger than at least 75% of the craters on both Callisto and Ganymede.**

15.

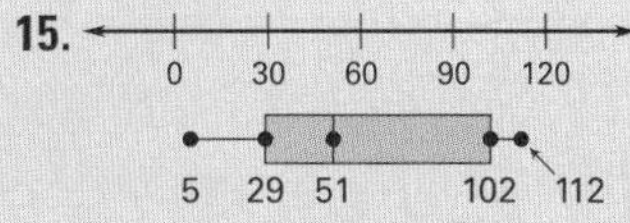

Avoiding Common Errors

Exercises 3–6, 11–13 Caution students to pay attention to the values they use to determine the median and quartiles. A common error is using the median to determine the quartiles when there is an odd number of values in the data set.

Mathematical Reasoning

Exercise 14 To get students started on this exercise, you may want to ask if two data sets can have the same range and the same mean, but different medians. Ask the students, as a class, to come up with an example.

Exercise 18 For additional information about the presidents of the United States, visit www.whitehouse.gov/history/presidents/index2.html

Teaching Strategy

Exercise 19 You may want to use this exercise to discuss outliers and interquartile range. First have students calculate outliers for Callisto and Ganymede and then point out how the outliers affect the range but not the interquartile range. Ask students to explain whether the range or the interquartile range best describes the spread of the data.

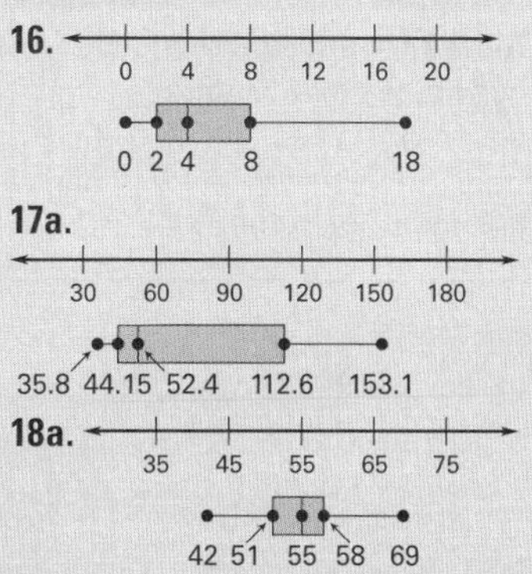

19a. ***Sample answer:*** **The craters on Ganymede are generally smaller than the craters on Callisto. The lower extreme, lower quartile, median, upper quartile, and upper extreme values are all lower for Ganymede than for Callisto.**

5 ASSESS AND RETEACH

Daily Homework Quiz

Transparency Available

1. Hiking trails (in miles) of moderate difficulty in Arizona's Mazatzal Wilderness Area are listed below. Make a box-and-whisker plot of the data.

   4.2, 5.7, 7, 3.3, 3.1, 3, 3.5, 3, 7.5, 4.2, 7.5, 6.6

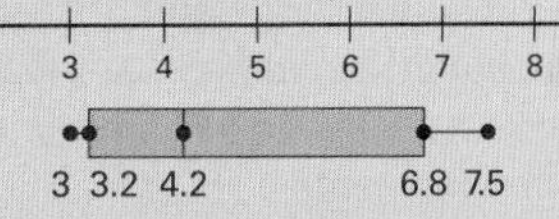

2. About what percent of the trails are greater than 4.2 miles in length? **50%**

Available at **classzone.com**

Diagnosis/Remediation

- Practice A, B, C in Chapter Resource Book
- Study Guide in Chapter Resource Book
- Practice Workbook
- @HomeTutor

Challenge

Additional challenge is available in the Chapter Resource Book.

Quiz

An easily-readable reduced copy of the quiz (with answers) on Lessons 13.5–13.8 from the Assessment Book can be found on p. 840F.

20, Quiz 4–6. See Additional Answers beginning on p. AA1.

C **20. CHALLENGE** The box-and-whisker plots show the heights (in inches) of singers in a chorus, according to their voice parts. A soprano part has the highest pitch, followed by alto, tenor, and bass, respectively. Draw a conclusion about voice parts and heights. *Justify* your conclusion. **See margin.**

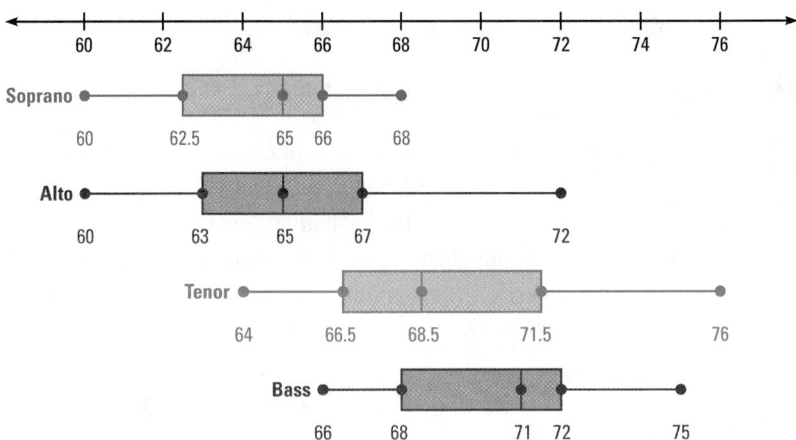

MIXED REVIEW

Make a stem-and-leaf plot of the data. *(p. 881)* **21, 22. See margin.**

21. 56, 55, 54, 57, 28, 28, 53, 52, 56, 28, 25, 23, 17, 51, 54, 23, 20, 10

22. 71, 60, 39, 43, 81, 32, 33, 41, 37, 34, 51, 41, 32, 34, 48, 35, 36, 58

Make a histogram of the data. *(p. 881)* **23, 24. See margin.**

23. 1.24, 2.45, 1.11, 2.09, 2.19, 1.99, 1.75, 1.65, 2.10, 2.30

24. 1.5, 5.12, 7.5, 7.1, 7.14, 9.7, 10.24, 1.3, 1.6, 1.6, 3.3, 3.12

QUIZ *for Lessons 13.5–13.8*

1. **HOTEL SURVEY** A hotel manager leaves guest comment cards in each room. Identify the population and classify the sampling method. *(p. 871)* **all the hotel's guests, self-selected**

In Exercises 2 and 3, find the range and mean absolute deviation of the data. Round to the nearest hundredth, if necessary. *(p. 875)*

2. 62, 63, 70, 40, 50, 60 **30, 8.33**
3. 14, 18, 22, 14, 14, 6, 17 **16, 3.43**
4. Make a histogram of the data: 44, 52, 60, 47, 65, 40, 49, 45, 32, 68, 39. *(p. 881)* **See margin.**
5. Make a stem-and-leaf plot of the data: 1.8, 2.2, 1.2, 2.8, 3.6, 3.3, 1.8, 2.2. *(p. 881)* **See margin.**
6. **TEST SCORES** The scores on a math exam are given below. Make a box-and-whisker plot of the data. Identify any outliers. *(p. 887)* **See margin.**

   76, 55, 88, 92, 79, 85, 90, 88, 85, 92, 100, 91, 90, 86, 88

21.

Stem	Leaves
1	0 7
2	0 3 3 5 8 8 8
3	
4	
5	1 2 3 4 4 5 6 6 7

Key: 1 | 0 = 10

22.

Stem	Leaves
3	2 2 3 4 4 5 6 7 9
4	1 1 3 8
5	1 8
6	0
7	1
8	1

Key: 3 | 2 = 32

23, 24. See Additional Answers beginning on p. AA1.

Graphing Calculator ACTIVITY *Use after Lesson 13.8*

@HomeTutor
classzone.com
Keystrokes

13.8 Draw Box-and-Whisker Plots

QUESTION **How can you use a graphing calculator to make a box-and-whisker plot?**

EXAMPLE **Make a box-and-whisker plot**

REPTILE SPECIES The number of known reptile species per 10,000 square kilometers in the countries of Asia (excluding the Middle East) and of Central America, South America, and the Caribbean are listed below. Make box-and-whisker plots of the numbers of species.

Asia: 36, 26, 49, 11, 32, 35, 27, 58, 91, 26, 8, 8, 12, 12, 23, 110, 4, 51, 41, 41, 62, 350, 77, 18, 81, 23, 18, 59

Central America, South America, and the Caribbean: 81, 125, 47, 69, 57, 107, 77, 73, 35, 123, 69, 116, 87, 37, 45, 53, 20, 124, 126, 35, 73, 60, 64

STEP 1 ***Enter the data***

Enter the data for Asia into List 1. Enter the data for Central America, South America, and the Caribbean into List 2.

STEP 2 ***Select box-and-whisker plot***

Go to the STAT PLOT screen and select the box-and-whisker plot for both Plot 1 and Plot 2. The Xlist for Plot 1 should be L_1, so that it displays the data from List 1. The Xlist for Plot 2 should be L_2, so that it displays the data from List 2. Make sure both plots are on.

STEP 3 ***Set the viewing window***

Press ZOOM 9 to set the window so that it shows all of the data.

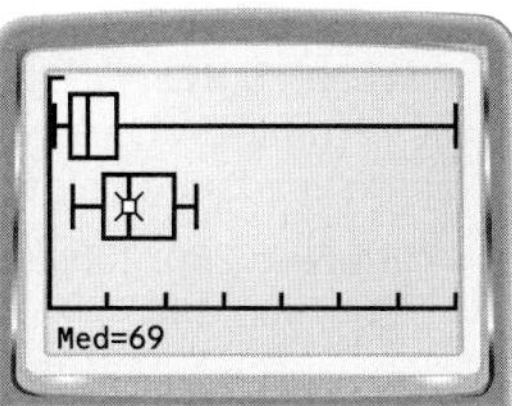

STEP 4 ***Graph***

Press GRAPH. Use the trace feature to examine the box-and-whisker plots more closely. Notice that the graphing calculator refers to the lower quartile as Q_1 and the upper quartile as Q_3.

DRAW CONCLUSIONS

1. **REPTILE SPECIES** *Compare* the number of reptile species per 10,000 square kilometers in the countries of Central America, South America, and the Caribbean with the number in Asia. **See margin.**

2. **BIRD SPECIES** The number of threatened bird species per 10,000 square kilometers in the countries of two regions are listed below. Make box-and-whisker plots of the data and compare the data for the two regions. **See margin.**

   Middle East and Northern Africa: 13, 8, 11, 14, 12, 8, 4, 3, 5, 2, 11, 5, 11, 7, 6, 14, 4, 13

   North and South America: 5, 50, 41, 27, 103, 18, 64, 53, 3, 26, 64, 2, 11, 22

1 PLAN AND PREPARE

Learn the Method

- Students will use a graphing calculator to make a box-and-whisker plot.
- After the activity, students can use a graphing calculator to check their solutions in Exercises 3–6 and 11–13 in Lesson 13.8.

Keystroke Help

Keystrokes for several models of calculators are available in blackline format in the *Chapter Resource Book.*

2 TEACH

Tips for Success

If necessary, tell students to adjust Xmin and Xmax in the viewing window so they can clearly see both plots.

Extra Example

The number of recorded green turtle nests and leatherback turtle nests during the years 1996–2004 on a Florida island are listed below. Make box-and-whiskers plots of the number of nests.

Green turtle: 31, 10, 93, 22, 166, 21, 106, 81, 70

Leatherback turtle: 13, 21, 7, 20, 21, 35, 16, 18, 6

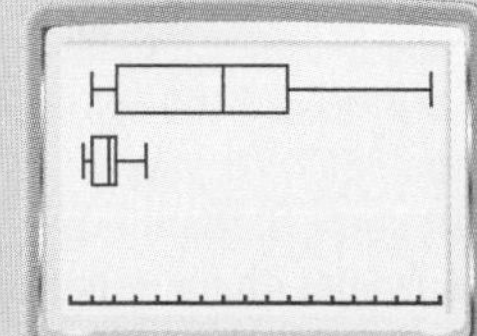

3 ASSESS AND RETEACH

What do the interquartile ranges of the two plots tell you? **The interquartile ranges tell you that the number of green turtle nests varied greatly during the 9-year period, while the number of leatherback turtle nests remained fairly consistent.**

1. ***Sample answer:*** **Although Asia has an outlier that is greater than any value in Central America, South America, and the Caribbean's data set, in general Asia's data is lower. The lower extreme, lower quartile, median, and upper quartile are all lower for Asia than for Central America, South America, and the Caribbean.**

2.

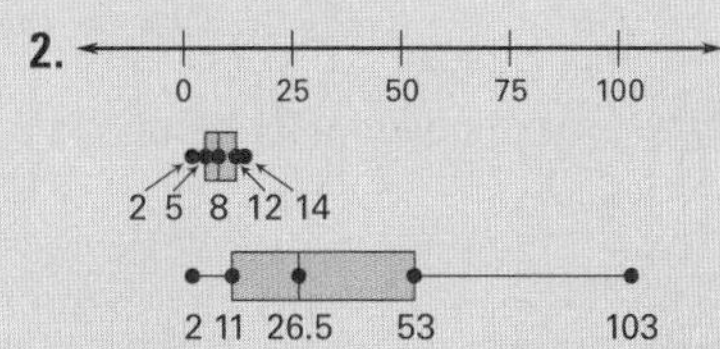

Sample answer: **Generally, there are more threatened bird species in North and South America than in the Middle East and Northern Africa. There is also a much greater range of values in North and South America.**

1a.

Age	People
20–29	III
30–39	𝍸
40–49	𝍸 I
50–59	𝍸 II
60–69	III

1b. 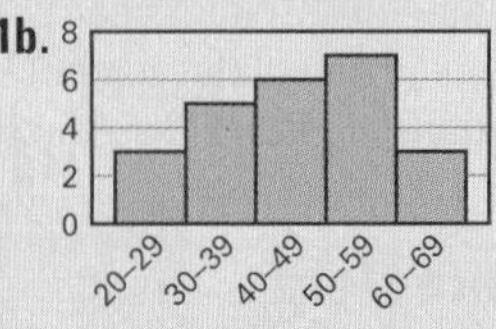

2a. population: all the doctor's patients, sampling method: systematic sample

2b. *Sample answer:* The sample is likely to be biased because those patients who cannot visit on Tuesdays cannot be represented, and they are likely to have different opinions about scheduling than those who can visit on Tuesdays.

4a. store A: mean: $257, median: $245, mode: $200, $260; store B: mean: $237.50, median: $210, mode: $200. *Sample answer:* The mean; the mean is not influenced by a very high or a very low price, so it is a good representation.

4b. store A: range: $350, mean absolute deviation: $63; store B: range: $250, mean absolute deviation: $57.50. *Sample answer:* Store A; it has a greater range and a greater mean absolute deviation.

4c. Yes. *Sample answer:* At store A, the interquartile range is 80, with an upper quartile of 280. All values at Store A greater than $400 are outliers, so the $500 DVD player is an outlier. At store B, the interquartile range is 60 with an upper quartile of 250. All values at store B above $340 are outliers, so the $350 and $400 DVD player are outliers.

MIXED REVIEW of Problem Solving

STATE TEST PRACTICE classzone.com

Lessons 13.5–13.8

1. **MULTI-STEP PROBLEM** The ages of people who attended an opening reception for a theater production are listed below.

   54, 25, 28, 64, 30, 42, 33, 50, 27, 35, 40, 39, 41, 52, 49, 48, 56, 60, 58, 37, 56, 45, 57, 62

   a, b. See margin.

   a. Make a frequency table of the data.

   b. Make a histogram of the data.

2. **MULTI-STEP PROBLEM** A doctor would like to extend her office hours to better accommodate her patients. She asks each patient who visits her office on Tuesday which day the patient thinks the hours should be extended. **a, b. See margin.**

   a. Identify the population and classify the sampling method.

   b. Tell whether the survey method used is likely to result in a biased sample.

3. **GRIDDED ANSWER** The average lengths (in hours) of several morning commutes are listed below. How many minutes is the mean commute? **37.5 min**

   0.25, 0.20, 0.50, 0.50, 0.50, 0.05, 0.65, 1.00, 1.50, 0.75, 0.50, 1.10, 0.60, 0.80, 1.00, 0.10

4. **EXTENDED RESPONSE** The prices (in dollars) of portable DVD players at two different stores are listed below.

   Store A: 280, 200, 260, 230, 200, 150, 300, 260, 500, 190

   Store B: 350, 190, 230, 250, 400, 200, 200, 220, 185, 150 **a–c. See margin.**

   a. Find the mean, median, and mode(s) of each data set. Which measure of central tendency best represents each data set? *Explain* your reasoning.

   b. Find the range and mean absolute deviation of each data set. Which store's prices are more spread out? *Explain.*

   c. Can any of the prices of the portable DVD players be considered outliers? *Explain* your reasoning.

5. **OPEN-ENDED** A clothing store sells several different styles of jeans. The mean price of the jeans is $27. The median price of the jeans is $27.50. The mode of the prices is $20. Make a list of prices of jeans that has these measures of central tendency. **See margin.**

6. **SHORT RESPONSE** The back-to-back stem-and-leaf plot below shows the lengths (in meters) of the eight best men's and women's final long jump results from the 2004 Olympics. *Compare* the lengths of the jumps by men with those by women. **See margin.**

Lengths (in meters) of Long Jump

Men		Women
	6	7 8 8 9
	7	0 0 0 1
6 5 3 3 2 2 2 0	8	

Key: 0 | 7 | 1 = 7.0 m, 7.1 m

7. **SHORT RESPONSE** The stem-and-leaf plot shows the number of games lost by 15 NCAA football coaches with the greatest career winning percentages after at least 10 years of coaching.

Stem	Leaves
1	1 2 3 6 7 7 8
2	1 3 3 4 5 9
3	6
4	9

Key: 2 | 1 = 21 games

   a. Make a box-and-whisker plot of the data. **See margin.**

   b. Tom Osborne had a winning percentage of 83.6% over his career and lost 49 games. Can the number of games lost by Tom Osborne be considered an outlier? *Explain* your reasoning. **Yes. *Sample answer:* The interquartile range is 9, and 49 is more than 9 • 1.5 = 13.5 years greater than the upper quartile of 25.**

5. *Sample answer:* 20, 20, 27, 28, 30, 37

6. *Sample answer:* The men jumped farther than the women.

7a. 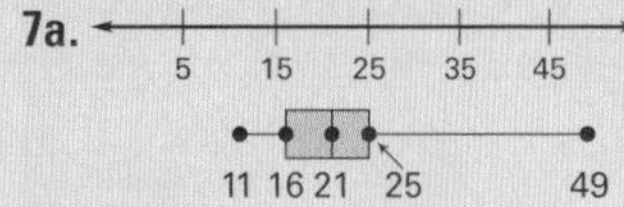

13 CHAPTER SUMMARY

BIG IDEAS — For Your Notebook

Big Idea 1

Finding Probabilities of Simple and Compound Events

To find $P(A)$ when...	
all outcomes are equally likely, use $P(A) = \frac{\text{Number of favorable outcomes}}{\text{Number of possible outcomes}}$	you perform an experiment, use $P(A) = \frac{\text{Number of successes}}{\text{Number of trials}}$

To find $P(A \text{ or } B)$ when...	...use this formula
events A and B have no common outcomes	$P(A \text{ or } B) = P(A) + P(B)$
events A and B have at least one common outcome	$P(A \text{ or } B) = P(A) + P(B) - P(A \text{ and } B)$

To find $P(A \text{ and } B)$ when...	...use this formula
events A and B are independent	$P(A \text{ and } B) = P(A) \cdot P(B)$
events A and B are dependent	$P(A \text{ and } B) = P(A) \cdot P(B \text{ given } A)$

Big Idea 2

Analyzing Sets of Data

You can find values that represent a typical data value using the following measures of central tendency:

mean, median, and mode

You can find values that describe the spread of data using the following measures of dispersion:

range, mean absolute deviation, and interquartile range

Big Idea 3

Making and Interpreting Data Displays

Use an appropriate display to show the distribution of a set of numerical data.

A **stem-and-leaf plot** organizes data based on their digits.

Stem	Leaves
1	0 1 1 2 3
2	0 0 0 2

Key: 1 | 0 = 10

A **histogram** shows the frequency of data on intervals of equal size, with no gaps or overlaps.

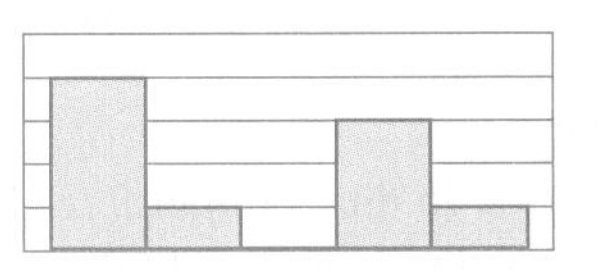

A **box-and-whisker plot** organizes data into four groups of approximately equal size.

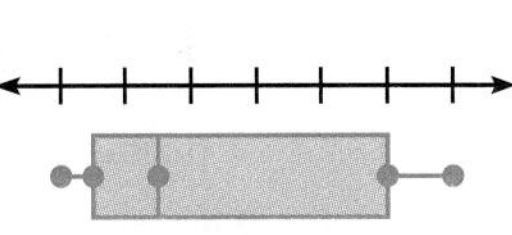

Additional Resources

The following resources are available to help review the materials in this chapter.

Chapter Resource Book

- Chapter Review Games and Activities
- Cumulative Practice, Chs. 1–13

Student Resources in Spanish

eWorkbook

@HomeTutor

Vocabulary Practice

Vocabulary practice is available at **classzone.com**

@HomeTutor
classzone.com
- Multi-Language Glossary
- Vocabulary Practice

Extra Example 13.1

A bag contains 12 green markers, 6 blue markers, and 8 yellow markers. You choose a marker at random. Find the probability you choose a blue marker. $\frac{3}{13}$

REVIEW KEY VOCABULARY

- outcome, event, *p. 843*
- sample space, *p. 843*
- probability of an event, *p. 843*
- theoretical, experimental probability, *p. 844*
- odds in favor, odds against, *p. 845*
- permutation, *p. 851*
- *n* factorial, *p. 852*
- combination, *p. 856*
- compound event, *p. 861*
- mutually exclusive events, *p. 861*
- overlapping events, *p. 861*
- independent events, *p. 862*
- dependent events, *p. 862*
- survey, *p. 871*
- population, *p. 871*
- sample: random, stratified random, systematic, convenience, self-selected, *p. 871*
- biased sample, *p. 872*
- biased question, *p. 872*
- mean, median, mode, *p. 875*
- measure of dispersion, *p. 876*
- range, *p. 876*
- mean absolute deviation, *p. 876*
- stem-and-leaf plot, *p. 881*
- frequency, frequency table, *p. 882*
- histogram, *p. 882*
- box-and-whisker plot, *p. 887*
- lower quartile, upper quartile, *p. 887*
- interquartile range, *p. 888*
- outlier, *p. 889*

VOCABULARY EXERCISES

Copy and complete the statement.

1. An event that combines two or more events is a(n) _?_. **compound event**
2. A possible result of an experiment is a(n) _?_. **outcome**
3. **WRITING** *Compare* theoretical probability and experimental probability.
   Sample answer: **Theoretical probability is based on knowing the likelihood of all possible outcomes of an event. Experimental probability is based on the results of an experiment.**

REVIEW EXAMPLES AND EXERCISES

Use the review examples and exercises below to check your understanding of the concepts you have learned in each lesson of Chapter 13.

13.1 Find Probabilities and Odds

pp. 843–848

EXAMPLE

A bag contains 15 red checkers and 15 black checkers. You choose a checker at random. Find the probability that you choose a black checker.

$$P(\text{black checker}) = \frac{\text{Number of black checkers}}{\text{Total number of checkers}} = \frac{15}{30} = \frac{1}{2}$$

EXERCISES

EXAMPLE 2 on p. 844 for Exs. 4–5

4. **CHECKERS** In the example above, suppose an extra red checker is added to the bag. Find the probability of randomly choosing a black checker. $\frac{15}{31}$
5. **BAG OF LETTERS** A bag contains tiles. Each tile has one letter from the word HAPPINESS on it. You choose a tile at random. What is the probability that you choose a tile with the letter S? $\frac{2}{9}$

13.2 Find Probabilities Using Permutations

pp. 851–855

EXAMPLE

You need to enter a 4 digit code in order to enter the building where you work. The digits are 4 different numbers from 1 to 5. You forgot the code and try to guess it. Find the probability that you guess correctly.

STEP 1 **Write** the number of possible outcomes as the number of permutations of 4 out of the 5 possible digits. This is ${}_5P_4$.

$${}_5P_4 = \frac{5!}{(5-4)!} = \frac{5!}{1!} = 5! = 5 \cdot 4 \cdot 3 \cdot 2 \cdot 1 = 120$$

STEP 2 **Find** the probability. Because only one of the permutations is the correct code, the probability that you guess the correct code is $\frac{1}{120}$.

EXERCISES

EXAMPLE 2 on p. 852 for Exs. 6–10

Evaluate the expression.

6. ${}_7P_6$ **5040** **7.** ${}_6P_2$ **30** **8.** ${}_8P_5$ **6720** **9.** ${}_{13}P_{10}$ **1,037,836,800**

10. MUSIC You downloaded 6 songs. You randomly choose 4 of these songs to play. Find the probability that you play the first 4 songs you downloaded in the order in which you downloaded them. $\frac{1}{360}$

13.3 Find Probabilities Using Combinations

pp. 856–859

EXAMPLE

For your government class, you must choose 3 states in the United States to research. You may choose your states from the 6 New England states. How many combinations of states are possible?

The order in which you choose the states is not important. So, to find the number of combinations of 6 states taken 3 at a time, find ${}_6C_3$.

$${}_6C_3 = \frac{6!}{(6-3)! \cdot 3!}$$ **Combinations formula**

$$= \frac{6 \cdot 5 \cdot 4 \cdot \cancel{3!}}{\cancel{3!} \cdot (3 \cdot 2 \cdot 1)}$$ **Expand factorials. Divide out common factor, 3!.**

$$= 20$$ **Simplify.**

EXERCISES

EXAMPLE 2 on p. 857 for Exs. 11–15

Evaluate the expression.

11. ${}_7C_6$ **7** **12.** ${}_6C_2$ **15** **13.** ${}_8C_5$ **56** **14.** ${}_{13}C_{10}$ **286**

15. TICKETS You win 5 tickets to a concert. In how many ways can you choose 4 friends out of a group of 9 to take with you to the concert? **126 ways**

Extra Example 13.2

The coach for the swimming team randomly chooses 2 of the 12 members of the team to talk to local reporters about an upcoming meet. What is the probability that the coach chooses you and your twin brother? $\frac{1}{132}$

Extra Example 13.3

Your dog has 6 puppies. You can choose 2 of the 6 to keep. How many choices of two puppies are possible? **15 choices**

Extra Examples 13.4

1. You roll a number cube. Find the probability that the number is 2 or an odd number. $\frac{2}{3}$

2. A bag contains 3 red chips, 2 white chips, 4 blue chips, and 6 yellow chips. You choose a chip at random and then return it to the bag. You choose another chip at random. What is the probability that both chips are red? $\frac{1}{25}$

13.4 Find Probabilities of Compound Events

pp. 861–867

EXAMPLE

The sections of the spinner shown all have the same area. You spin the spinner. Find the probability that the spinner stops on red or on an even number.

Because 24 is an even number on a red section, stopping on red and stopping on an even number are overlapping events.

$$P(\text{red or even}) = P(\text{red}) + P(\text{even}) - P(\text{red and even})$$

$$= \frac{3}{8} + \frac{3}{8} - \frac{1}{8}$$

$$= \frac{5}{8}$$

EXERCISES

EXAMPLES 1 and 2 on pp. 861–862 for Exs. 16–19

You spin the spinner shown above. Find the specified probability.

16. P(green or odd) $\frac{7}{8}$

17. P(blue or prime number) $\frac{3}{8}$

18. P(blue or even) $\frac{3}{4}$

19. P(red or multiple of 3) $\frac{5}{8}$

EXAMPLE

A bag contains 5 red marbles, 3 blue marbles, 6 white marbles, and 2 green marbles. You choose one marble at random, put the marble aside, then choose a second marble at random. What is the probability that both marbles are blue?

Because you do not replace the first marble, the events are dependent. Before you choose a marble, there are 16 marbles, and 3 of them are blue. After you choose a blue marble, there are 2 blue marbles among 15 marbles left.

$$P(\text{blue and then blue}) = P(\text{blue}) \cdot P(\text{blue given blue})$$

$$= \frac{3}{16} \cdot \frac{2}{15}$$

$$= \frac{6}{240}$$

$$= \frac{1}{40}$$

EXERCISES

EXAMPLES 3 and 4 on p. 863 for Exs. 20–21

You randomly choose 2 marbles from the bag described in the example above. Find the probability that both are green if:

20. you replace the first marble. $\frac{1}{64}$

21. you don't replace the first marble. $\frac{1}{120}$

@HomeTutor
classzone.com
Chapter Review Practice

13.5 Analyze Surveys and Samples

pp. 871–874

EXAMPLE

You want to determine what type of music is the favorite of students in your grade. You survey every third student from an alphabetical list of students in your grade. You ask each surveyed student, "What is your favorite type of music, classical or country?"

Identify the population and classify the sampling method. Tell whether the question is potentially biased. Explain your answer. If the question is potentially biased, rewrite it so that it is not.

The population is all students in your grade. Because you use the rule "survey every third student," the sample is a systematic sample.

The question is biased, because it does not allow students to choose a type of music other than classical or country. An unbiased question is "What is your favorite type of music?"

EXERCISES

EXAMPLE 1 on p. 871 for Ex. 22

22. **SURVEY** In the example above, suppose you create a questionaire and distribute one to every student in your grade. There is a box in the cafeteria where students can drop off completed questionaires during lunch. Identify the sampling method. **self-selected**

13.6 Use Measures of Central Tendency and Dispersion

pp. 875–878

EXAMPLE

The amounts of snowfall (in inches) in one town for 8 months of the year are listed below. Find the mean, median, and mode(s) of the data. Which measure of central tendency best represents the data?

0.5, 0.5, 1.5, 2.0, 3.5, 4.5, 16.5, 30.5

$$\bar{x} = \frac{0.5 + 0.5 + 1.5 + 2.0 + 3.5 + 4.5 + 16.5 + 30.5}{8} = \frac{59.5}{8} = 7.4375 \text{ inches}$$

The median is the mean of the two middle values, 2.0 and 3.5, or 2.75 inches.

The mode is 0.5 inch.

The median best represents the data. The mean is greater then most of the data values. The mode is less than most of the data values.

EXERCISES

EXAMPLES 1 and 2 on pp. 875–876 for Ex. 23

23. **BASEBALL STATISTICS** The numbers of home runs hit by baseball player Manny Ramirez against several different opposing teams over 3 seasons are 5, 1, 10, 5, 5, 4, 1, 0, 7, 2, 1, 1, 1, 9, 6, 1, 2, 6, 2, 19, 6, and 17.
   a. Find the mean, median, and mode(s) of the data. **about 5.045, 4.5, 1**
   b. Which measure of central tendency best represents the data? *Explain.* **See margin.**

Extra Example 13.5

You want to determine whether the students at your school think the cafeteria serves nutritious food. You randomly choose students standing in the cafeteria line during first period lunch. You ask each student, "Do you think the cafeteria should serve better food?"

Identify the population and classify the sampling method. Tell whether the question is potentially biased. Explain your answer. If the question is potentially biased, rewrite it so that it is not.

The population is all students at your school. The sampling method is convenience.

The question is biased because the word "better" is ambiguous. An unbiased question is "Do you think the cafeteria serves nutritious food?"

Extra Example 13.6

Your test scores for English and science are shown below. Compare the scores using the range and the mean absolute deviation.

English: 82, 76, 84, 82
Science: 91, 84, 88, 90
English: range is 8 and mean absolute deviation is 2.5
Science: range is 7 and mean absolute deviation is 2.25
The range of English test scores is greater. The mean absolute deviation for the English scores is also greater.

23b. Median. ***Sample answer:*** **The mode is much lower than many of the values, and the mean is affected by the two extreme values (17 and 19) that are much greater than the rest of the data. So, the median best represents the data.**

Extra Example 13.7

The back-to-back stem-and-leaf plot shows the prices (in dollars) of oak trees and maple trees at a nursery. Compare the prices of the two trees at the nursery.

Tree Prices

Oak		Maple
3 1 0	4	0 0 2 3 3
7 5 5	5	1 1 2 3 5 5
8 7 6 5 4	6	0 2 2
8 8 5 5	7	2

Key: 5 | 5 | 1 = \$55, \$51

The median price of oak trees is \$65, while the median price of maple trees is \$52. In general, oak trees cost more than maple trees at the nursery.

Extra Example 13.8

Make a box-and-whisker plot of the prices of oak trees in the extra example above.

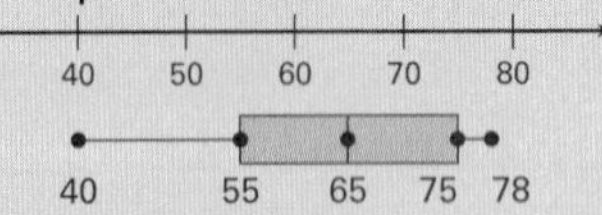

24.

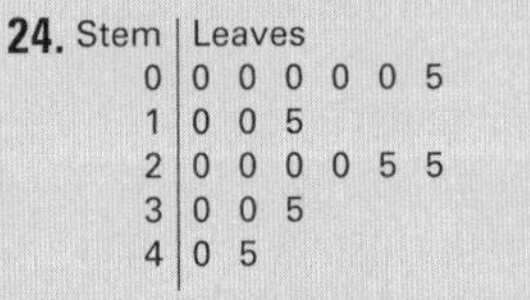

Stem	Leaves
0	0 0 0 0 0 5
1	0 0 5
2	0 0 0 0 5 5
3	0 0 5
4	0 5

Key: 1 | 0 = 10 minutes

25.

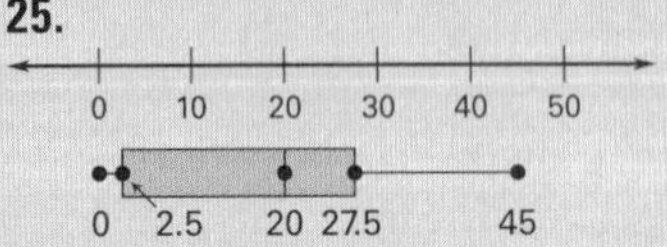

13.7 Interpret Stem-and-Leaf Plots and Histograms *pp. 881–885*

EXAMPLE

The prices (in dollars) of several books are listed below. Make a stem-and-leaf plot of the prices.

14, 15, 9, 19, 21, 29, 12, 25, 10, 8, 15, 13, 15, 20

STEP 1 **Separate** the data into stems and leaves

Book Prices

Stem	Leaves
0	9 8
1	4 5 9 2 0 5 3 5
2	1 9 0 5

Key: 1 | 4 = \$14

STEP 2 **Write** the leaves in increasing order.

Book Prices

Stem	Leaves
0	8 9
1	0 2 3 4 5 5 5 9
2	0 1 5 9

Key: 1 | 4 = \$14

EXERCISES

EXAMPLE 1 on p. 881 for Ex. 24

24. EXERCISING The minutes per day that the students in a class spend exercising are listed below. Make a stem-and-leaf plot of the data. **See margin.**

20, 25, 0, 10, 0, 30, 35, 20, 45, 25, 40, 0, 0, 0, 5, 10, 20, 15, 20, 30

13.8 Interpret Box-and-Whisker Plots *pp. 887–892*

EXAMPLE

Make a box-and-whisker plot of the book prices in the example above.

Order the data. Then find the median and quartiles.

Upper quartile — Median = 15 — Lower quartile

8 9 10 12 13 14 15 15 15 19 20 21 25 29

Plot the median, the quartiles, the maximum value, and the minimum value below a number line. Draw the box and the whiskers.

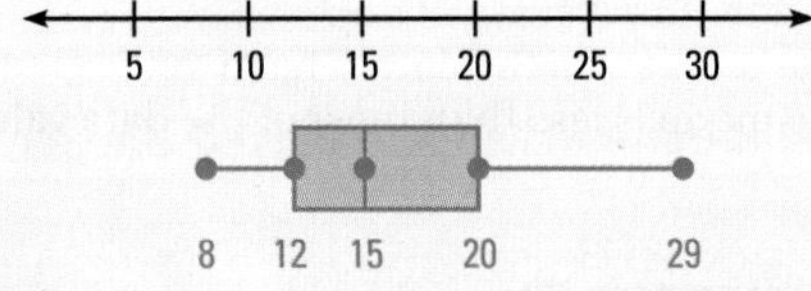

EXERCISES

EXAMPLE 1 on p. 887 for Ex. 25

25. EXERCISING Use the data in Exercise 24 to make a box-and-whisker plot of the minutes per day that the students in the class spend exercising. **See margin.**

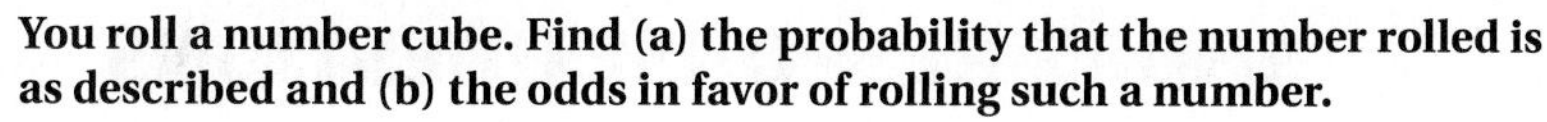

You roll a number cube. Find (a) the probability that the number rolled is as described and (b) the odds in favor of rolling such a number.

1. a 4 **a.** $\frac{1}{6}$ **b.** 1 : 5
2. an even number **a.** $\frac{1}{2}$ **b.** 1 : 1
3. a number less than 5 **a.** $\frac{2}{3}$ **b.** 2 : 1
4. a multiple of 3 **a.** $\frac{1}{3}$ **b.** 1 : 2

Evaluate the expression.

5. ${}_7P_2$ **42**
6. ${}_8P_3$ **336**
7. ${}_6C_3$ **20**
8. ${}_{12}C_7$ **792**

Tell whether the question can be answered using *combinations* or *permutations*. *Explain* your choice, then answer the question.

9. Permutations; order matters since there are first, second, and third places; 336 ways.

9. Eight swimmers participate in a race. In how many ways can the swimmers finish in first, second, and third place?
10. A restaurant offers 7 different side dishes. In how many different ways can you choose 2 side dishes? **Combinations; order does not matter since the side dishes can be selected in either order; 21 ways.**

In Exercises 11 and 12, refer to a bag containing 12 tiles numbered 1–12.

11. You choose a tile at random. What is the probability that you choose a number less than 10 or an odd number. $\frac{5}{6}$
12. You choose a tile at random, replace it, and choose a second tile at random. What is the probability that you choose a number greater than 3, then an odd number. $\frac{3}{8}$
13. **GOVERNMENT PROJECT** City officials want to know whether residents will support construction of a new library. This question appears on the ballot in the citywide election: "Do you support a tax increase to replace the old, deteriorating library with a brand new one?"Is the question potentially biased? *Explain* your answer. If the question is potentially biased, rewrite it so that it is not. **See margin.**
14. **BASKETBALL** The back-to-back stem-and-leaf plot shows the heights (in inches) of the players on a high school's basketball teams. **a–d. See margin.**

Basketball Players' Heights

Girls		Boys
9 7 7 6 6 5 3 3	6	9 9 9
3 2 1 1 0	7	0 0 0 2 4 4 6 6 7 7 7 8

Key: 3 | 6 | 9 = 63 in., 69 in.

a. Find the mean, median, and mode(s) of each data set. Which measure of central tendency best represents each data set? *Explain.*

b. Find the range and mean absolute deviation of each data set. Which team's heights are more spread out? *Explain.*

c. Make a box-and-whisker plot of each data set.

d. *Compare* the boys' heights with the girls' heights.

Additional Resources

Assessment Book

- Chapter Test, Levels A, B, C
- Standardized Chapter Test
- SAT/ACT Chapter Test
- Alternative Assessment

Test Generator

Chapter Test

Easily-readable reduced copies (with answers) of Chapter Test B, the Standardized Chapter Test, and the Alternative Assessment from the Assessment Book can be found on pp. 840F–840H.

14a. Girls: mean: about 67.92, median: 67, mode: 66, 67, and 71; Boys: mean: 73.2, median: 74, mode: 69, 70, and 77

14b. Girls: range: 10, mean absolute deviation: 2.84; Boys: range: 9, mean absolute deviation: 3.12. *Sample answer:* Boys; their range is less, but their mean absolute deviation is greater which indicates that, on the average, the heights are farther away from the mean.

14c.

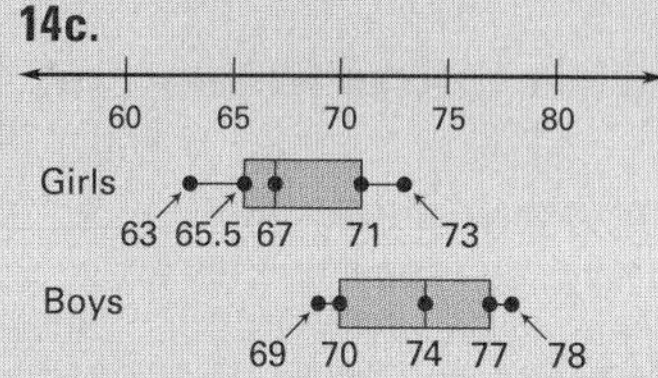

14d. *Sample answer:* Generally, the boys are taller than the girls. 50% of the boys are taller than all of the girls. Each group's data are almost equally dispersed, with the boy's having a slightly greater interquartile range.

13. Yes. *Sample answer:* The question suggests that the current library is old and deteriorating and that a new library would be an improvement; "Are you for or against a tax increase to build a new library to replace the old one?"

Using Rubrics

The rubric given on the pupil page is a sample of a three-level rubric. Other rubrics may contain four, five, or six levels. For more information on rubrics, see the *Differentiated Instruction Resources.*

Test-Taking Strategy

Encourage students to write down what they need to include when they are asked to display data in a graph. They should take a couple of minutes to think about the values or labels they need to show in their displays. After they have created the display, they can check it against their list to make sure that they have included all of the elements of the particular display. Tell students that using a checklist will increase their chances of getting full credit for the graph because it is easy to overlook a single element among many.

Avoiding Common Errors

Students often answer the questions in a short response test question, but fail to explain their answers. Remind students to check that they have answered all parts of the question.

Mathematical Reasoning

Tell students that it is a good idea to show their work so that a test reviewer can see how they arrived at their answers. They should show their work even if they use a calculator or mental math.

Scoring Rubric

Full Credit
- solution is complete and correct

Partial Credit
- solution is complete but has errors,

or
- solution is without error but incomplete

No Credit
- no solution is given,

or
- solution makes no sense

SHORT RESPONSE QUESTIONS

PROBLEM

The lengths (in inches) of several goldfish are listed below. Make a box-and-whisker plot of the lengths. Can any of the goldfish lengths be considered outliers? *Explain* why or why not.

8, 5, 4, 5, 4, 5, 4, 3, 4, 8

Below are sample solutions to the problem. Read each solution and the comments on the left to see why the sample represents full credit, partial credit, or no credit.

SAMPLE 1: Full credit solution

First, order the lengths from least to greatest.

3, 4, 4, 4, 4, 5, 5, 5, 8, 8

Then, plot the median, the quartiles, the maximum value, and the minimum value below a number line. Draw the box and whiskers.

The box-and-whisker plot is correct, and the student explained how it was drawn.

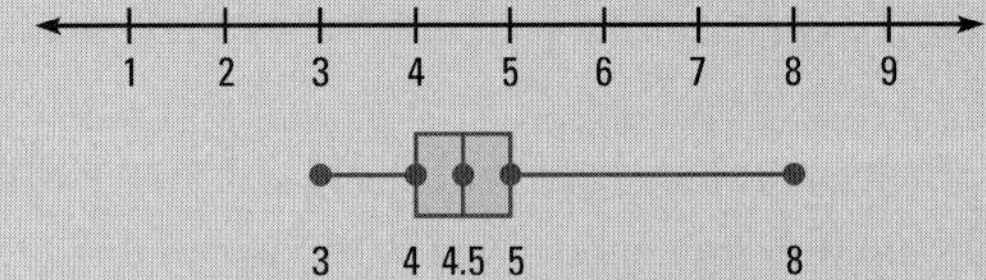

The interquartile range of the goldfish lengths is $5 - 4 = 1$, and 1.5 times the interquartile range is $1.5 \cdot 1 = 1.5$.

The question is answered correctly and includes an explanation.

A length that is less than $4 - 1.5 = 2.5$ would be an outlier. A length that is greater than $5 + 1.5 = 6.5$ would also an outlier. So, the two fish lengths of 8 inches are outliers.

SAMPLE 2: Partial credit solution

The box-and-whisker plot is incorrect. The student has not identified the median.

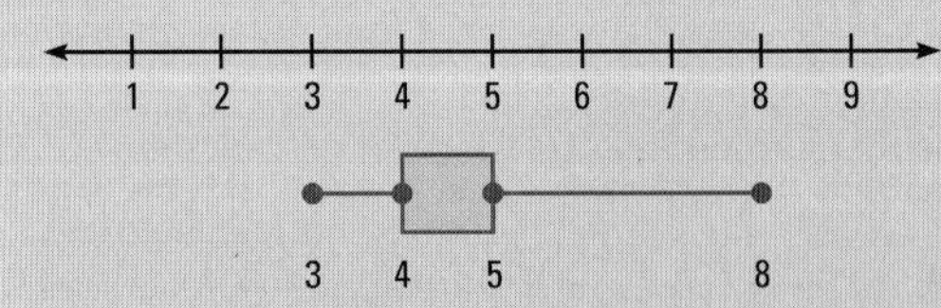

The answer and reasoning are correct.

The interquartile range of the lengths is $5 - 4 = 1$, and $1 \cdot 1.5 = 1.5$.

A length that is less than $4 - 1.5 = 2.5$ is an outlier. A length that is greater than $5 + 1.5 = 6.5$ is an outlier. So, the two fish lengths of 8 inches are outliers.

Sample 3: Partial credit solution

The box-and-whisker plot is correct.

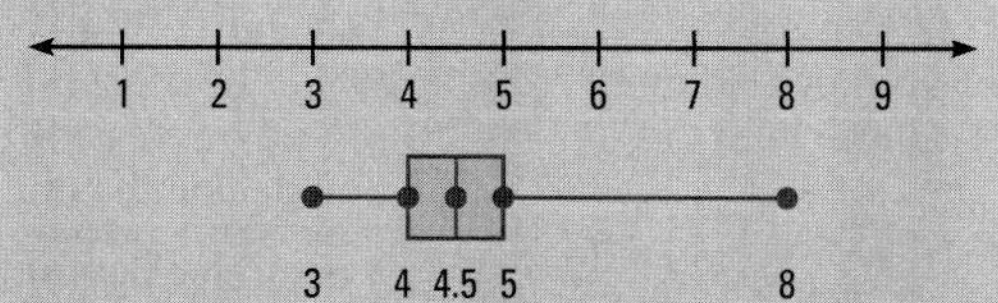

The answer is correct, but the reasoning is incorrect.

The interquartile range of the goldfish lengths is $5 - 4 = 1$.

A length that is less than $4 - 1 = 3$ is an outlier. A length that is greater than $5 + 1 = 6$ is an outlier. So, the two fish lengths of 8 inches are outliers.

Sample 4: No credit solution

There is no box-and-whisker plot. The answer is incorrect.

The value 3 is an outlier because it is a very small goldfish.

PRACTICE Apply the Scoring Rubric

Score the solution to the problem below as *full credit, partial credit,* or *no credit. Explain* your reasoning.

PROBLEM The number of runs scored by 13 players on a baseball team are listed below. Make a box-and-whisker plot of the data. Can any of the values be considered outliers? *Explain* why or why not.

24, 20, 20, 11, 17, 6, 16, 16, 6, 5, 1, 5, 4

1.

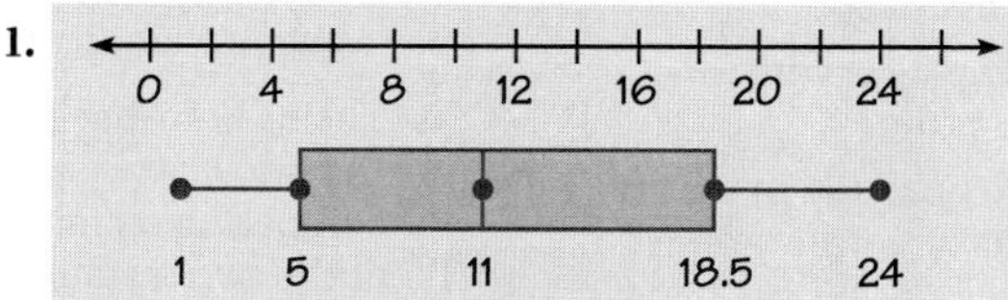

There are no outliers in the data set.

2.

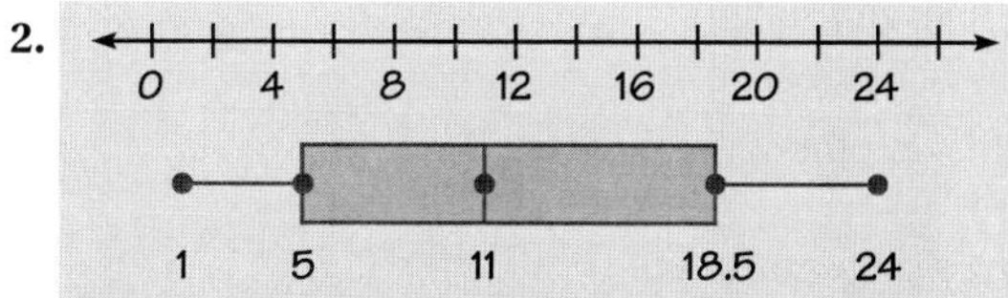

The interquartile range is 13.5, and $1.5 \cdot 13.5 = 20.25$. No values are less than $5 - 20.25 = -15.25$ or greater than $18.5 + 20.25 = 38.75$. So, there are no outliers.

Answers

1. Partial credit. ***Sample answer:*** **the box-and-whisker plot is correct, but there is no reasoning given for determining that there are no outliers.**

2. Full credit. ***Sample answer:*** **The box-and-whisker plot is correct, and the reasoning is correct.**

Answers

1a. 120 ways.

1b. $\frac{2}{5}$. *Sample answer:* Since the books are selected randomly, each book has an equal $\frac{1}{5}$ chance of being in the first, second, third, fourth, or fifth position. Since being selected first and being selected second are mutually exclusive, to find the probability that the longest book is first or second you can add the probability that it is selected first to the probability that it is selected second, $\frac{1}{5} + \frac{1}{5} = \frac{2}{5}$.

2a.

20 25 30 35 40

27 30.5 33 36 40

2b. No. *Sample answer:* The extreme values are less than 1.5 times the interquartile range from the nearest quartile.

3a. 232.1 sec, 251.5 sec, 136 sec and 270 sec.

3b. Median. *Sample answer:* The mean is affected by the outlier 46, and there are 2 modes.

4a. 56 pizzas.

4b. Combinations. *Sample answer:* It doesn't matter in which order you select the 3 toppings.

5a.

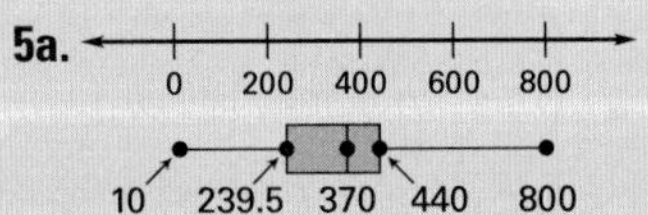

5b. $800. *Sample answer:* 800 is more than 1.5 times the interquartile range of 200.5 from the upper quartile, 440.

6a. *Sample answer:* You could select individuals sitting in randomly selected seats at a basketball game.

6b. *Sample answer:* What kind of food would you be most likely to buy at a basketball game? The question is unbiased because it does not stress any particular food.

7a. $\frac{9}{40}$

7b. $\frac{27}{40}$. *Sample answer:* $\frac{27}{40}$ is the sum of the answer from part (a) and the probability of selecting a medium short-sleeve T-shirt or a large long-sleeve T-shirt.

SHORT RESPONSE

1. Your English teacher gives you a list of 5 books that you are required to read over summer vacation. You read the books in a random order.
   a. In how many different ways can you read the 5 books?
   b. What is the probability that you read the longest book first or second? *Explain* how you found this probability.

2. The median ages (in years) of residents of 13 towns in a county are listed below.

   39, 35, 34, 40, 33, 30, 37,
   27, 33, 29, 33, 31, 35

   a. Make a box-and-whisker plot of the ages.
   b. Can any of the ages be considered outliers? *Explain* why or why not.

3. The lengths (in seconds) of songs on one CD are listed below.

   136, 249, 434, 136, 299,
   227, 270, 270, 46, 254

   a. Find the mean, median, and mode(s) of the song lengths.
   b. Which measure of central tendency best represents the data? *Explain.*

4. You are ordering a pizza with 3 toppings. There are 8 toppings available.
   a. How many possible pizzas with 3 toppings can you order?
   b. Did you answer the question in part (a) using combinations or permutations? *Explain* your choice.

5. The prices (in dollars) of several mobile phones sold by one retailer are listed below.

   350, 395, 429, 300, 569, 200, 500, 10,
   234, 245, 440, 50, 800, 390, 440, 338

   a. Make a box-and-whisker plot of the mobile phone prices.
   b. Which prices, if any, can be considered outliers? *Explain.*

6. You want to find out what kinds of food items would be most popular to sell to people who attend basketball games at your high school. You decide to conduct a survey.
   a. *Describe* how you could choose a representative sample.
   b. Write an unbiased question that you could use to collect information on what kinds of food items people would be most likely to purchase during a basketball game. *Explain* why your question is unbiased.

7. The student council has ordered T-shirts for everyone who participated in a recent fundraiser. The table below shows the number of each type of T-shirt ordered. You reach into the box of T-shirts and choose one at random.

	Medium	Large
Long sleeve	9	10
Short sleeve	8	13

   a. What is the probability that you choose a medium long-sleeve T-shirt?
   b. What is the probability that you choose a medium T-shirt or a long-sleeve T-shirt? *Explain* how this probability is related to the probability you found in part (a).

8. The back-to-back stem-and-leaf plot shows the prices (in dollars) of 15 dinners at two competing restaurants. *Compare* the prices at the two restaurants.

Dinner Prices

Restaurant A		Restaurant B
9 9 9 8	0	
7 7 5 5 2 2 1 0	1	0 2 2 3 5 6 6 8
1 0 0	2	1 2 4 4 5 5 5

Key: 0 | 2 | 1 = $20, $21

8. *Sample answer:* Generally, Restaurant B is more expensive. Restaurant A has cheaper options than does Restaurant B, and Restaurant B has several dinners that are more expensive than anything at Restaurant A.

MULTIPLE CHOICE

9. The odds in favor of an event are 3 : 4. What is the probability of the event?

Ⓐ $\frac{1}{4}$ Ⓑ $\frac{3}{7}$

Ⓒ 75% Ⓓ $\frac{3}{4}$

10. A bag contains 4 red marbles, 3 green marbles, and 5 blue marbles. You randomly choose a marble from the bag. What is the probability that you choose a blue marble?

Ⓐ $\frac{1}{5}$ Ⓑ $\frac{5}{12}$

Ⓒ $\frac{5}{11}$ Ⓓ $\frac{5}{7}$

11. You roll a number cube. What is the probability that you roll a multiple of 2 or a multiple of 3?

Ⓐ $\frac{1}{6}$ Ⓑ $\frac{1}{3}$

Ⓒ $\frac{2}{3}$ Ⓓ $\frac{5}{6}$

GRIDDED ANSWER

12. What is the value of ${}_4P_3$?

13. In how many ways can you arrange the letters in the word BEACH?

14. What is the range of the given data set?

32, 41, 29, 28, 40, 78, 56, 23, 61, 30

15. The stem-and-leaf plot shows the ages (in years) of members of one family. What is the median age (in years)?

0	8 9
1	0 4 6 7
2	0
3	9
4	2 3 3 4 5
5	
6	8 9

Key: 0 | 8 = 8 years

EXTENDED RESPONSE

16. A survey asked 500 teenagers where they would like to live. Of those surveyed, 150 teenagers would like to live in a large city. A participant in this survey is chosen at random.

a. What is the probability that the participant would like to live in a large city?

b. What are the odds in favor of the participant's wanting to live in a large city?

c. *Explain* how the probability in part (a) and odds in part (b) are related.

17. The histogram shows the diameters (in kilometers) of Jupiter's ten largest moons.

a. *Describe* the distribution of the data in the histogram. In your description, mention whether the data appear to be spread out or clumped in a certain way.

b. The diameters (in kilometers) of Saturn's ten largest moons are listed below.

97, 209, 256, 536, 560, 764, 2575, 180, 718, 110

Make a histogram of the diameters.

c. *Compare* the distribution of diameters of Jupiter's moons with the distribution of diameters of Saturn's moons.

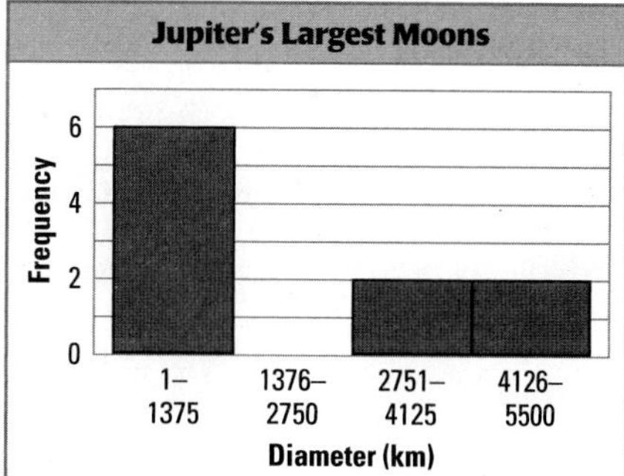

9. B
10. B
11. C
12. 24
13. 120 ways
14. 55
15. 39 yr
16a. $\frac{3}{10}$
16b. 3 : 7
16c. *Sample answer:* The odds in favor is the ratio of the numerator from part (a) to the denominator minus the numerator from part (a).
17a. *Sample answer:* Most of the data is clumped in the first interval. The remainder of the data is in the third and fourth intervals. So, most of the data is relatively small and the remainder is relatively large.
17b.

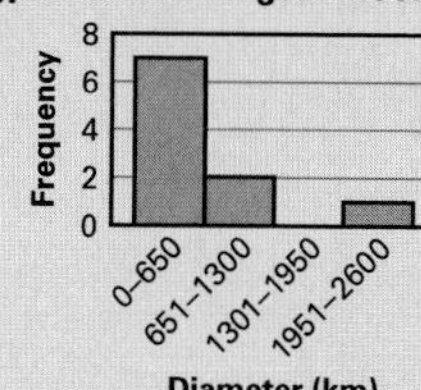

17c. *Sample answer:* Like Jupiter, most of the data for Saturn is clumped in the first interval. Relative to Jupiter, however, Saturn's moons are small. The largest of Saturn's moons would fall in the second interval in the Jupiter graph, and the majority of Saturn's moons are much smaller than this.

Additional Resources

A Cumulative Review for each of Chapters 11–13 is available in the Chapter Resource Book. A Cumulative Test for Chapters 8–13 and an End-of-Course Test for Chapters 1–13 are available in the Assessment Book.

7. 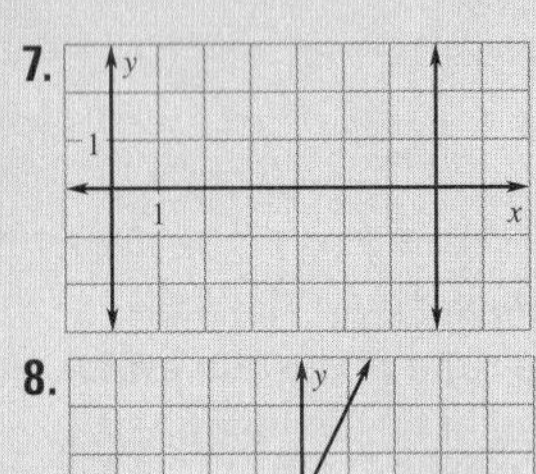

8. 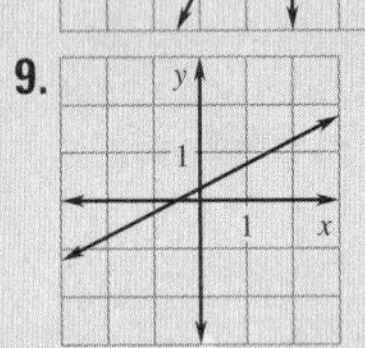

12. 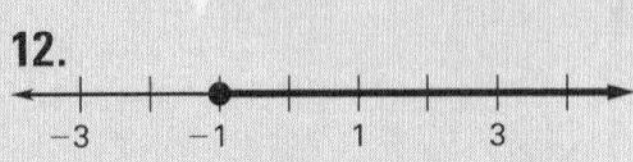

13. 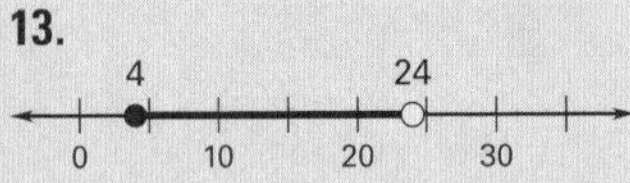

14. 

Evaluate the expression.

1. $2^4 \cdot 3 - 16 \div 4$ *(p. 8)* **44**
2. $|-125| - 34$ *(p. 80)* **91**
3. $\pm\sqrt{2025}$ *(p. 110)* **±45**

Solve the equation.

4. $7 - 2x = 13$ *(p. 141)* **−3**
5. $-8x + 15 + 5x = 9$ *(p. 148)* **2**
6. $5(2x + 3) = 4x$ *(p. 154)* **−2.5**

Graph the equation. **7–9. See margin.**

7. $x = 7$ *(p. 215)*
8. $y = 2x + 3$ *(p. 244)*
9. $4y - 2x = 1$ *(p. 244)*

Write an equation in slope-intercept form of the line with the given characteristics.

10. passes through $(-2, -8)$ and $(3, -5.5)$ *(p. 292)* $y = \frac{1}{2}x - 7$
11. slope: -8; passes through $(1, -5)$ *(p. 292)* $y = -8x + 3$

Solve the inequality. Graph your solution. **12–14. See margin for art.**

12. $4x - 6 \le 8x - 2$ *(p. 369)* $x \ge -1$
13. $-2 \le x - 6 < 18$ *(p. 380)* $4 \le x < 24$
14. $2x < 6$ *or* $4x \ge 8$ *(p. 380)* **all real numbers**

Solve the linear system.

15. $x = 4y + 3$, $2x - 4y = 7$ *(p. 435)* $(4, \frac{1}{4})$
16. $3x - 7y = 20$, $-11x + 10y = 5$ *(p. 451)* $(-5, -5)$
17. $-9x + 6y = 0$, $-12x + 8y = 5$ *(p. 451)* **no solution**

Simplify the expression. Write your answer using only positive exponents.

18. $(2x^3)^4 \cdot x^9$ *(p. 489)* $16x^{21}$
19. $(-9x^3)^2\left(-\frac{1}{4}x^6\right)$ *(p. 489)* $-\frac{81x^{12}}{4}$
20. $\frac{(3x)^{-3}y^3}{x^2y^{-1}}$ *(p. 503)* $\frac{y^4}{27x^5}$

Factor the polynomial.

21. $a^2 - 15a - 54$ *(p. 583)* $(a - 18)(a + 3)$
22. $-3b^2 - 22b - 7$ *(p. 593)* $-(3b + 1)(b + 7)$
23. $4f^2 + 4fg + g^2$ *(p. 600)* $(2f + g)^2$
24. $p^2(p - 5) + 9(5 - p)$ *(p. 606)* $(p - 5)(p - 3)(p + 3)$

Solve the equation.

25. $(x + 7)(x - 3) = 0$ *(p. 575)* $-7, 3$
26. $9x^2 - 28x + 3 = 0$ *(p. 652)* $\frac{1}{9}, 3$
27. $8x^2 + 7 = 36x - 9$ *(p. 663)* $\frac{1}{2}, 4$
28. $\sqrt{x + 8} + 10 = 2$ *(p. 729)* **no solution**

Find the distance between the two points. *(p. 744)*

29. $(5, 2), (7, 14)$ $2\sqrt{37}$
30. $(-8, 6), (5, 0)$ $\sqrt{205}$
31. $(2.5, 7), (2.5, -8)$ **15**

Find the sum, difference, product, or quotient.

32. $\frac{x - 2}{x + 5} \cdot \frac{x + 5}{x - 8}$ *(p. 802)* $\frac{x - 2}{x - 8}$
33. $\frac{x^3 - 16x}{x^2 + 3x} \div (x - 4)$ *(p. 802)* $\frac{x + 4}{x + 3}$
34. $\frac{16}{2x^4} \cdot \frac{7x^3}{2x}$ *(p. 802)* $\frac{28}{x^2}$
35. $\frac{2x}{3 - x} + \frac{x - 9}{3 - x}$ *(p. 812)* **−3**
36. $\frac{1}{x + 6} + \frac{4x}{x + 6}$ *(p. 812)* $\frac{4x + 1}{x + 6}$
37. $\frac{9}{x^2 - 3x} - \frac{3}{x - 3}$ *(p. 812)* $\frac{9 - 3x}{x^2 - 3x}$

Evaluate the expression.

38. ${}_6P_1$ *(p. 851)* **6**
39. ${}_8P_3$ *(p. 851)* **336**
40. ${}_7C_3$ *(p. 856)* **35**
41. ${}_{10}C_6$ *(p. 856)* **210**

42. You roll a number cube. What is the probability that you roll a 5? *(p. 843)* $\frac{1}{6}$

43. You roll a number cube. What is the probability that you roll a 2 or an even number? *(p. 861)* $\frac{1}{2}$

44. You choose a number from 1 to 20 at random. What is the probability that you choose a prime number? *(p. 843)* $\frac{2}{5}$

45. You choose a number from 1 to 20 at random. What is the probability that you choose a multiple of 6? *(p. 843)* $\frac{3}{20}$

46. A bag contains 2 red marbles, 4 green marbles, and 4 blue marbles. You choose one marble at random, put the marble back into the bag, then choose a second marble at random. What is the probability that you choose 2 red marbles? *(p. 861)* $\frac{1}{25}$

47. **MARATHON** Two runners are training for a marathon. When running a practice distance of 26.2 miles, one runner begins running 6 minutes after the other. The speed of the first runner is 11.4 miles per hour. The speed of the second runner is 12 miles per hour. After how many minutes does the second runner pass the first runner? *(p. 435)* ***Sample answer:* 120 min after the first runner starts**

48. **STONE ARCH** The shape of a stone arch can be modeled by the graph of the equation $y = -0.5x^2 + 4x + 4$ where x is the horizontal distance (in feet) from one end of the arch and y is its height (in feet) above the ground. What is the maximum height of the arch? *Explain* how you found your answer. *(p. 628)* **See margin.**

49. **GUY WIRE** A guy wire supports an antenna tower, as shown at the right. The bottom of the wire is secured in the ground 30 feet from the base of the tower. The top of the wire is secured to the tower at a height of 30 feet above the ground. How long is the wire? Round your answer to the nearest tenth of a foot. *(p. 737)* **42.4 ft**

30 ft
guy wire
30 ft

50. **HEATING RATES** An electric heater takes 8 minutes to heat an entire apartment to the desired temperature. A wood stove and an electric heater together take 6 minutes to heat the apartment. How many minutes does it take the wood stove alone to heat the apartment to the desired temperature? *(p. 820)* **24 min**

51. **FLIGHTS** You are traveling from Boston, Massachusetts, to Richmond, Virginia. The prices (in dollars) of airline tickets for different flights between the cities are listed below.

176, 191, 195, 197, 197, 204, 204, 204, 204,
204, 206, 206, 206, 206, 206, 217, 217, 221

a. What is the range of the prices? *(p. 875)* **$45**

b. Make a stem-and-leaf plot of the prices. *(p. 881)* **b–d. See margin.**

c. Make a box-and-whisker plot of the prices. *(p. 887)*

d. Can any of these prices be considered outliers? *Explain* why or why not. *(p. 887)*

48. 12 ft. *Sample answer:* The graph is a parabola with vertex at $x = -\frac{b}{2a} = 4$. When $x = 4$, the height of the arch is 12 feet.

51b.

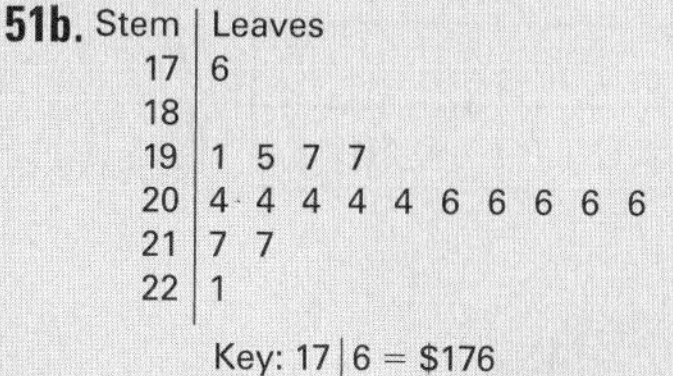

Stem	Leaves
17	6
18	
19	1 5 7 7
20	4 4 4 4 4 6 6 6 6 6
21	7 7
22	1

Key: 17 | 6 = $176

51c.

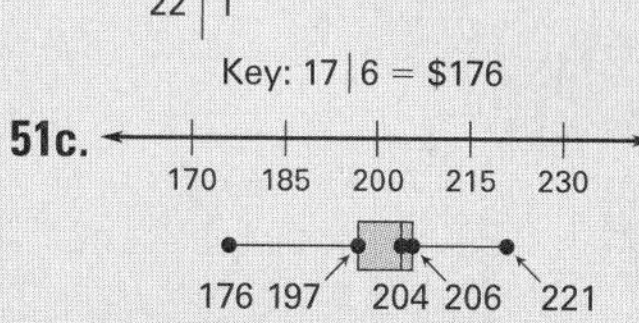

51d. Yes. *Sample answer:* The interquartile range is 9, so any data value more than 13.5 less than the lower quartile of 197 or greater than the upper quartile of 206 can be considered outliers. 176 and 221 are both outliers.

Additional Lessons

The additional lessons are associated with particular chapters as indicated below.

Lesson	Chapter
A	6
B	8
C	10

Additional Lessons

ADDITIONAL LESSONS

Algebra 1

The Additional Lessons extend the content taught in various chapters. The chapter with which a lesson is associated is noted next to the lesson's Goal statement.

Additional Lesson A Use Piecewise Functions

Use with Chapter 6

Key Vocabulary
- **piecewise function**
- **step function**

GOAL Graph and write piecewise functions.

A **piecewise function** is defined by at least two equations, each of which applies to a different part of the function's domain. An example is given below.

$$y = \begin{cases} x + 1, & \text{if } x < 0 \\ 2x - 1, & \text{if } x \geq 0 \end{cases}$$

The expression $x + 1$ gives the value of y when x is less than 0. The expression $2x - 1$ gives the value of y when x is greater than or equal to 0.

EXAMPLE 1 Graph a piecewise function

Graph the function: $y = \begin{cases} -x - 1, & \text{if } x \leq -1 \\ 3, & \text{if } -1 < x < 2 \\ 2x - 5, & \text{if } x \geq 2 \end{cases}$

Solution

STEP 1 To the left of $x = -1$, graph $y = -x - 1$. Use a closed dot at $(-1, 0)$ because the equation applies when $x = -1$.

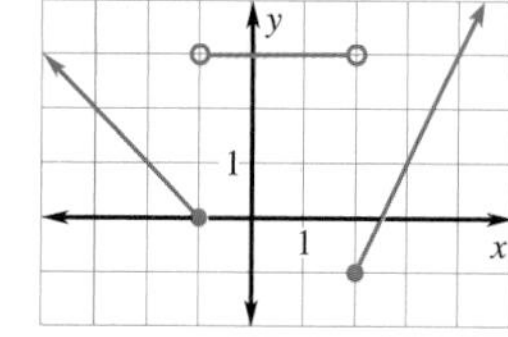

STEP 2 From $x = -1$ to $x = 2$, graph $y = 3$. Use open dots at $(-1, 3)$ and $(2, 3)$ because the equation does not apply when $x = -1$ or when $x = 2$.

STEP 3 To the right of $x = 2$, graph $y = 2x - 5$. Use a closed dot at $(2, -1)$ because the equation applies when $x = 2$.

EXAMPLE 2 Write a piecewise function

Write a piecewise function for the graph.

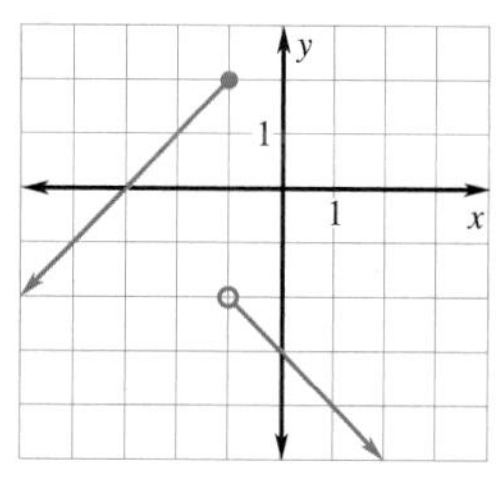

Solution

For $x \leq -1$, the graph is the line given by $y = x + 3$.

For $x > -1$, the graph is the line given by $y = -x - 3$.

▶ So, a piecewise function for the graph is as follows:

$$y = \begin{cases} x + 3, & \text{if } x \leq -1 \\ -x - 3, & \text{if } x > -1 \end{cases}$$

1. 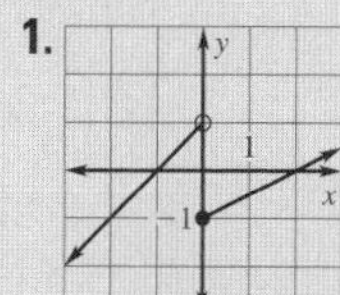

2. 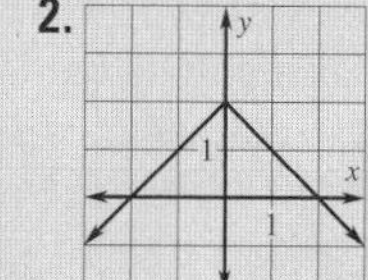

3. 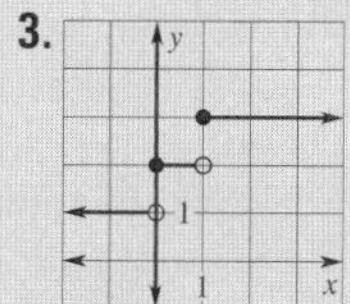

1 PLAN AND PREPARE

Warm-Up Exercises

1. Graph $y = x + 1$.

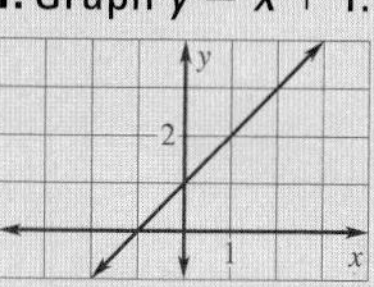

2. You have \$500 in an account, and add \$50 each month. Write an equation for the balance y (in dollars) after x months.
$y = 50x + 500$

2 FOCUS AND MOTIVATE

Essential Question

How do you graph a piecewise function? **Tell students they will learn how to answer this question by learning about piecewise functions.**

3 TEACH

Extra Example 1

Graph the function:

$f(x) = \begin{cases} x + 2, \text{ if } x \leq 0 \\ x - 1, \text{ if } x > 0 \end{cases}$

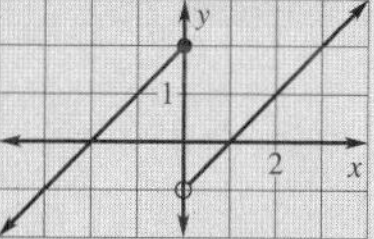

4. $y = \begin{cases} -x, \text{ if } x \leq 0 \\ -x + 1, \text{ if } x > 0 \end{cases}$

5. $y = \begin{cases} 1, \text{ if } x < -1 \\ 2x, \text{ if } -1 \leq x \leq 0 \\ -\frac{1}{2}x + 2, \text{ if } x > 0 \end{cases}$

6. $y = \begin{cases} 4, \text{ if } 0 < x \leq 1 \\ 3, \text{ if } 1 < x \leq 2 \\ 2, \text{ if } 2 < x \leq 3 \\ 1, \text{ if } 3 < x \leq 4 \end{cases}$

7. $P = \begin{cases} 20t, \text{ if } 0 \leq t \leq 40 \\ 30(t - 40) + 800, \text{ if } t > 40 \end{cases}$

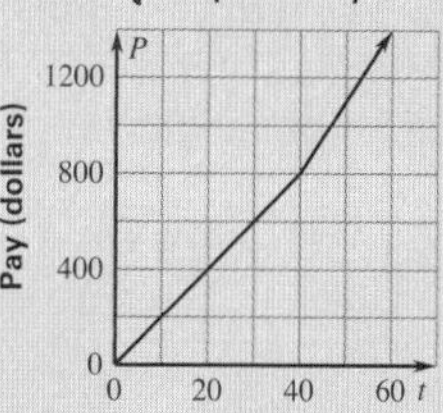

When $t = 46$, $P = \$980$.

Extra Example 2

Write a piecewise function for the graph.

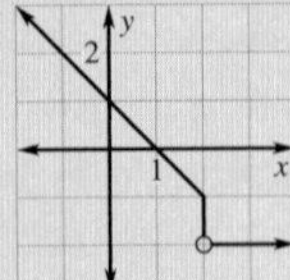

$f(x) = \begin{cases} 1 - x, \text{ if } x \le 2 \\ -2, \text{ if } x > 2 \end{cases}$

Extra Example 3

Ice time at a rink costs $10 for each hour or part of an hour between noon and 5 P.M. Use a table of values to write the cost C (in dollars) as a piecewise function of time t (in hours) you skate. Graph the function. What is the cost of skating for 3 hour and 15 minutes?

$C(t) = \begin{cases} 10, \text{ if } 0 < t \le 1 \\ 20, \text{ if } 1 < t \le 2 \\ 30, \text{ if } 2 < t \le 3 \\ 40, \text{ if } 3 < t \le 4 \\ 50, \text{ if } 4 < t \le 5 \end{cases}$

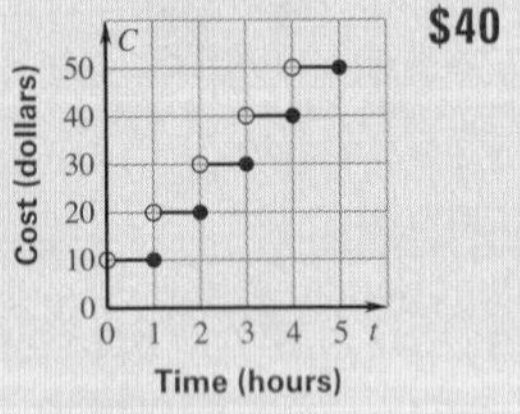

$40

Key Question to Ask for Example 3

- What are the domain and range of C? $0 < x \le 4$; 5, 10, 15, 20

4 PRACTICE AND APPLY

Avoiding Common Errors

Remind students that they can use the vertical line test to help them avoid including a point in more than one part of the functions's graph.

1–7. See p. A1.

8. The parent absolute value function is defined by two equations. For negative values of x, $|x| = -x$ and for nonnegative values of x, $|x| = x$; $y = \begin{cases} -x, \text{ if } x < 0 \\ x, \text{ if } x \ge 0 \end{cases}$

EXAMPLE 3 Solve a real-world problem

PARKING A parking garage charges $5.00 for each hour or fraction of an hour up to 4 hours per day. Make a table of values. Then write the cost C (in dollars) as a piecewise function of the time t (in hours) parked and graph the function. What is the cost of parking for 2 hours and 9 minutes?

Solution

Table

Time (hours)	Cost (dollars)
$0 < t \le 1$	5.00
$1 < t \le 2$	10.00
$2 < t \le 3$	15.00
$3 < t \le 4$	20.00

Function rule

$$C = \begin{cases} 5, & \text{if } 0 < t \le 1 \\ 10, & \text{if } 1 < t \le 2 \\ 15, & \text{if } 2 < t \le 3 \\ 20, & \text{if } 3 < t \le 4 \end{cases}$$

Graph

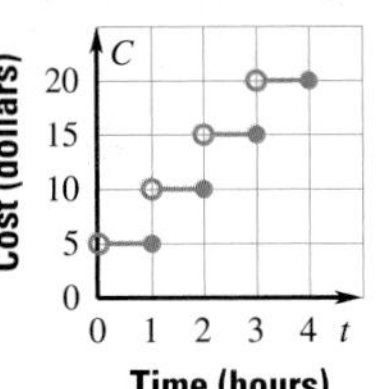

▶ Because 2 hours and 9 minutes is between 2 and 3 hours, the cost is $15.00.

STEP FUNCTIONS The function in Example 3 is called a *step function* because its graph resembles a set of stairs. A **step function** is a piecewise function that is defined by a constant value over each part of its domain.

PRACTICE

EXAMPLE 1 on p. A1 for Exs. 1–3

Graph the function. **1-9. See margin.**

1. $y = \begin{cases} x + 1, & \text{if } x < 0 \\ 0.5x - 1, & \text{if } x \ge 0 \end{cases}$

2. $y = \begin{cases} 2 + x, & \text{if } x < 0 \\ 2 - x, & \text{if } x \ge 0 \end{cases}$

3. $y = \begin{cases} 1, & \text{if } x < 0 \\ 2, & \text{if } 0 \le x < 1 \\ 3, & \text{if } x \ge 1 \end{cases}$

EXAMPLE 2 on p. A1 for Exs. 4–6

Write a piecewise function for the graph.

4. 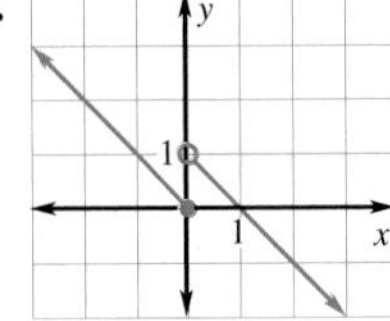

5. 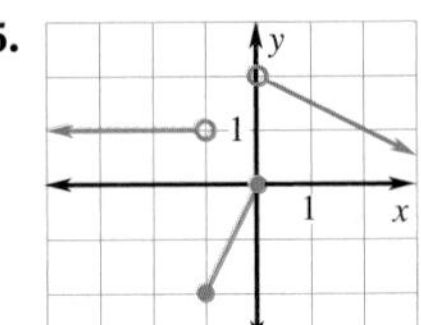

6. 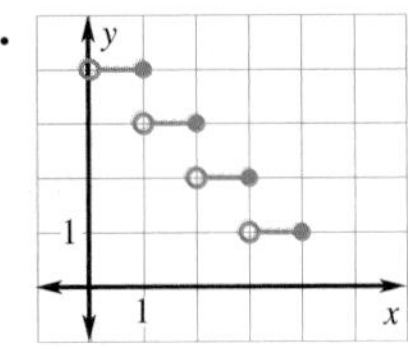

EXAMPLE 3 on p. A2 for Ex. 7

7. PAY Greg earns $20 per hour when he works 40 or fewer hours in a week. When he works more than 40 hours in a week, he earns $800 plus $30 per hour for each hour over 40. Write a piecewise function that gives his weekly pay P for working t hours. Graph the function. What is his pay for 46 hours?

8. REASONING *Explain* why the parent absolute value function $y = |x|$ is a piecewise function. Write a piecewise rule for the function.

9. REASONING The output y of the *greatest integer function* is the greatest integer less than or equal to the input value x. Graph the function for $-4 \le x < 4$. Is it a piecewise function? a step function? *Explain.*

9. 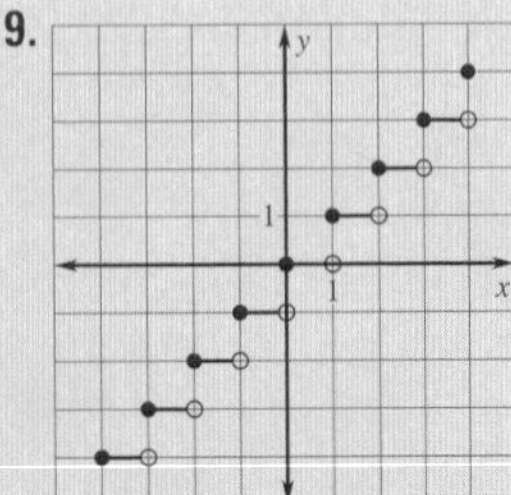

Yes; yes; the function is a piecewise function because, for every integer value of n, there is a unique equation that applies to the part of the domain defined by $n \le x < n + 1$. The function is a step function because it is defined by a constant value over each part of its domain.

Additional Lesson B Define Sequences Recursively

Use with Chapter 8

Key Vocabulary
- **recursive rule**

GOAL Write and graph recursively-defined sequences.

In Extensions 5.3 and 8.6, you learned how to define arithmetic and geometric sequences *explicitly.* An explicit rule gives a_n as a function of the term's position number n in the sequence. For example, an explicit rule for the arithmetic sequence 3, 5, 7, 9, . . . is $a_n = 3 + 2(n - 1)$, or $a_n = 2n + 1$.

You can also define arithmetic and geometric sequences *recursively.* A **recursive rule** gives the beginning term(s) of a sequence and a recursive equation that tells how a_n relates to preceding terms. For example, a recursive definition for the geometric sequence 2, 6, 18, 54, . . . is $a_1 = 2$ and $a_n = 3 \cdot a_{n-1}$.

REVIEW SEQUENCES
For help with arithmetic sequences, see p. 309. For help with geometric sequences, see p. 539.

KEY CONCEPT *For Your Notebook*

Recursive Equation for an Arithmetic Sequence

$a_n = a_{n-1} + d$ where d is the common difference

Recursive Equation for a Geometric Sequence

$a_n = r \cdot a_{n-1}$ where r is the common ratio

EXAMPLE 1 Write and graph recursively-defined sequences

Write the first five terms of the sequence. Then graph the sequence.

a. $a_1 = 5, a_n = a_{n-1} + 5$ **b.** $a_1 = 1, a_n = 2a_{n-1}$

Solution

a. $a_1 = 5$

$a_2 = a_1 + 5 = 5 + 5 = 10$

$a_3 = a_2 + 5 = 10 + 5 = 15$

$a_4 = a_3 + 5 = 15 + 5 = 20$

$a_5 = a_4 + 5 = 20 + 5 = 25$

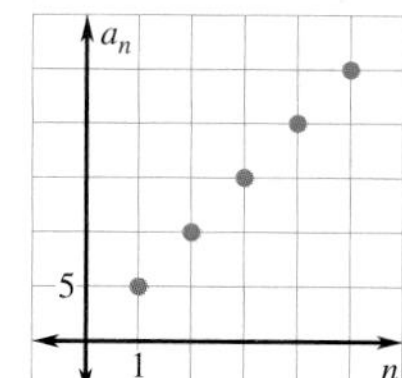

b. $a_1 = 1$

$a_2 = 2a_1 = 2(1) = 2$

$a_3 = 2a_2 = 2(2) = 4$

$a_4 = 2a_3 = 2(4) = 8$

$a_5 = 2a_4 = 2(8) = 16$

DRAW A GRAPH
A sequence is a discrete function. The points on the graph are not connected.

1 PLAN AND PREPARE

Warm-Up Exercises

Tell whether the sequence is *arithmetic* or *geometric*. Find the common difference or common ratio.

1. 10, 20, 30, 40, . . . **arithmetic; 10**
2. 0, −3, −6, −9, . . . **arithmetic; −3**
3. 3, 6, 12, 24, . . . **geometric; 2**
4. 125, 25, 5, 1, . . . **geometric; $\frac{1}{5}$**

2 FOCUS AND MOTIVATE

Essential Question

How do you write recursive rules for sequences? **Tell students they will learn how to answer this question by writing a value for the first term(s) and relating each other term to the preceding term(s).**

3 TEACH

Extra Example 1(a)

Write the first five terms of the sequence $a_1 = 8, a_n = a_{n-1} - 4$. Then graph the sequence. **8, 4, 0, −4, −8**

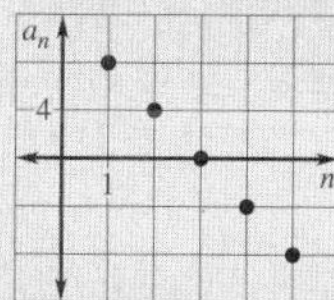

Extra Example 1(b)

Write the first five terms of the sequence $a_1 = -32, a_n = 0.5a_{n-1}$. Then graph the sequence.
−32, −16, −8, −4, −2

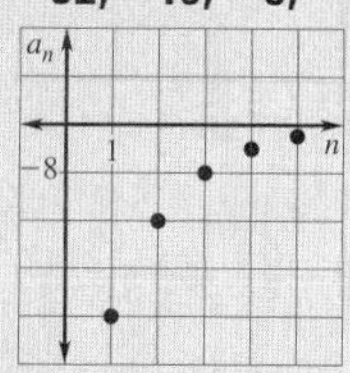

Extra Example 2

Write a recursive rule for the sequence.

a. 0, −11, −22, −33, −44, . . .
$a_1 = 0, a_n = a_{n-1} - 11$

b. 8, 20, 50, 125, 312.5, . . .
$a_1 = 8, a_n = 2.5a_{n-1}$

Extra Example 3

Write a recursive rule for the sequence 3, 4, 7, 11, 18, ...
$a_1 = 3, a_2 = 4, a_n = a_{n-1} + a_{n-2}$

1. 0, 2, 4, 6, 8

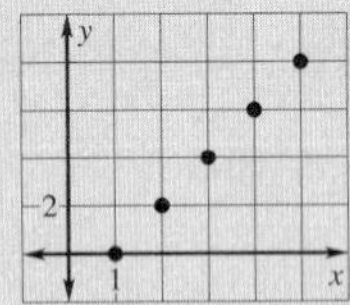

2. 10, 5, 0, −5, −10

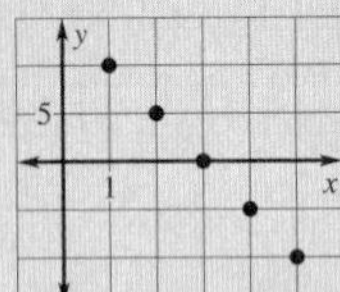

3. −3, 0, 3, 6, 9

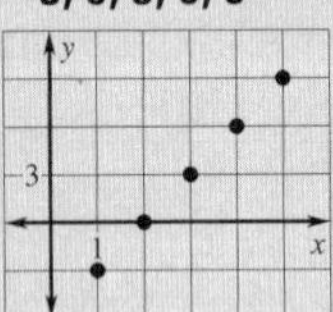

4. 1, 2, 3, 4, 5

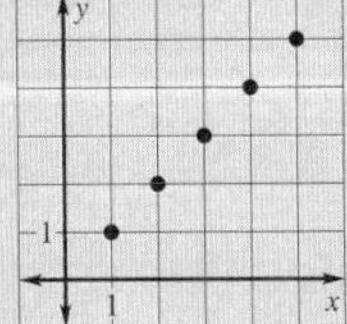

AVOID ERRORS

To write a recursive *rule* for a sequence, you must give both the beginning term(s) and the recursive *equation*.

EXAMPLE 2 Write recursive rules for sequences

Write a recursive rule for the sequence.

a. 2, 5, 8, 11, 14, . . . **b.** 16, 24, 36, 54, 81, . . .

Solution

a. The sequence is arithmetic with first term $a_1 = 2$ and common difference $d = 5 - 2 = 3$.

$a_n = a_{n-1} + d$ Recursive equation for a_n

$a_n = a_{n-1} + 3$ Substitute 3 for *d*.

▶ So, a recursive rule for the sequence is $a_1 = 2$, $a_n = a_{n-1} + 3$.

b. The sequence is geometric with first term $a_1 = 16$ and common ratio $r = \frac{24}{16} = 1.5$.

$a_n = r \cdot a_{n-1}$ Recursive equation for a_n

$a_n = 1.5a_{n-1}$ Substitute 1.5 for *r*.

▶ So, a recursive rule for the sequence is $a_1 = 16$, $a_n = 1.5a_{n-1}$.

SPECIAL SEQUENCES In special cases, you may be able to write a recursive rule for a sequence that is neither arithmetic nor geometric. Consider the following sequence, called the *Fibonacci sequence*: 1, 1, 2, 3, 5, 8, 13, ... Notice that the Fibonacci sequence is neither arithmetic nor geometric.

$$a_2 - a_1 = 1 - 1 = 0, \text{ while } a_3 - a_2 = 2 - 1 = 1.$$

$$\frac{a_2}{a_1} = \frac{1}{1} = 1, \text{ while } \frac{a_3}{a_2} = \frac{2}{1} = 2.$$

You can still write a recursive rule for the Fibonacci sequence, as shown in Example 3.

EXAMPLE 3 Write a recursive rule for a special sequence

Write a recursive rule for the sequence 1, 1, 2, 3, 5, 8, 13, ... Identify the next two terms of the sequence.

Solution

Look at sums of consecutive pairs of terms.

$a_1 + a_2 = 1 + 1 = 2$ 2 is the third term of the sequence.

$a_2 + a_3 = 1 + 2 = 3$ 3 is the fourth term of the sequence.

$a_3 + a_4 = 2 + 3 = 5$ 5 is the fifth term of the sequence.

Beginning with the third term, each term is the sum of the two previous terms.

▶ So, a recursive rule for the sequence is $a_1 = 1$, $a_2 = 1$, $a_n = a_{n-2} + a_{n-1}$. The next two terms after 13 are 8 + 13 = 21 and 13 + 21 = 34.

5. 8, 6, 4, 2, 0

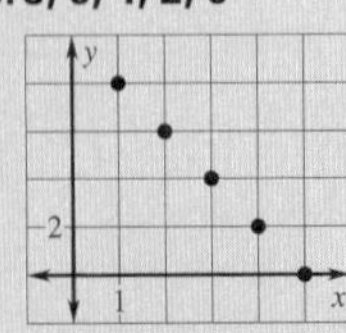

6. 8, 12, 18, 27, 40.5

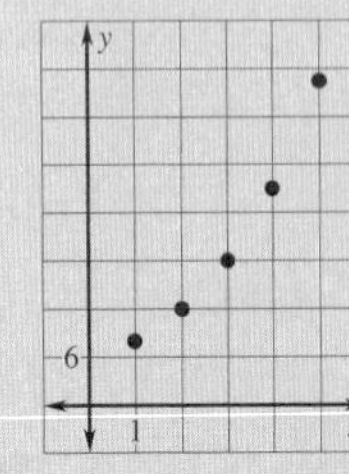

7. 1, 3, 9, 27, 81

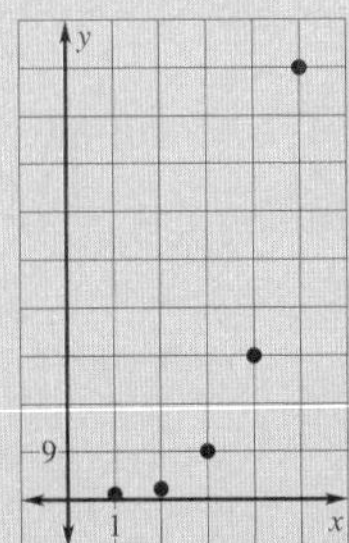

PRACTICE

EXAMPLE 1
on p. A3 for Exs. 1–9

Write the first five terms of the sequence. Then graph the sequence. **1-9. See margin.**

1. $a_1 = 0, a_n = a_{n-1} + 2$ **2.** $a_1 = 10, a_n = a_{n-1} - 5$ **3.** $a_1 = -3, a_n = a_{n-1} + 3$

4. $a_1 = 1, a_n = a_{n-1} + 1$ **5.** $a_1 = 8, a_n = a_{n-1} - 2$ **6.** $a_1 = 8, a_n = 1.5a_{n-1}$

7. $a_1 = 1, a_n = 3a_{n-1}$ **8.** $a_1 = 16, a_n = 0.5a_{n-1}$ **9.** $a_1 = -2, a_n = 2a_{n-1}$

EXAMPLE 2
on p. A4 for Exs. 10–18

Write a recursive rule for the sequence.

10. 8, 28, 48, 68, 88, ... **11.** 256, 64, 16, 4, 1, ... **12.** 0, −4, −8, −12, −16, ...

13. 3, 7, 11, 15, 19, ... **14.** 81, 27, 9, 3, 1, ... **15.** −5, −3, −1, 1, 3, ...

16. 16, 24, 36, 54, 81, ... **$a_1 = 16, a_n = 1.5a_{n-1}$** **17.** −2, 4, −8, 16, −32, ... **$a_1 = -2, a_n = -2a_{n-1}$** **18.** 0.5, 1.75, 3, 4.25, 5.5, ... **$a_1 = 0.5, a_n = a_{n-1} + 1.25$**

EXAMPLE 3
on p. A4 for Exs. 19–24

Write a recursive rule for the sequence. Identify the next two terms of the sequence. **19-24. See margin.**

19. 1, 3, 4, 7, 11, ... **20.** 1, 4, 4, 16, 64, ... **21.** 1, 1, 1, 3, 5, 9, ...

22. 10, 9, 1, 8, −7, 15, ... **23.** 64, 16, 4, 4, 1, ... **24.** 2, 4, 10, 24, 58, ...

. $a_1 = 8$, $a_n = a_{n-1} + 20$

. $a_1 = 256$, $a_n = 0.25a_{n-1}$

. $a_1 = 0$, $a_n = a_{n-1} - 4$

. $a_1 = 3$, $a_n = a_{n-1} + 4$

. $a_1 = 81$, $a_n = \frac{1}{3}a_{n-1}$

. $a_1 = -5$, $a_n = a_{n-1} + 2$

25. USING A SPREADSHEET You can use a spreadsheet to generate the terms of a sequence. **a. 3, 5, 7, 9, 11, 13, 15, 17, 19, 21**

A2	=A1+2		
	A	B	C
1	3		
2	5		
3			
4			

a. To generate the terms of the sequence $a_1 = 3, a_n = a_{n-1} + 2$, enter the value of a_1, 3, into cell A1. Then enter "=A1+2" into cell A2 as shown and use the *fill down* feature to generate the first ten terms of the sequence.

b. Use a spreadsheet to generate the first ten terms of the sequence $a_1 = 3, a_n = 4a_{n-1}$. (*Hint*: Enter "=4*A1" into cell A2.)
3, 12, 48, 192, 768, 3072, 12,288, 49,152, 196,608, 786,432

26. BACTERIA A population of bacteria doubles every hour. After 1 hour, there are 200 bacteria. Write a recursive rule for the number a_n of bacteria after n hours. How many bacteria are there after 6 hours?
$a_1 = 200, a_n = 2a_{n-1}$; 6400 bacteria

27. REASONING The explicit rule $a_n = a_1 + (n - 1)d$ defines an arithmetic sequence.

a. *Explain* why $a_{n-1} = a_1 + [(n - 1) - 1]d$. **This is the explicit rule with $n - 1$ substituted for n.**

b. *Justify* each step in showing that a recursive equation for the sequence is $a_n = a_{n-1} + d$.

$a_n = a_1 + (n - 1)d$ ____?____

$= a_1 + [(n - 1) + 0]d$ ____?____

$= a_1 + [(n - 1) - 1 + 1]d$ ____?____

$= a_1 + [((n - 1) - 1) + 1]d$ ____?____

$= a_1 + [(n - 1) - 1]d + d$ ____?____

$= a_{n-1} + d$ ____?____

b. Explicit rule r arithmetic seq.; ent. prop. of add.; v. prop. of add.; ssoc. prop. of ld.; dist. property; bst. prop. (from art (a))

4 PRACTICE AND APPLY

Avoiding Common Errors

Exercises 10–24 Students may write explicit rather than recursive rules. Remind them that recursive rules relate a_n to a preceding term or terms, so $a_n - 1$ should appear in the rule.

8. 16, 8, 4, 2, 1

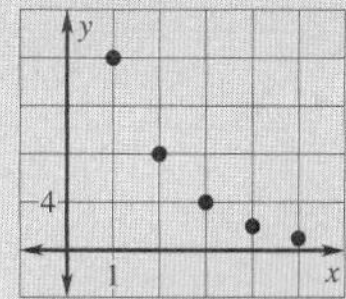

9. −2, −4, −8, −16, −32

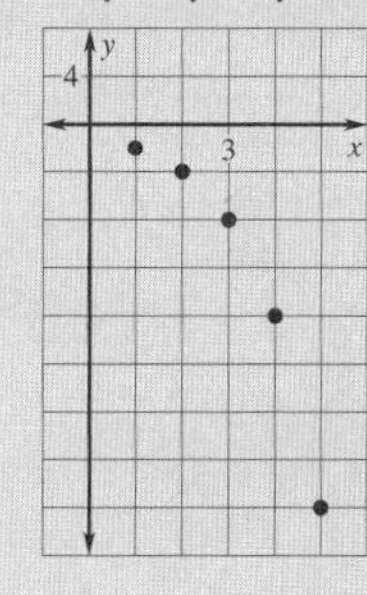

19. $a_1 = 1, a_2 = 3, a_n = a_{n-2} + a_{n-1}$; 18, 29

20. $a_1 = 1, a_2 = 4, a_n = (a_{n-2})(a_{n-1})$; 1024, 65,536

21. $a_1 = 1, a_2 = 1, a_3 = 1, a_n = a_{n-3} + a_{n-2} + a_{n-1}$; 17, 31

22. $a_1 = 10, a_2 = 9, a_n = a_{n-2} - a_{n-1}$; −22, 37

23. $a_1 = 64, a_2 = 16, a_n = \frac{a_{n-2}}{a_{n-1}}$; 4, 0.25

24. $a_1 = 2, a_2 = 4, a_n = a_{n-2} + 2a_{n-1}$; 140, 338

1 PLAN AND PREPARE

Warm-Up Exercises

Solve the inequality.

1. $x - 5 > -1$ **$x > 4$**

2. $2 - x \geq 3$ **$x \leq -1$**

Solve the equation.

3. $x^2 + 2x = 0$ **$-2, 0$**

4. $x^2 - 5x + 6 = 0$ **$2, 3$**

2 FOCUS AND MOTIVATE

Essential Question

How do you solve quadratic inequalities in one variable? **Tell students they will learn how to answer this question by learning to solve quadratic inequalities using tables and graphs.**

3 TEACH

Extra Example 1

Solve $x^2 + 3x < 4$ using a table.
$-4 < x < 1$

Key Question to Ask for Example 1

- How does the solution in Example 1 change if the inequality symbol changes to $\leq$?
  The solution changes to $-2 \leq x \leq 4$.

Additional Lesson C Solve Quadratic Inequalities

Use with Chapter 10

Key Vocabulary
- **quadratic inequality in one variable**

GOAL Use tables and graphs to solve quadratic inequalities in one variable.

A **quadratic inequality in one variable** can be written in one of these forms:

$ax^2 + bx + c < 0$ $\quad ax^2 + bx + c \leq 0$ $\quad ax^2 + bx + c > 0$ $\quad ax^2 + bx + c \geq 0$

You can use tables and graphs to solve quadratic inequalities.

EXAMPLE 1 Solve a quadratic inequality using a table

Solve $x^2 - 2x \geq 8$ using a table.

Solution

REVIEW SOLVING EQUATIONS
To review solving quadratic equations by factoring, see p. 643.

Rewrite the inequality as $x^2 - 2x - 8 \geq 0$. Then solve the related equation $x^2 - 2x - 8 = 0$ by factoring.

$x^2 - 2x - 8 = 0$ **Write equation.**

$(x - 4)(x + 2) = 0$ **Factor.**

$x = 4$ or $x = -2$ **Zero-product property**

Make a table of values for the expression $x^2 - 2x - 8$ using values of x less than -2, between -2 and 4, and greater than 4.

x	−4	−3	−2	−1	0	1	2	3	4	5	6
$x^2 - 2x - 8$	**16**	**7**	**0**	−5	−8	−9	−8	−5	**0**	**7**	**16**

Notice that $x^2 - 2x - 8 \geq 0$ when $x \leq -2$ or $x \geq 4$.

▸ The solution of $x^2 - 2x \geq 8$ is $x \leq -2$ or $x \geq 4$.

KEY CONCEPT *For Your Notebook*

Solving Quadratic Inequalities in One Variable by Graphing

STEP 1 **Write** the inequality in one of the following forms: $ax^2 + bx + c < 0$, $ax^2 + bx + c \leq 0$, $ax^2 + bx + c > 0$, or $ax^2 + bx + c \geq 0$.

STEP 2 **Write** the related function $y = ax^2 + bx + c$.

STEP 3 **Graph** the function $y = ax^2 + bx + c$.

- The solutions of $ax^2 + bx + c < 0$ are the x-coordinates of the points on the graph of $y = ax^2 + bx + c$ that lie below the x-axis.
- The solutions of $ax^2 + bx + c > 0$ are the x-coordinates of the points on the graph of $y = ax^2 + bx + c$ that lie above the x-axis.
- If the inequality symbol is $\leq$ or $\geq$, then the x-intercepts of the graph are also solutions.

EXAMPLE 2 Solve a quadratic inequality by graphing

Solve $x^2 - 2x < 3$ by graphing.

STEP 1 Write the inequality in the form $ax^2 + bx + c < 0$.

$x^2 - 2x < 3$ **Write original inequality.**

$x^2 - 2x - 3 < 0$ **Subtract 3 from each side.**

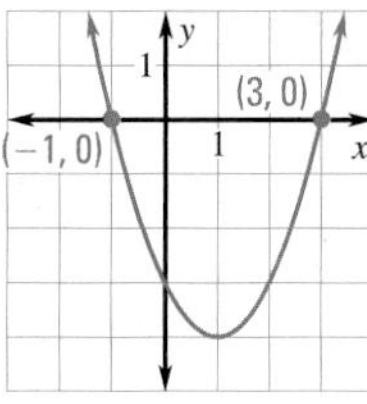

STEP 2 Write the related function $y = x^2 - 2x - 3$.

STEP 3 Graph the function $y = x^2 - 2x - 3$.

The x-intercepts are -1 and 3. The graph lies below the x-axis for x-values between -1 and 3.

▶ The solution of $x^2 - 2x < 3$ is $-1 < x < 3$.

EXAMPLE 3 Use a graphing calculator

Solve $-2x^2 + 3x \geq -4$ using a graphing calculator.

Graph the function $y = -2x^2 + 3x + 4$ and find its zeros.

REVIEW ZEROS
To review using a calculator to find zeros of a quadratic function, see p. 651.

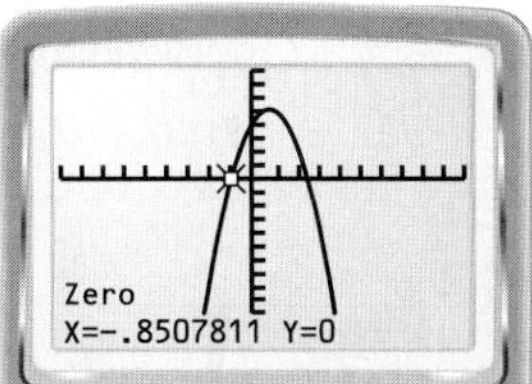

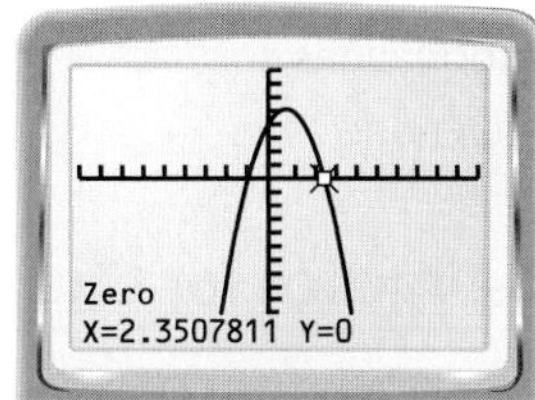

The x-intercepts are about -0.85 and about 2.35. The graph lies on or above the x-axis for x-values between about -0.85 and 2.35.

▶ The solution of $-2x^2 + 3x \geq -4$ is approximately $-0.85 \leq x \leq 2.35$.

PRACTICE

EXAMPLES 1–3
on pp. A6–A7 for Exs. 1–9

Solve the inequality using a table.

1. $x^2 - 7x + 6 > 0$ **$x < 1$ or $x > 6$**
2. $x^2 + x \leq 12$ **$-4 \leq x \leq 3$**
3. $x^2 + 7x < -10$ **$-5 < x < -2$**

Solve the inequality by graphing.

4. $x^2 - 3x > 4$ **$x < -1$ or $x > 4$**
5. $x^2 - 2x \geq 15$ **$x \leq -3$ or $x \geq 5$**
6. $2x^2 + 7x \leq -3$ **$-3 \leq x \leq -\frac{1}{2}$**

Solve the inequality using a graphing calculator. **7-9. See margin.**

7. $-2x^2 + x \geq -2$
8. $3x^2 + 2x > 4$
9. $x^2 - 4x + 1 < 0$

10. **KICKED BALL** A ball is kicked from the ground. The path can be modeled by $y = -0.05x^2 + 1.3x$ where x is the horizontal distance (in feet) from where the ball was kicked and y is the ball's height (in feet). Find the distances x for which the ball is high enough to go over an 8 foot fence. **$10 < x < 16$**

Extra Example 2

Solve $x^2 + 10x \geq -24$ by graphing. **$x \leq -6$ or $x \geq -4$**

Key Question to Ask for Example 2

- For a quadratic inequality, when are the x-intercepts of the related function solutions of the inequality? **When the inequality symbol is $\leq$ or $\geq$**

Extra Example 3

Solve $3x^2 - x > 8$ using a graphing calculator. **approximately $x < -1.47$ or $x > 1.81$**

4 PRACTICE AND APPLY

Graphing Calculator

Exercises 1–10 Remind students that after graphing the functions, they may have to adjust the viewing window so that the x-intercepts are visible. Then students should use the *zero* feature under the CALCULATE menu to find each zero.

7. Approximately $-0.78 \leq x \leq 1.28$
8. Approximately $x < -1.54$ or $x > 0.87$
9. Approximately $0.27 < x < 3.73$

Contents of Student Resources

Comparing and Ordering Decimals

A **number line** is a line whose points are associated with numbers. You can use a number line to compare and order decimals. From left to right, the numbers on a number line appear in order from least to greatest.

EXAMPLE **Copy and complete the statement using <, >, or =.**

a. 9.67 _?_ 9.59

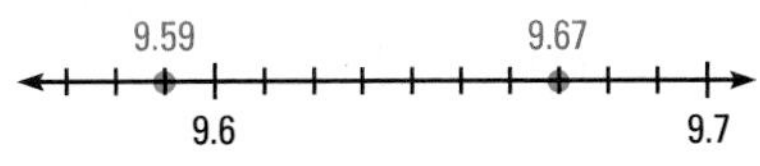

9.67 is to the right of 9.59, so 9.67 is greater than 9.59.

▸ 9.67 > 9.59

b. 0.08 _?_ 0.12

0.08 is to the left of 0.12, so 0.08 is less than 0.12.

▸ 0.08 < 0.12

EXAMPLE **Order the numbers 0.4, 0.56, 0.48, and 0.515 from least to greatest.**

Graph all the numbers on a number line.

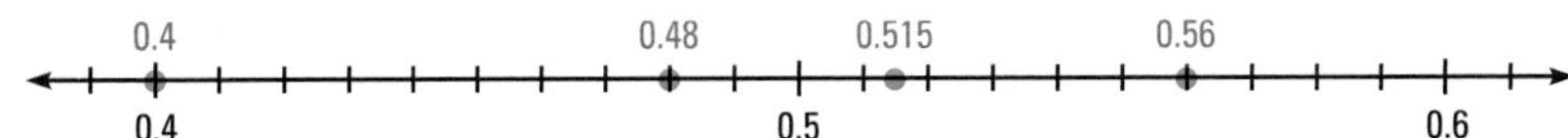

Write the numbers as they appear on the number line from left to right.

▸ The numbers in order from least to greatest are 0.4, 0.48, 0.515, and 0.56.

PRACTICE

Copy and complete the statement using <, >, or =.

1. 1.48 _?_ 1.413 >
2. 0.809 _?_ 0.81 <
3. 5.47 _?_ 5.43 >
4. 0.01 _?_ 0.005 >
5. 35.2 _?_ 35 >
6. 6.24 _?_ 6.2 >
7. 1.674 _?_ 1.678 <
8. 20.05 _?_ 20.3 <
9. 9.018 _?_ 9.017 >

Order the numbers from least to greatest.

10. 2.5, 2.3, 2.45, 2.38 **2.3, 2.38, 2.45, 2.5**
11. 7.01, 7.13, 7.3, 7.03 **7.01, 7.03, 7.13, 7.3**
12. 10.19, 10.2, 10, 10.4 **10, 10.19, 10.2, 10.4**
13. 0.3, 0.47, 0.9, 0.15 **0.15, 0.3, 0.47, 0.9**
14. 1.3, 1.05, 1.11, 1.0 **1.0, 1.05, 1.11, 1.3**
15. 12.6, 10.9, 11, 11.9 **10.9, 11, 11.9, 12.6**
16. 6.1, 6.89, 7.25, 7 **6.1, 6.89, 7, 7.25**
17. 3.1, 3.3, 0.3, 1.33 **0.3, 1.33, 3.1, 3.3**
18. 5.46, 5.4, 5.64, 5.6 **5.4, 5.46, 5.6, 5.64**

Factors and Multiples

A **prime number** is a whole number that is greater than 1 and has exactly two whole number factors, 1 and itself. A **composite number** is a whole number that is greater than 1 and has more than two whole number factors. The table below shows that the first five prime numbers are 2, 3, 5, 7, and 11.

Number	Product(s)	Factor(s)	Prime or composite?
1	1 • 1	1	Neither
2	1 • 2	1, 2	Prime
3	1 • 3	1, 3	Prime
4	1 • 4, 2 • 2	1, 2, 4	Composite
5	1 • 5	1, 5	Prime
6	1 • 6, 2 • 3	1, 2, 3, 6	Composite
7	1 • 7	1, 7	Prime
8	1 • 8, 2 • 4	1, 2, 4, 8	Composite
9	1 • 9, 3 • 3	1, 3, 9	Composite
10	1 • 10, 2 • 5	1, 2, 5, 10	Composite
11	1 • 11	1, 11	Prime
12	1 • 12, 2 • 6, 3 • 4	1, 2, 3, 4, 6, 12	Composite

When you write a composite number as a product of prime numbers, you are writing its **prime factorization**. You can use a **factor tree** to write the prime factorization of a number.

EXAMPLE **Write the prime factorization of 120.**

Write 120 at the top of your factor tree. Draw two branches and write 120 as the product of two factors. Continue to draw branches until all the factors are prime numbers (shown in red). Here are two possible factor trees for 120.

Start with $120 = 2 \cdot 60$.

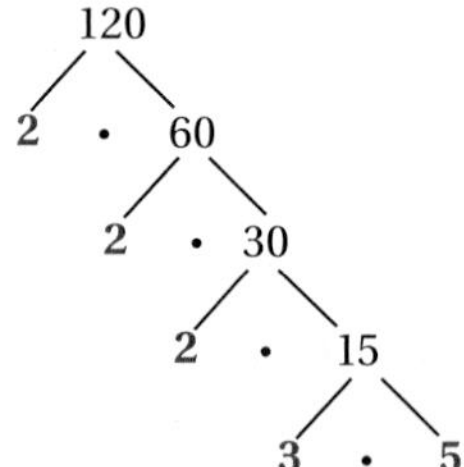

Start with $120 = 10 \cdot 12$.

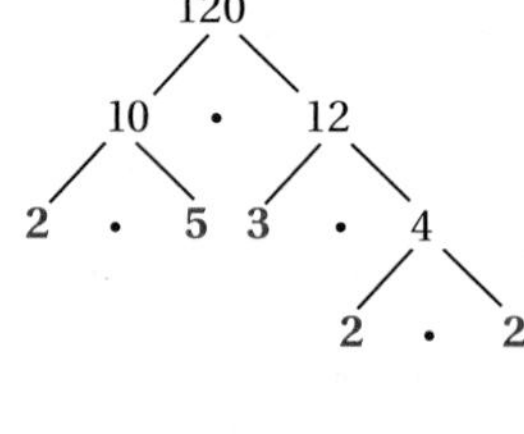

Both factor trees show that $120 = 2 \cdot 2 \cdot 2 \cdot 3 \cdot 5$, or $120 = 2^3 \cdot 3 \cdot 5$.

▶ The prime factorization of 120 is $2^3 \cdot 3 \cdot 5$.

For two or more nonzero whole numbers, a **common factor** is a whole number that is a factor of each number. The **greatest common factor (GCF)** of two or more nonzero whole numbers is the greatest of their common factors.

EXAMPLE **Find the greatest common factor of 30 and 42.**

Write the prime factorization of each number. The greatest common factor is the product of the common prime factors.

$30 = 2 \cdot 3 \cdot 5$ and $42 = 2 \cdot 3 \cdot 7$

The common prime factors are 2 and 3. The GCF is the product $2 \cdot 3 = 6$.

▶ The greatest common factor of 30 and 42 is 6.

A **multiple** of a whole number is the product of the number and any nonzero whole number. A **common multiple** of two or more whole numbers is a multiple of each number. The **least common multiple (LCM)** of two or more whole numbers is the least of their common multiples.

EXAMPLE **Find the least common multiple of 10 and 15.**

Write the prime factorization of each number. The least common multiple is the product of the factors, using each common prime factor only once.

$10 = 2 \cdot 5$ and $15 = 3 \cdot 5$

The common prime factor is 5. The LCM is the product $2 \cdot 3 \cdot 5 = 30$.

▶ The least common multiple of 10 and 15 is 30.

PRACTICE

Write the prime factorization of the number if it is not a prime number. If the number is prime, write *prime*.

1. 28 $2^2 \cdot 7$ **2.** 16 2^4 **3.** 11 prime **4.** 100 $2^2 \cdot 5^2$

5. 81 3^4 **6.** 49 7^2 **7.** 60 $2^2 \cdot 3 \cdot 5$ **8.** 53 prime

9. 180 $2^2 \cdot 3^2 \cdot 5$ **10.** 19 prime **11.** 51 $3 \cdot 17$ **12.** 72 $2^3 \cdot 3^2$

Find the greatest common factor of the pair of numbers.

13. 4, 8 **4** **14.** 5, 6 **1** **15.** 60, 18 **6** **16.** 2, 10 **2**

17. 36, 27 **9** **18.** 15, 21 **3** **19.** 12, 16 **4** **20.** 24, 108 **12**

21. 48, 88 **8** **22.** 8, 12 **4** **23.** 20, 28 **4** **24.** 3, 5 **1**

Find the least common multiple of the pair of numbers.

25. 6, 9 **18** **26.** 3, 8 **24** **27.** 5, 45 **45** **28.** 16, 20 **80**

29. 10, 65 **130** **30.** 12, 15 **60** **31.** 9, 30 **90** **32.** 8, 9 **72**

33. 2, 14 **14** **34.** 28, 32 **224** **35.** 7, 49 **49** **36.** 4, 6 **12**

SKILLS REVIEW HANDBOOK

Finding Equivalent Fractions and Simplifying Fractions

A **fraction** is a number of the form $\frac{a}{b}$ where a is the **numerator** and b is the **denominator**. The value of b cannot be 0.

The number lines show the graphs of two fractions, $\frac{1}{2}$ and $\frac{2}{4}$.

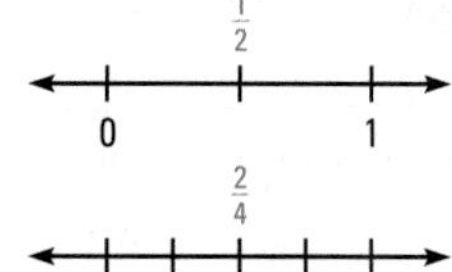

These fractions represent the same number. Two fractions that represent the same number are called **equivalent fractions**.

To write equivalent fractions, you can multiply or divide the numerator and the denominator by the same nonzero number.

EXAMPLE **Write two fractions that are equivalent to $\frac{6}{8}$.**

Multiply the numerator and denominator by 3.

$\frac{6}{8} = \frac{6 \times 3}{8 \times 3} = \frac{18}{24}$ **Equivalent fraction**

Divide the numerator and denominator by 2.

$\frac{6}{8} = \frac{6 \div 2}{8 \div 2} = \frac{3}{4}$ **Equivalent fraction**

A fraction is in **simplest form** when its numerator and its denominator have no common factors besides 1.

EXAMPLE **Write the fraction $\frac{10}{15}$ in simplest form.**

Divide the numerator and denominator by 5, the greatest common factor of 10 and 15.

$\frac{10}{15} = \frac{10 \div 5}{15 \div 5} = \frac{2}{3}$ **Simplest form**

PRACTICE

Write two fractions that are equivalent to the given fraction. 1–5. Sample answers are given.

1. $\frac{9}{12}$ $\frac{3}{4}$ and $\frac{18}{24}$
2. $\frac{4}{6}$ $\frac{2}{3}$ and $\frac{8}{12}$
3. $\frac{1}{2}$ $\frac{2}{4}$ and $\frac{3}{6}$
4. $\frac{2}{5}$ $\frac{4}{10}$ and $\frac{6}{15}$
5. $\frac{10}{14}$ $\frac{5}{7}$ and $\frac{20}{28}$

Write the fraction in simplest form.

6. $\frac{16}{24}$ $\frac{2}{3}$
7. $\frac{3}{12}$ $\frac{1}{4}$
8. $\frac{30}{48}$ $\frac{5}{8}$
9. $\frac{5}{40}$ $\frac{1}{8}$
10. $\frac{8}{20}$ $\frac{2}{5}$
11. $\frac{4}{16}$ $\frac{1}{4}$
12. $\frac{64}{72}$ $\frac{8}{9}$
13. $\frac{35}{100}$ $\frac{7}{20}$
14. $\frac{21}{81}$ $\frac{7}{27}$
15. $\frac{44}{55}$ $\frac{4}{5}$
16. $\frac{15}{20}$ $\frac{3}{4}$
17. $\frac{12}{28}$ $\frac{3}{7}$
18. $\frac{15}{39}$ $\frac{5}{13}$
19. $\frac{24}{78}$ $\frac{4}{13}$
20. $\frac{60}{96}$ $\frac{5}{8}$

Mixed Numbers and Improper Fractions

A **mixed number** is the sum of a whole number and a fraction. An **improper fraction** is a fraction with a numerator that is greater than or equal to the denominator.

The shaded part of the model at the right represents the mixed number $2\frac{1}{4}$ and the improper fraction $\frac{9}{4}$.

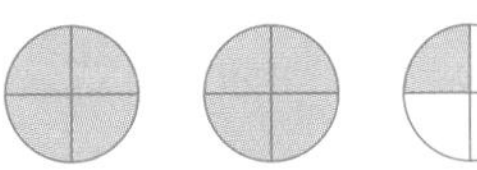

EXAMPLE Write $5\frac{7}{8}$ as an improper fraction.

$5\frac{7}{8} = 5 + \frac{7}{8}$ Definition of mixed number

$= \frac{40}{8} + \frac{7}{8}$ 1 whole $= \frac{8}{8}$, so 5 wholes $= \frac{40}{8}$.

$= \frac{47}{8}$ Add.

EXAMPLE Write $\frac{17}{5}$ as a mixed number.

$$\begin{array}{r} 3 \\ 5\overline{)17} \\ \underline{15} \\ 2 \end{array}$$

Divide the numerator by the denominator: $17 \div 5$.
The quotient is 3 and the remainder is 2.

▶ $\frac{17}{5} = 3\frac{2}{5}$ Write the remainder as a fraction, $\frac{\text{remainder}}{\text{divisor}}$.

PRACTICE

Write the mixed number as an improper fraction.

1. $1\frac{2}{3}$ $\frac{5}{3}$
2. $3\frac{1}{4}$ $\frac{13}{4}$
3. $10\frac{3}{10}$ $\frac{103}{10}$
4. $2\frac{3}{5}$ $\frac{13}{5}$
5. $4\frac{1}{2}$ $\frac{9}{2}$
6. $9\frac{1}{3}$ $\frac{28}{3}$
7. $1\frac{11}{12}$ $\frac{23}{12}$
8. $2\frac{3}{4}$ $\frac{11}{4}$
9. $6\frac{5}{8}$ $\frac{53}{8}$
10. $5\frac{9}{16}$ $\frac{89}{16}$
11. $8\frac{1}{8}$ $\frac{65}{8}$
12. $6\frac{3}{5}$ $\frac{33}{5}$
13. $7\frac{2}{9}$ $\frac{65}{9}$
14. $2\frac{3}{13}$ $\frac{29}{13}$
15. $12\frac{2}{3}$ $\frac{38}{3}$

Write the improper fraction as a mixed number.

16. $\frac{5}{2}$ $2\frac{1}{2}$
17. $\frac{12}{5}$ $2\frac{2}{5}$
18. $\frac{15}{8}$ $1\frac{7}{8}$
19. $\frac{25}{4}$ $6\frac{1}{4}$
20. $\frac{37}{3}$ $12\frac{1}{3}$
21. $\frac{7}{4}$ $1\frac{3}{4}$
22. $\frac{27}{8}$ $3\frac{3}{8}$
23. $\frac{29}{10}$ $2\frac{9}{10}$
24. $\frac{69}{16}$ $4\frac{5}{16}$
25. $\frac{54}{5}$ $10\frac{4}{5}$
26. $\frac{31}{4}$ $7\frac{3}{4}$
27. $\frac{22}{5}$ $4\frac{2}{5}$
28. $\frac{13}{3}$ $4\frac{1}{3}$
29. $\frac{43}{9}$ $4\frac{7}{9}$
30. $\frac{35}{11}$ $3\frac{2}{11}$

Adding and Subtracting Fractions

To add or subtract two fractions with the same denominator, write the sum or difference of the numerators over the denominator.

Sum and Difference Rules ($c \neq 0$)

$$\frac{a}{c} + \frac{b}{c} = \frac{a+b}{c} \qquad \frac{a}{c} - \frac{b}{c} = \frac{a-b}{c}$$

EXAMPLE **Add or subtract:** **a.** $\frac{1}{10} + \frac{3}{10}$ **b.** $\frac{7}{8} - \frac{3}{8}$

a. $\frac{1}{10} + \frac{3}{10} = \frac{4}{10}$ **Add numerators.**

$= \frac{2}{5}$ **Simplify.**

b. $\frac{7}{8} - \frac{3}{8} = \frac{4}{8}$ **Subtract numerators.**

$= \frac{1}{2}$ **Simplify.**

The **least common denominator (LCD)** of two fractions is the least common multiple of the denominators. To add or subtract two fractions with different denominators, use the LCD of the fractions to write equivalent fractions that have the same denominator.

EXAMPLE **Add:** $\frac{1}{4} + \frac{5}{6}$

The LCD of the fractions is 12, so write $\frac{1}{4}$ as $\frac{1 \times 3}{4 \times 3} = \frac{3}{12}$ and $\frac{5}{6}$ as $\frac{5 \times 2}{6 \times 2} = \frac{10}{12}$.

$\frac{1}{4} + \frac{5}{6} = \frac{3}{12} + \frac{10}{12}$ **Write equivalent fractions.**

$= \frac{13}{12}$ **Add.**

$= 1\frac{1}{12}$ **Write as a mixed number.**

PRACTICE

Add or subtract.

1. $\frac{1}{16} + \frac{3}{16}$ **$\frac{1}{4}$**
2. $\frac{1}{5} + \frac{2}{5}$ **$\frac{3}{5}$**
3. $\frac{7}{12} - \frac{5}{12}$ **$\frac{1}{6}$**
4. $\frac{2}{3} - \frac{1}{3}$ **$\frac{1}{3}$**
5. $\frac{5}{8} + \frac{3}{8}$ **1**
6. $\frac{3}{4} + \frac{3}{4}$ **$1\frac{1}{2}$**
7. $\frac{7}{8} - \frac{3}{8}$ **$\frac{1}{2}$**
8. $\frac{17}{20} + \frac{9}{20}$ **$1\frac{3}{10}$**
9. $\frac{7}{10} + \frac{1}{2}$ **$1\frac{1}{5}$**
10. $\frac{3}{10} + \frac{3}{5}$ **$\frac{9}{10}$**
11. $\frac{3}{8} - \frac{3}{16}$ **$\frac{3}{16}$**
12. $\frac{1}{3} + \frac{1}{10}$ **$\frac{13}{30}$**
13. $\frac{7}{12} - \frac{1}{16}$ **$\frac{25}{48}$**
14. $\frac{2}{3} - \frac{1}{4}$ **$\frac{5}{12}$**
15. $\frac{5}{6} + \frac{7}{8}$ **$1\frac{17}{24}$**
16. $\frac{3}{4} - \frac{5}{8}$ **$\frac{1}{8}$**
17. $\frac{3}{4} - \frac{1}{5}$ **$\frac{11}{20}$**
18. $\frac{5}{12} + \frac{2}{3}$ **$1\frac{1}{12}$**
19. $1 - \frac{1}{5}$ **$\frac{4}{5}$**
20. $4 - \frac{3}{16}$ **$3\frac{13}{16}$**
21. $2\frac{5}{8} + 4\frac{1}{8}$ **$6\frac{3}{4}$**
22. $2\frac{9}{10} - 1\frac{7}{10}$ **$1\frac{1}{5}$**
23. $1\frac{5}{6} + 3\frac{1}{6}$ **5**
24. $2\frac{1}{2} + 2\frac{3}{8}$ **$4\frac{7}{8}$**
25. $1\frac{3}{4} - \frac{11}{16}$ **$1\frac{1}{16}$**

Multiplying and Dividing Fractions

To multiply two fractions, write the product of the numerators over the product of the denominators.

Product Rule ($b, d \neq 0$)
$\frac{a}{b} \times \frac{c}{d} = \frac{ac}{bd}$

EXAMPLE **Multiply: $\frac{3}{5} \times \frac{7}{8}$**

$\frac{3}{5} \times \frac{7}{8} = \frac{3 \times 7}{5 \times 8}$ **Use product rule.**

$= \frac{21}{40}$ **Simplify.**

Two nonzero numbers whose product is 1 are **reciprocals**. For example, 6 and $\frac{1}{6}$ are reciprocals because $6 \times \frac{1}{6} = 1$. Every number except 0 has a reciprocal.

To divide by a fraction, multiply by its reciprocal.

Quotient Rule ($b, c, d \neq 0$)
$\frac{a}{b} \div \frac{c}{d} = \frac{a}{b} \times \frac{d}{c}$

EXAMPLE **Divide: $\frac{5}{7} \div \frac{3}{4}$**

The reciprocal of $\frac{3}{4}$ is $\frac{4}{3}$ because $\frac{3}{4} \times \frac{4}{3} = 1$, so multiply $\frac{5}{7}$ by $\frac{4}{3}$.

$\frac{5}{7} \div \frac{3}{4} = \frac{5}{7} \times \frac{4}{3}$ **Use quotient rule.**

$= \frac{20}{21}$ **Use product rule.**

PRACTICE

Multiply or divide.

1. $\frac{3}{4} \times \frac{2}{3}$ $\mathbf{\frac{1}{2}}$
2. $\frac{1}{5} \times \frac{5}{8}$ $\mathbf{\frac{1}{8}}$
3. $\frac{1}{6} \div \frac{1}{3}$ $\mathbf{\frac{1}{2}}$
4. $\frac{2}{3} \div \frac{2}{3}$ **1**
5. $\frac{9}{10} \div \frac{4}{5}$ $\mathbf{1\frac{1}{8}}$
6. $\frac{1}{12} \times \frac{3}{4}$ $\mathbf{\frac{1}{16}}$
7. $\frac{3}{8} \times \frac{1}{8}$ $\mathbf{\frac{3}{64}}$
8. $\frac{5}{6} \div \frac{1}{4}$ $\mathbf{3\frac{1}{3}}$
9. $\frac{1}{2} \times \frac{1}{4}$ $\mathbf{\frac{1}{8}}$
10. $\frac{7}{10} \div \frac{5}{8}$ $\mathbf{1\frac{3}{25}}$
11. $\frac{3}{4} \div \frac{1}{2}$ $\mathbf{1\frac{1}{2}}$
12. $\frac{5}{6} \times \frac{3}{10}$ $\mathbf{\frac{1}{4}}$
13. $\frac{2}{5} \div \frac{4}{5}$ $\mathbf{\frac{1}{2}}$
14. $\frac{9}{10} \times \frac{1}{3}$ $\mathbf{\frac{3}{10}}$
15. $\frac{1}{4} \div \frac{7}{8}$ $\mathbf{\frac{2}{7}}$
16. $\frac{3}{16} \times \frac{2}{5}$ $\mathbf{\frac{3}{40}}$
17. $\frac{2}{5} \div 20$ $\mathbf{\frac{1}{50}}$
18. $18 \times \frac{1}{3}$ **6**
19. $\frac{1}{10} \times 6$ $\mathbf{\frac{3}{5}}$
20. $24 \div \frac{3}{8}$ **64**
21. $5\frac{1}{2} \times \frac{9}{16}$ $\mathbf{3\frac{3}{32}}$
22. $8\frac{1}{4} \div \frac{3}{10}$ $\mathbf{27\frac{1}{2}}$
23. $1\frac{7}{8} \times 2\frac{1}{3}$ $\mathbf{4\frac{3}{8}}$
24. $3\frac{3}{4} \div 6\frac{1}{2}$ $\mathbf{\frac{15}{26}}$
25. $2\frac{1}{2} \div 1\frac{7}{8}$ $\mathbf{1\frac{1}{3}}$

915

Fractions, Decimals, and Percents

A **percent** is a fraction whose denominator is 100. The symbol for percent is %. In the model at the right, there are 100 squares in all, and 49 of the 100 squares are shaded. You can write the shaded part of the model as a fraction, a decimal, or a percent.

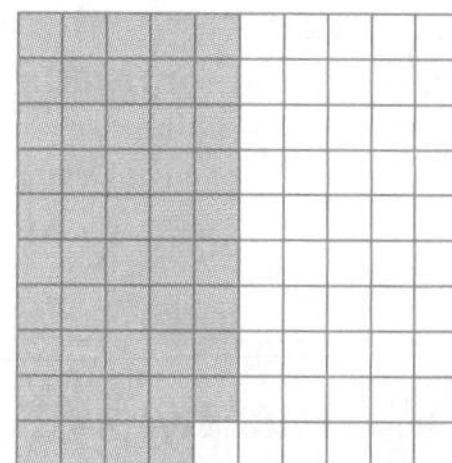

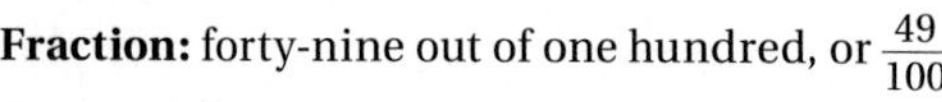

Fraction: forty-nine out of one hundred, or $\frac{49}{100}$

Decimal: forty-nine hundredths, or 0.49

Percent: forty-nine percent, or 49%

EXAMPLE **Write the fraction as a decimal: a. $\frac{1}{8}$ b. $\frac{5}{12}$**

a. $8\overline{)1.000}$ with quotient 0.125 **Divide.**

▶ $\frac{1}{8} = 0.125$

b. $12\overline{)5.00000...}$ with quotient 0.41666... **Divide.**

▶ $\frac{5}{12} = 0.41666... = 0.41\overline{6}$

EXAMPLE **Write the decimal as a fraction: a. 0.7 b. 0.32**

a. 0.7 = seven tenths

$= \frac{7}{10}$

b. 0.32 = thirty-two hundredths

$= \frac{32}{100}$

$= \frac{8}{25}$

To write a percent as a decimal, move the decimal point two places to the left and remove the percent sign.

EXAMPLE **Write the percent as a decimal: a. 16% b. 5%**

a. 16% = .16%

= 0.16

b. 5% = .05%

= 0.05

To write a decimal as a percent, move the decimal point two places to the right and write a percent sign.

EXAMPLE **Write the decimal as a percent: a. 0.83 b. 0.195**

a. 0.83 = 0.83.

= 83%

b. 0.195 = 0.19.5

= 19.5%

EXAMPLE **Write the percent as a fraction: a. 98% b. 5%**

a. $98\% = \frac{98}{100}$ **Definition of percent**

$= \frac{49}{50}$ **Simplify.**

b. $5\% = \frac{5}{100}$ **Definition of percent**

$= \frac{1}{20}$ **Simplify.**

To write a fraction as a percent, you may be able to rewrite the fraction using a denominator of 100. If the denominator of the fraction is not a factor of 100, you can first write the fraction as a decimal and then as a percent.

EXAMPLE **Write the fraction as a percent: a. $\frac{2}{5}$ b. $\frac{5}{8}$**

a. $\frac{2}{5} = \frac{2(20)}{5(20)}$ **Write as a fraction with denominator 100.**

$= \frac{40}{100} = 40\%$ **Write as a percent.**

b. $\frac{5}{8} = 0.625$ **Write as a decimal.**

$= 62.5\%$ **Write as a percent.**

The table below gives commonly used fractions, decimals, and percents written in increasing order.

$\frac{1}{100} = 0.01 = 1\%$	$\frac{1}{16} = 0.0625 = 6.25\%$	$\frac{1}{10} = 0.1 = 10\%$	$\frac{1}{8} = 0.125 = 12.5\%$
$\frac{1}{5} = 0.2 = 20\%$	$\frac{1}{4} = 0.25 = 25\%$	$\frac{1}{3} = 0.\overline{3} \approx 33.3\%$	$\frac{3}{8} = 0.375 = 37.5\%$
$\frac{2}{5} = 0.4 = 40\%$	$\frac{1}{2} = 0.5 = 50\%$	$\frac{3}{5} = 0.6 = 60\%$	$\frac{5}{8} = 0.625 = 62.5\%$
$\frac{2}{3} = 0.\overline{6} \approx 66.7\%$	$\frac{3}{4} = 0.75 = 75\%$	$\frac{4}{5} = 0.8 = 80\%$	$\frac{7}{8} = 0.875 = 87.5\%$

PRACTICE

Write the percent as a decimal and as a fraction.

1. 70% **0.7, $\frac{7}{10}$**
2. 12% **0.12, $\frac{3}{25}$**
3. 3% **0.03, $\frac{3}{100}$**
4. 55% **0.55, $\frac{11}{20}$**
5. 35% **0.35, $\frac{7}{20}$**
6. 9% **0.09, $\frac{9}{100}$**
7. 110% **1.1, $1\frac{1}{10}$**
8. 225% **2.25, $2\frac{1}{4}$**
9. 0.3% **0.003, $\frac{3}{1000}$**
10. 0.5% **0.005, $\frac{1}{200}$**

Write the decimal as a fraction and as a percent.

11. 0.28 **$\frac{7}{25}$, 28%**
12. 0.13 **$\frac{13}{100}$, 13%**
13. 0.05 **$\frac{1}{20}$, 5%**
14. 0.36 **$\frac{9}{25}$, 36%**
15. 0.52 **$\frac{13}{25}$, 52%**
16. 0.004 **$\frac{1}{250}$, 0.4%**
17. 0.025 **$\frac{1}{40}$, 2.5%**
18. 4 **$\frac{4}{1}$, 400%**
19. 1.5 **$\frac{3}{2}$, 150%**
20. 2.3 **$\frac{23}{10}$, 230%**

Write the fraction as a decimal and as a percent. Round decimals to the nearest thousandth. Round percents to the nearest tenth of a percent.

21. $\frac{3}{16}$ **0.188, 18.8%**
22. $\frac{1}{9}$ **0.111, 11.1%**
23. $\frac{61}{100}$ **0.61, 61%**
24. $\frac{3}{20}$ **0.15, 15%**
25. $\frac{19}{100}$ **0.19, 19%**
26. $\frac{17}{25}$ **0.68, 68%**
27. $\frac{9}{25}$ **0.36, 36%**
28. $\frac{5}{6}$ **0.833, 83.3%**
29. $\frac{4}{7}$ **0.571, 57.1%**
30. $\frac{5}{12}$ **0.417, 41.7%**

SKILLS REVIEW HANDBOOK

Mean, Median, and Mode

Three measures of central tendency are mean, median, and mode.

The **mean** of a data set is the sum of the values divided by the number of values.	The **median** of a data set is the middle value when the values are written in numerical order. If a data set has an even number of values, the median is the mean of the two middle values.	The **mode** of a data set is the value that occurs most often. A data set can have no mode, one mode, or more than one mode.

EXAMPLE **Find the mean, median, and mode(s) of the data in the table.**

Lengths of School Years	
Country	**School year (days)**
China	251
Korea	222
Taiwan	222
Japan	220
Israel	215
Switzerland	207
Canada	188
United States	178

Mean

Add the values. Then divide by 8, the number of values.

Sum = 251 + 222 + 222 + 220 + 215 + 207 + 188 + 178
= 1703

▸ Mean $= \frac{1703}{8} = 212.875$

Median

Write the values in order from least to greatest. Then find the middle value(s).

178, 188, 207, **215**, **220**, 222, 222, 251

Find the mean of the two middle values.

▸ Median $= \frac{215 + 220}{2} = \frac{435}{2} = 217.5$

Mode

Find the value that occurs most often.

▸ Mode = 222

PRACTICE

Find the mean, median, and mode(s) of the data.

1. Test scores: 90, 88, 95, 94, 87, 85, 92, 99, 100, 94 **92.4; 93; 94**
2. Daily high temperatures (°F) for a week: 68, 70, 67, 68, 75, 75, 74 **71°F; 70°F; 68°F and 75°F**
3. Ages of employees: 24, 52, 21, 55, 39, 49, 28, 33, 52, 41, 30, 64, 45 **41 yr; 41 yr; 52 yr**
4. Numbers of students in classes: 21, 24, 27, 28, 25, 18, 22, 25, 26, 22, 27, 20 **23.75; 24.5; 22, 25, and 27**
5. Movie ticket prices: $6.75, $7.50, $7.25, $6.75, $6.25, $7.50, $7.25, $6.75, $7 **$7; $7; $6.75**
6. Hourly rates of pay: $14.50, $8.75, $7, $11, $16.50, $18, $12, $10.25 **$12.25; $11.50; no mode**
7. Numbers of children in families: 0, 0, 1, 1, 1, 2, 2, 2, 2, 2, 3, 3, 4, 4, 4, 5 **2.25; 2; 2**
8. Ages of students in a high school class: 3 sixteen-year-olds, 10 seventeen-year-olds, and 7 eighteen-year-olds **17.2 yr; 17 yr; 17 yr**

The Coordinate Plane

Just as you use a number line to graph numbers, you use a *coordinate plane* to graph *ordered pairs* of numbers.

A **coordinate plane** has a horizontal ***x*-axis** and a vertical ***y*-axis** that intersect at a point called the **origin**. The origin is labeled *O*.

In an **ordered pair**, the first number is the ***x*-coordinate** and the second number is the ***y*-coordinate**. The coordinates of the origin are (0, 0). The ordered pair (4, 5) is graphed at the right.

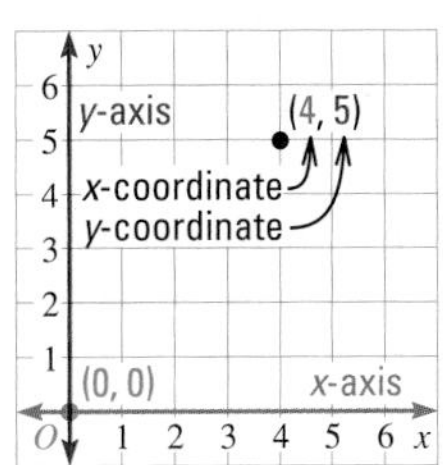

EXAMPLE **Give the coordinates of points *A* and *B*.**

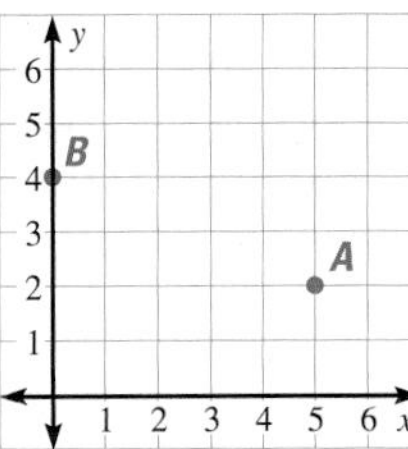

Point *A* is 5 units to the right of the origin and 2 units up, so the *x*-coordinate is 5 and the *y*-coordinate is 2.

▶ The coordinates of point *A* are (5, 2).

Point *B* is 0 units to the right or left of the origin and 4 units up, so the *x*-coordinate is 0 and the *y*-coordinate is 4.

▶ The coordinates of point *B* are (0, 4).

EXAMPLE **Plot the points *C*(1, 3) and *D*(3, 0) in a coordinate plane.**

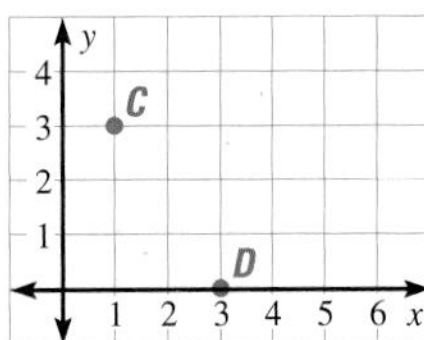

To plot the point *C*(1, 3), begin at the origin and move 1 unit to the right, then 3 units up.

To plot the point *D*(3, 0), begin at the origin and move 3 units right, then 0 units up.

PRACTICE

Give the coordinates of the point.

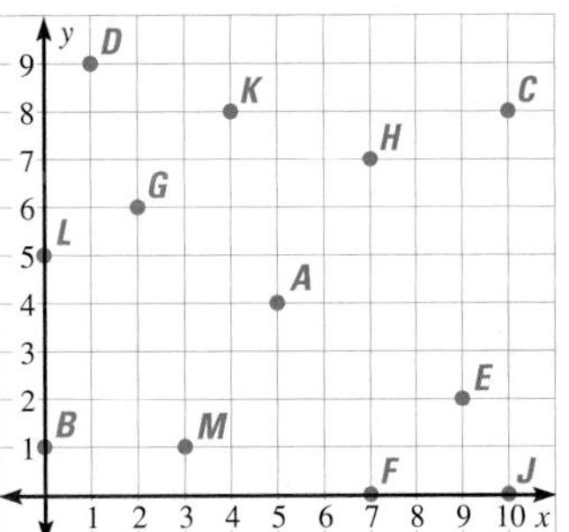

1. *A* (5, 4) **2.** *B* (0, 1) **3.** *C* (10, 8)

4. *D* (1, 9) **5.** *E* (9, 2) **6.** *F* (7, 0)

7. *G* (2, 6) **8.** *H* (7, 7) **9.** *J* (10, 0)

10. *K* (4, 8) **11.** *L* (0, 5) **12.** *M* (3, 1)

Plot the point in a coordinate plane.
13–24. See margin.

13. *M*(1, 7) **14.** *N*(2, 1) **15.** *P*(4, 4)

16. *Q*(0, 3) **17.** *R*(4, 0) **18.** *S*(6, 8)

19. *T*(3, 6) **20.** *U*(8, 4) **21.** *V*(7, 0)

22. *W*(0, 8) **23.** *X*(3, 5) **24.** *Z*(5, 6)

13–24.

1.

2.

3.

4.

5.

6.

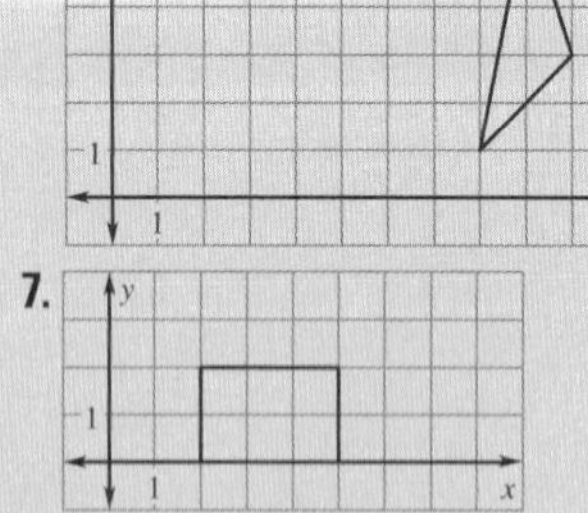

7.

Transformations

A **transformation** is a change made to the location, size, or shape of a figure. The new figure formed by a transformation is called an **image**. In this book, original figures are shown in blue and images in red.

A **translation** is a transformation in which each point of a figure moves the same distance in the same direction. A figure and its translated image are identical in size and shape.

EXAMPLE **Translate the triangle 4 units to the right and 1 unit up.**

From each vertex of the triangle, move 4 units to the right and 1 unit up to plot the image of the vertex. Draw segments connecting the images of the vertices.

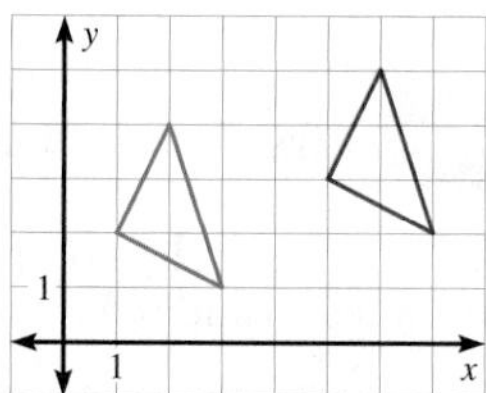

A **reflection** is a transformation in which a figure is reflected, or flipped, in a line, called the *line of reflection*. A figure and its reflected image are identical in size and shape.

EXAMPLE **Reflect the line segment in the given line.**

For each endpoint, find the distance from the endpoint to the line of reflection. Move the same distance on the opposite side of the line of reflection and plot the image point. Draw a segment connecting the image points.

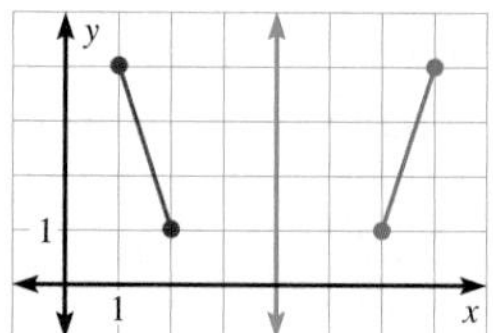

A **dilation** is a transformation in which a figure stretches or shrinks with respect to a fixed point called the *center of dilation*. (The examples and exercises below all have the origin as the center of dilation.) A figure and its dilated image have the same shape.

The **scale factor** of a dilation is the ratio of a side length of the image to the corresponding side length of the original figure. A figure *stretches* if its scale factor is greater than 1. A figure *shrinks* if its scale factor is between 0 and 1.

EXAMPLE **Dilate the rectangle using a scale factor of 3.**

Multiply each coordinate of each vertex by 3 to find the coordinates of the image. Plot the image of each vertex. Connect the image points to form a rectangle.

(1, 1) → **(3, 3)** (1, 2) → **(3, 6)**

(3, 2) → **(9, 6)** (3, 1) → **(9, 3)**

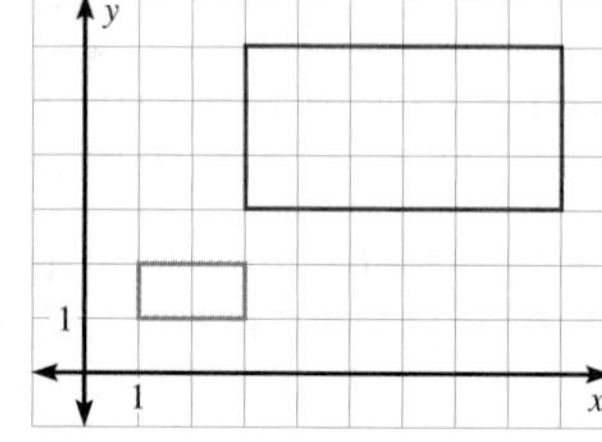

EXAMPLE Dilate the triangle using a scale factor of $\frac{1}{2}$.

Multiply each coordinate of each vertex by $\frac{1}{2}$ to find the coordinates of the image. Plot the image of each vertex. Connect the image points to form a triangle.

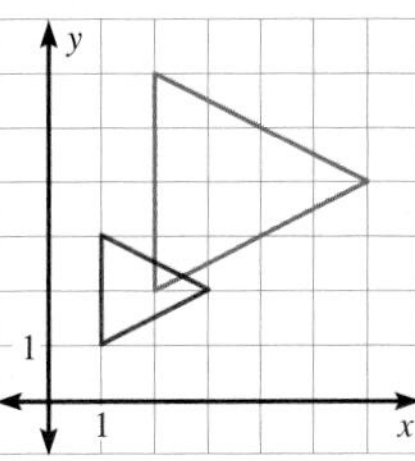

(2, 6) → **(1, 3)**

(2, 2) → **(1, 1)**

(6, 4) → **(3, 2)**

PRACTICE

The coordinates of the vertices of a polygon are given. Draw the polygon. Then find the coordinates of the vertices of the image after the specified translation, and draw the image. **1–5. See margin for art.**

1. (1, 5), (3, 4), (3, 1); translate 3 units to the right and 2 units up **(4, 7), (6, 6), (6, 3)**
2. (5, 0), (7, 0), (7, 2), (5, 2); translate 4 units to the left and 5 units up **(1, 5), (3, 5), (3, 7), (1, 7)**
3. (4, 4), (6, 4), (6, 7); translate 3 units to the left and 3 units down **(1, 1), (3, 1), (3, 4)**
4. (2, 1), (4, 1), (4, 6), (2, 6); translate 5 units to the right **(7, 1), (9, 1), (9, 6), (7, 6)**
5. (4, 5), (7, 2), (3, 3); translate 1 unit down **(4, 4), (7, 1), (3, 2)**

For the figure shown, find the coordinates of the vertices of the image after a reflection in the given line. Then draw the image. **6–8. See margin for art.**

6.

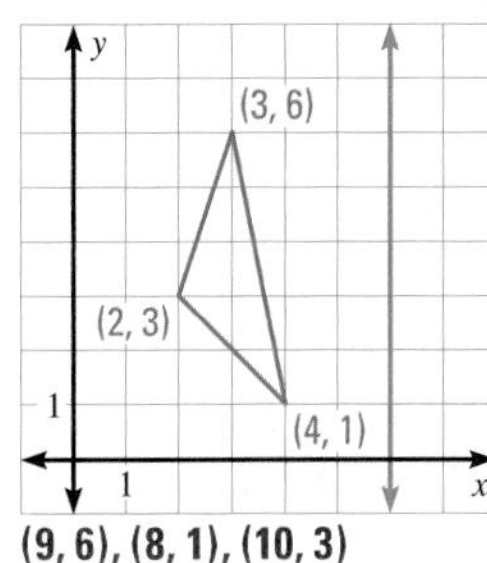

(9, 6), (8, 1), (10, 3)

7.

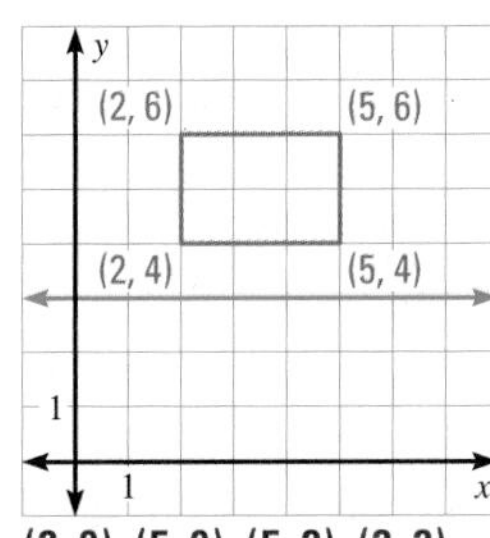

(2, 0), (5, 0), (5, 2), (2, 2)

8.

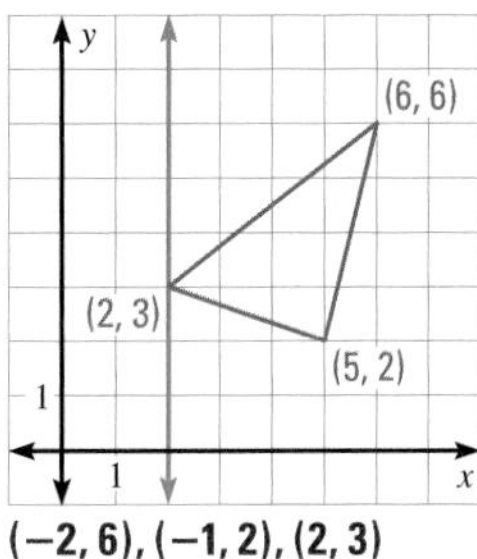

(−2, 6), (−1, 2), (2, 3)

The coordinates of the vertices of a polygon are given. Draw the polygon. Then find the coordinates of the vertices of the image after the specified dilation, and draw the image. **9–13. See margin for art.**

9. (1, 2), (2, 4), (5, 3); dilate using a scale factor of 2 **(2, 4), (4, 8), (10, 6)**
10. (2, 6), (6, 6), (6, 2), (2, 2); dilate using a scale factor of $\frac{1}{2}$ **(1, 3), (3, 3), (3, 1), (1, 1)**
11. (1, 3), (3, 3), (3, 1), (1, 1); dilate using a scale factor of 4 **(4, 12), (12, 12), (12, 4), (4, 4)**
12. (3, 9), (6, 9), (6, 3); dilate using a scale factor of $\frac{1}{3}$ **(1, 3), (2, 3), (2, 1)**
13. (0, 2), (4, 4), (6, 0); dilate using a scale factor of $1\frac{1}{2}$ **(0, 3), (6, 6), (9, 0)**

8. **9.**

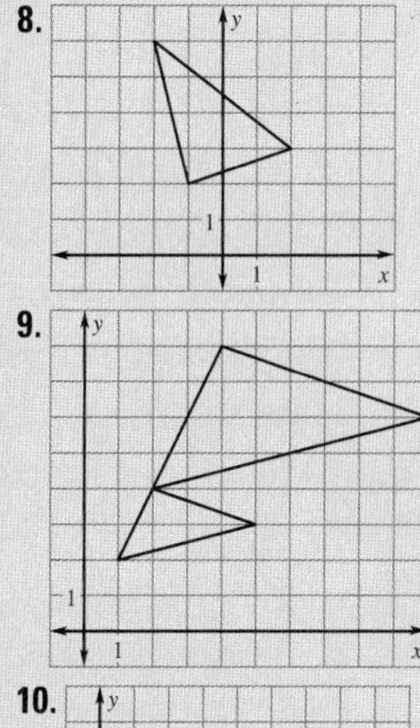

10.

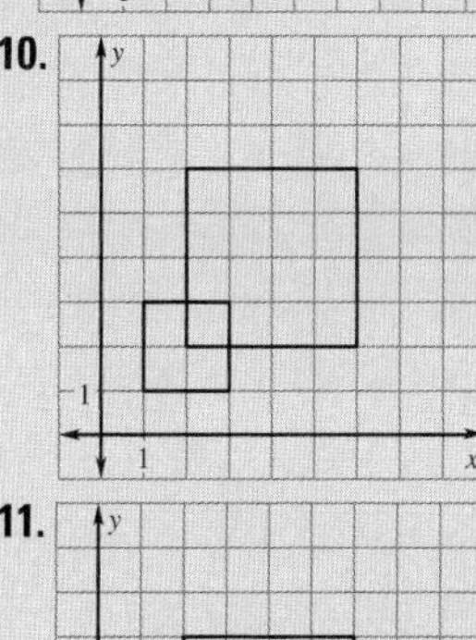

11. **12.**

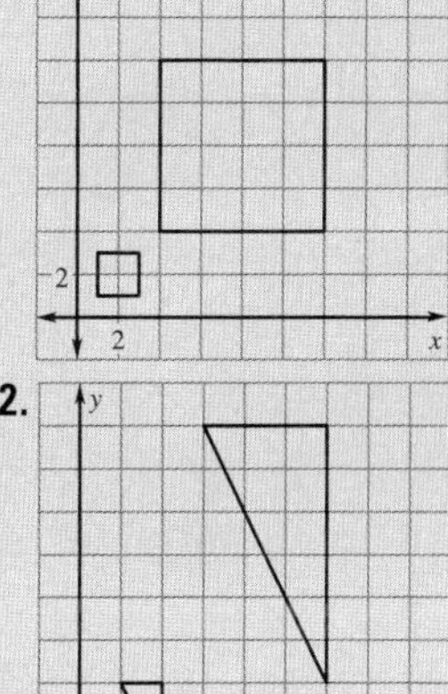

13.

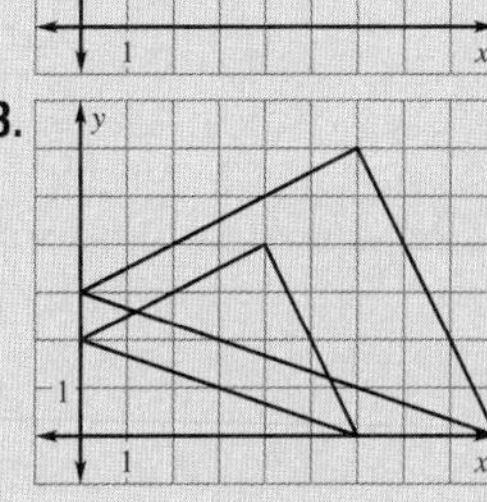

921

Perimeter and Area

The **perimeter** P of a figure is the distance around it.

Perimeter of a Square	Perimeter of a Rectangle	Perimeter of a Triangle
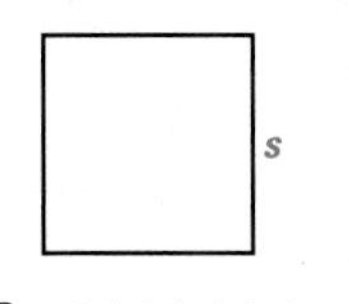	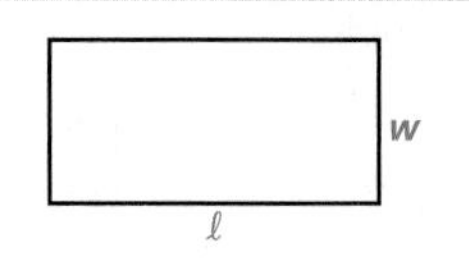	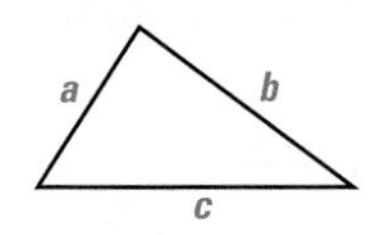
$P = s + s + s + s$ $= 4s$	$P = \ell + w + \ell + w$ $= 2\ell + 2w$	$P = a + b + c$

EXAMPLE **Find the perimeter of the figure.**

a. Square

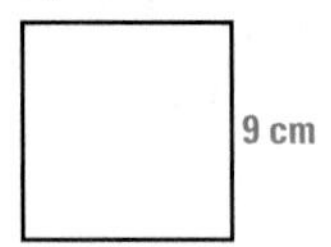

$P = 4s$

$= 4(9)$

$= 36$ cm

b. Rectangle

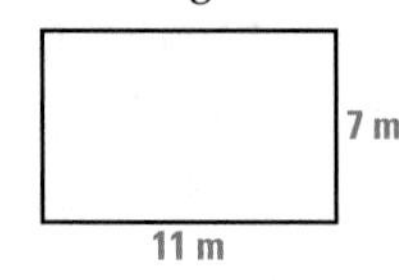

$P = 2\ell + 2w$

$= 2(11) + 2(7)$

$= 22 + 14 = 36$ m

c. Triangle

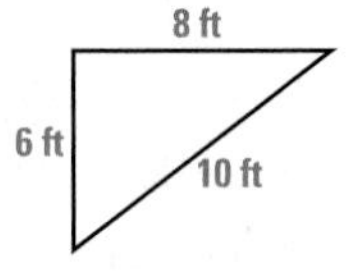

$P = a + b + c$

$= 6 + 8 + 10$

$= 24$ ft

The **area** A of a figure is the number of square units enclosed by the figure.

Area of a Square	Area of a Rectangle	Area of a Parallelogram
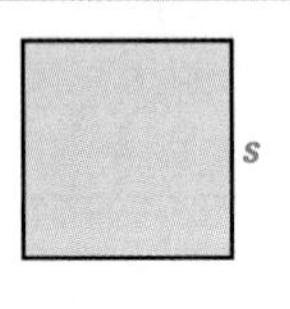	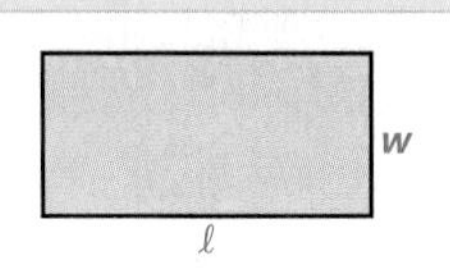	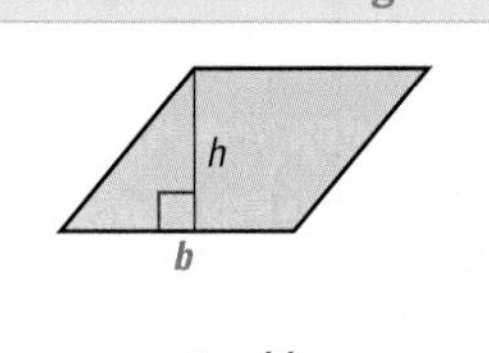 
$A = s^2$	$A = \ell w$	$A = bh$

Area of a Triangle	Area of a Trapezoid
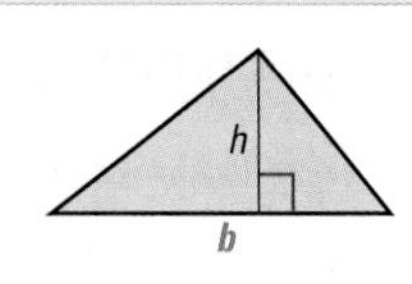	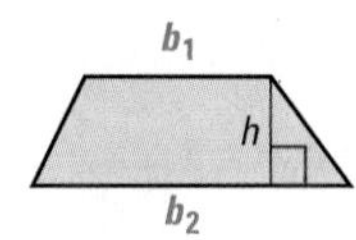
$A = \frac{1}{2}bh$	$P = \frac{1}{2}(b_1 + b_2)h$

EXAMPLE **Find the area of the figure.**

a. Rectangle

15 cm

9 cm

$A = \ell w$

$= 9(15)$

$= 135 \text{ cm}^2$

b. Triangle

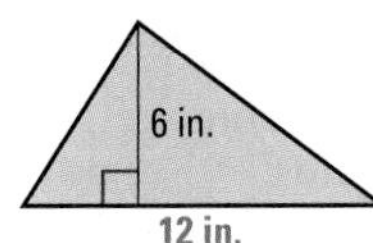

$A = \frac{1}{2}bh$

$= \frac{1}{2}(12)(6)$

$= 36 \text{ in.}^2$

c. Parallelogram

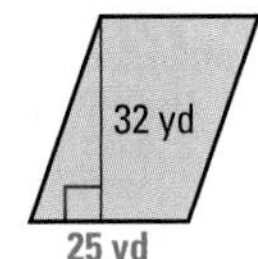

$A = bh$

$= 25(32)$

$= 800 \text{ yd}^2$

PRACTICE

Find the perimeter of the figure.

1. Square **36 ft**

2. Rectangle **28 mm**

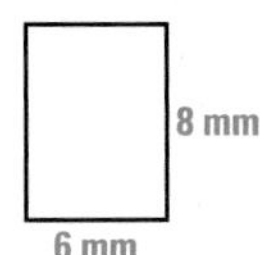

3. Triangle **20 ft**

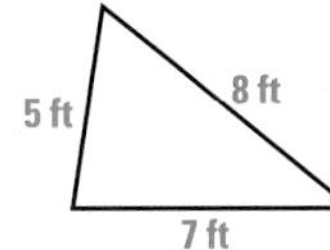

Find the area of the figure.

4. Square **400 in.^{2}**

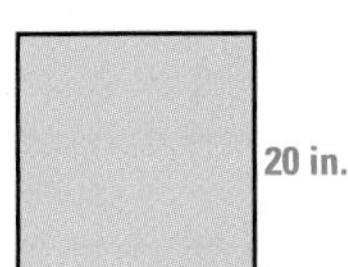

5. Rectangle **66 yd^2**

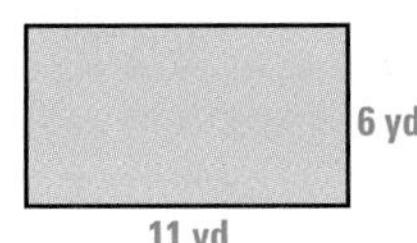

6. Triangle **52 m^2**

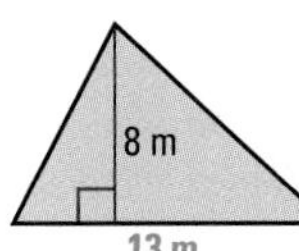

7. Parallelogram **110 in.^{2}**

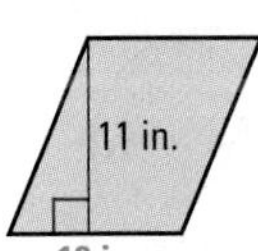

8. Trapezoid **130 m^2**

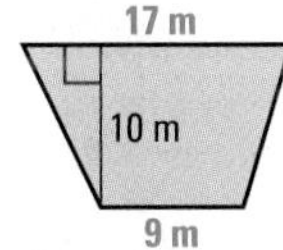

9. Parallelogram **21 ft^2**

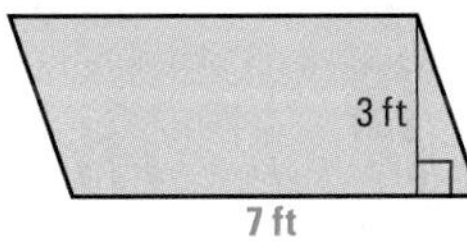

10. Trapezoid **234 m^2**

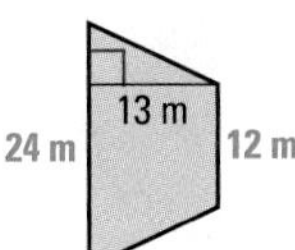

11. Triangle **70 yd^2**

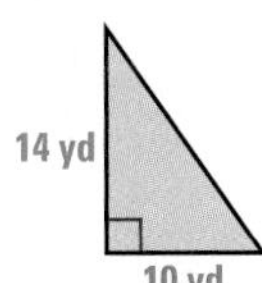

12. Rectangle **144 in.^{2}**

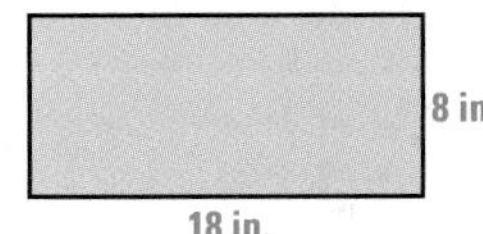

Circumference and Area of a Circle

A circle consists of all points in a plane that are the same distance from a fixed point called the **center**.

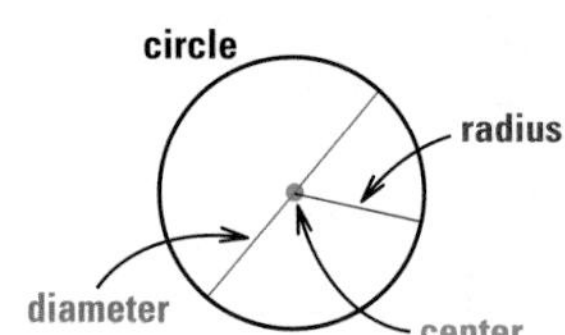

The distance between the center and any point on the circle is the **radius**. The distance across the circle through the center is the **diameter**. The diameter of a circle is twice its radius.

The **circumference** of a circle is the distance around the circle. For any circle, the ratio of its circumference to its diameter is π (pi), a number that is approximately equal to 3.14 or $\frac{22}{7}$.

Circumference and Area of a Circle

To find the circumference C of a circle with radius r or diameter d, use the formula $C = 2\pi r$ or $C = \pi d$.

To find the area A of a circle with radius r, use the formula $A = \pi r^2$.

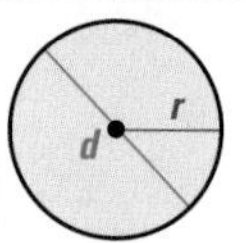

EXAMPLE **Find the circumference and area of the circle. Give your answers in terms of π and as decimals rounded to the nearest tenth.**

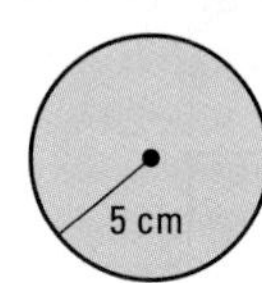

Circumference

$C = 2\pi r$

$= 2\pi(5)$

$= 10\pi$ cm **Exact answer**

$\approx 10(3.14)$

$= 31.4$ cm **Decimal approximation**

Area

$A = \pi r^2$

$= \pi(5^2)$

$= 25\pi$ cm^2 **Exact answer**

$\approx 25(3.14)$

$= 78.5$ cm^2 **Decimal approximation**

PRACTICE

Find the circumference and area of the circle. Give your answers in terms of π and as decimals rounded to the nearest tenth.

1.

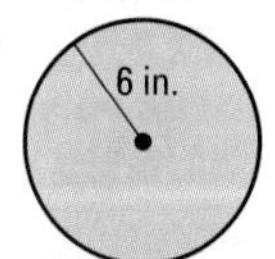

12π in. or 37.7 in., 36π in.^{2} or 113.0 in.^{2}

2. 3 cm

6π cm or 18.8 cm, 9π cm^2 or 28.3 cm^2

3. 8 in.

16π in. or 50.2 in., 64π in.^{2} or 201.0 in.^{2}

4.

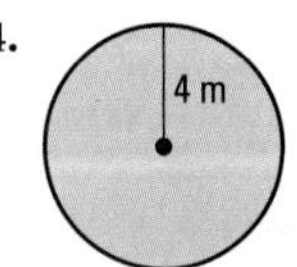

8π m or 25.1 m, 16π m^2 or 50.2 m^2

5.

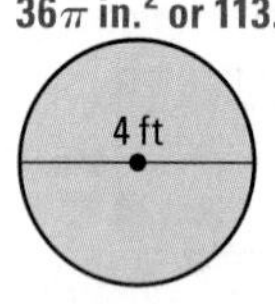

4π ft or 12.6 ft, 4π ft^2 or 12.6 ft^2

6.

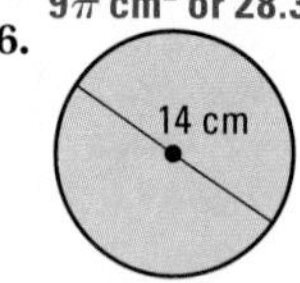

14π cm or 44.0 cm, 49π cm^2 or 153.9 cm^2

7.

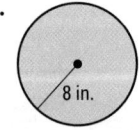

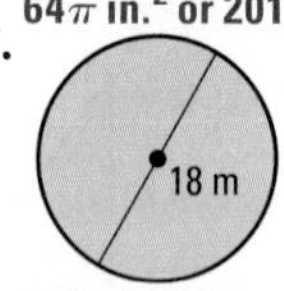

18π m or 56.5 m, 81π m^2 or 254.3 m^2

8. 2 ft

2π ft or 6.3 ft, π ft^2 or 3.1 ft^2

Surface Area and Volume

A **solid** is a three-dimensional figure that encloses part of space. The **surface area** S of a solid is the sum of the areas of all of its surfaces. The **volume** V of a solid is the amount of space that the solid occupies. In the formulas for surface area and volume, the number π (pi) is approximately equal to 3.14 or $\frac{22}{7}$.

Right Rectangular Prism

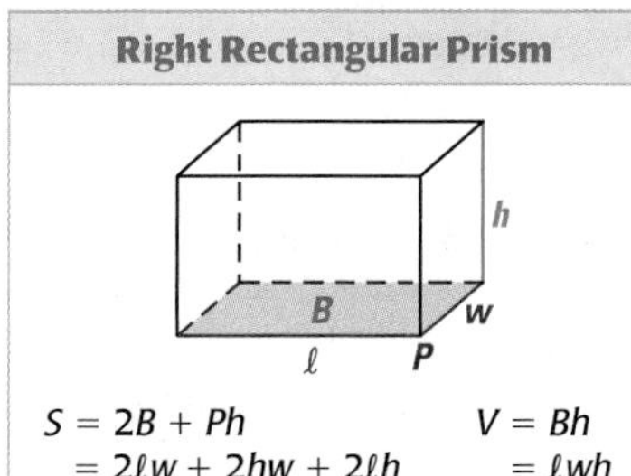

$S = 2B + Ph$ $\quad V = Bh$
$= 2\ell w + 2hw + 2\ell h$ $\quad = \ell wh$

Right Circular Cylinder

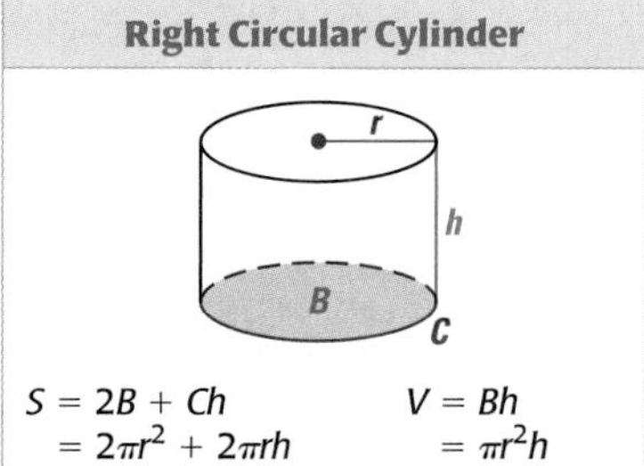

$S = 2B + Ch$ $\quad V = Bh$
$= 2\pi r^2 + 2\pi rh$ $\quad = \pi r^2 h$

Regular Pyramid

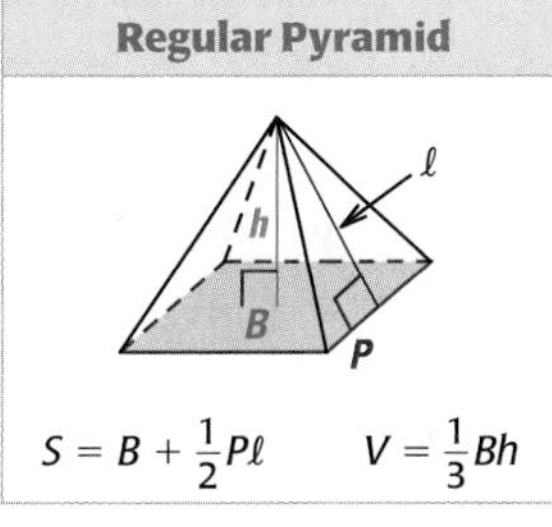

$S = B + \frac{1}{2}P\ell$ $\quad V = \frac{1}{3}Bh$

Right Circular Cone

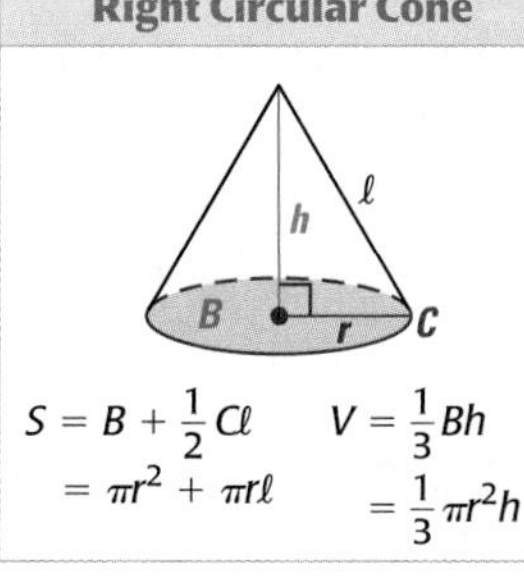

$S = B + \frac{1}{2}C\ell$ $\quad V = \frac{1}{3}Bh$
$= \pi r^2 + \pi r\ell$ $\quad = \frac{1}{3}\pi r^2 h$

Sphere

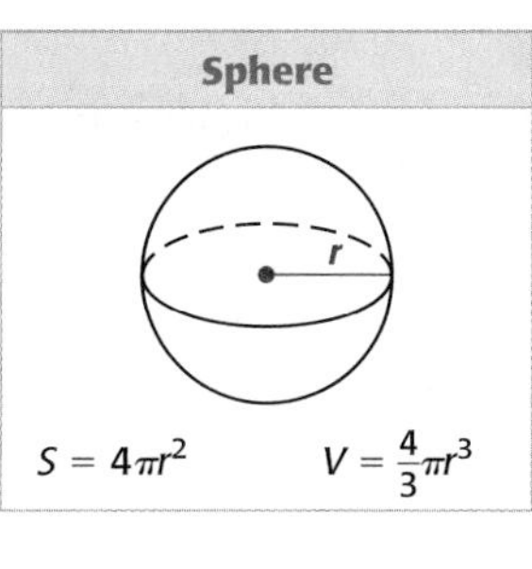

$S = 4\pi r^2$ $\quad V = \frac{4}{3}\pi r^3$

In this book, the adjectives *right* and *circular* will be assumed and therefore will not be used in naming solids.

EXAMPLE **Find the surface area of the solid.**

a. Sphere

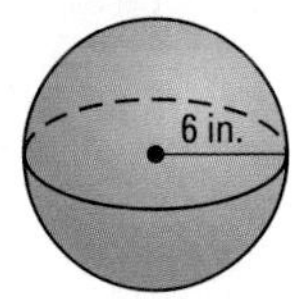

$S = 4\pi r^2$
$= 4\pi(6^2)$
$= 144\pi \text{ in.}^2$
$\approx 144(3.14)$
$\approx 452.2 \text{ in.}^2$

b. Cylinder

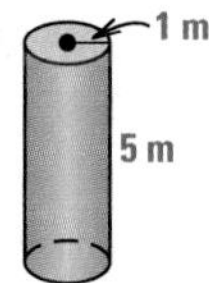

$S = 2\pi r^2 + 2\pi rh$
$= 2\pi(1^2) + 2\pi(1)(5)$
$= 2\pi + 10\pi$
$= 12\pi \text{ m}^2$
$\approx 12(3.14) \approx 37.7 \text{ m}^2$

c. Cone

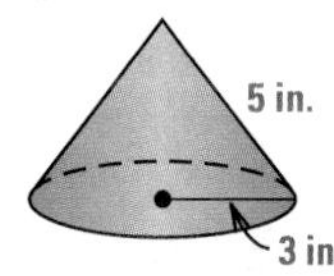

$S = \pi r^2 + \pi r\ell$
$= \pi(3^2) + \pi(3)(5)$
$= 9\pi + 15\pi$
$= 24\pi \text{ in.}^2$
$\approx 24(3.14) \approx 75.4 \text{ in.}^2$

925

EXAMPLE **Find the volume of the solid.**

a. Rectangular prism

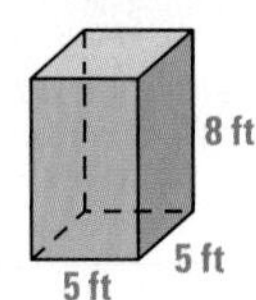

$V = Bh$

$= 25(8)$

$= 200 \text{ ft}^3$

b. Regular pyramid

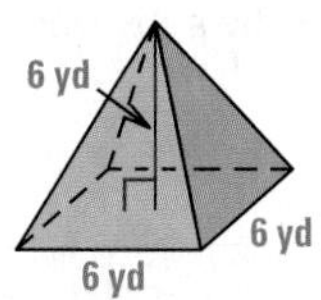

$V = \frac{1}{3}Bh$

$= \frac{1}{3}(36)6$

$= 72 \text{ yd}^3$

c. Cone

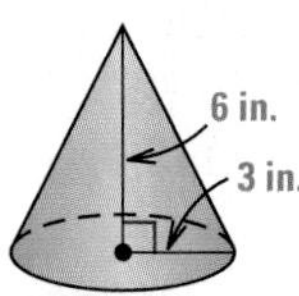

$V = \frac{1}{3}Bh$

$= \frac{1}{3}\pi(3^2)(6)$

$= 18\pi \text{ in.}^3$

$\approx 18(3.14) \approx 56.5 \text{ in.}^3$

PRACTICE

Find the surface area and volume of the solid. For spheres, cylinders, and cones, give your answers in terms of π and as decimals rounded to the nearest tenth.

1. Rectangular prism

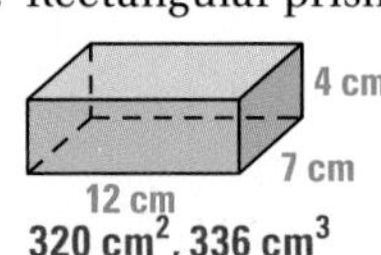

320 cm², 336 cm³

2. Cylinder **72π in.² or 226.1 in.², 80π in.³ or 251.2 in.³**

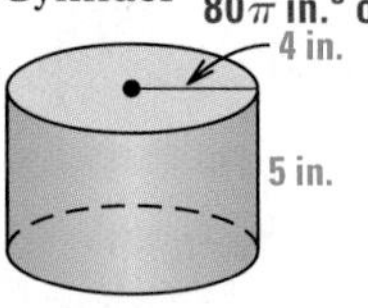

3. Sphere **900π m² or 2826 m², 4500π m³ or 14,130 m³**

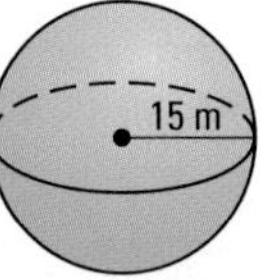

4. Cylinder **136π ft² or 427.0 ft², 208π ft³ or 653.1 ft³**

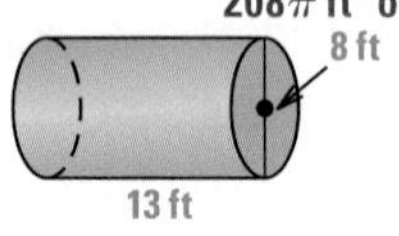

5. Cone **200π in.² or 628 in.², 320π in.³ or 1004.8 in.³**

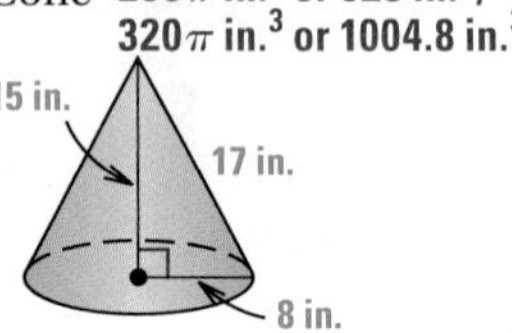

6. Rectangular prism

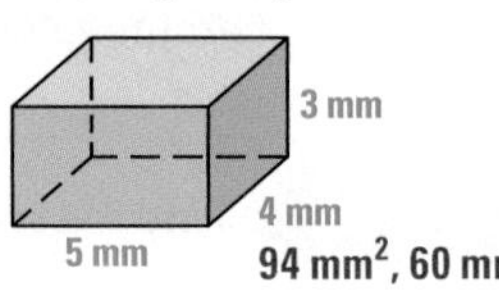

94 mm², 60 mm³

7. Regular pyramid **96 in.², 48 in.³**

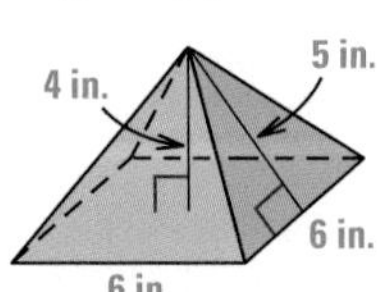

8. Sphere **100π in.² or 314 in.², $166\frac{2}{3}\pi$ in.³ or 523.3 in.³**

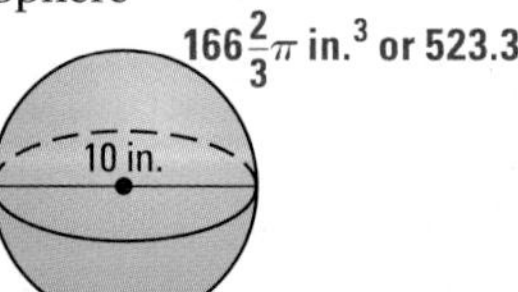

9. Cylinder **1888π in.² or 5928.3 in.², $11,008\pi$ in.³ or 34,565.1 in.³**

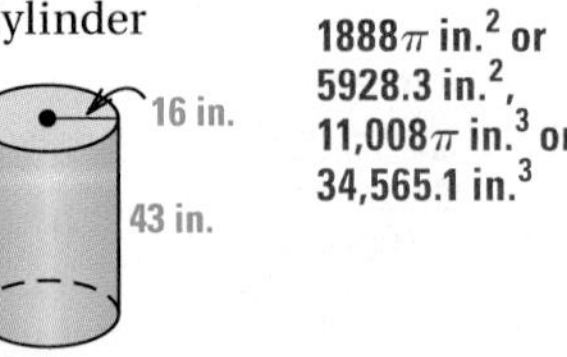

10. Rectangular prism **150 cm², 125 cm³**

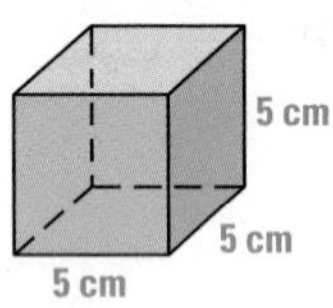

11. Cone **96π m² or 301.4 m², 96π m³ or 301.4 m³**

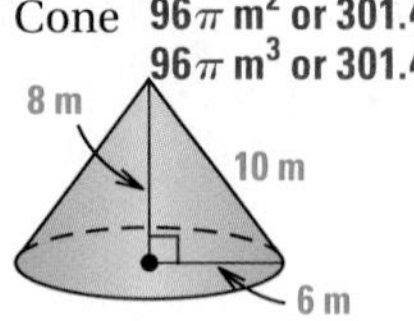

12. Regular pyramid **360 cm², 400 cm³**

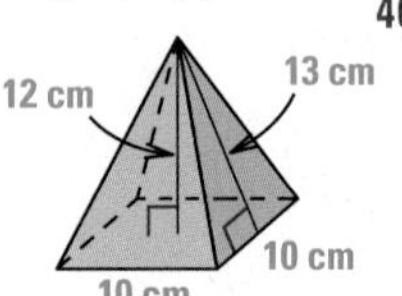

Converting Units of Measurement

The Table of Measures on page 956 gives many statements of equivalent measures. You can write two different conversion factors for each statement, as shown below. Each conversion factor is equal to 1.

Statement of Equivalent Measures	Conversion Factors
100 cm = 1 m	$\frac{100 \text{ cm}}{1 \text{ m}} = 1$ $\frac{1 \text{ m}}{100 \text{ cm}} = 1$

To convert from one unit of measurement to another, multiply by a conversion factor that will eliminate the starting unit and result in the desired unit.

Convert meters to centimeters:

Use $\frac{100 \text{ cm}}{1 \text{ m}}$.

$3 \cancel{\text{m}} \times \frac{100 \text{ cm}}{1 \cancel{\text{m}}} = 300 \text{ cm}$

Convert centimeters to meters:

Use $\frac{1 \text{ m}}{100 \text{ cm}}$.

$400 \cancel{\text{cm}} \times \frac{1 \text{ m}}{100 \cancel{\text{cm}}} = 4 \text{ m}$

Sometimes you need to use more than one conversion factor.

EXAMPLE **Copy and complete: 2 d = _?_ sec**

STEP 1 **Find** the appropriate statements of equivalent measures.

24 h = 1 d, 60 min = 1 h, and 60 sec = 1 min

STEP 2 **Write** the appropriate conversion factors: $\frac{24 \text{ h}}{1 \text{ d}}$, $\frac{60 \text{ min}}{1 \text{ h}}$, and $\frac{60 \text{ sec}}{1 \text{ min}}$

STEP 3 **Multiply** by the conversion factors:

$$2 \cancel{\text{d}} \times \frac{24 \cancel{\text{h}}}{1 \cancel{\text{d}}} \times \frac{60 \cancel{\text{min}}}{1 \cancel{\text{h}}} \times \frac{60 \text{ sec}}{1 \cancel{\text{min}}} = 172{,}800 \text{ sec}$$

▸ 2 d = 172,800 sec

PRACTICE

Copy and complete.

1. 300 sec = _?_ min **5**

2. 2.6 g = _?_ kg **0.0026**

3. 64 oz = _?_ lb **4**

4. 4 gal = _?_ qt **16**

5. 72 in. = _?_ ft **6**

6. 94 mm = _?_ cm **9.4**

7. 42 ft = _?_ yd **14**

8. 5 d = _?_ h **120**

9. 3 m = _?_ cm **300**

10. 2 yd = _?_ in. **72**

11. 70 L = _?_ mL **70,000**

12. 10 mi = _?_ ft **52,800**

13. 1.5 ton = _?_ lb **3000**

14. 4500 mL = _?_ L **4.5**

15. 15,000 mg = _?_ g **15**

Convert to common units as necessary and perform the indicated operation.

16. 42 g − 500 mg
41.5 g or 41,500 mg

17. $3\frac{2}{3}$ yd + 33 ft
$14\frac{2}{3}$ yd or 44 ft

18. $2\frac{1}{4}$ mi − 3960 ft
1.5 mi or 7920 ft

Converting Between Systems

To convert between metric and customary units, use the approximate relationships shown in the table. The symbol ≈ means is *approximately equal to.*

Length	Capacity	Weight
1 mm ≈ 0.0394 in.	1 mL ≈ 0.0338 fl oz	1 g ≈ 0.0353 oz
1 m ≈ 3.28 ft	1 L ≈ 1.06 qt	1 kg ≈ 2.2 lb
1 km ≈ 0.621 mi	1 kL ≈ 264 gal	

EXAMPLE **Copy and complete: 131 km ≈ ? mi. Round to the nearest whole number.**

STEP 1 **Find** the appropriate statement of equivalent measures: 1 km ≈ 0.621 mi

STEP 2 **Write** the appropriate conversion factor: $\frac{0.621 \text{ mi}}{1 \text{ km}}$

STEP 3 **Multiply** by the conversion factor:

$$131 \cancel{\text{km}} \times \frac{0.621 \text{ mi}}{1 \cancel{\text{km}}} = 81.351 \text{ mi} \approx 81 \text{ mi}$$

▸ 131 km ≈ 81 mi

EXAMPLE **Copy and complete: 124 lb ≈ ? kg. Round to the nearest whole number.**

STEP 1 **Find** the appropriate statement of equivalent measures: 1 kg ≈ 2.2 lb

STEP 2 **Write** the appropriate conversion factor: $\frac{1 \text{ kg}}{2.2 \text{ lb}}$

STEP 3 **Multiply** by the conversion factor:

$$124 \cancel{\text{lb}} \times \frac{1 \text{ kg}}{2.2 \cancel{\text{lb}}} = 56.\overline{36} \text{ kg} \approx 56 \text{ kg}$$

▸ 124 lb ≈ 56 kg

PRACTICE

Copy and complete the statement. Round to the nearest whole number.

1. 3.2 kL ≈ ? gal **845**
2. 25 mm ≈ ? in. **1**
3. 180 g ≈ ? oz **6**
4. 10 qt ≈ ? L **9**
5. 35 km ≈ ? mi **22**
6. 85 kg ≈ ? lb **187**
7. 12 ft ≈ ? m **4**
8. 14 oz ≈ ? g **397**
9. 30 L ≈ ? qt **32**
10. 15 m ≈ ? ft **49**
11. 2.5 mi ≈ ? km **4**
12. 8 fl oz ≈ ? ml **237**
13. 42 mm ≈ ? in. **2**
14. 39 mL ≈ ? fl oz **1**
15. 1300 gal ≈ ? kL **5**

Venn Diagrams and Logical Reasoning

A **Venn diagram** uses shapes to show how sets are related.

EXAMPLE **Draw a Venn diagram of the whole numbers less than 10 where set *A* consists of prime numbers and set *B* consists of even numbers.**

Whole numbers less than 10:
0, 1, 2, 3, 4, 5, 6, 7, 8, 9

Set *A*: 2, 3, 5, 7

Set *B*: 0, 2, 4, 6, 8

Both set *A* and set *B*: 2

Neither set *A* nor set *B*: 1, 9

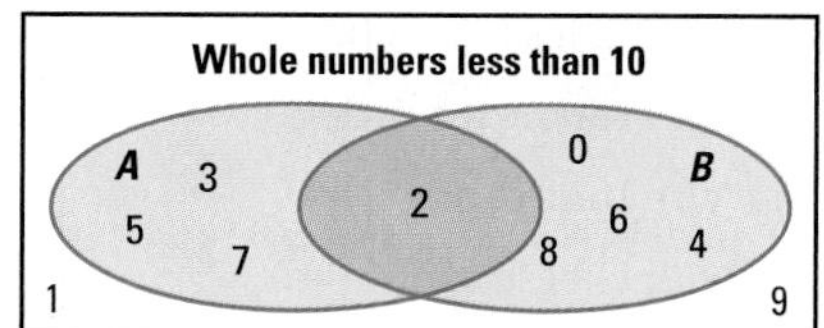

You can use a Venn diagram to answer questions about sets.

EXAMPLE **Use the Venn diagram above to answer the question.**

a. Is the statement below *true* or *false*? Explain.

No whole number less than 10 is prime.

▸ False. The whole number 2 is less than 10 and is prime.

b. Is the statement below *always, sometimes,* or *never* true? Explain.

A whole number less than 10 is either even or prime.

▸ Sometimes. Each of the numbers 0, 2, 3, 4, 5, 6, 7, and 8 are either even or prime, but the numbers 1 and 9 are not even and not prime.

PRACTICE

Draw a Venn diagram of the sets described. **1, 2. See margin.**

1. Of the whole numbers less than 10, set *A* consists of factors of 10 and set *B* consists of odd numbers.
2. Of the whole numbers less than 10, set *A* consists of factors of 6 and set *B* consists of even numbers.

Use the Venn diagrams you drew in Exercises 1 and 2 to answer the question.

3. Are the following statements *true* or *false*? Explain.
   a. *If a whole number less than 10 is odd, then it must be a factor of 10.*
   b. *A whole number less than 10 that is a factor of 10 must be odd.*
4. Are the following statements *always, sometimes,* or *never* true? Explain. **a, b. See margin.**
   a. *A whole number that is even and less than 10 is a factor of 6.*
   b. *A factor of 6 that is less than 10 is even.*

3a. False; there are whole numbers less than 10 that are odd but are not factors of 10, such as 3, 7, and 9.
3b. False; there is a whole number less than 10 that is a factor of 10 but is not odd, 2.

1.

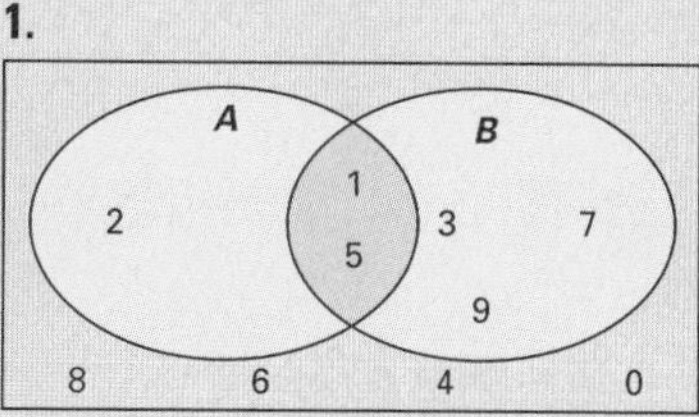

2.

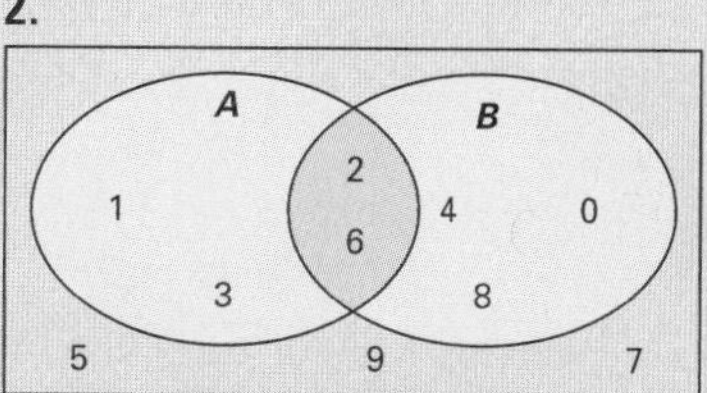

4a. Sometimes; there are whole numbers that are even and less than 10 that are factors of 6 such as 2 and 6, but there are also whole numbers that are even and less than 10 that are not factors of 6 such as 0, 4, and 8.

4b. Sometimes; there are factors of 6 that are less than 10 that are even such as 2 and 6, but there are also factors of 6 that are less than 10 that are odd such as 1 and 3.

Counting Methods

There are several methods for counting the number of possibilities in a situation.

EXAMPLE **Make a list to find the number of possible lunch specials.**

> **Lunch Special $6.95**
>
> Choose 1 soup and 1 sandwich.
>
> | Soups | Sandwiches |
> |---|---|
> | Chicken | Turkey |
> | Tomato | Tuna |
> | | Cheese |

Pair each soup with each sandwich.

Chicken soup with turkey sandwich

Chicken soup with tuna sandwich

Chicken soup with cheese sandwich

Tomato soup with turkey sandwich

Tomato soup with tuna sandwich

Tomato soup with cheese sandwich

Count the number of lunch specials in the list.

▶ There are 6 possible lunch specials.

EXAMPLE **Draw a tree diagram to find the number of possible lunch specials given the choices in the example above.**

Arrange the soups and sandwiches in a tree diagram.

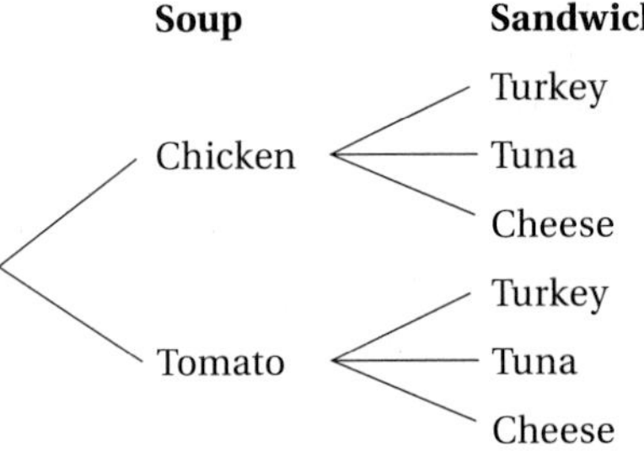

Lunch

Chicken soup, turkey sandwich

Chicken soup, tuna sandwich

Chicken soup, cheese sandwich

Tomato soup, turkey sandwich

Tomato soup, tuna sandwich

Tomato soup, cheese sandwich

▶ There are 6 possible lunch specials.

Another way to count the number of possible lunch specials described in the examples above is to multiply. Since there are 2 choices of soup and 3 choices of sandwich, there are $2 \times 3 = 6$ possible lunch specials. This method uses the counting principle.

> **The Counting Principle**
>
> If one event can occur in m ways, and for each of these ways a second event can occur in n ways, then the number of ways that the two events can occur together is $m \cdot n$.

The counting principle can be extended to three or more events.

EXAMPLE **Greta must choose a 4-digit password for her cell phone mailbox. Use the counting principle to find the number of possible 4-digit passwords.**

For each of the 4 digits in the password, there are 10 choices: 0, 1, 2, 3, 4, 5, 6, 7, 8, and 9.

10 choices for first digit	×	10 choices for second digit	×	10 choices for third digit	×	10 choices for fourth digit

$10 \times 10 \times 10 \times 10 = 10{,}000$

▸ There are 10,000 possible 4-digit passwords.

PRACTICE

In Exercises 1–3, use the indicated counting method to answer the question.

1. Andrew, Bettina, and Carl are triplets. In how many different ways can the triplets stand in a row for a photo? (Make a list.) **6 ways**
2. The sign at the right shows the color and size choices for school T-shirts. How many different types of school T-shirts are available? (Draw a tree diagram.) **12 types of T-shirts**
3. A 3-letter monogram consists of the first letter of a person's first name, middle name, and last name. For example, Matthew David Weaver's monogram is MDW. How many different 3-letter monograms are possible? (Use the counting principle.) **17,576 3-letter monograms**

School T-Shirts $9.99

Choose 1 color and 1 size.

Colors:	Sizes:
Black, Gold, or White	S, M, L, or XL

In Exercises 4–8, answer the question using any counting method you choose.

4. How many different pizzas with 2 different toppings are available for the large pizza special advertised at the right? **28 pizzas**
5. Lance must choose 4 characters for his computer password. Each character can be any letter A–Z or any digit 0–9. How many different computer passwords are possible? **1,679,616 computer passwords**
6. Mia must choose 3 whole numbers less than 50 for her locker combination. The numbers may be repeated. How many different locker combinations are possible? **125,000 locker combinations**
7. A restaurant offers a dinner special. You can choose a main course, a vegetable, and a salad from a choice of 6 main courses, 4 vegetables, and 3 salads. How many different dinners are available? **72 dinners**
8. Each day Scott walks, rides the bus, or gets a ride to school. He has each of the same possibilities for getting home each day. How many combinations of travel to and from school does Scott have? **9 combinations of travel**

Large Pizza Special

Any 2 toppings for $12.49

Pepperoni	Black olive
Sausage	Green pepper
Ground beef	Red onion
Extra cheese	Mushroom

SKILLS REVIEW HANDBOOK

Bar Graphs

You can use a **bar graph** to display and compare data that are in categories.

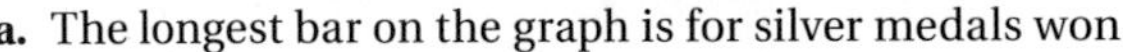

EXAMPLE **Use the bar graph, which shows the medals won by the United States in the 2004 Summer Olympics. (a) Did the United States win more gold medals, silver medals, or bronze medals? (b) How many more silver medals than bronze medals did the United States win?**

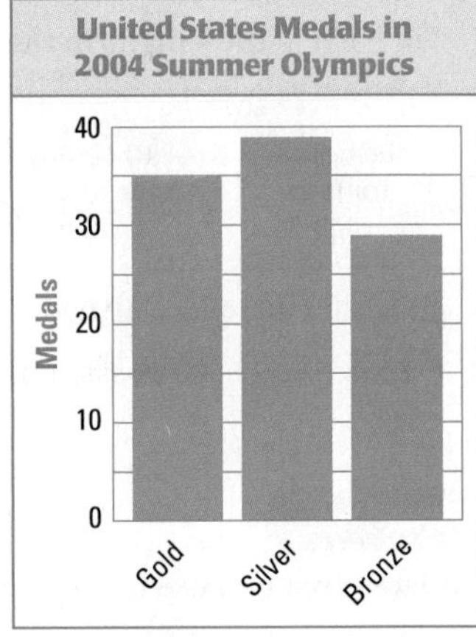

a. The longest bar on the graph is for silver medals won.

▶ The United States won more silver medals than any other type.

b. The bar for silver medals shows 39 silver medals won. The bar for bronze medals shows 29 bronze medals won.

$39 - 29 = 10$

▶ The United States won 10 more silver medals than bronze medals.

PRACTICE

In Exercises 1–3, use the bar graph above.

1. The United States won fewer of which type of medal than any other type? **bronze**
2. How many more silver medals than gold medals did the United States win? **4 more silver medals**
3. How many medals did the United States win altogether? **103 medals**

In Exercises 4–11, use the bar graph below, which shows the top medal-winning countries in the 2002 Winter Olympics.

4. Which country won the most medals? How many medals did it win? **Germany; 37 medals**
5. How many medals did Norway win? **25 medals**
6. Which two countries won 17 medals each? **Canada and Austria**
7. Which country won the same number of medals as France? **Switzerland**
8. How many countries won more than 15 medals? **5 countries**
9. Which country won twice as many medals as Austria? **United States**
10. How many medals did Russia and Italy win altogether? **26 medals**
11. How many medals did the top 3 medal-winning countries win? **96 medals**

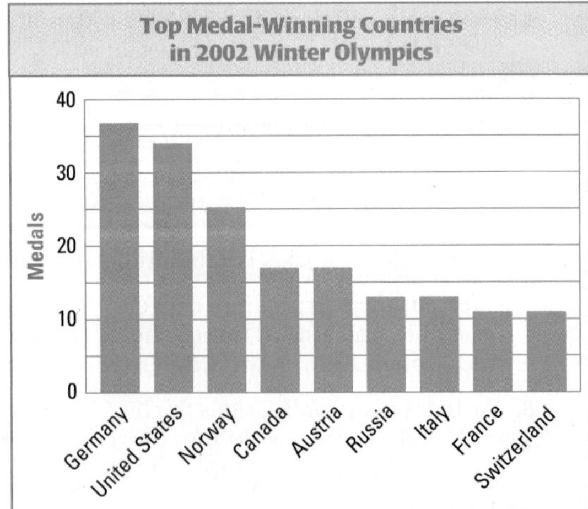

Line Graphs

You can use a **line graph** to show how numerical data change over time.

EXAMPLE **Use the line graph, which shows Charlie's weight from birth to 5 years old. (a) How much weight did Charlie gain in 5 years? (b) At what age did Charlie weigh 30 pounds? (c) In which year did Charlie gain the most weight?**

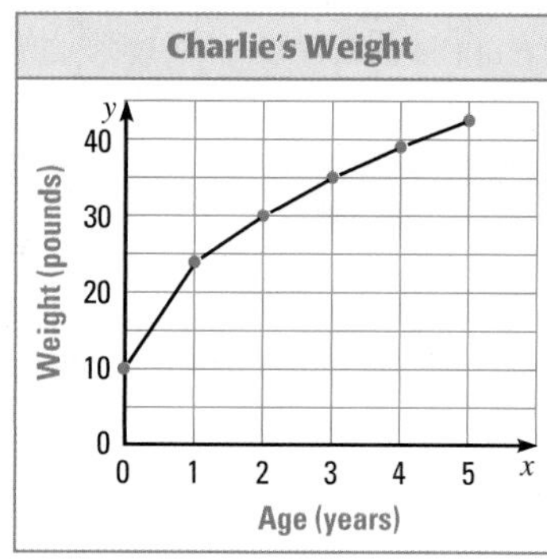

a. The lowest point on the graph shows that Charlie weighed 10 pounds at birth. The highest point on the graph shows he weighed 42.5 pounds at age 5.

$42.5 - 10 = 32.5$

▸ Charlie gained 32.5 pounds in 5 years.

b. The point on the graph to the right of 30 on the weight axis corresponds to an age of 2.

▸ Charlie weighed 30 pounds at age 2.

c. The graph is steepest from birth to age 1.

▸ Charlie gained the most weight in his first year.

PRACTICE

In Exercises 1–5, use the line graph above.

1. How much did Charlie weigh on his first birthday? **about 24 lb**
2. How old was Charlie when he weighed 40 pounds? **about 4.2 years old**
3. In which year did Charlie gain the least weight? **between ages 4 and 5**
4. How much weight did Charlie gain his first year? **about 14 lb**
5. How much weight did Charlie gain from age 1 to age 4? **about 15 lb**

In Exercises 6–14, use the line graph, which shows Abby's height from birth to 4 years old.

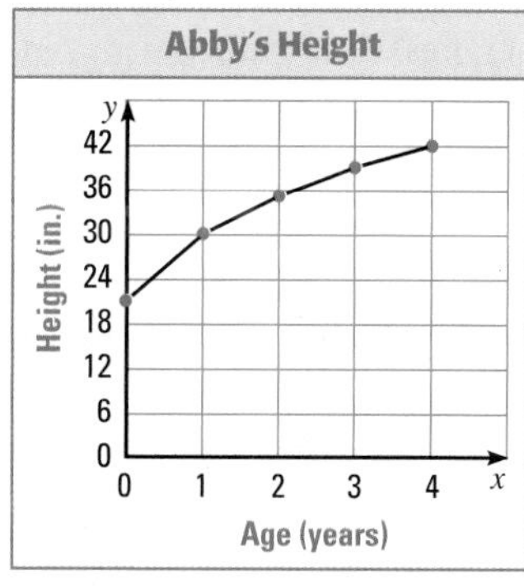

6. How tall was Abby when she was born? **about 21 in.**
7. How old was Abby when she was 35 inches tall? **about 2 years old**
8. In which year did Abby grow the most? **her first year**
9. In which year did Abby grow the least? **between ages 3 and 4**
10. How many inches did Abby grow from age 3 to age 4? **about 3 in.**
11. In which year did Abby grow 5 inches? **between ages 1 and 2**
12. How many inches did Abby grow in 4 years? **about 21 in.**
13. At what age was Abby's height double her height at birth? **about 4 yr**
14. If Abby maintains the same growth rate from age 4 to age 5 that she had from age 3 to age 4, how tall will she be when she is 5? **about 45 in.**

Circle Graphs

You can use a **circle graph** to display data as sections of a circle. The entire circle represents all of the data. The sections of the circle may be labeled using the actual data or the data expressed as fractions, decimals, or percents. When the data are expressed as fractions, decimals, or percents, the sum of the data is 1.

EXAMPLE **Use the circle graph, which shows the string musicians in a college orchestra. (a) What percent of the string musicians in the orchestra play the cello? (b) Which instrument do almost half the string musicians in the orchestra play?**

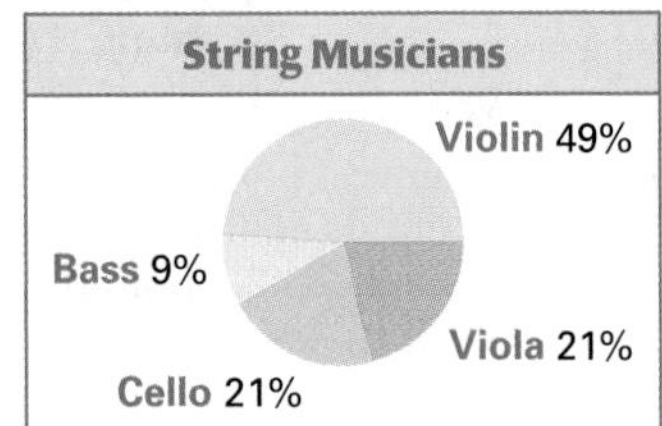

a. The cello section of the circle is labeled 21%.

▸ Of the string musicians in the orchestra, 21% play cello.

b. The violin section of the circle is labeled 49%, which is almost 50%. Also, the violin section of the circle is almost half the total area of the circle.

▸ Almost half of the string musicians in the orchestra play the violin.

PRACTICE

In Exercises 1–4, use the circle graph above.

1. What percent of the string musicians in the orchestra play the bass? **9%**
2. How does the number of string musicians who play the viola compare with the number of string musicians who play the cello? **They are equal.**
3. The violinists are divided evenly into two groups, first violin and second violin. What percent of the string musicians are in each of these groups? **24.5%**
4. If there are 57 string musicians in the orchestra, how many musicians play each type of instrument? **28 play violin, 12 play cello, 12 play viola, and 5 play bass**

In Exercises 5–10, use the circle graph, which shows the types of instruments played by musicians in a college band.

Band Musicians
Brass 37%
Woodwinds 52%
Percussion 8%
Other 3%

5. What percent of the musicians in the band play a brass instrument? **37%**
6. Which type of instrument do 8% of the musicians in the band play? **percussion**
7. Which type of instrument do more than half of the musicians in the band play? **woodwinds**

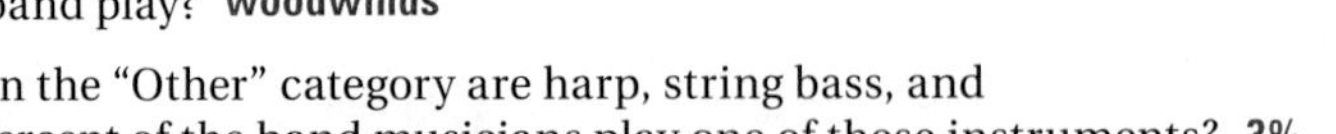

8. The instruments in the "Other" category are harp, string bass, and keyboard. What percent of the band musicians play one of these instruments? **3%**
9. In this band, which type of instrument is played by about 5 times as many musicians as play percussion instruments? **brass**
10. There are 91 musicians in the band. How many more musicians play a woodwind than play a percussion instrument? **40 more musicians**

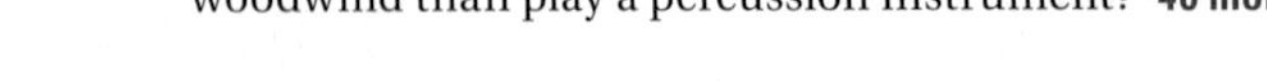

Misleading Data Displays

Data displays may be misleading because of the way in which they are drawn.

EXAMPLE ***Explain*** **why the data display may be misleading.**

a.

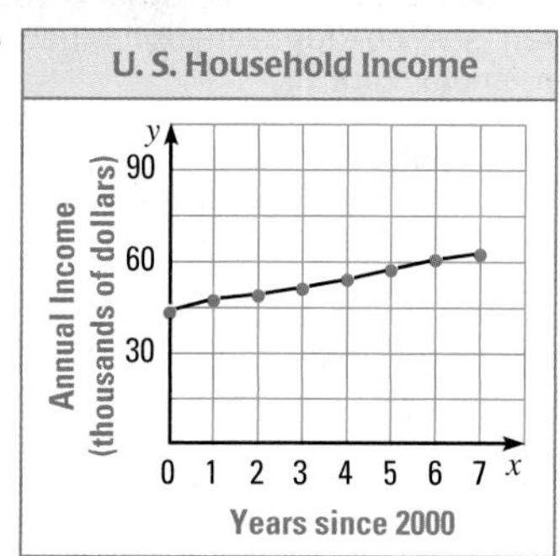

b.

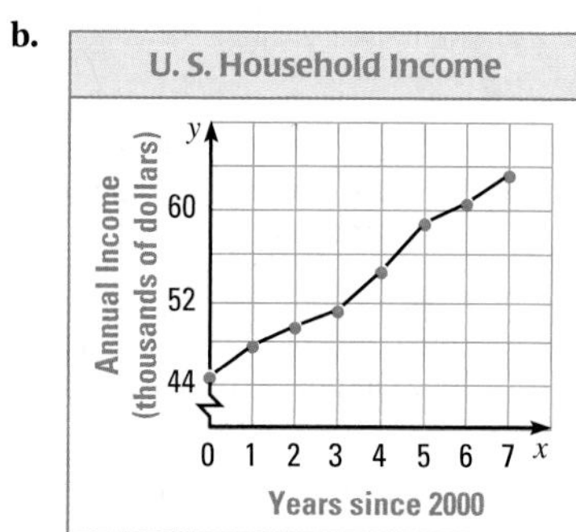

a. The large increments on the y-axis flatten the graph and make the increases seem insignificant.

b. The break in the y-axis stretches the graph and exaggerates the increases.

PRACTICE

Explain **why the data display may be misleading.** 1–4. See margin.

1.

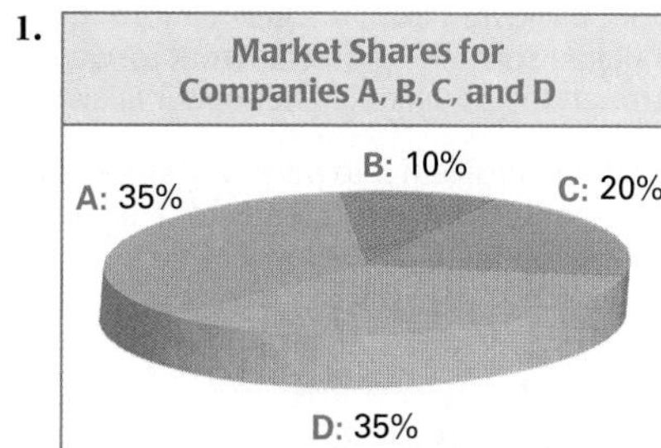

2.

Survey of 150 Voters

Should Main St. be renamed?

Yes : 40

No : 20

No response : 90

3.

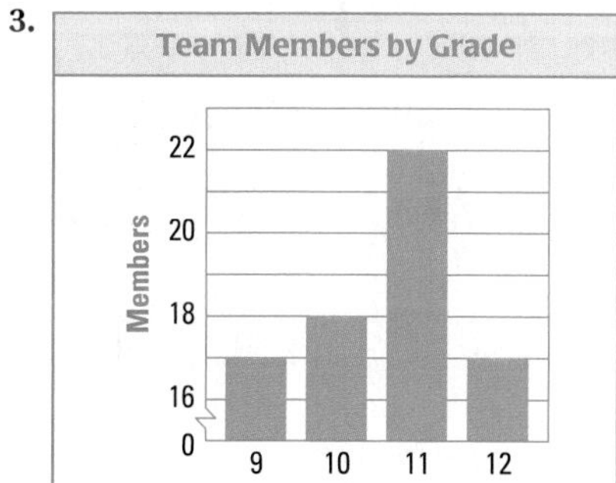

4.

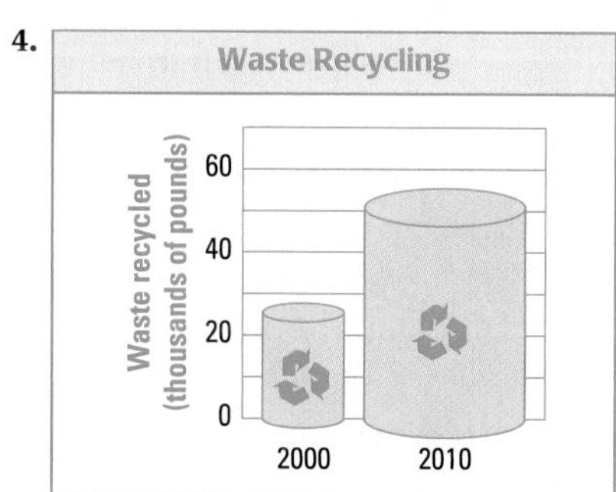

1. The graph is tilted, which exaggerates the prominence of the sector labeled "D." That sector looks larger than the one labeled "A" even though both sectors represent the same percentage of shares.
2. The graph shows only the sectors that represent *Yes* and *No* answers, which gives the impression that nearly half of the respondents answered *Yes*, and nearly one fourth answered *No*. Actually, just over one fourth of the respondents answered *Yes*, and just over 10% answered *No*.
3. The break in the y-axis stretches the graph and exaggerates the differences in the numbers of members in different grades. For example, although the bar for Grade 11 is 3.5 times as high as that for Grade 9, the number of members in Grade 11 is only about 1.3 times the number of members in Grade 9.
4. The cylinder that represents the amount of waste recycled in 2010 is twice as tall and has twice the diameter of the cylinder that represents 2000, which gives the visual impression that the amount of waste recycled in 2010 was 8 times the amount recycled in 2000, rather than twice the amount.

Problem Solving Strategies

The following are strategies that you can use to solve problems.

Strategy	When to use	How to use
Draw a diagram	Draw a diagram when a problem involves any relationships that you can represent visually.	Draw a diagram that shows the given information. Label any unknowns in your diagram and look for relationships between givens and unknowns.
Look for a pattern	Look for a pattern when a problem includes a series of numbers or diagrams that you need to analyze.	Look for a pattern in any given information. Apply, extend, or generalize the pattern to help you solve the problem.
Guess, check, and revise	Guess, check, and revise when you need a place to start or you want to see what happens for a particular number.	Make a reasonable guess. Check to see if your guess solves the problem. If it does not, revise your guess and check again.
Act it out	Act out a problem that involves any relationships that you can represent with physical objects and movement.	Act out the problem, using objects described in the problem or other items that represent those objects.
Make a list or table	Make a list or table when you need to record, generate, or organize information.	Generate a list systematically, accounting for all possibilities. Look for relationships across rows or down columns within a table.
Solve a simpler or related problem	Solve a simpler or related problem when a problem seems difficult and can be made easier by using simpler numbers or conditions.	Think of a way to make the problem easier. Solve the simpler or related problem. Use what you learned to help you solve the original problem.
Work backward	Work backward when a problem gives you an end result and you need to find beginning conditions.	Work backward from the given information until you solve the problem. Work forward through the problem to check your answer.
Break into parts	Break into parts when a problem cannot be solved all at once, but can be solved in parts or stages.	Break the problem into parts and solve each part. Put the answers together to help you solve the original problem.

EXAMPLE **Fletcher baked brownies in a rectangular pan that measures 9 inches by 13 inches. He wants to cut rectangular brownies that are at least 2 inches on each side, with all brownies the same size. What is the greatest number of brownies Fletcher can cut?**

Draw a diagram of the rectangular pan. Label the sides with their lengths. Think about each side of the rectangle.

$9 \div 2 = 4.5$, so cut 4 brownies along the 9 inch side.
Check: $9 \div 4 = 2.25$, and $2.25 > 2$.

$13 \div 2 = 6.5$, so cut 6 brownies along the 13 inch side.
Check: $13 \div 6 \approx 2.17$, and $2.17 > 2$.

Use your diagram to count the brownies: $4 \times 6 = 24$.

▶ The greatest number of brownies Fletcher can cut is 24.

PRACTICE

1. Four friends hosted a party. The table shows the amount of money each friend spent. The friends want to share the party expenses equally, and Pam will pay the entire amount she owes to one person. Who owes money to whom? **See margin.**

Person	Party expenses
Barb	$11 for drinks
Bonnie	$15 for food
Pam	$6 for invitations
Holly	$8 for decorations

2. Six people can be seated at a rectangular table, with one person at each end. How many people can be seated at five of these tables if they are placed end to end? **22 people**

3. Bob is 55 years old. In 5 years, Bob will be twice as old as his son. How old is Bob's son? **25 years old**

4. Maddie and Rob are sharing a pack of 25 pens. Maddie offers to let Rob have 3 pens for every 2 pens she gets. If they use the entire package of pens, how many pens will each person get? **Rob: 15 pens, Maddie: 10 pens**

5. In how many different ways can you make $.50 in change using quarters, dimes, and nickels? **10 ways**

6. The diagram shows two cuts through the center of a pizza. How many cuts through the center are needed to divide a pizza into 12 equal pieces? **6 cuts**

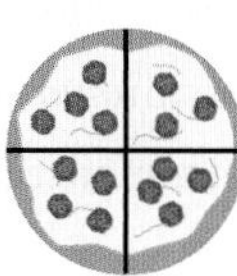

7. Deb is flying to Seattle. Her flight leaves at 4:15 P.M. She wants to arrive at the airport 2 hours early to check in and get through security. The taxi ride from her office to the airport takes about 30 minutes. What time should Deb ask the taxi driver to pick her up at the office? **1:45 P.M.**

8. Dan wants to enclose a rectangular area with a fence. He has 12 fence posts to use, and the fence posts will be placed 10 feet apart. The diagram shows a possible shape for the area. Find another shape that would use all the fence posts, placed 10 feet apart, and would increase the area by 100 square feet. **a square with 4 posts on each side**

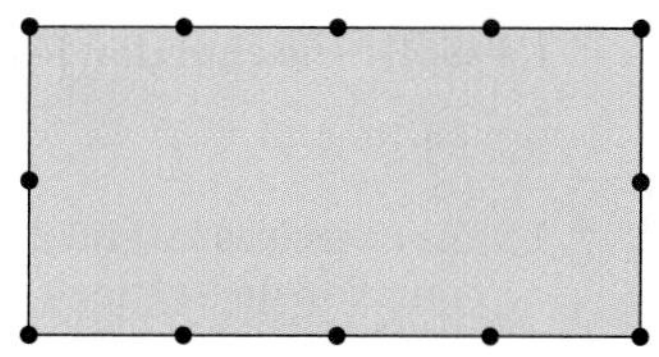

9. A soccer league has a 7 week season, and there are 7 teams in the league. Each team plays a game with every other team once during the season. How many soccer games must be played each week of the season? **3 soccer games per week**

10. Julia is setting up a display of cracker boxes at a grocery store. She wants one box in the top row, two boxes in the second row down, three boxes in the third row down, and so on, as shown. Each box is 8 inches tall, and her display will be 6 feet tall. How many cracker boxes will be in the display? **45 cracker boxes**

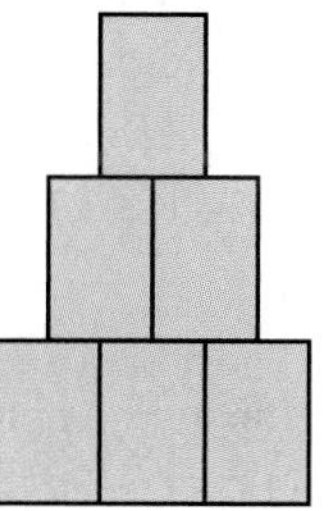

11. Five friends line up for tetherball. William is first in line, Mac is between Quinn and Benjamin, and Nate is next to William and Benjamin. Which friend is last in line? **Quinn**

12. The 4 members of the Buckner family usually drink 3 gallons of milk altogether each week. For 12 weeks in the summer, they will have a fifth family member staying with them. How many gallons of milk would you expect the 5 family members to drink over the 12 weeks? **45 gal**

1. Pam owes $4 that she can pay to Bonnie who is owed a total of $5. Holly should pay both Barb and Bonnie $1.

29. ***Sample answer:*** **You know the temperature in Quito in degrees Celsius and the temperature in Miami in degrees Fahrenheit. You need to find out which one is greater.**

30. ***Sample answer:*** **You know the rate and time Katherine walked each day. You need to find out the distance she walked during the 2 days.**

32.

Input	2	4	6	8
Output	7.5	10	12.5	15

33.–36.

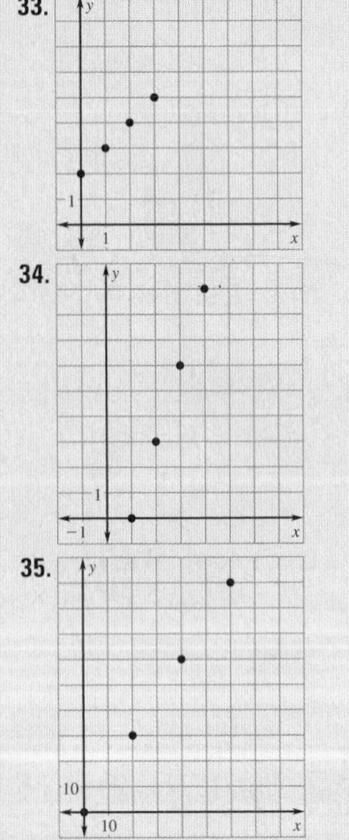

Extra Practice

Chapter 1

Evaluate the expression.

1.1 1. $k + 9$ when $k = 7$ **16** 2. $21 - x$ when $x = 3$ **18** 3. $3.5 + t$ when $t = 0.9$ **4.4** 4. $y - \frac{3}{8}$ when $y = \frac{7}{12}$ $\mathbf{\frac{5}{24}}$

5. $\frac{m}{4}$ when $m = 9.6$ **2.4** 6. $1.5t$ when $t = 2.3$ **3.45** 7. z^3 when $z = \frac{2}{3}$ $\mathbf{\frac{8}{27}}$ 8. p^4 when $p = 0.2$ **0.0016**

1.2 9. $25 - 7 + 8$ **26** 10. $67 - 3 \cdot 4$ **55** 11. $8^2 \div 4 + 12$ **28** 12. $9 + 6 \div 3$ **11**

13. $\frac{3^3 - 7}{2}$ **10** 14. $\frac{1}{3}(7 - 5.5)^2$ **0.75** 15. $3 + 4(3 + 24)$ **111** 16. $\frac{3}{5}[27 - (2 + 5)]^2$ **240**

1.3 Translate the verbal phrase into an expression.

17. $\frac{3}{4}$ of a number m $\mathbf{\frac{3}{4}m}$

18. the quotient of a number x and 7 $\mathbf{\frac{x}{7}}$

19. the difference of a number y and 3 $\mathbf{y - 3}$

20. 6 more than 3 times a number n $\mathbf{3n + 6}$

1.3 Write an expression for the situation.

21. Number of minutes left in a 45 minute class after m minutes have gone by $\mathbf{45 - m}$

22. Number of meters in c centimeters $\mathbf{\frac{c}{100}}$

1.4 Write an equation or an inequality.

23. The product of 12 and the difference of a number r and 4 is 72. $\mathbf{12 \cdot (r - 4) = 72}$

24. The difference of a number q and 18 is greater than 10 and less than 15. $\mathbf{10 < q - 18 < 15}$

1.4 Solve the equation using mental math.

25. $d - 13 = 25$ **38** 26. $12z = 96$ **8** 27. $23 - m = 7$ **16** 28. $\frac{k}{6} = 12$ **72**

1.5 In Exercises 29 and 30, identify what you know and what you need to find out. You do *not* need to solve the problem. **29, 30. See margin.**

29. One day the temperature in Quito, Ecuador, was 20°C. The temperature in Miami, Florida was 75°F. Which temperature was higher?

30. On Monday, Katherine walked at a rate of 0.08 mile per minute for 40 minutes. On Tuesday, she walked at a rate of 0.07 mile per minute for 50 minutes. How far did Katherine walk altogether?

1.6 31. Identify the domain and range of the function.
domain: 3, 4, 5, 6; range: 9, 11, 13, 15

Input	3	4	5	6
Output	9	11	13	15

1.6 32. The domain of the function $y = 1.25x + 5$ is 2, 4, 6, and 8. Make a table for the function. Identify the range of the function.
See margin for table; range: 7.5, 10, 12.5, 15.

1.7 Graph the function.
33–36. See margin.

33. $y = x + 2$; domain: 0, 1, 2, and 3

34. $y = 3x - 3$; domain: 1, 2, 3, and 4

35. $y = 1.5x$; domain: 0, 20, 40, and 60

36. $y = \frac{1}{4}x + 2$; domain: 0, 4, 8, and 12

Chapter 2

2.1 **Graph the numbers on a number line. Then tell which number is greater.** **1–4. See margin for art.**

1. 0 and −4 **0**
2. 2 and −2 **2**
3. −5 and −3 **−3**
4. −6 and 4 **4**

2.1 **Tell whether each number in the list is a whole number, an integer, or a rational number. Then order the numbers from least to greatest.** **5–7. See margin.**

5. $0.25, -\frac{1}{8}, -\frac{1}{10}, -\frac{1}{5}$
6. $-2.5, -3, \frac{5}{2}, -\frac{9}{4}$
7. $-4, 3, -5, 0$

2.2 **Find the sum.**

8. $-6 + 10$ **4**
9. $-25 + (-36)$ **−61**
10. $-75 + 58$ **−17**
11. $8 + (-15) + 7$ **0**
12. $-2.8 + 4.3$ **1.5**
13. $-8.2 + (-11.5)$ **−19.7**
14. $3\frac{2}{3} + \left(-5\frac{3}{8}\right)$ **$-1\frac{17}{24}$**
15. $-12\frac{3}{5} + 8\frac{1}{6}$ **$-4\frac{13}{30}$**

2.3 **Find the difference.**

16. $-17 - 20$ **−37**
17. $16 - (-50)$ **66**
18. $-9 - (-12)$ **3**
19. $\frac{4}{5} - \frac{1}{2}$ **$\frac{3}{10}$**
20. $-\frac{1}{2} - \frac{2}{3}$ **$-1\frac{1}{6}$**
21. $-\frac{1}{3} - \left(-\frac{3}{4}\right)$ **$\frac{5}{12}$**
22. $-6.4 - 15$ **−21.4**
23. $-12.8 - (-5.6)$ **−7.2**

2.3 **Evaluate the expression when $x = 1.5$ and $y = -4$.**

24. $y - x$ **−5.5**
25. $-y - (-x)$ **5.5**
26. $x - (10 - y)$ **−12.5**
27. $-7 - (x - y)$ **−12.5**

2.4 **Find the product.**

28. $-\frac{2}{3}(-36)$ **24**
29. $64\left(-\frac{5}{8}\right)$ **−40**
30. $-4.1(-3.5)$ **14.35**
31. $(1.1)(-0.5)(-4)$ **2.2**

2.4 **Identify the property illustrated.** **32–37. See margin.**

32. $(-5)(8)(2) = (-5)(2)(8)$
33. $6 \cdot (7 \cdot 2) = (6 \cdot 7) \cdot 2$
34. $1(mn) = mn$
35. $0 \cdot (134) = 0$
36. $y \cdot (-1) = (-1) \cdot y$
37. $(-1)(-9) = 9$

2.5 **Use the distributive property to write an equivalent expression.**

38. $8(x + 4)$ **$8x + 32$**
39. $5(6 - y)$ **$30 - 5y$**
40. $(m + 7)(-8)$ **$-8m - 56$**
41. $-3(k - 14)$ **$-3k + 42$**
42. $\frac{3}{5}(-15r - 5)$ **$-9r - 3$**
43. $\frac{7}{12}(24s + 12)$ **$14s + 7$**
44. $(9v - 18)\frac{1}{3}$ **$3v - 6$**
45. $-\frac{5}{6}(-6w - 30)$ **$5w + 25$**

2.6 **Find the quotient.**

46. $-35 \div 7$ **−5**
47. $-92 \div (-4)$ **23**
48. $36 \div \left(-\frac{3}{4}\right)$ **−48**
49. $-56 \div \left(-\frac{7}{8}\right)$ **64**
50. $\frac{5}{9} \div (-5)$ **$-\frac{1}{9}$**
51. $-\frac{5}{12} \div \frac{1}{2}$ **$-\frac{5}{6}$**
52. $-\frac{4}{3} \div \frac{4}{3}$ **−1**
53. $-\frac{5}{6} \div \left(-\frac{6}{5}\right)$ **$\frac{25}{36}$**

2.7 **Evaluate the expression.**

54. $-\sqrt{36}$ **−6**
55. $\pm\sqrt{400}$ **±20**
56. $\sqrt{6400}$ **80**
57. $\pm\sqrt{144}$ **±12**

2.7 **Approximate the square root to the nearest integer.**

58. $\sqrt{135}$ **12**
59. $-\sqrt{75}$ **−9**
60. $-\sqrt{160}$ **−13**
61. $\sqrt{250}$ **16**

EXTRA PRACTICE

1.

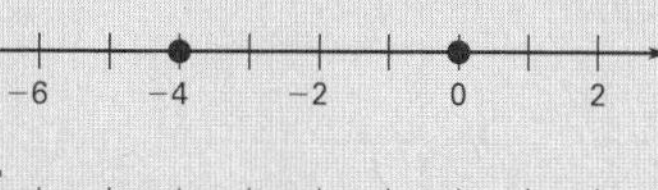

2.

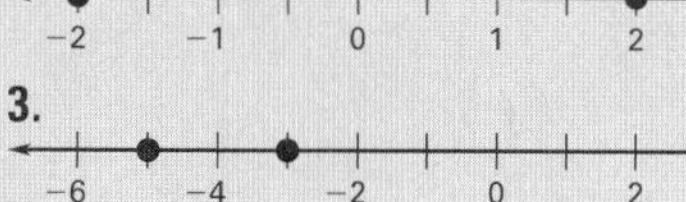

3.

4.

−6 −4 −2 0 2 4

5. Each number is a rational number; $-\frac{1}{5}, -\frac{1}{8}, -\frac{1}{10}, 0.25$.

6. −3: integer, rational number; the rest are rational numbers; $-3, -2.5, -\frac{9}{4}, \frac{5}{2}$.

7. −4: integer, rational number; 3: whole number, integer, rational number; −5: integer, rational number; 0: whole number, integer, rational number; −5, −4, 0, 3.

32. ~~Commutative~~ property of multiplication Associative

33. Associative property of multiplication

34. Identity property of multiplication

35. Property of zero

36. Commutative property of multiplication

37. Property of −1

Chapter 3

Solve the equation. Check your solution.

3.1
1. $x + 4 = 20$ **16**
2. $8 = m - 13$ **21**
3. $t + 2 = -10$ **−12**
4. $z - 8 = -7$ **1**
5. $7h = 63$ **9**
6. $-4t = -44$ **11**
7. $\frac{b}{4} = 13$ **52**
8. $\frac{y}{-3} = 8$ **−24**

3.2
9. $4x + 3 = 27$ **6**
10. $6m - 4 = 14$ **3**
11. $50 = 7y - 6$ **8**
12. $\frac{t}{4} - 3 = 9$ **48**
13. $\frac{x}{7} + 3 = -2$ **−35**
14. $6p - 2p = 28$ **7**

3.3
15. $6x + 3x + 8 = 35$ **3**
16. $12w - 5 - 3w = 40$ **5**
17. $4d - 3 - 2d = -15$ **−6**
18. $7m + 3(m + 2) = -24$ **−3**
19. $5x - 3(x - 5) = 13$ **−1**
20. $\frac{3}{4}(2y - 8) = 6$ **8**

3.4
21. $8x - 4 = 3x + 6$ **2**
22. $10 - 2x = 3x - 20$ **6**
23. $5 - 5x = 14 - 8x$ **3**
24. $3(2y - 5) = 4y - 7$ **4**
25. $9 + 4y = 2(3 - y)$ $-\frac{1}{2}$
26. $3x - 3 = \frac{3}{4}(2x + 12)$ **8**

3.5 Solve the proportion. Check your solution.

27. $\frac{7}{2} = \frac{x}{16}$ **56**
28. $\frac{m}{9} = \frac{6}{27}$ **2**
29. $\frac{z}{4} = \frac{48}{12}$ **16**
30. $\frac{30}{50} = \frac{t}{10}$ **6**

3.5 Write the sentence as a proportion. Then solve the proportion.

31. 5 is to 7 as 15 is to x. $\frac{5}{7} = \frac{15}{x}$; **21**
32. 9 is to 3 as x is to 12. $\frac{9}{3} = \frac{x}{12}$; **36**
33. g is to 9 as 16 is to 12. $\frac{g}{9} = \frac{16}{12}$; **12**
34. 6 is to 18 as y is to 3. $\frac{6}{18} = \frac{y}{3}$; **1**

3.6 Solve the proportion. Check your solution.

35. $\frac{12}{x} = \frac{6}{7}$ **14**
36. $\frac{6x}{4} = \frac{18}{12}$ **1**
37. $\frac{7}{x + 13} = \frac{4}{12}$ **8**
38. $\frac{y + 5}{y} = \frac{10}{8}$ **20**
39. $\frac{2x + 6}{x} = \frac{7}{2}$ **4**
40. $\frac{3b}{5b - 7} = \frac{8}{11}$ **8**
41. $\frac{8}{2x + 12} = \frac{6}{x + 8}$ **−2**
42. $\frac{4.8 - 2x}{8} = \frac{0.4 + x}{10}$ **1.6**

3.7 Use a proportion to answer the question.

43. What percent of 96 is 12? **12.5%**
44. What number is 35% of 18? **6.3**
45. 14 is 40% of what number? **35**
46. What percent of 125 is 30? **24%**

3.7 Use the percent equation to answer the question.

47. What number is 250% of 18? **45**
48. What percent of 58 is 8.7? **15%**
49. 30.1 is 35% of what number? **86**
50. What number is 70% of 250? **175**

3.8 Solve the literal equation for *x*. Then use the solution to solve the specific equation.

51. $ax - b = c$; $6x - 5 = 25$ $x = \frac{c + b}{a}$; **5**
52. $a(b - x) = c$; $2(8 - x) = -6$ $x = b - \frac{c}{a}$; **11**

3.8 Write the equation so that *y* is a function of *x*.

53. $5x + y = 10$ $y = -5x + 10$
54. $8x - 2y = 16$ $y = 4x - 8$
55. $7x + 3y = 6 - 5x$ $y = -4x + 2$
56. $21 = 6x + 7y$ $y = -\frac{6}{7}x + 3$

EXTRA PRACTICE

Chapter 4, p. 941

1.

2.

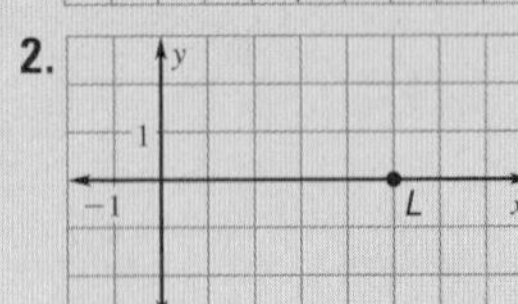

3.

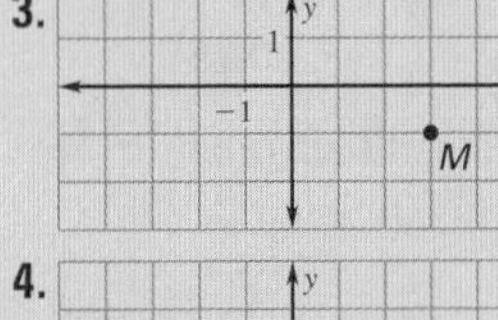

4.

5.

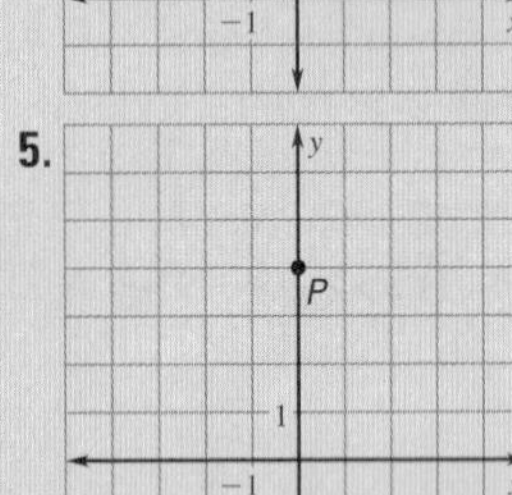

6.

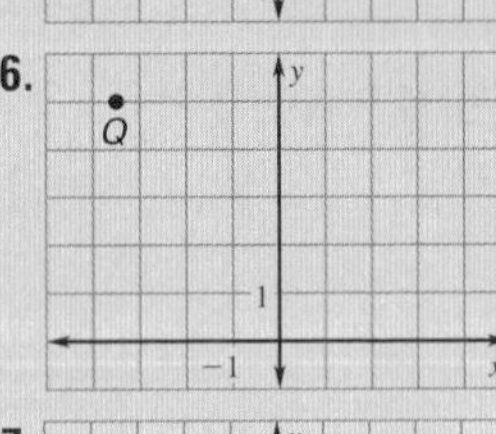

7.

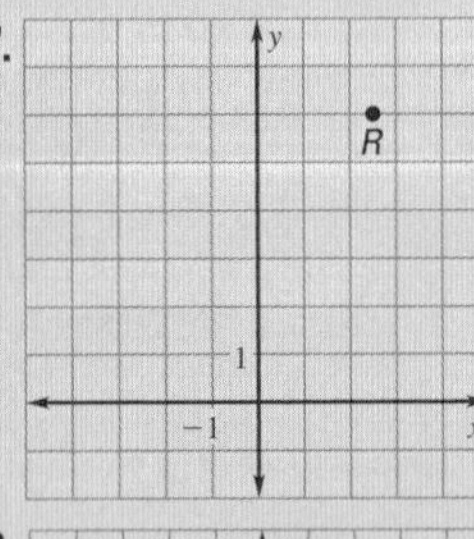

8.

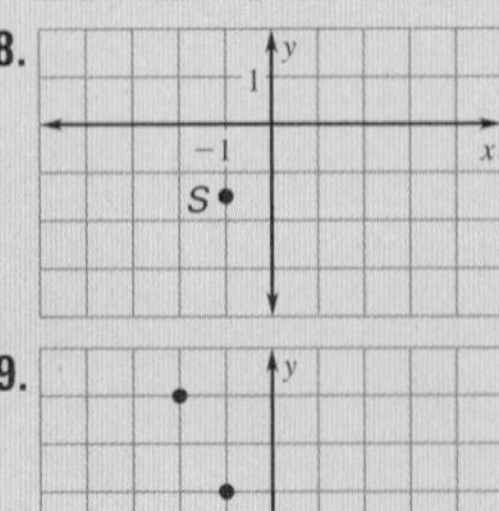

9.

10.

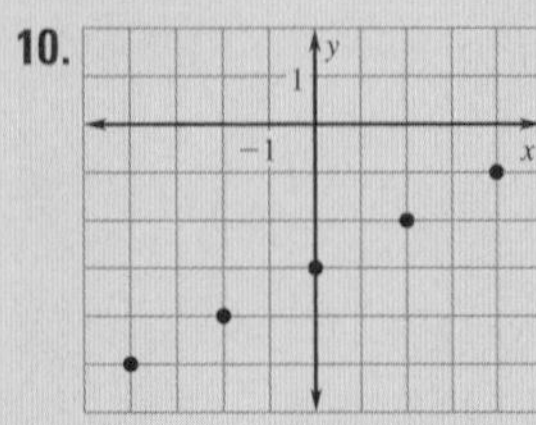

11.

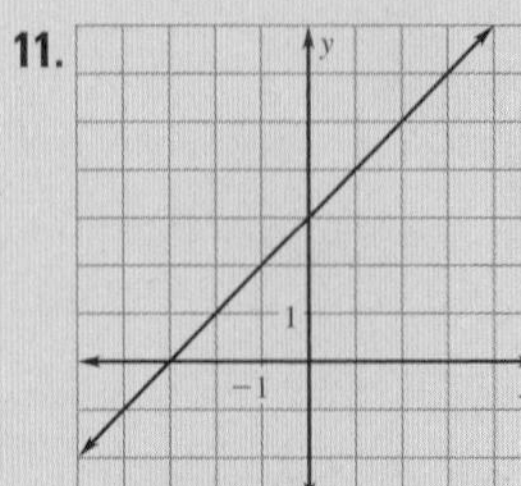

12.

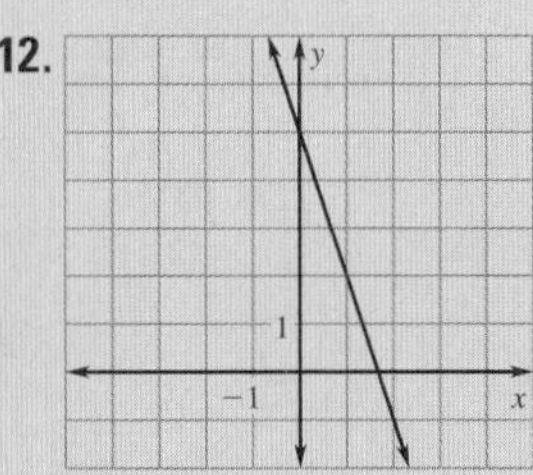

Chapter 4

4.1 Plot the point in a coordinate plane. *Describe* the location of the point. 1–8. See margin for art.

1. $K(-4, -2)$ Quadrant III
2. $L(5, 0)$ on the x–axis
3. $M(3, -1)$ Quadrant IV
4. $N(-2, 2)$ Quadrant II
5. $P(0, 4)$ on the y-axis
6. $Q(-3.5, 5)$ Quadrant II
7. $R(2.5, 6)$ Quadrant I
8. $S(-1, -1.5)$ Quadrant III

4.1 Graph the function with the given domain. Then identify the range of the function. 9, 10. See margin for art.

9. $y = -2x + 2$; domain: $-2, -1, 0, 1, 2$
range: $-2, 0, 2, 4, 6$
10. $y = \frac{1}{2}x - 3$; domain: $-4, -2, 0, 2, 4$
range: $-5, -4, -3, -2, -1$

4.2 Graph the equation. 11–18. See margin.

11. $y - x = 3$
12. $y + 3x = 5$
13. $y - 4x = 10$
14. $y = 4$
15. $2x - y = 0$
16. $3x + y = 0$
17. $3x + 2y = -6$
18. $x = 0.5$

4.3 Find the x-intercept and the y-intercept of the graph of the equation. 19–22. See margin.

19. $2x - y = 12$
20. $-5x - 2y = 20$
21. $-4x + 1.5y = 4$
22. $y = \frac{3}{4}x - 15$

4.3 Graph the equation. Label the points where the line crosses the axes. 23–26. See margin.

23. $y = 3x - 6$
24. $4x + 5y = -20$
25. $\frac{2}{3}x + \frac{1}{2}y = 10$
26. $0.3x - y = 6$

4.4 Find the slope of the line that passes through the points.

27. $(4, 2)$ and $(6, 8)$ **3**
28. $(-3, 0)$ and $(2, -5)$ **-1**
29. $(-5, 3)$ and $(-8, 10)$ **$-\frac{7}{3}$**
30. $(9, 4)$ and $(0, 1)$ **$\frac{1}{3}$**
31. $(-2, 5)$ and $(-2, 10)$ **no slope**
32. $(6, -4)$ and $(4, -4)$ **0**

4.5 Identify the slope and y-intercept of the line with the given equation. 33–36. See margin.

33. $y = 7x + 8$
34. $y = 10x - 6$
35. $y = 3 - 4x$
36. $y = x$

4.5 Rewrite the equation in slope-intercept form. Then identify the slope and the y-intercept of the line. 37–40. See margin.

37. $2x + y = 8$
38. $10x - y = 20$
39. $5x + 2y = 10$
40. $-2x - y = 3$

4.5 Graph the equation. 41–44. See margin.

41. $y = 2x - 4$
42. $y = -\frac{3}{4}x + 1$
43. $2x + y = 1$
44. $-2x + 3y = -9$

4.6 Graph the direct variation equation. 45–52. See margin.

45. $y = 2x$
46. $y = -x$
47. $y = 4x$
48. $5x + y = 0$
49. $x - 2y = 0$
50. $3x + y = 0$
51. $2y = 9x$
52. $y - \frac{5}{4}x = 0$

4.7 Find the value of x so that the function has the given value.

53. $f(x) = -7x - 3$; -17 **2**
54. $g(x) = 5x - 4$; 12 **$\frac{16}{5}$**
55. $t(x) = 3x + 1$; -11 **-4**

4.7 Graph the function. Compare the graph with the graph of $f(x) = x$. 56–59. See margin.

56. $m(x) = x - 2$
57. $t(x) = x + 4$
58. $z(x) = 6x$
59. $h(x) = -2x$

16.
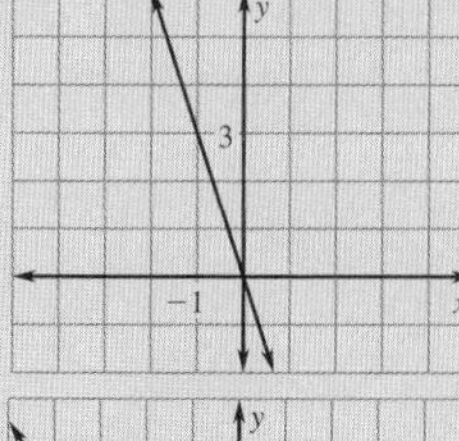

17.
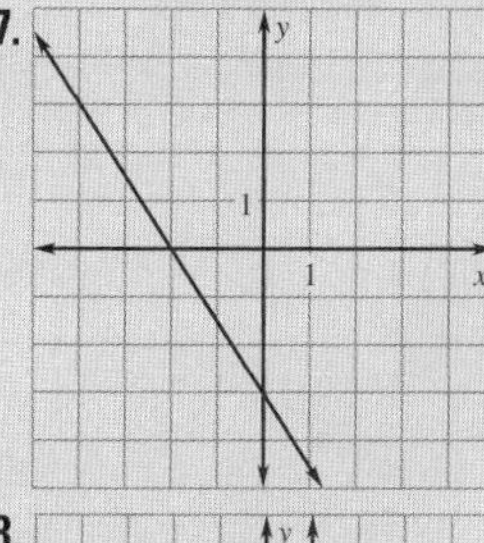

18.
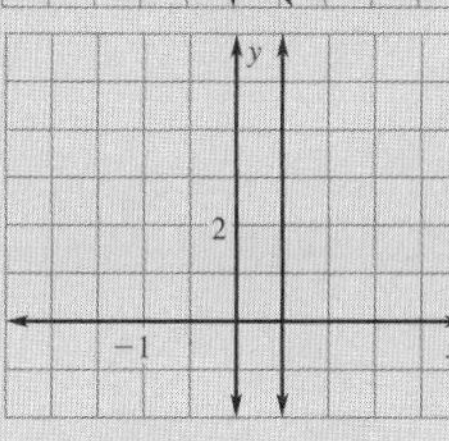

19. x-int: 6, y-int: -12
20. x-int: -4, y-int: -10
21. x-int: -1, y-int: $\frac{8}{3}$
22. x-int: 20, y-int: -15
23–26. See Additional Answers beginning on p. AA1.
33. slope: 7, y-intercept: 8
34. slope: 10, y-intercept: -6
35. slope: -4, y-intercept: 3
36. slope: 1, y-intercept: 0
37. $y = -2x + 8$; slope: -2, y-intercept: 8
38. $y = 10x - 20$; slope: 10, y-intercept: -20
39. $y = -\frac{5}{2}x + 5$; slope: $-\frac{5}{2}$, y-intercept: 5
40. $y = -2x - 3$; slope: -2, y-intercept: -3
41–52, 56–59. See Additional Answers beginning on p. AA1.

13.
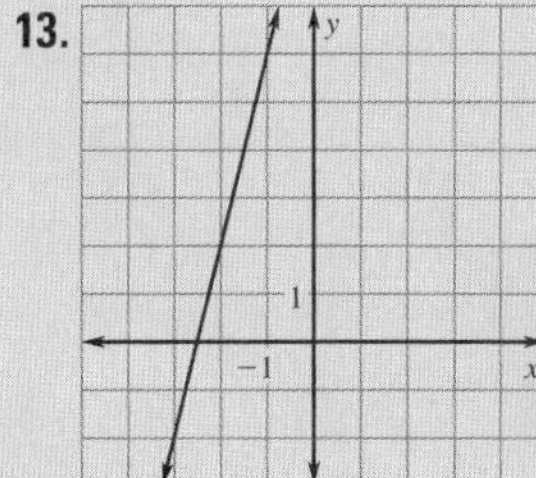

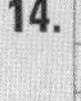

14.
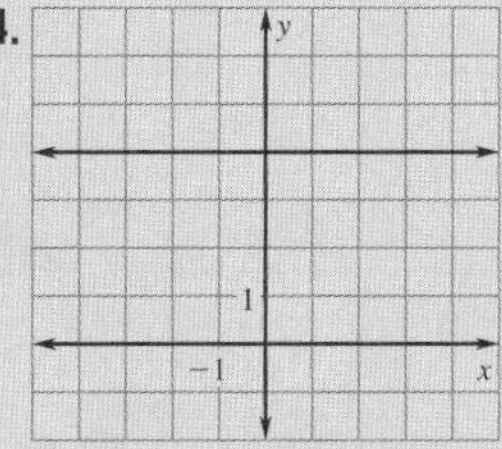

15.
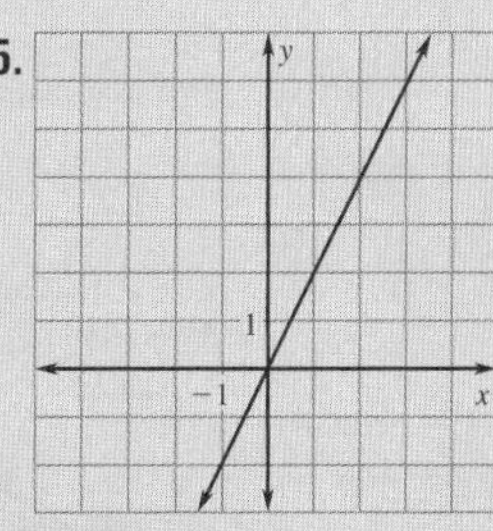

Chapter 5

5.1 Write an equation of the line with the given slope and y-intercept.

1. slope: 3
   y-intercept: 6
   $y = 3x + 6$
2. slope: -2
   y-intercept: 4
   $y = -2x + 4$
3. slope: 5
   y-intercept: -1
   $y = 5x - 1$
4. slope: -1
   y-intercept: -3
   $y = -x - 3$
5. slope: $\frac{1}{2}$
   y-intercept: -5
   $y = \frac{1}{2}x - 5$
6. slope: $-\frac{7}{10}$
   y-intercept: 8
   $y = -\frac{7}{10}x + 8$

5.2 Write an equation of the line that passes through the given point and has the given slope m.

7. $(3, 8)$; $m = 2$
   $y = 2x + 2$
8. $(-1, 5)$; $m = -4$
   $y = -4x + 1$
9. $(-6, 3)$; $m = \frac{2}{3}$
   $y = \frac{2}{3}x + 7$

5.2 Write an equation of the line that passes through the given points.

10. $(2, 4)$, $(5, 13)$
    $y = 3x - 2$
11. $(1, -2)$, $(-2, 13)$
    $y = -5x + 3$
12. $\left(2, \frac{1}{3}\right)$, $(6, 3)$
    $y = \frac{2}{3}x - 1$

5.3 Graph the equation. 13–15. See margin.

13. $y - 3 = -3(x + 4)$
14. $y + 5 = -2(x - 1)$
15. $y - 6 = \frac{2}{3}(x - 3)$

5.3 Write an equation in point-slope form of the line that passes through the given points. 16–18. See margin.

16. $(-4, 2)$, $(-2, 16)$
17. $(3, 9)$, $(-7, 4)$
18. $(10, -2)$, $(12, -6)$

5.4 Write an equation in standard form of the line that passes through the given point and has the given slope m or that passes through the two given points.

19. $(2, 7)$, $m = -4$
    $4x + y = 15$
20. $(5, 11)$, $m = 3$
    $3x - y = 4$
21. $(1, -2)$, $(-2, 4)$
    $2x + y = 0$

5.5 Write an equation of the line that passes through the given point and is parallel to the given line.

22. $(5, 4)$, $y = 3x + 5$
    $y = 3x - 11$
23. $(-3, -7)$, $y = -5x - 2$
    $y = -5x - 22$
24. $(8, -3)$, $y = \frac{3}{4}x + 5$
    $y = \frac{3}{4}x - 9$

5.5 Write an equation of the line that passes through the given point and is perpendicular to the given line.

25. $(-12, -2)$, $y = 3x + 2$
    $y = -\frac{1}{3}x - 6$
26. $(15, -11)$, $y = \frac{3}{5}x - 8$
    $y = -\frac{5}{3}x + 14$
27. $(7, -6)$, $4x + 6y = 7$
    $y = \frac{3}{2}x - \frac{33}{2}$

5.6 Make a scatter plot of the data in the table. Draw a line of fit. Write an equation of the line. 28, 29. See margin for art.

28.

x	1	2	3	3.5	4	4.5	5
y	20	35	40	55	60	45	60

Sample answer: $y = 10x + 10$

29.

x	10	20	30	40	50	60
y	55	45	45	40	35	20

Sample answer: $y = -\frac{5}{6}x + 70$

5.7 Make a scatter plot of the data. Find the equation of the best-fitting line. Approximate the value of y for $x = 7$. 30–31. See margin for art.

30.

x	0	2	4	6	8
y	0.5	3	4	5.5	7

$y = 0.78x + 0.9$; 6.36

31.

x	0	1	3	6	8
y	5	8	12	15	14

$y = 1.1x + 6.7$; 14.4

13.

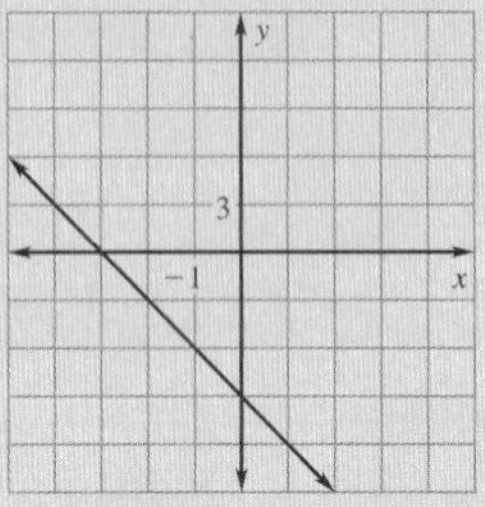

14.

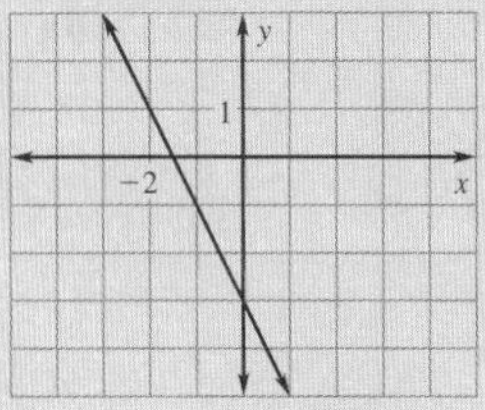

15.

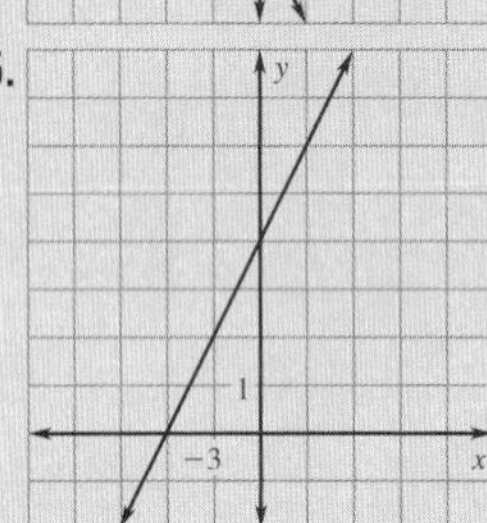

16–18. Sample answers are given.

16. $y - 2 = 7(x + 4)$
17. $y - 9 = \frac{1}{2}(x - 3)$
18. $y + 2 = -2(x - 10)$

28.

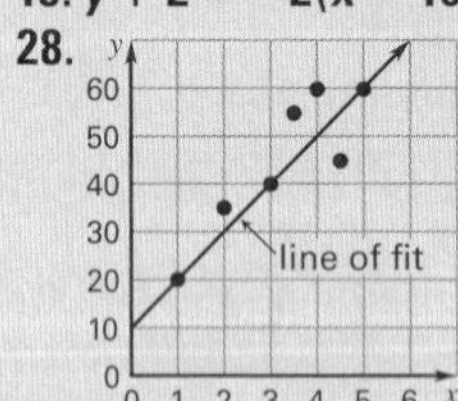

29.

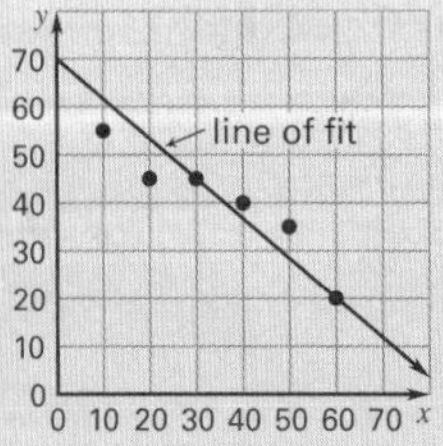

30.

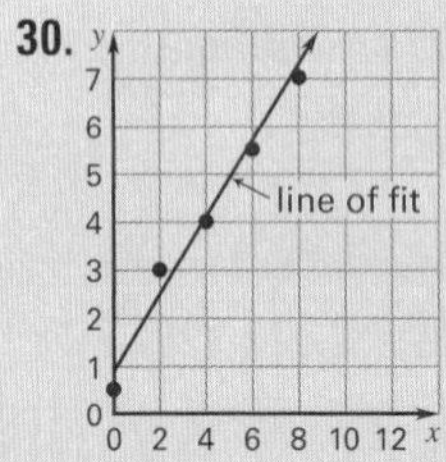

31.

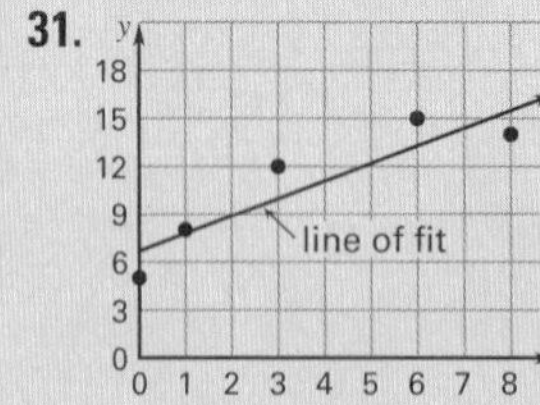

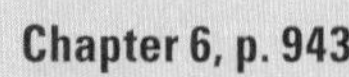

Chapter 6, p. 943

1.–3.

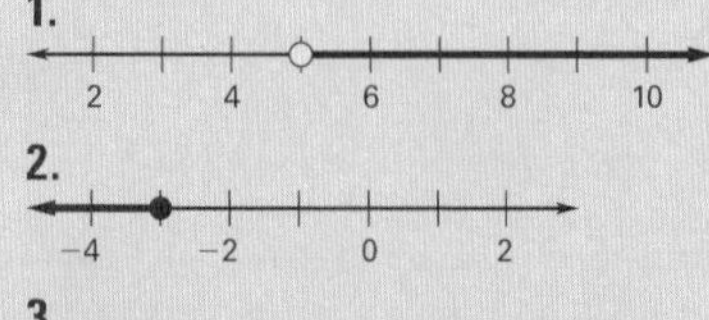

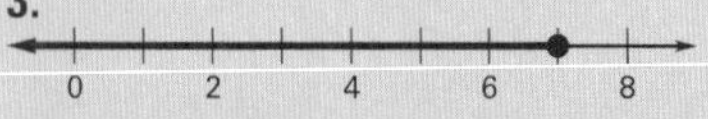

4.

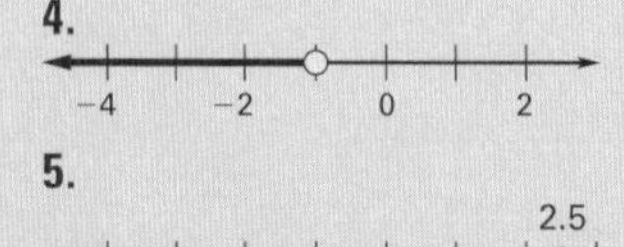

5.–6.

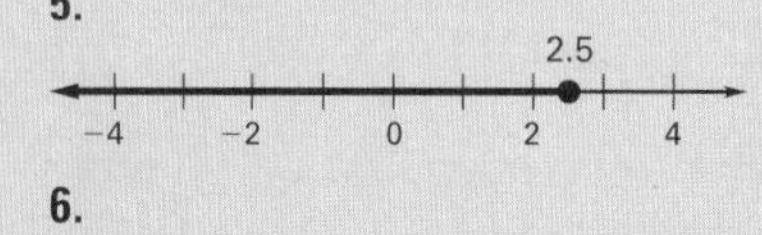

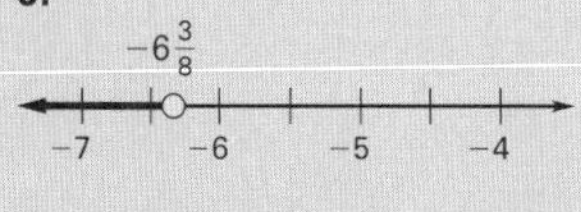

7.

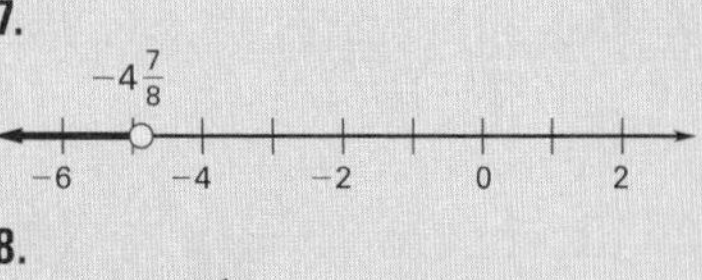

8.

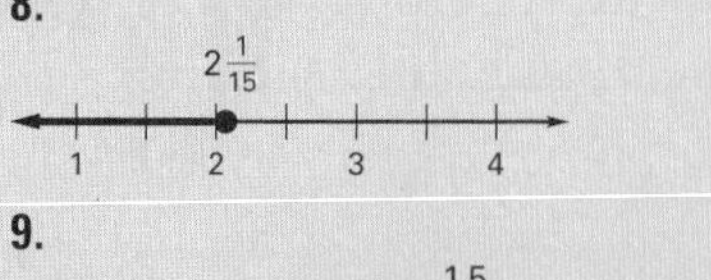

9.

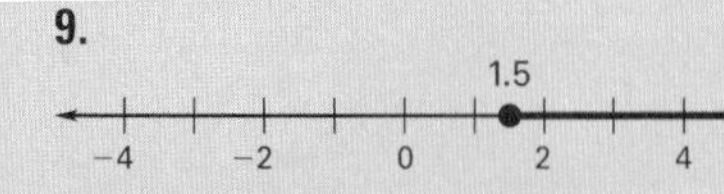

Chapter 6

Solve the inequality. Graph your solution. **1–24. See margin for art.**

6.1

1. $y - 2 > 3$ **$y > 5$**
2. $5 + x \le 2$ **$x \le -3$**
3. $4 \ge x - 3$ **$x \le 7$**
4. $m + 3 < 2$ **$m < -1$**
5. $2 + n \le 4\frac{1}{2}$ **$n \le 2\frac{1}{2}$**
6. $2\frac{3}{4} + n < -3\frac{5}{8}$ **$n < -6\frac{3}{8}$**
7. $1\frac{7}{8} > 6\frac{3}{4} + z$ **$z < -4\frac{7}{8}$**
8. $3\frac{2}{5} \ge 1\frac{1}{3} + k$ **$k \le 2\frac{1}{15}$**
9. $-8.5 \le t - 10$ **$t \ge 1.5$**
10. $r + 4 < -0.7$ **$r < -4.7$**
11. $-6.9 > -1.4 + y$ **$y < -5.5$**
12. $1.48 - m \ge -3.13$ **$m \le 4.61$**

6.2

13. $3p \le 27$ **$p \le 9$**
14. $-13t > 26$ **$t < -2$**
15. $\frac{x}{3} \ge 2$ **$x \ge 6$**
16. $\frac{y}{-2} < 5$ **$y > -10$**
17. $-6m \ge -9$ **$m \le \frac{3}{2}$**
18. $-3 \ge \frac{n}{2}$ **$n \le -6$**
19. $0.3z \le 2.4$ **$z \le 8$**
20. $25 > -2.5s$ **$s > -10$**
21. $4.8z \le 3.2$ **$z \le \frac{2}{3}$**
22. $0.09d < -1.8$ **$d < -20$**
23. $\frac{y}{0.3} > -15$ **$y > -4.5$**
24. $-1.8t < 9$ **$t > -5$**

6.3 Solve the inequality, if possible. Graph your solution. **25–33. See margin for art.**

25. $3x + 5 \ge 20$ **$x \ge 5$**
26. $6z - 5 < 13$ **$z < 3$**
27. $8(t + 4) > -8$ **$t > -5$**
28. $7 - 8n \le 4n - 17$ **$n \ge 2$**
29. $8(m + 2) < 4(5 + 2m)$ **all real numbers**
30. $6d - 4 - 3d \ge 14$ **$d \ge 6$**
31. $\frac{2}{3}y + 28 > 20 + 2y$ **$y < 6$**
32. $6(-5 + 3p) \ge 3(6p - 10)$ **all real numbers**
33. $\frac{5}{6}(12z - 24) > \frac{2}{5}(25z - 25)$ **no solution**

6.4 Solve the inequality. Graph your solution. **34–42. See margin for art.**

34. $2 \le y - 4 < 7$ **$6 \le y < 11$**
35. $-27 < 9x < 27$ **$-3 < x < 3$**
36. $2 < 6z - 10 < 20$ **$2 < z < 5$**
37. $15 < \frac{5}{9}(18a - 9) \le 30$ **$2 < a \le 3\frac{1}{2}$**
38. $2v > 12$ *or* $v + 2 < 6$ **$v > 6$ or $v < 4$**
39. $3r + 7 < -5$ *or* $32 \le 7r + 46$ **$r < -4$ or $r \ge -2$**
40. $-4m < 8$ *or* $2m - 2 < -12$ **$m > -2$ or $m < -5$**
41. $9t - 20 \ge 4t$ *or* $4 < \frac{1}{-2}t$ **$t \ge 4$ or $t < -8$**
42. $-n - 1 > 1$ *or* $2n + 8 > n + 8$ **$n < -2$ or $n > 0$**

6.5 Solve the equation, if possible.

43. $|x| = 8$ **± 8**
44. $|y| = -10$ **no solution**
45. $|m + 6| = 5$ **$-11, -1$**
46. $|4z - 2| = 14$ **$-3, 4$**
47. $|t - 7| = 21$ **$-14, 28$**
48. $6|z - 4| = 36$ **$-2, 10$**
49. $4|6s + 11| = -52$ **no solution**
50. $|r + 3| - 16 = -4$ **$-15, 9$**
51. $|5r| + 10 = 15$ **$-1, 1$**
52. $2|3s + 4| = 14$ **$-3\frac{2}{3}, 1$**
53. $-4|7v + 2| = 32$ **no solution**
54. $12\left|\frac{5}{6}w - 4\right| - 4 = 8$ **$3\frac{3}{5}, 6$**

6.6 Solve the inequality. Graph your solution. **55–66. See margin for art.**

55. $|x| \le 3$ **$-3 \le x \le 3$**
56. $|y| \ge 5$ **$y \le -5$ or $y \ge 5$**
57. $|s| > 1.2$ **$s < -1.2$ or $s > 1.2$**
58. $|q| < \frac{2}{5}$ **$-\frac{2}{5} < q < \frac{2}{5}$**
59. $|x + 2| > 6$ **$x < -8$ or $x > 4$**
60. $|y + 3| \le 5$ **$-8 \le y \le 2$**
61. $|8 - m| < 3$ **$5 < m < 11$**
62. $|4n - 1| \ge 7$ **$n \le -\frac{3}{2}$ or $n \ge 2$**
63. $3|p - 3| \le 12$ **$-1 \le p \le 7$**
64. $|3q + 2| - 3 \ge 8$ **$q \le -\frac{13}{3}$ or $q \ge 3$**
65. $2|5a - 1| + 3 \le 11$ **$-\frac{3}{5} \le a \le 1$**
66. $4\left|\frac{2}{3}c + 2\right| < 64$ **$-27 < c < 21$**

6.7 Graph the inequality. **67–78. See margin.**

67. $y \ge x + 5$
68. $y < x - 1$
69. $4x + y > 3$
70. $x \le -5$
71. $3(x - 8) \le 6y$
72. $2x - y \ge -2$
73. $y > 8$
74. $2(x - 1) \ge 1 - y$
75. $x - 8 \le y + 2$
76. $2x \ge -2y$
77. $3(y - 8) > x - 9$
78. $2(-x - 1) \ge 4 + y$

EXTRA PRACTICE

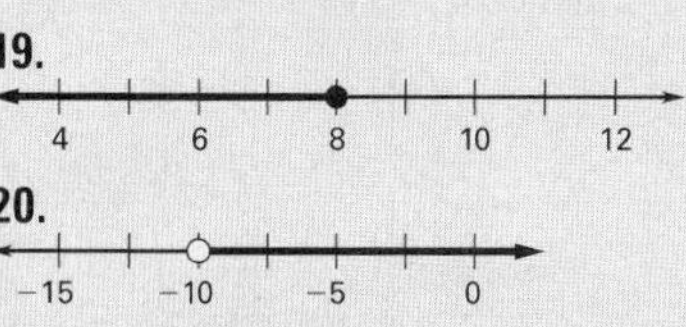

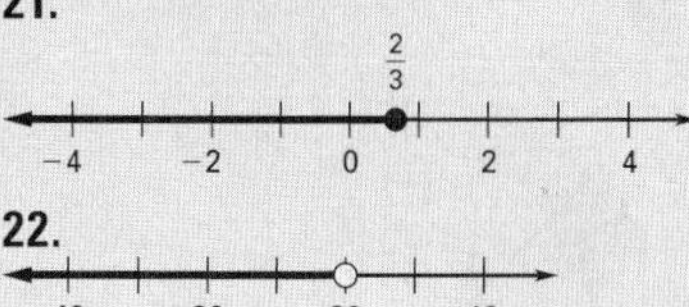

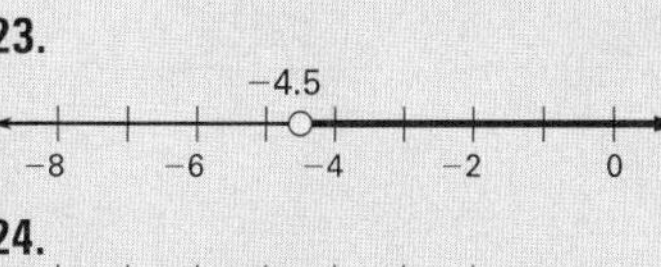

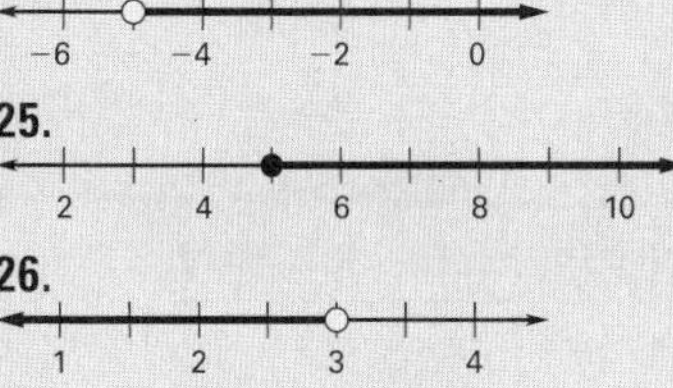

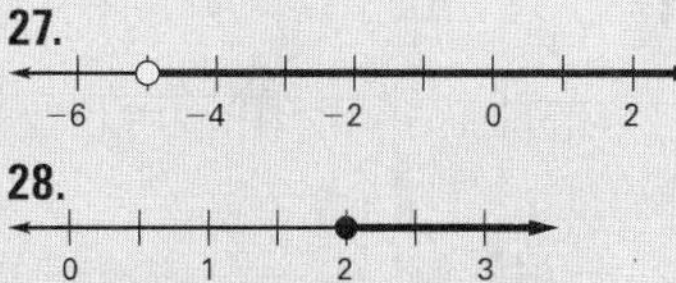

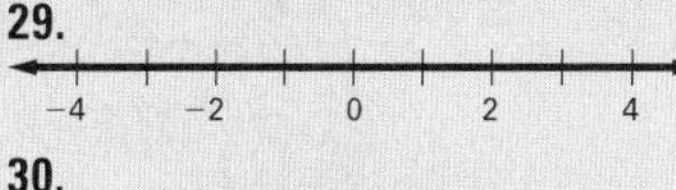

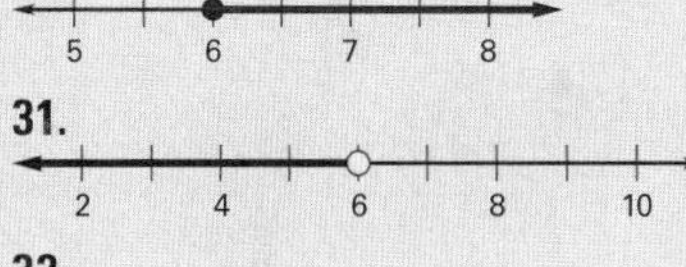

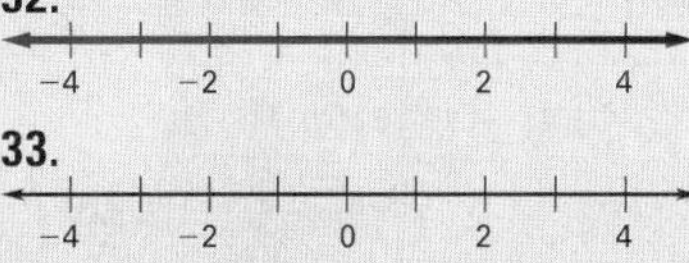

34–42, 55–78. See Additional Answers beginning on p. AA1.

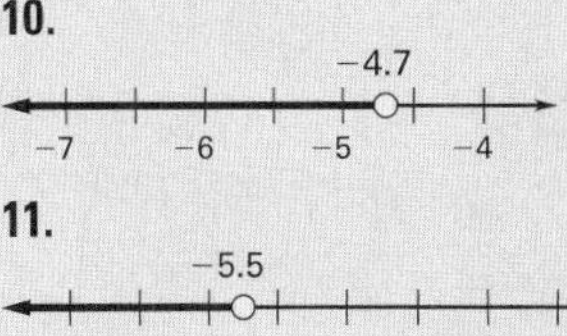

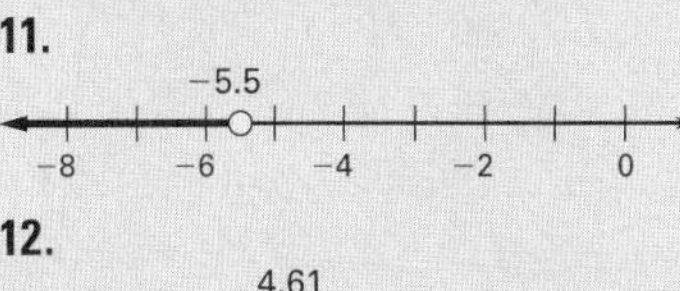

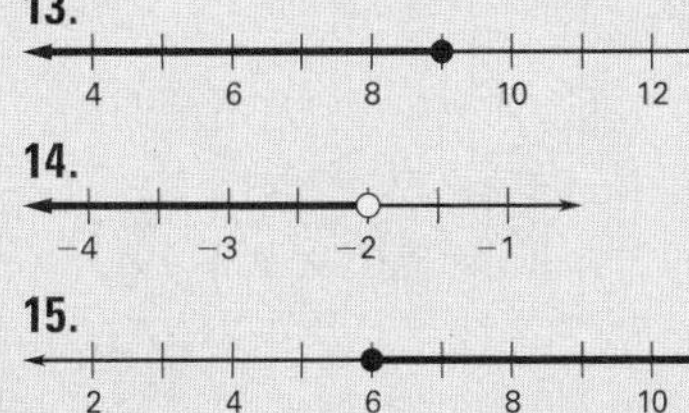

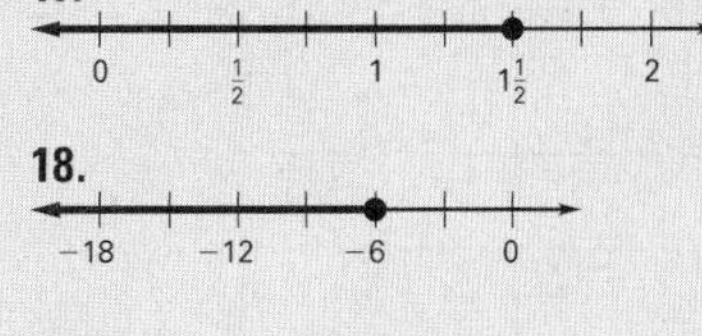

Chapter 7

7.1 Solve the linear system by graphing. Check your solution.

1. $y = x - 1$
   $y = -x + 5$ **(3, 2)**

2. $y = 3x + 12$
   $y = -4x - 2$ **(−2, 6)**

3. $x - y = 4$
   $x + y = -2$ **(1, −3)**

4. $4x - y = 10$
   $x = 4$ **(4, 6)**

5. $3x - 2y = -5$
   $4x + 3y = -18$ **(−3, −2)**

6. $\frac{2}{3}x + \frac{1}{3}y = \frac{16}{3}$
   $-\frac{2}{5}x + y = \frac{8}{5}$ **(6, 4)**

7.2 Solve the linear system using substitution.

7. $y = 2x + 6$
   $x = y - 3$ **(−3, 0)**

8. $y = 3x + 5$
   $x + y = -1$ $\left(-\frac{3}{2}, \frac{1}{2}\right)$

9. $x = 2y - 5$
   $2x - y = 11$ **(9, 7)**

10. $2x - y = 0$
    $x + 3y = -56$ **(−8, −16)**

11. $1.5x - 2.5y = 22$
    $x - y = 10$ **(3, −7)**

12. $\frac{1}{2}x + \frac{3}{4}y = 5$
    $x - \frac{1}{2}y = 6$ **(7, 2)**

Solve the linear system using elimination.

7.3

13. $x + 2y = 2$
    $-x + 3y = 13$ **(−4, 3)**

14. $3x - 4y = -16$
    $x - 4y = -40$ **(12, 13)**

15. $3x + 2y = -31$
    $5x + 2y = -49$ **(−9, −2)**

16. $5x + 4y = 6$
    $7x + 4y = 14$ $\left(4, -\frac{7}{2}\right)$

17. $10y - 3x = -41$
    $3x - 5y = 16$ **(−3, −5)**

18. $4x - 3y = 39$
    $7y = 4x - 79$ $\left(\frac{9}{4}, -10\right)$

7.4

19. $x + y = -3$
    $5x + 7y = -9$ **(−6, 3)**

20. $5x + 2y = -19$
    $10x - 7y = -16$ **(−3, −2)**

21. $8x - 3y = 61$
    $2x - 5y = -23$ **(11, 9)**

22. $4x - 3y = -2$
    $6x + 4y = 31$ $\left(\frac{5}{2}, 4\right)$

23. $5x - 2y = 53$
    $2x + 6y = 11$ $\left(10, -\frac{3}{2}\right)$

24. $15x - 8y = 6$
    $25x - 12y = 16$ $\left(\frac{14}{5}, \frac{9}{2}\right)$

7.5 Graph the linear system. Then use the graph to tell whether the linear system has *one solution*, *no solution*, or *infinitely many solutions*. 25–27. See margin for art.

25. $2x + y = -3$
    $y = -2x + 5$
    no solution

26. $2y - 4x = 10$
    $-2y - 2x = 8$
    one solution

27. $10x + 5y = -15$
    $y = -2x - 3$
    infinitely many solutions

7.5 Solve the linear system using substitution or elimination.

28. $y - 3x = 5$
    $x = y - 5$ **(0, 5)**

29. $2y - 3x = 36$
    $y = 3x - 12$ **(20, 48)**

30. $5x + 5y = -32$
    $3x + 3y = 14$ **no solution**

31. $4x + 6y = 11$
    $y = -\frac{2}{3}x + 7$ **no solution**

32. $3y - 3x = 12$
    $y = x - 4$ **no solution**

33. $x + 2y = -30$
    $y = \frac{1}{2}x + 15$ **(−30, 0)**

7.6 Graph the system of inequalities. 34–39. See margin.

34. $y \geq -5$
    $y \leq -2$

35. $x \geq -3$
    $y < 1$

36. $y < -2x - 3$
    $x - y > -4$

37. $x + 4y \geq -8$
    $y - 4x < 8$
    $x > -1$

38. $x > 3$
    $x < 5$
    $y > -2$
    $y \leq 0$

39. $x + y > 3$
    $x - y > 5$
    $x + 2y \leq 8$
    $x - 5y > 10$

EXTRA PRACTICE

25.

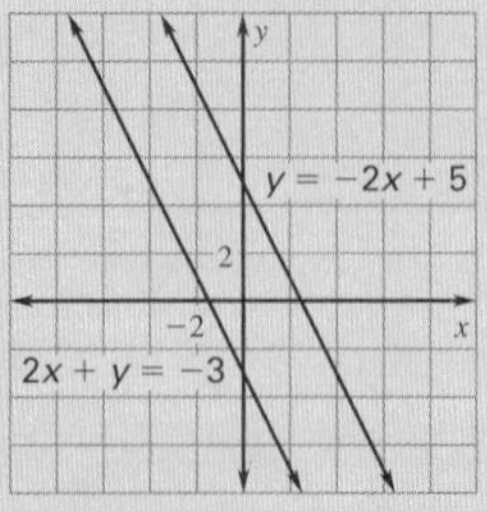

26.
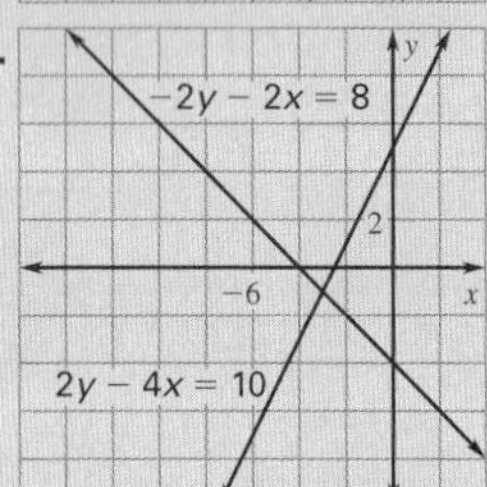

27.
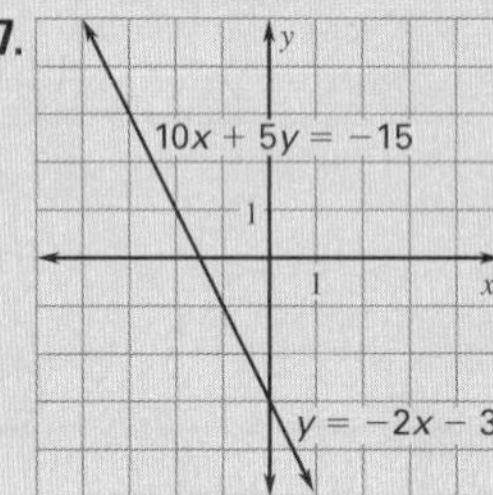

34.
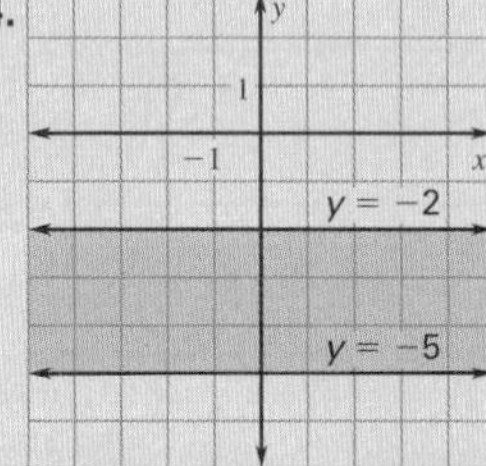

35.
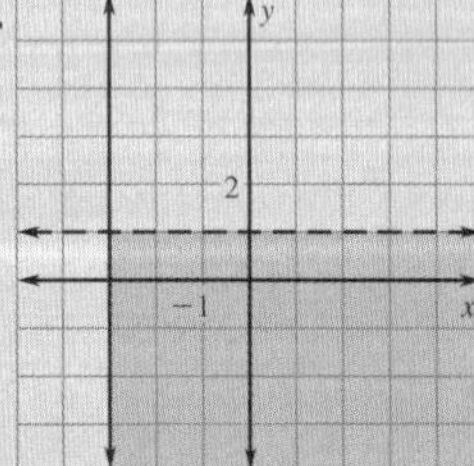

36.
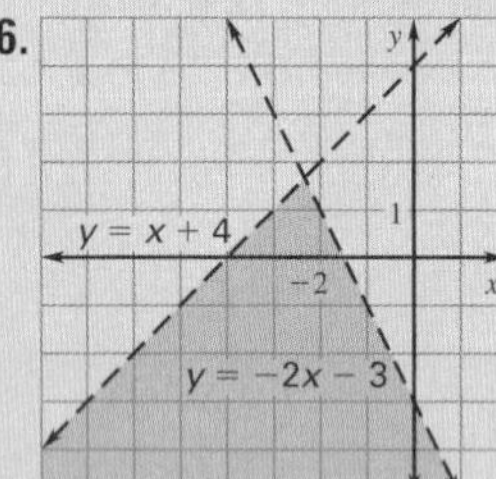

37.
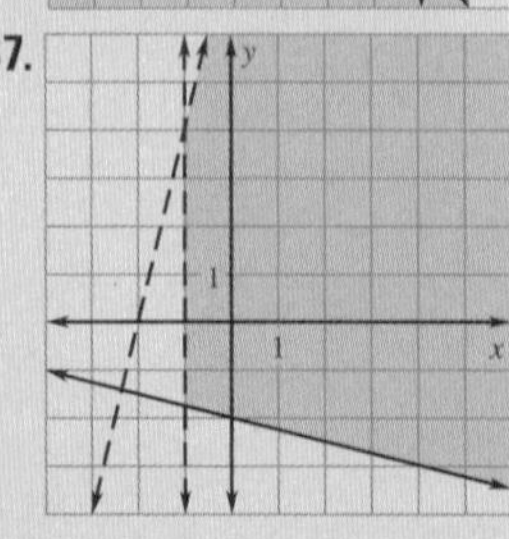

38.
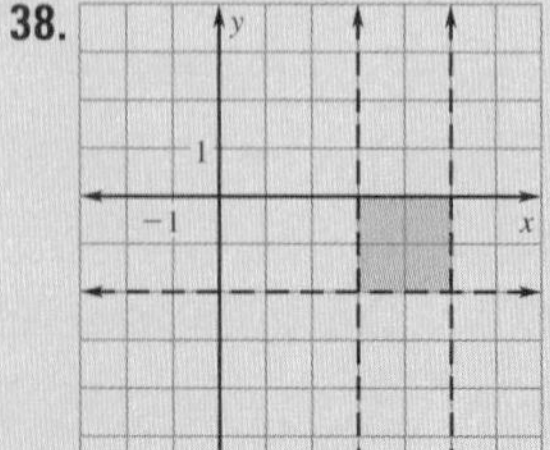

39.
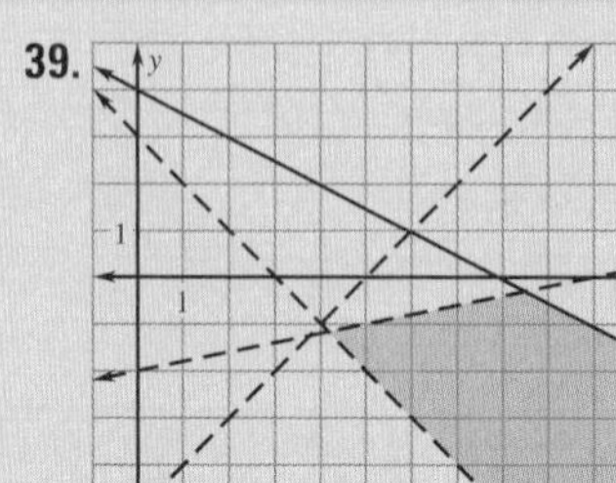

Chapter 8

Simplify the expression. In exercises involving numerical bases only, write your answer using exponents.

8.1 1. $5^3 \cdot 5^4$ $\mathbf{5^7}$ 2. $6 \cdot 6^7$ $\mathbf{6^8}$ 3. $(-2)^3 \cdot (-2)^6$ $\mathbf{(-2)^9}$ 4. $(2^8)^2$ $\mathbf{2^{16}}$

5. $[(-4)^3]^2$ $\mathbf{(-4)^6}$ 6. $(8 \cdot 4)^5$ $\mathbf{8^5 \cdot 4^5}$ 7. $m^5 \cdot m^2$ $\mathbf{m^7}$ 8. $n^2 \cdot n^4 \cdot n^5$ $\mathbf{n^{11}}$

9. $(y^3)^5$ $\mathbf{y^{15}}$ 10. $(-2x)^3$ $\mathbf{-8x^3}$ 11. $(3d^2)^3 \cdot 2d^2$ $\mathbf{54d^8}$ 12. $(-4s^2)^3(2s^3)^6$ $\mathbf{-4096s^{24}}$

8.2 13. $\frac{8^7}{8^2}$ $\mathbf{8^5}$ 14. $\frac{4^6 \cdot 4^2}{4^3}$ $\mathbf{4^5}$ 15. $\left(-\frac{2}{3}\right)^5$ $\mathbf{-\frac{2^5}{3^5}}$ 16. $10^{12} \cdot \frac{1}{10^7}$ $\mathbf{10^5}$

17. $7^9 \cdot \left(\frac{1}{7}\right)^4$ $\mathbf{7^5}$ 18. $\frac{1}{t^9} \cdot t^{13}$ $\mathbf{t^4}$ 19. $\left(\frac{p}{q}\right)^7$ $\mathbf{\frac{p^7}{q^7}}$ 20. $\left(\frac{6x^9}{3y^4}\right)^2$ $\mathbf{\frac{4x^{18}}{y^8}}$

21. $\left(\frac{4y^5}{3}\right)^3 \cdot \frac{1}{y^6}$ $\mathbf{\frac{64y^9}{27}}$ 22. $\left(\frac{2}{u^2}\right)^3 \cdot \left(\frac{3u^4}{z^2}\right)^4$ $\mathbf{\frac{648u^{10}}{z^8}}$ 23. $\left(\frac{5x^3y^4}{2x^2y}\right)^2$ $\mathbf{\frac{25x^2y^6}{4}}$ 24. $\frac{6a^4b^5}{ab} \cdot \left(\frac{2ab}{a^2b^2}\right)^3$ $\mathbf{48b}$

8.3 Evaluate the expression.

25. 3^{-4} $\mathbf{\frac{1}{81}}$ 26. $(-5)^{-3}$ $\mathbf{-\frac{1}{125}}$ 27. 7^0 $\mathbf{1}$ 28. $4^{-5} \cdot 4^3$ $\mathbf{\frac{1}{16}}$

29. $\left(\frac{1}{2}\right)^{-3}$ $\mathbf{8}$ 30. $(3^{-2})^3$ $\mathbf{\frac{1}{729}}$ 31. $\frac{1}{2^{-5}}$ $\mathbf{32}$ 32. $\frac{8^{-4}}{8^{-6}}$ $\mathbf{64}$

8.3 Simplify the expression. Write your answer using only positive exponents.

33. y^{-10} $\mathbf{\frac{1}{y^{10}}}$ 34. $(3c)^{-4}$ $\mathbf{\frac{1}{81c^4}}$ 35. $10b^{-3}c^5$ $\mathbf{\frac{10c^5}{b^3}}$ 36. $(2d^5e^{-2})^{-3}$ $\mathbf{\frac{e^6}{8d^{15}}}$

37. $\frac{x^{-4}}{y^{-5}}$ $\mathbf{\frac{y^5}{x^4}}$ 38. $\frac{1}{6t^{-5}u^3}$ $\mathbf{\frac{t^5}{6u^3}}$ 39. $\frac{3}{(-2z)^{-5}}$ $\mathbf{-96z^5}$ 40. $\frac{(2e)^{-4}g^5}{e^5g^{-3}}$ $\mathbf{\frac{g^8}{16e^9}}$

8.4 If the number is written in scientific notation, write it in standard form. If the number is written in standard form, write it in scientific notation.

41. 0.87 $\mathbf{8.7 \times 10^{-1}}$ 42. 378.4 $\mathbf{3.784 \times 10^2}$ 43. 0.000359 $\mathbf{3.59 \times 10^{-4}}$ 44. 465,000,000 $\mathbf{4.65 \times 10^8}$

45. 5.3×10^5 **530,000** 46. 1.67×10^{-4} **0.000167** 47. 8×10^{-6} **0.000008** 48. 9.0001×10^2 **900.01**

8.4 Evaluate the expression. Write your answer in scientific notation.

49. $\frac{3 \times 10^2}{8 \times 10^6}$ $\mathbf{3.75 \times 10^{-5}}$ 50. $(8.5 \times 10^{10})(3.7 \times 10^{-5})$ $\mathbf{3.145 \times 10^6}$ 51. $\frac{2.4 \times 10^{-5}}{6 \times 10^{-8}}$ $\mathbf{4 \times 10^2}$

Graph the function. **52–67. See margin.**

8.5 52. $y = 3^x$ 53. $y = 1.25^x$ 54. $y = \left(\frac{9}{4}\right)^x$ 55. $y = 5 \cdot 2^x$

56. $y = \frac{1}{3} \cdot 2^x$ 57. $y = -\frac{1}{2} \cdot 5^x$ 58. $y = -5 \cdot 2^x$ 59. $y = -\frac{1}{3} \cdot 4^x$

8.6 60. $y = \left(\frac{1}{3}\right)^x$ 61. $y = (0.2)^x$ 62. $y = 3 \cdot (0.2)^x$ 63. $y = 2 \cdot \left(\frac{1}{3}\right)^x$

64. $y = 4 \cdot \left(\frac{1}{3}\right)^x$ 65. $y = \frac{1}{2} \cdot \left(\frac{1}{3}\right)^x$ 66. $y = -2 \cdot \left(\frac{1}{3}\right)^x$ 67. $y = -\frac{3}{4} \cdot \left(\frac{1}{3}\right)^x$

8.6 68. Tell whether the table represents an exponential function. If so, write a rule for the function. **exponential; $y = 5 \cdot 2^x$**

x	−1	0	1	2	3
y	$\frac{5}{2}$	5	10	20	40

EXTRA PRACTICE

52.
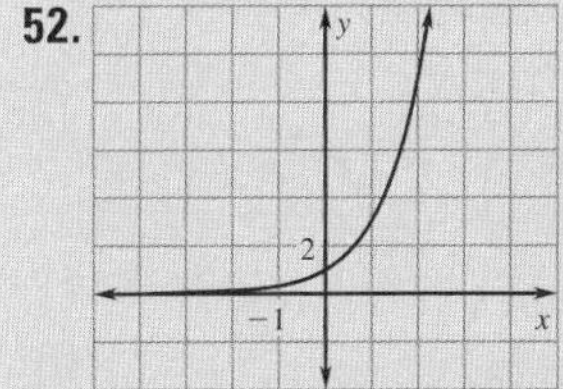

53.
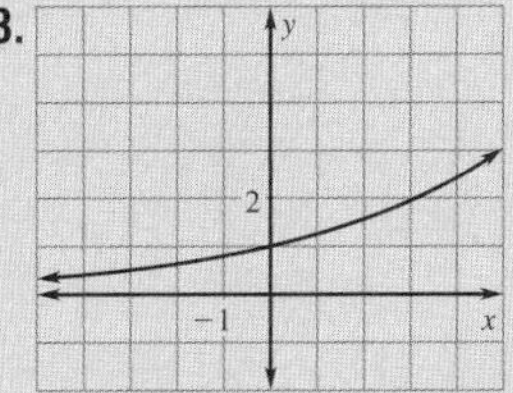

54.
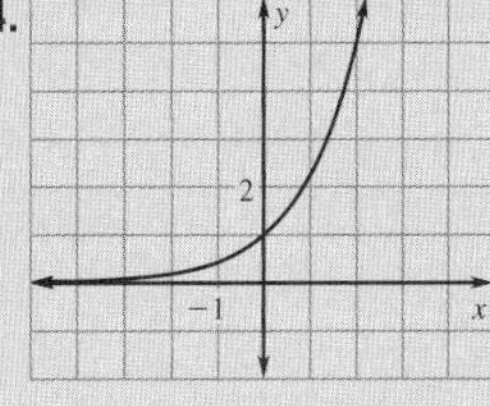

55.
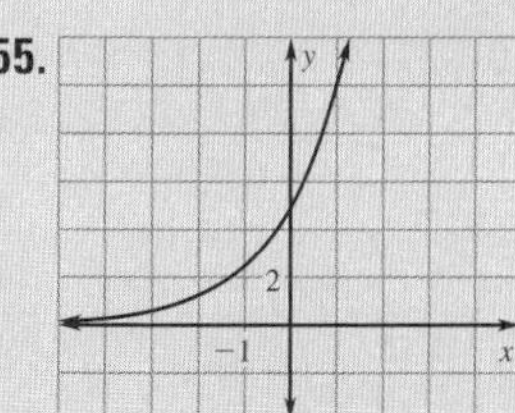

56.
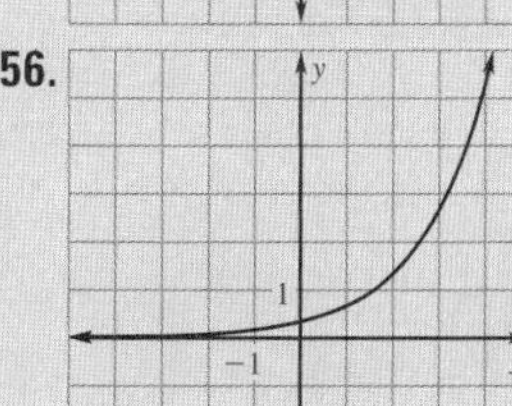

57.
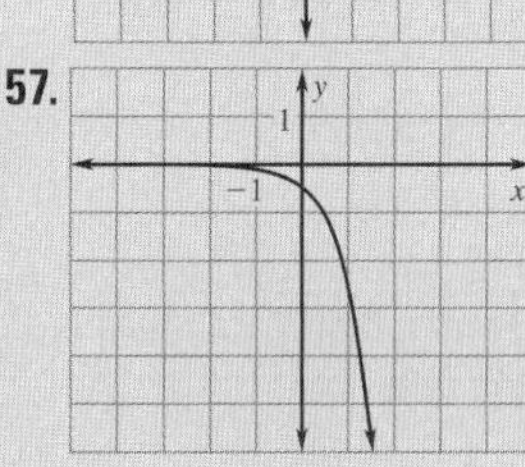

58.
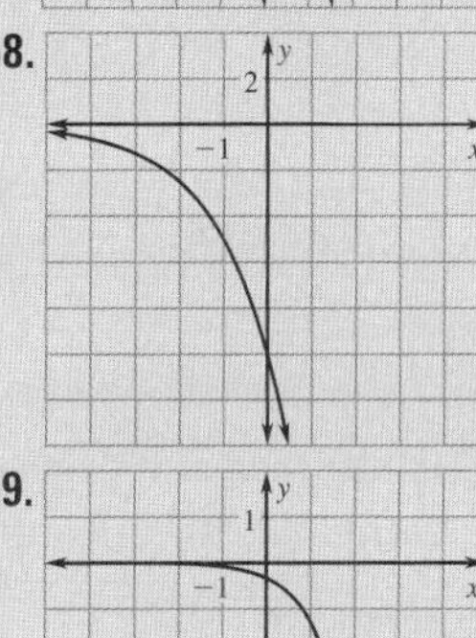

59.
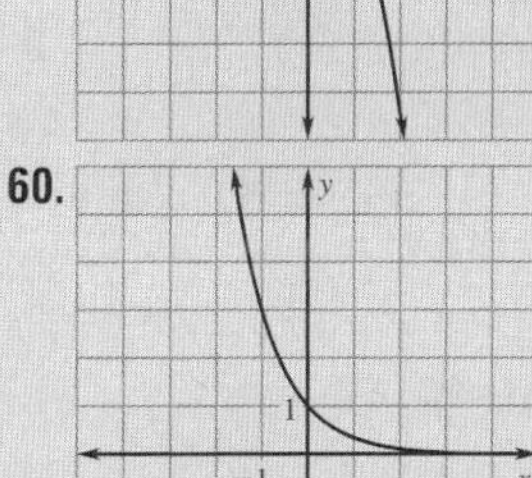

60.
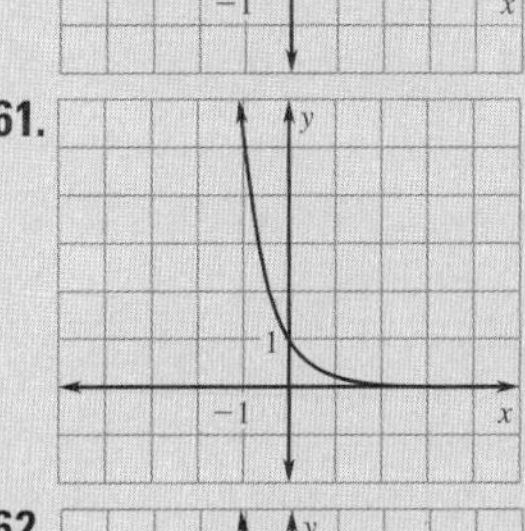

61.
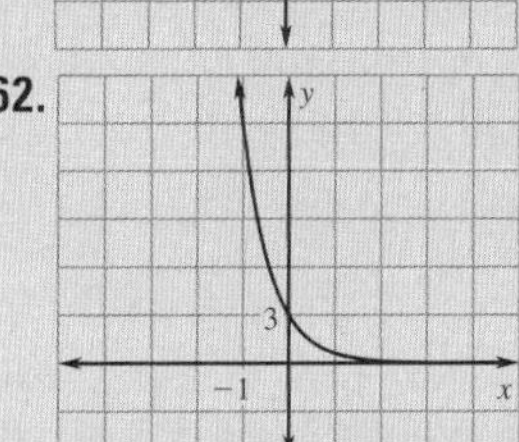

62.

63–67. See Additional Answers beginning on p. AA1.

Chapter 9

Find the sum or difference.

9.1

1. $(6x^2 + 7) + (x^2 - 9)$ **$7x^2 - 2$**
2. $(8y^2 - 3y - 10) + (-11y^2 + 2y - 7)$ **$-3y^2 - y - 17$**
3. $(10m^2 - 7m + 2) - (3m^2 - 2m + 5)$ **$7m^2 - 5m - 3$**
4. $(2t^3 - 3t^2 + 5t) - (6t^3 + 3t^2 - 5t)$ **$-4t^3 - 6t^2 + 10t$**
5. $(6b^3 + 12b^2 - b) - (15b^2 + 7b - 8)$ **$6b^3 - 3b^2 - 8b + 8$**
6. $(r^2 - 8 + 4r^3 + 5r) - (7r^3 - 3r^2 + 5)$ **$-3r^3 + 4r^2 + 5r - 13$**

Find the product.

9.2

7. $5x^4(2x^3 - 3x^2 + 5x - 1)$ **$10x^7 - 15x^6 + 25x^5 - 5x^4$**
8. $(x^2 + 4x + 2)(x + 7)$ **$x^3 + 11x^2 + 30x + 14$**
9. $(2x + 3)(4x + 2)$ **$8x^2 + 16x + 6$**
10. $(2x^2 - 5x + 6)(3x - 2)$ **$6x^3 - 19x^2 + 28x - 12$**
11. $(3x - 7)(x + 5)$ **$3x^2 + 8x - 35$**
12. $(9t - 2)(2t - 3)$ **$18t^2 - 31t + 6$**

9.3

13. $(x + 10)^2$ **$x^2 + 20x + 100$**
14. $(m + 8)(m - 8)$ **$m^2 - 64$**
15. $(4x - 2)(4x + 2)$ **$16x^2 - 4$**
16. $(3x - 4y)(3x + 4y)$ **$9x^2 - 16y^2$**
17. $(6 - 3t)(6 + 3t)$ **$36 - 9t^2$**
18. $(-11x - 4y)^2$ **$121x^2 + 88xy + 16y^2$**

9.4 Solve the equation.

19. $(m + 8)(m - 2) = 0$ **$-8, 2$**
20. $(2y - 6)(y + 3) = 0$ **± 3**
21. $(5y - 3)(2y - 4) = 0$ **$\frac{3}{5}, 2$**
22. $3b^2 + 9b = 0$ **$-3, 0$**
23. $-12m^2 - 3m = 0$ **$-\frac{1}{4}, 0$**
24. $14k^2 = 28k$ **$0, 2$**

9.5 Factor the trinomial.

25. $y^2 + 7y + 12$ **$(y + 3)(y + 4)$**
26. $x^2 - 12x + 35$ **$(x - 7)(x - 5)$**
27. $x^2 + 5x - 36$ **$(x - 4)(x + 9)$**
28. $q^2 + 3q - 40$ **$(q - 5)(q + 8)$**
29. $m^2 - 29m + 100$ **$(m - 25)(m - 4)$**
30. $y^2 + 14y - 72$ **$(y - 4)(y + 18)$**

9.5 Solve the equation.

31. $m^2 - 7m + 10 = 0$ **$2, 5$**
32. $p^2 - 7p = 18$ **$-2, 9$**
33. $z^2 - 13z + 24 = -12$ **$4, 9$**
34. $n^2 + 8 = 6n$ **$2, 4$**
35. $r^2 - 15r = -8r - 10$ **$2, 5$**
36. $c^2 - 8 = -13c + 6$ **$-14, 1$**

9.6 Factor the trinomial.

37. $-x^2 + 5x - 6$ **$-(x - 3)(x - 2)$**
38. $3k^2 - 10k + 8$ **$(3k - 4)(k - 2)$**
39. $4k^2 - 12k + 5$ **$(2k - 1)(2k - 5)$**
40. $6t^2 - 5t - 6$ **$(2t - 3)(3t + 2)$**
41. $-3s^2 - 7s - 2$ **$-(3s + 1)(s + 2)$**
42. $2v^2 - 5v + 3$ **$(2v - 3)(v - 1)$**

9.6 Solve the equation.

43. $-3x^2 + 14x - 8 = 0$ **$\frac{2}{3}, 4$**
44. $8t^2 + 6t = 9$ **$-\frac{3}{2}, \frac{3}{4}$**
45. $2x^2 + 3x - 2 = 0$ **$-2, \frac{1}{2}$**
46. $3p^2 - 28 = 17p$ **$-\frac{4}{3}, 7$**
47. $16m^2 - 1 = -15m$ **$-1, \frac{1}{16}$**
48. $t(6t - 7) = 3$ **$-\frac{1}{3}, \frac{3}{2}$**

9.7 Factor the polynomial.

49. $y^2 - 36$ **$(y + 6)(y - 6)$**
50. $9y^2 - 49$ **$(3y - 7)(3y + 7)$**
51. $12y^2 - 27$ **$3(2y - 3)(2y + 3)$**
52. $x^2 - 8x + 16$ **$(x - 4)^2$**
53. $4x^2 - 12x + 9$ **$(2x - 3)^2$**
54. $27x^2 - 36x + 12$ **$3(3x - 2)^2$**
55. $g^2 + 10g + 25$ **$(g + 5)^2$**
56. $9b^2 + 24b + 16$ **$(3b + 4)^2$**
57. $4w^2 + 28w + 49$ **$(2w + 7)^2$**

9.8 Factor the polynomial completely.

58. $2x^2 + 8x + 6$ **$2(x + 1)(x + 3)$**
59. $3z^2 - 16z + 5$ **$(3z - 1)(z - 5)$**
60. $5m^2 - 23m + 12$ **$(5m - 3)(m - 4)$**
61. $3y^3 + 15y^2 + 2y + 10$ **$(3y^2 + 2)(y + 5)$**
62. $30z^3 - 14z^2 - 8z$ **$2z(5z - 4)(3z + 1)$**
63. $98m^3 - 18m$ **$2m(7m - 3)(7m + 3)$**
64. $8h^2k - 32k$ **$8k(h - 2)(h + 2)$**
65. $2h^3 - 3h^2 - 18h + 27$ **$(h + 3)(h - 3)(2h - 3)$**
66. $-12z^3 + 12z^2 - 3z$ **$-3z(2z - 1)^2$**

Chapter 10, p. 947

1.

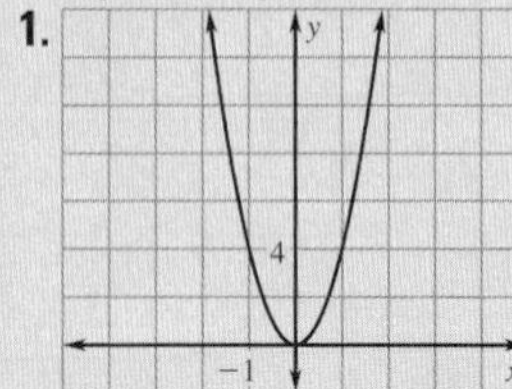

The graph is a vertical stretch by a factor of 4 of the graph of $y = x^2$.

2.

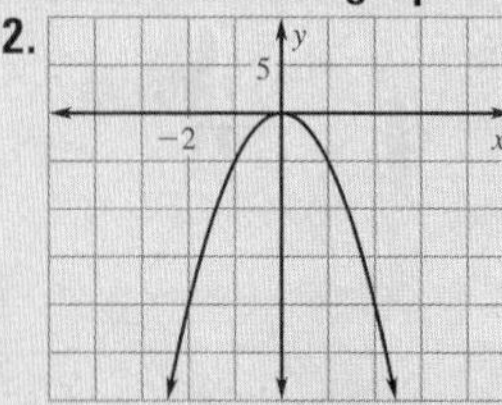

The graph is a vertical stretch by a factor of 5 and a reflection in the x-axis of the graph of $y = x^2$.

3.

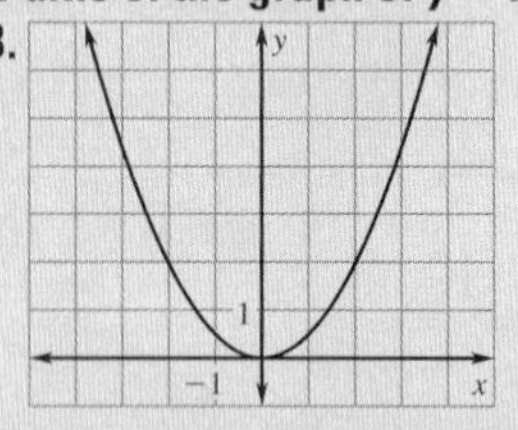

The graph is a vertical shrink by a factor of $\frac{1}{2}$ of the graph of $y = x^2$.

4.

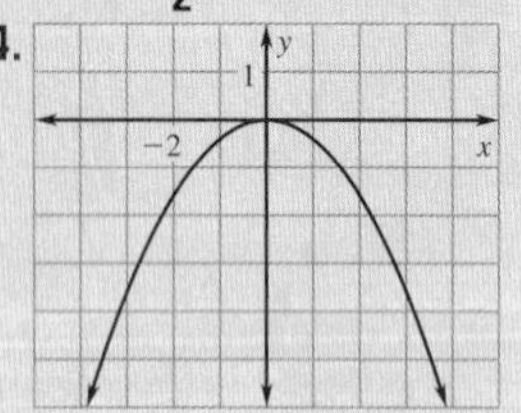

The graph is a vertical shrink by a factor of $\frac{2}{5}$ and a reflection in the x-axis of the graph of $y = x^2$.

5.

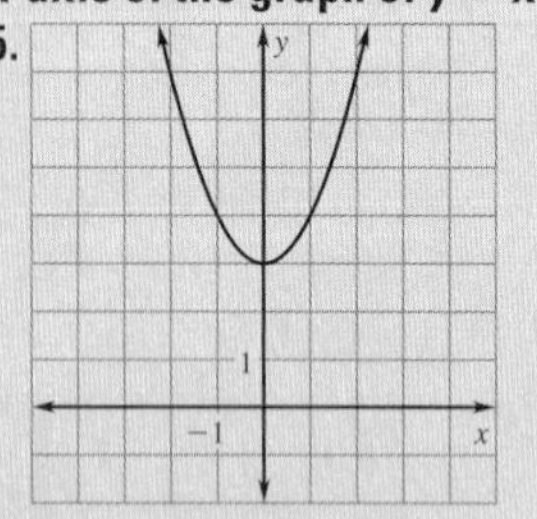

The graph is a vertical translation 3 units up of the graph of $y = x^2$.

6.

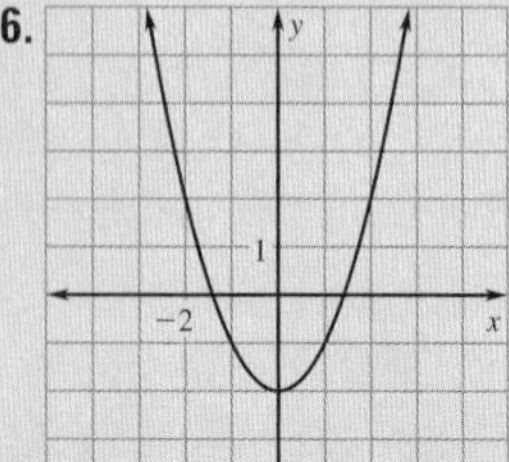

The graph is a vertical translation 2 units down of the graph of $y = x^2$.

7.

The graph is a vertical stretch by a factor of 3 and a vertical translation 4 units up of the graph of $y = x^2$.

Chapter 10

10.1 Graph the function. Compare the graph with the graph of $y = x^2$. 1–8. See margin.

1. $y = 4x^2$
2. $y = -5x^2$
3. $y = \frac{1}{2}x^2$
4. $y = -\frac{2}{5}x^2$
5. $y = x^2 + 3$
6. $y = x^2 - 2$
7. $y = 3x^2 + 4$
8. $y = -4x^2 - 3$

10.2 Graph the function. Label the vertex and axis of symmetry. 9–14. See margin.

9. $y = x^2 + 4x + 4$
10. $y = -x^2 - 2x + 3$
11. $y = 2x^2 - 6x + 5$
12. $y = 3x^2 + 12x + 8$
13. $y = -2x^2 + 6$
14. $y = \frac{3}{4}x^2 - 3x$

10.3 Solve the equation by graphing.

15. $x^2 + 3x - 10 = 0$ **−5, 2**
16. $x^2 + 14 = 9x$ **2, 7**
17. $-x^2 + 3x = -18$ **−3, 6**
18. $2x^2 + 3x - 20 = 0$ **$-4, \frac{5}{2}$**
19. $2x^2 + x = 6$ **$-2, \frac{3}{2}$**
20. $\frac{1}{2}x^2 - x = 12$ **−4, 6**

10.4 Solve the equation. Round the solutions to the nearest hundredth, if necessary.

21. $2x^2 - 20 = 78$ **±7**
22. $3y^2 + 16 = 4$ **no solution**
23. $16y^2 - 6 = 3$ **± 0.75**
24. $48 - x^2 = -52$ **±10**
25. $5m^2 - 5 = 10$ **±1.73**
26. $2 - 5t^2 = 4$ **no solution**

10.5 Solve the equation by completing the square. Round the solutions to the nearest hundredth, if necessary.

27. $x^2 + 4x - 21 = 0$ **−7, 3**
28. $g^2 - 10g = 24$ **−2, 12**
29. $w^2 - 7w + 6 = 0$ **1, 6**
30. $y^2 - \frac{3}{4}y = \frac{1}{4}$ **−0.25, 1**
31. $x^2 - 6x + 3 = 0$ **0.55, 5.45**
32. $4m^2 + 8m - 7 = 0$ **−2.66, 0.66**

10.6 Use the quadratic formula to solve the equation. Round the solutions to the nearest hundredth, if necessary.

33. $h^2 + 6h - 72 = 0$ **−12, 6**
34. $3x^2 - 7x + 2 = 0$ **0.33, 2**
35. $2k^2 - 5k + 2 = 0$ **0.5, 2**
36. $n^2 + 1 = 5n$ **0.21, 4.79**
37. $2z + 4 = 3z^2$ **−0.87, 1.54**
38. $5x^2 - 4x = 2$ **−0.35, 1.15**

10.7 Tell whether the equation has *two solutions*, *one solution*, or *no solution*.

39. $m^2 - 2m + 1 = 0$ **one solution**
40. $3x^2 + 6x + 2 = 0$ **two solutions**
41. $2q^2 + 3q + 5 = 0$ **no solution**
42. $\frac{3}{4}x^2 - x + 2 = 0$ **no solution**
43. $2w^2 - 5w + 6 = 8$ **two solutions**
44. $2y^2 + 10y - 5 = 3y^2 - 30$ **two solutions**

10.8 Tell whether the table of values represents a *linear function*, an *exponential function*, or a *quadratic function*. Then write an equation for the function. 45–48. See margin.

45.

x	−1	0	1	2	3
y	3	0	3	12	27

46.

x	0	1	2	3	4
y	−5	−2	1	4	7

47.

x	1	2	3	4	5
y	1	2	4	8	16

48.

x	−2	−1	0	1	2
y	18	14	10	6	2

9.
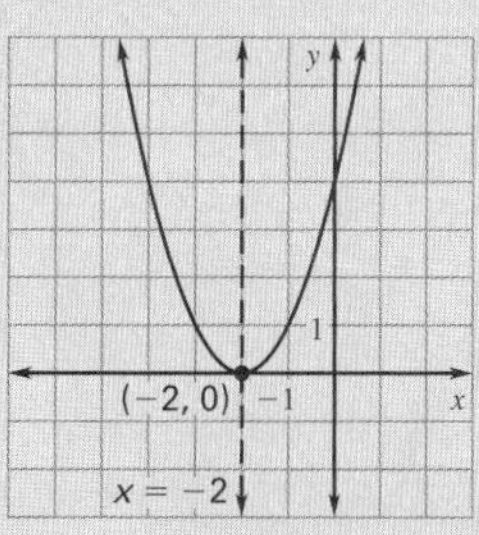

10.
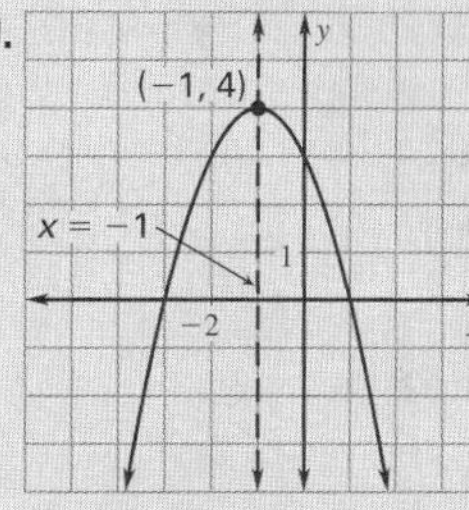

11.
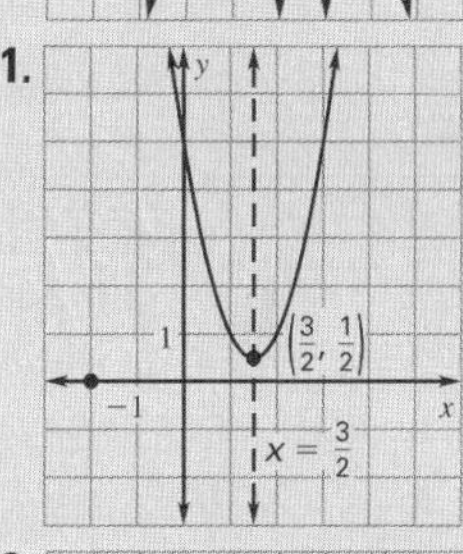

12.
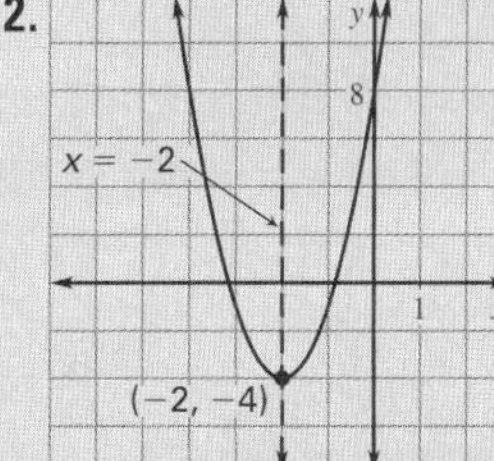

13.
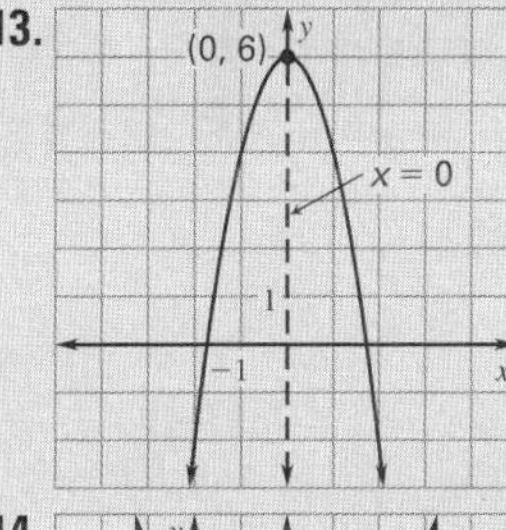

14.
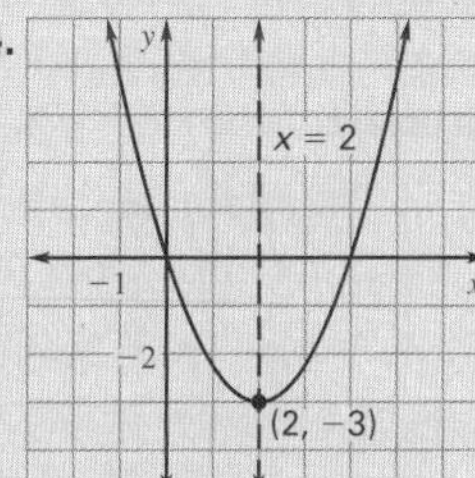

45. quadratic function; $y = 3x^2$
46. linear function; $y = 3x - 5$
47. exponential function; $y = 0.5 \cdot 2^x$
48. linear function; $y = -4x + 10$

8.
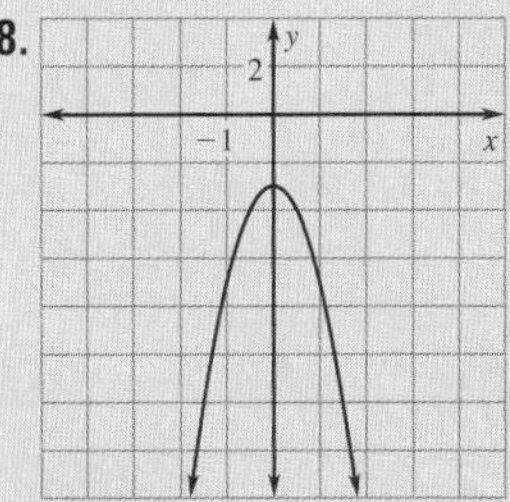

The graph is a vertical stretch by a factor of 4, a reflection in the *x*-axis, and a vertical translation of 3 units down of $y = x^2$.

1.

Domain: $x \geq 0$, range: $y \geq 0$; the graph is a vertical stretch by a factor of 6 of the graph of $y = \sqrt{x}$.

2. 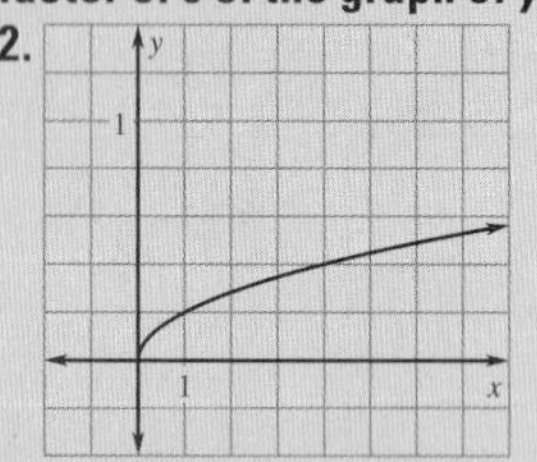

Domain: $x \geq 0$, range: $y \geq 0$; the graph is a vertical shrink by a factor of $\frac{1}{5}$ of the graph of $y = \sqrt{x}$.

3. 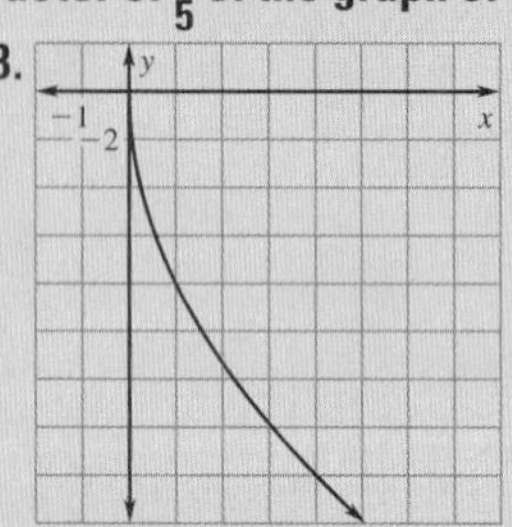

Domain: $x \geq 0$, range: $y \leq 0$; the graph is a vertical stretch by a factor of 8 and a reflection in the x-axis of the graph of $y = \sqrt{x}$.

4. 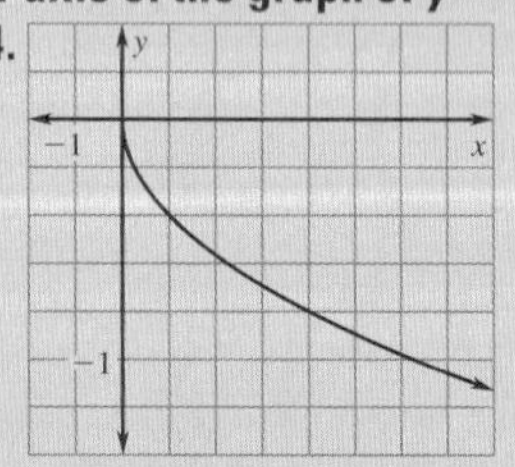

Domain: $x \geq 0$, range: $y \leq 0$; the graph is a vertical shrink by a factor of $\frac{2}{5}$ and a reflection in the x-axis of the graph of $y = \sqrt{x}$.

5. 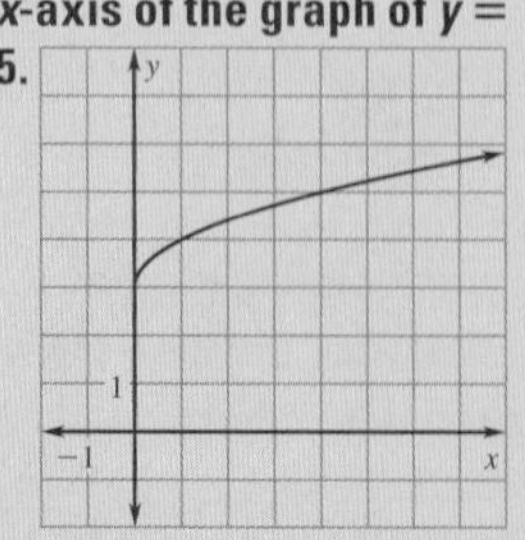

Domain: $x \geq 0$, range: $y \geq 3$; the graph is a vertical translation 3 units up of the graph of $y = \sqrt{x}$.

Chapter 11

EXTRA PRACTICE

11.1 Graph the function and identify its domain and range. Compare the graph with the graph of $y = \sqrt{x}$. **1–9. See margin.**

1. $y = 6\sqrt{x}$
2. $y = \frac{1}{5}\sqrt{x}$
3. $y = -8\sqrt{x}$
4. $y = -\frac{2}{5}\sqrt{x}$
5. $y = \sqrt{x} + 3$
6. $y = \sqrt{x} - 5$
7. $y = \sqrt{x - 2}$
8. $y = \sqrt{x + 5}$
9. $y = \sqrt{x - 4} + 2$

11.2 Simplify the expression.

10. $\sqrt{98}$ **$7\sqrt{2}$**
11. $\sqrt{300}$ **$10\sqrt{3}$**
12. $\sqrt{128x^3}$ **$8x\sqrt{2x}$**
13. $\sqrt{17} \cdot \sqrt{17}$ **17**
14. $\sqrt{112} \cdot \sqrt{63}$ **84**
15. $\sqrt{11g} \cdot 5\sqrt{g}$ **$5g\sqrt{11}$**
16. $4m\sqrt{m} \cdot \sqrt{5m}$ **$4m^2\sqrt{5}$**
17. $\sqrt{27x^5} \cdot \sqrt{48x}$ **$36x^3$**
18. $\sqrt{\frac{19}{49}}$ **$\frac{\sqrt{19}}{7}$**
19. $\sqrt{\frac{1}{6x^2}}$ **$\frac{\sqrt{6}}{6x}$**
20. $\frac{3}{\sqrt{5}}$ **$\frac{3\sqrt{5}}{5}$**
21. $\frac{\sqrt{7}}{\sqrt{8k}}$ **$\frac{\sqrt{14k}}{4k}$**
22. $\sqrt{\frac{5}{27}}$ **$\frac{\sqrt{15}}{9}$**
23. $2\sqrt{3} + \sqrt{7} + \sqrt{3}$ **$3\sqrt{3} + \sqrt{7}$**
24. $2\sqrt{11} + \sqrt{99}$ **$5\sqrt{11}$**
25. $\sqrt{45} + 3\sqrt{20}$ **$9\sqrt{5}$**
26. $\sqrt{3}(12 - \sqrt{15})$ **$12\sqrt{3} - 3\sqrt{5}$**
27. $3\sqrt{6}(4\sqrt{6} - \sqrt{600})$ **-108**
28. $(6 - \sqrt{7})(6 - \sqrt{7})$ **$43 - 12\sqrt{7}$**
29. $(4 - \sqrt{13})(10 + \sqrt{13})$ **$27 - 6\sqrt{13}$**

11.3 Solve the equation. Check for extraneous solutions.

30. $6\sqrt{x} - 30 = 0$ **25**
31. $\sqrt{8x} + 5 = 13$ **8**
32. $\sqrt{x + 3} + 5 = 16$ **118**
33. $3\sqrt{4x + 1} - 2 = 25$ **20**
34. $\sqrt{3x - 12} = \sqrt{5x - 26}$ **7**
35. $\sqrt{2x + 10} - \sqrt{x + 7} = 0$ **-3**
36. $\sqrt{\frac{1}{2}x + 10} - \sqrt{2x - 8} = 0$ **12**
37. $x = \sqrt{11x - 10}$ **1, 10**
38. $x = \sqrt{20 - x}$ **4**
39. $5x = \sqrt{20x - 3}$ **$\frac{1}{5}, \frac{3}{5}$**
40. $\sqrt{-4x + 5} = 3x$ **$\frac{5}{9}$**
41. $x + 1 = \sqrt{6 - 2x}$ **1**

11.4 Let a and b represent the lengths of the legs of a right triangle, and let c represent the length of the hypotenuse. Find the unknown length.

42. $a = 6, b = 8$ **$c = 10$**
43. $a = 10, c = 26$ **$b = 24$**
44. $b = 40, c = 41$ **$a = 9$**
45. $a = 2, c = 5$ **$b = \sqrt{21}$**
46. $a = 4, b = 7$ **$c = \sqrt{65}$**
47. $b = 8, c = 11$ **$a = \sqrt{57}$**

11.4 Tell whether the triangle with the given side lengths is a right triangle.

48. $a = 10, b = 24, c = 26$ **right triangle**
49. $a = 2, b = 4, c = 6$ **not a right triangle**
50. $a = 14, b = 15, c = 21$ **not a right triangle**
51. $a = 16, b = 30, c = 34$ **right triangle**
52. $a = 1.4, b = 4.8, c = 5$ **right triangle**
53. $a = 13, b = 84, c = 95$ **not a right triangle**

11.5 Find the distance between the two points.

54. (5, 10), (2, 6) **5**
55. (2, 8), (7, −4) **13**
56. (3, −3), (4, 1) **$\sqrt{17}$**
57. (6, 1.5), (2.5, −4) **$\sqrt{42.5}$**
58. $\left(1, \frac{2}{5}\right), \left(\frac{1}{2}, -\frac{4}{5}\right)$ **1.3**
59. $\left(-\frac{3}{8}, 1\right), \left(\frac{5}{8}, \frac{1}{2}\right)$ **$\frac{\sqrt{5}}{2}$**

11.5 Find the midpoint of the line segment with the given endpoints.

60. (6, −2), (8, −6) **(7, −4)**
61. (0, −5), (−4, 8) **(−2, 1.5)**
62. (0, −6), (0, 2) **(0, −2)**
63. (10, 0), (−8, 0) **(1, 0)**
64. (−5, −3), (−8, −7) **(−6.5, −5)**
65. $\left(5, -\frac{1}{2}\right), \left(8, -\frac{5}{2}\right)$ **$\left(6\frac{1}{2}, -1\frac{1}{2}\right)$**

6–9. See Additional Answers beginning on p. AA1.

Chapter 12

12.1 Graph the inverse variation equation. **1–4. See margin.**

1. $y = \frac{-1}{x}$ 2. $y = \frac{8}{x}$ 3. $y = \frac{12}{x}$ 4. $y = \frac{-14}{x}$

12.1 Given that y varies inversely with x, use the specified values to write an inverse variation equation that relates x and y. Then find the value of y when x = 2.

5. $x = 3, y = 4$ $\mathbf{y = \frac{12}{x}; 6}$ 6. $x = -2, y = 5$ $\mathbf{y = -\frac{10}{x}; -5}$ 7. $x = -4, y = -15$ $\mathbf{y = \frac{60}{x}; 30}$

8. $x = 8, y = -6$ $\mathbf{y = \frac{-48}{x}; -24}$ 9. $x = -7, y = -7$ $\mathbf{y = \frac{49}{x}; 24.5}$ 10. $x = -11, y = 11$ $\mathbf{y = \frac{-121}{x}; -60.5}$

12.2 Graph the function. **11–18. See margin.**

11. $y = \frac{6}{x}$ 12. $y = \frac{-6}{x}$ 13. $y = \frac{1}{5x}$ 14. $y = \frac{1}{x} + 6$

15. $y = \frac{1}{x-4}$ 16. $y = \frac{1}{x-5} + 3$ 17. $y = \frac{4}{x+2} - 3$ 18. $y = \frac{-2}{x+1} - 3$

12.3 Divide.

19. $(30x^4 - 12x^3 + 6x^2) \div (-6x)$ $\mathbf{-5x^3 + 2x^2 - x}$ 20. $(9y^2 + 3y - 6) \div (3y - 2)$ $\mathbf{3y + 3}$

21. $(3v^2 + 2v + 12) \div (v + 2)$ $\mathbf{3v - 4 + \frac{20}{v+2}}$ 22. $(-24w - 11 + 8w^2) \div (2 + 4w)$ $\mathbf{2w - 7 + \frac{3}{4w+2}}$

23. $(9m^2 - 6) \div (3m - 4)$ $\mathbf{3m + 4 + \frac{10}{3m-4}}$ 24. $(-2 + 25n^2) \div (2 + 5n)$ $\mathbf{5n - 2 + \frac{2}{5n+2}}$

12.4 Simplify the rational expression, if possible. State the excluded values. **25–32. See margin.**

25. $\frac{44x^3}{24x}$ 26. $\frac{3y+6}{y+2}$ 27. $\frac{3a-15}{4a-20}$ 28. $\frac{2b-8}{4-b}$

29. $\frac{r^2-2r-15}{r^2+r-6}$ 30. $\frac{s+3}{2s^2+3s-9}$ 31. $\frac{2m^2+8m-24}{3m^3+24m^2+36m}$ 32. $\frac{6n^3-18n^2}{3n^3-27n}$

Find the sum, difference, product, or quotient.

12.5 33. $\frac{x^2+3x-10}{2x-4} \cdot \frac{5x}{x^2+2x-15}$ $\mathbf{\frac{5x}{2x-6}}$ 34. $\frac{2y^6}{6y^3+8y^2} \cdot (3y+4)$ $\mathbf{y^4}$

35. $\frac{3r^2-12}{r-2} \div \frac{2r^2+7r+6}{2r^2-r-6}$ $\mathbf{3r - 6}$ 36. $\frac{3s^2+11s+10}{s+2} \div (-3s^2+s+10)$ $\mathbf{-\frac{1}{s-2}}$

12.6 37. $\frac{8}{5t} + \frac{3}{2t^2}$ $\mathbf{\frac{16t+15}{10t^2}}$ 38. $\frac{3}{u+2} + \frac{4}{2u+1}$ $\mathbf{\frac{10u+11}{(u+2)(2u+1)}}$

39. $\frac{3}{c^2-9} - \frac{2}{2c^2-3c-9}$ $\mathbf{\frac{4c+3}{(c+3)(c-3)(2c+3)}}$ 40. $\frac{k+4}{k^2+4k+4} - \frac{k-4}{k^2-k-6}$ $\mathbf{\frac{3k-4}{(k+2)^2(k-3)}}$

12.7 Solve the equation. Check your solution.

41. $\frac{2}{x+2} = \frac{x-5}{9}$ $\mathbf{-4, 7}$ 42. $\frac{y}{y-1} + \frac{1}{4} = \frac{6}{y-1}$ $\mathbf{5}$

43. $\frac{z}{z+3} + 2 = \frac{5}{z-1}$ $\mathbf{-\frac{7}{3}, 3}$ 44. $\frac{1}{w+5} - \frac{2}{w+3} = \frac{6}{w^2+5w+6}$ $\mathbf{-11, -4}$

45. $\frac{3}{h+4} - 4 = \frac{6}{h^2+h-12}$ $\mathbf{-3, \frac{11}{4}}$ 46. $\frac{2}{a+2} - \frac{5}{a+2} = \frac{4}{a^2+4a+4}$ $\mathbf{-\frac{10}{3}}$

EXTRA PRACTICE

1.
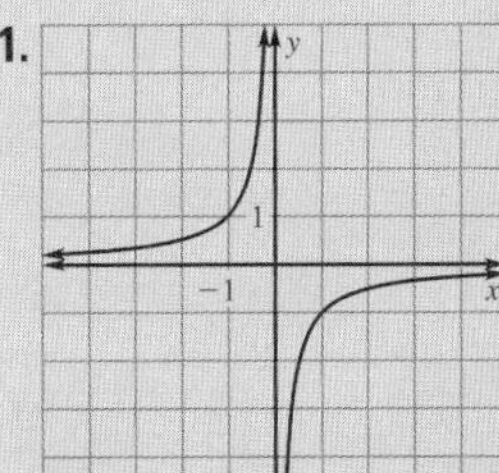

2.
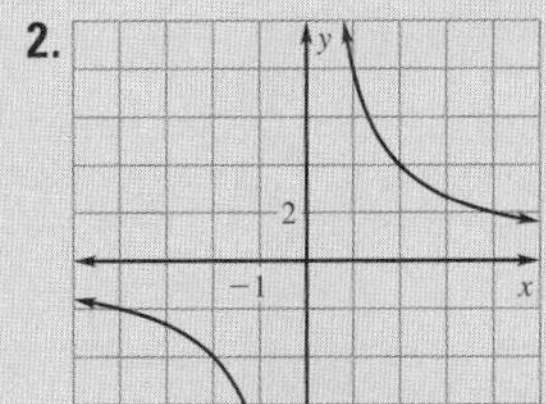

3.
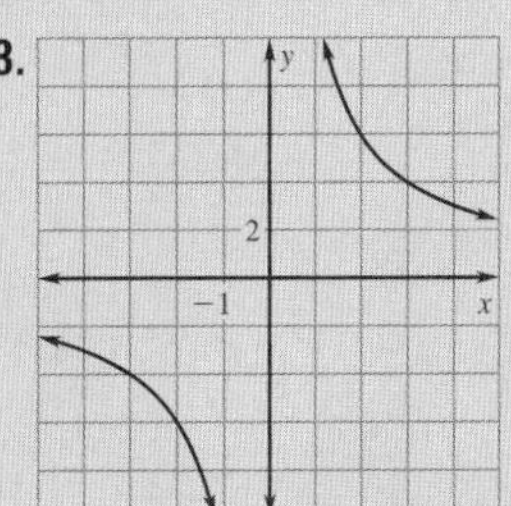

4.
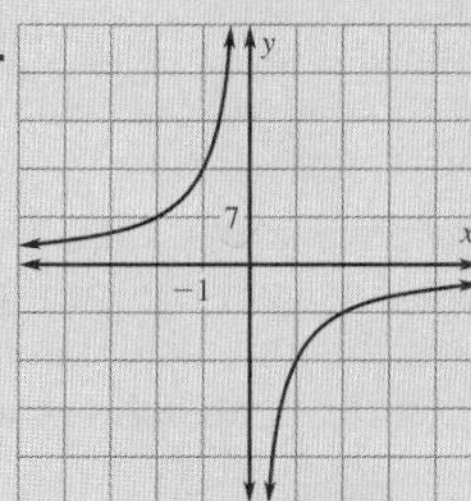

11.
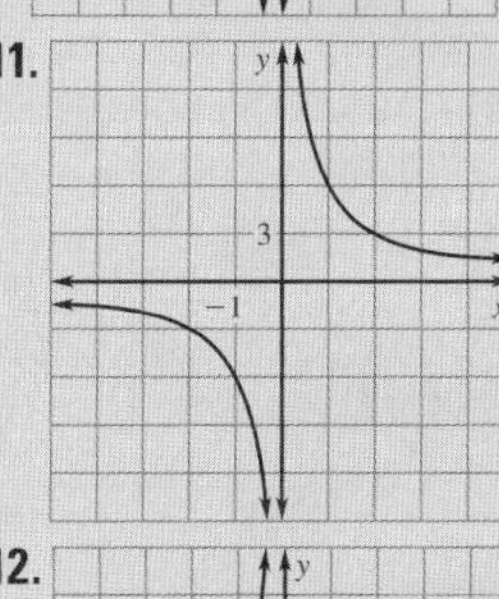

12.
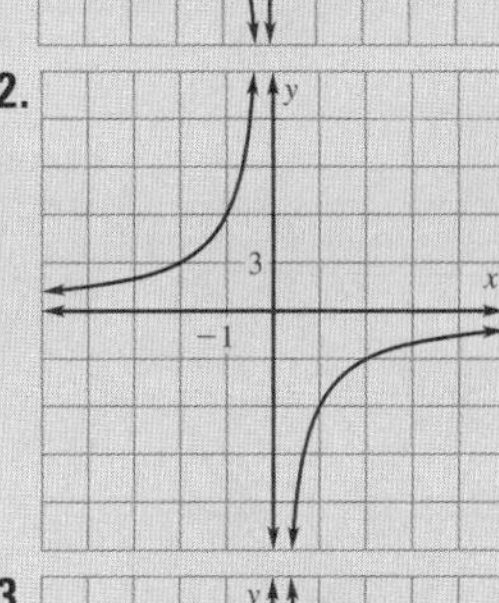

13.
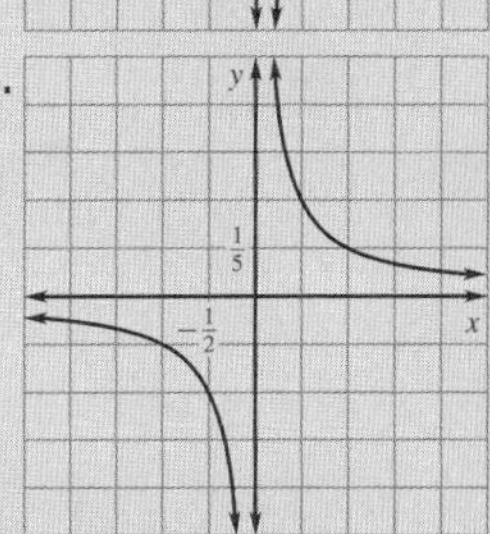

14–18. See Additional Answers beginning on p. AA1.

25. $\frac{11x^2}{6}$**, excluded value is 0.**

26. 3, excluded value is −2.

27. $\frac{3}{4}$**, excluded value is 5.**

28. −2, excluded value is 4.

29. $\frac{r-5}{r-2}$**, excluded values are 2 and −3.**

30. $\frac{1}{2s-3}$**, excluded values are −3 and** $\frac{3}{2}$**.**

31. $\frac{2m-4}{3m^2+6m}$**, excluded values are −6, −2, and 0.**

32. $\frac{2n}{n+3}$**, excluded values are −3, 0, and 3.**

18. population: parents or guardians of high school students, sampling method: systematic sample

19. Yes. *Sample answer:* The sampling method might be biased because only the parents or guardians of students are called and not other spectators.

20. Potentially biased. *Sample answer:* The question encourages the listener to agree with the researcher.

22. 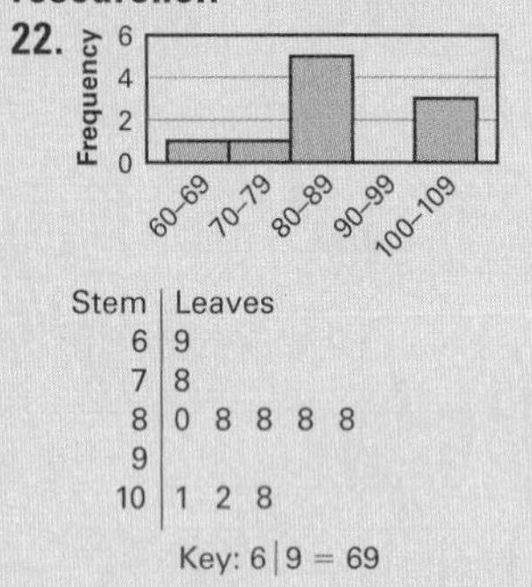

Stem	Leaves
6	9
7	8
8	0 8 8 8 8
9	
10	1 2 8

Key: 6 | 9 = 69

23. 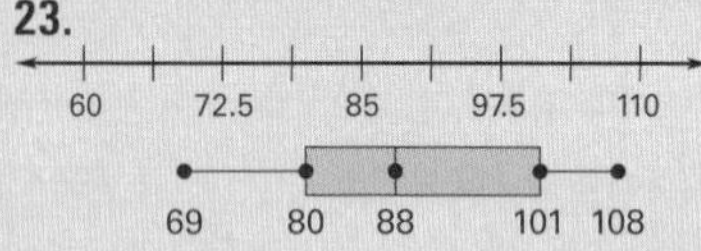

Chapter 13

13.1 In Exercises 1 and 2, use the following information. A bag contains 3 red, 3 blue, and 3 yellow marbles. You toss a coin and then draw a marble out of the bag at random.

1. Find the number of possible outcomes in the sample space. Then list the possible outcomes. **6 possible outcomes; heads, yellow; heads, red; heads, blue; tails, yellow; tails, red; tails, blue**

2. What is the probability that the coin shows tails and the marble is blue? $\frac{1}{6}$

13.1 **3.** You toss a coin 3 times. What are the odds against the coin's showing heads twice and tails once? **5 : 3**

13.2 **4.** In how many ways can you arrange the letters in the word SPRING? **720 ways**

5. In how many ways can you arrange 3 of the letters in the word TULIP? **60 ways**

13.2 Evaluate the expression.

6. 7! **5040** **7.** ${}_8P_3$ **336** **8.** ${}_{10}P_3$ **720** **9.** ${}_5P_5$ **120**

13.3 **10.** You can choose 3 books from a list of 5 books to read for English class. How many combinations of 3 books are possible? **10 combinations**

13.3 Evaluate the expression.

11. ${}_6C_2$ **15** **12.** ${}_7C_3$ **35** **13.** ${}_{10}C_4$ **210** **14.** ${}_{20}C_{15}$ **15,504**

13.4 In Exercises 15 and 16, you roll a number cube. Tell whether the events *A* and *B* are *mutually exclusive* or *overlapping*. Then find *P*(*A* or *B*).

15. Event *A*: Roll a 5. **Event *B*:** Roll a prime number. **overlapping; $\frac{1}{2}$**

16. Event *A*: Roll a 4. **Event *B*:** Roll a multiple of 3. **mutually exclusive; $\frac{1}{2}$**

13.4 **17.** A bag contains 3 red, 4 blue, and 5 yellow marbles. You randomly draw two marbles, one at a time. Find the probability that both are blue if **(a)** you replace the first marble and **(b)** you do not replace the first marble. **a. $\frac{1}{9}$ b. $\frac{1}{11}$**

13.5 In Exercises 18–20, use the following information. **18–20. See margin.**

Some parents want to gather information about updating the sound system in the high school auditorium. They obtain a list of high school students and call the parents or guardians of every 20th student on the list. The question they ask is "Don't you think the sound system in the high school auditorium needs updating?"

18. Identify the population and classify the sampling method.

19. Is the sampling method used likely to result in a biased sample? *Explain.*

20. Tell whether the question is potentially biased. *Explain* your answer.

In Exercises 21–23, use the following numbers of stories in the world's ten tallest buildings: 101, 88, 88, 108, 88, 88, 80, 69, 102, 78.

13.6 **21.** Find the mean, median, mode(s), range, and mean absolute deviation of the data. Round to the nearest hundredth, if necessary. **mean: 89, median: 88, mode: 88, range: 39, mean absolute deviation: 8.8**

13.7 **22.** Make a histogram and a stem-and-leaf plot of the data. **See margin.**

13.8 **23.** Make a box-and-whisker plot of the data. Identify any outliers. **See margin for art; no outliers.**

Symbols

Symbol	Meaning	Page
$3 \cdot x$ $3x$ $3(x)$	3 times x	2
$\frac{a}{b}$	a divided by b, $b \neq 0$	2
a^4	the fourth power of a, or $a \cdot a \cdot a \cdot a$	3
( )	parentheses—a grouping symbol	9
[ ]	brackets—a grouping symbol	9
=	is equal to	21
<	is less than	21
>	is greater than	21
≤	is less than or equal to	21
≥	is greater than or equal to	21
$\stackrel{?}{=}$	is equal to?	22
(x, y)	ordered pair	43
. . .	continues on	64
$-a$	the opposite of a	66
$\lvert a \rvert$	the absolute value of a	66
$\begin{bmatrix} 1 & 0 \\ 0 & 1 \end{bmatrix}$	matrix	94
$\frac{1}{a}$	the reciprocal of a, $a \neq 0$	103
≠	is not equal to	103
$\sqrt{a}$	the nonnegative square root of a, $a \geq 0$	110
±	plus or minus	110
≈	is approximately equal to	112
$a:b$	the ratio of a to b	162

Symbol	Meaning	Page
≅	is congruent to	174
~	is similar to	174
A'	the image of point A	213
m	slope	235
b	y-intercept	244
a	constant of variation	253
$f(x)$	the value of the function f at x	262
a^{-n}	$\frac{1}{a^n}$, $a \neq 0$	503
$\sqrt[3]{a}$	the cube root of a	510
$c \times 10^n$	scientific notation, $1 \leq c < 10$ and n is an integer	512
$P(A)$	the probability of an event A	844
$n!$	n factorial, or $n \cdot (n-1) \cdot \ldots \cdot 2 \cdot 1$, n is a nonnegative integer	852
$_nP_r$	the number of permutations of n objects taken r at a time, $r \leq n$	852
$_nC_r$	the number of combinations of n objects taken r at a time, $r \leq n$	856
$\overline{x}$	x bar, the mean of numerical data	875
σ^2	variance, the square of standard deviation	879
σ	standard deviation, the nonnegative square root of variance	879

Geometric Formulas

Pythagorean Theorem (p. 737)

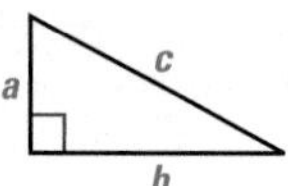

In a right triangle, $a^2 + b^2 = c^2$ where a and b are the lengths of the legs and c is the length of the hypotenuse.

Square (p. 924)

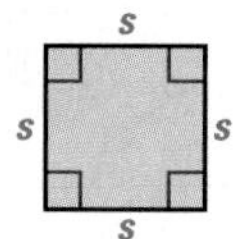
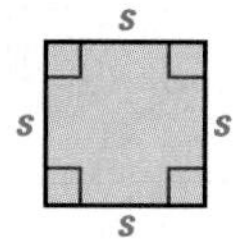

Area $A = s^2$

Perimeter $P = 4s$

Rectangle (p. 924)

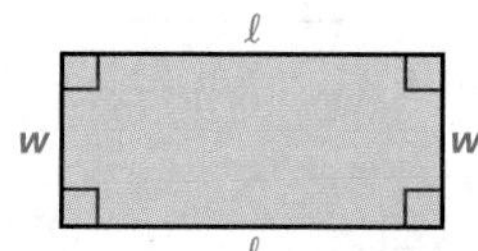

Area $A = \ell w$

Perimeter $P = 2\ell + 2w$

Parallelogram (p. 924)

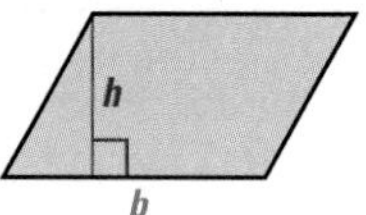

Area $A = bh$

Triangle (p. 924)

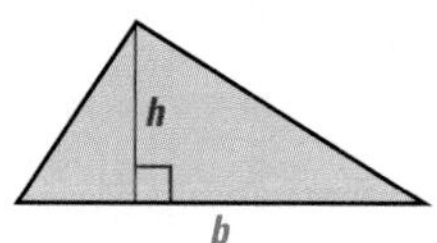

Area $A = \frac{1}{2}bh$

Trapezoid (p. 924)

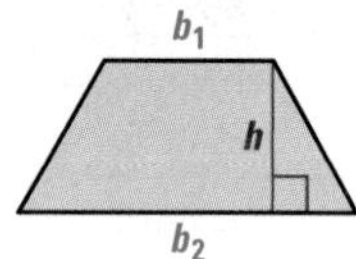

Area $A = \frac{1}{2}(b_1 + b_2)h$

Circle (p. 926)

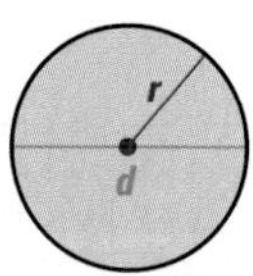

Circumference $C = \pi d$ or $C = 2\pi r$

Area $A = \pi r^2$

Prism (p. 927)

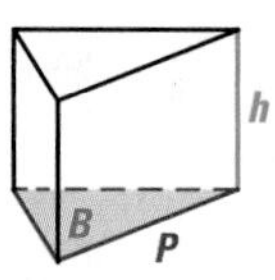

Surface Area $S = 2B + Ph$

Volume $V = Bh$

Cylinder (p. 927)

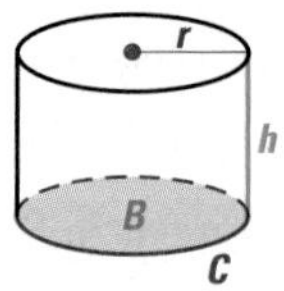

Surface Area $S = 2B + Ch = 2\pi r^2 + 2\pi rh$

Volume $V = Bh = \pi r^2 h$

Pyramid (p. 927)

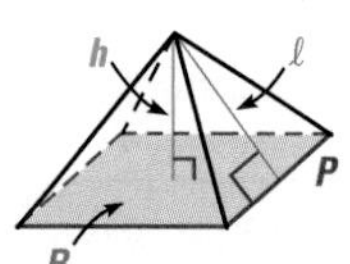

Surface Area $S = B + \frac{1}{2}P\ell$

Volume $V = \frac{1}{3}Bh$

Cone (p. 927)

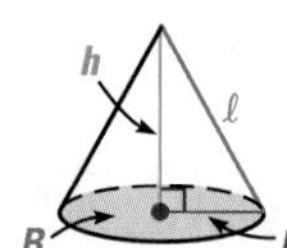
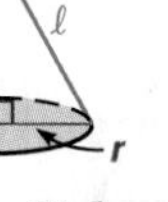

Surface Area $S = B + \frac{1}{2}C\ell = \pi r^2 + \pi r\ell$

Volume $V = \frac{1}{3}Bh = \frac{1}{3}\pi r^2 h$

Sphere (p. 927)

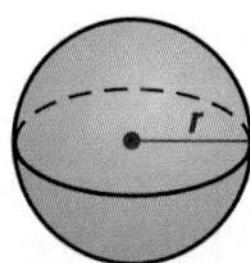

Surface Area $S = 4\pi r^2$

Volume $V = \frac{4}{3}\pi r^3$

TABLES

Other Formulas

Slope (p. 235)	The slope m of a nonvertical line passing through the two points (x_1, y_1) and (x_2, y_2) is $m = \frac{y_2 - y_1}{x_2 - x_1}$.
Compound interest (p. 523)	$y = a(1 + r)^t$ where y is the account balance, a is the initial investment, r is the annual interest rate (in decimal form), and t is the time in years.
Quadratic formula (p. 671)	The real-number solutions of the quadratic equation $ax^2 + bx + c = 0$ are $x = \frac{-b \pm \sqrt{b^2 - 4ac}}{2a}$ where $a \neq 0$ and $b^2 - 4ac \geq 0$.
Distance formula (p. 744)	The distance d between any two points (x_1, y_1) and (x_2, y_2) is $d = \sqrt{(x_2 - x_1)^2 + (y_2 - y_1)^2}$.
Midpoint formula (p. 745)	The midpoint M of the line segment with endpoints $A(x_1, y_1)$ and $B(x_2, y_2)$ is $M\left(\frac{x_1 + x_2}{2}, \frac{y_1 + y_2}{2}\right)$.
Theoretical probability (p. 844)	The probability of an event when all the outcomes are equally likely is $P(\text{event}) = \frac{\text{Number of favorable outcomes}}{\text{Total number of outcomes}}$.
Experimental probability (p. 844)	For repeated trials of an experiment, the probability of an event is $P(\text{event}) = \frac{\text{Number of successes}}{\text{Number of trials}}$.
Permutations (p. 852)	The number of permutations of n objects taken r at a time, where $r \leq n$, is given by ${}_nP_r = \frac{n!}{(n - r)!}$.
Combinations (p. 856)	The number of combinations of n objects taken r at a time, where $r \leq n$, is given by ${}_nC_r = \frac{n!}{(n - r)! \cdot r!}$.
Probability of mutually exclusive or overlapping events (p. 861)	If A and B are mutually exclusive events, then $P(A \text{ or } B) = P(A) + P(B)$. If A and B are overlapping events, then $P(A \text{ or } B) = P(A) + P(B) - P(A \text{ and } B)$.
Probability of independent or dependent events (p. 862)	If A and B are independent events, then $P(A \text{ and } B) = P(A) \cdot P(B)$. If A and B are dependent events, then $P(A \text{ and } B) = P(A) \cdot P(B \text{ given } A)$.

TABLES

953

Properties

Properties of Addition and Multiplication

Commutative Properties (pp. 75, 89) The order in which you add two numbers does not change the sum.	$a + b = b + a$
The order in which you multiply two numbers does not change the product.	$a \cdot b = b \cdot a$
Associative Properties (pp. 75, 89) The way you group three numbers in a sum does not change the sum.	$(a + b) + c = a + (b + c)$
The way you group three numbers in a product does not change the product.	$(a \cdot b) \cdot c = a \cdot (b \cdot c)$
Identity Properties (pp. 75, 89) The sum of a number and the additive identity, 0, is the number.	$a + 0 = 0 + a = a$
The product of a number and the multiplicative identity, 1, is the number.	$a \cdot 1 = 1 \cdot a = a$
Inverse Properties (pp. 75, 103) The sum of a number and its additive inverse, or opposite, is 0.	$a + (-a) = -a + a = 0$
The product of a nonzero number and its multiplicative inverse, or reciprocal, is 1.	$a \cdot \frac{1}{a} = \frac{1}{a} \cdot a = 1\ (a \neq 0)$
Distributive Property (p. 96) You can multiply a number and a sum by multiplying each term of the sum by the number and then adding these products. The same property applies to the product of a number and a difference.	$a(b + c) = ab + ac$ $(b + c)a = ba + ca$ $a(b - c) = ab - ac$ $(b - c)a = ba - ca$

TABLES

Properties of Equality

Addition Property of Equality (p. 134) Adding the same number to each side of an equation produces an equivalent equation.	If $x - a = b$, then $x - a + a = b + a$, or $x = b + a$.
Subtraction Property of Equality (p. 134) Subtracting the same number from each side of an equation produces an equivalent equation.	If $x + a = b$, then $x + a - a = b - a$, or $x = b - a$.
Multiplication Property of Equality (p. 135) Multiplying each side of an equation by the same nonzero number produces an equivalent equation.	If $\frac{x}{a} = b$ and $a \neq 0$, then $a \cdot \frac{x}{a} = a \cdot b$, or $x = ab$.
Division Property of Equality (p. 135) Dividing each side of an equation by the same nonzero number produces an equivalent equation.	If $ax = b$ and $a \neq 0$, then $\frac{ax}{a} = \frac{b}{a}$, or $x = \frac{b}{a}$.

Properties of Inequality

Addition and Subtraction Properties of Inequality (pp. 357, 358) Adding or subtracting the same number on each side of an inequality produces an equivalent inequality.	If $a < b$, then $a + c < b + c$ and $a - c < b - c$. If $a > b$, then $a + c > b + c$ and $a - c > b - c$.
Multiplication and Division Properties of Inequality (pp. 363, 364) Multiplying or dividing each side of an inequality by a *positive* number produces an equivalent inequality. Multiplying or dividing each side of an inequality by a *negative* number and *reversing the direction of the inequality symbol* produces an equivalent inequality.	If $a < b$ and $c > 0$, then $ac < bc$ and $\frac{a}{c} < \frac{b}{c}$. If $a < b$ and $c < 0$, then $ac > bc$ and $\frac{a}{c} > \frac{b}{c}$.

Properties of Exponents

Product of Powers Property (p. 489) To multiply powers having the same base, add the exponents.	$a^m \cdot a^n = a^{m+n}$
Power of a Power Property (p. 490) To find a power of a power, multiply exponents.	$(a^m)^n = a^{mn}$
Power of a Product Property (p. 490) To find a power of a product, find the power of each factor and multiply.	$(ab)^m = a^m b^m$
Quotient of Powers Property (p. 495) To divide powers having the same nonzero base, subtract exponents.	$\frac{a^m}{a^n} = a^{m-n}, a \neq 0$
Power of a Quotient Property (p. 496) To find a power of a quotient, find the power of the numerator and the power of the denominator and divide.	$\left(\frac{a}{b}\right)^m = \frac{a^m}{b^m}, b \neq 0$

Other Properties

Cross Products Property (p. 168) The cross products of a proportion are equal.	If $\frac{a}{b} = \frac{c}{d}$ $(b, d \neq 0)$, then $ad = bc$.
Product Property of Radicals (p. 719) The square root of a product equals the product of the square roots of the factors.	$\sqrt{ab} = \sqrt{a} \cdot \sqrt{b}$, $a \geq 0$ and $b \geq 0$
Quotient Properties of Radicals (p. 720) The square root of a quotient equals the quotient of the square roots of the numerator and denominator.	$\sqrt{\frac{a}{b}} = \frac{\sqrt{a}}{\sqrt{b}}$, $a \geq 0$ and $b > 0$

TABLES

955

Measures

Time	
60 seconds (sec) = 1 minute (min) 60 minutes = 1 hour (h) 24 hours = 1 day 7 days = 1 week 4 weeks (approx.) = 1 month	365 days, 52 weeks (approx.), 12 months = 1 year 10 years = 1 decade 100 years = 1 century

Metric	United States Customary
Length 10 millimeters (mm) = 1 centimeter (cm) 100 cm, 1000 mm = 1 meter (m) 1000 m = 1 kilometer (km)	**Length** 12 inches (in.) = 1 foot (ft) 36 in., 3 ft = 1 yard (yd) 5280 ft, 1760 yd = 1 mile (mi)
Area 100 square millimeters (mm^2) = 1 square centimeter (cm^2) 10,000 cm^2 = 1 square meter (m^2) 10,000 m^2 = 1 hectare (ha)	**Area** 144 square inches ($in.^2$) = 1 square foot (ft^2) 9 ft^2 = 1 square yard (yd^2) 43,560 ft^2, 4840 yd^2 = 1 acre (A)
Volume 1000 cubic millimeters (mm^3) = 1 cubic centimeter (cm^3) 1,000,000 cm^3 = 1 cubic meter (m^3)	**Volume** 1728 cubic inches ($in.^3$) = 1 cubic foot (ft^3) 27 ft^3 = 1 cubic yard (yd^3)
Liquid Capacity 1000 milliliters (mL), 1000 cubic centimeters (cm^3) = 1 liter (L) 1000 L = 1 kiloliter (kL)	**Liquid Capacity** 8 fluid ounces (fl oz) = 1 cup (c) 2 c = 1 pint (pt) 2 pt = 1 quart (qt) 4 qt = 1 gallon (gal)
Mass 1000 milligrams (mg) = 1 gram (g) 1000 g = 1 kilogram (kg) 1000 kg = 1 metric ton (t)	**Weight** 16 ounces (oz) = 1 pound (lb) 2000 lb = 1 ton
Temperature Degrees Celsius (°C) 0°C = freezing point of water 37°C = normal body temperature 100°C = boiling point of water	**Temperature Degrees Fahrenheit (°F)** 32°F = freezing point of water 98.6°F = normal body temperature 212°F = boiling point of water

TABLES

Squares and Square Roots

No.	Square	Sq. Root	No.	Square	Sq. Root	No.	Square	Sq. Root
1	1	1.000	**51**	2601	7.141	**101**	10,201	10.050
2	4	1.414	**52**	2704	7.211	**102**	10,404	10.100
3	9	1.732	**53**	2809	7.280	**103**	10,609	10.149
4	16	2.000	**54**	2916	7.348	**104**	10,816	10.198
5	25	2.236	**55**	3025	7.416	**105**	11,025	10.247
6	36	2.449	**56**	3136	7.483	**106**	11,236	10.296
7	49	2.646	**57**	3249	7.550	**107**	11,449	10.344
8	64	2.828	**58**	3364	7.616	**108**	11,664	10.392
9	81	3.000	**59**	3481	7.681	**109**	11,881	10.440
10	100	3.162	**60**	3600	7.746	**110**	12,100	10.488
11	121	3.317	**61**	3721	7.810	**111**	12,321	10.536
12	144	3.464	**62**	3844	7.874	**112**	12,544	10.583
13	169	3.606	**63**	3969	7.937	**113**	12,769	10.630
14	196	3.742	**64**	4096	8.000	**114**	12,996	10.677
15	225	3.873	**65**	4225	8.062	**115**	13,225	10.724
16	256	4.000	**66**	4356	8.124	**116**	13,456	10.770
17	289	4.123	**67**	4489	8.185	**117**	13,689	10.817
18	324	4.243	**68**	4624	8.246	**118**	13,924	10.863
19	361	4.359	**69**	4761	8.307	**119**	14,161	10.909
20	400	4.472	**70**	4900	8.367	**120**	14,400	10.954
21	441	4.583	**71**	5041	8.426	**121**	14,641	11.000
22	484	4.690	**72**	5184	8.485	**122**	14,884	11.045
23	529	4.796	**73**	5329	8.544	**123**	15,129	11.091
24	576	4.899	**74**	5476	8.602	**124**	15,376	11.136
25	625	5.000	**75**	5625	8.660	**125**	15,625	11.180
26	676	5.099	**76**	5776	8.718	**126**	15,876	11.225
27	729	5.196	**77**	5929	8.775	**127**	16,129	11.269
28	784	5.292	**78**	6084	8.832	**128**	16,384	11.314
29	841	5.385	**79**	6241	8.888	**129**	16,641	11.358
30	900	5.477	**80**	6400	8.944	**130**	16,900	11.402
31	961	5.568	**81**	6561	9.000	**131**	17,161	11.446
32	1024	5.657	**82**	6724	9.055	**132**	17,424	11.489
33	1089	5.745	**83**	6889	9.110	**133**	17,689	11.533
34	1156	5.831	**84**	7056	9.165	**134**	17,956	11.576
35	1225	5.916	**85**	7225	9.220	**135**	18,225	11.619
36	1296	6.000	**86**	7396	9.274	**136**	18,496	11.662
37	1369	6.083	**87**	7569	9.327	**137**	18,769	11.705
38	1444	6.164	**88**	7744	9.381	**138**	19,044	11.747
39	1521	6.245	**89**	7921	9.434	**139**	19,321	11.790
40	1600	6.325	**90**	8100	9.487	**140**	19,600	11.832
41	1681	6.403	**91**	8281	9.539	**141**	19,881	11.874
42	1764	6.481	**92**	8464	9.592	**142**	20,164	11.916
43	1849	6.557	**93**	8649	9.644	**143**	20,449	11.958
44	1936	6.633	**94**	8836	9.695	**144**	20,736	12.000
45	2025	6.708	**95**	9025	9.747	**145**	21,025	12.042
46	2116	6.782	**96**	9216	9.798	**146**	21,316	12.083
47	2209	6.856	**97**	9409	9.849	**147**	21,609	12.124
48	2304	6.928	**98**	9604	9.899	**148**	21,904	12.166
49	2401	7.000	**99**	9801	9.950	**149**	22,201	12.207
50	2500	7.071	**100**	10,000	10.000	**150**	22,500	12.247

English–Spanish Glossary

A

absolute deviation (p. 392) The absolute deviation of a number x from a given value is the absolute value of the difference of x and the given value: absolute deviation $= \lvert x - \text{given value} \rvert$	If the absolute deviation of x from 2 is 3, then $\lvert x - 2 \rvert = 3$.
desviación absoluta (pág. 392) La desviación absoluta de un número x con respecto a un valor dado es el valor absoluto de la diferencia entre x y el valor dado: desviación absoluta $= \lvert x - \text{valor dado} \rvert$	Si la desviación absoluta de x con respecto a 2 es 3, entonces $\lvert x - 2 \rvert = 3$.
absolute value (p. 66) The absolute value of a number a is the distance between a and 0 on a number line. The symbol $\lvert a \rvert$ represents the absolute value of a.	$\lvert 2 \rvert = 2$, $\lvert -5 \rvert = 5$, and $\lvert 0 \rvert = 0$
valor absoluto (pág. 66) El valor absoluto de un número a es la distancia entre a y 0 en una recta numérica. El símbolo $\lvert a \rvert$ representa el valor absoluto de a.	$\lvert 2 \rvert = 2$, $\lvert -5 \rvert = 5$, y $\lvert 0 \rvert = 0$
absolute value equation (p. 390) An equation that contains an absolute value expression.	$\lvert x + 2 \rvert = 3$ is an absolute value equation.
ecuación de valor absoluto (pág. 390) Ecuación que contiene una expresión de valor absoluto.	$\lvert x + 2 \rvert = 3$ es una ecuación de valor absoluto.
additive identity (p. 76) The number 0 is the additive identity, because the sum of any number and 0 is the number: $a + 0 = 0 + a = a$. **identidad aditiva** (pág. 76) El número 0 es la identidad aditiva ya que la suma de cualquier número y 0 es ese número: $a + 0 = 0 + a = a$.	$-2 + 0 = -2$, $0 + \frac{3}{4} = \frac{3}{4}$
additive inverse (p. 76) The additive inverse of a number a is its opposite, $-a$. The sum of a number and its additive inverse is 0: $a + (-a) = -a + a = 0$.	The additive inverse of -5 is 5, and $-5 + 5 = 0$.
inverso aditivo (pág. 76) El inverso aditivo de un número a es su opuesto, $-a$. La suma de un número y su inverso aditivo es 0: $a + (-a) = -a + a = 0$.	El inverso aditivo de -5 es 5, y $-5 + 5 = 0$.
algebraic expression (p. 2) An expression that includes at least one variable. Also called *variable expression.*	$5n$, $\frac{14}{y}$, $6 + c$, and $8 - x$ are algebraic expressions.
expresión algebraica (pág. 2) Expresión que incluye por lo menos una variable.	$5n$, $\frac{14}{y}$, $6 + c$ y $8 - x$ son expresiones algebraicas.

arithmetic sequence (p. 309) A sequence in which the difference between consecutive terms is constant.

2, 8, 14, 20, 26, . . . is an arithmetic sequence in which the difference between consecutive terms is 6.

progresión aritmética (pág. 309) Progresión en la que la diferencia entre los términos consecutivos es constante.

2, 8, 14, 20, 26, . . . es una progresión aritmética en la que la diferencia entre los términos consecutivos es 6.

asymptotes of a hyperbola (p. 767) Lines that a hyperbola approaches but does not intersect.

***See* hyperbola.**

asíntotas de una hipérbola (pág. 767) Rectas a las que la hipérbola se acerca pero sin cortarlas.

***Ver* hipérbola.**

axis of symmetry (p. 628) The line that passes through the vertex and divides the parabola into two symmetric parts.

eje de simetría (pág. 628) La recta que pasa por el vértice y divide a la parábola en dos partes simétricas.

The axis of symmetry of the graph of $y = -x^2 + 2x + 1$ is the line $x = 1$.

El eje de simetría de la gráfica de $y = -x^2 + 2x + 1$ es la recta $x = 1$.

B

base of a power (p. 3) The number or expression that is used as a factor in a repeated multiplication.

In the power 3^4, the base is 3.

base de una potencia (pág. 3) El número o la expresión que se usa como factor en la multiplicación repetida.

En la potencia 3^4, la base es 3.

best-fitting line (p. 335) The line that most closely follows a trend in data, found using technology.

mejor recta de regresión (pág. 335) La recta que se ajusta más a la tendencia de los datos y que se encuentra mediante tecnología.

The graph shows the best-fitting line for the data in the scatter plot.

La gráfica muestra la mejor recta de regresión para los datos del diagrama de dispersión.

biased question (p. 872) A question that encourages a particular response. **pregunta capciosa** (pág. 872) Pregunta que impulsa a dar una respuesta determinada.	**"Don't you agree that the voting age should be lowered to 16 because many 16-year-olds are responsible and informed?" is a biased question.** **"¿No estás de acuerdo en que se debe bajar la edad para votar a los 16 años ya que muchos jóvenes de 16 años son responsables y están bien informados?" es una pregunta capciosa.**
biased sample (p. 872) A sample that is not representative of the population. **muestra sesgada** (pág. 872) Muestra que no es representativa de la población.	**The members of a school's basketball team would form a biased sample for a survey about whether to build a new gym.** **Los miembros del equipo de baloncesto de una escuela formarían una muestra sesgada si participaran en una encuesta sobre si quieren que se construya un nuevo gimnasio.**
binomial (p. 555) A polynomial with two terms. **binomio** (pág. 555) Polinomio con dos términos.	$t^3 - 4t$ **and** $2x + 5$ **are binomials.** $t^3 - 4t$ **y** $2x + 5$ **son binomios.**
box-and-whisker plot (p. 887) A data display that organizes data values into four groups using the minimum value, lower quartile, median, upper quartile, and maximum value. **gráfica de frecuencias acumuladas** (pág. 887) Presentación de datos que organiza los valores de los datos en cuatro grupos usando el valor mínimo, el cuartil inferior, la mediana, el cuartil superior y el valor máximo.	0 10 20 30 40 50 8 19 26 37 45
branches of a hyperbola (p. 767) The two symmetrical parts of a hyperbola. **ramas de una hipérbola** (pág. 767) Las dos partes simétricas de la hipérbola.	***See*** **hyperbola.** ***Ver*** **hipérbola.**

C

coefficient (p. 97) The number part of a term with a variable part. **coeficiente** (pág. 97) La parte numérica de un término que tiene una variable.	**The coefficient of** $-6x$ **is** -6**.** **El coeficiente de** $-6x$ **es** -6**.**
combination (p. 856) A selection of objects in which order is *not* important. **combinación** (pág. 856) Selección de objetos en la que el orden *no* es importante.	**There are 6 combinations of two of the letters from the list A, B, C, D: AB, AC, AD, BC, BD, and CD.** **Hay 6 combinaciones de dos de las letras de la lista A, B, C, D: AB, AC, AD, BC, BD y CD.**

960

common difference (p. 309) The constant difference between consecutive terms of an arithmetic sequence. **diferencia común** (pág. 309) La diferencia constante entre los términos consecutivos de una progresión aritmética.	**2, 8, 14, 20, 26, . . . is an arithmetic sequence with a common difference of 6.** **2, 8, 14, 20, 26, . . . es una progresión aritmética con una diferencia común de 6.**
common ratio (p. 539) The ratio of any term of a geometric sequence to the previous term of the sequence. **razón común** (pág. 539) La razón entre cualquier término de una progresión geométrica y el término anterior de la progresión.	**The sequence 5, 10, 20, 40, . . . is a geometric sequence with common ratio 2.** **La progresión 5, 10, 20, 40, . . . es una progresión geométrica con una razón común de 2.**
completing the square (p. 663) The process of rewriting a quadratic expression so that it is a perfect square trinomial. **completar el cuadrado** (pág. 663) El proceso de escribir una expresión cuadrática de manera que sea un trinomio cuadrado perfecto.	**To write $x^2 - 16x$ as a perfect square trinomial, add $\left(\frac{-16}{2}\right)^2$, or $(-8)^2$. This gives $x^2 - 16x + (-8)^2 = (x - 8)^2$.** **Para escribir $x^2 - 16x$ como trinomio cuadrado perfecto, suma $\left(\frac{-16}{2}\right)^2$, o $(-8)^2$. Así resulta $x^2 - 16x + (-8)^2 = (x - 8)^2$.**
complex fraction (p. 810) A fraction that contains a fraction in its numerator, denominator, or both. **fracción compleja** (pág. 810) Fracción que contiene una fracción en su numerador, en su denominador o en ambos.	**$\frac{\frac{3x}{2}}{-6x^3}$ and $\frac{\frac{x^2-1}{x+1}}{x-1}$ are complex fractions.** **$\frac{\frac{3x}{2}}{-6x^3}$ y $\frac{\frac{x^2-1}{x+1}}{x-1}$ son fracciones complejas.**
compound event (p. 861) An event that combines two or more events, using the word *and* or the word *or*. **suceso compuesto** (pág. 861) Suceso que combina dos o más sucesos usando la palabra *y* o la palabra *o*.	**When you roll a number cube, the event "roll a 2 or an odd number" is a compound event.** **Cuando lanzas un cubo numerado, el suceso "salir el 2 ó número impar" es un suceso compuesto.**
compound inequality (p. 380) Two inequalities joined by *and* or *or*. **desigualdad compuesta** (pág. 380) Dos desigualdades unidas por *y* u *o*.	**$-2 < x$ *and* $x < 1$, which can be written as $-2 < x < 1$, is a compound inequality, as is $x < -1$ *or* $x > 0$.** **$-2 < x$ *y* $x < 1$, que puede escribirse $-2 < x < 1$, es una desigualdad compuesta, al igual que $x < -1$ *ó* $x > 0$.**
compound interest (p. 523) Interest that is earned on both an initial investment and on previously earned interest. **interés compuesto** (pág. 523) Interés obtenido tanto sobre la inversión inicial como sobre el interés conseguido anteriormente.	**You deposit \$250 in an account that earns 4% interest compounded yearly. After 5 years, your account balance is $y = 250(1 + 0.04)^5 \approx$ \$304.16.** **Depositas \$250 en una cuenta al 4% anual de interés compuesto. Después de 5 años, el balance de la cuenta es $y = 250(1 + 0.04)^5 \approx$ \$304.16.**

ENGLISH-SPANISH GLOSSARY

conditional statement (p. 66) A statement with a hypothesis and a conclusion.

enunciado condicional (pág. 66) Enunciado que tiene una hipótesis y una conclusión.

conditional statement
enunciado condicional

If $a > 0$, then $|a| = a$.

hypothesis / **hipótesis** — **conclusion** / **conclusión**

---

congruent figures (p. 174) Figures that have the same size and shape. The symbol ≅ indicates congruence.

figuras congruentes (pág. 174) Figuras que tienen igual tamaño y forma. El símbolo ≅ indica la congruencia.

$\triangle ABC \cong \triangle DEF$

---

conjecture (p. 117) A statement that is believed to be true but not yet shown to be true.

conjetura (pág. 117) Enunciado que se considera verdadero sin que haya sido demostrado todavía.

A conclusion reached using inductive reasoning is a conjecture.

Una conclusión que se saca mediante el razonamiento inductivo es una conjetura.

---

consistent dependent system (p. 459) A linear system with infinitely many solutions. The graphs of the equations of a consistent dependent system coincide.

sistema dependiente compatible (pág. 459) Sistema lineal con infinitas soluciones. Las gráficas de las ecuaciones de un sistema dependiente compatible coinciden.

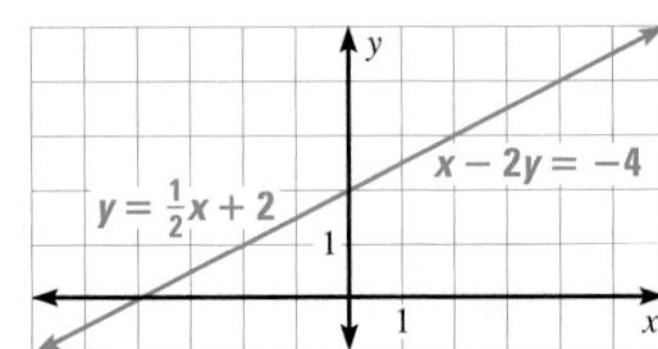

The linear system $x - 2y = -4$ and $y = \frac{1}{2}x + 2$ is a consistent dependent system because the graphs of the equations coincide.

El sistema lineal $x - 2y = -4$ e $y = \frac{1}{2}x + 2$ es un sistema dependiente compatible ya que las gráficas de las ecuaciones coinciden.

---

consistent independent system (p. 427) A linear system with exactly one solution. The graphs of the equations of a consistent independent system intersect.

sistema independiente compatible (pág. 427) Sistema lineal con una sola solución. Las gráficas de las ecuaciones de un sistema independiente compatible se cortan.

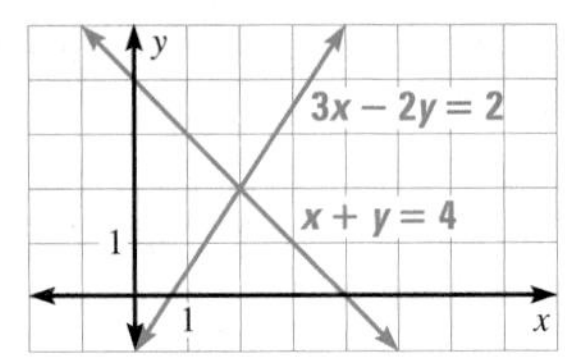

The linear system $3x - 2y = 2$ and $x + y = 4$ is a consistent independent system because the graphs of the equations intersect.

El sistema lineal $3x - 2y = 2$ y $x + y = 4$ es un sistema independiente compatible ya que las gráficas de las ecuaciones se cortan.

constant of variation (pp. 253, 765) The nonzero constant a in a direct variation equation $y = ax$ or in an inverse variation equation $y = \frac{a}{x}$. **constante de variación** (págs. 253, 765) La constante a distinta de cero de una ecuación de variación directa $y = ax$ o de una ecuación de variación inversa $y = \frac{a}{x}$.	**The constant of variation in the direct variation equation $y = \frac{2}{3}x$ is $\frac{2}{3}$, and the constant of variation in the inverse variation equation $y = \frac{-1}{x}$ is -1.** **La constante de variación de la ecuación de variación directa $y = \frac{2}{3}x$ es $\frac{2}{3}$, y la constante de variación de la ecuación de variación inversa $y = \frac{-1}{x}$ es -1.**
constant term (p. 97) A term with a number part but no variable part. **término constante** (pág. 97) Término que tiene una parte numérica sin variable.	**In the expression $3x + (-4) + (-6x) + 2$, the constant terms are -4 and 2.** **En la expresión $3x + (-4) + (-6x) + 2$, los términos constantes son -4 y 2.**
continuous function (p. 223) A function with a graph that is unbroken. **función continua** (pág. 223) Función con una gráfica no interrumpida.	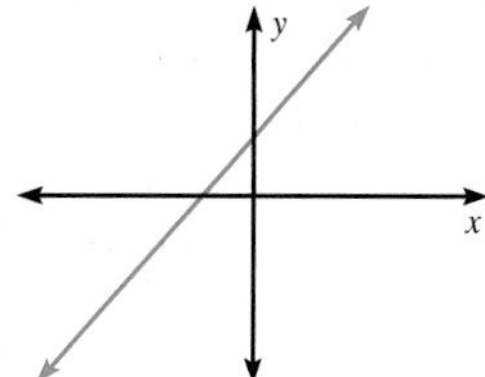
convenience sample (p. 871) A sample in which only members of a population who are easily accessible are selected. **muestra de conveniencia** (pág. 871) Muestra en la que se selecciona sólo a los miembros de una población fácilmente accesibles.	**You can select a convenience sample of a school's student population by choosing only students who are in your classes.** **Para seleccionar una muestra de conveniencia de la población de estudiantes de una escuela, puedes escoger sólo a los estudiantes que están en tus clases.**
converse of a conditional (p. 318) A statement formed by interchanging the hypothesis and the conclusion of the conditional. The converse of a true statement is not necessarily true. **recíproco de un condicional** (pág. 318) Enunciado formado al intercambiar la hipótesis y la conclusión del condicional. El recíproco de un enunciado verdadero no es necesariamente verdadero.	**The converse of the statement "If $x = 5$, then $\lvert x \rvert = 5$" is "If $\lvert x \rvert = 5$, then $x = 5$." The original statement is true, but the converse is false.** **El recíproco del enunciado "Si $x = 5$, entonces $\lvert x \rvert = 5$" es "Si $\lvert x \rvert = 5$, entonces $x = 5$". El enunciado original es verdadero, pero el recíproco es falso.**

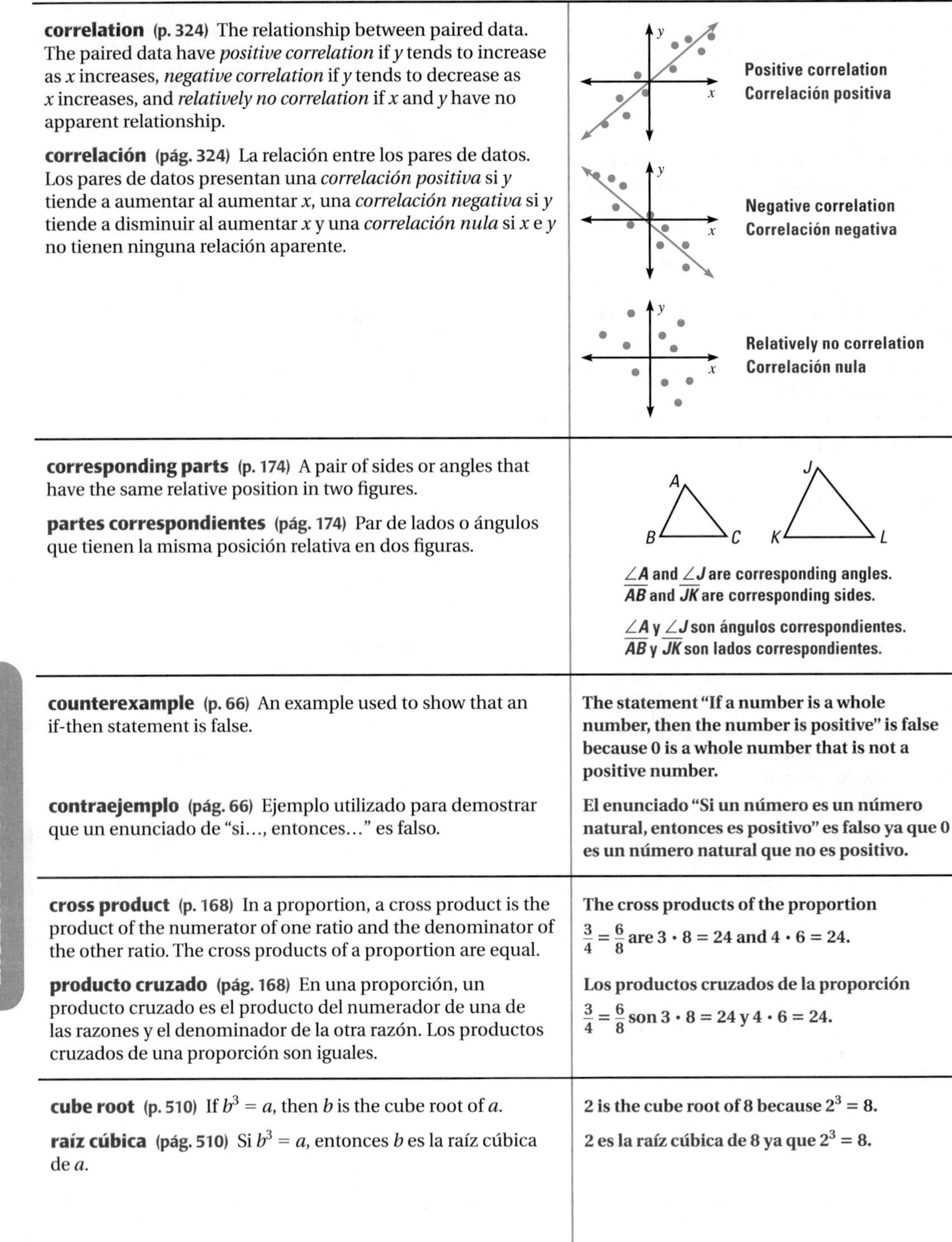

correlation (p. 324) The relationship between paired data. The paired data have *positive correlation* if y tends to increase as x increases, *negative correlation* if y tends to decrease as x increases, and *relatively no correlation* if x and y have no apparent relationship.

correlación (pág. 324) La relación entre los pares de datos. Los pares de datos presentan una *correlación positiva* si y tiende a aumentar al aumentar x, una *correlación negativa* si y tiende a disminuir al aumentar x y una *correlación nula* si x e y no tienen ninguna relación aparente.

Positive correlation
Correlación positiva

Negative correlation
Correlación negativa

Relatively no correlation
Correlación nula

corresponding parts (p. 174) A pair of sides or angles that have the same relative position in two figures.

partes correspondientes (pág. 174) Par de lados o ángulos que tienen la misma posición relativa en dos figuras.

$\angle A$ and $\angle J$ are corresponding angles.
$\overline{AB}$ and $\overline{JK}$ are corresponding sides.

$\angle A$ y $\angle J$ son ángulos correspondientes.
$\overline{AB}$ y $\overline{JK}$ son lados correspondientes.

counterexample (p. 66) An example used to show that an if-then statement is false.

The statement "If a number is a whole number, then the number is positive" is false because 0 is a whole number that is not a positive number.

contraejemplo (pág. 66) Ejemplo utilizado para demostrar que un enunciado de "si..., entonces..." es falso.

El enunciado "Si un número es un número natural, entonces es positivo" es falso ya que 0 es un número natural que no es positivo.

cross product (p. 168) In a proportion, a cross product is the product of the numerator of one ratio and the denominator of the other ratio. The cross products of a proportion are equal.

The cross products of the proportion $\frac{3}{4} = \frac{6}{8}$ are $3 \cdot 8 = 24$ and $4 \cdot 6 = 24$.

producto cruzado (pág. 168) En una proporción, un producto cruzado es el producto del numerador de una de las razones y el denominador de la otra razón. Los productos cruzados de una proporción son iguales.

Los productos cruzados de la proporción $\frac{3}{4} = \frac{6}{8}$ son $3 \cdot 8 = 24$ y $4 \cdot 6 = 24$.

cube root (p. 510) If $b^3 = a$, then b is the cube root of a.

2 is the cube root of 8 because $2^3 = 8$.

raíz cúbica (pág. 510) Si $b^3 = a$, entonces b es la raíz cúbica de a.

2 es la raíz cúbica de 8 ya que $2^3 = 8$.

ENGLISH-SPANISH GLOSSARY

D

decay factor (p. 534) The expression $1 - r$ in the exponential decay model $y = a(1 - r)^t$. **factor de decrecimiento** (pág. 534) La expresión $1 - r$ del modelo de decrecimiento exponencial $y = a(1 - r)^t$.	In the exponential decay model $P = 41(0.995)^t$, the decay factor is 0.995. En el modelo de decrecimiento exponencial $P = 41(0.995)^t$, el factor de decrecimiento es 0.995.
decay rate (p. 534) The variable r in the exponential decay model $y = a(1 - r)^t$. **tasa de decrecimiento** (pág. 534) La variable r del modelo de decrecimiento exponencial $y = a(1 - r)^t$.	In the exponential decay model $P = 41(0.995)^t$, the decay rate is 0.005, because $0.995 = 1 - 0.005$. En el modelo de decrecimiento exponencial $P = 41(0.995)^t$, la tasa de decrecimiento es 0.005 ya que $0.995 = 1 - 0.005$.
deductive reasoning (p. 118) A form of reasoning in which a conclusion is based on statements that are assumed or shown to be true. **razonamiento deductivo** (pág. 118) Tipo de razonamiento en el que una conclusión se basa en enunciados que se suponen o se demuestran verdaderos.	$(x + 2) + (-2)$ $= x + [2 + (-2)]$ Associative property of addition $= x + 0$ Inverse property of addition $= x$ Identity property of addition $(x + 2) + (-2)$ $= x + [2 + (-2)]$ Propiedad asociativa de la suma $= x + 0$ Propiedad del elemento inverso de la suma $= x$ Propiedad de identidad de la suma
degree of a monomial (p. 554) The sum of the exponents of the variables in the monomial. The degree of a nonzero constant term is 0. **grado de un monomio** (pág. 554) La suma de los exponentes de las variables del monomio. El grado de un término constante distinto de cero es 0.	The degree of $\frac{1}{2}ab^2$ is $1 + 2$, or 3. El grado de $\frac{1}{2}ab^2$ es $1 + 2$, ó 3.
degree of a polynomial (p. 554) The greatest degree of the terms of the polynomial. **grado de un polinomio** (pág. 554) El mayor grado de los términos del polinomio.	The polynomial $2x^2 + x - 5$ has a degree of 2. El polinomio $2x^2 + x - 5$ tiene un grado de 2.
dependent events (p. 862) Two events such that the occurrence of one event affects the occurrence of the other event. **sucesos dependientes** (pág. 862) Dos sucesos tales que la ocurrencia de uno de ellos afecta a la ocurrencia del otro.	A bag contains 3 red marbles and 5 white marbles. You randomly draw one marble, do not replace it, then randomly draw another marble. The events "draw a red marble first" and "draw a white marble second" are dependent events. Una bolsa contiene 3 canicas rojas y 5 blancas. Sacas al azar una canica sin reemplazarla y luego sacas al azar otra canica. Los sucesos "sacar primero una canica roja" y "sacar después una canica blanca" son sucesos dependientes.

dependent variable (p. 36) The output variable of a function. **variable dependiente** (pág. 36) La variable de salida de una función.	**In the function equation $y = x + 3$, y is the dependent variable.** **En la ecuación de función $y = x + 3$, y es la variable dependiente.**
dimensions of a matrix (p. 94) If a matrix has m rows and n columns, the dimensions of the matrix are written as $m \times n$. **dimensiones de una matriz** (pág. 94) Si una matriz tiene m filas y n columnas, las dimensiones de la matriz se escriben $m \times n$.	**The dimensions of a matrix with 2 rows and 3 columns are 2×3 ("2 by 3").** **Las dimensiones de una matriz con 2 filas y 3 columnas son 2×3 ("2 por 3").**
direct variation (p. 253) The relationship of two variables x and y if there is a nonzero number a such that $y = ax$. If $y = ax$, then y is said to vary directly with x. **variación directa** (pág. 253) La relación entre dos variables x e y si hay un número a distinto de cero tal que $y = ax$. Si $y = ax$, entonces se dice que y varía directamente con x.	**The equation $2x - 3y = 0$ represents direct variation because it is equivalent to the equation $y = \frac{2}{3}x$. The equation $y = x + 5$ does *not* represent direct variation.** **La ecuación $2x - 3y = 0$ representa una variación directa ya que es equivalente a la ecuación $y = \frac{2}{3}x$. La ecuación $y = x + 5$ *no* representa una variación directa.**
discrete function (p. 223) A function with a graph that consists of isolated points. **función discreta** (pág. 223) Función cuya gráfica consta de puntos aislados.	y x
discriminant (p. 678) The expression $b^2 - 4ac$ of the assciated equation $ax^2 + bx + c = 0$; also the expression under the radical sign in the quadratic formula. **discriminante** (pág. 678) La expresión $b^2 - 4ac$ de la ecuación asociada $ax^2 + bx + c = 0$; también es la expresión colocada bajo el signo radical de la fórmula cuadrática.	**The value of the discriminant of the equation $3x^2 - 2x - 7 = 0$ is:** $b^2 - 4ac = (-2)^2 - 4(3)(-7) = 88$ **El valor del discriminante de la ecuación $3x^2 - 2x - 7 = 0$ es:** $b^2 - 4ac = (-2)^2 - 4(3)(-7) = 88$
distance formula (p. 744) The distance d between any two points (x_1, y_1) and (x_2, y_2) is $d = \sqrt{(x_2 - x_1)^2 + (y_2 - y_1)^2}$. **fórmula de la distancia** (pág. 744) La distancia d entre dos puntos cualesquiera (x_1, y_1) y (x_2, y_2) es $d = \sqrt{(x_2 - x_1)^2 + (y_2 - y_1)^2}$.	**The distance d between $(-1, 3)$ and $(5, 2)$ is:** $d = \sqrt{(5 - (-1))^2 + (2 - 3)^2} = \sqrt{37}$ **La distancia d entre $(-1, 3)$ y $(5, 2)$ es:** $d = \sqrt{(5 - (-1))^2 + (2 - 3)^2} = \sqrt{37}$

ENGLISH-SPANISH GLOSSARY

distributive property (p. 96) A property that can be used to find the product of a number and a sum or difference: $a(b + c) = ab + ac$ $(b + c)a = ba + ca$ $a(b - c) = ab - ac$ $(b - c)a = ba - ca$ **propiedad distributiva** (pág. 96) Propiedad que sirve para hallar el producto de un número y una suma o una diferencia: $a(b + c) = ab + ac$ $(b + c)a = ba + ca$ $a(b - c) = ab - ac$ $(b - c)a = ba - ca$	**$3(4 + 2) = 3(4) + 3(2)$, $(8 - 6)4 = (8)4 - (6)4$**
domain of a function (p. 35) The set of all inputs of a function. **dominio de una función** (pág. 35) El conjunto de todas las entradas de una función.	***See* function.** ***Ver* función.**

E

element of a matrix (p. 94) Each number in a matrix. **elemento de una matriz** (pág. 94) Cada número de la matriz.	***See* matrix.** ***Ver* matriz.**
element of a set (p. 71) Each object in a set. Also called a *member* of a set. **elemento de un conjunto** (pág. 71) Cada objeto de un conjunto; llamado también *miembro* de un conjunto.	**5 is an element of the set of whole numbers, $W = \{0, 1, 2, 3, \ldots\}$.** **5 es un elemento del conjunto de los números naturales, $W = \{0, 1, 2, 3, \ldots\}$.**
empty set (p. 71) The set with no elements, written as $\emptyset$. **conjunto vacío** (pág. 71) El conjunto que no tiene ningún elemento, escrito $\emptyset$.	**The set of negative whole numbers $= \emptyset$.** **El conjunto de los números naturales negativos $= \emptyset$.**
equation (p. 21) A mathematical sentence formed by placing the symbol = between two expressions. **ecuación** (pág. 21) Enunciado matemático formado al colocar el símbolo = entre dos expresiones.	**$2k - 8 = 12$ is an equation.** **$2k - 8 = 12$ es una ecuación.**
equivalent equations (p. 134) Equations that have the same solution(s). **ecuaciones equivalentes** (pág. 134) Ecuaciones que tienen la misma solución o soluciones.	**$x + 7 = 4$ and $x = -3$ are equivalent equations.** **$x + 7 = 4$ y $x = -3$ son ecuaciones equivalentes.**

ENGLISH-SPANISH GLOSSARY

equivalent expressions **(p. 96)** Two expressions that have the same value for all values of the variable.

$3(x + 2) + x$ and $4x + 6$ are equivalent expressions.

expresiones equivalentes **(pág. 96)** Dos expresiones que tienen el mismo valor para todos los valores de la variable.

$3(x + 2) + x$ y $4x + 6$ son expresiones equivalentes.

equivalent inequalities **(p. 357)** Inequalities that have the same solutions.

$2t < 4$ and $t < 2$ are equivalent inequalities, because the solutions of both inequalities are all real numbers less than 2.

desigualdades equivalentes **(pág. 357)** Desigualdades con las mismas soluciones.

$2t < 4$ y $t < 2$ son desigualdades equivalentes ya que las soluciones de ambas son todos los números reales menores que 2.

evaluate an algebraic expression **(p. 2)** To find the value of an algebraic expression by substituting a number for each variable and performing the operation(s).

The value of $n - 1$ when $n = 3$ is $3 - 1 = 2$.

evaluar una expresión algebraica **(pág. 2)** Hallar el valor de una expresión algebraica sustituyendo cada variable por un número y realizando la operación o operaciones.

El valor de $n - 1$ cuando $n = 3$ es $3 - 1 = 2$.

event **(p. 843)** An outcome or a collection of outcomes.

When you roll a number cube, "roll an odd number" is an event.

suceso **(pág. 843)** Caso o colección de casos.

Cuando lanzas un cubo numerado, "salir número impar" es un suceso.

excluded value **(p. 794)** A number that makes a rational expression undefined.

3 is an excluded value of the expression $\frac{2}{x - 3}$ because 3 makes the value of the denominator 0.

valor excluido **(pág. 794)** Número que hace que una expresión racional sea indefinida.

3 es un valor excluido de la expresión $\frac{2}{x - 3}$ ya que 3 hace que el valor del denominador sea 0.

experimental probability **(p. 844)** A probability based on repeated trials of an experiment. The experimental probability of an event is the ratio of the number of successes (trials in which a favorable outcome occurs) to the number of trials.

You spin a spinner 20 times and it stops on yellow 3 times. The experimental probability that the spinner stops on yellow is $\frac{3}{20}$, 15%, or 0.15.

probabilidad experimental **(pág. 844)** Probabilidad basada en la realización repetida de las pruebas de un experimento. La probabilidad experimental de un suceso es la razón entre el número de resultados deseados (pruebas en las que se produce un caso favorable) y el número de pruebas.

Giras una ruleta 20 veces y ésta se detiene en el amarillo 3 veces. La probabilidad experimental de que la ruleta se detenga en el amarillo es $\frac{3}{20}$, 15% ó 0.15.

exponent **(p. 3)** The number or variable that represents the number of times the base of a power is used as a factor.

In the power 3^4, the exponent is 4.

exponente **(pág. 3)** El número o la variable que representa la cantidad de veces que se usa la base de una potencia como factor.

En la potencia 3^4, el exponente es 4.

exponential decay (p. 533) When $a > 0$ and $0 < b < 1$, the function $y = ab^x$ represents exponential decay. When a quantity decays exponentially, it decreases by the same percent over equal time periods. The exponential decay model is $y = a(1 - r)^t$.

decrecimiento exponencial (pág. 533) Cuando $a > 0$ y $0 < b < 1$, la función $y = ab^x$ representa el decrecimiento exponencial. Cuando una cantidad decrece de forma exponencial, disminuye en el mismo porcentaje durante períodos de tiempo iguales. El modelo de decrecimiento exponencial es $y = a(1 - r)^t$.

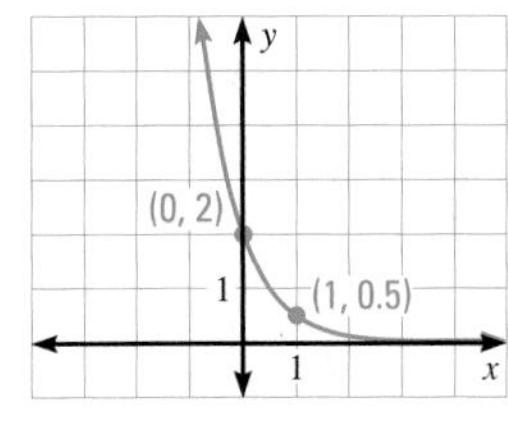

The function $y = 2(0.25)^x$ represents exponential decay. *See also* decay rate *and* decay factor.

La función $y = 2(0.25)^x$ representa el decrecimiento exponencial. *Ver también* tasa de decrecimiento *y* factor de decrecimiento.

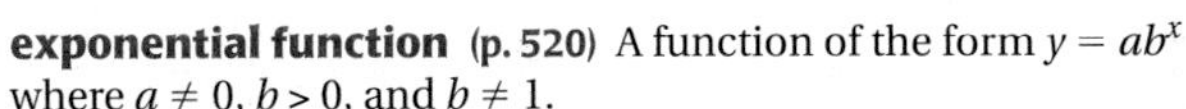

exponential function (p. 520) A function of the form $y = ab^x$ where $a \neq 0$, $b > 0$, and $b \neq 1$.

función exponencial (pág. 520) Función de la forma $y = ab^x$, donde $a \neq 0$, $b > 0$ y $b \neq 1$.

The functions $y = 2 \cdot 3^x$ and $y = -2 \cdot \left(\frac{1}{2}\right)^x$ are exponential functions.

See also exponential growth *and* exponential decay.

Las funciones $y = 2 \cdot 3^x$ e $y = -2 \cdot \left(\frac{1}{2}\right)^x$ son funciones exponenciales.

Ver también crecimiento exponencial *y* decrecimiento exponencial.

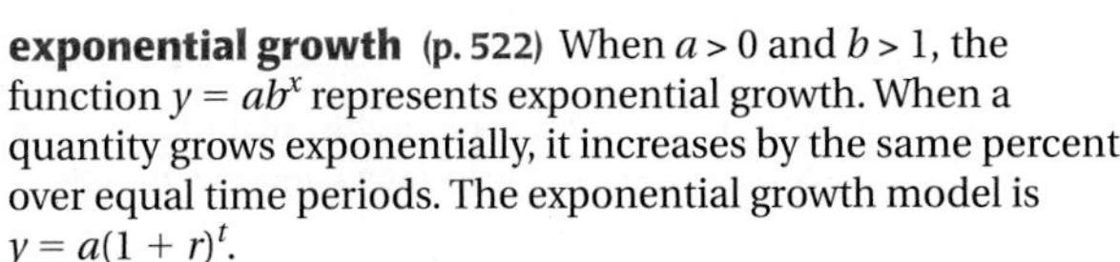

exponential growth (p. 522) When $a > 0$ and $b > 1$, the function $y = ab^x$ represents exponential growth. When a quantity grows exponentially, it increases by the same percent over equal time periods. The exponential growth model is $y = a(1 + r)^t$.

crecimiento exponencial (pág. 522) Cuando $a > 0$ y $b > 1$, la función $y = ab^x$ representa el crecimiento exponencial. Cuando una cantidad crece de forma exponencial, aumenta en el mismo porcentaje durante períodos de tiempo iguales. El modelo de crecimiento exponencial es $y = a(1 + r)^t$.

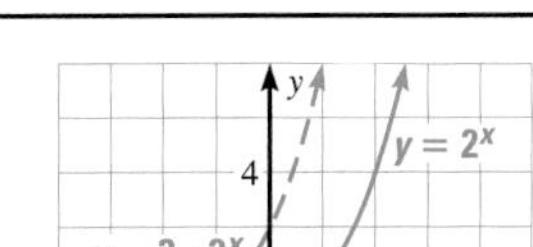

The functions $y = 3 \cdot 2^x$ and $y = 2^x$ represent exponential growth. *See also* growth rate *and* growth factor.

Las funciones $y = 3 \cdot 2^x$ e $y = 2^x$ representan el crecimiento exponencial. *Ver también* tasa de crecimiento *y* factor de crecimiento.

extraneous solution (p. 730) A solution of a transformed equation that is not a solution of the original equation.

solución extraña (pág. 730) Solución de una ecuación transformada que no es solución de la ecuación original.

When you square both sides of the radical equation $\sqrt{6 - x} = x$, the resulting equation has two solutions, 2 and -3, but -3 is an extraneous solution because it does not satisfy the original equation $\sqrt{6 - x} = x$.

Al elevar al cuadrado ambos miembros de la ecuación radical $\sqrt{6 - x} = x$, la ecuación resultante tiene dos soluciones, 2 y -3, pero -3 es una solución extraña ya que no satisface la ecuación original $\sqrt{6 - x} = x$.

F

factor by grouping (p. 606) To factor a polynomial with four terms by grouping, factor a common monomial from pairs of terms, and then look for a common binomial factor.

factorizar por grupos (pág. 606) Para factorizar por grupos un polinomio con cuatro términos, factoriza un monomio común a partir de los pares de términos y luego busca un factor binómico común.

$$\begin{aligned} x^3 + 3x^2 + 5x + 15 &= (x^3 + 3x^2) + (5x + 15) \\ &= x^2(x + 3) + 5(x + 3) \\ &= (x + 3)(x^2 + 5) \end{aligned}$$

---

factor completely (p. 607) A factorable polynomial with integer coefficients is factored completely if it is written as a product of unfactorable polynomials with integer coefficients.

factorizar completamente (pág. 607) Un polinomio que puede descomponerse en factores y que tiene coeficientes enteros está completamente factorizado si está escrito como producto de polinomios que no pueden descomponerse en factores y que tienen coeficientes enteros.

The polynomial $x^3 - x$ is *not* factored completely when written as $x(x^2 - 1)$ but is factored completely when written as $x(x + 1)(x - 1)$.

El polinomio $x^3 - x$ *no* está completamente factorizado cuando se escribe $x(x^2 - 1)$, pero sí está completamente factorizado cuando se escribe $x(x + 1)(x - 1)$.

---

family of functions (p. 263) A group of functions with similar characteristics.

familia de funciones (pág. 263) Grupo de funciones con características similares.

Functions that have the form $f(x) = mx + b$ constitute the family of linear functions.

Las funciones que tienen la forma $f(x) = mx + b$ constituyen la familia de las funciones lineales.

---

formula (p. 30) An equation that relates two or more quantities.

fórmula (pág. 30) Ecuación que relaciona dos o más cantidades.

The formula $d = rt$ relates the distance traveled to the rate of speed and travel time.

La fórmula $d = rt$ relaciona la distancia recorrida con la velocidad y el tiempo transcurrido.

---

frequency (p. 882) The frequency of an interval is the number of data values in that interval.

frecuencia (pág. 882) La frecuencia de un intervalo es el número de datos de valores que hay en ese intervalo.

***See* frequency table *and* histogram.**

***Ver* tabla de frecuencias *e* histograma.**

---

frequency table (p. 882) A data display that groups data into equal intervals with no gaps between intervals and no intervals overlapping.

tabla de frecuencias (pág. 882) Presentación de datos en la que se agrupan los datos en intervalos iguales sin que haya interrupciones entre los intervalos y sin intervalos superpuestos.

Prices Precios	Sandwiches Sándwiches
\$4.00–4.49	||||
\$4.50–4.99	||
\$5.00–5.49	
\$5.50–5.99	||||

ENGLISH-SPANISH GLOSSARY

970

function (p. 35) A function consists of:

- A set called the domain containing numbers called inputs, and a set called the range containing numbers called outputs.
- A pairing of inputs with outputs such that each input is paired with exactly one output.

función (pág. 35) Una función consta de:

- Un conjunto llamado dominio que contiene los números conocidos como entradas, y otro conjunto llamado rango que contiene los números conocidos como salidas.
- Una correspondencia entre las entradas y las salidas tal que a cada entrada le corresponde una sola salida.

The pairing in the table below is a function, because each input is paired with exactly one output.

La correspondencia que aparece en la tabla de abajo es una función ya que a cada entrada le corresponde una sola salida.

Input, x **Entrada, x**	0	1	2	3	4
Output, y **Salida, y**	3	4	5	6	7

The domain is the set of inputs: 0, 1, 2, 3, and 4.
The range is the set of outputs: 3, 4, 5, 6, and 7.

El dominio es el conjunto de entradas: 0, 1, 2, 3 y 4.
El rango es el conjunto de salidas: 3, 4, 5, 6 y 7.

function notation (p. 262) A way to name a function using the symbol $f(x)$ instead of y. The symbol $f(x)$ is read as "the value of f at x" or as "f of x."

notación de función (pág. 262) Forma de nombrar una función usando el símbolo $f(x)$ en lugar de y. El símbolo $f(x)$ se lee "el valor de f en x" o "f de x".

The function $y = 2x - 9$ can be written in function notation as $f(x) = 2x - 9$.

La función $y = 2x - 9$ escrita en notación de función es $f(x) = 2x - 9$.

G

geometric sequence (p. 539) A sequence in which the ratio of any term to the previous term is constant. The constant ratio is called the common ratio.

progresión geométrica (pág. 539) Progresión en la que la razón entre cualquier término y el término anterior es constante. La razón constante se llama razón común.

The sequence 5, 10, 20, 40, . . . is a geometric sequence with common ratio 2.

La progresión 5, 10, 20, 40, . . . es una progresión geométrica cuya razón común es 2.

graph of an equation in two variables (p. 215) The set of points in a coordinate plane that represent all solutions of the equation.

gráfica de una ecuación con dos variables (pág. 215) El conjunto de puntos de un plano de coordenadas que representa todas las soluciones de la ecuación.

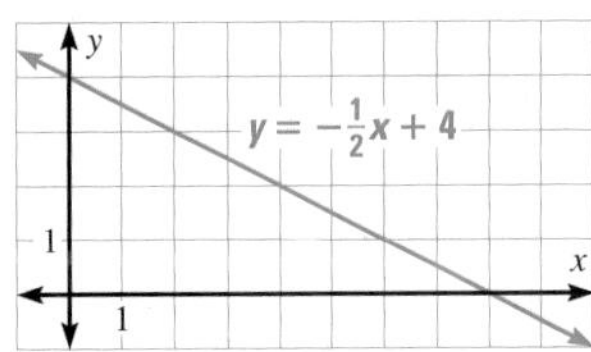

The line is the graph of the equation $y = -\frac{1}{2}x + 4$.

La recta es la gráfica de la ecuación $y = -\frac{1}{2}x + 4$.

971

graph of an inequality in one variable (p. 356) On a number line, the set of points that represent all solutions of the inequality.

gráfica de una desigualdad con una variable (pág. 356) En una recta numérica, el conjunto de puntos que representa todas las soluciones de la desigualdad.

−1 0 1 2 3 4

Graph of $x < 3$

Gráfica de $x < 3$

graph of an inequality in two variables (p. 405) In a coordinate plane, the set of points that represent all solutions of the inequality.

gráfica de una desigualdad con dos variables (pág. 405) En un plano de coordenadas, el conjunto de puntos que representa todas las soluciones de la desigualdad.

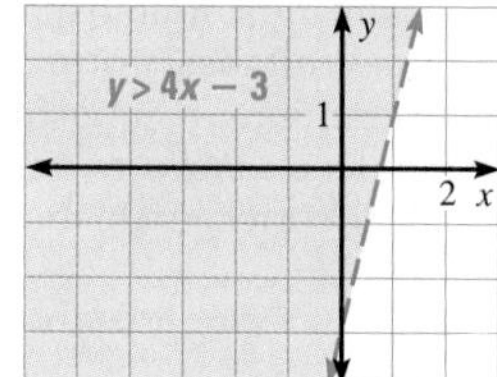

The graph of $y > 4x - 3$ is the shaded half-plane.

La gráfica de $y > 4x - 3$ es el semiplano sombreado.

graph of a system of linear inequalities (p. 466) The graph of all solutions of the system.

gráfica de un sistema de desigualdades lineales (pág. 466) La gráfica de todas las soluciones del sistema.

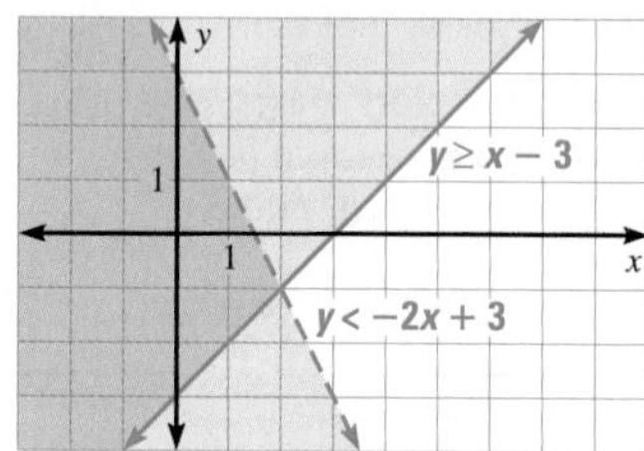

The graph of the system $y < -2x + 3$ and $y \geq x - 3$ is the intersection of the half-planes.

La gráfica del sistema $y < -2x + 3$ e $y \geq x - 3$ es la intersección de los semiplanos.

growth factor (p. 522) The expression $1 + r$ in the exponential growth model $y = a(1 + r)^t$.

factor de crecimiento (pág. 522) La expresión $1 + r$ del modelo de crecimiento exponencial $y = a(1 + r)^t$.

In the exponential growth model $C = 11{,}000(1.069)^t$, the growth factor is 1.069.

En el modelo de crecimiento exponencial $C = 11{,}000(1.069)^t$, el factor de crecimiento es 1.069.

growth rate (p. 522) The variable r in the exponential growth model $y = a(1 + r)^t$.

tasa de crecimiento (pág. 522) La variable r del modelo de crecimiento exponencial $y = a(1 + r)^t$.

In the exponential growth model $C = 11{,}000(1.069)^t$, the growth rate is 0.069.

En el modelo de crecimiento exponencial $C = 11{,}000(1.069)^t$, la tasa de crecimiento es 0.069.

H

half-plane (p. 405) In a coordinate plane, the region on either side of a boundary line.

semiplano (pág. 405) En un plano de coordenadas, la región situada a cada lado de una recta límite.

See **graph of an inequality in two variables.**

Ver **gráfica de una desigualdad con dos variables.**

histogram (p. 882) A bar graph that displays data from a frequency table. Each bar represents an interval, and the length of each bar indicates the frequency.

histograma (pág. 882) Gráfica de barras que presenta los datos de una tabla de frecuencias. Cada barra representa un intervalo, y la longitud de cada barra indica la frecuencia.

hyperbola (p. 767) The graph of the inverse variation equation $y = \frac{a}{x}$ $(a \neq 0)$ or the graph of a rational function of the form $y = \frac{a}{x-h} + k$ $(a \neq 0)$. A hyperbola has two symmetrical parts called branches. A hyperbola approaches but doesn't intersect lines called asymptotes.

hipérbola (pág. 767) La gráfica de la ecuación de variación inversa $y = \frac{a}{x}$ $(a \neq 0)$ o la gráfica de una función racional de la forma $y = \frac{a}{x-h} + k$ $(a \neq 0)$. La hipérbola tiene dos partes simétricas llamadas ramas. La hipérbola se acerca a las rectas llamadas asíntotas pero sin cortarlas.

The graph of $y = \frac{2}{x+1} - 3$ is a hyperbola. The asymptotes of the hyperbola are the lines $x = -1$ and $y = -3$.

La gráfica de $y = \frac{2}{x+1} - 3$ es una hipérbola. Las asíntotas de la hipérbola son las rectas $x = -1$ e $y = -3$.

hypotenuse (p. 737) The hypotenuse of a right triangle is the side opposite the right angle.

hipotenusa (pág. 737) La hipotenusa de un triángulo rectángulo es el lado opuesto al ángulo recto.

I

identity (p. 156) An equation that is true for all values of the variable.

identidad (pág. 156) Ecuación que es verdadera para todos los valores de la variable.

The equation $2x + 10 = 2(x + 5)$ is an identity.

La ecuación $2x + 10 = 2(x + 5)$ es una identidad.

if-then statement (p. 66) A conditional statement with an *if* part and a *then* part. The *if* part contains the hypothesis, and the *then* part contains the conclusion. **enunciado de "si..., entonces..."** (pág. 66) Enunciado condicional con una parte de *si* y otra de *entonces*. La parte de *si* contiene la hipótesis, y la parte de *entonces* contiene la conclusión.	If $a = -1$, then $\|a\| = 1$. The hypothesis is $a = -1$. The conclusion is $\|a\| = 1$. Si $a = -1$, entonces $\|a\| = 1$. La hipótesis es $a = -1$. La conclusión es $\|a\| = 1$.
inconsistent system (p. 459) A linear system with no solution. The graphs of the equations of an inconsistent system are parallel lines. **sistema incompatible** (pág. 459) Sistema lineal sin solución. Las gráficas de las ecuaciones de un sistema incompatible son rectas paralelas.	 The linear system $y = 2x + 1$ and $y = 2x - 3$ is inconsistent because the graphs of the equations are parallel lines. El sistema lineal $y = 2x + 1$ e $y = 2x - 3$ es incompatible ya que las gráficas de las ecuaciones son rectas paralelas.
independent events (p. 862) Two events such that the occurrence of one event has no effect on the occurrence of the other event. **sucesos independientes** (pág. 862) Dos sucesos tales que la ocurrencia de uno de ellos no afecta a la ocurrencia del otro.	You roll a number cube twice. The events "roll a 3 first" and "roll a 6 second" are independent events. Lanzas un cubo numerado dos veces. Los sucesos "salir primero el 3" y "salir después el 6" son sucesos independientes.
independent variable (p. 36) The input variable of a function. **variable independiente** (pág. 36) La variable de entrada de una función.	In the function equation $y = x + 3$, x is the independent variable. En la ecuación de función $y = x + 3$, x es la variable independiente.
inductive reasoning (p. 117) A form of reasoning in which a conclusion is based on several examples. **razonamiento inductivo** (pág. 117) Tipo de razonamiento en el que la conclusión se basa en varios ejemplos.	You add several pairs of odd numbers and notice that the sum is even. You conclude that the sum of any two odd numbers is even. Sumas varias parejas de números impares y observas que la suma es par. Sacas la conclusión de que la suma de dos números impares cualesquiera es par.
inequality (p. 21) A mathematical sentence formed by placing one of the symbols $<$, $\leq$, $>$, or $\geq$ between two expressions. **desigualdad** (pág. 21) Enunciado matemático formado al colocar uno de les siguentes símbolos entre dos expresiones: $<$, $\leq$, $>$ o $\geq$.	$6n \geq 24$ and $x - 2 < 7$ are inequalities. $6n \geq 24$ y $x - 2 < 7$ son desigualdades.

input (p. 35) A number in the domain of a function.

See **function.**

entrada (pág. 35) Número del dominio de una función.

Ver **función.**

---

integers (p. 64) The numbers . . . , −3, −2, −1, 0, 1, 2, 3, . . . , consisting of the negative integers, zero, and the positive integers.

−8 and 46 are integers.

$-8\frac{1}{2}$ and 46.2 are *not* integers.

números enteros (pág. 64) Los números . . . , −3, −2, −1, 0, 1, 2, 3, . . . , que constan de los números enteros negativos, cero y los números enteros positivos.

−8 y 46 son números enteros.

$-8\frac{1}{2}$ y 46.2 *no* son números enteros.

---

intercept form of a quadratic function (p. 641) A quadratic function in the form $y = a(x - p)(x - q)$ where $a \neq 0$. The x-intercepts of the graph of the function are p and q.

The quadratic function $y = -(x + 1)(x - 5)$ is in intercept form. The intercepts of the graph of the function are −1 and 5.

forma de intercepto de una función cuadrática (pág. 641) Función cuadrática de la forma $y = a(x - p)(x - q)$, donde $a \neq 0$. Los interceptos en x de la gráfica de la función son p y q.

La función cuadrática $y = -(x + 1)(x - 5)$ está en la forma de intercepto. Los interceptos de la gráfica de la función son −1 y 5.

---

interquartile range (p. 888) The difference of the upper and the lower quartiles of a data set.

The interquartile range of the data set below is 23 − 10 = 13.

lower quartile ↓ ... upper quartile ↓

8 10 14 17 20 23 50

rango intercuartílico (pág. 888) La diferencia entre el cuartil superior y el cuartil inferior de un conjunto de datos.

El rango intercuartílico del siguiente conjunto de datos es 23 − 10 = 13.

cuartil inferior ↓ ... cuartil superior ↓

8 10 14 17 20 23 50

---

intersection (p. 71) The intersection of two sets A and B is the set of all elements in *both* A and B. The intersection of A and B is written as $A \cap B$.

intersección (pág. 71) La intersección de dos conjuntos A y B es el conjunto de todos los elementos *tanto* de A *como* de B. La intersección de A y B se escribe $A \cap B$.

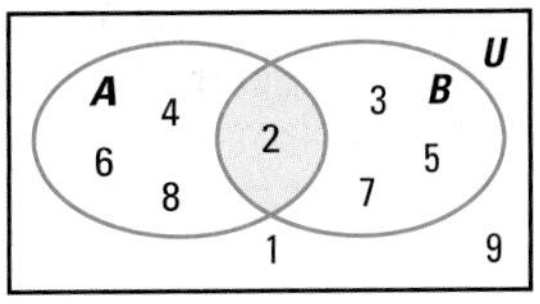

U; A: 4, 6, 8; B: 3, 5, 7; A ∩ B: 2; outside: 1, 9

$A \cap B = \{2\}$

---

inverse operations (p. 134) Two operations that undo each other.

Addition and subtraction are inverse operations. Multiplication and division are also inverse operations.

operaciones inversas (pág. 134) Dos operaciones que se anulan entre sí.

La suma y la resta son operaciones inversas. La multiplicación y la división también son operaciones inversas.

975

inverse variation (p. 765) The relationship of two variables x and y if there is a nonzero number a such that $y = \frac{a}{x}$. If $y = \frac{a}{x}$, then y is said to vary inversely with x.

variación inversa (pág. 765) La relación entre dos variables x e y si hay un número a distinto de cero tal que $y = \frac{a}{x}$. Si $y = \frac{a}{x}$, entonces se dice que y varía inversamente con x.

The equations $xy = 4$ and $y = \frac{-1}{x}$ represent inverse variation.

Las ecuaciones $xy = 4$ e $y = \frac{-1}{x}$ representan una variación inversa.

irrational number (p. 111) A number that cannot be written as the quotient of two integers. The decimal form of an irrational number neither terminates nor repeats.

número irracional (pág. 111) Número que no puede escribirse como cociente de dos números enteros. La forma decimal de un número irracional no termina ni se repite.

$\sqrt{945} = 30.74085\ldots$ is an irrational number. $1.666\ldots$ is *not* an irrational number.

$\sqrt{945} = 30.74085\ldots$ es un número irracional. $1.666\ldots$ *no* es un número irracional.

L

leading coefficient (p. 554) When a polynomial is written so that the exponents of a variable decrease from left to right, the coefficient of the first term is the leading coefficient.

coeficiente inicial (pág. 554) Cuando un polinomio se escribe de tal manera que los exponentes de una variable disminuyen de izquierda a derecha, el coeficiente del primer término es el coeficiente inicial.

The leading coefficient of the polynomial $2x^3 + x^2 - 5x + 12$ is 2.

El coeficiente inicial del polinomio $2x^3 + x^2 - 5x + 12$ es 2.

least common denominator (LCD) of rational expressions (p. 813) The product of the factors of the denominators of the rational expressions with each common factor used only once.

mínimo común denominador (m.c.d.) de las expresiones racionales (pág. 813) El producto de los factores de los denominadores de las expresiones racionales usando cada factor común una sola vez.

The LCD of $\frac{5}{(x-3)^2}$ and $\frac{3x+4}{(x-3)(x+2)}$ is $(x-3)^2(x+2)$.

El m.c.d. de $\frac{5}{(x-3)^2}$ y $\frac{3x+4}{(x-3)(x+2)}$ es $(x-3)^2(x+2)$.

legs of a right triangle (p. 737) The two sides that form the right angle.

catetos de un triángulo rectángulo (pág. 737) Los dos lados que forman el ángulo recto.

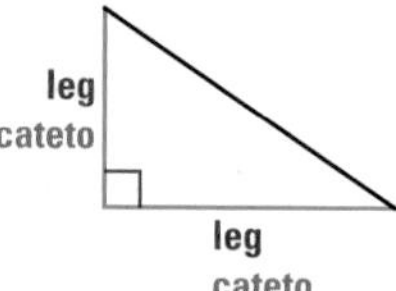

like terms (p. 97) Terms that have the same variable parts. Constant terms are also like terms.

términos semejantes (pág. 97) Términos que tienen las mismas variables. Los términos constantes también son términos semejantes.

In the expression $3x + (-4) + (-6x) + 2$, $3x$ and $-6x$ are like terms, and -4 and 2 are like terms.

En la expresión $3x + (-4) + (-6x) + 2$, $3x$ y $-6x$ son términos semejantes, y -4 y 2 también son términos semejantes.

976

line of fit (p. 325) A line used to model the trend in data having a positive or negative correlation. **recta de regresión** (pág. 325) Recta utilizada para representar la tendencia de los datos que presentan una correlación positiva o negativa.	The graph shows a line of fit for the data in the scatter plot. La gráfica muestra una recta de regresión para los datos del diagrama de dispersión.
linear equation (p. 216) An equation whose graph is a line. **ecuación lineal** (pág. 216) Ecuación cuya gráfica es una recta.	*See* standard form of a linear equation. *Ver* forma general de una ecuación lineal.
linear extrapolation (p. 336) Using a line or its equation to approximate a value outside the range of known values. **extrapolación lineal** (pág. 336) El uso de una recta o su ecuación para hallar por aproximación un valor situado fuera del rango de los valores conocidos.	X=11.75 Y=1200 The best-fitting line can be used to estimate that when $y = 1200$, $x \approx 11.75$. La mejor recta de regresión puede utilizarse para estimar que cuando $y = 1200$, $x \approx 11.75$.
linear function (p. 217) The equation $Ax + By = C$ represents a linear function provided $B \neq 0$. **función lineal** (pág. 217) La ecuación $Ax + By = C$ representa una función lineal siempre que $B \neq 0$.	The equation $2x - y = 3$ represents a linear function. The equation $x = 3$ does *not* represent a function. La ecuación $2x - y = 3$ representa una función lineal. La ecuación $x = 3$ *no* representa una función.
linear inequality in two variables (p. 405) An inequality that is the result of replacing the = sign in a linear equation with <, ≤, >, or ≥. **desigualdad lineal con dos variables** (pág. 405) Desigualdad que se obtiene al reemplazar el símbolo = de la ecuación lineal por <, ≤, > o ≥.	$x - 3y < 6$ is a linear inequality in two variables, x and y. $x - 3y < 6$ es una desigualdad lineal con dos variables, x e y.

ENGLISH-SPANISH GLOSSARY

977

linear interpolation (p. 335) Using a line or its equation to approximate a value between two known values.

interpolación lineal (pág. 335) El uso de una recta o su ecuación para hallar por aproximación un valor situado entre dos valores conocidos.

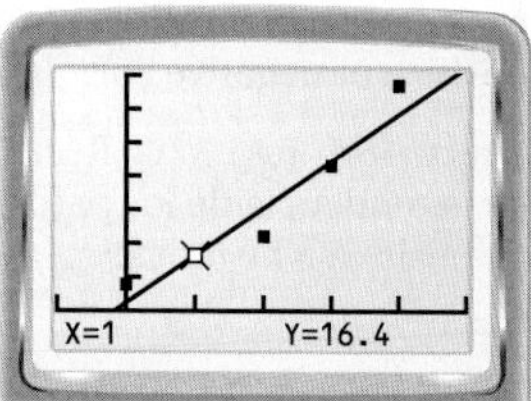

The best-fitting line can be used to estimate that when $x = 1$, $y \approx 16.4$.

La mejor recta de regresión puede utilizarse para estimar que cuando $x = 1$, $y \approx 16.4$.

linear regression (p. 335) The process of finding the best-fitting line to model a set of data.

regresión lineal (pág. 335) El proceso de hallar la mejor recta de regresión para representar un conjunto de datos.

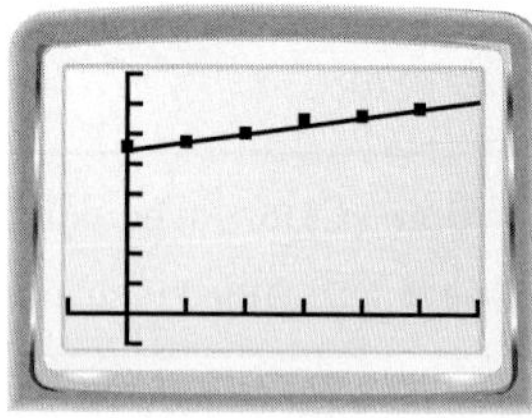

You can use a graphing calculator to perform linear regression on a data set.

Puedes usar una calculadora de gráficas para realizar una regresión lineal a un conjunto de datos.

literal equation (p. 184) An equation in which letters are used to replace the coefficients and constants of another equation.

ecuación literal (pág. 184) Ecuación en la que se usan letras para reemplazar los coeficientes y las constantes de otra ecuación.

The equation $5(x + 3) = 20$ can be written as the literal equation $a(x + b) = c$.

La ecuación $5(x + 3) = 20$ puede escribirse como la ecuación literal $a(x + b) = c$.

lower quartile (p. 887) The median of the lower half of an ordered data set.

cuartil inferior (pág. 887) La mediana de la mitad inferior de un conjunto de datos ordenados.

The lower quartile of the data set below is 10.

lower quartile ↓ median ↓

8 **10** 14 17 20 23 50

El cuartil inferior del siguiente conjunto de datos es 10.

cuartil inferior ↓ mediana ↓

8 **10** 14 17 20 23 50

M

matrix, matrices (p. 94) A rectangular arrangement of numbers in rows and columns. Each number in a matrix is an element, or *entry*.

matriz, matrices (pág. 94) Disposición rectangular de números colocados en filas y columnas. Cada número de la matriz es un elemento, o *entrada*.

$$A = \begin{bmatrix} 0 & 4 & -1 \\ -3 & 2 & 5 \end{bmatrix}$$ 2 rows / 2 filas

3 columns
3 columnas

Matrix *A* has 2 rows and 3 columns. The element in the first row and second column is 4.

La matriz *A* tiene 2 filas y 3 columnas. El elemento de la primera fila y la segunda columna es 4.

maximum value (p. 636) For $y = ax^2 + bx + c$ where $a < 0$, the y-coordinate of the vertex is the maximum value of the function.

valor máximo (pág. 636) Para $y = ax^2 + bx + c$ donde $a < 0$, la coordenada y del vértice es el valor máximo de la función.

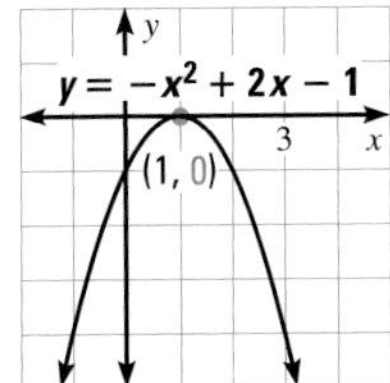

The maximum value of the function $y = -x^2 + 2x - 1$ is 0.

El valor máximo de la función $y = -x^2 + 2x - 1$ es 0.

mean (p. 875) For the numerical data set $x_1, x_2, \ldots, x_n$, the mean, or average, is:

$$\overline{x} = \frac{x_1 + x_2 + \ldots + x_n}{n}$$

media (pág. 875) Para el conjunto de datos numéricos $x_1, x_2, \ldots, x_n$, la media, o el promedio, es:

$$\overline{x} = \frac{x_1 + x_2 + \ldots + x_n}{n}$$

The mean of 5, 9, 14, 23 is $\frac{5 + 9 + 14 + 23}{4} = \frac{51}{4} = 12.75$.

La media de 5, 9, 14, 23 es $\frac{5 + 9 + 14 + 23}{4} = \frac{51}{4} = 12.75$.

mean absolute deviation (p. 876) The mean absolute deviation of the data set $x_1, x_2, \ldots, x_n$ is a measure of dispersion given by:

$$\frac{|x_1 - \overline{x}| + |x_2 - \overline{x}| + \ldots + |x_n - \overline{x}|}{n}$$

desviación absoluta media (pág. 876) La desviación absoluta media del conjunto de datos $x_1, x_2, \ldots, x_n$ es una medida de dispersión dada por:

$$\frac{|x_1 - \overline{x}| + |x_2 - \overline{x}| + \ldots + |x_n - \overline{x}|}{n}$$

The mean absolute deviation of the data set 3, 9, 13, 23 (with mean = 12) is:

$$\frac{|3 - 12| + |9 - 12| + |13 - 12| + |23 - 12|}{4} = 6$$

La desviación absoluta media del conjunto de datos 3, 9, 13, 23 (con media = 12)es:

$$\frac{|3 - 12| + |9 - 12| + |13 - 12| + |23 - 12|}{4} = 6$$

measure of dispersion (p. 876) A measure that describes the dispersion, or spread, of data.

medida de dispersión (pág. 876) Medida que describe la dispersión, o extensión, de los datos.

See range *and* mean absolute deviation.

Ver rango *y* desviación absoluta media.

median (p. 875) The median of a numerical data set is the middle number when the values are written in numerical order. If the data set has an even number of values, the median is the mean of the two middle values.

mediana (pág. 875) La mediana de un conjunto de datos numéricos es el número central cuando los valores se escriben en orden numérico. Si el conjunto de datos tiene un número par de valores, la mediana es la media de los dos valores centrales.

The median of 5, 9, 14, 23 is the mean of 9 and 14, or $\frac{9+14}{2} = 11.5$.

La mediana de 5, 9, 14, 23 es la media de 9 y 14, ó $\frac{9+14}{2} = 11.5$.

---

midpoint (p. 745) The midpoint of a line segment is the point on the segment that is equidistant from the endpoints.

punto medio (pág. 745) El punto medio de un segmento de recta es el punto del segmento que es equidistante de los extremos.

A M B

M is the midpoint of $\overline{AB}$.

M en el punto medio de $\overline{AB}$.

---

midpoint formula (p. 745) The midpoint M of the line segment with endpoints $A(x_1, y_1)$ and $B(x_2, y_2)$ is $M\left(\frac{x_1 + x_2}{2}, \frac{y_1 + y_2}{2}\right)$.

fórmula del punto medio (pág. 745) El punto medio M del segmento de recta cuyos extremos son $A(x_1, y_1)$ y $B(x_2, y_2)$ es $M\left(\frac{x_1 + x_2}{2}, \frac{y_1 + y_2}{2}\right)$.

The midpoint M of the line segment with endpoints $(-1, -2)$ and $(3, -4)$ is:

$$\left(\frac{-1+3}{2}, \frac{-2+(-4)}{2}\right) = (1, -3)$$

El punto medio M del segmento de recta cuyos extremos son $(-1, -2)$ y $(3, -4)$ es:

$$\left(\frac{-1+3}{2}, \frac{-2+(-4)}{2}\right) = (1, -3)$$

---

minimum value (p. 636) For $y = ax^2 + bx + c$ where $a > 0$, the y-coordinate of the vertex is the minimum value of the function.

valor mínimo (pág. 636) Para $y = ax^2 + bx + c$ donde $a > 0$, la coordenada y del vértice es el valor mínimo de la función.

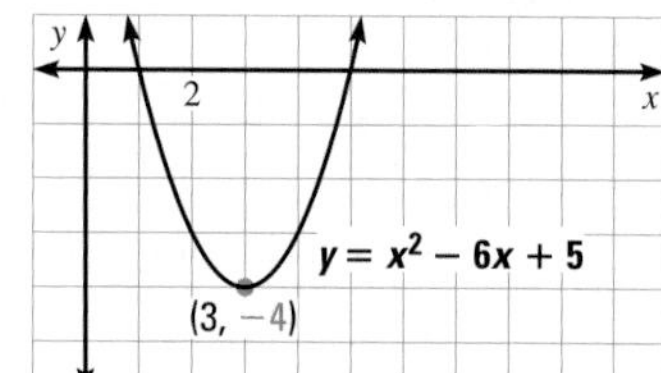

The minimum value of the function $y = x^2 - 6x + 5$ is -4.

El valor mínimo de la función $y = x^2 - 6x + 5$ es -4.

---

mode (p. 875) The mode of a data set is the value that occurs most frequently. There may be one mode, no mode, or more than one mode.

moda (pág. 875) La moda de un conjunto de datos es el valor que ocurre más veces. Puede haber una moda, más de una moda o ninguna moda.

The mode of the data set 4, 7, 9, 11, 11, 12, 18 is 11.

La moda del conjunto de datos 4, 7, 9, 11, 11, 12, 18 es 11.

980

monomial (p. 554) A number, variable, or the product of a number and one or more variables with whole number exponents. **monomio** (pág. 554) Un número, una variable o el producto de un número y una o más variables que tienen exponentes expresados por números naturales.	**$10, 3x, \frac{1}{2}ab^2$, and $-1.8m^5$ are monomials.** **$10, 3x, \frac{1}{2}ab^2$ y $-1.8m^5$ son monomios.**
multiplicative identity (p. 89) The number 1 is the multiplicative identity, because the product of any number and 1 is the number: $a \cdot 1 = 1 \cdot a = a$. **identidad multiplicativa** (pág. 89) El número 1 es la identidad multiplicativa ya que el producto de cualquier número y 1 es ese número: $a \cdot 1 = 1 \cdot a = a$.	**$3.6(1) = 3.6, 1(-7) = -7$**
multiplicative inverse (p. 103) The multiplicative inverse of a nonzero number a is its reciprocal, $\frac{1}{a}$. The product of a nonzero number and its multiplicative inverse is 1: $a \cdot \frac{1}{a} = \frac{1}{a} \cdot a = 1, a \neq 0$. **inverso multiplicativo** (pág. 103) El inverso multiplicativo de un número a distinto de cero es su recíproco, $\frac{1}{a}$. El producto de un número distinto de cero y su inverso multiplicativo es 1: $a \cdot \frac{1}{a} = \frac{1}{a} \cdot a = 1, a \neq 0$.	**The multiplicative inverse of $-\frac{1}{5}$ is -5 because $-\frac{1}{5} \cdot (-5) = 1$.** **El inverso multiplicativo de $-\frac{1}{5}$ es -5 ya que $-\frac{1}{5} \cdot (-5) = 1$.**
mutually exclusive events (p. 861) Events that have no common outcome. **sucesos mutuamente excluyentes** (pág. 861) Sucesos que no tienen ningún caso en común.	**When you roll a number cube, "roll a 3" and "roll an even number" are mutually exclusive events.** **Cuando lanzas un cubo numerado, "salir el 3" y "salir número par" son sucesos mutuamente excluyentes.**

N

n* factorial** (p. 852) For any positive integer n, n factorial, written $n!$, is the product of the integers from 1 to n; $0! = 1$. **factorial de *n (pág. 852) Para cualquier número entero positivo n, el factorial de n, escrito $n!$, es el producto de los números enteros de 1 a n; $0! = 1$.	**$5! = 5 \cdot 4 \cdot 3 \cdot 2 \cdot 1 = 120$**
negative exponent (p. 503) If $a \neq 0$, then a^{-n} is the reciprocal of a^n; $a^{-n} = \frac{1}{a^n}$. **exponente negativo** (pág. 503) Si $a \neq 0$, entonces a^{-n} es el recíproco de a^n; $a^{-n} = \frac{1}{a^n}$.	**$3^{-2} = \frac{1}{3^2} = \frac{1}{9}$**

ENGLISH-SPANISH GLOSSARY

981

negative integers (p. 64) The integers that are less than 0. **números enteros negativos** (pág. 64) Los números enteros menores que 0.	$-1, -2, -3, -4, \ldots$

O

odds against (p. 845) When all outcomes are equally likely, the odds against an event is the ratio of the number of unfavorable outcomes to the number of favorable outcomes. **probabilidad en contra** (pág. 845) Cuando todos los casos son igualmente posibles, la probabilidad en contra de que ocurra un suceso es la razón entre el número de casos desfavorables y el número de casos favorables.	When you roll a number cube, the odds against rolling a number less than 5 is $\frac{2}{4} = \frac{1}{2}$, or 1 : 2. Cuando lanzas un cubo numerado, la probabilidad en contra de que salga un número menor que 5 es $\frac{2}{4} = \frac{1}{2}$, ó 1 : 2.
odds in favor (p. 845) When all outcomes are equally likely, the odds in favor of an event is the ratio of the number of favorable outcomes to the number of unfavorable outcomes. **probabilidad a favor** (pág. 845) Cuando todos los casos son igualmente posibles, la probabilidad a favor de que ocurra un suceso es la razón entre el número de casos favorables y el número de casos desfavorables.	When you roll a number cube, the odds in favor of rolling a number less than 5 is $\frac{4}{2} = \frac{2}{1}$, or 2 : 1. Cuando lanzas un cubo numerado, la probabilidad a favor de que salga un número menor que 5 es $\frac{4}{2} = \frac{2}{1}$, ó 2 : 1.
open sentence (p. 21) An equation or an equality that contains an algebraic expression. **enunciado con variables** (pág. 21) Ecuación o desigualdad que contiene una expresión algebraica.	$2k - 8 = 12$ and $6n \geq 24$ are open sentences. $2k - 8 = 12$ y $6n \geq 24$ son enunciados con variables.
opposites (p. 66) Two numbers that are the same distance from 0 on a number line but are on opposite sides of 0. **opuestos** (pág. 66) En una recta numérica, dos números que están a la misma distancia de 0 pero en lados opuestos de 0.	4 units 4 units 4 unidades 4 unidades −6 −4 −2 0 2 4 6 4 and −4 are opposites. 4 y −4 son opuestos.
order of magnitude of a quantity (p. 491) The power of 10 nearest the quantity. **orden de magnitud de una cantidad** (pág. 491) La potencia de 10 más próxima a la cantidad.	The order of magnitude of 91,000 is 10^5, or 100,000. El orden de magnitud de 91,000 es 10^5, ó 100,000.

ENGLISH-SPANISH GLOSSARY

order of operations (p. 8) Rules for evaluating an expression involving more than one operation.	**To evaluate $24 - (3^2 + 1)$, evaluate the power, then add within the parentheses, and then subtract:** $24 - (3^2 + 1) = 24 - (9 + 1) = 24 - 10 = 14$
orden de operaciones (pág. 8) Reglas para evaluar una expresión relacionada con más de una operación.	**Para evaluar $24 - (3^2 + 1)$, evalúa la potencia, suma las cantidades entre paréntesis y después resta:** $24 - (3^2 + 1) = 24 - (9 + 1) = 24 - 10 = 14$
outcome (p. 843) A possible result of an experiment.	**When you roll a number cube, there are 6 possible outcomes: a 1, 2, 3, 4, 5, or 6.**
caso (pág. 843) Resultado posible de un experimento.	**Cuando lanzas un cubo numerado, hay 6 casos posibles: 1, 2, 3, 4, 5 ó 6.**
outlier (p. 889) A value that is widely separated from the rest of the data in a data set. Typically, a value that is greater than the upper quartile by more than 1.5 times the interquartile range or is less than the lower quartile by more than 1.5 times the interquartile range.	**The interquartile range of the data set below is $23 - 10 = 13$.** lower quartile ↓ (10), upper quartile ↓ (23) 8 **10** 14 17 20 **23** 50 **The data value 50 is greater than $23 + 1.5(13) = 42.5$, so it is an outlier.**
valor extremo (pág. 889) En un conjunto de datos, valor muy alejado del resto de los datos. Generalmente, un valor mayor que el cuartil superior en más de 1.5 veces el rango intercuartílico o menor que el cuartil inferior en más de 1.5 veces el rango intercuartílico.	**El rango intercuartílico del siguiente conjunto de datos es $23 - 10 = 13$.** cuartil inferior ↓ (10), cuartil superior ↓ (23) 8 **10** 14 17 20 **23** 50 **El valor 50 es mayor que $23 + 1.5(13) = 42.5$, por lo que es un valor extremo.**
output (p. 35) A number in the range of a function.	***See* function.**
salida (pág. 35) Número que pertenece al rango de una función.	***Ver* función.**
overlapping events (p. 861) Events that have at least one common outcome.	**When you roll a number cube, "roll a 3" and "roll an odd number" are overlapping events.**
sucesos de intersección (pág. 861) Sucesos que tienen al menos un caso en común.	**Cuando lanzas un cubo numerado, "salir el 3" y "salir número impar" son sucesos de intersección.**

parabola (p. 628) The U-shaped graph of a quadratic function.

parábola (pág. 628) La gráfica en forma de U de una función cuadrática.

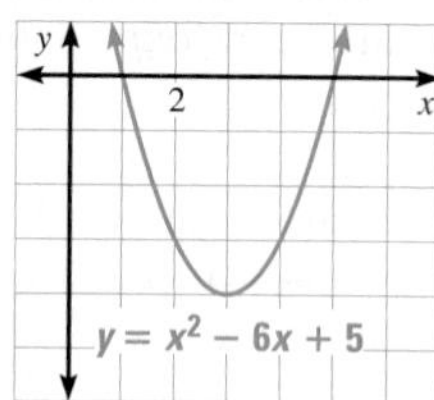

The graph of $y = x^2 - 6x + 5$ is a parabola.

La gráfica de $y = x^2 - 6x + 5$ es una parábola.

parallel lines (p. 246) Two lines in the same plane that do not intersect.

rectas paralelas (pág. 246) Dos rectas del mismo plano que no se cortan.

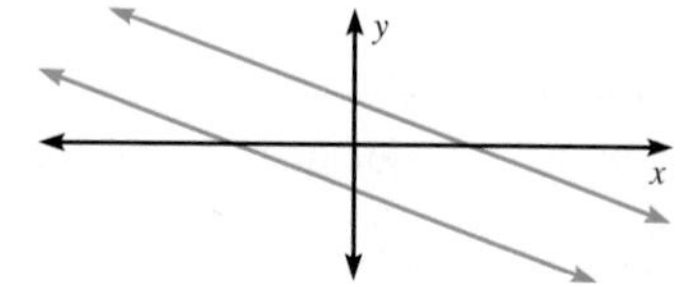

parent linear function (p. 263) The function $f(x) = x$, which is the most basic function in the family of linear functions.

función lineal básica (pág. 263) La función $f(x) = x$, que es la más básica de la familia de las funciones lineales.

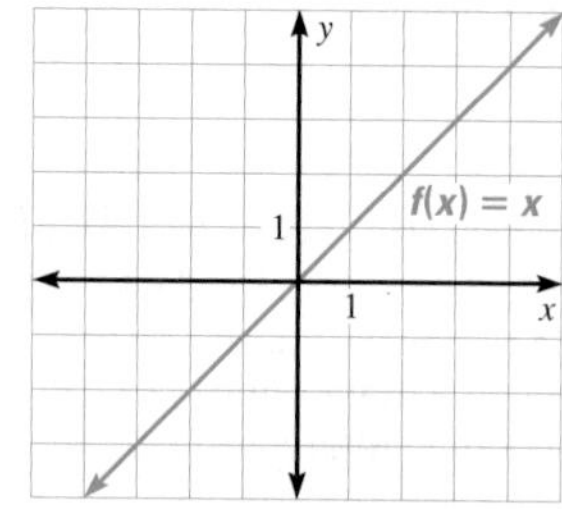

parent quadratic function (p. 628) The function $y = x^2$, which is the most basic function in the family of quadratic functions.

función cuadrática básica (pág. 628) La función $y = x^2$, que es la más básica de la familia de las funciones cuadráticas.

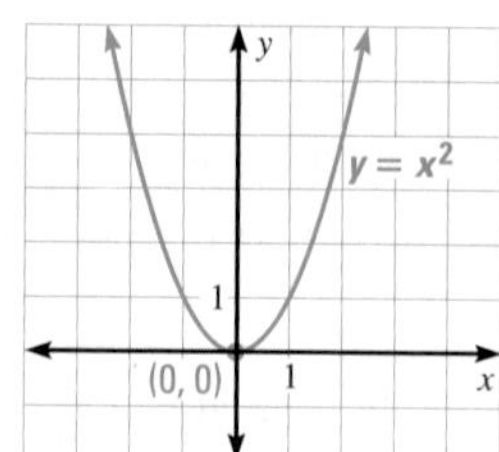

parent square root function (p. 710) The function $y = \sqrt{x}$, which is the most basic function in the family of square root functions.

función con raíz cuadrada básica (pág. 710) La función $y = \sqrt{x}$, que es la más básica de la familia de las funciones con raíz cuadrada.

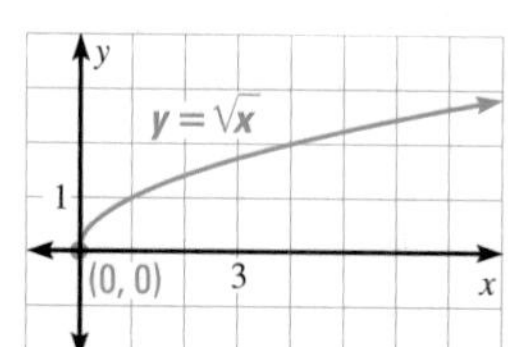

ENGLISH-SPANISH GLOSSARY

percent of change (p. 182) A percent that indicates how much a quantity increases or decreases with respect to the original amount. Percent of change, $p\% = \frac{\text{Amount of increase or decrease}}{\text{Original amount}}$	**The percent of change, $p\%$, from 140 to 189 is:** $p\% = \frac{189 - 140}{140} = \frac{49}{140} = 0.35 = 35\%$
porcentaje de cambio (pág. 182) Porcentaje que indica cuánto aumenta o disminuye una cantidad con respecto a la cantidad original. Porcentaje de cambio, $p\% = \frac{\text{Cantidad de aumento o disminución}}{\text{Cantidad original}}$	**El porcentaje de cambio, $p\%$, de 140 a 189 es:** $p\% = \frac{189 - 140}{140} = \frac{49}{140} = 0.35 = 35\%$
percent of decrease (p. 182) The percent of change in a quantity when the new amount of the quantity is less than the original amount.	***See* percent of change.**
porcentaje de disminución (pág. 182) El porcentaje de cambio de una cantidad cuando la nueva cantidad es menor que la cantidad original.	***Ver* porcentaje de cambio.**
percent of increase (p. 182) The percent of change in a quantity when the new amount of the quantity is greater than the original amount.	***See* percent of change.**
porcentaje de aumento (pág. 182) El porcentaje de cambio de una cantidad cuando la nueva cantidad es mayor que la cantidad original.	***Ver* porcentaje de cambio.**
perfect square (p. 111) A number that is the square of an integer.	**49 is a perfect square, because $49 = 7^2$.**
cuadrado perfecto (pág. 111) Número que es el cuadrado de un número entero.	**49 es un cuadrado perfecto ya que $49 = 7^2$.**
perfect square trinomials (p. 601) Trinomials of the form $a^2 + 2ab + b^2$ and $a^2 - 2ab + b^2$.	**$x^2 + 6x + 9$ and $x^2 - 10x + 25$ are perfect square trinomials.**
trinomios cuadrados perfectos (pág. 601) Trinomios de la forma $a^2 + 2ab + b^2$ y $a^2 - 2ab + b^2$.	**$x^2 + 6x + 9$ y $x^2 - 10x + 25$ son trinomios cuadrados perfectos.**
permutation (p. 851) An arrangement of objects in which order is important.	**There are 6 permutations of the numbers 1, 2, and 3: 123, 132, 213, 231, 312, and 321.**
permutación (pág. 851) Disposición de objetos en la que el orden es importante.	**Existen 6 permutaciones de los números 1, 2 y 3: 123, 132, 213, 231, 312 y 321.**
perpendicular lines (p. 319) Two lines in the same plane that intersect to form a right angle.	**Horizontal and vertical lines are perpendicular to each other.**
rectas perpendiculares (pág. 319) Dos rectas del mismo plano que al cortarse forman un ángulo recto.	**Las rectas horizontales y verticales son perpendiculares entre sí.**

point-slope form (p. 302) An equation of a nonvertical line written in the form $y - y_1 = m(x - x_1)$ where the line passes through a given point (x_1, y_1) and has a slope of m. **forma punto-pendiente** (pág. 302) Ecuación de una recta no vertical escrita en la forma $y - y_1 = m(x - x_1)$, donde la recta pasa por un punto dado (x_1, y_1) y tiene pendiente m.	The equation $y + 3 = 2(x - 4)$ is in point-slope form. The graph of the equation is a line that passes through the point $(4, -3)$ and has a slope of 2. La ecuación $y + 3 = 2(x - 4)$ está en la forma punto-pendiente. La gráfica de la ecuación es una recta que pasa por el punto $(4, -3)$ y tiene pendiente 2.
polynomial (p. 554) A monomial or a sum of monomials, each called a term of the polynomial. **polinomio** (pág. 554) Monomio o suma de monomios; cada uno se llama término del polinomio.	$9, 2x^2 + x - 5$, and $7bc^3 + 4b^4c$ are polynomials. $9, 2x^2 + x - 5$ y $7bc^3 + 4b^4c$ son polinomios.
population (p. 871) The entire group that you want information about. **población** (pág. 871) El grupo entero sobre el que se desea información.	A magazine invites its readers to mail in answers to a questionnaire rating the magazine. The population consists of all the magazine's readers. Una revista invita a sus lectores a enviar por correo las respuestas a un cuestionario sobre la calidad de la revista. La población está formada por todos los lectores de la revista.
positive integers (p. 64) The integers that are greater than 0. **números enteros positivos** (pág. 64) Los números enteros mayores que 0.	1, 2, 3, 4, . . .
power (p. 3) An expression that represents repeated multiplication of the same factor. **potencia** (pág. 3) Expresión que representa la multiplicación repetida del mismo factor.	81 is a power of 3, because $81 = 3 \cdot 3 \cdot 3 \cdot 3 = 3^4$. 81 es una potencia de 3 ya que $81 = 3 \cdot 3 \cdot 3 \cdot 3 = 3^4$.
probability of an event (p. 843) A number from 0 to 1 that measures the likelihood, or chance, that the event will occur. **probabilidad de un suceso** (pág. 843) Número de 0 a 1 que mide la posibilidad de que ocurra un suceso.	*See* experimental probability *and* theoretical probability. *Ver* probabilidad experimental *y* probabilidad teórica.
proportion (p. 163) An equation that states that two ratios are equivalent: $\frac{a}{b} = \frac{c}{d}$ where $b \neq 0$ and $d \neq 0$. **proporción** (pág. 163) Ecuación que establece que dos razones son equivalentes: $\frac{a}{b} = \frac{c}{d}$ donde $b \neq 0$ y $d \neq 0$.	$\frac{3}{4} = \frac{6}{8}$ and $\frac{11}{6} = \frac{x}{30}$ are proportions. $\frac{3}{4} = \frac{6}{8}$ y $\frac{11}{6} = \frac{x}{30}$ son proporciones.

ENGLISH-SPANISH GLOSSARY

Pythagorean theorem (p. 737) If a triangle is a right triangle, then the sum of the squares of the lengths a and b of the legs equals the square of the length c of the hypotenuse: $a^2 + b^2 = c^2$.

teorema de Pitágoras (pág. 737) Si un triángulo es rectángulo, entonces la suma de los cuadrados de las longitudes a y b de los catetos es igual al cuadrado de la longitud c de la hipotenusa: $a^2 + b^2 = c^2$.

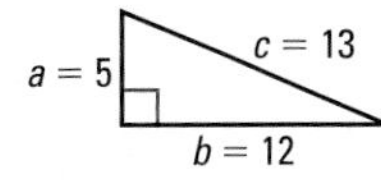

$5^2 + 12^2 = 13^2$

Q

quadrants (p. 206) The four regions into which the coordinate plane is divided by the x-axis and the y-axis.

cuadrantes (pág. 206) Las cuatro regiones en las que el eje de x y el eje de y dividen al plano de coordenadas.

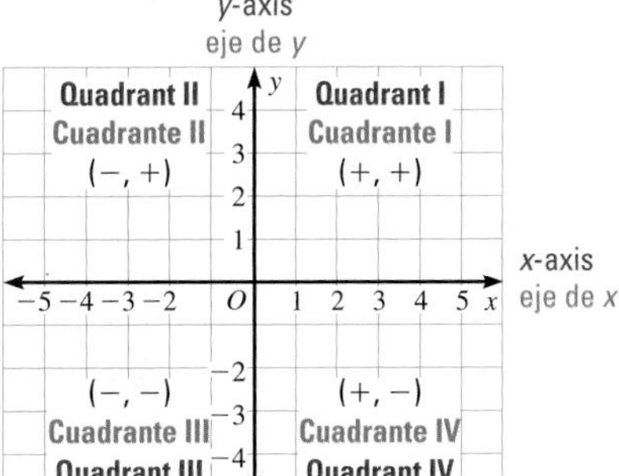

quadratic equation (p. 643) An equation that can be written in the standard form $ax^2 + bx + c = 0$ where $a \neq 0$.

ecuación cuadrática (pág. 643) Ecuación que puede escribirse en la forma general $ax^2 + bx + c = 0$, donde $a \neq 0$.

The equations $x^2 - 2x = 3$ and $0.1x^2 = 40$ are quadratic equations.

$x^2 - 2x = 3$ y $0.1x^2 = 40$ son ecuaciones cuadráticas.

quadratic formula (p. 671) The formula below that can be used to find the solutions of the quadratic equation $ax^2 + bx + c = 0$ where $a \neq 0$ and $b^2 - 4ac \geq 0$:

$$x = \frac{-b \pm \sqrt{b^2 - 4ac}}{2a}$$

fórmula cuadrática (pág. 671) La fórmula de abajo puede utilizarse para hallar las soluciones de la ecuación cuadrática $ax^2 + bx + c = 0$ donde $a \neq 0$ y $b^2 - 4ac \geq 0$:

$$x = \frac{-b \pm \sqrt{b^2 - 4ac}}{2a}$$

To solve $3x^2 + 5x - 8 = 0$, substitute 3 for a, 5 for b, and -8 for c in the quadratic formula:

$$x = \frac{-5 \pm \sqrt{5^2 - 4(3)(-8)}}{2(3)}$$

$x = 1$ or $x = -\frac{8}{3}$

Para resolver $3x^2 + 5x - 8 = 0$, sustituye a por 3, b por 5 y c por -8 en la fórmula cuadrática:

$$x = \frac{-5 \pm \sqrt{5^2 - 4(3)(-8)}}{2(3)}$$

$x = 1$ ó $x = -\frac{8}{3}$

quadratic function (p. 628) A nonlinear function that can be written in the standard form $y = ax^2 + bx + c$ where $a \neq 0$.

función cuadrática (pág. 628) Función no lineal que puede escribirse en la forma general $y = ax^2 + bx + c$, donde $a \neq 0$.

$y = 2x^2 + 5x - 3$ is a quadratic function.

$y = 2x^2 + 5x - 3$ es una función cuadrática.

R

radical equation (p. 729) An equation that contains a radical expression with a variable in the radicand. **ecuación radical** (pág. 729) Ecuación que contiene una expresión radical en cuyo radicando aparece una variable.	**$2\sqrt{x} - 8 = 0$ and $\sqrt{3x - 17} = \sqrt{x + 21}$ are radical equations.** **$2\sqrt{x} - 8 = 0$ y $\sqrt{3x - 17} = \sqrt{x + 21}$ son ecuaciones radicales.**
radical expression (p. 710) An expression that contains a radical, such as a square root, cube root, or other root. **expresión radical** (pág. 710) Expresión que contiene un radical, como una raíz cuadrada, una raíz cúbica u otra raíz.	**$3\sqrt{2x}$ and $\sqrt[3]{x - 1}$ are radical expressions.** **$3\sqrt{2x}$ y $\sqrt[3]{x - 1}$ son expresiones radicales.**
radical function (p. 710) A function that contains a radical expression with the independent variable in the radicand. **función radical** (pág. 710) Función que contiene una expresión radical y en cuyo radicando aparece la variable independiente.	**$y = \sqrt[3]{2x}$ and $y = \sqrt{x + 2}$ are radical functions.** **$y = \sqrt[3]{2x}$ e $y = \sqrt{x + 2}$ son funciones radicales.**
radicand (p. 110) The number or expression inside a radical symbol. **radicando** (pág. 110) El número o la expresión que aparece bajo el signo radical.	**The radicand of $\sqrt{9}$ and $-\sqrt{9}$ is 9.** **El radicando de $\sqrt{9}$ y $-\sqrt{9}$ es 9.**
random sample (p. 871) A sample in which every member of the population has an equal chance of being selected. **muestra aleatoria** (pág. 871) Muestra en la que cada miembro de la población tiene igual probabilidad de ser seleccionado.	**You can select a random sample of a school's student population by having a computer randomly choose 100 student identification numbers.** **Para seleccionar una muestra aleatoria de la población de estudiantes de una escuela, puedes usar la computadora para elegir al azar 100 números de identificación estudiantil.**
range of a data set (p. 876) The range of a numerical data set is a measure of dispersion. It is the difference of the greatest value and the least value. **rango de un conjunto de datos** (pág. 876) El rango de un conjunto de datos numéricos es una medida de dispersión. Es la diferencia entre los valores mayor y menor.	**The range of the data set 4, 7, 9, 11, 11, 12, 18 is $18 - 4 = 14$.** **El rango del conjunto de datos 4, 7, 9, 11, 11, 12, 18 es $18 - 4 = 14$.**
range of a function (p. 35) The set of all outputs of a function. **rango de una función** (pág. 35) El conjunto de todas las salidas de una función.	*See* **function.** *Ver* **función.**

ENGLISH-SPANISH GLOSSARY

rate (p. 17) A fraction that compares two quantities measured in different units. **relación** (pág. 17) Fracción que compara dos cantidades medidas en unidades diferentes.	$\frac{110 \text{ miles}}{2 \text{ hours}}$ and $\frac{55 \text{ miles}}{1 \text{ hour}}$ are rates. $\frac{110 \text{ millas}}{2 \text{ horas}}$ y $\frac{55 \text{ millas}}{1 \text{ hora}}$ son relaciones.
rate of change (p. 237) A comparison of a change in one quantity with a change in another quantity. In real-world situations, you can interpret the slope of a line as a rate of change. **relación de cambio** (pág. 237) Comparación entre el cambio producido en una cantidad y el cambio producido en otra cantidad. En situaciones de la vida real, se puede interpretar la pendiente de una recta como una relación de cambio.	You pay \$7 for 2 hours of computer use and \$14 for 4 hours of computer use. The rate of change is $\frac{\text{change in cost}}{\text{change in time}} = \frac{14-7}{4-2} = 3.5$, or \$3.50 per hour. Pagas \$7 por usar la computadora 2 horas y \$14 por usarla 4 horas. La relación de cambio es $\frac{\text{cambio en el costo}}{\text{cambio en el tiempo}} = \frac{14-7}{4-2} = 3.5$, o \$3.50 por hora.
ratio (p. 162) A comparison of two numbers using division. The ratio of a and b, where $b \neq 0$, can be written as a to b, as $a : b$, or as $\frac{a}{b}$. **razón** (pág. 162) Comparacion de dos números mediante la división. La razón entre a y b, donde $b \neq 0$, puede escribirse a a b, $a : b$ o $\frac{a}{b}$.	The ratio of 5 wins to 2 losses can be written as 5 to 2, as 5 : 2, or as $\frac{5}{2}$. La razón de 5 victorias a 2 derrotas puede escribirse 5 a 2, 5 : 2 ó $\frac{5}{2}$.
rational equation (p. 820) An equation that contains one or more rational expressions. **ecuación racional** (pág. 820) Ecuación que contiene una o más expresiones racionales.	The equations $\frac{6}{x+4} = \frac{x}{2}$ and $\frac{x}{x-2} + \frac{1}{5} = \frac{2}{x-2}$ are rational equations. $\frac{6}{x+4} = \frac{x}{2}$ y $\frac{x}{x-2} + \frac{1}{5} = \frac{2}{x-2}$ son ecuaciones racionales.
rational expression (p. 794) An expression that can be written as a ratio of two polynomials where the denominator is not 0. **expresión racional** (pág. 794) Expresión que puede escribirse como razón de dos polinomios, donde el denominador no es 0.	$\frac{x+8}{10x}$ and $\frac{5}{x^2-1}$ are rational expressions. $\frac{x+8}{10x}$ y $\frac{5}{x^2-1}$ son expresiones racionales.
rational function (p. 775) A function whose rule is given by a fraction whose numerator and denominator are polynomials and whose denominator is not 0. **función racional** (pág. 775) Función cuya regla viene dada por una fracción cuyo numerador y denominador son polinomios y cuyo denominador no es 0.	The equations $y = \frac{-1}{x}$ and $y = \frac{2x-1}{x-2}$ are rational functions. Las ecuaciones $y = \frac{-1}{x}$ e $y = \frac{2x-1}{x-2}$ son funciones racionales.

ENGLISH-SPANISH GLOSSARY

rational number (p. 64) A number that can be written as $\frac{a}{b}$ where a and b are integers and $b \neq 0$.

número racional (pág. 64) Número que puede escribirse $\frac{a}{b}$, donde a y b son números enteros y $b \neq 0$.

$4 = \frac{4}{1}, 0 = \frac{0}{1}, 2\frac{1}{3} = \frac{7}{3}, -\frac{3}{4} = \frac{-3}{4}$, and $0.6 = \frac{3}{5}$ are all rational numbers.

$4 = \frac{4}{1}, 0 = \frac{0}{1}, 2\frac{1}{3} = \frac{7}{3}, -\frac{3}{4} = \frac{-3}{4}$ y $0.6 = \frac{3}{5}$ son todos números racionales.

rationalizing the denominator (p. 721) The process of eliminating a radical from an expression's denominator by multiplying the expression by an appropriate form of 1.

racionalizar el denominador (pág. 721) El proceso de eliminar el radical del denominador de una expresión multiplicando la expresión por la forma apropiada de 1.

To rationalize the denominator of $\frac{5}{\sqrt{7}}$, multiply the expression by $\frac{\sqrt{7}}{\sqrt{7}}$:

$$\frac{5}{\sqrt{7}} = \frac{5}{\sqrt{7}} \cdot \frac{\sqrt{7}}{\sqrt{7}} = \frac{5\sqrt{7}}{\sqrt{49}} = \frac{5\sqrt{7}}{7}$$

Para racionalizar el denominador de $\frac{5}{\sqrt{7}}$, multiplica la expresión por $\frac{\sqrt{7}}{\sqrt{7}}$:

$$\frac{5}{\sqrt{7}} = \frac{5}{\sqrt{7}} \cdot \frac{\sqrt{7}}{\sqrt{7}} = \frac{5\sqrt{7}}{\sqrt{49}} = \frac{5\sqrt{7}}{7}$$

real numbers (p. 112) The set of all rational and irrational numbers.

números reales (pág. 112) El conjunto de todos los números racionales e irracionales.

$8, -6.2, \frac{6}{7}, \pi$, and $\sqrt{2}$ are real numbers.

$8, -6.2, \frac{6}{7}, \pi$ y $\sqrt{2}$ son números reales.

reflection (p. 213) A reflection flips a figure in a line.

reflexión (pág. 213) Una reflexión vuelca una figura en una recta.

y

x

line of reflection

recta de reflexión

relation (p. 49) Any pairing of a set of inputs with a set of outputs.

relación (pág. 49) Cualquier correspondencia establecida entre un conjunto de entradas y un conjunto de salidas.

The pairing in the table below is a relation, but it is *not* a function.

La correspondencia en la tabla de abajo es una relación, pero *no* es una función.

Input Entrada	4	4	5	6	7
Output Salida	0	1	2	3	4

roots (p. 575) The solutions of an equation in which one side is zero and other side is a product of polynomial factors.

raíces (pág. 575) Las soluciones de una ecuación en la que un lado es cero y el otro lado es el producto de factores polinómicos.

The roots of the equation $(x - 4)(x + 2) = 0$ are 4 and -2.

Las raíces de la ecuación $(x - 4)(x + 2) = 0$ son 4 y -2.

S

sample (p. 871) A part of a population. **muestra** (pág. 871) Parte de una población.	To predict the results of an election, a survey is given to a sample of voters. Para predecir los resultados de una elección, se realiza una encuesta entre una muestra de votantes.
sample space (p. 843) The set of all possible outcomes. **espacio muestral** (pág. 843) El conjunto de todos los casos posibles.	When you toss two coins, the sample space is heads, heads; heads, tails; tails, heads; and tails, tails. Cuando lanzas al aire dos monedas, el espacio muestral es cara, cara; cara, cruz; cruz, cara; y cruz, cruz.
scalar (p. 95) A real number by which you multiply a matrix. **escalar** (pág. 95) Número real por el que se multiplica una matriz.	*See* scalar multiplication. *Ver* multiplicación escalar.
scalar multiplication (p. 95) Multiplication of each element in a matrix by a real number, called a scalar. **multiplicación escalar** (pág. 95) Multiplicación de cada elemento de una matriz por un número real llamado escalar.	The matrix is multiplied by the scalar 3. $3\begin{bmatrix}1 & 2\\0 & -1\end{bmatrix}=\begin{bmatrix}3 & 6\\0 & -3\end{bmatrix}$ La matriz se multiplica por el escalar 3. $3\begin{bmatrix}1 & 2\\0 & -1\end{bmatrix}=\begin{bmatrix}3 & 6\\0 & -3\end{bmatrix}$
scale (p. 170) A ratio that relates the dimensions of a scale drawing or scale model and the actual dimensions. **escala** (pág. 170) Razón que relaciona las dimensiones de un dibujo a escala o un modelo a escala con las dimensiones reales.	The scale 1 in. : 12 ft on a floor plan means that 1 inch in the floor plan represents an actual distance of 12 feet. La escala 1 pulg : 12 pies en un diagrama de planta significa que 1 pulgada en el diagrama de planta representa una distancia real de 12 pies.
scale drawing (p. 170) A two-dimensional drawing of an object in which the dimensions of the drawing are in proportion to the dimensions of the object. **dibujo a escala** (pág. 170) Dibujo bidimensional de un objeto en el que las dimensiones del dibujo guardan proporción con las dimensiones del objeto.	A floor plan of a house is a scale drawing. El diagrama de planta de una casa es un dibujo a escala.
scale model (p. 170) A three-dimensional model of an object in which the dimensions of the model are in proportion to the dimensions of the object. **modelo a escala** (pág. 170) Modelo tridimensional de un objeto en el que las dimensiones del modelo guardan proporción con las dimensiones del objeto.	A globe is a scale model of Earth. El globo terráqueo es un modelo a escala de la Tierra.

991

scatter plot (p. 324) A graph used to determine whether there is a relationship or trend between paired data. **diagrama de dispersión** (pág. 324) Gráfica utilizada para determinar si hay una relación o tendencia entre los pares de datos.	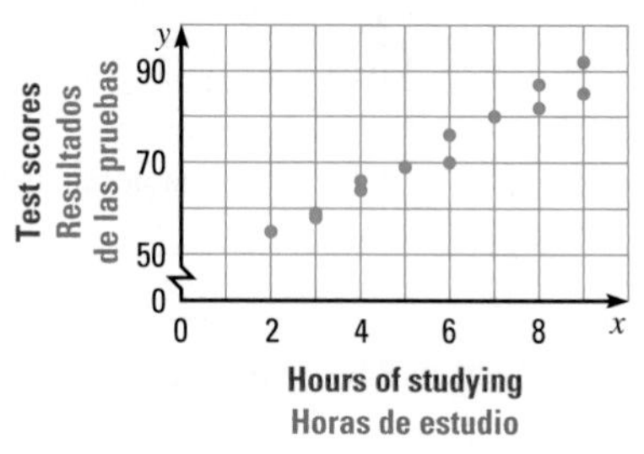
scientific notation (p. 512) A number is written in scientific notation when it is of the form $c \times 10^n$ where $1 \le c < 10$ and n is an integer. **notación científica** (pág. 512) Un número está escrito en notación científica cuando es de la forma $c \times 10^n$, donde $1 \le c < 10$ y n es un número entero.	Two million is written in scientific notation as 2×10^6, and 0.547 is written in scientific notation as 5.47×10^{-1}. El número dos millones escrito en notación científica es 2×10^6, y 0.547 escrito en notación científica es 5.47×10^{-1}.
self-selected sample (p. 871) A sample in which members of the population select themselves by volunteering. **muestra autoseleccionada** (pág. 871) Muestra en la que los miembros de la población se seleccionan a sí mismos ofreciéndose a participar.	You can obtain a self-selected sample of a school's student population by asking students to return surveys to a collection box. Para obtener una muestra autoseleccionada de la población de estudiantes de una escuela, puedes pedir a los estudiantes que hagan la encuesta que la depositen en un recipiente de recogida.
sequence (p. 309) An ordered list of numbers. **progresión** (pág. 309) Lista ordenada de números.	$-4, 1, 6, 11, 16, \ldots$ is a sequence. $-4, 1, 6, 11, 16, \ldots$ es una progresión.
set (p. 71) A collection of distinct objects. **conjunto** (pág. 71) Colección de objetos diferenciados.	The set of whole numbers is $W = \{0, 1, 2, 3, \ldots\}$. El conjunto de los números naturales es $W = \{0, 1, 2, 3, \ldots\}$.
similar figures (p. 174) Figures that have the same shape but not necessarily the same size. Corresponding angles of similar figures are congruent, and the ratios of the lengths of corresponding sides are equal. The symbol ~ indicates that two figures are similar. **figuras semejantes** (pág. 174) Figuras que tienen la misma forma pero no necesariamente el mismo tamaño. Los ángulos correspondientes de las figuras semejantes son congruentes, y las razones de las longitudes de los lados correspondientes son iguales. El símbolo ~ indica que dos figuras son semejantes.	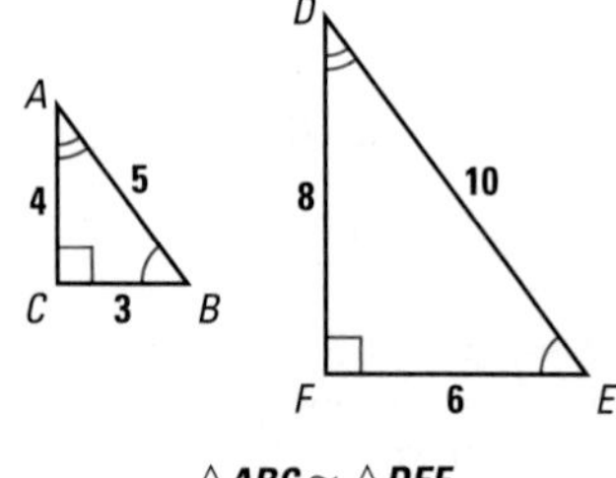 $\triangle ABC \sim \triangle DEF$

ENGLISH-SPANISH GLOSSARY

992

simplest form of a radical expression (p. 719) A radical expression that has no perfect square factors other than 1 in the radicand, no fractions in the radicand, and no radicals appearing in the denominator of a fraction. **forma más simple de una expresión radical** (pág. 719) Expresión radical que no tiene en el radicando fracciones ni factores cuadrados perfectos distintos de 1 y que no tiene radicales en el denominador de las fracciones.	In simplest form, $\sqrt{32}$ is written as $4\sqrt{2}$, and $\frac{5}{\sqrt{7}}$ is written as $\frac{5\sqrt{7}}{7}$. En la forma más simple, $\sqrt{32}$ se escribe $4\sqrt{2}$, y $\frac{5}{\sqrt{7}}$ se escribe $\frac{5\sqrt{7}}{7}$.
simplest form of a rational expression (p. 795) A rational expression whose numerator and denominator have no factors in common other than 1. **forma más simple de una expresión racional** (pág. 795) Expresión racional cuyo numerador y denominador no tienen más factores en común que el 1.	The simplest form of $\frac{2x}{x(x-3)}$ is $\frac{2}{x-3}$. La forma más simple de $\frac{2x}{x(x-3)}$ es $\frac{2}{x-3}$.
simulation (p. 849) An experiment that you can perform to make predictions about real-world situations. **simulación** (pág. 849) Experimento que se puede realizar para hacer predicciones sobre situaciones de la vida real.	Each box of Oaties contains 1 of 6 prizes. The probability of getting each prize is $\frac{1}{6}$. To predict the number of boxes of cereal you must buy to win all 6 prizes, you can roll a number cube 1 time for each box of cereal you buy. Keep rolling until you have rolled all 6 numbers. Cada paquete de Oaties contiene 1 de un total de 6 premios. La probabilidad de obtener cada premio es $\frac{1}{6}$. Para predecir el número de paquetes de cereales que debes comprar para poder conseguir los 6 premios, puedes lanzar un cubo numerado 1 vez por cada paquete de cereales que compres. Sigue lanzando el cubo hasta obtener los 6 números.
slope (p. 235) The slope m of a nonvertical line is the ratio of the vertical change (the *rise*) to the horizontal change (the *run*) between any two points (x_1, y_1) and (x_2, y_2) on the line: $m = \frac{y_2 - y_1}{x_2 - x_1}$. **pendiente** (pág. 235) La pendiente m de una recta no vertical es la razón del cambio vertical (*distancia vertical*) al cambio horizontal (*distancia horizontal*) entre dos puntos cualesquiera (x_1, y_1) y (x_2, y_2) de la recta: $m = \frac{y_2 - y_1}{x_2 - x_1}$.	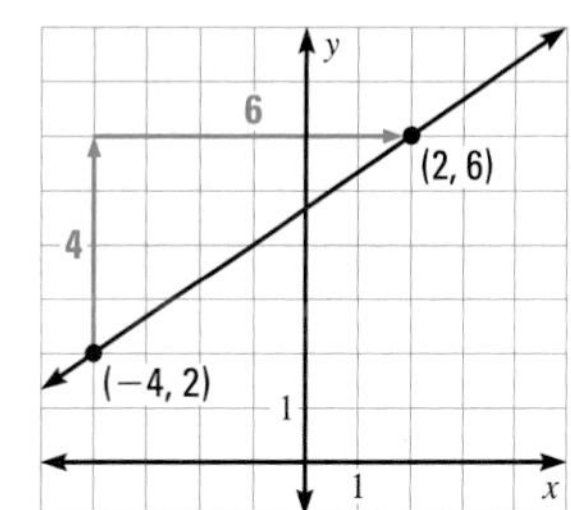 The slope of the line shown is $\frac{4}{6}$, or $\frac{2}{3}$. La pendiente de la recta indicada es $\frac{4}{6}$, ó $\frac{2}{3}$.

ENGLISH-SPANISH GLOSSARY

slope-intercept form (p. 244) A linear equation written in the form $y = mx + b$ where m is the slope and b is the y-intercept of the equation's graph.	**$y = 3x + 4$ is in slope-intercept form. The slope of the line is 3, and the y-intercept is 4.**
forma pendiente-intercepto (pág. 244) Ecuación lineal escrita en la forma $y = mx + b$, donde m es la pendiente y b es el intercepto en y de la gráfica de la ecuación.	**$y = 3x + 4$ está en la forma pendiente-intercepto. La pendiente de la recta es 3, y el intercepto en y es 4.**
solution of an equation in one variable (p. 22) A number that produces a true statement when substituted for the variable in an equation.	**The number 3 is a solution of the equation $8 - 2x = 2$, because $8 - 2(3) = 2$.**
solución de una ecuación con una variable (pág. 22) Número que, al sustituirse por la variable de la ecuación, produce un enunciado verdadero.	**El número 3 es una solución de la ecuación $8 - 2x = 2$ ya que $8 - 2(3) = 2$.**
solution of an equation in two variables (p. 215) An ordered pair that produces a true statement when the coordinates of the ordered pair are substituted for the variables in the equation.	**$(1, -4)$ is a solution of $3x - y = 7$, because $3(1) - (-4) = 7$.**
solución de una ecuación con dos variables (pág. 215) Par ordenado que, al ser sustituidas sus coordenadas por las variables de la ecuación, produce un enunciado verdadero.	**$(1, -4)$ es una solución de $3x - y = 7$ ya que $3(1) - (-4) = 7$.**
solution of an inequality in one variable (p. 22) A number that produces a true statement when substituted for the variable in an inequality.	**The number 3 is a solution of the inequality $5 + 3n \leq 20$, because $5 + 3(3) = 14$ and $14 \leq 20$.**
solución de una desigualdad con una variable (pág. 22) Número que, al sustituirse por la variable de la desigualdad, produce un enunciado verdadero.	**El número 3 es una solución de la desigualdad $5 + 3n \leq 20$ ya que $5 + 3(3) = 14$ y $14 \leq 20$.**
solution of an inequality in two variables x and y (p. 405) An ordered pair (x, y) that produces a true statement when the values of x and y are substituted into the inequality.	**$(-1, 2)$ is a solution of the inequality $x - 3y < 6$ because $-1 - 3(2) = -7$ and $-7 < 6$.**
solución de una desigualdad con las dos variables x e y (pág. 405) Par ordenado (x, y) que, al sustitutirse los valores de x e y en la desigualdad, produce un enunciado verdadero.	**$(-1, 2)$ es una solución de la desigualdad $x - 3y < 6$ ya que $-1 - 3(2) = -7$ y $-7 < 6$.**
solution of a system of linear equations (p. 427) An ordered pair that is a solution of each equation in the system.	**$(3, 2)$ is a solution of the system of linear equations $x + 2y = 7$, $3x - 2y = 5$ because each equation is a true statement when 3 is substituted for x and 2 is substituted for y.**
solución de un sistema de ecuaciones lineales (pág. 427) Par ordenado que es una solución de cada ecuación del sistema.	**$(3, 2)$ es una solución del sistema de ecuaciones lineales $x + 2y = 7$, $3x - 2y = 5$ ya que cada ecuación es un enunciado verdadero cuando x se sustituye por 3 e y se sustituye por 2.**

ENGLISH-SPANISH GLOSSARY

994

solution of a system of linear inequalities (p. 466) An ordered pair that is a solution of each inequality in the system.

(6, −5) is a solution of the system of inequalities

$$x - y > 7$$
$$2x + y < 8$$

because each inequality is a true statement when 6 is substituted for x and −5 is substituted for y.

solución de un sistema de desigualdades lineales (pág. 466) Par ordenado que es una solución de cada desigualdad del sistema.

(6, −5) es una solución del sistema de desigualdades

$$x - y > 7$$
$$2x + y < 8$$

ya que cada desigualdad es un enunciado verdadero cuando x se sustituye por 6 e y se sustituye por −5.

---

square root (p. 110) If $b^2 = a$, then b is a square root of a. The radical symbol $\sqrt{\ }$ represents a nonnegative square root.

The square roots of 9 are 3 and −3, because $3^2 = 9$ and $(-3)^2 = 9$. So, $\sqrt{9} = 3$ and $-\sqrt{9} = -3$.

raíz cuadrada (pág. 110) Si $b^2 = a$, entonces b es una raíz cuadrada de a. El signo radical $\sqrt{\ }$ representa una raíz cuadrada no negativa.

Las raíces cuadradas de 9 son 3 y −3 ya que $3^2 = 9$ y $(-3)^2 = 9$. Así pues, $\sqrt{9} = 3$ y $-\sqrt{9} = -3$.

---

square root function (p. 710) A radical function whose equation contains a square root with the independent variable in the radicand.

$y = 2\sqrt{x + 2}$ and $y = \sqrt{x} + 3$ are square root functions.

función con raíz cuadrada (pág. 710) Función radical representada por una ecuación con una raíz cuadrada en cuyo radicando aparece la variable independiente.

$y = 2\sqrt{x + 2}$ e $y = \sqrt{x} + 3$ son funciones con raíz cuadrada.

---

standard deviation (p. 879) The standard deviation of a numerical data set $x_1, x_2, \ldots, x_n$ is a measure of dispersion denoted by σ and computed as the square root of the variance.

$$\sigma = \sqrt{\frac{(x_1 - \bar{x})^2 + (x_2 - \bar{x})^2 + \ldots + (x_n - \bar{x})^2}{n}}$$

The standard deviation of the data set 3, 9, 13, 23 (with mean = 12) is:

$$\sigma = \sqrt{\frac{(3-12)^2 + (9-12)^2 + (13-12)^2 + (23-12)^2}{4}}$$
$$= \sqrt{53} \approx 7.3$$

desviación típica (pág. 879) La desviación típica de un conjunto de datos numéricos $x_1, x_2, \ldots, x_n$ es una medida de dispersión designada por σ y calculada como raíz cuadrada de la varianza.

$$\sigma = \sqrt{\frac{(x_1 - \bar{x})^2 + (x_2 - \bar{x})^2 + \ldots + (x_n - \bar{x})^2}{n}}$$

La desviación típica del conjunto de datos 3, 9, 13, 23 (con media = 12) es:

$$\sigma = \sqrt{\frac{(3-12)^2 + (9-12)^2 + (13-12)^2 + (23-12)^2}{4}}$$
$$= \sqrt{53} \approx 7.3$$

---

standard form of a linear equation (p. 216) $Ax + By = C$, where A, B, and C are real numbers and A and B are not both zero.

The linear equation $y = 2x - 3$ can be written in standard form as $2x - y = 3$.

forma general de una ecuación lineal (pág. 216) $Ax + By = C$, donde A, B y C son números reales, y A y B no son ambos cero.

La ecuación lineal $y = 2x - 3$ puede escribirse en la forma general como $2x - y = 3$.

standard form of a quadratic equation (p. 643) A quadratic equation in the form $ax^2 + bx + c = 0$ where $a \neq 0$. **forma general de una ecuación cuadrática** (pág. 643) Ecuación cuadrática de la forma $ax^2 + bx + c = 0$, donde $a \neq 0$.	**The quadratic equation $x^2 - 2x - 3 = 0$ is in standard form.** **La ecuación cuadrática $x^2 - 2x - 3 = 0$ está en la forma general.**
standard form of a quadratic function (p. 628) A quadratic function in the form $y = ax^2 + bx + c$ where $a \neq 0$. **forma general de una función cuadrática** (pág. 628) Función cuadrática de la forma $y = ax^2 + bx + c$, donde $a \neq 0$.	**The quadratic function $y = 2x^2 + 5x - 3$ is in standard form.** **La función cuadrática $y = 2x^2 + 5x - 3$ está en la forma general.**
stem-and-leaf plot (p. 881) A data display that organizes data based on their digits. **tabla arborescente** (pág. 881) Presentación de datos que organiza los datos basándose en sus dígitos.	Stem Raíces | Leaves Hojas 0 | 8 9 1 | 0 2 3 4 5 5 5 9 2 | 1 1 5 9 Key: Clave: 1 | 9 = \$19
stratified random sample (p. 871) A sample in which a population is divided into distinct groups, and members are selected at random from each group. **muestra aleatoria estratificada** (pág. 871) Muestra en la que la población está dividida en grupos diferenciados, y los miembros de cada grupo se seleccionan al azar.	**You can select a stratified random sample of a school's student population by having a computer randomly choose 25 students from each grade level.** **Para seleccionar una muestra aleatoria estratificada de la población de estudiantes de una escuela, puedes usar la computadora para elegir al azar a 25 estudiantes de cada grado.**
survey (p. 871) A study of one or more characteristics of a group. **encuesta** (pág. 871) Estudio de una o más características de un grupo.	**A magazine invites its readers to mail in answers to a questionnaire rating the magazine.** **Una revista invita a sus lectores a enviar por correo las respuestas a un cuestionario sobre la calidad de la revista.**
system of linear equations (p. 427) Two or more linear equations in the same variables; also called a *linear system*. **sistema de ecuaciones lineales** (pág. 427) Dos o más ecuaciones lineales con las mismas variables; llamado también *sistema lineal*.	**The equations below form a system of linear equations:** $x + 2y = 7$ $3x - 2y = 5$ **Las siguientes ecuaciones forman un sistema de ecuaciones lineales:** $x + 2y = 7$ $3x - 2y = 5$

ENGLISH-SPANISH GLOSSARY

system of linear inequalities in two variables (p. 466) Two or more linear inequalities in the same variables; also called a *system of inequalities.*	The inequalities below form a system of linear inequalities in two variables: $x - y > 7$ $2x + y < 8$
sistema de desigualdades lineales con dos variables (pág. 466) Dos o más desigualdades lineales con las mismas variables; llamado también *sistema de desigualdades.*	Las siguientes desigualdades forman un sistema de desigualdades lineales con dos variables: $x - y > 7$ $2x + y < 8$
systematic sample (p. 871) A sample in which a rule is used to select members of the population.	You can select a systematic sample of a school's student population by choosing every tenth student on an alphabetical list of all students at the school.
muestra sistemática (pág. 871) Muestra en la que se usa una regla para seleccionar a los miembros de la población.	Para seleccionar una muestra sistemática de la población de estudiantes de una escuela, puedes elegir a cada décimo estudiante de una lista ordenada alfabéticamente de todos los estudiantes de la escuela.

T

terms of an expression (p. 97) The parts of an expression that are added together.	The terms of the expression $3x + (-4) + (-6x) + 2$ are $3x$, -4, $-6x$, and 2.
términos de una expresión (pág. 97) Las partes de una expresión que se suman.	Los términos de la expresión $3x + (-4) + (-6x) + 2$ son $3x$, -4, $-6x$ y 2.
theoretical probability (p. 844) When all outcomes are equally likely, the theoretical probability of an event is the ratio of the number of favorable outcomes to the total number of possible outcomes. The probability of event *A* is written as *P*(*A*).	A bag of 20 marbles contains 8 red marbles. The theoretical probability of randomly choosing a red marble from the bag is $\frac{8}{20} = \frac{2}{5}$, 40%, or 0.4.
probabilidad teórica (pág. 844) Cuando todos los casos son igualmente posibles, la probabilidad teórica de un suceso es la razón entre el número de casos favorables y el número total de casos posibles. La probabilidad del suceso *A* se escribe *P*(*A*).	Una bolsa de 20 canicas contiene 8 canicas rojas. La probabilidad teórica de sacar al azar una canica roja de la bolsa es $\frac{8}{20} = \frac{2}{5}$, 40% ó 0.4.
transformation (p. 213) For a given set of points, a transformation produces an image by applying a rule to the coordinates of the points.	Translations, vertical stretches, vertical shrinks, and reflections are transformations.
transformación (pág. 213) Para un conjunto dado de puntos, una transformación produce una imagen al aplicar una regla a las coordenadas de los puntos.	Las traslaciones, las expansiones verticales, las contracciones verticales y las reflexiones son transformaciones.

translation (p. 213) A translation moves every point in a figure the same distance in the same direction.

traslación (pág. 213) Una traslación desplaza cada punto de una figura la misma distancia en la misma dirección.

$\triangle ABC$ is translated up 2 units.

$\triangle ABC$ es trasladada 2 unidades hacia arriba.

---

trinomial (p. 555) A polynomial with three terms.

trinomio (pág. 555) Polinomio con tres términos.

$2x^2 + x - 5$ is a trinomial.

$2x^2 + x - 5$ es un trinomio.

U

union (p. 71) The union of two sets A and B is the set of all elements in *either* A or B. The union of A and B is written as $A \cup B$.

unión (pág. 71) La unión de dos conjuntos A y B es el conjunto de todos los elementos en A *o* B. La unión de A y B se escribe $A \cup B$.

$A \cup B = \{2, 3, 4, 5, 6, 7, 8\}$

---

unit rate (p. 17) A rate in which the denominator of the fraction is 1 unit.

relación unitaria (pág. 17) Relación en la que el denominador de la fracción es 1 unidad.

$\frac{55 \text{ miles}}{1 \text{ hour}}$, or 55 mi/h, is a unit rate.

$\frac{55 \text{ millas}}{1 \text{ hora}}$, ó 55 mi/h, es una relación unitaria.

---

universal set (p. 71) The set of all elements under consideration, written as U.

conjunto universal (pág. 71) El conjunto de todos los elementos en cuestión, escrito U.

If the universal set is the set of positive integers, then $U = \{1, 2, 3, \ldots\}$.

Si el conjunto universal es el conjunto de los números enteros positivos, entonces $U = \{1, 2, 3, \ldots\}$.

---

upper quartile (p. 887) The median of the upper half of an ordered data set.

The upper quartile of the data set below is 23.

median ↓ (17), upper quartile ↓ (23)

8 10 14 17 20 23 50

cuartil superior (pág. 887) La mediana de la mitad superior de un conjunto de datos ordenados.

El cuartil superior del siguiente conjunto de datos es 23.

mediana ↓ (17), cuartil superior ↓ (23)

8 10 14 17 20 23 50

998

variable (p. 2) A letter that is used to represent one or more numbers. **variable** (pág. 2) Letra que sirve para representar uno o más números.	**In the expressions $5n$, $n + 1$, and $8 - n$, the letter n is the variable.** **En las expresiones $5n$, $n + 1$ y $8 - n$, la letra n es la variable.**
variance (p. 879) The variance of a numerical data set $x_1, x_2, \ldots, x_n$ is a measure of dispersion denoted by σ^2 and given by: $\sigma^2 = \frac{(x_1 - \bar{x})^2 + (x_2 - \bar{x})^2 + \ldots + (x_n - \bar{x})^2}{n}$ **varianza** (pág. 879) La varianza de un conjunto de datos numéricos $x_1, x_2, \ldots, x_n$ es una medida de dispersión designada por σ^2 y dada por: $\sigma^2 = \frac{(x_1 - \bar{x})^2 + (x_2 - \bar{x})^2 + \ldots + (x_n - \bar{x})^2}{n}$	**The variance of the data set 3, 9, 13, 23 (with mean = 12) is:** $\sigma^2 = \frac{(3 - 12)^2 + (9 - 12)^2 + (13 - 12)^2 + (23 - 12)^2}{4}$ $= 53$ **La varianza del conjunto de datos 3, 9, 13, 23 (con media = 12) es:** $\sigma^2 = \frac{(3 - 12)^2 + (9 - 12)^2 + (13 - 12)^2 + (23 - 12)^2}{4}$ $= 53$
verbal model (p. 16) A verbal model describes a real-world situation using words as labels and using math symbols to relate the words. **modelo verbal** (pág. 16) Un modelo verbal describe una situación de la vida real mediante palabras que la exponen y símbolos matemáticos que relacionan esas palabras.	**A verbal model and algebraic expression for dividing a dollars in a tip jar among 6 people:** **Un modelo verbal y una expresión algebraica utilizados para dividir entre 6 personas a dólares del recipiente de las propinas:** Amount in jar / Cantidad del recipiente ÷ Number of people / Número de personas a ÷ 6
vertex form of a quadratic function (p. 669) A quadratic function in the form $y = a(x - h)^2 + k$ where $a \neq 0$. The vertex of the graph of the function is (h, k). **forma de vértice de una función cuadrática** (pág. 669) Función cuadrática de la forma $y = a(x - h)^2 + k$, donde $a \neq 0$. El vértice de la gráfica de la función es (h, k).	**The quadratic function $y = -2(x + 1)^2 - 5$ is in vertex form. The vertex of the graph of the function is $(-1, -5)$.** **La función cuadrática $y = -2(x + 1)^2 - 5$ está en la forma de vértice. El vértice de la gráfica de la función es $(-1, -5)$.**

ENGLISH-SPANISH GLOSSARY

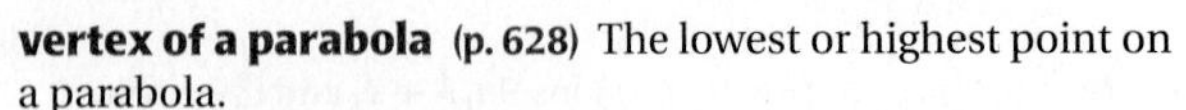

vertex of a parabola (p. 628) The lowest or highest point on a parabola.

vértice de una parábola (pág. 628) El punto más bajo o más alto de la parábola.

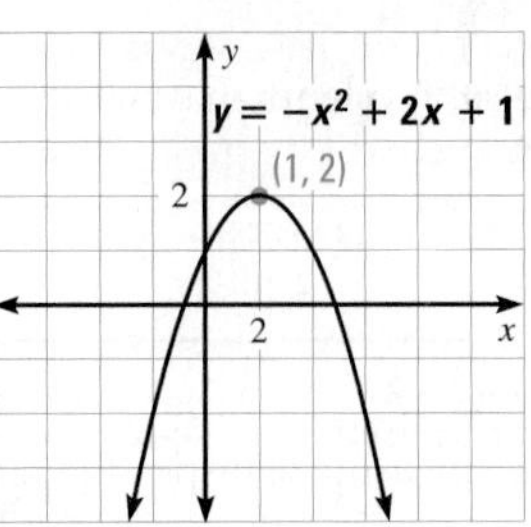

The vertex of the graph of $y = -x^2 + 2x + 1$ is the point (1, 2).

El vértice de la gráfica de $y = -x^2 + 2x + 1$ es el punto (1, 2).

vertical motion model (p. 577) A model for the height of an object that is propelled into the air but has no power to keep itself in the air.

The vertical motion model for an object thrown upward with an initial vertical velocity of 20 feet per second from an initial height of 8 feet is $h = -16t^2 + 20t + 8$ where h is the height (in feet) of the object t seconds after it is thrown.

modelo de movimiento vertical (pág. 577) Modelo para representar la altura de un objeto que es lanzado hacia arriba pero que no tiene potencia para mantenerse en el aire.

El modelo de movimiento vertical de un objeto lanzado hacia arriba con una velocidad vertical inicial de 20 pies por segundo desde una altura inicial de 8 pies es $h = -16t^2 + 20t + 8$, donde h es la altura (en pies) del objeto t segundos después del lanzamiento.

vertical shrink (p. 213) A vertical shrink moves every point in a figure toward the x-axis, while points on the x-axis remain fixed.

contracción vertical (pág. 213) La contracción vertical desplaza cada punto de una figura en dirección del eje de x, mientras los puntos del eje de x permanecen fijos.

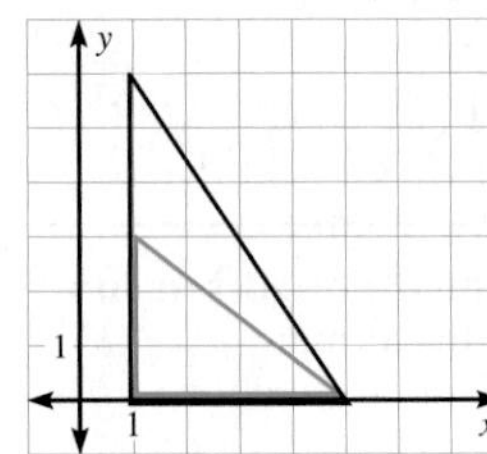

The black triangle is shrunk vertically to the green triangle.

El triángulo negro se contrae verticalmente hacia el triángulo verde.

vertical stretch (p. 213) A vertical stretch moves every point in a figure away from the x-axis, while points on the x-axis remain fixed.

expansión vertical (pág. 213) La expansión vertical desplaza cada punto de una figura alejándose del eje de x, mientras los puntos del eje de x permanecen fijos.

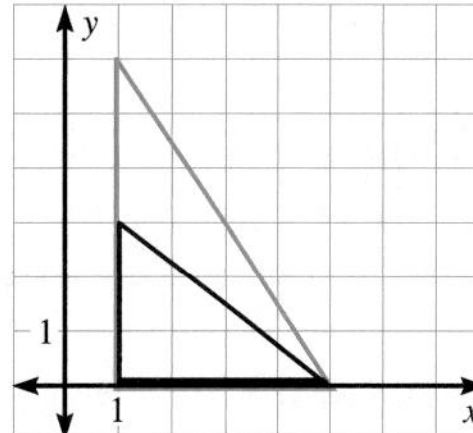

The black triangle is stretched vertically to the green triangle.

El triángulo negro se expande verticalmente hacia el triángulo verde.

whole numbers (p. 64) The numbers 0, 1, 2, 3, ...

0, 8, and 106 are whole numbers.
−1 and 0.6 are *not* whole numbers.

números naturales (pág. 64) Los números 0, 1, 2, 3, ...

0, 8 y 106 son números naturales.
−1 y 0.6 *no* son números naturales.

x-intercept (p. 225) The x-coordinate of a point where a graph crosses the x-axis.

intercepto en x (pág. 225) La coordenada x de un punto donde la gráfica corta al eje de x.

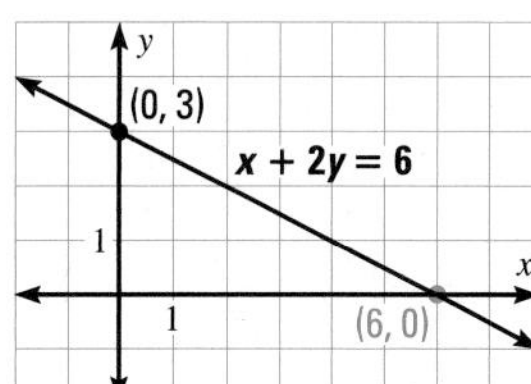

The x-intercept is 6.

El intercepto en x es 6.

y-intercept (p. 225) The y-coordinate of a point where a graph crosses the y-axis.

intercepto en y (pág. 225) La coordenada y de un punto donde la gráfica corta al eje de y.

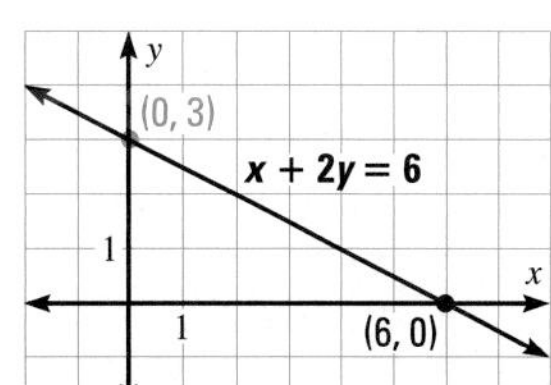

The y-intercept is 3.

El intercepto en y es 3.

ENGLISH-SPANISH GLOSSARY

Z

zero exponent (p. 503) If $a \neq 0$, then $a^0 = 1$. **exponente cero** (pág. 503) Si $a \neq 0$, entonces $a^0 = 1$.	$(-7)^0 = 1$
zero of a function (p. 337) An x-value for which $f(x) = 0$ (or $y = 0$). **cero de una función** (pág. 337) Un valor x para el que $f(x) = 0$ (o $y = 0$).	The zero of $f(x) = 2x - 4$ is 2 because $f(2) = 0$. El cero de $f(x) = 2x - 4$ es 2 ya que $f(2) = 0$.

Credits

Photography

Cover © Amy and Chuck Wiley/Wales/Index Stock Imagery/ Photolibrary.com; **Authors** *top* Meridian Creative Group; *top center* Robert C. Jenks, Jenks Studio; *bottom center* McDougal Littell; *bottom* Jerry Head Jr.; **Contents: Chapter 1** © J.D. Dallet/ A.G.E. Fotostock; **Chapter 2** © Natphotos/Digital Vision/Getty Images; **Chapter 3** © A. Witte/C. Mahaney/Getty Images; **Chapter 4** © Rick Havner/AP/Wide World Photos; **Chapter 5** © Joseph Sohm/Visions of America; **Chapter 6** © Morey Milbradt/ Brand X Pictures/Jupiterimages/Getty Images; **Chapter 7** © Kerrick James/Getty Images; **Chapter 8** JPL/NASA; **Chapter 9** © John Burcham/Getty Images; **Chapter 10** © Donald Miralle/ Getty Images; **Chapter 11** © Hisham F. Ibrahim/Getty Images; **Chapter 12** © Joseph Sohm, ChromoSohm Media Inc.; **Chapter 13** © Tom Carter/PhotoEdit; **Interior: 1** © Geoffrey Clifford/Getty Images; **2** © John C. Russell/Photonica/Getty Images; **4** McDougal Littell; **6** © Scott S. Warren/Aurora Photos; **8** © Royalty-Free/Comstock Images; **10** © David Young-Wolff/ PhotoEdit; **12** © Sue Ogrocki/AP/ Wide World Photos; **15** *printer* © PhotoDisc/Getty Images; **15** *photo* © Royalty-Free/Stockbyte; **17** © Steve Dunwell/Index Stock Imagery; **19** © Patrick Ward/ Corbis; **21** © Tommy Baynard; **23** © Seb Rogers/Alamy; **24** © Chris Collins/Corbis; **25** © Tommy Baynard; **27** © Don Smetzer/ Getty Images; **28** © Michael Stevens/Fog Stock; **32** © Scott Warren/Aurora Photos; **35** © Victoria Smith/HMH; **37** © Aneal Vohra/Index Stock Imagery; **42** McDougal Littell; **43** Lawrence Migdale/PIX/McDougal Littell; **47** © Marc Serota/Reuters/ Corbis; **51** © Derek Payne/Alamy; **62–63** © Altrendo/Getty Images; **64** © Evan Vucci/AP/Wide World Photos; **70** © John Chumack/Photo Researchers, Inc.; **74** © Brian Spurlock/ SportsChrome; **76** © Bob Krist/Corbis; **78** *center right* © LLC, FogStock/Index Stock Imagery; **80** © Stephen Alvarez/National Geographic Image Collection; **83** © Myrleen Ferguson Cate/ PhotoEdit; **85** © Ron Chapple/Getty Images; **86** © Gregory Bull/ AP/Wide World Photos; **88** © Natphoto/Getty Images; **90** © Peter Essick/Aurora Photos; **92** © Philip Coblentz/Getty Images; **96** © PhotoDisc/PunchStock; **98** © Howard Kingsnorth/cultura/ Corbis; **103** © Jonathan Ferrey/Getty Images; **104** © Duncan Adams/AP/Wide World Photos; **107** Photo courtesy of Mehgan Heaney-Grier, Freedive Champion & Jim Edds, photographer; **108** *both* USGS; **110** © Royalty-free/Corbis; **115** Photo from the New York Hall of Science/www.minotaurmazes.com; **130** *top* © Gary Bell/Oceanwide Images; **131** *center right* © Gary Bell/Getty Images; **134** © Barros & Barros/Getty Images; **137** © Anja Niedringhaus/AP/Wide World Photos; **139** *top right* Jay Penni Photography/McDougal Littell; **139** *bottom right* © Gary Bell/ Oceanwide Images ; **141** © Image Source/Getty Images; **143** © Royalty-Free/Corbis; **145** © M. Spencer Green/AP/Wide World Photos; **148** © Michael Newman/PhotoEdit; **150** © Jeff Foott/ PictureQuest; **154** © Mark Lennihan/AP/Wide World Photos; **161** © Moodboard/Corbis; **162** © Reuters/Corbis; **164** © Lowell Georgia/Corbis; **166** © Age Fotostock/Photolibrary; **168** © Michael S. Yamashita/Corbis; **176** © Reuters/Corbis; **178** © FoodCollection/Index Stock Imagery; **180** © Pat & Chuck Blackley/Alamy; **184** © Tony Garcia/SuperStock; **189** © Royalty-Free/Corbis; **204–205** © Rommel/Masterfile; **206** © Window Observational Research Facility/NASA; **208** © David J. & Janice L. Frent Collection/Corbis; **215** U.S. Navy photo; **220** © Bill Greene Globe Staff/The Boston Globe/Merlin-Net, Inc.; **225** © Alexis Rosenfeld/Photo Researchers, Inc.; **228** © Alexis Rosenfeld/ Photo Researchers, Inc.; **233** © Jim Cooper/AP/Wide World Photos; **234** *all* McDougal Littell; **235** © Kevin Fleming/Corbis; **237** *café* © Paul Edmondson/Getty Images; **237** (soup) © Judd Pilossof Photography; **241** © Kevin Fleming/Corbis; **244** © Getty Images/PhotoDisc; **245** © Kevin P. Casey/Corbis; **248** © Robert Laberge/Getty Images; **253** © Getty Images/PhotoDisc; **255** © The North Platte Telegraph, Kristina Jergensen/AP/Wide World Photos; **259** © Don Emmert/Staff/Getty Images; **262** © William Campbell/AP/Wide World Photos; **263** © altrendo nature/Getty Images; **267** © Scott Markewitz/Getty Images; **269** © Nicole Hill/ Rubberball/Corbis; **280–281** © Will & Deni McIntyre/Corbis; **282** Jay Penni Photography/McDougal Littell; **283** © Jim Cummins/Getty Images; **285** © Comstock Images/Alamy; **288** © Yann Arthus-Bertrand/Corbis; **292** © Tony Ashby/AFP/Getty Images; **295** © Lester Lefkowitz/Corbis; **302** © Ken Biggs/Getty Images; **307** © Royalty-Free/Corbis; **311** © The Photo Library Wales/Alamy; **313** © BananaStock/Alamy; **317** © Tom Stewart/ Corbis; **319** © Phillip Colla/www.OceanLight.com; **325** © Bob & Suzanne Clemenz; **327** © Tim Thompson/Corbis; **335** *both* © Nick Ut/AP/Wide World Photos; **337** © Cathrine Wessel/Corbis; **339** *bottom right* © Kevin Gilbert/Getty Images; **341** © Getty Images/PhotoDisc; **343** © David Middleton/Photo Researchers, Inc.; **354–355** © Ryan McVay/PhotoDisc/Getty Images; **356** © Royalty-Free/Corbis; **358** © Ralf-Finn Hestoft/Corbis; **360** © David Madison/Getty Images; **363** © Alan Becker/Getty Images; **365** © John Powell Photographer/Alamy; **368** © William Albert Allard/National Geographic Image Collection; **369** © Roy Toft/ Getty Images ; **371** © Eric Risberg/AP/Wide World Photos; **373** © Melanie Acevedo/Botanica/Jupiter Images; **375** © Eric Risberg/ AP/Wide World Photos; **380** Courtesy of www.apcamcar.com; **383** DLR/NASA; **386** Courtesy of Erik Heyl. U.S. Naval Historical Photograph; **389** © Photodisc/Getty Images; **390** © AP/Wide World Photos; **392** © Darren Sweet/PictureChasers.com; **394** © Patrik Giardino/Corbis; **398** © Jacqueline Malonson/Jax Photography; **402** © Michael Newman/PhotoEdit; **403** © D. Robert & Lorri Franz/Corbis; **405** © Greig Cranna/Index Stock Imagery; **408** © Keith Woods/Getty Images; **410** © Paul J. Sutton/ Duomo/Corbis; **413** © Thomas Hallstein/Outsight Photography; **424–425** © Joe Michl/Workbook Stock/Getty Images; **427** © View Stock/Alamy; **429** © Jose Carillo/PhotoEdit; **432** McDougal Littell; **433** *top left* © Royalty-Free/Corbis; **433** *top center* Elliptical Trainer photo courtesy of NordicTrack.com; **433** *top right* © Royalty-Free/Corbis; **435** © Gary Pearl/StockShot/Alamy; **437** Stockbyte/Getty Images; **444** © David Young-Wolff/ PhotoEdit; **449** © Michael Schmitt; **450** © Nick Rowe/PhotoDisc/ Getty Images; **451** © Oleg Boldyrev/Alamy; **456** © Ian O'Leary/ Dorling Kindersley/Getty Images; **458** © Dennis MacDonald/ PhotoEdit; **459** © Bobby Model/Getty Images; **466** © Dennis MacDonald/PhotoEdit; **471** © Comstock Images; **473** © Jeff Greenberg/A.G.E. Fotostock; **486–487** © Ron Kimball/Ron Kimball Stock; **489** © Digital Vision/Getty Images; **491** © Michael Busselle/Corbis; **493** © Royalty-Free/Getty Images; **495** © Arctic-Images/Corbis; **498** © Courtesy of NASA; **500** Akira Fujii/ESA; **503** © Robin Tinay Sallie/Akron Beacon Journal/AP/Wide World Photos; **505** *both* © Ted Kinsman/Photo Researchers, Inc.; **507** *center left* © Carlyn Iverson/Photo Researchers, Inc.; **507** *center right* © mediacolor's/Alamy; **512** © Brand X Pictures/ Getty Images; **516** © David Frazier/Corbis; **518** SOHO/NASA; **520** © Ron Kimball/Ron Kimball Stock; **522** © Michael Kelley/ Getty Images; **530** McDougal Littell; **531** © Cathrine Wessel/ Corbis; **534** © Pat O'Hara/Corbis; **537** *top* Scott Johnson/Indiana DNR/USFWS; **537** *bottom* © PhotoDisc/Getty Images; **538** © Jon Riley/Getty Images; **541** © PhotoDisc/Getty Images; **552–553** © Martin Harvey/Alamy; **554** © John Burcham/Getty Images; **556** © Rick Friedman/Corbis; **558** © Digital Vision/Corbis; **559** © Robert Galbraith/Reuters/Corbis; **562** © Neale Haynes/ ImageState/Alamy; **567** *photo* © PhotoDisc/Getty Images;

CREDITS

567 *frame* © PhotoSpin; **568** © Thinkstock/Getty Images; **569** © Alan Carey/Photo Researchers, Inc.; **571** *top left* © Ulrike Schanz/Animals Animals; **571** *top right* © Artville/Getty Images; **571** *center right* © Yann Arthus-Bertrand/Corbis; **573** *top* © Royalty-Free/Corbis; **573** *football* © PhotoDisc/Getty Images; **573** *grass* © PowerPhotos/PhotoSpin; **574** © Royalty-Free/Corbis; **575** © Aase Bjerner; **577** © George Holton/Photo Researchers, Inc.; **579** © James H. Robinson/Photo Researchers, Inc.; **583** © Richard Berenholtz/Corbis; **588** © Richard Berenholtz/Corbis; **593** © Brand X Pictures/Jupiter Images; **595** © Mike Powell/Getty Images; **598** *bottom right* © Martin Harvey/Natural History Photographic Agency; **598** *top left* © Richard Hutchings/Photo Researchers, Inc.; **598** *top center* © Kevin Peterson/Getty Images; **598** *top right* © Rubberball Productions/Getty Images; **600** © Scott Camazine/Alamy; **602** © HIRB/Index Stock Imagery; **606** © Lawrence M. Sawyer/Getty Images; **614** © Brian Drake/SportsChrome; **626–627** © Bill Stevenson/Alamy; **628** © Digital Vision/Getty Images; **631** © David Nunuk/Photo Researchers, Inc.; **635** © Dave G. Houser/Corbis; **637** © Dwight Cendrowski; **639** Stephen Finn/Alamy; **643** *top right* © Jeff Greenberg/PhotoEdit; **648** © Rhoda Peacher/R Photographs; **652** *top right* © Rhoda Peacher/R Photographs; **658** © Kim Karpeles; **661** © Amwell/Getty Images; **663** *center* © Jonathan Nourok/PhotoEdit; **671** © Adam Woolfitt/Corbis; **678** © Jeff Gross/Getty Images; **682** © Davis Barber/PhotoEdit; **684** © David A. Northcott/Corbis ; **687** © John Kelly/Getty Images; **689** © David A. Northcott/Corbis; **690** © Davies & Starr/Getty Images; **708–709** © Robert Holland/Getty Images; **710** © Michael Newman/PhotoEdit; **715** © Vince Streano/Corbis; **716** *top right* © Tim Zurowski/Corbis; **716** *top left* © Bill Gozansky/Alamy; **719** © John Elk/Elk Photography; **726** © Tony Freeman/PhotoEdit; **729** © PhotoDisc/Getty Images; **731** © Iconica/Photonica/Getty Images; **733** Jacques Descloitres/MODIS Rapid Response Team, NASA/GSFC; *right* **735** © StockShot/Alamy; **735** *left* © Philip Gould/Corbis; **737** © Joseph Pobereskin/Getty Images; **744** © Zig Urbanski/Alamy; **762–763** © Spike Walker/Stone/Getty Images; **765** *top right* © Dwight Cendrowski; **768** © Tony Freeman/PhotoEdit; **770** © Rhoda Peacher/R Photographs; **771** *both* © GK Hart/Vikki Hart/Getty Images; **772** *top right* © Lee Snider/Corbis; **775** © Matt York, Staff/AP/Wide World Photos; **778** © Richard Cummins/Corbis; **781** © Phillip Colla/www.OceanLight.com; **784** © Ace Stock Limited/Alamy; **787** © Michael Newman/PhotoEdit; **790** © Rubberball Productions/Getty Images; **791** © Scenics & Science/Alamy; **794** © Allana Wesley White/Corbis; **797** © Brand X Pictures/Getty Images; **799** © Zigy Kaluzny/Getty Images; **800** © Tom Stewart/Corbis; **802** © Adrees A. Latif/Reuters/Corbis; **807** © David Butow/Corbis; **808** © Ron Kuntz/Bettmann/Corbis; **809** © Bob Daemmrich/PhotoEdit; **812** © Michael Mahovlich/Masterfile; **820** © David Stoecklein/Corbis; **824** © Paul J. Sutton/Duomo/Corbis; **825** © Jim West/Jim West Photography; **840–841** © Comstock Production Department/Alamy; **840** *ball* © PhotoDisc/Getty Images; **843** © Michelle D. Bridwell/PhotoEdit; **847** © Royalty-Free/Corbis; **848** © Matt Brown/NewSport/Corbis; **851** © Mary Kate Denny/PhotoEdit; **856** © Don Smetzer/Getty Images; **857** *both* © Stockbyte/Royalty-Free; **861** © Tim Davis/Corbis; **870** © Dante Fenolio/Photo Researchers, Inc.; **871** © Chuck Eckert/Alamy; **872** © Tom Carter/PhotoEdit; **874** © David Young-Wolff/PhotoEdit; **875** © Adonica Sweet/PictureChasers.com; **876** © Alan Thornton/Getty Images; **878** © Leslie Parr/Getty Images; **881** © Paul Conklin/PhotoEdit; **882** © 2003 Robyn Beck/Staff/AFP/Getty; **885** © Bettmann/Corbis; **887** DLR/NASA; **894** © Mark Dadswell/Staff/Getty Images.

Illustration and Map

Argosy **1, 63, 131, 205, 281, 355, 425, 487, 553, 627, 631, 633, 709, 763, 841**; Steve Cowden **32, 40** *center*, **240, 258, 308, 323** *center right*, **440** *bottom center*, **446, 465, 615, 646, 654, 668, 675, 715, 733, 750, 752** *bottom left*, **781, 855**; Stephen Durke **634, 648** *center*, **658, 741** *both*, **741**; John Francis **815**; Patrick Gnan/Deborah Wolfe, Ltd. **228, 249, 323** *bottom right*, **468, 526, 567, 588** *both*, **588, 591, 742, 865**; Sharon and Joel Harris **514**; Mark Heine/Deborah Wolfe **28**; Steve McEntee **640, 683, 702**; Karen Minot **890**; Laurie O'Keefe **866**; Tony Randazzo **508, 604, 819**; Mark Schroeder **690**; Dan Stuckenschneider **20, 116, 145, 146, 152** *center*, **221, 231** *center*, **315, 361, 373, 381, 385, 411, 471, 494, 525, 564, 609, 612** *top right*, **612** *bottom right*, **612, 648** *bottom*, **667, 680, 725, 772** *both*, **772, 829, 862**; Matt Zang/American Artists **511, 657, 722, 749, 771, 891.**

Worked-Out Solutions

This section of the book provides step-by-step solutions to exercises with circled exercise numbers. These solutions provide models that can help guide your work with the homework exercises.

The separate **Selected Answers** section follows this section. It provides numerous answers that you can use to check your own answers.

Chapter 1

Lesson 1.1 (pp. 5–7)

19. three tenths to the fourth power; $(0.3)^4 = 0.3 \cdot 0.3 \cdot 0.3 \cdot 0.3$

35. $\left(\frac{3}{5}\right)^3 = \frac{3}{5} \cdot \frac{3}{5} \cdot \frac{3}{5} = \frac{27}{125}$

51. a. Total length $= 3.5 + 5.5 + 3 = 12$

The total length is 12 inches.

b. Evaluate $12f$ for $f = 12$: $12(12) = 144$

The area of water surface needed is 144 square inches.

Lesson 1.2 (pp. 10–12)

16. $\frac{1}{6}(6 + 18) - 2^2 = \frac{1}{6}(24) - 2^2$

$= \frac{1}{6}(24) - 4$

$= 4 - 4 = 0$

35. a. Total cost $= 3 \cdot 0.99 + 2 \cdot 9.95$

$= 2.97 + 19.90 = 22.87$

The total cost is \$22.87.

b. Amount of money left $= 25 - 22.87 = 2.13$

The amount you have left is \$2.13.

Lesson 1.3 (pp. 18–20)

11. 7 less than twice a number k

Less than is subtraction after the next term, and twice a number is two times a number. The expression is $2k - 7$.

21. 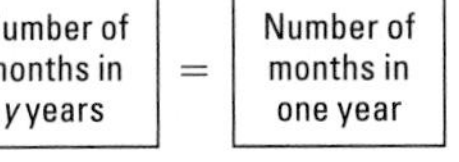

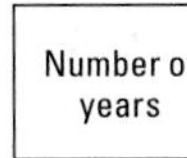

$\cdot$ Number of years

$= 12y$

The number of months is $12y$.

33. a. 48 ounce container:

$\frac{\$2.64}{48 \text{ ounces}} = \frac{\$2.64 \div 48}{48 \text{ ounces} \div 48} = \frac{\$.055}{1 \text{ ounce}}$

The unit rate is \$.055 per ounce.

64 ounce container:

$\frac{\$3.84}{64 \text{ ounces}} = \frac{\$3.84 \div 64}{64 \text{ ounces} \div 64} = \frac{\$.06}{1 \text{ ounce}}$

The unit rate is \$.06 per ounce.

b. Since \$.055 is less than \$.06, the 48 ounce container costs less per ounce.

c. Write a verbal model and an expression. Let n be the number of ounces.

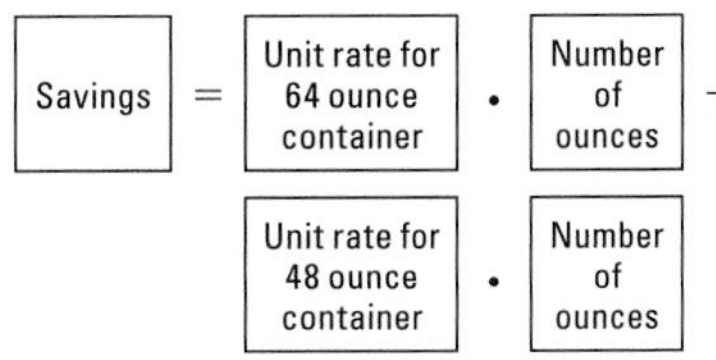

$= 0.06n - 0.055n$

Evaluate the expression when $n = 192$.

$0.06(192) - 0.055(192) = 0.96$

The amount of money you save is \$.96.

Lesson 1.4 (pp. 24–26)

7. 5 more than a number t is written as $t + 5$.

The product of 9 and the quantity 5 more than a number t is written as $9(t + 5)$.

The product of 9 and the quantity 5 more than a number t is less than 6 is written as $9(t + 5) < 6$.

WORKED-OUT SOLUTIONS

41. Write a verbal model. Then write an equation. Let w be the winning team's time.

U.S. team's time	$-$	Winning team's time	$=$	Difference in time

$173 - w = 6$

Use mental math to solve the equation. Think: 173 less what number is 6?

Because $173 - 167 = 6$, the solution is 167 hours.

Lesson 1.5 (pp. 31–33)

5. You know that the temperature in Rome, Italy, is 30°C, and the temperature in Dallas, Texas, is 83°F.

You want to find out which temperature is higher.

17. Step 1: You know the total weight of your backpack and its contents is $13\frac{3}{8}$ pounds. The total weight you want to carry is no more than 15 pounds. The weight of each bottle of water is $\frac{3}{4}$ pound. You want to find out how many extra bottles of water you can add to your backpack. First find the additional weight you can add to your backpack.

Step 2: Write a verbal model that represents what you want to find out. Then write an equation and solve it.

Step 3: Let w be the additional weight (in pounds) you can add to your backpack.

Desired weight of backpack	$-$	Current weight of backpack	$=$	Additional weight possible

$$15 - 13\frac{3}{8} = w$$

$$1\frac{5}{8} = w$$

You can carry an additional $1\frac{5}{8}$ pounds, and each bottle weighs $\frac{3}{4}$ pound.

$$1\frac{5}{8} \div \frac{3}{4} = \frac{13}{8} \times \frac{4}{3} = \frac{52}{24} = 2\frac{1}{6}$$

Since you cannot carry a fraction of a bottle, round down to 2 bottles.

Step 4: You know that 2 is a solution; check to see if 3 could be a solution. The additional bottle of water weighs $\frac{3}{4}$ pound. Since $14\frac{7}{8}$ pounds is only $\frac{1}{8}$ pound less than the maximum of 15 pounds, and $\frac{3}{4} > \frac{1}{8}$, adding another bottle weighing $\frac{3}{4}$ pound would make the total weight more than 15 pounds. Therefore, the number of extra bottles of water you can add to your backpack is 2 bottles.

Lesson 1.6 (pp. 38–40)

7. The pairing is not a function because the input $\frac{3}{4}$ is paired with two outputs, 3 and 5.

23. You have 10 quarters that you can use for a parking meter.

a. Each time you put 1 quarter in the meter, you have 1 less quarter, so the number of quarters left is a function of the number of quarters used.

b. Let y represent the number of quarters you have left.

Number of quarters you have left	$=$	Total number of quarters	$-$	Number of quarters you have used so far

$y = 10 - x$

The domain of the function is: 0, 1, 2, 3, 4, 5, 6, 7, 8, 9, and 10.

c. Make a table of inputs, x, and use $y = 10 - x$ to find the corresponding outputs.

Input, x	0	1	2	3	4	5
Output, y	10	9	8	7	6	5

Input, x	6	7	8	9	10
Output, y	4	3	2	1	0

The range of the function is: 0, 1, 2, 3, 4, 5, 6, 7, 8, 9, and 10.

Lesson 1.7 (pp. 46–48)

3. Make an input-output table using the given domain values.

x	0	1	2	3	4	5
y	3	4	5	6	7	8

Plot a point for each ordered pair (x, y).

17. Number of voters v as a function of time t in years since 1984.

Years since 1984	Voters	Voters (millions)
0	92,652,680	93
4	91,594,693	92
8	104,405,155	104
12	96,456,345	96
16	105,586,274	106

The t-values range from 0 to 16, so label the t-axis from 0 to 18 in increments of 2 units. The v-values (in millions) range from 93 to 106, so label the v-axis from 90 to 114 in increments of 4 units.

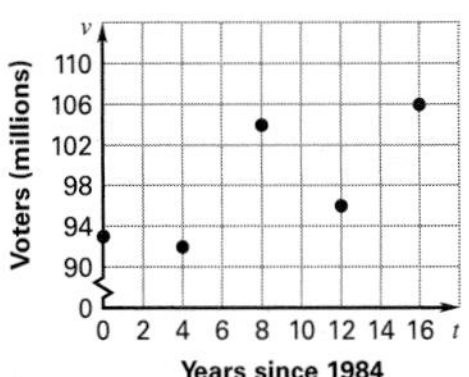

Chapter 2

Lesson 2.1 (pp. 67–70)

7. Graph −5 and −6 on a number line.

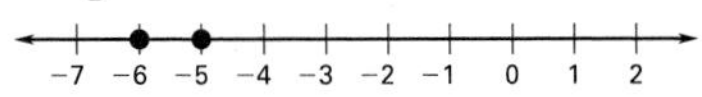

On the number line, −5 is to the right of −6, so $-5 > -6$. The number −5 is greater.

29. If $a = -6.1$, then $-a = -(-6.1) = 6.1$.

If $a = -6.1$, then $|a| = |-6.1| = 6.1$.

53. Graph the numbers on a number line.

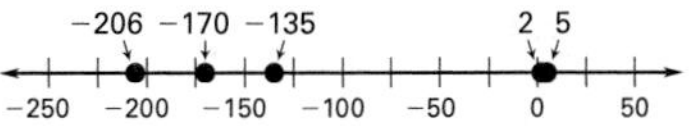

Read the numbers from left to right: −206, −170, −135, 2, 5.

From lowest elevation to highest elevation, the locations are Fondo, Frink, Alamorio, Calexico, and Date City.

Lesson 2.2 (pp. 77–79)

13. $-8.7 + 4.2 = -(|8.7| - |4.2|)$

$= -(8.7 - 4.2) = -4.5$

35. $-2.6 + (-3.4) + 7.6 = [-2.6 + (-3.4)] + 7.6$

$= -6 + 7.6 = 1.6$

55. a. You know the first lens has a strength of −4.75 diopters and the second lens has a strength of 6.25 diopters.

You want to know the strength of the new lens.

Calculate the sum of −4.75 and 6.25:

$-4.75 + 6.25 = 1.5$

The strength of the new lens is 1.5 diopters.

b. You know the first lens has a strength of −2.5 diopters and the second lens has a strength of −1.25 diopters.

You want to know the strength of the new lens.

Calculate the sum of −2.5 and −1.25:

$-2.5 + (-1.25) = -3.75$

The strength of the new lens is −3.75 diopters.

c. You know the first lens has a strength of 1.5 diopters and the second lens has a strength of −3.75 diopters. The greater the absolute value of the strength of a lens, the stronger the lens.

You want to know which new lens is stronger.

Find the absolute value of each lens in part (a) and part (b) and choose the greater.

$|1.5| = 1.5$ $|-3.75| = 3.75$

The new lens in part (b) has a greater absolute value, and is therefore stronger.

WORKED-OUT SOLUTIONS

Lesson 2.3 (pp. 82–84)

3. $13 - (-5) = 13 + 5 = 18$

21. When $x = 7.1$ and $y = -2.5$,

$$-y - (1.9 - x) = -(-2.5) - (1.9 - 7.1)$$
$$= 2.5 - [1.9 + (-7.1)]$$
$$= 2.5 - (-5.2)$$
$$= 2.5 + 5.2 = 7.7$$

43. Write a verbal model. Then write an equation.

Change in temperature	=	Temperature inside	−	Temperature outside

$C = i - t$

Substitute 12.2 for i and −2.4 for t.

$C = 12.2 - (-2.4)$

$C = 12.2 + 2.4 = 14.6$

The change in temperature is 14.6°C.

Lesson 2.4 (pp. 91–93)

11. $-1.9(3.3)(7) = (-6.27)(7) = -43.89$

31. $-2(-6)(-7z) = [-2(-6)](-7z)$

$$= 12(-7z)$$
$$= [12 \cdot (-7)]z$$
$$= -84z$$

51. Write a verbal model.

Total value	=	Original price per share	•	Number of shares	+
		Change in price per share	•	Number of shares	

Calculate the original price.

Original price = ($3.50)(50) = $175

Calculate the change in price.

Change in price = (−$.25)(50) = −$12.50

Calculate the total value.

Total value = (3.50)(50) + (−0.25)(50)

= 175 + (−12.50) = 162.50

The total value is $162.50.

Lesson 2.5 (pp. 99–101)

9. $(p - 3)(-8) = p(-8) - 3(-8) = -8p + 24$

23. Write the expression as a sum:
$7x^2 + (-10) + (-2x^2) + 5$

Terms: $7x^2$, −10, $-2x^2$, 5

Like terms: $7x^2$ and $-2x^2$; −10 and 5

Coefficients: 7, −2

Constant terms: −10, 5

51. Write a verbal model. Then write an equation.

Total cost	=	Number of movies rented	•	(Regular cost of a rental	−	Discount per movie)

$C = 3(r - 2)$ or $C = 3r - 6$

Find the value of C when $r = 3.99$.

$C = 3(3.99 - 2)$

$= 3(3.99) - 3(2)$

$= 11.97 - 6 = 5.97$

The total cost is $5.97.

Lesson 2.6 (pp. 106–108)

13. $-1 \div \left(-\frac{7}{2}\right) = -1 \cdot \left(-\frac{2}{7}\right) = \frac{2}{7}$

35. $\frac{9z - 6}{-3} = (9z - 6) \div (-3)$

$$= (9z - 6) \cdot \left(-\frac{1}{3}\right)$$
$$= 9z \cdot \left(-\frac{1}{3}\right) - 6 \cdot \left(-\frac{1}{3}\right)$$
$$= -3z + 2$$

53. To find the daily mean temperature for a day, find the sum of the high and low temperatures for that day and then divide the sum by 2.

Mean $= \frac{-10.6 + (-18.9)}{2} = \frac{-29.5}{2} = -14.75$

The daily mean temperature was −14.75°C.

Lesson 2.7 (pp. 113–116)

9. Since $50^2 = 2500$, $\pm\sqrt{2500} = \pm 50$.

19. Write a compound inequality that compares $-\sqrt{86}$ with both $-\sqrt{100}$ and $-\sqrt{81}$.

$-\sqrt{100} < -\sqrt{86} < -\sqrt{81}$

Take the square root of each number.

$-10 < -\sqrt{86} < -9$

Because 86 is closer to 81 than to 100, $-\sqrt{86}$ is closer to -9 than to -10. So $-\sqrt{86}$ is about -9.

47. You need to find the side length s of the mazes such that s^2 is the given area in square feet, so s is the positive square root of the area. Then identify the side length as rational or irrational.

Dallas: $s^2 = 1225$, $s = 35$; rational

San Francisco: $s^2 = 576$, $s = 24$; rational

Corona: $s^2 = 2304$, $s = 48$; rational

Waterville: $s^2 = 900$, $s = 30$; rational

The side lengths are 35 feet, 24 feet, 48 feet, and 30 feet. All the lengths are rational numbers.

Chapter 3

Lesson 3.1 (pp. 137–140)

13.
$$-2 = n - 6$$
$$-2 + 6 = n - 6 + 6$$
$$4 = n$$

55. Let w represent the width of the trampoline.

$$A = \ell \cdot w$$
$$187 = 17 \cdot w$$
$$\frac{187}{17} = \frac{17w}{17}$$
$$11 = w$$

The width of the trampoline is 11 feet.

Lesson 3.2 (pp. 144–146)

13.
$$7 = \frac{5}{6}c - 8$$
$$7 + 8 = \frac{5}{6}c - 8 + 8$$
$$15 = \frac{5}{6}c$$
$$\frac{6}{5} \cdot 15 = \frac{6}{5} \cdot \frac{5}{6}c$$
$$18 = c$$

19.
$$-32 = -5k + 13k$$
$$-32 = 8k$$
$$\frac{-32}{8} = \frac{8k}{8}$$
$$-4 = k$$

39. Write a verbal model. Then write an equation. Let h be the number of half-side advertisements.

Total budget = Cost per month • Number of full bus wrap advertisements + Cost per month • Number of half-side advertisements

$$6000 = 2000(1) + 800h$$
$$6000 = 2000 + 800h$$

Solve the equation.

$$6000 = 2000 + 800h$$
$$6000 - 2000 = 2000 - 2000 + 800h$$
$$4000 = 800h$$
$$\frac{4000}{800} = \frac{800h}{800}$$
$$5 = h$$

The museum can have 5 half-side advertisements.

WORKED-OUT SOLUTIONS

WS5

Lesson 3.3 (pp. 150–153)

17.

$$-3 = 12y - 5(2y - 7)$$
$$-3 = 12y - 10y + 35$$
$$-3 = 2y + 35$$
$$-3 - 35 = 2y + 35 - 35$$
$$-38 = 2y$$
$$\frac{-38}{2} = \frac{2y}{2}$$
$$-19 = y$$

39. Let x be the amount of space you should leave between posters (in feet).

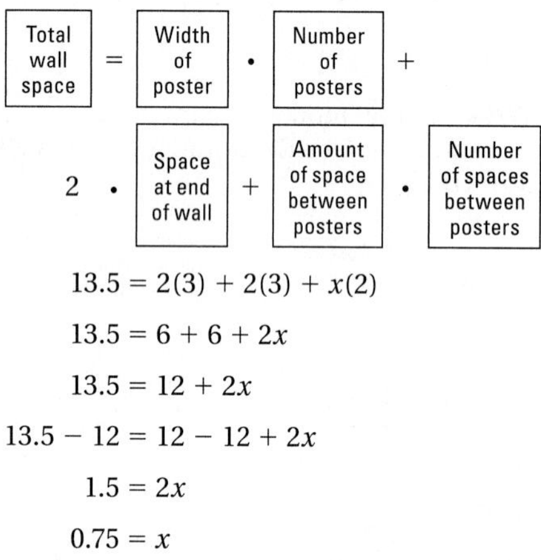

$$13.5 = 2(3) + 2(3) + x(2)$$
$$13.5 = 6 + 6 + 2x$$
$$13.5 = 12 + 2x$$
$$13.5 - 12 = 12 - 12 + 2x$$
$$1.5 = 2x$$
$$0.75 = x$$

You should leave 0.75 foot between each poster.

Lesson 3.4 (pp. 157–159)

13.

$$40 + 14j = 2(-4j - 13)$$
$$40 + 14j = -8j - 26$$
$$40 + 14j + 8j = -8j + 8j - 26$$
$$40 + 22j = -26$$
$$40 - 40 + 22j = -26 - 40$$
$$22j = -66$$
$$j = -3$$

51. Let x represent the number of years. So $33x$ represents the increase in the number of students taking Spanish, and $2x$ represents the decreased number of students who are taking French.

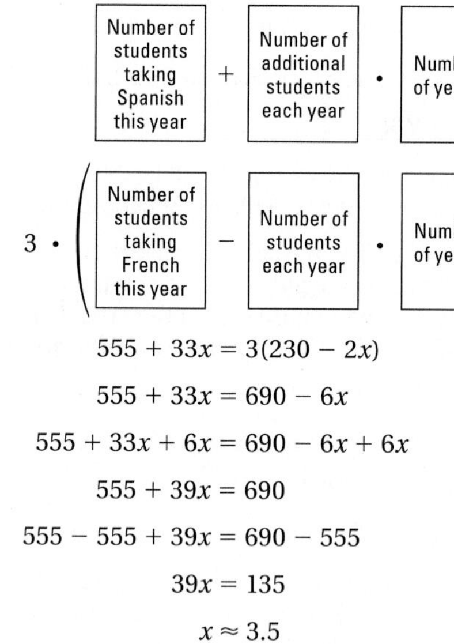

$$555 + 33x = 3(230 - 2x)$$
$$555 + 33x = 690 - 6x$$
$$555 + 33x + 6x = 690 - 6x + 6x$$
$$555 + 39x = 690$$
$$555 - 555 + 39x = 690 - 555$$
$$39x = 135$$
$$x \approx 3.5$$

So it will be after 3 more school years, or in about 4 years, when the number of students taking Spanish will be 3 times the number of students taking French.

Lesson 3.5 (pp. 165–167)

17.

$$\frac{16}{48} = \frac{n}{36}$$
$$36 \cdot \frac{16}{48} = 36 \cdot \frac{n}{36}$$
$$\frac{576}{48} = n$$
$$12 = n$$

49. Find the total number of pizzas: $96 + 144 + 240 = 480$.

The ratio of large pizzas to all pizzas is $\frac{\text{number of large pizzas}}{\text{total number of pizzas}} = \frac{240}{480} = \frac{1}{2}$.

Lesson 3.6 (pp. 171–173)

13. $\frac{11}{w} = \frac{33}{w+24}$

$11(w + 24) = 33w$

$11w + 264 = 33w$

$11w - 11w + 264 = 33w - 11w$

$264 = 22w$

$12 = w$

39. The ratio of model to height is $\frac{\text{height of model}}{\text{actual height}}$. Write and solve a proportion.

$\frac{1}{25} = \frac{x}{443.2}$

$443.2 = 25x$

$17.728 = x$

The height of the model is 17.728 meters.

Lesson 3.7 (pp. 179–181)

13. $a = p\% \cdot b$

$= 115\% \cdot 60$

$= 1.15 \cdot 60$

$= 69$ 69 is 115% of 60.

35. a. The survey shows that 36% of the 250 listeners who participated in the survey are "tired of" the song.

$a = p\% \cdot b$

$= 36\% \cdot 250$

$= 0.36 \cdot 250$

$= 90$

90 listeners are "tired of" the song.

b. The survey shows that 14% of the 250 listeners who participated in the survey "love" the song.

$a = p\% \cdot b$

$= 14\% \cdot 250$

$= 0.14 \cdot 250$

$= 35$

35 listeners "love" the song.

Lesson 3.8 (pp. 187–189)

17. $30 = 9x - 5y$

$30 + 5y = 9x - 5y + 5y$

$30 + 5y = 9x$

$30 - 30 + 5y = 9x - 30$

$5y = 9x - 30$

$y = \frac{9}{5}x - 6$

33. a. $C = 12x + 25$

$C - 25 = 12x + 25 - 25$

$C - 25 = 12x$

$\frac{C - 25}{12} = x$

b. \$145: $\frac{C - 25}{12} = x$

$\frac{145 - 25}{12} = x$

$10 = x$

For \$145, you bowled 10 league nights.

\$181: $\frac{C - 25}{12} = x$

$\frac{181 - 25}{12} = x$

$13 = x$

For \$181, you bowled 13 league nights.

\$205: $\frac{C - 25}{12} = x$

$\frac{205 - 25}{12} = x$

$15 = x$

For \$205, you bowled 15 league nights.

Chapter 4

Lesson 4.1 (pp. 209–212)

15. To plot $Q(-1, 5)$, begin at the origin. First move 1 unit to the left, then 5 units up. Point Q is in Quadrant II.

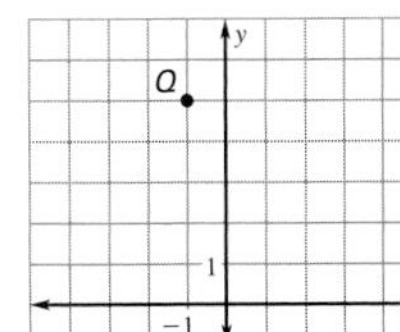

WORKED-OUT SOLUTIONS

WS7

25. First create a table of values by substituting the domain values into the function.

x	y = 2x − 5
−2	y = 2(−2) − 5 = −9
−1	y = 2(−1) − 5 = −7
0	y = 2(0) − 5 = −5
1	y = 2(1) − 5 = −3
2	y = 2(2) − 5 = −1

The table gives the ordered pairs (−2, −9), (−1, −7), (0, −5), (1, −3), and (2, −1).

Graph the function by plotting these points. The range of the function is the *y*-values from the table: −9, −7, −5, −3, −1.

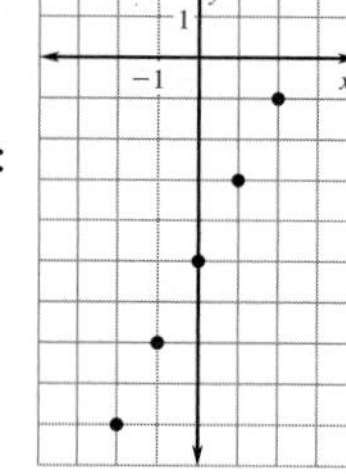

37. The table represents a function because there is exactly one low temperature for each day in the first week of February.

To graph the data, plot the ordered pairs (day, record low).

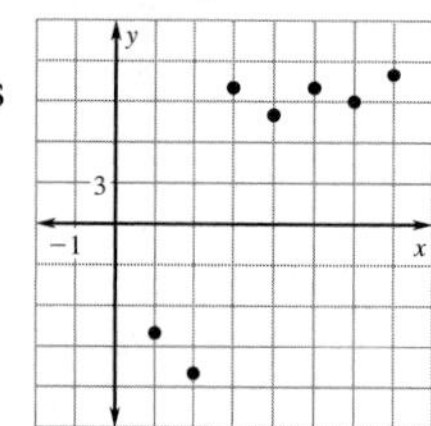

Lesson 4.2 (pp. 219–221)

3. Test (−2, 3):

$$2y + x = 4$$

$2(3) + (-2) \stackrel{?}{=} 4$ Substitute −2 for *x* and 3 for *y*.

$$6 + (-2) \stackrel{?}{=} 4$$

$$4 = 4 \checkmark$$

So, (−2, 3) is a solution of $2y + x = 4$.

11. First, solve the equation for *y*.

$$y + x = 2$$

$$y + x - x = 2 - x$$

$$y = 2 - x$$

Use this equation to create a table of values.

x	−2	−1	0	1	2
y	4	3	2	1	0

Plot at least three of the points whose ordered pairs (*x*, *y*) are indicated by the table. Draw a line through the plotted points.

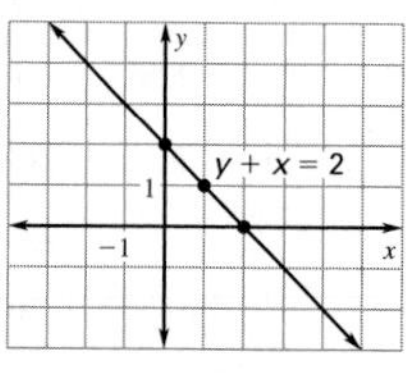

37. a.

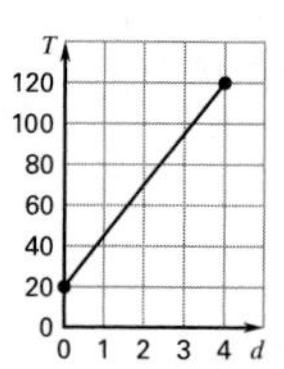

Since the scientist is studying the organisms in the first 4 kilometers of Earth's crust, the domain of the function is $0 \le d \le 4$. The range of the function is $20 \le T \le 120$. The temperature 4 kilometers from the surface is 120°C.

b. Notice in the table for part (a) that the temperatures between 20°C and 95°C occur when the distance from the surface is between 0 kilometers and 3 kilometers.

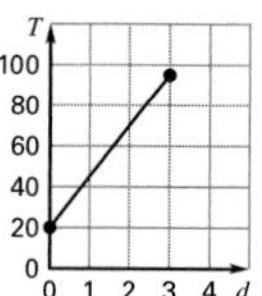

The domain of the function is now $0 \le d \le 3$ and the range is $20 \le T \le 95$. So this section of crust is 3 kilometers deep.

Lesson 4.3 (pp. 229–232)

21. Substitute 0 for *y* in $y = -4x + 3$ and solve for *x*.

$$0 = -4x + 3$$

$$-3 = -4x$$

$$\frac{3}{4} = x$$

The *x*-intercept is $\frac{3}{4}$.

Substitute 0 for *x* in $y = -4x + 3$ and solve for *y*.

$$y = -4(0) + 3 = 0 + 3 = 3$$

The *y*-intercept is 3.

Plot the two points that correspond to the intercepts and draw a line through them.

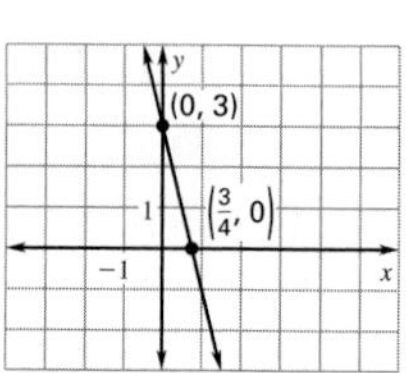

47. a. If $v = 0$ in the function $f = 180 - 1.5v$, then $f = 180 - 1.5(0)$, and $f = 180$. This is the intercept on the vertical axis, and it represents the area (in square feet) available for flowers when no vegetables are planted.

Letting $f = 0$ gives $0 = 180 - 1.5v$, $1.5v = 180$, and $v = 120$. This is the intercept on the horizontal axis, and it represents the area (in square feet) available for vegetables when no flowers are planted.

b. 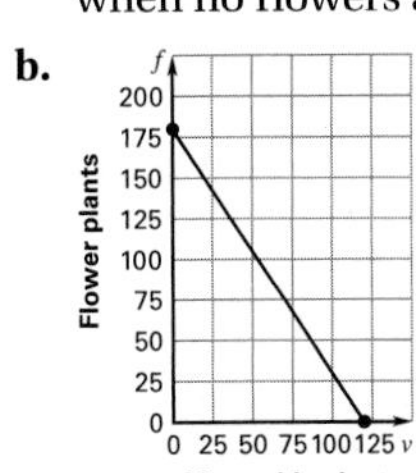

The domain is $0 \le v \le 120$. The range is $0 \le f \le 180$.

c. $f = 180 - 1.5(80)$ Substitute 80 for v.

$= 180 - 120 = 60$

There are 60 square feet left to plant flowers.

Lesson 4.4 (pp. 239–242)

11. Let $(x_1, y_1) = (1, 3)$ and $(x_2, y_2) = (3, -2)$.

$$m = \frac{y_2 - y_1}{x_2 - x_1} = \frac{-2 - 3}{3 - 1} = \frac{-5}{2} \text{ or } -\frac{5}{2}$$

37. a. $\text{rate of change} = \dfrac{\text{change in temperature}}{\text{change in time}}$

0–1.5 hours:
$\dfrac{1000 - 250}{1.5 - 0} = \dfrac{750}{1.5} = 500$ degrees per hour

1.5–2.5 hours:
$\dfrac{1300 - 1000}{2.5 - 1.5} = \dfrac{300}{1} = 300$ degrees per hour

2.5–4.65 hours:
$\dfrac{1680 - 1300}{4.65 - 2.5} = \dfrac{380}{2.15} \approx 177$ degrees per hour

4.65–8.95 hours:
$\dfrac{1920 - 1680}{8.95 - 4.65} = \dfrac{240}{4.3} \approx 56$ degrees per hour

The time interval with the greatest rate of change was from 0 hours to 1.5 hours.

b. The time interval that showed the least rate of change was from 4.65 hours to 8.95 hours.

Lesson 4.5 (pp. 247–250)

11.
$$4x + y = 1$$
$$4x - 4x + y = 1 - 4x$$
$$y = -4x + 1$$

The slope is -4 and the y-intercept is 1.

21. The equation $y = -6x + 1$ is in slope-intercept form. The slope is -6 and the y-intercept is 1. Locate the point (0, 1), which corresponds to the intercept. Use the slope to find a second point, $(1, -5)$. Draw a line through the points.

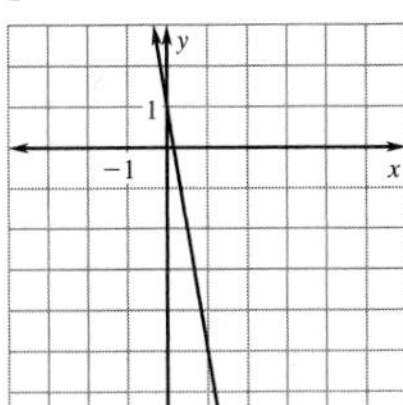

41. a. Graph: Distance (miles) d versus Time (hours) t, with lines $d = 65t$ and $d = 55t$.

b. On the graph, the vertical distance between the lines is about 30 when $t = 3$. To verify this estimate, substitute 3 in $d = 55t$: $d = 55(3) = 165$. Now substitute 3 in $d = 65t$: $d = 65(3) = 195$. Subtract: $195 - 165 = 30$. Driving at the maximum speed limit, a driver could travel 30 miles farther after 1995 than before 1995.

Lesson 4.6 (pp. 256–259)

7. Solve the equation for y: $8x + 2y = 0$

$$2y = -8x$$
$$y = -4x$$

Because $8x + 2y = 0$ can be written in the form $y = ax$, it does represent direct variation. The constant of variation is -4.

WS9

21. When solved for y, the equation is $y = -4x$. The slope of the line is the constant of variation, -4. The graph of a direct variation equation always passes through (0, 0). The slope can be used to locate a second point from the origin, like (1, −4). Draw a line through the points.

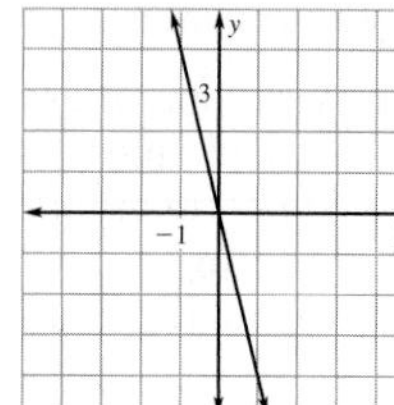

43. a. Compare the ratio $\frac{f}{w}$ or all three data pairs:

$$\frac{2.50}{10} = 0.25, \frac{3.75}{15} = 0.25, \frac{7.50}{30} = 0.25$$

Because the ratios are all equal, f varies directly with w.

b. Since $\frac{f}{w} = 0.25$, multiply both sides by w to obtain the direct variation equation $f = 0.25w$; the constant 0.25 represents $.25 per pound.

The computer weighs 18 pounds, so substitute 18 for w.

$f = 0.25(18) = 4.50$

The printer weighs 10 pounds, so substitute 10 for w.

$f = 0.25(10) = 2.50$

The total recycling fee for the computer and printer is $4.50 + $2.50 = $7.00.

Lesson 4.7 (pp. 265–268)

3. Substitute −2, 0, and 3 for x.

$f(-2) = 12(-2) + 1 = -24 + 1 = -23$

$f(0) = 12(0) + 1 = 0 + 1 = 1$

$f(3) = 12(3) + 1 = 36 + 1 = 37$

17. Substitute −13 for $j(x)$.

$$-13 = 4x + 11$$
$$-13 - 11 = 4x + 11 - 11$$
$$-24 = 4x$$
$$\frac{-24}{4} = \frac{4x}{4}$$
$$-6 = x$$

39. a. Create a table of values for the function.

x	f(x)
0	0.10(0) + 2.75 = 2.75
5	0.10(5) + 2.75 = 3.25
10	0.10(10) + 2.75 = 3.75
15	0.10(15) + 2.75 = 4.25
20	0.10(20) + 2.75 = 4.75

Use the ordered pairs given by the table to graph the function.

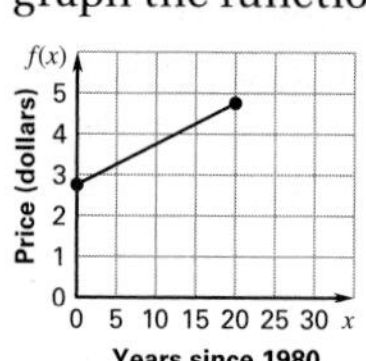

The domain of the function is $0 \le x \le 20$ and the range is $2.75 \le f(x) \le 4.75$.

b. Substitute 4.55 for $f(x)$.

$$4.55 = 0.10x + 2.75$$
$$4.55 - 2.75 = 0.10x + 2.75 - 2.75$$
$$1.8 = 0.10x$$
$$\frac{1.8}{0.10} = \frac{0.10x}{0.10}$$
$$18 = x$$

When $x = 18$, $f(x) = 4.55$. In 1998, 18 years after 1980, the average price of a movie ticket was $4.55.

Chapter 5

Lesson 5.1 (pp. 286–289)

11. Determine the slope: $m = \frac{\text{rise}}{\text{run}} = \frac{-1}{2} = \text{or } -\frac{1}{2}$.

The line crosses the y-axis at (0, 0), so the y-intercept is 0.

Substitute $-\frac{1}{2}$ for m and 0 for b in the slope-intercept form $y = mx + b$: $y = -\frac{1}{2}x$.

19. Calculate the slope:

$m = \frac{y_2 - y_1}{x_2 - x_1} = \frac{4 - 0}{0 - (-1)} = \frac{4}{1} = 4$.

The line crosses the y-axis at (0, 4), so the y-intercept is 4.

Substitute 4 for m and 4 for b in the slope-intercept form $y = mx + b$: $y = 4x + 4$.

47. Let C be the cost of a visit to the aquarium and t be the time parked there. The total cost C is given by the function $C = 3h + 30$, where h is the number of hours parked at the aquarium.

Evaluate the function for $h = 4$:
$C = 3(4) + 30 = 12 + 30 = 42$

The total cost is $42.

Lesson 5.2 (pp. 296–299)

5. The slope is given. To find the y-intercept, substitute the slope, -5, and the coordinates of the given point $(-4, 7)$ into the equation $y = mx + b$, and solve for b.

$$y = mx + b$$
$$7 = -5(-4) + b$$
$$7 = 20 + b$$
$$-13 = b$$

The equation of the line is $y = -5x - 13$.

11. Calculate the slope:
$m = \frac{y_2 - y_1}{x_2 - x_1} = \frac{7 - 4}{2 - 1} = \frac{3}{1} = 3.$

To find the y-intercept, substitute the slope, 3, and the coordinates of either given point into the equation $y = mx + b$, and solve for b. Using $(1, 4)$,

$$y = mx + b$$
$$4 = 3(1) + b$$
$$4 = 3 + b$$
$$1 = b$$

The equation of the line is $y = 3x + 1$.

49. Let T be the total time (in minutes) for cooking a roast that weighs p pounds and t be the extra time needed (in minutes). The equation $T = 30p + t$ models the situation.

For a 2 pound roast, the total time was 1 hour 25 minutes, or 85 minutes. Find the extra time t needed by substituting 85 for T and 2 for p, and solving for t.

$$85 = 30(2) + t$$
$$85 = 60 + t$$
$$25 = t$$

Find the value of T for a 3 pound roast by substituting 3 for p.

$T = 30(3) + 25 = 90 + 25 = 115$

You need 115 minutes, or 1 hour 55 minutes, to cook a 3 pound roast.

Lesson 5.3 (pp. 305–308)

3. Substitute 2 for x_1, 1 for y_1, and 2 for m in the point-slope form $y - y_1 = m(x - x_1)$:
$y - 1 = 2(x - 2)$.

39. The rate of change is given as $10,000 per year. Let y be the annual sales (in dollars) and x be the number of years since 1994. From the given information about 1997, one data pair is (3, 97000). Use the point-slope form of an equation.

$$y - y_1 = m(x - x_1)$$
$$y - 97000 = 10000(x - 3)$$
$$y - 97000 = 10000x - 30000$$
$$y = 10000x + 67000$$

To find the sales in 2000, use the equation above with $x = 2000 - 1994$, or 6.

$$y = 10000(6) + 67000$$
$$= 60000 + 67000 = 127000$$

The annual sales in 2000 were $127,000.

Lesson 5.4 (pp. 314–316)

17. Calculate the slope:
$m = \frac{y_2 - y_1}{x_2 - x_1} = \frac{-4 - 4}{4 - (-8)} = \frac{-8}{12}$ or $-\frac{2}{3}$.

Use either point to write an equation in point-slope form. Using $(-8, 4)$:

$$y - y_1 = m(x - x_1)$$
$$y - 4 = -\frac{2}{3}[x - (-8)]$$
$$y - 4 = -\frac{2}{3}(x + 8)$$

Rewrite the equation in standard form.

$$y - 4 = -\frac{2}{3}x - \frac{16}{3}$$
$$\frac{2}{3}x + y - 4 = -\frac{16}{3}$$
$$\frac{2}{3}x + y = -\frac{4}{3} \text{ (or } 2x + 3y = -4)$$

WORKED-OUT SOLUTIONS

39. a. Let n be the number of ounces in a box of wheat cereal.

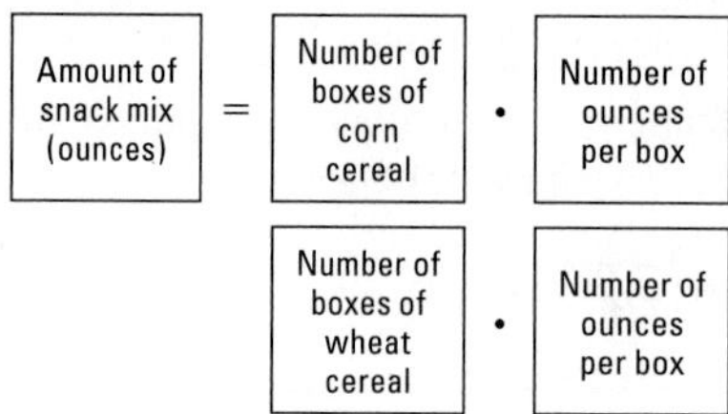

$120 = 5 \cdot 12 + 4 \cdot n$

$120 = 60 + 4n$

$60 = 4n$

$15 = n$

There are 15 ounces in a box of wheat cereal.

b. Let c be the number of boxes of corn cereal and let w be the number of boxes of wheat cereal you use. Use the verbal model from part (a).

$120 = c \cdot 12 + w \cdot 15$

$120 = 12c + 15w$ or $12c + 15w = 120$

c. Substitute different values for c and w in the equation for part (b).

If $c = 0$, then $12(0) + 15w = 120$, and $w = 8$; you can use 0 boxes of corn cereal and 8 boxes of wheat cereal.

If $c = 5$, then $12(5) + 15w = 120$, and $w = 4$; you can use 5 boxes of corn cereal and 4 boxes of wheat cereal.

If $c = 10$, then $12(10) + 15w = 120$, and $w = 0$; you can use 10 boxes of corn cereal and 0 boxes of wheat cereal.

Lesson 5.5 (pp. 321–323)

19. The slope of the line $y = 3x - 12$ is 3, so the slope of the perpendicular line is $-\frac{1}{3}$.

Use the slope $-\frac{1}{3}$ and the point $(-9, 2)$ to find the y-intercept of the line.

$y = mx + b$

$2 = -\frac{1}{3}(-9) + b$

$2 = 3 + b$

$-1 = b$

The equation of the line through $(-9, 2)$ that is perpendicular to the line $y = 3x - 12$ is $y = -\frac{1}{3}x - 1$.

33. a. Let w represent the weight of the blue whale calves and let d represent the number of days since birth.

The rate of change is 200 pounds per day. Use this value and the birth weights to write an equation for each calf.

First calf: $w_1 = 200d + 6000$
Second calf: $w_2 = 200d + 6250$

b. Substitute 30 for d in each equation from part (a).

$w_1 = 200(30) + 6000 = 12{,}000$

After 30 days, the first calf weighs 12,000 pounds.

$w_2 = 200(30) + 6250 = 12{,}250$

After 30 days, the second calf weighs 12,250 pounds.

c. The graphs of the equations in part (a) are parallel, since the two equations have the same slope, 200. The w-intercept of the second line is 250 greater than the w-intercept of the first line.

Lesson 5.6 (pp. 327–330)

7. The ordered pairs from the table are (1.2, 10), (1.8, 7), (2.3, 5), (3.0, −1), (4.4, −4), and (5.2, −8).

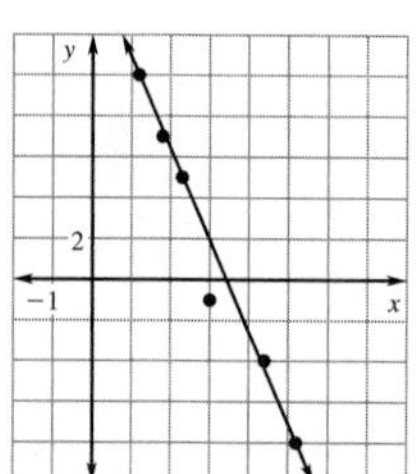

Use the points (1.2, 10) and (5.2, −8) to find the slope of the line of fit.

$m = \frac{y_2 - y_1}{x_2 - x_1} = \frac{-8 - 10}{5.2 - 1.2} = \frac{-18}{4} = -4.5.$

Use the slope −4.5 and the point (5.2, −8) to find the y-intercept of the line.

$y = mx + b$

$-8 = -4.5(5.2) + b$

$-8 = -23.4 + b$

$15.4 = b$

A line of fit is $y = -4.5x + 15.4$.

WORKED-OUT SOLUTIONS

WS12

17. a. The ordered pairs from the diagram are (86, −86), (80, −65), (75, −54), (70, −40), (65, −26), (60, −21), and (52, −4).

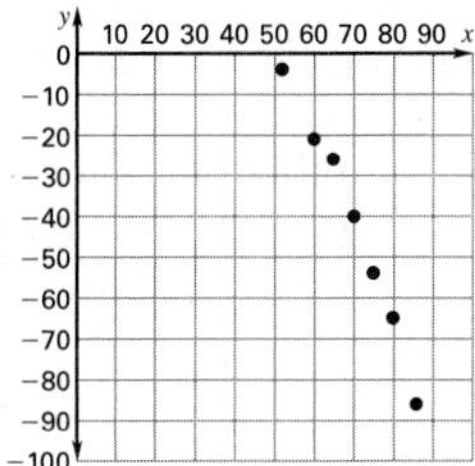

b. Draw a line that appears to fit the points.

Sample:

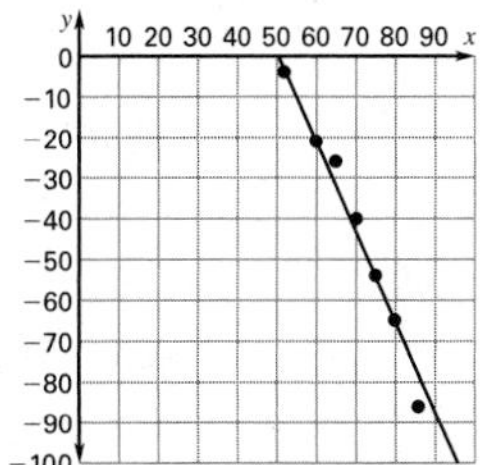

Use the points (60, −21) and (80, −65) to find the slope of the line of fit.

$$m = \frac{y_2 - y_1}{x_2 - x_1} = \frac{-21 - (-65)}{60 - 80} = \frac{44}{-20} = -2.2$$

Use the slope −2.2 and the point (80, −65) to find the y-intercept of the line.

$$y = mx + b$$
$$-65 = -2.2(80) + b$$
$$-65 = -176 + b$$
$$111 = b$$

A line of fit is $y = -2.2x + 111$.

c. The slope of the line of fit models the rate of change. So the temperature changes at an approximate rate of −2.2°C per kilometer of increasing altitude.

Lesson 5.7 (pp. 338–341)

3. Enter the data list on a graphing calculator. Create a scatter plot.

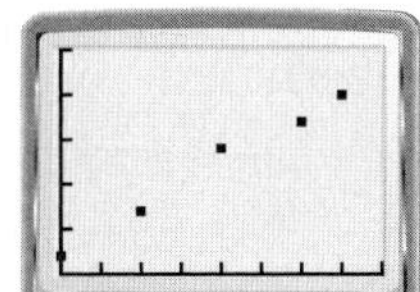

Perform a linear regression using the paired data. An equation of the best-fitting line is approximately $y = 2.6x + 2.5$.

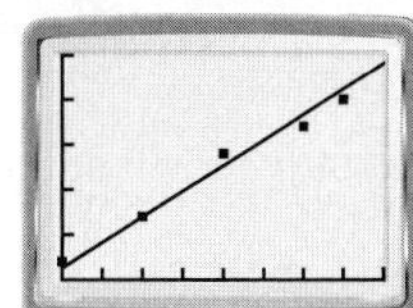

Graph the best-fitting line. Use the trace feature and arrow keys to find the value of y when $x = 5$. For $x = 5$, $y = 15.5$.

19. a. Enter the data list on a graphing calculator. Make a scatter plot.

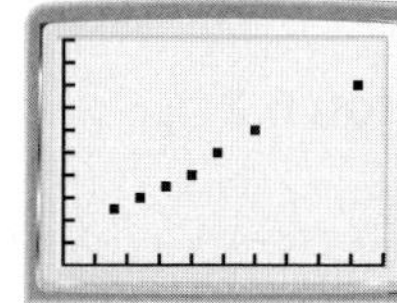

b. Perform a linear regression using the paired data. An equation of the best-fitting line is approximately $y = 0.03x + 1.23$ where y is the recommended space (in square feet) and x is a pig's weight (in pounds).

c. Evaluate $y = 0.03x + 1.23$ for $x = 250$.

$$y = 0.03(250) + 1.23 = 7.5 + 1.23 = 8.73$$

The model predicts that about 8.73 square feet of space is needed for a pig weighing 250 pounds.

Chapter 6

Lesson 6.1 (pp. 359–361)

7. The open circle means that 10 is not a solution of the inequality. Because the arrow points to the left, all numbers less than 10 are solutions. An inequality represented by the graph is $x < 10$.

15.

$$w + 14.9 > -2.7$$
$$w + 14.9 - 14.9 > -2.7 - 14.9$$
$$w > -17.6$$

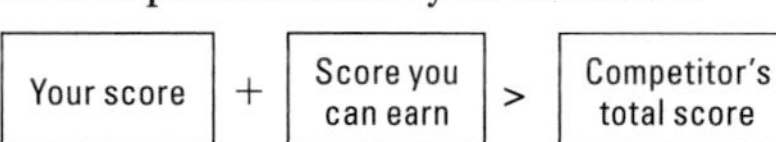

33. a. Let s represent score you can earn.

Your score	+	Score you can earn	>	Competitor's total score

$$129.49 + s > (127.04 + 129.98)$$
$$129.49 + s > 257.02$$
$$129.49 + s - 129.49 > 257.02 - 129.49$$
$$s > 127.53$$

The score you can earn must be greater than 127.53.

WORKED-OUT SOLUTIONS

b. Yes; since 128.13 > 127.53, you will beat your competitor.

No; since 126.78 < 127.53, you will not beat your competitor.

No; when your score is 127.53, you and your competitor will tie.

Lesson 6.2 (pp. 366–368)

5. $-6y < -36$

$\frac{-6y}{-6} > \frac{-36}{-6}$ Reverse the inequality symbol when dividing by −6.

$y > 6$

9. $\frac{g}{6} > -20$

$6 \cdot \frac{g}{6} > 6 \cdot (-20)$

$g > -120$

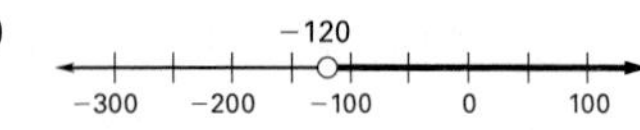

39. $48 \le 15 \cdot w$

$\frac{48}{15} \le \frac{15w}{15}$

$3.2 \le w$

The minimum width of the molding must be greater than or equal to 3.2 inches, or the width must be at least 3.2 inches.

Lesson 6.3 (pp. 372–374)

5. $8v - 3 \ge -11$

$8v \ge -8$

$v \ge -1$

19. $3(s - 4) \ge 2(s - 6)$

$3s - 12 \ge 2s - 12$

$3s \ge 2s$

$3s - 2s \ge 2s - 2s$

$s \ge 0$

39. a. The area of the habitat is (20 feet)(50 feet) = 1000 square feet. Since 500 square feet are needed for the first two swans, 1000 − 500 = 500 square feet are left for the other swans. 500 square feet can hold up to 500 ÷ 125 = 4 more swans; so, the maximum number of swans is 2 + 4 = 6 swans.

b. The area of the new habitat is [(20 + 20) feet][(50 + 20) feet] = (40 feet)(70 feet) = 2800 square feet. Since 2800 − 1000 = 1800, the additional area is 1800 square feet. 1800 square feet can hold up to 1800 ÷ 125 = 14.4 more swans; so the possible number of additional swans is at most 14 swans. The habitat can hold at most 14 more swans.

Lesson 6.4 (pp. 384–387)

7. Let s be the speed of a vehicle that is traveling within the posted speed limits.

$40 \le s \le 60$

11. Separate the compound inequality $-1 \le -4m \le 16$ into two inequalities.

$-1 \le -4m$ *and* $-4m \le 16$

$\frac{-1}{-4} \ge \frac{-4m}{-4}$ *and* $\frac{-4m}{-4} \ge \frac{16}{-4}$

$\frac{1}{4} \ge m$ *and* $m \ge -4$

The inequality can be written as $-4 \le m \le \frac{1}{4}$.

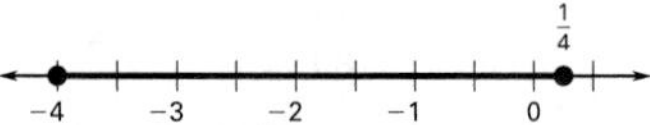

41. An inequality representing values for p is $0.02 \le p \le 0.04$.

$0.02 \le \frac{f}{d} \le 0.04$ Substitute $\frac{f}{d}$ for p.

$0.02 \le \frac{f}{160} \le 0.04$ Substitute 160 for w.

$3.2 \le f \le 6.4$

The possible amounts of food f eaten per day by a deer is greater or equal to 3.2 pounds and less than or equal to 6.4 pounds.

Lesson 6.5 (pp. 393–395)

11. Rewrite the absolute value equation $|3p + 7| = 4$ as two equations.

$3p + 7 = 4$ *or* $3p + 7 = -4$

$3p = -3$ *or* $3p = -11$

$p = -1$ *or* $p = -3\frac{2}{3}$

The solutions are −1 and $-3\frac{2}{3}$.

23. $|x - 1| + 5 = 2$

$|x - 1| = -3$

The absolute value of a number is never negative. So, there are no solutions.

45. a. Let s represent your friend's scores last year.

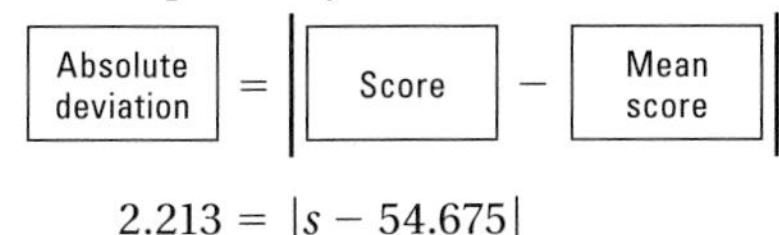

$2.213 = |s - 54.675|$

$2.213 = s - 54.675$

$56.888 = s$

or $-2.213 = s - 54.675$

$52.462 = s$

His least score earned was 52.462, and his greatest score was 56.888 points.

b. Let t represent your friend's scores this year. Find his greatest score for this year. Then find the difference between this year's greatest score and last year's greatest score.

$0.45 = |t - 56.738|$

$0.45 = t - 56.738$

$57.188 = t$

or $-0.45 = t - 56.738$

$56.288 = t$

His greatest score was 57.188 points. This score is 57.188 − 56.888, or 0.3 point more than his greatest score last year.

Lesson 6.6 (pp. 401–403)

9. Rewrite $|d + 4| \geq 3$ as a compound inequality.

$d + 4 \leq -3$ *or* $d + 4 \geq 3$

$d \leq -7$ *or* $d \geq -1$

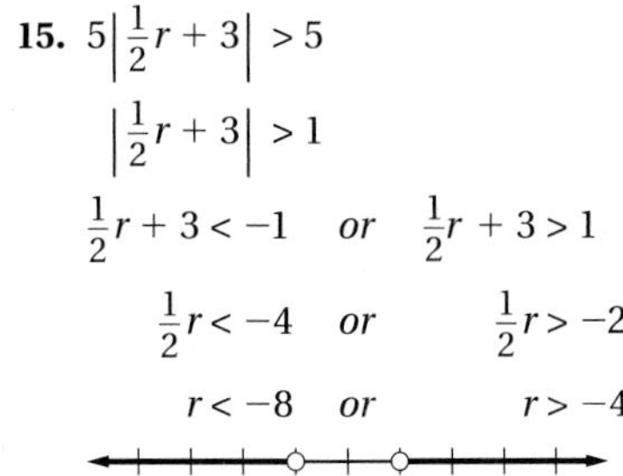

15. $5\left|\frac{1}{2}r + 3\right| > 5$

$\left|\frac{1}{2}r + 3\right| > 1$

$\frac{1}{2}r + 3 < -1$ *or* $\frac{1}{2}r + 3 > 1$

$\frac{1}{2}r < -4$ *or* $\frac{1}{2}r > -2$

$r < -8$ *or* $r > -4$

−14 −10 −6 −2 2

37. Let t represent the oven temperature.

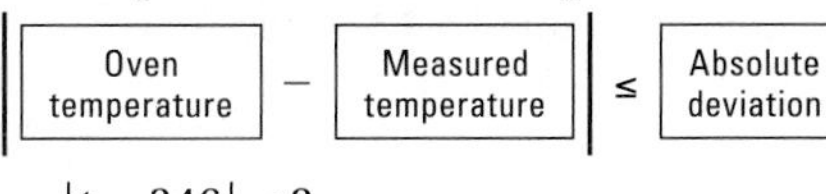

$|t - 346| \leq 2$

$-2 \leq t - 346 \leq 2$

$344 \leq t \leq 348$

The temperature is at least 344°F and at most 348°F. You should continue to preheat; the temperature is still below 350°F.

Lesson 6.7 (pp. 409–412)

5. Substitute −1 for x and −4 for y in the inequality $y - x > -2$.

$-4 - (-1) > -2$

$-3 > -2$ ✗

Since −3 is not greater than −2, the ordered pair (−1, −4) is not a solution.

19. Graph the equation $y = 3x + 5$. The symbol of the given inequality is <, so use a dashed line. Since the line does not pass through the origin, test the ordered pair (0, 0) in $y < 3x + 5$.

$0 < 3(0) + 5$

$0 < 5$ ✓

Shade the half-plane that contains (0, 0) because (0, 0) is a solution of the inequality.

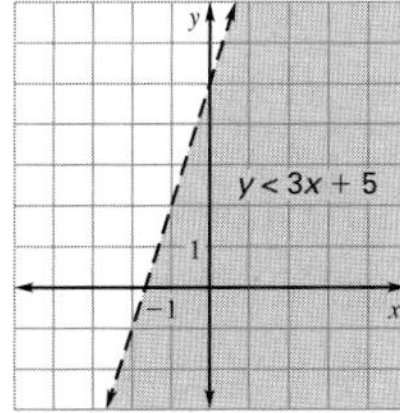

57. a. Let m be the number of muffins and let ℓ be the number of loaves of bread. An inequality modeling this situation is $\frac{1}{6}m + \frac{1}{2}\ell \leq 12$.

To graph $\frac{1}{6}m + \frac{1}{2}\ell \leq 12$, first graph the equation $\frac{1}{6}m + \frac{1}{2}\ell = 12$ in Quadrant I; the inequality symbol is ≤, so use a solid line.

Next, test (12, 12) in $\frac{1}{6}m + \frac{1}{2}\ell \leq 12$.

$\frac{1}{6}(12) + \frac{1}{2}(12) \leq 12$

$2 + 6 \leq 12$ ✓

WORKED-OUT SOLUTIONS

Finally, shade the part of Quadrant I that contains (12, 12), because (12, 12) is a solution of the inequality.

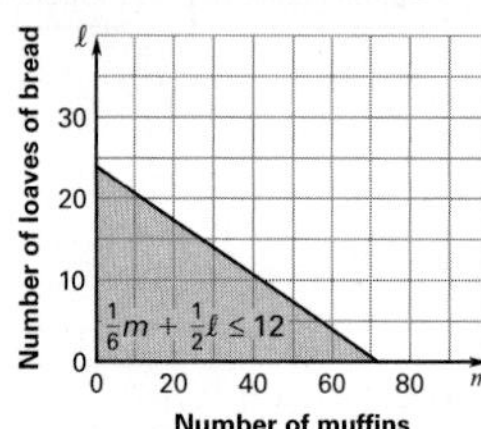

b. $\frac{1}{6}m + \frac{1}{2}(4) \le 12$ Substitute 4 for ℓ.

$\frac{1}{6}m + 2 \le 12$

$\frac{1}{6}m \le 10$

$m \le 60$

You can make up to 60 muffins.

Chapter 7

Lesson 7.1 (pp. 430–433)

15. Graph both equations.

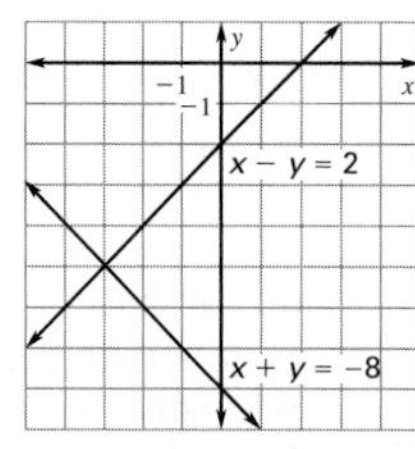

The lines appear to intersect at $(-3, -5)$.

Check: Substitute -3 for x and -5 for y in each equation.

$x - y = 2$	$x + y = -8$
$-3 - (-5) = 2$	$-3 + (-5) = -8$
$2 = 2$ ✓	$-8 = -8$ ✓

So, $(-3, -5)$ is the solution of the system.

31. The two lines appear to intersect at (50, 50). If the value of t is 50, then the year is 1990 + 50, or 2040. So, the percent of eighth graders who watch 1 hour or less of television will equal the percent of eighth graders who watch 1 hour or more of television in the year 2040.

Lesson 7.2 (pp. 439–441)

13. Solve $x + y = -3$ for x: $x = -y - 3$.

Substitute $-y - 3$ for x in the other equation and solve for y.

$5(-y - 3) + 2y = 9$

$-5y - 15 + 2y = 9$

$-3y - 15 = 9$

$-3y = 24$

$y = -8$

Substitute -8 for y in the equation $x = -y - 3$.

$x = -(-8) - 3 = 5$

The solution of the linear system is $(5, -8)$.

33. a. Write a system of two linear equations.

Use the given verbal model to write the first equation: $x \cdot 1.5 = y \cdot 1.2$, or $1.5x = 1.2y$.

Since the length of the dowel is 9 inches, the second equation is $x + y = 9$.

Solve $x + y = 9$ for x: $x = -y + 9$.

Substitute $-y + 9$ for x in the equation $1.5x = 1.2y$ and solve for y.

$1.5x = 1.2y$

$1.5(-y + 9) = 1.2y$

$-1.5y + 13.5 = 1.2y$

$13.5 = 2.7y$

$5 = y$

Substitute 5 for y in the equation $x = -y + 9$.

$x = -5 + 9 = 4$

The solution is (4, 5). So the string should be placed 4 inches from point A.

Lesson 7.3 (pp. 447–450)

17. Rewrite the first equation so that the x-term is first. Subtract the equations to eliminate the variable x, then solve for y.

$6x - 8y = 36$
$6x - y = 15$

$-7y = 21$

$y = -3$

Substitute −3 for y in either equation.

$6x - (-3) = 15$

$6x + 3 = 15$

$6x = 12$

$x = 2$

The solution of the linear system is (2, −3).

41. Write a system of equations. Let x be the cost of a monophonic ring tone and let y be the cost of a polyphonic ring tone.

$3 \cdot x + 2 \cdot y = 12.85$ ← Julie's total cost

$1 \cdot x + 2 \cdot y = 8.95$ ← Tate's total cost

Subtract the equations to eliminate y.

$$\begin{array}{r} 3x + 2y = 12.85 \\ x + 2y = \ \ 8.95 \\ \hline 2x = \ \ 3.90 \\ x = \ \ 1.95 \end{array}$$

Substitute 1.95 for x in either equation.

$1.95 + 2y = 8.95$

$2y = 7.00$

$y = 3.50$

The solution of the linear system is (1.95, 3.50). The cost of a monophonic ring tone is \$1.95 and the cost of a polyphonic ring tone is \$3.50.

Lesson 7.4 (pp. 454–457)

15. Begin by multiplying $9x + 2y = 39$ by 2 and $6x + 13y = -9$ by 3 so that the coefficient of x is the same in both equations. Then subtract the equations to eliminate x. Solve for y.

$9x + 2y = 39$ [×2] $18x + 4y = 78$

$6x + 13y = -9$ [×3] $18x + 39y = -27$

$-35y = 105$

$y = -3$

Substitute −3 for y in either original equations.

$9x + 2(-3) = 39$ Use the equation $9x + 2y = 39$.

$9x - 6 = 39$

$9x = 45$

$x = 5$ The solution is (5, −3).

39. Let x be the number of pies and y be the number of batches of applesauce.

$5x + 4y = 169$ ← Granny Smith apples

$3x + 2y = 95$ ← Golden Delicious apples

Now begin to solve the system by multiplying $5x + 4y = 169$ by 3 and $3x + 2y = 95$ by 5 so that the coefficient of x is the same in both equations. Then subtract the equations to eliminate x. Solve for y.

$5x + 4y = 169$ [×3] $15x + 12y = 507$

$3x + 2y = 95$ [×5] $15x + 10y = 475$

$2y = 32$

$y = 16$

Substitute 16 for y in either original equations.

$3x + 2(16) = 95$

$3x + 32 = 95$

$3x = 63$

$x = 21$

The solution is (21, 16). The apples can be used to make 21 pies and 16 batches of applesauce.

Lesson 7.5 (pp. 462–465)

11. 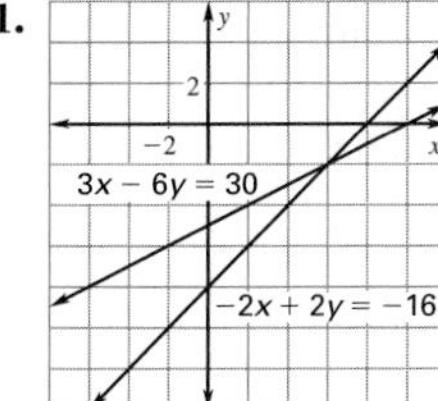

The lines intersect, so the linear system has one solution.

37. Write a system of equations. Let x be the cost of a coach ticket and let y be the cost of a business class ticket.

$150x + 80y = 22{,}860$ ← Washington, D.C.

$170x + 100y = 27{,}280$ ← New York City

Solve the linear system using elimination. Multiply the Washington, D.C. equation by 5 and the New York City equation by 4.

$750x + 400y = 114{,}300$

$680x + 400y = 109{,}120$

$70x = 5180$

$x = 74$

WORKED-OUT SOLUTIONS

Substitute 74 for x in either original equations.

$$170(74) + 100y = 27{,}280$$
$$12{,}580 + 100y = 27{,}280$$
$$100y = 14{,}700$$
$$y = 147$$

The solution is (74, 147). Since there is one solution to the system, there is enough information to determine the cost of one coach ticket.

Lesson 7.6 (pp. 469–472)

13. The graph of the system is the intersection of the two half-planes when both inequalities are graphed in the same coordinate plane.

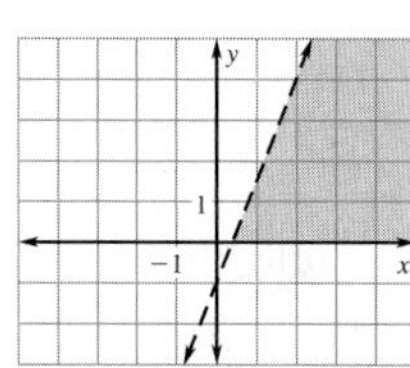

39. a. Let x be the person's age in years and let y be the target heart rate (in beats per minute). A person's maximum heart rate is given by $220 - x$, so 70% of this value is $0.7(220 - x)$ and 85% of this value is $0.85(220 - x)$. So the range for the target heart rate is given by the compound inequality $0.7(220 - x) \le y \le 0.85(220 - x)$, or $154 - 0.70x \le y \le 187 - 0.85x$. This compound inequality can be rewritten as the two inequalities $y \ge 154 - 0.70x$ and $y \le 187 - 0.85x$. The age range for which the heart rate calculations is valid is given as $20 \le x \le 65$.

The system of inequalities is:

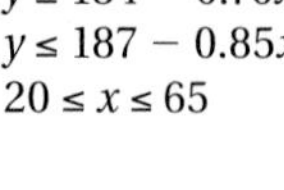

$y \ge 154 - 0.70x$
$y \le 187 - 0.85x$
$20 \le x \le 65$

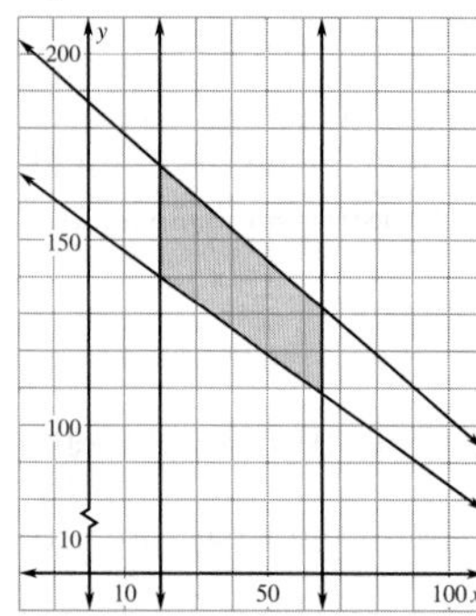

b. No; substituting 40 for x in the inequality $0.70(220 - x) \le y \le 0.85(220 - x)$ gives a range of $126 \le y \le 153$. Since 104 and 120 are both less than 126, his heart rate stays below 70% of the maximum heart rate and is not in the target range for his age.

Chapter 8

Lesson 8.1 (pp. 492–494)

31.
$$\begin{aligned}(-10x^6)^2 \cdot x^2 &= (-10 \cdot x^6)^2 \cdot x^2\\ &= (-10)^2 \cdot (x^6)^2 \cdot x^2\\ &= 100 \cdot x^{6 \cdot 2} \cdot x^2\\ &= 100 \cdot x^{12} \cdot x^2\\ &= 100 \cdot x^{12+2}\\ &= 100x^{14}\end{aligned}$$

55. a. For 10 ounces of gold, there are $10^1 \cdot 10^{23} = 10^{1+23}$, or 10^{24} atoms of gold; for 100 ounces of gold, there are $10^2 \cdot 10^{23} = 10^{25}$ atoms of gold; for 1000 ounces of gold, there are $10^3 \cdot 10^{23} = 10^{26}$ atoms of gold; for 10,000 ounces of gold, there are $10^4 \cdot 10^{23} = 10^{27}$ atoms of gold; and for 100,000 ounces of gold, there are $10^5 \cdot 10^{23} = 10^{28}$ atoms of gold.

b. The power of 10 closest to 96,000 is 10^5, or 100,000. So there were about $10^5 \cdot 10^{23} = 10^{5+23}$, or 10^{28} atoms of gold extracted from the mine.

Lesson 8.2 (pp. 498–501)

33.
$$\begin{aligned}\left(\frac{3x^3}{2y}\right)^2 \cdot \frac{1}{x^2} &= \frac{(3x^3)^2}{(2y)^2} \cdot \frac{1}{x^2}\\ &= \frac{3^2 \cdot (x^3)^2}{2^2 \cdot y^2} \cdot \frac{1}{x^2}\\ &= \frac{9x^6}{4y^2} \cdot \frac{1}{x^2}\\ &= \frac{9x^6}{4x^2y^2}\\ &= \frac{9x^4}{4y^2}\end{aligned}$$

51. Convert the speed of the spacecraft to kilometers per second.

$$\frac{10^4 \text{ m}}{1 \text{ sec}} \cdot \frac{1 \text{ km}}{10^3 \text{ m}} = \frac{10^{4-3} \text{ km}}{1 \text{ sec}} = \frac{10^1 \text{ km}}{1 \text{ sec}}$$

So the speed of the spacecraft is 10 kilometers per second.

Use the quotient of powers property to calculate the number of seconds it would take to make the trip.

$$\frac{10^{13}\text{ km}}{10^1\text{ km/sec}} = 10^{13-1}\text{ sec} = 10^{12}\text{ sec}$$

Calculate the number of seconds in a year (using 365 days = 1 year).

$$\frac{60\text{ sec}}{1\text{ min}} \cdot \frac{60\text{ min}}{1\text{ h}} \cdot \frac{24\text{ h}}{1\text{ day}} \cdot \frac{365\text{ day}}{1\text{ yr}} = \frac{31{,}356{,}000\text{ sec}}{1\text{ yr}}$$

Now convert the trip time, 10^{12} seconds, to years.

$$10^{12}\text{ sec} \div \frac{31{,}536{,}000\text{ sec}}{1\text{ yr}} \approx 31{,}710\text{ yr}$$

It would take about 31,710 years for the spacecraft to reach Alpha Centauri.

Lesson 8.3 (pp. 506–508)

11. $\left(\frac{2}{7}\right)^{-2} = \frac{1}{\left(\frac{2}{7}\right)^2} = \frac{1}{\frac{4}{49}} = \frac{49}{4}$

53. To find the number of red blood cells in the entire sample, multiply the sample size, 10^{-2} liter, by the ratio 10^7 red blood cells per 10^{-6} liter.

$$10^{-2}\text{ L} \cdot \frac{10^7\text{ red blood cells}}{10^{-6}\text{ L}}$$

$$= \frac{10^{-2} \cdot 10^7}{10^{-6}}\text{ red blood cells}$$

$$= 10^{-2+7-(-6)}\text{ red blood cells}$$

$$= 10^{11}\text{ red blood cells}$$

The entire sample would contain about 10^{11} red blood cells.

Lesson 8.4 (pp. 515–518)

3. Since 8.5 is already between 1 and 10, you move the decimal point 0 places and the exponent is 0: $8.5 = 8.5 \times 10^0$.

17. Since the exponent is 7, move the decimal point 7 places to the right: $7.5 \times 10^7 = 75{,}000{,}000$.

53. Divide the number of pounds of cotton by the number of acres.

$$\frac{9.7 \times 10^8}{6.9 \times 10^5} = \frac{9.7}{6.9} \times \frac{10^8}{10^5}$$

$$\approx 1.4058 \times 10^3 \approx 1405.8$$

The average number of pounds produced per acre was about 1406 pounds per acre.

Lesson 8.5 (pp. 523–527)

13. Make a table of values by choosing values for x and finding the corresponding values for y. The domain of the function is all real numbers.

x	−2	−1	0	1	2	3
y	$0.\overline{4}$	$0.\overline{6}$	1	1.5	2.25	3.375

Plot the points from the table and draw a smooth curve through them.

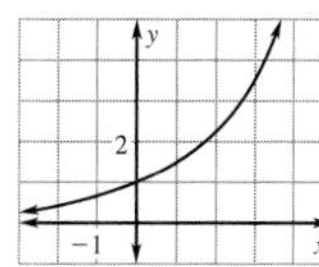

The table and the graph show that the range of the function is all positive real numbers.

41. a. Use the exponential growth model, $y = a(1 + r)^t$.

For tree 1 (with 6% = 0.06), substitute A for y, 154 for a, and 0.06 for r.

$A = 154(1 + 0.06)^t = 154(1.06)^t$

For tree 2 (with 10% = 0.1), substitute A for y, 113 for a, and 0.1 for r.

$A = 113(1 + 0.1)^t = 113(1.1)^t$

The functions are $A = 154(1.06)^t$ for tree 1 and $A = 113(1.1)^t$ for tree 2.

b.

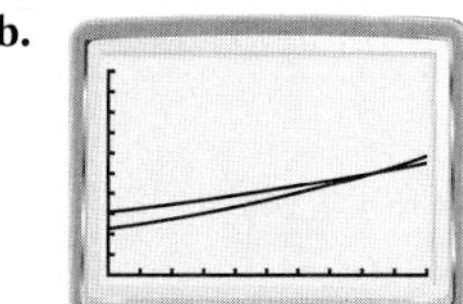

Using the *intersect* feature of the graphing calculator, the graphs intersect at about the point (8.4, 250.6). So, the trees will be the same height in about 8.4 years.

Lesson 8.6 (pp. 535–538)

7. Make a table of values by choosing values for x and finding the corresponding values for y. The domain of the function is all real numbers.

x	−2	−1	0	1	2
y	25	5	1	$\frac{1}{5}$	$\frac{1}{25}$

Plot the points from the table and draw a smooth curve through them.

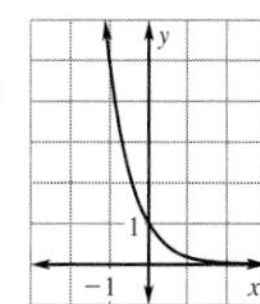

The table and the graph show that the range of the function is all positive real numbers.

WORKED-OUT SOLUTIONS

WORKED-OUT SOLUTIONS

49. Let V be the value of the boat (in dollars) and let t be the time (in years since 2003).

Use the exponential decay model, $y = a(1 - r)^t$, to write a function for the value of the boat over time. Substitute V for y, 4000 for a, and 0.07 for r.

$V = 4000(1 - 0.07)^t$

$= 4000(0.93)^t$

In 2006, the value of t is $2006 - 2003$, or 3.

$V = 4000(0.93)^3 \approx \$3217.43$

The value of the boat in 2006 is about \$3217. The family should not sell the boat, since the \$3000 offer is less than the value of the boat.

Chapter 9

Lesson 9.1 (pp. 557–559)

21. $(6c^2 + 3c + 9) - (3c - 5)$

$= 6c^2 + 3c + 9 - 3c + 5$

$= 6c^2 + (3c - 3c) + (9 + 5)$

$= 6c^2 + 14$

39. a. Add the models for the number of books of each type sold to find a model T for the total number (in millions) of books sold.

$T = A + J$

$= (9.5t^3 - 58t^2 + 66t + 500) + (-15t^2 + 64t + 360)$

$= 9.5t^3 + (-58t^2 - 15t^2) + (66t + 64t) + (500 + 360)$

$= 9.5t^3 - 73t^2 + 130t + 860$

b. To find the total number (in millions) of books sold in the years 1998 and 2002, substitute the number of years since 1998 for t in the model. Then compare the results.

For 1998, $t = 1998 - 1998 = 0$:

$M = 9.5(0)^3 - 73(0)^2 + 130(0) + 860 = 860$

There were 860 million books sold in 1998.

For 2002, $t = 2002 - 1998 = 4$:

$M = 9.5(4)^3 - 73(4)^2 + 130(4) + 860$

$= 9.5(64) - 73(16) + 130(4) + 860$

$= 608 - 1168 + 520 + 860$

$= 820$

There were 820 million books sold in 2002.

More books were sold in 1998 than in 2002.

Lesson 9.2 (pp. 565–568)

23. $(5x + 2)(-3x^2 + 4x - 1)$

$= 5x(-3x^2 + 4x - 1) + 2(-3x^2 + 4x - 1)$

$= -15x^3 + 20x^2 - 5x - 6x^2 + 8x - 2$

$= -15x^3 + (20x^2 - 6x^2) + (-5x + 8x) - 2$

$= -15x^3 + 14x^2 + 3x - 2$

51. a. Substitute 0 for t in each function:

$R = -336(0)^2 + 1730(0) + 12{,}300 = 12{,}300$

$P = 0.00351(0)^2 - 0.0249(0) + 0.171 = 0.171$

Since t is the number of years since 1997, the product $R \cdot P$ when $t = 0$ represents the amount (in million of dollars) spent in 1997 on sound recordings in the U.S. by people between 15 and 19 years old.

b. $R \cdot P = (-336t^2 + 1730t + 12{,}300) \cdot (0.00351t^2 - 0.0249t + 0.171)$

$= -336t^2(0.00351t^2 - 0.0249t + 0.171) + 1730t(0.00351t^2 - 0.0249t + 0.171) + 12{,}300(0.00351t^2 - 0.0249t + 0.171)$

$= -1.17936t^4 + 8.3664t^3 - 57.456t^2 + 6.0723t^3 - 43.077t^2 + 295.83t + 43.173t^2 - 306.27t + 2103.3$

$= -1.17936t^4 + (8.3664t^3 + 6.0723t^3) + (-57.456t^2 - 43.077t^2 + 43.173t^2) + (295.83t - 306.27t) + 2103.3$

$= -1.17936t^4 + 14.4387t^3 - 57.36t^2 - 10.44t + 2103.3$

So, $R \cdot P \approx -1.18t^4 + 14.4t^3 - 57.4t^2 - 10.4t + 2100$.

c. For 2002, $t = 2002 - 1997 = 5$. Substitute 5 for t in the equation for part (b).

$$R \cdot P \approx -1.18(5)^4 + 14.4(5)^3 - 57.4(5)^2 - 10.4(5) + 2100$$

$$\approx -1.18(625) + 14.4(125) - 57.4(25) - 10.4(5) + 2100$$

$$\approx -737.50 + 1800 - 1435 - 52 + 2100$$

$$\approx 1675.5$$

In 2002, people between the ages of 15 and 19 years old spent about 1680 million dollars (or $1,680,000,000) on sound recordings.

Lesson 9.3 (pp. 572–574)

11. $(t + 4)(t - 4) = t^2 - 4^2 = t^2 - 16$

41. a.

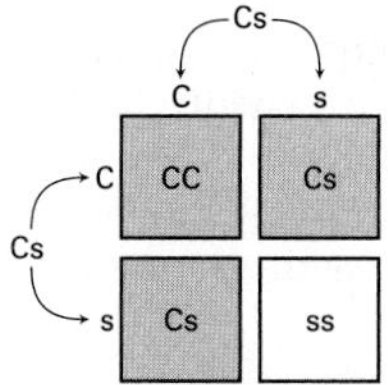

b. Model the gene from each parent with $0.5C + 0.5s$. There is an equal chance that the child inherits a straight thumb gene or a curved thumb gene from each parent. The possible gene combinations of the child can be modeled by $(0.5C + 0.5s)^2$, or

$$(0.5C)^2 + 2(0.5C)(0.5s) + (0.5s)^2$$

$$= 0.25C^2 + 0.5Cs + 0.25s^2$$

c. Consider the coefficients in the polynomial found in part (b). The coefficients show that 25% + 50% = 75% of the possible gene combinations will contain a C, and thus result in a child with a curved thumb.

Lesson 9.4 (pp. 578–580)

3. $(x - 5)(x + 3) = 0$

$x - 5 = 0$ *or* $x + 3 = 0$

$x = 5$ *or* $x = -3$

The solutions of the equation are 5 and −3.

55. a. The initial vertical velocity is given as 4.9 meters per second and the rabbit starts from the ground, so $v = 4.9$ and $s = 0$ in the vertical motion model.

$$h = -4.9t^2 + vt + s$$

$$= -4.9t^2 + 4.9t + 0$$

$$= -4.9t^2 + 4.9t$$

b. When the rabbit lands, its height above the ground is 0 meters. A reasonable domain for t can be found by substituting 0 for h and solving for t.

$$0 = -4.9t^2 + 4.9t$$

$$0 = 4.9t(-t + 1)$$

$4.9t = 0$ *or* $-t + 1 = 0$

$t = 0$ *or* $t = 1$

Since a height of 0 represents when the rabbit is on the ground, $t = 1$ second represents how long it takes for the rabbit to land back on the ground after jumping at $t = 0$ seconds. So, a reasonable domain is all real numbers greater than or equal to 0 and less than or equal to 1, or $0 \le t \le 1$.

WORKED-OUT SOLUTIONS

Lesson 9.5 (pp. 586–589)

7. In $z^2 + 8z - 48$, $c = -48$. Since c is negative, p and q must have different signs.

Factors of −48	Sum of factors	
−48, 1	−48 + 1 = −47	✗
48, −1	48 + (−1) = 47	✗
−24, 2	−24 + 2 = −22	✗
24, −2	24 + (−2) = 22	✗
−16, 3	−16 + 3 = −13	✗
16, −3	16 + (−3) = 13	✗
−12, 4	−12 + 4 = −8	✗
12, −4	12 + (−4) = 8	← Correct

So, $z^2 + 8z - 48 = (z + 12)(z - 4)$.

WORKED-OUT SOLUTIONS

61. Let x be the original length of the sides of the square photo. Then the length of the trimmed photo is $(x - 6)$ inches and its width is $(x - 5)$ inches. The formula $A = \ell \cdot w$ models the area of the trimmed photo which is 20 square inches.

$$A = \ell \cdot w$$
$$20 = (x - 6)(x - 5)$$
$$20 = x^2 - 11x + 30$$
$$0 = x^2 - 11x + 10$$
$$0 = (x - 10)(x - 1)$$
$$x - 10 = 0 \quad or \quad x - 1 = 0$$
$$x = 10 \quad or \quad x = 1$$

So, the original square photo had a side length of 10 inches or 1 inch. But an original length of 1 inch does not make sense in this situation, so the side length of the original square photo was 10 inches. Therefore, the perimeter of the original square photo was 4(10), or 40 inches.

Lesson 9.6 (pp. 596–599)

5. Factor −1 from each term of the trinomial: $-y^2 + 2y + 8 = -(y^2 - 2y - 8)$.

In $y^2 - 2y - 8$, $c = -8$. Since c is negative, the factors of c must have different signs.

Factors of −8	Possible factorization	Middle term when multiplied	
−8, 1	$(y - 8)(y + 1)$	$y - 8y = -7y$	✗
8, −1	$(y + 8)(y - 1)$	$-y + 8y = 7y$	✗
−4, 2	$(y - 4)(y + 2)$	$2y - 4y = -2y$	← Correct
4, −2	$(y + 4)(y - 2)$	$-2y + 4y = 2y$	✗

So, $y^2 - 2y - 8 = (y - 4)(y + 2)$. Therefore,

$$-y^2 + 2y + 8 = -(y^2 - 2y - 8)$$
$$= -(y - 4)(y + 2)$$

25. $4s^2 + 11s - 3 = 0$

$$(4s - 1)(s + 3) = 0$$
$$4s - 1 = 0 \quad or \quad s + 3 = 0$$
$$s = \frac{1}{4} \quad or \quad s = -3$$

61. Let w be the width of the Parthenon's base. Then $2w + 8$ is the length of the base. The formula $A = \ell \cdot w$ models the area of the rectangular base which is 2170 square meters.

$$A = \ell \cdot w$$
$$2170 = (2w + 8) \cdot w$$
$$2170 = 2w^2 + 8w$$
$$0 = 2w^2 + 8w - 2170$$
$$0 = 2(w^2 + 4w - 1085)$$
$$0 = 2(w + 35)(w - 31)$$
$$w + 35 = 0 \quad or \quad w - 31 = 0$$
$$w = -35 \quad or \quad w = 31$$

The solutions are −35 and 31.

Since the width cannot be negative, reject −35 as a solution. So, the width is 31 meters and the length is 2(31) + 8, or 70 meters. Therefore, the base of the Parthenon has length 70 meters and width 31 meters.

Lesson 9.7 (pp. 603–605)

11. $49a^2 + 14a + 1 = (7a)^2 + 2(7a \cdot 1) + 1^2$

$$= (7a + 1)^2$$

49. Use the vertical motion model with $h = 54$, $v = 56$, and $s = 5$.

$$h = -16t^2 + vt + s$$
$$54 = -16t^2 + 56t + 5$$
$$0 = -16t^2 + 56t - 49$$
$$0 = -(16t^2 - 56t + 49)$$
$$0 = -[(4t)^2 - 2(4t \cdot 7) + 7^2]$$
$$0 = -(4t - 7)^2$$
$$0 = (4t - 7)^2$$
$$4t - 7 = 0$$
$$t = 1.75$$

The ball reaches a height of 54 feet in 1.75 seconds. Since there is one solution for t, the ball reaches a height of 54 feet just once.

Lesson 9.8 (pp. 610–613)

13. $x^3 + x^2 + 2x + 2 = (x^3 + x^2) + (2x + 2)$

$= x^2(x + 1) + 2(x + 1)$

$= (x + 1)(x^2 + 2)$

23. $x^4 - x^2 = x^2(x^2 - 1) = x^2(x - 1)(x + 1)$

71. a. Substitute 0 for h in $h = -4.9t^2 + 3.9t + 1$.

$0 = -4.9t^2 + 3.9t + 1$

$0 = -(4.9t^2 - 3.9t - 1)$

$0 = -(4.9t + 1)(t - 1)$

$4.9t + 1 = 0$ *or* $t - 1 = 0$

$t \approx -0.20$ *or* $t = 1$

The zeros are 1 and about -0.2.

b. The zero $t \approx -0.2$ has no meaning in this situation because t represents time which cannot be negative. The zero $t = 1$ means that the pallino hits the ground (where $h = 0$) 1 second after it is thrown.

Chapter 10

Lesson 10.1 (pp. 632–634)

7. Make a table of values for $y = -2x^2$.

x	−2	−1	0	1	2
y	−8	−2	0	−2	−8

Plot the points from the table. Draw a smooth curve through the points.

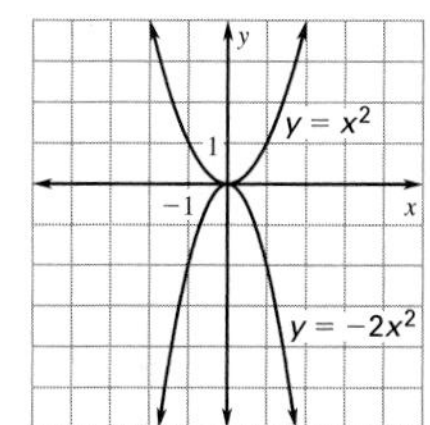

The graphs of $y = -2x^2$ and $y = x^2$ have the same vertex, (0, 0), and the same axis of symmetry, $x = 0$. However, the graph of $-2x^2$ is narrower than the graph of $y = x^2$, and it opens down. This is because the graph of $y = -2x^2$ is a vertical stretch (by a factor of 2) with a reflection in the x-axis of the graph of $y = x^2$.

41. a.

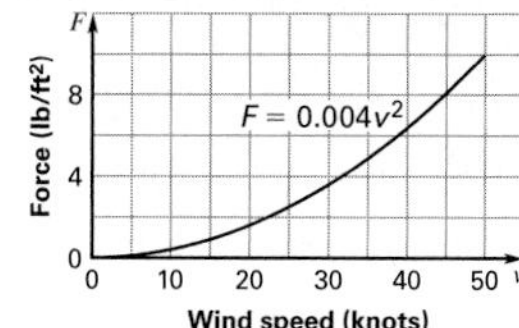

b. From the graph, the wind speed that will produce a force of 1 pound per square foot on a sail is about 16 knots. Using the function to check: $F = 0.004(16)^2 = 1.024$.

c. From the graph, the wind speed that will produce a force of 5 pounds per square foot on a sail is about 35 knots. Using the function to check: $F = 0.004(35)^2 = 4.9$.

Lesson 10.2 (pp. 638–640)

9. For $y = -\frac{2}{3}x^2 - 1$, $a = -\frac{2}{3}$ and $b = 0$.

$x = -\frac{b}{2a} = \frac{0}{2\left(-\frac{2}{3}\right)} = 0$

The axis of symmetry is $x = 0$.

The x-coordinate of the vertex, $-\frac{b}{2a}$, is 0. To find the y-coordinate, substitute 0 for x in the function and find y: $y = -\frac{2}{3}(0)^2 - 1 = -1$. The vertex is $(0, -1)$.

41. The highest point of each parabolic arch is at the vertex of the parabola. The height h is the y-coordinate of the vertex.

To find the x-coordinate of the vertex, use $x = -\frac{b}{2a}$ with $a = -0.0019$ and $b = 0.71$.

$x = -\frac{b}{2a} = -\frac{0.71}{2(-0.0019)} \approx 187$

Substitute 187 for x in the given equation to find the y-coordinate of the vertex.

$y = -0.0019(187)^2 + 0.71(187) \approx 66.3$

The height h at the highest point of the arch is about 66 feet.

WORKED-OUT SOLUTIONS

Lesson 10.3 (pp. 647–649)

5. Write the equation $x^2 + 6x = -8$ in standard form: $x^2 + 6x + 8 = 0$.

Graph the function $y = x^2 + 6x + 8$.

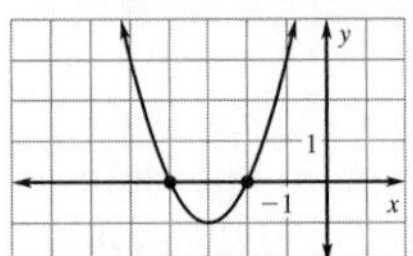

The x-intercepts are -4 and -2.

So, the solutions of $x^2 + 6x = -8$ are -4 and -2.

51. The width of the road can be found by finding the distance between the x-intercepts of the graph $y = -0.0017x^2 + 0.041x$.

Graph the function $y = -0.0017x^2 + 0.041x$ on a graphing calculator.

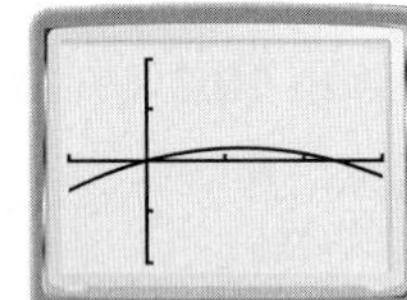

Use the *trace* feature of the graphing calculator to find the x-intercepts. There are two x-intercepts, one at 0 and one at approximately 24.12.

To the nearest tenth of a foot, the width of the road is 24.1 feet.

Lesson 10.4 (pp. 655–658)

25. $7c^2 = 100$

$$c^2 = \frac{100}{7}$$

$$c = \pm\sqrt{\frac{100}{7}}$$

$c \approx \pm 3.78$ Use a calculator.

59. First, solve the formula for D: $D = \pm\sqrt{\frac{w}{0.0018ds}}$.

Since D cannot be negative in this situation, use the positive square root only.

a. For amethyst, substitute 1 for w, 4.5 for d, and 2.65 for s.

$$D = \sqrt{\frac{1}{0.0018(4.5)(2.65)}} \approx 6.83$$

The diameter is about 6.8 millimeters.

b. For diamond, substitute 1 for w, 4.5 for d, and 3.52 for s.

$$D = \sqrt{\frac{1}{0.0018(4.5)(3.52)}} \approx 5.92$$

The diameter is about 5.9 millimeters.

c. For ruby, substitute 1 for w, 4.5 for d, and 4.00 for s.

$$D = \sqrt{\frac{1}{0.0018(4.5)(4.00)}} \approx 5.55$$

The diameter is about 5.6 millimeters.

Lesson 10.5 (pp. 666–668)

19.
$$z^2 + 11z = -\frac{21}{4}$$

$$z^2 + 11z + \left(\frac{11}{2}\right)^2 = -\frac{21}{4} + \left(\frac{11}{2}\right)^2$$

$$\left(z + \frac{11}{2}\right)^2 = -\frac{21}{4} + \frac{121}{4}$$

$$\left(z + \frac{11}{2}\right)^2 = 25$$

$$z + \frac{11}{2} = \pm 5$$

$$z = -\frac{11}{2} \pm 5$$

The solutions of the equation are $-\frac{11}{2} + 5 = -0.5$ and $-\frac{11}{2} - 5 = -10.5$.

47. a. Convert \$1,904,000 to thousands of dollars: $1,904,000 \div 1000 = 1904$.

Substitute 1904 for y in $y = 7x^2 - 4x + 392$: $1904 = 7x^2 - 4x + 392$.

$$7x^2 - 4x + 392 = 1904$$

$$7x^2 - 4x = 1512$$

$$x^2 - \frac{4}{7}x = 216$$

$$x^2 - \frac{4}{7}x + \left(\frac{2}{7}\right)^2 = 216 + \left(\frac{2}{7}\right)^2$$

$$\left(x - \frac{2}{7}\right)^2 = 216\frac{4}{49}$$

$$x - \frac{2}{7} = \pm\sqrt{216\frac{4}{49}}$$

$$x = \frac{2}{7} \pm \sqrt{216\frac{4}{49}}$$

Using a calculator, the solutions are about 14.99 and about -14.41.

The negative value does not make sense in this situation because the function does not model the years prior to 1985. So, the year when the average salary was \$1,904,000 was 1985 + 15, or 2000.

b. First, graph the function $y = 7x^2 - 4x + 392$ for $x \geq 0$. Then draw a dashed line at about $y = 1904$ until it intersects the curve. Draw a dashed line from this point down to the x-axis. The x-value here is about 15. So, the year when the average salary was \$1,904,000 is about 1985 + 15, or 2000.

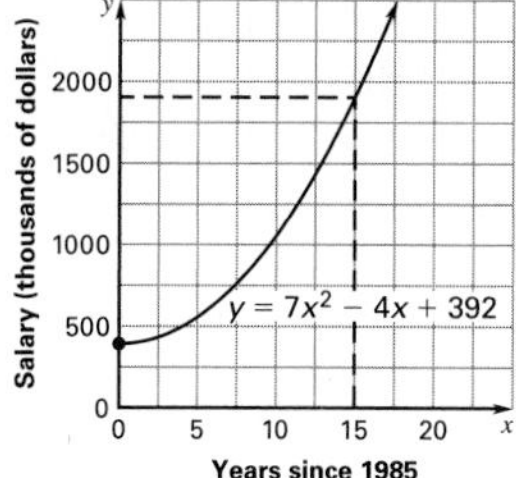

Lesson 10.6 (pp. 674–676)

19. Write $6z^2 = 2z^2 + 7z + 5$ in standard form: $4z^2 - 7z - 5 = 0$.

Use the quadratic formula, with $a = 4$, $b = -7$, and $c = -5$.

$$z = \frac{-(-7) \pm \sqrt{(-7)^2 - 4(4)(-5)}}{2(4)} = \frac{7 \pm \sqrt{129}}{8}$$

Using a calculator, the solutions are about 2.29 and about −0.54.

47. For 16,000,000 subscribers, $y = 16$ in the function.

$$16 = 0.7x^2 - 4.3x + 5.5$$

$$0 = 0.7x^2 - 4.3x - 10.5$$

Use the quadratic formula, with $a = 0.7$, $b = -4.3$, and $c = -10.5$.

$$x = \frac{-(-4.3) \pm \sqrt{(-4.3)^2 - 4(0.7)(-10.5)}}{2(0.7)}$$

$$= \frac{4.3 \pm \sqrt{47.89}}{1.4} \quad \text{Use a calculator.}$$

The solutions are about 8.01 and about −1.87.

The negative value does not make sense in this situation because the function does not model the years prior to 1985. So, the year when the number of subscribers was 16,000,000 was 1985 + 8, or 1993.

Lesson 10.7 (pp. 681–683)

9. Find the value of the discriminant. Substitute 25 for a, −16 for b, and 0 for c.

$$b^2 - 4ac = (-16)^2 - 4(25)(0) = 256$$

Since 256 > 0, the equation has two solutions.

47. In order for the child not to have to bend over, the height y of the arch must be at least 4 feet. Use the given quadratic equation with 4 substituted for y.

$$4 = -0.18x^2 + 1.6x$$

$$0 = -0.18x^2 + 1.6x - 4$$

Find the value of the discriminant. Substitute −0.18 for a, 1.6 for b, and −4 for c.

$$b^2 - 4ac = (1.6)^2 - 4(-0.18)(-4) = -0.32$$

Because the discriminant is negative, there are no solutions of the equation $0 = -0.18x^2 + 1.6x - 4$, meaning that the height of an arch is less than 4 feet. So, a child who is 4 feet tall would not be able to walk under one of the arches without having to bend over.

Lesson 10.8 (pp. 688–691)

7. 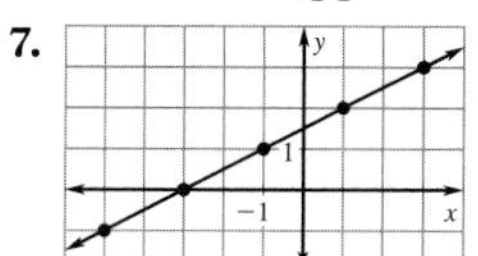 linear function

13.

x	−2	−1	0	1	2
y	−4	−1	0	−1	−4

First differences: +3 +1 −1 −3

Second differences: −2 −2 −2

The second differences are equal, so the table of values represents a quadratic function.

The equation has the form $y = ax^2$. Find the value of a by using the coordinates of a point (other than the origin) that lies on the graph, such as (−1, −1).

$$y = ax^2$$

$$-1 = a(-1)^2$$

$$-1 = a$$

An equation for the function is $y = -x^2$.

25. a. Troy: The population doubled every decade, so the data can be modeled by an exponential function. Union: The population increased by a fixed amount every decade, so the data can be modeled by a linear function.

b.

Decades since 1970	Troy's pop.
0	3000
1	6000
2	12,000
3	24,000
4	48,000

Decades since 1970	Union's pop.
0	3000
1	6000
2	9000
3	12,000
4	15,000

Troy: Ratios of successive y-values are equal. Union: First differences are constant.

c. Let P = population and n = number of decades since 1970. For 2030, $n = 6$. Troy: The population doubles, so $b = 2$. Use a data pair such as (1, 6000) to find a. Because $6000 = a(2^1)$, $a = 3000$. Then $P = 3000 \cdot 2^n$, and $P(6) = 3000 \cdot 2^6 = 192{,}000$. Union: The initial value is 3000 and the rate of change is 3000, so the linear function is $P = 3000n + 3000$, and $P(6) = 3000(6) + 3000 = 21{,}000$.

Chapter 11

Lesson 11.1 (pp. 713–716)

7. Make a table. Because the square root of a negative number is undefined, x must be nonnegative. So the domain of the function is $x \geq 0$.

x	0	1	2	3	4
y	0	1.5	2.1	2.6	3

Plot the ordered pairs from the table and then draw a smooth curve through the points. From the graph, it can seen that the range of the function is $y \geq 0$.

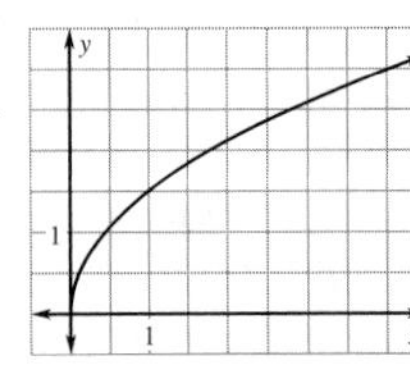

The graph of $y = \frac{3}{2}\sqrt{x}$ is a vertical stretch $\left(\text{by a factor of } \frac{3}{2}\right)$ of the graph of $y = \sqrt{x}$.

23. Make a table. Because the square root of a negative number is undefined, the value of $x - 1$ must be nonnegative: $x - 1 \geq 0$. So the domain of the function is $x \geq 1$.

x	1	2	3	4	5
y	0	1	1.4	1.7	2

Plot the ordered pairs from the table and then draw a smooth curve through the points.

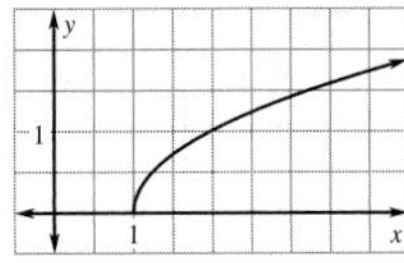

From the graph, it can seen that the range of the function is $y \geq 0$.

The graph of $y = \sqrt{x - 1}$ is a horizontal translation (of 1 unit to the right) of the graph of $y = \sqrt{x}$.

45. Because the square root of a negative number is undefined, h must be nonnegative. So the domain of the function is $s \geq 0$.

h	0	0.25	0.5	0.75	1
s	0	5.45	7.7	9.4	10.9

Plot the ordered pairs from the table and then draw a smooth curve through the points. From the graph, it can seen that the range of the function is $s \geq 0$.

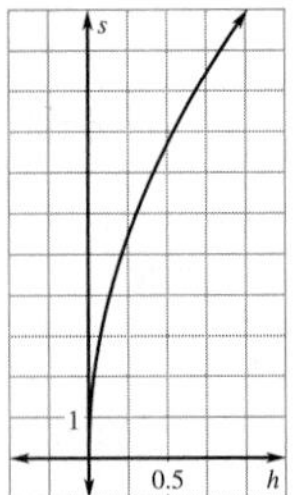

The maximum height reached is about 0.9 meter when the long jumper's speed before jumping is 10.25 meters per second.

Lesson 11.2 (pp. 723–726)

9. $\sqrt{81m^3} = \sqrt{81 \cdot m^2 \cdot m}$
$= \sqrt{81} \cdot \sqrt{m^2} \cdot \sqrt{m}$
$= 9m\sqrt{m}$

37. $9\sqrt{32} + \sqrt{2} = 9\sqrt{16 \cdot 2} + \sqrt{2}$
$= 9\sqrt{16} \cdot \sqrt{2} + \sqrt{2}$
$= 9 \cdot 4 \cdot \sqrt{2} + \sqrt{2}$
$= 36\sqrt{2} + \sqrt{2}$
$= (36 + 1)\sqrt{2}$
$= 37\sqrt{2}$

69. a. \$30 ÷ \$6 per square yard = 5 square yards

b. $s\text{ yd} = \sqrt{\frac{S\text{ yd}^2}{6}} = \sqrt{\frac{S}{6} \cdot \frac{\text{yd}^2}{1}}$

$= \sqrt{\frac{S}{6}} \cdot \sqrt{\frac{\text{yd}^2}{1}} = \sqrt{\frac{S}{6}}\text{ yd}$

Therefore $s\text{ yd} = \sqrt{\frac{S}{6}}\text{ yd}$, and the units check.

c. Substitute 5 for S in the formula $s = \sqrt{\frac{S}{6}}$:

$s = \sqrt{\frac{5}{6}} \approx 0.9.$

To the nearest tenth of a yard, the edge length of the largest footrest you can cover with 5 square yards of fabric is 0.9 yard.

Lesson 11.3 (pp. 732–734)

11. $\sqrt{6 - 2x} + 12 = 21$

$\sqrt{6 - 2x} = 9$

$6 - 2x = 81$

$-2x = 75$

$x = -\frac{75}{2}$, or $-37\frac{1}{2}$

37. Substitute 20 for y in the given function.

$\sqrt{18x + 272} = 20$

$18x + 272 = 400$

$18x = 128$

$x = \frac{128}{18}$, or about 7.1

So, the annual banana consumption in the United States reached 20 pounds per person in the year 1970 + 7, or 1977.

Lesson 11.4 (pp. 740–742)

9. $a^2 + b^2 = c^2$

$8^2 + 12^2 = c^2$ Substitute 8 for a and 12 for b.

$208 = c^2$

$\sqrt{208} = c$ Positive square root only.

$4\sqrt{13} = c$

23. Check to see if $a^2 + b^2 = c^2$ when $a = 2$, $b = 3$, and $c = 4$.

$2^2 + 3^2 \stackrel{?}{=} 4^2$

$4 + 9 \stackrel{?}{=} 16$

$13 \neq 16$ Not a right triangle

35. Check to see if $a^2 + b^2 = c^2$ when $a = 87$, $b = 173$, and $c = 190$.

$87^2 + 173^2 \stackrel{?}{=} 190^2$

$7569 + 29{,}929 \stackrel{?}{=} 36{,}100$

$37498 \neq 36100$

So, the triangle is not a right triangle. The sum of the squares of the lengths of the two shorter sides is not equal to the square of the length of the longest side.

Lesson 11.5 (pp. 747–750)

7. Let $(x_1, y_1) = (-4, 1)$ and $(x_2, y_2) = (3, -1)$.

$d = \sqrt{(x_2 - x_1)^2 + (y_2 - y_1)^2}$

$= \sqrt{(3 - (-4))^2 + (-1 - 1)^2}$

$= \sqrt{7^2 + (-2)^2} = \sqrt{53}$

23. Let $(x_1, y_1) = (6, -3)$ and $(x_2, y_2) = (4, -7)$.

$\left(\frac{x_1 + x_2}{2}, \frac{y_1 + y_2}{2}\right) = \left(\frac{6 + 4}{2}, \frac{-3 + (-7)}{2}\right) = (5, -5)$

49. a. The coordinates of the anchor are (2, 3), the coordinates of the sword are (9, 2), and the coordinates of the cup are (8, 5).

Distance between the anchor and sword: Let $(x_1, y_1) = (2, 3)$ and $(x_2, y_2) = (9, 2)$.

$d = \sqrt{(9 - 2)^2 + (2 - 3)^2}$

$= \sqrt{7^2 + (-1)^2} = \sqrt{50}$

Distance between the anchor and cup: Let $(x_1, y_1) = (2, 3)$ and $(x_2, y_2) = (8, 5)$.

$d = \sqrt{(8 - 2)^2 + (5 - 3)^2}$

$= \sqrt{6^2 + (2)^2} = \sqrt{40}$

Since $\sqrt{40} < \sqrt{50}$, the anchor and the cup are closer together.

b. By examining the survey grid, the belt buckle and the sword are closest together; they are 3 units, or 150 feet, apart.

Again, by examining the survey grid, the two objects farthest apart are either the anchor and cup or the anchor and sword. The result in part (a) shows that the anchor and the sword are farthest apart; they are $\sqrt{50}$ units, or $50\sqrt{50} \approx 354$ feet, apart.

Chapter 12

Lesson 12.1 (pp. 769–772)

17. Make a table by choosing several integer values of x and finding the values of y. Notice that x cannot be 0, and that y will never be 0.

x	−7	−5	−2	−1	0	1	2	5	7
y	1	1.4	3.5	7	—	−7	−3.5	−1.4	−1

Plot the points (x, y) from the table.

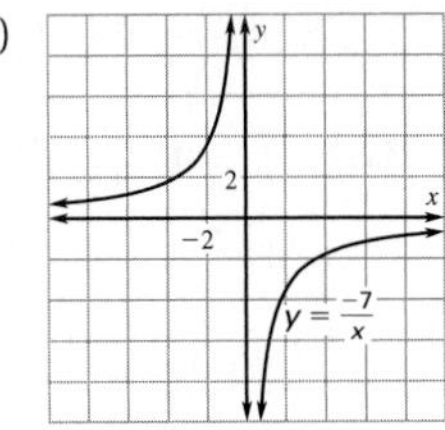

Connect the points in Quadrant II by drawing a smooth curve through them. Draw a separate curve though the points in Quadrant IV.

33. Because y varies inversely with x, the equation has the form $y = \frac{a}{x}$. Use the fact that $x = -22$ when $y = -6$ to find the value of a.

$-6 = \frac{a}{-22}$, so $a = -6(-22)$, or 132

An equation that relates x and y is $y = \frac{132}{x}$.
When $x = 2$, $y = \frac{132}{2}$, or 66.

57. a. An inverse variation equation can be used to model the data if each pair of points (ℓ, f) fits the same equation. Use $f = \frac{a}{\ell}$ to test the data.

For (42.1, 523): $523 = \frac{a}{42.1}$, so $a \approx 22{,}000$

For (37.5, 587): $587 = \frac{a}{37.5}$, so $a \approx 22{,}000$

For (33.4, 659): $659 = \frac{a}{33.4}$, so $a \approx 22{,}000$

For (31.5, 698): $698 = \frac{a}{31.5}$, so $a \approx 22{,}000$

Since the value of a is about the same for each pairing, the inverse equation $f = \frac{22{,}000}{\ell}$ can be used to model the data.

To graph $f = \frac{22{,}000}{\ell}$, make a table of values, plot the points (ℓ, f), and then draw a smooth curve through them. Use only positive values for ℓ since the length of a string cannot be negative.

ℓ	25	50	75	100
f	880	440	293.3	220

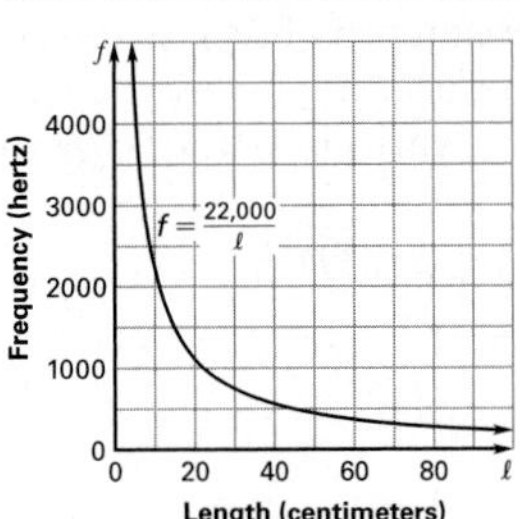

b. Use the equation found in part (a) with $\ell = 29.4$.

$f = \frac{22{,}000}{29.4} \approx 748.3$

The frequency is about 748 hertz.

c. The frequency increases as the length of the string decreases. Yes, the length in part (b), 29.4 centimeters, is shorter than those in the table, but it has the greatest frequency.

Lesson 12.2 (pp. 779–782)

7. Make a table of values for x and y.

x	$-\frac{1}{2}$	$-\frac{1}{4}$	0	$\frac{1}{4}$	$\frac{1}{2}$
y	$\frac{1}{2}$	1	—	−1	$-\frac{1}{2}$

Plot the points (x, y) from the table. Connect the points in Quadrant II by drawing a smooth curve through them. Draw a separate curve though the points in Quadrant IV.

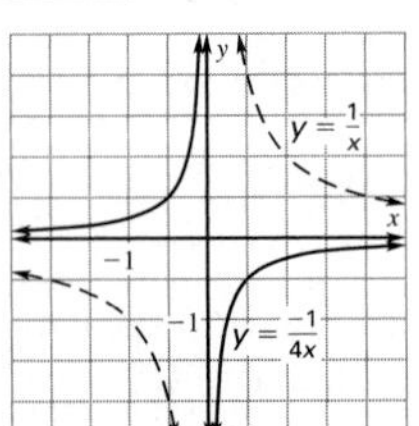

The graph of $y = \frac{-1}{4x}$ is a vertical shrink with a reflection in the x-axis of the graph of $y = \frac{1}{x}$.

WORKED-OUT SOLUTIONS

21. The vertical asymptote of the graph is $x = -7$ and the horizontal asymptote is $y = 5$. Plot several points on each side of the vertical asymptote, such as $(-9, 3)$, $(-8, 1)$, $(-5, 7)$, and $(-3, 6)$. Draw the two branches of the graph that pass through the plotted points and approach the asymptotes.

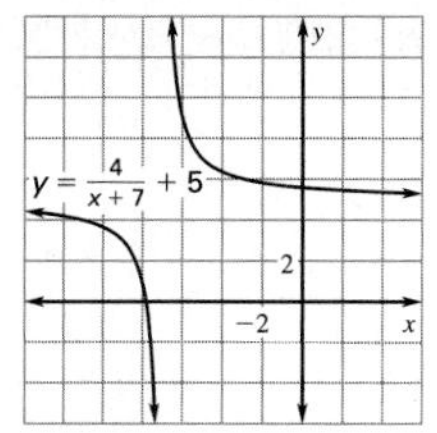

41. a. Use a verbal model to write an equation.

Average cost (dollars)	=	Total cost (dollars)	÷	(Number of additional rentals	+ 2)

$C = 22 \div (r + 2)$, or $C = \frac{22}{r + 2}$

b.

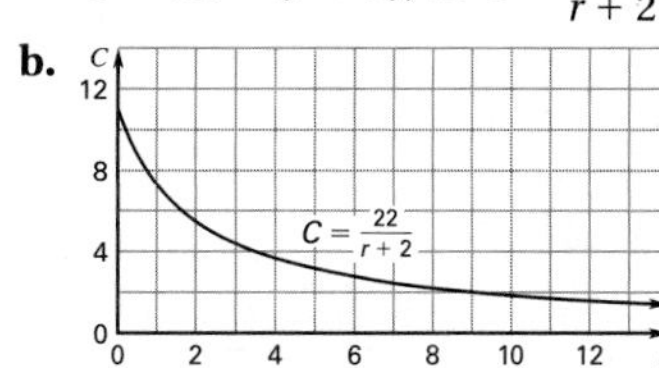

The graph shows that as the number of rentals increases, the average cost per rental decreases.

From the graph, the number of additional rentals needed per month so that the average cost is $1.50 per rental is 13 additional rentals.

Lesson 12.3 (pp. 788–791)

7.
$$\begin{array}{r} 3v + 5 \\ v - 2\overline{)3v^2 - v - 10} \\ \underline{3v^2 - 6v} \\ 5v - 10 \\ \underline{5v - 10} \\ 0 \end{array}$$

25. Rewrite the function in the form $y = \frac{a}{x - h} + k$.

$$\begin{array}{r} 2 \\ x - 1\overline{)2x - 4} \\ \underline{2x - 2} \\ -2 \end{array}$$

So, $y = \frac{-2}{x - 1} + 2$.

The asymptotes of the graph can be identified from the equation. The vertical asymptote is $x = 1$ and the horizontal asymptote is $y = 2$. Plot several points on each side of the vertical asymptote, such as $(-1, 3)$, $(0, 4)$, $(2, 0)$, and $(3, 1)$. Draw the two branches of the graph.

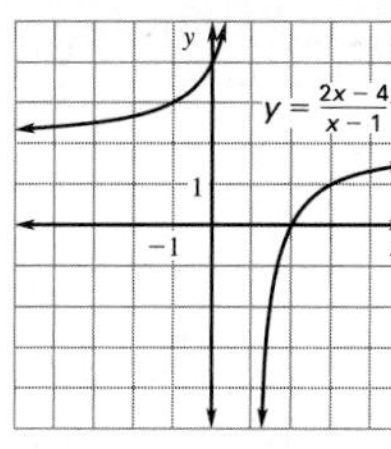

45. a. Since t is defined as the time for 1000 minutes or more, the domain of the function is $t \geq 1000$. The average cost C is found by adding the monthly fee to the product of the number of minutes over 1000 and the per-minute charge for those minutes, and then dividing that sum by the total number of minutes of use. The equation is $C = \frac{40 + 0.40(t - 1000)}{t}$, or $C = \frac{0.4t - 360}{t}$, where $t \geq 1000$.

b. Choose values of $t \geq 1000$.

t	1000	1100	1200	1300	1400	1500
C	0.04	0.073	0.10	0.123	0.143	0.16

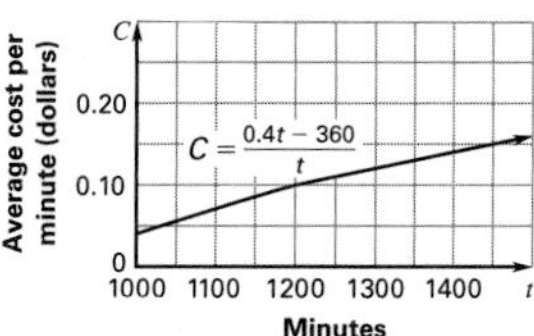

The average cost per minute increases as the number of minutes over 1000 increases.

c. From the graph you can see that the number of minutes used is about 1030 minutes if the average cost is $.05 per minute.

Lesson 12.4 (pp. 797–800)

9. The expression $\frac{-3}{2p^2 - p}$ is undefined when $2p^2 - p = 0$.

$2p^2 - p = 0$

$p(2p - 1) = 0$

$p = 0 \quad or \quad 2p - 1 = 0$

$p = \frac{1}{2}$

The excluded values are 0 and $\frac{1}{2}$.

WORKED-OUT SOLUTIONS

23. $\frac{h+3}{h^2-h-12} = \frac{h+3}{(h-4)(h+3)}$

$= \frac{\cancel{h+3}}{(h-4)\cancel{(h+3)}}$

$= \frac{1}{h-4}$

The excluded values are 4 and −3.

43. The percent of wood houses can be found by using the formula $p = \frac{W}{H}$.

$p = \frac{-20{,}200x + 366{,}000}{34{,}500x + 913{,}000} = \frac{-202x + 3660}{345x + 9130}$

To determine how the percent changed during the period 1990–2002, evaluate the function for several values of x.

For 1990, $x = 0$: $\frac{-202(0) + 3660}{345(0) + 9130} = \frac{3660}{9130} \approx 0.40$

In 1990, about 40% of new single-family houses were wood houses.

For 1994, $x = 4$: $\frac{-202(4) + 3660}{345(4) + 9130} = \frac{2852}{10{,}510} \approx 0.27$

In 1994, about 27% of new single-family houses were wood houses.

For 1998, $x = 8$: $\frac{-202(8) + 3660}{345(8) + 9130} = \frac{2044}{11{,}890} \approx 0.17$

In 1998, about 17% of new single-family houses were wood houses.

For 2002, $x = 12$:
$\frac{-202(12) + 3660}{345(12) + 9130} = \frac{1236}{13{,}270} \approx 0.09$

In 2002, about 9% of new single-family houses were wood houses.

The percent of wood houses decreased steadily from 1990 to 2002.

Lesson 12.5 (pp. 806–809)

5. $\frac{v^2 + v - 12}{5v + 10} \cdot \frac{-v - 2}{v^2 + 5v + 4}$

$= \frac{(v^2 + v - 12)(-v - 2)}{(5v + 10)(v^2 + 5v + 4)}$

$= \frac{\cancel{(v+4)}(v-3)(-1)\cancel{(v+2)}}{5\cancel{(v+2)}\cancel{(v+4)}(v+1)}$

$= \frac{-(v-3)}{5(v+1)}$

15. $\frac{2w^2 + 5w}{w^2 - 81} \div \frac{w^2}{w + 9} = \frac{2w^2 + 5w}{w^2 - 81} \cdot \frac{w + 9}{w^2}$

$= \frac{(2w^2 + 5w)(w + 9)}{(w^2 - 81)(w^2)}$

$= \frac{\cancel{(w)}(2w + 5)\cancel{(w+9)}}{\cancel{(w+9)}(w - 9)\cancel{(w)}(w)}$

$= \frac{2w + 5}{w(w - 9)}$

35. a. Use the formula $R = Y \div A$.

$R = \frac{860 + 1800x}{1 + 0.024x} \div \frac{230 + 380x}{1 + 0.014x}$

$= \frac{860 + 1800x}{1 + 0.024x} \cdot \frac{1 + 0.014x}{230 + 380x}$

$= \frac{(860 + 1800x)(1 + 0.014x)}{(1 + 0.024x)(230 + 380x)}$

$= \frac{\cancel{(10)}(86 + 180x)(1 + 0.014x)}{(1 + 0.024x)\cancel{(10)}(23 + 38x)}$

$= \frac{(86 + 180x)(1 + 0.014x)}{(1 + 0.024x)(23 + 38x)}$

b.

x	0	1	2	3	4	5	6
R	3.74	4.32	4.42	4.44	4.44	4.42	4.40

x	7	8	9	10	11	12
R	4.38	4.35	4.33	4.30	4.28	4.25

Smith's career rushing average increased for the first several years, and then began to decrease.

Lesson 12.6 (pp. 816–819)

7. $\frac{b}{b-3} + \frac{b+1}{b-3} = \frac{b + b + 1}{b-3} = \frac{2b+1}{b-3}$

29. $\frac{2j}{j^2 - 1} + \frac{j - 1}{j^2 - 7j + 6}$

$= \frac{2j}{(j-1)(j+1)} + \frac{j-1}{(j-1)(j-6)}$

$= \frac{2j(j-6)}{(j-1)(j+1)(j-6)} + \frac{(j - 1(j+1)}{(j-1)(j-6)(j+1)}$

$= \frac{2j(j-6) + (j-1)(j+1)}{(j-1)(j+1)(j-6)}$

$= \frac{2j^2 - 12j + j^2 - 1}{(j-1)(j+1)(j-6)}$

$= \frac{3j^2 - 12j - 1}{(j-1)(j+1)(j-6)}$

45. a. For $A \le 50$: $\frac{2A^2}{3} + \frac{200A}{3} = \frac{2A^2 + 200A}{3}$

For $A > 50$, $\frac{7A^2}{150} + (125A - 1367)$

$= \frac{7A^2}{150} + \frac{150(125A - 1367)}{150}$

$= \frac{7A^2 + 150(125A - 1367)}{150}$

$= \frac{7A^2 + 18{,}750A - 205{,}050}{150}$

b. For $A = 30$ ft^2, use the formula for $A \le 50$:

$W = \frac{2(30)^2 + 200(30)}{3} = \frac{7800}{3} = 2600$

The minimum weight this elevator must hold is 2600 pounds.

For $A = 60$ ft^2, use the formula for $A > 50$:

$W = \frac{7(60)^2 + 18{,}750(60) - 205{,}050}{150}$

$= \frac{945{,}150}{150} = 6301$

The minimum weight this elevator must hold is 6301 pounds.

Lesson 12.7 (pp. 823–826)

7. $\frac{2m}{m+4} = \frac{3}{m-1}$

$2m^2 - 2m = 3m + 12$

$2m^2 - 5m - 12 = 0$

$(2m + 3)(m - 4) = 0$

$2m + 3 = 0$ *or* $m - 4 = 0$

$m = -1\frac{1}{2}$ *or* $m = 4$

15. $\frac{z}{z+7} - 3 = \frac{-1}{z+7}$

$\frac{z}{z+7} \cdot (z + 7) - 3(z + 7) = \frac{-1}{z+7} \cdot (z + 7)$

$\frac{z\cancel{(z+7)}}{\cancel{z+7}} - 3(z + 7) = \frac{-1\cancel{(z+7)}}{\cancel{z+7}}$

$z - 3z - 21 = -1$

$-2z = 20$

$z = -10$

33. Let w be the number of cups of water needed.

$$\frac{\text{Cups of water in cleaning solution} + \text{Cups of water needed}}{\text{Cups of cleaning solution} + \text{Cups of water needed}} = \text{Desired fraction of water in mixture}$$

$\frac{7 + w}{9 + w} = \frac{5}{6}$

$(7 + w)6 = (9 + w)5$

$42 + 6w = 45 + 5w$

$w = 3$

You need to add 3 cups of water to the cleaning solution.

Chapter 13

Lesson 13.1 (pp. 846–848)

3. Use a tree diagram to find the possible outcomes in the sample space.

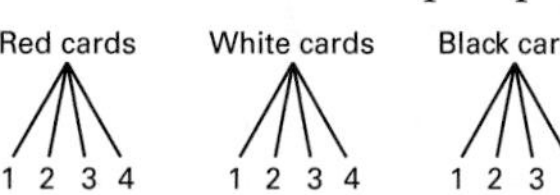

The sample space has 12 possible outcomes. The outcomes are: Red 1, Red 2, Red 3, Red 4, White 1, White 2, White 3, White 4, Black 1, Black 2, Black 3, Black 4.

21. Since there are 15 girls and 12 boys, there are a total of 27 students. So there are 27 possible outcomes.

$P(\text{boy}) = \frac{\text{Number of boys}}{\text{Total number of students}} = \frac{12}{27} = \frac{4}{9}$

Odds in favor of choosing a boy

$= \frac{\text{Number of boys}}{\text{Number of girls}} = \frac{12}{15} = \frac{4}{5}$

Sample answer: The probability and odds of choosing a boy are related because they each compare the number of favorable outcomes to another number. The probability of choosing a boy compares the number of boys to the total number of outcomes possible, while the odds of choosing a boy compare the number of boys to the total number of outcomes less the number of boys.

WORKED-OUT SOLUTIONS

Lesson 13.2 (pp. 853–855)

21. $_7P_3 = \frac{7!}{(7-3)!} = \frac{7!}{4!} = \frac{7 \cdot 6 \cdot 5 \cdot \cancel{4!}}{\cancel{4!}} = 210$

35. a. The total number of possible outcomes for the order on the first day is the number of permutations of the 4 student presenters on that day: $_4P_4 = 4!$.

The number of favorable outcomes (being chosen to be the first or second presenter) is the number of permutations of the 3 other presenters, given that you are chosen to be the first or second presenter. This is $_3P_3 = 3!$ if you are the first presenter and also $_3P_3 = 3!$ if you are the second presenter.

$P(\text{1st or 2nd presenter})$
$= P(\text{1st presenter}) + P(\text{2nd presenter})$

$= \frac{3!}{4!} + \frac{3!}{4!} = \frac{1}{4} + \frac{1}{4}, \text{ or } \frac{1}{2}$

The probability that you are the first or the second presenter is $\frac{1}{2}$.

b. The number of possible outcomes is still 4!. The number of favorable outcomes is again $_3P_3 = 3!$ for you being the second presenter and $_3P_3 = 3!$ for you being the third presenter.

$P(\text{2nd or 3rd presenter})$
$= P(\text{2nd presenter}) + P(\text{3rd presenter})$

$= \frac{3!}{4!} + \frac{3!}{4!} = \frac{1}{4} + \frac{1}{4}, \text{ or } \frac{1}{2}$

The probability that you are the second or the third presenter is $\frac{1}{2}$.

This answer is the same as the answer in part (a).

Lesson 13.3 (pp. 858–859)

7. $_8C_5 = \frac{8!}{(8-5)!5!} = \frac{8!}{3!5!} = \frac{8 \cdot 7 \cdot 6 \cdot \cancel{5!}}{3! \cdot \cancel{5!}} = 56$

25. a. The number of possible outcomes is the number of combinations of the 9 contestants taken 6 at a time, or $_9C_6$, because the order in which the contestants are chosen is not important.

$_9C_6 = \frac{9!}{(9-6)!6!} = \frac{9!}{3!6!} = \frac{9 \cdot 8 \cdot 7 \cdot \cancel{6!}}{3! \cdot \cancel{6!}} = 84$

There are 84 possible combinations of 6 players from the group of eligible contestants.

b. Find the number of favorable outcomes, those where you and your two friends are 3 of the 6 contestants selected to play. The order of the selections is not important. The favorable outcomes are those where only 3 of the other 6 eligible contestants are chosen. So the number of favorable combinations is $_6C_3 = 20$. Therefore, the probability that you and your friends are chosen is $\frac{20}{84}$, or $\frac{5}{21}$.

Lesson 13.4 (pp. 864–867)

5. Rolling an odd number on a number cube and rolling a number less than 5 are overlapping events as shown in the diagram. There are two numbers less than 5 that are odd, 1 and 3.

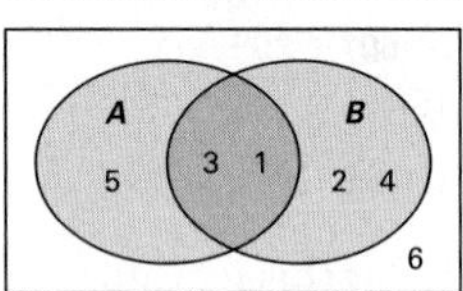

The probability of rolling an odd number is $\frac{3}{6} = \frac{1}{2}$, the probability of rolling a number less than 5 is $\frac{4}{6} = \frac{2}{3}$, and the probability of rolling a number that is both odd and less than 5 is $\frac{2}{6} = \frac{1}{3}$.

Using the formula for finding the probability of overlapping events,

$P(A \text{ or } B) = P(A) + P(B) - P(A \text{ and } B)$
$= \frac{3}{6} + \frac{4}{6} - \frac{2}{6} = \frac{5}{6}$

23. Let Event A be using a flipper to forage for food and let Event B be using the right flipper if the flipper wave technique is used. These two events are dependent.

$P(A) = 70\% = 0.7$ and
$P(B \text{ given } A) = 89\% = 0.89$

Using the formula for finding the probability of dependent events,

$P(A \text{ and } B) = P(A) \cdot P(B \text{ given } A)$
$= 0.7 \cdot 0.89 = 0.623, \text{ or } 62.3\%$

The probability that a walrus foraging for food uses a flipper and that it is the right flipper is 62.3%.

WORKED-OUT SOLUTIONS

Lesson 13.5 (pp. 873–874)

3. The population is all persons who dine at the restaurant. Because the diners ultimately decide whether or not to take part in the survey by mailing their comment cards, this is a self-selected sample.

15. No. *Sample answer:* The sample may be biased. It does not include fans who only listen to or watch games broadcast on radio or television. The sample is also self-selected. Fans in attendance have to choose to turn in their surveys in order to be counted.

Lesson 13.6 (pp. 877–878)

7. Mean:

$$\bar{x} = \frac{5.52 + 5.44 + 3.60 + 5.76 + 3.80 + 7.22}{6}$$

$$= \frac{31.34}{6} = 5.2233...$$

So, the mean of the data is $5.22\overline{3}$.

Median: The ordered list of numbers is: 3.60, 3.80, 5.44, 5.52, 5.76, 7.22. There are two middle values, 5.44 and 5.52. Therefore, the median is $\frac{5.44 + 5.52}{2} = 5.48$.

Each data value appears just once, so there is no mode.

19. a. The range of the pumpkin weights is the difference of the greatest value and the least value; $24 - 5 = 19$ pounds.

b. Mean: $\bar{x} =$

$$\frac{22 + 21 + 24 + 24 + 5 + 24 + 5 + 23 + 24 + 24}{10}$$

$$= \frac{196}{10} = 19.6$$

The mean of the pumpkin weights is 19.6 pounds.

Median: The ordered list of weights is: 5, 5, 21, 22, 23, 24, 24, 24, 24, 24. There are two middle values, 23 and 24. So, the median is 23.5 pounds.

Mode: The weight that occurs most frequently is 24 pounds.

c. The median best represents the data. *Sample answer:* The mode is the greatest data value and the mean is less than 8 of the 10 data values.

Lesson 13.7 (pp. 883–885)

3. First, separate the data into stems and leaves.

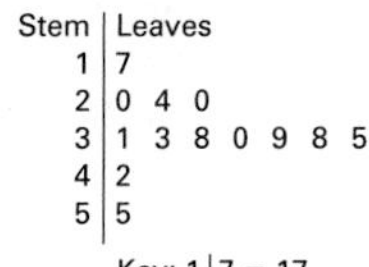

Stem	Leaves
1	7
2	0 4 0
3	1 3 8 0 9 8 5
4	2
5	5

Key: 1|7 = 17

Now rewrite the leaves in increasing order.

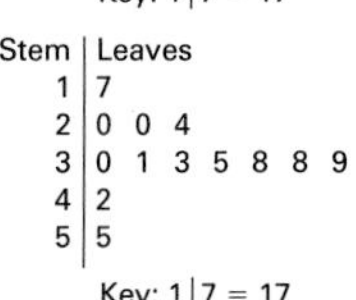

Stem	Leaves
1	7
2	0 0 4
3	0 1 3 5 8 8 9
4	2
5	5

Key: 1|7 = 17

19. a. Draw the bars of the histogram using the intervals from the frequency table.

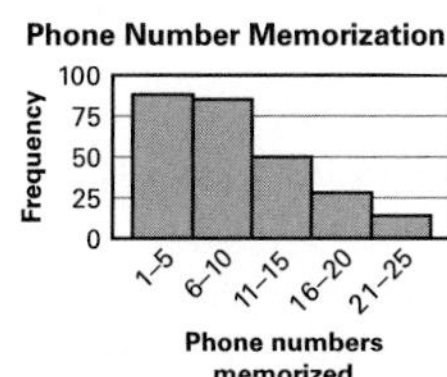

b. Use the table to determine the total number of people surveyed: $88 + 85 + 50 + 28 + 14 = 265$.

Determine the number of favorable outcomes. This number is the sum of the number of people in the 11–15 range, the 16–20 range, and the 21–25 range.

$$P(11\text{–}25) = \frac{\text{Number of favorable outcomes}}{\text{Total number of outcomes}}$$

$$= \frac{50 + 28 + 14}{265} = \frac{92}{265}$$

Lesson 13.8 (pp. 889–892)

3. Write the data in order from least to greatest. Find the median and the quartiles.

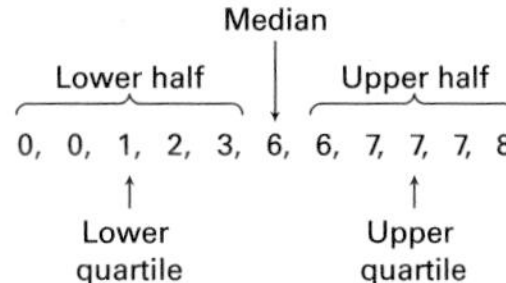

WORKED-OUT SOLUTIONS

Plot the median, the quartiles, the maximum value, and the minimum value below a number line. Draw a box from the lower quartile to the upper quartile. Draw a vertical line through the median. Draw a line segment from the side of the box to the maximum value and another from the other side of the box to the minimum value.

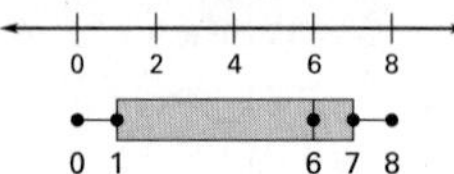

17. a. Order the data, and then find the median and the quartiles.

lower quartile: $\frac{\$38.4 + \$49.9}{2} = \$44.15$

median: $52.4

upper quartile: $\frac{\$107.0 + \$118.2}{2} = \$112.60$

Use the median, the quartiles, the maximum value, and the minimum value to draw the box-and-whisker plot.

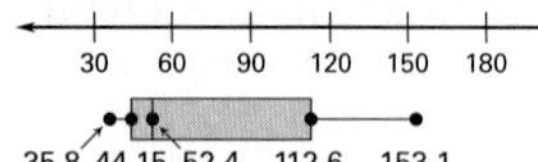

b. To check if any of the data are outliers, find the inner quartile range: $112.6 - 44.15 = 68.45$. An outlier would be any value greater than $1.5(68.45) + 112.6 = 215.275$ or less than $44.15 - 1.5(68.45) = -58.525$. Since all the data values are within these two values, there are no outliers. So, none of the states had retail sales that can be considered outliers.

WORKED-OUT SOLUTIONS

WS34

Chapter 1

1.1 Skill Practice (pp. 5–6) **1.** exponent: 12, base: 6 **3.** 60 **5.** 12 **7.** 12 **9.** 3 **11.** 10 **13.** $\frac{1}{3}$ **17.** seven to the third power, $7 \cdot 7 \cdot 7$ **19.** three tenths to the fourth power, $0.3 \cdot 0.3 \cdot 0.3 \cdot 0.3$ **21.** n to the seventh power, $n \cdot n \cdot n \cdot n \cdot n \cdot n \cdot n$ **23.** t to the fourth power, $t \cdot t \cdot t \cdot t$ **25.** The base was used as the exponent and the exponent was used as the base; $5^4 = 5 \cdot 5 \cdot 5 \cdot 5 = 625$. **27.** 100 **29.** 1331 **31.** 243 **33.** 1296 **35.** $\frac{27}{125}$ **37.** $\frac{1}{216}$ **39.** 1.21 **41.** 40.5 **43.** 9.6

1.1 Problem Solving (pp. 6–7) **49.** 162.5 cm **51. a.** 12 in. **b.** 144 $in.^2$ **53.** New England Patriots

1.2 Skill Practice (pp. 10–11) **1.** Square 4. **3.** 8 **5.** 14 **7.** $3\frac{3}{5}$ **9.** $63\frac{3}{4}$ **11.** 21 **13.** 73.5 **15.** $12\frac{1}{2}$ **17.** 48 **21.** $\frac{1}{2}$ was multiplied by 6 before squaring 6; $20 - \frac{1}{2} \cdot 6^2 = 20 - \frac{1}{2} \cdot 36 = 20 - 18 = 2$. **23.** 29 **25.** 126 **27.** 0.75 **29.** 3 **33.** $(2 \times 2 + 3)^2 - (4 + 3) \times 5$

1.2 Problem Solving (pp. 11–12) **35. a.** \$22.87 **b.** \$2.13 **37.** *Sample answer:* $(3 \times 4) + 5$ **39. a.** \$380, \$237.99; \$142.01 **b.** *Sample answer:* You could write an expression showing the difference of your income and expenses as $10s - (4.50m + 12.99)$.

1.2 Graphing Calculator Activity (p. 13) **1.** 5 **3.** 0.429 **5.** 0.188 **7.** 40.9 BMI units

1.3 Skill Practice (pp. 18–19) **1.** rate **3.** $x + 8$ **5.** $\frac{1}{2}m$ **7.** $7 - n$ **9.** $\frac{2t}{12}$ **11.** $2k - 7$ **15.** $4v$ **17.** $\frac{16}{p}$ **19.** $7 - d$ **21.** $12y$ **23.** 0.2 ft/sec **25.** 83.6 ft/sec **27.** Feet should cancel out; \$54. **29.** \$19.50 for 1 h

1.3 Problem Solving (pp. 19–20) **31.** $19.95t + 3$; \$102.75 **33. a.** \$.055, \$.06 **b.** 48 oz container **c.** \$.96 **35.** \$500 **37. a.** $12g + h + \frac{1}{4}c$ **b.** 247; 376.75; 242

1.4 Skill Practice (pp. 24–25) **1.** *Sample answer:* $3x + 5 = 20$ **3.** $42 + n = 51$ **5.** $9 - \frac{t}{6} = 5$ **7.** $9(t + 5) < 6$ **9.** $8 < b + 3 < 12$ **11.** $10 < t - 7 < 20$ **13.** $p \geq 12.99$ **15.** The wrong inequality symbol is used; $\frac{t}{4.2} \leq 15$. **17.** solution **19.** not a solution **21.** not a solution **23.** solution **25.** solution **27.** not a solution **29.** 5 **31.** 12 **33.** 9 **35.** $3x - 2 = x + 5$; solution

1.4 Problem Solving (pp. 25–26) **39.** 7.5 mi **41.** 167 h **43.** \$100 **45. a.** $6r + 5(10 - r) \geq 55$ **b.** Yes; you will earn \$30 running errands and \$25 walking dogs; $30 + 25 = 55$. **c.** Yes; if you work 10 hours running errands, you will earn \$60. You will not meet your goal if you work all 10 hours walking dogs.

1.5 Skill Practice (p. 31) **1.** *Sample answer:* $d = rt$ **3.** You know the cost of materials and the amount you hope to make. You need to find the amount you should charge for each collar. You need to know the number of collars you made, which is missing. **5.** You know the temperature in Rome and the temperature in Dallas. You know the formula to convert Fahrenheit temperatures to Celsius temperatures. You need to find the higher temperature. **7.** The formula for perimeter should be used, not area; $P = 2\ell + 2w$; $P = 2(200) + 2(150) = 700$; $\$10(700) = \$7000$. **9.** $P = I - E$

1.5 Problem Solving (pp. 32–33) **15.** 46.25 $in.^2$ **17.** 2 water bottles **19. a.** 960 ft **b.** 480 ft **21. a.**

Room size (feet)	1 by 1	2 by 2	3 by 3	4 by 4	5 by 5
Remaining area (square feet)	431	428	423	416	407

b. $1 \leq s \leq 5$; 5 ft

1.5 Problem Solving Workshop (p. 34)
1. 9 pieces of cake; Equation: Let c be the number of pieces of cake; $9c = 99$, $c = 11$. Diagram: Draw a diagram of a 9 inch by 11 inch pan and cut the cake into 3 inch by 3 inch pieces. From the diagram you see that you can cut 9 such pieces. The diagram shows that you cannot actually cut 11 square pieces because of the shape of the pan.

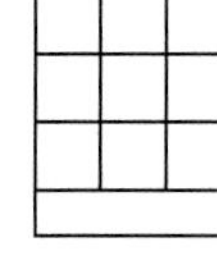

3. The equation should be $3x + 6 = 12$ because there are only 3 spaces between the 4 floats; $3(2) + 6 = 12$.

1.6 Skill Practice (pp. 38–39) **1.** input; output **3.** domain: 0, 1, 2, and 3, range: 5, 7, 15, and 44 **5.** domain: 6, 12, 21, and 42, range: 5, 7, 10, and 17 **7.** not a function **9.** The pairing is a function. Each input is paired with only one output.

11. *Sample:*

Input	Output
0	5
1	6
2	7
3	7
4	9
5	10

15.

Input	4	5	7	8	12
Output	7.5	8.5	10.5	11.5	15.5

range: 7.5, 8.5, 10.5, 11.5, and 15.5

17.

Input	4	6	9	11
Output	5	6	7.5	8.5

range: 5, 6, 7.5, and 8.5

19.

Input	0	2	4	6
Output	$\frac{1}{2}$	1	$1\frac{1}{2}$	2

range: $\frac{1}{2}$, 1, $1\frac{1}{2}$, and 2

21. $y = x - 8$

1.6 Problem Solving (pp. 39–40) **23. a.** the number of quarters left; the number of quarters used **b.** $y = 10 - x$; domain: 0, 1, 2, 3, 4, 5, 6, 7, 8, 9, and 10

c.

Input	0	1	2	3	4	5	6	7	8	9	10
Output	10	9	8	7	6	5	4	3	2	1	0

range: 0, 1, 2, 3, 4, 5, 6, 7, 8, 9, and 10

25. $y = 100 + 20m$; independent variable: m, the number of months; dependent variable: y, the amount of money saved; domain: $m > 0$, range: $y \geq 100$; $340

27. a.

2	3	4	5
A, B, C	D, E, F	G, H, I	J, K, L

6	7	8	9
M, N, O	P, Q, R, S	T, U, V	W, X, Y, Z

No; because there is more than one output for each input.

b.

A	B	C	D	E	F	G	H	I	J	K	L
2	2	2	3	3	3	4	4	4	5	5	5

M	N	O	P	Q	R	S	T	U	V	W	X	Y	Z
6	6	6	7	7	7	7	8	8	8	9	9	9	9

Yes; because there is only one output for each input.

1.6 Graphing Calculator Activity (p. 41) **1.** 50°F; scroll down until you see the output 10, look to see that the input is 50.

3.

Input	0	1	2	3
Output	5	5.75	6.5	7.25

5.

Input	1	2	3	4
Output	7	14.5	22	29.5

1.7 Skill Practice (pp. 46–47) **1.** domain; range

3. 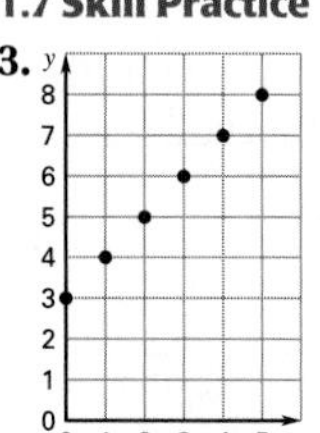

5. 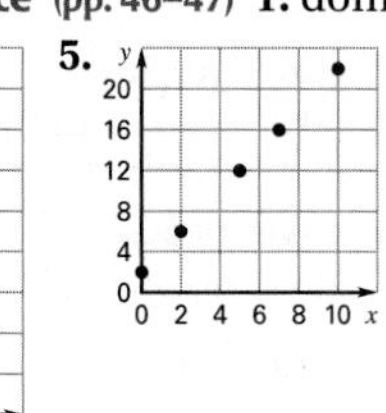

7. 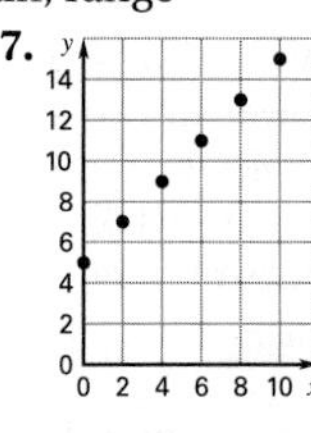

9. The domain and range are graphed backwards.

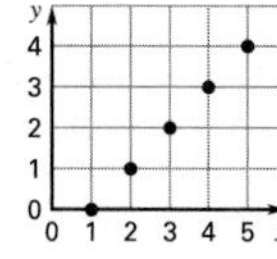

11. $y = 2x - 2$; domain: 1, 2, 3, and 4, range: 0, 2, 4, and 6

1.7 Problem Solving (pp. 47–48)

15.

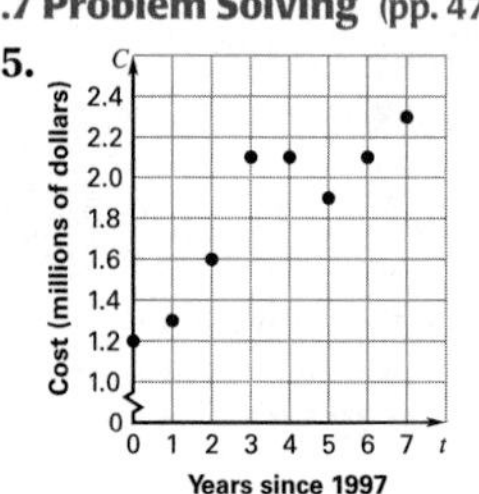

17.

Years since 1984	Voters	Voters (millions)
0	92,652,680	93
4	91,594,693	92
8	104,405,155	104
12	96,456,345	96
16	105,586,274	106

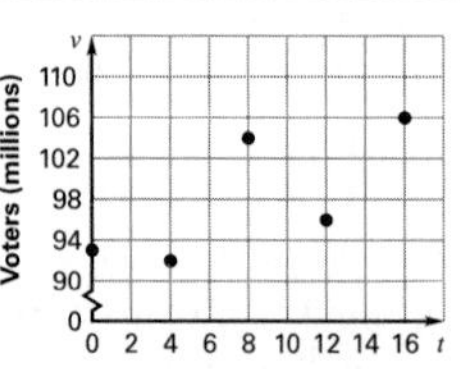

19. a. increases **b.** Yes; 27.5 grams is between the mass of an egg that is just under 38 millimeters long and an egg that is just over 38 millimeters long.

SA2

Extension (p. 50) **1.** function **3.** not a function **5.** function **7.** Not a function. *Sample answer:* There could be many students whose first names have 4 letters, for instance, but their last names could all have a different number of letters. **9.** Function; for each of your birthdays, you have only one height.

Chapter Review (pp. 53–56) **1.** 7, 12 **3.** algebraic expression **5.** 16 **7.** 10 **9.** 400 **11.** 25 in.^{2} **13.** 9 **15.** 8 **17.** $\frac{1}{3}$ **19.** 52 **21.** 18 **23.** $z - 5$ **25.** $3x^2$ **27.** $2.95n + 2.19$ **29.** $13 + t \geq 24$ **31.** solution **33.** 240 ft^2

35.

Input	10	12	15	20	21
Output	5	7	10	15	16

range: 5, 7, 10, 15, and 16

37. $y = x + 4$ **39.**

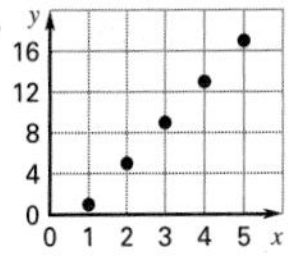

Chapter 2

2.1 Skill Practice (pp. 67–68) **1.** rational number **3.** Zero is in the set of whole numbers, but not in the set of positive integers. **5–13.** Check students' graphs. **5.** 7 **7.** -5 **9.** 5 **11.** -1 **13.** -2 **15.** 1.6: rational number, 1: whole number, integer, rational number, -4: integer, rational number, 0: whole number, integer, rational number; -4, 0, 1, 1.6 **17.** $-\frac{2}{3}$: rational number, -0.6: rational number, -1: integer, rational number, $\frac{1}{3}$: rational number; -1, $-\frac{2}{3}$, -0.6, $\frac{1}{3}$ **19.** 16: whole number, integer, rational number, -1.66: rational number, $\frac{5}{3}$: rational number, -1.6: rational number; -1.66, -1.6, $\frac{5}{3}$, 16 **21.** -4.99: rational number, 5: whole number, integer, rational number, $\frac{16}{3}$: rational number, -5.1: rational number; -5.1, -4.99, 5, $\frac{16}{3}$ **23.** -6, 6 **25.** 18, 18 **27.** -13.4, 13.4 **29.** 6.1, 6.1 **31.** $1\frac{1}{9}$, $1\frac{1}{9}$ **33.** $-\frac{3}{4}$, $\frac{3}{4}$ **35.** Hypothesis: a number is a positive integer, conclusion: the number is a whole number; true. **37.** Hypothesis: a number is positive, conclusion: its opposite is positive; false. *Sample answer:* The opposite of 2 is -2, a negative number. **41.** $-|-0.2|$ is a negative number. *Sample answer:* In the number $-|-0.2|$, remove both negative signs. **43.** 1 **45.** 1.75 **47.** 2.25 **49.** 1.5

2.1 Problem Solving (pp. 69–70) **53.** Fondo, Frink, Alamorio, Calexico, Date City **55.** -3.4; the absolute value of -3.4 is less than the absolute value of -3.8, so it is closer to 0, the exact pitch. **57. a.** 500 Hz **b.** The intensity decreases until 500 Hz and then increases. **59. a.** Sun, Sirius, Canopus, Arcturus, Capella, Achernar; Canopus, Achernar, Arcturus, Capella, Sirius, Sun **b.** Rigel's apparent magnitude is greater than the Sun's apparent magnitude, so it is dimmer than the Sun; Rigel's absolute magnitude is less than the Sun's absolute magnitude, so it is brighter than the Sun. **c.** No. *Sample answer:* The apparent magnitude of Arcturus is less than the apparent magnitude of Achernar, but the absolute magnitude of Arcturus is greater than the absolute magnitude of Achernar.

Extension (p. 72) **1.** {1, 3, 5, 6, 7, 9}, {3, 9} **3.** {0, 1, 2, 3, 4, 5, 6, 7, 8, 9, 10}, ∅ **5.** R = {2, 4, 6, 8, 10}, f = {(1, 2), (2, 4), (3, 6), (4, 8), (5, 10)} **7.** R = {4, 8, 12, 16, 20}, f = {(1, 4), (5, 8), (9, 12), (13, 16), (17, 20)} **9.** the set of integers, ∅

2.2 Skill Practice (pp. 77–78) **1.** 0 **3.** -8 **5.** 6 **7.** -13 **9.** -6 **11.** -20 **13.** -4.5 **15.** 6.6 **17.** -15.2 **19.** $7\frac{1}{15}$ **21.** $1\frac{16}{45}$ **23.** $-20\frac{23}{24}$ **25.** The numbers have different signs, so their absolute values should have been subtracted, $17 + (-31) = -14$. **27.** Associate property of addition **29.** Identity property of addition **31.** Commutative property of addition **33.** -49 **35.** 1.6 **37.** $5\frac{19}{60}$ **39.** -3 **41.** -9.5 **43.** $7\frac{23}{60}$ **45.** 0 **47.** 7.4 **49.** $-(-18) + (-18)$; 0

2.2 Problem Solving (pp. 78–79) **53.** 7°F **55. a.** 1.5 diopters **b.** -3.75 diopters **c.** part (b) **57. a.** your friend **b.** No, if you score 2 double eagles, you will have the same score.

2.3 Skill Practice (pp. 82–83) **1.** $-3 + (-6)$ **3.** 18 **5.** -8 **7.** 14.1 **9.** -25.8 **11.** $-\frac{1}{3}$ **13.** $\frac{3}{4}$ **15.** 8 was substituted for y instead of -8; $3 - (-8) + 2 = 3 + 8 + 2 = 13$. **17.** 4.6 **19.** 10.6 **21.** 7.7 **23.** 7.6 **25.** 1.8 **27.** 107°F **29.** -1280 m **31.** 127.1 mi **33.** 8 **35.** -4.2 **37.** 16.4 **39.** No; *Sample answer:* $5 - (3 - 2) = 4$, but $(5 - 3) - 2 = 0$ and $5 - 3 = 2$, but $3 - 5 = -2$.

SA3

2.3 Problem Solving (pp. 83–84)
43. 14.6°C **45. a.** $d = t - 342$

b.

t	d
341.7	−0.3
343.8	1.8
340.9	−1.1
342.7	0.7

341.7 and 340.9; you can tell if $t - 342$ is negative.
47. a. 6°; 19° **b.** −4°

2.3 Spreadsheet Activity (p. 85) **1.** 6 hand grips **3.** 4.902; the difference in the lengths has the smallest absolute value.

2.4 Skill Practice (pp. 91–92) **1.** 1 **3.** −28 **5.** 90 **7.** −36 **9.** 7 **11.** −43.89 **13.** −40 **15.** −80 **17.** $2\frac{2}{5}$ **19.** Multiplicative property of zero **21.** Identity property of multiplication **23.** Associative property of multiplication **25.** Identity property of multiplication **27.** Multiplicative property of −1 **29.** $18x$; $18x$, same signs, product is positive. **31.** $-84z$; $12(-7z)$, product of −2 and −6 is 12; $[12 \cdot (-7)]z$, associative property of multiplication; $-84(z)$, product of 12 and −7 is −84; $-84z$, multiply. **33.** $-40c$; $2(4)(-5c)$, product of $-\frac{1}{5}$ and −10 is 2; $8(-5c)$, product of 2 and 4 is 8; $[8 \cdot (-5)]c$, associative property of multiplication; $-40(c)$, product of 8 and −5 is −40; $-40c$, multiply. **35.** $16.8r^2$; $[-6r \cdot (-2.8)]r$, associative property of multiplication; $[-6 \cdot (-2.8) \cdot r]r$, commutative property of multiplication; $(16.8r)r$, product of −6 and −2.8 is 16.8; $16.8(r \cdot r)$, associative property of multiplication; $16.8r^2$, multiply **37.** −0.4 **39.** −12.6 **41.** −6.6 **43.** $-1(7) = -7$, not 7; $-1(7)(-3)(-2x) = -7(-3)(-2x) = 21(-2x) = -42x$ **45.** true **47.** true

2.4 Problem Solving (pp. 92–93) **51.** $162.50 **55. a.** $f = 11{,}250 + (-30t)$, $f = 135{,}000 + (-240t)$ **b.** 11,160 gal, 134,280 gal **c.** Rhododendron; 45,000 gal; the Rhododendron takes 375 hours to burn all of its fuel; the Spokane takes 562.5 hours to burn all of its fuel; to find the number of hours the Rhododendron will take to burn all its fuel, use the equations in part (a) and find the additive inverse of 11,250, then divide it by −30; to find the number of hours the Spokane will take to burn all its fuel, use the equations in part (a) and find the additive inverse of 135,000, then divide it by −240.

Extension (p. 95) **1.** $\begin{bmatrix} 16 & 4 \\ 8 & 12 \end{bmatrix}$ **3.** $\begin{bmatrix} -15 & -4 & -9 \\ -2 & 2 & -5 \end{bmatrix}$ **5.** Cannot be performed. **7.** $\begin{bmatrix} -28 & -49 \\ 3\frac{1}{2} & 3\frac{1}{9} \end{bmatrix}$ **9.** $\begin{bmatrix} -72 \\ 20.4 \\ 4.2 \end{bmatrix}$

11. $\begin{array}{cc} \text{Calcium (mg)} & \text{Potassium (mg)} \end{array}$ $\begin{bmatrix} 263.52 & 290.36 \\ 270.84 & 341.6 \\ 246.44 & 324.52 \end{bmatrix}$ **13.** $\begin{bmatrix} -41 & -99 \\ 78 & 91 \end{bmatrix}$

2.5 Skill Practice (pp. 99–100) **1.** 4, −9 **3.** The negative was not distributed to the −8; $5y - (2y - 8) = 5y - 2y + 8 = 3y + 8$. **5.** $4x + 12$ **7.** $5m + 25$ **9.** $-8p + 24$ **11.** $4r - 6$ **13.** $6v^2 + 6v$ **15.** $2x^2 - 6x$ **17.** $\frac{1}{4}m - 2$ **19.** $4n - 6$ **21.** terms: -7, $13x$, $2x$, 8; like terms: −7 and 8, $13x$ and $2x$; coefficients: 13, 2; constant terms: −7, 8 **23.** terms: $7x^2$, −10, $-2x^2$, 5; like terms: $7x^2$ and $-2x^2$, −10 and 5; coefficients: 7, −2; constant terms: −10, 5 **25.** terms: 2, $3xy$, $-4xy$, 6; like terms: 2 and 6, $3xy$ and $-4xy$; coefficients: 3, −4; constant terms: 2, 6 **29.** $5y$ **31.** $9a - 2$ **33.** $8r + 8$ **35.** $3m + 5$ **37.** $10w - 35$ **39.** $15s + 6$ **41.** $34 - 24w$; $72 - 108w$ **43.** $38.97 **45.** $11.88 **47.** $2(6 + x) + (x - 5)$; $3x + 7$

2.5 Problem Solving (pp. 100–101) **51.** $C = 3r - 6$; $5.97 **53.** $s = d(x + y + z) = dx + dy + dz$

2.5 Problem Solving Workshop (p. 102) **1.** $330 **3.** $287.50

2.6 Skill Practice (pp. 106–107) **1.** multiplicative inverse **3.** $-\frac{1}{18}$ **5.** −1 **7.** $-1\frac{1}{3}$ **9.** $-\frac{3}{13}$ **11.** −7 **13.** $\frac{2}{7}$ **15.** −3 **17.** $-2\frac{1}{2}$ **19.** $\frac{2}{7}$ **21.** −22 **25.** $-1\frac{2}{3}$ **27.** $2\frac{1}{4}$ **29.** $-2\frac{1}{5}$ **31.** 0.1 **33.** $3x - 7$ **35.** $-3z + 2$ **37.** $\frac{1}{2} - \frac{5}{2}q$ **39.** $3a + 1\frac{1}{4}$ **41.** $4 - 3c$ **43.** −2 was added instead of subtracted; $\frac{-15x - 10}{-5} = (-15x - 10) \cdot \left(-\frac{1}{5}\right) = -15x\left(-\frac{1}{5}\right) - 10\left(-\frac{1}{5}\right) = 3x + 2$ **45.** $-1\frac{1}{3}$ **47.** $\frac{1}{3}$

2.6 Problem Solving (pp. 107–108) **53.** −14.75°C **57. a.** −0.034 **b.** Yes; it will improve to −0.012. **c.** If the player had the same number of aces as service errors, then $a = e$, so $f = \frac{a - a}{s} = 0$; if all the serves were aces, a would be equal to s and e would be 0, so $f = \frac{s - 0}{s} = \frac{s}{s} = 1$; if all the serves were errors, then $e = s$ and $a = 0$, so $f = \frac{0 - s}{s} = \frac{-s}{s} = -1$.

2.7 Skill Practice (pp. 113–114) **1.** real numbers **3.** 2 **5.** −3 **7.** 14 **9.** ±50 **11.** −15 **13.** ±13 **15.** 3 **17.** −2 **19.** −9 **21.** 14 **25.** $-\sqrt{12}$: real number, irrational number, −3.7: real number, rational number, $\sqrt{9}$: real number, rational number, integer, whole number, 2.9: real number, rational number; −3.7, $-\sqrt{12}$, 2.9, $\sqrt{9}$

SELECTED ANSWERS

27. $\sqrt{8}$: real number, irrational number, $-\frac{2}{5}$: real number, rational number, -1: real number, rational number, integer, 0.6: real number, rational number, $\sqrt{6}$: real number, irrational number; -1, $-\frac{2}{5}$, 0.6, $\sqrt{6}$, $\sqrt{8}$ **29.** -8.3: real number, rational number, $-\sqrt{80}$: real number, irrational number, $-\frac{17}{2}$: real number, rational number, -8.25: real number, rational number, $-\sqrt{100}$: real number, rational number, integer; $-\sqrt{100}$, $-\sqrt{80}$, $-\frac{17}{2}$, -8.3, -8.25 **31.** If a number is a real number, then it is an irrational number; false. *Sample answer:* 3 is a real number and a rational number. **33.** If a number is an irrational number, then it is not a whole number; true. **35.** 2 **37.** -42 **39.** 63 **41.** B

2.7 Problem Solving (pp. 115–116) **45.** 60 in. **47.** 35 ft **49.** 2.2 ft **51. a.** 144 tiles **b.** 16 ft. *Sample answer:* If the homeowner can buy 144 tiles that are each 256 square inches, then the total area is (144 tiles)(256 square inches per tile) = 36,864 square inches. Divide 36,864 square inches by 144 square inches to find the number of square feet, 256 square feet. If the area of the square is 256 square feet, take the square root of 256 to find the side length, 16 feet.

Extension (p. 118) **1.** The sum is even. **3.** The sum is odd. **5.** Not closed **7.** Identity property of multiplication; Distributive property; Inverse property of multiplication; Property of zero

Chapter Review (pp. 121–124) **1.** terms: $-3x$, -5, $-7x$, -9; coefficients: -3, -7; constant terms: -5, -9; like terms: $-3x$ and $-7x$, -5 and -9 **3.** real number, rational number **5.** real number, rational number, integer **7.** -6, -5.2, $-\frac{3}{8}$, $-\frac{1}{4}$, 0.3 **9.** 0.2, 0.2 **11.** $-\frac{7}{8}$, $\frac{7}{8}$ **13.** 3 **15.** -3.5 **17.** $-1\frac{3}{14}$ **19.** $-\$.23$ million **21.** -10 **23.** -6.1 **25.** $-\frac{31}{36}$ **27.** $2\frac{1}{2}$ **29.** -60 **31.** -18 **33.** $6x$; $x \cdot (-18) = -\frac{1}{3}(-18)(x)$, commutative property of multiplication; $6(x)$, product of $-\frac{1}{3}$ and -18; $6x$, multiply **35.** 2.74 ft **37.** $-3y - 27$ **39.** $3x + 8$

41. $9n - 3\frac{1}{2}$ **43.** -14 **45.** $\frac{2}{3}$ **47.** $3x - 5$ **49.** $2n + 1$ **51.** -6 **53.** ± 15 **55.** -7 **57.** 17 **59.** $-\sqrt{4}$, -0.3, 0, 1.25, $\sqrt{11}$

Chapter 3

3.1 Skill Practice (pp. 137–138) **1.** inverse operations **3.** 3 **5.** 5 **7.** -3 **9.** 7 **11.** 17 **13.** 4 **17.** 4 **19.** 6 **21.** -15 **23.** 15 **25.** 48 **27.** 22 **29.** The student multiplied x by 100 to produce a number with a decimal part identical to the decimal part of x. When the student subtracted, the result was a whole number. **35.** -2.05 **37.** $\frac{5}{8}$ **39.** 0.06 **41.** 96 **43.** 12 **45.** -56 **47.** $\frac{3}{5}$ **49.** $54 = 12x$; 4.5 in.

3.1 Problem Solving (pp. 139–140) **53.** 1046.6 ft **55.** 11 ft **57. a.** $\frac{4}{7}x = 200$ **b.** Plants; if you solve the equation in part (a) you find that there are 350 species of birds.

59. a.

t	d
1	6.5
2	13
3	19.5
4	26
5	32.5

b. 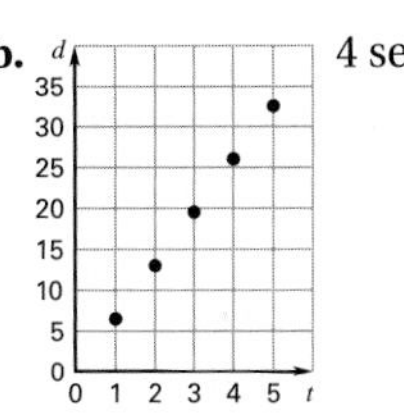

4 sec

c. $26 = 6.5t$; 4 sec **61. a.** 171 hits **b.** 215 hits **c.** No; if Mueller had fewer hits than Wells but had a higher batting average, he must have had fewer at bats than Wells.

3.2 Skill Practice (pp. 144–145) **1.** like terms **3.** 4 **5.** 2 **7.** -3 **9.** 6 **11.** 40 **13.** 18 **15.** 4 **17.** 9 **19.** -4 **23.** The division of $-2x + x$ by -2 is done incorrectly. *Sample answer:* If like terms are combined as the first step, the second line would be $-x = 10$ and the final result would be $x = -10$. **25.** $y = 2x + 4$; -7 **27.** 4 **29.** 5 **31.** 0.5 **33.** 15.9 **35.** 6.9

3.2 Problem Solving (pp. 145–146) **37.** 28 classes **39.** 5 half-side advertisements **41.** Yes; the equation $\$542 = \$50 + 6x$ gives the monthly cost of a guitar that costs $542. Solving the equation gives $x = \$82$ per month, so you can afford the guitar. **43. a.** $y = 12x$

b.

x (hours)	Marissa	Ryan	Total
1	5	7	12
2	10	14	24
3	15	21	36
4	20	28	48
5	25	35	60

SELECTED ANSWERS

c. about 4.5 h

3.2 Problem Solving Workshop (p. 147)
1. 7 players **3.** 4 chairs

3.3 Skill Practice (pp. 150–151) **1.** $\frac{5}{3}$ **3.** 3 **5.** 6 **7.** -2 **9.** -8 **11.** -8 **13.** 4 **15.** -9 **17.** -19 **19.** 12 **21.** -2 **23.** -9 **25.** -3 times -6 is 18, not -18; $5x - 3x + 18 = 2$, $2x + 18 = 2$, $2x = -16$, $x = -8$. **27.** 2 **29.** 3 **31.** -5 **33.** 2 **35.** 9.5 in., 6 in.; if you use the perimeter formula $P = 2\ell + 2w$ and substitute $3.5 + w$ for ℓ, the solution is $w = 6$.

3.3 Problem Solving (pp. 152–153) **39.** 0.75 ft **41. a.** 34 mo **b.** 307 ft per mo **c.** After the work crews merged; before the work crews merged they were working at a rate of $115 + 137 = 252$ feet per month, and after merging at a rate of 307 feet per month.

3.4 Skill Practice (pp. 157–158) **1.** identity **3.** -2 **5.** -4 **7.** -7 **9.** 8 **11.** -4 **13.** -3 **17.** *Sample answer:* Distribute the 3 to get $6z - 15 = 2z + 13$, then subtract $2z$ from each side to get $4z - 15 = 13$, next add 15 to each side to get $4z = 28$, finally divide each side by 4 to get $z = 7$. **19.** 2 **21.** -7 **23.** no solution **25.** no solution **27.** The 3 was not distributed to both terms; $3x + 15 = 3x + 15$, $15 = 15$, so the equation is an identity. **29.** *Sample answer:* $5x + 4 = 5x$; the number $5x$ cannot be equal to 4 more than itself. **31.** 2 **33.** -4 **35.** 6 **37.** identity **39.** 2 **41.** 10 **43.** identity **45.** 60

3.4 Problem Solving (pp. 158–159) **49.** 9 nights **51.** about 4 yr **53. a.** $23.4t = 24(t - 0.3)$; 12 sec **b.** about 4.4 sec **c.** No; it would take 12 seconds for the sheepdog to catch up to the collie and it only takes 4.4 seconds for the collie to complete the last leg.

3.4 Spreadsheet Activity (p. 160) **1.** 2 **3.** 4

3.5 Skill Practice (pp. 165–166) **1.** ratios **3.** no; 7 to 9 **5.** yes **7.** $\frac{6}{5}$ **9.** 22 **11.** 48 **13.** 15 **15.** 40 **17.** 12 **21.** Multiply each side by 6, not $\frac{1}{6}$; $6 \cdot \frac{3}{4} = 6 \cdot \frac{x}{6}$, $4\frac{1}{2} = x$. **23.** $\frac{3}{8} = \frac{x}{32}$; 12 **25.** $\frac{x}{4} = \frac{8}{16}$; 2 **27.** $\frac{b}{10} = \frac{7}{2}$; 35 **29.** $\frac{12}{18} = \frac{d}{27}$; 18 **31.** 1.8 **33.** 2.4 **35.** 4 **37.** 4 **39.** 2 **41.** 3.5 **43.** Yes. *Sample answer:* $\frac{3}{6} = \frac{4}{8}$

3.5 Problem Solving (pp. 166–167) **45.** $\frac{2}{145}$ **47.** $\frac{2}{5}$ **49.** $\frac{1}{2}$ **51.** 45 goals **53. a.** $\frac{10}{23}$ **b.** 110 lift tickets **c.** 40 snowboarders

3.6 Skill Practice (pp. 171–172) **1.** cross product **3.** 6 **5.** 24 **7.** 1 **9.** -49 **11.** 2 **13.** 12 **17.** Use the cross products property to multiply 4 by x and 16 by 3; $4 \cdot x = 3 \cdot 16$, $4x = 48$, $x = 12$. **19.** 15 **21.** 10 **23.** 5.5 **25.** -3.4 **27.** 4.2 **29.** -5.9 **31. a.** Multiplication property of equality **b.** Multiply **c.** Simplify

3.6 Problem Solving (pp. 172–173) **33.** 5 c **35.** 90 km **37.** 7.5 km **39.** 17.728 m **41.** 80 yd; find the actual length of the field by using the ratio 1 in. : 20 yd, then use that number to find the width of the soccer field by using the ratio 3 : 2.

Extension (p. 175) **1.** 24 in. **3.** 16 m **5.** 37.5 ft

3.7 Skill Practice (pp. 179–180) **1.** percent: 15, base: 360, part: 54 **3.** 36% **5.** 28 **7.** 150 **9.** 70% **11.** 6% **13.** 69 **15.** 25 **17.** 95 **21.** 76.5% needs to be changed to 0.765; $153 = 0.765 \cdot b$, $b = 200$. **23.** 96% **25.** 150 **27.** 6% **29.** 30% **31.** No. *Sample answer:* The area of the smaller square would be 16% of the area of the larger square because the percent needs to be squared.

3.7 Problem Solving (pp. 180–181) **33.** 8% **35. a.** 90 listeners **b.** 35 listeners **37.** 59.3%; 16.5%; 13.2%; 11.0% **39. a.** $48 **b.** $66.25 **c.** The bicycle in part (a); it will cost $192, the bicycle in part (b) will cost $198.75.

Extension (p. 183) **1.** increase; 25% **3.** decrease; 45% **5.** decrease; 33% **7.** 20.3 **9.** 35.2 **11.** 20% increase **13.** 48.0 people per square mile

3.8 Skill Practice (pp. 187–188) **1.** literal equation **3.** $x = \frac{c}{b - a}$; -2 **5.** $x = bc - a$; 9 **7.** $x = a(c - b)$; 28 **9.** b should have been subtracted from both sides, not added; $ax = -b$, $x = -\frac{b}{a}$. **11.** $y = 7 - 2x$ **13.** $4 - 3x = y$ **15.** $2 + \frac{6}{7}x = y$ **17.** $\frac{9}{5}x - 6 = y$ **19.** $y = \frac{1}{2}x + \frac{1}{3}$ **21.** $h = \frac{S - 2B}{P}$ **25.** $y = 18 - 5x$ **27.** $\ell = \frac{S}{\pi r} - r$; 13.03 cm **29.** *Sample answer:* You want to find how long it will take to drive 150 miles if you drive at an average rate of 55 miles per hour.

3.8 Problem Solving (pp. 188–189) **33. a.** $x = \frac{C - 25}{12}$ **b.** 10 nights; 13 nights; 15 nights **35.** Divide each side by the total bill, b, to get $\frac{a}{b} = p\%$.

Chapter Review (pp. 192–196) **1.** scale drawing **3.** If you collect like terms you get $10x = 10x$, so any value of x will make it true. **5.** Subtract $6x$ from each side, then divide each side by -2. **7.** 13 **9.** -15 **11.** -36 **13.** 2 **15.** 18 **17.** 5 **19.** 2 **21.** -6 **23.** 14 **25.** 1 **27.** -4 **29.** no solution **31.** 7 **33.** identity **35.** 3 **37. a.** 4 **b.** 116 **39.** 15 **41.** 10.5 **43.** 70 **45.** 28 **47.** 1 **49.** 10 **51.** 650 words **53.** 16.5 **55.** 37.5% **57.** 1500 general admission tickets **59.** $y = \frac{3}{2}x + 9$ **61. a.** $h = \frac{V}{\ell w}$ **b.** 15 in.

Cumulative Review (pp. 202–203) **1.** 27 **3.** 11 **5.** 42 **7.** solution **9.** not a solution **11.** not a solution **13.** $-6\frac{5}{6}$ **15.** -19.1 **17.** -21 **19.** 6 **21.** 3 **23.** 13.9 **25.** 58.8 **27.** -11 **29.** 6 **31.** $4\frac{2}{3}$ **33.** 3 **35.** 8.5 **37.** 15 **39.** 23 **41.** 1.2 **43.** 18 pieces **45.** $-\$.34$; $-\$.45$; $-\$.25$; \$1.02; \$.08 **47.** 140 people **49. a.** 2 players **b.** 7 players **c.** 11 players

Chapter 4

4.1 Skill Practice (pp. 209–210) **1.** 5; -3 **3.** $(3, -2)$ **5.** $(4, 4)$ **7.** $(4, -1)$ **9.** $(-5, 4)$ **11.** $(-4, -1)$

15–21.

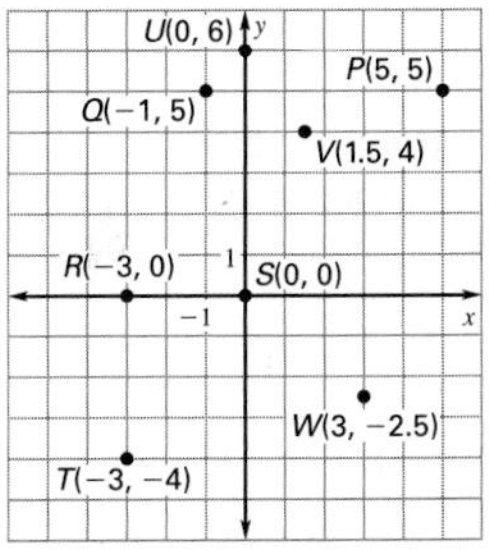

15. Quadrant II **17.** origin **19.** y-axis **21.** Quadrant IV

25.

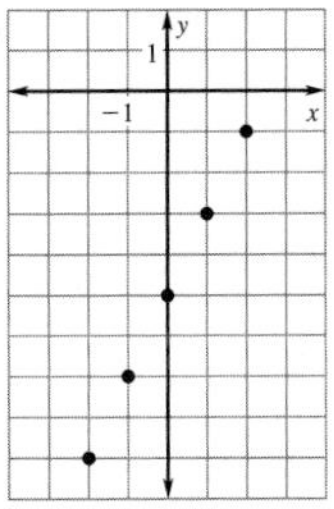

$-9, -7, -5, -3, -1$

27.

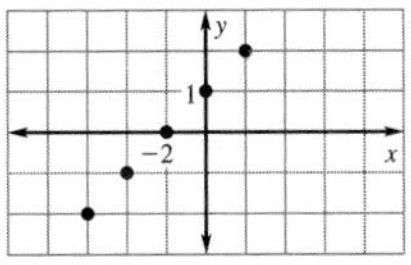

$-2, -1, 0, 1, 2$

29. Quadrant IV; the x-coordinate is positive and the y-coordinate is negative so the point is in Quadrant IV. **31.** Quadrant II; the x-coordinate is negative and the y-coordinate is positive so the point is in Quadrant II. **33.** If the x-coordinate is 0, then the point is on the y-axis. If the y-coordinate is 0, then the point is on the x-axis.

4.1 Problem Solving (pp. 210–212)

37. There is exactly one low temperature for each day in February.

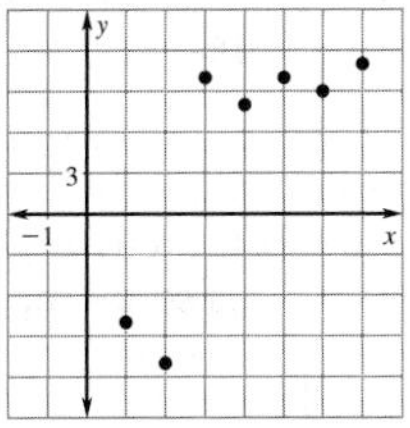

39. a.

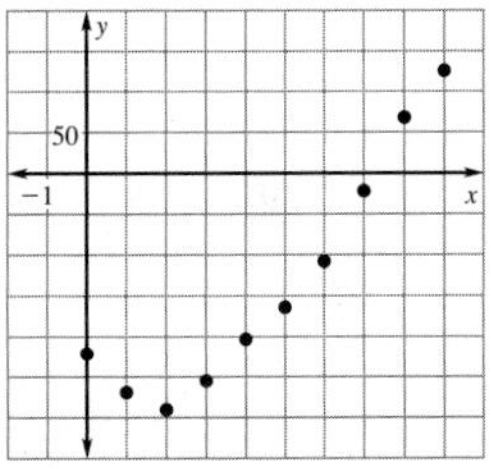

b. *Sample answer:* From 1992 to 1999 the federal deficit was decreasing.

41. a.

Height (in.)		
Reported	Measured	Difference
70	68	2
70	67.5	2.5
78.5	77.5	1
68	69	−1
71	72	−1
70	70	0

Weight (lb)		
Reported	Measured	Difference
154	146	8
141	143	−2
165	168	−3
146	143	3
220	223	−3
176	176	0

b. $(2, 8)$, $(2.5, -2)$, $(1, -3)$, $(-1, 3)$, $(-1, -3)$, $(0, 0)$

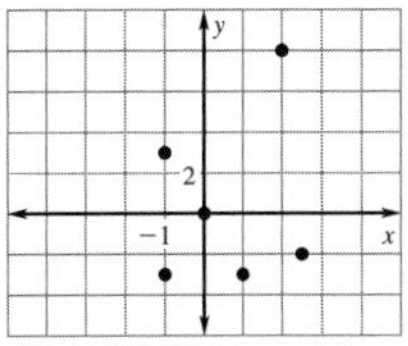

Extension (p. 214) **1.** Translation; a translation moves every point the same distance in the same direction so it will have the same shape and size as the original figure. **3.** Subtract 4 from each y-coordinate. **5.** Add 2 to each y-coordinate. **7.** (0, 1), (0, 3), (2, 3), (2, 1) **9.** (0, 0), (0, −2), (2, −2), (2, 0) **11.** (0, 0), (0, −1), (2, −1), (2, 0) **13.** (−1, 4), (−1, 6), (1, 6), (1, 4) **15.** Use the transformation $(x, y) \rightarrow (x, -y)$.

4.2 Skill Practice (pp. 219–220) **1.** linear function **3.** solution **5.** solution **7.** not a solution **9.** The 8 should be substituted for x and 11 for y, $11 - 8 \neq -3$, so (8, 11) is not a solution.

11.

$y + x = 2$

13.

$y - 3x = 0$

15.

$2y - 6x = 10$

17.

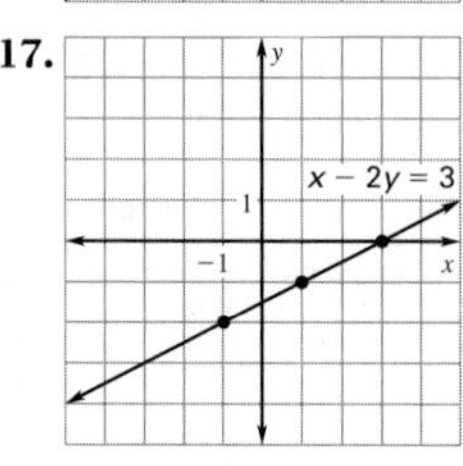

19.

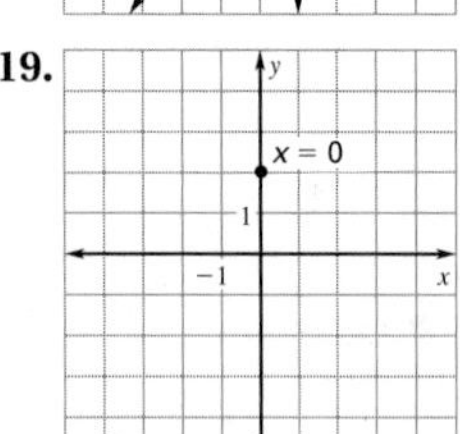

21.

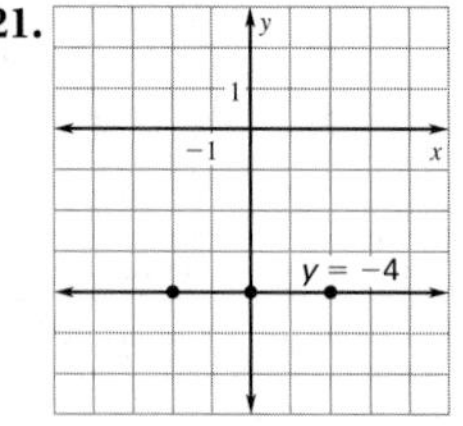

23. C **25.** B

27.

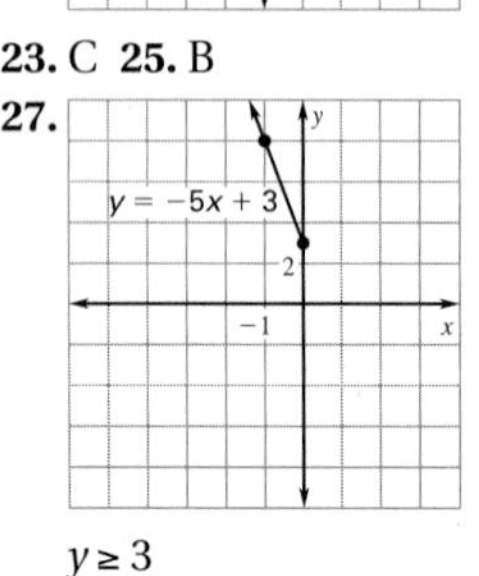

$y \geq 3$

29.

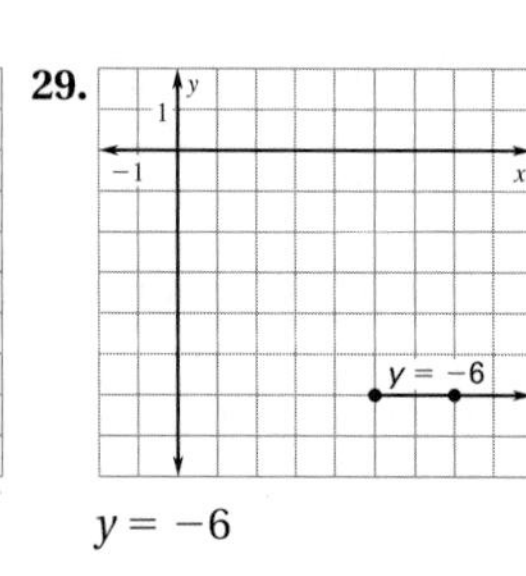

$y = -6$

31.

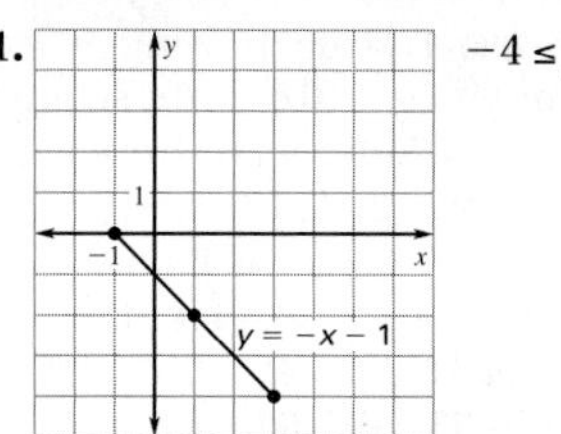

$-4 \leq y \leq 0$

4.2 Problem Solving (pp. 220–221)

35. $w = \frac{1}{2}f$

domain: $0 \leq f \leq 4$, range: $0 \leq w \leq 2$; 2 lb

37. a.

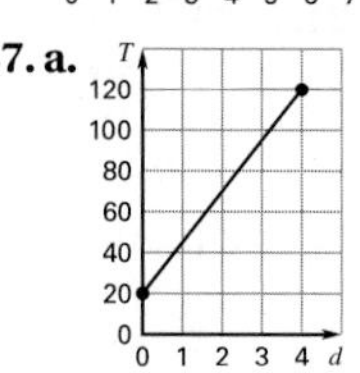

domain: $0 \leq d \leq 4$, range: $20 \leq T \leq 120$; 120°C

b.

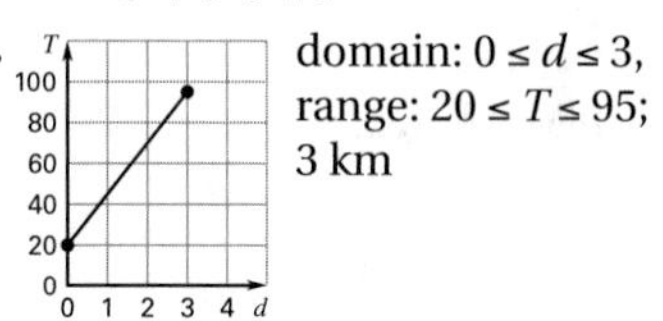

domain: $0 \leq d \leq 3$, range: $20 \leq T \leq 95$; 3 km

39. a.

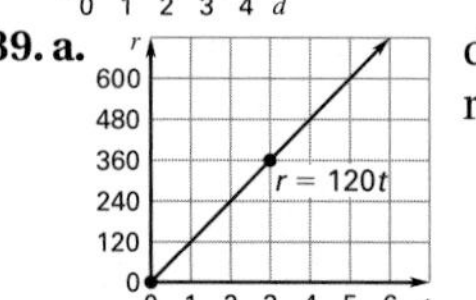

domain: $t \geq 0$, range: $r \geq 0$

b. Domain: $0 \leq t \leq 4$, range: $0 \leq r \leq 480$; the graph was a ray, but is now a segment.

41. a.

$y = 30$

$y = 2.5x$

4.2 Graphing Calculator Activity (p. 222) **1.** 5.6 **3.** −5.3

Extension (p. 224)

1.

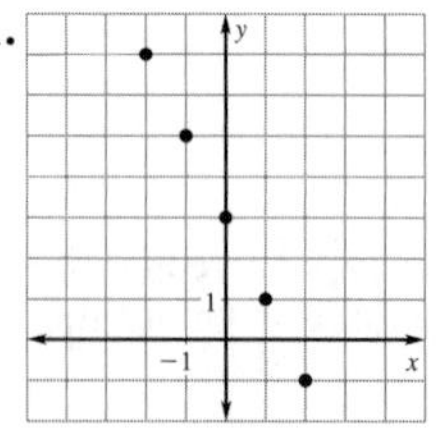

discrete

3. 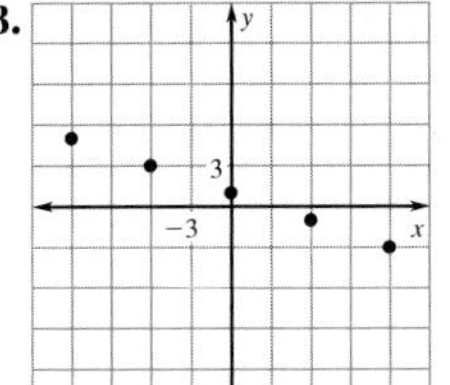 discrete

5. 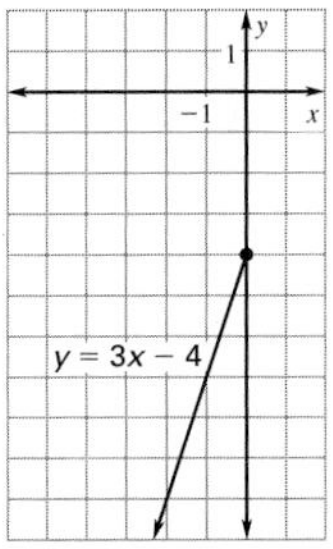 continuous

7. Discrete; you can only rent a whole number of DVDs.

9. Continuous; it makes sense to talk about the weight of water for any volume of water.

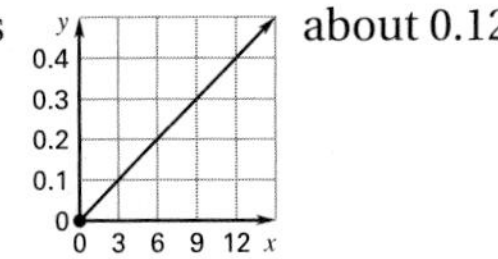

about 0.12

4.3 Skill Practice (pp. 229–230) **1.** x-intercept **3.** The intercepts are switched around; the x-intercept is -2, and the y-intercept is 1. **5.** 3, -3 **7.** 1, 4 **9.** 12, -3 **11.** 64, 4 **13.** $\frac{1}{2}$, 7 **15.** 20, -12

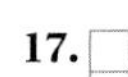

17. 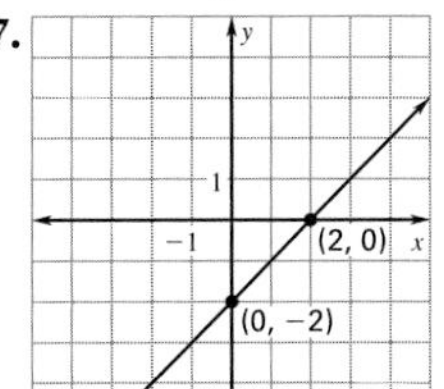

19. 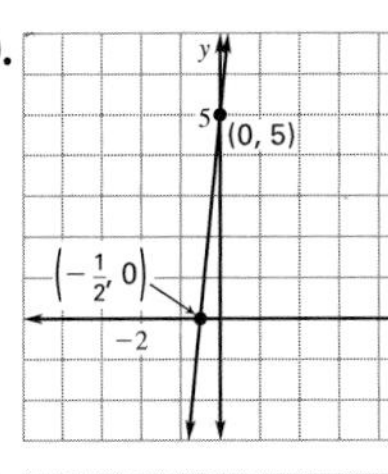

21. 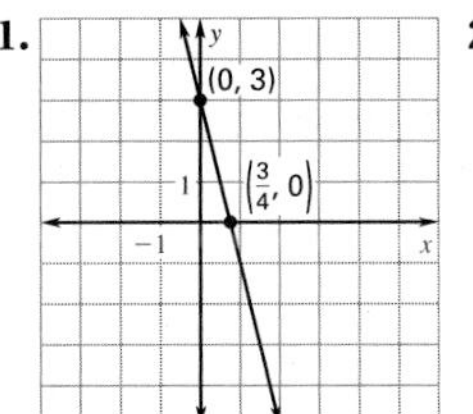

23. 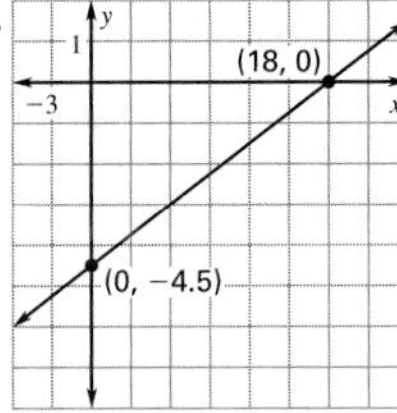

25. 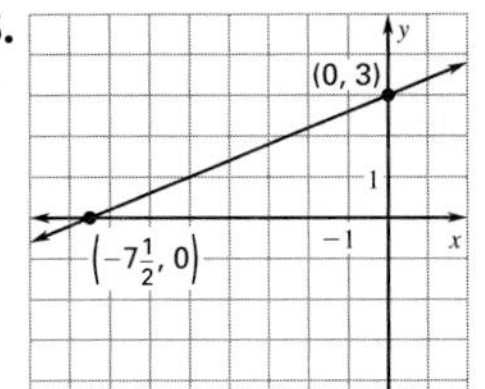

27. 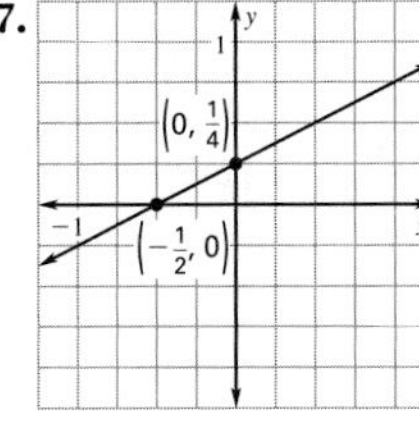

29. 3, -2

31. 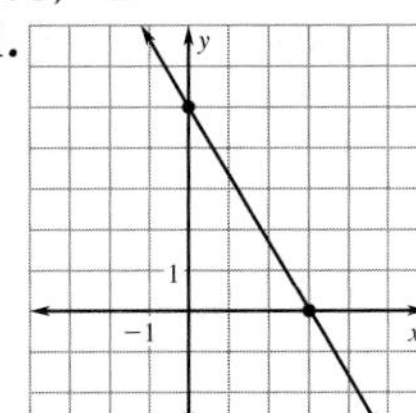

33. 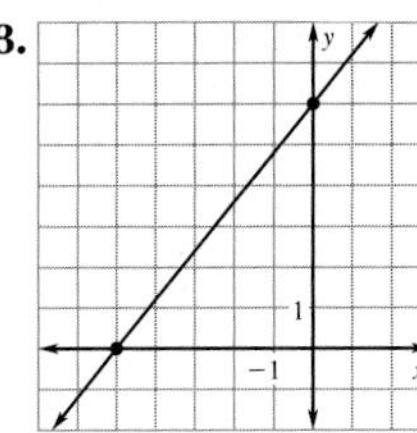

35. 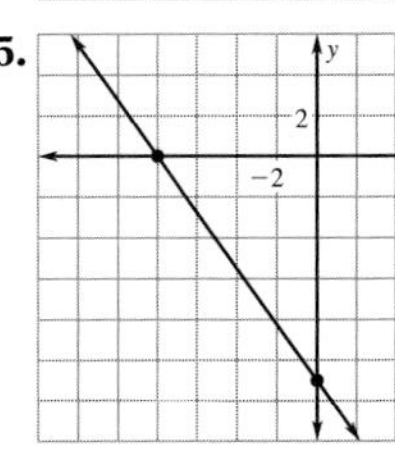

39. B **41.** Yes; yes; a horizontal line does not have an x-intercept if $y \neq 0$, a vertical line does not have a y-intercept if $x \neq 0$.

4.3 Problem Solving (pp. 230–232)

45. a. $x = 14$, $y = 7$

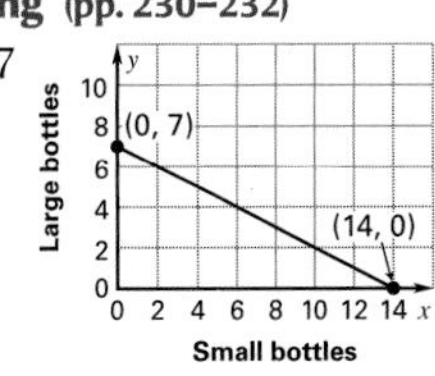

b. *Sample answer:* 2 and 6, 4 and 5, 6 and 4

47. a. v-intercept: 120, f-intercept: 180; the v-intercept means there are no flowers planted, the f-intercept means there are no vegetables planted.

b. 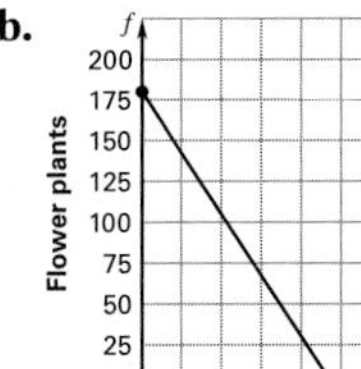

domain: $0 \leq v \leq 120$, range: $0 \leq f \leq 180$

c. 60 ft^2 **49.** 12.5 h. *Sample answer:* Since the tank will be empty when it needs to be refilled, replace w in the function with 0 and then solve the resulting equation for t.

4.4 Skill Practice (pp. 239–241) **1.** slope **3.** The denominator should be $2 - 5$, not $5 - 2$; $m = \frac{6-3}{2-5} = \frac{3}{-3} = -1$. **5.** undefined **7.** The slope was calculated using $\frac{\text{run}}{\text{rise}}$, not $\frac{\text{rise}}{\text{run}}$; $m = \frac{0-3}{12-6} = \frac{-3}{6} = -\frac{1}{2}$. **9.** undefined **11.** $-\frac{5}{2}$ **13.** 1 **15.** 0 **19.** \$2.25 per day; it costs \$2.25 per day to rent a movie. **21.** 0.3 **23.** 0.1 **25.** -15 **27.** -2 **29.** -3 **31.** -15 **33.** Yes; the slope of the line containing both points is -3.

SELECTED ANSWERS

4.4 Problem Solving (pp. 241–242) **37. a.** 0 h to 1.5 h **b.** 4.65 h to 8.95 h **39.** *Sample answer:* The elevation of the hiker increases for about 60 minutes, then stays the same for about 30 minutes, then decreases for the last 60 minutes.

4.5 Skill Practice (pp. 247–248) **1.** parallel **3.** 2, 1 **5.** −3, 6 **7.** $\frac{2}{3}$, −1 **11.** $y = -4x + 1$; −4, 1 **13.** $y = 2x + 3$; 2, 3 **15.** $y = -\frac{2}{5}x - 2$; $-\frac{2}{5}$, −2 **17.** B **19.** C

21. **23.**

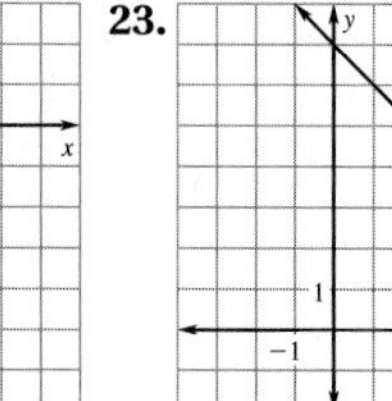

25. **27.**

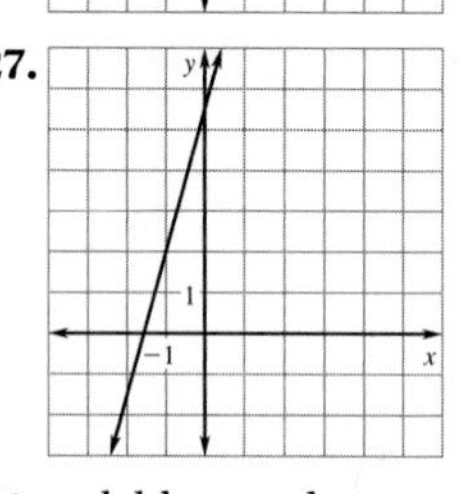

29.

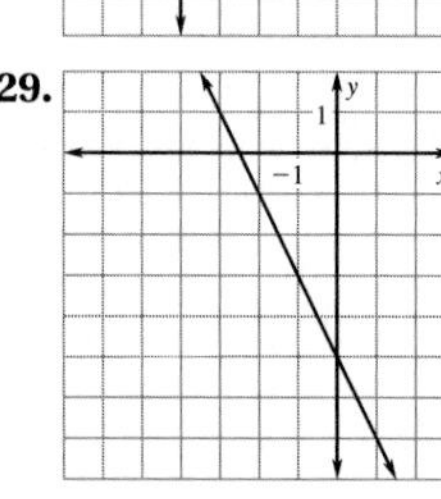

31. red, blue, and green **33.** Parallel; the slopes are both 3. **35.** Not parallel; the slopes are −4 and $-\frac{1}{4}$. **37.** −2

4.5 Problem Solving (pp. 248–250)

41. a.

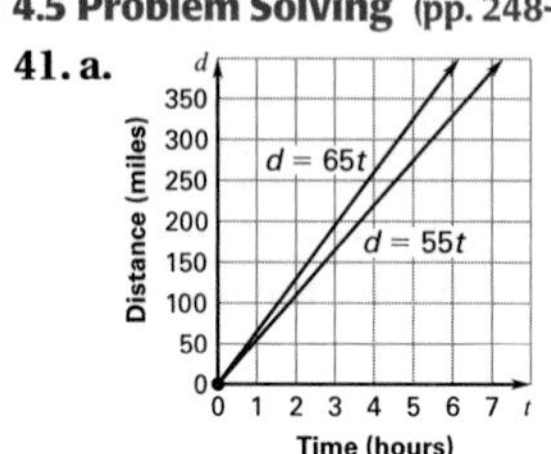

b. 30 mi

43. a.

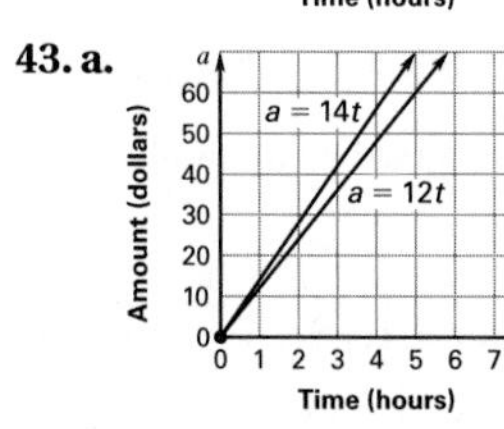

The slopes are the amount of money earned per hour, the *a*-intercepts show the amount of money made at 0 hours. **b.** $80

Extension (p. 252) **1.** −2 **3.** −4 **5.** $\frac{1}{2}$ **7.** 2000 **9.** 2000

4.6 Skill Practice (pp. 256–257) **1.** direct variation **3.** direct variation; 1 **5.** not direct variation **7.** direct variation; −4

11.

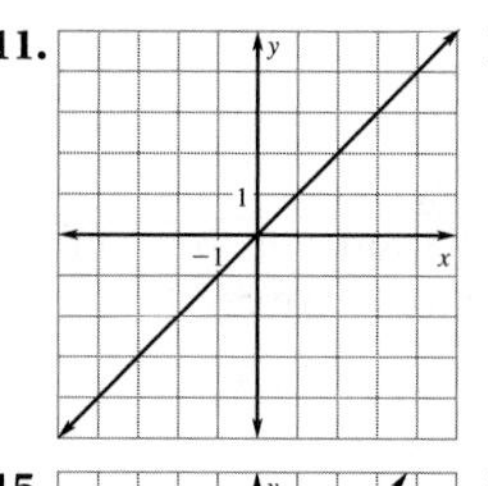

13.

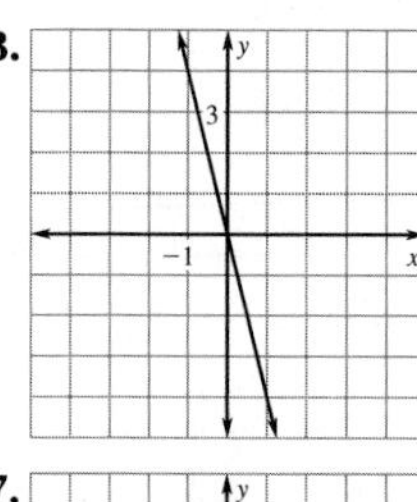

15.

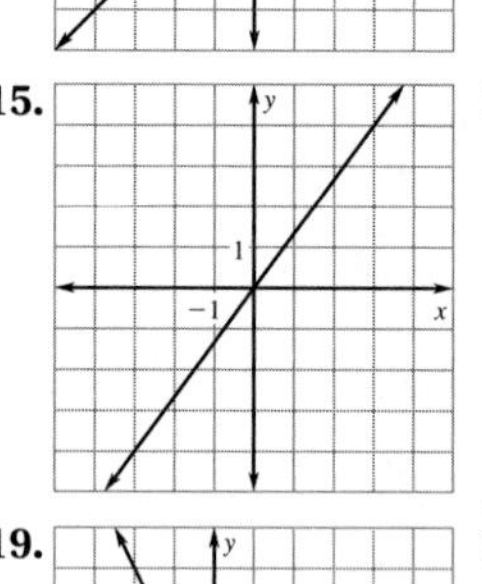

17.

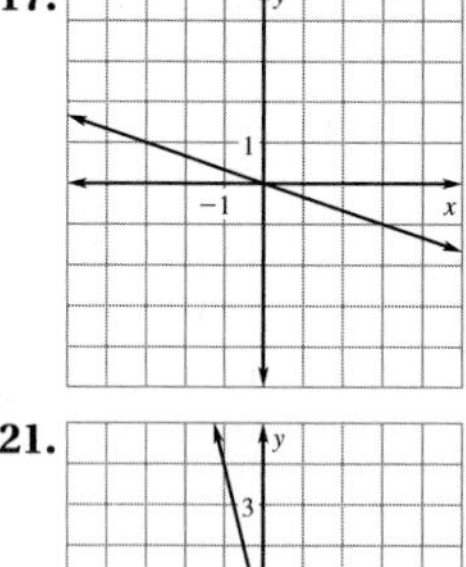

19. **21.**

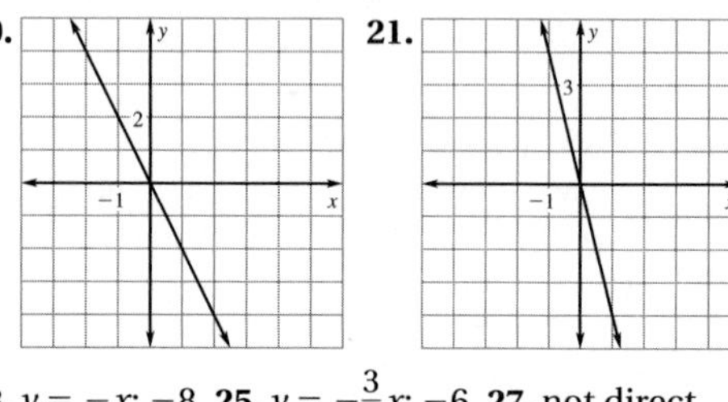

23. $y = -x$; −8 **25.** $y = -\frac{3}{4}x$; −6 **27.** not direct variation **29.** $y = 3x$ **31.** $y = \frac{1}{2}x$ **33.** $y = x$ **35.** $y = 4x$ **37.** $y = -\frac{7}{26}x$

4.6 Problem Solving (pp. 258–259) **41. a.** $v = \frac{3}{2}t$ **b.** 12 h **43. a.** Compare the ratios, $\frac{f}{w}$, for all data pairs (w, f). Since the ratios all equal 0.25, f varies directly with w. **b.** $f = 0.25w$; $.25 per pound; $7 **45. a.** *Sample answer:*

d	C (dollars)
1	1.5
2	3
3	4.5

b.

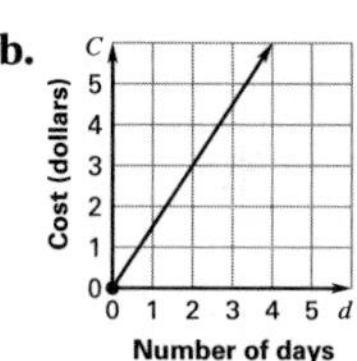

c. $C = 1.5d$; yes; it is in the form $y = ax$; $33.

SELECTED ANSWERS

4.6 Problem Solving Workshop (p. 261) **1.** 110 tbsp. *Sample answer:* Use the proportion $\frac{20}{100} = \frac{22}{x}$. **3.** Because 7 is half of 14, you can take half of 5.88 to find 7 words cost \$2.94. Because 21 is 3 times 7, multiply \$2.94 by 3 to get \$8.82. **5.** The proportion should be $\frac{6}{96} = \frac{10}{x}$; $\frac{6}{96} = \frac{10}{x}$, $960 = 6x$, $x = 160$.

4.7 Skill Practice (pp. 265–266) **1.** function notation **3.** $-23, 1, 37$ **5.** $14, -2, -26$ **7.** $13, 0, -19.5$ **9.** $2\frac{1}{5}, 3, 4\frac{1}{5}$ **11.** $-7\frac{1}{2}, -6, -3\frac{3}{4}$ **15.** 3 **17.** -6 **19.** -7.5 **21.** 3.5

23.

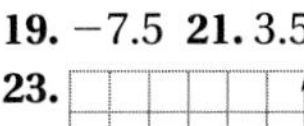

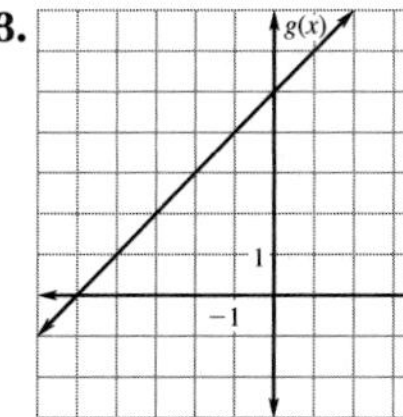

Because the graphs of g and f have the same slope, $m = 1$, the lines are parallel. The y-intercept of the graph of g is 5 more than the y-intercept of the graph of f.

25.

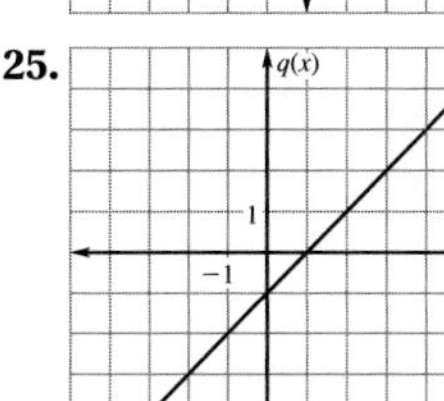

Because the graphs of q and f have the same slope, $m = 1$, the lines are parallel. The y-intercept of the graph of q is 1 less than the y-intercept of the graph of f.

27.

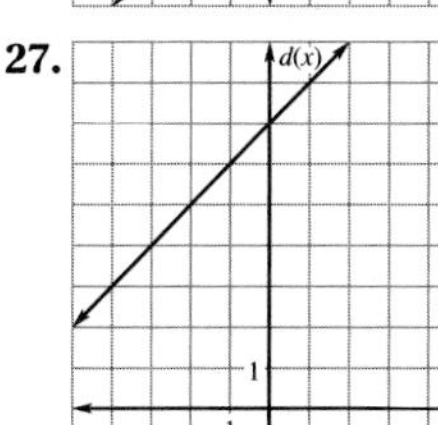

Because the graphs of d and f have the same slope, $m = 1$, the lines are parallel. The y-intercept of the graph of d is 7 more than the y-intercept of the graph of f.

29.

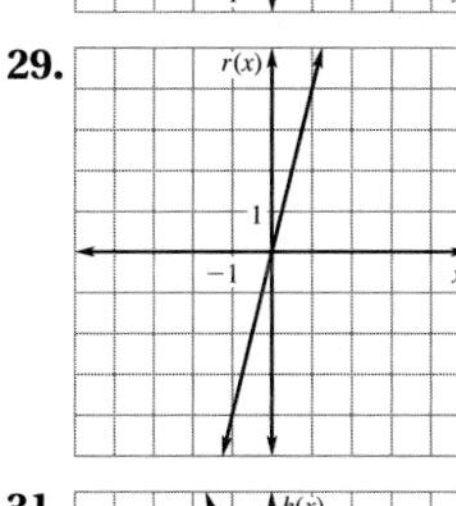

Because the slope of the graph of r is greater than the slope of the graph of f, the graph of r rises faster from left to right. The y-intercept for both graphs is 0, so both lines pass through the origin.

31. Because the slope of the graph of h is negative, the graph of h falls from left to right. The y-intercept for both graphs is 0, so both lines pass through the origin.

33.

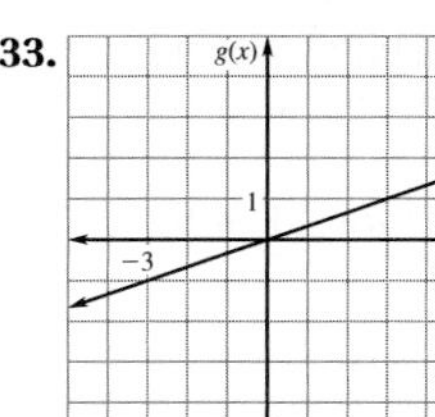

Because the slope of the graph of g is less than the slope of the graph of f, the graph of g rises slower from left to right. The y-intercept for both graphs is 0, so both lines pass through the origin.

37. Since the graphs of g and h have the same slope, $m = 0$, the lines are parallel. The y-intercept of the graph of h is 2 less than the y-intercept of the graph of g.

4.7 Problem Solving (pp. 267–268)

39. a.

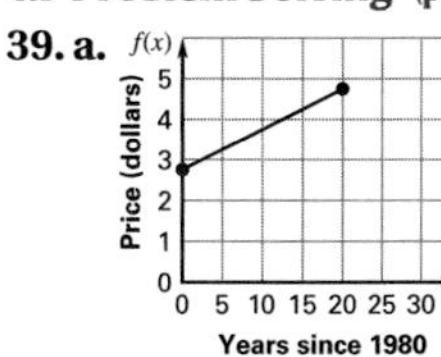

domain: $0 \le x \le 20$, range: $2.75 \le f(x) \le 4.75$ **b.** 18; in 1998, 18 years after 1980, the price of a movie ticket was \$4.55.

41.

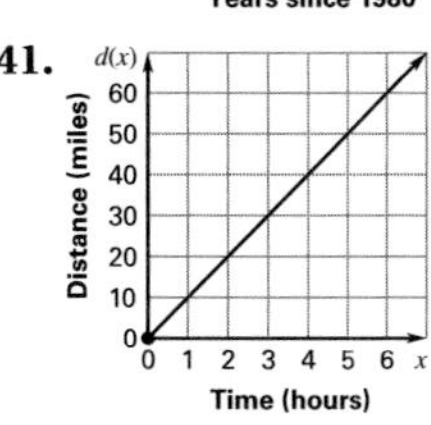

Domain: $x \ge 0$, range: $d(x) \ge 0$; 1.5 h; substitute 15 for $d(x)$ to get the equation $15 = 10x$, solve for x.

43.

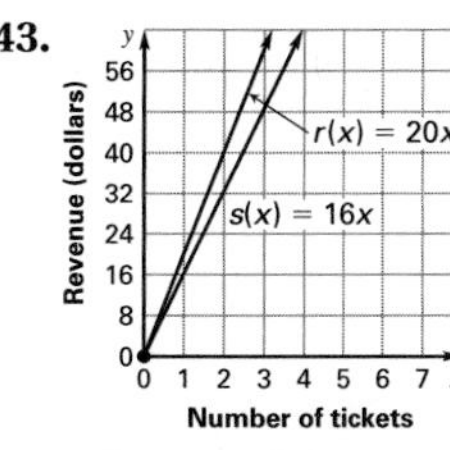

Because the slope of the graph of r is greater than the slope of the graph of s, the graph of r rises faster from left to right. The y-intercept for both graphs is 0, so both lines pass through the origin.

45. a. See graph in part (b); domain: $1 \le x \le 31$, range: $11.53 \le \ell(x) \le 12.43$.

b.

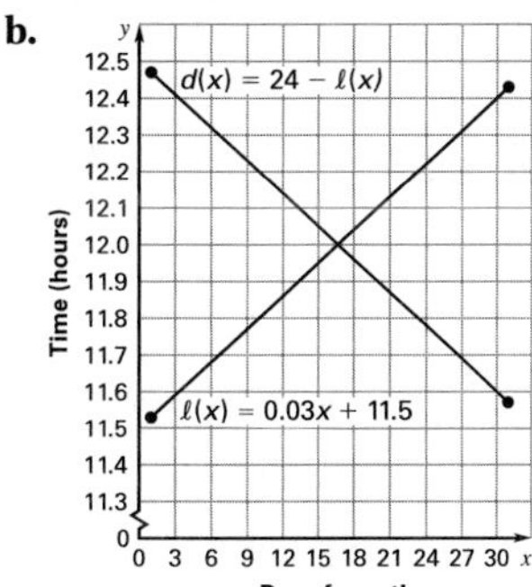

domain: $11.53 \le \ell(x) \le 12.43$, range: $11.57 \le d(x) \le 12.47$

SELECTED ANSWERS

Chapter Review (pp. 271–273) **1.** slope **3.** *Sample answer:* Make a table, use intercepts, and use the slope and y-intercept.

5–7.

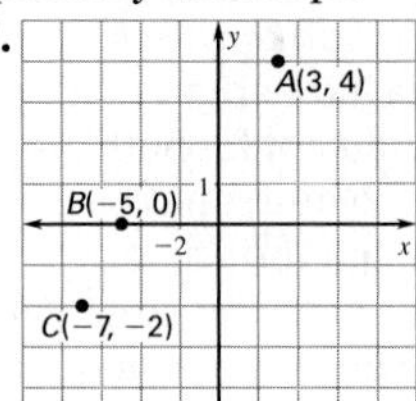

5. Quadrant I **7.** Quadrant III

9.

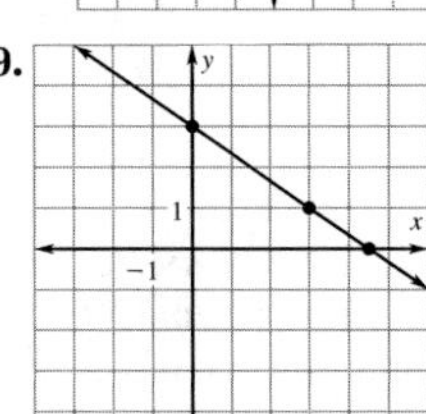

11.

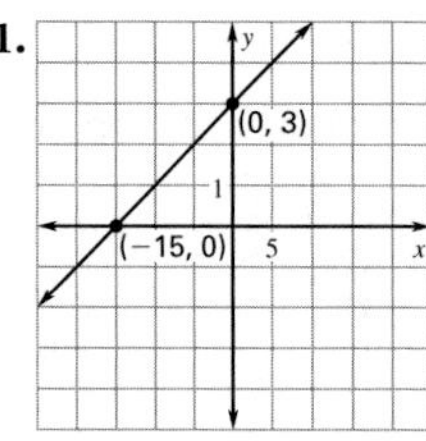

13.

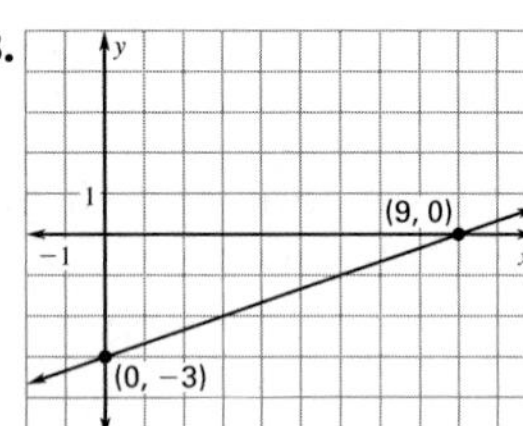

15. $-\frac{1}{3}$ **17.** -2

19.

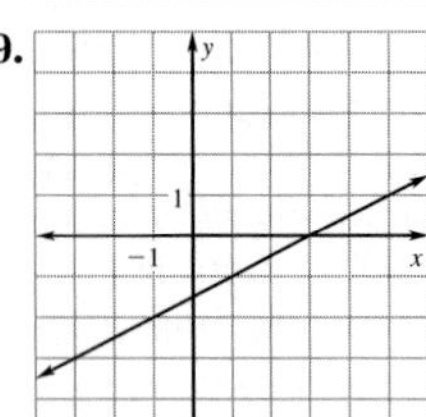

21.

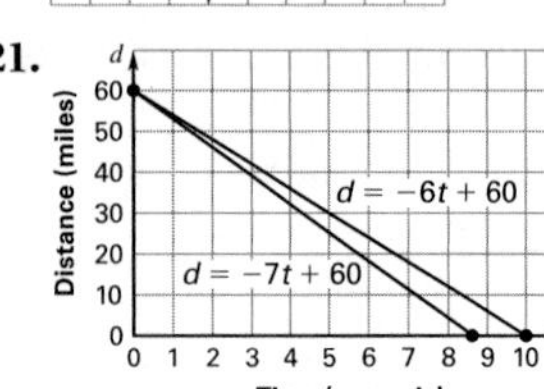

about 1.4 sec

23. direct variation; $-\frac{1}{2}$

25.

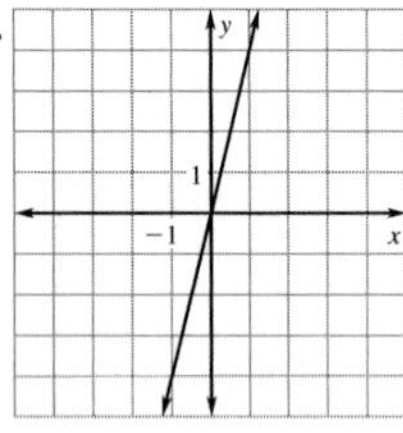

27.

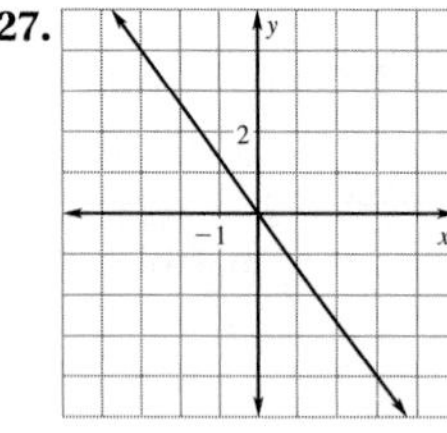

29. 11

31.

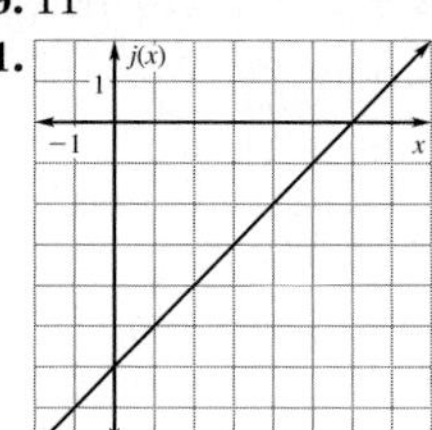

Because the graphs of j and f have the same slope, $m = 1$, the lines are parallel. The y-intercept of the graph of j is 6 less than the y-intercept of the graph of f.

33. Because the slope of the graph of t is greater than the slope of the graph of f, the graph of t rises faster from left to right. The y-intercept of the graph of t is 1 more than the y-intercept of the graph of f.

Chapter 5

5.1 Skill Practice (pp. 286–287) **1.** slope **3.** $y = 2x + 9$ **5.** $y = -3x$ **7.** $y = \frac{2}{3}x - 9$ **11.** $y = -\frac{1}{2}x$ **13.** $y = \frac{2}{3}x - 8$ **15.** $y = -2x - 2$ **17.** The slope should be $\frac{0-4}{5-0}$, $y = -\frac{4}{5}x + 4$. **19.** $y = 4x + 4$ **21.** $y = -\frac{4}{3}x$ **23.** $y = 2x - 2$ **25.** $y = -x - 5$ **27.** $y = -0.0625x + 4$ **29.** $y = -4x - 24$ **31.** $y = -2x + 7$ **33.** $y = -\frac{4}{5}x - 1$ **35.** $y = \frac{2}{3}x + 3$ **37.** $y = -3x + 9$ **39.** m changed from 2 to $-\frac{1}{3}$, and b changed from -1 to 1. **41.** $y = -2x + 1$ **43.** No; the slope of the line is undefined, the equation is $x = 3$, which is not in slope-intercept form.

5.1 Problem Solving (pp. 288–289) **45. a.** $C = 44m + 48$ **b.** $312 **47.** $C = 3h + 30$; $42

49. a.

x (years since 1970)	y (km^2)
0	5.2
10	4.1
20	3.0
30	1.9

b. The area of the glaciers changed −1.1 square kilometers between every 10 year interval. **c.** $y = -0.11x + 5.2$; -0.11 km^2

51. a. $t = 0.7d + 2$ **b.** 16 min

SELECTED ANSWERS

5.1 Graphing Calculator Activity (pp. 290–291)
1. $y = -2x + 5$ **3.** $y = 2x + 1.5$ **5.** $y = 1.5x + 2$ **7.** $y = 4x - 3$ **9.** $y = 0.5x + 1$; substitute 2 for x, 2 for y, and solve for b.

5.2 Skill Practice (pp. 296–297) **1.** y-intercept **3.** $y = 3x - 2$ **5.** $y = -5x - 13$ **7.** $y = -\frac{3}{4}x + 2$ **9.** -3 was substituted for x instead of y and 6 was substituted for y instead of x, $-3 = -2(6) + b$, $-3 = -12 + b$, $9 = b$. **11.** $y = 3x + 1$ **13.** $y = -\frac{2}{5}x - 1$ **15.** $y = -\frac{3}{4}x + \frac{35}{8}$ **17.** $y = 4x - 15$ **19.** $y = -\frac{1}{2}x + \frac{1}{2}$ **21.** $y = \frac{1}{3}x - \frac{4}{3}$ **23.** $y = -2x + 11$ **25.** $y = -\frac{1}{2}x + 8$ **27.** $y = x - 2$ **31.** $y = -\frac{2}{3}x + 6$ **33.** $y = 6x - 4$ **35.** Yes; you can substitute m and the coordinates of the point in $y = mx + b$, solve for b, and write the equation. **37.** Yes; you can find the slope of the line, then substitute the y-intercept for b, and write the equation. **39.** $y = \frac{9}{2}x - \frac{1}{2}$ **41.** The lines $y = \frac{3}{2}x - \frac{1}{2}$ and $y = \frac{9}{2}x - \frac{1}{2}$ and the lines $y = \frac{9}{2}x - \frac{1}{2}$ and $y = \frac{3}{2}x + \frac{11}{2}$ intersect because they have different slopes; the lines $y = \frac{3}{2}x - \frac{1}{2}$ and $y = \frac{3}{2}x + \frac{11}{2}$ will not intersect because they have the same slope, so they are parallel. **43.** The three points do not lie on the same line. If you find the equation of the line between two of the points and then check to see that the third point is a solution, you can see they do not lie on the same line. **45.** The three points do not lie on the same line. If you find the equation of the line between two of the points and then check to see that the third point is a solution, you can see they do not lie on the same line.

5.2 Problem Solving (pp. 298–299) **47.** $\frac{3}{4}$ ft/yr; 6 ft **49.** 115 min or 1 h 55 min; substitute 30 for m, 2 for x, and 85 for y into the equation $y = mx + b$ to find $b = 25$. Then substitute 3 for x into the equation $y = 30x + 25$ to solve for y. **51. a.** about 584 newspapers **b.** $y = 11.8x + 584$ **c.** about 938 newspapers **53. a.** $d = -18t + 234$

b.

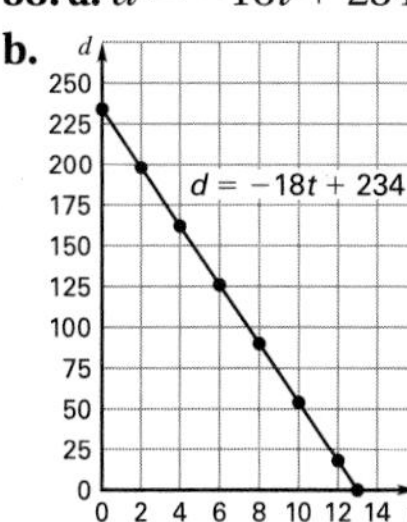

The slope is the rate that the hurricane is traveling, the y-intercept represents the distance from the town at 12 P.M.

c. 1 A.M.; find the t-intercept to find the value of t when the distance to the town is 0; substitute 0 for d and solve for t; $t = 13$, so you need to add 13 hours to 12 P.M. to get 1 A.M.

5.2 Problem Solving Workshop (p. 301) **1.** \$5; \$19 **3.** No; if the cost of the 60 inch bookshelf changes, the cost no longer increases at a constant rate. **5.** The student assumes that there is no fixed fee by using a proportion; $93 - 57 = 36$, $36 \div 2 = 18$, $57 + 18 = 75$.

5.3 Skill Practice (pp. 305–306) **1.** -2; $(-5, 5)$ **3.** $y - 1 = 2(x - 2)$ **5.** $y + 1 = -6(x - 7)$ **7.** $y - 2 = 5(x + 8)$ **9.** $y + 3 = -9(x + 11)$ **11.** $y + 12 = -\frac{2}{5}(x - 5)$ **13.** The form is $y - y_1$, so the left side should be $y - (-5)$ or $y + 5$; $y + 5 = -2(x - 1)$.

15. **17.**

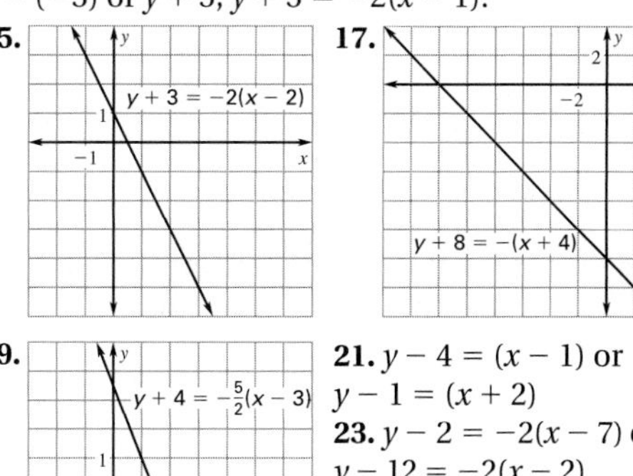

19.

y
y + 4 = −5/2(x − 3)
1
−1
x

21. $y - 4 = (x - 1)$ or $y - 1 = (x + 2)$ **23.** $y - 2 = -2(x - 7)$ or $y - 12 = -2(x - 2)$ **25.** $y + 1 = -\frac{3}{5}(x + 4)$ or $y + 7 = -\frac{3}{5}(x - 6)$

27. $y + 20 = 8(x + 3)$ or $y - 36 = 8(x - 4)$ **29.** A point was not substituted into the equation, the y-coordinates of the two points were substituted; $y - 2 = \frac{2}{3}(x - 1)$. **31.** No; because the increase is not at a constant rate, the situation cannot be modeled by a linear equation. **33.** No; because the increase is not at a constant rate, the situation cannot be modeled by a linear equation.

5.3 Problem Solving (pp. 307–308) **37. a.** $y = 130x + 530$ **b.** \$1570 **39.** $y = 10000x + 67000$; \$127,000 **41. a.** Since the cost increases at a constant rate of \$.49 per print, the situation can be modeled by a linear equation. **b.** *Sample answer:* $y - 1.98 = 0.49(x - 1)$ **c.** \$1.49 **d.** \$1.79 **43. a.** $y - 17.6 = -0.06(x - 60)$ **b.** 16.4 ft/sec

Extension (p. 310) **1.** yes; 2, -1 **3.** yes; -43, -50

5. **7.**

9.

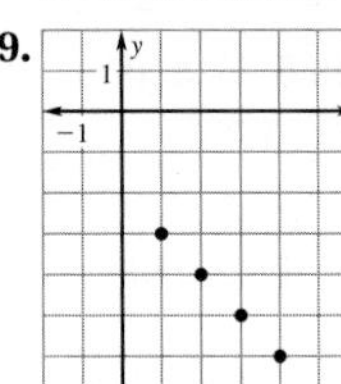

11. $a_n = 51 + (n - 1)21$; 2130 **13.** $a_n = \frac{1}{4} + (n - 1)\frac{1}{8}$; $12\frac{5}{8}$ **15.** $a_n = 1 + (n - 1)\frac{1}{3}$; 34

5.4 Skill Practice (p. 314) **1.** standard form **3.** point-slope form **5–9.** Sample answers are given. **5.** $2x + 2y = -20$, $3x + 3y = -30$ **7.** $x - 2y = -9$, $-2x + 4y = 18$ **9.** $3x - y = -4$, $6x - 2y = -8$ **11.** $-x + y = 5$ **13.** $2x + y = 5$ **15.** $\frac{3}{2}x + y = -10$ **17.** $\frac{2}{3}x + y = -\frac{4}{3}$ **19.** $-\frac{4}{3}x + y = -1$ **21.** $-\frac{1}{2}x + y = 1$ **23.** $y = 2$, $x = 3$ **25.** $y = 3$, $x = -1$ **27.** $y = 4$, $x = -1$ **29.** $(1, -4)$ was substituted incorrectly, 1 should be substituted for x and -4 substituted for y, $A(1) - 3(-4) = 5$, $A + 12 = 5$, $A = -7$. **31.** 4; $4x + 3y = 5$ **33.** -4; $-x - 4y = 10$ **35.** -5; $-5x - 3y = -5$

5.4 Problem Solving (pp. 315–316) **39. a.** 15 oz **b.** $12c + 15w = 120$ **c.** 10 corn, 0 wheat; 5 corn, 4 wheat; 0 corn, 8 wheat **41. a.** $100\ell + 40s = 1600$

b.

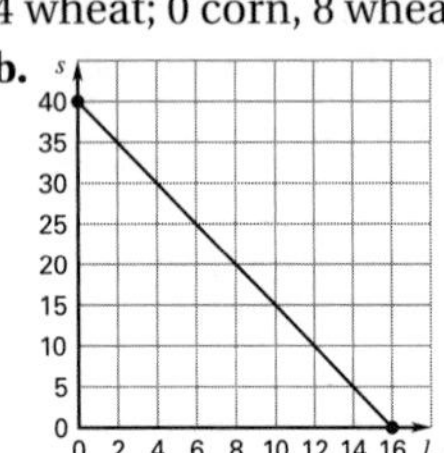

c.

Large rafts	Small rafts
16	0
14	5
12	10
10	15
8	20
6	25
4	30
2	35
0	40

5.5 Skill Practice (pp. 321–322) **1.** perpendicular **3.** $y = 2x + 5$ **5.** $y = -\frac{3}{5}x + 2$ **7.** $y = 6x + 1$ **9.** $y = 2x + 9$ **11.** $y = 3x + 30$ **13.** parallel: a and b; perpendicular: none **15.** parallel: none; perpendicular: a and b **17.** The line through points (6, 4) and (4, 1) is perpendicular to the line through points (1, 3) and (4, 1); the slope of the line through the points (6, 4) and (4, 1) is $\frac{3}{2}$, the slope of the line through the points (1, 3) and (4, 1) is $-\frac{2}{3}$. The slopes are negative reciprocals, so the lines are perpendicular. **19.** $y = -\frac{1}{3}x - 1$ **21.** $y = -2x + 24$ **23.** $y = -\frac{3}{4}x - 4$ **25.** $y = -\frac{1}{2}x - \frac{1}{2}$ **27.** (2, 1) was substituted incorrectly, 2 should be substituted for x, and 1 should be substituted for y; $1 = 2(2) + b$, $1 = 4 + b$, $-3 = b$.

5.5 Problem Solving (pp. 322–323) **33. a.** $w = 200d + 6000$; $w = 200d + 6250$ **b.** 12,000 lb; 12,250 lb **c.** The graphs of the lines are parallel because they have the same slope, 200. The w-intercept of the second line is 250 more than the w-intercept of the first line. **35.** Different registration fees; because the lines are parallel, the rate of change, the monthly fee, for each must be equal. Therefore, the students paid different registration fees.

5.6 Skill Practice (pp. 327–328) **1.** increase **3.** positive correlation **5.** negative correlation

7.

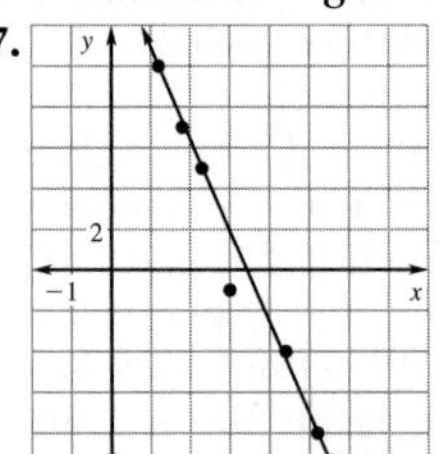

Sample answer: $y = -4.5x + 15.4$

9. The line does not have approximately half the data above it and half below it.

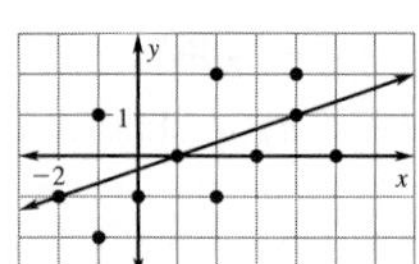

11. *Sample answer:* The amount of time driving a car and the amount of gas left in the gas tank

13.

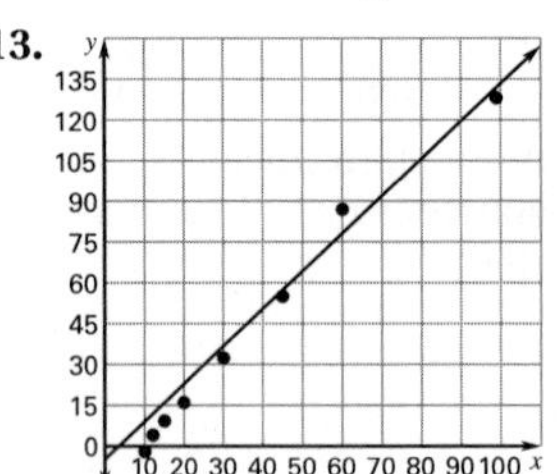

Positive correlation. *Sample answer:* $y = 1.49x - 13$

SELECTED ANSWERS

SA14

5.6 Problem Solving (pp. 329–330)

17. a. 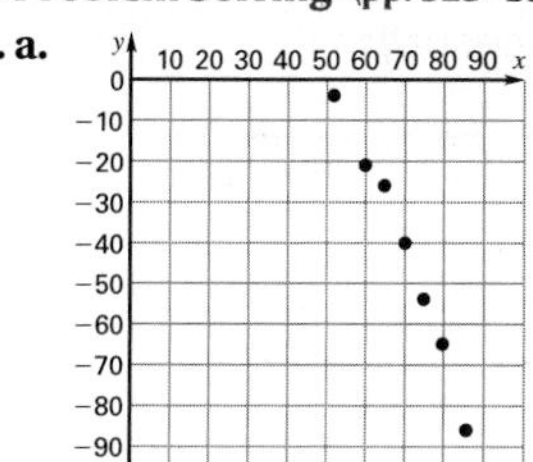

b. *Sample answer:* $y = -2.2x + 111$ **c.** *Sample answer:* -2.2 degrees per kilometer

19. *Sample answer:* $y = 12.6x + 32$

5.6 Graphing Calculator Activity (p. 332) **1.** See art in Exercise 3; negative correlation.

3. 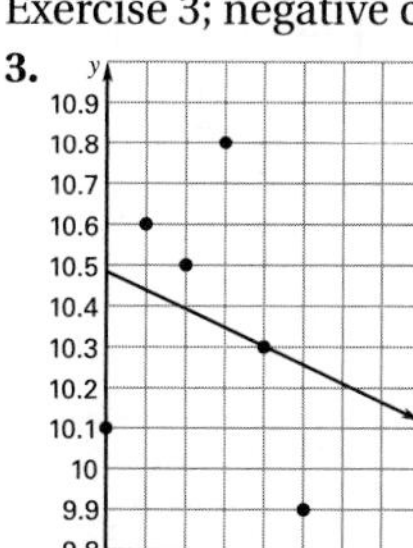

5. *Sample answer:* You cannot use the best-fitting line to predict future sales because the data do not show a strong correlation.

Extension (p. 333) **1.** about 0.927; The data show a strong positive correlation. While an increase in the number of minutes played may contribute to an increase in the number of points scored, there is not causation. The number of minutes played and the number of points scored may both be a result of the ability of the player. **3.** *Sample answer:* I think that as music downloads increase, sales of CDs decrease, so I would expect a strong negative correlation. The increase in the number of music downloads causes the decline in CD sales as users find downloading a more convenient way to obtain music.

5.7 Skill Practice (pp. 338–339) **1.** linear interpolation

3. 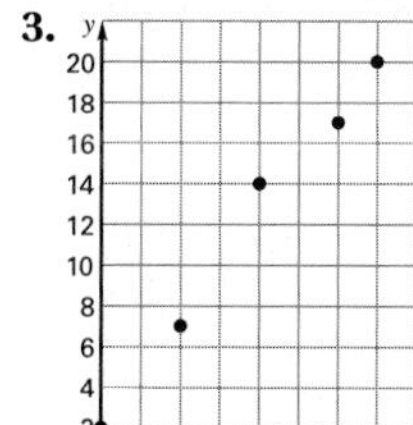

$y = 2.6x + 2.3$; 15.3

5. 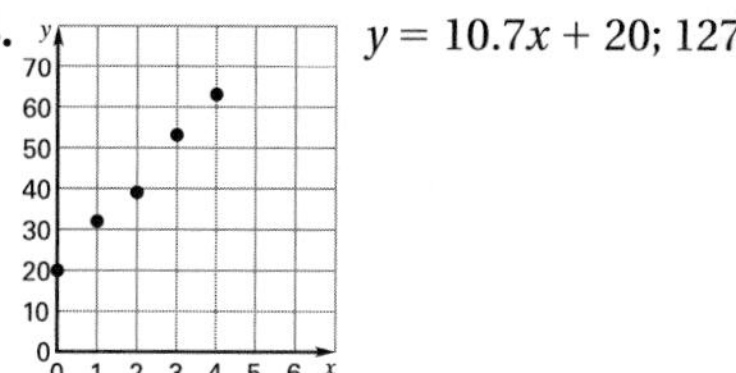

$y = 10.7x + 20$; 127

7. $2\frac{2}{3}$ **9.** -16 **11.** 1.5 **13.** To find the zero of a function, substitute 0 for *y*, not *x*; $0 = 2.3x - 2$, $2 = 2.3x$, $x = \frac{20}{23}$. **15.** *a* and *b* were not substituted correctly; $y = 4.47x + 23.1$.

5.7 Problem Solving (pp. 339–341)

19. a. 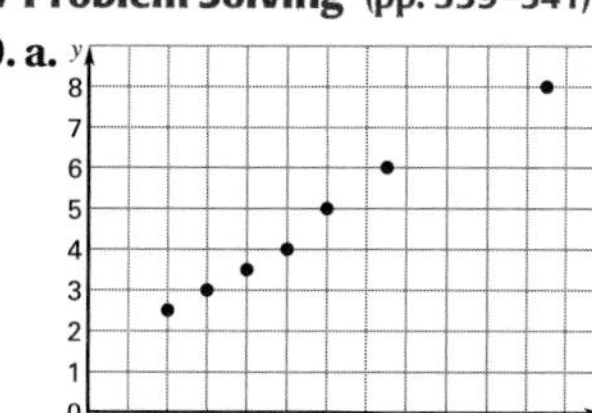

b. $y = 0.03x + 1.23$ **c.** about 8.73 ft^2 **21. a.** $y = -197.6x + 3542$ **b.** about 17.9; 17.9 years from 1985, or 2002, the number of people living in high noise areas will be 0; no.

5.7 Internet Activity (p. 342)

1. Answers may vary. **3.** Answers may vary.

Chapter Review (pp. 345–348) **1.** negative **3.** The zero of a function is the *x*-value of the function when $y = 0$; it is the *x*-intercept of the graph. **5.** $y = \frac{4}{9}x + 5$ **7.** $y = -1.25x + 25$; \$22.50 **9.** $y = x + 3$ **11.** $y - 7 = -6(x - 4)$ or $y - 1 = -6(x - 5)$ **13.** $y + 2 = -\frac{6}{11}(x + 3)$ or $y + 8 = -\frac{6}{11}(x - 8)$ **15.** $4x + y = -1$ **17.** $0.07r + 0.04s = 5$. *Sample answer:* 4 organza, 118 satin; 8 organza, 111 satin; 12 organza, 104 satin **19. a.** $y = -2x + 1$ **b.** $y = \frac{1}{2}x - 4$

21. 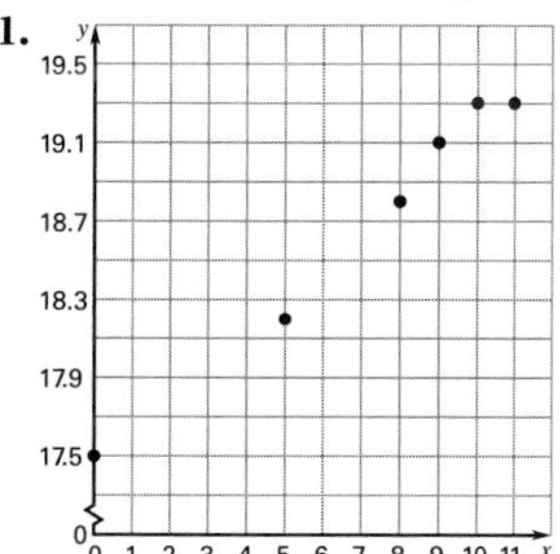

positive correlation

Chapter 6

6.1 Skill Practice (pp. 359–360) **1.** open, left of -8

3. $s \le 60$

5. $h > 48$

7. $x < 10$ **9.** $x \ge -2$

11. $y \ge -16$

13. $n \le -\frac{1}{5}$

15. $w > -17.6$

17. $s \ge 9$

19. $q > -1\frac{1}{6}$

21. $d > -6.84$

23. The number line should be shaded to the right of -3, not the left.

25. $n - 15 \le 37$; $n \le 52$

27. $x < 21.6$ **29.** No; no; there are infinitely many solutions of an inequality, so it is not possible to check them all. One solution might check in the inequality while another does not. For example, if you incorrectly solve $x + 7 > 10$ as $x > 2$, the solution $x = 4$ checks in the original inequality.

6.1 Problem Solving (pp. 360–361) **31.** more than 8350 points **33. a.** $s > 127.53$ **b.** Yes; no; no; $128.13 > 127.53$; $126.78 < 127.53$; when your score is 127.53, you and your competitor will tie.
35. *Sample answer:* You want to improve on your personal best of 16 points scored in a basketball game. In the first three quarters of the game, you scored 14 points. Write and solve an inequality to find the possible numbers of points that you can score in the fourth quarter to give yourself a new personal best; $x \ge 3$, if you score at least 3 points in the fourth quarter, you will have a new personal best.

37. a.

Original price, x ($)	19,459	19,989	20,549	22,679	23,999
Final price, y ($)	16,459	16,989	17,549	19,679	20,999

b. $x - 3000 \le 17{,}000$, $x \le 20{,}000$

6.2 Skill Practice (pp. 366–367)
1. Division property of inequality

3. $p \ge 7$ **5.** $y > 6$ **7.** $q < 28$ **9.** $g > -120$ **11.** $t \le -22.5$ **13.** $s \le -5$ **15.** $f < -0.25$ **17.** $c < -0.6$ **19.** $z \le -0.25$

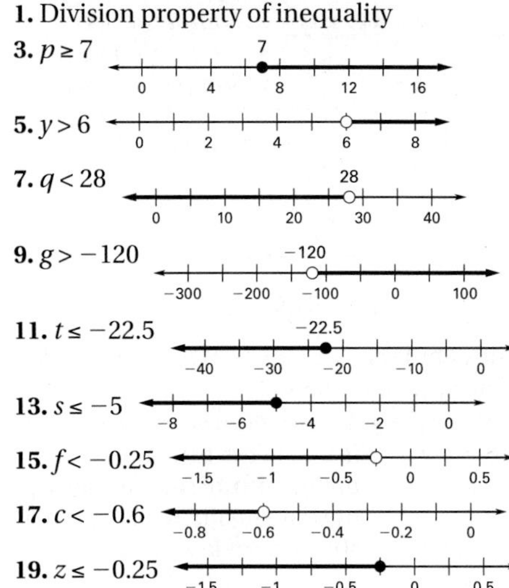

21. $j < -0.34$

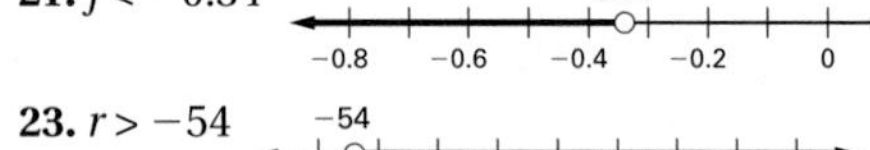

23. $r > -54$

25. $m > -24$

27. In both cases, you divide both sides of the inequality by a; when $a > 0$, you do not reverse the inequality symbol, but when $a < 0$, you do. **29.** Both sides of the inequality were multiplied by a positive number, so the inequality symbol should not have been reversed; $x \le -63$.

31. $-15y \le 90$; $y \ge -6$

33. $\frac{w}{24} \ge -\frac{1}{6}$; $w \ge -4$

6.2 Problem Solving (pp. 367–368) **37.** at least 200 words **39.** at least 3.2 **41. a.** $400h \le 6560$, $h \le 16.4$, no more than 16 horses **b.** No; the area added by increasing both the length and the width by 20 feet can be divided into 2 rectangles (80 feet by 20 feet and 82 feet by 20 feet) and 1 square (20 feet by 20 feet). The 400 square feet of the square is large enough to hold one horse, and the rectangular areas will be able to hold additional horses. **c.** no more than 23 horses; the area of the new corral is $(80 + 15)(82 + 15) = 9215$ square feet. Find the possible numbers of horses h the corral can hold by solving the inequality $9215 \ge 400h$; $h \le 23.04$.

SELECTED ANSWERS

SA16

6.3 Skill Practice (pp. 372–373)
1. equivalent inequalities
3. $x > 5$

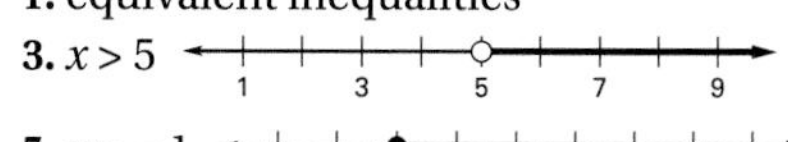

5. $v \geq -1$ **7.** $r \geq 1\frac{1}{7}$ **9.** $m > 3$ **11.** $p < \frac{1}{2}$ **13.** $d > -10$

15. The inequality symbol was not reversed when dividing both sides by -3; $x \leq -13$. **17.** all real numbers **19.** $s \geq 0$ **21.** all real numbers **23.** no solution **25.** no solution **27.** no solution
29. $3x + 4 < 40$; $x < 12$
31. $5x + 2x > 9x - 4$; $x < 2$
35. $\frac{1}{2} \cdot 8(x + 1) \leq 44$; $x \leq 10$

6.3 Problem Solving (pp. 373–374) **37.** at most 11 songs **39. a.** Up to 6 swans; the area of the habitat is (20 feet)(50 feet) = 1000 square feet. 500 square feet are needed for the first two swans and the remaining 1000 − 500 = 500 square feet can hold up to 500 ÷ 125 = 4 more swans; so, the maximum number of swans is 2 + 4 = 6 swans. **b.** at most 14 more swans

41. a.

Pitches per inning, p	15	16	17	18	19
Total number of pitches, t	98	101	104	107	110

b. $53 + 3p \leq 105$, $p \leq 17\frac{1}{3}$, at most 17 pitches

6.3 Problem Solving Workshop (p. 376) **1.** at least 9 batches **3.** at most 6 games **5.** less than 7.9 min/mi

Extension (p. 378) **1.** $x > 3$ **3.** $x < 213.75$

6.4 Skill Practice (pp. 384–385)
1. compound inequality
3. $2 < x < 6$
5. $-1.5 \leq x < 9.2$
7. $40 \leq s \leq 60$
9. $1 < x \leq 6$
11. $-4 \leq m \leq \frac{1}{4}$
13. $-\frac{1}{3} \leq p < 2$
15. $r < 2$ or $r \geq 7$
17. $v < -5$ or $v > 5$
19. $g < -2\frac{1}{3}$ or $g > 10$
21. 3 was subtracted from only two of the three expressions of the inequality; $1 < -2x < 6$, $-\frac{1}{2} > x > -3$.
23. $x + 5 < 8$ or $x - 3 > 5$; $x < 3$ or $x > 8$
25. $-8 \leq 3(x - 4) \leq 10$; $1\frac{1}{3} \leq x \leq 7\frac{1}{3}$
29. true **31.** False. *Sample answer:* $a = -4$ is a solution of $x > 5$ or $x \leq -4$, but it is not a solution of $x > 5$.

6.4 Problem Solving (pp. 385–387)
37. $-2600 \leq e \leq -100$
41. $3.2 \text{ lb} \leq f \leq 6.4 \text{ lb}$ **43. a.** $\frac{5}{9}(F - 32) < 0$ or $\frac{5}{9}(F - 32) > 100$, $F < 32°F$ or $F > 212°F$
b.

°F	23	86	140	194	239
°C	−5	30	60	90	115

23°F, 239°F

45. a. $8 \leq \frac{w}{300} \leq 10$, $2400 \leq w \leq 3000$; 2400 watts to 3000 watts **b.** Yes; no; the amplification per person for 350 people is $\frac{2900}{350} \approx 8.3$ watts, which is between 8 watts and 10 watts, the amplification per person for 400 people is $\frac{2900}{400} = 7.25$ watts, which is not between 8 watts and 10 watts. **c.** 4800 watts; because each person requires at least 8 watts of amplification, and you want to be sure to provide enough amplification for 600 people, you need at least 8(600) = 4800 watts of amplification.

6.4 Graphing Calculator Activity (p. 388) **1.** $4 < x < 7$; the graphs are the same. **3–7.** Displays should show the graphs of the following inequalities. **3.** $3 \leq x \leq 7$ **5.** $8 \leq x \leq 48$ **7.** $x \leq 4\frac{1}{2}$ or $x \geq 5$

SELECTED ANSWERS

SA17

6.5 Skill Practice (pp. 393–394) **1.** absolute value equation **3.** 5, −5 **5.** 0.7, −0.7 **7.** $\frac{1}{2}, -\frac{1}{2}$ **9.** 4, −10 **11.** $-1, -3\frac{2}{3}$ **13.** 2, −9 **15.** 4, 9 **17.** $8\frac{1}{2}, -3\frac{1}{2}$ **19.** $-\frac{1}{2}, -2\frac{1}{2}$ **21.** The absolute value symbol was removed without writing the second equation, $x + 4 = -13$; $x = 9$ or $x = -17$. **23.** no solution **25.** −4.5, −5.5 **27.** −3, 6 **29.** $13\frac{1}{2}, 14\frac{1}{2}$ **31.** $\frac{1}{4}, -1\frac{1}{4}$ **33.** 13, −3 **35.** −7.5, −10.7 **37.** The distance between x and 3 is 7, 10, −4; $x - 3 = 7$ *or* $x - 3 = -7$, 10, −4; the solutions are the same. **39.** $5|2x + 9| = 15$; −3, −6

6.5 Problem Solving (pp. 394–395) **43.** 235 sec, 245 sec **45. a.** 52.462 points, 56.888 points **b.** 0.3 point **47. a.** $p = |s - 450|$ **b.** 300 points, 600 points **49. a.** June 2005; November 2005 **b.** Yes; make a table of values for (m, p) using integer values of m from 0 to 8. Look for the lowest value of p in the table.

Extension (p. 397)

1. 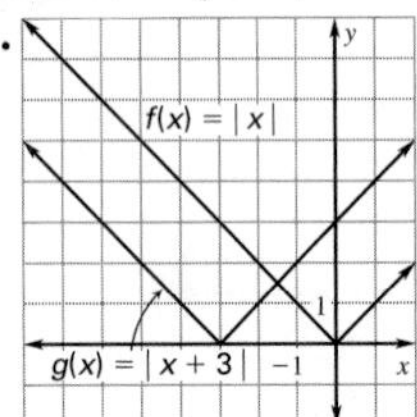

The graph of g is 3 units to the left of the graph of f.

3. 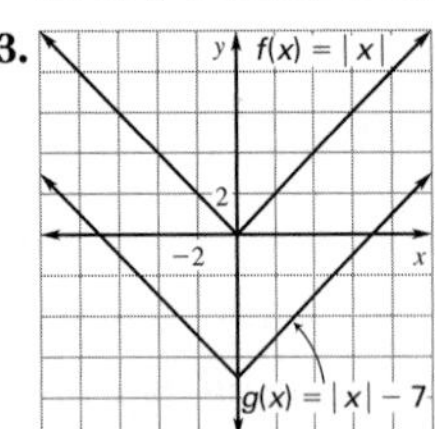

The graph of g is 7 units below the graph of f.

5. 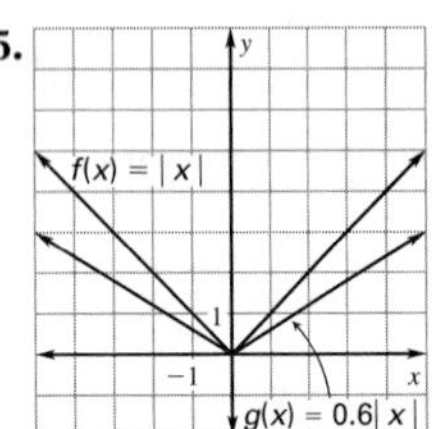

The graph of g opens up and is wider than the graph of f.

7. domain: all real numbers, range: $y \le 1$; (0, 1); maximum value: 1

6.6 Skill Practice (pp. 401–402) **1.** equivalent inequalities **3.** $-4 < x < 4$ **5.** $h < -4.5$ or $h > 4.5$ **7.** $-\frac{3}{5} \le t \le \frac{3}{5}$ **9.** $d \le -7$ or $d \ge -1$ **11.** $m < 8$ or $m > 20$ **13.** $c \le -3$ or $c \ge \frac{1}{2}$ **15.** $r < -8$ or $r > -4$ **17.** $u \le -3\frac{1}{5}$ or $u \ge 6\frac{2}{5}$ **19.** $v < 6$ or $v > 34$ **23.** The compound inequality should use *or*: $x + 4 > 13$ *or* $x + 4 < -13$; $x > 9$ *or* $x < -17$. **25.** $|x - 6| \le 4$; $2 \le x \le 10$ **27.** $|-4x - 7| + 3 > 10$; $x < -3.5$ *or* $x > 0$ **29.** true **31.** False. *Sample answer:* 20

6.6 Problem Solving (pp. 402–403) **35.** at least 470 words and at most 530 words **37.** $|t - 346| \le 2$, at least 344°F and at most 348°F; continue to preheat; the temperature is still below 350°F. **39. a.** 10.02 m/sec^2 **b.** 0.88 m/sec^2

6.7 Skill Practice (pp. 409–410) **1.** solution **3.** not a solution **5.** not a solution **7.** not a solution **9.** solution **11.** not a solution **13.** solution

17. **19.** **21.** **23.** **25.** **27.** **29.** **31.**

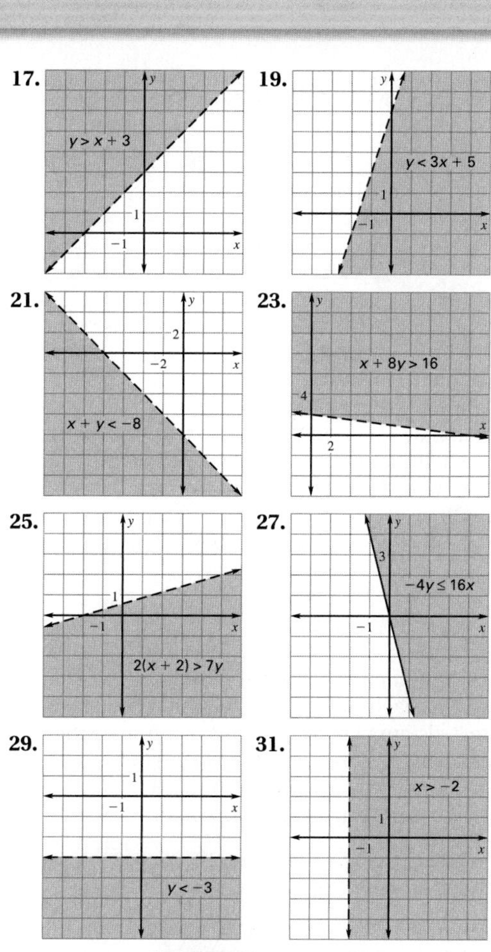

33. **35.**

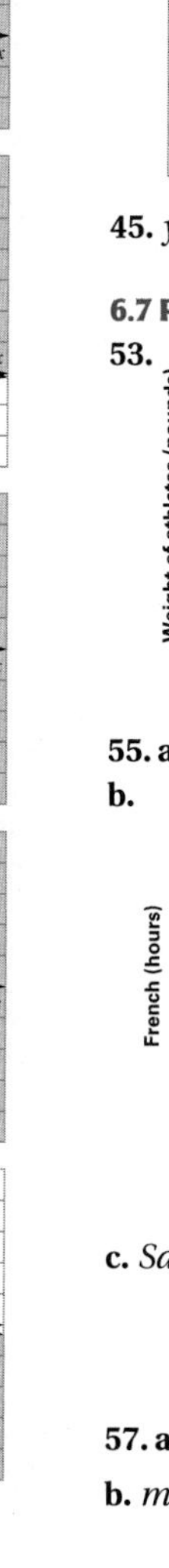

37. The wrong half-plane is shaded.

39. No; (0, 0) is a point on the boundary line $2x = -5y$.

41. $-2y \le x + 6$ **43.** $x + 4y < -3$

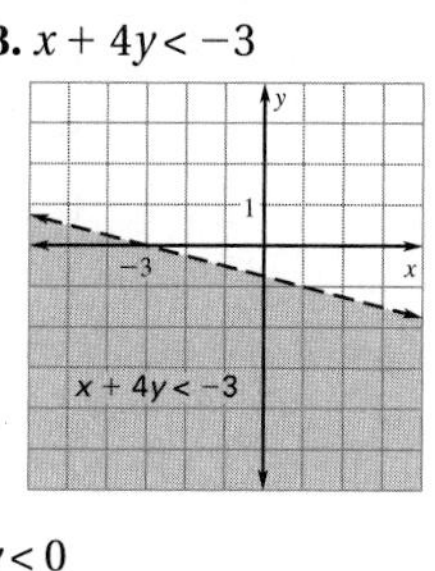

45. $y \le \frac{5}{7}x - \frac{9}{7}$ **47.** $y > 0$ **49.** $y < 0$

6.7 Problem Solving (pp. 410–412)

53.

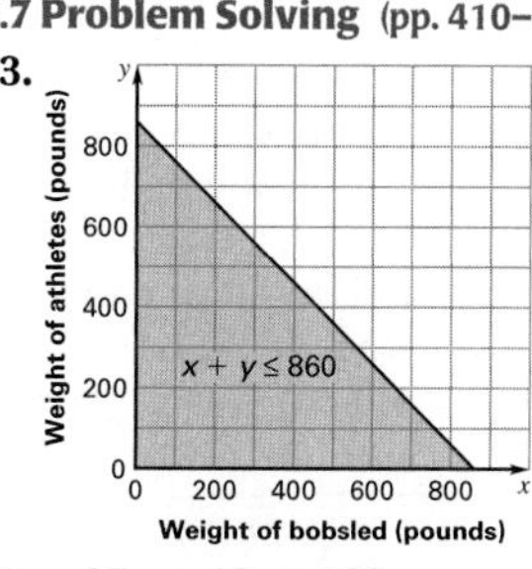

Sample answer: The solution (450, 400) means that the bobsled can weigh 450 pounds when the combined weight of the athletes is 400 pounds.

55. a. $15x + 10y \ge 100$

b.

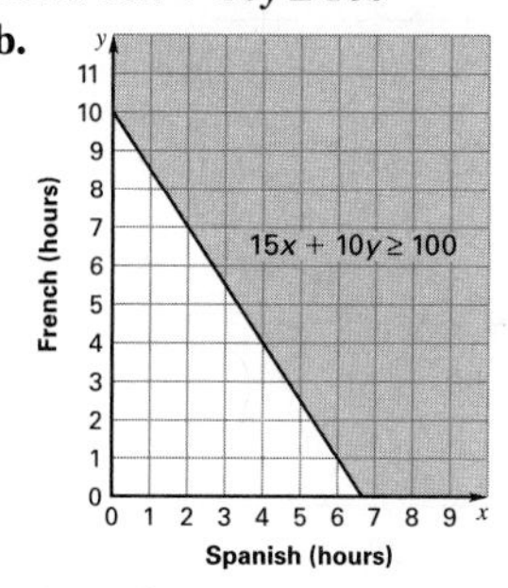

Sample answer: (4, 8), (5, 3), (6, 1)

c. *Sample answer:*

Spanish time (hours)	4	5	6
French time (hours)	8	3	1
Total earnings (dollars)	140	105	100

57. a. $\frac{1}{6}m + \frac{1}{2}\ell \le 12$

b. $m \le 60$

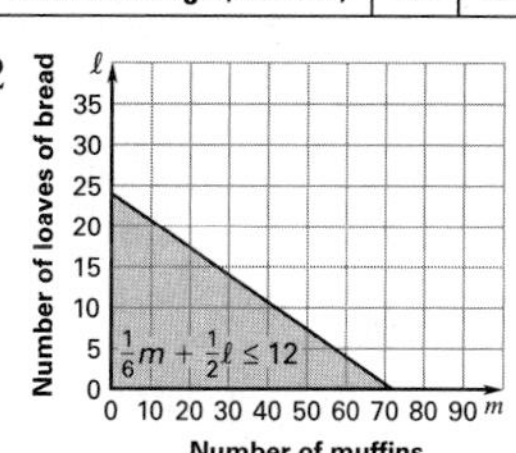

SELECTED ANSWERS

59. a. $x + y \le 30$

Sample answer: (20, 4), (25, 5), (26, 2)

b. Yes; no; (0, 30) means that you do not take a duffel and have a 30 pound bedroll, while (30, 0) means you take a 30 pound duffel and do not take a bedroll. You need to bring both a duffel and a bedroll.

Chapter Review (pp. 415–418) **1.** $|x - 19| = 8$ **3.** The boundary line is solid if the inequality symbol is ≤ or ≥, the boundary line is dashed if the inequality symbol is < or >; choose a test point that is not on the boundary line. If the ordered pair is a solution to the inequality, shade the half-plane that contains the test point; if it not a solution, shade the other half-plane.

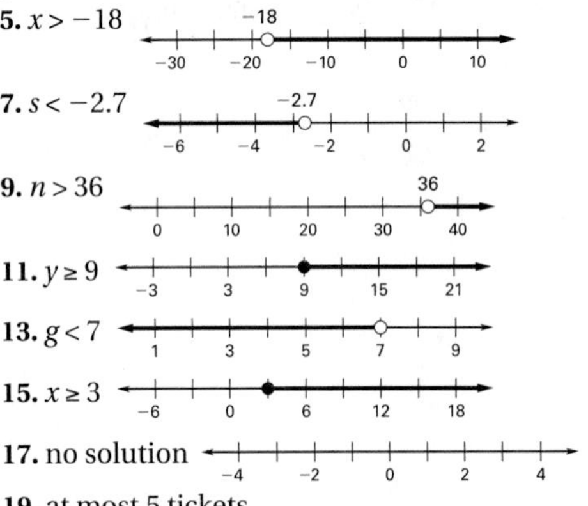

5. $x > -18$ **7.** $s < -2.7$ **9.** $n > 36$ **11.** $y \ge 9$ **13.** $g < 7$ **15.** $x \ge 3$ **17.** no solution

19. at most 5 tickets

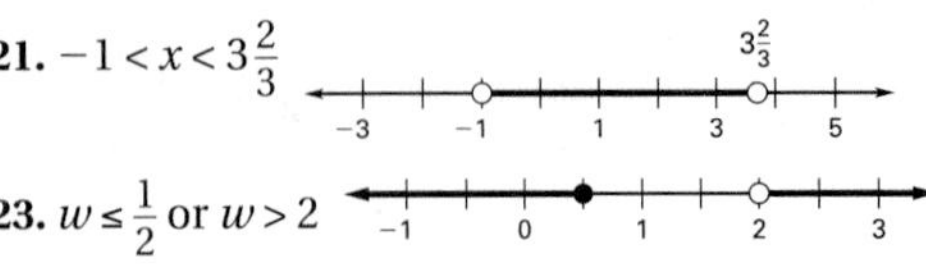

21. $-1 < x < 3\frac{2}{3}$

23. $w \le \frac{1}{2}$ or $w > 2$

25. −4, −8 **27.** 5, 1 **29.** $1\frac{1}{6}, \frac{1}{6}$

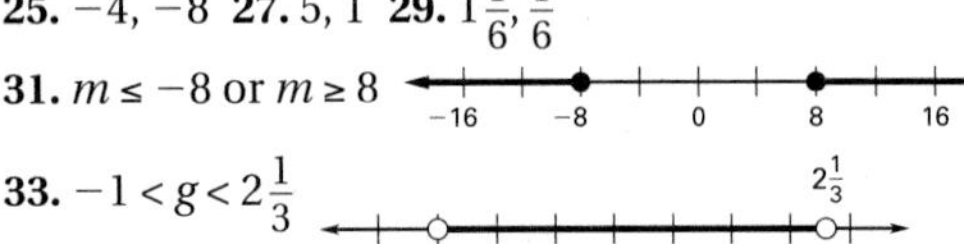

31. $m \le -8$ or $m \ge 8$

33. $-1 < g < 2\frac{1}{3}$

35. $j < -1\frac{1}{2}$ or $j > 10\frac{1}{2}$

37. solution **39.** solution

41.

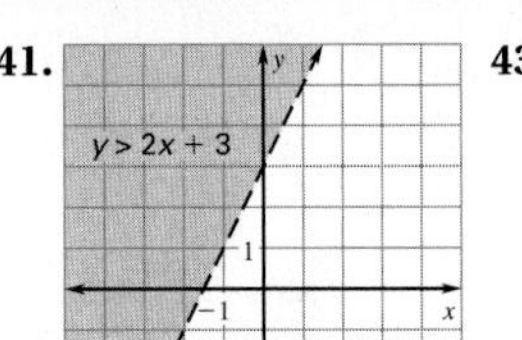

43.

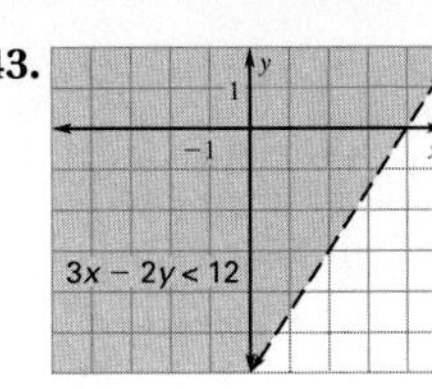

Chapter 7

7.1 Skill Practice (pp. 430–432) **1.** solution **3.** solution **5.** not a solution **9.** (4, 2) **11.** The solution (3, −1) does not satisfy Equation 2. The graph of Equation 2 is incorrect; if properly graphed, the lines would intersect at (−3, −3).

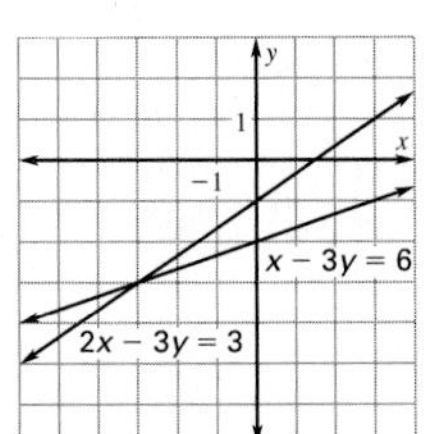

13. (4, 0) **15.** (−3, −5) **17.** (10, −15) **19.** (7, −5) **21.** (−5, 2) **23.** (3, 6) **25.** (4, 6) **27.** *Sample answer:* $m = 0$ and $b = 2$ **29. a.** 4 **b.** (4, 5) **c.** *Sample answer:* Each side of the equation is set equal to y. **d.** *Sample answer:* Set each side of the equation equal to y to create a system of two equations. Then solve the system using the graph-and-check method. The x-coordinate of the system's solution is the solution of the original equation.

7.1 Problem Solving (pp. 432–433) **31.** 2040 **33.** 15 small cards and 10 large cards **35. a.** $y = 5x + 15$, $y = 8x$

b.

Tickets	Cost for members	Cost for nonmembers
1	$20	$8
2	$25	$16
3	$30	$24
4	$35	$32
5	$40	$40
6	$45	$48

c.

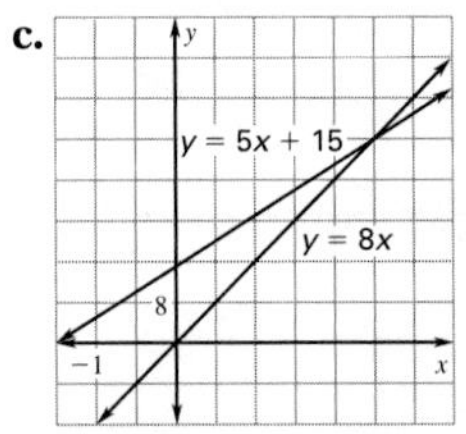

When you view 6 or more movies. *Sample answer:* The graph for a nonmember is below the graph for a member up through 4 movies. For 5 movies, the cost is the same. The graph for members is lower than the graph for nonmembers for 6 or more movies.

7.1 Graphing Calculator Activity (p. 434) **1.** (−1.5, 2.5) **3.** (0.2, −1.44)

7.2 Skill Practice (pp. 439–440) **1.** *Sample answer:* $y = x + 1, y = 2x + 1$ **3.** (5, 3) **5.** (2, −1) **7.** (−4, 5) **9.** (6, 7) **11.** (2, −2) **13.** (5, −8) **15.** (0, 2) **17.** (1.4, −4.4) **19.** *Sample answer:* In Step 3, 6 is substituted for y instead of x; $y = 9 - 3(6)$, $y = -9$, the solution is (6, −9). **21.** (4, −120) **23.** (3, 7) **25.** (6, −3) **27.** (0, −6) **29.** *Sample answer:* The graphs of the equations should intersect at the solution you found using the substitution method.

7.2 Problem Solving (pp. 440–441) **31.** 96 bags of popcorn; 48 pretzels **33.** 4 in. *Sample answer:* (4, 5) is the solution to the appropriate linear system, so x should equal 4. **35.** 50 milliliters of 1% hydrochloric acid solution and 50 milliliters of 5% hydrochloric acid solution **37.** Yes. *Sample answer:* The cheetah would have to run at 88 feet per second for 23.3 seconds to catch the gazelle.

7.2 Problem Solving Workshop (p. 442) **1.** 5 mi

7.3 Skill Practice (pp. 447–448) **1.** *Sample answer:* $x + y = 10, x - y = 5$ **3.** (1, 6) **5.** (−1, −5) **7.** (5, 7) **9.** (−1, 2) **11.** (5, 3) **13.** (4, 5) **17.** (2, −3) **19.** (−18, 4) **21.** (4, −3) **23.** *Sample answer:* The two equations should be subtracted rather than added; $6x = 8, x = \frac{4}{3}$. **25.** (26, 14) **27.** (−4, 12) **29.** (−2, 5) **31.** (5, 25) **33.** (−2, 8) **35.** $\ell = 4.5$ ft, $w = 2.5$ ft

7.3 Problem Solving (pp. 449–450) **39.** speed in still water: 4.6 m/sec, speed of current: 0.3 m/sec **41.** monophonic ring tone: $1.95, polyphonic ring tone: $3.50 **43. a.** flight to Phoenix: 400 mi/h, flight to Charlotte: 450 mi/h **b.** $s + w = 450, s - w = 400$; plane: 425 mi/h, wind: 25 mi/h

7.4 Skill Practice (pp. 454–455) **1.** 36 **3.** (1, 1) **5.** (5, −4) **7.** (2, 1) **9.** (−7, −12) **11.** (5, 6) **13.** (4, 4) **15.** (5, −3) **17.** $\left(4\frac{2}{7}, 5\right)$ **19.** *Sample answer:* The two equations should be subtracted rather than added; $-x = -9$, $x = 9$. **21.** (2, −1) **23.** $\left(-4\frac{5}{22}, -2\frac{1}{11}\right)$ **25.** (5, 4) **27.** (10, 2) **29.** (2, −1) **31.** $\left(\frac{1}{3}, -\frac{2}{3}\right)$ **33. a.** $2\ell + 2w = 18$, $6\ell + 4w = 46$; length: 5 in., width: 4 in. **b.** length: 15 in., width: 8 in.

7.4 Problem Solving (pp. 456–457) **37.** 5 hardcover books **39.** 21 pies, 16 batches of applesauce **41.** $16.50; a small costs $2.90, and a large costs $3.90; 3(2.90) + 2(3.90) = 16.50. **43.** $800; $1200

7.5 Skill Practice (pp. 462–464) **1.** inconsistent **3.** *Sample answer:* The lines have the same slope but different y-intercepts. **5.** B; one solution **7.** A; infinitely many solutions

9.

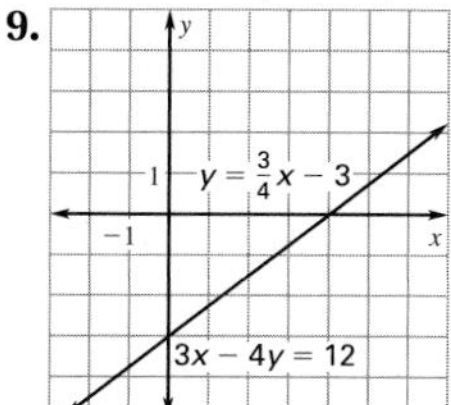

infinitely many solutions

11.

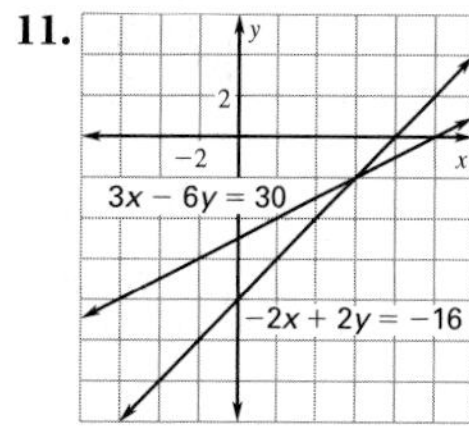

one solution

13.

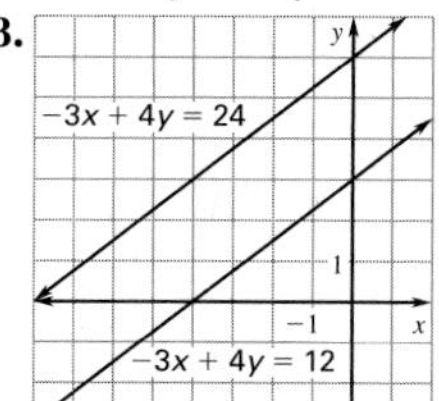

no solution

15. (−3, 4) **17.** (3, 7) **19.** (2, 2) **21.** no solution **23.** (0, 3) **27.** infinitely many solutions **29.** infinitely many solutions **31.** infinitely many solutions **33.** *Sample answer:* $7x - 8y = -9, 7x - 8y = 4$

7.5 Problem Solving (pp. 464–465) **37.** Yes. *Sample answer:* There is one solution to the resulting linear system. **39. a.** $d = \frac{t}{3}, d = \frac{t}{3} - 5$

b.

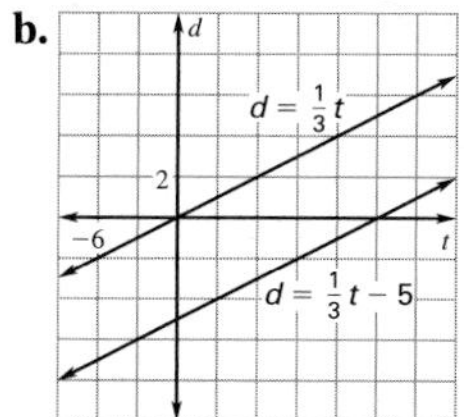

Sample answer: No, since the lines are parallel, the two climbers will never be at the same distance at the same time.

7.6 Skill Practice (pp. 469–470) **1.** solution **3.** not a solution **5.** not a solution **7.** A

9.

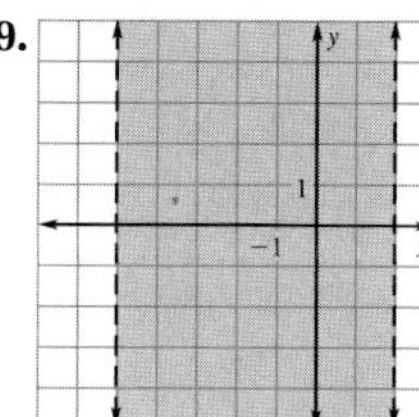

11.

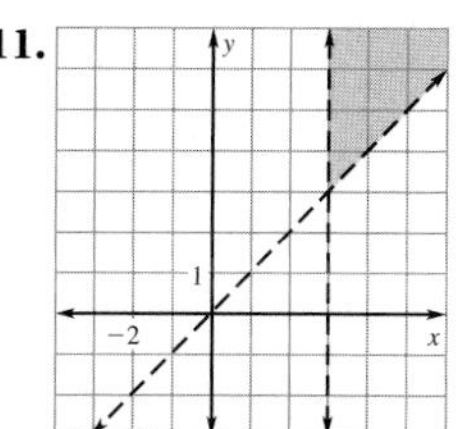

13.

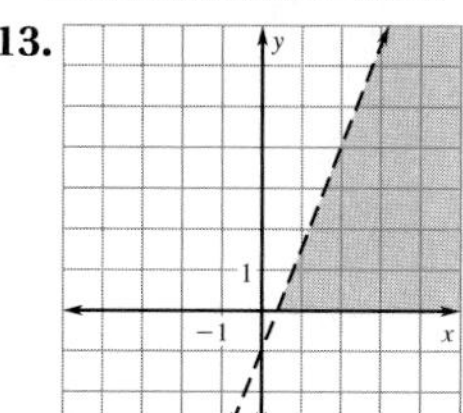

15.

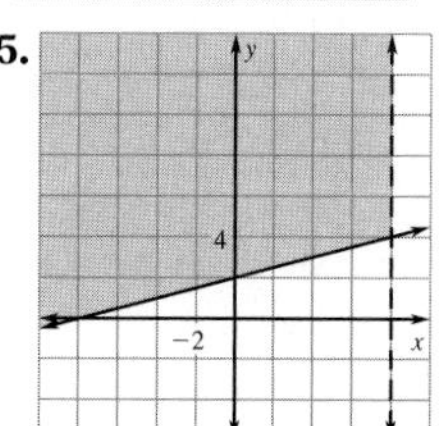

17. 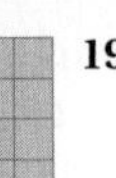

19. 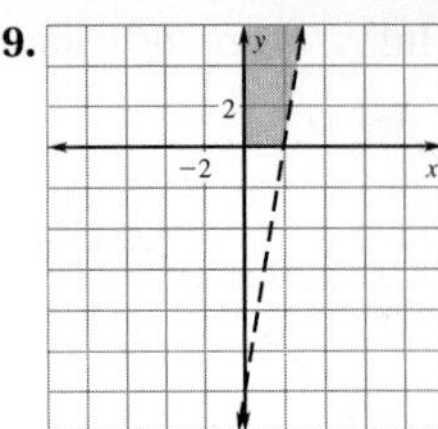

23. The graph is shaded to include $x + y > 3$, not $x + y < 3$.

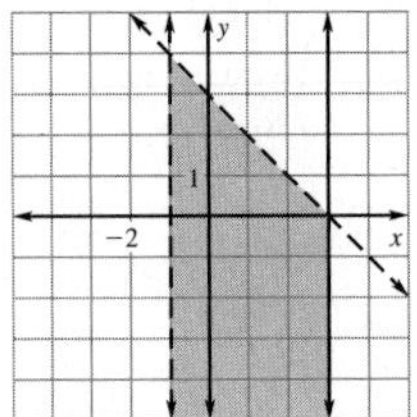

25. $y > -1, y < 4$ **27.** $y \leq 5x + 1, y > x - 2$ **29.** $y \leq x - 3$, $y > -2x - 1, y > -6$

31. 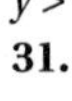

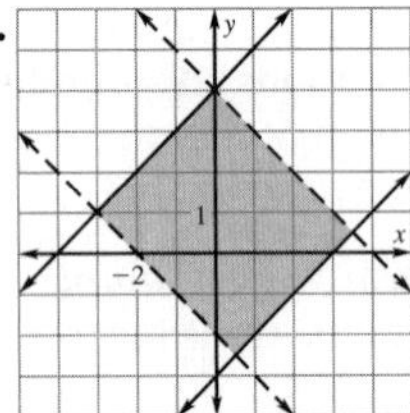

33. No; there are no possible values for x and y that satisfy both equations.

7.6 Problem Solving (pp. 471–472)

37. $14x + 7y < 70$, $x + y < 8, x \geq 0, y \geq 0$

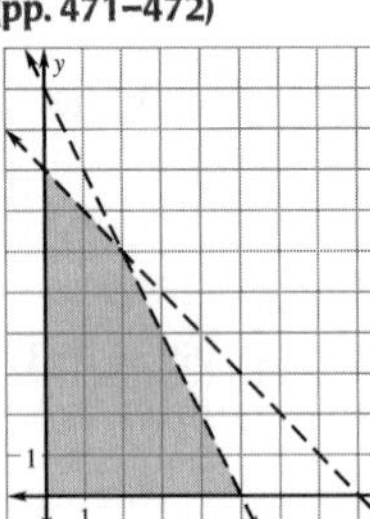

39. a. $20 \leq x \leq 65$, $154 - 0.7x \leq y \leq 187 - 0.85x$

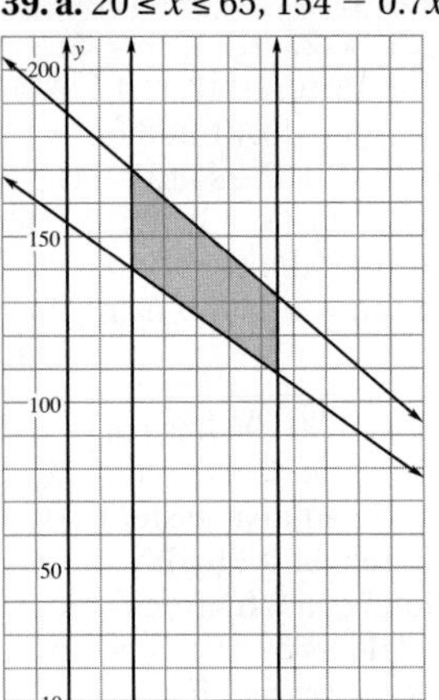

b. No. *Sample answer:* The heart rate is below 70% of the maximum heart rate.

Chapter Review (pp. 475–478) **1.** system of linear inequalities **3.** *Sample answer:* Graph each inequality then shade the region that is the intersection of the solutions to each inequality. Then check the solution with a test point. **5.** (2, −5) **7.** (4, −1) **9.** (5, 1) **11.** 4 tubes of paint, 8 brushes **13.** (1, −2) **15.** (6, 10) **17.** (−7, 8) **19.** (−2, 5) **21.** (4, 5) **23.** (1, 6) **25.** No solution. *Sample answer:* When the variables are eliminated, a false statement remains, which means there is no solution. **27.** One solution. *Sample answer:* The lines have different slopes, so there is only one solution.

29. 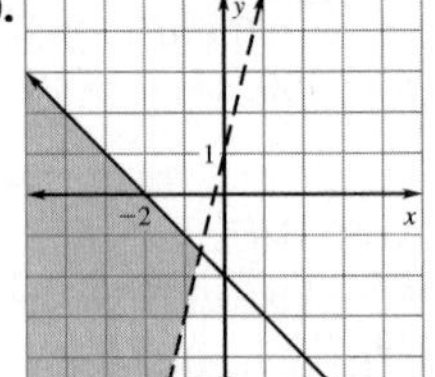

31. Let m represent the number of matinee movies and n represent the number of evening movies; $5m + 8n \leq 40, m \geq 0, n \geq 0$.

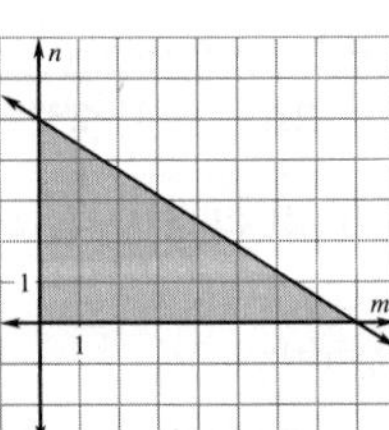

Cumulative Review (pp. 484–485) **1.** 62 **3.** 55 **5.** −50 **7.** solution **9.** not a solution **11.** solution **13.** $5y - 1$ **15.** $-g + 4$ **17.** $-3 + \frac{4}{7}x$ **19.** 29 **21.** −7 **23.** −3 **25.** −3 **27.** $4\frac{4}{9}$

SELECTED ANSWERS

29.

31. 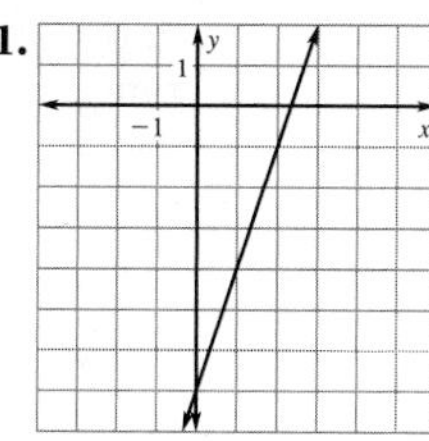

33.

35. $y = -x + 3$ **37.** $y + 10 = -2(x - 1)$ or $y - 2 = -2(x + 5)$ **39.** $y + 2 = \frac{10}{3}(x + 9)$ or $y - 8 = \frac{10}{3}(x + 6)$
41. $y - 4 = -\frac{1}{3}(x - 2)$ or $y - 2 = -\frac{1}{3}(x - 8)$
43. $x < -4$
45. $x \geq 7$
47. $x > -5$
49. $x \geq -6$
51. $-1 < x < 2$
53. $-5 < x < 5$

55. (1, 4) **57.** (2, −3) **59.** \$.02 **61. a.** The ratio $\frac{p}{\ell}$ is always the same, so p varies directly with ℓ. **b.** $p = 2.5\ell$ **63.** $-4 \leq F \leq 113$

Chapter 8

8.1 Skill Practice (pp. 492–493) **1.** order of magnitude **3.** 4^8 **5.** 3^4 **7.** $(-7)^9$ **9.** 2^{14} **11.** 3^{10} **13.** $(-5)^{12}$ **15.** $15^3 \cdot 29^3$ **17.** $132^6 \cdot 9^6$ **19.** x^6 **21.** z^6 **23.** x^{10} **25.** $(b - 2)^{12}$ **27.** $25x^2$ **29.** $49x^2y^2$ **31.** $100x^{14}$ **33.** $96d^{22}$ **35.** $12p^{19}$ **37.** $108x^{29}$ **39.** *Sample answer:* The exponents should be added, not multiplied; $c^1 \cdot c^4 \cdot c^5 = c^{1+4+5} = c^{10}$. **43.** 2 **45.** 2 **47.** $-3267x^{12}y^{13}$ **49.** $1000r^{17}s^6t^{17}$

8.1 Problem Solving (pp. 493–494) **53.** 10^{26} m

55. a.

Ounces of gold	10	100	1000	10,000	100,000
Number of atoms	10^{24}	10^{25}	10^{26}	10^{27}	10^{28}

b. $10^5 \cdot 10^{23}$; 10^{28} atoms **57.** 10^{27}

8.2 Skill Practice (pp. 498–499) **1.** base, exponent **3.** 5^4 **5.** 3^4 **7.** $(-4)^3$ **9.** 10^6 **11.** $\frac{1}{3^5}$ **13.** $\frac{5^4}{4^4}$ **15.** 7^7 **17.** 3^8 **21.** y^7 **23.** $\frac{a^9}{y^9}$ **25.** $\frac{p^4}{q^4}$ **27.** $-\frac{64}{x^3}$ **29.** $\frac{64c^3}{d^6}$ **31.** $\frac{x^4}{9y^6}$ **33.** $\frac{9x^4}{4y^2}$ **35.** $\frac{3m^7}{8n^6}$ **39.** 8 **41.** 4 **43.** $54s^3t^3$ **45.** $\frac{27x^{11}y^5}{25}$ **47.** Identity property of multiplication; Multiply fractions; Quotient of powers property

8.2 Problem Solving (pp. 500–501)

49. a.

Step	Number of new squares	Side length of new square
1	$4 = 4^1$	$\frac{1}{2} = \left(\frac{1}{2}\right)^1$
2	$16 = 4^2$	$\frac{1}{4} = \left(\frac{1}{2}\right)^2$
3	$64 = 4^3$	$\frac{1}{8} = \left(\frac{1}{2}\right)^3$
4	$256 = 4^4$	$\frac{1}{16} = \left(\frac{1}{2}\right)^4$

b. $\frac{4^4}{4^2}$; 16 times

51. about 31,710 yr **53.** 31^3 times greater

8.3 Skill Practice (pp. 506–507) **1.** Product of powers property and definition of zero exponent; the expression simplifies using the product of powers property to 3^0, which by definition equals 1. **3.** $\frac{1}{64}$ **5.** $-\frac{1}{3}$ **7.** 1 **9.** 1 **11.** $\frac{49}{4}$ **13.** undefined **15.** $\frac{1}{32}$ **17.** $\frac{1}{32}$ **19.** 27 **21.** $\frac{1}{243}$ **23.** $\frac{8}{3}$ **25.** 16 **27.** 3^0 is not equivalent to 0, but to 1; $-6 \cdot 3^0 = -6 \cdot 1 = -6$. **29.** $\frac{2}{y^3}$ **31.** $\frac{1}{121h^2}$ **33.** $\frac{5}{m^3n^4}$ **35.** 1 **37.** $\frac{1}{x^5y^2}$ **39.** $\frac{y^8}{15x^{10}}$ **41.** $243d^3$ **43.** $\frac{3x^{12}y^5}{4}$

8.3 Problem Solving (pp. 507–508) **51.** about 10^5 grains of rice **53.** about 10^{11} red blood cells

55. a.

Number of folds	0	1	2	3
Fraction of original area	1	$\frac{1}{2}$	$\frac{1}{4}$	$\frac{1}{8}$

b. $\left(\frac{1}{2}\right)^x$ where x is the number of folds **57. a.** 112.5 watts **b.** $I = 9d^{-2}$ **c.** The intensity is divided by 4.

Extension (p. 510) **1.** 1000 **3.** $\frac{1}{729}$ **5.** $\frac{1}{3}$ **7.** 81 **9.** $\frac{1}{216}$ **11.** $-\frac{1}{4}$ **13.** For $0 < x < 1$, $x^{1/2} < x^{-1/2}$; for $x = 1$, $x^{1/2} = x^{-1/2}$; for $x > 1$, $x^{1/2} > x^{-1/2}$.

8.4 Skill Practice (pp. 515–516) **1.** No; 0.5 is not a number greater than or equal to 1.0 and less than 10. **3.** 8.5×10^0 **5.** 8.24×10^1 **7.** 7.2×10^7

SELECTED ANSWERS

9. 1.06525×10^6 **11.** 1.06×10^9 **13.** 9×10^{14} **17.** 75,000,000 **19.** 30,300 **21.** 15,440,000,000 **23.** 0.00000000044 **25.** 0.0000000852 **27.** 0.0000012034 **29.** 6.7×10^3; 12,439; 2×10^4; 45,000 **31.** 9.8×10^{-6}; 0.00008; 0.0005; 5×10^{-3}; 8.2×10^{-3}; 0.04065 **33.** $<$ **35.** $=$ **37.** $>$ **39.** 6.6×10^{-4} **41.** 7.29×10^{-9} **43.** 3×10^{-3} **45.** 1.25×10^{-22} **47.** 1.96×10^6 **49.** *Sample answer:* 2.8×10^1 and 1×10^3; 1.12×10^6 and 4.0×10^1

8.4 Problem Solving (pp. 516–518) **51. a.** 1.4×10^{-4}; 2.5×10^{-1}; 1.67×10^2; 555 **b.** the elephant beetle and the walking stick **53.** 1406 pounds per acre **55. a.** About 3.67; the radius of Earth is about 3.67 times greater than the radius of the moon. **b.** About 49.30; the volume of Earth is about 49.30 times greater than the volume of the moon. **c.** The ratio of the volumes is the cube of the ratio of the radii. **57.** 4 in. by 6 in. **59. a.** 4.9 L **b.** about 2.58×10^6 L, about 2.58×10^7 L, about 2.06×10^8 L **c.** Underestimates. *Sample answer:* They are calculated when a person is at rest. When a person is not resting, the rate will go up.

8.4 Graphing Calculator Activity (p. 519) **1.** 2.7×10^{13} **3.** 2.5×10^{19} **5. a.** about 6.10×10^{18} g **b.** about 3.05×10^{41} atoms

8.5 Skill Practice (pp. 523–524) **1.** growth factor **3.** The graph would be a vertical stretch. *Sample answer:* Since the *y*-values of $y = 2 \cdot 5^x$ are double those of $y = 5^x$. **5.** $y = 125 \cdot 5^x$ **7.** $y = \frac{1}{9} \cdot 3^x$

9.

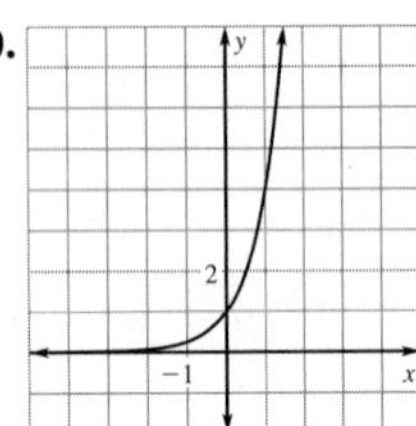

domain: all real numbers, range: all positive real numbers

11.

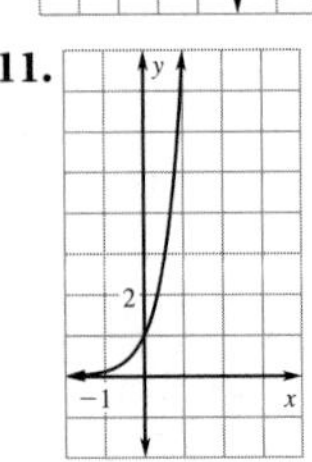

domain: all real numbers, range: all positive real numbers

13.

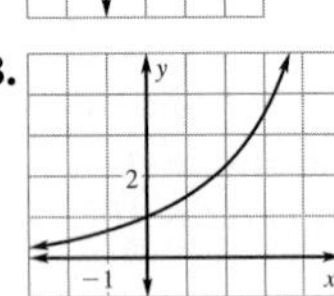

domain: all real numbers, range: all positive real numbers

15.

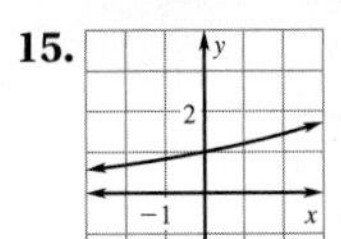

domain: all real numbers, range: all positive real numbers

17.

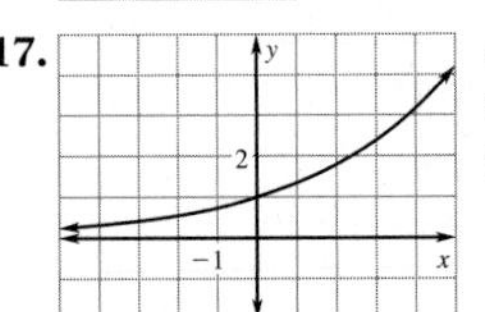

domain: all real numbers, range: all positive real numbers

19.

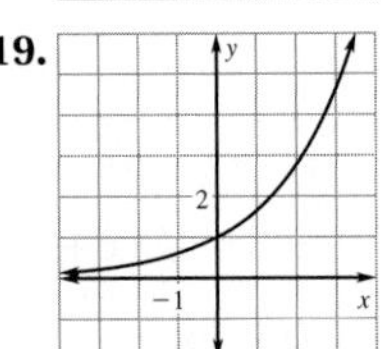

domain: all real numbers, range: all positive real numbers

21. The percent increase was not written as a decimal; $0.27(1 + 0.02)^3 = 0.27(1.02)^3 \approx \$.29$.

23.

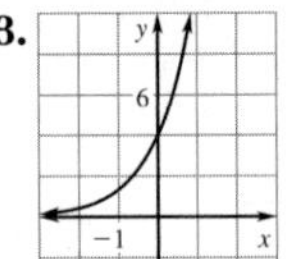

The graph is a vertical stretch.

25.

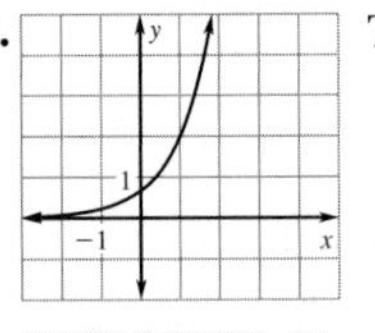

The graph is a vertical shrink.

27.

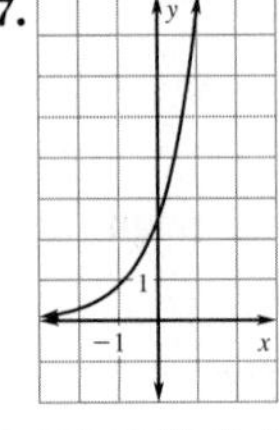

The graph is a vertical stretch.

29.

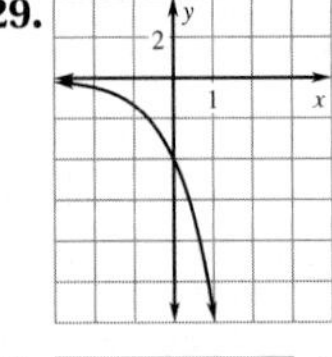

The graph is a vertical stretch with a reflection in the *x*-axis.

31.

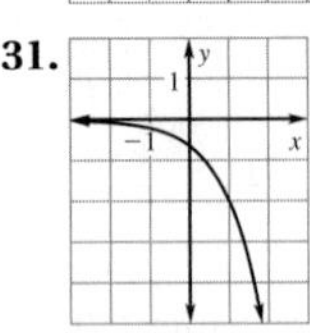

The graph is a vertical shrink with a reflection in the *x*-axis.

SELECTED ANSWERS

33. 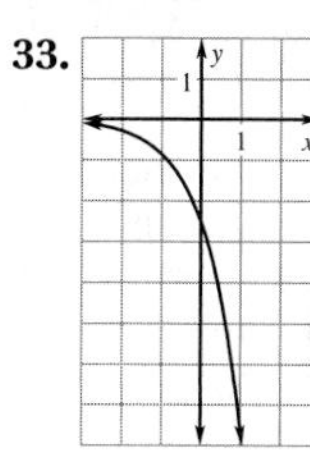 The graph is a vertical stretch with a reflection in the x-axis.

35. 200%. *Sample answer:* A growth rate of 200% would create a growth factor of $1 + 2 = 3$, which would represent the tripling of the population every year.

8.5 Problem Solving (pp. 525–527) **39. a.** Let x represent the number of years since 2001 and $f(x)$ represent the number of computers (in hundreds of millions); $f(x) = 6 \cdot (1.1)^x$. **b.** about 1,286,153,286 computers **41. a.** tree 1: $A = 154 \cdot (1.06)^t$, tree 2: $A = 113 \cdot (1.1)^t$

b. 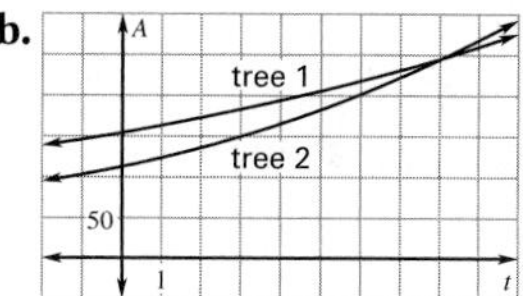

about 8.4 yr

45. $y = 25.96(1.059)^x$; about 145 Hz **47.** \$1266.77 **49.** \$1271.24

8.5 Problem Solving Workshop (pp. 528–529)
1. a. Let t represent the number of years since 1997 and F represent the bus fare; $F = 20(1.12)^t$. **b.** \$22.40 **c.** 2000. *Sample answer:* Make a table of values. **3. a.** $T = 7.5(1.039)^t$ **b.** about 37.4 million

8.6 Skill Practice (pp. 535–536) **1.** $1 - r$ **3.** exponential function; $y = 8 \cdot 4^x$ **5.** exponential function; $y = 2\left(\frac{1}{3}\right)^x$

7. 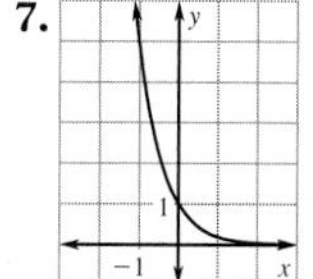 domain: all real numbers, range: all positive real numbers

9. 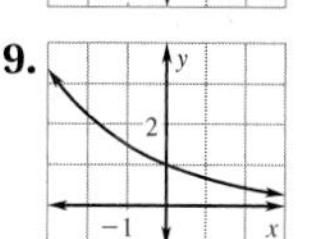 domain: all real numbers, range: all positive real numbers

11. 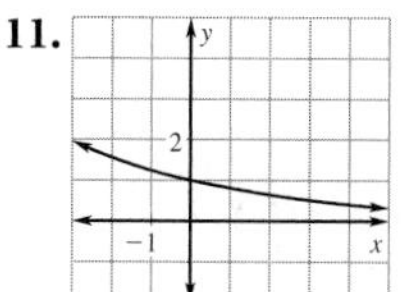 domain: all real numbers, range: all positive real numbers

13. 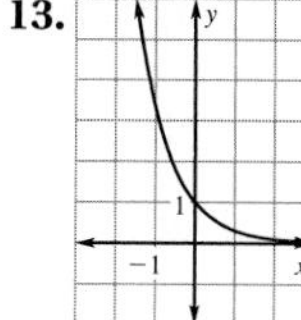 domain: all real numbers, range: all positive real numbers

15. 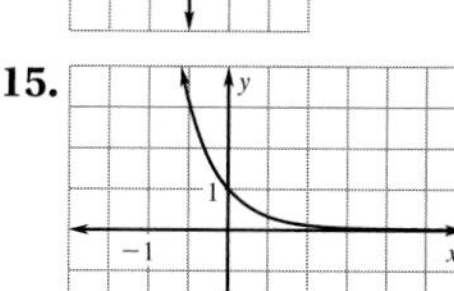 domain: all real numbers, range: all positive real numbers

17. 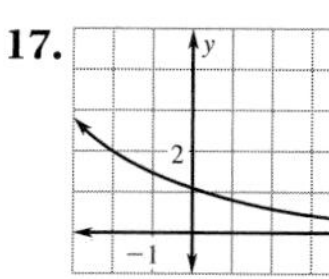 domain: all real numbers, range: all positive real numbers

21. 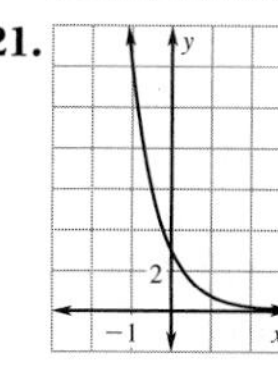 The graph is a vertical stretch.

23. 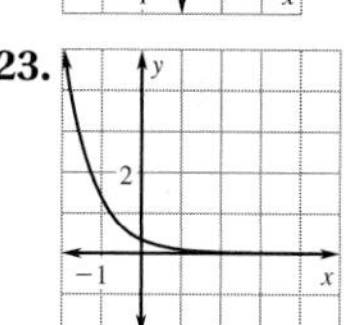 The graph is a vertical shrink.

25. 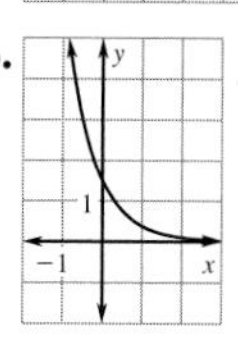 The graph is a vertical stretch.

27. 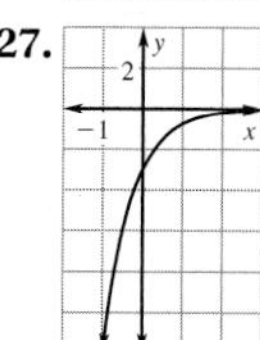 The graph is a vertical stretch with a reflection in the x-axis.

29. 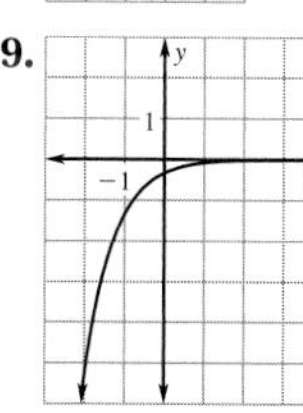 The graph is a vertical shrink with a reflection in the x-axis.

SA25

31. The graph is a vertical stretch with a reflection in the x-axis.

33. C **35.** initial amount: 90,000 people, decay factor: 0.975, decay rate: 2.5%; Let P represent the population and t represent the number of years; $P = 90{,}000(0.975)^t$. **37.** *Sample answer:* The decay rate, r, is 0.14. So the decay factor $(1 - r)$ should be 0.86, not 0.14; $y = 25{,}000(0.86)^t$. **39.** exponential decay; $y = 8 \cdot 0.6^x$ **41. a.** The graph is a vertical shrink. **b.** The graph is a vertical stretch with a reflection in the x-axis. **c.** The graph is a vertical shift up 1 unit. **45.** To find t, divide the number of days, 40, by the half-life, 10. Then $A = 100(0.5)^4 =$ 6.25 grams.

8.6 Problem Solving (pp. 537–538) **47.** Let V represent the value of the cell phone and t represent the number of years since purchase, $V = 125(0.8)^t$; \$64. **49.** No. *Sample answer:* The boat's value is about \$3217. **51. a.** decay factor: 0.9439, decay rate: 5.61% **b.** about 1.431 in. **c.** about 0.716 in. **53. a.** $y = 4(0.995)^x$, $y = 3.5(0.995)^x$

b.

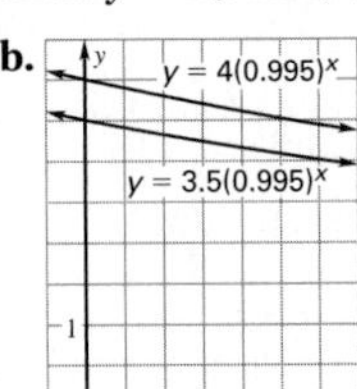

c. about 52 yr

Extension (p. 540)

1. geometric **3.** arithmetic

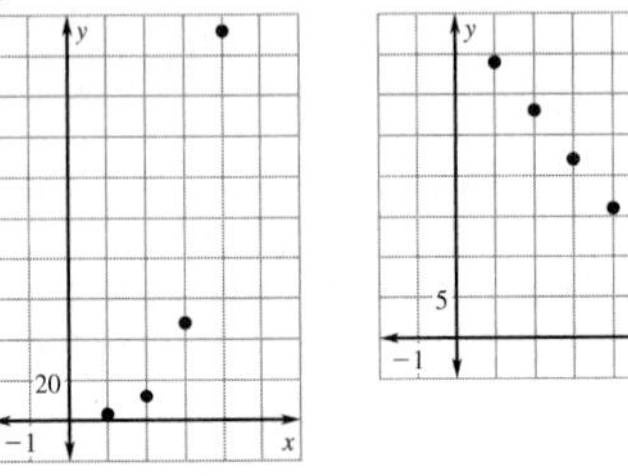

5. geometric

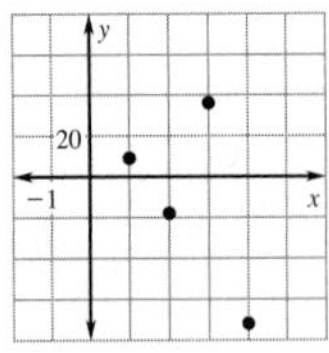

7. $a_n = (-5)^{n-1}$; 15,625 **9.** $a_n = 432\left(\frac{1}{6}\right)^{n-1}$; $\frac{1}{108}$

Chapter Review (pp. 543–546) **1.** decay, decay factor **3.** Exponential decay; $b = 0.85$ which is between 0 and 1, therefore it's exponential decay. **5.** Exponential growth; $b = 2.1$ which is greater than 1, therefore it's exponential growth. **7.** $(-3)^8$ **9.** y^{20} **11.** $(b + 2)^{24}$ **13.** $-64x^2y^2$ **15.** 10^{21} **17.** 5^3 **19.** 17^4 **21.** $\frac{49x^{10}}{y^4}$ **23.** $\frac{6r^{15}}{7s^5}$ **25.** 1 **27.** $\frac{27}{8}$ **29.** 10^6 **31.** 0.000075 **33.** 4.0625×10^{13}

35.

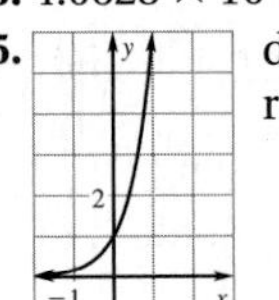

domain: all real numbers, range: all positive real numbers

37.

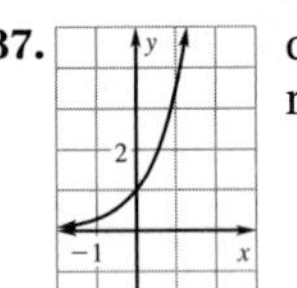

domain: all real numbers, range: all positive real numbers

39.

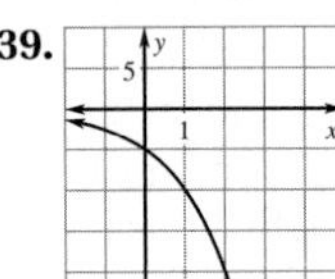

The graph is a vertical stretch with a reflection in the x-axis.

41. exponential decay; $y = 3 \cdot \left(\frac{1}{3}\right)^x$

Chapter 9

9.1 Skill Practice (pp. 557–558) **1.** monomial **3.** $9m^5$; 5, 9 **5.** $2x^2y^2 - 8xy$; 4, 2 **7.** $3z^4 + 2z^3 - z^2 + 5z$; 4, 3 **11.** not a polynomial; variable exponent **13.** polynomial; 1, binomial **15.** polynomial; 3, trinomial **17.** $13a^2 - 4$ **19.** $m^2 + 9m + 9$ **21.** $6c^2 + 14$ **23.** $-2n^3 + n - 12$ **25.** $-15d^3 + 3d^2 - 3d + 2$ **27.** Two unlike terms, $-4x^2$ and $8x$, were combined; $-2x^3 - 4x^2 + 8x + 1$. **29.** $3x^5$, $x + 2x^3 + x^2$, $1 - 3x + 5x^2$, $12x + 1$ **31.** $12x - 3$ **33.** $-x^2 + 10xy + y^2$ **35.** $6a^2b - 6a + 4b - 19$

SA26

9.1 Problem Solving (pp. 558–559) **37.** about 39,800,000 people **39. a.** $T = 9.5t^3 - 73t^2 + 130t + 860$ **b.** 1998; substitute $t = 0$ into the equation for T to find the number of books sold in 1998 to get 860 million books. Substitute 4 into the equation for T to find the number of books sold in 2002 to get 820 million books. More books were sold in 1998. **41. a.** $D = -0.44t^2 + 49t + 19.7$ **b.** about 855 decisions **c.** about 61%; Cy Young's career lasted $1911 - 1890 = 21$ years. To find the number of wins in his career, find the value of W when $t = 21$; about 525 wins. From part (b), we know that the total number of decisions in his career is about 855, so to find the percent of the decisions that were wins, find $525 \div 855 \approx 0.614$, or about 61%.

9.1 Graphing Calculator Activity (p. 560) **1.** $7x^2 + 2x + 1$ **3.** correct

9.2 Skill Practice (pp. 565–566) **1.** binomials **3.** $2x^3 - 3x^2 + 9x$ **5.** $4z^6 + z^5 - 11z^4 - 6z^2$ **7.** $9a^7 - 5a^6 - 13a^5$ **9.** $x^2 - x - 6$ **11.** $4b^2 - 31b + 21$ **13.** $12k^2 + 23k - 9$ **15.** The second term of the first binomial is -5, not 5, so the entries in the second row of the diagram should be $-15x$ and -5; $3x^2 - 14x - 5$. **17.** $y^2 + y - 30$ **19.** $77w^2 + 34w - 15$ **21.** $s^3 + 10s^2 + 19s - 20$ **23.** $-15x^3 + 14x^2 + 3x - 2$ **25.** $54z^3 - 21z^2 - 14z + 5$ **27.** $10r^2 + r - 3$ **29.** $8m^2 + 46m + 63$ **31.** $48x^2 - 88x + 35$ **33.** $3p^2 - 3p - 9$ **35.** $-3c^3 - 45c^2 + 23c - 10$ **37.** $2x^2 + x - 45$ **39.** $x^2 + 8x + 15$ **41.** $80 - 6x^2$ **43.** $2x^2 - 10x - 132$ **45.** $2x^4 - 11x^3 - 20x^2 - 7x$; graph $Y_1 = (x^2 - 7x)(2x^2 + 3x + 1)$ and $Y_2 = 2x^4 - 11x^3 - 20x^2 - 7x$ in the same viewing window. Because the graphs coincide, the expressions for Y_1 and Y_2 must be equivalent.

9.2 Problem Solving (pp. 567–568) **49. a.** $4x^2 + 84x + 440$ **b.** 840 in.^{2} **51. a.** \$12,300 million, 0.171; for $t = 0$, the amount of money (in millions of dollars) people between 15 and 19 years old spent on sound recordings in the U.S. in 1997 **b.** $R \cdot P \approx -1.18t^4 + 14.4t^3 - 57.4t^2 - 10.4t + 2100$ **c.** about \$1680 million **53. a.** *Sample answer:* $T = t + 90$; use the data points from 1995–1999: (5, 95), (6, 96), (7, 97), (8, 98), (9, 99). All these points lie on a line with slope $m = 1$; use any one of the points to find the y-intercept $b = 90$. The other data points, (0, 92), (10, 101), and (11, 102), lie close to the line $T = t + 90$. **b.** $V = -0.0015t^3 - 0.103t^2 + 2.949t + 6.21$ **c.** about 24.2 million households, about 22.2 million households

9.3 Skill Practice (p. 572) **1.** *Sample answer:* $x - 5$, $x + 5$ **3.** $x^2 + 16x + 64$ **5.** $4y^2 + 20y + 25$ **7.** $n^2 - 22n + 121$ **9.** The middle term of the product, $2(s)(-3) = -6s$, was left out; $s^2 - 6s + 9$. **11.** $t^2 - 16$ **13.** $4x^2 - 1$ **15.** $49 - w^2$ **19.** Use the sum and difference pattern to find the product $(20 - 4)(20 + 4)$. **21.** Use the square of a binomial pattern to find the product $(20 - 3)^2$. **23.** $r^2 + 18rs + 81s^2$ **25.** $9m^2 - 121n^2$ **27.** $9m^2 - 42mn + 49n^2$ **29.** $9f^2 - 81$ **31.** $9x^2 + 48xy + 64y^2$ **33.** $4a^2 - 25b^2$ **35.** $9x^2 - 0.25$ **37.** $9x^2 - 3x + 0.25$

9.3 Problem Solving (pp. 573–574)
41. a.

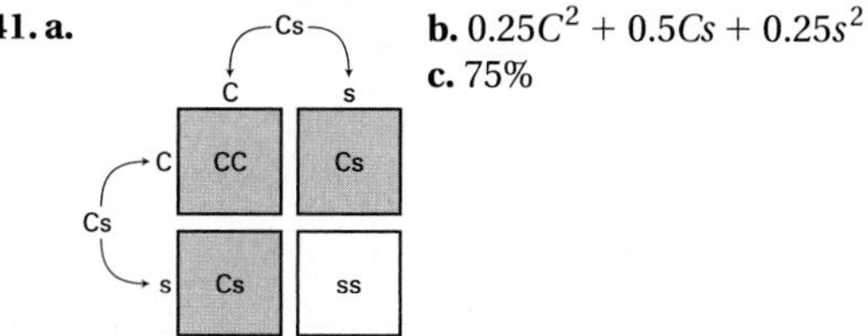

b. $0.25C^2 + 0.5Cs + 0.25s^2$ **c.** 75%

43. a. 88.1%; the areas of the four regions are: 2 complete passes: $0.655^2 \approx 0.429$ square units; 1 complete pass, 1 incomplete pass: $0.655(0.345) \approx 0.226$ square units; 1 incomplete pass, 1 complete pass: $0.345(0.655) \approx 0.226$ square units; and 2 incomplete passes: $0.345^2 \approx 0.119$ square units. The regions that involve at least one complete pass cover $0.429 + 0.226 + 0.226 = 0.881$ square units, or 88.1% of the whole square region. **b.** The outcome of each attempted pass is modeled by $0.655C + 0.345I$, so the possible outcomes of two attempted passes is modeled by $(0.655C + 0.345I)^2 = 0.429C^2 + 0.452CI + 0.119I^2$. Because any combination of outcomes with a C results in at least one completed pass, the coefficients of the first two terms show that 42.9% + 45.2% = 88.1% of the outcomes will have at least one completed pass, and the coefficient of the last term shows that 11.9% of the outcomes will have two incomplete passes.

9.4 Skill Practice (pp. 578–579) **1.** The vertical motion model is the equation $h = -16t^2 + vt + s$, where h is the height (in feet) of a projectile after t seconds in the air, given an initial vertical velocity of v feet per second and an initial height of s feet. **3.** 5, -3 **5.** 13, 14 **7.** 7, $-\frac{4}{3}$ **9.** ± 3 **11.** $-\frac{11}{3}$, -1 **13.** $-\frac{5}{2}$, $\frac{5}{7}$ **17.** $2(x + y)$ **19.** $s(3s^3 + 16)$ **21.** $7w^2(w^3 - 5)$ **23.** $5n(3n^2 + 5)$ **25.** $\frac{1}{2}x^4(5x^2 - 1)$ **27.** 0, -6 **29.** 0, $\frac{7}{2}$ **31.** 0, $-\frac{1}{3}$ **33.** 0, 2 **35.** 0, $\frac{5}{2}$ **37.** 0, $-\frac{2}{7}$ **41.** $2ab(4a - 3b)$ **43.** $v(v^2 - 5v + 9)$ **45.** $3q^2(2q^3 - 7q^2 - 5)$ **47.** 0, $\frac{1}{2}$

SELECTED ANSWERS

9.4 Problem Solving (pp. 579–580) **51.** about 0.69 sec **53.** 0, about 0.28; the zero $t = 0$ seconds means that the penguin begins at a height of 0 feet in the air as it leaves the water; the zero $t \approx 0.28$ second means that the penguin lands back in the water (at a height of 0 feet in the air) after about 0.28 second. **55. a.** $h = -4.9t^2 + 4.9t$ **b.** $0 \le t \le 1$; a reasonable domain for the function will cover the time from when the rabbit leaves the ground until the rabbit lands back on the ground; these times t are the zeros of the function, 0 seconds and 1 second. **57. a.** $w(w + 2) = w(10 - w)$ **b.** 4 ft **c.** 48 ft^2

9.5 Skill Practice (pp. 586–587) **1.** factors **3.** $(x + 3)(x + 1)$ **5.** $(b - 9)(b - 8)$ **7.** $(z + 12)(z - 4)$ **9.** $(y - 9)(y + 2)$ **11.** $(x + 10)(x - 7)$ **13.** $(m - 15)(m + 8)$ **15.** $(p + 16)(p + 4)$ **17.** $(c + 11)(c + 4)$ **19.** In order to have a product of $+24$, p and q must have the same sign; $(m - 6)(m - 4)$. **21.** 10, -3 **23.** -10, 5 **25.** -5, -4 **27.** -22, -1 **31.** -3, -2 **33.** 9, 5 **35.** 17, -3 **37.** 14, 2 **39.** -9, 8 **41.** -17, -2 **43.** 20 in., 5 in. **45.** 26 yd, 6 yd **47.** $(x - 2y)^2$ **49.** $(c + 9d)(c + 4d)$ **51.** $(a + 5b)(a - 3b)$ **53.** $(m - 7n)(m + 6n)$ **55.** $(g + 10h)(g - 6h)$

9.5 Problem Solving (pp. 588–589) **59.** 10 cm^2 **61.** 40 in.; the side lengths of the rectangular picture can be represented by $x - 5$ and $x - 6$; the area of the picture is 20 square inches, so to find the side length x of the original square picture, solve the equation $(x - 5)(x - 6) = 20$. The equation has two solutions, 10 and 1, but when $x = 1$ inch, both $x - 5$ and $x - 6$ are negative, which does not make sense in this situation. So, $x = 10$ inches, and the perimeter of the original picture was $4(10) = 40$ inches.

9.5 Problem Solving Workshop (p. 591) **1.** 2 ft **3.** 9 ft

9.6 Skill Practice (pp. 596–597) **1.** roots **3.** To factor the polynomial that has a leading coefficient of 1, $x^2 - x - 2$, you only need to find factors of the constant term, -2, that add to the coefficient of the middle term, -1. To factor the polynomial that has a leading coefficient that is not 1, $6x^2 - x - 2$, you must also take into account how the factors of the leading coefficient, 6, affect the coefficient of the middle term. **5.** $-(y - 4)(y + 2)$ **7.** $(5w - 1)(w - 1)$ **9.** $(6s + 5)(s - 1)$ **11.** $(2c - 1)(c - 3)$ **13.** $-(2h + 1)(h - 3)$ **15.** $(2x + 3)(5x - 9)$ **17.** $(3z + 7)(z - 2)$ **19.** $(2n + 3)(2n + 5)$ **21.** $(3y - 4)(2y + 1)$ **23.** $-\frac{7}{2}$, 5 **25.** $\frac{1}{4}$, -3 **27.** $\frac{3}{4}$, $-\frac{1}{2}$ **29.** $-\frac{1}{4}$, $\frac{2}{5}$ **31.** $\frac{1}{3}$, -5 **33.** $\frac{2}{5}$, 1 **35.** $\frac{11}{2}$, -3 **37.** $-\frac{4}{3}$, $\frac{1}{2}$ **39.** The factorization of the polynomial should be $(3x + 2)(4x - 1)$ instead of $(3x - 1)(4x + 2)$; $-\frac{2}{3}, \frac{1}{4}$. **41.** $9\frac{1}{2}$ in.; to find the width, solve the equation $w(4w + 1) = 3$ to get $w = \frac{3}{4}$ or $w = -1$. The width cannot be negative, so the width is $\frac{3}{4}$ inch. Then the length is $4\left(\frac{3}{4}\right) + 1 = 4$ inches, and the perimeter is $2\left(\frac{3}{4}\right) + 2(4) = 9\frac{1}{2}$ inches. **43.** 5, 7 **45.** $-\frac{7}{3}$, 2 **47.** $\frac{7}{2}$, $-\frac{3}{2}$ **49.** $-\frac{1}{4}$, $\frac{5}{2}$ **53.** $2x^2 - 9x - 5 = 0$; any root $x = \frac{r}{s}$ of $ax^2 + bx + c = 0$ comes from setting the factor $sx - r$ equal to 0 after $ax^2 + bx + c$ is written in factored form; so, the roots $-\frac{1}{2}$ and 5 come from the factors $2x - (-1)$, or $2x + 1$, and $x - 5$. The product of these factors is $(2x + 1)(x - 5) = 2x^2 - 10x + x - 5 = 2x^2 - 9x - 5$.

9.6 Problem Solving (pp. 598–599) **59. a.** $24x^2 + 48x + 24$ **b.** 4 cm, 2 cm **61.** 70 m, 31 m

9.7 Skill Practice (pp. 603–604) **1.** perfect square **3.** $(x + 5)(x - 5)$ **5.** $(9c + 2)(9c - 2)$ **7.** $-3(m + 4n)(m - 4n)$ **9.** $(x - 2)^2$ **11.** $(7a + 1)^2$ **13.** $\left(m + \frac{1}{2}\right)^2$ **15.** $4(c + 10)(c - 10)$ **17.** $(2s + 3r)(2s - 3r)$ **19.** $8(3 + 2y)(3 - 2y)$ **21.** $(2x)^2 - 3^2$ is in the form $a^2 - b^2$, so it must be factored using the difference of two squares pattern, not the perfect square trinomial pattern; $9(2x + 3)(2x - 3)$. **25.** -4 **27.** ± 3 **29.** -2 **31.** ± 12 **33.** $\pm\frac{7}{2}$ **35.** $\frac{5}{6}$ **37.** $\pm\frac{4}{3}$ **39.** 0, 1

9.7 Problem Solving (pp. 604–605) **47.** 2.5 sec **49.** Once; the ball's height (in feet) is modeled by the equation $h = -16t^2 + 56t + 5$, where t is the time (in seconds) since it was thrown. To find when the height is 54 feet, substitute 54 for h and solve the equation $54 = -16t^2 + 56t + 5$, or $16t^2 - 56t + 49 = 0$. Because the left side of the equation factors as a perfect square trinomial, $(4t - 7)^2$, the equation has only one solution, 1.75; so, the ball reaches a height of 54 feet only once, after 1.75 seconds. **51. a.** $4d^2 - 9$ **b.** 10 in.

SELECTED ANSWERS

9.8 Skill Practice (pp. 610–611) **1.** The polynomial is written as a monomial or as a product of a monomial and one or more prime polynomials. **3.** $(x - 8)(x + 1)$ **5.** $(z - 4)(6z - 7)$ **7.** $(b + 5)(b^2 - 3)$ **9.** $(x + 13)(x - 1)$ **11.** $(z - 1)(12 + 5z^2)$ **13.** $(x + 1)(x^2 + 2)$ **15.** $(z - 4)(z^2 + 3)$ **17.** $(a + 13)(a^2 - 5)$ **19.** $(5n - 4)(n^2 + 5)$ **21.** $(y + 1)(y + 5x)$ **23.** $x^2(x - 1)(x + 1)$ **25.** $3n^3(n - 4)(n + 4)$ **27.** $3c^7(5c - 1)(5c + 1)$ **29.** $8s^2(2s - 1)(2s + 1)$ **31.** cannot be factored **33.** $3w^2(w + 4)^2$ **35.** $(b - 5)(b - 2)(b + 2)$ **37.** $(9t - 1)(t^2 + 2)$ **39.** $7ab^3(a - 3)(a + 3)$ **43.** $-1, \pm 2$ **45.** $\frac{7}{4}, \pm 2$ **47.** $0, -5, -3$ **49.** $0, \pm 9$ **51.** $0, \pm 2$ **53.** $-\frac{1}{3}, \pm 1$ **55.** No; when the polynomial is factored completely, the equation becomes $(x + 2)(x^2 + 3) = 0$. When the factor $x^2 + 3$ is set equal to 0, the resulting equation, $x^2 + 3 = 0$, or $x^2 = -3$, has no real number solutions because x^2 cannot be negative. **57.** 12 yd, 4 yd, 2 yd **59.** $(2b - a)(2b - 3)(2b + 3)$ **61.** $(3x + 4)(2x - 1)$ **63.** $(4n - 3)(3n - 1)$ **65.** $(3w + 2)(7w - 2)$

9.8 Problem Solving (pp. 612–613) **69. a.** $4w^2 + 16w$ **b.** 4 in. long by 4 in. wide by 8 in. high **71. a.** 1, about -0.2 **b.** The zero $t \approx -0.2$ has no meaning because t, which represents time in seconds, cannot be negative in this situation. The zero $t = 1$ means that the ball lands on the ground 1 second after you throw it. **73. a.** $-h^3 + 5h^2 + 36h$ **b.** 4 in. long by 9 in. wide by 5 in. high, 3 in. long by 10 in. wide by 6 in. high **c.** 4 in. long by 9 in. wide by 5 in. high; the 4-inch long box has a surface area of 202 square inches and the 3-inch long box has a surface area of 216 square inches.

Chapter Review (pp. 616–620) **1.** degree of the polynomial **3.** A factorable polynomial with integer coefficients is factored completely if it is written as a product of unfactorable polynomials with integer coefficients. *Sample answer:* $3x(x - 4)(2x + 1)$ **5.** A **7.** $x^3 - 8x^2 + 15x$ **9.** $11y^5 + 4y^2 - y - 3$ **11.** $5s^3 - 7s + 13$ **13.** $x^3 - 5x^2 + 7x - 3$ **15.** $x^2 - 2x - 8$ **17.** $z^2 - 3z - 88$ **19.** $18n^2 + 27n + 7$ **21.** $3x^2 + 10x - 8$ **23.** $36y^2 + 12y + 1$ **25.** $16a^2 - 24a + 9$ **27.** $9s^2 - 25$ **29.** 0, 11 **31.** 0, 9 **33.** $0, \frac{1}{3}$ **35.** $(s + 11)(s - 1)$ **37.** $(a + 12)(a - 7)$ **39.** $(x + 8)(x - 4)$ **41.** $(c + 5)(c + 3)$ **43.** $\frac{1}{7}, 1$ **45.** $\frac{2}{3}, -2$ **47.** $-\frac{3}{2}, -3$ **49.** 3 sec **51.** $(z - 15)(z + 15)$ **53.** $12(1 - 2n)(1 + 2n)$ **55.** $(4p - 1)^2$ **57.** 1 sec **59.** $(y + 3)(y + x)$ **61.** $5s^2(s - 5)(s + 5)$ **63.** $2z(z + 6)(z - 5)$ **65.** $(2b + 3)(b - 2)(b + 2)$

Chapter 10

10.1 Skill Practice (pp. 632–633) **1.** parabola **3.** C **5.** B

7.

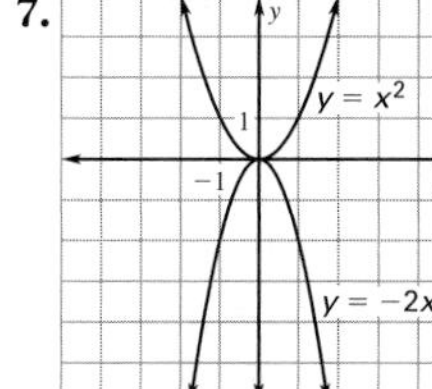

The graph is a vertical stretch (by a factor of 2) with a reflection in the x-axis of the graph of $y = x^2$.

9.

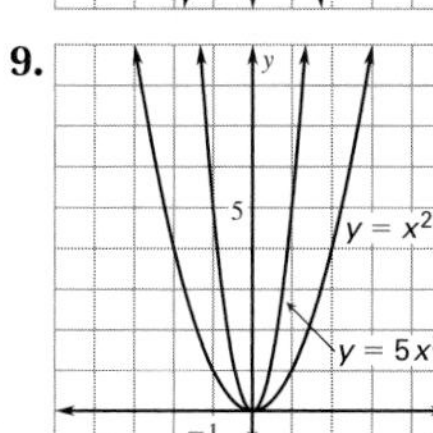

The graph is a vertical stretch (by a factor of 5) of the graph of $y = x^2$.

11.

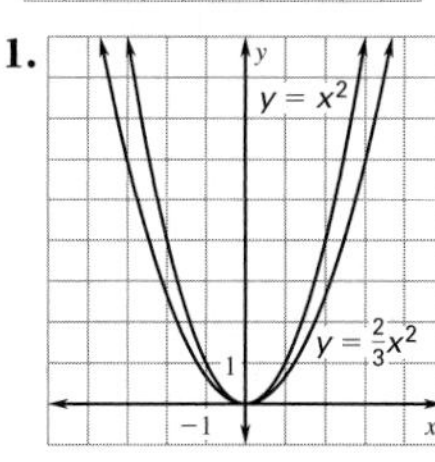

The graph is a vertical shrink $\left(\text{by a factor of } \frac{2}{3}\right)$ of the graph of $y = x^2$.

13.

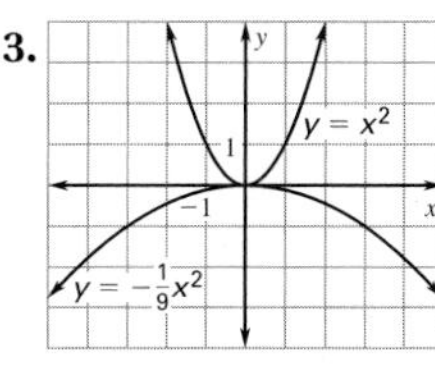

The graph is a vertical shrink $\left(\text{by a factor of } \frac{1}{9}\right)$ with a reflection in the x-axis of the graph of $y = x^2$.

15.

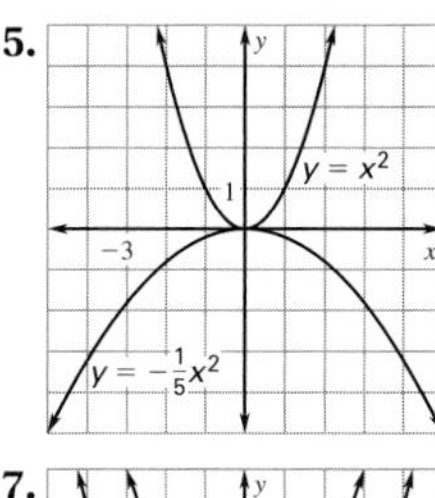

The graph is a vertical shrink $\left(\text{by a factor of } \frac{1}{5}\right)$ with a reflection in the x-axis of the graph of $y = x^2$.

17.

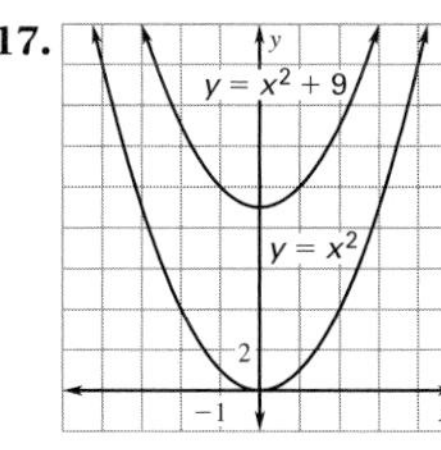

The graph is a vertical translation (of 9 units up) of the graph of $y = x^2$.

19. 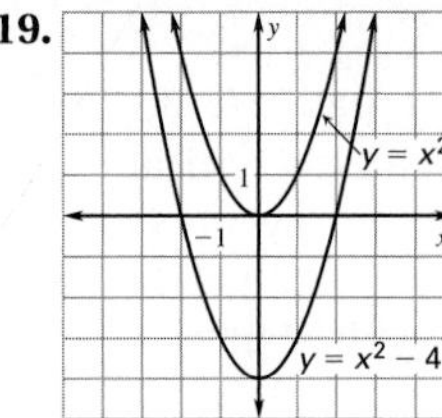

The graph is a vertical translation (of 4 units down) of the graph of $y = x^2$.

21. 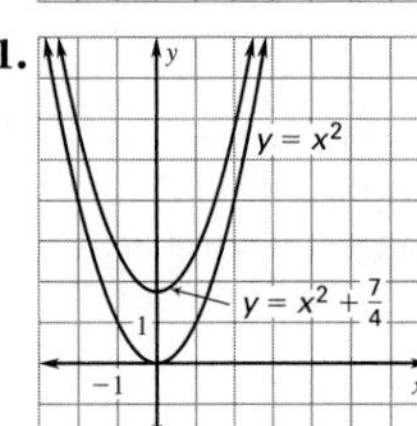

The graph is a vertical translation $\left(\text{of } \frac{7}{4} \text{ units up}\right)$ of the graph of $y = x^2$.

23. The graph of $y = x^2 - 2$ should be shifted 2 units down, not 2 units up. The vertex should be at $(0, -2)$.

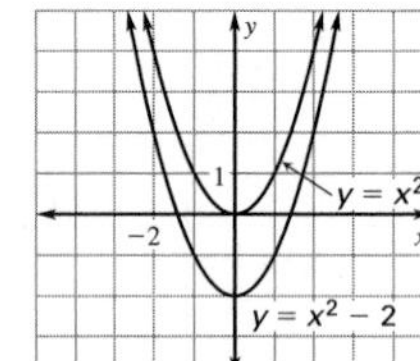

25. The graph is a reflection in the x-axis with a vertical translation (of 5 units up) of the graph of $y = x^2$.

27. 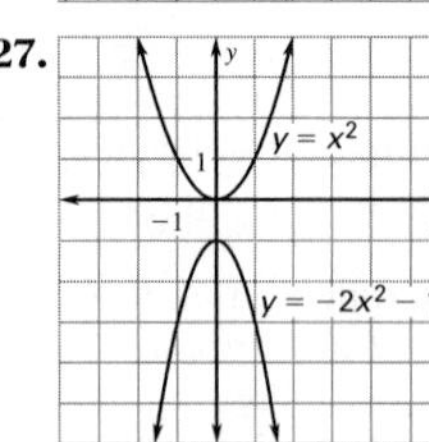

The graph is a vertical stretch (by a factor of 2) with a vertical translation (of 1 unit down) and a reflection in the x-axis of the graph of $y = x^2$.

29. 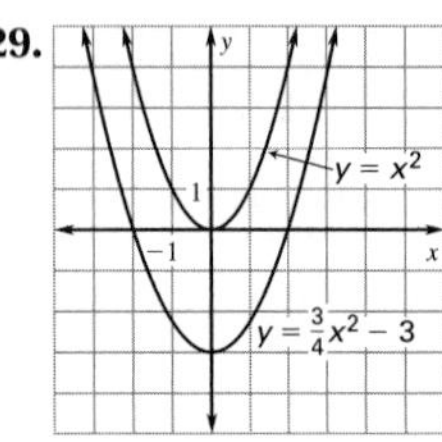

The graph is a vertical shrink $\left(\text{by a factor of } \frac{3}{4}\right)$ with a vertical translation (of 3 units down) of the graph of $y = x^2$.

31. 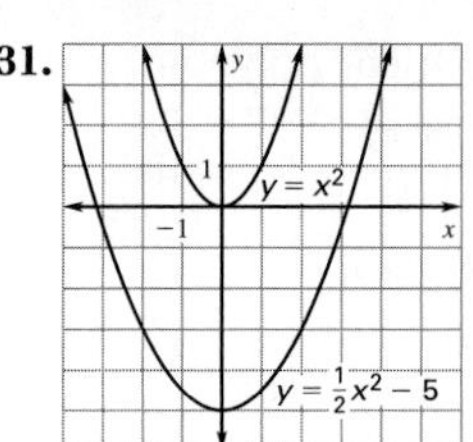

The graph is a vertical shrink $\left(\text{by a factor of } \frac{1}{2}\right)$ with a vertical translation (of 5 units down) of the graph of $y = x^2$.

35. Translate the graph of f 5 units down.

10.1 Problem Solving (pp. 633–634)

41. a. 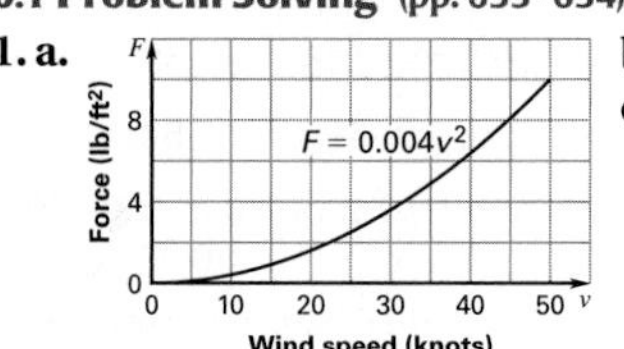

b. about 16 knots
c. about 35 knots

43. a. 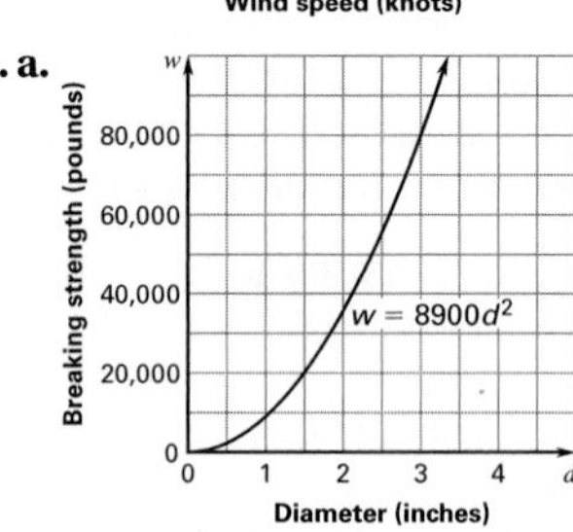

b. No. *Sample answer:* Let D be the diameter of a rope with 4 times the breaking strength of a rope with diameter d. Then $8900D^2 = 4(8900d^2)$; $D^2 = 4d^2$; $D = \sqrt{4d^2}$; $D = 2d$. Thus, the diameter of the rope with 4 times the breaking strength is only two times the diameter of the other rope.

10.2 Skill Practice (pp. 638–639) **1.** When the function is in standard form, $y = ax^2 + bx + c$, it will have a minimum value if $a > 0$ and a maximum value if $a < 0$. **3.** $x = 2$, $(2, -2)$ **5.** $x = 4$, $(4, 26)$ **7.** $x = -\frac{1}{2}, \left(-\frac{1}{2}, -\frac{3}{2}\right)$ **9.** $x = 0$, $(0, -1)$ **11.** $x = 6$, $(6, 7)$ **13.** The equation of the axis of symmetry is $x = \frac{-b}{2a}$, not $x = \frac{b}{2a}$; $x = \frac{-b}{2a} = \frac{-16}{2(2)}$, $x = -4$.

15. 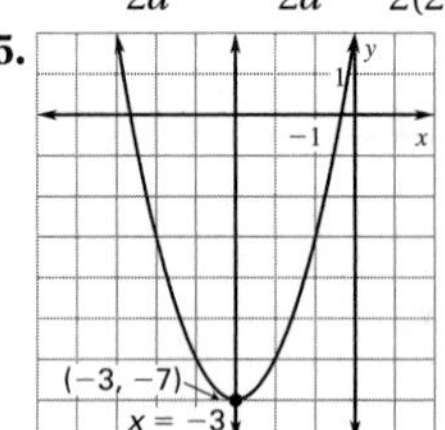

17. 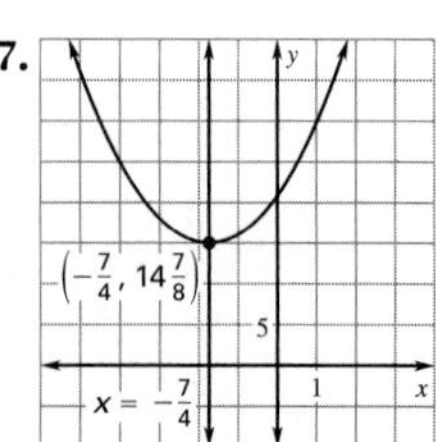

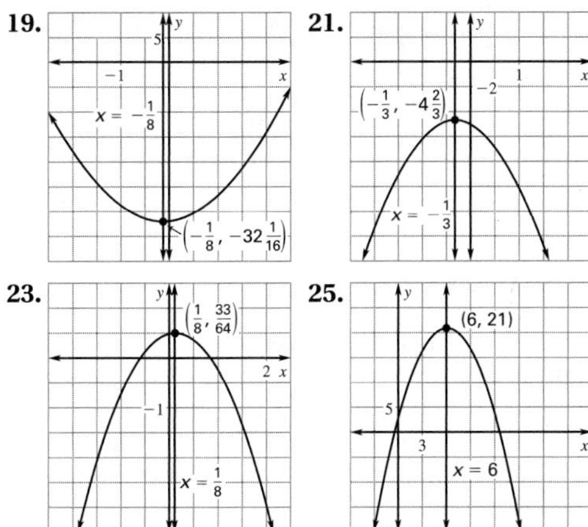

29. maximum value; 7 **31.** maximum value; −8
33. maximum value; $\frac{81}{8}$ **35.** maximum value; 54
37. The graph of $y = x^2 + 4x + 1$ is a horizontal translation (of 4 units left) of the graph of $y = x^2 - 4x + 1$.

10.2 Problem Solving (pp. 639–640) **41.** about 66 ft
43. about 243 ft

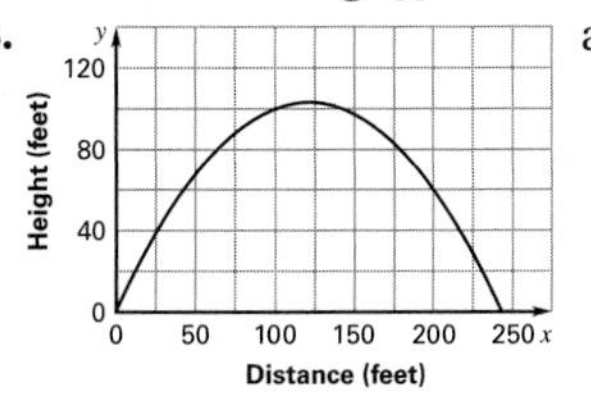

Extension (p. 642)

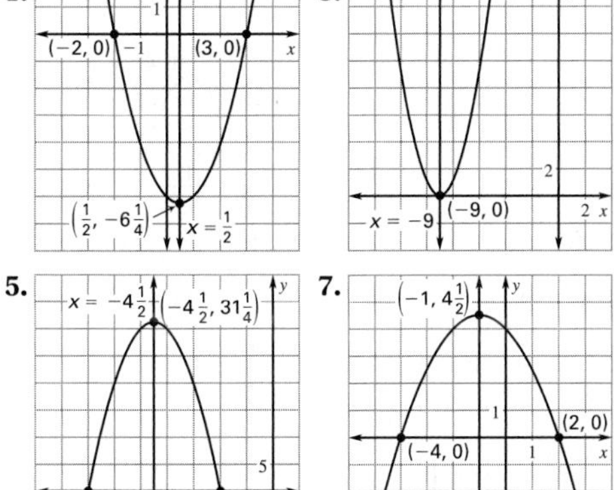

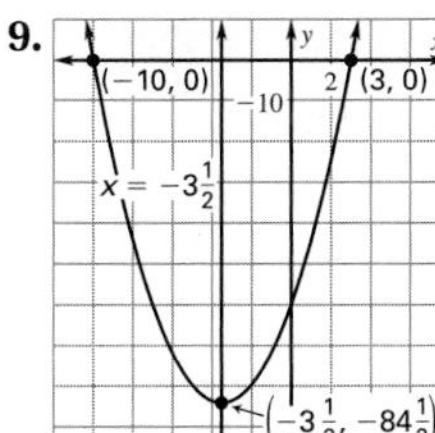

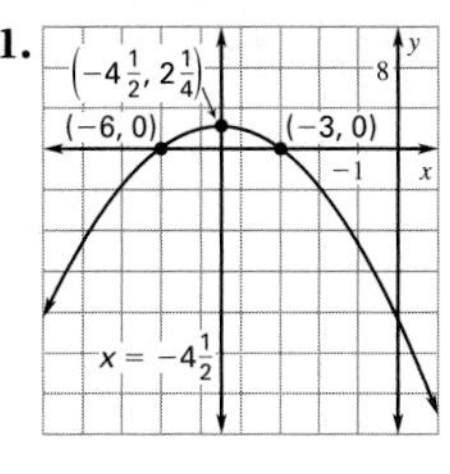

10.3 Skill Practice (pp. 647–648) **1.** $2x^2 - 9x + 11 = 0$ **3.** 4, 1 **5.** −4, −2 **7.** 8, −2 **9.** 3 **11.** −5 **13.** −7 **15.** no solution **17.** no solution **19.** −6, 2 **21.** Any solution of a quadratic equation is an x-intercept of the graph of the related quadratic function. The x-intercept of the function shown in the graph is 2, not 4; the only solution of the equation is 2. **23.** −3, 4 **25.** −5, 2 **27.** −5, 4 **29.** 1, 11 **31.** $-1\frac{1}{2}$, 1 **33.** $\frac{1}{2}$ **35.** no solution **37.** −3.4, −0.6 **39.** −1.4, 3.4 **41.** 0.8, 6.2 **43.** −1.3, 0.8 **45.** −4.7, −1.3

10.3 Problem Solving (pp. 648–649) **51.** 24.1 ft **53.** 16 ft; the distance from the nozzle to the circle is the distance between the x-intercepts of $y = -0.75x^2 + 6x$. Substitute 0 for y and solve for x: $0 = -0.75x^2 + 6x$ has solutions 0 and 8. The radius of the display circle is 8 feet, so the diameter is 16 feet.

10.3 Graphing Calculator Activity (pp. 650–651)
1. $1\frac{2}{3}$ **3.** −3.75 **5.** about −3.5 **7.** −1.11, 3.61 **9.** −1.61, 5.61 **11.** 0.90, 2.18 **13.** −7.03, 2.15 **15.** 0; the maximum or minimum value of a quadratic function occurs at the vertex of the parabola that is the graph of the function. When a quadratic function has only one zero, its graph has only one x-intercept, which must also be the x-coordinate of the vertex of the parabola. Then the y-coordinate of the vertex is 0, so the maximum or minimum value of the function is 0.

10.4 Skill Practice (pp. 655–656) **1.** square root **3.** ±1 **5.** ±10 **7.** 0 **9.** $\pm\frac{1}{2}$ **11.** $\pm\frac{7}{3}$ **13.** 0 **17.** ±2.65 **19.** no solution **21.** 0 **23.** ±2.24 **25.** ±3.78 **27.** ±1.32

SA31

31. Negative numbers do not have real number square roots, so $\pm\sqrt{-\frac{11}{7}}$ are not real numbers; there is no solution. **33.** 0.76, 5.24 **35.** −8.16, −1.84 **37.** −16.65, −11.35 **39.** −5.69, 3.69 **41.** ±4 **43.** ±1.41 **45.** 0.37, 13.63 **47.** 12 in. **49.** 11.66 ft **51.** $\pm\frac{6}{5}$, or ±1.2. *Sample answer:* Rewrite the decimal as a fraction and then take square roots of each side of the equation: $x^2 = \frac{144}{100}$, so $x = \pm\sqrt{\frac{144}{100}} = \pm\frac{12}{10} = \pm\frac{6}{5}$ or ±1.2.

10.4 Problem Solving (pp. 657–658) **59. a.** 6.8 mm **b.** 5.9 mm **c.** 5.6 mm **61. a.** $D = 4 \pm \sqrt{\frac{16V}{L}}$ **b.** 11.1 in., 10.7 in., 10.3 in., 10.0 in.

10.4 Problem Solving Workshop (p. 660) **1.** about 1.5 sec **3. a.** $V = 25x^2$ **b.** length: about 9 in., width: 5 in., height: about 1.8 in.

c.

Height, x (inches)	1.7	1.8	1.9
Width (inches)	5	5	5
Length, $5x$ (inches)	8.5	9	9.5
Volume, V (cubic inches)	72.25	81	90.25

The volume in the table closest to 83 cubic inches is 81 cubic inches. To the nearest tenth of an inch, the height of the box is about 1.8 inches. The length of the box is $5x \approx 9$ inches, and the width is 5 inches. **5.** To rewrite the equation $6 = -16t^2 + 54$ so that one side is 0, you must subtract 6 from each side; $0 = -16t^2 + 48$, replace 48 with the closest perfect square, 49. $0 = -16t^2 + 49 = -(16t^2 - 49) = -(4t + 7)(4t - 7)$, so the approximate solutions of this equation are $\pm\frac{7}{4}$. Disregard the negative solution because time cannot be negative; so, it takes about $\frac{7}{4}$, or 1.75, seconds for the shoe to hit the net.

10.5 Skill Practice (pp. 666–667) **1.** completing the square **3.** 9; $(x + 3)^2$ **5.** 4; $(x - 2)^2$ **7.** $\frac{9}{4}$; $\left(x - \frac{3}{2}\right)^2$ **9.** 1.44; $(x + 1.2)^2$ **11.** $\frac{4}{9}$; $\left(x - \frac{2}{3}\right)^2$ **13.** −12, 2 **15.** −6, 12 **17.** −7, 3 **19.** −10.5, −0.5 **21.** −0.80, 8.80 **23.** −2.5, −0.5 **27.** The perfect square trinomial $x^2 - 2x + 1$ factors as $(x - 1)^2$ not $(x + 1)^2$, $(x - 1)^2 = 5$, $x - 1 = \pm\sqrt{5}$, $x = 1 \pm \sqrt{5}$. **29.** −11.57, −0.43 **31.** −1.91, 0.91 **33.** −0.96, 6.96 **35.** 0.79, 2.21 **37.** −3.68, −0.32 **39.** −0.25, 0.75 **41.** 4.87

10.5 Problem Solving (pp. 667–668) **45.** 3 ft **47. a.** $1904 = 7x^2 - 4x + 392$, 2000

b.

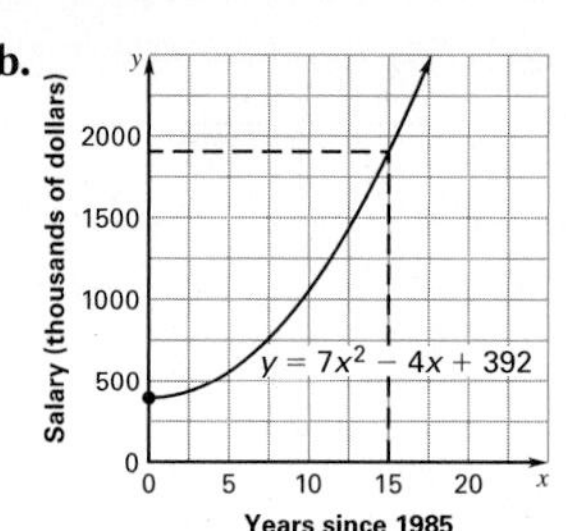

When $y \approx 1904$, the value of x is about 15. So the year 2000 (1985 + 15) found in part (a) is correct.

49. Yes; to find the number of days x after which the stock price was $23.50 per share, substitute 23.5 for y and solve for x by completing the square to find that the solutions are 10 and 30. You could have sold the stock for $23.50 per share 10 days after you purchased it.

Extension (p. 670)

1.

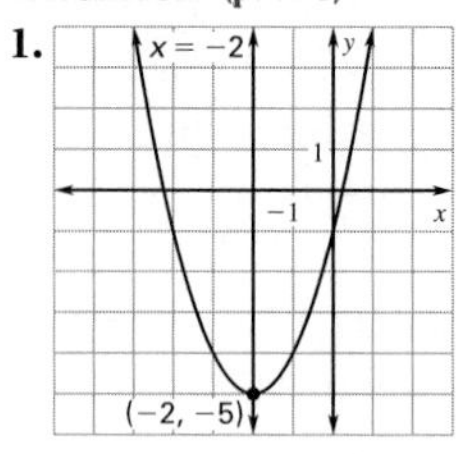

3.

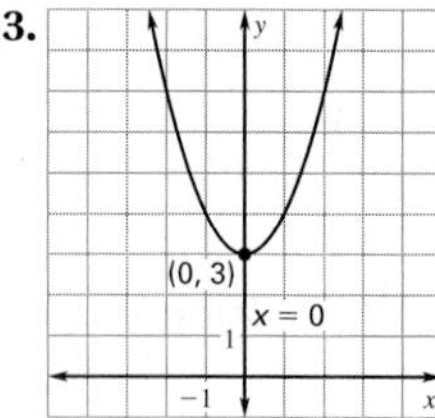

5.

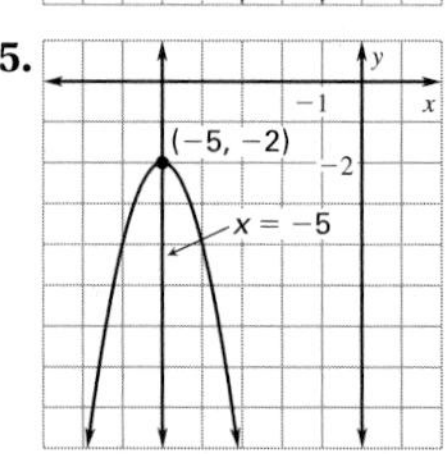

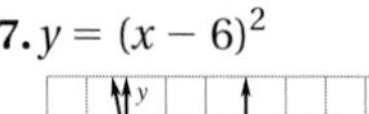
7. $y = (x - 6)^2$

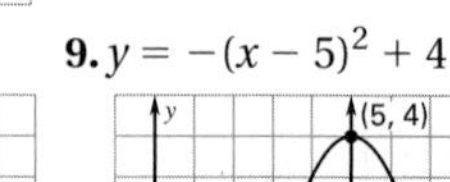
9. $y = -(x - 5)^2 + 4$

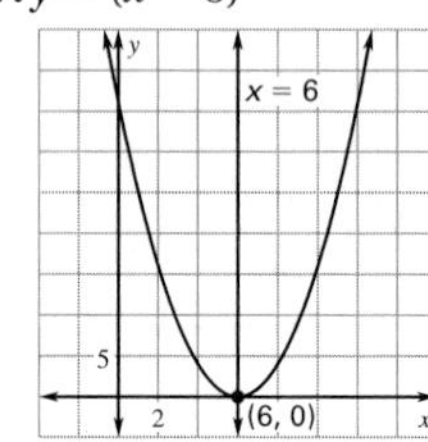

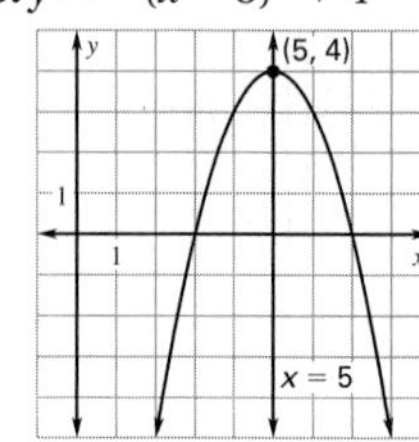

11. $y = -3(x + 1)^2 + 2$

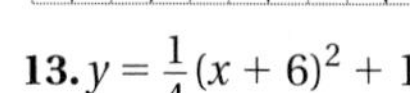
13. $y = \frac{1}{4}(x + 6)^2 + 1$

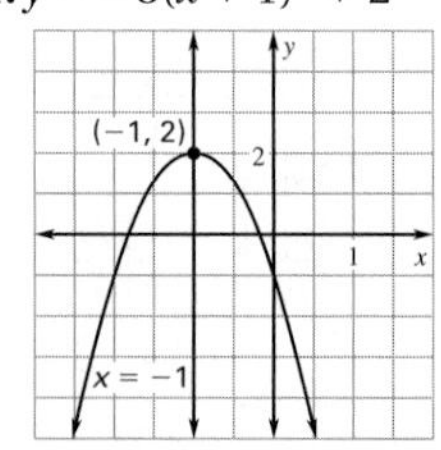

SELECTED ANSWERS

10.6 Skill Practice (pp. 674–675) **1.** quadratic formula **3.** $-13, 8$ **5.** $-2, 2.33$ **7.** $-3.27, 4.27$ **9.** -2.5 **11.** $-0.63, 2.13$ **13.** $-2, 7$ **15.** $-1, 1.29$ **17.** $3.27, 6.73$ **19.** $-0.54, 2.29$ **21.** $-0.66, 1.09$ **23.** $-1.77, -0.57$ **27.** Before identifying the values of *a*, *b*, and *c*, the equation must be written in standard form $ax^2 + bx + c = 0$; $-2x^2 + 3x - 1 = 0$, so $c = -1$, not 1; $x = \frac{-3 \pm \sqrt{3^2 - 4(-2)(-1)}}{2(-2)}$, $x = \frac{-3 \pm \sqrt{1}}{-4}$, $x = \frac{1}{2}$ and $x = 1$. **29–33.** Sample answers are given. **29.** Using square roots, the equation can be written in the form $x^2 = d$. **31.** Factoring, the expression $m^2 + 5m + 6$ factors easily. **33.** Quadratic formula, the equation does not factor easily. **35.** 4 **37.** 6 **39.** $-1.94, 2.19$ **41.** $-0.41, 2.41$ **43.** 5; 13 m by 7 m

10.6 Problem Solving (pp. 675–676)

47. 1993 **49. a.** 2001 **b.**

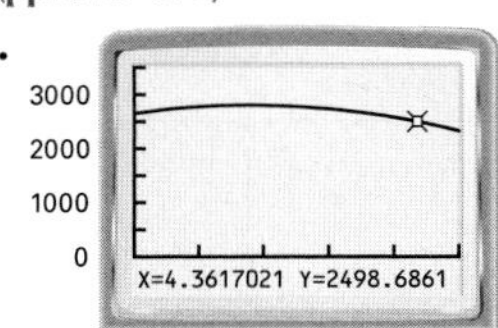

10.7 Skill Practice (pp. 681–682) **1.** $x = \frac{-b \pm \sqrt{b^2 - 4ac}}{2a}$, $b^2 - 4ac$ should be circled. **3.** no solution **5.** two solutions **7.** one solution **9.** two solutions **11.** two solutions **13.** one solution **15.** two solutions **17.** no solution **21.** Before calculating the discriminant, the equation must be written in standard form: $3x^2 - 7x + 5 = 0$. Thus, *c* is 5, not -4, so $b^2 - 4ac = (-7)^2 - 4(3)(5) = 49 - 60 = -11$; the equation has no solution. **23.** 2 **25.** 0 **27.** 0 **29.** 1 **31–33.** Sample answers are given for parts (a) and (c). **31. a.** 0 **b.** 1 **c.** 2 **33. a.** 8 **b.** 9 **c.** 10 **35.** On; the value of the discriminant is $(-6)^2 - 4(3)(3) = 0$, so the graph has exactly one *x*-intercept. A parabola that has exactly one *x*-intercept must have its vertex on the *x*-axis. **37.** Below; $a < 0$, so the graph opens down. The value of the discriminant is $(10)^2 - 4(-15)(-25) = -1400 < 0$, so the graph has no *x*-intercepts; a parabola that opens down and has no *x*-intercepts must have its vertex below the *x*-axis. **39.** On; the value of the discriminant is $(-24)^2 - 4(9)(16) = 0$, so the graph has exactly one *x*-intercept; a parabola that has exactly one *x*-intercept must have its vertex on the *x*-axis. **41. a.** $314 = 2w^2 + 40w + 64$ **b.** 2 **c.** $-25, 5$; the width *w* cannot be negative, so the solution -25 meters does not make sense in the context of the problem. The solution 5 meters makes sense in the context of the problem.

10.7 Problem Solving (pp. 682–683) **45. a.** Substitute 25 for *y* in the equation and then write the resulting quadratic equation in standard form: $25 = 0.06x^2 - 4x + 87$, or $0 = 0.06x^2 - 4x + 62$. Evaluate the discriminant: $b^2 - 4ac = (-4)^2 - 4(0.06)(62) = 1.12$. Since the discriminant is positive, we know that the equation $25 = 0.06x^2 - 4x + 87$ does have solutions, so it is possible for a parakeet to consume 25 milliliters of oxygen per gram of body mass per hour. **b.** 24.5 km/h and 42.2 km/h **47.** No; to determine if there is any point of the arch at a height of 4 feet, substitute 4 for *y* in the equation and then determine if the equation has any positive solutions. The equation is $4 = -0.18x^2 + 1.6x$, or $0 = -0.18x^2 + 1.6x - 4$. Evaluate the discriminant: $b^2 - 4ac = (1.6)^2 - 4(-0.18)(-4) = -0.32$. Since the discriminant is negative, we know the equation has no solution; thus, a child who is 4 feet tall cannot walk under one of the arches without having to bend over. **49. a.** $h = -16t^2 + 32t + 6$ **b.** no **c.** yes; about 0.8 sec and about 1.4 sec

10.8 Skill Practice (pp. 688–689) **1.** exponential function **3.** B **5.** A **7.** linear function **9.** exponential function **11.** quadratic function **13.** quadratic function; $y = -x^2$ **15.** linear function; $y = 3x + 1$ **17.** exponential function; $y = 4\left(\frac{1}{4}\right)^x$ **19.** The *x*- and *y*-values were reversed when substituting the coordinates of the ordered pair (2, 10) into the equation $y = ax^2$. Substituting 2 for *x* and 10 for *y* gives $10 = a(2)^2$, $a = 2.5$; so, the equation is $y = 2.5x^2$. **21.** $A = \left(\frac{\sqrt{3}}{4}\right)s^2$; $25\sqrt{3}$ cm^2

10.8 Problem Solving (pp. 689–691)

23. linear function; $y = 0.34x + 24.6$ **25. a.** Troy: Population doubled every decade; data can be modeled by an exponential function. Union: Population increased by a fixed amount every decade; data can be modeled by a linear function.

b.

Decades since 1970	Troy's pop.
0	3000
1	6000
2	12,000
3	24,000
4	48,000

Decades since 1970	Union's pop.
0	3000
1	6000
2	9000
3	12,000
4	15,000

Troy: Ratios of successive *y*-values are equal. Union: First differences are constant. **c.** Let P = population and n = number of decades since 1970. Troy: $P = 3000 \cdot 2^n$, 192,000; Union: $P = 3000n + 3000$, 21,000

SELECTED ANSWERS

27. a. quadratic function; $\ell = 0.82t^2$ **b.** 0.205 ft **c.** The period decreases by about 71%. For example, consider $t = 4$ for $\ell = 13.12$. To find t for 50% of ℓ, solve $0.5(13.12) = 0.82t^2$; $t \approx 2.83$, and $\frac{2.83}{4} = 0.708$, so the period decreased by about 71%. Consider $t = 2$ for $\ell = 3.28$. To find t for 50% of ℓ, solve $0.5(3.28) = 0.82t^2$; $t \approx 1.41$, and $\frac{1.41}{2} = 0.705$, so the period decreased by about 71%. Consider $t = 1$ for $\ell = 0.82$. To find t for 50% of ℓ, solve $0.5(0.82) = 0.82t^2$; $t \approx 0.707$, and $\frac{0.707}{1} = 0.707$, so the period decreased by about 71%.

10.8 Graphing Calculator Activity (pp. 692–693)
1. $y = 15{,}600(0.866)^x$; about \$5698
3. $y = 179(0.987)^x$, $y = 0.040x^2 - 4.13x + 197$

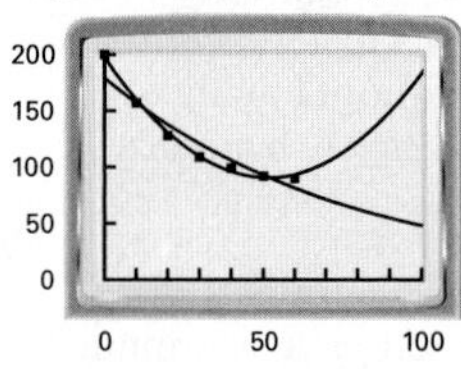

The exponential model; although the quadratic model appears to fit the given data points more closely than the exponential model does, the graph shows that after the last data point, (60, 90), the quadratic model implies increasing temperatures as time goes on, while the exponential model shows gradually decreasing temperatures as time goes on; the exponential model is a more accurate model of what will happen as the hot chocolate continues to cool.

Chapter Review (pp. 696–700)
1. axis of symmetry **3.** maximum
5.

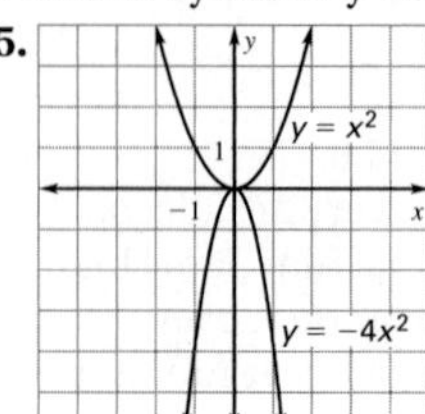

The graph is a vertical stretch (by a factor of 4) with a reflection in the x-axis of the graph of $y = x^2$.

7.

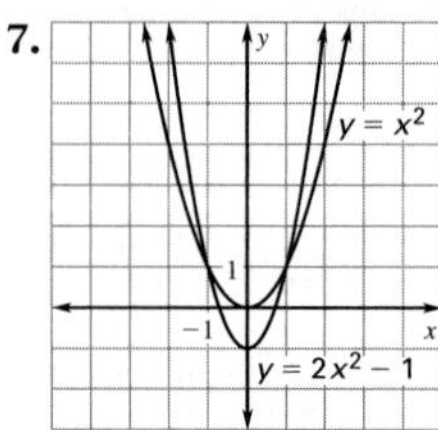

The graph is a vertical stretch (by a factor of 2) with a vertical translation (of 1 unit down) of the graph of $y = x^2$.

9.

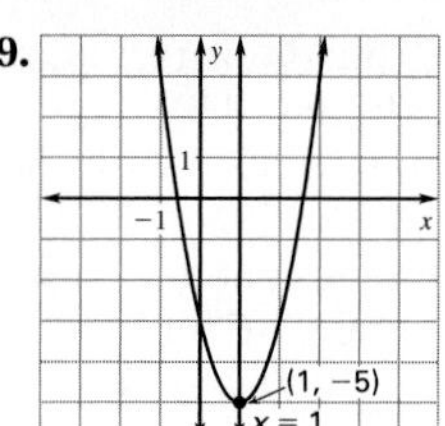

11. no solution **13.** $-8, 1$ **15.** no solution **17.** ± 0.76 **19.** 2.71, 5.29 **21.** $0.32, -6.32$ **23.** $-0.62, 1.62$ **25.** $-3.89, 0.39$ **27.** 0.16, 1.24 **29.** $-1.22, 1$ **31.** no solution **33.** two solutions **35.** two solutions **37.** exponential function

Cumulative Review (pp. 706–707) **1.** 3 **3.** 0.2 **5.** -1
7.

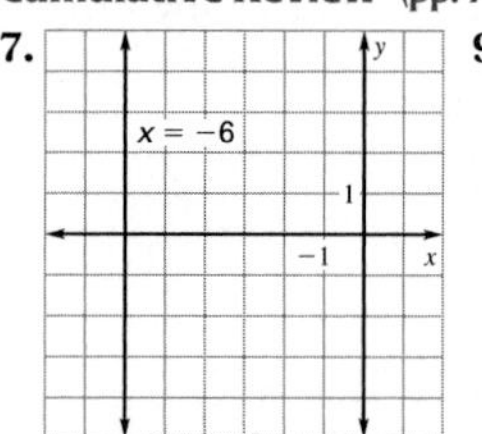

9.

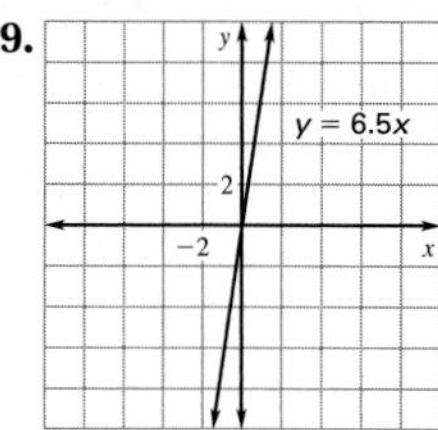

11.

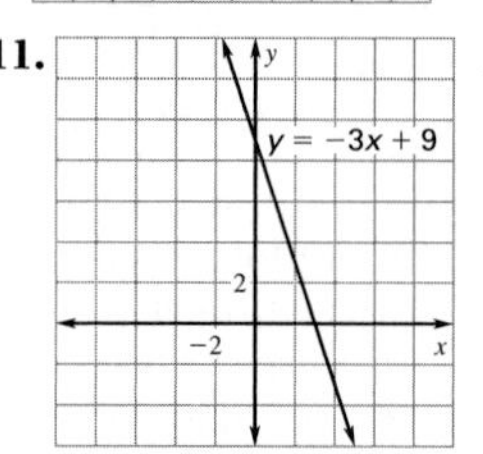

13.

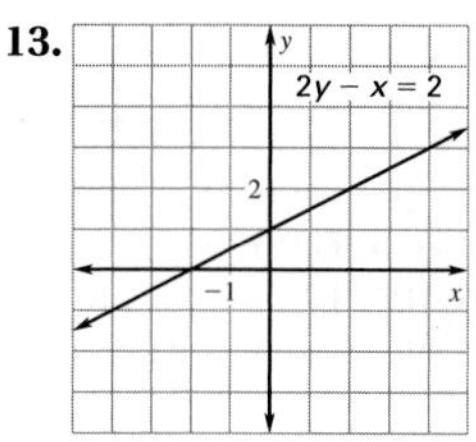

15. $y = \frac{1}{5}x + 3$ **17.** $y = -2x + 19$
19. $x < -36$

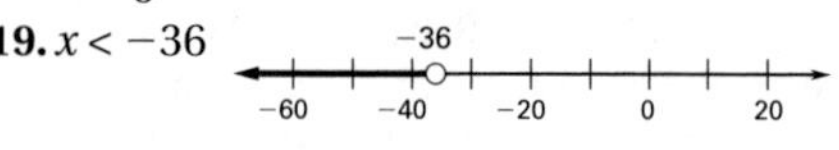

21. $b \geq -1$
23. $-\frac{3}{2} \leq c \leq 7$

25. all real numbers **27.** $-729r^3$ **29.** $\frac{81x^3}{y^2}$
31.

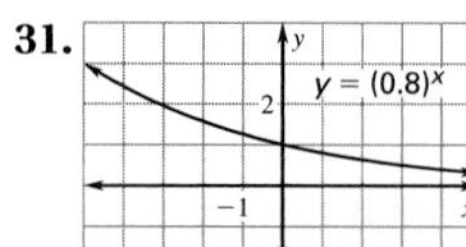

33. $-x^2 + 12x + 12$ **35.** $2z^2 + 11z - 63$
37. $-3q^3 + 11q - 2$ **39.** $4k^2 - 44k + 121$
41. $(x + 12)(x - 6)$ **43.** $(5d + 6)^2$
45. $(z - 6)(z + 2)(z - 2)$

SELECTED ANSWERS

47. 

49. 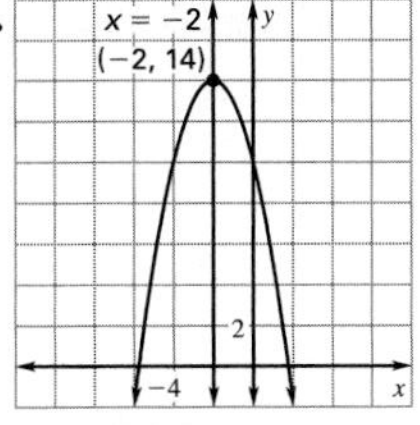

51. ±3.32 **53.** 0.5, 3 **55.** −0.57, 1 **57.** $475
59. length 19 in., width: 8 in.

61. a. 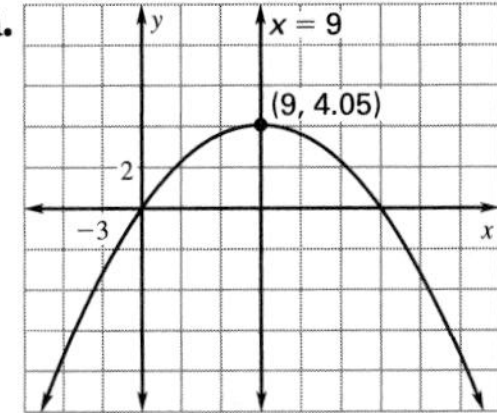

b. 18 ft

Chapter 11

11.1 Skill Practice (pp. 713–714) **1.** radical function

3. 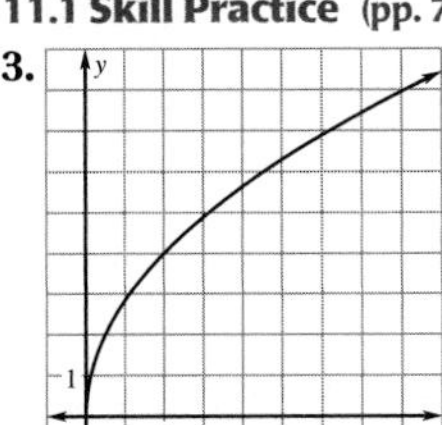
domain: $x \geq 0$, range: $y \geq 0$; vertical stretch by a factor of 4

5. 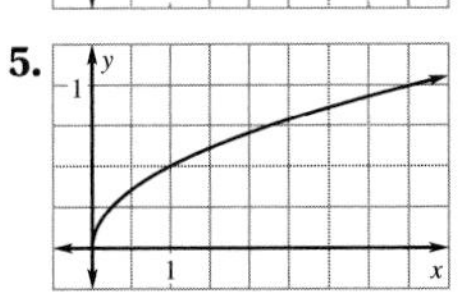
domain: $x \geq 0$, range: $y \geq 0$; vertical shrink by a factor of 0.5

7. 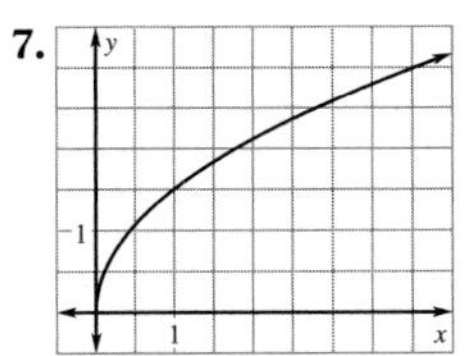
domain: $x \geq 0$, range: $y \geq 0$; vertical stretch by a factor of $\frac{3}{2}$

9. 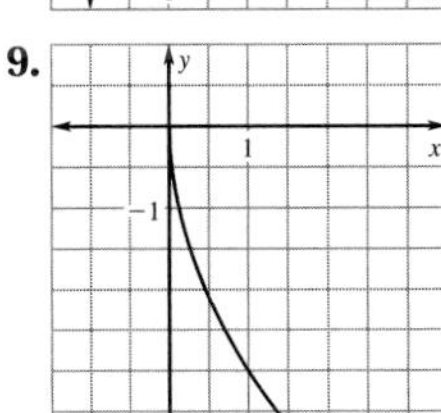
domain: $x \geq 0$, range: $y \leq 0$; vertical stretch by a factor of 3 with a reflection in the x-axis

11. 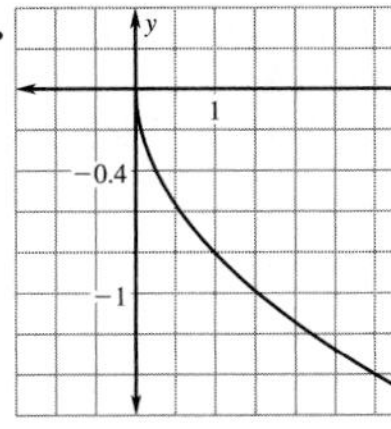
domain: $x \geq 0$, range: $y \leq 0$; vertical shrink by a factor of 0.8 with a reflection in the x-axis

13. 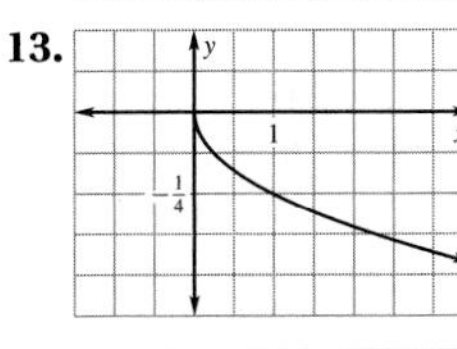
domain: $x \geq 0$, range: $y \leq 0$; vertical shrink by a factor of $\frac{1}{4}$ with a reflection in the x-axis

17. 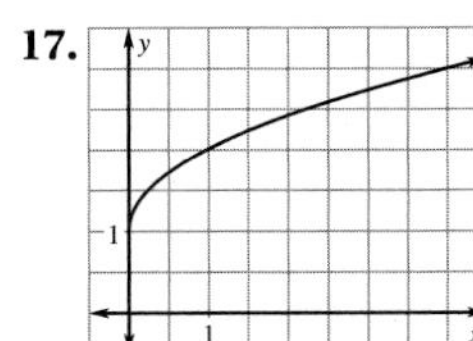
domain: $x \geq 0$, range: $y \geq 1$; vertical translation 1 unit up

19. 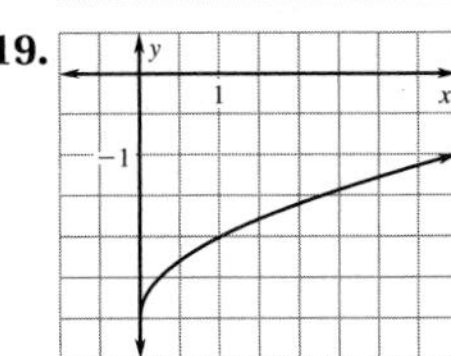
domain: $x \geq 0$, range: $y \geq -3$; vertical translation 3 units down

21. 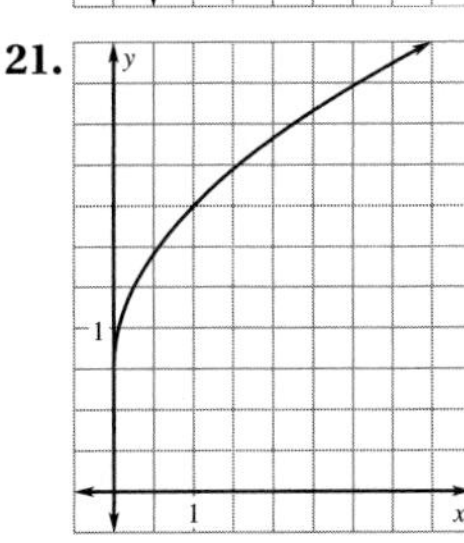
domain: $x \geq 0$, range: $y \geq \frac{3}{4}$; vertical translation $\frac{3}{4}$ unit up

23. 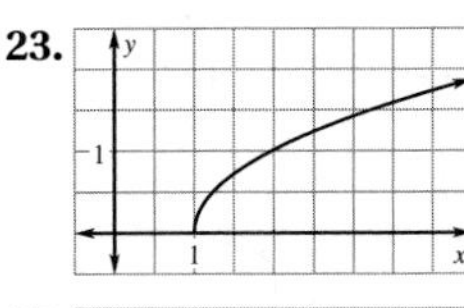
domain: $x \geq 1$, range: $y \geq 0$; horizontal translation 1 unit right

25. 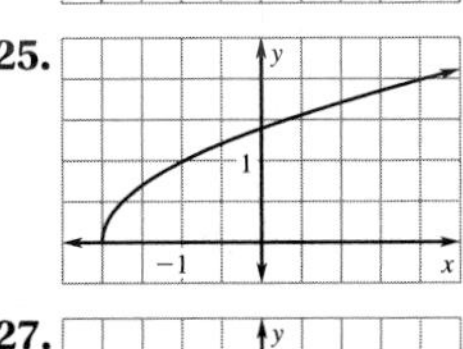
domain: $x \geq -2$, range: $y \geq 0$; horizontal translation 2 units left

27. 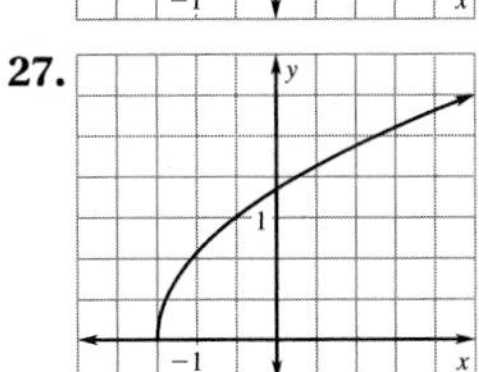
domain: $x \geq -1.5$, range: $y \geq 0$; horizontal translation 1.5 units left

31. 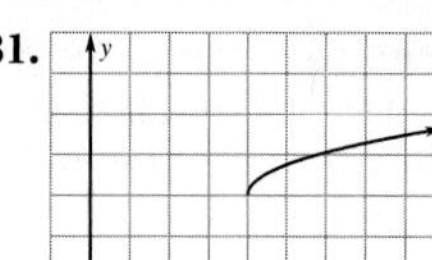

33. 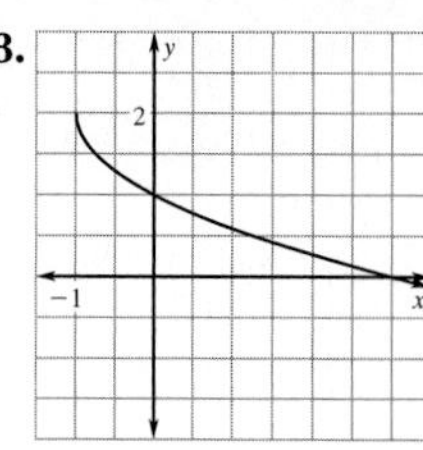

35. 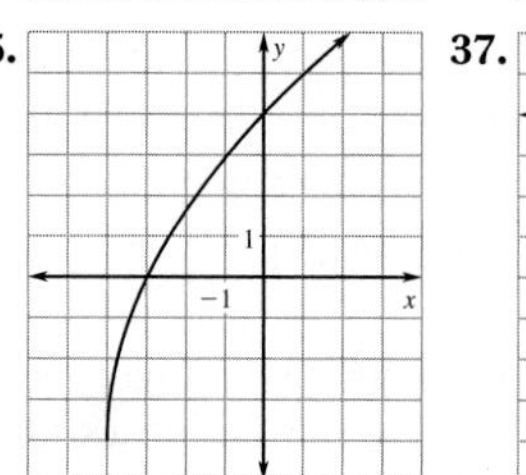

37. 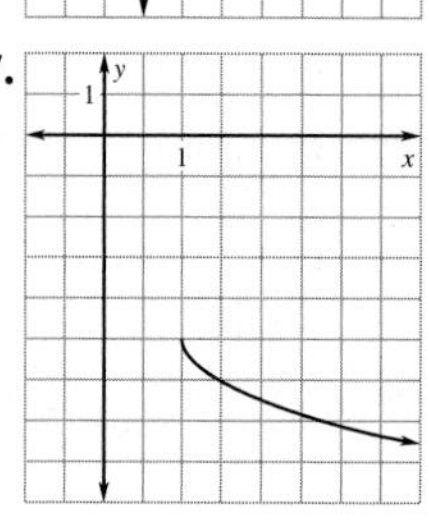

11.1 Problem Solving (pp. 715–716)

43. a. 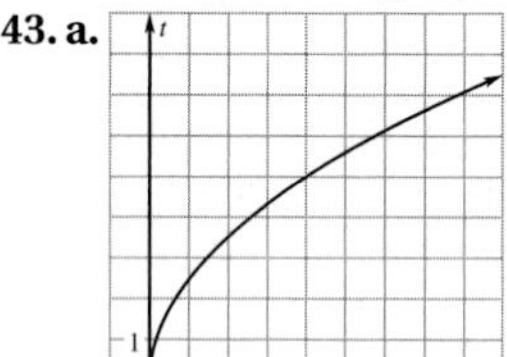

domain: $h \geq 0$, range: $t \geq 0$

b. about 1024 ft

45. 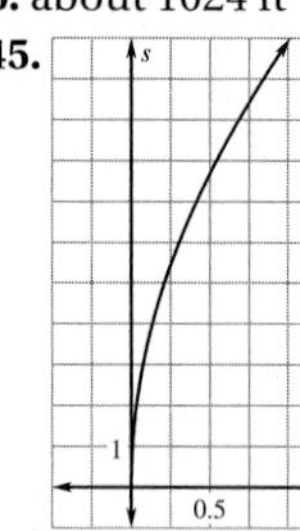

domain: $h \geq 0$, range: $s \geq 0$; about 0.9 m

47. a. 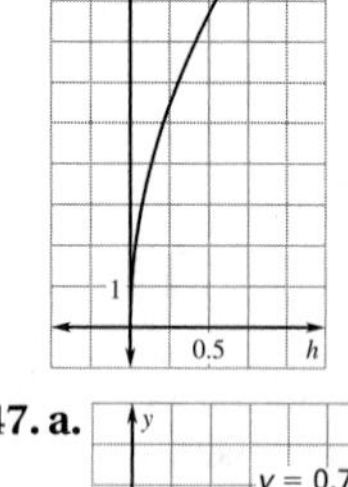

blue-winged teal's domain: $x \geq 0$, range: $y \geq 0$, northern pintail's domain: $x \geq 0$, range: $y \geq 0$

b. blue-winged teal: about 2 hectares, northern pintail: 25 hectares

11.1 Graphing Calculator Activity (p. 717)

1. 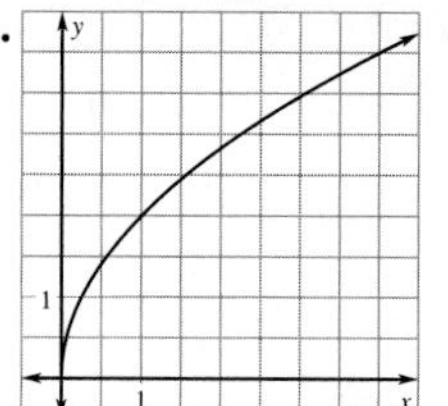

domain: $x \geq 0$, range: $y \geq 0$

3. 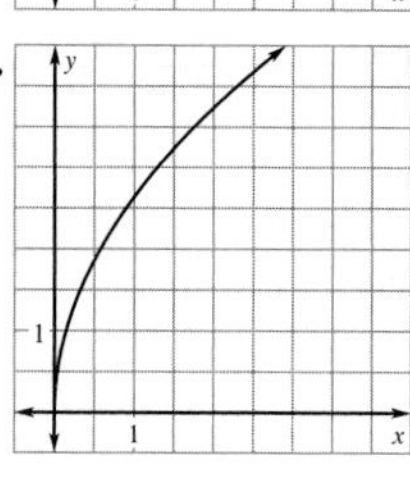

domain: $x \geq 0$, range: $y \geq 0$

5. 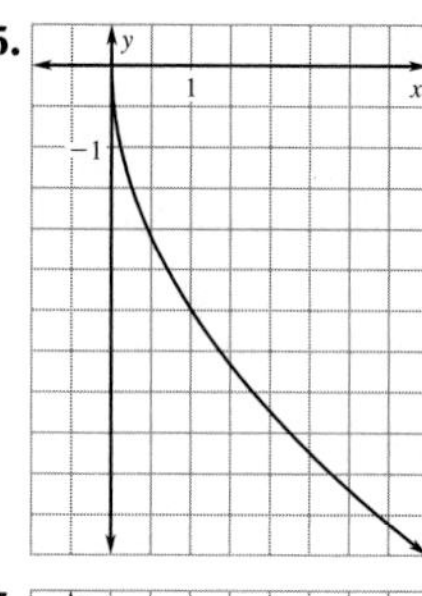

domain: $x \geq 0$, range: $y \leq 0$

7. 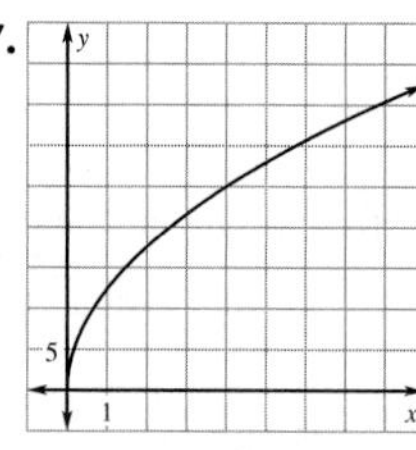

domain: $x \geq 0$, range: $y \geq 0$

9. 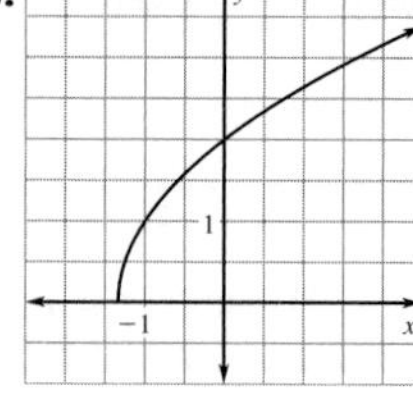

domain: $x \geq -\frac{4}{3}$, range: $y \geq 0$

11. 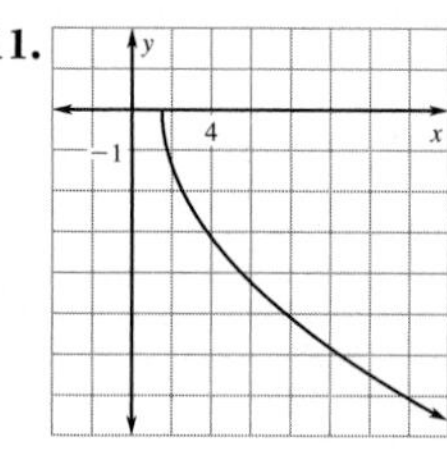

domain: $x \geq \frac{3}{2}$, range: $y \leq 0$

13. a. 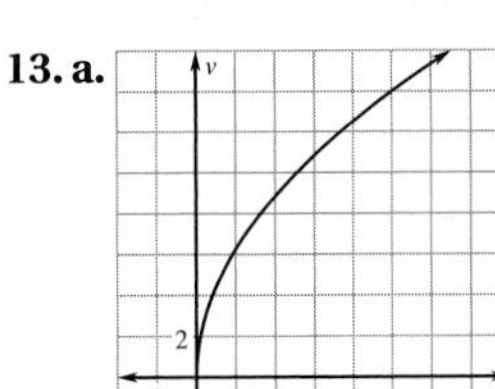 domain: $h \ge 0$, range: $v \ge 0$

b. about 154.3 m

11.2 Skill Practice (pp. 723–724) **1.** rationalizing the denominator **3.** $2\sqrt{5}$ **5.** $4\sqrt{6}$ **7.** $5\sqrt{5b}$ **9.** $9m\sqrt{m}$ **11.** $5\sqrt{6}$ **13.** $2x\sqrt{7}$ **15.** $2a^2b^2\sqrt{b}$ **17.** mn **19.** $\frac{2}{7}$ **21.** $\frac{a\sqrt{a}}{11}$ **25.** *Sample answer:* Simplify $\sqrt{45}$ to $\sqrt{9} \cdot \sqrt{5} = 3\sqrt{5}$. Then multiply $3\sqrt{5} \cdot \sqrt{5} = 3 \cdot 5 = 15$. Or, combine the expressions to create $\sqrt{45 \cdot 5} = \sqrt{225} = 15$. **27.** $\frac{4\sqrt{3}}{3}$ **29.** $\frac{\sqrt{13}}{13}$ **31.** $\frac{\sqrt{2x}}{2x}$ **33.** $\frac{2\sqrt{6n}}{3n^2}$ **35.** $-5\sqrt{5}$ **37.** $37\sqrt{2}$ **39.** $7\sqrt{7} - 5\sqrt{14}$ **41.** $21\sqrt{2} + 6\sqrt{6}$ **43.** $18 - \sqrt{2}$ **45.** $6\sqrt{7} + 6\sqrt{3} + 2\sqrt{14} + 2\sqrt{6}$ **47.** $16s^3t\sqrt{2rt}$ **49.** $\frac{h\sqrt{10gf}}{5f^2}$ **51.** $\frac{\sqrt{5}}{10}$ **53.** $\frac{3\sqrt{x} + 4x\sqrt{x}}{x^2}$ **55.** $\frac{\sqrt{7} - 1}{6}$ **57.** $\frac{7\sqrt{10} + 2\sqrt{5}}{47}$ **59.** $\frac{\sqrt{\pi S}}{2\pi}$ **61.** $\frac{\sqrt{2WC}}{C}$ **63.** Because $a > 0$, $a \cdot a < a \cdot b$. Similarly, $a \cdot b < b \cdot b$. Then $a^2 < ab < b^2$, so $\sqrt{a^2} < \sqrt{ab} < \sqrt{b^2}$, or $a < \sqrt{ab} < b$. That is, $\sqrt{ab}$ is between a and b on a number line. **65.** $-x$

11.2 Problem Solving (pp. 725–726) **67.** about 9.54% **69. a.** 5 yd^2 **b.** The side length s is in yd, and $\sqrt{\frac{S}{6}}$ is $\sqrt{\text{yd}^2} = \text{yd}$. **c.** 0.9 yd **71. a.** $S = \frac{\sqrt{hw}}{60}$ **b.** Yes. *Sample answer:* If the mass stays the same, then the greater the height the greater the body surface area will be.

Extension (pp. 727–728) **1.** $-2 - \sqrt{2}, -2 + \sqrt{2}$ **3.** $-4 - 2\sqrt{2}, -4 + 2\sqrt{2}$ **5.** $-1 - \frac{2\sqrt{3}}{3}, -1 + \frac{2\sqrt{3}}{3}$ **7.** $\frac{1}{5} - \frac{\sqrt{11}}{5}, \frac{1}{5} + \frac{\sqrt{11}}{5}$ **9.** $\frac{1}{2} - \frac{\sqrt{13}}{2}, \frac{1}{2} + \frac{\sqrt{13}}{2}$ **11.** $\frac{7}{2} - \frac{\sqrt{61}}{2}, \frac{7}{2} + \frac{\sqrt{61}}{2}$ **13.** $2 - \sqrt{2}, 2 + \sqrt{2}$ **15.** $-\frac{\sqrt{6}}{3}, \frac{\sqrt{6}}{3}$ **17.** $-\frac{1}{6} - \frac{\sqrt{73}}{6}, -\frac{1}{6} + \frac{\sqrt{73}}{6}$ **21.** Sum: $-\frac{b}{a}$, product: $\frac{c}{a}$. *Sample answer:* $y = 2x^2 - 4x + 1$

11.3 Skill Practice (pp. 732–733) **1.** extraneous solution **3.** 4 **5.** 48 **7.** 29 **9.** 8 **11.** $-\frac{75}{2}$ **13.** 47 **15.** -2 **17.** 7 **19.** no real solutions **23.** 1 **25.** $\frac{3}{8}, \frac{1}{2}$ **27.** -2 **29.** *Sample answer:* The solution $x = -9$ does not check in the original equation, so it is an extraneous solution. The only real solution is $x = 2$. **31.** no real solutions **33.** $\frac{16}{5}$

11.3 Problem Solving (pp. 733–734) **37.** 1977 **39.** 2.1 m

11.4 Skill Practice (pp. 740–741) **1.** hypotenuse **3.** $b = 4$ **5.** $c = \sqrt{61}$ **7.** $c = 8\sqrt{2}$ **9.** $c = 4\sqrt{13}$ **11.** $a = 8$ **13.** $a = 1.6$ **17.** 2, 4 **19.** 3, 4, 5, or 7, 24, 25 **21.** 2 in., 6 in. **23.** not a right triangle **25.** not a right triangle **27.** right triangle **31.** *Sample answer:* Let $m = 3$ and $n = 6$. Then $a = 6^2 - 3^2 = 27$, $b = 2(3)(6) = 36$, $c = 6^2 + 3^2 = 45$; substitute the values from the equation for a, b, and c in the Pythagorean theorem: $(n^2 - m^2)^2 + (2mn)^2 = (n^2 + m^2)^2$. Simplify to $n^4 - 2m^2n^2 + m^4 + 4m^2n^2 = n^4 + 2m^2n^2 + m^4$; $-2m^2n^2 + 4m^2n^2 = 2m^2n^2$; $2 = 2$. The equations are equal, so by the converse of the Pythagorean theorem, the lengths a, b, and c are a Pythagorean triple.

11.4 Problem Solving (pp. 741–742) **33.** 16 ft **35.** No; the sum of the squares of the two shorter sides is not equal to the square of the longer side. **37. a.** $\sqrt{6}$ **b.** $\sqrt{8}$ **c.** $\sqrt{n + 1}$. *Sample answer:* A list of the hypotenuse lengths for the first few triangles is $\sqrt{2}, \sqrt{3}, \sqrt{4}, \sqrt{5}, \ldots$. A general formula for this series is $c_n = \sqrt{n + 1}$.

11.5 Skill Practice (pp. 747–748) **1.** midpoint **3.** 1 **5.** 5 **7.** $\sqrt{53}$ **9.** $2\sqrt{17}$ **11.** $\sqrt{397}$ **13.** $\sqrt{73}$ **17.** 1, 25 **19.** -11, 1 **21.** -7, 15 **23.** $(5, -5)$ **25.** $(1, -4)$ **27.** $(-11, -6)$ **29.** $(-2, 0)$ **31.** $(-8, -4.5)$ **33.** $(-21, -33)$ **35.** *Sample answer:* The square of the difference in the x values and the square of the difference in the y values should be added, not subtracted; $d = \sqrt{(3 - (-17))^2 + (8 - (-2))^2} = \sqrt{400 + 100} = \sqrt{500} = 10\sqrt{5}$. **39.** $(8, -2)$ **41.** right triangle **43.** not a right triangle **45.** *Sample answer:* Use the distance formula to find the distance between the midpoint and each of the endpoints. If they are equal, the midpoint is equidistant from each endpoint.

11.5 Problem Solving (pp. 748–750) **47. a.** 10 mi **b.** $\sqrt{2}$ times greater **49. a.** the anchor and the cup **b.** the belt buckle and the sword; the anchor and the sword **51.** Yes; yes; all of them; the quadrilateral is a square.

11.5 Problem Solving Workshop (p. 751) **1. a.** Natural History Museum **b.** 0.24 mi

Chapter Review (pp. 754–756) **1.** It is a vertical stretch by a factor of 3 of the graph of $y = \sqrt{x}$. **3.** converse of the Pythagorean theorem

5.

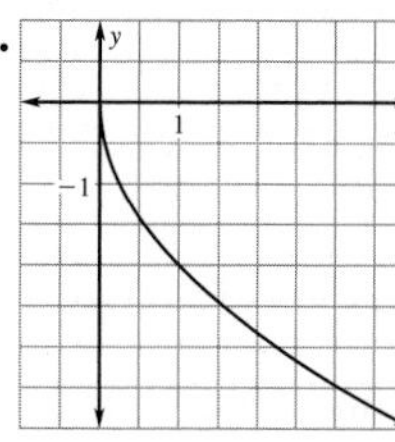

domain: $x \geq 0$, range: $y \leq 0$; vertical stretch by a factor of 2 with a reflection in the x-axis

7.

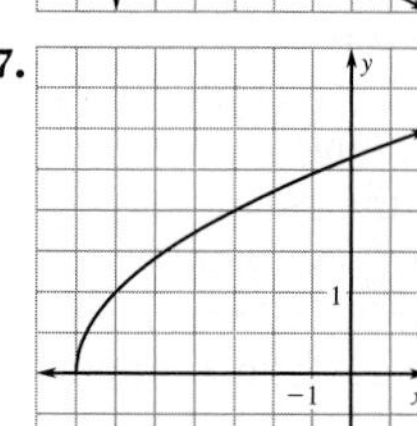

domain: $x \geq -7$, range: $y \geq 0$; horizontal translation of 7 units to the left

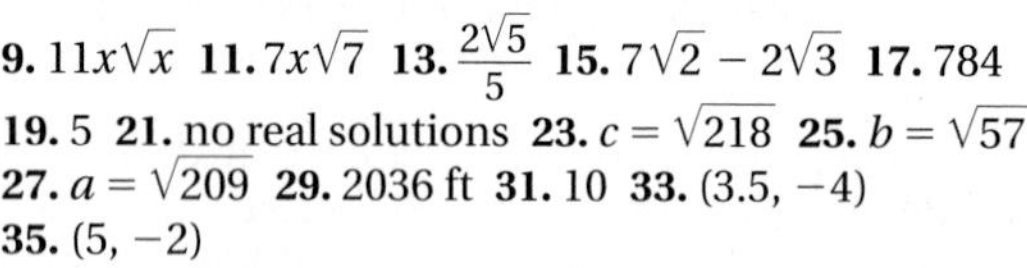

9. $11x\sqrt{x}$ **11.** $7x\sqrt{7}$ **13.** $\frac{2\sqrt{5}}{5}$ **15.** $7\sqrt{2} - 2\sqrt{3}$ **17.** 784 **19.** 5 **21.** no real solutions **23.** $c = \sqrt{218}$ **25.** $b = \sqrt{57}$ **27.** $a = \sqrt{209}$ **29.** 2036 ft **31.** 10 **33.** $(3.5, -4)$ **35.** $(5, -2)$

Chapter 12

12.1 Skill Practice (pp. 769–770) **1.** -3 **3.** direct variation **5.** neither **7.** inverse variation **9.** direct variation **11.** inverse variation **13.** direct variation

15. **17.**

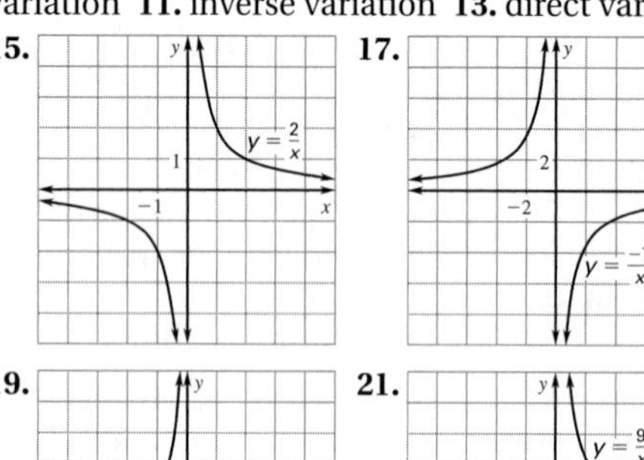

19. **21.**

23.

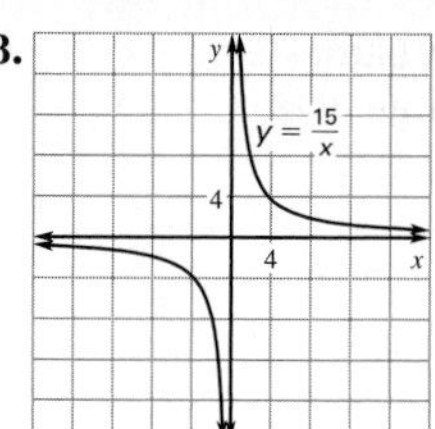

25.

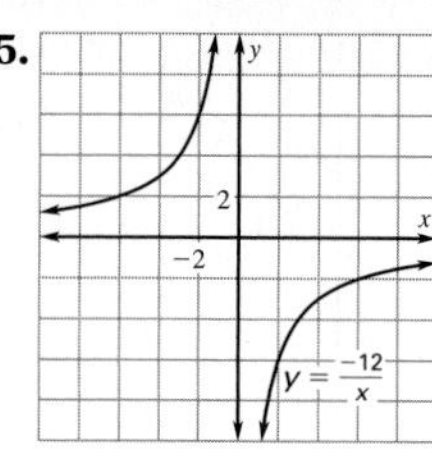

27. An inverse variation equation is in the form $y = \frac{a}{x}$, not $y = ax$; $8 = \frac{a}{2}$, $16 = a$. The correct inverse variation equation is $y = \frac{16}{x}$. **29.** $y = \frac{21}{x}$; 10.5 **31.** $y = \frac{-13}{x}$; -6.5 **33.** $y = \frac{132}{x}$; 66 **35.** $y = \frac{-18}{x}$; -9 **37.** $y = \frac{20}{x}$; 10 **39.** $y = \frac{70}{x}$; 35 **41.** $y = \frac{66}{x}$; 33 **45.** not inverse variation **47.** inverse variation; $y = \frac{-24}{x}$ **49.** $2\pi r = C$; direct variation **51.** $Bh = 400$; inverse variation

12.1 Problem Solving (pp. 770–772)

55. $d = \frac{175{,}000}{p}$; 350 units

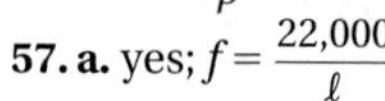

57. a. yes; $f = \frac{22{,}000}{\ell}$

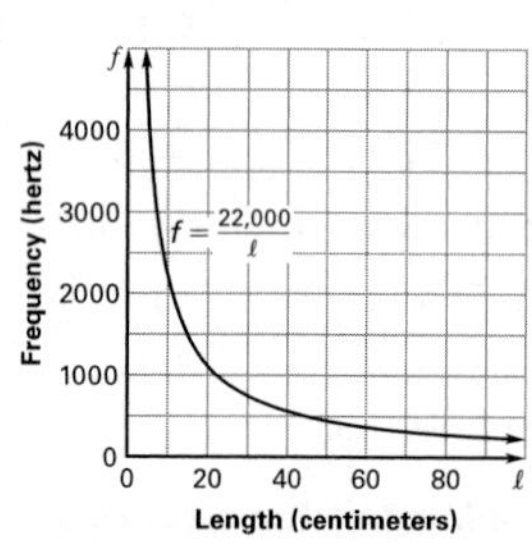

b. about 748 Hz **c.** The frequency increases; yes.

59. a. $s = \frac{35}{a}$ inverse variation

b. 4; when $s = 4$, the diameter of the aperture is $a = \frac{35}{4} = 8.75$ millimeters, and when $s = 8$, the diameter of the aperture is $a = \frac{35}{8} = 4.375$ millimeters.

SELECTED ANSWERS

SA38

12.2 Skill Practice (pp. 779–780) **1.** $x = 3, y = -6$

3. Domain: all real numbers except 0, range: all real numbers except 0; the graph is a vertical stretch of the graph of $y = \frac{1}{x}$.

5.

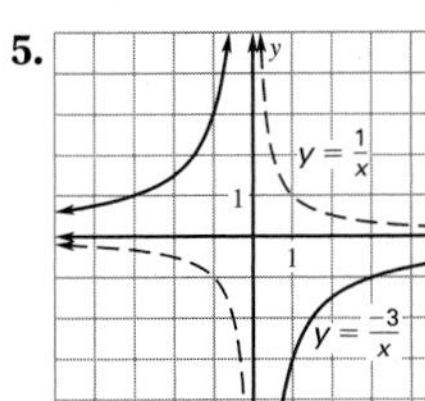

Domain: all real numbers except 0, range: all real numbers except 0; the graph is a vertical stretch of the graph of $y = \frac{1}{x}$ that is then reflected in the x-axis.

7.

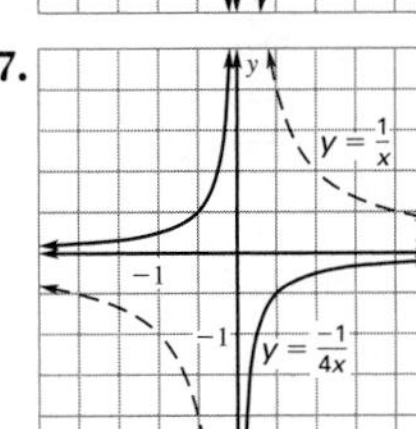

Domain: all real numbers except 0, range: all real numbers except 0; the graph is a vertical shrink of the graph of $y = \frac{1}{x}$ that is then reflected in the x-axis.

9.

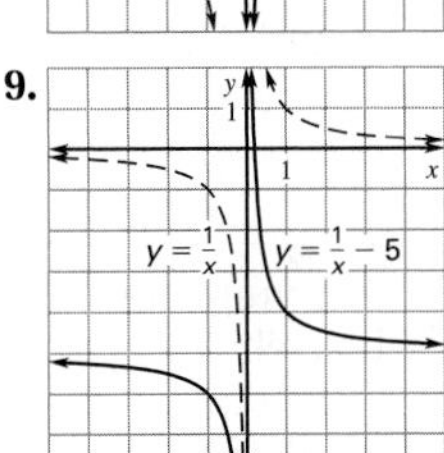

Domain: all real numbers except 0, range: all real numbers except -5; the graph is a vertical translation (of 5 units down) of the graph of $y = \frac{1}{x}$.

11.

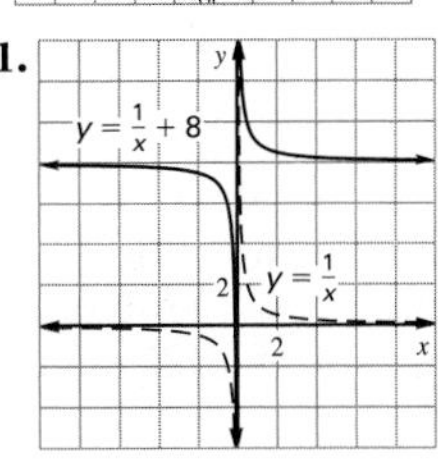

Domain: all real numbers except 0, range: all real numbers except 8; the graph is a vertical translation (of 8 units up) of the graph of $y = \frac{1}{x}$.

13.

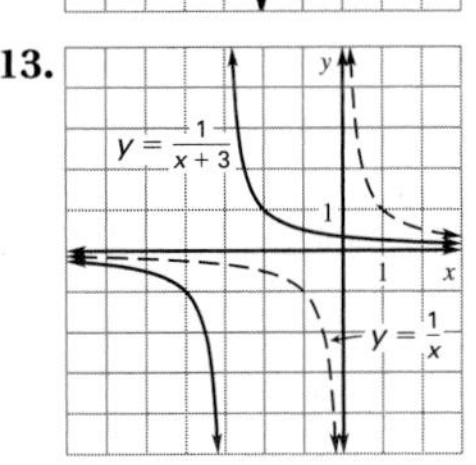

Domain: all real numbers except -3, range: all real numbers except 0; the graph is a horizontal translation (of 3 units left) of the graph of $y = \frac{1}{x}$.

15.

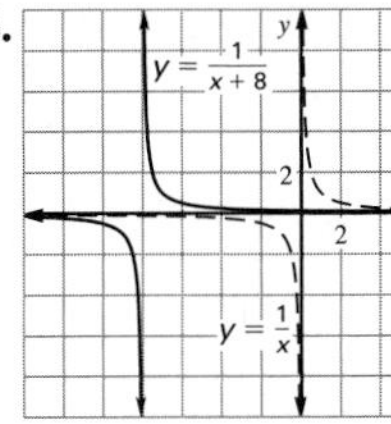

Domain: all real numbers except -8, range: all real numbers except 0; the graph is a horizontal translation (of 8 units left) of the graph of $y = \frac{1}{x}$.

17.

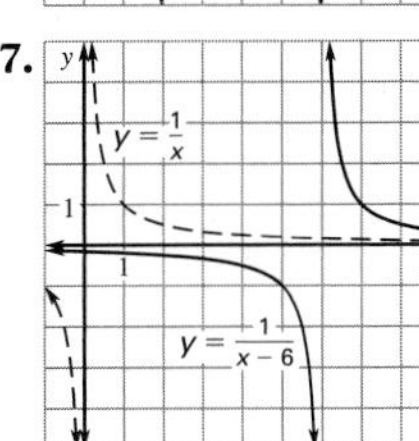

Domain: all real numbers except 6, range: all real numbers except 0; the graph is a horizontal translation (of 6 units right) of the graph of $y = \frac{1}{x}$.

19.

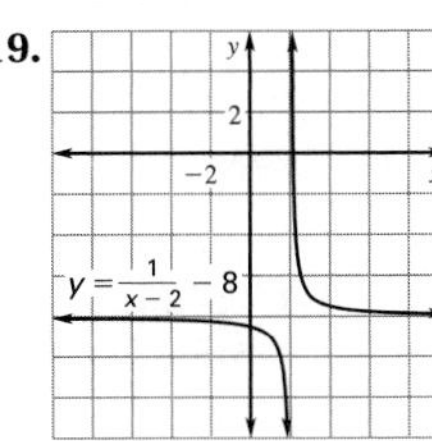

21.

23.

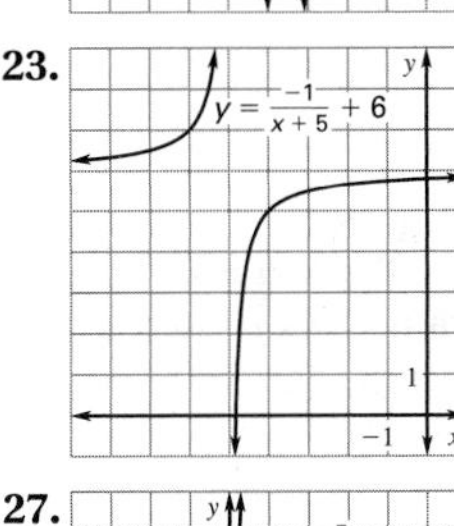

25.

27.

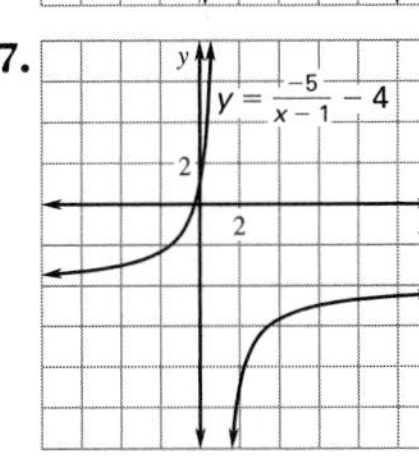

29. *Sample answer:* $y = \frac{1}{x+1} + 2$ **31.** To identify the asymptotes of the hyperbola, write its equation in the form $y = \frac{a}{x-h} + k$: $y = \frac{-2}{x-6} + 7$; thus the horizontal asymptote is $y = 7$, not $y = -7$. **33.** $y = \frac{-28}{x+2} + 5$ **35.** $y = \frac{-28}{x+4} - 4$

SELECTED ANSWERS

SA39

37. a. $h = \dfrac{100}{b_2 + 4}$

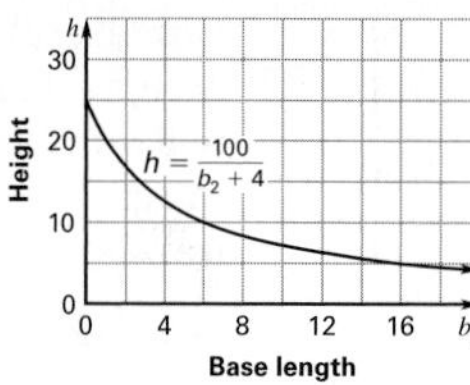

domain: $b_2 > 0$, range: $0 < h < 25$ **b.** about 13

12.2 Problem Solving (pp. 780–782)

39. $C = \dfrac{900}{p} + 400$

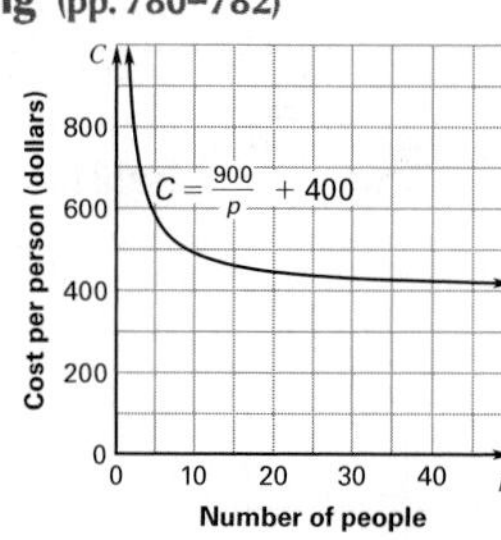

41. a. $C = \dfrac{22}{r + 2}$

b.

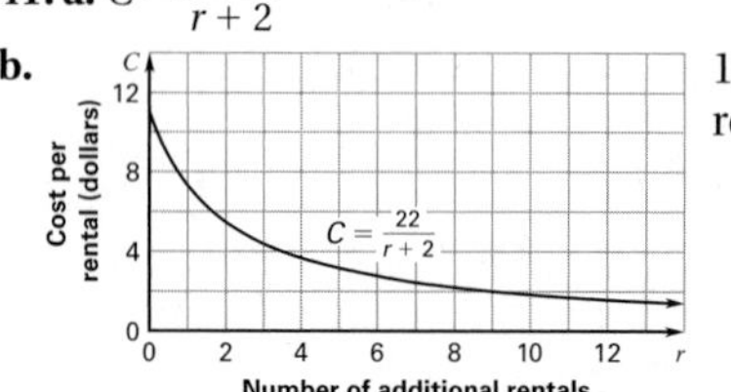

13 additional rentals

43.

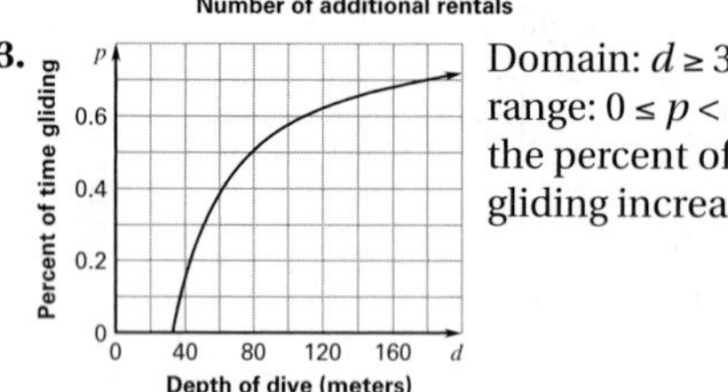

Domain: $d \geq 32.8$, range: $0 \leq p < 0.859$; the percent of time gliding increases.

12.3 Skill Practice (pp. 788–789) **1.** monomial **3.** $2x^2 - 3x + 4$ **5.** $-2r^3 + 5r + 12$ **7.** $3v + 5$ **9.** $m - 4$ **11.** $a - 4 + \dfrac{-1}{a - 1}$ **13.** $3p - 13 + \dfrac{18}{3 + p}$ **15.** $x + 3 + \dfrac{-12}{6 + x}$ **17.** $-t - 3 + \dfrac{-4}{t - 3}$ **21.** When subtracting $8x - 24$ from $8x - 9$, the result is $-9 - (-24) = -9 + 24 = 15$; $(8x - 9) \div (x - 3) = 8 + \dfrac{15}{x - 3}$.

23.

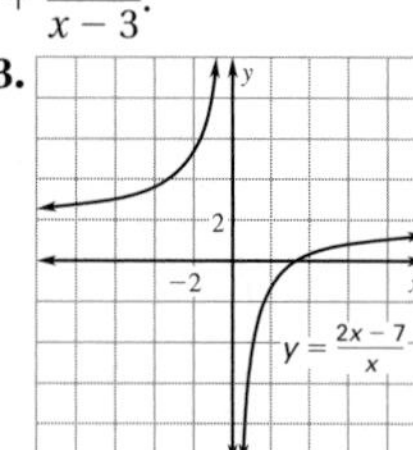

25.

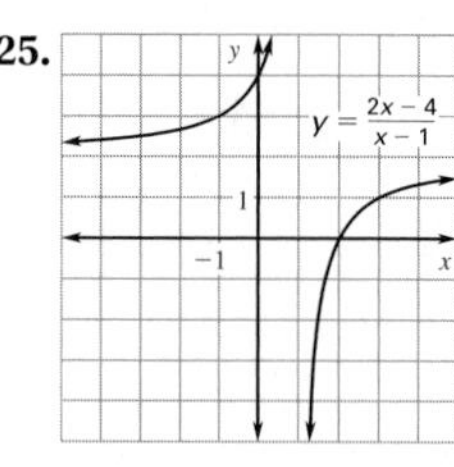

27.

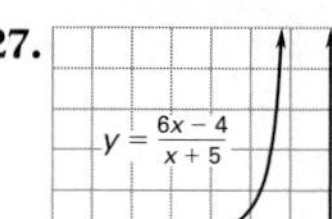
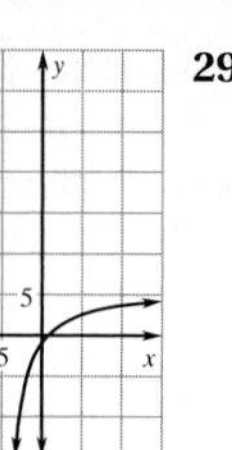

29.

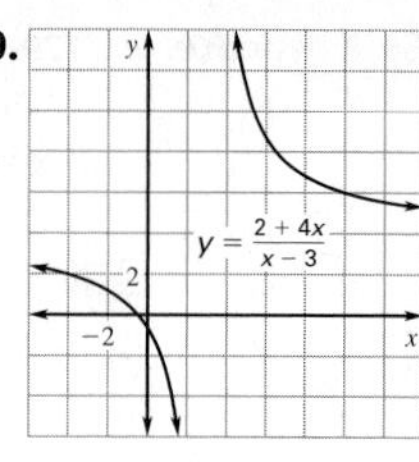

31. $\dfrac{7}{6} + \dfrac{2}{\ell}$ **35.** 10 **37.** -5

12.3 Problem Solving (pp. 789–791)

43. $C = \dfrac{80 + 3d}{d}$

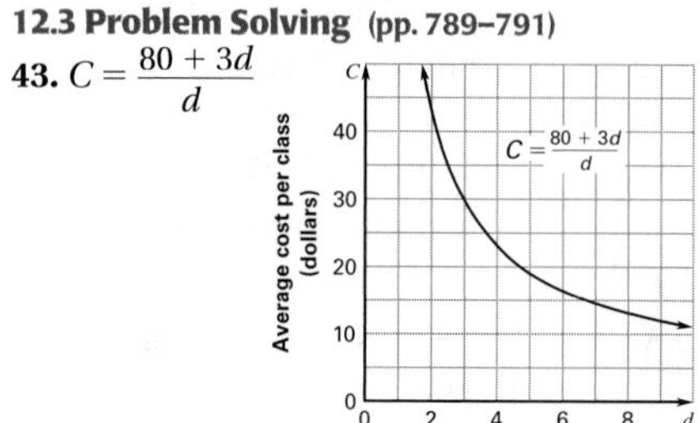

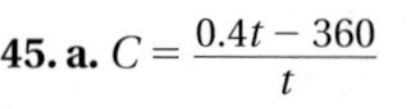

45. a. $C = \dfrac{0.4t - 360}{t}$

b.

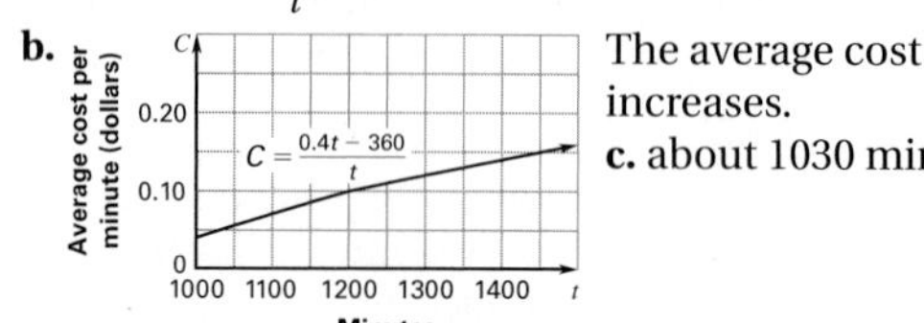

The average cost increases. **c.** about 1030 min

47. a.

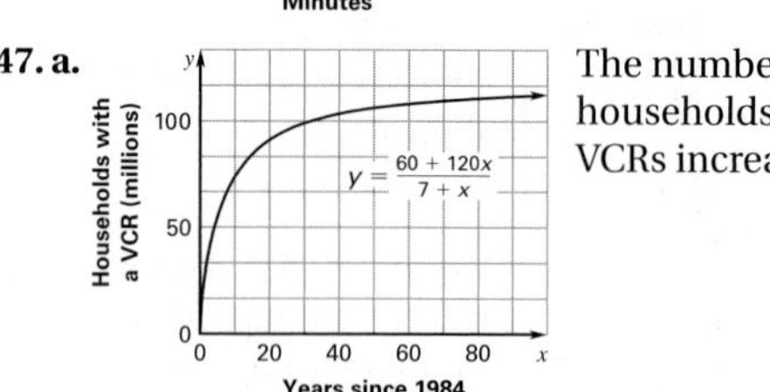

The number of households with VCRs increased.

b. No; as x increases, the graph of the function approaches its horizontal asymptote $y = 120$ from below, so the value of y will never exceed 120 million if this model applies to years beyond 2000.

49. a. $y = \dfrac{2r + 2\ell}{r\ell}$

SELECTED ANSWERS

b. More efficient; the graph in part (a) shows that as the length increases, the ratio decreases, implying that the microorganism becomes more efficient at performing metabolic tasks. **c.** The microorganism's efficiency would increase. *Sample answer:* Suppose the length is fixed at 50 micrometers. Then $y = \frac{2r + 100}{50r}$, or $y = \frac{2}{r} + 0.04$. This equation has the same graph as the graph shown in part (a); from the graph we see that as the radius increases, the ratio decreases, implying that the microorganism's efficiency increases.

12.3 Graphing Calculator Activity (pp. 792–793)

1. 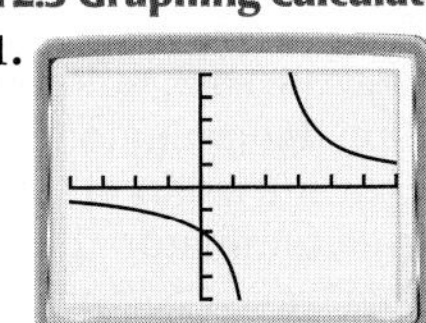 vertical: $x = 2$, horizontal: $y = 0$

3. 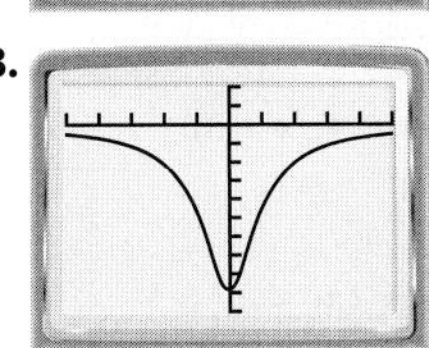 vertical: none, horizontal: $y = 0$

5. 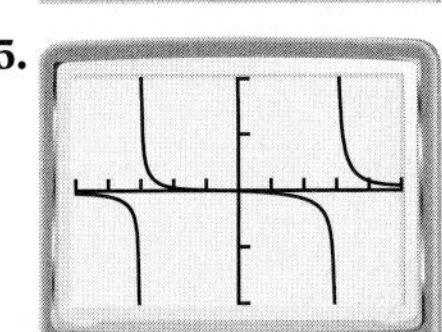 vertical: $x = -3, x = 3$, horizontal: $y = 0$

9. 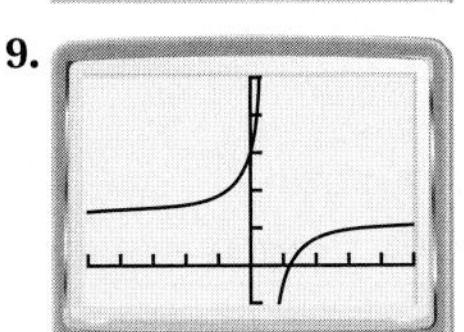 vertical: $x = 1$, horizontal: $y = 5$

11. 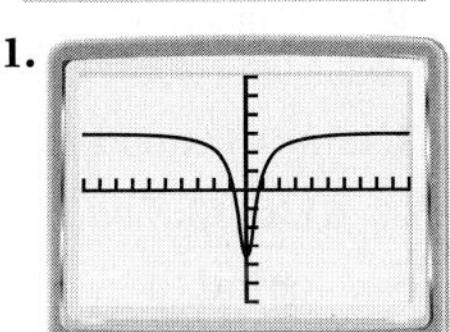 vertical: none, horizontal: $y = 3$

13. 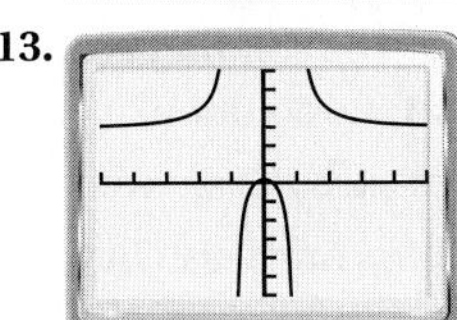 vertical: $x = -1, x = 1$, horizontal: $y = 3$

15. Vertical lines $x = a$, where a is an x-value that makes the denominator of the rational function equal to 0. **17.** $y = a$, where a is the quotient of the leading coefficient of the numerator and the leading coefficient of the denominator.

12.4 Skill Practice (pp. 797–798) **1.** excluded value **3.** none **5.** -1 **7.** none **9.** $0, \frac{1}{2}$ **11.** When finding the excluded values you must find the values for which the denominator of the original expression, $2x^2 - 11x + 12$, is 0; the excluded values are $\frac{3}{2}$ and 4. **13.** $\frac{2x}{5}$; none **15.** $-3a$; 0 **17.** 3; -11 **19.** -2; 3 **21.** $\frac{2}{f^2 - 9}$; ± 3 **23.** $\frac{1}{h - 4}$; $-3, 4$ **25.** $\frac{-6}{2w - 5}$; $0, \frac{5}{2}$ **27.** 3; 0, 4 **29.** $\frac{s + 8}{s - 1}$; $-8, 1$ **31.** $\frac{1}{m^2 + 5m}$; $0, -5$ **33.** No; the two expressions do not have the same excluded values; the excluded values for $\frac{x^2 + x}{x^2 - 1}$ are ± 1, while the excluded values for $\frac{x^2}{x^2 - x}$ are 0 and 1. The expressions are not equivalent for $x = 0$ and for $x = -1$. **37.** $\frac{3(x + 2)}{x(x + 6)}$

12.4 Problem Solving (pp. 799–800)

41. $p = \frac{3x^2 - 12}{22x^2 + 2500}$; about 11% **43.** $p = \frac{-202x + 3660}{345x + 9130}$; the percent of wood houses decreased.

45. a. $R = \frac{37{,}500 + 2500x}{125 + x}$; about \$522 million

b. 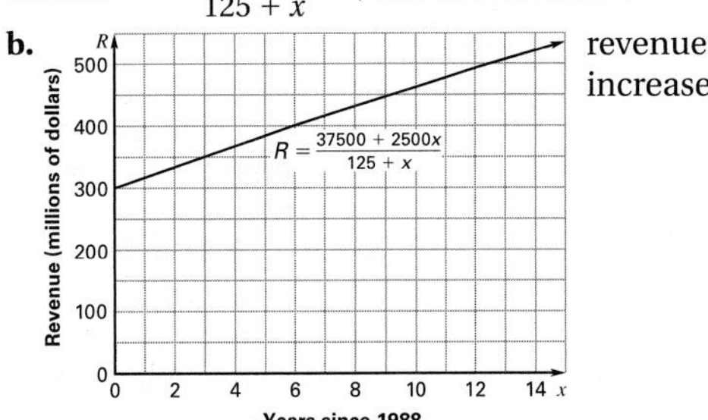

revenue increased

c. No; if the price per copy of printed music went up during the period 1988–2002, then the revenue may have increased without the number of copies sold increasing.

SELECTED ANSWERS

12.5 Skill Practice (pp. 806–807) **1.** multiplicative inverse **3.** $\frac{15}{14p^2}$ **5.** $\frac{-(v-3)}{5(v+1)}$ **7.** $\frac{x+4}{2x+1}$ **9.** $\frac{-3m}{m-2}$

11. To divide by the rational expression $\frac{15x^3}{2}$, you must multiply by its multiplicative inverse, $\frac{2}{15x^3}$; $\frac{x^3}{5} \cdot \frac{2}{15x^3} = \frac{2x^3}{75x^3} = \frac{2}{75}$. **13.** $\frac{20r^3}{9}$ **15.** $\frac{2w+5}{w(w-9)}$ **17.** $\frac{a+5}{3a^2}$

19. 1 **23.** $8x^2 \cdot \frac{1}{2x^3}$; $\frac{4}{x}$ **25.** $\frac{1}{x^2-3x-4} \div \frac{2}{x^2-1}$; $\frac{x-1}{2(x-4)}$

27. *Sample answer:* $\frac{x^2-2x-3}{x^2-2x-8}$, $\frac{x^2-9x+20}{x^2-4x-5}$

29. $(x-1)(x-3)$. *Sample answer:* 0

12.5 Problem Solving (pp. 807–809)

33. $p = \frac{100 + 2.2x}{(1-0.014x)(1500+63x)}$; about 7%

35. a. $R = \frac{(86+180x)(1+0.014x)}{(1+0.024x)(23+38x)}$

b.

Year	1990	1991	1992	1993	1994	1995	1996
Rushing average, *R* (yards per attempt)	3.74	4.32	4.42	4.44	4.44	4.42	4.40

Year	1997	1998	1999	2000	2001	2002
Rushing average, *R* (yards per attempt)	4.38	4.35	4.33	4.30	4.28	4.25

Smith's career rushing average increased for the first several years and then began to decrease.

37. a. $T = \frac{4700 - 74x}{(1-0.053x)(0.015x^2+4.1)}$

b.

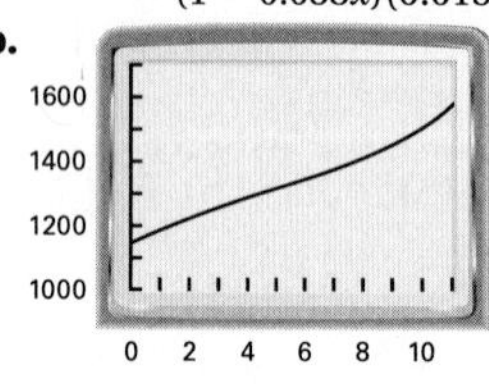

The number of tickets increased. No; the graph only shows how the *ratio* of the gross revenue and the ticket prices changed. *R* and *P* could go up and/or down while their ratio increases.

c.

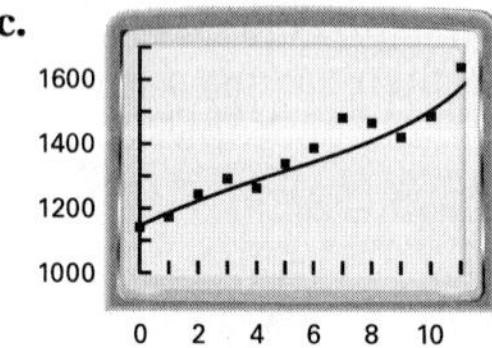

The points of the scatter plot are very close to the graph of the model for all years except 1998, 1999, and 2002.

Extension (p. 811) **1.** $\frac{3x^3}{28}$ **3.** $\frac{x}{2(x-3)(x-7)}$ **5.** $x^2(x-1)$ **7.** $\frac{5(x+4)}{2}$ **9.** $\frac{2(x+3)(x-1)}{5(3x+1)}$ **11.** $\frac{3(r+\ell)}{rh}$

13. No; $\frac{\frac{a}{b}}{c} = \frac{a}{b} \div c = \frac{a}{b} \cdot \frac{1}{c} = \frac{a}{bc}$ and $\frac{a}{\frac{b}{c}} = a \div \frac{b}{c} = \frac{a}{1} \cdot \frac{c}{b} = \frac{ac}{b}$. Thus, $\frac{\frac{a}{b}}{c} \neq \frac{a}{\frac{b}{c}}$.

12.6 Skill Practice (pp. 816–817) **1.** least common denominator **3.** $\frac{1}{x}$ **5.** $\frac{4}{z}$ **7.** $\frac{2b+1}{b-3}$ **9.** $\frac{-1}{m^2+1}$ **11.** $\frac{3r+1}{r^2+r-7}$ **13.** $60v^3$ **15.** $(s+2)(s-1)$ **17.** $(u+7)(u+1)(u-3)$ **19.** To rewrite each rational expression using the least common denominator, you must multiply its numerator by the factor of the LCD that is missing from the denominator: the numerator $5x$ should be multiplied by $(x+3)$ and the numerator 2 should be multiplied by $(x-4)$; $\frac{5x}{x-4} + \frac{2}{x+3} = \frac{5x(x+3)}{(x-4)(x+3)} + \frac{2(x-4)}{(x-4)(x+3)} = \frac{5x^2+15x+2x-8}{(x-4)(x+3)} = \frac{5x^2+17x-8}{(x-4)(x+3)}$.

21. $\frac{149}{33y}$ **23.** $\frac{5r^2-17r}{(r-2)(r-3)}$ **25.** $\frac{4c^2+13c+30}{(c-6)(3c+10)}$ **27.** $\frac{-20f^2+7f+12}{7f(f+4)}$ **29.** $\frac{3j^2-12j-1}{(j+1)(j-1)(j-6)}$ **31.** $\frac{-v^2+6v+20}{(2v+5)(v-3)(v+5)}$ **33.** $\frac{S-2\ell w}{2(\ell+w)}$ **35.** $\frac{15x^2+120x+20}{(x-2)(x+8)}$ **37.** $\frac{-3x^2+29x-4}{x-9}$ **39.** $y = \frac{-4x-16}{x+2}$

12.6 Problem Solving (pp. 817–819) **43.** $t = \frac{400r-1000}{r(r-5)}$; about 8.4 h **45. a.** $\frac{2A^2+200A}{3}$; $\frac{7A^2+18{,}750A-205{,}050}{150}$ **b.** 2600 lb; 6301 lb **47.** $f = \frac{2.5+0.215x}{5.3+0.30x}$; about 58%

12.7 Skill Practice (pp. 823–824) **1.** rational equation **3.** ± 10 **5.** $-1\frac{1}{2}$ **7.** $-1\frac{1}{2}$, 4 **9.** -6, 5 **11.** 6 **13.** The distributive property must be used to find the product of 5 and $(4x+1)$; $5(4x+1) = 3(8x-1)$, $20x+5 = 24x-3$, $8 = 4x$, $2 = x$. The solution is 2. **15.** -10 **17.** -22 **19.** $2 \pm 2\sqrt{3}$ **21.** no solution **23.** $-\frac{1}{5}$, -1 **25.** All real numbers except 2; 2; two fractions with equal denominators must also have equal numerators, so $x = 2$, and the denominator of both fractions is $2 - a$. The equation has this one solution as long as the denominator $2 - a$ is not 0; so, the equation has no solution when $a = 2$.

27. a. $\left(\frac{8}{3}, 9\right)$, $(-2, -5)$ **b.**

29. No; suppose that $\frac{x+a}{x+1+a} = \frac{x}{x+1}$. Then, using the cross products property, $(x + 1)(x + a) = x(x + 1 + a)$; $x^2 + xa + x + a = x^2 + x + xa$; $x^2 + x(a + 1) + a = x^2 + x(1 + a)$. Then, subtracting $x^2 + x(1 + a)$ from both sides gives the result $a = 0$; so, the only value of a for which the equation is true is 0.

12.7 Problem Solving (pp. 824–826) **31.** 50 consecutive shots **33.** 3 c **35. a.** $\frac{30}{t} + \frac{30}{1.5t} = 1$; 50 min **b.** Change each 30 to 20, and change 1.5 to 1; 40 min. **c.** Because you now both rake at the same rate, whenever you work together, the time it takes to rake a portion of the lawn will be half the time it takes either of you to rake that portion alone. Suppose you rake together for m minutes. Then you each rake $\frac{m}{40}$ of the lawn, and together you rake $\frac{m}{40} + \frac{m}{40} = \frac{2m}{40} = \frac{m}{20}$ of the lawn. To rake $\frac{m}{20}$ of the lawn alone would take you $2m$ minutes. **37.** From 8 psi to 7 psi; substitute the given psi values for p in the given equation and then solve for a: for $p = 10$, $a \approx 10{,}722$; for $p = 9$, $a \approx 13{,}536$; for $p = 8$, $a \approx 16{,}600$; for $p = 7$, $a \approx 19{,}948$. The change in altitude when the atmospheric pressure changes from 10 psi to 9 psi is about $13{,}536 - 10{,}722 = 2814$, and the change in altitude when the atmospheric pressure changes from 8 psi to 7 psi is about $19{,}948 - 16{,}600 = 3348$.

12.7 Problem Solving Workshop (p. 828) **1.** \$1250 **3.** 6 free throws **5.** 75 min

Chapter Review (pp. 831–834) **1.** asymptote **3.** $x = -2$, $y = -4$ **5.** $y = \frac{63}{x}$, 12.6 **7.** inverse variation; $y = \frac{-8}{x}$

9.

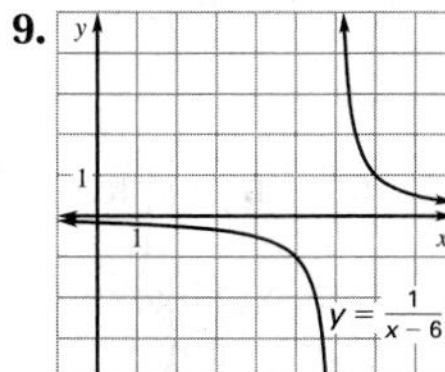

11. $x + 5$ **13.** $z - 1 + \frac{4}{z+5}$

15. $a = \frac{500 + 2d}{d}$

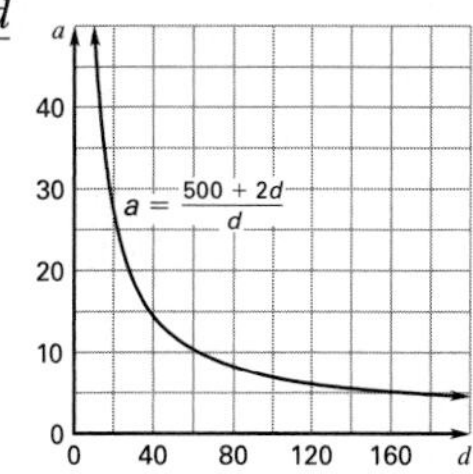

17. $-2, 6$ **19.** $\frac{m-3}{4}$; 0 **21.** $\frac{-(r+2)}{r+1}$; $-1, 2$ **23.** $\frac{21v^7}{4}$ **25.** $\frac{-8x+33}{5x-3}$ **27.** $\frac{5c^2 - 13c - 48}{(c+1)(c-4)(c+2)}$ **29.** $-6, 9$ **31.** $\frac{-21}{5}$

Chapter 13

13.1 Skill Practice (pp. 846–847) **1.** probability **3.** 12 outcomes; R1, R2, R3, R4, W1, W2, W3, W4, B1, B2, B3, B4 **5.** 48; HHH1, HHH2, HHH3, HHH4, HHH5, HHH6, HHT1, HHT2, HHT3, HHT4, HHT5, HHT6, HTH1, HTH2, HTH3, HTH4, HTH5, HTH6, HTT1, HTT2, HTT3, HTT4, HTT5, HTT6, THH1, THH2, THH3, THH4, THH5, THH6, THT1, THT2, THT3, THT4, THT5, THT6, TTH1, TTH2, TTH3, TTH4, TTH5, TTH6, TTT1, TTT2, TTT3, TTT4, TTT5, TTT6 **7.** $\frac{9}{10}$ **9.** $\frac{1}{10}$ **11.** $\frac{3}{7}$ or 3 : 7 **13.** *Sample answer:* Odds in favor is the number of favorable outcomes divided by the number of unfavorable outcomes; odds in favor of a multiple of 3 = $\frac{\text{Number of favorable outcomes}}{\text{Number of unfavorable outcomes}} = \frac{9}{1}$ or 9 : 1. **15.** *Sample answer:* Rolling a standard number cube and getting a 0, flipping a coin and getting heads or tails. **17.** *Sample answer:* route A; The experimental probability that he will encounter heavy traffic on route A is 0.25, and the experimental probability that he will encounter heavy traffic on route B is 0.375.

13.1 Problem Solving (pp. 847–848) **19.** $\frac{1}{7}$ **21.** $\frac{4}{9}$; $\frac{4}{5}$. *Sample answer:* The probability and odds of choosing a boy are related because both compare the number of boys to another number. The probability of choosing a boy compares the number of boys to the total number of outcomes, while the odds of choosing a boy compare the number of boys to the total number of outcomes minus the number of boys.

SELECTED ANSWERS

SA43

Extension (p. 850) **1.** Answers will vary. **3.** *Sample answer:* There are 3 prizes to win, but since the prizes do not have an equal likelihood of being won, generating a list of random integers from 1 to 3 would not represent the situation. The probability of winning a CD is $\frac{1}{6}$, so if there were only 3 possible outcomes in the simulation you could not represent winning a CD properly.

13.2 Skill Practice (pp. 853–854) **1.** permutation **3. a.** 2 ways **b.** 2 ways **5. a.** 24 ways **b.** 12 ways **7. a.** 120 ways **b.** 20 ways **9. a.** 120 ways **b.** 20 ways **11.** *Sample answer:* 5 people are running in a race. How many different results can there be for first and second place? **13.** 6 **15.** 120 **17.** 3,628,800 **19.** 6,227,020,800 **21.** 210 **23.** 720 **25.** 1 **27.** 6,375,600 **29.** The denominator should be $(5 - 3)! = 2!$, not $3!$; ${}_5P_3 = \frac{5!}{(5-3)!} = \frac{5!}{2!} = 60$.

13.2 Problem Solving (pp. 854–855) **35. a.** $\frac{1}{2}$. *Sample answer:* Make a list of possible permutations, count the number in which you are first or second, and divide it by the total number of outcomes. **b.** $\frac{1}{2}$; the answers are the same. **37.** $\frac{1}{720}$

13.3 Skill Practice (p. 858) **1.** combination **3.** 20 combinations **5.** *Sample answer:* The answer given is for ${}_9P_4$, not ${}_9C_4$; ${}_9C_4 = \frac{9!}{(9-4)! \cdot 4!} = \frac{9!}{5! \cdot 4!} = 126$. **7.** 56 **9.** 28 **11.** 330 **13.** 15,504 **17.** Permutations; since the roles are different, the order in which students are selected for the roles matters; 720 ways. **19.** Permutations; the arrangement of people in the car matters; 120 ways. **21.** ${}_nC_r = {}_nP_r \cdot \frac{1}{r!}$. *Sample answer:* To find the number of combinations, you find the number of permutations and then divide by the number of ways the items being chosen can be arranged, or $r!$.

13.3 Problem Solving (p. 859) **23.** 840 burritos **25. a.** 84 combinations **b.** $\frac{5}{21}$. *Sample answer:* There are 84 possible outcomes of the choice. Find the number of combinations that include you and your 2 friends. After you and your friends are chosen, 3 other contestants from a pool of 6 can be chosen in any combination, so the number of favorable combinations is ${}_6C_3 = 20$. The probability that you and your friends are chosen is $\frac{20}{84} = \frac{5}{21}$.

13.3 Graphing Calculator Activity (p. 860) **1.** 35 **3.** 120 **5.** 15,120 **7.** 6,652,800 **9. a.** 3276 groups **b.** 6 ways

13.4 Skill Practice (pp. 864–865) **1.** dependent **3.** mutually exclusive; $\frac{2}{3}$ **5.** overlapping; $\frac{5}{6}$ **7.** To find the probability that you draw a yellow *or* a blue marble, the individual probabilities should be added, not multiplied; $\frac{7}{16} + \frac{5}{16} = \frac{12}{16} = \frac{3}{4}$. **9.** independent; $\frac{1}{36}$ **11.** independent; $\frac{1}{12}$ **15.** $\frac{1}{64}$ **17.** The second-draw probabilities are incorrect. There are 31 pieces left; 1 is a king. *P*(king given king) $= \frac{1}{31}$, *P*(not king given king) $= \frac{30}{31}$, *P*(king given not king) $= \frac{2}{31}$, *P*(not king given not king) $= \frac{29}{31}$. **19.** 69%

13.4 Problem Solving (pp. 866–867) **23.** 62.3%

25. a.

Mon	Tues	Wed	Thurs	Fri	Sat	Sun
st. gov.		st. gov.				
tutor			tutor	tutor	tutor	

b.

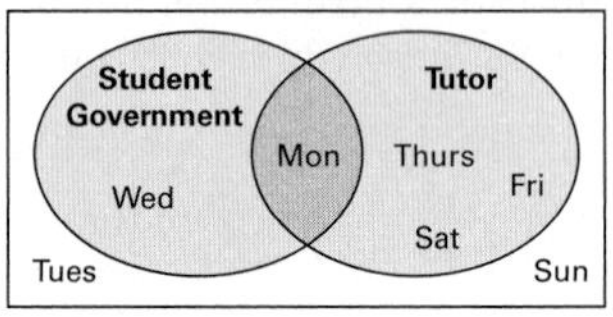

Student Government
Tutor
Mon
Wed
Thurs
Fri
Sat
Tues
Sun

c. $\frac{5}{7}$

13.4 Problem Solving Workshop (pp. 868–869) **1.** $\frac{4}{15}$ **3.** $\frac{1}{16}$. *Sample answer:* The third friend can arrive any time in a 20 minute span, and I will be away from the house for 15 of those minutes. The probability is $\frac{1}{4}$ that I will be home when the third friend arrives. Since the three friends arrive independently of each other, you can multiply the probability that you are home when the other two friends arrive by $\frac{1}{4}$ to calculate the probability that you are home when all three friends arrive; $\frac{1}{4} \cdot \frac{1}{4} = \frac{1}{16}$. **5.** *Sample answer:* The times at which the raffles are announced are independent, so the two probabilities should be calculated separately and then multiplied; $\frac{10}{30} \cdot \frac{25}{30} = \frac{1}{3} \cdot \frac{5}{6} = \frac{5}{18}$.

13.5 Skill Practice (p. 873) **1.** systematic **3.** people who have eaten at the restaurant, self-selected **5.** passengers of the airline, random **7.** Not likely. *Sample answer:* The sample should represent the neighborhood. **9.** Not potentially biased. *Sample answer:* This question simply presents the two choices.

SA44

11. *Sample answer:* The new question presumes that the driving age should be changed, and does not present the option that it should remain the same; "What do you think about the current driving age?"

13.5 Problem Solving (p. 874) **13.** *Sample answer:* This question is phrased to prompt people into agreeing that the athletic field is more important than the science lab; "Which do you think the school needs more: a new athletic field or a new science lab?" **15.** No. *Sample answer:* The sample may be biased. It does not include fans who only listen to or watch games on radio or television. The sample is also self-selected. Fans in attendance have to choose to turn in their surveys in order to be counted. **17.** *Sample answer:* Obtain a list of everyone at the school and select names randomly using a random number generator. "How many hours per day do you study?"; This question is unbiased because it does not prompt respondents to give any particular answer.

13.6 Skill Practice (p. 877) **1.** mode **3.** 3, 3, 1 **5.** 22, 21, no mode **7.** 5.223, 5.48, no mode **11.** 65, 21.2 **13.** 70, 12.56 **15.** 0.85, 0.23 **17.** *Sample answer:* The range only considers the two extreme values, while the mean absolute deviation is affected by all of the values.

13.6 Problem Solving (pp. 877–878) **19. a.** 19 **b.** 19.6 lb, 23.5 lb, 24 lb **c.** Median. *Sample answer:* The mode is the greatest data value and the mean is less than 8 of the 10 data values. **21. a.** The range for Team 2 is 56 and the range for Team 1 is 52, so the scores for Team 2 cover a slightly wider range. **b.** The mean absolute deviation for Team 1 is 15.75 and the mean absolute deviation for Team 2 is 22.5, so the scores for Team 2 are more dispersed.

Extension (pp. 879–880) **1.** 6.3, 2.5 **3.** 76,656.6; 276.9 **5.** 29.1 **7. a.** 5.6 **b.** *Sample answer:* Since 136 is much greater than the mean, the standard deviation will increase. **c.** 17.7. *Sample answer:* The standard deviation more than tripled, so the prediction was correct.

13.7 Skill Practice (pp. 883–884) **1.** frequency

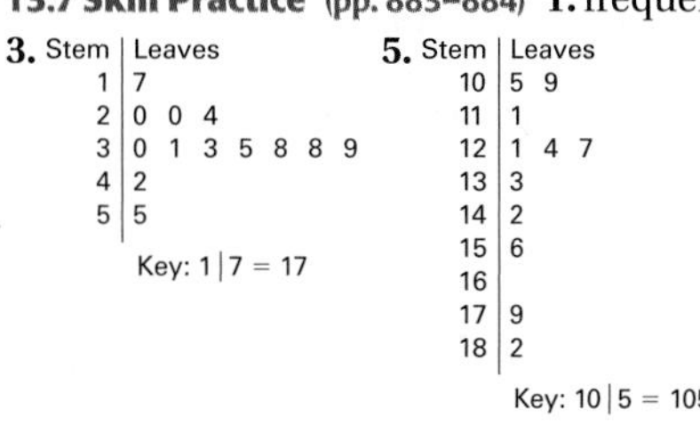

3.

Stem	Leaves
1	7
2	0 0 4
3	0 1 3 5 8 8 9
4	2
5	5

Key: 1 | 7 = 17

5.

Stem	Leaves
10	5 9
11	1
12	1 4 7
13	3
14	2
15	6
16	
17	9
18	2

Key: 10 | 5 = 105

7. There is no key given for the stem-and-leaf plot; Key: 1 | 8 = 18.

11. **13.**

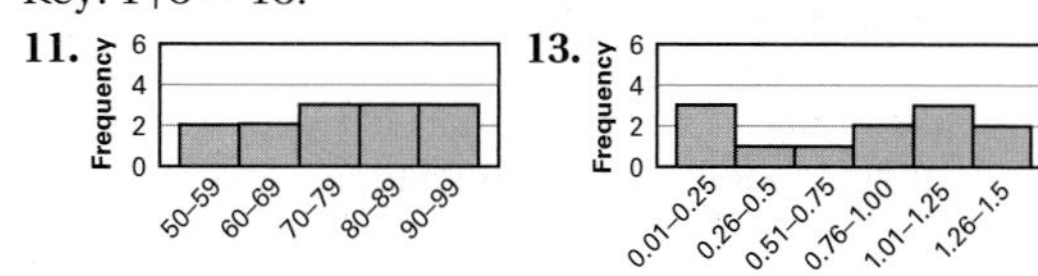

15. *Sample answer:* The given data range from 10 to 21, so a stem-and-leaf plot would place all the data into only two intervals, making it difficult to see the distribution of the data. The histogram could use more than two intervals.

13.7 Problem Solving (pp. 884–885)

17.

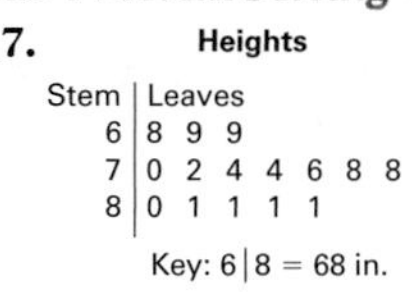

Heights

Stem	Leaves
6	8 9 9
7	0 2 4 4 6 8 8
8	0 1 1 1 1

Key: 6 | 8 = 68 in.

19. a.

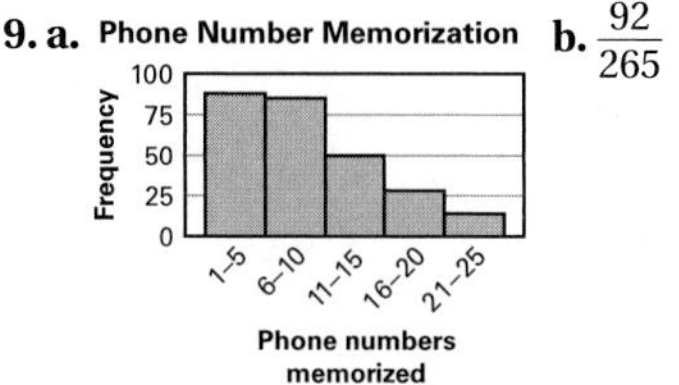

b. $\frac{92}{265}$

21. a.

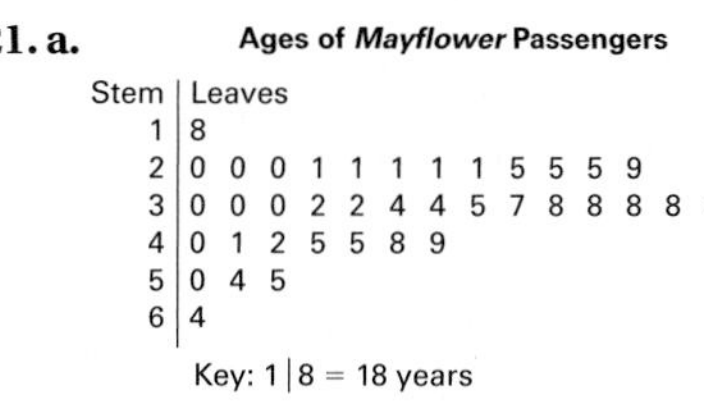

Ages of *Mayflower* Passengers

Stem	Leaves
1	8
2	0 0 0 1 1 1 1 1 5 5 5 9
3	0 0 0 2 2 4 4 5 7 8 8 8 8
4	0 1 2 5 5 8 9
5	0 4 5
6	4

Key: 1 | 8 = 18 years

b. median: 34 yr, range: 46 yr **c.** $\frac{1}{3}$. *Sample answer:* Since 13 of the 39 passengers or $\frac{1}{3}$ of them were ages 18–29, we can predict that another passenger about whom we have no information has a $\frac{1}{3}$ probability of being in that age group.

13.7 Graphing Calculator Activity (p. 886) **1.** *Sample answer:* The majority of the data are at the lower end of the scale, between 3000 and 12,000, with the highest frequency between 3000 and 6000.

13.8 Skill Practice (pp. 889–890) **1.** the difference of the upper quartile and the lower quartile

3.

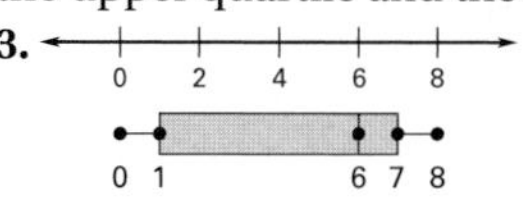

SELECTED ANSWERS

5. 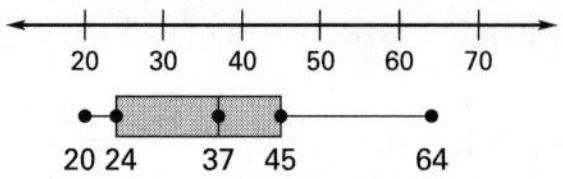

7. *Sample answer:* The upper quartile is incorrect. The upper quartile should be the median of 8 and 10, or 9.

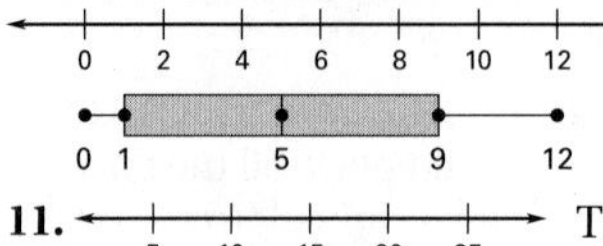

11. 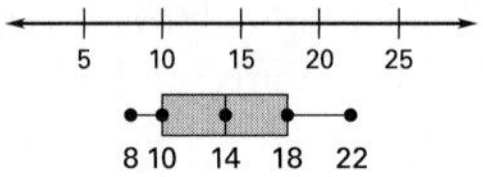

There are no outliers.

13. 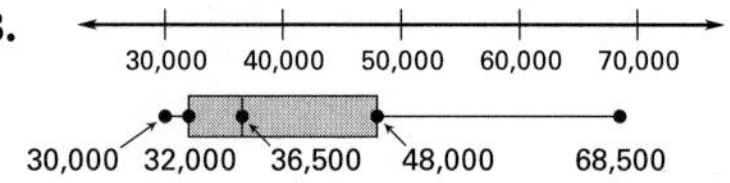

There are no outliers.

13.8 Problem Solving (pp. 890–892)

15. 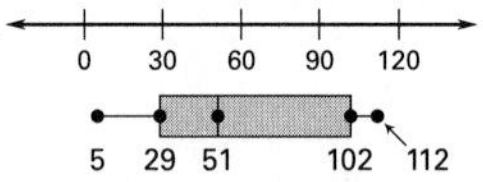

17. a. 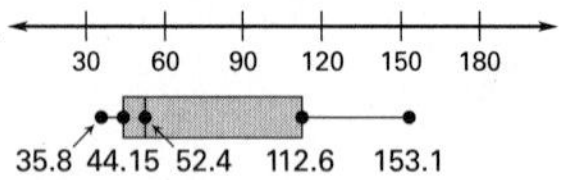

b. none

19. a. *Sample answer:* The craters on Ganymede are generally smaller than the craters on Callisto. The lower extreme, lower quartile, median, upper quartile, and upper extreme values are all lower for Ganymede than for Callisto. **b.** *Sample answer:* Chesapeake Bay is larger than between 50% and 75% of the craters on both Callisto and Ganymede. **c.** *Sample answer:* Vredefort is larger than at least 75% of the craters on both Callisto and Ganymede.

Chapter Review (pp. 896–900) **1.** compound event **3.** *Sample answer:* Theoretical probability is based on knowing the likelihood of all possible outcomes of an event. Experimental probability is based on the results of an experiment. **5.** $\frac{2}{9}$ **7.** 30 **9.** 1,037,836,800 **11.** 7 **13.** 56 **15.** 126 ways **17.** $\frac{3}{8}$ **19.** $\frac{5}{8}$ **21.** $\frac{1}{120}$ **23. a.** about 5.045, 4.5, 1 **b.** Median. *Sample answer:* The mode is much lower than many of the values, and the mean is affected by the two extreme values (17 and 19) that are much greater than the rest of the data. So, the median best represents the data.

25. 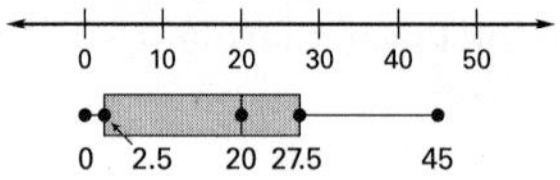

Cumulative Review (pp. 906–907) **1.** 44 **3.** ± 45 **5.** 2

7. 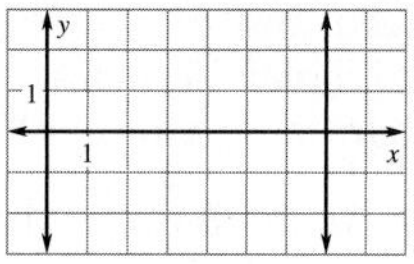

9. 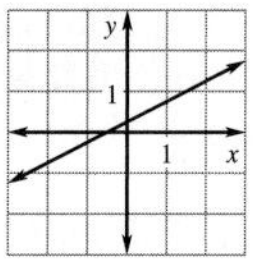

11. $y = -8x + 3$

13. $4 \le x < 24$ 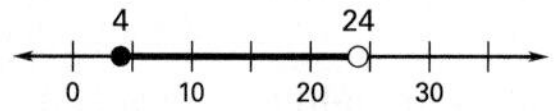

15. $\left(4, \frac{1}{4}\right)$ **17.** no solution **19.** $\frac{-81x^{12}}{4}$ **21.** $(a - 18)(a + 3)$ **23.** $(2f + g)^2$ **25.** $-7, 3$ **27.** $\frac{1}{2}, 4$ **29.** $2\sqrt{37}$ **31.** 15 **33.** $\frac{x + 4}{x + 3}$ **35.** -3 **37.** $\frac{9 - 3x}{x^2 - 3x}$ **39.** 336 **41.** 210 **43.** $\frac{1}{2}$ **45.** $\frac{3}{20}$ **47.** *Sample answer:* 120 min after the first runner starts **49.** 42.4 ft **51. a.** \$45

b.

Stem	Leaves
17	6
18	
19	1 5 7 7
20	4 4 4 4 4 6 6 6 6
21	7 7
22	1

Key: 17 | 6 = \$176

c. 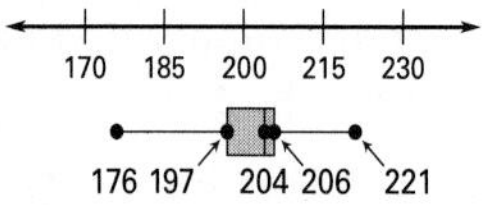

d. Yes. *Sample answer:* The interquartile range is 9, so any data value more than 13.5 less than the lower quartile of 197 or greater than the upper quartile of 206 can be considered outliers. 176 and 221 are both outliers.

Skills Review Handbook

Comparing and Ordering Decimals (p. 909) **1.** > **3.** > **5.** > **7.** < **9.** > **11.** 7.01, 7.03, 7.13, 7.3 **13.** 0.15, 0.3, 0.47, 0.9 **15.** 10.9, 11, 11.9, 12.6 **17.** 0.3, 1.33, 3.1, 3.3

Factors and Multiples (pp. 910–911) **1.** $2^2 \cdot 7$ **3.** prime **5.** 3^4 **7.** $2^2 \cdot 3 \cdot 5$ **9.** $2^2 \cdot 3^2 \cdot 5$ **11.** $3 \cdot 17$ **13.** 4 **15.** 6 **17.** 9 **19.** 4 **21.** 8 **23.** 4 **25.** 18 **27.** 45 **29.** 130 **31.** 90 **33.** 14 **35.** 49

Finding Equivalent Fractions and Simplifying Fractions (p. 912) **1–5.** Sample answers are given. **1.** $\frac{3}{4}$ and $\frac{18}{24}$ **3.** $\frac{2}{4}$ and $\frac{3}{6}$ **5.** $\frac{5}{7}$ and $\frac{20}{28}$ **7.** $\frac{1}{4}$ **9.** $\frac{1}{8}$ **11.** $\frac{1}{4}$ **13.** $\frac{7}{20}$ **15.** $\frac{4}{5}$ **17.** $\frac{3}{7}$ **19.** $\frac{4}{13}$

Mixed Numbers and Improper Fractions (p. 913) **1.** $\frac{5}{3}$ **3.** $\frac{103}{10}$ **5.** $\frac{9}{2}$ **7.** $\frac{23}{12}$ **9.** $\frac{53}{8}$ **11.** $\frac{65}{8}$ **13.** $\frac{65}{9}$ **15.** $\frac{38}{3}$ **17.** $2\frac{2}{5}$ **19.** $6\frac{1}{4}$ **21.** $1\frac{3}{4}$ **23.** $2\frac{9}{10}$ **25.** $10\frac{4}{5}$ **27.** $4\frac{2}{5}$ **29.** $4\frac{7}{9}$

SELECTED ANSWERS

Adding and Subtracting Fractions (p. 914) **1.** $\frac{1}{4}$ **3.** $\frac{1}{6}$ **5.** 1 **7.** $\frac{1}{2}$ **9.** $1\frac{1}{5}$ **11.** $\frac{3}{16}$ **13.** $\frac{25}{48}$ **15.** $1\frac{17}{24}$ **17.** $\frac{11}{20}$ **19.** $\frac{4}{5}$ **21.** $6\frac{3}{4}$ **23.** 5 **25.** $1\frac{1}{16}$

Multiplying and Dividing Fractions (p. 915) **1.** $\frac{1}{2}$ **3.** $\frac{1}{2}$ **5.** $1\frac{1}{8}$ **7.** $\frac{3}{64}$ **9.** $\frac{1}{8}$ **11.** $1\frac{1}{2}$ **13.** $\frac{1}{2}$ **15.** $\frac{2}{7}$ **17.** $\frac{1}{50}$ **19.** $\frac{3}{5}$ **21.** $3\frac{3}{32}$ **23.** $4\frac{3}{8}$ **25.** $1\frac{1}{3}$

Fractions, Decimals, and Percents (pp. 916–917) **1.** 0.7, $\frac{7}{10}$ **3.** 0.03, $\frac{3}{100}$ **5.** 0.35, $\frac{7}{20}$ **7.** 1.1, $1\frac{1}{10}$ **9.** 0.003, $\frac{3}{1000}$ **11.** $\frac{7}{25}$, 28% **13.** $\frac{1}{20}$, 5% **15.** $\frac{13}{25}$, 52% **17.** $\frac{1}{40}$, 2.5% **19.** $\frac{3}{2}$, 150% **21.** 0.188, 18.8% **23.** 0.61, 61% **25.** 0.19, 19% **27.** 0.36, 36% **29.** 0.571, 57.1%

Mean, Median, and Mode (p. 918) **1.** 92.4; 93; 94 **3.** 41 yr; 41 yr; 52 yr **5.** \$7; \$7; \$6.75 **7.** 2.25; 2; 2

The Coordinate Plane (p. 919) **1.** (5, 4) **3.** (10, 8) **5.** (9, 2) **7.** (2, 6) **9.** (10, 0) **11.** (0, 5)

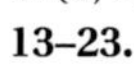
13–23.

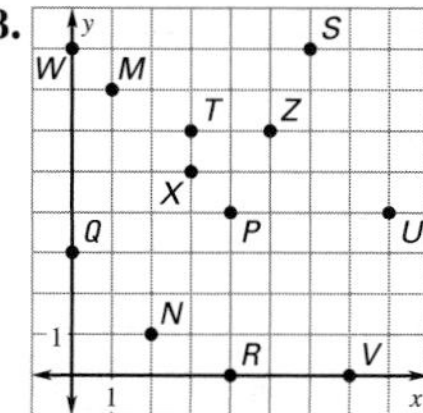

Transformations (pp. 920–921)

1.

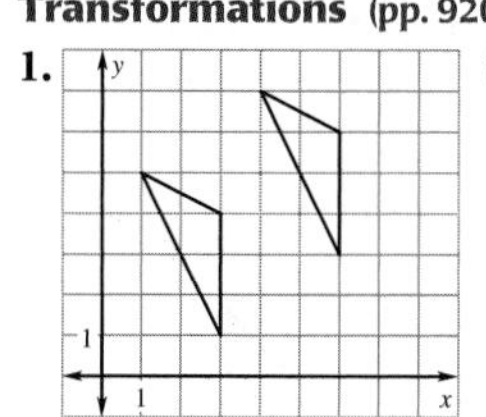

(4, 7), (6, 6), (6, 3)

3.

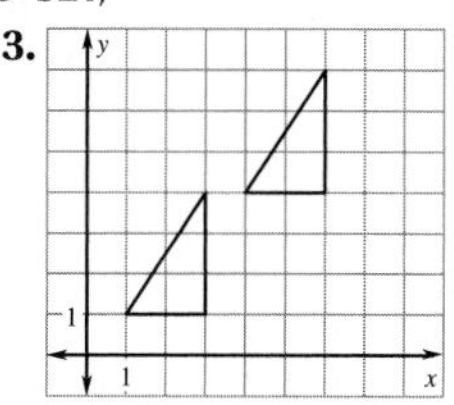

(1, 1), (3, 1), (3, 4)

5.

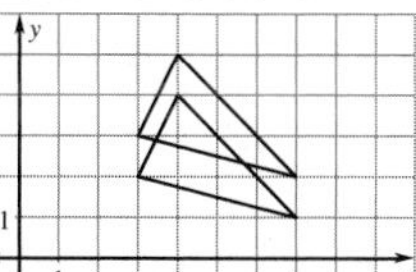

(4, 4), (7, 1), (3, 2)

7. (2, 0), (5, 0), (5, 2), (2, 2)

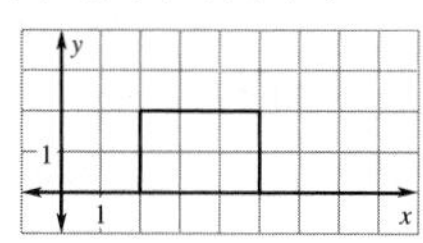

9.

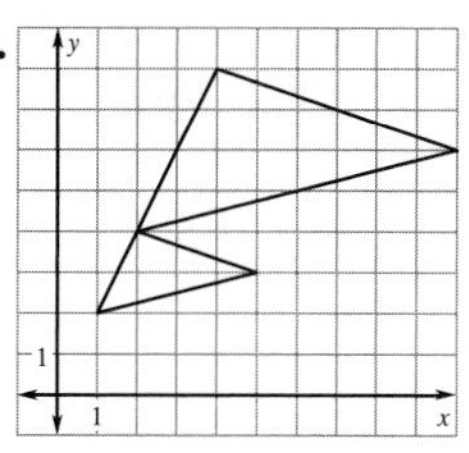

(2, 4), (4, 8), (10, 6)

11.

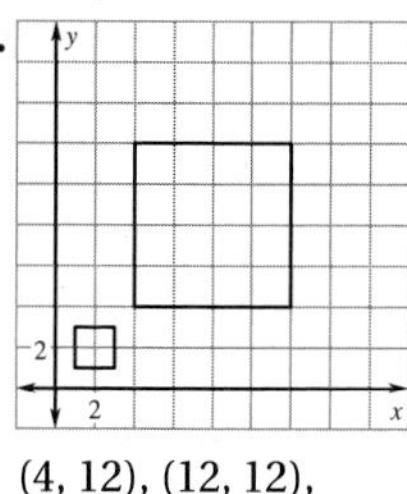

(4, 12), (12, 12), (12, 4), (4, 4)

13.

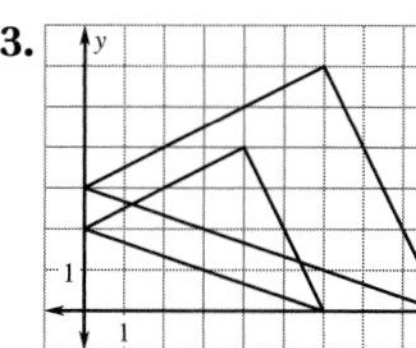

(0, 3), (6, 6), (9, 0)

Perimeter and Area (pp. 922–923) **1.** 36 ft **3.** 20 ft **5.** 66 yd^2 **7.** 110 $in.^2$ **9.** 21 ft^2 **11.** 70 yd^2

Circumference and Area of a Circle (p. 924) **1.** 12π in. or 37.7 in., 36π $in.^2$ or 113.0 $in.^2$ **3.** 16π in. or 50.2 in., 64π $in.^2$ or 201.0 $in.^2$ **5.** 4π ft or 12.6 ft, 4π ft^2 or 12.6 ft^2 **7.** 18π m or 56.5 m, 81π m^2 or 254.3 m^2

Surface Area and Volume (pp. 925–926) **1.** 320 cm^2, 336 cm^3 **3.** 900π m^2 or 2826 m^2, 4500π m^3 or 14,130 m^3 **5.** 200π $in.^2$ or 628 $in.^2$, 320π $in.^3$ or 1004.8 $in.^3$ **7.** 96 $in.^2$, 48 $in.^3$ **9.** 1888π $in.^2$ or 5928.3 $in.^2$, $11{,}008\pi$ $in.^3$ or 34,565.1 $in.^3$ **11.** 96π m^2 or 301.4 m^2, 96π m^3 or 301.4 m^3

Converting Units of Measurement (p. 927) **1.** 5 **3.** 4 **5.** 6 **7.** 14 **9.** 300 **11.** 70,000 **13.** 3000 **15.** $14\frac{2}{3}$ yd or 44 ft

Converting Between Systems (p. 928) **1.** 845 **3.** 6 **5.** 22 **7.** 4 **9.** 32 **11.** 4 **13.** 2 **15.** 5

Venn Diagrams and Logical Reasoning (p. 929)

1.

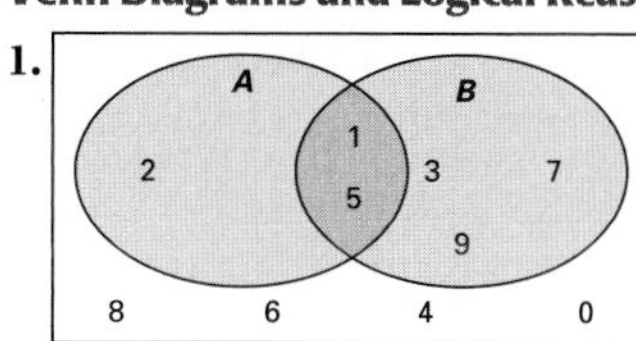

3. a. False; there are whole numbers less than 10 that are odd but are not factors of 10, such as 3, 7, and 9. **b.** False; there is a whole number less than 10 that is a factor of 10 but is not odd, 2.

SELECTED ANSWERS

Counting Methods (pp. 930–931) **1.** 6 ways **3.** 17,576 3-letter monograms **5.** 1,679,616 computer passwords **7.** 72 dinners

Bar Graphs (p. 932) **1.** bronze **3.** 103 medals **5.** 25 medals **7.** Switzerland **9.** United States **11.** 96 medals

Line Graphs (p. 933) **1.** about 24 lb **3.** between ages 4 and 5 **5.** about 15 lb **7.** about 2 years old **9.** between ages 3 and 4 **11.** between ages 1 and 2 **13.** about 4 yr

Circle Graphs (p. 934) **1.** 9% **3.** 24.5% **5.** 37% **7.** woodwinds **9.** brass

Misleading Data Displays (p. 935) **1.** The angle at which the graph is displayed emphasizes the region at the front. Although regions A and D represent the same percent of the data, region D appears larger. **3.** The break in the vertical axis exaggerates the differences in the data.

Problem Solving Strategies (pp. 936–937) **1.** Pam owes \$4 that she can pay to Bonnie who is owed a total of \$5. Holly should pay both Barb and Bonnie \$1. **3.** 25 years old **5.** 10 ways **7.** 1:45 P.M. **9.** 3 soccer games per week **11.** Quinn

Extra Practice

Chapter 1 (p. 938) **1.** 16 **3.** 4.4 **5.** 2.4 **7.** $\frac{8}{27}$ **9.** 26 **11.** 28 **13.** 10 **15.** 111 **17.** $\frac{3}{4}m$ **19.** $y - 3$ **21.** $45 - m$ **23.** $12 \cdot (r - 4) = 72$ **25.** 38 **27.** 16 **29.** *Sample answer:* You know the temperature in Quito in degrees Celsius and the temperature in Miami in degrees Fahrenheit. You need to find out which one is greater. **31.** domain: 3, 4, 5, 6; range: 9, 11, 13, 15

33. **35.**

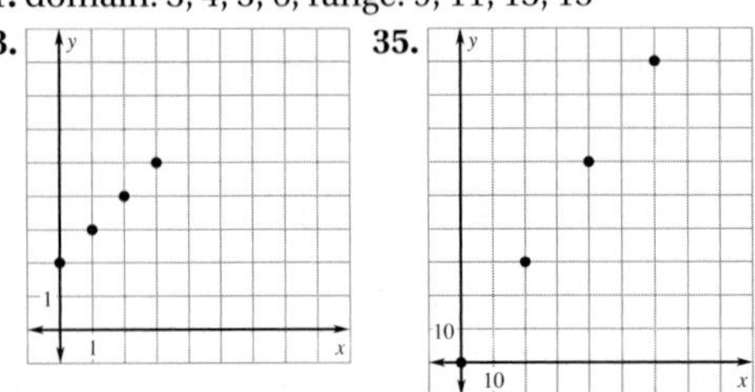

Chapter 2 (p. 939)

1. **3.**

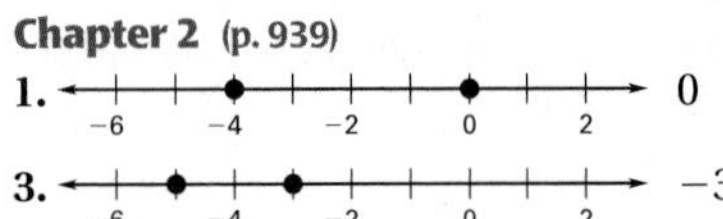

5. Each number is a rational number; $-\frac{1}{5}, -\frac{1}{8}, -\frac{1}{10}$, 0.25. **7.** −4: integer, rational number; 3: whole number, integer, rational number; −5: integer, rational number; 0: whole number, integer, rational number; −5, −4, 0, 3. **9.** −61 **11.** 0 **13.** −19.7 **15.** $-4\frac{13}{30}$ **17.** 66 **19.** $\frac{3}{10}$ **21.** $\frac{5}{12}$ **23.** −7.2 **25.** 5.5 **27.** −12.5 **29.** −40 **31.** 2.2 **33.** Associative property of multiplication **35.** Property of zero **37.** Property of −1 **39.** $30 - 5y$ **41.** $-3k + 42$ **43.** $14s + 7$ **45.** $5w + 25$ **47.** 23 **49.** 64 **51.** $-\frac{5}{6}$ **53.** $\frac{25}{36}$ **55.** ±20 **57.** ±12 **59.** −9 **61.** 16

Chapter 3 (p. 940) **1.** 16 **3.** −12 **5.** 9 **7.** 52 **9.** 6 **11.** 8 **13.** −35 **15.** 3 **17.** −6 **19.** −1 **21.** 2 **23.** 3 **25.** $-\frac{1}{2}$ **27.** 56 **29.** 16 **31.** $\frac{5}{7} = \frac{15}{x}$; 21 **33.** $\frac{g}{9} = \frac{16}{12}$; 12 **35.** 14 **37.** 8 **39.** 4 **41.** −2 **43.** 12.5% **45.** 35 **47.** 45 **49.** 86 **51.** $x = \frac{c + b}{a}$; 5 **53.** $y = -5x + 10$ **55.** $y = -4x + 2$

Chapter 4 (p. 941)

1. **3.**

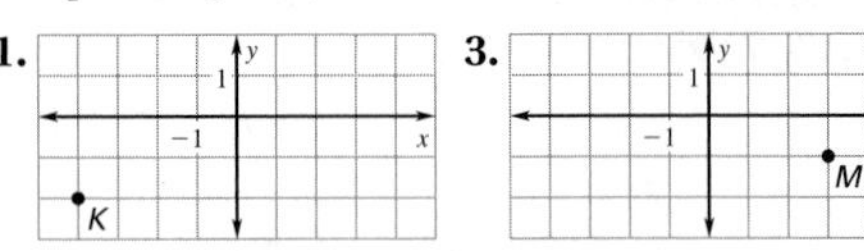

Quadrant III Quadrant IV

5. **7.**

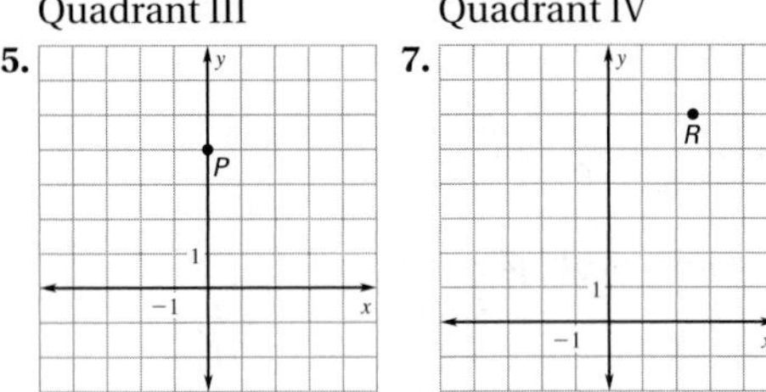

on the y-axis Quadrant I

9. **11.**

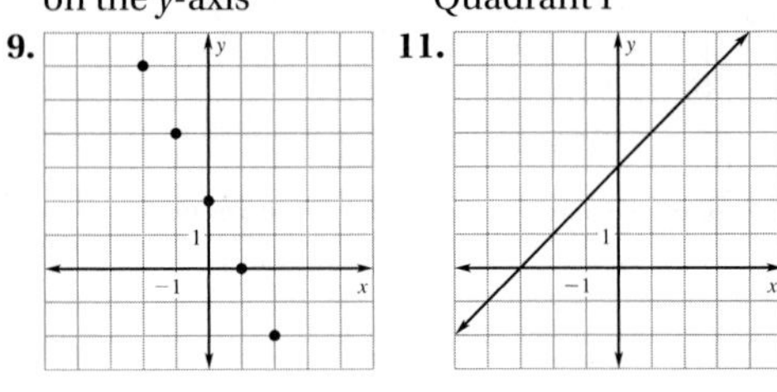

range: −2, 0, 2, 4, 6

17.

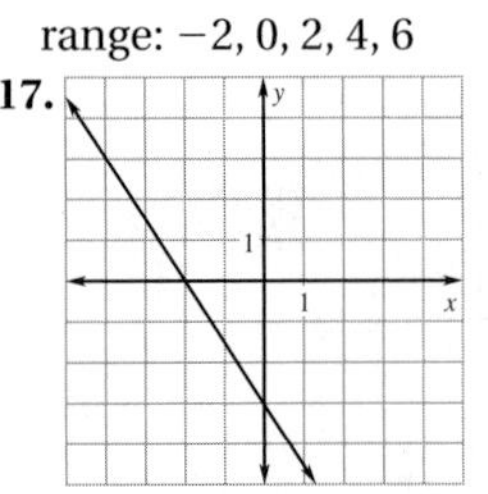

19. x-intercept: 6, y-intercept: −12 **21.** x-intercept: −1, y-intercept: $\frac{8}{3}$

23.

25. 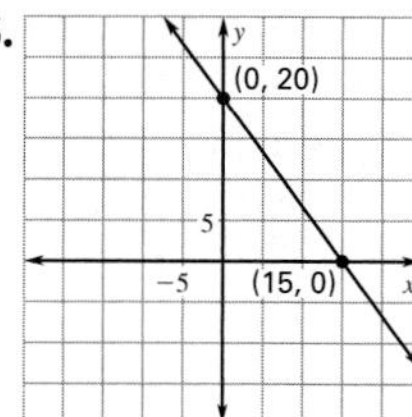

27. 3 **29.** $-\frac{7}{3}$ **31.** no slope **33.** slope: 7, y-intercept: 8 **35.** slope: −4, y-intercept: 3 **37.** $y = -2x + 8$; slope: −2, y-intercept: 8 **39.** $y = -\frac{5}{2}x + 5$; slope: $-\frac{5}{2}$, y-intercept: 5

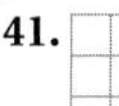

41. 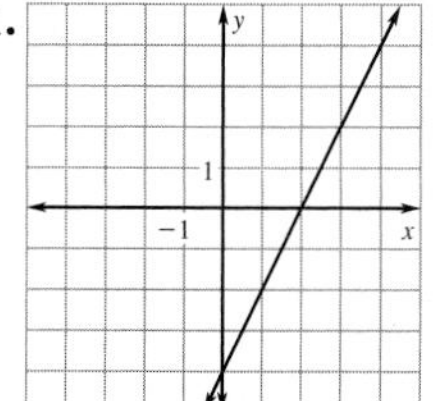

43. 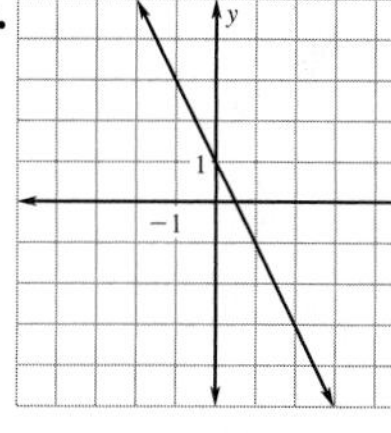

45. 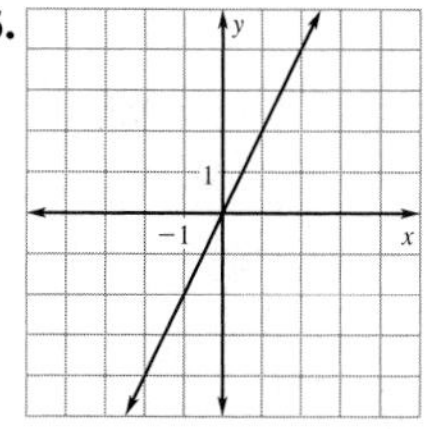

47. 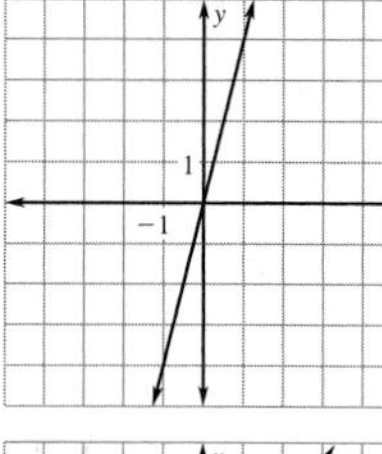

49.

51. 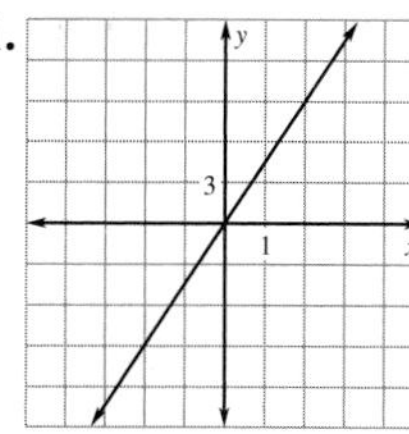

53. 2 **55.** −4

57. 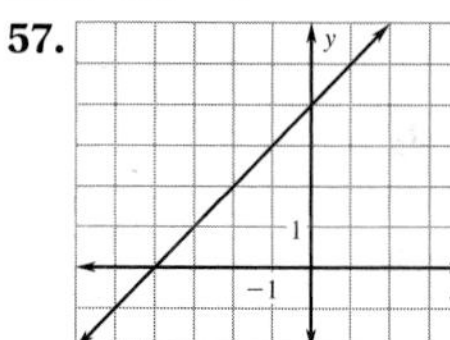

The graph is a vertical translation 4 units up of $f(x) = x$.

59. 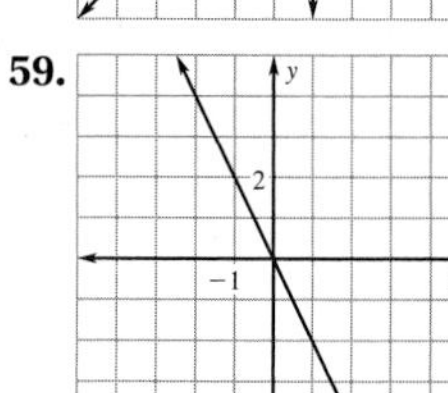

The graph is a vertical stretch by a factor of 2 with a reflection in the x-axis of $f(x) = x$.

Chapter 5 (p. 942) **1.** $y = 3x + 6$ **3.** $y = 5x - 1$ **5.** $y = \frac{1}{2}x - 5$ **7.** $y = 2x + 2$ **9.** $y = \frac{2}{3}x + 7$ **11.** $y = -5x + 3$

13. 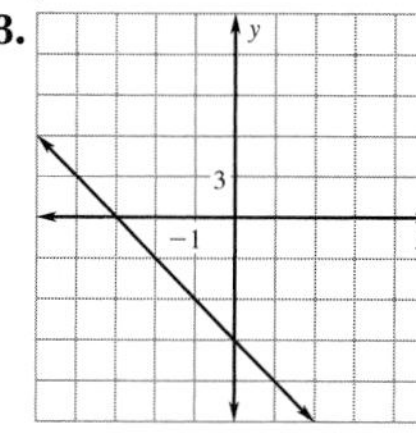

15. 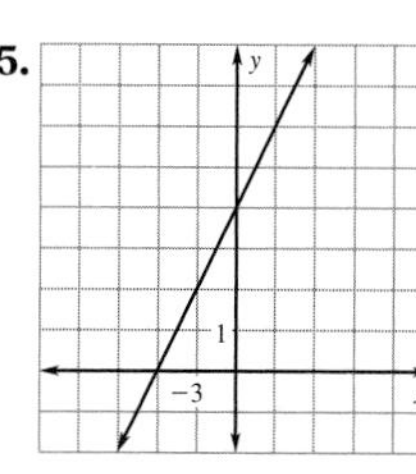

17. *Sample answer:* $y - 9 = \frac{1}{2}(x - 3)$ **19.** $4x + y = 15$ **21.** $2x + y = 0$ **23.** $y = -5x - 22$ **25.** $y = -\frac{1}{3}x - 6$ **27.** $y = \frac{3}{2}x - \frac{33}{2}$

29. *Sample answer:* $y = -\frac{5}{6}x + 70$

31. 

$y = 1.1x + 6.7$; 14.4

Chapter 6 (p. 943)

1. $y > 5$

3. $x \le 7$

5. $n \le 2\frac{1}{2}$

7. $z < -4\frac{7}{8}$

9. $t \ge 1.5$

11. $y < -5.5$

13. $p \le 9$

15. $x \ge 6$

17. $m \le \frac{3}{2}$

19. $z \le 8$

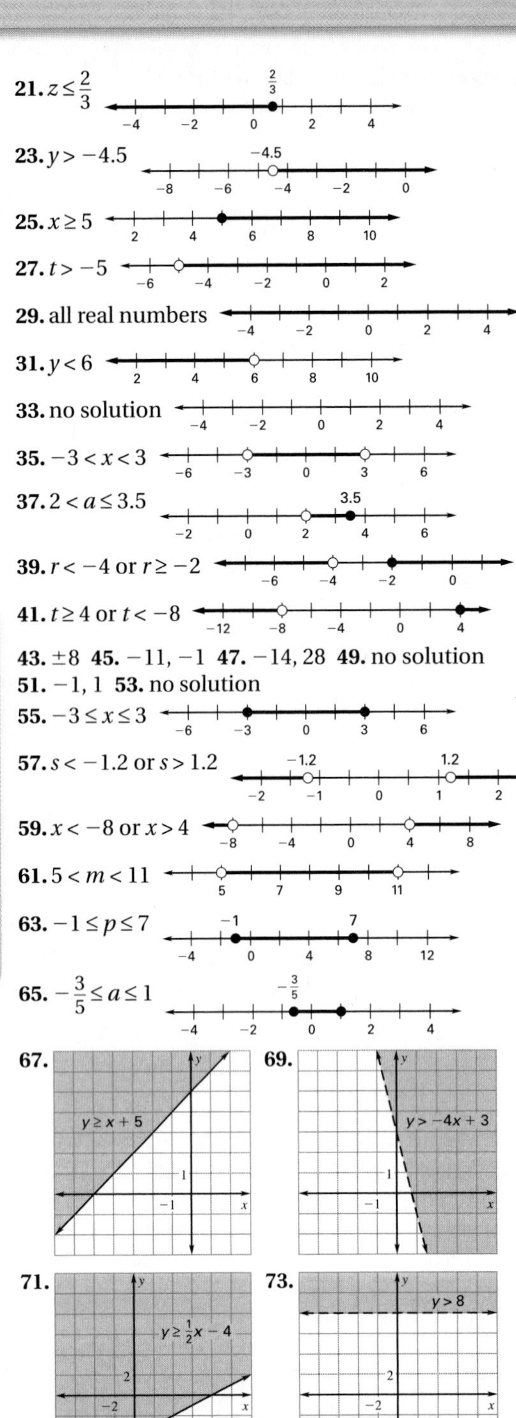

21. $z \leq \frac{2}{3}$

23. $y > -4.5$

25. $x \geq 5$

27. $t > -5$

29. all real numbers

31. $y < 6$

33. no solution

35. $-3 < x < 3$

37. $2 < a \leq 3.5$

39. $r < -4$ or $r \geq -2$

41. $t \geq 4$ or $t < -8$

43. ± 8 **45.** $-11, -1$ **47.** $-14, 28$ **49.** no solution **51.** $-1, 1$ **53.** no solution

55. $-3 \leq x \leq 3$

57. $s < -1.2$ or $s > 1.2$

59. $x < -8$ or $x > 4$

61. $5 < m < 11$

63. $-1 \leq p \leq 7$

65. $-\frac{3}{5} \leq a \leq 1$

67. $y \geq x + 5$ **69.** $y > -4x + 3$

71. $y \geq \frac{1}{2}x - 4$ **73.** $y > 8$

75.

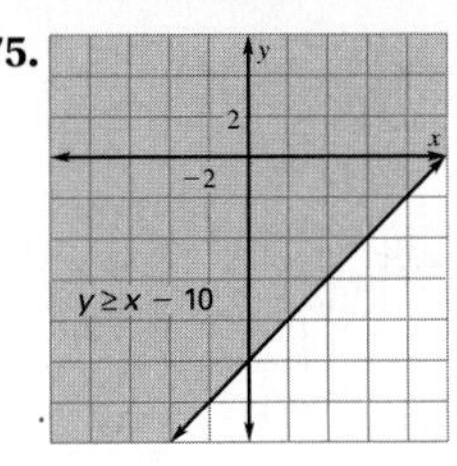

77.

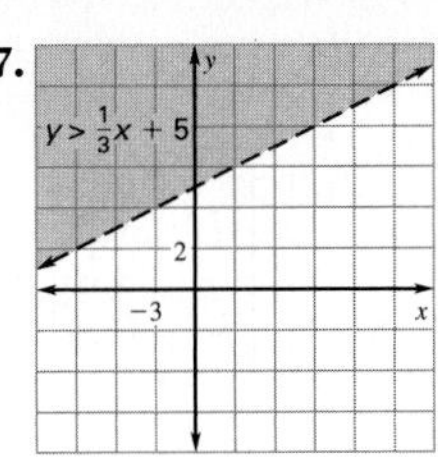

Chapter 7 (p. 944) **1.** $(3, 2)$ **3.** $(1, -3)$ **5.** $(-3, -2)$ **7.** $(-3, 0)$ **9.** $(9, 7)$ **11.** $(3, -7)$ **13.** $(-4, 3)$ **15.** $(-9, -2)$ **17.** $(-3, -5)$ **19.** $(-6, 3)$ **21.** $(11, 9)$ **23.** $\left(10, -\frac{3}{2}\right)$

25.

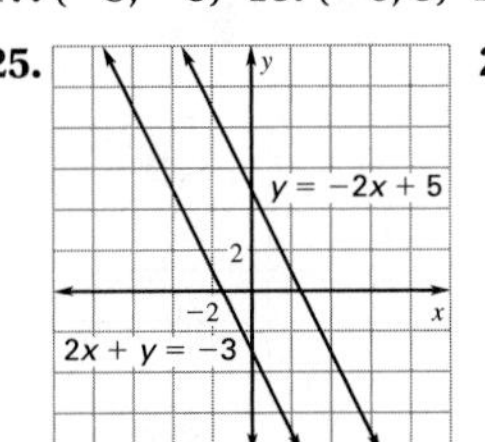

no solution

27.

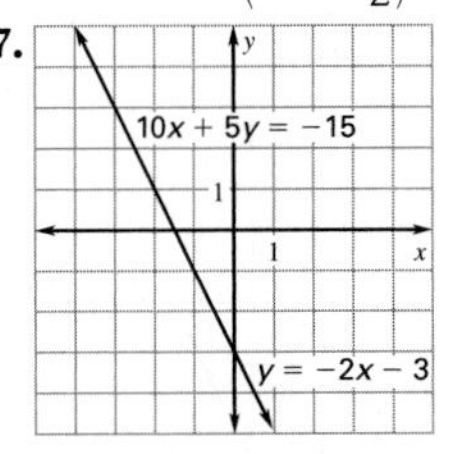

infinitely many solutions

29. $(20, 48)$ **31.** no solution **33.** $(-30, 0)$

35.

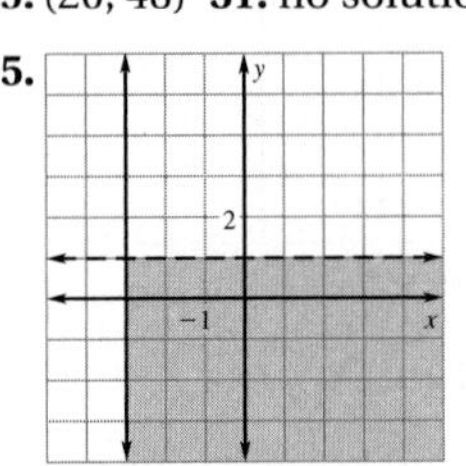

37.

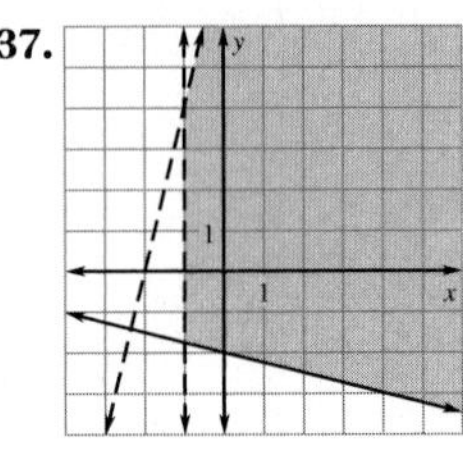

39.

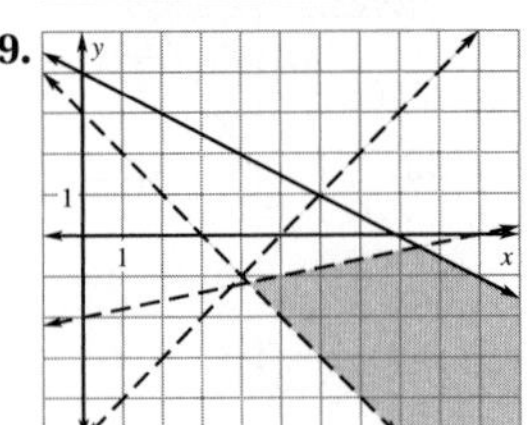

Chapter 8 (p. 945) **1.** 5^7 **3.** $(-2)^9$ **5.** $(-4)^6$ **7.** m^7 **9.** y^{15} **11.** $54d^8$ **13.** 8^5 **15.** $-\frac{2^5}{3^5}$ **17.** 7^5 **19.** $\frac{p^7}{q^7}$ **21.** $\frac{64y^9}{27}$ **23.** $\frac{25x^2y^6}{4}$ **25.** $\frac{1}{81}$ **27.** 1 **29.** 8 **31.** 32 **33.** $\frac{1}{y^{10}}$ **35.** $\frac{10c^5}{b^3}$ **37.** $\frac{y^5}{x^4}$ **39.** $-96z^5$ **41.** 8.7×10^{-1} **43.** 3.59×10^{-4} **45.** 530,000 **47.** 0.000008 **49.** 3.75×10^{-5} **51.** 4×10^2

53.

55. 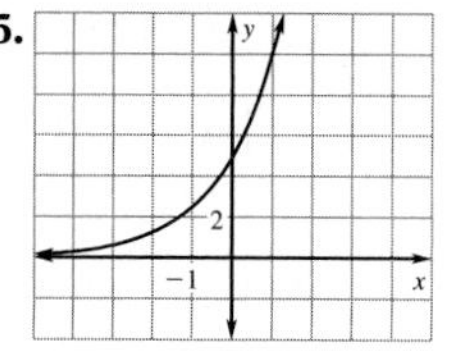

57. 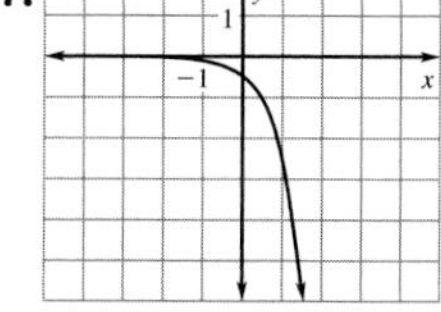

59. 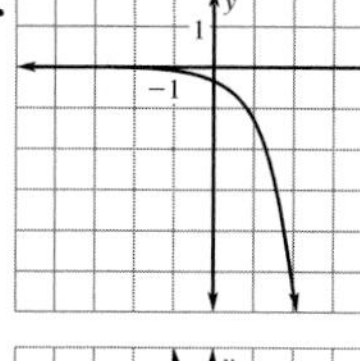

61.

63. 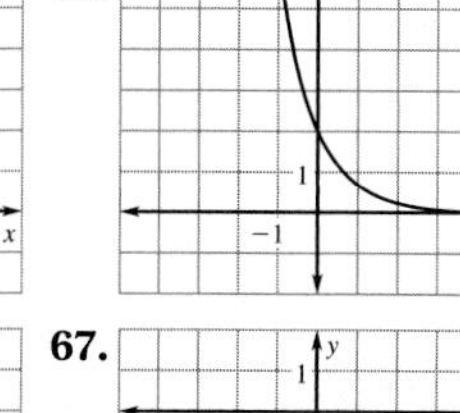

65.

67. 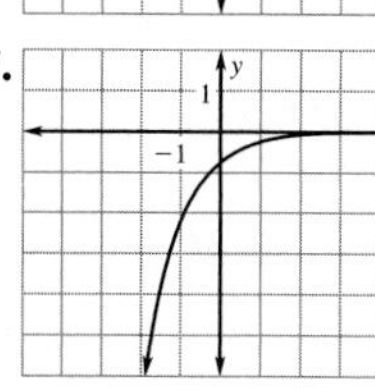

Chapter 9 (p. 946) **1.** $7x^2 - 2$ **3.** $7m^2 - 5m - 3$ **5.** $6b^3 - 3b^2 - 8b + 8$ **7.** $10x^7 - 15x^6 + 25x^5 - 5x^4$ **9.** $8x^2 + 16x + 6$ **11.** $3x^2 + 8x - 35$ **13.** $x^2 + 20x + 100$ **15.** $16x^2 - 4$ **17.** $36 - 9t^2$ **19.** $-8, 2$ **21.** $\frac{3}{5}, 2$ **23.** $-\frac{1}{4}, 0$ **25.** $(y + 3)(y + 4)$ **27.** $(x - 4)(x + 9)$ **29.** $(m - 25)(m - 4)$ **31.** 2, 5 **33.** 4, 9 **35.** 2, 5 **37.** $-(x - 3)(x - 2)$ **39.** $(2k - 1)(2k - 5)$ **41.** $-(3s + 1)(s + 2)$ **43.** $\frac{2}{3}, 4$ **45.** $-2, \frac{1}{2}$ **47.** $-1, \frac{1}{16}$ **49.** $(y + 6)(y - 6)$ **51.** $3(2y - 3)(2y + 3)$ **53.** $(2x - 3)^2$ **55.** $(g + 5)^2$ **57.** $(2w + 7)^2$ **59.** $(3z - 1)(z - 5)$ **61.** $(3y^2 + 2)(y + 5)$ **63.** $2m(7m - 3)(7m + 3)$ **65.** $(h + 3)(h - 3)(2h - 3)$

Chapter 10 (p. 947)

1. 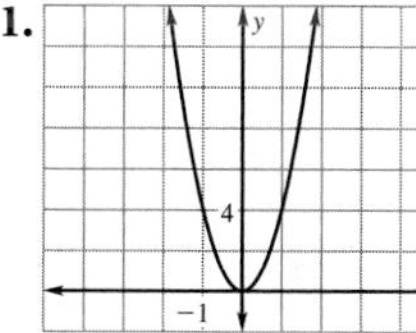

The graph is a vertical stretch by a factor of 4 of the graph of $y = x^2$.

3. 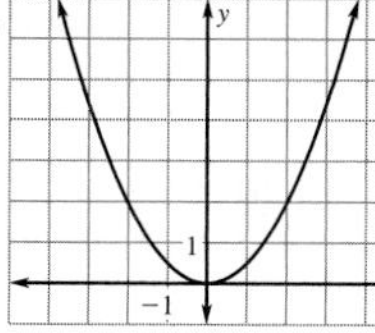

The graph is a vertical shrink by a factor of $\frac{1}{2}$ of the graph of $y = x^2$.

5. 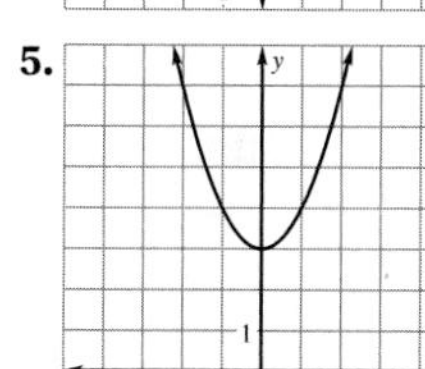

The graph is a vertical translation 3 units up of the graph of $y = x^2$.

7. 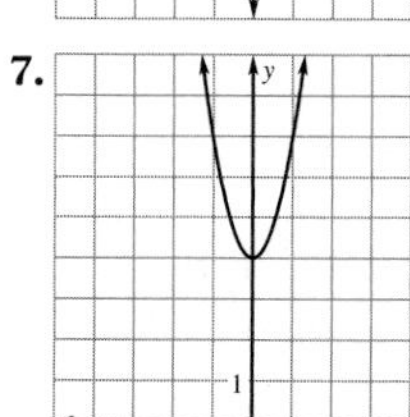

The graph is a vertical stretch by a factor of 3 with a vertical translation 4 units up of the graph of $y = x^2$.

9. 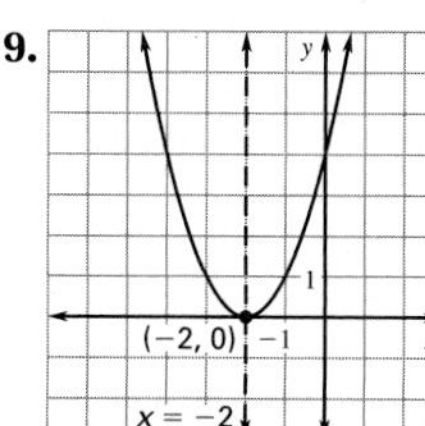

11. 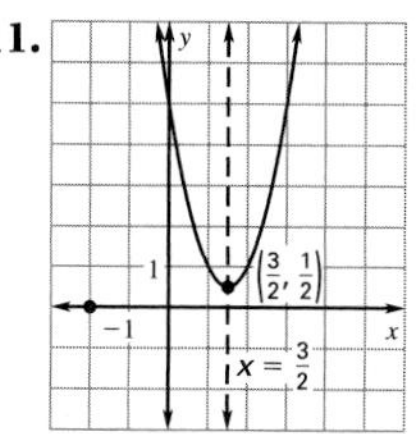

13. 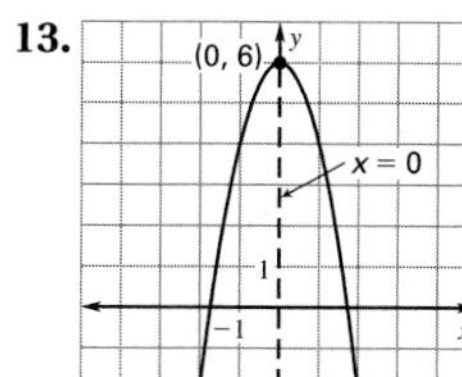

15. $-5, 2$ **17.** $-3, 6$ **19.** $-2, \frac{3}{2}$ **21.** ± 7 **23.** ± 0.75 **25.** ± 1.73 **27.** $-7, 3$ **29.** 1, 6 **31.** 0.55, 5.45 **33.** $-12, 6$ **35.** 0.5, 2 **37.** $-0.87, 1.54$ **39.** one solution **41.** no solution **43.** two solutions **45.** quadratic function; $y = 3x^2$ **47.** exponential function; $y = 0.5 \cdot 2^x$

Chapter 11 (p. 948)

1. 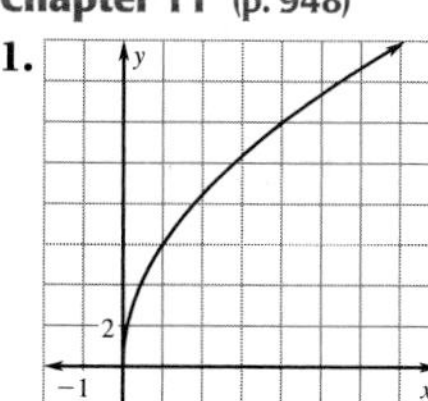

Domain: $x \geq 0$, range: $y \geq 0$; the graph is a vertical stretch by a factor of 6 of the graph of $y = \sqrt{x}$.

SELECTED ANSWERS

3. Domain: $x \geq 0$, range: $y \leq 0$; the graph is a vertical stretch by a factor of 8 with a reflection in the x-axis of the graph of $y = \sqrt{x}$.

5. 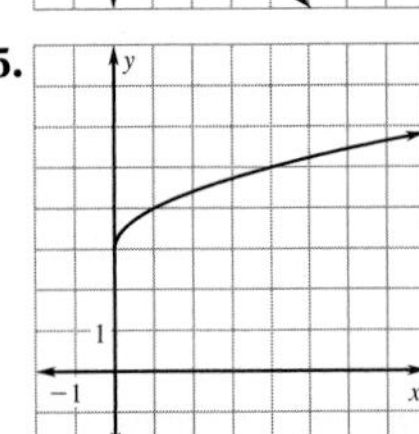

Domain: $x \geq 0$, range: $y \geq 3$; the graph is a vertical translation 3 units up of the graph of $y = \sqrt{x}$.

7. 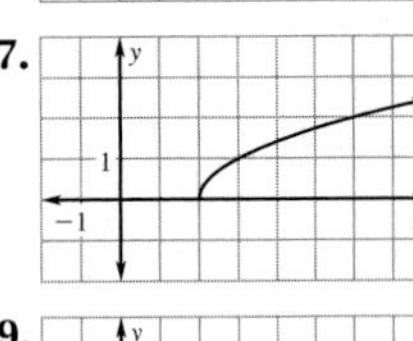

Domain: $x \geq 2$, range: $y \geq 0$; the graph is a horizontal translation 2 units right of the graph of $y = \sqrt{x}$.

9. 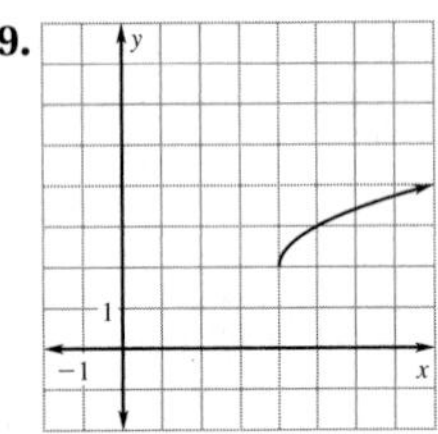

Domain: $x \geq 4$, range: $y \geq 2$; the graph is a vertical translation 2 units up and a horizontal translation 4 units right of the graph of $y = \sqrt{x}$.

11. $10\sqrt{3}$ **13.** 17 **15.** $5g\sqrt{11}$ **17.** $36x^3$ **19.** $\frac{\sqrt{6}}{6x}$ **21.** $\frac{\sqrt{14k}}{4k}$ **23.** $3\sqrt{3} + \sqrt{7}$ **25.** $9\sqrt{5}$ **27.** -108 **29.** $27 - 6\sqrt{13}$ **31.** 8 **33.** 20 **35.** -3 **37.** 1, 10 **39.** $\frac{1}{5}, \frac{3}{5}$ **41.** 1 **43.** $b = 24$ **45.** $b = \sqrt{21}$ **47.** $a = \sqrt{57}$ **49.** not a right triangle **51.** right triangle **53.** not a right triangle **55.** 13 **57.** $\sqrt{42.5}$ **59.** $\frac{\sqrt{5}}{2}$ **61.** $(-2, 1.5)$ **63.** $(1, 0)$ **65.** $\left(6\frac{1}{2}, -1\frac{1}{2}\right)$

Chapter 12 (p. 949)

1. 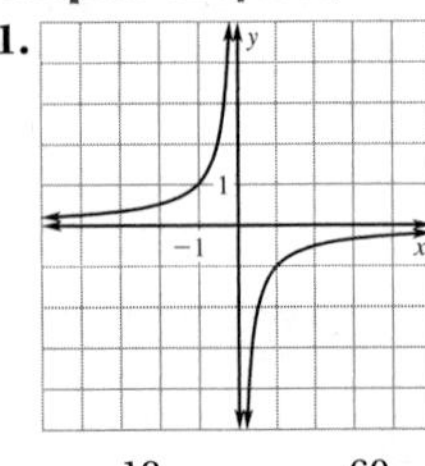

3.

5. $y = \frac{12}{x}$; 6 **7.** $y = \frac{60}{x}$; 30 **9.** $y = \frac{49}{x}$; 24.5

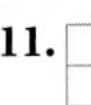

11. 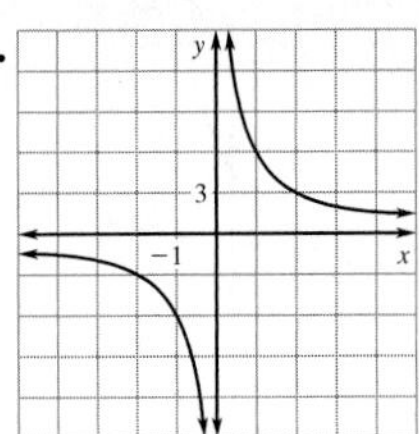

13. 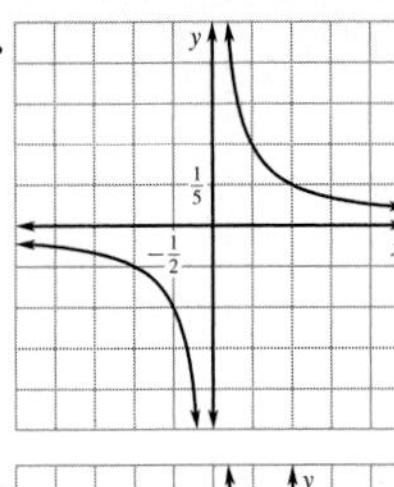

15.

17. 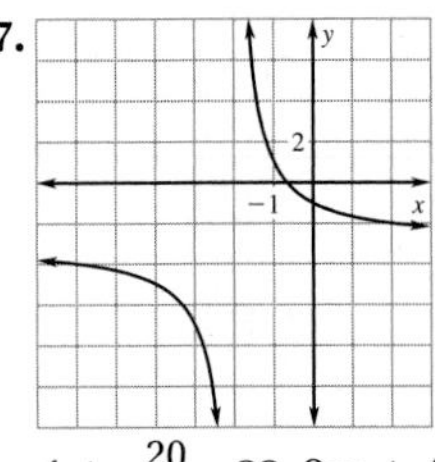

19. $-5x^3 + 2x^2 - x$ **21.** $3v - 4 + \frac{20}{v + 2}$ **23.** $3m + 4 + \frac{10}{3m - 4}$ **25.** $\frac{11x^2}{6}$, excluded value is 0. **27.** $\frac{3}{4}$, excluded value is 5. **29.** $\frac{r - 5}{r - 2}$, excluded values are 2 and -3. **31.** $\frac{2m - 4}{3m^2 + 6m}$, excluded values are -6, -2, and 0. **33.** $\frac{5x}{2x - 6}$ **35.** $3r - 6$ **37.** $\frac{16t + 15}{10t^2}$ **39.** $\frac{4c + 3}{(c + 3)(c - 3)(2c + 3)}$ **41.** $-4, 7$ **43.** $-\frac{7}{3}, 3$ **45.** $-3, \frac{11}{4}$

Chapter 13 (p. 950) **1.** 6 possible outcomes; heads, yellow; heads, red; heads, blue; tails, yellow; tails, red; tails, blue **3.** 5:3 **5.** 60 ways **7.** 336 **9.** 120 **11.** 15 **13.** 210 **15.** overlapping; $\frac{1}{2}$ **17. a.** $\frac{1}{9}$ **b.** $\frac{1}{11}$ **19.** No. *Sample answer:* The systematic sample should produce an unbiased sample of parents or guardians of high school students. **21.** mean: 89, median: 88, mode: 88, range: 39, mean absolute deviation: 8.8

23. 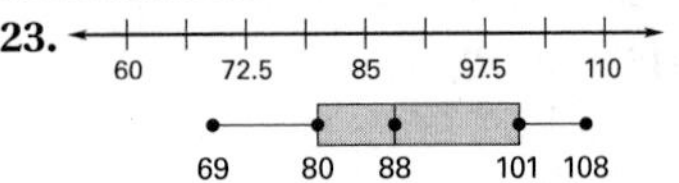

There are no outliers.

Teacher's Edition Index

Pupil's Edition in black
Teacher's Edition in blue

A

INDEX

B

INDEX

INDEX

E

F

G

INDEX

INDEX

INDEX

N

INDEX

Q

R

S

T

INDEX

Additional Answers

Chapter 1

1.5 Skill Practice (p. 31) 4. You know Paul's rate and the time that he ran for each of the two days, and you know Jen's rate and the time that she ran the second day. You need to find the total distance Paul ran. Jen's rate and time are irrelevant. **5.** You know the temperature in Rome and the temperature in Dallas. You know the formula to convert Fahrenheit temperatures to Celsius temperatures. You need to find the higher temperature. **6.** The formula for perimeter is wrong; $P = 2\ell + 2w$; $P = 2(200) + 2(150) = 700$; $\$10(700) = \$7000$. **7.** The formula for perimeter should be used, not area; $P = 2\ell + 2w$; $P = 2(200) + 2(150) = 700$; $\$10(700) = \$7000$.

1.6 Problem Solving (pp. 39–40)

27. a.

2	3	4	5
A, B, C	D, E, F	G, H, I	J, K, L

6	7	8	9
M, N, O	P, Q, R, S	T, U, V	W, X, Y, Z

No; because there is more than one output for each input.

b.

A	B	C	D	E	F	G	H	I	J	K	L
2	2	2	3	3	3	4	4	4	5	5	5

M	N	O	P	Q	R	S	T	U	V	W	X	Y	Z
6	6	6	7	7	7	7	8	8	8	9	9	9	9

Yes; because there is only one output for each input.

1.7 Skill Practice (pp. 46–47)

3. 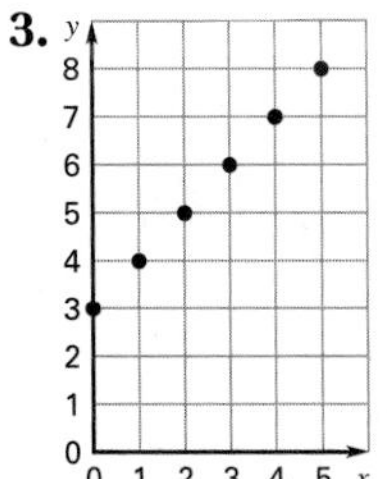

4. 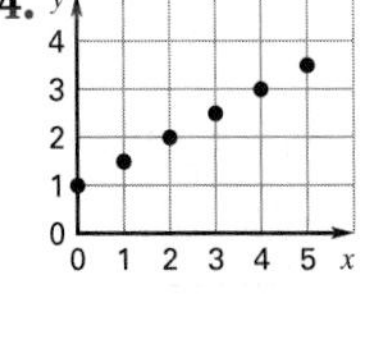

5. 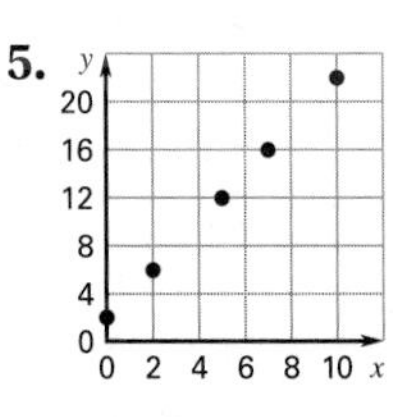

6. 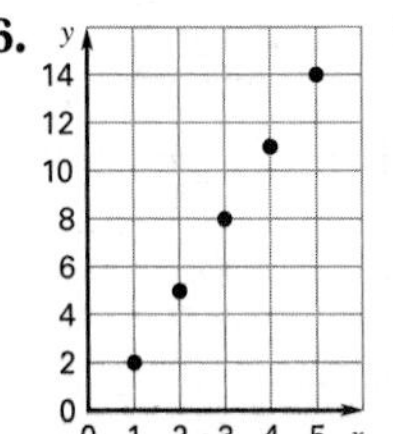

7. 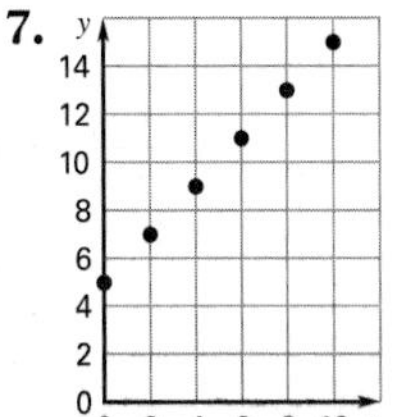

8. 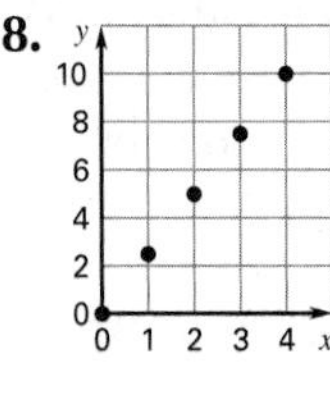

1.7 Problem Solving (pp. 47–48) 20. a. *Sample answer:* Count the number of blocks between the men's and women's times. Each block represents 10 minutes.

Quiz for Lessons 1.6–1.7 (p. 48)

1.

Input	0	2	3	4	5
Output	12	8	6	4	2

4. 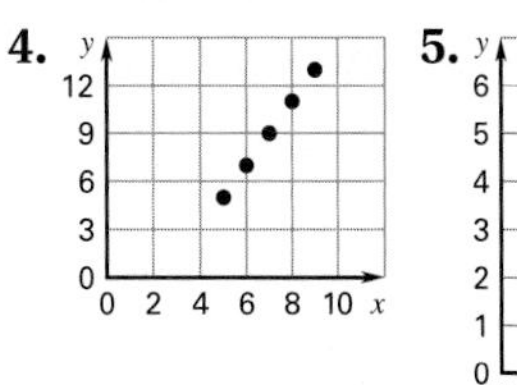

5. 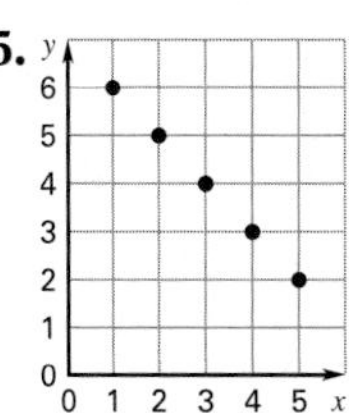

Chapter 2

2.1 Skill Practice (pp. 67–68) 52. $a < 0$; $a > 0$; $a = 0$. *Sample answer:* When a number a is negative, its opposite will be positive, which is greater than a. When a number a is positive, its opposite will be negative, which is less than a. When a is 0, its opposite is 0, which is equal to a.

2.3 Spreadsheet Activity (p. 85)

Step 2.

	A	B	C
1	Grip	Length (in.)	Difference
2	1	4.878	−0.122
3	2	4.902	−0.098
4	3	5.115	0.115
5	4	5.13	0.13
6	5	4.877	−0.123
7	6	4.874	−0.126
8	7	4.799	−0.201
9	8	4.819	−0.181
10	9	4.879	−0.121
11	10	5.124	0.124

4.

	A	B	C
1	Grip	Length (in.)	Difference
2	1	4.871	−0.129
3	2	5.019	0.019
4	3	5.112	0.112
5	4	4.987	−0.013
6	5	5.067	0.067
7	6	4.899	−0.101
8	7	4.859	−0.141
9	8	5.132	0.132
10	9	5.126	0.126
11	10	5.093	0.093

2.4 Skill Practice (pp. 91–92) **28.** $16y$; $y(16)$, product of -2 and -8; $16y$, commutative property of multiplication **29.** $18x$; $18x$, same signs, product is positive. **30.** $-3q$; $\left[\frac{3}{5}(-5)\right]q$, associative property of multiplication; $-3(q)$, product of $\frac{3}{5}$ and -5 is -3; $-3q$, multiply. **31.** $-84z$; $12(-7z)$, product of -2 and -6 is 12; $[12 \cdot (-7)]z$, associative property of multiplication; $-84(z)$, product of 12 and -7 is -84; $-84z$, multiply. **32.** $42z$; $20(-2.1)(-z)$, product of -5 and -4 is 20; $-42(-z)$, product of 20 and -2.1 is -42; $42z$, multiply. **33.** $-40c$; $2(4)(-5c)$, product of $-\frac{1}{5}$ and -10 is 2; $8(-5c)$, product of 2 and 4 is 8; $[8 \cdot (-5)]c$, associative property of multiplication; $-40(c)$, product of 8 and -5 is -40; $-40c$, multiply. **34.** $5t^2$; $(t)(-t)(-5)$, commutative property of multiplication; $-t^2(-5)$, product of t and $-t$ is $-t^2$; $(-5)(-t^2)$, commutative property of multiplication; $5t^2$, multiply. **35.** $16.8r^2$; $[-6r \cdot (-2.8)]r$, associative property of multiplication; $[-6 \cdot (-2.8) \cdot r]r$, commutative property of multiplication; $(16.8r)r$, product of -6 and -2.8 is 16.8; $16.8(r \cdot r)$, associative property of multiplication; $16.8r^2$, multiply. **36.** $-\frac{3}{10}m^2$; $-\frac{3}{10}(-m)(-m)$, product of $\frac{1}{3}$ and $-\frac{9}{10}$ is $-\frac{3}{10}$; $-\frac{3}{10}m^2$, multiply.

2.5 Problem Solving Workshop (p. 102) **3.** \$287.50; Method 1: Write an equation for a, the total amount earned as a function of d, the number of hours spent making deliveries; $a = 9.50d + 8(35 - d)$ or $a = 1.5d + 280$. Substitute 5 for d, giving you $a =$ \$287.50; Method 2: Break the problem into parts. Find the amount earned working 5 hours making deliveries: \$9.50 per hour • 5 hours = \$47.50. Find the number of hours spent working at the register: 35 hours − 5 hours = 30 hours. Find the amount earned working at the register for 30 hours: \$8 per hour • 30 hours = \$240. Add the amount earned making deliveries to the amount earned working at the register: \$47.50 + \$240 = \$287.50.

2.7 Skill Practice (pp. 113–114) **24.** $\sqrt{49}$: real number, rational number, integer, whole number, 8: real number, rational number, integer, whole number, $-\sqrt{4}$: real number, rational number, integer, -3: real number, rational number, integer; $-3, -\sqrt{4}, \sqrt{49}, 8$ **25.** $-\sqrt{12}$: real number, irrational number, -3.7: real number, rational number, $\sqrt{9}$: real number, rational number, integer, whole number, 2.9: real number, rational number; $-3.7, -\sqrt{12}, 2.9, \sqrt{9}$ **26.** -11.5: real number, rational number, $-\sqrt{121}$: real number, rational number, integer, -10: real number, rational number, integer, $\frac{25}{2}$: real number, rational number, $\sqrt{144}$: real number, rational number, integer, whole number; $-11.5, -\sqrt{121}, -10, \sqrt{144}, \frac{25}{2}$ **27.** $\sqrt{8}$: real number, irrational number, $-\frac{2}{5}$: real number, rational number, -1: real number, rational number, integer, 0.6: real number, rational number, $\sqrt{6}$: real number, irrational number; $-1, -\frac{2}{5}, 0.6, \sqrt{6}, \sqrt{8}$ **28.** $-\frac{8}{3}$: real number, rational number, $-\sqrt{5}$: real number, irrational number, 2.6: real number, rational number, -1.5: real number, rational number, $\sqrt{5}$: real number, irrational number; $-\frac{8}{3}, -\sqrt{5}, -1.5, \sqrt{5}, 2.6$ **29.** -8.3: real number, rational number, $-\sqrt{80}$: real number, irrational number, $-\frac{17}{2}$: real number, rational number, -8.25: real number, rational number, $-\sqrt{100}$: real number, rational number, integer; $-\sqrt{100}, -\sqrt{80}, -\frac{17}{2}, -8.3, -8.25$

2.7 Problem Solving (pp. 115–116)

52. a.

Quotient of pyramids	Quotient of area of bases	Quotient of side length of bases
$\frac{\text{Khafre}}{\text{Menafaure}}$	3.9	2.0
$\frac{\text{Khufu}}{\text{Menafaure}}$	4.6	2.1
$\frac{\text{Khufu}}{\text{Khafre}}$	1.2	1.1

The quotient of the areas is the square of the quotient of the side lengths.

Chapter 3

3.2 Problem Solving (pp. 145–146)

43. b.

x (h)	Marissa	Ryan	Total
1	5	7	12
2	10	14	24
3	15	21	36
4	20	28	48
5	25	35	60

3.2 Problem Solving Workshop (p. 147)

1. 7 players; Method 1: Use the equation $600 + 25x = 775$ to get $x = 7$; Method 2: Make a table that lists the number of non-members and the amount the team would pay. The team has 7 members who are not club members.

Non-members	Total fee (dollars)
0	600
1	625
2	650
3	675
4	700
5	725
6	750
7	775

3. 4 chairs; Method 1: Use the equation $220 + 35x = 370$ to get $x \approx 4.3$; Method 2: Make a table that lists the number of chairs and the total cost of the table and chairs; because you cannot afford $395 for 5 chairs, you can afford to buy 4 chairs.

Chairs	Total cost (dollars)
1	255
2	290
3	325
4	360
5	395

3.4 Problem Solving (pp. 158–159)

52. b.

Visits	Members' cost (dollars)	Non-members' cost (dollars)
5	380	80
10	400	160
15	420	240
20	440	320
25	460	400
30	480	480
35	500	560

3.4 Spreadsheet Activity (p. 160)

4. a–b.

	A	B	C	D
1	Possible solutions	Left side	Right side	Difference
2	0	38.5	0	38.5
3	1	33.7	6.2	27.5
4	2	28.9	12.4	16.5
5	3	24.1	18.6	5.5
6	4	19.3	24.8	−5.5
7	5	14.5	31	−16.5
8	6	9.7	37.2	−27.5
9	7	4.9	43.4	−38.5
10	8	0.1	49.6	−49.5
11	9	−4.7	55.8	−60.5
12	10	−9.5	62	−71.5

Chapter 4

4.1 Guided Practice (pp. 206–208)

3–6.

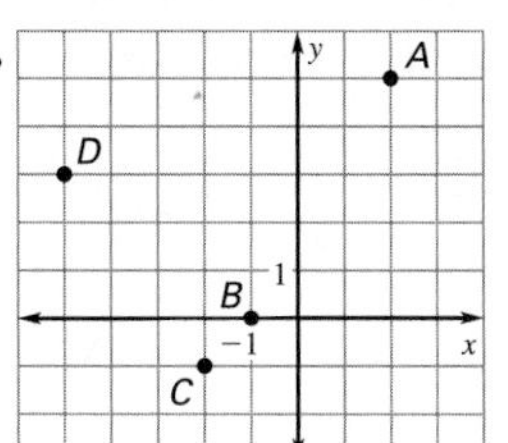

7.

4.1 Skill Practice (pp. 209–210)

29. Quadrant IV; the x-coordinate is positive and the y-coordinate is negative so the point is in Quadrant IV. **30.** Quadrant IV; the x-coordinate is positive and the y-coordinate is negative so the point is in Quadrant IV. **31.** Quadrant II; the x-coordinate is negative and the y-coordinate is positive so the point is in Quadrant II. **32.** Quadrant III; the x-coordinate is negative and the y-coordinate is negative so the point is in Quadrant III.

4.2 Guided Practice (pp. 215–218)

2.

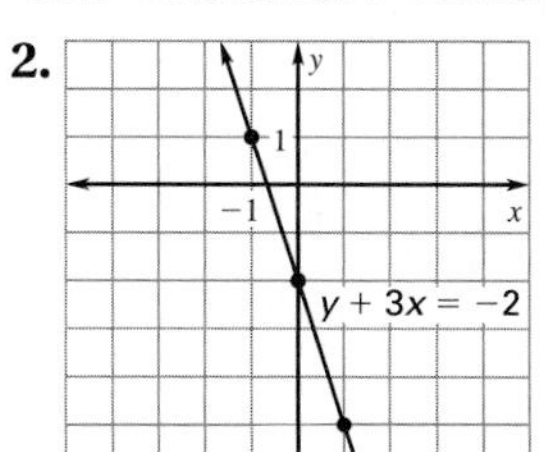

3.

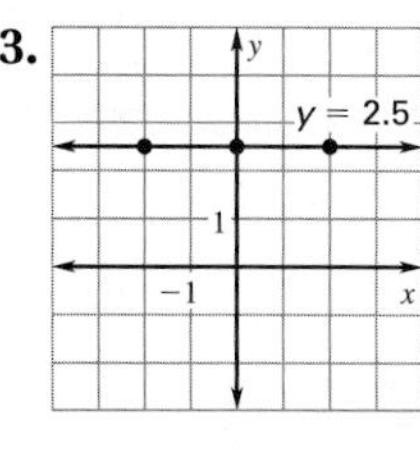

4.

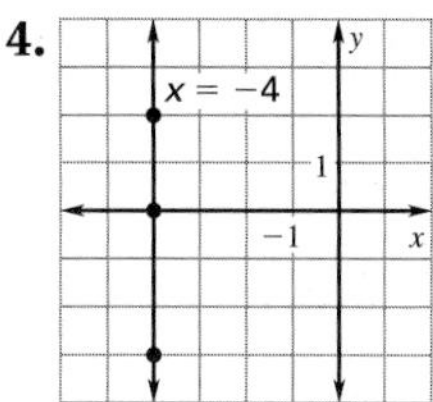

4.2 Skill Practice (pp. 219–220)

11.

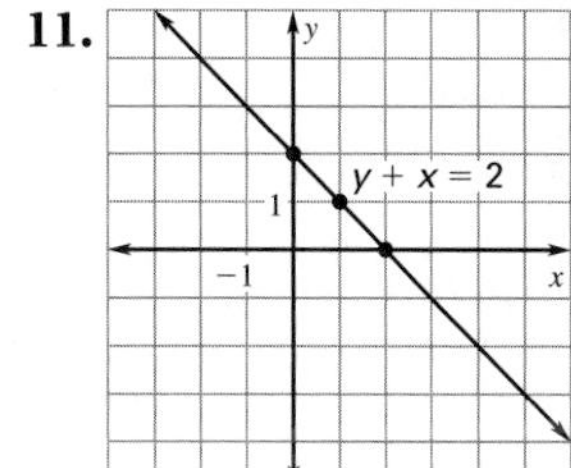

12.

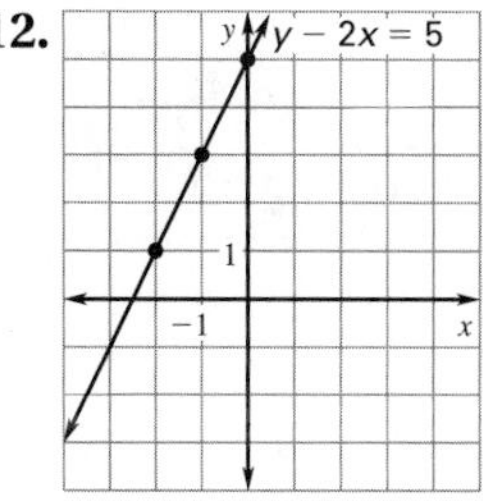

13.

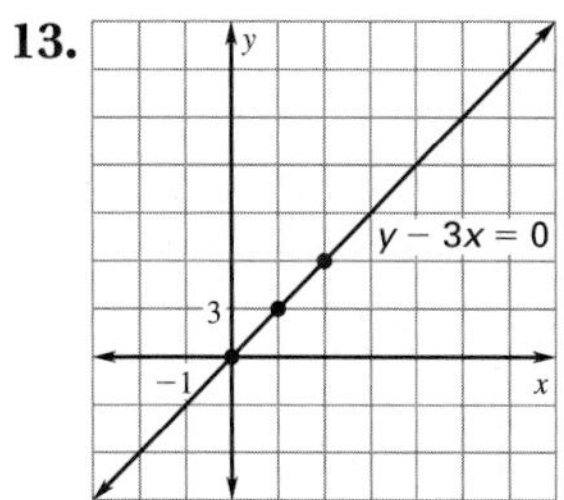

14.

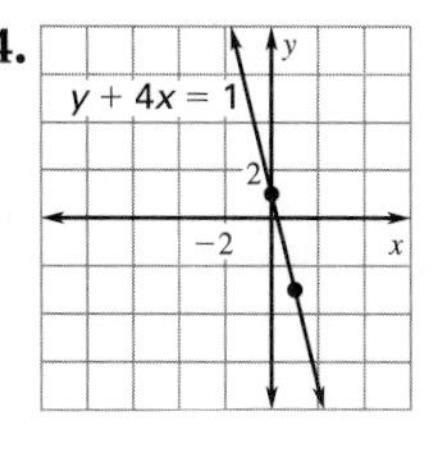

15.

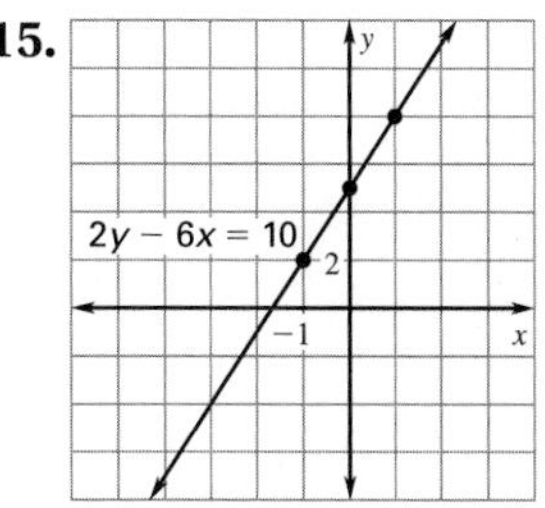

16.

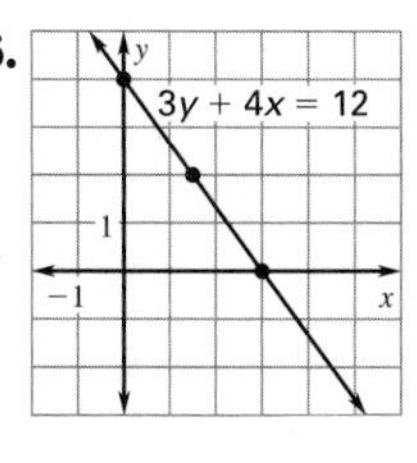

ADDITIONAL ANSWERS

17. 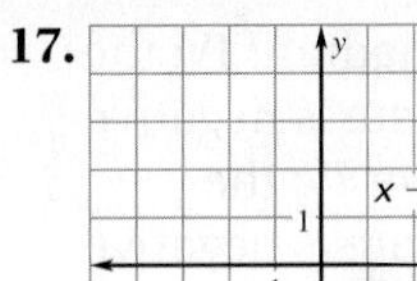

18. 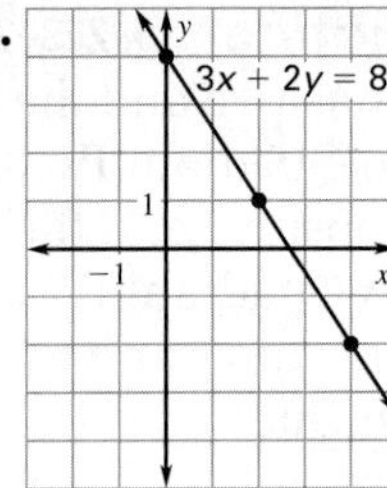

19. 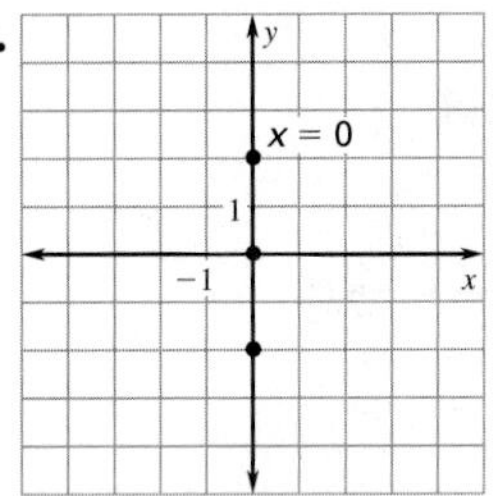

20. 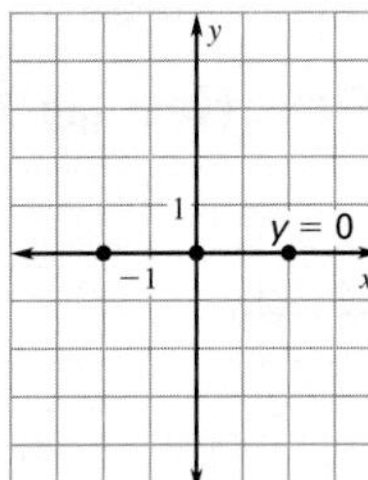

21. 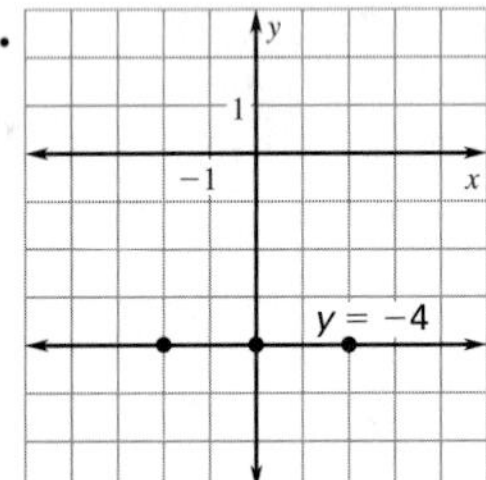

22. 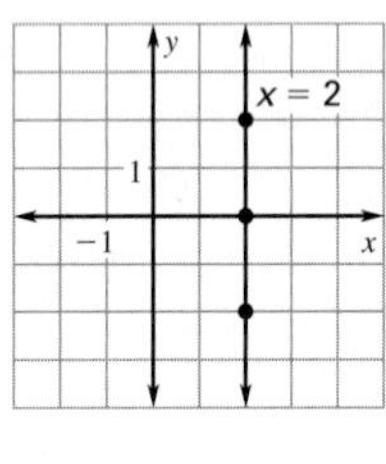

26. 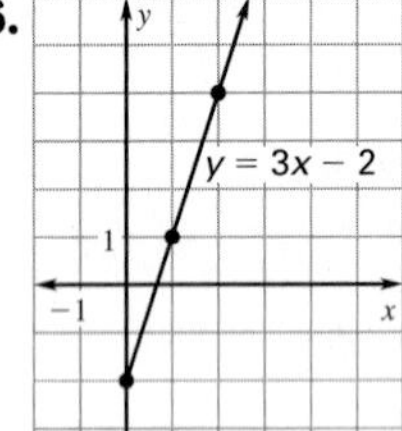

27. 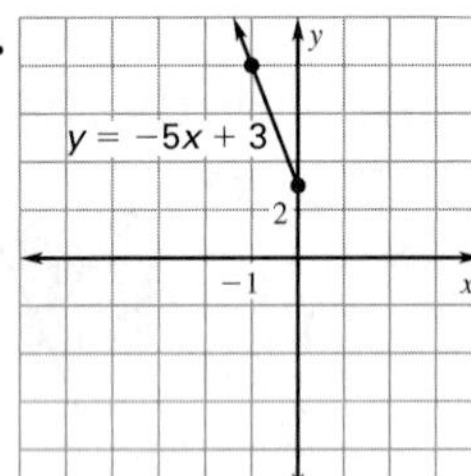

28. 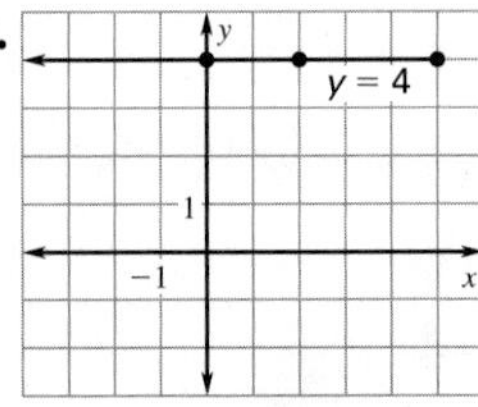

29. 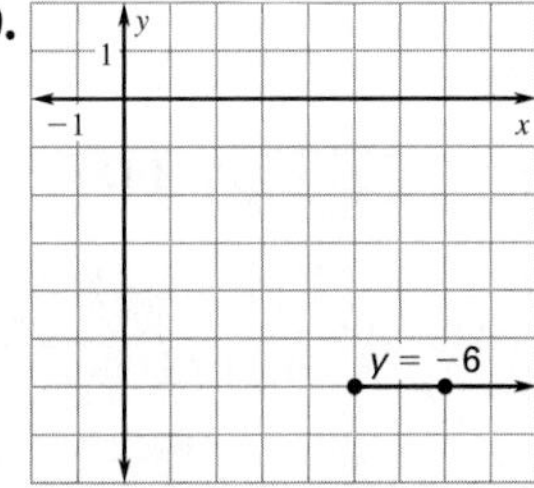

30. 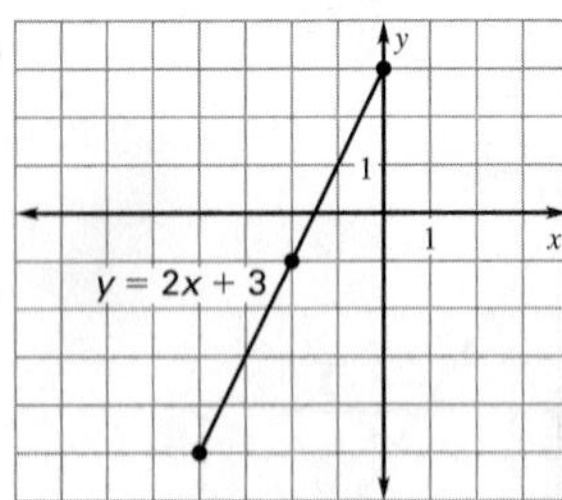

31. 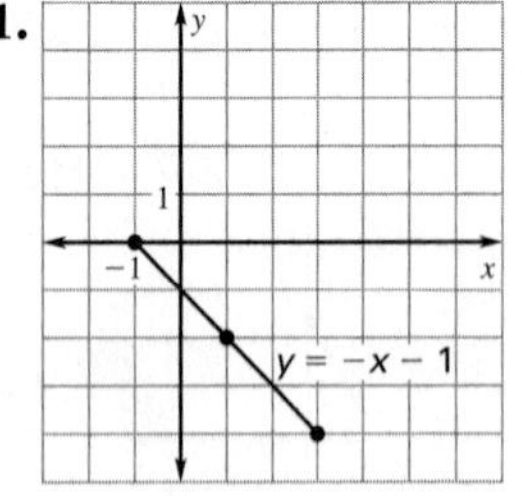

4.2 Problem Solving (pp. 220–221)

40. a.

t (seconds)	h (feet)
0	5
1	19
2	33
3	47
4	61
5	75
6	89
7	103
8	117
9	131
10	145

b. 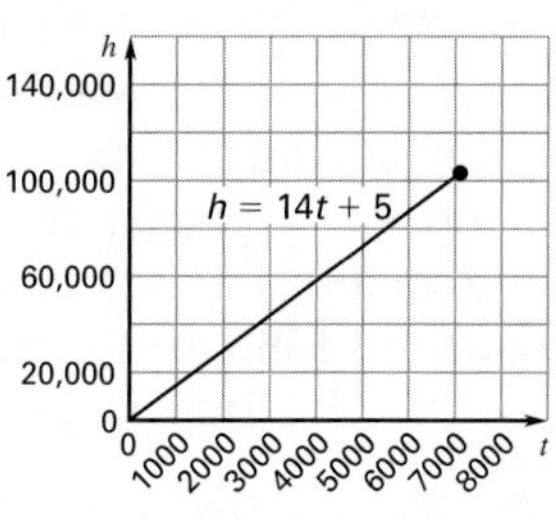

41. a. 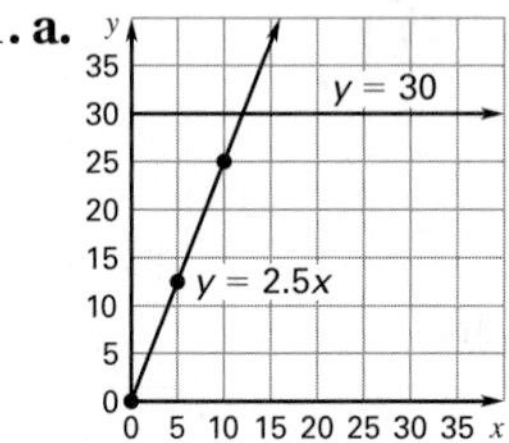

Extension (p. 224)

1. 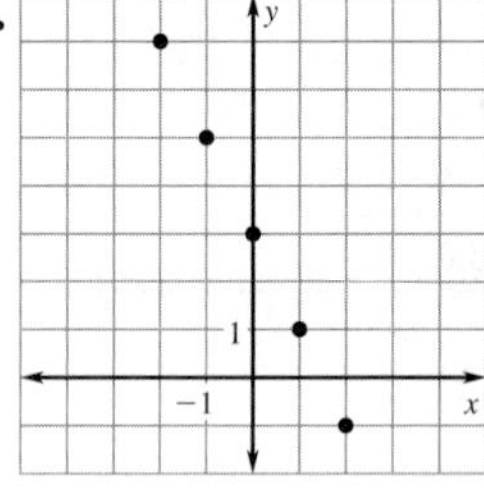

2. 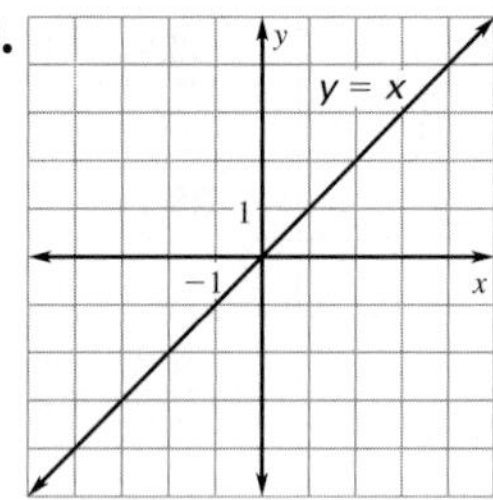

3. 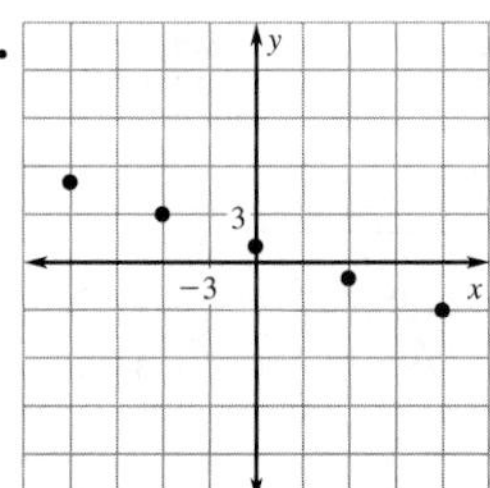

4. 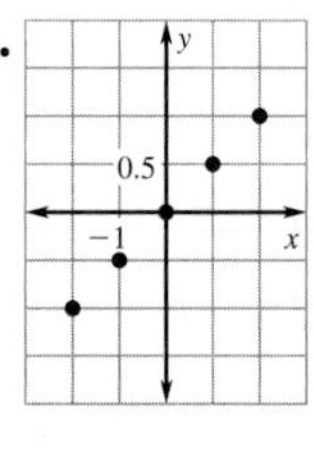

5. 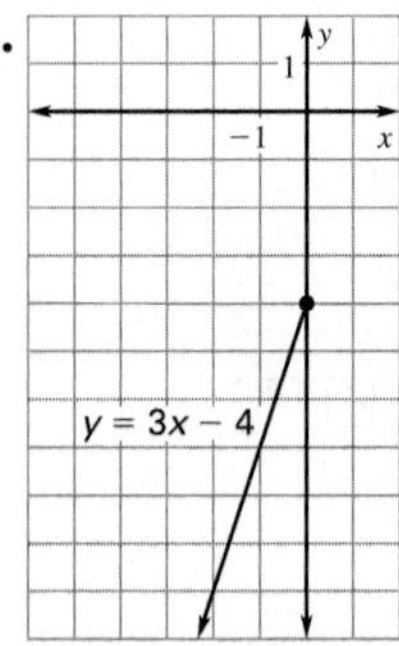

6. 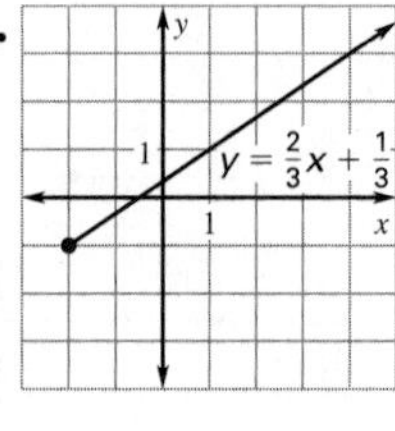

4.3 Skill Practice (pp. 229–230)

16.
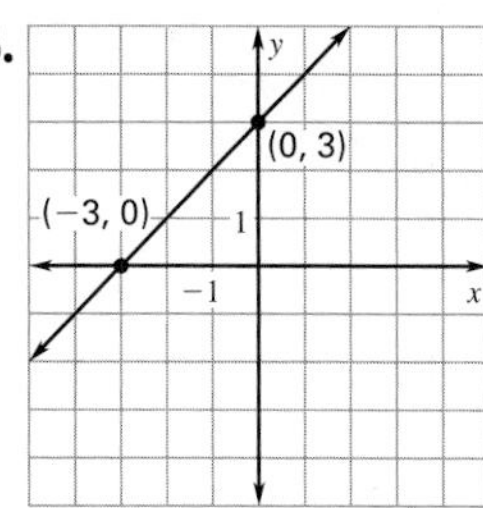

17.
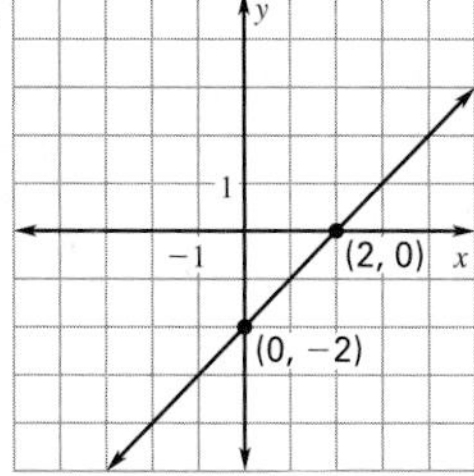

18.
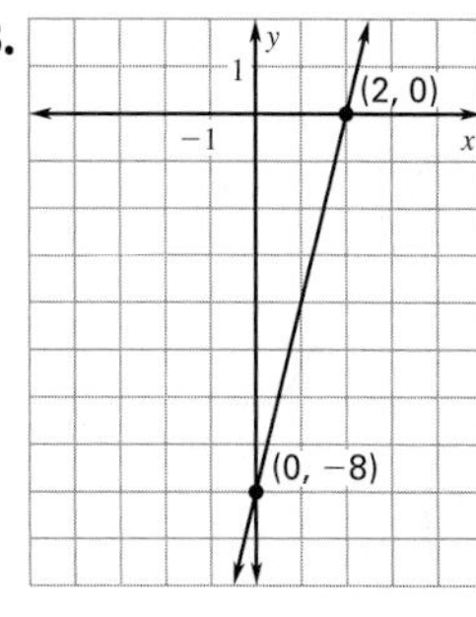

19.
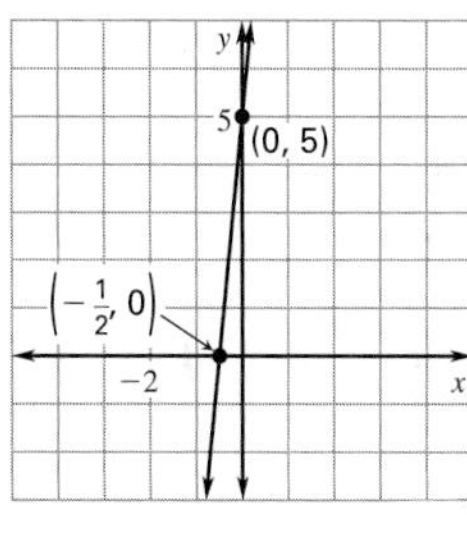

20.
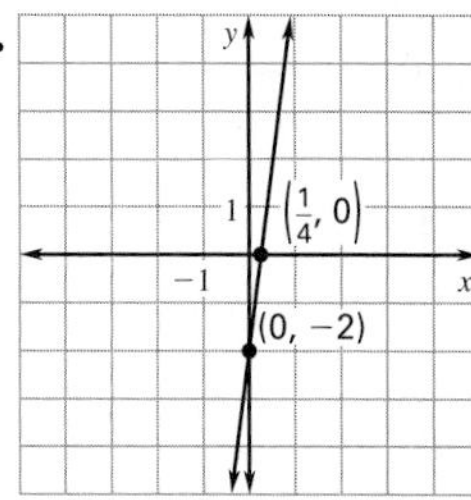

21.
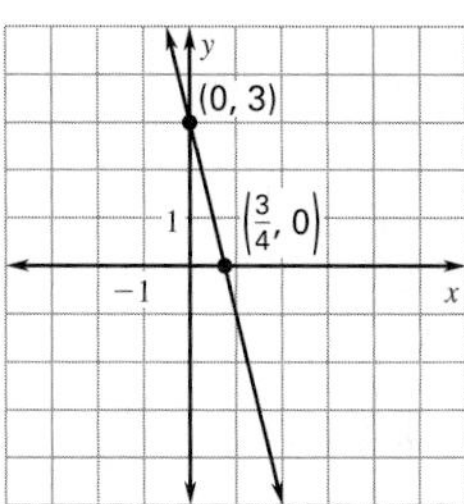

22.
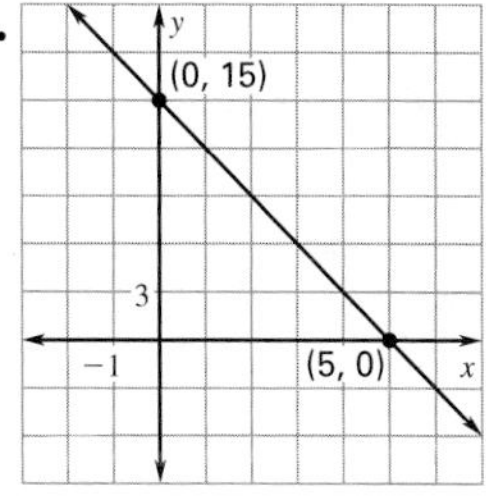

23.
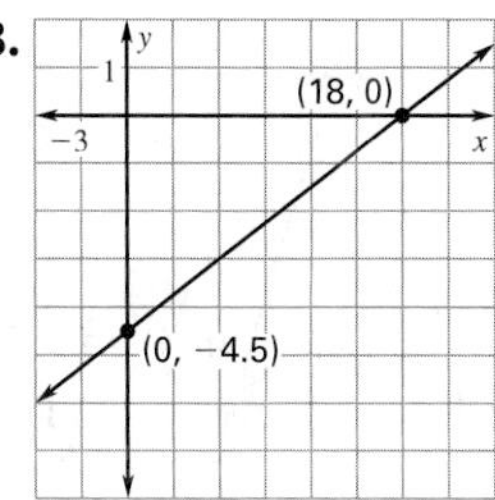

24.
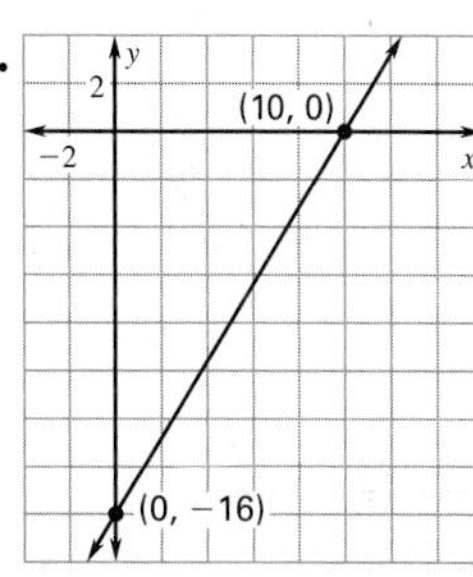

25.
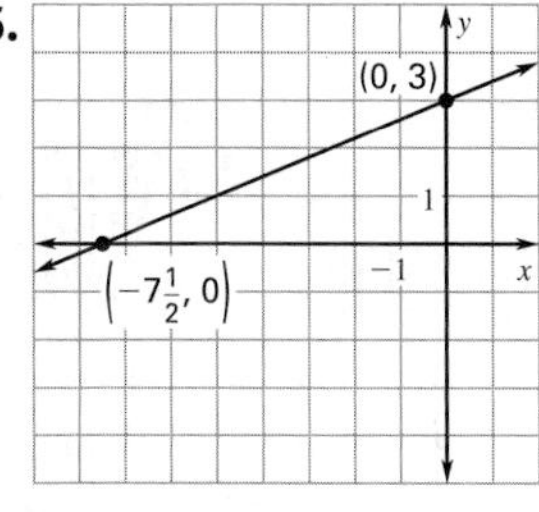

26.
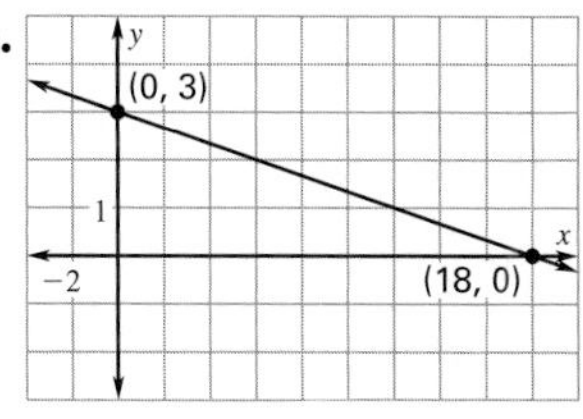

27.
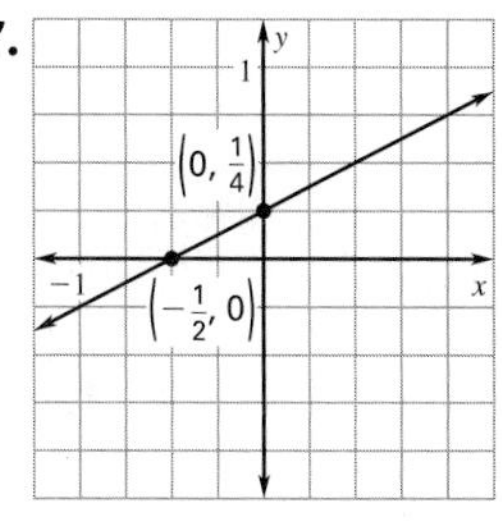

4.3 Problem Solving (pp. 230–232)

50. b.
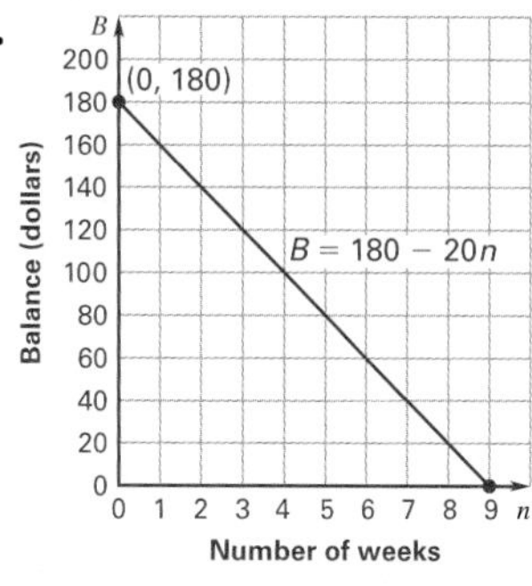

Quiz for Lessons 4.1–4.3 (p. 232)

1–3.
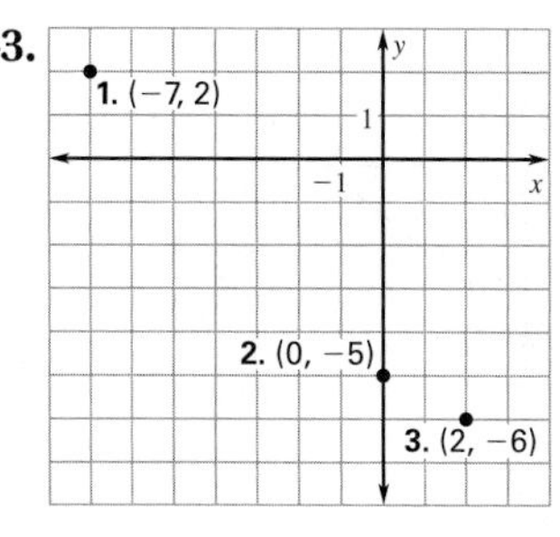

4.
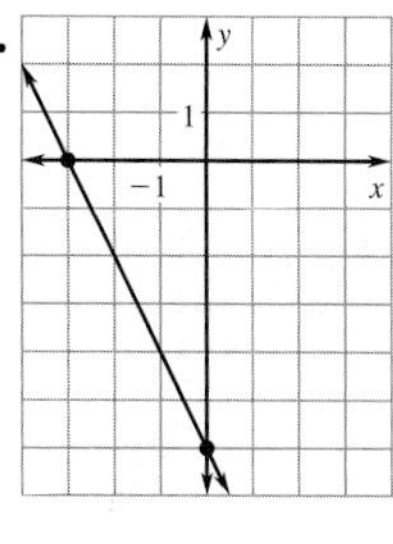

5.
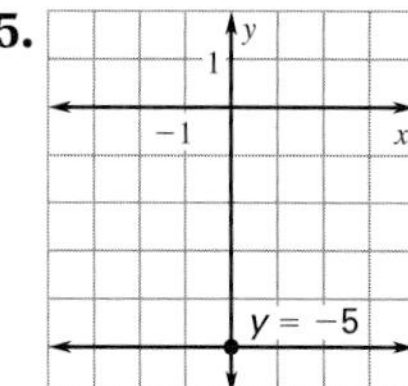

6.
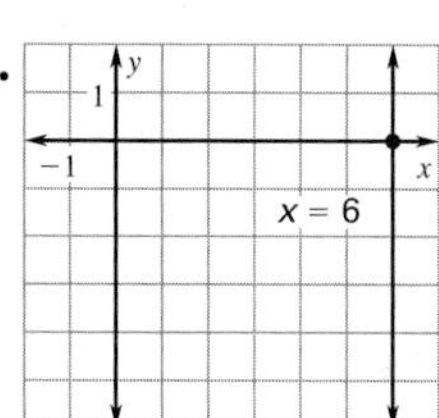

13.
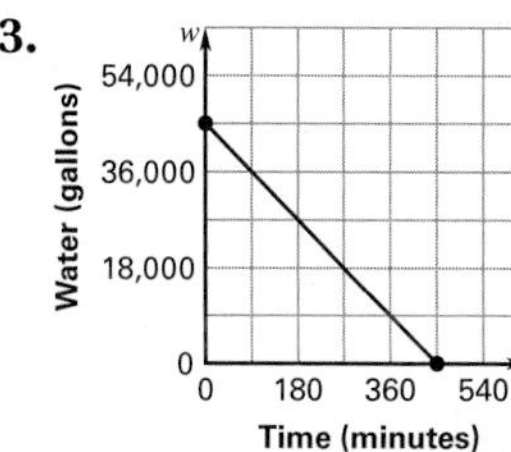

4.4 Problem Solving (pp. 241–242)

41. a.
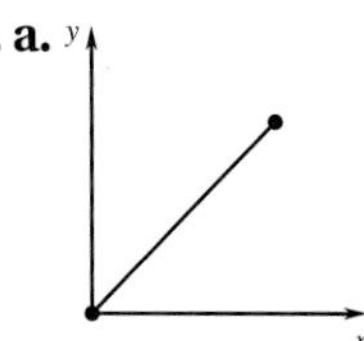

b.
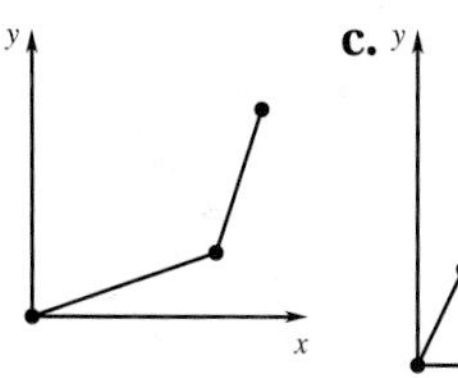

c.
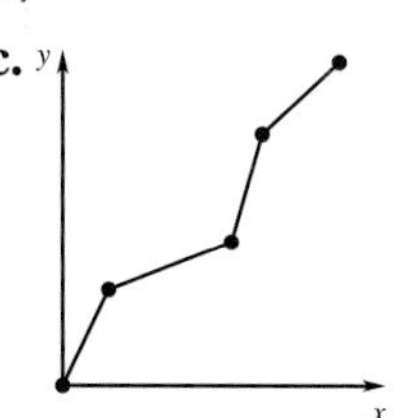

4.5 Guided Practice (pp. 244–246)

4.
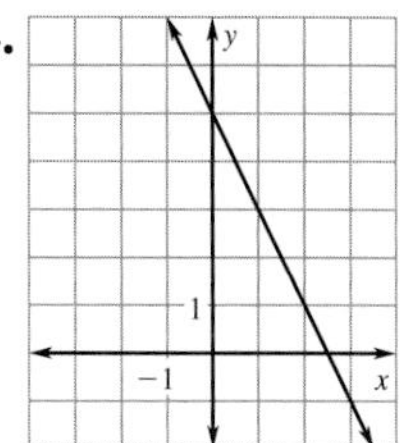

4.5 Problem Solving (pp. 248–250)

45. a.

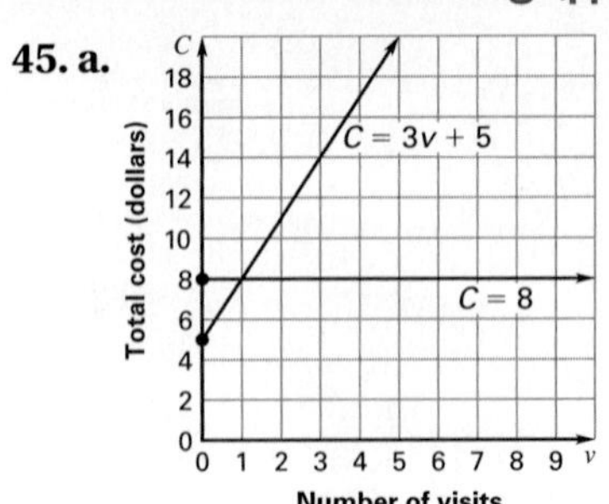

Quiz for Lessons 4.4–4.5 (p. 250)

7.

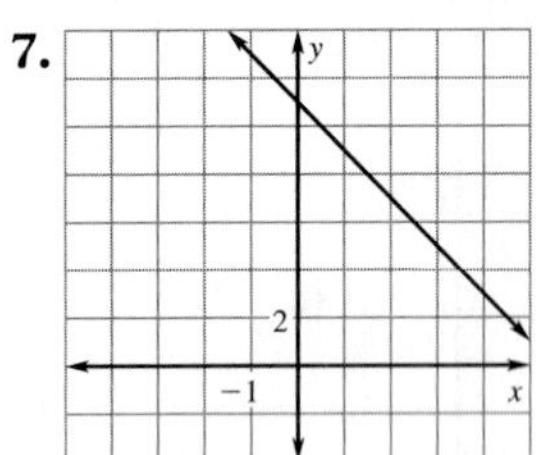

8.

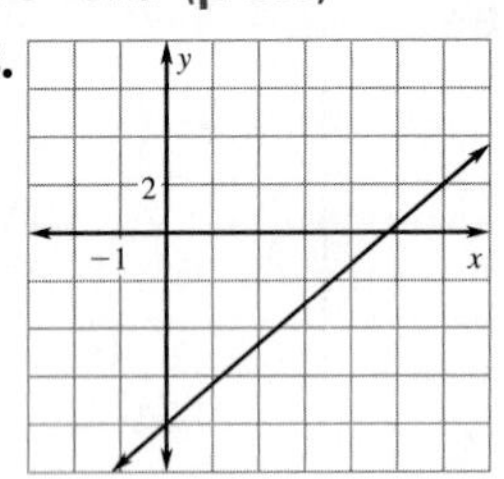

9.

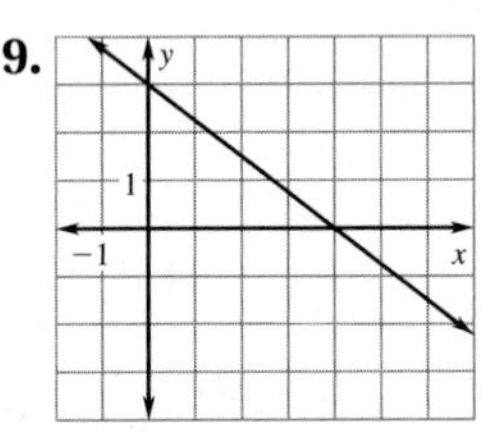

10. a.

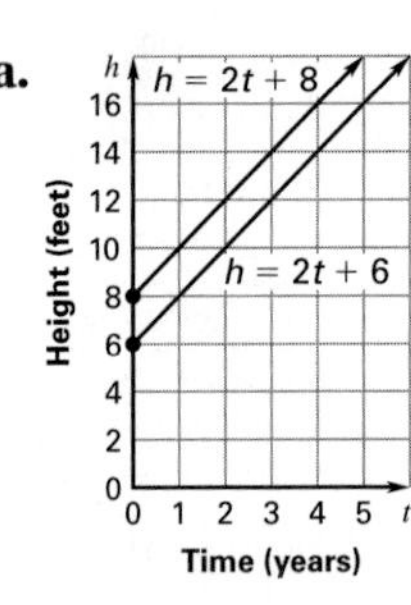

4.6 Skill Practice (pp. 256–257)

11.

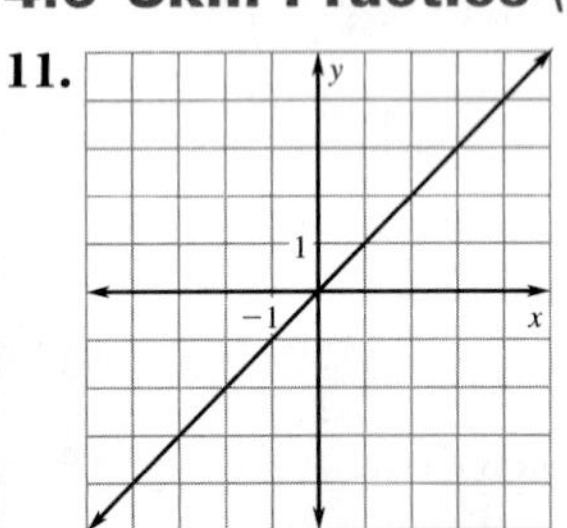

12.

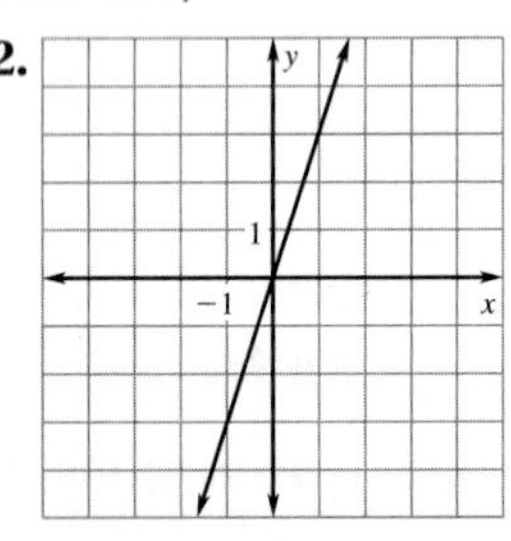

13.

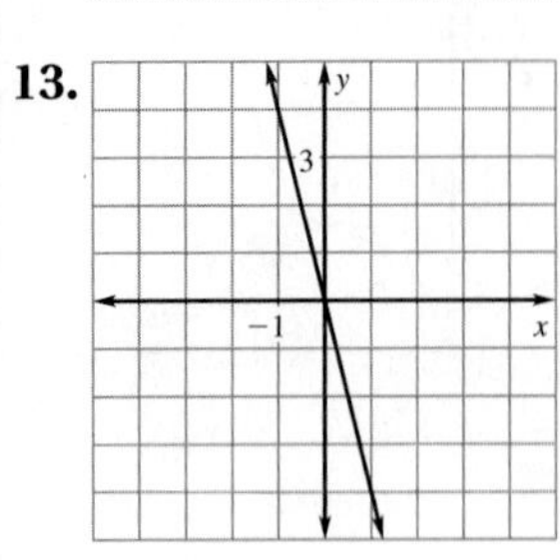

14.

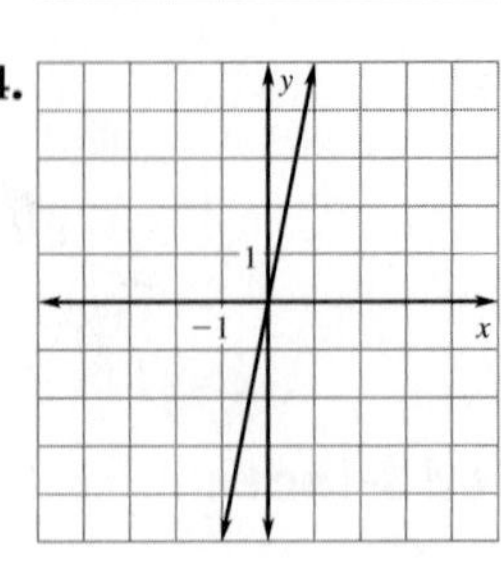

15.

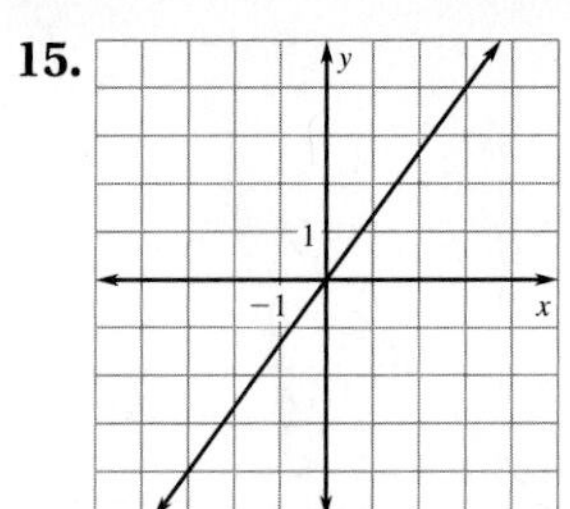

16.

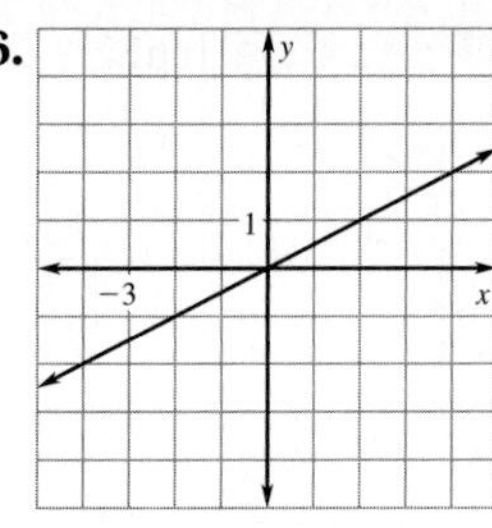

17.

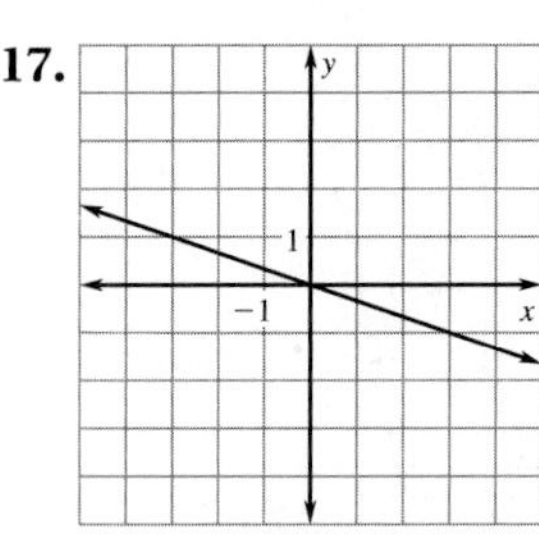

18.

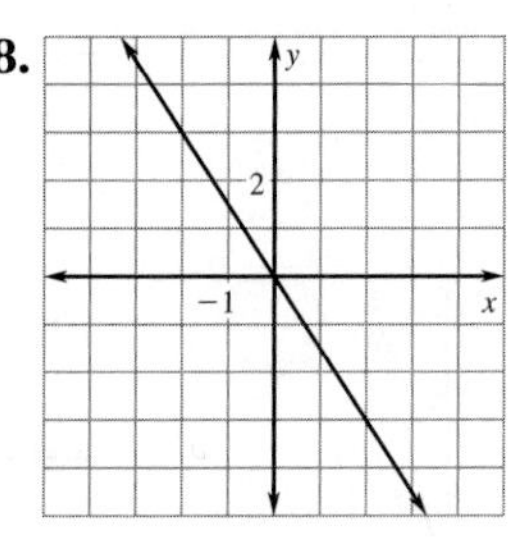

19.

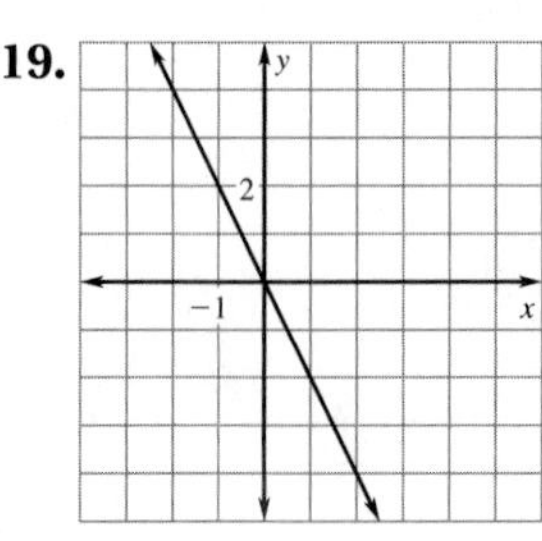

20.

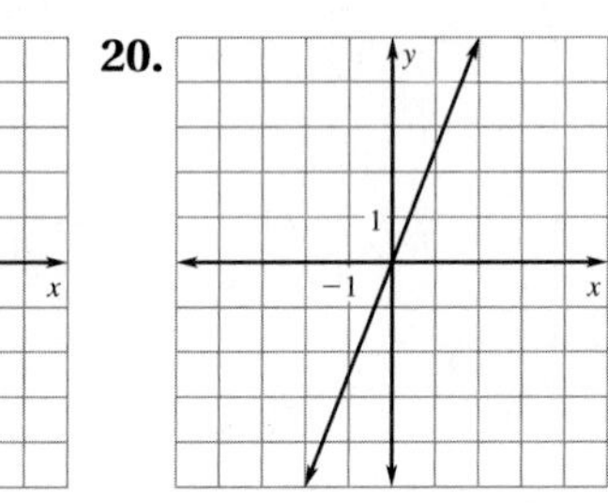

21.

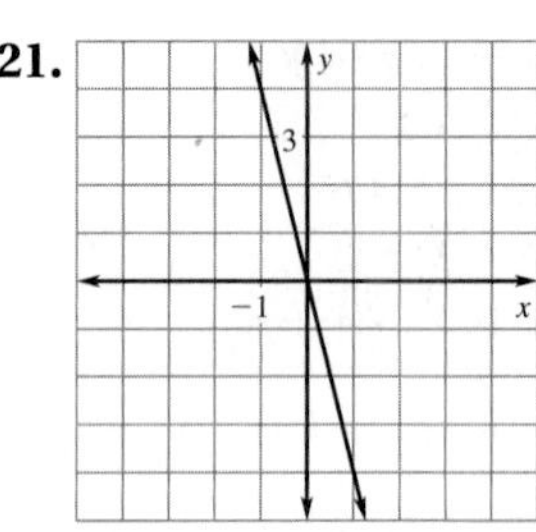

22.

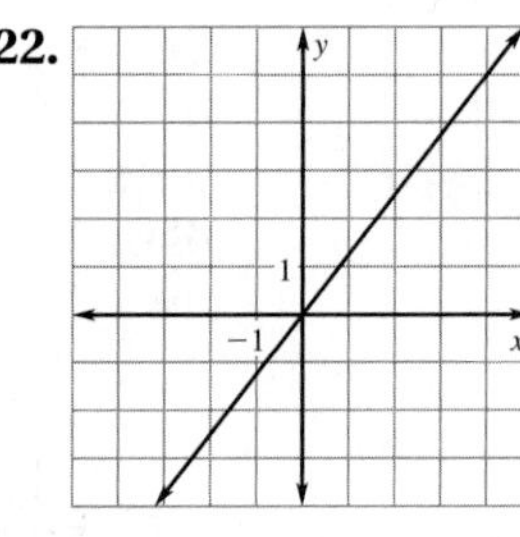

4.6 Mixed Review (p. 259)

48.

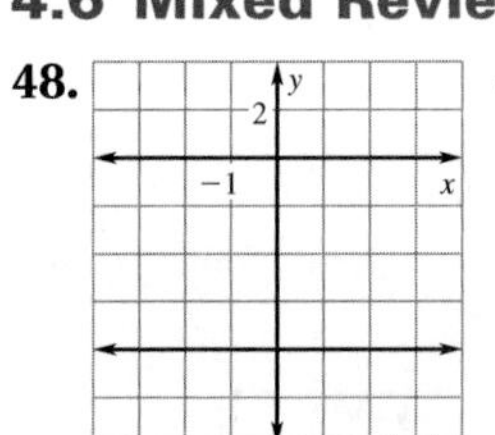

49.

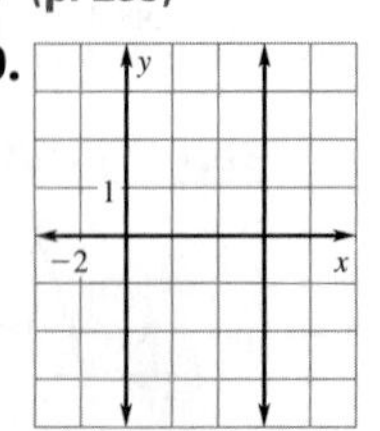

50.

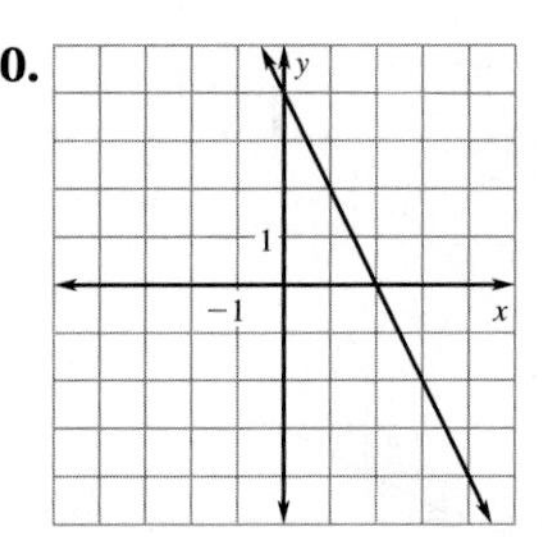

51.

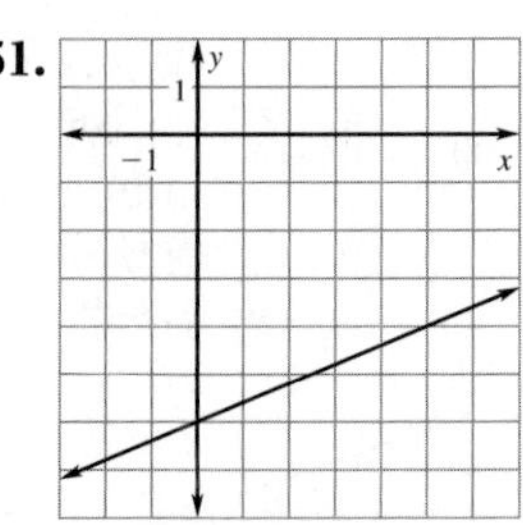

ADDITIONAL ANSWERS

52. 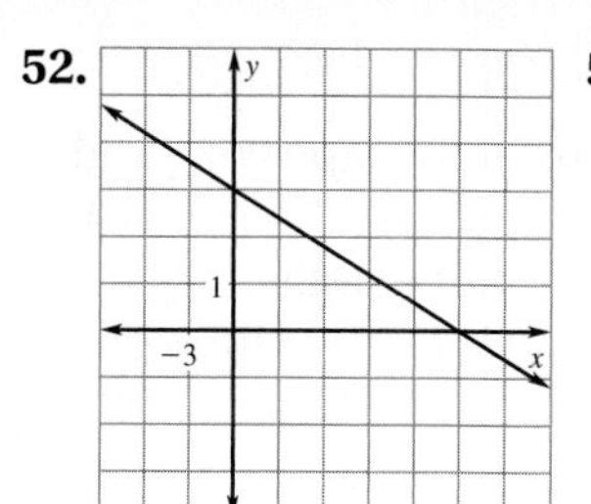

53. 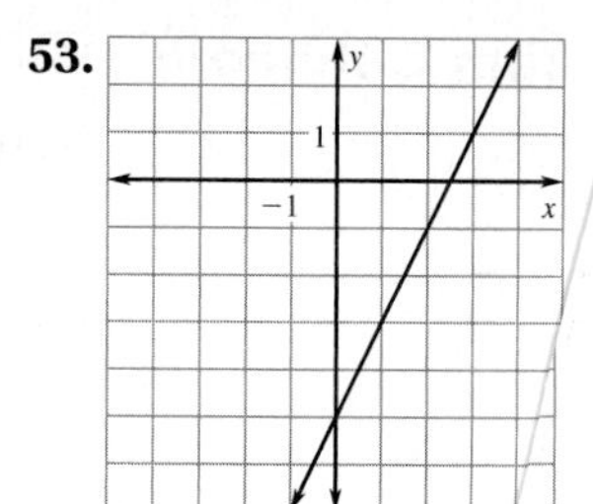

54. 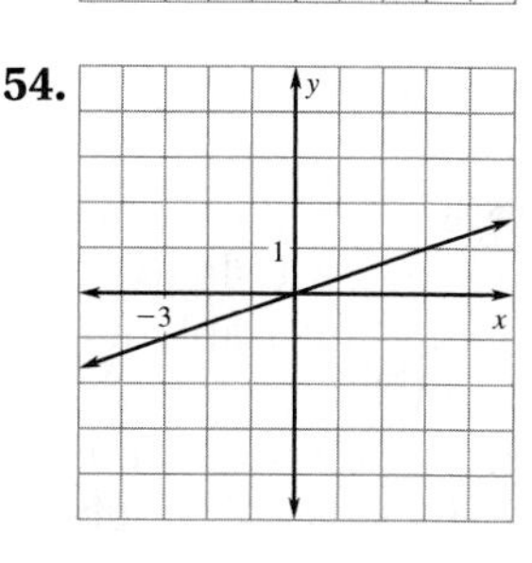

55. 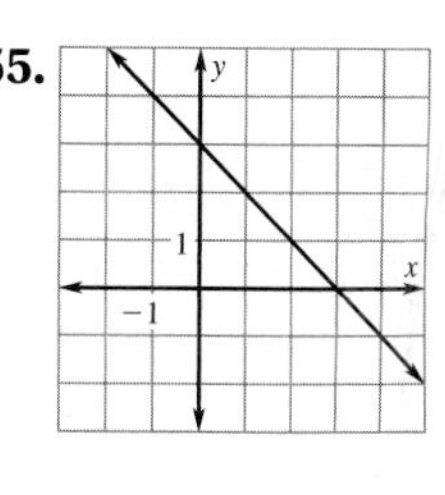

56. 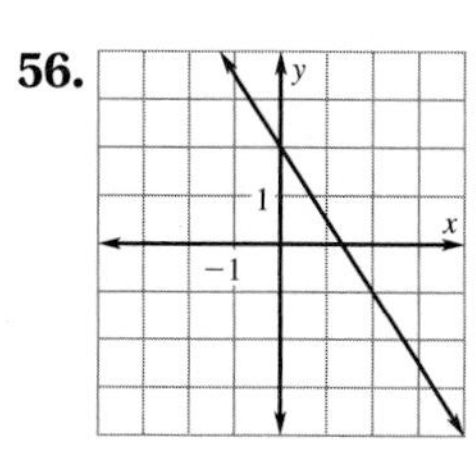

4.7 Skill Practice (pp. 265–266)

23. 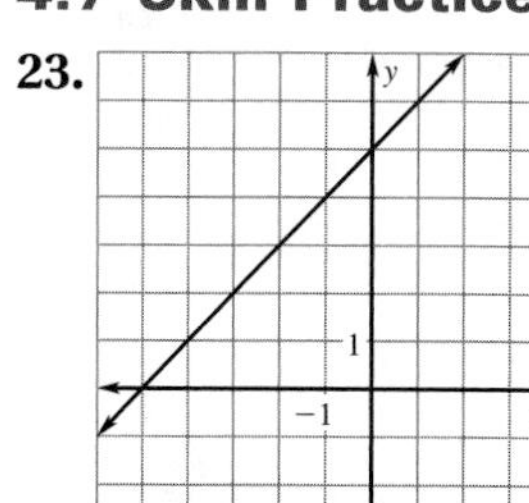

Because the graphs of g and f have the same slope, $m = 1$, the lines are parallel. The y-intercept of the graph of g is 5 more than the y-intercept of the graph of f.

24. 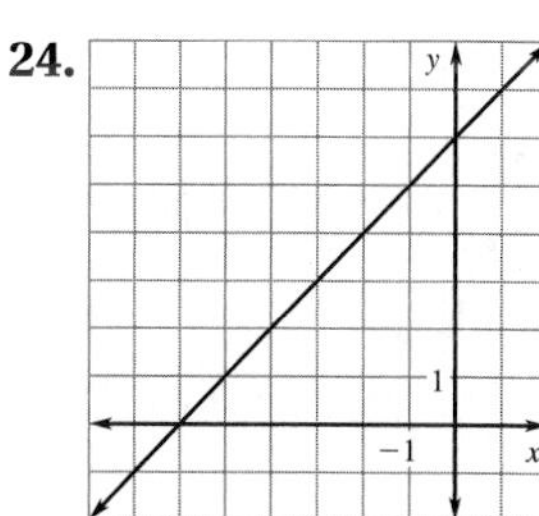

Because the graphs of h and f have the same slope, $m = 1$, the lines are parallel. The y-intercept of the graph of h is 6 more than the y-intercept of the graph of f.

25. 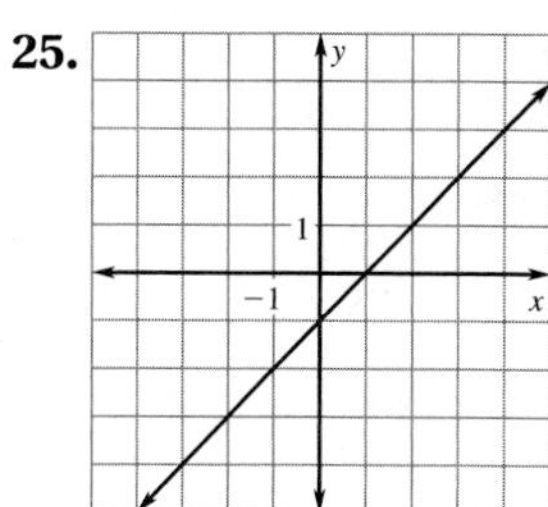

Because the graphs of q and f have the same slope, $m = 1$, the lines are parallel. The y-intercept of the graph of q is 1 less than the y-intercept of the graph of f.

26. 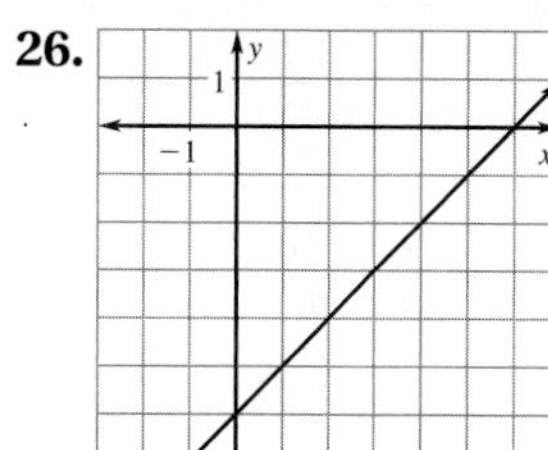

Because the graphs of m and f have the same slope, $m = 1$, the lines are parallel. The y-intercept of the graph of m is 6 less than the y-intercept of the graph of f.

27. 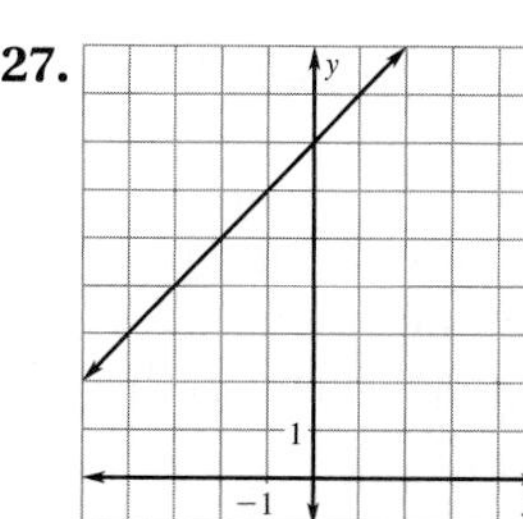

Because the graphs of d and f have the same slope, $m = 1$, the lines are parallel. The y-intercept of the graph of d is 7 more than the y-intercept of the graph of f.

28. 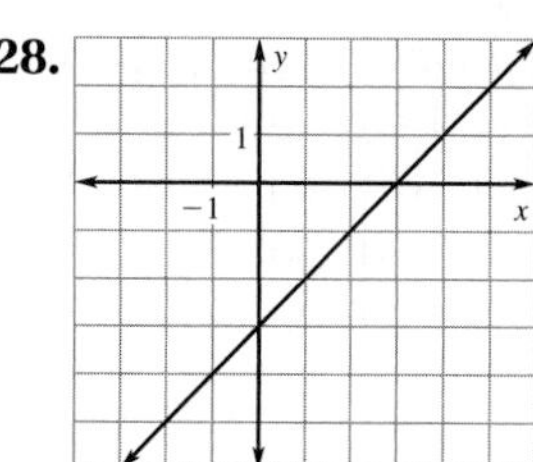

Because the graphs of t and f have the same slope, $m = 1$, the lines are parallel. The y-intercept of the graph of t is 3 less than the y-intercept of the graph of f.

29. 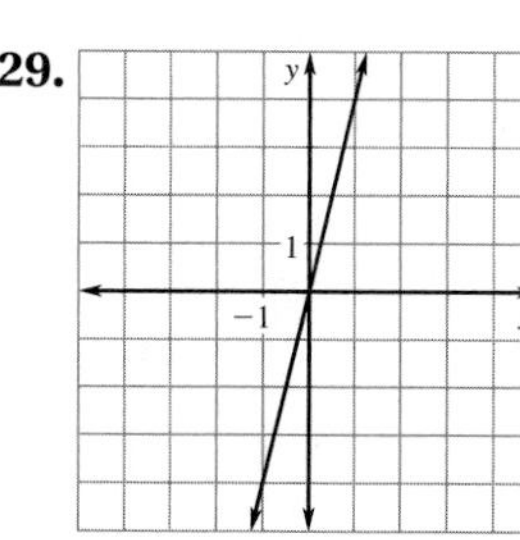

Because the slope of the graph of r is greater than the slope of the graph of f, the graph of r rises faster from left to right. The y-intercept for both graphs is 0, so both lines pass through the origin.

30. 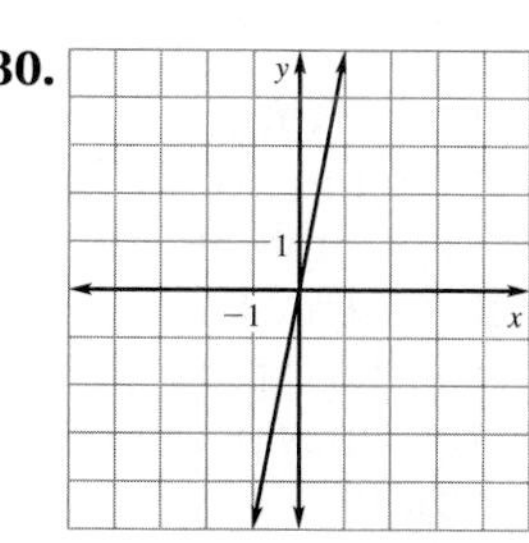

Because the slope of the graph of w is greater than the slope of the graph of f, the graph of w rises faster from left to right. The y-intercept for both graphs is 0, so both lines pass through the origin.

31. 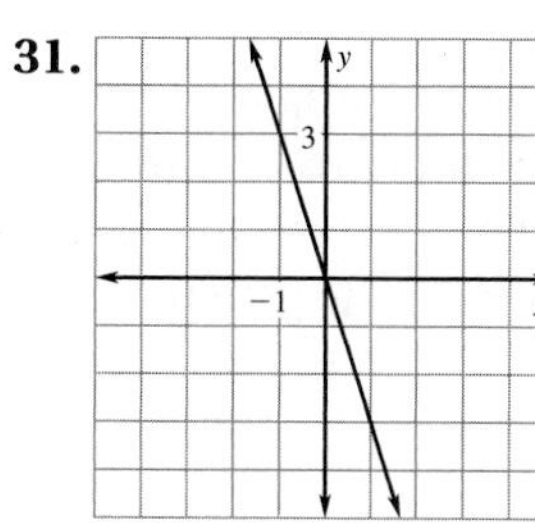

Because the slope of the graph of h is negative, the graph of h falls from left to right. The y-intercept for both graphs is 0, so both lines pass through the origin.

32. 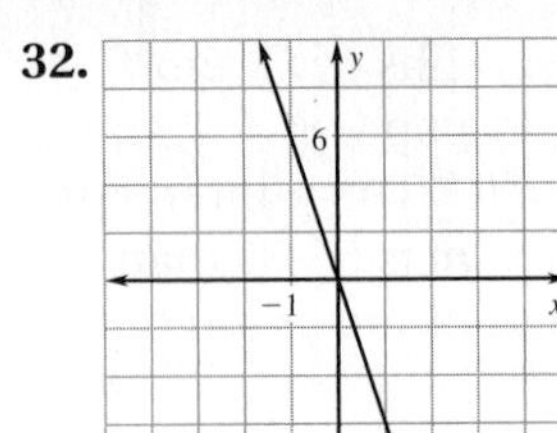

Because the slope of the graph of k is negative, the graph of k falls from left to right. The y-intercept for both graphs is 0, so both lines pass through the origin.

33. 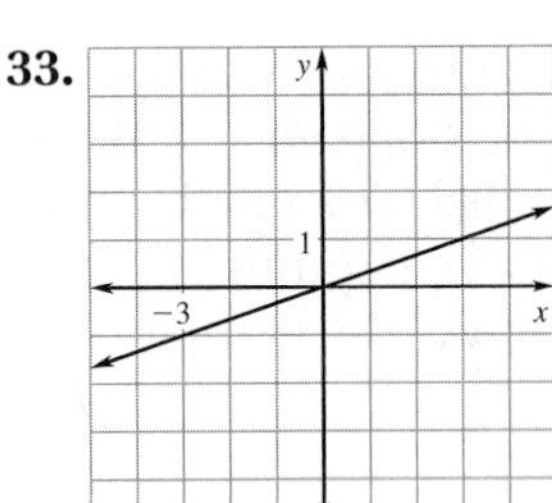

Because the slope of the graph of g is less than the slope of the graph of f, the graph of g rises slower from left to right. The y-intercept for both graphs is 0, so both lines pass through the origin.

34. 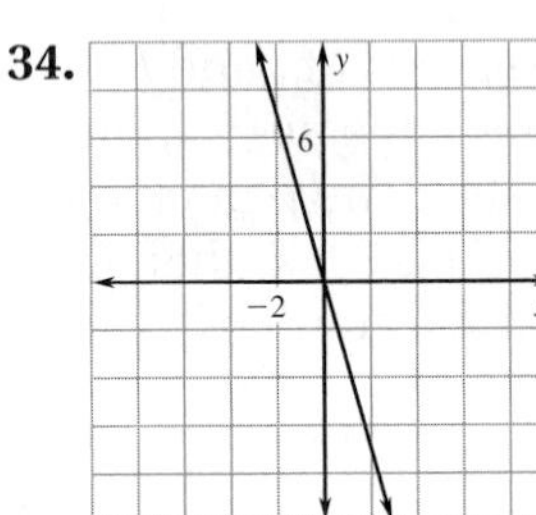

Because the slope of the graph of m is negative, the graph of m falls from left to right. The y-intercept for both graphs is 0, so both lines pass through the origin.

36. a. 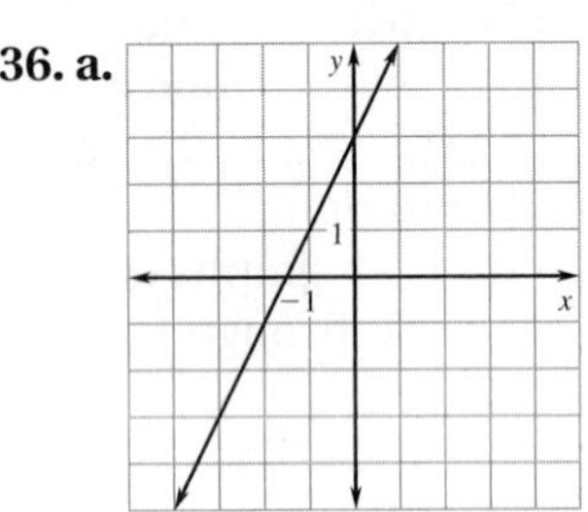

b. 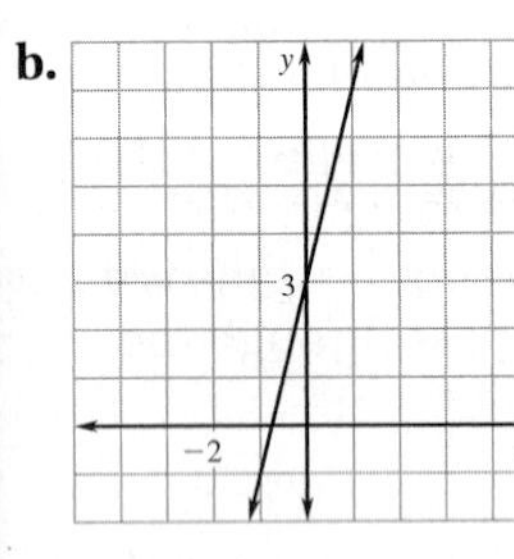

Because the slope of the graph of g is greater than the slope of the graph of f, the graph of g rises faster from left to right. The y-intercept for both graphs is the same, so both lines pass through the point (0, 3).

c. 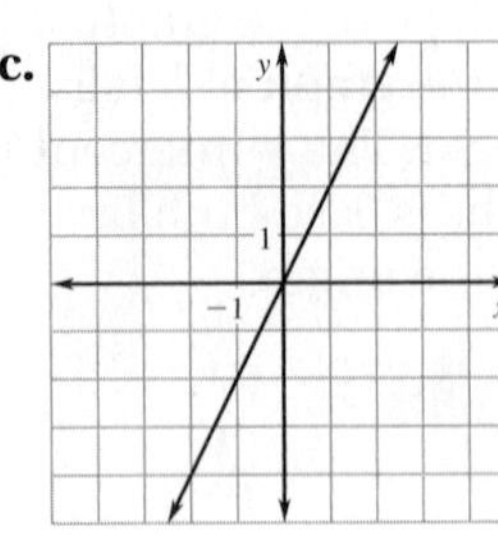

Because the graphs of h and f have the same slope, $m = 2$, the lines are parallel. The y-intercept of the graph of h is 3 less than the y-intercept of the graph of f.

4.7 Problem Solving (pp. 267–268)

42. 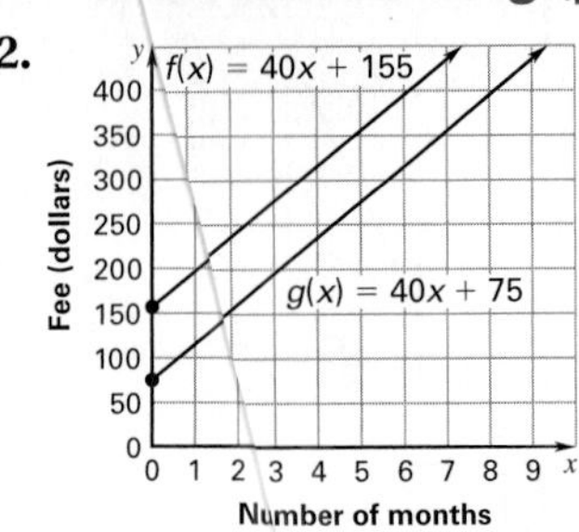

Because the graphs of g and f have the same slope, $m = 40$, the lines are parallel. The y-intercept of the graph of g is 80 less than the y-intercept of the graph of f.

43. 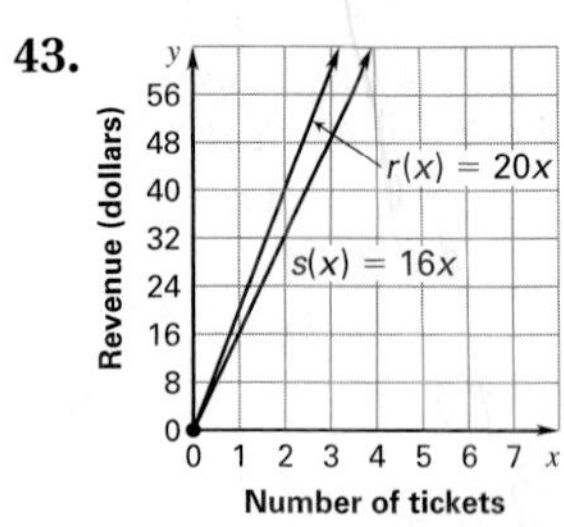

Because the slope of the graph of r is greater than the slope of the graph of s, the graph of r rises faster from left to right. The y-intercept for both graphs is 0, so both lines pass through the origin.

45. b. 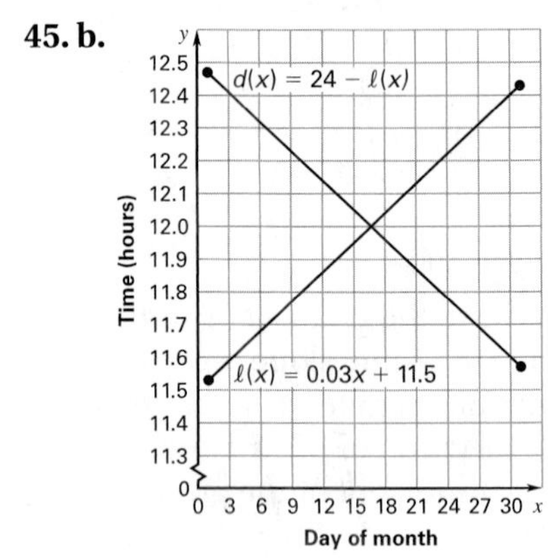

4.7 Mixed Review (p. 268)

55. 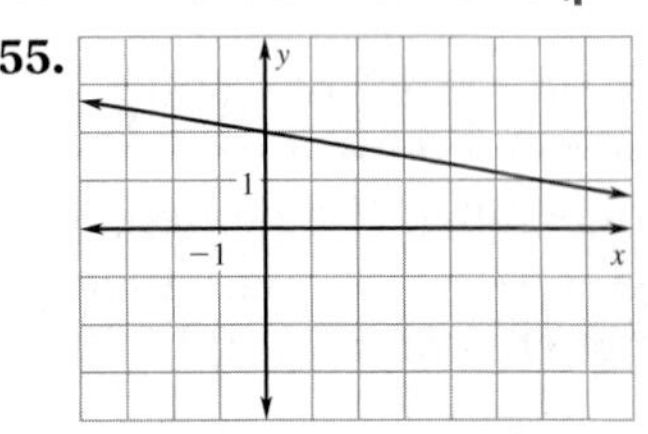

56. 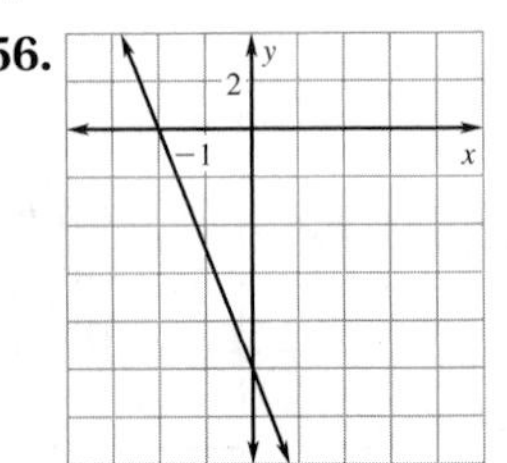

57. 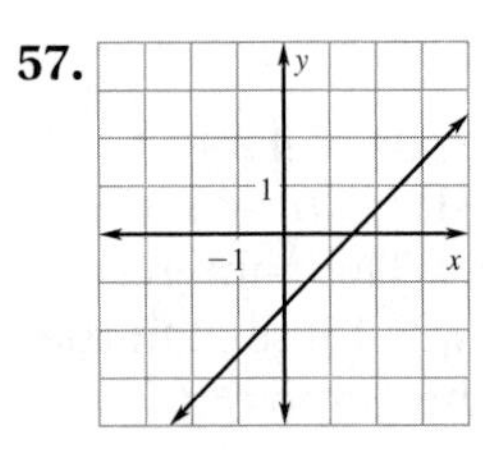

58. 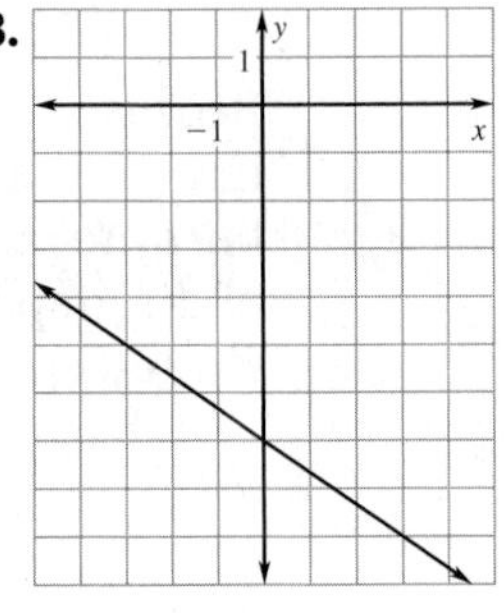

59.

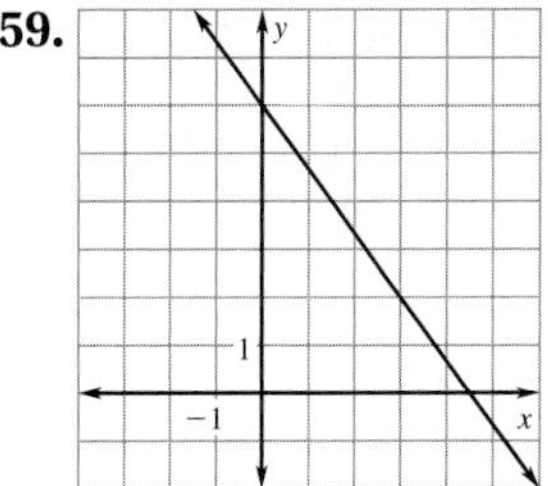

60.

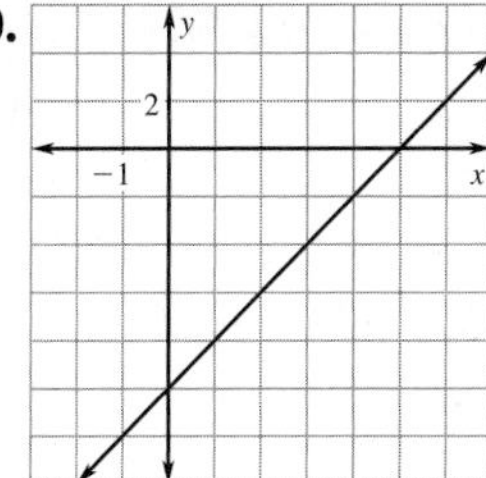

Quiz for Lessons 4.6–4.7 (p. 268)

8.

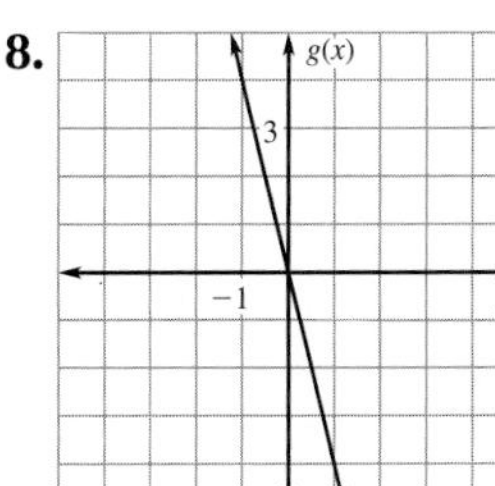

Because the slope of the graph of g is negative, the graph of g falls from left to right. The y-intercept for both graphs is 0, so both lines pass through the origin.

9.

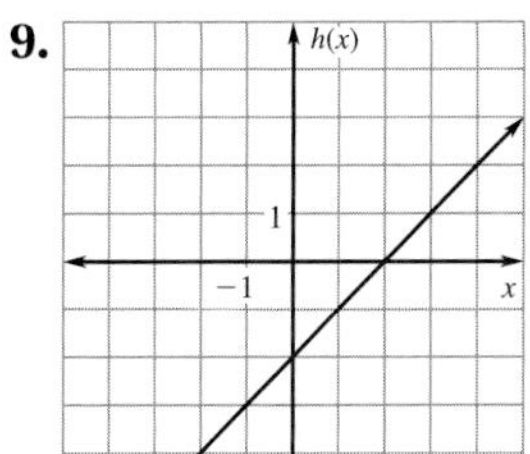

Because the graphs of h and f have the same slope, $m = 1$, the lines are parallel. The y-intercept of the graph of h is 2 less than the y-intercept of the graph of f.

Chapter Review (pp. 271–274)

31.

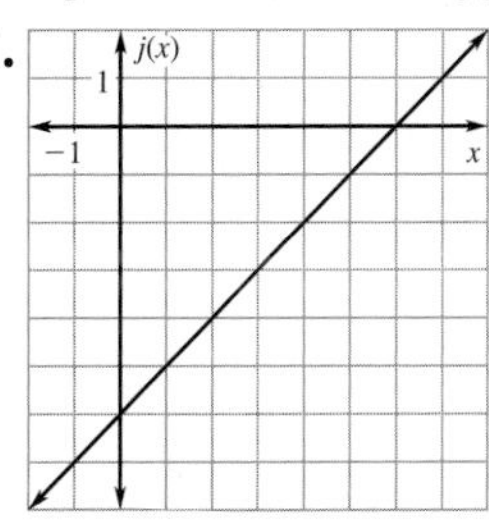

Because the graphs of j and f have the same slope, $m = 1$, the lines are parallel. The y-intercept of the graph of j is 6 less than the y-intercept of the graph of f.

32.

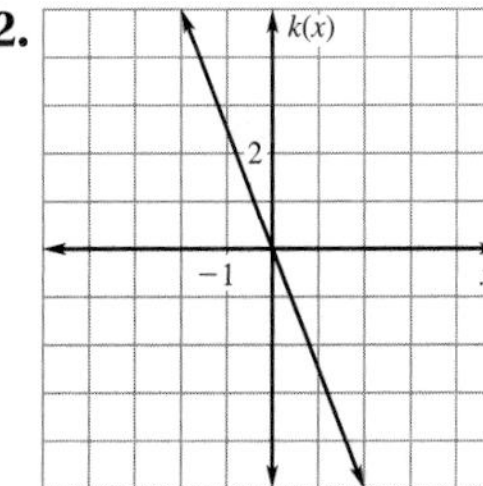

Because the slope of the graph of k is negative, the graph of k falls from left to right. The y-intercept for both graphs is 0, so both lines pass through the origin.

33.

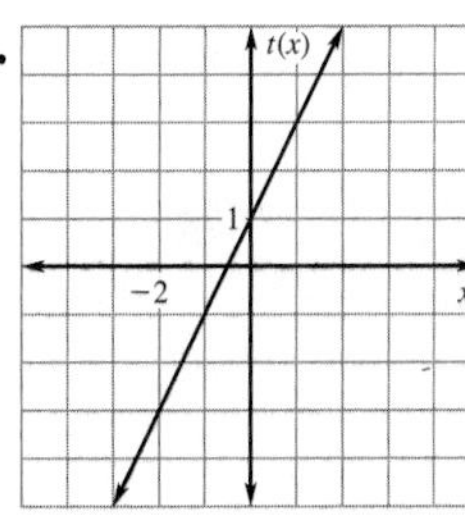

Because the slope of the graph of t is greater than the slope of the graph of f, the graph of t rises faster from left to right. The y-intercept of the graph of t is 1 more than the y-intercept of the graph of f.

Chapter Test (p. 275)

16.

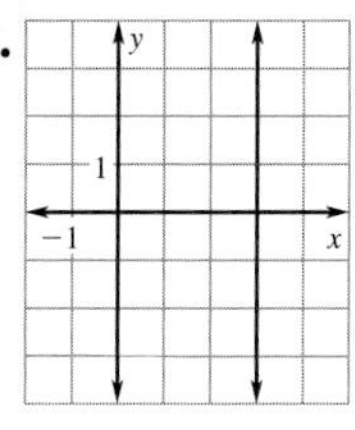

17.

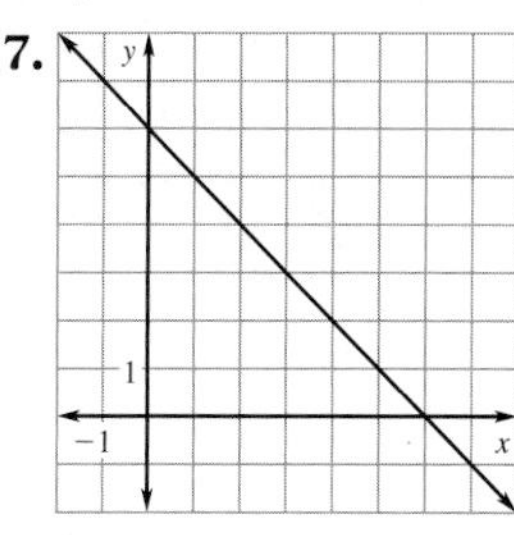

18.

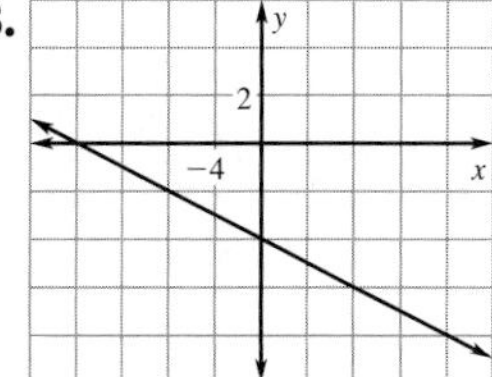

Chapter 5

5.3 Guided Practice (pp. 302–305)

2.

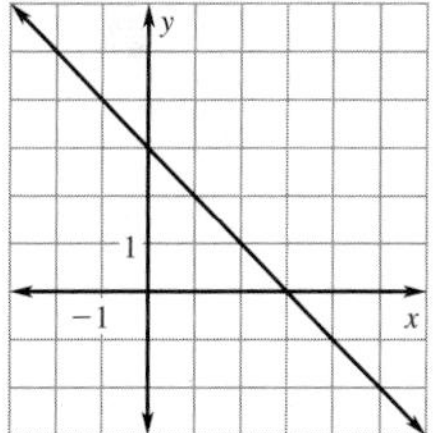

5.3 Skill Practice (pp. 305–306) **31.** No; because the increase is not at a constant rate, the situation cannot be modeled by a linear equation. **32.** Yes; because the rate is increasing at a constant rate, the situation can be modeled by a linear equation. *Sample answer:* $y - 1.2 = \frac{1}{5}(x - 1)$. **33.** No; because the increase is not at a constant rate, the situation cannot be modeled by a linear equation. **34.** Yes; because the rate is decreasing at a constant rate, the situation can be modeled by a linear equation. *Sample answer:* $y - 16 = -3(x + 3)$.

5.3 Mixed Review (p. 308)

48.

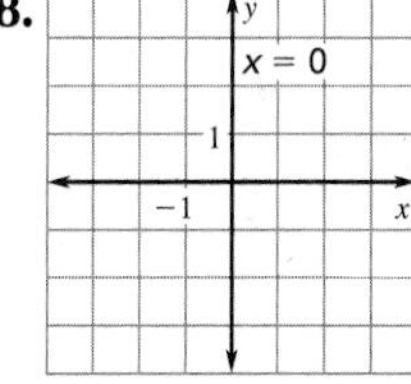

49.

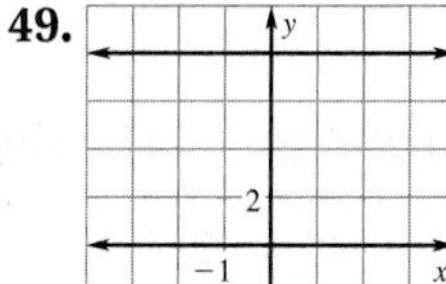

50.
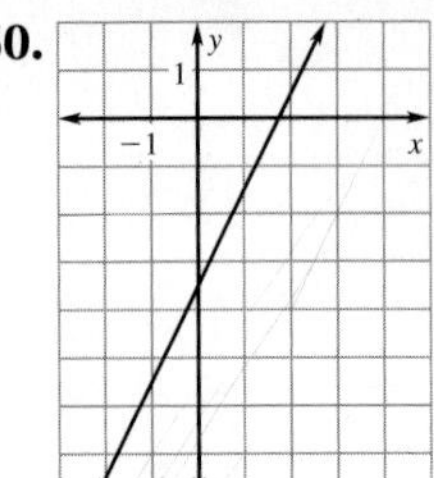

51.
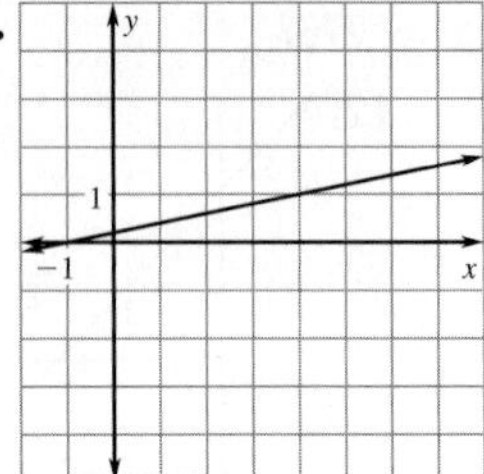

52.
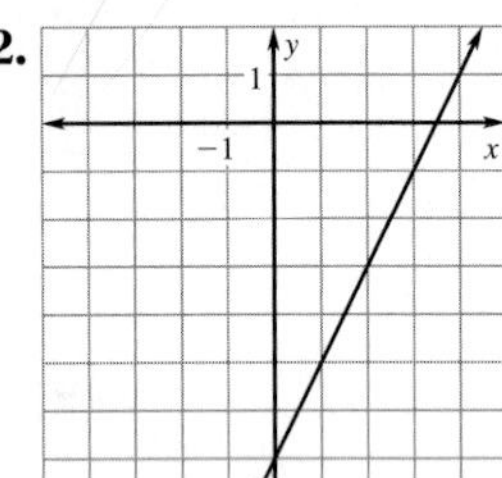

53.
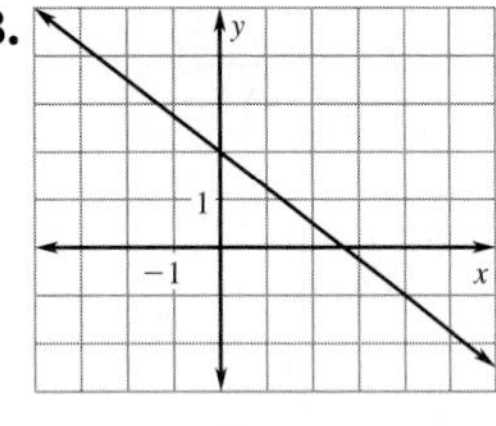

Extension (p. 310)

4.
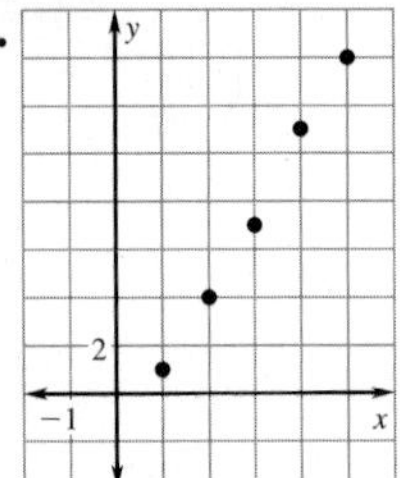

5.
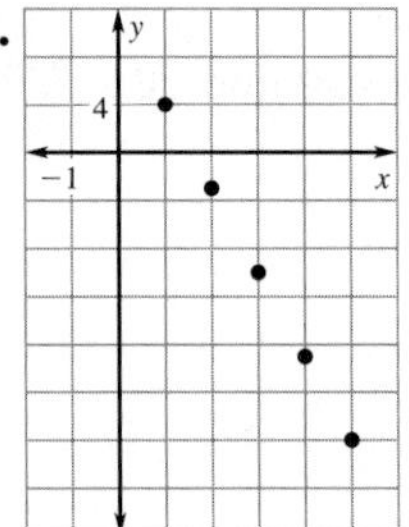

6.
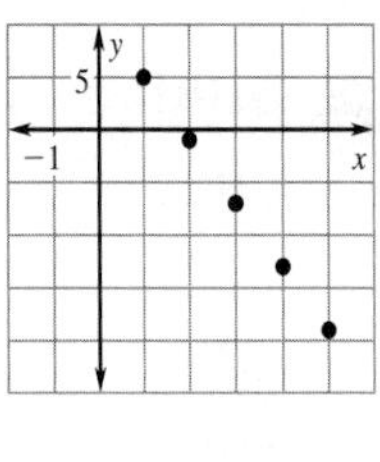

7.
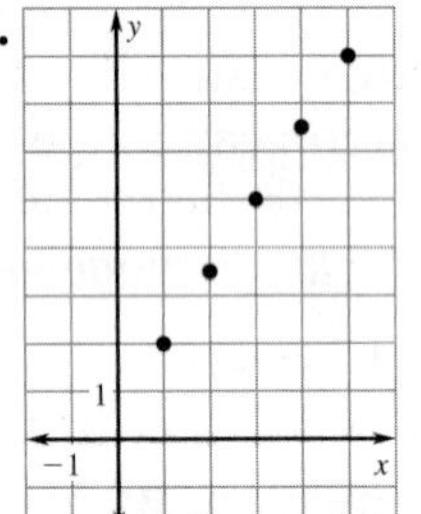

8.
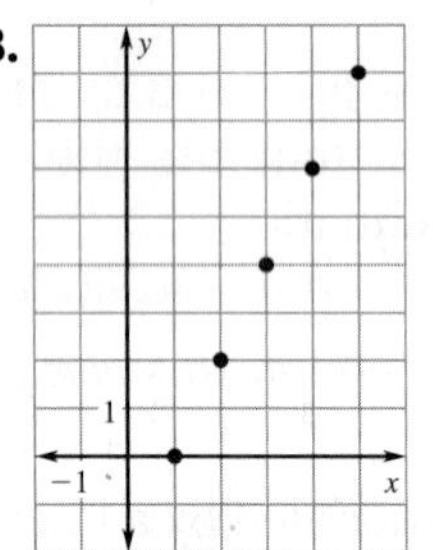

9.
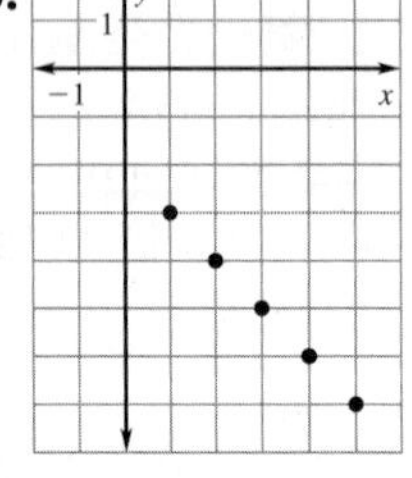

5.4 Skill Practice (p. 314) **5–10.** Sample answers are given. **5.** $2x + 2y = -20$, $3x + 3y = -30$ **6.** $x + 2y = 3$, $10x + 20y = 30$ **7.** $x - 2y = -9$, $-2x + 4y = 18$ **8.** $-3x - 4y = 2$, $-6x - 8y = 4$ **9.** $3x - y = -4$, $6x - 2y = -8$ **10.** $2x - 4y = 5$, $-4x + 8y = -10$

5.4 Problem Solving (pp. 315–316)

43. *Sample answer:*

Length (ft)	Width (ft)
5	25
10	20
15	15
20	10
25	5

Quiz for Lessons 5.1–5.4 (p. 316) **7. a.** $y - 2 = x + 5$ or $y - 3 = x + 4$ **b.** $-x + y = 7$ **8. a.** $y + 9 = \frac{4}{3}(x + 6)$ or $y + 1 = \frac{4}{3}x$ **b.** $-\frac{4}{3}x + y = -1$ **9. a.** $y - 1 = 4(x - 1)$ or $y - 9 = 4(x - 3)$ **b.** $-4x + y = -3$

Chapter 6

6.1 Guided Practice (pp. 357–358)

1.
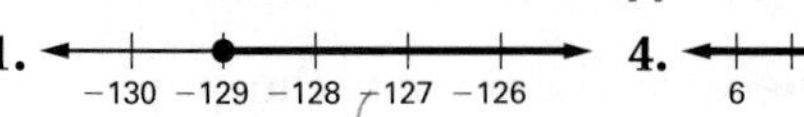

4.
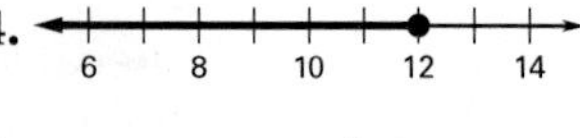

5. 4.2; 2 3 4 5 6

6. $-\frac{1}{2}$; −3 −2 −1 0 1

6.1 Skill Practice (pp. 359–360)

10. −2 −1 0 1 2

11. −18 −16 −14 −12 −10

12. $-4\frac{1}{4}$; −6 −5 −4 −3 −2

13. $-\frac{1}{5}$; −1 0 1 2 3

14. −15.8; −17 −16 −15 −14 −13

15. −17.6; −18 −16 −14 −12

16. −3 −2 −1 0 1

17. 7 9 11 13 15

18. 5 7 9 11 13

19. $-1\frac{1}{6}$; −4 −2 0 2 4

20. 8.8; 0 2 4 6 8 10

21. −6.84; −8 −6 −4 −2

22. −13 −12 −11 −10 −9

23. −5 −4 −3 −2 −1

6.1 Problem Solving (pp. 360–361) **36.** 2 axles: $w \le 19{,}800$ lb, 3 axles: $w \le 39{,}800$ lb, 4 axles: $w \le 54{,}800$ lb, 5 axles: $w \le 65{,}800$ lb; no; the total weight, 34,200 pounds, would exceed the maximum weight allowed, 34,000 pounds.

37. a.

Original price, x ($)	19,459	19,989	20,549	22,679	23,999
Final price, y ($)	16,459	16,989	17,549	19,679	20,999

6.2 Skill Practice (pp. 366–367)

3.

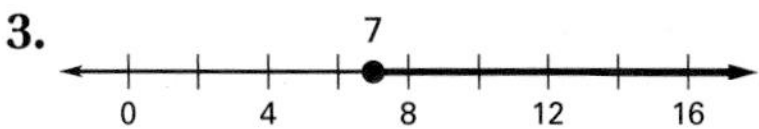

4.

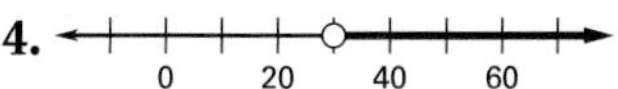

5. 0 2 4 6 8

6. −400 −200 0 200 400

7. 28; 0 10 20 30 40

8. 0 4 8 12 16

9. −120; −300 −200 −100 0 100

10. −2 0 2 4 6

11. −22.5; −40 −30 −20 −10 0

12. −27; −40 −30 −20 −10 0

13. −8 −6 −4 −2 0

14. 32; −40 −20 0 20 40

15. −1.5 −1 −0.5 0 0.5

16. −37.2; −40 −30 −20 −10 0

17. −0.8 −0.6 −0.4 −0.2 0

18. 0.49; −1.5 −1 −0.5 0 0.5

19. −1.5 −1 −0.5 0 0.5

20. 37.5; 0 20 40 60 80

21.

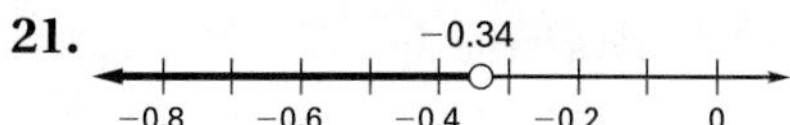

22. 45; 0 20 40 60 80

23. −54; −60 −40 −20 0 20

24. −0.38; −0.8 −0.6 −0.4 −0.2 0

25. −24; −30 −20 −10 0 10

26. 0.61; 0 0.2 0.4 0.6 0.8

6.2 Problem Solving (pp. 367–368) **41. b.** No; the area added by increasing both the length and the width by 20 feet can be divided into 2 rectangles (80 feet by 20 feet and 82 feet by 20 feet) and 1 square (20 feet by 20 feet). The 400 square feet of the square is large enough to hold one horse, and the rectangular areas will be able to hold additional horses.

Quiz for Lessons 6.1–6.2 (p. 368)

1. **2.**

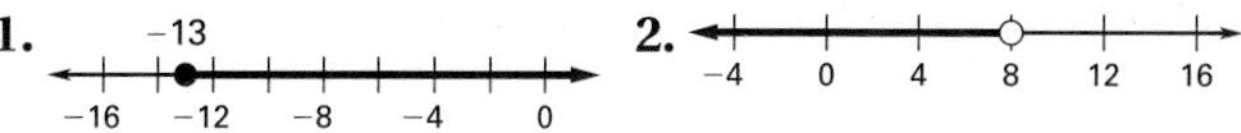

3. **4.**

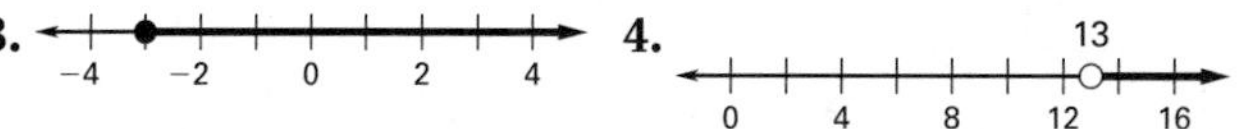

5. −4 0 4 8 12

6. −31; −40 −20 0 20 40

7. −13; −16 −12 −8 −4 0

8. 28; −40 −20 0 20 40

9. −48; −80 −60 −40 −20 0

6.3 Problem Solving (pp. 373–374)

41. a.

Pitches per inning, p	15	16	17	18	19
Total number of pitches, t	98	101	104	107	110

42. c. More than \$875; for price $p > 175$, the tax paid in the 4% sales tax state is $0.04p$, and the tax paid in the other state is $0.05(p - 175)$, or $0.05p - 8.75$. To find the values of p for which the first expression is less than the second, solve the inequality $0.04p < 0.05p - 8.75$ to get $p > \frac{8.75}{0.01}$, or $p > 875$. Check $p = \$900$: The tax paid in the 4% sales tax state is $0.04(\$900) = \$36$ and the tax paid in the other state is $0.05(\$900 - \$175) = \$36.25$.

ADDITIONAL ANSWERS

6.3 Problem Solving Workshop (pp. 375–376) **2.** At most 4 games; Method 1: Work backward. Begin with \$400 and subtract the cost of the console to find out how much money you have to spend on games: \$400 − \$259 = \$141. Make a table of values showing the amount of money you have left after buying various numbers of games.

Number of games bought	Amount of money left
0	\$141
1	\$112
2	\$83
3	\$54
4	\$25

After buying 4 games, you will not have enough money left to buy a fifth. You can buy at most 4 games. Method 2: Use a graph. Write and graph an equation that gives the total amount of money y you spend as a function of the number of games x that you buy: $y = 29x + 259$. Graph $y = 400$ on the same coordinate plane.

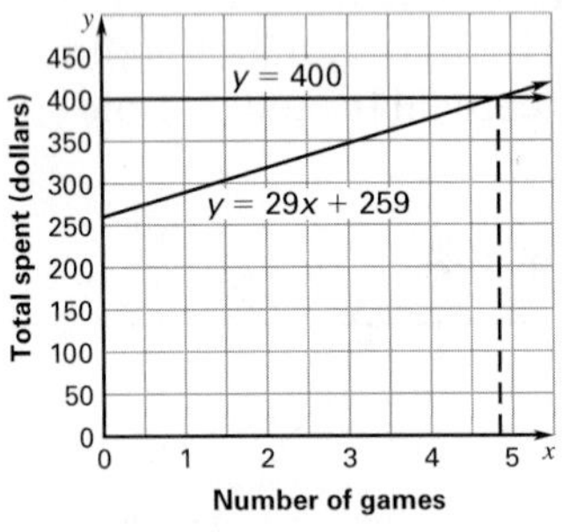

The graphs intersect between $x = 4$ and $x = 5$. Because you can spend at most \$400, the solutions are the x-coordinates of the points on the graph of $y = 29x + 259$ that lie on or below the graph of $y = 400$. Only integer values of x make sense in this situation, so you can buy at most 4 games. **4.** At most 7 weeks; Method 1: Work backward. Begin with \$247 and make a table of values showing the amount of money you have left in your account after various numbers of \$20 withdrawals.

Number of \$20 withdrawals	Amount of money left in account
0	\$247
1	\$227
2	\$207
3	\$187
4	\$167
5	\$147
6	\$127
7	\$107
8	\$87

If you make \$20 withdrawals for 8 weeks your account balance will fall below the required \$100, so you can make \$20 withdrawals for at most 7 weeks. Method 2: Use a graph. Write and graph an equation that gives the total amount of money y in your account as a function of the number x of \$20 withdrawals that you make: $y = -20x + 247$. Graph $y = 100$ on the same coordinate plane.

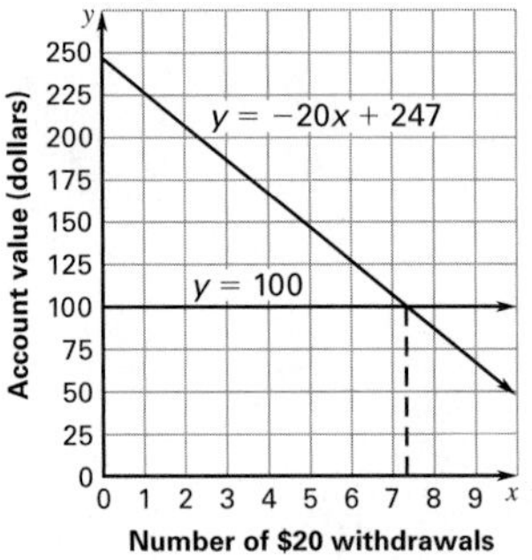

The graphs intersect between $x = 7$ and $x = 8$. Because your account must have at least \$100, the solutions are the x-coordinates of the points on the graph of $y = -20x + 247$ that lie on or above the graph of $y = 100$. Only integer values of x make sense in this situation, so you can make \$20 withdrawals for at most 7 weeks.

6.4 Guided Practice (pp. 380–383)

1. **2.**

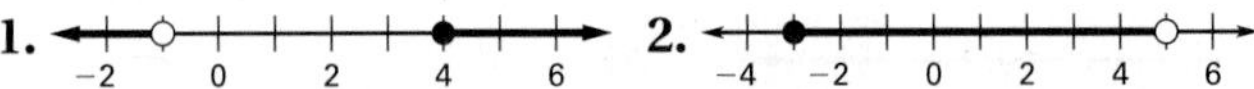

3. 4.5

4. 9

5.

6.

6.4 Skill Practice (pp. 384–385)

9.

10.

11.

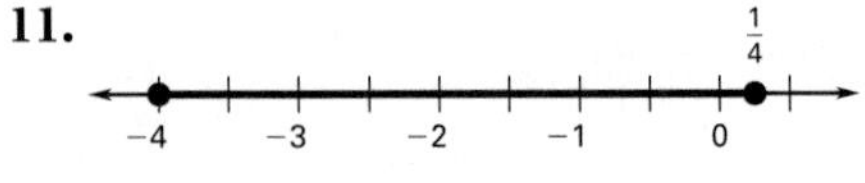

12.

13.

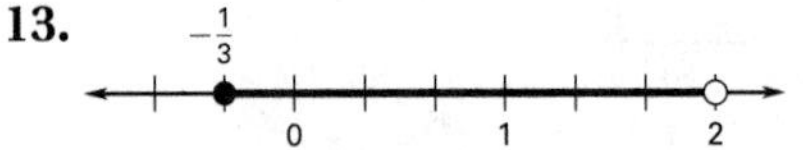

14.

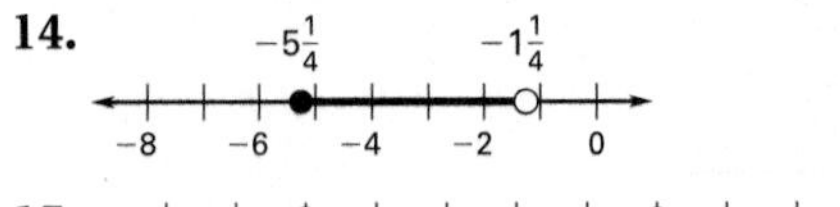

15.

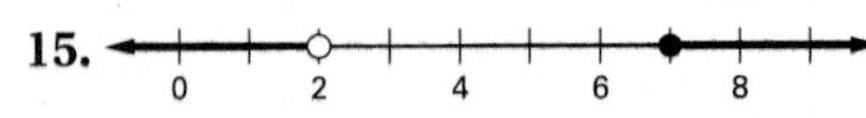

16.

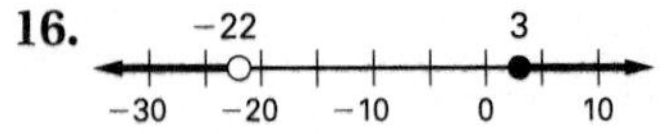

17. 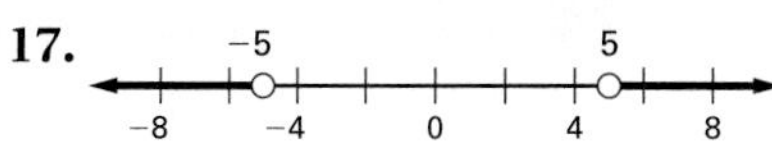

18. 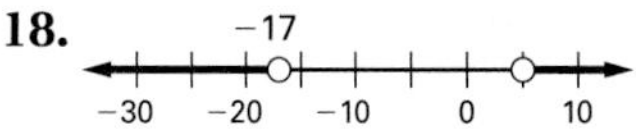

19. 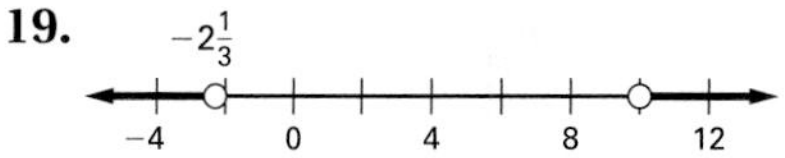

20. 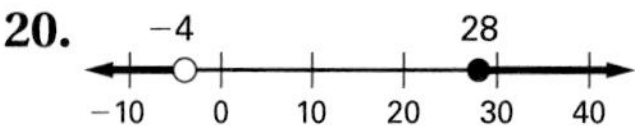

Extension (pp. 396–397)

1. 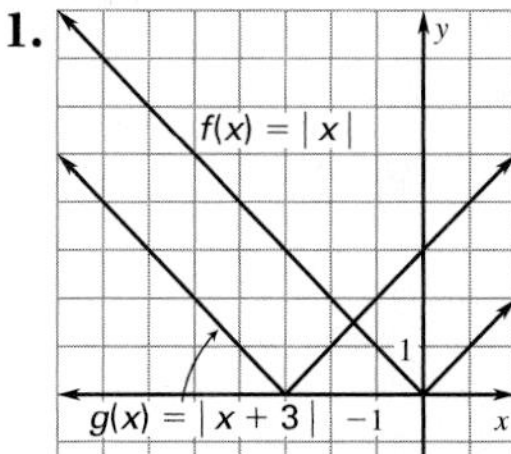

The graph of g is 3 units to the left of the graph of f.

2. 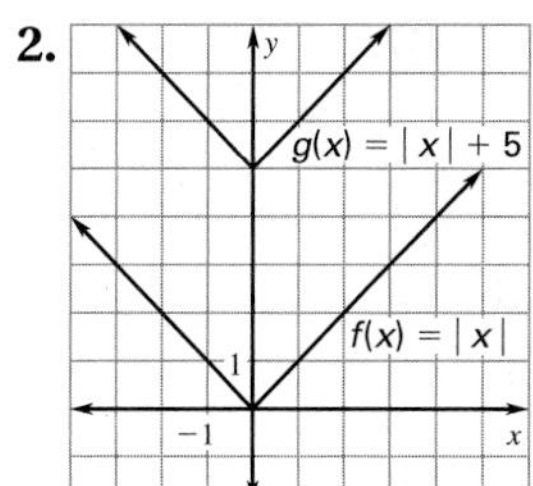

The graph of g is 5 units above the graph of f.

3. 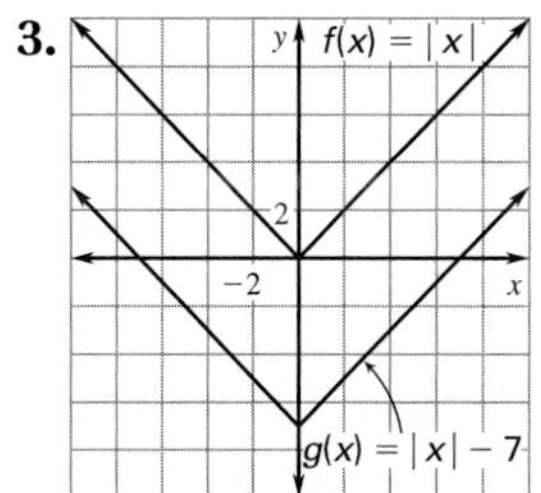

The graph of g is 7 units below the graph of f.

4. 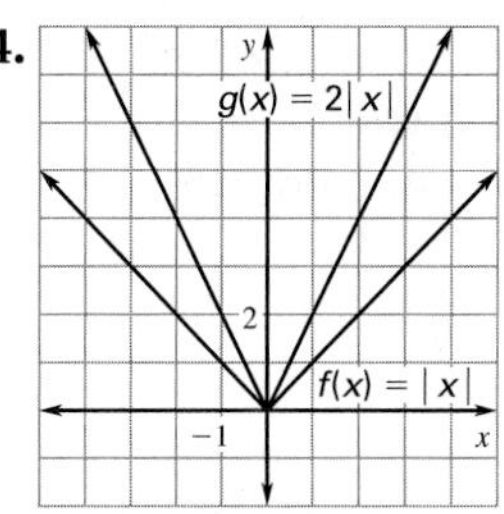

The graph of g opens up and is narrower than the graph of f.

5. 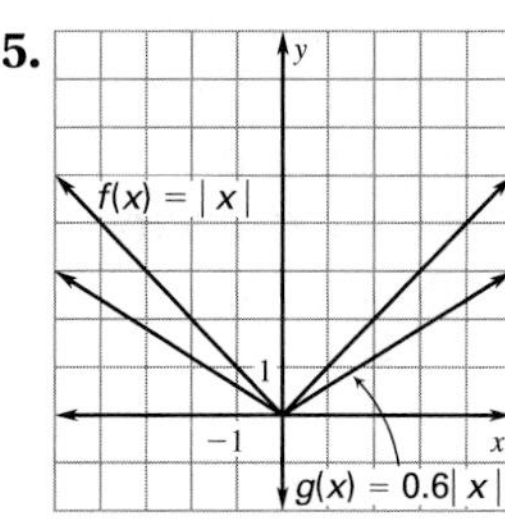

The graph of g opens up and is wider than the graph of f.

6. 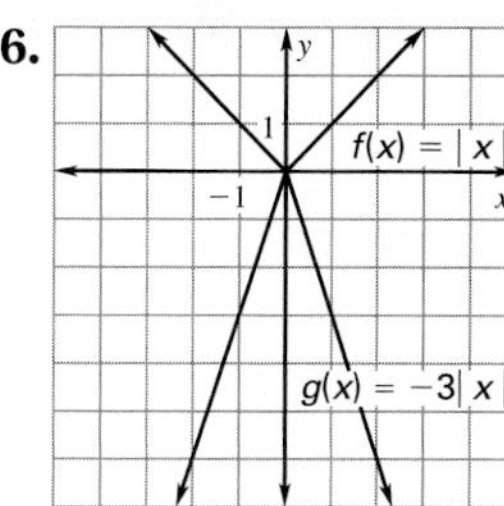

The graph of g opens down and is narrower than the graph of f.

6.6 Problem Solving (pp. 402–403)

38. a.

Measured compression, p (lb)	275	325	375	425	475
Absolute deviation from 350 (lb)	75	25	25	75	125

6.6 Mixed Review (p. 403)

42. 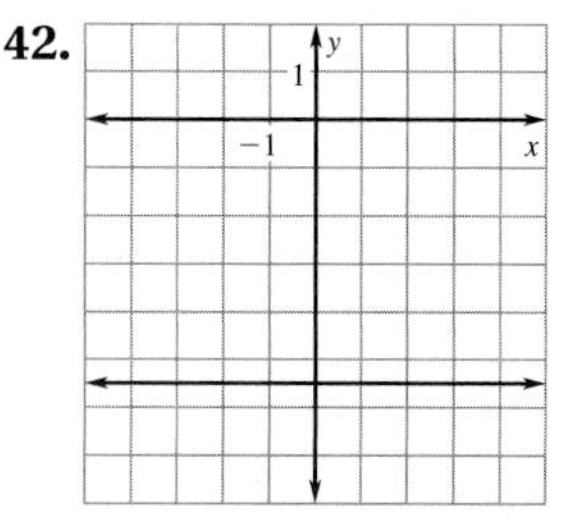

43. 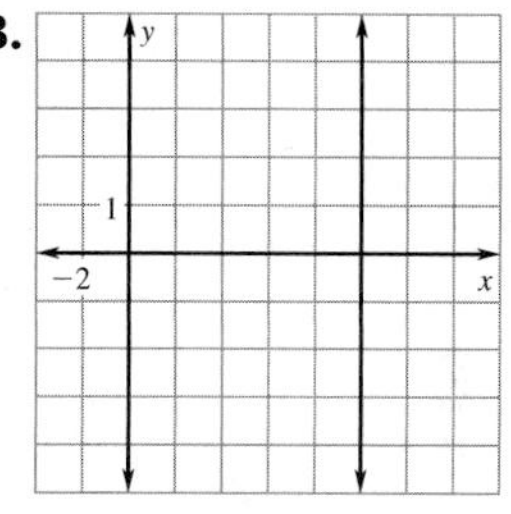

44. 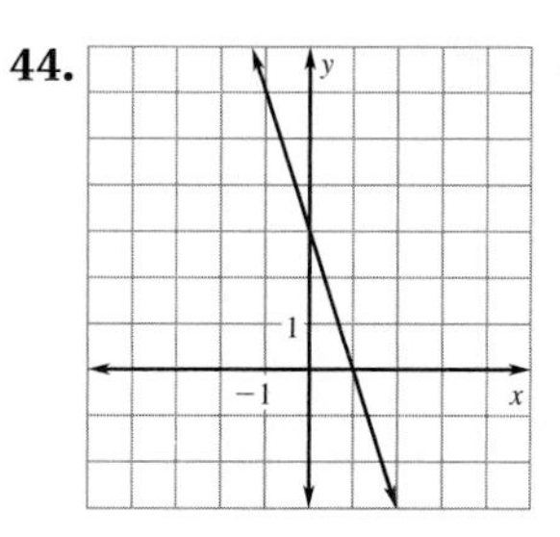

45. 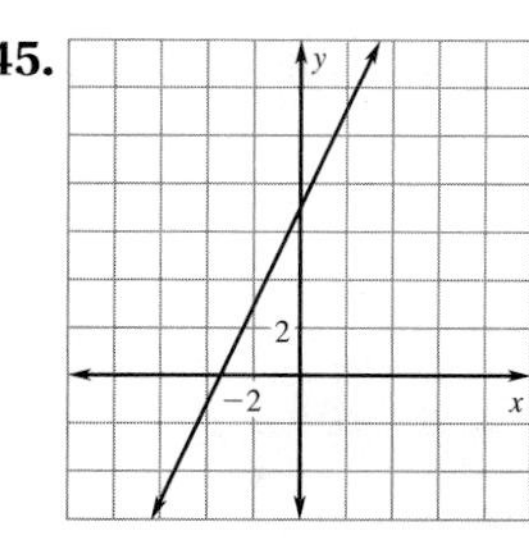

46. 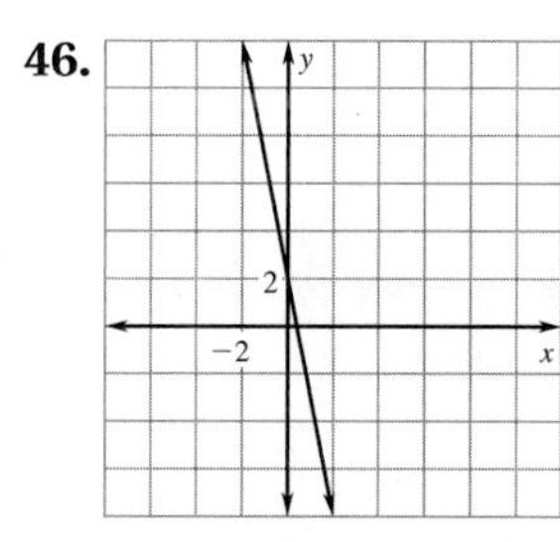

47. 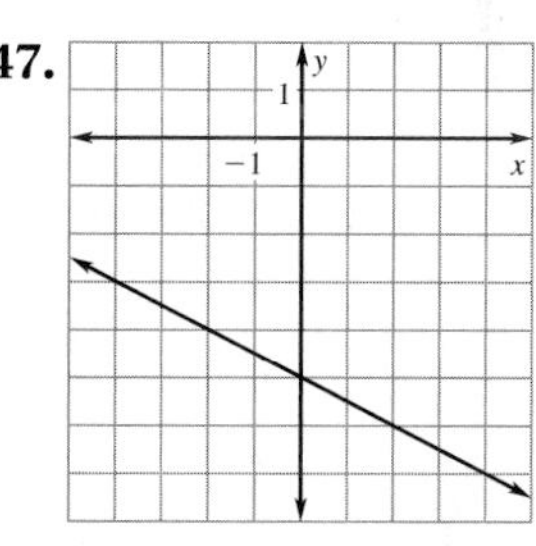

6.7 Skill Practice (pp. 409–410)

17. 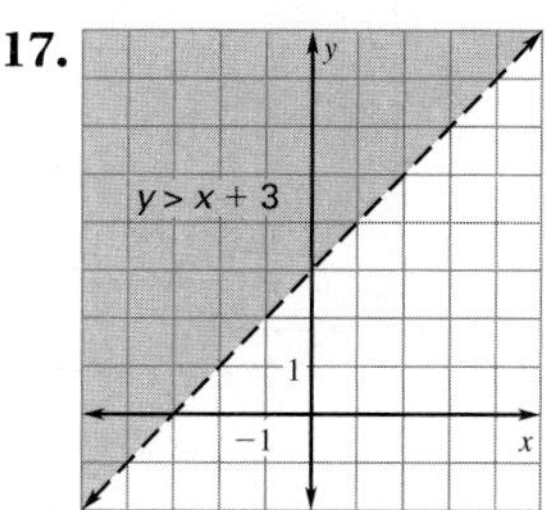

18. 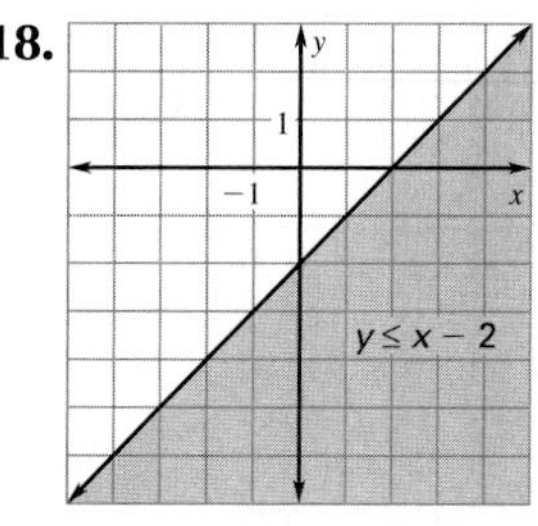

ADDITIONAL ANSWERS

19.
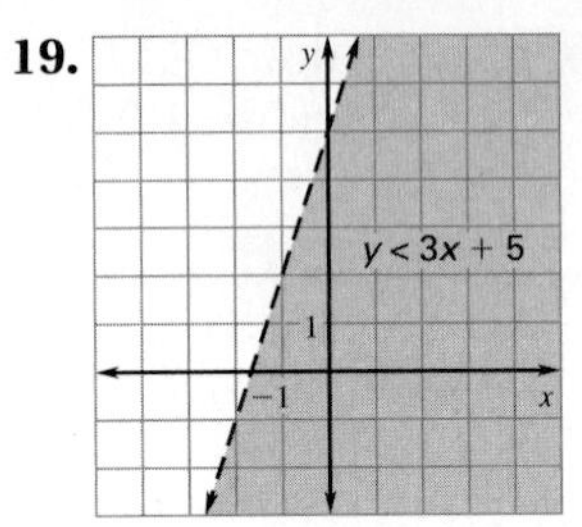

20.
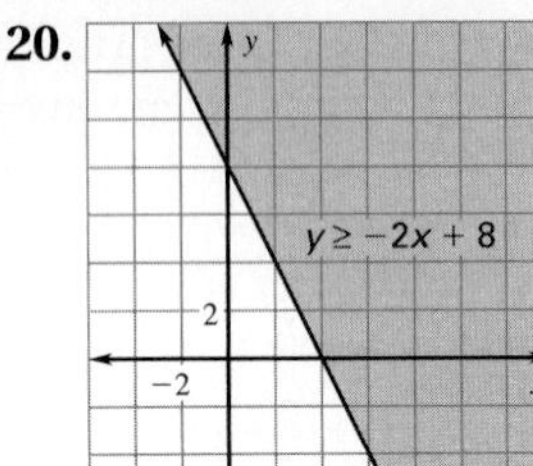

21.
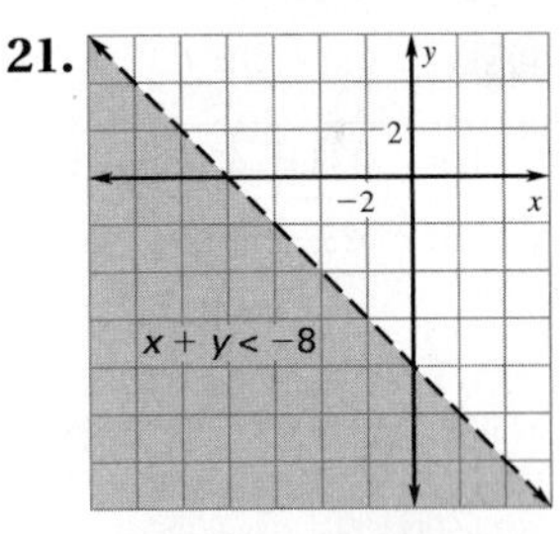

22.
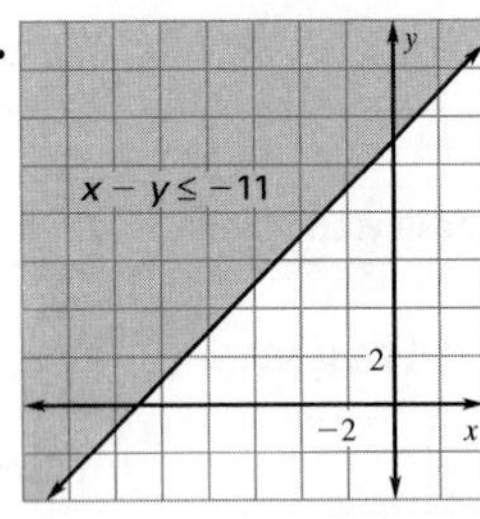

23.
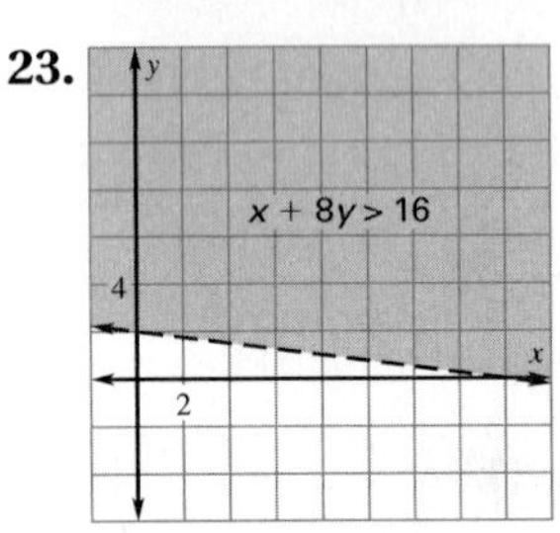

24.
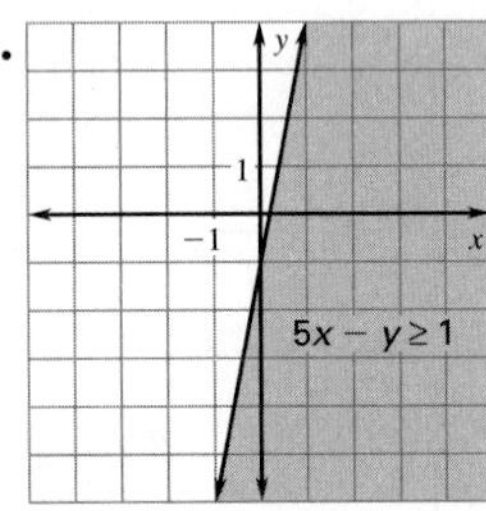

25.
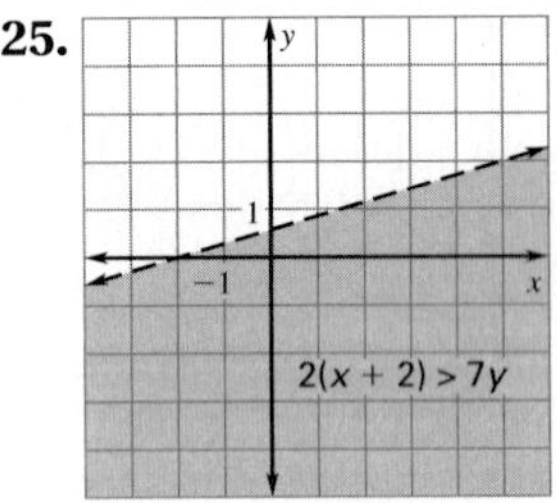

26.
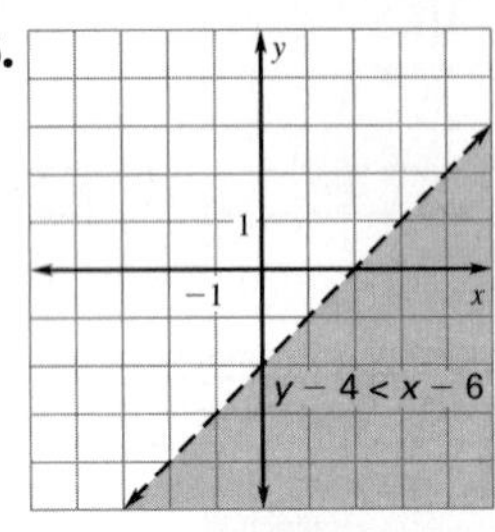

27.
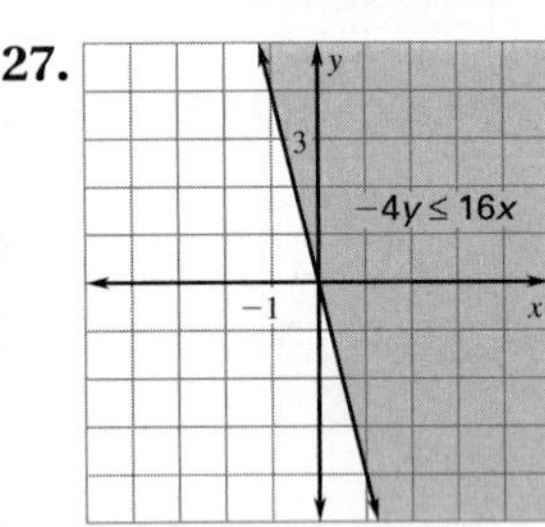

28.
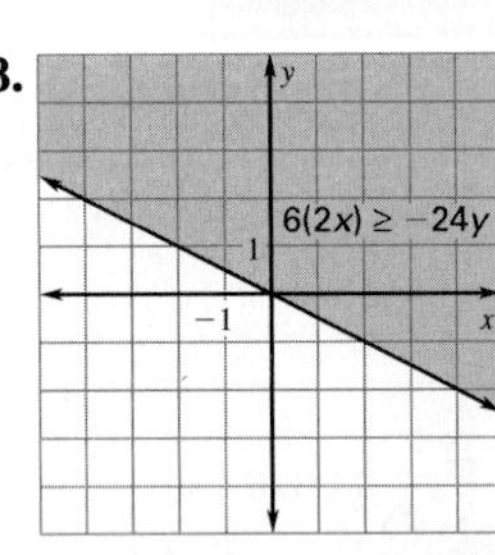

29.
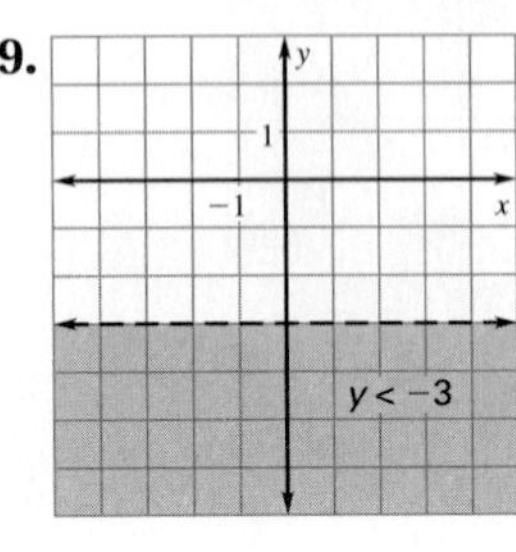

30.
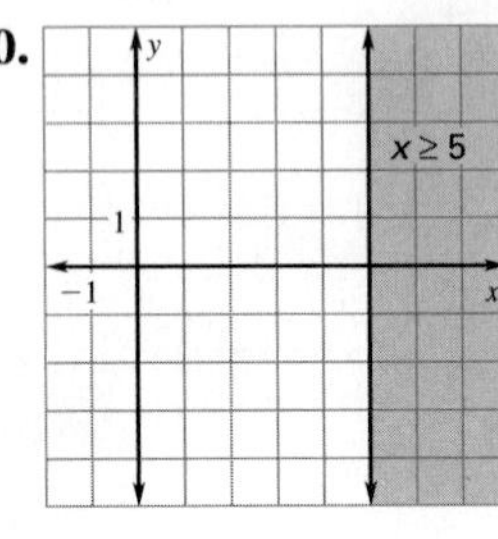

31.
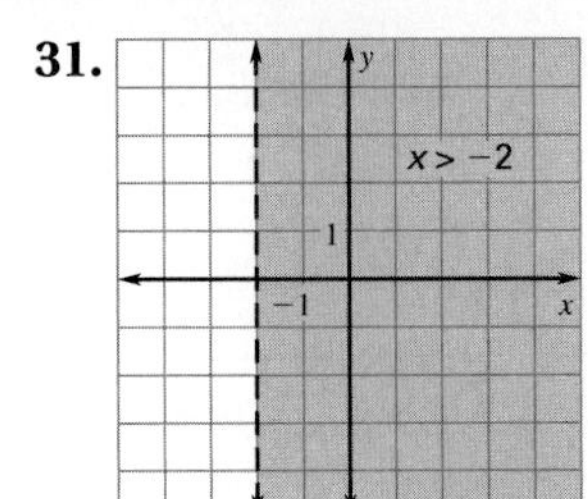

32.
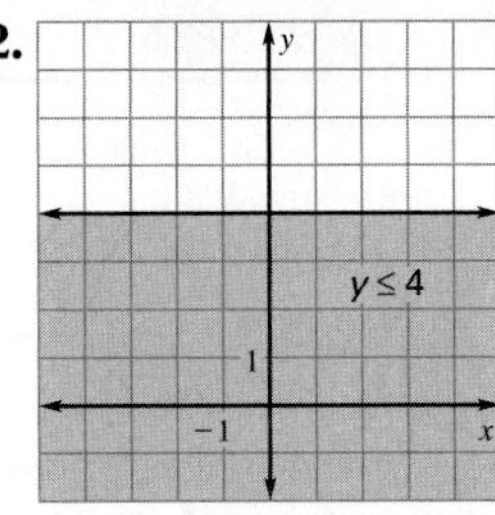

33.
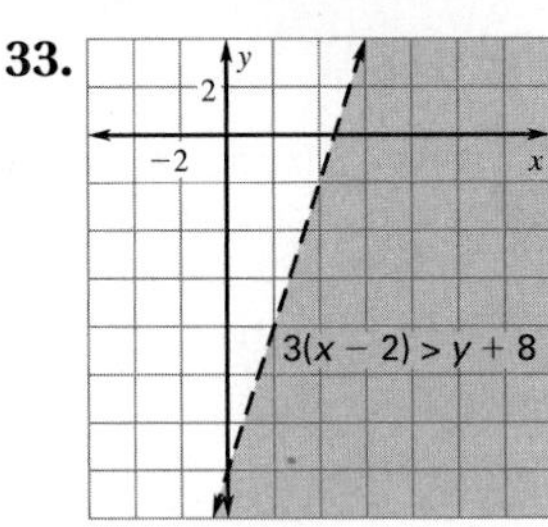

34.
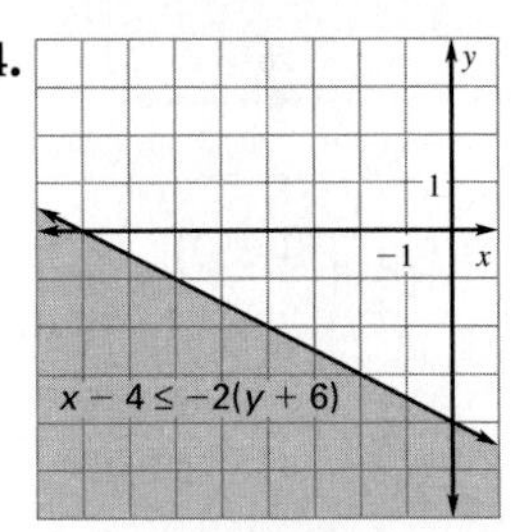

35.
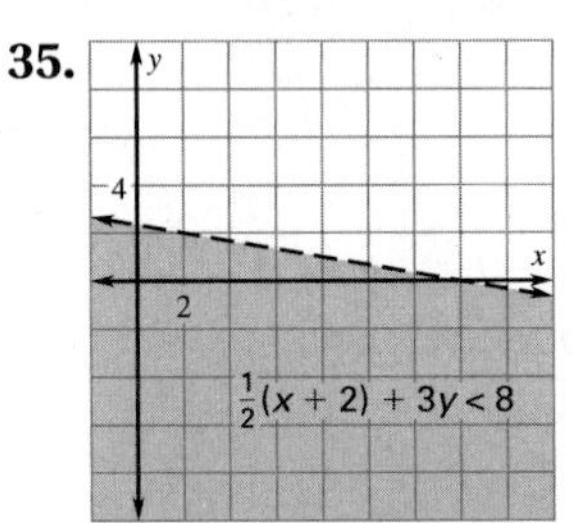

36.
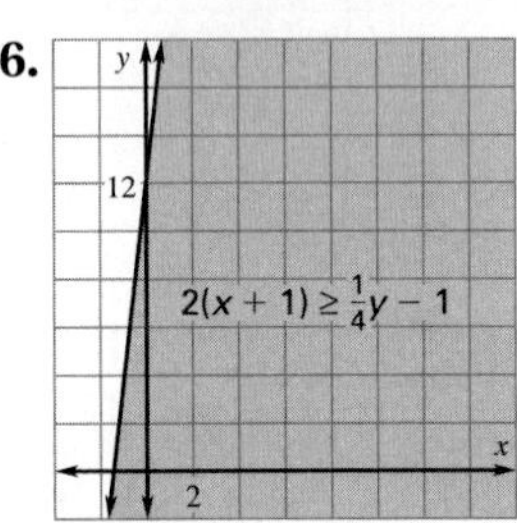

37.
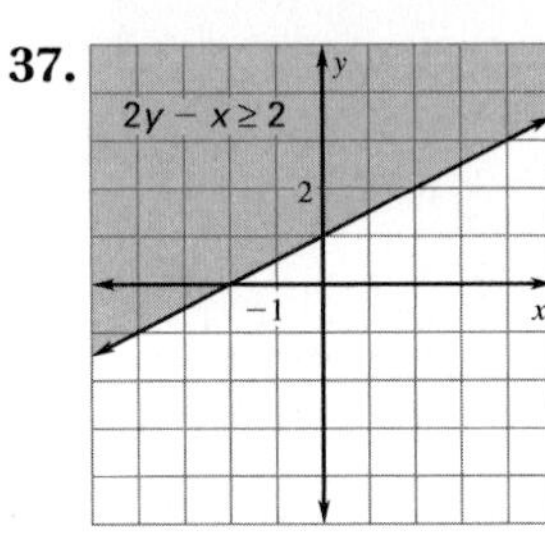

38.
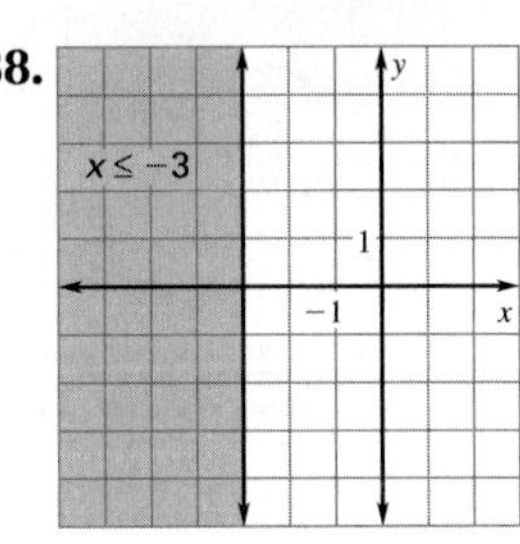

6.7 Problem Solving (pp. 410–412)

53.
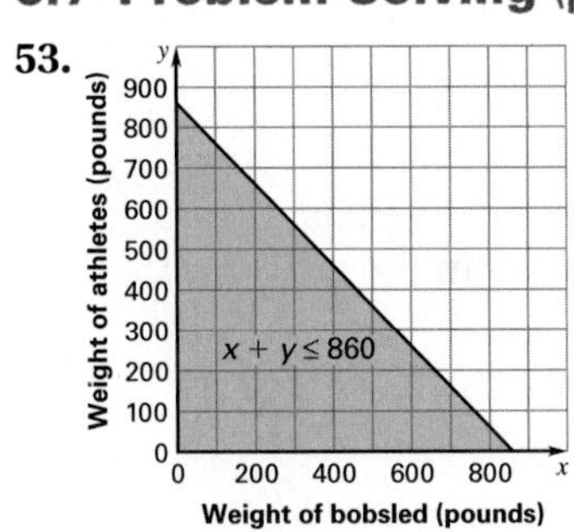

Sample answer: The solution (450, 400) means that the bobsled can weigh 450 pounds when the combined weight of the athletes is 400 pounds.

54.
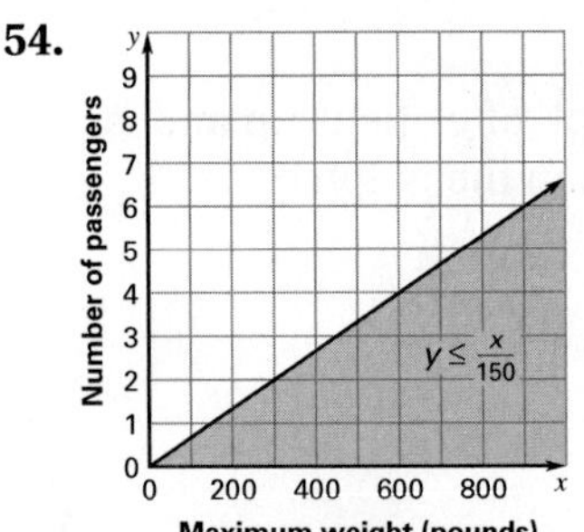

Sample answer: The solution (1200, 8) means that the elevator can have 8 passengers when the elevator's maximum weight capacity is 1200 pounds.

60. a.

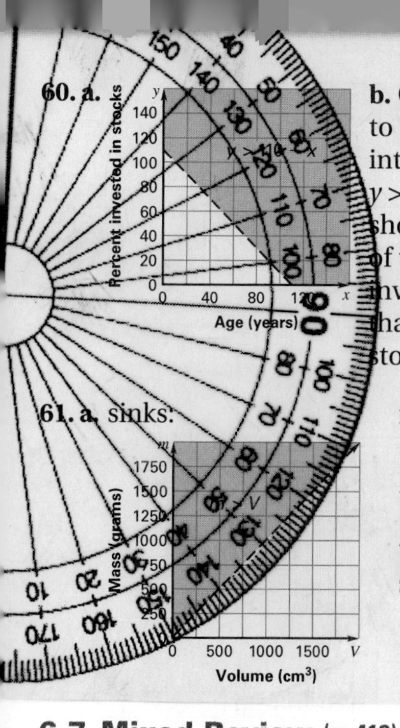

b. Greater than 80% and up to 100%; substitute $x = 30$ into the inequality to get $y > 110 - 30$, so the investor should invest more than 80% of the money in stocks. The investor cannot invest more than 100% of the money in stocks.

61. a. sinks:

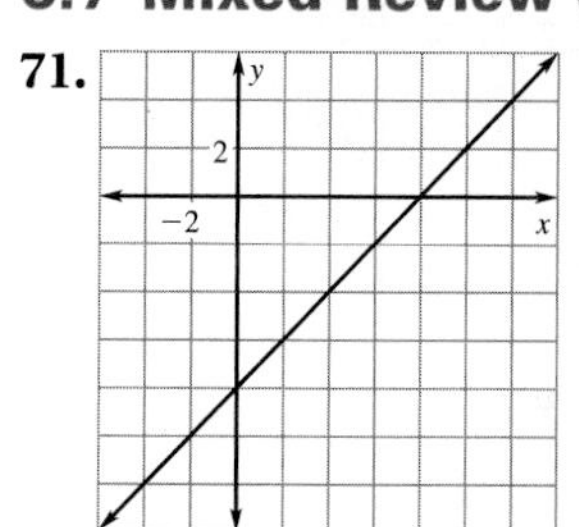

floats:

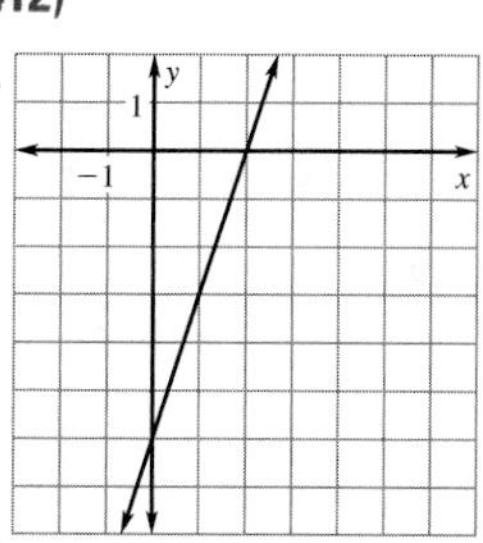

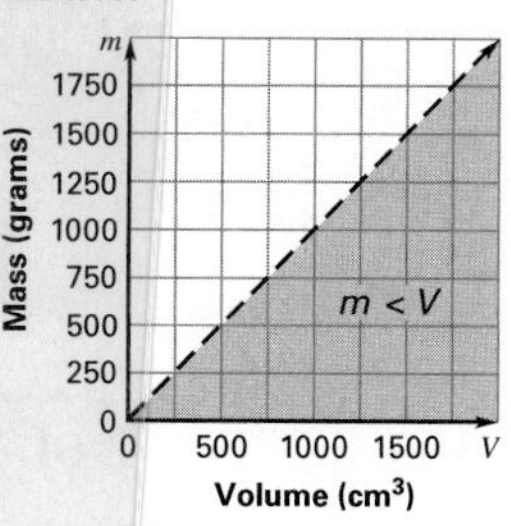

6.7 Mixed Review (p. 412)

71.

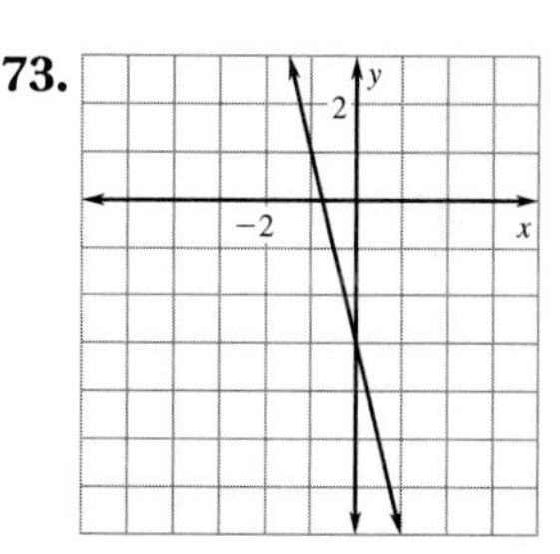

72.

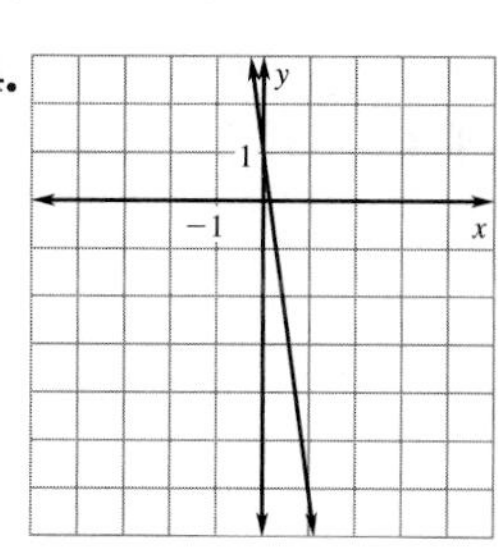

73.

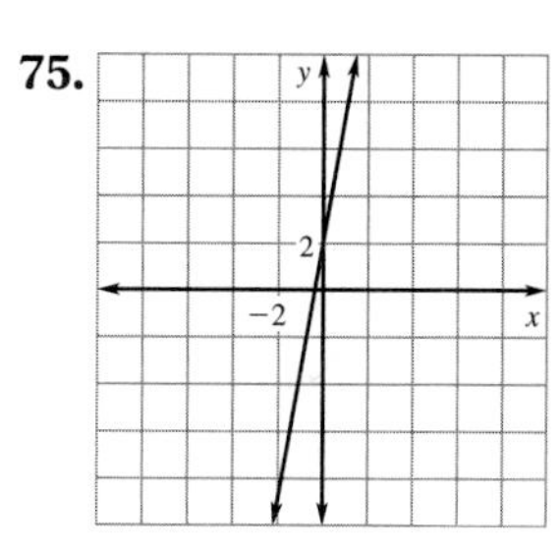

74.

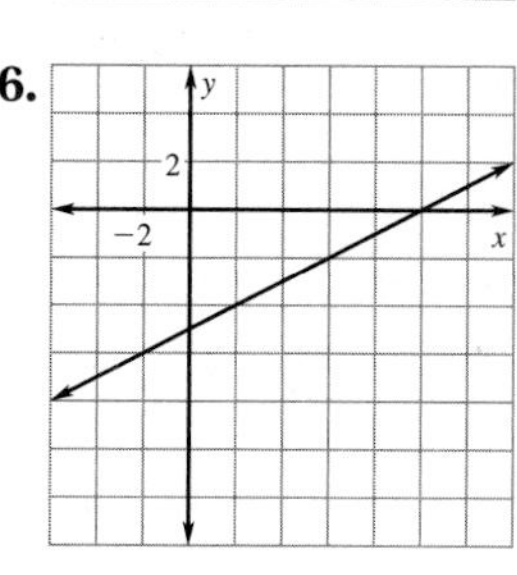

75.

76.

Quiz for Lessons 6.5–6.7 (p. 412)

4. **5.**

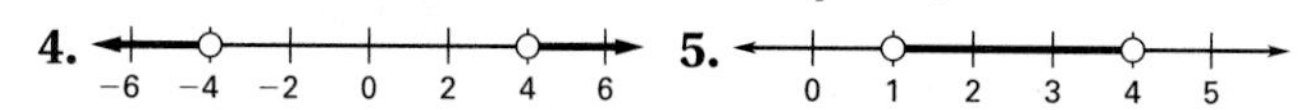

6.

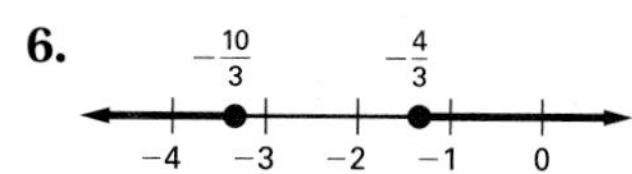

7.

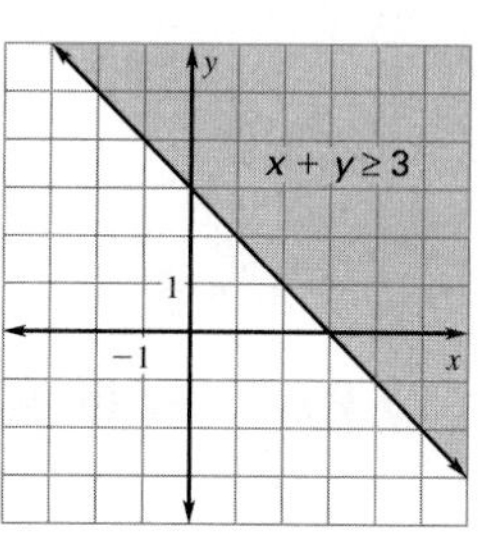

8.

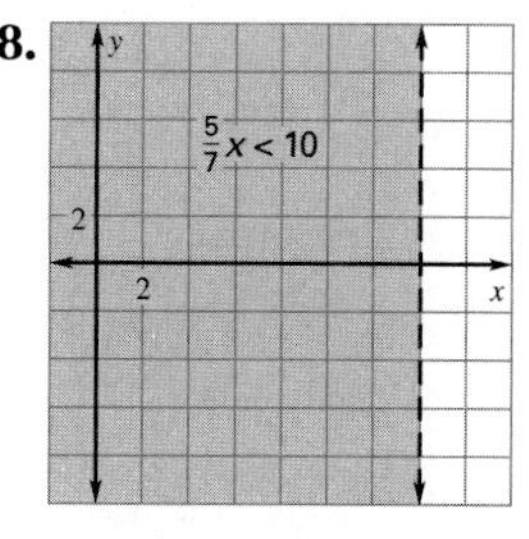

9.

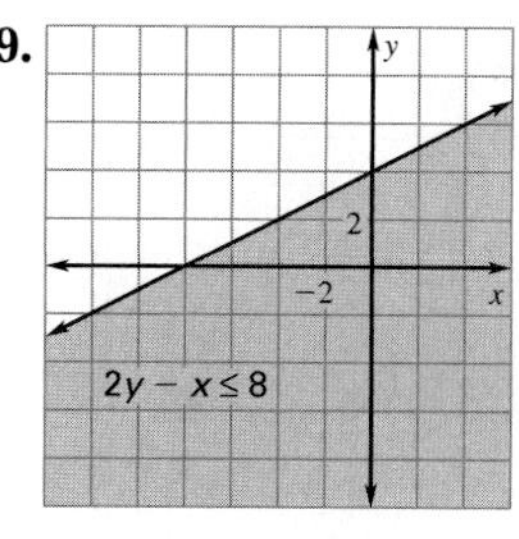

Chapter Test (p. 419)

29.

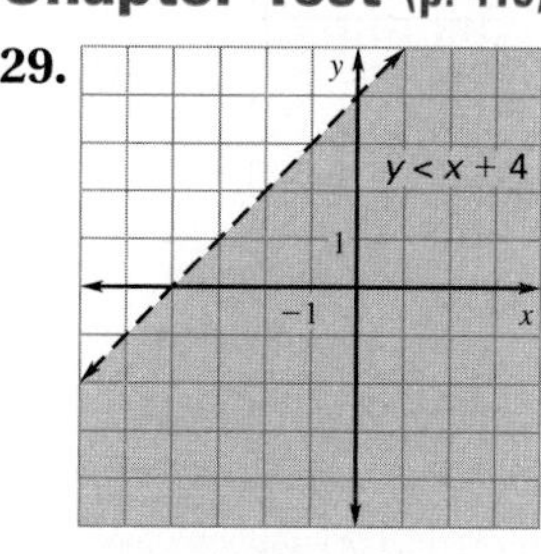

30.

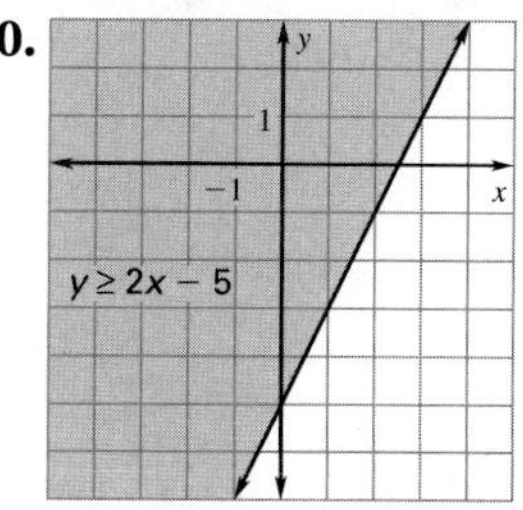

31.

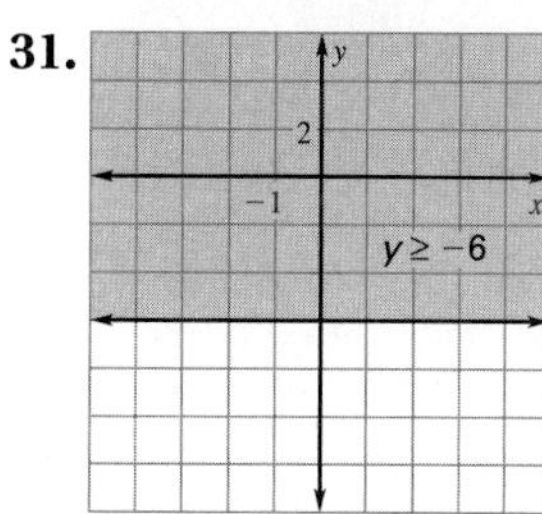

Chapter 7

7.3 Mixed Review (p. 450)

46.

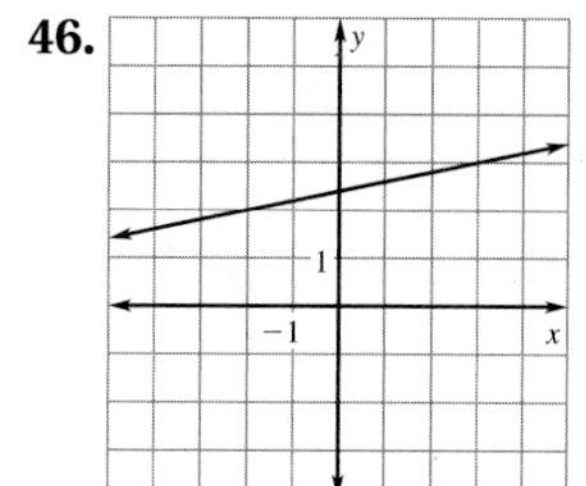

47.

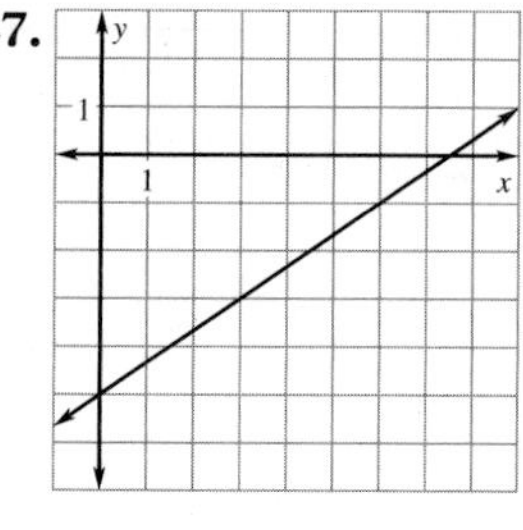

ADDITIONAL ANSWERS

48. 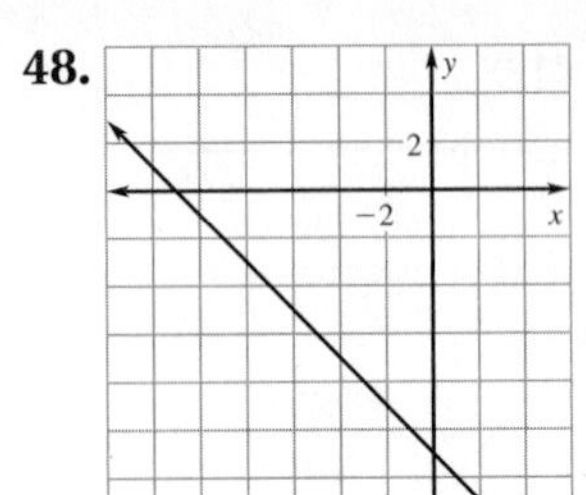

49. 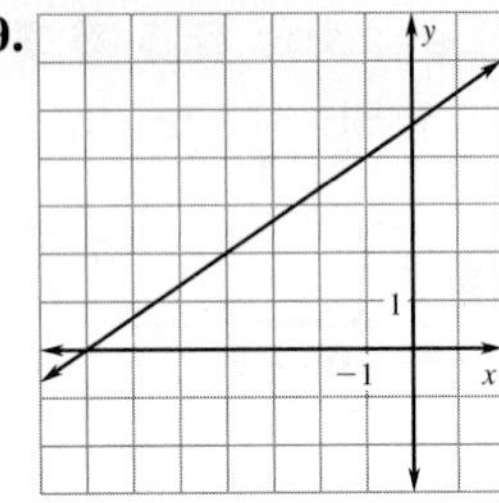

7.4 Mixed Review (p. 457)

45. 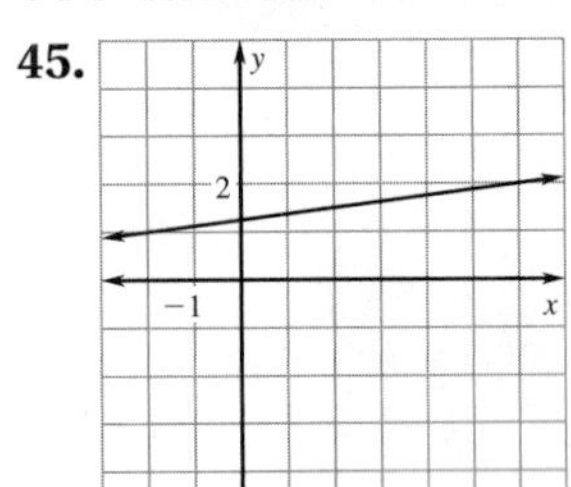

46. 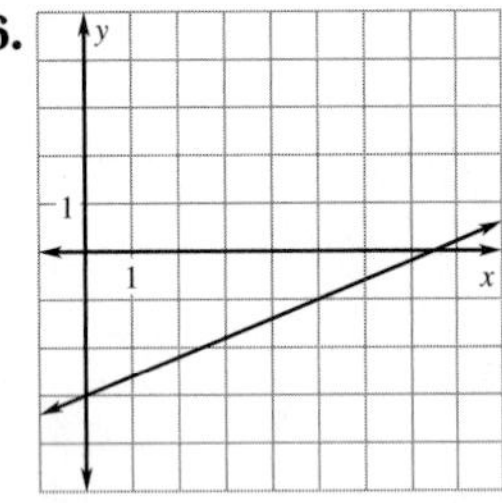

47. 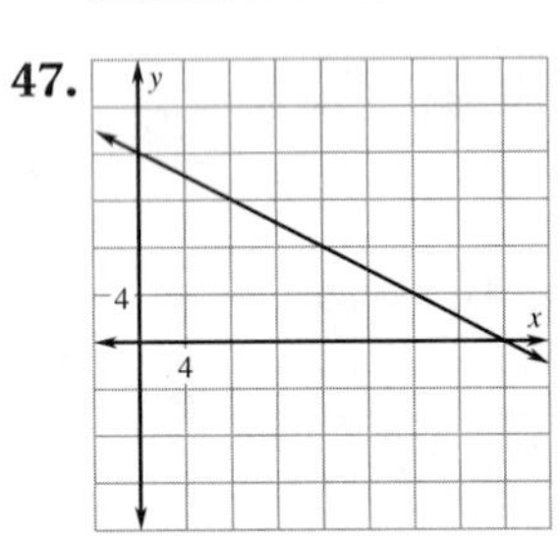

48. 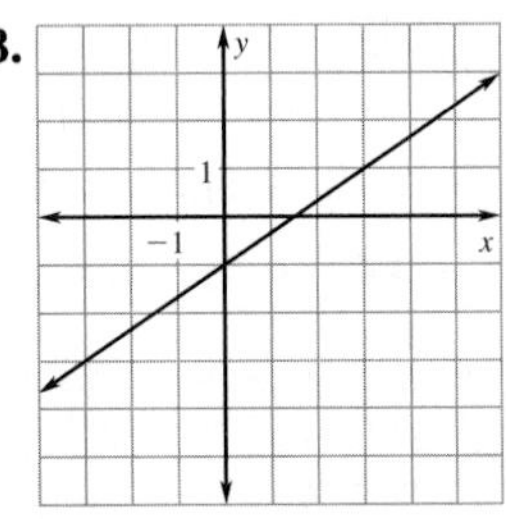

49. 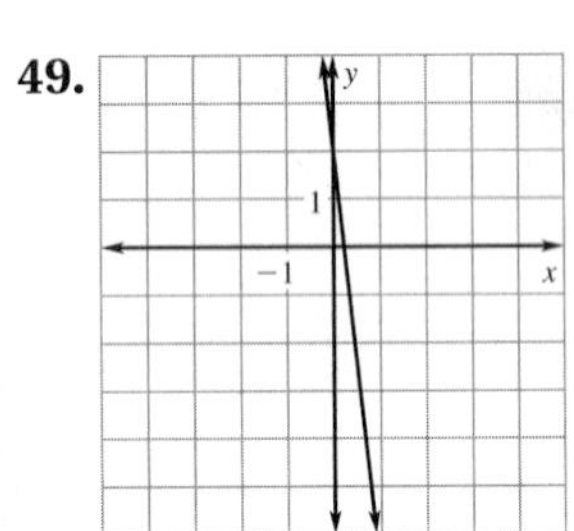

50. 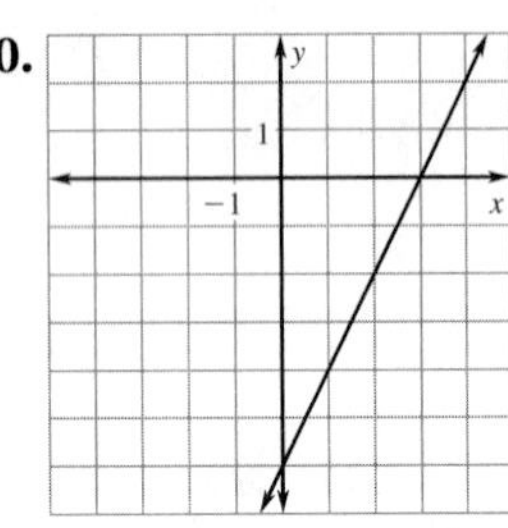

7.5 Mixed Review (p. 465)

46. 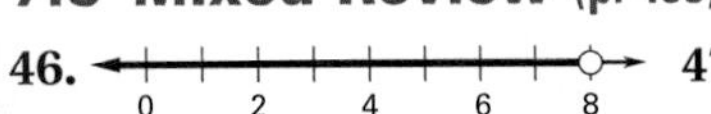

47. 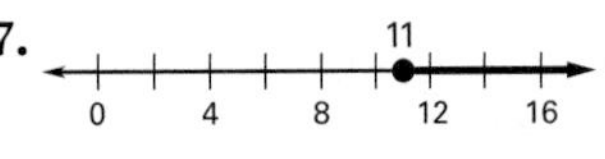

48. 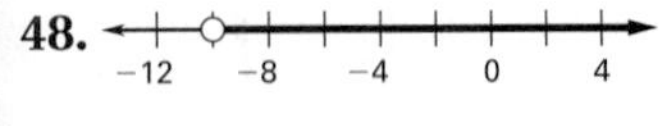

49. 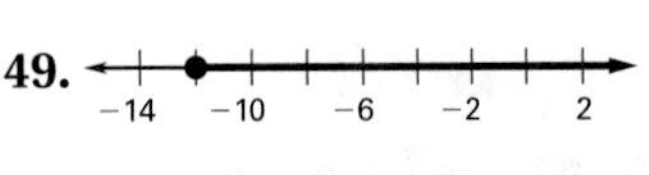

50. 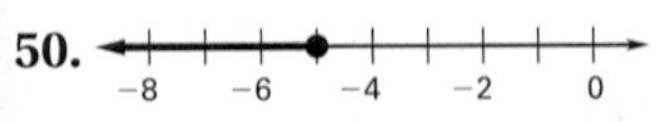

51. 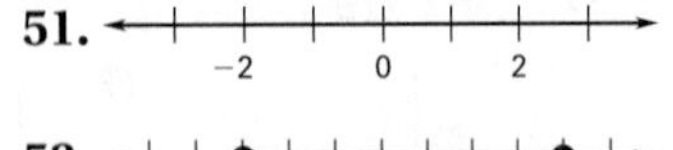

52. −5

53.

54. 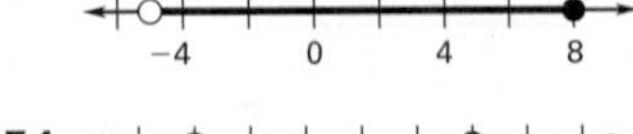

55. 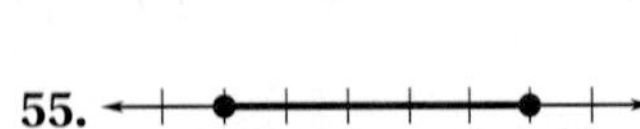

56. 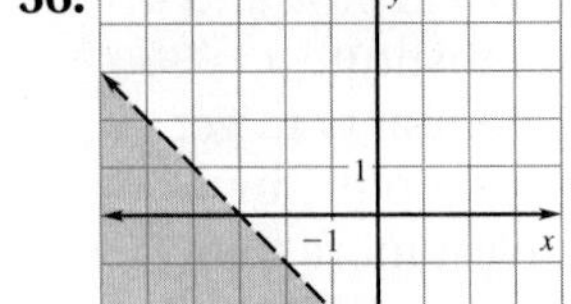

57. 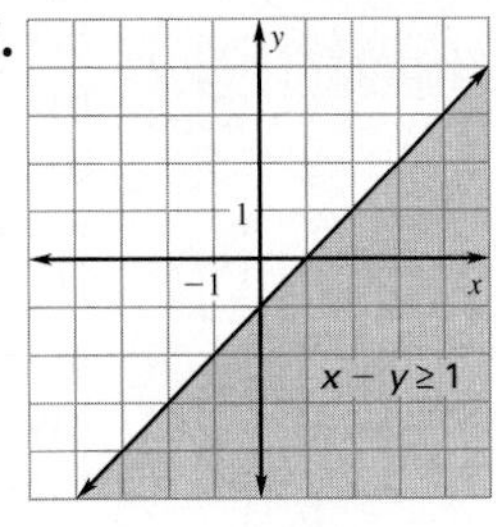

58. 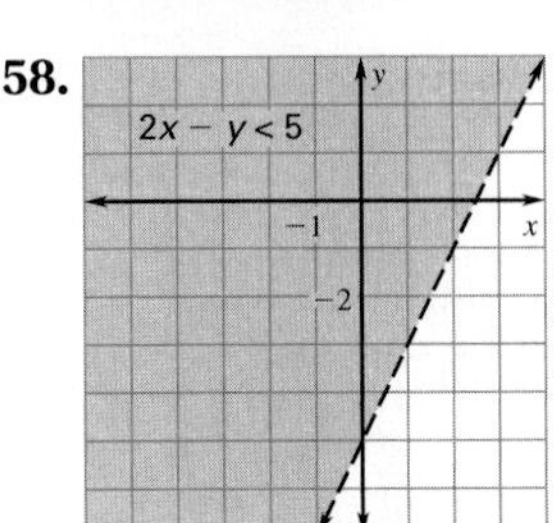

59. 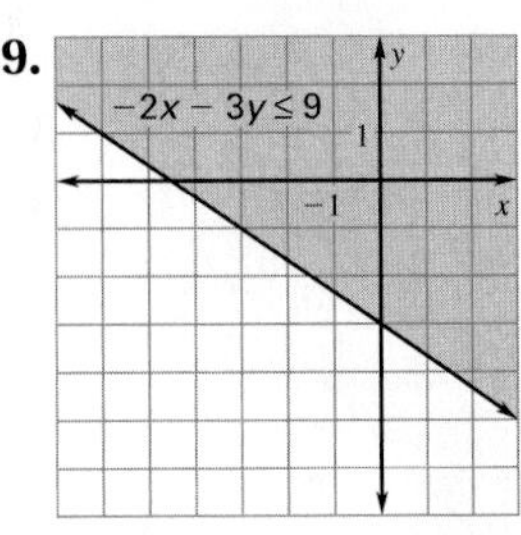

60. 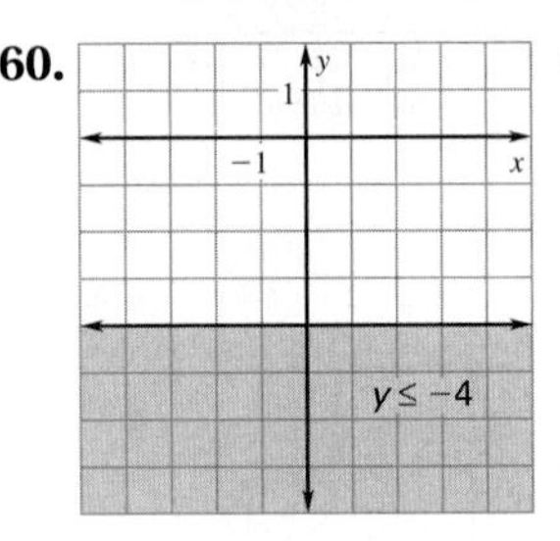

61. 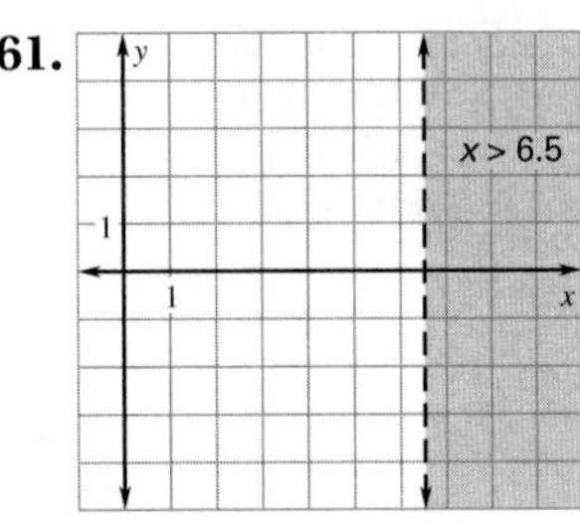

7.6 Guided Practice (pp. 467–468)

1. 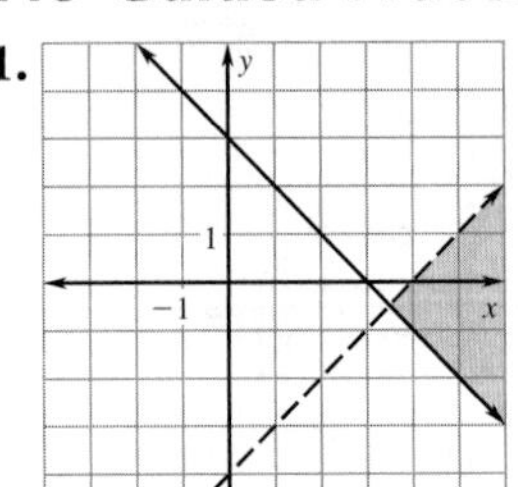

2. 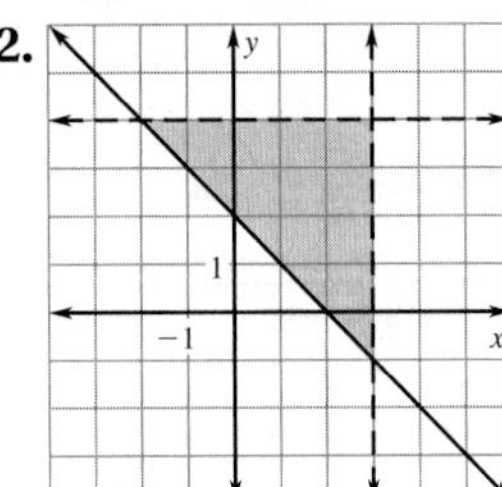

3. 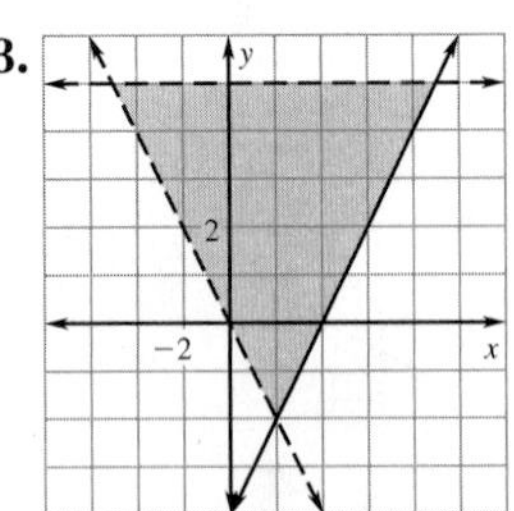

7.6 Skill Practice (pp. 469–470)

9. 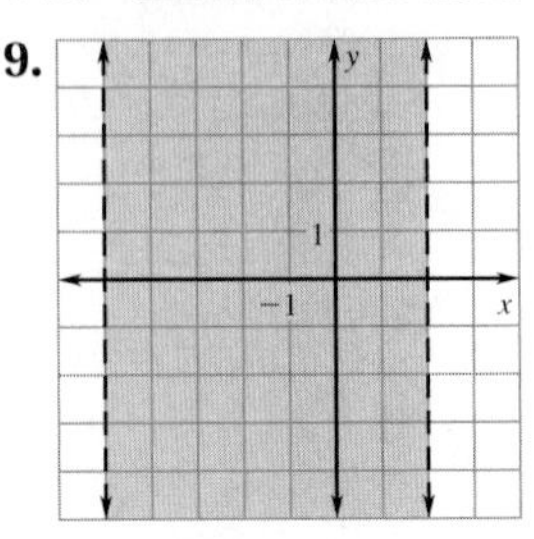

10. 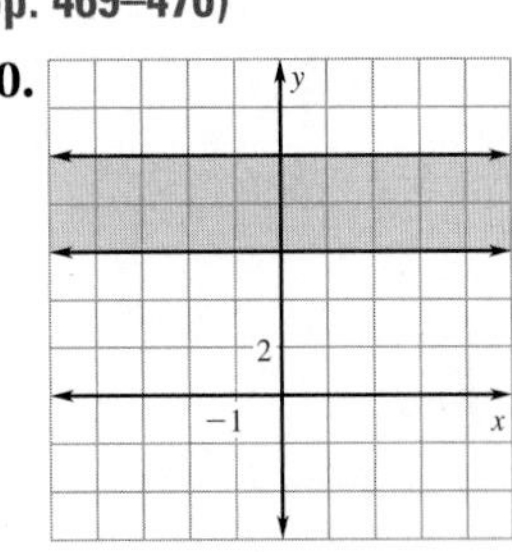

ADDITIONAL ANSWERS

11.
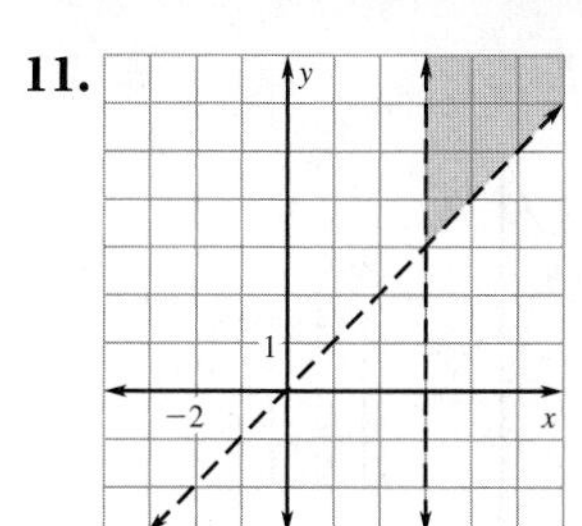

12.
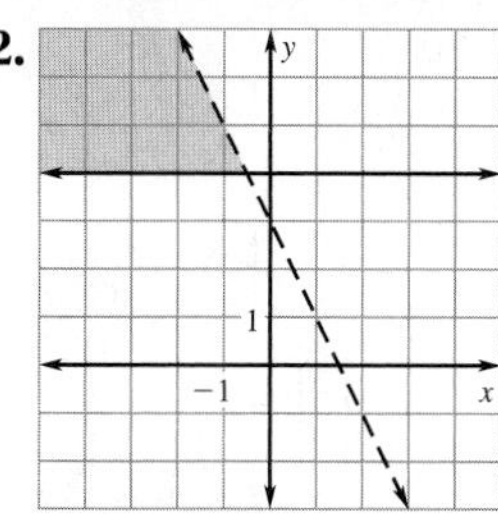

13.
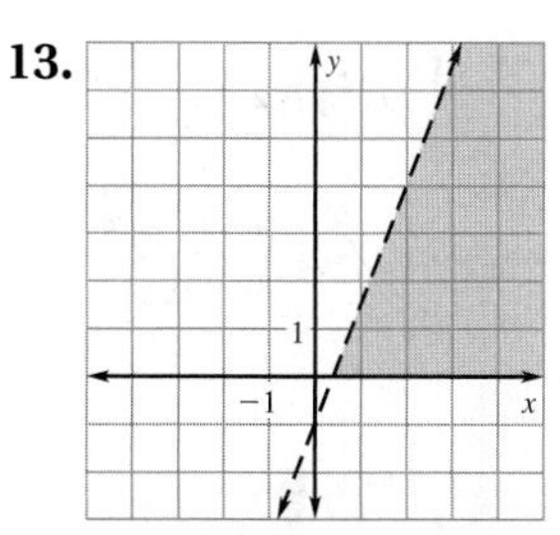

14.
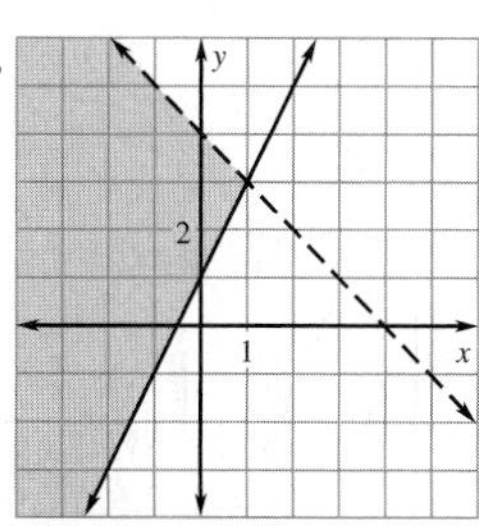

15.
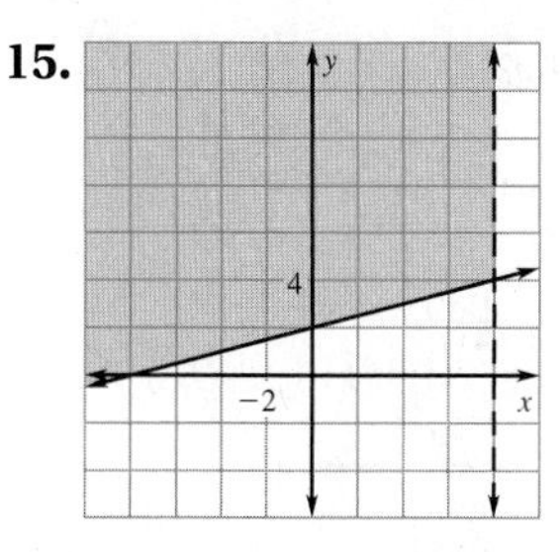

16.
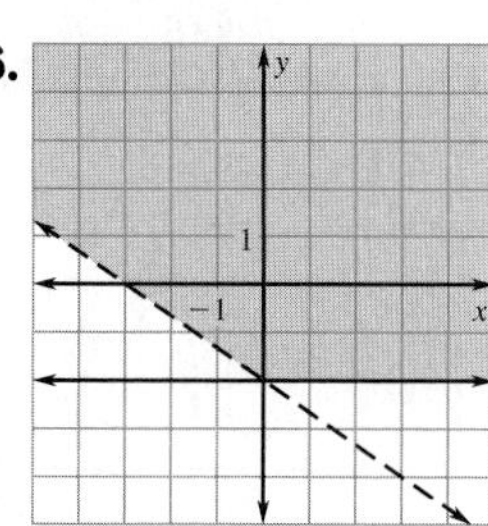

17.
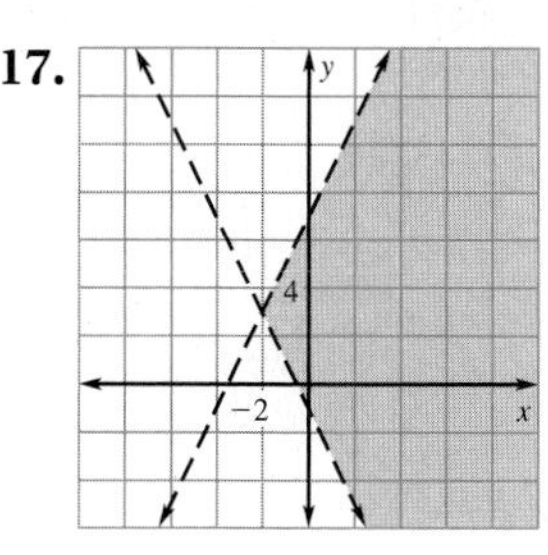

18.
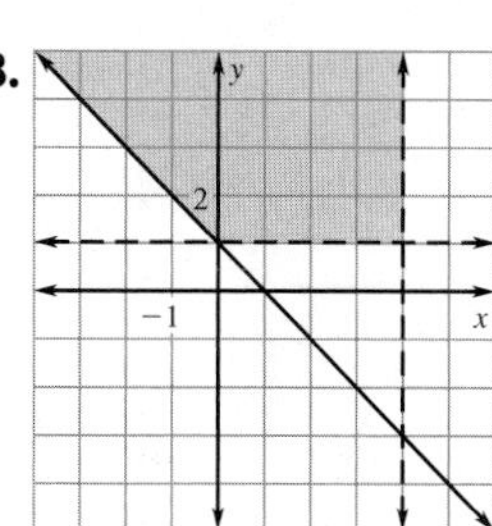

19.
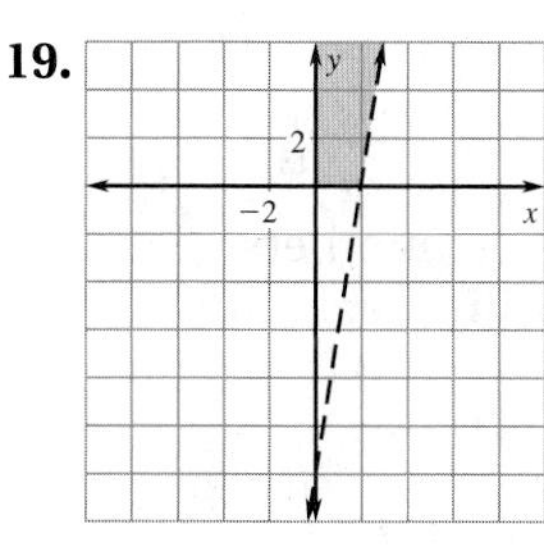

20.
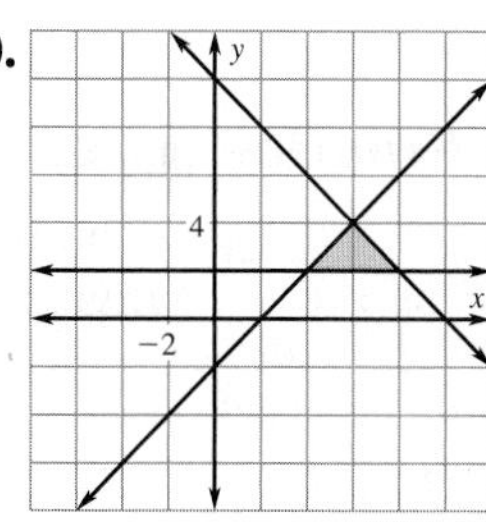

7.6 Problem Solving (pp. 471–472)

41. a.
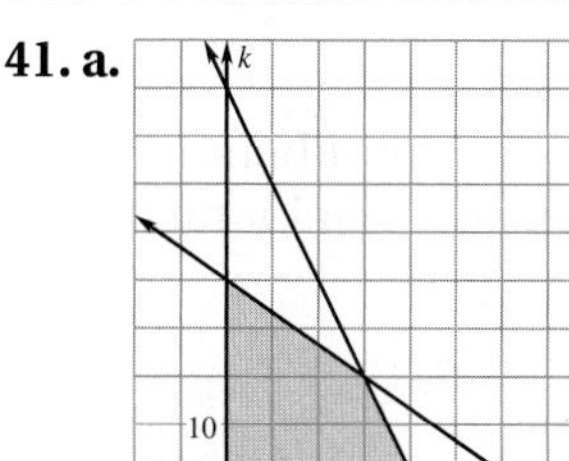

Quiz for Lessons 7.5–7.6 (p. 472)

1.
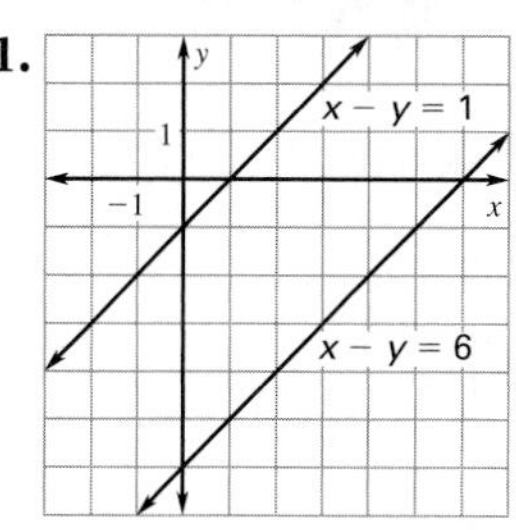

2.
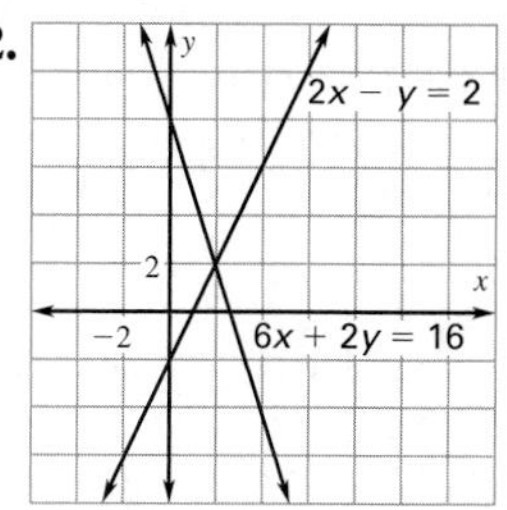

3.
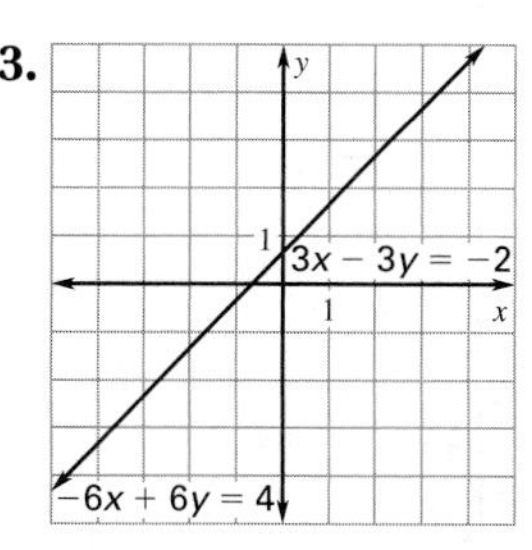

4.
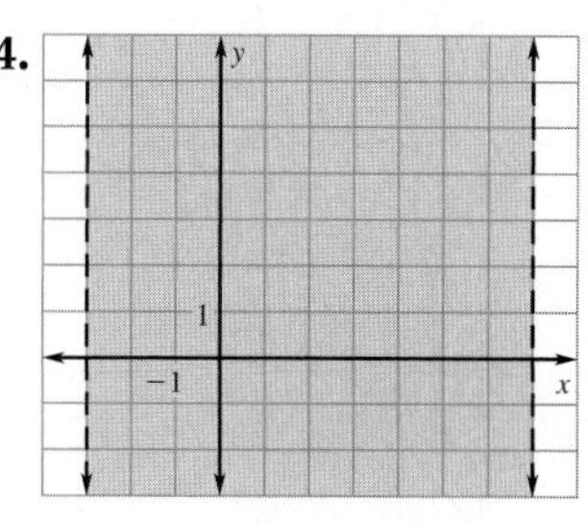

5.
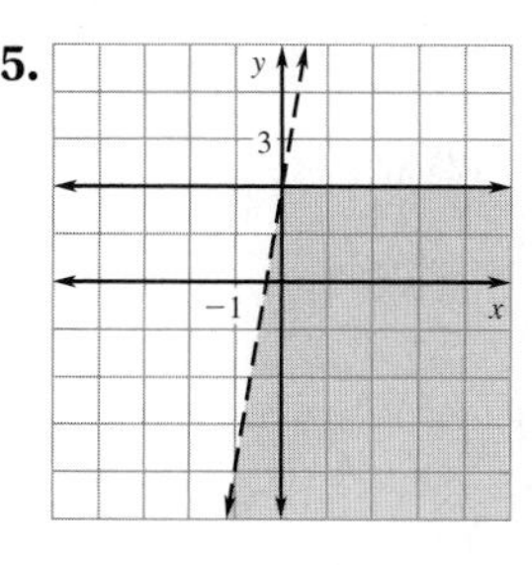

6.
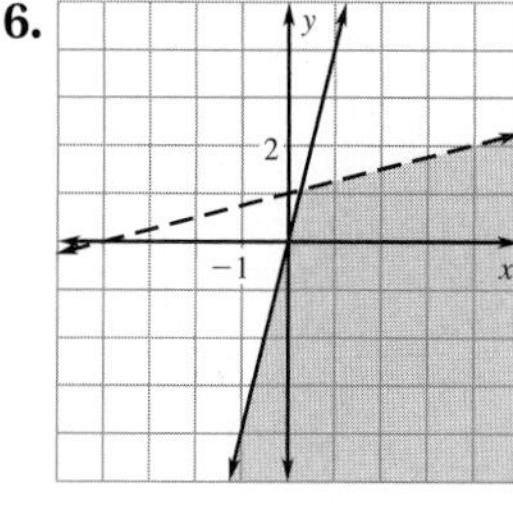

7.
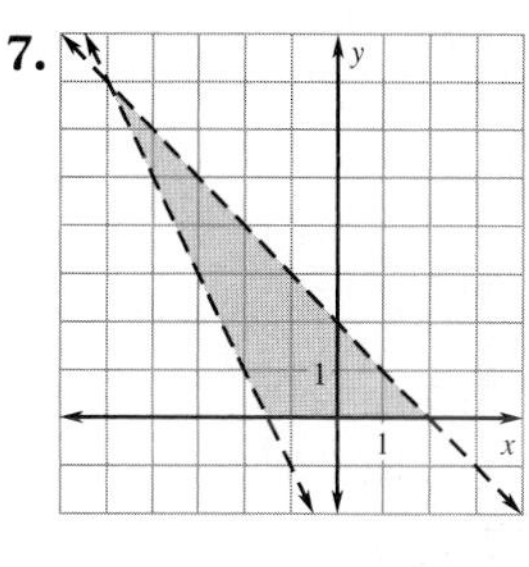

8.
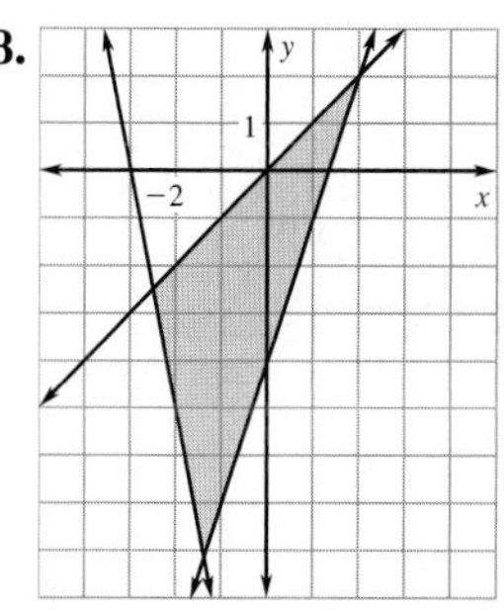

9.
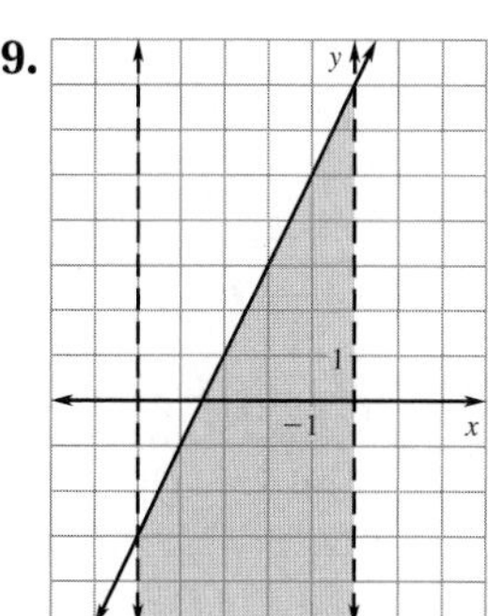

Chapter 8

8.1 Mixed Review (p. 494)

66. 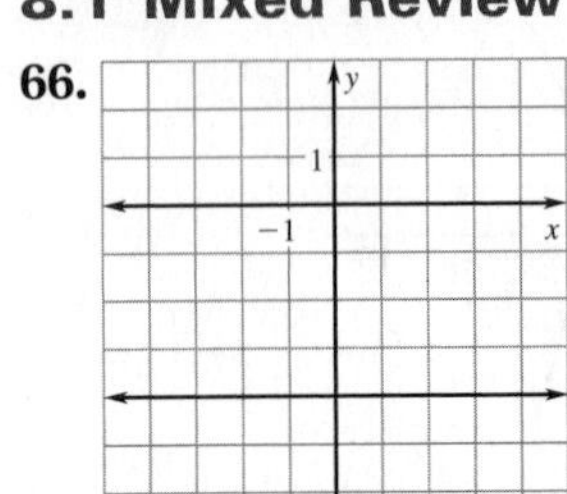

67. 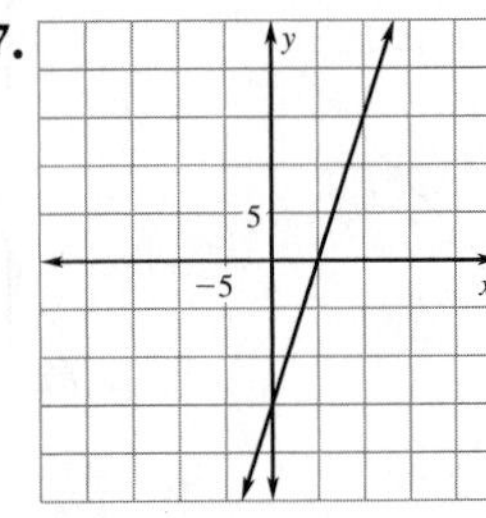

68. 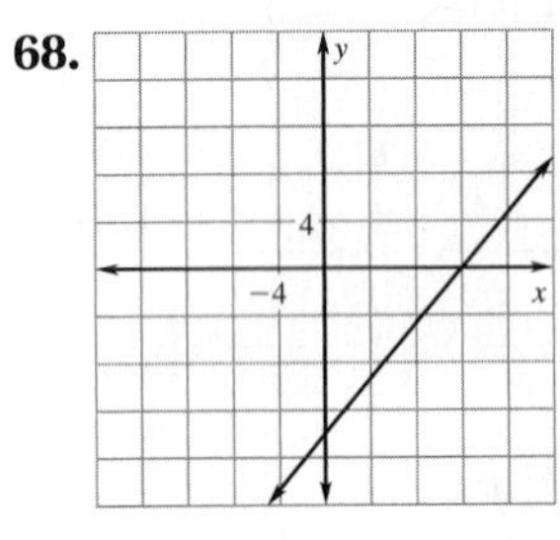

69. 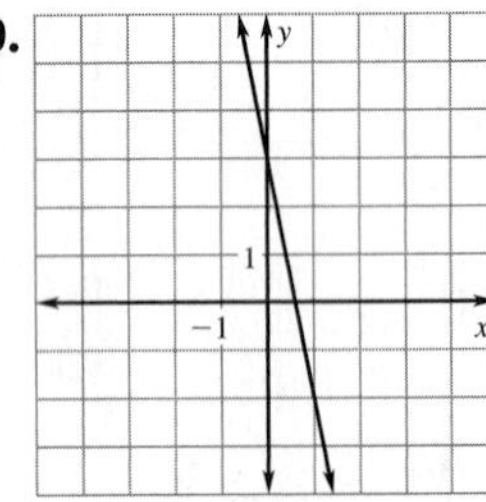

70. 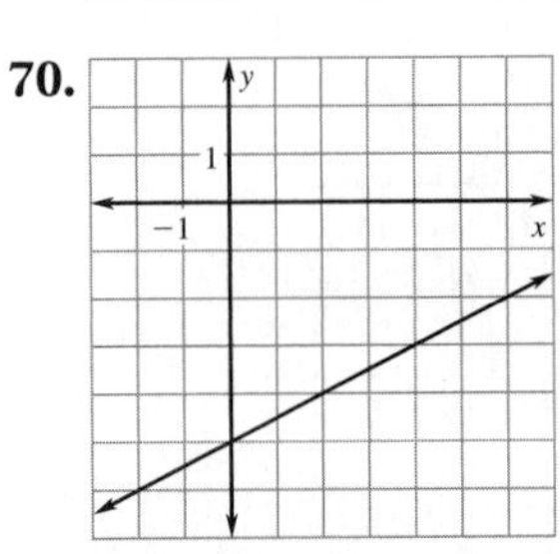

71. 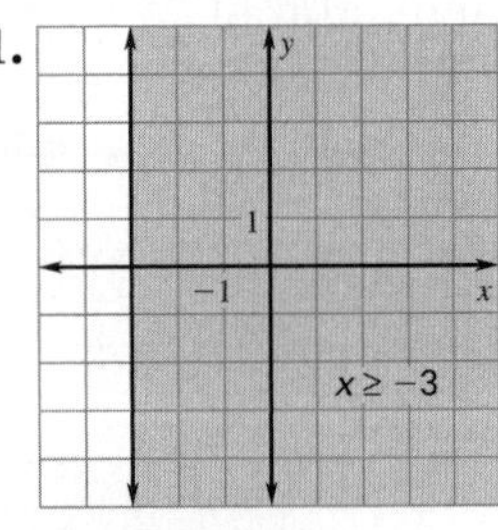

72. 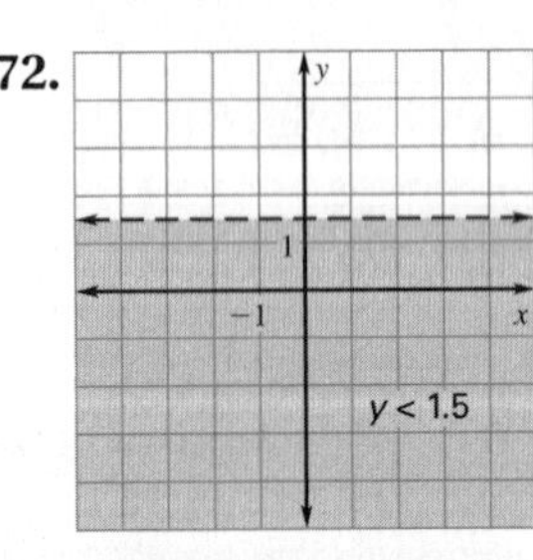

73. 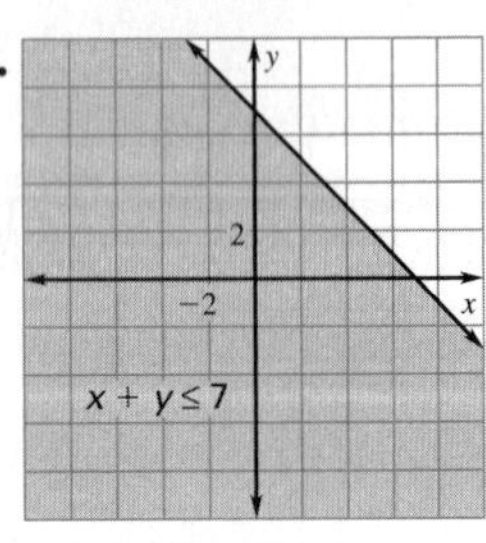

74. 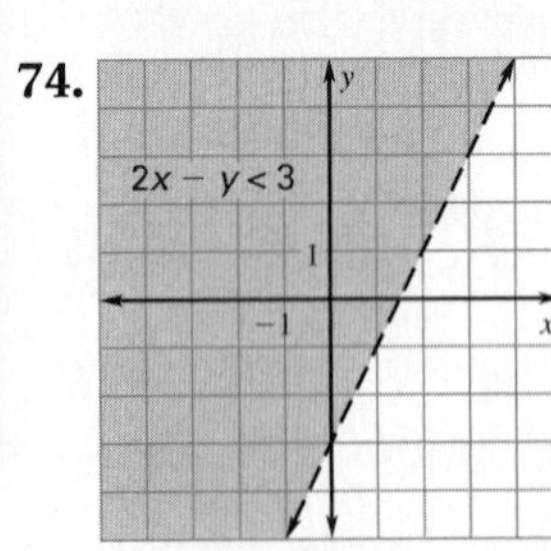

8.4 Mixed Review (p. 518)

69. 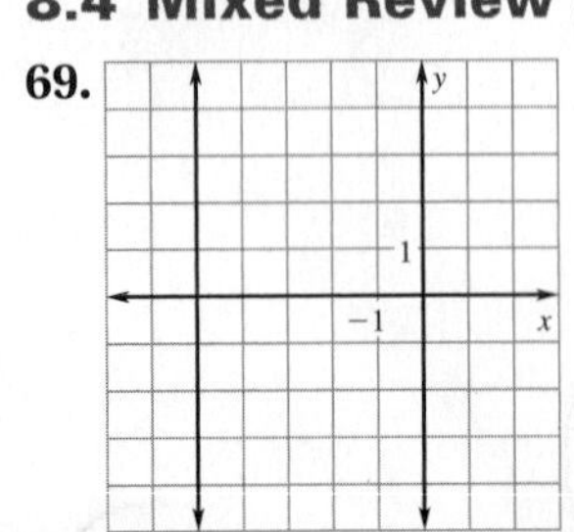

70. 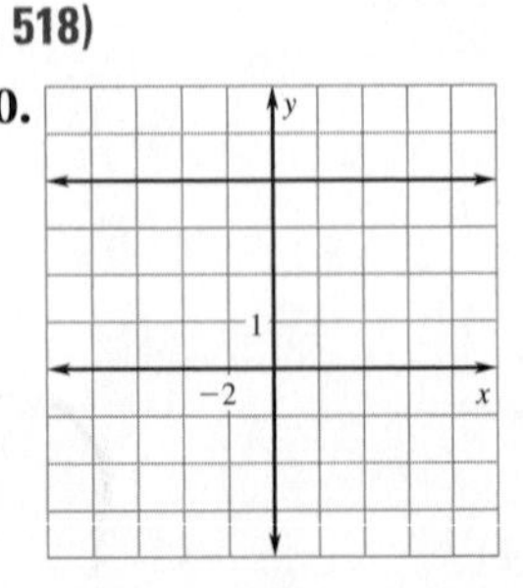

71. 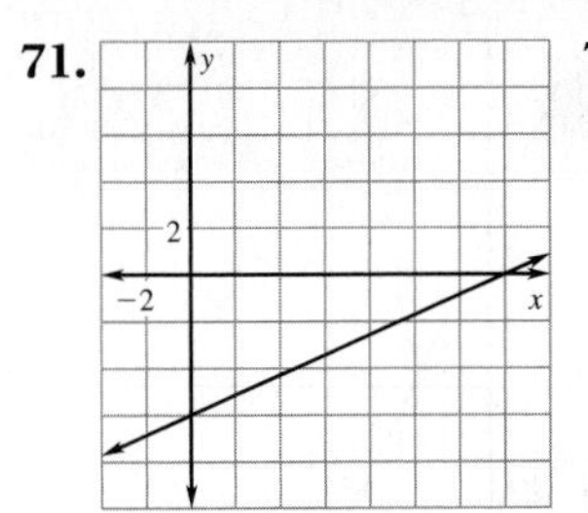

72. 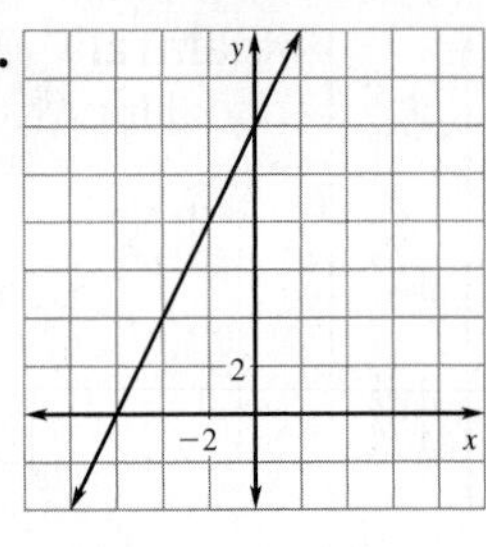

73. 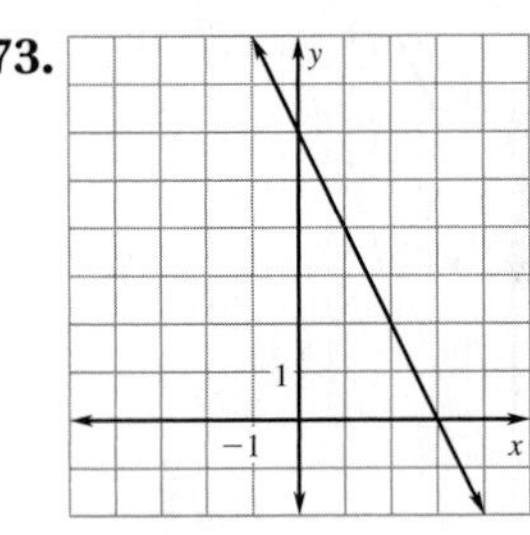

74. 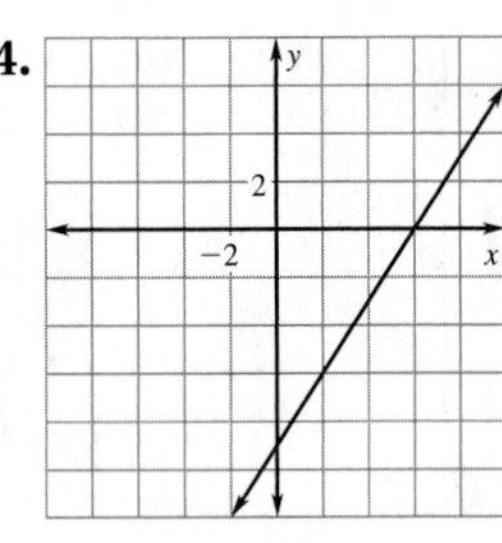

8.5 Guided Practice (pp. 520–523)

2. 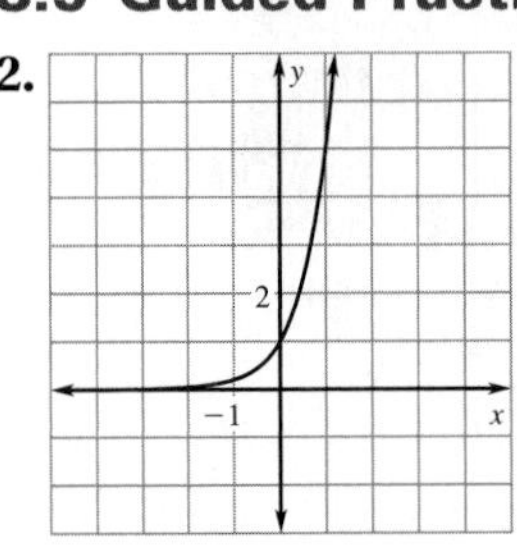

3. 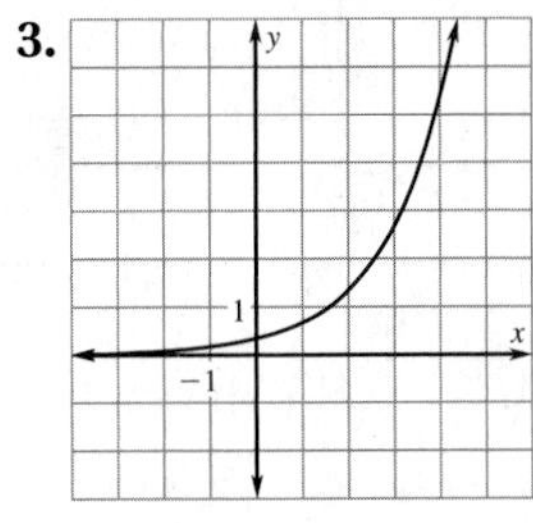

4. 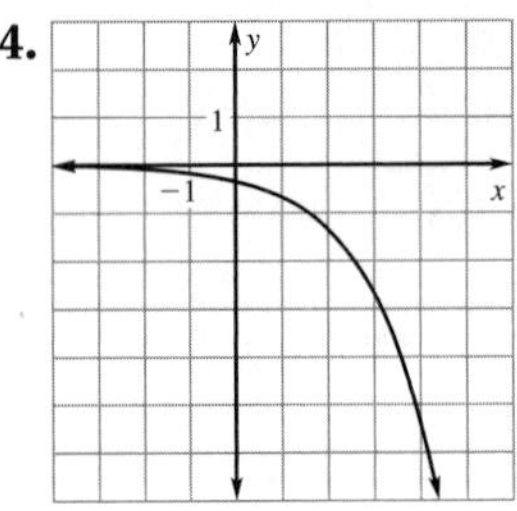

8.5 Skill Practice (pp. 523–524)

9. 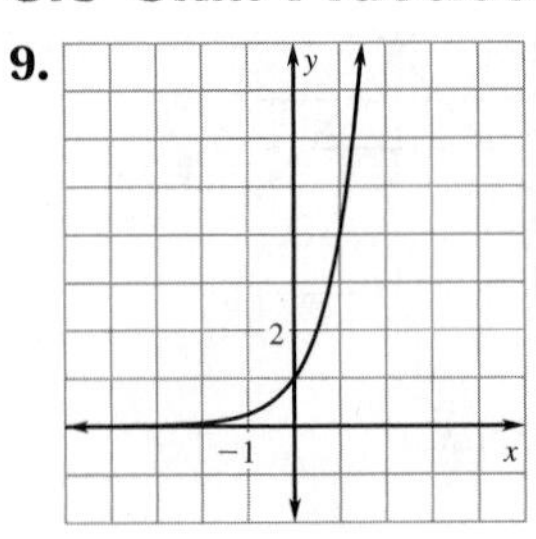

domain: all real numbers,
range: all positive real numbers

10. 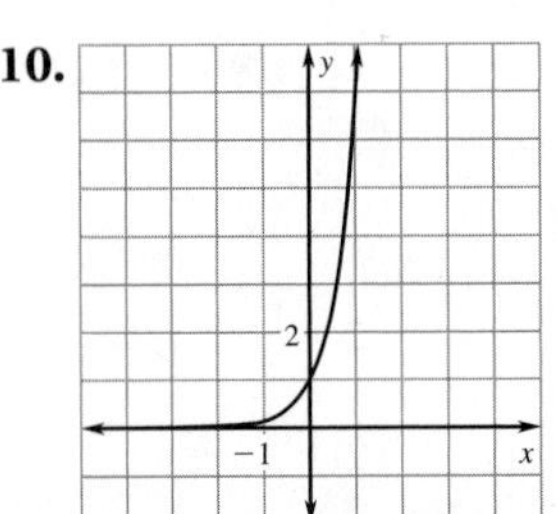

domain: all real numbers,
range: all positive real numbers

11. 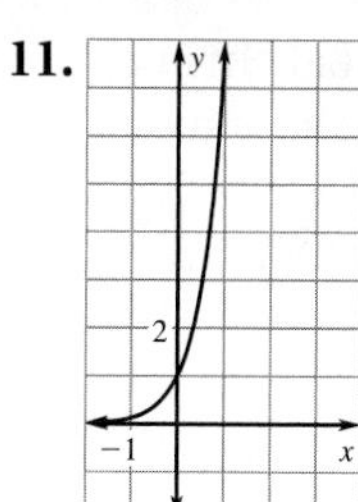

domain: all real numbers, range: all positive real numbers

12. 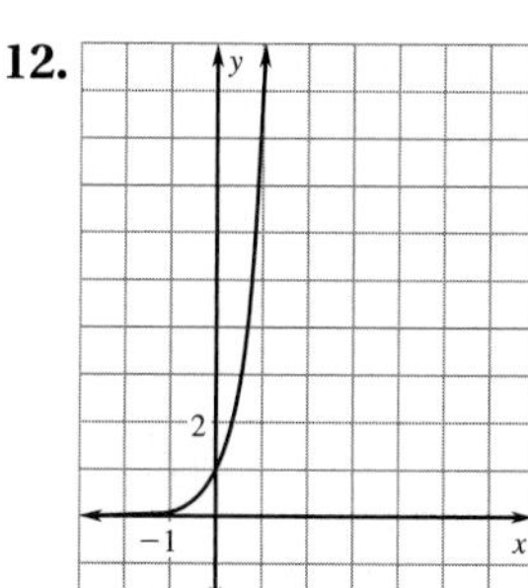

domain: all real numbers, range: all positive real numbers

13. 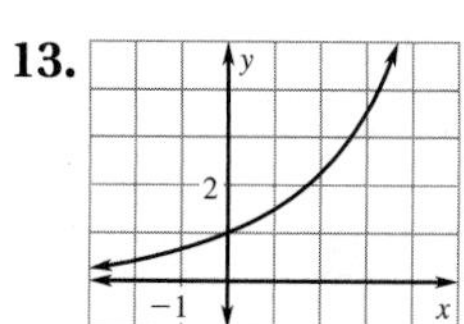

domain: all real numbers, range: all positive real numbers

14. 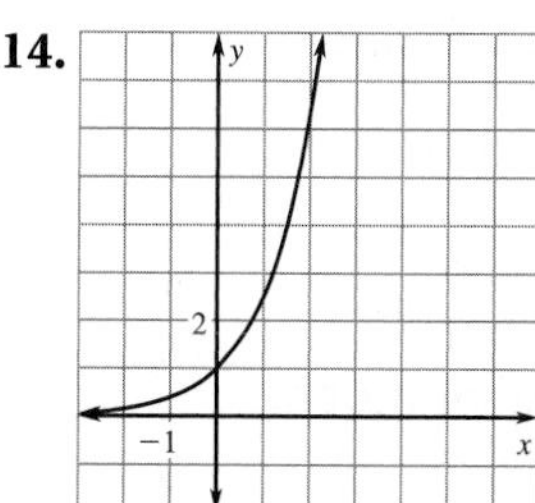

domain: all real numbers, range: all positive real numbers

15. 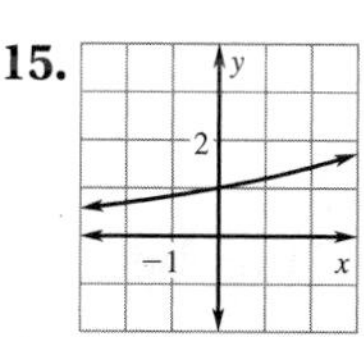

domain: all real numbers, range: all positive real numbers

16. 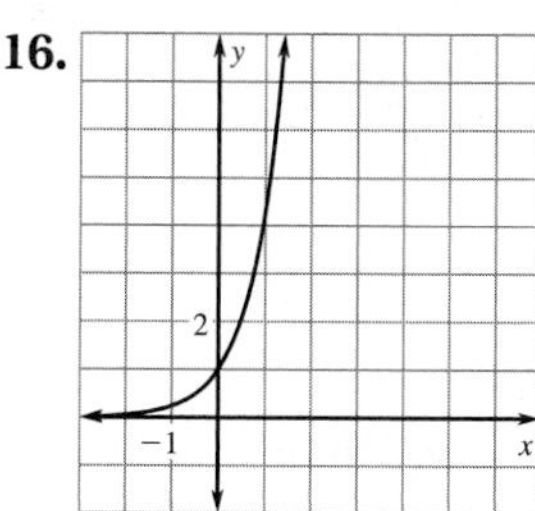

domain: all real numbers, range: all positive real numbers

17. 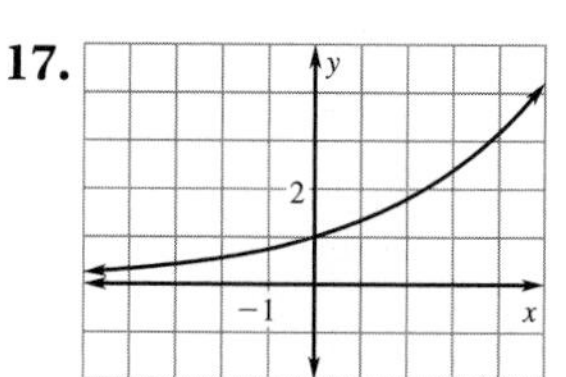

domain: all real numbers, range: all positive real numbers

18. 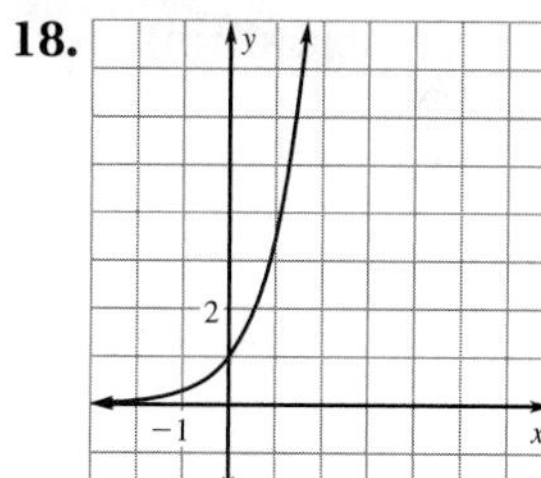

domain: all real numbers, range: all positive real numbers

19. 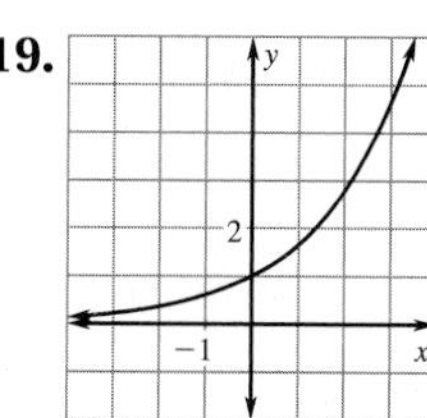

domain: all real numbers, range: all positive real numbers

20. 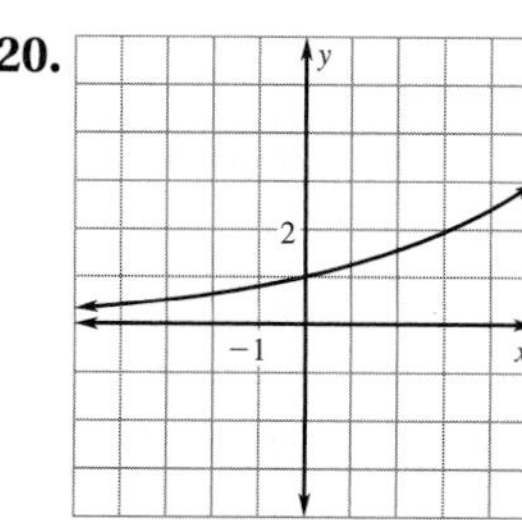

domain: all real numbers, range: all positive real numbers

22. 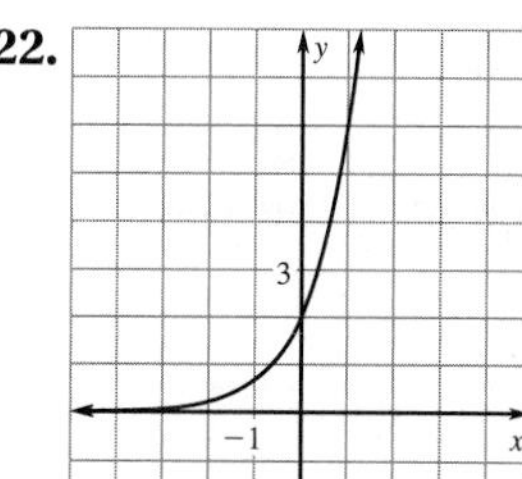

The graph is a vertical stretch.

23. 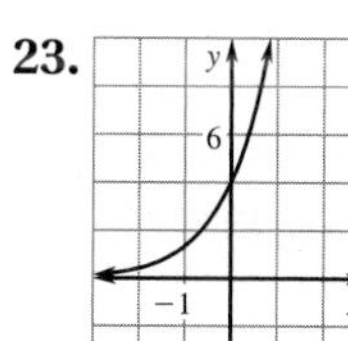

The graph is a vertical stretch.

24. 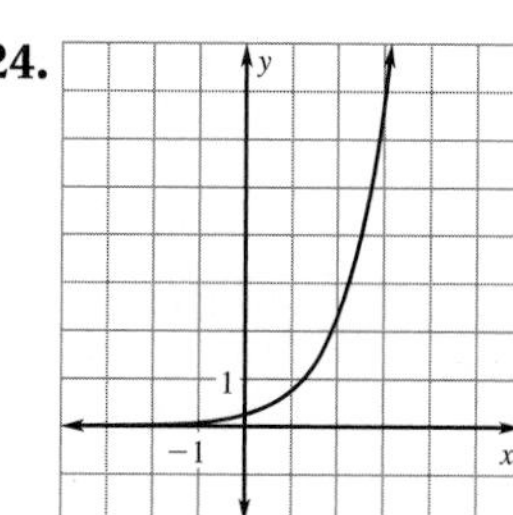

The graph is a vertical shrink.

25. 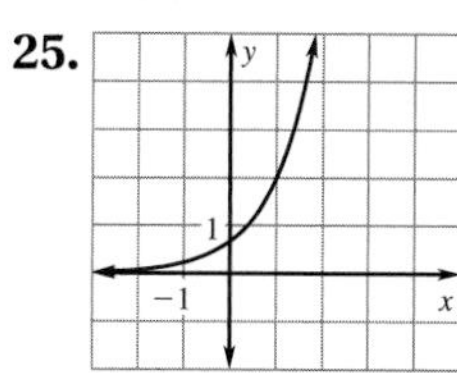

The graph is a vertical shrink.

26. 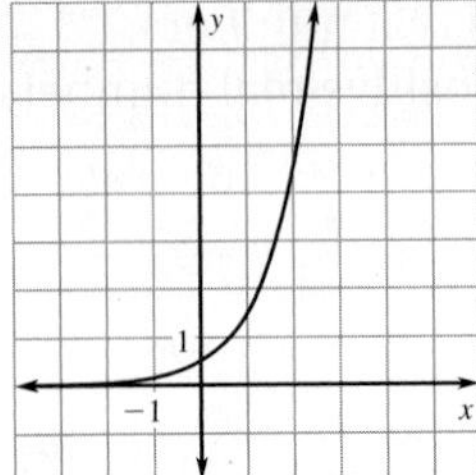 The graph is a vertical shrink.

27. 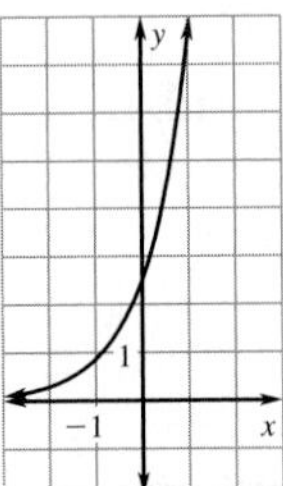 The graph is a vertical stretch.

28. 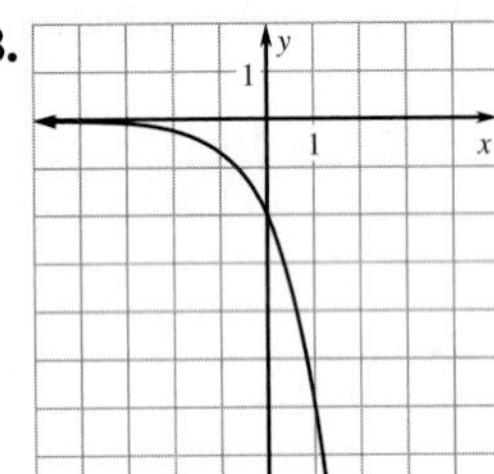 The graph is a vertical stretch with a reflection in the x-axis.

29. 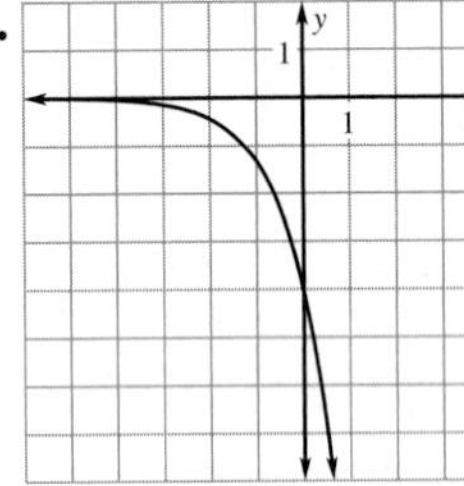 The graph is a vertical stretch with a reflection in the x-axis.

30. 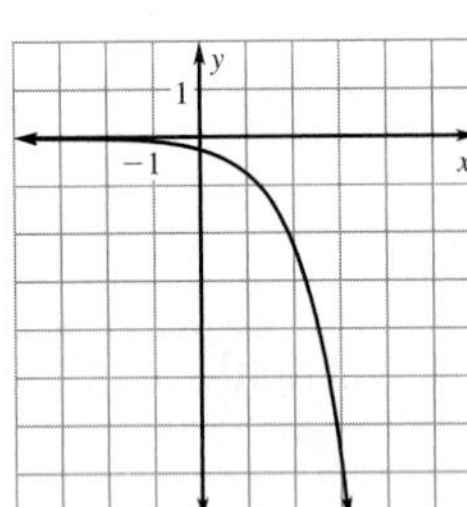 The graph is a vertical shrink with a reflection in the x-axis.

31. 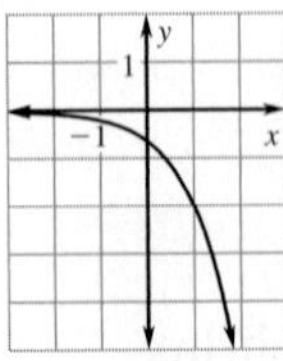 The graph is a vertical shrink with a reflection in the x-axis.

32. 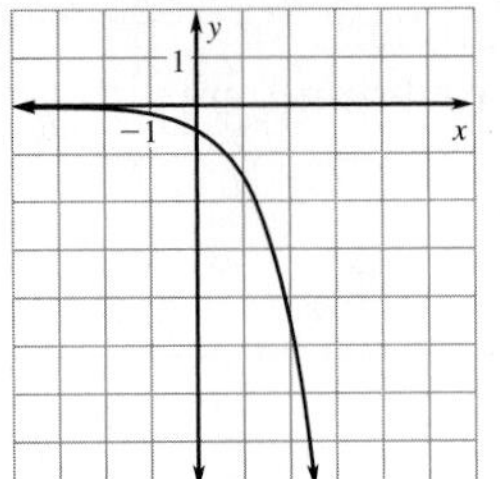 The graph is a vertical shrink with a reflection in the x-axis.

33. 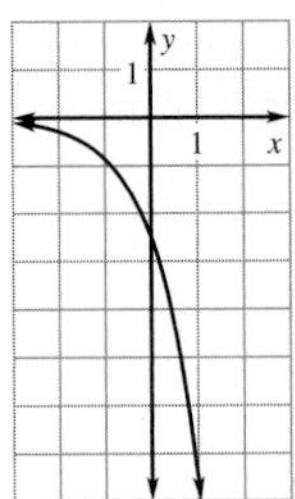 The graph is a vertical stretch with a reflection in the x-axis.

8.6 Guided Practice (pp. 531–534)

2. 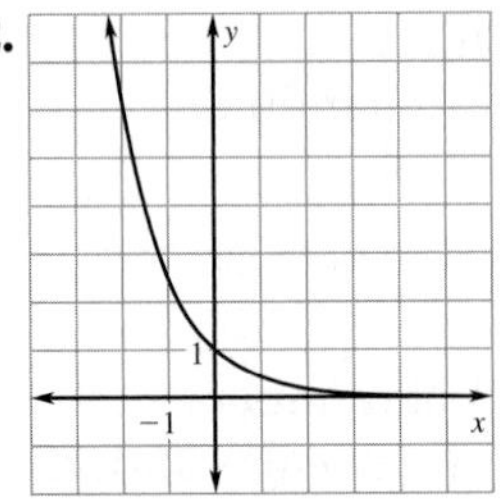

3. 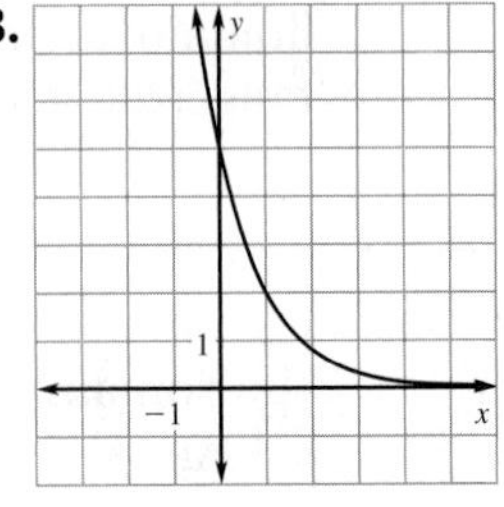

8.6 Skill Practice (pp. 535–536)

7. 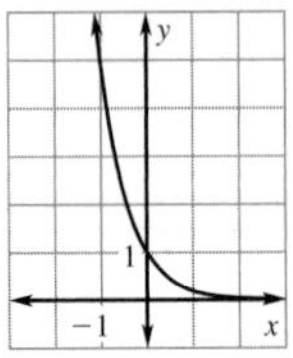 domain: all real numbers, range: all positive real numbers

8. 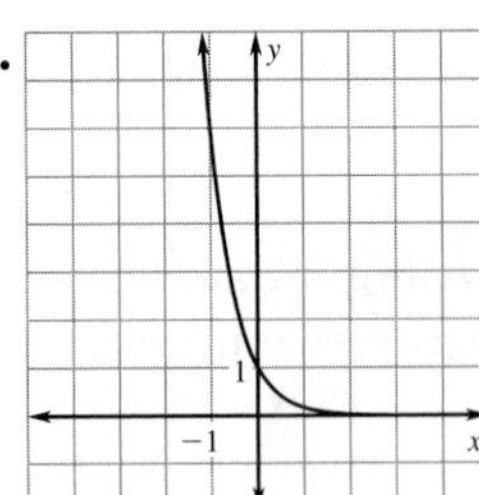 domain: all real numbers, range: all positive real numbers

9. 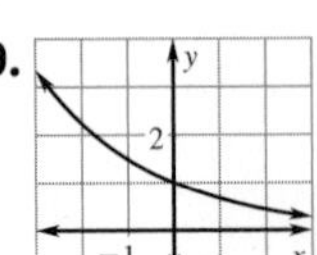 domain: all real numbers, range: all positive real numbers

ADDITIONAL ANSWERS

10. 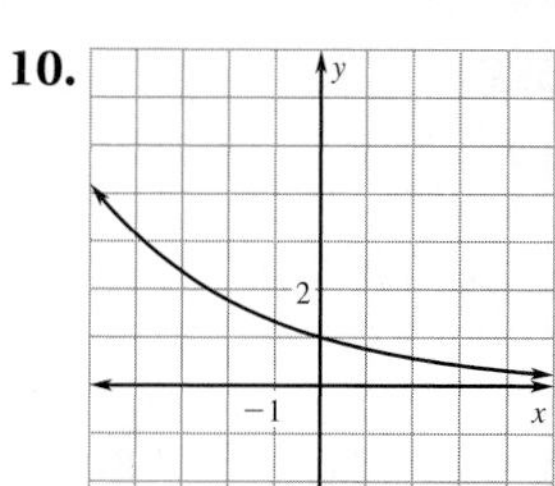

domain: all real numbers, range: all positive real numbers

11. domain: all real numbers, range: all positive real numbers

12. domain: all real numbers, range: all positive real numbers

13. domain: all real numbers, range: all positive real numbers

14. 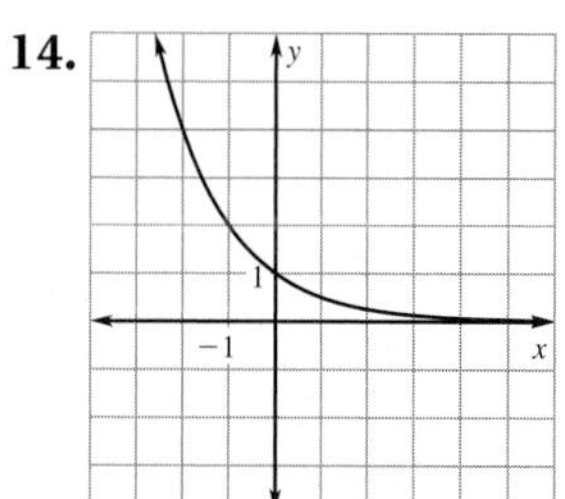

domain: all real numbers, range: all positive real numbers

15. 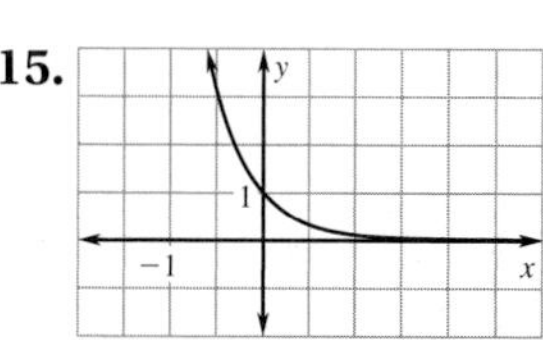

domain: all real numbers, range: all positive real numbers

16. 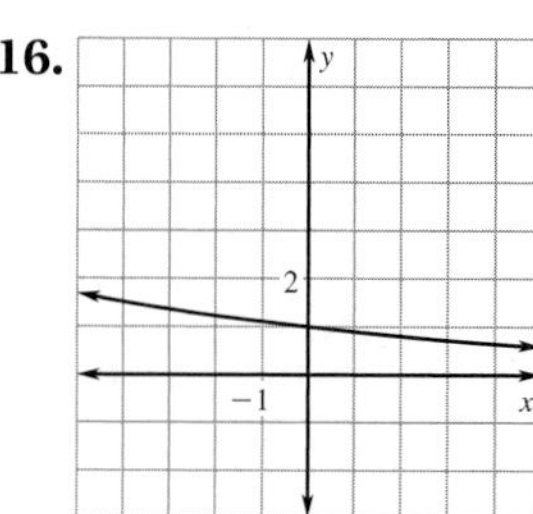

domain: all real numbers, range: all positive real numbers

17. domain: all real numbers, range: all positive real numbers

18. 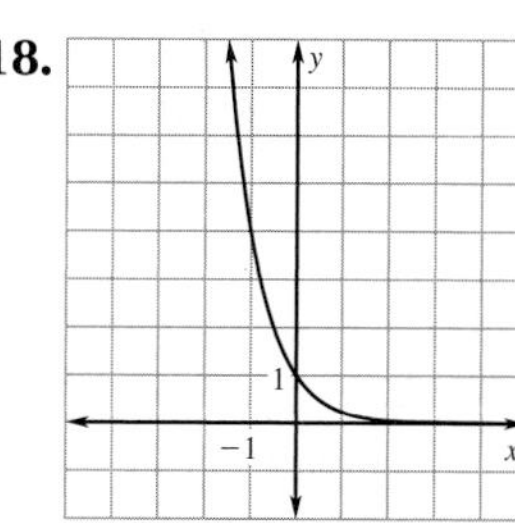

domain: all real numbers, range: all positive real numbers

20. 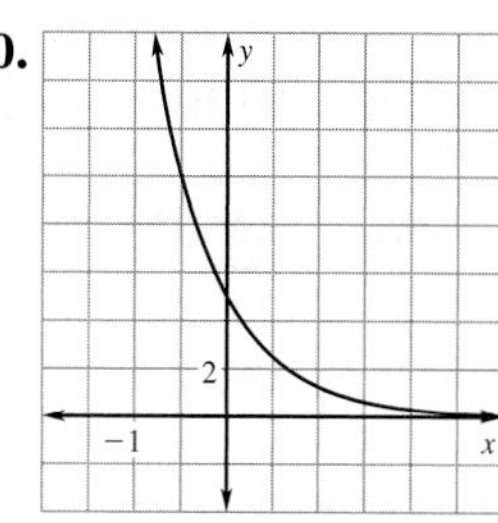

The graph is a vertical stretch.

21. 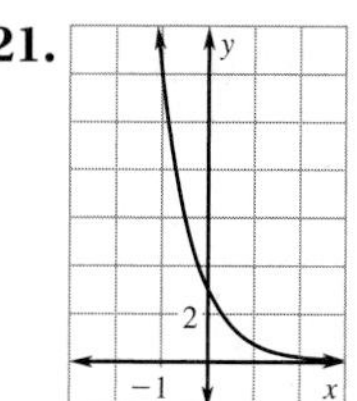

The graph is a vertical stretch.

22. 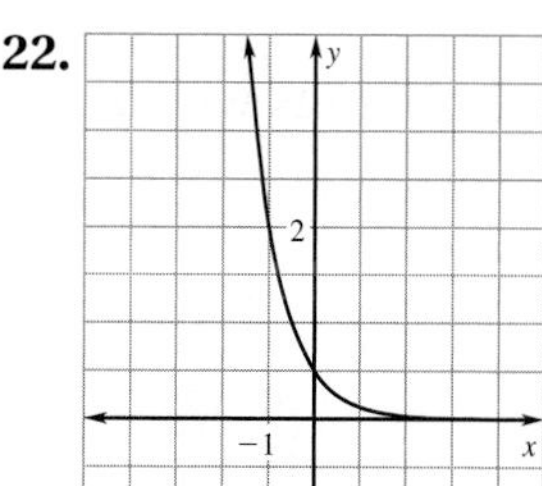

The graph is a vertical shrink.

23. 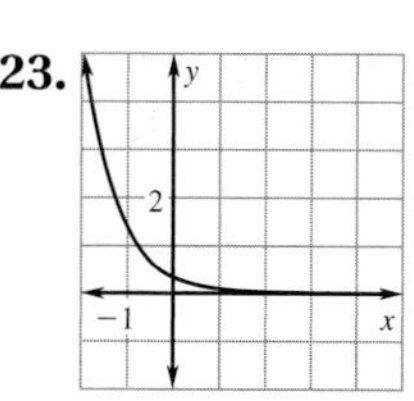

The graph is a vertical shrink.

24. 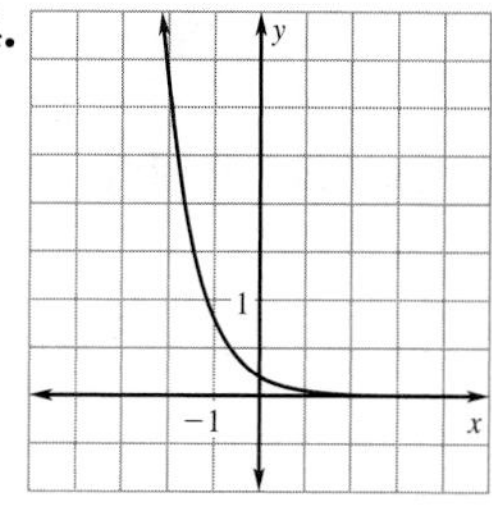

The graph is a vertical shrink.

25. 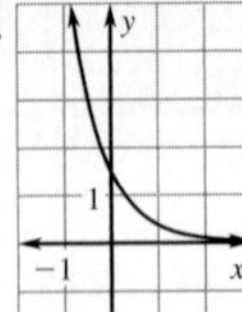

The graph is a vertical stretch.

26. 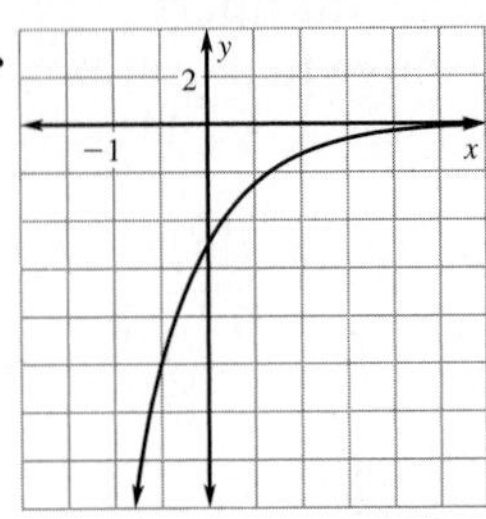

The graph is a vertical stretch with a reflection in the x-axis.

27. 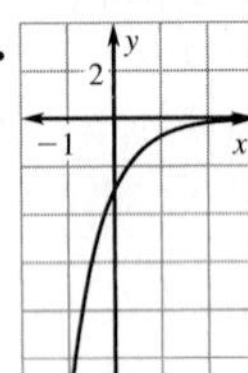

The graph is a vertical stretch with a reflection in the x-axis.

28. 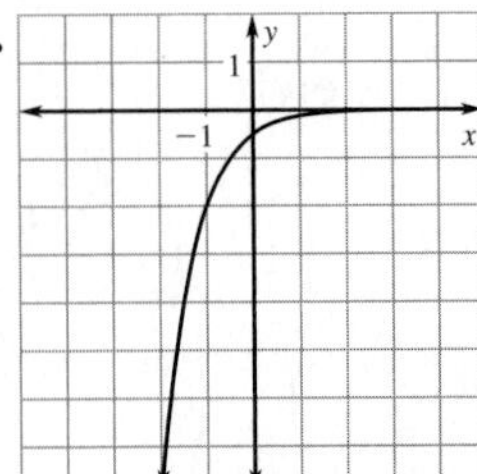

The graph is a vertical shrink with a reflection in the x-axis.

29. 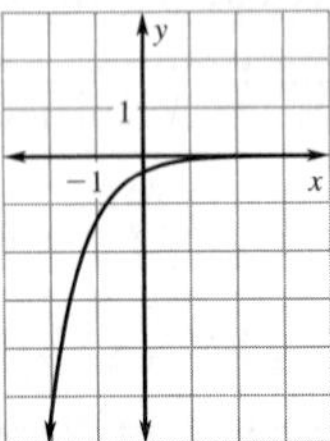

The graph is a vertical shrink with a reflection in the x-axis.

30. 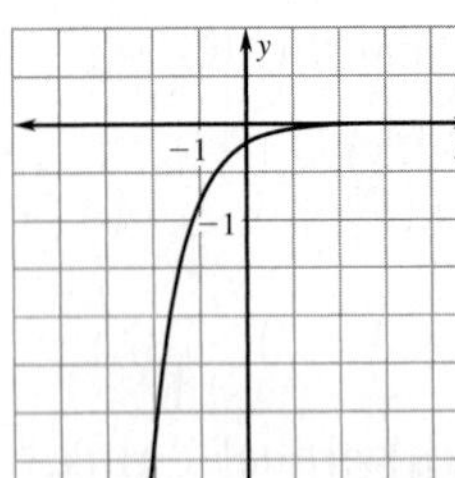

The graph is a vertical shrink with a reflection in the x-axis.

31. 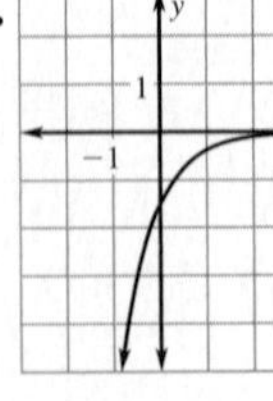

The graph is a vertical stretch with a reflection in the x-axis.

Quiz for Lessons 8.5–8.6 (p. 538)

1. 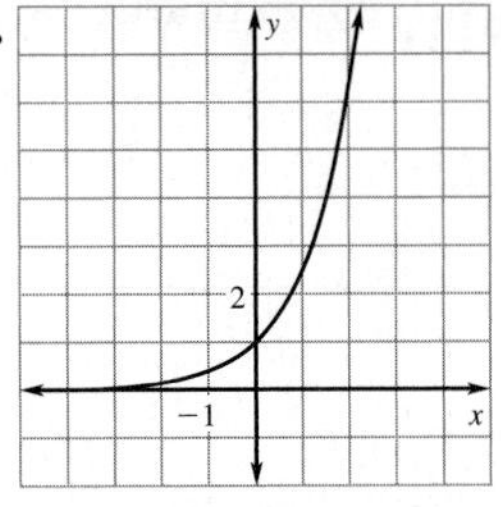

2. 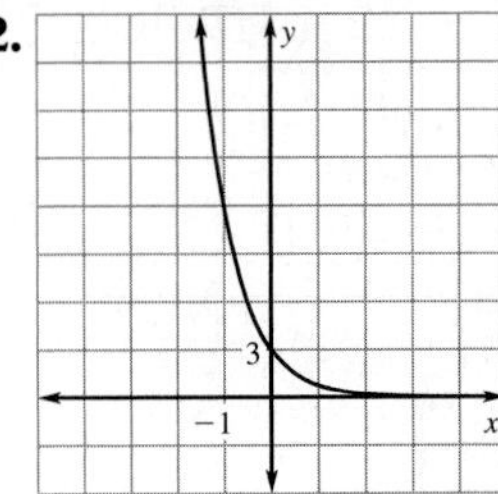

3. 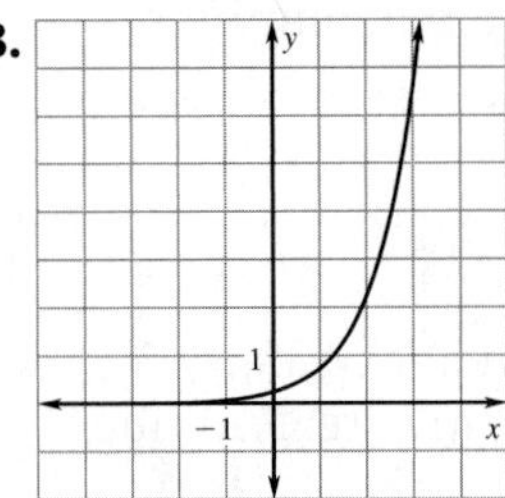

4. 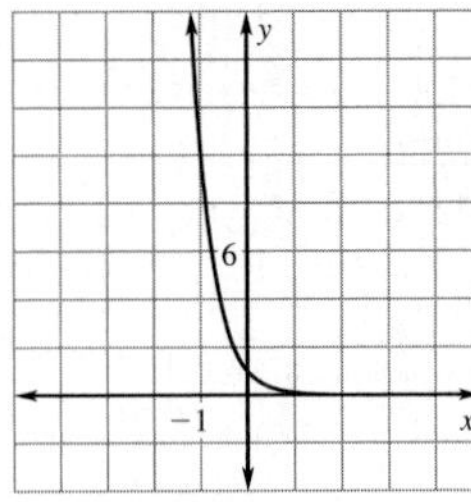

5. 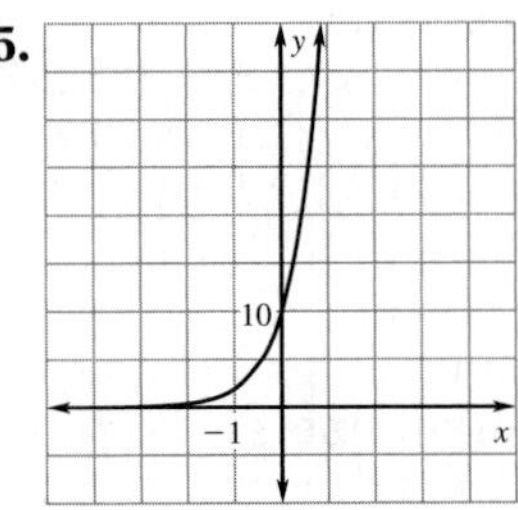

6. 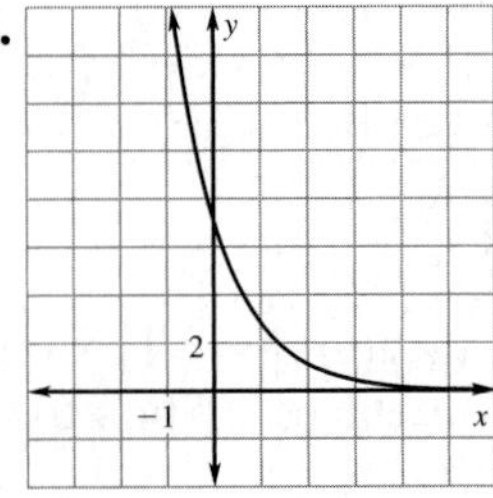

Extension (p. 540)

1. 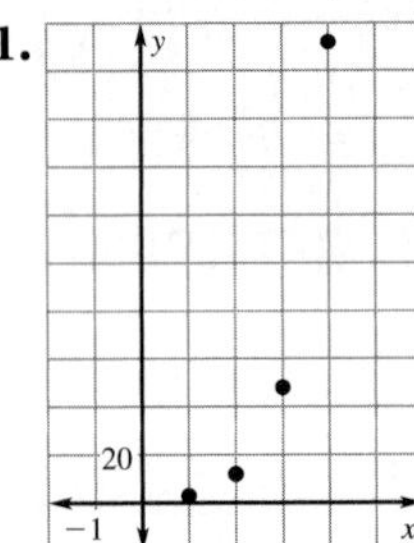

2. 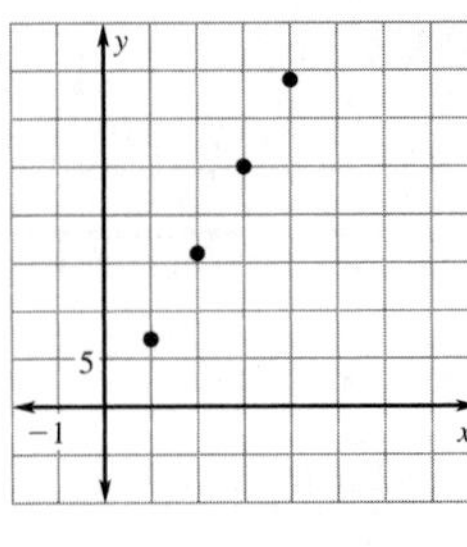

3. 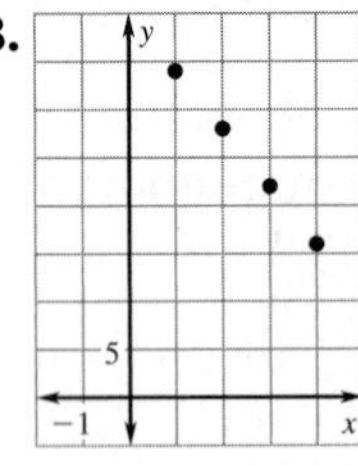

4. 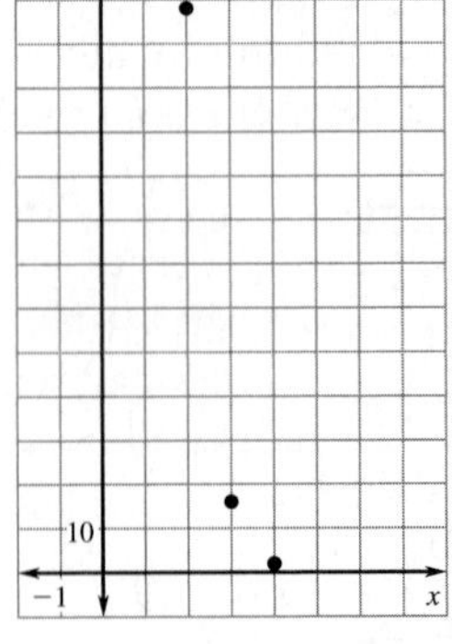

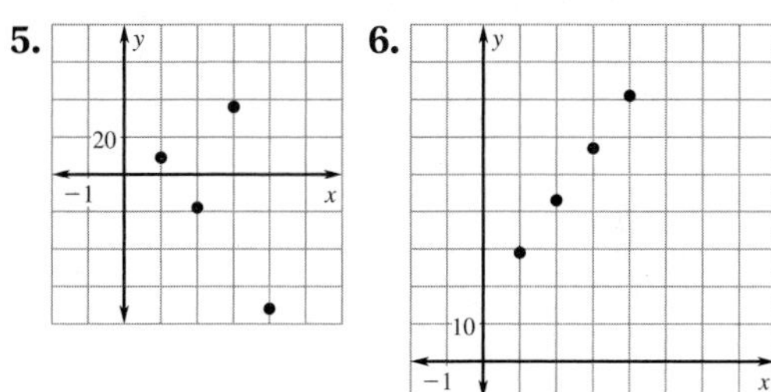

Chapter 9

9.1 Mixed Review (p. 559)

49.
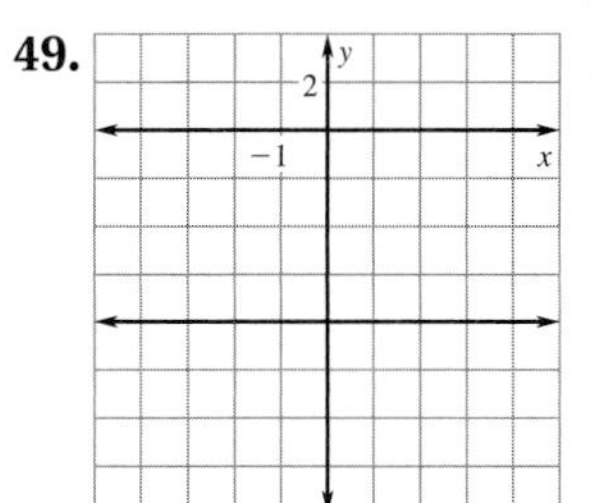

50.
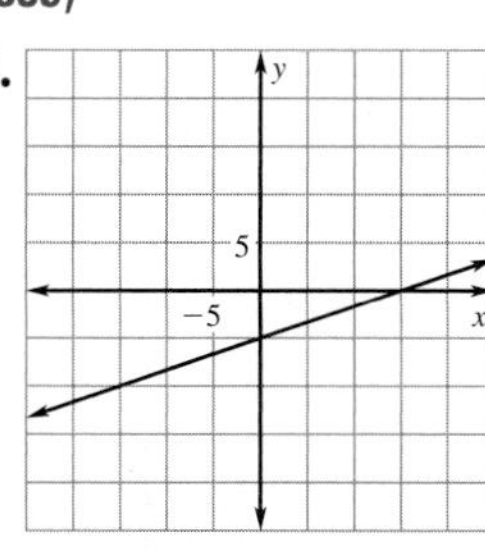

51.
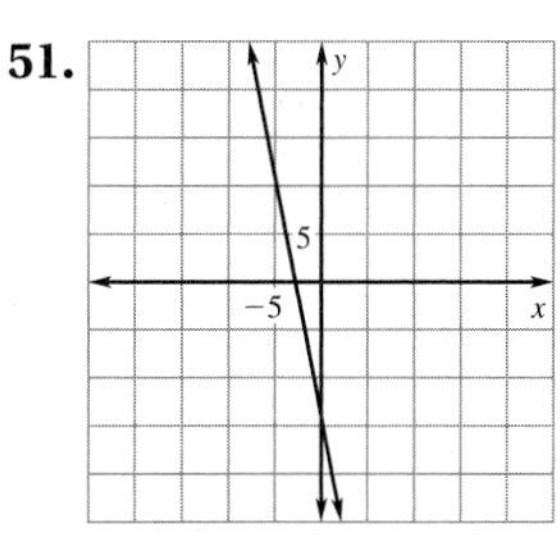

52.
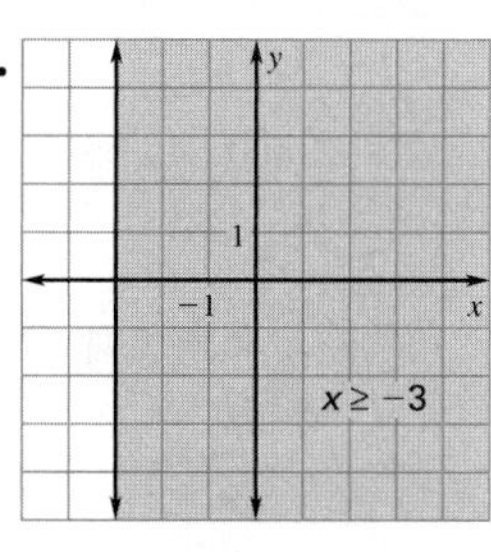

53.
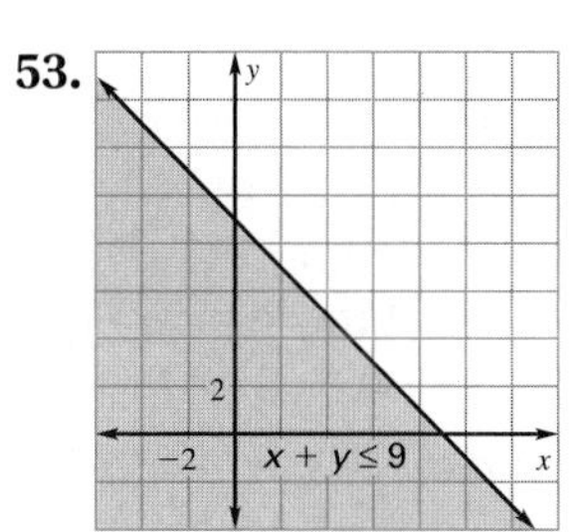

54.
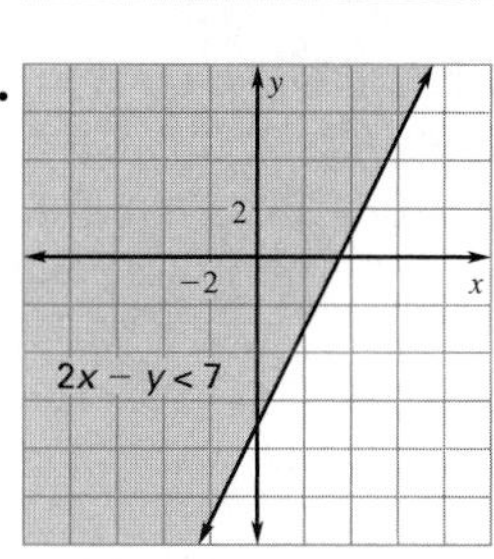

9.2 Investigating Algebra Activity (p. 561)

1.
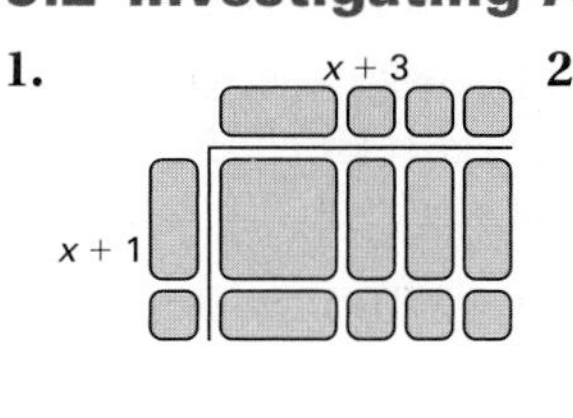

2.
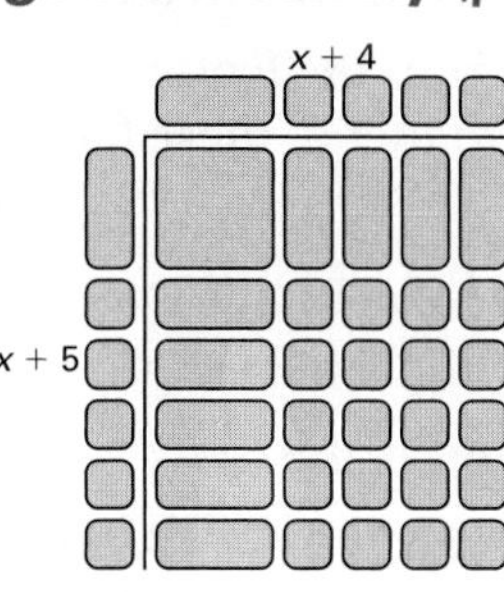

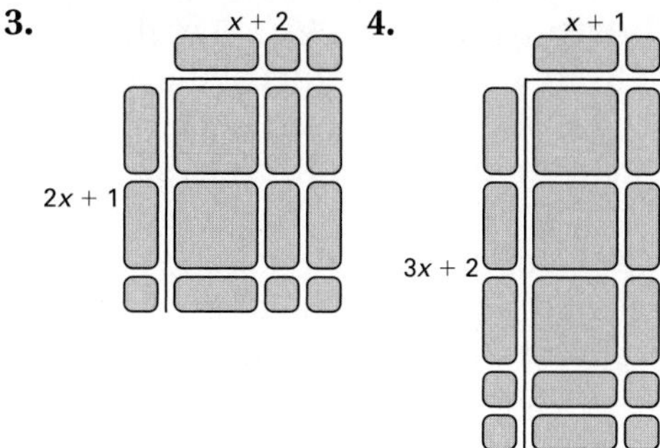

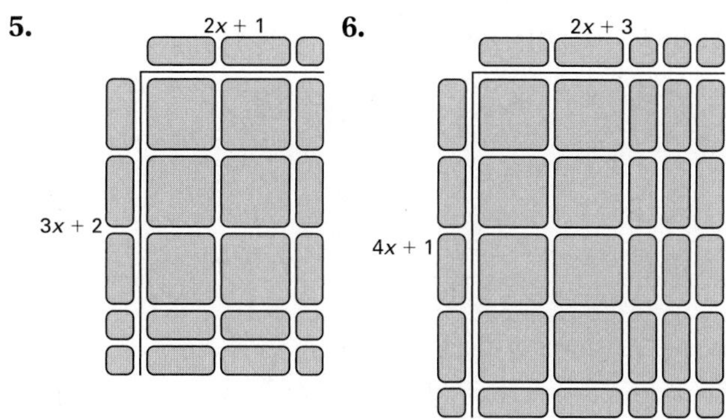

9.3 Skill Practice (p. 572) **2.** The square of a binomial is a trinomial. To find the first term of the trinomial, square the first term of the binomial. To find the second term of the trinomial, find twice the product of the terms of the binomial, using the sign of the second term. To find the third term of the trinomial, square the second term of the binomial.

9.3 Problem Solving (pp. 573–574) **43. a.** 88.1%; the areas of the four regions are: 2 complete passes: $0.655^2 \approx 0.429$ square units; 1 complete pass, 1 incomplete pass: $0.655(0.345) \approx 0.226$ square units; 1 incomplete pass, 1 complete pass: $0.345(0.655) \approx 0.226$ square units; and 2 incomplete passes: $0.345^2 \approx 0.119$ square units. The regions that involve at least one complete pass cover $0.429 + 0.226 + 0.226 = 0.881$ square units, or 88.1% of the whole square region. **b.** The outcome of each attempted pass is modeled by $0.655C + 0.345I$, so the possible outcomes of two attempted passes is modeled by $(0.655C + 0.345I)^2 = 0.429C^2 + 0.452CI + 0.119I^2$. Because any combination of outcomes with a C results in at least one completed pass, the coefficients of the first two terms show that 42.9% + 45.2% = 88.1% of the outcomes will have at least one completed pass, and the coefficient of the last term shows that 11.9% of the outcomes will have two incomplete passes.

9.4 Problem Solving (pp. 579–580) **59. a.** 8 ft; the zeros of the function, 0 and 8, are the x-intercepts of the graph, which represent the edges of the base of the doorway. The distance between 0 and 8 on the x-axis is 8 units, so the width of the doorway at its base is 8 feet. **b.** 8 ft; the center of the base is the midpoint of the segment joining the x-intercepts 0 and 8, so at the center of the base $x = 4$. The doorway's highest point will be the point $(4, y)$ on the graph of $y = -0.5x(x - 8)$. Substitute $x = 4$ into the equation for y to find the height: $y = -0.5(4)(4 - 8) = 8$ feet.

9.5 Investigating Algebra Activity (p. 582)

2. **3.**

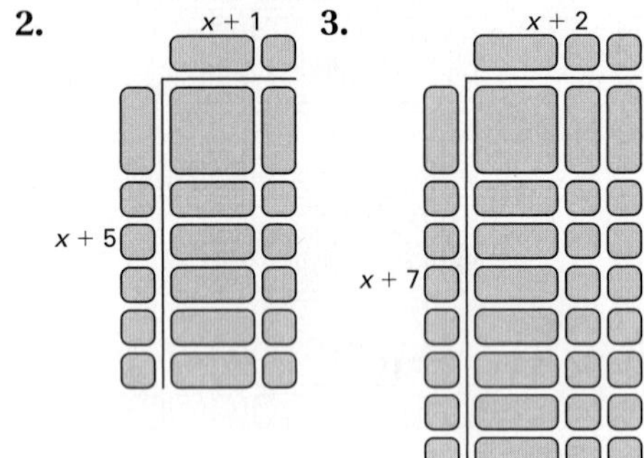

4. **5.**

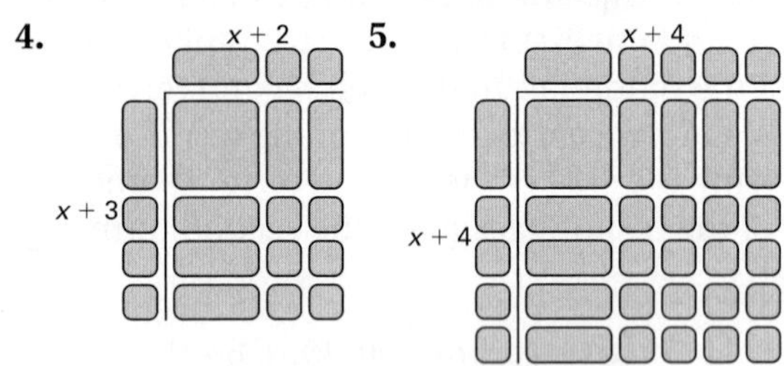

6. **7.**

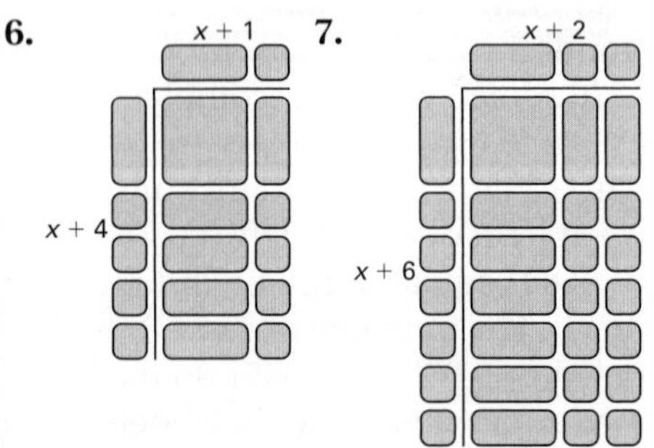

9.6 Investigating Algebra Activity (p. 592)

2. **3.**

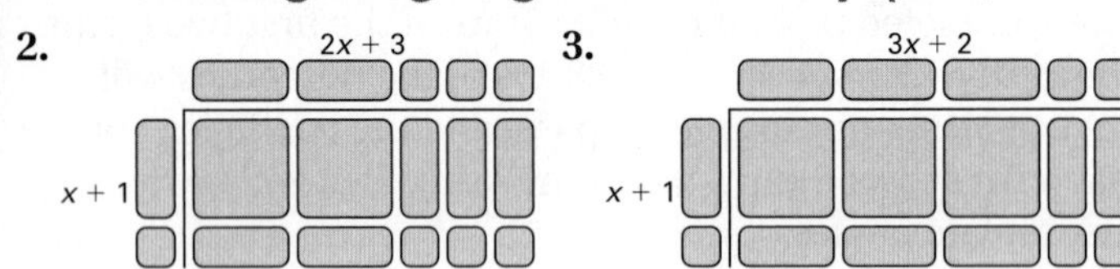

4.

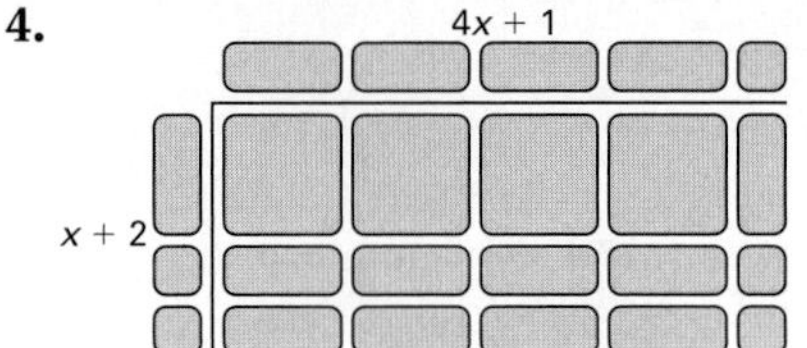

5.

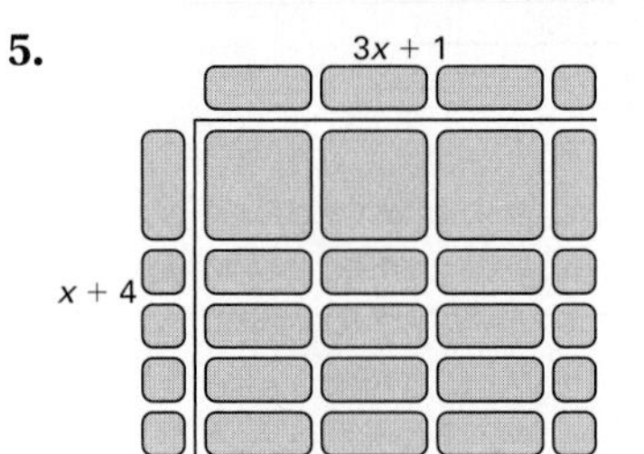

6.

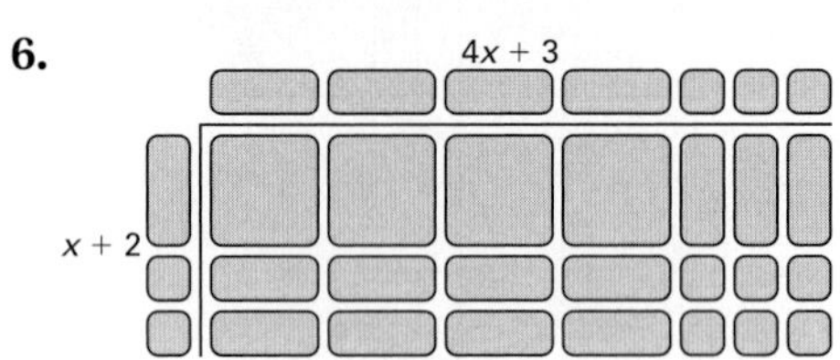

7.

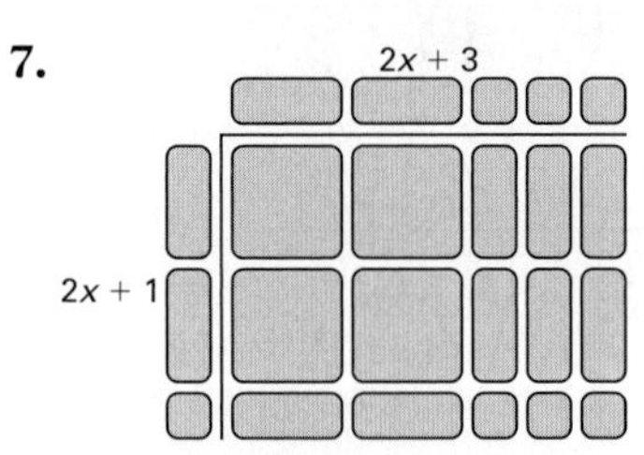

9.6 Skill Practice (pp. 596–597) **52.** $x^2 + x - 6 = 0$; any root $x = r$ of $x^2 + bx + c = 0$ comes from setting the factor $x - r$ equal to zero after $x^2 + bx + c$ is written in factored form; so, the roots -3 and 2 come from the factors $x - (-3)$, or $x + 3$, and $x - 2$. The product of these factors is $(x + 3)(x - 2) = x^2 - 2x + 3x - 6 = x^2 + x - 6$. **53.** $2x^2 - 9x - 5 = 0$; any root $x = \frac{r}{s}$ of $ax^2 + bx + c = 0$ comes from setting the factor $sx - r$ equal to zero after $ax^2 + bx + c$ is written in factored form; so, the roots $-\frac{1}{2}$ and 5 come from the factors $2x - (-1)$, or $2x + 1$, and $x - 5$. The product of these factors is $(2x + 1)(x - 5) = 2x^2 - 10x + x - 5 = 2x^2 - 9x - 5$. **54.** $12x^2 + 13x + 3 = 0$; any root $x = \frac{r}{s}$ of $ax^2 + bx + c = 0$ comes from setting the factor $sx - r$ equal to zero after $ax^2 + bx + c$ is written in factored form; so, the roots $-\frac{3}{4}$ and $-\frac{1}{3}$ come from the factors $4x - (-3)$, or $4x + 3$, and $3x - (-1)$, or $3x + 1$. The product of these factors is $(4x + 3)(3x + 1) = 12x^2 + 4x + 9x + 3 = 12x^2 + 13x + 3$.

9.7 Problem Solving (pp. 604–605) **52. d.** 6 rows; let $x =$ the number of chairs in the last row, so that the sum of the odd integers from 15 to x is 120. x can be written in the form $2n - 1$. 15 is the eighth odd integer and x is the nth odd integer, so the sum of the odd integers from 15 to x can be found as described in part (c): the sum of the first n odd integers minus the sum of the first 7 odd integers, $n^2 - 7^2$, or $n^2 - 49$. The total number of chairs is to be 120, so this leads to the equation $n^2 - 49 = 120$, or $n^2 - 169 = 0$. This equation has two solutions, 13 and -13. Disregard the solution -13 because n cannot be negative in this situation. So, x is the thirteenth odd integer. The numbers of chairs in the rows go from the eighth odd integer (15) to the thirteenth odd integer (25). There are $13 - 8 + 1 =$ 6 rows of chairs.

9.7 Mixed Review (p. 605)

62.
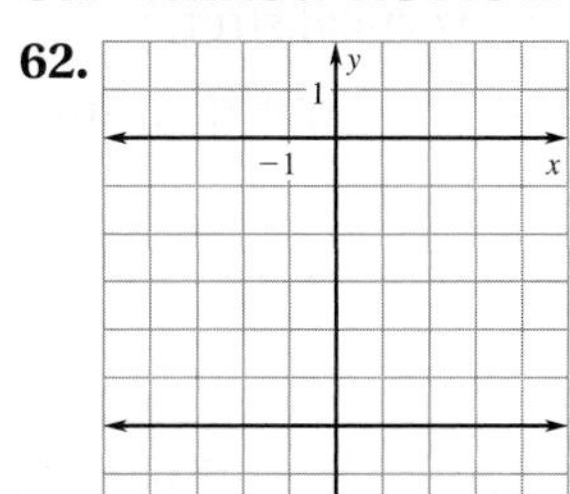

63.
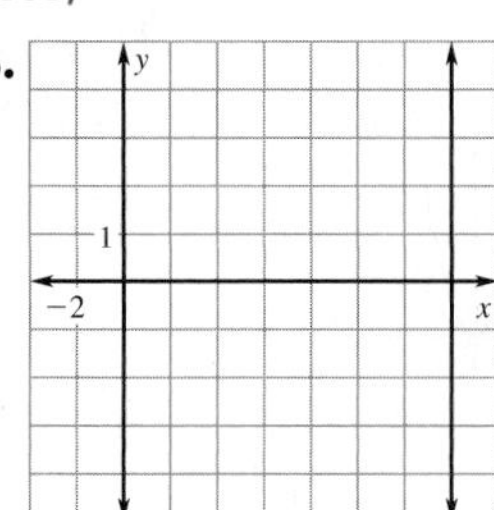

64.
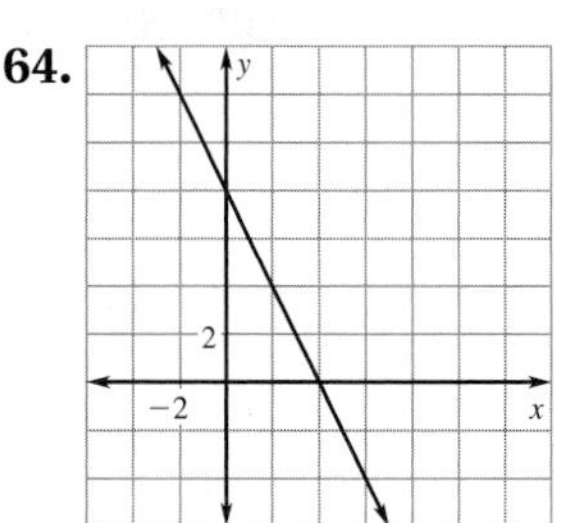

65.
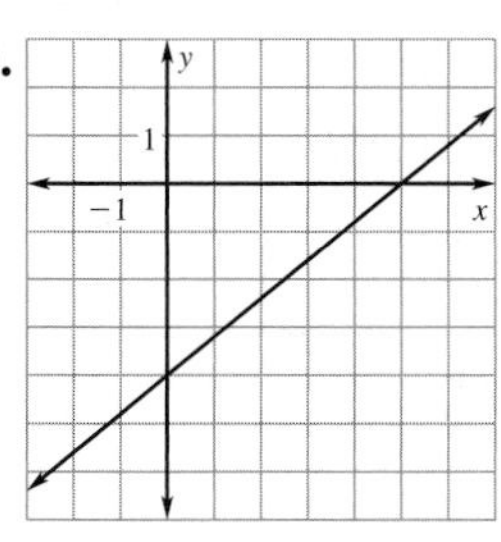

66.
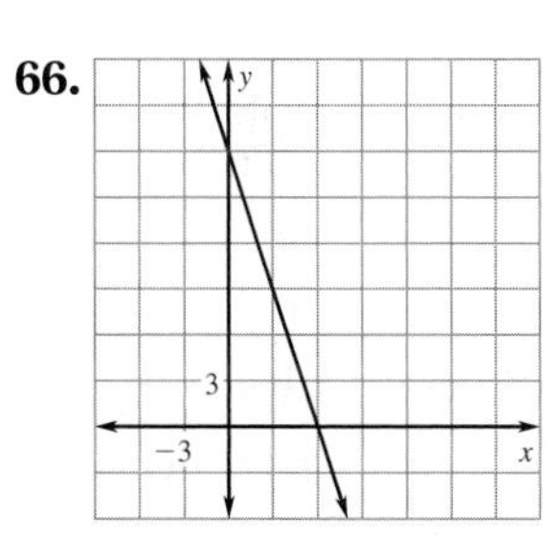

67.
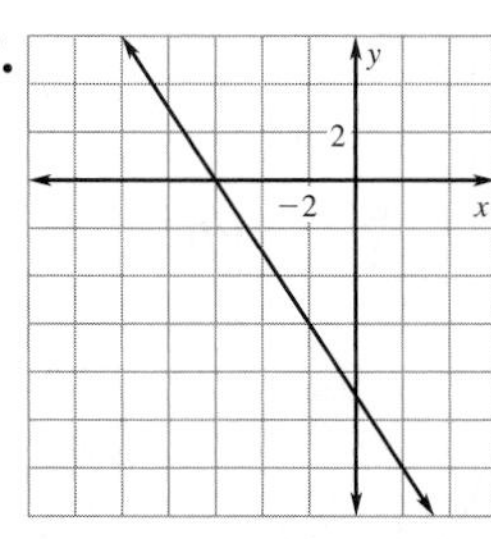

68.
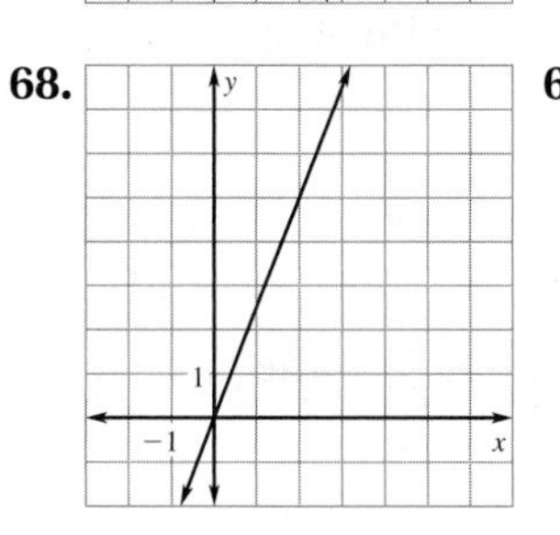

69.
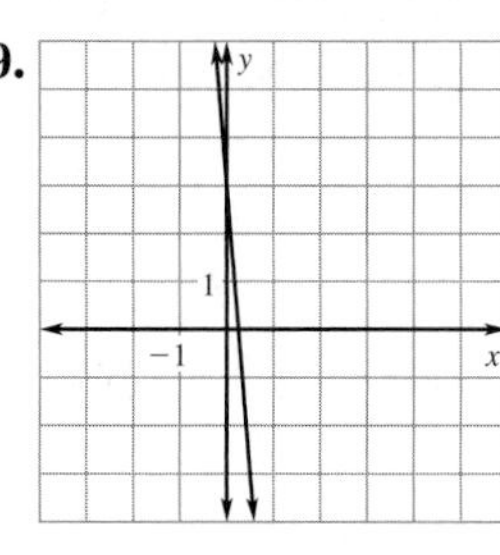

70.
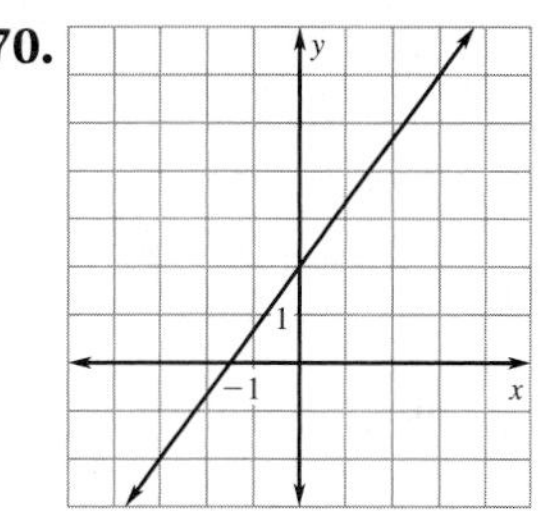

9.8 Mixed Review (p. 613)

75.
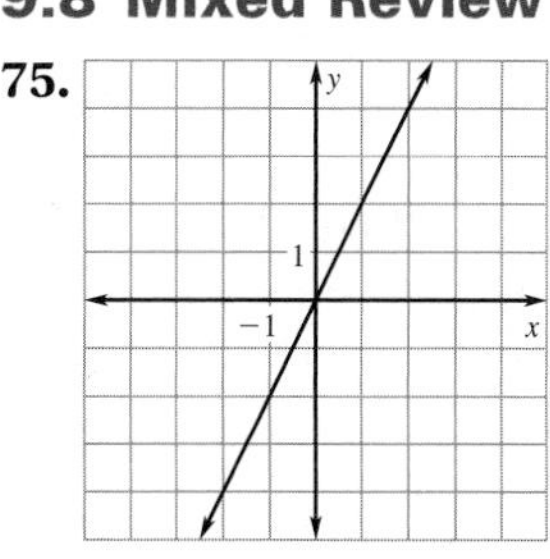

76.
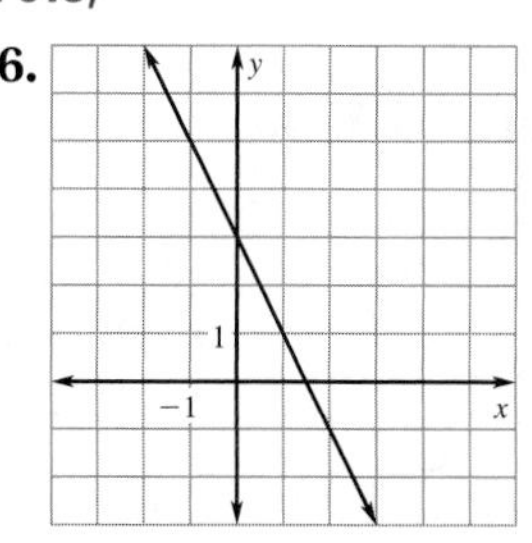

77.
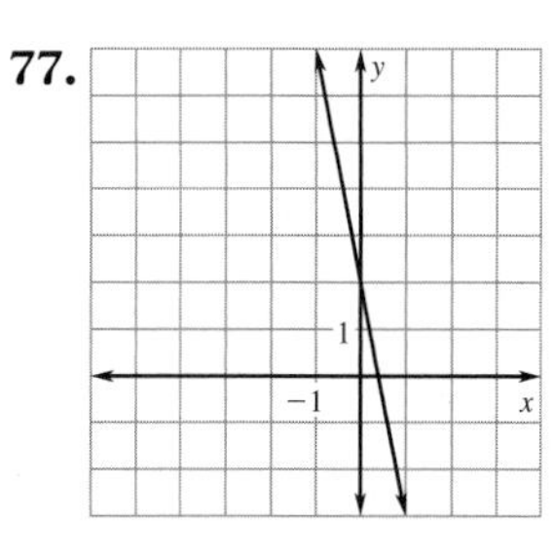

78.
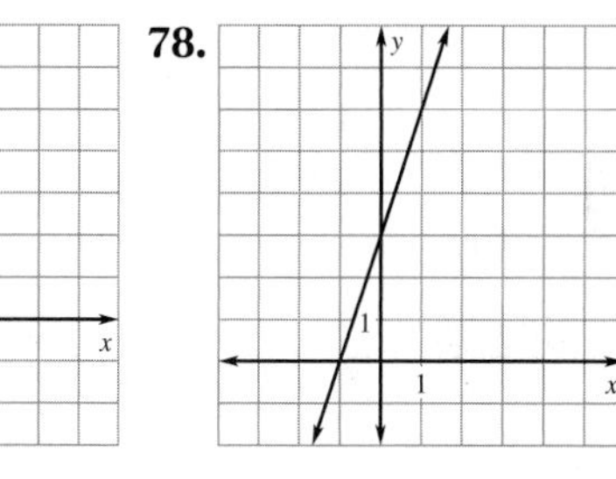

79.
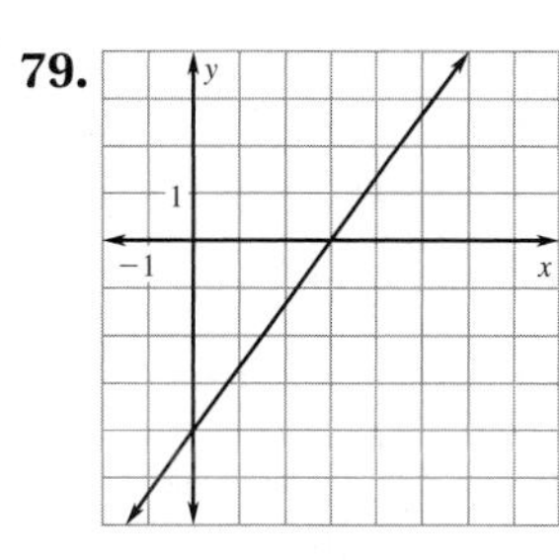

80.
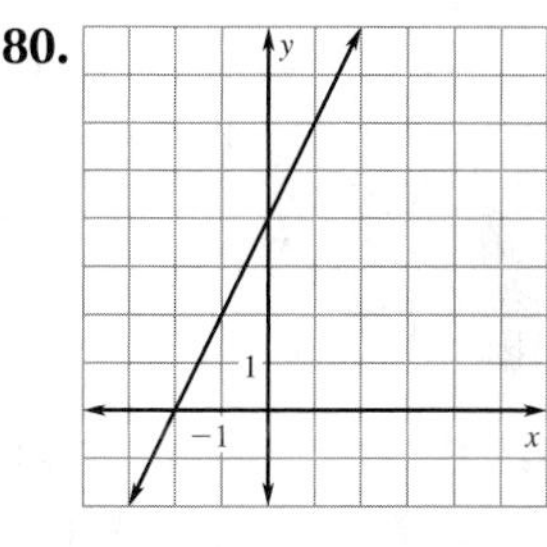

81.
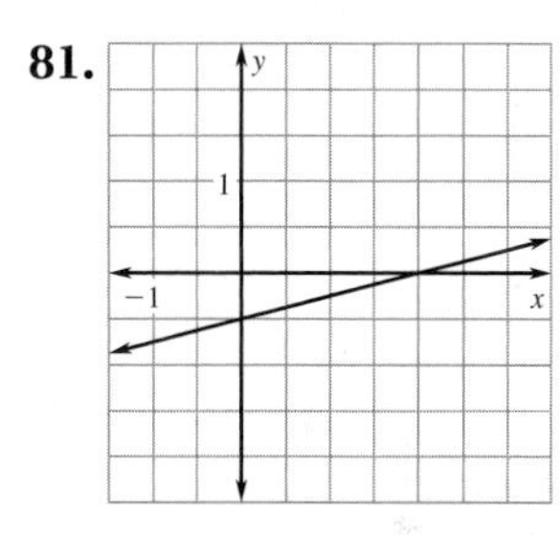

82.
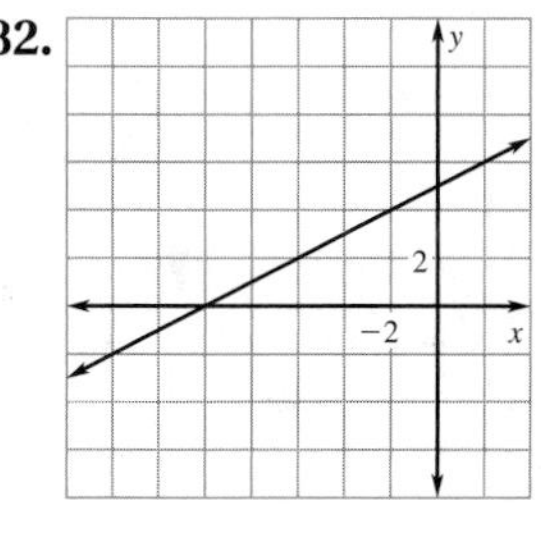

83.
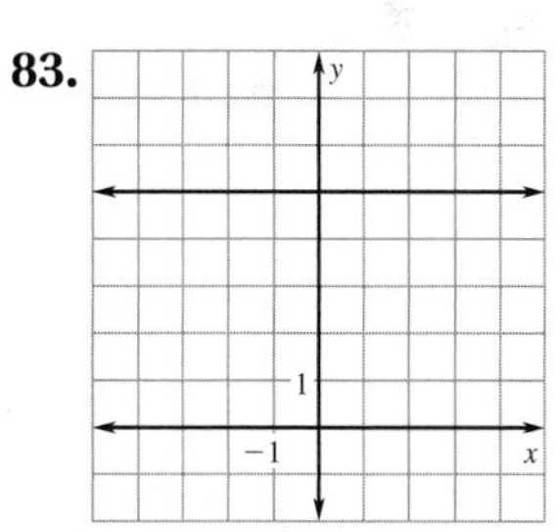

84.
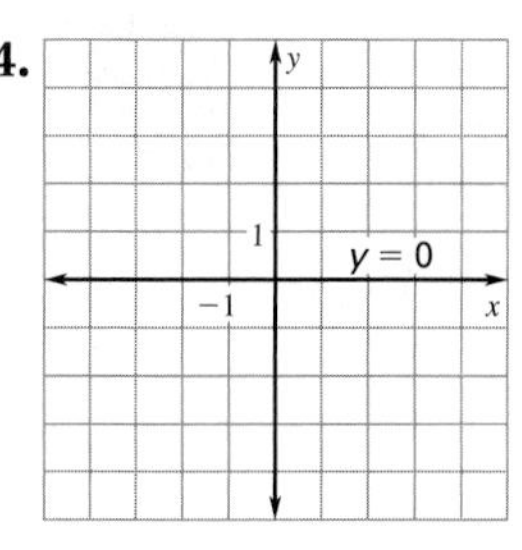

85.

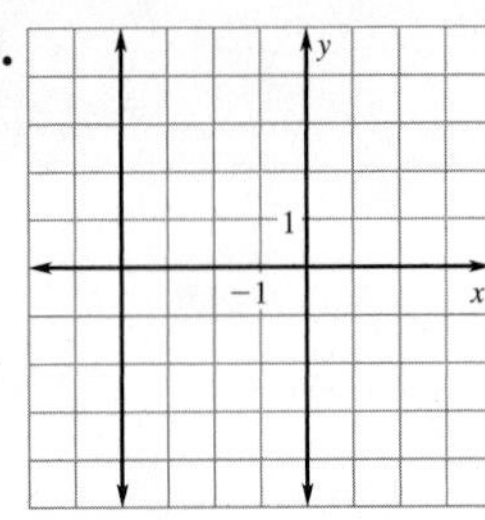

86.

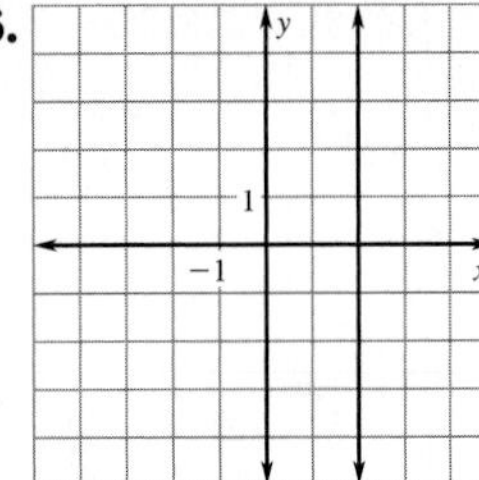

Chapter 10

10.1 Guided Practice (pp. 629–631)

1. The graph is a vertical stretch (by a factor of 4) with a reflection in the x-axis of the graph of $y = x^2$.

2. The graph is a vertical shrink $\left(\text{by a factor of } \frac{1}{3}\right)$ of the graph of $y = x^2$.

3.

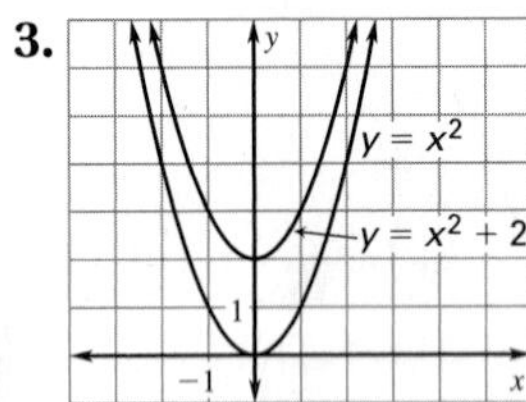

The graph is a vertical translation (of 2 units up) of the graph of $y = x^2$.

10.1 Skill Practice (pp. 632–633)

6.

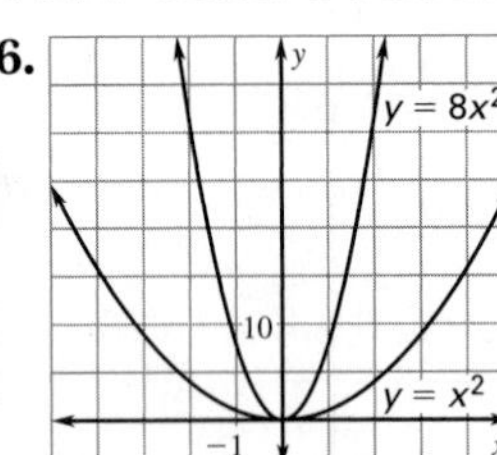

The graph is a vertical stretch (by a factor of 8) of the graph of $y = x^2$.

7.

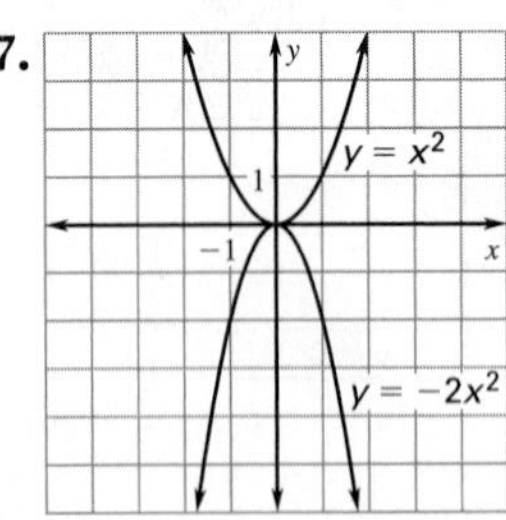

The graph is a vertical stretch (by a factor of 2) with a reflection in the x-axis of the graph of $y = x^2$.

8.

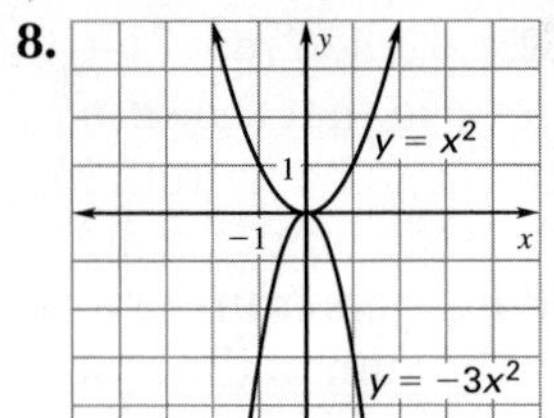

The graph is a vertical stretch (by a factor of 3) with a reflection in the x-axis of the graph of $y = x^2$.

9.

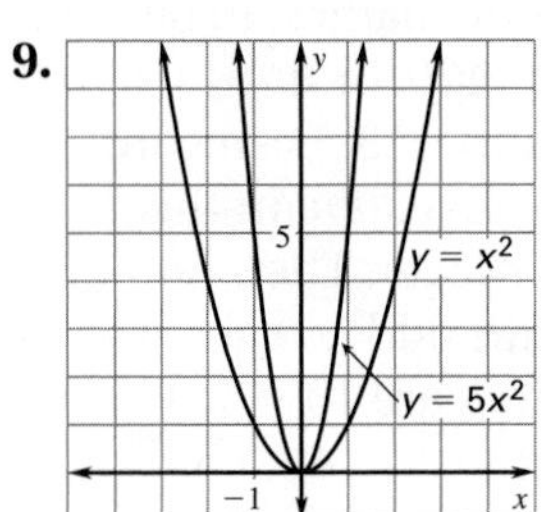

The graph is a vertical stretch (by a factor of 5) of the graph of $y = x^2$.

10.

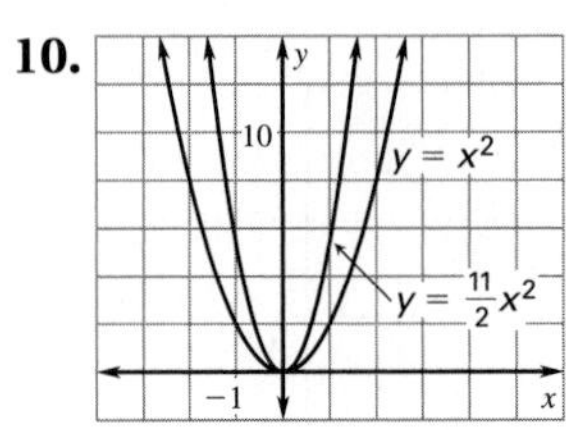

The graph is a vertical stretch $\left(\text{by a factor of } \frac{11}{2}\right)$ of the graph of $y = x^2$.

11.

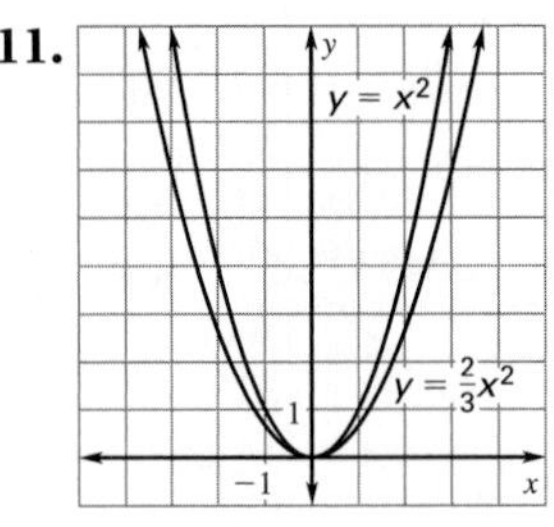

The graph is a vertical shrink $\left(\text{by a factor of } \frac{2}{3}\right)$ of the graph of $y = x^2$.

12.

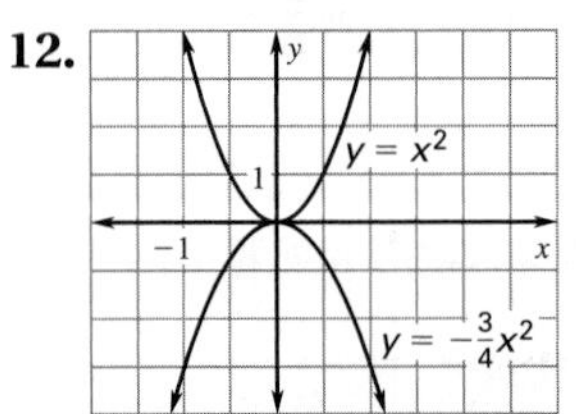

The graph is a vertical shrink $\left(\text{by a factor of } \frac{3}{4}\right)$ with a reflection in the x-axis of the graph of $y = x^2$.

13.

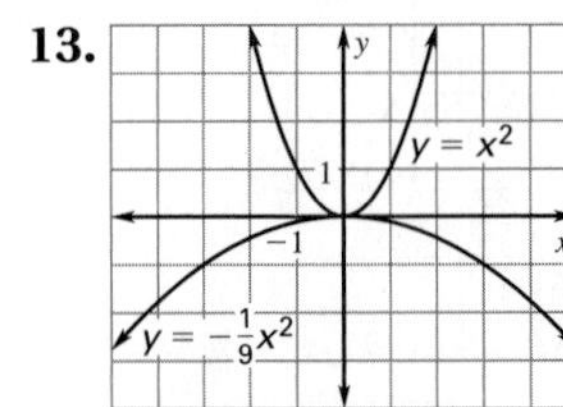

The graph is a vertical shrink $\left(\text{by a factor of } \frac{1}{9}\right)$ with a reflection in the x-axis of the graph of $y = x^2$.

14.

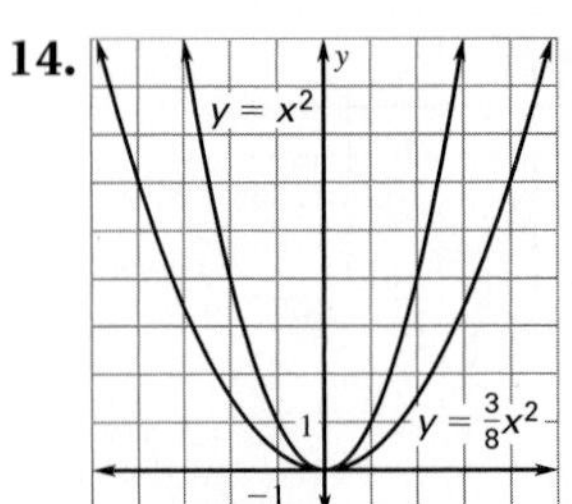

The graph is a vertical shrink $\left(\text{by a factor of } \frac{3}{8}\right)$ of the graph of $y = x^2$.

15. 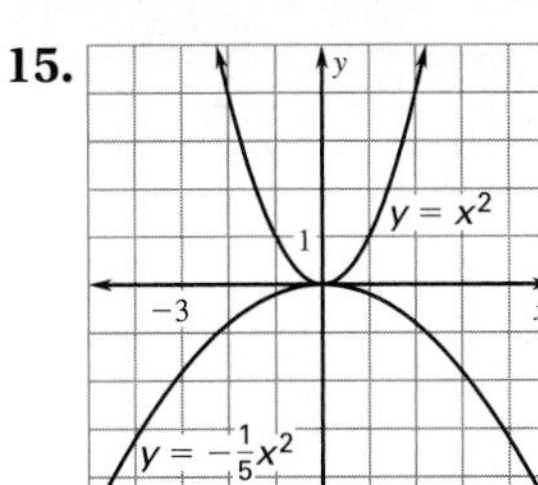
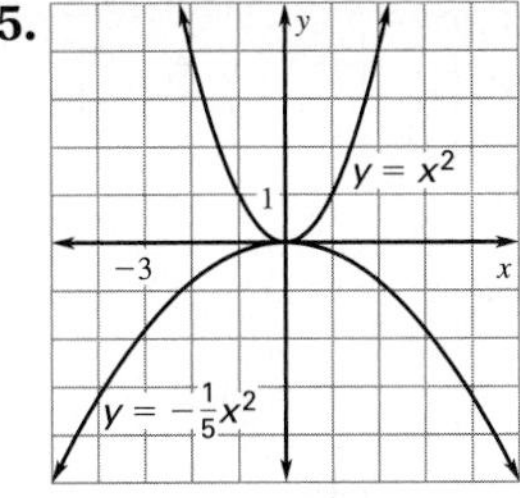

The graph is a vertical shrink $\left(\text{by a factor of } \frac{1}{5}\right)$ with a reflection in the x-axis of the graph of $y = x^2$.

16. 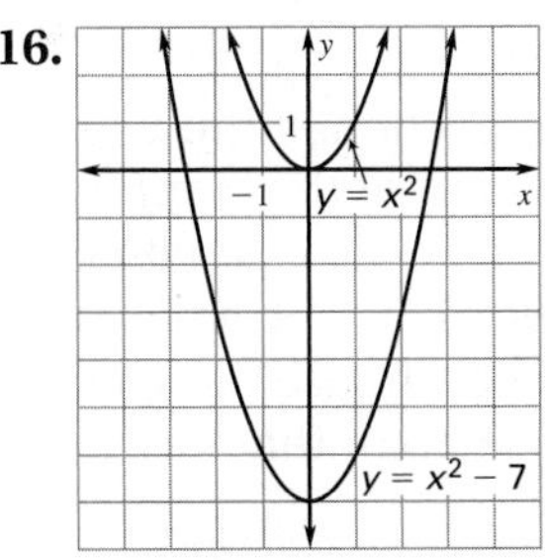

The graph is a vertical translation (of 7 units down) of the graph of $y = x^2$.

17. 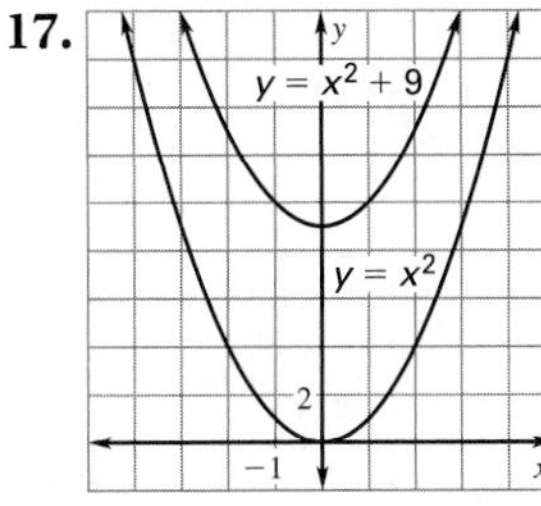

The graph is a vertical translation (of 9 units up) of the graph of $y = x^2$.

18. 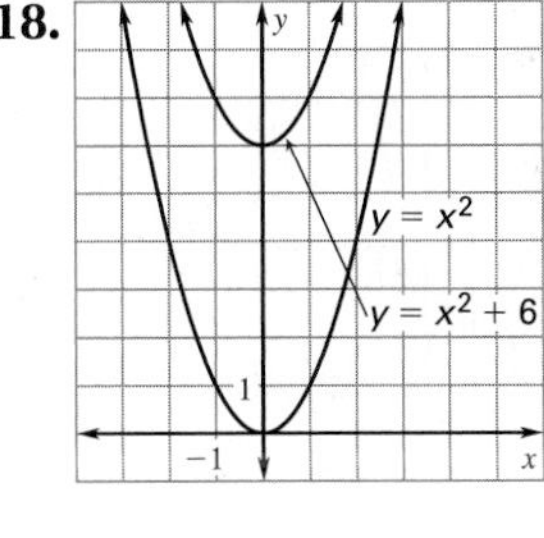

The graph is a vertical translation (of 6 units up) of the graph of $y = x^2$.

19. 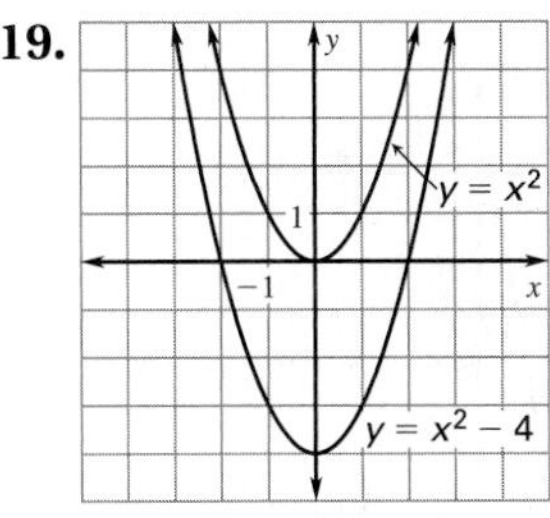

The graph is a vertical translation (of 4 units down) of the graph of $y = x^2$.

20. The graph is a vertical translation (of 1 unit down) of the graph of $y = x^2$.

21. 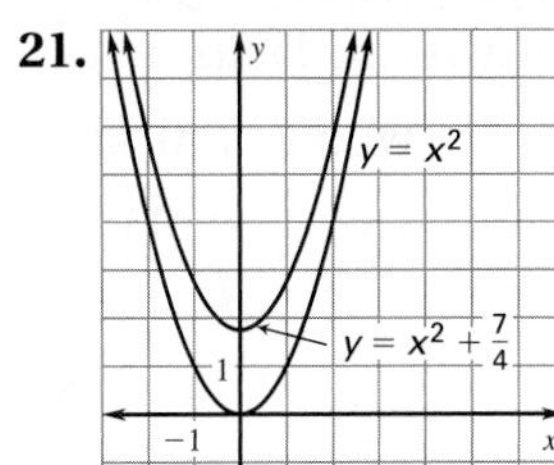

The graph is a vertical translation $\left(\text{of } \frac{7}{4} \text{ units up}\right)$ of the graph of $y = x^2$.

24. 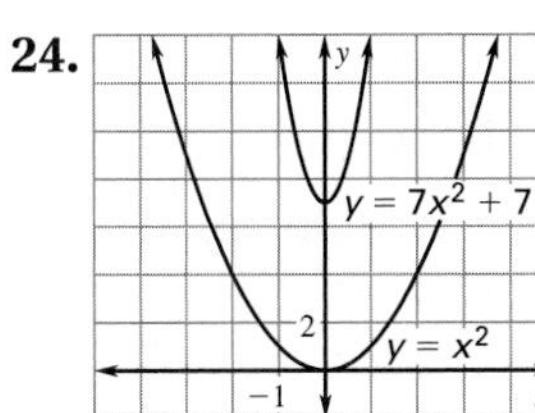

The graph is a vertical stretch (by a factor of 7) with a vertical translation (of 7 units up) of the graph of $y = x^2$.

25. 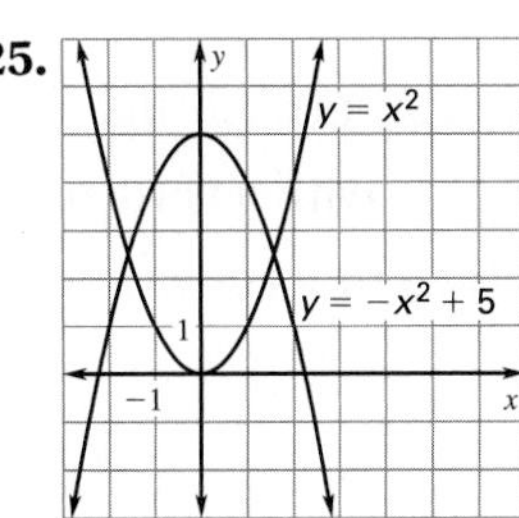

The graph is a reflection in the x-axis with a vertical translation (of 5 units up) of the graph of $y = x^2$.

26. 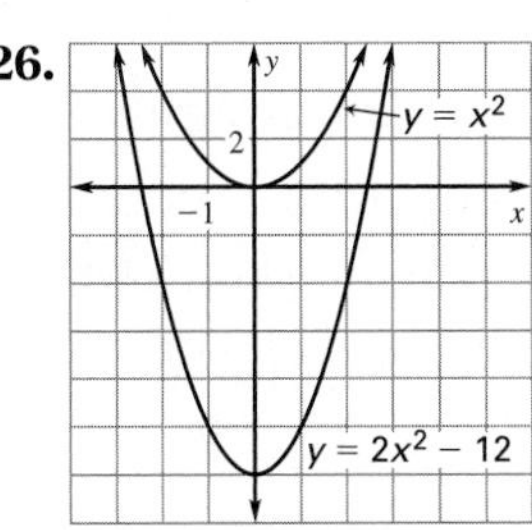

The graph is a vertical stretch (by a factor of 2) with a vertical translation (of 12 units down) of the graph of $y = x^2$.

27. 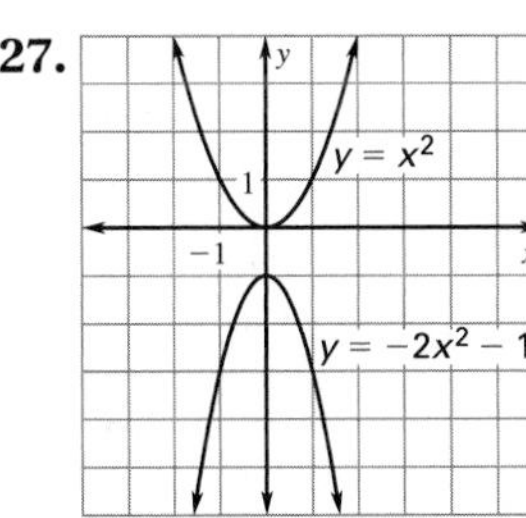

The graph is a vertical stretch (by a factor of 2) with a vertical translation (of 1 unit down) and a reflection in the x-axis of the graph of $y = x^2$.

28. 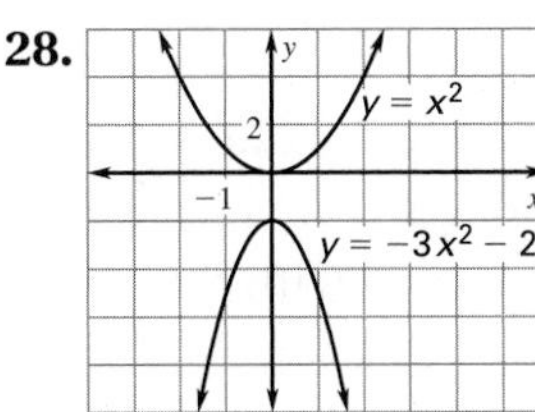

The graph is a vertical stretch (by a factor of 3) with a vertical translation (of 2 units down) and a reflection in the x-axis of the graph of $y = x^2$.

ADDITIONAL ANSWERS

29. 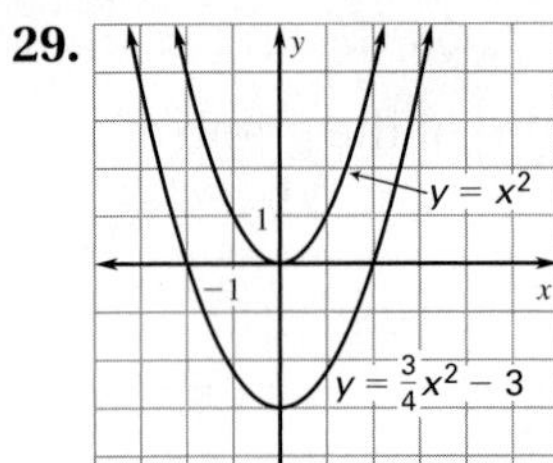

The graph is a vertical shrink $\left(\text{by a factor of } \frac{3}{4}\right)$ with a vertical translation (of 3 units down) of the graph of $y = x^2$.

30. 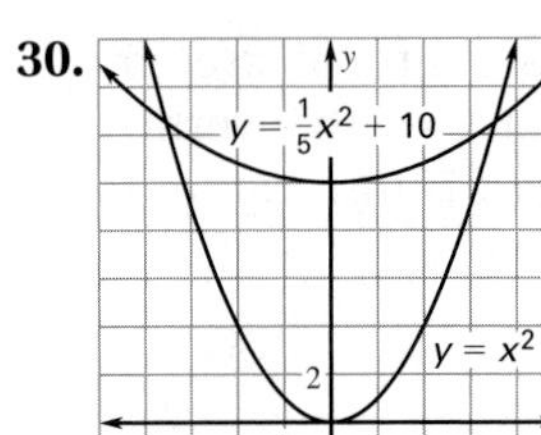

The graph is a vertical shrink $\left(\text{by a factor of } \frac{1}{5}\right)$ with a vertical translation (of 10 units up) of the graph of $y = x^2$.

31. 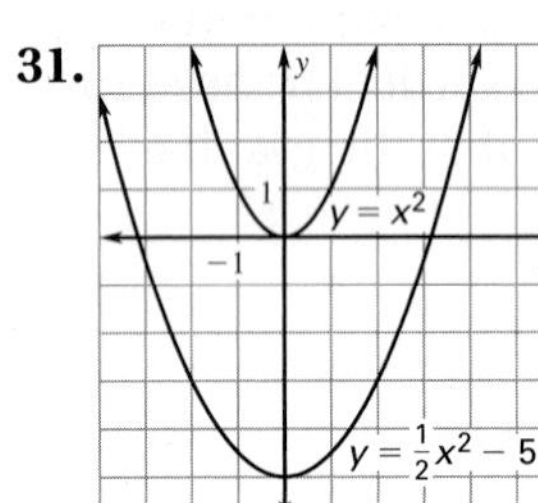

The graph is a vertical shrink $\left(\text{by a factor of } \frac{1}{2}\right)$ with a vertical translation (of 5 units down) of the graph of $y = x^2$.

32. 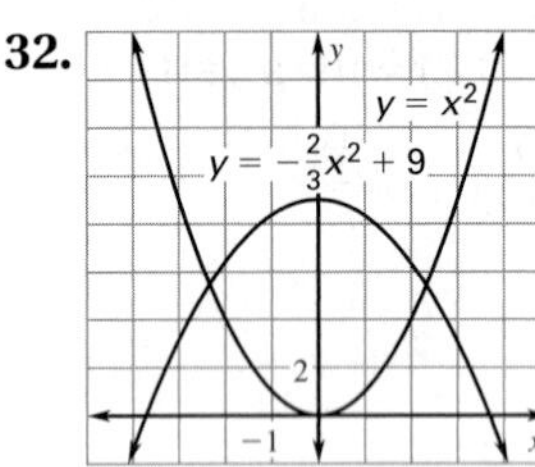

The graph is a vertical shrink $\left(\text{by a factor of } \frac{2}{3}\right)$ with a vertical translation (of 9 units up) and a reflection in the x-axis of the graph of $y = x^2$.

10.1 Problem Solving (pp. 633–634)

43. a. 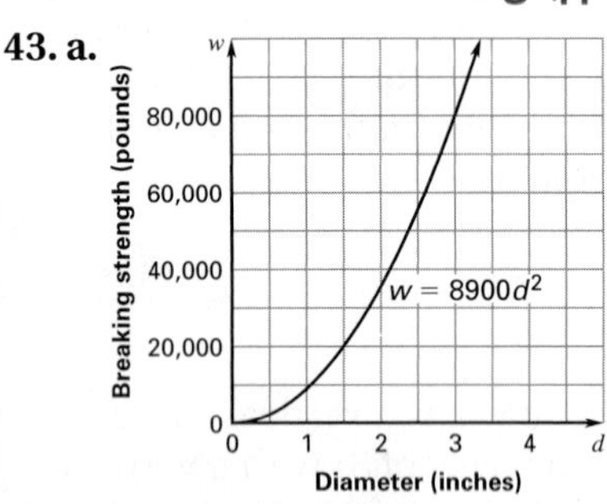

b. No. *Sample answer:* Let D be the diameter of a rope with 4 times the breaking strength of a rope with diameter d. Then $8900D^2 = 4(8900d^2)$; $D^2 = 4d^2$; $D = \sqrt{4d^2}$; $D = 2d$. Thus, the diameter of the rope with 4 times the breaking strength is only two times the diameter of the other rope.

44. a. 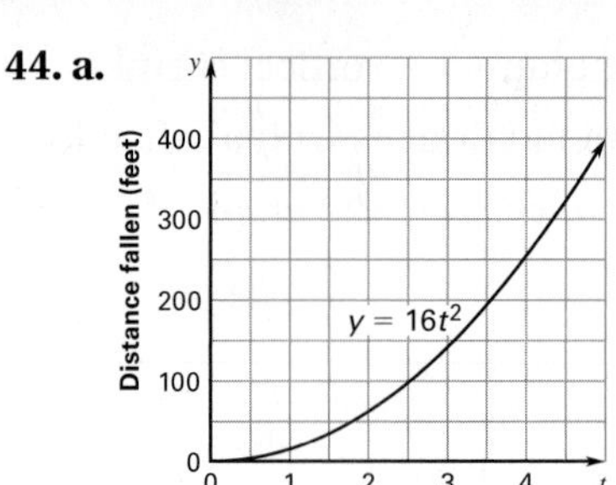

b. 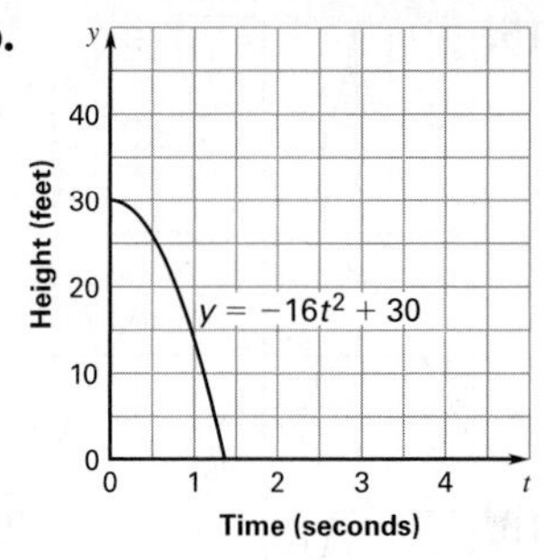

c. The graph of $y = -16t^2 + 30$ is a reflection in the x-axis and a vertical translation (of 30 units up) of the graph of $y = 16t^2$. To use the graph of $y = -16t^2 + 30$, estimate the t-value of the point that has a y-value of 20 feet, which is the height of the egg after it falls 10 feet. To use the graph of $y = 16t^2$, estimate the t-value of the point that has a y-value of 10 feet.

10.2 Skill Practice (pp. 638–639)

15. 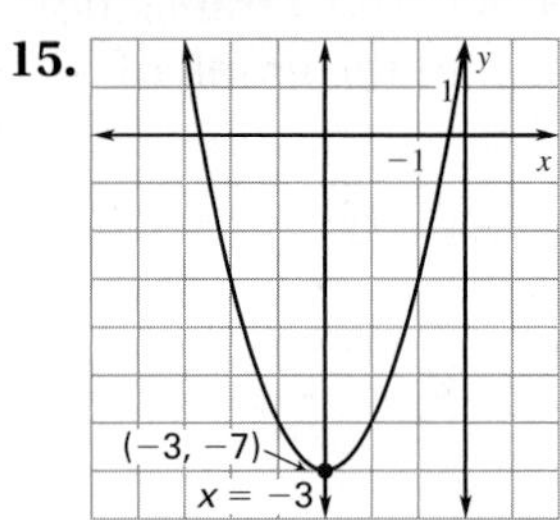

16. 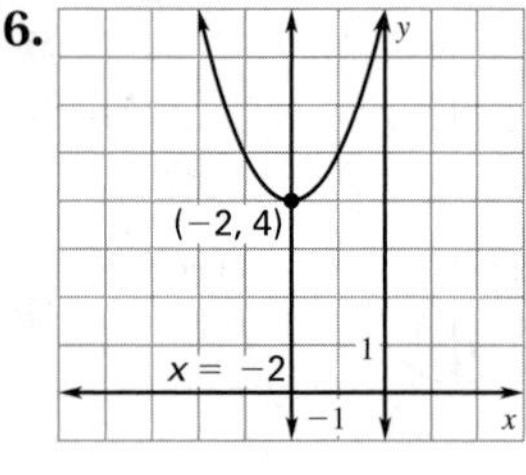

17. 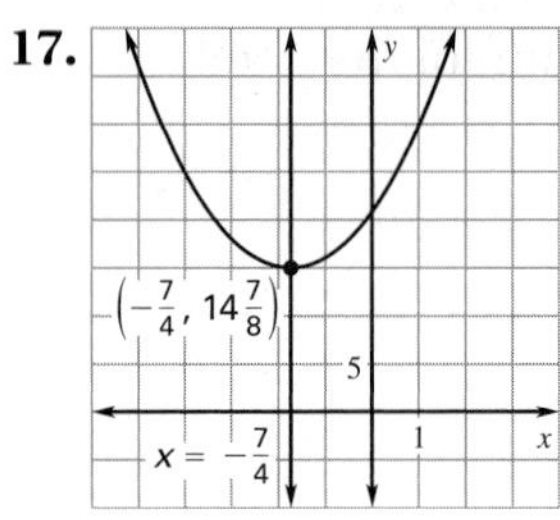

18. 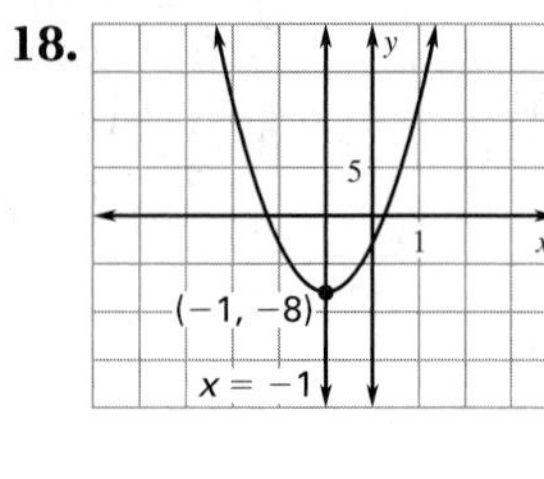

19. 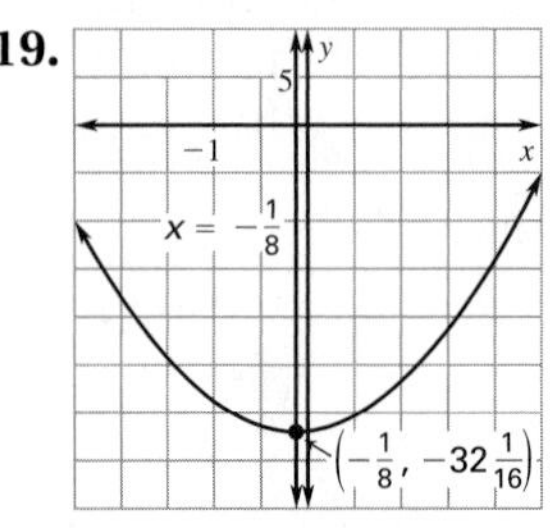

20. 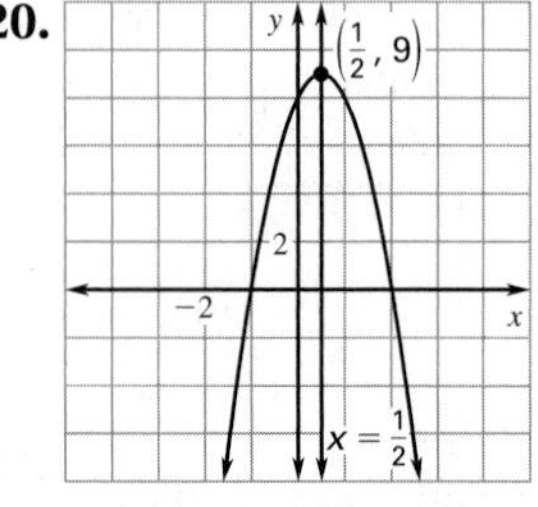

21. 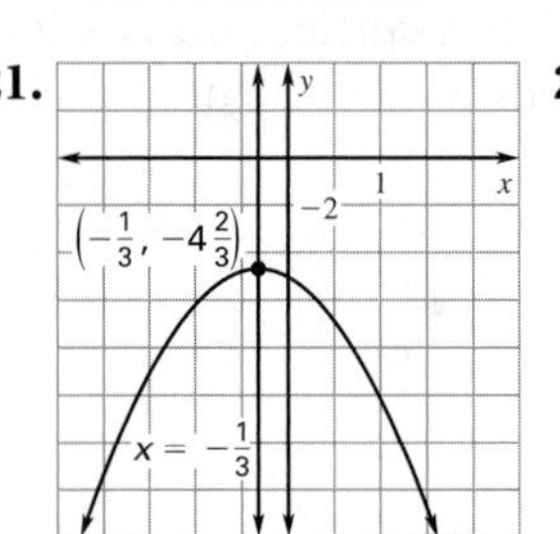

22. 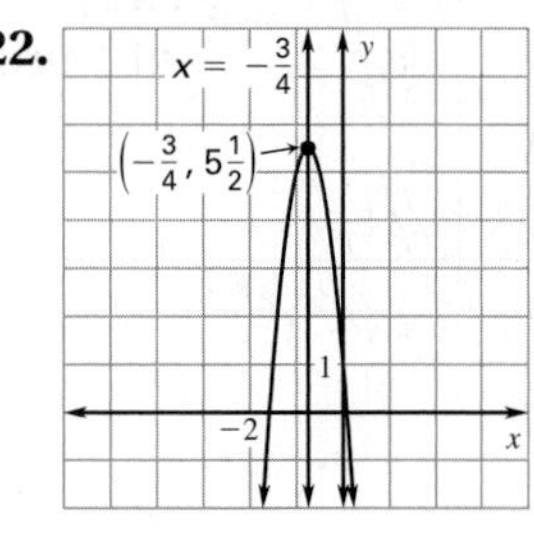

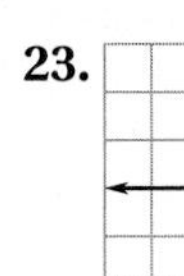

23.

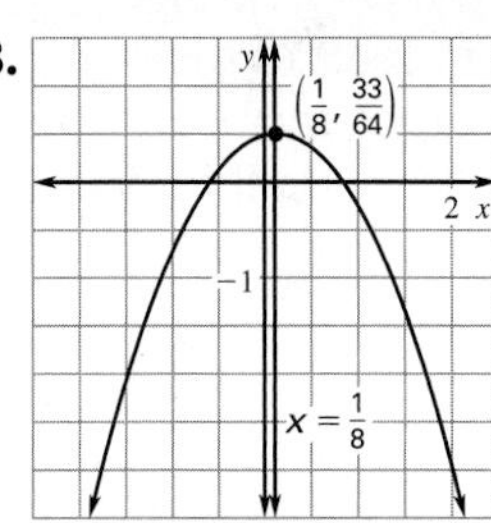

24.

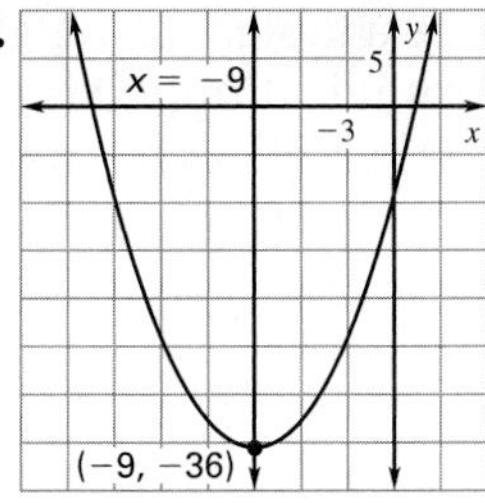

25.

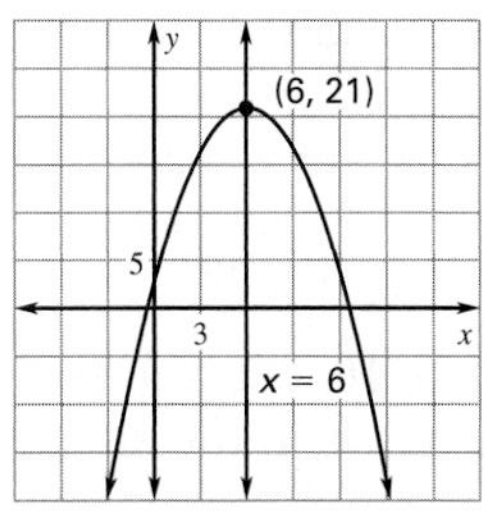

26.

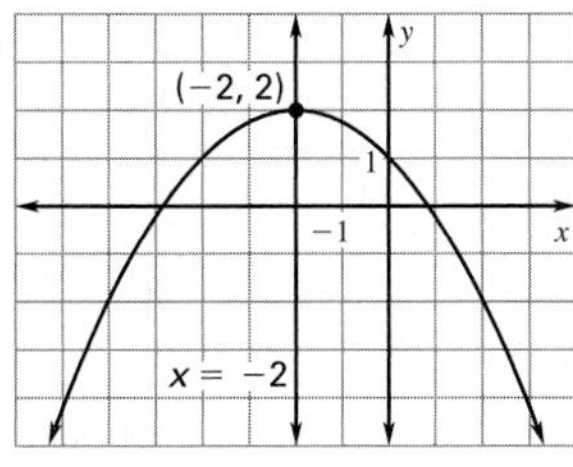

10.2 Problem Solving (pp. 639–640)

43.

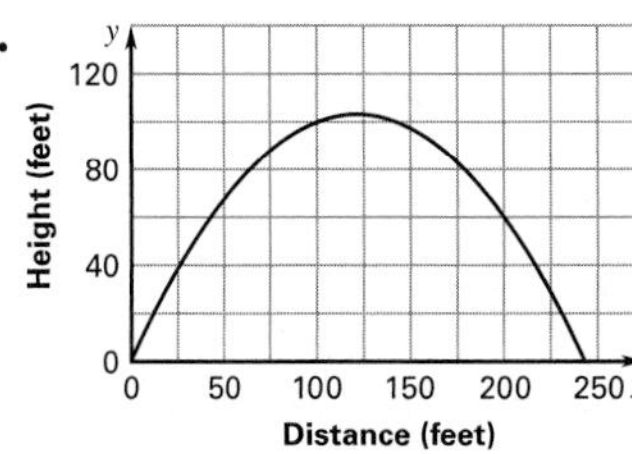

Extension (p. 642)

1.

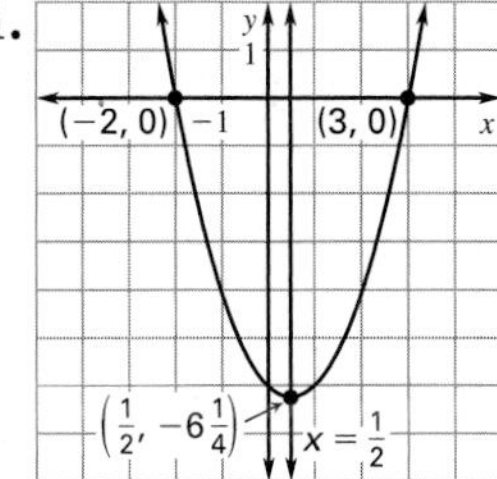

2.

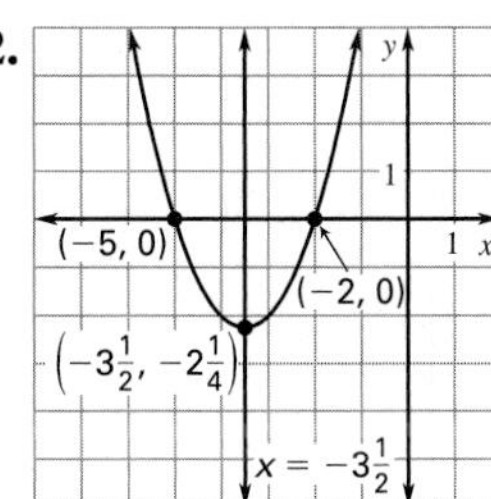

3.

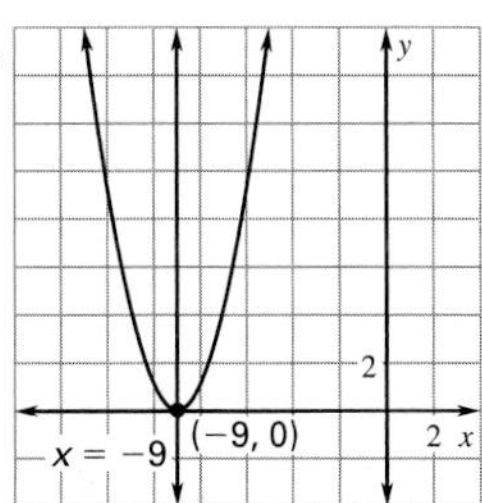

4.

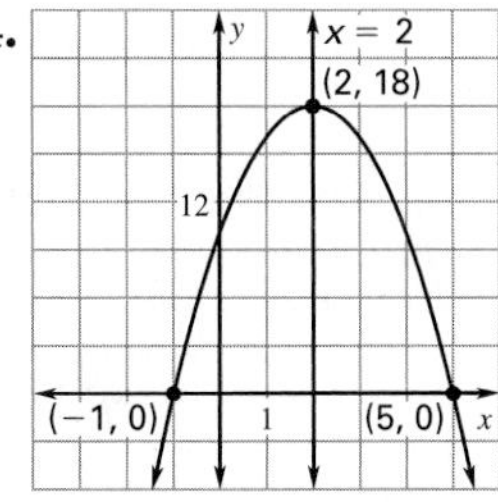

5.

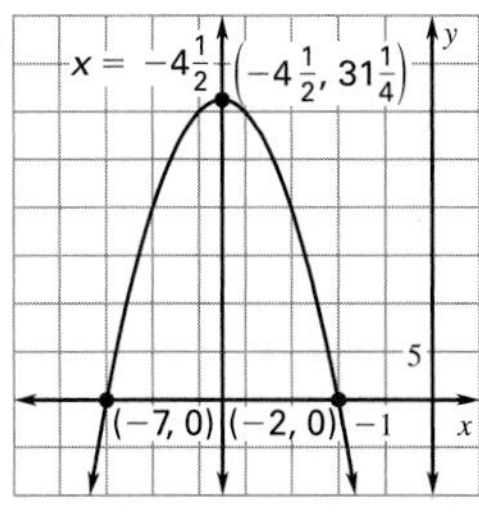

6.

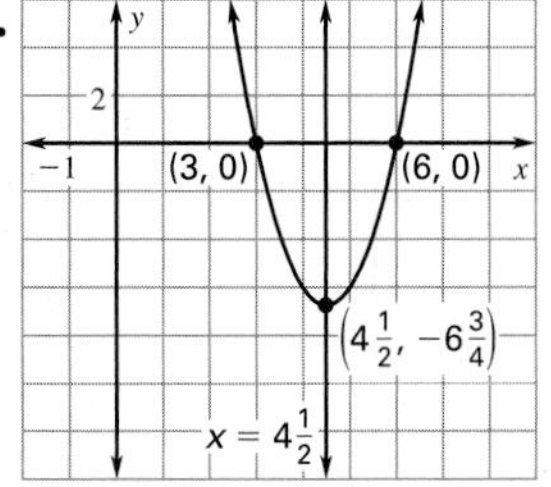

7.

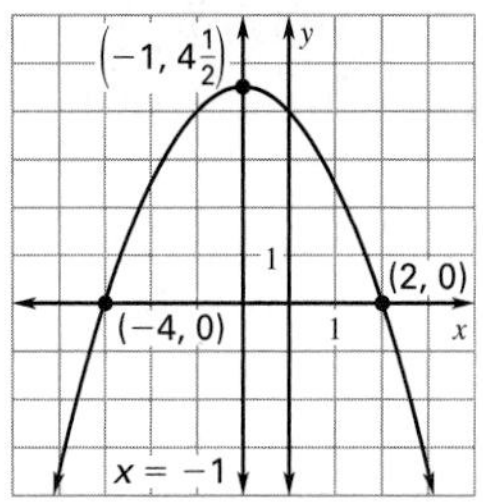

8.

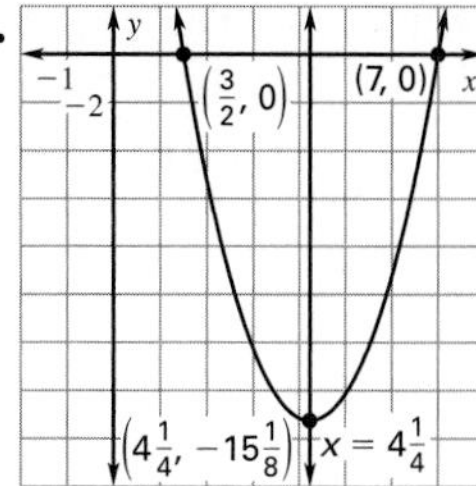

9.

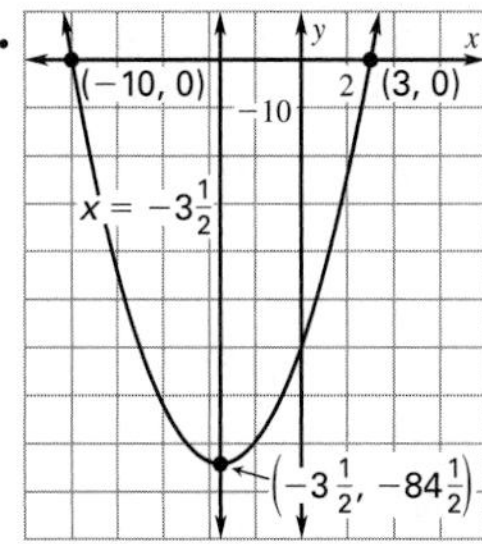

10.

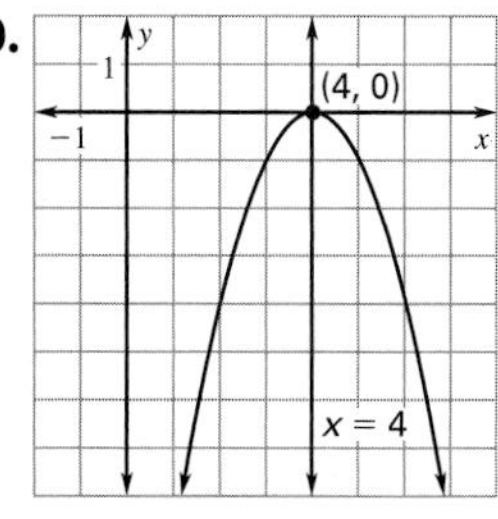

11.

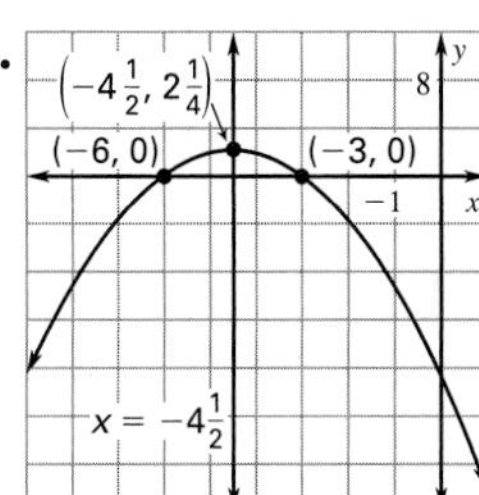

12.

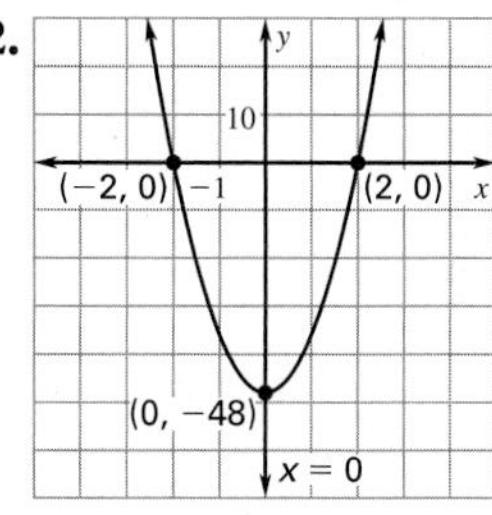

Quiz for Lessons 10.1–10.3 (p. 649)

1.

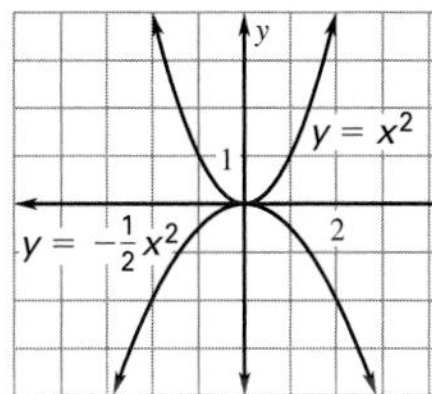

The graph is a vertical shrink $\left(\text{by a factor of } \frac{1}{2}\right)$ with a reflection in the x-axis of the graph of $y = x^2$.

2. 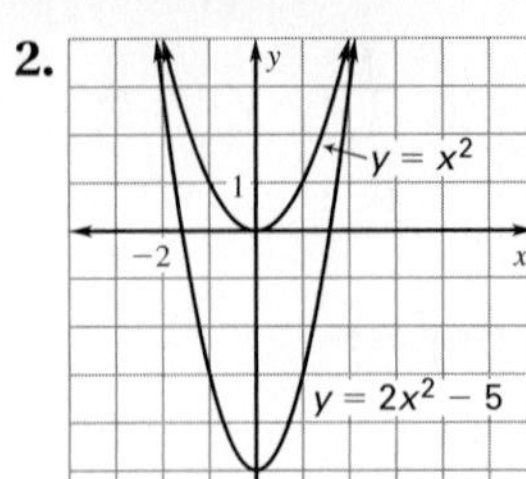

The graph is a vertical stretch (by a factor of 2) with a vertical translation (of 5 units down) of the graph of $y = x^2$.

3. 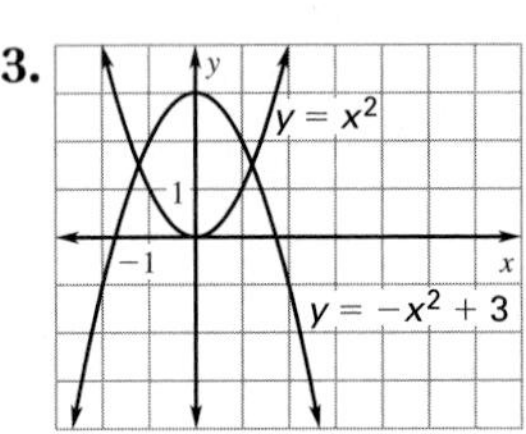

The graph is a vertical translation (of 3 units up) with a reflection in the x-axis of the graph of $y = x^2$.

4. 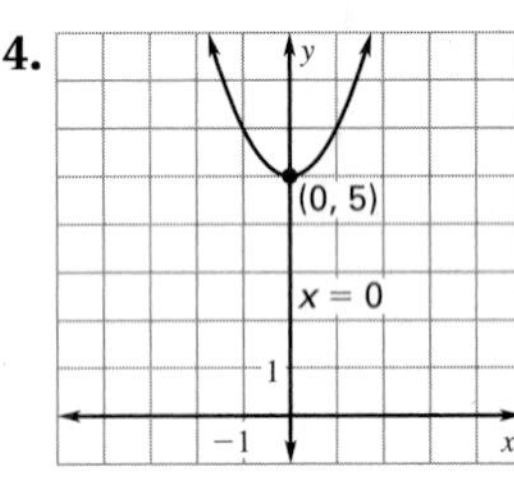

5. 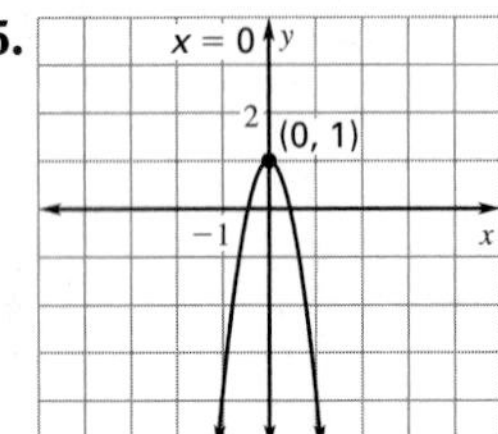

6. 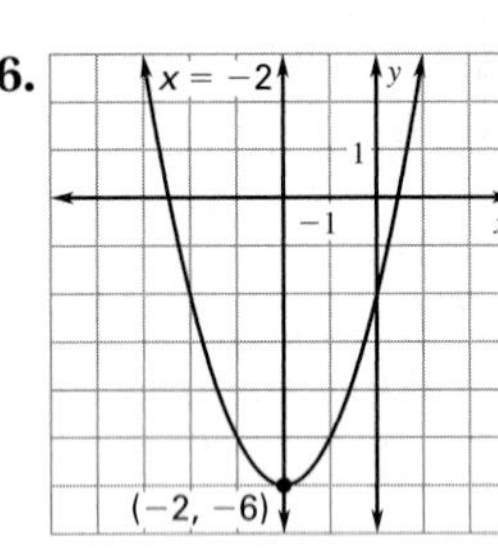

7. 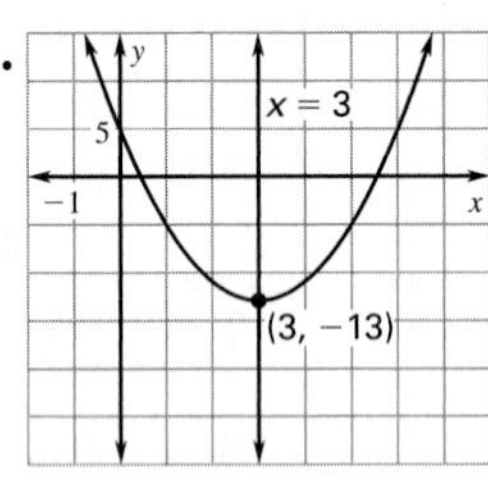

8. 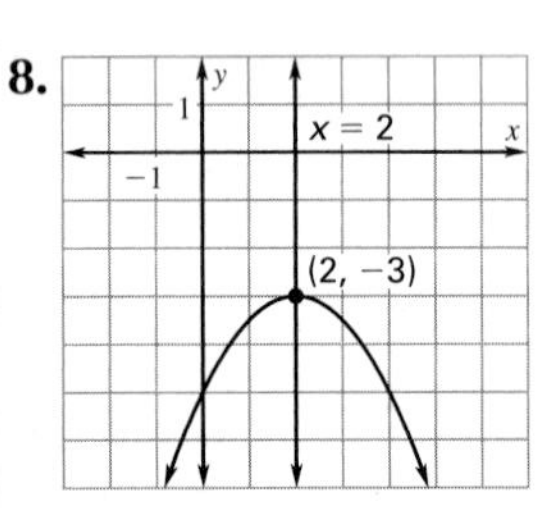

9. 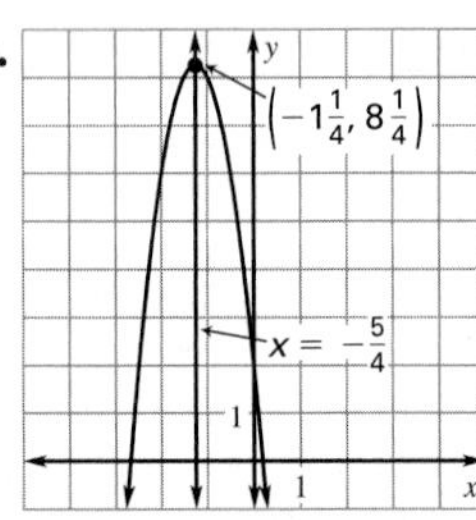

10.4 Problem Solving Workshop (p. 660) **1.** About 1.5 sec; Method 1: Use factoring. The height h (in feet) of the ball t seconds after it is dropped is modeled by $h = -16t^2 + 45$. To find the time it takes the ball to reach a height of 10 feet, substitute 10 for h and solve for t: $10 = -16t^2 + 45$, or $0 = -16t^2 + 35$. Replace 35 with the closest perfect square and factor: $0 = -16t^2 + 36$; $0 = -4(4t^2 - 9)$; $0 = -4(2t + 3)(2t - 3)$; $2t + 3 = 0$ *or* $2t - 3 = 0$; $t = -\frac{3}{2}$ or $t = \frac{3}{2}$. The time cannot be negative, so disregard the negative solution; the ball is in the air about 1.5 seconds.

Method 2: Use a table. The height h (in feet) of the ball t seconds after it is dropped is modeled by $h = -16t^2 + 45$. Make a table that shows the height h of the ball for values of t in increments of 1 second:

Time, t (sec)	0	1	2
Height, h (ft)	45	29	−19

Look in the table for the time interval in which the ball reaches a height of 10 feet; this happens between 1 and 2 seconds. Make a second table using increments of 0.1 second:

Time, t (sec)	1.0	1.1	1.2	1.3	1.4	1.5
Height, h (ft)	29.00	25.64	21.96	17.96	13.64	9

The height in the table that is closest to 10 feet is 9 feet. To the nearest tenth of a second, the ball is in the air for about 1.5 seconds.

3. b. length: about 9 in., width: 5 in., height: about 1.8 in.

c.

Height, x (in.)	1.7	1.8	1.9
Width (in.)	5	5	5
Length, $5x$ (in.)	8.5	9	9.5
Volume, V (in.^{3})	72.25	81	90.25

The volume in the table closest to 83 cubic inches is 81 cubic inches. To the nearest tenth of an inch, the height of the box is about 1.8 inches. The length of the box is $5x \approx 9$ inches, and the width is 5 inches.

Extension (p. 670)

1. 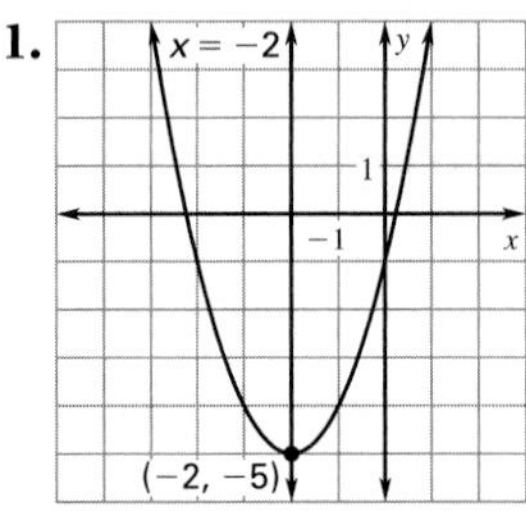

2. 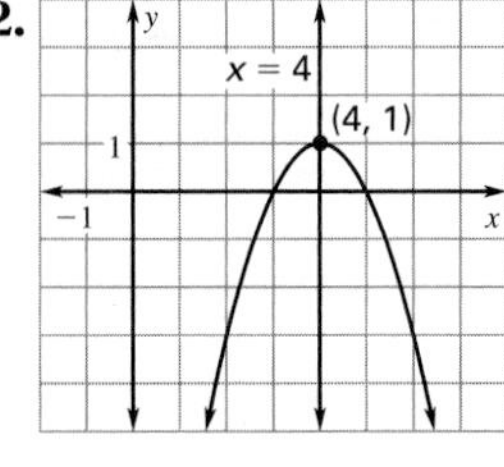

3. 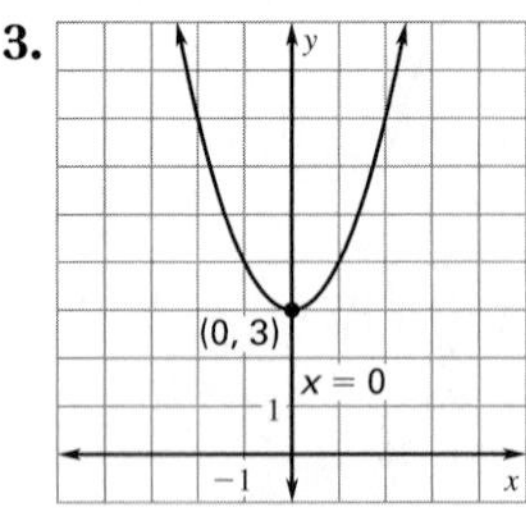

4. 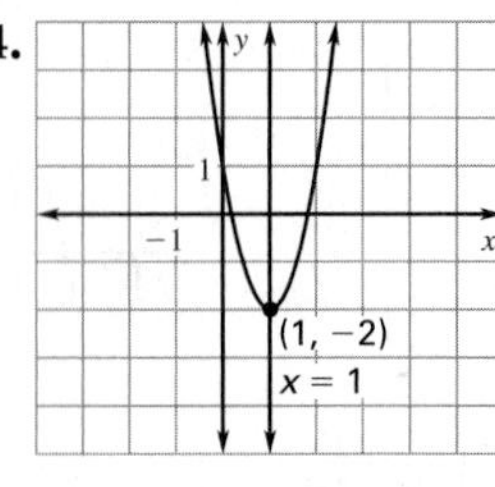

5. 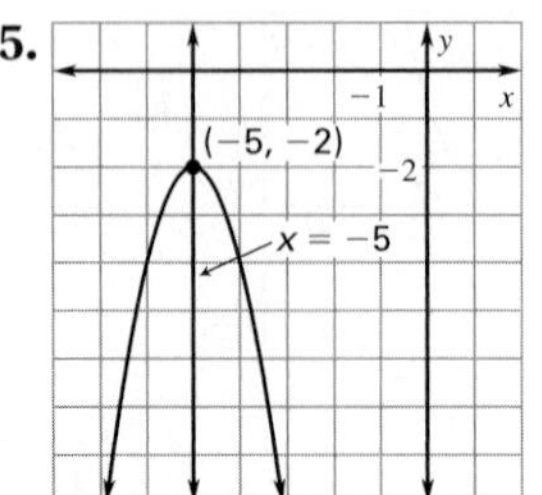

6. 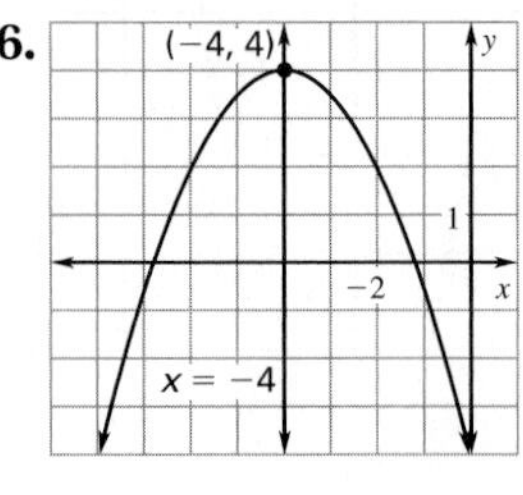

ADDITIONAL ANSWERS

7. $y = (x - 6)^2$

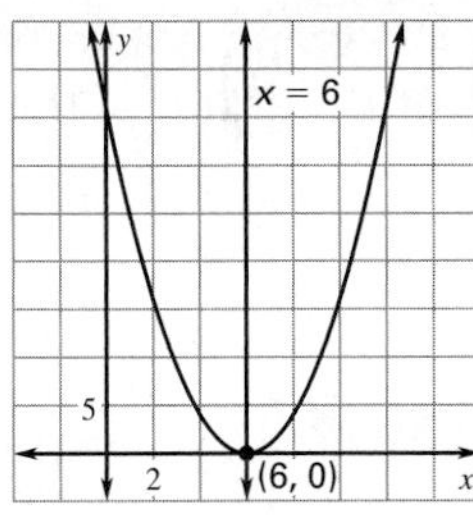

8. $y = (x + 4)^2 - 1$

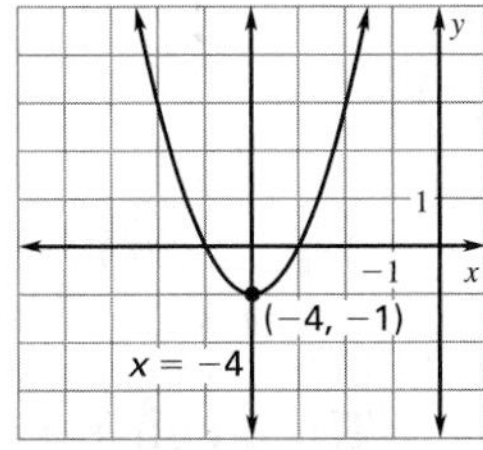

9. $y = -(x - 5)^2 + 4$

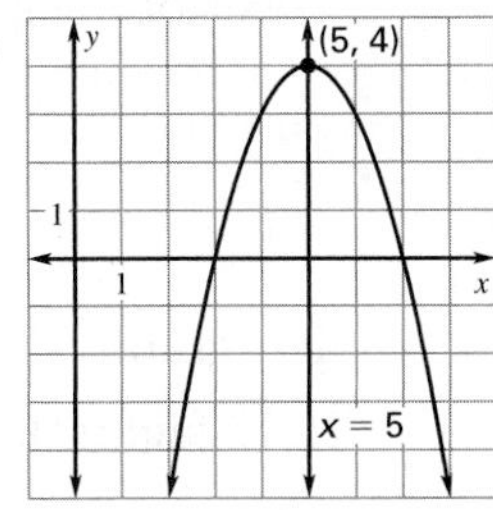

10. $y = 2(x - 3)^2 + 1$

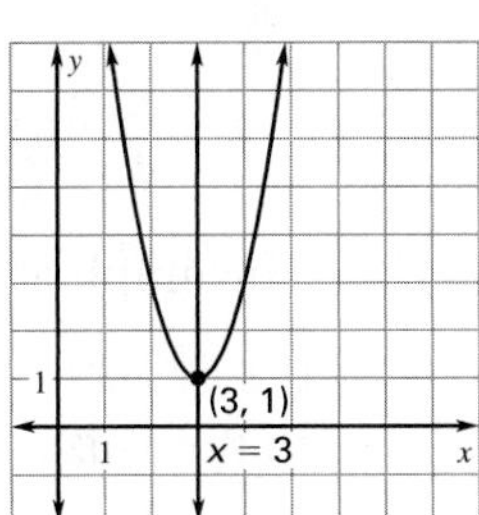

11. $y = -3(x + 1)^2 + 2$

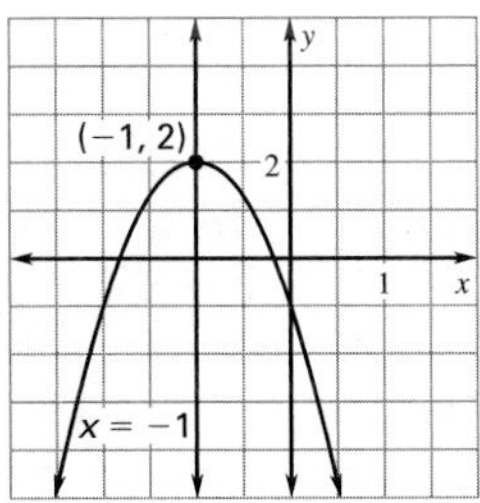

12. $y = -\frac{1}{2}(x + 6)^2 - 3$

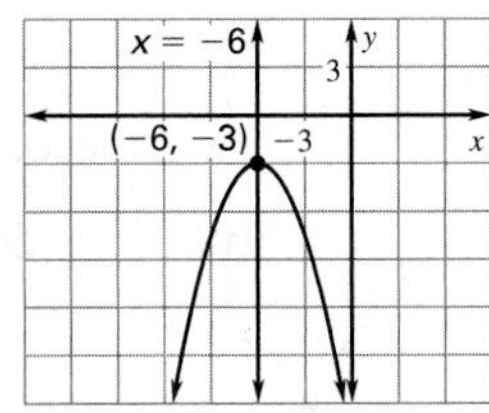

10.6 Mixed Review (p. 676)

56.

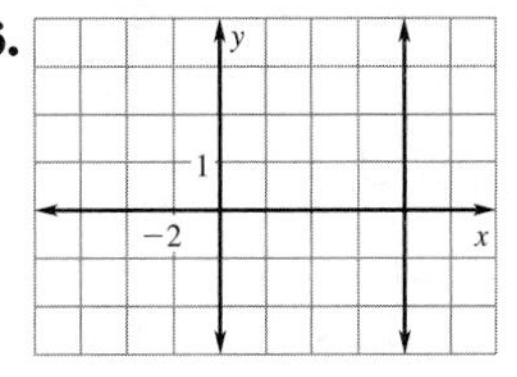

57.

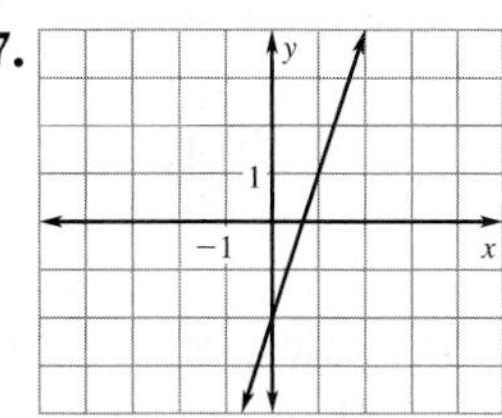

58.

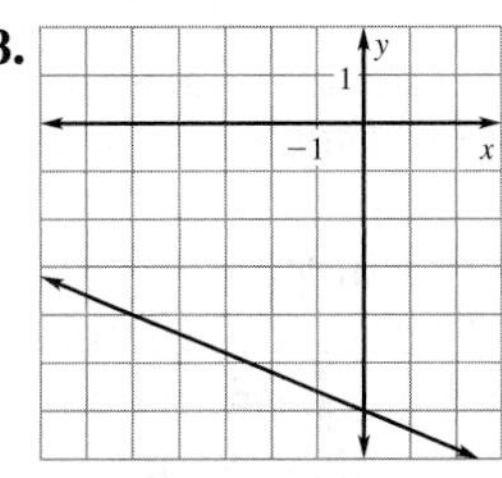

59.

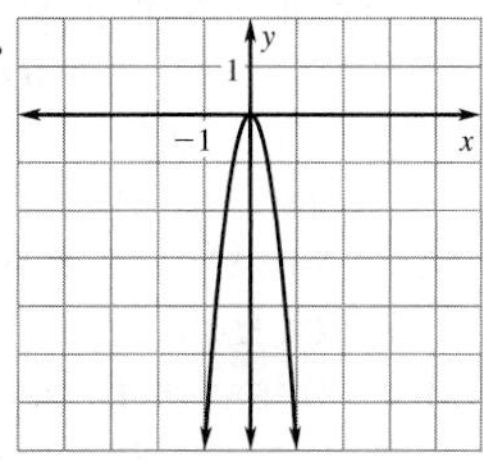

60.

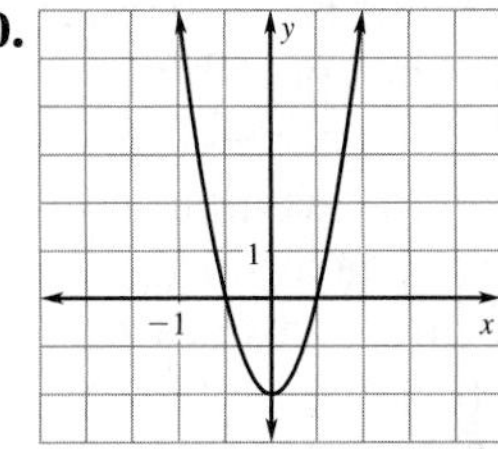

61.

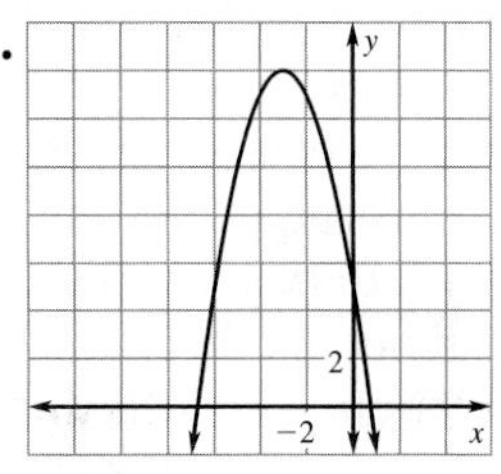

10.7 Investigating Algebra Activity (p. 677)

2. When $b^2 - 4ac$ is positive, $b^2 - 4ac$ has two square roots, one positive and one negative, so there are two different solutions to the quadratic equation $ax^2 + bx + c = 0$: $\frac{-b + \sqrt{b^2 - 4ac}}{2a}$ and $\frac{-b - \sqrt{b^2 - 4ac}}{2a}$. When $b^2 - 4ac$ is zero, $\sqrt{b^2 - 4ac} = 0$, so there is only one solution to the quadratic equation $ax^2 + bx + c = 0$: $\frac{-b \pm 0}{2a} = -\frac{b}{2a}$. When $b^2 - 4ac$ is negative, there is a negative number under the radical in the quadratic formula. Because negative numbers do not have real-number square roots, the quadratic formula cannot be evaluated and the quadratic equation $ax^2 + bx + c = 0$ has no real solution.

10.7 Skill Practice (pp. 681–682) **41. c.** −25, 5; the width w cannot be negative, so the solution −25 meters does not make sense in the context of the problem. The solution 5 meters does makes sense in the context of the problem.

42. a. $k < \frac{1}{24}$ **b.** $\frac{1}{24}$ **c.** $k > \frac{1}{24}$ **43. a.** $k < -3$ *or* $k > 3$ **b.** ± 3 **c.** $-3 < k < 3$ **44. a.** $k > -\frac{25}{64}$ **b.** $-\frac{25}{64}$ **c.** $k < -\frac{25}{64}$

10.7 Problem Solving (pp. 682–683) **45. a.** Substitute 25 for y in the equation and then write the resulting quadratic equation in standard form: $25 = 0.06x^2 - 4x + 87$, or $0 = 0.06x^2 - 4x + 62$. Evaluate the discriminant: $b^2 - 4ac = (-4)^2 - 4(0.06)(62) = 1.12$. Since the discriminant is positive, we know that the equation $25 = 0.06x^2 - 4x + 87$ does have solutions, so it is possible for a parakeet to consume 25 milliliters of oxygen per gram of body mass per hour.

47. No; to determine if there is any point of the arch at a height of 4 feet, substitute 4 for y in the equation and then determine if the equation has any positive solutions. The equation is $4 = -0.18x^2 + 1.6x$, or $0 = -0.18x^2 + 1.6x - 4$. Evaluate the discriminant: $b^2 - 4ac = (1.6)^2 - 4(-0.18)(-4) = -0.32$. Since the discriminant is negative, we know the equation has no solution; thus, a child who is 4 feet tall cannot walk under one of the arches without having to bend over. **50. b.** Yes; no; \$28,900; to decide if a weekly revenue of \$28,000 is possible, check the discriminant of the equation $28{,}000 = -100x^2 + 1400x + 24{,}000$, or $0 = -100x^2 + 1400x - 4000$. The discriminant is 360,000. Since the discriminant is positive, it may be possible to receive a weekly revenue of \$28,000. To decide if a weekly revenue of \$30,000 is possible, check the discriminant of the equation $30{,}000 = -100x^2 + 1400x + 24{,}000$, or $0 = -100x^2 + 1400x - 6000$. The discriminant is $-440{,}000$. Since the discriminant is negative, it is not possible to receive a weekly revenue of \$30,000. Since $r = -100x^2 + 1400x + 24{,}000$ is equivalent to the quadratic equation $0 = -100x^2 + 1400x + (24{,}000 - r)$, the maximum revenue r will occur when this equation has exactly one solution, or when its discriminant is 0. Solve $1400^2 - 4(-100)(24{,}000 - r) = 0$ for r; $r = \$28{,}900$.

10.7 Mixed Review (p. 683)

51.
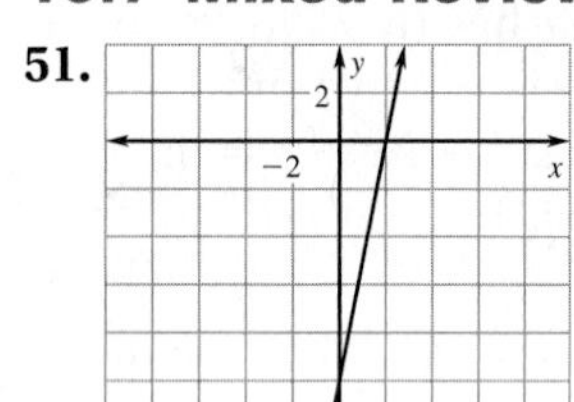

52.
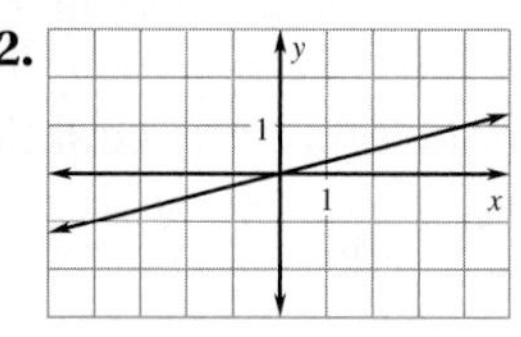

53.
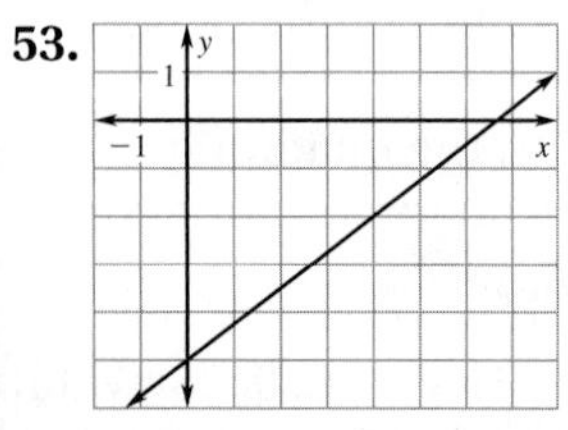

54.
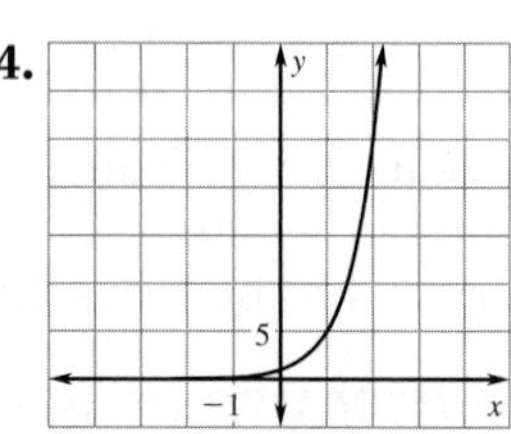

55.
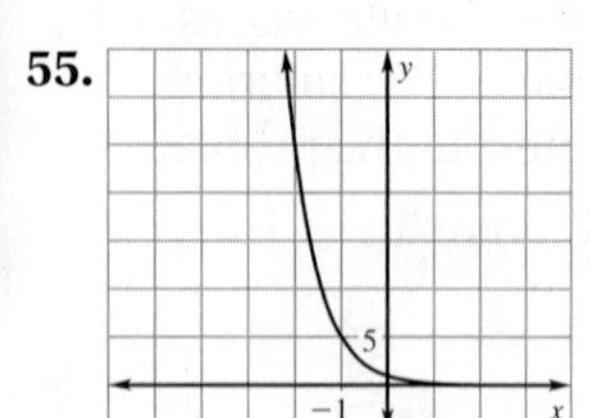

56.
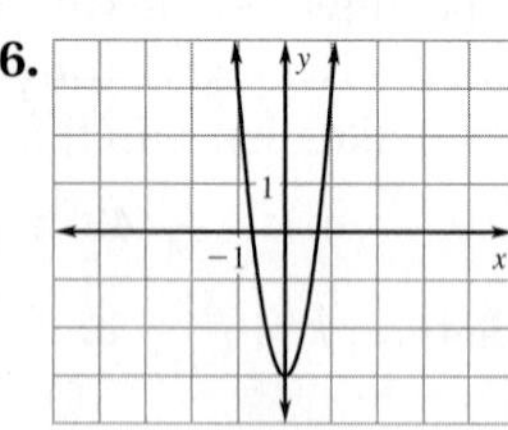

10.8 Mixed Review (p. 691)

35.
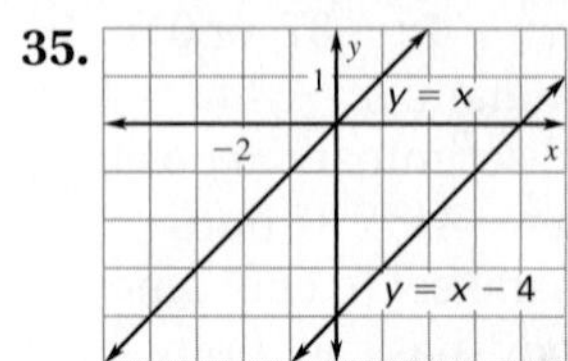

The graph is a vertical translation (of 4 units down) of the graph of $y = x$.

36.
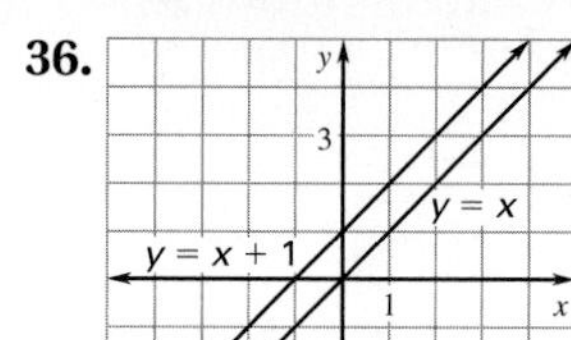

The graph is a vertical translation (of 1 unit up) of the graph of $y = x$.

37.
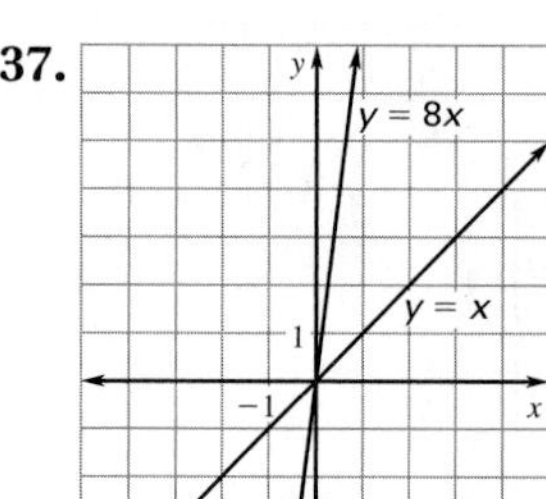

The graph is a vertical stretch (by a factor of 8) of the graph of $y = x$.

38.
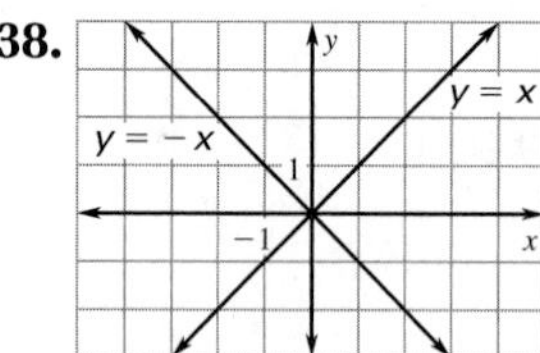

The graph is a reflection in the x-axis of the graph of $y = x$.

39.
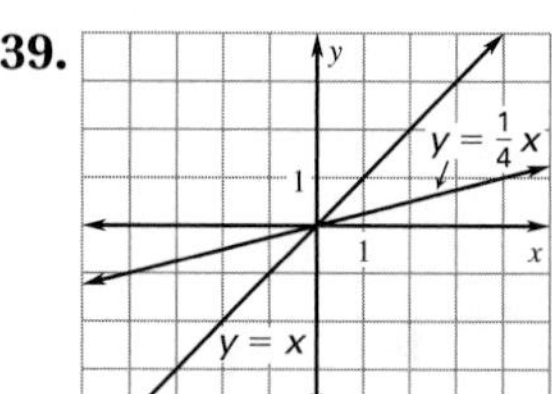

The graph is a vertical shrink $\left(\text{by a factor of } \frac{1}{4}\right)$ of the graph of $y = x$.

40.
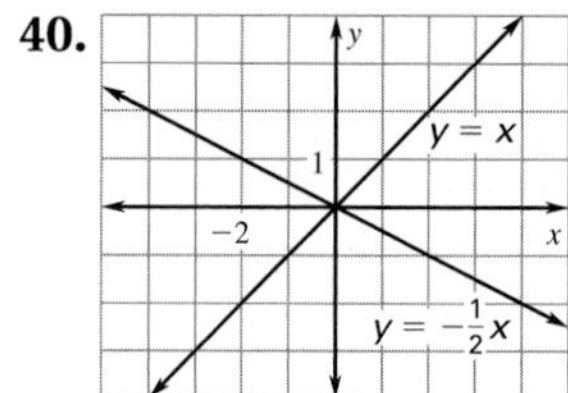

The graph is a vertical shrink $\left(\text{by a factor of } \frac{1}{2}\right)$ with a reflection in the x-axis of the graph of $y = x$.

41.
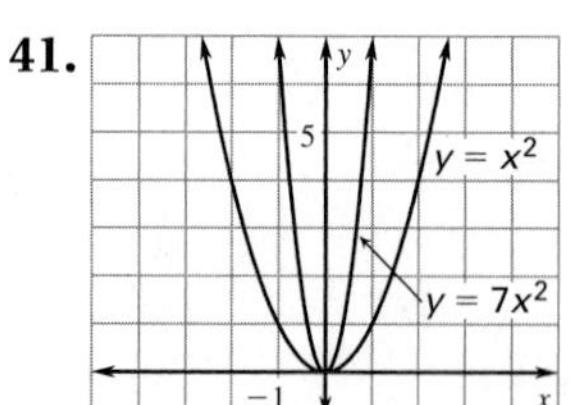

The graph is a vertical stretch (by a factor of 7) of the graph of $y = x^2$.

42.
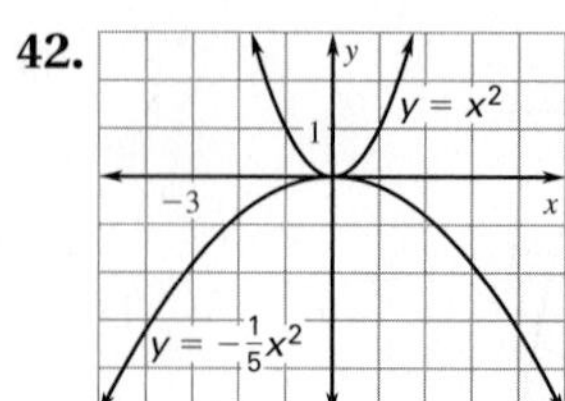

The graph is a vertical shrink $\left(\text{by a factor of } \frac{1}{5}\right)$ with a reflection in the x-axis of the graph of $y = x^2$.

ADDITIONAL ANSWERS

43. 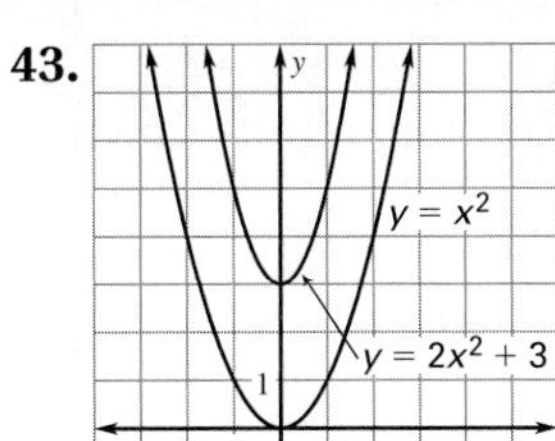

The graph is a vertical stretch (by a factor of 2) with a vertical translation (of 3 units up) of the graph of $y = x^2$.

Cumulative Review (pp. 706–707)

18. 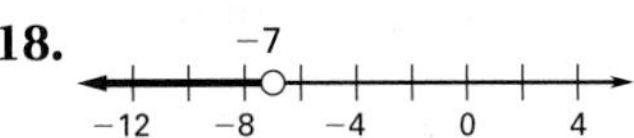

19. 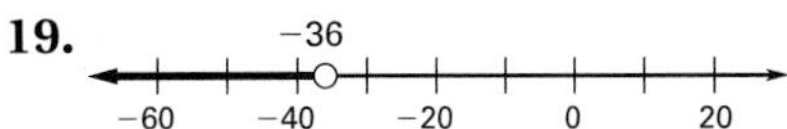

20.

21.

22.

23.

Chapter 11

11.1 Guided Practice (pp. 711–713)

1. 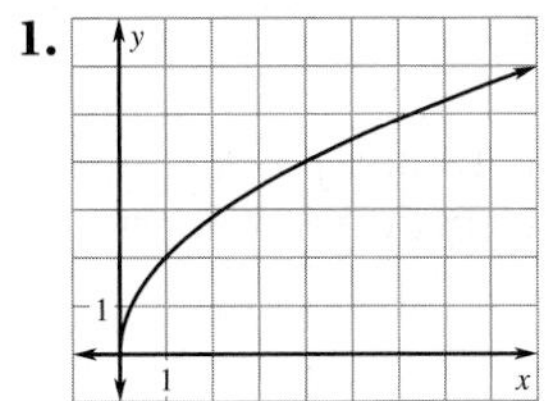
domain: $x \geq 0$, range: $y \geq 0$; vertical stretch by a factor of 2

2. 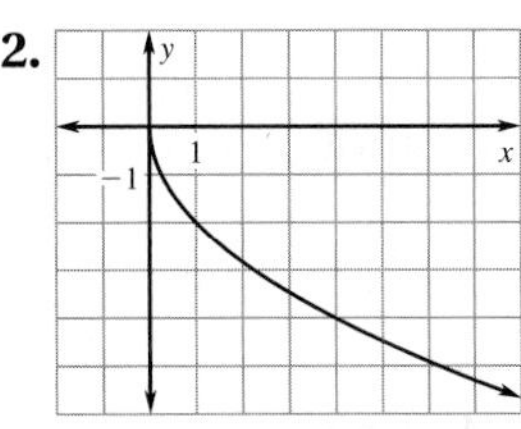
domain: $x \geq 0$, range: $y \leq 0$; vertical stretch by a factor of 2 and a reflection in the x-axis

3. 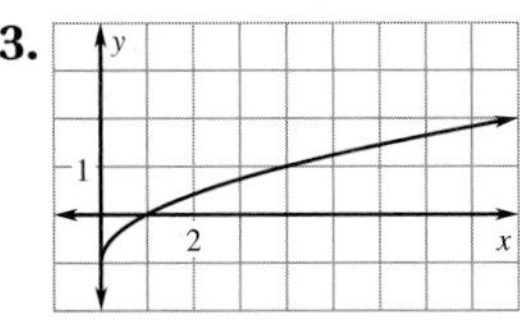
domain: $x \geq 0$, range: $y \geq -1$; vertical translation of 1 unit down

4. 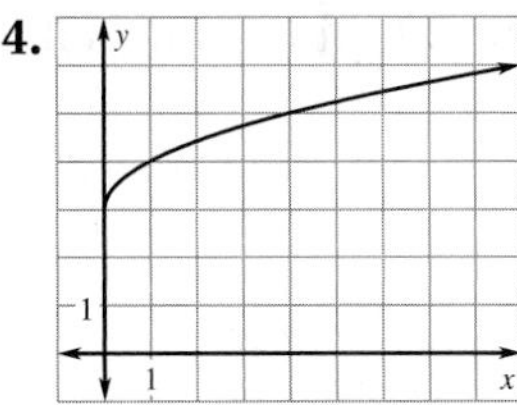
domain: $x \geq 0$, range: $y \geq 3$; vertical translation of 3 units up

11.1 Skill Practice (pp. 713–714)

3. 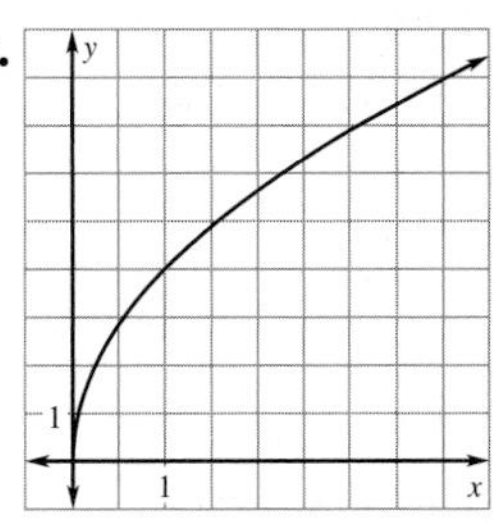
domain: $x \geq 0$, range: $y \geq 0$; vertical stretch by a factor of 4

4. 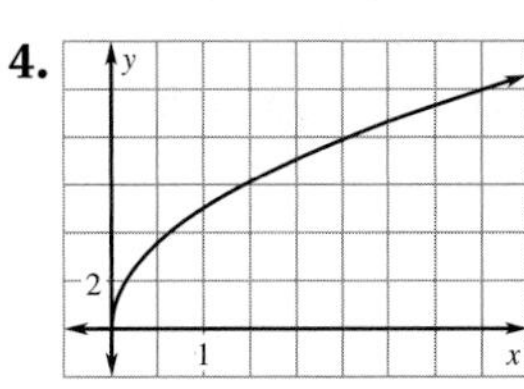
domain: $x \geq 0$, range: $y \geq 0$; vertical stretch by a factor of 5

5. 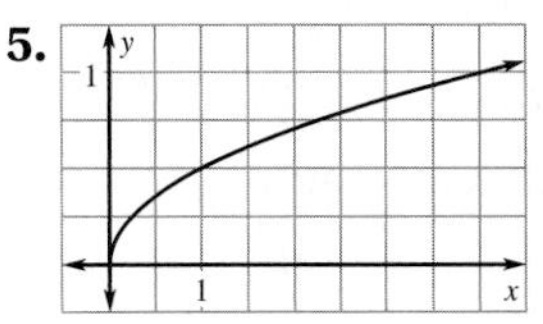
domain: $x \geq 0$, range: $y \geq 0$; vertical shrink by a factor of 0.5

6. 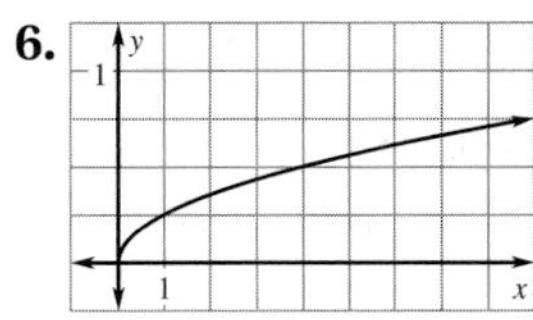
domain: $x \geq 0$, range: $y \geq 0$; vertical shrink by a factor of 0.25

7. 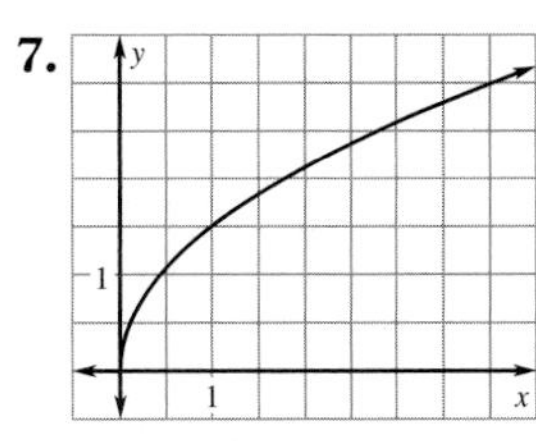
domain: $x \geq 0$, range: $y \geq 0$; vertical stretch by a factor of $\frac{3}{2}$

8. 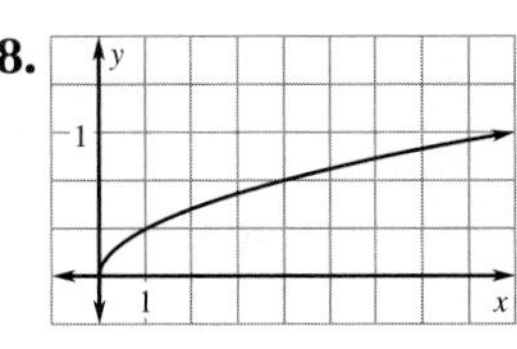
domain: $x \geq 0$, range: $y \geq 0$; vertical shrink by a factor of $\frac{1}{3}$

9. 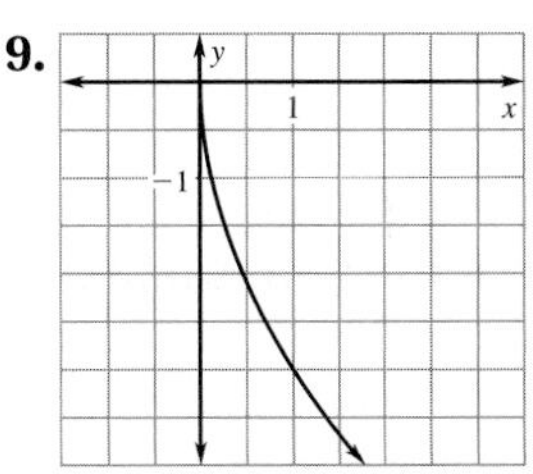
domain: $x \geq 0$, range: $y \leq 0$; vertical stretch by a factor of 3 with a reflection in the x-axis

10. 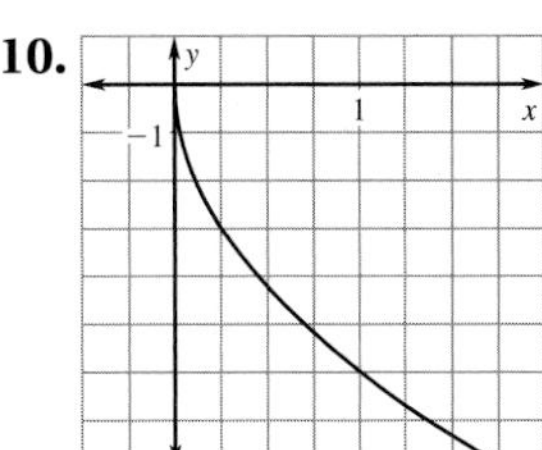
domain: $x \geq 0$, range: $y \leq 0$; vertical stretch by a factor of 6 with a reflection in the x-axis

11. 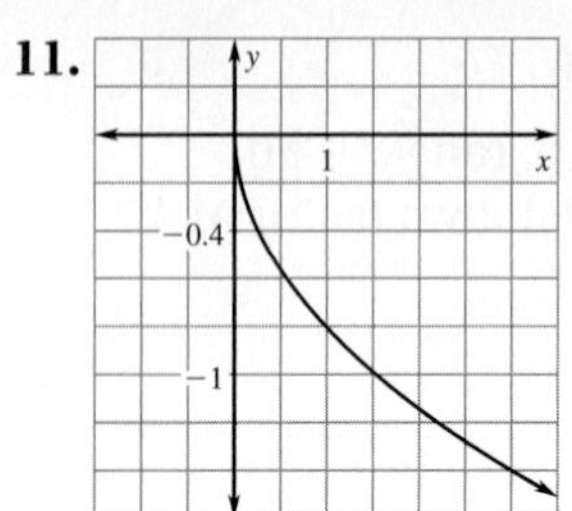

domain: $x \geq 0$, range: $y \leq 0$; vertical shrink by a factor of 0.8 with a reflection in the x-axis

12. 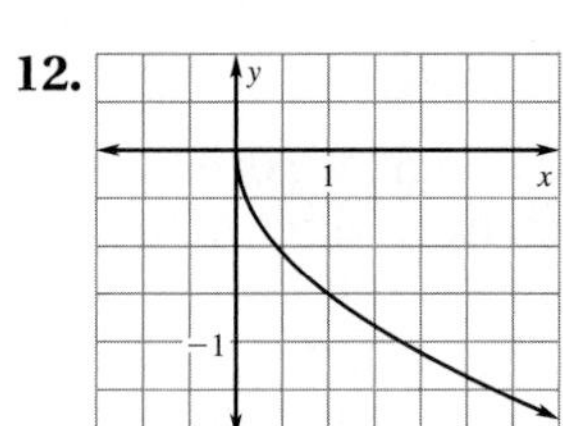

domain: $x \geq 0$, range: $y \leq 0$; vertical shrink by a factor of 0.75 with a reflection in the x-axis

13. 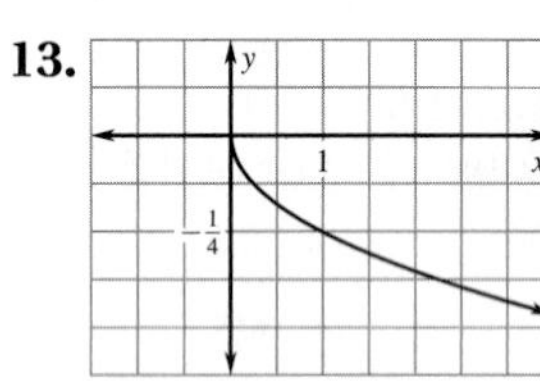

domain: $x \geq 0$, range: $y \leq 0$; vertical shrink by a factor of $\frac{1}{4}$ with a reflection in the x-axis

14. 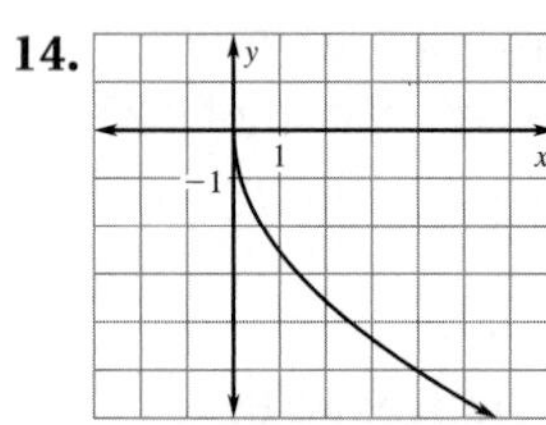

domain: $x \geq 0$, range: $y \leq 0$; vertical stretch by a factor of $\frac{5}{2}$ with a reflection in the x-axis

17. 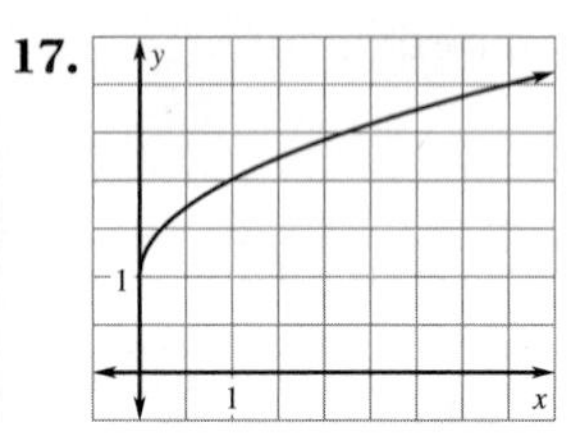

domain: $x \geq 0$, range: $y \geq 1$; vertical translation 1 unit up

18. 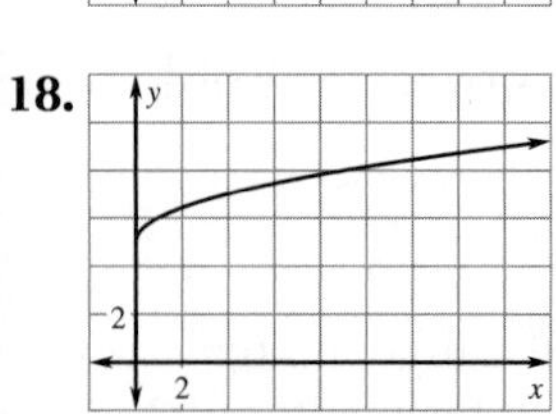

domain: $x \geq 0$, range: $y \geq 5$; vertical translation 5 units up

19. 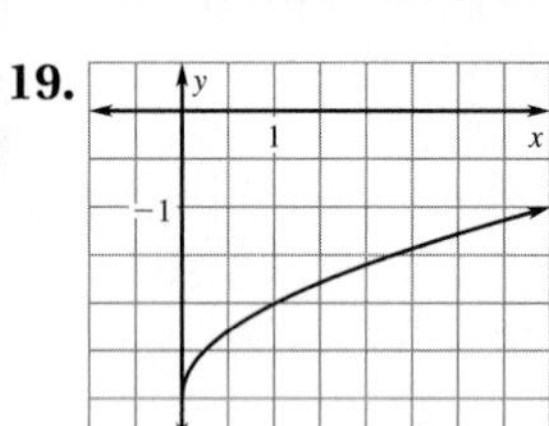

domain: $x \geq 0$, range: $y \geq -3$; vertical translation 3 units down

20. 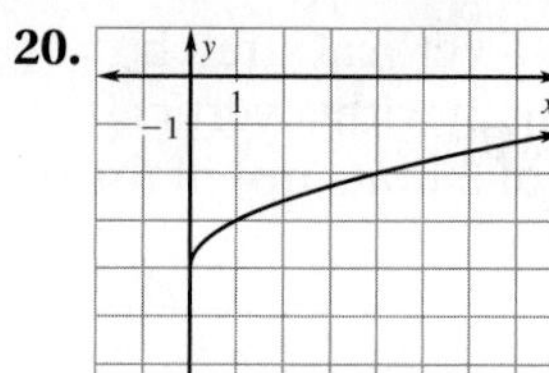

domain: $x \geq 0$, range: $y \geq -4$; vertical translation 4 units down

21. 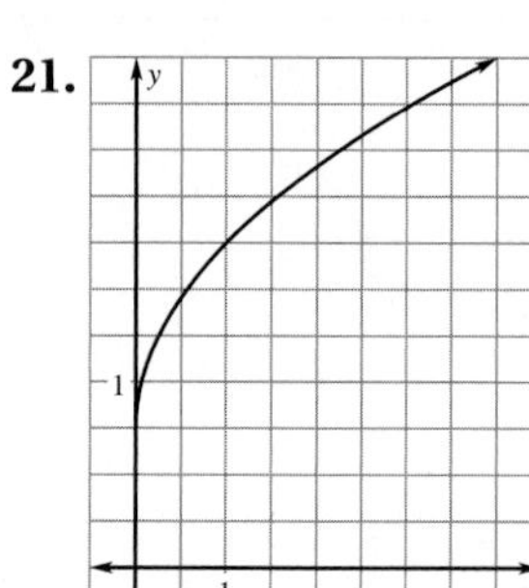

domain: $x \geq 0$, range: $y \geq \frac{3}{4}$; vertical translation $\frac{3}{4}$ unit up

22. 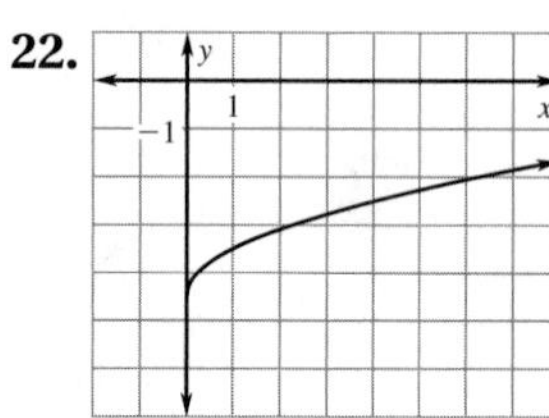

domain: $x \geq 0$, range: $y \geq -4.5$; vertical translation 4.5 units down

23. 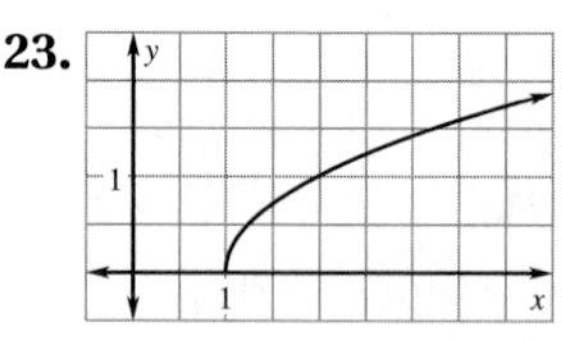

domain: $x \geq 1$, range: $y \geq 0$; horizontal translation 1 unit right

24. 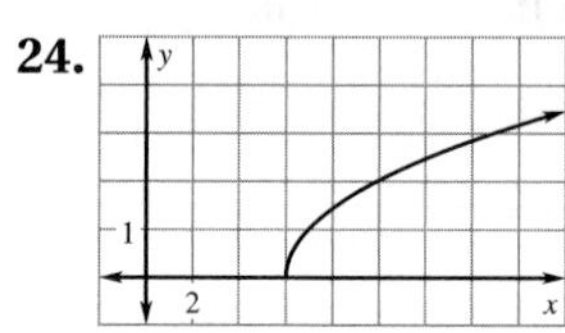

domain: $x \geq 6$, range: $y \geq 0$; horizontal translation 6 units right

25. 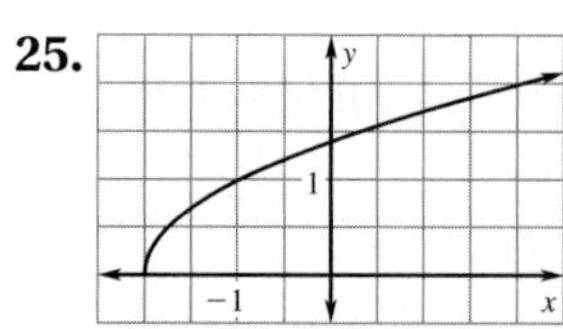

domain: $x \geq -2$, range: $y \geq 0$; horizontal translation 2 units left

26. 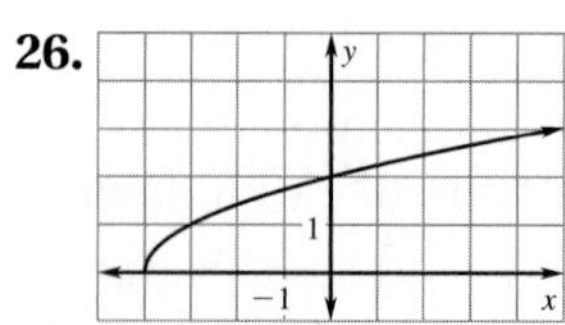

domain: $x \geq -4$, range: $y \geq 0$; horizontal translation 4 units left

27. 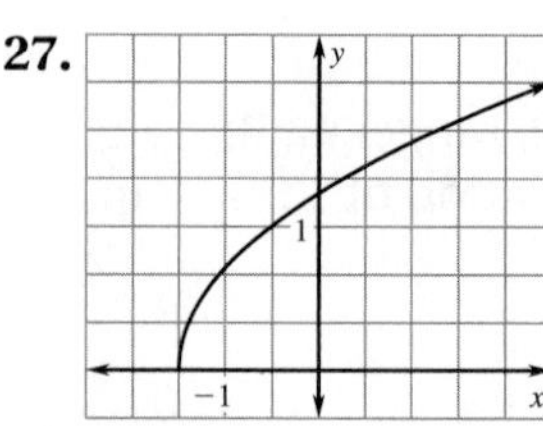

domain: $x \geq -1.5$, range: $y \geq 0$; horizontal translation 1.5 units left

28. 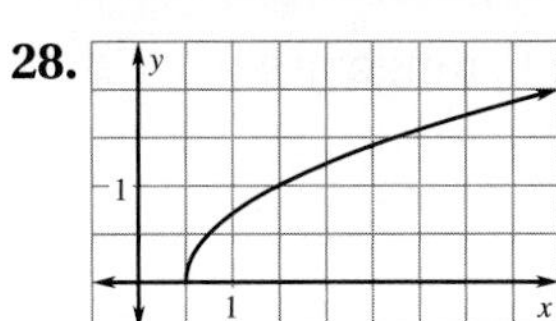

domain: $x \geq \frac{1}{2}$, range: $y \geq 0$; horizontal translation $\frac{1}{2}$ unit right

30. 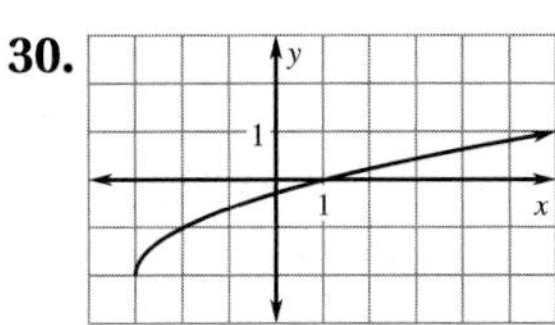

31. 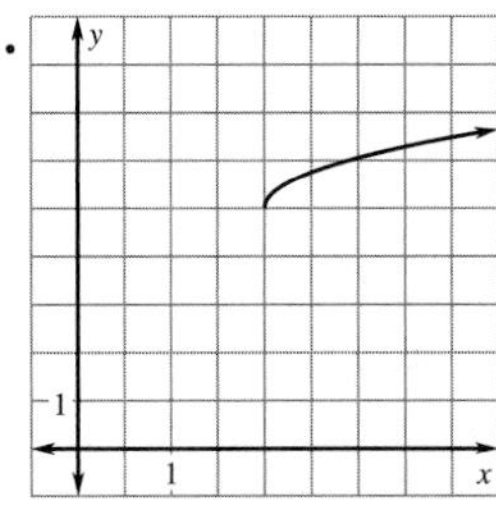

32. 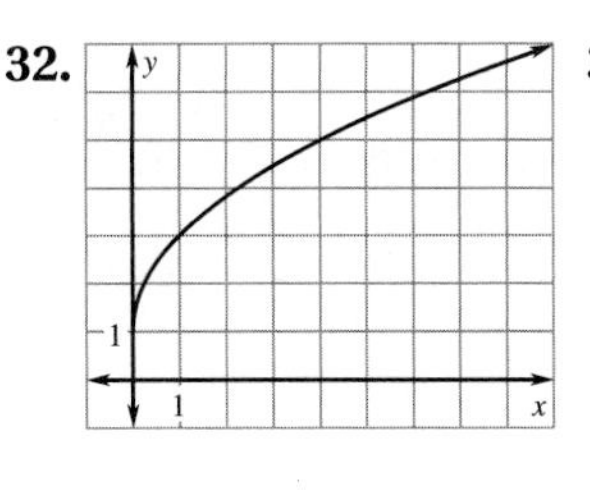

33. 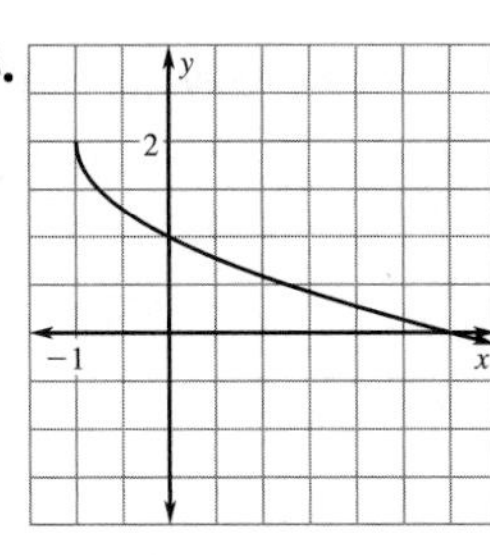

34. 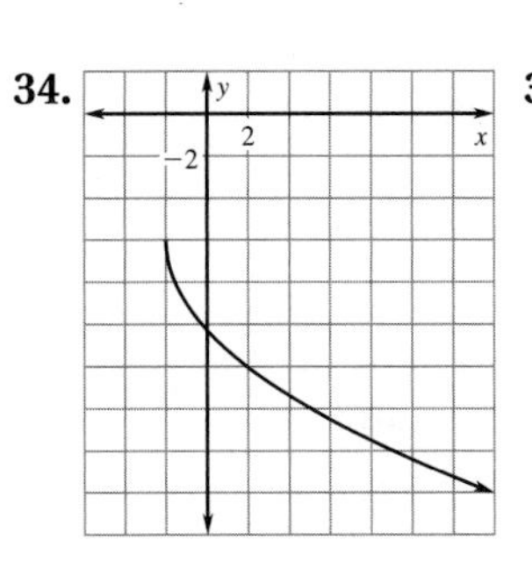

35. 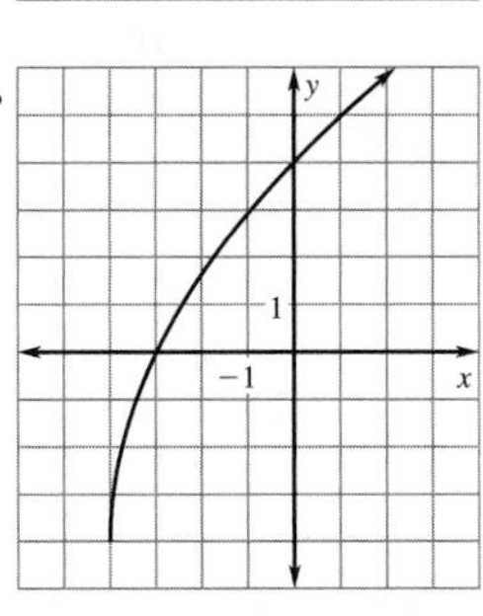

36. 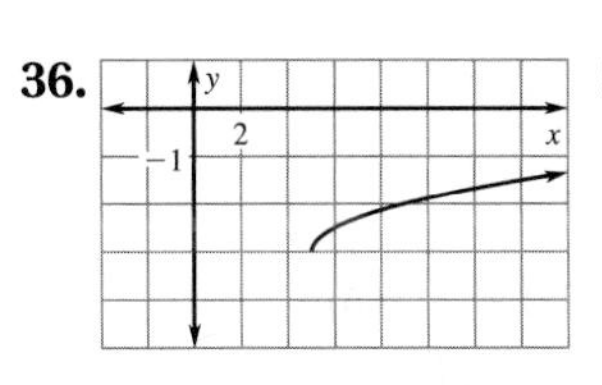

37. 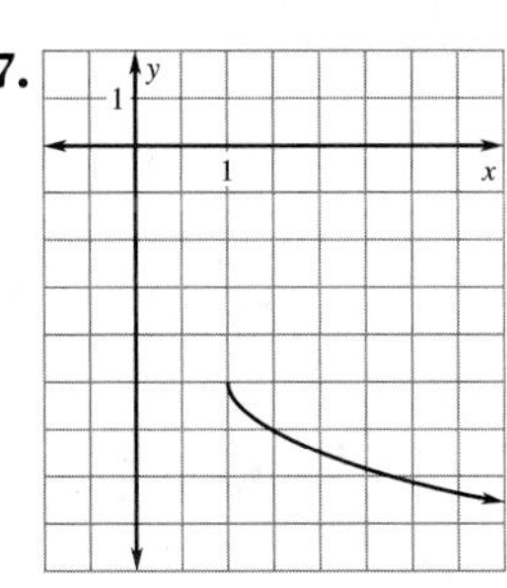

38. 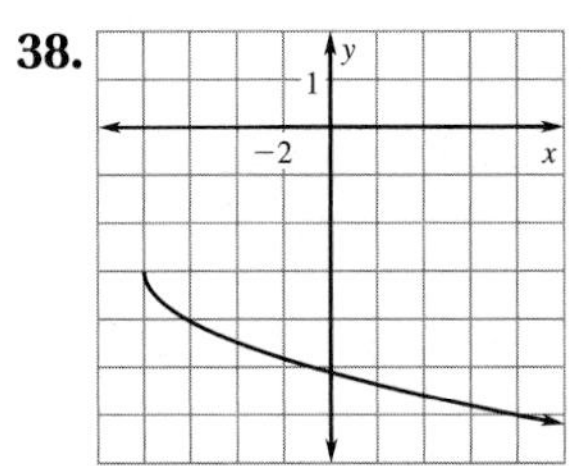

11.1 Problem Solving (pp. 715–716)

47. a. 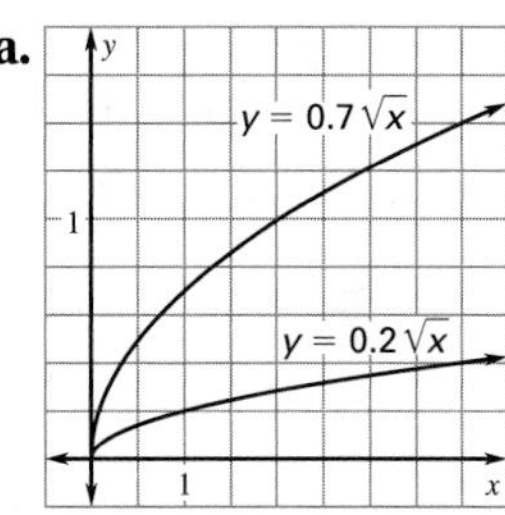

blue-winged teal's domain: $x \geq 0$, range: $y \geq 0$, northern pintail's domain: $x \geq 0$, range: $y \geq 0$

48. a. 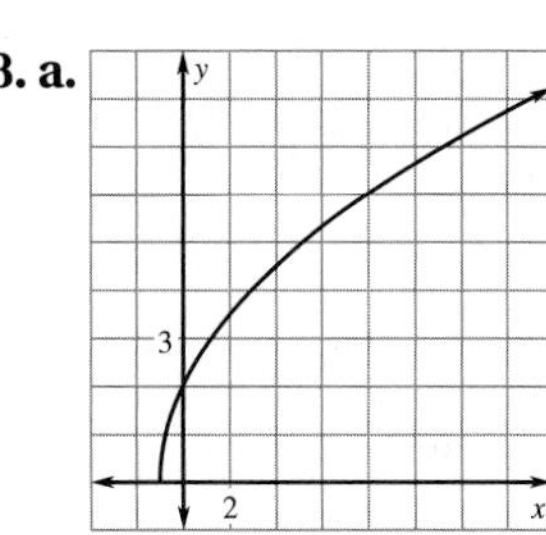

c. 1983; to find the year when the amount consumed doubled the amount consumed in 1980, solve the equation for $y = 4$; find $x = 3$, so 3 years after 1980, or 1983.

11.1 Graphing Calculator Activity (p. 717)

1. 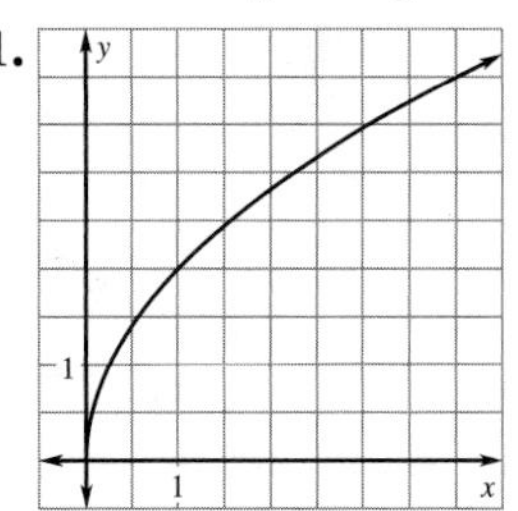

domain: $x \geq 0$, range: $y \geq 0$

2. 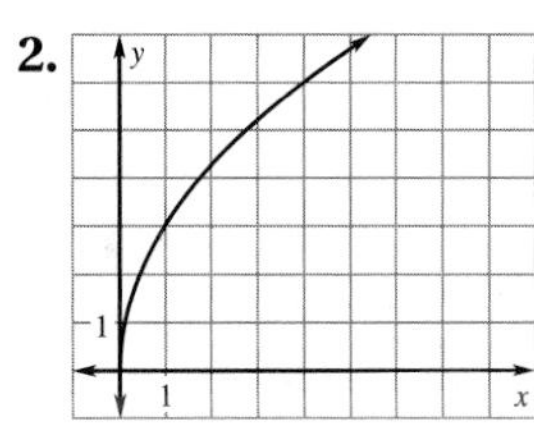

domain: $x \geq 0$, range: $y \geq 0$

3. 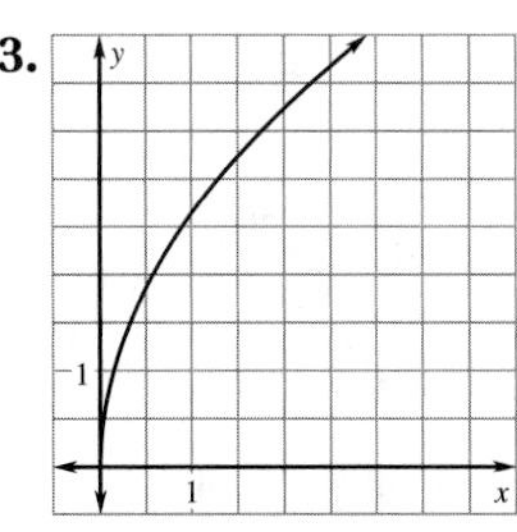

domain: $x \geq 0$, range: $y \geq 0$

4. 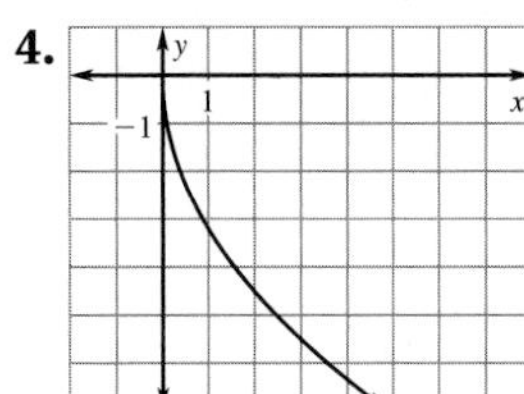

domain: $x \geq 0$, range: $y \leq 0$

5. 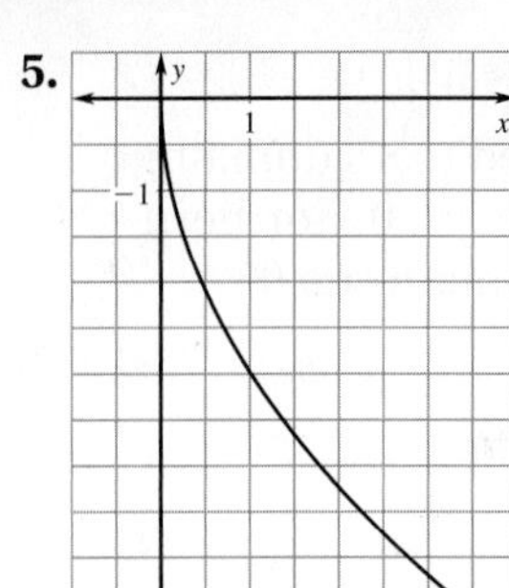

domain: $x \geq 0$, range: $y \leq 0$

6. 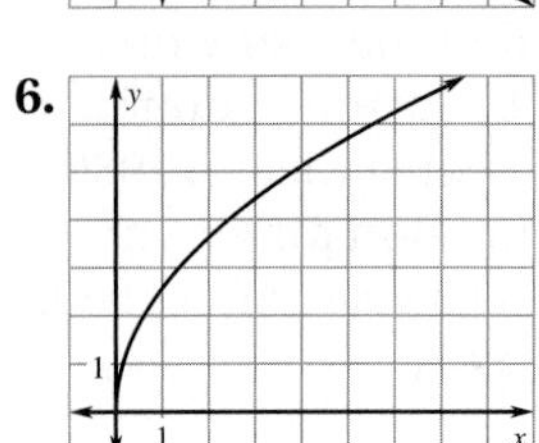

domain: $x \geq 0$, range: $y \geq 0$

7. 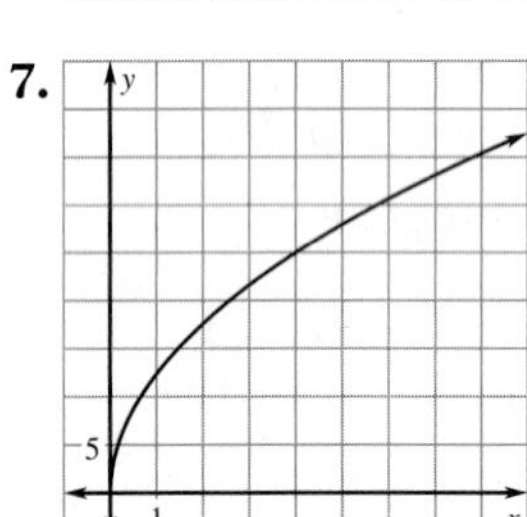

domain: $x \geq 0$, range: $y \geq 0$

8. 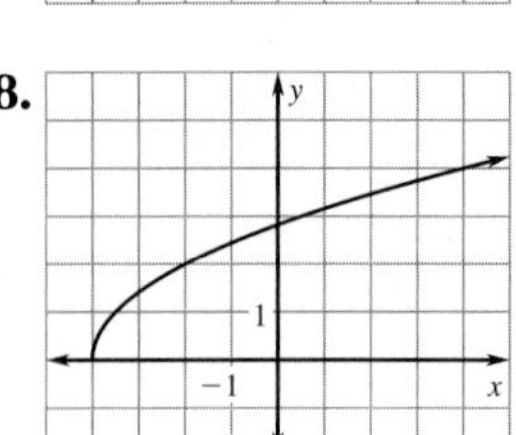

domain: $x \geq -4$, range: $y \geq 0$

9. 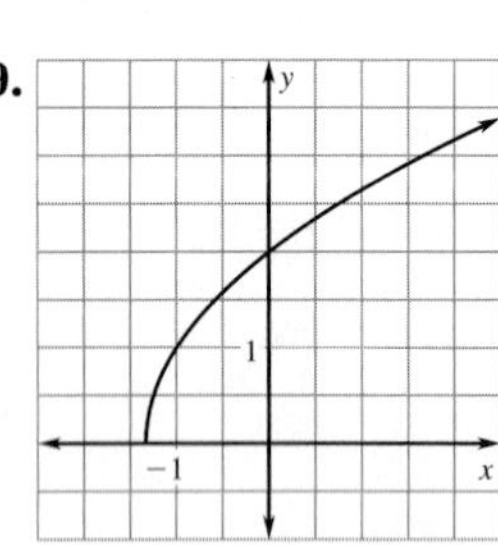

domain: $x \geq -\frac{4}{3}$, range: $y \geq 0$

10. 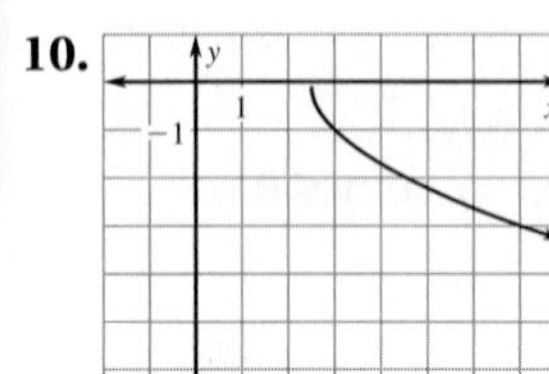

domain: $x \geq \frac{5}{2}$, range: $y \leq 0$

11. 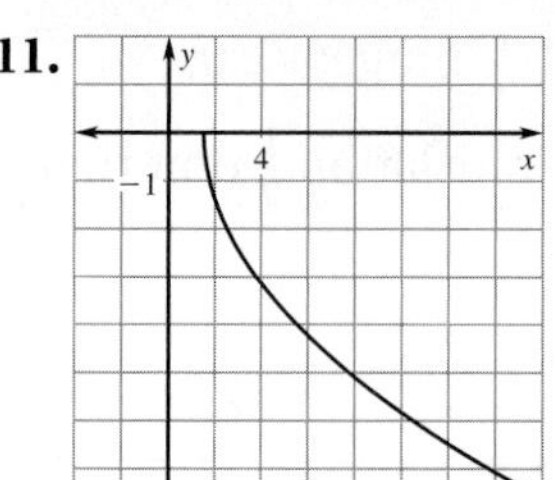

domain: $x \geq \frac{3}{2}$, range: $y \leq 0$

12. 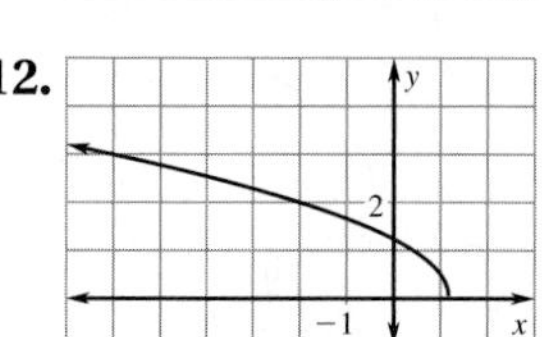

domain: $x \leq \frac{6}{5}$, range: $y \geq 0$

11.2 Mixed Review (p. 726)

73. 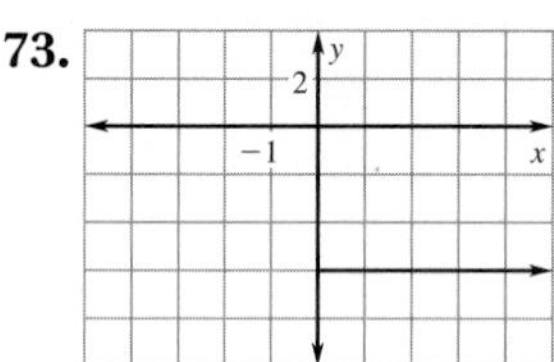

domain: $x \geq 0$, range: $y = -6$

74. 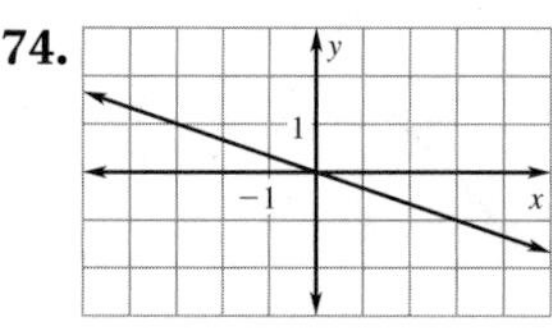

domain: all real numbers, range: all real numbers

75. 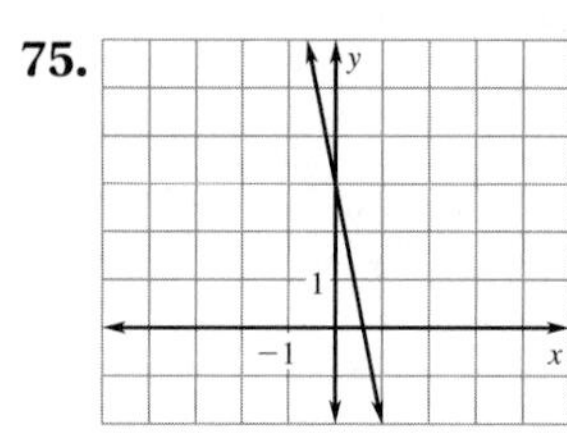

domain: all real numbers, range: all real numbers

76. 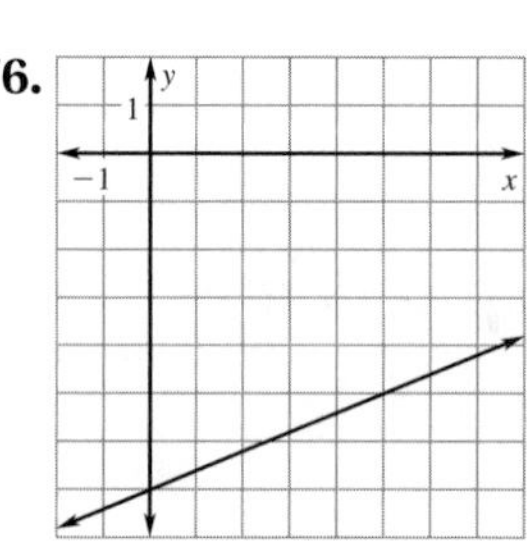

domain: all real numbers, range: all real numbers

77. 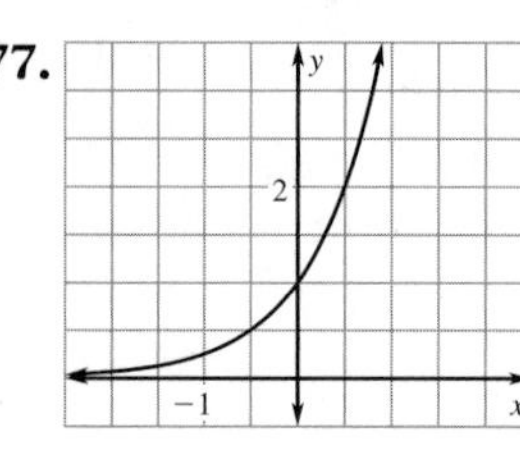

domain: all real numbers, range: $y > 0$

78. 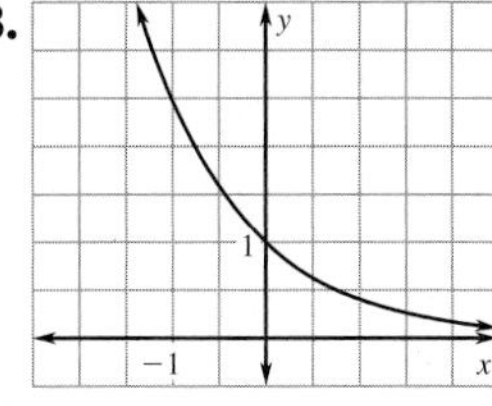

domain: all real numbers, range: $y > 0$

79. 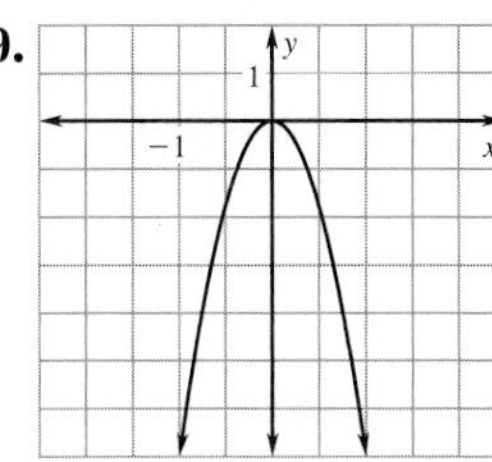

domain: all real numbers, range: $y \le 0$

80. 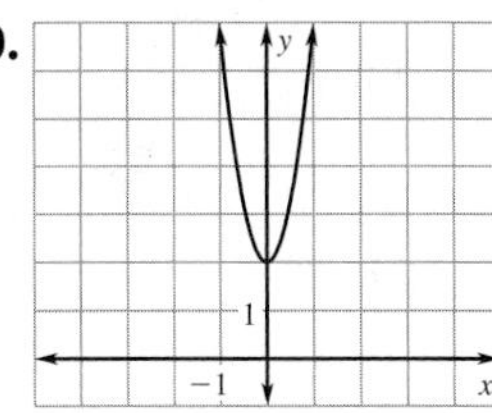

domain: all real numbers, range: $y \ge 2$

81. 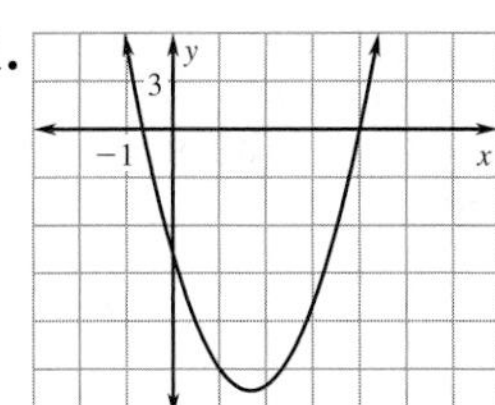

domain: all real numbers, range: $y \ge -\frac{49}{3}$

Extension (pp. 727–728)

19. Substitute $\frac{-b + \sqrt{b^2 - 4ac}}{2a}$ for x:

$$a\left(\frac{-b + \sqrt{b^2 - 4ac}}{2a}\right)^2 + b\left(\frac{-b + \sqrt{b^2 - 4ac}}{2a}\right) + c = 0$$

$$a\left(\frac{b^2 - 2b\sqrt{b^2 - 4ac} + b^2 - 4ac}{4a^2}\right) + \frac{-b^2 + b\sqrt{b^2 - 4ac}}{2a} + c = 0$$

$$\frac{b^2}{4a} - \frac{b\sqrt{b^2 - 4ac}}{2a} + \frac{b^2}{4a} - c - \frac{b^2}{2a} + \frac{b\sqrt{b^2 - 4ac}}{2a} + c = 0$$

$$0 = 0$$

Substitute $\frac{-b - \sqrt{b^2 - 4ac}}{2a}$ for x:

$$a\left(\frac{-b - \sqrt{b^2 - 4ac}}{2a}\right)^2 + b\left(\frac{-b - \sqrt{b^2 - 4ac}}{2a}\right) + c = 0$$

$$a\left(\frac{b^2 + 2b\sqrt{b^2 - 4ac} + b^2 - 4ac}{4a^2}\right) + \frac{-b^2 - b\sqrt{b^2 - 4ac}}{2a} + c = 0$$

$$\frac{b^2}{4a} + \frac{b\sqrt{b^2 - 4ac}}{2a} + \frac{b^2}{4a} - c - \frac{b^2}{2a} - \frac{b\sqrt{b^2 - 4ac}}{2a} + c = 0$$

$$0 = 0$$

22. $a \le 12$. *Sample answer:* For a quadratic equation to have one or two real solutions, the value of $b^2 - 4ac$ must be greater than or equal to 0. Substituting values and solving: $12^2 - 4 \cdot a \cdot 3 \ge 0$, $a \le 12$.

11.4 Mixed Review (p. 742)

39. 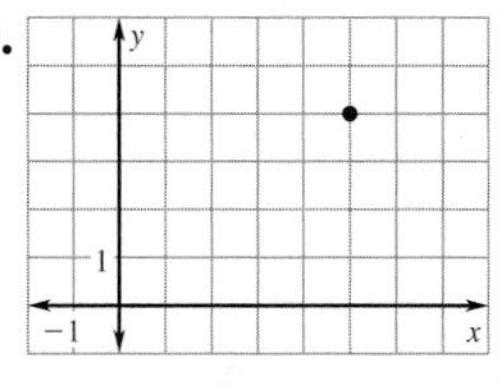

40. 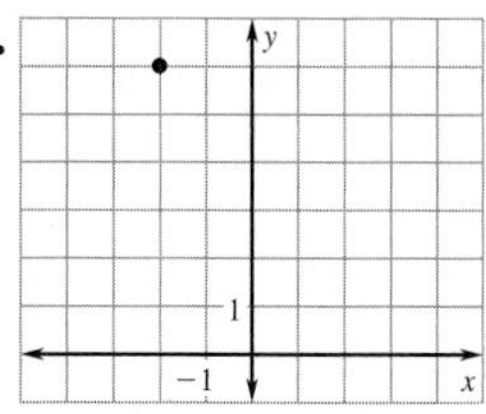

41. 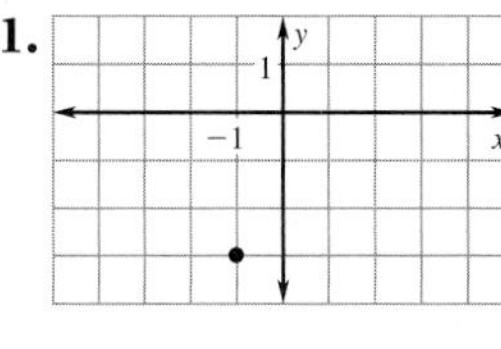

42. 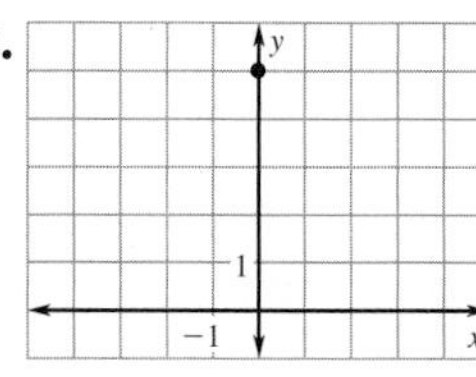

43. 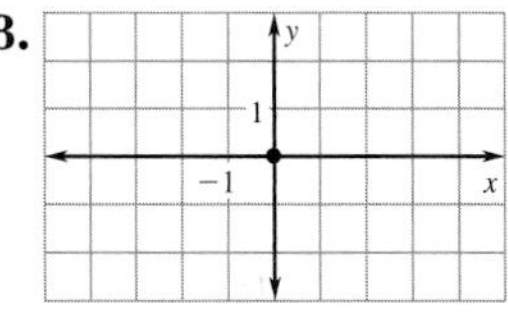

44. 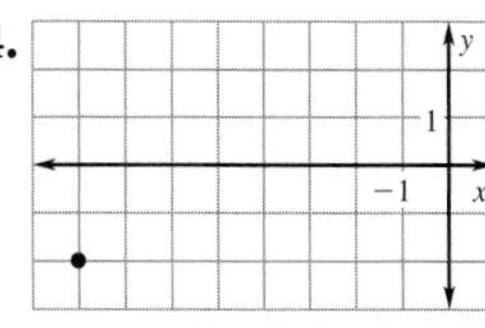

45. 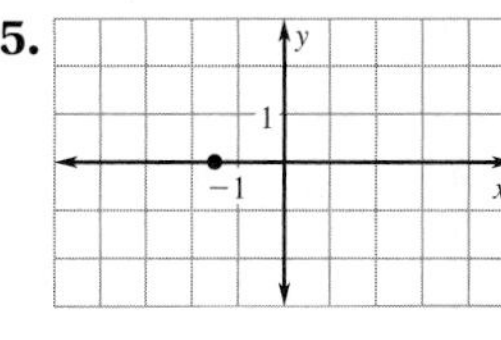

46. 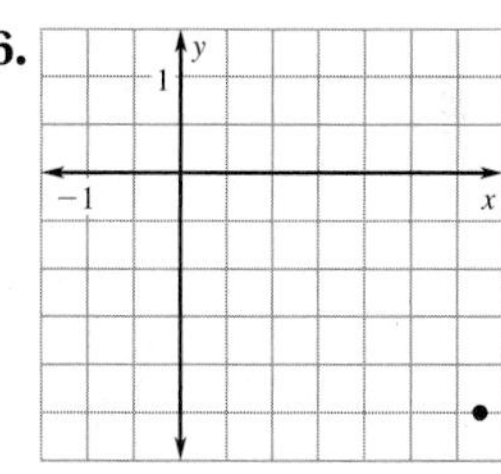

11.5 Mixed Review (p. 750)

59. 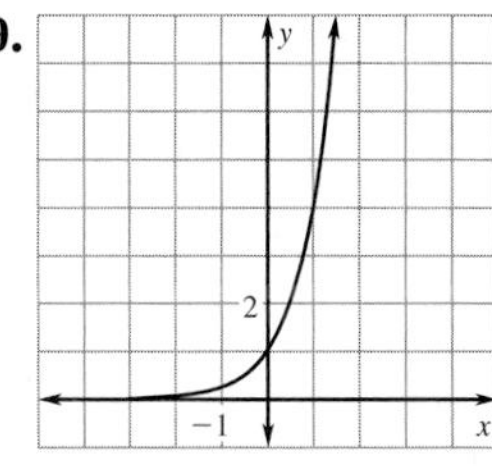

60. 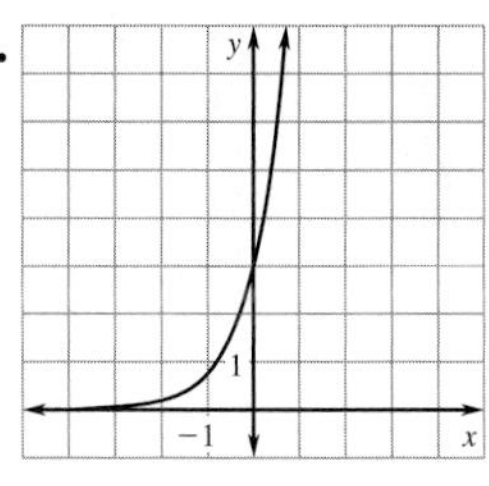

61. 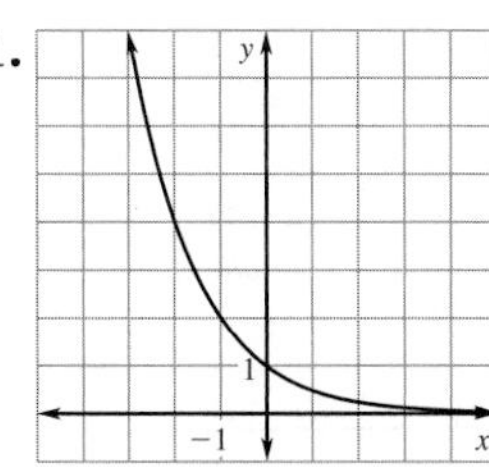

62. 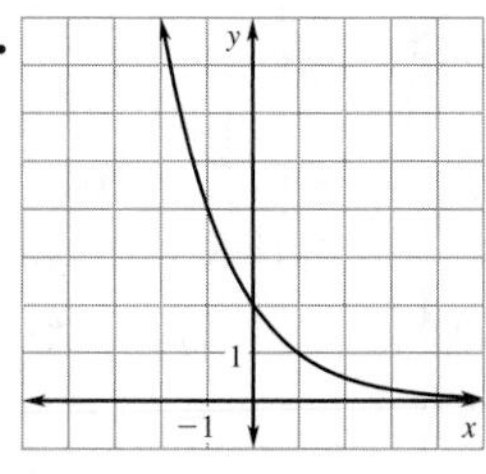

63. 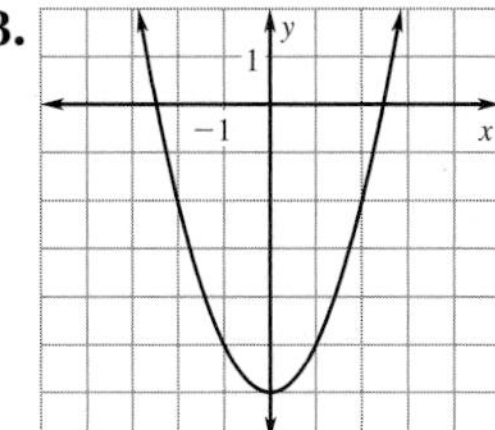

64. 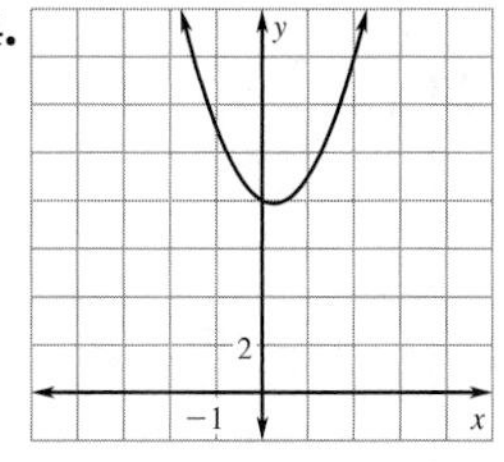

Chapter 12

12.1 Skill Practice (pp. 769–770)

15. 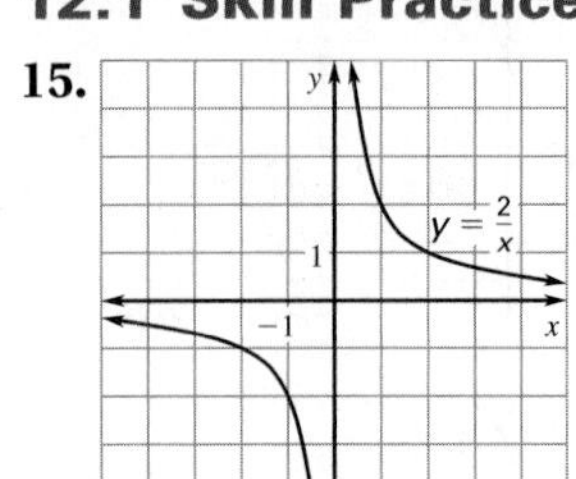

16. 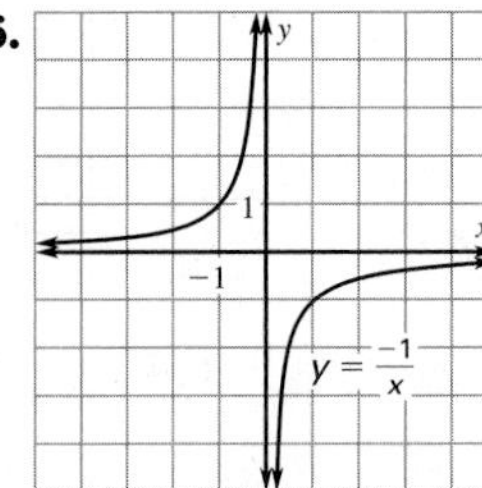

17. 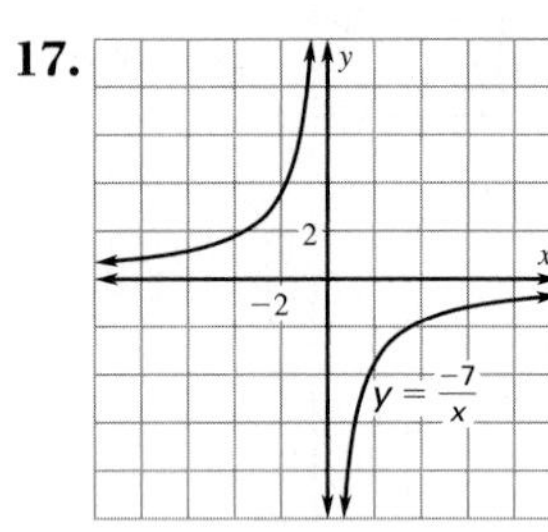

18. 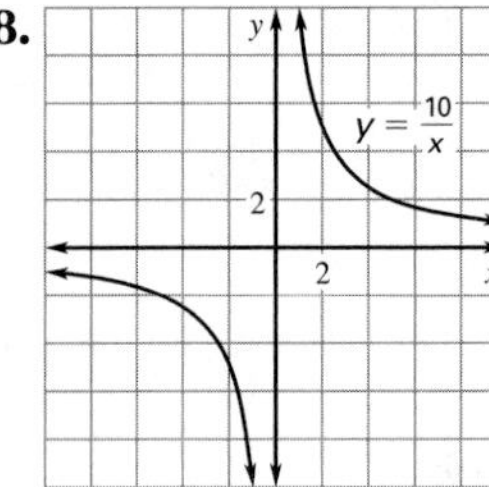

19. 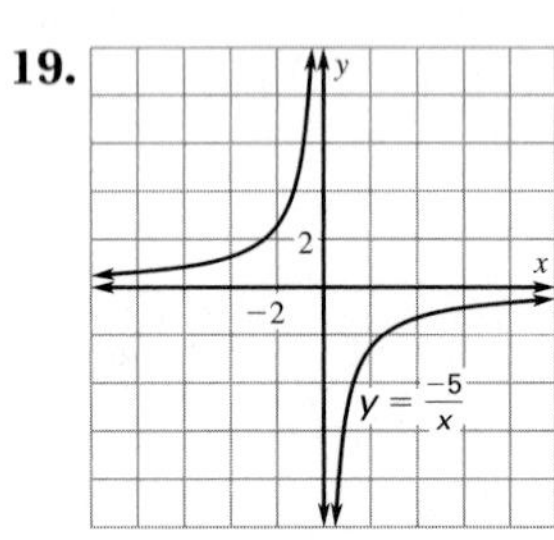

20. 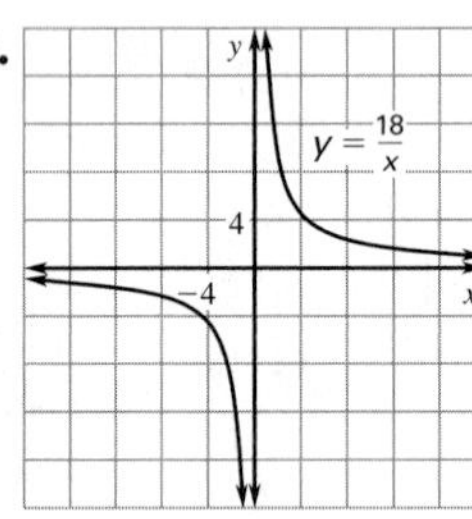

21. 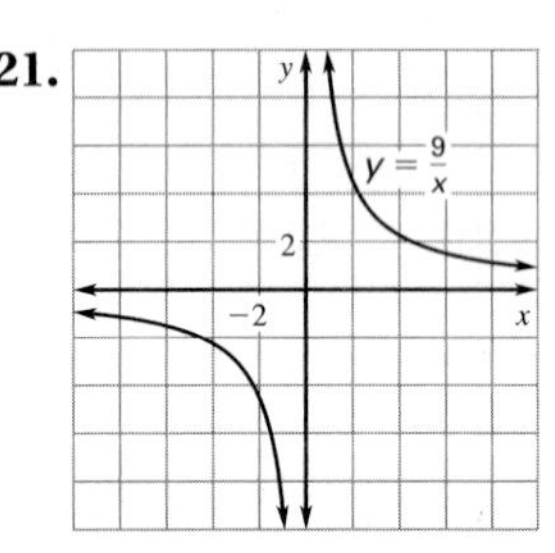

22. 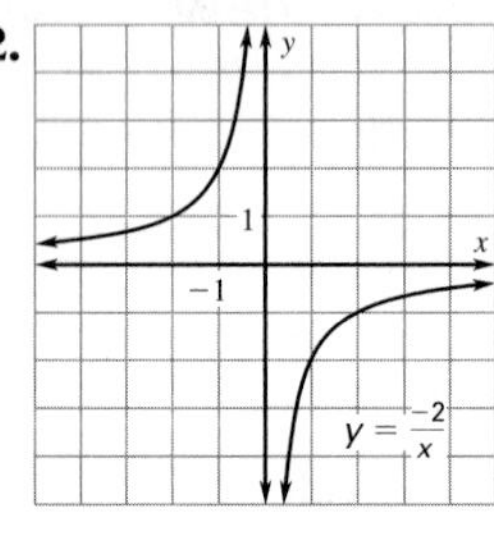

23. 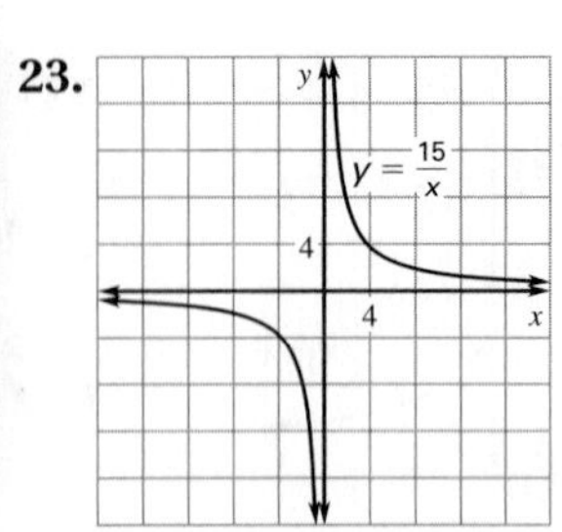

24. 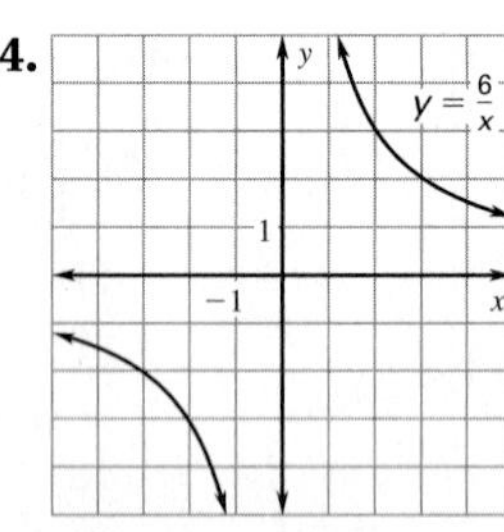

25. 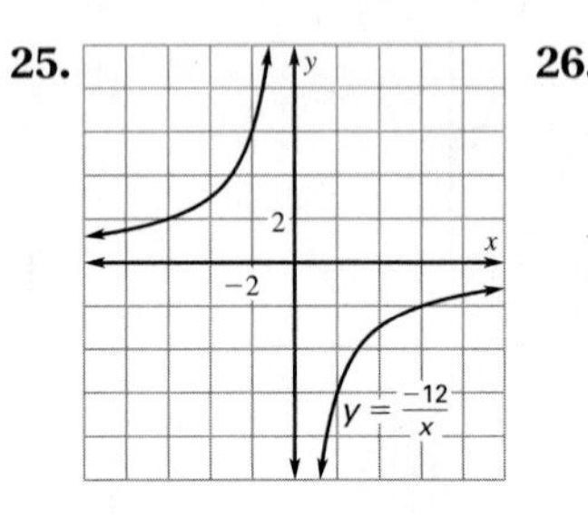

26. 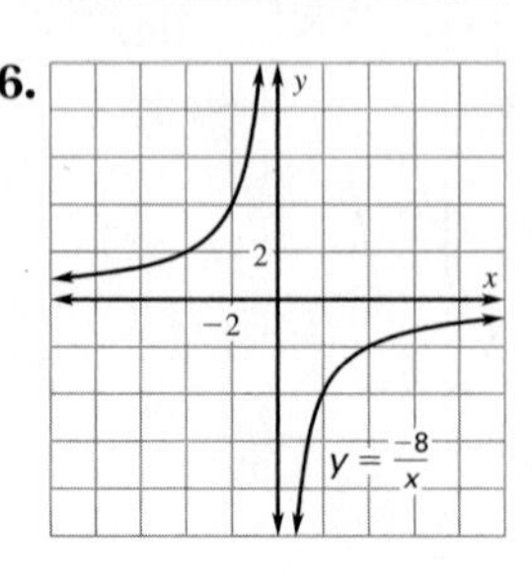

12.1 Mixed Review (p. 772)

63. 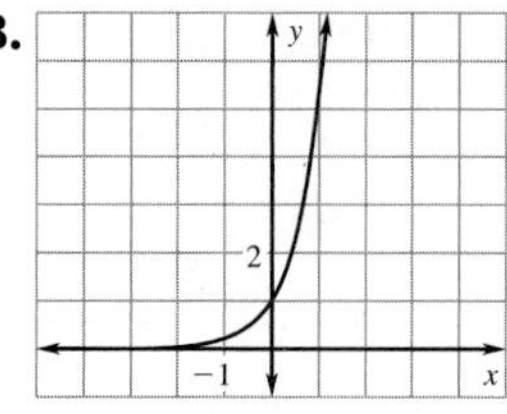
domain: all real numbers, range: $y > 0$

64. 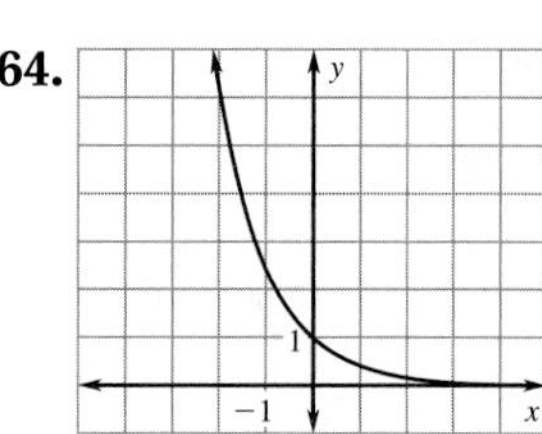
domain: all real numbers, range: $y > 0$

65. 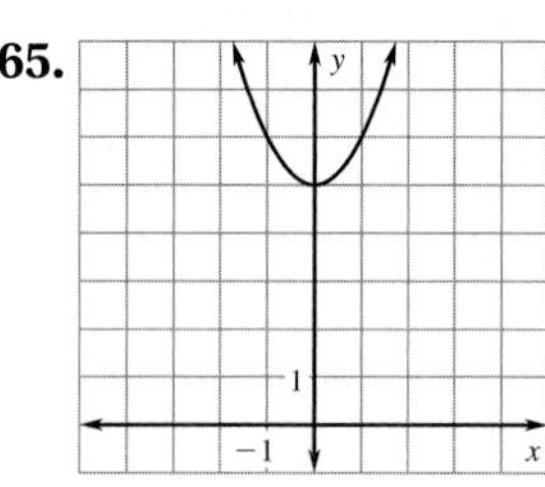
domain: all real numbers, range: $y \geq 5$

66. 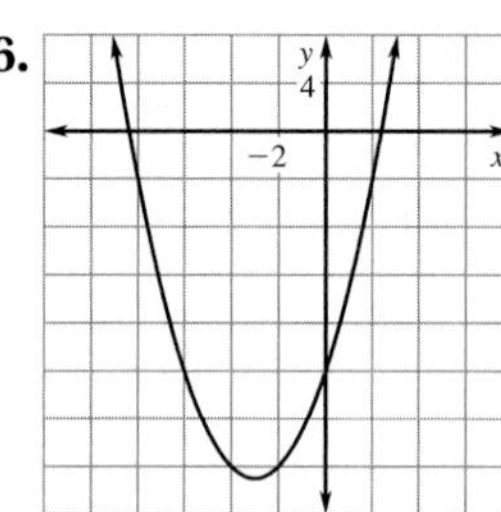
domain: all real numbers, range: $y \geq -29$

67. 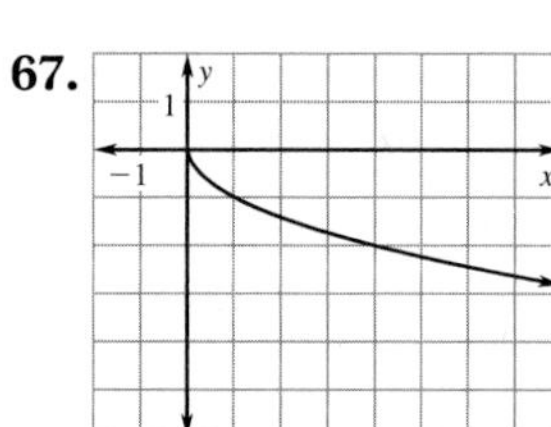
domain: $x \geq 0$, range: $y \leq 0$

68. 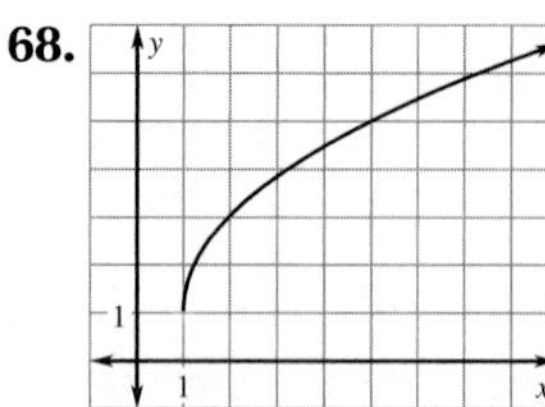
domain: $x \geq 1$, range: $y \geq 1$

12.2 Guided Practice (pp. 776–778)

1. 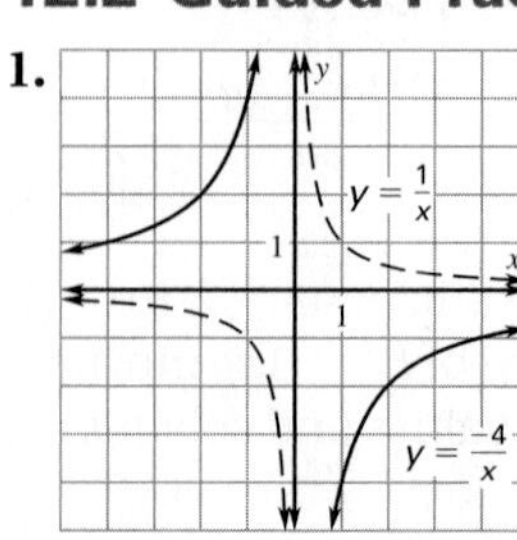

Domain: all real numbers except 0, range: all real numbers except 0; the graph is a vertical stretch of the graph of $y = \frac{1}{x}$ that is then reflected in the x-axis.

ADDITIONAL ANSWERS

2. 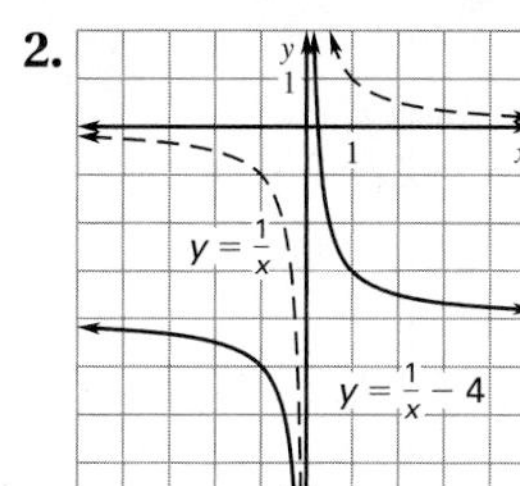

Domain: all real numbers except 0, range: all real numbers except −4; the graph is a vertical translation (of 4 units down) of the graph of $y = \frac{1}{x}$.

3. 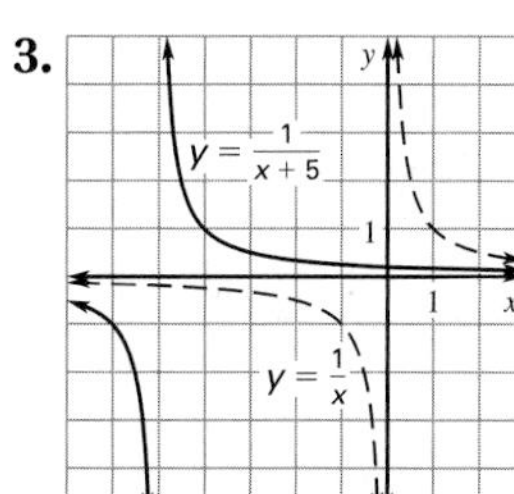

Domain: all real numbers except −5, range: all real numbers except 0; the graph is a horizontal translation (of 5 units left) of the graph of $y = \frac{1}{x}$.

4. The graph of $y = \frac{1}{x+3}$ is a horizontal translation (of 3 units left) of the graph of $y = \frac{1}{x}$.

12.2 Skill Practice (pp. 779–780)

3. 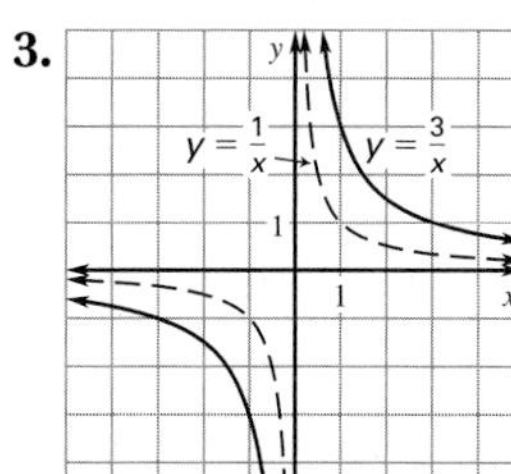

Domain: all real numbers except 0, range: all real numbers except 0; the graph is a vertical stretch of the graph of $y = \frac{1}{x}$.

4. 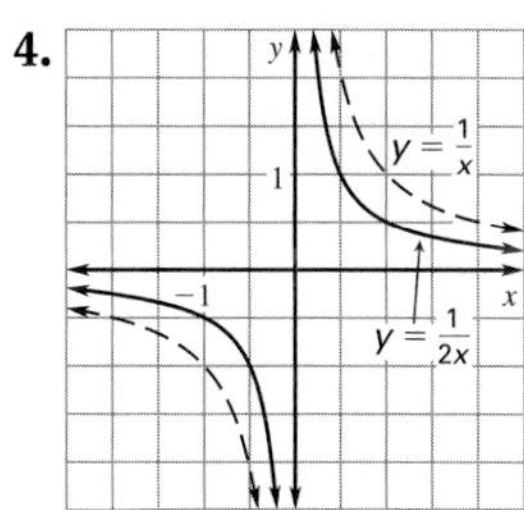

Domain: all real numbers except 0, range: all real numbers except 0; the graph is a vertical shrink of the graph of $y = \frac{1}{x}$.

5. 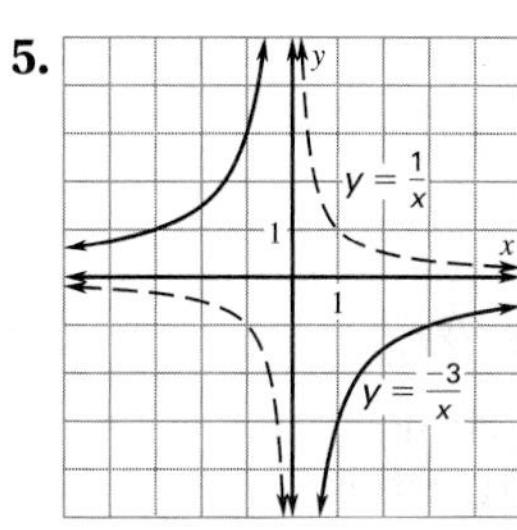

Domain: all real numbers except 0, range: all real numbers except 0; the graph is a vertical stretch of the graph of $y = \frac{1}{x}$ that is then reflected in the x-axis.

6. 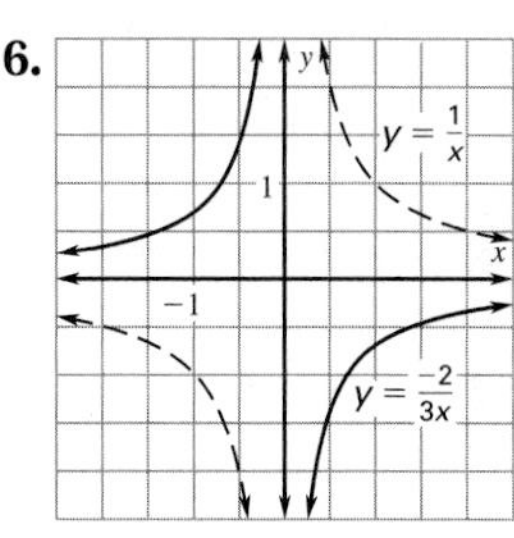

Domain: all real numbers except 0, range: all real numbers except 0; the graph is a vertical shrink of the graph of $y = \frac{1}{x}$ that is then reflected in the x-axis.

7. 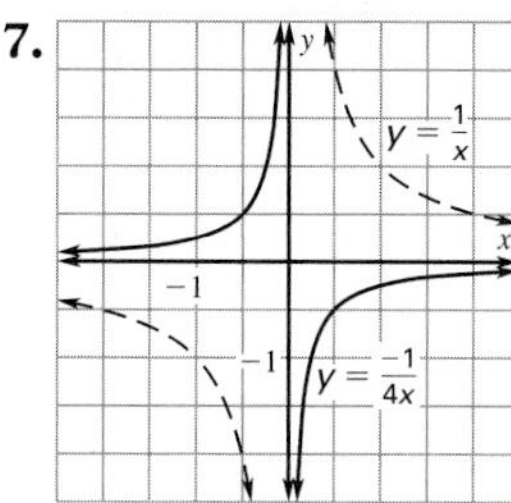

Domain: all real numbers except 0, range: all real numbers except 0; the graph is a vertical shrink of the graph of $y = \frac{1}{x}$ that is then reflected in the x-axis.

8. 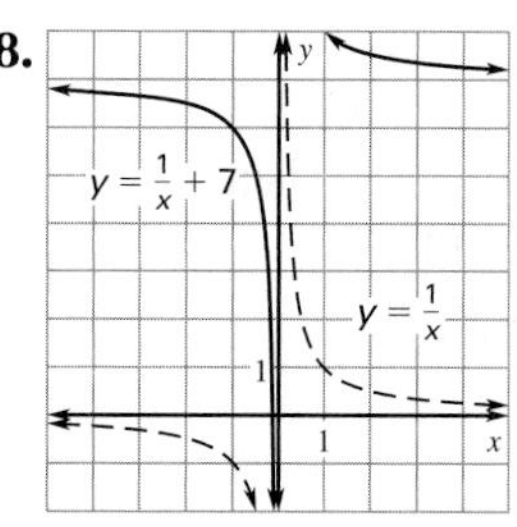

Domain: all real numbers except 0, range: all real numbers except 7; the graph is a vertical translation (of 7 units up) of the graph of $y = \frac{1}{x}$.

9. 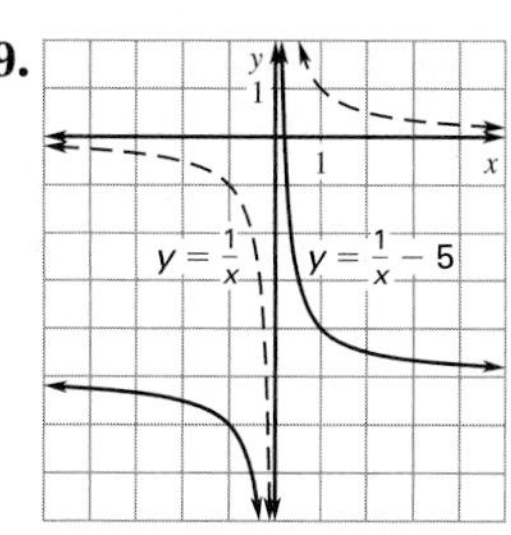

Domain: all real numbers except 0, range: all real numbers except −5; the graph is a vertical translation (of 5 units down) of the graph of $y = \frac{1}{x}$.

10. 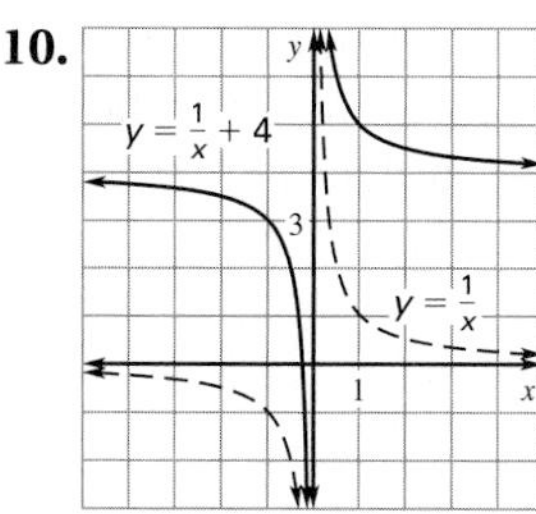

Domain: all real numbers except 0, range: all real numbers except 4; the graph is a vertical translation (of 4 units up) of the graph of $y = \frac{1}{x}$.

11. 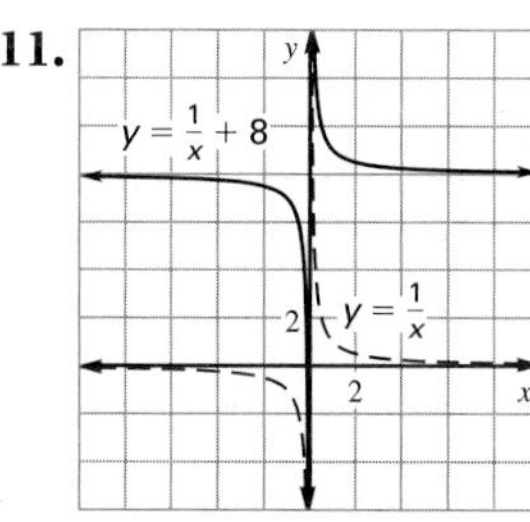

Domain: all real numbers except 0, range: all real numbers except 8; the graph is a vertical translation (of 8 units up) of the graph of $y = \frac{1}{x}$.

12. 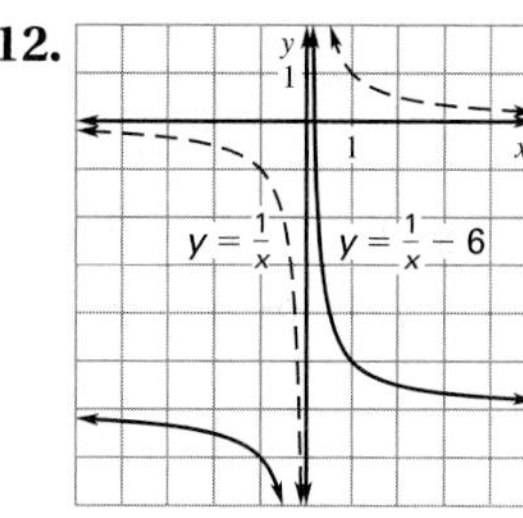

Domain: all real numbers except 0, range: all real numbers except −6; the graph is a vertical translation (of 6 units down) of the graph of $y = \frac{1}{x}$.

13. 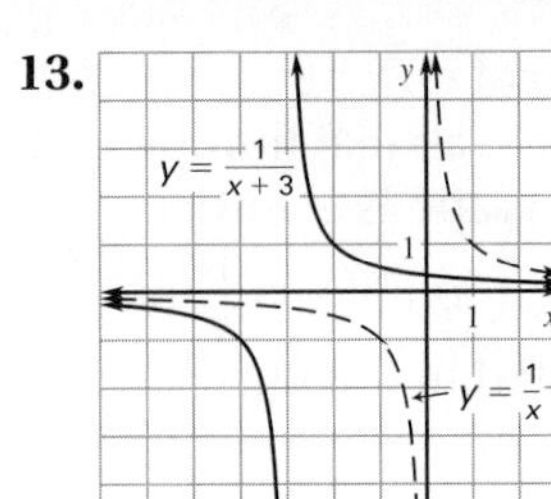

Domain: all real numbers except −3, range: all real numbers except 0; the graph is a horizontal translation (of 3 units left) of the graph of $y = \frac{1}{x}$.

14. 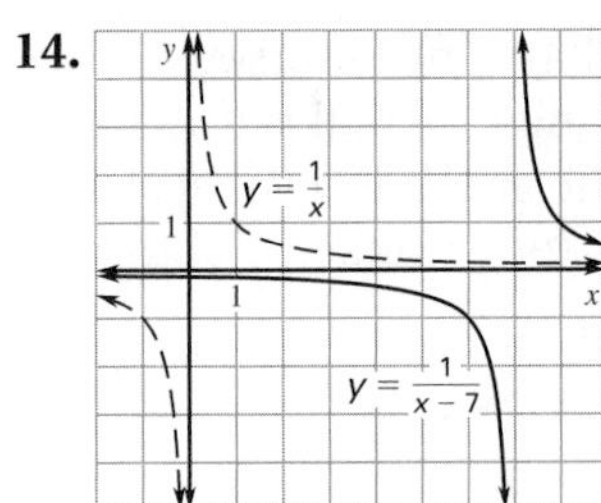

Domain: all real numbers except 7, range: all real numbers except 0; the graph is a horizontal translation (of 7 units right) of the graph of $y = \frac{1}{x}$.

15. 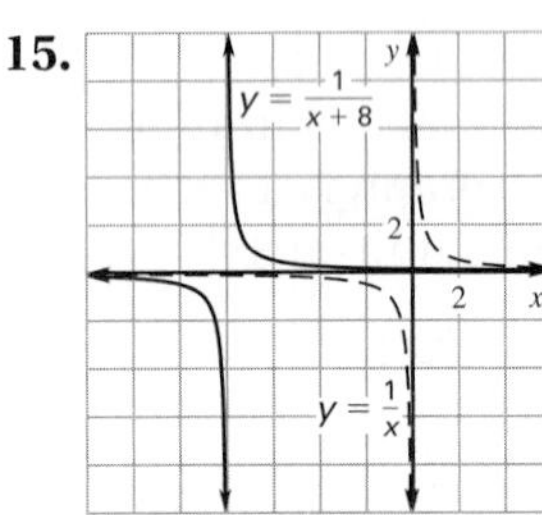

Domain: all real numbers except −8, range: all real numbers except 0; the graph is a horizontal translation (of 8 units left) of the graph of $y = \frac{1}{x}$.

16. 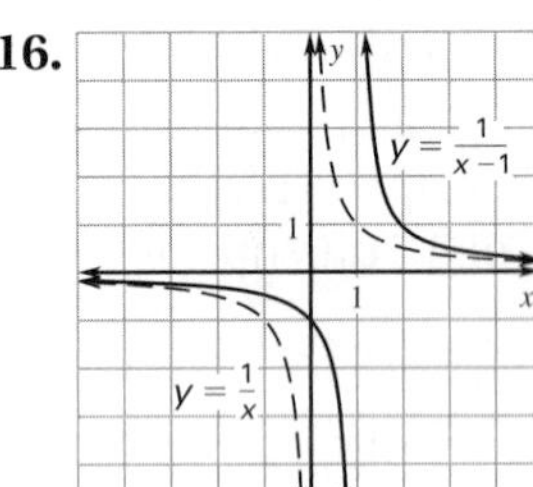

Domain: all real numbers except 1, range: all real numbers except 0; the graph is a horizontal translation (of 1 unit right) of the graph of $y = \frac{1}{x}$.

17. 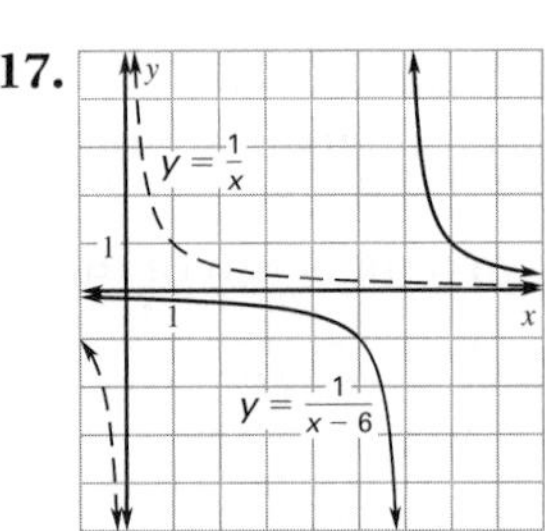

Domain: all real numbers except 6, range: all real numbers except 0; the graph is a horizontal translation (of 6 units right) of the graph of $y = \frac{1}{x}$.

19. 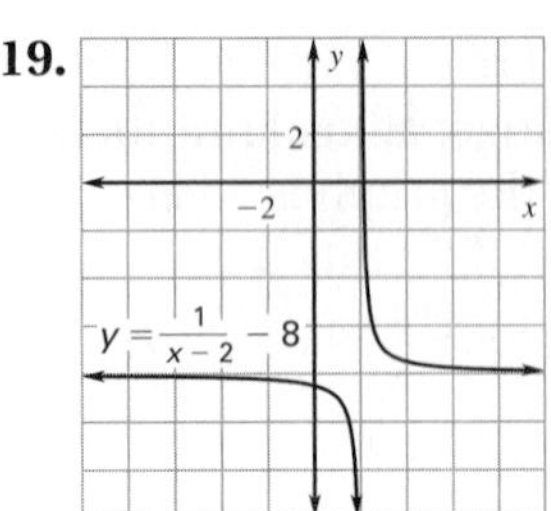

20.

21. 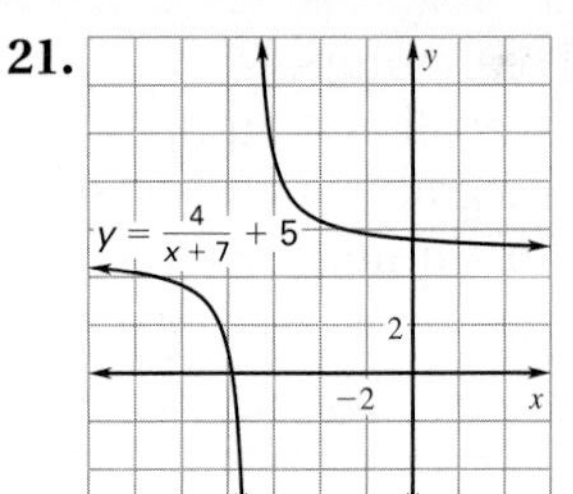

22. 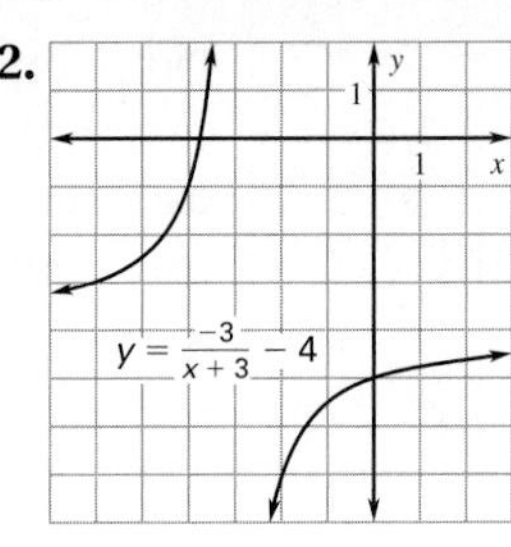

23. 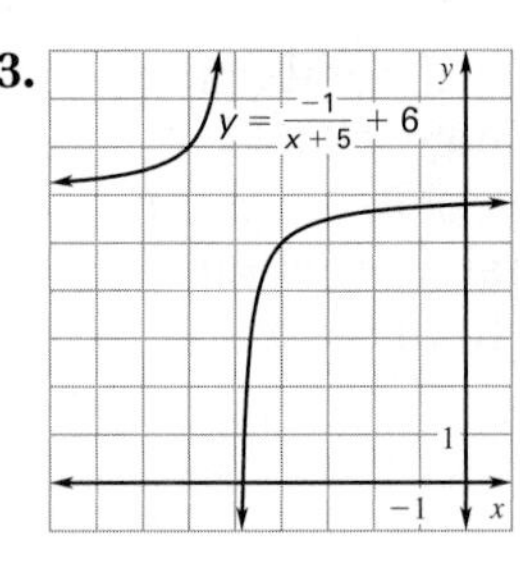

24. 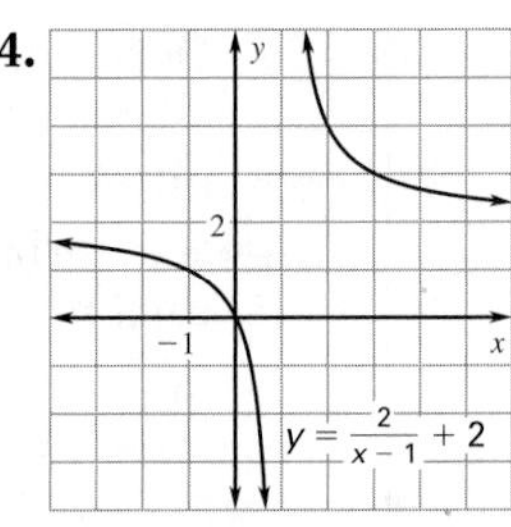

25. 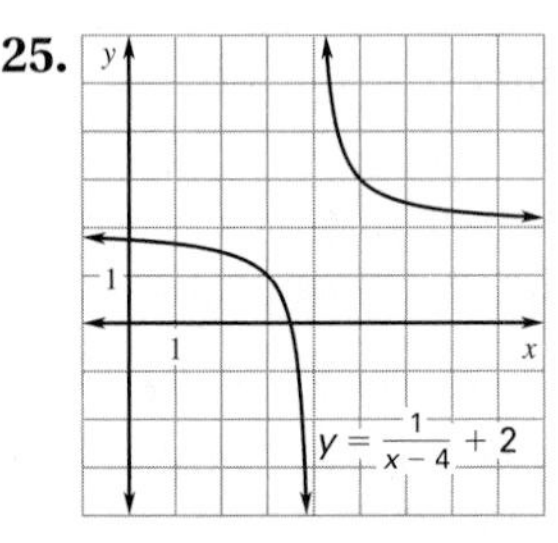

26. 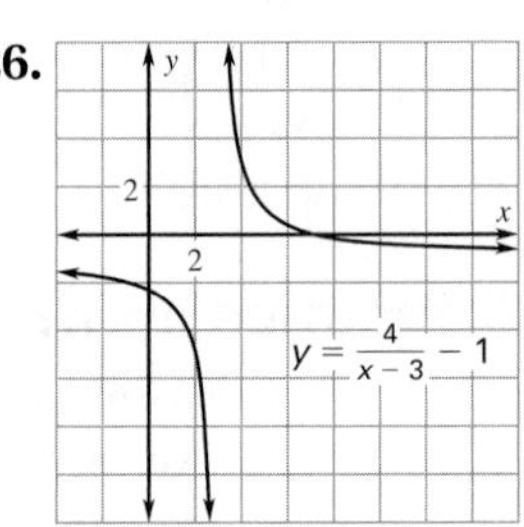

27. 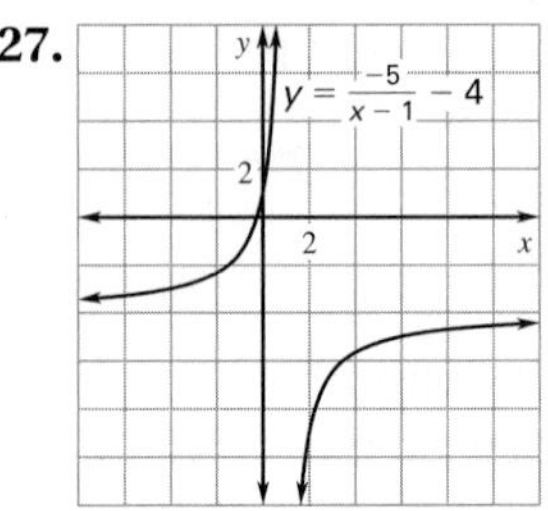

12.2 Problem Solving (pp. 780–782)

45. a. 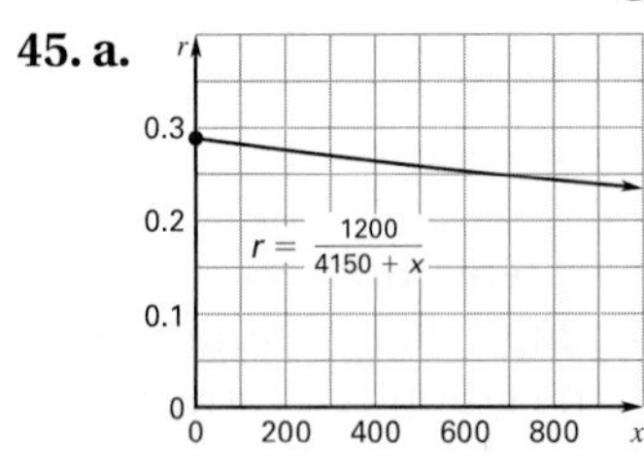

Quiz for Lessons 12.1–12.2 (p. 782)

7. 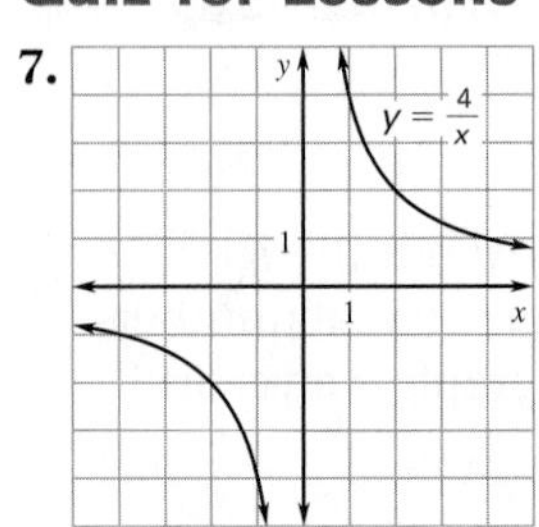

domain: all real numbers except 0, range: all real numbers except 0

8. 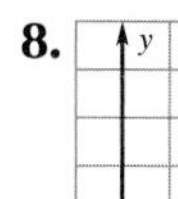
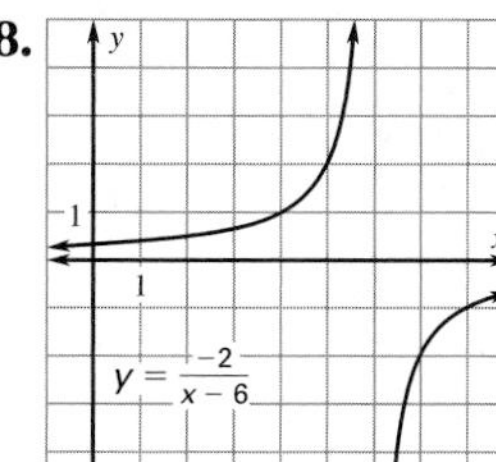

domain: all real numbers except 6, range: all real numbers except 0

9. 
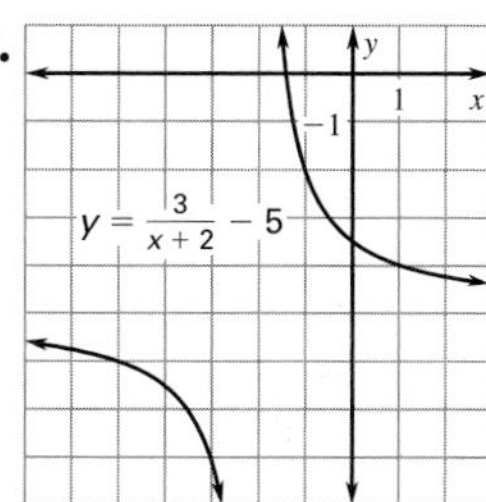

domain: all real numbers except −2, range: all real numbers except −5

12.3 Investigating Algebra Activity (p. 783)

2. $2x + 3$

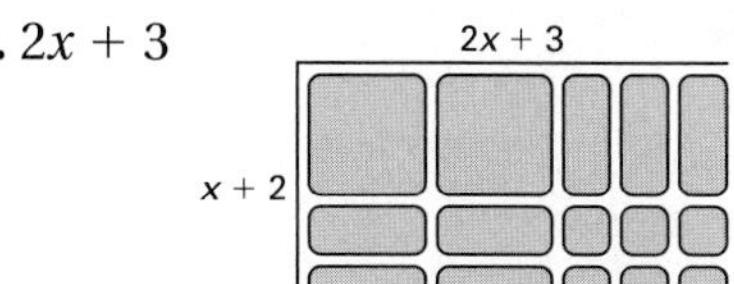

3. $2x + 3 + \frac{1}{x+3}$

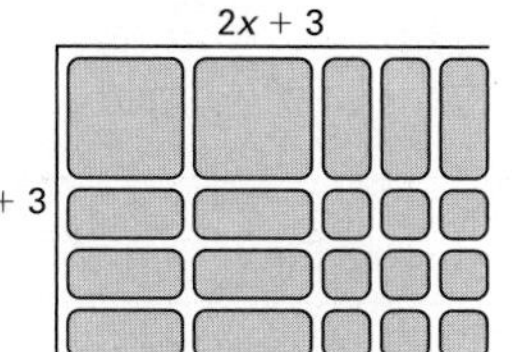

4. $2x + 1 + \frac{4}{2x+1}$

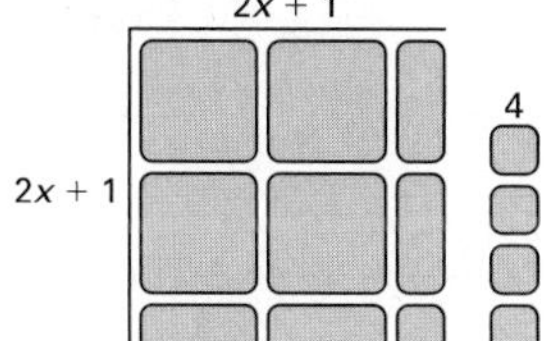

5. $x + 1 + \frac{4}{2x+3}$

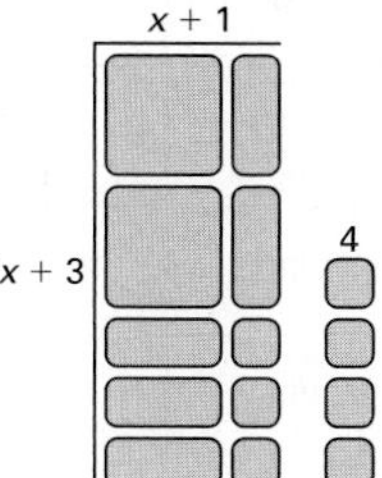

6. $3x + 1 + \frac{1}{x+2}$

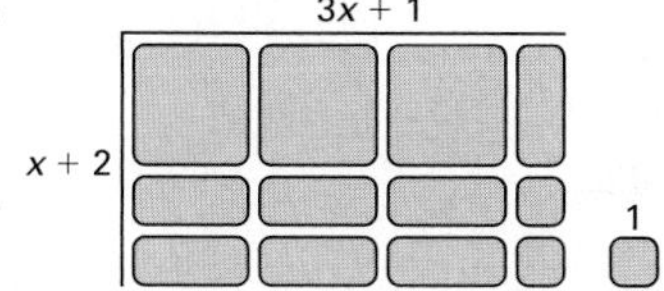

7. $4x + 2 + \frac{3}{x+1}$

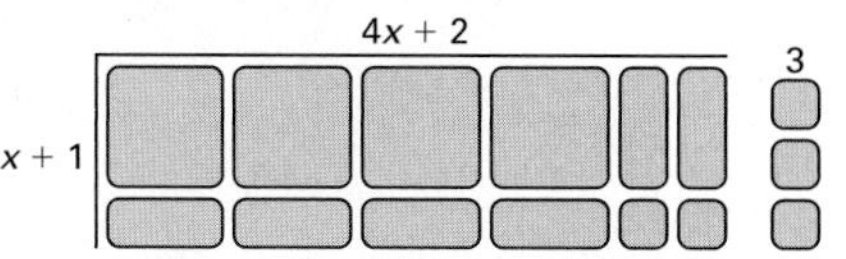

12.3 Skill Practice (pp. 788–789)

22. 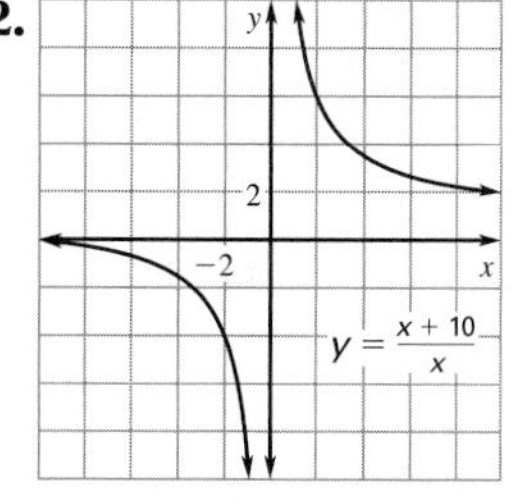

23. 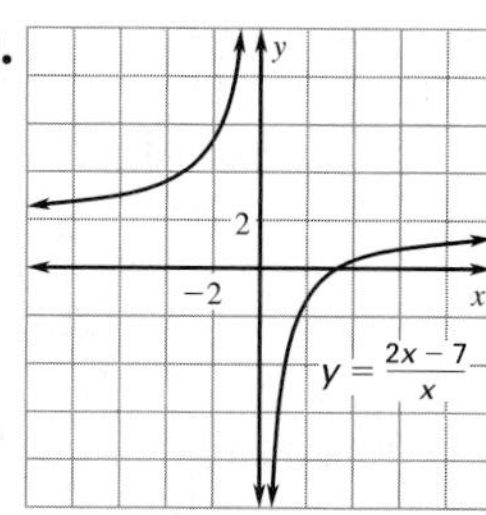

24. 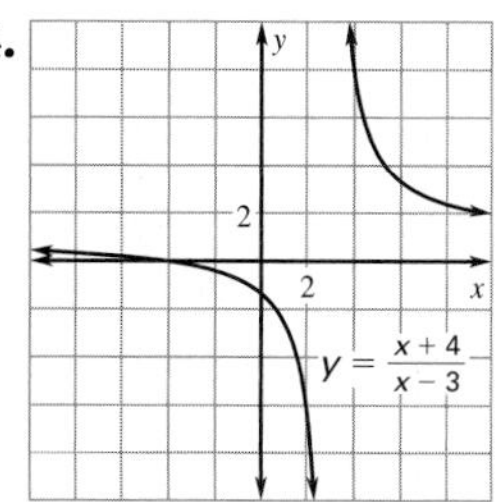

25. 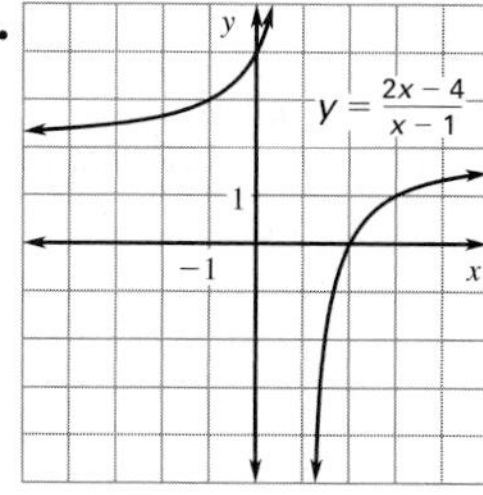

26. 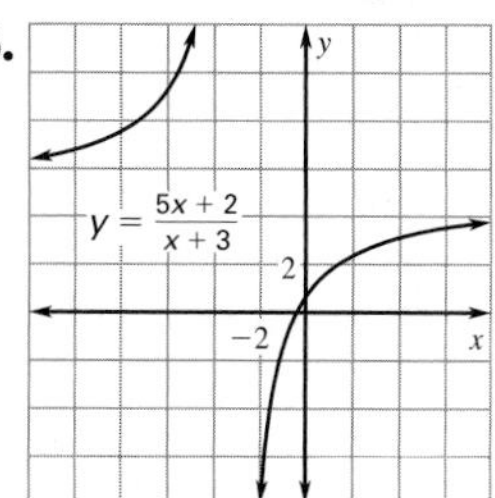

27. 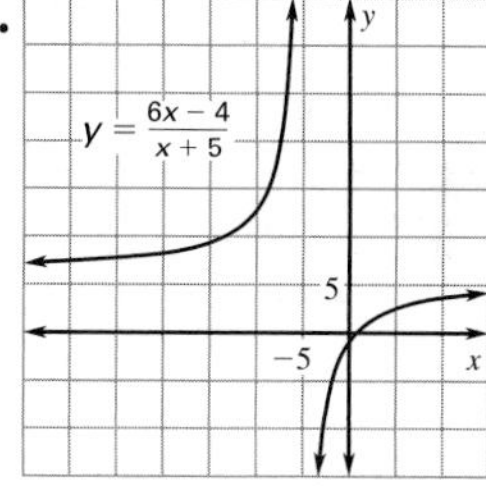

28. 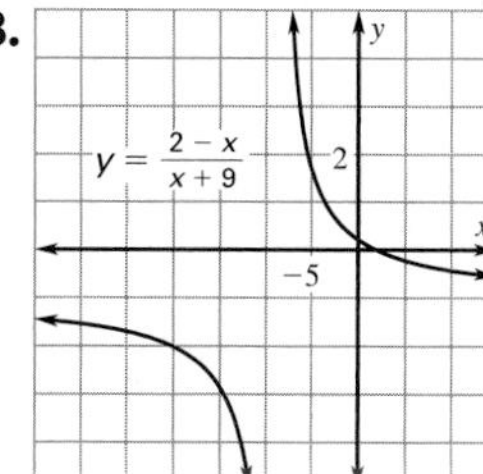

29. 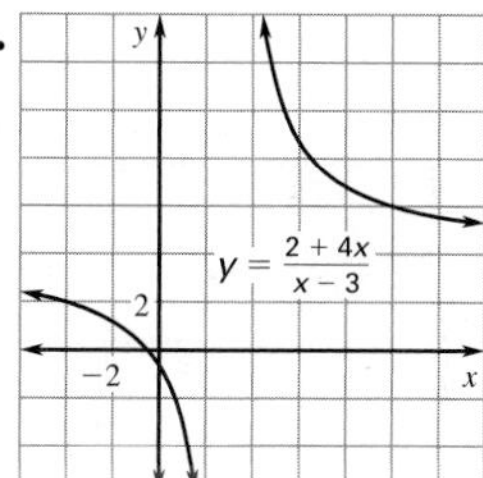

30. 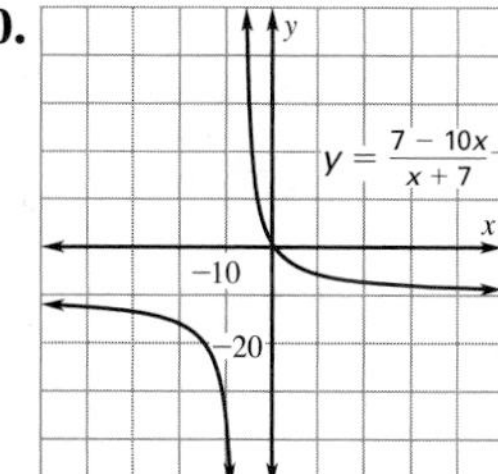

12.3 Problem Solving (pp. 789–791)

49. a. $y = \frac{2r + 2\ell}{r\ell}$;

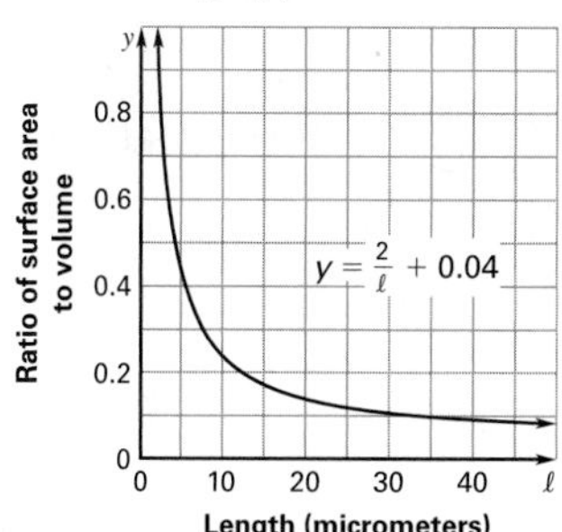

ADDITIONAL ANSWERS

b. More efficient; the graph in part (a) shows that as the length increases, the ratio decreases, implying that the microorganism becomes more efficient at performing metabolic tasks. **c.** The microorganism's efficiency would increase. *Sample answer:* Suppose the length is fixed at 50 micrometers. Then $y = \frac{2r + 100}{50r}$, or $y = \frac{2}{r} + 0.04$. This equation has the same graph as the graph shown in part (a); from the graph we see that as the radius increases, the ratio decreases, implying that the microorganism's efficiency increases.

12.3 Graphing Calculator Activity (pp. 792–793)

7.

	$y = \frac{8}{x-2}$	$y = \frac{4}{6x-7}$	$y = \frac{x-9}{x^2+1}$
Vertical asymptotes	$x = 2$	$x = \frac{7}{6}$	none
***x*-values for which *y* is undefined**	2	$\frac{7}{6}$	none
Horizontal asymptotes	$y = 0$	$y = 0$	$y = 0$
Degree of numerator	0	0	1
Degree of denominator	1	1	2

	$y = \frac{x+5}{x^2+4x+4}$	$y = \frac{x+1}{4x^2-36}$	$y = \frac{5}{10x^2+9}$
Vertical asymptotes	$x = -2$	$x = -3$, $x = 3$	none
***x*-values for which *y* is undefined**	−2	−3, 3	none
Horizontal asymptotes	$y = 0$	$y = 0$	$y = 0$
Degree of numerator	1	1	0
Degree of denominator	2	2	2

8. 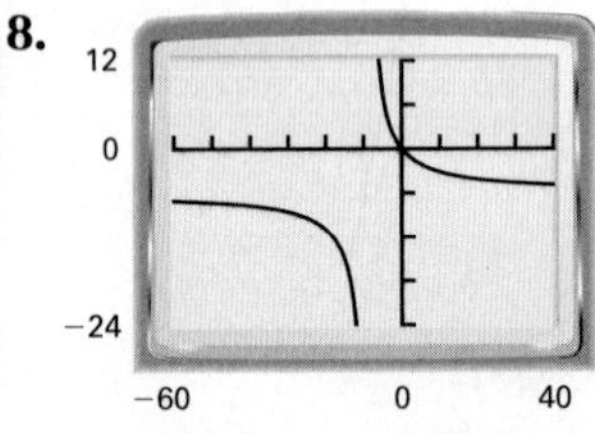

vertical: $x = -9$, horizontal: $y = -6$

9. 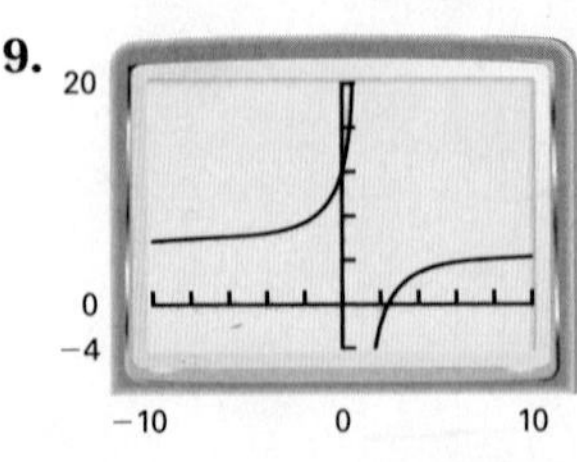

vertical: $x = 1$, horizontal: $y = 5$

10. 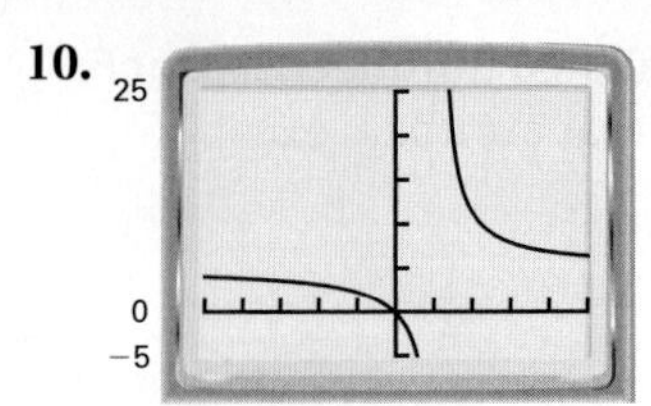

vertical: $x = \frac{9}{2}$, horizontal: $y = 5$

11. 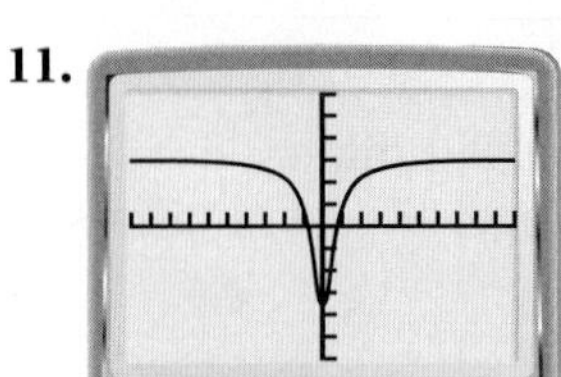
vertical: none, horizontal: $y = 3$

12. 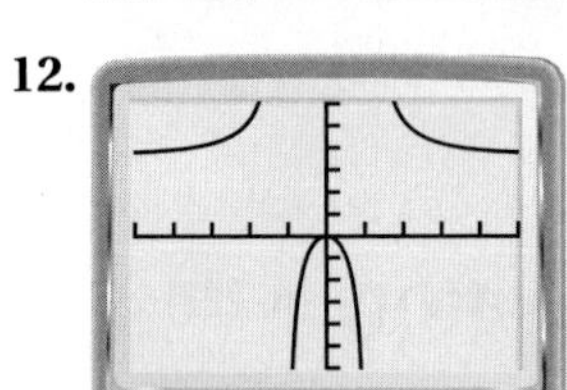
vertical: $x = \frac{-4}{3}$, $x = \frac{4}{3}$, horizontal: $y = 3$

13. 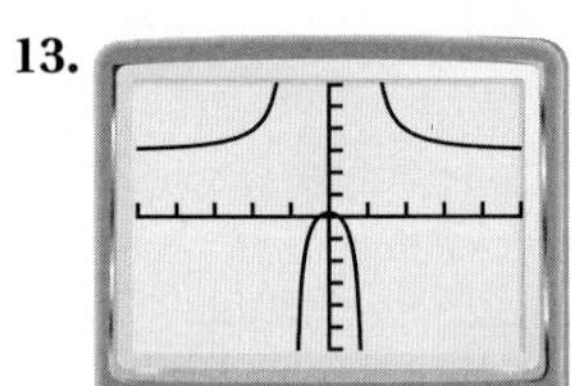
vertical: $x = -1$, $x = 1$, horizontal: $y = 3$

14.

	$y = \frac{-6x}{x+9}$	$y = \frac{5x-12}{x-1}$	$y = \frac{10x}{2x-9}$
Vertical asymptotes	$x = -9$	$x = 1$	$x = \frac{9}{2}$
***x*-values for which *y* is undefined**	−9	1	$\frac{9}{2}$
Horizontal asymptotes	$y = -6$	$y = 5$	$y = 5$
Degree of numerator	1	1	1
Degree of denominator	1	1	1
Quotient of leading coefficients	−6	5	5

	$y = \frac{12x^2-7}{4x^2+2}$	$y = \frac{27x^2-x}{9x^2-16}$	$y = \frac{18x^2-1}{6x^2-6}$
Vertical asymptotes	none	$x = \frac{-4}{3}$, $x = \frac{4}{3}$	$x = -1$, $x = 1$
***x*-values for which *y* is undefined**	none	$\frac{-4}{3}, \frac{4}{3}$	−1, 1
Horizontal asymptotes	$y = 3$	$y = 3$	$y = 3$
Degree of numerator	2	2	2
Degree of denominator	2	2	2
Quotient of leading coefficients	3	3	3

12.4 Problem Solving (pp. 799–800)

45. b.

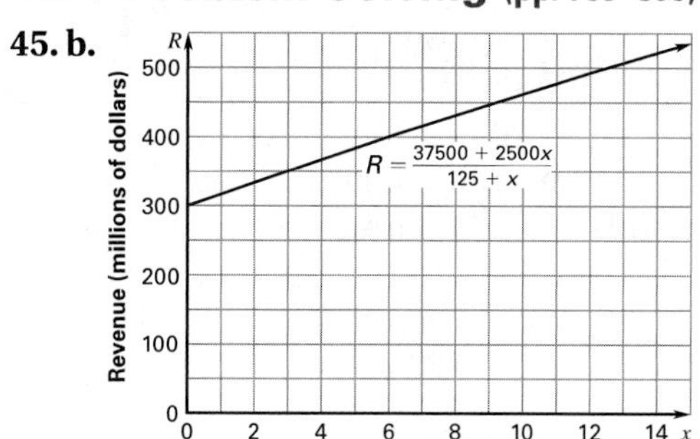

Quiz for Lessons 12.3–12.4 (p. 800)

3. **4.**

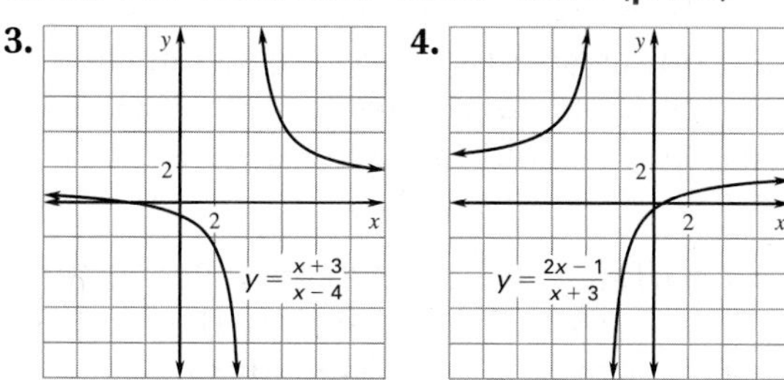

12.6 Skill Practice (pp. 816–817) **19.** To rewrite each rational expression using the least common denominator, you must multiply its numerator by the factor of the LCD that is missing from the denominator: the numerator $5x$ should be multiplied by $(x + 3)$ and the numerator 2 should be multiplied by $(x - 4)$; $\frac{5x}{x - 4} + \frac{2}{x + 3} =$ $\frac{5x(x + 3)}{(x - 4)(x + 3)} + \frac{2(x - 4)}{(x - 4)(x + 3)} = \frac{5x^2 + 15x + 2x - 8}{(x - 4)(x + 3)} =$ $\frac{5x^2 + 17x - 8}{(x - 4)(x + 3)}$.

12.7 Problem Solving Workshop (p. 828) **1.** \$1250; Method 1: Use a table. Make a table that shows the percent of Jill's investment money that is in the mutual fund after various amounts are added to the mutual fund.

Amount in mutual fund (\$)	Amount in all investments (\$)	Percent in mutual fund (%)
1000	10,000	10
1200	10,200	about 11.8
1400	10,400	about 13.5
1600	10,600	about 15
1800	10,800	about 16.7
2000	11,000	about 18.2
2050	11,050	about 18.6
2100	11,100	about 18.9
2150	11,150	about 19.3
2200	11,200	about 19.6
2250	11,250	20

Method 2: Reinterpret the problem. When 20% of Jill's investment money is in the mutual fund, $\frac{1}{5}$ of her money will be in the mutual fund and $\frac{4}{5}$ of her money will be in other accounts. The ratio of money in the mutual fund to money in other accounts (which is \$10,000 − \$1000 = \$9000) needs to be 1 : 4. Let a = amount of money (in dollars) added to the mutual fund and write a proportion: $\frac{1000 + a}{9000} = \frac{1}{4}$. Solving for a gives $a = 1250$, so Jill needs to add \$1250 to the mutual fund. **3.** 6 free throws; Method 1: Use a table. Make a table that shows the percent of free throw attempts made after various numbers of consecutive successful free throw attempts.

Number of consecutive successful free throw attempts	Total number of free throw attempts	Percent of free throw attempts made
12	30	40%
13	31	about 42%
14	32	about 44%
15	33	about 45%
16	34	about 47%
17	35	about 49%
18	36	50%

Method 2: Reinterpret the problem. When 50% of the free throw attempts have been successful, the number of attempts made will equal the number of attempts not made. After the first 30 attempts, the number of attempts made is $0.40(30) = 12$, and the number of attempts not made is $0.60(30) = 18$. Let n = number of consecutive successful free throw attempts and write an equation that shows that the number of attempts made and the number of attempts not made are equal: $12 + n = 18$. Solving for n gives $n = 6$, so the basketball player needs to make 6 consecutive free throws. **5.** 75 minutes; Method 1: Use a table. Make a table that shows the total time it takes you and your friend to shovel the driveway together for various amounts of time that it takes your friend to shovel the driveway alone.

Time m for your friend to shovel the driveway alone (min)	Time for you to shovel the driveway alone (min)	Time it takes to shovel the driveway together (min)
50	50	25
55	50	about 26
60	50	about 27
65	50	about 28
70	50	about 29
75	50	30

Method 2: Reinterpret the problem. Because you can shovel the driveway alone in 50 minutes, during each of the 30 minutes that you and your friend work together you shovel $\frac{1}{50}$ of the driveway. So, in 30 minutes you have shoveled $\frac{30}{50}$, or $\frac{3}{5}$ of the driveway. Your friend shovels $\frac{2}{5}$ of the driveway in 30 minutes, so 30 minutes is $\frac{2}{5}$ of the time that it will take your friend to shovel the whole driveway. Let m be the number of minutes it takes your friend to shovel the whole driveway and write an equation: $30 = \frac{2}{5}m$. Solving for m gives $m = 75$ minutes, so it takes your friend 75 minutes to shovel the driveway alone.

Chapter 13

13.1 Skill Practice (pp. 846–847) 13. *Sample answer:* Odds in favor is the number of favorable outcomes divided by the number of unfavorable outcomes; odds in favor of a multiple of $3 = \frac{\text{Number of favorable outcomes}}{\text{Number of unfavorable outcomes}} = \frac{9}{1}$ or 9 : 1. **21.** $\frac{4}{9}, \frac{4}{5}$. *Sample answer:* The probability and odds of choosing a boy are related because both compare the number of boys to another number. The probability of choosing a boy compares the number of boys to the total number of outcomes, while the odds of choosing a boy compare the number of boys to the total number of outcomes minus the number of boys.

13.2 Skill Practice (pp. 853–854) 31. b. There are the same number of permutations. *Sample answer:* The formula for n objects taken n at a time is $\frac{n!}{(n-n)!} = n!$, while the formula for n objects taken $n - 1$ at a time is $\frac{n!}{(n-(n-1))!} = \frac{n!}{1!} = n!$. Thus, both formulas are equal.

13.3 Skill Practice (p. 858) 20. ${}_6P_r \geq {}_6C_r$. *Sample answer:* The formula for ${}_6C_r$ is the same as ${}_6P_r$ multiplied by $\frac{1}{r!}$. For any value of $r > 1$, this will result in ${}_6C_r$ being less than ${}_6P_r$. If $r = 1$ or $r = 0$ then the values will be the same. **21.** ${}_nC_r = {}_nP_r \cdot \frac{1}{r!}$. *Sample answer:* To find the number of combinations, you find the number of permutations and then divide by the number of ways the items being chosen can be arranged, or $r!$. **22.** ${}_nC_{n-r} = \frac{n!}{[n-(n-r)]! \cdot (n-r)!} = \frac{n!}{r! \cdot (n-r)!} = \frac{n!}{(n-r)! \cdot r!} = {}_nC_r$. *Sample answer:* When you select a combination of r items from a group of n, you divide the group into 2 sections: a group of r selected items and
a group of $n - r$ items that were not selected. Since each combination you select results in a unique combination of items not selected, the number of combinations of r items you can select from a group of n is the same as the number of combinations of $(n - r)$ items you cannot select in the group of n.

13.3 Problem Solving (p. 859) 27. $\frac{351}{142{,}506} \approx 0.25\%$. *Sample answer:* The number of possible groups chosen is ${}_{30}C_5 = 142{,}506$. To find the number of groups that include me and my 2 best friends, find the number of combinations of students to fill the remaining group once me and my 2 best friends have been chosen, or ${}_{27}C_2 = 351$. There are 351 favorable groups out of 142,506 possible groups.

13.5 Guided Practice (pp. 871–872) 2. a. Yes. *Sample answer:* All the people sampled were visiting a soccer game, so they may be more likely than the American population to be interested in soccer. **b.** Yes. *Sample answer:* The question suggests that soccer is popular and may encourage respondents to say they are interested in soccer. *Sample answer:* "How interested or disinterested are you in soccer?"

13.6 Problem Solving (pp. 877–878) 22. c. Range: 219, mean absolute deviation: 50.7. *Sample answer:* The range is much higher than the mean which indicates that the data covers a wide spread of values. The mean absolute deviation tells you that the data points are not very close to the mean. **23.a.** *Sample answer:* Mean: add the data values and divide by the number of data values. Median: count from left to right or from right to left to locate the middle data values. Mode(s): find the data value(s) with the greatest number of Xs; 2, 2, 1 and 3. **b.** 2; whether you find the sum of the data values by simply adding them, or by first multiplying each distinct value by its weight and finding that sum, the result is the same.

13.7 Guided Practice (pp. 881–883)

4. *Sample:*

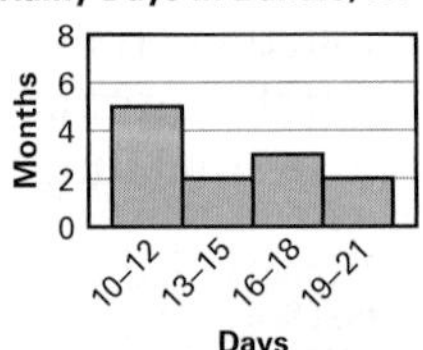

13.7 Skill Practice (pp. 883–884)

10. *Sample answer:* The range 20–29 even though it has a frequency of 0 needs to be included on the axis. Without it the histogram gives a distorted view of the spread of data.

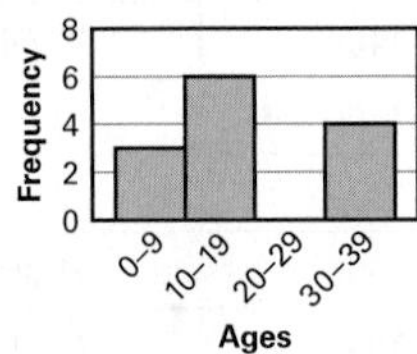

ADDITIONAL ANSWERS

11. 12. 13. 14.

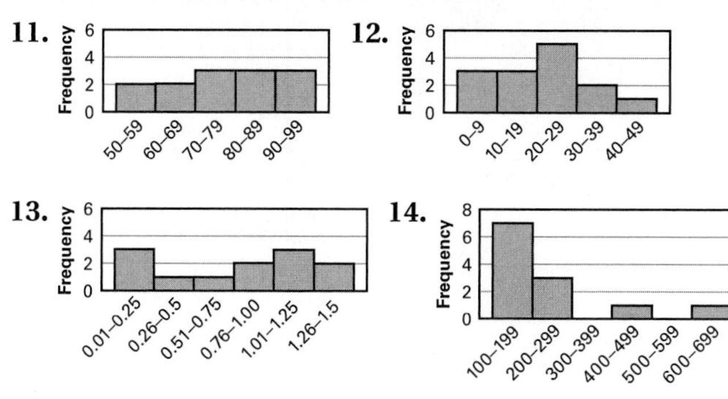

13.7 Problem Solving (pp. 884–885)

17. 18.

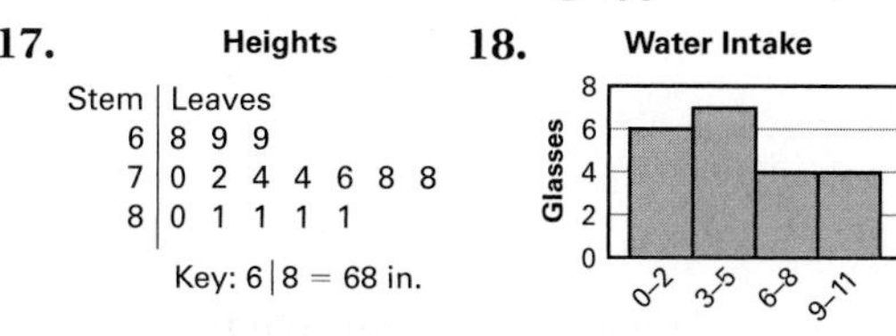

19. a.

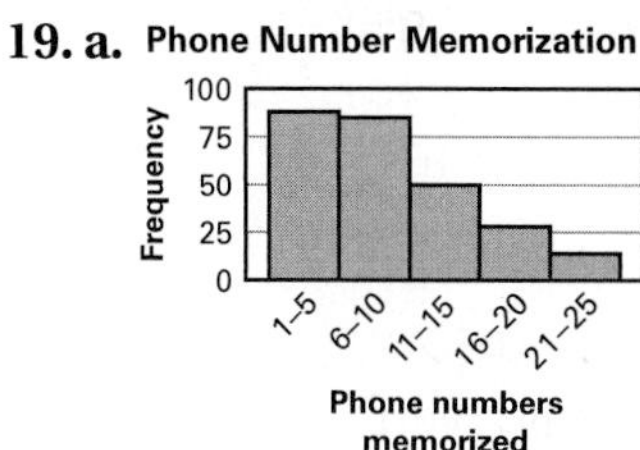

21. a.

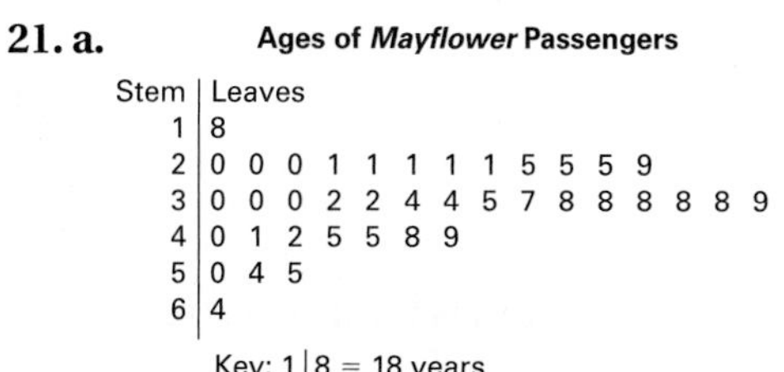

Ages of Mayflower Passengers
Stem | Leaves
1 | 8
2 | 0 0 0 1 1 1 1 1 5 5 5 9
3 | 0 0 0 2 2 4 4 5 7 8 8 8 8 8 9
4 | 0 1 2 5 5 8 9
5 | 0 4 5
6 | 4
Key: 1|8 = 18 years

22. The entries in the last column of the cumulative frequency table are 9, 20, 31, 38, and 39.

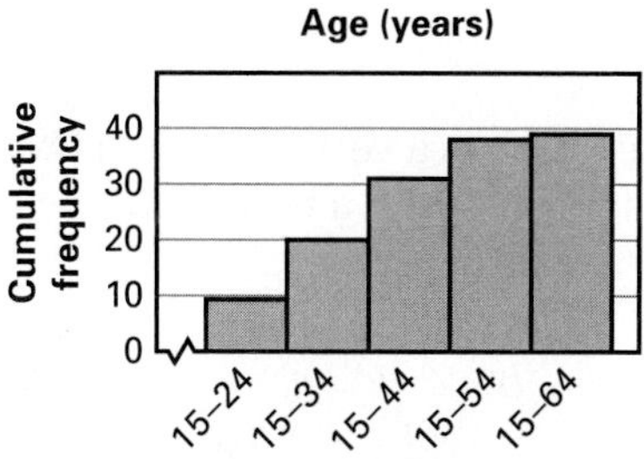

13.8 Skill Practice (pp. 889–890)

2. *Sample answer:* Find the interquartile range and multiply it by 1.5. Add the result to the upper quartile, and subtract it from the lower quartile. Any data values outside these values are outliers.

13.8 Problem Solving (pp. 890–892)

20. *Sample answer:* Generally, the lower the voice part the taller the singer in the chorus. 50% of the bass parts are between 68 and 72 inches, while 50% of the tenors are between 66.5 and 71.5 inches, 50% of the altos are between 63 and 67 inches, and sopranos are the shortest with 50% between 62.5 and 66 inches. Around 75% of all bass singers are taller than all sopranos and around 50% of tenors are taller than all sopranos.

13.8 Mixed Review (p. 892)

23. 24.

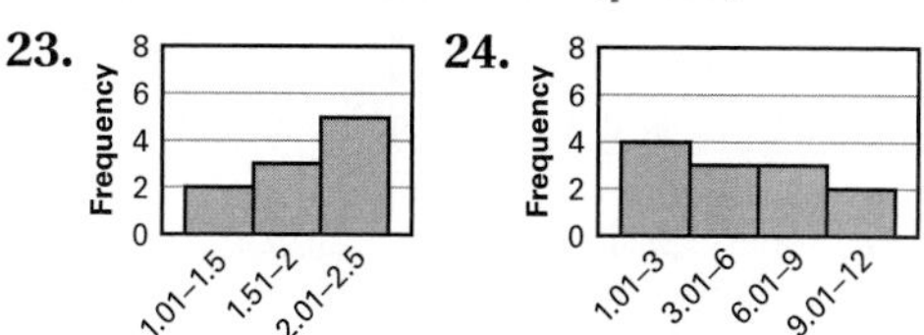

Quiz for Lessons 13.5–13.8 (p. 892)

4. 5. 6.

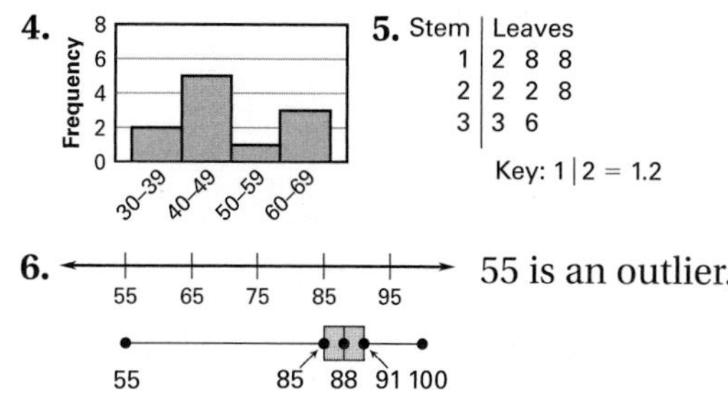

55 is an outlier.

Additional Lessons

Piecewise Functions (p. A2)

7. $P = \begin{cases} 20t, \text{ if } 0 \le t \le 40 \\ 30(t - 40) + 800, \text{ if } t > 40 \end{cases}$

When $t = 46$, $P = \$980$

8. The parent absolute value function is defined by two equations. For negative values of x, $|x| = -x$ and for nonnegative values of x, $|x| = x$; $y = \begin{cases} -x, \text{ if } x < 0 \\ x, \text{ if } x \ge 0 \end{cases}$.

9.

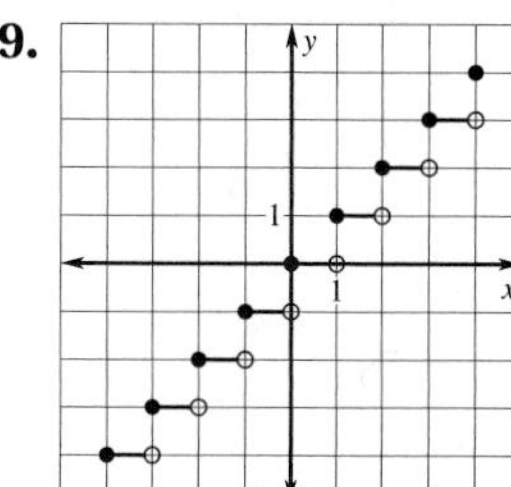

Yes; yes; the function is a piecewise function because, for every integer value of n, there is a unique equation that applies to the part of the domain defined by $n \le x < n + 1$. The function is a step function because it is defined by a constant value over each part of its domain.

Extra Practice

Chapter 4 (p. 941)

23.
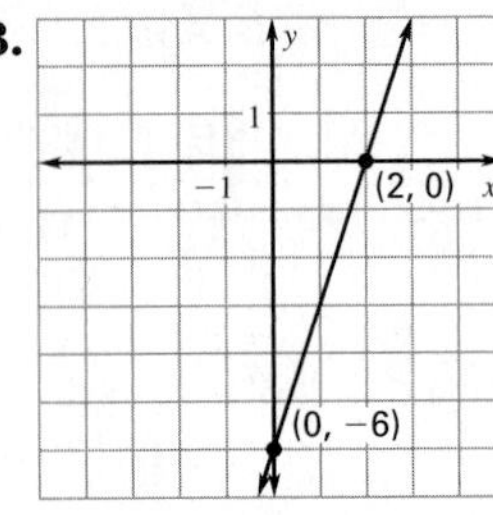

24.
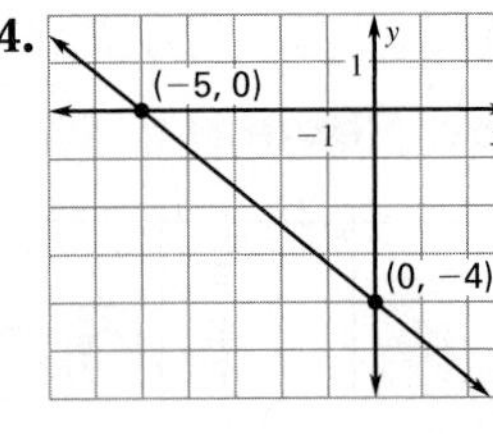

25.
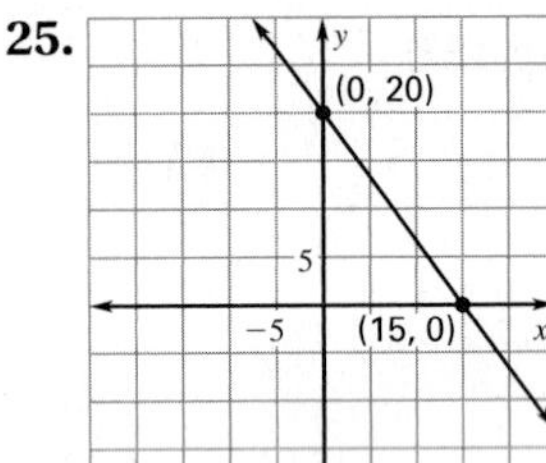

26.
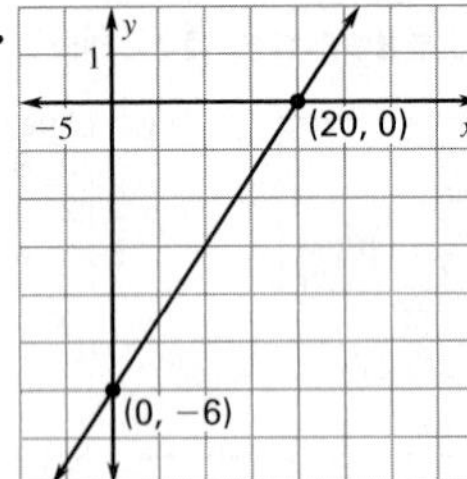

41.
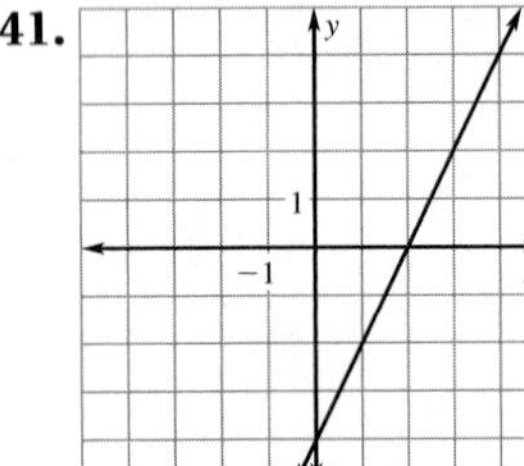

42.
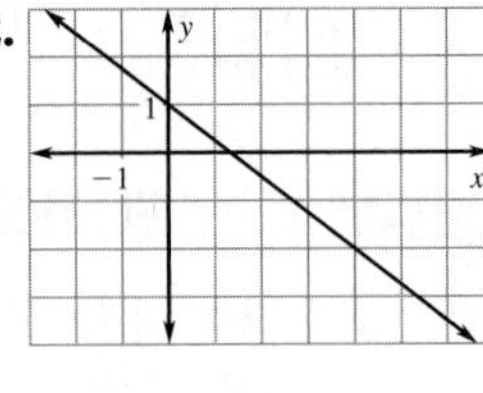

43.
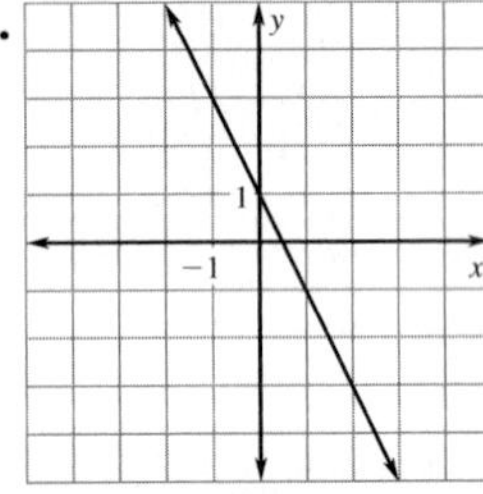

44.
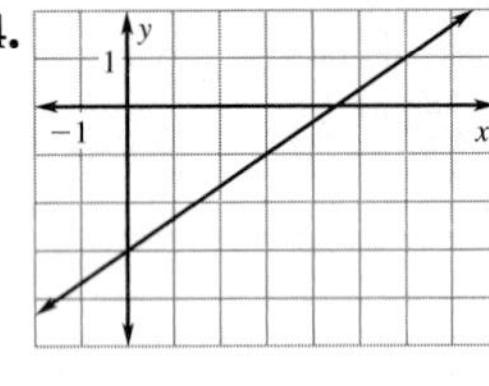

45.
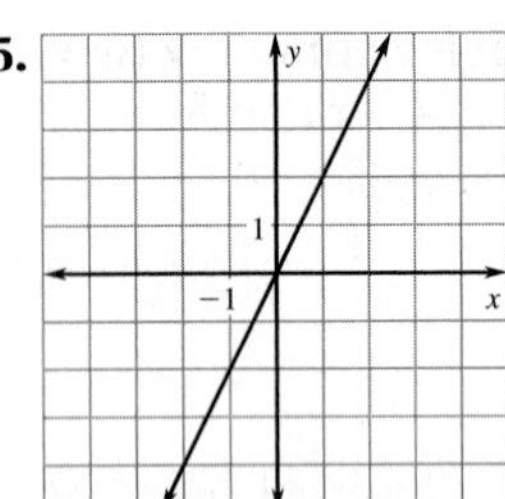

46.
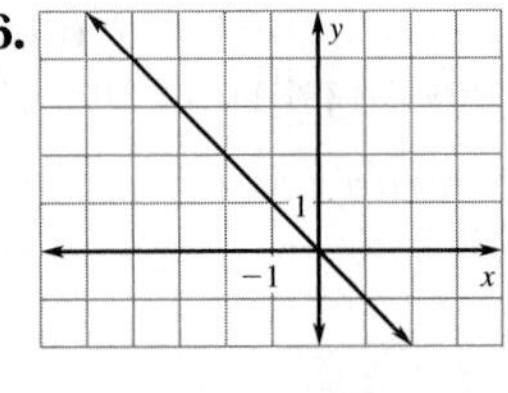

47.
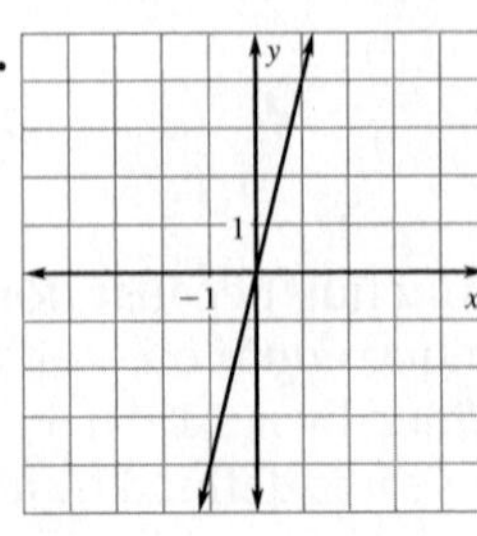

48.
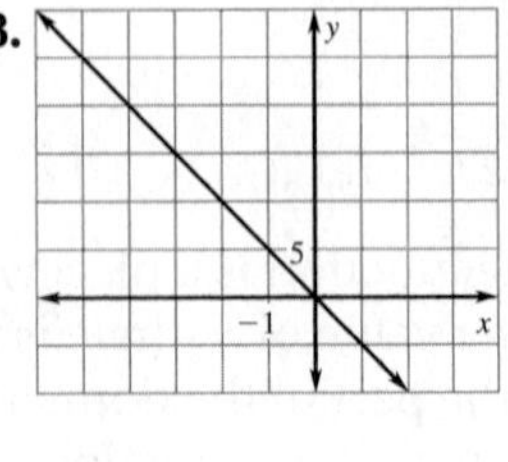

49.
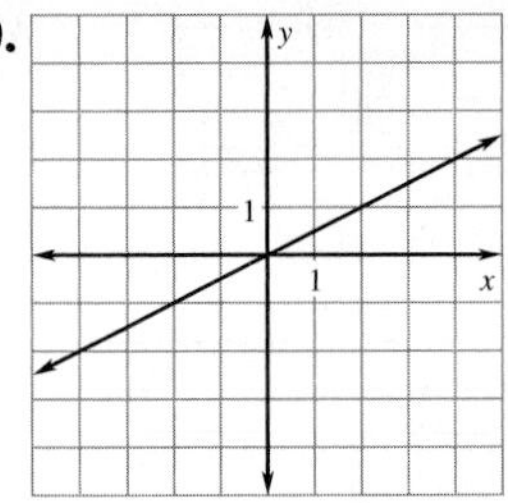

50.
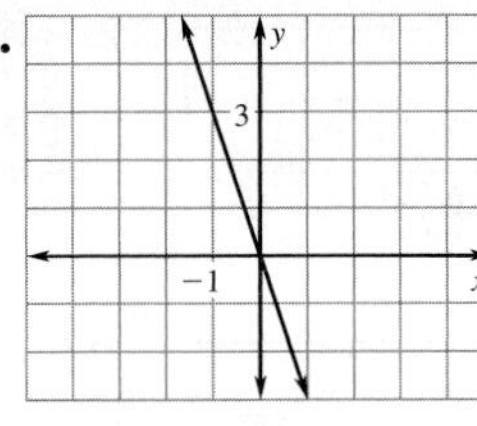

51.
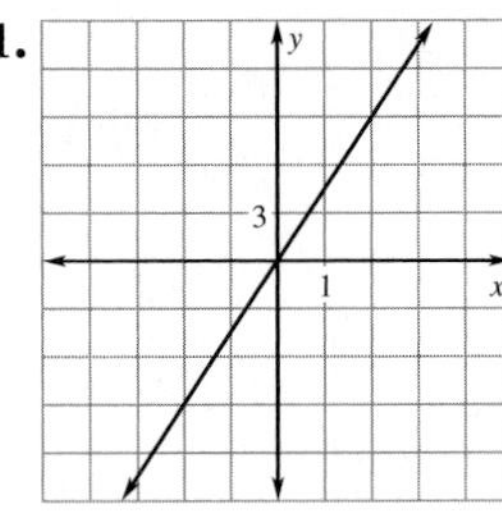

52.
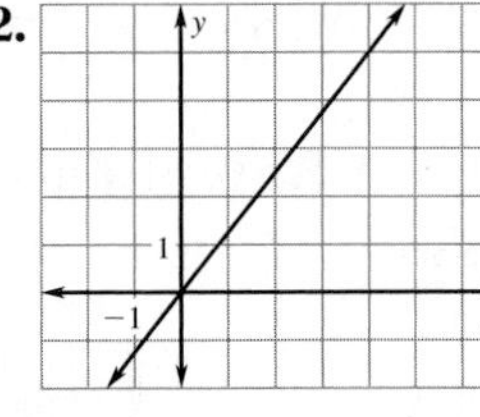

56.
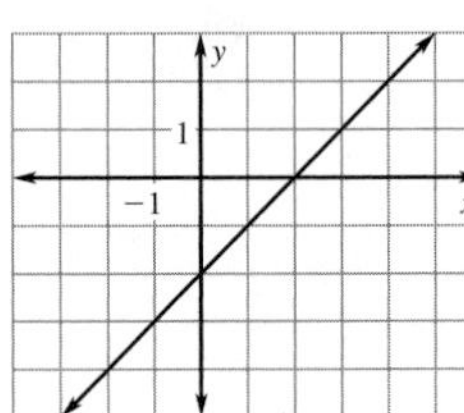

The graph is a vertical translation 2 units down of $f(x) = x$.

57.
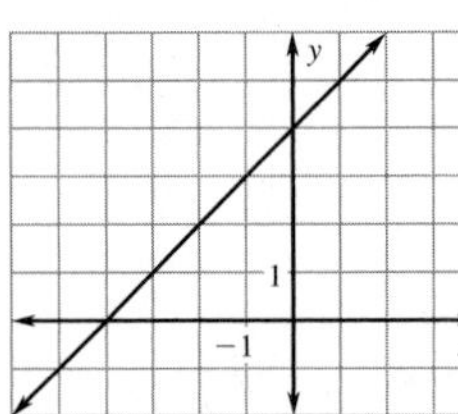

The graph is a vertical translation 4 units up of $f(x) = x$.

58.
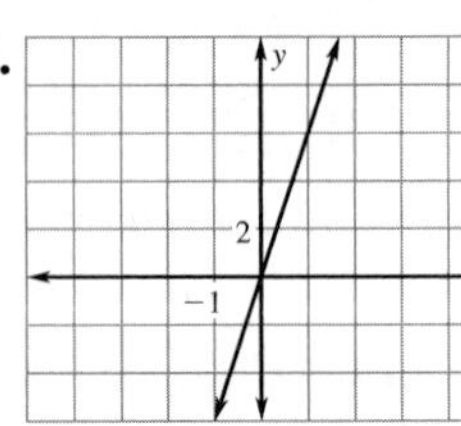

The graph is a vertical stretch by a factor of 6 of $f(x) = x$.

59.
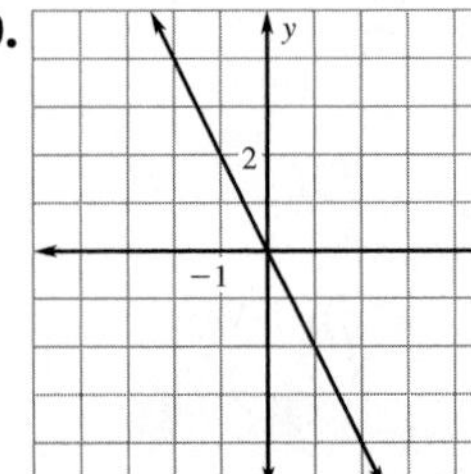

The graph is a vertical stretch by a factor of 2 and a reflection in the x-axis of $f(x) = x$.

Chapter 6 (p. 943)

34.
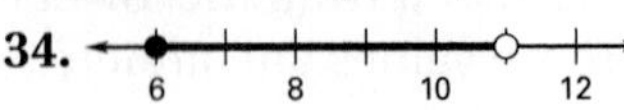

35.
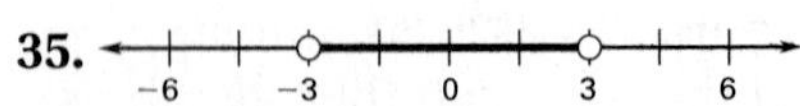

36.
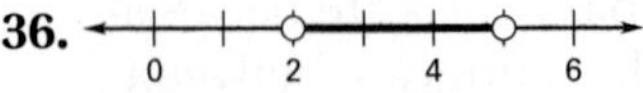

37. 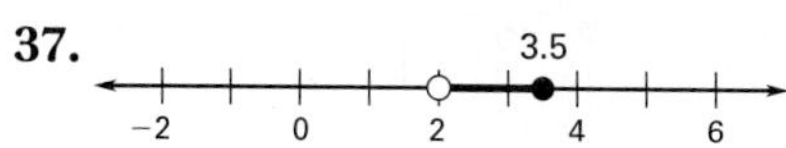

38. 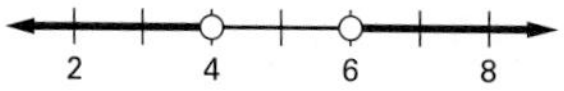 2 4 6 8

39. 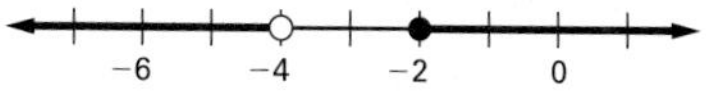 −6 −4 −2 0

40. 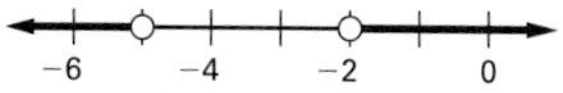 −6 −4 −2 0

41. 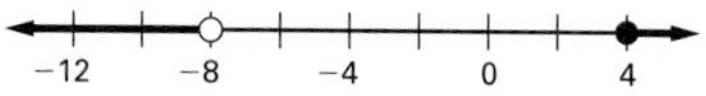 −12 −8 −4 0 4

42. 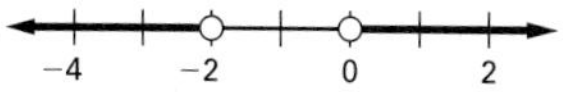 −4 −2 0 2

55. 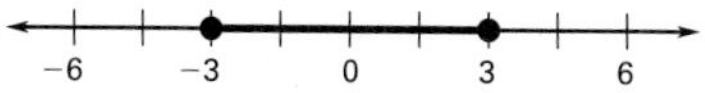 −6 −3 0 3 6

56. 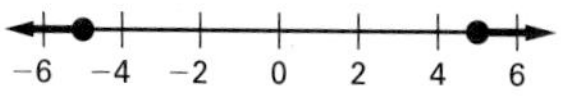 −6 −4 −2 0 2 4 6

57. 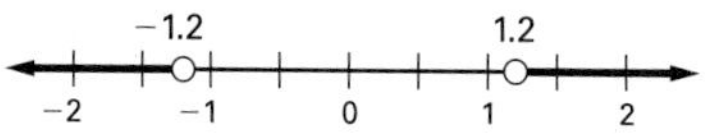 −1.2 1.2
−2 −1 0 1 2

58. 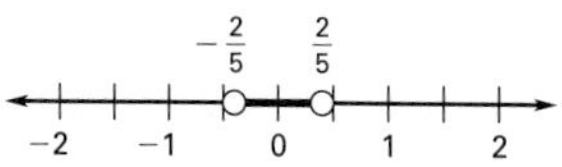 $-\frac{2}{5}$ $\frac{2}{5}$
−2 −1 0 1 2

59. 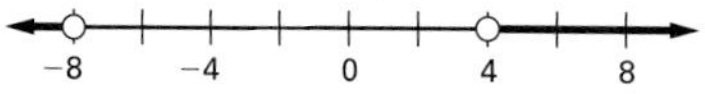 −8 −4 0 4 8

60. 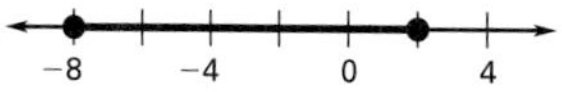 −8 −4 0 4

61. 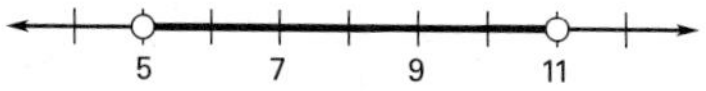 5 7 9 11

62.  $-\frac{3}{2}$
−2 0 2 4

63. 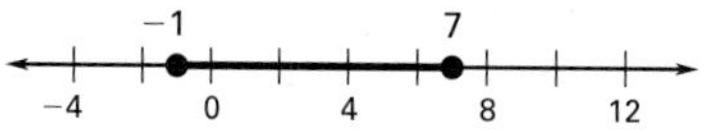 −1 7
−4 0 4 8 12

64. 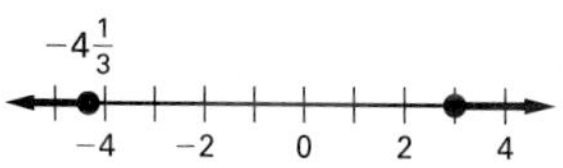 $-4\frac{1}{3}$
−4 −2 0 2 4

65. 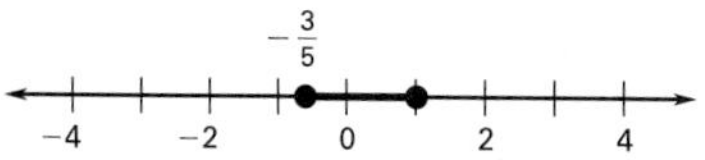 $-\frac{3}{5}$
−4 −2 0 2 4

66. 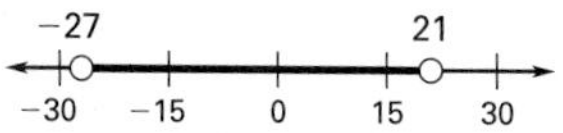 −27 21
−30 −15 0 15 30

67. 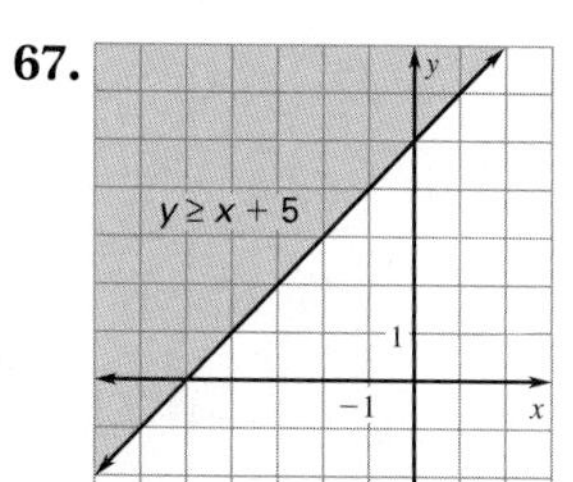

68. 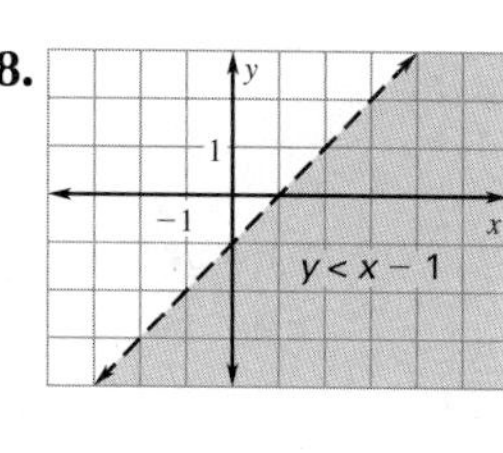

69. 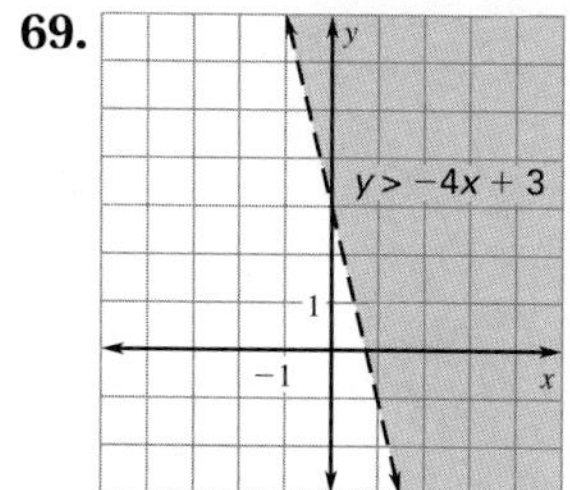

70. 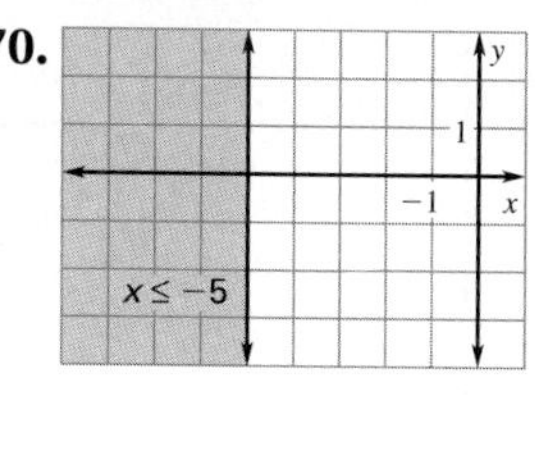

71. 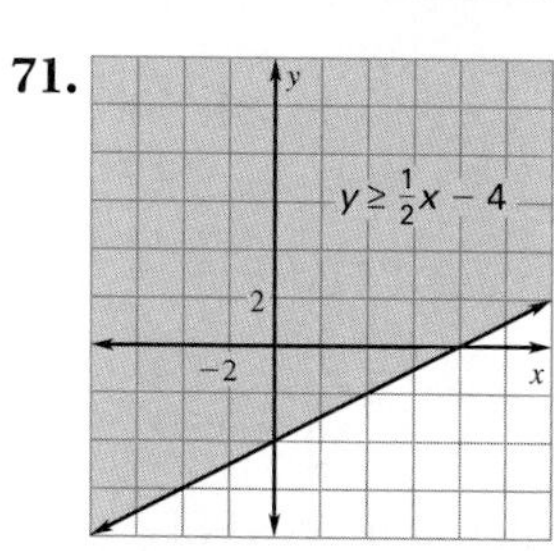

72. 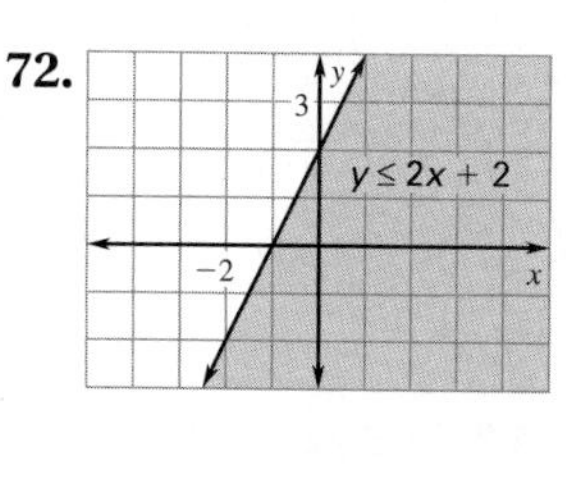

73. 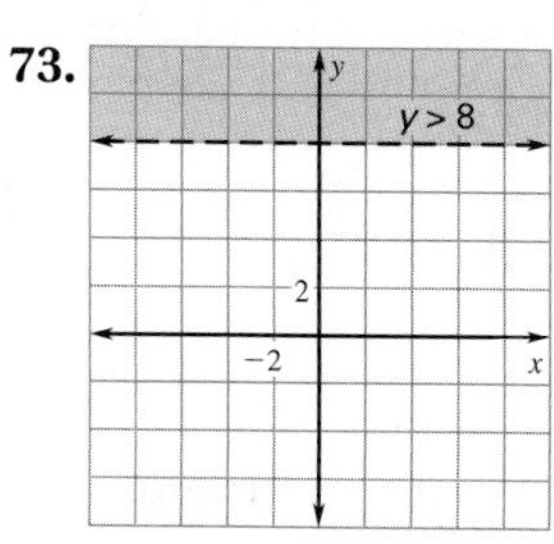

74. 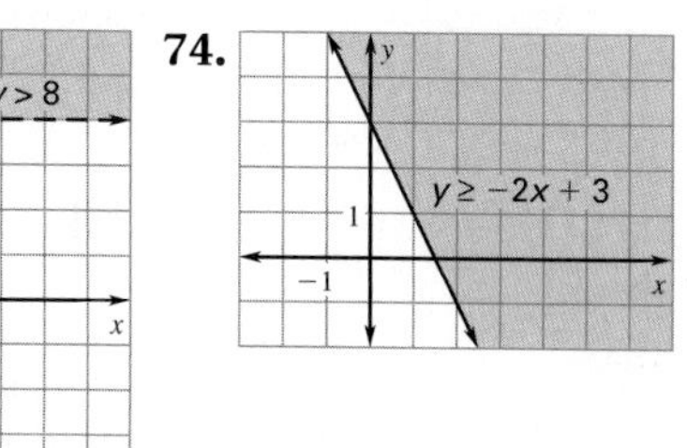

75. 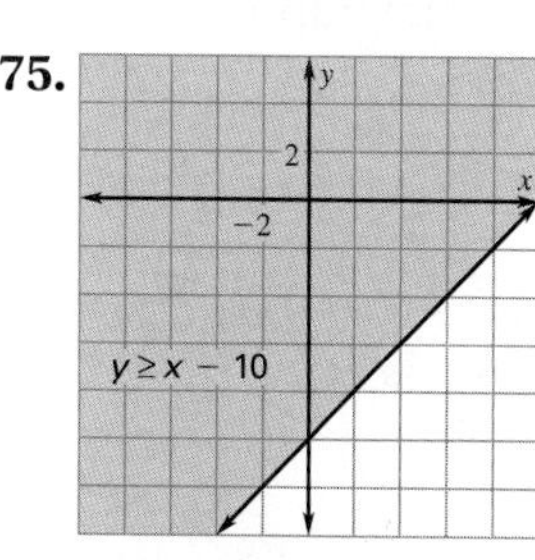

76. 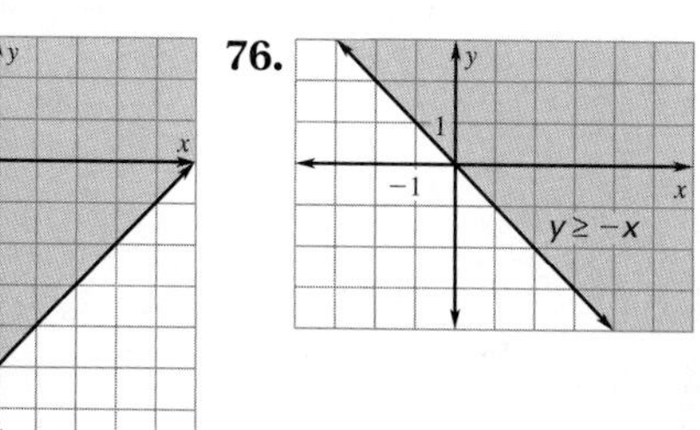

77. 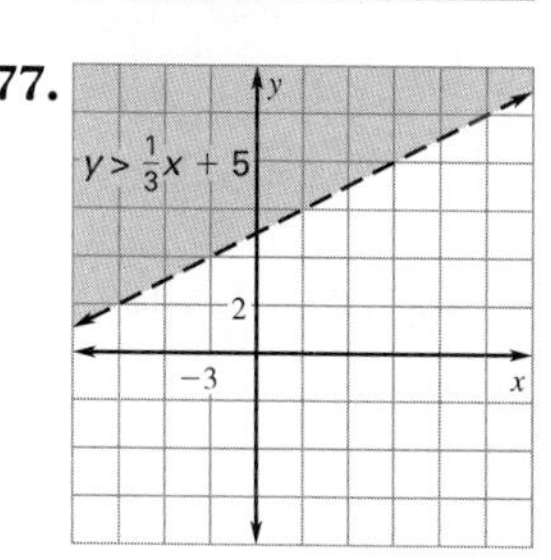

78. 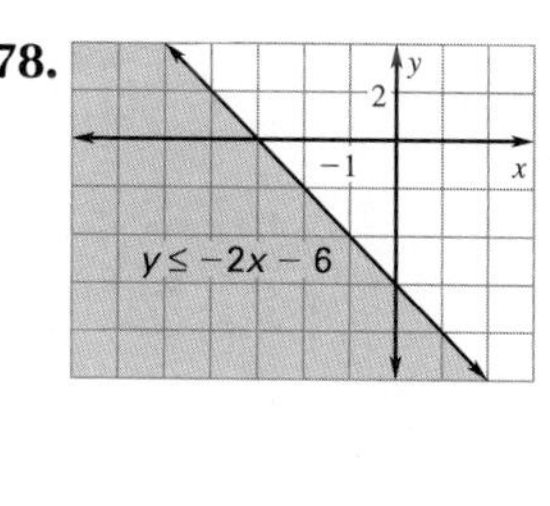

Chapter 8 (p. 945)

63. 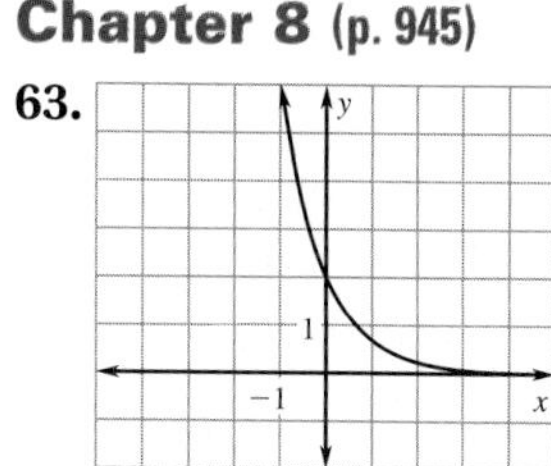

64. 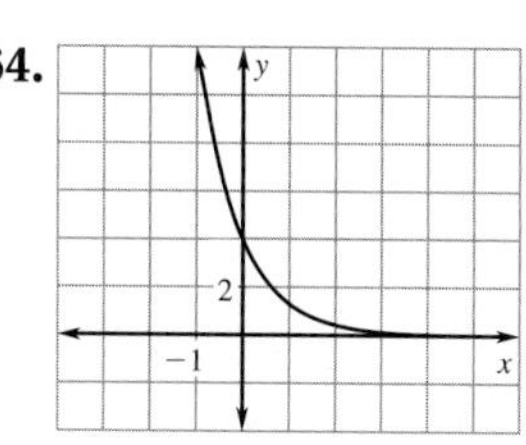

ADDITIONAL ANSWERS

65. 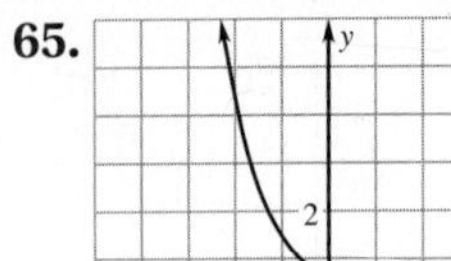

66. 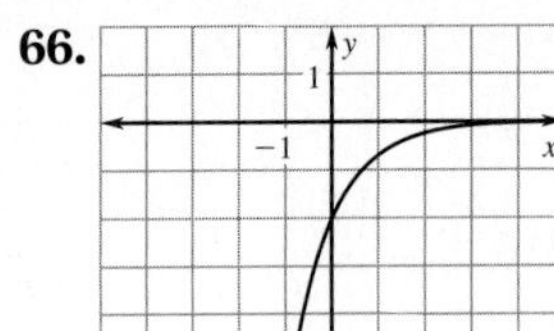

67. 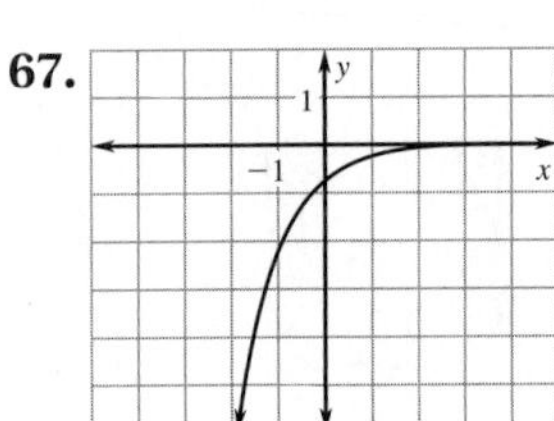

Chapter 11 (p. 948)

6. 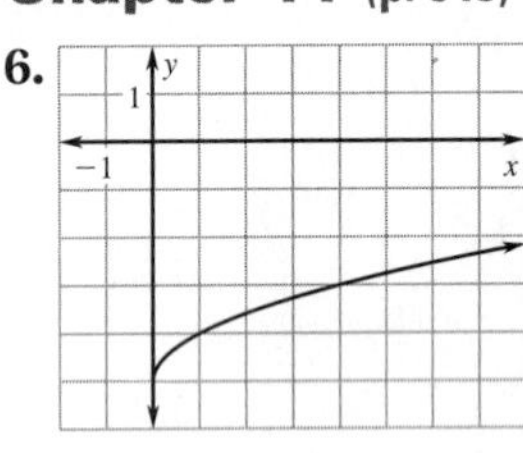

Domain: $x \geq 0$, range: $y \geq -5$; the graph is a vertical translation 5 units down of the graph of $y = \sqrt{x}$.

7. 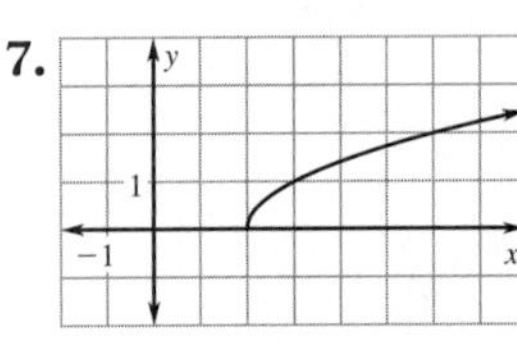

Domain: $x \geq 2$, range: $y \geq 0$; the graph is a horizontal translation 2 units right of the graph of $y = \sqrt{x}$.

8. 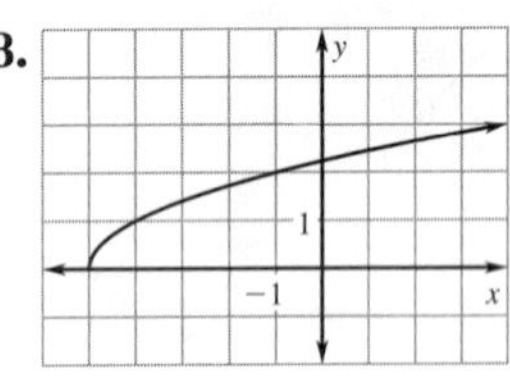

Domain: $x \geq -5$, range: $y \geq 0$; the graph is a horizontal translation 5 units left of the graph of $y = \sqrt{x}$.

9. 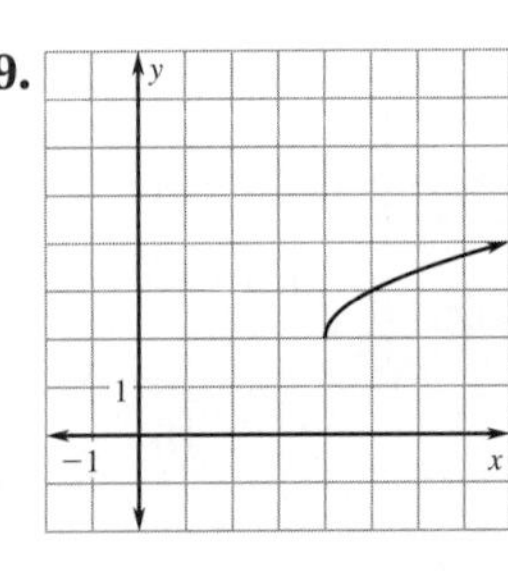

Domain: $x \geq 4$, range: $y \geq 2$; the graph is a vertical translation 2 units up and a horizontal translation 4 units right of the graph of $y = \sqrt{x}$.

Chapter 12 (p. 949)

14. 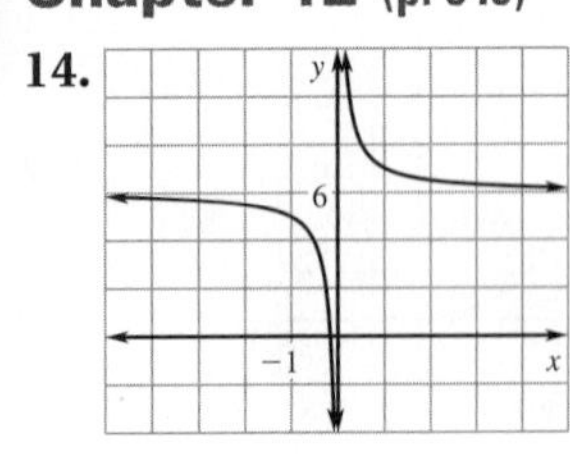

15. 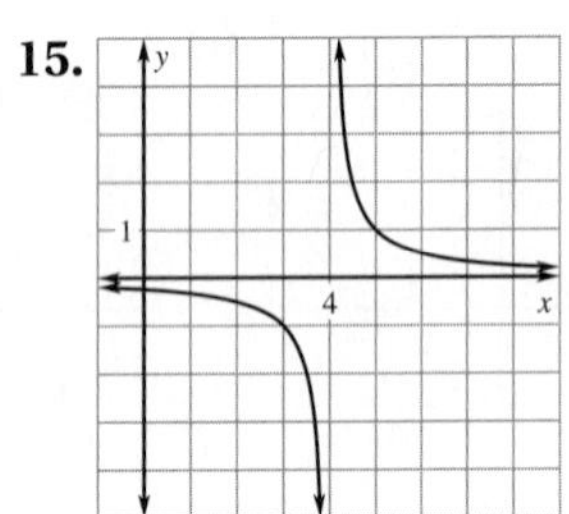

16. 17. 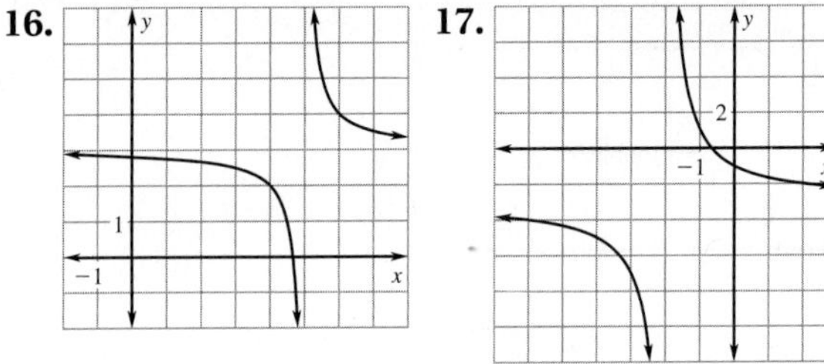

18. 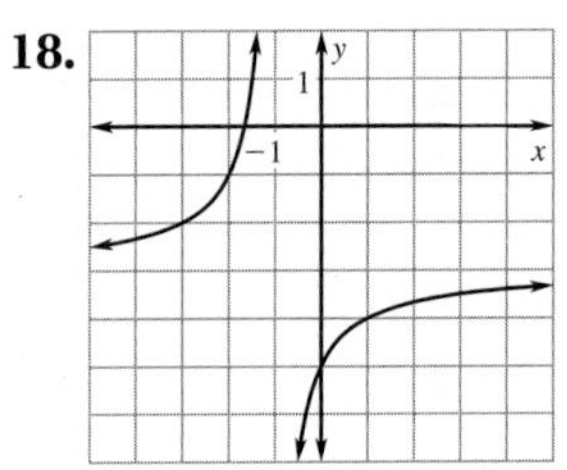

Symbols

Relation Symbols

Symbol	Meaning
$=$	is equal to
$<$	is less than
$>$	is greater than
$\leq$	is less than or equal to
$\geq$	is greater than or equal to
$\stackrel{?}{=}$	is equal to?
$\neq$	is not equal to
$\approx$	is approximately equal to

Set Symbols

Symbol	Meaning
$\{1, 2\}$	set with 1 and 2 as elements
U	universal set
$\varnothing$	empty set
$A \cup B$	union of sets A and B
$A \cap B$	intersection of sets A and B

Operation Symbols

Symbol	Meaning
$ab, a \cdot b, a(b)$	product of a and b
$\frac{a}{b}$	quotient of a and b, $b \neq 0$
$\frac{1}{a}$	reciprocal of a, $a \neq 0$
$-a$	opposite of a
$\lvert a \rvert$	absolute value of a
a^n	nth power of a
$\sqrt{a}$	nonnegative square root of a, $a \geq 0$
$\sqrt[3]{a}$	cube root of a

Other Symbols

Symbol	Meaning
$f(x)$	value of the function f at x, or f of x
a_n	nth term of a sequence

Measures

METRIC (SI)

Length

1 kilometer (km) = 1000 meters (m)
1 meter = 100 centimeters (cm)
1 centimeter = 10 millimeters (mm)

Capacity

1 kiloliter (kL) = 1000 liters (L)
1 liter = 1000 milliliters (mL)

Mass

1 kilogram (kg) = 1000 grams (g)
1 gram = 1000 milligrams (mg)

U.S. CUSTOMARY

Length

1 mile (mi) = 1760 yards (yd)
1 yard = 3 feet (ft)
1 foot = 12 inches (in.)

Capacity

1 gallon (gal) = 4 quarts (qt)
1 quart = 2 pints (pt)
1 pint = 2 cups (c)
1 cup = 8 fluid ounces (fl oz)

Weight

1 ton = 2000 pounds (lb)
1 pound = 16 ounces (oz)

TIME

1 century = 100 years
1 decade = 10 years
1 year = 12 months
1 year ≈ 52 weeks
1 year ≈ 365 days
1 week = 7 days
1 day = 24 hours (h)
1 hour = 60 minutes (min)
1 minute = 60 seconds (sec)

GYNECOLOGY AND OBSTETRICS

HEMATOLOGY/ONCOLOGY

Ferri's CLINICAL ADVISOR

2006

Ferri's CLINICAL ADVISOR

Instant Diagnosis and Treatment

FRED F. FERRI, M.D., F.A.C.P.

Clinical Professor
Department of Community Health
Brown Medical School
Providence, Rhode Island

ELSEVIER
MOSBY

ELSEVIER
MOSBY

1600 John F. Kennedy Blvd.
Suite 1800
Philadelphia, Pennsylvania 19103-2899

Notice

Knowledge and best practice in this field are constantly changing. As new research and experience broaden our knowledge, changes in practice, treatment and drug therapy may become necessary or appropriate. Readers are advised to check the most current information provided (i) on procedures featured or (ii) by the manufacturer of each product to be administered, to verify the recommended dose or formula, the method and duration of administration, and contraindications. It is the responsibility of the practitioner, relying on their own experience and knowledge of the patient, to make diagnoses, to determine dosages and the best treatment for each individual patient, and to take all appropriate safety precautions. To the fullest extent of the law, neither the Publisher nor the Editors assumes any liability for any injury and/or damage to persons or property arising out or related to any use of the material contained in this book.

ISBN-13: 978-0-323-03448-7
ISBN-10: 0-323-03448-9

Senior Acquisitions Editor: Rolla Couchman
Publishing Services Manager: Julie Eddy
Project Manager: Joy Moore
Senior Book Designer: Teresa McBryan

Printed in United States of America

Last digit is the print number: 9 8 7 6 5 4 3 2

Section Editors

MICHAEL BENATAR, M.B.Ch.B., D.Phil.
Assistant Professor of Neurology
Department of Neurology
Emory University
Atlanta, Georgia
Section I

GEORGE T. DANAKAS, M.D., F.A.C.O.G.
Clinical Assistant Professor
Department of Obstetrics and Gynecology
State University of New York at Buffalo
Buffalo, New York
Section I

MITCHELL D. FELDMAN, M.D., M.Phil.
Associate Professor of Clinical Medicine
Division of General Internal Medicine
University of California, San Francisco
San Francisco, California
Section I

FRED F. FERRI, M.D., F.A.C.P.
Clinical Professor
Department of Community Health
Brown Medical School
Providence, Rhode Island
Sections I-V

JOSEPH R. MASCI, M.D.
Director of Medicine
Elmhurst Hospital Center
Professor of Medicine
Mount Sinai School of Medicine
Elmhurst, New York
Section I

LONNIE R. MERCIER, M.D.
Clinical Instructor
Department of Orthopedic Surgery
Creighton University School of Medicine
Omaha, Nebraska
Section I

PETER PETROPOULOS, M.D., F.A.C.C.
Clinical Assistant Professor
Brown Medical School
Department of Veterans Affairs
Providence, Rhode Island
Section I

IRIS TONG, M.D.
Clinical Assistant Professor
Brown Medical School
Attending Physician
Women's Health Associates
Division of General Internal Medicine
Rhode Island Hospital
Providence, Rhode Island
Section I

TOM J. WACHTEL, M.D.
Physician-in-Charge
Division of Geriatrics
Rhode Island Hospital
Professor of Community Health and Medicine
Brown Medical School
Providence, Rhode Island
Section I

Contributors

SONYA S. ABDEL-RAZEQ, M.D.
Clinical Assistant Instructor
Department of Obstetrics and Gynecology/Resident Education
State University of New York at Buffalo
Women's and Children's Hospital
Buffalo, New York

PHILIP J. ALIOTTA, M.D., M.S.H.A., F.A.C.S.
Clinical Instructor
Department of Urology
School of Medicine and Biomedical Sciences
State University of New York at Buffalo
Buffalo, New York
Medical Director
Center for Urologic Research of Western New York
Williamsville, New York

GEORGE O. ALONSO, M.D.
Director
Department of Infection Control
Elmhurst Hospital Center
Elmhurst, New York
Instructor in Medicine
Mount Sinai School of Medicine
New York, New York

MEL L. ANDERSON, M.D., F.A.C.P.
Clinical Assistant Professor of Medicine
Brown Medical School
Providence, Rhode Island

ETSUKO AOKI M.D., Ph.D.
Fellow of General Internal Medicine
Rhode Island Hospital
Providence, Rhode Island

PATRICIA AREAN, Ph.D.
Associate Professor
Department of Psychiatry
University of California, San Francisco
San Francisco, California

VASANTHI ARUMUGAM, M.D.
Assistant Professor
Department of Medicine
Mount Sinai School of Medicine
New York, New York
Attending Physician
Division of Infectious Diseases/Department of Medicine
Elmhurst Hospital Center
Elmhurst, New York

AMAAR ASHRAF, M.D.
Assistant Professor
Department of Medicine
Mount Sinai School of Medicine
New York, New York
Attending Physician
Division of Infectious Diseases
Elmhurst Hospital Center
Elmhurst, New York

SUDEEP KAUR AULAKH, M.D., C.M., F.R.C.P.C.
Associate Professor of Medicine
Albany Medical College
Albany, New York

MICHAEL BENATAR, M.B.Ch.B., D.Phil.
Assistant Professor of Neurology
Department of Neurology
Emory University
Atlanta, Georgia

LYNN BOWLBY, M.D.
Attending Physician
Division of General Internal Medicine
Rhode Island Hospital
Clinical Instructor of Medicine
Brown Medical School
Providence, Rhode Island

WILLIAM F. BOYD, M.D., M.P.H.
Staff Physician
North Shore Medical Park
Peabody, Massachusetts

MANDEEP K. BRAR, M.D.
Clinical Assistant Professor
Department of Obstetrics and Gynecology
State University of New York at Buffalo
Buffalo, New York

GAURAV CHOUDHARY, M.D.
Assistant Professor of Medicine
Brown Medical School
Providence, Rhode Island

JENNIFER CLARKE, M.D.
Assistant Professor of Medicine and Obstetrics and Gynecology
Brown Medical School
Physician, Rhode Island Hospital
Providence, Rhode Island

MARIA A. CORIGLIANO, M.D., F.A.C.O.G.
Clinical Assistant Professor
Department of Obstetrics and Gynecology
State University of New York at Buffalo
Buffalo, New York

KAROLL CORTEZ, M.D.
Pediatric Oncology Branch
National Cancer Institute, National Institutes of Health
Bethesda, Maryland

JOHN E. CROOM, M.D., Ph.D.
Clinical Fellow in Neurology
Harvard Medical School
Beth Israel Deaconess Medical Center
Boston, Massachusetts

CLAUDIA L. DADE, M.D.
Attending Physician
Division of Infectious Diseases
Elmhurst Hospital Center
Elmhurst, New York
Instructor in Medicine
Mount Sinai School of Medicine
New York, New York

GEORGE T. DANAKAS, M.D., F.A.C.O.G.
Clinical Assistant Professor
Department of Obstetrics and Gynecology
State University of New York at Buffalo
Buffalo, New York

ALEXANDRA DEGENHARDT, M.D.
Clinical Fellow, Multiple Sclerosis Center
Department of Neurology
Beth Israel Deaconess Medical Center
Boston, Massachusetts

AMAR DESAI, M.D., M.P.H.
Resident Physician
Department of Internal Medicine
University of California, San Francisco
San Francisco, California

PRIYA DESAI, M.D., M.S.P.H.
Resident Physician/Clinical Consultant
University of California, San Francisco
San Francisco, California

JOSEPH DIAZ, M.D.
Assistant Professor of Medicine
Division of General Internal Medicine
Memorial Hospital of Rhode Island
Brown Medical School
Providence, Rhode Island

CHRISTINE M. DUFFY, M.D., M.P.H.
Fellow, Center for Gerontology and Health Care Research
Brown University
Providence, Rhode Island

JEFFREY S. DURMER, M.D., Ph.D.
Assistant Professor, Department of Neurology
Director, Emory Sleep Laboratory
Director, Egleston Children's Hospital Sleep Clinic
Emory University School of Medicine
Atlanta, Georgia

JANE V. EASON, M.D.
Attending Physician
Division of Infectious Diseases
Elmhurst Hospital Center
Elmhurst, New York
Instructor in Medicine
Mount Sinai School of Medicine
New York, New York

STUART EISENDRATH, M.D.
Professor of Clinical Psychiatry
University of California, San Francisco
San Francisco, California

RIF S. EL-MALLAKH, M.D.
Associate Professor
Department of Psychiatry and Behavioral Sciences
University of Louisville School of Medicine
Louisville, Kentucky

GREGORY J. ESPER, M.D.
Clinical Instructor and Research Fellow in Neuromuscular Disease
Beth Israel Deaconess Medical Center
Department of Neurology
Harvard Medical School
Boston, Massachusetts

MARILYN FABBRI, M.D.
Instructor
Department of Medicine
Mount Sinai School of Medicine
New York, New York
Attending Physician
Division of Infectious Diseases/Department of Medicine
Elmhurst Hospital Center
Elmhurst, New York

MARK J. FAGAN, M.D.
Director
Medical Primary Care Unit
Rhode Island Hospital
Associate Professor of Medicine
Brown Medical School
Providence, Rhode Island

GIL FARKASH, M.D.
Assistant Clinical Professor
State University of New York at Buffalo
School of Medicine
Buffalo, New York

MITCHELL D. FELDMAN, M.D., M.Phil.
Associate Professor of Clinical Medicine
University of California, San Francisco
Division of General Internal Medicine
San Francisco, California

FRED F. FERRI, M.D., F.A.C.P.
Clinical Professor
Department of Community Health
Brown Medical School
Providence, Rhode Island

Contributors

TAMARA G. FONG, M.D., Ph.D.
Instructor in Neurology
Beth Israel Deaconess Medical Center
Harvard Medical School
Boston, Massachusetts

GLENN G. FORT, M.D., M.P.H.
Clinical Associate Professor of Medicine
Brown Medical School
Chief
Infectious Diseases
Our Lady of Fatima Hospital
North Providence, Rhode Island

REBEKAH LESLIE GARDNER, M.D.
Department of Internal Medicine
University of California, San Francisco Medical Center
San Francisco, California

GENNA GEKHT, M.D.
Chief Resident in Neurology
Department of Neurology
Emory University
Atlanta, Georgia

DAVID R. GIFFORD, M.D., M.P.H.
Assistant Physician, Division of Geriatrics
Rhode Island Hospital
Assistant Professor of Community Health and Medicine
Brown Medical School
Providence, Rhode Island

JENNIFER ROHR GILLETT, M.D., M.P.H.
Primary Care Resident
Department of Internal Medicine
University of California, San Francisco
San Francisco, California

GEETHA GOPALAKRISHNAN, M.D.
Assistant Professor of Medicine
Brown Medical School
Providence, Rhode Island

NANCY R. GRAFF, M.D.
Associate Clinical Professor
Department of Pediatrics
University of California, San Diego
San Diego, California

REBECCA A. GRIFFITH, M.D.
Attending Physician
Department of Medicine
Morristown Memorial Hospital
Morristown, New Jersey

JOSEPH GRILLO, M.D.
Fellow, Department of Infectious Diseases
Roger Williams Medical Center
Providence, Rhode Island

MICHELE HALPERN, M.D.
Attending Physician, Division of Infectious Diseases
Sound Shore Medical Center of Westchester
New Rochelle, New York
Clinical Assistant Professor of Medicine
New York Medical College
Valhalla, New York

MUSTAFA A. HAMMAD, M.D.
Clincal Neurophysiology Fellow
Department of Neurology
Emory University
Atlanta, Georgia

SAJEEV HANDA, M.D.
Director
Division of Hospitalist Medicine
Rhode Island Hospital
Clinical Instructor of Medicine
Brown Medical School
Providence, Rhode Island

MIKE HARPER, M.D.
Associate Professor of Medicine
Division of Geriatrics
Department of Medicine
San Francisco Veterans Affairs Medical Center
University of California, San Diego
San Diego, California

TAYLOR HARRISON, M.D.
Neuromuscular Fellow
Department of Neurology
Emory University
Atlanta, Georgia

SHARON S. HARTMAN, M.D., Ph.D.
Clinical Associate
Department of Neurology
Emory University
Atlanta, Georgia

MEREDITH HELLER, M.D.
Department of Internal Medicine
University of California, San Francisco
San Francisco, California

JENNIFER ROH HUR, M.D.
Clinical Instructor
Brown Internal Medicine Residency Program
Brown Medical School
Providence, Rhode Island

JASON IANNUCCILLI, M.D.
Department of Medicine
Brown Medical School
Providence, Rhode Island

RICHARD S. ISAACSON, M.D.
Resident in Neurology
Beth Israel Deaconess Medical Center
Harvard Medical School
Boston, Massachusetts

JENNIFER JEREMIAH, M.D.
Clinical Associate Professor of Medicine
Brown Medical School
Providence, Rhode Island

MICHAEL P. JOHNSON, M.D.
Staff Physician
Division of General Internal Medicine
Rhode Island Hospital
Assistant Professor of Medicine
Brown Medical School
Providence, Rhode Island

BREE JOHNSTON, M.D., M.P.H.
Associate Professor of Medicine
Division of Geriatrics
Department of Medicine
Veterans Affairs Medical Center
University of California, San Diego
San Diego, California

MELVYN KOBY, M.D.
Associate Clinical Professor of Medicine
Department of Ophthalmology
University of Louisville School of Medicine
Louisville, Kentucky

DAVID KURSS, M.D., F.A.C.O.G.
Clinical Assistant Professor
Department of Obstetrics and Gynecology
State University of New York at Buffalo
Buffalo, New York

JOSEPH J. LIEBER, M.D.
Associate Director of Medicine
Chief, Medical Consultation Service
Elmhurst Hospital Center
Clinical Associate Professor of Medicine
Mount Sinai School of Medicine
New York, New York

CHUN LIM, M.D., PH.D.
Department of Neurology
Beth Israel Deaconess Medical Center
Boston, Massachusetts

ZEENA LOBO, M.D.
Attending Physician
Division of Infectious Diseases
Elmhurst Medical Center
Elmhurst, New York

RACHAEL LUCATORTO, M.D.
University of California, San Francisco,
San Francisco, California

MICHAEL MAHER, M.D.
Assistant Professor of Internal Medicine
Brown University School of Medicine
Rhode Island Hospital
Providence, Rhode Island

ACHRAF A. MAKKI, M.D. M.Sc.
Resident
Department of Neurology
Emory University
Atlanta, Georgia

JOSEPH R. MASCI, M.D.
Director of Medicine
Elmhurst Hospital Center
Professor of Medicine
Mount Sinai School of Medicine
Elmhurst, New York

DANIEL T. MATTSON, M.D., M.S.C.(Med.)
Clinical Fellow in Neurology
Beth Israel Deaconess Medical Center
Harvard Medical School
Boston, Massachusetts

MAITREYI MAZUMDAR, M.D., M.P.H.
Clinical Fellow in Neurology
Harvard Medical School
Children's Hospital of Boston
Boston, Massachusetts

KELLY McGARRY, M.D.
Associate Program Director
General Internal Medicine Residency Program
Rhode Island Hospital
Assistant Professor of Medicine
Brown Medical School
Providence, Rhode Island

LYNN McNICOLL, M.D.
Assistant Professor of Medicine
Brown Medical School
Geriatrician, Division of Geriatrics
Rhode Island Hospital
Providence, Rhode Island

LONNIE R. MERCIER, M.D.
Clinical Instructor
Department of Orthopedic Surgery
Creighton University School of Medicine
Omaha, Nebraska

DENNIS J. MIKOLICH, M.D.
Chief
Division of Infectious Diseases
VA Medical Center
Clinical Associate Professor of Medicine
Brown Medical School
Providence, Rhode Island

ANASTASIA MISAKIAN, M.D.
Division of General Internal Medicine
University of California, San Francisco
San Francisco, California

Contributors

MICHELE MONTANDON
University of California, San Francisco
San Francisco, California

TAKUMA NEMOTO, M.D.
Research Associate Professor of Surgery
State University of New York at Buffalo
Buffalo, New York

JAMES J. NG, M.D.
Staff Physician
The Vancouver Clinic
Vancouver, Washington

GAIL M. O'BRIEN, M.D.
Medical Director
Adult Ambulatory Services
Rhode Island Hospital
Clinical Associate Professor of Medicine
Brown Medical School
Providence, Rhode Island

CAROLYN J. O'CONNOR, M.D.
Internal Medicine
Primary Care of Southbury
Danbury Hospital
Southbury, Connecticut

ALEXANDER OLAWAIYE, M.D.
Clinical Instructor
Department of Obstetrics and Gynecology/Resident Education
State University of New York at Buffalo
Women's and Children's Hospital
Buffalo, New York

MICHAEL K. ONG, M.D. Ph.D.
VA Ambulatory Care Fellow
VA Palo Alto Health Care System
Centers for Health Policy and Primary Care Outcomes Research
Stanford University
Stanford, California

PRANAV M. PATEL, M.D.
Clinical Associate Instructor, Division of Cardiology
Department of Medicine
Brown Medical School
Providence, Rhode Island

MINA B. PANTCHEVA, M.D.
Resident
Internal Medicine
Roger Williams Medical Center
Providence, Rhode Island

PETER PETROPOULOS, M.D., F.A.C.C.
Clinical Assistant Professor
Brown Medical School
Department of Veterans Affairs
Providence, Rhode Island

MICHAEL PICCHIONI, M.D.
Attending Physician
Patient Care
High Street Health Center
Springfield, Maryland

PAUL A. PIRRAGLIA, M.D., M.P.H.
Assistant Professor of Medicine
Brown University
Rhode Island Hospital
Providence, Rhode Island

MAURICE POLICAR, M.D.
Chief of Infectious Diseases
Elmhurst Hospital Center
Elmhurst, New York
Assistant Professor of Medicine
Mount Sinai School of Medicine
New York, New York

ARUNDATHI G. PRASAD, M.D.
Clinical Instructor
Department of Obstetrics and Gynecology/Resident Education
State University of New York at Buffalo
Women's and Children's Hospital
Buffalo, New York

HEMCHAND RAMBERAN, M.D.
Resident, Internal Medicine
Memorial Hospital of Rhode Island
Brown Medical School
Providence, Rhode Island

VICTOR I. REUS, M.D.
Professor of Psychiatry
Department of Psychiatry
Langley Porter Psychiatric Institute
University of California, San Francisco
San Francisco, California

HARLAN G. RICH, M.D.
Director of Endoscopy
Rhode Island Hospital
Associate Professor of Medicine
Brown Medical School
Providence, Rhode Island

LUTHER K. ROBINSON, M.D.
Associate Professor of Pediatrics
Director, Dysmorphology and Clinical Genetics
State University of New York at Buffalo
Buffalo, New York

JASON M. SATTERFIELD, Ph.D.
Director
Behavioral Medicine
Associate Professor of Clinical Medicine
University of California, San Francisco
San Francisco, California

SEAN I. SAVITZ, M.D.
Clinical Fellow in Neurology
Harvard Medical School
Chief Resident in Neurology
Beth Israel Deaconess Medical Center
Boston, Massachusetts

JACK L. SCHWARTZWALD, M.D.
Clinical Assistant Professor of Medicine
Rhode Island Hospital
Providence, Rhode Island

HARVEY M. SHANIES, M.D., Ph.D.
Director of Critical Care Medicine
Vassar Brothers Medical Center
Poughkeepsie, New York

DEBORAH L. SHAPIRO, M.D.
Chief
Division of Rheumatology
Elmhurst Hospital Center
Elmhurst, New York
Clinical Assistant Professor of Medicine
Mount Sinai School of Medicine
New York, New York

CLIFFORD MILO SINGER, M.D.
Associate Professor of Psychiatry and Neurology
Medical Director of the Oregon Geriatric Education Center
Clinical Director of Geriatric Psychiatry
Oregon Health and Science University
Sleep and Mood Disorders Laboratory
Portland, Oregon

U. SHIVRAJ SOHUR, M.D., Ph.D.
Clinical Fellow in Neurology
Harvard Medical School
Chief Resident in Neurology
Beth Israel Deaconess Medical Center
Boston, Massachusetts

JENNIFER SOUTHER, M.D.
Attending Physician
Department of Family Practice
Memorial Hospital of Rhode Island
Pawtucket, Rhode Island

ANNE SPAULDING, M.D.
Centers for Disease Control
Atlanta, Georgia

MICHELLE STOZEK, M.D.
Clinical Instructor
Division of General Internal Medicine
Rhode Island Hospital
Clinical Instructor
Brown Medical School
Providence, Rhode Island

JULIE ANNE SZUMIGALA, M.D.
Clinical Instructor
Department of Obstetrics and Gynecology
State University of New York at Buffalo
Buffalo, New York

DOMINICK TAMMARO, M.D.
Associate Director
Categorical Internal Medicine Residency
Co-Director
Medicine-Pediatrics Residency
Division of General Internal Medicine
Rhode Island Hospital
Associate Professor of Medicine
Brown Medical School
Providence, Rhode Island

PETER E. TANGUAY, M.D.
Ackerly Professor of Child & Adolescent Psychiatry (Emeritus)
Department of Psychiatry and Behavioral Sciences
University of Louisville School of Medicine
Louisville, Kentucky

IRIS TONG, M.D.
Clinical Assistant Professor
Brown Medical School
Attending Physician
Women's Health Associates
Division of General Internal Medicine
Rhode Island Hospital
Providence, Rhode Island

EROBOGHENE E. UBOGU, M.B.B.S. (Hons.)
Assistant Professor of Neurology
Case Western Reserve University School of Medicine
Staff Neurologist
Louis Stokes Cleveland Veterans Affairs Medical Center
Cleveland, Ohio

NICOLE J. ULLRICH, M.D., Ph.D.
Clinical Fellow in Neurology/Neurooncology
Children's Hospital Boston
Boston, Massachusetts

CRAIG VAN DYKE, M.D.
Chair, Department of Psychiatry
University of California, San Francisco
San Francisco, California

TOM J. WACHTEL, M.D.
Physician-in-Charge
Division of Geriatrics
Rhode Island Hospital
Professor of Community Health and Medicine
Brown Medical School
Providence, Rhode Island

Contributors

DENNIS M. WEPPNER, M.D., F.A.C.O.G.
Associate Professor of Clinical Gynecology/Obstetrics
State University of New York at Buffalo
Clinical Chief
Department of Gynecology/Obstetrics
Millard Fillmore Hospital
Buffalo, New York

LAUREL M. WHITE, M.D.
Clinical Assistant Professor
Department of Obstetrics and Gynecology
Division of Maternal Fetal Medicine
State University of New York at Buffalo
Buffalo, New York

JOHN M. WIECKOWSKI, M.D., PH.D., F.A.C.O.G.
Director
Reproductive Medicine and In Vitro Fertilization
Williamsville, New York

DAVID P. WILLIAMS, M.D.
Neurophysiology Fellow, Department of Neurology
Emory University
Atlanta, Georgia

WEN-CHIH WU, M.D.
Assistant Professor of Medicine
Brown Medical School
Cardiologist
Providence VA Medical Center
Providence, Rhode Island

BETH J. WUTZ, M.D.
Clinical Assistant Professor of Medicine
Division of Internal Medicine/Pediatrics
Kajeida Health–Buffalo General Hospital
State University of New York at Buffalo
Buffalo, New York

MADHAVI YERNENI, M.D.
Staff Physician, Academic Medical Center
Miriam Hospital
Pawtucket, Rhode Island

JOHN Q. YOUNG, M.D., M.P.P.
Langley Porter Psychiatric Institute
University of California, San Francisco
San Francisco, California

CINDY ZADIKOFF, M.D.
Fellow, Movement Disorders
Morton and Gloria Shulman Movement Disorders Center
Toronto Western Hospital
Toronto, Ontario

SCOTT J. ZUCCALA, D.O., F.A.C.O.G.
Staff Physician
Mercy Hospital of Buffalo
Buffalo, New York

To

OUR FAMILIES

Their constant support and encouragement
made this book a reality

Preface

This book is intended to be a clear and concise reference for physicians and allied health professionals. It is available in clinical text and CD-ROM format. Its user-friendly format was designed to provide a fast and efficient way to identify important clinical information and to offer practical guidance in patient management. The book is divided into five sections and an appendix, each with emphasis and clinical information.

The tremendous success of the previous editions and the enthusiastic comments from numerous colleagues have brought about several positive changes. Each section has been significantly expanded from prior editions, bringing the total number of medical topics covered in this book to more than 1000. Illustrations have been added to several topics to enhance recollection of clinically important facts. A detailed table of contents facilitates identification and retrieval of topics. The use of ICD-9CM codes in all the topics will expedite claims submission and reimbursement.

Section I describes in detail 675 medical disorders. Twenty-five new topics ranging from neuropathic pain to amnestic disorders and encephalopathy have been added to the 2006 edition. Others such as body inclusion myositis and arachnid bites and stings have been completely redone. A new section editor has also been added for this edition. Medical topics in this section are arranged alphabetically, and the material in each topic is presented in outline format for ease of retrieval. Key, quick-access information is consistently highlighted, clinical photographs are used to further illustrate selected medical conditions, and relevant ICD-9CM codes are listed. Most references focus on current peer-reviewed journal articles rather than outdated textbooks and old review articles. Topics in this section use the following structured approach:

1. Basic Information (Definition, Synonyms, ICD-9CM Codes, Epidemiology and Demographics, Physical Findings and Clinical Presentation, Etiology)
2. Diagnosis (Differential Diagnosis, Workup, Laboratory Tests, Imaging Studies)
3. Treatment (Nonpharmacologic Therapy, Acute General Rx, Chronic Rx, Disposition, Referral)
4. Pearls and Considerations (Comments, References)

Section II includes the differential diagnosis, etiology, and classification of signs and symptoms. This section has been expanded to 401 topics for the 2006 edition. It is a practical section that allows the user investigating a physical complaint or abnormal laboratory value to follow a "workup" leading to a diagnosis. The physician can then easily look up the presumptive diagnosis in Section I for the information specific to that illness.

Section III includes clinical algorithms to guide and expedite the patient's workup and therapy. This section has been significantly expanded for the 2006 edition with the addition of 36 new algorithms and a complete revision of 15 others. Many physicians describe it as particularly valuable in today's managed care environment.

Section IV includes normal laboratory values and interpretation of results of commonly ordered laboratory tests. By providing interpretation of abnormal results, this section facilitates the diagnosis of medical disorders and further adds to the comprehensive, "one stop" nature of our text.

Section V focuses on preventive medicine and offers essential guidelines from the U.S. Preventive Services Task Force. Information in this section includes recommendations for the periodic health examination, screening for major diseases and disorders, patient counseling, and immunization and chemoprophylaxis recommendations.

The **Appendix** contains common definitions used in Complementary and Alternative Medicine (CAM), a listing of frequently used herbals with documented or suspected risks, and selected resources for complementary/alternative medicine. CAM has gained tremendous popularity; however, the gap between allopathy and CAM remains substantive. With the material in this appendix we hope to lessen the current scarcity of exposure of allopathic physicians to the diversity of CAM therapies.

As practicing physicians, we all realize the importance of patient education and the need for clear communication with our patients. Toward that end, the CD-ROM package contains not only the entire book contents with hyperlinks to drug information, but also includes easy-to-use, practical patient instruction sheets, organized alphabetically and covering the majority of the topics in this book. Several new patient instruction sheets have been added to the 2006 edition. These Patient Teaching Guides (PTGs) are available in English and Spanish and can be easily customized and printed from any computer. They are a valuable addition to patient care and are useful to improve physician-patient communication, patient satisfaction, and quality of care. For ease of identification, each clinical topic in Section I of the book with a corresponding patient teaching guide on the CD is marked with "PTG" icon after the topic name in the running head. In addition, the cross-references to the CD are included in the table of contents. The CD-ROM version of Clinical Advisor 2006 also contains several PTGs unrelated to section I topics.

I believe that we have produced a state of the art information system with significant differences from existing texts. It contains five sections, which could be sold separately based on their content, yet are available under a single cover, offering the reader a tremendous value. I hope that the Clinical Advisor's user-friendly approach, its numerous unique features, and yearly updates will make our book and CD-ROM, as well as the PDA ancillary, valuable medical references not only to primary care physicians, but also to physicians in other specialties, medical students, and allied health professionals.

Fred F. Ferri, M.D.

Contents

Detailed Contents

Section I Diseases and Disorders

PTG indicates that a patient teaching guide is available on the companion CD-ROM.

Section II Differential Diagnosis

Section III Clinical Algorithms

Section IV Laboratory Tests and Interpretation of Results

Section V Clinical Preventive Services

PART A

The Periodic Health Examination

PART B

Immunizations and Chemoprophylaxis

Appendix Complementary and Alternative Medicine

Additional PTGS on CD-ROM not Linked to Topics in Section I

SECTION I

Diseases and Disorders

BASIC INFORMATION

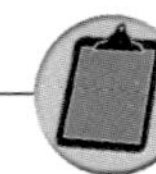

DEFINITION

Abruptio placentae is the separation of placenta from the uterine wall before delivery of the fetus. There are three classes of abruption based on maternal and fetal status, including an assessment of uterine contractions, quantity of bleeding, fetal heart rate monitoring, and abnormal coagulation studies (fibrinogen, PT, PTT).

- Grade I: mild vaginal bleeding, uterine irritability, stable vital signs, reassuring fetal heart rate, normal coagulation profile (fibrinogen 450 mg %)
- Grade II: moderate vaginal bleeding, hypertonic uterine contractions, orthostatic blood pressure measurements, unfavorable fetal status, fibrinogen 150 mg % to 250 mg %
- Grade III: severe bleeding (may be concealed), hypertonic uterine contractions, overt signs of hypovolemic shock, fetal death, thrombocytopenia, fibrinogen <150 mg %

ICD-9CM CODES
641.2 Premature separation of placenta

EPIDEMIOLOGY & DEMOGRAPHICS

INCIDENCE (IN U.S.): 1/86-206 births; incidence by grade: I = 40%, II = 45%, III = 15%; 80% occur before the onset of labor

RISK FACTORS: Hypertension (greatest association), trauma, polyhydramnios, multifetal gestation, smoking, use of crack cocaine, chorioamnionitis, preterm premature rupture of membranes

RECURRENCE RATE: 5% to 17%; with two prior episodes, 25%

PHYSICAL FINDINGS & CLINICAL PRESENTATION

- Triad of uterine bleeding (concealed or per vagina), hypertonic uterine contractions or signs of preterm labor, and evidence of fetal compromise exists.
- More than 80% of cases have external bleeding; 20% of cases have no bleeding but have indirect evidence of abruption, such as failed tocolysis for preterm labor.
- Tetanic uterine contractions are found in only 17% of cases, unless grade II or III abruption.

ETIOLOGY

- Primary etiology: unknown
- Hypertension: found in 40% to 50% of grade III abruptions
- Rapid decompression of uterine cavity, such as is found with polyhydramnios or multifetal gestation
- Blunt external trauma (motor vehicle accident, spousal abuse)

DIAGNOSIS

DIFFERENTIAL DIAGNOSIS

Placenta previa, cervical or vaginal trauma, labor, cervical cancer, rupture of membranes. The differential diagnosis of vaginal bleeding in pregnancy is described in Section II.

WORKUP

- Initial assessment should evaluate for the source of bleeding, ruling out placenta previa and associated conditions that contraindicate any type of vaginal examination (e.g., pelvic speculum examination).
- Continuous fetal heart monitoring is indicated for all viable gestations (60% incidence of fetal distress in labor); may show early signs of maternal hypovolemia (late decelerations or fetal tachycardia) before overt maternal vital sign changes.
- Actual amount of blood loss is often greater than initially perceived because of the possibility of concealed retroplacental bleeding and the apparent "normal" vital signs. The relative hypervolemia of pregnancy initially protects the gravida until late in the course of bleeding, when abrupt and sudden cardiovascular collapse can occur without warning.

LABORATORY TESTS

- Baseline Hgb and Hct help quantify blood loss and, even more important, with every four to six determinations can demonstrate significant trends during expectant management.
- Coagulation profile: platelets, fibrinogen, prothrombin, and partial thromboplastin time. DIC can develop with severe abruption. If fibrinogen is <150 mg %, estimated blood loss equals 2000 ml, and if fibrinogen is <100 mg %, consider FFP to prevent further bleeding.
- Type and antibody screen is important to identify Rh-negative patients who may need Rh immune globulin.

IMAGING STUDIES

Ultrasound should include fetal presentation and status, amniotic fluid volume, placental location, as well as any evidence of hematoma (retroplacental, subchorionic, or preplacental).

TREATMENT

Treatment is dependent on gestational age of the fetus, severity of the abruption, and maternal status. Stabilization of the mother is the first priority.

ACUTE GENERAL Rx

- Initial assessment for signs of maternal hemodynamic compromise or hemorrhagic shock; large-bore intravenous access, with crystalloid fluid resuscitation using a replacement of 3 ml LR solution for every 1 ml estimated blood loss.
- Indwelling Foley catheter to monitor urine output and maternal volume status, with a goal of 30 ml/hr urine output.
- Assess fetal status and gestational age using sonogram and continuous fetal heart rate monitoring.
- Because of the unpredictable nature of abruptions, cross-matched blood should be made available during the initial resuscitation period.

CHRONIC Rx

- In the term fetus or where lung maturity has been documented, delivery is indicated.
- In the preterm fetus or with an immature lung profile, consideration should be given for betamethasone 12.5 mg IM q24h for two doses and then delivery, depending on the severity of the abruption and the likelihood of fetal complications from preterm birth.
- C-section should be reserved for cases of fetal distress or for standard obstetric indications.
- In select cases, such as severe prematurity with a stable mother and mild contractions, magnesium sulfate can be used for tocolysis, 6 g IV loading dose then 3 g/hr maintenance, to allow for course of steroids.

DISPOSITION

Because of the unpredictable nature of abruptions, expectant management should occur only under controlled circumstances.

REFERRAL

Abruptio placentae places mother and fetus in a high-risk situation and should be managed by a qualified obstetrician in a facility with capability for neonatal and maternal resuscitation and ability to perform emergency C-sections.

AUTHOR: **SCOTT J. ZUCCALA, D.O.**

BASIC INFORMATION

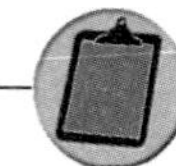

DEFINITION

A brain abscess is a focal, intracerebral infection that begins as a localized area of cerebritis and develops into a collection of pus surrounded by a well-vascularized capsule.

ICD-9CM CODES
324.0 Brain abscess

EPIDEMIOLOGY & DEMOGRAPHICS

- Quite uncommon (occur about 2% as commonly as brain tumors)
- Occur at any age.
- Peak incidences in preadolescence and middle age.
- Most common source of underlying infection: contiguous spread from the paranasal sinuses, middle ear, or teeth.
- Headache is usually localized to the side of the abscess, onset can be gradual or severe; present in 70% of cases.

PHYSICAL FINDINGS & CLINICAL PRESENTATION

- Classic triad: fever, headache, and focal neurologic deficit are present in 50% of cases.
- Fever is present in only 50% of patients.
- Focal neurologic findings (e.g., seizures, hemiparesis, aphasia, ataxia) depend on the location of the abscess and are seen in 30% to 50% of cases.
- Papilledema is present in 25% of cases.
- Presence of adjacent infections (dental abscess, otitis media, and sinusitis) may be a clue to the underlying diagnosis and should be sought in any suspected case.
- Time course from symptom onset to presentation ranges from hours in fulminant cases to more than 1 mo; 75% present in the first 2 wk.
- The nonspecific presentation of a brain abscess warrants that clinicians maintain a high index of suspicion.

ETIOLOGY

- Brain abscesses arise from:
  Contiguous infection
  Hematogenous spread from a remote site
- They are classified based on the likely portal of entry.

Likely source of abscess:

A. Contiguous focus or primary infection (55% of all brain abscesses):
   1. Paranasal sinus: occur in frontal lobe; streptococci, *Bacteroides, Haemophilus,* and *Fusobacterium* species
   2. Otitis media/mastoiditis: occur in temporal lobe and cerebellum; streptococci, Enterobacteriaceae, *Bacteroides,* and *Pseudomonas* species
   3. Dental sepsis: occur in frontal lobe; mixed *Fusobacterium, Bacteroides,* and *Streptococcus* species
   4. Penetrating head injury: site of abscess depends on site of wound; *Staphylococcus aureus, Clostridium* species, Enterobacteriaceae species
   5. Postoperative: *Staphylococcus epidermidis* and *S. aureus,* Enterobacteriaceae, and Pseudomonadaceae

B. Hematogenous spread/distant site of infection (25% of all brain abscesses): abscesses most commonly multiple, especially in middle cerebral artery distribution; infecting organisms depend on source.
   1. Congenital heart disease: streptococci, *Haemophilus* species
   2. Endocarditis: *S. aureus,* viridans streptococci
   3. Urinary tract: Enterobacteriaceae, Pseudomonadaceae
   4. Intraabdominal: streptococci, Enterobacteriaceae, anaerobes
   5. Lung: streptococci, *Actinomyces* species, *Fusobacterium* species
   6. Immunocompromised host: *Toxoplasma* species, fungi, Enterobacteriaceae, *Nocardia* species, tuberculosis, listeriosis

C. Cryptogenic (unknown source): 20% of all brain abscesses

DIAGNOSIS

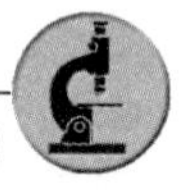

DIFFERENTIAL DIAGNOSIS

- Other parameningeal infections: subdural empyema, epidural abscess, thrombophlebitis of the major dural venous sinuses and cortical veins
- Embolic strokes in patients with bacterial endocarditis
- Mycotic aneurysms with leakage
- Viral encephalitis (usually resulting from herpes simplex)
- Acute hemorrhagic leukoencephalitis
- Parasitic infections: toxoplasmosis, echinococcosis, cysticercosis
- Metastatic or primary brain tumors
- Cerebral infarction
- CNS vasculitis
- Chronic subdural hematoma

WORKUP

Physical examination, laboratory tests, and imaging studies

LABORATORY TESTS

- WBC counts are elevated in 60% of patients.
- ESR is usually elevated, but may be normal.
- Blood cultures are most often negative (10% positive).
- Lumbar puncture is contraindicated in patients with suspected abscess (20% die or suffer neurologic decline).
- The yield of Gram stain and culture of material aspirated at time of surgical drainage approaches 100%.

IMAGING STUDIES

- MRI is the diagnostic procedure of choice; provides superior detail compared with CT scan (higher sensitivity and specificity than CT scan, but not always immediately available).
- CT scan (Fig. 1-1) with intravenous contrast is still an excellent test (sensitivity 95% to 99%).
- Serial CT or MRI scanning is recommended to follow the response to therapy.

TREATMENT

Effective treatment involves a combination of empiric antibiotic therapy and timely excision or aspiration of the abscess.

ACUTE GENERAL Rx

- If evidence of edema or mass effect, treatment of elevated intracranial pressure is paramount (includes hyperventilation of the mechanically ventilated patient, dexamethasone, mannitol).
- Medical therapy is never a substitute for surgical intervention to relieve increased intracranial pressure. Neurologic deterioration usually mandates surgery.
- Steroids should be limited to patients with severe cerebral edema or midline shift.

MEDICAL Rx

If abscess <2.5 cm and patient is neurologically stable and conscious, may start antibiotics and observe. Empiric antibiotic therapy guided by:

- Abscess location
- Suspicion of primary source
- Presence of single or multiple abscesses
- Patient's underlying medical conditions (e.g., HIV, immunocompromised)

Selection of empiric antibiotic therapy:

- Primary infection or contiguous source:
  1. Otitis media/mastoiditis, sinusitis, dental infection: third-generation cephalosporin (cefotaxime 2 g q6h IV or ceftriaxone 2 g q12h IV) plus metronidazole 7.5 mg/kg q6h IV or 15 mg/kg q12h IV
  2. Dental infection: penicillin G 6 million units q6° plus metronidazole
  3. Head trauma or postcranial surgery: third-generation cephalosporin plus metronidazole and nafcillin or vancomycin 1 g q12h IV
- Hematogenous spread (congenital heart disease, endocarditis, urinary tract, lung, intraabdominal): nafcillin or vancomycin plus metronidazole plus third-generation cephalosporin

Duration of antibiotic therapy is unclear. Most recommend parenteral treatment for 4 to 8 wk, with repeated neuroimaging to ensure adequate treatment. (Imaging suggested every wk for first 2 wk of therapy, then every 2 wk until antibiotics finished, and then every 2 to 4 mo for 1 yr to monitor for disease recurrence.)

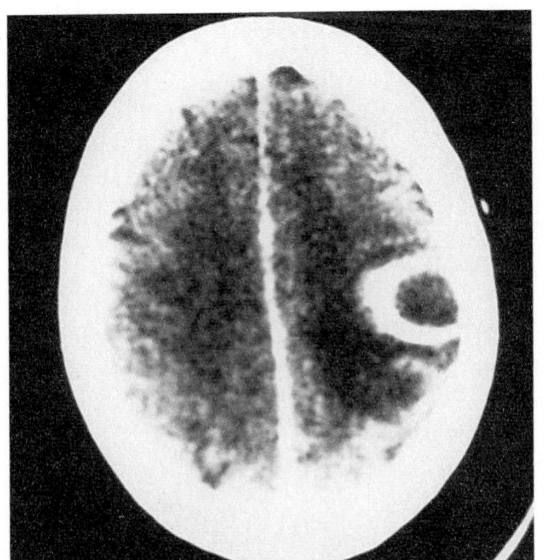

FIGURE 1-1 Computed tomography (CT) scan showing a brain abscess. A woman presented to physicians after a focal seizure followed by headache and weakness of the arm. Dental work had been performed several weeks before. CT scan revealed a contrast-enhanced, ringlike mass surrounded by edema. It is not possible on this scan to differentiate tumor from abscess. At surgery a well-encapsulated abscess was encountered. (From Andreoli TE [ed]: *Cecil essentials of medicine,* ed 4, Philadelphia, 1997, WB Saunders.)

SURGICAL Rx

- Two indications:
  1. Collect specimens for culture and sensitivity
  2. Reduce mass effect
- Stereotactic biopsy or aspirate of the abscess if surgically feasible
- Essential to selection of targeted antimicrobial coverage
- Timing and choice of surgery depends on:

  Primary infection source
  Number and location of the abscesses
  Whether the procedure is diagnostic or therapeutic
  Neurologic status of the patient

DISPOSITION

- Prompt diagnostic consideration, early institution of appropriate antimicrobial therapy, and advanced neuroradiologic imaging have reduced the mortality resulting from brain abscesses from 40% to 80% in the preantibiotic era to 10% to 20% at present.
- Morbidity is usually manifest as persistent neurologic sequelae (seizures, intellectual or behavioral impairment, motor deficits) seen in 20% to 60% of patients.

REFERRAL

Consultation with a neurosurgeon is mandatory.

SUGGESTED READINGS

Calfee DP, Wispelwey B: Brain abscess, *Semin Neurol* 20(3):353, 2000.

The rational use of antibiotics in the treatment of brain abscess: Report by the "Infection in Neurosurgery" Working Party of the British Society for Antimicrobial Chemotherapy, *Br J Neurosurg* 14(6):525, 2000.

AUTHOR: **KELLY MCGARRY, M.D.**

BASIC INFORMATION

DEFINITION

Breast abscess is an acute inflammatory process resulting in the formation of a collection of pus. Typically there is painful erythematous mass formation in the breast, occasionally with draining through the overlying skin or nipple duct opening.

SYNONYMS

Subareolar abscess
Lactational or puerperal abscess

ICD-9CM CODES
6.110 Abscess of the breast
675.0 Abscess of the nipple related to childbirth
675.1 Abscess of the breast related to childbirth

EPIDEMIOLOGY & DEMOGRAPHICS

- 10% to 30% of all breast abscesses are lactational.
- Acute mastitis occurs in 2.5% of nursing mothers, with 1 in 15 of these women developing abscess.

PHYSICAL FINDINGS & CLINICAL PRESENTATION

Painful erythematous induration involving the part of the breast leading to fluctuant abscess

ETIOLOGY

- Lactational abscess: milk stasis and bacterial infection leading to mastitis, then to abscess, with *Staphylococcus aureus* the most common causative agent
- Subareolar abscess:
  1. Central ducts involved, with obstructive nipple duct changes leading to bacterial infection
  2. Cultured organisms mixed, including anaerobes, staphylococci, streptococci, and others

DIAGNOSIS

DIFFERENTIAL DIAGNOSIS

- Inflammatory carcinoma
- Advanced carcinoma with erythema, edema, and/or ulceration
- Rarely, tuberculous abscess
- Hydradenitis of breast skin
- Sebaceous cyst with infection

WORKUP

- Clinical examination sufficient
- If abscess suspected, referral to surgeon for incision, drainage, and biopsy
- If possible abscess or advanced carcinoma, referral for workup required

LABORATORY TESTS

- Perform C&S test of abscess contents.
- If mammogram or ultrasound prevented by discomfort, perform after resolution of abscess if required.

TREATMENT

NONPHARMACOLOGIC THERAPY

- Established abscess: incision and drainage, preferably with general anesthesia
- Biopsy of abscess cavity wall to exclude carcinoma

ACUTE GENERAL Rx

- Antibiotics: the pathogen is generally staphylococci in lactational abscess. Recommended initial antibiotic therapy is with nafcillin or oxacillin 2 g q4h IV or cefazolin 1g q8h IV.
- If acute mastitis is treated early, resolution without drainage is possible.
- Subareolar abscess: broad-spectrum antibiotic treatment and drainage are needed to control acute phase.

CHRONIC Rx

Further surgical treatment for recurrences or fistula

DISPOSITION

- Lactational abscess: possible to continue breast-feeding without apparent risk of infection to the infant
- Subareolar abscess:
  1. Notorious for recurrence or complication of fistula formation
  2. Patient informed and referred for subsequent care

REFERRAL

- If abscess drainage required
- For surgical consultation if subareolar abscess involved

SUGGESTED READINGS

Schwarz RJ, Shrestha R: Needle aspiration of breast abscesses, *Am J Surg* 182(2):117, 2001.
Tan YM, Yeo A, Chia KH, Wong CY: Breast abscess as the initial presentation of squamous cell of the breast, *Eur J Surg Oncol* 28(1):91, 2002.

AUTHOR: **TAKUMA NEMOTO, M.D.**

BASIC INFORMATION

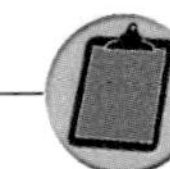

DEFINITION

Liver abscess is a necrotic infection of the liver usually classified as pyogenic or amebic.

SYNONYMS

Pyogenic hepatic abscess
Amebic hepatic abscess

ICD-9CM CODES
572.0 Abscess of liver

EPIDEMIOLOGY & DEMOGRAPHICS

- Worldwide, amebic liver abscess is more common than pyogenic liver abscess.
- In the U.S., pyogenic liver abscess is more common than amebic liver abscess.
- Incidence of pyogenic liver abscess is 8 to 15 cases per 100,000 population.
- Amebic liver abscesses complicate amebic colitis in nearly 10% of cases.
- Most abscesses occur on the right lobe of the liver.
- More common in men than women. Male:female ratio of 2:1.
- Most common in fourth to sixth decade of life.

PHYSICAL FINDINGS & CLINICAL PRESENTATION

- Fever, chills, and sweats
- Anorexia with weight loss
- Nausea, vomiting, and diarrhea
- Cough with pleuritic chest pain
- Right upper quadrant abdominal pain
- Hepatomegaly
- Splenomegaly
- Jaundice
- Pleural effusions, rales, and friction rubs may be present

ETIOLOGY

- Pyogenic liver abscess is usually polymicrobial (*E. coli* (33%), *K. pneumoniae* (18%), *Streptococcal Sp* (37%), *P. aeruginosa, Proteus, Bacteroides* (24%), *Fusobacterium, Actinomyces,* gram-positive anaerobes and *S. aureus*).
- Amebic hepatic abscess is caused by the parasite *Entamoeba histolytica*.
- Pyogenic liver abscess occurs from:
  1. Biliary disease with cholangitis (accounts for approximately 21% to 30%)
  2. Gallbladder disease with contiguous spread to the liver
  3. Diverticulitis or appendicitis with spread via the portal circulation
  4. Hematogenous spread via the hepatic artery
  5. Penetrating wounds
  6. Cryptogenic
  7. Infection via portal system (portal pyemia)
  8. No causes found in approximately half of cases
  9. Incidence increased in patients with diabetes and metastatic cancer
- Amebiasis is usually due to fecal-oral contamination and invades the intestinal mucosa gaining entry into the portal system to reach the liver.

DIAGNOSIS

The diagnosis of liver abscess requires a high index of suspicion after a detailed history and physical examination. Imaging studies, microbiologic, serologic, and percutaneous techniques (e.g., aspiration) confirm the presence of a liver abscess.

DIFFERENTIAL DIAGNOSIS

- Cholangitis
- Cholecystitis
- Diverticulitis
- Appendicitis
- Perforated viscus
- Mesentery ischemia
- Pulmonary embolism
- Pancreatitis

WORKUP

- The workup of a liver abscess should focus on differentiating between amebic and pyogenic causes.
- Features suggesting an amebic cause are travel to an endemic area, single abscess rather than multiple abscesses, subacute onset of symptoms, and absence of conditions predisposing to pyogenic liver abscess as highlighted under "Etiology."
- Laboratory studies are not specific but useful as adjunctive tests.
- Imaging studies cannot differentiate between the two, and bacteriologic cultures may be sterile in 50% of the cases.

LABORATORY TESTS

- CBC showing leukocytosis
- Liver function tests: alkaline phosphatase is most commonly elevated (95% to 100%); AST and ALT elevated in 50% of cases; elevated bilirubin (28% to 30%); decreased albumin
- PT (INR) prolonged (70%)
- Blood cultures positive in 50% of cases
- Aspiration (50% sterile)
- Stool samples for *E. histolytica* trophozoites (positive in 10% to 15% of amebic liver abscess cases)
- Serologic testing for *E. histolytica* does not differentiate acute from old infections

IMAGING STUDIES

- Chest x-ray examination abnormal in 50% of the cases showing elevated right hemidiaphragm, subdiaphragmatic air fluid levels, pleural effusions, and consolidating infiltrates.
- Ultrasound (80% to 100% sensitivity in detecting abscesses) seen as round or oval hypoechogenic mass.
- CT scans more sensitive in detecting hepatic abscesses and contiguous organ extension (Fig. 1-2). Imaging study of choice.

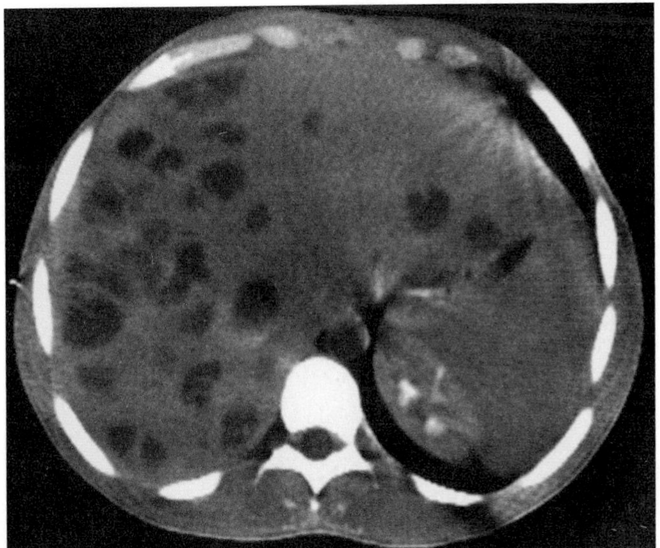

FIGURE 1-2 CT scan demonstrating multiple pyogenic liver abscesses in a 25-year-old man. (From Goldman L, Bennett JC [ed]: *Cecil textbook of medicine,* ed 21, Philadelphia, 2000, WB Saunders.)

- Most liver abscesses are single; however, multiple liver abscesses are seen with systemic bacteremia.

TREATMENT

NONPHARMACOLOGIC THERAPY

- The management of pyogenic liver abscess differs from that of amebic liver abscess.
- Medical management is the cornerstone of therapy in amebic liver abscess, whereas early intervention in the form of surgical therapy or catheter drainage and parenteral antibiotics is the rule in pyogenic liver abscess.

ACUTE GENERAL Rx

- Percutaneous drainage under CT or ultrasound guidance is essential in the treatment of pyogenic liver abscesses.
- Aspiration of hepatic amebic abscesses is not required unless there is no response to treatment or a pyogenic cause is being considered.
- Antibiotic treatment for pyogenic liver abscess initially is empirical triple therapy with penicillin, aminoglycoside, and metronidazole.
  1. In severely ill patients, parenteral antibiotics with cefotaxime or piperacillin/tazobactam and metronidazole for 2 wk followed by a 4- to 6-wk PO therapy is recommended.
  2. Clindamycin with an aminoglycoside or imipenem alone are alternative choices.
- Antibiotic coverage for amebic liver abscesses includes:
  1. Metronidazole 750 mg PO tid for 10 days
  2. Dehydroemetine 1 mg/kg/day IM for 5 days followed by chloroquine 1 g/day for 2 days; then 500 mg/day for 2 to 3 wk can be used as an alternative to metronidazole

CHRONIC Rx

- If fever persists for 2 wk despite percutaneous drainage and antibiotic therapy as outlined under "Acute General Rx," or if there is failure of aspiration or failure of percutaneous drainage, surgery is indicated.
- In patients failing intravenous antibiotics and percutaneous drainage, hepatic artery antibiotic infusion can be considered.
- In patients with evidence of metastatic disease that is causing biliary obstruction, a gastroenterology consultation for ERCP and stenting should be considered.

DISPOSITION

- Most patients with pyogenic liver abscesses defervesce within 2 wk of treatment with antibiotics and drainage.
- Pyogenic liver abscess cure rates using percutaneous drainage and antibiotics have been reported to be between 88% and 100%.
- Mortality of untreated pyogenic liver abscess is nearly 100%.
- Most patients with amebic liver abscesses defervesce within 4 to 5 days of treatment.
- Amebic liver abscess mortality rate is <1% unless complications occur (see under Comments).

REFERRAL

Infectious disease, gastroenterology, interventional radiology, and general surgical consultations are recommended in any patient with a single hepatic abscess or multiple abscesses.

PEARLS & CONSIDERATIONS

COMMENTS

- Complications of pyogenic and amebic liver abscesses include:
  1. Pleuropulmonary extension resulting in empyema, abscess, and fistula formation
  2. Peritonitis
  3. Purulent pericarditis
  4. Sepsis

SUGGESTED READINGS

Blessman J et al: Treatment of amoebic liver abscess with metronidazole alone or in combination with ultrasound guided needle aspiration: a comparative, prospective and randomized study, *Trop Med Int Health* 8(11):1030, 2003.

Krige JE, Beckingham IJ: ABC of diseases of liver, pancreas, and biliary system, *BMJ* 322(7285):537, 2001.

Kurland JE et al: Pyogenic and amebic liver abscess, *Curr Gastroenterol Rep* 6(4):273, 2004.

Lodhi S et al: Features distinguishing amebic from pyogenic liver abscess: a review of 577 adult cases, *Trop Med Int Health* 9(6):718, 2004.

Matoba M et al: Intremittent hepatic artery antibiotic infusion therapy for pyogenic liver abscess, *Acta Radiol* 4(5):13, 2004.

Sharma MP, Ahuja V: Management of amebic and pyogenic liver abscess, *Indian J Gastroenterol Suppl* 1:C33, 2001.

Yu SC et al: Treatment of pyogenic liver abscess: prospective randomized comparison of catheter drainage and needle aspiration, *Hepatology* 39(9):932, 2004.

AUTHORS: **HEMCHAND RAMBERAN, M.D.**, and **PETER PETROPOULOS, M.D.**

BASIC INFORMATION

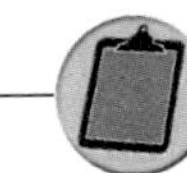

DEFINITION

A lung abscess is an infection of the lung parenchyma resulting in a necrotic cavity containing pus.

SYNONYMS

Pulmonary abscess

ICD-9CM CODES
513.0 Abscess of lung

EPIDEMIOLOGY & DEMOGRAPHICS

- Incidence has decreased over the last 30 years as a result of antibiotic therapy.
- Lung abscess in patients age 50 and over is associated with primary lung neoplasia in 30% of the cases.
- Lung abscesses commonly coexist with empyemas.
- Risk factor population includes patients with:
  1. Alcohol-related problems
  2. Seizure disorders
  3. Cerebrovascular disorders with dysphagia
  4. Drug abuse
  5. Esophageal disorders (e.g., scleroderma, esophageal carcinoma, etc.)
  6. Poor oral hygiene
  7. Obstructive malignant lung disease
  8. Bronchiectasis

PHYSICAL FINDINGS & CLINICAL PRESENTATION

- Symptoms are generally insidious and prolonged, occurring for weeks to months
- Fever, chills, and sweats
- Cough
- Sputum production (purulent with foul odor)
- Pleuritic chest pain
- Hemoptysis
- Dyspnea
- Malaise, fatigue, and weakness
- Tachycardia and tachypnea
- Dullness to percussion, whispered pectoriloquy, and bronchophony

ETIOLOGY

- The most important factor predisposing to lung abscess is aspiration.
- Following aspiration as a major predisposing factor is periodontal disease.
- Lung abscess is rare in an edentulous person.
- Approximately 90% of lung abscesses are caused by anaerobic microorganisms (*Bacteroides fragilis, Fusobacterium nucleatum, Peptostreptococcus,* microaerophilic *Streptococcus*).
- In most cases anaerobic infection is mixed with aerobic or facultative anaerobic organisms (*S. aureus, E. coli, K. pneumoniae, P. aeruginosa*).
- Parasitic organisms including Paragonimus westermani and Entamoeba histolytica.
- Fungi including *Aspergillus, Cryptococcus, Histoplasma, Blastomyces,* and *Coccidioides.*
- Immunocompromised hosts may become infected with *Aspergillus,* mycobacteria, *Nocardia,* and *Rhodococcus equi.*

DIAGNOSIS

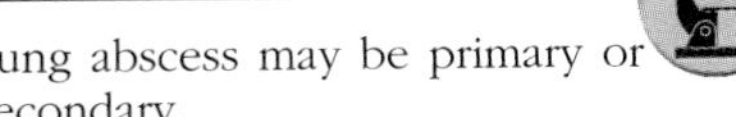

Lung abscess may be primary or secondary.
- Primary lung abscess refers to infection from normal host organisms within the lung (e.g., aspiration, pneumonia).
- Secondary lung abscess results from other preexisting conditions (e.g., endocarditis, underlying lung cancer, pulmonary emboli).

Lung abscess may be acute or chronic.
- Acute lung abscess is present if symptoms are of less than 4 to 6 wk.
- Chronic lung abscess is present if symptoms are greater than 6 wk.

DIFFERENTIAL DIAGNOSIS

The differential diagnosis is similar to cavitary lung lesions:
- Bacterial (anaerobic, aerobic, infected bulla, empyema, actinomycosis, tuberculosis)
- Fungal (histoplasmosis, coccidioidomycosis, blastomycosis, aspergillosis, cryptococcosis)
- Parasitic (amebiasis, echinococcosis)
- Malignancy (primary lung carcinoma, metastatic lung disease, lymphoma, Hodgkin's disease)
- Wegener's granulomatosis, sarcoidosis, endocarditis, and septic pulmonary emboli

WORKUP

- The workup of a patient with lung abscess attempts to elicit a primary or a secondary cause.
- Blood tests are not specific in diagnosing lung abscesses.
- Most diagnoses are made from imaging studies; however, to diagnose a specific cause bacteriologic studies are needed.

LABORATORY TESTS

- CBC with leukocytosis
- Bacteriologic studies
  1. Sputum Gram stain and culture (commonly contaminated by oral flora)
  2. Percutaneous transtracheal aspiration
  3. Percutaneous transthoracic aspiration
  4. Fiberoptic bronchoscopy using bronchial brushings or bronchoalveolar lavage is the most widely used intervention when trying to obtain diagnostic bacteriologic cultures
- Blood cultures on some occasions may be positive
- If an empyema is present, obtaining empyema fluid via thoracentesis may isolate the organism

IMAGING STUDIES

- Chest x-ray examination makes the diagnosis of lung abscess showing the cavitary lesion with an air fluid level.
- Lung abscesses are most commonly found in the posterior segment of the right upper lobe.
- Chest CT scan can localize and size the lesion and assist in differentiating lung abscesses from other pathologic processes (e.g., tumor, empyema, infected bulla, etc.) (Fig. 1-3).

TREATMENT

NONPHARMACOLOGIC THERAPY

- Oxygen therapy
- Postural drainage
- Respiratory therapy maneuvers

ACUTE GENERAL Rx

- Penicillin 1 to 2 million units IV q4h until improvement (e.g., afebrile, decrease in sputum production, etc.) followed by penicillin VK 500 mg PO qid for the next 2 to 3 wk but usually requiring longer 6- to 8-wk courses.
- Metronidazole is given with penicillin at doses of 7.5 mg/kg IV q6h followed by PO 500 mg bid to qid dosing.
- Clindamycin is an alternative choice if concerned about penicillin-resistant organisms. The dose is 600 mg IV q8h until improvement, followed by 300 mg PO q6h.

CHRONIC Rx

- Bronchoscopy to assist with drainage and/or diagnosis is indicated in patients who fail to respond to antibiotics or if there is suspected underlying malignancy.
- Surgery is indicated on rare occasions (<10%) in patients with complications of lung abscess (see Comments).

DISPOSITION

- More than 95% of patients are cured with the use of antibiotics alone.
- Complications of lung abscesses include:
  1. Empyema
  2. Massive hemoptysis
  3. Pneumothorax
  4. Bronchopleural fistula
- Mortality is low in community-acquired lung abscess (2.5%).
- Hospital-acquired lung abscess carries a high mortality rate (65%).

REFERRAL

If lung abscess is present, consultation with pulmonary and infectious disease specialist is recommended.

PEARLS & CONSIDERATIONS

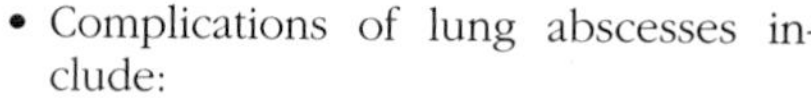

COMMENTS

- Complications of lung abscesses include:
  1. Empyema
  2. Bronchopleural fistula
  3. Hepatobronchial fistula
  4. Brain abscess
  5. Bronchiectasis
- Refractory cases are usually the result of:
  1. Large cavity size (>6 cm)
  2. Recurrent aspiration
  3. Thick-walled cavities
  4. Underlying lung carcinoma
  5. Empyema formation
- Necrotizing pneumonia is similar to a lung abscess but differs in size (<2 cm in diameter) and number (usually multiple suppurative cavitary lesions)

SUGGESTED READINGS

Cassiere HA, Niederman MS: Aspiration pneumonia, lipoid pneumonia, and lung abscess. In Baum GL et al: *Textbook of pulmonary diseases,* ed 6, New York, 1998, Lippincott-Raven.

Finegold SM: Lung abscess. In *Mandell, Douglas, and Bennett's principles and practice of infectious diseases,* ed 5, New York, 2000, Churchill Livingstone.

Hirshberg B, Sklair-Levi M, Nir-Paz R et al: Factors predicting mortality of patients with lung abscess, *Chest* 115:746, 1999.

Mwandumba HC, Beeching NJ: Pyogenic lung infections: factors for predicting clinical outcome of lung abscess and thoracic empyema, *Curr Opin Pulm Med* 6(3):234, 2000.

Rowe S, Cheadle WG: Complications of nosocomial pneumonia in the surgical patient, *Am J Surg* 179(2A suppl):63s, 2000.

Wiedemann HP, Rice TW: Lung abscess and empyema, *Semin Thorac Cardiovasc Surg* 7:119, 1995.

AUTHORS: **JOSEPH GRILLO, M.D.,** and **DENNIS J. MIKOLICH, M.D.**

A

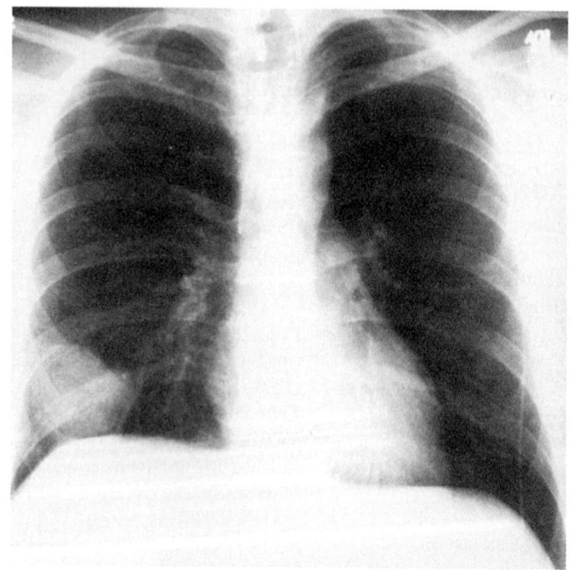

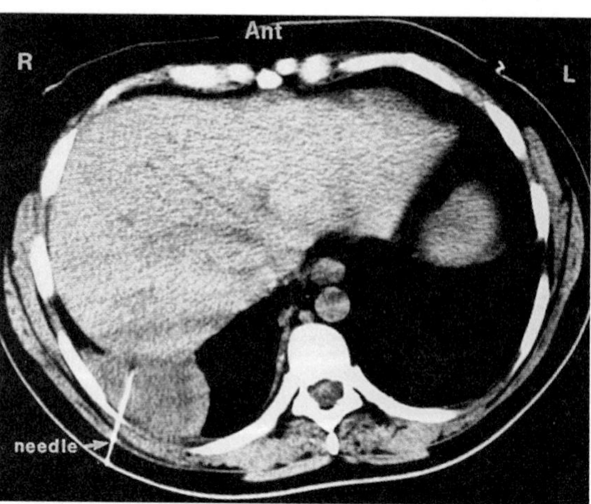

B

FIGURE 1-3 Lung abscess. On a chest radiograph, a lung abscess may look to be a solid rounded lesion **(A),** or, if it has a connection with the bronchus, there may be an air fluid level in a thick-walled cavitary lesion. CT scanning **(B)** can be used to localize the lesion and to place a needle for drainage and aspiration of contents for culture. (From Mettler FA [ed]: *Primary care radiology,* Philadelphia, 2000, WB Saunders.)

BASIC INFORMATION

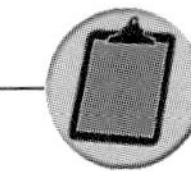

DEFINITION

Pelvic abscess is an acute or chronic infection, most commonly involving the pelvic viscera, initially localized and thus creating its own unique environment, so that treatment and possible cure require specific therapy. There are four categories based on etiologic factors:

- Ascending infection, spreading from cervix through endometrial cavity to adnexa, forming a tuboovarian complex
- Infection occurring in the puerperium, which spreads to the adnexa from the endometrium or myometrium via hematogenous or lymphatic route
- Abscess complicating pelvic surgery
- Involvement of the pelvic viscera secondary to spread from contiguous organs, such as appendicitis or diverticulitis

SYNONYMS

Tuboovarian abscess (TOA)
Vaginal cuff abscess

ICD-9CM CODES
614.2 Salpingitis and oophoritis not specified as acute, subacute, or chronic

EPIDEMIOLOGY & DEMOGRAPHICS

INCIDENCE:

- 34% of hospitalized patients with PID
- 1% to 2% of patients undergoing hysterectomy, most with vaginal approach
- Peak incidence third to fourth decade
- 25% to 50% are nulliparous

RISK FACTORS: Same risk factors as for PID, although in 30% to 50% of patients there is no prior history of salpingitis before abscess forms.

PHYSICAL FINDINGS & CLINICAL PRESENTATION

- Abdominal or pelvic pain (90%)
- Fever or chills (50%)
- Abnormal bleeding (21%)
- Vaginal discharge (28%)
- Nausea (26%)
- Up to 60% to 80% present in the absence of fever or leukocytosis; lack of these findings should not rule out diagnosis

ETIOLOGY

- Mixed flora of anaerobes, aerobes, and facultative anaerobes, such as *E. coli, B. fragilis, Prevotella* species, aerobic streptococci, *Peptococcus,* and *Peptostreptococcus.*
- *N. gonorrhoeae* and *Chlamydia* are the major etiologic factors in cervicitis and salpingitis but are rarely found in abscess cavity cultures.
- In elderly patients consider diverticular disease.

DIAGNOSIS

DIFFERENTIAL DIAGNOSIS

- Pelvic neoplasms, such as ovarian tumors and leiomyomas
- Inflammatory masses involving adjacent bowel or omentum, such as ruptured appendicitis or diverticulitis
- Pelvic hematomas, as may occur after C-section or hysterectomy
- Section III, Fig. 3-140 describes the diagnostic approach to patients with a pelvic mass; the differential diagnosis of pelvic mass is described in Section II.
- The differential diagnosis of pelvic pain is described in Section II.
- Physical examination
- Sonogram or CT scan: commonly employed because, owing to associated pain and guarding, a suboptimal abdominal or pelvic examination is the rule rather than the exception
- Most common cause of preventable death: physician delay in diagnosis

LABORATORY TESTS

- CBC including WBC with differential, Hgb, and Hct
- Aerobic as well as anaerobic cultures of cervix, blood, urine, sputum, peritoneal cavity (if entered), and abscess cavity before starting antibiotics
- Pregnancy test in patients of reproductive age if the possibility of pregnancy exists

IMAGING STUDIES

- Sonogram: noninvasive, inexpensive study to confirm diagnosis, estimate size of abscess, and monitor response to therapy; sensitivity >90%
- CT scan: used for both diagnosis and therapy (CT-guided drainage)
  1. Primary focus where sonogram provided insufficient information, as with intraabdominal vs. pelvic abscesses
  2. Success rate with CT-guided abscess drainage: unilocular, 90%; multilocular, 40%

TREATMENT

Major concerns:

1. Desire for future fertility
2. Likelihood of rupture of abscess, with resulting peritonitis, septic shock, and morbid sequelae

ACUTE GENERAL Rx

- Decision as to whether patient requires immediate surgery (uncertain diagnosis or suspicion of rupture) or management with IV antibiotics, reserving surgery for those with inadequate clinical response (e.g., 48 to 72 hr of therapy, with persistent fever or leukocytosis, increasing size of mass, or suspicion of rupture)
- Poor response to medical therapy in those with adnexal masses >8 cm, bilateral disease, or immunocompromise
- Antibiotic combinations:
  1. Clindamycin 900 mg IV q8h or metronidazole 500 mg IV q6-8h plus gentamicin either 5 to 7 mg/kg q24h or 1.5 mg/kg q8h
  2. Alternatives: ampicillin sulbactam 3 g IV q6h or cefoxitin 2 g IV q6h or cefotetan 2 g IV q12h plus doxycycline 100 mg IV q12h
- During medical management, high index of suspicion for acute rupture, such as acute worsening of abdominal pain or new-onset tachycardia and hypotension, mandating immediate surgical intervention after patient stabilization
- Surgical options:
  1. Laparoscopy with drainage and irrigation
  2. Transvaginal colpotomy (abscess must be midline, dissect rectovaginal septum, and be adherent to vaginal fornix)
  3. Laparotomy, including total abdominal hysterectomy with bilateral salpingo-oophorectomy or unilateral salpingo-oophorectomy
  4. Evidence of ruptured TOA 5 surgical emergency

DISPOSITION

- Of patients treated with medical therapy, response in 75%, with a 50% pregnancy rate
- No response in 30% to 40%; can be treated with either CT-guided drainage or surgical intervention, keeping in mind that unilateral adnexectomy may give equal chance of cure vs. hysterectomy, yet preserve reproductive potential

REFERRAL

If patient has a TOA, refer to gynecologist.

PEARLS & CONSIDERATIONS

COMMENTS

If *Actinomyces* species is isolated from culture, treatment with penicillin is required for an extended period (6 wk to 3 mo).

SUGGESTED READING

Aimakhu CO, Olayemi O, Odukogbe AA: Surgical management of pelvic abscess: laparotomy versus colpotomy, *J Obstet Gynaecol* 23(1):71, 2003.

AUTHOR: **SCOTT J. ZUCCALA, D.O.**

BASIC INFORMATION

DEFINITION

A perirectal abscess is a localized inflammatory process that can be associated with infections of soft tissue and anal glands based on anatomic location. Perianal and perirectal abscesses may be simple or complex, causing suppuration. Infections in these spaces may be classified as superficial perianal or perirectal with involvement in the following anatomic spaces: ischiorectal, intersphincteric, pestianal, and supralevator (Fig. 1-4).

SYNONYMS

Rectal abscess
Perianal abscess
Anorectal abscess

ICD-9CM CODES
566 Perirectal abscess

EPIDEMIOLOGY & DEMOGRAPHICS

INCIDENCE (IN U.S.): Commonly encountered
PREDOMINANT SEX: Male > female
PREDOMINANT AGE: All ages
PEAK INCIDENCE: Not seasonal; common
GENETICS: None known

PHYSICAL FINDINGS & CLINICAL PRESENTATION

- Localized perirectal or anal pain—often worsened with movement or straining
- Perirectal erythema or cellulitis
- Perirectal mass by inspection or palpation
- Fever and signs of sepsis with deep abscess
- Urinary retention

ETIOLOGY

Polymicrobial aerobic and anaerobic bacteria involving one of the anatomic spaces (see Definition), often associated with localized trauma
Microbiology: most bacteria are polymicrobial, mixed enteric and skin flora
Predominant anaerobic bacteria:
- *Bacteroides fragilis*
- *Peptostreptococcus spp.*
- *Prevotella spp.*
- *Fusobacterium spp.*
- *Porphyromonas spp.*
- *Clostridium spp.*

Predominant aerobic bacteria:
- *Staphylococcus aureus*
- *Streptococcus spp.*
- *Escherichia coli*

DIAGNOSIS

Many patients will have predisposing underlying conditions including:
- Malignancy or leukemia
- Immune deficiency
- Diabetes mellitus
- Recent surgery
- Steroid therapy

DIFFERENTIAL DIAGNOSIS

- Neutropenic enterocolitis
- Crohn's disease (inflammatory bowel disease)
- Pilonidal disease
- Hidradenitis suppurativa
- Tuberculosis or actinomycosis; Chagas' disease
- Cancerous lesions
- Chronic anal fistula
- Rectovaginal fistula
- Proctitis—often STD-associated, including:
  Syphilis
  Gonococcal
  Chlamydia
  Chancroid
  Condylomata acuminata
- AIDS-associated:
  Kaposi's sarcoma
  Lymphoma
  CMV

WORKUP

- Examination of rectal, perirectal/perineal areas
- Rule out necrotic process and crepitance suggesting deep tissue involvement
- Local aerobic and anaerobic culture
- Blood cultures if toxic, febrile, or compromised
- Possible sigmoidoscopy

IMAGING STUDIES

Usually not indicated unless extensive disease abscess

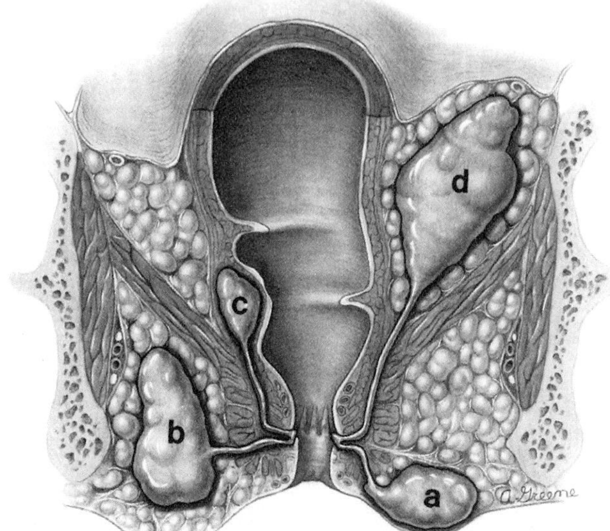

FIGURE 1-4 Common sites of anorectal abscesses: perianal **(a)**, ischiorectal **(b)**, intersphincteric **(c)**, and supralevator **(d)**. (From Noble J [ed]: *Textbook of primary care medicine,* ed 2, St Louis, 1996, Mosby.)

TREATMENT

- Incision and drainage of abscess
- Debridement if necrotic tissue
- Rule out need for fistulectomy
- Local wound care—packing
- Sitz baths

Antibiotic treatment: Directed toward coverage for mixed skins and enteric flora

Outpatient—oral:	Amoxicillin clavulanic acid (Augmentin) Ciprofloxacin plus metronidazole or clindamycin
Inpatient—intravenous:	Ampicillin/sulbactam (Unasyn) Cefotetan Piperacillin/Tazobactam Imipenem

SUGGESTED READINGS

Nelson RL et al: Prevalence of benign anorectal disease in a randomly selected population, *Dis Colon Rectum* 88:341, 1994.
Nomikos IN: Anorectal abscesses: need for accurate anatomical localization of the disease, *Clin Anat* 10:239, 1997.

AUTHOR: **DENNIS J. MIKOLICH, M.D.**

BASIC INFORMATION

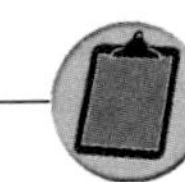

DEFINITION

Definition from the Federal Child Abuse Prevention and Treatment Act (CAPTA): any recent act or failure to act on the part of a parent or caretaker which results in death, serious physical or emotional harm, sexual abuse or exploitation of a child; or an act or failure to act which presents an imminent risk of serious harm to a child.

- Neglect: failure to provide for the basic needs of a child (e.g., food, shelter, supervision)
  1. Medical neglect: failure to provide basic medical or mental health care
  2. Educational neglect: failure to meet educational needs
- Physical abuse: injury inflicted by an adult intentionally or in the course of excessive discipline
- Sexual abuse: sexual act inflicted by parent or caretaker, includes exploitation and pornography
- Emotional abuse: pattern of behavior of caretaker toward a child that impairs emotional development, such as verbal abuse, cruelty, or exposure to domestic violence

SYNONYMS

- Child maltreatment
- Physical abuse
- Sexual abuse
- Battered child syndrome
- Shaken baby syndrome
- Shaken impact syndrome
- Abusive head trauma

ICD-9CM CODES
995.5 Child maltreatment
995.50 Child abuse, unspecified
995.51 Child abuse, emotional or psychologic
995.52 Child neglect
995.53 Child abuse, sexual
995.54 Child abuse, physical
995.55 Shaken infant syndrome
995.59 Multiple forms of child abuse

EPIDEMIOLOGY & DEMOGRAPHICS

INCIDENCE (IN U.S., 2002): Any reports of incidence are underestimates because many cases are never recognized or reported. These are collected based on CPS state aggregates.

- Annual incidence of 12.3 child victims/1000 children in the general population. This is decreased from 13.4 child victims/1000 children in 1990.
- Types of abuse by percentage. Note that this adds to greater than 100% because many children are subject to more than one type of victimization.
  1. Neglect 60.5%
  2. Physical abuse 18.6%
  3. Sexual abuse 9.9%
  4. Emotional abuse 6.5%
  5. Other 18.9%
- There is an estimate of 1400 child deaths per yr due to abuse and neglect.
- Overall annual death rate due to abuse or neglect is estimated to be 2 deaths/100,000 children.
- One third of these are due to neglect.
- 76% of these children are <4 yr of age.
- Most fatalities are suffered at the hand of one or both parents (79%).
- Many child abuse fatalities are underreported because of misdiagnosis or variations in state definitions and coding.
- More than 80% of abused children are victimized by their parents.
- One fifth of adult women report history of molestation or sexual assault as a child or adolescent.

VARIATIONS BY SEX:

- There is a slight predominance of females as victims.
- However, infant boys have a higher death rate: 19/100,000 boys versus 12/100,000 girls.

AGE:
Youngest children have the highest rates of victimization.

- 0-3 yr, 16 victims/1000 children
- 4-7 yr, 13.7/1000
- 8-11 yr, 11.9/1000
- 12-15 yr, 10.6/1000
- 16-17 yr, 6/1000

GENETICS:
No known genetic factors

ETIOLOGY

Multiple factors contribute to the incidence. No factor or combination of factors can definitively predict which children will be victimized.
Factors contributing to risk of abuse or neglect:

- Parent
  1. Substance abuse
  2. Mental illness
  3. Intellectual impairment
  4. Parental history of being abused as a child
  5. Domestic violence
- Child
  1. Low birth weight or prematurity
  2. Chronic physical disability
- Family
  1. Social isolation
  2. Poor parent-child bonding
  3. Stress: unemployment, chronic or severe illness, eviction, arrest, poverty
- Community/society
  1. Limited transportation
  2. Limited daycare
  3. Unsafe neighborhoods
  4. Poverty

DIAGNOSIS

DIFFERENTIAL DIAGNOSIS

PRESENTATION:

- Patterned bruising (e.g., loop-shaped, square, oval) is indicative of being struck with an object.
- Injury observed is incompatible with the history provided.
- History of injury provided is incompatible with the developmental capabilities of the child.
- There is delay in seeking care for a significant injury (e.g., callus formation on a fracture, eschar formation on a burn).
- Accidental injuries are most common over bony prominences: forehead, elbows, knees, shins; soft, fleshy areas are more common for inflicted injury: buttocks, thighs, upper arms.
- Bruising is rare in healthy precruising infants and warrants further investigation.
- There are multiple significant injuries of different ages.
- Infant with clinically significant head trauma attributed to a trivial cause (e.g., a short fall). Often associated with retinal hemorrhages and skeletal fractures is indicative of shaken baby syndrome or abusive head trauma.
- Certain fractures in infants without a history of significant trauma (e.g., MVA) are characteristic of abuse: metaphyseal, rib, sternum, scapula, vertebral body.
- Inflicted contact burns are indicated by an impression of the burning object: lighter, iron, cigarette.
- Inflicted immersion burns are indicated by "stocking" burns of the feet or "glove" burns of the hands. Stocking burns are often associated with buttocks/perineal burns from immersion of a minor in a flexed position.
- Most sexual abuse victims will have a normal or nonspecific genital examination. A normal genital examination does not mean the child was not abused. History is the most important part of the diagnosis.
- The identification of a sexually transmitted disease in a prepubertal child who is beyond the neonatal period is suggestive of sexual abuse. Reporting and further careful investigation are warranted.

In all categories, accidental injury is the most common entity to be distinguished from abuse.
Bruising

- Bleeding disorder (ITP, hemophilia, leukemia, hemorrhagic disease of the newborn, Von Willebrand's disease)
- Connective tissue disorder (Ehlers Danlos, vasculitis)
- Pigments (Mongolian spots)

- Dermatitis (phytophotodermatitis, nickel allergy)
- Folk treatment (coining, cupping)

Burns
- Chemical burn
- Impetigo
- Folk treatment (moxibustion)
- Dermatitis (phytophotodermatitis)

Intracranial hemorrhage
- Bleeding disorder
- Perinatal trauma (should resolve by 4 wk)
- AVM rupture
- Glutaric aciduria

Fractures
- Osteogenesis imperfecta
- Ricketts
- Congenital syphilis
- Very low birth weight

Sexual abuse
- Lichen sclerosis et atrophicus
- Congenital abnormalities
- Urethral prolapse
- Hemangioma
- Nonsexually acquired infection (group A strep, shigella)

LABORATORY TESTS

EVALUATION:

History and physical
- Careful history from all caretakers and child.
- Scene investigation may be necessary.
- Complete physical examination.
- Sexual abuse: magnified examinations by a trained professional is the standard for evaluation and evidence collection.

Laboratory tests for physical abuse
- CBC with differential and platelets.
- PT, aPTT.
- SGPT, amylase, UA.
- Skeletal survey for all children <2 yr of age; for 2- to 5-yr-olds, done only for severe abuse.
- Noncontrast head CT scan for all children <1 yr of age; for children >1 yr of age, clinical judgment should be used.
- Head MRI for children with significant abusive head trauma. This is used as an adjunct a few days after initial head CT.
- Abdominal CT scan if indicated by clinical examination or laboratory evaluation.

Laboratory tests for sexual abuse
- If within 72 hr of acute sexual assault/abuse, swabs are obtained for sperm, acid phosphatase, P30, MHS-5 antigen, blood group typing, DNA testing. Also collect samples of hair, blood, or saliva if present.
- For adolescent victims of acute assault, appropriate specimens should be collected from sites of penetration for GC and chlamydia. Nucleic acid amplification tests may be used. In females, wet mount for BV and trichomonas should also be done. Serum should be obtained for HIV, hepatitis B and syphilis testing acutely. If negative, HIV and syphilis testing should be repeated 6, 12, and 24 wk after the assault.
- Child victims should have specimens collected if considered high risk for an STD. Specimens should be collected for GC and chlamydia culture, wet mount, and blood for serologic testing (HIV, hepatitis B, syphilis) in the following cases:
  1. Vaginal discharge or genital ulcer
  2. Perpetrator is known to have an STD or be at high risk for an STD
  3. A sibling or adult in the same household has a known STD
  4. High prevalence of STDs in the community
  5. Evidence of ejaculation is present on the examination
  6. Child or parent requests testing

TREATMENT

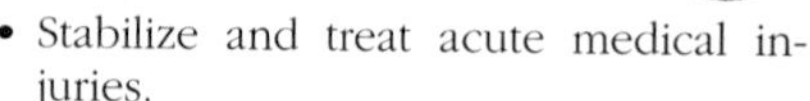

ACUTE GENERAL Rx

- Stabilize and treat acute medical injuries.
- Report to Child Protective Services. HIPAA allows reports for suspected child abuse without parental authorization.
- Early report to law enforcement for suspected physical abuse or sexual abuse. This allows for scene investigation.
- Disposition, once medically stable, is dependent on CPS. The child cannot be returned home if the environment is not safe.
- Physician should remain available to discuss with investigators. This is often critical to determining the outcome of the case and placement of the child.
- For adolescent victims of acute sexual assault, empirically treat for GC, chlamydia, trichomonas, and BV. Pregnancy prophylaxis should also be offered. Hepatitis B immunization should be offered if not previously given. HIV prophylaxis is offered in certain situations depending on local epidemiology and risk.

CHRONIC Rx

- Often dependent on CPS and court-ordered interventions
- Treatment of parental mental illness
- Treatment of parental substance abuse, including requirements for random drug testing
- Instruction for parents in behavior management skills including appropriate limit setting and discipline
- Anger management classes
- Ongoing individual and family therapy
- May need long-term placement in foster care before it is safe to return home

DISPOSITION

- Victims of chronic abuse and neglect have more mental illness (depression, suicide, PTSD, eating disorders)
- Victims have more cognitive difficulties and often have impaired academic performance
- Victims are more likely to become aggressive
- Victims, as adults, are more likely to have adverse physical health outcomes (cardiovascular disease, cancer, STDs)
- Victims of abusive head trauma:
  1. One third die.
  2. One third have severe disability.
  3. One third appear normal in the short term.

PEARLS & CONSIDERATIONS

PREVENTION

- Home visitation to high-risk families during pregnancy and infancy has shown positive outcomes.
- Anticipatory guidance at health visits to teach normal developmental expectations and appropriate discipline.
- Screening to identify at-risk or abused children.
- Targeted education in the newborn nursery for shaken baby prevention has been shown to be effective.
- Substance abuse prevention and treatment.
- Identification and intervention for domestic violence before children are born.

SUGGESTED READINGS

American Academy of Pediatrics: Diagnostic imaging of child abuse, *Pediatrics* 105:1345, 2000.

American Academy of Pediatrics: Shaken baby syndrome: rotational cranial injuries-technical report, *Pediatrics* 108:206, 2001.

American Academy of Pediatrics: When inflicted skin injuries constitute child abuse, *Pediatrics* 110:644, 2002.

Sirotnak AP, Grigsby T, Krugman RD: Physical abuse of children, *Pediatr Rev* 25:264, 2004.

United States Department of Health and Human Services: What is child abuse and neglect? 2004. Available at http://nccanch.acf.hhs.gov/pubs/factsheets/whatiscan.pdf.

AUTHOR: **NANCY R. GRAFF, M.D.**

BASIC INFORMATION

DEFINITION

Drug abuse is a recurring pattern of harmful use of a substance despite adverse consequences in work, school, relationships, the legal system, or personal health. This may occur concurrently with or independently from *substance dependence,* in which the impairment or distress is more pervasive and that often (though not necessarily) includes physical dependence and withdrawal symptoms. (See Table 1-1.)

SYNONYMS

Substance abuse
Addiction

ICD-9CM CODES
Defined by specific substance F10-F19 (DSM-IV code is also defined by specific substance 291-292, 303-305).

EPIDEMIOLOGY & DEMOGRAPHICS

INCIDENCE (IN U.S.): Alcohol or drug dependence: 5%-10%
PREVALENCE (IN U.S.): 15% of patients in primary care practice have "at-risk" pattern of drug and/or alcohol use
PREDOMINANT SEX: Males > females
PREDOMINANT AGE:
- Problematic use of substances may begin in early life (8 to 10 yr)
- The mean age of onset of problem drinking is about 25 yr for men and 30 yr for women

PEAK INCIDENCE:
- For most substances: 15 to 30 yr of age
- Men: average >20 yr of heavy drinking
- Women: average 15 yr of heavy drinking

GENETICS
There is evidence of nonspecific genetic factors.

PHYSICAL FINDINGS & CLINICAL PRESENTATION

- Polysubstance use is common.
- Anxiety, depression, insomnia, cognitive and memory dysfunction, and behavioral problems are frequent.
- Alcohol and cocaine abuse associated with violence and accidents (more than half of all murderers and their victims are intoxicated at the time of the crime).
- Alcohol withdrawal can be present with seizures and delirium.

ETIOLOGY

Two models of addiction:
- Conditioning—substance use paired with enforcing and triggering stimuli.
- Homeostatic—either preexisting abnormalities or drug-induced abnormalities lead to initial or continued use of the drug.

DIAGNOSIS

DIFFERENTIAL DIAGNOSIS

- Psychiatric disorders such as depression, mania, social phobia, or other anxiety disorders that coexist or occur as a consequence of substance abuse.
- Rule out seizure disorder, underlying illness in persons presenting with substance use, and seizure.

WORKUP

- A thorough history is crucial for diagnosis of any substance abuse disorder.
- The physician's history-taking style and techniques strongly affect patient's willingness to participate in future treatment activities.
- A structured approach is generally preferable. For example:
  1. Ask about alcohol or drug use in past year.
  2. Use a short screening instrument such as the two-item screen ("In the last year, have you ever drank or used drugs more than you meant to? Have you felt you wanted or needed to cut down on your drinking or drug use in the last year?").
  3. Ask about quantity and frequency. For example, the National Institute on Alcohol and Alcoholism declares that problem drinking for men is defined as more than 14 drinks/wk or more than 4 drinks on any one occasion; for women and anyone older than 65 years, the limits are 7 drinks and no more than 3 on any one occasion.
- Observation of problematic behavior during intoxication or withdrawal is diagnostic.
- Physical examination findings are limited. Odor of alcohol or intoxication is worrisome and indicates a high likelihood of drug or alcohol disorder.

LABORATORY TESTS

- Consider toxicology screen or blood alcohol level.
- Elevated mean corpuscular volume and α–glutamyltransferase are most sensitive indicators of alcohol intake.

IMAGING STUDIES

Not helpful in routine diagnosis and management of substance abuse, but possibly useful in the management of sequelae of substance abuse (e.g., brain scan to evaluate the alcohol abuse–associated increased risk of subdural hematomas or increased evidence of cerebral atrophy).

TREATMENT

NONPHARMACOLOGIC THERAPY

- Nonpharmacologic strategies have greatest documented efficacy. Effective nonpharmacologic interventions generally include advice, feedback, goal setting, and additional contacts for further assistance and support.
- Relapse prevention by avoidance of trigger stimuli or by uncoupling trigger stimuli from substance ingestion.
- Self-help groups such as Alcoholics Anonymous, Narcotics Anonymous, and Al-Anon.

ACUTE GENERAL Rx

- Detoxification is an important first step in substance abuse treatment. Its goals are to facilitate withdrawal and reduce symptoms, initiate abstinence, and refer the patient into ongoing treatment.
- Benzodiazepines, particularly long-acting ones, are safe and effective in acute alcohol withdrawal.
- Anticonvulsants, particularly carbamazepine, are used effectively in Europe.
- ß-Blockers and clonidine generally should be avoided in alcohol withdrawal; they may mask markers of the severity of the withdrawal (blood pressure and pulse rate).
- Clonidine alleviates the discomfort of opiate and nicotine withdrawal.
- The use of opiates for detoxification is legally restricted to inpatient settings and specially licensed outpatient programs.

CHRONIC Rx

- Disulfiram (Antabuse) provokes acetaldehyde accumulation after alcohol ingestion, producing a toxic state manifest by nausea, headache, flushing, and respiratory distress. Randomized trials generally have not demonstrated efficacy.
- Naltrexone helps reduce craving for alcohol. Naltrexone can be a useful adjunct to substance abuse counseling or rehabilitation programs, as one of many tools that clinicians and patients use. Randomized treatment studies are equivocal. Naltrexone does not increase the chance of staying completely abstinent but rather reduces the intensity or frequency of any drinking that does occur. Alcohol-dependent individuals who are most likely to benefit from naltrexone appear to be those with close relatives who also had alcohol problems, or those who have stronger urges to drink or who are more limited in cognitive abilities.

- Adjunctive use of antidepressants or lithium is helpful when substance use is associated with anxiety and mood symptoms.

DISPOSITION

- Substance abuse is a chronic relapsing illness.
- The goal of treatment is always abstinence, but success of treatment is measured by return of function and increasing duration between relapses.
- When substance abuse is complicated by another psychiatric illness, prognosis for both conditions is quite poor.
- Abuse of one substance increases likelihood for abuse of other substances.

REFERRAL

- Physicians should refer any patients who do not make good progress on changing substance use patterns.
- Intensive substance abuse treatment is nearly always indicated in substance-dependent individuals.
- Individuals with coexisting primary psychiatric illness and substance abuse nearly always require the care of a specialist.

SUGGESTED READINGS

Fiellin DA, O'Connor P: Office-based treatment of opioid-dependent patients, *N Engl J Med* 347:817, 2002.

Kosten TR, O'Connor PG: Management of drug and alcohol withdrawal, *N Engl J Med* 348(18):1786, 2003.

Naimi TS et al: Binge drinking among U.S. adults, *JAMA* 289:70, 2003.

Whitlock EP et al: Behavioral counseling interventions in primary care to reduce risky/harmful alcohol use by adults: a summary of the evidence for the U.S. Preventive Services Task Force, *Ann Intern Med* 140(7):557, 2004.

AUTHOR: **MITCHELL D. FELDMAN, M.D., M.PHI.**

TABLE 1-1 Diagnostic Criteria for Dependence and Drug Abuse

Dependence (>3 needed)	Abuse (>1 for 12 mo)
1. Tolerance	1. Recurrent substance use resulting in failure to fulfill major role obligations at work, school, or home
2. Withdrawal	2. Recurrent substance use in situations in which it is physically hazardous
3. The substance is often taken in larger amounts over a longer period than intended	3. Recurrent substance-related legal problems
4. Any unsuccessful effort or a persistent desire to cut down or control substance use	4. Continued substance use despite having persistent or recurrent social or interpersonal problems caused or exacerbated by the effects of the substance
5. A great deal of time is spent in activities necessary to obtain the substance or recover from its effects	Never met criteria for dependence
6. Important social, occupational, or recreational activities given up or reduced because of substance use	
7. Continued substance use despite knowledge of having had persistent or recurrent physical or psychological problems that are likely to be caused or exacerbated by the substance	

From Goldman L, Bennett JC (eds): *Cecil textbook of medicine*, ed 21, Philadelphia, 2000, WB Saunders.

BASIC INFORMATION

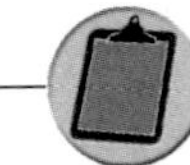

DEFINITION

Elder abuse is the willful infliction of physical pain or injury; emotional pain, injury, humiliation, or intimidation; exploitation or misappropriation of money or property; or neglect by the designated caregiver. In general, three basic categories of elder abuse exist: domestic elder abuse (or abuse in the home); institutional elder abuse (abuse that occurs in nursing homes, foster homes, group homes, board and care facilities); and self-neglect.

Seven types of abuse are described:

- Physical abuse: inflicting of physical pain or injury, including hitting, slapping, or restraining
- Sexual abuse: inflicting of nonconsensual sexual activity of any kind
- Psychologic abuse: inflicting mental anguish, including intimidation, humiliation, ridicule, or threats through verbal or nonverbal means
- Financial abuse: improper use of the resources of any older person without the elder's consent for another's benefit
- Abandonment: desertion of an elderly person by the responsible caregiver
- Neglect: failure to fulfill a caretaking obligation, including provision of food, a safe living environment, health care, hygiene, or basic custodial care
- Self-neglect: behavior of an elderly person that threatens the elder's health or safety

There is considerable variation between states regarding the definitions of abuse and reporting requirements for specific subtypes of abuse.

SYNONYMS

Geriatric abuse
Battered elder syndrome

ICD-9CM CODES
995.81 Adult maltreatment syndrome

EPIDEMIOLOGY & DEMOGRAPHICS

U.S. INCIDENCE & PREVALENCE: Unknown, statistics are thought to underreport the problem significantly. There were estimated to be 1 million victims of elder abuse in 1996; if self-neglect is included, that number increases to more than 2 million (National Center on Elder Abuse).

- Some experts estimate that only 1 of 14 abuse incidents are reported.
- In 1996 there were about 300,000 reports of domestic elder abuse.
- Neglect is the most common form of elder mistreatment.

PREDOMINANT AGE: Risk increases as level of disability increases

PEAK INCIDENCE: >80 yr old

RISK FACTORS: (Victim)

- Poor health
- Impaired cognition
- Social isolation

RISK FACTORS: (Perpetrator)

- Substance abuse
- Mental illness
- Dependence on the victim
- Being an involuntary or ill-equipped caregiver
- History of violence

CLINICAL PRESENTATION

- Physical abuse with multiple injuries at various stages with implausible or inconsistent descriptions of their origins; injuries are usually to head, neck, chest, breast, and abdomen.
- Extreme fear, hypervigilance, or withdrawal.
- Evidence of poor nutrition or hygiene.
- Toxicologic evidence of unprescribed medications.
- Poor adherence, frequent no-shows.

DIAGNOSIS

DIFFERENTIAL DIAGNOSIS

- Advancing dementia
- Depression or other psychiatric disorders
- Malnutrition due to intrinsic causes
- Conscious nonadherence
- Financial hardship
- Falling
- Diogenes syndrome

WORKUP

- Interview patient separately from the suspected abuser.
- Build trust; patients may be reticent.
- Ask direct questions.
- Be aware that physical findings are usually unexplained injuries or burns.
- Pelvic examination if sexual abuse suspected.

LABORATORY TESTS

- If sexual abuse suspected, screening for sexually transmitted diseases
- Toxicology screens or therapeutic drug monitoring

IMAGING STUDIES

X-rays as indicated by physical presentation

TREATMENT

NONPHARMACOLOGIC THERAPY

Reporting abuse to Adult Protective Services is mandatory in most states. This also provides the physician access to specialized personnel who can aid in evaluation and disposition.

- Separate patient and abuser.
- If the burden of care appears to be the major factor in contributing to abuse, referral to respite services, if available, can be useful.

Patient and caregiver may benefit from screening and treatment for depression, substance abuse, anxiety, mental illness, or cognitive impairment.

ACUTE GENERAL Rx

As indicated for injury or pain relief

DISPOSITION

In emergencies, hospitalization may be required. If the patient's level of disability does not allow for independent living, institutionalization may be required. Guidelines vary at the state and county levels regarding guardianship and conservatorship requirements.

REFERRAL

Adult Protective Services (mandatory in most states)

PEARLS & CONSIDERATIONS

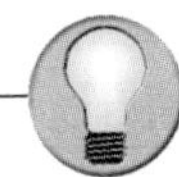

COMMENTS

Consider home visit if abuse, neglect, or self-neglect is suspected.

PREVENTION

- Screen for caregiver stress.
- Respite services, if possible.
- Make financial arrangements and arrange durable power of attorney for health care and finances while patient still cognitively intact.

PATIENT/FAMILY EDUCATION

Alzheimer's Association for caregivers of patients with dementia

SUGGESTED READINGS

Fulmer T et al: Progress in elder abuse screening and assessment instruments, *J Am Geriatr Soc* 52(2):297, 2004.

Jogerst GJ et al: Domestic elder abuse and the law, *Am J Public Health* 93:2131, 2003.

Levine JM: Elder neglect and abuse. A primer for primary care physicians, *Geriatrics* 58(10):37,42, 2003.

National Center on Elder Abuse: http://www.elderabusecenter.org.

AUTHORS: **BREE JOHNSTON, M.D., M.P.H.,** and **MIKE HARPER, M.D.**

Acetaminophen Poisoning (PTG)

BASIC INFORMATION

DEFINITION

Acetaminophen poisoning is a disorder manifested by hepatic necrosis, jaundice, somnolence, and potential death if not treated appropriately. Pathologically there is hepatic necrosis.

SYNONYMS

Paracetamol poisoning

ICD-9CM CODES
965.4 Acetaminophen poisoning

EPIDEMIOLOGY & DEMOGRAPHICS

- Potentially toxic ingestions of acetaminophen-containing medications exceed 100,000 cases annually.
- Death rate is approximately 1/1000 persons. Nearly 50% of exposures occur in children <6 yr.
- Hepatic necrosis is most likely to occur in people who are chronically malnourished, who regularly abuse alcohol, and who are using other potentially hepatotoxic medications.

PHYSICAL FINDINGS & CLINICAL PRESENTATION

- The physical examination may vary depending on the number of hours lapsed from the ingestion of acetaminophen.
- Initially, symptoms may be mild or absent and may consist of diaphoresis, malaise, nausea, and vomiting.
- After the initial 12 to 24 hr, patient may complain of RUQ pain with associated vomiting, diaphoresis, and subsequent somnolence.
- In massive overdoses, jaundice may occur within the initial 72 hr.
- Subsequent coma, somnolence, and confusion follow and can ultimately lead to death if not treated appropriately.

ETIOLOGY

The amount of acetaminophen necessary for hepatic toxicity varies with the patient's body size and hepatic function. Using standardized nomograms calculating the acetaminophen plasma level and the number of hours after ingestion, the clinician can determine potential hepatic toxicity.

DIAGNOSIS

DIFFERENTIAL DIAGNOSIS

- Liver disease from alcohol abuse or hepatitis
- Ingestion of other hepatotoxic substances

WORKUP

Initial workup is aimed at confirming acetaminophen overdose with plasma acetaminophen level and assessment of hepatic damage and potential damage to other organ systems, such as kidneys, pancreas, and heart (see "Laboratory Tests"). An acetaminophen ingestion algorithm is described in Section III.

LABORATORY TESTS

- Initial laboratory evaluation consists of plasma acetaminophen level with a second level drawn approximately 4 to 6 hr after the initial level. Subsequent levels can be obtained q2-4h until the levels stabilize or decline. These levels can be plotted using the Rumack-Matthew nomogram (see acetaminophen ingestion algorithm in Section III) to calculate potential hepatic toxicity.
- Transaminases (AST, ALT), bilirubin level, PT, BUN, and creatinine should be initially obtained on all patients.
- Serum and urine toxicology screen for other potential toxic substances is also recommended on admission.

TREATMENT

NONPHARMACOLOGIC THERAPY

Consultation with Poison Control Center for management recommendations is recommended in patients with large ingestions of acetaminophen and/or ingestion of other toxic substances. A toxic dose of acetaminophen usually exceeds 7.5 g in the adult or 140 mg/kg.

ACUTE GENERAL Rx

- Perform gastric lavage and administer activated charcoal if the patient is seen within 1 hr of ingestion or the clinician suspects polydrug ingestion.
- Determine blood levels 4 hr after ingestion; if in the toxic range, start *N*-acetylcysteine (Mucomyst), 140 mg/kg PO as a loading dose, followed by 70 mg/kg PO q4h for 48 hr. (*N*-Acetylcysteine therapy should be started within 24 hr of acetaminophen overdose.) If charcoal therapy was initially instituted, lavage the stomach and recover as much charcoal as possible; then instill *N*-acetylcysteine, increasing the loading dose by 40%.
- Monitor acetaminophen level; use graph to plot possible hepatic toxicity.
- Provide adequate IV hydration (e.g., $D_5$1/2NS at 150 ml/hr).
- If acetaminophen level is nontoxic, acetylcysteine therapy may be discontinued.

DISPOSITION

Most patients will recover fully without persisting hepatic abnormalities. Hepatic failure is particularly unusual in children <6 yr.

REFERRAL

Psychiatric referral is recommended following intentional ingestions.

AUTHOR: **FRED F. FERRI, M.D.**

BASIC INFORMATION

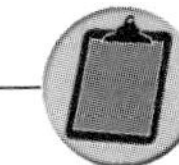

DEFINITION

Achalasia is a motility disorder of the esophagus characterized by inadequate relaxation of the lower esophageal sphincter (LES) and ineffective peristalsis of esophageal smooth muscle. The result is functional obstruction of the esophagus.

SYNONYMS

Esophageal achalasia
Esophageal cardiospasm

ICD-9CM CODES
530.0 Achalasia

EPIDEMIOLOGY & DEMOGRAPHICS

- Annual incidence is about 1 in 100,000 persons.
- Although the onset of symptoms may occur at any age, it is more common in persons 30 to 50 yr old.
- Men and women are affected equally.

PHYSICAL FINDINGS & CLINICAL PRESENTATION

Symptoms:
- Difficulty belching
- Dysphagia to both solids and liquids
- Chest pain and/or heartburn
- Globus
- Frequent hiccups
- Vomiting of undigested food
- Symptoms of aspiration such as nocturnal cough; possible dyspnea and pneumonia

Physical findings:
- Focal lung examination abnormalities and wheezing also possible

ETIOLOGY

- Etiology is poorly understood.
- This motility disorder may be due to autoimmune degeneration of the esophageal myenteric plexus, as association with the HLA class II antigen, DQw1, has been noted.
- Herpes zoster and measles virus have been implicated, but the association has not been confirmed.

DIAGNOSIS

DIFFERENTIAL DIAGNOSIS

- Angina
- Bulimia
- Anorexia nervosa
- Gastric bezoar
- Gastritis
- Peptic ulcer disease
- Postvagotomy dysmotility
- Esophageal disease:
  GERD
  Sarcoidosis
  Amyloidosis
  Esophageal stricture
  Esophageal webs and rings
  Scleroderma
  Barrett's esophagus
- Chagas' disease
  Esophagitis
  Diffuse esophageal spasm
- Malignancy:
  Esophageal cancer
  Infiltrating gastric cancer
  Lung cancer
  Lymphoma

WORKUP

- Physical examination and laboratory analyses to rule out other causes and assess complications
- Imaging studies and manometry for diagnosis

LABORATORY TESTS

- Assessment of nutritional status with albumin and prealbumin if indicated
- CBC, ECG, stress test, stool and emesis for occult blood if diagnosis is in doubt

IMAGING STUDIES

Barium swallow with fluoroscopy may demonstrate the following findings:
- Uncoordinated or absent esophageal contractions
- An acutely tapered contrast column ("bird's beak," Fig. 1-5)
- Dilation of the distal (smooth muscle portion) esophagus
- Esophageal air fluid level

Manometry may be indicated if barium swallow is inconclusive. Characteristic abnormalities are as follows:
- Low-amplitude disorganized contractions
- High intraesophageal resting pressure
- High LES pressure
- Inadequate LES relaxation after swallow

Direct visualization by endoscopy can rule out other causes of dysphagia.

TREATMENT

Three modalities of treatment:
- Medical:
  Smooth muscle relaxants including nitrates and calcium channel blockers are effective in up to 70% of patients. Botulinum toxin injection will benefit up to 90% of patients but will require repeat injections.
- Mechanical dilation:
  Fixed or pneumatic dilators may benefit up to 90%. Esophageal rupture or perforation is a rare complication that can be managed conservatively in some stable patients.
- Surgical:
  Open and thoracoscopic esophagomyotomy is available and effective (90%). This approach currently offers the most durable symptom relief. About 10% of patients undergoing surgery will have symptomatic reflux disease.

DISPOSITION

Prognosis is excellent in patients who respond to therapy, but in some patients more than one treatment modality may be necessary. In long-standing disease or inadequately treated disease, there is an increased risk of squamous cell carcinoma. Chronic GERD, as a result of treatment, may be complicated by Barrett's esophagus and malignant transformation.

REFERRAL

Choice of and response to therapy will determine referral. Some surgeons may not be facile with thoracoscopic procedures.

SUGGESTED READINGS

Harris AM et al: Achalasia management, outcome and surveillance in a specialist unit, *Br J Surg* 87(3):364, 2000.
Spiess AE, Kahrilas PJ: Treating achalasia, *JAMA* 280:638, 1998.
Vaezi MF, Richter JE: Practice guidelines: diagnosis and management of achalasia, *Am J Gastroenterol* 94(12):3406, 1999.
Vaezi MF et al: Botulinum toxin versus pneumatic dilatation in the treatment of achalasia: a randomized trial, *Gut* 44:231, 1999.

AUTHORS: **JAMES J. NG, M.D.**, and **PAUL A. PIRRAGLIA, M.D., M.P.H.**

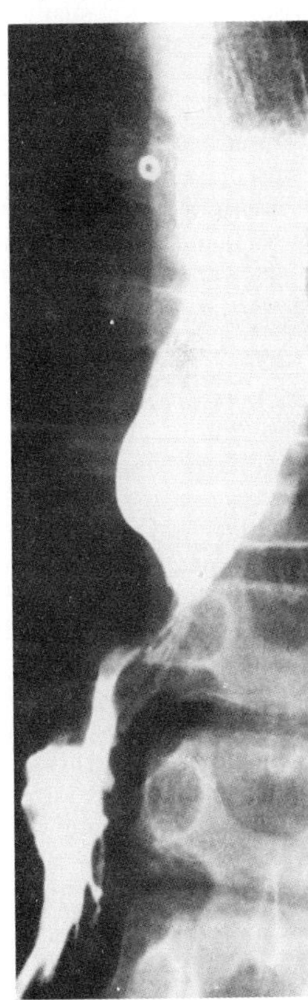

FIGURE 1-5 Classic appearance of achalasia of the esophagus. The dilated esophagus ends in a narrow segment. (From Hoekelman R [ed]: *Primary pediatric care,* ed 3, St Louis, 1997, Mosby.)

Achilles Tendon Rupture

BASIC INFORMATION

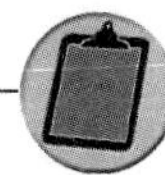

DEFINITION

Achilles tendon rupture refers to the loss of continuity of the *tendo Achillis,* usually from attrition.

ICD-9CM CODES
845.09 Achilles tendon rupture

EPIDEMIOLOGY & DEMOGRAPHICS

PREDOMINANT AGE: 30 to 55 yr

PHYSICAL FINDINGS & CLINICAL PRESENTATION

Injury often occurs during an activity that puts great stress on the tendon. Sudden "pop" is often felt followed by weakness and swelling.

- Patient walks flat-footed and is unable to stand on the ball of the foot.
- Tenderness and hemorrhage are present at the site of injury, and a sulcus is usually palpable but may be obscured by an organizing clot if the examination is delayed.
- Although active plantar flexion is usually lost, some plantar flexion occasionally remains because of the activity of the other posterior compartment muscles.
- Thompson's test is usually positive. Test measures plantar flexion of the foot when the calf is squeezed with the patient kneeling on a chair; normal foot plantarflexes with calf compression, but movement is absent when *tendo Achillis* is ruptured.
- Excessive passive dorsiflexion of the foot is also present on the injured side (Fig. 1-6).

ETIOLOGY

- Relative hypovascularity predisposing to tendon rupture in several tendons (Achilles, biceps, and supraspinatus)
- With advancing age, vascular supply to the tendon further compromised
- Repetitive trauma leading to degeneration of this critical area and weakness
- Rupture of *tendo Achillis* usually 2.5 to 5 cm from the insertion of the tendon into the os calcis
- Most common causative event leading to rupture: sudden dorsiflexion of the plantar flexed foot (landing from a height) or sudden pushing off with the weight on the forefoot

DIAGNOSIS

DIFFERENTIAL DIAGNOSIS

- Incomplete (partial) *tendo Achillis* rupture
- Partial rupture of gastrocnemius muscle, often medial head (previously thought to be "plantaris tendon rupture")

WORKUP

- Clinical diagnosis of *tendo Achillis* rupture is usually obvious.
- If bony injury is suspected, plain roentgenograms are indicated.
- Other studies are usually unnecessary.

TREATMENT

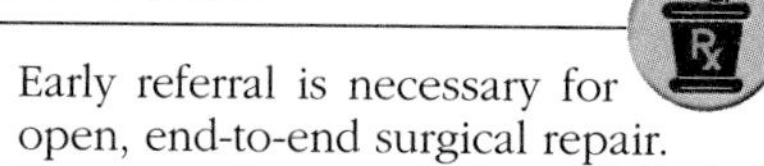

- Early referral is necessary for open, end-to-end surgical repair.
- If surgery is contraindicated, a short leg cast applied with the foot in equinus may allow healing.
- In cases of neglected rupture, reconstruction is usually indicated.
- Physical therapy is helpful after repair to restore strength and flexibility.

DISPOSITION

- Prognosis for recovery after surgical repair of the acute rupture is good, but recurrence is not uncommon regardless of treatment.
- *Tendo Achillis* must be protected from excessive activity for up to 1 yr.
- Results of reconstruction for neglected cases are worse than with primary repair.
- Return to work with limited weight-bearing is possible in 2 to 4 weeks.

SUGGESTED READINGS

Bhandari M et al: Treatment of acute Achilles tendon rupture: a systematic overview and metaanalysis, *Clin Orthop* (400):190, 2002.

Kocher MS et al: Operative versus nonoperative management of acute achilles tendon rupture: expected-value decision analysis, *Am J Sports Med* 30(6):783, 2002.

Maffulli N, Kader D: Tendinopathy of tendo Achillis, *J Bone Joint Surg Br* 84(1):1, 2002.

Mazzone MF, McCue T: Common conditions of the Achilles tendon, *Am Fam Physician* 65(9):1805, 2002.

Roberts C, Deliss L: Acute rupture of tendo Achillis, *J Bone Joint Surg Br* 84(4):620, 2002.

Schepsis AA, Jones H, Haas AL: Achilles tendon disorders in athletes, *Am J Sports Med* 30(2):287, 2002.

Wallace RG, Traynor IE et al. Combined conservative and orthotic management of acute ruptures of the Achiles tendon. *J Bone Joint Surg* 86A:1198, 2004.

Wong J, Barrass V, Maffulli N: Quantitative review of operative and nonoperative management of Achilles tendon ruptures, *Am J Sports Med* 30(4):565, 2002.

AUTHOR: **LONNIE R. MERCIER, M.D.**

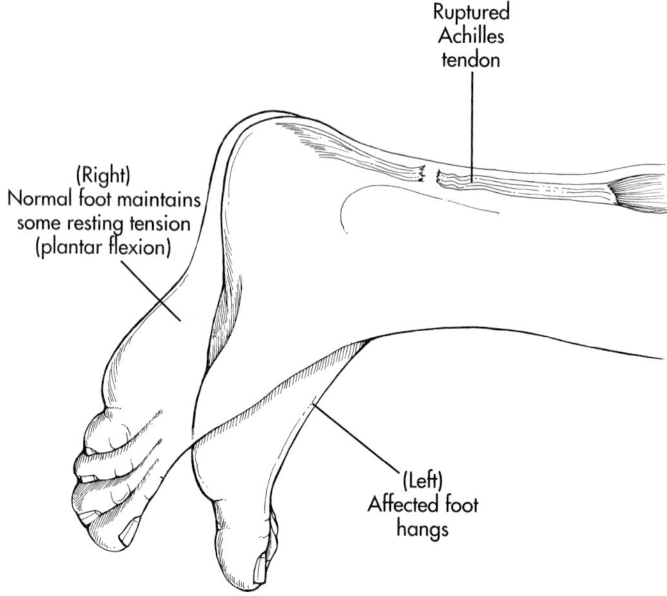

FIGURE 1-6 Observation of Achilles tendon rupture. The patient is asked to lie prone on the examining table with feet hanging off the end. The intact leg retains inherent plantar flexion, whereas on the injured side, the foot hangs straight down with gravity. (From Scudieri G [ed]: *Sports medicine: principles of primary care,* St Louis, 1997, Mosby.)

BASIC INFORMATION

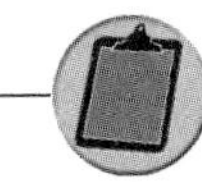

DEFINITION

Acne vulgaris is a chronic disorder of the pilosebaceous apparatus caused by abnormal desquamation of follicular epithelium leading to obstruction of the pilosebaceous canal, resulting in inflammation and subsequent formation of papules, pustules, nodules, comedones, and scarring. Acne can be classified by the type of lesion (comedonal, papulopustular, and nodulocystic). The American Academy of Dermatology classification scheme for acne denotes the following three levels:

1. Mild acne: characterized by the presence of few to several papules and pustules but no nodules.
2. Moderate acne: presence of several to many papules and pustules along with nodules.
3. Severe acne: presence of numerous or extensive papules and pustules as well as many nodules.

SYNONYMS

Acne

ICD-9CM CODES
706.1 Acne vulgaris

EPIDEMIOLOGY & DEMOGRAPHICS

- Acne is the most common skin disease in the U.S.
- It is most common in teenagers (highest incidence between ages of 16 and 18 yr).

PHYSICAL FINDINGS & CLINICAL PRESENTATION

- Open comedones (blackheads), closed comedones (whiteheads)
- Greasiness (oily skin)
- Presence of scars from prior acne cysts
- Various stages of development and severity may be present concomitantly
- Common distribution of acne: face, back, and upper chest
- Inflammatory papules, pustules, and ectatic pores

ETIOLOGY

- Overactivity of the sebaceous glands and blockage in the ducts. The obstruction leads to the formation of comedones, which can become inflamed because of overgrowth of *Propionibacterium acnes*.
- Exacerbated by environmental factors (hot, humid, tropical climate), medications (e.g., iodine in cough mixtures, hair greases), industrial exposure to halogenated hydrocarbons.

DIAGNOSIS

DIFFERENTIAL DIAGNOSIS

- Gram-negative folliculitis
- Staphylococcal pyoderma
- Acne rosacea
- Drug eruption
- Sebaceous hyperplasia
- Angiofibromas, basal cell carcinomas, osteoma cutis
- Occupational exposures to oils or grease
- Steroid acne

WORKUP

History and physical examination:

- Inquire about previous treatment
- Careful drug history
- Family history, history of cyclic menstrual flares
- History of use of cosmetics and cleansers
- Oral contraceptive use

LABORATORY TESTS

- Laboratory evaluation is generally not helpful.
- Patients who are candidates for therapy with isotretinoin (Accutane) should have baseline liver enzymes, cholesterol, and triglycerides checked, because this medication may result in elevation of lipids and liver enzymes.
- A negative serum pregnancy test or two negative urine pregnancy tests should also be obtained in females 1 wk before initiation of isotretinoin; it is also imperative to maintain effective contraception during and 1 mo after therapy with isotretinoin ends because of its teratogenic effects. Pregnancy status should be rechecked at monthly visits.
- In female patients if hyperandrogenism is suspected, levels of dehydroepiandrosterone sulfate (DHEAS), testosterone (total and free), and androstenedione should be measured. Generally for women with regular menstrual cycles, serum androgen measurements are not necessary.

TREATMENT

NONPHARMACOLOGIC THERAPY

- Blue light (ClearLight therapy system) can be used for treatment of moderate inflammatory acne vulgaris. Light in the violet/blue range can cause bacterial death by a photoreaction in which porphyrins react with oxygen to generate reactive oxygen species, which damage the cell membranes of *P. acnes*. Treatment usually consists of 15 min exposures twice weekly for 4 wk.

ACUTE GENERAL Rx

Treatment generally varies with the type of lesions (comedones, papules, pustules, cystic lesions) and the severity of acne.

- Comedones can be treated with retinoids or retinoid analogs. Topical retinoids are comedolytic and work by normalizing follicular keratinization. Commonly available agents are Adapalene (Differin, 0.1% gel or cream, applied once or twice daily), Tazarotene (Tazorac 0.1% cream or gel applied daily), tretinoin (Retin-A 0.1% cream or 0.025 gel applied once qhs), tretinoin microsphere (Retin-A Micro, 0.1% gel, applied at hs). Tretinoin is inactivated by UV light and oxydized by benzoyl peroxide, therefore it should only be applied at night and not used concomitantly with benzoyl peroxide. Tretinoin is pregnancy category C, tazarotene is pregnancy category X. Salicylic acid preparations (e.g., Neutrogena 2% wash) have keratolytic and antiinflammatory properties and are also useful in the treatment of comedones. Large open comedones (blackheads) should be expressed.
- Patients should be reevaluated after 4 to 6 wk. Benzoyl peroxide gel (2.5% or 5%) may be added if the comedones become inflamed or form pustules. The most common adverse effects are dryness, erythema, and peeling. Topical antibiotics (erythromycin, clindamycin lotions or pads) can also be used in patients with significant inflammation. They reduce *P. acnes* in the pilosebaceous follicle and have some antiinflammatory effects. The combination of 5% benzoyl peroxide and 3% erythromycin (Benzamycin) or 1% clindamycin with 5% benzoyl peroxide (Benzaclin) are highly effective in patients who have a mixture of comedonal and inflammatory acne lesions.
- Pustular acne can be treated with tretinoin and benzoyl peroxide gel applied on alternate evenings; drying agents (sulfacetamide-sulfa lotions [Novacet, Sulfacet]) are also effective when used in combination with benzoyl peroxide; oral antibiotics (doxycycline 100 mg qd or erythromycin 1 g qd given in 2 to 3 divided doses) are effective in patients with moderate to severe pustular acne; patients not responding well to these antibiotics can be switched over to minocycline 50 to 100 mg bid; however, this medication is more expensive.

- Patients with nodular cystic acne can be treated with systemic agents: antibiotics (erythromycin, tetracycline, doxycycline, minocycline), isotretinoin (Accutane), or oral contraceptives. Periodic intralesional triamcinolone (Kenalog) injections by a dermatologist are also effective. The possibility of endocrinopathy should be considered in patients responding poorly to therapy.
- Isotretinoin is indicated for acne resistant to antibiotic therapy and severe acne; dosage is 0.5 to 1 mg/kg/day in 2 divided doses (maximum of 2 mg/kg/day); duration of therapy is generally 20 wk for a cumulative dose ≥120 mg/kg for severe cystic acne; before using this medication patients should undergo baseline laboratory evaluation (see "Laboratory Tests"). This drug is absolutely contraindicated during pregnancy because of its teratogenicity. It should be used with caution in patients with history of depression. In order to prescribe this drug, physicians must be a registered member of the manufacturer's System to Manage Accutane-Related Teratogenicity (SMART) program.
- Azelaic acid is a bacteriostatic dicarboxylic acid used to normalize keratinization and reduce inflammation.
- Oral contraceptives reduce androgen levels and therefore sebum production. They represent a useful adjunctive therapy for all types of acne in women and adolescent girls. Commonly used agents are norgestimate/ethinyl estradiol (Ortho Tri-Cyclen) and drospirenone/ethinyl estradiol (Yasmin).

REFERRAL

Referral for intralesional injection and dermabrasion should be considered in patients with severe acne unresponsive to conventional therapy.

PEARLS & CONSIDERATIONS

- Gram-negative folliculitis should be suspected if inflammatory acne worsens after several months of oral antibiotic therapy.
- Acne may worsen during the first 3 to 4 weeks of retinoid therapy before improving.

COMMENTS

Indications for systemic therapy of acne are:

- Painful deep papules or nodules
- Extensive lesions
- Active acne with severe scarring or hyperpigmentation
- Patient's morale

Patients should be educated that in most cases acne can be controlled but not cured and that at least 4 to 6 wk of initial therapy should be required before significant improvement is noted.

SUGGESTED READINGS

Feldman S et al: Diagnosis and treatment of acne, *Am Fam Physician* 69:2123, 2004.

Haider A, Shaw JC: Treatment of acne vulgaris, *JAMA* 292:726, 2004.

AUTHOR: **FRED F. FERRI, M.D.**

BASIC INFORMATION

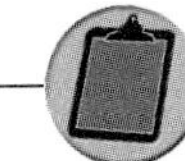

DEFINITION

Acoustic neuroma is a benign proliferation of the Schwann cells that cover the vestibular branch of the eighth cranial nerve (CN VIII). Symptoms are commonly a result of compression of the acoustic branch of CN VIII, the facial nerve (CN VII), and the trigeminal nerve (CN V). The glossopharyngeal nerve (CN IX) and vagus nerve (CN X) are less commonly involved. In extreme cases, compression of the brainstem may lead to obstruction of cerebrospinal fluid (CSF) outflow and elevated intracranial pressure (ICP).

SYNONYMS

Vestibular schwannoma

ICD-9CM CODES
225.1 Acoustic neuroma

EPIDEMIOLOGY & DEMOGRAPHICS

Annual incidence is about 1 in 100,000 patients per year. There may be a slight female predominance. The tumor most commonly presents in the fifth and sixth decades.

PHYSICAL FINDINGS & CLINICAL PRESENTATION

- Most frequently unilateral hearing loss and/or tinnitus. Also balance problems, vertigo, facial pain (trigeminal neuralgia) and weakness, difficulty swallowing, fullness or pain of the involved ear. Headache may occur.
- With elevated ICP, patients may also suffer from vomiting, fever, and visual changes.
- Hearing loss is the most common presenting complaint and is usually high frequency.

ETIOLOGY

The etiology is incompletely understood, but long-term exposure to acoustic trauma has been implicated. Bilateral acoustic neuromas may be inherited in an autosomal dominant manner as part of neurofibromatosis type 2. This disease is associated with a defect on chromosome 22q1.

DIAGNOSIS

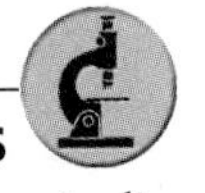

DIFFERENTIAL DIAGNOSIS

Benign positional vertigo, Meniere's disease, trigeminal neuralgia, cerebellar disease, normal-pressure hydrocephalus, presbycusis, glomus tumors, vertebrobasilar insufficiency, ototoxicity from medications, and other tumors: meningioma, glioma, facial nerve schwannoma, cavernous hemangioma, metastatic tumors

WORKUP

Physical examination, laboratory analysis, and imaging studies

PHYSICAL EXAMINATION

- A detailed neurologic examination with special attention to the cranial nerves is crucial.
- Otoscopic evaluation may help to rule out other causes of hearing loss.

LABORATORY TESTS

- Audiometry is useful, often shows asymmetric, sensorineural, high frequency hearing loss.
- CSF protein may be elevated.

IMAGING STUDIES

- MRI with gadolinium is the preferred test. It can detect tumors as small as 2 mm in diameter.
- CT scan with contrast can detect tumors 1 cm in diameter or larger (Fig. 1-7).

TREATMENT

Treatment decisions should be based on the size of the tumor, rate of growth (older patients tend to have slower-growing tumors), degree of neurologic deficit, desire to preserve hearing, life expectancy, age of the patient, and surgical risk. A combination of treatments can also be employed.

- Surgery is the definitive treatment. Choice of approach (middle cranial fossa, translabyrinthine, or retromastoid suboccipital) may vary depending on the size of the tumor, amount of residual hearing desired, and degree of surgical risk that can be tolerated. Partial resection is sometimes undertaken to minimize the risk of injury to nearby structures. Intraoperative facial nerve monitoring is recommended.
- Radiation therapy (stereotactic radiotherapy, stereotactic radiosurgery, or proton beam radiotherapy) is useful for tumors <3 cm in diameter or for those in whom surgery is not an option. Radiotherapy following partial resection has also been used to minimize complications.
- Observation with MRI every 6 to 12 mo may be appropriate for frail patients with small tumors, but risk of unrecoverable hearing loss may increase if surgery is delayed. Age alone is not a contraindication to surgery.

DISPOSITION

Hearing can be preserved at near preoperative levels in more than two thirds of patients with small- to medium-sized tumors.

REFERRAL

Prompt referral to an ENT specialist or neurosurgeon who is facile with all three surgical approaches is recommended.

SUGGESTED READINGS

Kondziolka D et al: Long-term outcomes after radiosurgery for acoustic neuromas, *N Engl J Med* 339:1426, 1999.

Pitts LH, Jackler RK: Treatment of acoustic neuromas, *N Engl J Med* 339:1471, 1998.

Poen JC et al: Fractionated stereotactic radiosurgery and preservation of hearing in patients with vestibular schwannoma: a preliminary report, *Neurosurgery* 45(6):1299, 1999.

Schmidt RJ et al: The sensitivity of auditory brainstem response testing for the diagnosis of acoustic neuroma, *Arch Otolaryngol Head Neck Surg* 127(1):19, 2001.

AUTHORS: **PAUL PIRRAGLIA, M.D.,** and **JAMES J. NG, M.D.**

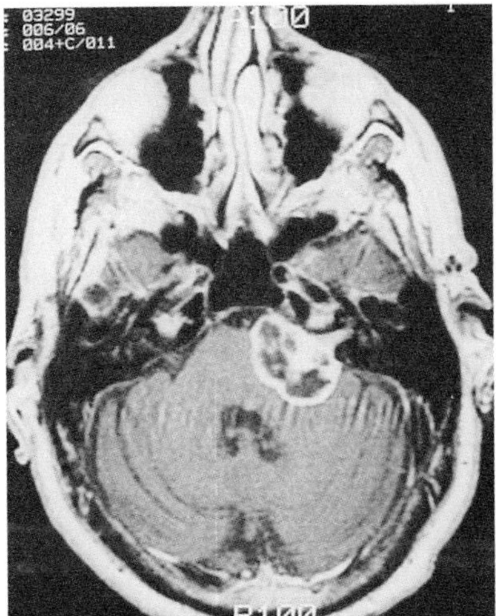

FIGURE 1-7 Acoustic schwannoma. Axial, postcontrast-enhanced T1 weighted image demonstrates an inhomogeneously contrast-enhancing mass in the left cerebellopontine angle with extension into the left internal auditory canal. There is associated displacement of the brainstem. (From Specht N [ed]: *Practical guide to diagnostic imaging,* St Louis, 1998, Mosby.)

BASIC INFORMATION

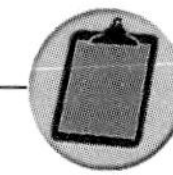

DEFINITION

Acquired immunodeficiency syndrome (AIDS) is a disorder caused by infection with the human immunodeficiency virus, type 1 (HIV-1) and marked by progressive deterioration of the cellular immune system, leading to secondary infections or malignancies.

SYNONYMS

AIDS

ICD-9CM CODES
042.9 AIDS, unspecified

EPIDEMIOLOGY & DEMOGRAPHICS

INCIDENCE (IN U.S.):
- 27.1 cases/100,000 persons
- Varies widely by location
- 85% of cases in large cities

PREVALENCE (IN U.S.): 62 cases/ 100,000 persons
PREDOMINANT SEX: Males 84%, females 16% (through 1998).
40% of newly reported U.S. cases in 1999 were in females.
PREDOMINANT AGE: 80% between ages 20 and 40 yr
PEAK INCIDENCE: See Incidence
GENETICS:
- Familial disposition: Although there is no proven genetic predisposition, individuals with deletions in the CCR5 gene are immune from infection with macrophage tropic virus (the predominant virus in sexual transmission).
- Congenital infection:
  1. Transmittable from an infected mother to the fetus in utero in as many as 30% of pregnancies.
  2. No specific congenital malformations associated with infection; low birth weight and spontaneous abortion are possible.
- Neonatal infection: transmission possible to the neonate intrapartum or postpartum through breast-feeding.

PHYSICAL FINDINGS & CLINICAL PRESENTATION

- Nonspecific findings: fever, weight loss, anorexia
- Specific syndromes:
  1. Seen in association with opportunistic infection and malignancies, so-called indicator diseases (see Box 1-1)
  2. Most common:
     Respiratory infections (*Pneumocystis carinii* pneumonia, TB, bacterial pneumonia, fungal infection)
     CNS infections (toxoplasmosis, cryptococcal meningitis, TB)
     GI (cryptosporidiosis, isosporiasis, cytomegalovirus); Sections II and III describe organisms associated with diarrhea in patients with AIDS
     Eye infections (cytomegalovirus, toxoplasmosis)
     Kaposi's sarcoma (cutaneous or visceral) or lymphoma (nodal or extranodal)
- Possibly asymptomatic
- Diagnosis of AIDS if T-lymphocyte subset analysis demonstrating CD4 cell count <200 or <14% of total lymphocyte in the presence of proven HIV infection even in the absence of other infections
- The various manifestations of HIV infection are described in Section II

ETIOLOGY

- Caused by infection with human immunodeficiency virus, type 1 (HIV-1)
- Transmitted by heterosexual or male homosexual contact, needle-sharing (during IV drug use), transfusion of contaminated blood or blood products, and from infected mother to fetus or neonate as described previously

DIAGNOSIS

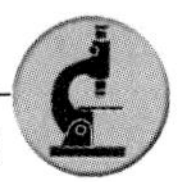

DIFFERENTIAL DIAGNOSIS

- Other wasting illnesses mimicking the nonspecific features of AIDS:
  1. TB
  2. Neoplasms
  3. Disseminated fungal infection
  4. Malabsorption syndromes
  5. Depression
- Other disorders associated with dementia or demyelination producing encephalopathy, myelopathy, or neuropathy

WORKUP

Prompt evaluation of respiratory, CNS, GI complaints

LABORATORY TESTS

- HIV antibody testing
- T-lymphocyte subset analysis: performed to determine the degree of immunodeficiency
- Viral load assay: to plan long-term antiviral therapy consider genotype or phenotype sensitivity testing for patients failing therapy
- CSF examination: for meningitis
- Serologic tests for syphilis, hepatitis B, hepatitis C, and toxoplasmosis
- Genotypic resistance testing: used to assess for primary resistance in naïve patients and secondary resistance in patients failing a regimen
- Eye exam: to evaluate for CMV retinitis in patients with CD counts <50 cells/mm³
- Cryptococcal antigen: part of the evaluation in AIDS patients with CD4 <100 cells/mm³ who have fever, diffuse pneumonia, or symptoms of meningitis

BOX 1-1 Conditions Included in the 1993 AIDS Surveillance I Case Definition

Bacterial infections, multiple or recurrent*
Candidiasis of bronchi, trachea, or lungs
Candidiasis, esophageal
Cervical cancer, invasive†
Coccidioidomycosis, disseminated or extrapulmonary
Cryptococcosis, extrapulmonary
Cryptosporidiosis, chronic intestinal (>1-mo duration)
Cytomegalovirus disease (other than liver, spleen, or nodes)
Cytomegalovirus retinitis (with loss of vision)
Encephalopathy, HIV related
Herpes simplex, chronic ulcer(s) (>1-mo duration); or bronchitis, pneumonitis, or esophagitis
Histoplasmosis, disseminated or extrapulmonary
Isoporiasis, chronic intestinal (>1-mo duration)
Kaposi's sarcoma
Lymphoid interstitial pneumonia and/or pulmonary lymphoid hyperplasia*
Lymphoma, Burkitt's (or equivalent term)
Lymphoma, primary, of brain
Mycobacterium avium-intracellulare complex or *Myobacterium kansasii,* disseminated or extrapulmonary
Mycobacterium tuberculosis, any site (pulmonary† or extrapulmonary)
Mycobacterium, other species or unidentified species, disseminated or extrapulmonary
Pneumocystis carinii pneumonia
Pneumonia, recurrent†
Progressive multifocal leukoencephalopathy
Salmonella septicemia, recurrent
Toxoplasmosis of brain
Wasting syndrome of HIV infection

*Children younger than 13 years.
†Added in the 1993 expansion of the AIDS surveillance case definition for adolescents and adults.

IMAGING STUDIES

- Cerebral CT for encephalopathy or focal CNS complications (e.g., toxoplasmosis, lymphoma)
- Pulmonary gallium scanning to aid in the diagnosis of a *Pneumocystis carinii* pneumonia
- Baseline chest x-ray

TREATMENT

NONPHARMACOLOGIC THERAPY

- Maintain adequate caloric intake
- Encourage good oral hygiene, regular dental care

ACUTE GENERAL Rx

Acute management of opportunistic infections and malignancies is reviewed elsewhere in this text under specific AIDS-related disorders.

CHRONIC Rx

For all HIV-infected patients, particularly those meeting the case definition of AIDS:

- Preventive therapy for *Pneumocystis carinii* pneumonia and TB (see specific chapters elsewhere in this text). With the advent of modern antiretroviral therapy many patients have experienced substantial restoration of cellular immune function. It has become clear that preventive therapy for *Pneumocystis carinii* and *Mycobacterium avium* complex as well as suppressive therapy for cytomegaloviral and cryptococcal infection can often be safely withdrawn if the CD4 cell count rises above 200 for at least 6 months.
- Antiretroviral therapy employing combinations of nucleoside derivative agents: zidovudine (AZT), didanosine (DDI), zalcitabine (DDC), lamivudine (3TC), stavudine (D4T), abacavir in addition to protease inhibitors (saquinavir, indinavir, nelfinavir, agenerase, ritonavir/lopinavir, atazanavir) nonnucleoside reverse transcriptase inhibitors (nevirapine, delavirdine, efavirenz) or the nucleotide agent tenofovir according to current recommendations based on clinical stage and viral load studies. The protease inhibitor ritonavir is often used, in low dose, in combination with other protease inhibitors to obtain more sustained drug levels. See Tables 1-2 through 1-6.
- An approach to evaluating chronic diarrhea in patients with HIV infection, the approach to the acutely ill HIV-infected patient, and the evaluation of respiratory complaints are described in Section III, Fig. 3-91. Approach to a patient with a suspected CNS lesion is also described in Section III.
- Genotypic resistance testing should be strongly considered for any patient failing antiretroviral therapy. Poor adherence to therapy, however, often underlies virologic failure.

REFERRAL

All patients with AIDS: to a physician knowledgeable and experienced in the management of the disease and its complications

SUGGESTED READINGS

Hermsen ED, Wynn HE, McNabb J: Discontinuation of prophylaxis for HIV-associated opportunistic infections in the era of highly active antiretroviral therapy, *Am J Health Syst Pharm* 61(3):245, 2004.

Kantor R et al: Evolution of resistance to drugs in HIV-1-infected patients failing antiretroviral therapy, *AIDS* 18(11):1503, 2004.

Klein MB et al: The impact of initial highly active antiretroviral therapy on future treatment sequences in HIV infectiion, *AIDS* 18(14):1895, 2004.

Monier PL, Wilcox R: Metabolic complications associated with the use of highly active antiretroviral therapy in HIV-1-infected adults, *Am J Med Sci* 328(1):48, 2004.

Volberding PA: Initiating HIV therapy: timing is critical, controversial, *Postgrad Med* 115(2):15, 2004.

Wang C et al: Mortality in HIV-seropositive versus—seronegative persons in the era of highly active antiretroviral therapy: implications for when to initiate therapy, *J Infect Dis* 190(6):1046, 2004.

AUTHOR: **JOSEPH R. MASCI, M.D.**

TABLE 1-2 **Approved Nucleoside Reverse Transcriptase Inhibitors**

Agent	Trade name	Oral bioavailability (%)	Serum half-life (H)	Intracellular half-life of triphosphate (H)	Elimination	Dose*	Availabiility	Major adverse effects‡
Zidovudine	Retrovir	63	1.1	3-4	Hepatic glucuronidation Renal excretion	Adults: 200 mg PO q8h or 300 mg PO q12h Pediatric: 90-180 mg/m² PO q6-12h, up to adult dose	300-mg tablets 100-mg capsules 10-mg/ml syrup 10-mg/ml solution for IV infusion	Headache Insomnia Gastrointestinal intolerance Fatigue Anemia Neutropenia Myositis
Didanosine	Videx EC	40	1.5	8-24	Cellular metabolism	Adult ≥60 kg: 400 mg PO qd; buffered tablets or enteric coated capsule 200 mg PO q12h; buffered tablets	25-mg, 50-mg, 100-mg, 150-mg chewable tablets	Diarrhea Abdominal discomfort Nausea Peripheral neuropathy Pancreatitis
					Renal excretion	Adult <60 kg: 250 mg PO qd; buffered tablets or enteric tablets or enteric coated capsule 125 mg PO q12h; buffered tablets	100-mg, 167-mg, 250-mg powder packets	
						Pediatric: 90-150 mg/m² PO q12h of solution up to adult dose	10-mg/ml solution	
Zalcitabine	Hivid	87	1.2	2.6	Renal excretion	Adult: 0.75 mg PO q8h	0.375-mg, 0.75-mg tablets	Peripheral neuropathy Pancreatitis Oral ulcers
Stavudine	Zerit	86	1.1	3	Renal excretion	Adult ≥60 kg: 40 mg PO q12h Adult <60 kg: 30 mg PO q12h Pediatric: 1 mg/kg q12h, up to adult dose	15-mg, 20-mg, 30-mg, 40-mg capsules 1-mg/ml solution	Peripheral neuropathy
Lamivudine	Epivir	86	2.5	11-14	Renal excretion	Adult: 150 mg PO q12h 300mg PO qd Pediatric: 4 mg/kg PO q12h, up to adult dose	150-mg, 300-mg tablets 10-mg/ml solution	Headache Fatigue
Abacavir	Ziagen	83	1.5	3.3	Hepatic glucuronidation and carboxylation	Adult: 300 mg PO q12h Pediatric: 8 mg/kg PO q12h, up to adult dose	300-mg tablets 20-mg/ml solution	Hypersensitivity reaction
Zidovudine + Lamivudine	Combivir†					Adult: One tablet PO q12h	300-mg zidovudine/150-mg lamivudine tablet	
Zidovudine + Lamimudine + Abacavir	Trizivir	—	—	—	—	Adult: One tablet PO q12h	300-mg zidovudine/150-mg lamivudine 300-mg abacavir	Hypersensitivity reaction (due to abacavir)

Adapted from Mandell GL: *Mandell, Douglas, and Bennett's principles and practice of infectious diseases,* ed 5, New York, 2000, Churchill Livingstone.
*Neonatal dose may differ significantly from pediatric dose described here.
†Pharmacokinetic properties, adverse effects, and drug interactions are similar to those of lamivudine and zidovudine used separately.
‡All nucleoside reverse transcriptase inhibitors may also be associated with rare occurrence of potentially fatal lactic acidosis and hepatomegaly with steatosis.

TABLE 1-2 Approved Nucleoside Reverse Transcriptase Inhibitors—cont'd

Agent	Trade name	Oral bioavailability (%)	Serum half-life (H)	Elimination	Dose*	Availabiility	Major adverse effects‡
Nevirapine	Viramune	>90	>24	Hepatic cytochrome P450	Adult: 200 mg PO qd for 14 d, then 200 mg PO q12h if no rash develops Pediatric: 120 mg/m2 PO qd for 14 d then increase to 120-200 mg/m2 PO q12h if no rash develops, up to adult dose	200-mg tablets	Rash Elevated hepatic transaminases
Delavirdine	Rescriptor	85	5.8	Hepatic cytochrome P450	Adult: 400 mg PO q8h	100-mg, 200-mg tablets	Rash Dizziness
Efavirenz	Sustiva		>24	Hepatic cytochrome P450	Adult: 600 mg PO qd	50 mg-, 100 mg-, 200 mg, 600-mg capsules	Headache Rash

*Neonatal dose may differ significantly from pediatric dose described here.

TABLE 1-3 Approved Protease Inhibitors

Agent	Trade name	Oral bioavailability (%)	Serum half-life (H)	Elimination	Dose*	Availabiility	Major adverse effects†
Saquinavir (soft gel capsule)	Fortovase		1-2	Hepatic cytochrome P450	Adult: 1200 mg PO q8h	200-mg soft gel capsules	Nausea Diarrhea Abdominal discomfort
Saquinavir (hard capsule)	Invirase	4	1-2	Hepatic cytochrome P450	Adult: When used in combination with ritonavir, 400-600 mg PO q12h When used in combination with ritonavir, 1000/100 mg SQV/RTV PO bid or 400/400 mg SQV/RTV PO bid	200-mg hard capsules	Nausea Diarrhea Abdominal discomfort
Ritonavir	Norvir	70	3.2	Hepatic cytochrome P450	Adult: 300 mg PO q12h with escalation over 1-2 wk to 600 mg PO q12h Pediatric: 250 mg/m2 of solution PO q12h with escalation over 1-2 wk to 400 mg/m2 PO q12h, up to adult dose	100-mg capsules 80-mg/ml solution	Nausea, vomiting Diarrhea Abdominal discomfort Circumoral or peripheral paresthesias Fatigue Altered taste Hypercholesterolemia Hypertriglyceridemia Elevated hepatic transaminases
Indinavir	Crixivan	60-65	1.8	Hepatic cytochrome P450	Adults: 800 mg PO q8h When used in combination with ritonavir, 400/400 mg or 800/100 mg or 800/200 mg IDV/RTV PO bid	200-mg, 400-mg capsules	Nausea Abdominal discomfort Nephrolithiasis Hyperbilirubinemia Diarrhea
Nelfinavir	Viracept	20-80	3.5-5	Hepatic cytochrome P450	Adult: 750 mg PO q8h Pediatric: 20-30 mg/kg q8h, up to adult dose	250-mg tablets 50-mg/g powder	Nausea, vomiting Rash
Amprenavir	Agenerase		9	Hepatic cytochrome P450	Adult: Capsule 1200 mg PO q12h When used in combination with ritonavir, 600/100 mg APV/RTV PO q12 or 1200/200 mg APV/RTV PO qd Pediatric: Capsule 20 mg/kg PO q12h or 15 mg/kg PO q8h, up to adult dose; solution 22.5 mg/kg PO q12h or 17 mg/kg PO q8h, up to 2800	50-mg, 150-mg capsules 15 mg/ml solution	
Lopinavir/ritonavir	Kaletra	Not yet established	5-6	Hepatic cytochrome P450	3 capsules 2×/day	Soft-gel capsules 133.3 mg lopinavir 33.3 mg ritonavir	Diarrhea, pancreatitis
Atazanavir	Reyataz	Not yet established	7	Hepatic	400 mg PO qd. When dosed with ritonavir, 300/100 mg ATZ/RTV PO qd	100-mg, 150-mg, 200-mg capsules	Hyperbilirubinemia

Adapted from Mandell GL: *Mandell, Douglas, and Bennett's principles and practice of infectious diseases,* ed 5, New York, 2000, Churchill Livingstone.
*Neonatal dose may differ significantly from pediatric dose described here.
†All protease inhibitors may be associated with hyperglycemia and changes in body fat distribution. They may also be associated with rare episodes of hemorrhage in persons with hemophilia.

TABLE 1-4 Approved Nucleotide Reverse Transcriptase Inhibitor

Agent	Trade name	Oral bio-availability (%)	Serum half-life (H)	Elimination	Dose	Availability	Major adverse effects
Tenofovir	Viread	25	—	Renal	300 mg/d	300-mg tablet	Nausea, vomiting, diarrhea

TABLE 1-5 Therapy for Opportunistic Infections in Patients with HIV Infection

Clinical disease	Drug	Dose	Route	Interval	Duration
Pneumocystis pneumonia	Trimethoprim with sulfamethoxazole *or*	5 mg/kg with 25 mg/kg	PO, IV	q8h	21 d
	Trimethoprim plus dapsone	300 mg	PO	18h	21 d
	or	100 mg	PO	qd	
	Pentamidine *or*	3-4 mg/kg	IV (IM)	qd	21 d
	Atovaquone *or*	750 mg	PO	q12h	21 d
	Clindamycin plus primaquine	300-450 mg	PO, IV	q6h	21 d
	or	15 mg	PO	qd	
	Trimetrexate plus leucovorin	45 mg/m²	IV	q24h	21 d
		20 mg/m²	PO, IV	q6h	
	Prednisone (adjunctive therapy for severe episode)	40 mg	PO	q12h*	21 d
Pneumocystis pneumonia (maintenance)	Trimethoprim plus sulfamethoxazole *or*	1 single- or double-strength tablet	PO	q24h	Lifelong¶
	Dapsone	100 mg	PO	q24h	Lifelong
Toxoplasmosis	Sulfadiazine plus pyrimethamine	1-2 g	PO	q6h	Lifelong
	plus leucovorin	100 mg†	PO	qd	Lifelong
	or	10-25 mg	PO, IV	qd	Lifelong
	Clindamycin plus pyrimethamine	450-600 mg	PO	q6h	Lifelong
		50-100 mg†	PO	qd	Lifelong
Cryptosporidiosis	Paromomycin	1.0 g	PO	bid	Lifelong
Microsporidiosis	Albendazole	400 mg	PO	bid	Lifelong
Isosporiasis	Trimethoprim wih sulfamethoxazole	160 mg	PO, IV	q6h	10 d
	followed by	800 mg			
	Trimethoprim plus sulfamethaxazole	160 mg	PO	bid	14 d
Candidiasis		800 mg			
Oral	Fluconazole	100-200 mg	PO, IV	q24h	5-10 d
Esophageal	Fluconazole	100-400 mg	PO, IV	q24h	14-21 d
Vaginal	Fluconazole	150 mg	PO	—	one dose
Coccidioidomycosis (Pulmonary)	Amphotericin B *followed by*	0.5-1.0 mg/kg	IV	q24h	≥56 d
	Itraconazole	300 mg	PO	bid	3 d
	followed by	200 mg	PO	bid	Lifelong
	Fluconazole	400-800 mg	PO	q24h	Lifelong
Cryptococcal infection	Amphotericin B with flucytosine	0.7 mg/kg with	IV	q24h	≥14 d
	followed by	25 mg/kg	PO	q6h	≥14 d
	Fluconazole *followed by*	400 mg	PO	q24h	8 wk
	Fluconazole	200 mg	PO	q24h	Lifelong
Histoplasmosis	Amphotericin B *followed by*	0.5-1.0 mg/kg	IV	q24h	≥28-56 d
	Itraconazole	200 mg	PO	q24h	Lifelong
Herpes simplex	Acyclovir *or*	200 mg	PO	5/d	10-14 d
	Famciclovir *or*	125-250 mg	PO	q12h	10-14 d
	Valacyclovir	500 mg	PO	q12h	10-14 d
Varicella-zoster virus					
Dermatomal	Acyclovir *or*	800 mg	PO	5/d	7-10 d
	Famciclovr *or*	500 mg	PO	q8h	7-10 d
	Valacyclovir	1000 mg	PO	q8h	7-10 d
Disseminated	Acyclovir	10-12 mg/kg	IV	q8h	7-14 d

From Mandell GL: *Mandell, Douglas, and Bennett's principles and practice of infectious diseases*, ed 5, New York, 2000, Churchill Livingstone.
*Prednisone, 40 mg q12h × 5 d, followed by 20 mg bid × 5 d, followed by 20 mg qd × 11 d.
†Following a single loading dose of pyrimethamine, 200 mg.
‡With probenecid as described in package insert.
§With pyridoxine 50 mg PO qd.
¶For patients who have sustained response to HAART (see text for criteria for discontinuation of maintenance therapy).

TABLE 1-5 Therapy for Opportunistic Infections in Patients with HIV Infection—cont'd

Clinical disease	Drug	Dose	Route	Interval	Duration
Cytomegalovirus	Ganciclovir	5 mg/kg	IV	q12h	14-21 d
	followed by				
	Ganciclovir	5 mg/kg	IV	q24h	Lifelong¶
	or				
	Foscarnet	60 mg/kg	IV	q8h	14-21 d
	followed by				
	Foscarnet	90-120 mg/kg	IV	q24h	Lifelong¶
	or				
	Ganciclovir implant	—	—	q6-9m	Lifelong¶
	or				
	Cidofovir‡	5 mg/kg	IV	qwk	2 wk
	followed by	5 mg/kg	IV	q2wk	Lifelong¶
Mycobacterium tuberculosis	Isoniazid§	300 mg	PO, IM	q24h	At least 6 mo
	and				
	Rifampin	600 mg	PO, IV	q24h	At least 6 mo
	and				
	Ethambutol	15-25 mg/kg	PO	q24h	Depends on sensitivity
	and				
	Pyrazinamide	15-25 mg/kg	PO	q24h	2 mo
Mycobacterium avium complex	Clarithromycin	500 mg	PO	q12h	Lifelong¶
	Ethambutol	15 mg/kg	PO	q24h	Lifelong
Bartonella (Rochalimaea) spp.	Erythromycin	500 mg	PO	q6h	≥12 wk
	or				
	Doxycycline	100 mg	PO	q12h	≥12 wk

From Mandell GL: *Mandell, Douglas, and Bennett's principles and practice of infectious diseases,* ed 5, New York, 2000, Churchill Livingstone.
*Prednisone, 40 mg q12h × 5 d, followed by 20 mg bid × 5 d, followed by 20 mg qd ×11 d.
†Following a single loading dose of pyrimethamine, 200 mg.
‡With probenecid as described in package insert.
§With pyridoxine 50 mg PO qd.
¶For patients who have sustained response to HAART (see text for criteria for discontinuation of maintenance therapy).

TABLE 1-6 Prophylaxis for Human Immunodeficiency Virus–Related Opportunistic Infections

Pathogen	Indication for prophylaxis	First choice	Alternatives	Comments
Pneumocystis	CD4+ <200/mm³ Persistent unexplained fever Chronic oropharyngeal candidiasis	Trimethoprim-sulfamethoxazole, 1 DS qd or SS	Dapsone, 50 mg qd, + pyrimethamine, 50 mg/wk Dapsone alone (100 mg qd) Aerosolized pentamidine	SS tablets are effective and may be less toxic than DS. Aerosol pentamidine should be delivered by Respirgard nebulizer.
Mycobacterium avium complex	CD4+ <100/mm3	Clarithromycin, 500 mg bid	Azithromycin (1200 mg qwk) Rifabutin, 300 mg qd	Rifabutin increases hepatic metabolism of other drugs.
Toxoplasma	No consensus	Trimethoprim-sulfamethoxazole, 1 DS qd	—	Pyrimethamine alone is not effective.
Mycobacterium tuberculosis	PPD >5 mm "High risk"	Sensitive: Isoniazid, 300 mg × 9 mo Resistant: ?	Rifampin* 600 mg, or Rifabutin* 300 mg, and pyrizinamide (15-25 mg/kg qd × 2 mo)	For resistant strains, two-drug regimens using combinations of rifampin, pyrazinamide, or a quinolone can be considered.
Candida	Multiple recurrences	Fluconazole, 200 mg daily		
Herpes simplex	Multiple recurrences	Acyclovir, 200 mg qd 3-4 ×/day Famciclovir, 125 mg PO bid Valacyclovir, 500 mg PD bid	Itraconazole, 100 mg qd —	Include pyridoxine, 500 mg qd for isoniazid-containing regimens. Recommended only if recurrences are severe or frequent.
Cytomegalovirus	None	—	—	Oral ganciclovir is not recommended currently.
Pneumococcus	All patients	Pneumovax	—	Trimethoprim-sulfamethoxazole, clarithromycin, and azithromycin appear to prevent some disease.
Influenza	All patients	Influenza vaccine	—	—

From Mandell GL: *Mandell, Douglas, and Bennett's principles and practice of infectious diseases,* ed 5, New York, 2000, Churchill Livingstone.
DS, Double strength; *PPD,* purified protein derivative; SS, single strength.
*For patients receiving *HAART,* dose adjustments may be necessary.

BASIC INFORMATION

DEFINITION

Acromegaly is a chronic debilitating disease with an insidious onset, resulting from the effects of either hypersecretion of growth hormone (GH) or increased amounts of an insulin-like growth factor I (IGF-I).

SYNONYMS

Marie's disease

ICD-9CM CODES
253.0 Acromegaly

EPIDEMIOLOGY & DEMOGRAPHICS

INCIDENCE: 3 to 4 new cases/ 1,000,000 persons
PREVALENCE: 50 to 60 cases/1 million persons, with some estimates as high as 90 cases/1 million persons
PREDOMINANT SEX: No sexual predominance
MEAN AGE AT DIAGNOSIS: Males: 40 yr; females: 45 yr
RISK FACTORS
- Increased mortality, primarily from cardiovascular and respiratory causes
- Death in 50% of untreated patients by age 50 yr (twice the rate of the general population)
- Increased prevalence of colon carcinoma and other malignancies

PHYSICAL FINDINGS & CLINICAL PRESENTATION

- Coarse features resulting from growth of soft tissue
- Coarse, oily skin
- Hands and feet that are spadelike, fleshy, and moist
- Prognathism, which can give an underbite
- Carpal tunnel syndrome
- Excessive sweating
- Arthralgias and severe osteoarthritis
- History of increased hat, glove, and/or shoe size
- Hypertension
- Skin tags
- Muscle weakness and decreased exercise capacity
- Headache, often severe
- Diabetes mellitus
- Visual field defects

ETIOLOGY

Cause is usually a pituitary adenoma, affecting the anterior lobe.

DIAGNOSIS

DIFFERENTIAL DIAGNOSIS

Ectopic production of growth hormone–releasing hormone (GHRH) from a carcinoid or other neuroendocrine tumor

WORKUP

1. First screening test: measure serum IGF-I level.
   a. Direct measurement of the GH level is not as useful, because it is secreted in a pulsatile fashion and a random level may be falsely normal.
   b. Upper limits of a normal IGF-I level, depending on the assay: >380 ng/ml or 2.5 U/ml.
2. Failure to suppress serum GH to less than 2 ng/ml after 100 g oral glucose is considered conclusive.
   a. Patients may show suppression of GH or a paradoxical response.
   b. Patients will not suppress GH to 2 ng/ml or less (the normal response).
   c. GHRH level >300 ng/ml is indicative of an ectopic source of GH.

LABORATORY TESTS

- Elevated serum phosphate
- Elevated urine calcium

IMAGING STUDIES

- Imaging studies of choice: MRI of the pituitary and hypothalamus
- CT of the pituitary and hypothalamus used initially

TREATMENT

SURGERY

Treatment of choice: transsphenoidal microsurgical adenomectomy
- Surgical failure rate: about 13.3% for microadenomas (tumors <10 mm) and 11.1% for macroadenomas (tumors >10 mm confined to the sella)
- Preoperative IGF-I level: indicator of surgical outcome with higher levels in the surgical failure group

RADIOTHERAPY

- Irradiation to reduce further growth of the tumor in most patients
- Major complication: hypopituitarism, which may occur in up to 50% of patients; this complication is more likely in patients who had surgery irradiation

MEDICAL Rx

- Indicated when patients have failed surgical therapy, when surgery is contraindicated, and in patients waiting for the effects of radiotherapy to begin
- Octreotide
  1. A somatostatin analog given tid at a dose of 100 mg subcutaneously
  2. Important side effects: biliary sludge and gallstones; nausea, cramps, and steatorrhea; suppression of GH levels to about 5 mg/L in 52% of patients; IGF-I levels normalized to about 53%
  3. Important in the preoperative shrinkage of pituitary tumors and softening of adenomatous tissue
- Bromocriptine
  1. A dopamine analog given at a dosage of 10 to 60 mg PO tid to qid
  2. Less effective than octreotide
  3. Important advantages: less expensive than octreotide and taken orally
  4. Important side effects: orthostatic hypotension, lightheadedness, nausea, constipation, and nasal stuffiness
  5. Suppresses GH levels to <5 mg/L in about 20% of patients; normalizes GH levels in approximately 10%, and shrinks pituitary adenomas in 10% to 20%; IGF-I levels normalized to about 10%
- Pegvisomant is a growth hormone receptor antagonist that has shown promising results in the treatment of acromegaly.

CHRONIC Rx

Combination of bromocriptine and octreotide may be synergistic, allowing a lower combination dosage than alone.

DISPOSITION

- Patients receiving radiotherapy need long-term follow-up to monitor the potential development of hypopituitarism.
- Continuation of medical therapy should be based on the normalization of IGF-I levels.

SUGGESTED READINGS

Melmad S et al: Current status and future opportunities for controlling acromegaly, *Pituitary* 5(3):185, 2002.

Trainer PJ et al: Treatment of acromegaly with the growth hormone-receptor antagonist pegvisomant, *N Engl J Med* 342:1172, 2000.

AUTHOR: **BETH J. WUTZ, M.D.**

BASIC INFORMATION

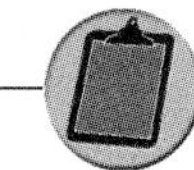

DEFINITION

Actinomycosis is an indolent, slowly progressive infection caused by both anaerobic or microaerophilic bacteria that normally colonize the mouth, vagina, and colon. Actinomycosis is characterized by the formation of painful abscesses, soft tissue infiltration, and draining sinuses.

SYNONYMS

Actinomyces infection

ICD-9CM CODES
039.9 Actinomycosis

EPIDEMIOLOGY & DEMOGRAPHICS

- Actinomycosis is worldwide in distribution.
- Commonly found as normal flora of the oral cavity (within gingival crevices, tonsillar crypts, periodontal pockets, dental plaques, and carious teeth), pharynx, tracheobronchial tree, gastrointestinal tract, and female urogenital tract.
- Incidence 1:300,000.
- Males infected more often than females 3:1.
- Can occur at any age but commonly seen in midlife.
- Incidence has decreased since the 1950s and is attributed to better oral hygiene and antibiotics.

PHYSICAL FINDINGS & CLINICAL PRESENTATION

Actinomycosis can affect any organ. Although not typically considered as opportunistic pathogens, *Actinomyces* species capitalize on tissue injury or mucosal breach to invade adjacent structures in the head and neck regions. As a result, dental infections and oromaxillofacial trauma are common antecedent events. Characteristic manifestations include:

- Cervicofacial disease (most common site):
  1. Occurs in the setting of poor dental hygiene, recent dental surgery, or minor oral trauma
  2. Painful soft tissue swelling commonly seen at the angle of the mandible
  3. Fever, chills, and weight loss
  4. Trismus
  5. Soft tissue facial infection with sinus tract or fistula formation
- Thoracic disease:
  1. Can involve the lungs, pleura, mediastinum, or chest wall.
  2. Presumed secondary to aspiration of *Actinomyces* organisms in patients with poor oral hygiene.
  3. Fever, cough, weight loss, and pleuritic chest pains are common symptoms.
  4. Signs of pneumonia or pleural effusion may be present.
  5. With extension beyond the lungs to mediastinal structures and the chest wall, signs and symptoms of pericarditis, empyema, chest wall sinus drainage, and tracheoesophageal fistula can all occur (Fig. 1-8).
- Abdominal disease:
  1. Occurs most commonly after appendectomy, perforated bowel, diverticulitis, or surgery to the gastrointestinal tract.
  2. Lesions develop most commonly in the ileocecal valve, causing abdominal pain, fever, weight loss, and a palpable mass.
  3. Extension may occur to the liver, causing jaundice and abscess formation.
  4. Sinus tracts to the abdominal wall can occur.
- Pelvic disease:
  1. Commonly occurs by extension from abdominal disease of the ileocecal valve to the right adnexa (80% of cases).
  2. Endometritis.

ETIOLOGY

- Actinomycosis is most commonly caused by *Actinomyces israelii.* Other causes are *A. naeslundii, A. odontolyticus, A. viscosus, A. meyeri,* and *A. gerencseriae.*
- *Actinomyces* are gram-positive, non-spore-forming, anaerobic or microaerophilic rods.
- Actinomycosis infections are polymicrobial, usually associated with *Streptococcus, Bacteroides, Eikenella corrodens, Enterococcus,* and *Fusobacterium.*
- Infects individuals only after entry into disrupted mucosa or tissue injury.

A

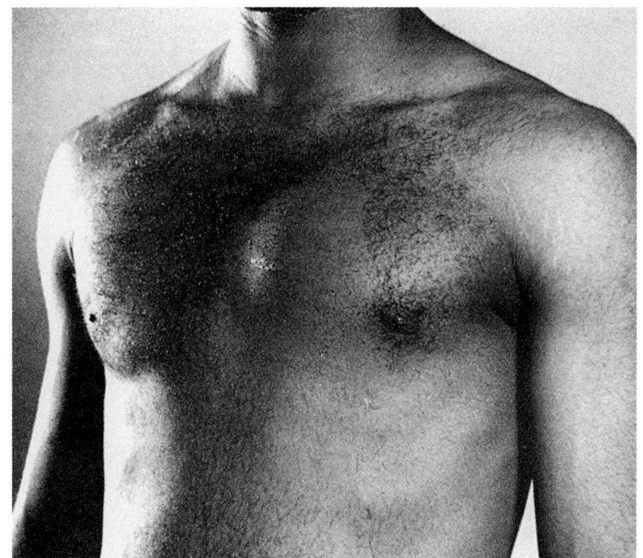

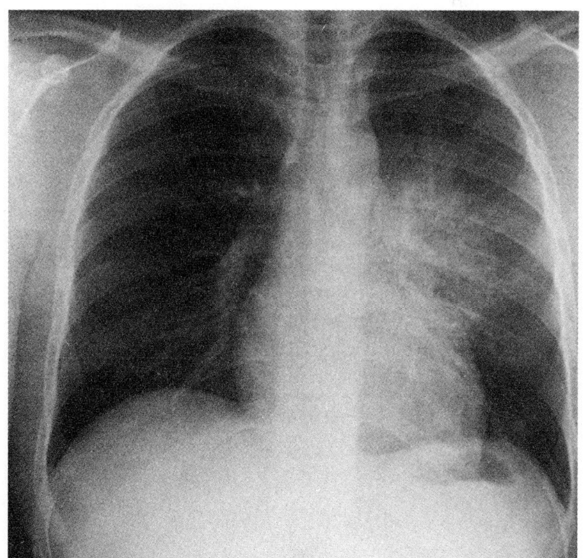

B

FIGURE 1-8 Thoracic actinomycosis. A, Initial presentation with a bulging mass lesion in the chest wall with a central sinus tract. **B,** The chest radiograph with the associated pulmonary infiltrate. (From Gorbach SL: *Infectious diseases,* ed 2, Philadelphia, 1998, WB Saunders.)

DIAGNOSIS

Isolating the bacteria in the proper clinical setting makes the diagnosis of actinomycosis.

DIFFERENTIAL DIAGNOSIS

Nocardiosis, botryomycosis, chromomycosis, intestinal tuberculosis, ameboma, Crohn's disease, colon cancer, and other causes of acute, subacute, or chronic infections of the lung, abdomen, hepatic, GI, GU, musculoskeletal, and CNS system.

WORKUP

The workup includes obtaining specimens either by aspirating abscesses, excising sinus tracts, or tissue biopsies.

LABORATORY TESTS

- Isolating "sulfur granules" from tissue specimens or draining sinuses confirms the diagnosis of actinomycosis. *Actinomyces* are noted for forming characteristic sulfur granules in infected tissue but not in vitro. The term *sulfur granule* is a misnomer, reflecting only the yellow color of the granule in pus, because the granules are not composed of any sulfur at all.
  1. Sulfur granules are nests of *Actinomyces* species. Sulfur granules may be macroscopic or microscopic (Fig. 1-9).
  2. Sulfur granules are crushed and stained for identification of *Actinomyces* organisms and may take up to 3 wk to grow in culture media.

IMAGING STUDIES

- Imaging studies are useful adjunctive tests in localizing the site and spread of infection.
  1. Chest x-ray examination
  2. CT scan of the head, chest, abdomen, and pelvic areas is useful

TREATMENT

NONPHARMACOLOGIC THERAPY

- Incision and drainage of abscesses
- Excision of sinus tract

ACUTE GENERAL Rx

- Penicillin 10 to 20 million units per day in 4 divided doses for 4 to 6 wk.
- In penicillin-allergic patients, erythromycin, tetracycline, clindamycin, or cephalosporins (depending on the type of penicillin allergy) are reasonable alternatives.
- Chloramphenicol 50 to 60 mg/kg/day has been used for CNS actinomycosis.

CHRONIC Rx

- Following 4 to 6 wk IV penicillin, oral penicillin V 500 mg PO qid for 6 to 12 mo.
- Treatment of associated microorganisms is not needed.

DISPOSITION

- Clinical actinomycosis, if not treated, spreads to contiguous tissues and structures ignoring tissue planes. Hematogenous spread, although possible, is rare.
- Actinomycosis is very sensitive to antibiotics but requires chronic long-term treatment to prevent relapse.

REFERRAL

If the diagnosis of actinomycosis is suspected, consultation with an infectious disease specialist is suggested. General surgical consultation for excision of sinus tracts and abscess incision and drainage is recommended.

PEARLS & CONSIDERATIONS

COMMENTS

- There is no person-to-person transmission of *Actinomyces.*
- Isolation of the organism in an asymptomatic individual does not mean the person has actinomycosis. Active symptoms must be present to make the diagnosis.
- Pelvic actinomycosis has been associated with use of an intrauterine device (IUD).
- Actinomycosis can also involve the CNS, causing multiple brain abscesses.

SUGGESTED READINGS

Jacobs RF, Schutze GE: Actinomycosis. In Behrman RE (Ed), *Nelson Textbook of Pediatrics,* ed 16, Philadelphia, 2000, WB Saunders, p. 823.

Russo TA: Agents of actinomycosis. In *Mandell, Douglas, and Bennett's principles and practice of infectious diseases,* ed 5, New York, 2000, Churchill Livingstone.

Smego RA, Foglia G: Actinomycosis, *Clin Infect Dis* 26:1255, 1998.

AUTHORS: **JOSEPH F. GRILLO, M.D.,** and **DENNIS MIKOLICH, M.D.**

A

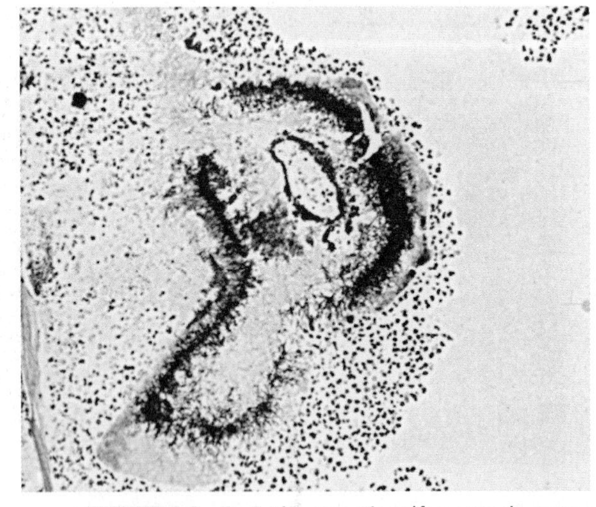

B

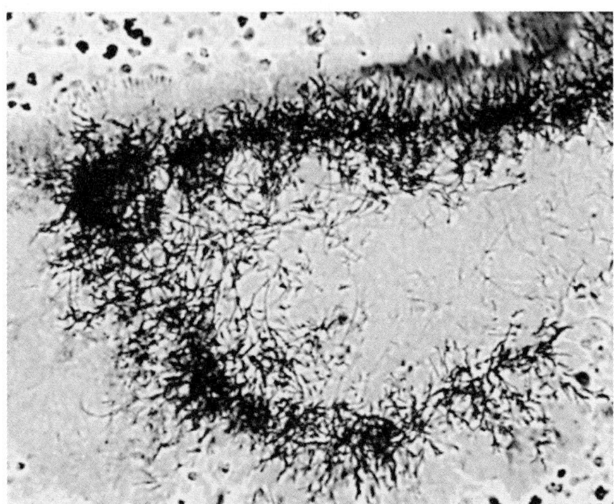

FIGURE 1-9 **A,** Actinomycotic sulfur granule surrounded by inflammatory cells (Brown-Brenn stain, ×250). **B,** Increased magnification (×1000) demonstrates the delicate, branched filaments of *Actinomyces.* (From Mandell GL [ed]: *Mandell, Douglas, and Bennett's principles and practice of infectious diseases,* ed 5, New York, 2000, Churchill Livingstone.)

BASIC INFORMATION

DEFINITION

Acute respiratory distress syndrome (ARDS) is a form of noncardiogenic pulmonary edema that results from acute damage to the alveoli. It is characterized by acute diffuse infiltrative lung lesions with resulting interstitial and alveolar edema, severe hypoxemia, and respiratory failure. The definition of ARDS includes the following three components:

1. A ratio of Pao_2 to Fio_2 ≤ 200 regardless of the level of PEEP
2. The detection of bilateral pulmonary infiltrates on frontal chest x-ray
3. Pulmonary artery wedge pressure (PAWP) ≤ 18 mm Hg or no clinical evidence of elevated left atrial pressure on the basis of chest radiograph or other clinical data

The cardinal feature of ARDS, refractory hypoxemia, is caused by formation of protein-rich alveolar edema after damage to the integrity of the lung's aveolar-capillary barrier.

SYNONYMS

ARDS

Adult respiratory distress syndrome

ICD-9CM CODES

518.82 Acute respiratory distress syndrome

EPIDEMIOLOGY & DEMOGRAPHICS

In the U.S. there are 125,000 to 150,000 ARDS cases/yr.

Incidence is 1.5 to 8.3 cases/ 100,000/yr.

About 50% of patients who develop ARDS do so within 24 hours of the inciting event.

PHYSICAL FINDINGS & CLINICAL PRESENTATION

- Signs and symptoms
  1. Dyspnea
  2. Chest discomfort
  3. Cough
  4. Anxiety
- Physical examination
  1. Tachypnea
  2. Tachycardia
  3. Hypertension
  4. Coarse crepitations of both lungs
  5. Fever may be present if infection is the underlying etiology

ETIOLOGY

- Sepsis (>40% of cases)
- Aspiration: near drowning, aspiration of gastric contents (>30% of cases)
- Trauma (>20% of cases)
- Multiple transfusions, blood products
- Drugs (e.g., overdose of morphine, methadone, heroin; reaction to nitrofurantoin)
- Noxious inhalation (e.g., chlorine gas, high O_2 concentration)
- Post-resuscitation
- Cardiopulmonary bypass
- Pneumonia
- Burns
- Pancreatitis
- A history of chronic alcohol abuse significantly increases the risk of developing ARDS in critically ill patients

DIAGNOSIS

DIFFERENTIAL DIAGNOSIS

- Cardiogenic pulmonary edema
- Viral pneumonitis
- Lymphangitic carcinomatosis

WORKUP

The search for an underlying cause should focus on treatable causes (e.g., infections such as sepsis or pneumonia)

- ABGs
- Hemodynamic monitoring
- Bronchoalveolar lavage (selected patients)

LABORATORY TESTS

- ABGs:
  1. Initially: varying degrees of hypoxemia, generally resistant to supplemental oxygen
  2. Respiratory alkalosis, decreased Pco_2
  3. Widened alveolar-arterial gradient
  4. Hypercapnia as the disease progresses
- Bronchoalveolar lavage:
  1. The most prominent finding is an increased number of polymorphonucleocytes.
  2. The presence of eosinophilia has therapeutic implications, because these patients respond to corticosteroids.
- Blood and urine cultures

IMAGING STUDIES

Chest x-ray examination (Fig. 1-10).

- The initial chest radiogram might be normal in the initial hours after the precipitating event.
- Bilateral interstitial infiltrates are usually seen within 24 hr; they often are more prominent in the bases and periphery.
- "White out" of both lung fields can be seen in advanced stages.
- CT scan of chest: diffuse consolidation with air bronchograms, bullae, pleural effusions. Pneumomediastinum and pneumathoraces may also be present.

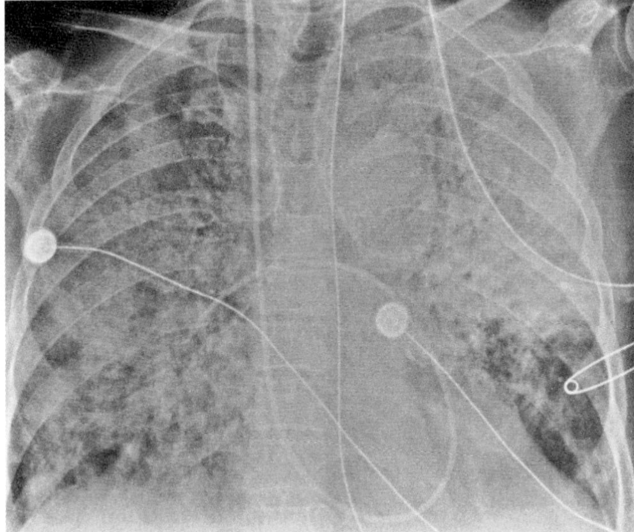

FIGURE 1-10 ARDS. AP radiograph in an elderly woman reveals widespread consolidation with air bronchograms. The heart size is normal. There are no pleural effusions. (From McLoud TC: *Thoracic radiology: the requisites,* St Louis, 1998, Mosby.)

TREATMENT

NONPHARMACOLOGIC THERAPY

Hemodynamic monitoring:

- Hemodynamic monitoring can be used for the initial evaluation of ARDS (in ruling out cardiogenic pulmonary edema) and its subsequent management. Recent studies, however, have shown that clinical management involving the early use of pulmonary artery catheters in patients with ARDS did not significantly affect mortality and morbidity.
- Although no dynamic profile is diagnostic of ARDS, the presence of pulmonary edema, a high cardiac output and a low pulmonary capillary wedge pressures (PCWP) is characteristic of ARDS.
- It is important to remember that partially treated intravascular volume overload and flash pulmonary edema can have the hemodynamic features of ARDS; filling pressures can also be elevated by increased intrathoracic pressures or with fluid administration; cardiac function can be depressed by acidosis, hypoxemia, or other factors associated with sepsis.

Ventilatory support: mechanical ventilation is generally necessary to maintain adequate gas exchange (see Section III, Fig. 3-6). A low tidal volume and low plateau pressure ventilator strategy is recommended to avoid ventilator-induced injury. Assist-control is generally preferred initially with the following ventilator settings:

- Fio_2 1.0 (until a lower value can be used to achieve adequate oxygenation). When possible, minimize oxygen toxicity by maintaining Fio_2 at <60%.
- Tidal volume: Set initial tidal volume at 5-6 ml/kg of body weight. Aim to maintain plateau pressure (Pplat) at <30 mm Hg.
- PEEP 5 cm H_2O or greater (to increase lung volume and keep alveoli open). PEEP should be applied in small increments of 3 to 5 cm H_2O (up to a maximum of 15 cm H_2O) to achieve acceptable arterial saturation (≥ 0.9) with nontoxic FiO_2 values (<0.6) and acceptable airway plateau pressures (> 30-35 cm H_2O). It is important to remember that an increase in PEEP may lower cardiac output and, despite improvement in PaO_2, may actually have a negative effect on tissue oxygenation (the major determinants of tissue oxygenation are Hb, percent saturation, and cardiac output).
- Inspiratory flow: 60 L/min.
- Ventilatory rate: high ventilatory rates of 20 to 25 breaths/min are often necessary in patients with ARDS because of their increased physiologic deadspace and smaller lung volumes. Patients must be monitored for excessive intrathoracic gas trapping ("auto-PEEP" or "intrinsic-PEEP") that can depress cardiac output.

ACUTE GENERAL Rx

Identify and treat precipitating conditions:

- Blood and urine cultures and trial of antibiotics in presumed sepsis (routine administration of antibiotics in all cases of ARDS is not recommended).
- Prompt repair of bone fractures in patients with major trauma.
- Bowel rest and crystalloid resuscitation in pancreatitis.
- Fluid management: optimal fluid and hemodynamic management of patients with ARDS is patient specific; generally, administration of crystalloids is recommended if a downward trend in PCWP is associated with diminished cardiac index, resulting in prerenal azotemia, oliguria, and relative tachycardia; on the other hand, if PCWP increases with little or no change in cardiac index, one should begin diuretic therapy and use low-dose dopamine (2 to 4 μg/kg/min) to maintain natriuresis and support adequate renal flow.
- Positioning the patient: changes in position can improve oxygenation by improving the distribution of perfusion to ventilated lung regions; repositioning (lateral decubitus positioning) should be attempted in patients with hypoxemia that is not responsive to other medical interventions. Placing patients with acute respiratory failure in a prone position improves their oxygenation but does not improve their survival.
- Corticosteroids: routine use of corticosteroids in ARDS is not recommended; corticosteroids may be beneficial in patients with many eosinophils in the bronchoalveolar lavage fluid; systemic infections should be ruled out or adequately treated before administration of corticosteroids.
- Nutritional support: nutritional support, preferably administered by the enteral route, is necessary to maintain adequate colloid oncotic pressure and intravascular volume. The inclusion of eicosapentaenoic acid from fish oil may be beneficial in improving ventilation requirements and length of stay in patients with ARDS.
- Tracheostomy: tracheostomy is warranted in patients requiring >2 wk of mechanical ventilation; discussion regarding tracheostomy should begin with patient (if alert and oriented) and family members/legal guardian, after 5 to 7 days of ventilatory support.
- Some form of DVT prophylaxis is indicated in all patients with ARDS.
- Stress ulcer prophylaxis with sucralfate suspension (via NG tube), or IV proton pump inhibitors (PPIs) or IV H_2 blockers.
- The use of surfactant remains controversial. Patients who receive surfactant have a greater improvement in gas exchange in the initial 24-hour period than patients who receive standard therapy alone; however, the use of exogenous surfactant does not improve survival.

DISPOSITION

- Prognosis for ARDS varies with the underlying cause. Prognosis is worse in patients with chronic liver disease, nonpulmonary organ dysfunction, sepsis, and advanced age.
- Elevated values of deadspace fraction $[(Paco_2\text{-}Peco_2)/Paco_2]$ (normal is <0.3) is associated with an increased risk of death.
- Overall mortality varies between 32% and 45%. The majority of deaths are attributable to sepsis or multiorgan dysfunction rather than primary respiratory causes.

REFERRAL

Surgical referral for tracheostomy (see "Acute General Rx").

SUGGESTED READINGS

Piantadosi CA, Schwartz DA: The acute respiratory distress syndrome, *Ann Intern Med* 141:460, 2004.

Spragg RG et al: Effect of recombinant surfactant Protein C-based surfactant on the acute respiratory distress syndrome. *N Engl J Med* 351:884, 2004.

The National Heart, Lung, and Blood Institute ARDS Clinical Trials Network, Higher versus Lower Positive End-Expiratory pressures in patients with the Acute Respiratory Distress Syndrome, *N Engl J Med* 351:327, 2004.

Udobi KF et al: Acute respiratory distress syndrome, *Am Fam Physician* 67:315, 2003.

AUTHOR: **FRED F. FERRI, M.D.**

BASIC INFORMATION

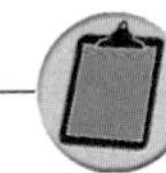

DEFINITION

Addison's disease is characterized by inadequate secretion of corticosteroids resulting from partial or complete destruction of the adrenal glands.

SYNONYMS

Primary adrenocortical insufficiency
Adrenal insufficiency

ICD-9CM CODES
255.4 Addison's disease

EPIDEMIOLOGY & DEMOGRAPHICS

PREVALENCE: 5 cases/100,000 persons
PREDOMINANT SEX: Female:male ratio of 2:1

PHYSICAL FINDINGS & CLINICAL PRESENTATION

- Hyperpigmentation: more prominent in palmar creases, buccal mucosa, pressure points (elbows, knees, knuckles), perianal mucosa, and around areolas of nipples
- Hypotension
- Generalized weakness
- Amenorrhea and loss of axillary hair in females

ETIOLOGY

- Autoimmune destruction of the adrenal glands (80% of cases)
- Tuberculosis (15% of cases)
- Carcinomatous destruction of the adrenal glands
- Adrenal hemorrhage (anticoagulants, trauma, coagulopathies, pregnancy, sepsis)
- Adrenal infarction (arteritis, thrombosis)
- AIDS (adrenal insufficiency develops in 30% of patients with AIDS)
- Other: sarcoidosis, amyloidosis, postoperative, fungal infections

DIAGNOSIS

DIFFERENTIAL DIAGNOSIS

Sepsis, hypovolemic shock, acute abdomen, apathetic hyperthyroidism in the elderly, myopathies, GI malignancy, major depression, anorexia nervosa, hemochromatosis, salt-losing nephritis, chronic infection

WORKUP

- If the clinical picture is highly suggestive of adrenocortical insufficiency, the diagnosis can be made with the rapid ACTH (Cortrosyn) test:
  1. Give 250 mg ACTH by IV push and measure cortisol levels at 0 and 30 min.
  2. Cortisol level <18 mg/dl at 30 or 60 min is suggestive of adrenal insufficiency.
  3. Measure plasma ACTH. A high ACTH level confirms primary adrenal insufficiency.
- Secondary adrenocortical insufficiency (caused by pituitary dysfunction) can be distinguished from primary adrenal insufficiency by the following:
  1. Normal or low plasma ACTH level following rapid ACTH (Cortrosyn test)
  2. Absence of hyperpigmentation
  3. No significant impairment of aldosterone secretion (because aldosterone secretion is under control of the renin-angiotensin system)
  4. Additional evidence of hypopituitarism (e.g., hypogonadism, hypothyroidism)

LABORATORY TESTS

- Increased potassium, decreased sodium and chloride
- Decreased glucose
- Increased BUN/creatinine ratio (prerenal azotemia)
- Mild normocytic, normochromic anemia, neutropenia, lymphocytosis, eosinophilia (significant dehydration may mask hyponatremia and anemia)
- PPD and antiadrenal antibodies

IMAGING STUDIES

- Chest x-ray examination may reveal a small heart.
- Abdominal x-ray film: adrenal calcifications may be noted if the adrenocortical insufficiency is secondary to TB or fungus.
- Abdominal CT scan: small adrenal glands generally indicate either idiopathic atrophy or long-standing TB, whereas enlarged glands are suggestive of early TB or potentially treatable diseases.

TREATMENT

NONPHARMACOLOGIC THERAPY

- Perform periodic monitoring of serum electrolytes, vital signs, and body weight; liberal sodium intake is suggested.
- Periodic measurement of bone density may be helpful in identifying patients at risk for the development of osteoporosis.

Patients should carry a Medic Alert bracelet and an emergency pack containing hydrocortisone 100 mg ampule, syringe, and needle. Patients and partners should be educated on how to give IM injection in case of vomiting or coma.

ACUTE GENERAL Rx

Addisonian crisis is an acute complication of adrenal insufficiency characterized by circulatory collapse, dehydration, nausea, vomiting, hypoglycemia, and hyperkalemia.

1. Draw plasma cortisol level; do not delay therapy while waiting for confirming laboratory results.
2. Administer hydrocortisone 50-100 mg IV q6h for 24 hr; if patient shows good clinical response, gradually taper dosage and change to oral maintenance dose (usually prednisone 7.5 mg/day).
3. Provide adequate volume replacement with D_5NS solution until hypotension, dehydration, and hypoglycemia are completely corrected. Large volumes (2 to 3 L) may be necessary in the first 2 to 3 hr to correct the volume deficit and hypoglycemia and to avoid further hyponatremia.

Identify and correct any precipitating factor (e.g., sepsis, hemorrhage).

CHRONIC Rx

- Give hydrocortisone 15 to 20 mg PO every morning and 5 to 10 mg in late afternoon or prednisone 5 mg in morning and 2.5 mg hs.
- Give oral fludrocortisone 0.05 mg/day to 0.20 mg/day: this mineralocorticoid is necessary if the patient has primary adrenocortical insufficiency. The dose is adjusted based on the serum sodium level and the presence of postural hypotension or marked orthostasis.
- Instruct patients to increase glucocorticoid replacement in times of stress and to receive parenteral glucocorticoids if diarrhea or vomiting occurs. Typical supplementation varies from 25 mg PO qd of hydrocortisone for minor medical and surgical stress to 50-100 mg IV hydrocortisone every 8 hr for sepsis-induced hypotension or shock.
- The administration of dehydroepiandrosterone 50 mg PO qd improves well-being and sexuality in women with adrenal insufficiency.

SUGGESTED READINGS

Cooper MS, Stewart PM: Corticosteroid insufficiency in acutely ill patients, *N Engl J Med* 348:727, 2003.

Dorin RI et al: Diagnosis of adrenal insufficiency, *Ann Intern Med* 139:194, 2003.

AUTHOR: **FRED F. FERRI, M.D.**

Alcoholism (PTG)

BASIC INFORMATION

DEFINITION

Although it is impossible to define alcoholism precisely, among the commonly used screening instruments for this disorder are the CAGE questionnaire, short Michigan Alcoholism Screening Test (SMAST), National Council on Alcoholism criteria, and DSM-IV-R criteria. Moderate drinking has been defined as two standard drinks (e.g., 12 oz of beer) per day and one drink per day for women and persons older than 65 years of age.

Although not generally included under the alcoholism topic, hazardous or at-risk drinking should also be considered. For men, *at-risk drinking* is defined as greater than 14 drinks/week or more than 4 drinks/occasion. For women, at-risk drinking is defined as about half that given for men.

The American Psychiatric Association defines diagnostic criteria for *alcohol withdrawal* as follows:

A. Cessation of (or reduction in) alcohol use that has been heavy and prolonged.

B. Two (or more) of the following, developing within several hours to a few days after criterion A:
   1. Autonomic hyperactivity (e.g., sweating or pulse rate >100 beats/min)
   2. Increased hand tremor
   3. Insomnia
   4. Nausea and vomiting
   5. Transient visual, tactile, or auditory hallucinations or illusions
   6. Psychomotor agitation
   7. Anxiety
   8. Grand mal seizures

C. The symptoms in criterion B cause clinically significant distress or impairment in social, occupational, or other important areas of functioning.

The symptoms are not due to a general medical condition and are not better accounted for by another mental disorder.

SYNONYMS

Alcohol abuse
Substance abuse

ICD-9CM CODES
303.9 Alcoholism

EPIDEMIOLOGY & DEMOGRAPHICS

INCIDENCE (IN U.S.):

- The clinical history suggests alcohol problems in 15% to 20% of patients in primary care and patients that are hospitalized. In the U.S. alcohol abuse generates nearly $185 billion in annual economic costs.
- 20% achieve abstinence without help, 70% achieve sobriety for 1 yr.

PREVALENCE (IN U.S.): 7% of population 18 yr or older

PREDOMINANT SEX:

- Lifetime risk for males 8% to 10%
- Lifetime risk for females 3% to 5%

PEAK INCIDENCE: 20 to 40 yr

GENETICS: More common with a family history of alcoholism and in patients of Irish, Scandinavian, and Native American descent

PHYSICAL FINDINGS & CLINICAL PRESENTATION

- Recurring minor trauma
- GI bleeding from gastris and/or varices
- Pancreatitis (acute and chronic)
- Liver disease
- Odor of alcohol on breath
- Tremulousness
- Tachycardia
- Peripheral neuropathy
- Recent memory loss

ETIOLOGY

- Social and genetic factors important
- Risk factors:
  1. Broken homes
  2. Unemployment
  3. Divorce
  4. Recurrent depression
  5. Addiction to another substance, including tobacco

DIAGNOSIS

WORKUP

- Several screening tests (CAGE, AUDIT, TWEAK, CRAFFT, SMAST) are available. The four-item CAGE (feeling need to Cut down, Annoyed by criticism, Guilty about drinking, and need for an Eye-opener in the morning) is the most popular screening test in primary care. A positive response should lead to further questioning. The sensitivity of the CAGE ranges from 43% to 94% and its specificity ranges from 70% to 97%. The five-item TWEAK scale (Tolerance, Worry, Eye-openers, Amnesia, [K] cut down) and the T-ACE questionnaire (Tolerance, Annoyance, Cut down, Eye-opener) are designed to screen pregnant women for alcohol misuse. They detect lower levels of alcohol consumption that may pose risks during pregnancy. The CRAFFT questionnaire (riding in Car with someone who was drinking, using alcohol to Relax, using alcohol while Alone, Forgetfulness, criticism from Friends and Family, Trouble) is useful as a screening tool for adolescents. Its sensitivity is 92% and specificity 64% for alcohol abuse. Screening tools are available at the National Institute on Alcohol Abuse and Alcoholism Web site: http://www.niaaa.nih.gov/publications/niaaa-guide.
- Blood studies (see "Laboratory Tests")

LABORATORY TESTS

- γ-Glutamyltransferase (GGTP), generally elevated
- Liver transaminases (ALT, AST), often elevated, may be normal or low in advanced liver disease
- Low albumin level, hypophosphatemia, hypomagnesemia from malnutrition
- CBC reveals elevated mean corpuscular volume (MCV) from toxic effect of alcohol on erythrocyte development on nutritional deficiencies
- Stool for occult blood may be positive secondary to gastritis, or variceal bleeding

IMAGING STUDIES

Indicated only if there is a history of trauma. CT or ultrasound of abdomen may reveal fatty liver or cirrhosis in advanced stages.

TREATMENT

NONPHARMACOLOGIC THERAPY

- Complete abstinence
- Depression, if present, should be treated at same time ETOH is withdrawn

ACUTE GENERAL Rx

Alcohol withdrawal syndrome occurs when a person stops ingesting alcohol after prolonged consumption. It can result in four possible clinical patterns depending on the severity of the patient's alcohol abuse and the time interval from the patient's previous alcohol ingestion. Blood ethanol level decreases by 20 mg/dL/hr in a normal person. Although discussed separately in the text, these alcohol withdrawal states blend together in real life.

1. **Tremulous state:** (early alcohol withdrawal, "impending DTs," "shakes," "jitters")
   a. Time interval: usually occurs 6 to 8 hr after the last drink or 12 to 48 hr after reduction of alcohol intake; becomes most pronounced at 24 to 36 hr
   b. Manifestation: tremors, mild agitation, insomnia, tachycardia; symptoms are relieved by alcohol
   c. Inpatient treatment
      (1) Admit to medical floor (private room); monitor vital signs q4h; institute seizure precautions; maintain adequate sedation.

(2) Administer lorazepam as follows:
  (a) Day 1: 2 mg PO q4h while awake and not lethargic
  (b) Day 2: 1 mg PO q4h while awake and not lethargic
  (c) Day 3: 0.5 mg PO q4h while awake and not lethargic
  (d) NOTE: Hold sedation for lethargy or abnormal vital or neurologic signs. The preceding doses are only guidelines; it is best to titrate the dose case by case
(3) In patients with mild to moderate withdrawal and without history of seizures, individualized benzodiazepine administration (rather than a fixed-dose regimen) results in lower benzodiazepine administration and avoids unnecessary sedation. The Clinical Institute Withdrawal Assessment-Alcohol (CIWA-A) scale can be used to measure the severity of alcohol withdrawal. It consists of 10 items: nausea; tremor; autonomic hyperactivity; anxiety; agitation; tactile, visual, and auditory disturbances; headache; and disorientation. Each item is assigned a score from 0 to 7. For example in the "agitation" category 0 indicates normal activity, 7 indicates that the patient constantly thrashes about, for the category of "tremor," 0 indicates that tremor is not present, 7 tremor is severe, even with arms not extended. The maximum total score is 67. When the CIWA-A score is ≥8, patients are usually given 2 to 4 mg of lorazepam hourly.
(4) β-Adrenergic blockers: β-blockers are useful for controlling BP and tachyarrhythmias. However, they do not prevent progression to more serious symptoms of withdrawal and if used, should not be administered alone but in conjunction with benzodiazepines. β-Blockers should be avoided in patients with contraindications to their use (e.g., bronchospasm, bradycardia, or severe CHF). Centrally acting α-adrenergic agonists such as clonidine ameliorate symptoms in patients with mild-to-moderate withdrawal but do not reduce delirium or seizures.
(5) Vitamin replacement: thiamine 100 mg IV or IM for at least 5 days, plus PO multivitamins. The IV administration of glucose can precipitate Wernicke's encephalopathy in alcoholics with thiamine deficiency; therefore thiamine administration should precede IV dextrose
(6) Hydration PO or IV (high-caloric solution): if IV, glucose with Na^+, K^+, Mg^{2+}, and phosphate replacement prn
(7) Laboratory studies
  (a) CBC, platelet count, INR
  (b) Electrolytes, glucose, BUN, creatinine
  (c) GGTP, ALT, AST
  (d) Phosphorus and magnesium
  (e) Serum vitamin B_{12} and folic acid (if megaloblastic features in blood smear)
(8) Diagnostic imaging: generally not necessary; if subdural hematoma is suspected (evidence of trauma, persistent lethargy), a CT scan should be ordered.
(9) Social rehabilitation: group therapy such as Alcoholics Anonymous; identification and treatment of social and family problems should be initiated during the patient's hospital stay.

2. **Alcoholic hallucinosis**
  a. Manifestations: usually hallucinations are auditory, but occasionally hallucinations are visual, tactile, or olfactory; usually there is no clouding of sensorium as in delirium (clinical presentation may be mistaken for an acute schizophrenic episode). Disordered perceptions become most pronounced after 24 to 36 hr of abstinence.
  b. Treatment: same as for DTs (see Withdrawal seizures).
3. **Withdrawal seizures** ("rum fits")
  a. Time interval: usually occurs 7 to 30 hr after cessation of drinking, with a peak incidence between 13 and 24 hr.
  b. Manifestations: generalized convulsions with loss of consciousness; focal signs are usually absent; consider further investigation with CT scan of head and EEG if clearly indicated (e.g., presence of focal neurologic deficits, prolonged postictal confusion state). In addition, in a febrile patient who is having a seizure or altered mental state, a lumbar puncture is necessary.
  c. Treatment
    (1) Diazepam 2.5 mg/min IV until seizure is controlled (check for respiratory depression or hypotension) may be beneficial for prolonged seizure activity; IV lorazepam 1 to 2 mg every 2 hr can be used in place of diazepam. Generally withdrawal seizures are self-limited and treatment is not required; the use of phenytoin or other anticonvulsants for short-term treatment of alcohol withdrawal seizures is not recommended.
    (2) Thiamine 100 mg IV, followed by IV dextrose, should also be administered.
    (3) Electrolyte imbalances (↑ Mg^{2+}, ↓ K^+, ↑/↓ Na^+, ↓ PO_4^{-3}) that may exacerbate seizures should be corrected.
4. **DTs:**
  a. Time interval: variable; usually occurs within 1 wk after reduction or cessation of heavy alcohol intake and persists for 1 to 3 days. Peak incidence is 72 hr and 96 hr after the cessation of alcohol consumption.
  b. Manifestations: profound confusion, tremors, vivid visual and tactile hallucinations, autonomic hyperactivity; this is the most serious clinical presentation of alcohol withdrawal (mortality is approximately 15% in untreated patients).
  c. Treatment
    (1) Admission to a detoxification unit where patient can be observed closely
    (2) Vital signs q30min (neurologic signs, if necessary)
    (3) Use of lateral decubitus or prone position if restraints are necessary
    (4) NPO: NG tube for abdominal distention may be necessary but should not be routinely used
    (5) Laboratory studies: same as for early alcohol withdrawal
    (6) Vigorous hydration (4-6 L/day): IV with glucose (Na^+, K^+, PO_4^{-3}, and Mg^{2+} replacement)
    (7) Vitamins: thiamine, 100 mg IV qd. The initial dose of thiamine should precede the administration of IV dextrose; multivitamins (may be added to the hydrating solution)

(8) Sedation: Control of agitation should be achieved using rapid-acting sedative-hypnotic agents in adequate doses to maintain light somnolence for the duration of delirium.
   (a) Initially: lorazepam 2 to 5 mg IM/IV repeated prn
   (b) Maintenance (individualized dosage): chlordiazepoxide, 50 to 100 mg PO q4-6h, lorazepam 2 mg PO q4h, or diazepam 5 to 10 mg PO tid; withhold doses or decrease subsequent doses if signs of oversedation are apparent
   (c) Midazolam is also effective for managing DTs. Its rapid onset (sedation within 2 to 4 min of IV injection) and short duration of action (approximately 30 min) make it an ideal agent for titration in continuous infusion.
(9) Treatment of seizures (as previously described)
(10) Diagnosis and treatment of concomitant medical, surgical, or psychiatric conditions

CHRONIC Rx

- See "Referral."
- Pharmacotherapies for alcoholism include the opiate antagonists (naltrexone 50 mg PO qd or nalmefene 10 to 40 mg qd), disulfiram, acamprosate, and SSRIs.

DISPOSITION

See "Referral."

REFERRAL

- To Alcoholics Anonymous or Adult Children of Alcoholics
- Family members to Al-Anon or Al-A-Teen
- Many cities have Salvation Army Adult Rehabilitation centers; all patients accepted, regardless of ability to pay

PEARLS & CONSIDERATIONS

COMMENTS

- Relative indications for inpatient alcohol detoxification are as follows: history of DTs or withdrawal seizures, severe withdrawal symptoms, concomitant psychiatric or medical illness, pregnancy, multiple previous detoxifications, recent high levels of alcohol consumption, and lack of reliable support network.
- The cure rate for alcoholism is very disappointing, regardless of the modality. Only those who want to be helped will be helped. An effective strategy for the primary care physician is a prominently displayed sign in the office that states, "If you think you consume too much alcoholic beverage, please discuss it with me." Those who do open up the discussion can be given the facts in a nonjudgmental way and often can be helped. All too often, problem drinkers lie on the questionnaire until they face a life-threatening health issue—and even then denial often reigns supreme.

SUGGESTED READINGS

Bayard M et al: Alcohol withdrawal syndrome, *Am Fam Physician* 69:1443, 2004.

Daeppen JB et al: Symptom-triggered vs fixed-schedule doses of benzodiazepine for alcohol withdrawal: a randomized treatment trial, *Arch Intern Med* 162:1117, 2002.

Enoch ME, Goldman D: Problem drinking and alcoholism: diagnosis and treatment, *Am Fam Physician* 65:441, 2002.

Fleming MF et al: Brief physician advise for problem drinkers: long-term efficacy and benefit-cost analysis, *Alcohol Clin Exp Res* 26:36, 2002.

Kosten TR, O'Connor PG: Management of drug and alcohol withdrawal, *N Engl J Med* 348:1786, 2003.

Krystal JH et al: Naltrexone in the treatment of alcohol dependence, *N Engl J Med* 345:1734, 2001.

Mayo-Smith MF et al: Management of alcohol withdrawal delirium, *Arch Intern Med* 164:1405, 2004.

Moyer A et al: Brief interventions for alcohol problems: a meta-analytic review of controlled investigations in treatment-seeking populations, *Addiction* 97:279, 2002.

Nicholas JM et al: The effect of controlled drinking in alcoholic cardiomyopathy, *Ann Intern Med* 136:192, 2002.

O'Connor PG, Schotrenfeld RS: Patients with alcohol problems, *N Engl J Med* 9:592, 1998.

Schneekloth TD et al: Point prevalence of alcoholism in hospitalized patients: continuing challenges of detection, assessment, and diagnosis, *Mayo Clin Proc* 76:460, 2001.

U.S. Preventive Services Task Force: Screening and behavioral counseling interventions in primary care to reduce alcohol misuse: recommendation statement, *Ann Intern Med* 140:554, 2004.

White IR et al: Alcohol consumption and mortality: modelling risks for men and women at different ages, *BMJ* 325:191, 2002.

AUTHOR: **FRED F. FERRI, M.D.**

BASIC INFORMATION

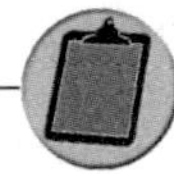

DEFINITION

Primary aldosteronism is a clinical syndrome characterized by hypokalemia, hypertension, low plasma renin activity (PRA), and excessive aldosterone secretion.

SYNONYMS

Hyperaldosteronism
Conn's syndrome

ICD-9CM CODES
255.1 Primary aldosteronism

EPIDEMIOLOGY & DEMOGRAPHICS

INCIDENCE/PREVALENCE: 1% to 2% of patients with hypertension; more common in females

PHYSICAL FINDINGS & CLINICAL PRESENTATION

- Generally asymptomatic
- If significant hypokalemia is present, possible muscle cramping, weakness, paresthesias
- Hypertension
- Polyuria, polydipsia

ETIOLOGY

- Aldosterone-producing adenoma (>60%)
- Idiopathic hyperaldosteronism (>30%)
- Glucocorticoid-suppressible hyperaldosteronism (<1%)
- Aldosterone-producing carcinoma (<1%)

DIAGNOSIS

DIFFERENTIAL DIAGNOSIS

- Diuretic use
- Hypokalemia from vomiting, diarrhea
- Renovascular hypertension
- Other endocrine neoplasm (pheochromocytoma, deoxycorticosterone-producing tumor, renin-secreting tumor)

WORKUP

In patients with hypokalemia and a low PRA, confirming tests for primary hyperaldosteronism include the following:
- 24-hr urine test for aldosterone and potassium levels (potassium >40 mEq and aldosterone >15 μg).
- Captopril test: administer 25 to 50 mg of captopril (ACE inhibitor) and measure plasma renin and aldosterone levels 1 to 2 hr later. A plasma aldosterone level >15 ng/dl confirms the diagnosis of primary aldosteronism. This test is more expensive and is best reserved for situations in which the 24-hr urine for aldosterone is ambiguous.
- 24-hr urinary tetrahydroaldosterone (<65 μg/24 hr) and saline infusion test (plasma aldosterone >10 ng/dl) can also be used in ambiguous cases.
- The renin-aldosterone stimulation test (posture test) is helpful in differentiating IHA from aldosterone-producing adenoma (APA). Patients with APA have a decrease in aldosterone levels at 4 hr, whereas patients with IHA have an increase in their aldosterone levels.
- As a screening test for primary aldosteronism, an elevated plasma aldosterone-renin ratio (ARR), drawn randomly from patients on hypertensive drugs, is predictive of primary aldosteronism (positive predictive value 100% in a recent study). ARR is calculated by dividing plasma aldosterone (mg/dl) by plasma renin activity (mg/ml/hour). ARR >100 is considered elevated.
- Bilateral adrenal venous sampling may be done to localize APA when adrenal CT scan is equivocal. In APA, ipsilateral/contralateral aldosterone level is >10:1, and ipsilateral venous aldosterone concentration is very high (>1000 ng/dl).
- A diagnostic evaluation of hypertensive patients with suspected aldosteronism is described in Section III, Hyperaldosteronism.

LABORATORY TESTS

Routine laboratory tests can be suggestive but are not diagnostic of primary aldosteronism. Common abnormalities are:
- Spontaneous hypokalemia or moderately severe hypokalemia while receiving conventional doses of diuretics
- Possible alkalosis and hypernatremia

IMAGING STUDIES

- Adrenal CT scans (with 3-mm cuts) may be used to localize neoplasm.
- Adrenal scanning with iodocholesterol (NP-59) or 6-beta-iodomethyl-19-norcholesterol after dexamethasone suppression. The uptake of tracer is increased in those with aldosteronoma and absent in those with idiopathic aldosteronism and adrenal carcinoma.

TREATMENT

NONPHARMACOLOGIC THERAPY

- Regular monitoring and control of blood pressure
- Low-sodium diet, tobacco avoidance, maintenance of ideal body weight, and regular exercise program

ACUTE GENERAL Rx

- Control of blood pressure and hypokalemia with spironolactone, amiloride, or ACE inhibitors
- Surgery (unilateral adrenalectomy) for APA

CHRONIC Rx

Chronic medical therapy with spironolactone, amiloride, or ACE inhibitors to control blood pressure and hypokalemia is necessary in all patients with bilateral idiopathic hyperaldosteronism.

DISPOSITION

Unilateral adrenalectomy normalizes hypertension and hypokalemia in 70% of patients with APA after 1 yr. After 5 yr, 50% of patients remain normotensive.

REFERRAL

Surgical referral for unilateral adrenalectomy following confirmation of unilateral APA or carcinoma

PEARLS & CONSIDERATIONS

COMMENTS

Frequent monitoring of blood pressure and electrolytes postoperatively is necessary, because normotension after unilateral adrenalectomy may take up to 4 mo.
- Recent investigations regarding serum aldosterone and the incidence of hypertension in nonhypertensive persons indicate that increased aldosterone levels within the physiologic range predispose to the development of hypertension.

SUGGESTED READING

Vasan RS et al: Serum aldosterone and the incidence of hypertension in nonhypertensive persons, *N Engl J Med* 351:33, 2004.

AUTHOR: **FRED F. FERRI, M.D.**

Alpha-1-Antitrypsin Deficiency (PTG)

BASIC INFORMATION

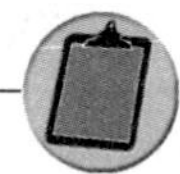

DEFINITION

Alpha-1-antitrypsin deficiency is a genetic deficiency of the protease inhibitor, alpha-1-antitrypsin, that results in a predisposition to pulmonary emphysema and hepatic cirrhosis.

SYNONYMS

AAT

ICD-9CM CODES
277.6 Alpha-1-antitrypsin deficiency

EPIDEMIOLOGY & DEMOGRAPHICS

- Felt to be underrecognized
- Affects approximately 80,000-100,000 Americans (including symptomatic and asymptomatic)
- Accounts for approximately 2% of COPD cases in Americans
- One in 10 individuals of European descent carry one of two mutations that may result in partial alpha-1-antitrypsin deficiency

PHYSICAL FINDINGS & CLINICAL PRESENTATION

- Physical findings and clinical presentation are varied and dependent upon phenotype (see "Etiology")
- Most often affects the lungs but can also involve liver and skin
- Classically associated with early-onset, severe, lower-lobe predominant emphysema; bronchiectasis may also be seen
- Symptoms are similar to "typical" COPD presentation (dyspnea, cough, sputum production).
- Liver involvement includes neonatal cholestasis, cirrhosis in children and adults, and primary carcinoma of the liver
- Panniculitis is the major dermatologic manifestation

ETIOLOGY

- Degree of alpha-1-antitrypsin deficiency is dependent on phenotype.
- "MM" represents the normal genotype and is associated with alpha-1-antitrypsin levels in the normal range.
- Mutation most commonly associated with emphysema is Z, with homozygote (ZZ) resulting in approximately 85% deficit in plasma alpha-1-antitrypsin concentrations.
- Development of emphysema is believed to be a result from an imbalance between the proteolytic enzyme, elastase, produced by neutrophils, and alpha-1-antitrypsin, which normally protects lung elastin by inhibiting elastase.
- Deficiency of alpha-1-antitrypsin increases risk of early-onset emphysema, but not all alpha-1-antitrypsin deficient individuals will develop lung disease.
- Smoking increases risk and accelerates onset of COPD.
- Liver disease is caused by pathologic accumulation of alpha-1-antitrypsin in hepatocytes.
- Similar to lung disease, skin involvement is thought to be secondary to unopposed proteolysis in skin.

DIAGNOSIS

DIFFERENTIAL DIAGNOSIS

See COPD
See cirrhosis

WORKUP

- Suspicion for alpha-1-antitrypsin deficiency usually results from emphysema developing at an early age and with basilar predominance of disease.
- Suspicion for alpha-1-antitrypsin deficiency resulting in liver disease or skin involvement may arise when other more common etiologies are excluded.

LABORATORY TESTS

- Serum level of alpha-1-antitrypsin is decreased or not detected in lung disease.
- Investigate possibility of abnormal alleles with genotyping.
- Pulmonary function testing is generally consistent with "typical" COPD.

IMAGING STUDIES

- Chest x-ray examination shows characteristic emphysematous changes at lung bases.
- High-resolution chest CT usually confirms the lower-lobe predominant emphysema and may also show significant bronchiectasis.

TREATMENT

NONPHARMACOLOGIC THERAPY

- Avoidance of smoking is paramount
- Avoidance of other environmental and occupational exposures that may increase risk of COPD

ACUTE GENERAL Rx

Acute exacerbations of COPD secondary to alpha-1-antitrypsin deficiency are treated in a similar fashion to "typical" COPD exacerbations.

CHRONIC Rx

- The goal of treatment in alpha-1-antitrypsin deficiency is to increase serum alpha-1-antitrypsin levels above a minimum, "protective" threshold.
- Although there are several therapeutic options under investigation, IV administration of pooled human alpha-1-antitrypsin is currently the only approved method to raise serum alpha-1-antitrypsin levels.
- Organ transplantation for patients with end-stage lung or liver disease is also an option.

DISPOSITION

Prognosis of patients with alpha-1-antitrypsin deficiency will depend on phenotype and level of deficiency.

REFERRAL

- Pulmonary and hepatology referrals for advanced lung and liver disease, or if replacement therapy is contemplated (e.g., moderate-severe lung disease)
- Lung and liver transplantation in suitable cases

PEARLS & CONSIDERATIONS

- The liver damage arising from the mutation is not from a deficiency in alpha-1-antitrypsin but from a pathologic accumulation of alpha-1-antitrypsin in hepatocytes.
- Consider alpha-1-antitrypsin deficiency in patients presenting with lower-lobe predominant emphysema; in most smokers without alpha-1-antitrypsin deficiency, emphysema predominates in the upper lobes.

SUGGESTED READINGS

Carell RW, Lomas DA: Alpha-1-antitrypsin deficiency: a model for conformational diseases, *N Engl J Med* 346(1):45, 2002.

Needham M, Stockley RA: Alpha-1-antitrypsin deficiency. 3:Clinical manifestations and natural history, *Thorax* 59(5):441, 2004.

AUTHOR: **JOSEPH A. DIAZ, M.D.**

BASIC INFORMATION

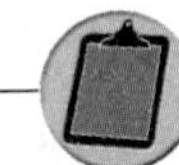

DEFINITION

Altitude sickness refers to a spectrum of illnesses related to hypoxia occurring in people rapidly ascending to high altitudes. Common acute syndromes occurring at high altitudes include acute mountain sickness, high-altitude pulmonary edema, and high-altitude cerebral edema (see Table 1-7).

SYNONYMS

Acute mountain sickness (AMS)
High-altitude pulmonary edema (HAPE)
High-altitude cerebral edema (HACE)

ICD-9CM CODES
289 Mountain sickness, acute
993.2 High altitude, effects

EPIDEMIOLOGY & DEMOGRAPHICS

- More than 30 million people are at risk of developing altitude sickness.
- Acute mountain sickness is the most common of the altitude diseases.
- In Summit County, Colorado, the incidence of acute mountain sickness was 22% at altitudes of 1850 to 2750 m (7000 to 9000 ft) and 42% at altitudes of 3000 m (10,000 ft).
- Approximately 0.01% of tourists to Colorado ski resorts experience HAPE or HACE.
- Men are 5 times more likely to develop HAPE than women.
- AMS and HACE affect men and women equally.

PHYSICAL FINDINGS & CLINICAL PRESENTATION

Acute mountain sickness
- Occurs within hours to a few days after rapid ascent over 8000 ft (2500 m)
- Headache is the most common symptom
- Dizziness and lightheadedness
- Nausea, vomiting, and loss of appetite
- Fatigue
- Sleep disturbance
- AMS can evolve into HAPE and HACE

Pulmonary edema (Fig. 1-11 and Section III, High-Altitude Pulmonary Edema)
- Occurs usually during the second night after rapid ascent over 8000 ft (2500 m)
- Dyspnea at rest
- Dry cough
- Chest tightness
- Tachycardia, tachypnea, rales, cyanosis with pink-tinged frothy sputum

High-altitude cerebral edema
- Usually presents several days after AMS
- Confusion, irritability, drowsiness, stupor, hallucinations
- Headache, nausea, vomiting
- Ataxia, paralysis, and seizures
- Coma and death may develop within hours of the first symptoms

ETIOLOGY

- As one ascends to altitudes above sea level, the atmospheric pressure decreases. Although the percentage of oxygen in the air remains the same, the partial pressure of oxygen decreases with altitude.
- Thus the cause of altitude sickness is primarily hypoxia resulting from low partial pressures of oxygen.
- The body responds to low oxygen partial pressures through a process of acclimatization (see "Comments").

DIAGNOSIS

The diagnosis of altitude sickness is made by clinical presentation and physical findings described previously.

TABLE 1-7 High-Altitude Sickness

	Acute Mountain Sickness	High-altitude pulmonary edema	High-altitude cerebral edema
Diagnostic findings	Nausea, vomiting, headache, lethargy, sleep disturbance, tinnitus, vertigo	Shortness of breath, tachypnea, tachycardia, cough, variable cyanosis	Headache, mental confusion, delirium, ataxia, hallucination, seizure, focal neurologic signs, coma
Onset	4-6 hr after reaching high altitude	24-96 hr	48-72 hr
Altitude	>8000 ft	8000-14,000 ft	Usually >12,000 ft
Ancillary data (in addition to those indicated for diagnostic evaluation)	ABG Chest x-ray study Electrolytes	ABG Chest x-ray study ECG Bleeding screen	ABG Electrolytes CT head
Differential considerations			
Trauma	Concussion	Pulmonary contusion	Head
Infection	Gastroenteritis Respiratory or CNS infection	Pneumonia	Meningitis Encephalitis
Metabolic		Uremia	Diabetic ketoacidosis Uremia Encephalopathy ↓↑ Na^+, ↑ Ca^{++}
Intoxication	Salicylates	Multiple	Narcotics
Vascular		CHF	Subarachnoid hemorrhage
Management (all respond to descent)			
Admit	Variable	Yes	Yes
Oxygen	Yes	Yes	Yes
Acetazolamide	Prophylactic	Prophylactic	Prophylactic
Bronchodilator	No	Yes	No
Steroids	Controversial	Yes	Yes
Ventilation with PEEP	No	Yes, if severe	Hyperventilation

From Barkin RM, Rosen P: *Emergency pediatrics,* St Louis, 1999, Mosby.
ABG, Arterial blood gas; *CHF,* congestive heart failure; *CNS,* central nervous system; *CT,* computed tomography; *ECG,* electrocardiogram; *PEEP,* peak end-expiratory pressure.

DIFFERENTIAL DIAGNOSIS

- Dehydration
- Carbon monoxide poisoning
- Hypothermia
- Infection
- Substance abuse
- Congestive heart failure
- Pulmonary embolism
- Cerebrovascular accident

WORKUP

Typically the diagnosis is self-evident after history and physical examination. Laboratory tests and imaging studies help monitor cardiopulmonary and CNS status in patients admitted to the intensive care unit for pulmonary and/or cerebral edema.

LABORATORY TESTS

Laboratory tests are not very useful in diagnosing altitude sickness.

IMAGING STUDIES

CXR showing Kerley B-lines and patchy edema (see Fig. 1-11)

CT scan of the head showing diffuse or patchy edema

TREATMENT

NONPHARMACOLOGIC THERAPY

- Stop the ascent to allow acclimatization or start to descend until symptoms have resolved.
- Oxygen 4 to 6 L/min is used for severe AMS, HAPE, and HACE.
- Portable hyperbaric bags are useful if available at the site.
- Avoid dehydration.

ACUTE GENERAL Rx

- Aspirin 325 mg PO q6h can be used for headaches in AMS.
- Acetazolamide 125 mg to 250 mg PO bid has been shown to alleviate symptoms of AMS and HAPE.
- Nifedipine 10 mg sublingual followed by long-acting nifedipine 30 mg bid is used for patients with HAPE who cannot descend immediately.
- Dexamethasone 4 mg PO every 6 hr is used in patients with severe AMS, HAPE, and HACE.

CHRONIC Rx

- Prevention therapy is the most prudent therapy.
  1. Slow, staged ascent to avoid altitude sickness.
  2. Start the ascent below 8000 ft.
  3. Ascend 1000 ft/day and rest.
  4. Spend 2 nights at the same altitude every 3 days.
  5. Sleep at lower heights than the altitude climbed ("climb high, sleep low").
  6. Prophylactic therapy with acetazolamide 750 mg daily or dexamethasone 8 to 16 mg daily decreases the risk of developing AMS. The drugs are used until acclimatization occurs.
  7. Prophylactic inhalation of a β-adrenergic agonist, salmeterol 125 mcg every 12 hr, or the use of slow-release nifedipine 20 mg bid reduces the risk of HAPE in susceptible individuals.

DISPOSITION

- AMS improves over a period of 2 to 3 days.
- HAPE is the most common cause of death among the altitude illnesses.
- More than 60% of patients with HAPE will have recurrence of symptoms on subsequent climbs.
- Neurologic deficits may persist for weeks but eventually resolve. If coma occurs, prognosis is poor.

REFERRAL

Cardiology and neurology referrals are made in patients with pulmonary edema and CNS findings, respectively.

PEARLS & CONSIDERATIONS

COMMENTS

- Acclimatization is the process whereby the body adapts to hypoxia by optimizing oxygen delivery to cells. Adaptive mechanisms include:
  1. Hyperventilation to increase O_2 in the setting of hypoxia
  2. Tachycardia secondary to hypoxemia
  3. Pulmonary hypertension developed to improve ventilation-perfusion mismatch
  4. Cerebral vasodilation to increase blood flow to the brain
  5. Rise in hemoglobin and hematocrit
- Risk factors for the development of altitude sicknesses are:
  1. Rapid ascent
  2. Strenuous exertion on arrival
  3. Obesity
  4. Previous history of altitude sickness
  5. Male gender
- Physical fitness is not protective against high-altitude illness.
- HAPE is characterized by elevated pulmonary pressures resulting in protein-rich, hemorrhagic exudates into the lung alveoli.

SUGGESTED READINGS

Dumont L, Mardirosoff C, Tramer MR: Efficacy and harm of pharmacological prevention of acute mountain sickness: quantitative systematic review, *BMJ* 321:267, 2000.

Hachett PH, Roach RC: High-altitude illness, *N Engl J Med* 345:107, 2001.

Hackett P, Rennie D: High altitude pulmonary edema, *JAMA* 287:2275, 2002.

Sartori C et al: Salmeterol for the prevention of high-altitude pulmonary edema, *N Engl J Med* 346:1631, 2002.

Swenson ER et al: Pathogenesis of high-altitude pulmonary edema, *JAMA* 287:2228, 2002.

AUTHOR: **PETER PETROPOULOS, M.D.**

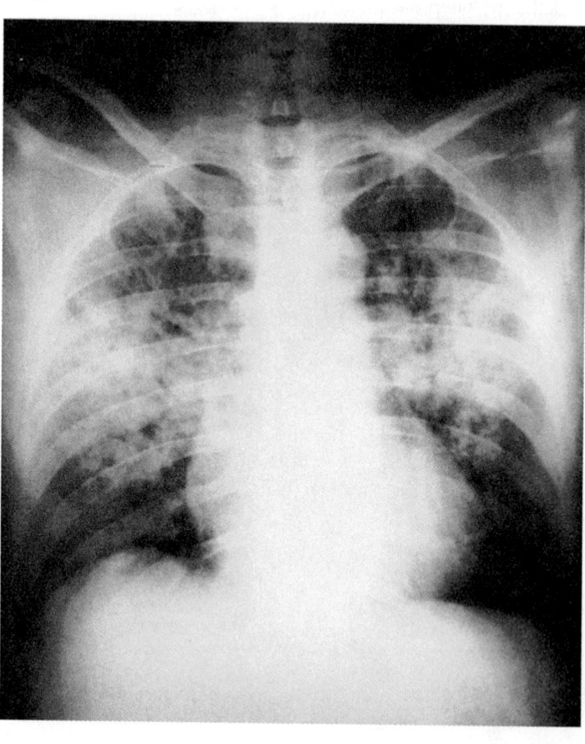

FIGURE 1-11 Chest radiograph showing high-altitude pulmonary edema. (From Strauss RH [ed]: *Sports medicine,* ed 2, Philadelphia, 1991, WB Saunders.)

BASIC INFORMATION

DEFINITION

Dementia is a syndrome characterized by progressive loss of previously acquired cognitive skills including memory, language, insight, and judgment. Alzheimer's disease (AD) accounts for the majority (50% to 75%) of all cases of dementia.

ICD-9CM CODES
331.0 Alzheimer's disease
290.0 Senile dementia, uncomplicated

EPIDEMIOLOGY & DEMOGRAPHICS

INCIDENCE: Risk doubles every 5 yr after the age of 65; above the age of 85 the incidence is about 8%

PREVALENCE: Currently an estimated 4 million Americans have AD; 5% of patients are over the age of 65; 35% to 50% of patients are over the age of 85

PREDOMINANT SEX: Female

PHYSICAL FINDINGS & CLINICAL PRESENTATION

- Spouse or other family member, not the patient, often notes insidious memory impairment.
- Patients have difficulties learning and retaining new information, handling complex tasks (e.g., balancing the checkbook), and have impairments in reasoning, judgment, spatial ability and orientation (e.g., difficulty driving, getting lost away from home).
- Atypical presentations include early and severe behavioral changes, focal findings on examination, parkinsonism, hallucinations, falls, or onset of symptoms younger than the age of 65.

DIAGNOSIS

There is no definitive imaging or laboratory test for the diagnosis of dementia; rather, diagnosis is dependent on clinical history, a thorough physical and neurological examination, and use of reliable and valid diagnostic criteria (i.e., DSM-IV or NINDCS-ADRDA) such as the following:

- Loss of memory and one or more additional cognitive abilities, including *aphasia* (disturbance in language), *apraxia* (impaired ability to carry out motor activities despite intact motor function), *agnosia* (failure to recognize or identify objects despite intact sensory function), or disturbance in executive function (e.g., planning, organizing, sequencing, abstracting)
- Impairment in social or occupational functioning that represents a decline from a previous level of functioning and results in significant disability
- Deficits that do not occur exclusively during the course of delirium
- Insidious onset and gradual progression of symptoms
- Cognitive loss documented by neuropsychological tests
- No physical signs, neuroimaging, or laboratory evidence of other diseases that can cause dementia (i.e., metabolic abnormalities, medication or toxin effects, infection, stroke, Parkinson's disease, subdural hematoma, or tumors)
- Deficits do not occur exclusively during the course of a delirium
- The disturbance is not better accounted for by another Axis I disorder

Patients with isolated memory loss who lack functional impairment at home or work do not meet criteria for dementia but may have a mild cognitive impairment (MCI). Identifying patients with MCI is important because patients with MCI may have a slightly higher rate of progression to dementia.

DIFFERENTIAL DIAGNOSIS

- Cancer (brain tumor, meningeal neoplasia)
- Infection (AIDS, neurosyphilis, PML)
- Metabolic (EtOH, hypothyroidism, B_{12} deficiency)
- Organ failure (dialysis dementia, Wilson's disease)
- Vascular disorder (chronic SDH)
- Depression

WORKUP

History and general physical examination:

- Medication use should always be reviewed for drugs that may cause mental status changes
- Patients should be screened for depression, because it can sometimes mimic dementia but also often occurs as a coexisting condition and should be treated
- On examination, look for signs of metabolic disturbance, presence of psychiatric features, or focal neurologic deficits

Mental status testing:

Brief mental status testing can be done easily and quickly in the office. Most commonly used is the Folstein Mini-mental status examination (MMSE). The MMSE is widely available in many reference books and on the Internet. A MMSE score <24 (scores range from 0 to 30, with lower scores reflecting poorer performance) suggests dementia; however, results must be interpreted with caution. The MMSE is not sensitive enough to detect mild dementia, or dementia in patients with high baseline IQ. Scores may be spuriously low in patients with limited education, poor motor function, African American or Hispanic ethnicity, poor language skills, or impaired vision. If the MMSE is not available, mental status testing should include tests that assess the following cognitive functions:

- *Orientation:* ask the patient to give the day, date, month, year, and place, and to name the current president
- *Attention:* ask patient to recite the months of the year forwards and in reverse
- *Verbal recall:* ask the patient to remember four items; test for recall after a 1- and 5-min delay
- *Language:* ask patient to write and then read a sentence; have the patient name both common and less common objects
- *Visual-Spatial:* ask the patient to draw a clock and to set the hands of the clock at 11:10

Patients with AD typically have trouble with verbal recall, plus visual-spatial and/or language deficits. Attention is usually preserved until the late stages of AD, so consider alternate diagnoses in patients who do poorly on tests of attention.

Patients should be referred for formal neuropsychological testing to confirm screening mental status testing, especially for those patients who have an atypical history and/or clinical presentation, nondiagnostic performance on screening mental status testing, or high baseline IQ. Formal testing may help to differentiate AD from other causes of dementia, such as diffuse Lewy body disease, fronto-temporal dementia, vascular dementia, and pseudodementia.

LABORATORY TESTS

- CBC
- Serum electrolytes
- Glucose
- BUN/creatinine
- Liver and thyroid function tests
- Serum vitamin B_{12} and methylmalonic acid
- Syphilis serology, if high clinical suspicion
- Lumbar puncture if history or signs of cancer, suspicion of infectious process, or when the clinical presentation is unusual (i.e., rapid progression of symptoms)
- EEG if there is history of seizures, episodic confusion, rapid clinical decline, or suspicion of Creutzfeldt-Jakob disease
- Measurement of Apolipoprotein E genotyping, CSF tau and amyloid, and functional imaging including positron emission tomography (PET) or scanning proton emission computed tomography (SPECT) are not routinely indicated

IMAGING STUDIES

CT scan or MRI to rule out hydrocephalus and mass lesions, including subdural hematoma.

TREATMENT

NONPHARMACOLOGIC THERAPY

- Patient safety, including risks associated with impaired driving, wandering behavior, leaving stoves unattended, and accidents, must be addressed with the patient and family early and appropriate measures implemented.
- Family education and support may help reduce need for skilled nursing facility, and reduce caregiver stress, depression, and burnout.

ACUTE GENERAL Rx

None

CHRONIC Rx

1. Symptomatic treatment of memory disturbance:
   a. Cholinesterase inhibitors (ChEI): this class of medication is FDA-approved for the treatment of mild to moderate AD (MMSE 10-26). Clinical studies have demonstrated small improvements in memory, language, and ability to perform activities of daily living. Medication may also help to reduce symptoms of agitation and aggressiveness. At present there are no data supporting superiority of one cholinesterase inhibitor over another. Common side effects include nausea, diarrhea, and anorexia and may be bothersome enough to require a slower escalation of dosage, or switching to another agent. There may be some benefit in severe AD, though this has not yet been established.
      - Donepezil (Aricept): dose is 5 mg qd for 4 to 6 wk, then increase to 10 mg qd
      - Rivastigmine (Exelon): dose is 1.5 mg bid with food, and then increased as tolerated by 1.5 mg bid until target dose of 3-6 mg bid
      - Galantamine (Reminyl): dose is 4 mg bid with food, then increasing by 4 mg bid until target dose of 8-12 mg bid

   b. NMDA receptor antagonist: Memantine (Namenda) is FDA-approved for the treatment of moderate to severe AD. Clinical studies have demonstrated improvement in function and cognition, and possibly a delay in disease progression. Combination therapy of memantine with ChEI has added benefits in moderate to severe AD patients compared to use of ChEI alone. There may be symptomatic benefit of monotherapy in mild AD but additional studies are still needed. Common side effects include constipation, dizziness, or headache. Memantine is contraindicated in patients with renal insufficiency or history of seizures.
      - Memantine (Namenda): dose is 5 mg qd, increasing dose by 5 mg each week to target dose of 10 mg bid.
2. Symptomatic treatment of behavioral disturbances
   - Wandering, hoarding or hiding objects, repetitive questioning, withdrawal, and social inappropriateness often respond to behavioral therapies.
   - Agitation, delusions, or hallucinations:
      - Olanzapine (Zyprexa) 2.5 mg qd to bid; may increase by 2.5 mg to maximum dose to 15 mg/day as needed
      - Quetiapine (Seroquel) 25 mg bid, increase by 25 mg per day every 2 days as needed, maximum dose 250 mg 3 times daily as needed
   - Depression:
      - Citalopram (Celexa): 10 mg qd; may increase to 20 mg after 1-2 wk
      - Sertraline (Zoloft): 25-50 mg qd; may increase by 25-50 mg qd every wk to maximum dose of 200 mg qd
      - Tricyclic antidepressants are generally avoided because of anticholinergic properties
3. Other agents:
   - Vitamin E: 1000 IU given twice daily may delay progression in patients with moderate disease.
   - Use of estrogen, NSAIDs, or ginkgo biloba is not routinely recommended.

PEARLS & CONSIDERATIONS

The physician must make a thorough search for the treatable causes of dementia.

Current American Academy of Neurology practice parameters recommend:

- Treat cognitive symptoms of AD with cholinesterase inhibitors and Vitamin E
- Treat agitation, psychosis, and depression
- Encourage caregivers to participate in educational programs and support groups

COMMENTS

For additional information for patients, families, and clinicians:

Alzheimer's Association (http://www.alzheimers.org; 800-272-3900)

Alzheimer's Disease Education and Referral Center (http://www.alzheimers.org; 800-438-4380)

SUGGESTED READINGS

Doody RS, Stevens JC, Beck C, et al: Management of dementia (an evidence-based review): report of the Quality Standards Subcommittee of the American Academy of Neurology, *Neurology* 56:1154, 2001.

DSM-IV: Diagnostic and statistical manual of mental disorders, ed 4, Washington, DC, 1994, American Psychiatric Association.

Folstein MF, Folsein SE, McHugh PR: "Mini-mental state": a practical method for grading the cognitive state of patients for the clinician, *J Psychiatr Res* 12:189, 1975.

Kawas CH: Early Alzheimer's disease, *N Engl J Med* 349(11):1056, 2003.

Knopman DS, DeKosky ST, Cummings JL, et al: Diagnosis of dementia (an evidence-based review): report of the Quality Standards Subcommittee of the American Academy of Neurology, *Neurology* 56:1143, 2001.

McKhann G et al: Clinical diagnosis of Alzheimer's disease: report of the NINCDS-ADRDA work group under the auspices of Department of Health and Human Services Task Force on Alzheimer's disease, *Neurology* 34:939, 1984.

Reisberg B, Doody R, Stoffler A, et al: Memantine in moderate-to-severe Alzheimer's disease, *N Engl J Med* 348:1333, 2003.

Sano M, Ernesto C, Thomas RG, et al: A controlled trial of selegiline, alpha-tocopherol, or both as treatment for Alzheimer's disease, *N Engl J Med* 336:1216, 1997.

Tariot PN, Farlow MR, Grossberg GT et al: Memantine treatment in patients with moderate to severe Alzheimer disease already receiving donepezil: a randomized controlled trial, *JAMA* 291:317, 2004.

AUTHOR: **TAMARA G. FONG, M.D, PH.D.**

BASIC INFORMATION

DEFINITION

Amaurosis fugax (AF) is a temporary loss of monocular vision caused by transient retinal ischemia. Distinguished from an ischemic optic neuropathy (usually anterior) in which visual loss is permanent.

ICD-9CM CODES
362.34 Amaurosis fugax

EPIDEMIOLOGY & DEMOGRAPHICS

INCIDENCE (IN U.S.): An uncommon presentation of carotid artery disease
PEAK INCIDENCE: 55 yr and older

PHYSICAL FINDINGS & CLINICAL PRESENTATION

- Onset is sudden, typically lasting seconds to minutes, and often accompanied by scotomas such as a shade or curtain being pulled over the front of the eye (usually downward).
- Vision loss can be complete or quadrantic.
- There are usually no physical findings.
- Acute stage: cholesterol emboli may be seen in retinal artery (Hollenhorst plaque): carotid bruits or other evidence of generalized atherosclerosis.
- If embolus is cardiac in origin, atrial fibrillation is often present.

ETIOLOGY

Usually embolic from the internal carotid artery or the heart but may also be due to vasculitis, such as giant cell arteritis (GCA), or hyperviscosity syndromes, such as sickle cell disease, that cause ischemia in the vascular territory of the ophthalmic artery

DIAGNOSIS

DIFFERENTIAL DIAGNOSIS

The differential diagnosis of transient monocular visual loss includes the following:

- Retinal migraine: in contrast to amaurosis, the onset of visual loss develops more slowly, usually over a period of 15-20 min.
- Transient visual obscurations (TVOs) occur in the setting of papilledema; intermittent rises in intracranial pressure briefly compromise optic disc perfusion and cause transient visual loss lasting 1-2 s and the episodes may be binocular.

If the visual loss persists at the time of evaluation (i.e., vision has not yet recovered), then the differential diagnosis should be broadened to include:

- Anterior ischemic optic neuropathy—arteritic (classically GCA) or nonarteritic
- Central retinal vein occlusion

WORKUP

Because amaurosis is usually due to emboli, the workup should focus on embolic sources; however, GCA should always be considered as well.

- Careful examination of retina; embolus may be visible and confirm the diagnosis (Fig. 1-12)
- Auscultation of arteries for bruits
- Examination of all pulses and for temporal artery tenderness
- Inquire about symptoms of GCA (scalp tenderness, jaw claudication)
- Examine for signs of hemispheric stroke resulting from ICA disease (contralateral limb and face weakness and/or sensory loss, aphasia, etc.)

LABORATORY TESTS

- CBC with ESR and CRP
- Serum chemistries, including lipid profile
- ECG and consider cycling cardiac enzymes
- Hypercoagulable workup is discretionary based on younger age and history

IMAGING STUDIES

- Carotid Dopplers followed by MRA or four-vessel angiography as indicated.
- Transthoracic echocardiography (TTE) is indicated to screen for embolization in patients with evidence of heart disease and in patients without an evident source for their transient neurologic deficit. Transesophageal echocardiography (TEE) is more sensitive for detecting cardiac sources of embolization (ventricular mural thrombus, atrial appendage, patent foramen ovale, aortic arch).
- Consider MRI of the brain with diffusion-weighted imaging to look for ischemic injury.

TREATMENT

NONPHARMACOLOGIC THERAPY

- Diet (decrease saturated fatty acids and high-cholesterol foods)
- Exercise
- Cessation of tobacco use

ACUTE GENERAL Rx

- Investigate as an emergency.
- Give aspirin if etiology is presumed embolic.
- If GCA is suspected, start prednisone and refer for temporal artery biopsy within 48 hr (see Section I, "Giant Cell Arteritis").

CHRONIC Rx

- Reduce risks by carotid endarterectomy or stent if stenosis >70%.
- Control hypertension and manage vascular risk factors.
- Antiplatelet therapy.
- Consider starting an HMG CoA reductase inhibitor.

DISPOSITION

Among patients with >50% carotid stenosis who do not undergo carotid endarterectomy, those who present with transient monocular blindness have about a 10% risk of stroke in 3 yr compared with a 20% risk in patients who present with a hemispheric transient ischemic attack (TIA).

REFERRAL

- Recommend referral to a neurologist for an evaluation and workup.
- If significant carotid stenosis, consider carotid endarterectomy or carotid stenting for the following:
  1. High-grade (≥70%) stenosis
  2. Multiple TIAs despite medical therapy, in the setting of high-grade or ulcerative disease

SUGGESTED READINGS

Barnett HJ et al: Benefit of carotid endarterectomy in patients with symptomatic moderate or severe stenosis. North American Symptomatic Carotid Endarterectomy Trial Collaborators, *N Engl J Med* 339:1415, 1998.

Benauente O et al: Prognosis after transient monocular blindness associated with carotid-artery stenosis, *N Engl J Med* 345:1084, 2001.

Murtha T, Stasheff SF: Visual dysfunction in retinal and optic nerve disease, *Neurol Clin* 21:445, 2003.

AUTHOR: **SEAN I. SAVITZ, M.D.**

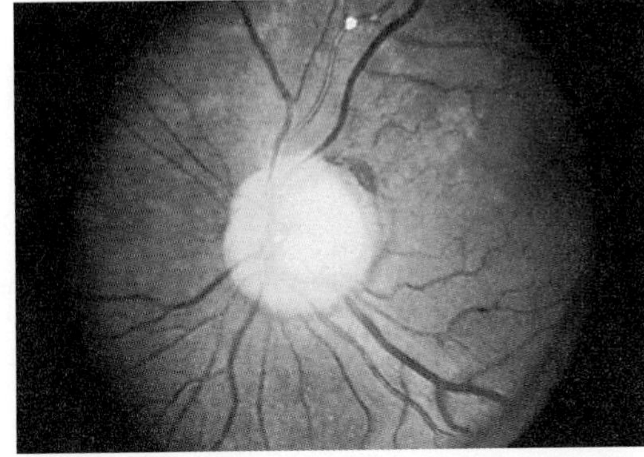

FIGURE 1-12 A cholesterol crystal embolus lodged at an arterial bifurcation. (From Stein JH [ed]: *Internal medicine,* ed 5, St Louis, 1998, Mosby.)

BASIC INFORMATION

DEFINITION

Amblyopia refers to a decrease in vision in one or both eyes in the presence of an otherwise normal ophthalmologic examination.

SYNONYMS

Deprivation amblyopia
Occlusion amblyopia
Strabismus amblyopia
Refractive amblyopia
Organic or toxic amblyopias
Lazy eye

ICD-9CM CODES
368.00 Amblyopia

EPIDEMIOLOGY & DEMOGRAPHICS

INCIDENCE (IN U.S.): 1% to 4% of the general population
PREVALENCE (IN U.S.): High incidence in premature infants with drug-dependent mothers and in neurologically impaired children
PREDOMINANT SEX: None
PREDOMINANT AGE: Childhood
PEAK INCIDENCE: Childhood

PHYSICAL FINDINGS & CLINICAL PRESENTATION

Decreased vision using best refraction in the presence of normal corneal, lens, retinal, and optic nerve appearance (Fig. 1-13)

ETIOLOGY

- Visual deprivation
- Strabismus
- Occlusion with patching
- Refractive error organic lesions in the nervous system
- Toxins

DIAGNOSIS

DIFFERENTIAL DIAGNOSIS

- Central nervous system (CNS) disease (brainstem)
- Optic nerve disorders
- Corneal or other eye diseases

WORKUP

- Complete eye examination to find cause of amblyopia or deprivation of vision
- Motility evaluation

LABORATORY TESTS

Usually none

IMAGING STUDIES

Usually not necessary unless CNS lesion suspected

TREATMENT

NONPHARMACOLOGIC THERAPY

- Glasses or prisms to align eyes with minor deviations and improve vision
- Patches, mechanical vs atropine—Patching and atropine both work. Atropine 1% is used daily for 6 months; patching is used 6 hr/day for 6 months. Patching may be more effective. Fifty percent get best vision improvement by 16 weeks.
- Removal of the cause of the amblyopia if possible
- Surgery to align the eyes or remove obstruction to vision

CHRONIC Rx

Patching or optics, including prisms and atropine most effective in 3 to 7 yr olds only; minimal or no help after 7 yrs old

DISPOSITION

Immediate patching, alternating eyes daily

REFERRAL

To ophthalmologist if vision is compromised

PEARLS & CONSIDERATIONS

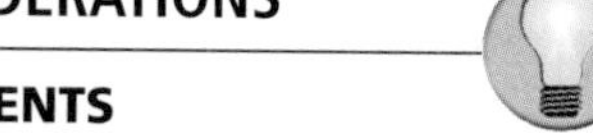

COMMENTS

The earlier the referral, the better the outcome.

SUGGESTED READINGS

Donahue SP et al: Screening for amblyopia in preverbal children, *Ophthalmology* 108:1711, 2001.
Gottlob I, Awan M. Proudlock F: The role of compliance in 2 vs 6 hrs of patching in children with amblyopia, *Arch Ophthalmol* 122(3):422, 2004.
Holmes JM et al: The amblyopia treatment study visual acuity testing protocol, *Arch Ophthalmol* 119:1345, 2001.
Pediatric Eye Disease Investigator Group: The clinical profile of moderate amblyopia in children younger than 7 years old, *Arch Ophthalmol* 120:281, 2003.
Quinn GE, Beck RW, Holmes JM et al: Recent advances in the treatment of amblyopia. *Pediatrics* 113(6):1800, 2004.
The Pediatric Eye Disease Investigator Group: A randomized trial of atropine vs patching for treatment of moderate amblyopia in children, *JAMA* 287:2145, 2002.
Williams C et al: Amblyopia treatment outcomes after screening before or at age 3 years: follow up from randomized trial, *BMJ* 324:1549, 2002.

AUTHOR: **MELVYN KOBY, M.D.**

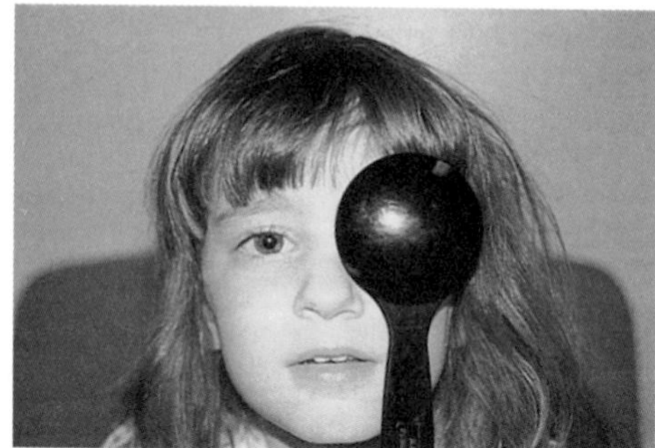

A

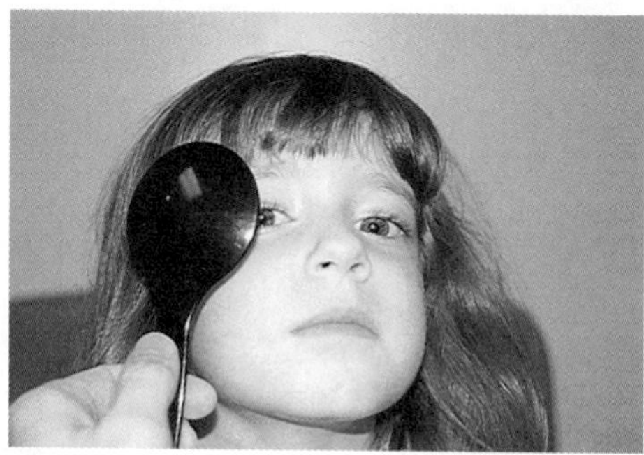

B

FIGURE 1-13 **A,** This child happily fixes with her right eye and does not object if the left eye is covered. **B,** When the right eye is covered she moves her head away and tries to remove the cover, demonstrating a fixation preference for the right eye and amblyopia of the left eye. (From Hoekelman R [ed]: *Primary pediatric care,* ed 3, St Louis, 1997, Mosby.)

BASIC INFORMATION

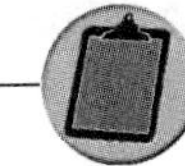

DEFINITION

Amebiasis is an infection caused by the protozoal parasite *Entamoeba histolytica*. Although primarily an infection of the colon, amebiasis may cause extraintestinal disease, particularly liver abscess.

SYNONYMS

Amebic dysentery (when severe intestinal infection)

ICD-9CM CODES
006.9 Amebiasis

EPIDEMIOLOGY & DEMOGRAPHICS

INCIDENCE (IN U.S.): Highest in institutionalized patients, sexually active homosexual men
PREVALENCE (IN U.S.): 4% (80% of infections asymptomatic)
PREDOMINANT SEX:
- Equal sex distribution in general
- Striking male predominance of liver abscess

PREDOMINANT AGE: Second through sixth decades
PEAK INCIDENCE: Peaks at age 2 to 3 yr and >40 yr
GENETICS: Infection more likely to be fulminant in young infants

PHYSICAL FINDINGS & CLINICAL PRESENTATION

- Often nonspecific
- Approximately 20% of cases symptomatic
  1. Diarrhea, which may be bloody
  2. Abdominal and back pain
- Abdominal tenderness in 83% of severe cases
- Fever in 38% of severe cases
- Hepatomegaly, RUQ tenderness, and fever in almost all patients with liver abscess (may be absent in fulminant cases)

ETIOLOGY

- Caused by the protozoal parasite *E. histolytica* (Fig. 1-14)
- Transmission by the fecal-oral route
- Infection usually localized to the large bowel, particularly the cecum where a localized mass lesion (ameboma) may form
- Extraintestinal infection in which the organism invades the bowel mucosa and gains access to the portal circulation

DIAGNOSIS

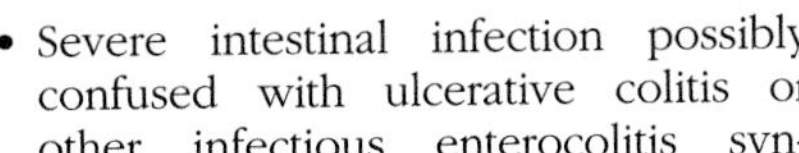

DIFFERENTIAL DIAGNOSIS

- Severe intestinal infection possibly confused with ulcerative colitis or other infectious enterocolitis syndromes, such as those caused by *Shigella, Salmonella, Campylobacter*, or invasive *Escherichia coli*
- In elderly patients: ischemic bowel possibly producing a similar picture

WORKUP

- Three stool specimens over a period of 7 to 10 days to exclude the diagnosis (sensitivity 50% to 80%)
- Concentration and staining the specimen with Lugol's iodine or methylene blue to increase the diagnostic yield
- Available culture (rarely necessary in routine cases)

LABORATORY TESTS

- Stool examination is generally reliable.
- Mucosal biopsy is occasionally necessary.
- Serum antibody may be detected and is particularly sensitive and specific for extraintestinal infection or severe intestinal disease.
- Aspiration of abscess fluid is used to distinguish amebic from bacterial abscesses.

IMAGING STUDIES

Abdominal imaging studies (sonography or CT scan) to diagnose liver abscess

TREATMENT

ACUTE GENERAL Rx

- Metronidazole (750 mg PO tid for 10 days) is used in the treatment of mild to severe intestinal infection and amebic liver abscess; it may be administered intravenously when necessary.
- Follow with iodoquinol (650 mg PO tid for 20 days) to eradicate persistent cysts.
- For asymptomatic patients with amebic cysts on stool examination, use iodoquinol or paromomycin (500 mg PO tid for 7 days).
- Avoid antiperistaltic agents in severe intestinal infections to avoid risk of toxic megacolon.
- Liver abscess is generally responsive to medical management but surgical intervention indicated for extension of liver abscess into pericardium or, occasionally, for toxic megacolon.

DISPOSITION

Host immunity incomplete and reinfection rate high for patients remaining at risk

REFERRAL

- For consultation with infectious diseases specialist for extraintestinal infection or persistent or relapsing intestinal infection
- For surgical consultation:
  1. For toxic megacolon
  2. For impending rupture of or extension of liver abscess into adjacent structures

PEARLS & CONSIDERATIONS

COMMENTS

- Infection with other intestinal parasites, particularly *Giardia lamblia*, may coexist with amebiasis.

SUGGESTED READINGS

Haque R et al: Amebiasis, *N Engl J Med* 348(16):1565, 2003.
Stanley SL: Protective immunity to amebiasis: new insights and new challenges, *J Infect Dis* 184(4):504, 2001.

AUTHOR: **JOSEPH R. MASCI, M.D.**

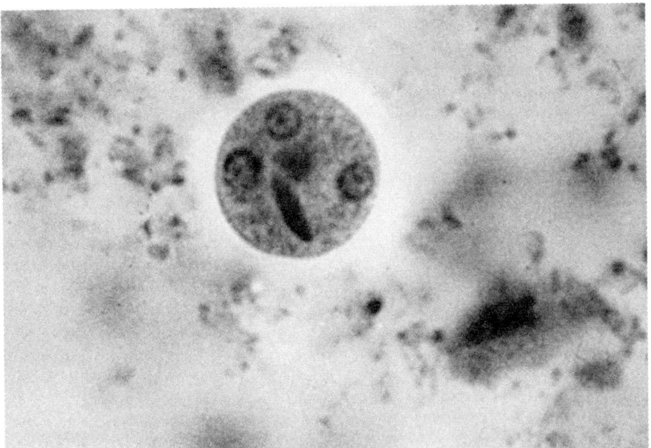

FIGURE 1-14 Mature cyst of Entamoeba histolytica. Three of the four nuclei are seen in the plane of focus of this photomicrograph. (From Mandell GL [ed]: *Mandell, Douglas, and Bennett's principles and practice of infectious diseases*, ed 5, New York, 2000, Churchill Livingstone.)

BASIC INFORMATION

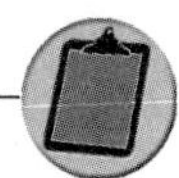

DEFINITION

The acquired inability to learn new information or recall new information. The impairment compromises personal, social, or occupational functioning. Disorder is not secondary to delirium or dementia.

SYNONYMS

Wernicke-Korsafoff syndrome
Amnesia

ICD-9CM CODES
780.9 Amnesia (retrograde); memory disturbance, loss or lack
DSM-IV-TR codes
294 Amnestic disorder due to . . . [indicate the general medical condition]
294.8 Amnestic disorder NOS

EPIDEMIOLOGY & DEMOGRAPHICS

- Data not available on true incidence or lifetime risk.
- Transient global amnesia onset usually over age 50.
- Genetic defect for thiamine metabolism has been described in some patients.

CLINICAL PRESENTATION

History
- Diagnosis dependent upon history.
- The inability to learn or recall new information is the key feature of this disorder.
- Mini mental status examination useful. Patients unable to recall events that transpire during the interview but may have a normal digit span and be able to follow the conversation.
- Patients unable to recall events subsequent to the onset of the amnesia.
- Individuals may learn new motor tasks but are unable to recall those learning experiences.
- Amnesia generally has both anterograde and retrograde components.

ETIOLOGY

- Traumatic brain injury
- Focal tumors or infarction
- Herpes simplex encephalitis
- Cerebral anoxia
- Korsakoff's syndrome (thiamine deficiency)
- Carbon monoxide poisoning
- Transient amnesia may arise from concussion, acute intoxications, seizures, transient global amnesia, and post-ECT.

DIAGNOSIS

DIFFERENTIAL DIAGNOSIS

- Dementia
- Delirium
- Major depression
- Benign senescent forgetfulness

WORKUP

- Complete medical history and mental status testing
- Neuropsychologic testing

LABORATORY TESTS

None

IMAGING STUDIES

- No specific or diagnostic features of amnestic disorder are detectable on imaging.
- Brain MRI indicates specific atrophy in diencephalic structures in Korsakoff's syndrome.

TREATMENT

NONPHARMACOLOGIC THERAPY

- Cognitive rehabilitation to promote recovery from brain injury may be helpful.
- Supervised living to ensure appropriate long-term care.

ACUTE GENERAL Rx

Initial treatment with thiamine, antiviral medication, aspirin, etc. directed to the underlying etiology

CHRONIC Rx

No known effective treatments for amnestic disorder to reverse or ameliorate memory deficits.

COMPLEMENTARY & ALTERNATIVE MEDICINE

None

DISPOSITION

Amnesias may be chronic or transient, depending upon etiology.

REFERRAL

Refer for neuropsychologic testing.

PEARLS & CONSIDERATIONS

COMMENTS

In Korsakoff's syndrome, anterograde amnesia (disturbance in acquisition of new information) is more prominent than retrograde amnesia (problems remembering old information).

PREVENTION

High-dose vitamins for prevention of Wernicke-Korsakoff syndrome

PATIENT/FAMILY EDUCATION

Respite care and in-home services for family care-givers

SUGGESTED READINGS

Oscar-Berman M et al: Comparisons of Korsakoff and non-Korsakoff alcoholics on neuropsychological tests of prefrontal brain functioning, *Alcohol Clin Exp Res* 28(4):667, 2004.

Vik PW et al: Cognitive impairment in substance abuse, *Psychiatr Clin North Am* 27(1):97, 2004.

AUTHOR: **MITCHELL D. FELDMAN, M.D., M.PHIL.**

BASIC INFORMATION

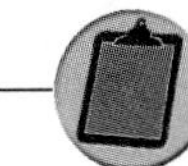

DEFINITION

Amyloidosis is a generic term describing the deposition of amyloid fibrils in body tissues. *Amyloid* is an amorphous, eosinophilic material; it is birefringent and usually extracellular. Electron microscopy reveals nonbranching fibrils that are soluble and relatively resistant to proteolytic digestion. There are two major forms of acquired systemic amyloidosis:

- AA, associated with chronic inflammatory diseases (e.g., rheumatoid arthritis) and amyloid deposits in kidneys, liver, and spleen
- AL (formerly known as primary amyloidosis) affecting the kidneys, heart, liver, intestines, skin, peripheral sensory nervous system, spleen, and lungs

ICD-9CM CODES
277.3 Amyloidosis

EPIDEMIOLOGY & DEMOGRAPHICS

- Amyloidosis affects primarily males between the ages of 60 and 70 yr.
- There are between 1500 and 3500 new cases annually in the U.S.
- The most common type in the U.S. is immunoglobulin light chain related (AL) occurring in 5 to 12 persons/yr in the U.S.

PHYSICAL FINDINGS & CLINICAL PRESENTATION

- Findings are variable with organ system involvement. Symmetric polyarthritis, peripheral neuropathy, and carpal tunnel syndrome may be present with joint involvement.
- Signs and symptoms of nephrotic syndrome may be present with renal involvement.
- Fatigue and dyspnea may occur with pulmonary involvement.
- Diarrhea, macroglossia (20% of patients), malabsorption, hepatomegaly, and weight loss may occur with GI involvement.
- Cardiac involvement is common and can lead to predominantly right-sided CHF, JVD, peripheral edema, and hepatomegaly.
- Vascular involvement can result in easy bleeding and periorbital purpura ("raccoon-eyes").

ETIOLOGY

In patients with amyloidosis, a soluble circulating protein (serum amyloid P [SAP]) is deposited in tissues as insoluble β-pleated sheets. The source of amyloid protein is a population of monoclonal plasma cells in the bone marrow. There are several chemically documented amyloidoses that can be principally subdivided into:

1. Acquired systemic amyloidosis (immunoglobulin light chain, multiple myeloma, hemodialysis amyloidosis)
2. Heredofamilial systemic (polyneuropathy, familial Mediterranean fever)
3. Organ-limited (Alzheimer's disease)
4. Localized endocrine (pancreatic islet, medullary thyroid carcinoma)

DIAGNOSIS

DIFFERENTIAL DIAGNOSIS

Variable, depending on the organ involvement:

- Renal involvement (toxin- or drug-induced necrosis, glomerulonephritis, renal vein thrombosis)
- Interstitial lung disease (sarcoidosis, connective tissue disease, infectious etiologies)
- Restrictive cardiac (endomyocardial fibrosis, viral myocarditis)
- Carpal tunnel (rheumatoid arthritis, hypothyroidism, overuse)
- Mental status changes (multiinfarct dementia)
- Peripheral neuropathy (alcohol abuse, vitamin deficiencies, diabetes mellitus)

WORKUP

Diagnostic approach is aimed at demonstration of amyloid deposits in tissues. This may be accomplished with rectal biopsy (positive in >60% of cases). Renal, myocardial, and bone marrow biopsy are other options. Abdominal fat pad biopsy can also be diagnostic; however, its yield is low and it should generally be reserved for evaluation of patients with peripheral neuropathy who also have findings associated with systemic amyloidosis.

LABORATORY TESTS

- Initial laboratory evaluation should include CBC, TSH, renal functions studies, ALT, AST, alkaline phosphatase, bilirubin, urinalysis, and serum and urine protein immunoelectrophoresis.
- Various laboratory abnormalities include proteinuria (found in >70% of cases), anemia, renal insufficiency, liver function abnormalities, hypothyroidism (10% to 20% of patients), and elevated monoclonal proteins. The finding of a monoclonal light chain in the serum or urine is very useful for diagnosis.
- DNA analysis is necessary for the diagnosis of hereditary amyloidosis.

IMAGING STUDIES

- Chest x-ray may reveal hilar adenopathy and mediastinal adenopathy.
- Two-dimensional Doppler echocardiography to study diagnostic filling is useful to evaluate for cardiac involvement.
- Nuclear imaging with technetium-labeled aprotinin may detect cardiac amyloidosis. SAP scintigraphy has high sensitivity for the detection of amyloid deposits in liver, spleen, kidneys, adrenal glands, and bones.

TREATMENT

ACUTE GENERAL Rx

- Therapy is variable, depending on the type of amyloidosis. Amyloidosis associated with plasma cell disorders may be treated with melphalan and prednisone, along with colchicine. Colchicine may also be effective in renal amyloidosis.
- Treatment of AL amyloidosis with high-dose melphalan and stem-cell transplantation may result in hematologic remission and improved 5-yr survival.
- Promising results have been found with the use of a molecule known as CPHPC given IV or SC in amyloidosis. This molecule has been shown effective in reducing circulating levels of SAP.

CHRONIC Rx

Renal transplantation is needed in patients with renal amyloidosis. Peritoneal dialysis in place of hemodialysis in patients with renal failure may improve hemodialysis amyloidosis by clearing β-2 microglobulin.

DISPOSITION

Prognosis is determined primarily by the presence or absence of cardiac involvement and with the form of amyloidosis:

- In reactive amyloidosis, eradication of the predisposing disease slows and can occasionally reverse the progression of amyloid disease. Survival of 5 to 10 yr after diagnosis is not uncommon.
- Patients with familial amyloidotic polyneuropathy generally have a prolonged course lasting 10 to 15 yr.
- Amyloidosis associated with immunocytic processes carries the worst prognosis (life expectancy <1 yr).
- The progression of amyloidosis associated with renal hemodialysis can be improved with newer dialysis membranes that can pass β-2 microglobulin.
- Median survival in patients with overt CHF is approximately 6 mo, 30 mo without CHF.

SUGGESTED READING

Skinner M et al: High-Dose melphalan and autologous stem-cell transplantation in patients with AL amyloidosis: an 8-year study, *Ann Intern Med* 140:85, 2004.

AUTHOR: **FRED F. FERRI, M.D.**

Amyotrophic Lateral Sclerosis 

BASIC INFORMATION

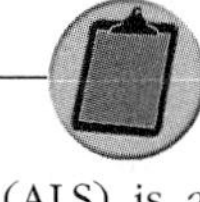

DEFINITION

Amyotrophic lateral sclerosis (ALS) is a progressive, degenerative neuromuscular condition of undetermined etiology affecting corticospinal tracts and anterior horn cells resulting in dysfunction of both upper motor neurons (UMN) and lower motor neurons (LMN), respectively.

ICD-9CM CODES
335.20 Amyotrophic lateral sclerosis

EPIDEMIOLOGY & DEMOGRAPHICS

INCIDENCE: 0.5 to 2 cases/100,000 persons. Onset is usually between the ages of 50 and 70 years. The male:female ratio is 2:1.

PREVALENCE: 5 in 100,000 persons

PHYSICAL FINDINGS & CLINICAL PRESENTATION

- Lower motor neuron signs (weakness, hypotonia, wasting, fasciculations, hyporeflexia or areflexia)
- Upper motor neuron signs (loss of fine motor dexterity, spasticity, extensor plantar responses, hyperreflexia, clonus)
- Preservation of extraocular movements, sensation, bowel and bladder function
- Dysarthria, dysphagia, pseudobulbar affect, frontal lobe dysfunction
- ALS comprises approximately 90% of adult-onset motor neuron disease. Other presentations of motor neuron disease include progressive muscular atrophy, primary lateral sclerosis, progressive bulbar palsy, progressive pseudobulbar palsy, and ALS-parkinsonism-dementia complex.

ETIOLOGY

- 90% to 95% of all cases are sporadic; of the familial cases, approximately 20% are associated with a genetic defect in the copper-zinc superoxide dismutase enzyme (SOD1).

DIAGNOSIS

DIFFERENTIAL DIAGNOSIS

- Multifocal motor neuropathy with conduction block (MMN)
- Cervical spondylotic myelopathy with polyradiculopathy
- Spinal stenosis with compression of lumbosacral nerve roots
- Chronic inflammatory demyelinating polyneuropathy with CNS lesions
- Syringomyelia
- Syringobulbia
- Foramen magnum tumor
- Spinal muscular atrophy (SMA)
- Late-onset hexosaminidase A deficiency
- Polyglucosan body disease
- Bulbospinal muscular atrophy (Kennedy's disease)
- Monomyelic amyotrophy
- ALS-like syndromes have been reported in the setting of lead intoxication, HIV, hyperparathyroidism, hyperthyroidism, lymphoma, and B_{12} deficiency

WORKUP

- EMG and nerve conduction studies
- Lumbar puncture to assess protein, serum GM-1 Ab if MMN suspected
- Assessment of respiratory function (FVC, NIF)

LABORATORY TESTS

- B_{12}, thyroid function, PTH, HIV may be considered
- Serum protein and immunofixation electrophoresis
- DNA studies for SMA or bulbospinal atrophy, hexosaminidase levels in pure LMN syndrome
- 24-hour urine for lead if indicated

IMAGING STUDIES

- Craniospinal neuroimaging contingent upon clinical scenario
- Modified barium swallow to evaluate aspiration risk

TREATMENT

NONPHARMACOLOGIC THERAPY

- Noninvasive positive pressure ventilation improves quality of life and increases tracheostomy-free survival
- PEG placement improves caloric and fluid status, eases medication administration, and may prolong life on the order of 1-4 mo
- Nutrition, speech therapy, physical and occupational therapy services
- Suction device for sialorrhea
- Communication may be eased with computerized assistive devices
- Early discussion of living will, recusitation orders, desire for PEG and tracheostomy, potential long-term care options
- Encourage contact with local support groups

ACUTE GENERAL Rx

Riluzole (Rilutek), a glutamate antagonist, is the only medication approved to extend tracheostomy-free survival in patients with ALS. Dosage is 50 mg q12h, at least 1 hr before or 2 hr after meals. Shown to prolong survival by 2-3 mo. Manufacturer recommends checking ALT at an initial frequency of once a month for 3 months, followed by once every 3 months until the first year of therapy is completed. ALT should be checked periodically thereafter.

CHRONIC Rx

- Glycopyrrolate or amitryptyline to help with sialorrhea (propranolol or metoprolol if secretions are thick in addition to sialorrhea)
- Relief of spasticity with baclofen, tizanadine, clonazepam
- Treatment of pseudobulbar affect with amitriptyline, sertraline (Zoloft), dextromethorphan

DISPOSITION

- Mean duration of symptoms is 3 to 5 yr.
- About 20% of patients survive >5 yr.

REFERRAL

- Referral to a neurologist experienced in neuromuscular disease is recommended to confirm the diagnosis.
- GI referral for PEG placement is recommended while forced vital capacity (FVC) remains >50% to minimize the risks inherent to the procedure.

PEARLS & CONSIDERATIONS

COMMENTS

- Patient education material may be obtained through the following:
  ALS Association, 21021 Ventura Boulevard, Suite 321, Woodland Hills, CA 91364, phone: (800) 782-4727; or the Muscular Dystrophy Association, 3561 East Sunrise Drive, Tucson, AZ 85718-3204, phone: (800) 572-1717, www.mdausa.org/.

SUGGESTED READINGS

Bradley WG et al: Current management of ALS: comparison of the ALS CARE Database and the AAN Practice Parameter. The American Academy of Neurology, *Neurology* 57(3):500, 2001.

Miller RG et al: Practice parameter: the care of the patient with amyotrophic lateral sclerosis (an evidence-based review), *Muscle Nerve* 22(8):1104, 1999.

Rowland LP, Shneider NA: Amyotrophic lateral sclerosis, *N Engl J Med* 344:1688, 2001.

AUTHOR: **TAYLOR HARRISON, M.D.**

BASIC INFORMATION

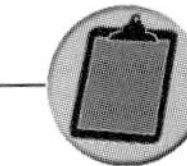

DEFINITION

An anaerobic infection is caused by one of a group of bacteria that require a reduced oxygen tension for growth.

ICD-9CM CODES
See specific condition.

PHYSICAL FINDINGS & CLINICAL PRESENTATION

- May occur at any site, but most are anatomically related to mucosal surfaces
- Should be suspected when there is foul-smelling tissue, soft-tissue gas, necrotic tissue, or abscesses
- Head and neck
  1. Odontogenic infections from dental or soft tissue possibly progressing to periapical abscesses, at times extending to bone
  2. Both anaerobic and aerobic pathogens in chronic sinusitis, chronic mastoiditis, and chronic otitis media
  3. Peritonsillar abscess possible
  4. Complications: deep neck space infections, brain abscesses, mediastinitis
- Pleuropulmonary
  1. May involve anaerobes present in the oropharynx
  2. Aspiration more common in persons with altered mental status or seizures
  3. Anaerobic bacteria more likely in those with gingivitis or periodontitis
  4. Manifestations: necrotizing pneumonia, empyema, lung abscess
- Intraabdominal
  1. Disruption of intestinal integrity leading to infection involving anaerobic bacteria
  2. Bacteria from colonic neoplasm, perforated appendicitis, diverticulitis, or bowel surgery, causing bacteremia, peritonitis, at times intraabdominal abscesses
  3. Resulting infections usually mixed, containing both anaerobes and aerobes
- Female genital tract
  1. Anaerobes in bacterial vaginosis, salpingitis, endometritis, pelvic abscesses, septic abortion; infections tend to be mixed
  2. Possible pelvic thrombophlebitis when resolving pelvic infection is accompanied by new or persistent fever
- Other anaerobic infections
  1. Skin and soft-tissue infection at any site
  2. More commonly associated infections: synergistic gangrene, bite wound infections, infected decubitus ulcers
  3. Clinical significance of anaerobes in diabetic foot infections unclear
  4. Anaerobic bacteremia uncommon with source usually intraabdominal, followed by female genital tract, pleuropulmonary, and head and neck infections
  5. Osteomyelitis especially when associated with decubitus ulcers or vascular insufficiency
  6. Facial bone osteomyelitis from adjacent infections of the teeth or sinuses

ETIOLOGY

- Most commonly endogenous, arising from bacteria that normally line mucosal surfaces
- Disruption of mucosal barriers resulting from various conditions (trauma, ischemia, surgery, perforation), with infection occurring when organisms gain access to normally sterile sites, causing tissue destruction and abscess formation
- Synergy between different anaerobes or between anaerobes and aerobes important
- Most commonly involved: gram-negative anaerobic bacilli

DIAGNOSIS

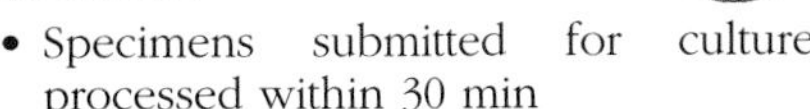

WORKUP

- Specimens submitted for culture processed within 30 min
- Large volume of material more likely to have significant growth; swabs less efficient for transporting infected material
- Blood cultures—preferably before antibiotic administration

LABORATORY TESTS

- Elevated WBC count, with extremely high WBC counts sometimes seen with pseudomembranous colitis
- Positive stool *C. difficile* toxin assay
- Increased lactate levels in ischemia or perforation
- Possible positive blood or wound cultures, but failure to grow anaerobes in culture may be common, attributed to inadequate culturing techniques and/or fastidious organisms

IMAGING STUDIES

- Plain film of an affected area to show gas in tissues, free air resulting from a perforated viscus, or an air/fluid level inside an abscess
- Ultrasound, CT scan, or MRI to reveal abscesses or tissue destruction

TREATMENT

NONPHARMACOLOGIC THERAPY

- Removal of necrotic tissue
- Drainage of abscesses (accomplished by CT scan–guided percutaneous drainage)

ACUTE GENERAL Rx

Oral antibiotics with anaerobic activity: clindamycin, metronidazole, and chloramphenicol

- Broader spectrum of activity with amoxicillin/clavulanate
- Penicillin VK in odontogenic infections
- Oral metronidazole for *C. difficile*–associated diarrhea, with oral vancomycin reserved for recurrent or recalcitrant infections

Parenteral antibiotics for more serious illness

- IV clindamycin, metronidazole, and chloramphenicol
- Cephalosporins (anaerobic or mixed infections): cefoxitin and cefotetan
- Extended-spectrum penicillins (e.g., piperacillin) and combination β-lactamase plus β-lactamase inhibitor drugs
  1. Significant anaerobic activity, plus various degrees of broad-spectrum coverage
  2. Include ampicillin/sulbactam, ticarcillin/clavulanate, and piperacillin/tazobactam
- Imipenem: a broad-spectrum agent with extensive anaerobic activity
- Actinomycosis treated with penicillin for 6 to 12 mo
- SMX/TMP and fluoroquinolones: ineffective

PEARLS & CONSIDERATIONS

COMMENTS

- Chloramphenicol is associated with aplastic anemia, although this is an extremely rare complication.
- Imipenem is a possible cause of thrombocytopenia and may lower the seizure threshold, especially in elderly patients with renal insufficiency.

SUGGESTED READINGS

Giamarellou H: Anaerobic infection therapy, *Int J Antimicrob Agents* 16:341, 2000.

Ortiz E, Sande MA: Routine use of anaerobic blood cultures: are they still indicated? *Am J Med* 108:445, 2000.

AUTHOR: **MAURICE POLICAR, M.D.**

Anal Fissure

BASIC INFORMATION

DEFINITION

A fissure is a tear in the epithelial lining of the anal canal (i.e., from the dentate line to the anal verge).

SYNONYMS

Anorectal fissure
Anal ulcer

ICD-9CM CODES
565.0 Anal fissure

EPIDEMIOLOGY & DEMOGRAPHICS

- Can occur at any age
- Most common in young and middle-aged adults
- Occurs in men > women
- Women more likely to have anterior fissure than men (10% vs. 1%, respectively)
- Most common cause of rectal bleeding in infants
- Common in women before and after childbirth

PHYSICAL FINDINGS & CLINICAL PRESENTATION

With separation of the buttocks will see a tear in the posterior midline or, less frequently, in the anterior midline (Fig. 1-15)

- Acute anal fissure:
  1. Sharp burning or tearing pain exacerbated by bowel movements
  2. Bright-red blood on toilet paper, a streak of blood on the stool or in the water
- Chronic anal fissure:
  1. Pruritus ani
  2. Pain seldom present
  3. Intermittent bleeding
  4. Sentinel tag at the caudal aspect of the fissure, hypertrophied anal papilla at the proximal end
- Underlying disease possible if the fissure:
  1. Is ectopically located
  2. Extends proximal to the dentate line
  3. Is broad-based or deep
  4. Is especially purulent

ETIOLOGY

- Most initiated after passage of a large, hard stool
- May result from frequent defecation and diarrhea
- Bacterial infections: TB, syphilis, gonorrhea, chancroid, lymphogranuloma venereum
- Viral infections: herpes simplex virus, cytomegalovirus, human immunodeficiency virus
- Inflammatory bowel disease (IBD): Crohn's disease, ulcerative colitis
- Trauma: surgery (hemorrhoidectomy), foreign bodies, anal intercourse
- Malignancy: carcinoma, lymphoma, Kaposi's sarcoma

DIAGNOSIS

DIFFERENTIAL DIAGNOSIS

- Proctalgia fugax
- Thrombosed hemorrhoid

WORKUP

- Digital rectal examination after lubricating the entire anus with anesthetic jelly (i.e., 2% lidocaine) and waiting 5 to 10 min
- Anoscopy
- Proctosigmoidoscopy to exclude inflammatory or neoplastic disease
- Biopsy if doubt exists about the etiology of the condition
- All studies done under adequate anesthesia

IMAGING STUDIES

- Colonoscopy or barium enema: if diagnosis of IBD or malignancy is suspected
- Small bowel series: occasionally obtained for similar reasons
- Biopsy to reveal caseating granuloma if TB is suspected
- Wet prep with darkfield examination to demonstrate treponemes if syphilis is suspected

TREATMENT

NONPHARMACOLOGIC THERAPY

- Sitz baths
- High-fiber diet
- Increased oral fluid intake

ACUTE GENERAL Rx

- Bulk-producing agent (e.g., Metamucil)/stool softener
- Local anesthetic jelly (may exacerbate pruritus ani)
- Nitroglycerin ointment
- Suppositories *not* recommended
- Surgery

CHRONIC Rx

- Surgery: lateral internal anal sphincterotomy
- Topical glyceryl trinitrate ointment
- Injection of botulinum toxin (an injection into each side of the internal anal sphincter) is effective in healing chronic anal fissures in more than 90% of patients.

DISPOSITION

Outpatient surgery

REFERRAL

- If fissure does not resolve with conservative therapy in 4 to 6 wk
- If patient prefers surgery for acute fissure
- If patient has chronic fissure

PEARLS & CONSIDERATIONS

COMMENTS

HIV-positive patients should be referred to clinicians who are well versed in the myriad infectious and neoplastic conditions that masquerade as anal ulcers in these patients.

SUGGESTED READINGS

Brisinda G et al: A comparison of injection of botulinum toxin and topical nitroglycerin ointment for the treatment of chronic anal fissure, *N Engl J Med* 341:65, 1999.

Pfenninger JL, Zainea GG: Common anorectal conditions, *Am Fam Physician* 64:77, 2001.

AUTHOR: **GEORGE T. DANAKAS, M.D.**

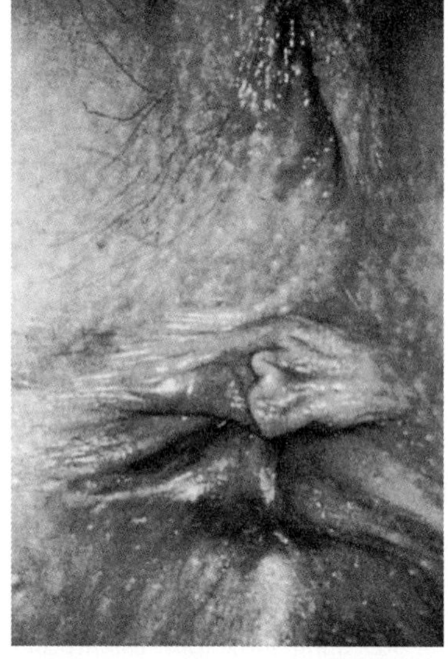

FIGURE 1-15 Lateral anal fissure. (In Seidel HM et al: *Mosby's guide to physical examination,* ed 3, St Louis, 1995, Mosby. Courtesy Gershon Efron, MD, Sinai Hospital of Baltimore.)

BASIC INFORMATION

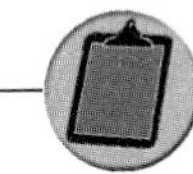

DEFINITION

Anaphylaxis is a sudden-onset, life-threatening event characterized by bronchial contractions in conjunction with hemodynamic changes. Its clinical presentation may include respiratory, cardiovascular, cutaneous, or gastrointestinal manifestations.

SYNONYMS

Anaphylactoid reaction is closely related to anaphylaxis. It is caused by release of mast cells and basophil mediators triggered by non–IgE-mediated events.

ICD-9CM CODES
995.0 Anaphylactic shock
995.60 Anaphylaxis due to food
999.4 Anaphylaxis due to immunization
977.9 Anaphylaxis due to drugs
989.5 Anaphylaxis following stings

EPIDEMIOLOGY & DEMOGRAPHICS

INCIDENCE: 20,000 to 50,000 persons/yr in the U.S. Anaphylaxis rates are 0.0004% for food, 0.7% to 10% for penicillin, 0.22% to 1% for radiocontrast media, and 0.5% to 5% after insect stings. It is estimated that 1 in every 3000 inpatients in U.S. hospitals develops an anaphylactic reaction.

PHYSICAL FINDINGS & CLINICAL PRESENTATION

- Urticaria, pruritus, skin flushing, angioedema, weakness, dizziness
- Dyspnea, cough, malaise, difficulty swallowing
- Wheezing, tachycardia, diarrhea
- Hypotension, vascular collapse

ETIOLOGY

Virtually any substance may induce anaphylaxis in a given individual.

- Commonly implicated medications are antibiotics, insulin, allergen extracts, opiates, vaccines, NSAIDs, contrast media, streptokinase
- Foods and food additives, nuts, egg whites, shellfish, fish, milk, fruits, and berries
- Blood products, plasma, immunoglobulin, cryoprecipitate, whole blood
- Venoms such as snake venom, fire ant venom, bee sting (*Hymenoptera* stings)
- Latex

DIAGNOSIS

DIFFERENTIAL DIAGNOSIS

- Endocrine disorders (carcinoid, pheochromocytoma)
- Globus hystericus, anxiety disorder
- Systemic mastocytosis
- Pulmonary embolism, serum sickness, vasovagal reactions
- Severe asthma (the key clinical difference is the abrupt onset of symptoms in anaphylaxis without a history of progressive worsening of symptoms)
- Septic shock or other form of shock
- Airway foreign body

WORKUP

Workup is aimed mainly at eliminating other conditions that may mimic anaphylaxis (e.g., vasovagal syncope may be differentiated by the presence of bradycardia as opposed to the tachycardia seen in anaphylaxis; the absence of hypoxemia in ABG analysis may be useful to exclude pulmonary embolism or foreign body aspiration).

LABORATORY TESTS

- Laboratory evaluation is generally not helpful, because the diagnosis of anaphylaxis is a clinical one.
- ABG analysis may be useful to exclude pulmonary embolism, status asthmaticus, and foreign body aspiration.
- Elevated serum and urine histamine levels can be useful for diagnosis of anaphylaxis, but these tests are not commonly available.

IMAGING STUDIES

Generally not helpful.

- Chest x-ray is indicated in patients presenting with acute respiratory compromise.
- Radiologic evaluation for epiglottitis is useful in patients with acute respiratory compromise.
- ECG should be considered in all patients with sudden loss of consciousness or complaints of chest pains or dyspnea and in any elderly patient.

TREATMENT

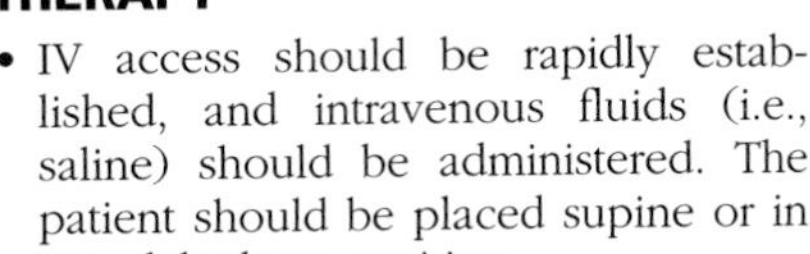

NONPHARMACOLOGIC THERAPY

- IV access should be rapidly established, and intravenous fluids (i.e., saline) should be administered. The patient should be placed supine or in Trendelenburg position.
- Supplemental oxygen and cardiac monitoring are also recommended.

ACUTE GENERAL Rx

- Epinephrine should be rapidly administered as an SC or IM injection at a dose of 0.01 ml/kg of aqueous epinephrine 1:1000 (maximum adult dose 0.3 to 0.5 ml). The dose may be repeated approximately q5-10 min if there is persistence or recurrence of symptoms. Endotracheal epinephrine should be considered if IV access is not possible during life-threatening reactions.
- Administration of H_1- and H_2-receptor antagonists is also recommended in the initial treatment of anaphylaxis.
  1. Administer diphenhydramine 50 to 75 mg IV or IM.
  2. Cimetidine 300 mg IV over 3 to 5 min, or ranitidine 50 mg IV, should be given initially; subsequent doses of H_1- and H_2-blockers can be given orally q6h for 48 hr.
- Corticosteroids are not useful in the acute episode because of their slow onset of action; however, they should be administered in most cases to prevent prolonged or recurrent anaphylaxis. Commonly used agents are hydrocortisone sodium succinate 250 to 500 mg IV q4-6h in adults (4 to 8 mg/kg for children) or methylprednisolone 60 to 125 mg IV in adults (1 to 2 mg/kg in children).
- Aerosolized β-agonists (i.e., albuterol, 2.5 mg, repeat prn 20 min) are useful to control bronchospasm.
- Additional useful agents in specific circumstances: atropine for refractory bradycardia, dopamine for refractory hypotension (despite volume expansion), and glucagon in patients on β-blocking drugs.

PEARLS & CONSIDERATIONS

COMMENTS

- Patient education regarding the nature of the illness and preventive measures is recommended. A documented history of previous anaphylactic episodes or known anaphylaxis triggers is the most reliable method of identifying individuals at risk.
- Prescription for prefilled epinephrine syringe (EpiPen) should be given, and the patient should be instructed on the use of this emergency epinephrine kit in case of recurrent anaphylactic episodes.
- Patients should also be advised to carry or wear Medic Alert ID describing substances that have caused anaphylaxis.
- Avoidance of radiologic contrast is also recommended.
- Venom immunotherapy immediately after a sting is effective and recommended for up to 5 yr after the anaphylactic incident.

SUGGESTED READING

Tang AW: A practical guide to anaphylaxis, *Am Fam Physician* 68:1325, 2003.

AUTHOR: **FRED F. FERRI, M.D.**

Anemia, Aplastic (PTG)

BASIC INFORMATION

DEFINITION

Aplastic anemia is a bone marrow failure resulting from a variety of causes and characterized by stem cell destruction or suppression leading to pancytopenia.

SYNONYMS

Refractory anemia
Hypoplastic anemia

ICD-9CM CODES
284.9 Aplastic anemia
284.8 Acquired aplastic anemia
284.0 Congenital aplastic anemia

EPIDEMIOLOGY & DEMOGRAPHICS

- There is no predominant age or sex for the acquired form.
- The annual incidence of aplastic anemia in the U.S. is 3 to 9 cases/1 million persons.

PHYSICAL FINDINGS & CLINICAL PRESENTATION

- Skin pallor, ecchymosis, petechiae, retinal hemorrhage
- Possible fever, mouth and tongue ulceration, pharyngitis
- Possible short stature or skeletal and nail anomalies in the congenital form
- Possible audible systolic ejection murmur with profound anemia

ETIOLOGY

- In most patients with acquired aplastic anemia, bone marrow failure results from immunologically mediated, active destruction of blood-forming cells by lymphocytes.
- Common etiologic factors in aplastic anemia:
  Toxins (e.g., benzene, insecticides)
  Drugs (e.g., Felbatol, cimetidine, busulfan and other myelosuppressive drugs, gold salts, chloramphenicol, sulfonamides, trimethadione, quinacrine, phenylbutazone)
  Ionizing irradiation
  Infections (e.g., hepatitis C, HIV)
  Idiopathic
  Inherited (Fanconi's anemia)
  Other: immunologic, pregnancy

DIAGNOSIS

DIFFERENTIAL DIAGNOSIS

- Bone marrow infiltration from lymphoma, carcinoma, myelofibrosis
- Severe infection
- Hypoplastic acute lymphoblastic leukemia in children
- Hypoplastic myelodysplastic syndrome or hypoplastic acute myeloid leukemia in adults
- Hypersplenism
- Hairy cell leukemia

WORKUP

- Diagnostic workup consists primarily of bone marrow aspiration and biopsy and laboratory evaluation (CBC and examination of blood film).
- Bone marrow examination generally reveals paucity or absence of erythropoietic and myelopoietic precursor cells; patients with pure red cell aplasia demonstrate only absence of RBC precursors in the marrow.

LABORATORY TESTS

- CBC reveals pancytopenia. Macrocytosis and toxic granulation of neutrophils may also be present. Isolated cytopenias may occur in the early stages.
- Reticulocyte count reveals reticulocytopenia.
- Additional initial laboratory evaluation should include Ham test to exclude paroxysmal nocturnal hemoglobinuria (PNH) and testing for hepatitis C.

IMAGING STUDIES

- Chest x-ray examination
- Abdominal sonogram or CT scan to evaluate for splenomegaly
- Radiography of hand and forearm in patients with constitutional anemia
- CT scan of thymus region if thymoma-associated RBC aplasia is suspected

TREATMENT

NONPHARMACOLOGIC THERAPY

- Discontinuation of any offending drugs or agents
- Evaluation for bone marrow transplantation

ACUTE GENERAL Rx

- Aggressive treatment of neutropenic fevers with parenteral broad-spectrum antibiotics
- Platelet and RBC transfusions prn; however, avoidance of transfusions in patients who are candidates for bone marrow transplantation
- Immunosuppressive therapy with antithymocyte globulin (ATG) and/or cyclosporine (CSP); ATG in combination with prednisone (1 to 2 mg/kg/day initially) to avoid complications of serum sickness
- Transplantation of allogeneic marrow or peripheral blood stem cell transplantation from a histocompatible sibling usually cures the underlying bone marrow failure
- In patients with severe aplastic anemia who are not candidates for allogeneic bone marrow, use of high-dose cyclophosphamide therapy without bone marrow transplantation represents a third treatment option for initial treatment of aplastic anemia.

CHRONIC Rx

- Long-term patient monitoring with physical examination and routine laboratory evaluation to screen for relapse.
- ATG with CSP restore hematopoiesis in approximately two thirds of patients; however, recovery of blood cell count is often incomplete, recurrent pancytopenia requires retreatment. In some patients, myelodysplasia is a late complication of immunosuppressive therapy.
- Patients refractory to immunosuppression have a poor long-term outlook and should consider unrelated stem cell transplantation.
- There is little justification for either a therapeutic trial of corticosteroids as primary treatment or for their long-term use to prevent bleeding.

DISPOSITION

- Patients with severe aplastic anemia who have marrow transplants before the onset of transfusion-induced sensitization have an excellent probability of long-term survival and normal life; age is a significant factor; the incidence of graft vs. host disease increases with age and is >90% in patients >30 yr of age.
- Following bone marrow transplantation from an HLA-identical sibling, >70% of patients are long-term survivors and can be considered cured.
- Response to immunosuppression in aplastic anemia is independent of age, but treatment is associated with increased mortality in older patients.
- Overall 5-yr survival rate for aplastic anemia is now 70% to 90%.

REFERRAL

Hematology referral is indicated in all patients with aplastic anemia.

AUTHOR: **FRED F. FERRI, M.D.**

BASIC INFORMATION

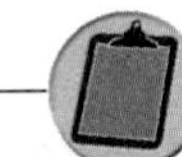

DEFINITION

Autoimmune hemolytic anemia (AIHA) is anemia secondary to premature destruction of red blood cells caused by the binding of autoantibodies and/or complement to red blood cells.

ICD-9CM CODES
283.0 Autoimmune hemolytic anemia

EPIDEMIOLOGY & DEMOGRAPHICS

Autoimmune hemolytic anemia is most common in women <50 yr.

PHYSICAL FINDINGS & CLINICAL PRESENTATION

- Pallor, jaundice
- Tachycardia with a flow murmur may be present if anemia is pronounced
- Most common presentation is dyspnea and fatigue
- Patients with intravascular hemolysis may present with dark urine and back pain
- The presence of hepatomegaly, and/or lymphadenopathy suggests an underlying lymphoproliferative disorder or malignancy; splenomegaly may indicate hypersplenism as a cause of hemolysis

ETIOLOGY

- Warm antibody mediated: IgG (often idiopathic or associated with leukemia, lymphoma, thymoma, myeloma, viral infections, and collagen-vascular disease)
- Cold antibody mediated: IgM and complement in majority of cases (often idiopathic, at times associated with infections, lymphoma, or cold agglutinin disease)
- Drug induced: three major mechanisms:
  1. Antibody directed against Rh complex (e.g., methyldopa)
  2. Antibody directed against RBC-drug complex (hapten induced, e.g., penicillin)
  3. Antibody directed against complex formed by drug and plasma proteins; the drug-plasma protein-antibody complex causes destruction of RBCs (innocent bystander, e.g., quinidine).

DIAGNOSIS

DIFFERENTIAL DIAGNOSIS

- Hemolytic anemia caused by membrane defects (paroxysmal nocturnal hemoglobinuria, spur-cell anemia, Wilson's disease)
- Non–immune mediated (microangiopathic hemolytic anemia, hypersplenism, cardiac valve prosthesis, giant cavernous hemangiomas, march hemoglobinuria, physical agents, infections, heavy metals, certain drugs [nitrofurantoin, sulfonamides])

WORKUP

Evaluation consists primarily of laboratory evaluation to confirm hemolysis and to exclude other causes of the anemia. Although most cases of AIHA are idiopathic, potential causes should always be sought.

LABORATORY TESTS

- Initial laboratory tests: CBC (anemia), reticulocyte count (elevated), liver function studies (elevated indirect bilirubin, LDH), evaluation of peripheral smear, Coombs' test (positive direct Coombs' test indicates presence of antibodies or complement on the surface of RBC, positive indirect Coombs' test implies presence of anti-RBC antibodies freely circulating in the patient's serum), haptoglobin level (decreased)
- IgG antibody and IgM antibody
- Hepatitis serology, ANA
- Urinary tests may reveal hemosiderinuria or hemoglobinuria

IMAGING STUDIES

- Chest x-ray
- CT scan of chest and abdomen to rule out lymphoma should also be considered

TREATMENT

NONPHARMACOLOGIC THERAPY

- Discontinuation of any potentially offensive drugs
- Plasmapheresis-exchange transfusion for severe life-threatening cases only
- Avoid cold exposure in patients with cold antibody

ACUTE GENERAL Rx

- Prednisone 1 to 2 mg/kg/day in divided doses initially in warm antibody autoimmune hemolytic anemia. Corticosteroids are generally ineffective in cold antibody autoimmune hemolytic anemia
- Splenectomy in patients responding inadequately to corticosteroids when RBC sequestration studies indicate splenic sequestration
- Immunosuppressive drugs and/or immunoglobulins only after both corticosteroids and splenectomy (unless surgery is contraindicated) have failed to produce an adequate remission
- Danazol, usually used in conjunction with corticosteroids (may be useful in warm antibody autoimmune hemolytic anemia)
- Immunosuppressive drugs (azathioprine, cyclophosphamide) may be useful in warm antibody autoimmune hemolytic anemia but are indicated only after both corticosteroids and splenectomy (unless surgery is contraindicated) have failed to produce an adequate remission

DISPOSITION

Prognosis is generally good unless anemia is associated with underlying disorder with a poor prognosis (e.g., leukemia, myeloma).

REFERRAL

Hematology referral in all cases of AIHA
Surgical referral for splenectomy in refractory cases

PEARLS & CONSIDERATIONS

COMMENTS

- The direct Coombs' test (also known as the direct antiglobulin test {DAT}) demonstrates the presence of antibodies or complement on the surface of RBCs and is the hallmark of autoimmune hemolysis.
- Warm AIHA is often associated with autoimmune diseases whereas cold AIHA often follows viral infections (e.g., mononucleosis) and *Mycoplasma pneumoniae* infections.
- HIV can induce both warm and cold AIHA.

SUGGESTED READINGS

Dhaliwal G et al: Hemolytic anemia, *Am Fam Physician* 69:2599, 2004.
Gehrs BC, Friedberg RC: Autoimmune hemolytic anemia, *Am J Hematol* 69:258, 2002.

AUTHOR: **FRED F. FERRI, M.D.**

Anemia, Iron Deficiency (PTG)

BASIC INFORMATION

DEFINITION

Iron deficiency anemia is anemia secondary to inadequate iron supplementation or excessive blood loss.

ICD-9CM CODES
280.9 Iron deficiency anemia
648.2 Iron deficiency anemia complicating pregnancy

EPIDEMIOLOGY & DEMOGRAPHICS

- Dietary iron deficiency occurs often in infants as a result of unsupplemented milk diets. It is also commonly seen in women during their reproductive years, as a result of heavy menstrual periods, and during pregnancy (increased demand).
- Iron deficiency is the most common nutritional deficiency worldwide.
- The prevalence of iron deficiency is greatest among toddlers ages 1-2 yr, (7%) adolescents, and adult families ages 12-49 yr (9%-16%).

PHYSICAL FINDINGS & CLINICAL PRESENTATION

- Most patients have a normal examination.
- Skin pallor and conjunctival pallor may be present.

ETIOLOGY

- Blood loss from GI or menstrual bleeding (GU blood loss less often the cause)
- Dietary iron deficiency (rare in adults)
- Poor iron absorption in patients with gastric or small bowel surgery
- Repeated phlebotomy
- Increased requirements (e.g., during pregnancy)
- Other: traumatic hemolysis (abnormally functioning cardiac valves), idiopathic pulmonary hemosiderosis (iron sequestration in pulmonary macrophages), paroxysmal nocturnal hemoglobinuria (intravascular hemolysis)

DIAGNOSIS

DIFFERENTIAL DIAGNOSIS

- Anemia of chronic disease
- Sideroblastic anemia
- Thalassemia trait

WORKUP

Diagnostic workup consists primarily of laboratory evaluation. Most patients with iron deficiency anemia are asymptomatic in the early stages. With progressive anemia, the major complaints are fatigue, dizziness, exertional dyspnea, pagophagia (ice eating), and pica. Patient's history may also suggest GI blood loss (melena, hematochezia, hemoptysis).

LABORATORY TESTS

- Laboratory results vary with the stage of deficiency.
- Absent iron marrow stores and decreased serum ferritin are the initial abnormalities.
- Decreased serum iron and increased TIBC are the next abnormalities.
- Hypochromic microcytic anemia is present with significant iron deficiency.
- Peripheral smear in patients with iron deficiency generally reveals microcytic hypochromic RBCs with a wide area of central pallor, anisocytosis, and poikilocytosis when severe.
- Laboratory abnormalities consistent with iron deficiency are low serum ferritin level, elevated RBC distribution width (RDW) with values generally >15, low MCV, elevated TIBC, and low serum iron.
- The reticulocyte hemoglobin content (CHr) may be a good screening test for iron deficiency. It can be measured on an automated hematology analyzer and represents a relatively inexpensive and fast way to detect iron deficiency.

TREATMENT

NONPHARMACOLOGIC THERAPY

Patients should be instructed to consume foods containing large amounts of iron, such as liver, red meat, and legumes.

ACUTE GENERAL Rx

- Treatment consists of ferrous sulfate 325 mg PO qd for at least 6 mo. Calcium supplements can decrease iron absorption; therefore, these two medications should be staggered.
- Parenteral iron therapy is reserved for patients with poor tolerance, noncompliance with oral preparations, or malabsorption.
- Transfusion of packed RBCs is indicated in patients with severe symptomatic anemia (e.g., angina) or life-threatening anemia.

CHRONIC Rx

Patients should be instructed to continue their iron supplements for at least 6 mo or longer to correct depleted body iron stores.

DISPOSITION

Most patients respond rapidly to iron supplementation with improvement in CBC and general well-being. GI side effects from oral iron therapy are common and may require decreased dose to once every other day.

REFERRAL

GI referral for evaluation of GI malignancy is recommended in all patients with iron deficiency and suspected GI blood loss.

PEARLS & CONSIDERATIONS

COMMENTS

If the diagnosis of iron deficiency anemia is made, it is mandatory to try to locate the suspected site of iron loss.

SUGGESTED READING

Tefferi A: Anemia in adults: a contemporary approach to diagnosis, *Mayo Clin Proc* 78:1274, 2004.

AUTHOR: **FRED F. FERRI, M.D.**

BASIC INFORMATION

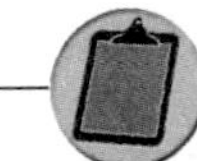

DEFINITION

Pernicious anemia is an autoimmune disease resulting from antibodies against intrinsic factor and gastric parietal cells.

SYNONYMS

Megaloblastic anemia resulting from vitamin B_{12} deficiency

ICD-9CM CODES
281.0 Pernicious anemia

EPIDEMIOLOGY & DEMOGRAPHICS

- Increased incidence in females and older adults (diagnosis is unusual before age 35 yr)
- The overall prevalence of undiagnosed PA over age 60 yr is 1.9%
- Prevalence is highest in women (2.7%), particularly in black women (4.3%)
- Increased incidence of autoimmune disease (e.g., type 1 DM, Graves' disease, Addison's disease), *Helicobacter pylori* infection

PHYSICAL FINDINGS & CLINICAL PRESENTATION

- Mucosal pallor, glossitis
- Peripheral sensory neuropathy with paresthesias initially and absent reflexes in advanced cases
- Loss of joint position sense, pyramidal or long track signs
- Possible splenomegaly and mild hepatomegaly
- Generalized weakness and delirium/dementia

ETIOLOGY

- Antigastric parietal cell antibodies in >70% of patients, antiintrinsic factor antibodies in >50% of patients
- Atrophic gastric mucosa

DIAGNOSIS

DIFFERENTIAL DIAGNOSIS

- Nutritional vitamin B_{12} deficiency
- Malabsorption
- Chronic alcoholism (multifactorial)
- Chronic gastritis related to *H. pylori* infection
- Folic acid deficiency
- Myelodysplasia

WORKUP

- The clinical presentation of pernicious anemia varies with the stage. Initially, patients may be asymptomatic. In advanced stages, patients may present with impaired memory, depression, gait disturbances, paresthesias, and complaints of generalized weakness.
- Investigation consists primarily of laboratory evaluation.
- Endoscopy and biopsy for atrophic gastritis may be performed in selected cases.
- Diagnosis is crucial because failure to treat may result in irreversible neurologic deficits.

LABORATORY TESTS

- CBC generally reveals macrocytic anemia and leukopenia with hypersegmented neutrophils.
- MCV is generally significantly elevated in the advanced stages.
- Reticulocyte count is low/normal.
- Falsely low serum cobalamin levels can occur in patients with severe folate deficiency, in patients using high doses of ascorbic acid, and when cobalamin levels are measured following nuclear medicine studies (radioactivity interferes with cobalamin RIA measurement).
- Falsely high normal levels in patients with cobalamin deficiency can occur in severe liver disease or chronic granulocytic leukemia.
- The absence of anemia or macrocytosis does not exclude the diagnosis of cobalamin deficiency. Anemia is absent in 20% of patients with cobalamin deficiency, and macrocytosis is absent in >30% of patients at the time of diagnosis. It can be blocked by concurrent iron deficiency or anemia of chronic disease and may be masked by thalassemia trait.
- Schilling test is abnormal in part I; part II corrects to normal after administration of intrinsic factor.
- Laboratory tests used for detecting cobalamin deficiency in patients with normal vitamin B_{12} levels include serum and urinary methylmalonic acid level (elevated), total homocysteine level (elevated), intrinsic factor antibody (positive).
- An increased concentration of plasma methylmalonic acid (P-MMA) does not predict clinical manifestations of vitamin B_{12} deficiency and should not be used as the only marker for diagnosis of B_{12} deficiency.
- Additional laboratory abnormalities can include elevated LDH, direct hyperbilirubinemia, and decreased haptoglobin.

TREATMENT

NONPHARMACOLOGIC THERAPY

Avoid folic acid supplementation without proper vitamin B_{12} supplementation.

ACUTE GENERAL Rx

Traditional therapy of a cobalamin deficiency consists of IM injections of vitamin B_{12} 1000 μg/wk for the initial 4 to 6 wk followed by 1000 μg/mo IM indefinitely. When hematologic parameters have returned to normal range, intranasal cyanocobalamin may be used in place of IM cyanocobalamin. The initial dose of intranasal cyanocobalamin (Nascobal) is one spray (500 μg) in one nostril once per week. Monitor response and increase dose if serum B_{12} levels decline. Consider return to intramuscular vitamin B_{12} supplementation if decline persists.

CHRONIC Rx

Parenteral vitamin B_{12} 1000 μg/mo or intranasal cyanocobalamin 500 μg/wk (see "Acute General Rx") for the remainder of life

DISPOSITION

Anemia generally resolves with appropriate treatment. Neurologic deficits, if present at diagnosis, may be permanent.

REFERRAL

GI referral for endoscopy upon diagnosis of pernicious anemia and surveillance endoscopy every 5 yr to rule out gastric carcinoma

PEARLS & CONSIDERATIONS

COMMENTS

- Patients must understand that therapy is lifelong.
- Self-injection of vitamin B_{12} may be taught in selected patients.
- Oral cobalamin (1000 mcg/day) has been reported as also being effective in mild cases of pernicious anemia because about 1% of an oral dose is absorbed by passive diffusion, a pathway that does not require intrinsic factor.

AUTHOR: **FRED F. FERRI, M.D.**

BASIC INFORMATION

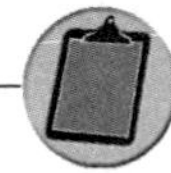

DEFINITION

Sideroblastic anemias are blood disorders resulting from defective heme synthesis and are classified as hereditary, acquired, and reversible.

SYNONYMS

- Primary hereditary sideroblastic anemia
- Primary acquired refractory anemia with ringed sideroblasts (RARS)
- Reversible sideroblastic anemias

ICD-9CM CODES
285.0 Sideroblastic anemia

EPIDEMIOLOGY & DEMOGRAPHICS

- Hereditary sideroblastic anemia, being sex-linked, primarily affects males.
- Primary acquired sideroblastic anemia is usually a disease of the elderly.

PHYSICAL FINDINGS & CLINICAL PRESENTATION

The symptoms for sideroblastic anemia are the same for any anemia:

- Symptoms include fatigue, weakness, palpitations, shortness of breath, headaches, irritability, and chest pain.
- Physical findings may include pallor, tachycardia, hepatosplenomegaly, S_3, JVD, and rales.

ETIOLOGY

- The exact cause in many cases of hereditary and primary acquired sideroblastic anemias remains unknown. However, in some cases the underlying molecular defect may involve genes encoding:
  5-aminolevulinate synthase enzyme (ALAS2)
  Mitochondrial iron transporter (ABC7)
  Ferrochelatase
  Cytochrome oxidase
  Mitochondrial proteins (e.g., Pearson Marrow-Pancrease Syndrome)
- Primary hereditary sideroblastic anemia may be inherited as a sex-linked recessive disease.
- Secondary acquired sideroblastic anemia can be caused by alcohol, isoniazid, pyrazinamide, cycloserine, chloramphenicol, and copper deficiency.

DIAGNOSIS

DIFFERENTIAL DIAGNOSIS

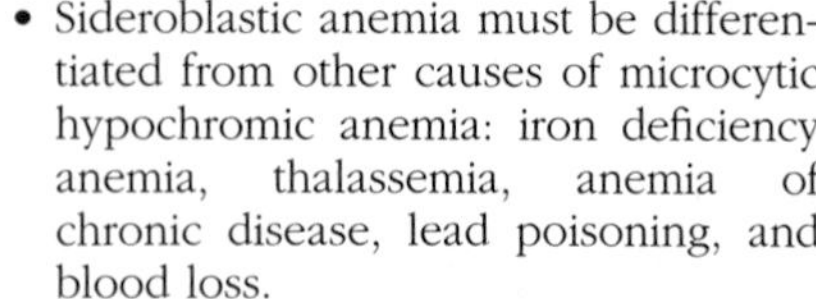

- Sideroblastic anemia must be differentiated from other causes of microcytic hypochromic anemia: iron deficiency anemia, thalassemia, anemia of chronic disease, lead poisoning, and blood loss.
- Tissue iron overload from sideroblastic anemia may act similar to hereditary hemochromatosis with liver cirrhosis, diabetes, congestive heart failure, and cardiac arrhythmias.

WORKUP

The diagnostic workup of suspected sideroblastic anemia includes laboratory evaluation and bone marrow aspiration and biopsy.

LABORATORY TESTS

- Sideroblastic anemias are characterized by hypochromic anemia (low Hgb, low Hct, low MCV, high RDW).
- Iron, TIBC, ferritin, free erythrocyte protoporphyrin (FEP), copper, and zinc levels may all assist in the diagnosis of sideroblastic anemias.
- Peripheral smear: dimorphic large and small cells revealing "Pappenheimer bodies" or siderocytes when stained for iron.
- Bone marrow shows the classic ringed sideroblasts not seen in normal bone marrow tissue (Fig. 1-16). The ringed sideroblasts represent iron storage in the mitochondria of normoblasts.

TREATMENT

NONPHARMACOLOGIC THERAPY

- Avoid alcohol.
- Secondary sideroblastic anemia due to isoniazid, pyrazinamide, and cycloserine can expect a full recovery by withdrawing the medication and by the use of vitamin B_6 (50 to 200 mg/day).

ACUTE GENERAL Rx

- Hereditary sideroblastic anemia:
  1. Nearly 35% of patients receiving vitamin B_6 (50 to 200 mg/day) will improve their red blood cell to near normal values.
  2. The remainder of patients will require blood transfusions to treat symptoms of anemia.
- Primary acquired sideroblastic anemia:
  1. Most patients do not respond to vitamin B_6.
  2. Erythropoietin has shown some success in improving the anemia.
  3. Blood transfusions are indicated for patients with symptomatic anemia.

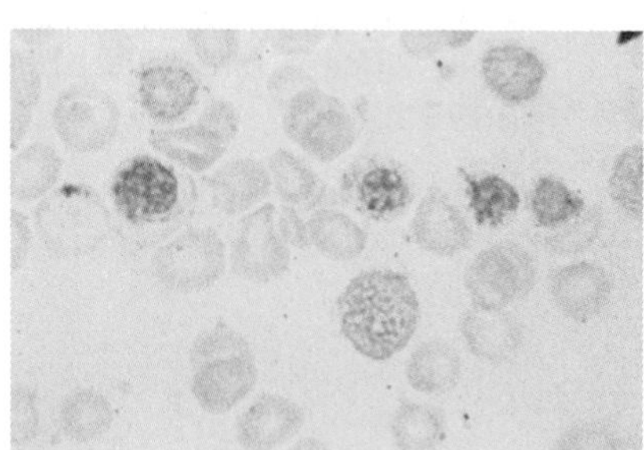

FIGURE 1-16 Prussian blue iron stain of the bone marrow shows ringed sideroblasts. (From Goldman L, Bennett JC [eds]: *Cecil textbook of medicine,* ed 21, Philadelphia, 2000, WB Saunders.)

CHRONIC Rx

- Hereditary sideroblastic anemia:
  1. Organ dysfunction resulting from iron overload will require periodic phlebotomies.
  2. In advanced cases, desferrioxamine 40 mg/kg/day IV is given.
- Primary acquired sideroblastic anemia:
  1. As in the hereditary form, periodic phlebotomies are indicated when serum iron levels increase to >500 μg/L and desferrioxamine is used in patients requiring frequent blood transfusions.

DISPOSITION

- Hereditary sideroblastic anemia:
  1. With previously mentioned treatment, prognosis is good for a normal life expectancy.
- Primary acquired sideroblastic anemia:
  1. In patients with anemia alone, life expectancy is normal. In patients dependent on blood transfusions, one can expect morbidity from organ dysfunction.
  2. Some patients with acquired sideroblastic anemia can go on to develop leukemia.

REFERRAL

- Hematology

PEARLS & CONSIDERATIONS

COMMENTS

- Sideroblastic anemia can be thought of as an iron-loading anemia secondary to defective heme synthesis. Protein enzymes necessary for heme synthesis are located in the mitochondria of erythroid cells. A decrease in the activity of these enzymes (D-aminolevulinic acid synthetase, ferrochelatase) impedes protoporphyrin formation and the incorporation of iron into protoporphyrin preventing heme synthesis. Iron continues to be absorbed from the GI tract accumulating in the mitochondria surrounding the nucleus of the normoblast and forming the "ringed sideroblast."
- Vitamin B_6, pyridoxal phosphate, is a required cofactor in heme synthesis, and drugs such as isoniazid, cycloserine, and pyrazinamide can inhibit its function.

SUGGESTED READINGS

Aleindor T, Bridges KR: Sideroblastic anemias, *Br J Haematol* 116(4):733, 2002.

Bottomley SS: Sideroblastic anemias. In Lee GR, Floerster J, Lukens J et al. (Eds), *Wintrobe's Clinical Hematology,* ed 10, Baltimore, 1999, Williams and Wilkins, p.1022.

AUTHOR: **PETER PETROPOULOS, M.D.**

BASIC INFORMATION

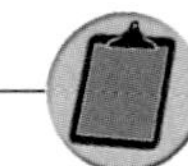

DEFINITION

An abdominal aortic aneurysm is a permanent localized dilation of the abdominal aortic artery to at least 50% when compared with the normal diameter. The normal diameter in men is 2.3 cm, and in women it is 1.9 cm.

SYNONYMS

AAA

ICD-9CM CODES
441.4 Aneurysm, abdominal (aorta)
441.3 Ruptured abdominal aortic aneurysm

EPIDEMIOLOGY & DEMOGRAPHICS

- The incidence of abdominal aortic aneurysms has been rising from 12.2 cases/100,000 persons in 1951 to 36.2 cases/100,000 persons in 1980.
- The prevalence ranges from 2% to 5% in men >60 yr.
- AAA is predominantly a disease of the elderly, affecting men > women (4:1).
- Rupture of an abdominal aortic aneurysm is the tenth leading cause of death in men >55 yr (15,000 deaths/yr in the U.S.).

PHYSICAL FINDINGS & CLINICAL PRESENTATION

- The physical exam although not very sensitive for AAA <5 cm in size has a sensitivity of 82% for detecting AAA >5 cm.
- Pulsatile epigastric mass that may or may not be tender.
- Abdominal pain radiating to the back, flank, and groin. The pain is thought to be caused by rapid expansion of the aneurysm as it stretches the overlying peritoneum.
- Early satiety, nausea and vomiting due to compression of adjacent bowel.
- Venous thrombosis from iliocaval venous compression.
- Discoloration and pain of the feet with distal embolization of the thrombus within the aneurysm embolizes.
- Flank and groin pain from ureteral obstruction and hydronephrosis.
- Shock, hypoperfusion, abdominal distention if rupture occurs.
- Rare presentations include hematemesis or melena with abdominal and back pain in patients with aortoenteric fistulas. Aortocaval fistula produces loud abdominal bruits.

ETIOLOGY

Multifactorial
- Atherosclerotic (degenerative or nonspecific)
- Genetic (e.g., Ehlers-Danlos syndrome)
- Trauma
- Cystic medial necrosis (Marfan's syndrome)
- Arteritis, inflammatory
- Mycotic, infected (syphilis)

DIAGNOSIS

DIFFERENTIAL DIAGNOSIS

Almost 75% of abdominal aneurysms are asymptomatic and are discovered on routine examination or serendipitously when ordering studies for other complaints. This must be considered in the differential of anyone presenting with abdominal pain or back pain.

IMAGING STUDIES

- Abdominal ultrasound is nearly 100% accurate in identifying an aneurysm and estimating the size to within 0.3 to 0.4 cm. It is not very good in estimating the proximal extension to the renal arteries or involvement of the iliac arteries.
- CT scan is recommended for preoperative aneurysm imaging and estimating the size to within 0.3 mm. There are no false-negatives, and the CT scan can localize the proximal extent, detect the integrity of the wall, and rule out rupture.
- Angiography gives detailed arterial anatomy, localizing the aneurysm relative to the renal and visceral arteries. This is the definitive preoperative study for surgeons.
- MRI can also be used, but it is more expensive and not as readily available.

TREATMENT

NONPHARMACOLOGIC THERAPY

- Despite lack of data substantiating reduction in expansion rate through treatment of cardiac risk factors, nonpharmacologic treatment continues to focus on risk factor modification (diet and exercise for blood pressure, cholesterol, and diabetes, and abstinence from tobacco).
- Serial studies have shown that expansion rates are faster in current smokers than ex-smokers.
- Definitive treatment depends on the size of the aneurysm (see "Chronic Rx").

ACUTE GENERAL Rx

Abdominal aortic rupture is an emergency. Surgery is the only chance for survival.

CHRONIC Rx

- Upon diagnosing an AAA, surveillance ultrasound for sizing with recommendations for prophylactic surgery for AAA >5.5 cm remains safe with very low rates of AAA rupture (<1%).
- The most commonly used predictor of rupture is the maximum diameter of the abdominal aortic aneurysm. For AAA with baseline diameters <3.5 cm, 4.0 cm, 4.5 cm, and 5 cm, the recommended screening intervals are 36, 24, 12, and 3 months respectively.
- Recent randomized trials found no reduction in mortality from repairing abdominal aortic aneurysms smaller than 5.5 cm in patients at low operative risk.
- For aneurysms 5.5 cm or greater, prosthetic graft replacement is recommended, providing there is no contraindication (e.g., MI within 6 mo, refractory CHF, life expectancy <2 yr, severe residual from CVA).
- For the high-risk patient deemed inoperable for such major surgery, endovascular stent-anchored grafts under local anesthesia have provided an alternative approach.

DISPOSITION

- The risk of rupture is 0% per year in aneurysms <4 cm, 0.6%-1%/yr in aneurysms 4.0-5.5 cm, 4.4%/yr in aneurysms 5.5-5.9 cm, 10.2%/yr in aneurysms 6.0-6.9 cm, and 32.5%/yr in aneurysms >7 cm.
- Mortality after rupture is >90%. Of those patients who reach the hospital, it is estimated 50% will survive compared with a 4% mortality rate for elective repair of the nonruptured aorta.

REFERRAL

Vascular surgical referral should be made in asymptomatic patients with aneurysms 4 cm or greater or in rapidly expanding aneurysms of 0.7-1 cm/yr, especially if symptoms are present.

PEARLS & CONSIDERATIONS

COMMENTS

- Most abdominal aortic aneurysms are infrarenal. Surgical risk is increased in patients with coexisting coronary artery disease, pulmonary disease (Pao_2 <50 mm Hg, FEV_1 <1l), liver cirrhosis, and chronic renal failure (Cr >3 mg/dl). Detailed cardiac workup with radionuclide perfusion studies for ischemia and aggressive perioperative hemodynamic monitoring help identify high-risk patients and decrease postoperative complications.
- It is estimated that abdominal aortic aneurysms <5 cm expand at a rate of 0.4 cm/yr.
- The use of the β-blocker propranolol has demonstrated a trend toward fewer surgeries in patients with asymptomatic small abdominal aortic aneurysms (3.0-5.0 cm).

SUGGESTED READINGS

Lederle FA et al: Rupture rate of large abdominal aortic aneurysms in patients refusing or unfit for elective repair, *JAMA* 287:2968, 2002.

Lederle FA et al: Immediate repair compared with surveillance of small abdominal aortic aneurysms, *N Engl J Med* 346:1437, 2002.

Lederle FA: Ultrasonographic screening for abdominal aortic aneurysm, *Ann Intern Med* 139:516, 2003.

Powell J, Brady A: Detection, management and prospects for medical treatment of small abdominal aortic aneurysms, *Arterioscler Thromb Vasc Biol* 24:241, 2004.

Powell J, Greenhalgh R: Small abdominal aortic aneurysms, *N Engl J Med* 348:1895, 2003.

Sparks AR et al: Imaging of abdominal aortic aneurysms, *Am Fam Physician* 65:1565, 2002.

The Propranolol Aneurysm Trial Investigators: Propranolol for small abdominal aortic aneurysms: results of a randomized trial, *J Vasc Surg* 35:72, 2002.

The United Kingdom Small Aneurysm Trial Participants: Long-term outcomes of immediate repair compared with surveillance of small abdominal aortic aneurysms, *N Engl J Med* 346:1445, 2002.

AUTHORS: **PRANAV M. PATEL, M.D.,** and **WEN-CHIH WU, M.D.**

BASIC INFORMATION

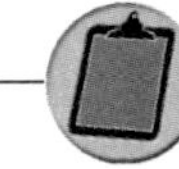

DEFINITION

Angina pectoris is characterized by discomfort that occurs when myocardial oxygen demand exceeds the supply. Myocardial ischemia can be asymptomatic (silent ischemia), particularly in diabetics. Angina can be classified as follows:

1. CHRONIC (STABLE):
   - Usually follows a precipitating event (e.g., climbing stairs, sexual intercourse, a heavy meal, emotional stress, cold weather)
   - Generally same severity as previous attacks; relieved by the customary dose of nitroglycerin
   - Caused by a fixed coronary artery obstruction secondary to atherosclerosis
2. UNSTABLE (REST OR CRESCENDO, CORONARY SYNDROME):
   - Recent onset
   - Increasing severity, duration, or frequency of chronic angina
   - Occurs at rest or with minimal exertion
3. PRINZMETAL'S VARIANT:
   - Occurs at rest
   - Manifests electrocardiographically as episodic ST-segment elevations
   - Caused by coronary artery spasms with or without superimposed coronary artery disease
   - Patients also more likely to develop ventricular arrhythmias
4. MICROVASCULAR ANGINA (SYNDROME X):
   - Refers to patients with normal coronary angiograms and no coronary spasm but chest pain resembling angina and positive exercise test
   - Defective endothelium-dependent dilation in the coronary microcirculation contributing to the altered regulation of myocardial perfusion and the ischemic manifestations in these patients
   - Excellent prognosis
5. OTHER:

Angina due to aortic stenosis and idiopathic hypertrophic subaortic stenosis, cocaine-induced coronary vasoconstriction.

6. Refractory Angina:
   - Refers to patients who despite optimal medical therapy have both angina and objective evidence of ischemia and are not considered candidates for revascularization.
   - Current FDA-approved therapies consist of enhanced external counterpulsation (EECP), transcutaneous electrical nerve stimulation (TENS), and invasive therapies such as spinal cord stimulation, transmyocardial revascularization, and percutaneous myocardial revascularization. Although some of these therapies may improve symptoms and quality of life, they have not been shown to improve mortality.

FUNCTIONAL CLASSIFICATION

- New York Heart Association Functional Classification of Angina:
  Class I—Angina only with unusually strenuous activity.
  Class II—Angina with slightly more prolonged or rigorous activity than usual.
  Class III—Angina with usual daily activity.
  Class IV—Angina at rest.
- Grading of Angina by the Canadian Cardiovascular Society Classification System:
  Class I—Ordinary physical activity does not cause angina, such as walking, climbing stairs. Angina (occurs) with strenuous, rapid, or prolonged exertion at work or recreation.
  Class II—Slight limitation of ordinary activity. Angina occurs on walking or climbing stairs rapidly; walking uphill; walking or stair climbing after meals, in cold, in wind, or under emotional stress; or only during the few hours after awakening. Angina occurs on walking more than two blocks on the level and climbing more than one flight of ordinary stairs at a normal pace and in normal condition.
  Class III—Marked limitations of ordinary physical activity. Angina occurs on walking one to two blocks on the level and climbing one flight of stairs in normal conditions and at a normal pace.
  Class IV—Inability to carry on any physical activity without discomfort—anginal symptoms may be present at rest.

ICD-9CM CODES
411.1 Angina, stable
413 Angina pectoris
413.1 Prinzmetal's angina
413.9 Angina, unspecified

EPIDEMIOLOGY & DEMOGRAPHICS

- Angina is most common in middle-aged and elderly males.
- Females are usually affected after menopause.
- Prevalence of angina pectoris in people older than 30 yr is >3%.
- Within 12 mo of initial diagnosis, 10% to 20% of patients with diagnosis of stable angina progress to MI or unstable angina.

PHYSICAL FINDINGS & CLINICAL PRESENTATION

- Although there is significant individual variation, most patients complain of substernal chest pain (pressure, tightness, heaviness, sharp pain, sensation similar to intestinal gas or dysphagia).
- The pain is of short duration (30 sec to 30 min), nonpleuritic, and often accompanied by shortness of breath, nausea, diaphoresis, and numbness or pain in the left arm, jaw, or shoulder.

ETIOLOGY

UNCONTROLLABLE RISK FACTORS FOR ANGINA:
- Advanced age
- Male sex
- Genetic predisposition

MODIFIABLE RISK FACTORS FOR ANGINA:
- Smoking (risk is almost double)
- Hypertension (risk is double if systolic blood pressure is >180 mm Hg)
- Hyperlipidemia
- Impaired glucose tolerance or diabetes mellitus
- Obesity (weight >30% over ideal)
- Hypothyroidism
- Left ventricular hypertrophy (LVH)
- Sedentary lifestyle
- Oral contraceptive use
- Cocaine use (Cocaine is used by >5,000,000 Americans regularly and is responsible for >64,000 ER evaluations yearly to rule out myocardial ischemia.)
- Low serum folate levels (Folate is required for conversion of homocysteine to methionine. Hyperhomocysteinemia has a toxic effect on vascular endothelium and interferes with proliferation of arterial wall smooth muscle cells. Folate deficiencies are associated with an increased risk of fatal coronary heart disease.)
- Elevated homocysteine levels. Elevated plasma homocysteine level is a strong and independent risk factor for CHD events especially in patients with type 2 DM
- Elevated levels of highly sensitive C-reactive protein (hs-CRP, cardio CRP)
- Elevated levels of lipoprotein-associated phospholipase A2
- Elevated fibrinogen levels
- Depression
- Vasculitis
- Low level of RBC glutathione peroxidase 1 activity

DIAGNOSIS

DIFFERENTIAL DIAGNOSIS

Noncardiac pain mimicking angina may be caused by:

- Pulmonary diseases (pulmonary hypertension, pulmonary embolism, pleurisy, pneumothorax, pneumonia)
- GI disorders (peptic ulcer disease, pancreatitis, esophageal spasm or spontaneous esophageal muscle contraction, esophageal reflux, cholecystitis, cholelithiasis)
- Musculoskeletal conditions (costochondritis, chest wall trauma, cervical arthritis with radiculopathy, muscle strain, myositis)
- Acute aortic dissection
- Herpes zoster
- Anxiety disorder

WORKUP

- In patients presenting with chest pain, the probability of CAD should be estimated on the basis of patient age, sex, cardiovascular risk factors, and pain characteristics.
- The most important diagnostic factor is the history. Chest pain or left arm pain or discomfort reproducing previously documented angina and a known history of CAD or MI are indicative of high likelihood of actue coronary syndrome.
- The physical examination is of little diagnostic help and may be totally normal in many patients, although the presence of an S_4 gallop is suggestive of ischemic chest pain. Transient mitral regurgitation, hypotension, diaphoresis, and rales indicate a high likelihood of acute coronary syndrome.
- An ECG taken during the acute episode may show transient T-wave inversion or ST-segment depression or elevation, but more than 50% of patients with chronic stable angina have normal results on resting ECG.
- Patients with intermediate or high probability should undergo risk stratification through further testing. Treadmill exercise tolerance test is useful to identify patients with coronary artery disease who would benefit from cardiac catheterization. Stress echocardiogram or radionuclide testing (e.g., thallium, Persantine, dobutamine) are useful and sensitive in the detection of myocardial ischemia.
- Although invasive, coronary angiography remains the gold standard for the identification of clinically significant coronary artery disease. Coronary magnetic resonance angiography can also detect coronary artery disease of the proximal and middle segments. This noninvasive approach, where available, can be used to reliably identify (or rule out) left main coronary artery or three-vessel disease.

LABORATORY TESTS

- Initial laboratory tests in patients with chronic stable angina should include hemoglobin, fasting glucose, and fasting lipid panel.
- Cardiac isoenzymes (CK-MB q8h × 2) should be obtained to rule out MI in patients presenting with acute chest pain.
- Cardiac troponin I and T are specific markers of myocardial necrosis and are useful in evaluating patients with acute chest pain. Elevation of either of these proteins in the setting of an acute coronary syndrome identifies patients with a several-fold increased risk of death in subsequent weeks. Patients with negative troponin assays on arrival in the ER and repeated 4 hr later are at a low level of risk for cardiac events within the following 30 days, and most of these patients can be safely discharged from the ER. Troponin T tests can be false-positive in patients with renal failure, sepsis, rhabdomyolysis, fibrin clots, and heterophile antibodies. The presence of jaundice or the concurrent use of heparin can result in underestimation of troponin.
- Cardio-CRP (hs-CRP)—elevation of cardio-CRP is a relatively moderate predictor of coronary heart disease and it adds prognostic information to that conveyed by the Framingham risk score. However, based on current data, it may be premature to adapt widespread assessment of cardio-CRP and of the other markers noted below.
- CD40 ligand, an immunomodulator, is an important contributor to the inflammatory process that leads to atherosclerosis and thrombosis. In patients with unstable coronary artery disease, elevation of soluble CD 40 ligand is useful to identify patients who are at high risk for cardiac events.
- Circulating interleukin-6 (IL-6), a cytokine with both proinflammatory and antiinflammatory effects, is a strong independent marker of increased mortality in unstable coronary artery disease and identifies patients who benefit most from a strategy of early intervention.
- New markers for risk stratification in acute coronary syndromes based on neurohormonal activation and inflammation have recently been identified. A single measurement of B-type natriuretic peptide, a natriuretic and vasodilative peptide regulated by ventricular wall tension and stored mainly in the ventricular myocardium, obtained in the first few days after the onset of ischemic symptoms, provides predictive information for risk stratification in acute coronary syndromes. Pregnancy-associated plasma protein A (PAPP-A), which is found in both men and women, is an activator of insulin-like growth factor I (IGF-I), and may be a marker for unstable plaques. Elevated plasma levels of PAPP-A may identify patients with unstable angina in the absence of elevations of either troponin I or C-reactive protein.
- Plasma myeloperoxidase measurement may be a potentially useful lab test for stratification of patients presenting with chest pain. An elevated single initial measurement of plasma myeloperoxidase in patients presenting with chest pain independently predicts the early risk of MI, and the risk of major adverse events in the following 1 mo and 6 mo periods.

IMAGING STUDIES

- Echocardiography is indicated in patients with systolic murmur suggestive of aortic stenosis, mitral valve prolapse, or hypertrophic cardiomyopathy. It is also useful in the detection of ischemia-induced regional wall motion abnormalities or mitral regurgitation. Echocardiography combined with treadmill exercise (stress echo) or pharmacologic stress with dobutamine can be used to detect regional wall abnormalities that occur during myocardial ischemia associated with CAD.
- Coronary angiography is performed to define the location and extent of coronary disease; this is indicated in selected patients who are candidates for CABG surgery or angioplasty.
- Noninvasive methods for assessing myocardial viability to predict which patients will have increased LVEF and improved survival after revascularization include positron-emission tomography, dobutamine echocardiography, and contrast-enhanced MRI. Additional studies are needed to determine the cost effectiveness of these studies in patients with ischemic cardiomyopathy.

TREATMENT

NONPHARMACOLOGIC THERAPY

- Aggressive modification of preventable risk factors (weight reduction in obese patients, regular aerobic exercise program, correction of folate deficiency, low-cholesterol and low-sodium diet, cessation of tobacco use)
- Diets using nonhydrogenated unsaturated fats as the predominant form of dietary fat, whole grains as the main form of carbohydrates, an abundance of fruits and vegetables, and adequate omega-3-fatty acids are optimal for prevention of coronary heart disease

- Correction of possible aggravating factors (e.g., anemia, hypertension, diabetes mellitus, hyperlipidemia, thyrotoxicosis, hypothyroidism)

ACUTE GENERAL Rx

The major classes of antiischemic agents are nitrates, β-adrenergic blockers, calcium channel blockers, aspirin, and heparin; they can be used alone or in combination.

- Nitrates cause venodilation and relaxation of vascular smooth muscle; the decreased venous return from venodilation decreases diastolic ventricular wall tension (preload) and thereby reduces mechanical activity (and myocardial oxygen consumption) during systole. Relaxation of vascular smooth muscle increases coronary blood flow and reduces systemic pressure. Tolerance to nitrates can be minimized by avoiding sustained blood levels with a daily nitrate-free period (e.g., omission of bedtime dose of oral isosorbide dinitrate or 12 hr on/12 hr off transdermal nitroglycerin therapy). Nitrates are relatively contraindicated in patients with hypertrophic obstructive cardiomyopathy, and should also be avoided in patients with severe aortic stenosis.
- β-Adrenergic blockers achieve their major antianginal effect by reducing heart rate and systolic blood pressure. Absent contraindications, they should be regarded as initial therapy for stable angina for all patients. Their dose should generally be adjusted to reduce the resting heart rate to 50-60 beats/min.
- Calcium channel blockers play a major role in preventing and terminating myocardial ischemia induced by coronary artery spasm. They are particularly effective in treating microvascular angina. Short-acting calcium channel blockers should be avoided. Calcium channel blockers should generally also be avoided after complicated MI (CHF) and in patients with CHF secondary to systolic dysfunction (unless necessary to control heart rate).
- Aspirin: give initial dose of at least 160 mg/day followed by 81 to 325 mg/day. Aspirin inhibits cyclooxygenics and synthesis of thromboxane A_2 and reduces the risk of adverse cardiovascular events by 33% in patients with unstable angina. Patients intolerant to aspirin can be treated with the antiplatelet agent clopidogrel. Clopidogrel acts by irreversibly blocking the P2Y12 adenosine diphosphate receptor on the platelet surface, thereby interrupting platelet activation and aggregation.
- Heparin is useful in patients with unstable angina and reduces the frequency of MI and refractory angina. Patients with unstable angina treated with aspirin plus heparin have a 32% reduction in the risk of MI and death compared with those treated with aspirin alone; therefore, unless heparin is contraindicated, most hospitalized patients with unstable angina should be treated with both aspirin and heparin. Enoxaparin (low–molecular weight heparin) 1 mg bid SC is as effective as continuous unfractionated heparin in reducing the incidence of unstable angina. It is usually given for 3-8 days, or until coronary revascularization is performed. Longer administration does not provide additional cardiac benefits and may increase risk of hemorrhage.
- Early administration of platelet glycoprotein IIb/IIIa receptor antagonists is useful in addition to aspirin and heparin in patients with unstable angina, in high-risk patients with positive troponin tests, or those undergoing percutaneous revascularization. Abciximab, the first GP IIb/IIa inhibitor, is an important component of percutaneous revascularization. Started in the catheterization lab, it reduces the incidence of ischemic events. Abciximab is contraindicated in patients for whom an early invasive strategy is not planned. Contraindications to the use of GP IIb/IIa inhibitors are: severe hypertension (>180/110), internal bleeding within 30 days, history of intracranial hemorrhage, neoplasm, NVM, aneurysm, CVA within 30 days or history of hemorrhagic CVA, thrombocytopenin (<100 k), acute pericarditis, history or symptoms suggestive of aortic dissection, and major surgical procedures or severe physical trauma within previous month.

CHRONIC Rx

Use of lipid-lowering drugs is recommended in patients with coronary heart disease and in patients with hyperlipidemia refractory to diet and exercise. Among patients who have recently had an acute coronary syndrome, an intensive lipid-lowering statin regimen to reduce LDL cholesterol to <70 mg/dL provides greater protection against death or major cardiovascular events than does a standard regimen. Statins also decrease the level of the inflammatory marker hs-CRP independently of the magnitude of change in lipid parameters.

REFERRAL

Surgical therapy:

CABG surgery is recommended for patients with left main coronary disease, for those with symptomatic three-vessel disease, and for those with left ventricular EF <40% and critical (>70% stenosis) in all three major coronary arteries. Surgical therapy improves prognosis, particularly in diabetic patients with multivessel disease.

Minimally invasive direct coronary artery bypass (MIDCAB) is a variation of CABG for patients in whom sternotomy and cardiopulmonary bypass is either contraindicated or unnecessary. In this procedure the left internal mammary is anastomosed to the LAD through a thoracic incision without cardiopulmonary bypass. This operation is generally performed for patients with only single-vessel CAD.

The Port-Access Procedure is another type of minimally invasive technique.

Angioplasty and coronary stents:

Percutaneous coronary intervention (PCI) should be considered for patients with one- or two-vessel disease that does not involve the main left coronary artery and in whom ventricular function is normal or near normal. Patients selected for PCI should also be candidates for CABG. The types of lesions best suited for angioplasty are proximal lesions, noncalcified, concentric, and preferably shorter than 5 mm (should not exceed 10 mm). Approximately 80% of patients show immediate benefit after PCI. The frequency of abrupt closure postangioplasty can be reduced by pretreatment with IV glycoprotein IIb/IIIa receptor inhibitors, which block the final common pathway of platelet aggregation. In patients with clinically documented acute coronary syndrome who are treated with GP IIb/IIa inhibitors, even small elevations in cTmI and cTmT identify high-risk patients who derive a large clinical benefit from an early invasive strategy. Abciximab (ReoPro) and eptifibatide (Integrilin) are approved for use before and during percutaneous coronary interventions. They are expensive (>$1400 per dose of abciximab) and can cause thrombocytopenia in 0.5% to 1% of patients. Platelet counts should be monitored for 24 hours after starting glycoprotein IIb/IIIa inhibitors. Reversal of thrombocytopenia (e.g., patients undergoing emergency CABG) can be achieved with platelet transfusions.

The development of *coronary stents* has broadened the number of patients who can be treated in the cardiac laboratory. Cardiac stents are currently used in nearly 95% of all percutaneous interventional lesions. The rate of restenosis may be reduced by placing a stent electively in primary atheromatous lesions. In patients with symptomatic isolated stenosis of the proximal left anterior descending artery, stenting has advantages over standard coronary angioplasty in that it is associated with both a lower rate of restenosis and a better clinical outcome. The major limitations of stenting are subacute thrombosis, restenosis within the stent, bleeding complications when anticoagulants are used post-stenting, and higher cost ($1500 average unit price). The combination of aspirin and clopidogrel is effective in preventing coronary stent thrombosis. Vitamin therapy to lower homocysteine levels has been recommended by some for the prevention of restenosis after coronary angioplasty, however, recent reports indicate that the administration of folate, vitamin B_6, and vitamin B_{12} after coronary stenting may increase the risk of in-stent restenosis and the need for target-vessel revascularization. Stents coated with sirolimus have been shown to dramatically reduce the incidence of stent restenosis by inhibiting the growth of endothelium and fibrosis within the lumen of the stent on the short term. Stents coated with paclitaxel, which inhibits cellular replication and reduces proliferation and migration of endothelial smooth muscle cells, are also effective in reducing the incidence of restenosis.

CO2 laser revascularization:
This operation is performed only in selected centers and consists of placing 1-mm laser channels in the heart muscle. It may be indicated in selected Class III or Class IV angina patients who are failing maximum medical therapy and are not amenable to any other PTCA or coronary bypass surgery.

PEARLS & CONSIDERATIONS

COMMENTS

Although nitrate responsiveness is usually an integral part of a diagnostic strategy for chronic stable chest pain, recent reports question its value and conclude that in a general population admitted for chest pain, relief of pain after nitroglycerin treatment does not predict active coronary artery disease and should not be used to guide diagnosis in the acute care setting.

SUGGESTED READINGS

Aviles RJ et al: Troponin T levels in patients with acute coronary syndromes, with or without renal dysfunction, *N Engl J Med* 346:2047, 2002.

Blankenberg S et al: Glutathione Peroxidase 1 activity and cardiovascular events in patients with coronary artery disease, *N Engl J Med* 349:1605, 2003.

Brennan ML et al: Prognostic value of myeloperoxidase in patients with chest pain, *N Engl J Med* 349:1595, 2003.

Buffon A et al: Widespread coronary inflammation in unstable angina, *N Engl J Med* 347:5, 2002.

Glassman AH et al: Sertraline treatment of major depression in patients with acute MI or unstable angina, *JAMA* 288:701, 2002.

Heeschen C et al: Soluble CD 40 ligand in acute coronary syndromes, *N Engl J Med* 348:1104, 2003.

Henrikson C et al: Chest pain relief by nitroglycerin does not predict active coronary artery disease, *Ann Intern Med* 139:979, 2003.

Hu F, Willet W: Optimal diets for prevention of coronary heart disease, *JAMA* 288:2569, 2002.

Kushner I, Sehgal A: Is high-sensitivity C-Reactive protein an effective screening test for cardiovascular risk? *Arch Intern Med* 162:867, 2002.

Lange H et al: Folate therapy and in-stent restenosis after coronary stenting, *N Eng J Med* 350:2673, 2004.

Levinson SS, Elin RJ: What is c-reactive protein telling us about coronary artery disease, *Arch Intern Med* 162:389, 2002.

Moses JW et al: Sirolimus-eluting stents versus standard stents in patients with stenosis in a native coronary artery, *N Engl J Med* 349:1315, 2003.

Ridker PM et al: Plasma homocysteine concentration, statin therapy, and the risk of first acute coronary events, *Circulation* 105:1776, 2002.

Ridker PM et al: Comparison of C-reactive protein and low-density lipoprotein cholesterol levels in the prediction of first cardiovascular events, *N Engl J Med* 347:1557, 2002.

Sabatine MS et al: Multimarker approach to risk stratification in non-ST elevation acute coronary syndromes: simultaneous assessment of troponin I, C-reactive protein, and B-type natriuretic peptide, *Circulation* 105:1760, 2002.

Serruys PW et al: Fluvastatin for prevention of cardiac events following successful first percutaneous coronary intervention, *JAMA* 287:3215, 2002.

Snow V et al: Evaluation of primary care patients with chronic stable angina: Guidelines from the American College of Physicians, *Ann Intern Med* 141:57 and 562, 2004.

Soinio M et al: Elevated plasma homocysteine level is an independent predictor of coronary artery disease events in patients with type 2 DM, *Ann Intern Med* 140:94, 2004.

Yang EHC et al: Current and future treatment strategies for refractory angina, *Mayo Clin Proc* 79(10):1284, 2004.

AUTHOR: **FRED F. FERRI, M.D.**

Angioedema (PTG)

BASIC INFORMATION

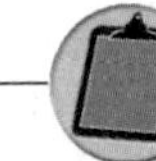

DEFINITION

- The cutaneous swelling caused by the release of vasoactive mediators is called urticaria and angioedema.
- Urticaria causes edema of the superficial dermis.
- Angioedema involves the deep layers of the dermis and the subcutaneous tissue.

SYNONYMS

Angioneurotic edema

ICD-9CM CODES
995.1 Angioedema (allergic)
277.6 Angioedema (hereditary)

EPIDEMIOLOGY & DEMOGRAPHICS

- Approximately 20% of the population experiences urticaria and/or angioedema at some time during life.
- Race: No predilection.
- Sex: More occurrences in women than men.
- Angioedema can occur together with urticaria (40%) or alone (20%); the remaining 40% have urticaria alone
- Angioedema commonly occurs after adolescence in the third decade of life.
- Incidence of hereditary angioedema is 1/150,000 persons.

PHYSICAL FINDINGS & CLINICAL PRESENTATION

- Angioedema may be acute or chronic.
  1. Acute angioedema is defined as symptoms lasting 6 wk.
  2. Chronic angioedema is defined as symptoms lasting >6 wk.
- Urticaria is commonly known as "hives" and is:
  1. Pruritic
  2. Palpable
  3. Erythematous
  4. Millimeters to centimeters in size
  5. Multiple in number
  6. Fades within 12 to 24 hr
  7. Reappears at other sites
- Angioedema is characterized by the following:
  1. Nonpruritic
  2. Burning
  3. Not well demarcated
  4. Involves eyelids (Fig. 1-17), lips, tongue, and extremities
  5. Can involve the larynx causing respiratory distress
  6. Resolves slowly

ETIOLOGY

- Angioedema, with or without urticaria, is classified as acquired (allergic or idiopathic) or hereditary.
- Angioedema is primarily due to mast cell activation and degranulation with release of vasoactive mediators (e.g., histamine, serotonin, bradykinins) resulting in postcapillary venule inflammation, vascular leakage, and edema in the deep layers of the dermis and subcutaneous tissue.
- Pathologically angioedema has both immunological and nonimmunological mediated mechanisms.
  1. Immunoglobulin E (Ig E)-mediated angioedema may result from antigen exposure (e.g., foods [milk, eggs, peanuts, shell fish, tomatoes, chocolate, sulfites] or drugs [penicillin, aspirin, NSAIDs, phenytoin, sulfonamides]).
  2. Complement-mediated angioedema involving immune complex mechanisms can also lead to mast cell activation that manifests as serum sickness.
  3. Hereditary angioedema is an autosomal dominant disease caused by a deficiency of C1 esterase inhibitor (C1-INH). C1-INH is a protease inhibitor that is normally present in high concentrations in the plasma. C1-INH serves many functions, one of which is to inhibit plasma kallikrein, a protease that cleaves kininogen and releases bradykinin. A deficiency in C1-INH results in excess concentration of kininogen and the subsequent release of kinin mediators.
  4. Acquired angioedema is usually associated with other diseases, most commonly B-cell lympho-proliferative disorders, but may also result from the formation of autoantibodies directed against C1 inhibitor protein.
  5. Other causes of angioedema include infection (e.g., herpes simplex, hepatitis B, coxsackie A and B, streptococcus, candida, ascaris, and strongyloides), insect bites and stings, stress, physical factors (e.g., cold, exercise, pressure, and vibration), connective tissue diseases (e.g., SLE, Henoch-Schönlein purpura), and idiopathic causes. ACE inhibitors can increase kinin activity and lead to angioedema.

DIAGNOSIS

A detailed history and physical examination usually establishes the diagnosis of angioedema. Extensive lab testing is of limited value.

DIFFERENTIAL DIAGNOSIS

The differential diagnosis of angioedema includes:

1. Cellulitis
2. Hypothyroidism
3. Contact dermatitis
4. Atopic dermatitis
5. Mastocytosis
6. Granulomatous cheilitis
7. Bullous pemphigoid
8. Urticaria pigmentosa
9. Anaphylaxis
10. Erythema multiforme
11. Epiglottitis
12. Peritonsillar abscess

WORKUP

- An extensive workup searching for the cause of angioedema is often unrevealing (90%).
- Workup including diagnostic blood tests and allergy testing is performed based on the history and physical examination.

LABORATORY TESTS

- CBC, ESR, and urinalysis are sometimes helpful as part of the initial evaluation
- Stools for ova and parasites
- Serology testing
- C4 levels are reduced in acquired and hereditary angioedema (occuring without urticaria). If C4 levels are low, C1-INH levels and activity should be obtained

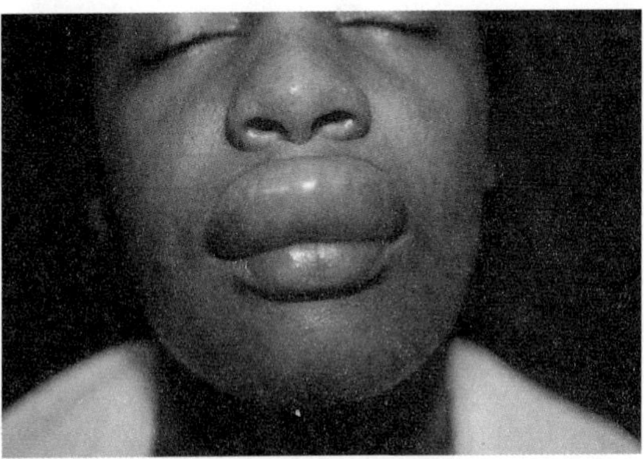

FIGURE 1-17 Angioedema of the upper lip, with severe swelling of deeper tissues. (From Goldstein BG, Goldstein AO: *Practical dermatology,* ed 2, St Louis, 1997, Mosby.)

- Skin and radioallergosorbent (RAST) testing may be done if food allergies are suspected
- Skin biopsy is usually done in patients with chronic angioedema refractory to corticosteroid treatment

TREATMENT

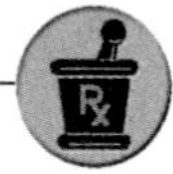

NONPHARMACOLOGIC THERAPY

- Eliminate the offending agent
- Avoid triggering factors (e.g., cold, stress)
- Cold compresses to affected areas

ACUTE GENERAL Rx

- Acute life-threatening angioedema involving the larynx is treated with:
  1. Epinephrine 0.3 mg in a solution of 1:1000 given SC
  2. Diphenhydramine 25 to 50 mg IV or IM
  3. Cimetidine 300 mg IV or ranitidine 50 mg IV
  4. Methylprednisolone 125 mg IV
- Mainstay therapy in angioedema is H1 antihistamines.
  1. Diphenhydramine 25 to 50 mg q6h
  2. Chlorpheniramine 4 mg q6h
  3. Hydroxyzine 10 to 25 mg q6h
  4. Cetirizine 5 to 10 mg qd
  5. Loratadine 10 mg qd
  6. Fexofenadine 60 mg qd
- H2 antihistamines can be added to H1 antihistamines.
  1. Ranitidine 150 mg bid
  2. Cimetidine 400 mg bid
  3. Famotidine 20 mg bid
- Tricyclic antidepressants
  1. Doxepin 25 to 50 mg qd can be tried.
- Corticosteroids are rarely required for symptomatic relief of acute angioedema.

CHRONIC Rx

- Chronic angioedema is treated as described under "Acute General Rx."
- Corticosteroids are used more often in chronic angioedema.
- Prednisone 1 mg/kg/day for 5 days and then tapered over a period of weeks.
- Androgens are used for the treatment of hereditary angioedema.

DISPOSITION

- Antihistamines achieve symptomatic relief in more than 80% of patients with angioedema.
- In chronic angioedema, corticosteroids are given in addition to antihistamines.
- A small percentage of people will have recurrence of symptoms after steroid treatment.
- Chronic angioedema can last for months and even years.

REFERRAL

Dermatology consultation is recommended in patients with chronic angioedema, hereditary angioedema, and recurring angioedema.

PEARLS & CONSIDERATIONS

ACE inhibitors can cause angioedema up to many months after initiation.

COMMENTS

- Identifying a cause for angioedema in patients is often difficult and met with frustration.
- Chronic angioedema, unlike acute angioedema, is rarely caused by an allergic reaction.

SUGGESTED READINGS

Joint Task Force on Practice Parameters: The diagnosis and management of urticaria: a practice parameter. Part I: acute urticaria/angioedema. Part II: chronic urticaria/angioedema, *Ann Allergy Asthma Immunol* 85(6 pt 2):521, 2000.

Kamboj S et al: Hereditary angioedema: a rare but potentially lethal disease, *J La State Med Soc* 154(3):121, 2002.

Kaplan AP: Clinical practice: chronic urticaria and angioedema, *N Engl J Med* 346(3):175, 2002.

AUTHOR: **MEL ANDERSON, M.D.**

BASIC INFORMATION

DEFINITION

Ankle fractures involve the lateral, medial, or posterior malleolus of the ankle and may occur either alone or in some combination. Associated ligamentous injuries are included.

ICD-9CM CODES
824.8 Ankle fracture (malleolus) (closed)
824.2 Lateral malleolus fracture (fibular)
824.0 Medial malleolus fracture (tibial)

PHYSICAL FINDINGS & CLINICAL PRESENTATION

- Deformity usually dependent on extent of displacement
- Pain, tenderness, and hemorrhage at the site of injury
- Gentle palpation of ligamentous structures (especially deltoid ligament) to determine the extent of soft tissue injury
- Evaluation of distal neurovascular status; results recorded

ETIOLOGY

- The ankle depends on its ligamentous and bony support for stability. The joint, or *mortise,* is an inverted U with the dome of the talus fitting into the medial and lateral malleoli. The posterior margin of the tibia is often called the *third* or *posterior malleolus.*
- Most common ankle fractures are the result of eversion or lateral rotation forces on the talus (in contrast to common sprains, which are caused usually by inversion).

DIAGNOSIS

IMAGING STUDIES

Standard AP and lateral views accompanied by an AP taken 15° internally rotated. The last view is taken to properly visualize the mortise.

TREATMENT

All fractures: elevation and ice to control swelling for 48 to 72 hr.

ACUTE GENERAL Rx

- Clinical and roentgenographic assessment of the status of the ankle mortise and stability of the injury is mandatory to determine treatment.
- There is potential for displacement if both sides of the joint are significantly injured (e.g., fracture of the lateral malleolus with deltoid ligament injury).
- Deviation of the position of the talus in the mortise could lead to traumatic arthritis.
- If there is no widening of the ankle mortise, many injuries can be safely treated with simple casting without reduction:
  1. Undisplaced or avulsion fractures of either malleolus below the ankle joint line:
     a. Stability of the joint is not compromised and a short leg walking cast or ankle support is sufficient.
     b. Weight bearing is allowed as tolerated.
     c. In 4 to 6 wk, protection may be discontinued.
  2. Isolated undisplaced fractures of the medial, lateral, or posterior malleolus:
     a. Usually stable and require only the application of a short leg walking cast with the ankle in the neutral position or fracture cast boot.
     b. Immobilization should be continued for 8 wk.
     c. Fracture line of lateral malleolus may persist roentgenographically for several months, but immobilization beyond 8 wk is usually unnecessary.
     d. Undisplaced bimalleolar fractures are treated with a long leg cast flexed 30° at the knee to prevent motion and displacement of the fracture fragments. In 4 wk, a short leg walking cast may be applied for an additional 4 wk.
  3. Isolated fractures of the lateral malleolus that are slightly displaced:
     a. May be treated with casting if no medial injury is present.
     b. A below-knee walking cast is applied with ankle in the neutral position and weight bearing is allowed as tolerated.
     c. Six weeks of immobilization is sufficient.
     d. If medial tenderness is present, suggesting deltoid ligament rupture, a carefully molded cast may suffice if weight bearing is not allowed and the patient is followed closely for signs of instability, especially after swelling recedes. If significant widening of the medial ankle mortise (increase in the "medial clear space") develops as a result of lateral displacement of the talus, referral for possible reduction is indicated.
     e. If signs of instability are already present at initial examination (widening of the medial clear space with medial tenderness), referral is indicated.
  4. Undisplaced fracture of the distal fibular epiphysis:
     a. Often diagnosed clinically.
     b. There is tenderness over the epiphyseal plate.
     c. Roentgenographic findings are often negative.
     d. A short leg walking cast is applied for 4 wk.
     e. Growth disturbance is rare.
  5. Isolated posterior malleolar fractures involving less than 25% of the joint surface on the lateral roentgenogram:
     Safely treated by applying a short leg walking cast or fracture brace. (Fractures involving >25% of the weight-bearing surface should be referred because of the potential for instability and subsequent traumatic arthritis.)

CHRONIC Rx

- Early motion is encouraged through a home exercise program.
- Protection from reinjury is appropriate for 4 to 6 wk following cast or brace removal.
- Temporary increase in lower extremity swelling that frequently occurs after short leg cast removal may benefit from the use of support hose.

DISPOSITION

Significant factors involved in the development of traumatic arthritis:
- Amount of joint trauma at the time of injury
- Eventual position of the talus in the mortise

Fracture nonunion is uncommon unless displacement is significant.

REFERRAL

Orthopedic consultation for:
- Unstable ankle joint
- Widened ankle mortise
- Posterior malleolar fracture over 25% of joint with incongruity
- Marked displacement of fracture fragment

SUGGESTED READINGS

Hasselman CT, Vogt MT et al: Foot and ankle fractures in elderly white women: incidence and risk factors, *J Bone Joint Surg* 85:820, 2003.

Kay RM, Matthys GA: Pediatric ankle fractures: evaluation and treatment, *J Am Acad Orthop Surg* 9:268, 2001.

Makwana NK et al: Conservative versus operative treatment for displaced ankle fractures in patients over 55 years of age, *J Bone Joint Surg* 83(B):525, 2001.

Michelson JD: Ankle fractures resulting from rotational injuries, *J Am Acad Orthop Surg* 11:403, 2003.

AUTHOR: **LONNIE R. MERCIER, M.D.**

BASIC INFORMATION

DEFINITION

An ankle sprain is an injury to the ligamentous support of the ankle. Most (85%) involve the lateral ligament complex (Fig. 1-18). The anterior inferior tibiofibular (AITF) ligament, deltoid ligament, and interosseous membrane may also be injured. Damage to the tibiofibular syndesmosis is sometimes called a *high sprain* because of pain above the ankle.

ICD-9CM CODES
845.00 Sprain, ankle or foot

EPIDEMIOLOGY & DEMOGRAPHICS

PREVALENCE: 1 case/10,000 people each day

PREDOMINANT SEX: Varies according to age and level of physical activity

PHYSICAL FINDINGS & CLINICAL PRESENTATION

- Often a history of a "pop"
- Variable amounts of tenderness and hemorrhage
- Possible abnormal anterior drawer test (pulling the plantar flexed foot forward to determine if there is any abnormal increase in forward movement of the talus in the ankle mortise) (Fig. 1-19)
- Inversion sprains: tender laterally; syndesmotic injuries: area of tenderness is more anterior and proximal
- Evaluation of motor function (Fig. 1-20)

ETIOLOGY

- Lateral injuries usually result from inversion and plantar flexion injuries.
- Eversion and rotational forces may injure the deltoid or AITF ligament or the interosseous membrane.

DIAGNOSIS

DIFFERENTIAL DIAGNOSIS

- Fracture of the ankle or foot, particularly involving the distal fibular growth plate in the immature patient
- Avulsion fracture of the fifth metatarsal base

WORKUP

- History and clinical examination are usually sufficient to establish the diagnosis.
- Plain radiographs are always needed.

IMAGING STUDIES

Roentgenographic evaluation
1. Usually normal but always performed
2. Should include the fifth metatarsal base
3. All minor avulsion fractures noted

Varying opinions on the usefulness of arthrograms, tenograms, and stress films

TREATMENT

ACUTE GENERAL Rx

Ankle sprains are often graded I, II, or III, according to severity, with Grade III injury implying complete rupture. The first line of treatment is described by the mnemonic device, *RICE:*
- Rest
- Ice
- Compression
- Elevation
- Varying opinions regarding the initial use of NSAIDs
- In 48 to 72 hr, active range of motion and weight bearing as tolerated
- In 4 to 5 days, exercise against resistance added
- Possible cast immobilization for some patients who require early independent walking; short leg orthoses also available for the same purpose
- Surgery is rarely recommended, even for Grade III sprains; reports of equally satisfactory outcomes with nonsurgical treatment

CHRONIC Rx

- Lateral heel and sole wedge to prevent inversion
- Protective taping or bracing during vigorous activities (Fig. 1-21)
- Strengthening exercises

DISPOSITION

- Lateral sprains of any severity may cause lingering symptoms for weeks and months.
  1. Some syndesmotic sprains take even longer to heal.
  2. Heterotopic ossification may even develop in the interosseous membrane, but long-term results do not seem to be affected by such ossification.
- Continuing lateral symptoms may require surgical reconstruction, although late traumatic arthritis or chronic instability is rare regardless of treatment.

REFERRAL

For orthopedic consultation for cases that fail to respond to conservative treatment

PEARLS & CONSIDERATIONS

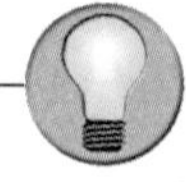

COMMENTS

If healing seems delayed (more than 6 wk), the following conditions should be considered:
1. Talar dome fracture
2. Reflex sympathetic dystrophy
3. Chronic tendinitis
4. Peroneal tendon subluxation
5. Other occult fracture
6. Peroneal weakness (poor rehabilitation)
7. A "high" (syndesmotic) sprain

Repeat plain roentgenograms, bone scan, or MRI may be indicated.

SUGGESTED READINGS

Bachman LM, Kolb E et al: Accuracy of Ottawa ankle rules to exclude fractures of the ankle and mid-foot: systematic review, *BMJ* 326:417, 2003.

Dahners LE, Mullis BH: Effects of nonsteroidal anti-inflammatory drugs on bone formation and soft tissue healing, *J Am Acad Orthop Surg* 12:139, 2004.

Judd DB, Kim DH: Foot fractures misdiagnosed as ankle sprains, *Am Fam Physician* 66:785, 2002.

Mizel MS, Hecht PJ et al: Evaluation and treatment of chronic ankle pain, *J Bone Joint Surg* 86A:622, 2004.

Wolfe M et al: Management of ankle sprains, *Am Fam Physician* 63:83, 2001.

AUTHOR: **LONNIE R. MERCIER, M.D.**

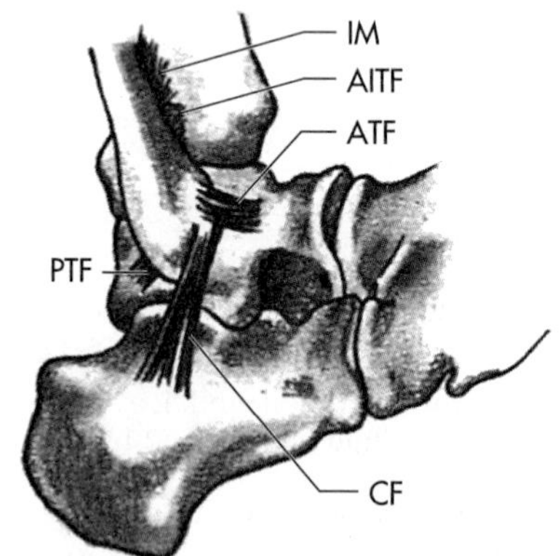

FIGURE 1-18 The lateral ankle ligaments, anterior and posterior talofibular *(ATF, PTF)* and calcaneofibular *(CF)*. Also shown are the anterior inferior tibiofibular ligament *(AITF)* and the beginning of the interosseous membrane *(IM)*. (From Mercier LR [ed]: *Practical orthopaedics,* ed 4, St Louis, 1995, Mosby.)

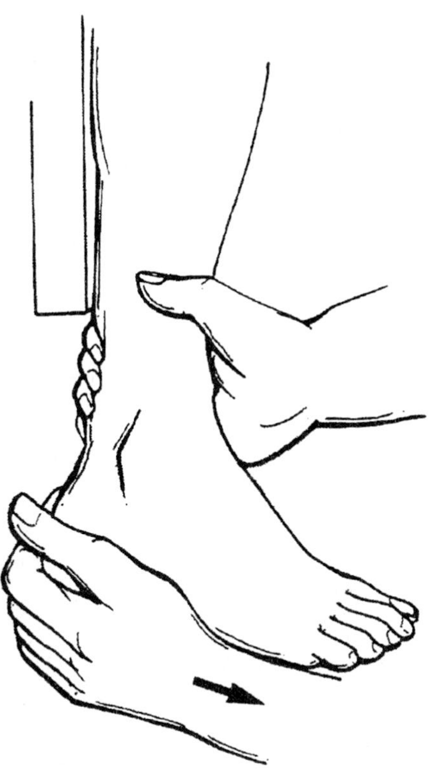

FIGURE 1-19 Anterior drawer test of the ankle (tests the integrity of the anterior talofibular ligament). (From Brinker MR, Miller MD: *Fundamentals of orthopaedics,* Philadelphia, 1999, WB Saunders.)

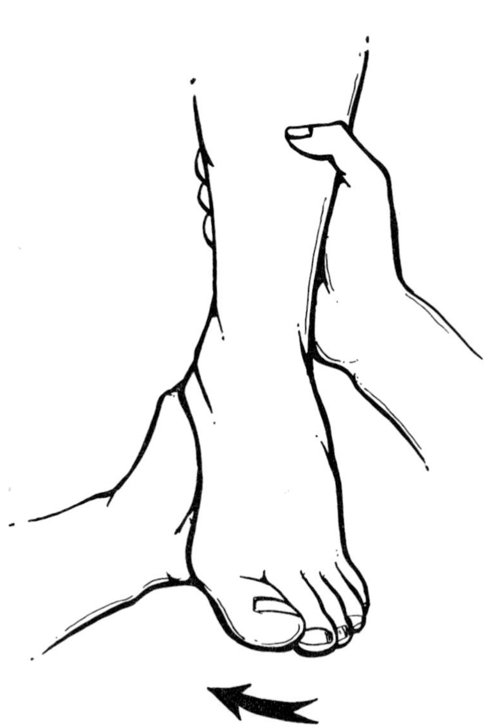

FIGURE 1-20 Talar tilt test (inversion stress) of the ankle (tests the integrity of the anterior talofibular ligament and the calcaneofibular ligament). (From Brinker MR, Miller MD: *Fundamentals of orthopaedics,* Philadelphia, 1999, WB Saunders.)

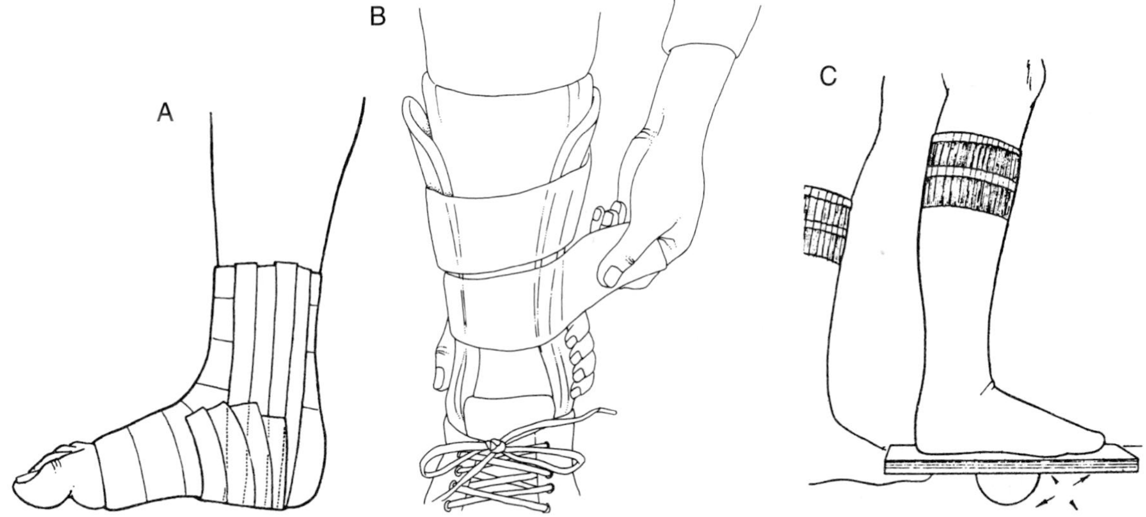

FIGURE 1-21 **A,** The most effective method of supporting most acute ankle sprains is by using an Ace wrap reinforced with 1-in medial and lateral tape strips. The anterior and posterior aspects of the ankle are left free to allow the patient to flex and extend the ankle. The patient is encouraged to bear weight with crutches. **B,** Diagram of an air splint. Straps are adjusted to heel size, the lower straps are wrapped about the ankle, and the side extensions are centered. The splint is then pressurized and straps adjusted until comfortable support and pressure are attained. **C,** As the ankle pain subsides, about the third to fifth day, balancing exercises can begin to allow the patient to regain ankle proprioception and avoid recurrent instability problems. (From Jardon OM, Mathews MS: Orthopedics. In Rakel RE [ed]: *Textbook of family practice,* ed 5, Philadelphia, 1995, WB Saunders.)

Ankylosing Spondylitis (PTG)

BASIC INFORMATION

DEFINITION

Ankylosing spondylitis is a chronic inflammatory condition involving the sacroiliac joints and axial skeleton characterized by ankylosis and enthesitis (inflammation at tendon insertions). It is one of a group of several overlapping syndromes, including spondylitis associated with Reiter's syndrome, psoriasis, and IBD. Patients are typically seronegative for the rheumatoid factor, and these disorders are now commonly called *rheumatoid variants* or *seronegative spondyloarthropathies*.

SYNONYMS

Marie-Strümpell disease

ICD-9CM CODES
720.0 Ankylosing spondylitis

EPIDEMIOLOGY & DEMOGRAPHICS

PREVALENCE: 0.15% of male population (rare in blacks)

PREDOMINANT AGE AT ONSET: 15 to 35 yr

PREDOMINANT SEX: Male:female ratio of 10:1

PHYSICAL FINDINGS & CLINICAL PRESENTATION

- Morning stiffness
- Fatigue, weight loss, anorexia, and other systemic complaints in more severe forms
- Bilateral sacroiliac tenderness (sacroiliitis)
- Limited lumbar spine motion (Fig. 1-22)
- Loss of chest expansion measured at the nipple line <2.5 cm, reflecting rib cage involvement
- Occasionally, peripheral joint involvement (large joints are more commonly affected)
- Possible extraskeletal manifestations affecting the cardiovascular system (aortic insufficiency, heart block, cardiomegaly), lungs (pulmonary fibrosis), and eye (uveitis)
- Tenderness at tendon insertion sites
- Radiation below the knee is rare

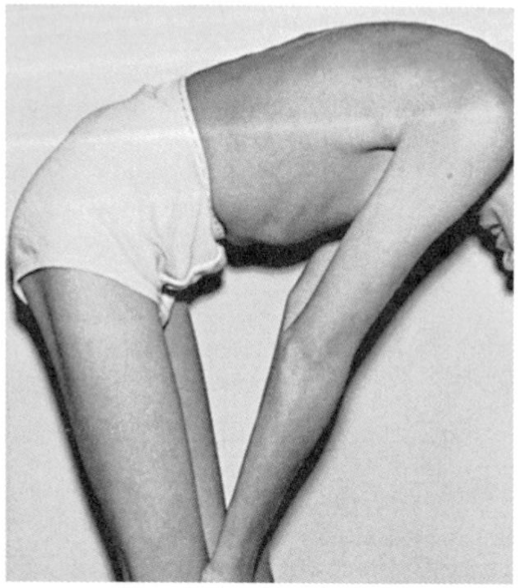

FIGURE 1-22 Loss of lumbodorsal spine mobility in a boy with ankylosing spondylitis: the lower spine remains straight when the patient bends forward. (From Behrman RE: *Nelson textbook of pediatrics,* Philadelphia, 1996, WB Saunders.)

ETIOLOGY

Unknown. Genetic factors play an important role. Destructive changes probably due to release of cytokines and tumor necrosis factor.

DIAGNOSIS

DIFFERENTIAL DIAGNOSIS

- Other spondyloarthropathies
- A clinical algorithm for the evaluation of back pain is described in Section III.

WORKUP

The modified New York criteria are often used for diagnosis:
- Low back pain of at least 3 mo duration improved by exercise and not relieved by rest
- Limitation of lumbar spine movement in sagittal and frontal planes
- Decreased chest expansion below normal values for age and sex
- Bilateral sacroiliitis of minimal grade or greater
- Unilateral sacroiliitis of moderate grade or greater

LABORATORY TESTS

- Elevated sedimentation rate, CRP
- Absence of rheumatoid factor and ANA
- Possible mild hyperchromic anemia
- Presence of HLA/B27 antigen in >90% of patients (although this antigen is often present in the general population)

IMAGING STUDIES

- Early roentgenographic features are those of bilateral sacroiliitis on plain films.
- Vertebral bodies may become demineralized and a typical "squaring off" occurs.
- With progression, calcification of the annulus fibrosus and paravertebral ligaments develop, giving rise to the so-called bamboo spine appearance.
- End result may be a forward protruding cervical spine and fixed dorsal kyphosis.
- MRI may be helpful in detecting early inflammatory lesions.

TREATMENT

NONPHARMACOLOGIC THERAPY

- Exercises primarily to maintain flexibility; general aerobic activity also important
- Postural training
  1. Patients must be instructed to sit in the erect position and to avoid stooping; otherwise, a flexion contracture of the spine may develop, which can become so severe that the patient cannot see forward.
  2. Sleeping should be in the supine position on a firm mattress; pillows should not be placed under the head or knees.

CHRONIC Rx

- NSAIDs: indomethacin is often successful in relieving symptoms; newer nonsteroidal agents may be tried as well.
- New research into the use of tumor necrosis factor antagonists such as etanercept appears promising.

DISPOSITION

- Most patients have a normal life span.
- The usual course of the disease is not life-threatening, but death may occur as a result of aortic insufficiency or secondary amyloidosis with renal disease.

REFERRAL

- Orthopedic consultation for pain or deformity
- Ophthalmologic consultation for ocular complications
- Rheumatology consultation for uncontrolled symptoms

PEARLS & CONSIDERATIONS

COMMENTS

Years may pass between the onset of symptoms and the ultimate diagnosis because of the frequency of nonspecific low back pain from other disorders.

SUGGESTED READINGS

Bennett DL, Ohashi E, El-Khoury GY: Spondyloarthropathies: ankylosing spondylitis and psoriatic arthritis, *Radiol Clin North Am* 42:121, 2004.

Gorman JD et al: Treatment of ankylosing spondylitis by inhibition of tumor necrosis factor alpha, *N Engl J Med* 346:1349, 2002.

Kataria RK, Brent LH: Spondyloarthropatries, *Am Fam Physician* 69:2853, 2004.

Liu Y, Cortinovis D, Stone MA: Recent advances in the treatment of the spondyloarthropathies, *Curr Opin Rheumatol* 16:357, 2004.

Maksymowych WP: Ankylosing spondylitis: not just another pain in the back, *Can Fam Phys* 50:205, 2004.

AUTHOR: **LONNIE R. MERCIER, M.D.**

BASIC INFORMATION

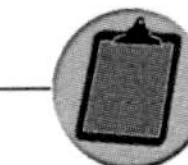

DEFINITION

A fistula is an inflammatory tract with a secondary (external) opening in the perianal skin and a primary (internal) opening in the anal canal at the dentate line. It originates in an abscess in the intersphincteric space of the anal canal. Fistulas can be classified as follows:

1. Intersphincteric: fistula track passes within the intersphincteric plane to the perianal skin; most common
2. Transsphincteric: fistula track passes from the internal opening, through the internal and external sphincter, and into the ischiorectal fossa to the perianal skin; frequent
3. Suprasphincteric: after passing through the internal sphincter, fistula tract passes above the puborectalis and then tracts downward, lateral to the external sphincter, into the ischiorectal space to the perianal skin; uncommon; if abscess cavity extends cephalad, a supralevator abscess possibly palpable on rectal examination
4. Extrasphincteric: fistula tract passes from the rectum, above the levators, through the levator muscles to the ischiorectal space and perianal skin; rare

With a horseshoe fistula, the tract passes from one ischiorectal fossa to the other behind the rectum.

SYNONYMS

Fistula-in-ano

ICD-9CM CODES

565.1 Anal fistula

EPIDEMIOLOGY & DEMOGRAPHICS

- Common in all ages
- Occurs equally in men and women
- Associated with constipation
- Pediatric age group: more common in infants; boys > girls

PHYSICAL FINDINGS & CLINICAL PRESENTATION

- Acute stage: perianal swelling, pain, and fever
- Chronic stage: history of rectal drainage or bleeding; previous abscess with drainage
- Tender external fistulous opening, with 2 to 3 cm of the anal verge, with purulent or serosanguineous drainage on compression; the greater the distance from the anal margin, the greater the probability of a complicated upward extension
- Goodsall's rule:
  1. Location of the internal opening related to the location of the external opening.
  2. With external opening anterior to an imaginary line drawn horizontally across the midpoint of the anus: fistulous tract runs radially into the anal canal.
  3. With opening posterior to the transanal line: tract is usually curvilinear, entering the anal canal in the posterior midline.
  4. Exception to this rule: an external, anterior opening that is >3 cm from the anus. In this case the tract may curve posteriorly and end in the posterior midline.
- If perianal abscess recurs, presence of a fistula is suggested

ETIOLOGY

- Most common: nonspecific cryptoglandular infection (skin or intestinal flora)
- Fistulas more common when intestinal microorganisms are cultured from the anorectal abscess
- Tuberculosis
- Lymphogranuloma venereum
- Actinomycosis
- Inflammatory bowel disease (IBD): Crohn's disease, ulcerative colitis
- Trauma: surgery (episiotomy, prostatectomy), foreign bodies, anal intercourse
- Malignancy: carcinoma, leukemia, lymphoma
- Treatment of malignancy: surgery, radiation

DIAGNOSIS

DIFFERENTIAL DIAGNOSIS

- Hidradenitis suppurativa
- Pilonidal sinus
- Bartholin's gland abscess or sinus
- Infected perianal sebaceous cysts

WORKUP

- Digital rectal examination:
  1. Assess sphincter tone and voluntary squeeze pressure
  2. Determine the presence of an extraluminal mass
  3. Identify an indurated track
  4. Palpate an internal opening or pit
- Gentle probing of external orifice to avoid creating a false tract; 50% do not have clinically detectable opening
- Anoscopy
- Proctosigmoidoscopy to exclude inflammatory or neoplastic disease
- All studies done under adequate anesthesia

LABORATORY TESTS

- CBC
- Rectal biopsy if diagnosis of IBD or malignancy suspected; biopsy of external orifice is useless

IMAGING STUDIES

- Colonoscopy or barium enema if:
  1. Diagnosis of IBD or malignancy is suspected
  2. History of recurrent or multiple fistulas
  3. Patient <25 yr old
- Small bowel series: occasionally obtained for reasons similar to above
- Fistulography: unreliable; but may be helpful in complicated fistulas

TREATMENT

NONPHARMACOLOGIC THERAPY

Sitz baths

ACUTE GENERAL Rx

- Treatment of choice: surgery
- Broad-spectrum antibiotic given if:
  1. Cellulitis present
  2. Patient is immunocompromised
  3. Valvular heart disease present
  4. Prosthetic devices present
- Stool softener/laxative

CHRONIC Rx

- Surgery
- Surgical goals are as follows:
  1. Cure the fistula
  2. Prevent recurrence
  3. Preserve sphincter function
  4. Minimize healing time
- Methods for the management of anal fistulas: fistulotomy, setons, rectal advancement flaps, colostomy

DISPOSITION

Outpatient surgery

REFERRAL

Refer to a surgeon with expertise in this area.

PEARLS & CONSIDERATIONS

COMMENTS

- HIV-positive and diabetic patients with perirectal abscesses/fistulas are true surgical emergencies.
- Risk of septicemia, Fournier's gangrene, and other septic complications make immediate drainage imperative.

SUGGESTED READING

Pfenninger JL, Zainea GG: Common anorectal condition, *Am Fam Physician,* 64:22, 2001.

AUTHOR: **GEORGE T. DANAKAS, M.D.**

BASIC INFORMATION

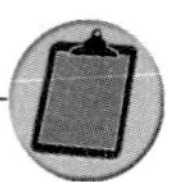

DEFINITION

Anorexia nervosa is a psychiatric disorder characterized by abnormal eating behavior, severe self-induced weight loss, and a specific psychopathology (see "Workup").

ICD-9CM CODES
307.1 Anorexia nervosa

EPIDEMIOLOGY & DEMOGRAPHICS

INCIDENCE/PREVALENCE (IN U.S.):
- Anorexia nervosa occurs in 0.2% to 1.3% of the general population, with an annual incidence of 5 to 10 cases/100,000 persons.
- Participation in activities that promote thinness (athletics, modeling) are associated with a higher incidence of anorexia nervosa.

PREDOMINANT SEX: Female:male ratio is 9:1. Approximately 0.5% to 1% of women between the ages of 15 and 30 yr have anorexia nervosa.

PREDOMINANT AGE: Adolescence to young adulthood is the predominant age. Mean age of onset is 17 yr.

PHYSICAL FINDINGS & CLINICAL PRESENTATION

Primary care physicians must be skilled at recognizing this disorder because patients with mild cases usually present with nonspecific symptoms such as asthenia, cold intolerance, lack of energy, or dizziness. The physical examination may be normal in the early stages or in mild cases. Patients with moderate to severe anorexia have the following physical characteristics:
- Patient is emaciated and bundled in clothing.
- Skin is dry and has excessive growth of lanugo. Skin may also be yellow-tinged from carotenodermia.
- Brittle nails, thinning scalp hair are present.
- Bradycardia, hypotension, hypothermia, and bradypnea are common.
- Female fat distribution pattern is no longer evident.
- Axillary and pubic hair is preserved.
- Peripheral edema may be present.

ETIOLOGY

- Etiology is unknown, but probably multifactorial (sociocultural, psychologic, familial, and genetic factors).
- A history of sexual abuse has been reported in as many as 50% of patients with anorexia nervosa.
- Psychologic factors: anorexics often have an incompletely developed personal identity. They struggle to maintain a sense of control over their environment, they usually have a low self-esteem, and they lack the sense that they are valued and loved for themselves.

DIAGNOSIS

DIFFERENTIAL DIAGNOSIS

- Depression with loss of appetite
- Schizophrenia
- Conversion disorder
- Occult carcinoma, lymphoma
- Endocrine disorders: Addison's disease, diabetes mellitus, hypothyroidism or hyperthyroidism, panhypopituitarism
- GI disorders: celiac disease, Crohn's disease, intestinal parasitosis
- Infectious disorders: AIDS, TB
- A clinical algorithm for the evaluation of anorexia is described in Section III

WORKUP

- A diagnosis can be made using the following DSM-IV diagnostic criteria for anorexia nervosa:
  1. Refusal to maintain body weight (BW) at or above a minimally normal weight for age and height (e.g., weight loss leading to maintenance of BW <85% of that expected or failure to make expected weight gain during a period of growth, leading to BW <85% of that expected)
  2. Intense fear of gaining weight or becoming fat, even though underweight
  3. Disturbance in the way in which BW or shape is experienced, undue influence of BW or shape on self-evaluation, or denial of the seriousness of the current low BW
  4. In postmenarchal females, amenorrhea, that is, the absence of at least three consecutive menstrual cycles (A woman is considered to have amenorrhea if her periods occur only following hormone, [e.g., estrogen] administration.)

Specify type:

Restricting type: During the current episode of anorexia nervosa, the person has not regularly engaged in binge-eating or purging behavior (i.e., self-induced vomiting or the misuse of laxatives, diuretics, or enemas).

Binge-eating/purging type: During the current episode of anorexia nervosa, the person has regularly engaged in binge-eating or purging behavior (i.e., self-induced vomiting or the misuse of laxatives, diuretics, or enemas).

- The SCOFF questionnaire is a useful screening tool used in England for eating disorders. It consists of the following five questions:
  1. Do you make yourself *S*ick because you feel full?
  2. Have you lost *C*ontrol over how much you eat?
  3. Have you lost more than *O*ne stone (about 6 kg) recently?
  4. Do you believe yourself to be *F*at when others say you are thin?
  5. Does *F*ood dominate your life?
- A positive response to two or more questions has a reported sensitivity of 100% for anorexia and bulimia, and an overall specificity of 87.5%.
- In college-aged females a positive response to any of the following screening questions also warrants further evaluation:
  1. How many diets have you been on in the past year?
  2. Do you think you should be dieting?
  3. Are you dissatisfied with your body size?
  4. Does your weight affect the way you think about yourself?
- Baseline ECG should be performed on all patients with anorexia nervosa. Routine monitoring of patients with prolonged QT interval is necessary; sudden death in these patients is often caused by ventricular arrhythmias related to QT interval prolongation.
- A DEXA scan to screen for osteopenia should be considered after 6 months of amenorrhea in patients suspected of anorexia nervosa.

LABORATORY TESTS

- In mild cases, laboratory findings might be completely normal.
- Endocrine abnormalities:
  1. Decreased FSH, LH, T_4, T_3, estrogens, urinary 17-OH steroids, estrone, and estradiol
  2. Normal free T_4, TSH
  3. Increased cortisol, GH, rT_3, T_3RU
  4. Absence of cyclic surge of LH
- Leukopenia, thrombocytopenia, anemia, reduced ESR, reduced complement levels, and reduced CD4 and CD8 cells may be present.
- Metabolic alkalosis, hypocalcemia, hypokalemia, hypomagnesemia, hypercholesterolemia, and hypophosphatemia may be present.
- Increased plasma β-carotene levels are useful to distinguish these patients from others on starvation diets.

TREATMENT

NONPHARMACOLOGIC THERAPY

- A multidisciplinary approach with psychologic, medical, and nutritional support is necessary.
- A goal weight should be set and the patient should be initially monitored at least once a week in the office setting. The target weight is 100% of ideal BW for teenagers and 90% to 100% for older patients.
- Weight gain should be gradual (1 to 3 lb/wk) to prevent gastric dilation. Begin with 800 to 1200 kcal in frequent small meals (to avoid bloating sensation), then increase calories to 1500 to 3000 depending on height and age.
- Add, as necessary, vitamin and mineral supplements
- In severe cases, total parenteral nutrition must be used (starting at 800 to 1200 kcal/day)
- Electrolyte levels should be strictly monitored.
- Mealtime should be a time for social interaction, not confrontation.
- Postprandially, sedentary activities are recommended. The patient's access to a bathroom should be monitored to prevent purging.

ACUTE GENERAL Rx

- Criteria to decide on the appropriate initial course of treatment for patients with anorexia nervosa are usually based on the presence of complications, percentage of ideal body weight, and severity of body image distortion.
- Outpatient treatment is adequate for most patients.
- Indications for hospitalization are described in the "Referral" section.
- Medically stable patients who are within 85% of ideal body weight can be followed up by the primary care physician at 3- or 4-wk intervals, which can be lengthened as the patient improves.
- Pharmacologic treatment generally has no role in anorexia nervosa unless major depression or another psychiatric disorder is present. SSRIs can be used to alleviate the depressed mood and moderate obsessive-compulsive behavior in some individuals.

CHRONIC Rx

- Psychotherapy continued for years and focused specifically on self-image, family and peer interactions, and relapse prevention is an integral part of a successful recovery.
- Family therapy is also recommended, especially in younger patients.

DISPOSITION

- The long-term prognosis is generally poor and marked by recurrent exacerbations. The percentage of patients with anorexia nervosa who fully recover is modest. Most patients continue to suffer from a distorted body image, disordered eating habits, and psychic difficulties.
- Most patients with anorexia nervosa will recover menses within 6 months of reaching 90% of their ideal body weight. It is important to note that patients with anorexia nervosa can become pregnant despite amenorrhea.
- Mortality rates vary from 5% to 20% and are six times that of peers without anorexia. Frequent causes of death are electrolyte abnormalities, starvation, or suicide.
- Factors that predict improved outcome in patients with eating disorders include early age at diagnosis, brief interval before initiation of treatment, good parent-child relationships, and having other healthy relationships wtih friends or therapists.
- A prolonged QT interval is a marker for risk of sudden death.

REFERRAL

Hospitalization should be considered in the following situations:

1. Severe dehydration or electrolyte imbalance
2. ECG abnormalities (prolonged QT interval, arrhythmias)
3. Significant physiologic instability (hypotension, orthostatic changes)
4. Intractable vomiting, purging, or bingeing
5. Patient having suicidal thoughts
6. Weight loss exceeds 30% of ideal BW and is unresponsive to outpatient treatment
7. Rapidly progressing weight loss (>2 lbs in a week)
8. Failure to progress in nutritional rehabilitation in outpatient treatment

SUGGESTED READINGS

American Psychiatric Association: Practice guideline for the treatment of patients with eating disorders, *Am J Psychiatry* 157(suppl):4, 2000 (revision).

Anstine D, Grinenko D: Rapid screening for disordered eating in college-aged females in the primary care setting, *J Adolesc Health* 26:338, 2000.

Becker AE et al: Eating disorders, *N Engl J Med* 340:1092, 1999.

Herzog DB et al: Comorbidity and outcome in eating disorders, *Psychiatr Clin North Am* 19:843, 1996.

Mehler PS: Diagnosis and care of patients with anorexia nervosa in primary care setting, *Ann Intern Med* 134:1048, 2001.

Morgan JF et al: The SCOFF questionnaire: assessment of a new screening tool for eating disorders, *BMJ* 319:1467, 1999.

Pritts SD, Susman J: Diagnosis of eating disorders in primary care, *Am Fam Physician* 67:297, 2003.

AUTHOR: **FRED F. FERRI, M.D.**

BASIC INFORMATION

DEFINITION

Anthrax is an acute infectious disease caused by the spore-forming bacterium *Bacillus anthracis.*

ICD-9CM CODES
0.22.0 Cutaneous anthrax
0.22.1 Inhalation anthrax
0.22.2 Gastrointestinal anthrax
022.3 Sepsis from anthrax

EPIDEMIOLOGY & DEMOGRAPHICS

- Anthrax most commonly occurs in hoofed animals and can only incidentally infect humans who come in contact with infected animals or animal products. Between 20,000 and 100,000 cases of cutaneous anthrax occur worldwide annually. In the U.S. the annual incidence was about 130 cases before 2001.
- Until the recent bioterrorism attack in 2001, most cases of anthrax occurred in industrial environments (contaminated raw materials used in manufacturing process) or in agriculture.
- In 2001 there were more than 20 confirmed cases of anthrax resulting from bioterrorism, most of which were associated with handling of contaminated mail. Inhalation anthrax is the most lethal form of anthrax and results from inspiration of 8000-50,000 spores of *Bacillus anthracis.* Before 2001 there had not been a case of inhalation anthrax in the U.S. for 20 years.
- Direct person-to-person spread of anthrax is extremely unlikely, if it occurs at all; therefore, there is no need to immunize or treat contacts of persons ill with anthrax, such as household contacts, friends, or co-workers, unless they also were exposed to the same source of infection.

PHYSICAL FINDINGS & CLINICAL PRESENTATION

Symptoms of disease vary depending on how the disease was contracted, but usually occur within 7 days after exposure. The serious forms of human anthrax are inhalation anthrax, cutaneous anthrax, and intestinal anthrax.

- **Inhalation anthrax** begins with a brief prodrome resembling a viral respiratory illness followed by development of hypoxia and dyspnea, with radiographic evidence of mediastinal widening. Host factors, dose of exposure, and chemoprophylaxis may affect the duration of the incubation period. Initial symptoms include mild fever, muscle aches, and malaise and may progress to respiratory failure and shock; meningitis often develops.
- **Cutaneous anthrax** is characterized by a skin lesion evolving from a papule, through a vesicular stage, to a depressed black eschar. The incubation period ranges from 1-12 days. The lesion is usually painless, but patients also may have fever, malaise, headache, and regional lymphadenopathy. The eschar dries and falls off in 1-2 wk with little scarring.
- **Gastrointestinal anthrax** is characterized by severe abdominal pain followed by fever and signs of septicemia. Bloody diarrhea and signs of acute abdomen may occur. This form of anthrax usually follows after eating raw or undercooked contaminated meat and can have an incubation period of 1-7 days. Gastric ulcers may occur and may be associated with hematemesis. An oropharyngeal and an abdominal form of the disease have been described. Involvement of the pharynx is usually characterized by lesions at the base of the tongue, dysphagia, fever, and regional lymphadenopathy. Lower bowel inflammation typically causes nausea, loss of appetite, and fever followed by abdominal pain, hematemesis, and bloody diarrhea.

ETIOLOGY

The disease is caused by *Bacillus anthracis,* a gram-positive, spore-forming bacillus. It is aerobic, nonmotile, nonhemolytic on sheep's blood agar, and grows readily at temperature of 37° C, forming large colonies with irregularly tapered outgrowths (a Medusa's head appearance). In the host it appears as single organisms or chains of two or three bacilli.

DIAGNOSIS

DIFFERENTIAL DIAGNOSIS

- Inhalation anthrax must be distinguished from influenza-like illness (ILI) and tularemia. Most cases of ILI are associated with nasal congestion and rhinorrhea, which are unusual in inhalation anthrax. Additional distinguishing factors are the usual absence of abnormal chest x-ray in ILI (see below).
- Cutaneous anthrax should be distinguished from staphylococcal disease, ecthyma, ecthyma gangrenosum, plague, brown recluse spider bite, and tularemia.
- The differential diagnosis of gastrointestinal anthrax includes viral gastroenteritis, shigellosis, and yersiniosis.

LABORATORY TESTS

- Presumptive identification is based on Gram stain of material from skin lesion, CSF, or blood showing encapsulated gram-positive bacilli.
- Confirmatory tests are performed at specialized labs. Virulent strains grow on nutrient agar in the presence of 5% CO_2. Susceptibility to lysis by gamma phage or DFA staining of cell-wall polysaccharide antigen are also useful confirmatory tests.
- Nasal swab culture to determine inhalation exposure is of limited diagnostic value. A negative result does not exclude the possibility of exposure. It may be used by public health officials to assist in epidemiologic investigations of exposed persons to evaluate the dispersion of spores.
- Serologic testing by enzyme-linked immunosorbent assay (ELISA) can confirm the diagnosis.
- A skin test (Anthracin Test) that detects anthrax cell-mediated immunity is also available in specialized labs.

IMAGING STUDIES

Chest x-ray usually reveals mediastinal widening. Additional findings include infiltrates and pleural effusion.

TREATMENT

NONPHARMACOLOGIC THERAPY

IV hydration and ventilator support may be necessary in inhalation anthrax

ACUTE GENERAL THERAPY

- Most naturally occurring *B. anthracis* strains are sensitive to penicillin. The FDA has approved penicillin, doxycycline, and ciprofloxacin for the treatment of inhalational anthrax infection.
- Table 1-8 describes a treatment protocol for inhalation anthrax.
- Initial postexposure prophylaxis therapy in adults is with ciprofloxacin, 500 mg PO bid or doxycycline 100 mg bid. The total duration of treatment is 60 days.

CHRONIC Rx

None

DISPOSITION

- Case fatality estimates for inhalation anthrax are extremely high (>90%).
- The case fatality rate for cutaneous anthrax is 20% without and <1% with antibiotic treatment.
- The case fatality rate for gastrointestinal anthrax is estimated to be 25% to 60%.

REFERRAL

Consultation with an infectious disease specialist is recommended in all cases of anthrax. Local state authorities should also be notified of suspected cases of anthrax.

PEARLS & CONSIDERATIONS

COMMENTS

- Postexposure prophylaxis: If the exposure to *B. anthracis* is confirmed and anthrax vaccine is available, 3 doses of the vaccine should be given at 0, 2, and 4 wk, and antibiotics should be continued throughout the 4-wk period. If vaccine is not available, antibiotics should be continued for 60 days.
- Preexposure vaccination is limited to groups at risk for repeated exposures to *B. anthracis* spores, such as bioterrorism level-B laboratories and workers who will be making repeated entries into known *B. anthracis* spore-contaminated areas.
- The U.S. anthrax vaccine is an inactivated cellfree product licensed to be given in a 6-dose series.

SUGGESTED READINGS

Inglesby TV et al: Anthrax as a biological weapon, 2002, *JAMA* 287:2236, 2002.

Hupert N et al: Accuracy of screening for inhalational anthrax after a bioterrorist attack, *Ann Intern Med* 139:337, 2003.

Interim guidelines for investigation of and response to *Bacillus anthracis* exposures, *MMWR* 50:987, 2001.

Post-exposure anthrax prophylaxis, *Med Lett Drugs Ther* 43:91, 2001.

Swartz MN: Recognition and management of anthrax: an update, *N Engl J Med* 345:1621, 2001.

Use of anthrax vaccine for pre-exposure vaccination, *MMWR Morb Mortal Wkly Rep* 51:1024, 2002.

AUTHOR: **FRED F. FERRI, M.D.**

TABLE 1-8 Inhalation Anthrax Treatment Protocol[a,b]

Category	Initial therapy (intravenous)[c,d]	Duration
Adults	Ciprofloxacin 400 mg every 12 hr[a] **or** Doxycycline 100 mg every 12 hr[f] **and** One or two additional antimicrobials[d]	IV treatment initially.[e] Switch to oral antimicrobial therapy when clinically appropriate: Ciprofloxacin 500 mg PO bid **or** Doxycycline 100 mg PO bid Continue for 60 days (IV and PO combined)[g]
Children	Ciprofloxacin 10-15 mg/kg every 12 hr[h,i] **or** Doxycyclinef,j: >8 yr and >45 kg: 100 mg every 12 hr >8 yr and ≤45 kg: 2.2 mg/kg every 12 hr ≤8 yr: 2.2 mg/kg every 12 hr **and** One or two additional antimicrobials[d]	IV treatment initially.[e] Switch to oral antimicrobial therapy when clinically appropriate: Ciprofloxacin 10-15 mg/kg PO every 12 hr[i] **or** Doxycyclinej: >8 yr and >45 kg: 100 mg PO bid >8 yr and ≤45 kg: 2.2 mg/kg PO bid ≤8 yr: 2.2 mg/kg PO bid Continue for 60 days (IV and PO combined)[g]
Pregnant women[k]	Same for nonpregnant adults (the high death rate from the infection outweighs the risk posed by the antimicrobial agent)	IV treatment initially. Switch to oral antimicrobial therapy when clinically appropriate.[b] Oral therapy regimens same for nonpregnant adults
Immunocompromised persons	Same for nonimmunocompromised persons and children	Same for nonimmunocompromised persons and children

MMRW 5:987, 2001.

[a]For gastrointestinal and oropharyngeal anthrax, use regimens recommended for inhalational anthrax.

[b]Ciprofloxacin or doxycycline should be considered an essential part of first-line therapy for inhalational anthrax.

[c]Steroids may be considered as an adjunct therapy for patients with severe edema and for meningitis based on experience with bacterial meningitis of other etiologies.

[d]Other agents with in vitro activity include rifampin, vancomycin, penicillin, ampicillin, chloramphenicol, imipenem, clindamycin, and clarithromycin. Because of concerns of constitutive and inducible beta-lactamases in *Bacillus anthracis*, penicillin and ampicillin should not be used alone. Consultation with an infectious disease specialist is advised.

[e]Initial therapy may be altered based on clinical course of the patient; one or two antimicrobial agents (e.g., ciprofloxacin or doxycycline) may be adequate as the patient improves.

[f]If meningitis is suspected, doxycycline may be less optimal because of poor central nervous system penetration.

[g]Because of the potential persistence of spores after an aerosol exposure, antimicrobial therapy should be continued for 60 days.

[h]If intravenous ciprofloxacin is not available, oral ciprofloxacin may be acceptable because it is rapidly and well absorbed from the gastrointestinal tract with no substantial loss by first-pass metabolism. Maximum serum concentrations are attained 1-2 hours after oral dosing but may not be achieved if vomiting or ileus are present.

[i]In children, ciprofloxacin dosage should not exceed 1 g/day.

[j]The American Academy of Pediatrics recommends treatment of young children with tetracyclines for serious infections (e.g., Rocky Mountain spotted fever).

[k]Although tetracyclines are not recommended during pregnancy, their use may be indicated for life-threatening illness. Adverse effects on developing teeth and bones are dose related; therefore, doxycycline might be used for a short time (7-14 days) before 6 months of gestation.

Antiphospholipid Antibody Syndrome

BASIC INFORMATION

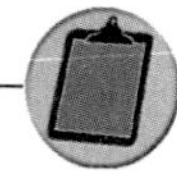

DEFINITION

The antiphospholipid antibody syndrome (APS) is characterized by arterial or venous thrombosis and/or pregnancy loss AND the presence of antiphospholipid antibodies (aPL). APL are antibodies directed against either phospholipids or proteins bound to anionic phospholipids. Four types of aPL have been characterized:

- False-positive serologic tests for syphilis
- Lupus anticoagulants
- Anticardiolipin antibodies
- Anti-β2 glycoprotein-1 antibodies

The syndrome is referred to as primary APS when it occurs alone and as secondary APS when in association with SLE, other rheumatic disorders, or certain infections or medications. APS can affect all organ systems and includes venous and arterial thrombosis, recurrent fetal losses, and thrombocytopenia.

ICD-9CM CODES
795.79 Antiphospholipid antibody syndrome

EPIDEMIOLOGY & DEMOGRAPHICS

- 1% to 5% of healthy subjects have anticardiolipin and lupus anticoagulant antibodies.
- 12% to 30% of patients with systemic lupus erythematosus have anticardiolipin antibodies and 15% to 34% have lupus anticoagulant antibodies.
- Some APS-positive families exist, and HLA studies have suggested associations with HLA DR7, DR4, and Dqw7 plus Drw53.
- Other risk factors: underlying SLE and collagen-vascular diseases; other autoimmune disorders including rheumatoid arthritis, Sjögren's syndrome, Behçet's syndrome, and ITP; drug-induced; and AIDS.
- Most individuals are otherwise healthy and have no underlying medical condition.
- Several studies assessing presence of aPL in patients with cardiovascular and cerebrovascular disease have found a higher than expected prevalence of antibody.

PHYSICAL FINDINGS & CLINICAL PRESENTATION

Associated conditions and effects on various systems of APS include:

- **Thrombosis:** patients with APS are at risk for both venous and arterial thromboses, although venous thromboses are more common, occurring as the initial manifestation of APS in approximately 30% of APS patients. Of all patients with venous thrombosis, 5% to 20% have aPL. The most common site for deep vein thrombosis is the calf, but thromboses may also occur in the renal, hepatic, axillary, subclavian, vena cava, and retinal veins. The most common site of arterial thrombosis is the cerebral vessels. Other common sites are the coronary, renal, mesenteric arteries, and arterial bypass. Recurrent thrombosis is common with APS
- **Central Nervous System:** stroke, TIA, migraine, multiinfarct dementia, epilepsy, movement disorders, transverse myelopathy, depression, and Guillain-Barré syndrome
- **Pulmonary:** pulmonary embolism and infarction, pulmonary HTN, ARDS, intraalveolar pulmonary hemorrhage, a postpartum syndrome characterized by fever, pleuritic chest pain, dyspnea, and patchy infiltrates with pleural effusion on CXR
- **Cardiology:** Libman-Sacks endocarditis, intracardiac thrombosis, CAD, MI
- **Gastrointestinal:** abd pain, GI bleed secondary to ischemia, splenic or pancreatic infarction, hepatic vein thrombosis, Budd-Chiari syndrome (second most common cause of BCS)
- **Renal:** proteinuria, acute renal failure, HTN, renal infarct, renal artery or vein thrombosis, postpartum hemolytic-uremic syndrome
- **Hematology:** thrombocytopenia, hemolytic anemia
- **Endocrine:** Addison's disease secondary to adrenal hemorrhage and less frequently thrombosis
- **Cutaneous:** livedo reticularis, cutaneous necrosis, skin ulcerations, gangrene of digits
- **Obstetrics:** recurrent spontaneous abortion (secondary to placental vessel thrombosis and ischemia)
- **Catastrophic APS:** widespread thrombotic disease with visceral damage

ETIOLOGY

- APL react with negatively charged phospholipids
- Range of possible mechanisms of thrombosis includes effects of aPL on platelet membranes, endothelial cells, and clotting components such as prothrombin, protein C or S
- Recently shown that prephospholipids are not immunogenic and that a binding protein (β_2-glycoprotein I) may be the key immunogen in the APS

DIAGNOSIS

Diagnostic criteria of APS include at least one clinical criterion and at least one laboratory criterion:

- *Clinical:*
  1. venous, arterial, or small vessel thrombosis OR
  2. morbidity with pregnancy defined as
  - fetal death at >10 wks gestation OR
  - premature births before 34 wks gestation secondary to eclampsia, preeclampsia, or severe placental insufficiency OR
  - three or more unexplained consecutive spontaneous abortions at <10 wks gestation
- *Laboratory:*
  1. IgG and/or IgM anticardiolipin antibody in medium or high titers OR
  2. lupus anticoagulant activity found on two or more occasions, at least 6 wk apart

DIFFERENTIAL DIAGNOSIS

- Other hypercoagulable states (inherited or acquired)
- Inherited: ATIII, protein C, S deficiencies, Factor V Leiden, prothrombin gene mutation
- Acquired: heparin-induced thrombopathy, myeloproliferative syndromes, cancer, hyperviscosity
- Homocysteinemia
- Nephrotic syndrome

WORKUP

History of thrombosis and/or pregnancy loss and laboratory testing

LABORATORY TESTS

Laboratory testing indicated in:

- Patient with underlying SLE or collagen-vascular disease with thrombosis
- Patient with recurrent, familial, or juvenile DVT or thrombosis in an unusual location (mesenteric or cerebral)
- Possibly in patients with lupus or lupuslike disorders in high-risk situations (e.g., surgery, prolonged immobilization, pregnancy)

Abnormal tests include:

- False-positive test for syphilis (RPR/VDRL)
- Lupus anticoagulant activity, demonstrated by prolongation of apTT that does not correct with 1:1 mixing study
- Presence of anticardiolipin antibodies (ELISA for anticardiolipin is most sensitive and specific test [>80%])
- Presence of anti β_2-glycoprotein I antibody

PROGNOSIS

Limited data on natural history in untreated patients. APS patients are at risk for recurrent thrombosis. Initial arterial thrombosis tends to be followed by arterial events and initial venous thrombosis tends to be followed by venous events. Catastrophic APS is associated with a high mortality rate, approaching 50%. Incidence of developing catastrophic APS is approximately 0.8% among APS patients.

TREATMENT

ACUTE GENERAL Rx

- Treatment of APS: Positive aPL and major thrombotic events or recurrent thrombotic events:
  - Initial anticoagulation with heparin, then lifelong warfarin treatment, INR 3-4
  - One prospective analysis of 147 patients (Khamashta MA et al, 1995) comparing intermediate-to-high intensity warfarin therapy (INR>3.0) to low-intensity warfarin (INR<3.0) to aspirin demonstrated that:
    - Aspirin alone appears to be of no benefit for the thrombotic manifestations of APS.
    - Low-intensity warfarin (INR<3.0), with or without low-dose aspirin, reduced the rate of thrombosis from 30%/yr to 23%/yr.
    - High-intensity warfarin (INR>3.0) reduced the risk of thrombosis from 30%/yr to 1.3%/yr.
  - A recent randomized, double blind trial (Crowther et al., 2003) of 114 APS patients who were randomized to receive warfarin therapy to achieve an INR 2.0-3.0 vs. an INR of 3.0-4.0 demonstrated:
    - No difference in thrombosis rate or bleeding events and therefore moderate-intensity warfarin may be appropriate for patients with APS
- Prophylaxis for (+) aPL: Asymptomatic patients with abnormal laboratory results, no previous thrombosis:
  - Questionable whether ASA (81 mg) is effective
  - No routine prophylaxis
  - Antithrombotic prophylaxis for major surgery, prolonged immobilization, and pregnancy
  - Avoid oral contraceptive pills in women with (+) aPL

Pregnant women:

- Who are positive for aPL antibodies, without history of nonplacental thrombotic event (e.g., DVT) or positive for aPL antibodies with history of <3 spontaneous abortions:
  - ASA, 81 mg at conception and SQ heparin 10,000 IU q12h at time of documented viable intrauterine pregnancy (approximately 7 wk gestation).
  - A mid-interval PTT should be checked and should be normal or similar to baseline before therapy.
- Who carry a diagnosis of APS and who should already be chronically anticoagulated:
  - Warfarin should be discontinued secondary to its teratogenic effects
  - ASA, 81 mg and heparin SQ to PTT of 1.5 to 2 × control value
  - IVIG and prednisone have also been used with success if aspirin and heparin fail.

CHRONIC Rx

Cerebral features of lupus may be more related to thrombosis than inflammation and may respond better to anticoagulants than immunosuppression.

SUGGESTED READINGS

Crowther MA et al: A comparison of two intensities of warfarin for the prevention of recurrent thrombosis in patients with the antiphospholipid antibody syndrome, *N Engl J Med* 359(12):1133, 2003.

Khamashta MA et al: The management of thrombosis in the antiphospholipid-antibody syndrome, *N Engl J Med* 332(15):993, 1995.

Levine JS et al: The antiphospholipid syndrome, *N Engl J Med* 346:752, 2002.

Ruiz-Irastorza G et al: Bleeding and recurrent thrombosis in definite antiphospholipid syndrome, *Arch Intern Med* 162:1164, 2002.

AUTHOR: **IRIS TONG, M.D.**

Anxiety (Generalized Anxiety Disorder) (PTG)

BASIC INFORMATION

DEFINITION

GAD is most likely to present in combination with other psychiatric and medical conditions. GAD commonly presents with excessive anxiety, fear, and worry for most of the time, continuously for at least 6 mo. The subjective anxiety must be accompanied by at least three somatic symptoms (e.g., restlessness, irritability, sleep disturbance, muscle tension, difficulty concentrating, or fatigability). Because worry is also a symptom of depression, officially, GAD is not present if there is a concurrent Major Depression. However, the field is recognizing that the two conditions can coexist, and research on the commonalities are being conducted.

SYNONYMS

Anxiety neurosis
Chronic anxiety
GAD

ICD-9CM CODES
F41.1 (DSM-IV Code 300.02)

EPIDEMIOLOGY & DEMOGRAPHICS

INCIDENCE (IN U.S.): 31% in 1 yr

PREVALENCE (IN U.S.):
- In general population: prevalence of 5% lifetime
- In primary care setting: 3% (It is the most common anxiety disorder in this setting.)

PREDOMINANT SEX: Females are more frequently affected (2:1 ratio), but they present for treatment less frequently (3:2 female:male).

PREDOMINANT AGE:
- 30% of patients report onset of symptoms before age 11 yr.
- 50% of patients have onset before age 18 yr.

PEAK INCIDENCE: Chronic condition with onset in early life

GENETICS: Concordance rates in dizygotic twins and monozygotic twins are not different (0% to 5%), but detailed analysis of 1033 female twin pairs finds that heredity contributes about 30% of the factors that may cause GAD.

PHYSICAL FINDINGS & CLINICAL PRESENTATION

- Report of being "anxious" all of their lives
- Excessive worry, usually regarding family, finances, work, or health
- Sleep disturbance, particularly early insomnia
- Muscle tension (typically in the muscles of neck and shoulders)
- Headaches (muscle tension)
- Difficulty concentrating
- Day form of fatigue
- Gastrointestinal symptoms compatible with IBD (one third of patients)
- Physical consequences of anxiety are the driving force for patients seeking medical attention
- Comorbid psychiatric illness (e.g., dysthymia or major depression) and substance abuse (e.g., alcohol abuse) are frequent

ETIOLOGY

- There is no clear etiology.
- Several hypotheses centering on neurotransmitter (catecholamines, indolamines) and developmental psychology are used as framework for treatment recommendations.
- Risk factors include a family history, increase in stress, history of physical or emotional trauma and medical illness.

DIAGNOSIS

DIFFERENTIAL DIAGNOSIS

- Wide range of psychiatric and medical conditions; however, for a diagnosis of GAD to be made a person must experience anxiety with coexisting physical symptoms the majority of the time continuously for at least 6 mo
- Cardiovascular and pulmonary disease
- Hyperthyroidism
- Parkinson's disease
- Myasthenia gravis
- Consequence of recreational drug use (e.g., cocaine, amphetamine, and PCP) or withdrawal (e.g., alcohol or benzodiazepines)

WORKUP

- History: required for diagnosis
- Physical examination: confirm the patient's physical complaints
- Exclusion of organic basis for the complaints possibly requiring additional workup
- Physical cause should be suspected if anxiety follows recent changes in medication

TREATMENT

NONPHARMACOLOGIC THERAPY

- Cognitive-behavioral therapy
- Relaxation training
- Biofeedback
- Psychodynamic psychotherapy

NOTE: Studies directly comparing medications with psychotherapy are not available, but the general clinical impression is that the psychotherapies are probably superior to pharmacotherapies.

ACUTE GENERAL Rx

- Acute treatment is rarely indicated because GAD is a chronic condition.
- Occasionally, patients are in acute distress, requiring physician to respond quickly; benzodiazepines are given under these conditions as drug of choice for both daytime anxiety and initial insomnia.

NOTE: Caution should be taken in prescribing benzodiazepines because of the propensity for misuse and dependence in this population. If provided, the patient should be educated about the use of other medications and the risks in using benzodiazepines.

CHRONIC Rx

- SSRIs and venlafaxine are also effective in generalized anxiety disorders and are typically given as a first line treatment. These are particularly useful if comorbid depression is present.
- If used and prescribed with supervision, benzodiazepines can provide long-term symptom control with only occasional problems with tolerance or abuse; however, tolerance to benzodiazepines is common and for this reason they have fallen from a first line treatment to second line treatment for GAD. Further, the rate of relapse after discontinuation of benzodiazepines may be twice the rate after discontinuation of the available nonbenzodiazepine anxiolytic buspirone.
- Buspirone is effective without any potential for tolerance or abuse.
- Sedating antidepressants are also useful in ameliorating initial insomnia.

DISPOSITION

- This condition is chronic with periodic exacerbations.
- Treatment is given to provide a significant degree of improvement, but symptoms and dysfunction may persist.
- The risk for suicide is higher than general population.

REFERRAL

- If the symptoms are refractory to treatment
- If the case is complicated with a comorbid psychiatric condition
- If treatment response is suboptimal with residual dysfunction

SUGGESTED READINGS

Fricchione G: Clinical practice. Generalized anxiety disorder, *N Engl J Med* 351(7):675, 2004.

Goodman WK: Selecting pharmacotherapy for generalized anxiety disorder, *J Clin Psychiatry* 65(suppl 13):8, 2004.

Lang AJ: Treating generalized anxiety disorder with cognitive-behavioral therapy, *J Clin Psychiatry* 65(suppl 13):14, 2004.

Rouillon F: Long term therapy of generalized anxiety disorder, *Eur Psychiatry* 19(2):96, 2004.

AUTHORS: **PATRICIA AREAN, PH.D.,** and **MITCHELL D. FELDMAN, M.D., M.PHIL.**

BASIC INFORMATION

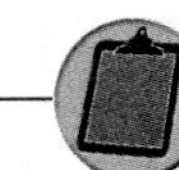

DEFINITION

Aortic dissection occurs when an intimal tear allows blood to dissect between medial layers of the aorta.

ICD-9CM CODES
441.00 Aortic dissection
444.01 Aortic dissection, thoracic

SYNONYMS

Dissecting aortic aneurysm, unspecified site

EPIDEMIOLOGY & DEMOGRAPHICS

PREDOMINANT SEX: Males > females
PEAK INCIDENCE: Ages 60 to 80
RISK FACTORS: Hypertension, atherosclerosis, and family history of aortic aneurysms. Others include inflammatory diseases that cause a vasculitis, disorders of collagen (Marfan syndrome, Ehlers-Danlos syndrome), bicuspid aortic valve, aortic coarctation, Turner's syndrome, crack cocaine, and trauma.

CLASSIFICATION

Based on the fact that the majority of aortic dissections originate in the ascending or descending aorta, three major classifications (Fig. 1-23):

- DeBakey type I ascending and descending aorta, II ascending aorta, III descending aorta
- Stanford type A ascending aorta (proximal), type B descending aorta (distal)

PHYSICAL FINDINGS & CLINICAL PRESENTATION

- Sudden onset of very severe chest pain, at its peak at onset
- Little radiation to neck, shoulder, or arm
- Sharp, tearing or ripping pain
- Ascending aortic dissection with anterior chest pain
- Descending aortic dissection with back pain
- Syncope, abdominal pain, CHF, malperfusion may occur
- Most with severe hypertension, 25% with hypotension (SBP <100), which can indicate bleeding, cardiac tamponade, or severe aortic regurgitation
- Pulse and blood pressure differentials common (38%) caused by partial compression of subclavian arteries
- Cardiac and neurological systems are most commonly involved organ systems
- Aortic regurgitation in 18% to 50% of cases of proximal dissection
- Myocardial ischemia caused by coronary artery compression
- Cerebral ischemia/stroke in 5% to 10% of patients

ETIOLOGY

- Unknown, risk factors known. Chronic HTN affects arterial wall composition
- Medial degeneration of aorta appears to be the culprit
- Aortic dissection reflects systemic illness of vasculature

DIAGNOSIS

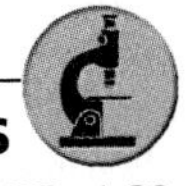

DIFFERENTIAL DIAGNOSIS

- Known as the great imitator: PE, ACS, AS, pericarditis, cholecystitis
- Acute MI needs to be ruled out
- Aortic insufficiency
- Nondissecting aortic aneurysm

LABORATORY TESTS

ECG: Helpful to rule out MI, generally nonspecific findings.
Serum biochemical marker: Smooth muscle myosin heavy chain high first 6 hr after onset.

IMAGING STUDIES

- Chest x-ray may show widened mediastinum (62%) nonspecific, and displacement of aortic intimal calcium.
- Transesophageal echocardiography, sensitivity 97% to 100%, can detect aortic insufficiency and pericardial effusion; study of choice in unstable patients, but operator dependent.
- MRI, sensitivity 90% to 100%, gold standard, but length of test and difficult access not suitable for stable intubated patients. Gives best information for surgeons.
- CT, sensitivity 83% to 100%, involves IV contrast.
- Aortography rarely done now.
- Transthoracic echocardiography, poor sensitivity.

TREATMENT

ACUTE GENERAL Rx

- Admit to ICU for hemodynamic monitoring.
- Propanolol 1 mg every 3-5 minutes or metoprolol 5 mg IV every 5 minutes, followed by Nitroprusside 0.3-10 mg/kg/min, with target SBP 100-120.
- Decrease contractility and BP with IV β-blocker, β-blocker is cornerstone of treatment.
- IV Labetalol can be used instead, 20 mg IV, then 40-80 mg every 10 min.
- IV calcium channel blockers or ACE inhibitors may be used.
- Proximal dissections require emergent surgery. (Type I, II, + A) to prevent rupture or pericardial effusion.
- Distal dissections are treated only medically unless distal organ involvement or impending rupture occurs (Type III + B).
- Endovascular stent placement is a new treatment, especially for older high-risk surgical patients.

CHRONIC Rx

Chronic aortic dissection (>2 wks) followed with aggressive BP control

DISPOSITION

- Natural history of untreated aortic dissection is 85% mortality within 2 wk.
- Proximal aortic dissection is a surgical emergency. Time is critical; mortality is 1% to 3% per hr.
- Patients who are postsurgical repair or have chronic aneurysm should be followed with imaging at 1, 3, 6, 9, and 12 months.
- Overall, in-hospital mortality is 30% in patients with proximal dissections and 10% in patients with distal dissections.

REFERRAL

For ICU management and surgery

SUGGESTED READINGS

Hagan PG et al: The international registry of acute aortic dissection: new insights into an old disease, *JAMA* 283:897, 2000.
Khan IA et al: Clinical, diagnostic, and management perspectives of aortic dissection, *Chest* 122(1):311, 2002.
Moore AG et al: Choice of CT, TEE, MRI and aortography in acute AD: IRAD, *Am J Cardiology* 89:1235, 2002.
Nienaber CA: Aortic dissection: New frontiers in diagnosis and management, Part I and II, *Circulation,* 108(6):772, 2003.

AUTHOR: **LYNN BOWLBY, M.D.**

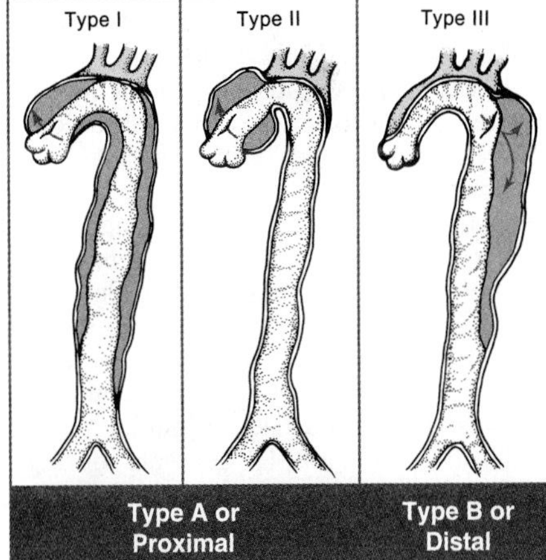

FIGURE 1-23 Classification systems for aortic dissection. (From Isselbacher EM, Eagle KA, DeSanctis RW: Disease of the aorta. In Braunwald E [ed]: *Heart disease: a textbook of cardiovascular medicine,* ed 5, Philadelphia, 1997, WB Saunders.)

BASIC INFORMATION

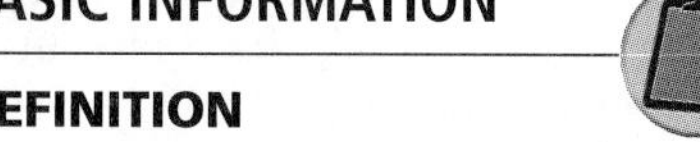

DEFINITION

Aortic regurgitation is retrograde blood flow into the left ventricle from the aorta secondary to incompetent aortic valve.

SYNONYMS

Aortic insufficiency
AI
AR

ICD-9CM CODES
424.1 Aortic valve disorders

EPIDEMIOLOGY & DEMOGRAPHICS

- The most common cause of isolated severe aortic regurgitation is aortic root dilation.
- Infectious endocarditis is the most frequent cause of acute aortic regurgitation.

PHYSICAL FINDINGS & CLINICAL PRESENTATION

The clinical presentation varies depending on whether aortic insufficiency is acute or chronic. Chronic aortic insufficiency is well tolerated (except when secondary to infective endocarditis), and the patients remain asymptomatic for years. Common manifestations after significant deterioration of left ventricular function are dyspnea on exertion, syncope, chest pain, and CHF. Acute aortic insufficiency manifests primarily with hypotension caused by a sudden fall in cardiac output. A rapid rise in left ventricular diastolic pressure results in a further decrease in coronary blood flow.

Physical findings in chronic aortic insufficiency include the following:

- Widened pulse pressure (markedly increased systolic blood pressure, decreased diastolic blood pressure) is present.
- Bounding pulses, head "bobbing" with each systole (de Musset's sign) are present; "water hammer" or collapsing pulse (Corrigan's pulse) can be palpated at the wrist or on the femoral arteries ("pistol shot" femorals) and is caused by rapid rise and sudden collapse of the arterial pressure during late systole; capillary pulsations (Quincke's pulse) may occur at the base of the nail beds.
- A to-and-fro "double Duroziez" murmur may be heard over femoral arteries with slight compression.
- Popliteal systolic pressure is increased over brachial systolic pressure ≥40 mm Hg (Hill's sign).
- Cardiac auscultation reveals:
  1. Displacement of cardiac impulse downward and to the patient's left
  2. S_3 heard over the apex
  3. Decrescendo, blowing diastolic murmur heard along left sternal border
  4. Low-pitched apical diastolic rumble (Austin-Flint murmur) caused by contrast of the aortic regurgitant jet with the left ventricular wall
  5. Early systolic apical ejection murmur

In patients with acute aortic insufficiency both the wide pulse pressure and the large stroke volume are absent. A short blowing diastolic murmur may be the only finding on physical examination.

ETIOLOGY

- Infective endocarditis
- Rheumatic fibrosis
- Trauma with valvular rupture
- Congenital bicuspid aortic valve
- Myxomatous degeneration
- Syphilitic aortitis
- Rheumatic spondylitis
- SLE
- Aortic dissection
- Fenfluramine, dexfenfluramine
- Takayasu's arteritis, granulomatous arteritis

DIAGNOSIS

DIFFERENTIAL DIAGNOSIS

- Patent ductus arteriosus, pulmonary regurgitation, and other valvular abnormalities
- The differential diagnosis of cardiac murmurs is described in Section II

WORKUP

- Echocardiogram, chest x-ray, ECG, and cardiac catheterization (selected patients)
- Medical history and physical examination focused on the following clinical manifestations:
  1. Dyspnea on exertion
  2. Syncope
  3. Chest pain
  4. CHF

IMAGING STUDIES

- Chest x-ray
  1. Left ventricular hypertrophy (chronic aortic regurgitation)
  2. Aortic dilation
  3. Normal cardiac silhouette with pulmonary edema: possible in patients with acute aortic regurgitation
- ECG: left ventricular hypertrophy
- Echocardiography: coarse diastolic fluttering of the anterior mitral leaflet; LVH in patients with chronic aortic regurgitation
- Cardiac catheterization: assesses degree of left ventricular dysfunction, confirms the presence of a wide pulse pressure, assesses surgical risk, and determines if there is coexistent coronary artery disease

TREATMENT

NONPHARMACOLOGIC THERAPY

- Avoidance of competitive sports and strenuous activity
- Salt restriction

ACUTE GENERAL Rx

MEDICAL:

- Digitalis, diuretics, ACE inhibitors, and sodium restriction for CHF; nitroprusside in patients with acute aortic regurgitation
- Long-term vasodilator therapy with ACE inhibitors or nifedipine for reducing or delaying the need for aortic valve replacement in asymptomatic patients with severe aortic regurgitation and normal left ventricular function
- Bacterial endocarditis prophylaxis for surgical and dental procedures

SURGICAL: Reserved for:

- Symptomatic patients with chronic aortic regurgitation despite optimal medical therapy
- Patients with acute aortic regurgitation (i.e., infective endocarditis) producing left ventricular failure
- Evidence of systolic failure:
  1. Echocardiographic fractional shortening <25%
  2. Echocardiographic and diastolic dimension >55 mm
  3. Angiographic ejection fraction <50% or end-systolic volume index (ESVI) >60 ml/m2
- Evidence of diastolic failure:
  1. Pulmonary pressure >45 mm Hg systolic
  2. Left ventricular end-diastolic pressure (LVEDP) >15 mm Hg at catheterization
  3. Pulmonary hypertension detected on examination
- In general, the "55 rule" has been used to determine the timing of surgery: surgery should be performed before EF <55% or end-systolic dimension >55 mm.

REFERRAL

Surgical referral (see "Acute General Rx" for indications)

PEARLS & CONSIDERATIONS

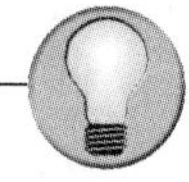

COMMENTS

The operative mortality rate for aortic regurgitation is 3% to 5%.

AUTHOR: **FRED F. FERRI, M.D.**

SECTION I

BASIC INFORMATION

DEFINITION

Aortic stenosis is obstruction to systolic left ventricular outflow across the aortic valve. Symptoms appear when the valve orifice decreases to <1 cm^2 (normal orifice is 3 cm^2). The stenosis is considered severe when the orifice is <0.5 cm^2/m^2 or the pressure gradient is 50 mm Hg or higher.

SYNONYMS

Aortic valvular stenosis
AS

ICD-9CM CODES
424.1 Aortic valvular stenosis

EPIDEMIOLOGY & DEMOGRAPHICS

- Aortic stenosis is the most common valve lesion in adults in Western countries.
- Calcific stenosis (most common cause in patients >60 yr old) occurs in 75% of patients.

PHYSICAL FINDINGS & CLINICAL PRESENTATION

- Rough, loud systolic diamond-shaped murmur, best heard at base of heart and transmitted into neck vessels; often associated with a thrill or ejection click; may also be heard well at the apex
- Absence or diminished intensity of sound of aortic valve closure (in severe aortic stenosis)
- Late, slow-rising carotid upstroke with decreased amplitude
- Strong apical pulse
- Narrowing of pulse pressure in later stages of aortic stenosis
- Some patients with aortic stenosis experience bleeding into their GI tract or skin. This is caused by an acquired defect in von Willebrandt factor. Aortic valve replacement restores normal hemostasis.

ETIOLOGY

- Rheumatic inflammation of aortic valve
- Progressive stenosis of congenital bicuspid valve (found in 1%-2% of population)
- Idiopathic calcification of the aortic valve
- Congenital (major cause of aortic stenosis in patients <30 yr)

DIAGNOSIS

DIFFERENTIAL DIAGNOSIS

- Hypertrophic cardiomyopathy
- Mitral regurgitation
- Ventricular septal defect
- Aortic sclerosis. Aortic stenosis is distinguished from aortic sclerosis by the degree of valve impairment. In aortic sclerosis, the valve leaflets are abnormally thickened but obstruction to outflow is minimal.

WORKUP

- Echocardiography
- Chest x-ray examination, ECG
- Cardiac catheterization in selected patients (see "Imaging Studies")
- Medical history focusing on symptoms and potential complications:
  1. Angina
  2. Syncope (particularly with exertion)
  3. CHF
  4. GI bleeding: in patients with associated hemorrhagic telangiectasia (AVM)

IMAGING STUDIES

- Chest x-ray examination
  1. Poststenotic dilation of the ascending aorta
  2. Calcification of aortic cusps
  3. Pulmonary congestion (in advanced stages of aortic stenosis)
- ECG:
  1. Left ventricular hypertrophy (found in >80% of patients)
  2. ST-T wave changes
  3. Atrial fibrillation: frequent
- Doppler echocardiography: thickening of the left ventricular wall; if the patient has valvular calcifications, multiple echoes may be seen from within the aortic root and there is poor separation of the aortic cusps during systole. Gradient across the valve can be estimated but is less precise than with cardiac catheterization.
- Cardiac catheterization: indicated in symptomatic patients; it confirms the diagnosis and estimates the severity of the disease by measuring the gradient across the valve, allowing calculation of the valve area. It also detects coexisting coronary artery stenosis that may need bypass at the same time as aortic valve replacement.

TREATMENT

NONPHARMACOLOGIC THERAPY

- Strenuous activity should be avoided.
- Sodium restriction if CHF is present.

GENERAL Rx

MEDICAL:

- Diuretics and sodium restriction are needed if CHF is present; digoxin is used only to control rate of atrial fibrillation.
- ACE inhibitors are relatively contraindicated.
- Calcium channel blocker verapamil may be useful only to control rate of atrial fibrillation.
- Antibiotic prophylaxis is necessary for surgical and dental procedures.

SURGICAL:

- Valve replacement is the treatment of choice in symptomatic patients because the 5-yr mortality rate after onset of symptoms is extremely high, even with optimal medical therapy; valve replacement is indicated if cardiac catheterization establishes a pressure gradient >50 mm Hg and valve area <1 cm^2.
- Balloon aortic valvotomy for adult acquired aortic stenosis is useful only for palliation.

DISPOSITION

- 15% to 20% of patients with severe aortic stenosis die before age 20 yr.
- The 5-yr survival rate in adults is 40%.
- The average duration of symptoms before death is as follows: angina, 60 mo; syncope, 36 mo; CHF, 24 mo.
- About 75% of patients with symptomatic aortic stenosis will be dead 3 yr after onset of symptoms unless the aortic valve is replaced.

REFERRAL

- Surgical referral for valve replacement in symptomatic patients. However, the presence of moderate or severe valvular calcification, together with a rapid increase in aortic-jet velocity, identifies patients with a very poor prognosis who should be considered for early valve replacement rather than have surgery delayed until symptoms develop.
- Surgical mortality rate for valve replacement is 3% to 5%; however, it varies with patient's age (>8% in patients >75 yr old).
- Balloon valvuloplasty is useful in infants and children or poor surgical candidates who do not have calcified valve apparatus; it can be done as an intermediate procedure to stabilize high-risk patients before surgery.
- When performed in adults who have calcified valves, balloon valvuloplasty is useful only for short-term reduction in severity of aortic stenosis when surgery is contraindicated, because restenosis occurs rapidly.

SUGGESTED READINGS

Alpert JS: Aortic stenosis, a new face for an old disease, *Arch Intern Med* 163:1769, 2003.

Carabello BA: Aortic stenosis, *N Engl J Med* 346:677, 2002.

Vincentelli A et al: Acquired von Willebrand syndrome in aortic stenosis, *N Engl J Med* 349: 343, 2003.

AUTHOR: **FRED F. FERRI, M.D.**

BASIC INFORMATION

DEFINITION

Appendicitis is the acute inflammation of the appendix.

ICD-9CM CODES
540.9 Appendicitis
540.0 Appendicitis with generalized peritonitis

EPIDEMIOLOGY & DEMOGRAPHICS

- Appendicitis occurs in 10% of the population, most commonly between the ages of 10 and 30 yr.
- More than 250,000 appendectomies are performed in the U.S. each year.
- It is the most common abdominal surgical emergency.
- Incidence of appendicitis has declined over the past 30 yr.
- Male:female ratio is 3:2 until mid-20s; it equalizes after age 30 yr.

PHYSICAL FINDINGS & CLINICAL PRESENTATION

- Abdominal pain: initially the pain may be epigastric or periumbilical in nearly 50% of patients; it subsequently localizes to the RLQ within 12 to 18 hr. Pain can be found in back or right flank if appendix is retrocecal or in other abdominal locations if there is malrotation of the appendix.
- Pain with right thigh extension (psoas sign), low-grade fever: temperature may be >38° C if there is appendiceal perforation.
- Pain with internal rotation of the flexed right thigh (obturator sign) is present.
- RLQ pain on palpation of the LLQ (Rovsing's sign): physical examination may reveal right-sided tenderness in patients with pelvic appendix.
- Point of maximum tenderness is in the RLQ (McBurney's point).
- Nausea, vomiting, tachycardia, cutaneous hyperesthesias at the level of T12 can be present.

ETIOLOGY

Obstruction of the appendiceal lumen with subsequent vascular congestion, inflammation, and edema; common causes of obstruction are:

- Fecaliths: 30% to 35% of cases (most common in adults)
- Foreign body: 4% (fruit seeds, pinworms, tapeworms, roundworms, calculi)
- Inflammation: 50% to 60% of cases (submucosal lymphoid hyperplasia [most common etiology in children, teens])
- Neoplasms: 1% (carcinoids, metastatic disease, carcinoma)

DIAGNOSIS

DIFFERENTIAL DIAGNOSIS

- Intestinal: regional cecal enteritis, incarcerated hernia, cecal diverticulitis, intestinal obstruction, perforated ulcer, perforated cecum, Meckel's diverticulitis
- Reproductive: ectopic pregnancy, ovarian cyst, torsion of ovarian cyst, salpingitis, tuboovarian abscess, Mittelschmerz endometriosis, seminal vesiculitis
- Renal: renal and ureteral calculi, neoplasms, pyelonephritis
- Vascular: leaking aortic aneurysm
- Psoas abscess
- Trauma
- Cholecystitis
- Mesenteric adenitis

WORKUP

- Patients presenting with RLQ pain, nausea, vomiting, anorexia, and RLQ rebound tenderness should undergo prompt clinical and laboratory evaluation. Imaging studies are generally not necessary in typical appendicitis. They are useful when the diagnosis is uncertain. Laparoscopy may be useful as both a diagnostic and a therapeutic modality.

LABORATORY TESTS

- CBC with differential reveals leukocytosis with a left shift in 90% of patients with appendicitis. Total WBC count is generally lower than 20,000/mm^3. Higher counts may be indicative of perforation. Less than 4% have a normal WBC and differential. A low Hgb and Hct in an older patient should raise suspicion for GI tract carcinoma.
- Microscopic hematuria and pyuria may occur in <20% of patients.

IMAGING STUDIES

- Spiral CT of the right lower quadrant of the abdomen has a sensitivity of >90% and an accuracy >94% for acute appendicitis. A distended appendix, periappendiceal inflammation, and a thickened appendiceal wall are indicative of appendicitis.
- Ultrasonography has a sensitivity of 75% to 90% for the diagnosis of acute appendicitis. Ultrasound is useful, especially in younger women when diagnosis is unclear. Normal ultrasonographic findings should not deter surgery if the history and physical examination are indicative of appendicitis.

TREATMENT

NONPHARMACOLOGIC THERAPY

- NPO
- Do not administer analgesics or antibiotics until the diagnosis is made (may mask signs of peritonitis).

ACUTE GENERAL Rx

- Urgent appendectomy (laparoscopic or open), correction of fluid and electrolyte imbalance with vigorous IV hydration and electrolyte replacement
- IV antibiotic prophylaxis to cover gram-negative bacilli and anaerobes (ampicillin-sulbactam [Unasyn] 3 g IV q6h or piperacillin-tazobactam [Zosyn] 4.5 g IV q8h in adults)

PEARLS & CONSIDERATIONS

COMMENTS

- Perforation is common (20% in adult patients). Indicators of perforation are pain lasting >24 hr, leukocytosis >20,000/mm^3, temperature >102° F, palpable abdominal mass, and peritoneal findings.
- In general, prognosis is excellent. Mortality is <1% in young adults without complications; however, it exceeds 10% in elderly patients with ruptured appendix.
- In approximately 20% of patients who undergo exploratory laparatomy because of suspected appendicitis, the appendix is normal.

SUGGESTED READINGS

Paulson EK et al: Suspected appendicitis, *N Engl J Med* 348:236, 2003.

Teresawa T et al: Systematic review: Computed tomography and ultrasonography to detect acute appendicitis in adults and adolescents, *Ann Intern Med* 141:537, 2004.

AUTHOR: **FRED F. FERRI, M.D.**

BASIC INFORMATION

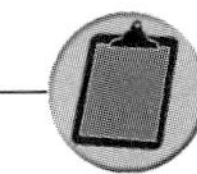

DEFINITION

The prototype of granulomatous arthritis is tuberculous arthritis. Atypical mycobacteria, sarcoidosis, and sporotrichosis can cause granulomatous involvement of the synovium, but these entities are much less common.

SYNONYMS

Tuberculous arthritis
Pott's disease

ICD-9CM CODES
711.40 Arthropathy associated with other bacterial disease
730.88 Other infection involving bone

EPIDEMIOLOGY & DEMOGRAPHICS

INCIDENCE (IN U.S.): Unknown
PREVALENCE (IN U.S.): Unknown
PREDOMINANT SEX: Male = female
PREDOMINANT AGE: Rare in childhood
PEAK INCIDENCE: No seasonal predilection

PHYSICAL FINDINGS

- Often no constitutional symptoms (fever and weight loss)
- Possibly no clinical or radiographic evidence of pulmonary TB
- Spinal infection most often in the thoracic or upper lumbar area, with back pain as the most common symptom
- Considerable local muscle spasm possible
- Kyphosis and neurologic symptoms resulting from spinal cord compression in advanced disease
- Chronic monoarticular arthritis in the peripheral joints
- Single joint involved in 85% of patients
- Pain, swelling, limitation of motion, and joint stiffness less dramatic than in acute bacterial arthritis; possibly present for months to years
- Seen more often in persons from developing countries, elderly patients, and hemodialysis patients

ETIOLOGY

- Hematogenous spread of organisms from a distant site of infection or by direct spread from bone
- Most commonly affected area: 50% of cases in the spine; next most commonly affected area: large joints (knee and hip)
- Primary infection beginning in the lungs and spreading to the highly vascular synovium
- Tuberculous osteomyelitis commonly involving an adjacent joint
- In peripheral joints, a granulomatous reaction in the synovium causing joint effusion and eventual destruction of underlying bone
- In the spine, infection of the intervertebral disk spreading to adjacent vertebrae
- Osteomyelitis of vertebrae causing collapse, kyphosis, or gibbous deformity, and possibly paraspinal "cold" abscess

DIAGNOSIS

DIFFERENTIAL DIAGNOSIS

- Sarcoidosis
- Fungal arthritis
- Metastatic cancer
- Primary or metastatic synovial tumors

WORKUP

- High index of suspicion needed
- Gold standard: synovial biopsy
- Joint aspiration and culture of the synovial fluid performed while awaiting biopsy
- Positive synovial fluid smear for acid-fast bacilli in 20% of cases; positive culture in 80%
- Elevated synovial fluid protein, low glucose
- Considerable variation in synovial fluid WBC count, but values of 10,000 to 20,000 cells/mm^3 typical; may be predominantly polymorphonuclear leukocytes
- Usually positive tuberculin skin test
- Anergy in elderly patients or in advanced disease
- In spinal infections, percutaneous or open biopsy to obtain accurate C&S data

LABORATORY TESTS

Peripheral WBC count and ESR are elevated but nonspecific.

IMAGING STUDIES

- Plain radiographs of the affected joint
  1. Typically demonstrate bony destruction with little new bone formation
  2. Osteopenia and soft tissue swelling in early infections
  3. Later, erosions at the joint margins
  4. In the spine, disk space narrowing with vertebral collapse (wedging) causing characteristic kyphosis
- CT scan: useful in early diagnosis of infections of the spine and to detect paraspinal abscess
- Technetium and gallium scintigraphic scans: may be positive, but do not permit differentiation from inflammation or osteoarthritis

TREATMENT

NONPHARMACOLOGIC THERAPY

Encourage range-of-motion exercises of the affected joint to prevent contractures.

ACUTE GENERAL Rx

- Combination chemotherapy
  1. If sensitive TB suspected, give isoniazid 5 mg/kg/day (maximum 300 mg/day) plus rifampin 10 mg/kg/day (maximum 600 mg/day) for at least 6 mo and pyrazinamide 15 to 30 mg/kg/day (maximum 2 g/day) for at least the first 2 mo plus ethambutol 15 to 25 mg/kg/day until sensitivity results are available.
  2. Most patients are treated successfully with chemotherapy alone.
  3. Urgent surgical intervention is necessary if spinal cord compression causes neurologic changes.
- Surgical debridement in cases of extensive bone involvement

CHRONIC Rx

In long-standing extensive disease, arthrodesis of weight-bearing joints

DISPOSITION

Loss of cartilage and destruction of underlying bone if treatment is not initiated promptly

REFERRAL

- To a physician experienced in the management of TB
- For consultation with an infectious diseases specialist if drug resistance is suspected or documented
- For neurosurgical and/or orthopedic consultation if neurologic impairment suspected

PEARLS & CONSIDERATIONS

COMMENTS

- As TB has become more prevalent in the U.S. in the last 10 to 20 yr, TB arthritis and osteomyelitis have also become more common.

SUGGESTED READINGS

Emery P et al: Detection of *Mycobacterium tuberculosis* group organisms in human and mouse joint tissue by reverse transcriptase PCR: prevalence in diseased synovial tissue suggests lack of specific association with rheumatoid arthritis, *Infect Immun* 69(30):1821, 2001.

Miyata K, Kanzaki T: Early onset sarcoidosis masquerading as juvenile rheumatoid arthritis, *J Am Acad Dermatol* 43:969, 2001.

Shanahan EM, Hanley SD: Tuberculosis of the wrist, *Arth Rheum* 42(12):2724, 1999.

van de Loo FA et al: Deficiency of NADPH oxidase components p47phox and gp91phox caused granulomatous synovitis and increased connective tissue destruction in experimental arthritis models, *Am J Pathol* 163(4):1525, 2003.

AUTHOR: **DEBORAH L. SHAPIRO, M.D.**

Arthritis, Infectious 

BASIC INFORMATION

DEFINITION

Bacterial arthritis is a highly destructive form of joint disease most often caused by hematogenous spread of organisms from a distant site of infection. Direct penetration of the joint as a result of trauma or surgery and spread from adjacent osteomyelitis may also cause bacterial arthritis. Any joint in the body may be affected. Gonococcal arthritis causes a distinct clinical syndrome and is often considered separately.

SYNONYMS

Septic arthritis
Pyogenic arthritis

ICD-9CM CODES
711 Pyogenic arthritis, site unspecified

EPIDEMIOLOGY & DEMOGRAPHICS

INCIDENCE (IN U.S.): Unknown
PREVALENCE (IN U.S.): Unknown
PREDOMINANT SEX: Gonococcal arthritis in males
PREDOMINANT AGE: Gonococcal arthritis in sexually active adults
PEAK INCIDENCE:
- Gonococcal arthritis: young adults
- Other bacterial causes: all ages

PHYSICAL FINDINGS & CLINICAL PRESENTATION

- Hallmark: acute onset of a swollen, painful joint
- Limited range of motion of the joint
- Effusion, with varying degrees of erythema and increased warmth around the joint
- Single joint affected in 80% to 90% of cases of nongonococcal arthritis
- Gonococcal dermatitis-arthritis syndrome
  1. Typical pattern is a migratory polyarthritis or tenosynovitis
  2. Small pustules on the trunk or extremities
- Febrile patient at presentation
- Most commonly affected joints in adult: knee and hip, but any joint may be involved; in children: hip

ETIOLOGY

- Bacteria spread from another locus of infection
  1. Highly vascular synovium is invaded by hematogenously spread bacteria.
  2. WBC enzymes cause necrosis of synovium, cartilage, and bone.
  3. Extensive joint destruction is rapid if infection is not treated with appropriate IV antibiotics and drainage of necrotic material.
- Predisposing factors: rheumatoid arthritis, prosthetic joints, advanced age, immunodeficiency
- The most common nongonococcal organisms are *Staphylococcus aureus,* β-hemolytic streptococci, and gram-negative bacilli.

DIAGNOSIS

DIFFERENTIAL DIAGNOSIS

- Gout
- Pseudogout
- Trauma
- Hemarthrosis
- Rheumatic fever
- Adult or juvenile rheumatoid arthritis
- Spondyloarthropathies such as Reiter's syndrome
- Osteomyelitis
- Viral arthritides
- Septic bursitis

WORKUP

- Joint aspiration, Gram stain, and culture of the synovial fluid
- Immediate arthrocentesis before other studies are undertaken or antibiotics instituted

LABORATORY TESTS

- Joint fluid analysis
  1. Synovial fluid leukocyte count is usually elevated >50,000 cells/mm^3 with a differential count of 80% or more polymorphonuclear cells.
  2. Counts are highly variable, with similar findings in gout, pseudogout, or rheumatoid arthritis.
  3. The differential diagnosis of synovial fluid abnormalities is described in Section II.
- Blood cultures
- Culture of possible extraarticular sources of infection
- Elevated peripheral WBC count and ESR (nonspecific)

IMAGING STUDIES

- X-ray examination of the affected joint to rule out osteomyelitis
- CT scan for early diagnosis of infections of the spine, hips, and sternoclavicular and sacroiliac joints
- Technetium and gallium scintigraphic scans (positive, but do not permit differentiation of infection from inflammation)
- Indium-labeled WBC scans (less sensitive, but more specific)

TREATMENT

NONPHARMACOLOGIC THERAPY

- Affected joints aspirated daily to remove necrotic material and to follow serial WBC counts and cultures
- If no resolution with IV antibiotics and closed drainage: open debridement and lavage, particularly in nongonococcal infections
- Prevention of contractures:
  1. After acute stage of inflammation, range-of-motion exercises of the affected joint
  2. Physical therapy helpful

ACUTE GENERAL Rx

- IV antibiotics immediately after joint aspiration and Gram stain of the synovial fluid
- For infections caused by gram-positive cocci: penicillinase-resistant penicillin, such as nafcillin (2 g IV q4h), unless there is clinical suspicion of methicillin-resistant *Staphylococcus aureus,* in which case vancomycin (1 g IV q12h)
- Infections caused by gram-negative bacilli: treated with a third-generation cephalosporin or an antipseudomonal penicillin plus an aminoglycoside, pending C&S results
- For suspected gonococcal infection, including young adults when the synovial fluid Gram stain is nondiagnostic: ceftriaxone 1 g IV q24h

CHRONIC Rx

See indications for surgical drainage.

DISPOSITION

- With prompt treatment, complete resolution is expected.
- Delay in treatment may result in permanent destruction of cartilage and loss of function of the affected joint.

REFERRAL

To an orthopedist for open drainage if the infected joint fails to improve on appropriate antibiotics and closed aspiration

PEARLS & CONSIDERATIONS

COMMENTS

- Any patient with an acute monoarticular arthritis should undergo an urgent joint aspiration to rule out septic arthritis, even if there is a history of gout.

SUGGESTED READINGS

Lidgren L et al: Infection and arthritis: infection of prosthetic joints, *Best Pract Clin Rheumatol* 17(2):209, 2003.

McGill PE: Geographically specific infections and arthritis, including rheumatic syndromes associated with certain fungi and parasites, *Brucella* species and *Mycobacterium leprae, Best Pract Res Clin Rheumatol* 17(2): 289, 2003.

Nade S: Septic arthritis, *Best Pract Clin Rheumatol* 17(2):183, 2003.

AUTHOR: **DEBORAH L. SHAPIRO, M.D.**

BASIC INFORMATION

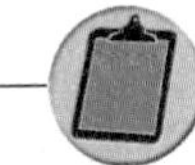

DEFINITION

Juvenile rheumatoid arthritis is arthritis beginning before the age of 16 yr.

SYNONYMS

Still's disease
Juvenile chronic arthritis
Juvenile polyarthritis

ICD-9CM CODES
714.3 Juvenile chronic polyarthritis

EPIDEMIOLOGY & DEMOGRAPHICS

PREVALENCE (IN U.S.): 250,000 to 300,000 cases

PREVALENT SEX: Female:male ratio of 2:1

PREVALENT AGE: Two peak incidences, between ages of 1 and 3 yr and ages 8 and 12 yr.

PHYSICAL FINDINGS & CLINICAL PRESENTATION

Usually one of three types:

SYSTEMIC OR ACUTE FEBRILE JUVENILE RHEUMATOID ARTHRITIS (20% OF CASES):

- Characterized by extraarticular manifestations, especially spiking fevers and a typical rash that frequently appears in the evening and may be elicited by gently scratching the skin in susceptible areas (Koebner's phenomenon)
- Possible splenomegaly, generalized lymphadenopathy, pericarditis, and myocarditis
- Often, minimal articular findings overshadowed by systemic symptoms

PAUCIARTICULAR OR OLIGOARTICULAR FORM (50% OF CASES):

- Involves fewer than five joints
- Usually involves the larger joints, such as the knees, elbows, and ankles
- Systemic features often minimal, and only one to three joints usually involved
- Rarely causes impairment but chronic iridocyclitis develops in approximately 30% of cases with this form, and permanent loss of vision will develop in a high percentage of these patients (Fig. 1-24)
- Accelerated growth of the affected limb from chronic hyperemia possibly resulting in a temporary leg length discrepancy that is eventually equalized in most cases on control of the inflammation

POLYARTICULAR JUVENILE RHEUMATOID ARTHRITIS (30% OF CASES):

- Involves five or more joints
- Resembles the adult disease in its symmetric involvement of the small joints of the hands and feet (Fig. 1-25)
- Cervical spine involvement common and may produce marked loss of motion
- Early closure of the ossification centers of the mandible, often producing a markedly receding chin, a characteristic of this form
- Systemic manifestations similar to the febrile variety but not as dramatic

ETIOLOGY

Unknown. There is increasing evidence that the inflammation and destruction of bone and cartilage that occurs in many rheumatic diseases are the result of the activation, by some unknown mechanism, of proinflammatory cells that infiltrate the synovium. These cells, in turn, release various substances, such as cytokines and tumor necrosis factor (TNF) alpha, which subsequently cause the pathologic changes typical of this group of diseases. Many of the newer therapeutic agents are directed at the suppression of these final mediators of inflammation.

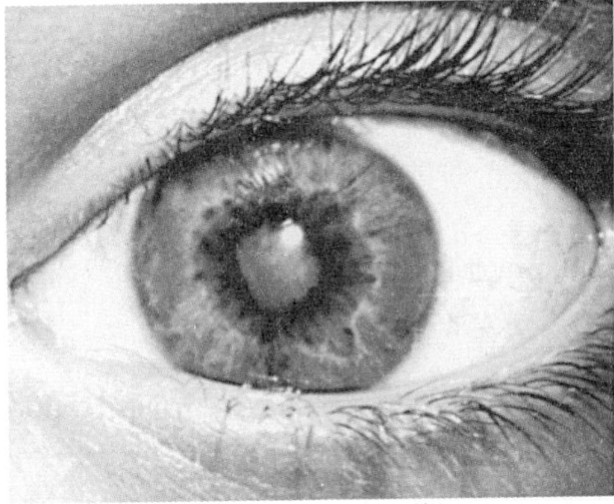

FIGURE 1-24 Chronic iridocyclitis of juvenile rheumatoid arthritis. Extensive posterior synechiae have resulted in a small, irregular pupil. There is a well-developed cataract and early band keratopathy at the medial and lateral margins of the cornea. (From Behrman RE [ed]: *Nelson textbook of pediatrics,* ed 16, Philadelphia, 2000, WB Saunders.)

A

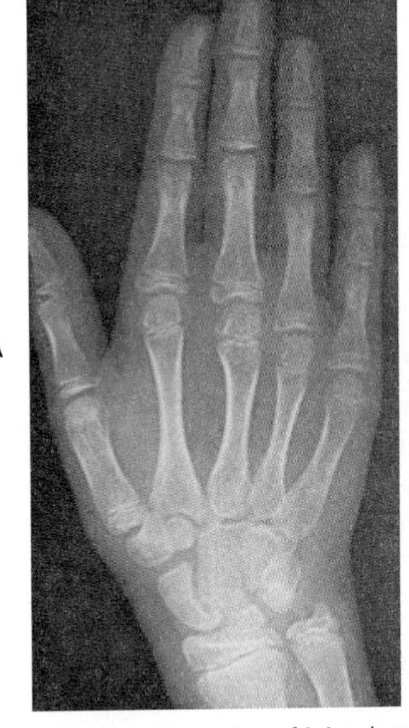

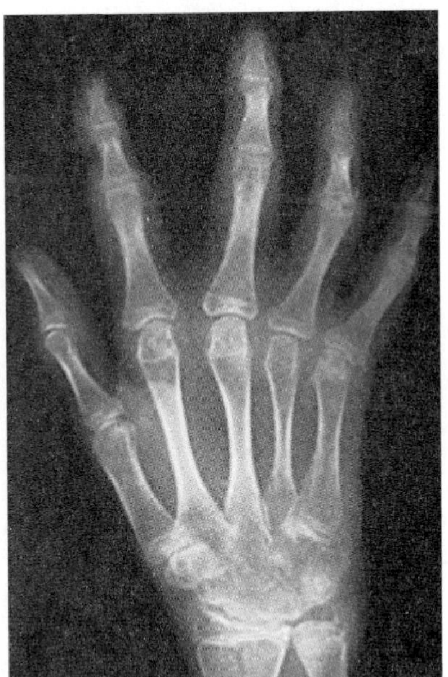

B

FIGURE 1-25 Progression of joint destruction in a girl with rheumatoid factor-positive juvenile rheumatoid arthritis despite doses of corticosteroids sufficient to suppress symptoms in the interval between A and B. **A,** Roentgenogram of the hand at onset. **B,** Roentgenogram 4 years later, showing a loss of articular cartilage and destruction changes in the distal and proximal interphalangeal and metacarpophalangeal joints and destruction and fusion of wrist bones. (From Behrman RE [ed]: *Nelson textbook of pediatrics,* ed 16, Philadelphia, 2000, WB Saunders.)

DIAGNOSIS

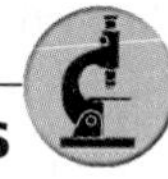

DIFFERENTIAL DIAGNOSIS

- Infectious causes of fever
- SLE
- Rheumatic fever
- Drug reaction
- Serum sickness
- "Viral arthritis"
- Lyme arthritis

WORKUP

Initial laboratory and imaging studies are often nonspecific in children with rheumatoid arthritis.

LABORATORY TESTS

- Increased ESR
- Low-grade anemia
- Very high peripheral WBC count
- Rheumatoid factor: rarely demonstrable in the serum of children
- Antinuclear antibodies: often found in children with ocular complications

IMAGING STUDIES

- Roentgenographic findings are similar to those in adult, with soft tissue swelling and osteoporosis early in the disease.
- Joint destruction is less frequent.
- Bony erosion and cyst formation may be present as a result of synovial hypertrophy.

TREATMENT

NONPHARMACOLOGIC THERAPY

Proper management requires close cooperation among primary physician, therapist, rheumatologist, and orthopedist.

- Rest
- Physical and occupational therapy
- Patient and family education
- Proper diet and weight maintenance

ACUTE GENERAL Rx

- NSAIDs
- DMARDs and biologic response modifiers (BMRs)
- Intraarticular steroids
- Systemic corticosteroids

DISPOSITION

- Complete remission occurs in the majority of patients and may occur at any age.
- 70% to 85% of children regain normal function.
- Mortality rate is 2%.
- Children with a protracted systemic phase of the disease are most at risk for developing serious intercurrent infection and potentially fatal amyloidosis.
- Myocarditis may develop in the systemic form.
- Blindness is the most serious complication of the pauciarticular form; joint deformity is the most serious problem of polyarticular disease.

REFERRAL

- Early rheumatology consultation
- For ophthalmology consultation when ocular involvement is suspected (frequent eye examinations, especially in oligoarticular form)
- For orthopedic consultation for corrective surgery

PEARLS & CONSIDERATIONS

COMMENTS

Patient information on juvenile rheumatoid arthritis can be obtained from the National Arthritis Foundation, 1330 West Peachtree Street, Atlanta, GA 30309; 800-283-7800.

SUGGESTED READINGS

Edwards JC, Szczepanski L et al: Efficacy of β-cell-targeted therapy with rituximab in patients with rheumatoid arthritis, *N Engl J Med* 350:2572, 2004.

Gardner GC, Kadel NJ: Ordering and interpreting rheumatologic laboratory tests, *J Am Acad Orthop Surg* 11:600, 2003.

Lovell D: Biologic agents for the treatment of juvenile rheumatoid arthritis: Current status, *Paediatr Drugs* 6:137, 2004.

Olsen JC: Juvenile idiopathic arthritis: an update *WMJ* 102:45, 2003.

Olsen NJ, Stein CM: New drugs for rheumatoid arthritis, *N Engl J Med* 350:2167, 2004.

Ravelli A, Martini A: Early predictors of outcome in juvenile idiopathic arthritis, *Clin Exp Rheumatol* 21:89, 2004.

AUTHOR: **LONNIE R. MERCIER, M.D.**

BASIC INFORMATION

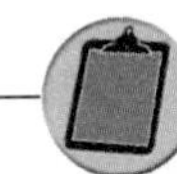

DEFINITION

Psoriatic arthritis is an inflammatory spondyloarthritis occurring in patients with psoriasis who are usually seronegative for rheumatoid factor. It is often included in a class of disorders called *rheumatoid variants* or *seronegative spondyloarthropathies*.

ICD-9CM CODES
696.0 Psoriatic arthritis

EPIDEMIOLOGY & DEMOGRAPHICS

PREVALENCE: 5% to 10% of patients with psoriasis (psoriasis affects 1% to 1.5% of general population)
PREVALENT SEX: Males = females
PREVALENT AGE: 30 to 55 yr

PHYSICAL FINDINGS & CLINICAL PRESENTATION

- Usually gradual clinical onset
- Asymmetric involvement of scattered joints
- Selective involvement of the DIP joints (described in "classic" cases but present in only 5% of patients; Fig. 1-26)
- Symmetric arthritis similar to RA in 15% of patients
- Possible development of predominant sacroiliitis in a small number of cases
- Advanced form of hand involvement (arthritis mutilans) in some patients
- Dystrophic changes in the nails (pitting, ridging) in many patients with DIP involvement

ETIOLOGY

Unknown. Destructive changes probably due to release of cytokines and tumor necrosis factor.

DIAGNOSIS

DIFFERENTIAL DIAGNOSIS

- Rheumatoid arthritis
- Erosive osteoarthritis
- Gouty arthritis
- Ankylosing spondylitis
- The differential diagnosis of spondyloarthropathies is described in Section II.

WORKUP

- Early diagnosis may be difficult to establish because the arthritis may develop before skin lesions appear.
- Laboratory studies show no specific abnormalities in most cases.

LABORATORY TESTS

- Slight elevation of ESR
- Possible mild anemia
- Possible HLA-B27 antigen (especially in patients with sacroiliitis)

IMAGING STUDIES

- Peripheral joint findings similar to those in rheumatoid arthritis but erosive changes in the distal phalangeal tufts characteristic of psoriatic arthritis
- Bony osteolysis; periosteal new bone formation
- Changes in axial skeleton: sacroiliitis, development of vertebral syndesmophytes (osteophytes) that often bridge adjacent vertebral bodies
- Paravertebral ossification
- Spinal changes: do not have same appearance as ankylosing spondylitis; however, spine abnormalities are less common than sacroiliitis

TREATMENT

NONPHARMACOLOGIC THERAPY

- Rest
- Splinting
- Joint protection
- PT

ACUTE GENERAL Rx

- NSAIDs
- Occasional intraarticular steroid injections
- DMARDs: rarely are required

DISPOSITION

- Different from rheumatoid arthritis in both prognosis and response to treatment
- Generally, mild joint symptoms in psoriatic arthritis
- Disease-free intervals lasting for several years in many patients

REFERRAL

Orthopedic consultation for painful joint deformity.

SUGGESTED READINGS

Bennett DL, Ohashi K, El-Khoury GY: Spondyloarthropathies: ankylosing spondylitis and psoriatic arthritis, *Radiol Clin North Am* 42:121, 2004.

Kataria RK, Brent LH: Spondyloarthiopathies, *Am Fam Phys* 69:2853, 2004.

Liu Y, Cortinovis D, Stone MA: Recent advances in the treatment of the spondyloarthropathies, *Curr Opin Rheumatol* 16:357, 2004.

Strober BE, Clarke S: Etanercept for the treatment of psoriasis: combination therapy with other modalities, *J Drugs Dermatol* 3:270, 2004.

Taylor WJ: Assessment of outcome in psoriatic arthritis, *Curr Opin Rheumatol* 16:350, 2004.

AUTHOR: **LONNIE R. MERCIER, M.D.**

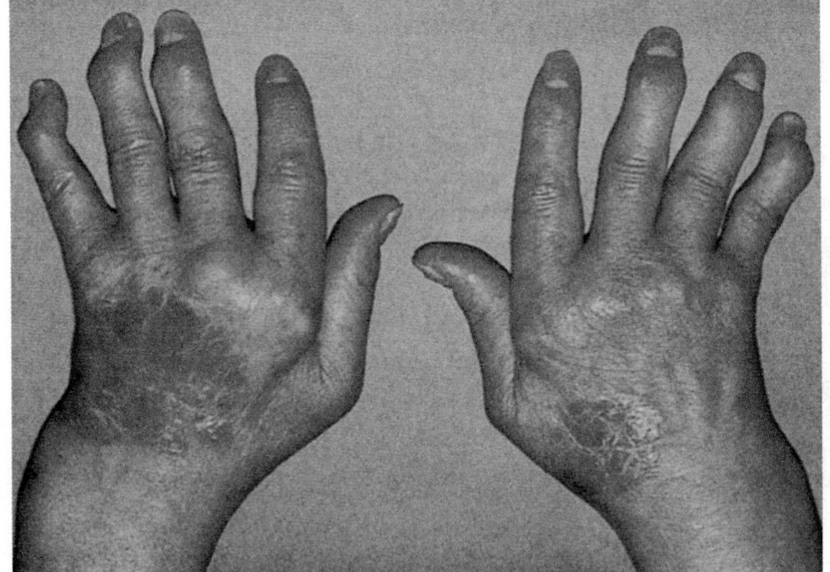

FIGURE 1-26 The hands of a woman with symmetric polyarthritis. Initially, this was indistinguishable from rheumatoid disease, but note the distal interphalangeal joint involvement, which is uncommon in rheumatoid arthritis, as well as the skin psoriasis. (From Klippel J, Dieppe P, Ferri F [eds]: *Primary care rheumatology,* London, 1999, Mosby.)

BASIC INFORMATION

DEFINITION

Rheumatoid arthritis (RA) is a systemic disorder characterized by chronic joint inflammation that most commonly affects peripheral joints. This process results in the development of pannus, a destructive tissue that damages cartilage.

ICD-9CM CODES
714.0 Rheumatoid arthritis

EPIDEMIOLOGY & DEMOGRAPHICS

PREVALENCE: 5 cases/1000 adults
PREVALENT AGE: 35 to 45 yr
PREDOMINANT SEX:

- Female:male ratio of 3:1
- After age 50 yr, sex difference less marked

PHYSICAL FINDINGS & CLINICAL PRESENTATION

- Usually gradual onset; common prodromal symptoms of weakness, fatigue, and anorexia
- Initial presentation: multiple symmetric joint involvement, most often in the hands and feet, usually MCP, MTP, and PIP joints (Fig. 1-27)
- Joint effusions, tenderness, and restricted motion usually present early in the disease
- Eventual characteristic deformities: subluxations, dislocations, and joint contractures
- Extraarticular findings:
  1. Tendon sheaths and bursae frequently affected by chronic inflammation
  2. Possible tendon rupture
  3. Rheumatoid nodules over bony prominences such as the elbow and shaft of the ulna
  4. Splenomegaly, pericarditis, and vasculitis
  5. Findings of carpal tunnel syndrome resulting from flexor tenosynovitis

ETIOLOGY

Unknown. There is increasing evidence that the inflammation and destruction of bone and cartilage that occurs in many rheumatic diseases are the result of the activation by some unknown mechanism of proinflammatory cells that infiltrate the synovium. These cells, in turn, release various substances, such as cytokines and tumor necrosis factor (TNF) alpha, which subsequently cause the pathologic changes typical of this group of diseases. Many of the newer therapeutic agents are directed at the suppression of these final mediators of inflammation.

DIAGNOSIS

DIFFERENTIAL DIAGNOSIS

- SLE
- Seronegative spondyloarthropathies
- Polymyalgia rheumatica
- Acute rheumatic fever
- Scleroderma

According to the American College of Rheumatology, RA exists when four of seven criteria are present, with criteria 1 to 4 being present for at least 6 wk.

1. Morning stiffness over 1 hr
2. Arthritis in three or more joints with swelling
3. Arthritis of hand joints with swelling
4. Symmetric arthritis
5. Rheumatoid nodules
6. Roentgenographic changes typical of RA
7. Positive serum rheumatoid factor

LABORATORY TESTS

- Increase in rheumatoid factor in 80% of cases (rheumatoid factor also present in the normal population)
- Possible mild anemia
- Usually, elevated acute phase reactants (ESR, C-reactive protein)
- Possible mild leukocytosis
- Usually, turbid joint fluid, which forms a poor mucin clot; elevated cell count, with an increase in polymorphonuclear leukocytes

IMAGING STUDIES

Plain radiography

- Usually reveals soft-tissue swelling and osteoporosis early (Fig. 1-28)
- Eventually, joint space narrowing, erosion, and deformity visible as a result of continued inflammation and cartilage destruction

TREATMENT

NONPHARMACOLOGIC THERAPY

Proper management requires close cooperation among primary physician, therapist, rheumatologist, and orthopedist.

- Patient education is important.
- Rest with proper exercise and splinting can prevent or correct joint deformities.

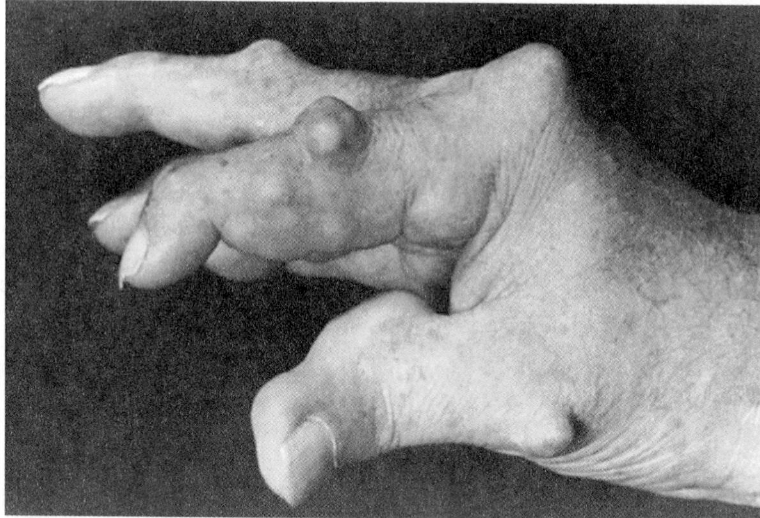

FIGURE 1-27 Rheumatoid arthritis. Hand of a 60-year-old man with seropositive rheumatoid arthritis. There are fixed deformities and gross rheumatoid nodules. (From Canoso JJ: *Rheumatology in primary care,* Philadelphia, 1997, WB Saunders.)

- Maintain proper diet and control obesity.

CHRONIC Rx

- NSAIDs: commonly used as the initial treatment to relieve inflammation (drug of choice for most patients: aspirin, but other NSAIDs also effective)
- Disease-modifying drugs (DMARDs): are traditionally begun when NSAIDs are not effective; current recommendations favor early aggressive treatment with DMARDs, seeking to minimize long-term joint damage. Commonly used agents are methotrexate, cyclosporine, hydroxychloroquine, sulfasalazine, leflunomide, and infliximab. Most of these are associated with potential toxicity and require close monitoring. They are also usually slow-acting drugs that require more than 8 wk to become effective (see Table 1-9)
- Oral prednisone
- Intrasynovial steroid injections
- Etanercept (Enbrel), a tumor necrosis factor α-blocker, is indicated in moderately to severely active RA in patients who respond inadequately to DMARDs. The combination of etanercept and methotrexate has been reported to be effective and promising in the treatment of RA.

DISPOSITION

- Remissions and exacerbations are common, but condition is chronically progressive in the majority of cases.
- Joint degeneration and deformity often lead to disability.
- Early diagnosis and treatment are important and can improve quality of life.

REFERRAL

Early referral to rheumatologist
Orthopedic consultation for corrective surgery

SUGGESTED READINGS

Chen AL, Joseph TN, Zuckerman JD: Rheumatoid arthritis of the shoulder, *J Am Acad Orthop Surg* 11:12, 2003.

Cohen S et al: Treatment of rheumatoid arthritis with anakinra, a recombinant human interleukin-1 receptor antagonist, in combination with methotrexate: results of a twenty-four-week, multicenter, randomized, double-blind, placebo controlled trial, *Arthritis Rheum* 46:614, 2002.

Dayer J-M, Bresnihan B: Targeting interleukin-1 in the treatment of rheumatoid arthritis, *Arthritis Rheum* 46:574, 2002.

Edwards JC, Szczepanski L et al: Efficacy of β-cell-targeted therapy with ritaximab in patients with rheumatoid arthritis, *N Engl J Med* 350:2572, 2004.

Gardner GC, Kadel MJ: Ordering and interpreting rheumatologic laboratory tests, *J Am Acad Orthop Surg* 11:60, 2003.

Genovese MC et al: Etanercept versus methotrexate in patients with early rheumatoid arthritis: two-year radiographic and clinical outcomes, *Arthritis Rheum* 46:1443, 2002.

Kremer JM: Rational use of new and existing disease-modifying agents in rheumatoid arthritis, *Ann Intern Med* 134:695, 2001.

Olsen NJ, Stein CM: New drugs for rheumatoid arthritis, *N Engl J Med* 350:2167, 2004.

Maini SR: Infliximab treatment of rheumatoid arthritis, *Rheum Dis Clin North Am* 30:329, 2004.

Smith JB, Haynes MK: Rheumatoid arthritis: a molecular understanding, *Ann Intern Med* 136:908, 2002.

Van Everdingen AA et al: Low dose prednisone therapy for patients with early active rheumatoid arthritis: clinical efficacy, disease-modifying properties, and side effects, *Ann Intern Med* 136:1, 2002.

AUTHOR: **LONNIE R. MERCIER, M.D.**

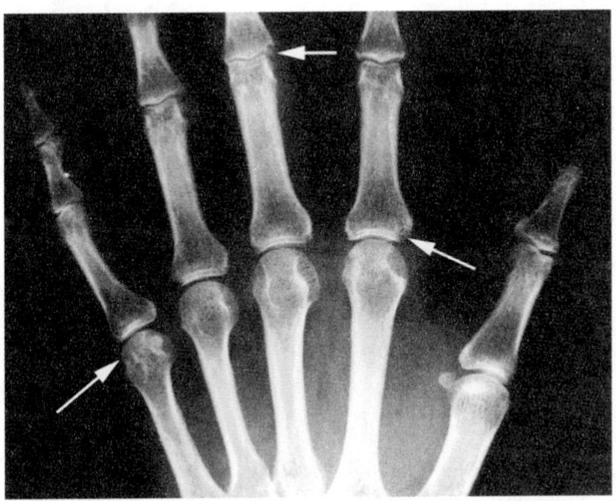

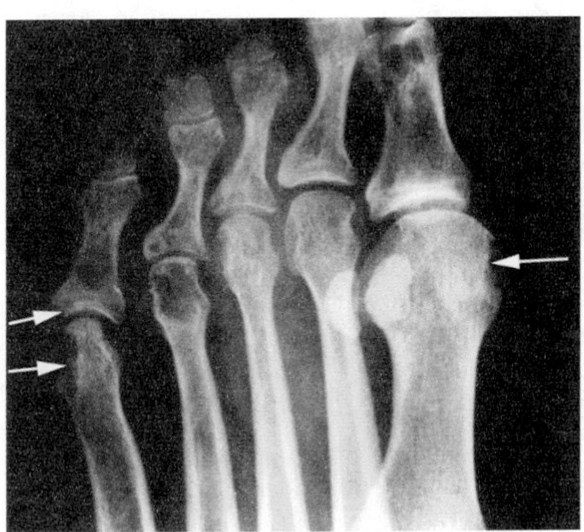

FIGURE 1-28 Rheumatoid arthritis. A, Periarticular osteopenia and marginal erosions in MCPs and a PIP (*arrows*). **B,** In the same patient, marginal erosions at metatarsal heads. (From Canoso JJ [ed]: *Rheumatology in primary care,* Philadelphia, 1997, WB Saunders.)

TABLE 1-9 **Selected Disease-Modifying Antirheumatic Drugs**

Type/Generic (Trade) Name	Recommended Dosages	Toxic effects	Recommended monitoring
Gold compounds (Myochrysine)	IM: 10 mg followed by 25 mg 1 wk later, then 25-50 mg wkly until there is toxicity, major clinical improvement, or cumulative dose = 1 g. If effective, interval between doses is increased.	Pruritus, dermatitis (frequent—$\frac{1}{3}$ of pts), stomatitis, nephrotoxicity, blood dyscrasias, "nitritoid" reaction: flushing, weakness, nausea, dizziness 30 min after injection.	CBC, platelet count before every other injection. Urinalysis before each dose.
Aurothioglucose (Solganal)	IM: 10 mg; 2nd and 3rd doses 25 mg, 4th and subsequent 50 mg. Interval between doses: 1 wk. If improvement, no toxicity→decrease dose to 25 mg or increase interval between doses.	Dermatitis, stomatitis, nephrotoxicity, blood dyscrasias.	CBC, platelet count every 2 wk. Urinalysis before each dose.
Auranofin (Ridaura)	Oral: 3 mg bid or 6 mg qd. May increase to 3 mg tid after 6 months.	Loose stools, diarrhea (up to 50%), dermatitis.	Baseline CBC, platelet count, U/A, renal, liver function, at onset then CBC with platelet count, U/A 9 months.
Antimalarial Hydroxychloroquine (Plaquenil)	Oral: 400-600 mg qd with meals then 200-400 mg qd.	Retinopathy, dermatitis, muscle weakness, hypoactive DTRs, CNS.	Ophthalmologic examination every 3 months (visual acuity, slitlamp, funduscopic, visual field tests), neuromuscular examination.
Penicillamine (Cuprimine, Depen)	Oral: 125-250 mg qd, then increasing at monthly intervals doses to max 750-1000 mg by 125-250 mg.	Pruritus, rash/mouth ulcers, bone marrow depression, proteinuria, hematuria, hypogeusia, myesthenia, myositis, GI distress, pulmonary toxicity, teratogenic.	CBC every 2 weeks until dose stable, then every month. U/A weekly until dose stable, then every month. HCG as needed.
Methotrexate (Rheumatrex)	Oral: 7.5-15 mg weekly.	Pulmonary toxicity, ulcerative stomatitis, leukopenia, thrombocytopenia, GI distress, malaise, fatigue, chills, fever, CNS, elevated LFTs/liver disease, lymphoma, infection.	CBC with platelet count, LFTs weekly × 6 wk then monthly LFTs, U/A periodically, HCG as needed.
Azathioprine (Imuran)	Oral: 50-100 mg qd, increase at 4-wk intervals by 0.5 mg/kg/d up to 2.5 mg/kg/d.	Leukopenia, thrombocytopenia, GI, neoplastic if previous Rx with alkylating agents.	CBC with platelet count, wkly × 1 mo, 2×/mo. × 2 mo, then monthly, HCG as needed.
Sulfasalazine (Azulfidine)	Oral: 500 mg daily then increase up to 3 g daily.	GI, skin rash, pruritus, blood dyscrasias, oligospermia.	CBC, U/A q 2 wk × 3 mo, then monthly × 9 mo, then every 6 mo.
Alkylating agents Cyclophosphamide (Cytoxan)	Oral: 50-100 mg daily up to 2.5 mg/kg/d.	Leukopenia, thrombocytopenia, hematuria, GI, alopecia, rash, bladder cancer, non-Hodgkin's lymphoma, infection.	CBC with platelet count, regularly. HCG as needed.
Chlorambucil (Leukeran)	Oral: 0.1-0.2 mg/kg/d.	Bone marrow suppression, GI, CNS, infection.	CBC with platelet count every wk. WBCs 3-4 days after each CBC during 1st 3-6 wk at therapy. HCG as needed.
Cyclosporine (Sandimmune)	Oral 2.5-5 mg/kg/d.	Nephrotoxicity, tremor, hirsutism, hypertension, gum hyperplasia.	Renal function, liver function.
Pyrimidine, synthesis inhibitors Leflunomide (Arava)	Loading dose: 100 mg/d for 3 days. Maintenance therapy: 20 mg/d; if not tolerated, 10 mg/d.	Hepatotoxicity, carcinogenesis. Immunosuppression, long half-life.	LFTs every month, drug levels after discontinuation (after 1 month therapy, remains in blood for 2 years without use of cholestyramine).

From Rakel RE (ed): *Principles of family practice,* ed 6, Philadelphia, 2002, WB Saunders.

Bid, Twice a day; *CBC,* complete blood count; *CNS,* central nervous system; *DTR,* deep tendon reflex; *GI,* gastrointestinal; *HCG,* human chorionic gonadotropin; *IM,* intramuscular; *LFT,* liver function test; *qd,* every day; *tid,* three times a day; *U/A,* urinalysis; *WBC,* white blood cell count.

BASIC INFORMATION

DEFINITION

Asbestosis is a slowly progressive diffuse interstitial fibrosis resulting from dose-related inhalation exposure to fibers of asbestos.

ICD-9CM CODES
501 Asbestosis

EPIDEMIOLOGY & DEMOGRAPHICS

- In U.S.: 5 to 10 new cases/100,000 persons/yr
- Prolonged interval (20 to 30 yr) between exposures to inhaled fibers and clinical manifestations of disease
- Most common in workers involved in the primary extraction of asbestos from rock deposits and in those involved in the fabrication and installation of products containing asbestos (e.g., naval shipyards in World War II, installation of floor tiles, ceiling tiles, acoustic ceiling coverings, wall insulation, and pipe coverings in public buildings)

PHYSICAL FINDINGS & CLINICAL PRESENTATION

- Insidious onset of shortness of breath with exertion is usually the first sign of asbestosis.
- Dyspnea becomes more severe as the disease advances; with time, progressively less exertion is tolerated.
- Cough is frequent and usually paroxysmal, dry, and nonproductive.
- Scant mucoid sputum may accompany the cough in the later stages of the disease.
- Fine end respiratory crackles (rales, crepitations) are heard more predominantly in the lung bases.
- Digital clubbing, edema, jugular venous distention are present.

ETIOLOGY

Inhalation of asbestos fibers

DIAGNOSIS

DIFFERENTIAL DIAGNOSIS

- Silicosis
- Siderosis, other pneumonoconioses
- Lung cancer
- Atelectasis

WORKUP

Documentation of exposure history, diagnostic imaging, pulmonary function testing

LABORATORY TESTS

- Generally not helpful
- Possible mild elevation of ESR, positive ANA and RF (These tests are nonspecific and do not correlate with disease severity or activity.)
- Pulmonary function testing: decreased vital capacity, decreased total lung capacity, decreased carbon monoxide gas transfer
- ABGs: hypoxemia, hypercarbia in advanced stages

IMAGING STUDIES

Chest x-ray (Fig. 1-29):
- Small, irregular shadows in lower lung zones
- Thickened pleural, calcified plaques (present under diaphragms and lateral chest wall)

CT scan of chest confirms the diagnosis.

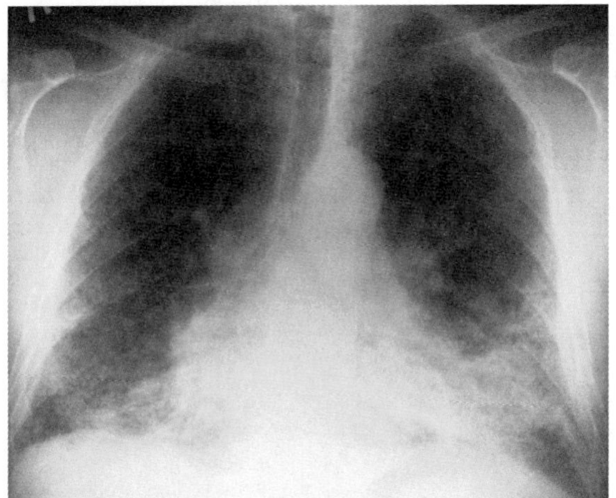

FIGURE 1-29 Asbestosis. PA radiograph shows coarse linear opacities at both lung bases obscuring the cardiac borders. (From McLoud TC: *Thoracic radiology: the requisites,* St Louis, 1998, Mosby.)

TREATMENT

NONPHARMACOLOGIC THERAPY

- Smoking cessation, proper nutrition, exercise program to maximize available lung function
- Home oxygen therapy prn
- Removal of patient from further asbestos fiber exposure

GENERAL Rx

- Prompt identification and treatment of respiratory infections
- Supplemental oxygen on a prn basis
- Annual influenza vaccination, pneumococcal vaccination

DISPOSITION

- There is no specific treatment for asbestosis.
- Death is usually secondary to respiratory failure from cor pulmonale.
- Patients with asbestosis have increased risk for mesotheliomas, lung cancer, and TB. Recent reports indicate that the risk of asbestos-induced lung cancer may be overestimated.
- Survival in patients following development of mesothelioma is 4 to 6 yr.

REFERRAL

To pulmonologist initially

PEARLS & CONSIDERATIONS

COMMENTS

Patient information on asbestosis can be obtained from the American Lung Association, 1740 Broadway, New York, NY 10019.

SUGGESTED READING

Camus M et al: Nonoccupational exposure to chrysotile asbestos and the risk of lung cancer, *N Engl J Med* 338:1565, 1998.

AUTHOR: **FRED F. FERRI, M.D.**

BASIC INFORMATION

DEFINITION

Ascariasis is a parasitic infection caused by the nematode *Ascaris lumbricoides*. The majority of those infected are asymptomatic; however, clinical disease may arise from pulmonary hypersensitivity, intestinal obstruction, and secondary complications.

ICD-9CM CODES
127.0 Ascariasis

EPIDEMIOLOGY & DEMOGRAPHICS

INCIDENCE (IN U.S.):
- Unknown
- Three times the infection rates found in blacks as in whites

PREVALENCE (IN U.S.): Estimated at 4,000,000, the majority of which live in the rural southeastern part of the country

PREDOMINANT SEX: Both sexes probably equally affected, with a possible slight female preponderance

PREDOMINANT AGE: Most common in children, with estimated mean age of approximately 5 yr based on surveys in highly endemic areas

PEAK INCIDENCE: Unknown

NEONATAL INFECTION:
Probable transmission, though not specifically studied

PHYSICAL FINDINGS & CLINICAL PRESENTATION

- Occurs approximately 9 to 12 days after ingestion of eggs (corresponding to the larva migration through the lungs)
- Nonproductive cough
- Substernal chest discomfort
- Fever
- In patients with large worm burdens, especially children, intestinal obstruction associated with perforation, volvulus, and intussusception
- Migration of worms into the biliary tree giving clinical appearance of biliary colic and pancreatitis as well as acute appendicitis with movement into that appendage
- Rarely, infection with *A. lumbricoides* producing interstitial nephritis and acute renal failure
- In endemic areas in Asia and Africa, malabsorption of dietary proteins and vitamins as a consequence of chronic worm intestinal carriage

ETIOLOGY

- Transmission is usually hand to mouth, but eggs may be ingested via transported vegetables grown in contaminated soil.
- Eggs are hatched in the small intestine, with larvae penetrating intestinal mucosa and migrating via the circulation to the lungs.
- Larval forms proceed through the alveoli, ascend the bronchial tree, and return to the intestines after swallowing, where they mature into adult worms.
- Estimated time until the female adult worm to begin producing eggs is 2 to 3 mo.
- Eggs are passed out of the intestines with feces.
- Within human host, adult worm lifespan is 1 to 2 yr.

DIAGNOSIS

DIFFERENTIAL DIAGNOSIS

- Radiologic manifestations and eosinophilia to be distinguished from drug hypersensitivity and Löffler's syndrome
- The differential diagnosis of intestinal helminths is described in Section II

LABORATORY TESTS

- Examination of the stool for *Ascaris* ova
- Expectoration or fecal passage of adult worm
- Eosinophilia: most prominent early in the infection and subsides as the adult worm infestation established in the intestines
- Anti-ascaris IgG4 blood levels by ELISA is a sensitive and specific marker of infection and may be useful in the evaluation of treatment
- Malondialdehyde levels clearly increase in patients infected with *A. lumbricoides*

IMAGING STUDIES

- Chest x-ray examination to reveal bilateral oval or round infiltrates of varying size (Löffler's syndrome); NOTE: infiltrates are transient and eventually resolve.
- Plain films of the abdomen and contrast studies to reveal worm masses in loops of bowel
- Ultrasonography and endoscopic retrograde cholangiopancreatography (ERCP) to identify worms in the pancreaticobiliary tract

TREATMENT

NONPHARMACOLOGIC THERAPY

Aggressive IV hydration, especially in children with fever, severe vomiting, and resultant dehydration

ACUTE GENERAL Rx

- Mebendazole (Vermox)
  1. Drug of choice for intestinal infection with *A. lumbricoides*
  2. 100 mg PO tid given for 3 days
- Albendazole, given as a single 400-mg dose PO
- Both mebendazole and albendazole are contraindicated in pregnancy.
- Pyrantel pamoate (Antiminth)
  1. Given at a dose of 11 mg/kg PO (maximum dose of 1 g/day)
  2. Considered safe for use in pregnant women
- Piperazine citrate
  1. Recommended in cases of intestinal or biliary obstruction
  2. Administered as a syrup, given via nasogastric tube, a 150 mg/kg loading dose, followed by six doses of 65 mg/kg q12h
  3. Considered safe in pregnancy, but cannot be given concurrently with chlorpromazine
- Complete obstruction should be managed surgically.

DISPOSITION

Overall prognosis is good.

REFERRAL

- To gastroenterologist in cases of visualized pancreaticobiliary tract or appendiceal obstruction
- To surgeon in cases of complete obstruction or suspected secondary complication (e.g., perforation or volvulus)

PEARLS & CONSIDERATIONS

COMMENTS

- Hepatic abscess, containing both viable and dead worms, complicating *Ascaris*-induced biliary duct disease has been documented.
- Given the known transmission of the parasite, routine hand washing and proper disposal of human waste would significantly decrease the prevalence of this disease.

SUGGESTED READINGS

Amjad N et al: An unusual presentation of acute cholecystitis: biliary ascariasis *Hosp Med* 62(6):370, 2001.

Kilic E et al: Serum malondialdehyde level in patients infected with *Ascaris lumbricoides*, *World J Gastroenterol* 9(10):2332, 2003.

Rodriguez EJ et al: Ascariasis causing small bowel volvulus, *Radiographics* 23(5):1291, 2003.

Sangkhathat S et al: Massive gastrointestinal bleeding in infants with ascariasis, *J Pediatr Surg* 38(11):1696, 2003.

Santra A et al: Serodiagnosis of ascariasis with specific IgG4 antibody and its use in an epidemiological study, *Trans R Soc Trop Med Hyg* 95(3):289, 2001.

AUTHOR: **GEORGE O. ALONSO, M.D.**

BASIC INFORMATION

DEFINITION

Cell death in components of bone: hematopoietic fat marrow and mineralized tissue.

SYNONYMS

Osteonecrosis, avascular necrosis

ICD-9CM CODES
733.40 Aseptic necrosis
733.43 Aseptic necrosis of femoral condyle
733.42 Aseptic necrosis of femoral head
733.41 Aseptic necrosis of humeral head
733.44 Aseptic necrosis of talus

EPIDEMIOLOGY & DEMOGRAPHICS

- 15,000 new cases per year in the U.S.
- Associated conditions:
  1. Corticosteroid treatment: 35%
  2. Alcohol abuse: 22%
  3. Idiopathic and other: 43%
- Common sites involved
  1. Femoral head
  2. Femoral condyle
  3. Humeral head
  4. Navicular and lunate wrist bones
  5. Talus

PHYSICAL FINDINGS & CLINICAL PRESENTATION

- May be asymptomatic
- Pain in the involved area exacerbated by movement or weight bearing
- Decreased range of motion as the disease progresses
- Functional limitation

ETIOLOGY

Final common pathway of conditions that lead to impairment of the blood supply to the involved bone.

Stages:

Stage 0
- Asymptomatic
- Normal imaging
- Histologic findings only (i.e., silent osteonecrosis)

Stage 1
- Asymptomatic or symptomatic
- Normal x-ray and CT scan
- Abnormal bone scan and/or MRI

Stage 2
- Abnormal x-rays and/or CT scan including linear sclerosis, focal bead mineralization, cysts; however, the overall architecture of the involved bone is normal

Stage 3
- Early evidence of mechanical bone failure (subchondral fracture), but the overall shape of the bone is still intact

Stage 4
- Flattening or collapse of the bone

Stage 5
- Joint space narrowing

Stage 6
- Extensive joint destruction

DIAGNOSIS

DIFFERENTIAL DIAGNOSIS

- None in late stages
- Early: any condition causing focal musculoskeletal pain including arthritis, bursitis, tendinitis, myopathy, neoplastic bone and joint diseases, traumatic injuries, pathologic fractures

IMAGING STUDIES See Fig. 1-30.

1. X-ray: insensitive early in the course. The earliest changes include diffuse osteopenia, areas of radiolucency with sclerotic border, and linear sclerosis. Later a subchondral lucency (crescent sign) indicates subchondral fracture. More advanced cases reveal flattening, collapsed bone and abnormal bone contour. In late disease, osteoarthritic changes are seen.
2. Bone scan:
   - Early: "cold" area
   - Later: increased radionuclide uptake as a result of remodeling
   - Sensitivity in early disease is only 70% and specificity is poor
3. CT scan: may reveal central necrosis and area of collapse before those are visible in x-ray.
4. MRI: the most sensitive technology to diagnose early aseptic necrosis. The first sign is a margin of low signal. An inner border of high signal associated with a low-signal line is specific of aseptic necrosis ("double line sign"). Sensitivity is 75%-100%.

TREATMENT

PREVENTION

- Management of etiologic conditions
- Minimize corticosteroid use

MEDICAL TREATMENT

- Decrease weight bearing of affected area
- Pulsing electromagnetic fields applied externally (still experimental)
- Peripheral vasodilators (e.g., dihydrogotamine) (unproven)

SURGICAL TREATMENT

- Core decompression: effectiveness 35%-95% in early phases
- Bone grafting
- Osteotomies
- Joint replacement

PROGNOSIS

- When diagnosed at an early stage treatment is appropriate in all cases because 85%-90% can be expected to progress to a more advanced stage
- Contralateral joint involvement is common (30%-70%)

SUGGESTED READING

Mazieres R: *Osteonecrosis:* In Klippel JH, Dieppe PA (eds): *Rhematology,* ed 2, St. Louis, 1998, Mosby.

AUTHOR: **TOM J. WACHTEL**

A

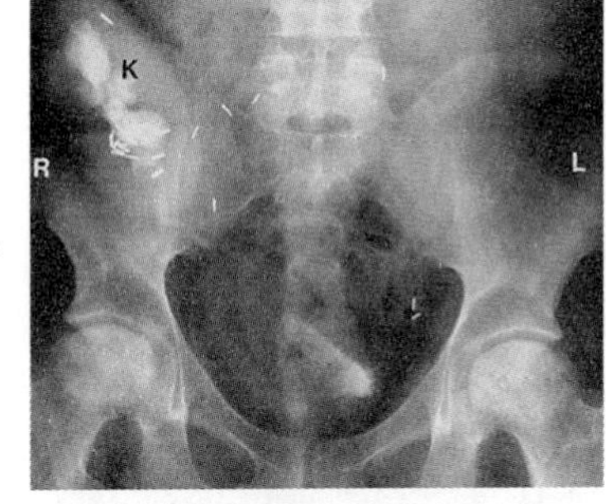

B

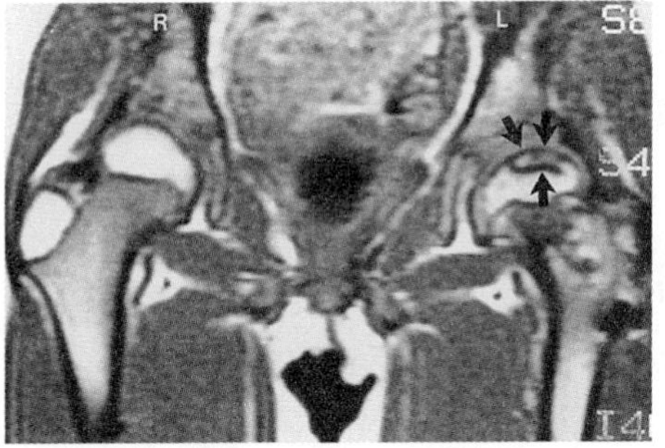

FIGURE 1-30 Aseptic necrosis of the hips. **A,** Aseptic necrosis can occur from a number of causes, including trauma and steroid use. In this patient, an anteroposterior view of the pelvis shows a transplanted kidney (K) in the right iliac fossa. Use of steroids has caused this patient to have bilateral aseptic necrosis. The femoral heads are somewhat flattened, irregular, and increased in density. **B,** Aseptic necrosis in a different patient is demonstrated on an MRI scan as an area of decreased signal (*arrows*) in the left femoral head. This is the most sensitive method for detection of early aseptic necrosis. (From Mettler FA [ed]: *Primary care radiology,* Philadelphia, 2000, WB Saunders).

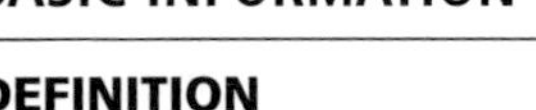

BASIC INFORMATION

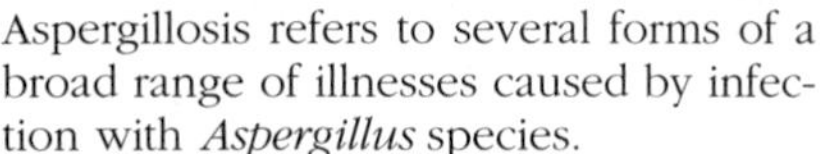

DEFINITION

Aspergillosis refers to several forms of a broad range of illnesses caused by infection with *Aspergillus* species.

ICD-9CM CODES
117.3 Aspergillosis
117.3 Aspergillosis with pneumonia
117.3 *Aspergillus (flavus) (fumigatus)* (infection) *(terreus)*

EPIDEMIOLOGY & DEMOGRAPHICS

- *Aspergillus* species are ubiquitous in the environment internationally and occur as a mold found in soil
- Cause a variety of illness from hypersensitivity pneumonitis to disseminated overwhelming infection in immunosuppressed patients
- Incidence of invasive aspergillosis is increasing with advances in the treatment of life threatening diseases: aggressive chemotherapy; bone marrow and organ transplantation
- Frequently cultured from samples obtained in hospital wards from unfiltered outside air circulating through open windows
- Reaches the patient by airborne conidia (spores) that are small enough (2.5 to 3 μm) to reach the alveoli on inhalation
- Can also invade the nose and paranasal sinuses, external ear, or traumatized skin
- The clinical syndrome and pathologic spectrum of *Aspergillus* lung disease is dependent on the underlying lung architecture, the host's immune response, and the degree of inoculum.

ETIOLOGY

- *Aspergillus fumigatus* is the usual cause.
- *A. flavus* is the second most important species, particularly in invasive disease of immunosuppressed patients and in lesions beginning in the nose and paranasal sinuses. *A. niger* can also cause invasive human infection.

ALLERGIC ASPERGILLOSIS:

- Represents a hypersensitivity pneumonitis
- Presents as cough, dyspnea, fever, chills, and malaise typically 4 to 8 hr after exposure
- Repeated attacks can lead to granulomatous disease and pulmonary fibrosis

ALLERGIC BRONCHOPULMONARY ASPERGILLOSIS (ABPA):

- Symptoms occur most commonly in atopic individuals during the third and fourth decades of life
- Hypersensitivity reaction of the airways to *Aspergillus* fungal antigens present in the bronchial tree
- Results from an initial type I (immediate hypersensitivity) and a type III reaction (immune complexes), which is most likely responsible for the roentgenographic features and more destructive changes of the bronchi
- Underdiagnosed pulmonary disorder in patients with asthma and cystic fibrosis

ASPERGILLOMAS ("FUNGUS BALLS"):

- In the absence of invasion or significant immune response, *Aspergillus* can colonize a preexisting cavity, causing pulmonary aspergilloma
- Forms masses of tangled hyphal elements, fibrin, and mucus
- Patients typically have a history of chronic lung disease, tuberculosis, sarcoidosis, or emphysema
- Manifests commonly as hemoptysis: blood-streaked sputum to active bleeding necessitating surgical reaction
- Many are asymptomatic

INVASIVE ASPERGILLOSIS:

- Patients with prolonged and profound granulocytopenia or impaired phagocytic function are predisposed to rapidly progressive *Aspergillus* pneumonia
- Lungs typically manifest a necrotizing bronchopneumonia, ranging from small areas of infiltrate to intensive bilateral hemorrhagic infarction
- Most common presentation is that of unremitting fever and a new pulmonary infiltrate despite broad-spectrum antibiotic therapy in an immunosuppressed patient
- Dyspnea and nonproductive cough are common; sudden pleuritic pain and tachycardia, sometimes with a pleural rub, may mimic pulmonary embolism; hemoptysis is uncommon
- Roentgenograms may reveal patchy bronchopneumonic, nodular densities, consolidation, or cavitation
- Immunocompromised patients: invasive pulmonary *Aspergillus* (IPA) generally is acute and evolves over days to weeks; less commonly, patients with normal or only mild abnormalities of their immune systems may develop a more chronic, slowly progressive form of IPA

EXTRAPULMONARY DISSEMINATION:

- Cerebral infarction from hematogenous dissemination may occur in immunosuppressed individuals
- Abscess formation may occur from direct extension of invasive disease in the sinuses
- Esophageal or gastrointestinal ulcerations caused by *Aspergillus* may occur in the immunosuppressed host
- Fatal perforation of the viscus or bowel infarction may occur
- Necrotizing skin ulcers involving the extremities (Fig. 1-31)
- Osteomyelitis
- Endocarditis

Patients with AIDS and a CD4 count of below 50 mm^3 have increased susceptibility to invasive aspergillosis.

DIAGNOSIS

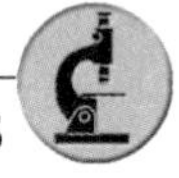

DIFFERENTIAL DIAGNOSIS

- Tuberculosis
- Cystic fibrosis
- Carcinoma of the lung
- Eosinophilic pneumonia
- Bronchiectasis
- Sarcoidosis
- Lung abscess

WORKUP

Physical examination and laboratory evaluation

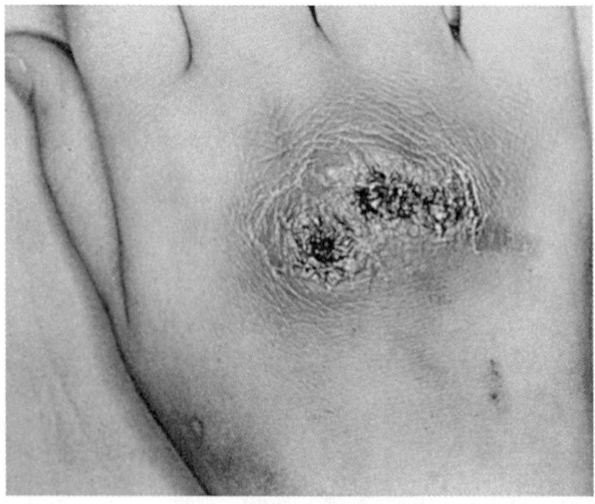

FIGURE 1-31 Cutaneous aspergillosis in a patient with acute leukemia and marked neutropenia. The lesion developed at the site where a steel needle had been left for several days of intravenous infusion. (From Mandell GL [ed]: *Mandell, Douglas, and Bennett's principles and practice of infectious diseases,* ed 5, New York, 2000, Churchill Livingstone.)

LABORATORY TESTS

ALLERGIC BRONCHOPULMONARY ASPERGILLOSIS:

1. Peripheral blood eosinophilia and an elevated total serum IgE level
2. Skin test with *Aspergillus* antigenic extract usually is positive but is nonspecific
3. *Aspergillus* serum precipitating antibody is present in 70% to 100% of cases
4. Sputum cultures may be positive for *Aspergillus* spp. but are nonspecific

ASPERGILLOMAS:

1. Sputum culture
2. Serum precipitating antibody

INVASIVE ASPERGILLOSIS: Definitive diagnosis requires the demonstration of tissue invasion as seen on a biopsy specimen (i.e., septate, acute branching hyphae) or a positive culture from the tissue obtained by an invasive procedure such as transbronchial biopsy.

1. Sputum and nasal cultures: in high-risk patients a positive culture is strongly suggestive of invasive aspergillosis.
2. Serologic studies not helpful, rarely elevated in patients with invasive disease
3. Blood cultures: usually negative
4. Lung biopsy is necessary for definitive diagnosis
5. Biopsy and culture of extrapulmonary lesions

IMAGING STUDIES

ALLERGIC BRONCHOPULMONARY ASPERGILLOSIS:

- Chest roentgenograms show a variety of abnormalities from small, patchy, fleeting infiltrates (commonly in the upper lobes) to lobar consolidation and/or cavitation
- A majority of patients eventually develop central bronchiectasis

ASPERGILLOMAS: Chest roentgenograms or CT scans usually show the characteristic intracavity mass partially surrounded by a crescent of air (Fig. 1-32).

INVASIVE ASPERGILLOSIS: Chest roentgenograms and CT scanning may reveal cavity formation.

TREATMENT

ACUTE GENERAL Rx

ALLERGIC BRONCHOPULMONARY ASPERGILLOSIS:

- Prednisone (0.5 to 1 mg/kg PO) until the chest roentgenogram has cleared, followed by alternate-day therapy at 0.5 mg/kg PO (3 to 6 mo)
- If a patient is corticosteroid dependent, prophylaxis for the prevention of *Pneumocystis carinii* infection and maintenance of bone mineralization should be considered
- Bronchodilators and physiotherapy
- Serial chest roentgenograms and serum IgE useful in guiding treatment
- Itraconazole 200 mg po bid for 4 to 6 mo, then taper over 4 to 6 mo; may be considered as a corticosteroid sparing agent or if corticosteroids are ineffective

ASPERGILLOMAS:

- Controversial and problematic; the optimal treatment strategy is unknown
- Up to 10% of aspergillomas may resolve clinically without overt pharmacologic or surgical intervention
- Observation for asymptomatic patients
- Surgical resection/arterial embolization for those patients with severe hemoptysis or life-threatening hemorrhage
- For those patients at risk for marked hemoptysis with inadequate pulmonary reserve, consider itraconazole 200 to 400 mg/day PO

INVASIVE ASPERGILLOSIS:

- Amphotericin B deoxycholate 0.8 to 1.2 mg/kg IV qd to a total dose of 2 to 2.5 g; itraconazole 200 to 400 mg/d PO for 1 yr
- Amphotericin B lipid complex (ABLC) 5 mg/kg IV qd in those intolerant of or refractory to amphotericin B
- Amphotericin B colloidal dispersion (ABCD) 3 to 6 mg/kg IV qd; stepwise approach in those who have failed amphotericin B
- Liposomal amphotericin B (L-AMB) 3 to 5 mg/kg IV q day; stepwise approach is indicated as empiric therapy for presumed fungal infection in febrile neutropenic patients who are refractory to or intolerant of amphotericin B
- Itraconazole 200 mg IV bid × 4 doses followed by 200 mg IV qd or 200 mg tid for 4 days, then 200 mg bid PO—first-line therapy if not taking p450 inducers. Levels may be obtained to ensure compliance and adequate absorption.
- Voriconazole 6 mg/kg IV bid followed by 6 mg/kg IV for up to 27 days, then 400 mg/day PO for up to 24 wk. Note that the optimal dose regimens have yet to be defined
  Posaconazole and Ravuconazole are two new azoles that are currently under investigation
- Caspofungins (Candigas) is the first of a new class of antifungals, the echinocandins approved by the FDA for the treatment of invasive aspergillosis in patients who fail to respond to or are unable to tolerate other antifungal drugs. The recommended dosage is 70 mg on the first day and 50 mg daily thereafter, given as a single dose IV over 1 hr. The two other echinocandins under investigation are micafungin and anidulafungin
- Because azoles and echinocandins target different cellular sites, combination therapy may have additive activity against *Aspergillus sp.* This is still under investigation.
- Cytokine therapy may offer future treatment options in conjunction with the currently available antifungals

REFERRAL

Consultation with an infectious diseases specialist is highly recommended.

SUGGESTED READINGS

Ferry TG, Yates RR: Aspergillomas: should we treat them all? *Infect Dis Clin Pract* 7:122, 1998.

Herbrecht R et al: Voriconazole versus amphotericin B for primary therapy of invasive aspergillosis, *N Engl J Med* 347:408, 2002.

Marr KA et al: Combination antifungal therapy for invasive aspergillosis, *CID* 39:797, 2004.

Steinbach WJ, Stevens DA: Review of newer antifungal and immunomodulatory strategies for invasive aspergillosis, *Clin Infect Dis* 37(Supp 3):S 157, 2003.

Stevens DA et al: Practice guidelines for diseases caused by aspergillus, *CID* 30:696, 2000.

Vlaharis N, Ausamit T: Diagnosis and treatment of allergic bronchopulmonary aspergillosis, *Mayo Clinic Proc* 76:30, 2001.

AUTHOR: **SAJEEV HANDA, M.D.**

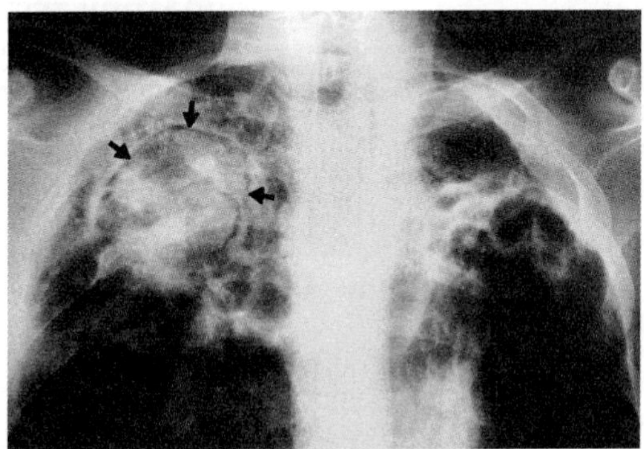

FIGURE 1-32 Fungus ball or mycetoma caused by Aspergillus. Coned-down PA view of the chest of a patient with biapical fibrocavitary tuberculosis accompanied by volume loss. There is a mass in a large right upper-lobe cavity with air dissecting into the cavity producing "air crescents" (*arrows*). (From McLoud TC: *Thoracic radiology: the requisites,* St Louis, 1998, Mosby.)

BASIC INFORMATION

DEFINITION

The American Thoracic Society defines asthma as a "disease characterized by an increased responsiveness of the trachea and bronchi to various stimuli and manifested by a widespread narrowing of the airways that changes in severity either spontaneously or as a result of treatment." *Status asthmaticus* can be defined as a severe continuous bronchospasm.

SYNONYMS

Bronchospasm
Reactive airway disease
Bronchial asthma

ICD-9CM CODES
493.9 Asthma, unspecified
493.1 Intrinsic asthma
493.0 Extrinsic asthma

EPIDEMIOLOGY & DEMOGRAPHICS

- Asthma affects 5% to 12% of the population and accounts for over 450,000 hospitalizations and nearly 2 million emergency department visits yearly in the U.S.
- It is more common in children (10% of children, 5% of adults).
- 50% to 80% of children with asthma develop symptoms before 5 yr of age.
- Overall asthma mortality in the U.S. is 20 per 1 million persons.

PHYSICAL FINDINGS & CLINICAL PRESENTATION

Physical examination varies with the stage and severity of asthma and may reveal only increased inspiratory and expiratory phases of respiration. Physical examination during status asthmaticus may reveal:

- Tachycardia and tachypnea
- Use of accessory respiratory muscles
- Pulsus paradoxus (inspiratory decline in systolic blood pressure >10 mm Hg)
- Wheezing: absence of wheezing (silent chest) or decreased wheezing can indicate worsening obstruction
- Mental status changes: generally secondary to hypoxia and hypercapnia and constitute an indication for urgent intubation
- Paradoxic abdominal and diaphragmatic movement on inspiration (detected by palpation over the upper part of the abdomen in a semirecumbent position): important sign of impending respiratory crisis, indicates diaphragmatic fatigue
- The following abnormalities in vital signs are indicative of severe asthma:
  1. Pulsus paradoxus >18 mm Hg
  2. Respiratory rate >30 breaths/min
  3. Tachycardia with heart rate >120 beats/min

ETIOLOGY

- Intrinsic asthma: occurs in patients who have no history of allergies; may be triggered by upper respiratory infections or psychologic stress
- Extrinsic asthma (allergic asthma): brought on by exposure to allergens (e.g., dust mites, cat allergen, industrial chemicals)
- Exercise-induced asthma: seen most frequently in adolescents; manifests with bronchospasm following initiation of exercise and improves with discontinuation of exercise
- Drug-induced asthma: often associated with use of NSAIDs, β-blockers, sulfites, certain foods and beverages
- There is a strong association of the ADAM 33 gene with asthma and bronchial hyperresponsiveness

DIAGNOSIS

DIFFERENTIAL DIAGNOSIS

- CHF
- COPD
- Pulmonary embolism (in adult and elderly patients)
- Foreign body aspiration (most frequent in younger patients)
- Pneumonia and other upper respiratory infections
- Rhinitis with postnasal drip
- TB
- Hypersensitivity pneumonitis
- Anxiety disorder
- Wegener's granulomatosis
- Diffuse interstitial lung disease

WORKUP

Medical history, physical examination, pulmonary function studies and peak flow meter determination, blood gas analysis and oximetry (during acute bronchospasm), chest radiography if infection is suspected

LABORATORY TESTS

Laboratory tests can be normal if obtained during a stable period. The following laboratory abnormalities may be present during an acute bronchospasm:

- ABGs can be used in staging the severity of an asthmatic attack:

Mild: decreased Pa_{O_2} and Pa_{CO_2}, increased pH

Moderate: decreased Pa_{O_2}, normal Pa_{CO_2}, normal pH

Severe: marked decreased Pa_{O_2}, increased Pa_{CO_2}, and decreased pH

- CBC, leukocytosis with "left shift" may indicate the existence of bacterial infection.
- Sputum: eosinophils, Charcot-Leyden crystals, PMNs, and bacteria may be found on Gram stain in patients with pneumonia.
- Useful diagnostic tests for asthma:
  1. Pulmonary function studies: during acute severe bronchospasm, FEV1 is <1 L and peak expiratory flow rate (PEFR) <80 L/min
  2. Methacholine challenge test
  3. Skin test: to assess the role of atopy (when suspected)

IMAGING STUDIES

- Chest x-ray: usually normal, may show evidence of thoracic hyperinflation (e.g., flattening of the diaphragm, increased volume over the retrosternal air space)
- ECG: tachycardia, nonspecific ST-T wave changes are common during an asthmatic attack; may also show cor pulmonale, right bundle-branch block, right axial deviation, counter-clockwise rotation

TREATMENT

NONPHARMACOLOGIC THERAPY

- Avoidance of triggering factors (e.g., salicylates, sulfites)
- Encouragement of regular exercise (e.g., swimming)
- Patient education regarding warning signs of an attack and proper use of medications (e.g., correct use of inhalers)

GENERAL Rx

The Expert Panel of the National Asthma Education and Prevention Program (NAEPP) based on the classification of asthma severity recommends the following stepwise approach in the pharmacologic management of asthma in adults and children older than 5 yr:

STEP 1 (MILD INTERMITTENT ASTHMA): No daily medications are needed.

- Short-acting inhaled β_2-agonists as needed (e.g., albuterol [Ventolin, Proventil], terbutaline [Brethaire], bitolterol [Tornalate], pirbuterol [Maxair])

STEP 2 (MILD PERSISTENT ASTHMA): Daily treatment may be needed.

- Low-dose inhaled corticosteroid (e.g., beclomethasone [Beclovent, Vanceril], flunisolide [AeroBid], triamcinolone [Azmacort]) can be used.
- Cromolyn (Intal) or nedocromil (Tilade) can also be used.
- Additional considerations for long-term control are the use of the leukotriene receptor antagonist montelukast (Singulair).
- Quick relief of asthma can be achieved with short-acting inhaled β_2-agonists (see Step 1).

STEP 3 (MODERATE PERSISTENT ASTHMA): Daily medication is recommended.

- Low-dose or medium-dose inhaled corticosteroids (see Step 2) plus long-acting inhaled β_2-agonist (salmeterol [Serevent]), or long-acting oral β_2-agonists (e.g., albuterol, sustained-release tablets). Salmeterol is also available as a dry powder inhaler (Discus) that does not require a spacer device; the dosage is one puff bid. A salmeterol-fluticasone combination for the Discus inhaler (Advair) is now available and simplifies therapy for patients with asthma. It generally should be reserved for patients with at least moderately severe asthma not controlled by an inhaled corticosteroid alone.
- Use short-acting inhaled β-agonists on a prn basis for quick relief.

STEP 4 (SEVERE PERSISTENT ASTHMA):

- Daily treatment with high-dose inhaled corticosteroids plus long-acting inhaled β-agonists (e.g., long-acting oral β_2-agonist plus long-term systemic corticosteroids [e.g., methylprednisolone, prednisolone, prednisone] can be used.
- Short-acting β_2-agonists can be used on a prn basis for quick relief.

Treatment of *status asthmaticus* is as follows:

- Oxygen generally started at 2 to 4 L/min via nasal cannula or Venti-Mask at 40% FiO_2; further adjustments are made according to the ABGs.
- Bronchodilators: various agents and modalities are available. Inhaled bronchodilators are preferred when they can be administered quickly. Parenteral administration of sympathomimetics (e.g., SC epinephrine) when necessary should be accompanied by electrocardiographic monitoring.
- Albuterol (Proventil, Ventolin): 0.5 to 1 ml (2.5 to 5 mg) in 3 ml of saline solution tid or qid via nebulizer is effective.
- Corticosteroids
  1. Early administration is advised, particularly in patients using steroids at home.
  2. Patients may be started on hydrocortisone (Solu-Cortef) 2.5 to 4 mg/kg or methylprednisolone (Solu-Medrol) 0.5 to 1 mg/kg IV loading dose, then q6h prn; higher doses may be necessary in selected patients (particularly those receiving steroids at home); steroids given by inhalation (e.g., beclomethasone 2 inhalations qid, maximum 20 inhalations/day) are also useful for controlling bronchospasm and tapering oral steroids and should be used in all patients with severe asthma.
  3. Rapid but judicious tapering of corticosteroids will eliminate serious steroid toxicity; long-term low-dose methotrexate may be an effective means of reducing the systemic corticosteroid requirement in some patients with severe refractory asthma.
  4. The most common errors regarding steroid therapy in acute bronchospasms are the use of "too little, too late" and too rapid tapering with return of bronchospasm.
- IV hydration: judicious use is necessary to avoid CHF in elderly patients.
- IV antibiotics are indicated when there is suspicion of bacterial infection (e.g., infiltrate on chest x-ray, fever, or leukocytosis).
- Intubation and mechanical ventilation are indicated when previous measures fail to produce significant improvement.
- General anesthesia: halothane may reverse bronchospasm in a severe asthmatic who cannot be ventilated adequately by mechanical means.
- IV magnesium sulfate supplementation in children with low or borderline-low magnesium levels may improve acute bronchospasm. Several reports in recent literature point to the beneficial effect on bronchospasm with a 20-min infusion of 40 mg/kg, up to a maximum of 2 g of magnesium sulfate in patients with acute asthma attack.

REFERRAL

Box 1-2 describes indications for referral to an asthma specialist.

Comments

- Inhaled low dose corticosteroids are the single most effective therapy for adult patients with asthma who require more than an occasional use of short acting β_2-agonists to control their asthma.
- Leukotriene modifiers/receptor agonists represent a reasonable alternative in adults unable or unwilling to use corticosteroids; however, these agents are less effective than monotherapy with inhaled corticosteroids.
- Patients who remain symptomatic despite inhaled corticosteroids benefit from the addition of long-acting β_2-agonists.
- In patients with allergies and elevated serum IgE levels use of anti-IgE therapy is beneficial.

SUGGESTED READINGS

Braun-Fahrlander C et al: Environmental exposure to endotoxin and its relation to asthma in school-age children, *N Engl J Med* 347:869, 2002.

Ciarallo L et al: Higher dose IV magnesium therapy for children with moderate to severe acute asthma, *Arch Pediatr Adol Med* 154:979, 2000.

Diette GB et al: Asthma in older patients: factors associated with hospitalization, *Arch Intern Med* 162:1123, 2002.

Holgate ST: Therapeutic options for persistent asthma, *JAMA* 285:2637, 2001.

Mintz M: Asthma update: Part I. Diagnosis, monitoring, and prevention of disease progression, *Am Fam Physician* 70:893, 2004.

National Asthma Education and Prevention Program: *Expert panel report 2: guidelines for diagnosis and management of asthma,* Bethesda, Md, 1997, National Institutes of Health.

National Asthma Education and Prevention Program (NAEPP): Expert panel report: guidelines for the diagnosis and management of asthma—update on selected topics 2002, *J Allergy Clin Immunol* 110(suppl 5):5161, 2002.

Naureckas ET, Solway J: Mild asthma, *N Engl J Med* 345:1257, 2001.

Sin DD et al: Pharmacological management to reduce exacerbations in adults with asthma, *JAMA* 292:367, 2004.

Wood RA: Pediatric asthma, *JAMA* 288:745, 2002.

AUTHOR: **FRED F. FERRI, M.D.**

BOX 1-2 Possible Indications for Referral to an Asthma Specialist

Severe, acute asthma that has caused loss of consciousness, hypoxia, respiratory failure, convulsions, or near death

Poorly controlled asthma as indicated by admission to a hospital, frequent need for emergency care, need for oral corticosteroids, absence from school or work, disruption of sleep, interference with quality of life

Severe, persistent asthma requiring step 4 care (consider for patients who require step 3 care)

Patient less than 3 years old who requires step 3 or 4 care (consider for patient less than 3 years old who requires step 2 care)

Requirement for continuous oral corticosteroids or high-dose inhaled corticosteroids or more than two short courses of oral corticosteroids within 1 year

Need for additional diagnostic testing such as allergy skin testing, rhinoscopy, provocative challenge, complete pulmonary function testing, bronchoscopy

Consideration for immunotherapy

Need for additional education regarding asthma, complications of asthma and treatment of asthma, problems with adherence to management recommendations, or allergen avoidance

Uncertainty of diagnosis

Complications of asthma, including sinusitis, nasal polyposis, aspergillosis, severe rhinitis, vocal cord dysfunction, gastroesophageal reflux

Modified from National Asthma Education and Prevention Program, National Heart, Lung, and Blood Institute, Expert Panel Report 2: Guidelines for the diagnosis and management of asthma. Washington, DC, NIH Pub No 97-4051, July 1997.

BASIC INFORMATION

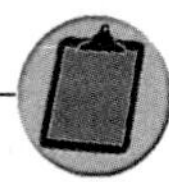

DEFINITION

Astrocytoma is a specific subtype of glioma, which refers to brain neoplasia arising from glial precursor cells within the CNS (astrocytes, oligodendrocytes, ependymal cells). Astrocytoma arises from astrocytes within the CNS and can be generally subclassified as low-grade (diffuse fibrillary astrocytoma) or high-grade (glioblastoma multiforme) tumor.

SYNONYMS

Astroglial neoplasms

ICD-9CM CODES
191.9 Astrocytoma, unspecified site

EPIDEMIOLOGY & DEMOGRAPHICS

- Incidence of primary brain tumors is 6/100,000 persons. Among these, low-grade astrocytoma is the most common.
- Approximately 18,000 primary brain tumors are diagnosed each year in the United States.
- In adults, glioblastoma is the most common brain tumor, followed by meningioma and astrocytoma. In children, astrocytomas are second only to medulloblastoma.
- Astrocytomas can be found at all ages, with an early peak between 0 to 4 years of age, followed by a trough between the ages of 15 to 24, and then a steady rise in incidence occurs.
- Low-grade astrocytomas represent about 15% of gliomas in adults and about 25% of all gliomas of the cerebral hemispheres in children. Average incidence is slightly less than 1 per 100,000 population per year in both groups.
- Peak age incidence of low-grade astrocytoma is 34 yr.
- Peak age incidence of anaplastic astrocytoma is 41 yr.
- Peak age incidence of glioblastoma is 53 yr.

PHYSICAL FINDINGS & CLINICAL PRESENTATION

The presenting symptoms of astrocytoma depend, in part, on the location of the lesion and its rate of growth. Astrocytomas classically present with any one or more of the following features:

- Headache (less frequent)
- New-onset seizure (>50%)
- Nausea and vomiting
- Focal neurologic deficit (less frequent)
- Change in mental status
- Papilledema (rare)

ETIOLOGY

- The specific etiology of astrocytoma is unknown.
- Genetic abnormalities leading to defective tumor-suppressing genes or activation of protooncogenes has been proposed. Loss of the CDKN2 gene on chromosome 9p has been associated with progression to higher grades in patients with low-grade astrocytomas.
- Genetic heterogeneity is common within these tumors, suggesting accumulation of genetic abnormalities and a multistep mechanism of progression to higher grades.

DIAGNOSIS

A provisional diagnosis of astrocytoma is made on clinical grounds and radiographic imaging studies. Tissue pathology is needed to establish the diagnosis and to grade the astrocytoma. Astrocytomas are commonly graded by the World Health Organization (WHO) or the Saint Anne–Mayo grading system.

- WHO grades astrocytomas as follows:
  1. Grade I: juvenile pilocytic astrocytoma, subependymal giant cell astrocytoma, and pleomorphic xanthoastrocytoma
  2. Grade II: low-grade astrocytoma (LGA)
  3. Grade III: anaplastic astrocytoma
  4. Grade IV: glioblastoma multiforme (GBM)
- The Saint Anne–Mayo system grades astrocytomas according to the presence or absence of four histologic features: nuclear atypia, mitoses, endothelial proliferation, and necrosis.
  1. Grade I tumors have none of the features.
  2. Grade II tumors have one feature.
  3. Grade III tumors have two features.
  4. Grade IV tumors have three or more features.
- Grades I and II astrocytomas are commonly called low-grade astrocytomas.
- Grades III and IV astrocytomas are called high-grade malignant astrocytomas.

DIFFERENTIAL DIAGNOSIS

The differential diagnosis is vast and includes any cause of headache, seizures, change in mental status, and focal neurologic deficits.

WORKUP

- A CT scan or MRI of the head essentially makes the diagnosis of an intracranial brain tumor. However, tissue is needed to establish a diagnosis of astrocytoma.
- Stereotactic biopsy under CT or MRI guidance has been shown to be a relatively safe and accurate method for diagnosis of LGA.
- In the presence of mass effect, either clinically or radiologically, craniotomy with open biopsy and tumor debulking is more appropriate than sterotactic biopsy to establish a tissue diagnosis.

LABORATORY TESTS

Blood tests are not very specific in the diagnosis of astrocytoma.

IMAGING STUDIES

- MRI is the diagnostic imaging study of choice. MRI and MRA are used to locate the margins of the tumor, distinguish vascular masses from tumors, detect low-grade astrocytomas not seen by CT scan, and provide clear views of the posterior fossa.

- Low-grade astrocytomas usually show mass effect and blurring of anatomic boundaries due to their infiltrative nature. Cystic change, focal calcification, or extension into contralateral structures may also be seen.
- High-grade astrocytomas are typically more associated with enhancement after IV contrast administration due to disruption of the blood-brain barrier. Only about 8% to 15% of LGAs enhance.
- PET scanning and MR spectroscopy are newer imaging modalities that may also play a role in tumor grading and in determining an appropriate site for biopsy.

ACUTE GENERAL Rx

- Controversy exists as to proper management of LGA. Almost all studies to date have been retrospective and flawed by patient and treatment selection bias.
- Nonsurgical observation is one treatment option that may be justified if risks of surgical or radiation treatment are greater than risks of medical treatment of presenting symptoms. Patients who may benefit most from observation are those who are at a young age with no or minimal neurologic deficit, and who present with seizures. This course of treatment rests on certainty of an accurate diagnosis on clinical and imaging grounds.
- Surgical morbidity and mortality is related to tumor location. Patients with deep tumors or tumors in eloquent cortex are at high risk for neurologic deterioration from surgical resection or biopsy.
- Surgery remains the initial treatment of almost all astrocytomas, particularly if the tumor is in an anatomically accessible location. Surgery helps in:
  1. Establishing a pathologic diagnosis
  2. Debulking the tumor
  3. Alleviating intracranial pressure
  4. Offering complete excision with hope for a cure
- Before surgery, dexamethasone 10 mg IV is given followed by 4-6 mg IV q6h.
- Phenytoin 300 mg qd is used for seizure control.

CHRONIC Rx

- Radiation therapy is used postoperatively in patients with low-grade astrocytoma (controversial) and in high-grade astrocytoma. Some authorities recommend waiting for symptoms to occur after surgery in patients with low-grade astrocytoma before using XRT.
- A prospective, randomized controlled trial has shown no survival benefit in treating LGA with adjuvant chemotherapy.
- Chemotherapeutic drugs carmustine and lomustine have been used with some effect in patients with high-grade astrocytoma.
- High-dose chemotherapy followed by autologous bone marrow transplantation is a consideration.

DISPOSITION

- Approximately 10% to 35% of astrocytomas (usually grade I pilocytic astrocytomas) are amenable to complete surgical excision and cure.
- In low-grade astrocytomas, the tumor is more infiltrative and therefore not amenable to complete excision. Nevertheless, most studies recommend surgery to remove as much of the tumor burden as possible.
- The prognosis of patients with low-grade astrocytoma is highly variable. A median of 7 yr is cited.
- Young age at diagnosis is by far the most important prognostic factor correlating with long survival. Other factors associated with a more favorable prognosis include good clinical condition at the time of diagnosis, seizure as a presenting symptom, and small preoperative tumor volume.
- Patient presentation with focal neurologic deficit or changes in personality/mental status is indicative of worse prognosis. Large preoperative tumor volume and high mitotic activity index are associated with a poorer prognosis in terms of overall and progression-free survival.
- Malignant astrocytomas, grades III and IV, usually require surgery for debulking. It is not known from prospective studies if surgery improves survival; however, retrospective studies suggest a survival benefit in the surgically treated group.
- Median survival for patients with high-grade astrocytomas is 2 yr for anaplastic type and 1 yr for glioblastoma multiforme.
- Most LGAs typically progress to higher-grade tumors, and progression to higher grades occurs more rapidly in older patients. WHO grade I astrocytomas do not usually progress to higher-grade tumors.

REFERRAL

A team of specialty consultations is indicated in patients diagnosed with astrocytoma. A neurosurgeon, radiation oncologist, and neurooncologist are all needed to assist in establishing the diagnosis and to provide immediate and follow-up treatment.

PEARLS & CONSIDERATIONS

COMMENTS

- Anaplastic astrocytomas and glioblastomas constitute >60% of all primary brain tumors.
- Approximately two thirds of LGA will progress to higher-grade lesions, but it is not possible to predict histologically which tumors will progress.
- It has not been proven that earlier treatment of LGA produces an increase in patient survival as measured from the time of diagnosis.
- Other treatment modalities including stereotaxic radiosurgery using a gamma knife and interstitial brachytherapy are available.

SUGGESTED READINGS

Black PM: Brain tumors: Part 1, *N Engl J Med* 324(21):1471, 1991.

Black PM: Brain tumors: Part 2, *N Engl J Med* 324(22):1555, 1991.

Burton EC, Prados MD: Malignant gliomas, *Curr Opin Oncol* 1(5):459, 2000.

Kaye AH, Walter DG: Low grade astrocytomas: controversies in management, *J Clin Neurosci* 7(6):475, 2000.

AUTHORS: **JASON IANNUCILLI, M.D.,** and **PETER PETROPOULOS, M.D.**

BASIC INFORMATION

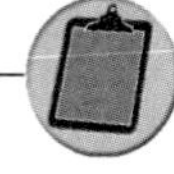

DEFINITION

An autosomal recessive disorder of childhood characterized by progressive cerebellar ataxia, choreoathetosis, telangiectasias of the skin and conjunctiva (see Fig. 1-33), increased sensitivity to ionizing radiation, and a predisposition to malignancies.

ICD-9CM CODES
334.8 Ataxia telangiectasia

EPIDEMIOLOGY & DEMOGRAPHICS

INCIDENCE: 1/40,000 live births (most common of the degenerative ataxias)
PREDOMINANT SEX: Males = Females
PEAK INCIDENCE: Childhood
GENETICS: Autosomal recessive, chromosome 11q22-q23. The defective gene product is *ATM,* a protein kinase that is thought to be a regulator of cell cycle checkpoint in response to DNA damage. Virtually every kindred has a distinct mutation.

PHYSICAL FINDINGS & CLINICAL PRESENTATION

- Children show normal early development until they start to walk, when gait and truncal ataxia become apparent.
- These findings are soon accompanied by polyneuropathy, progressive apraxia of eye movements, choreoathetosis, mild diabetes mellitus, growth failure, and signs of premature aging (graying of the hair).
- Telangiectatic lesions occur in the outer parts of the bulbar conjunctivae, over the ears, on exposed parts of the neck, on the bridge of the nose, and in the flexor creases of the forearms.
- Recurrent sinopulmonary infections occur secondary to impaired humoral and cellular immunity in about 70% of children
- Increased frequency of cancers is noted in approximately 20% of patients, most frequently acute lymphocytic leukemia or lymphoma.

DIAGNOSIS

DIFFERENTIAL DIAGNOSIS (OF EARLY ONSET ATAXIAS)

- Friedreich's ataxia
- Abetalipoproteinemia (Bassen-Kornzweig Syndrome)
- Acquired Vitamin E deficiency
- Early onset cerebellar ataxia with retained reflexes (EOCA)
- Ataxia associated with biochemical abnormalities: associated with ceroid lipofuscinosis, xeroderma pigmentosa, Cockayne's syndrome, adrenoleukodystrophy, metachromatic leukodystrophy, mitochondrial disease, sialidosis, Niemann Pick

WORKUP

- Patients should be evaluated for serum immunoglobulin levels (IgA, IgG, IgE and IgG subclasses), which are decreased or absent
- Karyotype: high incidence of chromosomal breaks, especially on chromosome 14; genetic testing for ATM protein and gene is now available
- CT or MRI scans will show cerebellar atrophy
- Fibroblasts can be screened in vitro for x-ray sensitivity and radioresistant DNA synthesis
- Pathology shows cerebellar degeneration, loss of pigmented neurons, and posterior column degeneration in the spinal cord

TREATMENT

- Supportive, no effective treatment to date
- Surveillance for infections and neoplasms; consider gamma-globulin injections to supplement immune system
- Minimize radiation as may induce further chromosomal damage and lead to neoplasms
- Physical and occupational therapy

PROGNOSIS

- 67% of children die by age 20, typically from infection or neoplasm

SUGGESTED READINGS

Boutwood J: Ataxia telangiectasia gene mutations in leukemia and lymphoma, *J Clin Pathol* 54:512, 2001.
Meyn MS: Ataxia-telangiectasia, cancer and the pathobiology at the AMT gene, *Clin Genet* 55(5):289, 1999.
Nowak-Wegrzyn A: Immunodeficiency and infections in ataxia-telangiectasia, *J Pediatr* 144:505, 2004.
Rotman G: ATM: from gene to function, *Hum Mol Genet* 7:1555, 1998.

AUTHORS: **NICOLE J. ULLRICH, M.D., PH.D.,** and **MAITREYI MAZUMDAR, M.D.**

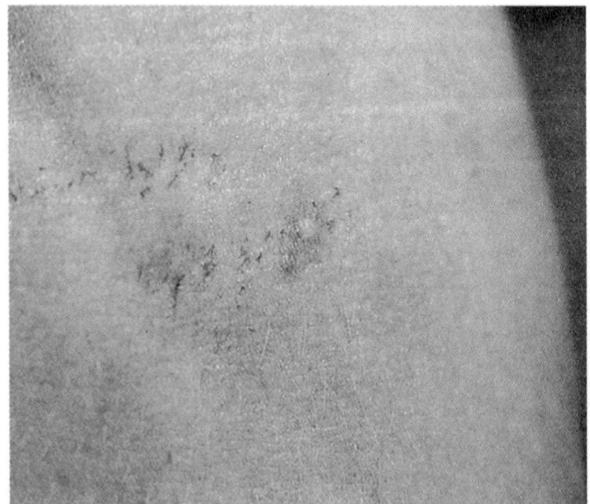

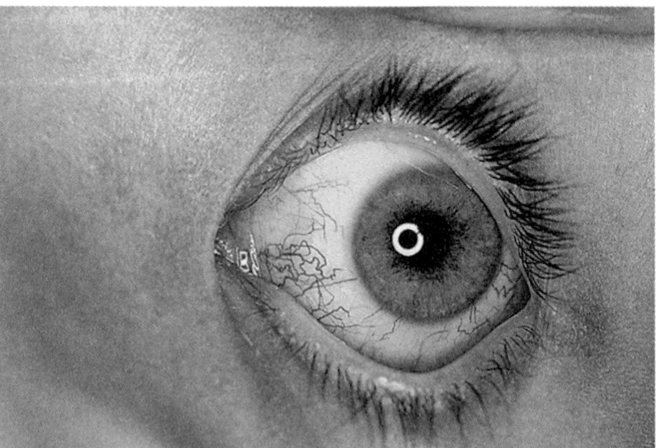

FIGURE 1-33 Ataxia telangiectasia. (From Callen JP [ed]: *Color atlas of dermatology,* ed 2, Philadelphia, 2000, WB Saunders.)

BASIC INFORMATION

DEFINITION

Atelectasis is the collapse of lung volume.

ICD-9CM CODES
518.0 Atelectasis

EPIDEMIOLOGY & DEMOGRAPHICS

- Occurs frequently in patients receiving mechanical ventilation with higher Fio_2
- Dependent regions of the lung are more prone to atelectasis: they are partially compressed, they are not as well ventilated, and there is no spontaneous drainage of secretions with gravity

PHYSICAL FINDINGS & CLINICAL PRESENTATION

- Decreased or absent breath sounds
- Abnormal chest percussion
- Cough, dyspnea, decreased vocal fremitus and vocal resonance
- Diminished chest expansion, tachypnea, tachycardia

ETIOLOGY

- Mechanical ventilation with higher Fio_2
- Chronic bronchitis
- Cystic fibrosis
- Endobronchial neoplasms
- Foreign bodies
- Infections (e.g., TB, histoplasmosis)
- Extrinsic bronchial compression from neoplasms, aneurysms of ascending aorta, enlarged left atrium
- Sarcoidosis
- Silicosis
- Anterior chest wall injury, pneumothorax
- Alveolar injury (e.g., toxic fumes, aspiration of gastric contents)
- Pleural effusion, expanding bullae
- Chest wall deformity (e.g., scoliosis)
- Muscular weaknesses or abnormalities (e.g., neuromuscular disease)
- Mucus plugs from asthma, allergic bronchopulmonary aspergillosis, postoperative state

DIAGNOSIS

DIFFERENTIAL DIAGNOSIS

- Neoplasm
- Pneumonia
- Encapsulated pleural effusion
- Abnormalities of brachiocephalic vein and of the left pulmonary ligament

WORKUP

- Chest x-ray (Fig. 1-34)
- CT scan and fiberoptic bronchoscopy (selected patients)

IMAGING STUDIES

- Chest x-ray will confirm diagnosis.
- CT scan is useful in patients with suspected endobronchial neoplasm or extrinsic bronchial compression.
- Fiberoptic bronchoscopy (selected patients) is useful for removal of foreign body or evaluation of endobronchial and peribronchial lesions.

TREATMENT

NONPHARMACOLOGIC THERAPY

- Deep breathing, mobilization of the patient
- Incentive spirometry
- Tracheal suctioning
- Humidification
- Chest physiotherapy with percussion and postural drainage

ACUTE GENERAL Rx

- Positive-pressure breathing (CPAP by face mask, positive end-expiratory pressure [PEEP] for patients on mechanical ventilation)
- Use of mucolytic agents (e.g., acetylcysteine [Mucomyst])
- Recombinant human DNase (dornase alpha) in patients with cystic fibrosis
- Bronchodilator therapy in selected patients

CHRONIC Rx

Chest physiotherapy, humidification of inspired air, frequent nasotracheal suctioning

DISPOSITION

Prognosis varies with the underlying etiology.

REFERRAL

- Bronchoscopy for removal of foreign body or plugs unresponsive to conservative treatment
- Surgical referral for removal of obstructing neoplasms

PEARLS & CONSIDERATIONS

COMMENTS

Patients should be educated that frequent changes of position are helpful in clearing secretions. Sitting the patient upright in a chair is recommended to increase both volume and vital capacity relative to the supine position.

AUTHOR: **FRED F. FERRI, M.D.**

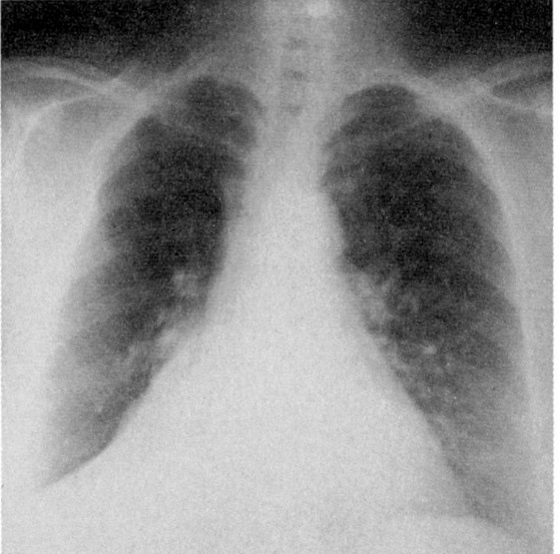

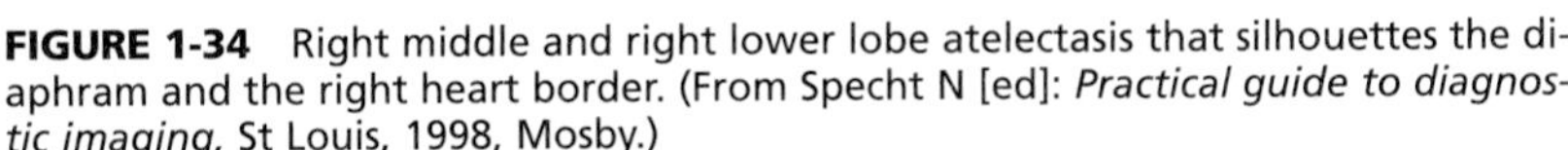

FIGURE 1-34 Right middle and right lower lobe atelectasis that silhouettes the diaphram and the right heart border. (From Specht N [ed]: *Practical guide to diagnostic imaging,* St Louis, 1998, Mosby.)

Atrial Fibrillation (PTG)

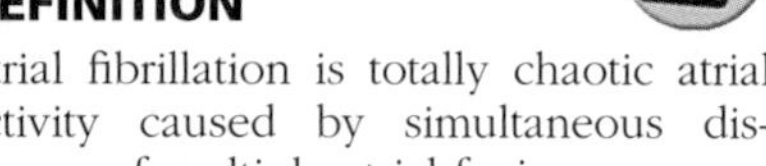

BASIC INFORMATION

DEFINITION

Atrial fibrillation is totally chaotic atrial activity caused by simultaneous discharge of multiple atrial foci.

SYNONYMS

AF
A-fib

ICD-9CM CODES
427.31 Atrial fibrillation

EPIDEMIOLOGY & DEMOGRAPHICS

The prevalence of atrial fibrillation increases with age, from 2% in the general population, to 5% in patients older than 60 yr, to 9% of those aged 80 years or older

PHYSICAL FINDINGS & CLINICAL PRESENTATION

Clinical presentation is variable:

- Most common complaint: palpitations
- Fatigue, dizziness, light-headedness in some patients
- A few completely asymptomatic patients
- Cardiac auscultation revealing irregularly irregular rhythm

ETIOLOGY

- Coronary artery disease
- MS, MR, AS, AR
- Thyrotoxicosis
- Pulmonary embolism, COPD
- Pericarditis
- Myocarditis, cardiomyopathy
- Tachycardia-bradycardia syndrome
- Alcohol abuse
- MI
- WPW syndrome
- Other causes: left atrial myxoma, atrial septal defect, carbon monoxide poisoning, pheochromocytoma, idiopathic, hypoxia, hypokalemia, sepsis, pneumonia

DIAGNOSIS

DIFFERENTIAL DIAGNOSIS

- Multifocal atrial tachycardia
- Atrial flutter
- Frequent atrial premature beats

WORKUP

New-onset atrial fibrillation: ECG, echocardiogram, Holter monitor (selected patients), and laboratory evaluation

LABORATORY TESTS

- TSH, free T_4
- Serum electrolytes

IMAGING STUDIES

- ECG (see Fig. 1-35 for "Atrial flutter and atrial fibrillation")
  1. Irregular, nonperiodic wave forms (best seen in V1) reflecting continuous atrial reentry
  2. Absence of P waves
  3. Conducted QRS complexes showing no periodicity
- Echocardiography to evaluate left atrial size and detect valvular disorders
- Holter monitor: useful only in selected patients to evaluate paroxysmal atrial fibrillation

TREATMENT

NONPHARMACOLOGIC THERAPY

- Avoidance of alcohol in patients with suspected excessive alcohol use
- Avoidance of caffeine and nicotine

ACUTE GENERAL Rx

New-onset atrial fibrillation

- If the patient is hemodynamically unstable, perform synchronized cardioversion following immediate conscious sedation with a rapid short-acting sedative (e.g., midazolam).
- If the patient is hemodynamically stable, treatment options include the following:
  1. Diltiazem 0.25 mg/kg given over 2 min followed by a second dose of 0.35 mg/kg 15 min later if the rate is not slowed. May then follow with IV infusion 10 mg/hr (range 5-15 mg/hr). Onset of action following IV administration is usually within 3 min, with peak effect most often occurring within 10 min. After the ventricular rate is slowed, the patient can be changed to oral diltiazem 60 to 90 mg q 6 hr.
  2. Verapamil 2.5 to 5 mg IV initially, then 5 to 10 mg IV 10 min later if the rate is still not slowed. After the ventricular rate is slowed, the patient can be changed to oral verapamil 80 to 120 mg q 6-8 h.
  3. Esmolol, metoprolol, atenolol are b-blockers that are available in IV preparations that can be used in atrial fibrillation.
  4. Other medications useful for converting atrial fibrillation to sinus rhythm are ibutilide, flecainide, propafenone, disopyramide, amiodarone, and quinidine.
  5. Digoxin is not a very potent AV nodal blocking agent and cannot be relied upon for acute control of the ventricular response. When used, give 0.5 mg IV loading dose (slow), then 0.25 mg IV 6 hr later. A third dose may be needed after 6 to 8 hr; daily dose varies from 0.125 to 0.25 mg (decrease dosage in patients with renal insufficiency and elderly patients). Digoxin should be avoided in Wolff-Parkinson-White patients with atrial fibrillation. Procainamide is the preferred pharmacologic agent in these patients.
- IV heparin or SC low-molecular-weight heparin.
- Cardioversion is indicated if the ventricular rate is >140 bpm and the patient is symptomatic (particularly in acute MI, chest pain, dyspnea, CHF) or when there is no conversion to normal sinus rhythm after 3 days of pharmacologic therapy. The likelihood of cardioversion-related clinical thromboembolism is low in patients with atrial fibrillation lasting <48 hr. Patients with atrial fibrillation lasting >2 days have a 5% to 7% risk of clinical thromboembolism if cardioversion is not preceded by several weeks of warfarin therapy. However, if transesophageal echocardiography reveals no atrial thrombus, cardioversion may be performed safely after only a short period of anticoagulant therapy. Anticoagulant therapy should be continued for at least 1 mo after cardioversion to minimize the incidence of adverse thromboembolic events following conversion from atrial fibrillation to sinus rhythm.
- Anticoagulate with warfarin (unless patient has specific contraindications).
- Long-term anticoagulation with warfarin (adjusted to maintain an INR of 2 to 3) is indicated in all patients with atrial fibrillation and associated cardiovascular disease, including the following:
  1. Rheumatic valvular disease (MS, MR, AI)
  2. Aortic stenosis
  3. Prostatic mitral valve
  4. History of previous embolism

5. Known cardiac thrombus
6. CHF
7. Cardiomyopathy with poor left ventricular function
8. Nonrheumatic heart disease (e.g., hypertensive cardiovascular disease, coronary artery disease, ASD)

- Anticoagulation is generally not recommended in young patients with lone atrial fibrillation (no associated cardiovascular disease).
- Aspirin 325 mg/day may be a suitable alternative to warfarin in patients >70 yr with increased risk of bleeding.
- Ximelagran is a promising new oral direct thrombin inhibitor not currently FDA approved that is also effective for stroke prevention in patients with nonvalvular atrial fibrillation. Its advantages over warfarin are no need to titrate dose and no routine coagulation monitoring.
- Medical cardioversion:
  1. Attempts at medical (pharmacologic) intervention should be considered only after proper anticoagulation because cardioversion can lead to systemic emboli. Following successful cardioversion, anticoagulation with warfarin should be continued for 4 wk.
  2. Useful agents for medical cardioversion are quinidine, flecainide, propafenone, amiodarone, ibutilide, sotalol, dofetilide, and procainamide.
  3. Amiodarone appears to be the most effective agent for converting to sinus rhythm in patients who do not respond to other agents. Amiodarone therapy should be considered for patients with recent atrial fibrillation and structural heart disease, particularly those with left ventricular dysfunction. Amiodarone should also be considered for patients with refractory conditions who do not have heart disease, before therapies with irreversible effects such as AV nodal ablation are attempted.

CHRONIC Rx

- Anticoagulation with warfarin (see "Acute General Rx")
- Rate control with atenolol, metoprolol, verapamil, or diltiazem

DISPOSITION

Factors associated with maintenance of sinus rhythm following cardioversion:

- Left atrium diameter <60 mm
- Absence of mitral valve disease
- Short duration of atrial fibrillation

REFERRAL

Surgical treatment of atrial fibrillation:

- The maze procedure with its recent modifications creating electrical barriers to the macroreentrant circuits that are thought to underlie atrial fibrillation is being performed with good results in several medical centers (preservation of sinus rhythm in >95% of patients without the use of long-term antiarrhythmic medication). Clear indications for its use remain undefined. Generally surgery is reserved for patients with rapid heart rate refractory to pharmacologic therapy or who cannot tolerate pharmacologic therapy.
- Catheter-based radiofrequency ablation procedures designed to eliminate atrial fibrillation represent newer approaches to atrial fibrillation.
- Implantable pacemakers and defibrillators that combine pacing and cardioversion therapies to both prevent and treat atrial defibrillation are likely to have an increasing role in the future management of atrial fibrillation.

PEARLS & CONSIDERATIONS

COMMENTS

The American Academy of Family Physicians and the American College of Physicians provide the following recommendations for the management of newly detected atrial fibrillation:

1. Rate control with chronic anticoagulation is the recommended strategy for the majority of patients with atrial fibrillation. Rhythm control has not been shown to be superior to rate control (with chronic anticoagulation) in reducing morbidity and mortality and may be inferior in some patient subgroups to rate control. Rhythm control is appropriate when based on other special considerations, such as patient symptoms, exercise tolerance, and patient preference.
2. Patients with atrial fibrillation should receive chronic anticoagulation with adjusted-dose warfarin, unless they are at low risk of stroke or have a specific contraindication to the use of warfarin (thrombocytopenia, recent trauma or surgery, alcoholism).
3. For patients with atrial fibrillation, the following drugs are recommended for their demonstrated efficacy in rate control during exercise and while at rest: atenolol, metoprolol, diltiazem, and verapamil (drugs listed alphabetically by class). Digoxin is only effective for rate control at rest and therefore should only be used as a second-line agent for rate control in atrial fibrillation.
4. For those patients who elect to undergo acute cardioversion to achieve sinus rhythm in atrial fibrillation, both direct-current cardioversion and pharmacologic conversion are appropriate options.
5. Both transesophageal echocardiography with short-term prior anticoagulation followed by early acute cardioversion (in absence of intracardiac thrombus) with postcardioversion anticoagulation versus delayed cardioversion with pre- and post-anticoagulation are appropriate management strategies for those patients who elect to undergo cardioversion.

Most patients converted to sinus rhythm from atrial fibrillation should not be placed on rhythm maintenance therapy since the risks outweigh the benefits. In a selected group of patients whose quality of life is compromised by atrial fibrillation, the recommended pharmacologic agents for rhythm maintenance are amiodarone, disopyramide, propafenone, and sotalol (drugs listed in alphabetical order). The choice of agent depends on specific risk of side effects based on patient characteristics.

SUGGESTED READINGS

Cooper JM et al: Implantable devices for the treatment of atrial fibrillation, *N Engl J Med* 346:2062, 2002.

Ezekowitz M, Falk RH: The increasing need for anticoagulation therapy to prevent stroke in patients with atrial fibrillation, *Mayo Clin Proc* 79(7):904, 2004.

Hart RG: Atrial fibrillation and stroke prevention, *N Engl J Med* 349:1015, 2003.

Hilek E et al: Effect of intensity of oral anticoagulation on stroke severity and mortality in atrial fibrillation. *N Engl J Med* 349:1019, 2003

Klein AL et al: Use of transesophageal echocardiography to guide cardioversions in patients with atrial fibrillation, *N Engl J Med* 344:1411, 2001.

Petersen P et al: Ximelagran versus warfarin for stroke prevention in patients with nonvalvular atrial fibrillation. SPORTIF II: A dose-guiding, tolerability, and safety study, *J Am Coll Cardiol* 41:1445, 2003.

Snow V et al: Management of newly detected atrial fibrillation: a clinical practice guideline from the Academy of Family Physicians and the American College of Physicians, *Ann Intern Med* 139:1009, 2003.

AUTHOR: **FRED F. FERRI, M.D.**

Atrial Flutter 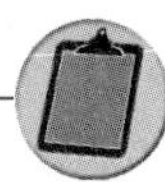

BASIC INFORMATION

DEFINITION

Atrial flutter is a rapid atrial rate of 280 to 340 bpm with varying degrees of intraventricular block. It is a macrorentrant tachycardia, most often involving right atrial tissue.

ICD-9CM CODES
427.32 Atrial flutter

EPIDEMIOLOGY & DEMOGRAPHICS

Atrial flutter is common during the first week after open heart surgery.

PHYSICAL FINDINGS & CLINICAL PRESENTATION

- Fast pulse rate (approximately 150 bpm)
- Symptoms of cardiac failure, lightheadedness, and angina pectoris

ETIOLOGY

- Atherosclerotic heart disease
- MI
- Thyrotoxicosis
- Pulmonary embolism
- Mitral valve disease
- Cardiac surgery
- COPD
- Atrial flutter can also occur spontaneously or as a result of organization of atrial fibrillation from antiarrhythmic therapy

DIAGNOSIS

DIFFERENTIAL DIAGNOSIS

- Atrial fibrillation
- Paroxysmal atrial tachycardia

WORKUP

- ECG
- Laboratory evaluation

LABORATORY TESTS

- Thyroid function studies
- Serum electrolytes

IMAGING STUDIES

ECG (Fig. 1-35)

- Regular, "sawtooth," or "F" wave pattern, best seen in II, III, and AVF and secondary to atrial depolarization
- AV conduction block (2:1, 3:1, or varying)

TREATMENT

NONPHARMACOLOGIC THERAPY

- Valsalva maneuver or carotid sinus massage usually slows the ventricular rate (increases grade of AV block) and may make flutter waves more evident.
- Electrical cardioversion is given at low energy levels (20 to 25 J).

ACUTE GENERAL Rx

- In absence of cardioversion, IV diltiazem or digitalization may be tried to slow the ventricular rate and convert flutter to fibrillation. Esmolol, verapamil, and adenosine may also be effective.
- Atrial pacing may also terminate atrial flutter.
- Atrial flutter is frequently associated with intermittent atrial fibrillation. It may be prudent to anticoagulate patients with atrial flutter and coexisting medical disorders (e.g., diabetes mellitus, hypertension, cardiac disease) before cardioversion. Anticoagulation should also be considered for all patients with atrial flutter who are older than 65 years of age.

CHRONIC Rx

- Chronic atrial flutter may respond to amiodarone.
- Radiofrequency ablation to interrupt the atrial flutter is very effective for patients with chronic or recurring atrial flutter and is generally considered first line therapy in those with recurrent episodes of atrial flutter.

DISPOSITION

- More than 85% of patients convert to regular sinus rhythm following cardioversion with as little as 25 to 50 J.
- Lone atrial flutter has a stroke risk at least as high as lone atrial fibrillation and carries a higher risk for subsequent development of atrial fibrillation than in the general population.

REFERRAL

For radiofrequency ablation in patients with chronic or recurring atrial flutter

PEARLS & CONSIDERATIONS

COMMENTS

- Lone atrial flutter has a stroke risk at least as high as lone atrial fibrillation and carries a higher risk for subsequent development of atrial fibrillation than in the general population.
- Anticoagulation should be considered for all patients with atrial flutter who are older than 65 years of age.

SUGGESTED READING

Halligan SC et al: The natural history of long atrial flutter, *Ann Int Med* 140:265, 2004.

AUTHOR: **FRED F. FERRI, M.D.**

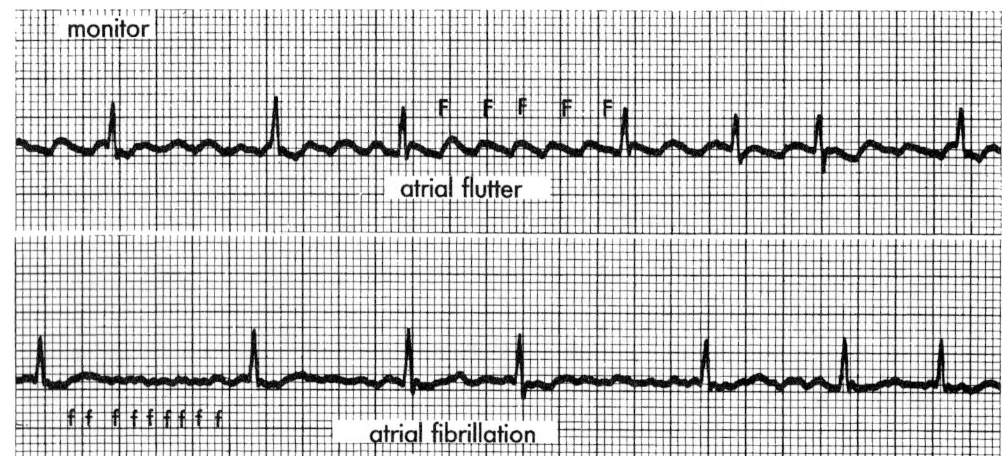

FIGURE 1-35 Atrial flutter and fibrillation. Notice the sawtooth waves with atrial flutter *(F)* and the irregular fibrillatory waves with atrial fibrillation *(f)*. (From Goldberger AL [ed]: *Clinical electrocardiography,* ed 5, St Louis, 1994, Mosby.)

BASIC INFORMATION

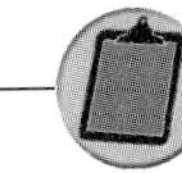

DEFINITION

- Atrial myxoma is a benign neoplasm of mesenchymal origin, and is the most common primary tumor of the heart

ICD-9CM CODES
212.7 Benign neoplasm, heart

EPIDEMIOLOGY & DEMOGRAPHICS

- Atrial myxomas account for 50% of all primary tumors of the heart.
- Approximately 75% of myxomas arise from the left atrium in close relationship to the fossa ovalis. Up to 15% of myxomas arise from the right atrium, with the remaining 10% arising from the left ventricle or from multiple sites.
- The prevalence of atrial myxoma is approximately 75 cases/1 million autopsies.
- Average age of sporadic cases is 56 yr.
- Average age of familial cases is 25 yr.
- 70% of sporadic cases occur in females.

PHYSICAL FINDINGS & CLINICAL PRESENTATION

Patients with atrial myxomas characteristically present in one of three ways:

- Mechanical valve obstruction (e.g., mitral or tricuspid valve)
  1. Dyspnea on exertion
  2. Orthopnea
  3. Paroxysmal nocturnal dyspnea
  4. Edema
  5. Dizziness, lightheadedness, or syncope
  6. Elevated jugular venous pressure
  7. Loud S1, increased intensity of the P2 component of S2 secondary to pulmonary hypertension
  8. Systolic murmurs of mitral regurgitation or tricuspid regurgitation and diastolic murmurs of mitral stenosis or tricuspid stenosis, depending on which chamber the myxoma arises from
  9. Third heart sound called a "tumor plop"
  10. Atrial fibrillation with an irregularly irregular pulse
- Systemic embolization may occur in up to 30% of cases leading to:
  1. Cerebrovascular accidents
  2. Pulmonary embolism
  3. Paradoxical embolism
- Constitutional symptoms
  1. Fever
  2. Weight loss
  3. Arthralgias
  4. Raynaud phenomenon

ETIOLOGY

- Most cases (90%) of atrial myxomas are sporadic with no known cause. In the remaining 10% of cases a familial pattern occurs having an autosomal dominant transmission. Some patients with familial cardiac myxomas have "Carney's syndrome," which consists of myxomas in other locations, skin pigmentation, and tumors of endocrine origin.

DIAGNOSIS

DIFFERENTIAL DIAGNOSIS

- Mitral stenosis
- Mitral regurgitaiton
- Tricuspid stenosis
- Tricuspid regurgitation
- Pulmonary hypertension
- Endocarditis
- Vasculitis
- Left atrial thrombus
- Pulmonary embolism
- Cerebrovascular accidents
- Collagen-vascular disease
- Carcinoid heart disease
- Ebstein's anomaly

WORKUP

A high index of suspicion is needed to make the diagnosis of atrial myxoma because the clinical manifestations are similar to many common cardiovascular and pulmonary diseases.

LABORATORY TESTS

Although not very specific, the following laboratory values may be abnormal in patients with atrial myxomas:

- CBC: anemia, polycythemia, thrombocytopenia may occur
- Erythrocyte sedimentation rate, C-reactive protein, and serum immunoglobulins are commonly elevated
- ECG: patients with atrial myxomas may have findings of left atrial enlargement, right atrial enlargement, atrial fibrillation, atrial flutter, premature ventricular contractions, ventricular tachycardia, and ventricular fibrillation

IMAGING STUDIES

- Echocardiography: initial imaging procedure of choice in suspected cases of atrial myxoma
- Chest x-ray examination: altered cardiac contour and chamber enlargement
- Transesophageal echocardiography: may pick up masses not visualized by transthoracic echocardiography
- MRI: Aids in delineating size, shape, and tumor characterizations
- Cardiac catheterization: usually not needed in diagnosing atrial myxoma; however, may be required in some circumstances to rule out coronary artery disease

TREATMENT

NONPHARMACOLOGIC THERAPY

None

ACUTE GENERAL THERAPY

- Surgical excision is the treatment of choice.
- Surgery should be done promptly because sudden death can occur while waiting for the procedure (see "Disposition").

CHRONIC Rx

Postoperative arrhythmias and conductions abnormalities were present in 26% of patients and can be treated according to standard convention.

DISPOSITION

- Surgical results have reported a 95% survival rate after a follow-up of 3 yr.
- Up to 5% of sporadic cases of atrial myxoma may recur within the first 6 yr after surgery.
- Up to 20% of familial cases of atrial myxoma may recur after surgery.
- Sudden death has been reported to occur in up to 15% of patients with atrial myxoma, with death resulting from coronary or systemic embolization or by obstruction of blood flow at the mitral or tricuspid valve.

REFERRAL

- Consultation with a cardiologist is recommended in the initial workup of a patient with signs and symptoms of valvular obstruction and/or systemic embolization thought to arise from the heart.
- Once the noninvasive workup has revealed a cardiac tumor, consultation with a cardiovascular surgeon is recommended for prompt surgical excision.

PEARLS & CONSIDERATIONS

COMMENTS

Although recurrence of atrial myxoma is rare following operative excision, yearly echocardiograms should be performed.

SUGGESTED READINGS

Bhan A et al: Surgical experience with intracardiac myxomas: long-term follow-up, *Ann Thorac Surg* 66:810, 1998.

Centofanti P et al: Primary cardiac tumors: early and late results of surgical treatment in 91 patients, *Ann Thorac Surg* 68:1235, 1999.

Pérez de Isla L et al: Diagnosis and treatment of cardiac myxomas by transesophageal echocardiography, *Am J Cardiol* 90(12):1419, 2002.

Pinede L, Duhaut P, Loire R: Clinical presentation of left atrial cardiac myxoma. A series of 112 consecutive patients, *Medicine* 80:159, 2001.

Pucci A et al: Histopathologic and clinical characterization of cardiac myxoma: review of 53 cases from a single institution, *Am Heart J* 140:134, 2000.

AUTHORS: **GAURAV CHOUDHARY, M.D.**, and **WEN-CHIH WU, M.D.**

Atrial Septal Defect

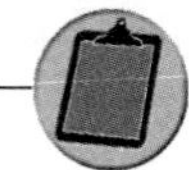

BASIC INFORMATION

DEFINITION

Atrial septal defect (ASD) is an abnormal opening in the atrial septum that allows for blood flow between the atria. There are several forms (Fig. 1-36):

- Ostium primum: defect low in the septum
- Ostium secundum: occurs mainly in the region of the fossa ovalis
- Sinus venous defect: less common form, involves the upper part of the septum

SYNONYMS

ASD

ICD-9CM CODES
429.71 Atrial septal defect

EPIDEMIOLOGY & DEMOGRAPHICS

- 80% of cases of ASD involve persistence of ostium secundum.
- Incidence is higher in females.
- ASD accounts for 8% to 10% of congenital heart abnormalities.

PHYSICAL FINDINGS & CLINICAL PRESENTATION

- Pansystolic murmur best heard at apex secondary to mitral regurgitation (ostium primum defect)
- Widely split S_2
- Visible and palpable pulmonary artery pulsations
- Ejection systolic flow murmur
- Prominent right ventricular impulse
- Cyanosis and clubbing (severe cases)
- Exertional dyspnea
- Patients with small defects: generally asymptomatic

ETIOLOGY

Unknown

DIAGNOSIS

DIFFERENTIAL DIAGNOSIS

- Primary pulmonary hypertension
- Pulmonary stenosis
- Rheumatic heart disease
- Mitral valve prolapse
- Cor pulmonale

WORKUP

- ECG
- Chest x-ray examination
- Echocardiography
- Cardiac catheterization

IMAGING STUDIES

- ECG
  1. Ostium primum defect: left axis deviation, RBBB, prolongation of PR interval
  2. Sinus venous defect: leftward deviation of P axis
  3. Ostium secundum defect: right axis deviation, right bundle-branch block
- Chest x-ray: cardiomegaly, enlargement of right atrium and ventricle, increased pulmonary vascularity, small aortic knob
- Echocardiography with saline bubble contrast and Doppler flow studies: may demonstrate the defect and the presence of shunting. Transesophageal echocardiography is much more sensitive than transthoracic echocardiography in identifying sinus venous defects and is preferred by some for the initial diagnostic evaluation
- Cardiac catheterization: confirms the diagnosis in patients who are candidates for surgery. It is useful if the patient has some anatomic finding on echocardiography that is not completely clear or has significant elevation of pulmonary artery pressures

TREATMENT

NONPHARMACOLOGIC THERAPY

Avoidance of strenuous activity in symptomatic patients

GENERAL Rx

- Children and infants: closure of ASD before age 10 yr is indicated if pulmonary:systemic flow ratio is >1.5:1.
- Adults: closure is indicated in symptomatic patients with shunts >2:1.
- Surgery should be avoided in patients with pulmonary hypertension with reversed shunting (Eisenmenger's syndrome) because of increased risk of right heart failure.
- Transcatheter closure is advocated in children when feasible.
- Prophylactic β-blocker therapy to prevent atrial arrhythmias should be considered in adults with ASD.
- Surgical closure is indicated in all patients with ostium primum defect and significant shunting unless patient has significant pulmonary vascular disease.

DISPOSITION

- Mortality is high in patients with significant ostium primum defect.
- Patients with small shunts have a normal life expectancy.
- Surgical mortality varies with the age of the patient and the presence of cardiac failure and systolic pulmonary artery hypertension; mortality ranges from <1% in young patients (<45 yr old) to >10% in elderly patients with presence of heart failure and systolic pulmonary hypertension.
- Preoperative atrial fibrillation is a risk factor for immediate postoperative and long-term atrial fibrillation.
- Thromboembolism after surgical repair of an ASD in an adult can occur in the early postoperative period. Giving early postoperative anticoagulation in patients >35 yr of age at the time of ASD repair and continuing it for at least 6 mo will decrease the risk.

SUGGESTED READING

Moodie DS, Sterba R: Long-term outcomes excellent for ASD repair in adults, *Cleve Clin J Med* 67:591, 2000.

AUTHOR: **FRED F. FERRI, M.D.**

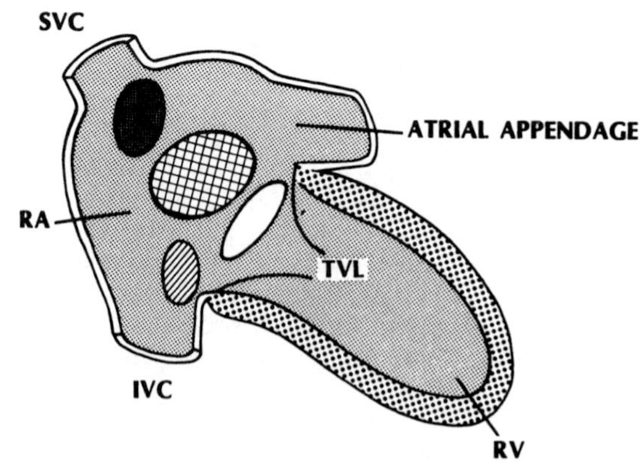

FIGURE 1-36 Location of the four types of atrial septal defect. SVC, *Superior vena cava;* RA, *right atrium;* IVC, *inferior vena cava;* RV, *right ventricle;* TVL, *tricuspid valve leaflet.* (From Noble J [ed]: *Primary care medicine,* ed 2, St Louis, 1996, Mosby.)

BASIC INFORMATION

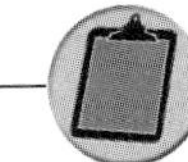

DEFINITION

Attention deficit hyperactivity disorder (AD/HD) is a chronic disorder of attention/concentration and/or hyperactivity/impulsivity. Symptoms must be present in early childhood, last at least 6 mo, and cause functional impairment in multiple settings.

SYNONYMS

Hyperactivity, attention deficit disorder (ADD)

ICD-9CM CODES
ICD-9: 314.XX; ICD-10: F90.X

EPIDEMIOLOGY & DEMOGRAPHICS

PEAK INCIDENCE: Diagnosis is usually first made in school-aged children (6-9 years).

PREVALENCE: 3% to 9% of school-aged children and 2% to 5% of adults.

PREDOMINANT SEX: Among children, male predominance with ratio of 2:1 to 4:1. Among adults, ratio is closer to 1:1. (Sex difference may reflect referral bias.)

PREDOMINANT AGE: Some symptoms must occur before age 7. Symptoms (especially hyperactivity) tend to diminish with age. Greater than 70% continue to meet criteria in adolescence and an estimated 40% to 65% have some symptoms in adulthood.

GENETICS: Strong polygenetic component. First-degree relatives of AD/HD patients have 5 times greater risk of AD/HD relative to controls. Studies suggest potential involvement of several genes including those associated with dopamine metabolism/transmission.

RISK FACTORS: Possible environmental/epidemiologic risk factors include in utero tobacco/drug exposure or hypoxia, low birth weight, prematurity, pregnancy complications, lead exposure, family dysfunction, low SES.

PHYSICAL FINDINGS & CLINICAL PRESENTATION

- Three types:
  1. Predominantly inattentive: difficulty organizing, planning, remembering, concentrating, starting/completing tasks; symptoms may not be present during preferred activities.
  2. Predominantly hyperactive-impulsive: edgy/restless, talkative, disruptive/intrusive, disinhibited, impatient.
  3. Combined.
- Usually diagnosed in elementary school when achievement is compromised and behavioral problems are not tolerated. Children with academic underproductivity, problems with peer and family relations, or discipline issues are often referred for evaluation.
- Adults with substance abuse or other addictions, multiple traffic violations, or frequent life failures should be screened.
- Up to 50% may have associated disorders such as psychiatric diagnoses (oppositional defiant disorder, conduct disorder, depression, anxiety), learning disabilities, substance abuse, and criminal behavior.

ETIOLOGY

Strongest evidence exists for genetic inheritance. Other theories include abnormal metabolism of brain catecholamines, structural brain abnormalities, and environmental factors (see earlier).

DIAGNOSIS

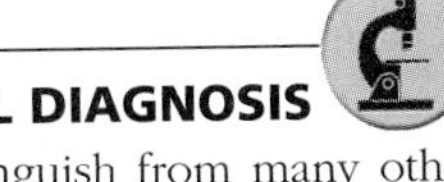

DIFFERENTIAL DIAGNOSIS

Difficult to distinguish from many other conditions because of symptom overlap and high frequency of comorbid conditions:

- Medical: visual/hearing impairment, seizure disorder, head injury, sleep disorder, medication interactions, mental retardation, developmental delay, thyroid abnormalities, lead toxicity.
- Psychiatric: depression, bipolar disorder, anxiety, obsessive-compulsive disorder, conduct disorder, posttraumatic stress disorder, substance abuse, antisocial personality disorder, Tourette syndrome, tics.
- Psychosocial: mismatch of learning environment with ability, family dysfunction, abuse/neglect.

WORKUP

- Clinical diagnosis requiring a series of office visits or an extended, multidisciplinary team evaluation.
- Clinical interview should include assessment of symptoms and impact on work/school and relationships; developmental history; personal and family psychiatric history including substance abuse; social history including family dysfunction; medical history.
- Thorough physical examination should be performed to uncover medical causes for symptoms, coexisting conditions, and contraindications to treatment.
- Many patients will not display symptoms during an office visit and may under- or over-report symptoms. Therefore, information from collateral sources (parents, partners, teachers) is crucial to diagnosis.
- Self-rating scales and standardized symptom-specific questionnaires from collateral sources can aid in diagnosis and in assessing response to treatment.
- No single diagnostic test can confirm diagnosis. Laboratory or imaging studies should be undertaken only if indicated by history or physical examination.
- Ancillary testing (e.g., IQ/achievement testing, language evaluation, and mental health assessment) may be indicated based on clinical findings and may require referral.

TREATMENT

NONPHARMACOLOGIC THERAPY

- Data comparing the efficacy of behavioral or educational therapy versus pharmacologic management are limited. Prevailing opinion favors a multimodal approach in which nonpharmacologic therapies can be used to target comorbid conditions or behaviors that have not responded to medication.
- Educational interventions are recommended, particularly in the setting of learning disabilities. Children with AD/HD are entitled to reasonable educational accommodations under a 504 Plan or the Individuals with Disabilities Education Act.
- Behavioral interventions (e.g., goal setting and rewards systems) show short-term efficacy and are endorsed by most national organizations (e.g., American Academy of Pediatrics, American Medical Association). Time management and organizational skills appear useful (but have not been studied).
- Psychotherapy (cognitive behavioral, group, social skills, and parent training) may be beneficial, particularly when there is coexisting psychiatric disease.
- Many support/advocacy groups exist that provide education and other resources (e.g., Children and Adolescents with AD/HD, National ADD Association, American Academy of Child and Adolescent Psychiatry).

ACUTE GENERAL Rx

- Most studies on treatment of AD/HD performed in children. Limited data on adults.
- Mainstay of treatment is drug therapy, particularly stimulants and atomoxetine. Second-line therapies include antidepressants and alpha-agonists.
- Stimulants:
  1. Release/block uptake of dopamine and norepinephrine.
  2. Include short- and long-acting methylphenidate (Ritalin, Concerta), dextroamphetamine/amphetamine combinations (Adderall). Pemoline (Cyclert) is no longer recommended because of hepatotoxicity.
  3. Do not cause euphoria or lead to addiction when taken as directed.
  4. Improve cognition, inattention, impulsiveness/hyperactivity, and driving skills. Limited effect on academic performance, learning, and emotional problems.
  5. Side effects are mild, reversible, and dose dependent. Include anorexia, weight loss, sleep disturbances, increased heart rate/blood pressure, nervousness/irritability, headache, onset or worsening of motor tics, reduction of growth velocity (but not adult height). Do not worsen seizures in patients on adequate anticonvulsant therapy. Rebound of symptoms can occur with withdrawal of medication.
  6. All equally effective; however, not all patients improve with stimulants. Patients who do not respond well to one stimulant may respond to another.
- Atomoxetine (Strattera):
  1. Selective norepinephrine reuptake inhibitor that is approved for use in patients >6 years old.
  2. Efficacy/safety of long-term use has not been studied.
  3. Side effects: gastrointestinal upset, sleep disturbance, decreased appetite, dizziness, sexual side effects in men, cost, lengthy titration.
- Antidepressants (bupropion, imipramine, nortriptyline):
  1. May be useful in patients with coexisting psychiatric disorders.
  2. Studies comparing efficacy versus stimulants are inconclusive.
  3. Side effects: arrhythmias, anticholinergic effects, lowering of seizure threshold.
- Alpha-agonists (clonidine, guanfacine):
  1. May reduce symptoms but are not as effective as stimulants.
  2. Side effects: sedation, headache, bradycardia, hypotension.
- Use of medications, particularly stimulants (which are monitored under the Controlled Substance Act), require frequent monitoring.

COMPLIMENTARY & ALTERNATIVE MEDICINE

Complimentary and alternative treatments include dietary modifications (low sugar, Kaiser-Permanente, Feingold), herbal and vitamin or mineral supplements, vision therapy, EEG biofeedback, and others. None have been consistently shown to be beneficial in randomized trials. Controlled trials are underway.

DISPOSITION

- While symptoms may change over time, for many patients, AD/HD represents a chronic condition that requires lifelong management.
- Patients are at higher risk for academic underachievement, lower SES, work and relationship difficulties, high-risk behavior, and psychiatric comorbidities.

REFERRAL

- Diagnosis complicated by difficult-to-treat comorbid psychiatric conditions, developmental disorders, or mental retardation.
- Lack of adequate response to stimulants/atomoxetine.

PEARLS & CONSIDERATIONS

COMMENTS

Some consider AD/HD one end of a spectrum of normal behavior. Concern stems from overdiagnosis and overtreatment, particularly with the use of psychostimulants. Thus, the diagnosis requires strict adherence to DSM-IV criteria, corroboration of symptoms from other sources, and referral to specialists in the setting of complicated or unclear diagnoses.

PREVENTION

Patients are at risk for accidental injury and engaging in high-risk behavior. Emphasize screening and education to reduce risk.

PATIENT/FAMILY EDUCATION

Medication adherence and management of controlled substances, role of behavioral/environmental therapies, existence of support groups and other resources (e.g., Children and Adults with Attention Deficit/Hyperactivity Disorder: http://www.chadd.org; Attention Deficit Disorders Association: http://www.add.org; Parents Helping Parents: http://www.php.org).

SUGGESTED READINGS

American Academy of Pediatrics: Clinical practice guideline: diagnosis and evaluation of the child with attention deficit/hyperactivity disorder, *Pediatrics* 105:1158, 2000.

Connors CK: *Conners' Parent and Teacher Rating Scales,* North Tonawanda, NY, 1997, Multi-Health Systems Inc.

Joshi SV: Psychostimulants, atomoxetine, and alpha-agonists in the treatment of ADHD. In Steiner H (ed.): *Handbook of mental health interventions in children and adolescents: an integrated developmental approach,* San Francisco, 2004, Jossey-Bass.

MTA Cooperative Group: A 14-month randomized clinical trial of treatment strategies for attention deficit/hyperactivity disorder, *Arch Gen Psychiatry* 56:1073, 1999.

National Initiative for Children's Healthcare Quality AD/HD Practitioner's Toolkit: http://www.nichq.org.

Pliszka SR, Texas Consensus Conference Panel on Medication Treatment of Childhood Attention Deficit/Hyperactivity Disorder: the Texas children's medication algorithm project: report of the Texas consensus of conference panel on medication treatment of childhood attention-deficit/hyperactivity disorder, *J Am Acad Child Adolesc Psychiatry* 39:908, 2000.

Wilens TE, Faraone SV, Biederman J: Attention deficit/hyperactivity disorder in adults, *JAMA* 292:619, 2004.

AUTHOR: **ANASTASIA MISAKIAN, M.D.**

SECTION I

BASIC INFORMATION

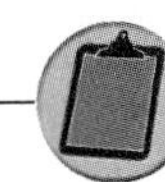

DEFINITION

Autistic spectrum disorders (ASD) encompass a whole spectrum of developmental disorders characterized by impairment in several behavioral domains. There is usually impairment in the development of language, communication, and reciprocal social interaction along with a restricted behavioral repertoire, with onset before age 3 yr.

SYNONYMS

Autism
Early infantile autism
Childhood autism
Kanner's autism
Pervasive developmental disorder

ICD-9CM CODES
F84.0 Autistic disorder (DSM-IV coded 299.0 Autistic disorder)

EPIDEMIOLOGY & DEMOGRAPHICS

PREVALENCE (IN U.S.): 3 to 6/1000 of ASD (2 to 5/10,000 if restricted to autism alone)
PREDOMINANT SEX: Male:female ratio of 3-4:1
PREDOMINANT AGE: Lifelong illness
PEAK INCIDENCE: Before age 3 yr
GENETICS:

- Unknown genetic component; risk for sibling of affected individual: increases to 3%
- 60% concordance for classic autism in monozygotic twins

PHYSICAL FINDINGS & CLINICAL PRESENTATION

- Marked impairment in the understanding and use of both verbal and nonverbal communication (probably underlies the profound impairment in social interaction)
- Stereotypic behavior or language
- Sensory overload and avoidance of novel stimuli is typical.

ETIOLOGY

- Majority of cases are not associated with a medical condition.
- There is a significant increase in comorbid seizure disorder (25%) and mental retardation.
- Autism is sometimes associated with other neurologic conditions (e.g., encephalitis, tuberous sclerosis, phenylketonuria, fragile X, and others), suggesting that it may result from nonspecific neuronal injury.
- There appears to be no relationship between childhood vaccination and the development of autism.

DIAGNOSIS

DIFFERENTIAL DIAGNOSIS

- Rett's syndrome: occurs in females, exhibits head growth deceleration, loss of previously acquired motor skills, and incoordination
- Childhood disintegration disorder: development normal until age 2 yr, followed by regression
- Childhood-onset schizophrenia: follows period of normal development
- Asperger's syndrome: lacks the language developmental abnormalities of autism
- Isolated symptoms of autism: when occurring in isolation, defined as disorders (i.e., selective mutism, expressive language disorder, mixed receptive-expressive language disorder, or stereotypic movement disorder)

WORKUP

- Rule out underlying medical condition
- Diagnostic instruments based on questionnaires and observation noting scales (e.g., Autism Diagnostic Interview) may be helpful.

LABORATORY TESTS

- PKU screen (usually done at birth in the U.S.)
- Chromosome analysis to rule out fragile X in both boys and girls (carrier girls may exhibit mild symptoms)
- IQ testing to help determine functional level of child

IMAGING STUDIES

- EEG to diagnose coexisting seizure disorder (a normal EEG does not rule out a seizure disorder.)
- Head CT scan or MRI to rule out tuberous sclerosis
- Possible BAER to rule out hearing deficit

TREATMENT

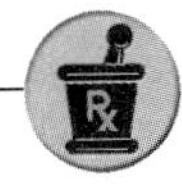

NONPHARMACOLOGIC THERAPY

- A behavioral training program that is consistent in both the home and school environments is important.
- Educational needs should focus on language and social development.
- Most children need a highly structured environment.
- Educating the parents and teachers is of great value.

ACUTE GENERAL Rx

- Haloperidol or other high-potency neuroleptics are helpful in reducing aggression and stereotypy. Atypical neuroleptics, such as risperidone, also reduce aggression and irritability.
- Atypical neuroleptics, such as risperidone, reduce aggression and irritability and improve overall behavioral symptoms.
- Selective serotonin reuptake inhibitors may be useful in children with coexisting depression or with marked obsessive or ritualistic behaviors. Current evidence does not support use of one SSRI over another.
- Buspirone reported to reduce aggression, hyperactivity and repetitive behaviors.
- Valproic acid and carbamazepine are preferred to phenytoin or phenobarbital for seizure control.

CHRONIC Rx

- Extended use of all medications used for acute management
- Pharmacotherapy is palliative only, not curative.
- Potential for tardive dyskinesia with chronic use of neuroleptics
- Large doses of vitamin B_6 and magnesium supplementation (mild ameliorating effect)

DISPOSITION

- Most children (70%) will require some degree of assistance as adults, will not be able to work, and will not achieve proper social adjustment.
- Some 10% (particularly if IQ is in the normal range and speech is achieved by age 5 yr) may have a reasonable outcome.
- Children with Asperger's syndrome may have a very good outcome despite ongoing symptoms.

REFERRAL

Assistance may be needed in diagnosis, management, parental teaching, or intervention with the school system.

COMMENTS

A center devoted to the study of autism: http://www.ucdmc.ucdavis.edu/mindinstitute/.

SUGGESTED READINGS

Goldson E: Autism spectrum disorders: An overview, *Adv Pediatrics* 51:63, 2004.
Muhle R, Trentacoste SV, Rapic I: The genetics of autism, *Pediatrics* 113(5):472, 2004.
Research Units on Pediatric Psychopharmacology Autism Network: Risperidone in children with autism and serious behavioral problems, *N Engl J Med* 347:314, 2002.

AUTHOR: **MITCHELL D. FELDMAN, M.D.**

BASIC INFORMATION

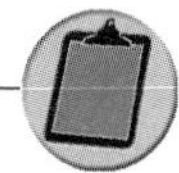

DEFINITION

Babesiosis is a tick-transmitted protozoan disease of animals, caused by intraerythrocytic parasites of the genus *Babesia.* Humans are incidentally infected, resulting in a nonspecific febrile illness.

ICD-9CM CODES
088.82 Babesiosis

EPIDEMIOLOGY & DEMOGRAPHICS

INCIDENCE (IN U.S.): Unknown
PREVALENCE (IN U.S.):
- In areas of high endemicity, seropositivity ranging from 9% (Rhode Island) to 21% (Connecticut)
- Highest number of reported cases in New York

PREDOMINANT SEX: Males (most likely through increased exposure to vectors during recreational or occupational activities)
PREDOMINANT AGE: Severity apparently increasing with age $>$40 yr
PEAK INCIDENCE: Spring and summer months, May through September
GENETICS: None known
CONGENITAL INFECTION: At least one case of probable vertical transmission
NEONATAL INFECTION: At least two cases of perinatal transmission

PHYSICAL FINDINGS & CLINICAL PRESENTATION

- Incubation period 1 to 4 wk, or 6 to 9 wk in transfusion-associated disease
- Gradual onset of irregular fever, chills, diaphoresis, headache, myalgia, arthralgia, fatigue, and dark urine
- On physical examination: petechiae, frank or mild hepatosplenomegaly, and jaundice
- Infection with *B. divergens* producing a more severe illness with a rapid onset of symptoms and increasing parasitemia progressing to massive intravascular hemolysis and renal failure

ETIOLOGY

- Vector: Deer tick, *Ixodes scapularis* (also known as *I. dammini*)
  1. Feeds on rodents during the spring and summer while in its larval and nymphal stages and on deer as an adult
  2. During the warmer months in endemic areas, humans are readily infected while engaging in outdoor activities
- *B. microti,* along with *B. divergens* and *B. bovis,* account for most human infections.
- In the U.S., cases caused by *B. microti* are acquired on offshore islands of the northeastern coast, including Nantucket Island, Cape Cod, and Martha's Vineyard in Massachusetts; Block Island in Rhode Island; and Long Island, Fire Island, and Shelter Island in New York; as well as the nearby mainland including Connecticut and New Jersey.
- Sporadic cases reported from California, Georgia, Maryland, Minnesota, Virginia, Wisconsin, and most recently the WA-1 strain from Washington State and the MO-1 strain from Missouri.
- *B. divergens* and *B. bovis* are implicated in human disease in Europe, where the disease remains rare and predominantly associated with asplenia.
- Majority of cases are symptomatic.
- May be transmissible by transfusion, through platelets and erythrocytes.
- Mixed infections (*B. microti* and *Borrelia burgdorferi*) are estimated to occur in 10% (Rhode Island and Connecticut) to 60% (New York) of cases.

DIAGNOSIS

DIFFERENTIAL DIAGNOSIS

- Amebiasis
- Ehrlichiosis
- Hepatic abscess
- Leptospirosis
- Malaria
- Salmonellosis, including typhoid fever
- Acute viral hepatitis
- Hemorrhagic fevers

WORKUP

Should be suspected in any febrile patient living or traveling in an endemic area, irrespective of exposure history to ticks or tick bites, especially if asplenic

LABORATORY TESTS

- CBC to reveal mild to moderate pancytopenia
- Abnormally elevated serum chemistries, including creatinine, liver function profile, lactate dehydrogenase, and direct and total bilirubin levels
- Urinalysis to reveal proteinuria and hemoglobinuria
- Examination of Giemsa- or Wright-stained thick and thin blood films for intraerythrocytic parasites
  1. In its classic, though infrequently seen, form a "tetrad" or "Maltese Cross" composed of four daughter cells attached by cytoplasmic strands is observed.
  2. More commonly, smaller forms composed of a single chromatin dot are eccentrically located within bluish cytoplasm.
  3. Parasitized erythrocytes may be multiply infected but not enlarged, or they may show evidence of pigment deposition, seen with Plasmodium species.
- Diagnosis achieved serologically by indirect immunofluorescence assay (IFA) is specific for *B. microti.*
  1. Titer of $\geq$1:64 is indicative of seropositivity, whereas one $\geq$1:256 is considered diagnostic of acute infection.
  2. Assay is hampered by the inability to distinguish between exposed patients and those who are actively infected.
  3. Immunoglobulin M indirect immunofluorescent-antibody test may be highly sensitive and specific for diagnosis.
  4. Babesial DNA by polymerase chain reaction (PCR) has comparable sensitivity and specificity to microscopic analysis of thin blood smears.

TREATMENT

NONPHARMACOLOGIC THERAPY

Supportive care with adequate hydration

ACUTE GENERAL Rx

- In patients with intact spleens: predominantly asymptomatic or if symptomatic, generally self-limited
- Therapy reserved for the severely ill patient, especially if asplenic or immunosuppressed
- Combination of quinine sulfate 650 mg PO tid plus clindamycin 600 mg PO tid (1.2 g parenterally bid) taken for 7 to 10 days: effective but may not eliminate parasites
- Combination of atovaquone 750 mg every 12 hr and azithromycin 500 mg on day 1 and 250 mg per day thereafter for 7 days appears to be as effective as a regimen of clindamycin and quinine with fewer adverse reactions
- Exchange transfusions in addition to antimicrobial therapy: successful treatment for severe infections in asplenic patients associated with high levels of *B. microti* or *B. divergens* parasitemia

DISPOSITION

Prognosis is usually good and fatal outcomes are rare.

REFERRAL

- For prompt consultation with an infectious disease specialist if the diagnosis is acutely suspected, especially in the asplenic, elderly, or immunocompromised patient

- For hospitalization for the severely ill patient who may require exchange transfusions in addition to antibiotic therapy

PEARLS & CONSIDERATIONS

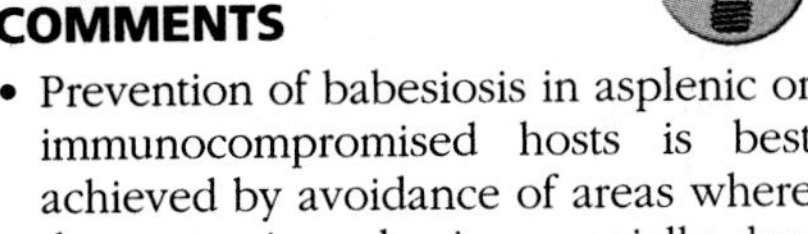

COMMENTS

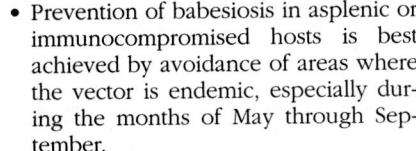

- Prevention of babesiosis in asplenic or immunocompromised hosts is best achieved by avoidance of areas where the vector is endemic, especially during the months of May through September.
- If residence or travel in endemic areas is unavoidable, advise patients to perform daily cutaneous self-examination, wear light-colored clothing (to facilitate removal of ticks), and apply tick repellent (diethyltoluamide and dimethylphthalate) to skin or clothing.
- Advise a daily inspection for ticks in family pets (e.g., cats and dogs).
- Infection with *B. divergens,* especially in the asplenic patient, is often fatal.
- At least one case of concurrent babesiosis and Lyme disease has been documented.
- Clindamycin and quinine has been successfully used to treat Babesiosis during the third trimester of pregnancy without incurring apparent adverse effect on the fetus.

SUGGESTED READINGS

Cable RG, Leiby DA: Risk and prevention of transfusion-transmitted babesiosis and other tick-borne diseases, *Curr Opin Hematol* 10(6):405, 2003.

Gelfand JA, Callahan MV: Babesiosis: an update on epidemiology and treatment, *Curr Infect Dis Rep* 5(1):53, 2003.

Krause PJ: Babesiosis diagnosis and treatment, *Vector Borne Zoonotic Dis* 3(1):45, 2003.

AUTHOR: **GEORGE O. ALONSO, M.D.**

BASIC INFORMATION

DEFINITION

Baker's cyst refers to a fluid-filled popliteal bursa located along the medial border of the popliteal fossa.

SYNONYMS

Popliteal cyst

ICD-9CM CODES

727.51 Baker's cyst (knee)

EPIDEMIOLOGY & DEMOGRAPHICS

- Popliteal cysts occur at all ages.
- Incidence of Baker's cysts is unknown.
- Between 2% to 6% of all patients thought to have clinical DVT turn out to have symptomatic Baker's cysts.
- Approximately 5% of MRIs of the knees reveal popliteal cysts.

PHYSICAL FINDINGS & CLINICAL PRESENTATION

- Pain in the popliteal space
- Knee swelling
- Leg edema
- Prominence of the popliteal fossa
- Decreased range of motion of the knee
- Locking of the knee
- Foucher's sign: The cyst becomes hard with knee extension and soft with knee flexion.
- Neuropathic lancinating pains radiating from the knee down the back of the leg.
- Deep vein thrombosis (DVT)

ETIOLOGY

- Baker's cysts are believed to represent fluid distention of the bursal sac separating the semimembranous tendon from the medial head of the gastrocnemius.
- In children, Baker's cysts are thought to be secondary to trauma and irritation of the knee.
- In adults, Baker's cysts are usually associated with pathologic changes of the knee joint:
  1. Rheumatoid arthritis
  2. Osteoarthritis of the knee
  3. Meniscal tears
  4. Patellofemoral chondromalacia
  5. Fracture
  6. Gout
  7. Pseudogout
  8. Infection (tuberculosis)

DIAGNOSIS

Baker's cysts, like deep vein thrombosis, are very difficult to diagnose on clinical grounds alone. In fact, Baker's cyst frequently mimics a DVT and is sometimes called *pseudothrombophlebitis syndrome.*

DIFFERENTIAL DIAGNOSIS

- DVT
- Popliteal aneurysms
- Abscess
- Tumors
- Lymphadenopathy
- Varicosities
- Ganglion

WORKUP

Anyone suspected of having a popliteal cyst should undergo imaging studies to exclude other causes.

LABORATORY TESTS

Blood tests are not very specific in the diagnosis of Baker's cysts.

IMAGING STUDIES

- Plain x-ray (AP and lateral views) may show calcification in a solid tumor or in the posterior meniscal area.
- Ultrasound is easy, cost effective, and excludes other causes of popliteal fossa pathology.
- MRI of the knee identifies coexisting joint pathology (e.g., osteoarthritis, torn meniscus).
- Noninvasive venous studies to rule out DVT.

TREATMENT

Treatment is directed at the underlying pathology leading to the formation of the popliteal cyst.

NONPHARMACOLOGIC THERAPY

- Rest
- Strenuous activity avoidance
- Knee immobilization possibly necessary in some cases

ACUTE GENERAL Rx

- NSAIDs, ibuprofen 400 to 800 mg PO tid, or naproxen 250 to 500 mg PO bid can be used to treat Baker's cyst caused by RA, gout, and pseudogout.
- Intraarticular injection or injection of the cyst with corticosteroids, triamcinolone acetonide 40 mg is sometimes tried.

CHRONIC Rx

- Surgical procedures addressing the underlying cause or aimed at the cyst include:
  1. Arthroscopic surgery to remove loose cartilaginous fragment
  2. Partial or total meniscectomy
  3. Open excision of the cyst (Fig. 1-37)

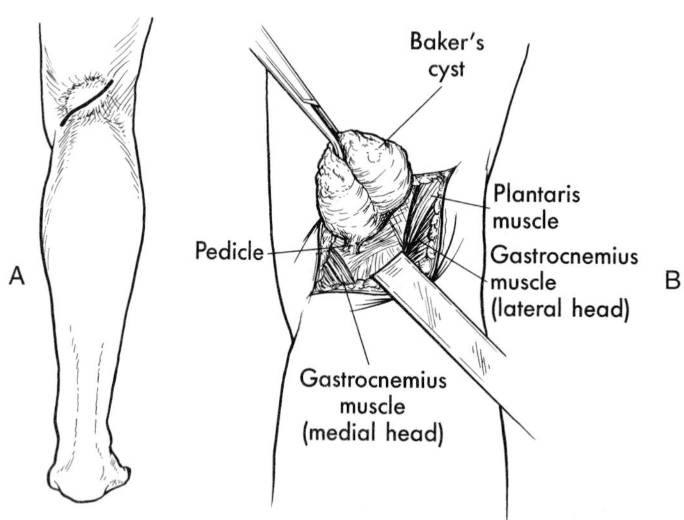

FIGURE 1-37 Removal of midline Baker's cyst. **A,** Skin incision. **B,** After being exposed, pedicle is clamped, ligated, divided, and inverted. (Redrawn and modified from Meyerding HW, Van Demark GE: JAMA 122:858, 1943.)

DISPOSITION

- Baker's cyst may spontaneously resolve without treatment.
- Complications of Baker's cysts are:
  1. Rupture
  2. DVT
  3. Nerve impingement

REFERRAL

Because Baker's cysts are commonly the result of underlying rheumatologic causes, a consultation with rheumatology is often recommended.

PEARLS & CONSIDERATIONS

COMMENTS

- Popliteal cysts was first described in 1877 by Baker in connection with disease of the knee joint.
- Baker's cyst and DVT can coexist. It is imperative to exclude the diagnosis of DVT before discharging the patient from the emergency room, hospital, or office.
- In the setting of meniscus injury, Baker's cysts commonly originate from the posterior horn of the medial meniscus with or without a tear.

SUGGESTED READINGS

Drescher MJ, Smally AJ: Thrombophlebitis and pseudothrombophlebitis in the ED, *Am J Emerg Med* 15(7):683, 1997.

Handy JR: Popliteal cysts in adults: a review, *Semin Arthritis Rheum* 31(2):108, 2001.

Stone KR et al: The frequency of Baker's cysts associated with meniscal tears, *Am Sports Med* 24(5):670, 1996.

Torreggiani WC et al: The imaging spectrum of Baker's (Popliteal) cysts, *Clin Radiol* 57(8):681, 2002.

AUTHOR: **PETER PETROPOULOS, M.D.**

BASIC INFORMATION

DEFINITION

Balanitis is an inflammation of the superficial tissues of the penile head (Fig. 1-38).

ICD-9CM CODES
112.2 Balanitis

EPIDEMIOLOGY & DEMOGRAPHICS

INCIDENCE (IN U.S.): Unknown
PREVALENCE (IN U.S.): Unknown
PREDOMINANT SEX: Exclusive to males
PEAK INCIDENCE: All ages, especially in sexually active men

PHYSICAL FINDINGS & CLINICAL PRESENTATION

- Itching and tenderness
- Pain, dysuria, and local edema
- Rarely, ulceration and lymph node enlargement
- Severe ulcerations leading to superimposed bacterial infections
- Inability to void: unusual, but a more distressing and serious complication

ETIOLOGY

- Poor hygiene, causing erosion of tissue with erythema and promoting growth of *Candida albicans*
- Sexual contact, urinary catheters, and trauma
- Allergic reactions to condoms or medications

DIAGNOSIS

DIFFERENTIAL DIAGNOSIS

- Leukoplakia
- Reiter's syndrome
- Lichen planus
- Balanitis xerotica obliterans
- Psoriasis
- Carcinoma of the penis
- Erythroplasia of Queyrat

WORKUP

- Sexually active males: assessment for evidence of other sexually transmitted diseases
- Biopsy if lesions do not heal

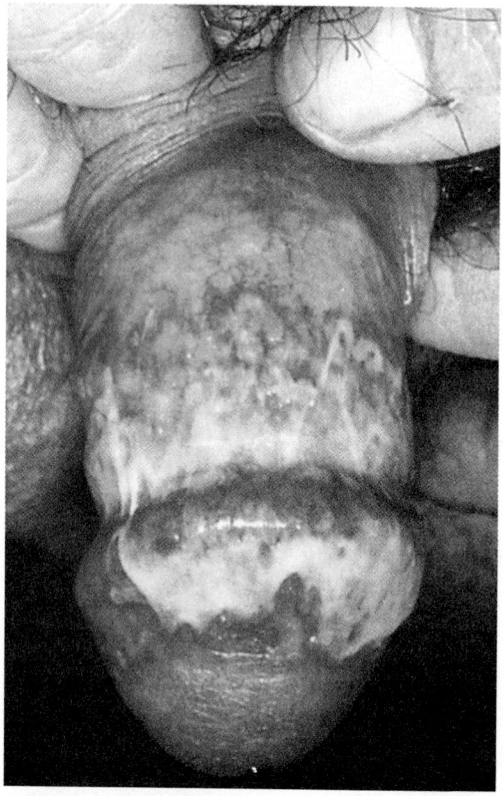

FIGURE 1-38 ***Candida*** **balanitis.** The moist space between the skin surfaces of the uncircumcised penis is an ideal environment for *Candida* infection. This thick white exudates is typical of a severe acute infection. (From Habif TP: *Clinical dermatology: a color guide to diagnosis and therapy,* ed 3, St Louis, 1996, Mosby.)

LABORATORY TESTS

- VDRL
- Serum glucose
- Wet mount
- KOH prep
- Microculture

TREATMENT

NONPHARMACOLOGIC THERAPY

- Maintenance of meticulous hygiene
- Retraction and bathing of prepuce several times a day
- Warm sitz baths to ease edema and erythema
- Consideration of circumcision, especially when symptoms are severe or recurrent
- With Foley catheters, strict catheter care strongly advised

MEDICATIONS

- Analgesics, such as acetaminophen and/or codeine
- Clotrimazole 1% cream applied topically twice daily to affected areas
- Bacitracin or Neosporin ointment applied topically 4 times daily
- With more severe bacterial superinfection: cephalexin 500 mg PO qid
- Topical corticosteroids added 4 times daily if dermatitis severe
- Patients with suspected urinary tract infections: trimethoprim-sulfa DS twice daily or ciprofloxacin 500 mg PO bid after obtaining appropriate cultures

REFERRAL

- For surgical evaluation for circumcision if symptoms are recurrent, especially if phimosis or meatitis occurs (NOTE: Severe phimosis with an inability to void may require prompt slit drainage.)
- For biopsy to rule out other diagnosis such as premalignant or malignant lesions if lesions are not healing

SUGGESTED READINGS

Bielan B: What's your assessment? *Candida* balanitis, *Dermatol Nurs* 15(2):134, 2003.
Buechner SA: Common skin disorders of the penis, *BJU Int* 90(5):498, 2002.
Bunker CB: Topics in penile dermatology, *Clin Exp Dermatol* 26(6):469, 2001.
Huntley JS et al: Troubles with the foreskin: one hundred consecutive referrals to paediatric surgeons, *J R Soc Med* 96(9):449, 2003.

AUTHOR: **JOSEPH J. LIEBER, M.D.**

BASIC INFORMATION

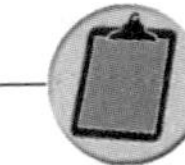

DEFINITION

Barrett's esophagus occurs when the squamous lining of the lower esophagus is replaced by metaplastic, intestinalized columnar epithelium. The condition is associated with an increased risk of adenocarcinoma of the esophagus.

SYNONYMS

Intestinal metaplasia of the lower esophagus

ICD-9CM CODES
530.85 Barrett's esophagus

EPIDEMIOLOGY & DEMOGRAPHICS

- Male predominance with a 4:1 ratio of men to women
- Mean age of onset is 40 yr with a mean age of diagnosis of 55 to 60 yr
- Occurs more frequently in Caucasians and Hispanics than in African Americans with a ratio of 10-20:1
- Mean prevalence of 5% to 15% in patients undergoing endoscopy for symptoms of GERD

PHYSICAL FINDINGS & CLINICAL PRESENTATION

Symptoms:
- Typically, chronic (>5 yr) heartburn
- May be an incidental finding in patients undergoing endoscopy for indications unrelated to GERD
- Dysphagia for solid food
- Less frequent: chest pain, hematemesis, or melena

Physical findings:
- Nonspecific
- Ranges from epigastric tenderness on palpation to completely normal

ETIOLOGY

- Metaplasia is thought to result from re-epithelialization of esophageal tissue injured secondary to, and in the background of, chronic gastroesophageal reflux (Fig. 1-39).
- Patients with Barrett's tend to have more severe esophageal motility disturbances (decreased lower esophageal sphincter pressure, ineffective peristalsis) and greater esophageal acid exposure on 24-hour pH monitoring than GERD patients without Barrett's.
- Intraesophageal bile (duodenogastroesophageal) reflux may also play a role in the pathogenesis.
- Familial clustering of GERD and Barrett's suggests a genetic predisposition for the disease.
- The progression from metaplasia to carcinoma is associated with a number of changes in gene structure and expression.

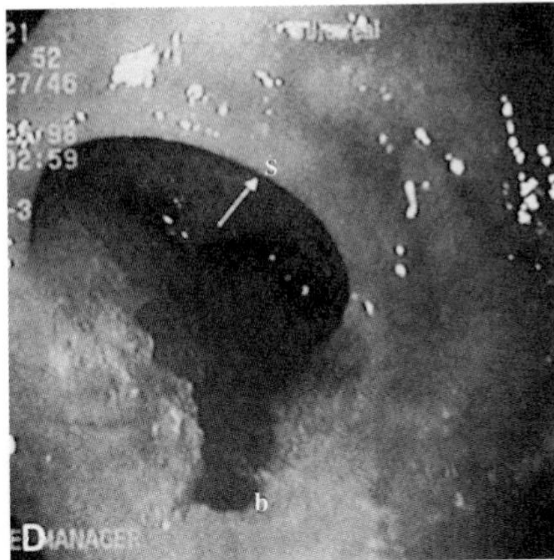

FIGURE 1-39 Endoscopic view of the distal esophagus from a patient with gastroesophageal reflux disease showing a tongue of Barrett's mucosa (*b*) and a Schatzki's ring (*s*) (*arrow*). (From Goldman L, Bennett JC [eds]: *Cecil textbook of medicine,* ed 21, Philadelphia, 2000, WB Saunders.)

DIAGNOSIS

DIFFERENTIAL DIAGNOSIS

- GERD, uncomplicated
- Erosive esophagitis
- Gastritis
- Peptic ulcer disease
- Angina
- Malignancy
- Stricture or Schatzki's ring

WORKUP

- Endoscopy with biopsy necessary for diagnosis.
- Diagnosis requires the presence of intestinal metaplasia in columnar epithelium displaced proximal to the gastroesophageal junction (see Fig. 1-40). Longer segment Barrett's is more readily diagnosed, but the length of the segment does not define the diagnosis.
- Intestinal metaplasia of the gastric cardia is not considered Barrett's and does not appear to convey the same risk of malignant transformation.
- Imaging studies are nonspecific and insensitive for the diagnosis
- Screening for *H. pylori* infection in patients with GERD and Barrett's esophagus is not recommended.

TREATMENT

The primary therapeutic goal is to control GERD symptoms and maintain healed mucosa.

NONPHARMACOLOGIC THERAPY

Same as treatment for GERD alone (lifestyle modifications, elevating the head of the bed, avoiding chocolate, tobacco, caffeine, mints, avoiding certain drugs [see Gastroesophageal reflux disease]); however, chronic acid suppression is often necessary to control symptoms and promote healing.

ACUTE GENERAL Rx

- Proton pump inhibitors (PPIs) are most effective at relieving symptoms and healing mucosal injury.
- Adequate control of GERD symptoms in patients with Barrett's esophagus may or may not completely control intraesophageal acid exposure. Some studies have suggested that normalization of intraesophageal acid exposure may lead to either regression of Barrett's or reduce the risk of dysplasia. Large-scale longitudinal studies that would support a general recommendation of aggressive pH control and monitoring have not been performed or reported.
- If asymptomatic and incidentally found to have Barrett's esophagus, medication use may be considered for the above-mentioned reasons.

CHRONIC Rx

- Thermal ablation techniques, photodynamic therapy, and endoscopic mucosal resection have all been suggested as possible approaches in patients with Barrett's and high-grade dysplasia, either in conjunction with aggressive surveillance, or as an alternate to surgery in poor operative candidates. All of these options have significant risks and run the risk of residual intestinal metaplasia.
- Antireflux surgery may be considered for management of GERD and associated sequelae. Surgical resection is offered for multifocal high-grade dysplasia, or carcinoma.

SCREENING

- GERD highly prevalent in general population
- Only 4% to 10% of patients with reflux symptoms develop Barrett's esophagus
- Patients with chronic GERD symptoms should be considered for a one-time endoscopy to exclude the presence of Barrett's. Because many patients with Barrett's are asymptomatic, some will be missed; however, general population screening is not currently recommended.

DISPOSITION

- Overall, 30 to 50 times increased risk of adenocarcinoma of the esophagus in patients with Barrett's esophagus than in general population
- This risk corresponds to 500 cancers per yr per 100,000 persons with Barrett's esophagus
- Specifics of frequency of monitoring is controversial, no prospective controlled studies to prove that surveillance increases life expectancy
- ACG recommends that patients with Barrett's undergo surveillance endoscopy and systematic 4-quadrant biopsy at intervals determined by the presence and grade of dysplasia. All mucosal abnormalities should be biopsied as well. Patients who have had two endoscopies showing no evidence of dysplasia should have follow-up every 3 years. Patients with low-grade dysplasia should have extensive mucosal sampling, and then follow-up every year. Patients with high-grade dysplasia should have expert confirmation and extensive mucosal sampling. Consideration may be given to intensive surveillance every 3 months for patients with focal high-grade dysplasia. Patients with multifocal high-grade dysplasia or carcinoma should be considered for resection, or ablation if not an operative candidate.
- Patients should be treated aggressively for GERD before surveillance.

REFERRAL

- For endoscopy with biopsy in patients with chronic GERD symptomatology who have not had previous endoscopy
- For surveillance in those with a previous biopsy-proven diagnosis of Barrett's esophagus
- For those with high-grade dysplasia, biopsies should be confirmed by an expert pathologist; patients should be offered intensive surveillance or esophageal resection; ablative therapy may be considered either as part of a research protocol, or if not an operative candidate

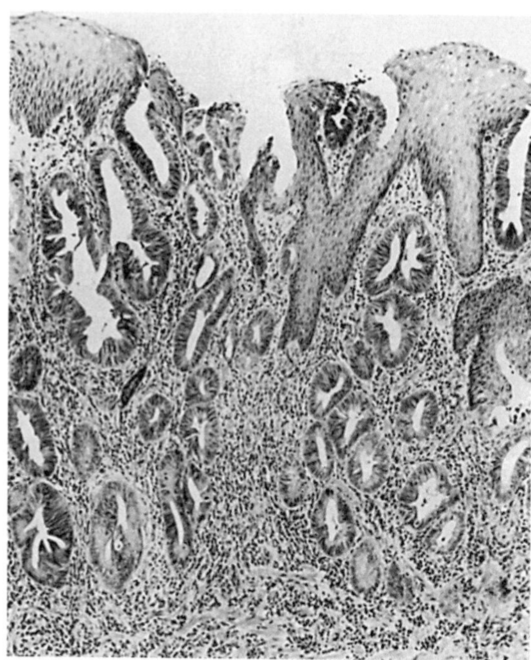

FIGURE 1-40 Epithelial metaplasia (original magnification, x16). The esophageal mucosa consists of columnar epithelium (Barrett's esophagus) intermixed with squamous epithelium. (Photomicrograph courtesy Frank Mitros, M.D., Department of Pathology, University of Iowa. From Stein JH [ed]: *Internal medicine,* ed 5, St Louis, 1998, Mosby.)

SUGGESTED READINGS

Bammer T et al: Rationale for surgical therapy of Barrett esophagus, *Mayo Clin Proc* 76:335, 2001.

Cameron A: Management of Barrett's esophagus, *Mayo Clin Proc* 73:5, 1998.

Falk GW: Barret's esophagus, *Gastroenterology* 122:1569, 2002.

Falk GW: Current challenges in Barrett's esophagus, *Cleve Clin J Med* 68:415, 2001.

Hirota WK: Specialized intestinal metaplasia, dysplasia, and cancer of the esophagus: prevalence and clinical date, *Gastroenterology* 116:277, 1999.

Morales TG, Sampliner RE: Barrett's esophagus, *Arch Intern Med* 159:1411, 1999.

Oatu-Lasear R, Fitzgerald RC, Triadafilopoulas G: Differentiation and proliferation in Barrett's esophagus and the effects of acid suppression, *Gastroenterology* 117:327, 1999.

Provenzale D, Schmitt C, Wong JB: Barrett's esophagus: a new look at surveillance based on emerging estimates of cancer risk, *Am J Gastroenterol* 94:2043, 1999.

Rajan E, Burgart LJ, Gostout CJ: Endoscopic and histologic diagnosis of Barrett esophagus, *Mayo Clin Proc* 76:217, 2001.

Samplinear RE and the Practice Parameters Committee of the American College of Gastroenterology: Updated guidelines for the diagnosis, surveillance, and therapy of Barrett's esophagus, *Am J Gastroenterol* 97:1888, 2002.

Shaheen N et al: Gastroesophageal reflux, Barrett esophagus, and esophageal cancer: clinical applications, *JAMA* 287(15):1982, 2002.

Sharma P: Short segment Barrett esophagus and specialized columnar mucosa at the gastroesophageal junction, *Mayo Clin Proc* 76:331, 2001.

Spechler SJ, Barr B: Review article: screening and surveillance of Barrett's esophagus: what is a cost-effective framework? *Aliment Pharmacol Ther* 19(Suppl 1):49, 2004.

Spechler SJ: Barrett's esophagus, *N Engl J Med* 346:836, 2002.

Wang KK, Samplinear RE: Mucosal ablation therapy of Barrett esophagus, *Mayo Clin Proc* 76:433, 2001.

Wijnhoven BPL et al: Molecular biology of Barrett's adenocarcinoma, *Ann Surg* 233: 322, 2001.

AUTHOR: **HARLAN G. RICH, M.D.**

Basal Cell Carcinoma

BASIC INFORMATION

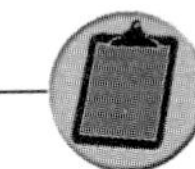

DEFINITION

Basal cell carcinoma (BCC) is a malignant tumor of the skin arising from basal cells of the lower epidermis and adnexal structures. It may be classified as one of six types (nodular, superficial, pigmented, cystic, sclerosing or morpheaform, and nevoid). The most common type is nodular (21%); the least common is morpheaform (1%); a mixed pattern is present in approximately 40% of cases. Basal cell carcinoma advances by direct expansion and destroys normal tissue.

SYNONYMS

BCC

ICD-9CM CODES
179.9 Basal cell carcinoma, site unspecified
173.3 Basal cell carcinoma, face
173.4 Basal cell carcinoma, neck, scalp
173.5 Basal cell carcinoma, trunk
173.6 Basal cell carcinoma of the limb
173.7 Basal cell carcinoma, lower limb

EPIDEMIOLOGY & DEMOGRAPHICS

- Most common cutaneous neoplasm in humans (>400,000 cases/yr)
- 85% appear on the head and neck region
- Most common site: nose (30%)
- Increased incidence with age >40 yr
- Increased incidence in men
- Risk factors: fair skin, increased sun exposure, use of tanning salons with ultraviolet A or B radiation, history of irradiation (e.g., Hodgkin's disease), personal or family history of skin cancer, impaired immune system

PHYSICAL FINDINGS & CLINICAL PRESENTATION

Variable with the histologic type:

- Nodular: dome-shaped, painless lesion that may become multilobular and frequently ulcerates (rodent ulcer); prominent telangiectatic vessels are noted on the surface; border is translucent, elevated, pearly white (Fig. 1-41); some nodular basal cell carcinomas may contain pigmentation, giving an appearance similar to a melanoma.
- Superficial: circumscribed scaling black appearance with a thin raised pearly white border; a crust and erosions may be present; occurs most frequently on the trunk and extremities.
- Morpheaform: flat or slightly raised yellowish or white appearance (similar to localized scleroderma); appearance similar to scars, surface has a waxy consistency.

ETIOLOGY

Sun exposure and use of tanning salons with equipment that emits ultraviolet A or B radiation

DIAGNOSIS

DIFFERENTIAL DIAGNOSIS

- Keratoacanthoma
- Melanoma (pigmented basal cell carcinoma)
- Xeroderma pigmentosa
- Basal cell nevus syndrome
- Molluscum contagiosum
- Sebaceous hyperplasia
- Psoriasis

WORKUP

Biopsy to confirm diagnosis

TREATMENT

NONPHARMACOLOGIC THERAPY

Avoidance of excessive tanning, use of sunscreens to prevent damage from excessive sun exposure

ACUTE GENERAL Rx

Variable with tumor size, location, and cell type:

- Excision surgery: preferred method for large tumors with well-defined borders on the legs, cheeks, forehead, and trunk.
- Mohs' micrographic surgery: preferred for lesions in high-risk areas (e.g., nose, eyelid), very large primary tumors, recurrent basal cell carcinomas, and tumors with poorly defined clinical margins.
- Electrodesiccation and curettage: useful for small (<6 mm) nodular basal cell carcinomas.
- Cryosurgery with liquid nitrogen: useful in basal cell carcinomas of the superficial and nodular types with clearly definable margins; no clear advantages over the other forms of therapy; generally reserved for uncomplicated tumors.
- Radiation therapy: generally used for basal cell carcinomas in areas requiring preservation of normal surround tissues for cosmetic reasons (e.g., around lips); also useful in patients who cannot tolerate surgical procedures or for large lesions and surgical failures.
- Photodynamic therapy uses a skin cream (Metvix, known as methyl aminolevulinate cream) and concentrated light to activate the cream, which kills cancer cells is used in Europe and Australia but not yet FDA-approved in the U.S.
- Imiquimod (Aldara) 5% cream can be used for treatment of small, superficial BCCs of the trunk and extremities. Efficacy rate is approximately 80%. Its main advantage is lack of scarring, which must be weighed against higher cure rates with surgical intervention.

CHRONIC Rx

Periodic evaluation for at least 5 yr because of increased risk of recurrence of another basal cell carcinoma (>40% risk within 5 yr of treatment)

DISPOSITION

- More than 90% of patients are cured.
- A lesion is considered low risk if it is <1.5 cm in diameter, is nodular or cystic, is not in a difficult-to-treat area (H zone of face), and has not been previously treated.
- Nodular and superficial basal cell carcinomas are the least aggressive.
- Morpheaform lesions have the highest incidence of positive tumor margins (>30%) and the greatest recurrence rate.

AUTHOR: **FRED F. FERRI, M.D.**

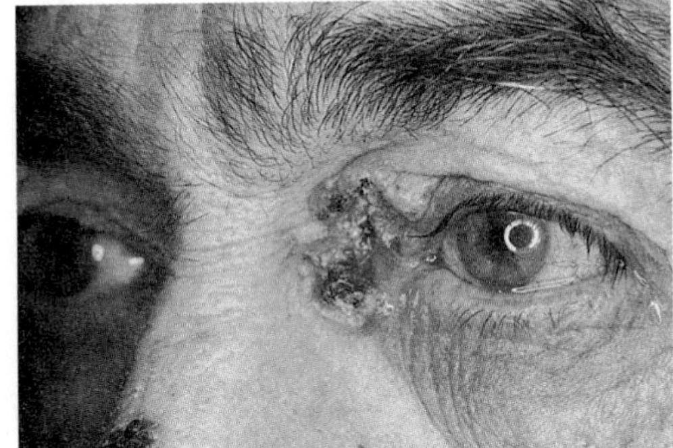

FIGURE 1-41 Basal cell carcinoma. Note rolled translucent border and central ulceration in typical facial location. (From Noble J et al: *Textbook of primary care medicine*, ed 3, St Louis, 2001, Mosby.)

BASIC INFORMATION

DEFINITION

Behçet's disease is a chronic, relapsing, inflammatory disorder characterized by the presence of recurrent oral aphthous ulcers, genital ulcers, uveitis, and skin lesions (Figs. 1-42 and 1-43).

ICD-9CM CODES
136.1 Behçet's syndrome

EPIDEMIOLOGY & DEMOGRAPHICS

Behçet's disease is observed in two different geographic locations.

- One region consists of Japan, Korea, Turkey, and the Mediterranean basin.
    1. Prevalence ranges from 1:7000 to 1:10,000.
    2. Turkey has the highest prevalence at 80 to 370 cases per 100,000.
- The second region consists of North America and Northern Europe.
    1. Prevalence ranges from 1:20,000 to 1:100,000.
    2. Prevalence of Behçet's disease in the U.S. is 0.12 to 0.33 cases per 100,000.
- In these regions the prevalence of HLA-B51 is higher in patients with Behçet's disease
- Males = females

PHYSICAL FINDINGS & CLINICAL PRESENTATION

- Behçet's disease typically affects individuals in the third to fourth decade of life and primarily presents with painful aphthous oral ulcers. The ulcers occur in crops measuring 2 to 10 mm in size and are found on the mucous membrane of the cheek, gingiva, tongue, pharynx, and soft palate
- Genital ulcers are similar to the oral ulcers
- Decreased vision secondary to uveitis, keratitis, or vitreous hemorrhage, or occlusion of the retinal artery or vein may occur
- Skin findings include nodular lesions, which are histologically equally divided to erythema nodosum-like lesions superficial thrombophlebitis, and acne lesions, which are also presented at sites uncommon for ordinary acne (arms and legs)
- Arthritis and arthralgias
- CNS meningeal findings including headache, fever, and stiff neck can occur. Cerebellar ataxia and pseudobulbar palsy occur with involvement of the brainstem
- Vasculitis leading to both arterial and venous inflammation or occlusion can result in signs and symptoms of a myocardial infarction, intermittent claudication, deep vein thrombosis, hemoptysis, and aneurysm formation

ETIOLOGY

The etiology of Behçet's disease is unknown. An immune-related vasculitis is thought to lead to many of the manifestations of Behçet's disease. What triggers the immune response and activation is not yet known.

DIAGNOSIS

According to the International Study Group for Behçet's disease, the diagnosis of Behçet's disease is established when recurrent oral ulceration is present along with at least two of the following in the absence of other systemic diseases:

- Recurrent genital ulceration
- Eye lesions
- Skin lesions
- Positive pathergy test

DIFFERENTIAL DIAGNOSIS

- Ulcerative colitis
- Crohn's disease
- Lichen planus
- Pemphigoid
- Herpes simplex infection
- Benign aphthous stomatitis
- SLE
- Reiter's syndrome
- Ankylosing spondylitis
- AIDS
- Hypereosinophilic syndrome.
- Sweet's syndrome

WORKUP

The diagnosis of Behçet's disease is a clinical diagnosis. Laboratory tests and x-ray imaging may be helpful in working up the complications of Behçet's disease or excluding other diseases in the differential.

LABORATORY TESTS

There are no diagnostic laboratory tests for Behçet's disease.

IMAGING STUDIES

CT scan, MRI, and angiography are useful for detecting CNS and vascular lesions

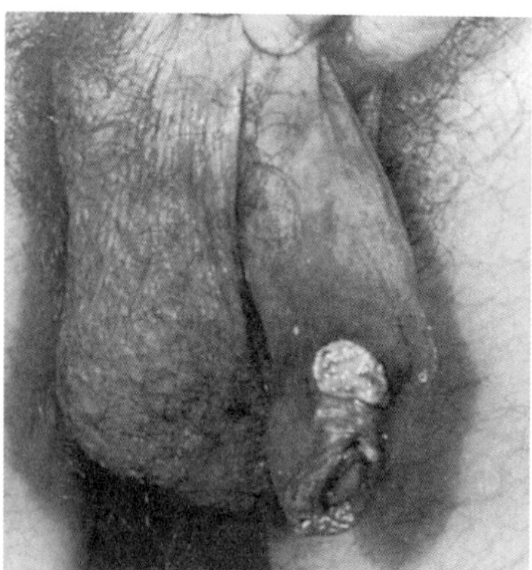

FIGURE 1-42 Behçet's syndrome. Painful prepuceal ulcer in a male with superficial thrombophlebitis, oral ulcers, and bowel vasculitis. (From Canoso J: *Rheumatology in primary care,* Philadelphia, 1997, WB Saunders.)

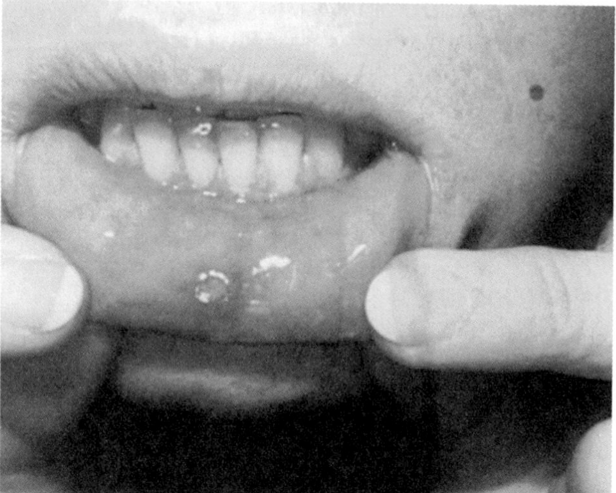

FIGURE 1-43 Behçet's syndrome. Painful aphthous inner lower lip ulcer in a 30-year-old Chinese woman with relapsing oral and genital ulcers and uveitis. She did well on low-dose prednisone plus colchicines. (From Canoso J: *Rheumatology in primary care,* Philadelphia, 1997, WB Saunders.)

TREATMENT

Treatment is directed at the patient's clinical presentation (e.g., mucocutaneous lesions, ocular lesions, arthritis, GI, CNS, or vascular lesions).

NONPHARMACOLOGIC THERAPY

Supportive care

ACUTE GENERAL Rx

- Oral and genital ulcers
  1. Topical corticosteroids (e.g., triamcinolone acetonide ointment applied tid)
  2. Tetracycline tablets 250 mg dissolved in 5 cc water and applied to the ulcer for 2 to 3 min
  3. Colchicine 0.5 to 1.5 mg/kg/day PO
  4. Thalidomide 100 to 300 mg PO daily
  5. Dapsone 100 mg PO daily
  6. Pentoxifylline 300 mg/day PO
  7. Azathioprine 1-2.5 mg/kg/day PO
  8. Methotrexate 7.5-25 mg/wk PO or IV
- Ocular lesions
  1. Anterior uveitis is treated by an ophthalmologist with topical corticosteroids (e.g., betamethasone drops 1 to 2 drops tid). Topical injection with dexamethasone 1 to 1.5 mg has also been tried
  2. Infliximab 5 mg/kg single dose
- CNS disease
  1. Chlorambucil 0.1 mg/kg/day is used in the treatment of posterior uveitis, retinal vasculitis, or CNS disease. Patients not responding to chlorambucil can be tried on cyclosporine 5 to 7 mg/kg/day.
  2. In CNS vasculitis, cyclophosphamide 2 to 3 mg/kg/day is used. Prednisone can be used as an alternative.
- Arthritis
  1. NSAIDs (e.g., ibuprofen 400 to 800 mg tid PO or indomethacin 50 to 75 mg/day PO)
  2. Sulfasalazine 1 to 3 g/day PO is an alternative treatment
- GI lesions
  1. Sulfasalazine 1 to 3 g/day PO
  2. Prednisone 40 to 60 mg/day PO
- Vascular lesions
  1. Prednisone 40 to 60 mg/day PO
  2. Cytotoxic agents as mentioned previously
  3. Heparin 5000 to 20,000 U/day followed by oral warfarin

CHRONIC Rx

- Chronic therapy is usually continued for approximately 1 yr after remission.
- Surgery may be indicated in patients with complications of bowel perforation, vascular occlusive disease, and aneurysm formation.

DISPOSITION

- The aphthous oral ulcers last 1 to 2 wk, recurring more frequently than genital ulcers.
- Approximately 25% of patients with ocular lesions become blind.
- The disease course is unpredictable.
- Complications include:
  1. Meningitis
  2. Cerebrovascular accident (stroke)
  3. Aneurysm rupture
  4. Peripheral lower-extremity ischemia
  5. Mesenteric ischemia
  6. Myocardial infarction

REFERRAL

If the diagnosis of Behçet's disease is suspected, a referral to both rheumatology and ophthalmology is indicated because the disease is so rare.

PEARLS & CONSIDERATIONS

COMMENTS

The pathergy test refers to the formation of a papule or pustule of 2 mm or more in size after oblique insertion of a sterile 20- or 25-gauge needle into the skin.

SUGGESTED READINGS

International Study Group for Behçet's Disease: Criteria for diagnosis of Behçet's disease, *Lancet* 335:1078, 1990.

Meador R, Ehrlich E, Von Feldt JM: Behçet's disease: immunopathologic and therapeutic aspects, *Curr Rheumatol Rep* 4(1):47, 2002.

Saenz A et al: Pharmacotherapy for Behçet's syndrome, *Cochrane Database Syst Rev* 2:CD001084, 2000.

Sakane T et al: Behcet's disease, *N Engl J Med* 341(17):1284, 1999.

Sfikakis PP et al: Effect of infliximab on sight-threatening panuveitis in Behçet's disease, *Lancet* (358):295, 2001.

Yazici H: Behçet's syndrome: an update, *Curr Rheumatol Rep* (5):195, 2003.

AUTHORS: **JOSEPH GRILLO, M.D.,** and **DENNIS MIKOLICH, M.D.**

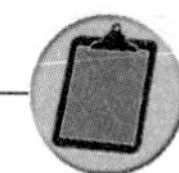

BASIC INFORMATION

DEFINITION

Bell's palsy is an idiopathic, isolated, usually unilateral facial weakness in the distribution of the seventh cranial nerve (<1% of the facial palsies are bilateral)

SYNONYMS

Idiopathic facial paralysis

ICD-9CM CODES
351.0 Bell's palsy

EPIDEMIOLOGY & DEMOGRAPHICS

INCIDENCE: 13-34 cases/100,000 persons

RISK FACTORS:

- Pregnancy (especially third trimester/first postpartum week)
- Ages 15 to 45 yr
- Diabetes (present in 5%-10% of patients)
- Travel to area endemic for Lyme disease

PHYSICAL FINDINGS & CLINICAL PRESENTATION

- Unilateral paralysis of the upper and lower facial muscles (asymmetric eye closure, brow, and smile). Upward rolling of eye on attempted eye closure ("Bell's phenomenon")
- Ipsilateral loss of taste
- Ipsilateral ear pain, usually 2-3 days before presentation
- Increased or decreased unilateral eye tearing
- Hyperacusis
- Subjective ipsilateral facial numbness
- In about 8% of cases, other cranial neuropathies may occur

ETIOLOGY

- Most cases are idiopathic.
- The cause is often viral (herpes simplex).
- Herpes zoster can cause Bell's palsy in association with herpetic blisters affecting the outer ear canal or the area behind the ear (Ramsay-Hunt Syndrome).
- Bell's palsy can also be one of the manifestations of Lyme disease.

DIAGNOSIS

DIFFERENTIAL DIAGNOSIS

- Neoplasms affecting the base of the skull or the parotid gland
- Bacterial infectious process (meningitis, otitis media, osteomyelitis of the base of the skull)
- Brainstem stroke
- Multiple sclerosis
- Sarcoidosis
- Head trauma with fracture of temporal bone
- Other: Guillain-Barré, carcinomatous or leukemic meningitis, leprosy, Melkersson-Rosenthal syndrome

WORKUP

Bell's palsy is a clinical diagnosis. A focused history and neurologic examination will confirm the diagnosis.

LABORATORY TESTS

- Fasting blood sugar to evaluate for diabetes
- Consider CBC, VDRL, ESR, ACE in selected patients
- Lyme titer in endemic areas

IMAGING STUDIES

- Contrast-enhanced MRI to exclude neoplasms is indicated only in patients with atypical features or course.
- Chest x-ray examination may be useful to exclude sarcoidosis or to rule out TB in selected patients before treating with steroids.

TREATMENT

NONPHARMACOLOGIC THERAPY

- Reassure patient that the disease is most likely a result of a virus attacking the nerve, not a stroke. It is also important to inform the patient that the prognosis is usually good.
- Avoid corneal drying by applying skin tape to the upper lid to keep the palpebral fissure narrowed. Lacri-Lube ophthalmic ointment at night and artificial tears during the day are also useful to prevent excessive drying.

ACUTE GENERAL Rx

- Although the benefits of corticosteroid therapy remain unproven, most practitioners use a brief course of prednisone therapy. Combination therapy with acyclovir and prednisone may possibly be effective in improving clinical recovery.
- If used, prednisone therapy should be started within 24-48 hr of symptom onset.
- Optimal steroid dose is unknown. Prednisone can be given as one 50-mg tablet qd for 7 days without tapering or can be started at 80 mg and tapered by 5 mg/day until finished. A Medrol dose-pack may also be given. A randomized controlled trial of patients treated with high dose IV steroids within 72 hr compared with placebo found a significant improvement in recovery rate and time to return to work but no statistical difference in final outcome.
- There is preliminary evidence for the effectiveness of methylcobalamin (active form of vitamin B_{12}) and hyperbaric oxygen, but these have not yet received widespread acceptance.
- Botulin toxin may be helpful for the treatment of synkinesis and hemifacial spasm, two of the late sequelae of Bell's palsy.

CHRONIC Rx

Patients should be monitored for evidence of corneal abrasion and ulceration or hemifacial spasm. Physical therapy including moist heat and massage may be beneficial.

DISPOSITION

- 71% of patients should recover completely. Prognosis is improved for those with clinical improvement within 3 wk and with less severity of symptoms at onset.
- Recovery begins within 3 wk in 85% of patients, with the remainder having some improvement within 3-6 mo.
- Recurrence is experienced in 5% of Bell's palsy cases.

REFERRAL

- Persistent redness or irritation of the eye requires referral to an ophthalmologist.
- Neurology referral is recommended if diagnosis is unclear or if the clinical course is atypical.

SUGGESTED READINGS

Benatar M, Edlow JA: The spectrum of cranial neuropathy in patients with Bell's palsy, *Arch Intern Med* 164:2283, 2004).

Grogan PM: Practice parameter: steroids, acyclovir, and surgery for Bell's palsy (an evidence-based review): report of the Quality Standards Subcommittee of the American Academy of Neurology, *Neurology* 56(7):830, 2001.

Holland NJ, Weiner GM: Recent developments in Bell's palsy, *Br J Med* 329:553, 2004.

Jabor, MA, Gianoli, G: Management of Bell's palsy, *J La State Med Soc* 148:279, 1996.

Lagalla G et al: Influence of early high-dose steroid treatment on Bell's palsy evolution, *Neurol Sci* 23:107, 2002.

Mountain, RE, et al: The Edinburgh facial palsy clinic: a review of three years' activity, *J R Coll Surg Edinb* 39:275, 1994.

Peitersen, E: The natural history of Bell's palsy, *Am J Otol* 4:107, 1982.

AUTHOR: **RICHARD ISAACSON, M.D.**

BASIC INFORMATION

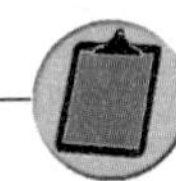

DEFINITION

Bipolar disorder is an episodic, recurrent, and frequently progressive condition in which the afflicted individual experiences at least one episode of mania characterized by at least 1 wk of continuous symptoms of elevated, expansive, or irritable mood in association with three or four of the following:

- Decreased need for sleep
- Grandiosity
- Pressured speech
- Subjective or objective flight of ideas
- Distractibility
- Increased level of goal-directed activity
- Problematic behavior

Most individuals with bipolar disorder will also experience one or more episodes of major depression over their lifetime or have symptoms of a depressive episode commingled with those of mania (mixed episode).

SYNONYMS

Manic-depression
Cycloid psychosis

ICD-9CM CODES
296.4-6 Circular manic, circular depressed, circular type mixed

EPIDEMIOLOGY & DEMOGRAPHICS

INCIDENCE (IN U.S.): Approximately 1.5% of the population

PREVALENCE (IN U.S.): 0.4% to 1.6%

PREDOMINANT SEX: Equal distribution among male and female

PREDOMINANT AGE: Lifelong condition with age of onset 14 to 30 yr

PEAK INCIDENCE: Onset in 20s

GENETICS:

- Concordance rates for monozygotic twins: 0.7 to 0.8, for dizygotic twins: 0.2
- Risk of affective disorder in offspring with one affected parent with bipolar disorder: 27%-29%, with two affected parents: 50%-74%
- Heritability estimate of 0.85
- Although no specific causal mutations have been identified, candidate gene loci have been reported on chromosomes 4, 5, 8, 18, and 21, as well as others

PHYSICAL FINDINGS & CLINICAL PRESENTATION

- Mania associated with psychomotor activation that is usually goal directed but not necessarily productive
- Elevated and frequently labile mood
- Flight of ideas with rapid, loud, pressured speech
- Psychosis with delusions, hallucinations, and formal thought disorder possible
- Depressive episodes resembling major depression (see "Major Depression"); however, retardation usually extreme
- Catatonia possible in severe cases

ETIOLOGY

- Unknown
- Hypotheses:
  1. Abnormalities of receptor and membrane function
  2. Alteration of cAMP, MAP kinase, protein kinase C, and glycine synthase kinase-3 signal transduction pathways
  3. Alteration in cell survival pathways

DIAGNOSIS

DIFFERENTIAL DIAGNOSIS

- Secondary manias caused by medical disorders (e.g., hyperthyroidism, AIDS, stroke, Cushing's syndrome) are frequent.
- First onset of mania after age 50 yr is suggestive of secondary mania.
- Less severe, and possibly distinct, conditions of bipolar type II and cyclothymia are possible.
- Comorbidity with substance abuse or dependency may confound diagnostic assessment and treatment.
- Cross-sectional examination of acutely manic patient can be confused with schizophreniform or a paranoid psychosis.

WORKUP

- History
- Physical examination
- Mental status examination
- Mood Disorder Questionnaire (MDQ)

LABORATORY TESTS

Because of high rate of secondary manias, initial evaluation to confirm health of all major organ systems (routine chemistries, complete blood count, urinalysis, sedimentation rate)

IMAGING STUDIES

- Consider brain imaging if late onset or if neurologic exam is abnormal
- Neuroimaging may show evidence of ventricular enlargement or increased white matter hyperintensities

TREATMENT

NONPHARMACOLOGIC THERAPY

- Cognitive-behavioral and family-focused psychoeducational psychotherapy to help patients cope with consequences of the disease, improve adherence with medications, and identify possible environmental triggers
- Bright light therapy in the northern latitudes in individuals exhibiting a seasonal pattern of winter depression
- Lifestyle "regularization"

ACUTE GENERAL Rx

- First-line agents for acute mania: lithium 1500-1800 mg/day (0.8-1.2 meq/L), valproate 1000-1500 mg/day (50-125 μg/mL), carbamazepine 600-800 mg/day (4-12 μg/mL).
- Useful adjuncts to acute treatment: olanzapine 10-20 mg/day, risperidone 2-4 mg/day, quetiapine 350-700 mg/day, ziprasidone 40-60 mg/day, and aripiprazole 10-30 mg/day, and benzodiazepines: lorazepam 1-2 mg/q4 hr, clonazepam 1-2 mg/q4 hr.
- Traditional antidepressants can induce manic episodes and exacerbate mania in mixed episodes.
- Lamotrigine may have acute antidepressant benefit.

CHRONIC Rx

- Goal of long-term treatment: prevention of relapse or episode recurrence
- Best agents for prophylaxis of mania: lithium, valproate and olanzapine (carbamazepine/oxcarbazepine possibly beneficial)
- Best agents for prophylaxis of depression: lamotrigine and lithium
- Role of atypical antipsychotics in maintenance unclear
- Long-term use of antidepressants: frequently destabilizes patient and leads to more frequent relapses

DISPOSITION

- Course is variable.
- More than 90% of patients having a single manic episode are likely to experience others.
- Uncontrolled manic or depressive episodes can lead to additional episodes ("illness begets illness").
- Lifetime rate of suicide attempts; 29%, risk of completed suicide increased 15% to 20%. Lithium treatment shown to specifically decrease suicidal risk.
- Psychosocioeconomic consequences of both mania and depression can be severe and disabling.

REFERRAL

- If use of antidepressant contemplated
- If patient is severely manic, rapid cycling, or suicidal, or is in a bipolar, mixed episode

SUGGESTED READINGS

Belmaker RH: Bipolar disorder, *N Engl J Med* 351(5):476, 2004.

Berns GS, Nemeroff CB: The neurobiology of bipolar disorder, *Am J Med Genet* 123C(1):76, 2003.

Geddes J: Bipolar disorder, *Evidence-Based Mental Health* 6(4):101, 2003.

Jones S: Psychotherapy of bipolar disorder: a review, *J Affect Disord* 80(2-3):101, 2004.

Mathew CA, Reus VI: Genetic linkage in bipolar disorder, *CNS Spectr* 8(12):891, 2003.

AUTHOR: **VICTOR I. REUS, M.D.**

BASIC INFORMATION

DEFINITION

A bite wound can be animal or human, accidental or intentional.

ICD-9CM CODES
879.8 Bite wound, unspecified site

EPIDEMIOLOGY & DEMOGRAPHICS

- Bite wounds account for 1% of emergency department visits.
- More than 1 million bites occur in humans annually in the U.S.
- Dog bites account for 85% to 90% of all bites and result in 10 to 20 fatalities yearly in the U.S.; cat bites, 10% to 20%. Typically the animal is owned by the victim.
- Infection rates are highest for cat bites (30% to 50%), followed by human bites (15% to 30%) and dog bites (5%).
- The extremities are involved in 75% of bites.

PHYSICAL FINDINGS & CLINICAL PRESENTATION

- The appearance of the bite wound is variable (e.g., puncture wound, tear, avulsion).
- Cellulitis, lymphangitis, and focal adenopathy may be present in infected bite wounds.
- Patient may experience fever and chills.

ETIOLOGY

- Increased risk of infection: human and cat bites, closed fist injuries, wounds involving joints, puncture wounds, face and lip bites, bites with skull penetration, bites in immunocompromised hosts
- Most frequent infecting organisms:
  1. *Pasteurella* spp.: responsible for majority of infections within 24 hr of dog (*P. canis*) and cat (*P. multocida, P. septica*) bites
  2. *Capnocytophaga canimorsus* (formerly DF-2 bacillus): a gram-negative organism responsible for late infection, usually following dog bites
  3. Gram-negative organisms (*Pseudomonas, Haemophilus*): often found in human bites
  4. *Streptococcus* spp., *Staphylococcus aureus*
  5. *Eikenella corrodens* in human bites

DIAGNOSIS

DIFFERENTIAL DIAGNOSIS

- Bite from a rabid animal (often the attack is unprovoked)
- Factitious injury

WORKUP

- Determination of the time elapsed since the patient was bitten, status of rabies immunization of the animal, and underlying medical conditions that might predispose the patient to infection (e.g., DM, immunodeficiency)
- Documentation of bite site, notification of appropriate authorities (e.g., police department, animal officer)

LABORATORY TESTS

- Generally not necessary
- Hct if there has been significant blood loss
- Wound cultures (aerobic and anaerobic) if there is evidence of sepsis or victim is immunocompromised patient; cultures should be obtained before irrigation of the wound but after superficial cleaning

IMAGING STUDIES

X-rays are indicated when bony penetration is suspected or if there is suspicion of fracture or significant trauma; x-rays are also useful for detecting presence of foreign bodies (when suspected).

TREATMENT

NONPHARMACOLOGIC THERAPY

- Local care with debridement, vigorous cleansing, and saline irrigation of the wound; debridement of devitalized tissue
- High-pressure irrigation to clean bite wound and ensure removal of contaminants (e.g., use saline solution with a 30- to 35-ml syringe equipped with a 20-gauge needle or catheter with tip of syringe placed 2 to 3 cm above the wound)
- Avoid blunt probing of wounds (increased risk of infection)

ACUTE GENERAL Rx

- Avoid suturing of hand wounds and any wounds that appear infected
- Puncture wounds should be left open
- Give antirabies therapy and tetanus immune globulin (250 to 500 units IM in limb controlateral to toxoid) and toxoid (adult or child older than 5 years old: 0.5 ml DT given IM, child less than 5 years old 0.5 ml DPT IM) as needed
- Use empiric antibiotic therapy in high-risk wounds (e.g., cat bite, hand bites, face bites, genital area bites, bites with joint or bone penetration, human bites, immunocompromised host): amoxicillin-clavulanate 500 to 875 mg bid for 7 days or cefuroxime 250 to 500 mg bid for 7 days
- In hospitalized patients, IV antibiotics of choice are cefoxitin 1 to 2 g q6h, ampicillin-sulbactam 1.5 to 3 g q6h, ticarcillin-clavulanate 3 g q6h, or ceftriaxone 1 to 2 g q24h
- Prophylactic therapy for persons bitten by others with HIV and hepatitis B (see Section V)

DISPOSITION

- Prognosis is favorable with proper treatment.
- Important prognostic factors are type and depth of wound, which compartments are entered, and pathogenicity of inoculated bacteria.
- Punctures that are difficult to irrigate adequately, carnivore bites over vital structures (arteries, nerves, joints), and tissue crushing that cannot be debrided have a worse prognosis.
- In general, human bites have a higher complication and infection rate than do animal bites.
- Nearly 50% of the anaerobic gram-negative bacilli isolated from human bite wounds may be penicillin resistant and beta-lactamase positive.

REFERRAL

- Hospitalization and IV antibiotic therapy for infected human bites; bites with injury to joints, nerves, or tendons; or any animal bites unresponsive to oral therapy.
- In the outpatient setting, bite wounds should be reevaluated within 48 hr to assess for signs of infection.

SUGGESTED READINGS

Broder J et al: Human bites, *Am J Med* 22:10, 2004.

Presutti RJ: Prevention and treatment of dog bites, *Am Fam Physician* 63:1567, 2001.

AUTHOR: **FRED F. FERRI, M.D.**

BASIC INFORMATION

DEFINITION

Injury resulting from snake biting a human.

ICD-9CM CODES
989.5 Venomous poisoning

EPIDEMIOLOGY & DEMOGRAPHICS

- 45,000 snake bites occur annually in the United States. Of the 8000 caused by poisonous snakes, approximately 9 to 15 result in fatality (i.e., ~1%-2%). Children, the elderly, and those in whom treatment has been delayed are at highest risk.
- In the United States at least one species of poisonous snake has been identified in every state except Alaska, Hawaii, and Maine. The majority of venomous snakes are members of the family Crotalidae, which includes rattlesnakes, copperheads, and cottonmouths. The Elapidae family, which includes the coral snake, accounts for the remainder.

PHYSICAL FINDINGS & CLINICAL PRESENTATION

In addition to local tissue injury, envenomation may affect the renal, neurologic, gastrointestinal, vascular, and coagulation systems. Species-specific signs and symptoms include:

CROTALIDAE (PIT VIPERS): Signs and symptoms:

- Fang punctures (see "Diagnosis")
- Pain within 5 min
- Edema within 30 min
- Erythema of site and adjacent tissues +/− lymphangitis

If no edema or erythema is manifested within 4 to 8 hr after a confirmed Crotalidae snakebite, it is safe to assume envenomation did not occur.

Systemic manifestations may include:

- Perioral paresthesias, metallic taste, and tingling of fingers or toes (especially with rattlesnake bites)
- Fasciculations (local or generalized)
- Chills, fever, hypotension (due to increased vascular permeability), nausea, vomiting, headache, weakness

ELAPIDAE (CORAL SNAKES): Signs and symptoms:

- Local symptoms are far less pronounced (little or no pain/swelling immediately after the bite)

Systemic symptoms predominate, but onset may be delayed for 1 to 5 hr. Examples include:

- Ptosis
- Dysphagia
- Dysarthria
- Intense salivation
- Loss of DTRs and respiratory depression (late manifestations)

DIAGNOSIS

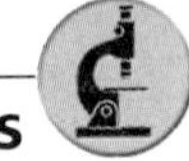

DIFFERENTIAL DIAGNOSIS

- Harmless snake bite
- Scorpion bite
- Insect bite
- Cellulitis
- Laceration or puncture wound

NOTE: Harmless snakebites are usually characterized by four rows of small scratches (teeth in upper jaw) separated from two rows of scratches (teeth in lower jaw). This is in distinction to venomous snake bites, which should have puncture wounds produced by the snake's fangs, whether other teeth marks are noted.

WORKUP

An estimated 25% of venomous snake bites do not result in envenomation, but observation is critical in all suspected cases:

- Clinical and laboratory evaluation are used to assess the severity of envenomation
- A nonstandardized classification system for grading envenomations was developed by Russell in 1964:
  - Minimal: confined to the site of the bite, no significant systemic symptoms or signs, no laboratory abnormalities
  - Moderate: manifestations extend beyond the site of the bite, but no life-threatening systemic symptoms
  - Severe: extensive limb involvement, severe systemic symptoms and signs, or significant laboratory abnormalities (including abnormal coagulation studies)

Determination of severity is based on the most severe symptom, sign, or laboratory result. Continual reassessment is indicated throughout the observation period because grading may change.

LABORATORY TESTS

- For all suspected envenomations, obtain CBC (with peripheral smear and platelet count) DIC screen (PT, PTT, fibrinogen, fibrin degradation products, D-dimer), ECG, and urinalysis
- For more severe bites, consider: LFTs, sedimentation rate, serum electrolytes, BUN, Cr, creatine kinase (r/o rhabdomyolysis), ABG, and type and crossmatch
- Other: Consider CXR in cases with severe envenomation or in patients >40 yr with underlying cardiopulmonary disease; x-ray of bite site for retained fangs (poor sensitivity); head CT if concern is raised for intracranial hemorrhage

TREATMENT

ACUTE GENERAL Rx

IN THE FIELD: For a suspected snakebite

- Immobilize affected part below level of the heart.
- Remove any constricting items. Local pressure has been advocated for elapid bites, particularly in Australia, as a means of delaying absorption of neurotoxins. However, crotalid bites are far more common in the U.S.A, and these frequently have tissue-necrosing venom, which will yield more damage with local pressure. Thus, as with incision and suction techniques, use by those without specialized training in snake-bite management is discouraged.
- DO NOT apply ice; keep victim warm.
- Avoid alcohol, stimulants (caffeine) or agents that can suppress mental status.
- Transport immediately to nearest medical facility and contact poison control center.

IN THE HOSPITAL:

- Establish intravenous access
- Obtain time of bite and description of snake if possible
- Obtain past medical history; ask about allergies to horse serum in those previously treated for snake bite
- Record vital signs: BP, HR, T, RR
- Inspect site of bite for fang marks, local symptoms
- Measure circumference of bitten part at two or more proximal sites and compare with unaffected limb; repeat every 15 to 20 min
- Neurologic examination
- Gauge the severity of the bite and decide whether administration of antivenom is necessary
- For minimal envenomation without progressive manifestations
  1. Clean and immobilize affected part
  2. Immunize against tetanus
  3. Observe patient for at least 8 to 12 hr. If, after this period, local and systemic sequelae are absent and lab values remain normal, the likelihood of significant envenomation is low, and the patient can be discharged from the acute setting
- Patients who have progressive symptoms (local or systemic) and/or moderate to severe envenomation should be considered for antivenom. The high incidence of allergic reactions argues against its use in less severe cases.
- Antivenom is most effective when given within 4 hr of the bite and least effective if delayed beyond 12 hr.

Once the decision is made to use antivenom:

- Prepare epinephrine 0.5-1.0 ml of a 0.1% solution to be administered in case of a hypersensitivity reaction to the antivenom. (Prophylactic antihistamines are not efficacious.)
- Most centers now have sheep immunoglobulin-based antivenom (Crofab) for crotalid bites. (A potent, safe, sheep-based antivenom for elapid bites exists but is not yet approved in the U.S.) Sheep-based antivenoms are very safe, but repeat administration may be necessary owing to a short half-life. An initial IV dose of 4 to 6 vials (depending on the size and age of the patient and the severity of the bite) is infused over 60 min. If the patient has not responded after 1 hr, a repeat dose of 4 to 6 vials is indicated. Additionally, patients with coagulopathic relapse (fibrinogen <50, platelets <25 K, INR >3.0, or PTT >50 sec) require repeat doses of two vials q6hrs until resolution occurs. Up to ⅔ of patients with initial coagulopathy will require relapse dosing. Help in using the antivenom is available around the clock by calling 877-377-3784.
- Horse serum-based antivenoms are available for both crotalid and elapid (coral snake), but it runs a much higher risk of hypersensitivity reactions such as anaphylaxis and serum sickness. (Skin testing is available, but it is not recommended because it is not completely reliable and may delay time to administration beyond the most effective period.) For treatment considerations, see "Complications". Guidelines to dosage of horse serum-based antivenom are as follows:
- For pit viper bites
  - Mild 5 vials
  - Moderate 10 vials
  - Severe 15 vials
  - Shock 20 vials
- For coral snake bites (different formulation)
  - 3 vials, if symptoms evolve, repeat with 5 vials
- Zoos with exotic snakes are required to maintain a supply of snake-specific antivenom on their premises

Other considerations:

- Initial dose of antivenom should be repeated until progression of symptoms has abated, but observation of bitten part should be continued for another 48 hr
- Children require more antivenom; increase dose by 50%
- Pregnancy is not a contraindication to antivenom
- Immunize against tetanus if no booster within past 5 yr; if never immunized, give immunoglobulin as well as toxoid
- Manage pain as needed (acetaminophen, codeine, meperidine)
- Avoid sedation in Mojave rattlesnake, eastern diamondback rattlesnake, and coral snake bites
- Antibiotics reserved for moderate to severe cases; use those with broad-spectrum coverage (which includes gram-negatives, i.e., quinolone derivatives)

DISPOSITION

Prognosis is good with prompt evaluation and treatment.

REFERRAL

To medical facility with ICU for administration of antivenom

PEARLS & CONSIDERATIONS

COMPLICATIONS

Most frequent complication of treated envenomations is serum sickness; occurs 7 to 14 days after antivenom administration and is characterized by fever, rash, arthralgias, and lymphadenopathy. It can be treated with PO prednisone 60 mg/day, tapered over 7 to 10 days. Acutely, there is the risk of anaphylaxis to antivenom as mentioned previously. This occurs within 30 min and is treated with

- IV epinephrine
- IV diphenhydramine
- IV hydrocortisone

Injuries also result from

- Tourniquet placement
- Cryotherapy

National poison-control hotline: (800)222-1222

SUGGESTED READINGS

Gold BS et al: Bites of venomous snakes, *N Engl J Med* 347:347, 2002.

Juckett G, Honcox JG: Venomous snakebites in the United States: management review and update, *Am Fam Physician* 65:1367, 2002.

The Medical Letter: A new snake antivenom, *Med Lett Drugs Ther* 43:55, 2001.

AUTHORS: **JACK SCHWARZWALD, M.D.**, and **REBECCA A. GRIFFITH, M.D.**

BASIC INFORMATION

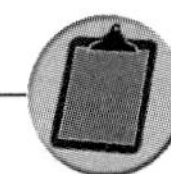

DEFINITION

There are two major classes of arthropods: insects and arachnida. This chapter will focus on the class arachnida. Arachnid bites consist of bites caused by:
- Spiders
- Scorpions
- Ticks

ICD-9CM CODES
E905.1 Venomous spiders (black widow spider, brown spider, tarantula)
E905.2 Scorpion
989.5 Bites of venomous snakes, lizards, and spiders; tick paralysis
E906.4 Bite of nonvenomous arthropod; insect bite NOS

EPIDEMIOLOGY & DEMOGRAPHICS

- Spiders: ubiquitous; only three types potentially significantly harmful:
  1. Sydney funnel web spider—Australia
  2. Black widow—worldwide (not Alaska)
  3. Brown recluse—most common (South Central U.S.)
- Scorpions: various warm climates: Africa, Central South America, Middle East, India; in U.S.: Texas, New Mexico, California, Nevada
- Ticks: woodlands

PHYSICAL FINDINGS & CLINICAL PRESENTATION

Spiders:
- Sydney funnel web—atrataxin toxin
  1. Piloerection, muscle spasms leading to tachycardia, HTN, increased intracranial pressure, coma
- Black widow—females toxic
  1. Initial reaction: local swelling, redness (two fang marks) leading to local piloerection, edema, urticaria, diaphoresis, lymphangitis
  2. Pain in limb leading to rest of body (chest pain, abdominal pain)
  3. Systemic SX: headache, fever, chills, GI upset, hemolysis, renal tubular necrosis, DIC possible.
- Brown Recluse
  1. Minor sting or burn.
  2. Wound may become pruritic and red with a blanched center with vesicle. Can necrose, especially in fatty areas. Leaves eschar, which sloughs and leaves ulcer, can take months to heal.

Scorpions:
- Sting leading to sympathetic and parasympathetic stimulation: HTN, bradycardia, vasoconstriction, pulmonary edema, reduced coronary blood flow, priapism, inhibition of insulin
- Also possible: tachycardia, arrhythmia, vasodilation, bronchial relaxation, excessive salivation, vomiting, sweating, bronchoconstriction

Ticks: U.S., Europe, Asia
- Very small (<1 mm). Must be attached >36 hours to transmit disease.
- Lyme disease—most common
  1. Early: erythema migrans 60% to 80% of cases
  2. 7 to 10 days: mild to moderate constitutional symptoms—disseminated—secondary skin lesions, fever, adenopathy, constitutional symptoms, facial palsy, peripheral neuropathy, lymphocytic meningitis, meningoencephalitis, cardiac manifestations

DIAGNOSIS

DIFFERENTIAL DIAGNOSIS:

Cellulitis
Urticaria
Other tick-borne illnesses:
- Babesiosis
- Tick-borne relapsing fever
- Tularemia
- Rocky Mountain spotted fever
- Ehrlichiosis
- Colorado tick fever
- Tick paralysis

WORKUP

Physical examination: thorough skin examination may reveal fang marks, attached ticks, black eschar.

TREATMENT

Spiders:
- Sydney funnel web
  1. Pressure, immobilization immediately, supportive care, antivenin
- Black widow
  1. Rarely fatal. Treatment based on severity of symptoms.
  2. All should get on oxygen, IV, cardiac monitor, tetanus prophylaxis.
  3. Symptomatic/supportive therapy.
  4. 10% calcium gluconate for muscle cramps (controversial).
  5. Antivenin only for more severe reactions. Antivenin carries risk of anaphylaxis.
  6. Dose: one vial in 100 ml 0.9% saline over 20 to 30 minutes.
  7. Skin test before use; give antihistamines with use.
- Brown recluse
  1. Pain management, tetanus, supportive treatment.
  2. No consensus regarding best treatment. Some evidence for hyperbaric oxygen.

Scorpions:
- Fluids, supportive care, species-specific antivenin (equine based, risk serum sickness)—controversial.

Ticks:
- Prophylactic: tick >36 hours: doxycycline 200 mg—single dose
- Early localized disease
  1. Treatment of choice in children: amoxicillin x 10 to 14 days. Doxycycline preferred in patients with possible concurrent ehrlichiosis.
  2. Early disseminated: treatment depends on manifestation.
  3. Late disease: may require longer-term/IV therapy. Controversial for neurologic disease. (See chapter on Lyme disease for further details.)

DISPOSITION

- For patients with systemic reactions, send home with emergency epinephrine kit.
- If severe or anaphylactic reaction, admit and observe for 48 hours for cardiac, renal, or neurologic problems.

REFERRAL

- For patients with systemic reactions, refer to allergist for immunotherapy; 95% to 98% effective in preventing anaphylaxis.

SUGGESTED READINGS

Farhat D: Arachnidism, *Topics in Emergency Medicine* 22(2):1, 2000.
Hayes P: Current concepts: how can we prevent Lyme disease? *N Engl J Med* 348(24): 2424, 2003.

AUTHOR: **GAIL O'BRIEN, M.D.**

BASIC INFORMATION

DEFINITION

Most stinging insects belong to the Hymenoptera order and include yellow jackets (most common cause of reactions), bumble bees, sweat bees, wasps, harvester ants, fire ants, and the Africanized honey bee "killer bee." Brown recluse spiders, although they are not insects, are another common cause of bites. The usual effect of a sting is to cause intense local pain, some immediate erythema, and often a small area of edema by injecting venom. Allergic reactions can be either local or generalized leading to anaphylactic shock. The majority of reactions occur within the first 6 hr after the sting or bite, but a delayed presentation may occur up to 24 hr.

SYNONYMS

Venom allergy

ICD-9CM CODES
989.5 Stings (bees, wasps)
989.5 Bites (fire ant, brown recluse spider)

EPIDEMIOLOGY & DEMOGRAPHICS

PREVALENCE (OF BEE STINGS AND INSECT BITES):
- Unknown
- Between 0.4% and 4% of the population is allergic to the venom of one or more stinging insects
- Most anaphylactic reactions occur in those most likely to be exposed including children, males, outdoor workers
- Bites by fire ants and brown recluse spiders are less likely to cause systemic disease

INCIDENCE (IN U.S.): 50 to 150 people die each year from insect sting anaphylaxis; anaphylaxis occurs more often within 10 to 30 min of a sting. Delayed reactions are rare occurring only in <0.3% of stings.

PHYSICAL FINDINGS & CLINICAL PRESENTATION

Stings:
- Cutaneous: the skin is the most common site of an allergic reaction. Manifestations include flushing, urticaria, pruritus, and angioedema.
- Respiratory: hoarseness, difficulty speaking, choking, throat tightness or tingling may progress to stridor, laryngeal edema, laryngospasm, and bronchoconstriction. This is the leading cause of anaphylactic death.
- Cardiovascular: manifestations include tachycardia, hypotension, arrhythmia, in some cases progressing to profound hypovolemic shock. Myocardial infarction is rare. Cardiac manifestations are the second leading cause of death from anaphylaxis.
- Other symptoms: abdominal pain, nausea, vomiting, and diarrhea.

Fire ant bites:
- Wheal and flare response followed by circularly arrayed pustules

ETIOLOGY

Stings:
- Most systemic reactions to insect stings are classic IgE-mediated allergic reactions.
- Reactions occur in previously sensitized patients who have produced high titers of IgE antibody to insect venom antigens.
- Sensitization to wasp venom requires only a few stings and can occur after a single sting.
- Sensitization to bee venom occurs mainly in people who have been stung frequently by bees.

Bites:
Fire ant venom contains proteins toxic to the skin.

DIAGNOSIS

DIFFERENTIAL DIAGNOSIS

- Stings: cellulitis, bites
- Bites: stings, cellulitis

WORKUP

History is essential for accurate diagnosis including timing of sting or bite and type of insect (bee, wasp, spider, or ant) if known.

LABORATORY TESTS

- Skin test: either skin prick test or intradermal with bee and wasp venom.
- Measurement of serum bee-specific or wasp-specific IgE measured by radioallergosorbent tests (RAST) or other assays.

TREATMENT

ACUTE GENERAL Rx

Sting:
- Removal of the stinger most readily performed with a flat tool like a credit card, cleansing, and application of ice
- Treatment with oral antihistamines if limited reaction. Topical corticosteroids may provide some relief of inflammation
- Patients with previous reactions or multiple stings to the mouth or neck should be evaluated in an emergency department
- Treatment for larger swellings and associated systemic symptoms is IM antihistamines, intravenous corticosteroids, adrenaline, IM epinephrine, and IV fluids

Bite:
- Supportive
- Application of ice

DISPOSITION

Sting:
Prognosis for a limited reaction is excellent. Anywhere from 20% to 80% of patients who have had generalized reaction to a sting will have no such reaction on subsequent sting and there is no evidence that the next sting will necessarily cause a more severe reaction. The reasons for the variable outcome include patient's immune status at the time of sting, dose of venom injected, and site of sting.
Bite:
Prognosis for fire ant bite is excellent. Large lesions from brown recluse spider bites may take months to heal.

FURTHER MANAGEMENT

Patients with a history of sting allergies should carry syringes preloaded with epinephrine (EpiPen) and oral antihistamines to take if they are stung again. Consider a referral to an allergist for immunotherapy. Risk of subsequent anaphylaxis with immunotherapy falls to <3%. Venom immunotherapy for 3 to 5 yr induces long-term protection in most patients.

SUGGESTED READINGS

Annila I: Bee venom allergy, *Clin Exp Allergy* 30(12):1682, 2000.
Ewan PW: ABC of allergies: venom allergy, *BMJ* 316(7141):1365, 1998.
Greco: Hymenoptera stings, *Top Emerg Med* 22(2):37, 2000.
Neugut AI et al: Anaphylaxis in the United States: an investigation into its epidemiology, *Arch Intern Med* 161(1):15, 2001.
Youlton L: Insect sting reactions, *Clin Exp Dermatol* 24(4):338, 2000.

AUTHORS: **ANNE W. MOULTON, M.D.,** and **JENNIFER JEREMIAH, M.D.**

BASIC INFORMATION

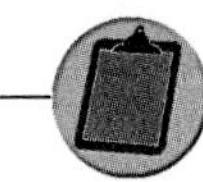

DEFINITION

Bladder cancer is a heterogeneous spectrum of neoplasms ranging from non–life-threatening, low-grade, superficial papillary lesions to high-grade invasive tumors, which often have metastasized at the time of presentation. It is a field change disease in which the entire urothelium from the renal pelvis to the urethra may be susceptible to malignant transformation. *Types:* Transitional cell carcinoma (TCCa), squamous cell carcinoma, and adenocarcinoma.

ICD-9CM CODES
Primary: 188.9
Secondary: 198.1
CIS: 233.7
Benign: 223.3
Uncertain behavior: 236.7
Unspecified: 239.4

EPIDEMIOLOGY & DEMOGRAPHICS

Each year approximately 54,000 new cases are diagnosed and more than 12,000 deaths are attributed to bladder cancer.

Until 1990, the incidence of bladder cancer in the U.S. was rising. Since 1990, the incidence of bladder cancer is decreasing at a rate of 0.8% per year (1.2% among men and 0.4% among women).

PREDOMINANT SEX: In males, it is the fourth most common cancer; it accounts for 10% of all cancers. In females, it is the eighth most common cancer; it accounts for 4% of all cancers.

RISK: The lifetime risk of developing bladder cancer is 2.8% in white males, 0.9% in black males, 1% in white females, and 0.6% in black females.

Smoking:
- Users of "black" tobacco in place of "blond" tobacco have a twofold to threefold increase in developing bladder cancer.
- Smoking risk is based on consumption:

With a twofold to threefold increase for subjects smoking at least 10 cigarettes per day

The risk increases again when the daily consumption rises above 40-60 cigarettes per day
- Smokers of low-tar and nicotine cigarettes have a lower risk when compared with higher tar and nicotine cigarettes.
- Unfiltered cigarettes have a 50% increased risk of bladder cancer compared with those who smoke filtered cigarettes.
- Pipe smokers have a lower risk of bladder cancer compared with cigarette smokers.
- Cigar smoking, snuff, and chewing tobacco, although implicated in nonurologic cancers, are not believed to influence bladder cancer risk.

Diet:
- Diets rich in beef, pork, and animal fat consumption increase risk of bladder cancer.
- There is no indication that consumption of nonbeer alcoholic drinks contributes to bladder cancer development.
- Beer consumption has been linked to bladder cancer development as a result of the presence of nitrosamines in the beer. Similarly, these nitrosamines have been implicated in the development of rectal cancer.
- Drinking coffee is not believed to contribute to bladder cancer risk. There is additional evidence that coffee consumption is protective for colorectal cancers, possibly by diminishing fecal transit time.

PEAK INCIDENCE: Incidence increases with age, high >60 yr, uncommon <40 yr.

GENETICS: It is thought to be multifactorial in etiology, involving both genetic and environmental interactions. Overall, it is estimated that approximately 20% to 25% of the male population in the U.S. with bladder cancer has the disease as a result of occupational exposure.

DISTRIBUTION: In North America, transitional cell carcinomas comprise 93%, squamous cell carcinomas comprise 6%, and adenocarcinomas account for 1% of bladder cancers.

PATHOGENESIS: Two pathways exist for bladder cancer (TCCa):
1. Papillary superficial disease occasionally leading to invasive cancer (75%)
2. Carcinoma-in-situ (CIS) and solid invasive cancer with high risk of disease progression (25%)

Two distinct forms of "Superficial Cancer" exist:

T_a Papillary low-grade tumor. High rate of recurrence. Disease progression occurs 5%

T_1 Higher-grade papillary tumors that infiltrate the lamina propria. Often associated with flat CIS that may involve the urothelium diffusely. Disease progression occurs between 30% to 50%

Subdivided into:

T_{1a} Penetration of tumor up to the muscularis mucosae. Disease progression 5.3%

T_{1b} Penetration of tumor through the muscularis mucosae. Disease progression 53%

Flat CIS:

Entirely different and separate pathway of cancer development whose mechanism is manifested by dysplasia, which leads to the occurrence of poorly differentiated malignant cells that replace or undermine the normal urothelium and extend along the plane of the bladder wall. It penetrates the basement membrane and lamina propria in 20% to 30% of the cases and is associated with the development of solid tumor growth. A defect in chromosome 17p53 occurs in 50% of the cases.

At presentation, 72% of cancers are localized to the bladder, 20% of the cancers extend to the regional lymph nodes, and 3% present with distant metastases. 80% of superficial TCCa recur with up to 30% progressing to a higher stage or grade. Younger patients most commonly develop low-grade papillary noninvasive TCCa and are less likely to have recurrences when compared with older patients with similar lesions. Involvement of the upper tracts with tumor occurs in 25% to 50% of the cases.

STAGING (BASED ON THE TNM SYSTEM):

T_0 No tumor in specimen
T_{is} CIS
T_a Papillary TCCa noninvasive
T_1 Papillary TCCa into lamina propria
T_2 TCCa invasive of superficial ms
T_{3a} Invasive of deep ms
T_{3b} Invasive of perivesical fat
T_{4a} Invasive of adjacent pelvic organ
T_{4b} Invasive of pelvic wall with fixation

Invasive of nodal status:
N_0 No nodal involvement
N_{1-3} Pelvic nodes
N_4 Nodes above bifurcation
N_x Unknown

Invasive of metastatic status:
M_0 No distant metastases
M_1 Distant metastases
M_x Unknown

MOLECULAR EPIDEMIOLOGY: TCCa is usually a field change disease with tumors arising at different times and sites in the urothelium, suggesting a polyclonal etiology of bladder cancer. Bladder cancers have been associated with abnormalities on chromosomes 1, 4, 11, 5, 7, 3, 9, 21, 18, 13, 8; with alterations in suppressor genes P53, retinoblastoma gene, and P16; and with alterations in oncogenes H-ras and epidermal growth factor receptor.

PHYSICAL FINDINGS

- Gross painless hematuria
- Microhematuria
- Frequency, urgency, occasional dysuria

With locally invasive to distant metastatic disease, the presentation can include:
- Abdominal pain
- Flank pain

- Lymphedema
- Renal failure
- Anorexia
- Bone pain

ETIOLOGY

Bladder cancer is a potentially preventable disease associated with specific etiologic factors:

- Cigarette smoking is associated with 25% to 65% of the cases. The risk of developing a TCCa is 2 to 4 times higher in smokers than in nonsmokers, and that risk persists for many years, being equal to nonsmokers only after 12 to 15 yr of smoking abstinence. Smoking tobacco is associated with tumors that are characterized by higher histologic grade, increased tumor stage, increase in the numbers of tumor present, and increased tumor size.
- Occupational exposures: dye workers, textile workers, tire and rubber workers, petroleum workers
- Chemical exposure: O-toluidine, 2-naphthylamine, benzidine, 4-aminobiphenyl, and nitrosamines
- Exposure to HPV type 16

Squamous carcinomas are associated with:

- Schistosomiasis
- Urinary calculi
- Indwelling catheters
- Bladder diverticula

Miscellaneous causes:

- Phenacetin abuse
- Cyclophosphamide
- Pelvic irradiation
- Tuberculosis

Adenocarcinomas are associated with:

- Exstrophy
- Endometriosis
- Neurogenic bladder
- Urachal abnormalities
- As a secondary site for distant metastases from other organs (i.e., colon cancer)

DIAGNOSIS

- History and physical examination
- Urinalysis
- Cystoscopy with bladder barbotage and biopsy
- Transurethral resection of bladder tumor(s)
- There is insufficient evidence to determine whether a decrease in mortality from bladder cancer occurs with hematuria testing, urinary cytology, or a variety of other tests on exfoliated urinary cells or other substances.
- In addition to urinary cytologies and bladder barbotage, BTA, NMP22, and Fibrin Degradation Products (FDP) have been approved by the FDA as bladder cancer tumor markers. No marker has general, widespread acceptance because the results are affected by the presence of stents, recent urologic manipulation, stones, infection, bowel interposition, and prostatitis creating false-positive results.

DIFFERENTIAL DIAGNOSIS

- Urinary tract infection
- Frequency-urgency syndrome
- Interstitial cystitis
- Stone disease
- Endometriosis
- Neurogenic bladder

LABORATORY TESTS

RADIOLOGIC TESTS:

- IVP, renal ultrasound, retrograde pyelography, CT scan, and MRI.
- One or a combination of studies can be used. In the absence of skeletal symptoms, bone scan is not recommended.

TREATMENT

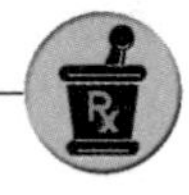

NONPHARMACOLOGIC THERAPY

- Initially, transurethral resection of bladder tumor (TURBT)
- Loop biopsy of the prostatic urethra if high-grade TCCa is suspected
- If superficial disease, follow-up protocol with repeat TURBT and/or the use of intravesical agents is recommended
- For advanced bladder cancer, radical cystectomy with urethrectomy (unless orthotopic diversion is planned) and either ileal loop conduit or orthotopic diversion

BLADDER PRESERVATION APPROACHES: Following cystectomy for muscle invasive disease, 50% or more of the patients will develop metastases. Most patients develop metastases at distant sites, a third relapse locally. Bladder preservation management is offered in those individuals who refuse surgery or who might not be suitable radical cystectomy patients. Bladder-sparing protocols include extensive TURBT or partial cystectomy with external beam or interstitial radiotherapy and systemic chemotherapy. Radiotherapy as a single treatment modality is not effective. The best predictor of successful bladder preservation is a complete response following the combination of initial TURBT and two cycles of CMV (cisplatin, methotrexate, vinblastine) chemotherapy seen with stages T2-T3a.

INDICATIONS FOR PARTIAL CYSTECTOMY:

- Tumor within a bladder diverticulum
- Solitary, primary, and muscle-invasive or high-grade lesion of a region of the bladder that allows complete excision with adequate surgical margins
- Inability to adequately resect tumor by TURBT alone because of size or location
- Tumor overlying a ureteral orifice requiring ureteral reimplantation
- Biopsy of a radiation-induced ulceration
- Palliation of severe local symptoms
- Patient refusal of urinary diversion
- Poor-risk patient who is not a diversion candidate

Contraindications:

- Multiple tumors
- CIS
- Cellular atypia on biopsy
- Prostatic invasion
- Invasion of the trigone
- Inability to achieve adequate surgical margins
- Prior radiotherapy
- Inability to maintain adequate bladder volume after resection
- Evidence of extravesical tumor extension
- Poor surgical risk

ACUTE GENERAL Rx

INDICATIONS FOR INTRAVESICAL CHEMOTHERAPY:

- High-grade tumor
- Tumor size >5 cm
- Tumor multiplicity
- Presence of CIS
- Positive urinary cytologies following a resection
- Incomplete tumor resection

Intravesical agents: thiotepa, Adriamycin, mitomycin C, AD-32, BCG, interferon, bropirimine, Epodyl, interleukin-2, and keyhole-limpet hemocyanin. Photodynamic therapy with hematoporphyrin derivatives has also been used.

INDICATIONS FOR CYSTECTOMY:

- Large tumors not amenable to complete TURBT
- High-grade tumor
- Multiple tumors with frequent recurrences
- Diffuse CIS not responsive to intravesical chemotherapy
- Prostatic urethra involvement
- Irritative bladder symptoms with upper tract deterioration
- Muscle-invasive disease
- Disease outside of the bladder

SYSTEMIC CHEMOTHERAPY: Used as neoadjuvant and adjuvant therapy for systemic disease. The most effective agents are cisplatin, methotrexate, vinblastine, Adriamycin (MVAC). Other agents include mitoxantrone, vincristine, etoposide (VP16), 5FU, ifosfamide, Taxol, gemcitabine, Piritrexim, and gallium nitrate. Chemotherapy in combination can provide palliation and modest survival benefit.

RADIOTHERAPY: Conflicting reports suggest that superficial bladder cancer is more sensitive to radiotherapy. Squamous changes within the tumor and secretion of human chorionic gonadotropin by the lesion are associated with poor response to radiotherapy. Only 20% to 30% of patients with invasive bladder cancer can be cured by external beam radiation therapy alone. It is used in combination with surgery or with systemic agents to treat bladder cancer primarily in those patients who are not surgical candidates or who refuse surgery.

CHRONIC Rx

FOLLOW-UP RECOMMENDATIONS FOR SUPERFICIAL BLADDER CANCER:

- Cystoscopy, bladder barbotage, and bimanual examination every 3 mo for 2 yr, then every 6 mo for 2 yr, and annually thereafter.
- Upper tract studies are based on the risk of upper tract tumor development, generally every 2 to 5 yr.

FOLLOW-UP RECOMMENDATIONS FOR ADVANCED DISEASE:

Bladder Preservation:

- Cystoscopy, barbotage, bimanual examination, biopsy (when indicated), every 3 mo for 2 yr, then every 6 mo for 2 yr, yearly thereafter.
- CT scan of abdomen and pelvis every 6 mo for 2 yr in addition to chest x-ray examination, liver function testing, and serum creatinine.

Cystectomy with Ileal Loop/Orthotopic Bladder:

- Neobladder endoscopy and IVP yearly.
- CT scan of abdomen and pelvis every 6 mo for 2 yr in addition to chest x-ray examination, liver function tests, and serum creatinine.
- Loopogram every 6 mo for 2 yr, then yearly.

BOX 1-3 American Urological Association Guideline Recommendations

1. Undiagnosed bladder tumor: obtain a histologic diagnosis of the tumor: Transurethral resection of the tumor is the most common method.
2. Stage Ta or T1 cancer: Complete surgical eradication of all visible tumors. The lesion can be treated with electrocautery resection, fulguration, or laser ablation. Adjuvant intravesical therapy is recommended for patients with carcinoma-in-situ, T1, or high-grade Ta tumors. The agent recommended is BCG or mitomycin C. Cystectomy is an option for this set of tumors because of risk of progression to muscle-invasive disease even after intravesical chemotherapy.

An increased risk of disease progression is associated with large tumor, high-grade tumor, location of the tumor in a site that is poorly accessible to complete resection, diffuse disease, infiltration of lymphatic or vascular spaces, and prostatic urethral involvement.

3. Carcinoma-in-situ or high-grade T1 cancer and prior intravesical chemotherapy: Cystectomy is the recommendation based on the panel's expert opinion rather than evidence from outcomes data. The data show a substantial risk of progression to muscle-invasive cancer in patients with diffuse carcinoma-in-situ and high-grade T1 tumors. The response to intravesical chemotherapy in terms of altering this disease progression is unknown, and as a result of this, cystectomy is an option for the afflicted patient.

American Urological Association, Guideline Division, 1120 North Charles Street, Baltimore, MD 21201.

PEARLS & CONSIDERATIONS

COMMENTS

- The most useful prognostic parameters for bladder tumor recurrence and subsequent cancer progression are tumor grade, depth of tumor penetration, multifocal tumors, frequency of recurrence, tumor size, CIS, lymphatic invasion, papillary or solid tumor configuration.
- Box 1-3 describes the American Urological Association Guideline Recommendations for bladder cancer.

SUGGESTED READINGS

Lamm DL et al: Megadose vitamins in bladder cancer: a double-blind clinical trial, *J Urol* 151:21, 1994.

Messing EM: In Walsh PC et al. (eds): *Campbell's urology*, ed 8, Philadelphia, 2002, WB Saunders.

AUTHOR: **PHILIP J. ALIOTTA, M.D., M.S.H.A.**

BASIC INFORMATION

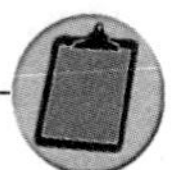

DEFINITION

Blastomycosis is a systemic pyogranulomatous disease caused by a dimorphic fungus, *Blastomyces dermatitidis*.

ICD-9CM CODES
116.0 Blastomycosis
116.0 Primary pulmonary
116.1 Brazilian
116.1 South American
116.2 Keloidal
117.5 European

EPIDEMIOLOGY & DEMOGRAPHICS

Most patients reside in the southeastern and south central states, especially those bordering the Mississippi and Ohio River valleys, the Midwestern states, and Canadian provinces bordering the Great Lakes. Rare cases have been reported outside the United States. Widely disseminated disease is most common in immunocompromised hosts, especially those with acquired immunodeficiency syndrome (AIDS). Initial infections result from the inhalation of conidia into the lungs, although primary cutaneous blastomycosis has been reported after dog bites, albeit infrequently.

PHYSICAL FINDINGS & CLINICAL PRESENTATION

- Acute infection: 50% symptomatic, median incubation 30 to 45 days, symptoms are nonspecific: mimic influenza or bacterial infection with abrupt onset of myalgias, arthralgias, chills and fever; transient pleuritic pain, cough that is initially nonproductive; resolution within 4 wk is usual
- Chronic or recurrent infection: indolent and progressive; manifestations are diverse including pulmonary or extrapulmonary disease

Pulmonary manifestations: Symptoms and signs of chronic pneumonia: productive cough, hemoptysis, pleuritic chest pain, weight loss, low-grade pyrexia

Extrapulmonary manifestations:

1. Cutaneous: most common; may occur with or without pulmonary disease. Two different lesions:
   Verrucous: beginning as a small papulopustular lesion on exposed body areas that may develop into an eschar with peripheral microabscesses
   Ulcerative
   Subcutaneous nodules (cold abscesses) may also occur.
2. Bone and joint: 10% to 50% of patients have osteolytic lesions; affects long bones, vertebrae, and ribs; lesions may present with a contiguous soft-tissue abscess or draining sinus that may spread to a joint, resulting in a pyarthrosis
3. Genitourinary: 10% to 30% of patients; prostatic involvement is most common and may manifest as obstruction; epididymis and testes may also be affected
4. Central nervous system: 5% normal host; 40% AIDS patients; meningitis and abscess formation

ETIOLOGY

B. dermatitidis exists in warm, moist soil that is rich in organic material. When these microfoci are disturbed, the aerosolized spores or conidia are inhaled into the lungs. Disease at other sites is a result of dissemination from the initial pulmonary infection; the latter may be acute or chronic.

DIAGNOSIS

DIFFERENTIAL DIAGNOSIS

PULMONARY INFECTION:

- Tuberculosis
- Bronchogenic carcinoma
- Histoplasmosis
- Bacterial pneumonia

CUTANEOUS INFECTION:

- Bromoderma
- Pyoderma gangrenosum
- *Mycobacterium marinum* infection
- Squamous cell carcinoma
- Giant keratoacanthoma

WORKUP

- Physical examination and laboratory evaluation
- Definitive diagnosis established by culture

LABORATORY TESTS

- Presumptive diagnosis can be made by visualizing the distinctive yeast forms in clinical specimens
- Culture: on Sabouraud's or more enriched media
  1. Aspirated material from abscesses
  2. Skin scrapings
  3. Prostatic secretions (urine culture with prostatic massage)
- Direct examination of clinical specimens
  1. Wet preparation with 10% KOH
  2. Histopathology: typically demonstrates pyogranulomas; yeast identification requires special stains
- Serologic tests: currently, a negative serologic test cannot be used to exclude blastomycosis, nor should a positive titer be an indication to start treatment

IMAGING STUDIES

In chronic disease, chest radiographic findings are nonspecific, but lobar or segmental alveolar infiltrates, especially of the upper lobes, are most common and may progress to cavitation.

TREATMENT

ACUTE BLASTOMYCOSIS

- Indication for chemotherapy remains controversial in patients with acute pulmonary blastomycosis.
- Because the acute form may be benign and self-limited, patients may be closely observed.
- Some patients progress to chronic infection with attendant significant morbidity and therefore may require treatment.
- Patients who are immunocompromised or have extrapulmonary disease or progressive pulmonary disease should be treated.

CHRONIC BLASTOMYCOSIS

- Itraconazole 200 mg IV bid × 4 doses followed by 200 mg IV qd or itraconazole 200 to 400 mg/day for 6 mo remains the drug of choice except for those patients with CNS disease or with fulminant illness who require amphotericin B.
- Amphotericin B: total dose of 1.5 to 2.5 g IV is recommended in immunocompromised patients, those with life-threatening disease or CNS disease, or those for whom azole treatment has failed. In addition, amphotericin B is the only drug approved for treating blastomycosis in pregnant women.
- Amphotericin B lipid complex (ABLC) 5 mg/kg/day IV may be considered in patients who are intolerant of or refractory to amphotericin.
- Fluconazole 400 mg/day to 800 mg/day PO for 6 mo in those who cannot take itraconazole or who are unable to tolerate a full course of amphotericin B.
- Ketoconazole 400 mg/day PO for 6 mo is an alternative in mild-moderate disease.
- Surgery may be indicated with antifungal therapy for drainage of large abscesses.

PROGNOSIS

- Before the development of antifungal chemotherapy, the disease had a progressive course with eventual extrapulmonary disease and a mortality exceeding 60%.
- Relapse rate for patients treated with amphotericin B is 5%; relapse is more common in AIDS patients.

SUGGESTED READINGS

Chapman SW et al: Practice guidelines for the management of patients with blastomycosis, *Clin Infect Dis* 30:679, 2000.
Martynowicz MA et al: Pulmonary blastomycosis: an appraisal of diagnostic techniques, *Chest* 121(3):768, 2002.

AUTHOR: **SAJEEV HANDA, M.D.**

BASIC INFORMATION

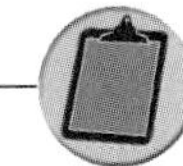

DEFINITION

Blepharitis is an acute or, most often, chronic inflammation of the eyelid margins that is often refractory to treatment.

ICD-9CM CODES
373.0 Blepharitis

PHYSICAL FINDINGS & CLINICAL PRESENTATION

- Chronically infected lids are usually diffusely erythematous, with collarettes (fibrin exudate) at the base of the lashes (Fig. 1-44).
- Lid margins thicken over time, with associated loss of eyelashes (madarosis), misdirected growth of lashes (trichiasis), and overflow or inspissation of the meibomian glands.
- Associated conjunctivitis with erythema and edema is frequent, but it is usually without discharge.
- Chalazia may develop.
- Superficial punctate erosions of the inferior corneal epithelium are common.
- More severe findings, such as corneal pannus, ulcerative keratitis, or lid ectropion, are less common.

ETIOLOGY

Multiple: bacterial and nonbacterial causes
- Staphylococcal infection
- Seborrheic dermatitis
- Rosacea
- Dry eye (keratoconjunctivitis sicca): includes a decrease in tear volume and/or increased rate of evaporation
- Meibomian gland dysfunction: normally there is keratinization of the meibomian gland duct; hyperkeratinization can plug up the duct.
- Two categories of blepharitis:
  1. Anterior blepharitis, most often associated with staphylococcal infection or seborrheic dermatitis
  2. Posterior blepharitis, associated with meibomian gland dysfunction

NOTE: Most often bacteria isolated from blepharitis patients are normal skin microflora, but in greater amounts (mostly *S. epidermidis* and *P. acnes*). (*S. aureus* and coagulase-negative staphylococci can be cultured from the eyelid margins of 10%-35% and 90%-95% of healthy persons, respectively.)

DIAGNOSIS

DIFFERENTIAL DIAGNOSIS

- Keratoconjunctivitis sicca
- Eyelid malignancies
- Herpes simplex blepharitis
- Molluscum contagiosum
- Phthiriasis palpebrarum
- Phthirus pubis (pubic lice)
- Demodex folliculorum (transparent mites)
- Allergic blepharitis

WORKUP

Scrapings of the eyelids to show polymorphonuclear leukocytes and gram-positive cocci

LABORATORY TESTS

Eyelid cultures and antibiotic sensitivity testing (usually not done unless patient fails to respond to initial treatment regimen)

TREATMENT

NONPHARMACOLOGIC THERAPY

- Lid scrubs are the oldest and most effective treatment.
- Alkaline soaps may be beneficial; alcohol and some detergents may be effective in removing surface lipids and microflora.
- Hot compresses applied to closed lids for 5 to 10 min: heat loosens debris from lid margins and increases meibomian gland fluidity.
- Firm massage of the lid margins to enhance the flow of secretions from glands, followed by cleansing of the lids with cotton-tipped applicators dipped in a 50:50 mixture of baby shampoo and water.
- Lashes and lid margins scrubbed vigorously while the eyelids are closed, followed by thorough rinsing.
- Following local massage and cleansing, the mainstay of treatment is application of topical antibiotic ointment to the eyelid margins.

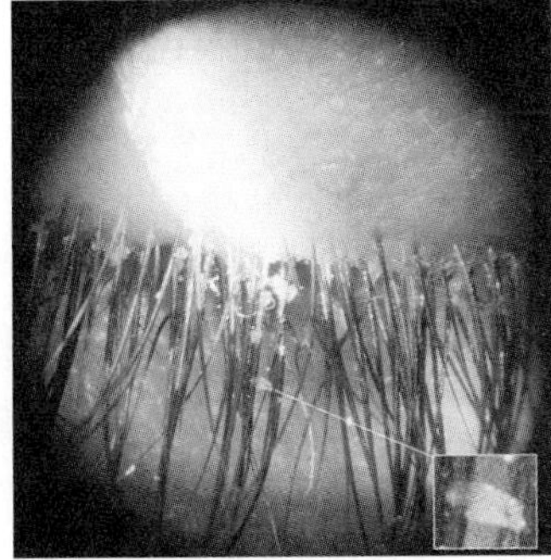

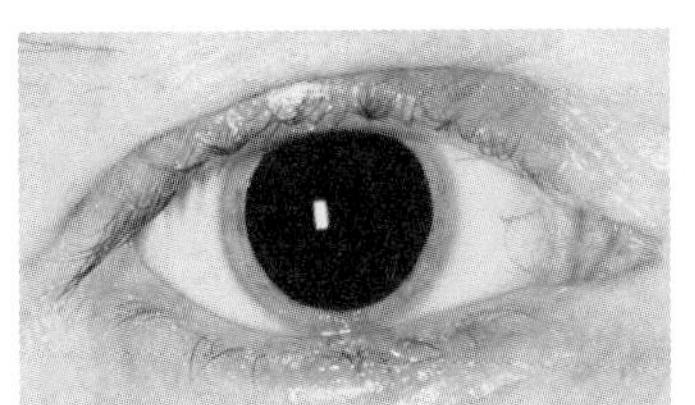

FIGURE 1-44 **A,** Seborrheic blepharitis. The typical scales (scurf) are translucent and easily removed. **B,** Staphylococcal blepharitis showing the typical lid margin erythema and discharge. (From Palay D [ed]: *Ophthalmology for the primary care physician,* St Louis, 1997, Mosby.)

- Antibiotics must be in ointment form for lids and drops or ointment for the ocular surface.
  1. Most effective topical antibiotics available are bacitracin and erythromycin ophthalmic ointments; also effective are many aminoglycosides and fluoroquinolones.
  2. Ointment is applied 1 to 4 times daily, depending on the severity of inflammation, for 1 to 2 wk.
  3. Treatment is continued once daily, at bedtime, for another 4 to 8 wk.
  4. Treatment is continued for 1 mo after all signs of inflammation have disappeared.

For patients with rosacea:
1. Tetracycline 250 mg orally 4 times daily or doxycycline 100 mg orally tid along with local treatment
2. Dosing reduced to once daily for several months, depending on the clinical situation

Recalcitrant cases with antibiotic resistance:
1. Vancomycin eye drops 1%
2. Ciprofloxacin or ofloxacin eyedrops

CHRONIC Rx

By definition, this is a chronic condition for which there is frequently no cure. This is complicated by the fact that long-term use of antibiotics results in development of resistance and cross-resistance.

Some newer agents being evaluated are flavonoid-type compounds (resveratrol, silymarin), which have antioxidant properties (may have a role in reducing the inflammatory response), azelaic acid, and glycolic acid (used to treat acne and has antikeratinizing effects).

Adapalene gel is also useful in treating acne; it has antiinflammatory properties and an antiproliferative effect on keratinocytes.

DISPOSITION

This condition is often refractory to treatment, and often requires prolonged courses of treatment. It is important that patients receive adequate education about treatment and compliance.

REFERRAL

To an ophthalmologist if patient fails to respond to local therapy.

SUGGESTED READINGS

Kaiserman I: Severe allergic blepharoconjunctivitis induced by a dye for eyelashes and eyebrows, *Ocul Immunol Inflamm* 11(2):149, 2003.

McCulley JP, Shine WE: Changing concepts in the diagnosis and management of blepharitis: cornea 19(5):650, 2000.

Tsao CH et al: Monthly recurrent herpes simplex virus blepharitis in a boy for more than 10 years, *Infection* 31(4):257, 2003.

AUTHORS: **JANE V. EASON, M.D.** and **JOSEPH R. MASCI, M.D.**

Body Dysmorphic Disorder

BASIC INFORMATION

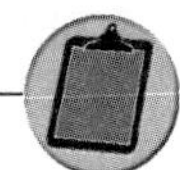

DEFINITION

Body Dysmorphic Disorder (BDD) is a somatoform disorder characterized by a preoccupation with a minor or imagined defect in physical appearance that causes significant impairment in social or occupational functioning. Although comorbid psychiatric conditions such as anorexia nervosa or depression may occur with body dysmorphic disorder, diagnosis of this condition necessitates a preoccupation not otherwise explained by another mental disorder.

SYNONYMS

Dysmorphophobia
Body dysmorphia

ICD-9CM CODES
306.9 Unspecified psychophysiomal function
DSM-IV: 300.7

EPIDEMIOLOGY & DEMOGRAPHICS

- Affects about 1%-2% of the population.
- Incidence among cosmetic surgery patients, 2%-7%.
- Onset is generally adolescence and young adulthood.
- Equal prevalence among males and females.
- No known genetic predisposition.

CLINICAL PRESENTATION

- Patients have an excessive preoccupation (obsession) with a perceived or minor defect in their appearance. Any part of the body may be a focus of concern, although skin, hair, body odor, and nose shape and size are the most common.
- The patient usually appears physically normal; if a defect is present, the patient's reaction to it is disproportionate to its severity.
- May engage in compulsive behaviors such as frequent mirror checking, excess grooming, camouflaging, skin picking, and repeatedly measuring or feeling the perceived defect, and seek constant reassurance about the perceived defect.
- Most patients experience some impairment in functioning.

ETIOLOGY

Unknown, though comorbid mental disorders associated with BDD include major depression, obsessive-compulsive disorder (OCD), generalized anxiety disorder, agoraphobia, trichotillomania, eating disorders.

DIAGNOSIS

DIFFERENTIAL DIAGNOSIS

- Often goes unrecognized and undiagnosed because of patient's reluctance to divulge symptoms.
- BDD has many features in common with OCD.
- In clinical settings, up to 60% of patients with BDD have major depression.
- Anorexia nervosa.
- Obsessive-compulsive disorder.
- Anxiety D/O.
- Social phobia.
- Hypochondriasis.

WORKUP

- Organic etiology should be assessed with MMSE.
- Body Dysmorphic Disorder Examination Self-Report used in clinical trials.

LABORATORY TESTS

None

IMAGING STUDIES

None

TREATMENT

NONPHARMACOLOGIC THERAPY

Cognitive behavioral therapy (particularly exposure and response prevention)

ACUTE GENERAL Rx

Precautions/hospitalization if actively suicidal

CHRONIC Rx

- High-dose selective serotonin reuptake inhibitors (SSRIs).
- Other agents (neuroleptic, TCAs, anticonvulsants) not as beneficial.
- Cognitive behavioral therapy highly recommended as stand-alone or along with SSRIs.

COMPLEMENTARY & ALTERNATIVE MEDICINE

None known

DISPOSITION

Outpatient therapy

REFERRAL

Refer for psychiatric evaluation if diagnosis is suspected.

PEARLS & CONSIDERATIONS

COMMENTS

- Compliments and reassurance rarely lessen the patient's fear or dislike of his or her appearance.
- Patients often have an unrealistic expectation of improvement regarding plastic surgery, and surgery itself provides little to no relief.
- Almost one third of patients with BDD attempt suicide.

PREVENTION

No known methods

PATIENT/FAMILY EDUCATION

- Consider therapy with family members, spouse, significant others.
- Body Dysmorphic Disorder Central: http://www.BDDCentral.com

SUGGESTED READINGS

American Psychiatric Association: *Diagnostic and Statistical Manual of Mental Disorders,* ed 4, Washington, DC, American Psychiatric Association, 1994.

Buhlman U et al: Selective processing of emotional information in body dysmorphic disorder, *J Anxiety Disord* 16(3):289, 2002.

Guggenheim FG: Somatoform disorders. In Sadock BJ, Sadock VA (eds): *Kaplan & Sadock's Comprehensive Textbook of Psychiatry,* vol. 1, Philadelphia, 2000, Lippincott Williams & Wilkins.

HealthyPlace.Com Eating Disorders Community: http://www.healthyplace.com/Communities/Eating_Disorders/peacelovehope/bdd.html

Phillips KA: Body dysmorphic disorder: clinical aspects and treatment strategies, *Bull Menninger Clin* 62(4 Suppl A):A33, 1998.

AUTHORS: **JENNIFER ROHR GILLETT, M.D., M.P.H.,** and **MITCHELL D. FELDMAN, M.D., M.PHIL.**

BASIC INFORMATION

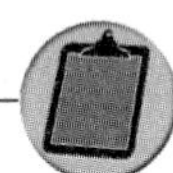

DEFINITION

Primary malignant bone tumors are invasive, anaplastic, and have the ability to metastasize. Most arise from the marrow (myeloma), but tumors may develop from bone, cartilage, fat, and fibrous tissues. Leukemia and lymphoma are excluded from this discussion.

FIBROSARCOMA AND LIPOSARCOMA: Extremely rare. They are similar to those tumors arising in soft tissue.

OSTEOSARCOMA: A rare primary malignant tumor of bone characterized by malignant tumor cells that produce osteoid or bone. Several variants have been described: parosteal sarcoma, periosteal sarcoma, multicentric, and telangiectatic forms.

CHONDROSARCOMA: A malignant cartilage tumor that may develop primarily or secondarily from transformation of a benign osteocartilaginous exostosis or enchondroma.

EWING'S SARCOMA: A malignant tumor of unknown histogenesis.

MULTIPLE MYELOMA: A neoplastic proliferation of plasma cells.

SYNONYMS

Multiple myeloma:
1. Plasma cell myeloma
2. Plasmacytoma

ICD-9CM CODES
203.0 Multiple myeloma
170.9 Neoplasma, bone (periosteum), primary malignant
M9180/3 Osteosarcoma
N9220/3 Chondrosarcoma
M9260/3 Ewing's sarcoma

EPIDEMIOLOGY & DEMOGRAPHICS

MULTIPLE MYELOMA:
- The most common tumor in bone
- Age at onset: usually >40 yr
- Male:female ratio of 2:1

OSTEOGENIC SARCOMA:
- Average age at onset: 10 to 20 yr
- Males > females
- Parosteal sarcoma in older patients

CHONDROSARCOMA:
- Age at onset: 40 to 60 yr
- Male:female ratio of 2:1

EWING'S SARCOMA:
- Age at onset: 10 to 15 yr

PHYSICAL FINDINGS

MULTIPLE MYELOMA:
- May present as a systemic process or, less commonly, as a "solitary" lesion
- Early manifestations: anorexia, weight loss, and bone pain; majority of cases present initially with back pain that often leads to the detection of a destructive skeletal lesion
- Other organ systems eventually become involved, resulting in more bone pain, anemia, renal insufficiency, and/or bacterial infections, usually as a result of the dysproteinemia typical of this disorder
- Possible secondary amyloidosis, leading to cardiac failure or nephrotic syndrome

OSTEOSARCOMA:
- Most originating in the metaphysis
- 50% to 60% around the knee
- Possible pain and swelling, but otherwise healthy patient
- Osteosarcoma in conjunction with Paget's disease, manifested primarily as a sudden increase in bone pain

CHONDROSARCOMA:
- Tumor most commonly involving the pelvis, upper femur, and shoulder girdle
- Painful swelling

EWING'S SARCOMA:
- Painful soft tissue mass often present
- Possibly increased local heat
- Midshaft of a long bone usually affected (in contrast to other tumors)
- Weight loss, fever, and lethargy

DIAGNOSIS

DIFFERENTIAL DIAGNOSIS

- Osteomyelitis
- Metastatic bone disease

The age of the patient and the initial radiographic features often determine the next appropriate diagnostic steps.

LABORATORY TESTS

- Slightly elevated alkaline phosphatase in osteosarcoma
- In Ewing's sarcoma: reflective of systemic reaction; include anemia, an increase in WBC count, and an elevated sedimentation rate
- In multiple myeloma:
  1. Bence Jones protein in the urine
  2. Anemia and elevated sedimentation rate
  3. Characteristic dysproteinemia on serum protein electrophoresis
  4. Diagnostic feature: peak in the electrophoretic pattern suggestive of a monoclonal gammopathy
  5. Rouleaux formation in the peripheral blood smear
  6. Often, presence of hypercalcemia, but alkaline phosphatase levels usually normal

IMAGING STUDIES

- Classic osteogenic sarcoma penetrates the cortex early in many cases.
  1. A blastic (dense), lytic (lucent), or mixed response may be seen in the affected bone.
  2. An aggressive perpendicular sunburst pattern may be present as a result of periosteal reaction, and peripheral Codman's triangles are often noted.
  3. Margins of the tumor are poorly defined.
- Speckled calcifications in a destructive radiolucent lesion are usually suggestive of chondrosarcoma.
- Ewing's sarcoma is characterized radiographically by mottled, irregular destructive changes with periosteal new bone formation. The latter may be multilayered, producing the typical "onion skin" appearance.
- Typical roentgenographic finding in multiple myeloma is the "punched out" lesion with sharply demarcated edges.
  1. Multiple lesions are usual.
  2. Diffuse osteoporosis may be the only finding in many cases.
  3. Pathologic fractures are common.

TREATMENT

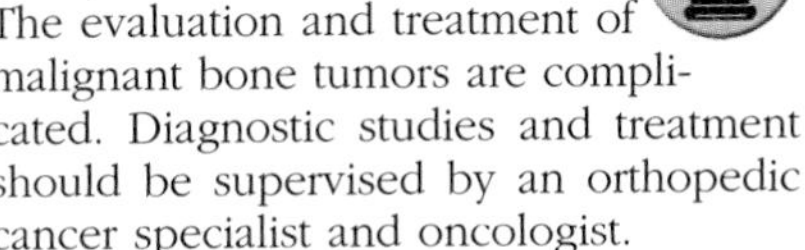

The evaluation and treatment of malignant bone tumors are complicated. Diagnostic studies and treatment should be supervised by an orthopedic cancer specialist and oncologist.

DISPOSITION

- In the past 20 yr, dramatic improvements have been made in the treatment protocols for osteosarcoma with the use of adjuvant multidrug regimens and limb-sparing surgery.
- Early diagnosis is important because most tumors have not metastasized at the time of the initial presentation.
- 70% 5-yr survival rates have been obtained in some series.
- Prognosis of multiple myeloma remains poor despite new therapies.
  1. Complete remissions are uncommon.
  2. Survival with a solitary lesion may be long, but most patients succumb after a median of 3 yr.
- Prognosis for Ewing's sarcoma has improved with a combination of chemotherapy, local resection, and radiation therapy.
- Chondrosarcomas are not sensitive to chemotherapy or radiation, and prognosis will depend on the grade of the tumor and the ability to obtain an adequate resection.

SUGGESTED READINGS

Heyman D et al: Bisphosphonates: new therapeutic agents for the treatment of bone tumors, *Trends Mol Med* 10(7):337, 2004.

Martinez MA et al: Ewings sarcoma: histopathological and immunohistochemical study, *Orthopedics* 26:723, 2003.

Meyer JS, Mackenzie W: Malignant bone tumors and limb-salvage surgery in children, *Pediatr Radiol* 34(8):606, 2004.

Wittig JC et al: Osteosarcoma: a multidisciplinary approach to diagnosis and treatment, *Am Fam Physician* 65:1123, 2002.

Zeytoonian T et al: Distal lower extremity sarcomas: frequency of occurrence and patient survival rate, *Foot Ankle Int* 25(5):325, 2004.

AUTHOR: **LONNIE R. MERCIER, M.D.**

Borderline Personality Disorder

BASIC INFORMATION

DEFINITION

Borderline personality disorder (BPD) is characterized by a pervasive pattern of instability in interpersonal relationships, self-image, affect regulation, and impulse control that causes significant subjective distress or impairment of functioning. The individual must meet five or more of the following criteria:

1. Frantic efforts to avoid real or imagined abandonment
2. Unstable and intense personal relationships characterized by alternating between extremes of idealization and devaluation
3. Identity disturbance characterized by an unstable self-image
4. Impulsivity in at least two areas that are potentially self-damaging (e.g., overspending, sex, substance abuse, binge eating, reckless driving)
5. Recurrent suicidal behavior, gestures, threats, or self-mutilating behavior
6. Affective instability due to a marked reactivity of mood
7. Chronic feelings of emptiness
8. Inappropriate, intense anger, or difficulty controlling anger
9. Transient, stress-related paranoid ideation or severe dissociative symptoms

SYNONYMS

None

ICD-9CM CODES
301.83 Borderline personality

EPIDEMIOLOGY & DEMOGRAPHICS

PREVALENCE: Affects about 1% to 2% of the general population and up to 10% of psychiatric outpatients
PREDOMINANT SEX: Female (3:1)
PREDOMINANT AGE: 20s
GENETICS: Five times as likely if BPD is present in first-degree relative. An increased prevalence of mood disorders and substance abuse disorders is also found in first-degree relatives of persons with BPD.
RISK FACTORS: Association with childhood physical, sexual, or emotional abuse and/or neglect

CLINICAL PRESENTATION

- Patients experience a pervasive sense of loneliness and emptiness.
- Intense emotions with difficulty returning to emotional baseline.
- All-or-nothing, either-or cognitive style that is represented by a phenomenon known as "splitting," in which patient sees situations or people as all good or all bad.
- Difficulty in maintaining commitment to long-term goals; history of numerous stormy relationships and multiple jobs.
- Reacts with rage, panic, despair to actual or perceived abandonment; may present with suicidality or self-mutilating behavior in response to recent stressor.
- Attempts to block the experience of pain, which may induce feelings of derealization, depersonalization, changes in consciousness, and/or brief psychotic reactions with delusions and hallucinations.
- Substance use, gambling, overspending, eating binges, and/or self-mutilation as a way to escape intensely painful affect.
- Some patients may display psychotic symptoms.

ETIOLOGY

- Interaction of psychosocial adversity plus genetic factors
- Hypotheses:
  1. Genetic: increased risk if first-degree relative with BPD.
  2. Biologic: abnormalities in limbic system and other areas of the brain cause emotional dysregulation. Serotonergic functioning appears to be disturbed.
  3. Environmental: history of childhood abuse or neglect.

DIAGNOSIS

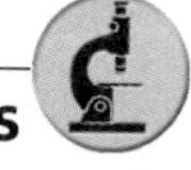

DIFFERENTIAL DIAGNOSIS

- Histrionic and narcissistic personality disorders share some common features.
- Dysthymia and other depressive disorders: requires a stability of affective symptoms not seen in BPD.
- Bipolar disorder: mood changes in BPD are often triggered by stressors and are less sustained than in bipolar disorder.
- Substance abuse or dependence: often induces impulsive, emotionally labile behavior.
- Posttraumatic stress disorder: individuals with BPD often have history of trauma but do not avoid the feared stimulus or reexperience the trauma as do individuals with PTSD.
- Mild cases of schizophrenia may superficially resemble BPD.
- Alcohol abuse is common.

WORKUP

- History (often helpful to gather collateral information from family and friends)
- Physical examination
- Mental status examination

IMAGING STUDIES

- Structural and functional MRI demonstrate abnormalities in the amygdala and hippocampus. PET scans reveal altered metabolism in prefrontal cortex. Imaging is not recommended as part of routine evaluation.

TREATMENT

NONPHARMACOLOGIC THERAPY

- Few randomized trials have assessed psychosocial interventions for BPD.
- Dialectical behavior therapy (DBT), a variation of cognitive behavior therapy (CBT), has the most empirical support from randomized trials. The goal of DBT is to help patients to control impulses and angry outbursts and to develop social skills.
- Definite structure and firm limit setting are required.

ACUTE GENERAL Rx

- Low-dose antipsychotics to control impulsivity, brief psychotic episodes.

CHRONIC Rx

- SSRIs if concurrent mood disorder. Fluoxetine may be helpful in reducing anger.
- Low-dose antipsychotics.
- Mood stabilizers (lithium, valproate, carbamazepine).
- Medications have low to moderate effectiveness and are most effective in improving symptoms of impulsivity, mood instability, and self-destructive behavior.

COMPLEMENTARY & ALTERNATIVE MEDICINE

- No evidence of efficacy in BPD.

DISPOSITION

- Course is variable. The most unstable period is typically in early adulthood; the majority of patients achieve greater stability in social/occupational functioning later in life but often continue to have difficulty maintaining intimate relationships.
- There is no evidence of progression to schizophrenia, but patients have a high incidence of episodes of major depressive disorder.

REFERRAL

- If use of pharmacotherapy contemplated
- If patient is severely impaired in daily function or suicidal

PEARLS & CONSIDERATIONS

COMMENTS

Guidelines for physician management of patients with BPD:

- Consider frequent, brief, scheduled visits for needy, demanding, or somaticizing patients with BPD.
- Validate the patient's feelings while stating the expectation of behavior control.
- Be matter-of-fact; avoid expressing extreme emotions.
- Be alert to the risk of suicide and assess suicide risk often.
- Convey a demeanor of competence but openly acknowledge minor errors.
- Have a low threshold for seeking psychiatric consultation.

PREVENTION

- Suicidality should be actively and consistently monitored.

SUGGESTED READINGS

American Psychiatric Association practice guidelines for the treatment of patients with BPD:
http://www.psych.org/psych_pract/treatg/pg/borderline_revisebook_index.cfm.

Gross R et al: Borderline personality disorder in primary care, *Arch Intern Med* 162:53, 2002.

Lieb K et al: Borderline personality disorder, *Lancet* 364(9432):453, 2004.

Livesley WJ: A practical approach to the treatment of patients with borderline personality disorder, *Psychiatr Clin North Am* 23:1, 2000.

AUTHORS: **MITCHELL D. FELDMAN, M.D., M.PHIL.,** and **MICHELE MONTANDON, M.D.**

BASIC INFORMATION

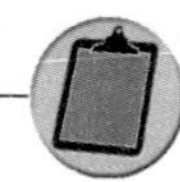

DEFINITION

Botulism is an illness caused by a neurotoxin produced by *Clostridium botulinum*. Three types of disease can occur: foodborne botulism, wound botulism, and infant intestinal botulism. Recent concern has increased about a possible fourth type of disease: inhalational botulism. Does not occur naturally, but may occur as a result of bioterrorism.

ICD-9CM CODE
005.1 Botulism

EPIDEMIOLOGY & DEMOGRAPHICS

INCIDENCE (IN U.S.): Approximately 24 cases/yr of foodborne illness, 3 cases/yr of wound botulism, and 71 cases/yr of infant botulism

PHYSICAL FINDINGS & CLINICAL PRESENTATION

- Symptoms usually begin 12 to 36 hr following ingestion.
- Severity of illness is related to the quantity of toxin ingested.
- Significant findings:
  1. Cranial nerve palsies, with ocular and bulbar manifestations being most frequent (diplopia, ophthalmoplegia, ptosis, dysphagia, dysarthria, and dry mouth)
  2. Usually bilateral nerve involvement that may progress to a descending flaccid paralysis
  3. Typically, absence of sensory findings; sensorium intact
  4. GI symptoms (nausea, vomiting, diarrhea, or cramps)
  5. Usually no fever
- Wound botulism
  1. Occurs mostly in injecting drug users (subcutaneous heroin injection—"skin popping") or with traumatic injury.
  2. Presentation is similar to that of foodborne disease, except for a longer incubation period and the absence of GI symptoms.
  3. Wound infection is not always apparent, but injection sites frequently reveal cellulitis, draining pus, or abscess formation.

ETIOLOGY

- Cause is one of several types of neurotoxins (usually A, B, or E) produced by *C. botulinum*, an anaerobic, gram-positive bacillus. Spore production guarantees survival of the organism in extreme conditions. Botulinum toxin is the most powerful neurotoxin known.
- Disease results from absorption of toxin into the circulation from a mucosal surface or wound. Botulinum toxin does not penetrate intact skin.
- In foodborne variety, disease is caused by ingestion of preformed toxin. Although rapidly inactivated by heat, the toxin can survive the proteolytic environment of the stomach.
- In wound botulism, toxin is elaborated by organisms that contaminate a wound. Most cases reported are from California.
- In infant botulism, toxin is produced by organisms in the GI tract.
- Inhalational botulism has been demonstrated experimentally in primates. This manufactured form results from aerosolized toxin, and has been attempted by bioterrorists.

DIAGNOSIS

DIFFERENTIAL DIAGNOSIS

- Myasthenia gravis
- Guillain-Barré syndrome
- Tick paralysis
- CVA

WORKUP

- Search made for toxin and the organism (see "Laboratory Tests")
- Electrophysiologic studies (EMG) may aid in the diagnosis

LABORATORY TESTS

- Samples of food and stool are cultured for the organism.
- Food, serum, and stool are sent for toxin assay.

TREATMENT

NONPHARMACOLOGIC THERAPY

- Supportive care with intubation if respiratory failure occurs
- Debridement of the wound in wound botulism

ACUTE GENERAL Rx

- Give trivalent equine botulinum antitoxin as early as possible. Once a clinical diagnosis is made, antitoxin should be administered before laboratory confirmation.
  1. Give one vial by IM injection and one vial IV.
  2. The antitoxin is available from the Centers for Disease Control and Prevention [(404) 639-2206 or (404) 639-2888]; it is derived from horse serum, so there is a significant incidence of serum sickness.
  3. Skin testing, and possible desensitization, is recommended before treatment.
- Give wound botulism patients penicillin, 2 million U IV q4h.

CHRONIC Rx

- Supportive
- Rehabilitation/physical therapy

DISPOSITION

- Highest mortality in the first case in an outbreak, with subsequent cases receiving rapid treatment
- Complete recovery for most individuals

REFERRAL

Immediate for all cases to an ER and an infectious disease consultant

PEARLS & CONSIDERATIONS

COMMENTS

- Routine cooking inactivates the toxin, but spores are resistant to environmental factors. At room temperature, spores can germinate and produce toxin.
- Most outbreaks are associated with home-canned foods, especially vegetables.
- Patients must be closely monitored for progression to respiratory paralysis.
- There is increasing concern over the potential use of botulinum toxin as a biologic weapon, either by the enteric route or by aerosolization.
- Notify public health authorities.

SUGGESTED READINGS

Amon SS et al: Botulinum toxin as a biological weapon, *Jama* 285(8):1059, 2001.

Bhidayasiri R, Choi YM, Nishimura R: Wound botulism, *Postgrad Med J* 80:240, 2004.

Bleck TP: *Clostridium botulinim* (botulism). In Mandell GL, Bennett JE, Dolin R (eds): *Principles and practice of infectious diseases,* ed 5, New York, 2000, Churchill Livingstone.

Cherington M: Botulism: update and review, *Semin Neurol* 24:155, 2004.

AUTHOR: **MAURICE POLICAR, M.D.**

BASIC INFORMATION

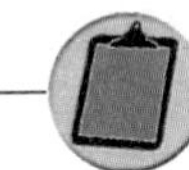

DEFINITION

Brain neoplasms are primary (nonmetastatic) tumors arising from one of many different cell types within the central nervous system. Specific tumors subtypes and prognosis depend on the tumor cell of origin and pattern of growth.

SYNONYMS

Brain tumors
Primary tumors of the central nervous system

ICD-9CM CODES
225.0 Brain neoplasm (benign)
239.2 Brain neoplasm (unspecified)

EPIDEMIOLOGY & DEMOGRAPHICS

INCIDENCE (IN U.S.): Approx. 8 cases/100,000 persons/yr. In 2002, the Central Brain Tumor Registry data estimated approximately 39,550 new cases of both malignant and benign brain tumors in the U.S. Primary brain neoplasms account for ~2% of all cancers, ~20% of all cancers in children >15 yr. Most common cause of cancer death in children up to 15 yr.

PREDOMINANT SEX: Male/female = 3/2, except for meningiomas: Female/male = 3/1

PREDOMINANT AGE: Male: 75+ yr; female: 65 to 74 yr

GENETICS

Most primary CNS neoplasms are sporadic; 5% are associated with hereditary syndromes that predispose to neoplasia. The most common of these include:

- Li Fraumeni syndrome → p53 mutation on chromosome 17q13 → gliomas
- Von Hippel-Lindau → VHL, chromosome 3p25 → hemangioblastoma
- Tuberous sclerosis → TSC1/TSC2 (chromosome 9q34/16p13) → subependymal giant cell astrocytoma
- Neurofibromatosis type 1 → NF1, chromosome 17q11 → neurofibroma, optic nerve glioma, meningioma
- Neurofibromatosis type 2 → NF2, chromosome 22q12 → schwannoma, meningioma, ependymoma
- Retinoblastoma → pRB, chromosome 13q → retinoblastoma
- Gorlin's syndrome → chromosome 9q31 → desmoplastic medulloblastoma

PHYSICAL FINDINGS & CLINICAL PRESENTATION

- In general, the location, size, and rate of growth will determine the symptoms and signs with development of progressive focal signs and symptoms. Even within a tumor subtype, clinical presentation may vary.
- Headache is a common problem for patients with brain tumors and may be a presenting symptom in 20% and develop later in 60%.
- Seizures in 33% of patients, particularly with brain metastases and low grade gliomas.
- Symptoms and signs of hydrocephalus and raised intracranial pressure (headache, vomiting [particularly in children], clouding of consciousness, papilledema).
- Patients may also present with subtle behavioral changes or cognitive and visual-spatial dysfunction.

ETIOLOGY

- Most cases are idiopathic, though specific chromosomal abnormalities have been implicated in some tumor types.
- Exposure to ionizing radiation has been implicated in the genesis of meningiomas, gliomas, nerve sheath tumors. No convincing evidence has linked CNS tumors with trauma, occupation, diet, electromagnetic fields.

DIAGNOSIS

- Most common tumors in children → astrocytoma, medulloblastoma, ependymoma
- Most common adult tumors → Glioblastoma multiforma, anaplastic astrocytoma, meningioma

DIFFERENTIAL DIAGNOSIS

- Stroke
- Abscess/parasitic cyst
- Demyelinating disease—multiple sclerosis, postinfectious encephalomyelitis
- Metastatic tumors
- Primary central nervous system lymphoma

LABORATORY TESTS

- CSF cytology may yield histologic diagnosis and test for tumor markers (for pineal tumors)
- NB: LP must never be performed if there is concern for increased ICP

IMAGING STUDIES

- A neuroradiologist is able to diagnose tumor type with considerable accuracy, but most tumors should be biopsied for 100% accuracy.
- MRI with gadolinium enhancement is highly sensitive, though CT scan is useful if calcification or hemorrhage suspected.
- MR spectroscopy is used to define metabolic composition of an area of interest and may be useful to contrast areas of tumor progression from radiation necrosis.
- PET scan is helpful to distinguish neoplastic lesions (with high rate of metabolism) from other lesions such as demyelination or radiation necrosis (with a much lower metabolic rate). May be useful to help map functional areas of the brain before surgery or radiation.
- Functional MRI is now used in perioperative planning for patients whose lesion is in vital regions, such as those responsible for speech, language, and motor control.

HISTOPATHOLOGY

- Ultimately, only a histologic examination can provide the exact diagnosis.
- There are several different classification schema. Typically, diagnosis is based on histopathology, according to the predominant cell type and grading based on the presence or absence of standard pathologic features.
- Advances in molecular biology are facilitating genetic classification, since both oncogenes and tumor suppressor genes play critical roles in tumor pathogenesis.

TREATMENT

NONPHARMACOLOGIC THERAPY

- Surgical removal or debulking is the initial treatment of choice.
- Biopsy alone is performed if the tumor is located in eloquent regions of brain or is inaccessible; this is essential for histopathologic diagnosis. Biopsy can be performed under CT or MRI guidance using stereotactic localization.
- If the tumor is of a benign nature (e.g., meningioma, acoustic neuroma), no further therapy is usually required.

ACUTE GENERAL Rx

- Steroids (e.g., dexamethasone 4 mg PO q6h) may be used as a temporizing measure to reduce edema. In addition, steroids may be used following surgery or during radiation therapy.
- Anti-seizure medications have been used perioperatively and to control seizures resulting from focal lesions.

CHRONIC Rx

- Depending on tumor type, chemotherapy may be necessary.
- Chemotherapy (combination or single agent) may be used before, during, or after surgery and radiation therapy. (In children, chemotherapy is often used to delay radiation therapy.)
- Radiation is useful for certain types of tumors: Conventional radiation uses external beams over a period of weeks, whereas stereotactic radiosurgery delivers a single, high dose of radiation to a well-defined area (usually <1 cm).
- Long-term effects of radiation therapy include radiation necrosis (particularly of white matter), blood vessel hyalinization, secondary tumors (usually meningiomas, sarcomas and malignant astrocytomas). Radiosensitizers may help to increase the therapeutic effect of radiation therapy.

DISPOSITION/PROGNOSTIC FACTORS

- Tumor histology/histologic diagnosis (WHO/grading system), including number of mitoses, capillary endothelial proliferation and necrosis (NB: there can be a high degree of morbidity based on tumor location, even with more benign histology)
- Age of the patient and Karnofsky performance score have predictive value for prognosis; for all histologic subtypes of brain tumors, pediatric and young adult patients have a better survival. In general, younger age, high performance status, and lower pathologic grade have more favorable prognosis.
- Terminal events typically result from raised intracranial pressure

REFERRAL

- All cases warrant evaluation by an oncologist and neurosurgeon.
- Patients should be evaluated for physical and occupational therapy.
- Children should undergo neuropsychological evaluations and screening for learning disabilities.

SUGGESTED READINGS

Bittar RG: Presurgical motor and somatosensory cortex mapping with functional magnetic resonance imaging and position emission tomography, *J Neurosurg* 91:915, 1999.

Burton EC, Prados MD: Malignant gliomas, *Curr Opin Oncol* 1(5):459, 2000.

Cascino GD: Epilepsy and brain tumors: implications for treatment, *Epilepsia* 31 (Suppl 3):S37, 1990.

Chao ST: The sensitivity and specificity of FDG PET in distinguishing recurrent brain tumor from radionecrosis in patients treated with stereotactic radiosurgery, *Int J Cancer* 96:191, 2001.

Kleihues P: Pathology and genetics of tumors of the nervous system. In Kleihues P, Cavenee WK (eds): *International Agency for Research on Cancer,* Lyon, 2000, p. 22.

Wrensch M: Epidemiology of primary brain tumors: current concepts and review of the literature, *NeuroOncol* 4:278, 2002.

AUTHOR: **NICOLE J. ULLRICH, M.D., PH.D.**

BASIC INFORMATION

DEFINITION

The term *breast cancer* refers to invasive carcinoma of the breast, whether ductal or lobular.

SYNONYMS

Carcinoma of the breast

ICD-9CM CODES
174.9 Malignant neoplasm female breast

EPIDEMIOLOGY & DEMOGRAPHICS

- Nearly exclusively the disease of women, with only 1% of breast cancers in males
- Steady increase in its incidence in the U.S., with 205,000 new patients annually
- Annual mortality of 40,000
- Risk steadily increases with age
- Genetically defined group of women with BRCA-1 or BRCA-2 identified to carry lifetime risk as high as 85%

PHYSICAL FINDINGS

- Increasing number of small breast cancers found by mammograms
- Patients usually completely free of physical findings
- Palpable tumors possibly as small as 1 cm or even smaller
- Size of the mass and its location measured and documented
- Skin and/or nipple retraction and skin edema/erythema/ulcer/satellite nodule
- Nodal enlargement in axilla and supraclavicular areas
- Advanced disease: clinical signs of pleural effusion and/or hepatomegaly
- Rare instances: clear, serous, or bloody discharge only symptom
- Nipple evaluation (see "Paget's disease of the breast")

ETIOLOGY

- Precise mechanism of carcinogenesis not understood
- Possibly interaction of ovarian estrogen, nonovarian estrogen, estrogens of exogenous origin with breast tissue of varied carcinogenic susceptibility to develop cancer
- Other known or suspected variables: childbearing, breast-feeding practice, diet, physical activities, body mass, alcoholic intake
- Have identified families with known high risk
- Women with BRCA-1 and BRCA-2 associated with high risk

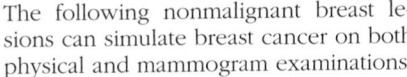

DIAGNOSIS

DIFFERENTIAL DIAGNOSIS

The following nonmalignant breast lesions can simulate breast cancer on both physical and mammogram examinations:
1. Fibrocystic changes
2. Fibroadenoma
3. Hamartoma

A
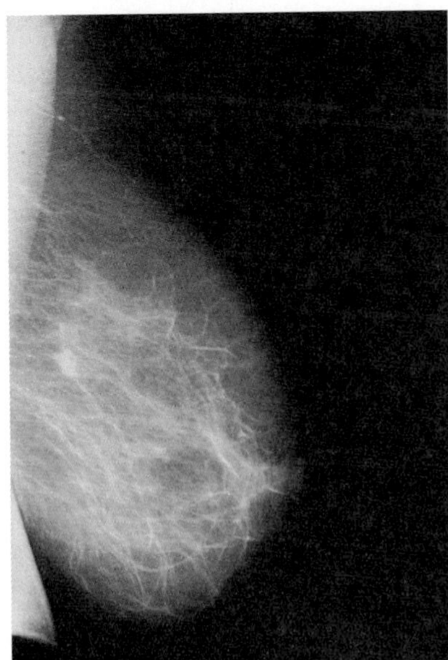
B
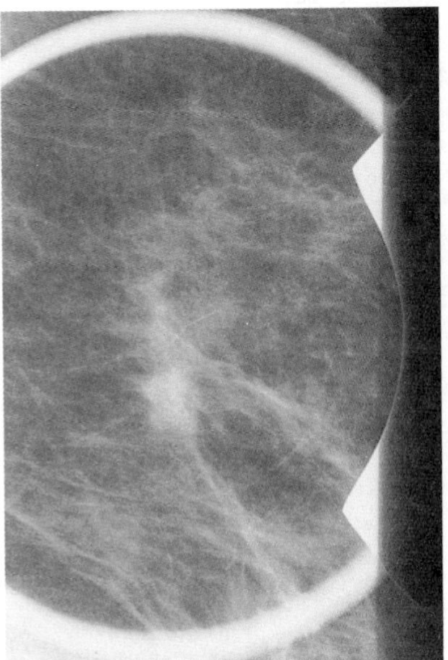

FIGURE 1-45 **A,** Right mediolateral and, **B,** spot magnification view from routine screening mammography demonstrates a small, ill-defined mass with minimal spiculation. This was nonpalpable, and biopsy demonstrated infiltrating ductal carcinoma. (From Specht N [ed]: *Practical guide to diagnostic imaging,* St Louis, 1998, Mosby.)

IMAGING STUDIES

Mammograms: 30% to 50% of breast cancers detected by screening mammograms only as a spiculated mass, a mass with or without microcalcifications, or a cluster of microcalcifications (Fig. 1-45)

WORKUP

- Physical examination:
  1. Mass detected by patient or medical professional: workup required
  2. Negative mammogram: breast cancer not ruled out
  3. Sonogram: to demonstrate mass to be cyst, usually eliminating need for further workup
- To establish diagnosis:
  1. Positive aspiration cytology on a clinically and mammographically malignant mass—highly accurate but still requires open biopsy confirmation
  2. Stereotactic core needle biopsy diagnosis: reliable with invasive carcinoma identified, but negative or equivocal results require careful evaluation
  3. Atypical hyperplasia or in situ carcinoma found by core needle biopsy: open surgical biopsy confirmation still required
  4. Excisional or incisional biopsy: establishes diagnosis
- NOTE: Do not rely on negative mammogram or negative aspiration cytology to exclude malignancy. Make appropriate referral. Obtain imaging studies such as bone scan, chest x-ray examination, CT scan of abdomen, or CT scan of liver.
- Breast radiologic evaluation and an algorithm for breast cancer screening and evaluation are described in Section III. The differential diagnosis of breast lumps is described in Section II.

TREATMENT

NONPHARMACOLOGIC THERAPY

- Early breast cancer: primarily surgical or surgical and radiotherapeutic
- Choice in 60% to 70% of women between modified mastectomy and breast-conserving treatment, which consists of lumpectomy, axillary staging with sentinel node biopsy or axillary dissection, and breast irradiation

ACUTE GENERAL Rx

- May require adjuvant chemotherapy or endocrine therapy
- Evaluation and treatment by medical oncologist

CHRONIC Rx

Follow-up required after proper treatment of primary breast cancer includes:
1. Periodic clinical evaluations
2. Annual mammograms
3. Other tests as indicated
4. Patient instruction in monthly breast self-examination technique

DISPOSITION

- Prognosis after curative therapy: depends on size of tumor, extent of nodal metastasis, and pathologic grade of tumor
  1. Patient with 1-cm tumor with no axillary node metastasis: 10-yr disease-free survival rate of 90%
  2. Patient with 3-cm tumor with metastasis in four nodes: 10-yr disease-free survival rate of 15% if no systemic adjuvant therapy given
  3. Outlook for most patients is between these extremes
- Systemic adjuvant therapy: improves prognosis significantly

REFERRAL

Referral is necessary as soon as breast cancer is even remotely suspected.

PEARLS & CONSIDERATIONS

Breast cancer in pregnancy and lactation:
1. Frequency in women 40 yr old or younger reported to be 15%
2. May carry worse prognosis because disease discovery delayed by engorged and nodular breast changes and/or because disease progression more rapid in pregnancy
3. Survival rates similar to those for nonpregnant early-stage breast cancer patients in same age group
4. Mass usually found by patient or obstetrician
5. Expedient workup recommended, including mammography and sonography
6. Diagnosis to be made without delay
7. Choice of mastectomy or lumpectomy with axillary dissection for treatment
8. Adjuvant chemotherapy delayed until third trimester or after delivery
9. Irradiation to breast after lumpectomy delayed until after delivery

Duct carcinoma in situ (DCIS, intraductal carcinoma):
1. "New" disease mostly found by mammogram as cluster of microcalcification and/or density
2. Less often, presents as palpable mass or nipple discharge
3. Before mammogram screening, DCIS accounted for 1% of all breast cancers
4. Now, 15% to 20% or even higher proportion present with DCIS
5. Formerly treated with mastectomy, now lumpectomy
6. Cure rates 98% to 99%
7. No axillary dissection required
8. With radiation, breast recurrences reduced
9. Mastectomy possibly required with extensive and/or high-grade DCIS
10. Systemic adjuvant treatment is not indicated

Inflammatory carcinoma:
1. Rare but rapidly progressive and often lethal form of breast cancer
2. Presents as erythematous and edematous breast resembling mastitis
3. Biopsy required, including skin
4. Treatment with combination chemotherapy followed by surgery and radiation therapy
5. Prognosis once dismal, now 5-yr disease-free survival in 50% of patients

COMMENTS

- Patient education material can be obtained from the following:
  1. SHARE: Self-Help for Women with Breast Cancer, 19 W 44th Street, No 415, New York, NY 10036-5902.
  2. Y-ME National Organization of Breast Cancer Information and Support, 18220 Harwood Avenue, Homewood, IL 80430.
- Breast radiologic evaluation, evaluation of nipple discharge, and evaluation of palpable mass are described in Section III.

SUGGESTED READINGS

Boyd NF et al: Heritability of mammographic density, a risk factor for breast cancer, *N Engl J Med* 347:886, 2002.

Graham J et al: Stressful life experiences and risk of relapse of breast cancer: observational cohort study, *BMJ* 324:1420, 2002.

Hellekson KL: NIH statement on adjuvant therapy for breast cancer, *Am Fam Physician* 63:1857, 2001.

Humphrey LL et al: Breast cancer screening: a summary of the evidence for the U.S. Preventive Services Task Force, *Ann Intern Med* 137:347, 2002.

Kinsinger LS et al: Chemoprevention of breast cancer: a summary of the evidence for U.S. Preventive Services Task Force, *Ann Intern Med* 137:59, 2002.

Marchbanks PA et al: Oral contraceptives and the risk of breast cancer, *N Engl J Med* 346:2025, 2002.

Miller AB et al: The Canadian National Breast Screening Study—1: breast cancer mortality after 11 to 16 years of follow-up, *Ann Intern Med* 137:305, 2002.

Pruthi S: Detection and evaluation of palpable breast mass, *Mayo Clin Proc* 76:641, 2001.

Rebbeck TR et al: Prophylactic oophorectomy in carriers of BRCA1 or BRCA2 mutations, *N Engl J Med* 346:1616, 2002.

Slamon DJ et al: Use of chemotherapy plus a monoclonal antibody against HER2 for metastatic breast cancer that overexpresses HER2, *N Engl J Med* 344(11):783, 2001.

The ATAC Trialists' Group: Anastrozole alone or in combination with tamoxifen versus tamoxifen alone for adjuvant treatment of postmenopausal women with early breast cancer: first results of the ATAC randomized trial, *Lancet* 359:2131, 2002.

U.S. Preventive Services Task Force: Chemoprevention of breast cancer. Recommendations and rationale, *Ann Intern Med* 137:56, 2002.

Van 't Veer LJ et al: Gene expression profiling predicts clinical outcome of breast cancer, *Nature* 415:530, 2002.

AUTHOR: **TAKUMA NEMOTO, M.D.**

BASIC INFORMATION

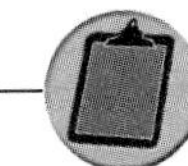

DEFINITION

Breech presentation exists when the fetal longitudinal axis is such that the cephalic pole occupies the uterine fundus. Three types exist, with respective percentages at term, frank (48% to 73%, flexed hips, extended thighs), complete (4.6% to 11.5%, flexed hips and knees), and footling (12% to 38%, hips extended).

ICD-9CM CODES
652.2 Breech presentation without mention of version

EPIDEMIOLOGY & DEMOGRAPHICS

INCIDENCE: Gestational age dependent: 3% to 4% overall, 14% at 29 to 32 wk, 33% at 21 to 24 wk

PERINATAL MORTALITY: 9% to 25%, or three to five times increase over vertex presentation at term. If one corrects for the associated increase in congenital anomalies and complications of prematurity, the morbidity and mortality approach that of the vertex presentation at term regardless of route of delivery.

PHYSICAL FINDINGS & CLINICAL PRESENTATION

- Maintain a high index of suspicion
- Lack of presenting part on vaginal examination
- Fetal heart tones heard above the umbilicus
- Leopold maneuvers revealing mobile fetal part in the uterine fundus

ETIOLOGY

- Abnormal placentation (fundal), uterine anomalies (fibroids, septa), pelvic or adnexal masses, alterations in fetal muscular tone, or fetal malformations
- Associated conditions: trisomy 13, 18, 21, Potter syndrome, myotonic dystrophy, prematurity

DIAGNOSIS

DIFFERENTIAL DIAGNOSIS

Vertex, oblique, or transverse lie

WORKUP

- If possible, determine reason for breech presentation, history of uterine anomalies, gestational age, or associated fetal congenital anomalies.
- Assess fetal status, by either continuous fetal heart rate monitoring or ultrasound.
- Assess pelvis to determine feasibility of vaginal delivery.
- Assess risk for safety of vaginal vs. abdominal delivery.

IMAGING STUDIES

Ultrasound to evaluate for:

- Fetal anomalies, such as hydrocephalus
- Placental location
- Position of fetal head relative to spine (check for hyperextension)
- Estimated fetal weight (2500 to 3800 g)
- Type of breech (frank, complete, footling)

CRITERIA FOR TRIAL OF LABOR

- Estimated fetal weight 2000 to 3800 g
- Frank breech
- Adequate pelvis
- Flexed fetal head
- Continuous fetal monitoring
- Normal progress of labor
- Bedside availability of anesthesia and capability for immediate C-section
- Informed consent
- Obstetrician trained in vaginal breech delivery

CRITERIA FOR C-SECTION

- Estimated fetal weight <1500 g or >4000 g
- Footling presentation (20% risk of cord prolapse, usually late in course of labor)
- Inadequate pelvis
- Hyperextended fetal head (21% risk of spinal cord injury)
- Nonreassuring fetal status
- Abnormal progress of labor
- Lack of trained obstetrician

TREATMENT

ACUTE GENERAL Rx

- Vaginal delivery in selected patient: allow maternal expulsive forces to deliver fetus until scapula visible (avoiding traction); with flexion and/or Piper forceps, deliver fetal head
- Perform C-section for the above-mentioned reasons
- External cephalic version, success 60% to 75%, after 37 wk, contraindicated with placental abruption, low-lying placenta, maternal hypertension, previous uterine incision, multiple gestation, nonreassuring fetal status
- Adequate pelvic/cervical relaxation essential for vaginal breech (i.e., need anesthesia in-room during birth [delivery] with uterine relaxants on hand [NTG, terbutaline])

COMPLICATIONS

- Head entrapment: leading cause of death (with the exception of anomalous fetuses), 88 cases/1000 deliveries, avoid by maintaining flexion of fetal head, use of Piper forceps or Dührssen's incisions. Before 36 wk, HC > AC, thus fetal predisposition. Tentorial tears secondary to hyperextended head. Association with trisomy 21 in 3% to 5% of cases. Avoid hyperextension of head during delivery.
- Cord prolapse: usually occurs late in the course of labor. Incidence depends on type of breech—frank (0.5%), complete (4% to 5%), footling (10%).
- Nuchal arm: arm extended above fetal head, occurs when there is undue traction before delivery of fetal scapulas. Treatment depends on bringing trapped arm across infant's face.

DISPOSITION

If confounding variables are corrected for, such as prematurity and associated congenital anomalies (6.3% of breeches vs. 2.4% in general population), route of delivery plays a less important role in fetal outcome than previously thought.

REFERRAL

An obstetrician trained in delivery of the vaginal breech is a prerequisite for attempting vaginal route, although it must be explained to the patient that with C-section certain risks (such as hyperextension of the fetal head with resultant spinal cord injury) may be minimized but not eliminated.

PEARLS & CONSIDERATIONS

COMMENTS

For breech presentation, in general, mortality is increased thirteenfold and morbidity sevenfold. The main reasons are an increase in congenital anomalies, perinatal hypoxia, birth injury, and prematurity.

There is no contraindication to induction of labor in the breech presentation, nor is labor prohibited in a primigravida.

AUTHOR: **SCOTT J. ZUCCALA, D.O.**

Bronchiectasis (PTG)

BASIC INFORMATION

DEFINITION

Bronchiectasis is the abnormal dilation and destruction of bronchial walls, which may be congenital or acquired.

ICD-9CM CODES
494.0 Bronchiectasis

EPIDEMIOLOGY & DEMOGRAPHICS

- Cystic fibrosis is responsible for nearly 50% of all cases of bronchiectasis.
- Acquired primary bronchiectasis is uncommon because of rapid diagnosis of pulmonary infections and frequent use of antibiotics.
- Effective childhood immunizations have led to a significant decrease in the incidence of bronchiectasis resulting from pertussis.

PHYSICAL FINDINGS & CLINICAL PRESENTATION

- Moist crackles at lung bases
- Cough with expectoration of large amount of purulent sputum
- Fever, night sweats, generalized malaise, weight loss
- Hemoptysis
- Halitosis, skin pallor
- Clubbing (infrequent)

ETIOLOGY

- Cystic fibrosis
- Lung infections (pneumonia, lung abscess, TB, fungal infections, viral infections)
- Abnormal host defense (panhypogammaglobulinemia, Kartagener's syndrome, AIDS, chemotherapy)
- Localized airway obstruction (congenital structural defects, foreign bodies, neoplasms)
- Inflammation (inflammatory pneumonitis, granulomatous lung disease, allergic aspergillosis)

DIAGNOSIS

DIFFERENTIAL DIAGNOSIS

- TB
- Asthma
- Chronic bronchitis or chronic sinusitis
- Interstitial fibrosis
- Chronic lung abscess
- Foreign body aspiration
- Cystic fibrosis
- Lung carcinoma

WORKUP

- Sputum for Gram stain and C&S, chest x-ray examination, bronchoscopy, spirometry
- Spirometry reveals reduced ration of FEV_1 to FVC, normal or slightly reduced FVC, and a reduced FEV_1

LABORATORY TESTS

- Sputum for Gram stain, C&S, and acid-fast bacteria (AFB)
- CBC with differential (leukocytosis with left shift, anemia)
- Serum protein electrophoresis to evaluate for hypogammaglobulinemia
- Antibody test for aspergillosis
- Sweat test in patients with suspected cystic fibrosis

IMAGING STUDIES

- Chest x-ray examination: hyperinflation, crowded lung markings, small cystic spaces at the base of the lungs
- High-resolution CT scan of the chest has become the best tool to detect cystic lesions and exclude underlying obstruction from neoplasm. The CT study should be a noncontrast study with the use of 1 to 1.5 mm window every 1 cm with acquisition time of 1 sec. Typical findings on CT include dilation of airway lumen, lack of tapering of an airway toward periphery, ballooned cysts at the end of bronchus, and varicose constrictions along airways.
- Bronchography is rarely used and may be considered only when surgery is contemplated.
- Pulmonary function tests generally reveal obstructive or mixed ventilatory defect.
- Bronchoscopy may be helpful to evaluate hemoptysis, rule out obstructive lesions, and remove mucus plugs.

TREATMENT

NONPHARMACOLOGIC THERAPY

- Postural drainage (reclining prone on a bed with the head down on the side) and chest percussion with use of inflatable vests or mechanical vibrators applied to the chest may enhance removal of respiratory secretions
- Adequate hydration
- Supplemental oxygen for hypoxemia

ACUTE GENERAL Rx

- Antibiotic therapy is based on the results of sputum, Gram stain, and C&S; in patients with inadequate or inconclusive results, empiric therapy with amoxicillin/clavulanate 500 mg to 875 mg q12h, TMP-SMX q12h, doxycycline 100 mg bid, or cefuroxime 250 mg bid for 10 to 14 days is recommended.
- Bronchodilators are useful in patients with demonstrable airflow obstruction.

CHRONIC Rx

- Avoidance of tobacco
- Maintenance of proper nutrition and hydration
- Prompt identification and treatment of infections
- Pneumococcal vaccination and annual influenza vaccination

DISPOSITION

Prognosis is variable with severity of the disease and underlying etiology of bronchiectasis.

REFERRAL

Surgical referral for partial lung resection in patients with localized severe disease unresponsive to medical therapy or in patients with massive hemoptysis

SUGGESTED READING

Barker AF: Bronchiectasis, *N Engl J Med* 346:1383, 2002.

AUTHOR: **FRED F. FERRI, M.D.**

BASIC INFORMATION

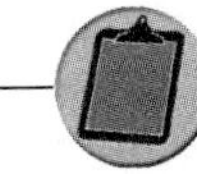

DEFINITION

Acute bronchitis is the inflammation of trachea and bronchi.

ICD-9CM CODES
466.0 Acute bronchitis

EPIDEMIOLOGY & DEMOGRAPHICS

- Highest incidence in smokers, older adults, young children, and in winter months
- In the U.S. there are nearly 30 million ambulatory visits annually for cough, leading to more than 12 million diagnoses of "bronchitis"

PHYSICAL FINDINGS & CLINICAL PRESENTATION

- Cough, usually worse in the morning, often productive. Mainly caused by transient bronchial hyperresponsiveness
- Low-grade fever
- Substernal discomfort worsened by coughing
- Postnasal drip, pharyngeal injection
- Rhonchi that may clear after cough, occasional wheezing

ETIOLOGY

- Viral infections are the leading cause of bronchitis (rhinovirus, influenza virus, adenovirus, respiratory syncytial virus)
- Atypical organisms (*Mycoplasma, Chlamydia pneumoniae*)
- Bacterial infections (*Haemophilus influenzae, Moraxella, Streptococcus pneumoniae*)

DIAGNOSIS

DIFFERENTIAL DIAGNOSIS

- Pneumonia
- Asthma
- Sinusitis
- Bronchiolitis
- Aspiration
- Cystic fibrosis
- Pharyngitis
- Cough secondary to medications
- Neoplasm (elderly patients)
- Influenza
- Allergic aspergillosis
- GERD
- CHF (in elderly patients)
- Bronchogenic neoplasm

WORKUP

Seldom necessary (e.g., to rule out pneumonia, neoplasm)

LABORATORY TESTS

- Tests are generally not necessary.
- CBC may reveal mild leukocytosis.
- Sputum culture, Gram stain, and blood cultures are generally not indicated.

IMAGING STUDIES

Chest x-ray examination is usually reserved for patients with suspected pneumonia, influenza, or underlying COPD and no improvement with therapy.

TREATMENT

NONPHARMACOLOGIC THERAPY

- Avoidance of tobacco and other pulmonary irritants
- Increased fluid intake
- Use of vaporizer to increase room humidity

ACUTE GENERAL Rx

- Inhaled bronchodilators (e.g., albuterol, metaproterenol) prn for 1 to 2 wk in patients with wheezing or troublesome cough. Inhaled albuterol has been proven effective in reducing the duration of cough in adults with uncomplicated acute bronchitis
- Cough suppression with guaifenesin; addition of codeine for cough suppression (e.g., Robitussin-AC) if cough is severe and is significantly interrupting patient's sleep pattern
- Use of antibiotics (TMP-SMX, amoxicillin, doxycycline, cefuroxime) for acute bronchitis is generally not indicated; should be considered only in patients with concomitant COPD and purulent sputum or in patients unresponsive to prolonged conservative treatment
- Antibiotics are overused in patients with acute bronchitis (70% to 90% of office visits for acute bronchitis result in treatment with antibiotics); this practice pattern is contributing to increases in resistant organisms

CHRONIC Rx

Avoidance of tobacco and other pulmonary irritants

DISPOSITION

- Complete recovery within 7 to 10 days in most patients
- Patients should be informed to expect to have a cough for 10 to 14 days after the visit

REFERRAL

For pulmonary function testing only in patients with recurrent bronchitis and suspected underlying asthma

PEARLS & CONSIDERATIONS

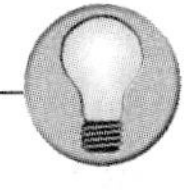

COMMENTS

- Intervention studies reveal that patient and physician education are effective in reducing the use of antibiotic therapy.
- It is helpful to refer to acute bronchitis as a "chest cold." Patients should be informed that antibiotics are probably not going to be beneficial and may result in significant side effects.

SUGGESTED READINGS

Evans AT et al: Azithromycin for acute bronchitis: a randomized, double-blind, controlled trial, *Lancet* 359:1648, 2002.

Knutson D, Braun C: Diagnosis and management of acute bronchitis, *Am Fam Physician* 65:2039, 2002.

Macfarlane J et al: Reducing antibiotic use for acute bronchitis in primary care: blinded, randomized controlled trial of patient information leaflet, *BMJ* 324:91, 2002.

Poole PJ, Black PN: Mucolytic agents for chronic bronchitis. *Cochrane Database Syst Rev* 2:CD001287, 2001.

Smucny JJ et al: Are beta-2 agonists effective treatment for acute bronchitis or acute cough in patients without underlying pulmonary disease? A systematic review, *J Fam Pract* 50:945, 2001.

AUTHOR: **FRED F. FERRI, M.D.**

BASIC INFORMATION

DEFINITION

Brucellosis is a zoonotic infection caused by one of four species of *Brucella*. It commonly presents as a nondescript febrile illness.

SYNONYMS

Malta fever
Bang's disease

ICD-9CM CODES
023.9 Brucellosis

EPIDEMIOLOGY & DEMOGRAPHICS

INCIDENCE (IN U.S.): About 100 cases/yr (may be underreported)
PREDOMINANT SEX: Male
PREDOMINANT AGE: Adult
CONGENITAL INFECTION: Recent evidence suggests a high rate of spontaneous abortions in untreated pregnant women during the first and second trimesters.
NEONATAL INFECTION: Can occur if mother is infected during pregnancy.

PHYSICAL FINDINGS

- Incubation period is 1 wk to 3 mo.
- Patients may be asymptomatic or have nonspecific symptoms such as fever, sweats, malaise, weight loss, and depression.
- Bacteremic patients may have arthralgias or arthritis. Patients may rarely present with abdominal pain.
- Fever is the most common finding.
- Hepatomegaly, splenomegaly, or lymphadenopathy is possible.
- Localized disease:
  1. Related to a single organ
  2. Includes endocarditis, meningitis, and osteomyelitis (especially vertebral)

Chronic hepatosplenic suppurative brucellosis (CHSB) presents with hepatic or splenic abscesses. This form is thought to be a reactivation and can occur years after the acute infection.

ETIOLOGY

- Caused by infection with *Brucella* species:
  1. Most commonly *melitensis,* but also *suis, abortus,* or *canis*
  2. A small, gram-negative coccobacillus
- Acquired through breaks in the skin or by inhalation or ingestion of organisms.
- Most cases occur after exposure to animals (sheep, goats, swine, cattle, or dogs), or animal products (i.e., milk, hides, tissue).
- Most cases (in U.S.) occur in men with occupational exposure to animals (farmers, ranchers, veterinarians, abattoir workers).
- Laboratory acquisition is possible.
- May occur in tourists to other countries who ingest goat milk or cheese.

DIAGNOSIS

DIFFERENTIAL DIAGNOSIS

Many febrile conditions without localizing manifestations (i.e., TB, endocarditis, typhoid fever, malaria, autoimmune diseases)

WORKUP

- Cultures of blood, bone marrow, or other tissue (lymph node, liver) should be sent and held for 4 wk, because *Brucella* grows slowly in vitro.
- Granulomas on biopsy are suggestive of diagnosis.

LABORATORY TESTS

- WBC count: normal or low
- Serology:
  1. Serum agglutination test (SAT) to detect antibodies to *B. abortus, melitensis,* and *suis*
  2. Specific antibody test to identify antibodies to *B. canis*
  3. False-negative SAT possibly resulting from a prozone effect
  4. Two different serologic tests are usually sent to avoid a false-negative result; Complement fixation or Brucella ELISA's may be used for confirmation

Serologic studies may be nondiagnostic in CHSB.

IMAGING STUDIES

- Radiographs to show splenic calcifications in chronic disease
- Bone scan and radiographs of the spine to suggest osteomyelitis
- Ultrasound or CT scan of the abdomen to show an enlarged liver or spleen
- Echocardiogram to reveal vegetations in endocarditis

In CHSB, abscesses and calcifications may be seen in the liver and spleen.

TREATMENT

NONPHARMACOLOGIC THERAPY

- Drainage of abscesses
- Valve replacement for endocarditis

ACUTE GENERAL Rx

Combination antibiotics required:

- Doxycycline 100 mg PO bid plus streptomycin 15 mg/kg IM qd for 6 wk
- Less effective: doxycycline 100 mg PO bid plus rifampin 600 mg PO qd or sulfamethoxazole 800 mg/trimethoprim 160 mg one DS tablet PO qid

Courses <6 wk are associated with higher relapse rates; longer courses are recommended for complicated disease.

CHRONIC Rx

See "Acute General Rx."

DISPOSITION

Relapse is possible weeks to months after the completion of therapy, usually because of noncompliance with a prolonged medical regimen or a persistent focus of infection that requires surgical drainage.
Reactivation with CHSB has been reported up to 35 yr after initial illness.

REFERRAL

For all cases to an infectious disease specialist

PEARLS & CONSIDERATIONS

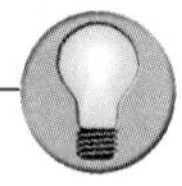

COMMENTS

- Alert the microbiology laboratory to the possibility of *Brucella.*
- Do not use doxycycline in children or pregnant women.
- Avoid aminoglycosides in pregnant women.

SUGGESTED READINGS

Al Dahouk et al: Laboratory-based diagnosis of brucellosis—a review of the literature. Part I: Techniques for direct detection and identification of Brucella spp, *Clin Lab* 49:487, 2003.
Ariza J et al: Current understanding and management of chronic hepatosplenic suppurative brucellosis, *Clin Infect Dis* 32(7):995, 2001.
Memish Z et al: *Brucella* bacteremia: clinical and laboratory observations in 160 patients, *J Infect Dis* 40:59, 2000.
Sarinas PS, Chitkara RK: Brucellosis, *Semin Respir Infect* 18:168, 2003.

AUTHOR: **MAURICE POLICAR, M.D.**

BASIC INFORMATION

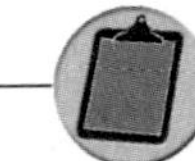

DEFINITION

Forcible clenching or grinding of the teeth during sleep or wakefulness, often leading to damage of the teeth.

ICD-9CM CODES
306.8 Bruxism

EPIDEMIOLOGY & DEMOGRAPHICS

Occurs in 15% of children and 75% of adults

PHYSICAL FINDINGS & CLINICAL PRESENTATION

Complaints of grinding of teeth from sleep partner or members of the family. In many cases, the masticatory system will adapt to the phenomenon, but in severe cases nearly every part of the masticatory system may be damaged. Excessive wearing of dentition is the most common physical finding. Tender or hypoatrophied masticatory muscles may also be observed.

ETIOLOGY

Cause is quite controversial. Possible causes in the literature include occlusal discrepancies, anatomy of the bony structures of the orofacial region, part of the sleep arousal response, disturbances of the central dopaminergic system, smoking, alcohol, drugs, stress, and personality.

DIAGNOSIS

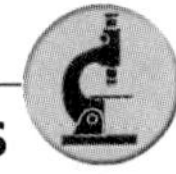

DIFFERENTIAL DIAGNOSIS

- Dental compression syndrome
- Temporomandibular joint disorders
- Chronic orofacial pain disorders
- Oral motor disorders
- Malocclusion

WORKUP

History should have an emphasis on sleep habits, including excessive snoring, pain in the temporal mandibular region, interview with close family members, health habits, personality quirks. Physical examination of the teeth and masticatory muscles is mandatory. Sleep studies in selected cases may be helpful.

LABORATORY TESTS

None indicated unless a systemic disease suspected (e.g., infection, autoimmune)

IMAGING STUDIES

X-ray studies of teeth and temporomandibular joints

TREATMENT

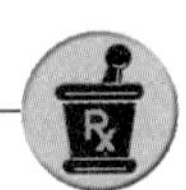

NONPHARMACOLOGIC THERAPY

Biofeedback, psychological counseling, and elimination of harmful health habits have been used with limited success.

GENERAL Rx

- Oral splints; a nightguard to protect teeth may be useful
- Correction of malocclusion
- Pain management (e.g., gabapentin, ibuprofen)
- Medication to relieve anxiety and improve sleep (e.g., benzodiazepine or trazodone at hs)

DISPOSITION

Referral to dentist mandatory if damage to teeth evident.

PEARLS & CONSIDERATIONS

Like any poorly understood disease, treatment is often unsatisfactory and subject to quackery.

SUGGESTED READINGS

Attansio R: An overview of bruxism and its management, *Dent Clin North Am* 41(2):229, 1997.

Dae TT, Lavigne EJ: Oral splints: the crutches for temporomandibular disorders and bruxism, *Crit Rev Oral Biol Med* 9(3):345, 1998.

Lopbezoo F, Naeije M: Bruxism is mainly regulated centrally, not peripherally, *J Oral Rehabil* 28(12):1085, 2001.

AUTHOR: **FRED F. FERRI, M.D.**

Budd-Chiari Syndrome

BASIC INFORMATION

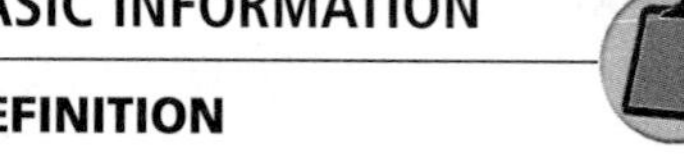

DEFINITION

Budd-Chiari syndrome (BCS) is a rare disease defined by the obstruction of hepatic venous outflow anywhere from the small hepatic veins to the junction of the inferior vena cava and the right atrium. Primary BCS is defined by endoluminal obstruction as seen in thromboses or webs. Secondary BCS is when the obstruction is due to nonvascular invasion (malignancy or parasitic masses) or extrinsic compression (tumor, abscess, cysts).

SYNONYMS

Hepatic vein thrombosis
Obliterative hepatocavopathy
Hepatic venous outflow obstruction

ICD-9CM CODES
453.0 Budd-Chiari syndrome

EPIDEMIOLOGY & DEMOGRAPHICS

BCS is a rare disorder. Clinical presentation and characteristics vary with geography. IVC thrombosis of an indolent course is more common in the Far East and more often complicated by hepatocellular carcinoma. Women are more commonly affected. Average age is 35, although the young and elderly can also be affected. In the U.S., BCS is more commonly associated with primary myeloproliferative disorders, underlying hypercoagulable states, IVC membranes, and tumors. Underlying factors contributing to BCS can be identified in approximately 75% of cases, and the finding of multiple causes in the same patient is quite common.

PHYSICAL FINDINGS & CLINICAL PRESENTATION

Variable according to the degree, location, acuity of obstruction, and presence of collateral circulation

- Fulminant/Acute: (uncommon) severe RUQ abdominal pain, fever, nausea, vomiting, jaundice, hepatomegaly, ascites, marked elevation in serum aminotransferases and drop in coagulation factors, and encephalopathy. Early recognition and treatment are essential to survival.
- Subacute/Chronic: (more common) vague abdominal discomfort, gradual progression to hepatomegaly, portal hypertension with or without cirrhosis; late-onset ascites, lower extremity edema, esophageal varices, splenomegaly, coagulopathy, hepatorenal syndrome, and rarely, encephalopathy.
- Asymptomatic: usually discovered incidentally.

ETIOLOGY

Myeloproliferative disease—often discovered in cases of initially idiopathic BCS, 20% to 53%

- Polycythemia vera
- Essential thrombocytosis
- Myelofibrosis

Hypercoagulable states—can coexist with other causes, up to 31%

- Protein C deficiency
- Protein S deficiency
- Antithrombin III deficiency
- Activated protein C resistance/Factor V Leiden mutation
- Prothrombin gene mutation
- Methylene-tetrahydrofolate reductase mutation
- Antiphospholipid antibody syndrome
- Homocysteinemia
- Pregnancy
- Oral contraceptive pills
- Sickle cell anemia

Infection:

- Liver abscess
- Filariasis
- Schistosomiasis
- Hydatid cyst
- Syphilis
- Tuberculosis
- Aspergillosis

Malignancy—<5%

- Adrenal carcinoma
- Ovarian
- Bronchogenic
- Renal-cell carcinoma
- Hepatocellular carcinoma
- Leiomyosarcoma
- Metastatic cancer

Other:

- Sarcoid
- Behçet's disease
- Paroxysmal nocturnal hemoglobinuria
- IVC membrane/congenital web
- Abdominal trauma
- Ulcerative colitis
- Celiac disease
- Dacarbazine therapy
- Idiopathic

DIAGNOSIS

DIFFERENTIAL DIAGNOSIS

- Shock liver/ischemic hepatitis
- Viral hepatitis
- Toxic hepatitis
- Hepatic veno-occlusive disease (sinusoidal obstruction syndrome)
- Alcoholic hepatitis
- Cholecystitis
- Cardiac cirrhosis (i.e., chronic right-sided heart failure)
  Tricuspid regurgitation
  Right atrial myxoma
  Constrictive pericarditis
- Alcoholic cirrhosis
- Cirrhosis of other etiologies:
  Wilson's
  Hemochromatosis
  α-1-Antitrypsin deficiency
  Autoimmune

WORKUP

History, physical examination, laboratory analysis, and imaging studies

LABORATORY TESTS

Assessment of liver injury and function:

- Serum aminotransferases, prothrombin time, albumin, bilirubin

Diagnostic tests (directed by history):

- CBC, bone marrow biopsy, viral hepatitis panel, α-1-antitrypsin, serum iron, transferrin saturation, alkaline phosphatase, ceruloplasmin, toxicology screen, antismooth muscle antibody, antimitochondrial antibody, and double-stranded DNA antibody. Tests for hypercoagulable states (particularly Protein C, S, and antithrombin deficiencies) may be difficult to interpret as many levels are abnormal because of liver dysfunction. Family studies may be the only way to identify a primary hypercoagulable disorder. Evaluation of ascitic fluid reveals a high serum-ascitic fluid albumin gradient (SAAG), mimicking the ascitic fluid in patients with cardiac disease.

IMAGING STUDIES

- Color and pulsed Doppler U/S—diagnostic sensitivity of >75%, first line test.
- MRI with gadolinium contrast—better than contrast enhanced CT, second line test.
- Venography—gold standard but invasive and mainly indicated to guide percutaneous or surgical intervention, confirm the classic spider web pattern caused by collateral venous flow, and look for BCS in cases of high clinical suspicion when initial studies are negative.
- Liver biopsy—not necessary to diagnose BCS but may be helpful in patients with cirrhosis in whom the diagnosis remains uncertain and the differential still includes sinusoidal obstruction syndrome, cirrhosis of other origins, and malignancy. Of note, long-standing BCS is characterized by large, regenerative nodules in the liver that are indistinguishable from hepatocellular carcinoma on imaging.

TREATMENT

ASYMPTOMATIC Rx

- Treatment of the underlying disorder.
- Anticoagulation may improve prognosis.

ACUTE DISEASE Rx

- Supportive measures.
- Angioplasty and stenting, in situ thrombolysis, or removal of IVC webs to decompress the portal circulation, all combined with anticoagulation may be indicated for acute BCS in patients in stable condition.
- TIPSS (transjugular intrahepatic portosystemic stent shunt) may be a decompression option but can be especially hazardous in BCS patients because of the high prevalence of hepatic vein thromboses.
- Liver transplant may be indicated for fulminant BCS or patients that fail the previous therapies.

CHRONIC DISEASE Rx

- Lifelong anticoagulation.
- Treatment of underlying myeloproliferative or other disorders.
- Treatment of liver dysfunction and complications related to portal hypertension.
- Invasive interventions should be reserved for symptomatic patients who do not improve with medical therapy.
- Liver transplantation.
- Shunt thrombosis is a common complication.

DISPOSITION

Prognosis is variable and dependent on multiple factors including time to recognition and treatment, etiology, acuity, the type of intervention, and the condition of the patient at the time of treatment. Generally, risk for decompensation and death has been reported as highest within the first 1-2 years after diagnosis. Patients surviving beyond 2 years have been reported to have an excellent 10-year survival rate.

REFERRAL

Fulminant presentations should immediately be referred to a center capable of liver transplantation. All cases benefit from referral to a hepatologist, hematologist, an interventional radiologist, and a surgeon specializing in hepatobiliary disease.

SUGGESTED READINGS

Janssen HLA et al: Budd Chiari syndrome: a review by an expert panel, *J Hepatol* 38(3):364, 2003.

Menon KVN, Shah V, Kamath PS: The Budd-Chiari syndrome, *N Engl J Med* 350(6):578, 2004.

Valla DC: The diagnosis and management of the Budd-Chiari syndrome: consensus and controversies, *Hepatology* 38(4):793, 2003.

AUTHOR: **JENNIFER R. HUR, M.D.**

Bulimia Nervosa 

BASIC INFORMATION

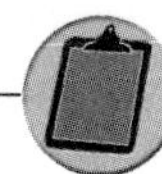

DEFINITION

Bulimia nervosa is a prolonged illness characterized by a specific psychopathology.

ICD-9CM CODES
783.6 Bulimia

EPIDEMIOLOGY & DEMOGRAPHICS

INCIDENCE/PREVALENCE: Affects 1% to 3% of female adolescents and young adults

PREDOMINANT SEX: Female:male ratio of 10:1

PREDOMINANT AGE: Adolescence to young adulthood; mean age of onset: 17 yr

PHYSICAL FINDINGS & CLINICAL PRESENTATION

- Parotid and salivary gland swelling
- Scars on the back of the hand and knuckles (Russell's sign) from rubbing against the upper incisors when inducing vomiting
- Eroded enamel, particularly on the lingual surface of the upper teeth; pyorrhea and other gum disorders possible
- Petechial hemorrhages of the cornea, soft palate, or face possibly noted after vomiting
- Loss of gag reflex, well-developed abdominal musculature
- Usually no emaciation; normal physical examination possible

ETIOLOGY

Etiology is unknown but likely multifactorial (sociocultural, psychologic, familial factors). Bulimia is much more common in Western societies where there is a strong cultural pressure to be slender. According to the American Psychiatric Association, patients with eating disorders display a broad range of symptoms that occur along a continuum between those of anorexia nervosa and bulimia.

DIAGNOSIS

DIFFERENTIAL DIAGNOSIS

- Schizophrenia
- GI disorders
- Neurologic disorders (seizures, Kleine-Levin syndrome, Klüver-Bucy syndrome)
- Brain neoplasms
- Psychogenic vomiting

WORKUP

- The following questions are useful to screen patients for bulimia:
  1. "Are you satisfied with your eating habits?"
  2. "Do you ever eat in secret?"
- Answering "no" to the first question and/or "yes" to the second question has 100% sensitivity and 90% specificity for bulimia. The SCOFF questionnaire can also be used as a screening tool for eating disorders (see "Anorexia Nervosa").
- A diagnosis can be made using the following DSM-IV diagnostic criteria for bulimia nervosa:
  1. Recurrent episodes of binge eating (rapid consumption of a large amount of food in a discrete period)
  2. A feeling of lack of control over eating behavior during the eating binges
  3. Self-induced vomiting, use of laxatives or diuretics, strict dieting or fasting, or rigorous exercise to prevent weight gain
  4. A minimum of two binge-eating episodes a week for at least 3 mo
  5. Persistent overconcern with body shape and weight

LABORATORY TESTS

- Electrolyte abnormalities secondary to vomiting (hypokalemia and metabolic alkalosis) or to diarrhea from laxative abuse (hypokalemia and hyperchloremic metabolic acidosis)
- Hyponatremia, hypocalcemia, hypomagnesemia (caused by laxative abuse)
- Elevated cortisol, decreased LH, decreased FSH

TREATMENT

NONPHARMACOLOGIC THERAPY

- Cognitive behavioral therapy to control abnormal behaviors
- Use of food diaries, nutritional counseling, and planning meals at least a day in advance is useful to counter abnormal eating behaviors
- Correction of electrolyte abnormalities

ACUTE GENERAL Rx

- SSRIs are generally considered to be the safest medication option in these patients. They are useful in severely depressed patients and in those who fail to benefit from cognitive behavioral therapy.
- Prompt recognition and treatment of complications:
  1. Ipecac cardiotoxicity from laxative abuse
  2. Electrolyte abnormalities (see Laboratory Tests)
  3. Esophagitis and Mallory-Weiss tears; esophageal rupture from repeated vomiting
  4. Aspiration pneumonia and pneumomediastinum
  5. Menstrual irregularities (including amenorrhea)
  6. GI abnormalities: acute gastric dilatation, pancreatitis, abdominal pain, constipation

CHRONIC Rx

- Psychotherapy continued for years and focused specifically on self-image and family and peer interactions is an integral part of successful recovery.
- Family therapy is also recommended, especially in younger patients.

DISPOSITION

Course is variable and marked by frequent recurrence of exacerbations.

REFERRAL

- In addition to the primary care physician, the multidisciplinary team should include a dietician, a psychiatrist, and a family therapist.
- Hospitalization should be considered for patients with severe electrolyte abnormalities or those with suicidal thoughts.

PEARLS & CONSIDERATIONS

COMMENTS

- Bulimia has a close association with depression, bipolar disorder, obsessive-compulsive disorder, alcoholism, and substance abuse.
- Bulimia should be considered in all patients (especially adolescents) with unexplained hypokalemia and metabolic alkalosis.

SUGGESTED READINGS

American Psychiatric Association: Practice guideline for the treatment of patients with eating disorders, *Am J Psychiatry* 157(suppl):4, 2000.

Bacaltchuk J, Hay P, Trefiglio R: Antidepressants versus psychological treatments and their combination for bulimia nervosa, *Cochrane Database Syst Rev* (4):CD003385, 2001.

Mehler PS: Bulimia nervosa, *N Engl J Med* 349:875, 2003.

Prits SD, Susman J: Diagnosis of eating disorders in primary care, *Am Fam Physician* 67:297, 2003.

AUTHOR: **FRED F. FERRI, M.D.**

BASIC INFORMATION

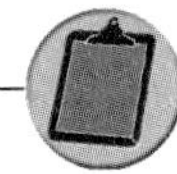

DEFINITION

Bullous pemphigoid refers to an autoimmune, subepidermal blistering disease seen in the elderly.

SYNONYMS

Subepidermal autoimmune bullous dermatoses

ICD-9CM CODES
694.5 Pemphigoid

EPIDEMIOLOGY & DEMOGRAPHICS

- Commonly seen in the elderly older than 70 yr
- Incidence 10/1 million
- Equal prevalence between males and females
- No racial predilection
- Most common of the autoimmune bullous dermatoses

PHYSICAL FINDINGS & CLINICAL PRESENTATION

History
- Bullous pemphigoid typically starts as an eczematous or urticarial rash on the extremities.
- Blisters form between 1 wk to several months.

Physical findings
- Anatomic distribution
  1. Flexor surfaces of the arms, legs, groin, axilla, and lower abdomen
  2. Spares the head and neck
  3. Rare involvement of mucous membranes
- Lesion configuration
  1. May be localized to the extremities or generalized
  2. Lesions irregularly grouped but sometimes can be serpiginous (Fig. 1-46)
- Lesion morphology
  1. Blistering bullae characteristic findings measuring anywhere from 5 mm to 2 cm in diameter
  2. Contains clear or bloody fluid
  3. Arises from normal skin or from an erythematous base
  4. Heals without scarring if denuded

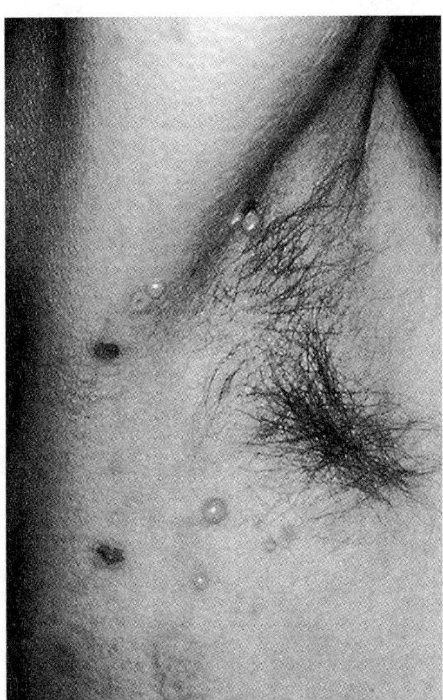

FIGURE 1-46 Bullous pemphigoid. Note intact bullae with erosions in aflexural distribution. (From Goldstein BG, Goldstein AO: *Practical dermatology,* ed 2, St Louis, 1997, Mosby.)

ETIOLOGY

Bullous pemphigoid is an autoimmune disease with IgG and/or C3 complement component reacting with antigens located in the basement membrane zone.

DIAGNOSIS

The diagnosis of bullous pemphigoid should be considered in any elderly individual with pruritic bullae.

DIFFERENTIAL DIAGNOSIS

- Cicatricial pemphigoid
- Herpes gestationis
- Epidermolysis bullosa acquisita
- Systemic lupus erythematosus
- Erythema multiforme
- Pemphigus
- Drug eruptions
- Pemphigoid nodularis

WORKUP

The clinical presentation and characteristic skin lesions assist in making the diagnosis of bullous pemphigoid. Specific laboratory tests, skin biopsy staining, and immunofluorescence studies confirm the diagnosis.

LABORATORY TESTS

- Antibodies to the basement membrane zone are detected in the serum in 70% of patients with bullous pemphigoid.
- Skin biopsy staining with hematoxylineosin reveals subepidermal blisters.
- Direct and indirect immunofluorescence studies to detect the presence of IgG and C3 immune complexes.
- Immunoelectron microscopy also reveals immune deposits on the basement membrane zone.

TREATMENT

Treatment of bullous pemphigoid is based on the degree of involvement and rate of disease progression.

NONPHARMACOLOGIC THERAPY

- Avoid scratching.
- Use mild soaps and emollients after bathing to prevent dryness of the skin.

ACUTE GENERAL Rx

- Systemic corticosteroids are considered the standard treatment for more advanced bullous pemphigoid
  1. Prednisone 1 mg/kg/day is usually recommended and is continued until new blister formation ceases. The dose is tapered to 20 to 40 mg. Thereafter, the dose is gradually tapered according to the clinical findings.
- Topical steroids in general have been used in patients with localized bullous pemphigoid; however, recently topical corticosteroid therapy has been found to be effective for both moderate and severe bullous pemphigoid and superior to oral corticosteroid.
- If patients cannot take corticosteroids, dapsone, combination tetracycline and nicotinamide or azathioprine can be tried.

CHRONIC Rx

- Combination prednisone and azathioprine protocols are available in the treatment of bullous pemphigoid.
- Cyclophosphamide can be considered in attempt to reduce chronic long-term use of corticosteroids.

DISPOSITION

- Mortality rates are estimated at 19% at 1 yr, 6% at 2 yr, and 28% to 30% at 3 yr.

REFERRAL

If bullous pemphigoid is suspected, a dermatology consultation is recommended to assist with decisions regarding diagnosis, monitoring, and therapy.

PEARLS & CONSIDERATIONS

COMMENTS

- Bullous pemphigoid has been associated with diabetes, multiple sclerosis, pernicious anemia, rheumatoid arthritis, lichen planus, psoriasis, and vitiligo.
- Not known to transform into malignancies or represent a dermatologic manifestation of harboring malignancies.

SUGGESTED READINGS

Joly P et al: A comparison of oral and topical corticosteroids in patients with bullous pemphigoid, *N Engl J Med* 346:321, 2002.

Korman NJ: Bullous pemphigoid: the latest in diagnosis, prognosis and therapy, *Arch Dermatol* 134(9):1137, 1998.

AUTHOR: **PETER PETROPOULOS, M.D.**

BASIC INFORMATION

DEFINITION

Burn injuries consist of thermal injuries (flames, scalds, cigarettes), as well as chemical, electrical, and radiation burns.

SYNONYMS

Thermal injury

ICD-9CM CODES
942-949 (by region, % burn)

EPIDEMIOLOGY & DEMOGRAPHICS

PREVALENCE (IN U.S.): 2 million people/yr, 70-80 thousand require hospitalization.
PREDOMINANT SEX: Male:female ratio of 2:1
PREVALENT AGE: first few years of life and then 20-29 year olds

PHYSICAL FINDINGS & CLINICAL PRESENTATION

- Burns are defined by size and depth.
- *First-degree burns (superficial)* involve the epidermis only and appear painful and red.
- *Second-degree burns* involve the dermis and appear blistered, moist, and red with two-point discrimination intact (*superficial partial-thickness*) or red and blanched white with only sensation of pressure intact (*deep partial thickness*).
- *Third-degree burns (full-thickness)* extend through the dermis with associated destruction of hair follicles and sweat glands. The skin is charred, pale, *painless,* and leathery. These burns are caused by flames, immersion scalds, chemical and high voltage injuries.
- The "rule of nines" is useful for rapidly assessing the extent of a burn. This rule is used to calculate the total burn surface area (TBSA) for second- and third-degree burns.

DIAGNOSIS

CLASSIFICATION

Major burns: Partial-thickness burns >25% TBSA (or 20% if younger than 10 or older than 50 yr); full-thickness burns >10% TBSA; burns crossing major joints or involving the hands, face, feet, or perineum; electrical or chemical burns; those complicated by inhalation injury, or involving high-risk patients (extremes of age/comorbid diseases)
Moderate burns: Partial-thickness burns >15% to 25% TBSA (or 10% in children and older adults); full-thickness burns >2% to 10% TBSA and not involving the specific conditions of major burns
Minor burns: Partial-thickness burns <15% TBSA or full-thickness burns <2% TBSA

WORKUP

Diagnosis is based on clinical findings.

LABORATORY STUDIES

- CBC, electrolytes, BUN, creatinine, and glucose
- Serial ABG and carboxyhemoglobin if smoke inhalation suspected
- Urinalysis, urine myoglobin, and CPK levels if concern for rhabdomyolysis

IMAGING STUDIES

Chest x-ray and bronchoscopy if smoke inhalation suspected

TREATMENT

Minor burns are amenable to outpatient treatment, whereas moderate and major burns should be treated in specialized burn care facilities according to the principles described below.

ACUTE GENERAL Rx

- Establish airway: inspect for inhalation injury and intubate for suspected airway edema (often seen 12 to 24 hr later); supplemental O_2
- Remove jewelry and clothing and place one or two large-bore peripheral IVs (if TBSA > 20%)
- Fluid resuscitation with Ringer's lactate at 2 to 4 ml/kg per %TBSA per 24 hr with half the calculated fluid given in the first 8 hr; may titrate to urine output of 0.5 to 1 ml/kg/hr
- Foley catheter and NG tube (20% of patients develop an ileus)
- Tetanus update
- Pain control
- Stress ulcer prophylaxis in high-risk patients
- Prophylactic antibiotics are not recommended; however, burn victims should be considered immunosuppressed
- High-voltage burn patients should have ECG monitoring because they are at increased risk for arrhythmia

BURN WOUND Rx

First-degree burns (e.g., sunburns) can be treated with cool compresses, antihistamines, emollients, and at times, a rapidly tapering dose of steroids.
Second-degree and third-degree burns:

- Wash burned skin with cool water or saline (1° to 5° C; immerse approximately 30 min if able) and cleanse with mild soap
- Sharp debridement of ruptured blisters (except palms and soles)
- There are several approaches to burn dressings after cleansing and debriding:
  1. Apply thin layer of antibiotic ointment (silver sulfadiazine can be used unless sulfa allergy or facial burn) and cover with a nonadherent dressing (e.g., Telfa or petroleum-soaked gauze) followed by a sterile gauze wrap. Wash wound and change dressing when dressing soaked.
  2. Apply saline-soaked gauze (Xeroform, Owen's), cover with 4 × 4 dressing and a bulky absorbent dressing such as Kerlex. Reevaluate in 5 to 7 days.
  3. Apply occlusive dressing (Duoderm, Tegaderm, Biobrane), remove in 7 to 10 days.
- Specialized care, such as excision and auto grafting is required for deep second-degree or third-degree burns.

DISPOSITION

- Respiratory injury, sepsis, and multiorgan failure may complicate severe burns.
- Scarring can be expected in many second-degree and all third-degree burns.

REFERRAL

Major and some moderate burns require referral to specialized burn centers for surgical debridement, grafting evaluation and rehabilitation

PEARLS & CONSIDERATIONS

COMMENTS

Burn victims need to be reassessed frequently because the examination can change significantly in the first 24-72 hr.

SUGGESTED READINGS

Edlich R, Moghtader J: Thermal burns. In Rosen P (ed): *Emergency medicine: concepts and clinical practice,* ed 4, vol 1, St Louis, 1998, Mosby.
Sheridan R: *Burn Care: Results of Technical and Organizational Progress,* JAMA 290(6):719, 2003.
Sheridan R: Burns. *Criti Care Med* 30(11)S;S500, 2002.

AUTHORS: **MICHAEL P. JOHNSON, M.D.,** and **MICHELLE STOZEK, M.D.**

BASIC INFORMATION

DEFINITION

Bursitis is an inflammation of a bursa and is usually aseptic. A *bursa* is a closed sac lined with a synovial-like membrane that sometimes contains fluid that is found or that develops in an area subject to pressure or friction.

SYNONYMS

Housemaid's knee (prepatellar bursitis)
Weaver's bottom (ischial gluteal bursitis)
Baker's cyst (gastrocnemius-semimembranosus bursa)

ICD-9CM CODES
726.19 Subacromial bursitis
726.33 Olecranon bursitis
726.5 Ischiogluteal bursitis (hip)
726.5 Iliopsoas bursitis (hip)
726.61 Anserine bursitis
726.5 Trochanteric bursitis
726.65 Prepatellar bursitis
727.51 Baker's cyst
726.79 Retrocalcaneal bursitis

PHYSICAL FINDINGS & CLINICAL PRESENTATION

- Swelling, especially if bursa is superficial (olecranon, prepatellar)
- Local tenderness with pain on pressure against bursa
- Pain with joint movement
- Referred pain
- Palpable occasional fibrocartilaginous bodies (most common in olecranon and prepatellar bursae)

ETIOLOGY

- Acute trauma
- Repetitive trauma
- Sepsis
- Crystalline deposit disease
- Rheumatoid arthritis

DIAGNOSIS

DIFFERENTIAL DIAGNOSIS

- Degenerative joint disease
- Tendinitis (sometimes occurs in conjunction with bursitis)
- Cellulitis (if bursitis is septic)
- Infectious arthritis

WORKUP

Aspiration with Gram stain and C&S

IMAGING STUDIES

- Plain radiography to rule out other potential or coexisting bone or joint problems (Fig. 1-47)
- MRI

TREATMENT

NONPHARMACOLOGIC THERAPY

- If chronic, elimination of cause of pressure or irritation
- Use of relief pads, avoidance of direct pressure
- Rest
- Elevation
- Ice for acute trauma

ACUTE GENERAL Rx

- Septic:
  1. Appropriate antibiotic coverage and drainage
  2. Aspiration of purulent fluid with a large-bore needle (if there is no rapid clinical response, incision and drainage are indicated)
- Nonseptic:
  1. Aspiration of blood from acute trauma
  2. Application of compression dressing

CHRONIC Rx

- Aspiration if excessive fluid volume present, followed by application of compression dressing to prevent fluid reaccumulation (repeat aspiration may be required)
- Steroid injection into bursa (1 ml of triamcinolone, 40 mg, mixed with 1 to 3 cc of Xylocaine depending on size of bursa)
- NSAIDs

DISPOSITION

- Many bursal sacs "dry up" eventually.
- Nonsurgical treatment is effective in most cases.

REFERRAL

For orthopedic consultation to assist in treatment of sepsis or for excision of chronic enlarged bursa when indicated

PEARLS & CONSIDERATIONS

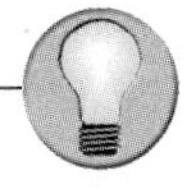

COMMENTS

- Injection of trochanteric bursa may require spinal needle in large patient.
- Sterile bursae should not be incised and drained because a chronic draining sinus tract may develop.
- Involvement of the iliopsoas bursa may cause groin pain, although the diagnosis is difficult to make because of the inaccessibility of the area to direct examination. (This also makes steroid injection impossible even if the diagnosis could be established.)

SUGGESTED READINGS

Floemer F, Morrison WB et al: MRI characteristics of olecranon bursitis, *Am J Roentgenol* 183:29, 2004.
Sofka CM, Adler RS: Sonography of cubital bursitis, *Am J Roengenal* 183:51, 2004.
Tortolani PJ, Carbone JJ, Quartaro LG: Greater trochantoric pain syndrome in patients referred to orthopedic spine specialists, *Spine* 2:251, 2002.
Van Mieghem IM, Boets A et al: Ischiogluteal bursitis: an uncommon type of bursitis, *Skeletal Radiol* 33:413, 2004.
Webner D, Drezner JA: Lesser trochanteric bursitis: a rare cause of anterior hip pain, *Clin J Sport Med* 14:242, 2004.

AUTHOR: **LONNIE R. MERCIER, M.D.**

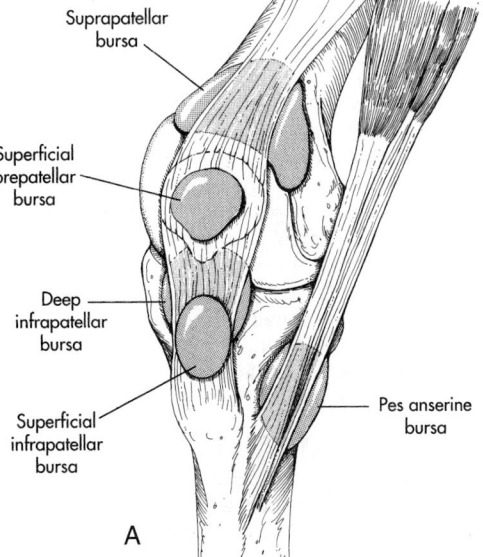

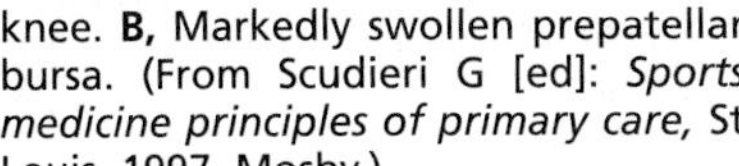

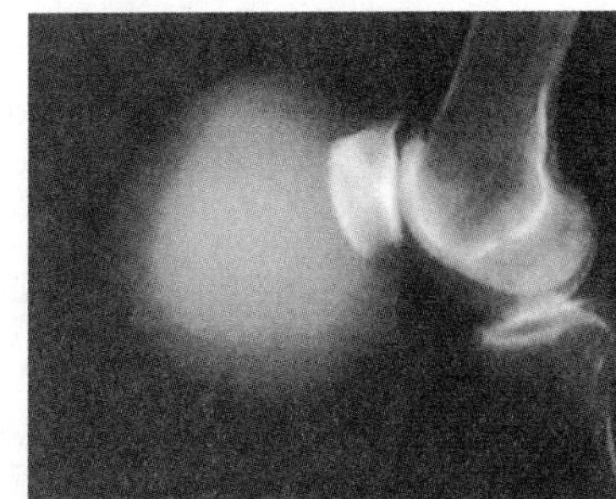

FIGURE 1-47 **A,** Bursae around the knee. **B,** Markedly swollen prepatellar bursa. (From Scudieri G [ed]: *Sports medicine principles of primary care,* St Louis, 1997, Mosby.)

BASIC INFORMATION

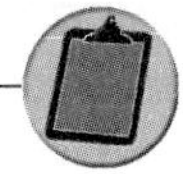

DEFINITION

Candidiasis is an inflammatory process involving the vulva and/or the vagina and is caused by superficial invasion of epithelial cells by *Candida* species.

SYNONYMS

Moniliasis
Thrush
Candidosis

ICD-9CM CODES
112.1 Moniliasis
112.0 Thrush
112 Candidosis

EPIDEMIOLOGY & DEMOGRAPHICS

- This is the second most common form of vaginitis in the U.S. 75% of women will have at least one episode of vulvovaginal candidiasis (VVC) during their childbearing years and about 45% will have a second attack. A small subpopulation of probably <5% of adult women has recurrent, often intractable episodes. *Candida* may be isolated in up to 20% of asymptomatic women of childbearing age.
- Factors that predispose to development of symptomatic VVC include pregnancy, antibiotic use, and diabetes. Antibiotic use disturbs normal vaginal flora and allows overgrowth of fungi; pregnancy and diabetes are associated with decrease in cell-mediated immunity.
- Factors associated with increased rates of asymptomatic vaginal colonization: pregnancy, high-estrogen oral contraceptives, uncontrolled diabetes mellitus, attendance at STD clinics.

UNCOMPLICATED VVC:
- Infrequent VVC
- Mild-to-moderate vaginitis and candida
- Likely to be *C. albicans*
- Nonimmunocompromised women

COMPLICATED VVC:
- Recurrent VVC
- Severe VVC
- Non-*albicans* candidiasis
- Women with uncontrolled diabetes, immunosuppression, or those who are pregnant

RX OF COMPLICATED VVC:
- Recurrent VVS: 7 to 14 days of topical therapy
- 150 mg fluconazole PO, repeat in 3 days
- Maintenance regimen
  1. Clotrimazole: 500-mg vaginal suppositories once weekly
  2. Ketoconazole: 100 mg once daily
  3. Fluconazole: 100 to 150 mg PO once weekly
  4. Itraconazole 400 mg/mo or 100 mg/day
  5. Continue one of the above regimens for 6 mo

COMPROMISED HOST:
- Treat with traditional antimycotics for at least 7 to 14 days
- Pregnancy: topical azoles recommended for 7 days
- HIV-infected women: fluconazole 200 mg/wk
- Not usually an STD

PHYSICAL FINDINGS & CLINICAL PRESENTATION

Symptoms of VVC consist of:
- Vulvar pruritus with vaginal discharge that typically resembles cottage cheese
- Erythema and edema of labia and vulvar skin; possible discrete pustulopapular peripheral lesions (satellite lesions)
- Vagina may be erythematous with an adherent, whitish discharge
- Cervix may appear normal
- Symptoms characteristically exacerbated in the week preceding menses with some relief after onset of menstrual flow

ETIOLOGY

- *Candida* are dimorphic fungi (spores and mycelial forms).
- *C. albicans* is responsible for 85% to 90% of vaginal yeast infections.
- *C. glabrata, C. tropicalis* (non-*albicans* species) also cause vaginitis and may be more resistant to conventional therapy.

DIAGNOSIS

DIFFERENTIAL DIAGNOSIS

- Bacterial vaginosis
- Trichomoniasis

WORKUP

- Usually normal vaginal pH (<4.5)
- Budding yeast forms or mycelia will appear in as many as 80% of cases. Saline wet prep of vaginal secretions usually is normal; may be increased in inflammatory cells in severe cases
- Whiff test negative (KOH)
- 10% KCl useful and more sensitive than wet mount for microscopic identification
- Can make a presumptive diagnosis based on symptomatology in the absence of microscopy-proven fungal elements if the pH and wet prep are normal. Fungal culture is recommended to confirm diagnosis
- In chronic/recurrent, burning replaces itching as prominent symptom. Confirm diagnosis with direct microscopy and culture. Many may actually have chronic or atrophic dermatitis. Test for HIV

LABORATORY TESTS

If sending cultures, send on Nickerson's media or semiquantitative slide-stix cultures. There is no reliable serologic technique for diagnosis.

TREATMENT

ACUTE GENERAL Rx

(UNCOMPLICATED)

TOPICAL BUTOCONAZOLE: 2% vaginal cream 5 g intravaginally for 3 days
- Butoconazole (sustained release)—5 gm intravaginally for 1 dose

TOPICAL CLOTRIMAZOLE:
- 1% cream 5 g intravaginally for 7 to 14 days
- 100-mg vaginal tablet for 7 days
- 100-mg vaginal tablets, two tablets for 3 days
- 500-mg vaginal tablet, single dose

TOPICAL MICONAZOLE:
- 2% cream 5 g intravaginally for 7 days
- 200-mg vaginal suppository for 3 days
- 100-mg vaginal suppository for 7 days

TOPICAL TIOCONAZOLE: 6.5% ointment 5 g intravaginally, single dose

TOPICAL TERCONAZOLE:
- 0.4% cream 5 g intravaginally for 7 days
- 0.8% cream 5 g intravaginally for 3 days
- 80-mg suppository for 3 days

ORAL FLUCONAZOLE: 150-mg single PO dose

CHRONIC Rx

Ketoconazole 400 mg PO qd or fluconazole 200 mg PO qd until symptoms resolve. Then maintenance on prophylactic doses of these agents for 6 mo (ketoconazole 100 mg/day, fluconazole 150 mg/wk).

DISPOSITION

If chronic or recurrent, consider screening for diabetes, HIV, or other immune deficiencies.

PEARLS & CONSIDERATIONS

COMMENTS

- Azoles are more effective than nystatin. Symptoms usually take 2 to 3 days to resolve. Adjunctive treatment with weak topical steroid such as 1% hydrocortisone cream may help with relief of symptoms.
- Creams and suppositories are oil based and may weaken latex condoms and diaphragms

SUGGESTED READINGS

Centers for Disease Control and Prevention: 2002 sexually transmitted diseases treatment guidelines, *MMWR Morb Mortal Wkly Rep* 51(RR-6), 2002.

Watson MC et al: Oral versus intra-vaginal imidazole and triazole anti-fungal treatment of uncomplicated vulvovaginal candidiasis (thrush), *Cochrane Database Syst Rev* (4):CD002845, 2001.

AUTHOR: **MARIA A. CORIGLIANO, M.D.**

BASIC INFORMATION

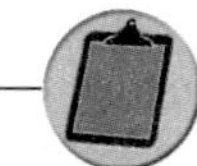

DEFINITION

Carbon monoxide is a colorless, odorless, tasteless, nonirritating gas. When inhaled it produces toxicity by causing cellular hypoxia.

ICD-9CM CODES
986 Carbon monoxide poisoning

EPIDEMIOLOGY & DEMOGRAPHICS

- Carbon monoxide poisoning is seen more frequently during the winter months.
- A leading cause of lethal poisoning in the U.S.

PHYSICAL FINDINGS & CLINICAL PRESENTATION

Depend on the severity and duration of exposure. The brain and heart are most sensitive to carbon monoxide poisoning.

- Presentation is often nonspecific. Mild to moderately severe poisoning may present with headache, fatigue, dizziness, nausea, dyspnea, confusion, or blurry vision. Severe poisoning may present with arrhythmias, myocardial ischemia, pulmonary edema, lethargy, ataxia, syncope, seizure, coma, or cherry-red skin.
- Symptoms of toxicity and prognosis do not correlate well with carboxyhemoglobin levels.

ETIOLOGY

Carbon monoxide toxicity results from tissue hypoxia and direct carbon monoxide mediated damage at the cellular level.

- Carbon monoxide binds to hemoglobin with an affinity 200 to 250 times greater than oxygen, thus displacing oxygen from hemoglobin and decreasing the oxygen-carrying capacity of blood.
- Carbon monoxide shifts the oxyhemoglobin curve to the left, thus decreasing oxygen release to tissue.
- Cellular respiration is depressed by inhibition of the mitochondrial cytochrome oxidase system.
- Cardiac function is depressed by direct binding to cardiac myoglobin.
- Neurologic toxicity is not explained by hypoxia alone and is thought to be related to the intracellular uptake of carbon monoxide, its role as a neural messenger, ischemic reperfusion injury of the brain, and delayed lipid peroxidation of brain tissue.

Carbon monoxide poisoning occurs when individuals are exposed to smoke from fires; motor vehicle exhaust; or the burning of wood, charcoal, or natural gas for cooking or heating in poorly ventilated areas.

- Methylene chloride (paint stripper) fumes are converted to carbon monoxide by the liver.

DIAGNOSIS

DIFFERENTIAL DIAGNOSIS

- Viral syndromes
- Cyanide
- Hydrogen sulfide
- Methemoglobinemia
- Amphetamines and derivatives
- Cocaine
- Cyclic antidepressants
- Phencyclidine (PCP)
- Phenothiazines
- Theophylline

WORKUP

History of exposure to carbon monoxide, physical examination, laboratory test

LABORATORY TESTS

- Carboxyhemoglobin level
  NOTE: CoHgb level >5% in nonsmoker confirms exposure. Heavy smokers may have levels of 10%
- Direct measurement of arterial oxygen saturation
  NOTE: Pulse oximetry and arterial blood gas may be falsely normal because neither measures oxygen saturation directly. Pulse oximetry is inaccurate because of the similar absorption characteristics of oxyhemoglobin and carboxyhemoglobin. An arterial blood gas is inaccurate because it measures oxygen dissolved in plasma (which is not affected by carbon monoxide) and then calculates oxygen saturation
- Electrolytes, glucose, BUN, creatinine, CPK, ABG (because lactic acidosis and rhabdomyolysis may develop)
- ECG (rule out ischemia)
- Pregnancy test (fetus at high risk)
- Consider toxicology screen

TREATMENT

ACUTE GENERAL Rx

- Remove from site of carbon monoxide exposure
- Ensure adequate airway
- Continuous ECG monitor
- 100% oxygen by tight-fitting nonrebreather mask or endotracheal tube (this decreases the half-life of carboxyhemoglobin from 4 to 6 hr to 60 to 90 min)
- Measure carboxyhemoglobin level every 2 to 4 hr
- Continue oxygen until carboxyhemoglobin level is less than 10%

Hyperbaric oxygen (3 ATM) decreases half-life of carbon monoxide to 20 to 30 min

- Controversial if there is any beneficial effect over regular 100% oxygen
- Recent study suggests patients with acute (<24 hr), symptomatic carbon monoxide poisoning treated with 3 hyperbaric O_2 sessions within 24 hr had lower rates of cognitive sequelae at 6 wk and 12 mo compared with those treated with normobaric O_2
- Consider for individuals with:
  1. Severe intoxication (carboxyhemoglobin >25%, neurologic symptoms or signs, ischemic ECG changes, severe metabolic acidosis, rhabdomyolysis, pulmonary edema, shock)
  2. Those who remain symptomatic after 2 to 4 hr of oxygen at room air
  3. Pregnant women with carboxyhemoglobin >15% or signs of fetal distress: lower threshold for treatment suggested given the higher affinity of carbon monoxide for fetal hemoglobin
- Consult local poison control center
- Consider concomitant poisoning with other toxic/irritant gases that may be present in smoke and/or thermal injury to the airway
- Identify source of exposure and determine if poisoning was accidental

DISPOSITION

- Depends on severity of exposure
- Survivors of severe poisoning are at 14% to 40% risk for neurologic sequelae ranging from parkinsonism to neuropsychiatric symptoms (personality and memory disorders). Neurologic deficits are usually apparent within 3 wk of poisoning, but may present months later. Brain MRI may show changes in the white matter and basal ganglia
- High risk of fetal demise

REFERRAL

- Regional poison control center
- +/− Hyperbaric chamber

SUGGESTED READINGS

Goldfrank LR et al: *Goldfrank's toxicologic emergencies,* ed 6, New York, 2002, McGraw-Hill.

Weaver LK et al: Hyperbaric oxygen for acute carbon monoxide poisoning, *N Engl J Med* 347:1057, 2002.

AUTHOR: **SUDEEP K. AULAKH, M.D., F.R.C.P.C.**

BASIC INFORMATION

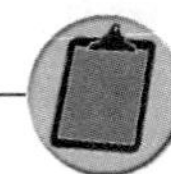

DEFINITION

Carcinoid syndrome is a symptom complex characterized by paroxysmal vasomotor disturbances, diarrhea, and bronchospasm. It is caused by the action of amines and peptides (serotonin, bradykinin, histamine) produced by tumors arising from neuroendocrine cells.

SYNONYMS

Flush syndrome
Argentaffinoma syndrome

ICD-9CM CODES
259.2 Carcinoid syndrome

EPIDEMIOLOGY & DEMOGRAPHICS

INCIDENCE: Carcinoid tumors are found incidentally in 0.5% to 0.75% of autopsies.

PHYSICAL FINDINGS & CLINICAL PRESENTATION

- Cutaneous flushing (75% to 90%)
  1. The patient usually has red-purple flushes starting in the face, then spreading to the neck and upper trunk.
  2. The flushing episodes last from a few minutes to hours (longer-lasting flushes may be associated with bronchial carcinoids).
  3. Flushing may be triggered by emotion, alcohol, or foods, or it may occur spontaneously.
  4. Dizziness, tachycardia, and hypotension may be associated with the cutaneous flushing.
- Diarrhea (>70%): often associated with abdominal bloating and audible peristaltic rushes
- Intermittent bronchospasm (25%): characterized by severe dyspnea and wheezing
- Facial telangiectasia
- Tricuspid regurgitation from carcinoid heart lesions

ETIOLOGY

- The carcinoid syndrome is caused by neoplasms originating from neuroendocrine cells.
- Carcinoid tumors are principally found in the following organs: appendix (40%); small bowel (20%; 15% in the ileum); rectum (15%); bronchi (12%); esophagus, stomach, colon (10%); ovary, biliary tract, pancreas (3%).
- Carcinoid tumors do not usually produce the syndrome unless liver metastases are present or the primary tumor does not involve the GI tract.

DIAGNOSIS

DIFFERENTIAL DIAGNOSIS

The carcinoid syndrome must be distinguished from idiopathic flushing (IF); patients with IF more often are females, younger, and with a longer duration of symptoms; palpitations, syncope, and hypotension occur primarily in patients with IF.

LABORATORY TESTS

- An algorithm for the diagnosis and treatment of carcinoid tumors is described in Section III.
- The biochemical marker for carcinoid syndrome is increased 24-hr urinary 5-hydroxyindoleacetic acid (5-HIAA), a metabolite of serotonin (5-hydroxytryptamine).
- False elevations can be seen with ingestion of certain foods (bananas, pineapples, eggplant, avocados, walnuts) and certain medications (acetaminophen, caffeine, guaifenesin, reserpine); therefore patients should be on a restricted diet and should avoid these medications when the test is ordered.
- Liver function studies are an unreliable indicator of liver involvement.

IMAGING STUDIES

- Chest x-ray examination is useful to detect bronchial carcinoids.
- CT scans of abdomen or a liver and spleen radionuclide scan is useful to detect liver metastases (palpable in >50% of cases).
- Iodine-123 labeled somatostatin (123-ISS) can detect carcinoid endocrine tumors with somatostatin receptors.
- Scanning with radiolabeled octreotide can visualize previously undetected or metastatic lesions.

TREATMENT

NONPHARMACOLOGIC THERAPY

Avoidance of ethanol ingestion (may precipitate flushing)

GENERAL Rx

- Surgical resection of the tumor can be curative if the tumor is localized or palliative and result in prolonged asymptomatic periods if metastases are present. Surgical manipulation of the tumor can, however, cause severe vasomotor abnormalities and bronchospasm (carcinoid crisis).
- Percutaneous embolization and ligation of the hepatic artery can decrease the bulk of the tumor in the liver and provide palliative treatment of tumors with hepatic metastases.
- Cytotoxic chemotherapy: combination chemotherapy with 5-fluorouracil and streptozotocin can be used in patients with unresectable or recurrent carcinoid tumors; however, it has only limited success.
- Control of clinical manifestations:
  1. Diarrhea usually responds to diphenoxylate with atropine (Lomotil).
  2. Flushing can be controlled by the combination of H_1- and H_2-receptor antagonists (e.g., diphenhydramine 25 to 50 mg PO q6h and ranitidine 150 mg bid).
  3. Somatostatin analogue (SMS 201-995) is effective for both flushing and diarrhea in most patients.
  4. Bronchospasm can be treated with aminophylline and/or albuterol.
- Nutritional support: supplemental niacin therapy may be useful to prevent pellagra, because the tumor uses dietary tryptophan for serotonin synthesis, resulting in a nutritional deficiency in some patients.
- Subcutaneous somatostatin analogues (octreotide 150 μg SC tid) have been used successfully for long-term control of symptoms in patients with unresectable neoplasms.
- Echocardiography and monitoring for right-sided CHF are recommended for patients with unresectable disease because endocardial fibrosis, involving predominantly the endocardium, chordae, and valves of the right side of the heart, can occur and result in right-sided CHF.

DISPOSITION

- Prognosis varies with the stage and location of the tumor.
- Carcinoids of the appendix and rectum have a low malignancy potential and rarely produce the clinical syndrome; metastases are also uncommon if the size of the primary lesion is <2 cm in diameter.

AUTHOR: **FRED F. FERRI, M.D.**

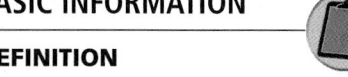

BASIC INFORMATION

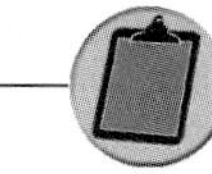

DEFINITION

Cardiac tamponade is a life-threatening, slow or rapid compression of the heart by fluid, blood, pus, or gas within the pericardial sac that impairs dilation and filling of the ventricles during diastole.

ICD-9CM CODES
423.9 Unspecified diseases of the pericardium

PHYSICAL FINDINGS & CLINICAL PRESENTATION

Acute cardiac tamponade (e.g., penetrating wounds, iatrogenic, aortic dissection)

1. Beck's triad
    a. Decrease in systemic arterial pressure
    b. Elevated central venous pressure
    c. Small, quiet heart

Chronic accumulating pericardial effusion leading to tamponade

1. Pericardial friction rub may be present
2. Tachypnea
3. Tachycardia (except in uremic or hypothyroid patients)
4. Raised jugular venous distention (prominent *x* descent with absent *y* descent) with peripheral venous distention in the forehead and scalp
5. Pulsus paradoxus defined as an inspiratory systolic fall in arterial pressure of 10 mm Hg or more during normal breathing
6. Soft heart sounds
7. May have absolute or relative hypotension

ETIOLOGY

Acute

1. Penetrating trauma
2. Aortic dissection
3. Myocardial rupture after treatment of MI with thrombolytics and/or heparin
4. Iatrogenic (central line and pacemaker insertions, postcoronary bypass surgery)

Chronic accumulating pericardial effusion leading to tamponade

1. Malignancy (e.g., lung, breast, lymphoma)
2. Viral pericarditis (e.g., coxsackie, HIV)
3. Uremia
4. Bacterial, fungal, and tuberculosis
5. Myxedema (rare)
6. Collagen-vascular disease (e.g., SLE, RA, scleroderma)
7. Radiation

DIAGNOSIS

DIFFERENTIAL DIAGNOSIS

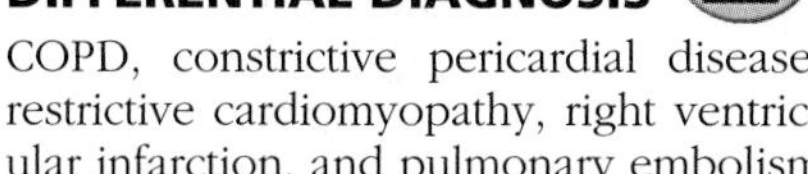

COPD, constrictive pericardial disease, restrictive cardiomyopathy, right ventricular infarction, and pulmonary embolism can all lead to elevated jugular venous pressure, decreased systemic pressure, and pulsus paradoxus.

WORKUP

Cardiac tamponade is a clinical diagnosis made at the bedside by noting the abovementioned physical findings. The echocardiogram will support the clinical diagnosis. Thereafter, one must pursue the etiology with specific laboratory work (see "Laboratory Tests").

LABORATORY TESTS

- Electrolytes, BUN, Cr, ESR, thyroid function tests, ANA, RF, PPD, blood cultures, viral titers, and pericardial fluid analysis and cultures will all help in identifying or excluding a possible etiology of the effusion leading to tamponade.
- 12-lead ECG findings are suggestive but not diagnostic.
    1. Low voltage (<5 mm QRS amplitude in the limb leads and <10 mm in the chest leads)
    2. PR depression or diffuse ST elevations if acute pericarditis is present
    3. Electrical alternans (alternating amplitude of the QRS complex in any or all leads)
    4. Sinus tachycardia

IMAGING STUDIES

- The chest x-ray examination is not very specific. The heart size can be normal in acute tamponade or massive (water bottle configuration) in slow-forming effusions. At least 200 ml of fluid must accumulate before the cardiac silhouette is affected.
- The echocardiogram can detect effusions as small as 20 ml and can strongly suggest tamponade physiology (collapse of the right atrium and right ventricle during diastole).
- Right-sided cardiac catheterization and intrapericardial pressure measurements confirm the diagnosis.
- Typical findings are diastolic equalization of pressures usually between 15 to 30 mm Hg (pulmonary artery pressure = right ventricular diastolic pressure = right atrial pressure = intrapericardial pressure).

TREATMENT

NONPHARMACOLOGIC THERAPY

Cardiac tamponade should be treated urgently. Avoid drugs that will reduce preload and exacerbate tamponade (e.g., nitrates, diuretics).

Large pericardial effusions without hemodynamic compromise can be managed conservatively with careful monitoring, treatment of the underlying cause, and surveillance echocardiography.

ACUTE GENERAL Rx

- The acute forms of tamponade as mentioned earlier (see "Etiology") usually require emergency pericardial fluid removal that is either catheter based or via surgical pericardiotomy.
- In the setting of cardiac arrest or code situation, one should also provide hemodynamic support with volume expansion (blood, saline, or dextran) and inotropic or vasopressor support.
- Avoid positive pressure ventilation and diuresis.

CHRONIC Rx

- Depends on etiology
- Semiacute treatment includes:
    1. Right-side heart catheter with pericardiocentesis. The catheter inside the pericardium can be left in place for 48 hr to allow for continued drainage until a more definitive procedure is performed or the etiology is resolved (e.g., dialysis for uremia, levothyroxine for myxedema).
- Other surgical drainage procedures include:
    1. Subxiphoid pericardial drainage
    2. Limited pericardiectomy draining the pericardial fluid into the left hemithorax
    3. Complete pericardiectomy

DISPOSITION

The prognosis of cardiac tamponade depends on the underlying cause.

REFERRAL

- Cardiology consultation is made if the clinical suspicion of tamponade exists.
- Cardiothoracic surgeon consultation should also be considered if clinically indicated.

PEARLS & CONSIDERATIONS

COMMENTS

As little as 200 ml of fluid can lead to acute cardiac tamponade, whereas in the chronic formation, the pericardial sac can hold up to 5 L of fluid before tamponade occurs.

SUGGESTED READINGS

Aikat S, Ghaffari S: A review of pericardial diseases: clinical, ECG and hemodynamic features and management, *Clev Clin J Med* 67(12):903, 2000.

Sagrista-Sauleda J, Angel J, Sanchez A et al: Effusive, constrictive pericarditis, *N Eng J Med* 350(5):469, 2004.

Spodick DH: Acute cardiac tamponade, *N Engl J Med* 349(7):684, 2003.

Spodick DH: Pathophysiology of cardiac tamponade, *Chest* 113(5):1372, 1998.

AUTHORS: **PRANAV M. PATEL, M.D.,** and **WEN-CHIH WU, M.D.**

 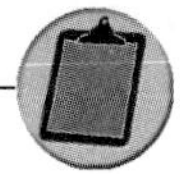

BASIC INFORMATION

DEFINITION

Cardiomyopathies are a group of diseases primarily involving the myocardium and characterized by myocardial dysfunction that is not the result of hypertension, coronary atherosclerosis, valvular dysfunction, or pericardial abnormalities. In dilated cardiomyopathy, the heart is enlarged, and both ventricles are dilated.

SYNONYMS

Congestive cardiomyopathy

ICD-9CM CODES
425.4 Other primary cardiomyopathies

EPIDEMIOLOGY & DEMOGRAPHICS

- The prevalence of dilated cardiomyopathy in the general adult population is approximately 1%.
- Incidence increases with age and approaches 10% at age 80 yr.

PHYSICAL FINDINGS & CLINICAL PRESENTATION

- Increased jugular venous pressure
- Small pulse pressure
- Pulmonary rales, hepatomegaly, peripheral edema
- S_3, S_4
- Mitral regurgitation, tricuspid regurgitation (less common)

ETIOLOGY

- Idiopathic
- Alcoholism (15% to 40% of all cases in Western countries)
- Collagen-vascular disease (SLE, RA, polyarteritis, dermatomyositis)
- Postmyocarditis
- Peripartum (last trimester of pregnancy or 6 mo postpartum)
- Heredofamilial neuromuscular disease
- Toxins (cobalt, lead, phosphorus, carbon monoxide, mercury, doxorubicin, daunorubicin)
- Nutritional (beriberi, selenium deficiency, carnitine deficiency, thiamine deficiency)
- Cocaine, heroin, organic solvents ("glue-sniffer's heart")
- Irradiation
- Acromegaly, osteogenesis imperfecta, myxedema, thyrotoxicosis, diabetes
- Hypocalcemia
- Antiretroviral agents (zidovudine, didanosine, zalcitabine)
- Phenothiazines
- Infections (viral [HIV], rickettsial, mycobacterial, toxoplasmosis, trichinosis, Chagas' disease)
- Hematologic (e.g., sickle cell anemia)

DIAGNOSIS

DIFFERENTIAL DIAGNOSIS

- Frank pulmonary disease
- Valvular dysfunction
- Pericardial abnormalities
- Coronary atherosclerosis
- Psychogenic dyspnea

WORKUP

- Chest x-ray examination, ECG, echocardiogram
- Medical history with emphasis on the following symptoms:
  1. Dyspnea on exertion, orthopnea, PND
  2. Palpitations
  3. Systemic and pulmonary embolism
- Cardiac troponin T levels: Persistently elevated troponin T levels are a marker of poor outcome in cardiomyopathy patients.

IMAGING STUDIES

CHEST X-RAY:
- Massive cardiac enlargement
- Interstitial pulmonary edema

ECG:
- Left ventricular hypertrophy with ST-T wave changes
- RBBB or LBBB
- Arrhythmias (atrial fibrillation, PVC, PAC, ventricular tachycardia)

ECHOCARDIOGRAM:
- Low ejection fraction with global akinesia

TREATMENT

NONPHARMACOLOGIC THERAPY

- Limit activity when CHF is present
- Treatment of underlying disease (SLE, alcoholism)

ACUTE GENERAL Rx

- Treat CHF (cause of death in 70% of patients) with sodium restriction, diuretics, ACE inhibitors, β-blockers, spironolactone, and digitalis.
- Vasodilators (combined with nitrates and ACE inhibitors) are effective agents in all symptomatic patients with left ventricular dysfunction
- Prevent thromboembolism with oral anticoagulants in all patients with atrial fibrillation and in patients with moderate or severe failure
- Low-dose β-blockade with carvedilol or other β-blockers may improve ventricular function by interrupting the cycle of reflex sympathetic activity and controlling tachycardia.
- Diltiazem and ACE inhibitors have also been reported to have a long-term beneficial effect in idiopathic dilated cardiomyopathy.
- Use antiarrhythmic treatment as appropriate. Empiric pharmacologic suppression of asymptomatic ventricular ectopy does not reduce risk of sudden death or improve long-term survival. In patients with severe left ventricular dysfunction and/or symptomatic and sustained ventricular tachycardia, the use of an automatic implantable cardioverter-defibrillator should be considered.
- Growth hormone administration has been shown to increase myocardial mass and reduce the size of the left ventricular chamber, resulting in improvement in hemodynamics and clinical status. This therapeutic approach remains controversial.
- Patients with dilated cardiomyopathy (LVEF <25%) and associated coronary atherosclerosis (angina, ECG changes, reversible defects on thallium scan) may benefit from surgical revascularization.

DISPOSITION

- Annual mortality is 20% in patients with moderate heart failure, and it exceeds 50% in patients with severe heart failure.
- The implantation of a cardioverter-defibrillator in patients with severe, nonischemic dilated cardiomyopathy already being treated with ACE inhibitors and β-blockers significantly reduces the risk of sudden death from arrhythmia.

REFERRAL

Consider heart transplant for young patients (<60 yr old) who are no longer responsive to medical therapy.

PEARLS & CONSIDERATIONS

COMMENTS

- Patients should be encouraged to restrict or eliminate alcohol and decrease sodium intake.
- Vulnerability to cardiomyopathy among chronic alcohol abusers is partially genetic and is related to the presence of angiotensin-converting-enzyme (ACE) DD genotype.

SUGGESTED READINGS

Kadish A et al: Prophylactic defibrillator implantation in patients with non-ischemic dilated cardiomyopathy, *N Engl J Med* 350:2151, 2004.

Lowes BD et al: Myocardial gene expression in dilated cardiomyopathy treated with beta-blocking agents, *N Engl J Med* 346:1357, 2002.

AUTHOR: **FRED F. FERRI, M.D.**

BASIC INFORMATION

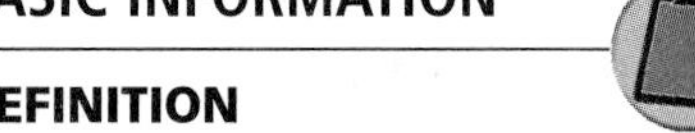

DEFINITION

Cardiomyopathies are a group of diseases primarily involving the myocardium and characterized by myocardial dysfunction that is not the result of hypertension, coronary atherosclerosis, valvular dysfunction, or pericardial abnormalities. In hypertrophic cardiomyopathy (HCM) there is marked hypertrophy of the myocardium and disproportionally greater thickening of the intraventricular septum than that of the free wall of the left ventricle (asymmetric septal hypertrophy [ASH]).

SYNONYMS

Idiopathic hypertrophic subaortic stenosis (IHSS)
Hypertrophic obstructive cardiomyopathy (HOCM)
ASH
HCM

ICD-9CM CODES
425.4 Cardiomyopathy, hypertrophic nonobstructive
425.1 Cardiomyopathy, hypertrophic obstructive
746.84 Cardiomyopathy, hypertrophic congenital

EPIDEMIOLOGY & DEMOGRAPHICS

- The disease occurs in two major forms:
  1. A familial form, usually diagnosed in young patients and gene mapped to chromosome 14q. It is caused by a missense mutation in 1 of at least 10 genes that encode the proteins of the cardiac sarcomere.
  2. A sporadic form, usually found in elderly patients
- The prevalence of phenotypically expressed HCM in the adult general population is 0.2% (most common genetic cardiovascular disease) and manifests with massive hypertrophy involving primarily the ventricular septum.

PHYSICAL FINDINGS & CLINICAL PRESENTATION

- Hypertrophic cardiomyopathy may be suspected on the basis of abnormalities found on physical examination. Classic findings include:
  1. Harsh, systolic, diamond-shaped murmur at the left sternal border or apex that increases with Valsalva maneuver and decreases with squatting
  2. Paradoxic splitting of S_2 (if left ventricular obstruction is present)
  3. S_4
  4. Double or triple apical impulse
- Increased obstruction can occur with:
  1. Drugs: digitalis, β-adrenergic stimulators (isoproterenol, dopamine, epinephrine), nitroglycerin, vasodilators, diuretics, alcohol
  2. Hypovolemia
  3. Tachycardia
  4. Valsalva maneuver
  5. Standing position
- Decreased obstruction is seen with:
  1. Drugs: β-adrenergic blockers, calcium channel blockers, disopyramide, α-adrenergic stimulators
  2. Volume expansion
  3. Bradycardia
  4. Hand grip exercise
  5. Squatting position
  - Clinical manifestations are as follows:
  1. Dyspnea
  2. Syncope (usually seen with exercise)
  3. Angina (decreased angina in recumbent position)
  4. Palpitations

ETIOLOGY

- Autosomal dominant trait with variable penetrance caused by mutations in any of 1 to 10 genes, each encoding proteins of cardiac sarcomere
- Sporadic occurrence

DIAGNOSIS

DIFFERENTIAL DIAGNOSIS

- Coronary atherosclerosis
- Valvular dysfunction
- Pericardial abnormalities
- Chronic pulmonary disease
- Psychogenic dyspnea

WORKUP

- The diagnosis can be confirmed by two-dimensional echocardiography. Continuous-wave Doppler echocardiography can be used to diagnose obstruction.
- ECG is abnormal in 75% to 95% of patients: left ventricular hypertrophy, abnormal Q waves in anterolateral and inferior leads.
- 24-hr Holter monitor to screen for potential lethal arrhythmias (principal cause of syncope or sudden death in obstructive cardiomyopathy) should be performed initially and annually.
- Exercise testing is indicated and can also provide prognostic information and should also be considered on an annual basis.

IMAGING STUDIES

- Chest x-ray: may be normal or may show cardiomegaly
- Two-dimensional echocardiography is used to establish the diagnosis. Findings include: ventricular hypertrophy, ratio of septum thickness to left ventricular wall thickness >1.3:1, increased ejection fraction.
- Magnetic resonance imaging may be of diagnostic value when echocardiographic studies are technically inadequate. MRI is also useful in identifying segmental LVH undetectable by echocardiography.

TREATMENT

NONPHARMACOLOGIC THERAPY

Advise avoidance of alcohol; alcohol use (even in small amounts) results in increased obstruction of the left ventricular outflow tract. Patients should also be advised on avoidance of dehydration and strenuous exertion.

GENERAL Rx

- Therapy for hypertrophic cardiomyopathy is directed at blocking the effect of catecholamines that can exacerbate dynamic left ventricualr outflow tract obstruction and avoidance of certain agents (e.g., vasodilator or diuretic agents), which can worsen the obstruction.
- Propranolol 160 to 240 mg/day. The beneficial effects of β-blockers on symptoms (principally dyspnea and chest pain) and exercise tolerance appear to be largely a result of a decrease in the heart rate with consequent prolongation of diastole and increased passive ventricular filling. By reducing the inotropic response, β-blockers may also lessen myocardial oxygen demand and decrease the outflow gradient during exercise, when sympathetic tone is increased.
- Verapamil also decreases left ventricular outflow obstruction by improving filling and probably reducing myocardial ischemia. It is used mainly as a second line agent in patients who cannot tolerate β-blockers. It should be used with caution in patients with symptomatic obstruction. Administration in the hospital setting is recommended in these patients.
- IV saline infusion in addition to propranolol or verapamil is indicated in patients with CHF.

- Disopyramide is a useful antiarrhythmic because it is also a negative inotrope resulting in further decrease in outflow gradient.
- Use antibiotic prophylaxis for surgical procedures.
- Avoid use of digitalis, diuretics, nitrates, and vasodilators.
- Encouraging results have been reported on the use of DDD pacing for hemodynamic and symptomatic benefit in patients with drug-resistant hypertrophic obstructive cardiomyopathy.
- Implantable defibrillators are a safe and effective therapy in HCM patients prone to ventricular arrhythmias. Their use is strongly warranted for patients with prior cardiac arrest or sustained spontaneous ventricular tachycardia. Implantation of a dual chamber pacemaker has not been shown to result in significant improvement in objective measures of exercise capacity.

DISPOSITION

HCM is not a static disease. Some adults may experience subtle regression in wall thickness while others (approximately 5% to 10%) paradoxically evolve into an end stage resembling dilated cardiomyopathy and characterized by cavity enlargement, LV wall thinning, and diastolic dysfunction. Patients with HCM are at increased risk of sudden death, especially if there is onset of symptoms during childhood. Left ventricular outflow at rest is also a strong, independent predictor of severe symptoms of heart failure and of death. Adult patients can be considered low risk if they have no symptoms or mild symptoms and also if they have none of the following:

- A family history of premature death caused by hypertrophic cardiomyopathy
- Nonsustained ventricular tachycardia during Holter monitoring
- A marked outflow tract gradient
- Substantial hypertrophy (>20 mm)
- Marked left atrial enlargement
- Abnormal blood pressure response during exercise

REFERRAL

- Surgical treatment (myotomy-myectomy involving resection of the basal septum) is reserved for patients who have both a large outflow gradient (≥50 mm Hg) and severe symptoms of heart failure that are unresponsive to medical therapy. The risk of sudden death from arrhythmias is not altered by surgery. When this operation is performed by experienced surgeons in tertiary referral centers the operative mortality is <2% and many patients are able to achieve near normal exercise capacity postoperatively.
- Nonsurgical reduction of interventricular septum represents a controversial therapeutic approach that can be used in patients with HCM refractory to pharmacologic treatment. This technique involves the injection of ethanol in the septal perforator branch of the left anterior descending coronary artery, producing a controlled myocardial infarction of the interventricular septum and thereby reducing the left ventricular outflow tract gradient. This method may lead to improvement in both subjective and objective measures of exercise capacity but is associated with a high incidence of heart block, often requiring permanent pacing in about one fourth of patients.

PEARLS & CONSIDERATIONS

COMMENTS

- Screening of first-degree relatives with two-dimensional echocardiography is indicated, particularly if adverse HCM-related events have occurred in the family. Annual screening is recommended for all adolescents from age 12 to 18. Periodic screening of all first-degree adult family members at 5-year intervals is recommended since hypertrophy may not be detected until the sixth decade of life.
- Future screening techniques may involve identification of mutations in the gene encoding the sarcomeric proteins.
- Mortality rate in HCM is approximately 1% to 2%.
- It is important to remember that HCM is predominantly a non-obstructive disease (75% of patients do not have a sizable resting outflow tract gradient).
- Patients should be instructed on need for bacterial endocarditis prophylaxis.

SUGGESTED READINGS

Maron BJ: Hypertrophic cardiomyopathy, a systematic review, *JAMA* 287:1308, 2002.

Maron MS et al: Effect of left ventricular outflow tract obstruction on clinical outcome in hypertrophic cardiomyopathy, *N Engl J Med* 348:295, 2003.

Nishimura RA, Holmes DR: Hypertrophic obstructive cardiomyopathy, *N Engl J Med* 350:1320, 2004.

Shamim W et al: Nonsurgical reduction of the interventricular septum in patients with hypertrophic cardiomyopathy, *N Engl J Med* 347:1326, 2002.

AUTHOR: **FRED F. FERRI, M.D.**

BASIC INFORMATION

DEFINITION

Cardiomyopathies are a group of diseases primarily involving the myocardium and characterized by myocardial dysfunction that is not the result of hypertension, coronary atherosclerosis, valvular dysfunction, or pericardial abnormalities. Restrictive cardiomyopathies are characterized by decreased ventricular compliance, usually secondary to infiltration of the myocardium.

ICD-9CM CODES
425.4 Other primary cardiomyopathies

EPIDEMIOLOGY & DEMOGRAPHICS

Relatively uncommon cardiomyopathy that is most frequently caused by amyloidosis (Fig. 1-48), myocardial fibrosis (after open heart surgery), and radiation

PHYSICAL FINDINGS & CLINICAL PRESENTATION

- Edema, ascites, hepatomegaly, distended neck veins
- Fatigue, weakness (secondary to low output)
- Kussmaul's sign: may be present
- Regurgitant murmurs
- Possible prominent apical impulse

ETIOLOGY

- Infiltrative and storage disorders (glycogen storage disease, amyloidosis, sarcoidosis, hemochromatosis)
- Scleroderma
- Radiation
- Endocardial fibroelastosis
- Endomyocardial fibrosis
- Idiopathic
- Toxic effects of anthracycline
- Carcinoid heart disease, metastatic cancers
- Diabetic cardiomyopathy
- Eosinophilic cardiomyopathy (Löffler's endocarditis)

DIAGNOSIS

DIFFERENTIAL DIAGNOSIS

- Coronary atherosclerosis
- Valvular dysfunction
- Pericardial abnormalities
- Chronic lung disease
- Psychogenic dyspnea

WORKUP

- Chest x-ray examination, ECG, echocardiogram
- Cardiac catheterization, MRI (selected cases)

IMAGING STUDIES

- Chest x-ray:
  1. Moderate cardiomegaly
  2. Possible evidence of CHF (pulmonary vascular congestion, pleural effusion)
- ECG:
  1. Low voltage with ST-T wave changes
  2. Possible frequent arrhythmias, left axis deviation, and atrial fibrillation
- Echocardiogram: increased wall thickness and thickened cardiac valves (especially in patients with amyloidosis)
- Cardiac catheterization to distinguish restrictive cardiomyopathy from constrictive pericarditis
  1. Constrictive pericarditis: usually involves both ventricles and produces a plateau of elevated filling pressures
  2. Restrictive cardiomyopathy: impairs the left ventricle more than the right (PCWP > RAP, PASP >50 mm Hg)
- MRI may also be useful to distinguish restrictive cardiomyopathy from constrictive pericarditis (thickness of the pericardium >5 mm in the latter)

TREATMENT

NONPHARMACOLOGIC THERAPY

Control CHF by restricting salt.

ACUTE GENERAL Rx

- Cardiomyopathy caused by hemochromatosis may respond to repeated phlebotomies to decrease iron deposition in the heart.
- Sarcoidosis may respond to corticosteroid therapy.
- Corticosteroid and cytotoxic drugs may improve survival in patients with eosinophilic cardiomyopathy.
- There is no effective therapy for other causes of restrictive cardiomyopathy.

CHRONIC Rx

Death usually results from CHF or arrhythmias; therefore therapy should be aimed at controlling CHF by restricting salt, administering diuretics, and treating potentially fatal arrhythmias.

DISPOSITION

Prognosis varies with the etiology of the cardiomyopathy.

REFERRAL

Cardiac transplantation can be considered in patients with refractory symptoms and idiopathic or familial restrictive cardiomyopathies.

AUTHOR: **FRED F. FERRI, M.D.**

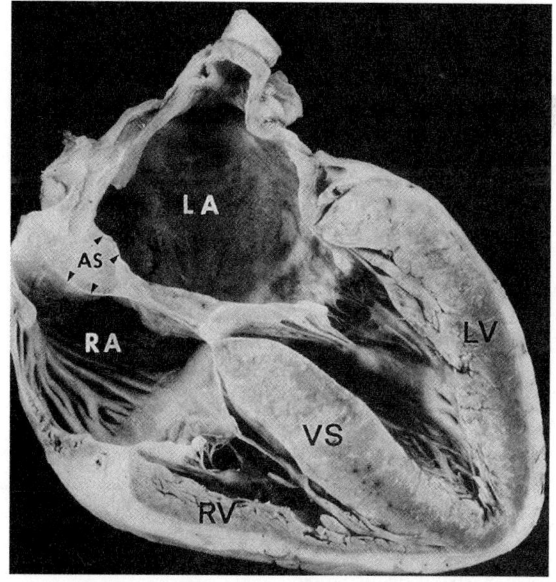

FIGURE 1-48 A necropsy specimen of an amyloid heart demonstrating the thickened ventricular septum *(VS)*, atrial septum *(AS)*, and free wall of the left ventricle *(LV)* and right ventricle *(RV)*, and the dilated left atrium *(LA)*. RA, Right atrium. (Courtesy Dr. William Edwards, Mayo Clinic, Rochester, MN. In Goldman L, Bennett JC [eds]: *Cecil textbook of medicine,* ed 22, Philadelphia, 2004, WB Saunders.)

BASIC INFORMATION

DEFINITION

Lightheadedness, dizziness, presyncope, or syncope in a patient with carotid sinus hypersensitivity is defined as *carotid sinus syndrome* (CSS). Carotid sinus hypersensitivity is the exaggerated response to carotid stimulation resulting in bradycardia, hypotension, or both.

SYNONYMS

Carotid sinus syncope
CSS

ICD-9CM CODES
337.0 Idiopathic peripheral autonomic neuropathy
Carotid sinus syncope or syndrome

EPIDEMIOLOGY & DEMOGRAPHICS

- Carotid sinus hypersensitivity accounts for 10% to 20% of presyncopal and syncopal episodes.
- Carotid sinus hypersensitivity is frequently associated with atherosclerosis.
- The incidence increases with age.
- Men are affected more often than women (2:1).
- Carotid sinus syndrome is rarely found before the age of 50 yr.

PHYSICAL FINDINGS & CLINICAL PRESENTATION

- Lightheadedness or presyncopal
- Syncope
- Usually associated with prodrome of nausea, warmth, pallor and/or diaphoresis
- Usually associated with sudden neck movements or tight fitting collars

Properly performed carotid sinus massage (CSM) at the bedside is diagnostic. This maneuver can elicit three types of responses in the appropriate patient (see Diagnosis).

1. Carotid sinus massage (CSM) should be done in the supine position while monitoring the patient's blood pressure by cuff and heart rate by ECG.
2. CSM should be performed on only one artery at a time.
3. CSM should be applied for approximately 5 sec.
4. The presence of carotid artery bruits or recent TIA or CVA is a relative contraindication to CSM.
5. Complications of visual disturbance and transient paresis occur in fewer than 1% of patients that CSM is performed upon.

ETIOLOGY

- Idiopathic
- Head and neck tumors (e.g., thyroid)
- Significant lymphadenopathy
- Carotid body tumors
- Prior neck surgery

DIAGNOSIS

- The diagnosis of CSS is made when carotid sinus hypersensitivity is diagnosed by CSM and no other cause of syncope is identified.
- CSM can elicit three types of responses that are diagnostic of carotid sinus hypersensitivity:
  1. Cardioinhibitory type: CSM producing asystole for at least 3 sec with reproduction of spontaneous symptoms and with abolition of symptoms when CSM is repeated after atropine infusion.
  2. Vasodepressor type: CSM producing (1) a decrease in systolic blood pressure of 50 mm Hg or 30 mm Hg in the presence of neurologic symptoms, (2) asystole is not exhibited and (3) neurologic symptoms remain unchanged after infusion of atropine.
  3. Mixed type: CSM producing both types of responses

DIFFERENTIAL DIAGNOSIS

Includes all causes of syncope, for example, cardiac tachyarrhythmias and bradyarrhythmias, cardiac valvular disease and obstructive cardiomyopathy, cerebrovascular events, seizures, drug-induced, autonomic dysfunction, orthostasis/hypovolemia, cough, micturition, hypoxemia, and hypoglycemia

WORKUP

The workup must exclude other causes of syncope as guided by the history and the physical examination. Blood tests, cardiac noninvasive studies (Holter, echocardiograms, ECG, tilt test, treadmill testing), cardiac invasive testing (electrophysiologic studies), EEG, and CT scan should be ordered in the appropriate clinical setting.

TREATMENT

NONPHARMACOLOGIC THERAPY

Avoidance of triggering factors such as straining or applying neck pressure from tight collars, shaving, or rapid head turning.

ACUTE GENERAL Rx

Treatment will vary according to the type of carotid hypersensitivity response (e.g., cardioinhibitory, vasodepressor, or mixed) and symptoms present (see Chronic Rx). Acute treatment is usually not needed, because most patients at presentation are hemodynamically stable but present with either a fall resulting in an injury (e.g., hip fracture, laceration) or a complaint of true syncope with no injury.

CHRONIC Rx

For asymptomatic carotid sinus hypersensitivity of either the cardioinhibitory or vasodepressor type, it is generally agreed that pacemaker implantation is not necessary.

It is necessary to ascertain the relative contribution of both cardioinhibitory and vasodepressor reflexes to CSS before concluding that permanent pacing is clinically indicated.

For patients with CSS with a cardioinhibitory response to CSM:

- Dual-chamber permanent pacemaker is indicated.
- Controversy exists as to whether to implant the pacemaker after the first syncopal episode or after a recurrent episode.

For patients with CSS with a vasodepressor response to CSM:

- Measures to maintain systolic blood pressure are tried:
  1. Sympathomimetics (ephedrine has been tried with success but has significant side effects, e.g., palpitations, tremors.)
  2. Fludrocortisone with its mineralocorticoid effect also has been tried with limited success.
  3. Elastic knee-high or thigh-high stockings help to maintain systolic blood pressure.
  4. Carotid sinus denervation is reserved for those patients refractory to the above mentioned treatment.

For patients with CSS with a mixed response to CSM:

- Dual-chamber permanent pacemaker and atropine can effectively treat the bradycardic response but have no major effect on the hypotensive response. The vasodepressor response should be treated as mentioned previously.

DISPOSITION

CSS occurs in the elderly population and presents with falls or syncope often resulting in injury. Up to 50% of the patients who present with symptoms will have recurrent symptoms. This is reduced in the group of patients for whom a pacemaker is indicated. In idiopathic cases there is no difference in survival in this group of patients when compared with the general population.

REFERRAL

Cardiology referral is indicated if a pacemaker is considered.

PEARLS & CONSIDERATIONS

COMMENTS

- The most common type of response to CSM in this population is cardioinhibitory response followed by mixed and vasodepressor responses.
- Prognosis depends on the underlying cause.

SUGGESTED READINGS

Goldschlanger N: Etiologic considerations in the patient with syncope and apparently normal heart, *Arch Intern Med* 163:151, 2003.

Kapoor WN: Current evaluation and management of syncope, *Circulation* 106(13):1606, 2002.

Kenny RA, Richardson DA: Carotid sinus syndrome and falls in older adults, *Am J Geriatr Cardiol* 10(2):97, 2001.

Puggioni E: Results and complications of the carotid sinus massage performed according to the "Methods of Symptoms," *Am J Cardio* 89:599, 2002.

AUTHORS: **PRANAV M. PATEL, M.D.,** and **WEN-CHIH WU, M.D.**

BASIC INFORMATION

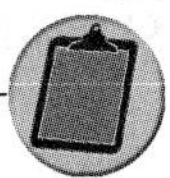

DEFINITION

Carpal tunnel syndrome is an entrapment neuropathy involving the median nerve at the wrist (Fig. 1-49). It is the most common entrapment neuropathy in the upper extremity.

ICD-9CM CODES
354.0 Carpal tunnel syndrome

EPIDEMIOLOGY & DEMOGRAPHICS

PREVALENT AGE: 30 to 60 yr (bilateral up to 50%)

PREVALENT SEX: Females are affected two to five times as often as males

PHYSICAL FINDINGS & CLINICAL PRESENTATION

- Nocturnal pain
- Occasional median nerve sensory impairment (often only index and long fingers)
- Positive Tinel's sign at wrist (tapping over the median nerve on the flexor surface of the wrist produces a tingling sensation radiating from the wrist to the hand)
- Positive Phalen's test (reproduction of symptoms after 1 min of gentle, unforced wrist flexion)
- Carpal compression test: Pressure with the examiner's thumb over the patient's carpal tunnel for 30 sec elicits symptoms
- Thenar atrophy in long-standing cases

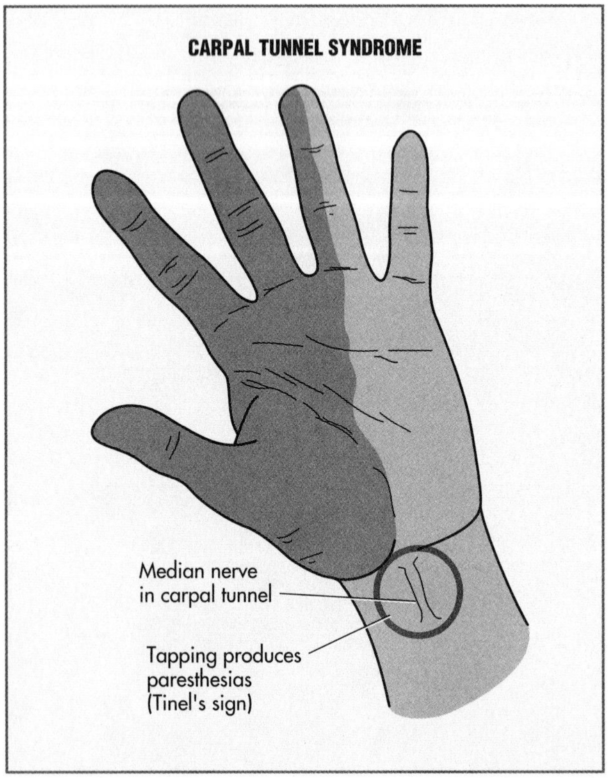

FIGURE 1-49 Distribution of pain and/or paresthesias (dark-shaded area) when the median nerve is compressed by swelling in the wrist (carpal tunnel). (From Arnett FC: Rheumatoid arthritis. In Andreoli TE [ed]: *Cecil essentials of medicine,* ed 4, Philadelphia, 1997, WB Saunders.)

ETIOLOGY

- Idiopathic in most cases
- Space-occupying lesions in carpal tunnel (tenosynovitis, ganglia, aberrant muscles)
- Often associated with hypothyroidism, hormonal changes of pregnancy
- Job-related mechanical overuse may be a risk factor
- Traumatic injuries to wrist

DIAGNOSIS

DIFFERENTIAL DIAGNOSIS

- Cervical radiculopathy
- Chronic tendinitis
- Vascular occlusion
- Reflex sympathetic dystrophy
- Osteoarthritis
- Other arthritides
- Other entrapment neuropathies

IMAGING STUDIES

Routine roentgenograms may be helpful in establishing cause or ruling out other conditions.

ELECTRODIAGNOSTIC STUDIES

Nerve conduction velocity tests and electromyography are useful in establishing the diagnosis and ruling out other syndromes.

TREATMENT

ACUTE GENERAL Rx

- Elimination of repetitive trauma
- Occupational splints or braces
- NSAIDs
- Injection of carpal canal on ulnar side of palmaris longus tendon at wrist flexor crease (avoiding median nerve)
- Low-dose oral corticosteroids (e.g., prednisolone 20 mg qd for 2 wk, followed by 10 mg qd for 2 more wk) are also effective for symptom relief in selected patients
- Stretching exercises

DISPOSITION

Prognosis is variable. Some cases resolve spontaneously. Relief from local injection appears transient and symptoms recur in the majority of cases following injection. Carpal tunnel syndrome is common in the third trimester of pregnancy, but symptoms subside after delivery in most cases, often dramatically. Symptoms may recur with subsequent pregnancies. Surgery is not recommended in pregnant patients because of the likelihood of spontaneous recovery.

REFERRAL

Surgical referral in cases of failed medical management or signs of motor weakness. Results of surgery usually excellent with return to full activity in 4-6 weeks.

SUGGESTED READINGS

Dias JJ, Burke FD et al: Carpal Tunnel Syndrome and work, *J Hand Surg* 29:329, 2004.

Geoghegan JM, Clark DI et al: Risk factors in carpal tunnel syndrome, *J Hand Surg* 29:315, 2004.

Gerritsen AM et al: Splinting vs surgery in the treatment of carpal tunnel syndrome, *JAMA* 288:1245, 2002.

Goodyear-Smith F, Arroll B: What can family physicians offer patients with carpal tunnel syndrome other than surgery? A systematic review of nonsurgical management, *Ann Fam Med* 2:267, 2004.

Hui AC, Wong SM et al: Long-term outcome of carpal tunnel syndrome after conservative treatment, *Int J Clin Pract* 58:337, 2004.

Katz JN, Simmons BP: Carpal tunnel syndrome, *N Engl J Med* 346:1807, 2002.

Lee DH, Claussen GC, Oh S: Clinical nerve conduction and needle electromyography studies, *J Am Acad Orthop Surg* 12:276, 2004.

Shum C et al: The role of fleyor tenosynovectomy in the operative treatment of carpal tunnel syndrome, *J Bone Joint Surg* 84(A):221, 2002.

Vjera AJ: Management of carpal tunnel syndrome, *Am Fam Physician* 68:265, 2003.

AUTHOR: **LONNIE R. MERCIER, M.D.**

BASIC INFORMATION

DEFINITION

Cataracts are the clouding and opacification of the normally clear crystalline lens of the eye. The opacity may occur in the cortex, the nucleus of the lens, or the posterior subcapsular region, but it is usually in a combination of areas.

SYNONYMS

Congenital cataracts (e.g., from rubella)
Metabolic cataracts (e.g., caused by diabetes)
Collagen-vascular disease cataracts (caused by lupus)
Hereditary cataracts
Age-related senile cataracts
Traumatic cataracts
Toxic or drug-induced cataracts (e.g., caused by steroids)

ICD-9CM CODES
366 Cataract

EPIDEMIOLOGY & DEMOGRAPHICS

INCIDENCE (IN U.S.): Highest cause of treatable blindness; cataract removal is the most frequent surgical procedure in patients >65 yr old (1.3 million operations/yr, with an annual cost of approximately $3 billion). By year 2020 expect over 30 million Americans to have cataracts. Of Americans >40, 20.5 million (17.2%) have cataracts. Of these, 5% have had surgery.

PREDOMINANT AGE: Elderly; some stage of cataract development is present in >50% of persons 65 to 74 yr old and 65% of those >75 yr old. Lens clouding begins at 39 to 40 yr old and then usually progresses either slowly or rapidly depending upon individual and health.

PEAK INCIDENCE:
- In early life: congenital and hereditary causes predominant
- In older age group: senile cataracts (after 40 yr of age)

GENETICS: Hereditary with such syndromes as galactosemia, homocystinuria, diabetes

PHYSICAL FINDINGS & CLINICAL PRESENTATION

Cloudiness and opacification of the crystalline lens of the eye (Fig. 1-50)

ETIOLOGY

- Heredity
- Trauma
- Toxins
- Age-related
- Drug-related
- Congenital
- Inflammatory
- Diabetes
- Collagen Vascular disease

DIAGNOSIS

DIFFERENTIAL DIAGNOSIS

- Corneal lesions
- Retinal lesions, detached retina, tumors
- Vitreous disease, chronic inflammation

WORKUP

- Complete eye examination, including slit lamp examination, funduscopic examination, and brightness acuity testing
- Complete physical exam for other underlying causes

LABORATORY TESTS

- Rarely, urinary amino acid screening and CNS imaging studies with congenital cataracts
- Fasting glucose in young adults with cataracts
- Diabetes, Cologen Vascular, other metabolic diseases in younger patients
- Genetic and hereditary evaluation

TREATMENT

There is no evidence that antioxidants or drugs will slow down or help cataracts.

NONPHARMACOLOGIC THERAPY

- Wait until vision is compromised before doing surgery.
- Surgery is indicated when corrected visual acuity in the affected eye is >20/30 in the absence of other ocular disease; however, surgery may be justified when visual acuity is better in specific situations (especially disabling glare, monocular diplopia). Surgery indicated when vision in one eye is greatly different from other and affects patient's life.

ACUTE GENERAL Rx

None necessary except when acute glaucoma or inflammation occurs.

CHRONIC Rx

- Change glasses as cataracts develop.
- Myopia is common, and glasses can be adjusted until surgery is contemplated.

DISPOSITION

Refer if sight compromised or inflamed red eye.

REFERRAL

Refer to ophthalmologist for evaluation extraction when vision is compromised (see Nonpharmacologic Therapy).

PEARLS & CONSIDERATIONS

Patients want to know five things about cataracts:
1. chance for vision improvement
2. when will vision improve
3. risk from surgery
4. effect of surgery
5. types of complications

COMMENTS

Success rate with surgery is 95% to 98%.

SUGGESTED READINGS

Congdon N et al: Prevalence of cataract and pseudophakia/aphakia among adults in the US, *Arch Ophthalmol* 122(4)487, 2004.
Consultation section: Cataract surgical problem, *J Cataract Refract Surg* 28:577, 2002.
Solomon R, Donninfeld ED: Recent advances and future frontiers in treating age-related cataracts, *JAMA* 290:248, 2003.
Wong TY et al: Relation of ocular trauma to cortical, nuclear and posterior subcapsular cataracts, *Br J Ophthalmol* 86:152, 2002.

AUTHOR: **MELVYN KOBY, M.D.**

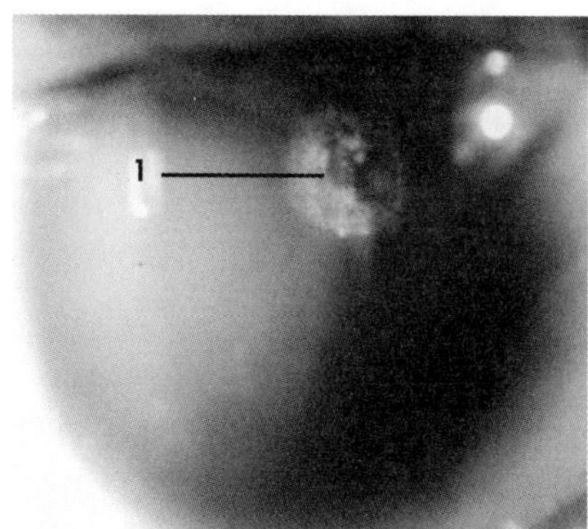

FIGURE 1-50 The central location of a posterior subcapsular cataract *(1).* (From Palay D [ed]: *Ophthalmology for the primary care physician,* St Louis, 1997, Mosby.)

BASIC INFORMATION

DEFINITION

Cat-scratch disease (CSD) is a syndrome consisting of gradually enlarging regional lymphadenopathy occurring after contact with a feline. Atypical presentations are characterized by a variety of neurologic manifestations as well as granulomatous involvement of the eye, liver, spleen, and bone. The disease is usually self-limiting, and recovery is complete; however, patients with atypical presentations, especially if immunocompromised, may suffer significant morbidity and mortality.

SYNONYMS

Cat-scratch fever
Benign inoculation lymphoreticulosis
Nonbacterial regional lymphadenitis

ICD-9CM CODES
078.3 Cat-scratch disease

EPIDEMIOLOGY & DEMOGRAPHICS

PREVALENCE: Unknown
INCIDENCE (IN U.S.):
- Unknown
- Majority of reported cases in children

PEAK INCIDENCE: August through January
GENETICS: Unknown

PHYSICAL FINDINGS & CLINICAL PRESENTATION

- Classic, most common finding: regional lymphadenopathy occurring within 2 wk of a scratch or contact with felines
- Tender, swollen lymph nodes most commonly found in the head and neck, followed by the axilla and the epitrochlear, inguinal, and femoral areas
- Erythematous overlying skin, showing signs of suppuration from involved lymph nodes
- On careful examination; evidence of cutaneous inoculation in the form of a nonpruritic, slightly tender pustule or papule (Fig. 1-51)
- Fever in most patients
- Malaise and headache in fewer than a third of patients
- Atypical presentations in fewer than 15% of cases
  1. Usually in association with lymphadenopathy and a low-grade or frank fever (>101° F, >38.3° C)
  2. Include granulomatous involvement of the conjunctiva (Parinaud's oculoglandular syndrome) and focal masses in the liver, spleen, and mesenteric nodes
- CNS involvement: neuroretinitis, encephalopathy, encephalitis, transverse myelitis, seizure activity, and coma
- Osteomyelitis in adults and children

ETIOLOGY

- Major cause: *Bartonella (Rochalimaea) henselae*
- Mode of transmission: predominantly by direct inoculation through the scratch, bite, or lick of a cat, especially a kitten
- Limited evidence in support of an arthropod (flea) as an alternative vector of infection arising from bacteremic felines
- Rarely, associated with dogs, monkeys, and inanimate objects with which a feline has been in recent contact
- Approximately 2 wk after introduction of the bacteria into the host, regional lymphatic tissues displaying granulomatous infiltration associated with gradual hypertrophy
- Possible dissemination to distant sites (e.g., liver, spleen, and bone), usually characterized by focal masses or discrete parenchymal lesions

DIAGNOSIS

DIFFERENTIAL DIAGNOSIS

Granulomas of this syndrome must be differentiated from those associated with tularemia, tuberculosis, sarcoidosis, sporotrichosis, toxoplasmosis, lymphogranuloma venerum, fungal diseases, and benign and malignant tumors.

WORKUP

Diagnosis should be considered in patients who present with a predominant complaint of gradually enlarging regional (focal) lymphadenopathy, often with fever and a recent history of having contact with a cat.

LABORATORY TESTS

- Three of four of the following criteria are required:
  1. History of animal contact in the presence of a scratch, dermal, or eye lesion
  2. Culture of lymphatic aspirate that is negative for other causes
  3. Positive CSD skin test
  4. Biopsied lymph node histology consistent with CSD
- Enhanced culture techniques and serologies will augment establishment of the diagnosis.
- Histopathologically, Warthin-Starry silver stain has been used to identify the bacillus.
- Routine laboratory findings:
  1. Mild leukocytosis or leukopenia
  2. Infrequent eosinophilia
  3. Elevated ESR
- Abnormalities of bilirubin excretion and elevated hepatic transaminases are usually secondary to hepatic obstruction by granuloma, mass, or lymph node.
- In patients with neurologic manifestations, lumbar puncture usually reveals normal CSF, although there may be a mild pleocytosis and modest elevation in protein.
- The diagnosis may be confirmed by specific enzyme immunoassay (EIA) in association with a history of cat contact and a typical clinical presentation.

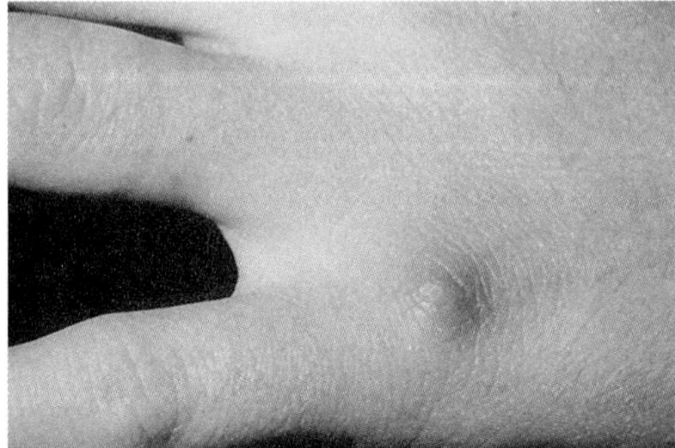

FIGURE 1-51 Primary lesion of cat-scratch disease is a tender papule occurring 3 to 10 days after a scratch. (From Noble J [ed]: *Primary care medicine,* ed 2, St Louis, 1996, Mosby.)

TREATMENT

NONPHARMACOLOGIC THERAPY

- Warm compresses to the affected nodes
- In cases of encephalitis or coma: supportive care

ACUTE GENERAL Rx

- There is no consensus over therapy, especially as the disease is self-limited in a majority of cases.
- It would be prudent to treat severely ill patients, especially if immunocompromised, with antibiotic therapy, because these patients tend to suffer dissemination of infection and increased morbidity.
- *Bartonella* is usually sensitive to aminoglycosides, tetracycline, erythromycin, and the quinolones.
- When the isolate is proven by culture, the patient should receive antibiotic therapy as directed by the obtained sensitivities.
- Antipyretics and NSAIDs may also be used.

DISPOSITION

Overall prognosis is good.

REFERRAL

- To an appropriate subspecialist to evaluate specific lesions
- For diagnostic aspiration or excision in presence of regional lymph-adenopathy, bone lesions, and mesenteric lymph nodes and organs
- To ophthalmologist for ocular granulomas
  1. Usually diagnosed clinically
  2. Rarely require excision

PEARLS & CONSIDERATIONS

COMMENTS

- A presentation of this syndrome, especially in patients with HIV infection or impaired cellular immunity, may be fever of unknown origin.
- Hepatic and splenic granulomas, coronary valve infections may offer few physical clues to diagnosis, emphasizing the need for a complete history.
- CSD should be considered in the differential diagnosis of school-aged children presenting with status epilepticus.
- Chronically immunocompromised patients considering the acquisition of a young feline should be made aware of the possible risk of infection.
- No signs of illness may be apparent in bacteremic kittens.

SUGGESTED READINGS

Gonzalez BE et al: Cat-scratch disease occurring in three siblings simultaneously, *Pediatr Infect Dis J* 22(5):467, 2003.

Koehler JE et al: Prevalence of Bartonella infection among human immunodeficiency virus-infected patients with fever, *Clin Infect Dis* 37(4):559, 2003.

Metzkor-Cotter E et al: Long-term serological analysis and clinical follow-up of patients with cat scratch disease, *Clin Infect Dis* 37(9):1149, 2003.

Mirakhur B et al: Cat scratch disease presenting as orbital abscess and osteomyelitis, *J Clin Microbiol* 41(8):3991, 2003.

Resto-Ruiz S, Burgess A, Anderson BE: The role of the host immune response in pathogenesis of Bartonella henselae, *DNA Cell Biol* 22(6):431, 2003.

Rolain JM et al: Cat scratch disease with lymphadenitis, vertebral osteomyelitis, and spleen abscesses, *Ann N Y Acad Sci* 990:397, 2003.

Rolain JM et al: Detection by immunofluorescence assay of Bartonella henselae in lymph nodes from patients with cat scratch disease, *Clin Diagn Lab Immunol* 10(4):686, 2003.

AUTHOR: **GEORGE O. ALONSO, M.D.**

Cavernous Sinus Thrombosis (PTG)

BASIC INFORMATION

DEFINITION

Cavernous sinus thrombosis (CST) is an uncommon diagnosis usually stemming from infections of the face or paranasal sinuses resulting in thrombosis of the cavernous sinus and inflammation of its surrounding anatomic structures, including cranial nerves III, IV, V (ophthalmic and maxillary branch), and VI, and the internal carotid artery.

SYNONYMS

Intracranial venous sinus thrombosis or thrombophlebitis

ICD-9CM CODES
325 Phlebitis and thrombophlebitis of intracranial venous sinus

EPIDEMIOLOGY & DEMOGRAPHICS

- Cavernous sinus thrombosis is rare in the postantibiotic era.
- Before antibiotics the mortality rate from cavernous sinus thrombosis was 80% to 100%.
- With antibiotics and early diagnosis, the mortality rates have fallen to <20%.
- Reported morbidity rates have also declined from between 50% and 70% to about 22% with improved methods of diagnosis and treatment.

PHYSICAL FINDINGS & CLINICAL PRESENTATION

- The clinical presentation of CST can be varied. Both acute, fulminant disease and indolent, subacute presentations have been reported in the literature.
- The most common signs of CST are related to anatomical structures affected within the cavernous sinus, notably cranial nerves III-VI, as well as symptoms resulting from impaired venous drainage from the orbit and eye.
- Classic presentations are abrupt onset of unilateral periorbital edema, headache, photophobia, and proptosis.

Other common signs and symptoms include:

- Ptosis
- Chemosis
- Cranial nerve palsies (III, IV, V, VI)
  1. Sixth nerve palsy is the most common.
  2. Sensory deficits of the ophthalmic and maxillary branch of the fifth nerve are common. Periorbital sensory loss and impaired corneal reflex may be noted.

Papilledema, retinal hemorrhages, and decreased visual acuity and blindness may occur from venous congestion within the retina.

- Fever, tachycardia, sepsis may be present.
- Headache with nuchal rigidity may occur.
- Pupil may be dilated and sluggishly reactive.

Infection can spread to contralateral cavernous sinus within 24-48 hr of initial presentation.

ETIOLOGY

- CST most commonly results from contiguous spread of infection from the sinuses (sphenoid, ethmoid, or frontal) or middle third of the face. Less common primary sites of infection include dental abscess, nares, tonsils, soft palate, middle ear, or orbit (orbital cellulitis).
- The highly anastomotic and valveless venous system of the paranasal sinuses allows retrograde spread of infection to the cavernous sinus via the superior and inferior ophthalmic veins.
- *Staphylococcus aureus* is the most common infectious microbe, found in 50% to 60% of the cases.
- *Streptococcus* is the second leading cause.
- Gram-negative rods and anaerobes may also lead to cavernous sinus thrombosis.
- Rarely, *Aspergillus fumigatus* and mucormycosis cause CST.

DIAGNOSIS

- The diagnosis of cavernous sinus thrombosis is made clinically, with imaging studies to confirm the clinical impression.
- Proptosis, ptosis, chemosis, and cranial nerve palsy beginning in one eye and progressing to the other eye establish the diagnosis.

DIFFERENTIAL DIAGNOSIS

- Orbital cellulitis
- Internal carotid artery aneurysm
- CVA
- Migraine headache
- Allergic blepharitis
- Thyroid exophthalmos
- Brain tumor
- Meningitis
- Mucormycosis
- Trauma

WORKUP

Cavernous sinus thrombosis is a clinical diagnosis with laboratory tests and imaging studies confirming the clinical impression.

LABORATORY TESTS

- CBC, ESR, blood cultures, and sinus cultures help establish and identify an infectious primary source.
- Lumbar puncture is necessary to rule out meningitis.

IMAGING STUDIES

- Sinus films are helpful in the diagnosis of sphenoid sinusitis. Opacification, sclerosis, and air-fluid levels are typical findings.
- Contrast-enhanced CT scan may reveal underlying sinusitis, thickening of the superior ophthalmic vein, and irregular filling defects within the cavernous sinus; however, findings may be normal early in the disease course.
- MRI using flow parameters and an MR venogram are more sensitive than CT scan, and are the imaging studies of choice to diagnose cavernous sinus thrombosis. Findings may include deformity of the internal carotid artery within the cavernous sinus, and an obvious signal hyperintensity within thrombosed vascular sinuses on all pulse sequences.
- Cerebral angiography can be performed, but it is invasive and not very sensitive.
- Orbital venography is difficult to perform, but it is excellent in diagnosing occlusion of the cavernous sinus.

TREATMENT

NONPHARMACOLOGIC THERAPY

Recognizing the primary source of infection (i.e., facial cellulitis, middle ear, and sinus infections) and treating the primary source expeditiously is the best way to prevent cavernous sinus thrombosis.

ACUTE GENERAL Rx

- Broad-spectrum intravenous antibiotics are used until a definite pathogen is found.
  1. Nafcillin 1.5 g IV q4h
  2. Cefotaxime 1.5 to 2 g IV q4h
  3. Metronidazole 15 mg/kg load followed by 7.5 mg/kg IV q6h

- Vancomycin may be substituted for Nafcillin if significant concern exists for infection by methicillin-resistant *Staphylococcus aureus* or resistant *Streptococcus pneumoniae*.
- Appropriate therapy should take into account the primary source of infection as well as possible associated complications such as brain abscess, meningitis, or subdural empyema.
- Anticoagulation with heparin is controversial. Retrospective studies show conflicting data. This decision should be made with subspecialty consultation.
- Steroid therapy is also controversial and is not recommended by many sources.

CHRONIC Rx

- Surgical drainage with sphenoidotomy is indicated if the primary site of infection is thought to be the sphenoid sinus.
- All patients with CST are usually treated with prolonged courses (3-4 wk) of IV antibiotics. If there is evidence of complications such as intracranial suppuration, 6-8 wk of total therapy may be warranted.
- All patients should be monitored for signs of complicated infection, continued sepsis, or septic emboli while antibiotic therapy is being administered.

DISPOSITION

- Cavernous sinus thrombosis can be a life-threatening, rapidly progressive infectious disease with high morbidity and mortality rates despite antibiotic use.
- Complications of untreated CST include extension of thrombus to other dural venous sinuses, carotid thrombosis with concomitant strokes, subdural empyema, brain abscess, or meningitis. Septic embolization may also occur to the lungs, resulting in ARDS, pulmonary abscess, empyema, and pneumothorax.
- Complications in treated patients include oculomotor weakness, blindness, pituitary insufficiency, and hemiparesis.

REFERRAL

If the diagnosis is suspected, this should be considered a medical emergency. Depending on the primary site of infection, appropriate consultation should be made (i.e., ENT, ophthalmology, and infectious disease).

PEARLS & CONSIDERATIONS

COMMENTS

Realizing the cavernous sinus lies just above and lateral to the sphenoid sinus and drains the middle portion of the face via the superior and inferior ophthalmic veins and knowing that cranial nerves III, IV, V, and VI pass alongside or through the cavernous sinus make the clinical findings and diagnosis easier to understand.

SUGGESTED READINGS

Cannon ML et al: Cavernous sinus thrombosis complicating sinusitis, *Pediatr Crit Care Med* 5(1):86, 2004.

Ebright JR et al: Septic thrombosis of the cavernous sinuses, *Arch Intern Med* 161:2671, 2001.

AUTHORS: **JASON IANNUCCILL, M.D.** and **PETER PETROPOULOS, M.D.**

BASIC INFORMATION

DEFINITION

Celiac disease is a chronic disease characterized by malabsorption and diarrhea precipitated by ingestion of food products containing gluten.

SYNONYMS

Gluten-sensitive enteropathy
Celiac sprue

ICD-9CM CODES
579.0 Celiac disease

EPIDEMIOLOGY & DEMOGRAPHICS

- Estimates of the incidence and prevalence of celiac sprue in the U.S. range from 50 to 500 cases/100,000 persons; it is highest in whites of northern European ancestry (1 in 300).
- Incidence is highest during infancy and the initial 36 mo (secondary to the introduction of foods containing gluten), in the third decade (frequently associated with pregnancy and severe anemia during pregnancy), and in the seventh decade.
- There is a slight female predominance.

PHYSICAL FINDINGS & CLINICAL PRESENTATION

- Physical examination may be entirely within normal limits.
- Weight loss, dyspepsia, short stature, and failure to thrive may be noted in children and infants.
- Weight loss, fatigue, and diarrhea are common in adults.
- Abdominal pain, nausea, and vomiting are unusual.
- Pallor as a result of iron deficiency anemia is common.
- Manifestations of calcium deficiency, such as tetany and seizures, are rare and can be exacerbated by coexistent magnesium deficiency.
- Angular cheilitis, aphthous ulcers, atopic dermatitis, and dermatitis herpetiformis are frequently associated with celiac disease.

ETIOLOGY

- Celiac sprue results from an inappropriate T-cell-mediated immune response against ingested gluten in genetically predisposed people. There is sensitivity to gliadin, a protein fraction of gluten found in wheat, rye, and barley.
- Recently a peptide that resists degradation by proteases in the small bowel was identified as the potential triggering molecule.

DIAGNOSIS

DIFFERENTIAL DIAGNOSIS

- IBD
- Laxative abuse
- Intestinal parasitic infestations
- Other: irritable bowel syndrome, tropical sprue, chronic pancreatitis, Zollinger-Ellison syndrome, cystic fibrosis (children), lymphoma, eosinophilic gastroenteritis, short bowel syndrome, Whipple's disease

WORKUP

Evaluation consists of laboratory tests followed by upper GI endoscopy with biopsy of duodenum or proximal jejunum.

LABORATORY TESTS

- Iron deficiency anemia (microcytic anemia, low ferritin level)
- Folic acid deficiency
- Vitamin B_{12} deficiency, hypomagnesemia, hypocalcemia
- Antigliadin IgA and IgG antibodies are elevated in >90% of patients; however, they are nonspecific. IgA endomysial antibodies are more specific for celiac sprue and are the best screening test for celiac disease, except in the case of patients with IgA deficiency. Tissue transglutinase autoantibody by ELISA is a newer serologic test for celiac sprue
- Biopsy of the small bowel is generally recommended to establish the diagnosis. It reveals absence or shortening of villi, intraepithelial lymphocytes, and crypt lengthening and hyperplasia. Several biopsy specimens should be obtained for proper diagnosis
- Tests for malabsorption are abnormal: fecal fat estimation for 72 hr is elevated (>7 g/day), D-xylose testing reveals malabsorption of sugar

IMAGING STUDIES

- Barium studies are usually unnecessary. Typical radiologic features include dilation of the small intestine with thickening or obliteration of the mucosal folds.
- Capsule endoscopy can also be used to evaluate the small intestinal mucosa, especially if future innovations will allow mucosal biopsy.

TREATMENT

NONPHARMACOLOGIC THERAPY

Patients should be instructed on gluten-free diet (avoidance of wheat, rye, and barley). Recent studies show that oats do not damage the mucosa in celiac disease.

GENERAL Rx

- Correct nutritional deficiencies with iron, folic acid, calcium, vitamin B_{12} as needed.
- Prednisone 20 to 60 mg qd gradually tapered is useful in refractory cases.
- Lifelong gluten-free diet is necessary.

DISPOSITION

- Prognosis is good with adherence to gluten-free diet. Rapid improvement is usually seen within a few days of treatment.
- Serial antigliadin or antiendomysial antibody tests can be used to monitor the patient's adherence to a gluten-free diet.
- Repeat small bowel biopsy following treatment generally reveals significant improvement. It is also useful to evaluate for increased risk of small bowel T-cell lymphoma in these patients (10%), especially in untreated patients.

REFERRAL

GI referral for small bowel biopsy.

PEARLS & CONSIDERATIONS

COMMENTS

- Some experts recommend a repeat biopsy only in selected patients who have an unsatisfactory response to a strict gluten-free diet.
- Celiac disease should be considered in patients with unexplained metabolic bone disease or hypocalcemia, especially because GI symptoms may be absent or mild. Clinicians should also consider testing children and young adults for celiac disease if unexplained weight loss, abdominal pain or distention, or chronic diarrhea is present.
- The prevalence of celiac disease in patients with dyspepsia is twice that of the general population. Screening for celiac disease should be considered in all patients with persistent dyspepsia.
- Celiac disease is associated with an increased risk for non-Hodgkin's lymphoma, especially of T-cell type and primarily localized in the gut.

SUGGESTED READINGS

Farrell RJ, Kelly CP: Celiac sprue, *N Engl J Med* 346:180, 2002.
Fasano A: Celiac disease, how to handle a clinical chameleon, *N Eng J Med* 348: 2568, 2003.
Hoffenberg EJ et al: A prospective study of the incidence of childhood celiac disease, *J Pediatr* 143:308, 2003.
Shan L et al: Structural basis for gluten intolerance in celiac sprue, *Science* 297:2275, 2002.

AUTHOR: **FRED F. FERRI, M.D.**

BASIC INFORMATION

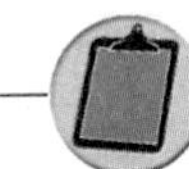

DEFINITION

Cellulitis is a superficial inflammatory condition of the skin. It is characterized by erythema, warmth, and tenderness of the area involved.

SYNONYMS

Erysipelas (cellulitis generally secondary to group A β-hemolytic streptococci)

ICD-9CM CODES
682.9 Cellulitis

EPIDEMIOLOGY & DEMOGRAPHICS

- Occurs most frequently in diabetics, immunocompromised hosts, and patients with venous and lymphatic compromise.
- Frequently found near skin breaks (trauma, surgical wounds, ulcerations, tinea infections). Edema, animal or human bites, subadjacent osteomyelitis, and bacteremia are potential sources of cellulites

PHYSICAL FINDINGS & CLINICAL PRESENTATION

Variable with the causative organism

- Erysipelas: superficial-spreading, warm, erythematous lesion distinguished by its indurated and elevated margin; lymphatic involvement and vesicle formation are common.
- Staphylococcal cellulitis: area involved is erythematous, hot, and swollen; differentiated from erysipelas by nonelevated, poorly demarcated margin; local tenderness and regional adenopathy are common; up to 85% of cases occur on the legs and feet.
- *H. influenzae* cellulitis: area involved is a blue-red/purple-red color; occurs mainly in children; generally involves the face in children and the neck or upper chest in adults.
- *Vibrio vulnificus:* larger hemorrhagic bullae, cellulitis, lymphadenitis, myositis; often found in critically ill patients in septic shock.

ETIOLOGY

- Group A β-hemolytic streptococci (may follow a streptococcal infection of the upper respiratory tract)
- Staphylococcal cellulitis
- *H. influenzae*
- *Vibrio vulnificus:* higher incidence in patients with liver disease (75%) and in immunocompromised hosts (corticosteroid use, diabetes mellitus, leukemia, renal failure)
- *Erysipelothrix rhusiopathiae:* common in people handling poultry, fish, or meat
- *Aeromonas hydrophila:* generally occurring in contaminated open wound in fresh water
- Fungi *(Cryptococcus neoformans):* immunocompromised granulopenic patients
- Gram-negative rods *(Serratia, Enterobacter, Proteus, Pseudomonas):* immunocompromised or granulopenic patients

DIAGNOSIS

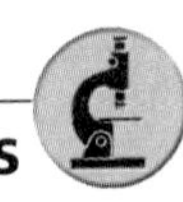

DIFFERENTIAL DIAGNOSIS

- Necrotizing fasciitis
- DVT
- Peripheral vascular insufficiency
- Paget's disease of the breast
- Thrombophlebitis
- Acute gout
- Psoriasis
- Candida intertrigo
- Pseudogout
- Osteomyelitis
- Insect bite
- Fixed drug eruption
- Rare causes: Vaccinia vaccination, Kawasaki disease, Well's syndrome, pyoderma gangrenosa, Sweet's syndrome, carcinoma erysipeloides, anaerobic myonecrosis

WORKUP

Physical examination and laboratory evaluation

LABORATORY TESTS

- Gram stain and culture (aerobic and anaerobic)
  1. Aspirated material from:
     a. Advancing edge of cellulitis
     b. Any vesicles
  2. Swab of any drainage material
  3. Punch biopsy (in selected patients)
- Blood cultures in hospitalized patients, in patients who have cellulitis superimposed on lymphedema, in patients with buccal or periorbital cellulitis, and in patients suspected of having a salt-water or fresh-water source of infection. Bacteremia is uncommon in cellulitis (positive blood cultures in only 4% of patients)
- ALOS titer (in suspected streptococcal disease)

Despite the previous measures, the cause of cellulitis remains unidentified in most patients.

IMAGING STUDIES

Radiologic examination is unnecessary in most cases of cellulitis. CT or MRI in patients with suspected necrotizing fasciitis (deep-seated infection of the subcutaneous tissue that results in the progressive destruction of fascia and fat).

TREATMENT

NONPHARMACOLOGIC THERAPY

Immobilization and elevation of the involved limb. Cool sterile saline dressings to remove purulence from any open lesion. Support stockings in patients with peripheral edema.

ACUTE GENERAL Rx

Erysipelas
- PO: dicloxacillin 500 mg PO q6h
- IV: cefazolin 1 g q6-8h or nafcillin 1.0 or 1.5 g IV q4-6h

NOTE: Use erythromycin, cephalosporins, clindamycin, or vancomycin in patients allergic to penicillin.

Staphylococcus cellulitis
- PO: dicloxacillin 250 to 500 mg qid
- IV: nafcillin, 1 to 2 g q4-6h
- Cephalosporins (cephalothin, cephalexin, cephradine) also provide adequate antistaphylococcal coverage except for MRSA
- Use vancomycin 1.0-2.0 g IV qd or linezolid 0.6 g IV q12h in patients allergic to penicillin or cephalosporins and in patients with methicillin-resistant *S. aureus* (MRSA). Daptomycin (Cubicin), a cyclic lipopeptide can be used as an alternative to vancomycin for complicated skin and skin structure infections. Usual dose is 4 mg/kg IV given over 30 min every 24 hr.

H. influenzae cellulitis
- PO: cefixime or cefuroxime
- IV: cefuroxime or ceftriaxone

Vibrio vulnificus
- Doxycycline 100 mg IV or PO bid +/− third-generation cephalosporin. Ciprofloxacin is an alternative antibiotic
- IV support and admission into ICU (mortality rate >50% in septic shock)

Erysipelothrix
- Penicillin

Aeromonas hydrophila
- Aminoglycosides
- Chloramphenicol
- Complicated skin and skin structure infections in hospitalized patients can be treated with daptomycin (cubicin) 4 mg/kg IV every 24 hr

DISPOSITION

Prognosis is good with prompt treatment.

REFERRAL

For surgical debridement in addition to antibiotics in patients with suspected necrotizing fasciitis

SUGGESTED READING

Swartz MN: Cellulitis, *N Engl J Med* 350:904, 2004.

AUTHOR: **FRED F. FERRI, M.D.**

Cerebral Palsy

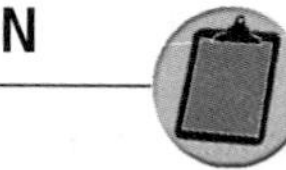

BASIC INFORMATION

DEFINITION

Cerebral palsy is a group of disorders of the central nervous system characterized by aberrant control of movement or posture, present since early in life and not the result of a recognized progressive or degenerative disease.

SYNONYMS

- Little's disease
- Congenital static encephalopathy
- Congenital spastic paralysis

ICD-9CM CODES
343 Infantile cerebral palsy
343.9 Infantile cerebral palsy, unspecified

EPIDEMIOLOGY & DEMOGRAPHICS
INCIDENCE (IN U.S.): 2-2.5 per 1000 live births
PREDOMINANT SEX: Male = female
PREDOMINANT AGE: Diagnosis made at 3-5 yr

PHYSICAL FINDINGS & CLINICAL PRESENTATION

- Monoplegia, diplegia, quadriplegia, hemiplegia
- Often hypotonic in newborn period, followed by development of hypertonia
- Spasticity
- Athetosis
- Delay in motor milestones
- Hyperreflexia
- Seizures
- Mental retardation

ETIOLOGY

Mulitfactorial, including low birthweight, congenital malformation, asphyxia, multiple gestation, intrauterine exposure to infection, neonatal stroke, hyperbilirubinemia

DIAGNOSIS

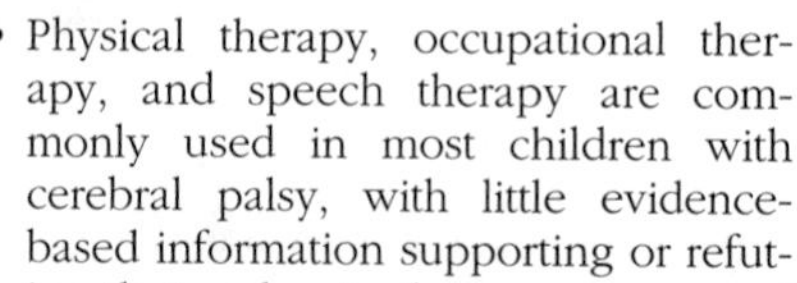

A clinical diagnosis always involves a motor deficit. Usual presenting complaint is that child is not reaching motor milestones at the appropriate chronological age. Medical history establishes that the child is not losing function. This history, combined with a neurological examination establishing that motor deficit is due to a cerebral abnormality, establishes the diagnosis of CP. Serial examinations may be necessary if the history is unreliable.

DIFFERENTIAL DIAGNOSIS

Other causes of neonatal hypotonia include muscular dystrophies, spinal muscular atrophy, Down syndrome, spinal cord injuries

WORKUP

- Laboratory tests are not necessary to establish the diagnosis, as it is based on history and physical examination.
- Workup is helpful for assessment of recurrence risk, implementation of prevention programs and medicolegal purposes.

IMAGING STUDIES

- Neuro-imaging is recommended if the etiology has not been established previously; for example, by perinatal imaging.
- MRI, when available, is preferred to CT scanning because of higher yield in suggesting an etiology, and timing of the insult leading to CP.

LABORATORY TESTS

- Metabolic and genetic testing should be considered if on follow-up, the child has (1) evidence of deterioration or episodes of metabolic decompensation, (2) no etiology determined by neuro-imaging, (3) family history of childhood neurologic disorder associated with CP, (4) developmental malformation on neuro-imaging
- If previous stroke seen on neuroimaging, consider evaluation for coagulopathy.
- An EEG should be obtained when a child with CP has a history suggestive of epilepsy, but is not recommended for the purpose of determining the etiology of CP.
- Children with CP should be screened for ophthalmologic and hearing impairments, speech and language disorders. Nutrition, growth and swallowing function should be monitored.

TREATMENT

NONPHARMACOLOGIC THERAPY

- Physical therapy, occupational therapy, and speech therapy are commonly used in most children with cerebral palsy, with little evidence-based information supporting or refuting their value in the management of cerebral palsy.
- Physical therapy is used to maintain or improve joint range of motion, facilitate weak muscles, inhibit spastic muscles and improve motor development and function.
- Orthotics and casting are used to increase musculotendinous length.

ACUTE GENERAL Rx

If present, treatment of seizures

CHRONIC Rx

- Treatment of seizures, as directed by seizure type. Initial treatment of partial seizures includes carbamazepine and oxcarbazepine. Treatment for generalized seizures includes dilantin and valproate.
- Intrathecal Baclofen is used for treatment of spasticity. Indications include arm and leg spasticity interfering with function. Each patient should undergo intrathecal baclofen trial before implantation of baclofen pump.
- Botulinum toxin A is also used for treatment of spasticity. Botulinum toxin A can be injected intramuscularly to produce selective and reversible chemodenervation at the neuromuscular junction. The amount depends on formulation of toxin, size of muscle, number of neuromuscular junctions, size, and weight of patient. Reported doses range from 2 to 29 units/kg.
- Surgical reduction of spasticity by dorsal rhizotomy, tendon lengthening and osteotomy.

REFERRAL

If the child has difficulty with spasticity, physical medicine and rehabilitation referrals are especially helpful.

PEARLS & CONSIDERATIONS

In full-term infants, history of traumatic delivery is usually not present.

SUGGESTED READINGS

Ashwal S et al: Practice parameter: diagnostic assessment of the child with cerebral palsy: report of the Quality Standards Subcommittee of the American Academy of Neurology and the Practice Committee of the Child Neurology Society, *Neurology* 62(6):851, 2004.

Koman LA, Smith BP, Shilt JS: Cerebral palsy, *Lancet* 363:1619, 2004.

Kuban KC, Leviton A: Cerebral palsy, *N Engl J Med* 330(3):188, 1994.

Nelson KB: The epidemiology of cerebral palsy in term infants, *Ment Retard Dev Disabil Res Rev* 8(3):146, 2002.

AUTHOR: **MAITREYI MAZUMDAR, M.D.**

BASIC INFORMATION

DEFINITION

Cervical cancer is penetration of the basement membrane and infiltration of the stroma of the uterine cervix by malignant cells.

ICD-9CM CODES
180 Malignant neoplasm of cervix uteri

EPIDEMIOLOGY & DEMOGRAPHICS

INCIDENCE: There are approximately 15,000 new cases annually, with 4000 to 5000 associated deaths. The U.S. has an age-adjusted mortality of 2.6 cases/ 100,000 persons for cervical cancer.
PREDOMINANCE: Higher incidence rates occur in developing countries. Among the U.S. population, Hispanics have a higher incidence than African Americans, who likewise have a higher incidence than whites.
RISK FACTORS: Smoking, early age at first intercourse, multiple sexual partners, immunocompromised state, nonbarrier methods of birth control, infection with high-risk HPV (types 16 and 18), multiparity.

PHYSICAL FINDINGS & CLINICAL PRESENTATION

- Unusual vaginal bleeding, particularly postcoital
- Vaginal discharge and/or odor
- Advanced cases may present with lower extremity edema or renal failure
- In early stages there may be little or no obvious cervical lesion, more advanced cases may present with large, bulky, friable lesions encompassing the majority of the vagina (Fig. 1-52)

ETIOLOGY

- Dysplastic cells progress to invasive carcinoma.
- Thought to be linked to the presence of HPV types 16, 18, 45, and 56 via interaction of E6 oncoproteins on p53 gene product.
- There may be an association between past infection with *Chlamydia trachomatis.*

DIAGNOSIS

DIFFERENTIAL DIAGNOSIS

- Cervical polyp or prolapsed uterine fibroid
- Preinvasive cervical lesions
- Neoplasia metastatic from a separate primary

WORKUP

- Thorough history and physical examination
- Pelvic examination with careful rectovaginal examination
- Colposcopy with directed biopsy and endocervical curettage
- Clinically staged, not surgically staged

LABORATORY TESTS

- CBC, chemistry profile
- Squamous cell carcinoma (SCC) antigen in research setting
- Carcinoembryonic antigen (CEA)

IMAGING STUDIES

- Chest x-ray examination
- IVP
- Depending on stage, may need cystoscopy, sigmoidoscopy or BE, CT scan or MRI, lymphangiography

TREATMENT

NONPHARMACOLOGIC THERAPY

- FIGO stage Ia: cone biopsy or simple hysterectomy
- FIGO stage Ib or IIa: type III radical hysterectomy and pelvic lymphadenectomy *or* pelvic radiation therapy
- Advanced or bulky disease: multimodality therapy (radiation, chemotherapy, and/or surgery); platinum use before radiation therapy as a fertizer

FIGURE 1-52 Carcinoma of cervix (gross specimen). (From Mishell D [ed]: *Comprehensive gynecology,* ed 3, St Louis, 1997, Mosby.)

ACUTE GENERAL Rx

Cervical cancer may present with massive and acute vaginal bleeding requiring volume and blood replacement, vaginal packing or other hemostatic modalities, and/or high-dose local radiotherapy.

CHRONIC Rx

- Physical examination with Pap smear every 3 mo for 2 yr, every 6 mo during the third to fifth year, and annually thereafter
- Chest x-ray examination annually

DISPOSITION

Five-year survival varies by stage:
- Stage I 60% to 90%
- Stage II 40% to 80%
- Stage III <60%
- Stage IV <15%

Early detection by Pap smear imperative to long-term improvements in survival.

REFERRAL

Gynecologic oncologist for all invasive disease

SUGGESTED READINGS

Anttila T et al: Serotypes of *Chlamydia trachomatis* and risk for development of cervical squamous cell carcinoma, *JAMA* 285:47, 2001.

Morris M et al: Pelvic radiation with concurrent chemotherapy compared with pelvic and para-aortic radiation for high-risk cervical cancer, *N Engl J Med* 340:1137, 1999.

Nuono J et al: New tests for cervical cancer screening, *Am Fam Physician* 64:780, 2001.

AUTHOR: **GIL FARKASH, M.D.**

BASIC INFORMATION

DEFINITION

Cervical disk syndromes refer to diseases of the cervical spine resulting from disk disorder, either herniation or degenerative change (spondylosis). When posterior osteophytes compress the anterior spinal cord, lower extremity symptoms may result, a condition termed *cervical spondylotic myelopathy*.

ICD-9CM CODES
722.4 Degenerative intervertebral cervical disk
722.71 Degenerative cervical disk with myelopathy

EPIDEMIOLOGY & DEMOGRAPHICS

PREVALENCE: 10% of general adult population (symptoms in 50% of population at some time in their life)
PREDOMINANT SEX: Male = female
PREDOMINANT AGE: 30 to 60 yr

PHYSICAL FINDINGS & CLINICAL PRESENTATION

- Neck pain, radicular symptoms, or myelopathy, either alone or in combination
- Limited neck movement
- Pain with neck motion, especially extension
- Referred unilateral interscapular pain, resulting in a local trigger point
- Radicular arm pain (usually unilateral), numbness, and tingling possible, most commonly involving the C6 (C5-C6 disk) or C7 (C6-C7 disk) nerve root
- Weakness and reflex changes (C6—biceps, C7—triceps)
- Myelopathy possibly resulting in gait disturbance, weakness, and even spasticity
- Sensory examination usually not helpful

ETIOLOGY

Unknown

DIAGNOSIS

DIFFERENTIAL DIAGNOSIS

- Rotator cuff tendinitis
- Carpal tunnel syndrome
- Thoracic outlet syndrome
- Brachial neuritis

A differential diagnosis for evaluation of neck pain is described in Section II.

WORKUP

In most cases, the diagnosis can be established on a clinical basis alone.
Section III, Cervical Disk Syndrome, describes an algorithm for a workup of suspected cases.

IMAGING STUDIES

- Plain roentgenograms within the first few weeks
  1. Usually normal in soft disk herniation
  2. With chronic degenerative disk disease, usually loss of height of the disk space, anterior and posterior osteophyte formation, and encroachment on the intervertebral foramen by osteophytes
- Myelography, CT scanning, and MRI indicated in patients whose symptoms do not resolve or when other spinal pathology suspected
- Electrodiagnostic studies to confirm the diagnosis or rule out peripheral nerve disorders

TREATMENT

NONPHARMACOLOGIC THERAPY

- Rest and cervical collar if needed
- Local modalities such as heat
- Physical therapy (Fig. 1-53)
- Avoid extreme range of motion exercises in degenerative disk disease

ACUTE GENERAL Rx

- NSAIDs
- "Muscle relaxants" for their sedative effect
- Analgesics as needed
- Epidural steroid injection for radicular pain

DISPOSITION

- Usually improve with time
- Surgical intervention in <5%

REFERRAL

Orthopedic or neurosurgical consultation for intractable pain or neurologic deficit

PEARLS & CONSIDERATIONS

COMMENTS

- Pain relief with physical therapy seems anecdotal and short-lived; any overall improvement usually parallels what would have probably occurred naturally.
- Sometimes carpal tunnel syndrome and cervical radiculopathy occur together; this is termed the *double-crush syndrome* and results from nerve compression at two separate levels. Proximal compression may decrease the ability of the nerve to tolerate a second, more distal compression.
- Surgical intervention is indicated primarily for relief of radicular pain caused by nerve root compression or for the treatment of myelopathy; it is generally not helpful when chief complaint is neck pain alone.
- In many cases of cervical spondylosis with myelopathy, the lower-extremity symptoms are much more disabling than the neck symptoms, a situation that can cause some difficulty in determining their etiology.

SUGGESTED READINGS

Benzel EC: Adjacent level disease, *J Neurosurg Spine* 100:1, 2004.
Edwards CC et al: Cervical myclopathy: current diagnostic and treatment strategies, *Spine* 3:68, 2003.
Emery SE: Cervical spondylotic myelopathy: diagnosis and treatment, *Am Acad Orthop Surg* 9:376, 2001.
Gorski JM, Schwartz LH: Shoulder impingement presenting as neck pain, *J Bone Joint Surg* 85A:635, 2003.
Nagano A et al: Surgical treatment of cervical myelopathy in patients aged over 80 years, *Orthopedics* 27:45, 2004.
Robinson LR: Role of neurophysiologic evaluation in diagnosis, *J Am Acad Orthop Surg* 8:190, 2000.

AUTHOR: **LONNIE R. MERCIER, M.D.**

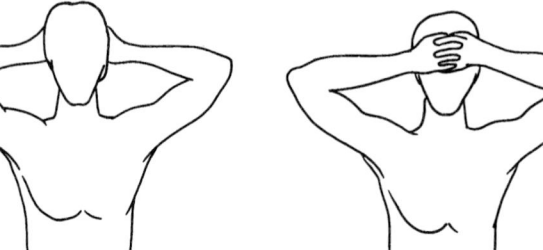

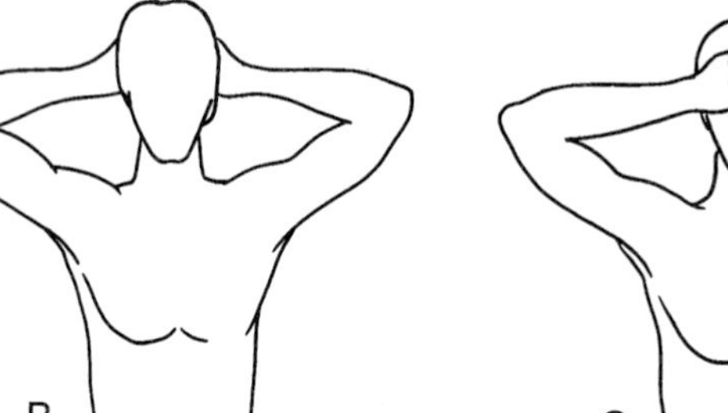

FIGURE 1-53 Isometric neck exercises. A, The hand is placed against the side of the head slightly above the ear, and pressure is gradually increased while resisting with the neck muscles and keeping the head in the same position. The position is held 5 sec, relaxed, and repeated five times. **B,** The exercise is performed on the other side and then from the back and front (C). The exercise should be performed three to four times daily. (From Mercier LR [ed]: *Practical orthopedics,* ed 4, St Louis, 1995, Mosby.)

BASIC INFORMATION

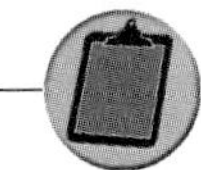

DEFINITION

Cervical dysplasia refers to atypical development of immature squamous epithelium that does not penetrate the basement epithelial membrane. Characteristics include increased cellularity, nuclear abnormalities, and increased nuclear to cytoplasm ratio. A progressive polarized loss of squamous differentiation exists beginning adjacent to the basement membrane and progressing to the most advanced stage (severe dysplasia), which encompasses the complete squamous epithelial layer thickness (Fig. 1-54).

Classification systems:

Modified Papanicolaou: Class I, II, III, IV, and V

Dysplasia: Normal, atypia (mild, moderate, and severe), carcinoma in situ, and cancer

CIN: Normal, atypia (CIN I, II, or III), and cancer

BETHESDA 2001 UPDATED CLASSIFICATION:

Interpretation/result (including specimen adequacy)

- Negative for intraepithelial lesion or malignancy
- Organisms (i.e., *Trichomonas vaginalis, Candida* sp., bacterial vaginosis), reactive cellular changes (inflammation), atrophy
- Epithelial cell abnormalities: atypical squamous cells (ASC), of undetermined significance (ASC-US), cannot exclude HSIL (ASC-H), LSIL (CIN 1 and HPV), HSIL (CIN 2 & 3, CIS), squamous cell carcinoma
- Glandular cell abnormalities: atypical glandular cells (AGC): *(specify endocervical, endometrial,* or *NOS),* atypical glandular cells, favor neoplastic *(specify endocervical, endometrial,* or *NOS)* endocervical adenocarcinoma in situ (AIS), adenocarcinoma
- Other: endometrial cells in a woman 40 yr of age

SYNONYMS

Class III or class IV Pap smear

Cervical intraepithelial neoplasia (CIN)

Low-grade or high-grade squamous intraepithelial lesion (LGSIL or HGSIL)

ICD-9CM CODES

622.1 Dysplasia of cervix (uteri)

EPIDEMIOLOGY & DEMOGRAPHICS

PEAK INCIDENCE:

- Age 35 yr
- Abnormal Pap smear rate revealing dysplasia approximates 2% to 5%, depending on population risk factors and false-negative rate variance
- False-negative rate approaching 40%
- Average age-adjusted incidence of severe dysplasia 35 cases/100,000 persons

PREVALENCE:

- Dysplasia: peak age, 26 yr (3600 cases/100,000 persons)
- CIS: peak age, 32 yr (1100 cases/100,000 persons)
- Invasive cancer: peak age, 77 yr (800 cases/100,000 persons)

PHYSICAL FINDINGS & CLINICAL PRESENTATION

- Cervical lesions associated with dysplasia usually are not visible to the naked eye; therefore physical findings are best viewed by colposcopy of a 3% acetic acid–prepared cervix.
- Patients evaluated by colposcopy are identified by abnormal cervical cytology screening from Pap smear screening
- Colposcopic findings:
  1. Leukoplakia (white lesion seen by the unaided eye that may represent condyloma, dysplasia, or cancer)
  2. Acetowhite epithelium with or without associated punctation, mosaicism, abnormal vessels
  3. Abnormal transformation zone (abnormal iodine uptake, "cuffed" gland openings)

ETIOLOGY

- Not clearly elucidated
- May be caused by abnormal reserve cell hyperplasia resulting in atypical metaplasia and dysplastic epithelium
- Strongly associated and initiated by oncogenic HPV infection (high-risk HPV types 16, 18, 31, 33, 35, 45, 51, 52, 56, and 58; low-risk HPV types 6, 11, 42, 43, and 44)

Risk factors:

1. Any heterosexual coitus
2. Coitus during puberty (T-zone metaplasia peak)
3. DES exposure
4. Multiple sexual partners
5. Lack of prior Pap smear screening

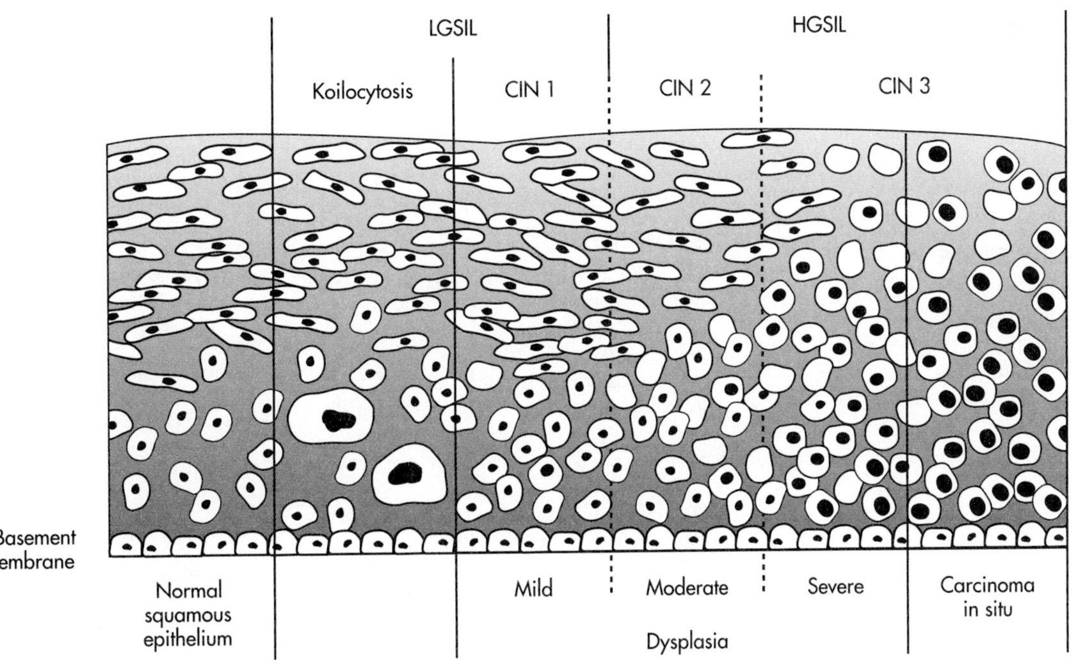

FIGURE 1-54 Diagram of cervical epithelium showing various terminologies used to characterize progressive degrees of cervical epithelium. (From Mishell D [ed]: *Comprehensive gynecology,* ed 3, St Louis, 1997, Mosby.)

6. History of STD
7. Other genital tract neoplasia
8. HIV
9. TB
10. Substance abuse
11. "High-risk" male partner (HPV)
12. Low socioeconomic status
13. Early first pregnancy
14. Tobacco use
15. HPV

DIAGNOSIS

DIFFERENTIAL DIAGNOSIS

- Metaplasia
- Hyperkeratosis
- Condyloma
- Microinvasive carcinoma
- Glandular epithelial abnormalities
- Adenocarcinoma in situ
- VIN
- VAIN
- Metastatic tumor involvement of the cervix

WORKUP

Periodic history and physical examination (including cytologic screening), depending on age, risk factors, and history of preinvasive cervical lesions

- Consider screening for sexually transmitted disease (Gc, *Chlamydia,* VDRL, HIV, HPV)
- Abnormal cytology (HSIL/LSIL, initial ASC/ASC-US/ASC-H in high-risk patients, recurrent in low-risk/postmenopausal patients) and grossly evident suspicious lesions; refer for colposcopy and possible directed biopsy/ECC (examination should include cervix, vagina, vulva, and anus)
- For glandular cell abnormalities (AGC): refer for colposcopy and possible directed biopsy/ECC, and consider endometrial sampling
- In pregnancy: abnormal cytology followed by colposcopy in the first trimester and at 28 to 32 wk; only high-grade lesions suspect for cancer biopsied; ECC contraindicated

LABORATORY TESTS

- Gc, *Chlamydia* to rule out STD
- Pap cytology screening (requires appropriate sampling, preparation, cytologist interpretation and reporting)
- Colposcopy and directed biopsy, ECC for indications (see Workup)
- HPV-DNA typing if identified abnormal cytology

IMAGING STUDIES

- Cervicography
- Computer-enhanced Pap cytology screening (e.g., PAPNET)

TREATMENT

NONPHARMACOLOGIC THERAPY

- Superficial ablative techniques (cryosurgery, CO_2 laser, and electrocoagulation diathermy) considered for colposcopy-identified dysplasia (moderate to severe dysplasia or CIS) and negative ECC; mild dysplasia followed conservatively in a compliant patient
- Cone biopsy (LEEP, CO_2 laser, "cold knife" cone biopsy) considered for colposcopy-identified dysplasia (moderate to severe dysplasia or CIS) and positive ECC or if there is a two-grade or more discrepancy between the Pap smear, colposcopy, and biopsy or ECC findings
- Hysterectomy if patient has completed child bearing and has persistent or recurrent severe dysplasia or CIS
- In pregnancy: treatment for cervical dysplasia deferred until after delivery

ACUTE GENERAL Rx

Topical 5-fluorouracil (5-FU) is rarely used for recurrent cervicovaginal lesions.

CHRONIC Rx

- Because of the risk for persistent and recurrent dysplasia, long-term follow-up is individualized based on patient risk factors, Pap smear and colposcopy results, treatment history, and presence of high-risk HPV (e.g., Pap smear q3-4mo/yr, then q6mo/1 yr, then annually [if all normal], or repeat colposcopy examination and treat as indicated).
- Mild dysplasia with negative ECC should be followed conservatively in a compliant patient as a majority of these lesions persist or regress.

DISPOSITION

- Because of the large numbers of women in high-risk groups, the prevalence of HPV, and the high false-negative Pap smear rate, routine Pap smear screening should be reinforced for all women, especially those with a history of cervical dysplasia.
- Success rates for treatment approach 80% to 90%.
- Detection of persistence of recurrence requires careful follow-up.
- Cervical treatment possibly results in infertility (cervical stenosis or incompetence), which requires careful consideration and discretion for use of LEEP and cone biopsy.
- Appropriate counseling and informed consent needed when considering any form of management of cervical dysplasia.
- There has been no case of cervical dysplasia progressing to invasive cancer with appropriate screening, diagnosis, treatment, and follow-up.

REFERRAL

- Patients with abnormal Pap cytology should not be followed by repeat Pap smear screening.
- Patients with identified abnormal cytology should be evaluated by a skilled colposcopist (defined as documented didactic and preceptorship training including 50 cases of identified pathology, ongoing colposcopy activity with a minimum of 2 cases/wk, Q.A. log, and periodic CME).
- If treatment is required, patient should be referred to a gynecologist or gynecologic oncologist skilled in the diagnosis and treatment of preinvasive cervical disease.

PEARLS & CONSIDERATIONS

COMMENTS

- Patient education material available from American College of Obstetricians and Gynecologists.

SUGGESTED READINGS

Nuono J et al: New tests for cervical cancer screening, *Am Fam Physician* 64:780, 2001.

Schlecht NF et al: Persistent human papillomavirus infection as a predictor of cervical intraepithelial neoplasia, *JAMA* 286:3106, 2001.

Solomon D et al: Comparison of three management strategies for patients with atypical squamous cells of undetermined significance: baseline results from a randomized trial, *J Natl Cancer Inst* 93:293, 2001.

Solomon D et al: The 2001 Bethesda system terminology for reporting results of cervical cytology, *JAMA* 287:2114, 2002.

Stoler MH: New Bethesda terminology and evidence-based management guidelines for cervical cytology findings, *JAMA* 287:2140, 2002.

Wright TC et al: 2001 consensus guidelines for the management of women with cervical cytological abnormalities, *JAMA* 287:2120, 2002.

AUTHOR: **DENNIS M. WEPPNER, M.D.**

BASIC INFORMATION

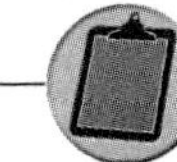

DEFINITION

A cervical polyp is a growth protruding from the cervix or endocervical canal. Polyps that arise from the endocervical canal are called *endocervical polyps*. If they arise from the ectocervix, they are called *cervical polyps*.

ICD-9CM CODES
622.7 Mucous polyp of cervix

EPIDEMIOLOGY & DEMOGRAPHICS

Cervical polyps are common. Found in approximately 4% of all gynecologic patients. Most commonly present in perimenopausal and multigravid women between the ages of 30 and 50 yr. Endocervical polyps are more common than cervical polyps and are almost always benign (Fig. 1-55). Malignant degeneration is extremely rare.

PHYSICAL FINDINGS & CLINICAL PRESENTATION

Polyps may be single or multiple and vary in size from being extremely small (a few mm) to large (4 cm). They are soft, smooth, reddish-purple to cherry-red in color. They bleed easily when touched. Very large polyps can cause some cervical dilation. There may be vaginal discharge associated with cervical polyps if the polyp has become infected.

ETIOLOGY

- Most unknown
- Inflammatory
- Traumatic
- Pregnancy

DIAGNOSIS

DIFFERENTIAL DIAGNOSIS

- Endometrial polyp
- Prolapsed myoma
- Retained products of conception
- Squamous papilloma
- Sarcoma
- Cervical malignancy

WORKUP

Polyps are most commonly asymptomatic and are usually found at the time of annual gynecologic pelvic examination. Polyps are also found in women who present for evaluation of intermenstrual or postcoital bleeding and for profuse vaginal discharge. Polyps are painless. Unless a patient has a bleeding abnormality that necessitates her being evaluated by a physician, polyps would go undiagnosed until her next Pap smear was obtained.

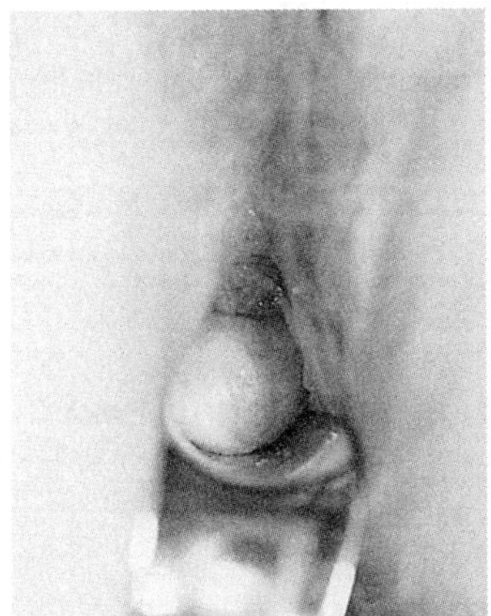

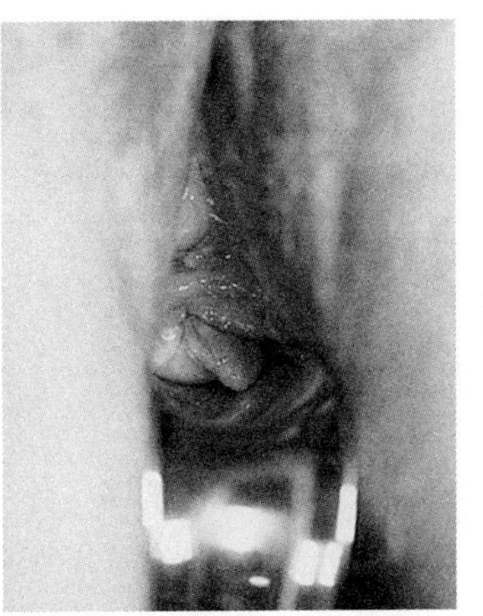

FIGURE 1-55 **A,** Fibroid polyp protruding through the external cervical os. **B,** Small endocervical polyp. (From Symonds EM, Macpherson MBA: *Color atlas of obstetrics and gynecology,* St Louis, 1994, Mosby.)

TREATMENT

NONPHARMACOLOGIC THERAPY

Simple surgical excision can be done in the office. The physician should be prepared for bleeding, which can easily be controlled with silver nitrate or Monsel's solution. Most commonly, a polyp is excised by grasping it at the stalk and twisting it off. Polyps can also be excised by electrocautery or, in the case of very large polyps, in an outpatient surgical suite. Sexual intercourse and tampon usage are to be avoided until the patient's follow-up visit. Also, douching is not to be performed.

ACUTE GENERAL Rx

Generally, no medication is needed.

CHRONIC Rx

Patient is followed up in 2 wk for recheck of the surgical excision site unless there is active bleeding, in which case she would be seen immediately. The cervix should be checked at the patient's routine gynecologic visits.

DISPOSITION

Because these are almost always benign, usually no further treatment is needed. Annual gynecologic examinations should be performed to check for any regrowths.

REFERRAL

To a gynecologist for removal of polyps

PEARLS & CONSIDERATIONS

COMMENTS

A Pap smear should be obtained before removing the polyp. If an abnormal Pap smear is obtained, more than likely the cause will be secondary to the polyp. If a colposcopic evaluation is needed, this should also be performed. During pregnancy, the cervix is highly vascularized. If the polyps are stable and benign-appearing, they should just be observed during the pregnancy and removed only if they are causing bleeding.

SUGGESTED READINGS

Copeland L: *Textbook of gynecology,* ed 2, Baltimore, 1999, Saunders.

Endo H et al: Cervical polyp with eccrine syringofibroadenoma-like features, *Histopathology* 42(3):301, 2003.

Rupke S: Family practice forum: clinical medicine. Evaluation and management of cervical polyps, *Hosp Pract* 33(6):81, 1998.

Scott PM: Procedures in family practice. Performing cervical polypectomy, *JAAPA* 12(6):81, 1999.

AUTHOR: **GEORGE T. DANAKAS, M.D.**

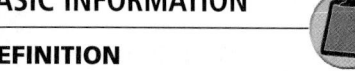

BASIC INFORMATION

DEFINITION

Cervicitis is an infection of the cervix. It may result from direct infection of the cervix, or it may be secondary to uterine or vaginal infection.

SYNONYMS

Endocervicitis
Ectocervicitis
Mucopurulent cervicitis

ICD-9CM CODES
616.0 Cervicitis
098.15 Acute gonococcal cervicitis
079.8 Chlamydia infection

EPIDEMIOLOGY & DEMOGRAPHICS

Cervicitis accounts for 20% to 25% of patients presenting with abnormal vaginal discharge, and this affects women only. It is most common in adolescents, but it can be found in any sexually active woman. Practicing unsafe sex with multiple sexual partners increases the risk of developing cervicitis, as well as other sexually transmitted diseases.

PHYSICAL FINDINGS

Cervicitis is usually asymptomatic or associated with mild symptoms. Copious purulent or mucopurulent in vaginal discharge (Fig. 1-56), pelvic pain, and dyspareunia may be present if cervicitis is severe. The cervix can be erythematous and tender on palpation during bimanual examination. The cervix may also bleed easily when obtaining cultures or a Pap smear. May have postcoital bleeding.

ETIOLOGY

- *Chlamydia*
- *Trichomonas*
- *Neisseria gonorrhoeae*
- Herpes simplex
- *Trichomonas vaginalis*
- Human papillomavirus

DIAGNOSIS

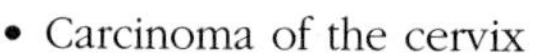

DIFFERENTIAL DIAGNOSIS

- Carcinoma of the cervix
- Cervical erosion
- Cervical metaplasia

WORKUP

The patient usually presents with a vaginal discharge or history of postcoital bleeding. Otherwise the patient is diagnosed asymptomatically during routine examination. On examination there is gross visualization of yellow, mucopurulent material on the cotton swab.

LABORATORY TESTS

On a smear there will be ten or more polymorphonuclear leukocytes per microscopic field. Positive Gram stain is found. Cultures should be obtained for *Chlamydia* and *N. gonorrhoeae*. Use a wet mount to look for trichomonads. Obtain a Pap smear.

TREATMENT

NONPHARMACOLOGIC THERAPY

Cervicitis is treated in an outpatient setting. Cryosurgery is an option for treatment of cervicitis with negative cultures and negative biopsies. Safe sex should be practiced with the use of condoms. Partners should be treated in all cases of infection proven by culture.

ACUTE GENERAL Rx

Because *Chlamydia* and *N. gonorrhoeae* make up >50% of the cause of infectious cervicitis, if it is suspected, treat without waiting for culture results. Administer ceftriaxone 125-mg IM single dose followed by doxycycline 100 mg PO bid for 7 days. If the patient is pregnant, treat with azithromycin (Zithromax) 1-g single dose instead of using doxycycline, which is contraindicated in pregnant or nursing mothers. Alternative treatments include: erythromycin base 500 mg PO qid for 7 days, erythromycin ethylsuccinate 800 mg PO qid for 7 days, ofloxacin 300 mg PO bid for 7 days, or levofloxacin 500 mg PO qd for 7 days. If *Trichomonas* is the etiologic agent, treat with metronidazole 2-g single dose. For herpes, treat with acyclovir 200 mg PO five times daily for 7 days.

DISPOSITION

Cervicitis responds well to antibiotics. Possible complications to watch for are a subsequent PID and infertility (found in 5% to 10% of patients). Repeat cultures should be performed after treatment. Sexual relations can be resumed after negative cultures.

REFERRAL

If subsequent PID develops, consider hospital admission for IV antibiotics.

PEARLS & CONSIDERATIONS

COMMENTS

Patient educational material can be obtained from local health clinics and clinics for sexually transmitted diseases.

SUGGESTED READING

Centers for Disease Control and Prevention: 2002 sexually transmitted diseases treatment guidelines, *MMWR Morb Mortal Wkly Rep* 51(RR-6), 2002.

AUTHOR: **GEORGE T. DANAKAS, M.D.**

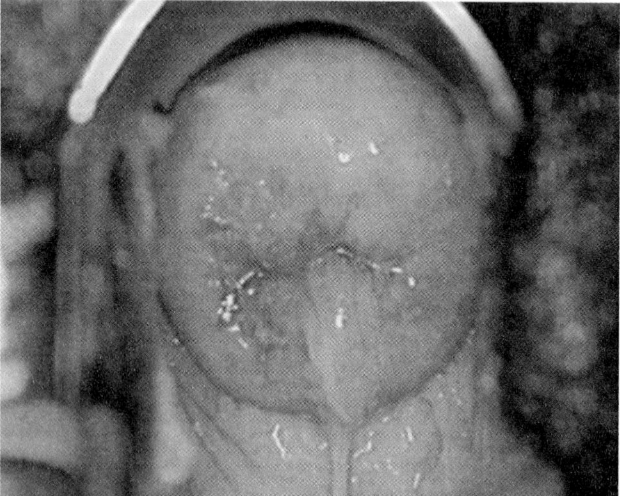

FIGURE 1-56 Colposcopy of a woman with mucopurulent cervicitis and purulent discharge from endocervical os. (Courtesy Dr. David Soper, Richmond, VA. From Mandell GL [ed]: *Mandell, Douglas, and Bennett's principles and practice of infectious diseases,* ed 5, New York, 2000, Churchill Livingstone.)

BASIC INFORMATION

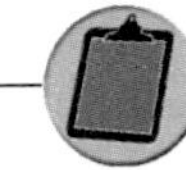

DEFINITION

Chagas' disease is an infection caused by the protozoan parasite *Trypanosoma cruzi*. The disease is characterized by an acute nonspecific febrile illness that may be followed, after a variable latency period, by chronic cardiac, GI, and neurologic sequelae.

SYNONYMS

American trypanosomiasis

ICD-9CM CODES
086.2 Chagas' disease

EPIDEMIOLOGY & DEMOGRAPHICS

INCIDENCE (IN U.S.):
- Four cases of autochthonous transmission in California and Texas
- In the last 2 decades, six cases of laboratory-acquired infection, three cases of transfusion-associated transmission, and nine cases of imported disease reported to the Centers for Disease Control and Prevention (none of the imported cases involving returning tourists)

PREVALENCE (IN U.S.): Based on regional seroprevalence studies in Hispanic blood donors, it is estimated that between 50,000 and 100,000 persons infected with *T. cruzi* are currently residing in the U.S.

PREDOMINANT SEX: Male = female

PREDOMINANT AGE:
- In highly endemic areas, mean age of acute infection: approximately 4 yr old
- Variable age distribution for both types of chronic disease, depending on geography
- Mean age of onset: usually between 35 and 45 yr

PEAK INCIDENCE: Unknown

GENETICS:

CONGENITAL INFECTION: Congenital transmission has been documented with attendant high fetal mortality and morbidity in surviving infants.

NEONATAL INFECTION: In rural areas, within substandard housing, transmission is likely to occur.

PHYSICAL FINDINGS & CLINICAL PRESENTATION

- Inflammatory lesion that develops about 1 wk after contamination of a break in the skin with infected insect feces (chagoma)
  1. Area of induration and erythema
  2. Usually accompanied by local lymphadenopathy
- Presence of Romaña's sign, which consists of unilateral painless palpebral and periocular edema, when conjunctiva is portal of entry
- Constitutional symptoms of fever, fatigue, and anorexia, along with edema of the face and lower extremities, generalized lymphadenopathy, and mild hepatosplenomegaly after the appearance of local signs of disease
- Myocarditis in a small portion of patients, sometimes with resultant CHF
- Uncommonly, CNS disease, such as meningoencephalitis, which carries a poor prognosis
- Symptoms and signs of disease persisting for weeks to months, followed by spontaneous resolution of the acute illness; patient then in the indeterminate phase of the disease (asymptomatic with attendant subpatent parasitemia and reactive antibodies to *T. cruzi* antigens)
- Chronic disease may become manifest years to decades after the initial infection:

1. Most common organ involved: heart, followed by GI tract, and to a much lesser extent the CNS
   a. Cardiac involvement takes the form of arrhythmias or cardiomyopathy, but rarely both.
   b. Cardiomyopathy is bilateral but predominantly affects the right ventricle and is often accompanied by apical aneurysms and mural thrombi.
   c. Arrhythmias are a consequence of involvement of the bundle of His and have been implicated as the leading cause of sudden death in adults in highly endemic areas.
   d. Right-sided heart failure, thromboembolization, and rhythm disturbances associated with symptoms of dizziness and syncope are characteristic.
2. Patients with megaesophagus: dysphasia, odynophagia, chronic cough, and regurgitation, frequently resulting in aspiration pneumonitis
3. Megacolon: abdominal pain and chronic constipation, which, when severe, may lead to obstruction and perforation
4. CNS symptoms: most often secondary to embolization from the heart or varying degrees of peripheral neuropathy

ETIOLOGY

- *T. cruzi*
  1. Found only in the Americas, ranging from the southern half of the U.S. to southern Argentina
  2. Transmitted to humans by various species of bloodsucking reduviid ("kissing") insects, primarily those of the genera *Triatoma, Panstrongylus,* and *Rhodnius*
  3. Usually found in burrows and trees where infected insects transmit the parasite to nonhuman mammals (e.g., opossums and armadillos), which constitute the natural reservoir
  4. Intrusion into enzootic areas for farmland, allowing insects to take up residence in rural dwellings, thus including humans and domestic animals in the cycle of transmission
  5. Initial infection of insects by ingesting blood from animals or humans that have circulating flagellated trypanosomes (trypomastigotes)
  6. Multiplication of ingested parasites in the insect midgut as epimastigotes, then differentiation into infective metacyclic trypomastigotes in the hindgut whereby the parasites are discharged with the feces during subsequent blood meals
  7. Transmission to the second mammalian host through contamination of mucous membranes, conjunctivae, or wounds with insect feces containing infected forms
- In the vertebrate host
  1. Movement of parasites into various cell types, intracellular transformation and multiplication in the cytoplasm as amastigotes, and thereafter differentiation into trypomastigotes
  2. Following rupture of the cell membrane, parasitic invasion of local tissues or hematogenous spread to distant sites, maintaining a parasitemia infective for vectors
- In addition to insect vectors, *T. cruzi* is transmitted through blood transfusions, transplacentally, and, occasionally, secondary to laboratory accidents

DIAGNOSIS

DIFFERENTIAL DIAGNOSIS

Acute disease
- Early African trypanosomiasis
- New World cutaneous and mucocutaneous leishmaniasis

Chronic disease
- Idiopathic cardiomyopathy
- Idiopathic achalasia
- Congenital or acquired megacolon

WORKUP

Principal considerations in diagnosis:
- A history of residence where transmission is known to occur
- Recent receipt of a blood product while in an endemic area
- Occupational exposure in a laboratory

LABORATORY TESTS

For acute diagnosis:
- Demonstration of *T. cruzi* in wet preparations of blood, buffy coat, or Giemsa-stained smears

- Xenodiagnosis, a technique involving laboratory-reared insect vectors fed on subjects with suspected infection thereafter examined for parasites, and culture of body fluids in liquid media to establish diagnosis
  1. Hampered by the length of time required for completion
  2. Of limited use in clinical decision making with regard to drug therapy
  3. Although xenodiagnosis and broth culture are considered to be more sensitive than microscopic examination of body fluids, sensitivities may not exceed 50%
- Recent advances in serologic testing include immunoblot assay, in situ indirect fluorescent antibody, PCR-based techniques, and an immunochromatographic assay (Chagas Stat Pak)

For chronic *T. cruzi* infection:

- Traditional serologic tests including: complement fixation (CF), indirect immunofluorescence (IIF), indirect hemagglutination, enzyme-linked immunosorbent assay (ELISA), and radioimmune precipitation assay
- Persistent problem with these tests: in addition to sensitivity and specificity, false-positive results
- Saliva ELISA may be useful as a screening diagnostic test in epidemiologic studies of chronic trypanosomiasis infection in endemic areas

TREATMENT

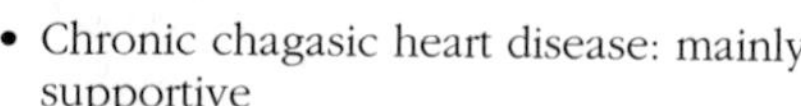

NONPHARMACOLOGIC THERAPY

- Chronic chagasic heart disease: mainly supportive
- Megaesophagus: symptoms usually amenable to dietary measures or pneumonic dilation of the esophagogastric junction
- Chagasic megacolon: in its early stages responsive to a high-fiber diet, laxatives, and enemas

ACUTE GENERAL Rx

Nifurtimox (Lampit, Bayer 2502):

- Only drug available in the U.S. for the treatment of acute, congenital, or laboratory-acquired infection
- Recommended oral dosage for adults: 8 to 10 mg/kg/day given in four divided daily doses and continued for 90 to 120 days
- Parasitologic cure in approximately 50% of those treated; should be begun as early as possible

Benznidazole, a nitroimidazole derivative:

- Has demonstrated similar efficacy as nifurtimox in limited trials
- Recommended oral dosage: 5 mg/kg/day for 60 days

CHRONIC Rx

- In patients with indeterminate phase or chronic disease: no evidence of benefit with pharmacologic therapy
- In patients exhibiting bradyarrhythmias: pacemakers
- In individuals with congestive heart failure:
  1. Treat with modalities appropriate for dilated, especially right-sided, cardiomyopathic disease.
  2. Cardiac transplant is a controversial alternative for end-stage cardiomyopathy; however, reactivation rate found to be low and amenable to therapy without subsequent infection of the allograft in one study.
  3. Myotomy or esophageal resection is reserved for patients with advanced disease.
- In advanced chagasic megacolon associated with chronic fecal impaction, perforation, or, less commonly, volvulus: surgical resection

DISPOSITION

Based on few prospective studies, most patients infected with *T. cruzi* will not develop symptomatic Chagas' disease.

REFERRAL

- For consultation with an infectious disease specialist or communication with the Centers for Disease Control and Prevention when the disease is acutely suspected
- To a cardiologist for pacemaker implantation for patients with bradyarrhythmias
- To a surgeon for symptomatic disease in individuals with chagasic megaesophagus or megacolon

PEARLS & CONSIDERATIONS

COMMENTS

- In recipients of solid organ or bone marrow transplants, patients with AIDS, or those receiving chemotherapy, there may be reactivation of indeterminate phase disease.
- Mortality predictors associated with chagasic cardiomyopathy include CHF, QT-interval dispersion, left ventricular (LV) end-systolic dimension, the presence of pathological Q waves, frequent PVCs, and isolated LAFB on ECG.
- Patients with chagasic esophageal disease have an increased incidence of esophageal malignancy.
- The use of pyrethroid-impregnated curtains may represent an option for the reduction or elimination of Chagas' disease transmission in certain endemic areas.
- A recent study suggests that male gender and detection of *T. cruzi* DNA in serum by PCR may portend a higher risk of progression for chronic cardiomyopathy.

SUGGESTED READINGS

Basquiera AL et al.: Risk progression to chronic Chagas cardiomyopathy: influence of male sex and of parasitemia detected by polymerase chain reaction, *Heart* 89(10):1186, 2003.

Herber O, Kroeger A: Pyrethroid-impregnated curtains for Chagas' disease control in Venezuela, *Acta Trop* 88(1):33, 2003.

Higuchi Mde L et al: Pathophysiology of the heart in Chagas' disease: current status and new developments, *Cardiovasc Res* 60(1):96, 2003.

Luquetti AO et al: Chagas' disease diagnosis: a multicentric evaluation of Chagas Stat-Pak, a rapid immunochromatographic assay with recombinant proteins of Trypanosoma cruzi, *Diagn Microbiol Infect Dis* 46(4):265, 2003.

Salles G et al: Prognostic value of QT interval parameters for mortality risk stratification in Chagas' disease: results of a long-term follow-up study, *Circulation* 108 (3):305, 2003.

Urbina JA, Docampo R: Specific chemotherapy of Chagas disease: controversies and advances, *Trends Parasitol* 19(11):495, 2003.

AUTHOR: **GEORGE O. ALONSO, M.D.**

BASIC INFORMATION

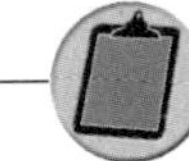

DEFINITION

Chancroid is a sexually transmitted disease characterized by painful genital ulceration and inflammatory inguinal adenopathy.

SYNONYMS

Soft chancre
Ulcus molle

ICD-9CM CODES
099.0 Chancroid

EPIDEMIOLOGY & DEMOGRAPHICS

- Exact incidence is unknown.
- Occurs more frequently in men (male:female ratio of 10:1).
- Clinical infection is rare in women.
- There is a higher incidence in uncircumcised men and in tropical and subtropical regions.
- Incubation period is 4 to 7 days but may take up to 3 wk.
- High incidence of HIV infection associated with chancroid.

PHYSICAL FINDINGS & CLINICAL PRESENTATION

- One to three extremely painful ulcers (Fig. 1-57), accompanied by tender inguinal lymphadenopathy (especially if fluctuant)
- May present with inguinal bubo and several ulcers
- In women: initial lesion in the fourchette, labia minora, urethra, cervix, or anus; inflammatory pustule or papule that ruptures, leaving a shallow, nonindurated ulceration, usually 1- to 2-cm diameter with ragged, undermined edges
- Unilateral lymphadenopathy develops 1 wk later in 50% of patients

ETIOLOGY

Haemophilus ducreyi, a bacillus

DIAGNOSIS

DIFFERENTIAL DIAGNOSIS

- Other genitoulcerative diseases such as syphilis, herpes, LGV, granuloma inguinale
- A clinical algorithm for the initial management of genital ulcer disease is described in Section III

WORKUP

Diagnosis based on history and physical examination is often inadequate. Must rule out syphilis in women because of the consequences of inappropriate therapy in pregnant women. Base initial diagnosis and treatment recommendations on clinical impression of appearance of ulcer and most likely diagnosis for population. Definitive diagnosis is made by isolation of organism from ulcers by culture or Gram stain.

LABORATORY TESTS

Darkfield microscopy, RPR, HSV cultures, *H. ducreyi* culture, HIV testing recommended

TREATMENT

NONPHARMACOLOGIC THERAPY

Fluctuant nodes should be aspirated through healthy adjacent skin to prevent formation of draining sinus. I&D not recommended, delays healing. Use warm compresses to remove necrotic material.

ACUTE GENERAL Rx

- Azithromycin 1 g PO (single dose) *or*
- Ceftriaxone 250 mg IM (single dose) *or*
- Ciprofloxacin 500 mg PO bid for 3 days *or*
- Erythromycin 500 mg PO qid for 7 days

NOTE: Ciprofloxacin is contraindicated in patients who are pregnant, lactating, or <18 yr.

- HIV-infected patients may need more prolonged therapy

DISPOSITION

- All sexual partners should be treated with a 10-day course of one of the previous regimens (see Acute General Rx).
- Patients should be reexamined 3 to 7 days after initiation of therapy. Ulcers should improve symptomatically within 3 days and objectively within 7 days after initiation of successful therapy.

PEARLS & CONSIDERATIONS

COMMENTS

In the U.S. HSV-1 and syphilis are the most common causes of genital ulcers, followed by chancroid, LGV, and granuloma inguinale.

SUGGESTED READING

Centers for Disease Control and Prevention: 2002 sexually transmitted diseases treatment guidelines, *MMWR Morb Mortal Wkly Rep* 51(RR-6), 2002.

AUTHOR: **MARIA A. CORIGLIANO, M.D.**

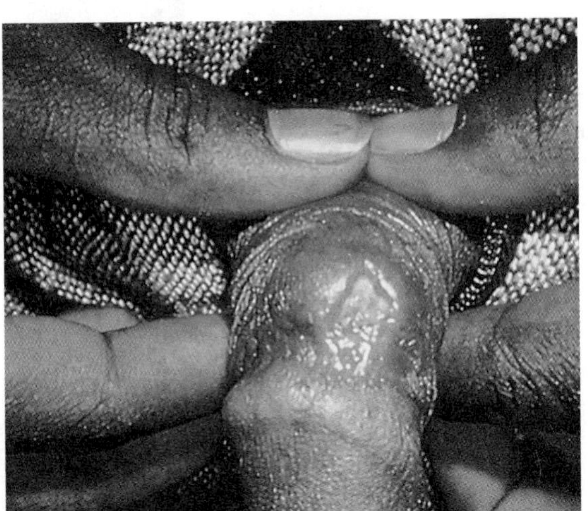

FIGURE 1-57 Chancroid. Note shaggy, ragged-edged ulcer with edema and exudative base. (Courtesy Beverly Sanders, M.D. From Goldstein B [ed]: *Practical dermatology,* ed 2, St Louis, 1997, Mosby.)

Charcot-Marie-Tooth Disease 

BASIC INFORMATION

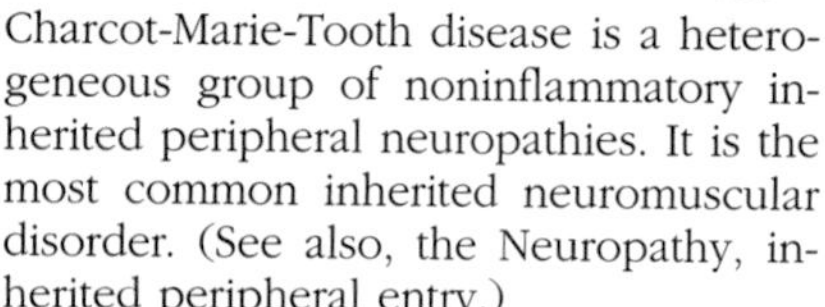

DEFINITION

Charcot-Marie-Tooth disease is a heterogeneous group of noninflammatory inherited peripheral neuropathies. It is the most common inherited neuromuscular disorder. (See also, the Neuropathy, inherited peripheral entry.)

SYNONYMS

Peroneal muscular atrophy
Hereditary motor and sensory neuropathy (HMSN)
Idiopathic dominantly inherited hypertrophic polyneuropathy

ICD-9CM CODES
356.1 Charcot-Marie-Tooth disease, paralysis, or syndrome

EPIDEMIOLOGY & DEMOGRAPHICS

PREDOMINANT AGE: Onset usually 10 to 20 yr but can be delayed to 50 to 60 yr
PREDOMINANT SEX: Male:female ratio of 3:1

PHYSICAL FINDINGS & CLINICAL PRESENTATION

- Variable presentation from family to family, but affected individuals in a family tend to have similar symptomatology
- Usually, gradual onset, with slowly progressive disorder
- Foot deformity producing a high arch (cavus) and hammertoes
- Atrophy of the lower legs producing a storklike appearance (muscle wasting does not involve the upper legs) (Fig. 1-58)
- Nerve enlargement
- Sensory loss or other neurologic signs, although the sensory involvement is usually mild
- Scoliosis
- Decreased proprioception that often interferes with balance and gait
- Painful paresthesias
- In late cases, possible involvement of hands
- Absence of DTRs in many cases
- Poorly healing foot ulcers in some patients

ETIOLOGY

Chronic segmental demyelination of peripheral nerves with hypertrophic changes caused by remyelination

DIAGNOSIS

DIFFERENTIAL DIAGNOSIS

- Other inherited neuropathies
- Toxic, metabolic, and nutritional polyneuropathies

WORKUP

- The early onset, slow progression, and familial nature of the disorder are usually sufficient to establish diagnosis.
- Electrophysiologic studies are often diagnostic and may also be helpful in defining various subtypes of this group of neuropathies.
- Occasionally, muscle and nerve (sural) biopsy may be required.

TREATMENT

ACUTE GENERAL Rx

- Genetic counseling
- Supportive physical therapy and occupational therapy
- Prevention of injury to limbs with diminished sensibility
- Bracing

CHRONIC Rx

Occasionally, surgery to add stability and restore a plantigrade foot

DISPOSITION

- Disability is usually mild and compatible with a long life.
- 10% to 20% of patients are asymptomatic.
- A small number of cases are nonambulators by the sixth or seventh decade.
- The condition is usually not life threatening.

REFERRAL

- For orthopedic consultation for bracing and treatment of deformity
- For genetic counseling

PEARLS & CONSIDERATIONS

COMMENTS

Patient information on Charcot-Marie-Tooth disease is available from the Muscular Dystrophy Association, 3300 East Sunrise Drive, Tucson, Arizona 85718; phone: 1-800-572-1717.

SUGGESTED READINGS

Chetlin RD, Gutmann L et al: Resistance training exercise and creatine in patients with Charcot-Marie-Tooth disease, *Muscle Nerve* 30:69, 2004.

Gemiynani F, Marbini A: Charcot-Marie-Tooth disease (CMT) distinctive phenotypic and genotypic features in CMT type 2, *J Neurol Sci* 184:1, 2001.

Pareyson D: Differential diagnosis of Charcot-Marie-Tooth disease and related neuropathies, *Neurol Sci* 25:72, 2004.

AUTHOR: **LONNIE R. MERCIER, M.D.**

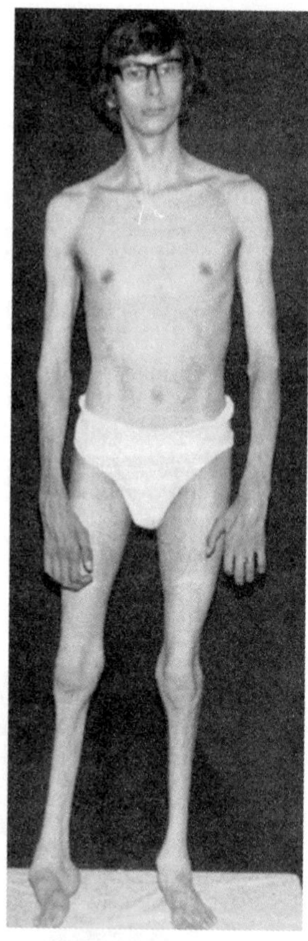

FIGURE 1-58 Patient with Charcot-Marie-Tooth disease showing marked wasting of calf muscles and intrinsic foot muscles. (From Dubowitz V: *Muscle disorders in childhood,* London, 1995, WB Saunders. In Goetz CG: *Textbook of clinical neurology,* Philadelphia, 1999, WB Saunders.)

BASIC INFORMATION

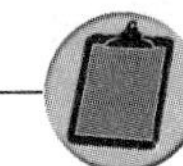

DEFINITION

Charcot's joint is a chronic, progressive joint degeneration, often devastating, seen most commonly in peripheral weight-bearing joints and vertebrae, which develops as a result of the loss of normal sensory innervation of the joint. It was described by Charcot as a result of tabes dorsalis.

SYNONYMS

Neuropathic arthropathy

ICD-9CM CODES
094.0 Charcot's arthropathy

EPIDEMIOLOGY & DEMOGRAPHICS

PREVALENCE:

- 1 case/750 patients with diabetes mellitus; 5 cases/100 of those with peripheral neuropathy (foot is most commonly involved)
- 20% to 40% of patients with syringomyelia (shoulder most commonly involved)
- 5% to 10% of patients with tabes dorsalis; usually >60 yr (spine, hip, and knee most commonly involved)

PHYSICAL FINDINGS & CLINICAL PRESENTATION

Neuropathic joint disease is relatively painless, often in spite of considerable destruction

- Often, diffusely warm, swollen, and occasionally erythematous involved joint, the latter suggesting sepsis
- Possible progression of joint instability; palpable osseous debris; crepitus common
- Often, frank dislocation, leading to bony deformity, especially in more superficial joints

ETIOLOGY

The most widely accepted theory is the "neurotraumatic" theory:

- Impairment and loss of joint sensitivity decreases the protective mechanism about the joint.
- Rapid destruction occurs.
- Chronic inflammation and repetitive effusions develop, eventually contributing to joint instability and incongruity.

DIAGNOSIS

DIFFERENTIAL DIAGNOSIS

- Osteomyelitis, cellulitis, abscess
- Infectious arthritis
- Osteoarthritis
- Rheumatoid and other inflammatory arthritides

WORKUP

- An underlying neurologic disorder must always be present.
- Diabetes mellitus with peripheral neuropathy is the most common cause (Fig. 1-59).
- Syringomyelia, tabes dorsalis, Charcot-Marie-Tooth disease, congenital indifference to pain, alcoholism, and spinal dysraphism can all lead to the disorder.

LABORATORY TESTS

In questionable cases, aspiration, sometimes including biopsy, to rule out sepsis

IMAGING STUDIES

Plain roentgenography

- Sufficient to establish diagnosis in most cases, especially if etiology is known
- Findings: variable degrees of destruction and dislocation

TREATMENT

ACUTE GENERAL Rx

- Protection of effusions, sprains, and fractures until all hyperemic response has resolved
- Braces, special shoes with molded inserts, and elevation of the extremity
- Patient education with avoidance of weight bearing when lower extremity joints are involved
- Surgery: only limited value

DISPOSITION

Once the full-blown neuropathic joint has developed, treatment is difficult.

SUGGESTED READINGS

Guyton GP, Saltzman CL: The diabetic foot: basic mechanisms of disease, *Instr Course Lect* 51:169, 2002.

Herbst SA, Jones KB, Saltzman CL: Pattern of diabetic neuropathic arthropathy associated with peripheral bone mineral density, *J Bone Joint Surg* 86:378, 2004.

Pakarinen TK et al: Charcot arthropathy of the diabetic foot: current concepts and review of 36 cases, *Scand J Surg* 91:195, 2002.

Slater RA et al: The diabetic Charcot foot, *Isr Med Assoc J* 6:280, 2004.

AUTHOR: **R. MERCIER, M.D.**

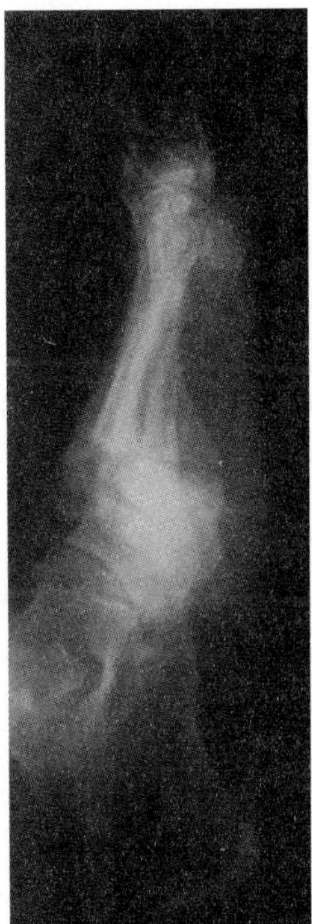

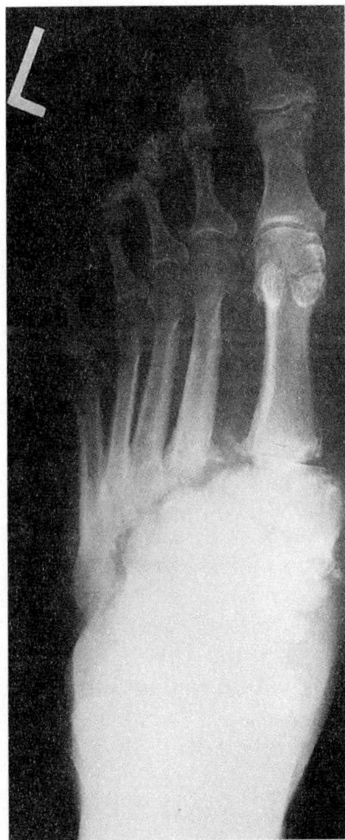

FIGURE 1-59 Diabetes mellitus and neuropathic arthritis. Note lateral displacement of metatarsals (*left*) and fragmentation and osseous debris (*right*). (From Goldman L, Bennett JC [eds]: *Cecil textbook of medicine,* ed 21, Philadelphia, 2000, WB Saunders.)

Chickenpox

BASIC INFORMATION

DEFINITION

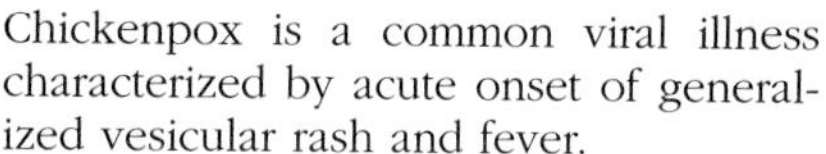

Chickenpox is a common viral illness characterized by acute onset of generalized vesicular rash and fever.

SYNONYMS

Varicella

ICD-9CM CODES

052.9 Varicella

EPIDEMIOLOGY & DEMOGRAPHICS

- Chickenpox is extremely contagious. More than 90% of unvaccinated contacts become infected.
- The incubation period of chickenpox ranges from 9 to 21 days.
- Peak incidence is in the springtime.
- The predominant age is 5 to 10 yr.
- Infectious period begins 2 days before onset of clinical symptoms and lasts until all lesions have crusted.
- Most patients will have lifelong immunity following an attack of chickenpox; protection from chickenpox following varicella vaccine is approximately 6 yr.

PHYSICAL FINDINGS & CLINICAL PRESENTATION

- Findings vary with the clinical course. Initial symptoms consist of fever, chills, backache, generalized malaise, and headache.
- Symptoms are generally more severe in adults.
- Initial lesions generally occur on the trunk (centripetal distribution) and occasionally on the face; these lesions consist primarily of 3- to 4-mm red papules with an irregular outline and a clear vesicle on the surface (dew drops on a rose petal appearance).
- Intense pruritus generally accompanies this stage.
- New lesion development generally ceases by the fourth day with subsequent crusting by the sixth day.
- Lesions generally spread to the face and the extremities (centrifugal spread).
- Patients generally present with lesions at different stages at the same time.
- Crusts generally fall off within 5 to 14 days.
- Fever is usually highest during the eruption of the vesicles; temperature generally returns to normal following disappearance of vesicles.
- Signs of potential complications (e.g., bacterial skin infections, neurologic complications, pneumonia, hepatitis) may be present on physical examination.
- Mild constitutional symptoms (e.g., anorexia, myalgias, headaches, restlessness) may be present (most common in adults).
- Excoriations may be present if scratching is prominent.

ETIOLOGY

Varicella-zoster virus (VZV) is a human herpes virus III that can manifest with either varicella or herpes zoster (i.e., shingles, which is a reactivation of varicella).

DIAGNOSIS

DIFFERENTIAL DIAGNOSIS

- Other viral infection
- Impetigo
- Scabies
- Drug rash
- Urticaria
- Dermatitis herpetiformis
- Smallpox

WORKUP

Diagnosis is usually made based on patient's history and clinical presentation.

LABORATORY TESTS

- Laboratory evaluation is generally not necessary.
- CBC may reveal leukopenia and thrombocytopenia.
- Serum varicella titers (significant rise in serum varicella IgG antibody level), skin biopsy, or Tzanck smear are used only when diagnosis is in question.

TREATMENT

NONPHARMACOLOGIC THERAPY

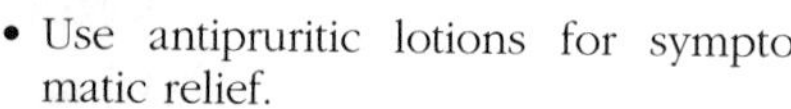

- Use antipruritic lotions for symptomatic relief.
- Avoid scratching to prevent excoriations and superficial skin infections.
- Use a mild soap for bathing; hands should be washed often.

ACUTE GENERAL Rx

- Use acetaminophen for fever and myalgias; aspirin should be avoided because of the increased risk of Reye's syndrome.
- Oral acyclovir (20 mg/kg qid for 5 days) initiated at the earliest sign (within 24 hr of illness) is useful in healthy, nonpregnant individuals 13 yr of age or older to decrease the duration and severity of signs and symptoms. Immunocompromised hosts should be treated with IV acyclovir 500 mg/m^2 or 10 mg/kg q8h IV for 7 to 10 days.
- Varicella-zoster immunoglobulin (VZIG) is effective in preventing chickenpox in susceptible individuals. Dose is 12.5 U/kg IM (up to a maximum of 625 U). May repeat dose 3 wk later if the exposure persists; VZIG must be administered as early as possible after presumed exposure.
- Varicella vaccine is available for children and adults; protection lasts at least 6 yr. Patients with HIV or other immunocompromised patients should not receive the live attenuated vaccine.
- Pruritus from chickenpox can be controlled with antihistamines (e.g., hydroxyzine 25 mg q6h) and oral antipruritic lotions (e.g., calamine).
- Oral antibiotics are not routinely indicated and should be used only in patients with secondary infection and infected lesions (most common infective organisms are *Streptococcus* sp. and *Staphylococcus* sp.).

DISPOSITION

- The course is generally benign in immunocompetent adults and children.
- Infants who develop chickenpox are incapable of controlling the infection and should be given varicella-zoster immunoglobulin or γ-globulin if VZIG is not available.

REFERRAL

Hospitalization and IV acyclovir are recommended for immunocompromised patients with chickenpox and for patients who develop neurologic complications or pneumonia.

PEARLS & CONSIDERATIONS

COMMENTS

- VZIG can be obtained from the nearest regional Red Cross Blood Center or the Centers for Disease Control and Prevention in Atlanta, Georgia.
- Varicella immunization (Varivax) is recommended for all who have not had chickenpox; dosage for adults and adolescents (>13 yr old) is two 0.5-ml doses 4 to 8 wk apart.

AUTHOR: **FRED F. FERRI, M.D.**

BASIC INFORMATION

DEFINITION

Genital infection with *Chlamydia trachomatis* may result in urethritis, epididymitis, cervicitis, and acute salpingitis, but often it is asymptomatic in women (see "Pelvic Inflammatory Disease"). In men, urethritis, mucopurulent discharge, dysuria, urethral pruritus.

ICD-9CM CODES
597.80 Urethritis
604.0 Epididymitis
616.0 Cervicitis
381.51 Acute salpingitis

EPIDEMIOLOGY & DEMOGRAPHICS

- *Chlamydia trachomatis* is the most common cause of sexually transmitted disease in the U.S. More than 4 million infections occur annually, although the exact number is unknown because reporting is not required in all states. Occurrence is common worldwide, and recognition has been increasing steadily over the last 2 decades in the U.S., Canada, Australia, and Europe.
- Most women with endocervical or urethral infections are asymptomatic.
- Up to 45% of cases of gonococcal infection may have concomitant chlamydial infection.
- Infertility or ectopic pregnancy can result as a complication from symptomatic or asymptomatic chronic infections of the endometrium and fallopian tubes.
- Conjunctival and pneumonic infection of the newborn may result from infection in pregnancy.
- In men 15% to 55% of cases are of *C. trachomatis*. Complications of nongonococcal urethritis in men infected with *C. trachomatis* include epididymitis and Reiter's syndrome.

PHYSICAL FINDINGS & CLINICAL PRESENTATION

Clinical manifestations may be similar to those of gonorrhea: mucopurulent endocervical discharge, with edema, erythema, and easily induced endocervical bleeding caused by inflammation of endocervical columnar epithelium. Less frequent manifestations may include bartholinitis, urethral syndrome with dysuria and pyuria, perihepatitis (Fitz-Hugh–Curtis syndrome).

ETIOLOGY

- *Chlamydia trachomatis,* serotypes D through K
- Obligate, intracellular bacteria
- Trichomonal vaginalis
- Mycoplasma genitalium
- HSV

DIAGNOSIS

DIFFERENTIAL DIAGNOSIS

Gonorrhea, nongonococcal urethritis (nonchlamydial etiologies)

WORKUP

Diagnosis based on laboratory demonstration of evidence of infection in intraurethral or endocervical swab by various tests. The intracellular organism is less readily recovered from the discharge.

LABORATORY TESTS

- Cell culture is the reference method for diagnosis (single culture sensitivity 80% to 90%), but it is labor intensive and takes 48 to 96 hr; it is not suited for large screening programs.
- Nonculture methods:
  Direct fluorescent antibody (DFA) tests
  Enzyme immunoassay (EIA)
  DNA probes
  Polymerase chain reaction (PCR)
- With the exception of PCR, the other tests are probably less specific than cell culture and may yield false-positive results.
- Because this is an intracellular organism, purulent discharge is not an appropriate specimen. An adequate sample of infected cells must be obtained.
- 10 WBCs per high-power field.

TREATMENT

Nongonococcal urethritis, urethritis, cervicitis, conjunctivitis (except for LGV):
- Azithromycin 1 g PO × 1 *or*
- Doxycycline 100 mg PO bid for 7 days
- Alternatives
  1. Erythromycin base 500 mg PO qid for 7 days *or*
  2. Erythromycin ethylsuccinate 800 mg PO qid for 7 days *or*
  3. Ofloxacin 300 mg PO bid for 7 days
  4. Levofloxacin 500 mg PO qd for 7 days

Infection in pregnancy:
- Erythromycin base 500 mg PO qid for 7 days *or*
- Amoxicillin 500 mg PO tid for 7 days

Alternatives:
1. Erythromycin base 250 mg PO qid for 7 days *or*
2. Erythromycin ethylsuccinate 800 mg PO qid for 7 days *or*
3. Erythromycin ethylsuccinate 400 mg PO qid for 14 days *or*
4. Azithromycin 1 g PO (single dose)

NOTE: Doxycycline and ofloxacin are contraindicated in pregnancy. Safety and efficacy of azithromycin are not established in pregnancy and lactation, although preliminary data indicate that it may be safe and effective. Erythromycin estolate is contraindicated in pregnancy because of drug-related hepatotoxicity.

FOLLOW UP:
Reculture after therapy completion and refer partners for evaluation and treatment.

RECURRENT AND PERSISTENT URETHRITIS:
Retreat noncompliant patients with the above regimens. If patient was initially complacent, recommended regimens: metronidazole 2 g PO in single dose plus erythromycin base 500 mg PO qid for 7 days or erythromycin ethylsuccinate 800 mg PO qid for 7 days.

DISPOSITION

See "Gonorrhea." In all patients being treated for chlamydia, presumptive treatment for concomitant infection with gonorrhea should be done. Also see Treatment in "Pelvic Inflammatory Disease."

SUGGESTED READING

Centers for Disease Control and Prevention: 2002 sexually transmitted diseases treatment guidelines, *MMWR Morb Mortal Wkly Rep* 51(RR-6), 2002.

AUTHOR: **MARIA A. CORIGLIANO, M.D.**

BASIC INFORMATION

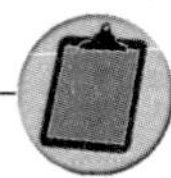

DEFINITION

Cholangitis refers to an inflammation and/or infection of the hepatic and common bile ducts associated with obstruction of the common bile duct.

SYNONYMS

Biliary sepsis
Ascending cholangitis
Suppurative cholangitis

ICD-9CM CODES
576.1 Cholangitis

EPIDEMIOLOGY & DEMOGRAPHICS

INCIDENCE (IN U.S.): Complicates approximately 1% of cases of cholelithiasis
PREVALENCE (IN U.S.): 2 cases/1000 hospital admissions
PREDOMINANT SEX:
- Females, for cholangitis secondary to gallstones
- Males, for cholangitis secondary to malignant obstruction and HIV infection

PREDOMINANT AGE: Seventh decade and older; unusual <50 yr of age
PEAK INCIDENCE: Seventh decade

PHYSICAL FINDINGS & CLINICAL PRESENTATION

- Usually acute onset of fever, chills, abdominal pain, tenderness over the RUQ of the abdomen, and jaundice (Charcot's triad)
- All signs and symptoms in only 50% to 85% of patients
- Often, dark coloration of the urine resulting from bilirubinuria
- Complications:
  1. Bacteremia (50%) and septic shock
  2. Hepatic abscess and pancreatitis

ETIOLOGY

Obstruction of the common bile duct causing rapid proliferation of bacteria in the biliary tree
- Most common cause of common bile duct obstruction: stones, usually migrated from the gallbladder
- Other causes: prior biliary tract surgery with secondary stenosis, tumor (usually arising from the pancreas or biliary tree), and parasitic infections from *Ascaris lumbricoides* or *Fasciola hepatica*
- Iatrogenic after contamination of an obstructed biliary tree by endoscopic retrograde cholangiopancreatoscopy (ERCP) or percutaneous transhepatic cholangiography (PTC)
- Primary sclerosing cholangitis (PSC)
- HIV-associated sclerosing cholangitis: associated with infection by CMV, *Cryptosporidium,* Microsporida, and *Mycobacterium avium* complex

DIAGNOSIS

DIFFERENTIAL DIAGNOSIS

- Biliary colic
- Acute cholecystitis
- Liver abscess
- PUD
- Pancreatitis
- Intestinal obstruction
- Right kidney stone
- Hepatitis
- Pyelonephritis

WORKUP

- Blood cultures
- CBC
- Liver function tests

LABORATORY TESTS

- Usually, elevated WBC count with a predominance of polynuclear forms
- Elevated alkaline phosphatase and bilirubin in chronic obstruction
- Elevated transaminases in acute obstruction
- Positive blood cultures in 50% of cases, typically with enteric gram-negative aerobes (e.g., *E. coli, Klebsiella pneumoniae*), enterococci, or anaerobes

IMAGING STUDIES

- Ultrasound:
  1. Allows visualization of the gallbladder and bile ducts to differentiate extrahepatic obstruction from intrahepatic cholestasis
  2. Insensitive but specific for visualization of common duct stones
- CT scan:
  1. Less accurate for gallstones
  2. More sensitive than ultrasound for visualization of the distal part of the common bile duct
  3. Also allows better definition of neoplasm
- ERCP:
  1. Confirms obstruction and its level
  2. Allows collection of specimens for culture and cytology
  3. Indicated for diagnosis if ultrasound and CT scan are inconclusive
  4. May be indicated in therapy (see Treatment)

TREATMENT

NONPHARMACOLOGIC THERAPY

Biliary decompression
- May be urgent in severely ill patients or those unresponsive to medical therapy within 12 to 24 hr
- May also be performed semielectively in patients who respond
- Options:
  1. ERCP with or without sphincterotomy or placement of a draining stent
  2. Percutaneous transhepatic biliary drainage for the acutely ill patient who is a poor surgical candidate
  3. Surgical exploration of the common bile duct

ACUTE GENERAL Rx

- Nothing by mouth
- Intravenous hydration
- Broad-spectrum antibiotics directed at gram-negative enteric organisms, anaerobes, and enterococcus: if infection is nosocomial, post-ERCP, or the patient is in shock, strong consideration of broader coverage to include hospital organisms such as *Pseudomonas aeruginosa,* resistant *Staphylococcus aureus,* and others

CHRONIC Rx

Repeated decompression may be necessary, particularly when obstruction is related to neoplasm.

DISPOSITION

Excellent prognosis if obstruction is amenable to definitive surgical therapy; otherwise relapses are common.

REFERRAL

- To biliary endoscopist if obstruction is from stones or a stent needs to be placed
- To interventional radiologist if external drainage is necessary
- To a general surgeon in all other cases
- To an infectious disease specialist if blood cultures are positive or the patient is in shock or otherwise severely ill

SUGGESTED READINGS

Gouma DJ: Management of acute cholangitis, *Dig Dis* 21(1):25, 2003.
Lipsett PA, Hitt HA: Acute cholangitis, *Front Biosci* 8(s1229-39), 2003.

AUTHOR: **MICHELE HALPERN, M.D.**

BASIC INFORMATION

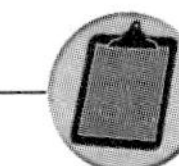

DEFINITION

Cholecystitis is an acute or chronic inflammation of the gallbladder generally secondary to gallstones (>95% of cases).

SYNONYMS

Gallbladder attack

ICD-9CM CODES

575.0 Acute cholecystitis
574.0 Calculus of the gallbladder with acute cholecystitis
575.1 Cholecystitis without mention of calculus

EPIDEMIOLOGY & DEMOGRAPHICS

- Acute cholecystitis occurs most commonly in females during the fifth and sixth decades.
- The incidence of gallstones is 0.6% in the general population and much higher in certain ethnic groups (>75% of Native Americans by age 60 yr).

PHYSICAL FINDINGS & CLINICAL PRESENTATION

- Pain and tenderness in the right hypochondrium or epigastrium; pain possibly radiating to the infrascapular region
- Palpation of the RUQ eliciting marked tenderness and stoppage of inspired breath (Murphy's sign)
- Guarding
- Fever (33%)
- Jaundice (25% to 50% of patients)
- Palpable gallbladder (20% of cases)
- Nausea and vomiting (>70% of patients)
- Fever and chills (>25% of patients)
- Medical history often revealing ingestion of large, fatty meals before onset of pain in the epigastrium and RUQ

ETIOLOGY

- Gallstones (>95% of cases)
- Ischemic damage to the gallbladder, critically ill patient (acalculous cholecystitis)
- Infectious agents, especially in patients with AIDS (CMV, *Cryptosporidium*)
- Strictures of the bile duct
- Neoplasms, primary or metastatic

DIAGNOSIS

DIFFERENTIAL DIAGNOSIS

- Hepatic: hepatitis, abscess, hepatic congestion, neoplasm, trauma
- Biliary: neoplasm, stricture
- Gastric: PUD, neoplasm, alcoholic gastritis, hiatal hernia
- Pancreatic: pancreatitis, neoplasm, stone in the pancreatic duct or ampulla
- Renal: calculi, infection, inflammation, neoplasm, ruptured kidney
- Pulmonary: pneumonia, pulmonary infarction, right-sided pleurisy
- Intestinal: retrocecal appendicitis, intestinal obstruction, high fecal impaction
- Cardiac: myocardial ischemia (particularly involving the inferior wall), pericarditis
- Cutaneous: herpes zoster
- Trauma
- Fitz-Hugh–Curtis syndrome (perihepatitis)
- Subphrenic abscess
- Dissecting aneurysm
- Nerve root irritation caused by osteoarthritis of the spine

WORKUP

Workup consists of detailed history and physical examination coupled with laboratory evaluation and imaging studies. No single clinical finding or laboratory test is sufficient to establish or exclude cholecystitis without further testing.

LABORATORY TESTS

- Leukocytosis (12,000 to 20,000) is present in >70% of patients.
- Elevated alkaline phosphatase, ALT, AST, bilirubin; bilirubin elevation >4 mg/dl is unusual and suggests presence of choledocholithiasis.
- Elevated amylase may be present (consider pancreatitis if serum amylase elevation exceeds 500 U).

IMAGING STUDIES

- Ultrasound of the gallbladder is the preferred initial test; it will demonstrate the presence of stones and also dilated gallbladder with thickened wall and surrounding edema in patients with acute cholecystitis.
- Nuclear imaging (HIDA scan) is useful for diagnosis of cholecystitis: sensitivity and specificity exceed 90% for acute cholecystis. This test is only reliable when bilirubin is <5 mg/dl. A positive test will demonstrate obstruction of the cystic or common hepatic duct; the test will not demonstrate the presence of stones.
- CT scan of abdomen is useful in cases of suspected abscess, neoplasm, or pancreatitis.
- Plain film of the abdomen generally is not useful, because <25% of stones are radiopaque.

TREATMENT

NONPHARMACOLOGIC THERAPY

Provide IV hydration; withhold oral feedings.

ACUTE GENERAL Rx

- Cholecystectomy (laparoscopic is preferred, open cholecystectomy is acceptable); conservative management with IV fluids and antibiotics (ampicillin-sulbactam [Unasyn] 3 g IV q6h *or* piperacillin-tazobactam [Zosyn] 4.5 g IV q8h) may be justified in some high-risk patients to convert an emergency procedure into an elective one with a lower mortality.
- ERCP with sphincterectomy and stone extraction can be performed in conjunction with laparoscopic cholecystectomy for patients with choledochal lithiasis; approximately 7% to 15% of patients with cholelithiasis also have stones in the common bile duct.
- IV fluids, broad-spectrum antibiotics, pain management (meperidine prn) should be used.

DISPOSITION

- Prognosis is good; elective laparoscopic cholecystectomy can be performed as outpatient procedure.
- Hospital stay (when necessary) varies from overnight with laparoscopic cholecystectomy to 4 to 7 days with open cholecystectomy.
- Complication rate is approximately 1% (hemorrhage and bile leak) for laparoscopic cholecystectomy and <0.5% (infection) with open cholecystectomy.

REFERRAL

Hospitalization and surgical referral in all patients with acute cholecystitis

PEARLS & CONSIDERATIONS

COMMENTS

- Patients should be instructed that stones may recur in bile ducts.
- Gallbladder aspiration in which all fluid visualized by ultrasound is aspirated represents a nonsurgical treatment when patients who are at high operative risk develop acute cholecystitis. Salvage cholecystectomy is reserved for nonresponders.

SUGGESTED READINGS

Cuschieri A: Management of patients with gallstones and ductal calculi, *Lancet* 360:739, 2002.

Trowbridge RL et al: Does this patient have acute cholecystitis? *JAMA* 289:80, 2003.

AUTHOR: **FRED F. FERRI, M.D.**

BASIC INFORMATION

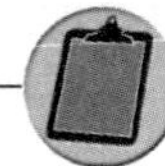

DEFINITION

Cholelithiasis is the presence of stones in the gallbladder.

SYNONYMS

Gallstones

ICD-9CM CODES
574.2 Calculus of the gallbladder without mention of cholecystitis
574.0 Calculus of the gallbladder with acute cholecystitis

EPIDEMIOLOGY & DEMOGRAPHICS

- Gallstone disease can be found in 20 million Americans. Of these, 2% to 3% (500,000 to 600,000) are treated with cholecystectomies each year.
- Annual medical expenditures for gallbladder surgeries in the U.S. exceed $5 billion.
- Incidence of gallbladder disease increases with age. Highest incidence is in the fifth and sixth decades. Predisposing factors for gallstones are female sex, pregnancy, age >40 yr, family history of gallstones, obesity, ileal disease, oral contraceptives, diabetes mellitus, rapid weight loss, estrogen replacement therapy.
- Patients with gallstones have a 20% chance of developing biliary colic or its complications at the end of a 20-yr period.

PHYSICAL FINDINGS & CLINICAL PRESENTATION

- Physical examination is entirely normal unless patient is having a biliary colic; 80% of gallstones are asymptomatic.
- Typical symptoms of obstruction of the cystic duct include intermittent, severe, cramping pain affecting the RUQ.
- Pain occurs mostly at night and may radiate to the back or right shoulder. It can last from a few minutes to several hours.

ETIOLOGY

- 75% of gallstones contain cholesterol and are usually associated with obesity, female sex, diabetes mellitus; mixed stones are most common (80%), pure cholesterol stones account for only 10% of stones.
- 25% of gallstones are pigment stones (bilirubin, calcium, and variable organic material) associated with hemolysis and cirrhosis. These tend to be black pigment stones that are refractory to medical therapy.
- 50% of mixed-type stones are radiopaque.

DIAGNOSIS

DIFFERENTIAL DIAGNOSIS

- PUD
- GERD
- IBD
- Pancreatitis
- Neoplasms
- Nonnuclear dyspepsia

LABORATORY TESTS

Generally normal unless patient has biliary obstruction (elevated alkaline phosphatase, bilirubin).

IMAGING STUDIES

- Ultrasound of the gallbladder will detect small stones and biliary sludge (sensitivity, 95%; specificity, 90%); the presence of dilated gallbladder with thickened wall is suggestive of acute cholecystitis.
- Nuclear imaging (HIDA scan) can confirm acute cholecystitis (>90% accuracy) if gallbladder does not visualize within 4 hr of injection and the radioisotope is excreted in the common bile duct.

TREATMENT

NONPHARMACOLOGIC THERAPY

Lifestyle changes (avoidance of diets high in polyunsaturated fats, weight loss in obese patients—however, avoid rapid weight loss)

ACUTE GENERAL Rx

- The management of gallstones is affected by the clinical presentation.
- Asymptomatic patients do not require therapeutic intervention.
- Surgical intervention is generally the ideal approach for symptomatic patients. Laparoscopic cholecystectomy is generally preferred over open cholecystectomy because of the shorter recovery period.
- Laparoscopic cholecystectomy after endoscopic sphincterectomy is recommended for patients with common bile duct stones and residual gallbladder stones. Where possible, single-stage laparoscopic treatments with removal of duct stones and cholecystectomy during the same procedure are preferable.
- Patients who are not appropriate candidates for surgery because of coexisting illness or patients who refuse surgery can be treated with oral bile salts: ursodiol (Actigall) 8 to 10 mg/kg/day in two to three divided doses for 16 to 20 mo, or chenodiol (Chenix) 250 mg bid initially, increasing gradually to a dose of 60 mg/kg/day. Candidates for oral bile salts are patients with cholesterol stones (radiolucent, noncalcified stones), with a diameter of ≤15 mm and having three or fewer stones. Candidates for medical therapy must have a functioning gallbladder and must have absence of calcifications on CT scans.
- Direct solvent dissolution with methyl *tert*-butyl ether (MTBE) can be used in patients with multiple stones with diameter ≥3 cm; this method should be used only by physicians experienced with contact dissolution. Administration of the solvent is either through percutaneous transhepatic placement of a catheter into the gallbladder or endoscopic retrograde catheter placement with subsequent continuous infusion and aspiration of the solvent either manually or by automatic pump system. MTBE is a powerful cholesterol solvent and can dissolve stones in a few hours (>90% dissolution over a 2-hr infusion).
- Extracorporeal shock wave lithotripsy (ESWL) is another form of medical therapy. It can be used in patients with stone diameter of ≤3 cm and having three or fewer stones.

DISPOSITION

- Recurrence rate after bile acid treatment is approximately 50% in 5 yr. Periodic ultrasound is necessary to assess the effectiveness of treatment.
- Gallstones recur after dissolution therapy with MTBE in >40% of patients within 5 yr.
- Following extracorporeal shock wave lithotripsy, stones recur in approximately 20% of patients after 4 yr.
- Patients with at least one gallstone <5 mm in diameter have a greater than fourfold increased risk of presenting with acute biliary pancreatitis. A policy of watchful waiting in such cases is generally unwarranted.
- A potential serious complication of gallstones is acute cholangitis. ERCP and endoscopic sphincterectomy (EC) followed by interval laparoscopic cholecystectomy is effective in acute cholangitis.

AUTHOR: **FRED F. FERRI, M.D.**

BASIC INFORMATION

DEFINITION

An acute diarrheal illness caused by *Vibrio cholerae.*

SYNONYMS

None

ICD-9CM CODES
001.0 Cholera

EPIDEMIOLOGY & DEMOGRAPHICS

INCIDENCE IN U.S. Previously, approximately 50 cases per year, mostly in travelers returning from endemic areas. From 1995 to 2000, 61 cases reported, 37 (61%) of which acquired outside the U.S.
PREDOMINANT SEX: None
PREDOMINANT AGE: In nonendemic areas, attack rates are equal in all age groups. In epidemic areas, children over the age of 2 yr are most commonly infected.
PEAK INCIDENCE:
None in the U.S.
Summer and fall in endemic areas
GENETICS: N/A
FAMILIAL DISPOSITION: N/A
CONGENITAL INFECTION: N/A
NEONATAL INFECTION: Illness is uncommon before the age of 2 yr, likely because of passive immunity.

PHYSICAL FINDINGS

Infection may result in asymptomatic illness or a mild diarrhea. The classic illness is described as the abrupt onset of voluminous watery diarrhea, which may lead to severe dehydration, acidosis, shock, and death. Vomiting may occur early in the illness, but fever and abdominal pain are usually absent. The typical "rice water" stools are pale with flecks of mucus and contain no blood. Muscle cramps may be prominent, and are the result of loss of fluid and electrolytes. Untreated illness results in hypovolemic shock, and death may occur in hours to days. With adequate fluid and electrolyte repletion, cholera is a self-limited illness that resolves in a few days. The use of antimicrobials can shorten the course of illness.

ETIOLOGY

The organism responsible for this illness is one of several strains of *V. cholerae.* Most infections result from the 01 serotype, the El Tor biotype. In the U.S., one outbreak occurred from the ingestion of illegally imported crab, and sporadic infection has been associated with the consumption of contaminated shellfish in Gulf Coast states. Most cases are seen in returning travelers. Transmission during epidemics is the result of the ingestion of contaminated water and, in some instances, contaminated food.

DIAGNOSIS

DIFFERENTIAL DIAGNOSIS

- Mild illness may mimic gastroenteritis resulting from a variety of etiologies.
- Sudden, voluminous diarrhea causing marked dehydration is uncommon in other illnesses.

WORKUP

Stool should be sent for culture and microscopy. Treatment should not be delayed while awaiting culture results.

LABORATORY TESTS

- WBC may be elevated, and hemoglobin may be increased as a result of hemoconcentration.
- Elevated bun and creatinine suggests prerenal azotemia. Hypoglycemia may occur. Stool cultures on appropriate media may grow the organism. Wet mount of stool under dark field or phase contrast microscopy shows organisms with characteristic darting motility.

IMAGING STUDIES

None

TREATMENT

NONPHARMACOLOGIC THERAPY

The mainstay of therapy is adequate fluid and electrolyte replacement. This can usually be achieved using oral rehydration solutions containing salts and glucose. Some patients may require intravenous fluid and electrolyte replacement.

ACUTE GENERAL Rx

- Antimicrobial therapy can decrease shedding of fluid and organisms and can shorten the course of illness
  1. Doxycycline 100 mg PO bid for 5 days, *or*
  2. Septra, one DS tablet PO bid for 5 days
- Resistance to Septra is increasing in travel-associated infections

CHRONIC Rx

It is likely that asymptomatic chronic carriers exist, however, because they are difficult to identify, and their role in transmission of disease appears to be rather limited, there is no recommendation for treatment of these individuals.

DISPOSITION

The mortality of adequately hydrated patients is less than 1%.

REFERRAL

If more than mild illness occurs

PEARLS & CONSIDERATIONS

COMMENTS

- There is currently no indication for vaccination of travelers to endemic areas. The risk of infection is small, protection from available vaccines is limited, and side effects are prominent and frequent.
- Doxycycline should not be used to treat children or pregnant women.

SUGGESTED READINGS

Ramakrishna BS et al: Amylase-resistant starch plus oral rehydration solution for cholera, *New Engl J Med* 342:308, 2000.

Steinberg EB et al: Cholera in the United States, 1995-2000: trends at the end of the twentieth century, *J Infect Dis* 184:799, 2001.

AUTHOR: **MAURICE POLICAR, M.D.**

Chronic Fatigue Syndrome

BASIC INFORMATION

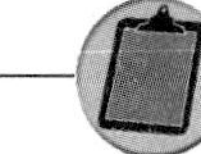

DEFINITION

Chronic fatigue syndrome (CFS) is characterized by four or more of the following symptoms, present concurrently for at least 6 mo:
- Impaired memory or concentration
- Sore throat
- Tender cervical or axillary lymph nodes
- Muscle pain
- Multijoint pain
- New headaches
- Unrefreshing sleep
- Postexertion malaise

SYNONYMS

Yuppie flu
CFS
Chronic Epstein-Barr syndrome

ICD-9CM CODES
780.7 Chronic fatigue syndrome
300.8 Neurasthenia

EPIDEMIOLOGY & DEMOGRAPHICS

PREVALENCE IN U.S.: 100 to 300 cases/100,000 persons
PREDOMINANT AGE: Young adulthood and middle age
PREDOMINANT SEX: Female > male

PHYSICAL FINDINGS & CLINICAL PRESENTATION

- There are no physical findings specific for CFS.
- The physical examination may be useful to identify fibromyalgia and other rheumatologic conditions that may coexist with CFS.

ETIOLOGY

- The etiology of CFS is unknown.
- Many experts suspect that a viral illness may trigger certain immune responses leading to the various symptoms. Most patients often report the onset of their symptoms with a flulike illness.
- Initial reports indicated a possible role of Epstein-Barr virus, but subsequent studies disproved this theory.

DIAGNOSIS

DIFFERENTIAL DIAGNOSIS

- Psychosocial depression, dysthymia, anxiety-related disorders, and other psychiatric diseases
- Infectious diseases (SBE, Lyme disease, fungal diseases, mononucleosis, HIV, chronic hepatitis B or C, TB, chronic parasitic infections)
- Autoimmune diseases: SLE, myasthenia gravis, multiple sclerosis, thyroiditis, RA
- Endocrine abnormalities: hypothyroidism, hypopituitarism, adrenal insufficiency, Cushing's syndrome, diabetes mellitus, hyperparathyroidism, pregnancy, reactive hypoglycemia
- Occult malignant disease
- Substance abuse
- Systemic disorders: chronic renal failure, COPD, cardiovascular disease, anemia, electrolyte abnormalities, liver disease
- Other: inadequate rest, sleep apnea, narcolepsy, fibromyalgia, sarcoidosis, medications, toxic agent exposure, Wegener's granulomatosis
- The differential diagnosis of fatigue is described in Section II

WORKUP

Because CFS is a clinical diagnosis and the symptoms are generally subjective, the history and physical examination are essential for excluding other causes of fatigue. A detailed mental status examination is necessary. Abnormalities should be further evaluated with appropriate psychiatric, psychologic, or neurologic examination. An algorithmic approach to the patient presenting with fatigue is described in Section III.

LABORATORY TESTS

- No specific laboratory tests exist for diagnosing CFS. Initial laboratory tests are useful to exclude other conditions that may mimic or may be associated with CFS.
  1. Screening laboratory tests: CBC, ESR, ALT, total protein, albumin, globulin, alkaline phosphatase, calcium, phosphorus, glucose, BUN, creatinine, electrolytes, TSH, and urinalysis are useful.
  2. Serologic tests for Epstein-Barr virus, *Candida albicans,* human herpesvirus 6, and other studies for immune cellular abnormalities are not useful; these tests are expensive and generally not recommended.
- Other tests may be indicated depending on the history and physical examination (e.g., ANA, RF in patients presenting with joint complaints or abnormalities on physical examination, Lyme titer in areas where Lyme disease is endemic).

IMAGING STUDIES

Generally not recommended unless history and physical examination indicate specific abnormalities (e.g., chest x-ray examination in any patient suspected of TB or sarcoidosis)

TREATMENT

NONPHARMACOLOGIC THERAPY

- Education and counseling help to develop realistic goals and expectations.
- Support groups (see "Chronic Rx") are useful.
- Patients should be reassured that the illness is not fatal and that most patients improve over time.
- An initially supervised exercise program to preserve and increase strength is beneficial for most patients and can improve symptoms.

ACUTE GENERAL Rx

Therapy is generally palliative. The following medications may be helpful:
- Antidepressants: The choice of antidepressant varies with the desired side effects. Patients with difficulty sleeping or fibromyalgia-like symptoms may benefit from low-dose tricyclics (doxepin 10 mg hs or amitriptyline 25 mg qhs). When sedation is not desirable, low-dose SSRIs (paroxetine 20 mg qd) often help alleviate fatigue and associated symptoms.
- NSAIDs can be used to relieve muscle and joint pain and headaches.
- Fludrocortisone as monotherapy for neurally mediated hypotension is no more efficacious than placebo.
- Low-dose hydrocortisone therapy provides a few benefits in quality of life; however, it is associated with frequent side effects and is not recommended.

"Alternative" medications (herbs, multivitamins, nutritional supplements) are very popular with many CFS patients but are generally not very helpful.

CHRONIC Rx

Psychiatric referral and treatment are helpful in coping with the disease in the majority of patients.

DISPOSITION

Moderate to complete recovery at 1 yr occurs in 22% to 60% of patients with CFS.

PEARLS & CONSIDERATIONS

COMMENTS

In CFS the symptoms are serious enough to reduce daily activities by >50% and in absence of any other medically identifiable disorders.

SUGGESTED READING

Koelle DM et al: Markers of viral infection in monozygotic twins discordant for chronic fatigue syndrome, *Clin Infect Dis* 35:518, 2002.

AUTHOR: **FRED F. FERRI, M.D.**

BASIC INFORMATION

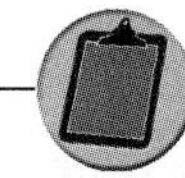

DEFINITION

A chronic demyelinating disease of the spinal nerve roots and peripheral nerves that is marked by sensory deficits and muscle weakness.

SYNONYMS

CIDP

RELATED DISORDERS

- Multifocal motor neuropathy with conduction block
- Lewis-Sumner syndrome
- Multifocal acquired demyelinating sensory and motor (MADSAM) neuropathy

ICD-9CM CODES

357.8 Inflammatory and toxic neuropathy, other (use for chronic inflammatory demyelinating polyneuropathy)

EPIDEMIOLOGY & DEMOGRAPHICS

PREVALENCE: 1.0 to 1.9 per 100,000

PREDOMINANT SEX: Male predominance

PREDOMINANT AGE: Most common in the fifth to seventh decade, although may also occur in children

CLINICAL PRESENTATION

- Onset is over weeks, months, or years.
- Symptoms may be both sensory (paresthesias, neuropathic pain, and numbness of the hands and feet) and motor (weakness).
- Postural instability, gait abnormalities, and proximal muscle weakness may become prominent late in the disease.
- Sensory findings on examination include impaired vibration and joint position sense more commonly than impaired light touch, pinprick, and temperature sensation.
- Muscle weakness is usually distal and symmetric, although may occasionally be asymmetric and more proximal than distal.
- Reflexes are usually reduced or absent.
- Cranial nerve abnormalities as well as bowel and bladder dysfunction are highly unusual.
- Autonomic dysfunction is rare, but may occur.

ETIOLOGY

CIDP occurs as a primary (idiopathic) form and may also occur in association with a number of systemic disorders.

- The idiopathic variety is most common and an autoimmune process is most likely.
- The most common systemic disorder associated with CIDP is a monoclonal gammopathy of undetermined significance (MGUS).
- Occasionally an underlying plasma cell dyscrasia such as Waldenstrom's macroglobulinemia, multiple myeloma, or osteosclerotic myeloma may be identified.
- An association with diabetes mellitus has been recognized more recently.
- CIDP may occasionally occur in the context of human immunodeficiency virus (HIV) and hepatitis B or C virus infection.

DIAGNOSIS

DIFFERENTIAL DIAGNOSIS

- Guillain-Barre syndrome (GBS)—the difference being that GBS evolves over a maximum of 4 wk and CIDP usually progresses over at least 8 wk.
- Diabetic neuropathy—the distinction can be made with electrodiagnostic studies, which show axonal physiology in diabetic neuropathy.
- Mononeuritis multiplex.
- Monoclonal gammopathy of undetermined significance, plasma cell dyscrasia, osteosclerotic myeloma, and HIV infection are not so much part of the differential diagnosis, but may coexist and so should always be sought.

WORKUP

Nerve conduction studies and electromyography—these should show evidence of primary demyelination (with or without secondary axonal loss).

LABORATORY TESTS

- Lumbar puncture
  1. Shows increased CSF protein (especially helpful if >100 mg/dl)
  2. There is little or no pleocytosis (<10 white cells)
- Serum protein electrophoresis and immunofixation electrophoresis to identify a small M-protein
- Urine protein electrophoresis
- Hepatitis and HIV serology
- Fasting blood sugar and/or glucose tolerance test
- Bone marrow biopsy if a monoclonal gammopathy is identified to exclude myeloma or other plasma cell dyscrasias

IMAGING STUDIES

Long bone skeletal survey to identify osteosclerotic myeloma

TREATMENT

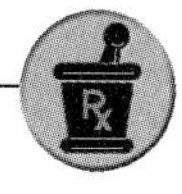

NONPHARMACOLOGIC THERAPY

- Physical and occupational therapy
- Ankle foot orthoses if there is significant weakness of ankle dorsiflexion

ACUTE GENERAL Rx

- The three primary treatment modalities for CIDP include high-dose oral corticosteroids, intravenous immunoglobulin (IVIg), and plasma exchange (PE).
- The benefit of each of these primary treatment modalities has been proven in randomized controlled trials, but their relative efficacies have not been evaluated.
- These three options for therapy should be discussed with the patient and a decision made to initiate therapy with one modality based on patient preference, tolerability of potential side effects, and cost (IVIg and PE are extremely expensive).
- IVIg is usually administered at a dose of 2g/kg divided over 3 to 5 days. Initial improvement is observed in two thirds of patients. If there has been incomplete improvement or no major improvement, it is advised to repeat the course of IVIg in 1 to 2 months. If there continues to be further improvement of symptoms after repeated administration of IVIg, monthly infusions may be necessary to maintain a response.
- PE is usually performed every other day for approximately 4 to 6 weeks. Like IVIg, plasma exchanges may be repeated on regular basis if therapeutic benefit has been established.

- Oral prednisone is usually initiated at a dose of ~1 mg/kg. High-dose prednisone dosing should be maintained until a clinical response is achieved, typically within 4 to 8 weeks, after which the dose may be slowly tapered. The goal is to maintain a clinical response with the lowest possible dose administered on an alternate-day regimen.

CHRONIC Rx

- IVIg, PE and/or prednisone are usually required on a chronic basis to maintain a clinical response. The frequency and dosing requirements must be determined on an individual basis.
- Steroid-sparing agents such as azathioprine, mycophenolate mofetil, methotrexate, cyclosporine, or cyclophosphamide may sometimes be necessary to reduce the maintenance dose of steroids or the frequency with which IVIg or PE is administered.

DISPOSITION

- Prognosis for functional recovery is quite variable, although most patients (70% to 80%) will be left with only minor disability (some difficulty with premorbid activities, but functionally independent) if treated aggressively with immunosuppressive therapy.
- Approximately 15% to 30% of patients will be left with moderate disability (i.e., require significant assistance with activities of daily living or with ambulation).
- In terms of the neuropathy, there is no clear evidence that the prognosis differs for patients with idiopathic forms of CIDP compared with those with CIDP associated with monoclonal proteins.
- Overall prognosis (not related to the neuropathy) may be worse in patients with multiple myeloma.
- Younger age, female gender, and the presence of a relapsing-remitting (rather than a monophasic progressive) course may portend a better prognosis.

REFERRAL

- Neurologist (preferably with expertise in the management of patients with neuromuscular disease)
- Physical therapy
- Occupational therapy
- Hematologist for further evaluation and management of associated plasma cell dyscrasia

PEARLS & CONSIDERATIONS

COMMENTS

- Electrophysiology (nerve conduction studies) are essential as they offer the best combination of sensitivity and specificity for the diagnosis of CIDP.
- Lumbar puncture for CSF analysis is also extremely helpful, especially if a markedly elevated protein without associated pleocytosis is found.

PREVENTION

There is no known preventative therapy.

PATIENT/FAMILY EDUCATION

CIDP is a chronic and often lifelong illness. It is often punctuated by long periods of remission and significant improvement. With appropriate therapy, patients often return to previous baseline level of functioning. Relapses, however, do occur. Chronic steroid use is a major cause of morbidity in patients with CIDP.

SUGGESTED READINGS

Adams R, Victor M: *Principles of Neurology,* New York, 1993, McGraw-Hill.

Bouchard C et al: Clinicopathologic findings and prognosis of chronic inflammatory demyelinating polyneuropathy, *Neurology* 52:498, 1999.

Noseworthy J et al: *Neurological Therapeutics Principles and Practice,* London and New York, 2003, Martin Dunitz.

Van Doorn PA et al: Intravenous immunoglobulin treatment in patients with chronic inflammatory demyelinating polyneuropathy, *Arch Neurol* 48:217, 1991.

AUTHOR: **GENNA GEKHT, M.D.**

BASIC INFORMATION

DEFINITION

Chronic obstructive pulmonary disease (COPD) is a disorder characterized by the presence of airflow limitation that is not fully reversible. COPD encompasses *emphysema,* characterized by loss of lung elasticity and destruction of lung parenchyma with enlargement of air spaces, and *chronic bronchitis,* characterized by obstruction of small airways and productive cough greater than 3 months' duration for more than 2 successive years. Patients with COPD are classically subdivided in two major groups based on their appearance:

1. "*Blue bloaters*" are patients with chronic bronchitis; the name is derived from the bluish tinge of the skin (secondary to chronic hypoxemia and hypercapnia) and from the frequent presence of peripheral edema (secondary to cor pulmonale); chronic cough with production of large amounts of sputum is characteristic.
2. "*Pink puffers*" are patients with emphysema; they have a cachectic appearance but pink skin color (adequate oxygen saturation); shortness of breath is manifested by pursed-lip breathing and use of accessory muscles of respiration.

SYNONYMS

COPD
Emphysema
Chronic bronchitis

ICD-9CM CODES
496 COPD
492.8 Emphysema

EPIDEMIOLOGY & DEMOGRAPHICS

- COPD affects 16 million Americans and is responsible for >80,000 deaths/yr.
- COPD is the fourth leading cause of death in the U.S. and is expected to become the third leading cause of death by 2020.
- Highest incidence is in males >40 yr.
- 16 million office visits, 500,000 hospitalizations, and >$18 billion in direct health care costs annually can be attributed to COPD.

PHYSICAL FINDINGS & CLINICAL PRESENTATION

- Blue bloaters (chronic bronchitis): peripheral cyanosis, productive cough, tachypnea, tachycardia
- Pink puffers (emphysema): dyspnea, pursed-lip breathing with use of accessory muscles for respiration, decreased breath sounds
- Possible wheezing in both patients with chronic bronchitis and emphysema
- Features of both chronic bronchitis and emphysema in many patients with COPD
- Acute exacerbation of COPD is mainly a clinical diagnosis and generally manifests with worsening dyspnea, increase in sputum purulence, and increase in sputum volume

ETIOLOGY

- Tobacco exposure
- Occupational exposure to pulmonary toxins (e.g., cadmium)
- Atmospheric pollution
- α-1 antitrypsin deficiency (rare; <1% of COPD patients)

DIAGNOSIS

DIFFERENTIAL DIAGNOSIS

- CHF
- Asthma
- Respiratory infections
- Bronchiectasis
- Cystic fibrosis
- Neoplasm
- Pulmonary embolism
- Sleep apnea, obstructive
- Hypothyroidism

WORKUP

Chest x-ray examination, pulmonary function testing, blood gases (in patients with acute exacerbation)

LABORATORY TESTS

- CBC may reveal leukocytosis with "shift to the left" during acute exacerbation.
- Sputum may be purulent with bacterial respiratory tract infections. Sputum staining and cultures are usually reserved for cases that are refractory to antibiotic therapy.
- ABGs: normocapnia, mild to moderate hypoxemia may be present.
- Pulmonary function testing (PFT): The primary physiological abnormality in COPD is an accelerated decline in forced expiratory volume in one second (FEV_1) from the normal rate in adults over 30 years of age of approximately 30 ml/yr to nearly 60 ml/yr. PFTs results in COPD reveal abnormal diffusing capacity, increased total lung capacity and/or residual volume, fixed reduction in FEV_1 in patients with emphysema; normal diffusing capacity, reduced FEV_1 in patients with chronic bronchitis. Patients with COPD can generally be distinguished from asthmatics by their incomplete response to albuterol (change in FEV_1 <200 ml and 12%) and absence of an abnormal bronchoconstrictor response to methacholine or other stimuli. However, nearly 40% of patients with COPD respond to bronchodilators.

IMAGING STUDIES

Chest x-ray:

- Hyperinflation with flattened diaphragm, tending of the diaphragm at the rib, and increased retrosternal chest space
- Decreased vascular markings and bullae in patients with emphysema
- Thickened bronchial markings and enlarged right side of the heart in patients with chronic bronchitis

TREATMENT

NONPHARMACOLOGIC THERAPY

- Weight loss in patients with chronic bronchitis.
- Avoidance of tobacco use and elimination of air pollutants.
- Supplemental oxygen, usually through a face mask to ensure oxygen saturation >90% measured by pulse oximetry.
- Pulmonary toilet: careful nasotracheal suction is indicated in patients with excessive secretions and inability to expectorate. Mechanical percussion of the chest as applied by a physical or respiratory therapist is ineffective with acute exacerbations of COPD.

GENERAL Rx

- Acute exacerbation of COPD can be treated with:
  1. Aerosolized β-agonists (e.g., metaproterenol nebulizer solution 5% 0.3 mL or albuterol nebulized 5% solution 2.5-5 mg).
  2. Anticholinergic agents, which have equivalent efficacy to inhaled β-adrenergic agonists. Inhalant solution of ipratropium bromide 0.5 mg can be administered every 4 to 8 hr.
  3. Short courses of systemic corticosteroids, which have been shown to improve spirometric and clinical outcomes. In the hospital setting give IV methylprednisolone 50- to 100-mg bolus, then q6-8h; taper as soon as possible. In the outpatient setting, oral prednisone 40 mg/day initially, decreasing the dose by 10 mg every other day is generally effective.
  4. Judicious oxygen administration (hypercapnia and further respiratory compromise may occur after high-flow oxygen therapy); use of a Venturi-type mask delivering an inspired oxygen fraction of 24% to 28% is preferred to nasal cannula.
  5. Noninvasive positive pressure ventilation delivered by a facial or nasal mask in the treatment of chronic restrictive thoracic disease may obviate the need for intratracheal intubation.
  6. The role of inhaled corticosteroids in COPD is controversial. Although some trials have demonstrated mild improvement in patients' symptoms and decreased frequency of exacerbations most pulmonologists believe that these drugs are ineffective in most patients with COPD but should be considered for patients with moderate to severe airflow limitation who have persistent symptoms despite optimal bronchodilator therapy.
  7. IV aminophylline administration is controversial and generally not recommended. When used, serum levels should be closely monitored to minimize risks of tachyarrhythmias.
- Antibiotics are indicated in suspected respiratory infection (e.g., increased purulence and volume of phlegm).
  1. *Haemophilus influenzae, Streptococcus pneumoniae* are frequent causes of acute bronchitis.
  2. Oral antibiotics of choice are azithromycin, levofloxacin, amoxicillin-clavulanate, and cefuroxime.
  3. The use of antibiotics is beneficial in exacerbations of COPD presenting with increased dyspnea and sputum purulence (especially if the patient is febrile).
- Guaifenesin may improve cough symptoms and mucus clearance; however, mucolytic medications are generally ineffective. Their benefits may be greatest in patients with more advanced disease.
- Intubation and mechanical ventilation may be necessary if previous measures fail to provide improvement.
- Lung volume reduction surgery has been proposed as a palliative treatment for severe emphysema. Overall it increases the chance of improved exercise capacity but does not confer a survival advantage over medical therapy. It is most beneficial in patients with both predominantly upper-lobe emphysema and low baseline exercise capacity.

In patients with end-stage emphysema who have an FEV_1 <25% of predicted normal value after administration of bronchodilator and additional complications such as severe hypoxemia, hypercapnia and pulmonary hypertension single lung transplantation should be considered a surgical option.

DISPOSITION

- Following the initial episode of respiratory failure, 5-yr survival is approximately 25%.
- Development of cor pulmonale or hypercapnia and persistent tachycardia are poor prognostic indicators.

PEARLS & CONSIDERATIONS

COMMENTS

- All patients with COPD should receive pneumococcal vaccine and yearly influenza vaccine.
- In assessing the severity of COPD, the forced expiratory volume in one second (FEV_1) is limited by the fact that it does not take into account the systemic manifestations of COPD. The BODE index (Body-mass index [B], degree of obstruction [O], dyspnea [D], and exercise capacity [E]) has been proposed as a multidimentional scale to better assess the morbidity and mortality associated with COPD. It is better than the FEV_1 at predicting the risk of death from any cause and from respiratory causes among patients with COPD.

SUGGESTED READINGS

Aaron SD et al: Outpatient oral prednisone after emergency treatment of chronic obstructive pulmonary disease, *N Engl J Med* 348:2618, 2003.

Anthonisen NR et al: Smoking and lung function of Lung Health Study participants after 11 years, *Am J Resp Crit Care Med* 166:675, 2002.

Celli B et al: The body-mass index, airflow obstruction, dyspnea, and exercise capacity index in chronic obstructive pulmonary disease, *N Engl J Med* 350:1005, 2004.

Hogg JC et al: The nature of small-airway obstruction in chronic obstructive pulmonary disease, *N Engl J Med* 350:2645, 2004.

Man PS et al: Contemporary management of chronic obstructive pulmonary disease, clinical applications, *JAMA* 290:2313, 2003.

National emphysema treatment trial research group: A randomized trial comparing lung-volume-reduction surgery with medical therapy for severe emphysema, *N Engl J Med* 348:2059, 2003.

Sethi S et al: New strains of bacteria and exacerbations of chronic obstructive pulmonary disease, *N Engl J Med* 347:465, 2002.

Sin DD et al: Contemporary management of chronic obstructive pulmonary disease, a scientific review, *JAMA* 290:2301, 2003.

Stoller JK: Acute exacerbations of chronic obstructive pulmonary disease, *N Engl J Med* 346:988, 2002.

Sutherland ER, Cherniak RM: Management of chronic obstructive pulmonary disease, *N Engl J Med* 350:2689, 2004.

AUTHOR: **FRED F. FERRI, M.D.**

BASIC INFORMATION

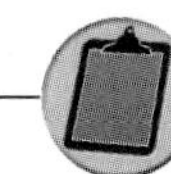

DEFINITION

Churg-Strauss syndrome (CSS) refers to a systemic vasculitis accompanied by severe asthma, hypereosinophilia, and necrotizing vasculitis with extravascular eosinophil granulomas.

SYNONYMS

Allergic angiitis and granulomatosis

ICD-9CM CODES
446.4 Angiitis, allergic granulomatous

EPIDEMIOLOGY & DEMOGRAPHICS

- Churg-Strauss syndrome was first described by Churg and Strauss in 1951 after reviewing a number of autopsy cases previously classified as polyarteritis nodosa.
- Churg-Strauss syndrome is a rare disease with an overall incidence of 2.4 to 4.0 per million population.
- At the Mayo Clinic, 90 cases were observed over a 19-year period from 1976 to 1995.
- There is no significant difference in incidence rate by gender, although some studies have shown a slight male predominance.
- CSS usually occurs between 14 and 75 years of age, with a mean age of 50 years, although cases have been reported in the pediatric population as young as 4 years of age.

PHYSICAL FINDINGS & CLINICAL PRESENTATION

The clinical picture of CSS typically consists of three partially overlapping phases:

1. The prodromal phase or allergic phase characterized by severe adult-onset asthma, with or without allergic rhinitis (70%), sinusitis, headache, cough, and wheezing. This phase can last several years.
2. The eosinophilic phase characterized by peripheral eosinophilia and eosinophilic infiltration of the lungs and GI tract producing signs and symptoms of cough, fever, anorexia, weight loss, sweats, malaise, nausea, vomiting, abdominal pain, and diarrhea.
3. The vasculitic phase, which may involve any organ, including the heart (most frequent), lung, peripheral nerves, kidney, lymph nodes, muscle, CNS, and skin, and manifesting in chest pain, dyspnea, hemophysis, migratory polyarthralgia, myalgias, peripheral neuropathy (mononeuritis multiplex), joint swelling, skin rash, and signs of CHF.

ETIOLOGY

- The cause of Churg-Strauss syndrome is unknown. A hypersensitivity allergic response to an unknown allergen has been proposed, with eosinophils and IgE playing a direct role in pathogenesis.
- The NIH investigated the observed relationship between asthma therapy and the development of CSS and found that symptoms of CSS typically appear as oral corticosteroids are being decreased or discontinued. Development of the vasculitis appeared to be unmasked by the tapering of corticosteroids and not triggered by leukotriene receptor-1 antagonists as previously reported.
- Reports of CSS developing in severe asthmatics after vaccination or desensitization therapy have led some authors to conclude that massive or nonspecific immunologic stimulation should be used with caution in patients with unstable asthma.
- Although similar and at times grouped with patients with polyarteritis nodosa (PAN) or Wegener's granulomatosis (WG), Churg-Strauss syndrome differs in that:
  1. Churg-Strauss syndrome vasculitis involves not only small-sized arteries but also veins and venules.
  2. Churg-Strauss syndrome, unlike PAN, predominantly involves the lung. Other organs affected include heart, GI, CNS, kidney, and skin.
  3. Kidney involvement is much less common in CSS than in WG. Pulmonary lesions in WG usually involve the upper respiratory tract, versus peripheral lung parenchymal in CSS.
  4. Churg-Strauss biopsy shows necrotizing vasculitis along with a granulomatous extravascular reaction infiltrated by eosinophils.

DIAGNOSIS

The American College of Rheumatology (ACR) has established criteria for the diagnosis of Churg-Strauss syndrome. At least four of the following six criteria must be met to make the diagnosis:

- Asthma
- Eosinophilia >10% on WBC count
- Mononeuropathy or polyneuropathy
- Migratory pulmonary infiltrates
- Paranasal sinus abnormalities
- Extravascular eosinophils

The presence of any four or more of the six criteria yields a sensitivity of 85% and a specificity of 99.7%. The combination of asthma and eosinophilia in patients with vasculitis was found by the ACR to be 90% sensitive and 99% specific for CSS.

DIFFERENTIAL DIAGNOSIS

- Polyarteritis nodosa
- Wegener's granulomatosis
- Sarcoidosis
- Loeffler syndrome
- Henoch-Schönlein purpura
- Allergic bronchopulmonary aspergillosis
- Rheumatoid arthritis
- Leukocytoclastic vasculitis

WORKUP

- If the clinical suspicion of Churg-Strauss is raised, further workup including blood tests, x-rays, and tissue biopsy help establish the diagnosis.

LABORATORY TESTS

- CBC with differential may reveal one diagnostic criterion: eosinophilia with counts ranging from 5,000 to 10,000 eosinophils/mm^3.
- ESR is usually elevated and a marker of inflammation.
- BUN/creatinine may be elevated, suggesting renal involvement.
- Urinalysis may show hematuria and proteinuria.
- 24-hour urine for protein if greater than 1 g/day is a poor prognostic factor.
- Antineutrophil cytoplasmic antibodies (ANCA), although not diagnostic of Churg-Strauss syndrome, are found in up to 70% of patients, usually with a perinuclear staining pattern.
- Stools may be occult blood positive because of enteric involvement during eosinophilic phase.
- AST, ALT, and CPK may indicate liver or muscle (skeletal or cardiac) involvement.
- RA and ANA may be positive.
- Biopsy substantiates the diagnosis. Necrotizing vasculitis and extravascular necrotizing granulomas, usually with eosinophilic infiltrates, are suggestive of CSS. The presence of eosinophils in extravascular tissues is most specific for CSS.

IMAGING STUDIES

- Chest x-ray is abnormal in 37% to 77% of the cases and can show asymmetrical patchy migratory infiltrates, interstitial lung disease, or nodular infiltrates (Fig. 1-60). Small pleural effusions are found in 29% of cases.
- Lung lesions in CSS are noncavitating, as opposed to those that are characteristic of Wegener's granulomatosis.
- Paranasal sinus films may reveal sinus opacification.
- Angiography is sometimes done in patients with mesenteric ischemia or renal involvement.

TREATMENT

NONPHARMACOLOGIC THERAPY

Oxygen therapy in severe asthmatic exacerbations

ACUTE GENERAL Rx

- Corticosteroids are the treatment of choice. Prednisone 1 mg/kg/day is the starting dose and is continued for 1-2 months. After clinically evident vasculitis resolves, prednisone is tapered progressively to 10 mg/day at 1 year.
- Although laboratory evidence of renal involvement is uncommon, it responds well to corticosteroid treatment and rarely progresses to renal failure.
- A drop in the eosinophil count and the ESR documents a response. Antineutrophil cytoplasmic antibodies does not reliably correspond with disease activity.

CHRONIC Rx

- Cyclophosphamide plus corticosteroids are used in patients with multiorgan involvement and poor prognostic factors.
- Many with persistent symptoms of asthma will require long-term corticosteroids even if vasculitis is no longer present.

DISPOSITION

- Clinical remissions are obtained in more than 90% of patients. Relapse occurs in 26%.
- With treatment, long-term prognosis is good, with a 5-year survival rate of 80% and 50% at 7 years. Despite successful treatment of Churg-Strauss syndrome, asthma generally remains persistent, and ischemic damage to peripheral nerves can be permanent.
- The 5-year survival of untreated Churg-Strauss is 25%.
- Death usually occurs from progressive refractory vasculitis, myocardial involvement (approximately 50% of deaths), or severe GI involvement (mesenteric ischemia, pancreatitis, etc.).
- Poor prognostic factors include:
  1. Renal insufficiency
  2. Proteinuria >1 g/day
  3. GI involvement
  4. Cardiac involvement
  5. CNS involvement (<25%) manifested as cerebral infarct or hemorrhage
  6. Weight loss of >10% body weight
  7. Age >50 years

REFERRAL

If a patient is suspected of having Churg-Strauss syndrome, a pulmonary referral for diagnosis and management is appropriate.

PEARLS & CONSIDERATIONS

COMMENTS

- The diagnosis of Churg-Strauss is many times missed initially, because asthma and rhinitis or sinusitis are very common and these symptoms can precede the onset of vasculitis by many years (mean 3-8 years, but up to 30 years has been reported).
- Churg-Strauss syndrome is distinguished from other vasculitides by the nearly universal presence of asthma that typically precedes all other symptoms.
- The asthma associated with CSS is distinct from common allergic asthma in that it typically has a late onset and a degree of eosinophilia that is much greater than typically seen in allergic asthma. The asthma of CSS is associated with very specific parenchymal lung lesions, and patients typically have no family history of allergies or asthma.
- Up to 77% of patients in the prodromal phase of CSS require oral steroids for asthma control.
- Nearly 50% of patients will experience improvement or dramatic remission of asthma symptoms shortly before or at the start of the vasculitic phase.
- Patients often experience constitutional symptoms of weight loss, fever, and malaise before specific organ involvement is clinically evident.
- Peripheral nerve involvement due to vasculitis of the vasa vasorum commonly manifests as mononeuritis multiplex. Patients may present with sudden foot or wrist drop, along with sensory deficits in the distribution of one or more distal nerves.
- Most patients with GI involvement are symptomatic. Gastroenteritis, acute abdomen, cholecystitis, hemorrhage, bowel perforation, and mesenteric ischemia have all been reported in patients with CSS.
- Cutaneous involvement is seen in 40% to 70% of cases of CSS, and manifests as palpable purpura, petechiae, and/or cutaneous nodules.
- In contrast to CSS, the eosinophilia in HES is usually refractory to steroid therapy, systemic vasculitis and granulomas are absent on biopsy, and endomyocardial fibrosis is a typical finding.
- Most patients with CSS respond to corticosteroid treatment and do not require cytotoxic therapy.

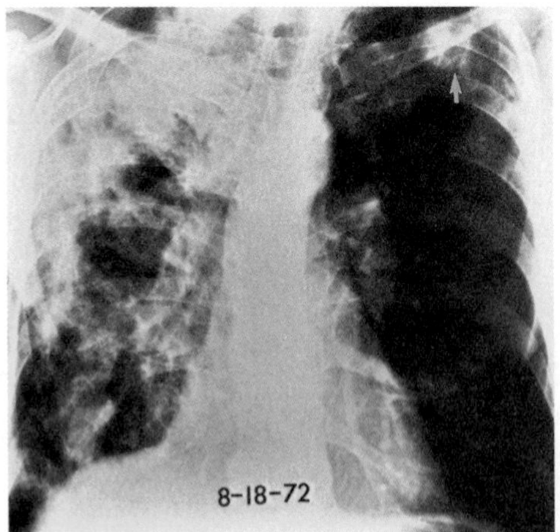

FIGURE 1-60 Allergic angitis and granulomatosis. PA chest radiograph demonstrates peripheral air-space consolidation in the right lung and a nodule (*arrow*) in the left upper lobe in this asthmatic patient. (From McLoud TC [ed]: *Thoracic radiology, the requisites,* St Louis, 1998, Mosby.)

SUGGESTED READINGS

Abril A, Calamia KT, Cohen MD: The Churg Strauss syndrome (allergic granulomatous angiitis): review and update, *Semin Arthritis Rheum* 33:106, 2003.

Conron M, Beynon HL: Churg-Strauss syndrome, *Thorax* 55(10):870, 2000.

Masi AT et al: American College of Rheumatology 1990 criteria for the classification of Churg-Strauss syndrome, *Arthritis Rheum* 33:1094, 1990.

Noth I, Strek ME, Leff AL: Churg-Strauss syndrome, *Lancet* 361(9357):587, 2003.

Vogel P, Schissel D: Churg-Strauss syndrome (allergic granulomatosis), eMedicine Journal 2(10), 2001. (http://www.emedicine.com).

Watts RA, Scott DG, Lane SE: Epidemiology of Wegener's granulomatosis, microscopic polyangiitis, and Churg-Strauss syndrome, *Cleve Clin J Med* 69(Suppl 2):SII84, 2002.

AUTHORS: **JASON IANNUCCILLI, M.D.,** and **PETER PETROPOULOS, M.D.**

BASIC INFORMATION

DEFINITION

Cirrhosis is defined histologically as the presence of fibrosis and regenerative nodules in the liver. It can be classified as micronodular, macronodular, and mixed; however, each form may be seen in the same patient at different stages of the disease. Cirrhosis manifests clinically with portal hypertension, hepatic encephalopathy, and variceal bleeding.

ICD-9CM CODES
571.5 Cirrhosis of the liver
571.2 Cirrhosis of the liver secondary to alcohol

EPIDEMIOLOGY & DEMOGRAPHICS

- Cirrhosis is the eleventh leading cause of death in the U.S. (death rate 9 deaths/100,000 persons/yr).
- Alcohol abuse and viral hepatitis are the major causes of cirrhosis in the U.S.

PHYSICAL FINDINGS & CLINICAL PRESENTATION

SKIN: Jaundice, palmar erythema (alcohol abuse), spider angiomata, ecchymosis (thrombocytopenia or coagulation factor deficiency), dilated superficial periumbilical vein (caput medusae), increased pigmentation (hemochromatosis), xanthomas (primary biliary cirrhosis), needle tracks (viral hepatitis)
EYES: Kayser-Fleischer rings (corneal copper deposition seen in Wilson's disease; best diagnosed with slit lamp examination), scleral icterus
BREATH: Fetor hepaticus (musty odor of breath and urine found in cirrhosis with hepatic failure)
CHEST: Possible gynecomastia in men
ABDOMEN: Tender hepatomegaly (congestive hepatomegaly), small, nodular liver (cirrhosis), palpable, nontender gallbladder (neoplastic extrahepatic biliary obstruction), palpable spleen (portal hypertension), venous hum auscultated over periumbilical veins (portal hypertension), ascites (portal hypertension, hypoalbuminemia)
RECTAL EXAMINATION: Hemorrhoids (portal hypertension), guaiac-positive stools (alcoholic gastritis, bleeding esophageal varices, PUD, bleeding hemorrhoids)
GENITALIA: Testicular atrophy in males (chronic liver disease, hemochromatosis)
EXTREMITIES: Pedal edema (hypoalbuminemia, failure of right side of the heart), arthropathy (hemochromatosis)
NEUROLOGIC: Flapping tremor, asterixis (hepatic encephalopathy), choreoathetosis, dysarthria (Wilson's disease)

ETIOLOGY

- Alcohol abuse
- Secondary biliary cirrhosis, obstruction of the common bile duct (stone, stricture, pancreatitis, neoplasm, sclerosing cholangitis)
- Drugs (e.g., acetaminophen, isoniazid, methotrexate, methyldopa)
- Hepatic congestion (e.g., CHF, constrictive pericarditis, tricuspid insufficiency, thrombosis of the hepatic vein, obstruction of the vena cava)
- Primary biliary cirrhosis
- Hemochromatosis
- Chronic hepatitis B or C
- Wilson's disease
- α-1 antitrypsin deficiency
- Infiltrative diseases (amyloidosis, glycogen storage diseases, hemochromatosis)
- Nutritional: jejunoileal bypass
- Others: parasitic infections (schistosomiasis), idiopathic portal hypertension, congenital hepatic fibrosis, systemic mastocytosis, autoimmune hepatitis, hepatic steatosis, IBD

DIAGNOSIS

WORKUP

In addition to an assessment of liver function, the evaluation of patients with cirrhosis should also include an assessment of renal and circulatory function. Diagnostic workup is aimed primarily at identifying the most likely cause of cirrhosis. The history is extremely important:

- Alcohol abuse: alcoholic liver disease
- History of hepatitis B (chronic active hepatitis, primary hepatic neoplasm, or hepatitis C)
- History of IBD (primary sclerosing cholangitis)
- History of pruritus, hyperlipoproteinemia, and xanthomas in a middle-aged or elderly female (primary biliary cirrhosis)
- Impotence, diabetes mellitus, hyperpigmentation, arthritis (hemochromatosis)
- Neurologic disturbances (Wilson's disease, hepatolenticular degeneration)
- Family history of "liver disease" (hemochromatosis [positive family history in 25% of patients], α-1 antitrypsin deficiency)
- History of recurrent episodes of RUQ pain (biliary tract disease)
- History of blood transfusions, IV drug abuse (hepatitis C)
- History of hepatotoxic drug exposure
- Coexistence of other diseases with immune or autoimmune features (ITP, myasthenia gravis, thyroiditis, autoimmune hepatitis)

LABORATORY TESTS

- Decreased Hgb and Hct, elevated MCV, increased BUN and creatinine (the BUN may also be "normal" or low if the patient has severely diminished liver function), decreased sodium (dilutional hyponatremia), decreased potassium (as a result of secondary aldosteronism or urinary losses). Evaluation of renal function should also include measurement of urinary sodium and urinary protein from a 24-hr urine collection.
- Decreased glucose in a patient with liver disease indicating severe liver damage
- Other laboratory abnormalities:
  1. Alcoholic hepatitis and cirrhosis: there may be mild elevation of ALT and AST, usually <500 IU; AST $>$ ALT (ratio $>2:3$).
  2. Extrahepatic obstruction: there may be moderate elevations of ALT and AST to levels <500 IU.
  3. Viral, toxic, or ischemic hepatitis: there are extreme elevations (>500 IU) of ALT and AST.
  4. Transaminases may be normal despite significant liver disease in patients with jejunoileal bypass operations or hemochromatosis or after methotrexate administration.
  5. Alkaline phosphatase elevation can occur with extrahepatic obstruction, primary biliary cirrhosis, and primary sclerosing cholangitis.
  6. Serum LDH is significantly elevated in metastatic disease of the liver; lesser elevations are seen with hepatitis, cirrhosis, extrahepatic obstruction, and congestive hepatomegaly.
  7. Serum γ-glutamyl transpeptidase (GGTP) is elevated in alcoholic liver disease and may also be elevated with cholestatic disease (primary biliary cirrhosis, primary sclerosing cholangitis).
  8. Serum bilirubin may be elevated; urinary bilirubin can be present in hepatitis, hepatocellular jaundice, and biliary obstruction.
  9. Serum albumin: significant liver disease results in hypoalbuminemia.
  10. Prothrombin time: an elevated PT in patients with liver disease indicates severe liver damage and poor prognosis.
  11. Presence of hepatitis B surface antigen implies acute or chronic hepatitis B.
  12. Presence of antimitochondrial antibody suggests primary biliary cirrhosis, chronic hepatitis.

13. Elevated serum copper, decreased serum ceruloplasmin, and elevated 24-hr urine may be diagnostic of Wilson's disease.
14. Protein immunoelectrophoresis may reveal decreased α-1 globulins (α-1 antitrypsin deficiency), increased IgA (alcoholic cirrhosis), increased IgM (primary biliary cirrhosis), increased IgG (chronic hepatitis, cryptogenic cirrhosis).
15 An elevated serum ferritin and increased transferrin saturation are suggestive of hemochromatosis.
16. An elevated blood ammonia suggests hepatocellular dysfunction; serial values, however, are generally not useful in following patients with hepatic encephalopathy because there is poor correlation between blood ammonia level and degree of hepatic encephalopathy.
17. Serum cholesterol is elevated in cholestatic disorders.
18. Antinuclear antibodies (ANA) may be found in autoimmune hepatitis.
19. Alpha fetoprotein: levels >1000 pg/ml are highly suggestive of primary liver cell carcinoma.
20. Hepatitis C viral testing identifies patients with chronic hepatitis C infection.
21. Elevated level of serum globulin (especially γ-globulins), positive ANA test may occur with autoimmune hepatitis.

IMAGING STUDIES

- Ultrasonography is the procedure of choice for detection of gallstones and dilation of common bile ducts.
- CT scan is useful for detecting mass lesions in liver and pancreas, assessing hepatic fat content, identifying idiopathic hemochromatosis, early diagnosing of Budd-Chiari syndrome, dilation of intrahepatic bile ducts, and detection of varices and splenomegaly.
- Technetium-99m sulfur colloid scanning is useful for diagnosing cirrhosis (there is a shift of colloid uptake to the spleen, bone marrow), identifying hepatic adenomas (cold defect is noted), diagnosing Budd-Chiari syndrome (there is increased uptake by the caudate lobe).
- ERCP is the procedure of choice for diagnosing periampullary carcinoma, common duct stones; it is also useful in diagnosing primary sclerosing cholangitis.
- Percutaneous transhepatic cholangiography (PTC) is useful when evaluating patients with cholestatic jaundice and dilated intrahepatic ducts by ultrasonography; presence of intrahepatic strictures and focal dilation is suggestive of PSC.
- Percutaneous liver biopsy is useful in evaluating hepatic filling defects, diagnosing hepatocellular disease or hepatomegaly, evaluating persistently abnormal liver function tests, and diagnosing hemachromatosis, primary biliary cirrhosis, Wilson's disease, glycogen storage diseases, chronic hepatitis, autoimmune hepatitis, infiltrative diseases, alcoholic liver disease, drug-induced liver disease, and primary or secondary carcinoma.

TREATMENT

NONPHARMACOLOGIC THERAPY

Avoid any hepatotoxins (e.g., ethanol, acetaminophen); improve nutritional status.

GENERAL Rx

- Correct any mechanical obstruction to bile flow (e.g., calculi, strictures).
- Provide therapy for underlying cardiovascular disorders in patients with cardiac cirrhosis.
- Remove excess body iron with phlebotomy and deferoxamine in patients with hemochromatosis.
- Remove copper deposits with D-penicillamine in patients with Wilson's disease.
- Long-term ursodiol therapy will slow the progression of primary biliary cirrhosis. It is, however, ineffective in primary sclerosing cholangitis.
- Glucocorticoids (prednisone 20 to 30 mg/day initially or combination therapy or prednisone and azathioprine) is useful in autoimmune hepatitis.
- Liver transplantation may be indicated in otherwise healthy patients (age <65 yr) with sclerosing cholangitis, chronic hepatitis cirrhosis, or primary biliary cirrhosis with prognostic information suggesting $<20\%$ chance of survival without transplantation; contraindications to liver transplantation are AIDS, most metastatic malignancies, active substance abuse, uncontrolled sepsis, uncontrolled cardiac or pulmonary disease.
- Treatment of complications of portal hypertension (ascites, esophagogastric varices, hepatic encephalopathy, and hepatorenal syndrome).

DISPOSITION

- Prognosis varies with the etiology of the patient's cirrhosis and whether there is ongoing hepatic injury. Mortality rate exceeds 80% in patients with hepatorenal syndrome.
- Two markers of portal hypertension, thrombocytopenia and splenomegaly, moderately increase the likelihood of large esophageal varices.
- If advanced cirrhosis is present and transplantation is not feasible, survival is 1 to 2 yr.

REFERRAL

- Hospital admission for bleeding varices, hepatic encephalopathy, or onset of hepatorenal syndrome
- Liver transplantation in suitable candidates is the only effective long-term treatment of complications resulting from cirrhosis

PEARLS & CONSIDERATIONS

COMMENTS

Thrombocytopenia and advanced Child-Pugh cases are associated with the presence of varices. These factors are useful to identify cirrhotic patients who benefit most from referral for endoscopic screening for varices.

SUGGESTED READINGS

Gines P et al: Management of cirrhosis and ascites, *N Engl J Med* 350:1645, 2004.

Ong JP et al: Correlation between ammonia levels and the severity of hepatic encephalopathy, *Am J Med* 114:189, 2003.

AUTHOR: **FRED F. FERRI, M.D.**

BASIC INFORMATION

DEFINITION

Primary biliary cirrhosis (PBC) is a chronic, variably progressive disease most often affecting women and characterized by destruction of the small intrahepatic bile ducts leading to portal inflammation, fibrosis, cirrhosis, and clinical liver failure. Two of the following three diagnostic criteria are pathognomonic for PBC: positive antimitochondrial antibody (AMA), compatible liver histology on biopsy, and a cholestatic pattern on liver function tests, all in the absence of extrahepatic biliary obstruction.

ICD-9CM CODES
571.6 Biliary cirrhosis

EPIDEMIOLOGY & DEMOGRAPHICS

- PBC affects all races and accounts for 0.6% to 2% of deaths from cirrhosis worldwide.
- Approximately 95% of patients are female.
- Prevalence estimates range from 19 to 151 cases per million population whereas incidence estimates range from 3.9 to 15 cases per million population per year. The previous observation that prevalence of PBC was highest in England and Scandinavia and extremely low in Africa and the Indian subcontinent is now recognized as an effect of epidemiologic reporting rather than a true difference in prevalence.
- Genetic factors are important in the development of PBC; however, there is no clear dominant or recessive pattern of inheritance. Prevalence in families with one affected member is estimated to be 100 times higher than the general population. There is a weak association between PBC and HLA-DR8.
- Onset typically occurs between the ages of 30 and 65.
- Up to 84% patients with PBC have at least one other autoimmune disorder, such as thyroiditis, Sjögren's syndrome, rheumatoid arthritis, Raynaud's phenomenon, or scleroderma.

ETIOLOGY

- Although the cause of PBC is still unknown, it is felt to be due to an environmental insult triggering an underlying genetic predisposition that results in the persistent T lymphocyte–mediated attack on intralobular bile duct epithelial cells.
- Recent studies have identified a peptide, an enzyme complex subunit (PDH E2) in the mitochondrial membrane, as a major autoantigen in the early pathogenesis of PBC. Patients with PBC have a 10-fold increased concentration of cytotoxic CD8+ lymphocytes recognizing this peptide in their livers as compared with their blood. Future therapies may be highly specific immunomodulation directed at these peptides.
- In addition to the T lymphocyte–mediated direct destruction of small bile ducts, secondary damage to hepatocytes may result from the accumulation of noxious substances such as bile acids.

PHYSICAL FINDINGS & CLINICAL PRESENTATION

Symptoms:

- 48% to 60% of patients may be asymptomatic. 40% to 100% of these patients will go on to develop symptoms.
- Fatigue (78% patients) and pruritus are the usual presenting symptoms.
- Pruritus is worse at night, under constricting, coarse garments; in association with dry skin; and in hot, humid weather. The cause is unknown; it is no longer felt to be due to the retention of bile acids in skin. Pruritus may first occur during pregnancy but is distinguished from pruritus of pregnancy because it persists into the postpartum period and beyond.
- Other common symptoms include hepatomegaly, jaundice, unexplained RUQ pain, splenomegaly, manifestations of portal hypertension, sicca symptoms, and scleroderma-like lesions.
- Musculoskeletal complaints caused by inflammatory arthropathy in 40% to 70% of patients: 5% to 10% develop chronic RA; 10% develop "arthritis of PBC."
- Steatorrhea may be seen in advanced disease.

Physical:

- Variable: dependent on stage of disease at time of presentation. Early may be completely normal.
- 25% to 50% have hypopigmentation of skin.
- Excoriations may be present.
- Hepatomegaly (70%) and splenomegaly (initially 35%) may be present in more advanced disease.
- Xanthomas and jaundice appear in advanced disease. Kayser-Fleischer rings are rare and result from copper retention.
- Late physical findings mirror those of cirrhosis: spider nevi, temporal and proximal limb wasting, ascites, and edema.

DIAGNOSIS

DIFFERENTIAL DIAGNOSIS

Drug-induced cholestasis

OTHER ETIOLOGIES OF CHRONIC LIVER DISEASE AND CIRRHOSIS:

- Alcoholic cirrhosis
- Viral hepatitis (chronic)
- Primary sclerosing cholangitis
- Autoimmune chronic active hepatitis
- Chemical/toxin-induced cirrhosis
- Other hereditary or familial disorders (e.g., CF, μ-1-antitrypsin deficiency)

WORKUP

- History, physical examination, laboratory evaluation, and liver biopsy

LABORATORY TESTS

- Antimitochondrial antibodies (found in 95% of patients with PBC and are 98% specific).
- Markedly elevated alkaline phosphatase (of hepatic origin).
- Elevated GGTP.
- Elevated serum IgM levels.
- Bilirubin normal early; increases with disease progression (direct and indirect) in 60% patients. Elevated serum bilirubin is a poor prognostic sign.
- Normal or slightly elevated aminotransferases, rarely more than 5× upper limit of normal. Have no prognostic significance.
- Markedly elevated serum lipids in more than 50%. Total cholesterol may exceed 1000 mg/dL. No increased risk of death from atherosclerosis seen, possibly due to very high HDL levels and low serum levels of Lp(a) lipoprotein.
- Elevated ceruloplasmin.
- Percutaneous liver biopsy confirms the diagnosis, allows staging, and indicates response to therapy.
- Histologic stage based on most advanced lesion present.
  Stage I—lymphocytic infiltration of the epithelial cells of the small bile ducts with granuloma-like lesions, limited to portal triads.
  Stage II—extension of inflammatory cells to periportal parenchyma, invasion by foamy macrophages, and development of biliary piecemeal necrosis.
  Stage III—fibrous septa link portal triads.
  Stage IV—frank cirrhosis. Hyaline deposits and accumulation of stainable copper are also seen.

- Associated disorders should be detected and treated. Up to 20% of patients have hypothyroidism, often with antitroglobulin and antimicrosomal antibodies. Asymptomatic renal tubular acidosis due to copper deposition in the kidney often occurs. Osteoporosis is often seen in patients with PBC and should be detected and treated. May develop deficiencies of fat-soluble vitamins, especially vitamin A.

IMAGING STUDIES

If history, physical examination, blood tests, and liver biopsy are all consistent with PBC, neither imaging nor cholangiography is necessary.

PROGNOSIS

- If symptomatic, progressive.
- Median survival asymptomatic: 10 to 16 yr; symptomatic: 7 yr.
- Neither presence nor titer of antimitochondrial antibodies predicts survival.
- Prognostic laboratory measures: serum bilirubin, albumin, prothrombin time.
- Presence of cirrhosis, increased risk for hepatocellular carcinoma.

TREATMENT

- Management decisions vary depending on clinical status of patient.
- No generally accepted treatment of underlying disease process.
- 20% of patients will not respond to medical therapy and proceed to liver transplantation.
- Treatment focuses on management of complications (pruritus, metabolic bone diseases, hyperlipidemia) because liver transplantation is the only definitive treatment for this disease.

ACUTE GENERAL Rx

- Ursodiol, colchicine, and methotrexate have shown encouraging though not overwhelming results.
- Ursodiol (12 to 15 mg/kg daily, divided or as one bedtime dose) may extend survival and lengthen the time before liver transplantation in early disease; normalizes bilirubin, may mask need for transplantation. Safe and well tolerated. Relieves pruritus in some patients although may initially exacerbate. Ineffective and may actually worsen patients with advanced disease.
- Colchicine (0.6 mg bid) and methotrexate (15 mg/wk) yield less impressive results but are still modestly effective. Patients with PBC on methotrexate need to be monitored for the development of interstitial pneumonitis, which resolves with discontinuation of the drug.
- Prednisone, azathioprine, penicillamine, and cyclosporine are no longer used because of limited efficacy and significant toxicity.
- For the pruritus of PBC, cholestyramine resin (4 g orally tid) reduces pruritus in most patients. Colestipol hydrochloride is also effective. Rifampin, ursodiol, and even naloxone benefit patients who fail treatment with cholestyramine.

CHRONIC Rx

- Diet low in neutral triglycerides and high in medium-chain triglycerides decreases steatorrhea and improves nutritional status.
- Treatment for acute bacterial cystitis, which occurs with greater frequency in these patients.
- Treatment for osteoporosis including calcium, vitamin D should be undertaken, although only liver transplantation results in improvement. Bisphosphonates may be helpful.
- Vitamin A, K, E deficiencies can be clinically important in advanced cases and respond to oral replacement.
- Liver transplantation is the definitive cure and appropriate referral should be sought. Indications for transplant include unacceptable quality of life and anticipated death in <1 yr, and are guided by the Mayo (MELD) scoring system.
- Liver transplant recipients with PBC are more likely to develop chronic rejection and less likely to be weaned from immunosuppressive therapy. After transplant, antimitochondrial antibody levels persist and histologic changes of PBC are seen in up to 50% of transplanted livers in 10 yr.
- With appropriate immunosuppression and despite histologic changes, patients who undergo transplant for PBC clinically do very well. 85% to 90% survival at 1 yr; survival rates thereafter resemble age/sex-matched healthy persons.

DISPOSITION

Definitive treatment requires liver transplantation; survival is 7 to 16 yr, dependent on symptoms at time of diagnosis.

REFERRAL

Gastroenterology and or hepatology referral for treatment, evaluation for liver transplantation, and potentially treatment of refractory variceal bleeding

SUGGESTED READINGS

Kaplan MM: Primary biliary cirrhosis (review), *N Engl J Med* 335:1570, 1996.

Kaplan MM: Primary biliary cirrhosis: past, present, and future, *Gastroenterology* 123(4):1392, 2002.

Levy C, Lindor KD: Management of osteoporosis, fat-soluble vitamin deficiencies, and hyperlipidemia in primary biliary cirrhosis, *Clin Liver Dis* 7(4):901, 2003.

MacQuillan GC, Neuberger J: Liver transplantation for primary biliary cirrhosis, *Clin Liver Dis* 7(4):941, ix, 2003.

Selmi C et al: Epidemiology and pathogenesis of primary biliary cirrhosis, *J Clin Gastroenterol* 38(3):264, 2004.

AUTHOR: **JENNIFER R. HUR, M.D.**

BASIC INFORMATION

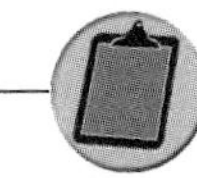

DEFINITION

Claudication refers to leg pain brought on by exertion and relieved with rest.

SYNONYMS

Intermittent claudication

ICD-9CM CODES
443.9 Peripheral vascular disease, unspecified
440.21 Intermittent claudication due to atherosclerosis

EPIDEMIOLOGY & DEMOGRAPHICS

INCIDENCE: 3 to 8 cases/1000 persons
PREVALENCE: 2% to 4% in the general population
RISK: Major risk factors of tobacco, hypertension, diabetes, and hypercholesterolemia increase the chance of developing claudication. Cigarette smoking is the major determinant of disease progression.

PHYSICAL FINDINGS & CLINICAL PRESENTATION

- Diminished pulses
- Bruits over the distal aorta, iliac or femoral arteries
- Pallor of the distal extremities on elevation
- Rubor with prolonged capillary refill on dependency
- Cool skin temperature
- Trophic changes of hair loss and muscle atrophy noted
- Nonhealing ulcers, necrotic tissue, and gangrene possible

ETIOLOGY

Primary cause of claudication is atherosclerosis with subsequent stenosis of peripheral vessels and ischemia to working muscle.

DIAGNOSIS

The history of buttock, thigh, or calf pain or fatigue brought on by exertion and relieved by rest along with the above mentioned physical findings makes the diagnosis of claudication fairly certain. Noninvasive studies help confirm the diagnosis.

DIFFERENTIAL DIAGNOSIS

Spinal stenosis (neurogenic claudication), muscle cramps, degenerative osteoarthritic joint disease particularly of the lumbar spine and hips, and compartment syndrome may all resemble claudication.

WORKUP

- Noninvasive vascular testing confirms the clinical impression of claudication and aids in locating the major occlusive site. Noninvasive testing uses continuous-wave Doppler to measure systolic arterial pressures and reports the ankle-brachial index (ABI) and segmental systolic pressures as well as Doppler waveforms.
- Ankle-brachial index (ABI): The ratio of ankle pressure to brachial pressure is usually about 1.
  1. In claudication, the ABI ranges from 0.5 to 0.8.
  2. In patients with rest pain or impending limb loss, ABI ≤0.3.
- Segmental systolic pressures usually are measured from the high thigh, above the knee, below the knee, and the ankle. Normally there should not be >20 mm Hg difference in pressures between adjacent segments. If the gradient is >20 mm Hg, significant narrowing is suspected in the intervening segment.
- Both ABI and segmental pressures can be done before and after exercise.

IMAGING STUDIES

- Duplex ultrasound can be used to locate the occluded areas and assess the patency of the distal arterial system or prior vein grafts.
- MRA and spiral CT angiography are further imaging techniques available.
- Angiography remains the gold standard for imaging peripheral arterial occlusion. Complications can occur, and the study should be done only if surgical reconstruction is being considered.

TREATMENT

NONPHARMACOLOGIC THERAPY

- Tobacco cessation is vital.
- Diet to control diabetes and blood pressure, as well as to reduce cholesterol, should be followed.
- Daily exercise must be emphasized. Exercise will increase walking distances before symptoms occur and improve functional status. Walking 30 to 60 min/day for 5 days at about 2 mi/hr is recommended.

ACUTE GENERAL Rx

Most patients with claudication respond to conservative management mentioned above. If this fails, medication can be tried (see Chronic Rx). Surgical reconstruction has its specific indications reserved for patients with impending limb loss or lifestyle altering claudication (see Chronic Rx).

CHRONIC Rx

- Pentoxifylline (Trental) and cilostazol (Pletal) have been approved for use in patients with intermittent claudication who have not responded well to conservative measures. Pentoxifylline 400 mg tid or cilostazol 100 mg bid for 3 mo should be tried. If there is no improvement in symptoms, the medicine should be discontinued.
- Surgical reconstruction is indicated in patients with refractory rest pain or lifestyle altering pain, nonhealing ulcers, or gangrene and in a select group of patients with functional disability. Common surgical procedures:
  1. Aortoiliofemoral reconstruction: perioperative mortality <3%
  2. Infrainguinal bypass (e.g., femoropopliteal, femorotibial): perioperative mortality, 2% to 5%
  3. Extraanatomic bypass (e.g., axillofemoral or femorofemoral bypass)
  4. Angioplasty is used on short, discrete stenotic lesions in the iliac or femoropopliteal artery
  5. Atherectomy, stents, and lasers are additional techniques

DISPOSITION

- Intermittent claudication progressing to an ischemic leg or limb loss is unusual, especially if maintaining the conservative treatment of exercise and abstaining from tobacco.
- The 5-yr risk for developing ischemic ulceration in patients treated for diabetes and with ABI <0.5 was 30% compared with only 5% in patients with neither characteristic.

REFERRAL

Consultation with the vascular surgeon is recommended in the patient with threatened limb loss, rest pain, nonhealing ulcers, functional disability from pain, and gangrene.

PEARLS & CONSIDERATIONS

- About 70% of patients with peripheral vascular disease will have concomitant coronary artery disease.
- β-blockers may worsen claudication symptoms.
- Patients with peripheral vascular disease may benefit from secondary cardiovascular prevention with clopidogrel more so than high-risk patients (CAPRIE trial).

COMMENTS

- Claudication is a marker for generalized atherosclerosis. This group of patients has a higher risk of death from cardiovascular events than from limb loss. This should be kept in mind when deciding to proceed with surgical evaluation. Every effort should be made toward conservative measures.
- The ABI is more closely associated with leg function in persons with peripheral arterial disease than is intermittent claudication or other leg symptoms.

SUGGESTED READINGS

Aquino R et al: Natural history of claudication: long-term serial follow-up study of 1244 claudicants, *J Vasc Surg* 34:962, 2002.

Hiatt WR: Drug therapy: medical treatment of peripheral arterial disease and claudication, *N Engl J Med* 344:1608, 2001.

McDermott MM et al: The ankle brachial index is associated with leg function and physical activity: the walking and leg circulation study, *Ann Intern Med* 136:873, 2002.

Stewart KJ, Hiatt WR, et al: Medical progress: exercise training for claudication, *N Engl J Med* 347:1941, 2002.

AUTHOR: **MEL ANDERSON, M.D.**

BASIC INFORMATION

DEFINITION

Cocaine is an alkaloid derived from the coca plant *Erythroxylon coca,* native to South America, which contains approximately 0.5% to 1% cocaine. The drug produces physiologic and behavioral effects when administered orally, intranasally, intravenously, or via inhalation following smoking. Cocaine has potent pharmacologic effects on dopamine, norepinephrine, and serotonin neurons in the central nervous system (CNS) involving alteration and blockade of cellular membrane transport and prevention of reputake.

SYNONYMS

Cocaine hydrochloride: topical solution (FDA approved as a topical anesthetic)
Free base: aqueous solution of cocaine hydrochloride converted to a more volatile base state by the addition of alkali, thereby extracting the cocaine base in a residue or precipitate
Crack: potent, purified smokable form; produces effects similar to those of intravenous administration
Street names include Bernice, Bernies, C, Cadillac or Champagne of drugs, Carrie, Cecil, Charlie, Coke, Dust, Dynamite, Flake, Gin, Girl, Gold dust, Green gold, Jet, Powder, Star dust, Paradise, Pimp's drug, Snowflake, Stardust, White girl
Liquid lady = alcohol + cocaine
Speedball = heroin + cocaine
Street measures: Hit (2-200 mg), snort, line, dose, spoon (approximately 1 g)

ICD-9CM CODES
304.2 Cocainism

EPIDEMIOLOGY & DEMOGRAPHICS

The 1993 National Household Survey on Drug Abuse estimated that 4.5 million Americans used cocaine in 1992, with 1.3 million reporting use at least monthly. By 1998 this had not significantly changed.
Between 1993 and 1994, intravenous cocaine and heroin abusers accounted for a major new group of persons with human immunodeficiency virus (HIV) in several metropolitan areas.
In 1999 an estimated 25 million Americans admitted that they used cocaine at least once, 3.7 million the previous year, and 1.5 million were current users. It is the most frequent cause of drug-related deaths reported by medical examiners.

PHYSICAL FINDINGS & CLINICAL PRESENTATION

PHASE I:

- CNS: euphoria, agitation, headache, vertigo, twitching, bruxism, nonintentional tremor
- Nausea, vomiting, fever, hypertension, tachycardia

PHASE II:

- CNS: lethargy, hyperreactive deep tendon reflexes, seizures (status epilepticus)
- Sympathetic overdrive: tachycardia, hypertension, hyperthermia
- Incontinence

PHASE III:

- CNS: flaccid paralysis, coma, fixed dilated pupils, loss of reflexes
- Pulmonary edema
- Cardiopulmonary arrest

Psychologic dependence manifests with habituation, paranoia, hallucinations (cocaine "bugs").

Central nervous system: cerebral ischemia and infarction, cerebral arterial spasm, cerebral vasculitis, cerebral vascular thrombosis, subarachnoid hemorrhage, intraparenchymal hemorrhage, seizures, cerebral atrophy, movement disorders

Cardiac: acute myocardial ischemia and infarction, arrhythmias and sudden death, dilated cardiomyopathy and myocarditis, infective endocarditis, aortic rupture

Pulmonary: (secondary to smoking crack cocaine) inhalation injuries: cartilage and nasal septal perforation, oropharyngeal ulcers; immunologically mediated diseases: hypersensitivity pneumonitis, bronchiolitis obliterans; pulmonary vascular lesions and hemorrhage, pulmonary infarction, pulmonary edema secondary to left ventricular failure, pneumomediastinum, and pneumothorax

Gastrointestinal: gastroduodenal ulceration and perforation; intestinal infarction and/or perforation, colitis

Renal: acute renal failure secondary to rhabdomyolysis and myoglobinuria; renal infarction; focal segmental glomerulosclerosis

Obstetric: placental abruption, low infant weight, prematurity, and microcephaly

Psychiatric: anxiety, depression, paranoia, delirium, psychosis, and suicide

ETIOLOGY

Cocaine may be absorbed through different routes with varying degrees of speed

- Nasal insufflation/snorting: 2.5 min
- Smoking: <30 sec
- Oral: 2 to 5 min
- Mucosal: <20 min
- Intravenous injection: <30 sec

DIAGNOSIS

DIFFERENTIAL DIAGNOSIS

- Methamphetamine ("speed") abuse
- Methylenedioxyamphetamine ("ecstasy") abuse
- Cathione ("khat") abuse
- Lysergic acid diethylamide (LSD) abuse

WORKUP

Physical examination and laboratory evaluation

LABORATORY TESTS

- Toxicology screen (urine): Cocaine is metabolized within 2 hr by the liver to major metabolites, benzoylecogonine and ecgonine methylester, which are excreted in the urine. Metabolites can be identified in urine within 5 min of IV use and up to 48 hr after oral ingestion
- Blood: CBC, electrolytes, glucose, BUN, creatinine, calcium
- ABG analysis
- ECG
- Serum creatinine kinase and troponin concentration

TREATMENT

There is no specific antidote and, at present, no drug therapy is uniquely effective in treating cocaine abuse and dependence. In addition, adulterants, contaminants, and other drugs may be admixed with street cocaine. Amantadine may provide effective treatment for cocaine-dependent patients with severe cocaine withdrawal symptoms, as well as the other dopamine agonist bromocriptine (1.5 mg PO tid), which may alleviate some of the symptoms of craving associated with acute cocaine withdrawal.

Cocaine Overdose 

ACUTE GENERAL Rx

Acute cocaine toxicity requires following advanced poisoning treatment and life support. A suspected "body-packer" should have an abdominal radiograph to detect the continued presence of cocaine-containing condoms in the intestinal tract. If present, gentle catharsis with charcoal and mineral oil should be performed with ICU admission and monitoring.

SPECIFIC TREATMENT

INHALATION: Wash nasal passages

AGITATION:
- Check STAT glucose
- Diazepam 15 to 20 mg PO IV for severe agitation

HYPERTHERMIA:
- Check rectal temperature, CK, electrolytes
- Monitor with continuous rectal probe; bring temperature down to 101°F within 30-45 minutes

RHABDOMYOLYISIS:
- Vigorous hydration with urine output at least 2 ml/kg
- Mannitol or bicarbonate for rhabdomyolysis resistant to hydration

SEIZURE MANAGEMENT (STATUS EPILEPTICUS):
- Diazepam 5 to 10 mg IV over 2 to 3 min, may be repeated every 10 to 15 min
- Lorazepam 2 to 3 mg IV over 2 to 3 min, may be repeated
- Phenytoin loading dose 15 to 18 mg/kg IV at a rate not to exceed 25 to 50 mg/min under cardiac monitoring
- Phenobarbital loading dose 10 to 15 mg/kg IV at a rate of 25 mg/min; an additional 5 mg/kg may be given in 30 to 45 min if seizures are not controlled.
- Refractory seizures, consider:
  Pancuronium 0.1 mg/kg IV
  Halothane general anesthesia
  Both require EEG monitoring to determine brain seizure activity.

HYPERTENSION:
- Consider arterial line for continuous BP monitoring
- Nifedipine 10 mg SL
- Labetalol 10 to 80 mg IV
- Propranolol 1 mg IV/q min, up to 6 mg
- Phentolamine may be required (unopposed adrenergic effects)
- If diastolic pressure >120 mm Hg: hydralazine hydrochloride 25 mg IM or IV; may repeat q1h
- If hypertension uncontrolled or hypertensive encephalopathy is present: sodium nitroprusside initially at 0.5 μg/kg/min not to exceed 10 μg/kg/min

CHEST PAIN:
- CXR, EKG, cardiac enzymes
- Benzodiazepines for agitation
- ASA and nitroglycerin for ischemic pain
- PTCA possibly better than thrombolysis for cocaine-associated MI

VENTRICULAR ARRHYTHMIAS:
- Antiarrhythmia agents should be used with caution during the early period after cocaine exposure as a result of their proarrhythmic and proconvulsant effects
- Propranolol 1 mg/min IV for up to 6 mg
- Lidocaine 1.5 mg/kg IV bolus followed by IV infusion (controversial: may cause seizures)
- Termination of ventricular arrhythmias may be resistant to lidocaine and even cardioversion
- $NaHCO_3^-$ is under investigation in cocaine-mediated conduction abnormalities and rhythm disturbances.

REFERRAL

Consider psychotherapy and/or behavioral therapy once stable.

SUGGESTED READING

Lange RA, Hillis LD: Cardiovascular complications of cocaine use, *N Engl J Med* 345:351, 2001.

AUTHOR: **SAJEEV HANDA, M.D.**

BASIC INFORMATION

DEFINITION

Coccidioidomycosis is an infectious disease caused by the fungus *Coccidioides immitis*. It is usually asymptomatic and characterized by a primary pulmonary focus with infrequent progression to chronic pulmonary disease and dissemination to other organs.

SYNONYMS

San Joaquin Valley fever

ICD-9CM CODES
114.0 Coccidioidax pneumonia
114.1 Cutaneous or extrapulmonary (primary) coccidioidomycosis
114.3 Disseminated or prostate occidioidomycosis
114.5 Pulmonary coccidioidomycosis
114.2 Meninges coccidioidomycosis
114.4 Chronic coccidioidomycosis

EPIDEMIOLOGY & DEMOGRAPHICS

PREVALENCE: Unknown
INCIDENCE (IN U.S.): Estimated annual infection rate 100,000 persons, predominantly in southwest U.S.
PREDOMINANT SEX: Males, between the ages of 25 to 55 yr
PEAK INCIDENCE: Unknown
GENETICS:
Familial Disposition: Unknown
Congenital Infection: Documented, but considered to occur rarely
Neonatal Infection:
- Occurs equally between the sexes
- Clinical disease more severe than in older children and adults

PHYSICAL FINDINGS & CLINICAL PRESENTATION

- Asymptomatic infections or illness consistent with a nonspecific upper respiratory tract infection in at least 60%
- Symptoms of primary infection—cough, malaise, fever, chills, night sweats, anorexia, weakness, and arthralgias (desert rheumatism)—in remaining 40% within 3 wk of exposure
- Skin rashes, such as erythema nodosum and erythema multiforme, usually with a significant female preponderance
- Scattered rales and areas that are dull on percussion with auscultation
- Spontaneous improvement within 2 wk of illness, with complete recovery usual
- Subsequent pulmonary residua in the form of pulmonary nodules and cavities in <10% of those patients with primary infection; half of these patients asymptomatic
- In a small portion of these patients: a progressive pneumonitis, often with a fatal outcome
- Some, especially if immunocompromised and/or diabetic, progressing to chronic pulmonary disease
- Over many years, granulomas rupture, leading to new cavity formation and continued fibrosis, often accompanied by hemoptysis
- Possible bronchiectasis with acute or chronic disease
- Disseminated or extrapulmonary disease in approximately 0.5% of acutely infected patients
  1. Early signs of probable dissemination: fever, malaise, hilar adenopathy, and elevated ESR persisting in the setting of primary infection
  2. Most organs are susceptible to dissemination, with heart and GI tract generally spared
- Musculoskeletal involvement
  1. Occurs one third of the time in disseminated disease
  2. Usually presents with local pain, swelling of a joint, bone, or muscle
  3. Majority of bone lesions unifocal and usually involve the skull, metacarpals, metatarsals, and tibia
  4. Vertebral column possibly affected with usually multiple lesions involving the arch and contiguous ribs and sparing the intravertebral disk
  5. Joint lesions predominantly unifocal, most commonly involving the ankle and knee, and often accompanying adjacent sites of osteomyelitis
- Meningeal involvement
  1. Occurs approximately one third of the time with dissemination
  2. Usually presents within 6 mo of primary infection or may appear concurrently
  3. Mass lesions rare, with approximately 40 cases reported this century
  4. Usually, absence of classic signs of meningeal irritation, but possible focal deficits, seizure activity, and stiff neck
  5. Most common complaint: headache
  6. Presenting symptoms: fever, weakness, confusion, lethargy, vomiting
- Cutaneous involvement, excluding rash
  1. Variable in appearance, taking the form of pustules, papules, plaques, nodules, ulcers, abscesses, or proliferative lesions
  2. Lesions most characteristically verrucous
  3. Dissemination and fatal outcomes most common in men, pregnant women, neonates, immunocompromised hosts, and individuals of dark-skinned races, especially those of African, Filipino, Mexican, and Native American ancestry

ETIOLOGY

- *Coccidioides immitis* is endemic to the American continent, including northern, central, and southern parts.
- In the U.S., most cases are acquired in Arizona, California, New Mexico, and Texas.
- Endemic areas coincide with the Lower Sonoran Life Zone, with semiarid climate, sparse flora, and alkaline soil.
- Fungus exists in the mycelial phase in soil, having barrel-shaped hyphae (arthroconidia).
- Windswept spores from easily fragmented arthroconidia are dispersed to infect other soil (saprophytic cycle) or are inhaled by animals, including rodents and humans.
- Arthrospore deposits in the alveoli, then fungus converts to thick-walled spherule.
- Internal spherical spores (endospores) are released through spherule rupture and mature into new spherules (parasitic cycle).
- Fungus incites a granulomatous reaction in host tissue, usually with caseation necrosis.

DIAGNOSIS

DIFFERENTIAL DIAGNOSIS

- Acute pulmonary coccidioidomycoses:
  1. Community-acquired pneumonias caused by *Mycoplasma* and *Chlamydia*
  2. Granulomatous diseases, such as *Mycobacterium tuberculosis* and sarcoidosis
  3. Other fungal diseases, such as *Blastomyces dermatitidis* and *Histoplasma capsulatum*
- Coccidioidomas: true neoplasms

WORKUP

- Suspected in patients with a history of residence or travel in an endemic area, especially during periods favorable to spore dispersion (e.g., dust storms and drought followed by heavy rains)
- Suspected with a patient history of handling fomites from endemic areas (e.g., fruit and cotton), as in textile workers or fruit handlers

LABORATORY TESTS

- CBC to reveal eosinophilia, especially with erythema nodosum
- Routine chemistries: usually normal but may reveal hyponatremia
- Elevated serum levels of IgE; associated with progressive disease
- CSF cell counts and chemistry: pleocytosis with mononuclear cell predominance associated with hypoglycorrhachia and elevated protein level
- Definitive diagnosis based on demonstration of the organism by culture from body fluids or tissues (Fig. 1-61)
  1. Greatest yield with pus, sputum, synovial fluid, and soft tissue aspirations, varying with the degree of dissemination
  2. Possible positive cultures of blood, gastric aspirate, pleural effusion, peritoneal fluid, and CSF, but less frequently obtained
  3. In patients with AIDS: failure of sputum cultures to grow the fungus, so pulmonary biopsy is needed
- Serologic evaluations
  1. Latex agglutination and complement fixation
  2. Elevated serum complement-fixing antibody (CFA) titers $\geq$1:32 (Smith and Saito) strongly correlated with disseminated disease, except with meningitis where lower titers seen
  3. Variable discriminating titers depending on method, so must be based on reference ranges provided
  4. In meningeal disease: CFA detected in CSF except with high serum CFA titers secondary to concurrent extraneural disease
  5. Enzyme-linked immunosorbent assay (ELISA) against a 33-kDa spherule antigen to detect and monitor CNS disease
- Coccidioidin, the mycelial phase antigen, and spherulin, the parasitic phase antigen
  1. Positive (>5 mm) 1 mo following onset of symptomatic primary infection
  2. Useful in assessing prior infection
  3. Negative skin test with primary infection: latent or future dissemination

IMAGING STUDIES

Chest x-ray examination:

- Reveals unilateral infiltrates, hilar adenopathy, or pleural effusion in primary infection
- Shows areas of fibrosis containing usually solitary, thin-walled cavities that persist as residua of primary infection
- Possible coccidioidoma, a coinlike lesion representing a healed area of previous pneumonitis

TREATMENT

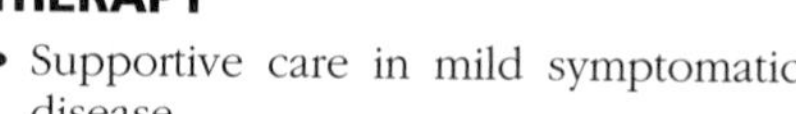

NONPHARMACOLOGIC THERAPY

- Supportive care in mild symptomatic disease
- In patients with extrapulmonary manifestations involving draining skin, joint, and soft tissue infection: local wound care to avoid possible bacterial superinfection

ACUTE GENERAL Rx

- In general, drug therapy is not required for patients with asymptomatic pulmonary disease and most patients with mild symptomatic primary infection.
- Chemotherapy is indicated under the following circumstances:
  1. Severe symptomatic primary infection
  2. High serum CFA titers
  3. Persistent symptoms >6 wk
  4. Prostration
  5. Progressive pulmonary involvement
  6. Pregnancy
  7. Infancy
  8. Debilitation
  9. Concurrent illness (e.g., diabetes, asthma, COPD, malignancy)
  10. Acquired or induced immunosuppression
  11. Racial group with known predisposition for disseminated disease
- Fluconazole
  1. Most commonly, oral therapy with 400 mg/day up to 1.2 g/day appears to be the drug of choice for meningeal and deep-seated mycotic infections.
  2. In patients with AIDS, fluconazole may be considered the drug of choice for initial and maintenance therapy.
  3. All patients with coccidioidal meningitis should continue azole therapy indefinitely.

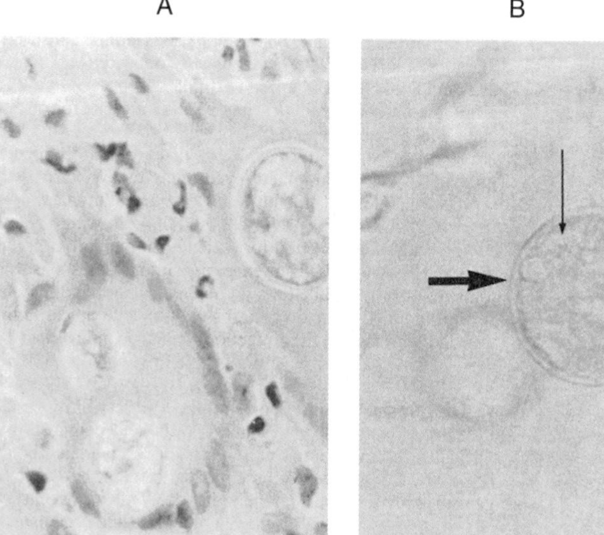

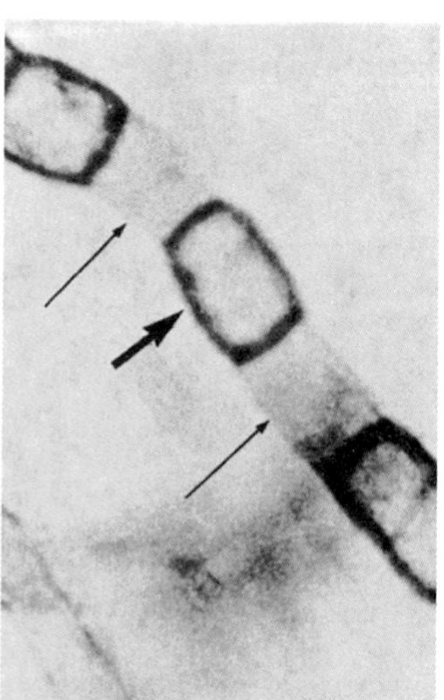

FIGURE 1-61 Morphologic appearance of Coccidioides immitis. A, Spherules within Langerhans' giant cells, shown by hematoxylin and eosin stain. **B,** Spherule in unstained potassium hydroxide preparation. The endospores within spherule *(small arrow)* and the clearly defined double wall of spherule *(large arrow)* are evident. **C,** Mycelial form with barrel-shaped arthroconidia *(large arrow)* spaced between intercalating "ghost cells" *(small arrows).* (From Stein JH [ed]: *Internal medicine,* ed 5, St Louis, 1998, Mosby.)

- Itraconazole
  1. 400 to 600 mg/day achieves 90% response rate in bone, joint, soft tissue, lymphatic, and genitourinary infections.
  2. Itraconazole may be more efficacious than fluconazole in the treatment of skeletal (bone) infections.
- For pulmonary infections, treatment with either fluconazole or itraconazole, given for 6 to 12 wk, appears to be equal in efficacy.
- Amphotericin B is the classic therapy for disseminated extraneural disease, dose 1 to 1.5 mg/kg/day, qd for the first week and qid thereafter, for a total dose of 1 to 2.5 g or until clinical and serologic remission is accomplished.
  1. Local instillation into body cavities such as sinuses, fistulae, and abscesses has been adjunct to therapy.
  2. Liposomal amphotericin B is probably equally effective, but further studies are needed.
  3. Duration of therapy for extraneural disease is undefined but probably about 1 yr.
- With meningeal disease:
  1. Intrathecal amphotericin B remains the traditional treatment modality, given alone or preceding the use of oral agents.
  2. Begin in doses of 0.01 to 0.025 mg/day, gradually increasing the dose as tolerated, to 0.5 mg/day with the patient in Trendelenburg's position.
  3. If given via Ommaya reservoir, as in ventriculitis, dose may be increased to 1.5 mg/day if tolerated.
  4. Concomitant parenteral therapy with amphotericin B is used for simultaneous extraneural disease as standard doses and with purely meningeal disease in smaller doses, although not strictly indicated.
  5. Intrathecal therapy is usually given three times a week for at least 3 mo, then discontinued or gradually tapered until once every 6 wk through 1 yr of therapy.
  6. Patients need routine monitoring of CSF, CFA, cell count, and chemistries for at least 2 yr following cessation of therapy.
- For osteomyelitis, soft-tissue closed space infections, and pulmonary fibrocavitary disease: surgical debridement, drainage, or resection, respectively, in addition to oral azole therapy or parenteral administration of amphotericin B

CHRONIC Rx

For chronically immunocompromised patients, lifelong therapy with oral azoles or amphotericin B

DISPOSITION

- Prognosis for primary symptomatic infection is good.
- Immunocompromised patients are most likely to have disseminated disease and higher morbidity and mortality.

REFERRAL

- To surgeon for the evaluation of chronic hemoptysis, enlarging cavitary lesions despite chemotherapy and intrapleural rupture, osteomyelitis, and other synovial or soft tissue closed space infections
- For neurosurgical consultation in patients with meningeal disease to establish the delivery route of intrathecal drug therapy

PEARLS & CONSIDERATIONS

COMMENTS

- Infected body fluids contained within a closed moist environment (e.g., sputum in a specimen cup) provide the opportunity for the fungus to revert to its hyphal form whereby spores may be made airborne on opening of the container. Purulent drainage into a cast, allowing conversion of fungus to the saprophytic phase, has been responsible for acute disease when the cast was opened and the spores were unintentionally made airborne.
- Patients with a remote history of exposure, especially if immunosuppressed by medication or disease, may reactivate primary disease and suffer rapid dissemination.
- Although cardiac disease is rare, constrictive pericarditis in the setting of disseminated coccidioidomycosis has been documented and is potentially fatal.
- Organ transplant recipients may develop disease if the transplant donor has unrecognized active coccidioidomycosis at the time of death.

SUGGESTED READINGS

Blair JE et al: Incidence and prevalence of coccidioidomycosis in patients with end-stage liver disease, *Liver Transpl* 9(8):843, 2003.

Caraway NP et al: Coccidioidomycosis osteomyelitis masquerading as a bone tumor. A report of 2 cases, *Acta Cytol* 47(5):777, 2003.

Chiller TM et al: Coccidioidomycosis, *Infect Dis Clin North Am* 17(1):41, 2003.

Copeland B, White D, Buenting J: Coccidioidomycosis of the head and neck, *Ann Otol Rhinol Laryngol* 112(1):98, 2003.

Crum NF et al: A cluster of disseminated coccidioidomycosis cases at a US military hospital, *Mil Med* 168(6):460, 2003.

Komotar RJ et al: Coccidioidomycosis of the brain, mimicking en plaque meningioma, *J Neurol Neurosurg Psychiatry* 74(6):806, 2003.

Visbal AL et al: Coccidioidal pericarditis: implications of surgical treatment in the elderly, *Ann Thorac Surg* 75(4):1328, 2003.

Wright PW et al: Donor-related coccidioidomycosis in organ transplant recipients, *Clin Infect Dis* 37(9):1265, 2003.

AUTHOR: **GEORGE O. ALONSO, M.D.**

BASIC INFORMATION

DEFINITION

Acute self-limited febrile illness caused by infection with a Coltivirus

ICD-9CM CODES
066.1 Colorado Tick Fever

EPIDEMIOLOGY & DEMOGRAPHICS

- Incidence: approximately 330 cases reported per year in the U.S.
- Demographics: children and adults of both genders
- Geography: Rocky Mountains at elevations of 4000 to 10,000 feet.
- Colorado has the highest incidence (see Fig. 1-62)

PHYSICAL FINDINGS & CLINICAL PRESENTATION

- Incubation: 3 to 4 days is usual, but can be up to 14 days
- First symptoms: fever, chills, severe headache, severe myalgias, and hyperesthetic skin
- Initial signs and symptoms
  1. Tick bite
  2. Fever and chills
  3. Headache
  4. Myalgias
  5. Weakness
  6. Prostration and indifference
  7. Injected conjunctivae
  8. Erythematous pharyngitis
  9. Lymphadenopathy
  10. Maculopapular or petechial rash

These first symptoms last for 1 wk or less but 50% of the cases experience a febrile relapse 2 to 3 days following an initial remission. Weakness and fatigue may persist for several months after the acute phase(s). This chronic phase is more likely in older patients.

In children, 5% to 10% of cases are complicated by aseptic meningitis. In adults, rare complications include pneumonia, hepatitis, myocarditis, and epididymoorchitis. Vertically transmitted fetal infection is possible.

ETIOLOGY & PATHOGENESIS

- Infectious agent: Coltiviruses; 7 species, including 3 in the U.S.
- Vector: wood tick, *Dermacentor andersoni*
- Pathogenesis: human transmission occurs via tick bite. Tick season spans from March to September. The virus infects marrow erythrocytic precursors, explaining the protracted disease course as viremia lasts for the lifespan of the infected RBC

DIAGNOSIS

DIFFERENTIAL DIAGNOSIS

Rocky Mountain spotted fever, influenza, leptospirosis, infectious mononucleosis, CMV infection, pneumonia, hepatitis, meningitis, endocarditis, scarlet fever, measles, rubella, typhus, Lyme disease, ITP, TTP, Kawasaki disease, toxic shock syndrome, vasculitis

WORKUP

Consider Colorado tick fever in the presence of the above symptoms associated with travel to an endemic area coupled with a history of tick exposure

LABORATORY TESTS

- CBC
  1. Leukopenia
  2. Atypical lymphocytes
  3. Moderate thrombocytopenia
- Virus identification in RBCs by indirect immunofluorescence
- Serology using ELISA, neutralization, or complement fixation

TREATMENT

- No specific therapy although Coltiviruses are sensitive to ribavirin
- Bedrest, fluids, acetaminophen
- Avoid aspirin because of thrombocytopenia
- Prevention: tick avoidance measures

SUGGESTED READING

Tsai TF: Coltiviruses (Colorado tick fever). In Mandell GL, Bennett JF, Dolin R (eds): *Principles and practice of infectious diseases,* ed 5, Philadelphia, 2000, Churchill Livingstone.

AUTHOR: **TOM J. WACHTEL, M.D.**

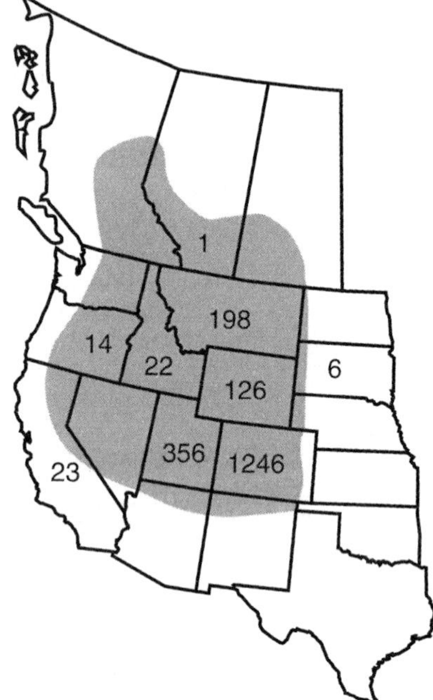

FIGURE 1-62 Geographic distribution of *Dermacentor andersoni* (wood ticks) and reported cases of Colorado tick fever, 1990-1996, United States and Canada. (From Mandell GL: *Mandell, Douglas, and Bennett's principles and practice of infectious diseases,* ed 5, New York, 2000, Churchill Livingstone.)

BASIC INFORMATION

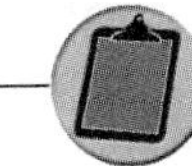

DEFINITION

Colorectal cancer is a neoplasm arising from the luminal surface of the large bowel: descending colon (40% to 42%), rectosigmoid and rectum (30% to 33%), cecum and ascending colon (25% to 30%), transverse colon (10% to 13%).

ICD-9CM CODES
154.0 Colorectal cancer

EPIDEMIOLOGY & DEMOGRAPHICS

- Colorectal cancer is the second leading cause of cancer deaths in the U.S. (>135,000 new cases and >50,000 deaths/yr).
- Peak incidence is in the seventh decade of life.
- 50% of rectal cancers are within reach of the examiner's finger, 50% of colon cancers are within reach of the flexible sigmoidoscope.
- Colorectal cancer accounts for 14% of all cases of cancer (excluding skin malignancies) and 14% of all yearly cancer deaths.
- Risk factors:
  1. Hereditary polyposis syndromes
     a. Familial polyposis (high risk)
     b. Gardner's syndrome (high risk)
     c. Turcot's syndrome (high risk)
     d. Peutz-Jeghers syndrome (low to moderate risk)
  2. IBD, both ulcerative colitis and Crohn's disease
  3. Family history of "cancer family syndrome"
  4. Heredofamilial breast cancer and colon carcinoma
  5. History of previous colorectal carcinoma
  6. Women undergoing irradiation for gynecologic cancer
  7. First-degree relatives with colorectal carcinoma
  8. Age >40 yr
  9. Possible dietary factors (diet high in fat or meat, beer drinking, reduced vegetable consumption)
  10. Hereditary nonpolyposis colon cancer (HNPCC): autosomal-dominant disorder characterized by early age of onset (mean age of 44 yr) and right-sided or proximal colon cancers, synchronous and metachronous colon cancers, mucinous and poorly differentiated colon cancers; it accounts for 1% to 5% of all cases of colorectal cancer
  11. Previous endometrial or ovarian cancer, particularly when diagnosed at an early age

PHYSICAL FINDINGS & CLINICAL PRESENTATION

- Physical examination may be completely unremarkable.
- Digital rectal examination can detect approximately 50% of rectal cancers.
- Palpable abdominal masses may indicate metastasis or complications of colorectal carcinoma (abscess, intussusception, volvulus).
- Abdominal distention and tenderness are suggestive of colonic obstruction.
- Hepatomegaly may be indicative of hepatic metastasis.

ETIOLOGY

Colorectal cancer can arise through two mutational pathways: microsatellite instability or chromosomal instability. Germline genetic mutations are the basis of inherited colon cancer syndromes; an accumulation of somatic mutations in a cell is the basis of sporadic colon cancer.

DIAGNOSIS

DIFFERENTIAL DIAGNOSIS

- Diverticular disease
- Strictures
- IBD
- Infectious or inflammatory lesions
- Adhesions
- Arteriovenous malformations
- Metastatic carcinoma (prostate, sarcoma)
- Extrinsic masses (cysts, abscesses)

WORKUP

- The clinical presentation of colorectal malignancies is initially vague and nonspecific (weight loss, anorexia, malaise). It is useful to divide colon cancer symptoms into those usually associated with right side of colon and those commonly associated with left side of colon, because the clinical presentation varies with the location of the carcinoma.

1. Right side of colon
   a. Anemia (iron deficiency secondary to chronic blood loss)
   b. Dull, vague, and uncharacteristic abdominal pain may be present or patient may be completely asymptomatic
   c. Rectal bleeding is often missed because blood is mixed with feces
   d. Obstruction and constipation are unusual because of large lumen and more liquid stools
2. Left side of colon
   a. Change in bowel habits (constipation, diarrhea, tenesmus, pencil-thin stools)
   b. Rectal bleeding (bright red blood coating the surface of the stool)
   c. Intestinal obstruction is frequent because of small lumen

- Early diagnosis of patients with surgically curable disease (Dukes' A, B) is necessary, because survival time is directly related to the stage of the carcinoma at the time of diagnosis. Appropriate screening recommendations are discussed in Section V.

CLASSIFICATION

Dukes' and UICC classification for colorectal cancer:

A Confined to the mucosa-submucosa (I)
B Invasion of muscularis propria (II)
C Local node involvement (III)
D Distant metastasis (IV)

LABORATORY TESTS

- Positive fecal occult blood test
- Newer modalities for early detection of colorectal neoplasms include the detection of mutations in the adenomatous polyposis coli (APC) gene from stool samples
- Microcytic anemia
- Elevated plasma carcinoembryonic antigen (CEA). CEA should not be used as a screening test for colorectal cancer because it can be elevated in patients with many other conditions (smoking, IBD, alcoholic liver disease). A normal CEA does not exclude the diagnosis of colorectal cancer
- Liver function tests

IMAGING STUDIES

- Colonoscopy with biopsy (primary assessment tool)
- CT scan of abdomen to assist in preoperative staging
- Chest x-ray examination to look for evidence of metastatic disease
- Air-contrast barium enema only in patients refusing colonoscopy or unable to tolerate colonoscopy

TREATMENT

GENERAL Rx

- Surgical resection: 70% of colorectal cancers are resectable for cure at presentation; 45% of patients are cured by primary resection.
- Radiation therapy is a useful adjunct to fluorouracil and levamisole therapy for stage II or III rectal cancers.
- Adjuvant chemotherapy with combination of 5-fluorouracil (5-FU) and levamisole substantially increases cure rates for patients with stage III colon cancer and should be considered standard treatment for all such patients and selected patients with high-risk stage II colon cancer.
- Leucovorin (folinic acid) enhances the effect of fluorouracil and is given together with it (FL). When given as adjuvant therapy after a complete resection in stage III disease, FL increases

overall 5-year survival from 51% to 64%. The use of adjuvant FL in stage II disease (no involvement of regional nodes) is controversial because 5 year overall survival is 80% for treated or untreated patients and the addition of FL only increases the probability of 5 year disease-free interval from 72% to 76%. For patients with standard-risk stage III tumors (e.g., involvement of one to three regional lymph nodes), FL alone or FL with oxaliplatin (Eloxatin, an inhibitor of DNA synthesis) are both reasonable choices. Generally reversible peripheral neuropathy is the main side effect of FL plus oxaliplatin.

- Irinotecan (Camptosar), a potent inhibitor of topoisomerase I, a nuclear enzyme involved in the unwinding of DNA during replication, can be used to treat metastatic colorectal cancer refractory to other drugs, including 5-FU; it may offer a few months of palliation but is expensive and associated with significant toxicity.
- Oxaliplatin can be used in combination with fluorouracil and leucovorin (FL) for patients with metastatic colorectal cancer whose disease has recurred or progressed despite treatment with fluorouracil/leucovorin plus irinotecan. FL plus oxaliplatin should be considered for high-risk patients with stage III cancers (e.g., >3 involved regional nodes [N2] or tumor invasion beyond the serosa [T4 lesion]).
- The monoclonal antibodies cetuximab [Erbitux] and bevacizumab [Avastatin] have also been approved by the FDA for advanced colorectal cancer. Bevacizumab is an angiogenesis inhibitor that binds and inhibits the activity of human vascular endothelial growth factor (VEGF). Cetuximab is an epidermal growth factor receptor [EGFR] blocker that inhibits the growth and survival of tumor cells that overexpress EGFR. Cetuximab has synergism with irinotecan and its addition to irinotecan in patients with advanced disease resistant to irinotecan increases response rate from 10% when cetuximab is used alone to 22% with combination of cetuximab and irinotecan. The addition of bevacizumab to FL in patients with advanced colorectal cancer has been reported to increase the response rate from 17% to 40%.
- In patients who undergo resection of liver metastases from colorectal cancer, postoperative treatment with a combination of hepatic arterial infusion of floxuridine and IV fluorouracil improves the outcome at 2 yr.

CHRONIC Rx

Follow-up is indicated with:

- Physician visits with a focus on the clinical and disease-related history, directed physical examination guided by this history, coordination of follow-up, and counseling every 3 to 6 mo for the first 3 yr then decreased frequency thereafter for 2 yr
- Colonoscopy yearly for the initial 2 yr, then every 3 yr
- CEA level should be obtained baseline; if elevated, it can be used postoperatively as a measure of completeness of tumor resection or to monitor tumor recurrence; if used to monitor tumor recurrence, CEA should be obtained every 3 to 6 mo for up to 5 yr. The role of CEA for monitoring patients with resected colon cancer has been questioned because of the small number of cures attributed to CEA monitoring despite the substantial cost in dollars and physical and emotional stress associated with monitoring

DISPOSITION

- The 5-yr survival varies with the stage of the carcinoma:
  1. Dukes' A 5-yr survival, >80%
  2. Dukes' B 5-yr survival, 60%
  3. Dukes' C 5-yr survival, 20%
  4. Dukes' D 5-yr survival, 3%
- Overall 5-yr disease-free survival is approximately 50% for colon cancer.
- High-frequency microsatellite instability in colorectal cancer is independently predictive of a relatively favorable outcome and, in addition, reduces the likelihood of metastases.
- In patients with Dukes' C (stage III) colorectal cancer there is improved 5-year survival among women treated with adjuvant chemotherapy (53% with chemotherapy vs. 33% without) and among patients with right-sided tumors treated with adjuvant chemotherapy.
- Retention of 18q alleles in microsatellite-stable cancers and mutation of the gene for the type I receptor for TGF-B1 in cancers with high levels of microsatellite instability point to a favorable outcome after adjuvant chemotherapy with fluorouracil-based regimens for stage II colon cancer.

REFERRAL

- Surgical referral for resection
- Oncology referral for adjuvant chemotherapy in selected patients
- Radiation oncology referral for patients with stage II or III rectal cancers

PEARLS & CONSIDERATIONS

COMMENTS

- Decreased fat intake to 30% of total energy intake, increased fiber, and fruit and vegetable consumption may lower colorectal cancer risk. Recent literature reports, however, do not support a protective effect from dietary fiber against colorectal cancer in women.
- Chemoprophylaxis with aspirin (81 mg/day) reduces the incidence of colorectal adenomas in persons at risk.
- The National Cancer Institute has published consensus guidelines for universal screening for hereditary nonpolyposis colon cancer (HNPCC) in patients with newly diagnosed colorectal cancer. Tumors in mutation carriers of HNPCC typically exhibit microsatellite instability, a characteristic phenotype that is caused by expansions or contractions of short nucleotide repeat sequences. These guidelines (Bethesda Guidelines) are useful for selective patients for microsatellite instability testing. Screening patients with newly diagnosed colorectal cancer for HNPCC is cost effective, especially if the benefits to their immediate relatives are considered.
- Expression of guanylyl cyclase C mRNA in lymph nodes is associated with recurrence of colorectal cancer in patients with stage II disease. Analysis of guanylyl cyclase mRNA expression by RT-PCR may be useful for colorectal cancer staging.
- The use of either annual or biennial fecal occult-blood testing significantly reduces the incidence of colorectal cancer.
- The detection of mutations in the adenomatous polyposis coli (APC) gene from stool samples is a promising new modality for early detection of colorectal neoplasms.

SUGGESTED READINGS

Andre T et al: Oxaliplatin, fluorouracil, and leucovorin as adjuvant treatment for colon cancer, *N Engl J Med* 350:2343, 2004.

Baron JA et al: A randomized trial of aspirin to prevent colorectal adenomas, *N Engl J Med* 348:891, 2003.

Cunningham D et al: Cetuximab monotherapy and cetuximab plus irinotecan in irinotecan-refractory metastatic colon cancer, *N Engl J Med* 351:337, 2004.

Hurwitz H et al: Bevacizumab plus irinotecan, fluorouracil, and leucovorin for metastatic colon cancer, *N Engl J Med* 350:2335, 2004.

Mayer R: Two steps forward in the treatment of colorectal cancer, *N Engl J Med* 350:2406, 2004.

Pfister D et al: Surveillance strategies after curative treatment of colorectal cancer, *N Engl J Med* 350:2375, 2004.

AUTHOR: **FRED F. FERRI, M.D.**

BASIC INFORMATION

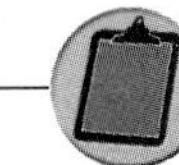

DEFINITION

Condyloma acuminatum is a sexually transmitted viral disease of the vulva, vagina, and cervix that is caused by the human papillomavirus (HPV).

SYNONYMS

Genital warts
Venereal warts
Anogenital warts

ICD-9CM CODES
078.11 Condyloma acuminatum

EPIDEMIOLOGY & DEMOGRAPHICS

- Seen mostly in young adults with a mean age of onset of 16 to 25 yr
- A sexually transmitted disease spread by skin-to-skin contact
- Highly contagious, with 25% to 65% of sexual partners developing it
- Virus shed from both macroscopic and microscopic lesions
- Average incubation time 2 mo (range: 1 to 8 mo)
- Predisposing conditions: diabetes, pregnancy, local trauma, and immunosuppression (e.g., transplant patients, those with HIV infection)

PHYSICAL FINDINGS & CLINICAL PRESENTATION (FIG. 1-63)

- Usually found in genital area, but can be present elsewhere
- Lesions usually in similar positions on both sides of perineum
- Initial lesions pedunculated, soft papules about 2 to 3 mm in diameter, 10 to 20 mm long; may occur as single papule or in clusters
- Size of lesions varies from pinhead to large cauliflower-like masses
- Usually asymptomatic, but if infected, can cause pain, odor, or bleeding
- Vulvar condyloma more common than vaginal and cervical
- There are four morphologic types: condylomatous, keratotic, papular, and flat warts

ETIOLOGY

- HPV DNA types 6 and 11 usually found in exophytic warts and have no malignant potential
- HPV types 16 and 18 usually found in flat warts and are associated with increased risk of malignancy
- Recurrence associated with persisting viral infection of adjacent normal skin in 25% to 50% of cases

DIAGNOSIS

DIFFERENTIAL DIAGNOSIS

- Abnormal anatomic variants or skin tags around labia minora and introitus
- Dysplastic warts

WORKUP

- Colposcopic examination of lower genital tract from cervix to perianal skin with 3% to 5% acetic acid
- Biopsy of vulvar lesions that lack the classic appearance of warts and that become ulcerated or fail to respond to treatment
- Biopsy of flat white or ulcerated cervical lesions

LABORATORY TESTS

- Pap smear
- Cervical cultures for *N. gonorrhoeae* and *Chlamydia*
- Serologic test for syphilis
- HIV testing offered
- Wet mount for trichomoniasis, *Candida albicans,* and *Gardnerella vaginalis*
- Testing for diabetes (blood glucose)

TREATMENT

NONPHARMACOLOGIC THERAPY

- Keep genital area dry and clean.
- Keep diabetes, if present, well controlled.
- Advise use of condoms to prevent spread of infection to sexual partner.

ACUTE GENERAL Rx

Keratolytic agents:

- Podophyllin
  1. Acts by poisoning mitotic spindle and causing intense vasospasm
  2. Applied directly to lesion weekly and washed off in 6 hr
  3. Used in minimal vulvar or anal disease
  4. Applied cautiously to nonkeratinized epithelial surfaces
  5. Contraindicated in pregnancy
  6. Discontinued if lesions do not disappear in 6 wk; switch to other treatment
- Trichloroacetic acid (30% to 80% solution)
  1. Acts by precipitation of surface proteins
  2. Applied twice monthly to lesion
  3. Indicated for vulvar, anal, and vaginal lesions; can be used for cervical lesions
  4. Less painful and irritating to normal tissue than podophyllin
- Fluorouracil
  1. Causes necrosis and sloughing of growing tissue
  2. Can be used intravaginally or for vulvar, anal, or urethral lesions
  3. Better tolerated; 3 g (two thirds of vaginal applicator) applied weekly for 12 wk
  4. Possible vaginal ulceration and erythema
  5. Patient's vagina examined after four to six applications
  6. 80% cure rate

Physical agents:

- Cryotherapy
  1. Can be used weekly for 3 to 6 wk
  2. 62% to 79% success rate
  3. Not suitable for large warts
- Laser therapy
  1. Done by physician with necessary expertise and equipment
  2. Painful; requires anesthesia
- Electrocautery or excision
  1. For recurrent, very large lesions
  2. Local anesthesia needed

Immunotherapy

- Interferon
  1. Injected intralesionally at a dose of 3 million U/m^2 three times weekly for 8 wk
  2. Side effects: fever, chills, malaise, headache

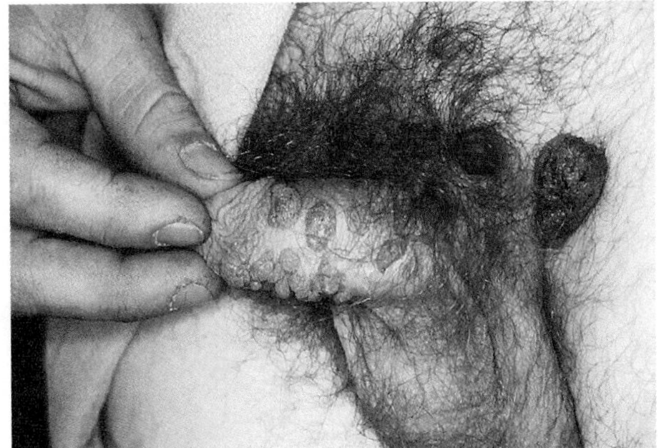

FIGURE 1-63 Condylomata. Verrucoid pigmented lesions on the penis. (From Noble J: *Primary care medicine,* ed 3, St Louis, 2001, Mosby.)

- Autologous vaccine
  1. Made from host's own condyloma acuminatum; not very effective
- Imiquimod 5% cream: increases wart clearance after 3 mo
- Interferon, topical: increases wart clearance at 4 wk

DISPOSITION

Follow closely with pelvic examinations and Pap smears every 3 mo for 6 mo, every 6 mo for 12 mo, and then yearly if no evidence of recurrence.

REFERRAL

Consult gynecologist in case of extensive lesions or lesions resistant to treatment with keratolytic agents (podophyllin and trichloroacetic acid).

SUGGESTED READINGS

Czegledy J: Sexual and non-sexual transmission of human papillomavirus, *Acta Microbiol Immunol Hung* 48(3-4):511, 2001.

Moore RA et al: Imiquimod for the treatment of genital warts: a quantitative systematic review, *BMC Infect Dis* 1(1):3, 2001.

Pearson GW, Langley RG: Topical imiquimod, *J Dermatolog Treat* 12(1):37, 2001.

AUTHOR: **GEORGE T. DANAKAS, M.D.**

BASIC INFORMATION

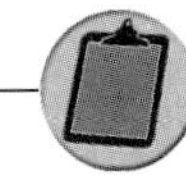

DEFINITION

Congestive heart failure is a pathophysiologic state characterized by congestion in the pulmonary and/or systemic circulation. It is caused by the heart's inability to pump sufficient oxygenated blood to meet the metabolic needs of the tissues.

CLASSIFICATION

The American College of Cardiology and the American Heart Association describe the following four stages of heart failure:

A. At high risk for heart failure, but without structural heart disease or symptoms of heart failure (e.g., CAD, hypertension)
B. Structural heart disease but without symptoms of heart failure
C. Structural heart disease with prior or current symptoms of heart failure
D. Refractory heart failure requiring specialized interventions

The New York Heart Association (NYHA) defines the following functional classes:

I. Asymptomatic
II. Symptomatic with moderate exertion
III. Symptomatic with minimal exertion
IV. Symptomatic at rest

SYNONYMS

CHF
Cardiac failure
Heart failure

ICD-9CM CODES
428.0 Congestive heart failure

EPIDEMIOLOGY & DEMOGRAPHICS

- CHF is the most common admission diagnosis (20%) in elderly patients.
- Heart failure occurs in 4.7 million persons in the U.S. and is the discharge diagnosis in 3.5 million hospitalizations annually.

PHYSICAL FINDINGS & CLINICAL PRESENTATION

The findings on physical examination in patients with CHF vary depending on the severity and whether the failure is right-sided or left-sided.

- Common clinical manifestations are:
  1. Dyspnea on exertion initially, then with progressively less strenuous activity, and eventually manifesting when patient is at rest; caused by increasing pulmonary congestion
  2. Orthopnea caused by increased venous return in the recumbent position
  3. Paroxysmal nocturnal dyspnea (PND) resulting from multiple factors (increased venous return in the recumbent position, decreased Pao_2, decreased adrenergic stimulation of myocardial function)
  4. Nocturnal angina resulting from increased cardiac work (secondary to increased venous return)
  5. Cheyne-Stokes respiration: alternating phases of apnea and hyperventilation caused by prolonged circulation time from lungs to brain
  6. Fatigue, lethargy resulting from low cardiac output
- Patients with failure of the left side of the heart will have the following abnormalities on physical examination: pulmonary rales, tachypnea, S_3 gallop, cardiac murmurs (AS, AR, MR), paradoxic splitting of S_2.
- Patients with failure of right side of the heart manifest with jugular venous distention, peripheral edema, perioral and peripheral cyanosis, congestive hepatomegaly, ascites, hepatojugular reflux.
- In patients with heart failure, elevated jugular venous pressure and a third heart sound are each independently associated with adverse outcomes.
- Acute precipitants of CHF exacerbations are: noncompliance with salt restriction, pulmonary infections, arrhythmias, medications (e.g., calcium channel blockers/antiarrhythmic agents), and inappropriate reductions in CHF therapy.

ETIOLOGY

LEFT VENTRICULAR FAILURE:

- Systemic hypertension
- Valvular heart disease (AS, AR, MR)
- Cardiomyopathy, myocarditis
- Bacterial endocarditis
- Myocardial infarction
- IHSS

Left ventricular failure is further differentiated according to systolic dysfunction (low ejection fraction) and diastolic dysfunction (normal or high ejection fraction), or "stiff ventricle." It is important to make this distinction because treatment is significantly different (see Treatment). Patients with heart failure and a normal ejection fraction have significant abnormalities in active relaxation and passive stiffness. In these patients, the pathophysiological cause of elevated diastolic pressures and heart failure is abnormal diastolic function.

- Common causes of systolic dysfunction are post-MI, cardiomyopathy, myocarditis.
- Causes of diastolic dysfunction are hypertensive cardiovascular disease, valvular heart disease (AS, AR, MR, IHSS), restrictive cardiomyopathy.

RIGHT VENTRICULAR FAILURE:

- Valvular heart disease (mitral stenosis)
- Pulmonary hypertension
- Bacterial endocarditis (right-sided)
- Right ventricular infarction

BIVENTRICULAR FAILURE:

- Left ventricular failure
- Cardiomyopathy
- Myocarditis
- Arrhythmias
- Anemia
- Thyrotoxicosis
- AV fistula
- Paget's disease
- Beriberi

DIAGNOSIS

DIFFERENTIAL DIAGNOSIS

- Cirrhosis
- Nephrotic syndrome
- Venous occlusive disease
- COPD, asthma
- Pulmonary embolism
- ARDS
- Heroin overdose
- Pneumonia

WORKUP

- Echocardiography plays a critical diagnostic role in patients with heart failure. Doppler echocardiography, which measures the velocity of intracardiac blood flow, is also helpful in the assessment of diastolic function.
- Standard 12-lead ECG is useful to diagnose ischemic heart disease and obtain information about rhythm abnormalities.
- Cardiac catheterization provides direct measurement of ventricular diastolic pressure and can demonstrate impaired relaxation and filling; however, it is invasive and indicated only in selected patients.

LABORATORY TESTS

- CBC (to rule out anemia, infections), BUN, creatinine, liver enzymes, TSH
- β-type natriuretic peptide is a cardiac neurohormone specifically secreted from the ventricles in response to volume expansion and pressure overload. Elevated levels are indicative of left ventricular dysfunction. Bedside measurement of β-type natriuretic peptide is useful in establishing or excluding the diagnosis of CHF in patients with acute dyspnea

IMAGING STUDIES

- Chest x-ray examination:
  1. Pulmonary venous congestion
  2. Cardiomegaly with dilation of the involved heart chamber
  3. Pleural effusions
- Two-dimensional echocardiography is useful to assess global and regional left ventricular function and estimate ejection fraction.
- Exercise stress testing may be useful for evaluating concomitant coronary disease and assess degree of disability. The decision to perform exercise stress testing should be individualized.
- Cardiac catheterization remains an excellent method to evaluate ventricular diastolic properties, significant coronary artery disease, or valvular heart disease; however, it is invasive. The decision to perform cardiac catheterization should be individualized.

TREATMENT

NONPHARMACOLOGIC THERAPY

- Determine if CHF is secondary to systolic or diastolic dysfunction and treat accordingly.
- Identify and correct precipitating factors (i.e., anemia, thyrotoxicosis, infections, increased sodium load, medical noncompliance).
- Decrease cardiac workload in patients with systolic dysfunction: restrict patients' activity only during periods of acute decompensation; the risk of thromboembolism during this period can be minimized by using heparin 5000 U SC q12h in hospitalized patients. In patients with mild to moderate symptoms aerobic training may improve symptoms and exercise capacity.
- Restrict sodium intake to ≤3 g/day.
- Restricting fluid intake to 2 L or less may be useful in patients with hyponatremia.

ACUTE GENERAL Rx

TREATMENT OF CHF SECONDARY TO SYSTOLIC DYSFUNCTION:

1. Diuretics: indicated in patients with systolic dysfunction and volume overload. The most useful approach to selecting the dose of, and monitoring the response to, diuretic therapy is by measuring body weight, preferably daily.
   a. Furosemide: 20 to 80 mg/day produces prompt venodilation and diuresis. IV therapy may produce diuresis when oral therapy has failed; when changing from IV to oral furosemide, doubling the dose is usually necessary to achieve an equal effect.
   b. Thiazides are not as powerful as furosemide but are useful in mild to moderate CHF.
   c. The addition of metolazone to furosemide enhances diuresis.
   d. Blockade of aldosterone receptors by spironolactone (12.5 to 25 mg qd) used in conjunction with ACE inhibitors reduces both mortality and morbidity in patients with severe CHF. It is generally not associated with hyperkalemia when used in low doses, however, serum electrolytes and renal function should be closely monitored after initiation of therapy and when changing doses. Spironolactone use should be considered in patients with recent or recurrent class IV (NYHA) symptoms.
   e. Frequent monitoring of renal function and electrolytes is recommended in all patients receiving diuretics.
2. ACE inhibitors:
   a. They cause dilation of the arteriolar resistance vessels and venous capacity vessels, thereby reducing both preload and afterload.
   b. They are associated with decreased mortality and improved clinical status when used in patients with CHF caused by systolic dysfunction. They are also indicated in patients with ejection fraction <40%.
   c. They can be used as first-line therapy or they can be added to diuretics in patients with CHF poorly controlled with only diuretic therapy.
   d. Therapy with ACE inhibitors should be initiated at low dose (e.g., captopril 6.25 mg tid or enalapril 2.5 mg bid) to prevent hypotension and rapidly titrated up to high doses if tolerated.
   e. Contraindications to use of ACE inhibitors are renal insufficiency (creatinine >3.0 or creatinine clearance <30 ml/min), renal artery stenosis, persistent hyperkalemia (K+ >5.5 mEQ/L), symptomatic hypotension, and history of adverse reactions (e.g., angioedema).
3. β-blockers: All patients with stable NYHA class II or III heart failure caused by left ventricular systolic dysfunction should receive a β-blocker unless they have a contraindication to its use or are intolerant to it. β-blockers are especially useful in patients who remain symptomatic despite therapy with ACE inhibitors and diuretics. Effective agents are carvedilol (Coreg) 3.125 mg bid, bisoprolol 1.25 mg qd, or metoprolol 12.5 mg bid initially, titrated upward as tolerated.
4. Angiotensin II receptor blockers (ARBS) block the A-II type 1 (AT) receptor, which is responsible for many of the deleterious effects of angiotensin II. These receptors are potent vasoconstrictors that may contribute to the impairment of LV function. ARBS are useful in patients unable to tolerate ACE inhibitors because of angioedema or intractable cough. They can also be used in combination with a β-blocker.
5. Digitalis may be useful because of its positive inotropic and vagotonic effects in patients with CHF secondary to systolic dysfunction; it is of limited value in patients with mild CHF and normal sinus rhythm. It is more beneficial in patients with rapid atrial fibrillation, severe CHF, or ejection fraction of <30%; it can be added to diuretics and ACE inhibitors in patients with severe CHF. In patients with chronic heart failure and normal sinus rhythm, digoxin does not reduce mortality, but it does reduce the rate of hospitalization both overall and for worsening heart failure. Digoxin has a narrow therapeutic window. Its beneficial effects are found with a low dose that results in a serum concentration of approximately 0.7 ng/ml. Higher doses may be detrimental.
6. Direct vasodilating drugs (nesiritide, hydralazine, isosorbide) are useful in the therapy of systolic dysfunction with CHF because they can reduce the systemic vascular resistance and pulmonary venous pressure, especially when used in combination. Nesiritide (Natrecor), a recombinant human brain, or B-type, natriuretic peptide has venous, arterial, and coronary vasodilatory properties that decrease preload and afterload and increase cardiac output without direct inotropic effects. In hospitalized patients with acutely decompensated CHF, the addition of IV nesiritide to standard care improves hemodynamic function (decreased PCWP) and self-reported symptoms more effectively than IV nitroglycerin. Usual nesiritide dosage is 2 mcg/kg IV bolus, then 0.01 mcg/kg/min.
7. Anticoagulants:
   a. Anticoagulation is not recommended for patients in sinus rhythm and no prior history of stroke, left ventricular thrombi, or arteriolar emboli.
   b. Anticoagulation therapy is appropriate for patients with heart failure and atrial fibrillation or a history of embolism.

8. Surgical revascularization should be considered in patients with both heart failure and severe limiting angina.
9. Antiarrhythmic therapy with amiodarone has a modest effect in reducing mortality in patients with CHF; however, it is not recommended for general use in CHF. Its benefits must be weighed against the risk for adverse effects, especially potentially fatal pulmonary toxicity.
10. Atriobiventricular pacing significantly improves exercise tolerance and quality of life in patients with chronic heart failure and intraventricular conduction delay.
11. Obstructive sleep apnea has an adverse effect on heart failure. Recognition and treatment of coexisting obstructive sleep apnea by continuous positive airway pressure reduces systolic blood pressure and improves left ventricular systolic function.

TREATMENT OF CHF SECONDARY TO DIASTOLIC DYSFUNCTION:

The initial treatment of diastolic heart failure should be directed at reducing the congestive state with the use of diuretics being careful not to avoid excessive diuresis. Long term goals are to control hypertension, tachycardia, congestion, and ischemia. Therapeutic options are determined by the cause.

1. Hypertension
   a. Calcium channel blockers (verapamil)
   b. ACE inhibitors
   c. β-blockers or verapamil to control heart rate and prolong diastolic filling
   d. Diuretics: vigorous diuresis should be avoided, because a higher filling pressure may be needed to maintain cardiac output in patients with diastolic dysfunction
   e. ARBs
2. Aortic stenosis
   a. Diuretics
   b. Contraindicated medications: ACE inhibitors, nitrates, digitalis (except to control rate of atrial fibrillation)
   c. Aortic valve replacement in patients with critical stenosis
3. Aortic insufficiency and mitral regurgitation
   a. ACE inhibitors increase cardiac output and decrease pulmonary wedge pressure. They are agents of choice along with diuretics.
   b. Hydralazine combined with nitrates can be used if ACE inhibitors are not tolerated.
   c. Surgery
4. IHSS
   a. β-blockers or verapamil
   b. Contraindicated medications (they increase outlet obstruction by decreasing the size of the left ventricle in end systole): diuretics, digitalis, ACE inhibitors, hydralazine
   c. Restoration of intravascular volume with IV saline solution if necessary in acute pulmonary edema
   d. DDD pacing is useful in selected patients

TREATMENT OF CHF SECONDARY TO MITRAL STENOSIS:

1. Diuretics
2. Control of the heart rate and atrial fibrillation with digitalis, verapamil, and/or β-blockers is critical to allow emptying of left atrium and relief of pulmonary congestion
3. Repairing or replacing the mitral valve is indicated if CHF is not readily controlled by the above measures
4. Balloon valvuloplasty is useful in selected patients

DISPOSITION

- Annual mortality ranges from 10% in stable patients with mild symptoms to >50% in symptomatic patients with advanced disease.
- Sudden death secondary to ventricular arrhythmias occurs in >40% of patients with heart failure.
- Cardiac transplantation has a 5-yr survival rate of >70% in many centers and represents a viable option in selected patients.
- The use of a left ventricular assist device in patients with advanced heart failure can result in a clinically meaningful survival benefit and improve quality of life. It is an acceptable alternative therapy in selected patients who are not candidates for cardiac transplantation.
- In patients with advanced heart failure and a prolonged QRS interval, cardiac-resynchronization therapy decreases the combined risk of death from any cause or first hospitalization and, when combined with an implantable defibrillator, significantly reduces mortality.

SUGGESTED READINGS

Aurigemma GP, Gaasch WH: Diastolic heart failure, *N Engl J Med* 351:1097, 2004.

Bristow MR et al: Cardiac-resynchronization therapy with or without an implantable defibrillator in advanced chronic heart failure, *N Engl J Med* 350:2140, 2004.

Cuffe MS et al: Short-term intravenous milrinone for acute exacerbation of chronic heart failure, *JAMA* 287:1541, 2002.

Goldstein S: Benefits of beta-blocker therapy in heart failure, *Arch Intern Med* 162:641, 2002.

Gutierrez C, Blanchard DG: Diastolic heart failure: Challenges of diagnosis and treatment, *Am Fam Physician* 69:2609, 2004.

Jessup M, Brozena S: Heart failure, *N Engl J Med* 348:2007, 2003.

King DE et al: Acute management of heart failure, *Am Fam Physician* 66:249, 2002.

Kukin ML: Beta blockers in chronic heart failure, *Mayo Clin Proc* 77:1199, 2002.

Maisel AS et al: Rapid measurement of B-type natriuretic peptide in the emergency diagnosis of heart failure, *N Engl J Med* 347:161, 2002.

Mueller C et al: Use of B-type natriuretic peptide in the evaluation and management of acute dyspnea, *N Engl J Med* 350:647, 2004.

Nohria A et al: Medical management of advanced heart failure, *JAMA* 287:628, 2002.

Pfeffer MA et al: Valsartan, captopril, or both in myocardial infarction complicated by heart failure, left ventricular dysfunction, or both, *N Engl J Med* 349:1893, 2003.

Publications Committee for the VMAC Investigators: Intravenous nesiritide vs nitroglycerin for the treatment of decompensated congestive heart failure, *JAMA* 287:1531, 2002.

Zile MR et al: Diastolic heart failure—abnormalities in active relaxation and passive stiffness of the left ventricle, *N Engl J Med* 350:1953, 2004.

AUTHOR: **FRED F. FERRI, M.D.**

Conjunctivitis

BASIC INFORMATION

DEFINITION

The term *conjunctivitis* refers to an inflammation of the conjunctiva resulting from a variety of causes, including allergies and bacterial, viral, and chlamydial infections.

SYNONYMS

"Red eye"
Acute conjunctivitis
Subacute conjunctivitis
Chronic conjunctivitis
Purulent conjunctivitis
Pseudomembranous conjunctivitis
Papillary conjunctivitis
Follicular conjunctivitis
Newborn conjunctivitis

ICD-9CM CODES
372.30 Conjunctivitis, unspecified

EPIDEMIOLOGY & DEMOGRAPHICS

INCIDENCE (IN U.S.): Newborn 1.6% to 12%

PREVALENCE (IN U.S.):

- Very common
- Often seasonal and can be extremely contagious

PREDOMINANT AGE: Occurs at any age

PEAK INCIDENCE: More common in the fall when viral infections and pollens increase

PHYSICAL FINDINGS & CLINICAL PRESENTATION

- Injection and chemosis of conjunctivae with discharge (Fig. 1-64)
- Cornea clear
- Vision often normal

ETIOLOGY

- Bacterial
- Viral
- Chlamydial
- Allergic
- Traumatic

DIAGNOSIS

DIFFERENTIAL DIAGNOSIS

- Acute glaucoma
- Corneal lesions
- Acute iritis
- Episcleritis
- Scleritis
- Uveitis
- Canalicular obstruction
- The differential diagnosis of red eye is described in Section II

WORKUP

- History and physical examination
- Reports of itching, pain, visual changes

LABORATORY TESTS

Cultures are useful if not successfully treated with antibiotic medications; initial culture is usually not necessary.

TREATMENT

NONPHARMACOLOGIC THERAPY

- Warm compresses if infective conjunctivitis
- Cold compresses in irritative or allergic conjunctivitis

ACUTE GENERAL Rx

- Antibiotic drops (e.g., levofloxacin, ofloxin, ciprofloxacin, tobramycin, gentamicin ophthalmic solution one or two drops q2-4h)
- Caution: be careful with corticosteroid treatment and avoid unless sure of diagnosis; corticosteroids can exacerbate infections
- Povidine-iodine (Betadine) eye drops when available

CHRONIC Rx

- Depends on cause
- If allergic, nonsteroidals such as Voltaren ophthalmic solution, mast cell stabilizers such as Alocril, Patanol, Zaditor are useful
- If infections, antibiotic drops (see Acute General Rx)
- Dry eyes need artificial tears, ristasis, lacrameal duct plugs when indicated

DISPOSITION

Follow carefully for the first 2 wk to make sure secondary complications do not occur.

REFERRAL

To ophthalmologist if symptoms refractory to initial treatment

PEARLS & CONSIDERATIONS

COMMENTS

- Red eyes are not just conjunctivitis when there is significant pain or loss of sight. However, it is usually safe to treat pain-free eyes and the normal seeing red eye with lid hygene and topical treatment.
- Beware of patients wearing soft contact lenses and of babies and the elderly.
- Do not use steroids indiscriminately; use only when the diagnosis is certain.

SUGGESTED READINGS

Bennett C: Treatment of viral conjunctivitis in children, *Am Fam Physician* 67(9):1873, 2003.

Fischer PR et al: Route of antibiotic administration for conjunctivitis, *Pediatr Infect Dis J* 21(10):989, 2002.

Nichols GR: The red eye, *N Engl J Med* 343(21):1577, 2000.

Sheikh A, Hurwitz B: Topical antibiotics for acute bacterial conjunctivitis: a systematic review, *Br J Gen Pract* 51:473, 2001.

AUTHOR: **MELVYN KOBY, M.D.**

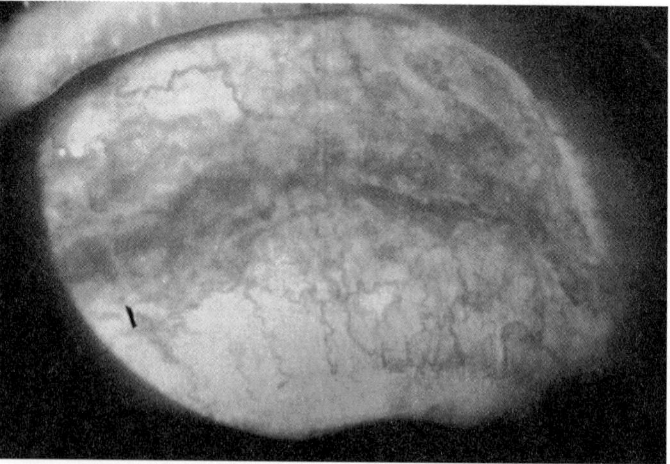

FIGURE 1-64 Conjunctival infection from viral conjunctivitis. (From Marx JA [ed]: *Rosen's emergency medicine,* ed 5, St Louis, 2002, Mosby.)

BASIC INFORMATION

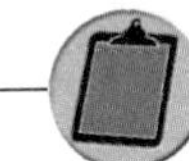

DEFINITION

Contraception refers to the various options that a sexually active couple have to prevent pregnancy. These options can be either medical or nonmedical and used by men or women or both. The options are as follows:

- No contraception: failure rate 85% both typical and perfect
- Abstinence
  1. 12.4% of unmarried men
  2. 13.2% of unmarried women
  3. More frequently practiced before age 17 yr
  4. No intercourse experienced by 13% of women ages 30 to 34 yr old
  5. Failure rate 0%
- Withdrawal
  1. Used in only 2% of sexually active women
  2. Failure rate with perfect use, 4%; with typical use, 19%
- Rhythm method (natural family planning)
  1. Failure rate with perfect use, 1% to 9%; with typical use, 20%
  2. Symptothermal type: mucus method and ovulation pain combined with basal body temperature
  3. Ovulation (Billings' method): takes into account mucus quality
  4. Basal body temperature method: uses biphasic temperature chart
  5. Lactation amenorrhea method: effective in fully breast-feeding women, especially 70 to 100 days after delivery; depends on number of feedings per day
- Barriers
  1. Diaphragm and cervical cap: failure rate 5% to 9% in nulliparous women, 20% in multiparous women
  2. Female condom: failure rate with perfect use, 5.1%; with typical use, 12.4%; FDA labeling states 25% failure rate
  3. Male condom: failure rate with perfect use, 3%, with typical use, 12%
  4. Spermicides (aerosols, foam, jellies, creams, tabs): failure rate with perfect use, 3%; with typical use, 21%
- Oral contraceptives
  1. Failure rate with perfect use, <1%; with typical use, 3%
  2. Come in combinations of estrogen/progestin or as progestin only
- Hormonal implants and injectables
  1. Norplant
     a. Most typically used in U.S.
     b. Failure rate in first 5 yr: 1%
     c. Failure rate after 6 yr: 2%
     d. May be extended to 7 yr use
  2. Depo-Provera: failure rate 0.3% in first year of use
  3. Lunelle (approved October 2000): failure rate 0.2% in first year
  4. Etonogestrel implant: 2-yr cumulative pregnancy rate 0%
  5. Nestorone-releasing single implant: not yet available
  6. Jadelle implant
- Mini pill (progesterone only pill)
  1. Failure rate with typical use, 1.1% to 13.2%
  2. With perfect use, 5 pregnancies/1000 women
- Emergency postcoital contraception
  1. Decreases pregnancy rate by 75% with women treated immediately postcoitally
  2. Involves hormonal use or IUD insertion
- IUD (available OTC in some states)
  1. Progestasert: failure rate with perfect use, 2%; with typical use, 3%
  2. Copper T (380-A): failure rate with perfect use, 0.8%; with typical use, 3%
  3. Levonorgestrel Intrauterine System (Mirena)
     a. 1-yr failure rate, 1%
     b. 5-yr cumulative failure rate, 0.71/100 women
- Female sterilization (tubal ligation): failure rate with perfect use, 0.2%; with typical use, 3%
- Male sterilization (vasectomy): failure rate of 0.1% in first year
- Vaginal ring (Nuva ring): failure rate pearl index 0.77
- Contraceptive patch (Orthoevra): failure rate 0.4% to 0.7%

SYNONYMS

Birth control
Family planning

ICD-9CM CODES
V25.01 Oral contraceptives
V25.02 Other contraceptive measures
V25.09 Family planning
V25.1 IUD
V25.2 Sterilization

EPIDEMIOLOGY & DEMOGRAPHICS

For women at risk for pregnancy, ranges for use of most commonly used birth control are dependent, as follows:

- Oral contraceptives: 3% (40 to 44 yr old) to 60% (20 to 24 yr old)
- Condoms: 9% (40 to 44 yr old) to 26% (15 to 19 yr old)
- Diaphragm: 0.8% (15 to 19 yr old) to 8% (30 to 34 yr old)
- Periodic abstinence: 0.7% (15 to 19 yr old) to 3% (35 to 39 yr old)
- Withdrawal: 1.1% (40 to 44 yr old) to 3% (20 to 30 yr old)
- IUD: 0% (15 to 19 yr old) to 3% (30 to 34 yr old)
- Spermicides: 0.8% (15 to 19 yr old) to 2.7% (35 to 39 yr old)
- No method: 6.3% (35 to 39 yr old) to 19.8% (15 to 19 yr old)
- Sterilization
  Female: 0.2% (15 to 19 yr old) to 47% (40 to 44 yr old)
  Male: 0.2% (15 to 19 yr old) to 21% (40 to 44 yr old)

Women are more likely to use contraception. The only two male forms available are condoms and vasectomy (sterilization).

DIAGNOSIS

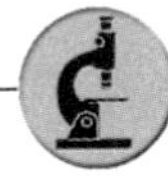

WORKUP

- Thorough medical history
- Thorough surgical history
- Obstetric history (fertility desired?)
- Gynecologic history, including:
  1. History of previous sexually transmitted diseases
  2. Number of partners
  3. Previous difficulties with contraception
  4. Frequency of intercourse
- Family history

LABORATORY TESTS

- Pap smear
- Cultures, aerobic and *Chlamydia*
- Pregnancy test if suspected pregnancy
- Lipid profile if family history of premature vascular event

TREATMENT

NONPHARMACOLOGIC THERAPY

- Male condoms
  1. 95% latex (rubber), 5% skin or natural membrane
  2. Proper use: place on an erect penis and leave one-half-inch empty space at the tip of the condom; use with non–oil-based lubricants
  3. Effectiveness increased when used with spermicides
- Female condoms
  1. Composed of polyurethane, with one end open and one end closed
  2. Proper use: place closed end over cervix, open end hanging out of vagina to cover penis and scrotum
  3. Highly effective against HIV
- Spermicides
  1. Types: nonoxynol, octoxynol
  2. Forms: jellies, creams, foams, suppositories, tablets, soluble films
  3. Proper use: put in immediately before intercourse; may be used with other barrier methods
- Diaphragm and cervical cap
  1. Must be fitted by practitioner, used with contraceptive gels, and refitted with weight gain or loss

2. Diaphragm sizes: 50 to 95 mm; cervical cap sizes: 22, 25, 28, and 31 mm
3. Proper use of diaphragm: put in immediately before intercourse and keep in for 6 hr after intercourse; must not remain in the vagina for longer than 24 hr
4. Proper use of cervical cap: fit over the cervix exactly; must not remain in place for longer than 48 hr

- Lactation amenorrhea method
  1. Depends on number of breast-feedings per day; effective as birth control for 6 mo if 15 or more feedings, lasting 10 min each, are accomplished daily
  2. Not a common practice in the U.S
- Withdrawal
  1. Withdrawal of the penis from the vagina before ejaculation
  2. Dependent on self-control
- Rhythm method
  1. Dependent on awareness of physiology of male and female reproductive tracts
  2. Sperm viable in vagina for 2 to 7 days
  3. Ovum life span 24 hr
- Sterilization
  1. Male:
     a. Vasectomy to interrupt vas deferens and block passage of sperm to seminal ejaculate
     b. Scalpel and nonscalpel techniques available
     c. More easily performed procedure than female sterilization and does not require general anesthesia
  2. Female:
     a. Leading method of birth control in U.S. in women older than 30 yr
     b. Interrupts fallopian tubes, blocking passage of ovum proximally and sperm distally through tube
     c. Several types; modified Pomeroy done during cesarean section or laparoscopic done in nonpregnant females most common
     d. Essure-tubal occlusion through hysteroscopic placement of micro-inserts into the fallopian tubes.

ACUTE GENERAL Rx

- Combination oral contraceptives
  1. Taken daily for 21 days, pill-free interval of 7 days
  2. Less than 50 μg ethynyl estradiol in most common combination oral contraceptives; progestins most commonly used in combination pills are norethindrone, levonorgestrel, norgestrel, norethindrone acetate, ethynodiol diacetate, norgestimate, or desogestrel; triphasic combination oral contraceptives (give varying doses of progestin and estrogens throughout cycle); monophasic oral contraceptives: offer same dose of progestin and estrogen throughout cycle, taken daily at same time; estrophasic pill (constant progesterone with variation of estrogen throughout the cycle)
  3. If pill taken with antibiotics, efficacy affected by inadequate gastrointestinal absorption in most cases; only rifampin truly reduces pill's effectiveness
  4. Increased body weight decreases effectiveness
- Mini pill
  1. Progestin only; taken without a break
  2. Causes much irregular bleeding because of the lack of estrogen effect on the lining of the uterus
- Hormonal implants and injectables
  1. Norplant
     a. Progestin only; inserted under the skin
     b. Six levonorgestrel implants placed subcutaneously in upper inner arm effective for 5 yr
  2. Depo-Provera
     a. Medroxyprogesterone acetate given every 3 mo in IM injection form
     b. Major side effect: irregular bleeding
     c. Fertility return possibly delayed up to 18 mo after discontinuation
  3. Lunelle: monthly injectable administered intramuscularly. Contains 0.5 ml aqueous, 5 mg estradiol cypionate and 25 mg medroxyprogesterone acetate
  4. Etonogestrel implant: single-rod release etonogestrel for 3 yr placed subdermally
- Postcoital contraception
  1. Done on emergency basis, usually secondary to noncompliance with birth control or failure of birth control (e.g., condom breakage) at the time of ovulation
  2. Methods:
     a. IUD insertion within 7 days of coitus
     b. Hormonal methods (combination pills and danazol) given within 48 hr of coitus
- IUD
  1. Device inserted into uterus to prevent sperm and ovum from uniting in fallopian tube
  2. Types available in the U.S.:
     a. Progestasert: a T-shaped device that is an ethylene vinyl acetate copolymer T; vertical stem contains 38 mg progesterone and must be changed yearly
     b. ParaGard (Copper T/380-A): a polyethylene T wrapped with a fine copper wire that is effective for 10 yr of use
     c Mirena Levonorgestrel Intrauterine System (LNGIUS): a T-shaped system with a chamber that contains LNG. Releases 20 μg per day; is effective for 5 yr
- Vaginal ring (brand name Nuvaring)
  1. Provides daily dose of 120 μg of etonogestrel and 15 μg ethinyl estradiol
  2. Stays in vagina 3 wk and removed the fourth
  3. Increased body weight decreases effectiveness
- Contraceptive patch (brand name Evra)
  1. Provides low daily dose of steroids
  2. Releases a progestin and estrogen (ethinyl estradiol)
  3. Patch size 20 cm^2
  4. Each patch contains 6 mg norelgestronin and delivers an estimated continuous systemic dose of 150 μg norelgestronin and 20 μg of ethinyl estradiol; common dose 250 μg/day progestin and 25 μg/day estrogen
  5. Worn 3 of 4 wk
  6. Increased body weight decreases effectiveness

CHRONIC Rx

- With all of the previously mentioned types of birth control, patient is followed at least yearly, or as necessary, if problems arise.
- Full history, physical examination, and Pap smear, including cultures when needed, are performed yearly.
- Patients with medical problems are followed about every 6 mo when taking hormonal therapy.

DISPOSITION

- Follow yearly or more frequently according to patient's side effects.
- Tailor birth control to patient according to different needs or side effects present at different times in life.

REFERRAL

With hormonal contraception, if neurologic or cardiac symptoms arise, stop method immediately, evaluate, and refer to internist when appropriate.

PEARLS & CONSIDERATIONS

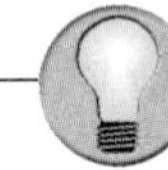

COMMENTS

- Patient education information available through American College of Obstetricians and Gynecologists (ACOG) at 1-800-673-8444 and through various drug companies representing and supplying the particular type of contraception.
- A clinical algorithm on the use of oral contraceptives is described in Section III, Contraceptive Use, Oral.

SUGGESTED READINGS

Clinical proceedings: *Association of Reproductive Health Professionals,* February 2001.

Dieben T: Efficacy cycle control and user acceptability of a novel combined contraceptive vaginal ring, *Obstet Gynecol* 100(3):585, 2002.

Gordon J: Transdermal contraception: a new technology for women, *The Female Patient* (Suppl):1, 2002.

Grimes DA: Switching emergency contraception to over-the-counter status, *N Engl J Med* 347:846, 2002.

Holt VL et al: Body weight and risk of oral contraceptive failure, *Obstet Gynecol* 99:820, 2002.

Sivin I, Moo-Young A: Recent developments in contraceptive implants at the population council contraception, 65(1):113, 2002.

AUTHOR: **MARIA A. CORIGLIANO, M.D.**

Conversion Disorder

BASIC INFORMATION

DEFINITION

A disturbance of bodily functioning that does not conform to current concepts of the anatomy and physiology of the central or peripheral nervous system, usually in the setting of stress. Patients do not willfully control their symptoms (which distinguishes them from factitious disorder or malingering).

SYNONYMS

Somatoform disorder (conversion disorder is a subset of this larger group)

ICD-9CM CODES
V61.10

EPIDEMIOLOGY & DEMOGRAPHICS

- Most frequent of the somatoform disorders
- Incidence estimated at 5-10/100,000 in general population, but 20-100/100,000 hospital inpatients
- All ages, including early childhood
- Women > men (ratios range from 2:1 to 5:1)
- Highest in rural areas, among undereducated, and in lower socioeconomic classes
- Predisposition includes axis I disorders (most commonly depression and anxiety) and axis II disorders (most commonly histrionic, passive-dependent, and passive-aggressive)

CLINICAL PRESENTATION

- May present in multiple ways, but usually involves pseudoneurologic signs or symptoms.
- Signs or symptoms usually do not correlate with known organic disease patterns, but do correlate with the patient's understanding of the disease pattern.
- Motor symptoms may include abnormal gait, weakness, paralysis, and involuntary movements, including seizures.
- Sensory deficits may include anesthesia (especially of extremities), blindness, and deafness.
- Visceral symptoms may include psychogenic vomiting, syncope, urinary retention, diarrhea, and pseudocyesis.
- All of the above occur in the setting of marked psychological stress.
- May last from hours to years.
- "Classic" features such as la belle indifference (patients do not seem to be disturbed by their signs or symptoms) or presence of secondary gains need not be present for diagnosis.

ETIOLOGY

- Complex interplay of neurologic and psychologic factors.
- Recent structural and functional brain imaging studies suggest defects in processing sensory and motor signals and improper communication with execution.

DIAGNOSIS

DIFFERENTIAL DIAGNOSIS

- Broad differential diagnosis depending on presenting signs and symptoms
- Myasthenia gravis
- Neurologic disorders (multiple sclerosis, CNS neoplasm, Guillain-Barré syndrome, amyotrophic lateral sclerosis, Parkinson's disease)
- Systemic lupus erythematosus
- Spinal cord compression
- Intracerebral hemorrhage
- Drug-induced dystonia
- HIV (or early manifestations of AIDS)
- Rule out other psychiatric disorders (major depressive episodes, posttraumatic stress disorder, factitious disorder, malingering, somatization disorder)

WORKUP

Thorough history and physical examination

LABORATORY TESTS

- No gold standard diagnostic tests exist; no single associated finding is pathognomonic.
- Other laboratory tests or procedures may be needed to rule out other etiologies (i.e., EEG for seizures, EMG for lower motor neuron paralysis, optokinetic drum test in blindness).

IMAGING STUDIES

As indicated by presenting signs and symptoms

TREATMENT

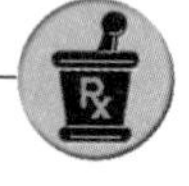

NONPHARMACOLOGIC THERAPY

- Treatment successes have been associated with a caring, long-term relationship with a physician in a safe, nonconfrontational approach.
- Physicians should discourage symptom retention by withdrawing attention from abnormal signs or symptoms.
- Physical and occupational therapy can be helpful for "retraining" the patient in normal behaviors.
- Psychotherapy should focus on developing appropriate coping mechanisms for stress.

ACUTE GENERAL Rx

- Recent studies have shown no additional benefit to hypnosis, although significant experience exists with barbiturate-induced hypnosis as a psychotherapeutic aid.
- Antidepressants may be helpful in treating comorbid mood or anxiety disorders.

CHRONIC Rx

See above.

DISPOSITION

Long-term follow-up is essential (about 25% of patients with conversion disorder will develop another episode).

PEARLS & CONSIDERATIONS

COMMENTS

- Good prognostic factors: sudden onset, presence of psychologic stressors at onset of symptoms, short duration between diagnosis and treatment, high level of intelligence, absence of other psychiatric or medical disorders, aphonia as the presenting symptom, and no ongoing compensation litigation.
- Poor prognostic factors: severe disability, long duration of symptoms, age >40 at symptom onset, and convulsions and paralysis as presenting symptoms.

SUGGESTED READINGS

Krem MM: Motor conversion disorders reviewed from a neuropsychiatric perspective, *J Clin Psychiatry* 65(6):783, 2004.

Hurwitz TA: Somatization and conversion disorder, *Can J Psychiatry* 49(3):172, 2004.

AUTHOR: **MEREDITH HELLER, M.D.**

BASIC INFORMATION

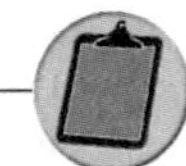

DEFINITION

Cor pulmonale refers to the enlargement of the right ventricle and deterioration of its function secondary to diseases affecting the lungs or pulmonary vasculature that cause pulmonary hypertension. Cor pulmonale may be acute or chronic.

SYNONYMS

- Acute cor pulmonale
- Chronic cor pulmonale

ICD-9CM CODES
415.0 Cor pulmonale, acute
416.9 Cor pulmonale, chronic

EPIDEMIOLOGY & DEMOGRAPHICS

- Cor pulmonale is the third most common cardiac disorder after the age of 50.
- More common in men than in women.

PHYSICAL FINDINGS & CLINICAL PRESENTATION

No symptoms are specific for cor pulmonale. Typically cor pulmonale presents according to the underlying disease process such as pulmonary embolism or COPD.

- Dyspnea, pleuritic chest pain, and cough
- Exertional angina (secondary to pulmonary artery stretching and right ventricular ischemia)
- Leg swelling
- Hemoptysis
- Wheezing and rales
- Tachypnea and tachycardia
- Cyanosis
- Hoarseness (due to compression of the left recurrent laryngeal nerve by dilated main pulmonary artery)
- Jugular venous distention with large V waves
- Holosystolic murmur heard best along the left parasternal line, fourth intercostal space and is augmented during inspiration (from associated tricuspid regurgitation)
- Increased intensity of pulmonic component of S2, which may be narrowly split (because of concomitant pulmonary hypertension)
- Diastolic pulmonary valve regurgitant murmur
- Pulsatile hepatomegaly
- Right upper quadrant abdominal discomfort and anorexia may occur secondary to passive hepatic congestion

ETIOLOGY

- The most frequent cause of cor pulmonale is emphysema or chronic bronchitis.
- Cor pulmonale is caused by pulmonary hypertension.
- Mechanisms leading to pulmonary hypertension include:
  1. Pulmonary vasoconstriction resulting from any condition causing alveolar hypoxia and/or acidosis
  2. Lung parenchymal disorders (e.g., emphysema, interstitial lung disease, pulmonary emboli)
  3. Conditions leading to increased bloom viscosity (e.g., polycythemia vera, Waldenstrom's macroglobulinemia)
  4. Idiopathic primary pulmonary hypertension
  5. Increased pulmonary blood flow (abnormal shunts)

DIAGNOSIS

The diagnosis of cor pulmonale is made in any patient with underlying evidence of pulmonary hypertension and findings of right-sided heart failure.

DIFFERENTIAL DIAGNOSIS

- Pulmonary thromboembolic disease
- Chronic obstructive pulmonary disease (COPD)
- Interstitial lung disease
- Neuromuscular diseases causing hypoventilation (e.g., ALS)
- Collagen-vascular disease (e.g., SLE, CREST, systemic sclerosis)
- Pulmonary venous disease
- Primary pulmonary hypertension

WORKUP

Any patient suspected of cor pulmonale should undergo a workup searching for an underlying pulmonary process resulting in pulmonary hypertension. Workup includes blood tests, chest x-ray, echocardiogram, MRI, and occasionally, right-side heart catheterization.

LABORATORY TESTS

- CBC may show erythrocytosis secondary to hypoxia
- Arterial blood gas (ABGs) confirming hypoxemia and acidosis or hypercapnia
- Pulmonary function tests

IMAGING STUDIES

- Chest x-ray may show evidence of COPD and pulmonary hypertension (e.g., RA, RV, and pulmonary enlargement)
- Electrocardiogram may reveal RVH, right atrial enlargement (p-pulmonale), right axis deviation or incomplete/complete RBBB.
- Echocardiogram with continuous, pulse, and color Doppler can estimate pulmonary artery pressure. M-mode and two-dimensional measures chamber size and wall thickness.
- Radionuclide ventriculography reveals depressed right ventricular ejection fraction.
- MRI is a sensitive test to measure right ventricular dimensions and detect hypertrophy.
- Right-side catheterization measures pulmonary artery pressures and vascular resistance. It also helps determine response to various therapies (e.g., oxygen, calcium blockers, angiotensin-converting enzyme inhibitors, etc.).

TREATMENT

The treatment of cor pulmonale is directed at the underlying etiology while at the same time reversing hypoxemia, hypercapnia, and acidosis. Management is also aimed at improving RV contraction and decreasing pulmonary artery vascular resistance.

NONPHARMACOLOGIC THERAPY

- Chest physiotherapy is beneficial in patients with COPD and infectious exacerbations.
- Continuous positive airway pressure (CPAP) is used in patients with obstructive sleep apnea.
- Long-term oxygen supplementation has improved survival in hypoxemic patients with COPD.
- Phlebotomy is reserved as adjunctive therapy in polycythemia patients (hematocrit >55%) who have acute decompensation of cor pulmonale. Phlebotomy has been shown to decrease mean pulmonary artery pressure and pulmonary vascular resistance.

ACUTE GENERAL Rx

- Pulmonary embolism is the most common cause of acute cor pulmonale. Treatment includes:
  1. Thrombolytic therapy (urokinase, tPA, streptokinase) in the hemodynamically unstable patient
  2. Heparin IV followed by warfarin therapy maintaining an INR between 2 and 3 is the standard therapy for pulmonary embolism (see "Pulmonary Embolism")

CHRONIC Rx

- Treatment of chronic cor pulmonale is directed at:
  1. The underlying cause (e.g., COPD, the most common cause of chronic cor pulmonale)
  2. The underlying pathologic process (e.g., pulmonary hypertension)
  3. The underlying pathologic sequelae (e.g., right ventricular [RV] failure)
- Cause
  1. COPD is treated in the standard fashion with metered dose inhalers (see "Chronic Obstructive Pulmonary Disease")
  - Theophylline and sympathomimetic amines may improve diaphragmatic excursion, myocardial contraction and pulmonary artery vasodilation.
- Rx of pulmonary hypertension
  1. Oxygen supplementation
  2. Vasodilators including nitroglycerine, calcium channel blockers, and angiotensin-converting enzyme inhibitors can be tried
- Rx of RV failure with diuretics (e.g., furosemide 40 to 80 mg PO qd and digoxin 0.25 mg PO qd)

DISPOSITION

- Nearly 50,000 people die each year from acute pulmonary embolism.
- The prognosis of patients with severe COPD and cor pulmonale is poor (survival <2 yr).

PEARLS & CONSIDERATIONS

COMMENTS

- Acute elevation of pulmonary artery pressures (30 to 40 mm Hg) results in:
  1. RV dilatation
  2. LV compression
  3. Decreased LV end-diastolic volume
  4. Decreased cardiac output
  5. Hypotension
  6. Mean pulmonary artery pressures >40 mm Hg usually signify a chronic underlying process.
- Right-sided heart disease resulting from disease of the left side of the heart or from congenital cardiac anomalies are not considered cor pulmonale.

SUGGESTED READINGS

MacNee W: Pathophysiology of cor pulmonale in chronic obstructive pulmonary disease, *Am J Respir Crit Care Med* 150:833, 1994.

Romano PM, Peterson S: The management of cor pulmonale, *Heart Dis* 2(6):431, 2000.

AUTHORS: **PRANAV M. PATEL, M.D.,** and **WEN-CHIH WU, M.D.**

BASIC INFORMATION

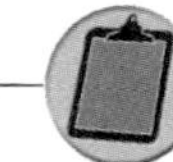

DEFINITION

A corneal abrasion is a loss of surface epithelial tissue of the cornea caused by trauma.

SYNONYMS

Corneal erosion
Corneal contusion

ICD-9CM CODES
918.1 Corneal abrasion

EPIDEMIOLOGY & DEMOGRAPHICS

INCIDENCE (IN U.S.): A universal problem
PREDOMINANT AGE: Any age
PEAK INCIDENCE: Childhood through active adulthood and older and debilitated patients

PHYSICAL FINDINGS & CLINICAL PRESENTATION

- Haziness of the cornea
- Disruption of the corneal surface (Fig. 1-65)
- Redness and infection of the conjunctiva
- Pain
- Light sensitivity
- Tearing
- Foreign body sensation
- Gritty feeling
- Pain on opening or closing eyes
- Sensation of a foreign body

ETIOLOGY

- Trauma (direct mechanical event)
- Foreign body
- Contact lenses
- Unknown etiology

DIAGNOSIS

DIFFERENTIAL DIAGNOSIS

- Acute angle glaucoma
- Herpes ulcers and other corneal ulcers
- Foreign body in the cornea (be certain it is not a keratitis)

WORKUP

- Fluorescein staining, slit lamp evaluation
- Assessment of visual acuity
- Intraocular pressure
- Rule out corneal laceration
- Rule out other eye pathology

TREATMENT

NONPHARMACOLOGIC THERAPY

- Patching
- Bandage
- Contact lenses
- Warm compresses
- Pressure dressing (controversial)
- Removal of any foreign particles if present

PHARMACOLOGIC THERAPY

- Cycloplegic drugs
- Antibiotics
- NSAIDs

ACUTE GENERAL Rx

- Topical antibiotics such as 10% sulfacetamide or Ocuflox qid
- Pressure patching of eye with eyelid closed
- Cycloplegics such as 5% homatropine

CHRONIC Rx

Topical antibiotics to prevent secondary infection

DISPOSITION

Follow-up in 24 hr and then every 3 days until abrasion has cleared and vision has returned to normal

REFERRAL

To ophthalmologist if patient experiences no relief within 24 hr

PEARLS & CONSIDERATIONS

COMMENTS

- Never give patient topical anesthetic to use at home because these can cause decomposition of the cornea and permanent damage.
- In children and adults, patching does not change speed of healing, but may feel more comfortable

SUGGESTED READINGS

Le Sage N et al: Efficiency of eye patching for traumatic corneal abrasions: a controlled clinical trial, *Ann Emerg Med* 78:129, 2001.
Michael JG et al: Management of corneal abrasion in children, *Ann Emerg Med* 40(1):67, 2002.
Wilson SA, Last A: Management of corneal abrasions, *Am Fam Physician* 70(1):123, 2004.

AUTHOR: **MELVYN KOBY, M.D.**

A

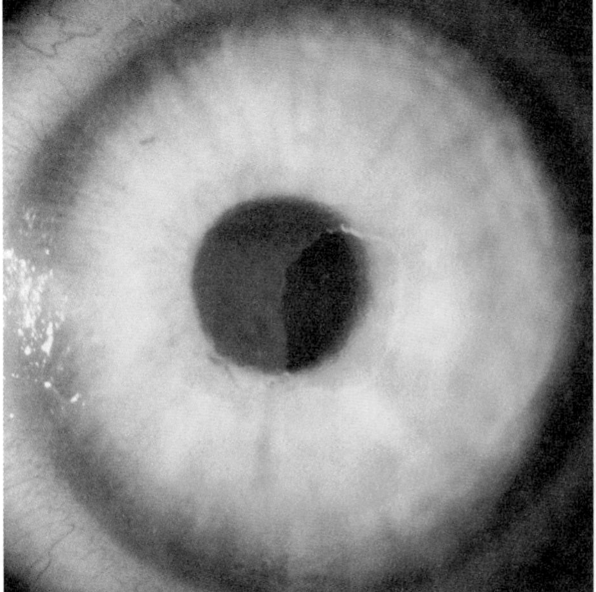

B

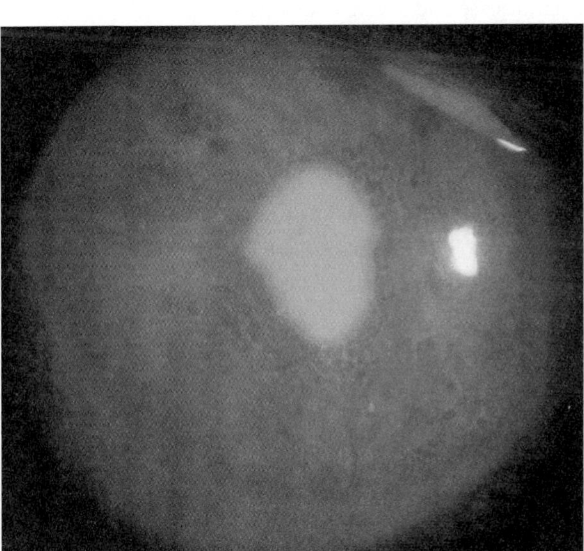

FIGURE 1-65 Corneal epithelial abrasion. A, Epithelial defect without fluorescein highlighting the defect. An irregularity in the otherwise smooth corneal surface is the key to identifying the defect if no fluorescein is available. **B,** Classic fluorescein staining of an epithelial defect. (From Palay D [ed]: *Ophthalmology for the primary care physician,* St Louis, 1997, Mosby.)

Corneal Ulceration

BASIC INFORMATION

DEFINITION

Corneal ulceration refers to the disruption of the corneal surface and/or deeper layers caused by trauma, contact lenses infection, degeneration, or other means.

SYNONYMS

Infectious keratitis with ulceration
Bacterial keratitis with ulceration
Viral keratitis with ulceration
Fungal keratitis with ulceration

ICD-9CM CODES
370.0 Corneal ulcer NOS

EPIDEMIOLOGY & DEMOGRAPHICS

INCIDENCE (IN U.S.): 4 to 6 cases/mo seen by average general ophthalmologist
PREVALENCE (IN U.S.): Common
PREDOMINANT SEX: Either
PREDOMINANT AGE: All ages

PHYSICAL FINDINGS

- Localized, well-demarcated, infiltrative lesion with corresponding focal ulcer (Fig. 1-66) or oval, yellow-white stromal suppuration with thick mucopurulent exudate and edema. Usually red, angry-looking eye with infiltration in surrounding area of cornea
- Eye possibly painful, with conjunctival edema and infection
- Sterile neurotrophic ulcers with tissue breakdown and no pain

ETIOLOGY

- Complication of contact lens wear, trauma, or diseases such as herpes simplex keratitis, keratoconjunctivitis sicca. Often associated with collagen vascular disease and severe exophthalmus and thyroid disease
- Viral causes often contagious

DIAGNOSIS

DIFFERENTIAL DIAGNOSIS

- *Pseudomonas* and pneumococcus and other bacterial infection—virulent
- *Moraxella, Staphylococcus, α-Streptococcus* infection—less virulent
- Herpes simplex infection or disease caused by other viruses
- Contact lens ulcers differ

WORKUP

- Fluorescein staining, slit lamp
- Appearance often typical
- Differentiate carefully with contact lens wearers
- Note previous eye surgery or laser vision correction

LABORATORY TESTS

Microscopic examination and culture of scrapings

TREATMENT

NONPHARMACOLOGIC THERAPY

- Warm compresses
- Bandage contact lenses
- Patching
- Stop contact lens wearing
- Remove eyelid crusting

GENERAL Rx

- Intense antibiotic and antiviral Rx
- NSAIDs
- Viroptic/Zymar

ACUTE GENERAL Rx

- An ophthalmic emergency
- Bacterial infection: subconjunctival cefazolin or gentamicin (topical Zymar, Vigomax, etc.)
- Fungal infection: hospitalization and topical application of antifungal agents
- Herpes—Vioptic and oral Rx

DISPOSITION

Ideally treated by an ophthalmologist if the patient does not rapidly respond to antibiotics (within 24 hr)

PEARLS & CONSIDERATIONS

- Always stop contact lens wearing
- Always refer ulcers to ophthalmologist
- Never treat with topical anesthetics or steroids

COMMENTS

Do not use topical steroids because herpes, fungal, or other ulcers may be aggravated, leading to perforation of the cornea. Antibiotics may delay response and result in overgrowth of nonbacterial (fungal and amoebic) pathogens.

SUGGESTED READINGS

Price FW: New pieces for the puzzle: nonsteroidal anti-inflammatory drugs and corneal ulcers, *J Cataract Refract Surg* 26(9):1263, 2000.

Schaefer F et al: Bacterial keratitis: a prospective clinical and microbiological study, *Br J Ophthalmol,* 85(7):42, 2001.

Stretton S, Gopinathan U, Willcox MD: Corneal ulceration in pediatric patients: a brief overview of progress in topical treatment, *Paediatr Drugs* 4(2):95, 2002.

Varaprasathan G et al: Trends in the etiology of infectious corneal ulcers at the F. I. Proctor Foundation, *Cornea* 23(4):360, 2004.

AUTHOR: **MELVYN KOBY, M.D.**

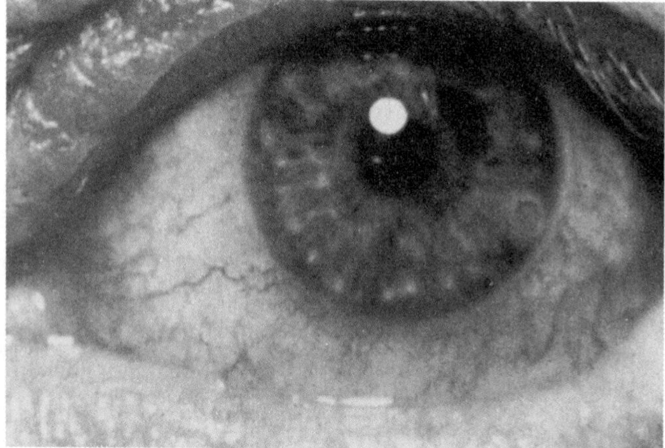

FIGURE 1-66 Peripherally located corneal ulcer. (From Marx JA [ed]: *Rosen's emergency medicine,* ed 5, St Louis, 2002, Mosby.)

Costochondritis (PTG)

BASIC INFORMATION

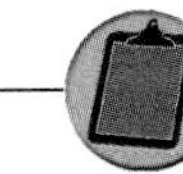

DEFINITION

Costochondritis is a poorly defined chest wall pain of uncertain cause.

SYNONYMS

- Benign chest wall pain syndrome
- Costosternal syndrome
- Costosternal chondrodynia

ICD-9CM CODES
733.6 Costochondritis

EPIDEMIOLOGY & DEMOGRAPHICS

PREVALENCE: Unknown
PREVALENT SEX: Women > men
PREVALENT AGE: Over age 40 yr

PHYSICAL FINDINGS & CLINICAL PRESENTATION

- Tenderness of costochondral junctions (second through fifth) and/or sternum
- Pain with coughing and deep breathing
- Both sides of chest equal in frequency of involvement

ETIOLOGY

- Unknown
- May be a form of regional fibrositis
- May be referred pain from cervical or thoracic spine

DIAGNOSIS

DIFFERENTIAL DIAGNOSIS

- Tietze's syndrome
- Cardiovascular disease
- GI disease
- Pulmonary disease
- Osteoarthritis (see Table 1-10)
- Cervical disc syndrome

WORKUP

- There are no laboratory or radiographic abnormalities.
- Testing to rule out or rule in more serious disorders is performed on a case-by-case basis.

TREATMENT

ACUTE GENERAL Rx

- Explanation, reassurance
- Tricyclic antidepressants for sleep disturbance (amitriptyline 10-25 mg)
- Aerobic exercise program
- NSAIDs for analgesia

DISPOSITION

- The duration of the disorder is variable.
- Spontaneous remission is the rule.

PEARLS & CONSIDERATIONS

COMMENTS

In spite of the name, no inflammation is present. After other, more serious conditions are ruled out, the treatment is strictly symptomatic and supportive.

SUGGESTED READINGS

Gregory PL, Biswas AC, Batt ME: Musculoskeletal problems of the chest wall in athletes, *Sports Med* 32:325, 2002.

Hiramuro-Shoji F, Wirth MA, Rockwood CA: Atraumatic conditions of the sternoclavicular joint, *J Shoulder Elbow Surg* 12:79, 2003.

Jenson S: Musculoskeletal causes of chest pain, *Am Fam Physician* 30:834, 2001.

AUTHOR: **LONNIE R. MERCIER, M.D.**

TABLE 1-10 Musculoskeletal Chest Pain

Disorder	Clinical Features	Comments
Tietze's syndrome	Pain and swelling of sternoclavicular joint or second or third costochondral junctions (usually left). Worse with cough and deep breathing. Local tenderness.	Traumatic cause? Rare.
Costochondritis	Pain and tenderness but no swelling. Costochondral junctions of ribs 2-5. Increased pain with cough and sneeze.	Sometimes associated with headache and hyperventilation.
Seronegative spondyloarthropathy (ankylosing spondylitis)	Sternoclavicular or manubriosternal joint. Worse in am. Relieved by activity. May be associated with swelling.	Local chest findings usually associated with other symptoms of ankylosing spondylitis such as sacroilitis. May need HLA-B27 antigen testing.
Cervical, thoracic disc disease	Referred regional pain from affected area. No local swelling. Often aggravated by spine motion and may be accompanied by radicular pain into arm if cervical or along intercostal nerve if thoracic.	May mimic chest disease if spinal complaints are minimal and referred or radicular symptoms predominate.
Fibromyalgia	Widespread pain with other sites involved. Symptoms often change in location. Local "tender points" but no swelling or objective findings.	Female:male ratio of 9:1. Prevalent age 30-50 yr
Osteoarthritis, sternoclavicular or manubriosternal joint	Dull, aching local pain with tenderness. Occasional bony joint enlargement with soft-tissue swelling.	Crepitus may rarely be present.

BASIC INFORMATION

DEFINITION

Craniopharyngiomas are tumors arising from squamous cell remnants of Rathke's pouch, located in the infundibulum or upper anterior hypophysis.

SYNONYMS

Subset of nonadenomatous pituitary tumors

ICD-9CM CODES
237.0 Craniopharyngioma

EPIDEMIOLOGY & DEMOGRAPHICS

PEAK INCIDENCE: Occurs at all ages; peak during the first two decades of life, with a second small peak occurring in the sixth decade.

PREDOMINANT SEX: Both sexes are usually equally affected.

Craniopharyngiomas represent 2% to 4% of intracranial neoplasms and 10% of central nervous system tumors in childhood.

PHYSICAL FINDINGS & CLINICAL PRESENTATION

- Presenting symptoms are usually related to the effects of a sella turcica mass. Approximately 75% of patients complain of headache and have visual disturbances.
- The usual visual defect is bitemporal hemianopsia. Optic nerve involvement with decreased visual acuity and scotomas and homonymous hemianopsia from optic tract involvement may also occur.
- Other symptoms include mental changes, nausea, vomiting, somnolence, or symptoms of pituitary failure. In adults, sexual dysfunction is the most common endocrine complaint, with impotence in males and primary or secondary amenorrhea in females. Diabetes insipidus is found in 25% of cases. In children, craniopharyngiomas may present with dwarfism.

ETIOLOGY

Craniopharyngiomas are believed to arise from nests of squamous epithelial cells that are commonly found in the suprasellar area surrounding the pars tuberalis of the adult pituitary.

DIAGNOSIS

DIFFERENTIAL DIAGNOSIS

- Pituitary adenoma
- Empty sella syndrome
- Pituitary failure of any cause
- Primary brain tumors (e.g., meningiomas, astrocytomas)
- Metastatic brain tumors
- Other brain tumors
- Cerebral aneurysm

LABORATORY TESTS

- Hypothyroidism (low TT_4, TT_3, T_3RU, FT_4, FT_3) with low TSH
- Hypercortisolism (low cortisol) with low ACTH
- Low sex hormones (testosterone, estriol) with low FSH and LH
- Diabetes insipidus (see "Diabetes Insipidus")
- Prolactin may be normal or slightly elevated
- Pituitary stimulation tests may be required in some cases

IMAGING STUDIES

- Visual field testing for bitemporal hemianopsia
- Skull film

Enlarged or eroded sella turcica (50%)
Suprasellar calcification (50%)

- Head CT scan or MRI (Fig. 1-67)

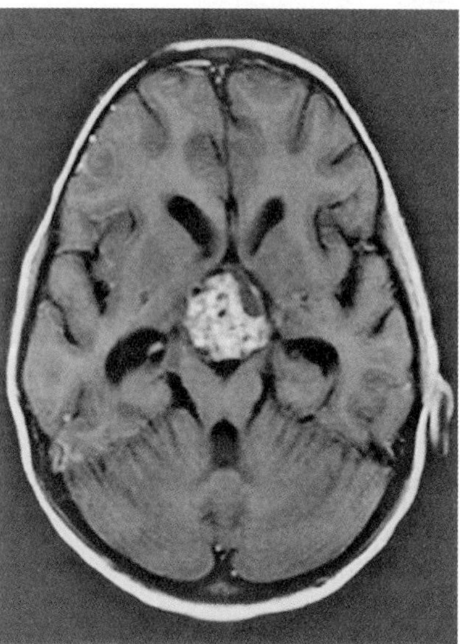

FIGURE 1-67 MRI scan of a craniopharyngioma, demonstrating a cystic contrast-enhancing mass in the suprasellar area extending upward and compressing the hypothalamus. (From Goetz CG: *Textbook of clinical neurology,* Philadelphia, 1999, WB Saunders.)

TREATMENT

- Surgical resection (curative or palliative)

Transsphenoidal surgery for small intrasellar tumors
Subfrontal craniotomy for most patients

- Postoperative radiation
- Intralesional ^{32}P irradiation or bleomycin for unresectable tumors

PROGNOSIS

- Operative mortality: 3% to 16% (higher with large tumors)
- Postoperative recurrence rate: 10% to 40%
- 5-yr and 10-yr survival: 88% and 76%, respectively, with surgery and radiation

SUGGESTED READINGS

Asa SL, Horvath E, Kovacs K: Craniopharyngiomas. In Mazzaferri EL, Samaan NA (eds): *Endocrine tumors,* Boston, 1993, Blackwell Scientific.

Leavens ME et al: Nonadenomatous intrasellar and parasellar neoplasms. In Mazzaferri EL, Samaan NA (eds): *Endocrine tumors,* Boston, 1993, Blackwell Scientific.

Melmed S: Evaluation of pituitary masses. In DeGroot LJ, Jameson JL (eds): *Endocrinology,* ed 4, Philadelphia 2001, WB Saunders.

AUTHOR: **TOM J. WACHTEL, M.D.**

BASIC INFORMATION

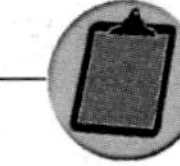

DEFINITION

Creutzfeldt-Jakob disease is a progressive, fatal, dementing illness caused by an infectious agent known as a *prion.*

SYNONYMS

Transmissible spongiform encephalopathy
Prion disease

ICD-9CM CODES
046.1 Creutzfeldt-Jakob disease

EPIDEMIOLOGY & DEMOGRAPHICS

- Incidence of 1 per 1,000,000 population per yr
- Peak age 60 yr (range 16-82 yr)
- 5%-10% familial, remaining cases are sporadic; iatrogenic cases (corneal transplants, dura mater allograft, human pituitary extract) very rare
- Normal prion protein gene found on human chromosome 20

PHYSICAL FINDINGS & CLINICAL PRESENTATION

- All patients present with cognitive deficits (dementing illness—memory loss, behavioral abnormalities, higher cortical function impairment).
- More than 80% will have myoclonus.
- Pyramidal tract signs (weakness), cerebellar signs (clumsiness), and extrapyramidal signs (parkinsonian features) are seen in more than 50% of the cases.
- Less common features include cortical visual abnormalities, abnormal eye movements, vestibular dysfunction, sensory disturbances, autonomic dysfunction, lower motor neuron signs, and seizures.

ETIOLOGY

Small proteinaceous infections particle (prion). Noninfectious prion protein (PrP) is a cellular protein found on the surfaces of neurons. Normal function is not known. Protein is converted to protease resistant and infectious agent (PrP^{sc}) by infectious prion protein (PrP^{sc}).

DIAGNOSIS

- Definite CJD: Neuropathologically confirmed spongiform encephalopathy in a case of progressive dementia.
- Probable CJD: History of rapidly progressive dementia (less than 2 yr) with typical EEG with at least two of the following clinical features: myoclonus, visual or cerebellar dysfunction, pyramidal or extrapyramidal features, akinetic mutism.
- Possible CJD: Same as probable CJD without EEG findings.

DIFFERENTIAL DIAGNOSIS

- Alzheimer's disease
- Frontotemporal dementia
- Dementia with Lewy bodies
- Vascular dementia
- Others (hydrocephalus, infectious, vitamin deficiency, endocrine)

A clinical algorithm for the evaluation of dementia is described in Section III, "Dementia."

WORKUP

- Evaluate for treatable causes of dementia (see "Alzheimer's Disease").
- Brain biopsy can be diagnostic, but it is usually not performed because there is no treatment or cure.

LABORATORY TESTS

- Presence of periodic sharp wave complexes on EEG in cases of rapidly progressive dementia has a sensitivity of 67% and a specificity of 86%.
- Presence of the 14,3,3 protein in CSF has a 95% positive predictive value with its absence having a 92% negative predictive value in cases of probable or possible CJD.

IMAGING STUDIES

MRI scan can show areas of restricted diffusion in the basal ganglia and cerebral cortex. MRI diffusion weighted imaging has a sensitivity of 92.3% and a specificity of 93.8% in cases of rapidly progressive dementia.

TREATMENT

NONPHARMACOLOGIC THERAPY

Full time caregiver and/or nursing home. Social work can be helpful with end of life discussions, family counseling, and optimizing appropriate home services.

ACUTE GENERAL Rx

No known therapy

CHRONIC Rx

No known therapy

DISPOSITION

The disease is fatal. Mean duration of illness is 8 mo (range 1-130 mo).

REFERRAL

Neurology for evaluation of any rapidly progressive dementia
Social work

PEARLS & CONSIDERATIONS

COMMENTS

- Related diseases in humans: Kuru, Fatal Familial Insomnia, Gerstmann-Sträussler-Scheinker syndrome, new-variant Creutzfeldt-Jacob disease.
- Related diseases in animals: Scrapie, bovine spongiform encephalopathy (Mad cow disease).

SUGGESTED READINGS

Brown P et al: Human spongiform encephalopathy: The National Institutes of Health series of 300 cases of experimentally transmitted disease, *Ann Neurol* 35:513, 1994.

Hsich G et al: The 14-3-3 brain protein in cerebrospinal fluid as a marker for transmissible spongiform encephalopathies, *N Engl J Med* 335:924, 1996.

Johnson RT, Gibbs CJ: Creutzfeldt-Jakob disease and related transmissible spongiform encephalopathies, *N Engl J Med* 339:1994, 1998.

Masters CL et al: Creutzfeldt-Jakob disease: patterns of worldwide occurrence and the significance of familial and sporadic clustering, *Ann Neurol* 5:177, 1979.

Shiga Y et al: Diffusion-weighted MRI abnormalities as an early diagnostic marker for Creutzfeldt-Jakob disease, *Neurology* 63:443, 2004.

Steinhoff BJ et al: Accuracy and reliability of periodic sharp wave complexes in Creutzfeldt-Jakob disease, *Arch Neurol* 53:162, 1996.

AUTHOR: **CHUN LIM, M.D., PH.D.**

BASIC INFORMATION

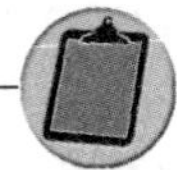

DEFINITION

Crohn's disease is an inflammatory disease of the bowel of unknown etiology, most commonly involving the terminal ileum and manifesting primarily with diarrhea, abdominal pain, fatigue, and weight loss.

SYNONYMS

Regional enteritis
Inflammatory bowel disease (IBD)

ICD-9CM CODES
555.9 Crohn's disease, unspecified site
555.0 Crohn's disease, small intestine
555.1 Crohn's disease involving large intestine

EPIDEMIOLOGY & DEMOGRAPHICS

PREVALENCE: 1 case/1000 persons; most common in Caucasians and Jews
- Crohn's disease affects approximately 380,000 to 480,000 persons in the U.S.
- Incidence: bimodal with a peak in the third decade of life and another one in the fifth decade

PHYSICAL FINDINGS & CLINICAL PRESENTATION

- Abdominal tenderness, mass, or distention
- Chronic or nocturnal diarrhea
- Weight loss, fever, night sweats
- Hyperactive bowel sounds in patients with partial obstruction, bloody diarrhea
- Delayed growth and failure of normal development in children
- Perianal and rectal abscesses, mouth ulcers, and atrophic glossitis
- Extraintestinal manifestations: joint swelling and tenderness, hepatosplenomegaly, erythema nodosum, clubbing, tenderness to palpation of the sacroiliac joints
- Symptoms may be intermittent with varying periods of remission

ETIOLOGY

Unknown. Pathophysiologically, Crohn's disease involves an immune system dysfunction.

DIAGNOSIS

DIFFERENTIAL DIAGNOSIS

- Ulcerative colitis
- Infectious diseases (TB, *Yersinia, Salmonella, Shigella, Campylobacter*)
- Parasitic infections (amebic infection)
- Pseudomembranous colitis
- Ischemic colitis in elderly patients
- Lymphoma
- Colon carcinoma
- Diverticulitis
- Radiation enteritis
- Collagenous colitis
- Fungal infections *(Histoplasma, Actinomyces)*
- Gay bowel syndrome (in homosexual patient)
- Carcinoid tumors
- Celiac sprue
- Mesenteric adenitis

LABORATORY TESTS

- Decreased Hgb and Hct from chronic blood loss, effect of inflammation on bone marrow, and malabsorption of vitamin B_{12}
- Hypokalemia, hypomagnesemia, hypocalcemia, and low albumin in patients with chronic diarrhea
- Vitamin B_{12} and folate deficiency
- Elevated ESR

ENDOSCOPIC EVALUATION

Endoscopic features of Crohn's disease include asymmetric and discontinued disease, deep longitudinal fissures, cobblestone appearance, presence of strictures. Crypt distortion and inflammation are also present. Granulomas may be present

IMAGING STUDIES

- Barium imaging studies reveal deep ulcerations (often longitudinal and transverse) and segmental lesions (skip lesions, strictures, fistulas, cobblestone appearance of mucosa caused by submucosal inflammation); "thumbprinting" is common, "string sign" in terminal ileum may be noted. Although the diagnosis may be suggested by radiographic studies, it should be confirmed by endoscopy and biopsy when possible.
- CT of abdomen is helpful in identifying abscesses and other complications.
- In 5% to 10% of patients with IBD, a clear distinction between ulcerative colitis and Crohn's disease cannot be made. Generally, Crohn's disease can be distinguished from ulcerative colitis by presence of transmural involvement and the frequent presence of noncaseating granulomas and lymphoid aggregates.

TREATMENT

The medical management of Crohn's disease is based on disease activity. According to Hanauer and Sanborn, disease activity can be defined as follows:

- Mild to moderate disease: The patient is ambulatory and able to take oral alimentation. There is no dehydration, high fever, abdominal tenderness, painful mass, obstruction, or weight loss of >10%.
- Moderate to severe disease: Either the patient has failed treatment for mild to moderate disease OR has more pronounced symptoms including fever, significant weight loss, abdominal pain or tenderness, intermittent nausea and vomiting, or significant anemia.
- Severe fulminant disease: Either the patient has persistent symptoms despite outpatient steroid therapy OR has high fever, persistent vomiting, evidence of intestinal obstruction, rebound tenderness, cachexia, or evidence of an abscess.
- Remission: The patient is asymptomatic OR without inflammatory sequelae, including patients responding to acute medical intervention.

NONPHARMACOLOGIC THERAPY

- Nutritional supplementation is needed in patients with advanced disease. TPN may be necessary in selected patients.
- Low-residue diet is necessary when obstructive symptoms are present.
- If diarrhea is prominent, increased dietary fiber and lowering of fat in the diet are sometimes helpful.
- Psychotherapy is useful for situational adjustment crises. A trusting and mutually understanding relationship and referral to self-help groups are very important because of the chronicity of the disease and the relatively young age of the patients.
- Avoid oral feedings during acute exacerbation to decrease colonic activity: a low-roughage diet may be helpful in early relapse.

ACUTE GENERAL Rx

- Sulfasalazine, 500 mg PO qid initially, increased qd or qod by 1 g until therapeutic dosages of 4 to 6 g/day are achieved. The oral salicylates, mesalamine (Asacol, Rowasa) are as effective as sulfasalazine and better tolerated but more expensive; they may be useful in patients allergic to the sulfa moiety of sulfasalazine molecule. Individuals with sulfa allergies should avoid sulfasalazine. Folate supplementation is recommended because sulfasalazine inhibits folate absorption.
- Corticosteroids have been the mainstay for treating moderate to severe active Crohn's disease. Prednisone 40 to 60 mg/day are useful for acute exacerbation. Steroids are usually tapered over approximately 2 to 3 mo. Some patients require a low dose for prolonged period of maintenance.

- Steroid analogues are locally active corticosteroids that target specific areas of inflammation in the GI tract. Budesonide (Entocort EC) is available as a controlled-release formulation and is approved for mild to moderate active Crohn's disease involving the ileum and/or ascending colon. The adult dose is 9 mg qd for a maximum of 8 wk.
- Immunosuppressants such as azathioprine (Imuran) 150 mg/day, methotrexate, or cyclosporine can be used for severe, progressive disease. In patients with Crohn's disease who enter remission after treatment with methotrexate, a low dose of methotrexate maintains remission.
- Metronidazole (Flagyl) 500 mg qid is useful for colonic fistulas and for treatment of mild to moderate active Crohn's disease. Ciprofloxacin 1 g qd has also been found effective in decreasing disease activity.
- Infliximab (Remicade), a chimeric monoclonal antibody targeting tumor necrosis factor-α, is effective in the treatment of enterocutaneous fistulas. This medication can induce clinical improvement in 80% of patients with Crohn's disease refractory to other agents. Its mechanism of action is incompletely understood. It is very costly. A PPD test should be done before using this medication.
- Natalizumab, a selective adhesion-molecule inhibitor, has been reported effective in increasing the rate of remission and response in patients with active Crohn's disease.
- Hydrocortisone (Cortenema) enema bid or tid is useful for proctitis.
- Most patients who have anemia associated with Crohn's disease respond to iron supplementation. Erythropoietin is useful in patients with anemia refractory to treatment with iron and vitamins.

CHRONIC Rx

- Monitor disease activity with symptom review and laboratory evaluation (CBC and sedimentation rate)
- Liver tests and vitamin B_{12} levels monitored on a yearly basis

DISPOSITION

- One tenth of patients have prolonged remission, three quarters have a chronic intermittent disease course, and one eighth have an unremitting course.

REFERRAL

- Surgical referral is needed for complications such as abscess formation, obstruction, fistulas, toxic megacolon, refractory disease, or severe hemorrhage. A conservative surgical approach is necessary, because surgery is not curative. Multiple surgeries may also result in short bowel syndrome.

SUGGESTED READINGS

Ghosh S et al: Natalizumab for active Crohn's disease, *N Engl J Med* 348:24, 2003.

Hanauer SB, Sanborn W: The management of Crohn's disease in adults, *Am J Gastroenterol* 96:635, 2001.

Knutson D et al: Management of Crohn's disease: a practical approach, *Am Fam Physician* 68:707, 2003.

Sands BE et al: Infliximab maintenance therapy for fistulizing Crohn's disease, *N Engl J Med* 350:876, 2004.

AUTHOR: **FRED F. FERRI, M.D.**

BASIC INFORMATION

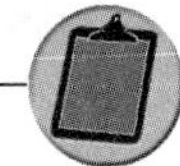

DEFINITION

Cryptococcosis is an infection caused by the fungal organism *Cryptococcus neoformans.*

ICD-9CM CODES
117.5 Cryptococcosis

EPIDEMIOLOGY & DEMOGRAPHICS

INCIDENCE (IN U.S.)

- 1 to 2 cases/1 million (non–HIV-infected) persons annually
- 6% to 7% in HIV-infected persons

PREDOMINANT SEX: Equal sex distribution when corrected for HIV status

PREDOMINANT AGE: Less than 2 yr of age; 20 to 40 yr of age

PEAK INCIDENCE: 20 to 40 yr (parallel to AIDS epidemic)

NEONATAL INFECTION: Very uncommon

PHYSICAL FINDINGS & CLINICAL PRESENTATION

- More than 90% present with meningitis; almost all have fever and headache.
- Meningismus, photophobia, mental status changes are seen in approximately 25%.
- Focal intracranial infection occurs in rare cases with focal deficit, increased intracranial pressure.
- Most common infections outside the CNS:
  1. In the lungs (fever, cough, dyspnea)
  2. In the skin (cellulitis, papular eruption)
  3. In the lymph nodes (lymphadenitis)
  4. Potential involvement of virtually any organ

ETIOLOGY

- Caused by the fungal organism *C. neoformans*
- Transmission by the respiratory route
- Disseminates to the CNS in most cases, usually without recognizable lung involvement
- Almost always in the setting of AIDS or other disorders of cellular immune function (hematologic malignancies, long-term corticosteroid therapy, immunosuppressive therapy following organ transplantation), or pregnancy
- Neutropenia alone poses a much lower risk of significant cryptococcal infection.

DIAGNOSIS

DIFFERENTIAL DIAGNOSIS

- Acute or subacute meningitis (caused by *Neisseria meningitidis, Streptococcus pneumoniae, Haemophilus influenzae, Listeria monocytogenes, Mycobacterium tuberculosis, Histoplasma capsulatum,* viruses)
- Intracranial mass lesion (neoplasms, toxoplasmosis, TB)
- Pulmonary involvement confused with *Pneumocystis carinii* pneumonia when diffuse or confused with TB or bacterial pneumonia when focal or involving the pleura
- Skin lesions confused with bacterial cellulitis or molluscum contagiosum

WORKUP

- Lumbar puncture to exclude cryptococcal meningitis.
- CT scan of the head when focal lesion or increased intracranial pressure is suspected.
- Biopsy of enlarged lymph nodes and skin lesions if feasible.

LABORATORY TESTS

- Culture and India ink stain (60% to 80% sensitive in culture-proven cases [Fig. 1-68]) examination of the CSF in all cases when CNS involvement is suspected
- Blood and serum cryptococcal antigen assay (>90% sensitivity and specificity)
- Culture and histologic examination of biopsy material

IMAGING STUDIES

- CT scan or MRI of the head if focal neurologic involvement is suspected
- Chest x-ray examination to exclude pulmonary involvement

TREATMENT

ACUTE GENERAL Rx

- Therapy is initiated with IV amphotericin B (0.5 mg/kg/day) with or without flucytosine.
- After stabilization (usually several weeks), consider fluconazole (200 to 400 mg qd PO) for additional 6 to 8 wk. Voriconazole, a newer imidazole compound, also has activity against most isolates.
- Alternative: IV fluconazole for initial therapy in patients unable to tolerate amphotericin B.
- If symptomatic increased intracranial pressure, consider therapeutic lumbar taps or intraventricular shunt.

CHRONIC Rx

Fluconazole (200 mg PO qd) is highly effective in preventing a relapse in HIV-infected patients.

DISPOSITION

Without maintenance therapy, relapse rate is >50% among AIDS patients.

REFERRAL

- For consultation with infectious diseases specialist in all cases
- For neurologic consultation if level of consciousness is depressed or focal lesion is present

PEARLS & CONSIDERATIONS

COMMENTS

Cryptococcosis is considered an AIDS-defining infection when it occurs in the absence of other known causes of immunodeficiency; thus all patients should be advised to be HIV tested and, if positive, referred for evaluation and follow-up by a physician experienced in the management of HIV infection.

SUGGESTED READINGS

Chandenier J et al: In vitro activity of amphotericin B, fluconazole and voriconazole against 162 Cryptococcous neoformans isolates from Africa and Cambodia, *Eur J Clin Microbiol Infect Dis* 23(6):506, 2004.

Pagano L et al: Cryptococcosis in patients with hematologic malignancies. A report from GIMEMA-infection, *Haematologica* 89(7): 852, 2004.

Powderly WG: Current approach to the acute management of cryptococcal infections, *J Infect Dis* 41:18, 2000.

AUTHOR: **JOSEPH R. MASCI, M.D.**

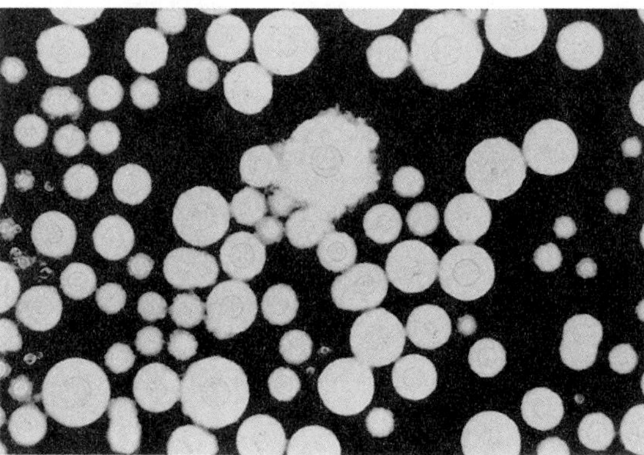

FIGURE 1-68 India ink preparation of cerebrospinal fluid revealing encapsulated cryptococci. Note the large capsules surrounding the smaller organisms. (From Andreoli TE [ed]: *Cecil essentials of medicine,* ed 4, Philadelphia, 1997, WB Saunders.)

BASIC INFORMATION

DEFINITION

Cryptorchidism is the failure of descent of the testes into the scrotum during fetal development. Cryptorchid testes neither reside in nor can be manipulated into the scrotum. Testes that can be manually manipulated into the scrotum are called retractile.

SYNONYMS

Undescended testis

ICD-9CM CODES
752.51 Cryptorchidism

EPIDEMIOLOGY & DEMOGRAPHICS

Cryptorchidism is the most common genitourinary disorder of male children. Approximately 30% of premature and 5% of full-term males will have an undescended testicle. Within the first year of life, most cryptorchid testes descend into the scrotum so that the incidence of cryptorchidism becomes approximately 1% in boys. Increased rates are associated with premature birth, low birth weight, and twinning. Associations have been seen with Kallmann's and Prader-Willi syndromes, pituitary hypoplasia, testicular feminization, and Reifenstein syndrome.

PHYSICAL FINDINGS & CLINICAL PRESENTATION

- Typically asymptomatic and is noted incidentally on screening examination
- The testis may be impalpable or palpable in a location other than the scrotum but usually along the path of normal descent (Fig. 1-69); in 80% of cases, the undescended testis will be palpable in the inguinal canal
- Associated with infertility and a 10- to 20-fold increase in risk of testicular cancer, which can occur in the contralateral descended testis. Testes that remain in an intraabdominal location are associated with a 40-fold increased risk of developing testicular carcinoma

ETIOLOGY

Normal testicular descent is a complex interplay between differential growth and endocrine, gubernaculum, and genitofemoral nerve function. Developmental problems among some or all of these are postulated in causing cryptorchidism.

DIAGNOSIS

DIFFERENTIAL DIAGNOSIS

- Retractile testis
- Ascended testis
- Dislocated testis
- Anorchia

WORKUP

Physical examination, hormonal challenge, imaging studies

PHYSICAL EXAMINATION

When properly done in a warm room, an examination identifies presence or absence of palpable testes and location of palpable testes. An examination should be done in both the supine and standing positions with adequate cremasteric relaxation to differentiate true cryptorchidism from retractile testes. Cryptorchid testes are often associated with an indirect inguinal hernia as the tunica vaginalis fails to close above the testis.

HORMONAL CHALLENGE

Administration of human chorionic gonadotropin (hCG) will confirm the presence of functioning testicular tissue. If the follicular stimulating hormone (FSH) level is 3× normal and there is no elevation of testosterone in response to hCG, functional testes are absent.

IMAGING

Ultrasound, CT scan, or MRI can be used to identify impalpable testes, but the sensitivity is inadequate. Inguinal exploration is not reliable. Laparoscopy is preferred and can be used therapeutically.

TREATMENT

Treatment of the undescended testicle can be hormonal, surgical, or both. Treatment is recommended as early as 6 mo of age and should be completed before age 2 yr because early treatment offers protection of fertility. Early referral to a pediatric urologist is recommended. There is no proof that placement of the undescended testicle into the scrotum reduces the risk of testicular cancer, but placement of both testes in the scrotum facilitates testicular examination.

FOLLOW-UP

- Repeat examination at 3 mo of age, because many testes will descend spontaneously. Spontaneous descent of true undescended testes is rare after 3 mo of age
- Lifelong testicular examination after puberty to screen for malignancy

HORMONAL Rx

Administration of hCG can cause testicular descent and is often tried before surgical intervention. hCG will cause retractile testes to remain in the scrotum.

SURGICAL Rx

Although the risk of testicular cancer is higher in men with cryptorchidism, the removal of all intraabdominal testes is not warranted. Orchiopexy, which is the surgical placement of an undescended testis into the scrotum, is a well-established operation for the palpable undescended testicle. For the nonpalpable testis, laparoscopic surgery is indicated to identify and locate the testis.

DISPOSITION

Prognosis is fair. Fertility and malignancy risks not greatly affected by treatment.

SUGGESTED READINGS

Dawson C, Whitfield H: ABC of urology. Common paediatric problems, *BMJ* 312(7041): 1291, 1996.

Docimo S, Silver R, Cromie W: The undescended testicle: diagnosis and management, *Am Fam Physician* 62:2037, 2000.

AUTHOR: **IRIS TONG, M.D.**

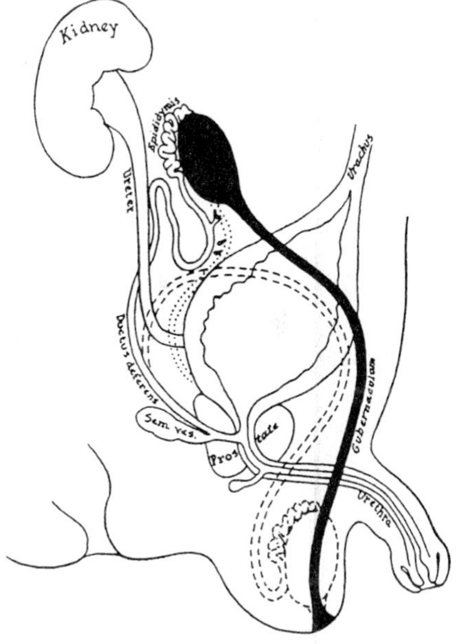

FIGURE 1-69 Undescended testes are common in male neonates with neuromuscular disease already symptomatic at birth, regardless of the etiology. The gubernaculums is a cylinder of striated muscle surrounding a core of smooth muscle that actively pulls the testicle into the scrotum in late gestation. Weakness of the gubernaculums in a generalized myopathy of fetal life prevents or delays the descent of the testis. (Reproduced with permission from Sarnat HB, Sarnat MS: Disorders of muscle in the newborn. In Moss AJ, Stern L [eds]: *Pediatrics update,* ed 4, New York, 1983, Elsevier-North Holland.)

BASIC INFORMATION

DEFINITION

The intracellular protozoan parasite *Cryptosporidium parvum* is associated with gastrointestinal disease and diarrhea, especially in AIDS patients or immunocompromised hosts. It is also associated with waterborne outbreak in immunocompetent hosts.

Other species, including *C. felis, C. muris,* and *C. meleagridis,* are now described to be pathogens as well.

SYNONYMS

Cryptosporidiosis

ICD-9CM CODES
00.7.4 Cryptosporidia infection

EPIDEMIOLOGY & DEMOGRAPHICS

PREVALENCE: Worldwide, especially third world countries; associated with poor hygiene as a waterborne pathogen

TRANSMISSION:
- Person to person (daycare, family members)
- Animal to person (pets, farm animals)
- Environmental (water-associated outbreaks, including travel associated with swimming in or drinking contaminated water)
- May be significant pathogen causing diarrhea in AIDS

INCIDENCE (IN U.S.):
- Approximately 2% in industrial countries, 5% to 10% in third world countries
- 10% to 20% HIV patients may excrete cyst in U.S.

PREDOMINANT SEX: Male = female

PHYSICAL FINDINGS & CLINICAL PRESENTATION

- Usually limited to gastrointestinal tract
- Diarrhea, severe abdominal pain (2 to 28 days)
- Impaired digestion, dehydration
- Fever, malaise, fatigue, nausea, vomiting
- Pneumonia if aspirated

ETIOLOGY

Cryptosporidium parvum, C. felis, C. muris, C. meleagridis

DIAGNOSIS

Clinical presentation of acute gastrointestinal illness, especially associated with HIV or with travel and waterborne outbreaks.

DIFFERENTIAL DIAGNOSIS

- *Campylobacter*
- *Clostridium difficile*
- *Entamoeba histolytica*
- *Giardia lamblia*
- *Salmonella*
- *Shigella*
- Microsporida
- Cytomegalovirus
- *Mycobacterium avium*

Disease may cause cholecystitis, reactive arthritis, hepatitis, pancreatitis, pneumonia in immunocompromised or HIV-infected patients.

WORKUP

- Stool evaluation looking for characteristic oocyst by modified acid-fast stain (Fig. 1-70)
- Serologic testing investigational
- May be seen in mucosal surfaces of GI lumen by biopsy

TREATMENT

- May be self-limited in normal host—often requiring hydration. Antidiarrhea agents Pepto-Bismol, Kaopectate, or loperamide may give symptomatic relief.
- Pharmacologic treatment with antibiotics has to date varying and usually poor response. Oocyst excretion reduction has been shown with paromomycin (1 g bid)/azithromycin and nitazoxanide therapy along with decreasing stool frequency. If treatment failure, consider metronidazole or Bactrim.
- Nitazoxanide elixir has been approved for the treatment of cryptosporidiosis in children ages 1 to 11 yr.
- Biliary cryptosporidiosis can be treated with antiretroviral therapy in the HIV setting.

SUGGESTED READINGS

Chen XM et al: Cryptosporidiosis, *N Engl J Med* 346:1723, 2002.

Rossignol JF, Ayoub A, Ayers, MS: Treatment of diarrhea caused by Cryptosporidium parvum. A prospective randomized, double-blind, placebo-controlled study of nitazoxanide, *J Infect Dis* 184:103, 2001.

Smith NH et al: Combination drug therapy for cryptosporidiosis in AIDS, *J Infect Dis* 178:900, 1998.

Tzipori S: Cryptosporidiosis: laboratory investigations and chemotherapy, *Adv Parasitol* 40:187, 1998.

AUTHORS: **GLENN G. FORT M.D.,** and **DENNIS J. MIKOLICH, M.D.**

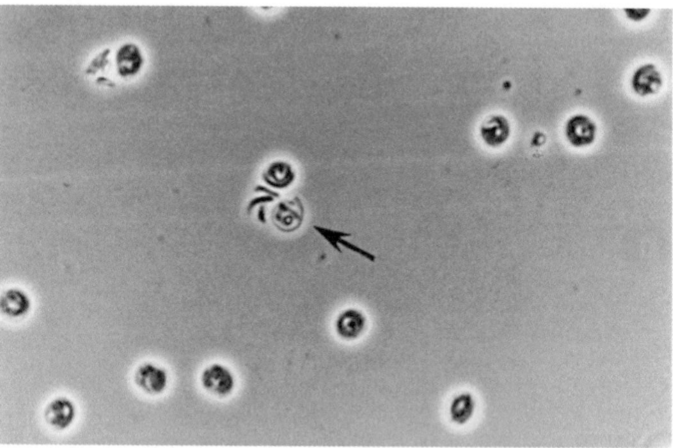

FIGURE 1-70 Human stool-derived Cryptosporidium oocysts. Excysting oocyst *(arrow)* is releasing three of its four sporozoites. (Phase-control microscopy x630.) (From Gorbach SL: *Infectious diseases,* ed 2, Philadelphia, 1998, WB Saunders.)

BASIC INFORMATION

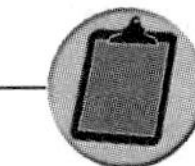

DEFINITION

Compression of the ulnar nerve behind the elbow (cubitus)

SYNONYMS

Tardy ulnar palsy

ICD-9CM CODES
354.2 Cubital tunnel syndrome

EPIDEMIOLOGY & DEMOGRAPHICS

Prevalent sex: Males = females

PHYSICAL FINDINGS & CLINICAL PRESENTATION

- Paresthesias and numbness along distribution of ulnar nerve (ulnar one and one-half fingers)
- Positive Tinel's sign at elbow
- Positive elbow flexion test (flexion of elbow with wrist extended for 30 sec may reproduce symptoms)
- May be diminished sensation to tip of small finger
- Ulnar nerve may be subluxable with elbow motion or by manipulation
- Cubitus valgus may be present if prior bony injury
- Interosseous weakness in long-standing cases with atrophy (Fig. 1-71)

ETIOLOGY

- Direct pressure
- Cubitus valgus deformity
- Subluxation of ulnar nerve
- Repeated stretching during throwing motion
- Elbow synovitis
- Local muscular hypertrophy

DIAGNOSIS

DIFFERENTIAL DIAGNOSIS

- Medial epicondylitis
- Medial elbow instability
- Carpal tunnel syndrome
- Cervical disc syndrome with radicular arm symptoms
- Ulnar nerve compression at wrist (Guyon's canal)

WORKUP

Diagnosis can usually be established clinically

IMAGING STUDIES

- Routine roentgenograms may be helpful in establishing cause or ruling out other conditions
- Electrodiagnostic studies: nerve conduction tests and electromyography are useful in establishing diagnosis and ruling out other syndromes

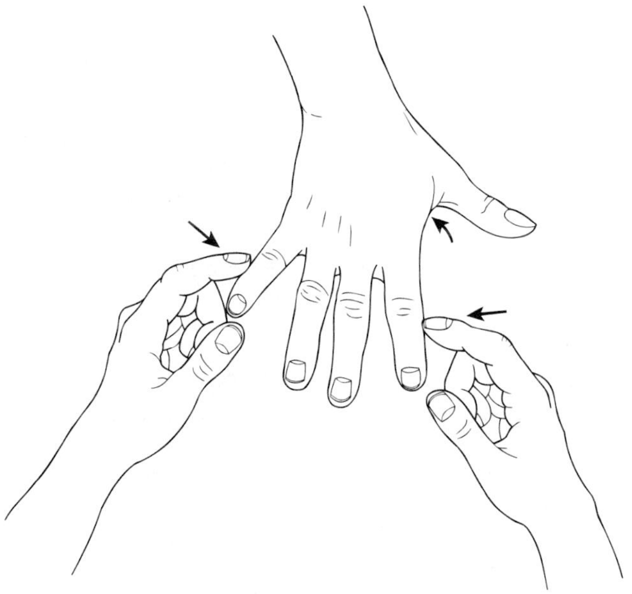

FIGURE 1-71 Testing for intrinsic (ulnar) motor weakness (fanning the fingers against resistance). Always look for atrophy of the first dorsal interosseus *(curved arrow)* when ulnar nerve lesions are suspected. (From Mercier LR: *Practical orthopedics,* ed 5, St Louis, 2000, Mosby.)

TREATMENT

GENERAL THERAPY

- Protect nerve from pressure
- Elbow pads
- Avoid prolonged elbow flexion (talking on phone with elbow bent)

DISPOSITION

- Prognosis is variable.
- Mild to moderate cases recover well if offending activity can be eliminated. If muscle atrophy has developed, recovery of strength may be incomplete in spite of treatment.
- Medical management may be continued as long as symptoms are controlled and no motor deficit has developed.

REFERRAL

Surgical referral in cases of failed medical management or if signs of motor impairment are present

SUGGESTED READINGS

Grana W: Medial epicondylitis and cubital tunnel syndrome in the throwing athlete, *Clin Sports Med* 20(3):541, 2001.

Kato H et al: Cubital tunnel syndrome associated with medial elbow ganglia and osteoarthritis of the elbow, *J Bone Joint Surg* 84(A):1413, 2002.

Lee DH, Claussen GC, Oh S: Clinical nerve conduction and needle electroonyography studies, *J Am Acad Orthop Surg* 12:276, 2004.

Park GY, Kim JM, Lee SM: The ultrasonographic and electro-diagnostic findings of ulnar neuropathy at the elbow, *Arch Phys Med Rehabil* 85:1000, 2004.

Sasaki J et al: Ultrasonographic assessment of ulnar collateral ligament and medial elbow laxity in college baseball players, *J Bone Joint Surg* 84(A):525, 2002.

AUTHOR: **LONNIE R. MERCIER, M.D.**

Cushing's Disease and Syndrome (PTG)

BASIC INFORMATION

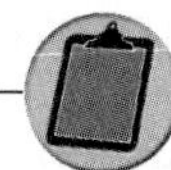

DEFINITION

- Cushing's syndrome is the occurrence of clinical abnormalities associated with glucocorticoid excess secondary to exaggerated adrenal cortisol production or chronic glucocorticoid therapy.
- Cushing's disease is Cushing's syndrome caused by pituitary ACTH excess.

ICD-9CM CODES
255.0 Cushing's disease or syndrome

PHYSICAL FINDINGS & CLINICAL PRESENTATION

- Hypertension
- Central obesity with rounding of the facies (moon facies); thin extremities
- Hirsutism, menstrual irregularities, hypogonadism
- Skin fragility, ecchymoses, red-purple abdominal striae, acne, poor wound healing, hair loss, facial plethora, hyperpigmentation (when there is ACTH excess)
- Psychosis, emotional lability, paranoia
- Muscle wasting with proximal myopathy

NOTE: The previous characteristics are not commonly present in Cushing's syndrome secondary to ectopic ACTH production. Many of these tumors secrete a biologically inactive ACTH that does not activate adrenal steroid synthesis. These patients may have only weight loss and weakness.

ETIOLOGY

- Iatrogenic from chronic glucocorticoid therapy (common)
- Pituitary ACTH excess (Cushing's disease; 60%)
- Adrenal neoplasms (30%)
- Ectopic ACTH production (neoplasms of lung, pancreas, kidney, thyroid, thymus; 10%)

DIAGNOSIS

DIFFERENTIAL DIAGNOSIS

- Alcoholic pseudo-Cushing's syndrome (endogenous cortisol overproduction)
- Obesity associated with diabetes mellitus
- Adrenogenital syndrome

WORKUP

- In patients with a clinical diagnosis of Cushing's syndrome the initial screening test is the overnight dexamethasone suppression test:
  1. Dexamethasone 1 mg PO given at 11 pm
  2. Plasma cortisol level measured 9 hr later (8 am)
  3. Plasma cortisol level <5 μg/100 ml excludes Cushing's syndrome
- Serial measurements (two or three consecutive measurements) of 24-hr urinary free cortisol and creatinine (to ensure adequacy of collection) are undertaken if overnight dexamethasone test is suggestive of Cushing's syndrome. Persistent elevated cortisol excretion (>300 μg/24 hr) indicates Cushing's syndrome.
- The low-dose (2 mg) dexamethasone suppression test is useful to exclude pseudo-Cushing's syndrome if the previous results are equivocal. CRH stimulation after low-dose dexamethasone administration (dexamethasone-CRH test) is also used to distinguish patients with suspected Cushing's syndrome from those who have mildly elevated urinary free cortisol level and equivocal findings.
- The high-dose (8 mg) dexamethasone test and measurement of ACTH by RIA are useful to determine the etiology of Cushing's syndrome.
  1. ACTH undetectable or decreased and lack of suppression indicates adrenal etiology of Cushing's syndrome.
  2. ACTH normal or increased and lack of suppression indicate ectopic ACTH production.
  3. ACTH normal or increased and partial suppression suggest pituitary excess (Cushing's disease).
- A single midnight serum cortisol (normal diurnal variation leads to a nadir around midnight) >7.5 μg/dl has been reported as 96% sensitive and 100% specific for the diagnosis of Cushing's syndrome.

LABORATORY TESTS

- Hypokalemia, hypochloremia, metabolic alkalosis, hyperglycemia, hypercholesterolemia
- Increased 24-hr urinary free cortisol (>100 μg/24 hr)

IMAGING STUDIES

- CT scan of adrenal glands in suspected adrenal Cushing's syndrome
- MRI of pituitary gland with gadolinium in suspected pituitary Cushing's syndrome
- Additional imaging studies to localize neoplasms of the lung, pancreas, kidney, thyroid, or thymus in patients with ectopic ACTH production

TREATMENT

GENERAL Rx

The treatment of Cushing's syndrome varies with its cause:

- Pituitary adenoma: transsphenoidal microadenomectomy is the therapy of choice in adults. Pituitary irradiation is reserved for patients not cured by transsphenoidal surgery. In children, pituitary irradiation may be considered as initial therapy, because 85% of children are cured by radiation. Stereotactic radiotherapy (photon knife or gamma knife) is effective and exposes the surrounding neuronal tissues to less irradiation than conventional radiotherapy. Total bilateral adrenalectomy is reserved for patients not cured by transsphenoidal surgery or pituitary irradiation.
- Adrenal neoplasm:
  1. Surgical resection of the affected adrenal
  2. Glucocorticoid replacement for approximately 9 to 12 mo after the surgery to allow time for the contralateral adrenal to recover from its prolonged suppression
- Bilateral micronodular or macronodular adrenal hyperplasia: bilateral total adrenalectomy
- Ectopic ACTH:
  1. Surgical resection of the ACTH-secreting neoplasm
  2. Control of cortisol excess with metyrapone, aminoglutethimide, mifepristone, or ketoconazole
  3. Control of the mineralocorticoid effects of cortisol and 11-deoxycorticosteroid with spironolactone
  4. Bilateral adrenalectomy: a rational approach to patients with indolent, unresectable tumors

DISPOSITION

Prognosis is favorable in patients with surgically amenable disease.

PEARLS & CONSIDERATIONS

COMMENTS

- Screening for MEN I should be considered in patients with Cushing's disease.
- An algorithm for the diagnosis of Cushing's syndrome is described in Section III.

SUGGESTED READING

Boscaro M et al: The diagnosis of Cushing's syndrome, *Arch Intern Med* 160:3045, 2000.

AUTHOR: **FRED F. FERRI, M.D.**

BASIC INFORMATION

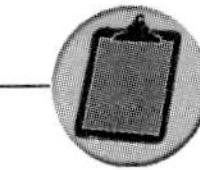

DEFINITION

Cystic fibrosis (CF) is an autosomal recessive disorder characterized by dysfunction of exocrine glands.

ICD-9CM CODES
277.0 Cystic fibrosis

EPIDEMIOLOGY & DEMOGRAPHICS

- It is the most common fatal hereditary disorder of caucasians in the U.S. (1 case/2500 caucasians).
- Median survival is 30 yr.

PHYSICAL FINDINGS & CLINICAL PRESENTATION

- Failure to thrive in children
- Increased anterior/posterior chest diameter
- Basilar crackles and hyperresonance to percussion
- Digital clubbing
- Chronic cough
- Abdominal distention
- Greasy, smelly feces

ETIOLOGY

Chromosome 7 gene mutation (CFTR gene) resulting in abnormalities in chloride transport and water flux across the surface of epithelial cells; the abnormal secretions cause obstruction of glands and ducts in various organs and subsequent damage to exocrine tissue (recurrent pneumonia, atelectasis, bronchiectasis, diabetes mellitus, biliary cirrhosis, cholelithiasis, intestinal obstruction, increased risk of GI malignancies)

DIAGNOSIS

DIFFERENTIAL DIAGNOSIS

- Immunodeficiency states
- Celiac disease
- Asthma
- Recurrent pneumonia

WORKUP

A diagnosis of CF requires a positive quantitative pilocarpine iontophoresis test with one or more phenotypic features consistent with CF (e.g., chronic suppurative obstructive lung disease, pancreatic insufficiency) or documented CF in a sibling or first cousin.

LABORATORY TESTS

- Pilocarpine iontophoresis ("sweat test"): diagnostic of cystic fibrosis in children if sweat chloride is >60 mmol/L (>80 mmol/L in adults) on two separate tests on consecutive days
- DNA testing may be useful for confirming the diagnosis and providing genetic information for family members.
- Sputum C&S and Gram stain (frequent bacterial infections with *Staphylococcus aureus, Pseudomonas, Haemophilus influenzae*)
- Low albumin level, increased 72-hr fecal fat excretion
- Pulse oxymetry or ABGs: hypoxemia
- Pulmonary function studies: decreased TLC, forced vital capacity, pulmonary diffusing capacity

IMAGING STUDIES

- Chest x-ray examination: may reveal focal atelectasis, peribronchial cuffing, bronchiectasis, increased interstitial markings, hyperinflation
- High-resolution chest CT scan: bronchial wall thickening, cystic lesions, ring shadows (bronchiectasis)

TREATMENT

NONPHARMACOLOGIC THERAPY

- Postural drainage and chest percussion
- Encouragement of regular exercise and proper nutrition
- Psychosocial evaluation and counseling of patient and family members

ACUTE GENERAL Rx

- Antibiotic therapy based on results of Gram stain and C&S of sputum (PO ciprofloxacin or floxacillin for *Pseudomonas,* cephalosporins for *S. aureus,* IV aminoglycosides plus ceftazidime for life-threatening *Pseudomonas* infections). Macrolides are also active against *pseudomona aeruginosa.* A recent study using azithromycin maintenance in children with CF for 6 mo found less use of additional antibiotics and improvement in some aspects of pulmonary function. Additional studies may be necessary to determine if azithromycin should be used as a primary therapy or rescue treatment
- Bronchodilators for patients with air flow obstruction
- Chronic pancreatic enzyme replacement
- Alternate-day prednisone (2 mg/kg) possibly beneficial in children with cystic fibrosis (decreased hospitalization rate, improved pulmonary function); routine use of corticosteroids not recommended in adults; among children with cystic fibrosis who have received alternate-day treatment with prednisone, boys, but not girls, have persistent growth impairment after treatment is discontinued
- Proper nutrition and vitamin supplementation
- Recombinant human deoxyribonuclease (DNase [Dornase alpha]) 2.5 mg qd or bid given by aerosol for patients with viscid sputum. It is useful to improve mucociliary clearance by liquefying difficult-to-clear pulmonary secretions. It is, however, very expensive (annual cost to the pharmacist is >$10,000); most beneficial in patients with FVC values >40% of predicted. Its cost can be decreased by using alternate-day rhDnase therapy
- Intermittent administration of inhaled tobramycin has been reported beneficial in CF
- Treatment of impaired glucose tolerance and diabetes mellitus

CHRONIC Rx

Pneumococcal vaccination, yearly influenza vaccination

DISPOSITION

- More than 50% of children with cystic fibrosis live beyond age 20 yr.
- Lung transplantation is the only definitive treatment; 3-yr survival following transplantation exceeds 50%.
- Obstructive azoospermia is present in >98% of postpubertal males.

REFERRAL

- To regional ambulatory care cystic fibrosis center
- For lung transplantation in selected patients
- For screening of family members with DNA analysis

PEARLS & CONSIDERATIONS

COMMENTS

- Genetic testing for CF should be offered to adults with a positive family history of CF, to couples currently planning a pregnancy, and to couples seeking prenatal care.
- Current research for therapeutic agents involves curcumin, a dietary supplement that is a mixture of compounds derived from the curry spice turmeric. It acts by inhibiting a calcium pump (sarcoplasmic reticulum Ca-ATPase) in the endoplasmic reticulum.

SUGGESTED READINGS

Egan ME et al: Curcumin, a major constituent of turmeric corrects cystic fibrosis, *Science* 304:600, 2004.

Kulich M et al: Improved survival among young patients with cystic fibrosis, *J Pediatr* 142:631, 2003.

Wilschanski M et al: Gentamicin-induced correction of CFTR function in patients with cystic fibrosis and CFTR stop mutations, *N Engl J Med* 349:1433, 2003.

Zeitlin P: Can curcumin cure cystic fibrosis?, *N Engl J Med* 351:606, 2004.

AUTHOR: **FRED F. FERRI, M.D.**

Cysticercosis (PTG)

BASIC INFORMATION

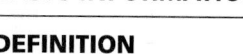

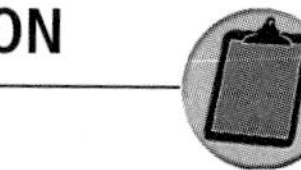

DEFINITION

Cysticercosis is an infection with the larval stage of the pork tapeworm (*Taenia solium*). Humans acquire cysticercosis through fecal-oral contamination with *T. solium* eggs from tapeworm carriers. Oncospheres (embryos) in the eggs are liberated by the action of gastric and intestinal fluids and cross the bowel wall, enter the bloodstream, and are carried to muscles and other tissues, including the central nervous system (neurocysticercosis). At small vessels, they establish and encyst as cysticerci reaching the size of about 1 cm in 2-3 months.

ICD-9CM CODES
123.1 Cysticercosis

EPIDEMIOLOGY & DEMOGRAPHICS

- *T. solium* infection and the resulting disease neurocysticercosis are endemic in less developed countries where pigs are raised as a food source.
- Neurocysticercosis is common throughout Latin America, most of Asia, sub-Saharan Africa, and parts of Oceania, and it is the greatest cause of acquired epilepsy worldwide. Neurocysticercosis is no longer an exotic disease in the U.S., and it accounts for up to 2% of neurologic and neurosurgical admissions in southern California and more than 1000 cases per year nationally.
- *T. solium* has a complex two-host life cycle. Humans are the only definitive host and harbor the adult worm in the intestine (taeniasis); however, both people and pigs can serve as intermediate hosts and harbor the larvae or cysticerci.

PHYSICAL FINDINGS & CLINICAL PRESENTATION

- Soft tissue deposition of cysts can cause local inflammation, which results in only minor morbidity compared with the damage possible in neurocysticercosis.
- Epilepsy caused by intracerebral cysts is the most common manifestation of neurocysticercosis (70% to 90% of cases). The patient with a seizure history often has no unusual physical findings.
- Less common: headache, nausea and vomiting resulting from increased intracranial pressure, and altered mental status, including psychosis.
- Inflammation around degenerating cysts can cause focal encephalitis, vasculitis, chronic meningitis, and cranial nerve palsies.
- Cysts can occur in the ventricles and cause hydrocephalus; more rarely, they can be found in the spinal cord and eye.

ETIOLOGY

Ingestion of the *T. solium* cysticerci in infected, undercooked pork results in human intestinal tapeworms, and excretion of eggs in the feces follows. Eggs can be ingested by the source patient or be transmitted via food handlers. Ingestion of the *T. solium* eggs leads to release of an oncosphere, which traverses the intestinal wall and enters the circulation. Oncospheres mature into cysticerci; these can be deposited in the soft tissue or the CNS. The presence of viable cysts in the CNS is usually asymptomatic. With time, inflammation around degenerating cysts causes symptoms dependent on the cysts' location, number, and size. Neurocysticercosis has been reported in AIDS patients; immunosuppression does not appear to increase the incidence of the infection.

DIAGNOSIS

DIFFERENTIAL DIAGNOSIS

- Idiopathic epilepsy
- Migraine
- Vasculitides
- Primary neoplasia of CNS
- Toxoplasmosis
- Brain abscess
- Granulomatous disease such as sarcoidosis

WORKUP

- Comprehensive clinical history
- Stool examination for ova if intestinal tapeworms also suspected
- Imaging studies (precedes laboratory tests if CNS involvement suspected)
- CSF examination
- Laboratory tests (serology)

LABORATORY TESTS

- CSF examination: may show pleocytosis, with lymphocytic or eosinophilic predominance; low glucose; elevated protein with neurocysticercosis.
- Immunotest: both serum and CSF can be studied for antibodies. Enzyme-linked immunoassay has a sensitivity and specificity of >90% when done in inflammatory CSF.

IMAGING STUDIES

- Head CT scan has been claimed to have a sensitivity and specificity of >95% and can show living cysticerci (hypodense lesions) and degenerating cysts (isodense or hyperdense lesions). Typically, there are multiple lesions. CT scan is the best method for detecting calcification associated with prior infection.
- Brain MRI is the most accurate technique to assess the degree of infection, the location, and the evolutionary stage of the parasites. It provides detailed images of living and degenerating cysts and perilesional edema as well as small cysts or those located in the ventricles, brainstem, and cerebellum.

TREATMENT

Cysticercosis outside the nervous system is a benign disorder and does not merit specific treatment. Neurocysticercosis, however, is associated with substantial morbidity and mortality.

A plan for treatment should follow a clear definition of the characteristics of the cysts and the degree of the immune response to the parasite.

- Inactive infection: patients with seizures and calcifications alone on neuroimaging studies are not thought to have viable parasites. Cysticidal therapy is usually not undertaken. Anticonvulsants can control seizures. For patients with hydrocephalus, ventriculoperitoneal shunting can resolve symptoms.
- Active parenchymal infection (most common form of presentation): eradication of cysts is less controversial for active disease. Anticonvulsants should be given to control seizures. Some argue that only treatment of seizures, not antiparasitic therapy, is needed.

- Extraparenchymal neurocysticercosis: refer to a neurosurgeon.
  1. Ventricular: usually presents with obstructive hydrocephalus. The mainstay of therapy is the rapid correction of hydrocephalus.
  2. Subarachnoid: associated with arachnoiditis. Diversion of CSF and steroid therapy may be needed.
- Cysticidal therapy: praziquantel has been the mainstay of therapy and is effective; albendazole is now being used more frequently, and it may have greater efficacy at a lesser cost than praziquantel. Currently accepted schemes are either praziquantel (50 mg/kg/day) divided into three doses for 15 days or albendazole (15 mg/kg/day) divided into three doses for 8 days with simultaneous administration of steroids. Shorter schemes of 1 day of praziquantel or 3 days of albendazole appear to be effective for patients with only one lesion, but not for those with many cysts.

NOTE: Praziquantel is metabolized via the cytochrome P-450 enzyme complex and levels may be reduced when given in combination with anticonvulsants. Levels can increase with cimetidine.

REFERRAL

Neurosurgical consultation if extraparenchymal neurocysticercosis or obstructive hydrocephalus is suspected

PEARLS & CONSIDERATIONS

PREVENTION

Eradication of taeniasis/cysticercosis is possible, as demonstrated in countries that were endemic earlier in this century. The disease disappears with implementation of meat inspection, improvement of pig husbandry, and betterment of sociocultural conditions.

SUGGESTED READING

Garcia HH et al: *Taenia solium* cysticercosis, *Lancet* 362:547, 2003.

AUTHOR: **KAROLL CORTEZ, M.D.**

Note: Dr. Cortez wrote this monograph while employed by the U.S. government; therefore it is public domain.

BASIC INFORMATION

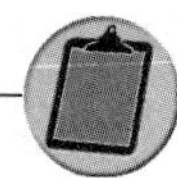

DEFINITION

Infection with cytomegalovirus (CMV), a herpes virus, is common in the general population, with multiple mechanisms for transmission, often during childhood and adolescence. CMV is associated with pregnancy and can be a congenital disease. CMV is also associated with immunocompromised states and may be life threatening.

SYNONYMS

CMV
Heterophil-negative mononucleosis
Cytomegalic inclusion disease virus

ICD-9CM CODES
078.5 CMV infection
771.1 Congenital or perinatal CMV infection
V01.7 Exposure to CMV

EPIDEMIOLOGY & DEMOGRAPHICS

- Seroprevalence is widespread: 40% to 100% antibody positivity in adults.
- Increased infection develops perinatally, in day care exposure, and then during reproductive age, related to sexual activity.

ROUTES OF TRANSMISSION

- Blood transfusions
- Sexually (STDs) via uterus, cervix, and semen
- Perinatally via breast milk
- Transplant of organs—bone marrow, kidneys, liver, heart, or lung

PHYSICAL FINDINGS & CLINICAL PRESENTATION

Children: Congenital—25% of infected children with symptoms if congenital:
- Jaundice
- Petechial rash
- Hepatosplenomegaly
- Lethargy
- Respiratory distress
- CNS involvement
- Seizures

Postnatal acquisition:
- CMV mononucleosis
- Pharyngitis
- Bronchitis
- Pneumonia
- Croup

Healthy adults:
Common
- May be asymptomatic
- CMV mononucleosis similar to EBV mononucleosis
- Fever—lasting 9 to 30 days—mean of 19 days

Less common
- Exudative pharyngitis
- Rare lymphadenopathy—splenomegaly
- Interstitial pneumonia (rare)
- Cervical adenopathy
- Nonspecific rash
- Thrombocytopenia/hemolytic anemia

Rare
- Hepatitis
- Guillain-Barré syndrome
- Meningoencephalitis
- Myocarditis
- Granulomatous hepatitis

Immunosuppressed patients:
- Febrile mononucleosis
- GI ulcerations, hepatitis, pneumonitis, retinitis, encephalopathy, meningoencephalopathy
- HIV associated—dementia, demyelination, retinitis (Fig. 1-72), acalculous cholecystitis, adrenalitis, diarrhea, enterocolitis, esophagitis
- Diabetes associated with pancreatitis
- Adrenalitis associated with HIV

ETIOLOGY

Cytomegalovirus infection can remain latent, reactive with immunosuppression.

DIAGNOSIS

DIFFERENTIAL DIAGNOSIS

Congenital:
- Acute viral, bacterial, parasitic infections including other congenitally transmitted agents (toxoplasmosis, rubella, syphilis, pertussis, croup, bronchitis)

Acquired:
- EBV mononucleosis
- Viral hepatitis—A, B, C
- Cryptosporidiosis

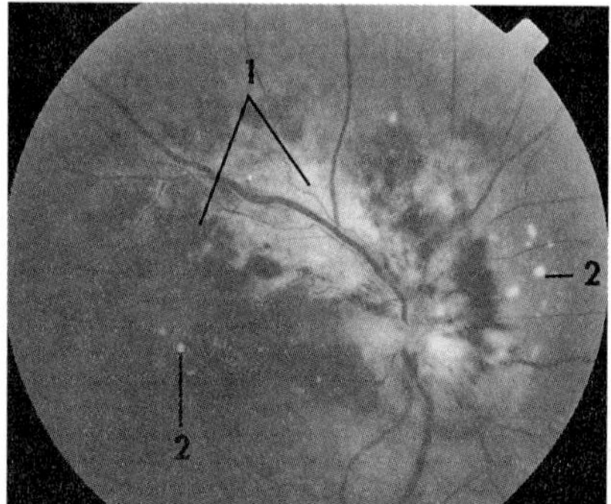

FIGURE 1-72 Sight-threatening CMV retinitis involves the macula and optic nerve of this HIV-positive young man. White, infected retina with intraretinal hemorrhage is present in the arcuate distribution of the nerve fiber layer *(1)*. A small amount of lipid exudation near the fovea and nasal to the optic nerve is also seen *(2)*. (From Palay D [ed]: *Ophthalmology for the primary care physician,* St Louis, 1997, Mosby.)

- Toxoplasmosis
- *Mycobacterium avium* infections
- Human herpesvirus 6
- Drug reaction
- Acute HIV infection

WORKUP

- Laboratory confirmation combined with clinical findings often with leukopenia, thrombocytopenia, lymphocytosis
- Demonstration of virus in tissue or serologic testing including CMV IgM antibodies, rising titers of complement fixation (CF) and indirect fluorescent antibody (IFA) or anticomplement IFA
- Funduscopic—necrotic patches with white granular component of retina
- Cultures—(viral) human fibroblast from urine, cervical swab, tissue buffy coat
- Biopsy—"owl's eye" inclusion bodies on tissue sample

IMAGING STUDIES

- Chest x-ray—if pneumonitis suspected, consider bronchoscopy
- Endoscopy—if GI involvement
- Funduscopy—retinitis
- CT scan/MRI—if CNS involvement

TREATMENT

NONPHARMACOLOGIC THERAPY

- Strict handwashing and education about standard precautions can control CMV transmission in health care facilities
- Highly active antiretroviral therapy (HAART) in patients with CD4 count $<50/mm^3$ for the goal of CD4 $>100/mm^3$ for a 3-6 mo period

ACUTE GENERAL Rx

For compromised hosts with CMV retinitis or pneumonitis:
- Ganciclovir 5 mg/kg bid IV × 21 days, then 5 mg/kg/day IV, or 1 g po tid or occular implant
- Foscarnet 60 mg/kg tid × 3 wk, then 90 mg/kg/day
- Cidofovir 5 mg/kg IV, repeat 1 wk later, then q2 wk IV
- Fomivirsen-salvage therapy for CMV retinitis 300 μg injected into vitreous

SUGGESTED READINGS

MacDonald JC et al: High active anti-retroviral therapy-related immune recovery in AIDS patients with cytomegalovirus retinitis, *Ophthalmology* 107:877, 2000.
Taylor GH: Cytomegalovirus, *Am Fam Physician* 67:3, 2003.
Whitcup SM: Cytomegalovirus retinitis in the era of highly active antiretroviral therapy, *JAMA* 283:653, 2000.

AUTHORS: **MINA PANTCHEVA, M.D.,** and **DENNIS J. MIKOLICH, M.D.**

BASIC INFORMATION

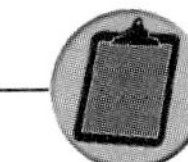

DEFINITION

Decubitus ulcers (pressure ulcers) are any damage to the skin and the underlying tissue or both that results from pressure, friction, or shearing forces that usually occur over bony prominences such as the sacrum or heels.

SYNONYMS

Pressure ulcers
Pressure sores
Bed sores
Sacral decubitus
Decubiti

ICD-9CM CODES
707.X Decubitus ulcers

EPIDEMIOLOGY & DEMOGRAPHICS

Pressure ulcers are present in 5% to 10% of patients in all health care settings: hospitals, nursing homes, and home-confined. Pressure ulcers are associated with significant morbidity and mortality. Pain occurs in two thirds of patients with stage II or greater pressure ulcers. Cellulitis, osteomyelitis, abscesses, and sepsis are all associated with pressure ulcers. One-year mortality approaches 40%.

PHYSICAL FINDINGS & CLINICAL PRESENTATION

All pressure ulcers should be staged according to the depth and type of tissue damage.

Stage I	Nonblanchable erythema of intact skin or boggy mushy feeling of skin
Stage II	Partial-thickness skin loss involving the epidermis, dermis, or both
Stage III	Full-thickness skin loss involving damage or necrosis of subcutaneous tissue that may extend down to, but not through, underlying fascia or muscle
Stage IV	Full-thickness skin loss with extensive destruction and tissue damage to muscle, bone, or supporting structures (e.g., tendons, joint capsule)

ETIOLOGY

- Prolonged unrelieved pressure often associated with impaired or restricted mobility
- Friction or shearing forces on skin

DIAGNOSIS

DIFFERENTIAL DIAGNOSIS

- Venous stasis ulcers
- Arterial ulcers
- Diabetic ulcers
- Skin cancer
- Cellulitis

WORKUP

All ulcers should have a description of the ulcer that includes the stage, location, and size and for stage III and IV a description of the wound bed (i.e., epithelialization, granulation tissue, necrotic tissue, eschar); the presence of any exudates, which includes type and amount; the wound edges (i.e., undermining, sinus tracts, tunneling, or fistulas); any signs of infection; and pain. In addition, pressure ulcer risk factors and their causes should be reassessed.

LABORATORY TESTS

Directed at identifying the cause of risk factors or any complications arising from the pressure ulcer (e.g., abscess or osteomyelitis); wound cultures of the wound bed are not helpful and should not be performed. Ultrasound has not yet been proven effective.

IMAGING STUDIES

MRI or bone scans may help identify osteomyelitis when clinically suspected.

TREATMENT

PREVENTION STRATEGIES

- Identify high-risk patients using standardized risk assessment scales such as the Bradon scale
- Routine skin inspection and good skin care for high-risk patients
- Minimize prolonged skin exposure to moisture, including urine and stool
- Avoid excessive drying and cracking of skin
- Reduce skin pressure through repositioning and pressure-reducing devices (e.g., foam mattresses, low air loss beds, pillows, or foam wedges when in bed and chair)
- Use adequate support surfaces while in bed and chair to prevent "bottoming out" (defined as less than 1 inch between patient and support surface measured by putting hand under support surface and feeling thickness to patient)
- Shear and friction reduction

MANAGEMENT STRATEGIES FOR PRESSURE ULCERS

- Pressure ulcers should be cleaned at each dressing change, and necrotic tissue should be debrided quickly as it delays wound healing.
- Wound irrigation should not exceed 15 psi and is best done with an 18-gauge angiocatheter.
- No one dressing or product is superior but should be used to keep ulcer bed moist and protect it from urine and stool.
- Avoid agents that are cytotoxic to epithelial cells (e.g., iodine, iodophor, sodium hypochlorite, hydrogen peroxide, acetic acid, and alcohol).
- Reduce pressure by using foam mattress, dynamic support surface (e.g., low-air-loss bed), and frequent repositioning (e.g., q2h).
- Hyperbaric oxygen, ultrasound, ultraviolet and low-energy radiation, either are ineffective or have not been extensively evaluated to conclude their efficacy.
- Growth factors appear promising but are second-line treatments if traditional approaches are ineffective.
- Correct poor nutrition.
- Minimize urinary and fecal incontinence.
- Use standardize assessment tool (e.g., PUSH tool) to monitor wound healing on weekly basis.

DISPOSITION

When systematic risk assessments are done and preventive measures are followed, most pressure ulcers can be prevented. Most pressure ulcers heal when appropriate management strategies are followed.

REFERRAL

- To physical and occupational therapists to improve bed and chair mobility
- Wounds with necrotic tissue to physicians, nurses, or physical therapists trained in sharp debridement
- To plastic surgeons for operative repair for large stage III or IV ulcers that do not respond to optimal care

SUGGESTED READINGS

Bergstrom A: prospective study on pressure sore risk among institutionalized elderly, *JAGS* 747, 1992.

Lyder C: Pressure ulcer prevention and management, *JAMA* 289(2):223, 2003.

National Pressure Ulcer Advisory Panel 9 (NPUAP): Pressure Ulcer Scale for Healing (PUSH), PUSH tool version 3.0 http://www.npuap.org/push3-0.htm

Pressure ulcers in adults: prediction and prevention, Clinical practice guideline No 3; Treatment of pressure ulcers, Clinical practice guideline No 4, AHCPR Publication No 92-0047 & 95-0652, Rockville, Md, 1994, US Department of Health and Human Services, Public Health Service, Agency for Health Care Policy and Research.

Thomas DR: The promise of topical growth factors in healing pressure ulcers, *Ann of Int Med* 139(8):694, 2003.

AUTHOR: **DAVID R. GIFFORD, M.D., M.P.H.**

Delirium Tremens

BASIC INFORMATION

DEFINITION

Delirium tremens refers to overactivity of the central nervous system after cessation of alcohol intake. The time interval is variable; it usually occurs within 1 wk after reduction or cessation of heavy alcohol intake and persists for 1 to 3 days.

SYNONYMS

Alcohol withdrawal syndrome
DTs
Alcoholic delirium

ICD-9CM CODES
291.00 Alcohol withdrawal delirium

EPIDEMIOLOGY & DEMOGRAPHICS

INCIDENCE (IN U.S.): Up to 500,000 cases annually
PREDOMINANT SEX: Male
PEAK INCIDENCE: 30 yr and older
PEAK AGE: Teenage years and older
GENETICS: More common with patients who have relatives who are alcoholics

PHYSICAL FINDINGS & CLINICAL PRESENTATION

- Initially: anxiety, insomnia, tremulousness
- Early: tachycardia, sweating, anorexia, agitation, headache, GI distress
- Late: seizures, visual hallucinations, delirium

ETIOLOGY

Alcoholism

DIAGNOSIS

DIFFERENTIAL DIAGNOSIS

Be alert for coexisting illness, trauma, and drug usage.

WORKUP

- Frequent rating of symptoms (hallucinations, tremor, sweating, agitation, orientation).
- The Clinical Institute Withdrawal Assessment-Alcohol (CIWA-A) scale can be used to measure the severity of alcohol withdrawal. It consists of the 10 following items:
  1. Nausea
  2. Tremor
  3. Autonomic hyperactivity
  4. Anxiety
  5. Agitation
  6. Tactile disturbances
  7. Visual disturbances
  8. Auditory disturbances
  9. Headache
  10. Disorientation

The maximum score is 67. When the CIWA-A score is ≥8, patients are usually given 2 to 4 mg of lorazepam hourly.

LABORATORY TESTS

- Electrolytes
- Close monitoring of glucose levels
- Drug screen

IMAGING STUDIES

CT scan of head if there is a history of head trauma

TREATMENT

NONPHARMACOLOGIC THERAPY

Refer to drug rehabilitation program after patient recovers.

ACUTE GENERAL Rx

1. Admission to a detoxification unit where patient can be observed closely
2. Vital signs q30min (neurologic signs, if necessary)
3. Use of lateral decubitus or prone position if restraints are necessary
4. NPO: NG tube for abdominal distention may be necessary but should not be routinely used
5. Vigorous hydration (4-6 L/day): IV with glucose (Na^+, K^+, PO_4^{-3}, and Mg^{2+} replacement)
6. Vitamins: thiamine, 100 mg IV qd. The initial dose of thiamine should precede the administration of IV dextrose; multivitamins (may be added to the hydrating solution)
7. Sedation
   a. Initially: lorazepam 2 to 5 mg IM/IV repeated prn
   b. Maintenance (individualized dosage): chlordiazepoxide, 50 to 100 mg PO q4-6h, lorazepam 2 mg PO q4h, or diazepam 5 to 10 mg PO tid; withhold doses or decrease subsequent doses if signs of oversedation are apparent
   c. Midazolam is also effective for managing DTs. Its rapid onset (sedation within 2 to 4 min of IV injection) and short duration of action (approximately 30 min) make it an ideal agent for titration in continuous infusion
8. Treatment of seizures: Diazepam 2.5 mg/min IV until seizure is controlled (check for respiratory depression or hypotension) may be beneficial for prolonged seizure activity; IV lorazepam 1 to 2 mg every 2 hr can be used in place of diazepam; generally, withdrawal seizures are self-limited and treatment is not required; the use of phenytoin or other anticonvulsants for short-term treatment of alcohol withdrawal seizures is not recommended
9. Diagnosis and treatment of concomitant medical, surgical, or psychiatric conditions

CHRONIC Rx

Alcoholics Anonymous has the best record in breaking addiction, but the results are still disappointing.

DISPOSITION

Refer to drug rehabilitation program.

REFERRAL

If cardiac arrhythmias are prominent or respiratory distress develops

PEARLS & CONSIDERATIONS

COMMENTS

This is a potentially lethal disease if not carefully treated. Mortality is 15% in untreated patients.

SUGGESTED READING

Kosten TR, O'Connor PG: Management of drug and alcohol withdrawal, *N Engl J Med* 348:1786, 2003.

AUTHOR: **FRED F. FERRI, M.D.**

BASIC INFORMATION

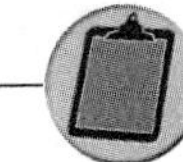

DEFINITION

A progressive neurodegenerative disease with core features of dementia accompanied or followed by parkinsonism.

SYNONYMS

Diffuse Lewy body disease, dementia with parkinsonism

ICD-9CM CODES
331.82 Dementia with Lewy bodies (DLB)

EPIDEMIOLOGY & DEMOGRAPHICS

- Now thought to be the second most common primary degenerative dementia, accounting for 10% to 15% of cases at autopsy
- Prevalence at age 65 estimated at 0.7%; at age 85 rises to 5.0%

CLINICAL PRESENTATION

- Most often dementia precedes appearance of parkinsonism by months to years. Occasionally parkinsonism precedes dementia; especially in this case there is clinical overlap between LBD and Parkinson's disease with dementia (PDD). There is debate whether LBD and PDD are actually a spectrum of the same disease, as pathologic findings are quite similar.
- Dementia is superficially quite similar to Alzheimer's disease. Early visual hallucinations (outside the setting of dopaminergic therapy) occur in up to 80% and are the major differentiating feature from AD. Typically the hallucinations are well formed and detailed.
- Fluctuations in performance, especially with regards to attention and alertness, are another key feature of the presentation. Can occur acutely, leading to misdiagnosis of vascular dementia presenting with stroke. These fluctuations may last hours or days.
- Parkinsonism is typically symmetrical and axially predominant, with little tremor but prominent gait impairment and postural instability.
- Parkinsonism not ubiquitous; up to 25% of cases diagnosed by autopsy had mild or no reported parkinsonian features.
- Rapid eye movement (REM) sleep behavior disorder and other related sleep abnormalities are common.

ETIOLOGY

- Uncertain; it is felt that DLB probably results from abnormal handling of alpha-synuclein with resulting aggregation of the protein inside neurons.
- Lewy bodies are eosinophilic intracellular inclusions, which contain alpha-synuclein and ubiquitin; it is not clear whether they are pathogenic.

DIAGNOSIS

DIFFERENTIAL DIAGNOSIS

- Parkinson's disease dementia (PDD)—differentiated from DLB in which dementia usually precedes parkinsonism. A somewhat arbitrary "1-year" rule is sometimes used to differentiate DLB from PDD in that if dementia presents within first year after the parkinsonism, DLB can still be diagnosed.
- Alzheimer's disease (AD)—differs from DLB in which visual hallucinations and parkinsonism are prominent.
- Atypical parkinsonian syndromes (multiple systems atrophy, progressive supranuclear palsy, corticobasal degeneration)—these syndromes have other features such as cerebellar degeneration, supranuclear gaze palsy, or asymmetrical limb apraxia that are not seen in DLB.
- Vascular dementia—differs from DLB in that despite the fluctuations in performance seen in DLB, there is no clear history of multiple strokes.
- Frontotemporal dementia (FTD, a.k.a. Pick's disease).
- Creutzfeldt-Jacob disease (CJD)—differs from DLB in that it is usually more rapidly progressive, can have cerebellar signs and symptoms, and often has distinctive EEG abnormalities.
- Toxic/metabolic/pharmacologic-related delirium.

WORKUP

- Diagnosis is largely clinical.
- Although dementia may be clinically similar to AD, detailed neuropsychologic testing can be helpful in bringing out prominent frontosubcortical and visuospatial deficits more typical of LBD.

LABORATORY TESTS

- Routine blood tests are normal but should be done to rule out treatable causes of dementia (e.g., B_{12}, TSH). In the setting of a fluctuation in performance, laboratory studies to rule out metabolic causes of delirium are appropriate.
- Spinal fluid analysis is normal; this may be helpful in more rapidly progressive cases if CJD is suspected.
- EEG may be helpful in the setting of fluctuations in performance to look for subclinical status epilepticus or other evidence of seizures, or if CJD is suspected.

IMAGING STUDIES

- Brain MRI is indicated mostly to look for multiple prior strokes suggestive of vascular dementia. In the setting of a sudden deterioration in performance, MRI with diffusion-weighted imaging may be needed to rule out acute stroke.
- Conventional neuroimaging is not diagnostic of DLB. Functional neuroimaging such as PET and SPECT show promise, but are not yet routinely indicated or available.

TREATMENT

NONPHARMACOLOGIC

Dementia-care education with physical and occupational therapy may be of benefit to both patients and caregivers.

ACUTE GENERAL Rx

None available

CHRONIC Rx

- Treatment of parkinsonism with levodopa can be partially successful, but because of risk of hallucinations the lowest effective dose should be used.
- Cholinesterase inhibitors are modestly effective for treating cognitive impairment (possibly better than in AD), as well as hallucinations, sleep impairments, and anxiety.
- Antipsychotic medications are helpful in treating hallucinations; however, older neuroleptic agents should be avoided in favor of low doses of newer "atypical" antipsychotics.

DISPOSITION

Median survival similar to AD.

REFERRAL

Referral to a general neurologist, dementia specialist, or movement disorders center is appropriate.

PEARLS & CONSIDERATIONS

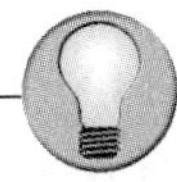

COMMENTS

- REM sleep behavior disorder is common in DLB (as it is in PD and multiple systems atrophy), but uncommon in Alzheimer's disease and frontotemporal dementia.
- LBD patients are unusually susceptible to extrapyramidal reactions to traditional neuroleptics, with sensitivity reactions in up to 50% of patients.

PREVENTION

None known

PATIENT/FAMILY EDUCATION

Comprehensive movement disorders website with disease information as well as links to support and discussion groups: http://www.wemove.org

SUGGESTED READINGS

McKeith I et al: Dementia with Lewy bodies, *Lancet Neurol* 3(1):19, 2004.

Rossor M: Primary degenerative dementia. In Bradley W et al (eds): *Neurology in Clinical Practice,* ed 3, Boston, 2000, Butterworth-Heinemann.

AUTHOR: **DAVID P. WILLIAMS, M.D.**

Dependent Personality Disorder

BASIC INFORMATION

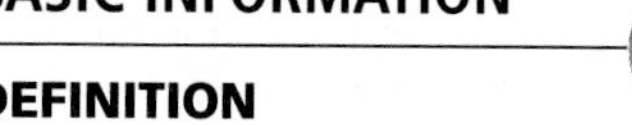

DEFINITION

Dependent personality disorder (DPD) is characterized by a pervasive and excessive need to be taken care of that leads to submissive and clinging behavior and fears of separation. PPD begins by early adulthood and causes significant distress or impairment in multiple domains of functioning. Individuals must meet five or more of the following criteria:

1. Difficulty making routine decisions (e.g., what color shirt to wear to work) without an excessive amount of advice and reassurance from others.
2. Need others to assume responsibility for most major areas of their life.
3. Difficulty expressing disagreement with others because of fear of loss of support or approval. Distinguish from realistic fears of retribution.
4. Difficulty initiating or completing projects on own because of a lack of self-confidence in abilities rather than lack of motivation or energy.
5. Excessive attempts to obtain nurturance and support from others. For example, will volunteer to do unpleasant tasks.
6. Feel uncomfortable or helpless when alone because of exaggerated fears of being unable to care for self.
7. Urgently seek another relationship for support when a close relationship ends.
8. Unrealistically preoccupied with being left to take care of self.

SYNONYMS

None

ICD-9CM CODES
301.6

EPIDEMIOLOGY & DEMOGRAPHICS

PREVALENCE: 0.5% in general population. Dependent traits, as opposed to the disorder itself, among the most often reported in outpatient mental health clinics.

PREDOMINANT SEX: Female (2:1) in clinical settings. Some studies suggest even sex distribution in the general population.

CLINICAL PRESENTATION

- Early onset and chronic course. Impairment often mild.
- On interview, will defer excessively to partner or parent.
- Indecision in routine decisions (e.g., what outfit to wear) without excessive reassurance.
- Depend on a parent or spouse to decide where they should live, work, and recreate and whom they should befriend.
- Need for others to function for them goes beyond age-appropriate and situation-appropriate requests for assistance.
- Will agree with objectionable opinions, submit to unreasonable requests, and not express appropriate anger or disappointment for fear of alienating the person without whom they believe they cannot function. As a result, relationships are often highly imbalanced.
- Convinced that they are not capable of independent function and present themselves as inept. Self-denigrating. But with assurance and support, they are likely to function adequately.
- Because they rely on the others to handle routine tasks, they often do not develop independent living skills, perpetuating their dependency.
- May tolerate verbal, physical, and sexual abuse, but this behavior indicative of DPD only when it can be established that other options are available to the person.
- Social relations tend to be limited to those few people on whom the person depends.

ETIOLOGY

- At this point, limited knowledge about role of genetic loading and neurobiologic vulnerability.
- Chronic physical illness or separation anxiety disorder may predispose for DPD.

DIAGNOSIS

DIFFERENTIAL DIAGNOSIS

- Dependency and personality changes arising as a consequence of an Axis I disorder such as mood disorders, social anxiety, panic disorder, and agoraphobia.
- Dependency arising as a consequence of a general medical condition.
- Most common comorbid Axis I conditions are major depressive and other mood disorders, anxiety disorders, including social phobia, and adjustment disorder.
- Most common comorbid personality disorders are histrionic, avoidant, and borderline. Each of these disorders is characterized by dependent features. DPD distinguished by its predominantly submissive, reactive, and clinging behavior:
  1 Borderline: also fears abandonment but reacts to abandonment with rage rather than urgent efforts to replace the relationship. Also, unstable relationships in borderline.
  2. Histronic: also strong need for reassurance with associated clinging, but behavior flamboyant with active demands for attention rather than docile and self-effacing.
  3. Avoidant: also experiences strong feelings of inadequacy but avoids contact until certain of acceptance rather than active seeking of connection.

WORKUP

- History—collateral information essential to establishing presence of longstanding interpersonal pattern in multiple domains of the patient's life.
- Physical examination.
- Mental status examination.

LABORATORY TESTS

Those tests necessary to rule out medical causes of personality changes

IMAGING STUDIES

Those necessary to rule out medical causes of personality changes

TREATMENT

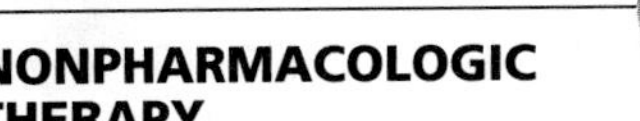

NONPHARMACOLOGIC THERAPY

- No randomized trials assessing treatment
- Cognitive behavioral and psychodynamic psychotherapy to diminish and better contain anxiety and to help patients develop sense of self as competent and requisite assertiveness skills

ACUTE GENERAL Rx

Benzodiazepines to control highly anxious states

CHRONIC Rx

- SSRIs and buspar for anxiety
- SSRIs for comorbid depression, social phobia, other anxiety disorders, and agoraphobia

COMPLEMENTARY & ALTERNATIVE MEDICINE

None

DISPOSITION

- Severity is variable and course is chronic.
- Impairments often mild.
- At increased risk for major depression, social phobia, and other anxiety.

REFERRAL

- If pharmacotherapy or psychotherapy contemplated
- If patient's functioning impaired

PEARLS & CONSIDERATIONS

COMMENTS

- DPD patients fear illness will lead to helplessness and abandonment by others.
- This fear of simultaneous helplessness and abandonment intensifies neediness and may lead to dramatic demands for urgent medical attention.
- When physicians do not respond as wanted, angry outbursts may ensue.
- Medical care can also become a means by which dependency needs are met. As a result, some of these patients may unconsciously or consciously prolong their illness for primary gain.
- Physicians often react to the extreme neediness with aversion and avoidance or overengagement leading to burnout.
- Management guidelines:
  1. Overall strategy is to provide reassurance and allay fear of abandonment.
  2. Specific strategies include scheduling frequent visits, noncontingent care (i.e., scheduling visits regardless of whether ill or not).
  3. Establish firm and realistic limits to availability as early as possible in treatment.
  4. Enlist other members of healthcare team for support.
  5. Encourage patient to develop additional, "outside" support systems.

SUGGESTED READINGS

Feder A, Robbins SW, Ostermeyer B: Personality disorders. In Feldman MD, Christensen JF (eds): *Behavioral Medicine in Primary Care,* 2003, New York, McGraw Hill.

Shea MT et al: Associations in the course of personality disorders and Axis I disorders over time, *J Abnorm Psychol* 113(4):499, 2004.

Ward RK: Assessment and management of personality disorders, *Am Fam Physician* 70(8):1505, 2004.

AUTHORS: **JOHN Q. YOUNG, M.D., M.P.P.,** and **CRAIG VAN DYKE, M.D.**

BASIC INFORMATION

DEFINITION

Major depression is an episodic, frequently recurrent syndrome. Criteria for major depression require that five of nine symptoms be present for a 2-week period. One of these nine symptoms must be either a persistent depressed mood (present most of the day nearly every day) or pervasive anhedonia (loss of interest or pleasure in living). Other symptoms include sleep disorder (insomnia or hypersomnia), appetite loss/gain or weight loss/gain, fatigue, psychomotor retardation or agitation, difficulty concentrating, feelings of guilt or low self-esteem, and recurrent thoughts of death or suicidal ideation.

SYNONYMS

Unipolar affective disorder
Melancholia
Manic-depressive illness, depressed type
Depressive episode

ICD-9CM CODES
296.2, 296.3, 311

EPIDEMIOLOGY & DEMOGRAPHICS

INCIDENCE (IN U.S.): 10% of men; 20% of women
PREVALENCE (IN U.S.): Point prevalence in a community sample is 3% of men; 4.5%-9.3% of women; 1% of children. Prevalence of 20%-40% in patients with comorbid medical conditions.
PREDOMINANT SEX: Female:male is 2:1; equal before puberty
PREDOMINANT AGE: 25 to 44 yr; 5% of adolescents
PEAK INCIDENCE: 30 to 40 yr; 13% of postpartum women
GENETICS:
- Clear evidence of familial predominance.
- Prevalence is 2-3 times greater among first-degree relatives of patients with major depression.
- Concordance among monozygotic twins is about 50%.
- No established pattern of inheritance.

PHYSICAL FINDINGS & CLINICAL PRESENTATION

- Clinical evaluation can be facilitated by organizing the major symptoms into four hallmarks: (1) depressed mood, (2) anhedonia, (3) physical symptoms (sleep disorder, appetite problem, fatigue, psychomotor changes), and (4) psychologic symptoms (difficulty concentrating or indecisiveness, guilt or low self-esteem, and hopelessness).
- A stressful life event, typically a serious loss, often precedes and triggers a depressive episode.
- However, the presence or absence of identifiable precipitants is irrelevant to the diagnosis of major depression.
- Patients often present with somatic complaints such as pain, fatigue, insomnia, dizziness, or gastrointestinal problems.
- May be associated with mood-congruent delusional thinking (paranoid and melancholic themes) in about 15% of individuals.
- May be associated with active or passive suicidal ideation.
- Among adolescents, serious misconduct may appear.
- Major depression is often misdiagnosed in elderly patients as signs of aging.

ETIOLOGY

- Major depression is a heterogeneous group of disorders probably arising from a variety of etiologic determinants.
- Genetic and family experiences both play roles though neither is a determining factor.
- Significant psychosocial stressors, especially involving loss, often trigger depression.
- Numerous biologic markers have been identified including endocrine and central nervous system factors, though none are considered causative.

DIAGNOSIS

DIFFERENTIAL DIAGNOSIS

- Other mental disorders such as anxiety disorders, somatoform disorders, obsessive-compulsive disorder, substance abuse, and personality disorders often present with symptoms similar to depression.
- It is critical to distinguish between a depressive episode occurring as part of a major depression and a depressive episode that is part of bipolar disorder.
- Approximately 10%-15% of depression is caused by general medical illness. General medical conditions with high prevalence of depression include Alzheimer's disease, Parkinson's disease, stroke, end-stage renal failure, cardiac disease (specifically coronary artery disease), HIV infection, and cancer.
- Some medical conditions can present as depression, for example, hypothyroidism or hyperthyroidism and neurosyphilis.
- Premenstrual dysphoric disorder.
- Elderly patients: depression often coexists with dementia.

WORKUP

- History: a careful medical history is required.
- Physical examination: there are no specific diagnostic signs of depression.
- Mental status examination.
- The two-item screener may enhance recognition of depression.
- The Patient Health Questionnaire (PHQ-9) has documented high sensitivity and specificity for the diagnosis of major depression (see http://www.depression-primarycare.org).

LABORATORY TESTS

- No laboratory studies can definitively diagnose depression.
- The following can be done to rule out other major organ system disease:
  1. Routine chemistries
  2. CBC with differential
  3. Thyroid function studies
  4. B_{12} levels.

IMAGING STUDIES

With unusual presentations (e.g., associated with new-onset severe headache, focal neurologic signs, a cognitive or sensory disturbance), the following are performed:

- EEG (diffuse slowing indicates metabolic encephalopathy)
- Anatomic brain imaging (CT scan or MRI)

TREATMENT

NONPHARMACOLOGIC THERAPY

- There is good evidence that cognitive behavioral therapy is as effective as antidepressant medication in achieving a significant reduction or remission of depression.
- Problem-solving and interpersonal psychotherapies have efficacy rates of 50%-60%.
- By 12 wk, psychotherapy and medication are equally effective.

ACUTE GENERAL Rx

- In selecting an antidepressant medication, the patient's concurrent medical or psychiatric illnesses, history of prior response, cost, and side effects should all be taken into account.
- Antidepressants are effective in about 60%-70% of cases.
- Selective serotonin reuptake inhibitors (SSRIs) generally are first-line agents.
- The acute phase of treatment lasts about 6-12 weeks and has as its goal the reduction and removal of signs and symptoms of depression.
- Therapy should be continued for 4-9 months after the full remission of symptoms.
- Treatment-refractory patients should be switched to an agent in a different class.
- Electroconvulsive therapy is still the most effective means available for the treatment of refractory depression.

CHRONIC Rx

- The risk of recurrence exceeds 90% in individuals having experienced three or more depressive episodes; for these individuals continuous prophylactic therapy is recommended.

DISPOSITION

- Major depression is a relapsing and remitting illness, characterized in most patients by recurrent episodes throughout life.
- Physical symptoms predict a favorable response to biologic intervention.
- Additional episodes are experienced by >60% of individuals having one depressive episode.
- Without treatment, episodes last an average of 6-12 months.

REFERRAL

- If treatment refractory
- If patient suicidal or psychotic

PEARLS & CONSIDERATIONS

COMMENTS

- All threats of suicide should be taken very seriously. Clinicians can use the mnemonic SAL: Is the method Specific? Is it Available? Is it Lethal?
- It is imperative to rule out bipolar affective disorder before initiating treatment with an antidepressant medication.
- Many patients and families are reluctant to accept the diagnosis of depression because of associated stigma.
- A two-question screener is as effective as longer screening instruments. A positive answer to one of the following two questions should lead to a full diagnostic assessment for depression.
  1. Over the past 2 weeks have you ever felt down, depressed, or hopeless?
  2. Over the past 2 weeks, have you felt little interest or pleasure in doing things?

SUGGESTED READINGS

Cole S et al: Depression. In MD Feldman, JF Christensen (eds): *Behavioral Medicine in Primary Care: A Practical Guide,* ed 2, New York, 2003, Lange Medical Books/McGraw-Hill.

Gilbody S et al: Educational and organizational interventions to improve the management of depression in primary care: a systematic review, *JAMA* 289:3145, 2003.

Kessler R et al: The epidemiology of major depressive disorder: results from the National Comorbidity Survey Replication (NCS-R), *JAMA* 289:3095, 2003.

Treatment for Adolescents with Depression Study Team: Fluoxetine, cognitive-behavioral therapy, and their combination for adolescents with depression: Treatment for Adolescents with Depression Study (TADS) randomized controlled trial, *JAMA* 292(7):807, 2004.

U.S. Preventive Services Task Force: Screening for depression: recommendations and rationale, *Ann Intern Med* 136:760, 2002.

Whooley MA, Simon GE: Managing depression in medical outpatients, *N Engl J Med* 343:1842, 2000.

AUTHOR: **MITCHELL D. FELDMAN, M.D., M.PHIL.**

BASIC INFORMATION

DEFINITION

De Quervain's tenosynovitis refers to a stenosing inflammatory process of the first dorsal retinacular compartment containing the tendons of the abductor pollicis longus (APL) and extensor pollicis brevis (EPB).

SYNONYMS

Stenosing tenosynovitis of the radial styloid
Stenosing tenovaginitis of the first dorsal compartment

ICD-9CM CODES
727.04 Tenosynovitis radial styloid

EPIDEMIOLOGY & DEMOGRAPHICS

- More common in women than in men (10:1)
- Usually occurs between the ages of 30 to 50
- Associated with rheumatoid arthritis
- Seen in occupations (e.g., clerical, assembly, and manual labor)

PHYSICAL FINDINGS & CLINICAL PRESENTATION

- Pain over the styloid process of the radius
- Swelling
- Positive Finkelstein's test (Fig. 1-73): stretching the tendons of the APL and EPB by clasping the thumb with the fingers and passive deviation of the wrist to the ulnar side. Provocation of pain is a positive sign
- Crepitance

ETIOLOGY

- The cause is usually repetitive use or overuse of the hands.

DIAGNOSIS

- The diagnosis of de Quervain's tenosynovitis is based on the clinical triad of:
  1. Tenderness over the radial styloid
  2. Swelling over the first dorsal retinacular compartment
  3. Positive Finkelstein's test (Fig. 1-73)
- Sometimes 1.5 cc of 1% Xylocaine can be injected into the tenosynovial sac, and if all three physical signs resolve, the diagnosis is confirmed.

DIFFERENTIAL DIAGNOSIS

- Carpal tunnel syndrome
- Ostearthritis
- Gout
- Infiltrative tenosynovitis
- Radiculopathy
- Compression neuropathy (e.g., superficial branch of the radial nerve "bracelet syndrome")
- Infection (e.g., tuberculosis, bacterial)

WORKUP

The workup of suspected de Quervain's tenosynovitis requires laboratory testing and x-rays to exclude other causes of wrist and hand pain.

LABORATORY TESTS

- ESR is usually normal in patients with de Quervain's tenosynovitis. If elevated, a search for an infectious or infiltrative cause should be pursued
- Aspiration with examination of the specimen under polarized microscope to rule out gout
- Gram stain and culture of aspirate to rule out infectious etiology

IMAGING STUDIES

- X-ray studies of the hand may show findings of osteoarthritis of the first carpometacarpal joint that can mimic de Quervain's tenosynovitis.

TREATMENT

NONPHARMACOLOGIC THERAPY

- Rest
- Splinting
- Physiotherapy

ACUTE GENERAL Rx

- Corticosteroid injection using 20 to 40 mg triamcinolone acetonide and 1% Xylocaine is effective in relieving pain.
- NSAIDs ibuprofen 800 mg tid or naproxen 500 mg bid can be tried in patients refusing steroid injection therapy.

CHRONIC Rx

- Surgical release is generally reserved for patients not responding to NSAIDs and corticosteroid injection therapy.

DISPOSITION

- Approximately 90% of patients have relief of symptoms with either single or multiple steroid injections.
- Complications of steroid injections include:
  1. Infection
  2. Tendon rupture
- Surgical control of symptoms occurs in 90% of cases.
- Complications of surgery include:
  1. Radial nerve damage
  2. Paresthesia (~10%)
  3. Neuroma

REFERRAL

Consultation with either a rheumatologist or an orthopedist is recommended in patients with de Quervain's tenosynovitis requiring injection therapy.

SUGGESTED READINGS

Chin DH, Jones NF: Repetitive motion hand disorder, *J Calif Dent Assoc* 30(2):149, 2002.
Saldana TS: Trigger digit: diagnosis and treatment, *J Am Acad Orthop Surg* 9(4):246, 2001.

AUTHOR: **PETER PETROPOULOS, M.D.**

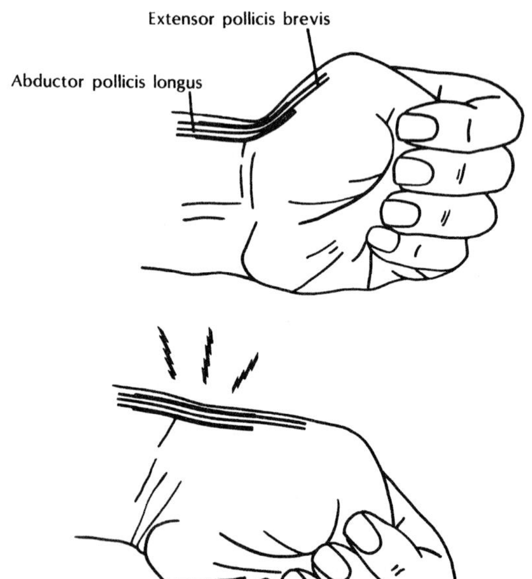

FIGURE 1-73 Finkelstein's test is positive in de Quervain's stenosing synovitis. Ulnar flexion of the wrist produces pain over the dorsal compartment containing the extensor policis brevis and abductor pollicis longus. (From Noble J [ed]: *Textbook of primary care medicine,* ed 2, St Louis, 1996, Mosby.)

BASIC INFORMATION

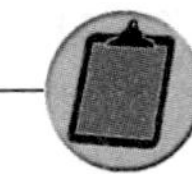

DEFINITION

Atopic dermatitis is a genetically determined eczematous eruption that is pruritic, symmetric, and associated with personal family history of allergic manifestations (atopy).

SYNONYMS

Eczema
Atopic neurodermatitis
Atopic eczema

ICD-9CM CODES
691.8 Atopic dermatitis

EPIDEMIOLOGY & DEMOGRAPHICS

- Incidence is between 5 and 25 cases/1000 persons.
- Highest incidence is among children (5%-10%). It accounts for 4% of acute care pediatric visits.
- Onset of disease before age 5 yr in 85% of patients.
- More than 50% of children with generalized atopic dermatitis develop asthma and allergic rhinitis by age 13 yr.
- Concordance in monozygotic twins is 86%.

PHYSICAL FINDINGS & CLINICAL PRESENTATION

- There are no specific cutaneous signs for atopic dermatitis, and there is a wide spectrum of presentations ranging from minimal flexural eczema to erythroderma.
- The primary lesions are a result of itching caused by severe and chronic pruritus. The repeated scratching modifies the skin surface, producing lichenification, dry and scaly skin, and redness.
- The lesions are typically on the neck, face, upper trunk, and bends of elbows and knees (symmetric on flexural surfaces of extremities).
- There is dryness, thickening of the involved areas, discoloration, blistering, and oozing.
- Papular lesions are frequently found in the antecubital and popliteal fossae.
- In children, red scaling plaques are often confined to the cheeks and the perioral and perinasal areas.
- Inflammation in the flexural areas and lichenified skin is a very common presentation in children.
- Constant scratching may result in areas of hypopigmentation or hyperpigmentation (more common in blacks).
- In adults, redness and scaling in the dorsal aspect of the hands or about the fingers are the most common expression of atopic dermatitis; oozing and crusting may be present.
- Secondary skin infections may be present (*Staphylococcus aureus,* dermatophytosis, herpes simplex).

ETIOLOGY

Unknown; elevated T-lymphocyte activation, defective cell immunity, and B cell IgE overproduction may play a significant role.

DIAGNOSIS

DIFFERENTIAL DIAGNOSIS

- Scabies
- Psoriasis
- Dermatitis herpetiform
- Contact dermatitis
- Photosensitivity
- Seborrheic dermatitis
- Candidiasis
- Lichen simplex chronicus
- Other: Wiskott-Aldrich syndrome, PKU, mycosis fungoides, ichthyosis, HIV dermatitis, nonnummular eczema, histiocytosis X

WORKUP

Diagnosis is based on the presence of three of the following major features and three minor features.

MAJOR FEATURES:
- Pruritus
- Personal or family history of atopy: asthma, allergic rhinitis, atopic dermatitis
- Facial and extensor involvement in infants and children
- Flexural lichenification in adults

MINOR FEATURES:
- Elevated IgE
- Eczema-perifollicular accentuation
- Recurrent conjunctivitis
- Ichthyosis
- Nipple dermatitis
- Wool intolerance
- Cutaneous *S. aureus* infections or herpes simplex infections
- Food intolerance
- Hand dermatitis (nonallergic irritant)
- Facial pallor, facial erythema
- Cheilitis
- White dermographism
- Early age of onset (after 2 mo of age)

LABORATORY TESTS

- Tests are generally not helpful.
- Elevated IgE levels are found in 80% to 90% of atopic dermatitis.
- Blood eosinophilia correlates with disease severity.

TREATMENT

NONPHARMACOLOGIC THERAPY

Avoidance of triggering factors:
- Sudden temperature changes, sweating, low humidity in the winter
- Contact with irritating substance (e.g., wool, cosmetics, some soaps and detergents, tobacco)
- Foods that provoke exacerbations (e.g., eggs, peanuts, fish, soy, wheat, milk)
- Stressful situations
- Allergens and dust
- Excessive hand washing
- Clip nails to decrease abrasion of skin

GENERAL Rx

- Emollients can be used to prevent dryness. Severely affected skin can be optimally hydrated by occlusion in addition to application of emollients.
- Topical corticosteroids (e.g., 1% to 2.5% hydrocortisone) may be helpful. Consider intermediate-potency steroids (e.g., triamcinolone, fluocinolone) for more severe cases and limit potent corticosteroids (e.g., betamethasone, desoximetasone, clobetasol) to severe cases.
- Pimecrolimus cream (Elidel) 1% applied bid is a steroid-free compound with antiinflammatory effects secondary to blockage of activated T-cell cytokine production. It is highly effective in atopic dermatitis without having the adverse effects associated with topical corticosteroids.
- Tacrolimus (Protopic) ointment (0.03% or 0.1%) applied bid represents another alternative to topical corticosteroids. It does not cause skin atrophy and may be particularly useful on the face and neck. It is a macrolide that decreases activation of T-lymphocytes, inhibits release of inflammatory mediators from cutaneous mast cells and basophils, and suppresses humoral and cell-mediated immune responses.
- Oral antihistamines (e.g., hydroxyzine, diphenhydramine) are effective in controlling pruritus and inducing sedation, restful sleep, and prevention of scratching during sleep. Doxepin and other tricyclic antidepressants also have antihistamine effect, induce sleep, and reduce pruritus.
- Oral prednisone, IM triamcinolone, Goeckerman regimen, PUVA are generally reserved for severe cases.
- Methotrexate, cyclosporine azathioprine, and systemic corticosteroids are sometimes tried for recalcitrant disease.

DISPOSITION

- Resolution occurs in approximately 40% of patients by adulthood.
- Most patients have a course characterized by remissions and intermittent flares.

SUGGESTED READINGS

Barnetson RC, Rogers M: Childhood atopic eczema, *BMJ* 324(7350):1376, 2002.

Ong et al: Endogenous antimicrobial peptides and skin infections in atopic dermatitis, *N Engl J Med* 347:1151, 2002.

AUTHOR: **FRED F. FERRI, M.D.**

Dermatitis, Contact (PTG)

BASIC INFORMATION

DEFINITION

Contact dermatitis is an acute or chronic skin inflammation, usually eczematous dermatitis resulting from exposure to substances in the environment. It can be subdivided into "irritant" contact dermatitis (nonimmunologic physical and chemical alteration of the epidermis) and "allergic" contact dermatitis (delayed hypersensitivity reaction).

SYNONYMS

Irritant contact dermatitis
Allergic contact dermatitis

ICD-9CM CODES
692 Contact dermatitis and other eczema

EPIDEMIOLOGY & DEMOGRAPHICS

- 20% of all cases of dermatitis in children are caused by allergic contact dermatitis.
- Rhus dermatitis (poison ivy, poison oak, and poison sumac) is responsible for most cases of contact dermatitis.
- Frequent causes of irritant contact dermatitis are soaps, detergents, and organic solvents.

PHYSICAL FINDINGS & CLINICAL PRESENTATION

IRRITANT CONTACT DERMATITIS:

- Mild exposure may result in dryness, erythema, and fissuring of the affected area (e.g., hand involvement in irritant dermatitis caused by exposure to soap, genital area involvement in irritant dermatitis caused by prolonged exposure to wet diapers).
- Eczematous inflammation may result from chronic exposure.

ALLERGIC CONTACT DERMATITIS:

- Poison ivy dermatitis can present with vesicles and blisters; linear lesions (as a result of dragging of the resins over the surface of the skin by scratching) are a classic presentation.
- The pattern of lesions is asymmetric; itching, burning, and stinging may be present.
- The involved areas are erythematous, warm to touch, swollen, and may be confused with cellulitis.

ETIOLOGY

- Irritant contact dermatitis: cement (construction workers), rubber, ragweed, malathion (farmers), orange and lemon peels (chefs, bartenders), hair tints, shampoos (beauticians), rubber gloves (medical, surgical personnel)
- Allergic contact dermatitis: poison ivy, poison oak, poison sumac, rubber (shoe dermatitis), nickel (jewelry), balsam of Peru (hand and face dermatitis), neomycin, formaldehyde (cosmetics)

DIAGNOSIS

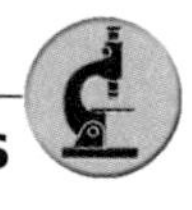

DIFFERENTIAL DIAGNOSIS

- Impetigo
- Lichen simplex chronicus
- Atopic dermatitis
- Nummular eczema
- Seborrheic dermatitis
- Psoriasis
- Scabies

WORKUP

- Medical history: gradual onset vs. rapid onset, number of exposures, clinical presentation, occupational history
- Physical examination: contact dermatitis in the neck may be caused by necklaces, perfumes, after-shave lotion; involvement of the axillae is often secondary to deodorants, clothing; face involvement can occur with cosmetics, airborne allergens, aftershave lotion

LABORATORY TESTS

- Patch testing is useful to confirm the diagnosis of contact dermatitis; it is indicated particularly when inflammation persists despite appropriate topical therapy and avoidance of suspected causative agent; patch testing should not be used for irritant contact dermatitis because this is a nonimmunologic-mediated inflammatory reaction.
- Gram stain and cultures are indicated only in cases of suspected secondary infection or impetigo.

TREATMENT

NONPHARMACOLOGIC THERAPY

Avoidance of suspected allergens

ACUTE GENERAL Rx

- Removal of the irritant substance by washing the skin with plain water or mild soap within 15 min of exposure is helpful in patients with poison ivy, poison oak, or poison sumac dermatitis.
- Cold or cool water compresses for 20 to 30 min five to six times a day for the initial 72 hr are effective during the acute blistering stage.
- Oral corticosteroids (e.g., prednisone 20 mg bid for 6 to 10 days) are generally reserved for severe, widespread dermatitis.
- IM steroids (e.g., Kenalog) are used for severe reactions and in patients requiring oral corticosteroids but unable to tolerate PO.
- Oral antihistamines (e.g., hydroxyzine 25 mg q6h) will control pruritus, especially at night; calamine lotion is also useful for pruritus; however, it can lead to excessive drying.
- Colloidal oatmeal (Aveeno) baths can also provide symptomatic relief.
- Patients with mild to moderate erythema may respond to topical steroid gels or creams.
- Patients with shoe allergy should change their socks at least once a day; use of aluminum chloride hexahydrate in a 20% solution (Drysol) qhs will also help control perspiration.
- Use hypoallergenic surgical gloves in patients with rubber and surgical glove allergy.

DISPOSITION

Allergic contact dermatitis generally resolves within 2 to 4 wk if reexposure to allergen is prevented.

REFERRAL

For patch testing in selected patients (see Laboratory Tests)

PEARLS & CONSIDERATIONS

COMMENTS

- Commercially available corticosteroid dose packs should be avoided, because they generally provide an inadequate amount of medication.

AUTHOR: **FRED F. FERRI, M.D.**

BASIC INFORMATION

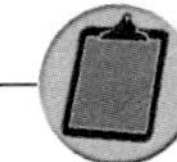

DEFINITION

Dermatitis herpetiformis (DH) is a rare, chronic skin disorder characterized by an intensely burning, pruritic, vesicular rash. It is strongly associated with gluten-sensitive enteropathy. Twenty percent to seventy percent of patients with dermatitis herpetiformis will have gastrointestinal symptoms, whereas approximately 10% of patients with celiac sprue will have dermatitis herpetiformis.

ICD-9CM CODES
694.0 Dermatitis herpetiformis

EPIDEMIOLOGY & DEMOGRAPHICS

PREVALENCE: 11.2 cases/100,000 persons in the U.S. The prevalence for celiac disease is 1 in 133 adults in the U.S.

PREDOMINANT AGE: Third and fourth decades

PREDOMINANT SEX: Slight male predominance

PREDOMINANT RACE: Rarely seen in Blacks/African Americans or Asians

GENETIC PREDISPOSITION: A specific HLA type, DQ2, is present in 90% of patients with celiac disease with or without DH. DQ8 is present in the remaining 10%. DQ2 is present in 16%-18% of the normal population. 11% of patients with DH have a first-degree relative with either DH or celiac disease.

PHYSICAL FINDINGS & CLINICAL PRESENTATION

- Pruritic, burning vesicles initially, frequently grouped (hence the name "herpetiform") (see Fig. 1-74)
- Symmetrically distributed on extensor surfaces: elbows, knees, scalp, nuchal area, shoulder, and buttocks; rarely found in mouth
- May evolve in time to intensely burning urticarial papules, vesicles, and rarely bullae
- Celiac-type permanent-tooth enamel defects found in 53% of patients

DIAGNOSIS

Diagnosis is confirmed histologically by the demonstration of IgA deposits found along the subepidermal basement membrane, in the dermal papillary tips, which is specific to the diagnosis of DH.

DIFFERENTIAL DIAGNOSIS

- Linear IgA bullous dermatosis (not associated with gluten-sensitive enteropathy)
- Herpes simplex infection
- Herpes zoster infection
- Bullous erythema multiforme
- Bullous pemphigoid

WORKUP

History of chronic diarrhea and pruritic, vesicular rash highly suggestive of diagnosis

LABORATORY TESTS

- Skin biopsy for immunofluorescence studies. Diagnosis is confirmed by IgA deposits along the subepidermal basement membrane. >90% will have granular or fibrillar IgA deposits in the dermal papillae. Multiple specimens may be needed to obtain positive findings because of the focal nature of deposits. Biopsies are taken from adjacent normal skin because the diagnostic Ig deposits are usually destroyed by the blistering process.
- Circulating antibody levels
  1. IgA antiendomysial antibody: found in 70% of patients with rash and who are not on gluten-free diet; in 100% of patients with rash and grade 3 to 4 flattening of intestinal mucosa; and in all patients with untreated celiac disease. Levels decrease to 0% when gluten is avoided for 3 mo.
  2. IgA antigliadin antibodies: found in 66% of patients; also present in patients with pemphigus and pemphigoid.
  3. IgA reticulin antibody: found in 36% of patients with DH.
  4. IgA antitissue transglutaminase: elevated levels in patients with DH as compared with patients with skin or intestinal diseases unrelated to DH.

TREATMENT

Patients may be given a trial of pharmacologic therapy if they are extremely uncomfortable. Symptoms are often dramatically relieved within hours or days of initiation of medical therapy.

ACUTE GENERAL Rx

PHARMACOLOGIC

- Dapsone: Initial dose of 100 to 150 mg PO qd. Itching and burning are controlled in 12 to 48 hr and new lesions stop appearing. The dosage is adjusted to the lowest level that provides ade-

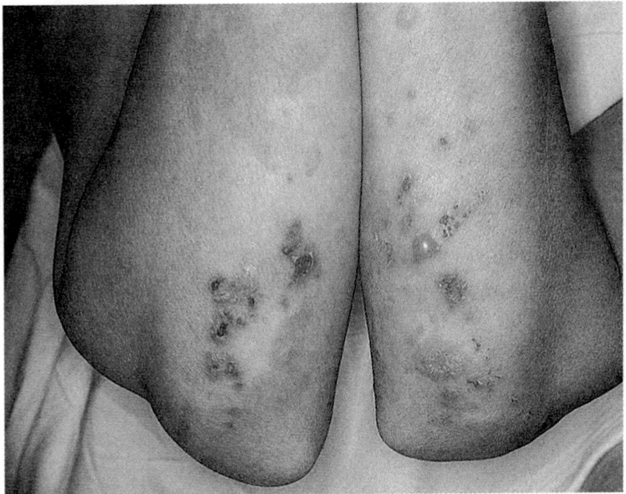

FIGURE 1-74 Dermatitis herpetiformis is an immunologically mediated blistering disease. There is a strong association of dermatitis herpetiformis with HLA-B8, DR3. Gluten-sensitive enteropathy is a common associated finding. The lesions are grouped (herpetiform) and extremely pruritic. (From Callen JP [ed]: *Color atlas of dermatology,* ed 2, Philadelphia, 2000, WB Saunders.)

quate relief, usually in the range of 50 to 200 mg/day; although some patients may require 25 mg/day, others may require 400 mg/day. Peripheral motor neuropathy can occur in the first few months of therapy. Paresthesias and weakness of the distal upper and lower extremities and footdrop are the most common manifestations. Symptoms slowly improve over months to years after dapsone is discontinued. Hemolysis, anemia, and methemoglobinemia occur to some degree in all patients receiving dapsone therapy. Patients at risk for having G6PD should have levels drawn before initiation as dapsone may cause severe hemolytic anemia in these patients. Probenecid blocks the renal excretion of dapsone, and rifampin increases the rate of its clearance.

- Sulfapyridine: Initial dosage 500 to 1500 mg/day. Sulfapyridine does not cause neuropathy, but it is associated with agranulocytosis and aplastic anemia. It also may cause severe hemolysis in patients with G6PD.
- Tetracycline: Successful treatment has been reported with tetracycline 500 mg PO qd-tid and minocycline 100 mg PO bid. Cessation resulted in a flare of the rash.
- Nicotinamide: Successful treatment has been reported with nicotinamide 500 mg PO bid-tid. Cessation resulted in a flare of the rash.
- *Topical Steroids:* may help but can cause skin irritation and atrophy with prolonged use.
- Nonsteroidal anti-inflammatory drugs and iodide can worsen skin inflammation.

NONPHARMACOLOGIC

- Gluten-free diet: for at least 6 mo, which will allow most patients to begin to decrease or discontinue sulfone therapy. The diet usually needs to be followed for 2 yr before medications can be discontinued. Although intestinal villous architecture improves, symptoms and lesions recur in 1 to 3 wk if a normal diet is resumed. Most patients need to follow diet indefinitely. Gluten is found in all grains except rice and corn.
- Elemental diet: Other dietary factors may also be important in dermatitis herpetiformis. Antigens stimulate the production of antibodies, leading to the formation of immune complexes. Most antigens that elicit a humoral immune response are proteins. Thus, a diet without full proteins, an elemental diet, is not likely to contain major antigens. A diet of amino acids, fat, and carbohydrates can produce a rapid benefit and allow a decrease in the dosage of dapsone within 2 wk.

CHRONIC Rx

Gluten-free diet

REFERRAL

To dermatologist for skin biopsy

PEARLS & CONSIDERATIONS

- There is an increased incidence of other autoimmune disorders, including thyroid disease, type 1 diabetes mellitus, systemic lupus erythematosus, vitiligo, and Sjögren's syndrome in patients with dermatitis herpetiformis.
- Small bowel lymphoma and nonintestinal lymphoma have been reported in patients with dermatitis herpetiformis and celiac disease.
- Linear IgA bullous dermatosis is not associated with gluten-sensitive enteropathy or with IgA antiendomysial Ab.

SUGGESTED READINGS

Dieterich W et al: Antibodies to tissue Transglutaminase as serologic markers in patients with dermatitis herpetiformis, *J Invest Dermatol* 113(1):133, 1999.

Kosann MK: Dermatitis herpetiformis, *Dermatology Online Journal* 9(4):8, 2003.

Zone JJ et al: Warning: bread may be harmful to your health, *Journal of the American Academy of Dermatology* 51(1 Suppl):S27, 2004.

AUTHOR: **IRIS L. TONG, M.D.**

BASIC INFORMATION

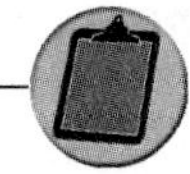

DEFINITION

Diabetes insipidus is a polyuric disorder resulting from insufficient production of antidiuretic hormone (ADH) (pituitary [neurogenic] diabetes insipidus) or unresponsiveness of the renal tubules to ADH (nephrogenic diabetes insipidus).

ICD-9CM CODES
253.5 Diabetes insipidus

EPIDEMIOLOGY & DEMOGRAPHICS

GENETICS:

- Nephrogenic diabetes insipidus can be inherited as sex-linked recessive.
- There is also a rare autosomal dominant form of neurogenic diabetes insipidus.

PHYSICAL FINDINGS & CLINICAL PRESENTATION

- Polyuria: urinary volumes ranging from 2.5 to 6 L/day
- Polydipsia (predilection for cold or iced drinks)
- Neurologic manifestations (seizures, headaches, visual field defects)
- Evidence of volume contractions

NOTE: The previous physical findings and clinical manifestations are generally not evident until vasopressin secretory capacity is reduced <20% of normal.

ETIOLOGY

NEUROGENIC DIABETES INSIPIDUS:

- Idiopathic
- Neoplasms of brain or pituitary fossa (craniopharyngiomas, metastatic neoplasms from breast or lung)
- Posttherapeutic neurosurgical procedures (e.g., hypophysectomy)
- Head trauma (e.g., basal skull fracture)
- Granulomatous disorders (sarcoidosis or TB)
- Histiocytosis (Hand-Schüller-Christian disease, eosinophilic granuloma)
- Familial (autosomal dominant)
- Other: interventricular hemorrhage, aneurysms, meningitis, postencephalitis, multiple sclerosis

NEPHROGENIC DIABETES INSIPIDUS:

- Drugs: lithium, amphotericin B, demeclocycline, methoxyflurane anesthesia
- Familial: X-linked
- Metabolic: hypercalcemia or hypokalemia
- Other: sarcoidosis, amyloidosis, pyelonephritis, polycystic disease, sickle cell disease, postobstructive

DIAGNOSIS

DIFFERENTIAL DIAGNOSIS

- Diabetes mellitus, nephropathies
- Primary polydipsia, medications (e.g., chlorpromazine)
- Osmotic diuresis (glucose, mannitol, anticholinergics)
- Psychogenic polydipsia, electrolyte disturbances

WORKUP

- The diagnostic workup is aimed at showing that the polyuria is caused by the inability to concentrate urine and determining whether the problem is secondary to decreased ADH or insensitivity to ADH. This is done with the water deprivation test:
  1. Following baseline measurement of weight, ADH, plasma sodium, and urine and plasma osmolarity, the patient is deprived of fluids under strict medical supervision.
  2. Frequent (q2h) monitoring of plasma and urine osmolarity follows.
  3. The test is generally terminated when plasma osmolarity is >295 or the patient loses ≥3.5% of initial body weight.
  4. Diabetes insipidus is confirmed if the plasma osmolarity is >295 and the urine osmolarity is <500.
  5. To distinguish nephrogenic from neurogenic diabetes insipidus, the patient is given 5 U of vasopressin (ADH) and the change in urine osmolarity is measured. A significant increase (>50%) in urine osmolarity following administration of ADH is indicative of neurogenic diabetes insipidus.
- A diagnostic algorithm for diabetes insipidus is described in Section III.

LABORATORY TESTS

- Decreased urinary specific gravity (≤1.005)
- Decreased urinary osmolarity (usually <200 mOsm/kg) even in the presence of high serum osmolality
- Hypernatremia, increased plasma osmolarity, hypercalcemia, hypokalemia

IMAGING STUDIES

MRI of the brain if neurogenic diabetes insipidus is confirmed

TREATMENT

NONPHARMACOLOGIC THERAPY

- Patient education regarding control of fluid balance and prevention of dehydration with adequate fluid intake
- Daily weight

ACUTE GENERAL Rx

Therapy varies with the degree and type of diabetes insipidus:

NEUROGENIC DIABETES INSIPIDUS:

1. Desmopressin acetate (DDAVP) 10 to 40 μg qd intranasally in one to three divided doses or in tablet form 0.1 or 0.2 mg. Usual oral dose is 0.1 to 1.2 mg/day in two to three divided doses Desmopressin is also available in injectable form given as 2 to 4 μg/day SC or IV in two divided doses
2. Vasopressin tannate in oil: 2.5 to 5 U IM q24-72h; useful for long-term management because of its long life
3. In mild cases of neurogenic diabetes insipidus, the polyuria may be controlled with HCTZ 50 mg qd (decreases urine volume by increasing proximal tubular reabsorption of glomerular infiltrate) or chlorpropamide (Diabinese) 100-250 mg qd; enhances the effect of vasopressin at the renal tubule

NEPHROGENIC DIABETES INSIPIDUS:

1. Adequate hydration
2. Low-sodium diet and chlorothiazide to induce mild sodium depletion
3. Polyuria of diabetes insipidus secondary to lithium can be ameliorated by using amiloride (5 mg PO bid initially, increased to 10 mg bid after 2 wk)

CHRONIC Rx

Patients should be aware of the danger of dehydration and the need for liberal water intake.

REFERRAL

Endocrinology evaluation for diagnostic testing

PEARLS & CONSIDERATIONS

COMMENTS

Patients should be instructed to wear a medical identification tag or bracelet identifying their medical illness.

SUGGESTED READING

Maghnie M et al: Central diabetes insipidus in children and young adults, *N Engl J Med* 343:998, 2000.

AUTHOR: **FRED F. FERRI, M.D.**

BASIC INFORMATION

DEFINITION

- Diabetes mellitus (DM) refers to a syndrome of hyperglycemia resulting from many different causes (see Etiology). It can be classified into type 1 (formerly IDDM) and type 2 (formerly NIDDM) DM. Because "insulin-dependent" and "non–insulin-dependent" refer to stage at diagnosis, when a type 2 diabetic needs insulin, he or she remains classified as type 2 and does not revert to type 1. Table 1-11 provides a general comparison of the two types of diabetes mellitus.
- The American Diabetes Association (ADA) defines DM as (1) a fasting plasma glucose ≥126 mg/dl or (2) a nonfasting plasma glucose ≥200 mg/dl or (3) an oral glucose tolerance test (OGTT) ≥200 mg/dl in the 2-hr sample. Furthermore, the ADA also defines a value of 110 mg/dl on fasting blood sugar as the upper limit of normal for glucose. A fasting glucose between 110 mg/dl and 126 mg/dl is classified as "Impaired Fasting Glucose" (IFG). When results of the oral glucose test are between 110 mg/dl and 200 mg/dl, the patient is also classified as having IFG.

SYNONYMS

IDDM (insulin-dependent diabetes mellitus)
NIDDM (non–insulin-dependent diabetes mellitus)
Type 1 diabetes mellitus (insulin-dependent diabetes mellitus)
Type 2 diabetes mellitus (non-insulin-dependent diabetes mellitus)

ICD-9CM CODES
250.0 Diabetes mellitus (NIDDM)
250.1 Insulin-dependent diabetes mellitus without complication (IDDM)

EPIDEMIOLOGY & DEMOGRAPHICS

- DM affects 5% to 7% of the U.S. population. Prevalence in Pima Indians is 35%.
- Incidence increases with age, with 2% in persons ages 20 to 44 yr to 18% in persons 65 to 74 yr of age.
- Diabetes accounts for 8% of all legal blindness and is the leading cause of end-stage renal disease in the U.S.
- Patients with diabetes are twice as likely as nondiabetic patients to develop cardiovascular disease.

PHYSICAL FINDINGS & CLINICAL PRESENTATION

1. Physical examination varies with the presence of complications and may be normal in early stages.
2. Diabetic retinopathy:
   a. Nonproliferative (background diabetic retinopathy):
      (1) Initially: microaneurysms, capillary dilation, waxy or hard exudates, dot and flame hemorrhages, AV shunts
      (2) Advanced stage: microinfarcts with cotton wool exudates, macular edema
   b. Proliferative retinopathy: characterized by formation of new vessels, vitreal hemorrhages, fibrous scarring, and retinal detachment
3. Cataracts and glaucoma occur with increased frequency in diabetics.
4. Peripheral neuropathy: patients often complain of paresthesias of extremities (feet more than hands); the symptoms are symmetric, bilateral, and associated with intense burning pain (particularly during the night).
   a. Mononeuropathies involving cranial nerves III, IV, and VI, intercostal nerves, and femoral nerves are also common.

TABLE 1-11 General Comparison of the Two Most Common Types of Diabetes Mellitus

	Type 1	Type 2
Previous terminology	Insulin-dependent diabetes mellitus (IDDM), type I, juvenile-onset diabetes	Non–insulin-dependent diabetes mellitus, type II, adult-onset diabetes
Age of onset	Usually <30 yr, particularly childhood and adolescence, but any age	Usually >40 yr, but any age
Genetic predisposition	Moderate; environmental factors required for expression; 35%-50% concordance in monozygotic twins; several candidate genes proposed	Strong; 60%-90% concordance in monozygotic twins; many candidate genes proposed; some genes identified in maturity-onset diabetes of the young
Human leukocyte antigen associations	Linkage to DQA and DQB, influenced by DRB (3 and 4) [DR2 protective]	None known
Other associations	Autoimmune; Graves' disease, Hashimoto's thyroiditis, vitiligo, Addison's disease, pernicious anemia	Heterogenous group, ongoing subclassification based on identification of specific pathogenic processes and genetic defects
Precipitating and risk factors	Largely unknown; microbial, chemical, dietary, other	Age, obesity (central), sedentary lifestyle, previous gestational diabetes
Findings at diagnosis	85%-90% of patients have one and usually more autoantibodies to ICA512/IA-2/IA-2β, GAD_{65}, insulin (IAA)	Possibly complications (microvascular and macrovascular) caused by significant preceeding asymptomatic period
Endogenous insulin levels	Low or absent	Usually present (relative deficiency), early hyperinsulinemia
Insulin resistance	Only with hyperglycemia	Mostly present
Prolonged fast	Hyperglycemia, ketoacidosis	Euglycemia
Stress, withdrawal of insulin	Ketoacidosis	Nonketotic hyperglycemia, occasionally ketoacidosis

From Andreoli TE (ed): *Cecil essentials of medicine,* ed 5, Philadelphia, 2001, WB Saunders.
GAD, Glutamic acid decarboxylase; *IA-2/IA-2β,* tyrosine phosphatases; *IAA,* insulin autoantibodies; *ICA,* islet cell antibody; *ICA512,* islet cell autoantigen 512 (fragment of IA-2).

b. Physical examination may reveal:
   (1) Decreased pinprick sensation, sensation to light touch, and pain sensation
   (2) Decreased vibration sense
   (3) Loss of proprioception (leading to ataxia)
   (4) Motor disturbances (decreased DTR, weakness and atrophy of interossei muscles); when the hands are affected, the patient has trouble picking up small objects, dressing, and turning pages in a book
   (5) Diplopia, abnormalities of visual fields
5. Autonomic neuropathy:
   a. GI disturbances: esophageal motility abnormalities, gastroparesis, diarrhea (usually nocturnal)
   b. GU disturbances: neurogenic bladder (hesitancy, weak stream, and dribbling), impotence
   c. Orthostatic hypotension: postural syncope, dizziness, lightheadedness
6. Nephropathy: pedal edema, pallor, weakness, uremic appearance. Neuropathy can be detected with a simple exam of the lower extremities using a 10-g monofilament to test sensation.
7. Foot ulcers: occur frequently and are usually secondary to peripheral vascular insufficiency, repeated trauma (unrecognized because of sensory loss), and superimposed infections. If a diabetic foot ulcer has been present for weeks and foot pulses are palpable, neuropathy should be considered a major cause.
8. Neuropathic arthropathy (Charcot's joints): bone or joint deformities from repeated trauma (secondary to peripheral neuropathy).
9. Necrobiosis lipoidica diabeticorum: plaquelike reddened areas with a central area that fades to white-yellow found on the anterior surfaces of the legs; in these areas the skin becomes very thin and can ulcerate readily.

ETIOLOGY

IDIOPATHIC DIABETES:

Type 1 DM
- Hereditary factors:
  1. Islet cell antibodies (found in 90% of patients within the first year of diagnosis)
  2. Higher incidence of HLA types DR3, DR4
  3. 50% concordance in identical twins
- Environmental factors: viral infection (possibly coxsackie virus, mumps virus)

Type 2 DM
- Hereditary factors: 90% concordance in identical twins
- Environmental factor: obesity

DIABETES SECONDARY TO OTHER FACTORS:
- Hormonal excess: Cushing's syndrome, acromegaly, glucagonoma, pheochromocytoma
- Drugs: glucocorticoids, diuretics, oral contraceptives
- Insulin receptor unavailability (with or without circulating antibodies)
- Pancreatic disease: pancreatitis, pancreatectomy, hemochromatosis
- Genetic syndromes: hyperlipidemias, myotonic dystrophy, lipoatrophy
- Gestational diabetes

DIAGNOSIS

Diagnosis is made on the basis of the following tests and should be confirmed by repeated testing on a different day:
1. Fasting glucose ≥126 mg/dl (ADA criteria)
2. Nonfasting plasma glucose ≥200 mg/dl

Use of glycosylated hemoglobin (Hb A1c) level is not recommended for diagnosis at this time by the ADA because of lack of standardization of hemoglobin Alc values and the imperfect correlation between HbAlc and fasting plasma glucose levels. However, some physicians use this test to make the diagnosis of diabetes mellitus if the random plasma glucose is >200 mg/dl and the hemoglobin Alc level is ≥2 standard deviations above the laboratory mean.

DIFFERENTIAL DIAGNOSIS
- Diabetes insipidus
- Stress hyperglycemia
- Diabetes secondary to hormonal excess, drugs, pancreatic disease

TREATMENT

NONPHARMACOLOGIC THERAPY

1. Diet
   a. Calories
      (1) The diabetic patient can be started on 15 calories/lb of ideal body weight; this number can be increased to 20 calories/lb for an active person and 25 calories/lb if the patient does heavy physical labor.
      (2) The calories should be distributed as 55% to 60% carbohydrates, 25% to 35% fat, and 15% to 20% protein.
      (3) The emphasis should be on complex carbohydrates rather than simple and refined starches and on polyunsaturated instead of saturated fats in a ratio of 2:1.
   b. Seven food groups
      (1) The exchange diet of the ADA includes protein, bread, fruit, milk, and low- and intermediate-carbohydrate vegetables.
      (2) The name of each exchange is meant to be all-inclusive (e.g., cereal, muffins, spaghetti, potatoes, rice are in the bread group; meats, fish, eggs, cheese, peanut butter are in the protein group).
      (3) The *glycemic index* compares the rise in blood sugar after the ingestion of simple sugars and complex carbohydrates with the rise that occurs after the absorption of glucose; equal amounts of starches do not give the same rise in plasma glucose (pasta equal in calories to a baked potato causes less of a rise than the potato): thus it is helpful to know the glycemic index of a particular food product.
      (4) Fiber: insoluble fiber (bran, celery) and soluble globular fiber (pectin in fruit) delay glucose absorption and attenuate the postprandial serum glucose peak; they also appear to lower the elevated triglyceride level often present in uncontrolled diabetics.
2. Exercise increases the cellular glucose uptake by increasing the number of cell receptors. The following points must be considered:
   a. Exercise program must be individualized and built up slowly.
   b. Insulin is more rapidly absorbed when injected into a limb that is then exercised, and this can result in hypoglycemia.
3. Weight loss: to ideal body weight if the patient is overweight

PHARMACOLOGIC THERAPY

- When the previous measures fail to normalize the serum glucose, oral hypoglycemic agents (e.g., metformin, glitazones, or a sulfonylurea) should be added to the regimen in type 2 DM. Table 1-12 describes commonly used oral hypoglycemic agents. The sulfonamides and the biguanide metformin are the oldest and most commonly used classes of hypoglycemic drugs.
- Metformin's primary mechanism is to decrease hepatic glucose output. Because metformin does not produce hypoglycemia when used as a monotherapy, it is preferred for most patients. It is contraindicated in patients with renal insufficiency.
- Sulfonylureas and repaglinide work best when given before meals because they increase the postprandial output of insulin from the pancreas. All sulfonylureas are contraindicated in patients allergic to sulfa.
- Acarbose and miglitol work by competitively inhibiting pancreatic amylase and small intestinal glucosidases delay gastrointestinal absorption of carbohydrates, thereby reducing alimentary hyperglycemia. The major side effects are flatulence, diarrhea, and abdominal cramps.
- Pioglitazone and rosiglitazone increase insulin sensitivity and are useful in addition to other agents in type 2 diabetics whose hyperglycemia is inadequately controlled. Serum transaminase levels should be obtained before starting therapy and monitored periodically.
- Insulin is indicated for the treatment of all type 1 DM and type 2 DM patients who cannot be adequately controlled with diet and oral agents. Table 1-13 describes commonly used types of insulin. The risks of insulin therapy include weight gain, hypoglycemia, and, in rare cases, allergic or cutaneous reactions. Replacement insulin therapy should mimic normal release patterns. Approximately 50% to 60% of daily insulin should be a basal type consisting of a long acting insulin (NPH, ultralente, glargine) injected once or twice daily, the remaining 40% to 50% should be short acting or rapid acting insulin (regular, aspart, lispro) to cover mealtime carbohydrates and correct elevated current glucose levels. Among long acting insulins, once-daily bed-

TABLE 1-12 Oral Antidiabetic Agents as Monotherapy

	Sulfonylureas	Biguanides	α-Glucosidase inhibitors	Thiazolidinediones	Meglitinides
Generic name	Glimepiride, glyburide, glipizide, chlorpropamide, tolbutamide	Metformin	Acarbose, miglitol	Troglitazone, rosiglitazone, pioglitazone	Repaglinide, nateglinide
Mode of action	↑↑ Pancreatic insulin secretion chronically	↓↓ HGP; ↓ peripheral IR; ↓ intestinal glucose absorption	Delays PP digestion of carbohydrates and absorption of glucose	↓↓ Peripheral IR; ↑↑ glucose disposal; ↓ HGP	↑↑ Pancreatic insulin secretion acutely
Preferred patient type	Diagnosis age >30 yr, lean, diabetes <5 yr, insulinopenic	Overweight, IR, fasting hyperglycemia, dyslipidemia	PP hyperglycemia	Overweight, IR, dyslipidemia, renal dysfunction	PP hyperglycemia, insulinopenic
Therapeutic effects					
↓ HBA_{1c}* (%)	1-2	1-2	0.5-1	0.8-1	1-2
↓ FPG* (mg/dl)	50-70	50-80	15-30	25-50	40-80
↓ PPG* (mg/dl)	~90	80	40-50	—	30
Insulin levels	↑	—	—	—	↑
Weight	↑	–/↓	—	–/↑	↑
Lipids	—	↓ LDL ↓↓ TG		↑ Large "fluffy" LDL ↓↓ TG ↑ HDL	—
Side effects	Hypoglycemia	Diarrhea, lactic acidosis	Abdominal pain, flatulence, diarrhea	Idiosyncratic hepatotoxicity with troglitazone; edema	Hypoglycemia (low-risk)
Dose(s)/day	1-3	2-3	1-3	1	1-4+
Maximum daily dose (mg)	Depends on agent	2550	150 (<60-kg bw) 300 (>60-kg bw)	Depends on agent	16 (repaglinide), 360 (nateglinide)
Range/dose (mg)	Depends on agent	500-1000	25-50 (<60-kg bw) 25-100 (>60-kg bw)	Depends on agent	0.5-4 (repaglinide), 60, 120 (nateglinide)
Optimal administration time	~30 min premeal (some with food, others on empty stomach)	With meal	With first bite of meal	With meal (breakfast)	Preferably <15 (0-30 min) premeals (omit if no meal)
Main site of metabolism/excretion	Hepatic/renal, fecal	Not metabolized/renal	Only 2% absorbed/fecal	Hepatic/fecal	Hepatic/fecal

Modified from Andreloi TE (ed): *Cecil essentials of medicine*, ed 5, Philadelphia, 2001, WB Saunders.

↑, Increased; ↓, decreased; —, unchanged; *bw*, body weight; *FPG*, fasting plasma glucose; *HDL*, high-density lipoprotein; *HGP*, hepatic glucose production; *IR*, insulin resistance; *LDL*, low-density lipoprotein; *PP*, postprandial; *PPG*, postprandial plasma glucose; *TG*, triglyceride.

*Values combined from numerous studies; values are also dose dependent.

TABLE 1-13 Types of Insulin

Insulin type	Generic name	Preprandial injection timing* (hr)	Onset* (hr)	Peak* (hr)	Duration* (hr)	Blood glucose (BG) nadir* (hr)
Rapid acting	Lispro†	0-0.2	0.2-0.5	0.5-2	<5	2-4
Short acting	Regular	0.5-(1)	0.3-1	2-6	4-8 (≤16)	3-7 (Pre-next meal)
	Lente		1-2	4-12		
Intermediate acting	NPH	0.5-(1)	1-3	6-15	16-26	6-13
Long acting‡	Ultralente	0.5-(1)	4-6	8-30	24-36	10-28
Mixed, short/intermediate acting	70/30					
	50/50	0.5-(1)	0.5-1	3-12	16-24	3-12

From Andreoli TE (ed): ***Cecil essentials of medicine,*** ed 5, Philadelphia, 2001, WB Saunders.
70/30, 70% NPH, 30% regular; ***50/50,*** 50% NPH, 50% regular; ***NPH,*** neutral protamine Hagedorn.
*Times depend on several factors including dose, anatomic site of injection, method (SQ, IM, IV), duration of diabetes, degree of insulin resistance, level of activity, and body temperature. Some time ranges are wide to include data from several separate studies. Preprandial injection depends on premeal BG values as well as insulin type. If BG is low, may need to inject insulin and eat immediately (carbohydrate portion of meal first). If BG is high, may delay meal after insulin injection and eat carbohydrate portion last.
†Insulin analogue with reversal of lysine and proline at positions 28 and 29 on the β chain.
‡Insulin glargine [rDNA origin] is a newer, once-daily insulin analog (Lantus) that provides 24-hour basal glucose-lowering with once-a-day bedtime dosing. Onset of action is 2-3 hr, duration of action is 24+ hr.

time insulin glargine is as effective as once- or twice-daily NPH but has a lower risk of nocturnal hypoglycemia and less weight gain. When using short acting insulins, insulin aspart and insulin lispro are more effective in lowering postprandial glucose levels than regular insulin.

- Combination therapy of various hypoglycemic agents is commonly used when monotherapy results in inadequate glycemic control.
- Continuous subcutaneous insulin infusion (CSII, or insulin pump) provides better glycemic control than does conventional therapy and comparable to or slightly better control than multiple daily injections. It should be considered for diabetes presenting in childhood or adolescence and during pregnancy.
- Low-dose ASA to decrease the risk of cerebrovascular disease is beneficial for diabetics over age 30 with other risk factors (hypertension, dyslipidemia, smoking, obesity).
- A fasting serum lipid panel should be obtained yearly on all adult diabetic patients. Strict lipid control (LDL <70 mg/dl) is indicated in all diabetics. Use of statins is often necessary to achieve therapeutic goals.

DISPOSITION

The Diabetes Control and Complications Trial (DCCT) proved that intensive treatment decreases the development and progression of complications of DM. In this trial, the risks of retinopathy, nephropathy, and neuropathy were decreased by 35% to 90%. Each patient should be made aware of these findings.

- Retinopathy occurs in approximately 15% of diabetic patients after 15 yr and increases 1%/yr after diagnosis.
- The frequency of neuropathy in type 2 diabetics approaches 70% to 80%. Gabapentin (900-3600 mg/day) is effective for the symptomatic treatment of peripheral neuropathic pain. Amitriptyline or carbamazepine are also modestly effective.
- Nephropathy occurs in 35% to 45% of patients with type 1 DM and in 20% of type 2 DM. The first sign of renal involvement in patients with DM is most often microalbuminuria, which is classified as incipient nephropathy. ACE inhibitors are effective in slowing the progression of renal disease in both type I and type II DM, independently of their reduction in blood pressure. ARBs and nondihydropyridine calcium channel blockers are also effective in protecting against the progression of nephropathy in diabetics, especially in type 2 DM.
- Infections are generally more common in diabetics because of multiple factors, such as impaired leukocyte function, decreased tissue perfusion secondary to vascular disease, repeated trauma because of loss of sensation, and urinary retention secondary to neuropathy.
- Diabetic ketoacidosis and hyperosmolar coma are described in detail in Section I.

REFERRAL

- Diabetic patients should be advised to have annual ophthalmologic examination. In type 1 DM, ophthalmologic visits should begin within 3 to 5 yr, whereas type 2 DM patients should be seen from disease onset.
- Podiatric care can significantly reduce the rate of foot infections and amputations in patients with DM. Noninfected neuropathic foot ulcers require debridement and reduction of pressure.

PEARLS & CONSIDERATIONS

COMMENTS

- Because normalization of serum glucose level is the ultimate goal, every patient should measure his or her blood glucose unless contraindicated by senility or blindness.
- For blood glucose monitoring, glucose oxidase strips are used in conjunction with a meter to give a digital reading. The testing can be done once day, but the time should be varied each day so that over time the serum glucose level before meals and at bedtime can be assessed frequently without pricking the patient's fingers four times daily.
- Glycosylated hemoglobin should be measured at least twice yearly; measurement of microalbumin in the urine on a yearly basis is also recommended.
- Creatining and serum-lipid panel should be obtained at least yearly in patients with diabetes.
- Underinsured children and those with psychiatric illness are at higher risk for acute complications in type 1 DM and require frequent monitoring and aggressive risk management with diet, exercise, and periodic laboratory evaluation.

SUGGESTED READINGS

American Diabetes Association Position Statement: Standards of medical care for patients with diabetes mellitus, *Diabetes Care* 25:S33, 2002.

Barr RG et al: Tests of glycemia for the diagnosis of type 2 diabetes mellitus, *Ann Intern Med* 137:263, 2002.

Beckman JA et al: Diabetes and atherosclerosis, *JAMA* 287:2570, 2002.

Boulton AJM et al: Neuropathic diabetic foot ulcers, *N Engl J Med* 351:48, 2004.

DeWitt DE, Hirsch IB: Outpatient insulin therapy in type 1 and type 2 DM, *JAMA* 289:2254, 2003.

Diabetes Control and Complications Trial (DCCT)/Epidemiology of Diabetes Interventions and Complications (EDIC) Research Group: Beneficial effects of intensive therapy of diabetes during adolescence: outcomes after the conclusion of the Diabetes Control and Complications Trial (DCCT), *J Pediatr* 139:804, 2001.

Diabetes Control and Complications Trial/ Epidemiology of Diabetes Interventions and Complications Research Group: Effect of intensive therapy on the microvascular complications of type 1 diabetes mellitus, *JAMA* 287:2563, 2002.

Holmboe ES: Oral antihyperglycemic therapy for type 2 diabetes, *JAMA* 287:373, 2002.

Mayfield J, White R: Insulin therapy for type 2 DM: Rescue, augmentation, and replacement of Beta cell function, *Am Fam Physician* 70:489, 2004.

Nathan DM: Initial management of glycemia in type 2 diabetes mellitus, *N Engl J Med* 347:1342, 2002.

Pickup J et al: Glycemic control with continuous subcutaneous insulin infusion compared with intensive insulin injections with type 1 diabetes: meta-analysis of randomized controlled trials, *BMJ* 324:705, 2002.

Remuzzi G et al: Nephropathy in patients with type 2 diabetes, *N Engl J Med* 346:1145, 2002.

Stern MP et al: Identification of persons at high risk for type 2 diabetes mellitus: do we need the oral glucose tolerance test? *Ann Intern Med* 136:575, 2002.

U.S. Preventive Services Task Force: Screening for type 2 DM in adults: recommendations and rationale, *Ann Intern Med* 138:212, 2003.

Zandbergen AM et al: Effect of losartan on microalbuminuria in normotensive patients with type 2 DM, *Ann Intern Med* 139:90, 2003.

AUTHOR: **FRED F. FERRI, M.D.**

BASIC INFORMATION

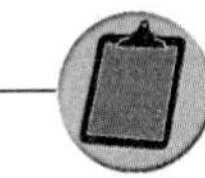

DEFINITION

Diabetic ketoacidosis (DKA) is a life-threatening complication of diabetes mellitus resulting from severe insulin deficiency and manifested clinically by severe dehydration and alterations in the sensorium.

SYNONYMS

DKA

ICD-9CM CODES

250.1 Diabetic ketoacidosis

EPIDEMIOLOGY & DEMOGRAPHICS

INCIDENCE/PREVALENCE: 46 episodes/10,000 diabetics; cause of 14% of all hospital admissions of diabetic patients
PREDOMINANT AGE: 1 to 25 yr

PHYSICAL FINDINGS & CLINICAL PRESENTATION

- Evidence of dehydration (tachycardia, hypotension, dry mucous membranes, sunken eyeballs, poor skin turgor)
- Clouding of mental status
- Tachypnea with air hunger (Kussmaul's respiration)
- Fruity breath odor (caused by acetone)
- Lipemia retinalis in some patients
- Possible evidence of precipitating factors (infected wound, pneumonia)
- Abdominal or CVA tenderness in some patients

ETIOLOGY

Metabolic decompensation in diabetics usually precipitated by an infectious process (up to 40% of cases). Poor compliance with insulin therapy and severe medical illness (e.g., CVA, MI) are other common causes. Cocaine abuse has been reported as a risk factor for DKA, particularly in patients with multiple admissions.

DIAGNOSIS

DIFFERENTIAL DIAGNOSIS

- Hyperosmolar nonketotic state (Table 1-14)
- Alcoholic ketoacidosis
- Uremic acidosis
- Metabolic acidosis secondary to methyl alcohol, ethylene glycol
- Salicylate poisoning

WORKUP

- Laboratory evaluation (see Laboratory Tests) to confirm diagnosis and evaluate precipitating factors
- Admission ECG to evaluate electrolyte abnormalities and rule out myocardial ischemia/infarction as a contributing factor

LABORATORY TESTS

- Glucose level reveals severe hyperglycemia (serum glucose generally >300 mg/dl).
- ABGs reveal acidosis: arterial pH usually <7.3 with Pco_2 <40 mm Hg.
- Serum electrolytes:
  1. Serum bicarbonate is usually <15 mEq/L.
  2. Serum potassium may be low, normal, or high. There is always significant total body potassium depletion regardless of the initial potassium level.
  3. Serum sodium is usually decreased as a result of hyperglycemia, dehydration, and lipemia. Assume 1.6 mEq/L decrease in extracellular sodium for each 100 mg/dl increase in glucose concentration.
  4. Calculate the anion gap (AG):

$$AG = Na^+ - (Cl^- + HCO^{-3})$$

In DKA the anion gap is increased; hyperchloremic metabolic acidosis may be present in unusual circumstances when both the glomerular filtration rate and the plasma volume are well maintained.

- CBC with differential, urinalysis, urine and blood cultures to rule out infectious precipitating factor.
- Serum calcium, magnesium, and phosphorus; the plasma phosphate and magnesium levels may be significantly depressed and should be rechecked within 24 hr because they may decrease further with correction of DKA.
- BUN and creatinine generally reveal significant dehydration.
- Amylase, liver enzymes should be checked in patients with abdominal pain.

TABLE 1-14 **A Comparison of Diabetic Ketoacidosis (DKA) and Hyperosmolar Nonketotic Syndrome (HNKS)**

Feature	DKA	HNKS
Age of patient	Usually <40 yr	Usually >60 yr
Duration of symptoms	Usually <2 days	Usually >5 days
Serum glucose concentration	Usually <800 mg/dl	Usually >800 mg/dl
Serum sodium concentration (Na^+)	More likely to be normal or low	More likely to be normal or high
Serum bicarbonate concentration (HCO_3^-)	Low	Normal
Ketone bodies	At least 4 + in 1:1 dilution	<2 + in 1:1 dilution
pH	Low	Normal
Serum osmolality	Usually <350 mOsm/kg	Usually >350 mOsm/kg
Cerebral edema	Occasionally clinical symptoms	Rarely (never?) clinical
Prognosis	3% to 10% mortality	10% to 20% mortality
Subsequent course	Insulin therapy required in almost all cases	Insulin therapy not required in most cases

From Andreoli TE (ed): *Cecil essentials of medicine*, ed 5, Philadelphia, 2001, WB Saunders.

IMAGING STUDIES

Chest x-ray is helpful to rule out infectious process. The initial chest x-ray may be negative if the patient has significant dehydration. Repeat chest x-ray examination after 24 hr if pulmonary infection is strongly suspected.

TREATMENT

NONPHARMACOLOGIC THERAPY

- Monitor mental status, vital signs, and urine output qh until improved, then monitor q2-4h.
- Monitor electrolytes, renal function, and glucose level (see Acute General Rx).

ACUTE GENERAL Rx

FLUID REPLACEMENT (THE USUAL DEFICIT IS 6 TO 8 L)

1. Do not delay fluid replacement until laboratory results have been received.
2. The initial fluid replacement should be with 0.9% NS until blood pressure and organ perfusion are restored (usually 1 L or more). In patients with severe hypernatremia (serum sodium > 160 mEq/L), 0.45 % saline infusion can be used. Careful monitoring for fluid overload is necessary in elderly patients and those with a history of CHF.
3. The rate of fluid replacement varies with the age of the patient and the presence of significant cardiac or renal disease.
   - The usual rate of infusion is 500 ml to 1 L over the first hour; 300 to 500 ml/hr for the next 12 hr.
   - Continue the infusion at a rate of 200 to 300 ml/hr, using 0.45% NS until the serum glucose level is <300 ml/dl, then change the hydrating solution to D_5W to prevent hypoglycemia, replenish free water, and introduce additional glucose substrate (necessary to suppress lipolysis and ketogenesis).

INSULIN ADMINISTRATION

1. The patient should be given an initial loading IV bolus of 0.15 to 0.2 U/kg of regular insulin followed by a constant infusion at a rate of 0.1 U/kg/hr (e.g., 25 U of regular insulin in 250 ml of 0.9% saline solution at 70 ml/hr equals 7 U/hr for a 70-kg patient).
2. Monitor serum glucose qh for the first 2 hr, then monitor q2-4h.
3. The goal is to decrease serum glucose level by 80 mg/dl/hr (following an initial drop because of rehydration); if the serum glucose level is not decreasing at the expected rate, double the rate of insulin infusion.
4. When the serum glucose level approaches 250 mg/dl, decrease the rate of insulin infusion to 2 to 3 U/hr and continue this rate until the patient has received adequate fluid replacement, HCO^-_3 is close to normal, and ketones have cleared.
5. Approximately 30 to 60 min before stopping the IV insulin infusion, administer an SC dose of regular insulin (dose varies with the patient's demonstrated insulin sensitivity); this SC dose of regular insulin is necessary because of the extremely short life of the insulin in the IV infusion.
6. When the patient is able to eat, NPH insulin 10-15 U is given in the morning and regular insulin is administered before each meal and at bedtime by using a sliding scale. In newly diagnosed diabetics, the total daily dose to maintain metabolic control ranges from 0.5 to 0.8 U/kg/day. Split dose therapy with regular and NPH insulin may be given, with two thirds of the total daily dose administered in the morning and one third in the evening.

ELECTROLYTE REPLACEMENT

Potassium Replacement: The average total potassium loss in DKA is 300 to 500 mEq.

- The rate of replacement varies with the patient's serum potassium level, degree of acidosis (decreased pH, increased potassium level), and renal function (potassium replacement should be used with caution in patients with renal failure).
- As a rule of thumb, potassium replacement may be started when there is no ECG evidence of hyperkalemia (tall, narrow, or tent-shaped T waves, decreased or absent P waves, short QT intervals, widening of QRS complex).
- In patients with normal renal function, potassium replacement can be started by adding 20 to 40 mEq KCl/L of IV hydrating solution if serum potassium is 4 to 5 mEq/L, more if serum potassium level is lower than 4 mEq/L.
- Monitor serum potassium level qh for the first 2 hr, then monitor q2-4h.

Phosphate Replacement: If the serum PO_4 is <1.5 mEq/L, give 2.5 mg/kg IV over 6 hr of elemental phosphate. Routine replacement of phosphate (in absence of laboratory evidence of significant hypophosphatemia) is not indicated. Rapid IV phosphate administration can cause hypocalcemia.

Magnesium Replacement: Replacement indicated only in the presence of significant hypomagnesemia or refractory hypokalemia.

BICARBONATE THERAPY: Routine use of bicarbonate in DKA is contraindicated, because it can worsen hypokalemia and intracellular acidosis and cause cerebral edema. Bicarbonate therapy should be used only if the arterial pH is <7. In these patients 44 to 88 mEq of sodium bicarbonate can be added to a liter of 0.45% NS q2-4h until pH increases >7. Use of bicarbonate therapy is particularly dangerous in the pediatric population. Children with DKA who have low partial pressures of arterial carbon dioxide and high serum urea nitrogen concentration at presentation and who are treated with bicarbonate are at increased risk for cerebral edema. Bicarbonate therapy in children with DKA should be limited to those with severe circulatory failure and a high risk of cardiac decompensation resulting from profound acidosis.

DISPOSITION

- Average mortality in DKA is 5% to 10%.
- In children <10 yr of age, DKA causes 70% of diabetes-related deaths.
- Cerebral edema occurs in 1% of episodes of DKA in children and is associated with a mortality rate of 40% to 90%.

REFERRAL

Patients with DKA should be admitted to the ICU.

PEARLS & CONSIDERATIONS

COMMENTS

- Although DKA occurs more commonly in type 1 DM, a significant proportion (>20%) occurs in patients with type 2 DM.
- 20% of DKA admissions involve newly diagnosed diabetes.
- Potential complications of DKA therapy include hypoglycemia, cerebral edema, cardiac arrhythmias, shock, MI, and acute pancreatitis.
- Underinsured children and those with psychiatric illness are at higher risk for DKA.

SUGGESTED READINGS

Glaser N et al: Risk factor for cerebral edema in children with diabetic ketoacidosis, *N Engl J Med* 344:264, 2001.

Newton CA, Raskin P: Diabetic ketoacidosis in type 1 and type 2 diabetes mellitus, *N Engl J Med* 164:1925, 2004.

AUTHOR: **FRED F. FERRI, M.D.**

BASIC INFORMATION

DEFINITION

Diabetic polyneuropathy (DPN) is an insidious and progressive length-dependent disorder of peripheral nerves (large, small, and autonomic fibers) that is secondary to diabetes and is characterized by distal and symmetric pain, numbness, tingling, and/or autonomic dysfunction. Other diabetic neuropathies may present with proximal and/or asymmetric pain and weakness.

SYNONYMS

Chronic distal symmetric polyneuropathy, diabetic neuropathy

ICD-9CM CODES
250.6 Diabetic polyneuropathy

EPIDEMIOLOGY & DEMOGRAPHICS

PREVALENCE (IN U.S.): 7.5% of diabetic patients at initial diagnosis and 40% (patients with type II diabetes) after 10 years of diabetes. Overall, 10%-64% of all diabetic patients.

PREDOMINANT SEX: Male diabetic patients have a higher incidence than female diabetic patients.

PREDOMINANT AGE: More common in patients older than 50 years of age.

PHYSICAL FINDINGS & CLINICAL PRESENTATION

- Tingling, buzzing, numbness, tightness, electric shock-like, hot, cold, and/or burning sensations starting in the feet bilaterally and slowly progressing to involve the hands. The level of impairment in the legs usually reaches above the knees before the hands are affected, and in severe cases the sensory disturbances may involve the anterior trunk and the vertex of the head. Symptoms are typically worse at night.
- Some patients report difficulties in opening jars, turning keys, foot slapping, toe scuffing, difficulty with stairs, getting up from a sitting or lying position, raising their arms above the shoulders, and falling.
- Autonomic dysfunction presents as dry skin, lack of or excessive sweating, poor dark adaptation, sensitivity to bright lights, postural lightheadedness, fainting, urinary urgency, incontinence, nocturnal diarrhea, constipation, vomiting, erectile and ejaculatory dysfunction in men, and loss of ability to reach sexual climax in women.
- Examination shows decreased pinprick, light touch, temperature, vibration, and proprioceptive sensations in a stoking and/or glove distribution with absent ankle reflexes. Gait abnormalities (sensory ataxia), anhidrosis, and unreactive pupils can be seen. Muscle weakness (of the distal muscles) can be seen in later stages.

OTHER DIABETIC NEUROPATHIES

Generalized:

- Hyperglycemic neuropathy: tingling, pain, and/or hyperesthesia in the feet of a patient with poor glycemic control that rapidly resolves by improving hyperglycemia.
- Insulin neuritis: severe pain (worse at night) that is difficult to control, which is seen in patients who are on insulin.
- Chronic inflammatory demyelinating polyneuropathy (CIDP): more common in patients with type I diabetes. It differs from idiopathic CIDP in that those patients are older, imbalance is more common, duration of symptoms at time of presentation is longer, more prominent secondary axonal loss on nerve conduction studies and less response to therapy.

Focal:

- Cranial neuropathies: abrupt painless sixth or third nerve palsy. Third nerve palsy is less common than sixth and half of the patients complain of retro-orbital pain and headache. The pupil is also spared because of central rather than peripheral ischemia of the nerve fascicle. Symptoms usually resolve within 6 months.
- Somatic mononeuropathies: focal neuropathies in the extremities caused by entrapment or compression of nerves including the median at the wrist (carpal tunnel syndrome), the ulnar at the elbow, or the common peroneal at the fibular head.
- Diabetic truncal radiculoneuropathy (thoracoabdominal radiculopathy): patients present with a unilateral (later becomes bilateral) focal contact hyperesthesia and stabbing, burning, belt-like pain in the same area (worse at night), focal weakness of the anterior abdominal wall muscles, and weight loss. Sensory deficits are seen in a dermatomal distribution. Most recover within months.
- Diabetic lumbosacral radiculoplexus neuropathy (Bruns-Garland syndrome or diabetic amyotrophy): patients present with an abrupt severe unilateral low back, hip, or anterior thigh pain. Asymmetric proximal weakness and muscle atrophy develop a few days to weeks later (initially unilateral then becomes bilateral) with marked weight loss.

ETIOLOGY

- Not fully understood.
- The polyol pathway theory: high blood glucose leads to high nerve glucose, which causes overactivity of the polyol pathway and a disturbance of axoplasmic transport.
- Microvascular ischemia and hypoxia theory: hyperglycemia causes endothelial cell hypertrophy of the blood vessel walls and capillary damage, which eventually causes ischemia of the central portion of the nerve fascicle.
- Nonenzymatic glycosylation theory: increased low-density lipoproteins (LDL) promote smooth muscle proliferation and atheroma formation.

DIAGNOSIS

DIFFERENTIAL DIAGNOSIS

- Idiopathic chronic inflammatory demyelinating polyneuropathy (CIDP)
- Amyloid neuropathy
- Vasculitic neuropathy
- Sarcoid neuropathy
- Alcoholic neuropathy
- Nutritional neuropathy
- Thyroid disease
- Toxic neuropathy
- Uremic neuropathy
- Idiopathic painful neuropathy

WORKUP

- A good history demonstrating the characteristic pattern of symmetrical sensory complaints in a patient with established diabetes or with symptoms suggestive of diabetes.
- A good physical examination showing absent ankle reflexes and sensory abnormalities (all or some modalities) in a stocking and/or glove distribution.
- Nerve conduction studies: distal symmetric predominately sensory polyneuropathy with axonal features (reduced response amplitudes).
- Electromyography: denervation (positive sharp waves and fibrillations) and reinnervation (high-amplitude, long-duration, and polyphasic motor unit potentials) changes in the distal muscles.

LABORATORY TESTS

- Serum protein electrophoresis, immunofixation electrophoresis
- Antinuclear antigen (ANA), rheumatoid factor (RF), double-stranded DNA (ds-DNA), erythrocyte sedimentation rate (ESR), scl-70, anti-Ro, and anti-La to rule out other autoimmune diseases
- Thyroid function test to rule out thyroid disease
- Complete blood count, serum electrolytes, B_{12}, and folate
- Fasting blood sugar, hemoglobin A1c, and/or glucose tolerance test

TREATMENT

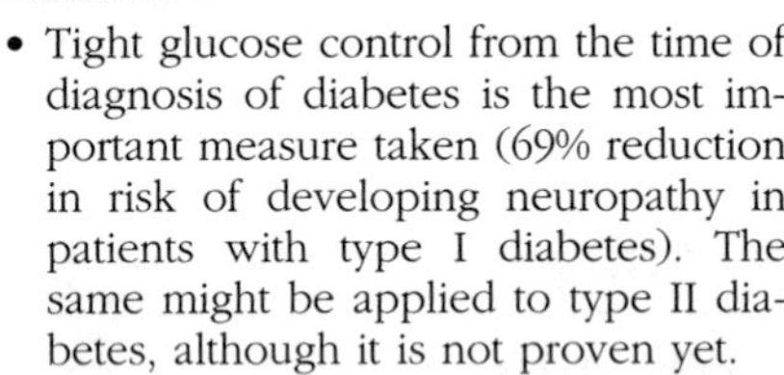

NONPHARMACOLOGIC THERAPY

- Tight glucose control from the time of diagnosis of diabetes is the most important measure taken (69% reduction in risk of developing neuropathy in patients with type I diabetes). The same might be applied to type II diabetes, although it is not proven yet.
- Frequent follow-up visits, foot inspection for ulcers, and education on foot care.

GENERAL Rx

Treatment of pain and paresthesias:
- Gabapentin 100-900 mg tid
- Amitriptyline, nortriptyline or imipramine 10-150 mg qhs
- Desipramine 10-150 mg qhs
- Oxcarbazepine 150-600 mg bid
- Topiramate 25-200 mg bid
- Lamitorigine 25-200 mg qd
- Carbamazepine 100-200 mg bid or tid
- Opiates if all else fails (Tramadol up to 400 mg a day)

DISPOSITION

Diabetes carries significant morbidity and complications. Patients with untreated diabetic peripheral neuropathy have higher morbidity and complication rates than those without neuropathy or those with treated neuropathy.

REFERRAL

- A neurologist or a neuromuscular specialist for neurophysiologic testing
- Podiatrist for yearly foot examination
- Ophthalmologist for yearly eye examination

PEARLS & CONSIDERATIONS

COMMENTS

Nerve (sural) biopsy should be considered if there is prominent early autonomic neuropathy (amyloid) or rapid multifocal clinical pattern suggesting a mononeuritis multiplex that may be due to vasculitis.

SUGGESTED READINGS

Katirji B et al: *Neuromuscular Disorders in Clinical Practice,* Boston, 2002, Butterworth-Heinemann.

Llewelyn G: The diabetic neuropathies: types, diagnosis and management, *J Neurol Neurosurg Psychiatry* 74:ii15, 2003.

AUTHOR: **MUSTAFA A. HAMMAD, M.D.**

BASIC INFORMATION

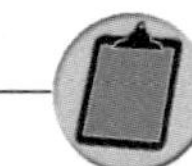

DEFINITION

Diffuse interstitial lung disease is a group of blood disorders involving the lung interstitium and characterized by inflammation of the alveolar structures and progressive parenchymal fibrosis.

SYNONYMS

Interstitial lung disease
ILD

ICD-9CM CODES
136.3 Acute interstitial lung disease
515 Chronic interstitial lung disease

EPIDEMIOLOGY & DEMOGRAPHICS

- The incidence of interstitial lung disease is 5 cases/100,000 persons
- There are >100 known disorders that can cause interstitial lung disease (see Etiology).

PHYSICAL FINDINGS & CLINICAL PRESENTATION

- The patient generally presents with progressive dyspnea and nonproductive cough; other clinical manifestations vary with the underlying disease process.
- Physical examination typically shows end respiratory dry rales (Velcro rales), cyanosis, clubbing, and right-sided heart failure.

ETIOLOGY

- Occupational and environmental exposure: pneumoconiosis, asbestosis, organic dust, gases, fumes, berylliosis, silicosis
- Granulomatous lung disease: sarcoidosis, infections (e.g., fungal, mycobacterial)
- Drug-induced: bleomycin, busulfan, methotrexate, chlorambucil, cyclophosphamide, BCNU (carmustine), gold salts, tetrazolium chloride, amiodarone, tocainide, penicillin, zidovudine, sulfonamide
- Radiation pneumonitis
- Connective tissue diseases: SLE, rheumatoid arthritis, dermatomyositis
- Idiopathic pulmonary fibrosis: bronchiolitis obliterans, interstitial pneumonitis, DIP
- Infections: viral pneumonia, *Pneumocystis* pneumonia
- Others: Wegener's granulomatosis, Goodpasture's syndrome, eosinophilic granuloma, lymphangitic carcinomatosis, chronic uremia, chronic gastric aspiration, hypersensitivity pneumonitis, lipoid pneumonia, lymphoma, lymphoid granulomatosis

DIAGNOSIS

DIFFERENTIAL DIAGNOSIS

- CHF
- Chronic renal failure
- Lymphangitic carcinomatosis
- Sarcoidosis
- Allergic alveolitis

WORKUP

Chest x-ray, ABGs, PFTs, bronchoscopy with bronchioloalveolar lavage, biopsy, laboratory evaluation

- Pulmonary function testing: findings are generally consistent with restrictive disease (decreased VC, TLC, and diffusing capacity).
- Bronchoscopy with bronchioloalveolar lavage may be useful to characterize the pulmonary inflammatory response; the effector cell population in patients with interstitial lung disease consists of two major cell types:
  1. Lymphocytes (e.g., sarcoidosis, berylliosis, silicosis, hypersensitive pneumonitis)
  2. Neutrophils (e.g., asbestosis, collagen-vascular disease, idiopathic pulmonary fibrosis)
- Open lung biopsy or transbronchial biopsy is useful to identify the underlying disease process and exclude neoplastic involvement; transbronchial biopsy is less invasive but provides less tissue for analysis (this factor may be important in patients with irregular pulmonary involvement).

LABORATORY TESTS

- ABGs provide only limited information; initially ABGs may be normal but with progression of the disease, hypoxemia may be present.
- Antineutrophil cytoplasmic antibody (c-ANCA) is frequently positive in Wegener's granulomatosis.
- Antiglomerular basement membrane (anti-GBM) and antipulmonary basement membrane antibody are often present in Goodpasture's syndrome.
- Pulmonary function testing: findings are generally consistent with restrictive disease (decreased VC, TLC, and diffusing capacity).
- Bronchoscopy with bronchioloalveolar lavage is useful to characterize the pulmonary inflammatory response; the effector cell population in patients with interstitial lung disease consists of two major cell types:
  1. Lymphocytes (e.g., sarcoidosis, berylliosis, silicosis, hypersensitive pneumonitis)
  2. Neutrophils (e.g., asbestosis, collagen-vascular disease, idiopathic pulmonary fibrosis)

IMAGING STUDIES

Chest x-ray may be normal in 10% of patients.

- Ground-glass appearance is often an early finding.
- A coarse reticular pattern is usually a late finding.
- CHF causing interstitial changes on chest x-ray must always be ruled out.
- Differential diagnosis of interstitial patterns include the following: pulmonary fibrosis, pulmonary edema, PCP, TB, sarcoidosis, eosinophilic granuloma, pneumoconiosis, and lymphangitic spread of carcinoma.
- Gallium-67 scanning plays a limited role in the evaluation of interstitial lung disease because it is not specific and a negative result does not exclude the disease (e.g., patients with end-stage fibrosis may have a negative scan).

TREATMENT

NONPHARMACOLOGIC THERAPY

Avoidance of tobacco and removal of any other offending agent (e.g., environmental exposure)

ACUTE GENERAL Rx

- Treatment of infectious process with appropriate antibiotic therapy
- Supplemental oxygen in patients with significant hypoxemia
- Corticosteroids in symptomatic patients with sarcoidosis
- Immunosuppressive therapy in selected cases (e.g., cyclophosphamide in patients with Wegener's granulomatosis)
- Treatment of any complications (e.g., pneumothorax, pulmonary embolism)

DISPOSITION

Overall mortality is 50% within 5 yr of diagnosis.

REFERRAL

- Surgical referral for biopsy
- Pulmonary referral for bronchoscopy and bronchoalveolar lavage (selected patients)
- Consider lung transplantation in selected patients with intractable end-stage ILD

PEARLS & CONSIDERATIONS

COMMENTS

Although open lung biopsy is the gold standard for diagnosis, it may be inappropriate in elderly patients; therefore individual consideration is advisable.

AUTHOR: **FRED F. FERRI, M.D.**

BASIC INFORMATION

DEFINITION

Acute or chronic consumption of digitalis leading to signs and symptoms of toxicity. May occur when serum levels are within the therapeutic range.

SYNONYMS

Cardiac glycosides: clinically available forms are digoxin and digitoxin

ICD-9CM CODES
972.1 Digitalis overdose

PHARMACOKINETICS

- Steady state levels (not peak levels) correlate with toxicity; digoxin reaches steady state 6 hr after ingestion

BIOAVAILABILITY: (1) digoxin about 80%, (2) digitoxin about 100%
VOLUME OF DISTRIBUTION: (1) digoxin 5 to 7 L/kg, (2) digitoxin 0.6 L/kg
HALF-LIFE: (1) digoxin 36 hr, (2) digitoxin 5 to 7 days
EXCRETION: (1) digoxin predominantly renal, (2) digitoxin predominantly hepatic
THERAPEUTIC LEVEL: (1) digoxin 0.8 to 2 ng/ml, (2) digitoxin 10 to 30 ng/ml

EPIDEMIOLOGY & DEMOGRAPHICS

- Digitalis toxicity occurs in up to 5% of individuals on therapy.
- Factors that potentiate toxicity: advanced age, renal insufficiency, cardiac or pulmonary disease, drugs that affect elimination (amiodarone, quinidine, verapamil, diltiazem, captopril, spironolactone, cyclosporine, erythromycin, clarithromycin, tetracyclines, indomethacin), coingestion of cardiotoxic drugs (β-blockers, calcium channel blockers, tricyclic antidepressants), hypokalemia, hypomagnesemia, hypercalcemia, hypoxemia, hypothyroidism, and volume depletion.

PHYSICAL FINDINGS & CLINICAL PRESENTATION

Cardiac, gastrointestinal, and central nervous systems are affected. Fatigue and weakness are common complaints.

CARDIAC
Any dysrhythmia; most frequently seen are increased automaticity and conduction delay

GI
Anorexia, nausea, vomiting, diarrhea, abdominal pain

CNS
Headache, dizziness, visual disturbance (scotoma, blurred vision, change in color perception, decreased visual acuity), confusion, hallucinations, delirium.

ETIOLOGY

Cardiac glycosides reversibly inhibit the function of the sodium-potassium ATPase pump resulting in increased myocardial contractility. Toxicity causes:

- **AV Block** by the following effects on the AV node:
  1. Decreased conduction velocity
  2. Increased refractory period
- **Extrasystoles and tachyarrhythmias** by the following effects on the atria and ventricles:
  1. Increased automaticity
  2. Increased excitability
  3. Decreased conduction velocity
  4. Decreased refractoriness

DIAGNOSIS

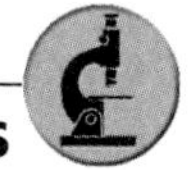

DIFFERENTIAL DIAGNOSIS

- β-Blockers
- Calcium channel blockers
- Clonidine
- Cyclic antidepressants
- Encainide and flecainide
- Procainamide
- Propoxyphene
- Quinidine
- Plants producing glycosides similar to digitalis (foxglove, oleander, lily of the valley)

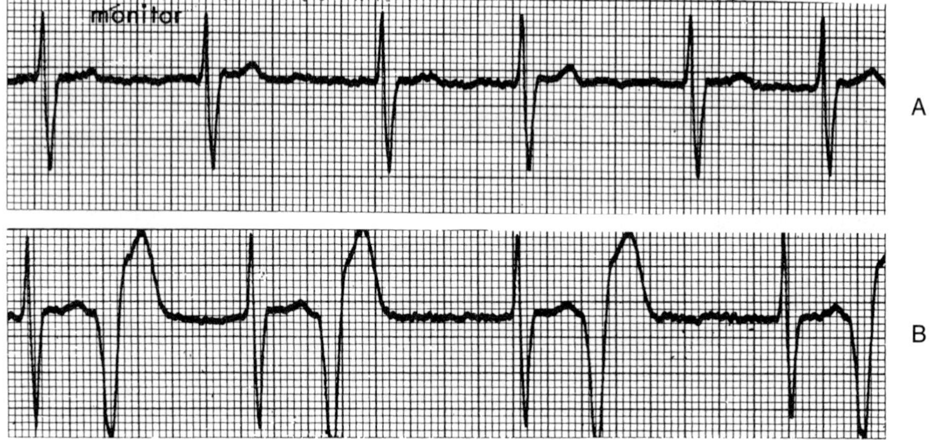

FIGURE 1-75 Ventricular bigeminy caused by digitalis toxicity. Ventricular ectopy is one of the most common signs of digitalis toxicity. The underlying rhythm in **(A)** is atrial fibrillation. In **(B)** each normal QRS is followed by a VPB. (From Goldberger AL [ed]: *Clinical electrocardiography,* ed 5, St Louis, 1994, Mosby.)

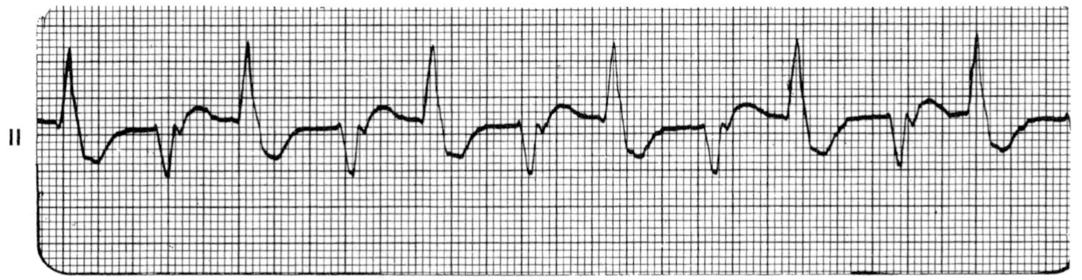

FIGURE 1-76 This digitalis-toxic arrhythmia is a special type of ventricular tachycardia (bidirectional tachycardia) with QRS complexes that alternate in direction from beat to beat. No P waves are present. (From Goldberger AL [ed]: *Clinical electrocardiography,* ed 5, St Louis, 1994, Mosby.)

WORKUP

History, physical examination, laboratory tests

LABORATORY TESTS

- Stat digoxin or digitoxin levels (may not correlate with severity of intoxication in acute ingestion)
- Electrolytes, BUN, creatinine, magnesium, calcium
- ECG (Figs. 1-75 and 1-76)

TREATMENT

NONPHARMACOLOGIC THERAPY

- Ensure adequate airway
- ECG monitor for 12 to 24 hr after ingestion

ACUTE GENERAL Rx

DECREASE TOXICITY:

- Acute toxicity: Activated charcoal if within 1 hr of ingestion, multiple doses may be indicated for digitoxin intoxication (because of significant enterohepatic circulation). Gastric emptying considered for massive acute overdose presenting <1 hr after ingestion.
- Treat hyperkalemia, hypokalemia and hypomagnesemia. In acute intoxication, patients may develop hyperkalemia, further increasing AV block.
- Fab fragments of digoxin-specific antibodies (Digibind):
  1. Specific antibodies that bind to digoxin and to a lesser extent digitoxin and other cardiac glycosides
  2. Initial response usually seen in 30 min, and complete reversal usually occurs within 4 hr
  3. Indications: hyperkalemia (≥5 mEq/L), life-threatening arrhythmia, massive overdose (acute ingestion of ≥10 mg digoxin or digoxin serum level ≥10 ng/ml 6 hr postingestion), coingestion of cardiotoxic drugs or plants containing cardiac glycosides
  4. Dosing: 1 vial (38 mg) of Fab fragments binds 0.5 mg of digoxin or digitoxin
     a. Digoxin **Acute ingestion:** number of vials = [ingested digoxin mg × 0.8]/ 0.5 **Chronic ingestion:** number of vials = [(serum digoxin level ng/ml) × weight kg]/100
     b. Digitoxin **Acute ingestion:** number of vials = (ingested digitoxin mg)/ 0.5 **Chronic ingestion:** number of vials = [(serum digitoxin level ng/ml) × weight kg]/1000
     c. If neither the amount ingested nor serum level are known, treat empirically:
        - acute intoxication—10 vials and repeat if needed
        - chronic toxicity—6 vials
  5. After use of Fab fragments the digoxin level is falsely elevated; accurate measurement of free digoxin level can be obtained by fluorescence polarization assay of protein-free ultrafiltrate
  6. Inactive complex excreted in urine, half-life of complex is 15 to 20 hr. In renal failure, consider plasma exchange (within 3 hr) to remove Fab-digoxin complex; theoretically, complexes may dissociate before excretion
  7. Class C for pregnancy
  8. Adverse effects of treatment: May undo desirable action of drug and exacerbate heart failure and increase ventricular response in previously controlled atrial fibrillation, hypokalemia, hypersensitivity reaction, and serum sickness
  9. Hemodialysis and hemoperfusion: not useful because of extensive tissue binding and large volume of distribution

COMPLICATIONS:

Hyperkalemia:
- Sodium bicarbonate
- Glucose and insulin
- Sodium polystyrene sulfonate (Kayexalate)
- Do not use calcium because it may worsen ventricular arrhythmias

Bradycardia and heart block:
- Atropine
- Temporary pacemaker if symptomatic

Supraventricular and ventricular tachycardia:
- Lidocaine or phenytoin: decrease ventricular automaticity without significantly slowing AV node conduction
- Avoid quinidine, bretylium, procainamide, and verapamil; may increase ventricular arrhythmias/AV node block
- Elective cardioversion is contraindicated, because it may precipitate ventricular fibrillation.

DISPOSITION

- Good with prompt treatment
- Chronic poisoning is associated with higher mortality than acute poisoning

SUGGESTED READING

Marx JA: *Rosen's emergency medicine: concepts and clinical practice,* ed 5, St Louis, 2002, Mosby.

AUTHOR: **SUDEEP K. AULAKH, M.D., F.R.C.P.C**

BASIC INFORMATION

DEFINITION

Diphtheria is an infection of the mucous membranes or skin caused by *Corynebacterium diphtheriae.*

ICD-9CM CODES
032.9 Diphtheria

EPIDEMIOLOGY & DEMOGRAPHICS

INCIDENCE (IN U.S.):
- Fewer than 5 cases/yr since 1980 (<0.002 cases/100,000 persons)
- Last culture-confirmed indigenous case in 1988

PREDOMINANT AGE: Adult years

PHYSICAL FINDINGS & CLINICAL PRESENTATION

RESPIRATORY DIPHTHERIA:
- Commonly presenting as pharyngitis, but any part of the respiratory tract may be involved, including the nasopharynx, larynx, trachea, or bronchi
- Areas of gray or white exudate coalescing to form a "pseudomembrane" that bleeds when removed
- Possible fever and dysphagia
- Complications: respiratory tract obstruction and pneumonia
- Systemic effects of the toxin: myocarditis and polyneuritis (frequently involving a bulbar distribution)
- Occurs mostly in nonimmune individuals; usually milder and less likely to be complicated in those adequately immunized

CUTANEOUS DIPHTHERIA:
- Usually complicates existing skin lesion (i.e., impetigo or scabies)
- Resembles the underlying condition

ETIOLOGY

- Caused by *C. diphtheriae,* an aerobic, gram-positive rod
- Transmitted by close contact through droplets of nasopharyngeal secretions
- Symptomatic disease of the respiratory system caused by toxin-producing strains (tox^+)
- Systemic effects of toxin: ranging from nausea and vomiting to polyneuropathy, myocarditis, and vascular collapse
- Presence of strains not producing toxin (tox^+) in the respiratory tract of asymptomatic carriers and in skin lesions of cutaneous diphtheria

DIAGNOSIS

DIFFERENTIAL DIAGNOSIS

- *Streptococcus* pharyngitis
- Viral pharyngitis
- Mononucleosis

WORKUP

- Presence of a pseudomembrane in the oropharynx suggestive of diagnosis (not always present)
- Gram stains of secretions to show club-shaped organisms, which appear as "Chinese letters"
- Nasolaryngoscopy to identify lesions in the nares, nasopharynx, larynx, or tracheobronchial tree
- Electrocardiogram
- Possible ICU monitoring

LABORATORY TESTS

- Cultures of mucosal lesions or of nasal discharge
  1. Positive culture for *C. diphtheriae* confirms the diagnosis.
  2. Laboratory is notified of the suspected diagnosis so that appropriate culture medium (Tinsdale agar) is used.
- Testing of all isolated organisms for toxin production

IMAGING STUDIES

- Chest x-ray examination to rule out pneumonia
- Bronchopneumonia has been described in fatal cases

TREATMENT

NONPHARMACOLOGIC THERAPY

- Intubation or tracheostomy if signs of respiratory distress occur
- Nasogastric or parenteral nutrition in those with bulbar signs
- ICU monitoring for patients with signs of systemic toxicity
- Cardiac pacing in patients with heart block
- Respiratory isolation

ACUTE GENERAL Rx

- Administration of diphtheria antitoxin once a clinical diagnosis is made
- If tests for hypersensitivity to horse serum are negative: 50,000 U given for mild to moderate disease or 60,000 to 120,000 U for critically ill patients
- IV infusion of antitoxin over 60 min
- Serum sickness in 10% of treated individuals; those with hypersensitivity to horse serum should be desensitized before administration of antitoxin
- Antibiotics to eradicate the organism in carriers or patients
- For respiratory diphtheria:
  1. Erythromycin 500 mg qid PO or IV or IM penicillin 600,000 U bid for 14 days
  2. Carriers or patients with cutaneous disease: erythromycin 500 mg PO qid or rifampin 600 mg PO qd for 7 days

CHRONIC Rx

Antibiotics to limit toxin production and eradicate carrier state, thereby preventing transmission

DISPOSITION

Complete recovery with adequate supportive measures and antitoxin

REFERRAL

- Hospitalization and referral to an infectious disease specialist for all suspected patients
- To an otolaryngologist for evaluation in cases of respiratory diphtheria
- All cases reported to the public health authorities

PEARLS & CONSIDERATIONS

COMMENTS

- Most cases are imported by travelers in epidemic areas, so recent epidemics in Europe are a cause for concern. A widespread epidemic of diphtheria began in 1990 in the former Soviet Union.
- Vaccination with diphtheria toxoid (attenuated toxin) is safe and effective in the form of DPT or Td; Td boosters should be given to adults every 10 yr.
- According to serologic studies, 20% to 60% of U.S. adults >20 yr of age are susceptible to diphtheria.

SUGGESTED READINGS

Bisgard KM et al: Respiratory diphtheria in the United States: 1980 through 1995, *Am J Pub Health* 88:787, 1998.

Hadfield TL et al: The pathology of diphtheria, *J Infect Dis* 181:s116, 2000.

Markina SS et al: Diphtheria in the Russian Federation in the 1990s, *J Infect Dis* 181 (Suppl 1):S27, 2000.

AUTHOR: **MAURICE POLICAR, M.D.**

BASIC INFORMATION

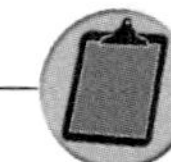

DEFINITION

Discoid lupus erythematosus (DLE) refers to a chronic cutaneous usually localized skin disorder sometimes associated with systemic lupus erythematosus (SLE). Erythematous plaque lesions with scaling, follicular plugging, atrophy, and scarring characterize DLE.

SYNONYMS

Chronic cutaneous lupus erythematosus

ICD-9CM CODES
695.4 Lupus erythematosus (local discoid)

EPIDEMIOLOGY & DEMOGRAPHICS

- Discoid lupus is more common in African Americans.
- DLE is more common in females, with peak incidence in the fourth decade of life.
- Less than 5% of patients with DLE progress to SLE.
- Approximately 10% to 20% of patients with SLE will also have discoid lupus skin lesions.

PHYSICAL FINDINGS & CLINICAL PRESENTATION

History
- Appearance of single or multiple asymptomatic plaque lesions (Fig. 1-77)

Physical findings
- Anatomic distribution
  1. DLE commonly involves the scalp, face, and ears but is not limited to these areas.
- Lesion configuration
  1. Irregularly grouped
- Lesion morphology
  1. Plaque lesions with scales
  2. Follicular plugging
  3. Atrophy
  4. Scarring
  5. Telangiectasia
- Color
  1. Erythematous
  2. Red to violaceous
  3. Hyperpigmentation or hypopigmentation
- Alopecia can occur and is permanent
- Urticaria (5%)
- May be associated with other criteria for SLE (e.g., oral ulcers, arthritis, pleuritis, pericarditis)

ETIOLOGY

The exact cause of DLE is not known, although an immune complex mediated mechanism is thought to be responsible.

DIAGNOSIS

Clinical inspection and skin biopsy usually establish the diagnosis of DLE.

DIFFERENTIAL DIAGNOSIS

- Psoriasis
- Lichen planus
- Secondary syphilis
- Superficial fungal infections
- Photosensitivity eruption
- Sarcoidosis
- Subacute cutaneous lupus erythematosus
- Rosacea
- Keratoacanthoma
- Actinic keratosis
- Dermatomyositis

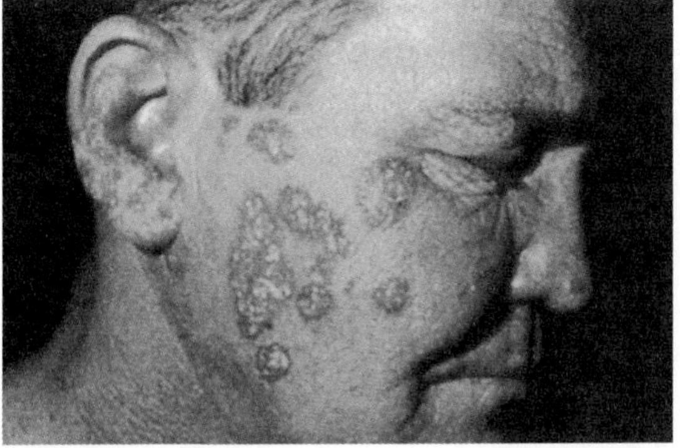

FIGURE 1-77 Scaling plaques with thick scales on the ear and face of a patient who has discoid lupus. (Courtesy Department of Dermatology, University of North Carolina at Chapel Hill. In Goldstein BG, Goldstein AO [eds]: *Practical dermatology,* ed 2, St Louis, 1977, Mosby.)

WORKUP

The workup for isolated DLE includes laboratory tests and x-rays looking for diagnostic criteria for SLE.

LABORATORY TESTS

Laboratory tests are done to exclude criteria for SLE. The following statements refer to patients having SLE with DLE.
- CBC is usually normal in isolated DLE.
- BUN/creatinine is normal.
- ESR is elevated in active disease associated with SLE.
- Urinalysis looking for proteinuria and hematuria.
- ANA may be positive in 20% of patients with isolated DLE.
- Anti-Ro (SS-A) autoantibodies are present in approximately 1% to 3% of patients.
- dsDNA and antiSm antibodies are rarely present.
- Complement levels may be low in patients with SLE but not in DLE.
- Skin biopsy shows degeneration of the basal cell layer with follicular plugging and atrophy of the epidermis.

IMAGING STUDIES

Chest x-ray examination is not specific in the diagnosis of DLE; however, it is helpful when assessing for SLE.

TREATMENT

NONPHARMACOLOGIC THERAPY

- The goals of management are to control existing lesions and limit scarring, and to prevent development of further lesions.
- Avoid sun exposure from 10 AM to 4 PM.
- Use sunscreens with sun protective factor (SPF) of at least 15.

ACUTE GENERAL Rx

- Topical steroid is first-line therapy for DLE.
- Intradermal steroid triamcinolone acetonide, 3 mg/ml with 1% Xylocaine is injected into the lesion.
- Hydroxychloroquine 400 mg PO qd for 1 mo, then decrease the dose to 200 mg qd. Treatment is continued for 3 to 6 mo.

CHRONIC Rx

- Dapsone 100 mg/day can be used in patients who fail to respond to topical steroid or hydroxychloroquine.
- Other alternatives include:
  1. Chloroquine 250-500 mg PO qd
  2. Auranofin 6 mg/day PO qd or divided bid; after 3 mo, may increase to 9 mg/day divided tid
  3. Thalidomide 100-300 mg PO hs, aq, and >1 hr pc

4. Azathioprine 1 mg/kg/day PO for 6-8 wk, increase by 5 mg/kg q4wk until response is seen or dose reaches 2.5 mg/kg/day
5. If all of the previous treatments fail, mycophenolate 1 g PO bid or interferon ∝-2b (2 million units/m^2 SQ 3 times/wk for 30 days) have been tried

DISPOSITION

- If left untreated, DLE is a chronic disorder that can lead to atrophy and scarring of the skin.
- A minority of patients with isolated cutaneous DLE progress to systemic lupus erythematosus. Prognosis is better in this group than unselected SLE patients.

REFERRAL

Patients with isolated DLE involving the face and scalp should be referred to a dermatologist. If associated with SLE, a rheumatology consultation is recommended.

PEARLS & CONSIDERATIONS

COMMENTS

- Cutaneous lesions account for 4 of the 11 criteria in the diagnosis of SLE (e.g., malar rash, discoid rash, photosensitivity, and oral ulcers).
- Cutaneous lupus erythematosus is classified as:
  1. Chronic cutaneous lupus erythematosus (discoid lupus is included in this category)
  2. Subacute cutaneous lupus erythematosus
  3. Acute cutaneous lupus erythematosus
- DLE lesions are not as photosensitive as the subacute cutaneous lesions.
- Rarely does DLE degenerate into a malignant nonmelanotic skin cancer.

SUGGESTED READINGS

Callen JP: Collagen vascular diseases, *Med Clin North Am* 82(6):1217, 1998.

Callen JP: Lupus erythematosus, discoid *e* Medicine Journal, 2(11) 2001 (www.emedicine.com).

Jessop S, Whitelaw D, Jordaan F: Drugs for discoid lupus erythematosus, *Cochrane Database Syst Rev* (1):CD002954, 2001.

Werth V: Current treatment of cutaneous lupus erythematosus, *Dermatology Online Journal* 7(1):2, 2001.

AUTHOR: **PETER PETROPOULOS, M.D.**

SECTION I

BASIC INFORMATION

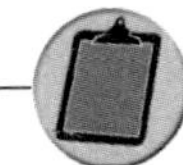

DEFINITION

Disseminated intravascular coagulation (DIC) is an acquired thromboembolic disorder characterized by generalized activation of the clotting mechanism, which results in the intravascular formation of fibrin and ultimately thrombotic occlusion of small and midsize vessels.

SYNONYMS

Consumptive coagulopathy
DIC
Defibrination syndrome

ICD-9CM CODES
286.6 Disseminated intravascular coagulation

EPIDEMIOLOGY & DEMOGRAPHICS

Greater than 50% of cases are associated with gram-negative sepsis or other septicemic infections.

PHYSICAL FINDINGS & CLINICAL PRESENTATION

- Wound site bleeding, epistaxis, gingival bleeding, hemorrhagic bullae
- Petechiae, ecchymosis, purpura
- Dyspnea, localized rales, delirium
- Oliguria, anuria, GI bleeding, metrorrhagia

ETIOLOGY

- Infections (e.g., gram-negative sepsis, Rocky Mountain spotted fever, malaria, viral or fungal infection)
- Obstetric complications (e.g., dead fetus, amniotic fluid embolism, toxemia, abruptio placentae, septic abortion, eclampsia)
- Tissue trauma (e.g., burns, hypothermia-rewarming)
- Neoplasms (e.g., adenocarcinomas [GI, prostate, lung, breast], acute promyelocytic leukemia)
- Quinine, cocaine-induced rhabdomyolysis
- Liver failure
- Acute pancreatitis
- Transfusion reactions
- Respiratory distress syndrome
- Other: SLE, vasculitis, aneurysms, polyarteritis, cavernous hemangiomas

DIAGNOSIS

DIFFERENTIAL DIAGNOSIS

- Hepatic necrosis: normal or elevated Factor VIII concentrations
- Vitamin K deficiency: normal platelet count
- Hemolytic uremic syndrome
- Thrombocytopenic purpura
- Renal failure, SLE, sickle cell crisis, dysfibrinogenemias

WORKUP

Diagnostic workup includes laboratory screening to confirm the diagnosis and exclude conditions noted in the differential diagnosis.

LABORATORY TESTS

- Peripheral blood smear generally shows RBC fragments and low platelet count.
- Coagulation factors are consumed at a rate in excess of the capacity of the liver to synthesize them, and platelets are consumed in excess of the capacity of the bone marrow megakaryocytes to release them. Diagnostic characteristics of DIC are increased PT, PTT, TT, fibrin split products, d-dimer; decreased fibrinogen level, thrombocytopenia.
- Coagulopathy secondary to DIC must be differentiated from that secondary to liver disease or vitamin K deficiency.
  1. Vitamin K deficiency manifests with prolonged PT and normal PTT, TT, platelet, and fibrinogen level; PTT may be elevated in severe cases.
  2. Patients with liver disease have abnormal PT and PTT; TT and fibrinogen are usually normal unless severe disease is present; platelets are usually normal unless splenomegaly is present.
  3. Factors V and VIII are low in DIC, but they are normal in liver disease with coagulopathy.

IMAGING STUDIES

Imaging studies are generally not useful. Chest x-ray may be helpful to exclude infectious processes in patients presenting with pulmonary symptoms such as dyspnea, cough, or hemoptysis.

TREATMENT

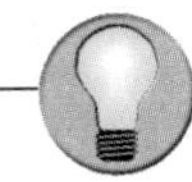

NONPHARMACOLOGIC THERAPY

No specific precautions regarding activity level are necessary unless thrombocytopenia is severe.

ACUTE GENERAL Rx

- Correct and eliminate underlying cause (e.g., antimicrobial therapy for infection).
- Give replacement therapy with FFP and platelets in patients with significant hemorrhage:
  1. FFP 10 to 15 ml/kg can be given with a goal of normalizing INR.
  2. Platelet transfusions are given when platelet count is <10,000 (or higher if major bleeding is present).
  3. Cryoprecipitate 1 U/5 kg is reserved for hypofibrinogen states.
  4. Antithrombin III treatment may be considered as a supportive therapeutic option in patients with severe DIC. Its modest results and substantial cost are limiting factors.
- Heparin therapy at a dose lower than that used in venous thrombosis (300 to 500 U/hr) may be useful in selected cases to increase neutralization of thrombin (e.g., DIC associated with acute promyelocytic leukemia, purpura fulminans, acral ischemia).

CHRONIC Rx

Follow-up management includes coagulation screening to assess factor replacement therapy. Laboratory abnormalities generally correct with treatment of the underlying disorder. Chronic laboratory monitoring is not required.

DISPOSITION

Mortality in severe DIC exceeds 75%. Death generally results from progression of the underlying disease and complications such as acute renal failure, intracerebral hematoma, shock, or cardiac tamponade.

REFERRAL

Hematology consultation is recommended in all cases of DIC.

PEARLS & CONSIDERATIONS

COMMENTS

The treatment of chronic DIC is controversial. Low-dose SC heparin and/or combination antiplatelet agents such as aspirin and dipyridamole may be useful.

AUTHOR: **FRED F. FERRI, M.D.**

BASIC INFORMATION

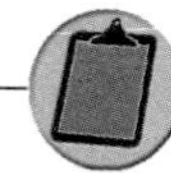

DEFINITION

- Colonic diverticula are herniations of mucosa and submucosa through the muscularis. They are generally found along the colon's mesenteric border at the site where the vasa recta penetrates the muscle wall (anatomic weak point).
- *Diverticulosis* is the asymptomatic presence of multiple colonic diverticula.
- *Diverticulitis* is an inflammatory process or localized perforation of diverticulum.

ICD-9CM CODES
562.10 Diverticulosis of colon
562.11 Diverticulitis of colon

EPIDEMIOLOGY & DEMOGRAPHICS

- Incidence of diverticulosis in the general population is 35% to 50%.
- Diverticulosis is more common in Western countries, affecting >30% of people >40 yr and >50% of people >70 yr.

PHYSICAL FINDINGS & CLINICAL PRESENTATION

- Physical examination in patients with diverticulosis is generally normal.
- Painful diverticular disease can present with LLQ pain, often relieved by defecation; location of pain may be anywhere in the lower abdomen because of the redundancy of the sigmoid colon.
- Diverticulitis can cause muscle spasm, guarding, and rebound tenderness predominantly affecting the LLQ.

ETIOLOGY

- Diverticular disease is believed to be secondary to low intake of dietary fiber.

DIAGNOSIS

DIFFERENTIAL DIAGNOSIS

- Irritable bowel syndrome
- IBD
- Carcinoma of colon
- Endometriosis
- Ischemic colitis
- Infections (pseudomembranous colitis, appendicitis, pyelonephritis, PID)
- Lactose intolerance

LABORATORY TESTS

- WBC count in diverticulitis reveals leukocytosis with left shift.
- Microcytic anemia can be present in patients with chronic bleeding from diverticular disease. MCV may be elevated in acute bleeding secondary to reticulocytosis.

IMAGING STUDIES

- Barium enema will demonstrate multiple diverticula and muscle spasm ("sawtooth" appearance of the lumen) in patients with painful diverticular disease. Barium enema can be hazardous and should not be performed in the acute stage of diverticulitis because it may produce free perforation.
- A CT scan of the abdomen can be used to diagnose acute diverticulitis; typical findings are thickening of the bowel wall, fistulas, or abscess formation.
- Evaluation of suspected diverticular bleeding:
  1. Arteriography if the bleeding is faster than 1 ml/min (advantage: the possible infusion of vasopressin directly into the arteries supplying the bleeding, as well as selective arterial embolization; disadvantages: its cost and invasive nature)
  2. Technetium-99m sulfa colloid
  3. Technetium-99m labeled RBC (can detect bleeding rates as low as 0.12 to 5 ml/min)

TREATMENT

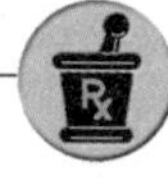

NONPHARMACOLOGIC THERAPY

- Increase in dietary fiber intake and regular exercise to improve bowel function
- NPO and IV hydration in severe diverticulitis; NG suction if ileus or small bowel obstruction is present

ACUTE GENERAL Rx

TREATMENT OF DIVERTICULITIS:

- Mild case: broad-spectrum PO antibiotics (e.g., Ciprofloxacin 500 mg bid to cover aerobic component of colonic flora and metronidazole 500 mg q6h for anaerobes) and liquid diet for 7 to 10 days
- Severe case: NPO and aggressive IV antibiotic therapy
  a. Ampicillin-sulbactam (Unasyn) 3 g IV q6h *or*
  b. Piperacillin-tazobactam (Zosyn) 4.5 g IV q8h *or*
  c. Ciprofloxacin 400 mg IV q12h plus metronidazole 500 mg IV q6h *or*
  d. Cefoxitin 2 g IV q8h plus metronidazole 500 mg IV q6h
- Life-threatening case: Imipenem 500 mg IV q6h *or* meropenem 1 g IV q8h
- Surgical treatment consisting of resection of involved areas and reanastomosis (if feasible); otherwise a diverting colostomy with reanastomosis performed when infection has been controlled; surgery should be considered in patients with:
  1. Repeated episodes of diverticulitis (two or more)
  2. Poor response to appropriate medical therapy (failure of conservative management)
  3. Abscess or fistula formation
  4. Obstruction
  5. Peritonitis
  6. Immunocompromised patients, first episode in young patient (<40 yr old)
  7. Inability to exclude carcinoma (10% to 20% of patients diagnosed with diverticulosis on clinical grounds are subsequently found to have carcinoma of the colon)

DIVERTICULAR HEMORRHAGE: 70% of diverticular bleeding occurs in the right colon.

1. Bleeding is painless and stops spontaneously in the majority of patients (60%); it is usually caused by erosion of a blood vessel by a fecalith present within the diverticular sac.
2. Medical therapy consists of blood replacement and correction of volume and any clotting abnormalities.
3. Colonoscopic treatment with epinephrine injections, bipolar coagulation, or both may prevent recurrent bleeding and decrease the need for surgery.
4. Surgical resection is necessary if bleeding does not stop spontaneously after administration of 4 to 5 U of PRBCs or recurs with severity within a few days; if attempts at localization are unsuccessful, total abdominal colectomy with ileoproctostomy may be indicated (high incidence of rebleeding if segmental resection is performed without adequate localization).

CHRONIC Rx

Asymptomatic patients with diverticulosis can be treated with a high-fiber diet or fiber supplements.

DISPOSITION

- Most patients with diverticulitis respond well to antibiotic management and bowel rest. Up to 30% of patients with diverticulitis will eventually require surgical management.
- Diverticular bleeding can recur in 15% to 20% of patients within 5 yr.

REFERRAL

Surgical referral when considering resection (see Acute General Rx)

AUTHOR: **FRED F. FERRI, M.D.**

BASIC INFORMATION

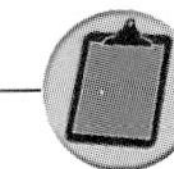

DEFINITION

Down syndrome is a disorder characterized by mental retardation and multiple organ defects that is caused by a chromosomal abnormality (trisomy 21).

SYNONYMS

Trisomy 21

ICD-9CM CODES
758.0 Down Syndrome

EPIDEMIOLOGY & DEMOGRAPHICS

INCIDENCE (IN U.S.): 1 in 800 births
PREVALENCE (IN U.S.): 300,000 persons
PREDOMINANT SEX: Male:female ratio of 1.3:1.0
PREDOMINANT AGE: Newborn to early adulthood
PEAK INCIDENCE: Newborn
GENETICS: Nondisjunction causing trisomy 21
PHYSICAL FINDINGS: (SEE FIG. 1-78)

- Microcephaly
- Flattening of occiput and face
- Upward slant to eyes with epicanthal folds
- Brushfield spots in iris
- Broad stocky neck
- Small feet, hands, digits
- Single palmar crease
- Hypotonia
- Short stature
- Associated with congenital heart disease, malformations of the GI tract, cataracts, hypothyroidism, hip dysplasia
- About half of children with Down syndrome are born with congenital heart disease, with the most common lesions being atrial septal defect and ventricular septal defect.
- Persistent primary congenital hypothyroidism is found in 1 in 141 newborns with Down syndrome, as compared with 1 in 4000 in the general population.
- Ophthalmologic disorders increase in frequency with age. Over 80% of children aged 5-12 have disorders that need monitoring or intervention, such as refractive errors, strabismus, or cataracts.

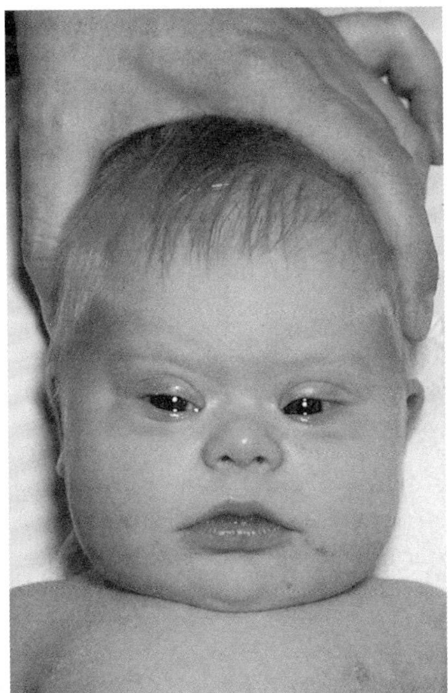

FIGURE 1-78 **Down syndrome.** Note depressed nasal bridge, epicanthal folds, mongoloid slant of eyes, low-set ears, and large tongue. (From Zitelli BJ, Davis HW: *Atlas of pediatric physical diagnosis,* ed 3, St Louis, 1997, Mosby.)

ETIOLOGY

Nondisjunction of chromosome 21

DIAGNOSIS

- Prenatal cytogenic diagnosis by amniocentesis or chorionic villus sampling
- Combined use of serum screening and fetal ultrasound testing for thickened nuchal fold has 80% detection rate with 5% false positives
- Postnatal chromosomal karyotype

TREATMENT

- Treatment consists of vigilant monitoring for comorbid states, such as obesity, hypothyroidism, leukemia, hearing loss, and valvular heart disease
- Thyroid screen at birth, at age 6 mo, and yearly thereafter
- Prevention of obesity with low-calorie, high-fiber diet
- Monitoring for hematologic problems
- Auditory brainstem responses in all newborns and aggressive testing for hearing loss in children with chronic otitis media
- Echocardiogram in all newborns and cardiac assessment of adolescents for development of mitral valve prolapse
- Ophthalmologic assessment by age 6 mo for congenital cataracts and annual exams for monitoring of refractive errors and strabismus
- Regular dental care
- Pelvic examination of women who are sexually active or who have menstrual problems
- Dermatologic issues such as folliculitis can become problematic in adolescents and require careful attention to hygiene and topical antibiotics.

REFERRAL

Down syndrome clinics use a preventive checklist to anticipate many clinical challenges.

COMMENTS

- Screening for atlantoaxial subluxation is controversial.
- Most patients develop neuropathologic changes typical of Alzheimer disease. Presenting symptoms include seizures, change in personality, focal neurologic signs, and apathy. If Alzheimer disease is suspected, screen for treatable diseases such as depression or hypothyroidism.
- This disease accounts for approximately one third of moderate to severe cases of mental retardation.
- Individuals with Down syndrome have a wide range of function, but all will have decrease in intelligence quotient in first decade of life.
- Deficiency of language production relative to other areas of development often causes substantial impairment.
- Individuals with Down syndrome have more behavioral and psychiatric problems than other children, but fewer than other individuals with mental retardation.
- Though increased maternal age is a risk factor, most children with Down syndrome are born to women under the age of 35 yr.

SUGGESTED READINGS

Roizen NJ: Medical care and monitoring for the adolescent with Down syndrome, *Adolesc Med* 13(2):345, 2002.

Roizen NJ, Patterson D: Down's syndrome, *Lancet* 361(9365):1281, 2003.

Torfs CP, Christianson RE: Anomalies in Down syndrome individuals in a large population-based registry, *Am J Med Genet* 77(5):431, 1998.

AUTHOR: **MAITREYI MAZUMDAR, M.D.**

Dumping Syndrome (PTG)

BASIC INFORMATION

DEFINITION

Dumping syndrome refers to the constellation of postprandial symptoms as a result of rapid delivery of stomach contents into the small bowel seen after definitive surgery for peptic ulcer disease.

SYNONYMS

Early postgastrectomy syndrome

ICD-9CM CODES
564.2 Postgastric surgery syndromes

EPIDEMIOLOGY & DEMOGRAPHICS

Incidence is 10% of all patients having gastric surgery.

- Vagotomy and pyloroplasty (8.5% to 20%)
- Vagotomy and antrectomy (4% to 27%)
- Subtotal gastrectomy (10% to 40%)
- Parietal cell vagotomy (3% to 5%)
- Affects males and females equally

PHYSICAL FINDINGS & CLINICAL PRESENTATION

Early dumping

- Symptoms start within 1 hr after eating food
- No symptoms in fasting state
- Nausea, vomiting, and belching
- Epigastric fullness, cramping, and diarrhea
- Dizziness, flushing, diaphoresis, and syncope
- Palpitations and tachycardia

Late dumping

- Symptoms occurring 1 to 3 hr after eating
- Diaphoresis
- Irritability
- Difficulty concentrating
- Tremulous

ETIOLOGY

Dumping syndrome occurs almost exclusively in patients having gastric surgery.

- Systemic symptoms are thought to be due to hypovolemia caused by rapid shifts of fluid from the intravascular space into the lumen of the bowel.
- Increase in vasoactive substances is thought to play a role in dumping syndrome.
- Late dumping symptoms are thought to be due to reactive hypoglycemia.

DIAGNOSIS

A detailed clinical history and evidence of prior gastric surgery usually makes the diagnosis of dumping syndrome. Oral glucose challenge test and radiographic imaging studies aid in establishing the diagnosis.

DIFFERENTIAL DIAGNOSIS

- Pancreatic insufficiency
- Inflammatory bowel disease
- Afferent loop syndromes
- Bile acid reflux after surgery
- Bowel obstruction
- Gastroenteric fistula

WORKUP

Typically the diagnosis is made on clinical grounds. In certain clinical settings (e.g., symptoms in patients with no prior history of gastric surgery), a workup, including oral glucose challenge and imaging studies, may be pursued.

LABORATORY TESTS

Oral glucose challenge test:

- Oral intake of 50 g of glucose is followed by serial measurements of heart rate, serum glucose, and hydrogen breath test every 15 min for 6 hr.
- An increase in the heart rate >12 beats/min and a rise in hydrogen breath excretion had a sensitivity of 94% and specificity >92%. A nadir blood glucose <3.3 mmol/L was present in 75% of late dumpers.

IMAGING STUDIES

- Upper GI series properly defines anatomy.
- Scintigraphic imaging documents rapid gastric emptying and may be useful in patients with dumping syndrome and no prior history of gastric surgery.

TREATMENT

NONPHARMACOLOGIC THERAPY

- Diet modification
  1. Divide calorie intake over six small meals
  2. Limit fluid intake with meals (try to avoid 30 min before meals)
  3. Decrease carbohydrate intake and avoid simple sugars
  4. Increase/supplement dietary fibers
  5. Avoid milk/milk products

ACUTE GENERAL Rx

- Acarbose 50 mg PO qd can be tried if dietary modification does not help.
- Octreotide 25 to 50 μg SC 30 min before meals is effective in relieving symptoms of dumping syndrome.
- Pectin and Guar have been used to increase viscocity of intraluminal contents and relieving symptoms from rapid emptying and absorption.

CHRONIC Rx

- Surgery is considered in patients with severe symptoms refractory to the above mentioned dietary and acute general treatment.
- Surgical procedures include: reconstruction of the pylorus, converting Billroth II to a Billroth I anastomosis, and a Roux-en-Y reconstruction.

DISPOSITION

- Dumping syndrome improves with time. Approximately 1% to 2% of patients will continue to have significant symptoms several months after surgery.
- Dietary modification effectively treats the majority of patients.

REFERRAL

- A GI consult is recommended in patients suspected of having dumping syndrome.
- If medical management is unsuccessful, a general surgical consultation is warranted.

PEARLS & CONSIDERATIONS

COMMENTS

- The majority of patients usually manifest with early dumping symptoms or combination of early and late symptoms. Few have late dumping symptoms alone.
- Octreotide has an inhibitory effect on the release of insulin and other vasoactive substances released by the gut. It also works by decreasing gastric emptying.

SUGGESTED READINGS

Hasler WL: Dumping syndrome, *Current Treat Options Gastroenterol* 5(2):139, 2002.

Imhof A et al: Reactive hypoglycemia due to late dumping syndrome: successful treatment with acarbose, *Swiss Med Wkly* 131(5-6):81, 2001.

Li-Ling J, Irving M: Therapeutic value of octreotide for patients with severe dumping syndrome: a review of randomized controlled trials, *Postgrad Med J* 77(909):441, 2001.

Vecht J, Masclee AAM, Lamers CBHW: The dumping syndrome: current insights into pathophysiology, diagnosis and treatment, *Scand J Gastroenterol* 32 (223):21, 1997.

AUTHOR: **HEMCHAND RAMBERAN, M.D.**

BASIC INFORMATION

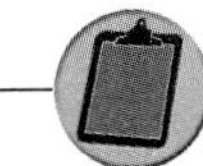

DEFINITION

Dupuytren's contracture is a disease of the palmar fascia characterized by nodular fibroblastic proliferation that often results in progressive contractures of the fascia and flexion deformity of the fingers.

ICD-9CM CODES
728.6 Dupuytren's contracture

EPIDEMIOLOGY & DEMOGRAPHICS

PREVALENCE: Varies depending on nationality
PREVALENT AGE: 40 to 60 yr
PREVALENT SEX: Male:female ratio of 10:1

PHYSICAL FINDINGS & CLINICAL PRESENTATION

- Usually asymptomatic
- Most common complaints: deformity and interference with the use of the hand by the flexed, contracted fingers (Fig. 1-79)
- Process usually begins in the ulnar side of the hand, often starting at the ring finger
- Isolated painless nodules that eventually harden and mature into a longitudinal cord that extends into the finger
- Lesion often begins in the distal palmar crease
- Overlying skin adherent to the fascia
- Later stages: fibrous cord begins to contract and pull the finger into flexion
- Possible involvement of other fingers, particularly small finger

ETIOLOGY

Unknown

DIAGNOSIS

DIFFERENTIAL DIAGNOSIS

Soft tissue tumor, tendon cyst

TREATMENT

NONPHARMACOLOGIC THERAPY

- Stretching exercises
- Local heat

DISPOSITION

Rate of development is variable.

REFERRAL

- If joint contracture begins to develop
- For excision of rare nodule that is painful (at any stage)

PEARLS & CONSIDERATIONS

COMMENTS

- Dupuytren's contracture develops earlier and more often in certain families.
- The disorder is more common in Scandinavians, and some Northern Europeans have a 25% prevalence over age 60 yr.
- About 5% of patients develop a similar condition elsewhere, such as Peyronie's disease or Ledderhose disease (involvement of the plantar fascia).
- Soft tissue "pads" in the knuckles may also be present.
- Individuals with these additional findings are considered to have Dupuytren's diathesis, and their disease is generally more severe and recurrent.

SUGGESTED READINGS

Frank PL: An update on Dupuytren's contracture, *Hosp Med* 62:678, 2001.
Khan AA et al: The role of manual occupation in the aetilogy of Dupuytren's disease in men in England and Wales, *J Hand Surg* 299(1):12, 2004.
McFarlane RM: On the origin and spread of Dupuytren's disease, *J Hand Surg* 27:385, 2002.
Ragsowansi RH, Britto JA: Genetic and epigenetic influence on the pathogenesis of Dupuytren's disease, *J Hand Surg* 26:1157, 2001.
Thurston AJ: Dupuytren's disease, *J Bone Joint Surg Br* 85(4):469, 2003.

AUTHOR: **LONNIE R. MERCIER, M.D.**

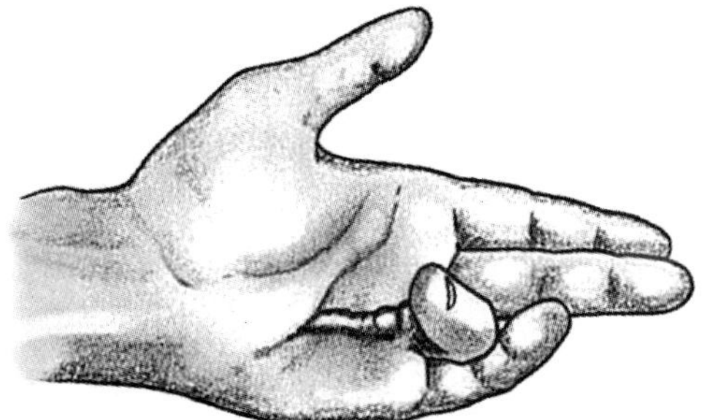

FIGURE 1-79 Dupuytren's contracture. A flexion deformity of the finger is present, with nodular thickening of the fascia to the ring finger.

Dysfunctional Uterine Bleeding (PTG)

BASIC INFORMATION

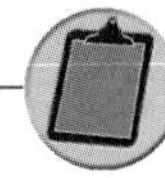

DEFINITION

Dysfunctional uterine bleeding (DUB) describes abnormal uterine bleeding in the absence of disease in the pelvis, pregnancy, or medical illness. Specific types of abnormal bleeding include the following:

- Hypermenorrhea: excessive bleeding in amount during normal duration of regular menstrual cycles.
- Hypomenorrhea: decreased bleeding in amount in regular menstrual cycles.
- Menorrhagia: regular normal intervals, excessive flow and duration.
- Metrorrhagia: irregular intervals, excessive flow and duration.
- Menometrorrhagia: irregular or excessive bleeding during menstruation and between periods.
- Oligomenorrhea: intervals greater than 35 days.
- Polymenorrhea: intervals less than 21 days.

SYNONYMS

DUB

ICD-9CM CODES

626 Disorders of menstruation and other abnormal bleeding from female genital tract
626.2 Hypermenorrhea
626.1 Hypomenorrhea
626.2 Menorrhagia
626.6 Metrorrhagia
626.2 Menometrorrhagia
626.1 Oligomenorrhea
626.2 Polymenorrhea

EPIDEMIOLOGY & DEMOGRAPHICS

- Most cases of DUB occur in postmenarchal and perimenopausal age groups.
- During reproductive age, <20% of abnormal bleeding results from anovulatory DUB.

PHYSICAL FINDINGS & CLINICAL PRESENTATION

- A clinical diagnosis of exclusion
- Thorough physical and pelvic examination to exclude the other causes of abnormal bleeding
  1. Includes thyroid, breasts, liver, presence or absence of ecchymotic lesions
  2. Patient possibly obese and hirsute (polycystic ovarian disease)
  3. No evidence of any vulvar, vaginal, cervical lesions, uterine (fibroid) or ovarian tumor, urethral caruncle, urethral diverticula, hemorrhoids, anal fissure, colorectal lesions
  4. Bimanual pelvic examination: normal-sized or slightly enlarged uterus

ETIOLOGY & PATHOGENESIS

- 90% is caused by anovulation.
- 10% is ovulatory in origin; can be caused by dysfunction of corpus luteum or midcycle bleeding.
- Section II describes the various causes of abnormal uterine bleeding.

DIAGNOSIS

DIFFERENTIAL DIAGNOSIS

- Pregnancy-related cause
- Anatomic uterine causes:
  1. Leiomyomas
  2. Adenomyosis
  3. Polyps
  4. Endometrial hyperplasia
  5. Cancer
  6. Sexually transmitted diseases
  7. Intrauterine contraceptive devices
- Anatomic nonuterine causes:
  1. Cervical neoplasia, cervicitis
  2. Vaginal neoplasia, adhesions, trauma, foreign body, atrophic vaginitis, infections, condyloma
  3. Vulvar trauma, infections, neoplasia, condyloma, dystrophy, varices
  4. Urinary tract: urethral caruncle, diverticulum, hematuria
  5. GI tract: hemorrhoids, anal fissure, colorectal lesions
- Systemic diseases:
  1. Exogenous hormone intake
  2. Coagulopathies: von Willebrand's disease, thrombocytopenia, hepatic failure
  3. Endocrinopathies: thyroid disorder, hypo- and hyperthyroidism, diabetes mellitus
  4. Renal diseases
- Section II describes a differential diagnosis of vaginal bleeding abnormalities.

WORKUP

- A detailed history and thorough physical examination, including a pelvic examination to exclude above mentioned causes.
- Clinical algorithms for the evaluation of vaginal bleeding are described in Section III, Bleeding, Vaginal.

LABORATORY TESTS

- CBC with platelets; possible iron deficiency anemia or thrombocytopenia
- Prothrombin (PT); partial thromboplastin and bleeding time if coagulopathy is suspected
- Serum human chorionic gonadotropin (hCG)
- Chemistry profile, including liver function tests
- Thyroid profile
- Stool testing for occult blood
- Urinalysis for hematuria
- Pap smear
- Cultures for gonorrhea and *Chlamydia*
- Serum gonadotropins and prolactin
- Serum androgens
- Endometrial biopsy in women >35 yr old, or earlier, if longstanding history of anovulatory bleeding
- Hysterogram and hysteroscopy

IMAGING STUDIES

- Pelvic ultrasound, including measurement of endometrial thickness
- Hydrosonogram

TREATMENT

NONPHARMACOLOGIC THERAPY

Increase iron intake in the form of pills and in a diet rich in iron.

ACUTE GENERAL Rx

- Progestational agents
  1. Progesterone in oil, 100 to 200 mg
  2. Medroxyprogesterone acetate, 20 to 40 mg qd for 15 days
  3. Megestrol acetate, 40 to 120 mg daily in divided doses × 15 days
  4. Oral contraceptives: any oral contraceptive pill, one tablet qid for 5 to 7 days, followed by one tablet low-dose estrogen qd for 21 days; causes one heavy withdrawal bleeding, should then be on cyclical Provera or continue on oral contraceptives
- Estrogens
  1. Conjugated estrogen (Premarin) 25 mg IV q4h until bleeding is under control (in cases of severe or life-threatening bleeding); maximum three doses
  2. For prolonged bleeding that is not life-threatening: Premarin 1.25 mg (Estrace 2 mg) q4h for 24 hr, followed by Provera to bring on withdrawal bleeding; then sequential regimen of estrogen and progestin (Premarin 1.25 mg qd for 24 days; Provera 10 mg for last 10 days) or oral contraceptives
- Surgical treatment
  1. Dilation and curettage (D&C) and hysteroscopy
  2. Endometrial ablation
  3. Hysterectomy

CHRONIC Rx

- Progestational agents
  1. Medroxyprogesterone acetate 10 mg qd for 12 days, then cyclically to induce monthly withdrawal bleeding
  2. Norethindrone 1 mg qd for 12 days
  3. Depo-Provera 150 mg IM and then 150 mg q3mo
  4. Oral contraceptives one tablet qd
- Clomiphene citrate: patients with anovulatory bleeding who want to become pregnant
- Others
  1. Antiprostaglandins
  2. Danazol
  3. Gonadotropin-releasing hormone analogs (GNRH)
  4. Human menopausal gonadotropin (HMG)
- Surgical treatment
  1. D&C and hysteroscopy
  2. Endometrial ablation
  3. Hysterectomy

DISPOSITION

Cyclical treatment on birth control pills or Provera for several cycles, then discontinue pill and watch patient for onset of regular menses

REFERRAL

To gynecologist in case of failure of treatment

PEARLS & CONSIDERATIONS

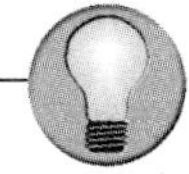

COMMENTS

Patient education material may be obtained from the American College of Obstetricians and Gynecologists, 409 12th Street SW, Washington, DC 20024-2188; phone (202) 638-5577.

SUGGESTED READINGS

Gallinat A, Nugent W: NovaSure impedance-controlled system for endometrial ablation, *J Am Assoc Gynecol Laparosc* 9(3):283, 2002.

Mihm LM et al: The accuracy of endometrial biopsy and saline sonohysterography in the determination of the cause of abnormal uterine bleeding, *Am J Obstet Gynecol* 186:858, 2002.

Mishell DR, Stenchever MA, Drogemuller W: *Comprehensive gynecology,* ed 3, St Louis, 1997, Mosby.

Speroff L: *Clinical gynecologic endocrinology and infertility,* ed 6, Baltimore, 1999, Williams & Wilkins.

AUTHOR: **MANDEEP K. BRAR, M.D.**

BASIC INFORMATION

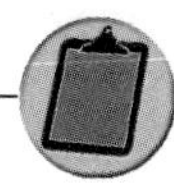

DEFINITION

Dysmenorrhea is pain with menstruation, usually as cramping and usually centered in the lower abdomen. It is defined as *primary dysmenorrhea* when there is no associated organic pathology and *secondary dysmenorrhea* when there is demonstrable organic pathology.

SYNONYMS

Menstrual cramps
Painful periods

ICD-9CM CODES
625.3 Dysmenorrhea

EPIDEMIOLOGY & DEMOGRAPHICS

Approximately 50% of menstruating women are affected by dysmenorrhea, with approximately 10% of them having severe dysmenorrhea with incapacitation for 1 to 3 days/mo. Dysmenorrhea is most common in the age group from 20 to 24 yr, and primary dysmenorrhea usually appears within 6 to 12 mo after menarche.

PHYSICAL FINDINGS & CLINICAL PRESENTATION

- Sharp, crampy, midline, lower abdomen pain without a lower quadrant or adnexal component but possible radiation to the lower back and upper thighs
- Unremarkable pelvic examination in nonmenstruating patient
- Accompanying symptoms: nausea, vomiting, headaches, anxiety, fatigue, diarrhea, fainting, and abdominal bloating
- Cramps usually lasting <24 hr and seldom lasting >2 to 3 days
- Secondary dysmenorrhea: dyspareunia is a common complaint, and bimanual pelvic-abdominal examination may demonstrate uterine or adnexal tenderness, fixed uterine retroflexion, uterosacral nodularity, a pelvic mass, or an enlarged, irregular uterus

ETIOLOGY

Prostaglandin $F_2\alpha$ (PG $F_2\alpha$) is the agent responsible for dysmenorrhea. It stimulates uterine contractions, cervical stenosis or narrowing, and increased vasopressin release. Behavior and psychologic factors have also been implicated in the etiology of primary dysmenorrhea. Primary dysmenorrhea only occurs in ovulatory cycles. Secondary dysmenorrhea is usually caused by endometriosis, adenomyosis, leiomyomas and, less commonly, chronic salpingitis, IUD use, or congenital or acquired outflow tract obstruction, including cervical stenosis.

DIAGNOSIS

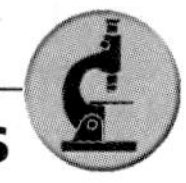

DIFFERENTIAL DIAGNOSIS

- Adenomyosis
- Adhesions
- Allen-Masters syndrome
- Cervical structures or stenosis
- Congenital malformation of müllerian system
- Ectopic pregnancy
- Endometriosis, endometritis
- Imperforate hymen
- IUD use
- Leiomyomas
- Ovarian cysts
- Pelvic congestion syndrome, PID
- Polyps
- Transverse vaginal septum

WORKUP

- Primary dysmenorrhea: characteristic history, physical examination normal with the absence of an identifiable cause of pelvic pain
- Secondary dysmenorrhea: history of onset generally >2 yr after menarche, physical examination may reveal uterine irregularity, cul-de-sac tenderness, or nodularity or pelvic masses

LABORATORY TESTS

- No specific tests diagnostic for dysmenorrhea
- Elevated WBC count in the presence of infection
- hCG to rule out ectopic pregnancy

IMAGING STUDIES

- Ultrasound scan of the pelvis to evaluate the presence of leiomyomas, ovarian cysts, or ectopic pregnancy
- Hysterosalpingogram to assess the uterine cavity to rule out endometrial polyps, submucosal or intraluminal leiomyomas

TREATMENT

NONPHARMACOLOGIC THERAPY

- Applying heat to the lower abdomen with hot compresses, heating pads, or hot water bottles seems to offer some relief.
- Other reassurance that this is a treatable condition.

ACUTE GENERAL Rx

- Nonsteroidal antiinflammatory drugs such as ibuprofen 400 to 600 mg q4-6h or naproxen sodium 550 mg q12h, mefenamic acid 500 mg initial dose followed by 250 mg q6h prn, aspirin 650 mg q4-6h, or oral contraceptives
- Nifedipine 30 mg qd in difficult cases of dysmenorrhea
- Magnesium supplements have been found likely to be beneficial
- Thiamine supplements may reduce pain
- Secondary dysmenorrhea: treatment directed to the specific underlying condition; surgery plays a greater role
- Endometriosis: use of nonsurgical approaches, such as using danazol, gonadotropin-releasing hormone agonists, and oral contraceptives

CHRONIC Rx

Acupuncture and transcutaneous electrical nerve stimulation (TENS) may be tried. In cases in which medical therapy has not worked, laparoscopy should be considered, as well as other surgical treatments depending on the secondary cause of the dysmenorrhea.

DISPOSITION

The majority of patients are satisfactorily treated with good outcomes. It is thought that primary dysmenorrhea generally improves with age and parity and that secondary dysmenorrhea usually has good results with adequate treatment. Possible chronic complications with primary dysmenorrhea that has not been adequately treated can lead to anxiety and depression. With certain causes of secondary dysmenorrhea infertility can become a problem.

REFERRAL

If a secondary cause of dysmenorrhea is revealed, refer to the appropriate specialist for further medical or surgical treatment (e.g., gynecologist, pain management center).

PEARLS & CONSIDERATIONS

COMMENTS

Patient education materials can be obtained through various pharmaceutical companies (e.g., booklet "Painful Periods" from Warner Lambert, Inc.)

AUTHOR: **GEORGE T. DANAKAS, M.D.**

Dyspareunia

BASIC INFORMATION

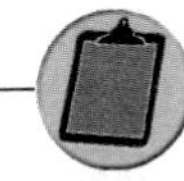

DEFINITION

Persistent and/or recurrent sexual intercourse associated pain

ICD-9CM CODES
625.0 Pain associated with female genital organs
302.76 Sexual deviations and disorders with functional dyspareunia, psychogenic dyspareunia

EPIDEMIOLOGY & DEMOGRAPHICS

PREVALENCE: 7% to 60% depending on definition
PREDOMINANT SEX: Female
AT-RISK POPULATION
No consistent findings regarding:
- Age
- Parity
- Educational status
- Race
- Income
- Marital status

RISK FACTORS
Lower:
- Frequency of intercourse
- Levels of desire and arousal
- Orgasmic response
- Physical and emotional satisfaction
- General happiness

HISTORICAL FACTORS
- Pain parameters
  1. Character
  2. Location (Introital/middle/deep)
  3. Onset
  4. Duration
  5. Timing
  6. Chronicity
  7. Cyclicity
  8. Recurrence
- Gynecologic history
  1. History of STD
  2. History of HSV or HPV
  3. Other sexual dysfunctions
  4. Prior abdominal or gynecologic surgery
  5. Prior pelvic or abdominal radiation
  6. History of endometriosis, fibroids
  7. History of genital/uterine prolapse
  8. History of gynecologic infection
  9. History of pelvic pain
  10. History of menopausal symptoms
  11. Sexual misinformation
- OB history
  1. Lacerations
  2. Episiotomy
- General medical causes
  1. History of chronic diseases
  2. GI or GU symptoms
  3. Medications
  4. History of psychological disorders
  5. History of dermatologic condition
  6. Religious beliefs
  7. Generalized anxiety

PHYSICAL FINDINGS & CLINICAL PRESENTATION

- Primary vs. secondary dyspareunia
  1. Latter with history of pain-free coitus
- Visual inspection
  1. Discoloration
  2. Ulcerations
  3. Discharge
  4. Prolapse
  5. Dysplastic changes
  6. Infestations
- Physical examination
  1. Sensitivity to light touch
  2. Tenderness to palpation
  3. Genital prolapse
     a. Uterus
     b. Bladder
     c. Cervix
     d. Vagina
     e. Adnexa
     f. Rectum
     g. Bowel
  4. Ridges/septum
  5. Levator muscle tone
  6. Evidence of previous surgery
  7. Vaginal length/depth/caliber constrictions

ETIOLOGY

- Pathology or alteration/reduction of genital-associated tissue
- Psychosocial factors
- Marital/relationship discord
- History of sexual abuse

DIAGNOSIS

DIFFERENTIAL DIAGNOSIS

(Not an exhaustive list)
- Congenital deformities (septa/agenesis)
- Imperforate hymen
- Menopausal changes
- Atrophic tissue
- Impaired lubrication
- Psychogenic
- Vaginismus
- Inadequate foreplay
- Endometriosis
- Levator ani myalgia
- Chronic pelvic pain
- Previous surgery (posterior colporrhaphy/perineorrhaphy)
  1. Alteration in vaginal length/depth/caliber
  2. Adhesions
- Infectious
  1. Human papilloma
  2. Herpes simplex
  3. Candidiasis
  4. Tinea cruris
  5. Acute/chronic salpingitis/endometritis
- Pelvic carcinoma
- Previous radiation
- Adnexal attachment or tubal prolapse
- Pelvic tumor
- Uterine prolapse/malpositions/enlargement/retroversion
- Genital prolapse
- Cystocele/rectocele/enterocele
- Urethral/bladder pathology
- Pelvic congestion
- Vulvar vestibulitis
- Postcoital cystitis
- Broad ligament pathology
- Neuroma at the site of previous episiotomy
- Previous sexual abuse
- Vulvodynia
- Contact or allergic dermatitis
- Vitamin A, B, or C deficiency
- Equestrian dyspareunia
- Interstitial cystitis
- Pudendal neuralgia
- Myofacial pain syndrome
- Rectal pathology
- Structural abnormalities/alterations
  1. Muscle
  2. Bone
  3. Ligament

WORKUP

- History and physical examination are key
- If needed
  1. Colposcopy
  2. Cystoscopy
  3. Consider laparoscopy for unexplained deep dyspareunia

LABORATORY TESTS

- ESR
- WBC
- Wet mount
- Cultures
  1. Cervical
     a. Gonorrhea
     b. Chlamydia
  2. Vaginal
  3. Lesions
  4. Urine
- Vulva/vaginal/cervical biopsy
- Pap smear
- Herpes simplex virus antibodies
- Gonadotropin levels

IMAGING STUDIES

Pelvic/abdominal ultrasonography

TREATMENT

NONPHARMACOLOGIC THERAPY

- Patient education
- Discontinue exacerbating activity and irritants
- Lubrication with colitis
- Coital position changes: female superior position
- Warm or cool soaks
- Reassurance to patient of nonmalignant condition

- Psychosocial interventions
  1. Systemic desensitization techniques
  2. Behavior modification
- Vaginal dilators
- Vaginal muscle exercises and relaxation techniques
- Excision of pathologic tissue
- Surgical correction of altered/reduced/deformed tissues

ACUTE GENERAL THERAPY

- Topical lidocaine
- Corticosteroids
- Antiinfective agents
- Trigger point injections
- Massage
- Acupuncture
- TENS
- Stress reduction techniques
- Safe sexual practices
- Hormonal replacement therapy
- Antiviral agents
- Intralesional interferon
- Mild analgesics
- Antidepressants

CHRONIC Rx

All the previous plus:

- Set supportive visits, as needed
- Oral contraceptives
- Regular sexual activity
- Balanced diet
- Vitamin supplementation
- Proper hygiene

DISPOSITION

Most patients will have a reduction and/or resolution of their symptoms by using the appropriate therapeutic approaches.

REFERRAL

A multidisciplinary approach using the expertise of psychologists, dermatologists, gynecologic surgeons, infectious disease specialists, or urologists is helpful.

PEARLS & CONSIDERATIONS

- Dyspareunia is a symptom complex resulting from a multitude of etiologies, some of which are acting simultaneously.
- Uncovering the etiology of dyspareunia is predominately based on a comprehensive history and physical examination.
- The differential diagnoses can be sorted into superficial, intermediate, and deep dyspareunia categories.
- As with the physical evaluation of any painful condition, attempt, by precise touching (moistened cotton swab), palpation, or applied pressure, to reproduce the patient's chief complaint.
- Performing a one-finger pelvic exam, without concurrent abdominal palpation, allows for a more precise assessment of the source of genital pain.
- Individualize therapy.
- Initiate and maintain an honest diagnosis and compassionate demeanor with the patient and her mate.
- Be open-minded, approachable, nonjudgmental, and diligent in your search for a solution to help these often silently suffering patients.

SUGGESTED READINGS

Helm LJ: Evaluation and differential diagnosis of dyspareunia, *Am Fam Physician* 63:1535, 2001.

Nichols D: *Reoperative gynecologic and obstetric surgery,* ed 2, St Louis, 1997, Mosby.

AUTHOR: **DAVID I. KURSS, M.D.**

BASIC INFORMATION

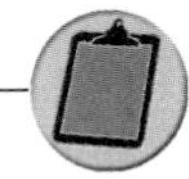

DEFINITION

Dystonia is characterized by involuntary muscle contractions (sustained or spasmodic) that lead to abnormal body movements or postures. Dystonia can be generalized or focal.

SYNONYMS

Blepharospasm
Oromandibular dystonia
Torticollis
Writer's cramp

ICD-9CM CODES
333.6 Dystonia musculorum deformans
335.7 Dystonia caused by drugs
333.7 Dystonia, torsion, symptomatic

EPIDEMIOLOGY & DEMOGRAPHICS

PREVALENCE: Estimated at 1 in 3000 persons.
PREDOMINANT SEX: Cervical dystonia has a 3:2 female preponderance.
PREDOMINANT AGE:
- Focal cervical dystonia usually has its onset in the fifth decade.
- Hereditary forms may have an onset in childhood or adulthood.

GENETICS: Autosomal dominant, autosomal recessive, and X-linked forms of dystonia have been identified.

PHYSICAL FINDINGS & CLINICAL PRESENTATION

Focal dystonias produce abnormal sustained muscle contractions in an area of the body:
- Neck (torticollis): most commonly affected site with a tendency for the head to turn to one side
- Eyelids (blepharospasm): involuntary closure of the eyelids
- Mouth (oromandibular dystonia): involuntary contraction of muscles of the mouth, tongue, or face
- Hand (writer's cramp) (Fig. 1-80)

Generalized dystonia affects multiple areas of the body and can lead to marked joint deformities.

ETIOLOGY

- Exact pathophysiology is unknown, thought to involve abnormalities of basal ganglia. Specifically, reduced and abnormal patterns of neuronal activity in the basal ganglia result in disinhibition of the motor thalamus and cortex leading to abnormal movement.
- Hereditary forms have been described, including the severe progressive form, dystonia musculorum deformans.
- Sporadic or idiopathic forms occur.
- Dystonia can occur secondary to other diseases such as CNS disease, hypoxia, kernicterus, Huntington's disease, Wilson's disease, Parkinson syndrome, lysosomal storage diseases.
- Acute dystonia can occur following treatment with drugs that block dopamine receptors, such as phenothiazines or butyrophenones.
- Tardive dyskinesia or dystonia can result from long-term treatment with antipsychotic drugs such as antimetics (e.g., phenothiazines) or antipsychotics (such as butyrophenones, e.g., haloperidol). It can also occur with levodopa, anticonvulsants, or ergots.

DIAGNOSIS

DIFFERENTIAL DIAGNOSIS

- Parkinson's disease
- Progressive supranuclear palsy
- Wilson's disease
- Huntington's disease
- Drug effects

WORKUP

History (including family history, birth history, medication use) and physical examination

LABORATORY TESTS

- Usually not helpful for establishing diagnosis
- Serum ceruloplasmin if Wilson's disease is suspected

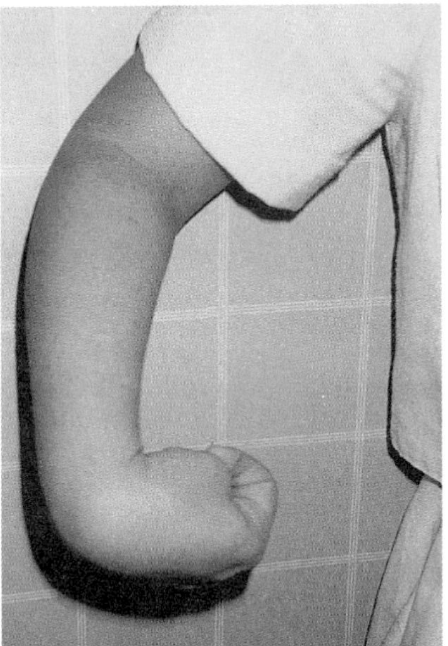

FIGURE 1-80 Focal dystonia of the distal right arm. (From Goldman L, Bennett JC [eds]: *Cecil textbook of medicine,* ed 21, Philadelphia, 2000, WB Saunders.)

IMAGING STUDIES

Primary dystonias are generally not associated with structural CNS abnormalities. CT scan or MRI of brain if a CNS lesion is suspected as a cause of secondary dystonia.

TREATMENT

NONPHARMACOLOGIC THERAPY

- Heat, massage, physical therapy to relieve pain
- Splints to prevent contractures

ACUTE Rx

For acute dystonic reactions to phenothiazines or butyrophenones: use diphenhydramine 50 mg IV or benztropine 2 mg IV

CHRONIC Rx

- Treatment is often ineffective.
- Slowly withdraw potentially offending agents.
- Diazepam, baclofen, or carbamazepine may be helpful.
- Trihexyphenidyl may be helpful in tardive dyskinesia or dystonia.
- Injections of botulinum toxin into the affected muscles can be used for refractory cases of focal dystonias.
- Surgical procedures including myectomy, rhizotomy, thalamotomy, or deep brain stimulation may be helpful for severe, refractory cases.

DISPOSITION

Spontaneous remission of focal cervical dystonia can occur, but dystonia is generally progressive and pharmacologic therapy is often ineffective.

REFERRAL

To neurologist for severe or refractory cases

SUGGESTED READING

Tan N-C et al: Hemifacial spasm and involuntary facial movements, *QJM* 95(8):493, 2002.

AUTHORS: **LYNN MCNICOLL, M.D.** and **MARK J. FAGAN, M.D.**

BASIC INFORMATION

DEFINITION

Echinococcosis is a chronic infection caused by the larval stage of several animal cestodes (flat worms) of the genus *Echinococcus*.

SYNONYMS

Hydatid disease

ICD-9CM CODES
122.9 *Echinococcus* infection

EPIDEMIOLOGY & DEMOGRAPHICS

INCIDENCE (IN U.S.): Seen primarily in immigrants; varies widely depending on areas of origin.
PREVALENCE (IN U.S.): See Incidence
PREDOMINANT SEX: Male = female
PREDOMINANT AGE: 20 to 50 yr of age
PEAK INCIDENCE: Presumed to be acquired in childhood or early adulthood in most cases.

PHYSICAL FINDINGS & CLINICAL PRESENTATION

- Signs of an enlarging mass lesion in a visceral site such as the liver, lungs, kidneys, bone, or CNS
- Occasional cyst rupture causing allergic manifestations such as urticaria, angioedema, or anaphylaxis that bring the patient to medical attention
- Incidental discovery of cysts by abdominal or thoracic imaging studies performed for other reasons

ETIOLOGY

- Four species of *Echinococcus: E. granulosus, E. multilocularis, E. oligarthrus,* and *E. vogeli.*
  1. *E. granulosus* is the cause of cystic hydatid disease.
  2. *E. multilocularis* and *E. vogeli* are the causes of alveolar and polycystic disease.
- The disease is transmitted to humans by infected canines (domestic or wild dogs, wolves, foxes) and seen most commonly in livestock-producing areas of the Middle East, Africa, Australia, New Zealand, Europe, and the Americas, including the southwestern U.S.
- Eggs are present in the feces of infected canines; human infection occurs by ingestion of viable eggs in contaminated food.
- It is common in many areas of the world, especially the Middle East.

DIAGNOSIS

DIFFERENTIAL DIAGNOSIS

- Cystic neoplasms
- Abscess (amebic or bacterial)
- Congenital polycystic disease

WORKUP

- Antibody assay
- Imaging study (CT scan, ultrasonography)
- Histologic examination of cyst or contents obtained by aspiration or resection (if possible) to confirm diagnosis

LABORATORY TESTS

Antibody assays (ELISA and Western blot): >90% sensitive and specific for liver cysts, but less accurate for cysts in other sites

IMAGING STUDIES

Ultrasonography and/or CT scan:
- Both are extremely sensitive for the detection of cysts, especially in the liver (Fig. 1-81).
- Both lack specificity and are inadequate to establish the diagnosis of echinococcosis with certainty.

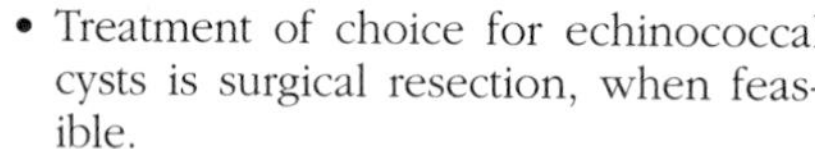

TREATMENT

NONPHARMACOLOGIC THERAPY

- Treatment of choice for echinococcal cysts is surgical resection, when feasible.
- If resection is not feasible, perform percutaneous drainage with instillation of 95% ethanol to prevent dissemination of viable larvae.
- Surgical therapy is followed by medical therapy with albendazole (see Acute General Rx).

ACUTE GENERAL Rx

For echinococcosis confined to the liver:
- Albendazole (400 mg bid for 28 days followed by 14 days of rest for at least three cycles)
- Mebendazole (50 to 70 mg/kg qd) if albendazole not available

CHRONIC Rx

See Acute General Rx.

DISPOSITION

- Long-term follow-up is necessary following surgical or medical therapy because of the high incidence of late relapse.
- Antibody assays and imaging studies are repeated every 6 to 12 mo for several years following successful surgical or medical therapy.

REFERRAL

- All patients for evaluation for possible surgical resection of cysts
- For consultation with a physician experienced in the medical and surgical management of echinococcosis

PEARLS & CONSIDERATIONS

COMMENTS

Surgical resection, if indicated, should be performed by surgeons experienced in the management of echinococcal cysts.

SUGGESTED READING

Eckert J, Deplazes P: Biological, epidemiological, and clinical aspects of echinococcosis, a zoonosis of increasing concern, *Clin Microbiol Rev* 17(1):107, 2004.

AUTHOR: **JOSEPH R. MASCI, M.D.**

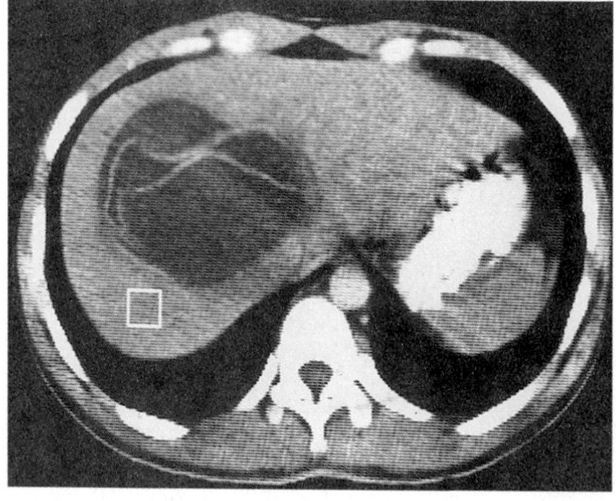

FIGURE 1-81 Computed tomography scan of an echinococcal cyst in a 25-year-old man, demonstrating the complex structure of the wall and the interior. (From Goldman L, Bennett JC [eds]: *Cecil textbook of medicine,* ed 21, Philadelphia, 2000, WB Saunders.)

BASIC INFORMATION

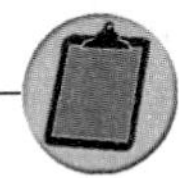

DEFINITION

Eclampsia is the occurrence of seizures or coma in a woman with preeclampsia, occurring at >20 wk gestation or <48 hr postpartum. Atypical eclampsia occurs at <20 wk gestation or as much as 14 days postpartum.

SYNONYMS

Toxemia
Seizures of pregnancy

ICD-9CM CODES
642.6 Eclampsia

EPIDEMIOLOGY & DEMOGRAPHICS

INCIDENCE: 1 case/150 to 3000 pregnancies; 2% to 4% of those with preeclampsia

RISK FACTORS: Multifetal gestation (3.6% in twin gestation), molar pregnancy, nonimmune hydrops fetalis, uncontrolled hypertension, preexisting hypertension, or renal disease

GENETICS: Increased incidence with first-degree relatives (sister or mother) having had eclampsia

PHYSICAL FINDINGS & CLINICAL PRESENTATION

- Seizure begins as facial twitching then spreads to generalized clonicotonic state, with cessation of respiration, followed by a postictal period of amnesia, agitation, and confusion.
- 40% have severe hypertension, 40% have mild to moderate hypertension, and 20% are normotensive.
- Generalized edema with rapid weight gain (>2 lb/wk) may be one of the earliest signs of eclampsia.
- Persistent occipital headache and hyperreflexia with clonus occur in 80% of patients with eclampsia; epigastric pain exists in 20% of these patients.

ETIOLOGY

Although the exact etiology is unknown, the common pathway relates to abnormalities in autoregulation of cerebral blood flow. This may involve transient vasospasm, ischemia, cerebral hemorrhage, and edema, occurring by a mechanism involving hypertensive encephalopathy, decreased colloid osmotic pressure, and prostaglandin imbalance.

DIAGNOSIS

DIFFERENTIAL DIAGNOSIS

- Preexisting seizure disorder
- Metabolic abnormalities (hypoglycemia, hyponatremia, hypocalcemia)
- Substance abuse
- Head trauma, infection (meningitis, encephalitis)
- Intracerebral bleeding or thrombosis
- Amniotic fluid embolism
- Space-occupying brain lesions or neoplasms
- Pseudoseizure

WORKUP

- Rule out other causes of seizures during pregnancy.
- Atypical presentations such as prolonged postictal state, status epilepticus, gestational age <20 wk or >48 hr postpartum, or signs of meningitis, substance abuse, or severe uncontrolled hypertension should prompt a search for other seizure etiologies.

LABORATORY TESTS

- Proteinuria: severe (49%), mild to moderate (29%), absent (22%)
- Hct: elevated secondary to hemoconcentration
- Platelet count: decreased; LFTs elevated in HELLP syndrome
- BUN and creatinine: elevated with renal involvement
- Serum electrolytes, glucose, calcium, toxicology profile: to rule out other causes of seizures
- Hyperuricemia: >6.9 mg/dl found in 70% of eclamptics
- ABG: maternal acidemia and hypoxia

IMAGING STUDIES

- CT scan or MRI indicated in atypical presentation, suspected intracerebral bleeding, focal neurologic deficit.
- There are abnormal findings, including cerebral edema, hemorrhage, and infarction, in 50% of patients.

TREATMENT

NONPHARMACOLOGIC THERAPY

- Airway protection (risk of aspiration)
- Supportive care during acute event

ACUTE GENERAL Rx

- Maintain airway, adequate oxygenation, and IV access.
- Fetal resuscitation, involving maternal oxygenation, left lateral positioning, and continuous fetal heart rate monitoring, is needed.
- Magnesium sulfate is drug of choice. Give magnesium sulfate 6 g IV load over 20 min, then 3 g/hr maintenance, for recurrent seizure prophylaxis. If repeated convulsion, may give an additional 2 g IV over 3 to 5 min. About 10% to 15% of patients will have a second seizure after initial loading dose. Check magnesium level 1 hr after loading dose, then q6h (therapeutic range 4 to 6 mg/dl). Antidote for toxicity is calcium gluconate 10 ml of 10% solution. Phenytoin has been used as an alternative in patients in whom magnesium sulfate is contraindicated (renal insufficiency, heart block, myasthenia gravis, hypoparathyroidism).
- Give sodium amobarbital 250 mg IV over 3 min for persistent seizures.
- Treat blood pressure if >160 mm Hg/110 mm Hg, with labetalol 20- to 40-mg IV bolus, hydralazine 10 mg IV, or nifedipine 10 to 20 mg sublingual q20min.
- Evaluate patient for delivery.

CHRONIC Rx

- The first priority is stabilization of the mother in terms of adequate oxygenation, hemodynamics, and laboratory abnormalities, such as associated coagulopathies.
- Cervical status and gestational age should be assessed. If unfavorable cervix and <30 wk consider C-section, otherwise consider induction.
- Controlled epidural is the anesthesia of choice for labor or C-section.
- Avoid general anesthesia in uncontrolled hypertension to minimize risk of catastrophic cerebral events.

DISPOSITION

The maternal mortality rate for eclampsia averages 5% to 6%. Morbidity is 25%, including placental abruption (10%), maternal apnea with fetal asphyxia, aspiration pneumonia, pulmonary edema (4%), renal failure, cardiopulmonary arrest, and coma.

REFERRAL

Because of the potential for serious permanent maternal and fetal sequelae, all cases should be managed by a team approach of obstetrician, neonatologist, and intensivist.

PEARLS & CONSIDERATIONS

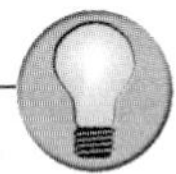

COMMENTS

- Eclampsia antepartum, 50%; intrapartum, 20%; and postpartum, 30%
- Postseizure there is an associated period of fetal bradycardia from 1 to 9 min; if there is evidence of fetal compromise beyond that time, consider alternative etiologies such as placental abruption (23% incidence).

SUGGESTED READING

Schroeder BM: ACOG practice bulletin on diagnosing and managing preeclampsia and eclampsia, *Am Fam Physician* 66:330, 2002.

AUTHOR: **SCOTT J. ZUCCALA, D.O.**

Ectopic Pregnancy

BASIC INFORMATION

DEFINITION

An ectopic pregnancy (EP) is one in which a fertilized ovum implants outside the endometrial lining of the uterus.

SYNONYMS

Abdominal pregnancy (1% to 2%)
Cervical pregnancy (0.5%)
Interstitial pregnancy (2% to 3%)
Ovarian pregnancy (1%)
Tubal pregnancy (97%)

ICD-9CM CODES
633 Ectopic pregnancy

EPIDEMIOLOGY & DEMOGRAPHICS

- 1% to 2% of pregnancies
- 13% of maternal deaths

PREVALENCE (IN U.S.): Increasing number of EPs; 17,800 reported cases in 1970 and 108,000 reported cases in 1992.
RISK FACTORS: Previous salpingitis, previous EP, previous tubal ligation, previous tuboplasty, IUD use, progestin-only pill, and assisted reproductive techniques

PHYSICAL FINDINGS & CLINICAL PRESENTATION

- Abdominal tenderness: 95%
- Adnexal tenderness: 87% to 99%
- Peritoneal signs: 71% to 76%
- Adnexal mass: 33% to 53%
- Enlarged uterus: 6% to 30%
- Shock: 2% to 17%
- Amenorrhea or abnormal vaginal bleeding: 75%
- Shoulder pain: 10%
- Tissue passage: 6% to 7%

ETIOLOGY

- Anatomic obstruction to zygote passage
- Abnormalities in tubal motility
- Transperitoneal migration of the zygote

DIAGNOSIS

DIFFERENTIAL DIAGNOSIS

- Corpus luteum cyst
- Rupture or torsion of ovarian cyst
- Threatened or incomplete abortion
- PID
- Appendicitis
- Gastroenteritis
- Dysfunctional uterine bleeding
- Degenerating uterine fibroids
- Endometriosis

WORKUP

1. The classic presentation of EP includes the triad of abnormal vaginal bleeding, pelvic pain, and an adnexal mass. Consider in all women with abdominal-pelvic pain and a positive pregnancy test
2. Culdocentesis is clinically useful when other diagnostic modalities are not readily available
   - Positive tap means nonclotting blood with Hct >12%.
   - Negative tap means clear or blood-tinged fluid.
   - Nondiagnostic tap means clotted blood or no fluid.
3. Laparoscopy

LABORATORY TESTS

- hCG: if normal IUP, 85% have doubling time of 2 days. If abnormal gestation, will show <66% increase of QhCG within 2 days. However, 13% of ectopic pregnancies have a normal doubling time (Section III, Ectopic Pregnancy)
- Progesterone: decreased production in EP, <5 ng/ml strongly predictive of abnormal pregnancy. If >25 ng/ml, strongly predictive of normal IUP
- Dropping Hct associated with tubal rupture
- Leukocytosis

IMAGING STUDIES

- Ultrasound: presence of an IUP rules out EP.
- If QhCG >6000 mIU/ml, should see IUP on abdominal scan, and QhCG >1500 mIU/ml for transvaginal scan.
- Findings on ultrasound in EP include:
  1. Empty uterus
  2. Adnexal mass
  3. Cul-de-sac fluid
  4. Fetal sac in tube
  5. Fetal cardiac activity in adnexa

TREATMENT

NONPHARMACOLOGIC THERAPY

Surgery: can be performed by laparoscopy if patient is stable or by laparotomy if patient is unstable. Salpingiosis: direct injection of chemotherapy into ectopic via laparoscopy, transvaginal ultrasound, or hysteroscopy.

- Conservative surgery-salpingostomy or segmental resection depends on tubal location and size of ectopic.
- Salpingectomy should be considered in the following circumstances:
  1. Ruptured tube
  2. Future fertility not desired
  3. Recurrent ectopic in the same tube
  4. Uncontrolled hemorrhage

ACUTE GENERAL Rx

- If the patient is stable and compliant may consider medical management with methotrexate. Patient should not have contraindications to methotrexate such as hepatic or renal disease, thrombocytopenia, leukopenia, or significant anemia. There should be no evidence of hemoperitoneum on transvaginal ultrasound. Ectopic should be <4 cm mass with QhCG <30,000 mIU/ml.
- Most common regimen is methotrexate 50 mg/m^2 body surface area. May require second dose or surgical intervention if QhCG increases or plateaus after 7 days.

CHRONIC Rx

Persistent EP results from residual trophoblastic tissue or secondary implantation after conservative surgery. There is a 5% incidence of persistent ectopic with conservative treatment.

DISPOSITION

If diagnosed and treated early (before rupture) prognosis is excellent for good recovery. Follow QhCG weekly until negative. Use reliable contraception until hCG negative. With subsequent pregnancies, follow QhCG and perform early ultrasound to confirm IUP. There is a 12% recurrence rate for EP.

REFERRAL

Should obtain gynecologic consultation if EP is suspected.

PEARLS & CONSIDERATIONS

COMMENTS

Patient information can be obtained through American College of Obstetricians and Gynecologists, 409 12th St SW, Washington, DC 20024-2188.

SUGGESTED READINGS

Della-Giustina D, Denny M: Ectopic pregnancy, *Emerg Med Clin North Am* 21(3):565, 2003.

Gracia CR, Barnhart KT: Diagnosing ectopic pregnancy: decision analysis comparing six strategies, *Obstet Gynecol* 97(3):464, 2001.

Lipscomb GH, Stovall TG, Ling FW: Nonsurgical treatment of ectopic pregnancy, *N Engl J Med* 343:1325, 2000.

AUTHOR: **GEORGE T. DANAKAS, M.D.**

BASIC INFORMATION

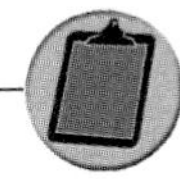

DEFINITION

Ehlers-Danlos syndrome (EDS) refers to a group of inherited, clinically variable, and genetically heterogeneous connective tissue disorders. EDS is characterized by skin hyperextensibility, skin fragility, joint laxity, and joint hyperextensibility. The revised classification scheme and diagnostic criteria (1998) are listed below.

ICD-9CM CODES
756.83 Ehlers-Danlos syndrome

EPIDEMIOLOGY & DEMOGRAPHICS

The prevalence of EDS is estimated to be about 1 in 5000 births, although it is somewhat higher in African Americans. Types I, II, and III are most prevalent. Types I and II account for approximately 80% of reported cases. In most cases, transmission is autosomal dominant except for V and IX (X-linked) and X and VIIC (autosomal recessive).

PHYSICAL FINDINGS & CLINICAL PRESENTATION

- Classic: (EDS I and II) hyperextensibility ("Gorlin's sign": ability to touch tip of tongue to nose), easy scarring and bruising ("cigarette-paper scars"), smooth, velvety skin, subcutaneous spheroids (small, firm cystlike nodules) along shins or forearms
- Hypermobility (EDS III): Joint hypermobility and some skin hypermobility with or without very smooth skin.
- Vascular (EDS IV): Thin, translucent skin with visible veins; marked bruising; pinched nose; acrogeria; spontaneous rupture of medium and large arteries and hollow organs, especially large intestine and uterus.
- Kyphoscoliotic (EDS VI): Characterized by joint hypermobility, progressive scoliosis; ocular fragility and possible globe rupture, mitral valve prolapse, and aortic dilation.
- Arthrochalasia (EDS VII A and B): Prominent joint hypermobility with subluxations, congenital hip dislocation, skin hyperextensibility, and tissue fragility.
- Dermatosparaxis (EDS VIIC): Severe skin fragility with decreased elasticity, bruising, hernias.
- Unclassified type:
  1. EDS V: Classic characteristics
  2. EDS VIII: Classic characteristics and periodontal disease
  3. EDS IX: Classic characteristics
  4. EDS X: Mild classic characteristics, mitral valve prolapse
  5. EDS XI: Joint instability

ETIOLOGY

Defects of collagen in extracellular matrices of multiple tissues (skin, tendons, blood vessels, and viscera) underlie all forms of EDS. EDS I and II are associated with defects in type V collagen, corresponding to mutations of the COL5A genes. EDS IV involves a deficiency in type III collagen, and several studies suggest that mutations of gene COL3A1 lead to this deficiency. EDS VIIA and VIIB result from a defect in type I collagen, caused by mutations in the COL1A1 and COL1A2 genes.

DIAGNOSIS

Diagnosis is based solely on clinical criteria. It is important to identify patients with EDS type IV because of the grave consequences of the disease.

DIFFERENTIAL DIAGNOSIS

Generally limited to types of EDSs. Some individuals with Marfan's syndrome have joint laxity. Some patients with osteogenesis imperfecta have joint laxity and easy bruising. Patients with joint hypermobility without skin changes are more likely to have familial joint hypermobility. Patients with autosomal dominant cutis laxa have skin redundancy and loss of elasticity but do not have easy bruising or tissue fragility.

WORKUP

Diagnosis is based solely on clinical criteria.

LABORATORY TESTS

- Limited biochemical assays and gene analyses are performed for known molecular defects.
- Plain radiographs may reveal calcified nodules along the shin or forearms, corresponding to the subcutaneous spheroids.
- Echocardiogram can identify MVP and aortic dilation.

TREATMENT

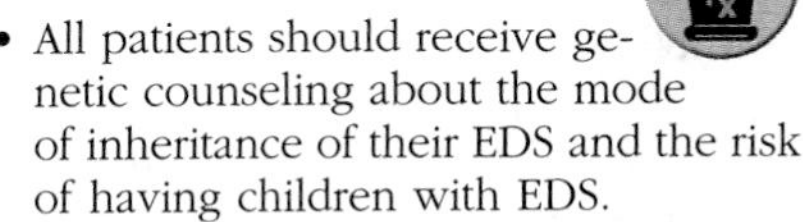

- All patients should receive genetic counseling about the mode of inheritance of their EDS and the risk of having children with EDS.
- Management of most skin and joint problems should be conservative and preventive. Joint hypermobility and pain in EDS usually does not require surgical intervention. Physical therapy to strengthen muscles is helpful. Surgical repair and tightening of joint ligaments can be performed but ligaments frequently will not hold sutures. Surgical intervention should be considered on an individual basis.
- Vascular type requires special surgical care because of increased friability of tissues. Women with EDS type IV should be counseled to avoid pregnancy.
- Patients should be advised to avoid contact sports, and elevated blood pressure should be aggressively treated.

DISPOSITION

Prognosis varies according to type of EDSs.

REFERRAL

Referral to cardiology, orthopedic surgery, and general surgery, and physical therapy as needed.

SUGGESTED READINGS

Pepin M et al: Clinical and genetic features of Ehlers-Danlos syndrome type IV, the vascular type, *N Engl J Med* 342:673, 2000.

Pyeritz R: Ehlers-Danlos syndrome, *N Engl J Med* 342(10):730, 2000

Pyeritz RE: Ehlers-Danlos syndromes. In Goldman L, Bennett JC (eds): *Cecil textbook of medicine,* ed 21, vol 1, Philadelphia, 2000, WB Saunders.

Shapiro, JR: Heritable disorders of structural proteins, *Kelley's textbook of rheumatology,* ed 6, Philadelphia, 2001, WB Saunders.

AUTHOR: **IRIS TONG, M.D.**

Ejaculation, Premature (PTG)

BASIC INFORMATION

DEFINITION

Premature ejaculation is a persistent or recurrent problem in which a male experiences orgasm or ejaculation in the early phases of sexual contact and before he wishes it. Other definitions have emphasized elapsed time after intromission (with durations of 30 sec to several min), number of thrusts, or rate of partner satisfaction. However, no absolute measure is applicable to the diverse numbers of men presenting with this problem.

SYNONYMS

Rapid ejaculation
Early ejaculation
Inadequate ejaculatory control

ICD-9CM CODES
F52.4 Premature ejaculation
(DSM-IV Code 302.75)

EPIDEMIOLOGY & DEMOGRAPHICS

PREVALENCE (IN U.S.): 7% to 40% of adult men
PREDOMINANT AGE: None defined
PEAK INCIDENCE: Adolescence and young adulthood
GENETICS: No identifiable genetic factors

PHYSICAL FINDINGS & CLINICAL PRESENTATION

- Complaint of ejaculation before, upon, or shortly after penetration
- Frequently associated anxiety related to either sexual activity or more generalized anxiety disorder
- Premature ejaculation secondary to a medical condition frequently associated with low anxiety, low desire, and/or erectile insufficiency

ETIOLOGY

- Increasingly thought to be a neurobiological phenomenon
- Different theoretical frameworks emphasizing anxiety related to performance or personal interactions, behavioral concepts of learned expectations related to early experience, or heightened penile sensitivity
- Organic factors are contributory in some individuals (e.g., abdominal or pelvic trauma or surgery, neuropathies, or urologic pathology such as prostatic urethritis)
- Emerging evidence that premature ejaculation is related to serotonergic neurotransmission

DIAGNOSIS

DIFFERENTIAL DIAGNOSIS

- In as many as 25% of men with complaints of premature ejaculation, partner is anorgasmic.
- In young adolescents, premature ejaculation may be normally experienced as a consequence of heightened excitation.

WORKUP

- History with a specific emphasis on sexual activities and beliefs
- Factors to be assessed include patient's subjective evaluation, degree of sexual satisfaction, and sense of control
- Collateral information from sexual partner when possible
- Additional history regarding surgery, trauma, and mycologic symptoms
- History of prescribed and recreational drugs (e.g., antidepressants, alcohol, opiates)

LABORATORY TESTS

Urinalysis and urine culture after prostatic massage to rule out prostatic infection

IMAGING STUDIES

None routinely indicated

TREATMENT

NONPHARMACOLOGIC THERAPY

- Behavioral and psychotherapeutic interventions: strongly guided by a specific theoretical framework; often inadequate data to suggest the superiority of any particular approach
- Use of condoms may reduce penile sensitivity
- Use of "pause-squeeze technique," (in which 4 sec of moderate pressure is applied to the frenulum to reduce ejaculatory urge) or "stop-start technique" may be helpful for some patients

GENERAL Rx

- Topical anesthetics increase ejaculatory latency.
- Anxiolytics (benzodiazepines) may be useful in individuals with anxiety.
- Selective serotonin reuptake inhibitors and clomipramine found to delay orgasm in men.
- Acute treatment with SSRIs not as effective as chronic use.
- Sildenafil may be superior to antidepressants in delaying ejaculation.

DISPOSITION

- Premature ejaculation is frequently a chronic, lifelong problem.
- There is gradual improvement with age but frequently a chronic, lifelong problem with few spontaneous remissions.

REFERRAL

Behavioral sex therapy or psychotherapy may be helpful to urologist if recurrent prostate infection is indicated

SUGGESTED READINGS

Bullard D, Caplan H: Sexual Problems. In Feldman MD, Christensen JF (eds): *Behavioral Medicine in Primary Care,* ed 2, New York, 2003, McGraw Hill.

Waldruger MD, Olivier B: Utility of selective serotonin reuptake inhibitors in premature ejaculation, *Curr Opin Investig Drugs* 5(7):743, 2004.

AUTHOR: **MITCHELL D. FELDMAN, M.D., M.PHIL.**

BASIC INFORMATION

DEFINITION

The three clinically significant disorders of ejaculation are ejaculatory failure, retrograde ejaculation, and premature ejaculation. Ejaculatory failure is the lack of production of seminal emission. Retrograde ejaculation is a backward flow of the emission into the bladder. Premature ejaculation is the inability to control ejaculation for sufficient time to allow adequate penetration and intercourse.

SYNONYMS

Ejaculation disorder
Sexual dysfunction
Male erectile disorder
Early or rapid ejaculation

ICD-9CM CODES
606.9 Male infertility unspecified
608.9 Unspecified disorder of male genital organs
302.72 Male erectile disorder
302.74 Orgasm inhibited male psychosexual
302.75 Premature ejaculation (psychosexual)

EPIDEMIOLOGY & DEMOGRAPHICS

Ejaculatory failure and retrograde ejaculation are disorders seen with diseases affecting the nervous system or as a result of anatomic genitourinary abnormalities. More commonly, disorders that result in erectile dysfunction (i.e., the inability to achieve or sustain an erection) can result in ejaculatory failure. Erectile dysfunction increases with age and impacts 80% of men in their eighties. Premature ejaculation is a common functional problem seen mostly in younger men. Up to 38% of men in the United States report premature ejaculation.

PHYSICAL FINDINGS & CLINICAL PRESENTATION

Varies with disorder:

- Ejaculatory failure: no ejaculate is expelled; physical findings may be normal or may reveal nervous system dysfunction (e.g., spinal cord injury) or anatomic abnormality (e.g., duct obstruction); results in infertility. If ejaculatory failure is secondary to erectile dysfunction (i.e., the inability to achieve or sustain an erection), differentiation between psychogenic and organic etiology is important. Nocturnal penile tumescence is normal in psychogenic disorders. In erectile dysfunction, evaluation for signs and symptoms of endocrinopathies is important.
- Retrograde ejaculation: no ejaculate is expelled at orgasm and subsequent bladder void reveals cloudy urine; physical examination is often normal but may reveal autonomic nervous system dysfunction or anatomic genitourinary abnormality; results in infertility.
- Premature ejaculation: ejaculation occurs quickly after excitation; physical examination is normal.

ETIOLOGY

- Anatomical lesions: duct obstruction, open or transurethral prostatectomy, urethral or bladder procedures, congenital urethral anomalies, vascular abnormality
- Neurologic disorders: spinal cord injury, cortical lesions, peripheral neuropathies
- Endocrinolopathies: thyroid disorder, hypogonadism, prolactinemia, diabetes
- Medications/substance abuse: antihypertensives, antidepressants, antipsychotics, histamine blockers, histamine blockers, nicotine, alcohol, marijuana
- Psychologic factors: depression, anxiety, psychotic disorders, social stressors

DIAGNOSIS

WORKUP

- History, physical examination, and laboratory analysis
- Imaging occasionally

HISTORY

- General: assess medication history (antihypertensives, antidepressants, antipsychotics, histamine blockers, nicotine, etc.), substance abuse (alcohol, marijuana, opiates, etc.), and past medical history.
- Genitourinary: assess history of genitourinary surgeries, infections, and abnormalities. Evaluate for symptoms of decreased libido, erectile dysfunction, nocturnal penile tumescence, and ejaculation timing and quantity.
- Neuro: assess history of spinal cord injury, cortical lesions, and peripheral neuropathies. Evaluate symptoms of changes in sensory or motor function.
- Endocrine: assess history of thyroid disorder, hypogonadism, prolactinemia, and diabetes. Evaluate for changes in weight, palpitation, tremor, fatigue, neck mass, decreased libido, erectile dysfunction, breast discharge, headaches, visual problems, polyuria, and polydipsia.
- Cardiovascular: assess history of coronary artery disease, arrhythmias, or peripheral vascular disease.
- Psych: assess history of depression, anxiety, and psychotic disorders. Evaluate social stressors and psychosexual history.

PHYSICAL EXAMINATION

- Psychologic: explore patient's mental status and relationship with partner.
- Neurologic: evaluate for sensory or motor deficits.
- Genitourinary: evaluate anatomic abnormality, testicular size, and prostate examination.
- Cardiovascular: evaluate blood pressure, peripheral pulse, heart rate, and rhythm.
- Other: evaluate for galactorrhea, visual field deficits, and goiter.

LABORATORY TESTS

- Postorgasmic urine should be evaluated for spermatozoa, viscosity, and fructose to differentiate ejaculatory failure from retrograde ejaculation. Evaluate for urinary or prostatic infection.
- Fasting blood glucose, TSH, testosterone, and prolactin.

IMAGING STUDIES

- Transrectal ultrasound or vasography can show dilated seminal vesicles or ejaculatory ducts if obstruction is present.
- Doppler studies to evaluate penile-brachial pressure index (evaluates loss of systolic blood pressure between arm and penis).
- Intracorporeal injections of prostaglandin E1 should be considered to distinguish vascular versus nonvascular etiologies. Erections achieved in patients with nonvascular etiologies.

TREATMENT

NONPHARMACOLOGIC THERAPY

- Ejaculatory failure: vibratory or electrical stimulation of emission.
- Retrograde ejaculation: viable sperm can be recovered from the bladder.
- Premature ejaculation: sex therapy.

GENERAL Rx

- Ejaculatory failure: offending drugs should be eliminated if possible. Sildenafil or vardenafil 1 hr before sexual activity may help for erectile dysfunction. Must avoid nitrates with this class of drugs. Intracavernosal injections of vasodilators (papaverine, alprostadil, or prostaglandin E1) can also be considered. If hypogonadism, consider testosterone replacement; if hypothyroid, consider thyroxine replacement; and if diabetes, blood glucose control, and cardiovascular risk assessment are important.
- Retrograde ejaculation: α-adrenergic sympathomimetics such as pseudoephedrine, ephedrine, or phenylpropanolamine may convert retrograde to antegrade ejaculation.
- Premature ejaculation: psychotropic medications such as sertraline, fluoxetine, and clomipramine have shown success in delaying premature ejaculation. Topical anesthetics such as lidocaine cream have also been used. Sildenafil (Viagra) or vardenafil (Levitra) 1 hr before sexual activity may help for premature ejaculation. Must avoid nitrates with this class of drugs.

SURGICAL Rx

- Correction of anatomic abnormalities, such as relieving obstruction or improving the competence of the internal urethral sphincter apparatus

REFERRAL

- All fertility issues and suspected anatomic problems should be referred to a urologist. Professional psychotherapy and sex therapy should be considered for some patients. Endocrine input should be considered for thyrotoxicosis, prolactinemia, diabetes, and hypogonadism.

SUGGESTED READINGS

Levine SB: Marital sexual dysfunction: ejaculation disturbance, *Ann Intern Med* 84(5):575, 1976.

Master VA, Turek PJ: Ejaculation physiology and dysfunction, *Urol Clin North Am* 28(2):363, 2001.

Miller TA: Diagnostic evaluation of erectile dysfunction, *Am Fam Physician* 611:95, 2000.

Murphy JB, Lipshultz LI: Abnormalities of ejaculation, *Urol Clin North Am* 14(3):583, 1987.

AUTHORS: **MICHAEL PICCHIONI, M.D.,** and **GEETHA GOPALAKRISHNAN, M.D.**

BASIC INFORMATION

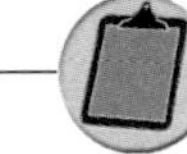

DEFINITION

Electrical injuries are wounds occurring as a result of contact with an electrical current.

SYNONYMS

None

ICD-9CM CODES
994.8 Electrical shock, nonfatal

EPIDEMIOLOGY & DEMOGRAPHICS

- Electrical injuries cause approximately 1000 deaths annually, with two thirds occurring in persons between 15 and 40 yr of age.
- Electrical injury ranks fifth as the cause of occupational fatalities.
- Electrical injuries account for 4% to 6.5% of all admissions to burn units.
- Deaths typically occur in the young.
- Most electrical burns in adults are occupationally related.
- Children commonly experience oral burns from electrical appliances.

PHYSICAL FINDINGS & CLINICAL PRESENTATION

- Depending on the extent of injury, the patient may be unconscious, seizing, or confused and unable to present a history
- Extensive burns (~10% to 25% of the body surface)
  1. Located over the entry and exit sites
  2. Most common entry sites are the hands and skull
  3. Most common exit sites are the heels
  4. "Kissing burns" over the flexor creases
  5. Superficial partial thickness
  6. Oral burns in children
  7. Bleeding from the labial artery may present 7 to 10 days after the injury
- Cardiac arrest (asystole or ventricular fibrillation) may be the initial presenting rhythm
- Pulseless extremities
- Fractures
- Compartment syndrome from severe muscle tissue damage
- Headaches
- Weakness and paresthesias
- Motor and sensory deficits

ETIOLOGY

- Electricity causes tissue injury by converting electrical energy into heat.
- The higher the electrical voltage, the greater the tissue destruction.
- The longer the duration of contact with the electrical source, the greater the damage.
  1. Direct current (DC) contact causes a single muscle contraction throwing the patient away from the source.
  2. Alternating current (AC) contact precipitates a tetanic contraction, not allowing the patient to withdraw from the source and prolonging the duration of contact.
  3. Therefore AC contact is more ominous than DC contact.
- Electrical injuries are arbitrarily divided into high voltage (1000 volts) and low voltage (500 volts).
- The entry and exit path the electrical current travels in the body determines which tissues are affected.

DIAGNOSIS

WORKUP

A detailed workup is indicated because the physical examination may not reveal the extent of damage that has occurred.

LABORATORY TESTS

- CBC
- Electrolytes
- BUN/creatinine
- Arterial blood gases
- Myoglobin
- Creatinine kinase CPK with isoenzyme fractionation
- Urinalysis including screening for myoglobinuria
- LFTs
- Type and cross-match
- EKG

IMAGING STUDIES

- C-spine films in patients with suspected spinal injury
- X-ray any suspicious area for bone fractures
- CT scan of the head and skull in patients with major head injury
- Technetium pyrophosphate scanning may locate areas of myonecrosis

TREATMENT

NONPHARMACOLOGIC THERAPY

- If at the scene of the injury, make sure the power source is turned off before approaching the victim
- Maintain urine output of at least 50 cc/hr with IV fluids
- Cardiac monitoring
- Oxygen
- Tetanus prophylaxis

ACUTE GENERAL Rx

- Alkalinization of the urine (sodium bicarbonate 50 mEq in 1 L of normal saline) is indicated in patients who are suspected of having myoglobinuria.
- Furosemide 20 to 40 mg PO or IV may be used to force diuresis.
- Mannitol 12.5 g/kg/hr assists in maintaining diuresis.
- Seizures are treated in the standard fashion.
- Treat burns with sulfadiazine silver dressings.

CHRONIC Rx

- Asymptomatic patients with a normal physical examination, negative urinalysis, and normal ECG findings may be discharged home with close follow-up.

DISPOSITION

- Patients with severe burns should be transferred to the regional burn center.
- Complications of electrical injuries include:
  1. Infection
  2. Renal failure from rhabdomyolysis
  3. Seizure disorder
  4. Fasciotomies
  5. Amputation
- Delayed neurologic damage may present as ascending paralysis, amytrophic lateral sclerosis, or transverse myelitis weeks to years after the injury.
- Vascular damage may also present in a delayed fashion.

REFERRAL

A general surgery consultation is recommended in any patient with significant electrical injuries and tissue damage. Plastic surgery is recommended in children with oral burns. Ophthalmology consultation is also recommended screening for cataract formation.

PEARLS & CONSIDERATIONS

COMMENTS

- Electrical injuries are caused by:
  1. Direct contact with the electrical source.
  2. Conversion of electrical energy to heat.
  3. Blunt trauma after being thrown from the electrical source or from continuous muscle contraction (tetany).
- Electrical burns are the most frequent cause of amputation in burn units.
- Cataract formation has been shown to occur within 1 to 24 mo following a high-voltage electrical injury in approximately 5% to 20% of patients.
- The absence of physical findings on the initial examination does not exclude extensive underlying tissue damage.

SUGGESTED READINGS

Fish RM: Electrical injury, part III: cardiac monitoring indications, the pregnant patient, and lightning, *J Emerg Med* 18(2):181, 2000.

Jeschke RJ, Herndon RE: Electrical injuries: a 30-year review, *J Trauma* 46(5):933, 1999.

AUTHOR: **PETER PETROPOULOS, M.D.**

BASIC INFORMATION

DEFINITION

Electromechanical dissociation (EMD) is the absence of effective cardiac output in the presence of organized electrical activity.

SYNONYMS

Pulseless electrical activity (PEA)

ICD-9CM CODES
426.89 Electromechanical dissociation

EPIDEMIOLOGY & DEMOGRAPHICS

- Less frequent than VT/VF, asystole
- May be last electrical activity of dying myocardium

PHYSICAL FINDINGS & CLINICAL PRESENTATION

PRIMARY EMD:
- Organized electrical activity (not VT/VF)
- No palpable pulse

SECONDARY EMD:
Primary EMD and may also have:
- Bradycardia: drug overdose
- Tachycardia: hypovolemia, massive PE
- Decreased JVP: hypovolemia
- Elevated JVP and no pulse with CPR: cardiac tamponade, massive PE, tension pneumothorax
- Absent unilateral breath sounds with mechanical ventilation and tracheal deviation: tension pneumothorax
- Cyanosis: hypoxia

ETIOLOGY

PRIMARY EMD: Myocardial excitation and contraction uncoupling secondary to advanced heart muscle disease
SECONDARY EMD: Because of changes in the loading conditions of the heart, ischemia, myocardial depressants
- Massive MI
- Massive PE
- Hypovolemia
- Cardiac tamponade
- Tension pneumothorax
- Hypothermia
- Hyperkalemia/hypokalemia
- Hypomagnesemia
- Hypoxia
- Acidosis
- Drug overdose: β-blockers, calcium channel blockers, digoxin, tricyclic antidepressants

DIAGNOSIS

DIFFERENTIAL DIAGNOSIS

- Pseudo-EMD
- Idioventricular rhythm
- Postdefibrillation idioventricular rhythm
- Ventricular escape rhythm
- Bradyasystolic rhythm

WORKUP

- Stabilizing patient and workup to establish etiology of EMD should proceed simultaneously
- History, physical examination, laboratory tests, imaging studies

LABORATORY TESTS

- Potassium, magnesium
- Arterial blood gas
- ECG (Fig. 1-82):

Low voltage: tamponade
Right heart strain: PE, pneumothorax
Arrhythmias: MI, metabolic abnormalities, drug effects
ST changes, Q waves: MI

IMAGING STUDIES

Guided by clinical suspicion of reversible causes and what can be performed without compromising patient safety:
- Chest x-ray: rule out pneumothorax
- Pulmonary arteriogram: rule out PE
- Echocardiogram: rule out pseudo-EMD, tamponade, valve dysfunction, and atrial myxoma
- Abdominal x-ray: rule out rupture of abdominal aortic aneurysm

TREATMENT

NONPHARMACOLOGIC THERAPY

- Activate emergency medical service system
- Begin CPR
- Intubate and ventilate
- Obtain IV access
- Continuous cardiac monitor
- Confirm absence of blood flow with Doppler ultrasound, arterial line, or bedside echocardiogram

ACUTE GENERAL Rx

NOTE: Epinephrine and atropine can be given via tracheal tube. Give 2 to 2.5 times the IV dose in 10 ml of normal saline or distilled water.
- Epinephrine 1 mg IV push, repeat q3-5min
- If bradycardic (<60 beats/min): atropine 1 mg IV q3-5min to a maximum of 3 mg
- If preexisting hyperkalemia: sodium bicarbonate 1 mEq/kg
- Treat specific cause if known

PROBABLY HELPFUL:
Sodium bicarbonate 1 mEq/kg if:
- Preexisting bicarbonate responsive acidosis
- Tricyclic antidepressant overdose
- Drug overdoses that respond to alkalization of urine

POSSIBLY HELPFUL:
Sodium bicarbonate 1 mEq/kg if:
- Intubated and prolonged arrest
- Successful resuscitation after prolonged arrest

Epinephrine at higher doses:
- 2 to 5 mg IV push q3-5min
- 1 mg, 3 mg, 5 mg IV push, 3 min apart
- 0.1 mg/kg IV push q3-5min

DISPOSITION

- Poor overall. Of hospitalized patients who develop EMD, <15% survive to discharge. Survival rates much lower in patients with prehospital EMD.
- Prompt treatment may be successful in secondary EMD.

SUGGESTED READINGS

ECG Guidelines: Part 6: advanced cardiovascular life support: section 7: algorithm approach to ACLS emergencies, *Circulation* 102(suppl I):I136, 2000.

Emergency Cardiac Care Committee and Subcommittees, American Heart Association: Guidelines for cardiopulmonary resuscitation and emergency cardiac care, part III: adult advanced cardiac life support, *JAMA* 268(16):2199, 1992.

AUTHOR: **SUDEEP K. AULAKH, M.D., F.R.C.P.C.**

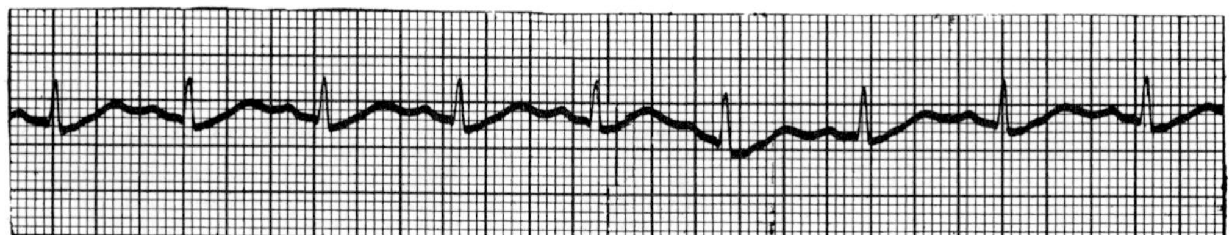

FIGURE 1-82 Sinus rhythm with electromechanical dissociation (EMD). Although the ECG showed sinus rhythm, the patient had no pulse or blood pressure. In this case the EMD was a result of depressed myocardial function after a cardiac arrest. (From Goldberg AL: *Clinical electrocardiography,* ed 5, St Louis, 1994, Mosby.)

BASIC INFORMATION

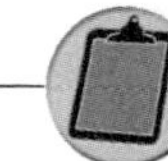

DEFINITION

An accumulation of pus in the pleural space, most often caused by bacterial infection.

ICD-9CM CODES
511.9

EPIDEMIOLOGY & DEMOGRAPHICS

Empyema occurs in a variety of clinical settings. Most often it is seen as a complication of bacterial pneumonia, especially in association with pneumococcal or anaerobic infection. Empyema may also occur as a complication of thoracic surgery, penetrating chest trauma, or bronchopleural fistulae resulting from malignancy or lung biopsy. Although pleural effusions occur in many other disease states, most notably congestive heart failure, end-stage liver disease, collagen-vascular, and malignancy, the term *empyema* refers to the presence of pus in the pleural space and does not encompass most pleural effusions.

PHYSICAL FINDINGS & CLINICAL PRESENTATION

The clinical presentation of empyema may be abrupt and dramatic or chronic and insidious depending on the etiologic agent and host factors. Empyema complicating pneumococcal pneumonia typically presents as progressive pleuritic chest pain, persistent fever, and other sustained signs and symptoms of infection. In the case of anaerobic empyema, particularly that caused by the actinomycetes, the clinical picture may be dominated by nonrespiratory symptoms and signs, such as weight loss, malaise, and a slowly enlarging chest wall mass. As a complication of thoracic trauma or surgery, empyema typically results from superinfection of blood or other material in the pleural space several days following the event.

The physical findings of empyema are those of pleural effusion. Decreased breath sounds and dullness to percussion over the involved part of the thorax is typical. Systemic signs of infection include fever, tachycardia, leukocytosis and, occasionally, warmth and erythema over the involved area.

ETIOLOGY

Empyema results from the accumulation of infected material within the pleural space. Infection of the lung parenchyma with *Streptococcosis pneumoniae, Hemophilus influenzae, Staphylococcus aureus, Legionella species,* or a variety of oral anaerobic bacteria.

DIAGNOSIS

DIFFERENTIAL DIAGNOSIS

- Uninfected parapneumonic effusion
- Congestive heart failure
- Malignancy involving the pleura
- Tuberculous pleurisy
- Collagen vascular disease (particularly rheumatoid lung and systemic lupus erythematosus)

LABORATORY TESTS

- Complete blood count; arterial blood gas
- Blood cultures
- Pleural fluid analysis including cell count and differential, LDH and protein levels, pH, Gram stain and culture. Empyema fluid is expected to have the characteristics of pleural exudates with a ratio of pleural fluid protein to serum protein of >0.5 or a ratio of pleural fluid LDH to serum LDH of >0.6. In addition, the presence of gross pus; visible organisms on Gram stain of the pleural fluid; pleural fluid glucose <50 mg/dL or pleural fluid pH below 7 are characteristic of empyema. Any of these latter findings justify immediate drainage by chest tube or surgery because of the high risk of loculation and progressive systemic infection.

IMAGING STUDIES

- Chest roentgenogram
- Lateral decubitus view to establish the presence of free fluid in the pleural space
- Computed tomography to establish the presence of fluid loculation, underlying mass lesions, and other intrathoracic pathology

TREATMENT

NONPHARMACOLOGIC THERAPY

Prompt drainage by thoracostomy (chest tube) or open thoracotomy

ACUTE GENERAL THERAPY

- Maintenance of drainage until infection controlled
- Antibiotics directed at suspected or proven bacterial or fungal pathogens
- Thoracoscopy or instillation of thrombolytic agents (streptokinase or urokinase) may be considered in refractory, loculated empyema.

CHRONIC THERAPY

- If thorough drainage cannot be accomplished, open thoracotomy with pleural decortication may be required.
- Lung function should be monitored following completion of therapy.

DISPOSITION

- Hospitalization
- Supplemental oxygen with ventilatory support if necessary

REFERRAL

Consultation by infectious diseases, pulmonary or thoracic surgical specialists may be appropriate.

PEARLS & CONSIDERATIONS

COMMENTS

- Empyema caused by actinomycetes may present with erosion through the chest wall and formation of a fistulous tract.
- Nosocomial infection caused by relatively resistant bacterial or fungal pathogens may result in empyema in patients with indwelling thoracostomy tubes.

SUGGESTED READINGS

De Hoyos A, Sundaresan S: Thoracic empyema, *Surg Clin North Am* 82(3):643, 2002.

Jaffe A, Cohen G: Thoracic empyema, *Arch Dis Child* 88(10):839, 2003.

Pierrepoint MJ et al: Pigtail catheter drain in the treatment of empyema thoracis, *Arch Dis Child* 87(4):331, 2002.

AUTHOR: **JOSEPH R. MASCI, M.D.**

BASIC INFORMATION

DEFINITION

Acute viral encephalitis is an acute febrile syndrome with evidence of meningeal involvement and of derangement of the function of the cerebrum, cerebellum, or brainstem.

SYNONYMS

Arboviral encephalitis
Brainstem encephalitis
Acute necrotizing encephalitis
Rasmussen encephalitis
Encephalitis lethargica

ICD-9CM CODES
049.9 Viral encephalitis NOS

EPIDEMIOLOGY & DEMOGRAPHICS

INCIDENCE (IN U.S.): About 20,000 cases/yr are reported to the CDC.
PREVALENCE (IN U.S.): Unknown
PREDOMINANT SEX: Male = female
PREDOMINANT AGE: Any age
PEAK INCIDENCE: Any age
GENETICS: No specific genetic or congenital predisposition

ETIOLOGY

- Can be caused by a host of viruses, with herpes simplex the most common virus identified
- Arboviruses: agents causing Eastern equine encephalitis, Western equine encephalitis, St. Louis encephalitis, Venezuelan equine encephalitis, California virus encephalitis, Japanese B encephalitis, Murray Valley and West Nile encephalitis, Russian spring-summer encephalitis, as well as other lesser known agents
- Also implicated: rabies-causing agents, CMV, Epstein-Barr, varicella-zoster, echo virus, mumps, adenovirus, coxsackie, rubeola, and herpes viruses
- Meningoencephalitis: acute retroviral infection

PHYSICAL FINDINGS & CLINICAL PRESENTATION

- Initially, fever and evidence of meningeal irritation
- Headache and stiff neck
- Later, development of signs of cortical dysfunction: lethargy, coma, stupor, weakness, seizures, facial weakness, as well as brainstem findings
- Cerebellar findings: ataxia, nystagmus, hypotonia; myoclonus, cranial nerve palsies, and abnormal tendon reflexes
- Patients with rabies: hydrophobia, anxiety, facial numbness, psychosis, coma, or dysarthria
- Rarely, movement disorders, such as chorea, hemiballismus, or dystonia
- Recall of a prodromal viral-like illness (this finding is not at all uniform)

DIAGNOSIS

DIFFERENTIAL DIAGNOSIS

- Bacterial infections: brain abscess, toxic encephalopathies, TB
- Protozoal infections
- Behçet's disease
- Lupus encephalitis
- Sjögren's syndrome
- Multiple sclerosis
- Syphilis
- Cryptococcus
- Toxoplasmosis
- Brucellosis
- Leukemic or lymphomatous meningitis
- Other metastatic tumors
- Lyme disease
- Cat-scratch disease
- Vogt-Koyanagi-Harada syndrome
- Mollaret's meningitis

WORKUP

- Lumbar puncture to reveal pleocytosis, usually lymphocytic although neutrophils may be seen early on
- Usually, elevated CSF protein
- Normal or low CSF glucose
- In herpes simplex encephalitis: RBCs and xanthochromia
- EEG changes showing periodic high-voltage sharp waves in the temporal regions and slow wave complexes suggestive of herpes encephalitis
- CT scan and MRI to reveal edema and hemorrhage in the frontal and temporal lobes
- Arboviral infections suspected during outbreaks in specific areas
- Rising titers of neutralizing antibodies from the acute to the convalescent stage demonstrated but often not helpful in the acutely ill patient
- Polymerase chain reaction that amplifies DNA from the CSF for herpes simplex encephalitis
- Rarely, brain biopsy to assist in the diagnosis; viral culture of cerebral tissue obtained if biopsy done
- Classic herpetic skin lesions suggestive of herpes encephalitis
- In diagnosing arboviral encephalitis:
  1. Presence of antiviral IgM within the first few days of symptomatic disease; detected and quantified by ELISA
  2. Unusual to recover an arbovirus from the blood or CSF

LABORATORY TESTS

- Aside from the lumbar puncture, most other laboratory studies are nonspecific.
- Skin lesions and urine may be cultured for herpes simplex and CMV.

TREATMENT

ACUTE GENERAL Rx

- Supportive care, frequent evaluation, and neurologic examination
- Ventilatory assistance for patients who are moribund or at risk for aspiration
- Avoidance of infusion of hypotonic fluids to minimize the risk of hyponatremia
- For patients who develop seizures: anticonvulsant therapy and follow-up in a critical care setting
- For comatose patients:
  1. Aggressive care to avoid decubiti, contractures, and DVT
  2. Close attention to weights, input/output, and serum electrolytes
- Acyclovir 30 mg/kg/day IV for 14 days for herpes simplex encephalitis
- Short courses of corticosteroids to control brain edema and prevent herniation
- In patients with suspected rabies:
  1. Human rabies immune globulin (HRIG) should be given at a dose of 20 U/kg.
  2. Active immunization may be stimulated by recently developed rabies vaccine, which is grown on a human diploid cell line (HDCV) and has reduced the number of doses needed to five.
  3. If suspect animal can be found, observe closely for 10 days to detect rabid behavior.
  4. If signs are seen, animal should be euthanized and its brain examined for signs of rabies.
- No specific pharmacologic therapy for most other viral pathogens

CHRONIC Rx

Some patients may develop permanent neurologic sequelae; these patients will gain benefit from intensive rehabilitation programs, including physical, occupational, and speech therapy.

SUGGESTED READINGS

Beckwith WH et al: Isolation of eastern equine encephalitis virus and West Nile virus from crows during increased arbovirus surveillance in Connecticut, 2000, *Am J Trop Med Hyg* 66(4):422, 2002.

Centers for Disease Control and Prevention: Provisional surveillance summary of the West Nile virus epidemic—United States, January-November, 2002, *MMWR Morb Mortal Wkly Rep* 51(50):1129, 2002.

Miravalle A, Roos KL: Encephalitis complicating smallpox vaccination, *Arch Neurol* 60(7):925, 2003.

Romero JR, Newland JG: Viral meningitis and encephalitis: traditional and emerging viral agents, *Semin Pediatr Infect Dis* 14(2):72, 2003.

Srey VH et al: Etiology of encephalitis syndrome among hospitalized children and adults in Takeo, Cambodia, 1999-2000, *Am J Trop Med Hyg* 66(2):200, 2002.

AUTHOR: **JOSEPH J. LIEBER, M.D.**

BASIC INFORMATION

DEFINITION

Clinical syndrome of global cognitive impairment that is characterized by impaired arousal, inattention, and disorientation.

SYNONYMS

Delirium, acute confusional state

ICD-9CM CODES
348.3 encephalopathy NOS
348.30 encephalopathy unspecified
348.31 metabolic encephalopathy
348.39 other encephalopathy
349.82 toxic encephalopathy

EPIDEMIOLOGY & DEMOGRAPHICS

POINT PREVALENCE: 1.1% of adults in the general population >55 years of age, 10%-40% of hospitalized elderly, and 60% of nursing home patients >75 years of age

RISK FACTORS: age, cancer, AIDS, terminal illness, bone marrow transplant, surgery

CLINICAL PRESENTATION

- The essential feature of encephalopathy is the patient's inability to maintain a coherent stream of thought or action.
- The history may often suggest a waxing and waning of the level of arousal and general cognitive ability.
- Because toxins and metabolic disturbances are common causes of encephalopathy, the history should focus on exposure to toxins (including medications) and symptoms suggesting a concurrent illness such as a urinary tract infection or pneumonia.
- Common to all encephalopathies is a fluctuating level of arousal, poor attention, and disorientation.
- Some patients may appear agitated and others lethargic.
- Delusions (fixed false beliefs) and hallucinations are common.
- Asterixis (negative myoclonus) is extremely common.
- Other physical findings may vary depending on the underlying cause of encephalopathy: fever, ascites, jaundice, and tachycardia.

ETIOLOGY

- The final common pathway of all causes of encephalopathy is widespread cortical and subcortical neuronal dysfunction. The causes may be structural or functional.
- Many conditions are reversible and carry a good prognosis if treated in a timely manner.
- Organ failure (e.g., hepatic encephalopathy, hypoxia, hypercapnia, uremia).
- Infection—systemic (e.g., urinary tract, pneumonia) or involving the central nervous system (e.g., meningitis, encephalitis).
- Toxin ingestion or withdrawal (e.g., alcohol, medications, recreational drugs).
- Metabolic disturbances—hyperosmolar states, hypernatremia, hyponatremia, hyperglycemia, hypoglycemia, hypercalcemia, hypophosphatemia, acidosis, alkalosis.
- Endocrinopathy—hyperthyroidism, hypothyroidism, Cushing's syndrome, adrenal insufficiency, pituitary failure.
- Neoplasm—tumors of the central nervous system, primary or metastatic. Also effect of distant tumors (e.g., paraneoplastic limbic encephalitis).
- Nutritional deficiency, mostly in alcoholics and chronically ill patients, such as vitamin B_{12} deficiency or folate deficiency (Wernicke's encephalopathy).
- Seizures—postictal state, nonconvulsive status epilepticus, complex partial seizures, absence seizures.
- Trauma—concussion, contusion, subdural hematoma, epidural hematoma, diffuse axonal injury.
- Vascular—both ischemic and hemorrhagic strokes, vasculitis, venous thrombosis.
- Others—hypertensive encephalopathy, postoperative, sleep deprivation.

DIAGNOSIS

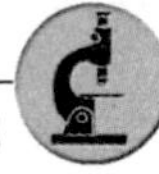

DIFFERENTIAL DIAGNOSIS

- Dementia—distinguished from encephalopathy by a history of slowly progressive cognitive decline over time (fluctuating cognitive function is rare except in diffuse Lewy body disease).
- Hypersomnia.
- Aphasia—distinguished from encephalopathy by virtue of it representing a specific disorder of language rather than a global disturbance of cognitive function.
- Depression.
- Psychosis—some overlap with encephalopathy as delusions and hallucinations may be common to both.
- Mania.
- Coma—a severe form of encephalopathy.
- Vegetative state—one potential outcome of coma; these patients appear awake (eyes are open) but there is no content to their consciousness.
- Akinetic mutism—these patients do not talk and do not move; there is little fluctuation in their state and there is no asterixis.
- Locked-in syndrome—may be distinguished from encephalopathy by the presence of fixed neurologic deficits (i.e., paralysis of all four limbs).

WORKUP

- EEG is helpful to confirm the presence of encephalopathy (diffuse slowing) and also to exclude nonconvulsive seizures.
- ECG to rule out arrhythmias.
- CXR to rule out pneumonia.

LABORATORY TESTS

- General chemistry—electrolytes, glucose, creatinine, ammonia, blood urea nitrogen, transaminases, amylase, lipase
- Arterial blood gases
- Complete blood count
- Drug screen and alcohol level
- Lumbar puncture if meningitis, encephalitis, or subarachnoid hemorrhage with negative imaging are suspected
- HIV testing
- Endocrine testing—cortisol level, thyroid function test
- Urine analysis and microscopy

IMAGING STUDIES

- Computed tomography to rule out bleeding, hydrocephalus, tumors
- Magnetic resonance imaging for suspected encephalitis, tumors, and acute strokes
- Magnetic resonance angiography/venography for strokes, arterial dissection, venous thrombosis
- Conventional angiography for CNS vasculitis and aneurysms

TREATMENT

NONPHARMACOLOGIC THERAPY

The best approach is to treat the underlying toxic or metabolic disturbance. The encephalopathy itself is a symptom of these underlying problems. In general, it is best to avoid treating the symptom of encephalopathy with antipsychotics or sedatives.

ACUTE GENERAL Rx

- Glucose if hypoglycemia
- Antibiotics in cases of infections (choice of an agent with good CNS penetration in cases of primary CNS infections)
- Insulin in hyperglycemic conditions
- Lactulose in hepatic encephalopathy
- Folate replacement when deficiency suspected
- Anticonvulsants if seizures likely
- Librium or diazepam for delirium tremens (alcohol withdrawal)

CHRONIC Rx

- Antiepileptics in patients with epilepsy
- Steroids/immunosuppressants in CNS vasculitis
- Antihypertensives in hypertensive encephalopathy

REFERRAL

- Most instances of encephalopathy are due to systemic disorders that can be managed by a general internist.
- Neurology, neurosurgery, or rheumatology may be appropriate depending on the underlying etiology.

PEARLS & CONSIDERATIONS

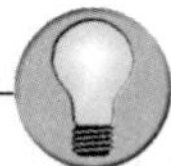

COMMENTS

- Encephalopathy is very common among elderly patients.
- It is a symptom not a disease.
- Usually it is reversible when underlying condition is addressed in timely manner.

SUGGESTED READINGS

Andrefsky J et al: Approach to the patient with acute confusional state (delirium/encephalopathy). In Biller J (ed): *Practical Neurology,* Philadelphia, 2002, Lippincott Williams & Wilkins.

Plum F, Posner J: The pathologic physiology of signs and symptoms of coma. In *The Diagnosis of Stupor and Coma,* New York, 1982, Oxford University Press.

AUTHOR: **ACHRAF A. MAKKI, M.D., M.SC.**

BASIC INFORMATION

DEFINITION

Encopresis is the voluntary or involuntary passage of stool into inappropriate places, in children over the developmental age of 4 yr, with the absence of direct physiologic causes. Occurs at least once per month for at least 3 months.

SYNONYMS

Functional incontinence of stool

ICD-9CM CODES
787.6 Incontinence of feces
307.7 Encopresis

EPIDEMIOLOGY & DEMOGRAPHICS

PREVALANCE (IN U.S.): 1% to 1.5% of children ages 5-8.
PREDOMINANT SEX: Male > female (ratio of 4:1)
PREDOMINANT AGE: 4 to 9 yr of age
PEAK INCIDENCE: 4 to 5 yr of age
GENETICS: Factors that contribute to slow gut motility may predispose to encopresis

PHYSICAL FINDINGS & CLINICAL PRESENTATION

- Most children attain fecal continence by the age of 4. In "primary encopresis," continence is never fully established, whereas in "secondary encopresis" incontinence is preceded by a year or more of continence.
- In secondary encopresis, constipation is generally severe, causing an overflow incontinence in which soft or liquid stool flows around the retained feces, often several times per day.
- When constipation and overflow incontinence are causative, defecation is usually uncomfortable or painful, so patient avoids defecation with consequent stool retention.
- Stool is usually poorly formed and leakage is continuous (occurring during sleep and wakefulness).
- Encopresis resolves when the constipation is resolved.
- In primary encopresis, stool is more likely to be normal in character.
- Soiling is intermittent and usually in a prominent location.
- Coexisting oppositional-defiant or conduct disorders are frequent.

ETIOLOGY

- Children with encopresis exhibit abnormal anorectal dynamics.
- Primary encopresis may be related to developmental delay of sphincter control whereas secondary encopresis develops in the setting of constipation.
- Approximately 96% of children will have bowel movements between three times daily to once every other day. When bowel movements are less frequent, stool becomes drier and harder and much more uncomfortable to pass. Children may avoid the discomfort by avoiding elimination, but this only results in worsening constipation. Soiling results from more liquid stool that leaks around the main stool mass.
- Constipation may begin gradually as a result of a slow decrease in elimination frequency or more acutely after an illness, dehydration, or prolonged bed rest.
- In encopresis without constipation and overflow incontinence, soiling is often intentional. This may occur in the setting of oppositional-defiant disorder or conduct disorder.
- Harsh or inconsistent toilet training and resultant anxiety may lead to retention of stool, constipation, and eventually encopresis.

DIAGNOSIS

DIFFERENTIAL DIAGNOSIS

- Hirschsprung's disease
- Endocrine disease (hypothyroidism)
- Cerebral palsy
- Myelomeningocele
- Pseudoobstruction
- Anorectal lesions (rectal stenosis)
- Malformations
- Trauma
- Rectal prolapse
- Hypothyroidism
- Medications

WORKUP

- History: pay particular attention to frequency of elimination, character of the stool, associated pain, and presence of enuresis (with which it is frequently associated).
- Evaluate child for other developmental or psychiatric problems.
- Physical examination: pay particular attention to the abdomen, anus, rectum, and saddle sensation.

LABORATORY TESTS

Consider thyroid function tests, electrolytes, calcium, urinalysis, and culture.

IMAGING STUDIES

- Abdominal imaging to determine extent of obstruction or megacolon
- Anorectal manometric studies to determine sphincter function if Hirschsprung's disease is suspected; if abnormal, followed up with a barium enema and rectal biopsy

TREATMENT

NONPHARMACOLOGIC THERAPY

- Behavioral and/or individual psychotherapy and family therapy.
- It is important to educate parents and children as to the nature of the problem and to defuse hostile or negative interactions between them.
- Biofeedback advocated by some to improve sphincter function

ACUTE GENERAL Rx

- In secondary encopresis, disimpaction with hypertonic phosphate (30 ml/5 kg body weight) or isotonic saline enemas
- Resistant cases: repeated instillation of 200 to 600 ml of milk of magnesia enemas
- If child does not permit enemas: oral disimpaction with large doses of mineral oil or lactulose until stool mass is cleared (NOTE: this is frequently more painful and more uncomfortable than an enema)

CHRONIC Rx

- Prevention of recurrence of constipation by increased dietary fiber and bulk agents and the use of laxatives (Senokot) and stool softeners (Colace)
- In immediate postdisimpaction period (3 mo following acute treatment) laxatives needed because bowel tone remains low
- In primary encopresis, continue with nonpunitive toilet training and encourage regular toilet times (the latter is also helpful in secondary encopresis)

DISPOSITION

In most cases encopresis is self-limited and of relatively brief duration

REFERRAL

If patient is resistant to treatment, complicated family factors are involved, or encopresis is purposeful.

SUGGESTED READINGS

Di Lorenzo C, Benninga MA: Pathophysiology of pediatric fecal incontinence, *Gastroenterology* 126(1 Suppl 1):S33, 2004.

Loening-Baucke V: Encopresis, *Curr Opin Pediatr* 5:570, 2002.

Schonwald A, Rappaport L: Consultation with the specialist: encopresis: assessment and management, *Pediatr Rev* 8:278, 2004.

AUTHORS: **MITCHELL D, FELDMAN, M.D., M.PHIL.**, and **RIF S. EL-MALLAKH, M.D.**

BASIC INFORMATION

DEFINITION

Infective endocarditis is an infection of the endocardial surface of the heart or mural endocardium.

ACUTE ENDOCARDITIS: Usually caused by *Staphylococcus aureus, Streptococcus pyogenes,* pneumococcus, and *Neisseria* organisms; classic clinical presentation of fever, positive blood cultures, vascular and immunologic phenomenon

SUBACUTE ENDOCARDITIS: Usually caused by viridans streptococci in the presence of valvular pathology; less toxic, often indolent presentation with lower fevers, night sweats, fatigue

INFECTIVE ENDOCARDITIS IN INJECTION DRUG USERS: Often involving *S. aureus* or *Pseudomonas aeruginosa* with variation that may be geographically influenced; tricuspid or multiple valvular involvement; high mortality rate of 50% to 60%

EARLY PROSTHETIC VALVE ENDOCARDITIS: Usually caused by *S. epidermidis* within 2 mo of valve replacement; other organisms include *S. aureus,* gram-negative bacilli, diphtheroids, *Candida* organisms

LATE PROSTHETIC VALVE ENDOCARDITIS: Typically develops >60 days after valvular replacement; involved organisms similar to early prosthetic valve endocarditis, including viridans streptococci, enterococci, and group D streptococci

NOSOCOMIAL ENDOCARDITIS: Secondary to intravenous catheters, TPN lines, pacemakers; coagulase negative staphylococci, *S. aureus,* and streptococci most common

SYNONYMS

Bacterial endocarditis

ICD-9CM CODES
421.0 Infective endocarditis
996.61 Prosthetic valve endocarditis

EPIDEMIOLOGY & DEMOGRAPHICS

INCIDENCE (IN U.S.): 1.7 to 3.8 cases/100,000 persons/yr

NOSOCOMIAL ENDOCARDITIS: 14% to 28% of cases

PREVALENCE (IN U.S.): 0.3 to 3 cases/1000 hospital admissions

PREDOMINANT SEX: Male > female

PREDOMINANT AGE: 45 to 65 yr

PEAK INCIDENCE: Females: often <35 yr old; males: 45 to 65 yr old

PHYSICAL FINDINGS & CLINICAL PRESENTATION

- Fever may be variable in presentation; may be high, hectic, or absent.
- Fever, chills, fatigue, and rigors occur in 25% to 80% of patients.
- Heart murmur may be absent in right-sided endocarditis.
- Embolic phenomenon with peripheral manifestations is found in 50% of patients.
- Skin manifestations include petechiae, Osler nodes, splinter hemorrhages, Janeway lesions.
- Splenomegaly is more common with subacute course.

ETIOLOGY

Streptococcal and staphylococcal infections are the most common causes of infective endocarditis. Variation in incidence may occur that is influenced by the patient's risk for developing infection.

ACUTE ENDOCARDITIS:
- *S. aureus*
- *Streptococcus pneumoniae*
- Streptococcal species and groups A through G
- *Haemophilus influenzae*

SUBACUTE ENDOCARDITIS:
- Viridans streptococci (α-hemolytic)
- *S. bovis*
- Enterococci
- *S. aureus*

ENDOCARDITIS IN IV DRUG ADDICTS:
- *S. aureus*
- *P. aeruginosa*
- *Candida* species
- Enterococci

PROSTHETIC VALVE (EARLY):
- *S. epidermidis*
- *S. aureus*
- Gram-negative bacilli
- Group D streptococci

PROSTHETIC VALVE (LATE):
- *S. epidermidis*
- Viridans streptococci
- *S. aureus*
- Enterococci and group D streptococci

NOSOCOMIAL ENDOCARDITIS:
- Coagulase negative *Staphylococcus*
- *S. aureus*
- Streptococci: viridans, group B, enterococcus

HACEK ORGANISMS:
- Fastidious gram-negative bacilli
- *Haemophilus parainfluenzae*
- *Haemophilus aphrophilus*
- *Actinobacillus actinomycetemcomitans*
- *Cardiobacterium hominis*
- *Eikenella corrodens*
- *Kingella kingae*

RISK FACTORS
- Poor dental hygiene
- Long-term hemodialysis
- Diabetes mellitus
- HIV infection
- Mitral valve prolapse

DIAGNOSIS

DIFFERENTIAL DIAGNOSIS

- Brain abscess
- FUO
- Pericarditis
- Meningitis
- Rheumatic fever
- Osteomyelitis
- Salmonella
- TB
- Bacteremia
- Pericarditis
- Glomerulonephritis

WORKUP

Physical examination to evaluate for the previous physical findings followed by laboratory testing (see Laboratory Tests)

LABORATORY TESTS

- Blood cultures: three sets in first 24 hr
- More culturing if patient has received prior antibiotic
- CBC (anemia possibly present, subacute)
- WBC (leukocytosis is higher in acute endocarditis)
- ESR (elevated)
- Positive rheumatoid factor (subacute endocarditis)
- False-positive VDRL
- Proteinuria, hematuria, RBC casts

IMAGING STUDIES

- Echocardiogram: two-dimensional
- Transesophageal echocardiography: more sensitive in detecting vegations if two-dimensional is negative, especially helpful with prosthetic valves or in detecting perivalvular disease

TREATMENT

Initial IV antibiotic therapy (before culture results) is aimed at the most likely organism:

- In patients with prosthetic valves or patients with native valves who are allergic to penicillin: vancomycin plus rifampin and gentamicin
- In IV drug users: nafcillin or oxacillin plus gentamicin; if MRSA, vancomycin plus gentamicin

- In native valve endocarditis: combination of penicillin and gentamicin; a penicillase-resistant penicillin (oxacillin or nafcillin) can be used if acute bacterial endocarditis is present or if *S. aureus* is suspected as one of the possible causative organisms; for Hacek organisms, treat with third-generation cephalosporin
- Ceftriaxone and an aminoglycoside for 2 wk can be used in streptococcus viridans endocarditis

Antibiotic therapy after identification of the organism should be guided by susceptibility testing.

PEARLS & CONSIDERATIONS

COMMENTS

For endocarditis prophylaxis refer to Section II and Tables 5-25 and 5-26.

SUGGESTED READINGS

DiSalvo G, Habib G, Pergola V: Echocardiography predicts embolic events in infective endocarditis, *J Am Coll Cardiol* 37:1069, 2001.

Heiro M et al: Diagnosis of infective endocarditis, *Arch Intern Med* 158:18, 1998.

Mylonakis E, Calderwood SB: Infective endocarditis in adults, *N Engl J Med* 345:1318, 2001.

AUTHORS: **GLENN G. FORT, M.D., AND DENNIS J. MIKOLICH, M.D.**

Endometrial Cancer 

BASIC INFORMATION

DEFINITION

Endometrial cancer is a malignant transformation of endometrial stroma and/or glands typified by irregular nuclear membranes, nuclear atypia, mitotic activity, loss of glandular pattern, irregular cell size (Fig. 1-83).

SYNONYMS

Uterine cancer (some forms)

ICD-9CM CODES
182 Malignant neoplasm of body of uterus

EPIDEMIOLOGY & DEMOGRAPHICS

INCIDENCE: 21.2 cases/100,000 persons; approximately 30,000 new cases annually

PREDOMINANCE: Median age at onset: 60 yr; only 5% occur in women <40 yr

RISK FACTORS: Obesity, diabetes, nulliparity, early menarche and late menopause, unopposed estrogen therapy, tamoxifen use, endometrial atypical hyperplasia

PHYSICAL FINDINGS & CLINICAL PRESENTATION

- Abnormal uterine bleeding or postmenopausal bleeding in 90%
- Pyometra or hematometra
- Abnormal Pap smear

ETIOLOGY

Endogenous or exogenous chronic unopposed estrogen stimulation of the endometrium

DIAGNOSIS

DIFFERENTIAL DIAGNOSIS

- Atypical hyperplasia
- Other genital tract malignancy
- Polyps
- Atrophic vaginitis
- Granuloma cell tumor
- Fibroid uterus

WORKUP

- Complete history and physical examination
- Endometrial biopsy or dilation and curettage
- Assessment of operative risk

LABORATORY TESTS

- CBC
- Chemistry profile including liver function tests
- Consider CA-125 level

IMAGING STUDIES

- Chest x-ray examination
- Possible CT scan, BE, and/or pelvic ultrasound
- Endovaginal ultrasound in postmenopausal women with vaginal bleeding

TREATMENT

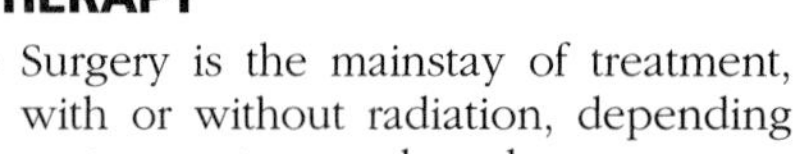

NONPHARMACOLOGIC THERAPY

- Surgery is the mainstay of treatment, with or without radiation, depending on tumor stage and grade.
- Surgery consists of pelvic washings, total abdominal hysterectomy and bilateral salpingo-oophorectomy, omental biopsy, and selective pelvic and periaortic lymphadenectomy, depending on stage and grade.
- Brachytherapy and/or teletherapy are added in an advanced stage.
- Chemotherapy (cisplatin, Adriamycin) or tamoxifen may also be used.

ACUTE GENERAL Rx

- A thorough workup should be completed before any therapy for endometrial cancer.
- Surgery is the treatment of choice.

CHRONIC Rx

- Physical and pelvic examination every 3 mo for 2 yr, then every 6 mo for 2 yr, annually thereafter
- Yearly Pap smear
- Hormone replacement (combination) a consideration in low-risk patients (stage I or early stage II)

DISPOSITION

The majority of cases present early, where the 5-yr survival is generally good:

Stage I 75% to 100%
Stage II 60%
Stage III 50%
Stage IV 20%

Some histologic types (clear cell, serous papillary) have poorer survival rates.

REFERRAL

A gynecologist may manage early-stage disease, otherwise refer to a gynecologic oncologist.

PEARLS & CONSIDERATIONS

COMMENTS

Estrogen replacement therapy (ERT) after surgery for endometrial cancer remains controversial. Recent data suggest that ERT does not increase endometrial cancer recurrence rates.

SUGGESTED READINGS

Smith-Bindman R et al: Endovaginal ultrasound to exclude endometrial cancer and other endometrial abnormalities, *JAMA* 280:1510, 1998.

Suriano KA et al: Estrogen replacement therapy in endometrial cancer patients, *Obstet Gynecol* 97:555, 2001.

Tabor A et al: Endometrial thickness as a test for endometrial cancer in women with postmenopausal vaginal bleeding, *Obstet Gynecol* 99:529, 2002.

AUTHOR: **GIL FARKASH, M.D.**

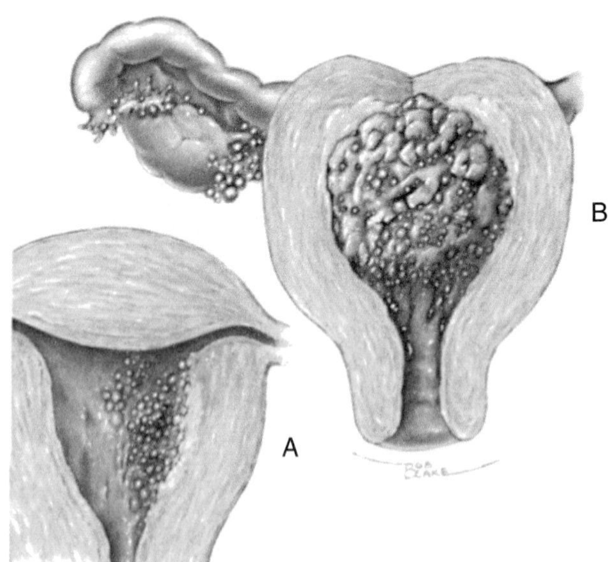

FIGURE 1-83 Carcinoma of the endometrium. A, Stage I. **B,** Stage III, myometrial invasion. (From Sabiston D: *Textbook of surgery,* ed 15, Philadelphia, 1997, WB Saunders.)

BASIC INFORMATION

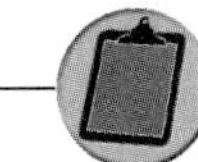

DEFINITION

Endometriosis is defined as the presence of functioning endometrial glands and stroma outside the uterine cavity (Fig. 1-84).

ICD-9CM CODES
617.9 Endometriosis

EPIDEMIOLOGY & DEMOGRAPHICS

PREVALENCE:

- In asymptomatic woman: 2%-22%
- Women with dysmenorrhea: 40%-60%
- Subfertile women: 20%-30%
- Incidence peaks at about age 40

MOST COMMON AGE AT DIAGNOSIS: 25 to 29 yr

GENETICS:

- Multifactorial inheritance pattern
- 6.9% occurrence rate in first-degree female relatives

PHYSICAL FINDINGS & CLINICAL PRESENTATION

- Classic triad is dysmenorrhea, dyspareunia, and infertility.
- Presence of pelvic pain *not correlated* with the total area of endometriosis, type of lesion, or volume of disease, but it *is correlated* with the depth of infiltration.
- Other symptoms include: Abnormal bleeding (premenstrual spotting, menorrhagia), cyclic abdominal pain, intermittent constipation/diarrhea, dyschezia, dysuria, hemeturia, urinary frequency.
- Rare manifestations: Catamenial hemothorax, bloody pleural effusion, massive ascitis occurring during menses.
- Most severe discomfort is associated with lesions >1 cm in depth.
- Bimanual examination may reveal tender uterosacral ligaments, cul-de-sac nodularity, induration of the rectovaginal septum, fixed retroversion of the uterus, adnexal mass, and generalized or localized tenderness.

ETIOLOGY

- Reflux and direct implantation theory: retrograde menstruation with implantation of viable endometrial cells to surrounding pelvic structures
- Coelomic metaplasia theory: transformation of multipotential cells of the coelomic epithelium into endometrium-like cells
- Vascular dissemination theory: transport of endometrial cells to distant sites via the uterine vascular and lymphatic systems
- Autoimmune disease theory: disorder of immune surveillance allows growth of endometrial implants

DIAGNOSIS

DIFFERENTIAL DIAGNOSIS

- Ectopic pregnancy
- Acute appendicitis
- Chronic appendicitis
- PID
- Pelvic adhesions
- Hemorrhagic cyst
- Hernia
- Psychologic disorder
- Irritable bowel syndrome
- Uterine leiomyomata
- Adenomyosis
- Nerve entrapment syndrome
- Scoliosis
- Muscular/skeletal strain
- Interstitial cystitis

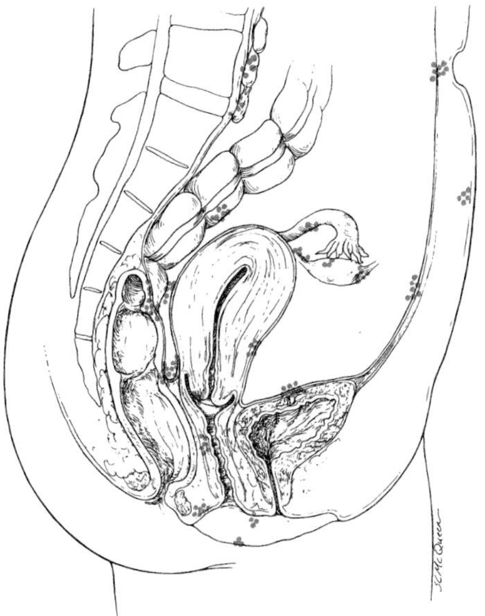

FIGURE 1-84 Common pelvic sites of endometriosis. (From Mishell D [ed]: *Comprehensive gynecology,* ed 3, St Louis, 1997, Mosby.)

WORKUP

- Thorough history and physical examination, including inquiry about physical and emotional abuse
- Colonoscopy if rectal bleeding present
- Laparoscopy for definitive diagnosis
- Revised American Fertility Society (RAFS) scale to classify endometriosis (since 1985):
  Stage I minimal
  Stage II mild
  Stage III moderate
  Stage IV severe

LABORATORY TESTS

Cancer antigen 125 (CA125)

- Also elevated in ovarian epithelial neoplasm, myomas, adenomyosis, acute PID, ovarian cysts, pancreatitis, chronic liver disease, menstruation, and pregnancy
- CA 125 value >35 U/ml: positive predictive value of 0.58 and a negative predictive value of 0.96 for the presence of endometriosis

IMAGING STUDIES

- Ultrasound: for evaluating adnexal mass; cannot reliably distinguish endometriomas from other benign or malignant ovarian conditions
- MRI:
  1. Highly accurate in detecting endometriomas
  2. Limited sensitivity in detecting diffuse pelvic endometriosis

TREATMENT

NONPHARMACOLOGIC THERAPY

Expectant management (observation for 5 to 12 mo) for stage I or stage II endometriosis-associated infertility

ACUTE GENERAL Rx

NSAIDs for symptomatic relief of dysmenorrhea

CHRONIC Rx

PHARMACOLOGIC MANAGEMENT:

Estrogen-progesterone:

- State of "pseudopregnancy" created by continuous use of combination oral contraceptives for 6 to 12 mo
- Breakthrough bleeding treated by administering conjugated estrogens 1.25 mg/day for 2 wk

Danazol:

- Initial dose 200 mg PO bid
- If no improvement within 6 wk, dosage increased to 300 or 400 mg PO bid

- Treatment generally continued for 6 mo, after which up to 90% of patients with mild to moderate endometriosis experience alleviation of pelvic pain
- Treatment begun after menses to avoid fetal exposure

Progestins:
- Medroxyprogesterone acetate 10 to 30 mg PO qd and occasionally up to 100 mg PO qd
- Alternatively, 100 mg IM q2wk for four doses, followed by 200 mg IM monthly for 4 mo
- Breakthrough bleeding treated with ethinyl estradiol (20 μg/day) or conjugated estrogens (1.25 mg/day) for 1 to 2 wk
- Comparison with danazol: progestins cost less, have a more tolerable side-effect profile, and have comparable efficacy with regard to pain relief, so are often the first-line drug

Gonadotropin-releasing hormone (GnRH) agonists:
- Use usually limited to 6 mo
- Leuprolide acetate depot 3.75 mg IM monthly *or* 11.25 mg IM q3mo
- *or* nafarelin 200 μg nasal puffs bid
- *or* goserelin 3.6 mg SC monthly
- As effective as danazol for relief of pelvic pain
- Add-back therapy for protection against vasomotor symptoms and bone loss: norethindrone acetate 5 mg PO qd alone *or* in combination with conjugated estrogen 0.625 mg PO qd
- Add-back therapy allows GnRH agonist use to be extended to 1 yr

Alternative therapy for inhibition of estrogen action currently under investigation are:
- Aromatase inhibitors: Anastrozole, Letrozole
- SERM: Raloxifene
- Agents enhancing cell-mediated immunity are: Cytokines (interleukin-12 and interferon-α-2b)
- Immunomodulators (Loxaribine, Levamisole)
- Antiinflamatory: Pentoxifylline

SURGICAL MANAGEMENT:

Conservative:
- Directed at enhancing fertility or treating pain unresponsive to first-line medical treatment
- Usually accomplished through laparoscopy
- Removal or destruction of endometriotic implants by excision, electrocautery, or laser
- Cystectomy for endometrioma
- LUNA (Laproscopic Uterosacral Nerve Abalation) for midline pain such as dysmenorrheal or dyspareunia
- Unless pregnancy is desired, patient is usually started on GnRH agonist therapy immediately after surgery
- For those desiring pregnancy, surgery alone results in significant increase in fertility

Definitive:
- Directed at relieving endometriosis-associated pain
- Total abdominal hysterectomy with bilateral salpingo-oophorectomy and complete excision or ablation of endometriosis
- Thorough abdominal exploration to ensure removal of all disease
- Must be prepared to manage possible GI and urinary tract endometriosis
- 90% effective in pain relief
- Estrogen replacement therapy (ERT) to be considered in all women undergoing definitive surgical management; after ERT, recurrence rate of 0% to 5% in women with endometriosis confined to the pelvis but 18% in women with bowel involvement

MANAGEMENT OF ENDOMETRIOSIS-ASSOCIATED INFERTILITY:

Conservative Surgery:
- Yields significantly increased pregnancy rate than does expectant management, in part because of correction of mechanical factors such as adhesions

Assisted Reproductive Technologies:
- Can be used to circumvent unknown mechanism of endometriosis-associated infertility
- Superovulation with clomiphene citrate or human menopausal gonadotropins; clomiphene citrate results in threefold pregnancy rate over either danazol or expectant management
- Further improvement with intrauterine insemination combined with superovulation
- In vitro fertilization if above mentioned unsuccessful

DISPOSITION

Tends to recur unless definitive surgery is performed

REFERRAL

To a reproductive endocrinologist for advanced surgical management or infertility management

PEARLS & CONSIDERATIONS

COMMENTS

Patient information can be obtained through the following organizations: Endometriosis Association, 8585 North 76th Place, Milwaukee, WI 53223, 414-355-2200 or 800-992-ENDO; Women's Reproductive Health Network, P.O. Box 30167, Portland, OR 97230-9067; phone: 503-667-7757.

SUGGESTED READINGS

Vignali M et al: Novel etiopathogenetic concept & clinical perspectives, *Fertility & Sterility,* Vol 78(4), Oct 2002.

Hornstein MD et al for the Lupron Addback Study Group: Leuprolide acetate depot and hormonal add-back in endometriosis: a 12-month study, *Obstet Gynecol* 91:16, 1998.

Olive DL, Pritts EA: Treatment of endometriosis, *N Engl J Med* 345:266, 2001.

Winkel CA: Evaluation and management of women with endometriosis, *Obstetrics and gynecology,* 102(2):397, 2003.

AUTHOR: **WAN J. KIM, M.D.**

BASIC INFORMATION

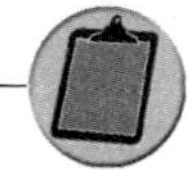

DEFINITION

Endometritis is defined as a uterine infection following delivery or abortion.

SYNONYMS

Endomyometritis
Endoperimetritis
Metritis

ICD-9CM CODES
615.9 Endometritis

EPIDEMIOLOGY & DEMOGRAPHICS

- Overall rate of postpartum infection: estimated between 1% and 8%
- Most common genital tract infection following delivery
- Usually presents early in postpartum period; more commonly seen following C-section than vaginal delivery; also seen with an incomplete abortion (spontaneous abortion, legal abortion, or illegal abortion)
- More common in preterm deliveries
- Possible following any uterine manipulation in the presence of an undiagnosed cervicitis or vaginitis

PHYSICAL FINDINGS & CLINICAL PRESENTATION

- Postpartum oral temperature >37.8° C
- Localized uterine tenderness, purulent or foul lochia; physical examination revealing uterine or parametrial tenderness
- Nonspecific signs and symptoms such as malaise, abdominal pain, chills, and tachycardia

ETIOLOGY

Endometritis is usually associated with multiple organisms: group A or B streptococci, *Staphylococcus aureus* and *Bacteroides* species, *Neisseria gonorrhoeae, Chlamydia trachomatis,* enterococci, *Gardnerella vaginalis, E. coli,* and *Mycoplasma.*

DIAGNOSIS

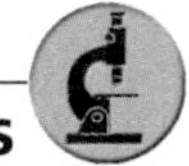

DIFFERENTIAL DIAGNOSIS

Causes of postoperative or postprocedural infections

WORKUP

Diagnosis based on symptoms of fever, malaise, abdominal pain, uterine tenderness, and purulent, foul vaginal discharge

LABORATORY TESTS

CBC, blood cultures, and uterine culture

IMAGING STUDIES

Ultrasound may be useful if retained products are considered a possible source of infection.

TREATMENT

ACUTE GENERAL Rx

- In treating endometritis after a vaginal delivery, ampicillin 2 g IV q6h plus gentamicin loading dose IV or IM (2 mg/kg of body weight), followed by a maintenance dose (1.5 mg/kg of body weight) q8h are used.
- Regimen should be continued for at least 48 hr after substantial clinical improvement. If response is not adequate, check cultures and treat with appropriate antibiotics (Table 1-15).
- Endometritis following C-section should be treated with ampicillin 2 g IV q6h plus gentamicin loading dose IV or IM (2 mg/kg of body weight), followed by a maintenance dose (1.5 mg/kg of body weight) q8h and clindamycin 900 mg IV q8h. If *Chlamydia* is one of the etiologic agents, add doxycycline 100 mg PO bid for completion of a 14-day course of therapy (if breast feeding, use erythromycin).

CHRONIC Rx

Watch for recurrent infection.

DISPOSITION

With appropriate antibiotic therapy, 95% to 98% cure rate

REFERRAL

For patients who do not respond within 48 to 72 hr of appropriate antibiotic therapy, obtain an infectious disease consult or gynecologic consultation.

SUGGESTED READINGS

Centers for Disease Control and Prevention: Sexually transmitted disease treatment guideline, *MMWR* 47(RR-1), 1998.
French LM, Smaill FM: Antibiotic regimens for endometritis after delivery, *Cochrane Database of Systematic Reviews* (1):CD001067, 2002.
Smaill F, Hofmeyr GJ: Antibiotic prophylaxis for cesarean section, *Cochrane Database of Systematic Reviews* (3):CD000933, 2002.

AUTHOR: **GEORGE T. DANAKAS, M.D.**

TABLE 1-15 **Identified Causes of Poor Response to Antibiotic Therapy in Patients with Endometritis**

Cause	Approximate prevalence (%)
Infected mass, including abscess, hematoma, septic pelvic thrombophlebitis, pelvic cellulitis, retained placenta	40-50
Resistant organisms, commonly enterococci, in a patient receiving clindamycin-aminoglycoside or a cephalosporin	20
Additional cause, including catheter phlebitis, inadequate dose of antibiotics	10
No cause evident but response to empirical change in antibiotic therapy	20-30

From Gorbach SL: Infectious diseases, ed 2, Philadelphia, 1998, WB Saunders.

BASIC INFORMATION

DEFINITION

Enuresis refers to the voiding of urine into clothes or in bed that is usually involuntary but occasionally intentional in individuals who are expected to be continent (i.e., >5 yr of age). The diagnosis is made if voiding occurs at least twice a week for 3 mo. Primary enuresis refers to enuresis without a period of continence. Secondary enuresis occurs after a period of normal bladder control.

SYNONYMS

Urinary incontinence
Bed-wetting

ICD-9CM CODES
F98.0
DMS-IV Code 307.6

EPIDEMIOLOGY & DEMOGRAPHICS

PREVALENCE (IN U.S.):
- Age 5: 7% of males and 3% of females
- Age 10: 3% of males and 2% of females
- Age 18: 1% of males and even fewer females

PREDOMINANT SEX: Twice as many males as females at all ages

PREDOMINANT AGE: By definition, enuresis does not begin before age 5 yr, at which time the prevalence is highest, and decreases steadily thereafter.

PEAK INCIDENCE: Early childhood, ages 5 to 10 yr

GENETICS:
- Approximately 75% of children with enuresis have a first-degree relative with enuresis.
- Significantly more common in monozygotic than dizygotic twins.

PHYSICAL FINDINGS & CLINICAL PRESENTATION

Three subtypes are defined:
- Nocturnal only: usually occurs in first third of sleep, frequently during REM sleep; child may recall a dream with voiding
- Diurnal only: more frequent in girls and rarely after age 9 yr; voiding occurs in early afternoon on school days
- Combined nocturnal and diurnal enuresis

ETIOLOGY

- Enuresis correlates with other maturational delays, particularly language, motor skills, and social development
- May be related to lax toilet training, stress, inability to concentrate urine, and altered smooth muscle physiology
- Diurnal enuresis associated with a higher rate of urinary tract infections
- Illness, hospitalization, family stressors may precipitate recurrent enuresis after period of dryness

DIAGNOSIS

DIFFERENTIAL DIAGNOSIS

- May be associated with encopresis and sleep disorders such as sleep terrors
- Must rule out organic causes associated with polyuria or urgency but may coexist if enuresis was present before or after treatment of the associated medical condition
- Medical causes of enuresis include: diabetes mellitus, diabetes insipidus, bladder outlet obstruction, urethral valves, meatal stenosis, cerebral palsy, spina bifida, pelvic mass, impacted stool, sedating medications, nocturnal seizures

WORKUP

History and physical examination to rule out anatomic abnormalities
Because children frequently experience shame, gentleness and care must be exercised when questioning or examining the child.

LABORATORY TESTS

- Urinalysis to determine specific gravity
- Urine culture to rule out urinary tract infection
- Serum studies to rule out diabetes and fluid balance abnormalities

IMAGING STUDIES

- In complicated cases: sleep studies may be useful
- If an anatomic abnormality suspected: renal ultrasound or IVP possibly indicated

TREATMENT

NONPHARMACOLOGIC THERAPY

Behavioral treatment:
- Alarm and pad technique—up to 80% cure rate, although 30% relapse
- Scheduled voiding to reduce the frequency of enuretic episodes
- Star charts to reward child for dry nights

ACUTE GENERAL Rx

- Desmopressin (DDAVP) administered intranasally at bedtime significantly reduces the incidence of bedwetting.
- Tricyclic antidepressants (Imipramine)—efficacy supported by randomized control trials. Use with care in children.
- Serotonin reuptake inhibitors: lack of adequate trials is notable.

DISPOSITION

- After age 5 yr, the rate of spontaneous remissions is 5% to 10%/yr.
- Usually the disorder resolves by adolescence.
- Fewer than 1% will experience enuresis as adults.

REFERRAL

If coexisting psychiatric condition complicates the course of treatment

SUGGESTED READINGS

Glazner CM, Evans JH: Simple behavioural and physical interventions for nocturnal enuresis in children, *Cochrane Database Syst Rev* (2), 2004.

Hjalmas K et al: Nocturnal enuresis: an international evidence based management strategy, *Urol* 171:2545, 2004.

Landgraf JM et al: Coping, commitment, and attitude: quantifying the everyday burden of enuresis on children and their families, *Pediatrics* 113(2):334, 2004.

AUTHORS: **MITCHELL D. FELDMAN, M.D., M. PHIL.,** and **RIF S. EL-MALLAKH, M.D.**

BASIC INFORMATION

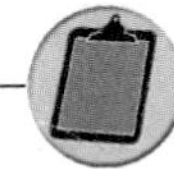

DEFINITION

Eosinophilic fasciitis is a rare inflammatory disease of the skin and subcutaneous tissue that is initially characterized by pain, swelling, and peripheral eosinophilia. This condition starts with erythema and edema on an extremity or on the trunk, and later it may progress to sclerosis of the dermis and subcutaneous fascia and contractures.

SYNONYMS

Shulman's syndrome

ICD-9CM CODES
728.89 Eosinophilic fasciitis

EPIDEMIOLOGY & DEMOGRAPHICS

- Males and females are affected equally.
- The disease most commonly presents in the fourth and fifth decades.

PHYSICAL FINDINGS & CLINICAL PRESENTATION

- Initial presentation consists of swelling and pain with or without erythema.
- The extremities are usually symmetrically involved.
- Upper extremities are more commonly affected than lower extremities.
- The face, fingers, and toes tend to be spared.
- The skin may appear deeply rippled with an orange-peel texture (peau d'oange).
- Sunken veins may be seen when the extremity is elevated (Fig. 1-85).
- The groove sign marks the borders of different muscle groups.
- Arthritis is found in 40% of cases.
- Chronic complications are carpal tunnel syndrome, which was seen in 23% of patients in one series, and flexion contractures.
- Hematological abnormalities other than eosinophilia are present in 10% of cases; these include aplastic anemia, amegakaryocytic thrombocytopenia, myeloproliferative disorders, myelodysplastic syndrome, leukemia, lymphoma, multiple myeloma.
- Spontaneous resolution or improvement has been reported after 2 to 5 yr.

ETIOLOGY

- The etiology is unclear. A defect in humoral immunity has been hypothesized to cause the disease.
- Elevated polyclonal IgG levels and immune complexes have been associated with the disease.

DIAGNOSIS

DIFFERENTIAL DIAGNOSIS

- Systemic or localized sclerosis
- Scleroderma-like disorders
- Chemical induced sclerosis
- Generalized lichen sclerosus et atrophicus
- Eosinophilia-myalgia syndrome
- Graft-versus-host disease
- Porphyria cutanea tarda
- Chronic Lyme borreliosis

WORKUP

- Physical examination to confirm characteristic distribution
- Consider bone marrow biopsy to rule out hematological malignancy
- Ultrasound sonography and MRI might be useful to detect the thickened fascia

LABORATORY TESTS

- Peripheral eosinophilia in up to 70%
- Elevated erythrocyte sedimentation rate (29%)
- Hypergammaglobulinemia (35%)
- Occasionally thrombocytopenia and anemia

DEEP TISSUE BIOPSY

Skin biopsy that penetrates to muscle is optimal for diagnosis:
- Epidermis is usually normal.
- Dermis may demonstrate mild inflammation with lymphocytes, histiocytes, plasma cells, and eosinophils with some fibrosis.
- Subcutaneous tissue shows moderate inflammation and sclerosis of fat septa.
- Muscle demonstrates perivascular mixed inflammatory cell infiltrate.

TREATMENT

- Although there are no controlled trials, oral steroids are effective in most patients, but the duration and extent of symptom reduction are variable.
- Methotrexate and cimetidine have also been used.
- Surgery is sometimes required to reduce contractures and maintain function.

DISPOSITION

Prognosis is generally good with frequent spontaneous regression and response to steroids. However, 10% may develop blood dyscrasias, and contractures are common.

REFERRAL

Dermatology referral may be needed for definitive diagnosis (biopsy). Functional impairment requires surgical evaluation.

SUGGESTED READINGS

Costenbader KH et al: Eosinophilic fasciitis presenting as pitting edema of the extremities, *Am J Med* 111(4):318, 2001.

Lakhanpal S et al: Eosinophilic fasciitis: clinical spectrum and therapeutic response in 52 cases, *Semin Arthritis Rheum* 17(4):221, 1988.

AUTHORS: **JAMES J. NG, M.D.,** and **ETSUKO AOKI, M.D., PH.D.**

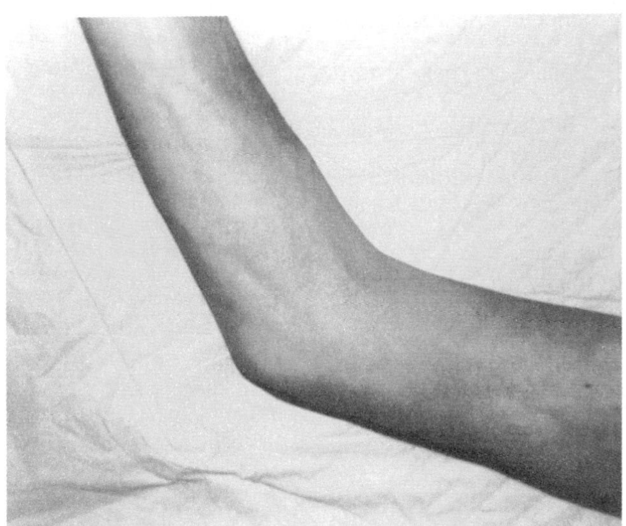

FIGURE 1-85 Eosinophilic fasciitis. This 29-year-old butcher had to stop working because of a generalized painful induration of his skin. Fingers were spared. As he raised his forearms, the collapsed veins appeared as grooves (the "groove sign"), which is pathognomonic of eosinophilic fasciitis. Four years later his condition subsided, leaving joint contractures. (From Canoso J: *Rheumatology in primary care,* Philadelphia, 1997, WB Saunders.)

Eosinophilic Pneumonias

BASIC INFORMATION

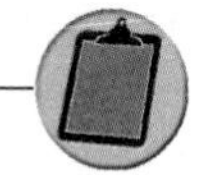

DEFINITION

Eosinophilic pneumonias are a group of disorders characterized by infiltrates on chest radiographs (x-rays), pulmonary parenchymal eosinophilia, and peripheral blood eosinophilia.

ICD-9CM CODES
518.3 Eosinophilic pneumonia

EPIDEMIOLOGY & DEMOGRAPHICS

Varies depending on the specific cause of the pneumonia

PHYSICAL FINDINGS & CLINICAL PRESENTATION

- Usually a combination of fever, cough, and shortness of breath
- Varies depending on the specific cause

ETIOLOGY

SIMPLE PULMONARY EOSINOPHILIA (LÖFFLER'S SYNDROME):
- Transient infiltrates
- Symptoms range from asymptomatic to dyspnea and dry cough
- Usually idiopathic
- May be secondary to parasitic infection or drugs such as nitrofurantoin or penicillin
- Therapy consists of removing the offending agent
- If idiopathic and severe symptoms, then give glucocorticoid therapy

CHRONIC EOSINOPHILIC PNEUMONIA:
- Idiopathic disease
- Presents with productive cough, dyspnea, malaise, weight loss, night sweats, and fever
- Progressive peripheral pulmonary infiltrates
- Blood eosinophilia is not always present
- Diagnose by bronchoalveolar lavage (BAL) or lung biopsy
- Spontaneous remission in 10% of cases
- Treatment with glucocorticoids is rapidly effective
- Relapses are common

ALLERGIC BRONCHOPULMONARY ASPERGILLOSIS:
- Hypersensitivity reaction to *Aspergillus*
- Occurs most often in patients with asthma and atopy
- Fever, flulike symptoms, myalgias, and lassitude
- Chest x-ray: infiltrates (sometimes migratory) and atelectasis
- Blood and sputum eosinophilia
- Diagnosis by:
  1. *Aspergillus* isolation from multiple sputum samples
  2. Positive skin test to *Aspergillus* antigen
  3. Elevated serum IgE
  4. *Aspergillus*-specific IgE and IgG antibodies
- Treatment: systemic corticosteroids

TROPICAL PULMONARY EOSINOPHILIA:
- Onset of asthma, fever, marked blood eosinophilia
- Basilar reticulonodular and alveolar infiltrates
- Presumed etiology: filariasis

PULMONARY VASCULITIS (ALLERGIC GRANULOMATOSIS AND ANGIITIS):
- Vasculitis and necrotizing granulomatous inflammation that involves many organ systems
- Blood eosinophilia and elevated IgE levels

HYPEREOSINOPHILIC SYNDROME:
- A disease of elevated eosinophils with no known cause
- Cardiac problems are the prominent clinical feature
- Pulmonary involvement results in fever, cough, weight loss, and wheezing
- Diagnosis of exclusion
- Check echocardiogram
- Treat with steroids if symptoms or cardiac abnormalities

ACUTE EOSINOPHILIC PNEUMONIA:
- Acute onset of cough, dyspnea, fever, tachypnea, and rales
- Patients often require mechanical ventilation
- Tends to affect the young
- Often blood eosinophilia
- Chest radiographs show alveolar infiltrates
- BAL eosinophils often >20%
- Glucocorticoid therapy often leads to rapid improvement
- Relapses are rare
- May be secondary to drugs or cigarette smoking

DIAGNOSIS

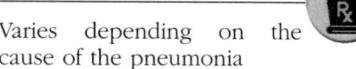

- Diagnosis varies depending on the specific cause of the eosinophilic pneumonia.
- Usually involves a combination of chest radiograph, peripheral eosinophil count, and BAL.

DIFFERENTIAL DIAGNOSIS

- Tuberculosis
- Brucellosis
- Fungal diseases
- Bronchogenic carcinoma
- Hodgkin's disease
- Immunoblastic lymphadenopathy
- Rheumatoid lung disease
- Sarcoidosis

WORKUP

Physical examination, laboratory tests, and bronchoscopy

LABORATORY TESTS

- WBC counts are often normal
- Often there is an increase in blood eosinophils
- BAL will often reveal an elevation in the eosinophil count

IMAGING STUDIES

Chest radiograph may show a variety of infiltrates depending on the cause of the eosinophilic pneumonia.

TREATMENT

- Varies depending on the cause of the pneumonia
- Remove offending agent or treat with appropriate antibiotic
- Steroids may be helpful in many cases and usually indicated; the doses and length of treatment clearly depend on etiology of symptoms and response to treatment as manifested by clinical improvement, radiologic clearing, and resolution of peripheral eosiniophilia
- Supportive respiratory care

REFERRAL

Consultation with a pulmonologist may be necessary if a BAL is needed to establish the diagnosis.

SUGGESTED READING

Allen JN et al: The eosinophilic pneumonias, *Sem Resp Crit Care Med* 23(2):127, 2002.

AUTHORS: **JENNIFER CLARKE, M.D.**, and **CAROLYN J. O'CONNOR, M.D.**

BASIC INFORMATION

DEFINITION

Epicondylitis is an inflammation of the musculotendinous origin of the common extensors at the lateral elbow or the flexor pronator group at the medial elbow.

SYNONYMS

Tennis elbow (lateral epicondylitis)
Golfer's elbow (medial epicondylitis)

ICD-9CM CODES
726.31 Medial epicondylitis
726.32 Lateral epicondylitis
723.4 Radial nerve neuralgia

EPIDEMIOLOGY & DEMOGRAPHICS

PREVALENCE: 10% to 15% of regular (2 hr/wk) tennis players
PREVALENT AGE: 20 to 40 yr
The lateral side is involved 5 times more often than the medial.

PHYSICAL FINDINGS & CLINICAL PRESENTATION

- Local tenderness over affected epicondyle
- Reproduction of pain by resistance against wrist extension (lateral) (Fig. 1-86) or flexion (medial)

ETIOLOGY

- Unknown
- Overuse probably causing minor tendinous tears resulting in inflammation
- Posterior interosseous nerve syndrome: compression of this nerve has occasionally been cited as a possible etiology, especially in cases that have failed traditional medical and surgical treatment. In this disorder, the site of tenderness is 2-3 cm distal to the epicondyle

DIAGNOSIS

DIFFERENTIAL DIAGNOSIS

- Cervical radiculopathy
- Intraarticular elbow pathology (osteoarthritis, osteochondritis dissecans, loose body)
- Radial nerve compression
- Ulnar neuropathy
- Medial collateral ligament instability

IMAGING STUDIES

Traction spur or minor soft tissue calcification may be present on plain radiography. Other studies are not usually needed.

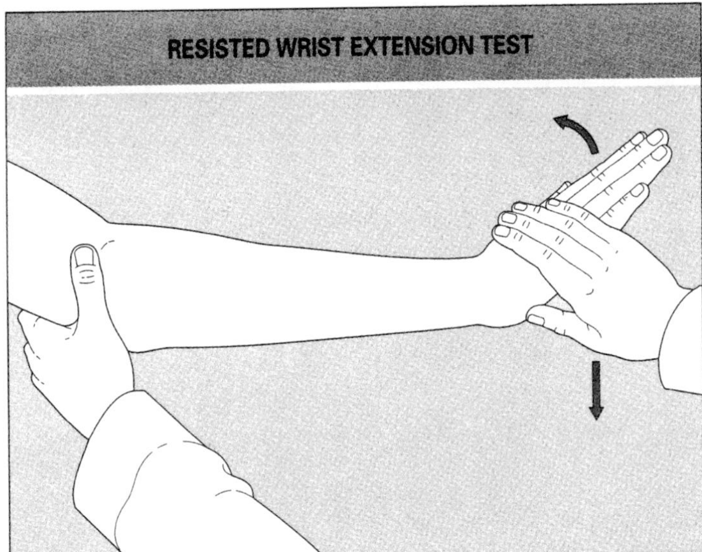

FIGURE 1-86 Resisted wrist extension to test for lateral epicondylitis. The examiner asks the patient to try to extend the wrist, but prevent movement by fixing the wrist; this puts tension on the lateral epicondyle without moving the elbow and reproduces the pain of lateral epicondylitis. (From Klippel J, Dieppe P, Ferri F [eds]: *Primary care rheumatology,* London, 1999, Mosby.)

TREATMENT

- Rest, restricted activities
- Ice after exercise
- Stretching exercise program
- NSAIDs
- Local steroid/lidocaine injection (Table 1-16), (Fig. 1-87)
- Counterforce brace
- Proper technique in sports activities
- Intermittent immobilization

DISPOSITION

Disorder is self-limited in most cases. Resolution of symptoms may take months to years.

REFERRAL

- If symptoms fail to respond to medical management
- For surgical consideration

SUGGESTED READINGS

Ashe MC, McCauley T, Khan KM: Tendinopathies in the upper extremity: A paradigm shift, *J Hand Ther* 17(8):329, 2004.
David TS: Medial elbow pain in the throwing athlete, *Orthopedics* 26:94, 2003.
Haake M et al: Extracorporeal shock wave therapy in the treatment of lateral epicondylitis, *J Bone Joint Surg* 84(A):1982, 2002.
Nirschl RP, Ashman ES: Tennis elbow tendinosis (epicondylitis), *Instr Course Lect* 53:587, 2004.
Rompe JD et al: Repetitive low-energy shock wave treatment for chronic lateral epicondylitis in tennis players, *Am J Sports Med* 32:734, 2004.
Smidt N et al: Corticosteroid injections, physiotherapy, or wait-and-see policy for lateral epicondylitis: a randomized controlled trial, *Lancet* 359:657, 2002.
Wang AA et al: Pain levels after injection of corticosteroid to hand and elbow, *Am J Orthop* 32:383, 2003.

AUTHOR: **LONNIE R. MERCIER, M.D.**

TABLE 1-16 **Guidelines for Common Steroid Injections**

Using 1 ml of the appropriate steroid, the volume is increased by the addition of local anesthetic. Injecting a "space" should not cause pain during the injection. If it does, the needle tip may be in the synovium, capsule, or fat pad, and the needle should be redirected or the shot may not be as effective. Injecting soft tissue should be performed slowly so as not to cause pain from the sudden volume pressure.

Site	Diagnosis	Needle size (gauge, inches)	Anesthetic volume (ml)
Subacromial bursa	Rotator cuff tendinitis	22,1½	4 to 5
Bicipital groove	Biceps tendinitis	22,1½	2 to 3
A-C joint	Arthritis	25,1½	1 to 2
L, M epicondyle	Epicondylitis	25,⅝	1.5
First extensor sheath	De Quervain's disease	25,⅝	1.5
Trochanteric bursa	Tendinitis	22, spinal	4 to 5
Knee joint	Arthritis	22,1½	5 to 10
Knee, soft tissue	Tendinitis	25,1½	3 to 4
Plantar fascia	Fasciitis	25,1½	1.0
Toe MPJ	Arthritis	25,⅝	1.5

From Mercier LR: ***Practical orthopedics,*** ed 5, St Louis, 2000, Mosby.

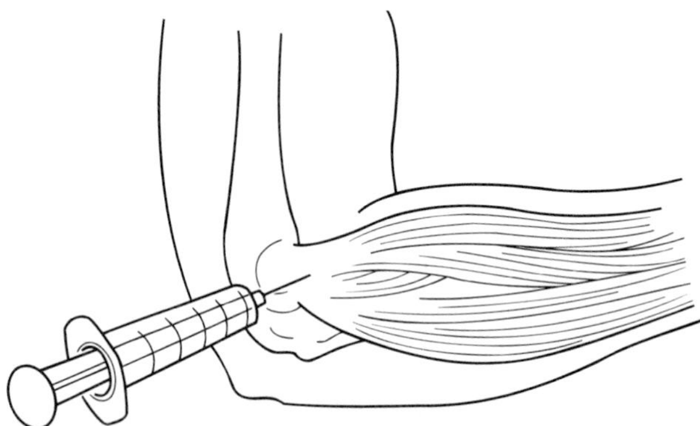

FIGURE 1-87 Soft-tissue injection for lateral epicondylitis. The patient is supine, and the elbow is flexed 90 degrees. A 25-gauge needle is used to inject the tender spot, which is usually about 1 cm distal to the bony epicondyle. (From Mercier L: *Practical orthopedics,* ed 5, St Louis, 2000, Mosby.)

BASIC INFORMATION

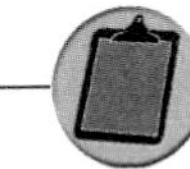

DEFINITION

Epididymitis is an inflammatory reaction of the epididymis caused by either an infectious agent or local trauma.

SYNONYMS

Nonspecific bacterial epididymitis
Sexually transmitted epididymitis

ICD-9CM CODES
604.90 Nonvenereal epididymitis
098.0 Gonococcal epididymitis

EPIDEMIOLOGY & DEMOGRAPHICS

INCIDENCE (IN U.S.): Cause of >600,000 visits to physicians per year
PREDOMINANT SEX: Exclusive to males
PREDOMINANT AGE: All ages affected but usually in sexually active men or older males
PEAK INCIDENCE: Sexually active years
CONGENITAL: Congenital urologic structural disorders possibly predisposing to infections

PHYSICAL FINDINGS & CLINICAL PRESENTATION

- Tender swelling of the scrotum with erythema, usually unilateral testicular pain and tenderness
- Dysuria and/or urethral discharge
- Fever and signs of systemic illness (less common)
- Pain and redness on scrotal examination
- Hydrocele or even epididymoorchitis, especially late
- Chronic draining scrotal sinuses with a "beadlike" enlargement of the vas deferens in tuberculous disease

ETIOLOGY

- In young, sexually active men, the most common infectious agents isolated are *N. gonorrhoeae* and *Chlamydia trachomatis.*
- In men >35 yr or with underlying urologic disease:
  1. Gram-negative aerobic rods are predominant.
  2. Similar organisms are found in men following invasive urologic procedures.
  3. Gram-positive cocci are rarely seen in these groups.
  4. Mycobacteria are also a cause of epididymitis.
- Young, prepubertal boys may present with epididymitis caused by coliform bacteria; almost always a complication of underlying urologic disease such as reflux.
- Recently, in AIDS patients, CMV and *Salmonella* epididymitis have been described. CMV may have a negative urine culture. Toxoplasmosis should also be considered as a cause of epididymitis in AIDS patients.

DIAGNOSIS

DIFFERENTIAL DIAGNOSIS

- Orchitis
- Testicular torsion, trauma, or tumor
- Epididymal cyst
- Hydrocele
- Varicocele
- Spermatocele
- Testicular torsion should be considered in all cases but is more common in adolescents and men without evidence of inflammation. If a diagnosis is in question, a specialist should be consulted immediately.

WORKUP

- Consideration of a full assessment of the urologic tract in patients with bacterial infection, especially if recurrent
- Imaging with sonogram or IVP (possibly procedures of choice)
- If discharge is present: cultures and Gram stain smear of urethral exudate
- In sexually active men: gonococcal cultures of the throat and rectum possibly of value
- If testicular torsion a consideration: radionuclear imaging
- Examination of first void uncentrifugal urine for leukocytes if the urethral Gram stain is negative. A culture and Gram-stained smear of this urine specimen should be obtained

LABORATORY TESTS

- Urinalysis and urine culture if dysuria is present or if urinary tract infection is suspected
- VDRL in sexually active men
- PPD placed and chest x-ray viewed if TB suspected
- Rarely, biopsy to assure the diagnosis of tuberculous epididymitis
- HIV testing and counseling

TREATMENT

ACUTE GENERAL Rx

- Ice packs and scrotal elevation for relief of pain
- Analgesia with acetaminophen with or without codeine or NSAIDs (such as ibuprofen or Naprosyn)
- Antibiotics to cover suspected pathogens
- In sexually active men, doxycycline 100 mg PO bid or tetracycline 500 mg PO qid for 10 days to cover both gonococci and chlamydiae; ceftriaxone 250 mg IM is a single dose may be adequate for gonococci alone
- Best treatment for older men with gram-negative bacteria and leukocyturia: ofloxacin 300 mg PO bid for 10 days or levofloxacin 500 mg PO qd for 10 days
- *Pseudomonas* covered by ciprofloxacin or ceftazidime (1 g IV q6-8h)
- Gentamicin in toxic-appearing patients (1 mg/kg IV q8h following a loading dose of 2 mg/kg): doses must be adjusted for renal function and these agents may be more toxic
- Vancomycin (1 g IV q12h) to cover suspected gram-positive infections
- Surgical aspiration of local abscesses or even open surgical drainage
- Diabetics: especially prone to develop more extensive scrotal infections, including Fournier's gangrene
- Reinforcement of compliance with antibiotics to avoid partial treatment

CHRONIC Rx

- Repair of underlying structural defects is considered especially if infections are severe or recur.
- Surgical repair of reflux in young boys should be undertaken promptly and at a young age when possible.
- Sex partners of patient should be referred for evaluation and treatment.

DISPOSITION

Usually self-limited

REFERRAL

- If abscess or chronic structural problems suspected
- If other diagnosis, such as testicular torsion, strongly considered

SUGGESTED READING

Centers for Disease Control and Prevention: 2002 Sexually transmitted diseases treatment guidelines. *MMWR* 51(RR-6), 2002.

AUTHOR: **JOSEPH J. LIEBER, M.D.**

 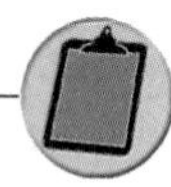

BASIC INFORMATION

DEFINITION

Epiglottitis is a rapidly progressive cellulitis of the epiglottis and adjacent soft tissue structures with the potential to cause abrupt airway obstruction.

SYNONYMS

Supraglottitis
Cherry-red epiglottitis

ICD-9CM CODES
464.30 Epiglottitis

EPIDEMIOLOGY

INCIDENCE (IN U.S.): Highest in young children, 2 to 4 yr old
INCIDENCE (IN U.S.): Unknown
PREDOMINANT SEX: Males
PEAK INCIDENCE: Peaks in young boys ages 2 to 4 yr, but it is reported in adults as well

PHYSICAL FINDINGS & CLINICAL PRESENTATION

- Irritability, fever, dysphonia, and dysphagia
- Respiratory distress, with child tending to lean up and forward
- Often, drooling or oral secretions
- Often, presence of tachycardia and tachypnea
- On visualization, edematous and cherry-red epiglottis
- Often, no classic barking cough as seen in croup
- Possibly fulminant course (especially in children), leading to complete airway obstruction

ETIOLOGY

- In children, *Haemophilus influenzae* type b is usual.
- In adults, *H. influenzae* can be isolated from blood and/or epiglottis (about 26% of cases).
- Pneumococci, streptococci, and staphylococci are also implicated.
- Role of viruses in epiglottitis unclear.

DIAGNOSIS

DIFFERENTIAL DIAGNOSIS

- Croup
- Angioedema
- Peritonsillar abscess
- Retropharyngeal abscess
- Diphtheria
- Foreign body aspiration
- Lingual tonsillitis

WORKUP

- Cultures of blood and urine
- Lateral neck radiograph to show an enlarged epiglottis, ballooning of the hypopharynx, and normal subglottic structures (Fig. 1-88)
  1. Radiographs are of only moderate sensitivity and specificity and take time to perform.
  2. Epiglottis should be visualized directly to secure diagnosis and only when prepared to urgently secure the airway.
  3. Visualization of the epiglottis may be safer in adults than in children.
- Cultures of the epiglottis

LABORATORY TESTS

- CBC: may reveal a leukocytosis with a shift to the left
- Chest x-ray examination: may reveal evidence of pneumonia in close to 25% of cases
- Cultures of blood, urine, and the epiglottis, as noted previously

TREATMENT

ACUTE GENERAL Rx

- Maintenance of adequate airway is critical.
- Early placement of an endotracheal or nasotracheal tube in a child is advised.
- Closely follow adult patient and defer intubation, provided the airway reveals no signs of obstruction.
- In children, visualization and intubation are best done in the most controlled environment, such as an operating room; pay close attention to vital signs, oxygen saturation, respiratory rate, input, and output, because abrupt deterioration can occur.
- *H. influenzae* in children may be less common thanks to the HIB vaccine.
- Use antibiotics such as ceftriaxone (80 to 100 mg/kg/day in two divided doses), cefotaxime (50 to 180 mg/kg/day in four divided doses), or ampicillin (200 mg/kg/day in four divided doses) with chloramphenicol (75 to 100 mg/kg/day in four divided doses).
- If possible, obtain cultures before initiating antibiotics, but do not delay antibiotic therapy if cultures cannot be obtained quickly.
- Treat adult patients with similar antibiotic regimens.
- Give close family contacts of the patient who are <4 yr old rifampin 20 mg/kg/day for 4 days (up to 600 mg/day) for prophylaxis.
- Role of epinephrine or corticosteroids in the management of epiglottitis is not firmly established.

REFERRAL

For effective management:
- Close cooperation between the pediatrician or internist, anesthesiologist, and otorhinolaryngologist, especially when epiglottis is visualized and when the patient requires endotracheal intubation
- Best managed in a critical care setting or ICU

SUGGESTED READINGS

Nakamura H et al: Acute epiglottitis: a review of 80 patients, *J Laryngol Otol* 115(1):31, 2001.

Sack JL, Brock CD: Identifying acute epiglottitis in adults: high degree of awareness, close monitoring are key, *Postgrad Med* 112(1):81, 2002.

AUTHOR: **JOSEPH J. LIEBER, M.D.**

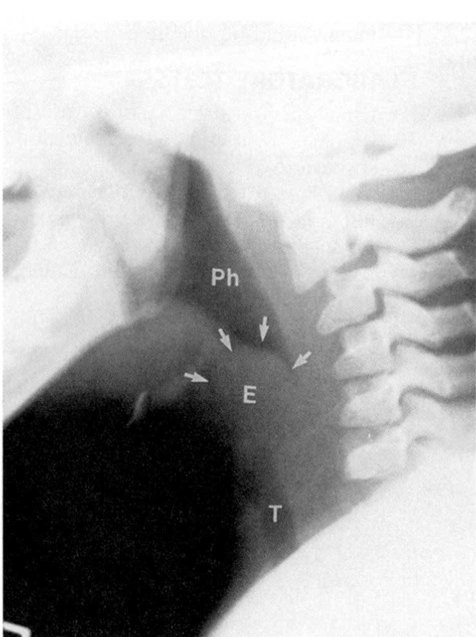

FIGURE 1-88 Epiglottitis. A lateral soft tissue view of the neck shows a ballooned pharynx *(Ph)* with swollen epiglottis *(E)* in the shape of a large thumbprint *(arrows)*. *T*, Trachea. (From Mettler FA [ed]: *Primary care radiology*, Philadelphia, 2000, WB Saunders.)

BASIC INFORMATION

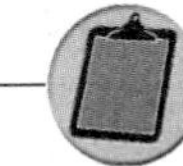

DEFINITION

Episcleritis is an inflammation of the episclera, or thin layer of vascular elastic tissue between the sclera and conjunctiva.

ICD-9CM CODES
379.0 Scleritis and episcleritis

EPIDEMIOLOGY & DEMOGRAPHICS

INCIDENCE (IN U.S.): Relatively rare in an ophthalmologic practice
PREDOMINANT SEX: None
PREDOMINANT AGE: 43 yr
PEAK INCIDENCE: Most common in middle and old age

PHYSICAL FINDINGS & CLINIAL PRESENTATION

- Red, vascular injection of conjunctiva with engorged and enlarged blood vessels beneath the conjunctions (Fig. 1-89)
- Pain in area of inflammation which is usually localized

ETIOLOGY

Associated with collagen-vascular diseases, vasculitis, trauma, often nonspecific

DIAGNOSIS

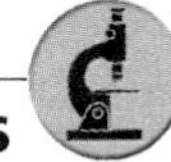

DIFFERENTIAL DIAGNOSIS

- Acute glaucoma
- Conjunctivitis
- Scleritis
- Subconjunctival hemorrhage
- Congenital or lymphoid masses
- The differential diagnosis of "red eye" is described in Section II.

WORKUP

Eye examination, general check-up for collagen vascular disease or other autoimmune diseases

LABORATORY TESTS

Studies for collagen-vascular disease (e.g., ANA, ESR, RF)

TREATMENT

NONPHARMACOLOGIC THERAPY

Warm compresses

ACUTE GENERAL Rx

- Topical steroids, 1% prednisolone if no glaucoma; nonsteroidals if there is a tendency for glaucoma
- NSAIDs: treat underlying systemic disease

CHRONIC Rx

NSAIDs such as Voltaren or Acular qid

DISPOSITION

Close follow-up needed

REFERRAL

To ophthalmologist if patient unresponsive to treatment after a few days

PEARLS & CONSIDERATIONS

COMMENTS

- Often associated with collagen vascular disease
- Usually related to systemic disease

SUGGESTED READINGS

Jabs DA et al: Episcleritis and scleritis: clinical features and treatment results, *Am J Ophthalmol* 130(4):469, 2000.

Paresio CE, Meier FM: Systemic disorders associated with episcleritis and scleritis, *Curr Opin Ophthalmology* 12(6):471, 2002.

Shaw C et al: Rheumatoid arthritis and ocular involvement, *J Indian Med Assoc* 101(9)537, 2003.

AUTHOR: **MELVYN KOBY, M.D.**

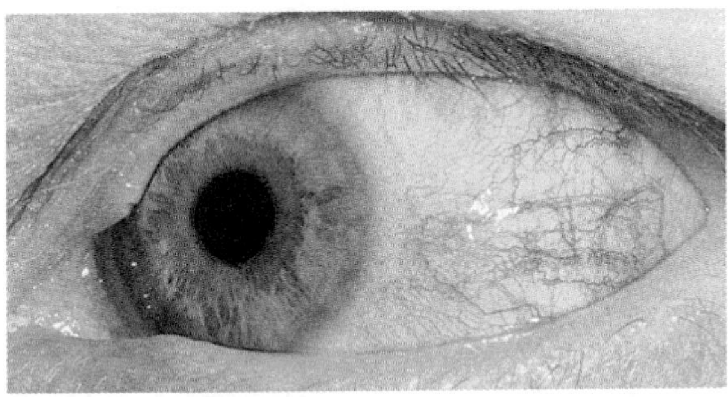

FIGURE 1-89 Nodular episcleritis in a patient with gout. (From Palay D [ed]: *Ophthalmology for the primary care physician,* St Louis, 1997, Mosby.)

BASIC INFORMATION

DEFINITION

Epistaxis is defined as bleeding from the nose or nasal hemorrhage and is classified as either anterior or posterior.

SYNONYMS

Nosebleed

ICD-9CM CODES
784.7 Epistaxis

EPIDEMIOLOGY & DEMOGRAPHICS

- Up to 60% of the population experiences at least one episode over a lifetime, and 6% of these patients will seek professional health care assistance to control the bleeding.
- Over 80% of cases of epistaxis are anterior in origin (Little's area) and occur from Kiesselbach's plexus (Fig. 1-90).
- Only 5% of patients with epistaxis have posterior bleeds.

PHYSICAL FINDINGS & CLINICAL PRESENTATION

- Nosebleed
- Hypotension and hemodynamic instability with acute severe epistaxis

ETIOLOGY

- Approximately 90% of epistaxes presenting to primary care physicians, emergency departments, and otolaryngologists are idiopathic.
- Other common causes of epistaxis can be either local or systemic in nature. Many cases of epistaxis are multifactorial in etiology.
  1. Cold, dry environment
  2. Trauma (nose picking, accidents, and physical altercations)
  3. Structural deformities (septal deviations/spurs, chronic perforations)
  4. Inflammatory (rhinosinusitis, nasal polyposis)
  5. Allergies
  6. Foreign bodies in the nasal cavity
  7. Tumors (juvenile angiofibroma)
  8. Irritants
  9. Hypertension
  10. Coagulopathy (hemophilia, von Willebrand's disease, thrombocytopenia)
  11. Osler-Weber-Rendu disease
  12. Renal failure
  13. Drugs: aspirin, NSAIDs, warfarin, and alcohol
  14. Blood vessel disorders (connective tissue disease, hereditary hemorrhagic telangiectasia)

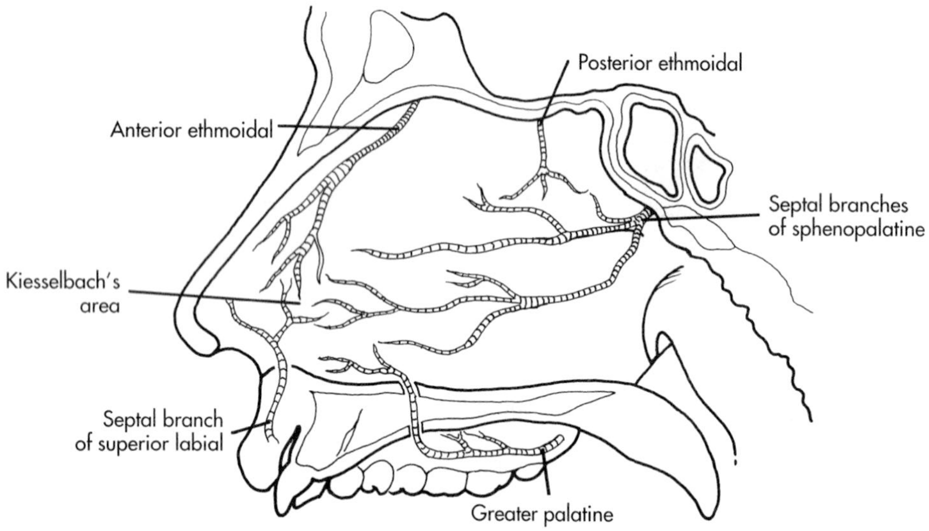

FIGURE 1-90 Kiesselbach's plexus on the anterior septum derives blood supply from the superior labial, descending palatine, and sphenopalatine arteries. (From Noble J: *Primary care medicine,* ed 3, St Louis, 2001, Mosby.)

DIAGNOSIS

- The diagnosis of epistaxis is self-evident; however, a good attempt should be made to directly visualize the source of bleeding to confirm the diagnosis.

DIFFERENTIAL DIAGNOSIS

- Pseudoepistaxis must be ruled out. Common extranasal sites of bleeding that can present with epistaxis include:
  1. Pulmonary hemoptysis
  2. Bleeding esophageal varices
  3. Tumor bleeding from the pharynx, larynx, or trachea

WORKUP

The diagnosis of epistaxis is self-evident. The workup should include laboratory blood testing to exclude obvious causes and type and cross in anticipation of transfusion if the bleeding is severe and cannot be stopped.

LABORATORY TESTS

- Hemoglobin and hematocrit
- Platelet count
- BUN/creatinine
- Coagulation studies (PT and PTT)
- Type and crossmatching of blood products

IMAGING STUDIES

X-ray studies are usually not helpful in the assessment of patients with epistaxis.

TREATMENT

NONPHARMACOLOGIC THERAPY

- Digital compression or pinching of the lower soft cartilaginous part of the nose for 10 min is the method of choice
- Cotton or tissue plug
- The patient should be sitting and leaning forward, breathing through the mouth, allowing blood to flow out of the nostrils as opposed to bending backward, which would allow the blood to flow down the throat
- Application of cold compresses to the bridge of the nose, causing a vasoconstrictive effect; the patient may also suck on ice to achieve this effect

ACUTE GENERAL Rx

Anterior Epistaxis

- Local vasoconstriction is performed by moistening a cotton pledget with either:
  1. 4% lidocaine with 1:1000 epinephrine
  2. 4% lidocaine with 1% phenylephrine (Neo-Synephrine)
  3. 4% lidocaine with 0.05% oxymetazoline (Afrin)

4. 4% cocaine or cocaine 25% in paraffin base ointment and inserting the pledget into the nasal cavity with bayonet forceps.
- Cauterization with silver nitrate is performed once hemostasis is achieved.
- Anterior nasal packing is needed when local measures are unsuccessful in controlling hemostasis. Nasal packing is performed under local anesthesia, and is done by inserting Vaseline gauze strips in layers from the floor of the nasal cavity to the front entrance of the nasal orifice. Enough pressure is placed to tamponade the epistaxis (Fig. 1-91).
- Other commercially available nasal packing using sponge packs that expand when exposed to blood or moisture can be used for anterior epistaxis.

Posterior Epistaxis
- Posterior nasal packing
  1. Commercially available nasal sponge packing can be applied
  2. Rolled gauze technique (see reference)
- Foley catheter balloon insertion into the nasopharynx can be tried in patients with posterior epistaxis (for the proper technique, please refer to the reference).

CHRONIC Rx
- If acute treatment fails to stop the bleeding or the site of bleeding cannot be located, electrocautery, or endoscopic cauterization can be used.
- Electrocautery is performed after suitable anesthesia such as application of a topical anesthetic followed by local anesthetic injection. Only one side of the nasal septum should be cauterized at a time as perforation can result from bilateral cauterization.
- Arterial ligation or embolization has been used in refractory posterior epistaxis.
- For cases involving irritated or inflamed mucosa, a conservative regimen of triamcinolone 0.025%, nemdyn, nasalate, or equivalent cream should be applied once a week, combined with nightly application of a small quantity of petroleum jelly to the septum before bedtime.

DISPOSITION
- Most cases of anterior epistaxis from Kiesselbach's plexus can be stopped by nasal compression and local vasoconstriction or cauterization.
- Nasal packing with gauze or sponge can control 90% of anterior epistaxis.

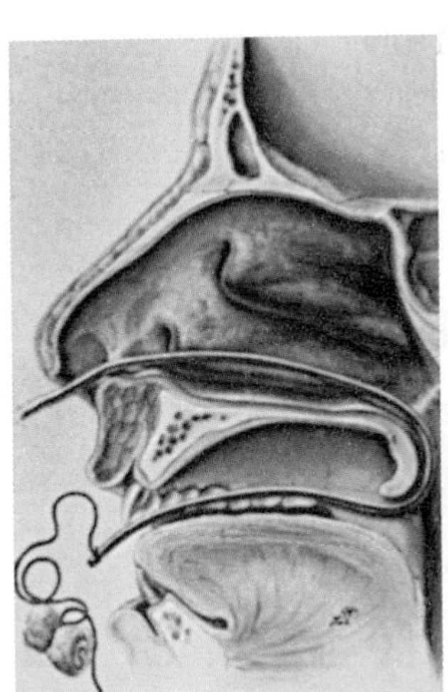
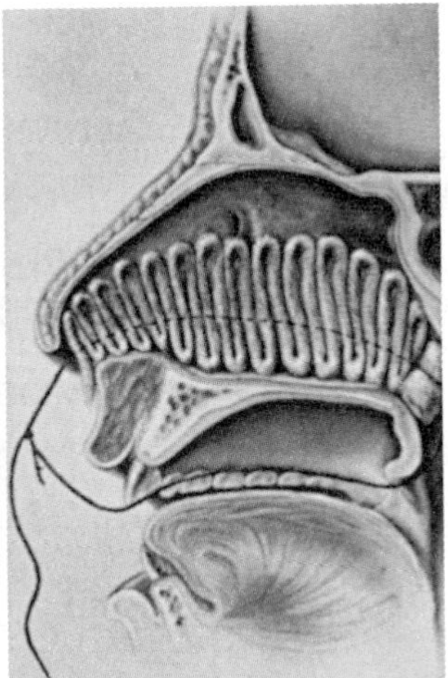

FIGURE 1-91 Packing of the nose for epistaxis with a postnasal pack and an anterior nose pack. (From Boies LR et al: *Fundamentals of otolaryngology: a textbook of ear, nose, and throat diseases,* ed 4, Philadelphia, 1964, WB Saunders.)

- Anterior and posterior packs are removed in 2 to 3 days.
- Although rare, epistaxis can lead to death by aspiration of blood, hemodynamic compromise from rapid excessive blood loss, or toxic shock syndrome.

REFERRAL
- If epistaxis cannot be controlled in the acute setting by the above mentioned nonpharmacologic and pharmacologic measures, ENT specialist should be called for assistance.
- ENT specialist should be consulted in any patient with posterior epistaxis requiring posterior packing.

PEARLS & CONSIDERATIONS

COMMENTS
- Silver nitrate cauterization, if done on both sides of the nasal septum, can lead to septal perforation and should be discouraged.
- If anterior nasal packing is done, broad-spectrum antibiotics (e.g., amoxicillin-clavulanate 250 mg PO tid or trimethoprim-sulfamethoxazole 1 tab PO bid) are used until the anterior packs are removed.
- Complications of nasal packing include
  1. Aspiration
  2. Dislodged packing
  3. Infection
  4. Nasal trauma

SUGGESTED READINGS

Bentley B: Nasal emergencies. In Cline DM et al (eds): *Emergency medicine: a comprehensive study guide,* ed 4, American College of Emergency Physicians, New York, 1996, McGraw-Hill.

Kotecha B et al: Management of epistaxis: a national survey, *Ann R Coll Surg Engl* 78:444, 1996.

Mahmood S, Lowe T: Management of epistaxis in the oral and maxillofacial surgery setting: an update on current practice, *Oral Surg Oral Med Oral Pathol Oral Radiol Endod* 95:23, 2003.

Parshen D, Stevens M: Management of epistaxis in general practice, *Aust Fam Physician* 31(8):717, 2002.

Pond F, Sizeland A: Epistaxis: strategies for management, *Aust Fam Physician* 29(10):933, 2000.

Tan LKS, Calhoun KH: Epistaxis, *Med Clin North Am* 83(1):43, 1999.

AUTHORS: **JASON IANNUCCILLI, M.D.,** and **PETER PETROPOULOS, M.D.**

Epstein-Barr Virus Infection

BASIC INFORMATION

DEFINITION

Epstein-Barr virus infection refers to a disease caused by Epstein-Barr virus (EBV), a human herpesvirus.

SYNONYMS

Infectious mononucleosis

ICD-9CM CODES
075 Mononucleosis

EPIDEMIOLOGY & DEMOGRAPHICS

INCIDENCE (IN U.S.): 45 cases/100,000 persons/yr of infectious mononucleosis (IM)

PREDOMINANT SEX: Neither, although peak incidence occurs about 2 years earlier in women

PREDOMINANT AGE:

- Infectious mononucleosis: occurs most commonly between the ages of 15 and 24 yr.
- EBV infection: occurs earlier in life in lower socioeconomic groups.

PHYSICAL FINDINGS

- Most EBV infections either are asymptomatic or cause a nonspecific illness.
- Incubation period is 1 to 2 mo, possibly followed by a prodrome of anorexia, malaise, headache, and chills; after several days, clinical triad of pharyngitis, fever, and adenopathy may appear, accompanied by fatigue and malaise.
- Pharyngitis is usually the most severe symptom; exudates are common.
- Lymphadenopathy is most prominent in the cervical region but may be diffuse.
- Splenomegaly is possible, most commonly during the second week of illness.
- Rash is uncommon, but will occur in nearly all patients who receive ampicillin.
- Possible IM presentation: fever and adenopathy without pharyngitis.
- Although complications may be severe, they are also uncommon and tend to resolve completely.
- Involvement of the hematologic, pulmonary, cardiac, or nervous systems possible; splenic rupture is rare.
- IM is usually a self-limited illness, but symptoms of malaise and fatigue may last months before resolving.
- Besides IM, EBV is also related to lymphoproliferative syndromes in transplant recipients and in AIDS patients.
- Increasing evidence showing an association between EBV infection and both African Burkitt's lymphoma and nasopharyngeal carcinoma.

ETIOLOGY

- Ubiquitous virus
- Prevalence is higher in lower socioeconomic groups than in age-matched controls in more affluent groups
- Infection during childhood is much less likely to cause significant illness
- Frequency of IM in late adolescence is attributed to the onset of social contact between the sexes
- Close personal contact is usually necessary for transmission, although EBV is occasionally transmitted by blood transfusion; transfer via saliva while kissing may be responsible for many cases

DIAGNOSIS

DIFFERENTIAL DIAGNOSIS

- Heterophile-negative infectious mononucleosis caused by CMV
- Although clinical presentation similar, CMV more frequently follows transfusion
- Bacterial and viral causes of pharyngitis
- Toxoplasmosis
- Acute retroviral syndrome of HIV
- Lymphoma

WORKUP

Heterophile antibody and CBC

LABORATORY TESTS

- Increased WBC common, with a relative lymphocytosis and neutropenia
- Hallmark of IM: atypical lymphocytes (not pathognomonic)
- Mild thrombocytopenia
- Falling Hct signaling splenic rupture
- Elevated hepatocellular enzymes and cryoglobulins in most cases
- Heterophile antibody
  1. As measured by the Monospot test, may be positive at presentation or may appear later in the course of illness.
  2. Negative test is repeated if clinical suspicion is high.
  3. A positive test has been reported with primary HIV infection.
- Virus-specific antibodies possibly responding to IM: determination of these EBV-specific antibodies is rarely necessary to diagnose IM

IMAGING STUDIES

Chest x-ray examination

- May rarely show infiltrates
- Possible elevated left hemidiaphragm with splenic rupture

TREATMENT

NONPHARMACOLOGIC THERAPY

- Supportive
- Rest advocated by some; impact on outcome not clear
- Splenectomy if rupture occurs
- Transfusions for severe anemia or thrombocytopenia

ACUTE GENERAL Rx

- Pharmacologic therapy is not indicated in uncomplicated illness
- Use of steroids
  1. Suggested in patients who have severe thrombocytopenia or hemolytic anemia, or impending airway obstruction resulting from enlarged tonsils
  2. Prednisone 60 to 80 mg PO qd for 3 days, then tapered over 1 to 2 wk
- There is no role for antiviral agents such as acyclovir in the management of IM.

CHRONIC Rx

An extremely rare, chronic form of IM with persistent fevers and other objective findings has been described and should be differentiated from chronic fatigue syndrome, which is not related to EBV.

DISPOSITION

Eventual resolution of all symptoms

REFERRAL

If more than mild illness

PEARLS & CONSIDERATIONS

COMMENTS

Avoidance of contact sports during the first month of illness, because splenic rupture can occur even in the absence of clinically detectable splenomegaly.

SUGGESTED READINGS

Auwaerter PG: Infectious mononucleosis in middle age, *JAMA* 281:454, 1999.

Cohen JI: Epstein-Barr virus infection, *N Engl J Med* 343:481, 2000.

Thorley-Lawson DA, Gross A: Persistence of the Epstein-Barr virus and the origins of associated lymphomas, *N Engl J Med* 350:1328, 2004.

Vidrih JA et al: Positive Epstein-Barr virus heterophile antibody tests in patients with primary human immunodeficiency virus infection, *Am J Med* 111(3):237, 2001.

AUTHOR: **MAURICE POLICAR, M.D.**

BASIC INFORMATION

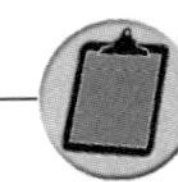

DEFINITION

Erectile dysfunction is the inability to achieve or sustain a penile erection of adequate rigidity to make intercourse possible.

SYNONYMS

Impotence
Male erectile disorder
Sexual dysfunction (a nonspecific term)

ICD-9CM CODES
F52.2 Male erectile disorder
(DSM-IV Code: 302.72
Male erectile disorder)

EPIDEMIOLOGY & DEMOGRAPHICS

PREVALENCE (IN U.S.):
- Increases with age.
- About 7% for men between 18 and 29 yr, 18% for men in their 50s, 25% for men in their 60s, 80% for men in their 80s.
- The Massachusetts Male Aging Study reports a 1989 prevalence as 52%, with 9.6% of respondents with complete erectile dysfunction; in 2000, the prevalence was 44%.
- Likely underestimated because of social stigma but the number of patients presenting to their doctor with this complaint has increased considerably with greater availability and awareness of oral therapy.

PREDOMINANT SEX: By definition, only in males
PREDOMINANT AGE: Increases with age
PEAK INCIDENCE: Over 70 yr old
CLINICAL PRESENTATION
- Psychogenic impotence: inability to obtain erection, inability to obtain or maintain an adequate erection, or the loss of erection before completion of sexual intercourse; nocturnal penile tumescence usually normal.
- Organic impotence: inability to obtain an erection or inability to obtain an adequate erection; nocturnal penile tumescence usually abnormal.

ETIOLOGY

- Psychogenic erectile dysfunction resulting from a wide range of experiential, historical, or even psychotic processes.
- Mental health disorders, particularly depression, widower syndrome, and performance anxiety are known psychogenic contributors.
- Organic impotence resulting from a wide variety of insults to neurologic, hormonal, or vascular structures. In approximately 40% of men >50 years of age, the primary cause of ED is related to atherosclerotic disease.
- Medications (antihypertensives, antidepressants, antipsychotics, histamine blockers, nicotine, alcohol, and others) are commonly causative.
- Endocrinopathies such as diabetes, hypogonadism, hypothyroidism or hyperthyroidism, and hyperprolactinemia.
- Neurogenic causes including spinal cord lesions, cortical lesions, and peripheral neuropathies.

DIAGNOSIS

DIFFERENTIAL DIAGNOSIS

- Treatment dependent on the etiology.
- Psychogenic dysfunction distinguished from organic.
- Etiology of organic dysfunction to be determined.
- Erectile dysfunction possible in the setting of another psychiatric condition (e.g., depression or obsessive-compulsive disorder).

WORKUP

- History (often including partner report) with a focus on risk factors (e.g., smoking, alcohol)
- Report of nocturnal erections
- Physical examination to rule out neuronal damage, direct penile damage (e.g., fibrosis), or testicular atrophy

LABORATORY TESTS

Evaluate for endocrine abnormalities with morning serum testosterone (total and free) and LH, dyslipidemia with lipid panel, HbA1c or fasting glucose, thyroid profile.

IMAGING STUDIES

Imaging studies rarely performed except in situations of pelvic trauma or surgery.

OTHER STUDIES

- Nocturnal penile tumescence very specific for distinguishing psychogenic versus organic causes.
- Vascular etiologies screened by the penile-brachial pressure index (measures the loss of systolic blood pressure between the arm and penis) or with Doppler studies.
- Neurogenic etiologies examined by the bulbocavernosus reflex or the pudendal-evoked response.
- Intracorporeal injection of prostaglandin E1 to distinguish vascular and nonvascular etiologies (erection is achieved in patients with nonvascular etiologies).

TREATMENT

NONPHARMACOLOGIC THERAPY

- Various psychotherapeutic approaches: cognitive behavioral therapy preferred because it is the most focused; success rates decrease with advancing age and duration of symptoms.
- Sex therapy and couples' therapy are used to address technical or social issues that contribute to impotence.
- Vacuum devices (70% to 90% effective) work for many men, but they are difficult to use and cumbersome.

ACUTE GENERAL Rx

- PDE5 inhibitors: sildenafil (Viagra) 50 mg approx 1 hr before sexual activity, most commonly used as first-line therapy. Tadalafil (Cialis) with broad period of responsiveness (to 36 hr) gives it enhanced patient convenience. Vardenafil (Levitra) 10 mg PO 1 hr before sexual activity; avoid concomitant use of nitrates.
- Intracavernosal injections of vasodilators (e.g., papaverine, alprostadil, or prostaglandin E1 pellet).
- Oral medications such as pentoxifylline and yohimbine (limited success).

CHRONIC Rx

- Psychogenic impotence: relatively uncommon and characterized objectively by nocturnal and morning erections and otherwise negative test results. PDE5 inhibitors effective in patients with depression because tissues, nerves, hormones, and vasculature normal. Full psychologic evaluation recommended before starting treatment so underlying problem is addressed.
- For men failing other approaches: penile prosthesis.
- Testosterone therapy in elderly hypogonadal males.

DISPOSITION

- When erectile dysfunction is secondary to an organic cause, it does not remit unless the organic cause is corrected; therefore, it is usually a chronic condition.
- Psychogenic acquired erectile dysfunction will remit spontaneously in 15% to 30% of the cases.
- Lifelong erectile dysfunction is usually a chronic and unremitting condition.
- Situational erectile dysfunction may remit with changes in social environment, but it usually recurs.

REFERRAL

If psychotherapy, sex therapy, or invasive organic treatment required

SUGGESTED READINGS

Fazio L et al: Erectile dysfunction: management update, *Can Med Assoc Jour* 170:1429, 2004.
Fink HA et al: Sildenafil for male erectile dysfunction, *Arch Intern Med* 162:1349, 2002.
Kalsi JS et al: Update on oral treatments for male erectile dysfunction, *J Eur Acad Dermatol Venereol* 18:267, 2004.
Miller TA: Diagnostic evaluation of erectile dysfunction, *Am Fam Physician* 61:95, 2000.

AUTHOR: **AMAR DESAI, M.D., M.P.H.**

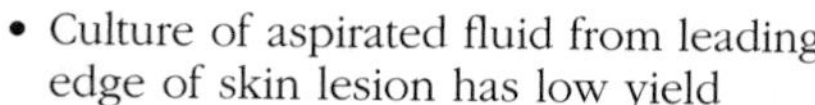

BASIC INFORMATION

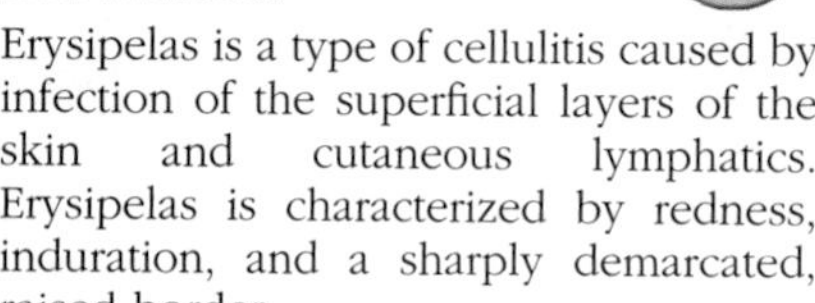

DEFINITION

Erysipelas is a type of cellulitis caused by infection of the superficial layers of the skin and cutaneous lymphatics. Erysipelas is characterized by redness, induration, and a sharply demarcated, raised border.

SYNONYMS

St. Anthony's fire

ICD-9CM CODES
035 Erysipelas

EPIDEMIOLOGY & DEMOGRAPHICS

Erysipelas occurs most often in the young or old, in patients with impaired lymphatic or venous drainage (mastectomy, saphenous vein harvesting), and in immunocompromised patients. Recurrence is relatively common.

PHYSICAL FINDINGS & CLINICAL PRESENTATION

- Distinctive red, warm, tender skin lesion with induration and a sharply defined, advancing, raised border is present (Fig. 1-92).
- Most common sites are lower extremities or face.
- Systemic signs of infection (fever) are often present.
- Vesicles or bullae may develop.
- After several days, lesions may appear ecchymotic.
- After 7 to 10 days desquamation of affected area may occur.

ETIOLOGY

- Usually group A β-hemolytic streptococci
- Less often group B, C, or G streptococci
- Rarely *Staphylococcus aureus*

COMPLICATIONS

- Abscess
- Necrotizing fasciitis
- Thrombophlebitis
- Gangrene
- Metastatic infection

DIAGNOSIS

DIFFERENTIAL DIAGNOSIS

- Other types of cellulitis
- Necrotizing fasciitis
- DVT
- Contact dermatitis
- Erythema migrans (Lyme disease)
- Insect bite
- Herpes zoster
- Erysipeloid
- Acute gout
- Pseudogout

WORKUP

History, physical examination, and laboratory evaluation

LABORATORY TESTS

Diagnosis is usually made by characteristic clinical setting and appearance.
- CBC and WBC often elevated
- Blood cultures positive in 5% of patients
- Gram stain and culture of any drainage from skin lesions
- Culture of aspirated fluid from leading edge of skin lesion has low yield

IMAGING STUDIES

- Duplex ultrasound for patients suspected of having DVT
- CT scan or MRI for patients with suspected necrotizing fasciitis

TREATMENT

NONPHARMACOLOGIC THERAPY

- Elevation of the affected limb
- Warm compresses

ACUTE GENERAL Rx

Typical erysipelas of extremity in nondiabetic patient:
- PO: penicillin V 250 mg to 500 mg qid
- IV: penicillin G (aqueous) 1 to 2 million units q6h

NOTE: Use erythromycin or cephalosporin in patients allergic to penicillin.
Facial erysipelas (include coverage for *Staphylococcus aureus*):
- PO dicloxacillin 500 mg q6h
- IV nafcillin or oxacillin 2 g q4h

DISPOSITION

Prognosis is good with antibiotic treatment, but recurrence is common.

REFERRAL

For surgical debridement for patients with necrotizing fasciitis or for drainage of abscess

AUTHORS: **GAIL O'BRIEN, M.D.**, and **MARK J. FAGAN, M.D.**

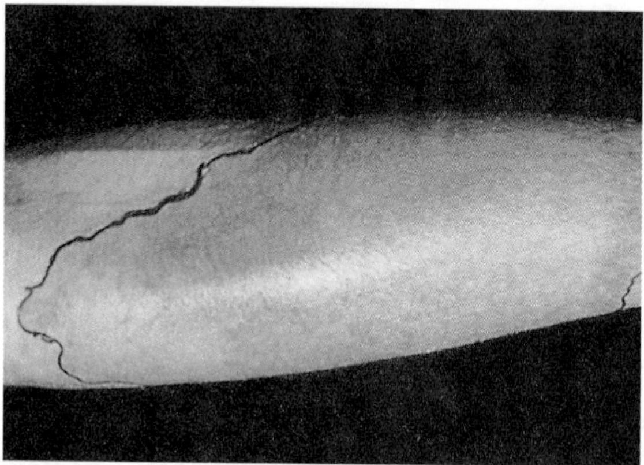

FIGURE 1-92 Erysipelas. Note well-demarcated erythematous plaque on arm. (From Goldstein B [ed]: *Practical dermatology,* ed 2,, St Louis, 1997, Mosby. Courtesy Department of Dermatology, University of North Carolina at Chapel Hill.)

SECTION I

BASIC INFORMATION

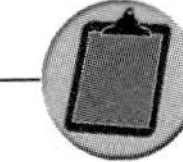

DEFINITION

Erythema multiforme is an inflammatory disease believed to be secondary to immune complex formation and subsequent deposition in the skin and mucous membranes.

SYNONYMS

EM

ICD-9CM CODES
695.1 Erythema multiforme

EPIDEMIOLOGY & DEMOGRAPHICS

- Predominant age: 20 to 40 yr
- Often associated with herpes simplex and other infectious agents, drugs, and connective tissue diseases

PHYSICAL FINDINGS & CLINICAL PRESENTATION

- Symmetric skin lesions with a classic "target" appearance (caused by the centrifugal spread of red maculopapules to circumference of 1 to 3 cm with a purpuric, cyanotic, or vesicular center) are present (Fig. 1-93).
- Lesions are most common in the back of the hands and feet and extensor aspect of the forearms and legs. Trunk involvement can occur in severe cases.
- Urticarial papules, vesicles, and bullae may also be present and generally indicate a more severe form of the disease.
- Individual lesions heal in 1 or 2 wk without scarring.
- Bullae and erosions may also be present in the oral cavity.

ETIOLOGY

- Immune complex formation and subsequent deposition in the cutaneous microvasculature may play a role in the pathogenesis of erythema multiforme.
- The majority of EM cases follow outbreaks of herpes simplex.
- In >50% of patients, no specific cause is identified.
- Erythema multiforme associated with bupropion use has been reported.

DIAGNOSIS

DIFFERENTIAL DIAGNOSIS

- Chronic urticaria
- Secondary syphilis
- Pityriasis rosea
- Contact dermatitis
- Pemphigus vulgaris
- Lichen planus
- Serum sickness
- Drug eruption
- Granuloma annulare

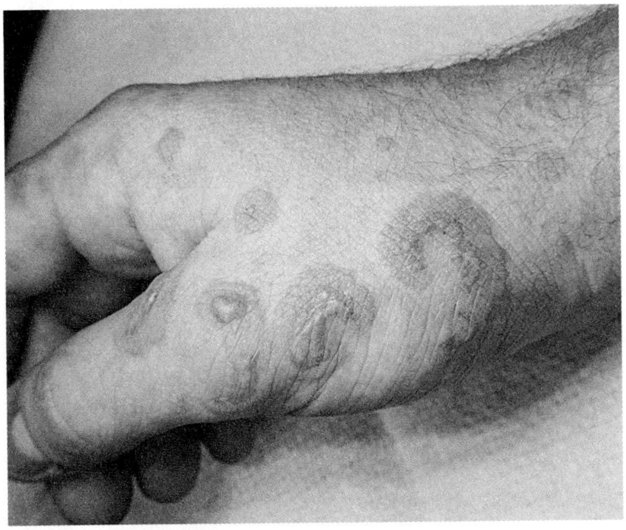

FIGURE 1-93 Iris and arcuate lesions of erythema multiforme. Note erythematous lesions with multiform configurations—target, arcuate, and vesicles. (From Noble J et al: *Textbook of primary care medicine,* ed 2, St Louis, 1995, Mosby.)

WORKUP

- Medical history with emphasis on drug ingestion
- Laboratory evaluation in patients with suspected collagen-vascular diseases
- Skin biopsy when diagnosis is unclear

LABORATORY TESTS

- CBC with differential
- ANA
- Serology for *Mycoplasma pneumoniae*
- Urinalysis

TREATMENT

NONPHARMACOLOGIC THERAPY

- Mild cases generally do not require treatment; lesions resolve spontaneously within 1 mo.
- Potential drug precipitants should be removed.

ACUTE GENERAL Rx

- Treatment of associated diseases (e.g., acyclovir for herpes simplex, erythromycin for *Mycoplasma* infection).
- Prednisone 40 to 80 mg/day for 1 to 3 wk may be tried in patients with many target lesions; however, the role of systemic steroids remains controversial.
- Levamisole, an immunomodulator, may be effective in treatment of patients with chronic or recurrent oral lesions (dose is 150 mg/day for 3 consecutive days used alone or in combination with prednisone).

DISPOSITION

The rash of EM generally evolves over a 2-wk period and resolves within 3 to 4 wk without scarring. A severe bullous form can occur (see "Stevens-Johnson syndrome").

REFERRAL

Hospital admission in patients with Stevens-Johnson syndrome

PEARLS & CONSIDERATIONS

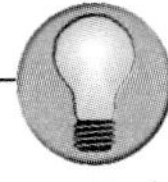

COMMENTS

The risk of recurrence of erythema multiforme exceeds 30%.

SUGGESTED READING

Lineberry TW et al: Bupropion-induced erythema multiforme, *Mayo Clin Proc* 76:664, 2001.

AUTHOR: **FRED F. FERRI, M.D.**

Erythema Nodosum

BASIC INFORMATION

DEFINITION

Erythema nodosum is an acute, tender, erythematous, nodular skin eruption resulting from inflammation of subcutaneous fat, often associated with bruising.

ICD-9CM CODES
695.2 Erythema nodosum
017.10 Erythema nodosum, tuberculous, NOS

EPIDEMIOLOGY & DEMOGRAPHICS

INCIDENCE: 2 to 3 cases per 100,000 persons per year
PEAK AGE: 25 to 40 yr
SEX DISTRIBUTION: Ratio of 3-4:1 (female:male)

PHYSICAL FINDINGS & CLINICAL PRESENTATION

- Acute onset of tender nodules typically located on shins (Fig. 1-94), occasionally seen on thighs and forearms
- The nodules are usually one eighth to 1 inch in diameter, but can be as large as 4 inches; they begin as light red lesions, then become darker and often ecchymotic. The nodules heal within 8 wk without ulceration
- Associated findings
  Fever
  Lymphadenopathy
  Arthralgia
  Signs of the underlying illness

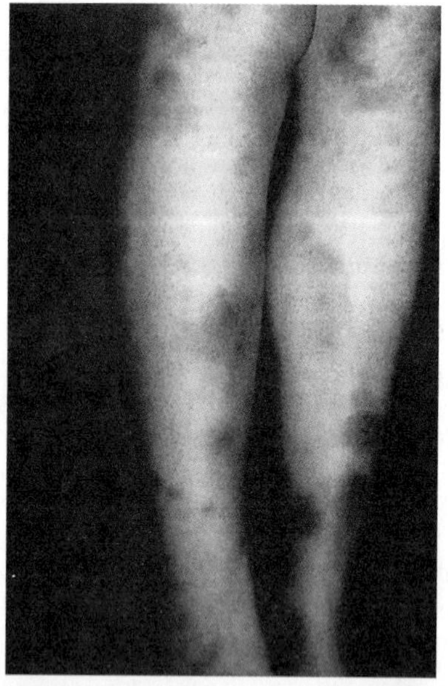

FIGURE 1-94 Erythema nodosum. (From Arndt KA et al: *Cutaneous medicine and surgery,* vol 1, Philadelphia, 1997, WB Saunders.)

ETIOLOGY

Cell-mediated hypersensitivity reaction seen more frequently in persons with HLA antigen B8. The lesion results from an exaggerated interaction between an antigen and cell-mediated immune mechanisms leading to granuloma formation.
Infections:

- Bacteria
  Streptococcal pharyngitis
  Salmonella enteritis
  Yersinia enteritis
  Psittacosis
  Chlamydia pneumoniae infection
  Mycoplasma pneumonia
  Meningococcal infection
  Gonorrhea
  Syphilis
  Lymphogranuloma venereum
  Tularemia
  Cat-scratch disease
  Leprosy
  Tuberculosis
- Fungi
  Histoplasmosis
  Coccidioidomycosis
  Blastomycosis
  Trichophyton verrucosum
- Viruses
  Cytomegalovirus
  Hepatitis B
  Epstein-Barr virus
- Drugs
  Sulfonamides
  Penicillins
  Oral contraceptives
  Gold salts
  Prazosin
  Aspirin
  Bromides
- Sarcoidosis
- Cancer, usually lymphoma
- Ankylosing spondylosis and reactive arthropathies (e.g., associated with inflammatory bowel disease)

DIAGNOSIS

DIFFERENTIAL DIAGNOSIS

- Insect bites
- Posttraumatic ecchymoses
- Vasculitis
- Weber-Christian disease
- Fat necrosis associated with pancreatitis

WORKUP

- Physical examination
- Diagnosis of underlying illness by history, physical examination, and laboratory tests as indicated

LABORATORY TESTS

- Erythrocyte sedimentation rate (ESR)
- Throat culture and antistreptolysin O titer
- PPD
- Others depending on index of suspicion

IMAGING STUDIES

- Chest x-ray for sarcoidosis and TB
- Skin biopsy in doubtful cases

Early lesion: inflammation and hemorrhage in subcutaneous tissue
Late lesion: giant cells and granulomata

TREATMENT

The disease is self-limited and treatment is symptomatic
- NSAIDs for pain
- Systemic steroids in severe cases

PROGNOSIS

Typical case:
- Pain for 2 wk
- Resolution within 8 wk

SUGGESTED READING

Dixey J: Erythema nodosum. In Klippel JH et al (eds): *Rheumatology,* St Louis, 1998, Mosby.

AUTHOR: **TOM J. WACHTEL, M.D.**

BASIC INFORMATION

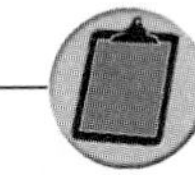

DEFINITION

Esophageal tumors are defined as benign and malignant tumors arising from the esophagus. Approximately 15% of esophageal cancers arise in the cervical esophagus, 50% in the middle third of the esophagus, and 35% in the lower third. Eighty-five percent of esophageal tumors are squamous cell carcinoma (arising from squamous epithelium). Adenocarcinomas arise from columnar epithelium in the distal esophagus, which have become dysplastic secondary to chronic gastric reflux.

ICD-9CM CODES
150.8 Esophageal cancer, NEC
150.9 Esophageal cancer, NOS
230.1 Carcinoma of esophagus, in situ

EPIDEMIOLOGY & DEMOGRAPHICS

Carcinomas of the esophageal epithelium, both squamous cell and adenocarcinoma, are by far the most common and important tumors of the esophagus. Benign neoplasms are much less common and include leiomyoma, papilloma, and fibrovascular polyps. Prevalence of esophageal carcinoma varies widely in different parts of world, from 7.6 cases per 100,000 persons in the U.S. to 130 cases per 100,000 persons in China. It occurs frequently within the so-called Asian "esophageal cancer belt," extending from the southern shore of the Caspian Sea to northern China, with certain high-incidence pockets in Finland, Ireland, SE Africa, and NW France. In the U.S., 13,900 new cases and 13,000 deaths occur per year, making it the seventh leading cause of death by cancer among men. Esophageal cancer is more common among blacks than whites and has a high male:female ratio of 3:1. It usually develops in the seventh and eighth decades of life and is an illness associated with lower socioeconomic status. More than 50% of patients are diagnosed with esophageal cancer at an advanced stage (unresectable or metastatic disease).

PHYSICAL FINDINGS & CLINICAL PRESENTATION

Symptoms and signs:
- Dysphagia: initially occurs with solid foods and gradually progresses to include semisolids and liquids; latter signs usually indicate incurable disease with tumor involving more than 60% of the esophageal circumference, and occurs in 74% of patients.
- Weight loss: more than many of patients present with weight loss usually of short duration. Weight loss >10% of body mass is an independent predictor of poor prognosis.
- Hoarseness: suggests recurrent laryngeal nerve involvement
- Odynophagia: an unusual symptom
- Cervical adenopathy: usually involving supraclavicular lymph nodes
- Dry cough: suggests tracheal involvement
- Aspiration pneumonia: caused by development of a fistula between the esophagus and trachea
- Massive hemoptysis or hematemesis: results from the invasion of vascular structures
- Advanced disease spreads to liver, lungs, and pleura
- Hypercalcemia: usually associated with squamous cell carcinoma because of the secretion of a tumor peptide similar to the parathyroid hormone

ETIOLOGY

Pathogenesis of esophageal cancers is felt to be due to chronic recurrent oxidative damage from any of the following etiological agents listed below, which cause inflammation, esophagitis, increased cell turnover and ultimately, initiation of the carcinogenic process.
Etiologic Agents:
- Excess alcohol consumption: accounts for 80% to 90% of esophageal cancer in the U.S., with whiskey being associated with a higher incidence than wine or beer
- Cigarette smoking: alcohol and tobacco use combined increase the risk substantially
- Other ingested carcinogens:
  Nitrates (converted to nitrites): South Asia, China
  Smoked opiates: Northern Iran
  Fungal toxins in pickled vegetables
- Mucosal damage:
  Long-term exposure to extremely hot tea
  Lye ingestion
- Radiation-induced strictures
- Chronic achalasia: incidence is seven times higher
- Host susceptibility secondary to precancerous lesions:
  Plummer-Vinson syndrome (Paterson-Kelly): glossitis with iron deficiency
  Congenital hyperkeratosis and pitting of palms and soles
- Chronic GERD leading to Barrett's esophagus and adenocarcinoma (whites are affected more than blacks)
- Possible association with celiac sprue or dietary deficiencies of molybdenum, zinc, vitamin A

DIAGNOSIS

DIFFERENTIAL DIAGNOSIS

- Achalasia of the esophagus
- Scleroderma of the esophagus
- Diffuse esophageal spasm
- Esophageal rings and webs

PHYSICAL EXAMINATION

- Monitor weight
- Findings are often limited to cervical and supraclavicular lymph nodes
- Signs of lung consolidation from aspiration pneumonia

LABORATORY TESTS

Complete blood cell count, chemistries, liver enzymes

IMAGING STUDIES

- Double contrast esophagogram effectively identifies large esophageal lesions (Fig. 1-95).
- In contrast to benign esophageal leiomyomata, which cause esophageal narrowing with preservation of normal mucosal pattern, esophageal carcinomas cause ragged ulcerating changes in the mucosa in association with deeper infiltration.
- Smaller tumors can be missed by esophagogram, therefore esophagoscopy is recommended.
- Esophagoscopy is performed to visualize tumor and obtain histopathologic confirmation. In conjunction, an endoscopic ultrasonogram is often performed to determine the depth of tumor invasion.
- This population is also at risk for cancers of head, neck, and lung; therefore endoscopic inspection of larynx, trachea, and bronchi should also be performed.
- Endoscopic biopsies fail to recover malignant tissue one third of the time, thus cytologic examination of tumor brushings should be routinely performed.
- Examination of the fundus of the stomach via retroflexion of the endoscope is also imperative.
- Chest and abdominal CT scan should be performed to determine the extent of tumor spread to mediastinum, paraaortic lymph nodes, and liver.

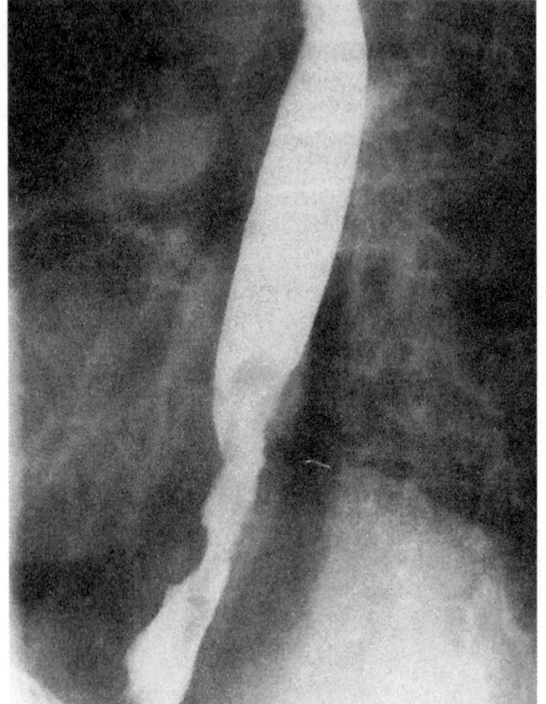

FIGURE 1-95 Barium swallow demonstrating the classic findings in cancer of the distal third of the espophagus. (From Nobel J [ed]: *Primary care medicine,* ed 2, St Louis, 1996, Mosby.)

TREATMENT

ACUTE GENERAL Rx

SURGICAL RESECTION:

- Surgical resection of squamous cell and adenocarcinoma of the lower third of the esophagus is done in most centers if there is no widespread metastasis.
- Less than 20% of patients who survive a total resection can be expected to survive after 5 yr. Usually stomach or colon is used for esophageal replacement.

POSSIBLE COMPLICATIONS OF SURGERY: Anatomic fistula (usually with colon interposition, subphrenic abscesses); respiratory complications are less common as a result of advances in surgical techniques, respiratory therapy, hyperalimentation, and anesthetic support during surgery. Cardiovascular complications are by far the most common including MI, CVA, and PE.

RADIATION THERAPY:

- Squamous cell carcinomas are more radiosensitive than adenocarcinoma, and radiation achieves good local control and is an excellent palliative modality for obstructive symptoms. Usually employed for tumors in upper third of esophagus, often for middle third tumors as well.
- About 40% of tumors cannot be destroyed even after 6000 rads.
- Palliative radiation therapy for bone metastasis is also effective.
- Single agent resulted in significant tumor regression in 15% to 25% of patients and combination chemotherapy including cisplatin achieved significant tumor reduction in 30% to 60% of patients.

COMPLICATIONS OF RADIATION THERAPY:

- Esophageal stricture, radiation-induced pulmonary fibrosis, transverse myelitis are the most feared complications.
- Radiation-induced cardiomyopathy and skin changes occur less frequently given modern techniques.
- Mucositis, GI toxicity, and myelosuppression occur frequently.
- Nephrotoxicity, ototoxicity and neurotoxicity can develop with cisplatin.

COMBINATION CHEMOTHERAPY, RADIATION Rx, AND SURGICAL Rx:

- Combination therapy has not been found to be associated with improved survival, however, many centers are using preoperative chemotherapy for many patients with esophageal cancer.
- Palliative procedures such as repeated endoscopic dilation, surgical placement of feeding tube, or polyvinyl prosthesis to bypass tumors have been used for surgically unresectable patients.

DISPOSITION

- Surgery: 5-yr survival rate is 48% in stages I and II, 20% in advanced stages.
- Radiation therapy: 5-yr survival rate is between 6% and 20%.
- Chemotherapy: Simple agent response rate 15% to 38%; combination response rate 80%.
- Combined modality: 18% response rate.
- Patients with stage IV disease receive palliative chemotherapy with a median survival of less than 1 year.

SUGGESTED READINGS

Enzinger PC, Mayer RJ: Esophageal cancer, *N Engl J Med* 349:2241, 2003.

Shaheen N et al: Gastroesophageal reflux, Barrett esophagus, and esophageal cancer: clinical applications, *JAMA* 287(15):1982, 2002.

AUTHORS: **LYNN MCNICOLL, M.D.,** and **MADHAVI YERNENI, M.D.**

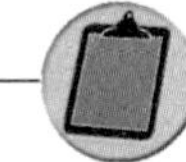

BASIC INFORMATION

DEFINITION

A predominantly postural and action tremor that is bilateral and tends to progress slowly over the years in the absence of other neurological abnormalities.

ICD-9CM CODES
333.1 Essential tremor

EPIDEMIOLOGY & DEMOGRAPHICS

About 415/100,000 in persons over 40 yr. No gender or racial predominance.

PHYSICAL FINDINGS & CLINICAL PRESENTATION

- Patients complain of tremor that is most bothersome when writing or holding something, such as a newspaper, or trying to drink from a cup. Worsens under emotional duress and drinking liquids
- Tremor, 4 to 12 Hz, bilateral postural and action tremor of the upper extremities. May also affect the head, voice, trunk, and legs. Typically is the same amplitude throughout the action, such as bringing a cup to the mouth. No other neurologic abnormalities on examination. Patients often note improvement with small amount of alcohol.

ETIOLOGY

Often an inherited disease, autosomal dominant; sporadic cases without a family history are frequently encountered

DIAGNOSIS

DIFFERENTIAL DIAGNOSIS

- Parkinson's disease—tremor is usually asymmetric, especially early on in the disease, and is predominantly a resting tremor. Patients with Parkinson's disease will also have increased tone, decreased facial expression, slowness of movement, and shuffling gait.
- Cerebellar tremor—an intention tremor that increases at the end of a goal-directed movement (such as finger to nose testing). Other associated neurologic abnormalities include ataxia, dysarthria, and difficulty with tandem gait.
- Drug-induced—there are many drugs that enhance normal, physiologic tremor. These include caffeine, nicotine, lithium, levothyroxine, β-adrenergic bronchodilators, valproate, and SSRIs.
- Wilson's Disease—wing-beating tremor that is most pronounced with shoulders abducted, elbows flexed, and fingers pointing towards each other. Usually there are other neurologic abnormalities including dysarthria, dystonia, and Keyser Fleischer rings on ophthalmologic examination.

WORKUP

- All imaging studies normal (MRI, CT) and are usually unnecessary unless there are other associated neurologic abnormalities
- Check TSH
- In patients younger than 40 yr with other neurologic abnormalities, send ceruloplasmin, Cu, 24-hr urine Cu to rule out Wilson's disease

TREATMENT

Do not need to treat essential tremor unless it is functionally impairing. Patients need to understand that treatments are only 40%-70% effective.

NONPHARMACOLOGIC THERAPY

Reduction of stress. Minimize use of caffeine. Small quantities of alcohol at social functions tend to be beneficial.

ACUTE GENERAL Rx

Can take a dose of propranolol (20-40 mg) in preparation for specific event.

CHRONIC Rx

First-line agents

- Propranolol: Usual starting dose is 30 mg. Usual therapeutic dose is 160-320 mg. Must be used with caution in those with asthma, depression, cardiac disease, and diabetes.
- Primidone: Usual starting dose is 12.5 to 25 mg hs. Usual therapeutic dose is between 62.5 and 750 mg daily. Sedation and nausea when first begin medication are biggest side effects.

Other agents

- Neurontin: 400 mg qhs, usual therapeutic dose is 1200-3600 mg
- Topamax: 25 mg qhs, may titrate up to about 400 mg
- Alprazolam: 0.75-2.75 mg

SURGICAL Rx

Thalamic deep brain stimulation contralateral to side of tremor

DISPOSITION

Patients should be reassured that the condition is not associated with other neurologic disabilities; however, it can become quite functionally disabling over time.

REFERRAL

This is a condition that usually can be treated by the primary care physician; however, if patient fails first-line therapies then patient should be referred to specialists for other drug trials and other possible surgical options.

PEARLS & CONSIDERATIONS

Essential tremor is the most common of all movement disorders.

SUGGESTED READINGS

Deuschel G, Volkmann J: Tremors: Differential diagnosis, pathophysiology, and therapy. In Jankovic J, Tolosa E (eds): *Parkinson's disease and movement disorders*, ed 4, 2002, pp. 270-291.

Louis ED: Essential tremor, *N Engl J Med* 345(12):887, 2001.

Zesiewicz TA et al: Phenomenology and treatment of tremor disorders. In Hurtig H, Stern M (eds): *Neurologic clinics: Movement disorders* 19:3, 2001, pp. 651-680.

AUTHOR: **CINDY ZADIKOFF, M.D.**

BASIC INFORMATION

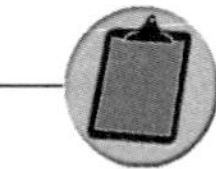

DEFINITION

Factitious physical disorder is one in which an individual intentionally strives to create signs or symptoms of disease. The individual may create signs or symptoms by (1) lying, (2) simulating (e.g., putting drops of blood into a urine sample), or (3) actually creating disease (e.g., injecting bacteria or medications). The primary aim is to achieve the patient role, and the individual may seek invasive diagnostic testing, surgery, and treatment. Munchausen syndrome is the most severe variant of factitious physical disorder and is exaggerated lying (pseudologia fantastica), sociopathy, geographic wandering from hospital to hospital, and a continuous life of patienthood.

SYNONYMS

Factitious disorder
Munchausen syndrome
Munchausen by proxy
Deliberate disability
Hospital addiction syndrome
Artifactual illness
Peregrinating problem patients
Dermatitis artefacta
Surreptitious illness

ICD-9CM CODES
300.19 Factitious disorder

EPIDEMIOLOGY & DEMOGRAPHICS

INCIDENCE (IN U.S.): Unknown
PREVALENCE (IN U.S.): Unknown but considerable in specific illnesses. For example, 3.3% of patients with fever of unknown origin have a factitious disorder.
PREDOMINANT SEX: Male:female ratio of 2:1 for Munchausen syndrome but 1:2 for individuals with non-Munchausen type of factitious physical disorder.
PREDOMINANT AGE: 30 to 40 yr
PEAK INCIDENCE: 30s
GENETICS: No genetic predisposition known.

PHYSICAL FINDINGS & CLINICAL PRESENTATION

- False complaints or self-inflicted injury or symptoms without clear secondary gain. The intentional aspect of the disorder is often evident, such as injecting bacteria to produce infection or taking medication to produce an abnormality.
- Presentation may be acute and dramatic but can be a chronic, recurring problem.
- Workup is usually negative for naturally occurring organic etiology.
- Clinical picture is atypical for the natural history of disease (e.g., an infection that fails to respond to multiple courses of appropriate antibiotics).

ETIOLOGY

- A history of significant childhood illness; physical or sexual abuse are thought to predispose.
- Personality disorders and psychodynamic factors often play a significant role.

DIAGNOSIS

The diagnosis can be made by (1) direct observation of fabrication, (2) the presence of signs or symptoms that contradict laboratory testing, (3) nonphysiologic response to treatment, (4) finding physical evidence of fabrication (e.g., syringes), and (5) recurrent patterns of illness exacerbation (e.g., just before discharge).

DIFFERENTIAL DIAGNOSIS

- Malingering: a clear secondary gain (e.g., financial gain or avoidance of unwanted duties) is present.
- Somatoform disorders or hypochondriasis: these disorders are produced unconsciously and are not intentionally produced.
- Self-injurious behavior is common in many other psychiatric conditions (e.g., borderline personality disorder, psychoses, or nonfatal suicide attempt as may occur in depression); in those conditions the patients confess the intentional self-harm and describe motivating factors; the main intent is the self-harm and not to attain the patient role as occurs in factitious disorder.
- May also present as Munchausen by proxy in which a mother (86% of time) or other caregiver induces illness in a child (52% between ages of 3 and 13 yr) for the purpose of obtaining medical attention. Motivations may be complex and may involve retaliation against a spouse in divorce cases. Mothers often have a history of somatoform, factitious, or personality disorder themselves.

WORKUP

- Workup is often dictated by the presenting complaints.
- No specific tests for Munchausen syndrome, although Minnesota Multiphasic Personality Inventory (MMPI) may show personality disorder with somatoform tendencies.
- Diagnosis may be made when the patient is caught in the act of lying or inducing an injury. The diagnosis often rests on organic workup failing to reveal a plausible natural organic disease. The failure of usual or even extensive treatment to ameliorate a condition is an important clue.

LABORATORY TESTS

- Laboratory testing often reveals inconsistencies.
- Other laboratory abnormalities may reflect the underlying factitious behavior (e.g., hypokalemia in an individual surreptitiously taking furosemide).

TREATMENT

NONPHARMACOLOGIC THERAPY

Two major approaches:

- Nonpunitive confrontation. Primary physician and psychiatrist conjointly meet with patient and say, "You must be in a lot of distress to be harming yourself as we believe you have been. We would like to help you deal with your distress more adaptively and get into psychiatric treatment."
- Avoid overt confrontation with patient but provide him or her with a face-saving way to recover. For example, a therapeutic double bind would involve saying, "There are two possibilities here, one is that you have a medical problem that should respond to the next intervention we do, or two, you have a factitious disorder. How you do will give us the answer."

Munchausen syndrome is the most severe variant and may be virtually impossible to treat except to avoid further invasive and iatrogenic disease.

ACUTE GENERAL Rx

Treatment of comorbid psychiatric disorders may be helpful. Treatment with antidepressants or psychotherapy may ameliorate the factitious behavior.

DISPOSITION

- Ultimate course is unknown.
- After being confronted with their behavior, patients may cease factitious behavior but more commonly seek other physicians or hospitals in the Munchausen variant. Other factitious disorder patients may enter psychotherapy, particularly when they have been given a face-saving approach with an avoidance of a humiliating confrontation (see earlier).
- Extensive medical workups and exploratory surgery are frequent.

REFERRAL

Always obtain psychiatric referral when diagnosis is made.

SUGGESTED READINGS

Feldman MD, Brown RM: Munchausen by proxy in an international context, *Child Abuse Negl* 26:509, 2002.
Krahn LE, Li H, O'Connor MK: Patients who strive to be ill: patients with factitious physical disorder, *Am J Psychiatry* 160:1163, 2003.
Turner J, Reid S: Munchausen's syndrome, *Lancet* 359:346, 2002.

AUTHOR: **STUART EISENDRATH, M.D.**

BASIC INFORMATION

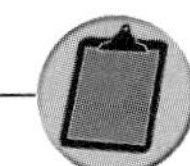

DEFINITION

Acute fatty liver of pregnancy (AFLP) is characterized histologically by microvesicular fatty cytoplasmic infiltration of hepatocytes with minimal hepatocellular necrosis.

SYNONYMS

Acute fatty metamorphosis
Acute yellow atrophy

ICD-9CM CODES
646.7 Liver disorders in pregnancy

EPIDEMIOLOGY & DEMOGRAPHICS

INCIDENCE:

- Approximately 1 in 10,000 pregnancies
- Equal frequencies in all races and at all maternal ages

AVERAGE GESTATIONAL AGE: 37 wk (range 28 to 42 wk)

RISK FACTORS:

- Primiparity
- Multiple gestation
- Male fetus

GENETICS: Some with a familial deficiency of long-chain 3-hydroxyacyl-CoA dehydrogenase (LCHAD)

PHYSICAL FINDINGS & CLINICAL PRESENTATION

- Initial manifestations
  1. Nausea and vomiting (70%)
  2. Pain in RUQ or epigastrium (50% to 80%)
  3. Malaise and anorexia
- Jaundice often in 1 to 2 wk
- Late manifestations
  1. Fulminant hepatic failure
  2. Encephalopathy
  3. Renal failure
  4. Pancreatitis
  5. GI and uterine bleeding
  6. Disseminated intravascular coagulation
  7. Seizures
  8. Coma
- Liver
  1. Usually small
  2. Normal or enlarged in preeclampsia, eclampsia, HELLP (hemolysis, elevated liver enzymes, and low platelets) syndrome, and acute hepatitis
  3. Coexistent preeclampsia in up to 46% of patients

ETIOLOGY

- Postulated that inhibition of mitochondrial oxidation of fatty acids may lead to microvesicular fatty infiltration of liver
- Fatty metamorphosis of preeclamptic liver disease thought to be of different etiology

DIAGNOSIS

DIFFERENTIAL DIAGNOSIS

- Acute gastroenteritis
- Preeclampsia or eclampsia with liver involvement
- HELLP syndrome
- Acute viral hepatitis
- Fulminant hepatitis
- Drug-induced hepatitis caused by halothane, phenytoin, methyldopa, isoniazid, hydrochlorothiazide, or tetracycline
- Intrahepatic cholestasis of pregnancy
- Gallbladder disease
- Reye's syndrome
- Hemolytic-uremic syndrome
- Budd-Chiari syndrome
- SLE

WORKUP

- A clinical diagnosis is based predominantly on physical and laboratory findings.
- Most definitive diagnosis is through liver biopsy with oil red O staining and electron microscopy.
- Liver biopsy is reserved for atypical cases only and only after any existing coagulopathy corrected with FFP.

LABORATORY TESTS

Tests to determine the following:

- Hypoglycemia (often profound <60)
- Hyperammonemia
- Elevated aminotransferases (usually <500 U/ml)
- Thrombocutopenia
- Leucocytosis (WBC count >15,000)
- Hyperbilirubinemia (usually <10 mg/dl)
- Low albumin
- Hypofibrinogenemia (<300 mg/dl)
- DIC (in 75%)

IMAGING STUDIES

- Ultrasound: best used to rule out other diseases in the differential diagnosis such as gallbladder disease
- CT scan: plays minimal role because of a high false-negative rate

TREATMENT

NONPHARMACOLOGIC THERAPY

- Patient is admitted to intensive care unit for stabilization.
- Fetus is delivered; spontaneous resolution usually follows delivery.
- Mode of delivery is based on obstetric indications and clinical assessment of disease severity.

ACUTE GENERAL Rx

- Decrease in endogenous ammonia through dietary protein restriction; neomycin 6 to 12 g/day PO to decrease presence of ammonia-producing bacteria; magnesium citrate 30 to 50 ml PO or enema to evacuate nitrogenous wastes from colon
- Administration of intravenous fluids with glucose to keep glucose levels >60 mg/dl
- Coagulopathy corrected with FFP
- Avoidance of drugs metabolized by liver
- Aggressive avoidance and treatment for nosocomial infections; consideration of prophylactic antibiotics
- Monitor closely for development of complications like hepatic encephalopathy, pulmonary edema, DIC, and respiratory arrest.

CHRONIC Rx

Orthotopic liver transplantation is the only treatment for irreversible liver failure.

DISPOSITION

- Before 1980, both maternal and fetal mortalities: approximately 85%
- After 1980, both maternal and fetal mortalities: below 20%
- Usually rapid return of liver function to normal after delivery
- Minimal risk of recurrence with future pregnancies

REFERRAL

- To tertiary health care facility as soon as diagnosis is suspected.
- Infants of mothers with AFLP should be evaluated for LCHAD deficiency.

SUGGESTED READINGS

Cunningham FG et al: Gastrointestinal disorders. In Cunningham FG et al (eds): *Williams' obstetrics*, ed 20, Stamford, Conn, 1997, Appleton & Lange.

Davidson KM: Acute fatty liver of pregnancy, *Postgrad Obstet Gynecol* 15:1, 1995.

Knox TA, Olans LB: Liver disease in pregnancy, *N Engl J Med* 335:569, 1996.

Sawai SK: Acute fatty liver of pregnancy. In Foley MR, Strong TH Jr: *Obstetric intensive care: a practical manual*, Philadelphia, 1997, WB Saunders.

Toro Ortiz JC et al: Acute fatty liver of pregnancy. *J Matern Fetal Neonatl Med* 12(4):277, 2003.

AUTHOR: **ARUNDATHI G. PRASAD, M.D.**

Felty's Syndrome

BASIC INFORMATION

DEFINITION

Felty's syndrome (FS) is defined as the triad of rheumatoid arthritis (RA), splenomegaly, and granulocytopenia. This definition requires some modification based on a number of subsequent reviews of the subject. The hallmark of FS is a persistent, idiopathic granulocytopenia, which is defined as a neutrophil count of <2000/mm³. Splenomegaly is extremely variable in its extent and varies over time. It is an extraarticular manifestation of seropositive RA in which recurrent local and systemic infections are the major source of morbidity and mortality.

ICD-9CM CODES
714.1 Felty's syndrome

EPIDEMIOLOGY & DEMOGRAPHICS

- FS occurs in less than 1% of patients with RA
- 60% to 80% are women
- Recognized in the fifth through seventh decades in patients who have had RA for 10 yr or more
- FS patients are more likely to have a family history of RA and HLA-DR4
- Rare in African Americans (low frequency of HLA-DR4)

PHYSICAL FINDINGS & CLINICAL PRESENTATION

- Rarely, splenomegaly and granulocytopenia are present before the arthritis.
- Articular involvement is usually more severe in patients with FS as compared with other patients with RA; however, one third may have relatively inactive synovitis with elevated ESR.
- Degree of splenomegaly varies and may be detectable only by imaging studies.
- The degree of splenomegaly has no correlation with the degree of granulocytopenia.
- FS patients have a greater frequency of extraarticular manifestations (nodules, weight loss, Sjögren's syndrome, etc.) than other patients with RA.
- Approximately 25% of patients have refractory leg ulcers, often associated with hyperpigmentation of the anterior tibia.
- Mild hepatomegaly is common (up to 68%).
- Patients with FS have a 20 times increased frequency of infections as compared with other RA patients.
- There is usually an adequate response to appropriate antibiotic therapy.

ETIOLOGY

The pathogenesis of FS is probably multifactorial and no clear explanation has been elucidated.

Proposed mechanisms of the granulocytopenia:

- Splenic sequestration and peripheral destruction of granulocytes secondary to immune complexes and antineutrophil antibodies
- Impaired granulopoiesis in bone marrow as a result of decreased cytokine production, presence of inhibitors, or humoral and cell-mediated immune suppression
- Excessive margination

DIAGNOSIS

DIFFERENTIAL DIAGNOSIS

- Systemic lupus erythematosus
- Drug reaction
- Myeloproliferative disorders
- Lymphoma/reticuloendothelial malignancies
- Hepatic cirrhosis with portal hypertension
- Sarcoidosis
- Tuberculosis
- Amyloidosis
- Chronic infections

WORKUP

Physical examination and laboratory evaluation

LABORATORY TESTS

- Complete blood count with differential, looking for:
  1. Granulocytopenia
  2. Mild to moderate anemia
  3. Mild thrombocytopenia
- ESR
- Bone marrow biopsy in most patients will show myeloid hyperplasia with an excess of immature granulocyte precursors ("maturation arrest")
- Rheumatoid factor: positive in 98%, usually high titer
- ANA: positive in 67%
- Antihistone antibody: positive in 83%
- HLA-DR4: positive in 95%
- Antineutrophil cytoplasmic antibodies (77%)
- Immunoglobulins: level may be higher than in RA patients
- Complement: level may be lower than in RA patients

IMAGING STUDIES

Ultrasonography or CT scan may be useful in diagnosing splenomegaly

TREATMENT

There is no uniformly effective therapy for FS.

ACUTE GENERAL Rx

Splenectomy
- Standard therapy since 1932
- Acutely reverses hematological abnormalities
- Ongoing infections may resolve after operation as the granulocyte count rises
- 25% to 30% will have recurrent granulocytopenia, but the granulocyte count usually remains above the presplenectomy level
- Improvement in frequency of recurrent infection variable and not correlated with hematological improvement
- Usually reserved for patients with profound granulocytopenia (<1000/mm³) and severe recurrent infections

Lithium
- Stimulates granulopoiesis
- Little evidence of long-term benefit or conclusive reduction in rate of infection
- Used as short-term therapy while awaiting response to other measures

Parenteral testosterone: Efficacy limited by toxicity, especially in women

Corticosteroids
- Pulse dosing is a potential alternative for short-term elevation of neutrophils
- Overwhelming infection is the main barrier to the use of corticosteroids

Antirheumatic drugs: Second-line drugs, may improve the granulocytopenia in FS
- Gold salt injections: Good hematological response—60%, partial response—20%
- Penicillamine: Controversial, should never be the first choice for FS
- Methotrexate: The frequency of infection may decrease, but still not well proven

Recombinant G-CSF
- Improves neutrophil count but not arthritis and anemia of FS
- May be useful as adjunctive therapy during serious infection or in preparation for surgery

Other immunosuppressants: Cyclophosphamide, cyclosporine, azathioprine, leflunomide, TNF-α: limited experience

REFERRAL

- To rheumatologist for treatment of RA
- To hematologist for treatment of granulocytopenia

SUGGESTED READINGS

Bowman SJ: Hematological manifestations of rheumatoid arthritis, *Scand J Rheumatol* 31(5):251, 2002.

Campion G et al: The Felty's syndrome: a case-matched study of clinical manifestations and outcome, serologic features, and immunogenetic associations, *Medicine (Baltimore)* 69(2):69, 1990.

Losenstein ED et al: Felty's and pseudo-Felty's syndromes, *Semin Arthritis Rheum* 21(3):129, 1991.

Spivak JL: Felty's syndrome: an analytical study, *John Hopkins Med* 141(3):156, 1977.

AUTHORS: **ETSUKO AOKI, M.D.,** and **REBECCA A. GRIFFITH, M.D.**

BASIC INFORMATION

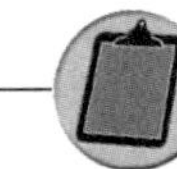

DEFINITION

A femoral neck fracture occurs within the capsule of the hip joint between the base of the head and the intertrochanteric line.

SYNONYMS

Intracapsular fracture
Subcapital fracture

ICD-9CM CODES
820.8 Femoral neck fracture

EPIDEMIOLOGY & DEMOGRAPHICS

PREVALENCE: Lifetime risk in women approximately 16%
PREVALENT SEX: Female:male ratio of 3:1
PREVALENT AGE: 90% over age 60

PHYSICAL FINDINGS & CLINICAL PRESENTATION

- A hip or groin pain
- Affected limb usually shortened and externally rotated in displaced fractures
- Impacted fractures: possibly no deformity and only mild pain with hip motion
- Mild external bruising

ETIOLOGY

- Trauma
- Age-related bone weakness, usually caused by osteoporosis
- Increased risk of fractures in elderly (decline in muscle function, use of psychotropic medication, etc.)

DIAGNOSIS

DIFFERENTIAL DIAGNOSIS

Osteoarthritis of hip
Pathologic fracture
Lumbar disc syndrome with radicular pain
Insufficiency fracture of pelvis

WORKUP

Diagnosis usually obvious based on clinical and radiographic findings

IMAGING STUDIES

- Standard roentgenograms consisting of an AP of the pelvis and a cross-table lateral of the hip to confirm the diagnosis (Fig. 1-96)
- If initial roentgenograms negative and diagnosis of an occult femoral neck fracture suspected, hospital admission and further radiographic assessment with either bone scanning or MRI
- Bone scanning most sensitive after 48 to 72 hr.

TREATMENT

- Orthopedic consultation
- Surgery indicated in most cases, usually within 24 hr
- DVT prophylaxis

DISPOSITION

- Mortality rate within 1 yr in elderly patients is 25% to 30%.
- Dementia is a particularly poor prognostic sign.

PEARLS & CONSIDERATIONS

COMMENTS

- Complications: nonunion and avascular necrosis
- Intracapsular fractures: occasionally occur in nonambulatory patients
  1. Usually treated nonsurgically, especially in the patient with dementia and limited pain perception
  2. Early bed-to-chair mobilization and vigilant nursing care to avoid skin breakdown
  3. Fracture usually pain free in a short time even if solid bony healing does not occur
- As a result of the increasing life span of the female population, femoral neck fractures are becoming more common. The initial physical examination and roentgenographic studies may be completely negative. Groin pain, sometimes quite severe, may be the only early clue to the diagnosis.
- The rate of hip fracture could be reduced by:
  1. Elimination of environmental hazards (poor lighting, loose rugs)
  2. Regular exercise for balance and strength
  3. Patient education about fall prevention
  4. Medication review to minimize side effects
  5. Prevention and treatment of osteoporosis

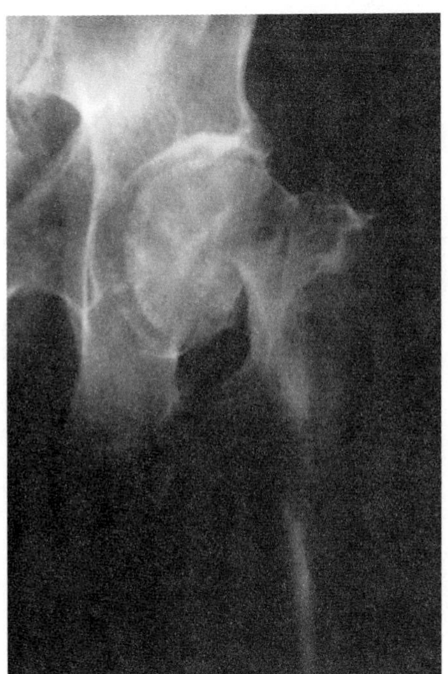

FIGURE 1-96 Femoral neck fracture. (From Scudieri G [ed]: *Sports medicine: principles of primary care*, St Louis, 1997, Mosby.)

SUGGESTED READINGS

Bettelli G et al: Relationship between mortality and proximal femur fractures in the elderly, *Orthopedics* 26:1045, 2003.
Feldstein AC et al: Older women with fractures: patients falling through the cracks of guideline recommended osteoporosis screening and treatment, *J Bone Joint Surg* 85A:2294, 2003.
Jain R et al: Comparison of early and delayed fixation of subcapital hip fractures in patients sixty years of age or less, *Bone Joint Surg* 84(A):1605, 2002.
Kaufman JD et al: Barriers and solutions to osteoporosis care in patients with a hip fracture, *J Bone Joint Surg* 85A:1837, 2003.
Lawrence VA et al: Medical complications and outcomes after hip fracture repair, *Ann Intern Med* 162:2053, 2003.
McClung MR et al: Effect of risedronate on the risk of hip fracture in elderly women. Hip Intervention Program Study Group, *N Engl J Med* 344(5):333, 2001.
McKinley JC, Robinson CM: Treatment of displaced intracapsular fractures with total hip arthroplasty, *J Bone Joint Surg* 84(A):2010, 2002.
Schoofs MW et al: Thiazide diuretics and the risk for hip fractures, *Ann Intern Med* 139:476, 2003.
Stevens JA, Olson S: Reducing falls and resulting hip fractures among older women, *Home Care Prov* 5(4):134, 2000.

AUTHOR: **LONNIE R. MERCIER, M.D.**

SECTION I

Fever of Undetermined Origin

BASIC INFORMATION

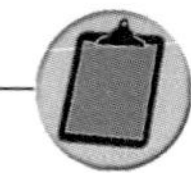

DEFINITION

Fever of undetermined origin (FUO) was defined by Petersdorf in 1961 as an illness characterized by temperatures surpassing 101° F on several occasions for more than 3 wk with no known cause despite extensive workup.

- Persistence for greater than 2 wk separates an FUO from an insignificant viral illness.
- Traditionally, diagnosis made only after at least a 1-wk inpatient workup.
- In contemporary practice, much of the workup is performed outpatient; taking time for a complete history and physical examination is still essential.
- Different settings—community vs. hospital vs. oncology ward—dictate duration needed for FUO designation.

ICD-9CM CODES
780.6 Pyrexia of undetermined origin

EPIDEMIOLOGY & DEMOGRAPHICS

Incidence is difficult to calculate because of inconsistent designation of febrile illnesses as FUO. The incidence of undiagnosed FUO has dropped to less than 10% in most recent studies.

ETIOLOGY

Classic (1 wk workup after 2 wk persistently febrile): Divided into infection, malignancy, collagen-vascular, and other etiology; proportion for each dependent on age, geography, host and microbial factors, hospital and health services. Etiology has also changed over time. A partial list of eventual etiologies, with most common diagnoses in *italics:*

- *Factitious fever, Munchausen syndrome*
- *Abscess: dental, abdominal, pelvic*
- *Lymphoma and leukemia*
- Endocarditis (especially caused by difficult-to-isolate organisms)
- Biliary tract infection
- Osteomyelitis
- Tuberculosis
- Whipple's disease
- Psittacosis
- Fungal: histoplasmosis, cryptomycosis
- Leishmaniasis
- Renal cell carcinoma, other solid malignancies
- Systemic lupus erythematosus
- Still's disease
- Hypersensitivity vasculitis
- Temporal arteritis
- Drug-induced fever
- Inflammatory bowel disease
- Sarcoidosis
- Granulomatous hepatitis
- Central fever (rare)

Neutropenic (PMN <500 and febrile >3 days): With blood cultures from onset negative, ruling out *Pseudomonas* and other gram-negative bacteremia, staphylococcal bacteremia from line infection; urinalysis and chest x-ray negative. Possible etiologies:

- Perianal infection
- Occult fungal infection
- Drug fever
- Cytomegalovirus infection in post-transplant patients or patients who are on immunosuppressants

HIV-associated: Etiology depends on CD4 count. HIV itself may be the cause. With low CD4 count—MAI bacteremia, non-Hodgkin's lymphoma

Nosocomial (febrile for 3 days in hospital): UTI, pneumonia, line-related bacteremia, *Clostridium difficile* diarrhea, or sinusitis secondary to intubation

- Noninfectious etiology: deep venous thrombosis, hematoma, drug fever

DIAGNOSIS

DIFFERENTIAL DIAGNOSIS

Factitious fever: body temperature not elevated when accurately measured.

WORKUP

- Accurate history and careful physical examination is essential
- Laboratory tests and radiologic examinations dependent on historical clues, physical findings
- "Shotgun" approach, ordering every test for every possibility, is rarely helpful
- Tests and procedures should be thoughtful, directed toward localizing signs and symptoms (Section III, Fever of Undetermined Origin).
- When in doubt, perform another complete history and physical examination

HISTORICAL CLUES

- Fever duration, tempo; inciting factors
- Associated symptoms: rash, myalgia, weight loss, pain
- Sick contacts
- Past medical history: HIV, malignancies, surgeries
- Medications
- Family history: tuberculosis in a relative, malignancies, familial Mediterranean fever
- Social history: daily routine, rural vs. urban, pets and animal contacts, arthropod bites, travel—recent and remote, socioeconomic status, occupation, military service, sexual history

PHYSICAL FINDINGS

- HEENT: rule out sinusitis, dental abscesses; examine eyes carefully
- Neck: check adenopathy
- Lungs: auscultate for rales
- Heart: listen for murmur
- Abdomen: check for organomegaly
- Rectal: examine for prostate tenderness
- Pelvic: rule out cervical motion tenderness, check for inguinal adenopathy
- Extremities: look for clubbing, splinter hemorrhages; examine IV access site
- Musculoskeletal: examine for joint effusions
- Skin: note any rashes, wounds

LABORATORY TESTS

- Base on historical clues and physical findings.
- Blood cultures, CBC, urinalysis, transaminases, PPD testing is important in most FUO workups.
- Base on leads from history, examination—whether need for serum antibody testing, lumbar puncture, thyroid function testing, stool culture and *C. difficile* assay, bone marrow biopsy, skin biopsy, ANA.
- May need to repeat laboratory examinations at regular intervals until diagnosis is established.

IMAGING STUDIES

- Base on historical clues and physical findings.
- Chest x-ray, abdominal CT scan are important eventually in most workups in which diagnosis is elusive.

TREATMENT

GENERAL Rx

Antibiotics and other treatment are indicated only after definitive or highly probable diagnosis is established, unless patient appears severely ill or septic.

DISPOSITION

Diagnoses are found in majority of fevers with initially undetermined origin. Some will continue to defy diagnosis for years.

REFERRAL

To an infectious disease specialist if no diagnosis after thoughtful workup

SUGGESTED READINGS

Mackowiak PA, Durack DT: Fever of unknown origin. In Mandel G, Bennett J, Dolin R (eds): *Principles and practice of infectious disease,* ed 5, Philadelphia, 2000, Churchill Livingstone.

Petersdorf R, Beeson P: Fever of unexplained origin: report of 100 cases, *Medicine* 40:1, 1961.

Roth AR, Basello GM: Approach to the adult patient with fever of unknown origin, *Am Fam Physician* 68:2223, 2003.

AUTHORS: **ETSUKO AOKI, M.D., PH.D.,** and **ANNE SPAULDING, M.D.**

BASIC INFORMATION

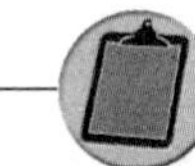

DEFINITION

Fibrocystic breast disease (FCD) is a "nondisease" that includes nonmalignant breast lesions such as microcystic and macrocystic changes, fibrosis, ductal or lobular hyperplasia, adenosis, apocrine metaplasia, fibroadenoma, papilloma, papillomatosis, and other changes. Atypical ductal or lobular hyperplasia is associated with a moderate increase in breast cancer risk.

SYNONYMS

Cystic changes
Chronic cystic mastitis
Mammary dysplasia

ICD-9CM CODES
610.0 Solitary cyst of the breast
610.1 Fibrocystic disease of the breast

EPIDEMIOLOGY & DEMOGRAPHICS

- Ubiquitous in premenopausal women after 20 yr of age
- Palpable nodular changes in the breast termed *FCD* clinically; such changes observable in more than half of adult women 20 to 50 yr of age

PHYSICAL FINDINGS & CLINICAL PRESENTATION

- Tender breasts
- Nodular areas
- Dominant mass
- Thickening
- Nipple discharge
- Can vary with menstrual cycle

ETIOLOGY

- Although frequently seen and diagnosed, mechanism of development not understood.
- Because found in majority of healthy breasts, regarded as nonpathologic process.
- With hormone replacement therapy, may be carried into menopausal age.

DIAGNOSIS

DIFFERENTIAL DIAGNOSIS

- If presenting as dominant mass or masses: exclude possible carcinoma.
- Carcinoma: detection is difficult with FCD, particularly among premenopausal women.
- If presenting with nipple discharge: differentiate from discharge of possible malignant origin.

WORKUP

- Exclude breast carcinoma if breast mass, thickening, discharge, and pain present.
- Perform biopsy of suspected area for histologic confirmation.

IMAGING STUDIES

Mammography and ultrasound studies required:

- For mammographic changes (suspicious densities, microcalcifications, architectural distortion): careful evaluation, including possibly biopsy to exclude breast cancer
- Ultrasound study: to establish cystic nature of clinical or mammographic mass lesion

TREATMENT

NONPHARMACOLOGIC THERAPY

- Not considered a "disease" and does not require treatment
- Surgical intervention diagnostic to eliminate possibility of breast cancer
- Periodic physician examination to follow patients with FCD who have pronounced nodular features
- Aspiration for palpable cysts (NOTE: Cysts often recur; repeat aspiration is not always required unless pain is a problem.)

ACUTE GENERAL Rx

Majority of women require no treatment.

CHRONIC Rx

For breast pain:

- Danocrine (Danazol): limited success reported
- Bromocriptine or tamoxifen: used less frequently
- Limited caffeine intake: not as successful in controlling pain or nodularity as originally suggested

DISPOSITION

- Careful evaluation to exclude suspicious changes for breast cancer, then reassurance and periodic reevaluation as required
- Regular self-examination, annual physician examination, and annual mammograms for women with atypical ductal or lobular hyperplasia

REFERRAL

- For further evaluation and/or biopsy if there are suspicious changes that may be associated with FCD (including changing of dominant mass or thickening, persistent or spontaneous discharge, suspicious mammographic changes or lesions)
- To alleviate anxiety associated with breast symptoms or changes

PEARLS & CONSIDERATIONS

COMMENTS

Patient education material is available from American College of Obstetricians and Gynecologists, 408 12th Street SW, Washington, DC 20024-2188.

SUGGESTED READING

Zera RT et al: Atypical hyperplasia, proliferative fibrocystic change, and exogenous hormone use, *Surgery* 130(4):732, 2001.

AUTHOR: **TAKUMA NEMOTO, M.D.**

BASIC INFORMATION

DEFINITION

Fibromyalgia is a poorly defined disorder characterized by multiple trigger points and referred pain.

SYNONYMS

Myofascial pain syndrome
Fibrositis
Psychogenic rheumatism
Nonarticular rheumatism
Fibromyalgia syndrome (FS)

ICD-9CM CODES
729.0 Rheumatism, unspecified and fibrositis
729.1 Myalgia and myositis, unspecified

EPIDEMIOLOGY & DEMOGRAPHICS

PREVALENCE: 1% to 2% of the general population

PREVALENT SEX: Female:male ratio of 9:1

PREVALENT AGE: 30 to 50 yr

PHYSICAL FINDINGS

Tender "nodules" and tender points (Fig. 1-97)

ETIOLOGY

- Unknown
- Pain magnification may play a role

DIAGNOSIS

DIFFERENTIAL DIAGNOSIS

- Polymyalgia rheumatica
- Referred discogenic spine pain
- Rheumatoid arthritis
- Localized tendinitis
- Connective tissue disease
- Osteoarthritis
- Thyroid disease
- Spondyloarthropathies

WORKUP

- Subsets of this disorder are often described:
  1. If symptoms develop in conjunction with other conditions (rheumatoid disease or acute stress)
  2. If findings are more regionally distributed, such as those in the neck following motor vehicle accidents
- The primary condition is often suggested by the following criteria from the American College of Rheumatology:
  1. History of widespread pain
  2. Pain in 11 of 18 selected tender spots on digital palpation (mainly in the spine, elbows, and knees)

LABORATORY TESTS

There are no abnormalities in fibromyalgia, but laboratory assessment may be required to rule out other conditions and may include:

- CBC, ESR, rheumatoid factor, ANA
- CPK, T_4

right left left right

1. Occiput
2. Low cervical
3. Trapezius
4. Supraspinatus
5. Second rib
6. Lateral epicondyle
7. Gluteal
8. Greater trochanter
9. Knees

right left

FIGURE 1-97 The sites of the 18 tender points of the 1990 ACR criteria for the classification of fibromyalgia. (From Conn R: *Current Diagnosis,* ed 9, Philadelphia, 1997, WB Saunders.)

TREATMENT

ACUTE GENERAL Rx

- Self-management
- Explanation, reassurance
- Tricyclic antidepressants for sleep disturbance (amitriptyline 10-25 mg)
- Aerobic and stretching exercise, particularly swimming
- Mild analgesics; avoidance of chronic narcotic use
- Trigger point injections
- Physical therapy

DISPOSITION

- Prognosis is uncertain.
- Symptoms come and go for years in spite of an aggressive multifaceted approach to treatment.

PEARLS & CONSIDERATIONS

COMMENTS

- Before making this diagnosis, all other more likely disorders should be ruled out.
- The term "fibrositis" is often used, but no inflammation has ever been found.
- The number of trigger points needed to establish the diagnosis is debated.

SUGGESTED READINGS

Clauw DJ: Elusive syndromes: treating the biologic basis of fibromyalgia and related syndromes, *Cleve Clin J Med* 68:830, 2001.

Crofford LJ: Pharmaceutical treatment options for fibromyalgia, *Curr Rheumatol Rep* 6:274, 2004.

Gracely RH et al: Functional magnetic resonance imaging evidence of augmented pain processing in fibromyalgia, *Arthritis Rheum* 46:1333, 2002.

Hakkinen A et al: Strength training induced adaptations in neuromuscular function of premenopausal women with fibromyalgia: comparison with healthy women, *Ann Rheum Dis* 60:21, 2001.

Richards SCM, Scott DL: Prescribed exercise in people with fibromyalgia: parallel group randomized controlled trial, *BMJ* 325:185, 2002.

Robinson RL et al: Depression and fibromyalgia: treatment and cost when diagnosed separately or concurrently, *J Rheumatol* 31:1621, 2004.

Worrel LM et al: Treating fibromyalgia with a brief interdisciplinary program: initial outcomes and predictors of response, *Mayo Clin Proc* 76:381, 2001.

AUTHOR: **LONNIE R. MERCIER, M.D.**

BASIC INFORMATION

DEFINITION

Fifth disease is a viral exanthem of childhood affecting primarily school-age children, which is caused by parvovirus B-19. Erythema infectiosum was the "fifth" in a series of described viral exanthems of childhood and is the most common clinical syndrome associated with parvovirus B-19.

SYNONYMS

Erythema infectiosum

ICD-9CM CODES
057.0 Fifth disease (eruptive)

EPIDEMIOLOGY & DEMOGRAPHICS

- Peak age range 5 to 18 yr old
- Peak incidence in late winter and spring, especially April and May
- Fifty to sixty percent of adults have demonstrated protective antibodies to parvovirus B-19

PHYSICAL FINDINGS & CLINICAL PRESENTATION

- Typical bright red nontender maxillary rash with circumoral pallor over cheeks, producing the classic "slapped cheek" appearance (Fig. 1-98)
- Reticular nonpruritic lacy, erythematous maculopapular rash over trunk and extremities lasting for up to several weeks after the acute episode. May be worsened by heat or sunlight
- Polyarthritis and arthralgias are commonly seen in older patients; less common in children. Arthritis involves small joints of extremities in symmetric fashion
- Mild fever seen in up to one third of patients

ETIOLOGY

Syndrome caused by parvovirus B-19, a single-stranded DNA virus, which has been reclassified in a new genus "erythrovirus." It remains the only accepted member of this genus, although new variants have recently been described. Designation as "parvovirus" is still common in recent literature

DIAGNOSIS

DIFFERENTIAL DIAGNOSIS

- Juvenile rheumatoid arthritis (Still's disease)
- Rubella, measles (rubeola), and other childhood viral exanthems
- Mononucleosis
- Lyme disease
- Acute HIV infection
- Drug eruption

WORKUP

- Diagnosis made by typical clinical picture
- Parvovirus B-19 IgM antibody seen in 90% of patients with acute illness

LABORATORY TESTS

- Complete blood count. Transient aplastic crisis is a syndrome distinct from fifth disease, which may be seen in patients with chronic hematologic illness (described with sickle cell disease, spherocytosis, and other hemolytic processes) or AIDS, who are infected with parvovirus B-19. It is usually self-limited and associated with prodrome of fever and malaise. Lasts for 1 to 2 wk followed by marrow recovery. Rash usually absent. These patients are highly infective.
- hCG in women of childbearing age. Infection during early pregnancy may result in fetal death (10%) or severe anemia but is usually asymptomatic and not associated with congenital malformations.
- Antibody testing usually not necessary. IgM levels may be elevated early in the course of the illness.
- Lyme titers, monospot performed.
- Testing for other viral diseases as indicated by clinical picture.
- Polymerase chain reaction (PCR) has been used for early, rapid diagnosis in immunocompromised patients.

TREATMENT

ACUTE GENERAL Rx

- Treatment is supportive only
- NSAIDs for arthralgias/arthritis
- Intravenous immunoglobulin and transfusion support may be used in patients with immunocompromised state with red cell aplasia
- Consider immunoglobulin treatment or prophylaxis in pregnancy

DISPOSITION & PROGNOSIS

- Self-limited illness lasting 1 to 2 wk
- Arthritis lasts for weeks. In some patients it may be chronic and develop into rheumatoid arthritis as adult
- Pregnant women should avoid contact with patients who have marrow suppression
- Patients with transient aplastic crisis or chronic parvovirus B-19 infection pose a risk for nosocomial spread and, when hospitalized, should be isolated with contact and respiratory precautions
- Children with fifth disease are not contagious and may attend school and day care
- Vaccine is under development

REFERRAL

- For signs of marrow suppression
- For signs of severe or erosive arthritis

SUGGESTED READINGS

Katta, R: Parvovirus B19: a review, *Dermatol Clin* 20(2):333, 2002.

Sabella C, Goldfarls J: Parvovirus B19 infections, *Am Fam Physician* 60(5):1455, 1999.

AUTHOR: **DOMINICK TAMMARO, M.D.**

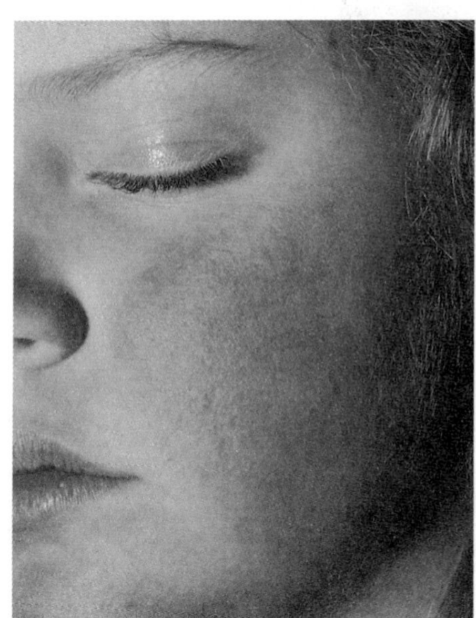

FIGURE 1-98 Fifth disease (erythema infectiosum). Facial erythema "slapped cheek." The red plaque covers the cheek and spares the nasolabial and the circumoral region. (From Habif TP: *Clinical dermatology: a color guide to diagnosis and therapy,* ed 3, St Louis, 1996, Mosby.)

BASIC INFORMATION

DEFINITION

Filariasis is a general term for an infection caused by nematodes (roundworms) of the genera *Wuchereria* and *Brugia,* found in the tropical and subtropical regions of the world. The disease is variably characterized by acute lymphatic inflammation or chronic lymphatic obstruction associated with intermittent fevers or recurrent episodes of dyspnea and bronchospasm.

SYNONYMS

Lymphatic filariasis

ICD-9CM CODES
125.0 Bancroftian
125.1 Brugian
125.9 Filariasis

EPIDEMIOLOGY & DEMOGRAPHICS

INCIDENCE (IN U.S.): Unknown
PREDOMINANT SEX: Male
PREDOMINANT AGE: For both males and females, risk is greatest between the ages of 15 to 35 yr.
PEAK INCIDENCE: Unknown

PHYSICAL FINDINGS & CLINICAL PRESENTATION

- Clinical manifestations result from acute lymphatic inflammation or chronic lymphatic obstruction.
- Many patients are asymptomatic despite the presence of microfilaremia.
- Episodes of lymphangitis and lymphadenitis are associated with fever, headache, and back pain.
- Acute funiculitis and epididymitis or orchitis may also be present; all usually resolve within days to weeks but tend to recur.
- Chronic infections may be associated with lymphedema, most commonly manifested by hydrocele.
- It is a progressive disease, leading to nonpitting edema and brawny changes that may involve a whole limb (Fig. 1-99).
- Elephantiasis occurs in about 10% of patients, with skin of the scrotum or leg becoming thickened and fissured; patient is thereafter plagued by recurrent ulceration and infection.
- Chyluria, a condition that develops when lymphatic vessels rupture into the urinary tract, may occur.

ETIOLOGY

Caused by one of three types of nematode parasites, all of which are transmitted to humans by mosquitoes.

- *W. bancrofti:* distributed in Africa, areas of Central and South America, the Pacific Islands, and the Caribbean Basin
- *B. malayi:* restricted to Southeast Asia
- *B. timori:* confined to the Indonesian archipelago

After bite of an infected mosquito:

- Filarial larvae move into lymphatic vessels and nodes, settling and maturing over 3 to 15 mo into adult male and female worms.
- After fertilization, the female nematode produces large numbers of larvae or microfilariae that enter into the blood stream via the lymphatics.
- Nocturnal periodicity, characteristic of *B. malayi,* is an increased presence of microfilariae in the circulation during the night.
- Microfilariae of *W. bancrofti* are maximal during late afternoon.
- Most microfilariae remain in the body as immature forms for 6 mo to 2 yr.
- Infected larvae are ingested by mosquitoes, then transmitted to humans where the microfilariae mature into new adult worms.

Acute and chronic inflammatory and granulomatous changes in the lymphatic channels:

- Result from complex interaction of adult worms and host's immune systems
- Eventually lead to fibrosis and obstruction
- Most likely to develop into obstructive lymphatic disease with recurrent exposure over many years

DIAGNOSIS

DIFFERENTIAL DIAGNOSIS

- Elephantiasis is distinguished from other causes of chronic lymphedema, including Milroy's disease, postoperative scarring, and lymphedema of malignancy.

WORKUP

Diagnosis is suspected in individuals who have resided in endemic areas for at least 3 to 6 mo or more and complain of recurrent episodes of lymphangitis, lymphadenitis, scrotal edema, or thrombophlebitis, with or without fever.

LABORATORY TESTS

- Demonstration of microfilariae on a blood smear for definitive diagnosis
- For patients from southeastern Asia: blood sample drawn at night, especially between midnight and 2 AM
- Occasionally, microfilaremia in chylous urine or hydrocele fluid
- Prominent eosinophilia only during periods of acute lymphangitis or lymphadenitis
- Serologic tests for antibody, including enzyme-linked immunosorbent assay and indirect fluorescent antibody (often unable to distinguish among the various forms of filariasis or between acute and remote infection)

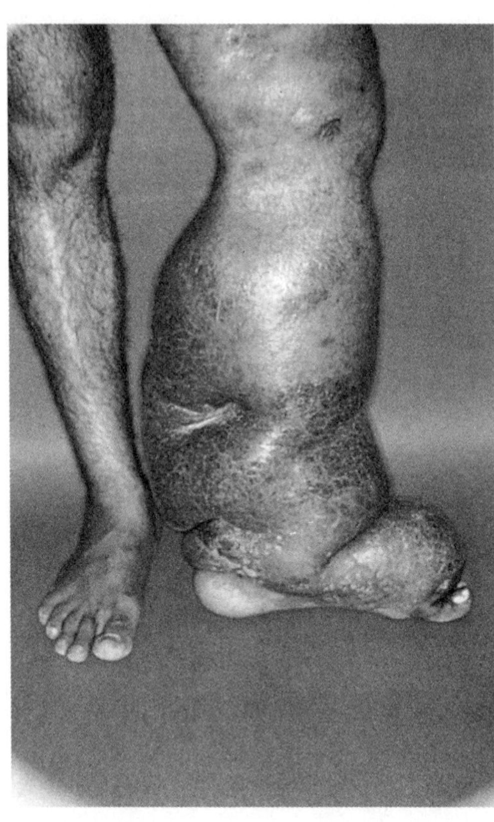

FIGURE 1-99 Filariasis that eventually leads to elephantiasis. Note massive swelling of the extremity. (From Goldstein B [ed]: *Practical dermatology,* ed 2, St Louis, 1997, Mosby.)

- Immunoassays (such as circulating filaria antigen [CFA]): more successful in antigen detection in patients who are microfilaremic than in those who are amicrofilaremic

IMAGING STUDIES

- Chest x-ray examination: reticular nodular infiltrates (tropical pulmonary eosinophilia syndrome)
- In men proven to be microfilaremic, scrotal ultrasonography to aid in the detection of adult worms
- Compared with adults, children with FS have more sleep disturbances, fewer tender points, and a better prognosis

TREATMENT

NONPHARMACOLOGIC THERAPY

- Standard of care for elephantiasis:
  1. Elevation of the affected limb
  2. Use of elastic stockings
  3. Local foot care
- General wound care for chronic ulcers and prevention of secondary infection

ACUTE GENERAL Rx

- Diethylcarbamazine citrate (DEC) to reduce microfilaremia by 90%
  1. Effect on adult worms, especially those of the *Wuchereria* species, less certain
  2. Given in an oral dose of 6 mg/kg qd for 12 to 14 days
- Ivermectin alone or in combination with diethylcarbamazine citrate to decrease microfilaremia
- Both drugs are similar in efficacy and tolerability; advantage of ivermectin: administration in a single oral dose of 200 μg/kg
- World Health Organization (WHO) recommendation: DEC given as a single dose, alone or (preferably) in combination with ivermectin as treatment in endemic areas

CHRONIC Rx

- Surgical drainage of hydroceles
- No satisfactory therapy for those patients with chyluria

DISPOSITION

Rarely fatal, but the psychologic impact of limb and scrotal deformities associated with elephantiasis is substantial.

REFERRAL

To a surgeon for management of hydrocele

PEARLS & CONSIDERATIONS

- Studies in endemic areas suggest that filarial-specific IgG1 is associated with amicrofilaremic states highest in children, regardless of sex.
- Levels of IgE and IgG4 increase with age and are associated with increased levels of microfilaremia.

COMMENTS

Individuals who intend to travel or reside in endemic areas should be advised to institute preventive measures such as the use of netting and insect repellents, especially at night.

SUGGESTED READINGS

Malhotra I et al: Influence of maternal filariasis on childhood infection and immunity to Wuchereria bancrofti in Kenya, *Infect Immun* 71(9):5231, 2003.

Rahmah N et al: Multicentre laboratory evaluation of Brugia Rapid dipstick test for detection of brugian filariasis, *Trop Med Int Health* 8(10):895, 2003.

Ramaiah KD et al: The prevalences of Wuchereria bancrofti antigenemia in communities given six rounds of treatment with diethylcarbamazine, ivermectin or placebo tablets, *Ann Trop Med Parasitol* 97(7):737, 2003.

Walther M, Muller R: Diagnosis of human filariases (except onchocerciasis), *Adv Parasitol* 53:149, 2003.

Watanabe K et al: Bancroftian filariasis in Nepal: a survey for circulating antigenemia of Wuchereria bancrofti and urinary IgG4 antibody in two rural areas of Nepal, *Acta Trop* 88(1):11, 2003.

AUTHOR: **GEORGE O. ALONSO, M.D.**

Folliculitis

BASIC INFORMATION

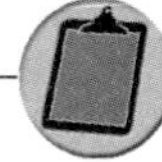

DEFINITION

Folliculitis is the inflammation of the hair follicle as a result of infection, physical injury, or chemical irritation.

SYNONYMS

Sycosis barbae

ICD-9CM CODES
704.8 Other specified diseases of hair and hair follicles

EPIDEMIOLOGY & DEMOGRAPHICS

- Staphylococcal folliculitis is the most common form of infectious folliculitis; it occurs most commonly in persons with diabetes.
- Sycosis barbae occurs most frequently in men who have commenced shaving.

PHYSICAL FINDINGS & CLINICAL PRESENTATION

- The lesions generally consist of painful yellow pustules surrounded by erythema; a central hair is present in the pustules.
- Patients with sycosis barbae may initially present with small follicular papules or pustules that increase in size with continued shaving; deep follicular pustules may occur surrounded by erythema and swelling; the upper lip is frequently involved (Fig. 1-100).
- "Hot tub" folliculitis occurs within 1 to 4 days following use of hot tub with poor chlorination, and it is characterized by pustules with surrounding erythema generally affecting torso, buttocks, and limbs.

ETIOLOGY

- *Staphylococcus* infection (e.g., sycosis barbae), *Pseudomonas aeruginosa* ("hot tub" folliculitis)
- Gram-negative folliculitis *(Klebsiella, Enterobacter, Proteus)* associated with antibiotic treatment of acne
- Chronic irritation of the hair follicle (use of cocoa butter or coconut oil, chronic irritation from workplace)
- Initial use of systemic corticosteroid therapy (steroid acne), eosinophilic folliculitis (AIDS patients), *Candida albicans* (immunocompromised patients)
- *Pityrosporum orbiculare*

DIAGNOSIS

DIFFERENTIAL DIAGNOSIS

- Pseudofolliculitis barbae (ingrown hairs)
- Acne vulgaris
- Dermatophyte fungal infections
- Keratosis biliaris
- Cutaneous candidiasis
- Superficial fungal infections
- Miliaris

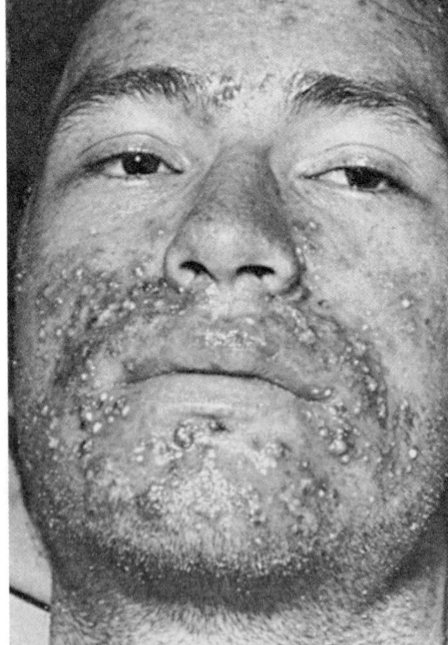

FIGURE 1-100 Folliculitis. Note the pustular eruption with small abscess formation in the hair-bearing areas of the face. General symptoms are usually absent. (From Mandell GL: *Mandell, Douglas, and Bennett's principles and practice of infectious diseases,* ed 5, New York, 2000, Churchill Livingstone.)

WORKUP

Physical examination and medical history (e.g., use of hot tub: "hot tub" folliculitis; adolescent patients who have started shaving: sycosis barbae; use of occlusive topical steroid therapy: *Staphylococcus* folliculitis).

LABORATORY TESTS

Gram stain is useful to identify the infective organisms in infectious folliculitis and to differentiate infectious folliculitis from noninfectious.

TREATMENT

NONPHARMACOLOGIC THERAPY

- Prevention of chemical or mechanical skin irritation
- Glycemic control in diabetics
- Proper chlorination of hot tubs and spas
- Shaving with a clean razor

ACUTE GENERAL Rx

- Cleansing of the area with chlorhexidine and application of saline compresses to involved area
- Application of 2% mupirocin ointment (Bactroban) for bacterial folliculitis affecting a limited area (e.g., sycosis barbae)
- Treatment of severe cases of *Pseudomonas* folliculitis with ciprofloxacin
- Treatment of *S. aureus* folliculitis with dicloxacillin 250 mg qid for 10 days

CHRONIC Rx

- Chronic nasal or perineal *S. aureus* carriers with frequent folliculitis can be treated with rifampin 300 mg bid for 5 days.
- Mupirocin (Bactroban ointment 2%) applied to nares bid is also effective for nasal carriers.

DISPOSITION

- Most cases of bacterial folliculitis resolve completely with proper treatment.
- Steroid folliculitis responds to discontinuation of steroids.

PEARLS & CONSIDERATIONS

COMMENTS

Patients should be instructed in good personal hygiene and avoidance of sharing razors, towels, and washcloths.

AUTHOR: **FRED F. FERRI, M.D.**

BASIC INFORMATION

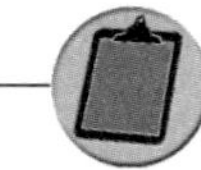

DEFINITION

Food poisoning is an illness caused by ingestion of food contaminated by bacteria and/or bacterial toxins.

ICD-9CM CODES
See specific illness.

EPIDEMIOLOGY & DEMOGRAPHICS

INCIDENCE (IN U.S.):
- Estimated range of 6 to 80 million cases/yr
- Majority of identifiable causes are bacterial

PREDOMINANT AGE: Varies with specific agent

PEAK INCIDENCE: Varies with specific organism
- Summer: *Staphylococcus aureus, Salmonella, Shigella*
- Summer and fall: *Clostridium botulinum, Vibrio parahaemolyticus*
- Spring and fall: *Campylobacter jejuni*
- Winter: *Clostridium perfringens, Yersinia*

NEONATAL INFECTION: Rare but severe with *Shigella*

PHYSICAL FINDINGS & CLINICAL PRESENTATION

- Any combination of GI symptoms and fever
- Specific organisms suspected on the basis of the incubation period and predominant symptoms, although a great deal of overlap exists
  1. Short incubation period (1 to 6 hr): involve the ingestion of preformed toxin; noninvasive
     a. *S. aureus:* nausea, profuse vomiting, and abdominal cramps common; diarrhea possible, but fever uncommon; usually resolves within 24 hr; foods implicated in outbreaks include meats, mayonnaise, and cream pastries
     b. *B. cereus:* two forms, a short incubation (emetic) form (characterized by vomiting and abdominal cramps in virtually all patients, diarrhea in one third of patients, fever uncommon) and a long incubation *(diarrheal)* form; illness usually mild, resolves within 12 hr; unrefrigerated rice most often implicated as vehicle
  2. Moderate incubation period (8 to 16 hr): involves the in vivo production of toxin; noninvasive
     a. *C. perfringens:* severe crampy abdominal pain and watery diarrhea common; fever and vomiting unlikely; symptoms usually resolving within 24 hr; outbreaks invariably related to cooked meat or poultry that is allowed to cool without refrigeration; most cases in the fall and winter months
     b. *B. cereus:* diarrheal (or long incubation) form most commonly beginning with diarrhea, abdominal cramps, and occasionally vomiting; fever uncommon; usually resolves within 24 hr; the responsible food is usually fried rice
  3. Long incubation period (>16 hr): some toxin-mediated, some invasive
     a. Toxin-producing organisms include:
        (1) *C. botulinum:* should be considered when a diarrheal illness coincides with or precedes paralysis; severity of illness related to the quantity of toxin ingested; characteristic cranial nerve palsies progressing to a descending paralysis; fever usually absent; usually associated with home-canned foods
        (2) Enterotoxigenic *E. coli* (ETEC): most common cause of travelers' diarrhea; after 1- to 2-day incubation period, abdominal cramps and copious diarrhea occur; vomiting and fever uncommon; usually resolves after 3 to 4 days; vehicle usually unbottled water or contaminated salad or ice
        (3) Enterohemorrhagic *E. coli* (EHEC): can cause severe abdominal cramps and watery diarrhea, which may eventually become bloody; bacteria (strain O157:H7) are noninvasive; no fever; illness may be complicated by hemolytic-uremic syndrome; associated with contaminated beef
        (4) *V. cholerae:* varies from a mild, self-limited illness to life-threatening cholera; diarrhea, nausea and vomiting, abdominal cramps, and muscle cramps; no fever; severe cases may progress to shock and death within hours of onset; survivors usually have resolution of symptoms in 1 wk; U.S. cases are either imported or result from ingestion of imported food
     b. Invasive organisms include:
        (1) *Salmonella:* associated most often with nontyphoidal strains; incubation period generally 12 to 48 hr; nausea, vomiting, diarrhea, and abdominal cramps typical; fever possible; outbreaks of gastroenteritis related to contaminated poultry, meat, and dairy products
        (2) *Shigella:* asymptomatic infection possible, but some with fever and watery diarrhea that may progress to bloody diarrhea and dysentery; with mild illness, usually self-limited, resolves in a few days; with severe illness, may develop complications; transmission usually from person to person but can occur via contaminated food or water
        (3) *C. jejuni:* the most common food-borne bacterial pathogen; incubation period is about 1 day, then a prodrome of fever, headache, and myalgias; intestinal phase marked by diarrhea associated with fever, malaise, and abdominal pain; diarrhea mild to profuse and bloody; usually resolves in about 7 days, but relapse is possible; associated with undercooked meats and poultry, unpasteurized dairy products, and drinking from freshwater streams

(4) *Y. enterocolitica* and *Y. pseudotuberculosis:* infrequent causes of enteritis in U.S.; children affected more often than adults; fever, diarrhea, and abdominal pain lasting 1 to 3 wk; some with mesenteric adenitis that mimics acute appendicitis; contaminated food or water is usually responsible
(5) *V. parahaemolyticus:* In U.S., most outbreaks in coastal states or on cruise ships during the summer months; incubation period usually <1 day, followed by explosive watery diarrhea in the majority of cases; nausea, vomiting, abdominal cramps, and headache also common; fever less common; usually resolves by 1 wk; related to ingestion of seafood
(6) Enteroinvasive *E. coli* (EIEC): a rare cause of disease in the U.S.; high incidence of fever and bloody diarrhea; may resemble bacillary dysentery
(7) *V. vulnificus:* may cause serious, often fatal illness in persons with chronic liver disease; GI symptoms usually absent, but fever, chills, hypotension, and hemorrhagic skin lesions possible; patients with liver disease or at increased risk of developing liver disease should avoid eating raw oysters

ETIOLOGY

Classically categorized as either inflammatory (invasive) or noninflammatory:

- Noninflammatory: *B. cereus, S. aureus, C. botulinum, C. perfringens, V. cholerae,* enterotoxigenic *E. coli* (ETEC), and enterohemorrhagic *E. coli* (EHEC); toxin-producing organisms that are noninvasive; fecal leukocytes are not seen.
- Inflammatory: *Campylobacter,* enteroinvasive *E. coli* (EIEC), *Salmonella, Shigella, V. parahaemolyticus,* and *Yersinia;* cause disease by invasion of intestinal tissue; fecal leukocytes are seen.

DIAGNOSIS

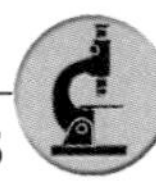

DIFFERENTIAL DIAGNOSIS

Gastroenteritis caused by viruses (Norwalk or rotavirus), parasites *(Amoeba histolytica, Giardia lamblia),* or toxins (ciguatoxins, mushrooms, heavy metals)

LABORATORY TESTS

- Test stool for fecal leukocytes to help narrow the differential diagnosis:
  1. Send stool for culture and for ova and parasites.
  2. Send stool for *C. difficile* toxin in patients with current or recent antibiotic use.
  3. NOTE: Some pathogens are not identified on routine stool culture; laboratory should be advised if *Yersinia, C. botulinum, Vibrio,* or enterohemorrhagic *E. coli* (O157:H7) are suspected.
  4. Finding *B. cereus, C. perfringens,* or *E. coli* in stool is of little value, because these may be part of the normal bowel flora.
- If botulism suspected, send food, serum, and stool for toxin assay.
- Blood cultures are needed for all febrile patients.

TREATMENT

NONPHARMACOLOGIC THERAPY

Adequate rehydration is the mainstay of therapy.

ACUTE GENERAL Rx

- Gastroenteritis caused by the following organisms requires no antimicrobial treatment: *B. cereus, S. aureus, C. perfringens, V. parahaemolyticus, Yersinia,* and enterohemorrhagic and enteroinvasive *E. coli.*
- The usual cause of traveler's diarrhea is enterotoxigenic *E. coli.* Although usually a self-limited illness, antibiotics can shorten the course.
  1. SMX/TMP one DS tab bid for 3 days
  2. Ciprofloxacin 500 mg PO bid for 3 days
- The mainstay of therapy for cholera is fluid replacement. Antibiotics should be given to decrease shedding and duration of illness.
  1. Doxycycline 100 mg PO bid for 3 days
  2. SMX/TMP one DS tab bid for 3 days
- Treatment is not indicated for *Salmonella* gastroenteritis. Patients who are at high risk of developing bacteremia may be treated for 48 to 72 hr (see "Salmonellosis").
- Although shigellosis tends to be a self-limited illness, antibiotics shorten the course of illness and may limit transmission of the illness (see "Shigellosis").
- Those with moderate or severe *Campylobacter* diarrhea may benefit from treatment.
  1. Erythromycin 500 mg PO qid for 5 days
  2. Ciprofloxacin 500 mg PO bid for 5 days
- *V. vulnificus* sepsis should be treated with:
  1. Doxycycline 100 mg IV bid for 2 wk
  2. Ceftazidime 2 g IV q8h for 2 wk
- For suspected botulism, antitoxin should be administered early (see "Botulism").

CHRONIC Rx

Patients with *Salmonella* infections may become carriers and may require treatment (see "Salmonellosis").

DISPOSITION

- Most infections are self-limited and do not require therapy.
- In immunocompromised host or patient with underlying disease, serious complications are possible.
- Postinfectious syndromes are important with some infections:
  1. Reiter's syndrome: *Salmonella, Shigella, Campylobacter, Yersinia;* more common in genetically susceptible host (HLA-B27+)
  2. Guillain-Barré syndrome: *Campylobacter*

REFERRAL

If more than a mild illness

PEARLS & CONSIDERATIONS

COMMENTS

- Grossly underreported and undiagnosed
- All cases to be reported to the local health department
- Table 2-74 compares incubation period, symptoms, and common vehicles for microbial causes of food poisoning.

SUGGESTED READING

Centers for Disease Control and Prevention: Diagnosis and management of foodborne illnesses: a primer for physicians, *MMWR Recomm Rep* 50(RR-2):1, 2001.

AUTHOR: **MAURICE POLICAR, M.D.**

BASIC INFORMATION

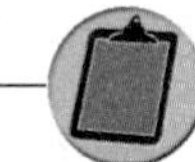

DEFINITION

Friedreich's ataxia is the most common neurodegenerative hereditary ataxic disorder, caused by degeneration of dorsal root ganglions, posterior columns, spinocerebellar and corticospinal tracts and large sensory peripheral neurons.

ICD-9CM CODES
334.0 Friedreich's ataxia

EPIDEMIOLOGY & DEMOGRAPHICS

INCIDENCE (IN U.S.): Estimated at 1 in 30,000 Caucasians
PREVALENCE (IN U.S.): 2-4/100,000. Carrier rate 1:120-1:160. Lower prevalence in Asians and people of African descent.
PREDOMINANT SEX: Male = Female
PEAK INCIDENCE: 8 to 15 yr
GENETICS: Autosomal recessive; 96% of affected patients are homozygous, 4% compound heterozygous (2 different mutations). Trinucleotide repeat expansion accounts for 98% of cases, while point mutations account for 2% of cases.

PHYSICAL FINDINGS

- Onset of progressive appendicular and gait ataxia, with absent muscle stretch reflexes in the lower extremities
- With disease progression (within 5 yr): dysarthria, distal loss of position and vibration sense, pyramidal leg weakness, areflexia in all 4 limbs, extensor plantar responses
- Common findings: progressive scoliosis, distal atrophy, pes cavus, and cardiomyopathy (symmetric concentric hypertrophic form in most cases)
- Insulin-requiring diabetes mellitus may occur in 10% of patients, with glucose intolerance occurring in an additional 10%-20%

ETIOLOGY

- Genetic: Frataxin gene is localized to the centromeric region of chromosome 9q13.
- Normal sequence has 6-27 repeats; abnormal sequence has 120-1700 GAA repeats.
- Frataxin deficiency leads to impaired mitochondrial iron homeostasis.

DIAGNOSIS

DIFFERENTIAL DIAGNOSIS

- Charcot-Marie-Tooth disease type (in early cases)
- Abetalipoproteinemia (Bassen-Kornzweig syndrome)
- Severe vitamin E deficiency with malabsorption
- Early-onset cerebellar ataxia with retained reflexes
- Autosomal dominant cerebellar ataxia (Spinocerebellar ataxia)

WORKUP

- Diagnostic criteria include electrophysiological evidence for a generalized axonal sensory neuropathy
- Electrocardiogram (ECG) shows widespread T-wave inversion and evidence of left ventricular hypertrophy in 65% of patients
- Sural nerve biopsy shows major loss of large myelinated fibers
- Specific gene testing for the expanded GAA trinucleotide repeat

LABORATORY TESTS

- EMG/NC
- ECG and echocardiogram
- Peripheral blood smear for acanthocytes
- Lipid profile
- Glucose levels (fasting or 2 hr postprandial; consider glucose tolerance test if necessary)
- Vitamin E levels (if necessary)

IMAGING STUDIES

MRI of the spinal cord may demonstrate spinal cord atrophy with essentially normal cerebrum, brainstem, and cerebellum (Fig. 1-101).

TREATMENT

NONPHARMACOLOGIC THERAPY

- Surgical correction of scoliosis and foot deformities in selected patients
- Prosthetic devices as required (e.g., ankle-foot orthosis for foot drop)
- Physical therapy
- Communication devices for patients with severe dysarthria

ACUTE GENERAL Rx

None established.
An antioxidant, idebenone (short-chain analogue of coenzyme Q10) administered orally at 5 to 10 mg/kg/day with or without vitamin E may improve outcomes in patients with cardiomyopathy without clinical deterioration. This treatment is experimental and research may be reviewed on www.idebenone.org.

Further research with various antioxidants and iron chelators is ongoing.

CHRONIC Rx

Chronic management of congestive heart failure required. Cardiac arrhythmias will warrant pacemaker implantation.

DISPOSITION

- Loss of ambulation typically occurs within 15 yr of symptom onset, and 95% are wheelchair bound by age 45 yr.
- Life expectancy is reduced, particularly if heart disease with/without diabetes mellitus is present. Mean survival from symptom onset is 36 years.

REFERRAL

- If uncertain about diagnosis
- For genetic counseling (recommended if available)

SUGGESTED READINGS

Alper G, Narayanan V: Friedreich's ataxia, *Pediatr Neurol* 28:335, 2003.
Voncken M, Ioannou P, Delatycki MB: Friedreich ataxia-update on pathogenesis and possible treatment, *Neurogenetics* 5:1, 2004.

AUTHOR: **EROBOGHENE E. UBOGU, M.D.**

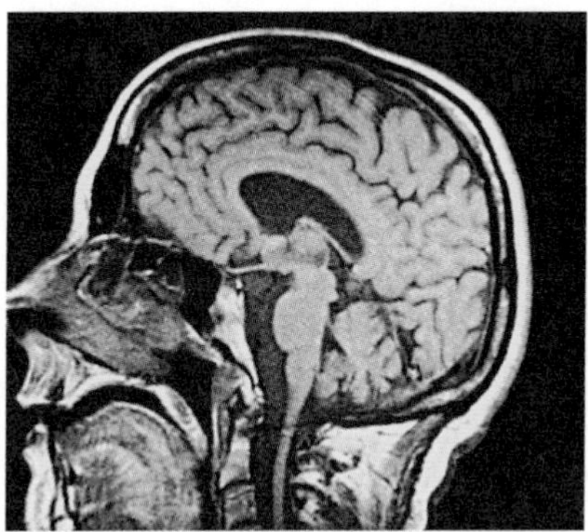

A

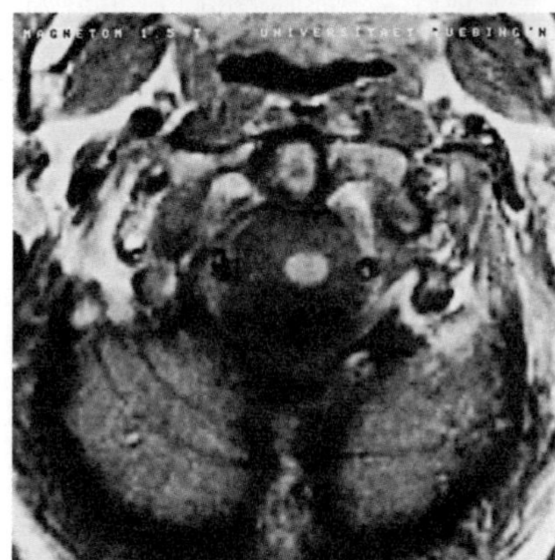

B

FIGURE 1-101 T1-weighted MRIs of the brain and cervical spinal cord in Friedreich's ataxia. The images are, **A,** midsagittal plane of the head and, **B,** an axial slice at the level of the dens axis. There is severe shrinkage of the cervical spinal cord. In contrast, the cerebellum and brainstem are of normal size. (From Goetz CG: *Textbook of clinical neurology,* Philadelphia, 1999, WB Saunders.)

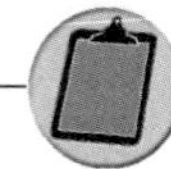

BASIC INFORMATION

DEFINITION

Frostbite represents tissue injury (or death) from freezing and vasoconstriction induced by severe environmental cold exposure.

SYNONYMS

Cold-induced tissue injury

ICD-9CM CODES
991.3 Frostbite

EPIDEMIOLOGY & DEMOGRAPHICS

- Environmental factors include wind chill factor, temperature, duration of exposure, altitude, and degree of wetness. Hands and feet account for 90% of all recorded injuries; earlobes, nose and male genitalia are also more susceptible.
- Host factors include extremes of age, immobility, history of cold injuries, lack of acclimatization, skin damage, psychiatric illness, atherosclerosis, malnutrition, tobacco use, sedative drugs (especially alcohol), fatigue, and wearing constricting clothing/footwear.

PHYSICAL FINDINGS & CLINICAL PRESENTATION

- Frostbite may be classified into degrees of injury or, more practically, into *superficial* and *deep* groups.
- *Superficial* frostbite involves the skin and subcutaneous tissue. The frozen part is waxy, white, and firm but soft and resilient below the surface when gently depressed. After rewarming, the frostbitten area may appear mottled and swollen, and superficial blisters with clear or milky fluid may form within 6 to 24 hr (Fig.1-102). There is no ultimate tissue loss.
- *Deep* frostbite extends into subcutaneous tissues and may involve muscles, nerves, tendons, or bones. The skin may be hard or wooden, without tissue resilience. Edema, cyanosis, hemorrhagic blisters (after 3 to 7 days), tissue necrosis, and gangrene may develop. Affected tissue has a poor prognosis.
- Patients initially experience numbness, prickling, and itching. More severe injury can produce paresthesias and stiffness, with burning or throbbing pain upon thawing.
- Severity of frostbite injury appears to correlate more with duration of exposure than ambient temperature.

DIAGNOSIS

- Diagnosis is clinically based on the appropriate environmental conditions.
- Other locally induced cold injuries include:

Pernio (chilblains): cold-induced vasculitis of dermal vessels often affecting dorsum of hands and feet and seen with repeated cold exposure to dry, cold temperatures.

Cold immersion (trench) foot: caused by ischemic injury resulting from sustained severe vasoconstriction in appendages exposed to wet cold at temperatures above freezing.

WORKUP

- Labwork not indicated unless patient has systemic hypothermia
- Wound and blood cultures in more severe cases
- Technetium scintigraphy, MRI, and MRA appear to be the most promising modalities for assessment of tissue viability, but a delay of 2 to 3 wk is generally required to reliably distinguish a level of debridement or amputation

TREATMENT

NONPHARMACOLOGIC THERAPY

- Remove constricting or wet clothing and gently insulate and immobilize the affected area.
- Avoid thawing if there is any risk of refreezing.
- Never rub or massage the affected area. Avoid dry heat.
- If there is associated hypothermia, core temperature must first be stabilized with warmed, humidified oxygen, heated IV saline (45° to 65° C), and warming blankets.

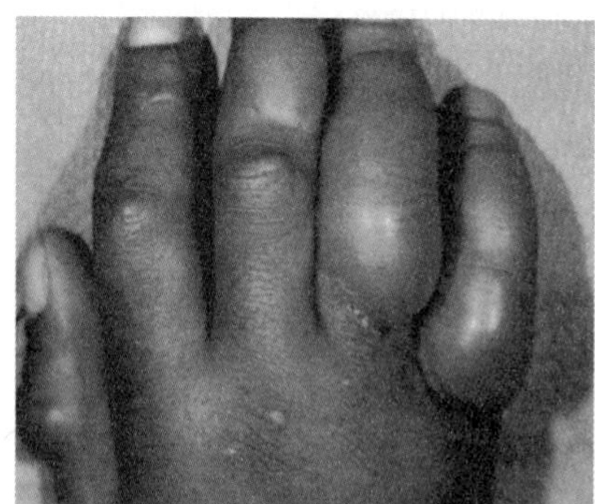

FIGURE 1-102 Large, clear frostbite blisters on the right hand. (From Rosen P [ed]: *Emergency medicine,* ed 4, St Louis, 1998, Mosby.)

ACUTE GENERAL Rx

- Immerse affected area in circulating warm water that is 40° to 42° C for 15 to 30 min, repeat until capillary refill returns and tissue is supple.
- IV narcotics for pain control during thawing.
- Cover injured tissue with dry, sterile, noncompressive and nonadherent dressings. Splint and elevate hands and feet to reduce edema and separate digits with cotton gauze.
- Td prophylaxis and topical antibiotics if potentially contaminated skin wound
- Streptococcal prophylaxis for 48 to 72 hr with IV penicillin for severe cases
- Topical aloe vera, thromboxane inhibitors, steroids, antiinflammatory agents, thrombolytics, and anticoagulants do not conclusively demonstrate a therapeutic benefit.

POST-THAW Rx

- Debride broken clear vesicles and avoid disrupting intact blisters (especially hemorrhagic ones) unless they interfere with the patient's functional status.
- Whirlpool hydrotherapy with an antiseptic for 20 to 30 min bid to tid for several weeks
- Gentle, progressive physical therapy after edema resolves
- Avoid all vasoconstrictors, including nicotine

DISPOSITION

A majority of patients experience long-term residual symptoms including neuropathic pain, sensory deficits, hyperhidrosis, secondary Raynaud's disease, edema, hair or nail deformities, and (rarely) arthritis.

REFERRAL

- Hospitalize if patient has systemic hypothermia or more than superficial frostbite.
- Early surgical intervention is not indicated. Surgical decisions regarding amputation should be deferred until there is clear demarcation of viable tissue (at least 3 to 4 weeks) unless refractory pain, sepsis, or gangrene occurs.

SUGGESTED READINGS

Danzl D: Frostbite. In Rosen P (ed): *Emergency medicine: concepts and clinical practice,* vol 1, ed 5, St Louis, 2002, Mosby.

Kare JA, Shneiderman A: Hyperthermia and hypothermia in the older population, *Top Emerg Med* 23(3):39, 2001.

Murphy JV et al: Frostbite: pathogenesis and treatment, *J Trauma Inj Infect & Crit Care,* 48(1):171, 2000.

Reamy B: Frostbite: review and current concepts, *J Am Board Fam Pract* 11(1):341, 1998.

Ulrich AS, Rathlev NK: Hypothermia and localized cold injuries, *Emerg Med Clin North Am* 22(2):281, 2004.

AUTHOR: **MICHAEL P. JOHNSON, M.D.**

Frozen Shoulder (PTG)

BASIC INFORMATION

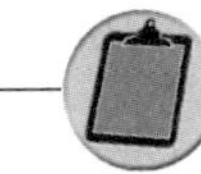

DEFINITION

Frozen shoulder is a condition unique to the shoulder and characterized by pain and restricted passive and active range of motion (Fig. 1-103).

SYNONYMS

Adhesive capsulitis
Periarthritis
Pericapsulitis
Check-rein shoulder

ICD-9CM CODES
726.0 Adhesive shoulder capsulitis

EPIDEMIOLOGY & DEMOGRAPHICS

PREVALENT AGE: Over 40 yr
PREVALENT SEX: Females > males

PHYSICAL FINDINGS & CLINICAL PRESENTATION

- Arm held protectively at the side with apprehension caused by pain
- Varying degrees of deltoid and spinatus atrophy
- Generalized shoulder tenderness
- Restricted active and passive shoulder motion of varying degrees

ETIOLOGY

- Unknown
- Fig. 1-103 illustrates the sequence of events terminating in frozen shoulder

DIAGNOSIS

DIFFERENTIAL DIAGNOSIS

- Secondary causes of shoulder stiffness (prolonged immobilization following trauma or surgery)
- Posterior shoulder dislocation
- Ruptured rotator cuff
- Glenohumeral osteoarthritis
- Rotator cuff inflammation
- Superior sulcus tumor
- Cervical disk disease
- Brachial neuritis

WORKUP

Laboratory and radiographic studies are generally normal.

TREATMENT

NONPHARMACOLOGIC THERAPY

Prevention is important. Shoulder motion should be maintained during those periods when the patient may be inactive as a result of illness or injury.

ACUTE GENERAL Rx

- Moist heat, sedation, and analgesics as needed
- A local steroid/lidocaine mixture injected into the subacromial space and joint (See Epicondylitis entry for guidelines to common steroid injections)
- Home exercise program
- Manipulation of shoulder under anesthesia (rarely needed)

DISPOSITION

- The initial stage of pain followed by stiffness may last several months; recovery phase may also last several months; complete recovery is usually the case.
- Recurrence in the same shoulder is rare, although the opposite limb may develop the same symptoms.
- Some patients have mild residual loss of movement but without any significant functional impairment.

REFERRAL

Orthopedic consultation in patients with resistant disease

PEARLS & CONSIDERATIONS

COMMENTS

- "Capsulitis" with an inflammatory infiltrate is not consistently found pathologically.
- Frozen shoulder is increased in patients with diabetes, thyroid disease, and recent cardiopulmonary conditions.
- Some cases present with findings of reflex sympathetic dystrophy.

SUGGESTED READINGS

Berghs BM, Sole-Molins X, Bunker TD: Arthroscopic release of adhesive capsulitis, *J Shoulder Elbow Surg* 13:180, 2004.
Harrast MA, Rao AG: The stiff shoulder, *Phys Med Rehabil Clin N Am* 15(3):557, 2004.
Kivimaki J, Pohjolainen T: Manipulation for frozen shoulder with and without steroid injection, *Arch Phys Med Rehabil* 82:1188, 2001.
Rundquist PJ et al: Shoulder kinematics in subjects with frozen shoulder, *Arch Phys Med Rehabil* 84(10):1473, 2003.
Wolf JM, Green A: Influence of comorbidity on self-assessment instrument scores of patients with idiopathic adhesive capsulitis, *J Bone Joint Surg* 84(A):1167, 2002.

AUTHOR: **LONNIE R. MERCIER, M.D.**

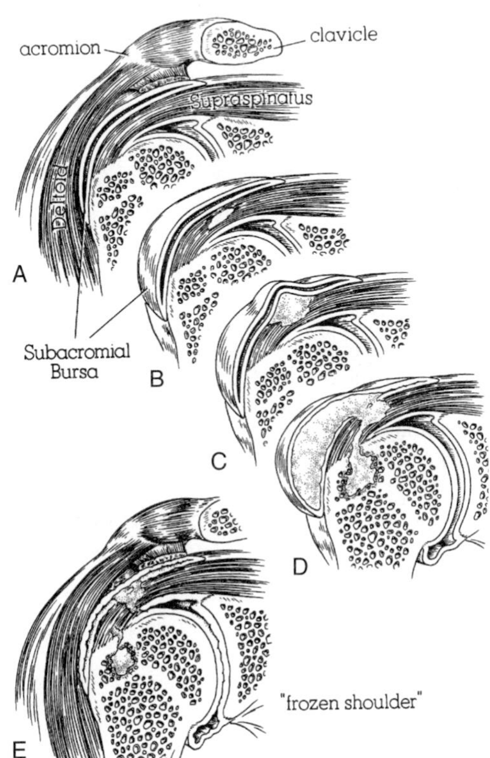

FIGURE 1-103 Sequence of events terminating in frozen shoulder. A, Normal structures of the shoulder. **B,** Supraspinatus tendonitis, sometimes calcific, in the "critical zone." **C,** Spread of inflammation to the tendon sheath and a bulge into the floor of the subacromial bursa. **D,** Rupture into the subacromial bursa and extension of the inflammatory process as an osteitis into the humeral head and greater tuberosity. **E,** Frozen shoulder with involvement of tendons, bursa, capsule, synovium, and muscle with fibrous contracture and markedly diminished volume of the shoulder joint space. (From Noble J [ed]: *Primary care medicine,* ed 2, St Louis, 1996, Mosby.)

Galactorrhea

BASIC INFORMATION

DEFINITION

Galactorrhea can be defined as inappropriate lactation (in absence of pregnancy and postpartum state) secondary to nonphysiologic augmentation of prolactin release.

ICD-9CM CODES
611.6 Galactorrhea

PHYSICAL FINDINGS AND CLINICAL PRESENTATION

- Milky discharge from nipples usually occurring bilaterally
- Evidence of chest wall irritation from ill-fitting clothing, herpes zoster, or atopic dermatitis may be present
- Visual field defects may be present with prolactinomas
- Evidence of acromegaly, Cushing's disease, or hypothyroidism when galactorrhea is secondary to these disorders

ETIOLOGY

- Medications (phenothiazines, metoclopramide, SSRIs, anxiolytics, buspirone, atenolol, valproic acid, conjugated estrogen and medroxyprogesterone, methyldopa, verapamil, H2 receptor blockers, octreotide, danazol, tricyclics, isoniazid, amphetamine, reserpine, opiates, sumatriptan, rimantadine, oral contraceptive formulations); after infancy, galactorrhea is usually medication-induced
- Breast stimulation (prolonged suckling), sexual intercourse
- Pituitary tumors (prolactinomas, craniopharyngiomas
- Chest wall irritation from ill-fitting clothing, herpes zoster, atopic dermatitis, burns
- Hypothyroidism (elevated TSH increases TRH, which increases prolactin)
- Increased stress, major trauma
- Chronic renal failure (decreased prolactin clearance)
- Cushing's disease
- Herbs (e.g. fennel, red clover, anise, red raspberry, marshmallow)
- Cannabis
- Spinal cord surgery or injury, or tumors
- Severe GERD, esophagitis (stimulation of thoracic nerves via cervical and thoracic ganglia)
- Breast surgery
- Idiopathic
- Neonatal ("witch's milk" produced by 2%-5% of neonates because of precipitous drop in maternal estrogen and progesterone postdelivery)
- Lymphomas, Hodgkin's disease, bronchogenic carcinoma, renal adenocarcinomas
- Sarcoidosis and other infiltrative disorders
- Tuberculosis affecting pituitary gland
- Pituitary stalk resection
- Multiple sclerosis
- Empty sella syndrome
- Acromegaly

DIAGNOSIS

DIFFERENTIAL DIAGNOSIS

- Intraductal papilloma
- Breast cancer
- Paget's disease of breast
- Breast abscess

WORKUP

- Complete history focusing on menstrual irregularity, infertility, previous pregnancies, duration of galactorrhea, medications, visual complaints, fatigue. Age of onset is also significant (e.g., prolactinoma most common between ages 20 to 35, neonatal galactorrhea is usually secondary to transplacental transfer of maternal estrogen)
- Physical examination: hirsutism, acne, obesity, visual field defects, goiter
- Breast exam for presence of nodules, evaluation of discharge (milky vs serosanguinous vs purulent)
- Laboratory testing and imaging studies (see "Laboratory Tests")

LABORATORY TESTS

- Prolactin level (elevated, usually >200 ng/ml in prolactinoma)
- Human chorionic gonadotropin level (positive in pregnancy)
- TSH, TRH (both elevated in hypothyroidism)
- BUN, creatinine (elevated in renal failure), glucose (elevated in Cushing's syndrome)
- Urinalysis (hematuria in renal cell carcinoma)
- Microscopic examination of nipple discharge (scant cellular material, numerous fat globules)

IMAGING STUDIES

- MRI of brain if prolactin level is elevated, amenorrhea is present or visual fields defects are detected on physical examination.
- High-resolution CT of brain with special cuts coronal cuts through the pituitary region may be helpful in patients with contraindications to MRI; however, it may miss small lesions.

TREATMENT

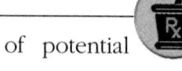

- Discontinuation of potential offending agents
- Avoidance of excessive breast stimulation
- Galactorrhea resulting from prolactinoma can be managed medically, surgically, or with careful surveillance depending on size and growth of tumor, associated symptoms and prolactin level. Please refer to "Prolactinoma" in Section I for additional information

REFERRAL

- Endocrine and surgical consultation if prolactinoma is detected

SUGGESTED READINGS

Leung A, Pacaud D: Diagnosis and management of galactorrhea, *Am Fam Physician* 70:543, 2004.

Pena KS, Rosenfeld JA: Evaluation and treatment of galactorrhea, *Am Fam Physician* 63:1763, 2001.

AUTHOR: **FRED F. FERRI, M.D.**

BASIC INFORMATION

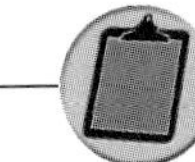

DEFINITION

Ganglia are cystic structures thought to derive from a tendon sheath or joint capsule.

ICD-9CM CODES
727.43 Ganglion

EPIDEMIOLOGY & DEMOGRAPHICS

- Ganglia are more common in women than men (3:1)
- Can occur at any age but usually occurs between second and fourth decades of life
- Most common soft tissue tumor of the hand and wrist

PHYSICAL FINDINGS & CLINICAL PRESENTATION

- Most ganglia occur on the dorsum of the wrist (50% to 70%) (Fig. 1-104).
- Volar wrist (18% to 20%) is the next most common site.
- Ganglia can also involve the proximal digital flexor tendons and the distal interphalangeal joints.
- Left and right hands are equally affected.
- Ganglia are usually solitary, firm, smooth, round, and fluctuant.
- Pain from mass effect or compression up against nearby structure may be present (e.g., median nerve and radial nerve).
- Hand numbness may be present.
- Patient may experience hand muscle weakness.
- Ganglia usually develop over a period of months but may arise suddenly.

ETIOLOGY

Ganglia are thought to derive from synovial herniation or expansion from the joint capsule or tendon sheath.

DIAGNOSIS

Direct inspection and localization of the cyst often is enough to make the diagnosis of ganglia.

DIFFERENTIAL DIAGNOSIS

- Lipoma
- Fibroma
- Epidermoid inclusion cyst
- Osteochondroma
- Hemangioma
- Infection (tuberculosis, fungi, and secondary syphilis)
- Gout
- Rheumatoid nodule
- Radial artery aneurysm

WORKUP

The workup of ganglia usually consists of history, physical examination, and x-ray imaging.

LABORATORY TESTS

Blood tests are not specific in the diagnosis of ganglia.

IMAGING STUDIES

- X-ray of the hand and wrist is done to rule out other bone or joint abnormalities.
- Ultrasound studies are helpful in the diagnosis of ganglia, demonstrating smooth cystic walls that may be septated.
- CT scan can be done if the ultrasound is equivocal.
- MRI, although not done often for the diagnosis of ganglia, aids in differentiating malignant bone lesions from cystic structures.
- Arthrography may demonstrate a communication between the joint and ganglia (not commonly done).

TREATMENT

Treatment is indicated for pain, muscle weakness, and cosmetic purposes.

NONPHARMACOLOGIC THERAPY

- Attempts to rupture the cyst by sharp blows with a book or with finger compression.
- Aspiration, heat, and sclerotherapy have been tried but met with high recurrence rates (60%).

ACUTE GENERAL Rx

- Aspiration with a large-bore needle (18-gauge) followed by injection of 20 to 40 mg of triamcinolone acetonide can be tried.
- This may be repeated if the ganglia recurs (35% to 40%).

CHRONIC Rx

Total ganglionectomy is the surgical procedure of choice.

DISPOSITION

- Ganglia spontaneously resolve in approximately 40% to 50% of cases.
- Aspiration with steroid injection is successful in approximately 65% of cases.
- Surgery provides cure in 85% to 95% of the cases.
- Complications of ganglia include:
  1. Carpal tunnel syndrome with pain and muscle atrophy
  2. Radial nerve impingement
  3. Radial artery compression
- Complications of ganglion surgery include:
  1. Infection
  2. Recurrence (5% to 15%) usually secondary to inadequate excision
  3. Reflex sympathetic dystrophy
  4. Scar formation

REFERRAL

It is best to refer patients with symptomatic ganglia to a hand surgeon.

PEARLS & CONSIDERATIONS

COMMENTS

- Ganglia synovial membrane maintains its secretory function. Aspiration of ganglia often demonstrates a viscous, mucinous clear fluid containing albumin, globulin, and hyaluronic acid.
- Dorsal ganglia usually originate from the scapholunate ligament.
- Volar ganglia typically originate between the tendons of the flexor carpi radialis and brachioradialis.

SUGGESTED READINGS

Ho PC et al: Current treatment of ganglion of the wrist, *Hand Surg* 6(1):49, 2001.

Thornburg LE: Ganglions of the hand and wrist, *J Am Acad Orthop Surg* 7(4):231, 1999.

Wang AA, Hutchinson DT: Longitudinal observation of pediatric hand and wrist ganglia, *J Hand Surg* 26(4):599, 2001.

AUTHOR: **PETER PETROPOULOS, M.D.**

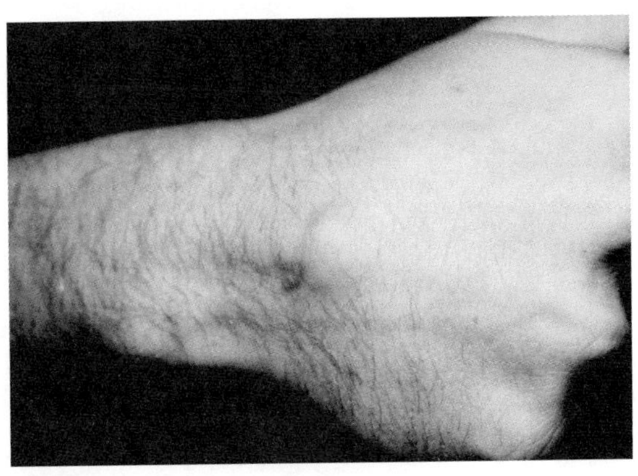

FIGURE 1-104 Round and firm ganglion cyst bulging from the dorsal aspect of the hand. (From Kelly WN: *Textbook of rheumatology,* ed 5, Philadelphia, 1997, WB Saunders.)

BASIC INFORMATION

DEFINITION

Gardner's syndrome is a variant of familial adenomatous polyposis (FAP), with prominent extraintestinal manifestations. It is an autosomal dominant condition characterized by:

- Adenomatous intestinal polyps
- Soft-tissue tumors
- Osteomas

ICD-9CM CODES
211.3 Gardner's syndrome

EPIDEMIOLOGY & DEMOGRAPHICS

- FAP accounts for less than 1% of all colorectal cancers.
- The entire GI tract may have polyps, but the malignant potential is highest in the colon. Individuals with Gardner's syndrome develop hundreds to thousands of colorectal adenomatous polyps.
- Polyps occur at a mean age of 16 yr.
- Cancer develops in 7% of individuals by age 21 yr, 50% by age 39 yr, and 90% by age 45 yr.
- Associated increased risk for other cancers: about 10% develop desmoid tumors and 10% develop duodenal periampullary cancer. Risk for brain (medulloblastoma), nasopharyngeal angiofibroma, thyroid, childhood hepatoblastoma, adrenal and pancreatic cancer is also increased.

CLINICAL PRESENTATION

Phenotypic variability seen in individuals and families with the same mutation. Soft tissue and bone abnormalities may precede intestinal disease.

- Congenital hypertrophy of the retinal pigment epithelium (often the first sign)
- Dental abnormalities: supernumerary or unerupted teeth
- Soft tissue lesions: epidermoid or sebaceous cysts, fibromas, lipomas, desmoid tumors
- Skull, mandible and long bone abnormalities
- Abdominal mass, occult blood in stool

ETIOLOGY

- Caused by mutations of the ade nomatous polyposis coli (APC) gene on chromosome 5q21; 300 mutations have been identified. The site of the mutation may explain the prominent extraintestinal lesions that differentiate Gardner's syndrome from other variants of FAP.
- Spontaneous mutations are responsible for 20%-30% of FAP cases.

DIAGNOSIS

In individuals with a family history, diagnosis is confirmed by >100 adenomatous polyps in the colon, >3 pigmented ocular lesions on fundoscopic examination, or genetic testing.

DIFFERENTIAL DIAGNOSIS

- FAP
- Turcot's syndrome
- Attenuated adenomatous polyposis coli
- Peutz-Jeghers syndrome
- Juvenile polyposis
- MYH polyposis

WORKUP

History, physical examination, laboratory tests, imaging studies

SCREENING/LABORATORY TESTS

Screening should be offered to first-degree relatives of affected individuals >10 yr of age and individuals with >100 colorectal adenomas.

PROTEIN TRUNCATION TESTING (PTT):

- Genetic testing consisting of serum *in vitro* synthesized protein assay.
- Able to identify a mutation in 80% of families with FAP. To ensure that the mutation affecting the family is identifiable, a family member known to have FAP should be tested first.
- If positive in the affected individual, family members can be screened and the test can differentiate with 100% accuracy affected and unaffected family members. If negative in the affected individual, screening family members will not be useful in determining disease status
- If there is no known family history, screening the individual in question is reasonable. A positive test rules in the condition, but a negative test does not rule it out.
- Other genetic tests (sequencing, linkage, single-strand conformation polymorphism testing) can be considered if PTT is not informative.

NOTE: Genetic counseling should be performed and written informed consent obtained before genetic testing.

ANNUAL PHYSICAL EXAM: Examine for extraintestinal lesions (thyroid nodule, abdominal mass, etc.) and obtain routine blood tests.

CONGENITAL HYPERTROPHY OF THE RETINAL PIGMENT EPITHELIUM: Lesions occur in some families and are a reliable indicator of affected status in these families.

IMAGING STUDIES

SIGMOIDOSCOPY

- Pedigrees with an identified APC mutation: positive genetic tests: annual sigmoidoscopy beginning at age 12 yr; negative genetic test: sigmoidoscopy at age 25 yr.
- Pedigrees with an unidentified APC mutation: family members should have annual sigmoidoscopy starting at age 12 yr; every 2 yr starting at age 25 yr; every 3 yr starting at age 35 yr; and then per age-appropriate guidelines starting at age 50.

UPPER GI ENDOSCOPY (INCLUDING THE AMPULLA OF VATER): Screening for gastric and duodenal polyps should begin once colonic polyps are detected and continue every 2 to 4 yr. Screen q1yr if polyps are present in the UGI tract.

ULTRASOUND: Screen children of affected parents q1yr (from infancy to 7 yr of age) with alpha-fetoprotein levels and liver ultrasound to r/o hepatoblastoma.

TREATMENT

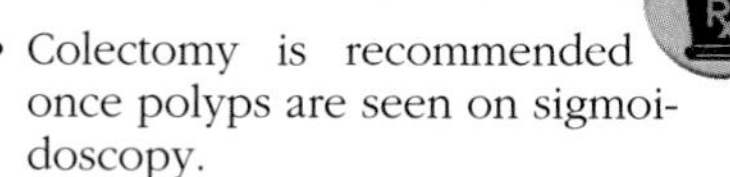

- Colectomy is recommended once polyps are seen on sigmoidoscopy.
- Regular screening of remaining GI tract and extraintestinal manifestations must continue after colectomy.

DISPOSITION

There is a 100% chance of colorectal cancer in untreated individuals. Many other neoplasms occur at higher rates.

REFERRAL

- GI for sigmoidoscopy
- Surgery for prophylactic colectomy at detection of polyps
- Genetic counseling

PEARLS & CONSIDERATIONS

- Sulindac (nonselective NSAID) and celecoxib (cox-2 inhibitor) have been found to cause polyp regression in individuals with FAP. Celecoxib is FDA approved for this indication. Whether cancer risk is changed is not clear. Neither replaces colon resection for cancer prevention.
- Desmoid tumors have been induced and promoted by surgical procedures and OCP use.

SUGGESTED READINGS

Cruz-Correa M, Giardiello FM: Diagnosis and management of hereditary colon cancer, *Gastroenterol Clin North Am* 31(2):537, 2002.

Giardiello FM, Brensinger JD, Petersen GM: American Gastroenterologic Association Practice Guidelines: AGA technical review on hereditary colorectal cancer and genetic testing, *Gastroenterology* 121(1):198, 2001.

AUTHOR: **SUDEEP K. AULAKH, M.D., F.R.C.P.C.**

BASIC INFORMATION

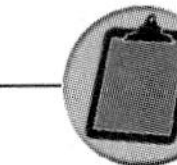

DEFINITION

Gastric cancer is an adenocarcinoma arising from the stomach.

SYNONYMS

Stomach cancer
Linitis plastica

ICD-9CM CODES
451 Malignant neoplasm of stomach

EPIDEMIOLOGY & DEMOGRAPHICS

- Annual incidence of gastric cancer in the U.S. is 7 cases/100,000 persons. The incidence is much higher in Japan, with rates as high as 80 cases/100,000 persons.
- Most gastric cancers arise in the antrum (35%).
- The incidence of distal stomach tumors has greatly declined whereas that of proximal tumors of the cardia and fundus is on the rise.
- Gastric cancer occurs most commonly in male patients >65 yr (70% of patients are >50 yr).
- Incidence of gastric cancer has been declining over the past 30 yr.
- Male:female ratio is 3:2.
- Familiar diffuse gastric cancer is a disease with autosomal dominant inheritance in which gastric cancer develops at a young age. Germ-line truncating mutations in the E-cadherin gene (CDH1) is found in these families.

PHYSICAL FINDINGS & CLINICAL PRESENTATION

- Medical history may reveal complaints of postprandial fullness with significant weight loss (70% to 80%), nausea/emesis (20% to 40%), dysphagia (20%), and dyspepsia, usually unrelieved by antacids; epigastric discomfort, usually lessened by fasting and exacerbated by food intake, is also common.
- Epigastric or abdominal mass (30% to 50%), epigastric pain.
- Skin pallor secondary to anemia.
- Hard, nodular liver: generally indicates metastatic disease to the liver.
- Hemoccult-positive stools.
- Ascites, lymphadenopathy, or pleural effusions: may indicate metastasis.

ETIOLOGY

Risk factors:

- Chronic *H. pylori* gastritis. Gastric cancer develops in persons infected with *H. pylori* but not in uninfected persons. Those with histologic findings of severe gastric atrophy, corpus-predominant gastritis, or intestinal metaplasia are at increased risk. Persons with *H. pylori* infection and duodenal ulcer are not at risk, whereas those with gastric ulcers, nonulcer dyspepsia, and gastric hyperplastic polyps are.
- Tobacco abuse, alcohol consumption
- Food additives (nitrosamines), smoked foods, occupational exposure to heavy metals, rubber, asbestos
- Chronic atrophic gastritis with intestinal metaplasia, hypertrophic gastritis, and pernicious anemia

DIAGNOSIS

DIFFERENTIAL DIAGNOSIS

- Gastric lymphoma (5% of gastric malignancies)
- Hypertrophic gastritis
- Peptic ulcer
- Reflux esophagitis

WORKUP

Upper endoscopy with biopsy will confirm diagnosis. Endoscopic ultrasonography in combination with CT scannning and operative lymph node dissection can be used in staging of the tumor.

LABORATORY TESTS

- Microcytic anemia
- Hemoccult-positive stools
- Hypoalbuminemia
- Abnormal liver enzymes in patients with metastasis to the liver
- Mutation-specific predictive genetic testing by PCR amplification followed by restriction—enzyme digestion and DNA sequencing for truncating mutations in the E-cadherin gene (CDH1) is recommended in families of patients with familiar diffuse cancer because gastric cancer develops in three of every four carriers of a mutant CDH1 gene.

IMAGING STUDIES

- Upper GI series with air contrast (90% accurate) should be considered only if endoscopy is not readily available
- Abdominal CT scan to evaluate for metastasis (70% accurate for regional node metastases)

TREATMENT

ACUTE GENERAL Rx

- Gastrectomy with regional lymphadenectomy is performed in patients with curative potential (<30% of patients at time of diagnosis). Post-op adjuvant chemoradiatiotherapy using 5-fluorouracil and leucovorin is now the standard of care for resected patients able to tolerate such treatment. Postoperative chemotherapy and radiotherapy, compared with surgical resection alone, can extend the survival of patients with gastric cancer in those who are able to complete adjuvant therapy.
- When surgical cure is not possible, palliative resection may prolong duration and quality of life.
- Chemotherapy (FAM: 5-fluorouracil, Adriamycin, and mitomycin C) may provide some palliation; however, it generally does not prolong survival. Chemotherapy with docetaxel, cisplatin, and 5-fluorouracil can be used for chemotherapy-naive patients with metastatic or locally recurrent gastric cancer.

DISPOSITION

- 5-yr survival rate of gastric carcinoma is 12% overall.
- 5-yr survival for early gastric cancers (usually detected incidentally with endoscopy in populations where screening is recommended) is >35%.

REFERRAL

Surgical referral for resection

PEARLS & CONSIDERATIONS

COMMENTS

- Gastrectomy patients will need vitamin B_{12} replacement. They are also at risk for dumping syndrome and should be advised to ingest frequent, small meals.
- Prophylactic gastrectomy should be considered in young asymptomatic carriers of germ-line truncating CDH1 mutations who belong to families with highly penetrant heredity diffuse gastric cancer.

SUGGESTED READINGS

Layke J, Lopez P: Gastric cancer: Diagnosis and treatment options, *Am Fam Physician* 69:1133, 2004.
McDonald JS: Chemotherapy in the management of gastric cancer, *JCO* 2768, 2003.

AUTHOR: **FRED F. FERRI, M.D.**

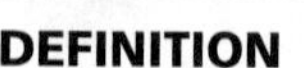

BASIC INFORMATION

DEFINITION

Histologically, gastritis refers to inflammation in the stomach. Endoscopically, "gastritis" refers to a number of abnormal features such as erythema, erosions, and subepithelial hemorrhages. Gastritis can also be subdivided into erosive, nonerosive, and specific types of gastritis with distinctive features both endoscopically and histologically.

SYNONYMS

Erosive gastritis
Hemorrhagic gastritis
Helicobacter pylori gastritis

ICD-9CM CODES
535.5 Gastritis (unless otherwise specified)
535.0 Gastritis, acute
535.3 Alcoholic gastritis
535.1 Atrophic (chronic) gastritis
535.4 Erosive gastritis
535.2 Hypertrophic gastritis

EPIDEMIOLOGY & DEMOGRAPHICS

- Erosive and hemorrhagic gastritis are most commonly seen in patients taking NSAIDs, alcoholics, and critically ill patients (usually on ventilator support).
- *H. pylori* infection with gastritis is believed to be present in 30% to 50% of the population; however, the majority are asymptomatic.
- The prevalence of *H. pylori* infection increases with age from <10% in Caucasians <40 yr old to >50% in patients >50 yr.

PHYSICAL FINDINGS & CLINICAL PRESENTATION

- Patients with gastritis generally present with nonspecific clinical signs and symptoms (e.g., epigastric pain, abdominal tenderness, bloating, anorexia, nausea [with or without vomiting]). Symptoms may be aggravated by eating.
- Epigastric tenderness in acute alcoholic gastritis (may be absent in chronic gastritis).
- Foul-smelling breath.
- Hematemesis ("coffee-ground" emesis).

ETIOLOGY

- Alcohol, NSAIDs, stress (critically ill patients usually on mechanical respiration), hepatic or renal failure, multiorgan failure
- Infection (bacterial, viral)
- Bile reflux, pancreatic enzyme reflux
- Gastric mucosal atrophy, portal hypertension gastropathy
- Irradiation

DIAGNOSIS

DIFFERENTIAL DIAGNOSIS

- Peptic ulcer disease
- GERD
- Nonulcer dyspepsia
- Gastric lymphoma or carcinoma
- Pancreatitis
- Gastroparesis

WORKUP

Diagnostic workup includes a comprehensive history and endoscopy with biopsy.

LABORATORY TESTS

- Serologic (IgG antibody to *H. pylori*) or breath test (^{13}C urea breath tests) for *H. pylori;* patients should not receive proton pump inhibitors for 2 wk before undergoing urea breath test for *H. pylori* infection. Serum antibody tests are not reliable because of a high rate of false-positive results and the fact that antibodies persist even after treatment. The urea breath test is more sensitive and specific; however, it is not readily available. Histologic evaluation of endoscopic biopsy samples is currently the gold standard for accurate diagnosis of *H. pylori* infection.
- Stool antigen test for *H. pylori* is useful to confirm successful eradication of *H. pylori* following treatment.
- Vitamin B_{12} level in patients with atrophic gastritis.
- Hct (low if significant bleeding has occurred).

IMAGING STUDIES

Upper GI series is generally insensitive for the detection of gastritis. Gastroscopy with biopsy is the gold standard diagnostic test and will also detect *H. pylori*.

TREATMENT

NONPHARMACOLOGIC THERAPY

- Avoidance of mucosal irritants such as alcohol and NSAIDs
- Lifestyle modifications with avoidance of tobacco and foods that trigger symptoms

ACUTE GENERAL Rx

- Eradication of infectious agents: *H. pylori* therapy with
  1. Proton pump inhibitors (PPI) bid (e.g., omeprazole 20 mg bid or lansoprazole 30 mg bid) *plus* clarithromycin 500 mg bid *and* amoxicillin 1000 mg bid for 7 to 10 days
  2. PPI bid *plus* amoxicillin 500 mg bid *plus* metronidazole 500 mg for 7 to 10 days
  3. PPI bid *plus* clarithromycin 500 mg bid *and* metronidazole 500 mg bid for 7 days
  4. Recent trials indicate that a 1-day quadruple therapy may be as effective as a 7-day triple therapy regimen. The 1-day quadruple therapy regimen consists of two tablets of 262 mg bismouth subsalicylate qid, one 500-mg metronidazole tablet qid, 2 grams of amoxicillin suspension qid, and two capsules of 30 mg of lansoprazole.
  5. Bismouth compound qid *plus* tetracycline 500 mg qid *and* metronidazole 500 mg qid for 14 days
- Prophylaxis and treatment of stress gastritis with sucralfate suspension 1 g orally q4-6h, H_2-receptor antagonists, or PPIs in patients on ventilator support
- Misoprostol (Cytotec) or PPIs in patients on chronic NSAIDs therapy

CHRONIC Rx

- Misoprostol 100 μg qid or Omeprazole 20 mg/qd in patients receiving chronic NSAIDs
- Avoidance of alcohol, tobacco, and prolonged NSAID use
- Surveillance gastroscopy in patients with atrophic gastritis (increased risk of gastric cancer)

DISPOSITION

- Prognosis is good with most cases resolving with treatment. Successful eradication of *H. pylori* infection can be achieved in >80% of patients with appropriate therapy.
- Undetectable stool antigen 4 wk after therapy accurately confirm cure of *H. pylori* infection in initially seropositive healthy subjects with reasonable sensitivity.
- Most patients with atrophic gastritis and intestinal metaplasia improve within 12 mo following successful *H. pylori* eradication.

SUGGESTED READINGS

Lara LF et al: One day quadruple therapy compared with 7-day triple therapy for helicobacter pylori infection, *Arch Intern Med* 163:2079, 2003.
Meurer L et al: Management of *helicobacter pylori* infection, *Am Fam Physician* 65:1327, 2002.
Suerbaum S, Michetti P: *Helicobacter pylori* infection, *N Engl J Med* 347:1175, 2002.
Vaira D et al: The stool antigen test for detection of *Helicobacter pylori* after eradication therapy, *Ann Intern Med* 136:280, 2002.

AUTHOR: **FRED F. FERRI, M.D.**

BASIC INFORMATION

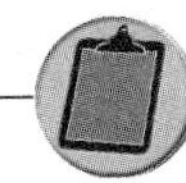

DEFINITION

Gastroesophageal reflux disease (GERD) is a motility disorder characterized primarily by heartburn and caused by the reflux of gastric contents into the esophagus.

SYNONYMS

Peptic esophagitis
Reflux esophagitis
GERD

ICD-9CM CODES
530.81 Gastroesophageal reflux disease
530.1 Esophagitis
787.1 Heartburn

EPIDEMIOLOGY & DEMOGRAPHICS

GERD is one of the most prevalent GI disorders. Nearly 7% of persons in the United States experience heartburn daily, 20% experience it monthly, and 60% experience it intermittently. Incidence in pregnant women exceeds 80%. Nearly 20% of adults use antacids or OTC H_2-blockers at least once a week for relief of heartburn.

PHYSICAL FINDINGS & CLINICAL PRESENTATION

- Physical examination: generally unremarkable
- Clinical signs and symptoms: heartburn, dysphagia, sour taste, regurgitation of gastric contents into the mouth
- Chronic cough and bronchospasm
- Chest pain, laryngitis, early satiety, abdominal fullness, and bloating with belching
- Dental erosions in children

ETIOLOGY

- Incompetent LES
- Medications that lower LES pressure (calcium channel blockers, β-adrenergic blockers, theophylline, anticholinergics)
- Foods that lower LES pressure (chocolate, yellow onions, peppermint)
- Tobacco abuse, alcohol, coffee
- Pregnancy
- Gastric acid hypersecretion
- Hiatal hernia (controversial) present in >70% of patients with GERD; however, most patients with hiatal hernia are asymptomatic

DIAGNOSIS

DIFFERENTIAL DIAGNOSIS

- Peptic ulcer disease
- Unstable angina
- Esophagitis (from infections such as herpes, *Candida*), medication induced (doxycycline, potassium chloride)
- Esophageal spasm (nutcracker esophagus)
- Cancer of esophagus

WORKUP

- Aimed at eliminating the conditions noted in the differential diagnosis and documenting the type and extent of tissue damage.
- Upper GI endoscopy is useful to document the type and extent of tissue damage in GERD and to exclude potentially malignant conditions such as Barrett's esophagus. The American College of Gastroenterology recommends endoscopy to screen for Barrett's esophagus in patients who have chronic GERD symptoms. The data demonstrating the cost-effectiveness of endoscopic screening remain controversial.

LABORATORY TESTS

- 24-hr esophageal pH monitoring and Bernstein test are sensitive diagnostic tests; however, they are not very practical and generally not done. They are useful in patients with atypical manifestations of GERD, such as chest pain or chronic cough.
- Esophageal manometry is indicated in patients with refractory reflux in whom surgical therapy is planned.

IMAGING STUDIES

Upper GI series can identify ulcerations and strictures; however, it may miss mucosal abnormalities. Only one third of patients with GERD have radiographic signs of esophagitis.

TREATMENT

NONPHARMACOLOGIC THERAPY

- Lifestyle modifications with avoidance of foods (e.g., citrus- and tomato-based products) and drugs that exacerbate reflux (e.g., caffeine, β-blockers, calcium channel blockers, α-adrenergic agonists, theophylline)
- Avoidance of tobacco and alcohol use
- Elevation of head of bed (4 to 8 in) using blocks
- Avoidance of lying down directly after late or large evening meals
- Weight reduction, decreased fat intake
- Avoidance of clothing that is tight around the waist

GENERAL Rx

- Proton pump inhibitors (PPIs) (esomeprazole 40 mg qd, omeprazole 20 mg qd, lansoprazole 30 mg qd, rabeprazole 20 mg qd, or pantoprazole 40 mg qd) are safe, tolerated, and very effective in most patients.
- H_2-Blockers (nizatidine 300 mg qhs, famotidine 40 mg qhs, ranitidine 300 mg qhs, or cimetidine 800 mg qhs) can be used but are generally much less effective than PPIs.
- Antacids (may be useful for relief of mild symptoms; however, they are generally ineffective in severe cases of reflux).
- Prokinetic agents (metoclopramide) are indicated only when PPIs are not fully effective. They can be used in combination therapy; however, side effects limit their use.
- For refractory cases: surgery with Nissen fundoplication. Potential surgical candidates should have reflux esophagitis documented by EGD and normal esophageal motility as evaluated by manometry. Surgery generally consists of reduction of hiatal hernia when present and placement of a gastric wrap around the GE junction (fundoplication). Although laparoscopic fundoplication is now widely used, surgery should not be advised with the expectation that patients with GERD will no longer need to take antisecretory medications or that the procedure will prevent esophageal cancer among those with GERD and Barrett's esophagus.
- Endoscopic radiofrequency heating of the GE junction (Stretta procedure) is a newer treatment modality for GERD patients unresponsive to traditional therapy. Its mechanism of action remains unclear. Endoscopy gastroplasty (EndoCinch procedure) also aims at treating GERD. Initial results appear encouraging; however, long-term studies are needed before recommending these procedures.

- Lifestyle modification must be followed lifelong, because this is generally an irreversible condition.

DISPOSITION

- The majority of the patients respond well to therapy.
- Recurrence of reflux is common if treatment is discontinued.
- Postsurgical complications occur in nearly 20% of patients (dysphagia, gas, bloating, diarrhea, nausea). Long-term follow-up studies also reveal that within 3 to 5 yr 52% of patients who had undergone antireflux surgery are taking antireflux medications again.

REFERRAL

- There is a strong and probably causal relation between symptomatic prolonged and untreated GERD, Barrett's esophagus, and esophageal adenocarcinoma. GI referral for upper endoscopy is needed when there are concerns about associated PUD, Barrett's esophagus, or esophageal cancer.
- Patients with Barrett's esophagus should undergo surveillance endoscopy with mucosal biopsy every 2 yr or less because the risk of developing adenocarcinoma of esophagus is at least 30 times greater than that of the general population.
- All children with dental erosions should be evaluated for GERD.

SUGGESTED READINGS

Heidelbaugh JL et al: Management of gastroesophageal reflux disease, *Am Fam Physician* 68:1311, 2003.

Kabrilas PJ: Radiofrequency energy treatment of GERD, *Gastroenterology* 125:970, 2003.

Shaheen N, Ransohoff DF: Gastroesophageal reflux, Barret esophagus, and esophageal cancer, *JAMA* 287:1972, 2002.

AUTHOR: **FRED F. FERRI, M.D.**

BASIC INFORMATION

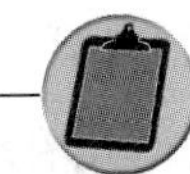

DEFINITION

Giant cell arteritis (GCA) is a segmental systemic granulomatous arteritis affecting medium- and large-sized arteries in individuals >50 years. Inflammation primarily targets extracranial blood vessels, and although the carotid system is usually affected, pathology in posterior cerebral artery has been reported.

SYNONYMS

Temporal arteritis
Cranial arteritis
Horton's disease

ICD-9CM CODES
446.5 Temporal arteritis

EPIDEMIOLOGY & DEMOGRAPHICS

PREVALENCE: 200 cases/100,000 persons; female-to-male predominance of two- to four-fold

INCIDENCE: 17 to 23.3 new cases/ 100,000 persons >50 yr

CLINICAL PRESENTATION & PHYSICAL FINDINGS

GCA can present with the following clinical manifestations:

- Headache, often associated with marked scalp tenderness
- Constitutional symptoms (fever, weight loss, anorexia, fatigue)
- Polymyalgia syndrome (aching and stiffness of the trunk and proximal muscle groups)
- Visual disturbances (transient or permanent monocular visual loss)
- Intermittent claudication of jaw and tongue on mastication

Important physical findings in GCA:

- Vascular examination: Tenderness, decreased pulsation, and nodulation of temporal arteries; diminished or absent pulses in upper extremities

ETIOLOGY

Vasculitis of unknown etiology

DIAGNOSIS

Clinical history and vascular examination are cornerstones of diagnosis. The presence of any three of the following five items allows the diagnosis of GCA with a sensitivity of 94% and a specificity of 91%:

- Age of onset >50 yr
- New-onset or new type of headache
- Temporal artery tenderness or decreased pulsation on physical examination
- Westergren ESR >50 mm/hr
- Temporal artery biopsy with vasculitis and mononuclear cell infiltrate or granulomatous changes

DIFFERENTIAL DIAGNOSIS

- Other vasculitic syndromes
- Nonarteritic Anterior Ischemic Optic Neuropathy (AION)
- Primary amyloidosis
- TIA, stroke
- Infections
- Occult neoplasm, multiple myeloma

WORKUP

LABORATORY TESTS

- ESR >50 mm/hr; however, up to 22.5% patients with GCA have normal ESR before treatment
- C-reactive protein is typically included in lab investigation; it has greater sensitivity than ESR
- Mild-to-moderate normochromic normocytic anemia, elevated platelet count
- IL-6 levels hold promise for a more sensitive modality, but at this stage remains experimental

IMAGING STUDIES

- Reliability of color duplex ultrasonography of temporal artery is controversial as it is thought that it does not improve diagnostic accuracy over careful physical examination
- Fluorescein angiogram of ophthalmic vessels may be warranted to differentiate between arteritic AION (i.e., GCA) and nonarteritic AION

TREATMENT

ACUTE GENERAL Rx

- Intravenous methylprednisolone (500-1000 mg qd for 3-5 days) is indicated in those with significant clinical manifestations (e.g., visual loss).
- Oral prednisone (1 mg/kg/day) may be used under less urgent circumstances or following the initial period of treatment with intravenous methylprednisolone. High-dose oral regimen should be continued at least until symptoms resolve and ESR returns to normal.
- Prednisone should be tapered gradually (~5 mg every other wk) initially and subsequently even more slowly (2.5 mg every 2-4 wk). Steroid treatment is usually required for at least 6 mo, and sometimes as much as 2 yr.
- Methotrexate or azathioprine may be added to the steroid regimen for their steroid-sparing effect, but efficacy is unproven.

DISPOSITION

If steroid therapy is initiated early, GCA has excellent prognosis; however, 20% of patients have permanent partial or complete loss of vision. Once there is visual loss, improvement is dismal: in one study, only 4% of eyes improved in both visual acuity and central visual field.

REFERRAL

- Surgical referral for biopsy of temporal artery
- Ophthalmology referral in patients with visual disturbances and following initiation of corticosteroid therapy
- Rheumatology referral for difficult cases

PEARLS & CONSIDERATIONS

COMMENTS

- The relationship between polymyalgia rheumatica and GCA is unclear, but the two may frequently coexist.
- Clinical picture rather than ESR should be the prime yardstick for continuing prednisone therapy.
- A rising ESR in a clinically asymptomatic patient with normal hematocrit should raise suspicion for alternate explanations (e.g., infections, neoplasms).
- Although pathologic findings on temporal artery biopsy are the gold standard for the diagnosis of GCA, the false-negative rate is around 9% (the false-negative rate may be lower in the hands of an experienced surgeon); in some cases, a second biopsy from the contralateral side may be required.
- GCA is associated with a markedly increased risk for the development of aortic aneurysm, which is often a late complication and may cause death. Annual chest radiograph in chronic CGA patients has been suggested, as well as emergent chest CT or MRI for clinical suspicion.

SUGGESTED READINGS

Please refer to references within these papers as well as associated 'Letters to the Editor' for further details.

Gold R et al: Therapy of neurological disorders in systemic vasculitis, *Sem Neurol* 23(2):207, 2003.

Hayreh SR et al: Visual improvement with corticosteroid therapy in giant cell arteritis. Report of large study and review of the literature, *Acta Opththalmol Scand* 80:355, 2002.

Hoffman GS et al: A multicenter, randomized, double-blind, placebo-controlled trial of adjuvant methotrexate for giant-cell arteritis, *Arthritis and Rheum* 46(5):1309, 2002.

Norborg E, Norborg C: Giant cell arteritis: epidemiological clues to its pathogenesis and an update on its treatment, *Rheumatol* 42:413, 2003.

Salvarani C et al: Polymyalgia rheumatica and giant-cell arteritis, *N Engl J Med* 347(4):261, 2002.

Smetana GW, Shmerling RH: Does this patient have temporal arteritis? *JAMA* 287:92, 2002.

AUTHOR: **U. SHIVRAJ SOHUR, M.D, PH.D.**

BASIC INFORMATION

DEFINITION

Giardiasis is an intestinal and/or biliary tract infection caused by the protozoal parasite *Giardia lamblia.*

ICD-9CM CODES
007.1 Giardiasis

EPIDEMIOLOGY & DEMOGRAPHICS

INCIDENCE (IN U.S.):
- Exact incidence unknown
- Frequently occurs in outbreaks

PREVALENCE (IN U.S.): 4%
PREDOMINANT SEX: Male = female
PREDOMINANT AGE:
- Preschool children, especially if in day care
- 20 to 40 yr old, especially among sexually active homosexual men

PEAK INCIDENCE:
- Varies with risk factors, outbreaks
- All age groups affected

GENETICS:
Familial Disposition: Patients with common variable immunodeficiency or X-linked agammaglobulinemia are at increased risk of infection.
Neonatal Infection: Rare; infection is common among preschool children in day care.

PHYSICAL FINDINGS & CLINICAL PRESENTATION

- More than 70% with one or more intestinal symptoms (diarrhea, flatulence, cramps, bloating, nausea)
- Fever in <20%
- Malaise, anorexia
- Chronic diarrhea, malabsorption, and weight loss
- GI bleeding is unusual
- Continuous or intermittent symptoms, lasting for weeks
- Of infected patients, 20% to 25% are asymptomatic

ETIOLOGY

Infection is acquired by ingestion of viable cysts of the organism, typically in contaminated water or by fecal-oral contact.

DIAGNOSIS

DIFFERENTIAL DIAGNOSIS

- Other agents of infective diarrhea (amebae, *Salmonella* sp., *Shigella* sp., *Staphylococcus aureus, Cryptosporidium,* etc.)
- Noninfectious causes of malabsorption

WORKUP

Stool specimen (three specimens yield 90% sensitivity) or duodenal aspirate for microscopic examination to establish diagnosis and exclude other pathogens (Fig. 1-105)

LABORATORY TESTS

- Serum albumin, vitamin B_{12} levels, and stool fat test to exclude malabsorption
- Serum antibody test if desired for epidemiologic purposes

IMAGING STUDIES

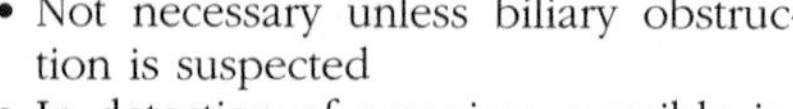

- Not necessary unless biliary obstruction is suspected
- In detection of organism, possible interference by barium in stool from radiographic studies

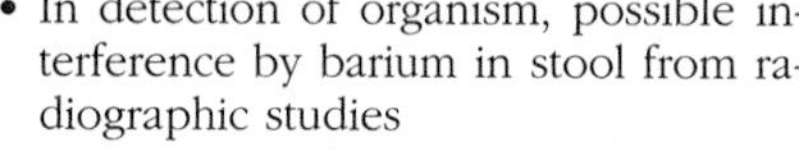

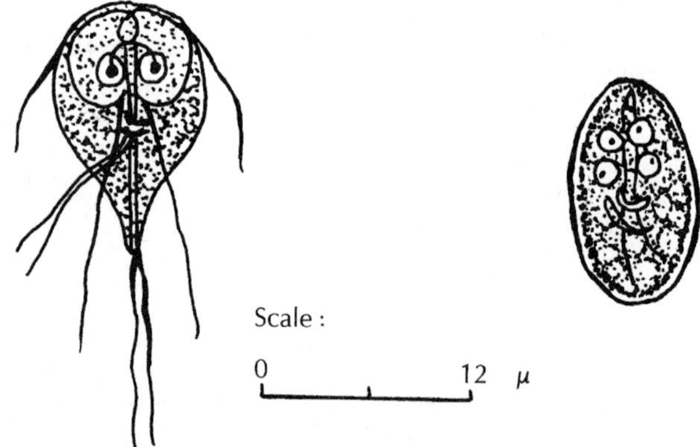

FIGURE 1-105 ***Giardia* organisms.** The trophozoite (*left*) is 12 to 15 μm long and has four pairs of flagella. This form is not commonly seen in stools. Cysts (*right*) are 9 to 19 μm long and may have two to four nuclei. (From Hoekelman R [ed]: *Primary pediatric care,* ed 3, St Louis, 1997, Mosby.)

TREATMENT

NONPHARMACOLOGIC THERAPY

Avoidance of milk products to reduce symptoms of transient lactase deficiency that occur in many patients

ACUTE GENERAL Rx

Adults:
- Metronidazole 250 mg PO three times daily for 7 days (metronidazole avoided in pregnancy) *or*
- Paromomycin 25 to 30 mg/kg/day in three doses for 5 to 10 days

CHRONIC Rx

May require retreatment

DISPOSITION

Reinfection is possible.

REFERRAL

For evaluation by gastroenterologist if malabsorption and weight loss do not resolve with therapy

PEARLS & CONSIDERATIONS

COMMENTS

Travelers to endemic areas (developing world, wilderness areas) should be cautioned to boil drinking water, or if this is impossible, use halogenated water purification tablets.

SUGGESTED READINGS

Grant J et al: Wheat germ supplement reduces cyst and trophozoite passage in people with giardiasis, *Am J Trop Med Hyg* 65(6):705, 2001.

Hoque ME et al: Nappy handling and risk of giardiasis, *Lancet* 357(9261):1017, 2001.

Lane S, Loyd D: Current trends in research into the waterborne parasite *Giardia, Crit Rev Microbiol* 28(2):123, 2002.

Minenoa T, Avery MA: Giardiasis: recent progress in chemotherapy and drug development, *Curr Pharm Des* 9(11):841, 2003.

Newman RD et al: A longitudinal study of *Giardia lamblia* infection in northeast Brazilian children, *Trop Med Int Health* 6(8):624, 2001.

AUTHOR: **JOSEPH R. MASCI, M.D.**

BASIC INFORMATION

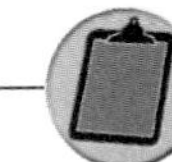

DEFINITION

Gilbert's disease is an autosomal dominant disease characterized by indirect hyperbilirubinemia caused by impaired glucuronyl transferase activity.

SYNONYMS

Gilbert's syndrome

ICD-9CM CODES
277.4 Gilbert's syndrome

EPIDEMIOLOGY & DEMOGRAPHICS

- Probable autosomal dominant disease affecting >5% of the U.S. population
- Male:female ratio of 3:1
- Most common hereditary hyperbirubinemia (genotypic prevalence 12%)

PHYSICAL FINDINGS & CLINICAL PRESENTATION

- No abnormalities on physical examination other than mild jaundice when bilirubin exceeds 3 mg/dl.
- A family history of unconjugated hyperbilirubinemia may be present.

ETIOLOGY

Decreased elimination of bilirubin in bile is caused by inadequate conjugation of bilirubin. Alcohol consumption and starvation diet can increase the bilirubin level. The pathogenesis of Gilbert's syndrome has been linked to a reduction in bilirubin UGT-1 gene (HUG-Brl) transcription resulting from a mutation in the promoter region.

DIAGNOSIS

DIFFERENTIAL DIAGNOSIS

- Hemolytic anemia
- Liver disease (chronic hepatitis, cirrhosis)
- Crigler-Najjar syndrome

WORKUP

- Most patients are diagnosed during or after adolescence, when isolated hyperbilirubinemia is detected as an incidental finding on routine biochemical testing
- Laboratory evaluation to exclude hemolysis and liver diseases as a cause of the elevated bilirubin level (Table 1-17)

LABORATORY TESTS

Elevated indirect (unconjugated) bilirubin (rarely exceeds 5 mg/dl)

TREATMENT

ACUTE GENERAL Rx

Treatment is generally unnecessary. Phenobarbital (if clinical jaundice is present) can rapidly decrease serum indirect bilirubin level.

DISPOSITION

Prognosis is excellent. Treatment is generally unnecessary.

REFERRAL

Referral is generally not necessary.

PEARLS & CONSIDERATIONS

COMMENTS

- Patients should be reassured about the benign nature of their condition.
- Fasting for 2 days or significant dehydration may raise the bilirubin level and result in the clinical recognition of jaundice.

AUTHOR: **FRED F. FERRI, M.D.**

TABLE 1-17 **Characteristic Patterns of Liver Function Tests**

Disorder	Bilirubin	Alkaline Phosphatase	AST	ALT	Prothrombin Time	Albumin
Gilbert's syndrome (abnormal bilirubin metabolism)	↑	NL	NL	NL	NL	NL
Bile duct obstruction (pancreatic cancer)	↑↑↑	↑↑↑	↑	↑	↑-↑↑	NL
Acute hepatocellular damage (toxic, viral hepatitis)	↑-↑↑↑	↑-↑↑	↑↑↑	↑↑↑	NL-↑↑↑	NL-↓↓
Cirrhosis	NL-↑	NL-↑	NL-↑	NL-↑	NL-↑↑	NL-↓↓

From Andreoli TE (ed): ***Cecil essentials of medicine,*** ed 4, Philadelphia, 1997, WB Saunders.
ALT, Alanine aminotransferase; ***AST,*** aspartate aminotransferase; ***NL,*** normal; ↑, increase; ↓, decrease (arrows indicate extent of change: ↑-↑↑↑, slight to large).

BASIC INFORMATION

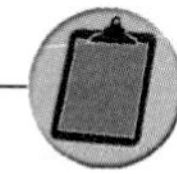

DEFINITION

Inflammation of the gums covering the maxilla and mandible

SYNONYMS

None

ICD-9CM CODE
523.1

EPIDEMIOLOGY & DEMOGRAPHICS

INCIDENCE IN US: N/A
PREVALENCE IN US: N/A
PREDOMINANT SEX: None
PREDOMINANT AGE: Adults
PEAK INCIDENCE: None
GENETICS: N/A
Familial Disposition: N/A
Congenital Infection: N/A
Neonatal Infection: N/A

PHYSICAL FINDINGS

Inflammation is usually painless. Bleeding may occur with minor trauma such as brushing teeth. A bluish discoloration of the gums and halitosis are sometimes present. Subgingival plaque may be seen on close examination, and in time, there is detachment of soft tissue from the tooth surface. Long-standing infection may lead to destructive periodontal disease, which may involve teeth and bones.

A dramatic form of gingivitis called *acute ulcerative necrotizing gingivitis* (ANUG or "trench mouth") can occur. This is manifested by acute, painful, inflammation of the gingivae, with bleeding, ulceration, and halitosis. At times this is accompanied by fever and lymphadenopathy.

Linear gingival erythema ("HIV Gingivitis") presents as a brightly inflamed band of marginal gingiva. It may be painful, with easy bleeding and rapid destruction.

Severe periodontitis can occur in patients with diabetes mellitus or HIV infection and in primary HIV infection (acute retroviral syndrome).

Pregnancy may be associated with an acute form of gingivitis. Gingivae become inflamed and hypertrophic; this is likely due to hormonal shifts.

ETIOLOGY

- A variety of organisms may be found in the environment of plaque. Anaerobes play a predominant role in periodontal disease.
- Improper hygiene and poorly fitting dentures may contribute to development of gingivitis.
- Excessive use of tobacco and alcohol may predispose individuals to gingival disease.
- In patients with HIV infection, gram-negative anaerobes, enteric organisms, and yeast predominate.
- Appropriate oral hygiene, such as flossing and tooth brushing, can prevent the accumulation of bacterial plaque.
- Once plaque is present, adequate hygiene becomes more difficult.

DIAGNOSIS

DIFFERENTIAL DIAGNOSIS

Gingival hyperplasia, which may be caused by phenytoin or nifedipine

WORKUP

Oral examination

LABORATORY TESTS

Elevated serum glucose in diabetics

IMAGING STUDIES

Radiographs of the teeth and facial bones may reveal extension of infection to these structures.

TREATMENT

NONPHARMACOLOGIC THERAPY

Removal of plaque, and at times, debridement of soft tissue

ACUTE GENERAL Rx

Penicillin VK, 500 mg po qid for 1 to 2 wk, *or*
Clindamycin, 300 mg po qid for 1 to 2 wk
For *linear gingival erythema,* clorhexidene rinses and nystatin rinses or troches may be used.

CHRONIC Rx

Extensive or recurrent infection may require periodic evaluation and debridement.

DISPOSITION

Continued inflammation can eventually lead to destruction of teeth and bone.

REFERRAL

Patients should be referred to a dentist or oral surgeon.

PEARLS & CONSIDERATIONS

COMMENTS

- Presence of periodontal disease is associated with an increased incidence of anaerobic pleuropulmonary infections.
- Existing data support the recommendation to change a toothbrush every 3 mo. Worn brushes seem to be less effective in plaque reduction.

SUGGESTED READINGS

Obernesser MS: Gingivitis and periodontitis syndromes, In *Up To Date,* Clinical reference CD, vol 8.1, 2000.

Sharma NC et al: Antiplaque and antigingivitis effectiveness of a hexetidine mouthwash, *J Clin Periodontol* 30(7):590, 2003.

Warren PR et al: A clinical investigation into the effect of toothbrush wear on efficacy, *J Clin Dent* 13:119, 2002.

AUTHOR: **MAURICE POLICAR, M.D**

BASIC INFORMATION

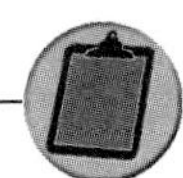

DEFINITION

Chronic open-angle glaucoma refers to optic nerve damage often associated with elevated intraocular pressure; it is a chronic, slowly progressive, usually bilateral disorder associated with visual loss, eye pain, and optic nerve damage. Now felt to be a primary disease of the optic nerve with high pressure a high risk factor for glaucoma.

SYNONYM

Chronic simple glaucoma

ICD-9CM CODES
365.1 Open-angle glaucoma

EPIDEMIOLOGY & DEMOGRAPHICS

INCIDENCE (IN U.S.): Third most common cause of visual loss (75% to 95% of all glaucomas are open angle.)

PREVALENCE (IN U.S.):
- Overall prevalence in U.S. population >40 yr of age is estimated to be 1.86%, with 1.57 million white and 398,000 black patients affected.
- 150,000 patients suffer bilateral blindness.
- Disease occurs in 2% of people >40 yr old.
- Prevalence is higher in diabetics, with high myopia, and among older persons.
- More common in blacks (3 × the age-adjusted prevalence than whites).

PREDOMINANT AGE:
- Persons >50 yr old
- Can occur in 30s and 40s

PEAK INCIDENCE:
- Increases after 40 yr
- Because of rapid aging of the U.S. population, expect 3 million cases by year 2020.

GENETICS:
- Four to six times higher incidence in blacks than whites
- No clear-cut hereditary patterns but a strong hereditary tendency

PHYSICAL FINDINGS

- High intraocular pressures and large optic nerve cup (OHTS study—very important)
- Cornea thickens faster in vision loss
- Abnormal visual fields
- Open-angle gonioscopy
- Red eye
- Restricted vision and field

ETIOLOGY

- Uncertain hereditary tendency
- Topical steroids
- Trauma
- Inflammatory
- High-dose oral corticosteroids taken for prolonged periods

DIAGNOSIS

DIFFERENTIAL DIAGNOSIS

- Other optic neuropathies
- Secondary glaucoma from inflammation and steroid therapy
- Red eye differential
- Trauma
- Contact lens injury

WORKUP

- Intraocular pressure
- Slit lamp examination
- Visual fields
- Gonioscopy
- Nerve fiber analysis—GDx, etc.
- Corneal thickness—very important in prognosis

LABORATORY TESTS

Blood sugar

IMAGING STUDIES

- Optic nerve photography—stereo photographs
- Visual field testing
- GDx (laser scan of nerve fiber layer)

TREATMENT

ACUTE GENERAL Rx

- β-Blockers (Timolol) qd to bid depending on individual response to drug
- Diamox 250 mg qid or pilocarpine
- Hyperosmotic agents (mannitol) in acute treatment
- Prostaglandins
- Laser trabeculoplasty (SLT) as needed
- Pilocarpine qid

CHRONIC Rx

- At least biannual checks of intraocular pressure and adjustment of medication
- Poor control = frequent examinations; good control = drugs
- Trabectalectomy
- Filter valves

DISPOSITION

Must be followed by ophthalmologist

REFERRAL

Immediately to ophthalmologist

PEARLS & CONSIDERATIONS

COMMENTS

- Glaucoma is a serious blinding disease. Must be followed professionally by an ophthalmologist.
- Early diagnosis and treatment may minimize visual loss.
- Glaucoma is not solely caused by increased intraocular pressure, because approximately 20% of patients with glaucoma have normal intraocular pressure, but high pressure is definitely a risk factor to be considered.

SUGGESTED READINGS

Gordon MO et al: Baseline factors that predict the onset of primary open-angle glaucoma, *Arch Ophthalmol* 120:714, 2002.

Heijl A et al: Reduction of intraocular pressure and glaucoma progression: Results from the early manifest glaucoma trial, *Arch Ophthalmol* 120:1268, 2002.

Higginbotham EJ et al: The Ocular Hypertension Treatment Study: topical medication delays or prevents primary open-angle glaucoma in African American individuals, *Arch Ophthalmol* 122(6):813, 2004.

Rezaie T et al: Adult-onset primary open-angle glaucoma caused by mutations in optineurin, Science 295:1077, 2002.

AUTHOR: **MELVYN KOBY, M.D.**

Glaucoma, Primary Closed-Angle

BASIC INFORMATION

DEFINITION

Primary closed-angle glaucoma occurs when elevated intraocular pressure is associated with closure of the filtration angle or obstruction in the circulating pathway of the aqueous humor.

SYNONYMS

Acute glaucoma
Pupillary block glaucoma
Narrow-angle glaucoma

ICD-9CM CODES
365.2 Primary angle-closure glaucoma

EPIDEMIOLOGY & DEMOGRAPHICS

INCIDENCE (IN U.S.):
- In 2% to 8% of all patients with glaucoma
- Higher incidence among those with hyperopia, small eyes, dense cataracts, shallow anterior chambers

PREDOMINANT SEX: Females > males
PREDOMINANT AGE: 50 to 60 yr
PEAK INCIDENCE: Greater after 50 yr of age; high association with hypopia, cataracts, and eye trauma
GENETICS: High family history

PHYSICAL FINDINGS & CLINICAL FINDINGS

- Hazy cornea (Fig. 1-106)
- Narrow angle
- Red eyes
- Pain
- Injection of conjunctiva
- Shallow anterior chamber
- Thick cataract
- Old trauma
- Chronic eye infections

ETIOLOGY

- Narrow angles with acute closure—blockage of circulatory path of the aqueous humor causing increase in interior ocular pressure

DIAGNOSIS

DIFFERENTIAL DIAGNOSIS

- High pressure
- Optic nerve cupping
- Field loss
- Shallow chamber
- Open-angle glaucoma
- Conjunctivitis
- Corneal disease-keratitis
- Uveitis
- Scleritis
- Allergies
- Contact lens wearing with irritation

WORKUP

- Intraocular pressure
- Gonioscopy
- Slit lamp examination
- Visual field examination
- GDx examination (laser scan of nerve fiber layer)
- Optic nerve evaluation
- Anterior chamber depth
- Cataract evaluation
- High hyperopia

LABORATORY TESTS

- Blood sugar and CBC (if diabetes or inflammatory disease is suspected)
- Visual field
- GDx nerve fiber analysis

A
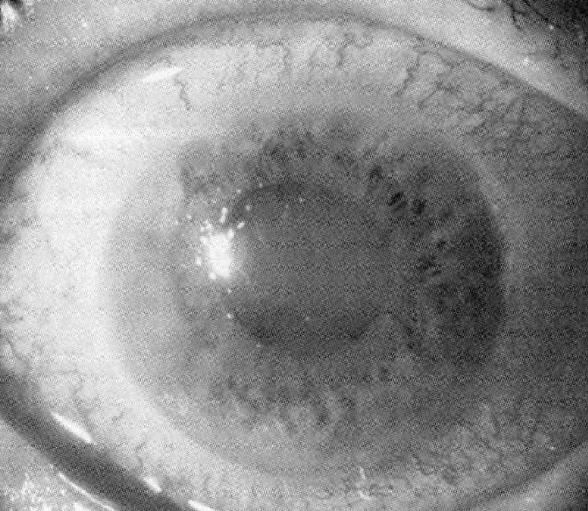

B
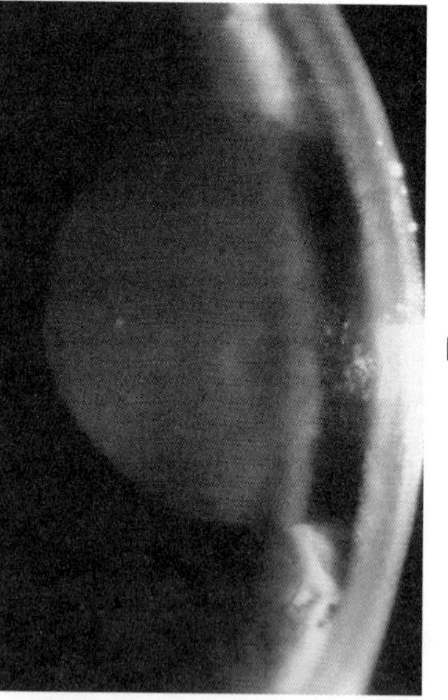

FIGURE 1-106 Acute angle-closure glaucoma. A, Acutely elevated pressure produces an inflamed eye with corneal edema (note fragmented light reflex) and a middilated pupil. **B,** Slit lamp examination shows a very shallow central anterior chamber (space between cornea and iris) and no peripheral chamber. (From Palay D [ed]: *Ophthalmology for the primary care physician,* St Louis, 1997, Mosby.)

IMAGING STUDIES

- Fundus photography
- Fluorescein angiography for neurovascular disease

TREATMENT

The goal of treatment is to acutely lower pressure on eye and keep it down.

NONPHARMACOLOGIC THERAPY

Laser iridotomy early in disease process

ACUTE GENERAL Rx

- IV mannitol
- Pilocarpine
- β-Blockers
- Diamox
- Laser iridotomy
- Anterior chamber paracentesis (as emergency treatment)

CHRONIC Rx

- Iridotomy
- Trabeculectomy
- Filter valves
- Other laser procedures

DISPOSITION

Refer to ophthalmologist immediately.

REFERRAL

This is an emergency—refer immediately to an ophthalmologist.

PEARLS & CONSIDERATIONS

COMMENTS

- Do not use antihistamines or vasodilators with narrow angle glaucoma.
- After iridotomy, the majority of patients will be totally cured and will need no further medication and have no visual loss.
- Lower socioeconomic status and higher levels of social deprivation are risk factors for delayed detection and probable worse outcomes in glaucoma.

SUGGESTED READINGS

Foster PJ et al: Defining "occludable" angles in population surveys: drainage angle width, peripheral anterior synechiae, and glaucomatous optic neuropathy in East Asian people, *Br J Opthalmol* 88(4):486, 2004.

Fraser S et al: Deprivation and late presentation of glaucoma: case control study, *BMJ* 322:638, 2001.

Gazzard G et al: Intraocular pressure and visual field loss in primary angle closure and primary open angle glaucomas, *Br J Ophthalmol* 87(6):720, 2003.

Kapur SB: The lens and angle-closure glaucoma, *J Cataract Refract Surg* 27(2):176, 2001.

Lam DS et al: Angle-closure glaucoma, *Opthalmology* 109:1, 2002.

AUTHOR: **MELVYN KOBY, M.D.**

Glenohumeral Dislocation (PTG)

BASIC INFORMATION

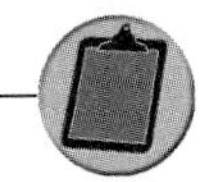

DEFINITION

Complete separation or displacement of the humeral head from the glenoid surface. (Partial separation is termed *subluxation.*) Most often the cause is traumatic, and the humeral head dislocates anterior and inferior. This may cause a tear of the glenoid labrum (the Bankart lesion). Less commonly, the head dislocates posteriorly.

Rarely, multidirectional instability may be present in which dislocation or subluxation, often bilateral, may occur in multiple directions, usually the result of excessive joint laxity and generally without trauma.

ICD-9CM CODES
831.01 Anterior
831.02 Posterior
831.03 Inferior
718.31 Recurrent
718.81 Instability

PHYSICAL FINDINGS & CLINICAL PRESENTATION

Traumatic
- The arm is held in external rotation with anterior dislocation, internal rotation with posterior dislocation.
- Little movement is possible without pain.
- The acromion may appear more prominent and there is absence of the normal "fullness" beneath the acromion.
- The status of the axillary nerve must always be checked (sensation to the middeltoid should be assessed).
- The apprehension test may become positive if anterior instability persists (pain and apprehension that the shoulder will dislocate when the relaxed arm is manually placed in the "throwing position" of external rotation and abduction).
- Recurrent episodes of anterior dislocation may occur with minor movement such as putting on a coat or turning a light off at night.

Multidirectional
- Often difficult to diagnose, especially if only subluxation occurs
- Recurrent episodes of giving out, weakness, often bilateral without trauma
- Sulcus sign often positive (the arms are pulled downward with the patient standing; a sulcus [indentation] will form between the acromion and humeral head, indicating excessive inferior movement of the head)
- Other signs of generalized joint laxity may be present, such as joint hyperextensibility and the ability of the patient to touch the thumb against the flexor aspect of the forearm

ETIOLOGY

- Trauma
- Generalized joint laxity (multidirectional)
- Seizures (posterior dislocations)

DIAGNOSIS

DIFFERENTIAL DIAGNOSIS

- Rotator cuff rupture
- Frozen shoulder (posterior dislocation)
- Suprascapular nerve paralysis
- Anterior instability

IMAGING STUDIES

- Acute shoulder injury: True AP roentgenogram plus lateral view of the glenohumeral joint, either transaxillary or transcapular
- MRI: To determine soft tissue status, especially the presence of Bankart lesion or rotator cuff tear; may be indicated following a second episode of dislocation
- Arthrogram: To determine if concurrent rotator cuff tear has occurred, especially in older patient

TREATMENT

- Reduction of the acute dislocation by gentle straight traction in the relaxed patient followed by light immobilization
- Gentle limited range of motion exercises as pain subsides followed by strengthening exercises at 2 wk

DISPOSITION

- Recurrence of anterior dislocation is common in the young; this patient may have to avoid the arm position associated with dislocation (external rotation with abduction)
- Primary dislocations in patients over 40 yr are not generally complicated by recurrence, but may result in shoulder stiffness and may have associated rotator cuff injuries
- There is an almost 100% recurrence after the third dislocation

REFERRAL

- Surgical reconstruction may be required in the recurrent dislocator

PEARLS & CONSIDERATIONS

COMMENTS

- It is important to know if there was an injury involved in the first episode and if a radiograph was taken to determine direction.
- Up to 50% of posterior dislocations are missed by the first examiner, usually the result of an inadequate lateral radiograph of the glenohumeral joint.
- "Voluntary" posterior dislocators should always be treated nonsurgically.
- Sports activities may be resumed when there is pain-free full flexibility and normal strength.
- Multidirectional instabilities are usually treated nonsurgically with strengthening exercises.

SUGGESTED READINGS

Cicak N: Posterior dislocation of the shoulder, *J Bone Joint Surg Br* 86(3):324, 2004.

McFarland EG et al: The effect of variation in definition on the diagnosis of multidirectional instability of the shoulder, *J Bone Joint Surg* 85A:2138, 2003.

Orlinski I et al: Comparative study of intra-articular lidocaine and intravenous meperidine/diazepam for shoulder dislocation, *J Emerg Med* 22:241, 2001.

Pagnini N, Dome DC: Surgical treatment of traumatic anterior shoulder instability in the American football players, *J Bone Joint Surg* 84(A):711, 2002.

Robinson CN, Kelly M, Wakefield AE: Redislocation of the shoulder during the first 6 weeks after a primary anterior dislocation: risk factor and results of treatment, *J Bone Joint Surg* 84:1552, 2002.

Robinson CM, Dobson RJ: Anterior instability of the shoulder after trauma, *J Bone Joint Surg Br* 86(4):469, 2004.

Sugaya H, Moriishi J, et al: Glenoid rim morphology in recurrent anterior glenohumeral instability, *J Bone Joint Surg* 85:878, 2003.

te Slaa RL et al: The prognosis following acute primary glenohumeral dislocation, *J Bone Joint Surg Br* (86)1:58, 2004.

AUTHOR: **LONNIE R. MERCIER, M.D.**

BASIC INFORMATION

DEFINITION

Acute glomerulonephritis is an immunologically mediated inflammation primarily involving the glomerulus that can result in damage to the basement membrane, mesangium, or capillary endothelium. Table 1-18 summarizes primary renal diseases that present as acute glomerulonephritis.

SYNONYMS

Postinfectious glomerulonephritis
Acute nephritic syndrome

ICD-9CM CODES
583.9 Glomerulonephritis, acute

EPIDEMIOLOGY & DEMOGRAPHICS

- Over 50% of cases involve children <13 yr old.
- Glomerulonephritis is the most common cause of chronic renal failure (25%).
- IgA nephropathy glomerulonephritis (Berger's disease) is the most common glomerulonephritis worldwide.

PHYSICAL FINDINGS & CLINICAL FINDINGS

- Edema (peripheral, periorbital, or pulmonary)
- Joint pains, oral ulcers, malar rash (frequently seen with lupus nephritis)
- Dark urine
- Hypertension
- Findings of palpable purpura in patients with Henoch-Schönlein purpura
- Heart murmurs may indicate endocarditis
- Impetigo, skin pallor, tenderness in the abdomen and/or back, pharyngeal erythema may be present

ETIOLOGY

Acute glomerulonephritis may be due to primary renal disease or a systemic disease. A number of pathogenic processes (e.g., antibody deposition, cell-mediated immune mechanisms, complement activation, hemodynamic alterations) have been implicated in the pathogenesis of glomerular inflammation. Medical disorders generally associated with glomerulonephritis are:

- Post group A β-hemolytic *Streptococcus* infection (other infectious etiologies including endocarditis and visceral abscess)
- Collagen-vascular diseases (SLE)
- Vasculitis (Wegener's granulomatosis, polyarteritis nodosa)
- Idiopathic glomerulonephritis (membranoproliferative, idiopathic, crescentic, IgA nephropathy)
- Goodpasture's syndrome
- Other cryoglobulinemia (Henoch-Schönlein purpura)
- Drug-induced (gold, penicillamine)
- Table 1-18 is a summary of primary renal diseases that present as acute glomerulonephritis

DIAGNOSIS

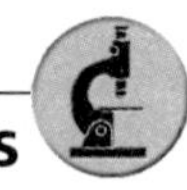

DIFFERENTIAL DIAGNOSIS

- Cirrhosis with edema and ascites
- CHF
- Acute interstitial nephritis
- Severe hypertension
- Hemolytic-uremic syndrome
- SLE, diabetes mellitus, amyloidosis, preeclampsia, sclerodermal renal crisis

WORKUP

Initial evaluation of suspected glomerulonephritis consists of laboratory testing.

LABORATORY TESTS

- Urinalysis (hematuria [dysmorphic erythrocytes and red cell casts], proteinuria)
- Serum creatinine (to estimate GFR), BUN
- 24-hr urine for protein excretion and creatinine clearance (to document degree of renal dysfunction and amount of proteinuria). Proteinuria in acute glomerulonephritis typically ranges from 500 mg/day to 3 g/day but nephrotic-range proteinuria (>3.5 g/day) may be present
- Streptococcal tests (Streptozyme), antistreptolysin O (ASO) quantitative titer (highest in 3 to 5 wk); ASO titer, however, is not related to severity of renal disease, duration, or prognosis
- Additional useful tests depending on the history: Anti-DNA antibodies (rule out SLE), CH_{50} level (if elevated, obtain C_3, C_4 levels), triglycerides, cryoglobulins, hepatitis B and C serologies, ANCA (antineutrophil cytoplasmic antibody), c-ANCA (in suspected cases of Wegener's granulomatosis), p-ANCA found in pauciimmune (lack of immune deposits) idiopathic rapidly progressive glomerulonephritis with or without systemic vasculitis, anti-glomerular basement membrane (type alpha[3] IV collagen) antibodies
- Hct (decrease in glomerulonephritis), platelet count (thrombocytopenia in cases of lupus nephritis)
- Anti-GBM antibody (in Goodpasture's syndrome)
- Blood cultures are indicated in all febrile patients

IMAGING STUDIES

- Chest x-ray: pulmonary congestion, Wegener's granulomatosis, and Goodpasture's syndrome
- Renal ultrasound if GFR is depressed to evaluate renal size and determine extent of fibrosis. A kidney size of <9 cm is suggestive of extensive scarring and low likelihood of reversibility
- Echocardiogram in patients with new cardiac murmurs or positive blood cultures to rule out endocarditis and pericardial effusion
- Renal biopsy and light, electron, and immunofluorescent microscopy to confirm diagnosis
- Kidney biopsy: generally reveals a granular pattern in poststreptococcal glomerulonephritis, linear pattern in Goodpasture's syndrome; absence of immune deposits suggests vasculitis; renal biopsy: although helpful to define the etiology of glomerulonephritis, is not usually essential. It is useful to determine the degree of inflammation and fibrosis. It is also especially important for patients with RPGN where prompt diagnosis and treatment is essential
- Immunofluorescence: generally reveals C_3; negative immunofluorescence suggests Wegener's granulomatosis, idiopathic crescentic glomerulonephritis, or polyarteritis nodosa
- Angiography or biopsy of other affected organs if systemic vasculitis is suspected

TREATMENT

NONPHARMACOLOGIC THERAPY

- Avoidance of salt if edema or hypertension is present
- Low-protein intake (approximately 0.5 g/kg/day) in patients with renal failure
- Fluid restriction in patients with significant edema
- Avoidance of high-potassium foods

ACUTE GENERAL Rx

- Correction of electrolyte abnormalities (hypocalcemia, hyperkalemia) and acidosis (if present)
- Treatment of streptococcal infection with penicillin (or erythromycin in penicillin-allergic patients)
- Furosemide in patients with significant hypertension and/or edema; hydralazine or nifedipine in patients with hypertension
- Immunosuppressive treatment in patients with heavy proteinuria or rapidly decreasing glomerular filtration rate (high-dose steroids, cyclosporin A, cyclophosphamide); corticosteroids generally not useful in poststreptococcal glomerulonephritis
- Fish oil (n-3 fatty acids) 12 g/day: may prevent or slow down loss of renal function in patients with IgA nephropathy

TABLE 1-18 **Summary of Primary Renal Diseases That Present as Acute Glomerulonephritis**

Diseases	Poststreptococcal glomerulonephritis (PSGN)	IgA nephropathy	Membranoproliferative glomerulonephritis	Idiopathic rapidly progressive glomerulonephritis (RPGN)
Clinical manifestations	All ages, mean 7 yr, 2:1 male	15-35 yr, 2:1 male	15-30 yr, 6:1 male	Mean 58 yr, 2:1 male
Age and sex	90%	50%	90%	90%
Acute nephritic syndrome	Occasionally	50%	Rare	Rare
Asymptomatic hematuria	10%-20%	Rare	Rare	10%-20%
Nephrotic syndrome	70%	30%-50%	Rare	25%
Hypertension	50% (transient)	Very rare	50%	60%
Acute renal failure	Latent period of 1-3 wk	Follows viral syndromes	Pulmonary hemorrhage; iron-deficiency anemia	None
Other				
Laboratory findings	↑ ASO titers (70%) Positive streptozyme (95%) ↓ C3-C9 Normal C1, C4	↑ Serum IgA (50%) IgA in dermal capillaries	Positive anti-GBM antibody	Positive ANCA
Immunogenetics	HLA-B12, D "EN" (9)*	HLA-Bw 35, DR4 (4)*	HLA-DR2 (16)*	None established
Renal pathology				
Light microscopy	Diffuse proliferation	Focal proliferation	Focal → diffuse proliferation with crescents	Crescentic GN
Immunofluorescence	Granular IgG, C3	Diffuse mesangial IgA	Linear IgG, C3	No immune deposits
Electron microscopy	Subepithelial humps	Mesangial deposits	No deposits	No deposits
Prognosis	95% resolve spontaneously 5% RPGN or slowly progressive	Slow progression in 25%-50%	75% stabilize or improve if treated early	75% stabilize or improve if treated early
Treatment	Supportive	None established	Plasma exchange, steroids, cyclophosphamide	Steroid pulse therapy

Modified from Goldman L, Ausiello D (eds): ***Cecil textbook of medicine***, ed 22, Philadelphia, 2004, WB Saunders.
ANCA, Antineutrophil cytoplasm antibody; ***GBM***, glomerular basement membrane; ***GN***, glomerulonephritis; ***Ig***, immunoglobulin.
*Relative risk.

- Plasma exchange therapy and immunosuppressive drugs (prednisone and cyclophosphamide): effective in Goodpasture's syndrome
- Short-term therapy with IV cyclophosphamide followed by maintenance therapy with mycophenolate mofetil or azathioprine is more efficacious and safer than long-term therapy with IV cyclophosphamide in patients with proliferative lupus nephritis

CHRONIC Rx

- Frequent monitoring of urinalysis, serum creatinine, and blood pressure in the initial 12 mo
- Monitoring for onset of hypertensive retinopathy, encephalopathy
- Aggressive treatment of infections, particularly streptococcal infections
- Dosage adjustment of all renally excreted medications

DISPOSITION

- Prognosis is generally related to histology with excellent prognosis in patients with minimal change glomerulonephritis and focal segmental proliferative glomerulonephritis; 25% to 30% of patients with mesangial IgA disease and membranous glomerulonephritis generally progress to chronic renal failure; >70% of patients with mesangial capillary glomerulonephritis will develop chronic renal failure.
- Generally prognosis is worse in patients with heavy proteinuria, severe hypertension, and significant elevations of creatinine.
- Recovery of renal function occurs within 8 to 12 wk in 95% of patients with poststreptococcal glomerulonephritis.

REFERRAL

- Nephrology consultation. The urgency for referral depends on the GFR. Urgent consultation is recommended if GFR is significantly abnormal, rapidly deteriorating, or if there are systemic symptoms
- Surgical referral for biopsy in selected cases

PEARLS & CONSIDERATIONS

COMMENTS

- Anticoagulation to prevent DVT should be considered in patients with a low level of physical activity.
- Monitoring of lipids and aggressive treatment of hyperlipidemias is recommended.
- Close monitoring of side effects of immunosuppressive drugs and complications of corticosteroids is necessary.

SUGGESTED READINGS

Contreras G et al: Sequential therapies for proliferative lupus nephritis, *N Engl J Med* 350:971, 2004.

Hricik D et al: Glomerulonephritis, *N Engl J Med* 339:888, 1998.

Madaio MP, Harrington JT: The diagnosis of glomerular diseases, *Arch Intern Med* 161:25, 2001.

AUTHOR: **FRED F. FERRI, M.D.**

BASIC INFORMATION

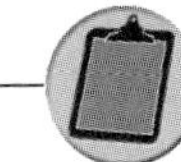

DEFINITION

Glossitis is an inflammation of the tongue that can lead to loss of filiform papillae.

ICD-9CM CODES
529.0 Glossitis

EPIDEMIOLOGY & DEMOGRAPHICS

Glossitis is seen more frequently in patients of lower socioeconomic status, malnourished patients, alcoholics, smokers, elderly patients, immunocompromised patients, and patients with dentures.

PHYSICAL FINDINGS & CLINICAL PRESENTATION

- The appearance of the tongue is variable depending on the etiology of the glossitis. Loss of filiform papillae results in red, smooth-surfaced tongue (Fig. 1-107).
- The tongue may appear pale in patients with significant anemia.
- Pain and swelling of the tongue may be present when glossitis is associated with infections, trauma, or lichen planus.
- Ulcerations may be present in patients with herpetic glossitis, pemphigus, or streptococcal infection.
- Excessive use of mouthwash may result in a "hairy" appearance of the tongue.

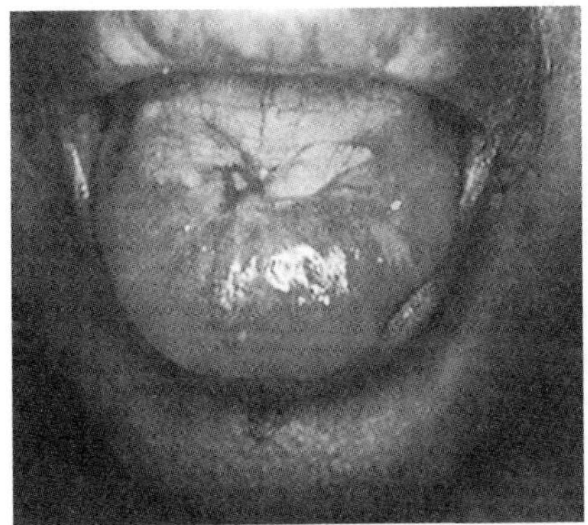

FIGURE 1-107 Glossitis. (From Seidel HM [ed]: *Mosby's guide to physical examination,* ed 4, St Louis, 1999, Mosby.)

ETIOLOGY

- Nutritional deficiencies (vitamin E, riboflavin, niacin, vitamin B_{12}, iron deficiency)
- Infections (viral, candidiasis, TB, syphilis)
- Trauma (generally caused by poorly fitting dentures)
- Irritation of the tongue secondary to toothpaste, medications, alcohol, tobacco, citrus
- Lichen planus, pemphigus vulgaris, erythema multiforme
- Neoplasms

DIAGNOSIS

DIFFERENTIAL DIAGNOSIS

- Infections
- Use of chemical irritants
- Neoplasms
- Skin disorders (e.g., Behçet's syndrome, erythema multiforme)

WORKUP

- Laboratory evaluation to exclude infectious processes, vitamin deficiencies, and systemic disorders
- Biopsy of lesion only when there is no response to treatment

LABORATORY TESTS

- CBC: Decreased Hgb and Hct, low MCV (iron deficiency anemia), elevated MCV (vitamin B_{12} deficiency)
- Vitamin B_{12} level
- 10% KOH scrapings in patients with white patches suspect for candidiasis

TREATMENT

NONPHARMACOLOGIC THERAPY

Avoidance of primary irritants such as hot foods, spices, tobacco, and alcohol

ACUTE GENERAL Rx

Treatment varies with the etiology of the glossitis.

- Malnutrition with avitaminosis: multivitamins
- Candidiasis: fluconazole 200 mg on day 1, then 100 mg/day for at least 2 wk or nystatin 400,000 U suspension qid for 10 days or 200,000 pastilles dissolved slowly in the mouth four to five times qd for 10 to 14 days
- Painful oral lesions: rinsing of the mouth with 2% lidocaine viscous, 1 to 2 tablespoons q4h prn; triamcinolone 0.1% applied to painful ulcers prn for symptomatic relief

CHRONIC Rx

- Lifestyle changes with elimination of tobacco, alcohol, and other primary irritants
- Dental evaluation for correction of ill-fitting dentures
- Correction of associated metabolic abnormalities such as hyperglycemia from diabetes mellitus

DISPOSITION

Most patients experience prompt improvement with identification and treatment of the cause of the glossitis.

REFERRAL

Surgical referral for biopsy of solitary lesions unresponsive to treatment to rule out neoplasm

PEARLS & CONSIDERATIONS

COMMENTS

If the primary cause of glossitis is not identified or cannot be corrected, enteric nutritional replacement therapy should be considered in malnourished patients.

AUTHOR: **FRED F. FERRI, M.D.**

BASIC INFORMATION

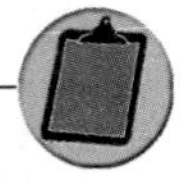

DEFINITION

Gonorrhea is a sexually transmitted bacterial infection with a predilection for columnar and transitional epithelial cells. It commonly manifests as urethritis, cervicitis, or salpingitis. Infection may be asymptomatic. It differs in males and females in course, severity, and ease of recognition.

SYNONYMS

Gonococcal urethritis
Gonococcal vulvovaginitis
Gonococcal cervicitis
Gonococcal bartholinitis
Clap
GC

ICD-9CM CODES
098 Gonococcal infections

EPIDEMIOLOGY & DEMOGRAPHICS

- The disease is common worldwide, affects both sexes, all ages, especially younger adults; highest incidence is in inner-city areas, with an estimated 3 million new cases annually.
- Asymptomatic anterior urethral carriage may occur in 12% to 50% of cases in men.
- Asymptomatic in 50% to 80% of cases in women. Most common dissemination by mucosal passage to fallopian tubes, resulting in PID in 10% to 15% of infected women. Hematogenous spread may result in septic arthritis and skin lesions. Conjunctivitis rarely occurs but may result in blindness if not rapidly treated. Infection can occur in both men and women in oropharynx and anorectally.
- 600,000 new infections/yr.

PHYSICAL FINDINGS & CLINICAL PRESENTATION

- Males: purulent discharge from anterior urethra with dysuria appearing 2 to 7 days after infecting exposure. May have rectal infection causing pruritus, tenesmus, and discharge or may be asymptomatic.
- Females: initial urethritis, cervicitis may occur a few days after exposure, frequently mild. In about 20% of cases, uterine invasion occurs after menstrual period with signs and symptoms of endometritis, salpingitis, or pelvic peritonitis. The patient may have purulent discharge, inflamed Skene's or Bartholin's glands.
- Classic presentation of acute gonococcal PID is fever, abdominal and adnexal tenderness, often absence of purulent discharge. Physical examination may be normal if asymptomatic.

ETIOLOGY

Neisseria gonorrhoeae is the gonococcus. Plasmids coding for β-lactamase render some strains resistant to penicillin or tetracycline (PPNG, TRNG). There is an increasing frequency of chromosomally mediated resistance to penicillin, tetracycline, and cefoxitin. In the Far East, high-level resistance to spectinomycin is endemic.

There is a rising number of cases of quinolone-resistant *N. gonorrhoeae* (QRNG) worldwide, with the expected number to rise in the U.S. from importation. As long as the total number of QNRG strains remains less than 1% of strains isolated, fluoroquinolones may still be used with confidence.

DIAGNOSIS

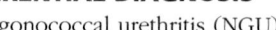

DIFFERENTIAL DIAGNOSIS

- Nongonococcal urethritis (NGU)
- Nongonococcal mucopurulent cervicitis
- *Chlamydia trachomatis*

WORKUP

- Diagnosis is dependent on bacteriologic investigation.
- Gram-negative intracellular diplococci are diagnostic in male urethral smears. There is a false-negative rate of 60% to 70% in female cervical or urethral smears. Culture is essential in women.

LABORATORY TESTS

- Gonorrhea culture on Thayer-Martin medium (Organism is fastidious, requires aerobic conditions with increased carbon dioxide atmosphere. Incubate ASAP.)
- Serologic testing for syphilis on all patients
- *Chlamydia* testing on all patients
- Offer of HIV counseling and testing

TREATMENT

ACUTE GENERAL Rx

Uncomplicated infections of the cervix, urethra, and rectum:
- Cefixime 400 mg PO × 1 dose *or*
- Ceftriaxone 125 mg IM × 1 dose *or*
- Ciprofloxacin 500 mg PO × 1 dose *or*
- Ofloxacin 400 mg PO × 1 dose *plus* azithromycin 1 g PO × 1 dose *or*
- Doxycycline 100 mg PO bid × 7 days
- Dual treatment with azithromax and doxycycline may prevent the development of antimicrobial resistant *N. gonorrhoeae*.

Alternatives: Spectinomycin 2 g IM × 1 dose
Quinolones:
- Gatifloxacin 400 mg PO × 1 dose
- Norfloxacin 800 mg PO × 1 dose
- Lomefloxacin 400 mg PO × 1 dose
- Not recommended for person <18 yr

Uncomplicated pharyngeal infection:
- Ceftriaxone 125 mg IM × 1 dose *or*
- Ciprofloxacin 500 mg PO × 1 dose *or*
- Ofloxacin 400 mg PO × 1 dose *plus* azithromycin 1 g PO × 1 dose *or*
- Doxycycline 100 mg PO bid × 7 days

Pregnancy: patients should not be treated with quinolones or tetracyclines. They should be treated with one of the previous recommended or alternative cephalosporins.

DISPOSITION

- Pregnant patients require test of cure (as do those treated with regimens other than ceftriaxone/doxycycline); reculture 4 to 7 days after treatment.
- Treatment failure in nonpregnant patients is rare, and test of cure is not required. Rescreening in 1 to 2 mo detects treatment failures and reinfections.
- Sexual partners should all be identified, examined, cultured, and receive presumptive treatment.

REFERRAL

PID reuiring hospitalization, disseminated gonococcal infection

PEARLS & CONSIDERATIONS

COMMENTS

- This is a reportable disease.

SUGGESTED READING

Centers for Disease Control and Prevention: 2002 sexually transmitted diseases treatment guidelines, *MMWR Morb Mortal Wkly Rep* 51(RR-6), 2002.

AUTHOR: **MARIA A. CORIGLIANO, M.D.**

SECTION I

BASIC INFORMATION

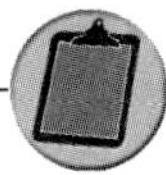

DEFINITION

Goodpasture's syndrome is characterized by idiopathic recurrence of alveolar hemorrhage and rapidly progressive glomerulonephritis. It can also be defined by the triad of glomerulonephritis, pulmonary hemorrhage, and antibody to basement membrane antigens.

ICD-9CM CODES
446.2 Goodpasture's syndrome

EPIDEMIOLOGY & DEMOGRAPHICS

- Goodpasture's syndrome affects predominantly young white male smokers.
- Male:female ratio is 6:1.
- Goodpasture's syndrome accounts for 5% of all cases of rapidly progressive glomerulonephritis.
- 80% of patients are HLA-BR2 positive.

PHYSICAL FINDINGS & CLINICAL PRESENTATION

- Dyspnea, cough, hemoptysis
- Skin pallor, fever, arthralgias (may be mild or absent at the time of initial presentation)

ETIOLOGY

Presence of glomerular basement membranes (GBM) antibody deposition in kidneys and lungs with subsequent pulmonary hemorrhage and glomerulonephritis.

DIAGNOSIS

DIFFERENTIAL DIAGNOSIS

- Wegener's granulomatosis
- SLE
- Systemic necrotizing vasculitis
- Idiopathic rapidly progressive glomerulonephritis
- Drug-induced renal pulmonary disease (e.g., penicillamine)

WORKUP

Laboratory evaluation, diagnostic imaging, immunofluorescence studies of renal biopsy

LABORATORY TESTS

- Presence of circulating serum anti-GBM antibodies
- Absence of circulating immunocomplexes, antineutrophils, cytoplasmic antibodies, and cryoglobulins
- Urinalysis revealing microscopic hematuria and proteinuria
- Elevated BUN and creatinine from rapidly progressive glomerulonephritis
- Immunofluorescence studies of renal biopsy material: linear deposits of anti-GBM antibody, often accompanied by C3 deposition
- Anemia from iron deficiency (secondary to blood loss and iron sequestration in the lungs)

IMAGING STUDIES

Chest x-ray: fluffy alveolar infiltrates, evidence of pulmonary hemorrhage (Fig. 1-108)

TREATMENT

ACUTE GENERAL Rx

- Plasma exchange therapy
- Immunosuppressive therapy with prednisone (1 mg/kg/day) and cyclophosphamide (2 mg/kg/day)
- Dialysis support in patients with renal failure

DISPOSITION

Life-threatening pulmonary hemorrhage and irreversible glomerular damage are the major causes of death.

REFERRAL

- Surgical referral for renal biopsy to guide the management
- Referral of patients with renal failure to dialysis center
- Consideration for renal transplantation in patients with end-stage renal failure

AUTHOR: **FRED F. FERRI, M.D.**

A

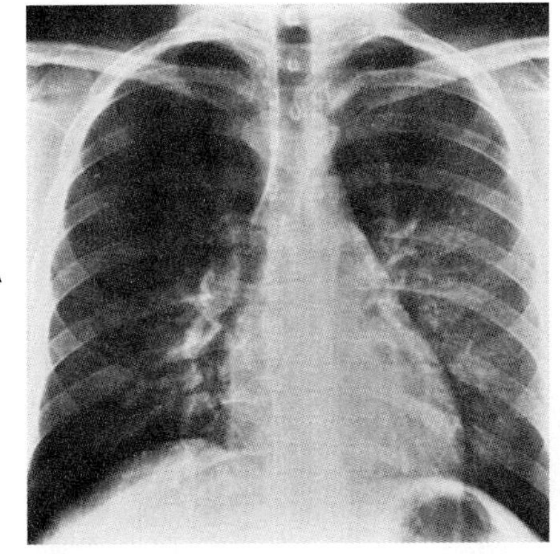

B

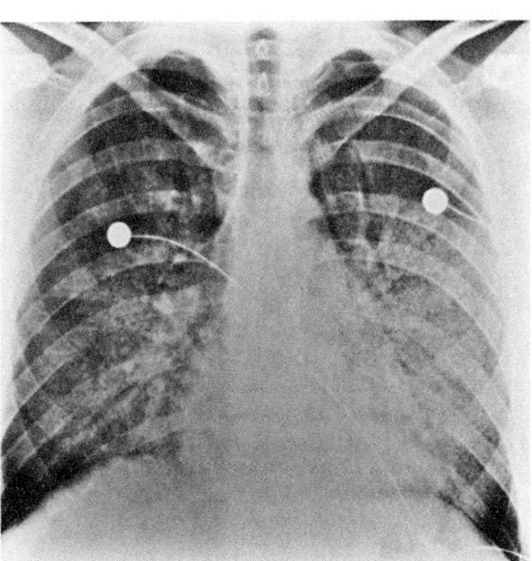

FIGURE 1-108 Goodpasture's syndrome. PA chest radiographs several days apart demonstrate consolidation in the left lung, **A,** which progressed to diffuse alveolar disease (consolidation), **B.** (From McLoud TC [ed]: *Thoracic radiology: the requisites,* St Louis, 1998, Mosby.)

BASIC INFORMATION

DEFINITION

Gout is a clinical disorder in which crystals of monosodium urate become deposited in tissue as a result of hyperuricemia. Gout and hyperuricemia can be classified as either primary or secondary if resulting from another disorder.

ICD-9CM CODES
274.9 Gout

EPIDEMIOLOGY & DEMOGRAPHICS

PREVALENCE: 3 cases/1000 persons
PREDOMINANT SEX: 95% males, rare in females before menopause
PREDOMINANT AGE: 30 to 50 yr

PHYSICAL FINDINGS & CLINICAL PRESENTATION

- Usually, initial attack in a single joint or an area of tenosynovium
- Mainly a disease of the lower extremities
- First site of involvement: classically, MP joint of the great toe
- Another common site of acute attack: extensor tenosynovium on the dorsum of the midfoot
- Severe pain and inflammation, which may be precipitated by exercise, dietary indiscretions, and physical or emotional stress
- Attacks following illness or surgery
- Presence of swelling, heat, redness, and other signs of inflammation (the physical findings simulating cellulitis)
- Exquisite soft tissue tenderness
- Fever, tachycardia, and other constitutional symptoms
- Eventually, deposits of urate crystals (tophi) in the subcutaneous tissue

ETIOLOGY

- Hyperuricemia and gout develop from excessive uric acid production, a decrease in the renal excretion of uric acid, or both.
- Primary gout results from an inborn error of metabolism and may be attributed to several biochemical defects.
- Secondary hyperuricemia may develop as a complication of acquired disorders (e.g., leukemia) or as a result of the use of certain drugs (e.g., diuretics).

DIAGNOSIS

DIFFERENTIAL DIAGNOSIS

- Pseudogout
- Rheumatoid arthritis
- Osteoarthritis
- Cellulitis
- Infectious arthritis

Section II describes the differential diagnosis of acute monoarticular and oligoarticular arthritis.

WORKUP

Hyperuricemia accompanying a typical history of monoarticular acute arthritis is usually sufficient to establish the diagnosis.

LABORATORY TESTS

- Mild leukocytosis
- Elevated ESR
- Hyperuricemia
- Synovial aspirate: usually cloudy and markedly inflammatory in nature; urate crystals in fluid: needle-shaped and birefringent under polarized light

IMAGING STUDIES

- Plain radiography to rule out other disorders
- No typical findings in early gouty arthritis but late disease possibly associated with characteristic punched-out lesions and joint destruction

TREATMENT

NONPHARMACOLOGIC THERAPY

- Modification of diet (avoidance of foods high in purines [e.g., anchovies, organ meat, liver, spinach, mushrooms, asparagus, oatmeal, cocoa, sweetbreads]) and lifestyle
- Treatment for obesity
- Moderation in alcohol intake, no more than two drinks per day
- Hypertension and its management requiring careful assessment and possibly nondiuretic drugs

ACUTE GENERAL Rx

- Quick-acting NSAIDs such as ibuprofen
- Colchicine (given PO or IV)
- Corticosteroids or ACTH for those who are intolerant of NSAIDs or colchicine
- Intraarticular cortisone when oral medication cannot be given
- General measures, such as rest, elevation, and analgesics as needed until acute pain subsides.
- Table 1-19 describes treatment options for gout

CHRONIC Rx

- Prevention is achieved through normalization of serum urate concentration.
- Uricosuric agents (e.g., probenecid) or xanthine oxidase inhibitors (allopurinol) are used in patients with recurrent attacks despite adequate dietary restrictions.
- A 24-hr urine collection is useful in deciding which antihyperuricemic agent is indicated. Allopurinol is generally used if the uric acid output is >900 mg/day on a regular diet. However, hyperuricemic therapy should not be started for at least 2 wk after the acute attack has resolved because it may prolong the acute attack and it can also precipitate new attacks by rapidly lowering the serum uric acid level.
- Urinary uric acid hypoexcretors (<700 mg/day) can be given probenecid (250 mg bid for 1 wk, then increased to 500 mg bid) to block absorption of uric acid. Probenecid should be started only after the acute attack of gout has completely subsided.
- Colchicine 0.6 mg bid is indicated for acute gout prophylaxis before starting hyperuricemic therapy. It is generally discontinued 6 to 8 wk after normalization of serum urate levels. Long-term colchicine therapy (0.6 mg qd or bid) may be necessary in patients with frequent gout attacks despite the use of uricosuric agents.
- Surgery usually limited to excision of large tophi and, occasionally, arthroplasty.

DISPOSITION

- Musculoskeletal complications are usually limited to joint disease.
- Surgical intervention may occasionally be indicated.
- Renal disease is the most frequent complication of gout after arthritis; most gouty patients develop renal disease as a result of parenchymal urate deposition but the involvement is only slowly progressive and often has no effect on life expectancy.
- Incidence of urolithiasis is increased, with 80% of calculi being uric acid stones.

REFERRAL

For orthopedic consultation when joint destruction has occurred

PEARLS & CONSIDERATIONS

COMMENTS

- No significant correlation between coronary artery disease and gout
- No indication to treat asymptomatic hyperuricemia
- Acute attacks of gout occasionally associated with normal levels of uric acid
- The main indication for prophylaxis is recurrent attacks of gouty joint inflammation, 3 or more per year

SUGGESTED READINGS

Agudelo CA, Wise CM: Gout: diagnosis, pathogenesis, and clinical manifestations, *Curr Opin Rheumatol* 13:234, 2001.

Riedel AA et al: Compliance with allopurinol therapy among managed care enrollees with gout: a retrospective analysis of administrative claims, *J Rheumatol* 31(8):1575, 2004.

Schlesinger N, Schumacher HR: Gout: can management be improved? *Curr Opin Rheumatol* 13:240, 2001.

Terkeltaub RA: Gout, *N Engl Med* 349:1647, 2003.

Velilla-Moliner J et al: Podagra, is it always gout? *Am J Emerg Med* 22(4):320, 2004.

Wallace KL et al: Increasing prevalence of gout and hyperuricemia over 10 years among older adults in a managed care population, *J Rheumatol* 31(8):1582, 2004.

AUTHOR: **LONNIE R. MERCIER, M.D.**

TABLE 1-19 Treatment of Gout

Acute gout	Interval gout	Long-term treatment
Therapeutic goal: Terminate acute inflammatory attack.	**Therapeutic goal:** Prevent recurrent attacks.	**Therapeutic goals:** Prevent attacks, resolve tophi, maintain serum urate at ≤6 mg/dl.
NSAIDs *(preferred):* Indomethacin, 50 mg qid, or ibuprofen, 800 mg tid (or other NSAIDs in full doses) ***(lower dose in renal insufficiency; contraindicated with peptic ulcer disease).***	**Colchicine, oral:** 0.6-1.2 mg daily as prophylaxis against recurrent attacks.	**Colchicine, oral:** 0.6-1.2 mg daily for 1-2 wk before initiating hypouricemic therapy and for several months afterward to prevent recurrent attacks during initial period of hypouricemic therapy.
OR		
Colchicine, oral *(used infrequently):* 0.6-1.2 mg (1-2 tablets), then 0.6 mg (1 tablet) q1-2h until attack subsides or until nausea, diarrhea, or GI cramping develops. Maximum total dose, 4-6 mg. If ineffective in 48 hr, do not repeat.	**Hypouricemic agent:** Start only if indicated by frequent attacks, severe hyperuricemia, presence of tophi, urolithiasis, or urate overexcretion.	**Allopurinol:** Dose variable; usually 300 mg once daily, but up to 900 mg may be needed in occasional patient; dose should be reduced to 100 mg daily or every other day in patients with renal insufficiency.
		OR
Colchicine, IV *(only if oral medication is precluded):* 1-2 mg in 20 ml 0.9% saline infused slowly ***(extravasation causes tissue necrosis);*** dose may be repeated once in 6 hr. Few GI symptoms with IV use. Maximum total dose, 4 mg per attack. Monitor blood counts	**Other:** Diet—moderate protein, low fat; avoid excessive alcohol. Treat hypertension if present. High fluid intake to promote uric acid excretion in a dilute urine (for uric acid overexcretors).	**Uricosuric agent** ***(reduced efficacy if creatinine clearance <80 ml; ineffective if <30 mL):*** Probenecid, 0.5-1 g bid, or sulfinpyrazone, 100 mg tid or qid; usually well tolerated, but may cause headache, GI upset, rash.
Steroids ***(if NSAIDs or colchicines are contraindicated or if oral medication is precluded, e.g., postoperatively):*** Triamcinolone acetonide, 60 mg IM, ***or*** ACTH, 40 U IM ***or*** 25 U by slow IV infusion, ***or*** prednisone, 20-40 mg daily. Intra-articular steroids may be used to treat a single inflamed joint: triamcinolone hexacetonide, 5-20 mg, or dexamethasone phosphate, 1-6 mg.		**Other:** Diet—moderate protein, low fat; avoid excessive alcohol. Treat hypertension if present. For uric acid overexcretors or when initiating uricosuric agent: high fluid intake, particularly at night, to promote uric acid excretion in a dilute urine. Acetazolamide, 250 mg at bedtime, may be used to keep urine pH >6.
Hypouricemic agents: Of no benefit for inflammatory attack and may initiate recurrent attack. Should not be started until attack has resolved, but ***ongoing use should not be interrupted during an attack.***		

From Goldman L, Ausiello D (eds): ***Cecil textbook of medicine,*** ed 22, Philadelphia, 2004, WB Saunders.

ACTH, Adrenocorticotropic hormone; ***bid,*** twice daily; ***GI,*** gastrointestinal; ***IM,*** intramuscularly; ***IV,*** intravenously; ***NSAIDs,*** nonsteroidal antiinflammatory drugs; ***q1-2h,*** every 1 to 2 hours; ***qid,*** four times daily; ***tid,*** three times daily.

BASIC INFORMATION

DEFINITION

A chronic, inflammatory disorder of the dermis.

ICD-9CM CODES
695.89 Granuloma annulare

EPIDEMIOLOGY & DEMOGRAPHICS

- Most common in children and young adults
- Female predominance (2:1)
- Disseminated form associated with diabetes mellitus
- Recurrent in 40% of affected individuals

PHYSICAL FINDINGS & CLINICAL PRESENTATION

- Start as small ring of colored skin or pale erythematous papules
- Coalesce and evolve into annular plaques over several weeks
- Plaques undergo central involution and increase in diameter over several months (0.5 to 5 cm) (Fig. 1-109)
- Most frequently found on the lateral and dorsal surfaces of the hands and feet
- Most lesions resolve spontaneously after several months

ETIOLOGY

Unknown, but may be related to vasculitis, trauma, monocyte activation, or delayed hypersensitivity.

DIAGNOSIS

DIFFERENTIAL DIAGNOSIS

- Tinea corporis
- Lichen planus
- Necrobiosis lipoidica diabeticorum
- Sarcoidosis
- Rheumatoid nodules
- Late secondary or tertiary syphilis

WORKUP

- Diagnosis is based on clinical appearance and presentation.
- Biopsy when diagnosis is unclear

LABORATORY TESTS

Biopsy shows collagen degeneration.

TREATMENT

NONPHARMACOLOGIC THERAPY

Reassurance

CHRONIC Rx

Intralesional steroid injection into elevated border with triamcinolone 2.5 to 10 mg/ml

DISPOSITION

Most lesions will resolve spontaneously within 2 yr.

REFERRAL

Dermatology referral recommended for symptomatic, disseminated disease

SUGGESTED READING

Hsu S et al: Differential diagnosis of annular lesions, *Am Fam Physician* 64:284, 2001.

AUTHOR: **JENNIFER R. SOUTHER, M.D.**

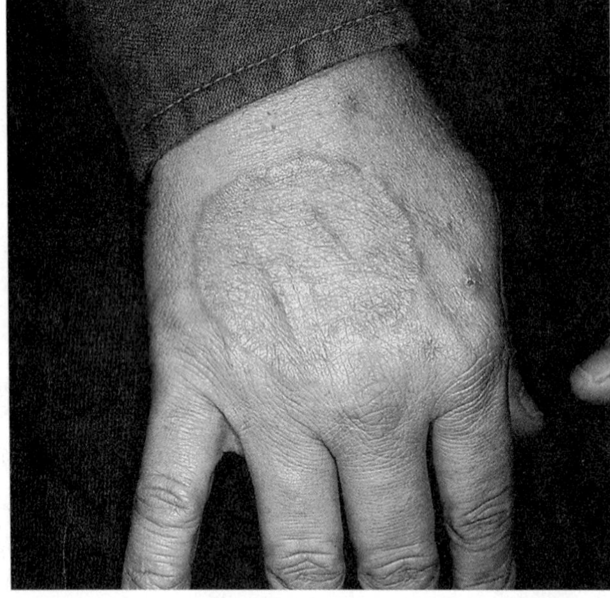

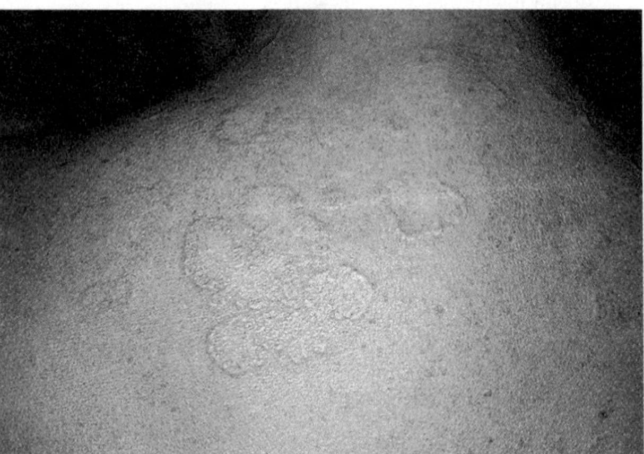

FIGURE 1-109 Granuloma annulare. (From Callen JP [ed]: *Color atlas of dermatology,* ed 2, Philadelphia, 2000, WB Saunders.)

BASIC INFORMATION

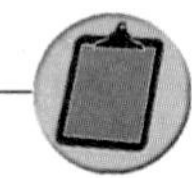

DEFINITION

Granuloma inguinale is caused by a gram-negative bacterium, *Calymmatobacterium granulomatis,* that may be sexually transmitted, possibly by anal intercourse. It can also be spread through close, chronic nonsexual contact.

SYNONYMS

Donovanosis

ICD-9CM CODES
099.2 Granuloma inguinale

EPIDEMIOLOGY & DEMOGRAPHICS

- Rare in the U.S. (<100 cases reported annually) and other developed countries
- Endemic in Australia, India, Caribbean, and Africa
- Can affect both males and females
- Incubation period is variable: 1 to 2 wk

PHYSICAL FINDINGS & CLINICAL PRESENTATION

- Indurated nodule is the primary lesion and is usually painless.
- Lesion erodes to granulomatous heaped ulcer (Fig. 1-110); progresses slowly.
- Pathogenic features are as follows:
  1. Large infected mononuclear cell containing many Donovan bodies
  2. Intracytoplasmic location

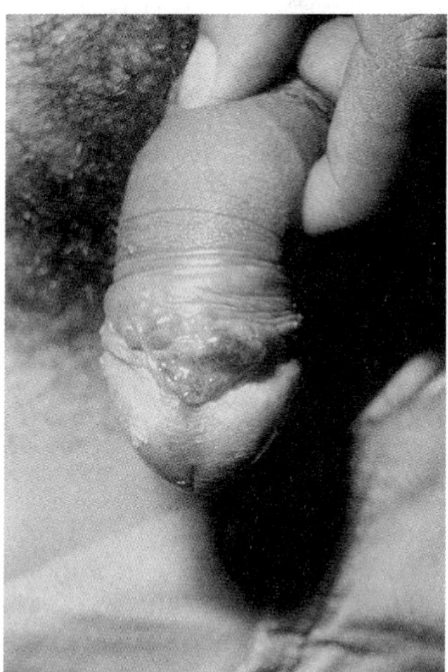

FIGURE 1-110 Involvement of the penis, with a beefy red, granulomatous ulceration in a patient with granuloma inguinale. (From Goldstein B [ed]: *Practical dermatology,* ed 2, St Louis, 1997, Mosby.)

ETIOLOGY

Calymmatobacterium granulomatis is a gram-negative bacillus that reproduces within PMNs, plasma cells, and histiocytes, causing the infected cells to rupture 20 to 30 organisms.

DIAGNOSIS

DIFFERENTIAL DIAGNOSIS

- Carcinoma
- Secondary syphilis: condylomata lata
- Amebiasis: necrotic ulceration
- Concurrent infections
- Lymphogranuloma venereum
- Chancroid
- Genital herpes

WORKUP

- Check for clinical manifestations.
  1. Lesions bleed easily.
  2. Lesions sharply defined and painless.
  3. Secondary infection may ensue.
  4. Inguinal involvement may cause pseudobuboes.
  5. Elephantiasis can result from obstruction of lymphatics.
  6. Suppuration and sinus formation are rare in female patients.
- Screen for other sexually transmitted diseases.
- Exclude other causes of lesions.
- Obtain stained, crushed prep from lesion.
- A clinical algorithm for evaluation of genital ulcer disease is described in Section III.

Section II describes the differential diagnosis of genital sores.

LABORATORY TESTS

Wright stain: observation of Donovan bodies (intracellular bacteria); organisms in vacuoles within macrophages

TREATMENT

ACUTE GENERAL Rx

Recommended regimens:
- Doxycycline 100 mg orally bid × 3 wk minimum
- Trimethoprim/sulfamethoxazole, one double-strength tablet orally bid × 3 wk minimum

Alternative regimens:
- Ciprofloxacin 750 mg PO bid × 3 wk
- Erythromycin base 500 mg PO od × 3 wk
- Azithromycin 1 g PO/wk × 3 wk
- All gentamycin 1 mg/kg IV q8h if no improvement within the first few days of therapy

CHRONIC Rx

If there is a poor initial response, extend treatment. Treatment of relapses is often necessary. Patients should be counseled to avoid risky sex practices and not resume having sex until infection is cleared.

DISPOSITION

Follow clinically until signs and symptoms have resolved, then routine annual or semiannual visits

REFERRAL

If response is poor, consider referral to infectious disease specialist.

PEARLS & CONSIDERATIONS

COMMENTS

- Sexual partners should be examined and offered therapy.
- Pregnant women should be treated with erythromycin regimen.
- Patient education material can be obtained from local and state health clinics and also from ACOG.

SUGGESTED READINGS

Centers for Disease Control and Prevention: 2002 sexually transmitted diseases treatment guidelines, *MMWR Morb Mortal Wkly Rep* 51(RR-6), 2002.

Mead PB et al: *Protocols for infectious diseases in obstetrics and gynecology,* ed 2, Cambridge, Mass, 2000, Blackwell Science.

AUTHOR: **GEORGE T. DANAKAS, M.D.**

BASIC INFORMATION

DEFINITION

Graves' disease is a hypermetabolic state characterized by thyrotoxicosis, diffuse goiter, and infiltrative ophthalmopathy (edema and inflammation of the extraocular muscles and an increase in orbital connective tissue and fat); infiltrative dermopathy characterized by lymphocytic infiltration of the dermis, accumulation of glycosaminoglycans, and edema is occasionally present.

SYNONYMS

Thyrotoxicosis

ICD-9CM CODES
242.0 Toxic diffuse goiter

EPIDEMIOLOGY & DEMOGRAPHICS

INCIDENCE/PREVALENCE: Hyperthyroidism affects 2% of women and 0.2% of men in their lifetimes. More than 80% of these cases are caused by Graves' disease.
PREDOMINANT AGE: Most common before age 50 yr
GENETICS: Increased prevalence of HLA-B8 and HLA-DR3 in whites with Graves' disease. Concordance rate is 20% among monozygotic twins.

PHYSICAL FINDINGS & CLINICAL FINDINGS

- Tachycardia, palpitations, tremor, hyperreflexia
- Goiter, exophthalmos (50% of patients), lid retraction, lid lag
- Nervousness, weight loss, heat intolerance, atrial fibrillation
- Increased sweating, brittle nails, clubbing of fingers
- Nervousness, weight loss, heat intolerance, and atrial fibrillation
- Localized dermopathy (1% to 2% of patients) is most frequent over the anterolateral aspects of the skin but can be found at other sites (especially after trauma)

ETIOLOGY

Autoimmune etiology: the activity of the thyroid gland is stimulated by the action of T cells, which induce specific B cells to synthesize antibodies against TSH receptors in the follicular cell membrane.

DIAGNOSIS

DIFFERENTIAL DIAGNOSIS

- Anxiety disorder
- Premenopausal state
- Thyroiditis
- Other causes of hyperthyroidism (e.g., toxic multinodular goiter, toxic adenoma)
- Other: metastatic neoplasm, diabetes mellitus, pheochromocytoma

WORKUP

The diagnostic workup includes a detailed medical history followed by laboratory and imaging studies. Patients often present with anxiety, heat intolerance, menstrual dysfunction, increased appetite, and weight loss. Elderly patients can have an atypical presentation (apathetic hyperparathyroidism). For additional information, refer to the topic "Hyperthyroidism."

LABORATORY TESTS

- Increased free thyroxine (T_4) and free triiodothyronine (T_3)
- Decreased TSH
- Presence of thyroid autoantibodies (useful in selected patients to differentiate Graves' disease from toxic nodular goiter)

IMAGING STUDIES

- 24-hr radioactive iodine uptake (RAIU): increased homogeneous uptake
- CT or MRI of the orbits is useful if there is uncertainty about the cause of ophthalmopathy

TREATMENT

NONPHARMACOLOGIC THERAPY

Patient education and discussion of therapeutic options

ACUTE GENERAL Rx

- Antithyroid drugs (ATDs) to inhibit thyroid hormone synthesis or peripheral conversion of T_4 to T_3
  1. Propylthiouracil (PTU) 50 to 100 mg q8h or methimazole (Tapazole) 10 to 20 mg q8h for 6 to 24 mo
  2. Side effects: skin rash (3% to 5%), arthralgias, myalgias, granulocytopenia (0.5%); rare side effects: aplastic anemia, hepatic necrosis (PTU), cholestatic jaundice (methimazole)
- Radioactive iodine (RAI)
  1. Treatment of choice for patients >21 yr of age and younger patients who have not achieved remission after 1 yr of ATD therapy
  2. Contraindicated during pregnancy and lactation
- Surgery: near-total thyroidectomy is rarely performed; indications: obstructing goiters despite RAI and ATD therapy, patients who refuse RAI and cannot be adequately managed with ATDs, and pregnant women inadequately managed with ATDs
- Adjunctive therapy: propranolol (20 to 40 mg q6h) to alleviate the β-adrenergic symptoms of hyperthyroidism (tachycardia, tremor); contraindicated in patients with CHF and bronchospasm
- Graves' ophthalmopathy: methylcellulose eye drops to protect against excessive dryness, sunglasses to decrease photophobia, systemic high-dose corticosteroids for severe exophthalmos; worsening of ophthalmopathy after RAI therapy often transient and can be prevented by the administration of prednisone

CHRONIC Rx

Patients undergoing treatment with ATDs should be seen every 1 to 3 mo until euthyroidism is achieved and every 3 to 4 mo while they are receiving ATDs.

DISPOSITION

- ATDs induce sustained remission in <60% of cases.
- The incidence of hypothyroidism post RAI is >50% within first year and 2%/yr thereafter.
- Complications of surgery include hypothyroidism (28% to 43% after 10 yr), hypoparathyroidism, and vocal cord paralysis (1%).
- Successful treatment of hyperthyroidism requires lifelong monitoring for the onset of hypothyroidism or the recurrence of thyrotoxicosis.
- RAI therapy is followed by the appearance or worsening of ophthalmopathy more often than is therapy with methimazole, particularly in patients who are cigarette smokers. It can be prevented with the administration of prednisone 0.5 mg/kg of body weight per day starting 2 to 3 days post RAI, continued for 1 mo, then tapered off over 2 mo.
- Mild to moderate ophthalmopathy often improves spontaneously. Severe cases can be treated with high-dose glucocorticoids, orbital irradiation, or both. Orbital decompression may be used in patients with optic neuropathy and exophthalmos.

SUGGESTED READING

Weetman AP: Graves' disease, *N Engl J Med* 343:1236, 2000.

AUTHOR: **FRED F. FERRI, M.D.**

BASIC INFORMATION

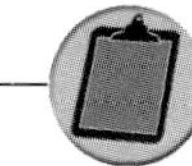

DEFINITION

Guillain-Barré syndrome (GBS) is an acute immune-mediated polyradiculoneuropathy (affects nerve roots and peripheral nerves), with predominant motor involvement. Maximal clinical weakness occurs within 4 wk of disease onset.

SYNONYMS

Acute polyneuropathy
Ascending paralysis
Postinfectious polyneuritis

ICD-9CM CODES
357.0 Guillain-Barré

EPIDEMIOLOGY & DEMOGRAPHICS

INCIDENCE: 0.6-1.9 cases/100,000 persons annually without geographical variation. Incidence increases with age. A slight peak in incidence occurs between late adolescence and early adulthood. A slight male preponderance (1.25:1) also exists.

PREDISPOSING FACTORS: Viral (HIV, CMV, EBV, influenza) and bacterial (*Campylobacter jejuni, Mycoplasma pneumonia*) infections; systemic illness (Hodgkin's lymphoma, immunizations)

PHYSICAL FINDINGS & CLINICAL PRESENTATION

- Symmetric weakness, initially involving proximal muscles, subsequently involving both proximal and distal muscles; difficulty in ambulating, getting up from a chair, or climbing stairs
- Depressed or absent reflexes bilaterally
- Minimal to moderate glove and stocking paresthesias/dysesthesia/anesthesia and/or back pain
- Pain (caused by involvement of posterior nerve roots) may be prominent
- Autonomic abnormalities (brady- or tachyarrhythmias, hypo- or hypertension)
- Respiratory insufficiency (caused by weakness of bulbar/intercostal muscles)
- Facial paresis, ophthalmoparesis, dysphagia (secondary to cranial nerve involvement)

ETIOLOGY

Unknown. Preceding infectious illness 1-4 wk before disease onset in 66% of patients. Humoral and cell-mediated immune attack of peripheral nerve myelin, Schwann cells; sometimes with axonal involvement

DIAGNOSIS

DIFFERENTIAL DIAGNOSIS

- Toxic peripheral neuropathies: heavy metal poisoning (lead, thallium, arsenic), medications (vincristine, disulfiram), organophosphate poisoning, hexacarbon (glue sniffer's neuropathy)
- Nontoxic peripheral neuropathies: acute intermittent porphyria, vasculitic polyneuropathy, infectious (poliomyelitis, diphtheria, Lyme disease); tick paralysis
- Neuromuscular junction disorders: myasthenia gravis, botulism, snake envenomations
- Myopathies; such as polymyositis, acute necrotizing myopathies caused by drugs
- Metabolic derangements such as hypermagnesemia, hypokalemia, hypophosphatemia
- Acute central nervous system disorders such as basilar artery thrombosis with brainstem infarction, brainstem encephalomyelitis, transverse myelitis, or spinal cord compression
- Hysterical paralysis or malingering

WORKUP

1. Exclude other causes based on clinical history, examination, and laboratory tests.
2. Lumbar puncture (may be normal in the first 1-2 wk of the illness)
    - Typical findings include elevated CSF protein with few mononuclear leukocytes (albuminocytologic dissociation) in 80%-90% of patients. Elevated CSF cell counts is an expected feature in cases associated with HIV seroconversion.
3. EMG/NCS: May be normal in the first 10-14 days of the disease. The earliest electrodiagnostic abnormality is prolongation or absence of H-reflexes.

LABORATORY TESTS

- CBC may reveal early leukocytosis with left shift. Electrolytes to exclude metabolic causes
- Heavy metal testing, urine porphyria screen, creatine kinase, HIV titers, neuroimaging of the brain and spinal cord if diagnosis uncertain

TREATMENT

NONPHARMACOLOGIC THERAPY

- Close monitoring of respiratory function (frequent measurements of vital capacity, negative inspiratory force and pulmonary toilet), because respiratory failure is the major complication in GBS
- Frequent repositioning of patient to minimize formation of pressure sores
- Prevention of thromboembolism with antithrombotic stockings and SC heparin (5000 U q12h) in nonambulatory patients
- Emotional support and social counseling

ACUTE GENERAL Rx

- Infusion of IV immunoglobulins (IVIg; 0.4 g/kg/day for 5 days). Always check serum IgA levels before infusion to prevent anaphylaxis in deficient patients.
- Early therapeutic plasma exchange (TPE or plasmapheresis: 200-250mL/kg over 5 sessions qod), started within 7 days of onset of symptoms, is beneficial in preventing paralytic complications in patients with rapidly progressive disease. It is contraindicated in patients with cardiovascular disease (recent MI, unstable angina), active sepsis, and autonomic dysfunction.
- Mechanical ventilation may be needed if FVC is <12 to 15 ml/kg, vital capacity is rapidly decreasing or is <1000 ml, negative inspiratory force <−20 cm H_2O, PaO_2 is <70, the patient is having significant difficulty clearing secretions or is aspirating.

CHRONIC Rx

- Ventilatory support: may be necessary in 10% to 20% of patients. Adequate fluid/electrolyte support and nutrition necessary, especially in patients with dysautonomia or bulbar dysfunction
- Aggressive nursing care to prevent decubiti, infections, fecal impactions, and pressure nerve palsies
- Monitoring and treatment of autonomic dysfunction (bradyarrhythmias or tachyarrhythmias, orthostatic hypotension, systemic hypertension, altered sweating)
- Treatment of back pain and dysesthesia with low-dose tricyclics, gabapentin, etc.
- Stress ulcer prevention in patients receiving ventilator support
- Physical and occupational therapy rehabilitation, including supportive devices

DISPOSITION

- Mortality is approximately 5%-10%. A recent study showed 62% complete recovery, 14% mild weakness, 9% moderate weakness, 4% bed-bound or ventilated, and 8% dead at 1 yr.

- Predictors for poor recovery (inability to walk independently at 1 yr): age >60 yr, preceding diarrheal illness, recent CMV infection, fulminant or rapidly progressing course, ventilatory dependence, reduced motor amplitudes (<20% normal), or inexcitable nerves on NCS.

REFERRAL

Tracheostomy may be necessary in patients with prolonged ventilatory support. Percutaneous endoscopic gastrostomy may be temporarily required.

PEARLS & CONSIDERATIONS

COMMENTS

Patient education information may be obtained from the Guillain-Barré Foundation International, Box 262, Wynnewood, PA 19096; phone: (610) 667-0131.

SUGGESTED READINGS

Gorson KC, Ropper AH: Guillain-Barré syndrome (acute inflammatory demyelinating neuropathy) and related disorders. In: Katirji B et al. (eds): *Neuromuscular disorders in clinical practice.* Boston, 2002, Butterworth-Heinemann.

Kuwabara S: Guillain-Barré syndrome: epidemiology, pathophysiology and management, *Drugs* 64:597, 2004.

AUTHOR: **EROBOGHENE E. UBOGU, M.D.**

BASIC INFORMATION

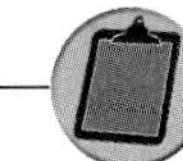

DEFINITION

Hand-foot-mouth (HFM) disease is a viral illness that is characterized by superficial lesions of the oral mucosa and of the skin of the extremities. HFM is transmitted primarily by the fecal oral route and is highly contagious. Although children are predominantly affected, adults are also at risk. This disease is usually self-limited and benign.

SYNONYMS

Vesicular stomatitis with exanthem
Coxsackievirus infection

ICD-9CM CODES
074.0 Hand-foot-mouth disease

EPIDEMIOLOGY & DEMOGRAPHICS

- Children under the age of 5 yr are at the highest risk and have the most severe cases
- HFM is usually found in children below the age of 10 yr.
- Close contacts of affected children, including family members and health care workers, are the most commonly affected adults.
- Outbreaks tend to occur during the summer.
- Infection leads to immunity, but a second episode may occur after infection with a different agent.

PHYSICAL FINDINGS & CLINICAL PRESENTATION

Symptoms:
- After a 4 to 6 day incubation period, patients may complain of odynophagia, sore throat, malaise, and fever (38.3-40° C).
- One to 2 days later the characteristic oral lesions appear.
- In 75% of cases, skin lesions on the extremities accompany these oral manifestations.
- 11% of adults have cutaneous findings.
- Lesions appear over the course of 1 or 2 days.

Physical findings:
- Oral lesions, usually between five and ten, are commonly found on the tongue, buccal mucosa, gingivae, and hard palate.
- Oral lesions initially start as 1- to 3-mm erythematous macules and evolve into gray vesicles on an erythematous base.
- Vesicles are frequently broken by the time of presentation and appear as superficial gray ulcers with surrounding erythema.
- Skin lesions of the hands and feet start as linear erythematous papules (3 to 10 mm in diameter) that evolve into gray vesicles that may be mildly painful (Fig. 1-111). These vesicles are usually intact at presentation and remain so until they desquamate within 2 wk.
- Involvement of the buttocks and perineum is present in 31% of cases.
- In rare cases, encephalitis, meningitis, myocarditis, poliomyelitis-like paralysis, and pulmonary edema may develop.
- Spontaneous abortion may occur if the infection takes place early in pregnancy.

ETIOLOGY

Coxsackievirus group A, type 16, was the first and is the most common viral agent isolated. Coxsackieviruses A5, A7, A9, A10, B1, B2, B3, B5, and enterovirus 71 have also been implicated.

DIAGNOSIS

DIFFERENTIAL DIAGNOSIS

- Aphthous stomatitis
- Herpes simplex infection
- Herpangina
- Behçet's disease
- Erythema multiforme
- Pemphigus
- Gonorrhea
- Acute leukemia
- Lymphoma
- Allergic contact dermatitis

WORKUP

The diagnosis is usually made on the basis of history and characteristic physical examination.

LABORATORY TESTS

Not indicated unless the diagnosis is in doubt
Throat culture or stool specimen may be obtained for viral testing

TREATMENT

ACUTE GENERAL Rx

- Palliative therapy is given for this usually self-limited disease.
- One small, uncontrolled case series reported a decrease in duration of symptoms in response to acyclovir.

DISPOSITION

Prognosis is excellent except in rare cases of CNS or cardiac involvement. Most are managed as outpatients.

REFERRAL

Not usually needed

SUGGESTED READINGS

Chang LY et al: Clinical features and risk of pulmonary edema after enterovirus-related hand, foot, and mouth disease, *Lancet* 354(9191):1682, 1999.

Weir E: Foot-and-mouth disease in animals and humans, *Can Med Assoc J*, 164(9):1338, 2001.

AUTHORS: **JAMES J. NG, M.D.**, and **JENNIFER JEREMIAH, M.D.**

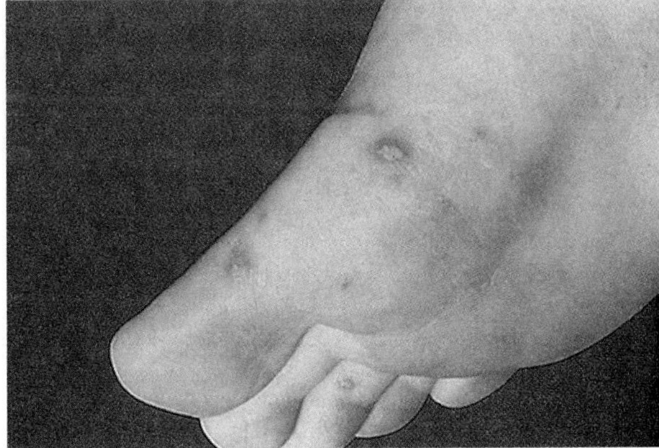

FIGURE 1-111 Hand-foot-mouth disease. Note oval lesions on an erythematous base. (From Goldstein B [ed]: *Practical dermatology,* ed 2, St Louis, 1997, Mosby.)

BASIC INFORMATION

DEFINITION

The term *cluster headache* refers to attacks of severe, strictly unilateral pain that is orbital, supraorbital, temporal, or in any combination of these sites, lasting 15 to 180 minutes, and occurring from once every other day to 8 times a day. The attacks are associated with one or more of the following, all of which are ipsilateral: conjunctival injection, lacrimation, nasal congestion, rhinorrhea, forehead and facial sweating, miosis, ptosis, eyelid edema. Most patients are restless or agitated during an attack.

ICD-9CM CODES
346.2 Variants of migraine

EPIDEMIOLOGY & DEMOGRAPHICS

- Estimated to occur in 0.05% to 1% of the population with males at least five times more common than females
- Peak age of onset between 20 and 40 yr
- Cluster headaches may be inherited (autosomal dominant) in about 5% of cases

PHYSICAL FINDINGS & CLINICAL PRESENTATION

- During attack: ipsilateral conjunctival injection, lacrimation, nasal congestion, rhinorrhea, facial sweating, Horner's syndrome.
- In contrast to migraine sufferers, patients are agitated and active during an attack.
- Permanent partial Horner's syndrome in 5% of patients; otherwise examination normal.

ETIOLOGY

Activation of the posterior hypothalamic grey matter resulting in trigeminal activation coupled with parasympathetic activation.

DIAGNOSIS

- Severe or very severe unilateral orbital, supraorbital and/or temporal pain lasting 15 to 180 minutes
- Frequency of every other day to 8 per day
- Headache is accompanied by at least one of the following (ipsilateral):
  1. conjunctival injection and/or lacrimation
  2. nasal congestion and/or rhinorrhea
  3. eyelid edema
  4. forehead and facial sweating
  5. miosis and/or ptosis
  6. restlessness or agitation

DIFFERENTIAL DIAGNOSIS

- Migraine
- Trigeminal neuralgia
- Temporal arteritis
- Postherpetic neuralgia
- Other trigeminal autonomic cephalagias
- Section II describes the differential diagnosis of headaches

WORKUP

Diagnosis is usually established by characteristic history.

IMAGING STUDIES

None, unless history or examination suggests focal neurological deficit

TREATMENT

NONPHARMACOLOGIC THERAPY

Avoidance of alcohol, histamine, nitroglycerine, or tobacco during clusters

ABORTIVE Rx

- Inhalation of 100% oxygen by face mask at 8 to 10 L/min for 15 min often aborts an attack.
- Triptans, cafergot or dihydroergotamine may abort an attack or prevent one if given just before a predictable episode. Acute episode is typically resolved before oral analgesics become effective, although indomethacin and other NSAIDS may also be effective in prolonged attacks.

PROPHYLAXIS Rx

Various medications have been tried without great success, although good responses may be obtained in up to 50% of cases. Examples include:

- Verapamil: up to 480 mg/day as tolerated (the drug of choice)
- Lithium: 200 mg tid with frequent monitoring and adjustment to maintain therapeutic serum level of 0.4 to 1 mEq/L. Equally effective as verapamil, but more side effects
- Methysergide: 1 to 2 mg tid; requires familiarity with the potential adverse effects and use of "drug holidays" to decrease risk of fibrosis
- Ergotamine tartrate: 3-4 mg/day during clusters
- Prednisone: 60 mg po qd x 1 wk followed by taper. Headaches can return during taper

DISPOSITION

Headache-free periods tend to increase with increasing age.

REFERRAL

Refractory cluster headaches

PEARLS & CONSIDERATIONS

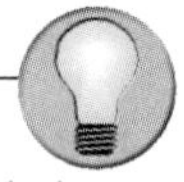

COMMENTS

- Cluster headaches are divided into episodic (attacks lasting up to 1 yr with greater than 1 mo pain-free periods) and chronic (>1 yr without remission).
- Cluster headaches now classified as a trigeminal autonomic cephalalgia (TAC). Other TAC includes paroxysmal hemicrania and short-lasting unilateral neuralgiform headache attacks with conjunctival injection and tearing (SUNCT).

SUGGESTED READINGS

Ekbom K, Hardebo JE: Cluster headache: aetiology, diagnosis and management, *Drugs* 62(1):61, 2002.

Headache Classification Committee of the International Headache Society: The International Classificaiton of Headache Disorders, *Cephalgia* 24:s1, 2004.

Weiss HD: The treatment of migraine and cluster headaches. In Johnson RT et al. (eds): *Current therapy in neurologic disease.* Philadelphia, 2002, Mosby.

AUTHOR: **CHUN LIM, M.D., PH.D.**

BASIC INFORMATION

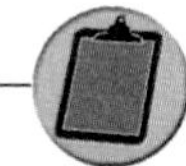

DEFINITION

Migraine headaches are recurrent headaches that are preceded by a focal neurological symptom (migraine with aura), occur independently (migraine without aura), or have atypical presentations (migraine variants). Migraine with aura is characterized by visual or sensory symptoms that typically develop or march over a period of 5 to 20 min. In both migraine with and without aura, the headache is typically unilateral, pulsatile, and associated with nausea and vomiting, photophobia and phonophobia.

ICD-9CM CODES
346 Migraine

EPIDEMIOLOGY & DEMOGRAPHICS

PREVALENCE (IN U.S.): Females: 18%; males: 6%

PREDOMINANT SEX: Female:male ratio of 3:1

INCIDENCE: Increases from infancy, peaks during the third decade of life then decreases

GENETICS:
- Familial predisposition, with over 50% of migraine sufferers having an affected family member
- Autosomal dominant transmission for some rare migraine variants (familial hemiplegic migraine, CADASIL)

PHYSICAL FINDINGS & CLINICAL PRESENTATION

- Normal between episodes
- Normal for migraine without aura. Focal motor or sensory abnormalities possible with migraine with aura or migraine variants
- Common aura types include scintillating scotomata, bright zigzags, homonymous visual disturbance such as paraethesias, speech disturbances, or hemiparesis (familial or sporadic hemiplegic migraine)

ETIOLOGY

A primary neuronal event resulting in a trigeminovascular reflex causing neurogenic inflammation. Serotonin, nitric oxide, and calcitonin-gene-related peptide also play a role but exact mechanism is unknown. Cortical spreading depression is responsible for the aura.

DIAGNOSIS

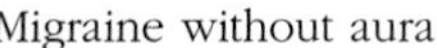

Migraine without aura
- 5 attacks fulfilling criteria
- Headache attacks lasting 4 to 72 hours
- Headache has at least two of the following characteristics:
  1. Unilateral location
  2. Pulsating quality
  3. Moderate or severe pain intensity
  4. Aggravation by or causing avoidance of routine physical activity
- During headache at least one of the following:
  1. Nausea and/or vomiting
  2. Photophobia and phonophobia

Migraine with aura
- At least two attacks
- Aura consisting of at least one of the following, but no motor weakness:
  1. Fully reversible visual symptoms including positive features and/or negative features.
  2. Fully reversible sensory symptoms including positive and/or negative features.
- At least two of the following:
  1. Homonymous visual symptoms and/or unilateral sensory symptoms.
  2. At least one aura symptom develops gradually over > 5 minutes and/or different aura symptoms occur in succession over > 5 minutes.

DIFFERENTIAL DIAGNOSIS

- Subarachnoid hemorrhage
- Cluster headache
- Chronic daily headaches (drug rebound headaches)
- Arteriovenous malformation
- Vasculitis
- Tumor
- Section II describes the differential diagnosis of headaches

WORKUP

- Generally no additional investigation is needed with recurrent, typical attacks with usual age of onset, family history, and a normal physical examination.
- If there is an unusual presentation and/or unexpected findings on examination, investigation for other causes is required.

LABORATORY TESTS

Lumbar puncture for history of abrupt onset headaches and uncertain diagnosis of migraine

IMAGING STUDIES

- Imaging should be done in patients with headaches and an unexplained abnormal finding on the neurological examination.
- Imaging should be considered in patients with rapidly increasing headache frequency, history of dizziness or incoordination, subjective numbness or tingling, headache causing wakening from sleep, or headaches worsening with Valsalva maneuver.

TREATMENT

Consider the use of a headache log/diary to identify triggers of headaches, to record efficacy of treatments, and to track history of the headaches.

NONPHARMACOLOGIC THERAPY

- Avoid any identifiable provoking factors: caffeine, tobacco, and alcohol may trigger attacks, as may dietary or other environmental precipitants (less common)
- Avoid stressors in life and minimize variations in daily routine with regular sleep, meals, and exercise
- Relaxation training and biofeedback

ACUTE ANALGESIC Rx

- Many oral agents are ineffective because of poor absorption secondary to migraine-induced gastric stasis. Nonoral route of administration should be selected in patients with severe nausea or vomiting
- Nonspecific treatment for pain.
- Acetaminophen, NSAIDS, combination analgesics, benzodiazepines, opioids, barbiturates

ACUTE ABORTIVE Rx

- Intravenous antiemetics (prochlorperazine, metoclopramide, domperidone). Acute dystonic reactions and akathisia are rare side effects. Generally not used as monotherapy
- Ergotamine and ergotamine combinations (PO/PR), and dihydroergotamine (DHE 45) (SC, IV, IM, Nasal) all have well-documented efficacy against migraines (less so with ergotamines). DHE 45 usually administered in combination with an antiemetic drug (Table 1-20)
- Triptans (SC, PO, and intranasal) now considered drug of choice for abortive therapy. Meta-analysis suggests that 10 mg rizatriptan, 80 mg eletriptan, and 12.5 mg almotriptan are most effective.
- Early administration improves effectiveness

PROPHYLAXIS Rx

- Prophylactic treatment is generally indicated when headaches occur more than once a week or when symptomatic treatments are contraindicated or not effective. They are most effective when initiated during headache-free period. All prophylaxis should be maintained for at least 3 mo before deeming the medication a failure.
- Well-established options for prophylactic treatment include β-blockers (propanolol, timolol, atenolol, metoprolol), tricyclic antidepressants (amitriptyline), and the antiepileptic drug valproic acid.

- Less established options include Ca-channel blockers, SSRI, the antiepileptic drugs gabapentin and topiramate.

DISPOSITION

After age 30 yr, 40% of patients are migraine free.

REFERRAL

If uncertain about diagnosis or treatment not effective

PEARLS & CONSIDERATIONS

- Avoid overuse of narcotics, barbiturates, caffeine, and benzodiazepines, as they are habit-forming.
- Chronic use of analgesic medications can result in drug-induced or rebound headaches.

SUGGESTED READINGS

Ferrari, MD et al: Oral triptans (serotonin 5-HT1B/1D agonist) in acute migraine treatment: a meta-analysis of 53 trials, *Lancet* 358:1668, 2001.

Ferrari MD et al: Migraine—current understanding and treatment, *N Engl J Med* 346:257, 2002.

Headache Classification Committee of the International Headache Society: The International Classificaiton of Headache Disorders, *Cephalgia* 24:s1, 2004.

Silberstein SD, for the US Headache Consortium: Practice parameter: Evidence-based guidelines for migraine headache (an evidence based review), *Neurology* 55:754, 2000.

AUTHOR: **CHUN LIM, M.D., PH.D.**

TABLE 1-20 **Abortive and Analgesic Therapy for Migraine***

Drug	Dose	Route
Triptans (serotonin agonists)		
Sumatriptan	6 mg, repeat in 2 hr (max 2 doses/day)	Subcutaneous
Sumatriptan	25 mg, 50 mg, repeat in 2 hr (max 200 mg/day)	Oral
Sumatriptan	5 mg and 20 mg, repeat in 2 hr (max 40 mg/day)	Nasal spray
Zolmitriptan	1.25, 2.5 mg, 5 mg, repeat in 2 hr (max 10 mg/day)	Oral
Zolmitriptan	5 mg, repeat in 2 hr (max 10 mg/day)	Nasal spray
Zolmitriptan	2.5, 5 mg, repeat in 2 hr (max 10 mg/day)	Orally disintegrating tab
Naratriptan	1 mg, 2.5 mg, repeat in 4 hr (max 5 mg/day)	Oral
Rizatriptan	5 mg, 10 mg, repeat in 2 hr (max 30 mg/day)	Oral
Almotriptan	6.25 mg, 12.5 mg, may repeat in 2 hr (max 25 mg/day)	Oral
Eletriptan	20 mg, 40 mg, may repeat in 2 hr (max 80 mg/day)	Oral
Frovatriptan	2.5 mg, may repeat in 2 hr (max 7.5 mg/day)	Oral
Ergotamine preparations		
Ergotamine and caffeine	2 tablets, may repeat 1 tab q30 min; max 6/day	Oral
Ergotamine and caffeine	1 suppository, repeat in 1 hr; max 2/day	Rectal
Ergotaminel	1 tablet, repeat in 1 hr; max 2/day	Sublingual
Dihydroergotamine	0.5-1.0 mg, repeat twice at 1-hr intervals (max 3 mg/attack)	Intramuscular
		Subcutaneous
		Intravenous
		Nasal spray
Sympathomimetics (with or without barbiturates or codeine)		
Isometheptene+dichloralphenazone+acetaminophen	1 to 2 capules, repeat in 4 hr, max 8/day	Oral
Nonsteroidal antiinflammatory drugs		
Acetaminophen+aspirin+caffeine	2 tablets, repeat in 6 hr, max 8/day	Oral
Naproxen	550-750 mg, repeat in 1 hr; max 3 times/wk	Oral
Meclofenamate	100-200 mg, repeat in 1 hr; max 3 times/wk	Oral
Flurbiprofen	50-100 mg, repeat in 1 hr; max 3 times/wk	Oral
Ibuprofen	200-300 mg, repeat in 1 hr; max 3 times/wk	Oral
Antiemetics		
Promethazine	50-125 mg	Oral
		Intramuscular
Prochlorperazine	1-25 mg	Oral
	2.5-25 mg (suppository)	Rectal
	5-10 mg	Intramuscular
Chlorpromazine	10-25 mg	Oral
	50-100 mg (suppository)	Rectal
	Up to 35 mg	Intravenous
Trimetobenzamide	250 mg	Oral
	200 mg	Rectal
Metoclopramide	5-10 mg	Oral
	10 mg	Intramuscular
	5-10 mg	Intravenous
Dimenhydrinate	50 mg	Oral

Modified from Wiederholt WC: ***Neurology for non-neurologists***, ed 4, Philadelphia, 2000, WB Saunders.

*For side effects and contraindications consult the manufacturer's drug insert before prescribing any of these drugs.

BASIC INFORMATION

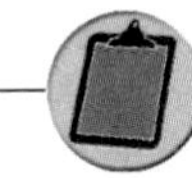

DEFINITION

Tension-type headaches (TTH) are recurrent headaches lasting 30 min to 7 days without nausea or vomiting and with at least two of the following characteristics: pressing or tightening quality (nonthrobbing), mild or moderate intensity, bilateral, and not aggravated by routine physical activity. The International Classification of Headache Disorders (ICHD-2) criteria includes three subtypes: infrequent episodic TTH (<1 day/month), frequent episodic TTH (1 to 14 days/month), and chronic TTH (15 days/month, perhaps without recognizable episodes).

SYNONYMS

Muscle contraction headache
Tension headache
Stress headache
Essential headache

ICD-9CM CODES
307.81 Tension headache

EPIDEMIOLOGY & DEMOGRAPHICS

INCIDENCE (IN U.S.):
- Undetermined
- Most common type of headache; as high as 70% of all headaches presenting to primary care physician

PREVALENCE (IN U.S.): Males: 63%/yr; females: 86%/yr
PREDOMINANT SEX: Females > males
PEAK INCIDENCE: Occurs at all ages
GENETICS: Not established

PHYSICAL FINDINGS & CLINICAL PRESENTATION

Pressure or "band-like" tightness all around the head, may be worse at the vertex. Cervical, paracervical and trapezius muscle spasm and/or percussion tenderness may be present. Scalp tenderness or hypersensitivity to pain also occurs. Symptoms suggestive of migraine are usually not present (e.g., throbbing pain, nausea/vomiting, visual complaints, aura). Either one symptom of photo or phonophobia does not exclude the diagnosis of TTH.

ETIOLOGY

- Unclear; little data to support postulated muscle contraction component. More recently has been thought of as a multifactorial disorder with several possible concurrent pathophysiological mechanisms
- No recent data to support the long-standing belief that these headaches arise from stress or other psychologic factors. However, components of stress, sleep deprivation, hunger, and eyestrain may exacerbate symptoms
- These headaches respond poorly to standard migraine therapy

DIAGNOSIS

DIFFERENTIAL DIAGNOSIS

- Migraine (would expect associated symptoms see "Headache, Migraine")
- Cervical spine disease
- Intracranial mass (may present with focal neurologic signs, seizures, or headache awakening patient from sleep)
- Idiopathic intracranial hypertension (found more often in obese women of child-bearing age, may have papilledema, visual loss, or diplopia)
- Rebound headache from overuse of analgesics
- Secondary headache (e.g., temporomandibular joint syndrome, thyrotoxicosis, polycythemia, drug side-effects)
- Migraine and tension-type headache may often coexist and may be difficult to differentiate (suggest headache calendar)
- Section II describes the differential diagnosis of headaches

WORKUP

- Thorough history and physical examination for any new-onset headache
- Neuroimaging should be performed when unexplained neurologic findings are present on exam or in cases of atypical new-onset sudden and severe headaches. Although data are insufficient, imaging studies may be considered if there is a change in the pattern, frequency, or severity of headaches but may be of lower yield

LABORATORY TESTS

- No routine tests
- ESR in elderly patients suspected of having cranial arteritis

IMAGING STUDIES

CT scan and/or MRI may be used to exclude intracranial pathology. MRI is better for imaging the posterior fossa. Contrast should be used if mass lesion is suspected.

TREATMENT

NONPHARMACOLOGIC THERAPY

- Relaxation training, biofeedback, heat
- Transcutaneous electrical nerve stimulation (TENS)
- Physical therapy including stretching exercises, massage, and ultrasound

ACUTE GENERAL Rx

Nonnarcotic analgesics with limited frequency to prevent drug-induced headache

CHRONIC Rx

- Tricyclic antidepressants (e.g., amitriptyline 10 to 150 mg hs) and SSRIs
- Avoid narcotics, limit NSAIDs, consider indomethacin; if related to cervical muscle spasm, may consider trial of muscle relaxants (e.g., Skelaxin 400-800 mg TID)

DISPOSITION

May not respond fully to treatment

REFERRAL

If uncertain about diagnosis or unexplained focal neurologic findings on examination

PEARLS & CONSIDERATIONS

It is imperative to avoid overuse of caffeine- and barbiturate-containing medications because of the risk of rebound headaches

SUGGESTED READINGS

Bendtsen L: Central sensitization in tension-type headache—possible pathophysiological mechanisms, *Cephalalgia* 20(5):486, 2000.

Headache Classification Committee of the International Headache Society. The International Classificaiton of Headache Disorders, *Cephalalgia* 24:1, 2004.

Holroyd KA et al: Management of chronic tension-type headache with tricyclic anti-depressant medication, stress management therapy, and their combination: a randomized controlled trial, *JAMA* 285(17):2208, 2001.

Jensen R: Pathophysiological mechanisms of tension-type headache: a review of epidemiological and experimental studies, *Cephalalgia* 19(6):602, 1999.

Lipton RB et al: Classificaiton of primary headaches, *Neurology* 63:427, 2004.

Millea P, Brodie J: Tension-type headache, *Am Fam Physician* 66:797, 2002.

Rollnik, JD, et al: Botulinum toxin type A and EMG: A key to the understanding of chronic tension-type headaches? *Headache* 41:985, 2001.

Silberstein, SD, Rosenberg, J: Multispecialty consensus on diagnosis and treatment of headache, *Neurology* 54:1553, 2000.

AUTHOR: **RICHARD S. ISAACSON, M.D.**

Heart Block, Complete

BASIC INFORMATION

DEFINITION

In complete heart block, there is complete blockage of all AV conduction. The atria and ventricles have separate, independent rhythms.

SYNONYMS

Third-degree AV block

ICD-9CM CODES
426.0 Complete heart block

EPIDEMIOLOGY & DEMOGRAPHICS

Over 100,000 permanent pacemakers are implanted worldwide each year for complete heart block.

PHYSICAL FINDINGS & CLINICAL PRESENTATION

Physical examination may be normal. Patients may present with the following clinical manifestations:

- Dizziness, palpitations
- Stokes-Adams syncopal attacks
- CHF
- Angina

ETIOLOGY

- Degenerative changes in His-Purkinje system
- Acute anterior wall MI
- Calcific aortic stenosis
- Cardiomyopathy
- Trauma
- Cardiovascular surgery
- Congenital

DIAGNOSIS

DIFFERENTIAL DIAGNOSIS

The differential diagnosis involves only the etiology. ECG will confirm diagnosis.

WORKUP

ECG:

- P waves constantly change their relationship to the QRS complexes (Fig. 1-112).
- Ventricular rate is usually <50 bpm (may be higher in congenital forms).
- Ventricular rate is generally lower than the atrial rate.
- QRS complex is wide.

TREATMENT

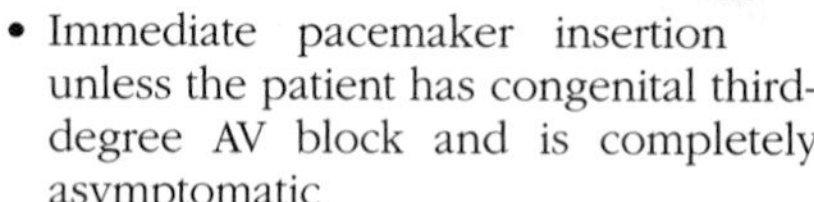

ACUTE GENERAL Rx

- Immediate pacemaker insertion unless the patient has congenital third-degree AV block and is completely asymptomatic
- Therapy of underlying etiology

CHRONIC Rx

Patients with permanent pacemakers need regular follow-up and pacemaker monitoring to ensure proper sensing.

DISPOSITION

Prognosis is favorable following insertion of pacemaker and related to the underlying etiology of complete AV block (e.g., MI, cardiomyopathy).

REFERRAL

Referral for implantation of permanent pacemaker

PEARLS & CONSIDERATIONS

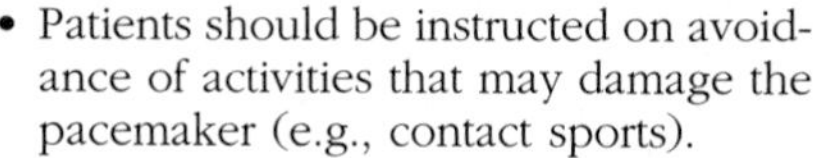

COMMENTS

- Patients should be instructed on avoidance of activities that may damage the pacemaker (e.g., contact sports).
- Common environmental causes of pacemaker malformation are electrocautery, transthoracic defibrillation, MRI, extracorporeal shock wave lithotripsy, transcutaneous electrical nerve stimulation, therapeutic radiation, ECT, diathermy, radiofrequency ablation for treatment of tachyarrhythmias.

SUGGESTED READING

Bayce M et al: Evolving indications for permanent pacemakers, *Ann Intern Med* 134:1130, 2001.

AUTHOR: **FRED F. FERRI, M.D.**

THIRD-DEGREE (COMPLETE) AV BLOCK

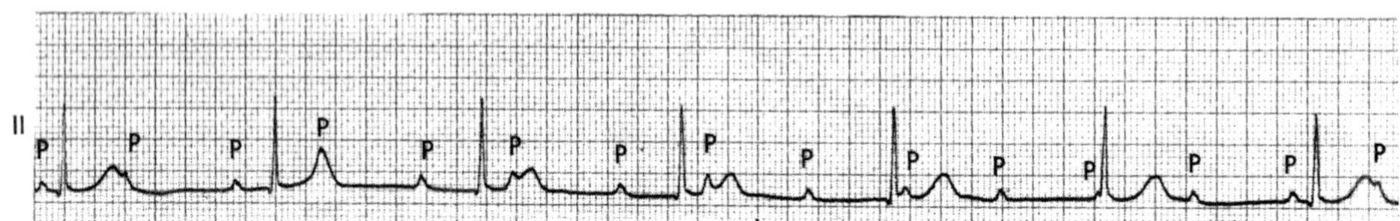

FIGURE 1-112 Third-degree complete AV heart block is characterized by independent atrial (*P*) and ventricular (QRS) activity. The atrial rate is always faster than the ventricular rate. The PR intervals are completely variable. Some P waves fall on the T wave, distorting its shape. Others may fall in the QRS complex and be "lost." Notice that the QRS complexes are of normal width, indicating that the ventricles are being paced from the AV junction. (From Goldberger AL [ed]: *Clinical electrocardiography,* ed 5, St Louis, 1994, Mosby.)

BASIC INFORMATION

DEFINITION

Second-degree heart block is the blockage of some (but not all) impulses from the atria to the ventricles. There are two types of second-degree AV block:

MOBITZ TYPE I (WENCKEBACH):

- There is a progressive prolongation of the PR interval before an impulse is completely blocked; the cycle repeats periodically.
- Cycle with dropped beat is less than two times the previous cycle.
- Site of block is usually AV node (proximal to the bundle of His).

MOBITZ TYPE II:

- There is a sudden interruption of AV conduction without prior prolongation of the PR interval.
- Site of block is infranodal.

SYNONYMS

Wenckebach block (Mobitz type I block)
Mobitz type II block

ICD-9CM CODES
426.13 Mobitz type I
426.12 Mobitz type II

EPIDEMIOLOGY & DEMOGRAPHICS

Mobitz type I block is more common and may occur in individuals with heightened vagal tone or secondary to some medications such as β-blockers or calcium channel blockers.

PHYSICAL FINDINGS & CLINICAL PRESENTATION

- Patients with Mobitz type I are usually asymptomatic.
- Sudden loss of consciousness without warning (Adams-Stokes attack) can occur in patients with Mobitz type II; however, it is much more common in patients with complete heart block.
- Irregular pulse with dropped beats is present (Mobitz type I).
- Irregular pulse with occasional dropped beats is present (Mobitz type II).

ETIOLOGY

MOBITZ TYPE I:

- Vagal stimulation
- Degenerative changes in the AV conduction system
- Ischemia at the AV nodes (particularly in inferior wall MI)
- Drugs (digitalis, quinidine, procainamide, adenosine, calcium channel blockers, β-blockers)
- Cardiomyopathies
- Aortic regurgitation
- Lyme carditis

MOBITZ TYPE II:

- Degenerative changes in the His-Purkinje system
- Acute anterior wall MI
- Calcific aortic stenosis

DIAGNOSIS

DIFFERENTIAL DIAGNOSIS

The ECG will distinguish between Mobitz type I and Mobitz type II block and other conduction abnormalities.

WORKUP

ECG, 24-hr Holter monitor (selected patients)

MOBITZ TYPE I (Fig. 1-113): ECG shows:

- Gradual prolongation of PR interval leading to a blocked beat
- Shortened PR interval after dropped beat

MOBITZ TYPE II: ECG shows:

- Fixed duration of PR interval
- Sudden appearance of blocked beats

TREATMENT

NONPHARMACOLOGIC THERAPY

Elimination of drugs that may induce AV block

ACUTE GENERAL Rx

MOBITZ TYPE I:

- Treatment generally is not necessary. This type of block is usually transient.
- If symptomatic (e.g., dizziness), atropine 1 mg (may repeat once after 5 min) may be tried to increase AV conduction; if no response, insert temporary pacemaker.
- If block is secondary to drugs (e.g., digitalis), discontinue the drug.
- If associated with anterior wall MI and wide QRS escape rhythm, consider insertion of temporary pacemaker.
- Significant AV block post-MI may be caused by adenosine produced by the ischemic myocardium. These arrhythmias (which may be resistant to conventional therapy such as atropine) may respond to theophylline (adenosine antagonist).

MOBITZ TYPE II:

- Pacemaker insertion is needed, because this type of block is usually permanent and often progresses to complete AV block.

DISPOSITION

Prognosis is good with insertion of pacemaker in patients with Mobitz type II.

REFERRAL

Referral for pacemaker insertion (see Acute General Rx)

PEARLS & CONSIDERATIONS

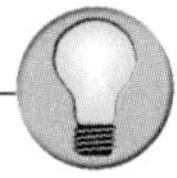

COMMENTS

Patients with Mobitz type I should be followed routinely for potential development of high-grade AV block.

SUGGESTED READING

Barold S, Hayes D: Second-degree atrioventricular block: a reappraisal, *Mayo Clin Proc* 76:44, 2001.

AUTHOR: **FRED F. FERRI, M.D.**

WENCKEBACH (MOBITZ TYPE I) SECOND-DEGREE AV BLOCK

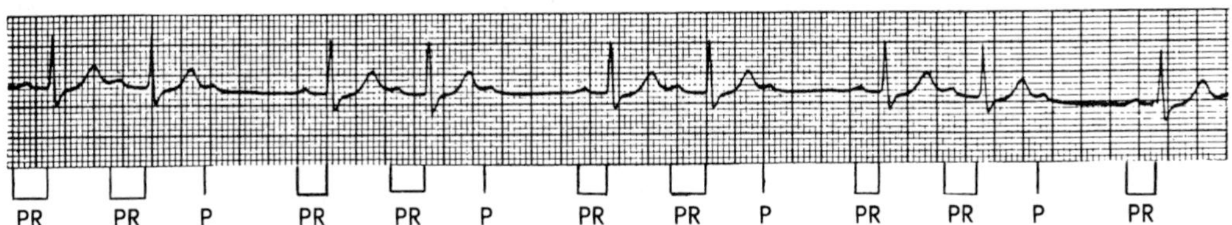

FIGURE 1-113 Wenckebach (Mobitz type I) second-degree AV block. Notice the progressive increase in PR intervals, with the third P wave in each sequence not followed by a QRS. Wenckebach block produces a characteristically syncopated rhythm with grouping of the QRS complexes (group beating). (From Goldberger AL [ed]: *Clinical electrocardiography,* ed 5, St Louis, 1994, Mosby.)

Heat Exhaustion and Heat Stroke 

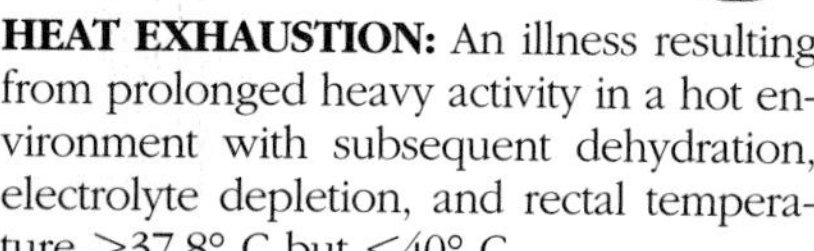

BASIC INFORMATION

DEFINITION

HEAT EXHAUSTION: An illness resulting from prolonged heavy activity in a hot environment with subsequent dehydration, electrolyte depletion, and rectal temperature >37.8° C but <40° C.

HEAT STROKE: A life-threatening heat illness characterized by extreme hyperthermia, dehydration, and neurologic manifestations (core temperature >40° C).

SYNONYMS

Heat illness
Hyperthermia

ICD-9CM CODES
992.0 Heat stroke
992.5 Heat exhaustion

EPIDEMIOLOGY & DEMOGRAPHICS

- Heat exhaustion and stroke occur more frequently in elderly patients, especially those taking diuretics or medications that impair heat dissipation (e.g., phenothiazines, anticholinergics, antihistamines, β-blockers).
- Incidence of heat stroke in United States is approximately 20 cases/ 100,000 population.

PHYSICAL FINDINGS & CLINICAL PRESENTATION

HEAT EXHAUSTION:
- Generalized malaise, weakness, headache, muscle and abdominal cramps, nausea, vomiting, hypotension, and tachycardia
- Rectal temperature is usually normal
- Sweating is usually present

HEAT STROKE:
- Neurologic manifestations (seizures, tremor, hemiplegia, coma, psychosis, and other bizarre behavior)
- Evidence of dehydration (poor skin turgor, sunken eyeballs)
- Tachycardia, hyperventilation
- Skin is hot, red, and flushed
- Sweating is often (not always) absent, particularly in elderly patients

ETIOLOGY

- Exogenous heat gain (increased ambient temperature)
- Increased heat production (exercise, infection, hyperthyroidism, drugs)
- Impaired heat dissipation (high humidity, heavy clothing, neonatal or elderly patients, drugs [phenothiazines, anticholinergics, antihistamines, butyrophenones, amphetamines, cocaine, alcohol, β-blockers])

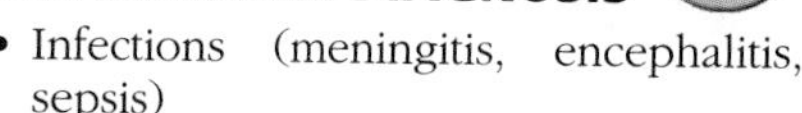

DIAGNOSIS

DIFFERENTIAL DIAGNOSIS

- Infections (meningitis, encephalitis, sepsis)
- Head trauma
- Epilepsy
- Thyroid storm
- Acute cocaine intoxication
- Malignant hyperthermia
- Heat exhaustion can be differentiated from heat stroke by the following:
  1. Essentially intact mental function and lack of significant fever in heat exhaustion
  2. Mild or absent increases in CPK, AST, LDH, ALT in heat exhaustion

WORKUP

- Heat stroke: comprehensive history, physical examination, and laboratory evaluation
- Heat exhaustion: in most cases, laboratory tests are not necessary for diagnosis

LABORATORY TESTS

Laboratory abnormalities may include the following:
- Elevated BUN, creatinine, Hct
- Hyponatremia or hypernatremia, hyperkalemia or hypokalemia
- Elevated LDH, AST, ALT, CPK, bilirubin
- Lactic acidosis, respiratory alkalosis (secondary to hyperventilation)
- Myoglobinuria, hypofibrinogenemia, fibrinolysis, hypocalcemia

TREATMENT

- Treatment of **heat exhaustion** consists primarily of placing the patient in a cool, shaded area and providing rapid hydration and salt replacement.
  1. Fluid intake should be at least 2 L q4h in patients without history of CHF.
  2. Salt replacement can be accomplished by using one-quarter teaspoon of salt or two 10-grain salt tablets dissolved in 1 L of water.
  3. If IV fluid replacement is necessary, young athletes can be given normal saline IV (3 to 4 L over 6 to 8 hr); in elderly patients, consider using $D_5\frac{1}{2}$NS IV with rate titrated to cardiovascular status.
- Patients with **heat stroke** should undergo rapid cooling.
  1. Remove the patient's clothes and place the patient in a cool and well-ventilated room.
  2. If unconscious, position patient on his or her side and clear the airway. Protect airway and augment oxygenation (e.g, nasal O_2 at 4 L/min to keep oxygen saturation >90%).
  3. Monitor body temperature every 5 min. Measurement of the patient's core temperature with a rectal probe is recommended. The goal is to reduce the body temperature to 39° C (102.2° F) in 30 to 60 min.
  4. Spray the patient with a cool mist and use fans to enhance airflow over the body (rapid evaporation method).
  5. Immersion of the patient in ice water, stomach lavage with iced saline solution, intravenous administration of cooled fluids, and inhalation of cold air are advisable only when the means for rapid evaporation are not available. Immersion in tepid water (15° C 59° F]) is preferred over ice water immersion to minimize risk of shivering.
  6. Use of ice packs on axillae, neck, and groin is controversial because they increase peripheral vasoconstriction and may induce shivering.
  7. Antipyretics are ineffective because the hypothalamic set point during heat stroke is normal despite the increased body temperature.
  8. Intubate a comatose patient, insert a Foley catheter, and start nasal O_2. Continuous ECG monitoring is recommended.
  9. Insert at least two large-bore IV lines and begin IV hydration with NS or Ringer's lactate.
  10. Draw initial lab studies: electrolytes, CBC, BUN, creatinine, AST, ALT, CPK, LDH, glucose, INR, PTT, platelet count, Ca^{2+}, lactic acid, ABGs.
  11. Treat complications as follows:
      a. Hypotension: vigorous hydration with normal saline or Ringer's lactate.
      b. Convulsions: diazepam 5 to 10 mg IV (slowly).
      c. Shivering: chlorpromazine 10 to 50 mg IV.
      d. Acidosis: use bicarbonate judiciously (only in severe acidosis).
  12. Observe for evidence of rhabdomyolysis, hepatic, renal, or cardiac failure and treat accordingly.

DISPOSITION

Most patients recover completely within 48 hr. Mortality can exceed 30% in patients with prolonged and severe hyperthermia.

SUGGESTED READINGS

Bouchama A, Knochel JP: Heat stroke, *N Engl J Med* 346:1978, 2002.
Wexler RK: Evaluation and treatment of heat-related illness, *Am Fam Physician* 65:230, 2002.

AUTHOR: **FRED F. FERRI, M.D.**

BASIC INFORMATION

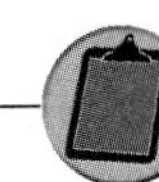

DEFINITION

The HELLP syndrome is a serious variant of preeclampsia. HELLP is an acronym for *H*emolysis, *E*levated *L*iver function, and *L*ow *P*latelet count. It is the most frequently encountered microangiopathy of pregnancy. There are three classes of the syndrome based on the degree of maternal thrombocytopenia as a primary indicator of disease severity.

Class 1: platelets 50,000/mm^3
Class 2: platelets >50,000/mm^3 to 100,000/mm^3
Class 3: platelets >100,000/mm^3

ICD-9CM CODES
642.50 HELLP, episode of care
642.51 HELLP, delivered
642.52 HELLP, delivered with postpartum complications
642.53 HELLP, antepartum complications
642.54 HELLP, postpartum complications

EPIDEMIOLOGY & DEMOGRAPHICS

- Among women with severe preeclampsia, 6% will manifest with one abnormality suggestive of HELLP syndrome, 12% will develop two abnormalities, and approximately 10% will develop all three.
- The HELLP Syndrome, like preeclampsia, is rare before 20 wk gestation.
- One third of all cases occur postpartum; of these, only 80% were diagnosed with preeclampsia before delivery.

RISK FACTORS: Women older than 35 yr, Caucasian, multiparity
RECURRENCE RATE: 3% to 25%

PHYSICAL FINDINGS & CLINICAL PRESENTATION

- Definitive laboratory criteria remain to be validated prospectively.
- Most commonly used criteria include hemolysis defined by the presence of an abnormal peripheral smear with schistocytes, lactate dehydrogenase (LDH) >600 U/L, and total bilirubin >1.2 mg/dl; elevated liver enzymes as serum aspartate aminotransferase (AST) >70 U/L and LDH >600 U/L; low platelet count as less than 100,000/mm^3.
- Although many women with HELLP syndrome will be asymptomatic, 80% report right upper quadrant pain and 50% to 60% present with excessive weight gain and worsening edema.

ETIOLOGY

As with other microangiopathies, endothelial dysfunction, with resultant activation of the intravascular coagulation cascade, has been proposed as the central pathogenesis of HELLP syndrome.

DIAGNOSIS

DIFFERENTIAL DIAGNOSIS

Appendicitis, gallbladder disease, peptic ulcer, enteritis, hepatitis, pyelonephritis, systemic lupus erythematosus, thrombotic thrombocytopenic purpura/hemolytic uremic syndrome, acute fatty liver of pregnancy.

WORKUP

Because the HELLP syndrome is a disease entity based on laboratory values, initial assessment is detailed as follows.

LABORATORY TESTS

- Initial assessment of suspected HELLP syndrome should include a complete blood count (CBC) to evaluate platelets, urinalysis, serum creatinine, LDH, uric acid, indirect and total bilirubin levels, and AST/ALT.
- Tests of prothrombin time, partial thromboplastin time, fibrinogen and fibrin split products are reserved for those women with a platelet count well below 100,000/mm^3.

IMAGING STUDIES

There are none to aid in diagnosis.

TREATMENT

Treatment is dependent on gestational age of the fetus, severity of HELLP, and maternal status. Stabilization of the mother is the first priority.

ACUTE GENERAL Rx

- Assess gestational age thoroughly. Fetal status should be monitored with nonstress tests, contraction stress tests, and/or biophysical profile
- Maternal status should be evaluated by history, physical examination, and laboratory testing
- Magnesium sulfate is administered for seizure prophylaxis regardless of blood pressure
- Blood pressure control is achieved with agents such as hydralazine or labetalol
- Indwelling Foley catheter to monitor maternal volume status and urine output

CHRONIC Rx

- In those pregnancies 34 wk or Class 1 HELLP syndrome, delivery, either vaginal or abdominal, within 24 hr is the goal.
- In the preterm fetus, corticosteroid therapy to enhance fetal lung maturation is indicated.
- Some reports have shown temporary amelioration of HELLP severity with the administration of high dose of steroids measured by increased urine output, improvement in platelet count and LFTs.
- Judicious use of blood products, especially in those requiring surgery.
- The patient requires intensive observation for 48 hr postpartum; laboratory levels should begin to improve during this time.

DISPOSITION

The natural history of this disorder is a rapidly deteriorating condition requiring close monitoring of maternal and fetal well-being.

REFERRAL

Preterm patients with the HELLP syndrome should be stabilized hemodynamically and transferred to a tertiary care center. Term patients can be treated at a local hospital depending on the availability of obstetric, neonatal, and blood banking services.

PEARLS & CONSIDERATIONS

Not all women with HELLP have hypertension or proteinuria.

SUGGESTED READINGS

Egerman RS, Sibai BM: HELLP syndrome, *Clin Obstet Gynecol* 42(2):381, 1999.
Magann EF, Martin JN: Twelve steps to optimal management of HELLP syndrome, *Clin Obstet Gynecol* 42(3):532, 1999.
Norwitz ER, Hsu CD, Repke JT: Acute complications of preeclampsia, *Clin Obstet Gynecol* 45(2):308, 2002.

AUTHOR: **SONYA S. ABDEL-RAZEQ, M.D.**

BASIC INFORMATION

DEFINITION

Hemochromatosis is an autosomal recessive disorder characterized by increased accumulation of iron in various organs (adrenals, liver, pancreas, heart, testes, kidneys, pituitary) and eventual dysfunction of these organs if not treated appropriately.

SYNONYMS

Bronze diabetes

ICD-9CM CODES
275.0 Hemochromatosis

EPIDEMIOLOGY & DEMOGRAPHICS

- Hemochromatosis is generally diagnosed in males in their fifth decade.
- Diagnosis in females is generally not made until 10 to 20 yr after menopause.
- Incidence in whites is approximately 1 in 300 persons.
- Most common genetic disorder in North European ancestry. Homozygosity for the C282Y mutation is now found in approximately 5 of every 1000 persons of European descent.

PHYSICAL FINDINGS & CLINICAL PRESENTATION

Examination may be normal; patient with advanced case may present with the following:

- Increased skin pigmentation
- Hepatomegaly, splenomegaly, hepatic tenderness, testicular atrophy
- Loss of body hair, peripheral edema, gynecomastia, ascites
- Amenorrhea (25% of females)
- Loss of libido (50% of males)
- Arthropathy
- Joint pain (44%)
- Fatigue (45%)

ETIOLOGY

Autosomal recessive disease linked to the region of the short arm of chromosome 6 encoding HLA-A*3; the gene HFE, which contains two missense mutations (C 282Y and H 63D), was recently identified.

DIAGNOSIS

DIFFERENTIAL DIAGNOSIS

- Hereditary anemias with defect of erythropoiesis
- Cirrhosis
- Repeated blood transfusions

WORKUP

Medical history, physical examination, and laboratory evaluation should be focused on affected organ systems (see Physical Findings). Liver biopsy is the gold standard for diagnosis; it reveals iron deposition in hepatocytes, bile ducts, and supporting tissues.

LABORATORY TESTS

- Transferrin saturation is the best screening test. Values >45% are an indication for further testing. When using transferring saturation to screen individuals <40 yr, a single test may not be sufficient and sequential measurements over a period of many years should be considered to detect hemochromatosis prior to onset of fibrosis or cirrhosis. Plasma ferritin is also a good indicator of total body iron stores but may be elevated in many other conditions (inflammation, malignancy). Some authors recommend measurement of both fasting transferrin saturation and serum ferritin level as initial tests for population-based screening to detect and treat hemochromatosis before iron loading occurs.
- Elevated AST, ALT, alkaline phosphatase.
- Hyperglycemia.
- Endocrine abnormalities (decreased testosterone, LH, FSH).
- Measurement of hepatic iron index (hepatic iron concentration [HIC] divided by age) in liver biopsy specimen can confirm diagnosis.
- Genetic testing (HFE genotyping for the C282Y and H63 D mutations) may be useful in selected patients with liver disease and suspected iron overload (e.g., patients with transferrin saturation >40%). Genetic testing should not be performed as part of initial routine evaluation for hereditary hemochromatosis. Once a patient has been identified, first-degree relatives of the index patient should also be screened. The HFE gene test is a PCR-based test usually performed on whole blood sample. Cost is approximately $150 to $200.

IMAGING STUDIES

CT scan or MRI of the liver is useful to exclude other etiologies and may in some cases show iron overload in the liver.

TREATMENT

NONPHARMACOLOGIC THERAPY

Weekly phlebotomies of one or two units of blood (each containing approximately 250 mg of iron) should be continued for several weeks until depletion of iron stores is achieved (ferritin level <50 μg/ml and transferring saturation <30%). Subsequent phlebotomies can be performed on a prn basis to maintain a transferrin saturation <50% and a ferritin level <100 μg/L.

ACUTE GENERAL Rx

Deferoxamine (iron chelating agent) is generally reserved for patients with severe hemochromatosis with diffuse organ involvement (e.g., liver disease, heart disease) and when phlebotomy is not possible. It is administered in a dose of 0.5 to 1 g IM qd or 20 mg SC over a 12- to 24-hr period with a constant infusion pump.

CHRONIC Rx

Phlebotomy on a prn basis depending on the Hct level; generally, Hct should not exceed 40%.

DISPOSITION

Prognosis is good if phlebotomy is started early (before onset of cirrhosis or diabetes mellitus); women can have the full phenotypic expression of the disease, including cirrhosis, and should also be aggressively treated.

REFERRAL

For liver biopsy if diagnosis is uncertain

PEARLS & CONSIDERATIONS

COMMENTS

- Patients with hemochromatosis and serum ferritin levels <1000 mcg/L are unlikely to have cirrhosis. Liver biopsy to screen for cirrhosis may be unnecessary in such patients.
- Cirrhotic patients must be periodically monitored (ultrasound or CT scan) because of their increased risk of hepatocellular carcinoma.
- HFE gene testing for C282Y mutation is a cost-effective method of screening relatives of patients with hereditary hemochromatosis.
- Established cirrhosis, hypogonadism, destructive arthritis, and insulin-dependent diabetes mellitus secondary to hemochromatosis cannot be reversed with repeated phlebotomy but their progress can be slowed.

SUGGESTED READINGS

Brandhagen DJ et al: Recognition and management of hereditary hemochromatosis, *Am Fam Physician,* 65:853, 2002.

Morrison ED et al: Serum ferritin level predicts advanced hepatic fibrosis among US patients with phenotypic hemochromatosis, *Ann Intern Med* 138:627, 2003.

Pietrangelo A: Hereditary hemochromatosis, a new look at an old disease, *N Engl J Med* 350:2383, 2004.

Waalen J et al: Prevalence of hemochromatosis-related symptoms among individuals with mutations in the HFE gene, *Mayo Clin Proc* 77:522, 2002.

AUTHOR: **FRED F. FERRI, M.D.**

BASIC INFORMATION

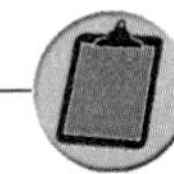

DEFINITION

Hemolytic-uremic syndrome refers to an acute syndrome characterized by hemolytic anemia, thrombocytopenia, and severe renal failure.

SYNONYMS

HUS

ICD-9CM CODES
283.11 Hemolytic-uremic syndrome

EPIDEMIOLOGY & DEMOGRAPHICS

- HUS affects mainly children younger than 10 yr old
- Incidence is 2.6 cases/100,000 in people younger than 5 yr of age
- Incidence is 0.97 cases/100,000 in people over the age of 18
- May be epidemic, most commonly occurring during the summer months
- Most common cause of acute renal failure in children
- In the United States 300 to 700 new cases occur each year

PHYSICAL FINDINGS & CLINICAL PRESENTATION

- HUS usually preceded by diarrhea in 90% of cases
- Bloody diarrhea (75%)
- Abdominal pain
- Vomiting
- Fever
- Irritability, lethargy, and seizures (10%)
- Hypertension
- Pallor
- Anuria or oliguria

ETIOLOGY

Pathologically, it is thought that thrombin generation (probably the result of accelerated thrombogenesis) and inhibition of fibrinolysis leads to renal arteriolar and capillary microthrombi preceding renal injury.
In children:

- *E. coli* serotype O157:H7 is the leading cause of HUS.
- The infection is acquired by eating undercooked red meat, especially hamburgers.

Other causes of HUS in children and adults are:

- Drugs (cyclosporine, mitomycin, tacrolimus, ticlopidine, clopidogrel, cisplatin, quinine, penicillin, penicillamine, oral contraceptives, and quinine used to treat muscle cramps)
- Infection (*Salmonella, Shigella, Yersinia, Campylobacter,* coxsackievirus, rubella, influenza virus, Epstein-Barr virus)
- Toxins
- Pregnancy (usually postpartum) and oral contraceptives
- HIV-associated thrombotic microangiopathy
- Pneumococcal infection

DIAGNOSIS

The triad of thrombocytopenia, acute renal failure, and microangiopathic hemolytic anemia establishes the diagnosis of HUS.

DIFFERENTIAL DIAGNOSIS

- The differential is vast, including all causes of bloody and nonbloody diarrhea because the GI symptoms usually precede the triad of HUS
- Thrombotic thrombocytopenic purpura
- Disseminated intravascular coagulation
- Prosthetic valve hemolysis
- Malignant hypertension
- Vasculitis

WORKUP

The workup for suspected HUS patients includes blood tests and stool cultures.

LABORATORY TESTS

- CBC with hemoglobin <10 g/dl
- Peripheral smear shows the hallmark microangiopathic hemolytic anemia with schistocytes, burr cells, and helmet cells
- Thrombocytopenia (platelet counts usually <60,000/mm^3)
- Reticulocyte count is high
- LDH level is elevated
- Haptoglobin is low
- Indirect bilirubin is elevated
- BUN and creatinine are elevated
- Urinalysis reveals proteinuria, microscopic hematuria, and pyuria
- Stool cultures for *E. coli* O157:H7 are positive in over 90% of cases if obtained during the first week of illness. After the first week only one third are positive

IMAGING STUDIES

Imaging studies are not very helpful in the diagnosis of HUS.

TREATMENT

The treatment of HUS is primarily supportive.

NONPHARMACOLOGIC THERAPY

- Blood transfusions for severe anemia
- Antibiotics should be avoided and are not indicated for the treatment of *E. coli* O157:H7
- Correction of electrolyte abnormalities

ACUTE GENERAL Rx

Hypertension control

CHRONIC Rx

For anuric or oliguric renal failure, dialysis may be required.

DISPOSITION

- Adults presenting with HUS have a worse prognosis than children do with HUS.
- Mortality rate is 5%.
- Morbidity includes:
  1. Proteinuria (31%)
  2. Renal insufficiency (31%)
  3. Hypertension (6%)

REFERRAL

- The local health department should be notified if the bacteria *E. coli* O157:H7 has been isolated.
- Consultation with hematology and nephrology specialist is recommended in patients with HUS.

PEARLS & CONSIDERATIONS

COMMENTS

- Hemolytic-uremic syndrome was first described by Gasser and colleagues in 1955.
- Children testing positive for the *E. coli* O157:H7 serotype should not return to school or day care facilities until two consecutive stools test negative for the microorganism.
- *E. coli* O157:H7 can be transmitted from person to person, therefore universal precautions and hand washing are recommended in preventing the spread of the infection.

SUGGESTED READINGS

Begue RE, Mehta D, Blecker U: *Escherichia coli* and the hemolytic-uremic syndrome, *South Med J* 91(9):798, 1998.
Boyce TG, Swerdlow DL, Griffin PM: *Escherichia coli* O157:H7 and the hemolytic-uremic syndrome, *N Engl J Med* 333(6):364, 1995.
Chandler WL et al: Prothrombotic coagulation abnormalities preceding the hemolytic-uremic syndrome, *N Engl J Med* 346:23, 2002.
Gordjani N et al: Hemolytic uremic syndromes in childhood, *Semin Thromb Hem* 23(3):281, 1997.
Medina PJ, Sipolis JM, George JN: Drug-associated thrombotic thrombocytopenic purpura-hemolytic uremic syndrome, *Curr Opin Hematol* 8:286, 2001.

AUTHORS: **PETER PETROPOULOS, M.D.,** and **DENNIS J. MIKOLICH, M.D.**

BASIC INFORMATION

DEFINITION

Hemophilia is a hereditary bleeding disorder caused by low factor VIII coagulant activity (hemophilia A) or low levels of Factor IX coagulant activity (hemophilia B).

SYNONYMS

Hemophilia A: Classic hemophilia, factor VIII deficiency hemophilia
Hemophilia B: Christmas disease, factor IX hemophilia

ICD-9CM CODES
286.0 Hemophilia A
286.1 Hemophilia B

EPIDEMIOLOGY & DEMOGRAPHICS

INCIDENCE/PREVALENCE (IN U.S.): Hemophilia A: 100 cases/1 million males, hemophilia B: 20 cases/1 million males
GENETIC FACTORS: Both hemophilias have an X-linked recessive pattern of inheritance with only males affected.

PHYSICAL FINDINGS & CLINICAL PRESENTATION

- The clinical features of hemophilia A and B are generally indistinguishable from each other.
- Bleeding is most commonly seen in joints (knees, ankles, elbows) resulting in hot, swollen, painful joints and subsequent crippling joint deformity.
- Bleeding can also occur into the muscles and the GI tract.
- Compartment syndromes can occur from large hematomas.
- Hematuria may be present.

ETIOLOGY

- Hemophilia A: low factor VIII coagulant (VIII:C) activity; can be classified as mild if factor VIII:C levels are >5%, moderate: levels are 1% to 5%, severe: levels are <1%.
- Hemophilia B: low levels of factor IX coagulant activity.
- Both disorders are congenital.
- Spontaneous acquisition of factor VIII inhibitors (acquired hemophilia) is rare.

DIAGNOSIS

DIFFERENTIAL DIAGNOSIS

- Other clotting factor deficiencies
- Platelet function disorders
- Vitamin K deficiency

WORKUP

Patients with mild hemophilia bleed only in response to major trauma or surgery and may not be diagnosed until young adulthood. Diagnostic workup includes laboratory evaluation (see Laboratory Tests).

LABORATORY TESTS

- Partial thromboplastin time (PTT) is prolonged.
- Reduced factor VIII:C level distinguishes hemophilia A from other causes of prolonged PTT.
- Factor VIII antigen, PT, fibrinogen level, and bleeding time are normal.
- Factor IX coagulant activity levels are reduced in patients with hemophilia B.
- Coagulation factor activity measurement is useful to correlate with disease severity: normal range is 50 to 150 U/dl; 5 to 20 U/dl indicates mild disease, 2 to 5 U/dl indicates moderate disease, and <2 U/dl indicates severe disease with spontaneous bleeding episodes.

TREATMENT

NONPHARMACOLOGIC THERAPY

- Avoidance of contact sports
- Patient education regarding their disease; promotion of exercises such as swimming
- Avoidance of aspirin or other NSAIDs
- Orthopedic evaluation and physical therapy evaluation in patients with joint involvement
- Hepatitis vaccination

ACUTE GENERAL Rx

HEMOPHILIA A:

- Reversal and prevention of acute bleeding in hemophilia A and B are based on adequate replacement of deficient or missing factor protein.
- The choice of the product for replacement therapy is guided by availability, capacity, concerns, and cost. Recombinant factors cost two to three times as much as plasma-derived factors, and the limited capacity to produce recombinant factors often results in periods of shortage. In the U.S., 60% of patients with severe hemophilia use recombinant products.
- Factor VIII concentrates are effective in controlling spontaneous and traumatic hemorrhage in severe hemophilia. The new recombinant factor VIII is stable without added human serum albumin (decreased risk of transmission of infectious agents).
- Recombinant activated factor VII is useful to stop spontaneous hemorrhages and prevent excessive bleeding during surgery in 75% of patients with inhibitors. Recommended dose is 90 μg/mg of body weight every 2-3 hr for treatment of life-threatening hemorrhage. It is, however, very expensive ($1 per μg).
- Desmopressin acetate 0.3 μg/kg q24h (causes release of factor VIII:C) may be used in preparation for minor surgical procedures in mild hemophiliacs.
- Aminocaproic acid (EACA, Amicar) 4 g PO q4h can be given for persistent bleeding that is unresponsive to factor VIII concentrate or desmopressin.

HEMOPHILIA B:

- Infuse factor IX concentrates. It is important to remember that factor IX concentrates contain other proteins that may increase the risk of thrombosis with recurrent use. Therefore factor IX concentrates must be used only when clearly indicated.
- Daily administration of oral cyclophosphamide and prednisone without empirical factor VIII therapy is an effective and well-tolerated treatment for acquired hemophilia.

CHRONIC Rx

- The aim of chronic treatment is to prevent spontaneous bleeding and to prevent excessive bleeding during any surgical intervention.
- Implantation of genetically altered fibroblasts that produce factor VIII is safe and well tolerated. This form is feasible in patients with severe hemophilia. Hemophilia will likely be the first common, severe genetic disease to be cured by gene therapy.

DISPOSITION

- Despite the advent of virally safe blood products and blood treatment programs, nearly 70% of hemophiliacs are HIV-seropositive. Survival is of normal expectancy in HIV-negative patients with mild disease.
- Intracranial bleeds are the second most common cause of death in hemophiliacs after AIDS. They are fatal in 30% of patients, occur in 10% of patients, and are generally secondary to trauma.

SUGGESTED READING

Mannucci PM, Tuddenham E: The hemophilias, from royal genes to gene therapy, *N Engl J Med* 344:1773, 2001.

AUTHOR: **FRED F. FERRI, M.D.**

Hemorrhoids (PTG)

BASIC INFORMATION

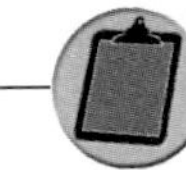

DEFINITION

A hemorrhoid is a varicose dilation of a vein of the superior or inferior hemorrhoidal plexus, resulting from a persistent increase in venous pressure. External hemorrhoids are below the pectinate line (inferior plexus). Internal hemorrhoids are above the pectinate line (superior plexus) (Fig. 1-114).

SYNONYMS

Piles

ICD-9CM CODES
455.6 Hemorrhoids

EPIDEMIOLOGY & DEMOGRAPHICS

Potential for development of symptomatic hemorrhoids in all adults

PREVALENCE: Estimated 50% of the adult population in the U.S.

PREDOMINANT SEX: Males = females

PHYSICAL FINDINGS & CLINICAL PRESENTATION

- Painless bleeding with defecation; bleeding is bright red and staining on toilet paper
- Perianal irritation
- Mucofecal staining of underclothes
- Acute external hemorrhoids: painful, swollen, and often thrombosed
- Pain on sitting, standing, or defecating (thrombosed hemorrhoid)
- Prolapse
- Constipation

ETIOLOGY

- Low-fiber, high-fat diet
- Chronic constipation and straining with defecation
- High resting anal sphincter pressures
- Pregnancy
- Obesity
- Rectal surgery (i.e., episiotomy)
- Prolonged sitting
- Anal intercourse

DIAGNOSIS

DIFFERENTIAL DIAGNOSIS

- Fissure
- Abscess
- Anal fistula
- Condylomata acuminata
- Hypertrophied anal papillae
- Rectal prolapse
- Rectal polyp
- Neoplasm

WORKUP

- Inspection
- Digital rectal examination
- Anoscopy
- Sigmoidoscopy

TREATMENT

NONPHARMACOLOGIC THERAPY

- Avoidance of constipation and straining with defecation
- Avoidance of prolonged sitting on toilet
- High-fiber diet (20 to 30 g/day)
- Increased fluid intake (six to eight glasses of water per day)
- Cleaning with mild soap and water after defecation
- Warm soaks or ice to soothe
- Sitz baths

ACUTE GENERAL Rx

- Fiber supplements to provide bulk (psyllium extracts or mucilloids)
- Medicated compresses with witch hazel
- Topical hydrocortisone (1% to 3% cream or ointment)
- Topical anesthetic spray
- Glycerin suppositories
- Stool softeners
- Surgically remove during first 72 hr after onset

CHRONIC Rx

- Rubber-band ligation
- Injection sclerotherapy
- Photocoagulation
- Cryodestruction
- Hemorrhoidectomy
- Anal dilation
- Laser or cautery hemorrhoidectomy
- Observance for complications: thrombosis, bleeding, infection, anal stenosis or weakness

DISPOSITION

Should resolve, but there is a high rate of recurrence

REFERRAL

To colorectal or general surgeon for any hemorrhoid that does not respond to conservative therapy

PEARLS & CONSIDERATIONS

COMMENTS

- Patients need to understand the importance of a healthy diet, regular exercise, and rectal hygiene.
- Stress the importance of avoiding prolonged sitting and straining on the toilet.
- Stress the need not to defer the urge to defecate.

SUGGESTED READING

Zuber TJ: Hemorrhoidectomy for thrombosed external hemorrhoids, *Am Fam Physician* 65:1629, 2002.

AUTHOR: **MARIA A. CORIGLIANO, M.D.**

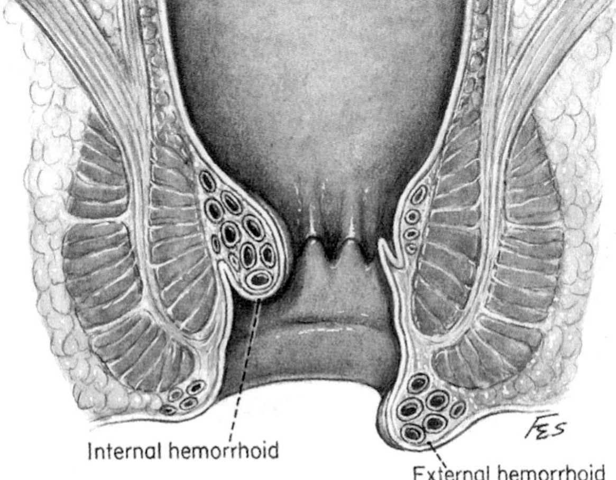

FIGURE 1-114 Anatomy of internal and external hemorrhoids. (From Noble J [ed]: *Textbook of primary care medicine,* ed 2, St Louis, 1996, Mosby.)

Henoch-Schönlein Purpura

BASIC INFORMATION

DEFINITION

Henoch-Schönlein purpura (HSP) is a systemic small vessel vasculitis characterized by palpable purpura in dependent areas (buttocks, legs), gastrointestinal bleeding and other symptoms, arthralgias, arthritis, and renal involvement.

SYNONYMS

Anaphylactoid purpura
Allergic purpura

ICD-9CM CODES

287.0 Henoch-Schönlein purpura

EPIDEMIOLOGY & DEMOGRAPHICS

HSP is the most common vasculitis seen in children and younger age groups. It has an annual incidence of 14 cases/ 100,000 population. It is seen mostly from 4 to 15 yr of age, although it can also be seen in older adolescents and young adults. A 2:1 male to female ratio exists. Peak incidence is seen in spring, although cases are seen throughout the year.

PHYSICAL FINDINGS & CLINICAL PRESENTATION

- Palpable purpura of dependent areas, especially lower extremities (Fig. 1-115), and areas subjected to pressure such as the beltline
- Subcutaneous edema
- Arthralgias and arthritis in 80% of patients
- GI symptoms are seen in approximately one third of patients. Common findings are nausea, vomiting, diarrhea, cramping, abdominal pain, hematochezia, and melena
- Anecdotally may follow upper respiratory infection
- Renal involvement is seen in up to 80% of older children, usually within the first month of illness. Less than 5% of cases progress to end-stage renal failure

ETIOLOGY

The presumptive etiology is exposure to a trigger antigen that causes antibody formation. Antigen-antibody (immune) complex deposition then occurs in arteriole and capillary walls of skin, renal mesangium, and GI tract. IgA deposition is most common. Antigen triggers postulated include drugs, foods, immunization, and upper respiratory and other viral illnesses. Serologic and pathologic evidence exists, suggesting an association between Parvovirus B19 and HSP. This association may explain observed cases of HSP, which does not respond to corticosteroids or other immunosuppressive therapy.

DIAGNOSIS

Diagnosis is made on clinical grounds. Skin manifestations are most common. Palpable purpura is seen in 70% of adult patients and is less pronounced in children, in whom GI complaints are more common. Skin biopsy will show leukocytoclastic vasculitis. The presence of two of the following four American College of Rheumatology criteria yields a diagnostic sensitivity of 87.1% and specificity of 87.7%:

- Palpable purpura unrelated to thrombocytopenia
- Age <20 yr at onset of first symptoms
- Bowel angina or ischemia
- Granulocytic infiltration of arteriole or venule walls on biopsy

DIFFERENTIAL DIAGNOSIS

Other forms of cutaneous or leukocytoclastic vasculitis:

- Polyarteritis nodosa
- Meningococcemia
- Thrombocytopenic purpura

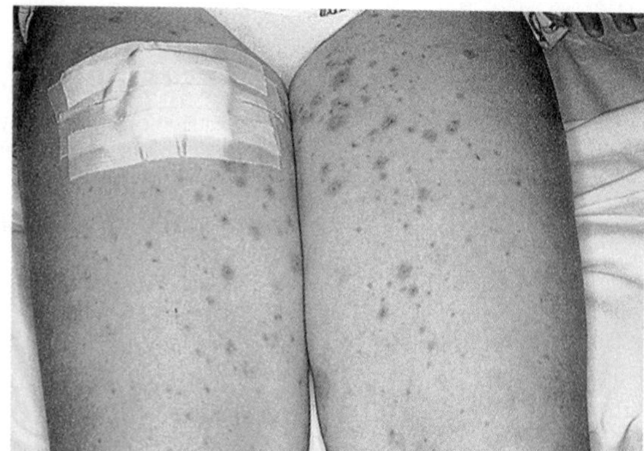

FIGURE 1-115 Henoch-Schönlein purpura on the lower extremities of a child. (Courtesy Medical College of Georgia, Division of Dermatology. From Goldstein B [ed]: *Practical dermatology,* ed 2, St Louis, 1997, Mosby.)

WORKUP

History, physical examination, laboratory testing to rule out other diagnostic considerations, and skin biopsy

LABORATORY TESTS

- Electrolytes, BUN, and creatinine
- Urinalysis
- CBC
- Prothrombin time, fibrinogen, and fibrin degradation products
- Blood cultures

Laboratory abnormalities are not specific for HSP. Leukocytosis and eosinophilia may be seen. IgA levels are elevated in approximately 50% of patients. Glomerulonephritis may be present and result in microscopic hematuria, proteinuria, and RBC casts.

IMAGING STUDIES

Imaging studies are not useful in diagnosis of HSP. Arteriography or magnetic resonance angiography may be helpful in distinguishing from polyarteritis nodosa.

TREATMENT

- Prednisone 1 mg/kg PO is given if renal or severe GI disease, although benefits are not clear
- Corticosteroids and azathioprine may be beneficial if rapidly progressive glomerulonephritis present. Pulse methylprednisolone therapy has also been proposed in patients with glomerulonephritis, mesenteric vasculitis, or pulmonary involvement
- NSAIDs for arthritis and arthralgias

NONPHARMACOLOGIC THERAPY

Supportive care with pain management, adequate hydration, and nutrition

DISPOSITION & PROGNOSIS

- Prognosis excellent with spontaneous recovery of most patients within 4 wk.
- End-stage renal disease occurs in 5% of patients. Chronic renal insufficiency is the most common long-term morbidity.
- GI complications include mesenteric infarction, perforation, and intussusception.
- Recurrences can occur.

REFERRAL

- For renal or gastrointestinal complications
- For severe clinical syndrome

SUGGESTED READINGS

Ballinger S: Henoch-Schonlein purpura, *Curr Opin Rheumatol* 15:591, 2003.
Dillon MJ: Henoch-Schönlein purpura (treatment and outcome), *Cleve Clin J Med* 69(Suppl 2):SII 121, 2002.

AUTHOR: **DOMINICK TAMMARO, M.D.**

BASIC INFORMATION

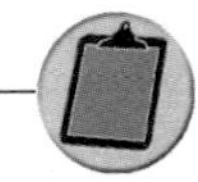

DEFINITION

Hepatic encephalopathy is an abnormal mental status occurring in patients with severe impairment of liver function and consequent accumulation of toxic products not metabolized by the liver.

SYNONYMS

Hepatic coma

ICD-9CM CODES
572.2 Hepatic encephalopathy

EPIDEMIOLOGY & DEMOGRAPHICS

INCIDENCE/PREVALENCE: Hepatic encephalopathy occurs in >50% of all cases of cirrhosis.

PHYSICAL FINDINGS & CLINICAL PRESENTATION

Hepatic encephalopathy can be classified in stages or grades 1 to 4:
- Grades 1 and 2: mild obtundation
- Grades 3 and 4: stupor to deep coma, with or without decerebrate posturing

The physical examination in hepatic encephalopathy varies with the stage and may reveal the following abnormalities:
- Skin: jaundice, palmar erythema, spider angiomata, ecchymosis, dilated superficial periumbilical veins (caput medusae) in patients with cirrhosis
- Eyes: scleral icterus, Kayser-Fleischer rings (Wilson's disease)
- Breath: fetor hepaticus
- Chest: gynecomastia in men with chronic liver disease
- Abdomen: ascites, small nodular liver (cirrhosis), tender hepatomegaly (congestive hepatomegaly)
- Rectal examination: hemorrhoids (portal hypertension), guaiac-positive stool (alcoholic gastritis, bleeding esophageal varices, PUD, bleeding hemorrhoids)
- Genitalia: testicular atrophy in males with chronic liver disease
- Extremities: pedal edema from hypoalbuminemia
- Neurologic: flapping tremor (asterixis), obtundation, coma with or without decerebrate posturing

ETIOLOGY

- Precipitating factors in patients with underlying cirrhosis (UGI bleeding, hypokalemia, hypomagnesemia, analgesic and sedative drugs, sepsis, alkalosis, increased dietary protein)
- Acute fulminant viral hepatitis
- Drugs and toxins (e.g., isoniazid, acetaminophen, diclofenac and other NSAIDs, statins, methyldopa, loratadine, PTU, lisinopril, labetalol, halothane, carbon tetrachloride, erythromycin, nitrofurantoin, troglitazone)
- Reye's syndrome
- Shock and/or sepsis
- Fatty liver of pregnancy
- Metastatic carcinoma, hepatocellular carcinoma
- Other: autoimmune hepatitis, ischemic venoocclusive disease, sclerosing cholangitis, heat stroke, amebic abscesses

DIAGNOSIS

DIFFERENTIAL DIAGNOSIS

- Delirium secondary to medications or illicit drugs
- CVA, subdural hematoma
- Meningitis, encephalitis
- Hypoglycemia
- Uremia
- Cerebral anoxia
- Hypercalcemia
- Metastatic neoplasm to brain
- Alcohol withdrawal syndrome

WORKUP

Exclude other etiologies with comprehensive history (obtained from patient, relatives, and others), physical examination, laboratory and imaging studies. A pertinent history should include exposure to hepatitis, ethanol intake, drug history, exposure to toxins, IV drug abuse, measles or influenza with aspirin use (Reye's syndrome), history of carcinoma (primary or metastatic).

LABORATORY TESTS

- ALT, AST, bilirubin, alkaline phosphatase glucose, calcium, electrolytes, BUN, creatinine, albumin
- CBC, platelet count, PT, PTT
- Serum and urine toxicology screen in suspected medication or illegal drug use
- Blood and urine cultures, urinalysis
- Venous ammonia level
- ABGs

IMAGING STUDIES

CT scan of head may be useful in selected patients to exclude other etiologies.

TREATMENT

NONPHARMACOLOGIC THERAPY

- Identification and treatment of precipitating factors
- Restriction of protein intake (30 to 40 g/day) to reduce toxic protein metabolites

ACUTE GENERAL Rx

REDUCTION OF COLONIC AMMONIA PRODUCTION:
- Lactulose 30 ml of 50% solution qid initially, dose is subsequently adjusted depending on clinical response. Ornithine aspartate 9 g tid is also effective.
- Neomycin 1 g PO q4-6h or given as a 1% retention enema solution (1 g in 100 ml of isotonic saline solution); neomycin should be used with caution in patients with renal insufficiency; metronidazole 250 mg qid may be as effective as neomycin and is not nephrotoxic; however, long-term use can be associated with neurotoxicity. Rifaximin 1200 mg/day is a viable alternative to metronidazole.
- A combination of lactulose and neomycin can be used when either agent is ineffective alone.

TREATMENT OF CEREBRAL EDEMA: Cerebral edema is often present in patients with acute liver failure, and it accounts for nearly 50% of deaths. Monitoring intracranial pressure by epidural, intraparenchymal, or subdural transducers and treatment of cerebral edema with mannitol (100 to 200 ml of 20% solution [0.3 to 0.4 g/kg of body weight]) given by rapid IV infusion is helpful in selected patients (e.g., potential transplantation patients); dexamethasone and hyperventilation (useful in head injury) are of little value in treating cerebral edema from liver failure

CHRONIC Rx

- Avoidance of any precipitating factors (e.g., high-protein diet, medications)
- Consideration of liver transplantation in selected patients with progressive or recurrent encephalopathy

DISPOSITION

Prognosis varies with the underlying etiology of the liver failure and the grade of encephalopathy (generally good for grades 1, 2; poor for grades 3, 4).

REFERRAL

The early stages of hepatic encephalopathy can be managed in the outpatient setting, whereas stages 3 or 4 require hospital admission.

PEARLS & CONSIDERATIONS

COMMENTS

Patients not responding to supportive therapy should be evaluated for liver transplantation.

AUTHOR: **FRED F. FERRI, M.D.**

Hepatitis A (PTG)

BASIC INFORMATION

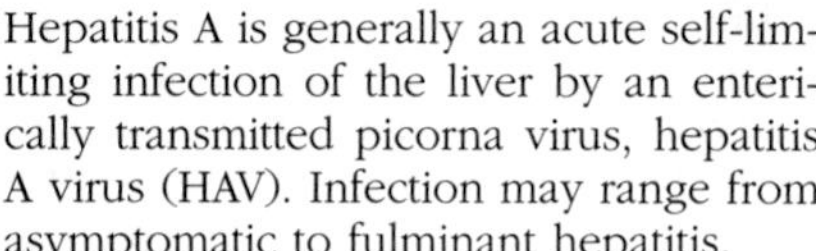

DEFINITION

Hepatitis A is generally an acute self-limiting infection of the liver by an enterically transmitted picorna virus, hepatitis A virus (HAV). Infection may range from asymptomatic to fulminant hepatitis.

ICD-9CM CODES
070.1 Hepatitis A

EPIDIMIOLOGY & DEMOGRAPHICS

INCIDENCE:

- It occurs worldwide, affecting 1.4 million people annually and accounting for 20%-40% of cases of viral hepatitis in U.S.
- The seroprevalence increases with age, ranging from 10% in individuals <5 yr to 74% in those >50 yr.
- In the U.S. average disease rate is approximately 15 cases/100,000 persons/yr.
- The incidence is relatively higher in some regions in the U.S., including Arizona, Alaska, California, Idaho, Nevada, New Mexico, Okalahoma, Oregon, South Dakota, and Washington.
- At-risk groups include:
  1. Residents and staff of group homes
  2. Children, employees of day care centers
  3. Persons who engage in oral-anal contact, regardless of sexual orientation
  4. Intravenous drug abusers
  5. Travel to endemic areas
  6. Areas of overcrowding, poor sanitation, inadequate sewage treatment

PREVALENCE

- Approximately three fourths of U.S. population has serologic evidence of prior infection
- Anti-HAV prevalence has inverse relation to income and household size

PREDOMINANT SEX: None, except higher infection rates seen in homosexual males who engage in oral-anal contact.

PREDOMINANT AGE/PEAK INCIDENCE

- In areas of high rates of hepatitis A, virtually all children are infected while younger than 10 yr, but disease is rare.
- In areas of moderate rates of hepatitis A, disease occurs in late childhood and young adults.
- In areas of low rates of hepatitis A, most cases occur in young adults.

INCUBATION PERIOD: Averages 30 days (15 to 50)

PHYSICAL FINDINGS & CLINICAL PRESENTATION

- Infection with HAV may have acute or subacute presentation, icteric or anicteric. Severity of illness seems to increase with age (90% of infection in children <5 yr may be subclinical)
- A preicteric, prodromal phase of approximately 1-14 days. 15% no apparent prodrome. Symptoms are usually abrupt in onset and may include anorexia, malaise, nausea, vomiting, fever, headache, abdominal pain
- Less common symptoms are chills, myalgias, arthralgias, upper respiratory symptoms, constipation, diarrhea, pruritis, urticaria
- Jaundice occurs in >70% of patients
- The icteric phase is preceded by dark urine
- Bilirubinuria is typically followed a few days later by clay-colored stools and icterus

PHYSICAL EXAM

- Jaundice
- Hepatomegaly
- Splenomegaly
- Cervical lymphadenopathy
- Evanescent rash
- Petechiae
- Cardiac arrhythmias

COMPLICATION

- Cholestasis
- Fulminant hepatitis
- Arthritis
- Myocarditis
- Optic neuritis
- Transverse myelitis
- Thrombocytopenic purpura
- Aplastic anemia
- Red cell aplasia
- Henoch-Schonlein purpura
- IgA dominant glomerulonephritis

ETIOLOGY

- Caused by HAV, a 27nm, nonenveloped, icosahedra, positive-stranded RNA virus
- Transmission is fecal-oral route, from person to person. Transmission requires close contact
- Parenteral transmission is considered rare
- Vertical transmission also reported

DIAGNOSIS

DIFFERENTIAL DIAGNOSIS

- Other hepatitis virus (B, C, D, E)
- Infectious mononucleosis
- Cytomegalovirus infection
- Herpes simplex virus infection
- Leptospirosis
- Brucellosis
- Drug-induced liver disease
- Ischemic hepatitis
- Autoimmune hepatitis

WORKUP

- IgM antibody specific for HAV
- Liver function tests; ALT and AST elevations are sensitive for liver damage but not specific for HAV
- Elevated ESR
- CBC; may find mild lymphocytosis

LABORATORY TESTS

- Diagnosis confirmed by IgM anti HAV; it is detectable in almost all infected patients at presentation and remains positive for 3 to 6 mo
- A fourfold rise in titer of total antibody (IgM and IgG) to HAV confirms acute infection
- HAV detection in stool and body fluids by electron microscopy
- HAV RNA detection in stool, body fluids, serum, and liver tissue
- ALT and AST usually more than eight times normal in acute infection
- Bilirubin usually five to 15 times normal
- Alkaline phosphatase minimally elevated but higher level in cholestasis
- Albumin and prothrombin time are generally normal, if elevated may herald hepatic necrosis

IMAGING STUDIES

- Rarely useful
- Sonogram (fulminant hepatitis)

TREATMENT

- Usually self-limited
- Supportive care
- Those with fulminant hepatitis may require hospitalization and treatment of associated complications
- Activity as tolerated
- Advise to avoid alcohol and hepatoxic drugs
- Patients with fulminant hepatitis should be assessed for liver transplantation

CHRONIC Rx

No chronic HAV and no chronic carrier state

DISPOSITION

Follow-up as outpatient

PREVENTION

- Improvement in hygiene and sanitation
- Heating food
- Avoidance of water and foods from endemic area

PASSIVE IMMUNIZATION

- Immunoglobulin provides protection against HAV through passive transfer of antibody
- Preexposure prophylaxis indicated for person traveling to endemic areas (0.6 ml protects for <5 mo)
- Postexposure prophylaxis indicated for persons with recent exposure (within 2 wk) to HAV and who have not been previously vaccinated. In high-risk patients vaccine may be administered with immunoglobulin

ACTIVE IMMUNIZATION

- There are several inactivated and attenuated hepatitis vaccines; only the inactivated vaccines are currently available for use and they have been found to be safe and highly immunogenic
- Protective antibody levels were reached in 94% to 100% of adults 1 mo after the first dose, similar results have been found for children and adolescents
- Theoretic analyses of antibody levels estimate duration of immunity to be 10 to 20 yr
- Vaccine should be considered for persons who are at risk: those traveling to or working in endemic areas, homosexual men, illegal drug users, persons with chronic liver disease, children in areas with high rates of hepatitis A infection

SUGGESTED READINGS

Jenson HB: The changing picture of hepatitis A in the United States, *Curr Opin Pediatr* 16(1):89, 2004.

Leach CT: Hepatitis A in the United States, *Pediatr Infect Dis J* 23(6):551, 2004.

Rezende G. et al: Viral and clinical factors associated with the fulminant course of hepatitis A infection, *Hepatology* 38:613, 2003.

AUTHOR: **VASANTHI ARUMUGAM, M.D.**

BASIC INFORMATION

DEFINITION

Hepatitis B is an acute infection of the liver parenchymal cells caused by the hepatitis B virus (HBV).

SYNONYMS

Serum hepatitis
Long incubation (30 to 180 days) Hepatitis

ICD-9CM CODES
070.3 Hepatitis B

EPIDEMIOLOGY & DEMOGRAPHICS

INCIDENCE (IN U.S.):

- Approximately 200,000 to 300,000 infections annually in U.S.
- Much higher incidence in Europe (approximately 1 million new cases annually) and in areas of high endemicity
- In U.S., transmission is mainly horizontal (percutaneous and mucous membrane exposure to infectious blood and other body fluids, [e.g., sexual transmission, either homosexual or heterosexual]); also from needle sharing amongst drug abusers; occupational exposure to contaminated blood and blood products; persons receiving transfusions of blood and blood products; hemodialysis patients

NOTE: improved screening of blood and blood products has greatly reduced, although not eliminated, the risk of post-transfusion HBV infection.

- In areas of high endemicity, transmission is largely vertical (perinatal): HBV exists in the blood and body fluids. Perinatal transmission from HBsAg-positive mothers is as high as 90%

PREVALENCE (IN U.S.):

- North America, Western Europe, and Australia are areas of low prevalence, <2%.
- Africa, Asia, and the Western Pacific region are areas of high prevalence, ≥8%.
- Southern and Eastern Europe have intermediate rates, 2% to 7%.
- Chronically infected persons, those with positive HBsAg for >6 mo, represent the major source of infection.
- Up to 95% of infants and children <5 yr of age, who typically have subclinical acute infection, will become chronic HBV carriers.
- Adults are more likely to have clinically evident acute infection, but only 1% to 5% will develop chronic infection.
- Approximately 0.1% with acute infection will develop fulminant acute hepatitis resulting in death.

PREDOMINANT SEX:

- Predominant in males because of increased intravenous drug abuse, homosexuality
- Females more commonly terminate in chronic carrier state

PREDOMINANT AGE: 20 to 45 yr

PEAK INCIDENCE: 30 to 45 yr of age, at rates of 5% to 20%

GENETICS:

Neonatal infection:

- Rare in U.S.
- High (up to 90%) in areas of high endemicity (only 5% to 10% of perinatal infections occur in utero)

PHYSICAL FINDINGS & CLINICAL PRESENTATION (FIG. 1-116)

- Often nonspecific symptoms
- Profound malaise
- Many asymptomatic cases
- Prodrome:
  1. 15% to 20% serum sickness (urticaria, rash, arthralgia) during early HBsAg
  2. HBsAg-Ab complex disease (arthritis, arteritis, glomerulonephritis)
- Hepatomegaly (87%) with RUQ tenderness
  1. Hepatic punch tenderness
  2. Splenomegaly: rare (10% to 15%)

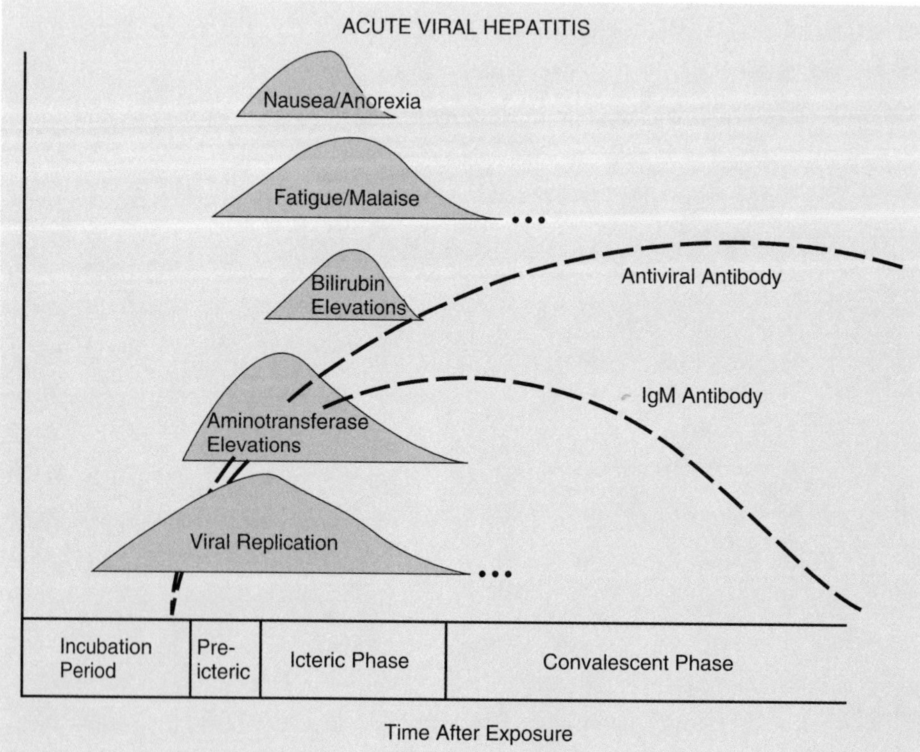

FIGURE 1-116 The typical course of acute viral hepatitis. (From Goldman L, Ausiello D [eds]: *Cecil textbook of medicine,* ed 22, Philadelphia, 2004, WB Saunders.)

- Jaundice, dark urine, with occasional pruritus
- Variable fever (when present, generally precedes jaundice and rapidly declines following onset of icteric phase)
- Spider angiomata: rare; resolves during recovery
- Rare polyarteritis nodosa, cryoglobulinemia

ETIOLOGY

- Caused by hepatitis B virus (42-nm hepadnavirus with an outer surface coat [HBsAg], inner nucleocapsid core [HBcAg; HBeAg]; DNA polymerase; and partially double-stranded DNA genome)
- Transmission by parenteral route (needle use, tattooing, ear piercing, acupuncture, transfusion of blood and blood products, hemodialysis, sexual contact), perinatal transmission
- Infection may result from contact of infectious material with mucous membranes and open skin breaks (e.g., HBV is stable and can be transmitted from toothbrushes, utensils, razors, baby toys, various medical equipment [respirators, endoscopes])
- Oral intake of infectious material may result in infection through breaks in the oral mucosa
- Food or water virtually never found to be sources of HBV infection
- Infection occurring primarily in liver, where necrosis probably results from cytotoxic T-cell response, direct cytopathic effect of HBcAg (core antigen), high-level HBsAg (surface antigen) expression, or co-infection with delta (D) hepatitis virus (RNA delta core within HBsAg envelope)
- Recovery (>90%):
  1. Fulminant hepatitis occurring in <1% (especially if coinfected with hepatitis D); 80% fatal
  2. Unusual (5%) prolonged acute disease for 4 to 12 mo, with recovery
  3. Overall fatality increases with age and viral inoculation (e.g., transfusions)
- Chronic infection (1% to 2%):
  1. Persistent carrier state without hepatitis (HBsAg positive)
  2. Chronic persistent hepatitis (CPH) (clinically well), or chronic active hepatitis (CAH) (HBsAg positive and HBeAg positive)
  3. Cirrhosis
  4. Hepatocellular carcinoma (especially after neonatal infection)
  5. Chronic infection: more common following low-dose exposure and mild acute hepatitis, with earlier age of infection, in males, or if immunosuppressed
  6. One third to one quarter of chronically infected will develop progressive liver disease (cirrhosis, hepatocellular carcinoma)

DIAGNOSIS

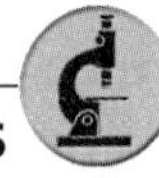

DIFFERENTIAL DIAGNOSIS

- Acute disease confused with other viral hepatitis infections (A, C, D, E)
- Any viral illness producing systemic disease and hepatitis (e.g., yellow fever, EBV, CMV, HIV, rubella, rubeola, coxsackie B, adenovirus, herpes simplex or zoster)
- Nonviral etiologies of hepatitis (e.g., leptospirosis, toxoplasmosis, alcoholic hepatitis, drug-induced [e.g., acetaminophen, INH], toxic hepatitis [carbon tetrachloride, benzene])

WORKUP

- Acute serum specimen for hepatitis B serology (HBsAg, HBsAb, HBcAb, HBeAg, HBeAb)
- LFTs
- CBC
- Liver biopsy: rarely indicated for diagnosis of fulminant viral hepatitis, chronic hepatitis, cirrhosis, carcinoma

LABORATORY TESTS

- Diagnosis of acute HBV infection is best confirmed by IgM HBcAb in acute or early convalescent serum.
  1. Generally, IgM present during onset of jaundice
  2. Coexisting HBsAg
- HBsAg and IgG-HBcAb during acute jaundice are strongly suggestive of remote HBV infection and another etiology for current illness.
- HBsAb alone is suggestive of immunization response.
- With recovery, HBeAg is rapidly replaced by HBeAb in 2 to 3 mo, and HBsAg is replaced by HBsAb in 5 to 6 mo.
- In chronic HBV hepatitis, HBsAg and HBeAg are persistent without corresponding Ab.
- In chronic carrier state, HBsAg is persistent, but HBeAg is replaced by HBe AB.
- HBcAb develops in all outcomes.
- HBeAg correlation with highest infectivity; appearance of HBeAb heralds recovery.
- LFTs:
  1. ALT and AST: usually more than eight times normal (often 1000 U/L) at onset of jaundice (minimal acute ALT/AST rises often followed by chronic hepatitis or hepatocellular carcinoma)
  2. Bilirubin: variably elevated in icteric viral hepatitis
  3. Alkaline phosphatase: minimally elevated (one to three times normal) acutely
- Albumin and prothrombin time:
  1. Generally normal
  2. If abnormal, possible harbinger of impending hepatic necrosis (fulminant hepatitis)
- WBC and ESR: generally normal

IMAGING STUDIES

- Rarely useful
- Sonogram to document rapid reduction in liver size during fulminant hepatitis or mass in hepatocellular carcinoma

TREATMENT

NONPHARMACOLOGIC THERAPY

- Symptomatic treatment as necessary
- Activity as tolerated
- High-calorie diet preferred; often best tolerated in morning

ACUTE GENERAL Rx

- In most cases of acute HBV infection no treatment necessary; >90% of adults will spontaneously clear infection
- Hospitalization advisable for any patient in danger from dehydration caused by poor oral intake, whose PT is prolonged, who has rising bilirubin level >15 to 20 μg/dl, or who has any clinical evidence of hepatic failure
- IV therapy needed (rarely) for hydration during severe vomiting
- Avoid hepatically metabolized drugs
- No therapeutic measures are beneficial
- Steroids not shown helpful

CHRONIC Rx

The aim of therapy in chronic HBV infection is to eradicate the virus.

The two modalities of therapy available to achieve this goal have been: immune modulators (interferon alpha) and antiviral agents in the form of nucleoside analogues (e.g., lamivudine, famciclovir).

- Until recently, IFN-α has been the mainstay of therapy. Its mechanism of action is to stimulate the immune system to attack HBV-infected hepatocytes, thus inhibiting viral protein synthesis.
- A 4-month course of treatment results in a 30% to 40% response with significant reduction of serum HBV DNA, normalization of ALT, and loss of HBeAg. Seroconversion from HBeAg to HBeAb occurs in 15% to 20%.
- Factors that increase the likelihood of response to IFN-α therapy include:
  1. Adult onset of infection
  2. High baseline ALT
  3. Low baseline HBV DNA
  4. Absence of cirrhosis
  5. Female
  6. HBeAg positive
- Infrequent relapse after successful completion of therapy

- 80% of patients who lose HBeAg during therapy lose HBsAg in the decade after therapy
- >50% of patients who do not seroconvert after initial therapy develop a delayed HBeAg seroconversion months to years after therapy
- Overall incidence of cirrhosis and hepatocellular carcinoma is decreased in those treated with IFN-α
- IFN-α is successful only in patients with an active immune response; therefore it is not effective in patients with HIV infection and organ transplant patients
- Asians respond poorly to IFN-α
- Treatment with IFN-α in general is also poorly tolerated: side effects include flulike symptoms, injection-site reactions, rash, weight loss, anxiety, depression, alopecia, thrombocytopenia, granulocytopenia, thyroid dysfunction
- Nucleoside analogues block viral replication by inhibiting HBV polymerase
- Lamivudine is, to date, the only one of these agents approved for treatment of chronic HBV infection; it has been shown to rapidly reduce HBV replication and suppress HBV DNA to undetectable levels after a few weeks of treatment, and treatment for 1 yr is as effective as IFN-α with respect to loss of HBeAg seroconversion to HBeAb and loss of HBV DNA
    1. It is better tolerated than IFN-α
    2. Easier administration: given orally
    3. Suppression of HBV replication regardless of sex, ethnicity, disease severity
- Other nucleoside agents under evaluation include famciclovir (found less effective than lamivudine), adefovir and adefovir dipivoxil, ganciclovir, lobucavir, entecavir, emtricitabine
- A problem with the antiviral therapies is emergence of resistant HBV strains (YMDD variants [tyrosine-methionine-aspartate-aspartate])
- Combination therapy with two or three nucleoside analogues or combination therapy with IFN-α currently under investigation
- Liver transplantation (consider for fulminant hepatitis)

DISPOSITION

- Follow-up as outpatient
- Acute disease: usually <6 wk
- Rare fatalities (fulminant hepatitis)
- Possible chronic carrier state, cirrhosis, hepatocellular carcinoma

REFERRAL

To infectious disease specialist and gastroenterologist for consultation regarding fulminant hepatitis or prolonged cholestasis, for cases of uncertain etiology, or for treatment of chronic active hepatitis

PEARLS & CONSIDERATIONS

COMMENTS

- Virus and HBsAg in high titers in blood for 1 to 7 wk before jaundice and for a variable time thereafter.
- Transmission is possible during entire period of HBsAg (and especially during HBeAg) in serum.
- Universal precautions should be followed for all contacts with blood or secretions/excretions contaminated with blood.
- Preventing before exposure:
    1. Lifestyle changes
    2. Meticulous testing of blood supply (although some chronically infected, infectious donors are HBsAg negative)
    3. Sterilization via steam or hypochlorite
    4. Hepatitis B vaccine for high-risk groups given IM in deltoid to induce HBsAb (response should be confirmed) is protective (>90% effective)
    5. Recommendation for universal childhood immunization with doses at birth, 1 mo, and 6 mo
- Prevention after exposure:
    1. HBV hyperimmune globulin (HBIG) given immediately after needlestick, within 14 days of sexual exposure, or at birth, followed by HBV vaccination
    2. Standard immune globulin: nearly as effective as HBIG

Section V, Tables 5-15 and 5-17 describe hepatitis B prophylaxis.

SUGGESTED READINGS

Jonas MM et al: Clinical trial of lamivudine in children with chronic hepatitis B, *N Engl J Med* 346(22):1706, 2002.

Lin KW, Kirchner JT: Hepatitis B, *Am Fam Physician* 69:75, 2004.

Maddrey WC: Hepatitis B: an important public health issue, *J Med Virol* 61:362, 2000.

Torresi J, Locarnini S: Antiviral chemotherapy for the treatment of hepatitis B virus infections, *Gastroenterol* 118:S83, 2000.

Weinberg MS et al: Preventing transmission of hepatitis B virus from people with chronic infection, *Am J Prev Med* 20(4):272, 2001.

AUTHOR: **JANE V. EASON, M.D.**

BASIC INFORMATION

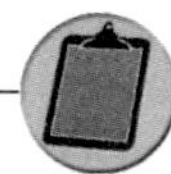

DEFINITION

Hepatitis C is an acute liver parenchymal infection caused by hepatitis C virus (HCV).

SYNONYMS

Transfusion-related non-A, non-B hepatitis (incubation period averages 6 wk, intermediate between hepatitis A and B)

ICD-9CM CODES
070.51 Other viral hepatitis

EPIDEMIOLOGY & DEMOGRAPHICS

Hepatitis C infection is the most common chronic blood-borne infection in the U.S.

INCIDENCE (IN U.S.):
- 150,000 new cases/yr (37,500, symptomatic; 93,000, later chronic liver disease; 30,700, cirrhosis)
- Approximately 9000 of these ultimately die of HCV infection; most common (40%) cause of nonalcoholic liver disease in U.S.

PREVALENCE (IN U.S.):
- Overall prevalence of anti-HCV is 1.8% (an estimated 3.9 million persons nationwide)
- Highest prevalence in hemophiliacs transfused before 1987 and injecting-drug users, 72% to 90%
- Among low-risk groups, prevalence 0.6%

PREDOMINANT SEX: Slight male predominance

PREDOMINANT AGE: Highest prevalence in 30 to 49 yr age group (65%)

PEAK INCIDENCE:
- 20 to 39 yr old
- African Americans and whites have similar incidence of acute disease; Hispanics have higher rates
- Prevalence substantially higher among non-Hispanic blacks than among non-Hispanic whites

GENETICS: Neonatal infection: Rare. Increased risk with maternal HIV-1 coinfection

PHYSICAL FINDINGS & CLINICAL PRESENTATION
- Symptoms usually develop 7 to 8 wk after infection (2 to 26 wk), but 70% to 80% of cases are subclinical.
- 10% to 20% report acute illness with jaundice and nonspecific symptoms (abdominal pain, anorexia, malaise).
- Fulminant hepatitis may rarely occur during this period.
- After acute infection, 15% to 25% have complete resolution (absence of HCV RNA in serum, normal ALT).
- Progression to chronic infection is common, 50% to 84%. 74% to 86% have persistent viremia; spontaneous clearance of viremia in chronic infection is rare. 60% to 70% of patients will have persistent or fluctuating ALT levels, 30% to 40% with chronic infection have normal ALT levels.
- 15% to 20% of those with chronic HCV will develop cirrhosis over a period of 20 to 30 yr; in most others chronic infection leads to hepatitis and varying degrees of fibrosis.
- 0.4% to 2.5% of patients with chronic infection develop hepatocellular carcinoma.
- 25% of patients with chronic infection continue to have an asymptomatic course with normal LFTs and benign histology.
- In chronic HCV infection, extrahepatic sequelae include a variety of immunologic and lymphoproliferative disorders (e.g., cryoglobulinemia, membranoproliferative glomerulonephritis, and possibly Sjögren syndrome, autoimmune thyroiditis, polyarteritis nodosa, aplastic anemia, lichen planus, porphyria cutanea tarda, B-cell lymphoma, others).

ETIOLOGY

- Caused by HCV (single-stranded RNA flavivirus)
- Most HCV transmission is parenteral
- In the U.S., advances in screening of blood and blood products in 1990 and 1992 have made transfusion-related HCV infection rare (the risk is estimated to be 0.001%/unit transfused)
- Injecting-drug use accounts for most HCV transmission in the U.S. (60% of newly acquired cases, 20% to 50% of chronically infected persons)
- Occupational needlestick exposure from an HCV-positive source has a seroconversion rate of 1.8% (range 0% to 7%)
- Nosocomial transmission rates (from surgery and procedures such as colonoscopy, hemodialysis) are extremely low
- Sexual transmission and maternal-fetal transmission are infrequent (estimated at 5%)
- No identifiable risk in 40% to 50% of community-acquired HIV infection
- HCV infection may stimulate production of cytotoxic T lymphocytes and cytokines (inf-γ), which likely mediate hepatic necrosis

DIAGNOSIS

DIFFERENTIAL DIAGNOSIS

- Other hepatitis viruses (A, B, D, E)
- Other viral illnesses producing systemic disease (e.g., yellow fever, EBV, CMV, HIV, rubella, rubeolae, coxsackie B, adenovirus, HSV, HZV)
- Nonviral hepatitis (e.g., leptospirosis, toxoplasmosis, alcoholic hepatitis, drug-induced hepatitis [acetaminophen, INH], toxic hepatitis)

WORKUP

- Acute hepatitis C antibody (Table 1-21)
- LFTs; CBC

NOTE: ALT is an easy and inexpensive test to monitor infection and efficacy of therapy. However, ALT levels may fluctuate or even be normal in active or chronic infection and even with cirrhosis, and ALT may remain elevated even after clearance of viremia.

- Liver biopsy with histologic staging is the gold standard for assessing the degree of disease activity and the likelihood of disease progression, and also help rule out other causes of liver disease.

LABORATORY TESTS

Diagnosis is often by exclusion, because it takes 6 wk to 12 mo to develop anti-HCV antibody (70% positive by 6 wk, 90% positive by 6 mo).

Diagnostic tests include serologic assays for antibodies and molecular tests for viral particles.

1. Enzyme immunoassay is the test for anti-HCV antibody:
   - The current version can detect antibody within 4 to 10 wk after infection
   - False-negative rate in low-risk populations is 0.5% to 1%
   - False-negatives also in immune-compromised persons, HIV-1, renal failure, HCV-associated essential mixed cryoglobulinemia
   - False positives in autoimmune hepatitis, paraproteinemia, and persons with no risk factors
2. Recombinant immunoblot is used to confirm positive enzyme immunoassays:
   - Recommended only in low-risk settings
3. Qualitative and quantitative HCV RNA tests using PCR:
   - Lower limit of detection is <100 copies HCV RNA/ml
   - Used to confirm viremia and to assess response to treatment
   - Qualitative PCR useful in patients with negative enzyme immunoassay in whom infection is suspected

TABLE 1-21 **Tests for Hepatitis C Virus (HCV) Infection**

Test/type	Application	Comments
Hepatitis C Virus Antibody (anti-HCV) EIA (enzyme immunoassay) Supplemental assay (i.e., recombinant immunoblot assay [RIBA])	Indicates past or present infection but does not differentiate among acute, chronic, or resolved infection All positive EIA results should be verified with a supplemental assay	Sensitivity ≥97% EIA alone has low-positive predictive value in low-prevalence populations
HCV RNA (Hepatitis C Virus Ribonucleic Acid)		
*Qualitative Tests**†		
Reverse transcriptase polymerase chain reaction (RT-PCR) amplification of HCV RNA by in-house or commercial assays (e.g., Amplicor HCV)	Detect presence of circulating HCV RNA Monitor patients on antiviral therapy	Detect virus as early as 1-2 wk after exposure Detection of HCV RNA during course of infection might be intermittent; a single negative RT-PCR is not conclusive False-positive and false-negative results might occur
*Quantitative Tests**†		
RT-PCR amplification of HCV RNA by in-house or commercial assays (e.g., Amplicor HCV Monitor) Branched chain DNA‡ (bDNA) assays (e.g., Quantiplex HCV RNA Assay)	Determine concentration of HCV RNA Might be useful for assessing the likelihood of response to antiviral therapy	Less sensitive than qualitative RT-PCR Should not be used to exclude the diagnosis of HCV infection or to determine treatment end point
*Genotype**†		
Several methodologies available (e.g., hybridization, sequencing)	Group isolates of HCV based on genetic differences, into 6 genotypes and >90 subtypes With new therapies, length of treatment might vary based on genotype	Genotype 1 (subtypes 1a and 1b) most common in U.S. and associated with lower response to antiviral therapy
*Serotype**		
EIA based on immunoreactivity to synthetic peptides (e.g., Murex HCV Serotyping 1-6 Assay)	No clinical utility	Cannot distinguish among subtypes Dual infections often observed

From ***MMWR Morb Mortal Rep Wkly*** 47(RR-19) 1998.
*Currently not U.S. Food and Drug Administration approved; lack standardization.
†Samples require special handling (e.g., serum must be separated within 2-4 hours of collection and stored frozen [−20° C or −70° C]; frozen samples should be shipped on dry ice).
‡Deoxyribonucleic acid.

- Quantitative tests use either branched-chain DNA or reverse transcription PCR; the latter is more sensitive

4. Viral genotyping can distinguish among genotypes 1, 2, and 3, which is helpful in choosing therapy; most of these tests use PCR (NOTE: genotypes 1, 2, and 3 predominate in the U.S. and Europe [1 is especially common in North America])
5. LFTs:
   - ALT and AST may be elevated to more than eight times normal in acute infection; in chronic infection ALT may be normal or fluctuate
   - Bilirubin may be 5 to 10 times normal
   - Albumin and prothrombin time generally normal; if abnormal, may be harbinger of impending hepatic necrosis
6. WBC and ESR are generally normal

IMAGING STUDIES

- Rarely useful
- Sonogram: rapid liver size reduction during fulminant hepatitis or mass in hepatocellular carcinoma

TREATMENT

NONPHARMACOLOGIC THERAPY

Activity and diet as tolerated

ACUTE GENERAL Rx

- Supportive care
- Avoid hepatically metabolized drugs
- Specific Rx for acute HCV infection
- Recent studies demonstrate that *early* treatment with IFN-α-2b during acute HCV infection prevents chronic infection. The aim is to decrease viral load early in infection and allow the patient's immune system to control viral replication, thus preventing progression to chronic infection. The primary end point was sustained virologic response, with absence of HCV RNA in serum 24 wk after completion of therapy.
- Further investigations are in progress.

CHRONIC Rx

- Response to therapy is influenced by HCV genotype. Patients with genotype 1 rarely respond to interferon alone, and response to combination therapy with interferon and ribavirin is less than for genotypes 2 and 3.
- IFN-α alone or combined with ribavirin have been the mainstays of therapy.
- IFN-α monotherapy for 12 to 18 mo achieves initial response (normalization of transaminases and undetectable HCV RNA) in 40%, but most have relapse after therapy; sustained response in only 6% to 21%; those with genotype 1 and those with cirrhosis at time of therapy have even lower response rates.

- Combination INF-α and ribavirin given thrice weekly has been shown to achieve sustained virologic response in up to 40% of patients. Those with genotype 1 and those with high viral loads required 48 wk of therapy to achieve optimal response (versus 24 wk for those with genotypes 2 and 3 and those with low viral loads).
- 49% of patients who relapse after IFN-α monotherapy have a sustained virologic response to IFN-α and ribavirin combination therapy. In those with contraindications to ribavirin, a more prolonged course of treatment with higher dose IFN-α or PEG-interferon may be an option.
- Both IFN-α and ribavirin have numerous contraindications (absolute and relative) to use and may cause a variety of side effects. IFN-α can cause flu-like symptoms, thrombocytopenia, granulocytopenia, rash, alopecia, anorexia, psychiatric disturbances, others. Ribavirin can cause hemolysis, nausea, anemia, nasal congestion, pruritus.
- In patients who fail to respond to IFN-α or combination therapy with ribavirin, <10% will respond to retreatment.
- Pegylated interferons are IFN-α with an attached polyethylene glycol molecule. The PEG molecule confers a longer half-life and extended therapeutic activity compared with IFN-α, and reduced dosing, once a week.
- Recent treatment trials have shown that pegylated interferon alone achieves higher response rates than does IFN-α alone in patients with chronic hepatitis C without cirrhosis, and in patients with chronic hepatitis C with cirrhosis or bridging fibrosis. Their enhanced efficacy over INF-α may be the result of a more vigorous immune response (e.g., increased hepatitis C-specific T-helper-1 response).
- Pegylated interferons can be used in the treatment of persons who cannot be treated with ribavirin.
- Optimal regimens with pegylated interferons have yet to be determined; currently trials are underway using pegylated interferon in combination with ribavirin.

Liver transplantation:

- Hepatitis C is the main indication for liver transplantation in the U.S.
- It is the only option for patients with deteriorating HCV-related cirrhosis and for some patients with hepatocellular carcinoma.
- Recurrent infection occurs in almost all patients with progressive fibrosis and cirrhosis; up to 20% progress to cirrhosis within 5 yr posttransplant.

Coinfection with HIV:

- These patients have a poor response to IFN-α alone.
- Consider initiating therapy for HCV before starting antiretrovirals, because immune reconstitution syndrome occurring with initiation of antiretrovirals may exacerbate HCV-related hepatitis.

DISPOSITION

- Follow-up as outpatient
- Monitor ALT levels as a clue for chronic disease
- Chronic carrier state, cirrhosis, hepatic carcinoma more common than with hepatitis A and B

PEARLS & CONSIDERATIONS

- More rapid progression of disease in persons who drink alcohol regularly, persons of advanced age at time of infection, and those coinfected with other viruses (HIV, hepatitis B).
- No preventive vaccine available; postexposure immune globulin may provide minimal protection.
- Preventive measures include use of universal precautions, careful screening of blood and blood products, lifestyle changes.

SUGGESTED READINGS

Centers for Disease Control: Hepatitis C, *MMWR Morb Mortal Wkly Rep* 51(RR-6), 2002.

Germer HH, Zein NN: Advances in the molecular diagnosis of hepatitis C and their implications, *Mayo Clin Proc* 76:911, 2001.

Hadziyannis JJ et al: Peginterferon α-2a and ribavirin combination therapy in chronic hepatitis C, *Ann Intern Med* 140:346, 2004.

Herrine SK: Approach to the patient with chronic hepatitis C virus infection, *Ann Intern Med* 136:747, 2002.

Jaeckel E et al: Treatment of acute hepatitis C with interferon alfa-2b, *N Engl J Med* 345(20):1452, 2001.

Lauer GM, Walker BD: Hepatitis C virus infection, *N Engl J Med* 345(1):41, 2001.

Sulkowski MS, Ray SC, Thomas DL: Needlestick transmission of hepatitis C, *JAMA* 287(18):2406, 2002.

AUTHOR: **JANE V. EASON, M.D.**

Hepatitis, Autoimmune

BASIC INFORMATION

DEFINITION

Autoimmune hepatitis is a chronic inflammatory condition of the liver, characterized by the presence of circulating autoantibodies. Three types have been described:

- Type 1 or "classic" autoimmune hepatitis is the most predominant form in the United States and are positive for either antinuclear antibodies (ANA) or antismooth muscle antibodies (ASMA). There is a bimodal age distribution: teenagers and adults between 50 and 70 years are most commonly affected.
- Type 2 is rare in the United States and primarily affects young children. Type 2 is characterized by the presence of antibodies to liver/kidney microsomes (anti-LKM).
- Type 3 is characterized by antibodies to soluble liver antigen or liver-pancreas antigen (anti-SLA/LP). There is also a bimodal age distribution associated with type 3.

SYNONYMS

Autoimmune chronic active hepatitis
Chronic active hepatitis
Lupoid hepatitis

ICD-9CM CODES
571.49 Chronic hepatitis

EPIDEMIOLOGY & DEMOGRAPHICS

- Type 1 can occur at any age
- Type 2 is more common in children
- More common in women
- Estimated 100,000 to 200,000 cases in U.S.
- Accounts for 5.9% of liver transplants in U.S.

PHYSICAL FINDINGS & CLINICAL PRESENTATION

- Varies from asymptomatic elevations of liver enzymes to advanced cirrhosis
- Symptoms may include fatigue, anorexia, nausea, abdominal pain, pruritus, and arthralgia
- Jaundice
- Hepatomegaly/splenomegaly
- Autoimmune findings may include arthritis, xerostomia, keratoconjunctivitis, cutaneous vasculitis, and erythema nodosum
- For patients presenting with advanced disease: ascites, edema, abnormal bleeding, jaundice

ETIOLOGY

- Exact etiology unknown; liver histology demonstrates cell-mediated immune attack against hepatocytes
- Presence of a variety of autoantibodies suggests an autoimmune mechanism
- Strong genetic predisposition

DIAGNOSIS

DIFFERENTIAL DIAGNOSIS

Acute Disease:

- Acute viral hepatitis (A, B, C, D, E, cytomegalovirus, Epstein-Barr, herpes)
- Chronic viral hepatitis (B, C)
- Toxic hepatitis (alcohol, drugs)
- Primary biliary cirrhosis
- Primary sclerosing cholangitis
- Hemochromatosis
- Nonalcoholic steatohepatitis
- SLE
- Wilson's disease
- Alpha-1-antitrypsin deficiency

WORKUP

- History and physical examination with attention to the presence of autoimmune abnormalities such as arthritis, vasculitis, or sicca syndrome
- LFTs
- Tests for autoantibodies
- Liver biopsy for establishing diagnosis and disease severity

LABORATORY TESTS

- Aminotransferases generally elevated, may fluctuate
- Bilirubin and alkaline phosphatase moderately elevated or normal
- Hypergammaglobulinemia usually present
- Circulating autoantibodies often present
  1. Rheumatoid factor
  2. Antinuclear antibodies (ANA)
     a. Present in 2/3 of patients
     b. Typical pattern is homogeneous or speckled
     c. Titer does not correlate with the stage, activity, or prognosis
  3. Antismooth muscle antibodies (ASMA)
     a. Present in 87% of patients
     b. Titer does not correlate with course or prognosis
  4. Antibodies to liver/kidney microsomes (anti-LKM)
     a. Typically found in patients who are ANA-negative and ASMA-negative
     b. Found in <1/25 of patients in U.S.
     c. Present in pediatric population and up to 20% of adults in Europe also present in patients with drug-induced hepatitis
  5. Autoantibodies against soluble liver antigen and liver-pancreas antigen (anti-SLA/LP)
     a. Present in 10% to 30% of patients
     b. Associated with higher rate of relapse after corticosteroid therapy
     c. Several studies suggest that patients with anti-SLA/LP have a more severe course
- Hypoalbuminemia and prolonged prothrombin time with advanced disease
- Liver biopsy reveals interface hepatitis, which consists of a lymphoplasmacytic inflammatory infiltrate that extends from the portal tract into the lobule.

IMAGING STUDIES

Ultrasound of liver and biliary tree to rule out obstruction or hepatic mass

TREATMENT

NONPHARMACOLOGIC THERAPY

Avoid alcohol and hepatotoxic drugs

CHRONIC Rx

- Initial treatment:
  1. Prednisone 60 mg PO/day or combination treatment with prednisone 30 mg PO/day plus azathiaprine 50 mg PO/day
  2. Combination therapy allows for lower prednisone doses and less steroid side effects
  3. Goal of therapy is remission (normalization of gammaglobulin and bilirubin, reduction of animotransferases to <2 times the upper limit of normal)

- Indications for treatment:
  1. Serum aminotransferase >10 times the upper limit of normal
  2. Serum aminotransferase >5 times the upper limit of normal, with serum gammaglobulin level twice the upper limit of normal
  3. Young age
  4. Histologic features of bridging necrosis or multiacinar necrosis
  5. Compensated cirrhosis:
     a. A 3- to 6-month treatment trial may be beneficial in patients with inflammation on liver biopsy
     b. Established cirrhosis or fibrosis is unlikely to resolve with therapy, but treatment may delay or obviate liver transplantation.
- Patients with decompensated cirrhosis usually do not benefit from corticosteroid therapy and should be considered for liver transplantation.
- Evaluation of treatment response:
  - Goal is normalization of serum transaminase levels.
  - Patients who normalize their transaminase levels may continue to have ongoing active hepatitis involving inflammation and fibrosis. 5%-10% of patients with normal transaminase levels progress to cirrhosis.
  - Histological improvement may lag behind clinical and laboratory improvement by as much as 6 mo.
  - Repeat liver biopsy should be considered after normalization of transaminase levels.
  - Complete normalization on biopsy is associated with 15% to 20% risk of relapse.
  - Persistent interface hepatitis is associated with 90% risk of relapse.

DISPOSITION

- Follow-up as outpatient
- Long-term treatment may be necessary for sustained remission
- 65% of patients achieve remission by 18 mo; 80% achieve remission by 3 yr
- Approximately 10% of patients fail to improve with therapy
- Patients who develop end-stage liver disease are candidates for liver transplantation

REFERRAL

To gastroenterologist for long-term management

PEARLS & CONSIDERATIONS

A variety of autoimmune conditions can be seen in association with autoimmune hepatitis, including thyroiditis, Graves' disease, ulcerative colitis, rheumatoid arthritis, uveitis, pernicious anemia, Sjögren's syndrome, mixed connective tissue disease, CREST syndrome, and vitiligo.

SUGGESTED READINGS

Al-Khalidi JA, Czaja AJ: Current concepts in the diagnosis, pathogenesis, and treatment of autoimmune hepatitis, *Mayo Clin Proc* 76:1237, 2001.

Luxon BA: Autoimmune hepatitis, *Postgraduate Medicine* 114(1):79, 2003.

AUTHORS: **IRIS TONG, M.D.**, and **MARK J FAGAN, M.D.**

Hepatocellular Carcinoma (Hepatoma) (PTG)

BASIC INFORMATION

DEFINITION

Hepatocellular carcinoma is a malignant tumor of the liver, arising from hepatocytes.

ICD-9CM CODES
155.0 Hepatocellular carcinoma

SYNONYMS

Hepatoma

EPIDEMIOLOGY & DEMOGRAPHICS

Fifth most common cancer worldwide. Incidence of hepatocellular carcinoma varies widely in parts of the world:

- Areas with high rates of hepatitis B and hepatitis C (Asia, sub-Saharan Africa) have correspondingly high rates of hepatocellular carcinoma.
- Males are affected more commonly than females.
- Peak incidence is in fifth and sixth decades in Western countries, earlier in areas with perinatal transmission of hepatitis B.
- Incidence rapidly growing in U.S. secondary to hepatitis C infection.

RISK FACTORS

- Chronic liver disease
- Cirrhosis
- Chronic hepatitis B or C infection, especially in the presence of HBeAg
- Hepatotoxins including alcohol, mycotoxins (aflatoxin B_1), high-dose anabolic steroids, vinyl chloride, possibly estrogen
- Systemic diseases affecting the liver such as alpha-1 antitrypsin deficiency, hemochromatosis, tyrosinemia

PHYSICAL FINDINGS & CLINICAL PRESENTATION

- One third of patients are asymptomatic.
- Signs of underlying cirrhosis are often present (e.g., weight loss, ascites).
- Previously compensated cirrhosis with new ascites, encephalopathy, jaundice or bleeding

DIAGNOSIS

DIFFERENTIAL DIAGNOSIS

- Metastatic tumor to liver
- Benign liver tumors such as adenomas, focal nodular hyperplasia, hemangiomas
- Focal fatty infiltration

WORKUP

- History with regard to risk factors (see Risk Factors)
- Physical examination with attention to signs of chronic liver disease
- Laboratory evaluation and imaging

LABORATORY TESTS

- LFTs
- Elevated alpha-fetoprotein in 70% of patients (sensitivity 40%-65%; specificity 80%-94%)
- Paraneoplastic syndromes associated with hepatocellular carcinoma may cause abnormalities such as hypercalcemia, hypoglycemia, and polycythemia

IMAGING STUDIES

Ultrasound, CT scan, or MRI. Ultrasound is favored over other imaging modalities because of lower cost. However, benign regenerative nodules can be difficult to distinguish from cancer by ultrasound. In the setting of nodular cirrhosis, ultrasound with arterial phase contrast or helical CT may be the preferred first-line screening method.

BIOPSY

Percutaneous biopsy under ultrasound or CT scan usually is diagnostic. Tissue diagnosis is the gold standard. However, HCC can be reliably diagnosed when:

- Confirmed by two imaging modalities when the nodule is >2 cm and has arterial hypervascularity

OR

- Single positive imaging method with AFP >400 μg/ml

SCREENING

Screening high-risk patients with ultrasound and α-fetoprotein q6months may identify hepatocellular carcinoma at an early stage. Screening at 6- to 12-mo intervals may be acceptable for healthy hepatitis B virus carriers without cirrhosis.

STAGING

According to the Barcelona-Clinic Liver Cancer (BCLC) staging classification, treatment is determined according to stage:

- Early stage: asymptomatic single tumor ≤5 cm or 3 nodules ≤3 cm
- Intermediate stage: patients with tumors that exceed early criteria but do not yet show cancer-related symptoms, vascular invasion, or metastases
- Advanced stage: patients with cancer-related symptoms
- End-stage: patients with advanced, symptomatic disease

TREATMENT

- For patients who are not candidates for surgical resection, percutaneous ethanol injection, transcatheter arterial chemotherapy with or without embolization of the tumor, or ultrasound-guided cryoablation can be used for local tumor control. Chemotherapy not used routinely for advanced disease. Treatment is based on tumor size and severity of symptoms.

According to the BCLC staging system, treatment is as follows:

1. Early stage: curative treatment (resection, liver transplantation, and/or percutaneous ablation). Elevated portal pressure is a predictor of poor outcome after resection. Among patients with elevated portal pressure who have <3 tumors which are <3 cm in size, surgical resection should be attempted, including transplantation or ablation.
2. Intermediate stage: optimal therapeutic approach is controversial. Outcome maybe improved with chemoembolization.
3. Advanced stage: No curative treatment. In the absence of metastatic disease, ablation is reasonable. Entry into clinical trials should be considered.
4. End-stage: palliative care

- Patients with advanced cirrhosis and small tumors should be considered for liver transplantation
- For patients with hepatitis C virus, associated hepatocellular carcinoma, postoperative treatment with interferon-alpha decreases the rate of tumor recurrence

DISPOSITION

- For unresectable tumors, prognosis is poor.
- Five-year survival following surgical resection ranges from 30%-50%.

REFERRAL

Referral to GI for treatment planning

PEARLS & CONSIDERATIONS

Prevention:

- Hepatitis B vaccination
- Eliminate aflatoxin contamination of food
- Decrease alcohol consumption
- Identify and treat hemochromatosis
- Interferon therapy in patients with hepatitis C reduces the risk of hepatocellular carcinoma

SUGGESTED READINGS

Anderson JM et al: Synopsis for the Yale workshop on hepatocellular carcinoma, *J Clin Gastroenterol* 35:S152, 2002.

Gupta S et al: Test characteristics of α-fetoprotein for detecting hepatocellular carcinome in patients with Hepatitis C: a systematic review and critical analysis, *Ann Intern Med* 139:46, 2003.

Kubo S et al: Effects of long-term post-operative interferon–alpha therapy on intrahepatic recurrence after resection of hepatitis C virus-related hepatocellular carcinoma: a randomized controlled trial, *Ann Intern Med* 134:963, 2001.

AUTHORS: **CHRISTINE DUFFY, M.D.**, and **IRIS TONG, M.D.**

BASIC INFORMATION

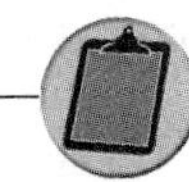

DEFINITION

Hepatorenal syndrome (HRS) is a condition of intense renal vasoconstriction resulting from loss of renal autoregulation occurring as a complication of severe liver disease. Criteria for hepatorenal syndrome are:

1. Serum creatinine concentration >1.5 mg/dl or 24 hr creatinine clearance <40 ml/min
2. Absence of shock, ongoing infection, and fluid loss, and no current treatment with nephrotoxic drugs
3. Absence of sustained improvement in renal function (decrease in serum creatinine to <1.5 mg/dl after discontinuation of diuretics and a trial of plasma expansion
4. Absence of proteinuria (<500 mg/day) or hematuria (<50 RBC/high power field)
5. Absence of ultrasonographic evidence of obstructive uropathy or parenchymal renal disease
6. Urinary sodium concentration <10 mmol/liter

There are two types of hepatorenal syndrome:

Type 1: progressive impairment in renal function as defined by a doubling of initial serum creatinine above 2.5 mg/dl in <2 wk

Type 2: stable or slowly progressive impairment of renal function not meeting the above criteria

SYNONYMS

Hepatic nephropathy
Oliguric renal failure of cirrhosis
HRS

ICD-9CM CODES
572.4 Hepatorenal syndrome

EPIDEMIOLOGY & DEMOGRAPHICS

The probability of HRS in patients with cirrhosis is 18% at 1 yr and 39% at 5 yr.

PHYSICAL FINDINGS & CLINICAL PRESENTATION

- Evidence of cirrhosis is usually present: jaundice, spider angiomas, splenomegaly, ascites, fetor hepaticus, pedal edema
- Hepatic encephalopathy: flapping tremor (asterixis), coma
- Tachycardia and bounding pulse
- Oliguria

ETIOLOGY

An exacerbation of end-stage liver disease, HRS may occur after significant reduction of effective blood volume (e.g., paracentesis, GI bleeding, diuretics) or in the absence of any precipitating factors.

DIAGNOSIS

DIFFERENTIAL DIAGNOSIS

- Prerenal azotemia: response to sustained plasma expansion is good (prompt diuresis with volume expansion).
- Acute tubular necrosis: urinary sodium >30, FENa >1.5%, urinary/plasma creatinine ratio <30, urine/plasma osmolality ratio = 1, urine sediment reveals casts and cellular debris, there is no significant response to sustained plasma expansion.

WORKUP

Patients with acute azotemia and oliguria in the setting of liver disease should undergo laboratory evaluation to differentiate HRS from acute tubular necrosis and volume challenge to differentiate HRS from prerenal azotemia if FENa <1%.

LABORATORY TESTS

- Obtain serum electrolytes, BUN, creatinine, osmolality, urinalysis, urinary sodium, urinary creatinine, urine osmolality.
- Calculate fractional excretion of sodium (FENa).
- In HRS: urinary sodium <10 mEq/L, FENa <1%, urinary plasma creatinine ratio >30, urinary-plasma osmolality ratio >1.5, urine sediment is unremarkable.

IMAGING STUDIES

Renal ultrasound may be indicated if renal obstruction is suspected.

TREATMENT

NONPHARMACOLOGIC THERAPY

Avoidance of precipitating factors

ACUTE GENERAL Rx

- Volume challenge (to increase mean arterial pressure) followed by large-volume paracentesis (to increase cardiac output and decrease renal venous pressure) may be useful to distinguish HRS from prerenal azotemia in patients with FENa <1%. In patients with prerenal azotemia, the increase in renal perfusion pressure and renal blood flow will result in prompt diuresis; the volume challenge can be accomplished by giving a solution of 100 g of albumin in 500 ml of isotonic saline.
- The only effective treatment of HRS is liver transplantation; ornipressin is used in some liver units to avoid further deterioration of renal function in patients awaiting liver transplantation. Generally dopamine and prostaglandins are ineffective in treating patients with hepatorenal syndrome.
- Vasopressin analogues may improve renal perfusion by reversing splanchnic vasodilation, which is the hallmark of HRS. Encouraging results were found in a recent study using continuous IV noradrenalin in combination with albumin and furosemide. In this study, reversal of HRS was achieved in 10 out of 12 patients.
- Treatment of hepatorenal syndrome with vasoconstrictors for 5 to 15 days in attempt to reduce serum creatinine to <1.5 mg/dl is as follows:
  1. Administration of one of the following drugs or drug combinations:
     a. Norepinephrine (0.5 to 3.0 mg/hr IV)
     b. Midodrine (7.5 mg PO tid, increased to 12.5 mg tid if needed) in combination with octretide (100 micrograms SC tid, increased to tid prn)
     c. Terlipressin (0.2 to 2.0 mg IV q 4-12 hr)
  2. Concomitant administration of albumin (1 g/kg IV on day 1, followed by 20 to 40 g daily)

DISPOSITION

Mortality rate exceeds 80%; liver transplantation is the only curative treatment.

REFERRAL

Referral for liver transplantation when indicated (see Comments)

PEARLS & CONSIDERATIONS

COMMENTS

Liver transplantation may be indicated in otherwise healthy patients (age preferably <65 yr) with sclerosing cholangitis, chronic hepatitis with cirrhosis, or primary biliary cirrhosis; contraindications to liver transplantation are AIDS, most metastatic malignancies, active substance abuse, uncontrolled sepsis, uncontrolled cardiac or pulmonary disease.

SUGGESTED READINGS

Duvoux C et al: Effects of noradrenalin and albumin in patients with type 1 hepatorenal syndrome: a pilot study, *Hepatology* 36:374, 2002.

Gines P et al: Management of cirrhosis and ascites, *N Engl J Med* 350:1646, 2004.

AUTHOR: **FRED F. FERRI, M.D.**

Herpangina (PTG)

BASIC INFORMATION

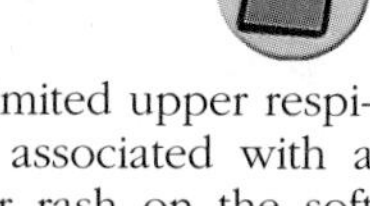

DEFINITION

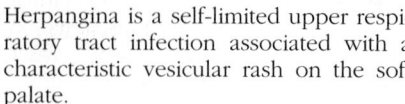

Herpangina is a self-limited upper respiratory tract infection associated with a characteristic vesicular rash on the soft palate.

ICD-9CM CODES
074.0 Herpangina

EPIDEMIOLOGY & DEMOGRAPHICS

INCIDENCE (IN U.S.): Unknown
PREVALENCE (IN U.S.): Unknown
PREDOMINANT SEX: Male = female
PREDOMINANT AGE: 3 to 10 yr
PEAK INCIDENCE: Summer outbreaks common

PHYSICAL FINDINGS & CLINICAL PRESENTATION

- Characterized by ulcerating lesions typically located on the soft palate (Fig. 1-117)
- Usually fewer than six lesions that evolve rapidly from a diffuse pharyngitis to erythematous macules and subsequently to vesicles that are moderately painful
- Fever, vomiting, and headache in the first few days of illness but subsiding spontaneously
- Pharyngeal lesions typical for several more days

ETIOLOGY

- Most caused by coxsackie A viruses (A2, A4, A5, A6, A10)
- Occasional cases caused by other viruses

DIAGNOSIS

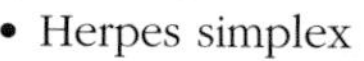

DIFFERENTIAL DIAGNOSIS

- Herpes simplex
- Bacterial pharyngitis
- Tonsillitis
- Aphthous stomatitis
- Hand-foot-mouth disease

WORKUP

Diagnosis is typically based on characteristic lesions on the soft palate.

LABORATORY TESTS

Viral and bacterial cultures of the pharynx to exclude herpes simplex infection and streptococcal pharyngitis if the diagnosis is in doubt

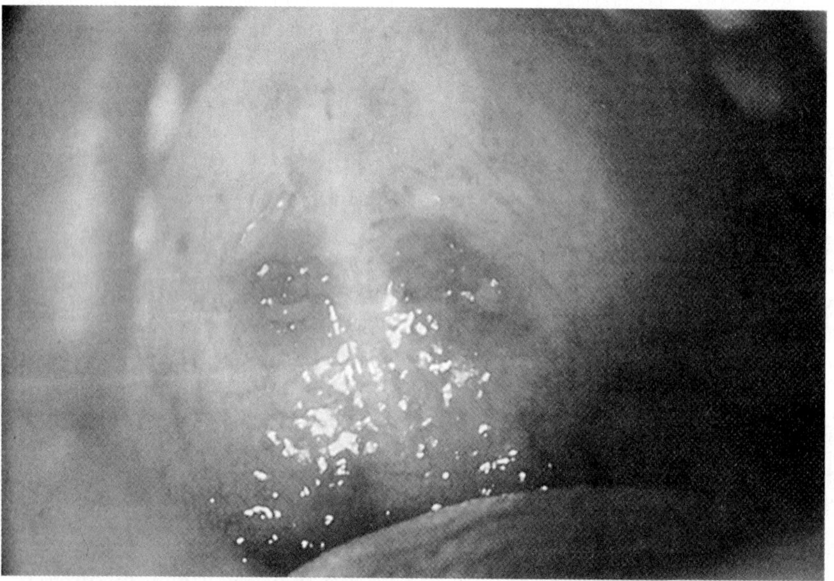

FIGURE 1-117 Herpangina with shallow ulcers in the roof of the mouth. (Courtesy Marshall Guill, M.D. From Goldstein B [ed]: *Practical dermatology,* ed 2, St Louis, 1997, Mosby.)

TREATMENT

- Symptomatic treatment for sore throat
- No antiviral therapy indicated

NONPHARMACOLOGIC THERAPY

Analgesic throat lozenges are helpful in some cases.

ACUTE GENERAL Rx

Antipyretics when indicated

CHRONIC Rx

Self-limited infection

DISPOSITION

- Generally, resolution of symptoms within 1 wk
- Persistence of fever or mouth lesions beyond 1 wk suggestive of an alternative diagnosis (see Differential Diagnosis)

REFERRAL

For consultation with otolaryngologist or infectious disease specialist if the diagnosis is in doubt

PEARLS & CONSIDERATIONS

COMMENTS

Household outbreaks may occur, especially during the summer months.

SUGGESTED READINGS

Chang LY et al: Risk factors of enterovirus 71 infection and associated hand, foot, and mouth disease/herpangina in children during an epidemic in Taiwan, *Pediatrics* 109(6):e88, 2002.

Stone MS: Viral exanthems, *Dermatol Online J* 9(3):4, 2003.

AUTHOR: **JOSEPH R. MASCI, M.D.**

BASIC INFORMATION

DEFINITION

Herpes simplex is a viral infection caused by the herpes simplex virus (HSV); HSV-1 is associated primarily with oral infections, whereas HSV-2 causes mainly genital infections; however, each type can infect any site; following the primary infection, the virus enters the nerve endings in the skin directly below the lesions and ascends to the dorsal root ganglia where it remains in a latent stage until it is reactivated.

SYNONYMS

Genital herpes
Herpes labialis
Herpes gladiatorum
Herpes digitalis

ICD-9CM CODES
054.10 Genital herpes
054.9 Herpes labialis

EPIDEMIOLOGY & DEMOGRAPHICS

- More than 85% of adults have serologic evidence of HSV-1 infection. The seroprevalence of adults with HSV-2 in the United States is 25%; however, only about 20% of these persons recall having symptoms of HSV infection.
- Most cases of eye or digital herpetic infections are caused by HSV-1.
- Frequency of recurrence of HSV-2 genital herpes is higher than HSV-1 oral labial infection.
- The frequency of recurrence is lowest for oral labial HSV-2 infections.
- The incidence of complications from herpes simplex (e.g., herpes encephalitis) is highest in immunocompromised hosts.

PHYSICAL FINDINGS

PRIMARY INFECTION:

- Symptoms occur from 3 to 7 days after contact (respiratory droplets, direct contact).
- Constitutional symptoms include low-grade fever, headache and myalgias, regional lymphadenopathy, and localized pain.
- Pain, burning, itching, and tingling last several hours.
- Grouped vesicles (Fig. 1-118) usually with surrounding erythema appear and generally ulcerate or crust within 48 hr.
- The vesicles are uniform in size (differentiating it from herpes zoster vesicles, which vary in size).
- During the acute eruption the patient is uncomfortable; involvement of lips and inside of mouth may make it unpleasant for the patient to eat; urinary retention may complicate involvement of the genital area.
- Lesions generally last from 2 to 6 wk and heal without scarring.

RECURRENT INFECTION:

- Generally caused by alteration in the immune system; fatigue, stress, menses, local skin trauma, and exposure to sunlight are contributing factors.
- The prodromal symptoms (fatigue, burning and tingling of the affected area) last 12 to 24 hr.
- A cluster of lesions generally evolve within 24 hr from a macule to a papule and then vesicles surrounded by erythema; the vesicles coalesce and subsequently rupture within 4 days, revealing erosions covered by crusts.
- The crusts are generally shed within 7 to 10 days, revealing a pink surface.
- The most frequent location of the lesions is on the vermilion border of the lips (HSV-1), the penile shaft or glans penis and the labia (HSV-2), buttocks (seen more frequently in women), fingertips (herpetic whitlow), and trunk (may be confused with herpes zoster).
- Rapid onset of diffuse cutaneous herpes simplex (eczema herpeticum) may occur in certain atopic infants and adults. It is a medical emergency, especially in young infants, and should be promptly treated with acyclovir.
- Herpes encephalitis, meningitis, and ocular herpes can occur in patients with immunocompromised status and occasionally in normal hosts.

ETIOLOGY

HSV-1 and HSV-2 are both DNA viruses.

DIAGNOSIS

DIFFERENTIAL DIAGNOSIS

- Impetigo
- Behçet's syndrome
- Coxsackie virus infection
- Syphilis
- Stevens-Johnson syndrome
- Herpangina
- Aphthous stomatitis
- Varicella
- Herpes zoster

WORKUP

Diagnosis is based on clinical presentation. Laboratory evaluation will confirm diagnosis.

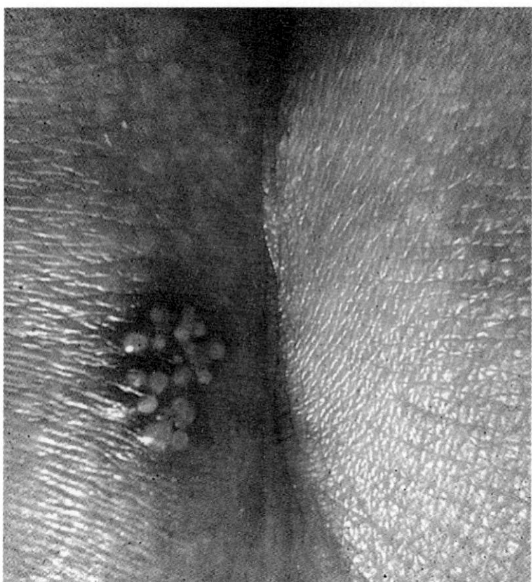

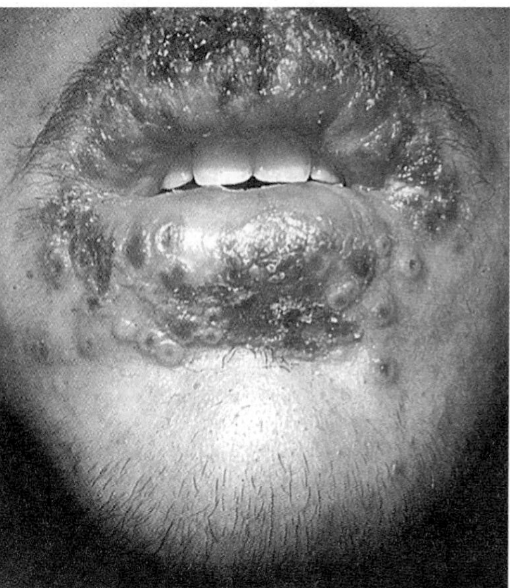

FIGURE 1-118 Herpes simplex. (From Scuderi G [ed]: *Sports medicine: principles of primary care,* St Louis, 1997, Mosby.)

LABORATORY TESTS

- Direct immunofluorescent antibody slide tests will provide a rapid diagnosis.
- Viral culture is the most definitive method for diagnosis; results are generally available in 1 or 2 days; the lesions should be sampled during the vesicular or early ulcerative stage; cervical samples should be taken from the endocervix with a swab.
- Tzanck smear is a readily available test; it will demonstrate multinucleated giant cells. However, it is not a very sensitive test.
- Pap smear will detect HSV-infected cells in cervical tissue from women without symptoms.
- Serologic tests for HSV: IgG and IgM serum antibodies. Antibodies to HSV occur in 50% to 90% of adults. Routine tests do not discriminate between antibodies that are HSV-1 and HSV-2; the presence of IgM or a fourfold or greater rise in IgG titers indicates a recent infection (convalescent sample should be drawn 2 to 3 wk after the acute specimen is drawn).

TREATMENT

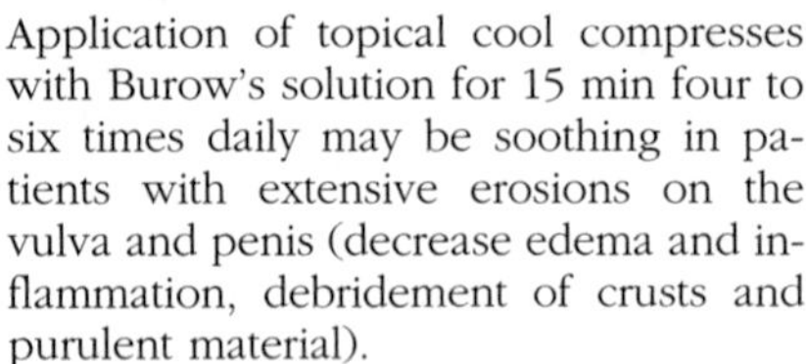

NONPHARMACOLOGIC THERAPY

Application of topical cool compresses with Burow's solution for 15 min four to six times daily may be soothing in patients with extensive erosions on the vulva and penis (decrease edema and inflammation, debridement of crusts and purulent material).

ACUTE GENERAL Rx

- Acyclovir ointment or cream (Zovirax) applied using finger-cot or rubber glove q3-6h (six times daily) for 7 days may be useful for the first clinical episode of genital herpes. Severe primary genital infections may be treated with IV acyclovir (5 mg/kg infused at a constant rate over 1 hr q8h for 7 days in patients with normal renal function) or oral acyclovir 200 mg five times daily for 10 days. Topical acyclovir 5% cream can also be used for herpes labialis; when started at the prodrome or papule stage, it decreases the duration of an episode by about one-half day.
- Valacyclovir caplets (Valtrex) can also be used for the initial episode of genital herpes (1 g bid for 10 days).
- Valacyclovir 2 g PO q12h for 1 day begun within the first symptoms of herpes labialis can modestly shorten its duration.
- Penciclovir 1% cream (Denavir) can be used for recurrent herpes labialis on the lips and face. It should be applied q2h while awake for 4 days. Treatment should be started at the earliest sign or symptom. Its use decreases healing time of orolabial herpes by about one day.
- Docosanol 10% cream (Abbreva), a long-chain saturated alcohol, inhibits fusion between the plasma membrane and the viral envelope, blocking viral entry and subsequent replication. It is available over the counter and, when applied at the first sign of recurrence of herpes labialis, may shorten the durations of the episode by about 12 hr.

CHRONIC Rx

- Recurrent episodes of genital herpes can be treated with acyclovir. A short course (800 mg tid for 2 days) is effective. Other treatment options include 800 mg PO bid for 3 to 5 days, generally started during the prodrome or within 2 days of onset of lesions; famciclovir (Famvir) is also useful for treatment of recurrent genital herpes (dose is 125 mg q12h for 5 days in patients with normal renal function) started at the first sign of symptoms, or valacyclovir (Valtrex) (dose is 500 mg q12h for 3 days in patients with normal renal function).
- Acyclovir-resistant mucocutaneous lesions in patients with HIV can be treated with foscarnet (40 to 60 mg/kg IV q8h in patients with normal renal function); HPMPC has also been reported to be effective in HSV infections resistant to acyclovir or foscarnet.
- Patients with 6 recurrences of genital herpes/year can be treated with valacyclovir 1 g qd, acyclovir 400 mg bid, or famciclovir 250 mg bid.

DISPOSITION

Most patients recover from the initial episode or recurrences without complications; immunocompromised hosts are at risk for complications (e.g., disseminated herpes simplex infection, herpes encephalitis).

REFERRAL

Hospital admission in patients with herpes encephalitis, herpes meningitis, and in immunocompromised hosts with diffuse herpes simplex infection
Ophthalmology referral in patients with suspected ocular herpes

PEARLS & CONSIDERATIONS

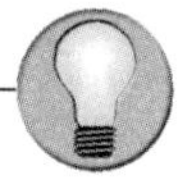

COMMENTS

- Provide patient education regarding transmission of HSV.
- Condom use offers significant protection against HSV-1 infection in susceptive women.
- Patients should be instructed on the use of condoms for sexual intercourse and on avoiding kissing or sexual intercourse until lesions are crusted.
- Patients should also avoid contact with immunocompromised hosts or neonates while lesions are present.
- Proper hand-washing techniques should be explained.
- Patients with herpes gladiatorum (cutaneous herpes in athletes involved in contact sports) should be excluded from participation in active sports until lesions have resolved.
- Many new HSV-2 infections are asymptomatic, but new symptoms may result from old infections.

SUGGESTED READINGS

Centers for Disease Control and Prevention: 2002 sexually transmitted diseases treatment guidelines, *MMWR Morb Mortal Wkly Rep* 51(RR-6), 2002.

Corey L et al: Once-daily valacyclovir to reduce the risk of transmission of genital herpes, *N Engl J Med* 350:11, 2004.

AUTHOR: **FRED F. FERRI, M.D.**

BASIC INFORMATION

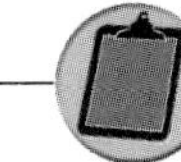

DEFINITION

Herpes zoster is a disease caused by reactivation of the varicella-zoster virus. Following the primary infection (chickenpox) the virus becomes latent in the dorsal root ganglia and reemerges when there is a weakening of the immune system (secondary to disease or advanced age).

SYNONYMS

Shingles

ICD-9CM CODES
053.9 Herpes zoster

EPIDEMIOLOGY & DEMOGRAPHICS

- Herpes zoster occurs during lifetime in 10% to 20% of the population.
- There is an increased incidence in immunocompromised patients (AIDS, malignancy), the elderly, and children who acquired chickenpox when younger than 2 mo.

PHYSICAL FINDINGS & CLINICAL PRESENTATION

- Pain generally precedes skin manifestation by 3 to 5 days and is generally localized to the dermatome that will be affected by the skin lesions.
- Constitutional symptoms are often present (malaise, fever, headache).
- The initial rash consists of erythematous maculopapules generally affecting one dermatome (thoracic region in majority of cases); some patients (<50%) may have scattered vesicles outside of the affected dermatome.
- The initial maculopapules evolve into vesicles and pustules by the third or the fourth day.
- The vesicles have an erythematous base, are cloudy, and have various sizes (a distinguishing characteristic from herpes simplex in which the vesicles are of uniform size).
- The vesicles subsequently become umbilicated and then form crusts that generally fall off within 3 wk; scarring may occur.
- Pain during and after the rash is generally significant.
- Secondary bacterial infection with *Staphylococcus aureus* or *Streptococcus pyogenes* may occur.
- Regional lymphadenopathy may occur.
- Herpes zoster may involve the trigeminal nerve (most frequent cranial nerve involved); involvement of the geniculate ganglion can cause facial palsy and a painful ear, with the presence of vesicles on the pinna and external auditory canal (*Ramsay Hunt syndrome*).

ETIOLOGY

Reactivation of varicella virus (human herpesvirus III)

DIAGNOSIS

DIFFERENTIAL DIAGNOSIS

- Rash: herpes simplex and other viral infections
- Pain from herpes zoster: may be confused with acute myocardial infarction, pulmonary embolism, pleuritis, pericarditis, renal colic

LABORATORY TESTS

Laboratory tests are generally not necessary (viral cultures and Tzanck smear will confirm diagnosis in patients with atypical presentation).

TREATMENT

NONPHARMACOLOGIC THERAPY

- Wet compresses (using Burow's solution or cool tap water) applied for 15 to 30 min 5 to 10 times a day are useful to break vesicles and remove serum and crust.
- Care must be taken to prevent any secondary bacterial infection.

ACUTE GENERAL Rx

- Gabapentin 300 to 1800 mg qd is effective in the treatment of pain and sleep interference associated with postherpetic neuralgia.
- Lidocaine patch 5% (Lidoderm) is also effective in relieving postherpetic neuralgia. Patches are applied to intact skin to cover the most painful area for up to 12 hr within a 24-hr period.
- Oral antiviral agents can decrease acute pain, inflammation, and vesicle formation when treatment is begun within 48 hr of onset of rash. Treatment options are:
  1. Acyclovir (Zovirax) 800 mg 5 times daily for 7 to 10 days
  2. Valacyclovir (Valtrex) 1000 mg tid for 7 days
  3. Famciclovir (Famvir) 500 mg tid for 7 days
- Immunocompromised patients should be treated with IV acyclovir 500 mg/m² or 10 mg/kg q8h in 1-hr infusions for 7 days, with close monitoring of renal function and adequate hydration; vidarabine (continuous 12-hr infusion of 10 mg/kg/day for 7 days) is also effective for treatment of disseminated herpes zoster in immunocompromised hosts.
- Patients with AIDS and transplant patients may develop acyclovir-resistant varicella-zoster; these patients can be treated with foscarnet (40 mg/kg IV q8h) continued for at least 10 days or until lesions are completely healed.
- Capsaicin cream (Zostrix) can be useful for treatment of postherpetic neuralgia. It is generally applied three to five times daily for several weeks after the crusts have fallen off.
- Sympathetic blocks (stellate ganglion or epidural) with 0.25% bupivacaine and rhizotomy are reserved for severe cases unresponsive to conservative treatment.
- Corticosteroids should be considered in older patients if there are no contraindications. Initial dose is prednisone 60 mg/day tapered over a period of 21 days. When used there is a decrease in the use of analgesics and time to resumption of usual activities, but there is no effect on the incidence and duration of postherpetic neuralgia.

DISPOSITION

- The incidence of postherpetic neuralgia (defined as pain that persists more than 30 days after onset of rash) increases with age (30% by age 40 yr, >70% by age 70 yr); antivirals reduce the risk of postherpetic neuralgia.
- Incidence of disseminated herpes zoster is increased in immunocompromised hosts (e.g., 15% to 50% of patients with active Hodgkin's disease).
- Immunocompromised hosts are also more prone to neurologic complications (encephalitis, myelitis, cranial and peripheral nerve palsies, acute retinal necrosis). The mortality rate is 10% to 20% in immunocompromised hosts with disseminated zoster.
- Motor neuropathies occur in 5% of all cases of zoster; complete recovery occurs in >70% of patients.

REFERRAL

- Hospitalization for IV acyclovir in patients with disseminated herpes zoster
- Patients with herpes zoster ophthalmicus should be referred to an ophthalmologist
- Surgical referral for rhizotomy in patients with severe pain unresponsive to conventional treatment
- Sympathetic blocks in selected patients

SUGGESTED READING

Gnann JW, Whitley RJ: Herpes zoster, *N Engl J Med* 347:340, 2002.

AUTHOR: **FRED F. FERRI, M.D.**

BASIC INFORMATION

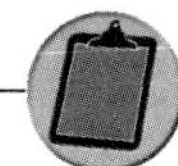

DEFINITION

A hiatal hernia is the herniation of a portion of the stomach into the thoracic cavity through the diaphragmatic esophageal hiatus.

SYNONYMS

Diaphragmatic hernias

ICD-9CM CODES
750.6 Hiatal hernia

EPIDEMIOLOGY & DEMOGRAPHICS

- Found in 50% of patients over the age of 50
- Increases with age
- More prevalent in Western countries than in Africa and Asia
- Sliding hiatal hernias are more common in women than men (4:1)
- Associated with diverticulosis (25%), esophagitis (25%), duodenal ulcers (20%), and gallstones (18%)
- More than 90% of patients with documented endoscopic esophagitis have hiatal hernias

PHYSICAL FINDINGS & CLINICAL PRESENTATION

Most patients with hiatal hernias are asymptomatic. Symptomatic patients present similar to patients with GERD.
- Heartburn
- Dysphagia
- Regurgitation
- Chest pain
- Postprandial fullness
- GI bleed
- Dyspnea
- Hoarseness
- Wheezing with bowel sounds heard over the left lung base

ETIOLOGY

- Hiatal hernias are classified as:
  1. Sliding (1-119, *A*), axial, or concentric hiatal hernia (most common type, 99%). The GE junction protrudes through the hiatus into the thoracic cavity
  2. Paraesophageal hernia (Fig. 1-119, *B*) (1%). The GE junction stays at the level of the diaphragm, but part of the stomach bulges into the thoracic cavity and stays there at all times, not being affected by swallowing
  3. Mixed (rare)
- Hiatal hernias are thought to develop from an imbalance between normal pulling forces of the esophagus through the diaphragmatic hiatus during swallowing and the supporting structures maintaining normal esophagogastric junction positioning in association with repetitive stretching that results in rupture of the phrenoesophageal membrane.

DIAGNOSIS

The diagnosis of hiatal hernia relies on history and imaging studies.

DIFFERENTIAL DIAGNOSIS

- Peptic ulcer disease
- Unstable angina
- Esophagitis (e.g., *Candida,* herpes, NSAIDs, etc.)
- Esophageal spasm
- Barrett's esophagus
- Schatzki's ring
- Achalasia
- Zenker's diverticulum
- Esophageal cancer

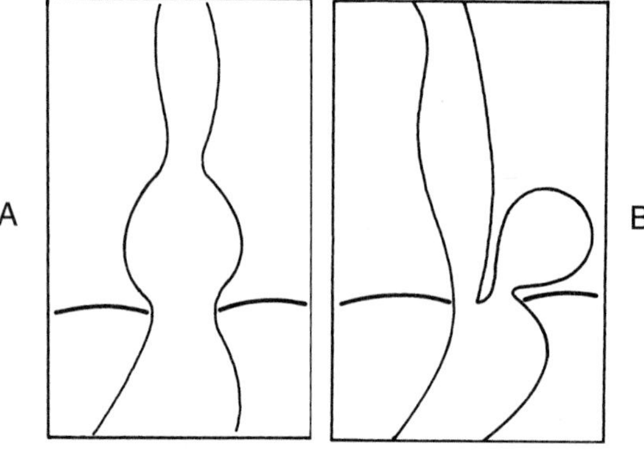

FIGURE 1-119 Types of esophageal hiatal hernia. A, Sliding hiatal hernia, the most common type. **B,** Paraesophageal hiatal hernia. (From Behrman RE: *Nelson textbook of pediatrics,* ed 16, Philadelphia, 2000, WB Saunders.)

WORKUP

- The workup is directed at excluding conditions noted in the differential diagnosis and documenting the presence of a hiatal hernia. Upper endoscopy may also be needed to exclude abnormal metaplasia, dysplasia, or neoplasia.
- A clinical algorithm for evaluation of heartburn is described in Section III.

LABORATORY TESTS

- Blood tests are not very specific in diagnosing hiatal hernias.
- Esophageal manometry, although not commonly done, can be used in establishing a diagnosis.

IMAGING STUDIES

- Barium contrast UGI series best defines the anatomic abnormality. A hiatal hernia is considered to be present if the gastric cardia is herniated 2 cm above the hiatus. UGI may reveal a tortuous esophagus.
- Upper GI endoscopy is useful to document the presence of a hiatal hernia and also to exclude common associated findings of esophagitis and Barrett's esophagus. A hiatal hernia can be found incidentally and is diagnosed if >2 cm of gastric rugal fold is seen above the margins of the diaphragmatic crura.

TREATMENT

NONPHARMACOLOGIC THERAPY

- Lifestyle modifications with avoidance of foods and drugs that decrease lower esophageal pressure (e.g. caffeine, chocolate, mint, calcium channel blockers, and anticholinergics)
- Weight loss
- Avoid large quantities of food with meals
- Sleep with the head of the bed elevated 4 to 6 in with blocks

ACUTE GENERAL Rx

- Antacids may be useful to relieve mild symptoms.
- H_2 antagonists (e.g., cimetidine 400 mg bid, ranitidine 150 mg bid, or famotidine 20 mg bid) can be used for symptomatic relief.
- If significant GERD is present with documented esophagitis by upper EGD, proton pump inhibitors (e.g., omeprazole 20 mg qd or lansoprazole 30 mg qd) are used. Refractory symptoms may require higher doses of PPI (e.g., BID dosing).
- Prokinetic agents (e.g., metoclopramide 10 mg taken 30 min before each meal) can be added to an H_2 antagonist or proton pump inhibitor.

CHRONIC Rx

- When indicated, surgery (laparoscopic or open) can be done in patients with refractory symptoms impairing quality of life and causing both intestinal (e.g., recurrent GI bleeds) and extraintestinal complications (e.g., aspiration pneumonia, asthma, and ENT complications).
- Prophylactic surgery is a consideration in all patients with paraesophageal hiatal hernias because they have a higher incidence of strangulation.

DISPOSITION

- More than 90% of patients with a hiatal hernia having GERD symptoms respond well to medical therapy.
- Complications of hiatal hernias are similar to complications occurring in patients with GERD:
  1. Erosive esophagitis
  2. Ulcerative esophagitis
  3. Barrett's esophagus
  4. Peptic stricture
  5. GI hemorrhage
  6. Extraintestinal complications

REFERRAL

All patients with documented hiatal hernia refractory to conventional H_2 antagonists, antacids, and proton pump inhibitors or having complications as mentioned previously should be referred to a gastroenterologist.

PEARLS & CONSIDERATIONS

COMMENTS

- Once in a lifetime upper endoscopy has been proposed in the literature to exclude Barrett's esophagus.
- Approximately 5% of patients with Barrett's esophagus go on to develop esophageal cancer.
- Yearly surveillance by upper EGD is recommended in patients with Barrett's esophagus.

SUGGESTED READINGS

Andujan JJ et al: Laparoscopic repair of large paraesophageal hernia is associated with low incidence of recurrence and reoperations, *Surg Endosc* 18(3):444, 2004.

Christensen J, Miftakhnr R: Hiatus hernia: a review of evidence for its origin in esophageal longitudinal muscle dysfunction, *Am J Med* 108(Suppl 4a):35, 2000.

Epstein FH: The esophagogastric junction, *N Engl J Med* 336(13):924, 1997.

Rosen M, Ponsky J: Laparoscopic repair of giant paraesophageal hernia: an update for internists, *Clev Clin J Med* 70(6):511, 2003.

Stylopoulos N, Rattner DW: Paraesophageal hernia: when to operate? *Adv Surg* 37:213, 2003.

Targarona EM et al: Midterm analysis of safety and quality of life after laparoscopic repair of paraesophageal hiatal hernia, *Surg Endosc* 18(7):1045, 2004.

AUTHORS: **HEMCHAND RAMBERAN, M.D.**

Histiocytosis X (PTG)

BASIC INFORMATION

DEFINITION

Histiocytosis X is a rare disorder characterized by the abnormal proliferation of pathologic Langerhans cells. These dendritic cells form characteristic infiltrates with eosinophils, lymphocytes, and other histiocytes that may be found in various organs.

SYNONYMS

- Eosinophilic granuloma
- Hand-Schuller-Christian disease
- Letterer-Siwe disease
- Langerhans cell histiocytosis
- Langerhans cell granulomatosis

ICD-9CM CODES
277.8 Histiocytosis X

EPIDEMIOLOGY & DEMOGRAPHICS

- Histiocytosis X is a rare disease in adults and is considered to be mainly a childhood disorder.
- In the pediatric population, it affects 2 to 5 per million population annually.
- The disease may affect any age group, from newborns to the elderly; however, peak incidence is from 1 to 4 yr.
- Affects males more often than females, 2:1.
- Disseminated histiocytosis X usually occurs before 2 yr of age.
- Approximately 50% of isolated eosinophilic granuloma cases occur before the age of 5.

PHYSICAL FINDINGS & CLINICAL PRESENTATION

- A characteristic feature of histiocytosis X is its variable clinical presentation. The clinical spectrum ranges from:
  1. A benign isolated bony lesion (eosinophilic granuloma).
  2. Multiple bone lesions with soft tissue gingival and oral mucosal involvement (Hand-Schüller-Christian disease).
  3. An aggressive disseminated disease infiltrating organs and causing organ dysfunction (Letterer-Siwe disease).
- Bone lesions (80% to 100%).
  1. May be isolated or multiple
  2. Painful, often worse at night
  3. Skull most often involved, followed by long bones; lesions rarely seen in small bones of hands and feet
  4. Proptosis
  5. Mastoiditis
  6. Loose teeth
  7. Gingival hypertrophy
- Skin is involved in >80% of patients with disseminated disease and in 30% of patients with less extensive disease.
  1. Seborrhea-like scaling of scalp, petechial and purpuric lesions, ulcers, and bronzing of the skin may occur.
  2. Common sites: scalp, neck, trunk, groin, and extremities.
- Lymphadenopathy (10%): cervical and inguinal.
- Lung involvement may manifest with cough, tachypnea, cyanosis, inspiratory crackles, pleural effusions, or pneumothorax. Diffuse emphysema associated with pulmonary fibrosis is the end stage of a mixed restrictive and obstructive pattern of disease.
- Pulmonary disease is very frequent in adults (usually as isolated disease), but can be seen in 23%-50% of children as well. In children, lung involvement always occurs as part of multisystem disease.
- Liver involvement manifesting as hepatomegaly with or without jaundice (50%-60%).
- Involvement of the biliary tree may be seen as biliary fibrosis or sclerosing cholangitis.
- Splenomegaly (5%).
- CNS involvement occurs in 25%-35% of patients, most often in those with multisystem disease. The most common cerebral site affected is the hypothalamic-neurohypophyseal region, where infiltration and destruction usually result in diabetes insipidus with insatiable thirst and urination. The second most common site of involvement is the cerebellum.
- Involvement of the thymus, parotid glands, and GI tract have been reported in rare cases.

ETIOLOGY

- The etiology of histiocytosis is unknown.
- Initially, histiocytosis was thought to represent an abnormal immune response to a virus or other stimulant resulting in the proliferation of pathologic Langerhans cells. More recent evidence suggests histiocytosis X as a monoclonal proliferative neoplastic disorder.
- In adults, pulmonary histiocytosis X appears to be primarily an immune-mediated reactive process and has been linked to cigarette smoking. Cigarette smoke had not been observed as a causative factor in other forms of histiocytosis X.

DIAGNOSIS

Tissue biopsy revealing pathologic Langerhans cells characterized by the presence of surface nucleoprotein, protein S-100, and CD1a antigen. "Birbeck granules" noted on electron microscopy establishes the diagnosis of histiocytosis X.

DIFFERENTIAL DIAGNOSIS

The differential diagnosis is extensive, including all causes of diabetes insipidus, lytic bone lesions, dermatitis, hepatomegaly, and lymphadenopathy.

WORKUP

The workup of patients suspected of having histiocytosis X includes blood tests and imaging studies to assess the extent of disease involvement.

LABORATORY TESTS

- CBC is not specific in the diagnosis of histiocytosis X but may reveal cytopenias in patients with bone marrow involvement.
- Electrolytes, BUN, creatinine, urinalysis, and urine and serum osmolality are helpful in the diagnosis of diabetes insipidus during fluid deprivation testing.
- LFTs may be elevated in patients with liver involvement.
- Bronchoalveolar lavage (BAL) may show increased numbers of CD1a-positive histiocytes or Langerhans cells in patients with pulmonary histiocytosis X.

IMAGING STUDIES

- X-ray studies of affected areas show lytic lesions with or without sclerotic margins.
- X-ray bone survey is done searching for other lesions.
- Bone scan complements the bone survey studies.
- Panoramic dental view of the mandible and maxilla for children with oral involvement.
- Chest x-ray can show interstitial reticulonodular infiltrates. This pattern typically progresses toward frank honeycombing fibrosis later in the course of the disease (Fig. 1-120).
- High-resolution CT scan of the chest confirms interstitial lung scarring, nodules, and cysts, and represents an excellent noninvasive means for diagnosis and follow-up of pulmonary histiocytosis X. Pulmonary cysts are bilateral and symmetric, showing slight upper-lobe predominance with relative sparing of the costophrenic angles.

- CT scans of the temporal bone looking at the mastoid, and inner and middle ear.
- Ultrasound of the abdomen may show hepatosplenomegaly.
- Conventional cholangiography or magnetic resonance cholangiopancreatography (MRCP) can confirm the presence of disease in patients suspected to have biliary involvement.
- MRI of the brain visualizing the hypothalamic-hypophyseal region in patients suspected of having diabetes insipidus.

TREATMENT

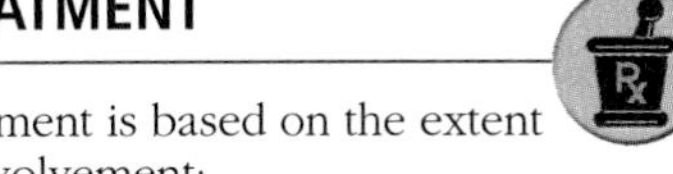

Treatment is based on the extent of involvement:

- Single-system disease:
  1. Single site: single bone lesion, isolated skin disease, or solitary lymph node
  2. Multiple site: multiple bone lesions, multiple lymph nodes
- Multiple disease: multiple organ involvement, with or without dysfunction

ACUTE GENERAL Rx

Isolated bone lesions can be treated by:

- Curettage at the time of diagnosis
- Intralesional steroid injection
- Radiation therapy

Single skin lesions are treated with:

- Topical steroid (e.g., triamcinolone acetonide) applied bid
- Nitrogen mustard in 20% solution

Solitary lymph node:

- Excision at the time of diagnosis
- Systemic oral prednisone

Multisystem disease treatment includes:

- Vinblastine 6 mg/m2 IV bolus qwk × 6 mo or etoposide 150 mg/m2 IV for 3 days q3wk for 6 mo plus
- Methylprednisolone 30 mg/kg per day for 3 days

CHRONIC Rx

- High-risk patients not responding to initial treatment should be considered for salvage therapy, including either bone marrow transplantation or combination cyclosporin A, antithymocyte globulin, and prednisolone.
- Diabetes insipidus is treated with DDAVP 0.1 mg to 0.8 mg PO or 1 spray bid to tid.
- Adults with isolated pulmonary histiocytosis X do not require aggressive treatment but may benefit from smoking cessation, as several reported cases of spontaneous resolution or improvement after smoking cessation have been reported in the literature.
- Empirical use of steroids, in either short pulses or longer exposures, has also been implicated in the treatment of pulmonary disease; however, data regarding effectiveness are still limited.
- Lung transplantation has been tried in both children and adults with advanced pulmonary disease and limited lung function, but failure rates are high because of local recurrence after transplantation.

DISPOSITION

- The course of histiocytosis X is often unpredictable and varies from spontaneous resolution to rapid progression and death, or multiple recurrences and regressions with risk for permanent sequelae.
- Patients with disease localized to only one organ system have a good prognosis and appear to need minimal, if any, treatment.
- Patients with multisystem disease have an increased risk for poor outcome, with a reported mortality rate of 10%-20% and 50% risk of life-impairing morbidity.
- A poor prognostic feature in the multisystem treatment group is the failure to respond to therapy in the first 6 wk.
- Multisystem disease patients categorized as low-risk group were patients >2 yr of age with no evidence of organ involvement (e.g., bone marrow, liver, lung, or spleen).
- Age of onset (<2 yr) with organ involvement is considered a high-risk group.
- In patients with disseminated histiocytosis X and <2 yr of age, the mortality rate is 30%.
- For patients with isolated pulmonary histiocytosis X, the 5-yr survival rate is around 80%.
- The association of histiocytosis X with other malignancies (e.g., ALL, acute nonlymphoblastic leukemia, and solid tumors) has been cited. It remains unclear if the associated malignancies result from the treatment of histiocytosis X or from chance events.

REFERRAL

- Patients with histiocytosis X require a multidisciplinary approach, including pediatric oncologist, radiation oncologists, oral maxillary surgeons, ENT specialists, audiology, dermatology, endocrinology, and family counseling.

PEARLS & CONSIDERATIONS

COMMENTS

- Dr. Alfred Hand, Jr., described the first case of histiocytosis X in 1893. Drs. Letterer, Siwe, Schüller, and Christian also described similar cases between 1915 and 1933.
- Dr. Louis Lichtenstein noted the similarities of the cases and coined the term "histiocytosis X."
- In 1987, the Histiocyte Society was formed, and the disease was officially termed "Langerhans cell histiocytosis."

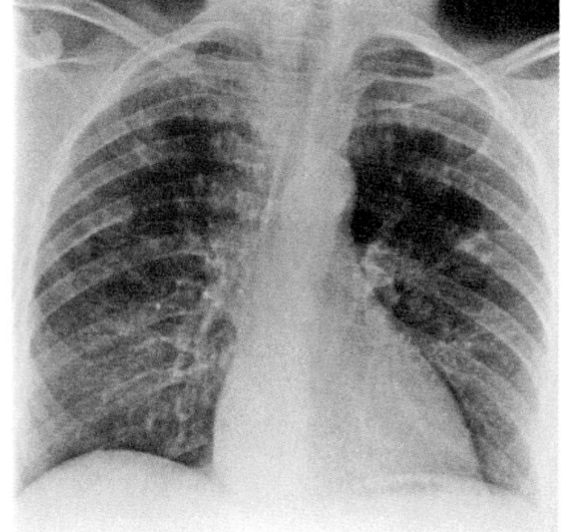

FIGURE 1-120 Histiocytosis X. There is a reticular nodular pattern in the upper lobes. The lung volumes are preserved. (From McLoud TC [ed]: *Thoracic radiology, the requisites,* St Louis, 1998, Mosby.)

SUGGESTED READINGS

Arico M: Langerhans cell histiocytosis in adults: more questions than answers? *Dur J Cancer* 40:1467, 2004.

Arico M, Egeler RM: Clinical aspects of Langerhans cell histiocytosis, *Hematol Oncol Clin North Am* 12(2):247, 1998.

Broadbent V, Gadner H: Current therapy for Langerhans cell histiocytosis, *Hematol Oncol Clin North Am* 12(2):327, 1998.

Coppes-Zantinga A, Egeler RM: The Langerhans cell histiocytosis X files revealed, *Br J Haematol* 116:3, 2002.

Lamper F: Langerhans cell histiocytosis: historical perspectives, *Hematol Oncol Clin North Am* 12(2):213, 1998.

Nicholson HS, Egeler RM, Nesbit ME: The epidemiology of Langerhans cell histiocytosis, *Hematol Oncol Clin North Am* 12(2):379, 1998.

Schmidt S et al: Extra-osseous involvement of Langerhan's cell histiocytosis in children, *Pediatr Radiol* 34:313, 2004.

Schmitz L, Favara BE: Nosology and pathology of Langerhans cell histiocytosis, *Hematol Oncol Clin North Am* 12(2):221, 1998.

AUTHORS: **JASON IANNUCCILL, M.D.,** and **PETER PETROPOULOS, M.D.**

BASIC INFORMATION

DEFINITION

Histoplasmosis is an infectious disease caused by the fungus *Histoplasma capsulatum,* which is usually asymptomatic and characterized by a primary pulmonary focus with occasional progression to chronic pulmonary histoplasmosis (CPH) or various forms of dissemination. Progressive disseminated histoplasmosis (PDH) may present with a diverse clinical spectrum, including adrenal necrosis, pulmonary and mediastinal fibrosis, and ulcerations of the oropharynx and GI tract. In those patients who are concurrently infected with the human immunodeficiency virus (HIV), it is a defining disease for acquired immunodeficiency syndrome (AIDS).

ICD-9CM CODES
115.90 Histoplasmosis
115.94 Histoplasmosis with endocarditis
115.91 Histoplasmosis with meningitis
115.93 Histoplasmosis with pericarditis
115.95 Histoplasmosis with pneumonia
115.92 Histoplasmosis with retinitis

EPIDEMIOLOGY & DEMOGRAPHICS

INCIDENCE (IN U.S.):
- Unknown for acute pulmonary disease
- For CPH, estimated at 1/100,000 cases in endemic areas
- For PDH in immunocompetent adults, estimated at 1/2000 cases of histoplasmosis

PREVALENCE: Unknown
PREDOMINANT SEX: Clinically evident disease is most common in males; male:female ratio of 4:1
PREDOMINANT AGE:
- CPH is most often seen in males >50 yr old with an associated history of COPD.
- Presumed ocular histoplasmosis syndrome (POHS) is most commonly diagnosed between ages of 20 and 40 yr.

PEAK INCIDENCE: Unknown

PHYSICAL FINDINGS & CLINICAL PRESENTATION

- Conidia are deposited in alveoli, then fungus is converted to a yeast in the initial focus of bronchopneumonia and spreads to regional lymph nodes and other organs, especially liver and spleen, via lymphatics.
- From 7 to 18 days after onset, granulomatous inflammatory response marking host's cellular immunity begins to contain the yeast in the form of discrete granulomas.
- In normal host, fungistasis is achieved slowly as granulomas undergo contraction and, later, fibrosis with frequent calcification.
- With maturation of specific cellular immunity, there is development of delayed-type cutaneous hypersensitivity to *Histoplasma* antigens, usually 3 to 6 wk after exposure.
- Clinical disease manifests in various forms, depending on host cellular immunity and inoculum size:
  1. Acute primary pulmonary histoplasmosis
     a. Overwhelming number of patients are asymptomatic.
     b. Most clinically apparent infections manifest by complaints of fever, headache, malaise, pleuritic chest pain, nonproductive cough, and weight loss.
     c. Less than 10%, mainly women, complain of arthralgias, myalgias, and skin manifestations such as erythema multiforme or erythema nodosum.
     d. Acute pericarditis presents in smaller percentage of patients.
     e. On auscultation findings are minimal; hepatosplenomegaly, seen sometimes in adults, is most commonly observed in children.
     f. With particularly heavy exposure, there is severe dyspnea, marked hypoxemia, impending respiratory failure.
     g. Most patients are asymptomatic within 6 wk.
  2. CPH
     a. Presents insidiously with low-grade fever, malaise, weight loss, cough, sometimes with blood-streaked sputum or frank hemoptysis.
     b. Most patients with cavitary lesions present with associated COPD or chronic bronchitis, masking underlying fungal disease.
     c. Tends to worsen preexisting pulmonary disease and further contribute to eventual respiratory insufficiency.
  3. PDH
     a. In both acute and subacute forms, constitutional symptoms of fever, fatigue, malaise, and weight loss are common.
     b. Acute form (seen most commonly in infants and children) is distinguished by predominance of respiratory symptoms, fevers consistently >101° F (38.3° C), generalized lymphadenopathy, marked hepatosplenomegaly, and fulminant course resembling septic shock associated with a high fatality rate.
     c. Subacute form is more common in adults and associated with lower temperatures, hepatosplenomegaly, oropharyngeal ulceration, focal organ involvement (including Addison's disease secondary to adrenal destruction, endocarditis, chronic meningitis, and intracerebral mass lesions).
     d. Course of subacute form is relentless, with untreated patient dying within 2 yr.
     e. Chronic PDH is found in adults and marked by gradual, often intermittent, symptoms of weight loss, weakness, easy fatigability; fever only uncommonly and usually of low grade when present; oropharyngeal ulcerations and hepatomegaly and/or splenomegaly in one third of patients.
     f. Less clinical evidence of focal organ involvement in chronic form than in subacute form.
     g. Natural history of chronic form protracted and intermittent, spanning months to years.
- Histoplasmoma
  1. A healed area of caseation necrosis surrounded by a fibrous capsule
  2. Usually asymptomatic
- Mediastinal fibrosis
  1. A rare consequence of a fibroblastic process that encases caseating mediastinal lymph nodes after primary histoplasma bronchopneumonia
  2. Progressive fibrosis producing severe retraction, compression, and distortion of mediastinal structures
  3. Constriction of the bronchi resulting in bronchiectasis, also esophageal stenosis associated with dysphagia, and superior vena cava syndrome
- POHS
  1. Diagnosis characterized by distinct clinical features, including atrophic choroidal scars and maculopathy in patient with a history suggestive of exposure to the fungus (e.g., residence in an endemic area)
  2. Patient complains of distortion or loss of central vision without pain, redness, or photophobia
  3. Usually no evidence of systemic infection except for a positive skin reaction to histoplasmin
- In patients with AIDS
  1. Possible presentation as overwhelming infection similar to acute PDH seen in children
  2. Constitutional symptoms: fever, weight loss, malaise, cough, dyspnea

3. About 10% with cutaneous maculopapular, erythematous eruptions or purpuric lesions on face, trunk, and extremities
4. Up to 20% with CNS involvement, manifesting as intracerebral mass lesions, chronic meningitis, or encephalopathy
5. Infrequent oropharyngeal ulceration

ETIOLOGY

- *H. capsulatum* is a dimorphic fungus present in temperate zones and river valleys around the world.
- In the U.S., it is highly endemic in southeastern, mid-Atlantic, and central states.
- Exists as mold at ambient temperature and favors surface soil enriched with bird or bat droppings.
- In endemic areas, contaminated dusty soil containing spores (microconidia) may be windswept or otherwise made airborne by sweeping, raking, or bulldozing, and then be inhaled.

DIAGNOSIS

DIFFERENTIAL DIAGNOSIS

- Acute pulmonary histoplasmosis
  1. *Mycobacterium tuberculosis*
  2. Community-acquired pneumonias caused by *Mycoplasma* and *Chlamydia*
  3. Other fungal diseases, such as *Blastomyces dermatitidis* and *Coccidioides immitis*
- Chronic cavitary pulmonary histoplasmosis: *M. tuberculosis*
- Yeast forms of histoplasmosis on tissue section: cysts of *Pneumocystis carinii,* which tend to be larger, extracellular, and do not display budding
- Intracellular parasites of *Leishmania* and *Toxoplasma* species: distinguishable by inability to take up methenamine silver
- Histoplasmomas: true neoplasms

WORKUP

- Suspect diagnosis in patients who present with an influenza-like illness and a history of residence or travel in an endemic area, especially if engaged in occupations (e.g., outside construction or street cleaning) or hobbies (e.g., cave exploring and aviary keeper) that increase the likelihood of exposure to fungal spores.
- Suspect diagnosis in immunosuppressed patients with remote history of exposure, especially if associated with characteristic calcifications on chest x-ray examination.

LABORATORY TESTS

- Demonstration of organism on culture from body fluid or tissues to make definitive diagnosis
  1. Especially high yield in patients with AIDS
  2. Characteristic oval yeast cells in neutrophils stained with Wright-Giemsa on peripheral smear
  3. Preparations of infected tissue with Gomori's silver methenamine for revealing yeast forms, especially in areas of caseation necrosis
- Serologic tests, including complement-fixing (CF) antibodies and immunodiffusion assays
  1. To establish previous infection and suggest active disease
  2. Possibly limited by inability to distinguish acute disease from remote infection and cross-reactivity with other fungi
- Detection of *Histoplasma* antigen in urine: may be influenced by infections with *Blastomyces* and *Coccidioides*
- Skin testing with histoplasmin: useful epidemiologically but essentially useless for diagnosis of acute disease
- In PDH
  1. Pancytopenia
  2. Marked elevations in alkaline phosphatase and alanine aminotransferase (ALT) common
  3. Most evident in acute and subacute forms and to a lesser extent in chronic form
- In chronic meningitis (majority of cases)
  1. CSF pleocytosis with either lymphocytes or neutrophils predominating
  2. Elevated CSF protein levels
  3. Hypoglycorrhachia

IMAGING STUDIES

- Chest x-ray examination in acute pulmonary histoplasmosis
  1. Singular or multiple patchy infiltrates, especially in the lower lung fields
  2. Hilar or mediastinal lymphadenopathy with or without pneumonitis
  3. Diffuse nodular or confluent bilateral miliary infiltrates characteristic of heavier exposure
  4. Infrequent pleural effusions, except when associated with pericarditis
- Chest x-ray examination in histoplasmoma: coin lesion displaying central calcification, ranging from 1 to 4 cm in diameter, predominantly located in the subpleural regions
- Chest x-ray examination in CPH:
  1. Upper lobe disease frequently associated with cavities (thick-walled, secondarily infected with an *Aspergillus* fungus ball)
  2. Preexisting calcifications in the hilum associated with peribronchial streaking extending to the parenchyma
- Chest x-ray examination in acute PDH: hilar adenopathy and/or diffuse nodular infiltrates
- CT scan of adrenals to reveal bilateral enlargement and low-attenuation centers

TREATMENT

NONPHARMACOLOGIC THERAPY

For life-threatening disease seen in acute disseminated disease or infection in patients with AIDS: supportive therapy with IV fluids

ACUTE GENERAL Rx

- No drug therapy is required for patients with asymptomatic pulmonary disease and most patients with mild symptomatic pulmonary disease.
- Brief course of therapy with ketoconazole 400 mg/day or itraconazole 200 mg/day PO for 3 to 6 wk may be beneficial in some patients with acute pulmonary distress.
- Same therapy appropriate for immunocompetent, mild to moderately symptomatic patients with CPH and subacute and chronic forms of PDH, but duration of therapy is longer, ranging for 6 to 12 mo.
- Use amphotericin B 0.7 to 1 mg/kg IV for 6 to 12 mo in patients hypersensitive to or intolerant of azole therapy.
- Do not give immunocompromised patients, especially those with AIDS, ketoconazole as primary therapy for disseminated histoplasmosis.
- Give amphotericin B for life-threatening disease or continued illness as a result of primary failure or relapse of adequate azole therapy.
  1. For acute pulmonary histoplasmosis associated with acute respiratory distress syndrome (ARDS), acute PDH, and histoplasma meningitis: dose of 0.7 to 1 mg/kg IV >4 hr
  2. End point of therapy for patient with complicated acute pulmonary disease: total dose of 500 mg
  3. End point for patient with acute PDH: total dose 35 mg/kg or 2.5 g total
  4. Concomitant administration of prednisone 60 to 80 mg/day beneficial for severe fungal hypersensitivity complicating acute pulmonary disease

- Endocarditis: surgical treatment is preferable, with excision of infected valve or graft combined with amphotericin for a total dose of 35 mg/kg or 2.5 g
- For pericardial disease:
  1. Antifungal therapy: no apparent benefit
  2. Best managed with NSAIDs
- For POHS:
  1. Antifungal therapy: no apparent benefit
  2. May respond to laser therapy

CHRONIC Rx

In patients with AIDS: lifelong suppressive therapy with either itraconazole, given 200 mg PO qd, or IV amphotericin B at a dose of 50 mg once weekly

DISPOSITION

- Most immunocompetent patients with acute histoplasmosis are asymptomatic.
- For those with chronic or progressive disease, especially if immunocompromised by virtue of disease or medication, outcome and favorable prognosis are dependent on prompt recognition of varied forms of disease and timely administration of appropriate antifungal drugs.

REFERRAL

- For consultation with infectious disease specialist in suspected cases of disseminated disease, especially if immunocompromised
- To a pulmonologist for patients with CPH form because progressive respiratory compromise usually results from chronic infection and underlying COPD
- For consultation with a thoracic surgeon for decompression procedures in patients symptomatic as a consequence of progressive mediastinal fibrosis

PEARLS & CONSIDERATIONS

- *H. capsulatum,* variety *duboisii,* also known as African histoplasmosis, is restricted to Senegal, Nigeria, Zaire, and Uganda.
- Unlike *H. capsulatum,* pulmonary forms of *duboisii* are not seen, and the disease is limited to the skin, soft tissues, and bone.

COMMENTS

- Patients living in endemic areas, especially if immunocompromised, should be advised to take appropriate respiratory precautions when sweeping or disposing of bird waste from rooftop or home aviaries.
- Appropriate respiratory precautions should also be taken when leisure traveling to areas that act as a natural haven for the fungus, such as bat caves.
- Immunocompetent hosts are generally unaware of fungal infection, but the immunocompromised suffer devastating consequences.

SUGGESTED READINGS

Ball SC: Histoplasmosis in a patient with AIDS, *AIDS Read* 13(3):112, 2003.

Kumar N et al: Adrenal histoplasmosis: clinical presentation and imaging features in nine cases, *Abdom Imaging* 28(5):703, 2003.

Quraishi NA et al: Histoplasmosis as the cause of a pathological fracture, *J Bone Joint Surg Br* 85(5):732, 2003.

Saccente M et al: Cerebral histoplasmosis in the azole era: report of four cases and review, *South Med J* 96(4):410, 2003.

Spencer WH et al: Detection of histoplasma capsulatum DNA in lesions of chronic ocular histoplasmosis syndrome, *Arch Ophthalmol* 121(11):1551, 2003.

Weinberg M et al: Severe histoplasmosis in travelers to Nicaragua, *Emerg Infect Dis* 9 (10):1322, 2003.

Wheat LJ, Kauffman CA: Histoplasmosis, *Infect Dis Clin North Am* 17(1):1, 2003.

AUTHOR: **GEORGE O. ALONSO, M.D.**

BASIC INFORMATION

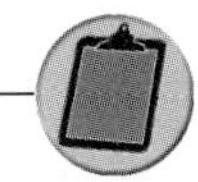

DEFINITION

Histrionic personality disorder is a cluster B personality disorder with a pervasive pattern of excessive emotionality and attention-seeking behavior that generally begins in early adulthood.

SYNONYMS

Hysterical personality disorder
Psychoinfantile personality disorder
Personality disorder (nonspecific)

ICD-9CM CODES
301.5 Histrionic personality disorder (ICD-9 and DSM IV Code)

EPIDEMIOLOGY & DEMOGRAPHICS

PREVALENCE (IN U.S.):

- Diagnosed more often in women; rarely found in men.
- Prevalence: 2%-3% for histrionic personality disorder; 10%-13% for personality disorders (unspecified).

PREDOMINANT SEX: Predominant in women. It is suggested that cultural factors (attention-seeking behavior and sexual forwardness not being acceptable in women) cause it to be more often diagnosed in women.

PREDOMINANT AGE: Generally begins in early childhood.

CLINICAL PRESENTATION

Features include five or more of the following:

1. Is uncomfortable in situations where he or she is not the center of attention.
2. Interaction with others is often characterized by inappropriate sexually seductive or provocative behavior.
3. Displays rapidly shifting and shallow expression of emotions.
4. Consistently uses physical appearance to draw attention to self.
5. Has a style of speech that is excessively impressionistic and lacking in detail.
6. Shows self-dramatization, theatricality, and exaggerated expression of emotion.
7. Is suggestible (i.e., easily influenced by others or circumstances).
8. Considers relationships to be more intimate than they actually are.

ETIOLOGY

Etiology is unknown; it is hypothesized that childhood events and genetics are contributory.

DIAGNOSIS

DIFFERENTIAL DIAGNOSIS

- Borderline personality disorder.
- Antisocial personality disorder.
- Narcissistic personality disorder.
- Dependant personality disorder.
- Personality change secondary to general medical condition.
- Symptoms may develop in association with chronic substance abuse.

WORKUP

- There is no formal test to establish diagnosis.
- Person's overall appearance, behavior, history, and psychologic evaluation are sufficient to make diagnosis using DSM-IV criteria.

LABORATORY TESTS

None

IMAGING STUDIES

None

TREATMENT

NONPHARMACOLOGIC THERAPY

- Long-term individual psychotherapy is treatment of choice.
- Individuals who suffer from this disorder are usually difficult to treat.
- Like most other personality disorders, people present for treatment only when stress or some other situational factor within their lives has made their ability to function and cope effectively impossible.
- Unlike other people who suffer from personality disorders, however, these individuals are much quicker to seek treatment and exaggerate their symptoms and difficulties in functioning.
- Patients tend to be more emotionally needy and are often reluctant to terminate therapy.

ACUTE GENERAL Rx

- As with most personality disorders, medications are not indicated except for the treatment of specific, concurrent Axis I diagnoses, such as depression.
- Care should be given when prescribing medications to someone who suffers from histrionic personality disorder because of the potential for using the medication to contribute to self-destructive or otherwise harmful behaviors.

DISPOSITION

- Therapy approaches should not be focused on the long-term personality change of the individual, but rather short-term alleviation of difficulties within the person's life.
- It should be stated at the onset of therapy that a "cure" is unlikely.

REFERRAL

Primarily treated by mental health professionals.

PEARLS & CONSIDERATIONS

COMMENTS

Suicidality should be assessed on a regular basis and suicidal threats and self-mutilation should not be ignored or dismissed.

PATIENT/FAMILY EDUCATION

Group and family therapy approaches are generally not recommended, because the individual who suffers from this disorder often draws attention to himself or herself and exaggerates every action and reaction.

SUGGESTED READINGS

Horowitz MJ: Personality disorder diagnosis, *Am J Psychiatry* 155:1464, 1998.
Internet Mental Health: http://www.mentalhealth.com.
National Library of Medicine, National Institutes of Health: http://www.nlm.nih.gov.
Stanley B et al: Are suicide attempters who self-mutilate a unique population? *Am J Psychiatry* 158:427, 2001.

AUTHOR: **PRIYA DESAI, M.D., M.S.P.H.**

Hodgkin's Disease (PTG)

BASIC INFORMATION

DEFINITION

Hodgkin's disease is a malignant disorder of lymphoreticular origin, characterized histologically by the presence of multinucleated giant cells (Reed-Sternberg cells) usually originating from B lymphocytes in germinal centers of lymphoid tissue.

ICD-9CM CODES
201.9 Hodgkin's disease, unspecified
201.4 Hodgkin's disease, lymphocyte predominance
201.5 Hodgkin's disease, nodular sclerosis
201.6 Hodgkin's disease, mixed cellularity
201.7 Hodgkin's disease, lymphocyte depletion

EPIDEMIOLOGY & DEMOGRAPHICS

- There is a bimodal age distribution (15 to 34 yr and >50 yr).
- Concordance for Hodgkin's disease in identical twins suggests that a genetic susceptibility underlies Hodgkin's disease in young adulthood.
- The disease is more common in males (in childhood Hodgkin's disease, >80% occurs in males), in Caucasians, and in higher socioeconomic groups.
- Overall incidence of Hodgkin's disease in the U.S. is approximately 4:100,000.

PHYSICAL FINDINGS & CLINICAL PRESENTATION

- Palpable lymphadenopathy, generally painless
- Most common site of involvement: neck region
- See Workup for description of common symptoms

ETIOLOGY

Unknown; evidence implicating Epstein-Barr virus remains controversial.

DIAGNOSIS

DIFFERENTIAL DIAGNOSIS

- Non-Hodgkin's lymphoma
- Sarcoidosis
- Infections (e.g., CMV, Epstein-Barr virus, toxoplasma, HIV)
- Drug reaction

WORKUP

Symptomatic patients with Hodgkin's disease usually present with the following manifestations:

- Fever and night sweats: fever in a cyclical pattern (days or weeks of fever alternating with afebrile periods) is known as Pel-Epstein fever
- Weight loss, generalized malaise
- Persistent, nonproductive cough
- Pain associated with alcohol ingestion, often secondary to heavy eosinophil infiltration of the tumor sites
- Pruritus
- Others: superior vena cava syndrome and spinal cord compression (rare)

Diagnosis can be made with lymph node biopsy. There are four main **histologic subtypes,** based on the number of lymphocytes, Reed-Sternberg cells, and the presence of fibrous tissue:

1. Lymphocyte predominance
2. Mixed cellularity
3. Nodular sclerosis
4. Lymphocyte depletion

Nodular sclerosis is the most common type and occurs mainly in young adulthood, whereas the mixed cellularity type is more prevalent after age 50 yr.

Staging for Hodgkin's disease follows the **Ann Arbor staging classification.**

Stage I: Involvement of a single lymph node region
Stage II: Two or more lymph node regions on the same side of the diaphragm
Stage III: Lymph node involvement on both sides of diaphragm, including spleen
Stage IV: Diffuse involvement of external sites
Suffix A: No systemic symptoms
Suffix B: Presence of fever, night sweats, or unexplained weight loss of 10% or more body weight over 6 mo
Suffix X: Indicates bulky disease >1⁄3 widening of mediastinum or >10 cm maximum dimension of nodal mass on a chest film

Proper staging requires the following:

- Detailed history (with documentation of "B symptoms" and physical examination)
- Surgical biopsy
- Laboratory evaluation (CBC, sedimentation rate, BUN, creatinine, alkaline phosphatase, LFTs, albumin, LDH, uric acid)
- Chest x-ray (PA and lateral)
- Bilateral bone marrow biopsy
- CT scan of the chest (when abnormal findings are noted on chest x-ray examination) and of the abdomen and pelvis to visualize the mesenteric, hepatic, portal, and splenic hilar nodes
- Bipedal lymphangiography in selected patients to define periaortic and iliac lymph node involvement
- Exploratory laparotomy and splenectomy (selected patients):
  1. Decision to perform staging laparotomy depends on the therapeutic plan; it is generally not indicated in patients who have a large mediastinal mass (these patients will generally be treated with combined chemotherapy and radiation). Staging laparotomy may also not be required in patients with clinical stage I or unlikely to have abdominal disease (e.g., females with supradiaphragmatic disease).
  2. Exploratory laparotomy and splenectomy may be used for patients with clinical stage I-IIA or IIB.
  3. It is useful in identifying patients who can be treated with irradiation alone with curative intent.
  4. Polyvalent pneumococcal vaccine should be given prophylactically to all patients before splenectomy (increased risk of sepsis from encapsulated organisms in splenectomized patients).
- Gallium scan

LABORATORY TESTS

See Workup.

IMAGING STUDIES

See Workup.

TREATMENT

ACUTE GENERAL Rx

The main therapeutic modalities are radiotherapy and chemotherapy; the indication for each vary with pathologic stage and other factors.

- Stage I and II: radiation therapy alone unless a large mediastinal mass is present (mediastinal to thoracic ratio ≥1.3); in the latter case, a combination of chemotherapy and radiation therapy is indicated.

- Stage IB or IIB: total nodal irradiation is often used, although chemotherapy is performed in many centers.
- Stage IIIA: treatment is controversial. It varies with the anatomic substage after splenectomy.
  1. III_1A and minimum splenic involvement: radiation therapy alone may be adequate.
  2. III_2 or III_1A with extensive splenic involvement: there is disagreement whether chemotherapy alone or a combination of chemotherapy and radiation therapy is the preferred treatment modality.
  3. IIIB and IVB: the treatment of choice is chemotherapy with or without adjuvant radiotherapy.

Various regimens can be used for combination of chemotherapy. Most oncologists prefer the combination of doxorubicin plus bleomycin plus vincristine plus dacarbazine (ABVD). Other commonly used regimens are MOPP, MOPP-ABV, MOPP-ABVD, MOPP-BAP.

- In patients with advanced Hodgkin's disease, increased-dose bleomycin, etoposide, doxorubicin, cyclophosphamide, vincristine, procarbazine, and prednisone (BEACOPP) offers better tumor control and overall survival than COPP-ABVD.

DISPOSITION

- The overall survival at 10 yr is approximately 60%.
- Cure rates as high as 75% to 80% are now possible with appropriate initial therapy.
- Poor prognostic features include presence of "B symptoms," advanced age, advanced stage at initial presentation, mixed-cellularity, and lymphocyte depletion histology.
- Chemotherapy significantly increases the risk of leukemia.
- The peak in risk of leukemia is seen approximately 5 yr after the initiation of chemotherapy.
- The risk of leukemia is greater for those who undergo splenectomy and for patients with advanced stages of Hodgkin's disease; the risk is unaffected by concomitant radiotherapy.
- Involved-field radiotherapy does not improve the outcome in patients with advanced-stage Hodgkin's lymphoma who have a complete remission after MOPP-ABV chemotherapy. Radiotherapy may benefit patients with a partial response after chemotherapy.
- Mediastinal irradiation increases the risk of subsequent death from heart disease caused by sclerosis of coronary artery secondary to irradiation. Risk increases with high mediastinal doses, minimal protective cardiac blocking, young age at irradiation, and increased duration of follow-up.
- Both chemotherapy and radiation therapy increase the risk of developing secondary solid tumors (e.g., carcinoma of the lung, breast, and stomach).

REFERRAL

- Surgical referral for lymph node biopsy
- Hematology/oncology referral

PEARLS & CONSIDERATIONS

COMMENTS

Young male patients should consider sperm banking before the initiation of therapy.

SUGGESTED READINGS

Aleman B et al: Involved-field radiotherapy for advanced Hodgkin's lymphoma, *N Engl J Med* 348:2396, 2003.

Diehl V et al: Standard and increased-dose BEACOPP chemotherapy compared with COPP-ABVD for advanced Hodgkin's disease, *N Engl J Med* 348:2386, 2003.

AUTHOR: **FRED F. FERRI, M.D.**

Hookworm

BASIC INFORMATION

DEFINITION

Hookworm is a parasitic infection of the intestine caused by helminths.

ICD-9CM CODES
126.35 Hookworm

EPIDEMIOLOGY & DEMOGRAPHICS

INCIDENCE (IN U.S.):
- Varies greatly in different areas of the U.S.
- Most common in rural areas of southeastern U.S.
- Poor sanitation and increased rainfall increase likelihood

PREVALENCE (IN U.S.): Varies from 10% to 90% in regions where it is found
PREDOMINANT AGE: Schoolchildren

PHYSICAL FINDINGS & CLINICAL PRESENTATION

- Nonspecific abdominal complaints
- Because these organisms consume host RBCs, symptoms related to iron-deficiency anemia, depending on the amount of iron in the diet and the worm burden
- Fatigue, tachycardia, dyspnea, and high-output failure
- Hypoproteinemia and edema from loss of proteins into the intestinal tract
- Unusual for pulmonary manifestations to occur when the larvae migrate through the lungs
- Skin rash at sites of larval penetration in some individuals without prior exposure

ETIOLOGY

Two species can cause this disease: *Necator americanus* and *Ancylostoma duodenale. N. americanus* is the predominant cause of hookworm in the U.S.
- Infection occurs via penetration of the skin by the larval form, with subsequent migration via the blood stream to the alveoli, up the respiratory tract, then into the GI tract
- Sharp mouth parts allow for attachment to intestinal mucosa

DIAGNOSIS

DIFFERENTIAL DIAGNOSIS

- Strongyloidiasis
- Ascariasis

WORKUP

Examine stool for hookworm eggs.

LABORATORY TESTS

CBC to show hypochromic, microcytic anemia; possible mild eosinophilia and hypoalbuminemia

IMAGING STUDIES

Chest x-ray examination: occasionally shows opacities

TREATMENT

NONPHARMACOLOGIC THERAPY

Prevention of disease by not walking barefoot and by improving sanitary conditions

ACUTE GENERAL Rx

- Mebendazole 100 mg PO bid for 3 days
- Iron supplementation may be helpful

DISPOSITION

Easily treated

REFERRAL

If diagnosis uncertain

PEARLS & CONSIDERATIONS

COMMENTS

Appropriate disposal of human wastes is important in controlling the disease in areas with a high prevalence of hookworm infestation.

SUGGESTED READINGS

Biegel Y et al: Clinical problem-solving: letting the patient off the hook, *N Engl J Med* 342:1658, 2000.

Grover JK et al: Antihelminthics: a review, *Trop Gastroenterol* 22:180, 2001.

AUTHOR: **MAURICE POLICAR, M.D.**

BASIC INFORMATION

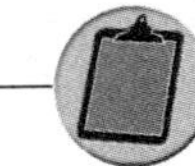

DEFINITION

A hordeolum is an acute inflammatory process affecting the eyelid and arising from the meibomian (posterior) or Zeis (anterior) glands. It is most often infectious and usually caused by *Staphylococcus aureus.*

SYNONYMS

Stye

ICD-9CM CODES
373.11 External hordeolum
373.12 Internal hordeolum

EPIDEMIOLOGY & DEMOGRAPHICS

INCIDENCE (IN U.S.): Unknown
PREVALENCE (IN U.S.): Unknown
PREDOMINANT SEX: No gender predilection
PREDOMINANT AGE: May occur at any age
PEAK INCIDENCE: May occur at any age
NEONATAL INFECTION: Rare in the neonatal period

PHYSICAL FINDINGS & CLINICAL PRESENTATION

- Abrupt onset with pain and erythema of the eyelid
- Localized, tender mass in the eyelid (Fig. 1-121)
- May be associated with blepharitis
- External hordeolum: points toward the skin surface of the lid and may spontaneously drain
- Internal hordeolum: can point toward the conjunctival side of the lid and may cause conjunctival inflammation

ETIOLOGY

- 75% to 95% of cases are caused by *S. aureus.*
- Occasional cases are caused by *Streptococcus pneumoniae,* other streptococci, gram-negative enteric organisms, or mixed bacterial flora.

DIAGNOSIS

DIFFERENTIAL DIAGNOSIS

- Eyelid abscess
- Chalazion
- Allergy or contact dermatitis with conjunctival edema
- Acute dacryocystitis
- Herpes simplex infection
- Cellulitis of the eyelid

LABORATORY TESTS

- Generally, none are necessary.
- If incision and drainage are performed, specimens should be sent for bacterial culture.

IMAGING STUDIES

None necessary

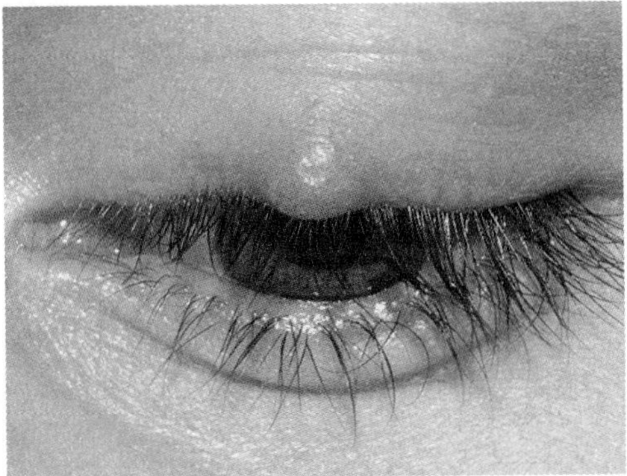

FIGURE 1-121 External stye. (From Palay D [ed]: *Ophthalmology for the primary care physician,* St Louis, 1997, Mosby.)

TREATMENT

NONPHARMACOLOGIC THERAPY

Usually responds to warm compresses

ACUTE GENERAL Rx

- Systemic antibiotics generally not necessary
- In refractory cases, an oral antistaphylococcal agent (e.g., dicloxacillin 500 mg PO qid) possibly helpful
- Topical erythromycin ophthalmic ointment applied to the lid margins two to four times daily until resolution
- Incision and drainage: rarely needed but should be considered for progressive infections

CHRONIC Rx

None necessary

DISPOSITION

- Usually sporadic occurrence
- Possible relapse if resolution is not complete

REFERRAL

- For evaluation by an ophthalmologist if visual acuity or ocular movement is affected or if the diagnosis is in doubt
- For surgical drainage if necessary

PEARLS & CONSIDERATIONS

COMMENTS

Seborrheic dermatitis may coexist with hordeolum.

SUGGESTED READINGS

Kiratli HK, Akar Y: Multiple recurrent hordeola associated with selective IgM deficiency, *J AAPOS* 5(1):60, 2001.

Maldonado M, Juberias J, Moreno-Montanes J: Extensive corneal epithelial defect associated with internal hordeolum after uneventful laser in situ keratomileusis, *J Cataract Refract Surg* 28(9):1700, 2002.

AUTHOR: **JOSEPH R. MASCI, M.D.**

Horner's Syndrome

BASIC INFORMATION

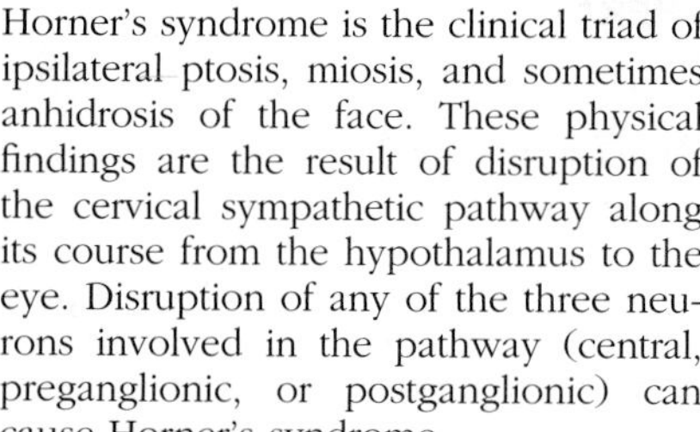

DEFINITION

Horner's syndrome is the clinical triad of ipsilateral ptosis, miosis, and sometimes anhidrosis of the face. These physical findings are the result of disruption of the cervical sympathetic pathway along its course from the hypothalamus to the eye. Disruption of any of the three neurons involved in the pathway (central, preganglionic, or postganglionic) can cause Horner's syndrome.

SYNONYMS

Oculosympathetic paresis

ICD-9CM CODES
337.9 Horner's syndrome

EPIDEMIOLOGY & DEMOGRAPHICS

- May occur congenitally
- Associated with vascular disease and neoplasms

PHYSICAL FINDINGS & CLINICAL PRESENTATION

- Ptosis results from loss of sympathetic tone to eyelid muscles.
- Miosis results from loss of sympathetic pupillodilator activity (Fig. 1-122). The affected pupil reacts normally to light and accommodation. Anisocoria is greater in darkness.
- The presence of anhidrosis is variable, and depends on the site of injury in the sympathetic pathway. Anhidrosis may occur with lesions affecting the central or preganglionic neurons.
- Conjunctival or facial hyperemia may occur on the affected side because of loss of sympathetic vasoconstrictor activity.
- In congenital Horner's syndrome, the iris on the affected side may fail to become pigmented, resulting in heterochromia of the iris, with the affected iris remaining blue-gray.

ETIOLOGY

Lesions affecting any of the neurons involved in the sympathetic pathway can cause Horner's syndrome.

Mechanical:
- Syringomyelia
- Trauma
- Benign tumors
- Malignant tumors (thyroid, Pancoast tumor)
- Metastatic tumor
- Lymphadenopathy
- Neurofibromatosis
- Cervical rib
- Cervical spondylosis

Vascular (ischemia, hemorrhage or AVM):
- Brainstem lesion: commonly occlusion of the posterior inferior cerebellar artery but almost any of the vessels may be responsible (vertebral; superior, middle or inferior lateral medullary arteries; superior or anterior inferior cerebellar arteries)
- Internal carotid artery aneurysm or dissection. Injury of other major vessels (carotid artery, subclavian artery, ascending aorta) can also cause Horner's syndrome
- Cluster headache, migraine

Miscellaneous:
- Congenital
- Demyelination (multiple sclerosis)
- Infection (apical TB, herpes zoster)
- Pneumothorax
- Iatrogenic (angiography, internal jugular/subclavian catheter, chest tube, surgery, epidural spinal anesthesia)
- Radiation

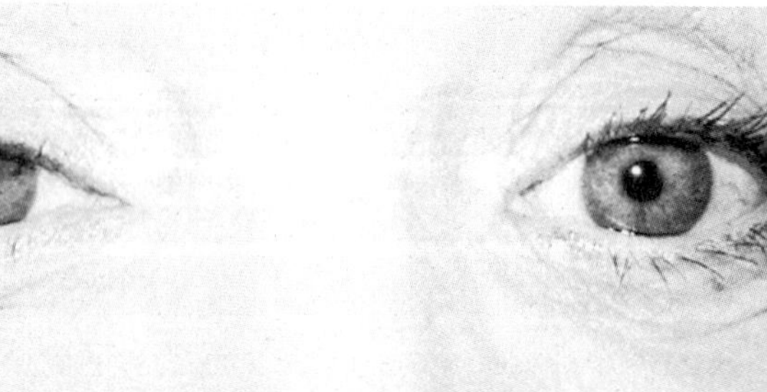

FIGURE 1-122 Horner's syndrome. The mild ptosis (1 to 2 mm) and the smaller pupil (in room light) can be seen on the affected right side. (From Palay D [ed]: *Ophthalmology for the primary care physician,* St Louis, 1997, Mosby.)

DIAGNOSIS

DIFFERENTIAL DIAGNOSIS

Causes of anisocoria (unequal pupils):
- Normal variant
- Mydriatic use
- Prosthetic eye
- Unilateral cataract
- Iritis

Disorders causing ptosis are described in Section II.

WORKUP

History, physical examination, and imaging

IMAGING STUDIES

- Chest CT scan to rule out lung tumors
- MRI of the head and neck to identify lesions affecting the central and cervical sympathetic pathway
- Ultrasound, CT angiography, or MR angiography to assess the vessels in the head and neck

TREATMENT

Treatment depends on underlying cause.

DISPOSITION

Prognosis depends on underlying cause. Horner's syndrome is an uncommon presentation for malignancy. In one study, 60% of cases were idiopathic.

REFERRAL

- Opthalmologist for confirmation of the diagnosis. Topical cocaine test: failure of pupillary dilation after cocaine eye drops confirms the presence of sympathetic denervation. Topical hydroxyamphetamine/pholedrine test: distinguishes central and preganglionic sympathetic lesions from postganglionic sympathetic lesions
- Vascular surgeon for carotid disease.
- Oncologist for Pancoast tumor.

AUTHORS: **MARK J. FAGAN, M.D.,** and **SUDEEP K. AULAKH, M.D., F.R.C.P.C.**

BASIC INFORMATION

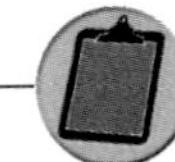

DEFINITION

Sudden onset of intense warmth that begins in the neck or face or in the chest and progresses to the neck and face, often associated with profuse sweating, anxiety, and palpitations

ICD-9CM CODES
627.2 Hot flashes

EPIDEMIOLOGY & DEMOGRAPHICS

- Hot flashes affect 75% of postmenopausal women.
- Most hot flashes begin 1 to 2 yr before menopause and resolve after 2 yr.
- 15% of women report duration of hot flashes longer than 15 yr.

PHYSICAL FINDINGS & CLINICAL PRESENTATION

- Profuse sweating and red blotching of skin may be noted during the vasomotor event.
- Palpitations and hyperreflexia may be present during the hot flash.
- Hot flushes typically last 1-5 min.
- Each hot flush is associated with increase in temperature, increased pulse rate, and increased blood flow into the hands and face.
- Episodes of hot flush during sleep are common and are referred to as "night sweats."
- There is considerable variation in the frequency of hot flashes. One third of women report more than 10 flushes per day.

ETIOLOGY

- Dysfunction of central thermoregulatory centers caused by changes in estrogen level at the time of menopause
- Tamoxifen use
- Chemotherapy-induced ovarian failure
- Androgen ablation therapy for prostate carcinoma

DIAGNOSIS

DIFFERENTIAL DIAGNOSIS

- Carcinoid syndrome
- Anxiety disorder
- Idiopathic flushing
- Lymphoma (night sweats)
- Hyperthyroidism
- Hyperhydrosis

WORKUP

Evaluation of hot flashes is aimed at excluding conditions listed in the differential diagnosis

LABORATORY TESTS

- FSH, LH
- TSH

TREATMENT

NONPHARMACOLOGIC THERAPY

- Behavioral interventions such as relaxation training and paced respiration have been reported effective in reducing symptoms in some women.
- Avoidance of caffeine, alcohol, and tobacco, and spicy foods may be beneficial.

GENERAL THERAPY

- Estrogen replacement therapy reduces hot flashes by 80%-90%. Estrogen therapy, however, is contraindicated in many women and others are fearful of its use. Potential risks and side effects should be considered before using estrogen in any patient. When using estrogen, it is best to use low-dose (e.g., Prempro [conjugated equine estrogen 0.45 mg or 0.3 mg plus medroxyprogesterone 1.5 mg]). Femring is an intravaginal ring that is changed every 3 mo and approved to treat vasomotor symptoms in women who have had a hysterectomy. It provides both local and systemic estrogen.
- Megestrol acetate, a progestational agent, is a safer alternative to estrogen in women with a history of breast or uterine cancer and in men receiving androgen ablation therapy for prostate cancer. Usual dose is 20 mg bid.
- The antidepressant venlaxefine has been reported to be 60% effective in reducing hot flashes and represents an alternative treatment modality in women unable or unwilling to use estrogens. Starting dose is 37.5 mg qd, increased as tolerated up to a maximum of 300 mg/day. Other antidepressants such as the SSRIs fluoxetine and paroxetine are also used by clinicians for hot flashes; however, they appear to be less effective than venlaxefine. A recent trial showed that paroxetine is an effective agent for diminishing hot flashes in men receiving androgen ablation therapy.
- The anticonvulsant gabapentin (300-1200 mg/day) represents another nonhormonal alternative in the treatment of hot flashes and can be used alone or in combination with venlafaxine.
- The antihypertensive clonidine is also effective in reducing the frequency of hot flashes. Adverse effects include dry mouth, sedation, and dizziness.
- Vitamin E (800 IU/day) may be effective in patients with mild symptoms that do not interfere with sleep or daily function.
- Soy protein (use of soy extracts which contain plant-derived estrogens [phytoestrogens]) is often used; however, clinical trials have not shown clear efficacy.
- Several classes of herbal remedies are available to patients and commonly used without significant benefit. Frequently used agents are *Cimicifuga racemosa* (black cohosh, snakeroot, bugbane), *angelica sinensis,* and evening primrose (evening star).

SUGGESTED READINGS

Fitzpatrick LA, Santen RJ: Hot flashes: the old and the new, what is really true? *Mayo Clin Proc* 77:1155, 2002.

Loprinzi CL et al: Pilot evaluation of Gabapentin for treating hot flashes, *Mayo Clin Proc* 77:1159, 2002.

Loprinzi Cl et al: Pilot evaluation of paroxetine for treating hot flashes in men, *Mayo Clin Proc* 79(10):1247, 2004.

Shanafelt TD et al: Pathophysiology and treatment of hot flashes, *Mayo Clin Proc* 77:1207, 2002.

Women's Health Initiative Investigators: Risks and benefits of estrogen plus progestin in healthy postmenopausal women: principal results from the Women's Health initiative randomized controlled trial, *JAMA* 288:321, 2002.

Sikon A, Thacker HL: Treatment options for menopausal hot flashes, *Cleveland Clinic J Med* 71:578, 2004.

AUTHOR: **FRED F. FERRI, M.D.**

Human Granulocytic Ehrlichiosis (PTG)

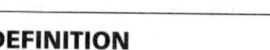

BASIC INFORMATION

DEFINITION

Human granulocytic ehrlichiosis (HGE) is a zoonotic infection of granulocytes, caused by an *Ehrlichia* species closely related to *E. phagocytophila, E. equi,* and *E. ewingii,* with multisystem manifestations.

ICD-9CM CODES
082-8 Other tick-borne rickettsiosis

EPIDEMIOLOGY & DEMOGRAPHICS

INCIDENCE (IN U.S.): Highest overall incidence in New York, New Jersey, Connecticut, Wisconsin, Minnesota, and northern California. >600 cases identified in the U.S. since 1990

PREDOMINANT SEX: Males outnumber females by 2 to 1

PREDOMINANT AGE: Most severe disease 50 to 70 yr

PEAK INCIDENCE: Occurs throughout the year, with peak incidence between May and July and again in November

PHYSICAL FINDINGS & CLINICAL PRESENTATION

- Most common initial symptoms
  1. Fever
  2. Chills, rigor
  3. Headache
  4. Myalgia
- Subsequent symptoms
  1. Anorexia, nausea
  2. Arthralgia
  3. Cough
  4. Confusion
  5. Abdominal pain
  6. Rash (erythematous to pustular) rare (<11%)
- Complications
  1. Hepatitis
  2. Interstitial pneumonitis
  3. Noncardiogenic pulmonary edema
  4. Renal and respiratory failure
  5. Bilateral facial palsy
  6. Meningitis

ETIOLOGY

- Obligate intracellular gram-negative bacterium (family *Rickettsiaceae,* genus *Ehrlichia*), closely related to *E. phagocytophila, E. equi* and *E. ewingii*
- Vector
  1. Almost certainly tick-borne, recently transmitted by infected blood
  2. Transmitted by *Ixodes scapularis* in the northeastern and upper midwestern states and *Ixodes pacificus* in the Pacific western states
  3. Tick exposure reported in >90% of patients, with approximately 60% reporting tick bite
- Mammalian host: deer, horses, dogs, white-footed mice, cattle, sheep, goats, bison
- Precise pathogenesis is unclear, although host inflammatory and immune responses may define final spectrum of disease beyond granulocytes, including hepatitis, interstitial pneumonitis, and nephritis with mild azotemia
- Between 6% and 21% of patients with HGE also have serologic evidence of other infection, both transmitted by *Ixodes* spp. tick bites
- Recovery is usual outcome; fatality rate of HGE is <1%

DIAGNOSIS

DIFFERENTIAL DIAGNOSIS

- Human monocytic ehrlichiosis (HME)
  1. Caused by *E. chaffeensis* (vector: tick *Amblyomma americanum,* possibly *Dermocenter variabilis*)
  2. Rash more common, sometimes petechial
  3. Morulae in monocytes
- Rocky Mountain spotted fever, Colorado tick fever, Q fever, relapsing fever
- Babesiosis
- Leptospirosis
- Typhus
- Lyme disease
- Legionnaire's disease
- Tularemia
- Typhoid fever, paratyphoid fever
- Brucellosis
- Viral hepatitis
- Enteroviral infections
- Meningococcemia
- Influenza
- Adenovirus pneumonia
- Infectious mononucleosis
- Thrombotic thrombocytopenic purpura
- Hematologic malignancy

WORKUP

- Acute blood samples for Giemsa-stained smears
- CBC
- Prothrombin time
- Acute serum samples for serology
- Chest x-ray examination
- Liver function and renal function tests
- MRI
- CSF analysis
- Bone marrow rarely needed

LABORATORY TESTS

- Giemsa-stained smear demonstrating morulae of *Ehrlichia* within granulocytes
- CBC progressive leukopenia and thrombocytopenia with nadir near day 7
- C reactive protein concentration is generally elevated
- LFT—twofold to fourfold increase in concentration of hepatic transaminases, elevated lactate dehydrogenase and alkaline phosphatase
- Elevated plasma creatinine concentration may be seen
- Serologic titer (IFA) >80 or fourfold increase in titer to *E. equi* antigen
- Polymerase chain reaction (PCR) to facilitate early diagnosis
- Culture on the first 7 days of illness
- Spinal tap for PCR analysis

IMAGING STUDIES

- Chest x-ray examination to show interstitial pneumonitis (unusual)
- MRI of the brain

TREATMENT

ACUTE GENERAL Rx

- Immediate therapy to limit extent of acute illness and complication
- Tetracycline and doxycycline have demonstrated marked activity against the HGE, although doxycycline has been preferred because of a better pharmacokinetic profile and better toleration by patient
- Rifampin is an alternative drug of choice

CHRONIC Rx

Probably unnecessary; undefined

PROGNOSIS

Poor prognostic indicators include:

1. Advanced age
2. Concomitant chronic illness (such as diabetes mellitus, collagen-vascular disease)
3. Lack of diagnosis recognition
4. Delayed onset of specific antibiotic therapy

DISPOSITION

- Follow-up as outpatient
- Repeat CBC every 2 to 4 wk until normal

REFERRAL

- For consultation with infectious diseases specialist and hematologist in suspected cases
- For coagulopathy

PEARLS & CONSIDERATIONS

COMMENTS

Duration of time tick must be attached to produce illness is at least 24 hr.

SUGGESTED READINGS

Low A, Turett G: Human granulocytic Ehrlichiosis presenting as acute abdomen in adult, *Clin Infect Dis* 37:1397, 2003.

Singh-Behl D et al: Tick-borne infections, *Dermatol Clin* 21(2):237, 2003.

AUTHOR: **VASANTHI ARUMUGAM, M.D.**

BASIC INFORMATION

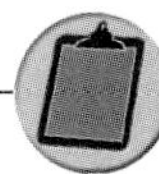

DEFINITION

The human immunodeficiency virus, type 1 (HIV) causes a chronic infection that culminates, usually after several years, in acquired immunodeficiency syndrome (AIDS).

SYNONYMS

Acquired immunodeficiency syndrome (AIDS) when a patient with HIV infection meets specific diagnostic criteria (see "Acquired Immunodeficiency Syndrome" in Section I)

ICD-9CM CODES
044.9 HIV, unspecified

EPIDEMIOLOGY & DEMOGRAPHICS

INCIDENCE (IN U.S.):
- No complete incidence data available.
- Greatest incidence is in metropolitan areas with population >500,000.

PREVALENCE (IN U.S.): Estimated at 1 to 2 million cases

PREDOMINANT SEX:
- Adults: Most recently, estimated to be 74% males, 24% females, but is changing toward more women
- Children: male = female

PREDOMINANT AGE: 80% of cases occur between ages 20 and 40 yr

PEAK INCIDENCE: Age 30 to 35 yr

GENETICS:

Familial Disposition: Although there is no proven genetic predisposition, individuals with deletions in the CCR5 gene are immune from infection with macrophage tropic virus (the predominant virus in sexual transmission).

Congenital Infection:
- 80% of childhood cases are caused by peripartum infection, which may occur in utero, during delivery, or after delivery via breast-feeding.
- No specific congenital abnormalities are associated with HIV infection, although risk of spontaneous abortion and low birth weight is greater.

Neonatal Infection:
- May occur during delivery or via breast-feeding
- Typically asymptomatic

PHYSICAL FINDINGS & CLINICAL PRESENTATION

- Signs and symptoms variable with stage of disease
- In acute infection:
  1. May cause a self-limited mononucleosis-like illness characterized by fever, sore throat, lymphadenopathy, headache, and a rash resembling roseola
  2. In a minority of acute cases: frank aseptic meningitis, Bell's palsy, or peripheral neuropathy
- Later in the course of infection, after a prolonged asymptomatic phase: nonspecific symptoms of lymphadenopathy, weight loss, diarrhea, and skin changes including seborrheic dermatitis, localized herpes zoster, or fungal infection
- Advanced disease: characterized by the infections and malignancies associated with acquired immunodeficiency syndrome (see specific disorders)
- Section II describes rheumatic syndromes in HIV infection
- Some studies suggest that HIV infection in women is associated with lower levels of viral load at comparable degrees of immunosuppression when compared with men. Further, women may, on average have higher CD4 lymphocyte counts at the time of AIDS diagnosis
- Another special consideration in women infected with HIV is the high incidence of human papillomavirus (HPV) coinfection and the risk for cervical neoplasm that this presents. Even women with normal Pap smears should have this test repeated after 6 mo and annually thereafter

ETIOLOGY

- RNA retrovirus (Fig. 1-123)
- Transmitted by sexual contact, shared needles, blood transfusion, or from mother to child during pregnancy, delivery, or breast-feeding
- Primary target of infection: CD4 lymphocyte
- Direct CNS involvement: manifested as encephalopathy, myelopathy, or neuropathy in advanced cases
- Renal failure, rheumatologic disorders, thrombocytopenia, or cardiac abnormalities

DIAGNOSIS

DIFFERENTIAL DIAGNOSIS

- Acute infection: mononucleosis or other respiratory viral infections
- Late symptoms: similar to those produced by other wasting illnesses such as neoplasms, TB, disseminated fungal infection, malabsorption, or depression
- HIV-related encephalopathy: confused with Alzheimer's disease or other causes of chronic dementia (cognitive impairment in HIV infection is described in Section II); myelopathy and neuropathy possibly resembling other demyelinating diseases such as multiple sclerosis

WORKUP

Diagnosis is established by voluntary testing for antibody to the virus, available through public health laboratories or private facilities.

LABORATORY TESTS

HIV antibody detected by a two-step technique:
- ELISA as a sensitive screening test
- Confirmation of positive ELISA tests with the more specific Western blot technique
- The CD4 count and HIV RNA PCR should be measured in all patients
- The CD4 count is a marker of current immune status
- The HIV RNA PCR (viral load) is predictive of disease progression

Fig. 1-124 describes the immunologic response to HIV infection

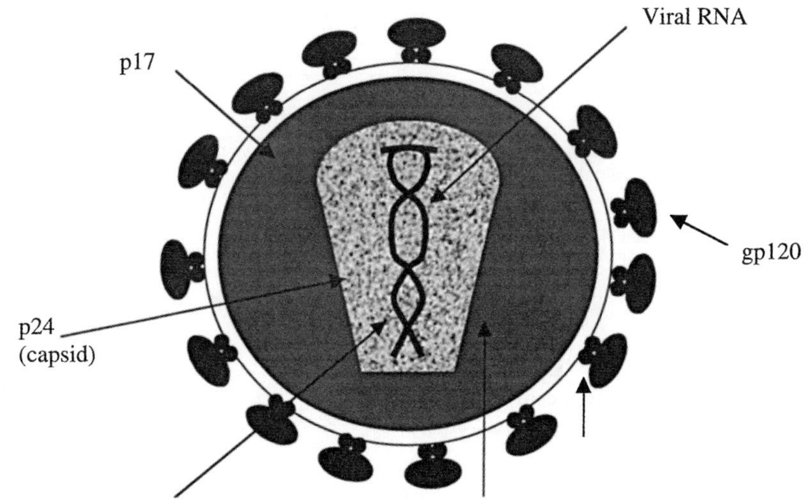

FIGURE 1-123 Locations of viral proteins and nucleic acids in the HIV-1 virion. (From Mandell GL [ed]: *Mandell, Douglas, and Bennett's principles and practice of infectious diseases,* ed 5, New York, Churchill Livingstone.)

TREATMENT

NONPHARMACOLOGIC THERAPY

Maintenance of adequate nutrition

ACUTE GENERAL Rx

- Acute management of opportunistic infections and malignancies (see AIDS-associated disorders, "*Pneumocystis carinii* pneumonia," "Cryptococcosis," "Tuberculosis," "Toxoplasmosis" elsewhere in this text)
- Acute HIV syndrome:
  1. Treat with combination antiretroviral therapy, consisting of one or more (usually two) nucleoside agents (zidovudine [AZT], didanosine [DDI], zalcitabine [DDC], lamivudine [3TC] abacavir, tenofovir) with a protease inhibitor (lopinavir, indinavir, saquinavir, nelfinavir aquerate), or nonnucleoside reverse transcriptase inhibitors (nevirapine, delavirdine, efavirenz). Protease inhibitors, particularly lopinavir, are often administered in combination with low-dose ritonavir for enhanced drug levels. A new protease inhibitor, atazanavir, has been associated with a relatively low incidence of lipid abnormalities and insulin resistance than other protease inhibitors.
  2. Recommended doses of these drugs and specific combinations are currently being assessed.

CHRONIC Rx

- Naïve chronically infected patients should be considered for therapy based on their current CD4 counts, likelihood for disease progression (viral loads), and ability to remain adherent with combination antiretroviral therapy. Please see current HIV treatment guidelines of the Department of Health and Human Services (http://www.aidsinfo.nih.gov/guidelines/).
  1. Patients with CD4 counts <200 cells/mm^3 should be treated regardless of viral load.
  2. Those with CD4 counts >350 cells/mm^3 should generally be observed without therapy; however, in cases of extremely elevated viral loads therapy should be considered.
  3. The benefits of therapy for patients with CD4 counts between 200-350 cells/mm^3 remains controversial, although most authorities recommend treatment.
  4. The current guidelines recommend the use of lamivudine (Epivir) 1 zidovudine (Retrovir) or tenofovir (Viread) or stavudine (Zerit) 1 lopinavir/ritonavir (Kaletra) or efavirenz (Sustiva) as the preferred initial antiretroviral regimen. Many alternative regimens and drugs are available.
- All patients should have genotypic resistance testing upon entry into medical care.
- Later antiretroviral regimen should be constructed based on past antiretroviral experience and the results of genotypic testing.
- Patients with CD4 lymphocyte count <200/mm^3 should be given preventive therapy for *Pneumocystis carinii* pneumonia (PCP) (see "*Pneumocystis carinii* pneumonia").
- Evaluation of chronic diarrhea in patients with HIV is described in Section III "HIV-Infected Patient, Acutely Ill.".
- Table 1-5 describes primary prophylaxis of opportunistic infections in adults and adolescents with HIV infection. Criteria for discontinuing and restarting opportunistic prophylaxis for adults with HIV infection is described in Section I, "Acquired Immunodeficiency Syndrome."
- HIV infection in a pregnant woman poses special challenges and considerations. Appropriate and timely antiretroviral therapy given to mother and newborn has been shown to dramatically reduce the risk of perinatal transmission of HIV. All pregnant women with newly diagnosed HIV infection should be offered antiretroviral therapy. Antiretroviral therapy should be initiated at the end of the first trimester, include zidovudine when possible, and continue through the baby's birth. The goal of therapy is to achieve an undetectable viral load. In women with viral loads persistently >1000 copies/ml despite appropriate ARV, C-section may further lower risk of transmission. Zidovudine (AZT) should also be given to the newborn for the first 6 wk of life, and mothers should completely avoid nursing. Efavirenz (Sustiva) should be avoided because of its potential teratogenic effects.

DISPOSITION

- Ongoing care consisting of frequent medical evaluations and T-lymphocyte subset analysis
- Long-term care focused on providing up-to-date antiretroviral therapy and prophylaxis of PCP and other opportunistic infections, as well as early detection of complications (see Section III)

REFERRAL

To a physician knowledgeable and experienced in the management of HIV infection and its complications

PEARLS & CONSIDERATIONS

COMMENTS

HIV chemoprophylaxis after occupational exposure is described in Section V, Tables 5-29 and 5-30.

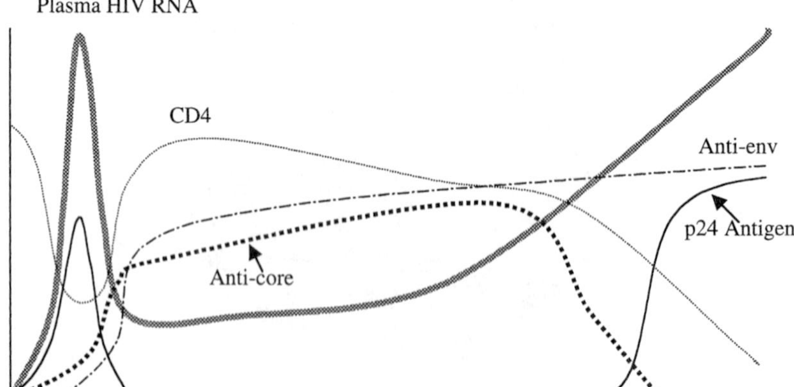

FIGURE 1-124 Course of human immunodeficiency virus infection. (From Mandell GL [ed]: *Mandell, Douglas, and Bennett's principles and practice of infectious diseases,* ed 5, New York, Churchill Livingstone.)

SUGGESTED READINGS

Kantor R et al: Evolution of resistance to drugs in HIV-1-infected patients failing antiretroviral therapy, AIDS 18(11):1503, 2004.

Klein MB et al: The impact of initial highly active antiretroviral therapy on future treatment sequences in HIV infection, AIDS 18(14):1895, 2004.

Monier PL, Wilcox R: Metabolic complications associated with the use of highly active antiretroviral therapy in HIV-1-infected adults, Am J Med Sci 328(1):48, 2004.

Volberding PA: Initiating HIV therapy: timing is critical, controversial, *Postgrad Med* 115(2):15, 2004.

Watts DH: Management of human immunodeficiency virus infection in pregnancy, *N Engl J Med* 346(24):1879, 2002.

Yeni PG: Antiretroviral treatment for adult HIV infection in 2002: updated recommendations of the International AIDS Society–USA panel, *JAMA* 288:222, 2002.

AUTHOR: **JOSEPH R. MASCI, M.D.**

SECTION I

BASIC INFORMATION

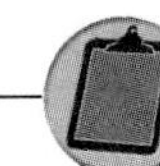

DEFINITION

Huntington's chorea is an inherited neurodegenerative disorder characterized by involuntary movements, psychiatric disturbance, and cognitive decline.

SYNONYMS

Huntington's disease

ICD-9CM CODES
333.4 Huntington's chorea

EPIDEMIOLOGY & DEMOGRAPHICS

PREVALENCE (IN U.S.): 4.1 to 5.4 cases/100,000 persons
PREDOMINANT SEX: Female = male
PREDOMINANT AGE: Adulthood
PEAK INCIDENCE: Late 30s and 40s, with onsets from age 2 to 70 yr
GENETICS: Autosomal dominant

PHYSICAL FINDINGS & CLINICAL PRESENTATION

- Chorea (irregular rapid, flowing, nonstereotyped involuntary movements). When there is a writhing quality, it is referred to as choreoathetosis. 90% of affected patients have chorea, but virtually any expression of basal ganglia dysfunction, including rigidity and dystonia, can be seen. Chorea is present early on and tends to decrease in end stages of disease.
- Dancelike, lurching gait, often caused by chorea.
- Westphal variant: cognitive dysfunction, bradykinesia, and rigidity. This variant is more commonly seen in juvenile onset HD.
- Oculomotor abnormalities are common early on and include increased latency of response and insuppressible eye blinking.
- Psychiatric disorders (can be present early on): depression is commonly seen. Also, obsessive-compulsive behaviors and aggression associated with impaired impulse control.

ETIOLOGY

- Trinucleotide repeat disorder.
- Unstable repeat results in CAG expansion.
- The responsible gene is the Huntington gene located on chromosome 4. Its function is not known.

DIAGNOSIS

DIFFERENTIAL DIAGNOSIS

- Drug-induced chorea—dopamine, stimulants, anticonvulsants, antidepressants, and oral contraceptives have all been known to cause chorea.
- Sydenham's chorea—decreased incidence with decline of rheumatic fever.
- Benign hereditary chorea—autosomal dominant with onset in childhood. There is no progression of symptoms and no associated dementia or behavioral problems.
- Senile chorea—probably vascular in origin.
- Wilson's disease—autosomal recessive; tremor, dysarthria, and dystonia are more common presentations than chorea. 95% of patients with neurologic manifestations will have Keyser-Fleischer rings.
- Neuroacanthocytosis—autosomal recessive. Chorea, dystonia, tics, and orolingual dyskinesias that can result in self-mutilation. Must look for acanthocytes in peripheral smear.
- Dentatorubropallidoluysian atrophy—autosomal dominant, triplet repeat disease. Presentation is variable and includes chorea, myoclonus, dementia, and ataxia. More common in Japan. Can be confirmed by genetic testing.
- Postinfectious.
- Systemic lupus erythematosus—can be the presenting feature of lupus. Only occurs in about 1% of individuals with lupus. Pathophysiology unknown.
- Chorea gravidarum—presents during first 4-5 mo of pregnancy and resolves after delivery.
- Paraneoplastic—seen most commonly in small cell lung cancer and lymphoma.

WORKUP

Onset of symptoms in an individual with an established family history requires no additional investigation.

LABORATORY TESTS

- Confirm diagnosis by chromosome analysis.
- If normal, obtain CBC with smear, ESR, electrolytes, serum ceruloplasmin, 24-hr urinary copper excretion, TFTs, ANA, LFTs, HIV, and ASO titer. Consider paraneoplastic markers.

IMAGING STUDIES

CT scan or MRI scan will show atrophy most notably in the caudate and putamen. Cortex is involved to a lesser extent. A normal scan does not exclude the diagnosis.

TREATMENT

NONPHARMACOLOGIC THERAPY

- Supportive counseling
- Physical and occupational therapy
- Home health care
- Genetic counseling

CHRONIC Rx

- Chorea does not need to be treated unless disabling
- Chorea may be diminished by low doses of neuroleptics (e.g., haloperidol 1 to 10 mg/day)
- Amantadine (up to 300-400 mg divided tid)
- Tetrabenazine. This is a dopamine depletor that is not currently available in the United States. Side effects include parkinsonism and depression
- Depression with suicidal ideation is common; may improve with tricyclic or SSRI antidepressants

DISPOSITION

Relentless course of variable duration leading to progressive disability and death

REFERRAL

- Should refer to psychiatry and neurology for treatment of mood disorders and movement disorders
- Genetic counselors

PEARLS AND CONSIDERATIONS

- Suicide rate is fivefold that of the general population.
- The number of repeats does correlate with age of onset but does not clearly correlate with disease severity. Interpretation of number of repeats is still difficult at this time and therefore it is debatable whether to disclose this information to patients.

SUGGESTED READINGS

Biglan K, Shoulson I: Huntington's disease. In Jankovic J, Tolosa E (eds): *Parkinson's disease and movement disorders.* Philadelphia, 2002, Lippincott Williams & Wilkins.

Higgins D: Chorea and its disorders, *Neuro Clin* 19(3):707, 2001.

AUTHOR: **CINDY ZADIKOFF M.D.**

Hydrocele

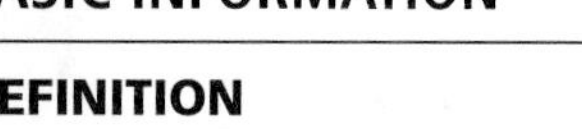

BASIC INFORMATION

DEFINITION

A hydrocele is a fluid collection in a serous scrotal space usually between the layers of the tunica vaginalis (Figs. 1-125 and 1-126).

ICD-9CM CODES
603.9 Hydrocele

PHYSICAL FINDINGS & CLINICAL PRESENTATION

Symptoms:
- Scrotal enlargement
- Scrotal heaviness or discomfort radiating to the inguinal area
- Back pain

Physical findings:
- Scrotal distention (testicle may be impossible to palpate)
- Transillumination

ETIOLOGY & PATHOGENESIS

Hydroceles may occur as a congenital abnormality where the processus vaginalis fails to close. In this case, an inguinal hernia is virtually always associated with the malformation. Congenital hydroceles are most common in infants and children. In adults, hydroceles are more frequently caused by infection, tumor, or trauma. Infection of the epididymis often results in the development of a secondary hydrocele. Tropical infections such as filariasis may produce hydroceles.

DIAGNOSIS

DIFFERENTIAL DIAGNOSIS

- Spermatocele
- Inguinoscrotal hernia
- Testicular tumor
- Varicocele
- Epididymitis

IMAGING

Scrotal ultrasound (useful to rule out a testicular tumor as the cause of the hydrocele)

TREATMENT

- No treatment if asymptomatic and testicle is thought to be normal
- Surgical repair

SUGGESTED READING

Rowland RG, Foster RS, Donohue JP: Scrotum and testis. In Gillenwater JY et al. (eds): *Adult and pediatric urology,* ed 3, St Louis, 1996, Mosby.

AUTHOR: **TOM J. WACHTEL, M.D.**

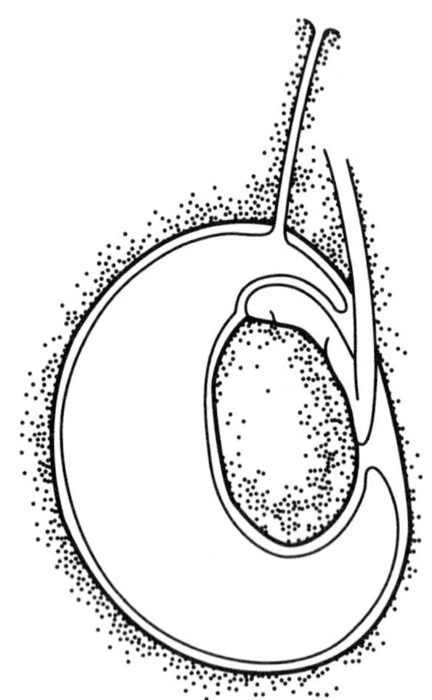

FIGURE 1-125 A hydrocele is a fluid collection in the serous space between the layers of the tunica vaginalis. The tunica vaginalis may or may not remain patent, allowing the hydrocele to communicate with the peritoneum.

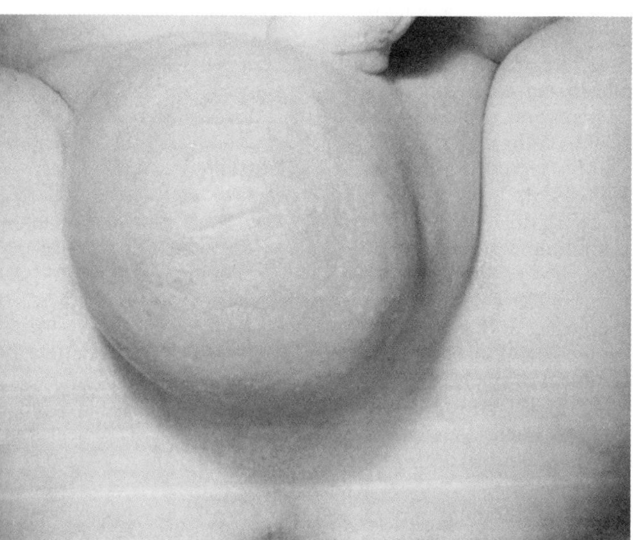

FIGURE 1-126 Newborn with large right hydrocele. (From Behrman RE: *Nelson textbook of pediatrics,* ed 16, Philadelphia, 2000, WB Saunders.)

BASIC INFORMATION

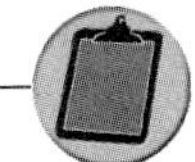

DEFINITION

Normal pressure hydrocephalus (NPH) is a syndrome of symptomatic hydrocephalus in the setting of normal CSF pressure. The classic clinical triad of NPH includes gait disturbance, cognitive decline, and incontinence.

ICD-9CM CODES
331.3 Communicating hydrocephalus

EPIDEMIOLOGY & DEMOGRAPHICS

PREDOMINANT SEX: Males = females
PREDOMINANT AGE: Fourth to sixth decades, but can occur at any age
INCIDENCE: 1 per 100,0000

PHYSICAL FINDINGS & CLINICAL PRESENTATION

- Gait difficulty: patients often have difficulty initiating ambulation, and the gait may be broad-based and shuffling, with the appearance that the feet are stuck to the floor (i.e., "magnetic gait" or "frontal gait disorder")
- Cognitive decline: mental slowing, forgetfulness and inattention without agnosia, aphasia, or other "cortical" disturbances
- Incontinence: initially may have urinary urgency; later incontinence develops. Occasionally fecal incontinence also occurs
- On physical examination, look for signs of disease that may mimic NPH

ETIOLOGY

- Approximately 50% of cases are idiopathic; remaining cases are from secondary causes, including prior subarachnoid hemorrhage, meningitis, trauma, or intracranial surgery.
- Symptoms are presumed to result from stretching of sacral motor and limbic fibers that lie near the ventricles, as dilation occurs.

DIAGNOSIS

DIFFERENTIAL DIAGNOSIS

- Alzheimer's disease with extrapyramidal features
- Cognitive impairment in the setting of Parkinson's disease or Parkinson's Plus syndromes
- Diffuse Lewy Body disease
- Frontotemporal dementia
- Cervical spondylosis with cord compromise in setting of degenerative dementia
- Multifactorial gait disorder
- Multi-infarct dementia

WORKUP

- **Large volume lumbar puncture:**
  1. Mental status testing and time to walk a prespecified distance (usually 25 feet) are measured, followed by removal of 30-50 ml of CSF.
  2. Retest of mental status and timed walking are done at 1 and 4 hr. Patients who have significant improvement in gait or mental status tend to have better surgical outcome; those with mild or negative response can have variable outcomes.
  3. Opening and closing pressure are measured; if pressure is elevated, alternative etiologies must be considered.
- Occasionally, continuous lumbar CSF drainage may be performed.
- CSF infusion and CSF pressure monitoring are sometimes used to help predict surgical outcome.

LABORATORY TESTS

CSF should be sent for routine fluid analyses to exclude other pathology.

IMAGING STUDIES

- CT scan or MRI can be used to document ventriculomegaly. The distinguishing feature of NPH is ventricular enlargement out of proportion to sulcal atrophy.
- MRI has advantages over CT, including better ability to visualize structures in the posterior fossa, visualize transependymal CSF flow, and to document extent of white matter lesions.
- Isotope cisternography and dynamic MRI studies have not been shown to be superior in predicting shunt outcome.

TREATMENT

NONPHARMACOLOGIC THERAPY

Some patients (30% of those with idiopathic NPH and 60% of patients with a known etiology) show significant improvement from shunting.
Factors that may predict positive outcome with surgery:

- NPH secondary to prior trauma, subarachnoid hemorrhage, or meningitis
- History of mild impairment in cognition <2 yr
- Onset of gait abnormality before cognitive decline
- Imaging demonstrates hydrocephalus without sulcal enlargement
- Transependymal CSF flow visualized on MRI

Factors that may predict negative outcome with surgery

- Extensive white matter lesions or diffuse cerebral atrophy on MRI
- Moderate to severe cognitive impairment
- Onset of cognitive impairment before gait disorder
- History of alcohol abuse

ACUTE GENERAL Rx

Shunting in selected patients

REFERRAL

Neurosurgical referral for shunting in appropriate patients

PEARLS & CONSIDERATIONS

Each of the cardinal symptoms of NPH are commonly seen in the elderly and occur in multiple disease processes; therefore differential diagnosis should always be considered carefully.

CAUTION

Shunt complications occur in 30%-40% of patients.

SUGGESTED READING

Vanneste JA: Diagnosis and management of normal-pressure hydrocephalus, *J Neurol* 247(1):5, 2000.

AUTHOR: **TAMARA G. FONG, M.D., PH.D.**

Hydronephrosis (PTG)

BASIC INFORMATION

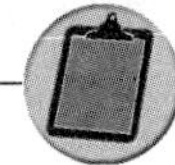

DEFINITION

Hydronephrosis is dilation of the renal pyelocalyceal system, most often as a result of impairment of urinary flow.

SYNONYMS

Hydroureter (dilation of ureter, often seen with hydronephrosis when obstruction is in lower urinary tract)
Urinary tract obstruction

ICD-9CM CODES
591 Acquired hydronephrosis
753.2 Congenital hydronephrosis

EPIDEMIOLOGY & DEMOGRAPHICS

Children usually have congenital malformations, whereas adults tend to have acquired defects as etiologies.

PHYSICAL FINDINGS & CLINICAL PRESENTATION

HISTORY:

- Pain is caused by distention of collecting system or renal capsule and is more related to the rate of onset than the degree of obstruction. It can vary in location from flank to lower abdomen to testes/labia. Pain in flank occurring only on micturition is highly suggestive of vesicoureteral reflux.
- Anuria can occur with total obstruction of urinary flow (bilateral hydronephrosis or unilateral if only one kidney is present).
- Polyuria or nocturia can occur with chronic (incomplete) obstruction because of deleterious effects on renal concentrating ability (nephrogenic diabetes insipidus).
- Urinary frequency, hesitancy, postvoid dribbling, and difficulty initiating stream are all symptoms that can occur with obstruction at or below the bladder (e.g., prostatic hyperplasia).
- Chronic urinary infections can either result from chronic urinary obstruction (organisms favoring growth with stasis of urine) or lead to conditions (e.g., urine pH changes) that favor stone formation and subsequent obstruction.

PHYSICAL EXAMINATION:

- Hypertension can be caused by increased renin release in acute or subacute obstruction
- Fever or CVA tenderness can suggest urinary tract infection
- Distended bladder or kidneys present
- Rectal examination should be done to evaluate prostate for size and nodularity and also to check rectal sphincter tone
- Pelvic examination is done to assess for vaginal anatomy, pelvic mass, or pelvic inflammatory disease (PID)
- Penile examination performed to rule out meatal stenosis or phimosis
- Bladder catheterization is needed to assess postvoid residual volume if urinary tract obstruction is considered. Should rule out postrenal obstruction in unexplained acute renal failure

ETIOLOGY

MECHANICAL IMPAIRMENTS:

- Congenital: ureteropelvic junction narrowing, ureterovesical junction narrowing, ureterocele, retrocaval ureter, bladder neck obstruction, urethral valves, urethral stricture, meatal stenosis
- Acquired:
  1. Intrinsic to urinary tract: calculi, inflammation, trauma, sloughed papillae, ureteral tumor, blood clots, prostatic hypertrophy or cancer, bladder cancer, urethral stricture, phimosis
  2. Extrinsic to urinary tract: gravid uterus, retroperitoneal fibrosis or tumor (e.g., lymphoma), aortic aneurysm, uterine fibroids, trauma (surgical or nonsurgical), PID, pelvic malignancies (e.g., prostate, colorectal, cervical, uterine, bladder)

FUNCTIONAL IMPAIRMENTS:

- Neurogenic bladder (often with adynamic ureter) can occur with spinal cord disease or diabetic neuropathy.
- Pharmacologic agents such as α-adrenergic antagonists and anticholinergic drugs can inhibit bladder emptying.
- Vesicoureteral reflux may occur.
- Pregnancy can cause hydroureter and hydronephrosis (right more often than left) as early as the second month. Hormonal effects on ureteral tone combine with mechanical factors.

DIAGNOSIS

DIFFERENTIAL DIAGNOSIS

- Urinary stones
- Neoplastic disease
- Prostatic hypertrophy
- Neurologic disease
- Urinary reflux
- Urinary tract infection
- Medication effects
- Trauma
- Congenital abnormality of urinary tract

LABORATORY TESTS

- Serum BUN and creatinine to assess for renal insufficiency (usually implies bilateral obstruction or unilateral obstruction of a solitary kidney)
- Electrolytes may reveal hypernatremia (if nephrogenic DI), hyperkalemia (from renal failure and effects on tubular function), or distal renal tubular acidosis
- Urinalysis and examination of sediment may reveal WBCs, RBCs, or bacteria in the appropriate setting (e.g., infection, stones), but often the sediment is normal in obstructive renal disease

IMAGING STUDIES

- Abdominal plain film of kidneys, ureters, and bladder is used to look for nephrocalcinosis or a radiopaque stone.
- Assess kidney and bladder size with ultrasound; contour of pyelocalyces and ureters. Ultrasound is about 90% sensitive and specific for hydronephrosis and is noninvasive, so it will not worsen preexisting renal insufficiency.
- Intravenous pyelogram (IVP) helps localize the site of obstruction when hydronephrosis is seen on ultrasound, but the contrast may have deleterious effects on the kidneys if there is renal insufficiency.
- Antegrade or retrograde urograms can be performed if renal failure is a concern with IVP and either of these two procedures could be extended to provide relief of the obstruction.
- Abdominal CT scan without IV contrast provides excellent localization of the site of obstruction.
- Voiding cystourethrogram is helpful in diagnosing vesicoureteral reflux and obstructions of the bladder neck or urethra.
- Magnetic resonance urography may be useful if contrast studies not feasible or other studies non-diagnostic.

TREATMENT

- Urgent treatment is required if urinary tract obstruction is associated with urinary tract infection, acute renal failure, or uncontrollable pain.

- Conservative management of calculi with IV fluid, IV antibiotics (if evidence of infection), and aggressive analgesia may be enough to treat acute unilateral urinary tract obstruction depending on the size (90% of stones <5 mm will pass spontaneously).
- Urethral catheter is adequate to relieve most obstructions at or distal to the bladder, but occasionally a suprapubic catheter will be required (e.g., impassable urethral stricture or urethral injury). Neurogenic bladder may require intermittent clean catheterization if frequent voiding and pharmacologic treatments are ineffective.
- Nephrostomy tube can be placed percutaneously to facilitate urinary drainage.
- Extracorporeal shock wave lithotripsy (ESWL) is used to fragment large stones to facilitate spontaneous passage or subsequent extraction (NOTE: ESWL is contraindicated in pregnancy).
- Nephroscopy is performed for extraction of proximal stones under direct vision.
- Cystoscopy with ureteroscopy is used for removal of distal ureteral stones using a loop or basket with or without fragmentation by ultrasonic or laser lithotripsy.
- Ureteral stents can be used for extrinsic and some intrinsic ureteral obstructions.
- Urethral dilation or internal urethrotomy can be used for urethral strictures.
- Nephrectomy or ureteral diversion may be required in severe cases (e.g., malignancy).
- Ureterovesical reimplantation can be used for reflux disease.
- Transurethral retrograde prostatectomy (TURP) is used for severe obstruction from benign prostatic hypertrophy (BPH).
- IV fluid and electrolyte replacement is needed; the patient must be monitored closely during the postobstructive diuresis (usually lasting several days to a week).

DISPOSITION

Aggressive treatment of infections and early relief of obstruction can usually prevent progressive loss of renal function; however, chronic bilateral obstruction (often from BPH) can lead to chronic renal failure.

REFERRAL

- Urologist consultation early for diagnostic and/or therapeutic procedures
- Oncologist if a neoplasm is diagnosed
- Gynecologist if pregnancy or female pelvic anatomy is involved

AUTHORS: **WILLIAM F. BOYD, M.D.,** and **PAUL A. PIRRAGLIA, M.D., M.P.H.**

Hypercholesterolemia 

BASIC INFORMATION

DEFINITION

Hypercholesterolemia refers to a blood cholesterol measurement >200 mg/dl. A cholesterol level of 200 to 239 mg/dl is considered borderline high, and a level of ≥240 mg/dl is considered to be a high cholesterol measurement.

SYNONYMS

Hypercholesteremia
Hypercholesterinemia
Type II familial hyperlipoproteinemia

ICD-9CM CODES
272.0 Hypercholesterolemia

EPIDEMIOLOGY & DEMOGRAPHICS

INCIDENCE/PREVALENCE:
- There are well over 100 million Americans with a total serum cholesterol >200 mg/dl.
- Elevated cholesterol requires drug therapy in about 60 million Americans.
- Incidence of heterozygous familial hypercholesterolemia: about 1:500.
- Incidence of homozygous familial hypercholesterolemia: about 1:1 million.
- Prevalence of hypercholesterolemia increases with increasing age.

GENETICS:
- Familial hypercholesterolemia: autosomal dominant disorder
- Familial combined hyperlipidemia: possibly an autosomal dominant disorder
- Multifactorial predilection: apparent in majority of affected individuals

RISK FACTORS:
- Dietary intake
- Genetic predisposition
- Sedentary lifestyle
- Associated secondary causes

PHYSICAL FINDINGS & CLINICAL PRESENTATION

- Most patients: no physical findings
- Possible findings particularly in the familial forms
  1. Tendon xanthomas
  2. Xanthelasma
  3. Arcus corneae
  4. Arterial bruits (young adulthood)

ETIOLOGY

Primary
1. Genetics
2. Obesity
3. Dietary intake

Secondary
1. Diabetes mellitus
2. Alcohol
3. Oral contraceptives
4. Hypothyroidism
5. Glucocorticoid use
6. Most diuretics
7. Nephrotic syndrome
8. Hepatoma
9. Extrahepatic biliary obstruction
10. Primary biliary cirrhosis

DIAGNOSIS

DIFFERENTIAL DIAGNOSIS

No real differential diagnosis; however, consider underlying secondary causes/etiologies for the elevated cholesterol.

LABORATORY TESTS

PRIMARY PREVENTION WITHOUT ATHEROSCLEROSIS OR DIABETES MELLITUS:
1. Total cholesterol <200 mg/dl, and the HDL >40: repeat in 5 yr.
2. Cholesterol 200 to 239 mg/dl and the HDL >40: discuss dietary modification, repeat in 1 to 2 yr.
3. Total cholesterol >240 mg/dl or the HDL <40 mg/dl: need a fasting lipid profile (cholesterol, HDL, triglycerides, from which an LDL can be calculated).
4. Fasting lipid profile with LDL <130 mg/dl and 1 or no risk factors: dietary guidance and repeat in 5 yr.
5. Fasting lipid profile with LDL 130 to 159 mg/dl (borderline high risk), and less than two risk factors for CAD: diet and exercise modification, with repeat profile in 12 wk.
6. Fasting lipid profile with LDL >160 mg/dl or borderline LDL and two or more risk factors for CAD: need drug therapy.

SECONDARY PREVENTION WITH ATHEROSCLEROSIS OR DIABETES MELLITUS:
1. All patients: fasting lipid profile
2. If LDL <100 mg/dl: instruction on diet and exercise, and repeat annually
3. If LDL >100 mg/dl: drug therapy required

SECONDARY PREVENTION WITH ATHEROSCLEROSIS AND DIABETES MELLITUS:
1. Now classified as very high risk
2. Fasting lipid profile for all patients
3. If LDL >70, drug therapy required

TREATMENT

NONPHARMACOLOGIC THERAPY

- First line of treatment: dietary therapy (see "Hyperlipoproteinemia")
- Dietary modifications
  1. Low-cholesterol, low-fat diet (fat intake to 30% or less of the total caloric intake)
  2. Saturated fats <7% of total calories
  3. No more than 200 mg/day of cholesterol
- Increased activity with aerobic exercise: encourage 20 to 30 min of aerobic exercise three to four times a week
- Smoking cessation encouraged
- Counseling on CAD risk factors

ACUTE GENERAL Rx

No acute treatment needed

CHRONIC Rx

- In primary prevention: needed for patients with LDL >160 mg/dl or LDL 130 to 159 mg/dl with two or more risk factors for CAD
- In secondary prevention: needed for patients with known CAD, vascular disease or diabetes mellitus, and LDL >70 mg/dl
- In primary prevention: considered in patients on dietary therapy with LDL >190 mg/dl with no risk factors, LDL >160 mg/dl with two or more risk factors, or HDL <30 mg/dl
- Medications that can be used (see Table 1-22):
  1. Bile acid sequestrants (poorly tolerated)
  2. Niacin (poorly tolerated)
  3. HMG-CoA reductase inhibitors ("statins")
  4. Fibric acids
  5. Medication tailored to the patient's lipid profile, lifestyle, and the medication's side-effect profile
- Cholesterol absorption inhibitors (ezetimibe)
- Bile acid sequestrants to lower LDL

SECTION I

- Niacin to lower LDL and triglycerides and raise HDL
- HMG-CoA reductase inhibitors to lower LDL
- Fibric acids work to lower triglycerides more than LDL

DISPOSITION

- After initiation of therapy, repeat laboratory tests in 4 to 6 wk, with modifications as necessary.
- Once goal is achieved, lifelong medication and monitoring are needed at least three to four times a year.
- Dietary modification is needed to continue with drug therapy.
- Repeat review for additional CAD risk factors.

PEARLS & CONSIDERATIONS

COMMENTS

See "Hyperlipoproteinemia."

SUGGESTED READINGS

Cleeman JI: Detection and evaluation of dyslipoproteinemia, *Endocrinol Metab Clin North Am* 27(3):597, 1998.

Illingworth DR: Management of hypercholesterolemia, *Med Clin North Am* 84(1):23, 2000.

National Cholesterol Education Program: Second Report on the Expert Panel on Detection, Evaluation, and Treatment of High Cholesterol in Adults (adult treatment panel IV), *JAMA* 285:2486, 2001.

Safeer R, Ugalat P: Cholesterol treatment guidelines update, *Am Fam Physician* 65:871, 2002.

AUTHOR: **BETH J. WUTZ, M.D.**

TABLE 1-22 Drugs Affecting Lipoprotein Metabolism

Drug class	Agents and daily doses	Lipid/lipoprotein effects		Side effects	Contraindications
HMG-CoA reductase inhibitors (statins)	Lovastatin (20-80 mg) Pravastatin (20-80 mg) Simvastatin (20-80 mg) Fluvastatin (20-80 mg) Atorvastatin (10-80 mg) Rosuvastain (5-40 mg)	LDL HDL TG	↓18%-55% ↑5%-15% ↓7%-30%	Myopathy Increased liver enzymes	Absolute: • Active or chronic liver disease Relative: • Concomitant use of certain drugs*
Bile acid sequestrants	Cholestyramine (4-16 g) Colestipol (5-20 g) Colesevelam (2.6-3.8 g)	LDL HDL TG	↓1.5%-30% ↑3%-5% No change or increase	Gastrointestinal distress Constipation Decreased absorption of other drugs	Absolute: • Dysbetalipoproteinemia • TG >400 mg/dl Relative: • TG >200 mg/dl
Nicotinic acid	Immediate release (crystalline) nicotinic acid (1.5-3 g), extended-release nicotinic acid (Niaspan) 1-2 g, sustained release nicotinic acid (1-2 g)	LDL HDL TG	↓5%-25% ↑15%-35% ↓20%-50%	Flushing Hyperglycemia Hyperuricemia (or gout) Upper GI distress Hepatotoxicity	Absolute: • Chronic liver disease • Severe gout Relative: • Diabetes • Hyperuricemia • Peptic ulcer disease
Fibric acids	Gemfibrozil (600 mg bid) Fenofibrate (160 mg qd) Clofibrate (1000 mg bid)	LDL *(may be increased in patients with high TG)* HDL TG	↓5%-20% ↑10%-20% ↓20%-50%	Dyspepsia Gallstones Myopathy	Absolute: • Severe renal disease • Severe hepatic disease
Cholesterol absorption inhibitors	Ezetimibe (10 mg QD)	LDL HDL TG	↓18% ↑1% ↓7%-8%	Abdominal pain myalgias	• Severe renal disease • Severe hepatic disease

Modified from The National Cholestrol Education Program, *JAMA* 285:2486, 2001.
CoA, Coenzyme A; *GI,* gastrointestinal; *HDL,* high-density lipoprotein; *HMG,* 3-hydroxy-3 methylglutanyl; *LDL,* low-density lipoprotein; *TG,* triglyceride.
*Cyclosporine, macrolide antibiotics, various antifungal agents, and cytochrome P-450 inhibitors (fibrates and niacin should be used with appropriate caution).

BASIC INFORMATION

DEFINITION

A hypercoagulable state is an inherited or acquired condition associated with an increased risk of thrombosis.

ICD-9CM CODES
289.8 Hypercoagulable state
795.79 Antiphospholipid antibody syndrome

EPIDEMIOLOGY & DEMOGRAPHICS

See Table 1-23
- Risk of thrombosis increases with age.
- Most people with a genetic defect or laboratory abnormality will not suffer thrombotic disease. Annual risk of thrombosis is <1%.
- About half of patients with thrombosis have a predisposing hereditary or acquired blood protein defect.
- Significant variation in the prevalence rates and thrombotic risks is reported in different studies. This may reflect variations in the prevalence of genetic defects, the presence of other unmeasured coagulation defects, or different populations.

HISTORY

A hypercoagulable state is strongly suggested by:
- Spontaneous thrombosis: absence of other medical conditions associated with increased risk of thrombosis
- <50 yr of age at first episode of thrombosis
- Family history of thrombosis: first-degree relative with thrombosis at <50 yr
- Recurrent thrombotic events
- Thrombosis in unusual anatomic location (i.e., portal, hepatic, mesenteric, or cerebral vein)
- Thrombosis in pregnancy, postpartum, or associated with oral contraceptive use
- Fetal loss associated with placental infarction, recurrent or severe placental abruption, severe intrauterine growth restriction, severe preeclampsia in 2nd or early 3rd trimester
- Warfarin-induced skin necrosis

PHYSICAL FINDINGS & CLINICAL PRESENTATION

- Thrombosis: arterial thrombosis is a rare complication of inherited thrombophilia.
- Medical conditions associated with increased risk of thrombosis.

ETIOLOGY

See Table 1-23.
- Often a multifactorial process with genetic, environmental, and acquired factors.
- Multiple genetic factor defects are not uncommon (1%-2% prevalence); often strong synergistic effect when multiple risk factors are present.
- Pregnancy complications may be caused by thrombosis of uteroplacental circulation: late fetal loss, severe intrauterine growth restriction, placental abruption/infarction, or severe early-onset preeclampsia.

COMMON INHERITED:

Factor V Leiden (FVL)
- Autosomal dominant mutation with low penetrance.
- Causes activated protein C resistance (APCR); 90% of APCR is caused by FVL mutation.
- Most common genetic risk factor for venous thrombosis; accounts for 40%-50% of inherited thrombophilia cases.
- Heterozygous carrier has sevenfold increased risk and homozygous carrier has eightyfold increased risk of thrombosis.
- OCP use and pregnancy induce APCR. Carriers have a fourfold to eightfold increased risk of thrombosis with OCP use and pregnancy. OCP use in heterozygous carriers is associated with a thirty-fivefold increased risk of thrombosis compared with noncarriers not using OCP.
- Accounts for about 40% of thrombotic events in pregnancy. Associated with second- and third-trimester fetal loss; severe intrauterine growth retardation; severe preeclampsia; and placental abruption.
- Risk of recurrent thrombotic events not well defined.

Prothrombin G20210A mutation
- Autosomal dominant mutation with low penetrance.
- Second most common inherited thrombophilia.
- Responsible for 17% of thrombosis in pregnancy. Associated with increased risk of fetal loss and possibly severe intrauterine growth retardation, severe preeclampsia, and placental abruption.
- OCP use in heterozygous carriers is associated with a sixteenfold increased risk of thrombosis compared with noncarriers not using OCP.

Hyperhomocysteinemia
- Can be inherited (most commonly an autosomal recessive mutation in methylene tetrahydrofolate reductase gene) but more often secondary to poor dietary intake. Deficiency of folate, vitamin B6, or vitamin B12 accounts for two thirds of cases.

TABLE 1-23 Hypercoagulable Conditions

	Prevalence in general population (%)	Prevalence in population with thrombosis (%)	Arterial (A)/ Venous (V) events	Fetal loss	Relative risk of thrombosis
FVL	• 6% of whites • Rare in nonwhites	12%-20%	V	yes	7
Prothrombin G20210A	• 2% of whites • Rare in nonwhites	6%	V	yes	3
AT	0.02 %	0.5%-1%	V	yes	25-50
PC	0.2%-0.3%	3%	V	yes	10-15
PS	1%-2%	3%	V	yes	2
Factor VIII (activity level >150%)	11%	25%	V		5 (activity level >150% compared with those with activity level <100%)
Hyperhomocysteinemia	5%-7%	10%	V+A		2.5 (if homocysteine level >95 percentile of control population)
Antiphospholipid antibody syndrome	1%-2%	5%-21%	V+A	yes	2-11

- Associated with increased rates of pregnancy complications, including fetal neural tube defects, severe preeclampsia, placental abruption, intrauterine fetal growth restriction, and stillbirth.

Factor VIII

- Levels >150% found to be associated with increased risk of venous thrombosis.
- Possibly an important risk factor for thrombosis in blacks.
- May be associated with increased risk of early pregnancy loss.

UNCOMMON INHERITED:

Protein C, protein S, antithrombin deficiency:

- Autosomal dominant inheritance.
- Decreased level or abnormal function.
- First episode of thrombosis usually in young adults.
- Increased risk of recurrent thrombosis.
- Associated with an eightfold increased risk of venous thrombosis in pregnancy/postpartum or with OCP use in carriers versus noncarriers.

Protein C and protein S:

- Lifetime risk of thromboembolic event is about 50%.
- Homozygous condition very rare, usually associated with lethal thrombosis in infancy.
- Risk of thrombosis in pregnancy/postpartum: 10%-30%. Associated with increased risk of fetal loss, and possibly severe preeclampsia.
- Associated with warfarin-induced skin necrosis, which occurs secondary to depletion of vitamin K-dependent anticoagulant factors sooner than procoagulant factors in the first few days of therapy.

Antithrombin (AT) deficiency:

- Most thrombogenic of the identified inherited factors. Lifetime risk of thromboembolic event is about 70%.
- Homozygous condition very rare, probably not compatible with normal fetal development.
- Risk of thrombosis in pregnancy 12%-60% and postpartum 11%-33%. Increases risk of pregnancy loss twofold to fivefold. Because of low prevalence, it is rarely the cause of fetal loss, intrauterine growth retardation, preeclampsia, or placental abruption.
- Associated with high recurrence risk of thrombosis; about 60% of individuals have recurrent thrombosis.
- Can cause heparin resistance.

Other possible causes: dysfibrinogenemia, heparin cofactor II, Factor XII, plasminogen deficiency, elevated lipoprotein(a) levels.

ACQUIRED:

Antiphospholipid antibody syndrome: most common cause of acquired thrombophilia.

- The antiphospholipid antibody syndrome (APS) is characterized by arterial or venous thromboembolism, or recurrent pregnancy loss, in association with antibodies to certain plasma proteins that are often bound to anionic phospholipids. This disorder is referred to as primary APS when these antibodies occur alone or secondary APS when they are found in association with systemic lupus erythematosus, other rheumatic diseases, or drugs (i.e., hydralazine, procainamide).
- Defined as the presence of at least one of the following clinical criteria and at least one of the following laboratory criteria:
    1. Clinical: either one or more episodes of venous, arterial, or small vessel thrombosis and/or morbidity with pregnancy (fetal loss after 10 wk of anatomically normal fetus; premature birth [<34 wk] of anatomically normal fetus as a result of preeclampsia or placental insufficiency; >3 fetal losses before 10 wk gestation in the absence of parental chromosomal abnormalities, or abnormal maternal hormones/anatomy).
    2. Laboratory: persistence of either anticardiolipin IgG or IgM antibodies at moderate to high levels (measured by a standardized enzyme-linked immunosorbent assay for b2-glycoprotein I-dependent anticardiolipin antibodies) and/or lupus anticoagulant activity (tested at least 6 wk apart).
- About two thirds of patients will have a venous thrombosis and one third will have an arterial thrombosis. An initial venous event is usually followed by venous events, and an initial arterial event is usually followed by arterial events.
- Thromboembolic events occur in up to 30% of people. Associated with high recurrence risk of thrombosis (as high as 70% reported).
- Presence of lupus anticoagulant may be more strongly associated with increased risk of thrombosis than elevated levels of anticardiolipin antibodies in primary APS.

Medical conditions associated with increased risk of thrombosis:

- Trauma
- Chronic medical illness: CHF, DM, obesity, nephrotic syndrome, inflammatory bowel disease, paroxysmal nocturnal hemoglobinuria, sickle cell anemia
- Pregnancy (fivefold increased risk of thrombosis compared with nonpregnant women), postpartum, OCP (fourfold increased risk of thrombosis with OCP use; risk about 2 times higher with third-generation versus second-generation OCP), HRT (twofold increased risk of thrombosis compared with nonusers), tamoxifen
- Immobilization, surgery (especially orthopedic), travel
- Myeloproliferative disorders
- Cancer: disease or treatment related
- Heparin-induced thrombocytopenia and thrombosis
- Cigarette smoking

DIAGNOSIS

WORKUP

- History, physical examination, laboratory tests.
- Varying recommendations on extent of workup. Little cost-effectiveness and outcomes data. It is currently not recommended that individuals with medical conditions associated with increased risk of thrombosis be screened for the inherited or acquired defects. A notable exception is made for thrombosis associated with pregnancy, postpartum, or OCP use.
- Currently, screening for Factor VIII is not suggested.

Venous thrombosis

Among individuals without medical conditions associated with increased thrombotic risk:

- Screen individuals for protein C, protein S, antithrombin deficiency, FVL, prothrombin G20210A mutation, hyperhomocysteinemia, and antiphospholipid antibodies if any of the following are present: <50 yr old at first episode of thrombosis, family history of thrombosis, recurrent thrombotic events, thrombosis in unusual anatomic location, life-threatening thrombotic event, warfarin-induced skin necrosis, thrombosis in pregnancy/postpartum/with OCP use or characteristic pregnancy complications.
- Screen all caucasians and all women on HRT for FVL, prothrombin G20210A mutation, hyperhomocysteinemia, and antiphospholipid antibodies.
- Screen all others for hyperhomocysteinemia and antiphospholipid antibodies.

Arterial thrombosis

- Screen for antiphospholipid antibody syndromes and hyperhomocysteinemia.
- Timing of workup.

- Ideally 2 wk after discontinuation of anticoagulation (except for antiphospholipid antibodies because this will influence duration of anticoagulation).

LABORATORY TESTS

- CBC, electrolytes, renal function, liver function tests, PT/PTT, PSA (in men >50 yr), urinanalysis

Note: acute thrombosis, anticoagulation, and many medical conditions can affect the results and must be considered in the interpretation of the workup.

- APCR: screen with second-generation clotting assay (using factor V-deficient plasma); in pregnancy, use genetic test for FVL mutation (PCR).
- Clotting assay affected by presence of increased factor VIII level or antiphospholipid antibodies, both can cause APCR.
- Prothrombin G20210A mutation: genetic test (PCR).
- Antithrombin deficiency: screen with functional assay (AT heparin cofactor assay). Immunologic assay may be used to differentiate types of AT deficiency.
- Protein C deficiency: functional assay (level and activity) and immunologic assay (level). Functional assay may be false positive if have APCR or elevated factor VIII level. Results may be unreliable if lupus anticoagulant is present.
- Protein S deficiency: screen with measurement of free and total levels. Functional assay (level and activity) and immunologic assay (free and total level). Results of functional assay affected by the presence of APCR and lupus anticoagulant.
- Antiphospholipid antibody syndrome: either of the following found on two occasions at least 6 wk apart
  1. Lupus anticoagulant: clotting assay
  2. Anticardiolipin antibody: IgG and/or IgM anticardiolipin antibody (measured by enzyme-linked immunosorbent assay for b2-glycoprotein I-dependent anticardiolipin antibodies)
- Hyperhomocysteinemia: fasting plasma homocysteine level (if normal but suspicion is high, can proceed with methionine loading test and genotyping for methylene tetrahydrofolate reductase).
- Factor VIII: clotting factor level.

IMAGING STUDIES

As appropriate to diagnose thrombosis and to rule out medical conditions associated with increased thrombotic risk

TREATMENT

NONPHARMACOLOGIC THERAPY

OCP/HRT use and smoking should be avoided.

PROPHYLAXIS

- Symptomatic and asymptomatic carriers (identified by family screening) should receive prophylactic anticoagulation in high-risk situations.
- Patients with antithrombin deficiency may benefit from antithrombin concentrates in the perioperative and postoperative periods.
- Patients with hyperhomocysteinemia should receive folic acid supplement (and vitamin B6 and B12 if deficient); this may decrease risk of thrombosis by decreasing plasma homocysteine levels.

Pregnancy prophylaxis

- HIGH RISK: Women with AT deficiency, homozygous FVL mutation, homozygous prothrombin G20210A mutation, protein C deficiency, combined defects, antiphospholipid antibodies, history of idiopathic venous thrombosis, or venous thrombosis during pregnancy or with OCP use: should receive full heparin anticoagulation throughout pregnancy.

LMWH is preferred because of less need for monitoring, and lower risk of osteopenia, thrombocytopenia, and hemorrhage. If LMWH is used, it should be changed to unfractionated heparin at 36 wk to decrease the risk of hematomas associated with epidural anesthesia during labor. Postpartum anticoagulation should be resumed for at least 6 wk. AT concentrates may be used during labor, delivery, and obstetric complications if deficiency is present.

- MODERATE RISK: Women who are heterozygous for protein S, heterozygous FVL mutation, and have a family history of thrombosis or heterozygous prothrombin G20210A mutation should receive prophylaxis during pregnancy and for 6 wk postpartum.
- LOW RISK: Women with a history of thrombosis associated with a nonrecurring risk factor and without inherited or acquired thrombophilia, asymptomatic heterozygous carriers of FVL mutation, or prothrombin G20210A mutation do not need prophylaxis in pregnancy. They should receive prophylactic anticoagulation for 6 wk postpartum.
- Women with antiphospholipid antibody syndrome and a history of nonplacental thrombosis should replace warfarin with full heparin anticoagulation preconception. Once pregnant, add ASA 81 mg/day. Postpartum resume warfarin anticoagulation.
- Women with antiphospholipid antibody syndrome but no history of nonplacental thrombosis should be treated with ASA 81 mg/day preconception and add unfractionated heparin 10,000 U s/c bid postconception. Adjust heparin to get midinterval PTT level similar to baseline (or use LMWH). Continue both until term. Anticoagulate with heparin or warfarin for 6 wk postpartum.

ACUTE GENERAL Rx

- Initial therapy is the same as for individuals without thrombophilia.

Venous thrombosis

- Unfractionated heparin or LMWH followed by warfarin. Continue heparin for at least 5 days or until INR is therapeutic for 48 hr, continue warfarin for 6 mo. Aim for INR of 2 to 3, unless antiphospholipid antibodies are present, in which case an INR of 3 to 3.5 is more protective.
- In pregnancy, full heparin anticoagulation for at least 4 mo, followed by prophylactic heparin for the remainder of the pregnancy. Prophylaxis with heparin or warfarin should be continued for at least 6 wk postpartum.

Arterial thrombosis

- Anticoagulation and surgical consult for definitive procedure.

Protein C deficiency

- Warfarin-induced skin necrosis: after full heparin or LMWH anticoagulation, begin gradual warfarin loading (2 mg qd for 3 days and increase by 2 to 3 mg qd until target INR is reached). Continue heparin for 5 to 7 days until warfarin-induced anticoagulation is achieved.
- Protein C concentrates may be used for deficiency states.

AT deficiency

- AT concentrates may be used if difficulty achieving anticoagulation (heparin resistance), severe thrombosis, or recurrent thrombosis despite adequate anticoagulation.

Lupus anticoagulant

- Low-molecular-weight heparin or unfractionated heparin (check heparin levels or antifactor Xa activity) followed by warfarin (INR 3 to 3.5).

Duration of therapy: must consider risk and benefit, risk of major bleeding 2% to 3%/yr in general population on anticoagulation but as high as 7% to 9%/yr in the elderly.
Indefinite anticoagulation suggested if:

- One spontaneous thrombosis associated with one of the following:
  1. Life-threatening thrombosis
  2. More than one genetic defect
  3. Presence of antithrombin deficiency or antiphospholipid antibodies
- Two or more spontaneous thrombosis

DISPOSITION

Depends on underlying condition

REFERRAL

Hematology, high-risk obstetrics

PEARLS & CONSIDERATIONS

Consider screening family members: may be able to decrease risk with lifestyle modification and provide prophylaxis in risk situations.
Interpreting workup: many medical conditions cause acquired abnormalities.

- Heparin therapy: antithrombin levels decrease by up to 30%.
- Warfarin therapy: protein C, protein S levels, and function decrease; antithrombin levels may increase.
- Antithrombin decrease with acute thrombosis (<10 days), surgery, liver disease, DIC, nephrotic syndrome, estrogen therapy (HRT, OCP).
- Protein S levels decrease with acute thrombosis (<10 days), surgery, liver disease, DIC, nephrotic syndrome, pregnancy (free and total levels may be reduced by 40%-60%), estrogen therapy (HRT, OCP).
- Protein C decreases with acute thrombosis (<10 days), surgery, liver disease, severe infection, and DIC. Levels increase with age and hyperlipidemia.
- APCR is increased with pregnancy (2nd and 3rd trimester) and estrogen therapy (HRT, OCP).
- Factor VIII levels increase with acute thrombosis (<10 days), pregnancy, and surgery.

SUGGESTED READINGS

Bauer KA: The thrombophilias: well-defined risk factors with uncertain therapeutic implications, *Ann Intern Med* 135:367, 2001.

Doyle NM, Monga M: Thromboembolic disease in pregnancy, *Obstet Gynecol Clin North Am* 31(2):319, 2004.

Haemostasis and Thrombosis Task Force, British Committee for Standards in Haematology: Investigation and management of heritable thrombophilia, *Br J Haematol* 114:512, 2001.

Marques MB, Triplett DA: When to suspect hypercoagulability and how to investigate it, *Ann Diagn Pathol* 5(3):177, 2001.

Shehata HA, Nelson-Piercy C, Khamashta MA: Antiphospholipid syndrome: management of pregnancy in antiphospholipid syndrome, *Rheum Dis Clin North Am* 27:643, 2001.

AUTHOR: **SUDEEP K. AULAKH, M.D., F.R.C.P.C.**

Hyperemesis Gravidarum

BASIC INFORMATION

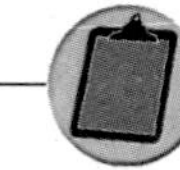

DEFINITION

Hyperemesis gravidarum is the persistent nausea and vomiting with onset in the first trimester of pregnancy, resulting in weight loss and fluid and electrolyte and acid-base imbalances.

ICD-9CM CODES
643.1 Hyperemesis gravidarum

EPIDEMIOLOGY & DEMOGRAPHICS

INCIDENCE: 0.5 to 10 cases/1000 pregnancies
GENETICS: No genetic disposition
RISK FACTORS:
- Multiple pregnancy
- Molar pregnancy
- Previous history of unsuccessful pregnancy
- Nulliparity
- Hyperemesis gravidarum in a prior pregnancy
- No correlation with race, socioeconomic status, or marital status

PEAK ONSET: 8 to 12 wk of gestation

PHYSICAL FINDINGS & CLINICAL PRESENTATION

- Weight loss
- Rapid heart rate
- Fall in blood pressure
- Dry mucous membranes
- Loss of skin elasticity
- Ketotic odor
- In severe cases, Wernicke's encephalopathy as a result of thiamine deficiency

ETIOLOGY

Specific etiology is unknown.

DIAGNOSIS

DIFFERENTIAL DIAGNOSIS

Pancreatitis, cholecystitis, hepatitis, pyelonephritis

WORKUP

Hyperemesis gravidarum is a diagnosis of exclusion. A detailed history and physical examination along with laboratory tests to rule out other causes of vomiting in early pregnancy are indicated.

LABORATORY TESTS

- Urinalysis to document ketonuria and proteinuria
- Urine C&S to rule out pyelonephritis
- Serum electrolytes to rule out electrolyte and acid-base imbalance
- Serum concentration of aminotransferases and bilirubin to rule out hepatitis
- Serum amylase to rule out pancreatitis
- Free T_4 and TSH (Elevated T_4 with suppressed TSH levels present in up to 60% of patients with hyperemesis gravidarum. This biochemical hyperthyroidism usually spontaneously resolves after 18 wk.)

IMAGING STUDIES

- Pelvic ultrasound examination to rule out multiple gestation and molar pregnancy
- Ultrasound of the gallbladder to rule out cholecystitis

TREATMENT

NONPHARMACOLOGIC THERAPY

- Reassurance
- Psychologic support
- Avoidance of foods that trigger nausea
- Frequent small meals once oral intake has resumed
- Accupressure with the use of a wrist band
- Ginger has been studied as a promising herbal remedy, but data are relatively sparse

ACUTE GENERAL Rx

- NPO
- Fluid and electrolyte replacement
- Parenteral vitamin supplementation
- Daily supplementation of thiamine 100 mg IM or IV to prevent Wernicke's encephalopathy
- Pyridoxine (vitamin B_6) 30 mg daily may reduce nausea. It should not exceed 25 mg/day.
- Antiemetics, such as promethazine (Phenergan) or droperidol (Inapsine), have not been found to be associated with fetal malformations when given in early pregnancy. Promethazine given as a low-dose continuous infusion of 25 mg in each liter of IV fluid has been shown to be very effective in controlling nausea and vomiting.
- Restart oral intake gradually no less than 48 hr after vomiting has ceased.

CHRONIC Rx

If the previous acute therapy does not resolve vomiting and oral intake is not feasible, parenteral hyperalimentation may be necessary.

DISPOSITION

- Untreated hyperemesis gravidarum can result in maternal renal and hepatic damage or death from fluid and electrolyte imbalance.
- Hyperemesis gravidarum with severe weight loss has been associated with lower average birth weight and with CNS malformations in neonates.

REFERRAL

For parenteral hyperalimentation if required

PEARLS & CONSIDERATIONS

COMMENTS

Although the specific etiology of hyperemesis gravidarum is not known, psychogenic causes proposed in older literature have been largely discredited. "Behavioral therapies" for hyperemesis gravidarum are inappropriate.

SUGGESTED READING

Strong T: Alternative therapies of morning sickness, *Clin Obstet Gynecol* 44:653, 2001.

AUTHOR: **LAUREL WHITE, M.D.**

BASIC INFORMATION

DEFINITION

Hypereosinophilic syndrome (HES) refers to a group of disorders of unknown cause characterized by sustained overproduction of eosinophils and organ dysfunction.

SYNONYMS

Idiopathic hypereosinophilic syndrome

ICD-9CM CODES
288.3 Hypereosinophilic syndrome

EPIDEMIOLOGY & DEMOGRAPHICS

- HES usually occurs between the ages of 20 and 50 yr
- Occurs in men more often than women (9:1)

PHYSICAL FINDINGS & CLINICAL PRESENTATION

- Clinical presentation of patients with HES may vary from an incidental finding of eosinophilia on peripheral blood smear to sudden onset of cardiac or neurologic symptoms.
- *Cardiac manifestations* (58%) include dyspnea, orthopnea, signs and symptoms of congestive heart failure, murmurs of mitral regurgitation or tricuspid regurgitation.
    1. Symptoms are the result of endocardial infiltration of eosinophils leading to tissue necrosis. Thrombosis of the damaged tissue ensues and ultimately results in scarring and fibrosis.
    2. The pathologic process may result in a restrictive cardiomyopathy, dilated cardiomyopathy, and valvular heart disease.
- *Neurologic manifestations* (54%) may be of three types:
    1. Thromboembolic (e.g., cardiac emboli or local vascular thrombosis)
    2. CNS dysfunction—confusion, loss of memory, ataxia, upper motor neuron signs, Babinski's sign, seizures, and behavior changes. The cause is unknown
    3. Peripheral neuropathy may be symmetric or asymmetric, sensory or mixed sensory and motor deficits
- *Pulmonary manifestations* (40%) include a chronic persistent nonproductive cough, shortness of breath, and dyspnea on exertion.
- *Cutaneous manifestations* (56%) usually include urticaria, angioedema, or erythematous pruritic papules and nodules.
- *GI manifestations* (23%) include diarrhea but findings of gastritis, colitis, pancreatitis, and hepatitis can occur.
- *Ocular manifestations* (23%) are thought to be due to microemboli causing visual disturbances (e.g., blurring).

ETIOLOGY

- The etiology of HES is unknown.
- HES is thought to be a composite of many diseases.

DIAGNOSIS

Criteria for the diagnosis of idiopathic HES include:

- Persistent eosinophilia of >1500 eosinophils/mm^3 for more than 6 mo
- Exclusion of other conditions causing eosinophilia (e.g., parasites, allergies)
- Signs and symptoms of organ system dysfunction (e.g., heart, liver, lung)

DIFFERENTIAL DIAGNOSIS

The differential includes all causes of peripheral blood eosinophilia. Parasitic infections (filariasis, schistosomiasis, ascariasis, trichinosis, etc.), coccidioidomycosis, cat-scratch disease, asthma, Churg-Strauss syndrome, allergic rhinitis, atopic dermatitis, drug reactions, aspergillosis, eosinophilic pneumonia, hypersensitivity pneumonitis, HIV, eosinophilic gastroenteritis, inflammatory bowel disease.

WORKUP

The workup of a patient who is suspected of having HES should exclude other causes mentioned in the Differential Diagnosis leading to peripheral eosinophilia.

LABORATORY TESTS

- CBC with total eosinophil count; often the total white cell count ranges from 10,000 to 30,000/mm^3 with eosinophilia of 30% to 70%
- Erythrocyte sedimentation rate (ESR)
- Electrolytes, BUN, and creatinine
- LFTs
- Urinalysis
- HIV assay
- Stools for ova and parasites × 3
- Serologic blood tests for parasitic infections (e.g., *Strongyloides*)
- Total IgE level
- Rheumatoid factor
- Bone marrow aspirate and biopsy
- Duodenal aspirate
- ECG

IMAGING STUDIES

- Chest x-ray may be clear or show infiltrates, effusions, or fibrotic scarring
- CT scan of chest, abdomen, and pelvis
- Echocardiogram can assess for ventricular function, valvular pathology including regurgitation and thrombi formation

TREATMENT

Treatment is usually not initiated unless there is evidence of organ involvement and therapy is designed at controlling organ damage.

NONPHARMACOLOGIC THERAPY

In patients with hypereosinophilia without organ involvement, serial echocardiograms are recommended at 6-mo intervals.

ACUTE GENERAL Rx

- In patients with organ involvement, initial therapy is with prednisone 1 mg/kg/day or 60 mg/day in adults.
- Patient's symptoms and peripheral eosinophil counts are monitored as a means of assessing response.
- Doses may be tapered to alternate day prednisone use in patients whose eosinophil counts have been suppressed.

CHRONIC Rx

- Patients not responding to corticosteroids, hydroxyurea 1 to 2 g/day may be tried.
- Hydroxyurea is aimed at reducing the total WBC count to <10,000/mm^3.
- If the disease continues to progress, vincristine, etoposide, interferon-α, cyclosporine, and leukapheresis are alternative choices.
- Anticoagulation with warfarin and/or antiplatelet agents is often used in patients with HES.
- If all else fails, bone marrow transplantation may be considered.

DISPOSITION

- Before the use of cardiac imaging (echo) and cardiac surgeries (valve replacement), patients with HES had a poor prognosis with a mean survival of 9 mo and a 3-yr survival of 12%.
- Deaths usually resulted from congestive heart failure, valvular endocarditis, and systemic embolization.
- Patients responding to corticosteroids (reduction of eosinophil counts to normal range) have a better prognosis than patients who do not respond to corticosteroids.
- There are now reports of 5-, 10-, and 15-yr survival rates.

REFERRAL

HES is a rare and complicated disorder requiring a multidisciplinary approach. Cardiology, neurology, pulmonary, ophthalmology, and hematology consultations should be requested in the appropriate clinical setting.

PEARLS & CONSIDERATIONS

COMMENTS

There is still much to be learned about HES. The etiology and exact mechanism of organ damage caused by eosinophils remains unknown, and research is ongoing to attempt to answer these and other questions.

SUGGESTED READINGS

Ackerman SJ: *Hematology basic principles and practice,* ed 3, New York, 2000, Churchill Livingstone.

Brito-Babapulle F: The eosinophilias, including the idiopathic hypereosinophilic syndrome, *Br J Haematol* 121:203, 2003.

Weller PF, Bubley GJ: The idiopathic hypereosinophilic syndrome, *Blood* 83(10):2749, 1994.

Weller PF, Dvorak AM: The idiopathic hypereosinophilic syndrome, *Arch Dermatol* 132(5):583, 1996.

AUTHOR: **DENNIS MIKOLICH, M.D.**

BASIC INFORMATION

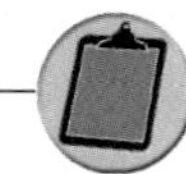

DEFINITION

Primary hyperlipoproteinemia refers to a group of genetic disorders of the lipid transport proteins in the blood, which manifests as abnormally elevated levels of cholesterol, triglycerides, or both in the serum of affected patients (Table 1-24).

SYNONYMS

Hyperlipidemia

ICD-9CM CODES
272.4 Hyperlipoproteinemia
272.3 Fredrickson type I
272.0 Fredrickson type IIa
272.2 Fredrickson type IIb, III
272.1 Fredrickson type IV
272.3 Fredrickson type V

EPIDEMIOLOGY & DEMOGRAPHICS

INCIDENCE:
- Variable depending on the genetic defect
- Spectrum spans the common familial hypercholesterolemia, with an incidence of 1:500, to the rare familial lipoprotein lipase deficiency

PREDOMINANT SEX: None

GENETICS:
- Familial lipoprotein lipase deficiency: autosomal recessive, resulting in an elevation in the plasma chylomicrons and triglycerides
- Familial apoprotein CII deficiency: autosomal recessive, resulting in increased serum chylomicrons, VLDL, and hypertriglyceridemia
- Familial type 3 hyperlipoproteinemia: single-gene defect requiring contributory factors to manifest
- Familial hypercholesterolemia: autosomal dominant defect of the LDL receptor resulting in an elevated serum cholesterol level and normal triglycerides
- Familial hypertriglyceridemia: common, autosomal dominant defect resulting in elevated VLDL and triglycerides
- Multiple lipoprotein–type hyperlipidemia: autosomal dominant, manifesting as isolated hypercholesterolemia, isolated hypertriglyceridemia, or hyperlipidemia
- Polygenic hypercholesterolemia: multifactorial
- Polygenic hyperalphalipoproteinemia: autosomal dominant or polygenic, causing an elevated HDL

PHYSICAL FINDINGS & CLINICAL PRESENTATION

- Familial lipoprotein lipase deficiency: recurrent bouts of abdominal pain in infancy, eruptive xanthomas, hepatomegaly, splenomegaly, lipemia retinalis
- Familial apoprotein CII deficiency: occasional eruptive xanthomas
- Familial type 3 hyperlipoproteinemia: after age 20 yr see xanthoma striata palmaris or tuberoeruptive xanthomas, xanthelasmas, arterial bruits at a young age, gangrene of the lower extremities at a young age
- Familial hypercholesterolemia: tendon xanthomas, arcus corneae, xanthelasma
- Familial hypertriglyceridemia: associated obesity; with exacerbations eruptive xanthomas can develop
- Multiple lipoprotein type hyperlipidemia: no discerning physical findings
- Polygenic hypercholesterolemia: no discerning physical findings
- Polygenic hyperalphalipoproteinemia: no discerning physical findings

ETIOLOGY

Genetic defects causing lipid abnormalities

TABLE 1-24 Classification of Lipoprotein Disorders by Phenotypes, Genotypes, and Corresponding Clinical Manifestations

	PLASMA LIPID LEVELS				
Phenotype	**Cholesterol**	**Triglyceride**	**Genotype**	**Xanthomas**	**Other Clinical Manifestations**
I	Normal or elevated	Elevated lipemia	Familial lipoprotein lipase deficiency, Apo C-II deficiency	Eruptive, tuberoeruptive	Recurrent abdominal pain, other gastrointestinal symptoms, hepatosplenomegaly
IIA	Normal	Elevated	FHC, familial combined hyperlipidemia—polygenic and sporadic hypercholesterolemia	Tendinous, xanthelasma, tuberous; planar (homozygous)	Premature CAD, arcus corneae, aortic stenosis (homozygous FHC), arthritic symptoms
IIB	Elevated	Elevated	Familial combined hyperlipidemia, FHC		
III	Elevated	Elevated	Familial dysbetalipoproteinemia	Planar (especially palmar), tuberous	Premature CAD and peripheral vascular disease, male > female, obesity, abnormal glucose tolerance, hyperuricemia, aggravated by hypothyroidism, good response to therapy
IV	Normal or elevated	Elevated	Familial hypertriglyceridemia, familial combined hyperlipidemia, sporadic hypertriglyceridemia	Usually none; rarely eruptive or tuberoeruptive	CAD and peripheral vascular disease, obesity, abnormal glucose tolerance, hyperuricemia, arthritic symptoms, gallbladder disease
V	Normal or elevated	Elevated	Homozygous FHC	Eruptive, tuberoeruptive	Recurrent abdominal pain, other gastrointestinal symptoms, hepatosplenomegaly, peripheral paresthesia

From Graber MA: The family practice handbook, ed 4, St Louis, 2001, Mosby.
CAD, Coronary artery disease; FHC, familial hypercholesterolemia.

Hyperlipoproteinemia, Primary (PTG)

DIAGNOSIS

DIFFERENTIAL DIAGNOSIS

Secondary causes of hyperlipoproteinemias:

- Diabetes mellitus
- Glycogen storage diseases
- Lipodystrophies
- Glucocorticoid use/excess
- Alcohol
- Oral contraceptives
- Renal disease
- Hepatic dysfunction

WORKUP

- Detailed family history for premature cardiac disease
- Recurrent pancreatitis
- Thorough physical examination

LABORATORY TESTS

- Lipoprotein analysis
- Lipoprotein electrophoresis

TREATMENT

NONPHARMACOLOGIC THERAPY

- Cornerstone of treatment: dietary therapy
- Familial lipoprotein lipase deficiency and familial apoprotein CII deficiency: fat-free diet
- Remainder of cases, except those with polygenic hyperalphalipoproteinemia: fat- and cholesterol-restricted diets

ACUTE GENERAL Rx

No acute treatment needed

CHRONIC Rx

- Familial lipoprotein lipase deficiency, polygenic hyperalphalipoproteinemia, or familial apoprotein CII deficiency: no chronic drug therapy
- Familial type 3 hyperlipoproteinemia: usually responds well to secondary causes being treated and diet therapy; if not, fibric acids may be tried
- Familial hypercholesterolemia: bile acid sequestrants, HMG-CoA reductase inhibitors, or niacin
- Familial hypertriglyceridemia: fibric acids
- Multiple lipoprotein type hyperlipidemia: drug therapy aimed at the predominant lipid abnormality noted
- Recent data suggest in patients with lipoprotein abnormalities that treatment goals should be based on non-HDLC rather than LDL-C

DISPOSITION

- Those with polygenic hyperalphalipoproteinemia: excellent prognosis for longevity
- Those with familial hypercholesterolemia, familial type 3 hypercholesterolemia, and multiple lipoprotein type hyperlipidemia: even with aggressive treatment, at high risk for accelerated atherosclerosis and CAD

PEARLS & CONSIDERATIONS

COMMENTS

Patient information is available through the American Heart Association.

See Tables 1-25 and 1-26 and Boxes 1-14 through 1-18.

SUGGESTED READINGS

Cleeman JI: Detection and evaluation of dyslipoproteinemia, *Endocrinol Metab Clin North Am* 27(3):597, 1998.

Davignon J, Genesh J, Jr: Genetics of lipoprotein disorders, *Endocrinol Metab Clin North Am* 27(3):521, 1998.

National Cholesterol Education Program: Second report on the Expert Panel on Detection, evaluation and treatment of high cholesterol in adults (adult treatment panel III), *JAMA* 285:2486, 2001.

AUTHOR: **BETH J. WUTZ, M.D.**

TABLE 1-25 **LDL Cholesterol Goals and Cutpoints for Therapeutic Lifestyle Changes (TLC) and Drug Therapy in Different Risk Categories**

Risk Category	LDL Goal (mg/dl)	LDL Level at Which to Initiate Therapeutic Lifestyle Changes (mg/dl)	IDLD Level at Which to Consider Drug Therapy (mg/dl)
CHD or CHD risk equivalents (10-yr risk >20%)	<100	≥100	≥130 (100-129: drug optional)*
2+ Risk factors (10-yr risk ≤20%)	<130	≥130	10-yr risk 10%-20%: ≥130 10-yr risk <10%: ≥160
0-1 Risk factor†	<160	≥160	≥190 (160-189: LDL-lowering drug optional)

From National Cholesterol Education Program Expert Panel on Detection, Evaluation, and Treatment of High Blood Cholesterol in Adults (Adult Treatment Panel III), National Institutes of Health, *JAMA* 285:2486, 2001.

CHD, Coronary heart disease; *LDL,* low-density lipoprotein.

*Some authorities recommend use of LDL-lowering drugs in this category if an LDL cholesterol level of <100 mg/dl cannot be achieved by therapeutic lifestyle changes. Others prefer use of drugs that primarily modify triglycerides and HDL (e.g., nicotinic acid or fibrate). Clinical judgment also may call for deferring drug therapy in this subcategory.

†Almost all people with 0-1 risk factor have a 10-year risk <10%; thus 10-year risk assessment in people with 0-1 risk factor is not necessary.

TABLE 1-26 **Comparison of LDL Cholesterol and Non-HDL Cholesterol Goals for Three Risk Categories**

Risk Category	LDL Goal (mg/dl)	Non-HDL Goal (mg/dl)
CHD and CHD risk equivalent (10-yr risk for CHD >20%)	<70	<130
Multiple (2+) risk factors and 10-yr risk ≤20%	<130	<160
0-1 Risk factor	<160	<190

From National Cholesterol Education Program Expert Panel on Detection, Evaluation, and Treatment of High Blood Cholesterol in Adults (Adult Treatment Panel III), National Institutes of Health, *JAMA* 285:2486, 2001.

CHD, Coronary heart disease; *HDL,* high-density lipoprotein; *LDL,* low-density lipoprotein.

BOX 1-14 Nutrient Composition of the Therapeutic Lifestyle Changes (TLC) Diet

Nutrient	Recommended Intake
Saturated fat*	<7% of total calories
Polyunsaturated fat	Up to 10% of total calories
Monounsaturated fat	Up to 20% of total calories
Total fat	25%-35% of total calories
Carbohydrate†	50%-60% of total calories
Fiber	20-30 g/day
Protein	Approximately 15% of total calories
Cholesterol	<200 mg/day
Total calories‡	Balance energy intake and expenditure to maintain desirable body weight/prevent weight gain

From National Cholesterol Education Program Expert Panel on Detection, Evaluation, and Treatment of High Blood Cholesterol in Adults (Adult Treatment Panel III), National Institutes of Health, *JAMA* 285:2486, 2001.

*Trans fatty acids are another LDL-raising fat that should be kept at a low intake.

†Carbohydrates should be derived predominantly from foods rich in complex carbohydrates, including grains, especially whole grains, fruits, and vegetables.

‡Daily energy expenditure should include at least moderate physical activity (contributing approximately 200 kcal/day).

BOX 1-15 ATP III Classification of LDL, Total, and HDL Cholesterol (mg/dl)

LDL cholesterol	
<100	Optimal
100-129	Near or above optimal
130-159	Borderline high
160-189	High
≥190	Very high
Total cholesterol	
<200	Desirable
200-239	Borderline high
≥240	High
HDL cholesterol	
<40	Low
≥60	High

From National Cholesterol Education Program Expert Panel on Detection, Evaluation, and Treatment of High Blood Cholesterol in Adults (Adult Treatment Panel III), National Institutes of Health, *JAMA* 285:2486, 2001.

ATP, Adult treatment panel; *HDL,* high-density lipoprotein, *LDL,* low-density lipoprotein.

BOX 1-16 Major Risk Factors (Exclusive of LDL Cholesterol) That Modify LDL Goals*

Cigarette smoking
Hypertension (blood pressure ≥140/90 mm Hg or on antihypertensive medication)
Low HDL cholesterol (<40 mg/dl)†
Family history of premature CHD (CHD in male first-degree relative (<55 yr; CHD in female first-degree relative <65 yr)
Age (men ≥45 yr; women ≥55 yr)

From National Cholesterol Education Program Expert Panel on Detection, Evaluation, and Treatment of High Blood Cholesterol in Adults (Adult Treatment Panel III), National Institutes of Health, *JAMA* 285:2486, 2001.

HDL, High-density lipoprotein; *LDL,* low-density lipoprotein.

*Diabetes is regarded as a coronary heart disese (CHD) risk equivalent.

†HDL cholesterol ≥60 mg/dl counts as a "negative" risk factor; its presence removes 1 risk factor from the total count.

BOX 1-17 Interventions to Improve Adherence

Focus on the Patient
Simplify medication regimens
Provide explicit patient instruction and use good counseling techniques to teach the patient how to follow the prescribed treatment
Encourage the use of prompts to help patients remember treatment regimens
Use systems to reinforce adherence and maintain contact with the patient
Encourage the support of family and friends
Reinforce and reward adherence
Increase visits for patients unable to achieve treatment goal
Increase the convenience and access to care
Involve patients in their care through self-monitoring

Focus on the Physician and Medical Office
Teach physicians to implement lipid treatment guidelines
Use reminders to prompt physicians to attend to lipid management
Identify a patient advocate in the office to help deliver or prompt care
Use patients to prompt preventive care
Develop a standardized treatment plan to structure care
Use feedback from past performance to foster change in future care
Remind patients of appointments and follow up missed appointments

Focus on the Health Delivery System
Provide lipid management through a lipid clinic
Utilize case management by nurses
Deploy telemedicine
Utilize the collaborative care of pharmacists
Execute critical care pathways in hospitals

From National Cholesterol Education Program Expert Panel on Detection, Evaluation, and Treatment of High Blood Cholesterol in Adults (Adult Treatment Panel III), National Institutes of Health, *JAMA* 285:2486, 2001.

BOX 1-18 Clinical Identification of the Metabolic Syndrome

RISK FACTOR	DEFINING LEVEL
Abdominal obesity* (waist circumference)†	
Men	>102 cm (>40 in)
Women	>88 cm (>35 in)
Triglycerides	≥150 mg/dl
High-density lipoprotein cholesterol	
Men	<40 mg/dl
Women	<50 mg/dl
Blood pressure	≥130/≥85 mm Hg
Fasting glucose	≥110 mg/dl

From National Cholesterol Education Program Expert Panel on Detection, Evaluation, and Treatment of High Blood Cholesterol in Adults (Adult Treatment Panel III), National Institutes of Health, *JAMA* 285:2486, 2001.

*Overweight and obesity are associated with insulin resistance and the metabolic syndrome. However, the presence of abdominal obesity is more highly correlated with the metabolic risk factors than is an elevated body mass index (BMI). Therefore, the simple measure of waist circumference is recommended to identify the body weight component of the metabolic syndrome.

†Some male patients can develop multiple metabolic risk factors when the waist circumference is only marginally increased, for example, 94-102 cm (37-40 in). Such patients may have strong genetic contribution to insulin resistance, and they should benefit from changes in life habits, similarly to men with categorical increases in waist circumference.

BASIC INFORMATION

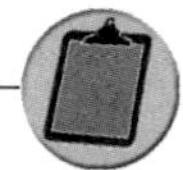

DEFINITION

Hyperosmolar coma (nonketotic hyperosmolar syndrome) is a state of extreme hyperglycemia, marked dehydration, serum hyperosmolarity, altered mental status, and absence of ketoacidosis.

SYNONYMS

Nonketotic hyperosmolar syndrome
Hyperosmolar nonketotic state

ICD-9CM CODES
250.2 Hyperosmolar coma

PHYSICAL FINDINGS & CLINICAL PRESENTATION

- Evidence of extreme dehydration (poor skin turgor, sunken eyeballs, dry mucous membranes)
- Neurologic defects (reversible hemiplegia, focal seizures)
- Orthostatic hypotension, tachycardia
- Evidence of precipitating factors (pneumonia, infected skin ulcer)
- Coma (25% of patients), delirium

ETIOLOGY

- Infections, 20% to 25% (e.g., pneumonia, UTI, sepsis)
- New or previously unrecognized diabetes (30% to 50%)
- Reduction or omission of diabetic medication
- Stress (MI, CVA)
- Drugs: diuretics (dehydration), phenytoin, diazoxide (impaired insulin secretion)

DIAGNOSIS

DIFFERENTIAL DIAGNOSIS

- Diabetic ketoacidosis
- The differential diagnosis of coma is described in Section II.

LABORATORY TESTS

- Hyperglycemia: serum glucose usually >600 mg/dl.
- Hyperosmolarity: serum osmolarity usually >340 mOsm/L.
- Serum sodium: may be low, normal, or high; if normal or high, the patient is severely dehydrated, because an elevated glucose draws fluid from intracellular space decreasing the serum sodium; the corrected sodium can be obtained by increasing the serum sodium concentration by 1.6 mEq/dl for every 100 mg/dl increase in the serum glucose level over normal.
- Serum potassium: may be low, normal, or high; regardless of the initial serum level, the total body deficit is approximately 5 to 15 mEq/kg.
- Serum bicarbonate: usually >12 mEq/L (average is 17 mEq/L).
- Arterial pH: usually >7.2 (average is 7.26); both serum bicarbonate and arterial pH may be lower if lactic acidosis is present.
- BUN: azotemia (prerenal) is usually present (BUN generally ranges from 60 to 90 mg/dl).
- Phosphorus: hypophosphatemia (average deficit is 70 to 140 mm).
- Calcium: hypocalcemia (average deficit is 50 to 100 mEq).
- Magnesium: hypomagnesemia (average deficit is 50 to 100 mEq).
- CBC with differential, urinalysis, blood and urine cultures should be performed to rule out infectious etiology.

IMAGING STUDIES

- Chest x-ray examination is useful to rule out infectious process. The initial chest x-ray may be negative if the patient has significant dehydration. Repeat chest x-ray examination after 24 hr of hydration if pulmonary infection is suspected.
- CT scan of head should be performed in patients with suspected CVA.

TREATMENT

NONPHARMACOLOGIC THERAPY

- Monitor mental status, vital signs, urine output qh until improved, then monitor q2-4h.
- Monitor electrolytes, renal function, and glucose level (see Acute General Rx).

ACUTE GENERAL Rx

- Vigorous fluid replacement: the volume and rate of fluid replacement are determined by renal and cardiac function. Typically, infuse 1000 to 1500 ml/hr for the initial 1 to 2 L; then decrease the rate of infusion to 500 ml/hr and monitor urinary output, blood chemistries, and blood pressure; use 0.9% NS (isotonic solution) if the patient is hypotensive or serum osmolarity is <320 mOsm/L; otherwise use 0.45% NS solution. Slower infusion rate may be used initially in patients with compromised cardiovascular or renal status.
- Replace electrolytes and monitor serum levels frequently (e.g., serum sodium and potassium q2h for the first 12 hr). Serum KCl replacement in patients with normal renal function and adequate urinary output is started when the serum potassium level is <5.2 mEq/L (e.g., 10 mEq KCl/hr if potassium level is 4 to 5.2 mEq/L). Continuous ECG monitoring and hourly measurement of urinary output are recommended.
- Correct hyperglycemia. The goal is for plasma glucose to decline by at least 75 to 100 mg/dl/hr.
  1. Vigorous IV hydration will decrease the serum glucose level in most patients by 80 mg/dl/hr; a regular insulin IV bolus (10 U) is often not necessary.
  2. Low-dose insulin infusion at 1 to 2 U/hr (e.g., 25 U of regular insulin in 250 ml of 0.9% saline solution at 20 ml/hr) until the serum glucose level approaches 300 mg/dl; then the patient is started on regular SC insulin with sliding scale coverage. If the plasma glucose does not decrease over 2 to 4 hr despite adequate fluid administration and urine output, consider doubling the hourly insulin dose.
  3. Glucose should be monitored q1-2h in the initial 12 hr.
- In the absence of renal failure, phosphate can be administered at a rate of 0.1 mmol/kg/hr (5 to 10 mmol/hr) to a maximum of 80 to 120 mmol in 24 hr. Magnesium replacement, in absence of renal failure, can be administered IM (0.05 to 0.10 ml/kg of 20% magnesium sulfate) or as IV infusion (4 to 8 ml of 20% magnesium sulfate [0.08 to 0.16 mEq/kg]). Repeat magnesium, phosphate, and calcium levels should be obtained after 12 to 24 hr.

DISPOSITION

Mortality in nonketotic hyperosmolar coma ranges from 20% to 50%.

PEARLS & CONSIDERATIONS

COMMENTS

The typical patient presenting with hyperosmolar coma is an elderly or bed-confined diabetic with impaired ability to communicate thirst who is evaluated after an interval of 1 to 2 wk of prolonged osmotic diuresis.

AUTHOR: **FRED F. FERRI, M.D.**

BASIC INFORMATION

DEFINITION

Primary hyperparathyroidism is an endocrine disorder caused by the excessive secretion of parathyroid hormone (PTH) from the parathyroid glands.

ICD-9CM CODES
252.0 Primary hyperparathyroidism
253.9 Ectopic hyperparathyroidism
588.8 Secondary hyperparathyroidism in chronic renal disease

EPIDEMIOLOGY & DEMOGRAPHICS

PREVALENCE: 1 case/1000 persons

PREDOMINANT AGE AND SEX:

- Primary hyperparathyroidism occurs most frequently in postmenopausal women; prevalence in this group may be as high as 3%. The condition is asymptomatic in >50% of patients
- Incidence: 1 case/1000 men and 2 to 3 cases/1000 women
- Primary hyperparathyroidism is the most frequent cause of hypercalcemia in ambulatory patients whereas malignancy is the most frequent cause of hypercalcemia in hospitalized patients.

GENETICS: Hyperparathyroidism can occur in conjunction with MEN I or II.

PHYSICAL FINDINGS & CLINICAL PRESENTATION

Primary hyperparathyroidism can be classified as asymptomatic (75% to 80%) and symptomatic. Physical examination may be entirely normal. The presence of signs and symptoms varies with the rapidity of development and degree of hypercalcemia. The following abnormalities may be present:

- GI: constipation, anorexia, nausea, vomiting, pancreatitis, ulcers
- CNS: confusion, obtundation, psychosis, lassitude, depression, coma
- GU: nephrolithiasis, renal insufficiency, polyuria, decreased urine-concentrating ability, nocturia, nephrocalcinosis
- Musculoskeletal: myopathy, weakness, osteoporosis, pseudogout, bone pain
- Other: hypertension, metastatic calcifications, band keratopathy (found in medial and lateral margin of the cornea), pruritus

ETIOLOGY

- A single adenoma is found in 80% of patients; 90% of the adenomas are found within one of the parathyroid glands, the other 10% are in ectopic sites (lateral neck, thyroid, mediastinum, retroesophagus).
- Parathyroid gland hyperplasia occurs in 20% of patients.
- Primary hyperthyroidism is associated with multiple endocrine neoplasia (MEN) I and II.

DIAGNOSIS

DIFFERENTIAL DIAGNOSIS

Other causes of hypercalcemia:

- Malignancy: neoplasms of breast, lung, kidney, ovary, pancreas; myeloma, lymphoma
- Granulomatous disorders (e.g., sarcoidosis)
- Paget's disease
- Vitamin D intoxication, milk-alkali syndrome
- Thiazide diuretics
- Other: familial hypocalciuric hypercalcemia, thyrotoxicosis, adrenal insufficiency, prolonged immobilization, vitamin A intoxication, recovery from acute renal failure, lithium administration, pheochromocytoma, disseminated SLE

WORKUP

- Persistent hypercalcemia and an elevated serum PTH confirm the diagnosis of primary hyperparathyroidism. Repeated measurements of serum calcium may be necessary because patients may not have persistently elevated serum calcium level. In malnourished patients, the serum calcium level needs to be corrected for low albumin levels by adding 0.8 mg/dl to the total serum calcium level for every 1.0 g/dl by which the serum albumin concentration is lower than 4 g/dl.
- The serum PTH level is the single best test for initial evaluation of confirmed hypercalcemia. The "intact" PTH (iPTH) is the best assay. The iPTH distinguishes primary hyperparathyroidism from hypercalcemia caused by malignancy when the serum calcium level is >12 mg/dl.
- A high level of urinary cyclic AMP is also suggestive of primary hyperparathyroidism.
- Parathyroid hormone–like protein (PLP) is increased in hypercalcemia associated with solid malignancies.
- ECG may reveal shortening of the QT interval secondary to hypercalcemia.

LABORATORY TESTS

- Elevated serum ionized calcium level, low serum phosphorus, and normal or elevated alkaline phosphatase
- Elevated urine calcium level (in contrast with very low urinary calcium levels seen in patients with familial hypocalciuric hypercalcemia)
- Possibly elevated serum chloride levels, decreased serum CO_2, hyperchloremic metabolic acidosis
- A serum albumin level should be obtained when measuring serum calcium and the calcium level should be adjusted (see above) in hypoalbuminemic patients
- The differential diagnosis of hypercalcemia is described in Section II

IMAGING STUDIES

- A bone survey may show evidence of subperiosteal bone resorption (suggesting PTH excess). The classic bone disease of primary hyperparathyroidism is *osteitis fibrosa cystica*.
- Parathyroid localization with technetium-99m sestamibi has been shown to have a high sensitivity and specificity for single adenomas.
- Screen for osteopenia with measurement of bone mineral density in all postmenopausal women.

TREATMENT

NONPHARMACOLOGIC THERAPY

- Unless contraindicated, patients should maintain a high intake of fluids (3 to 5 L/day) and sodium chloride (>400 mEq/day) to increase renal calcium excretion. Calcium intake should be 1000 mg/day.
- Potential hypercalcemic agents (e.g., thiazide diuretics) should be discontinued.
- Surgery is the only effective treatment for primary hyperparathyroidism. It is generally indicated in all patients under age 50 and patients with complications from hyperthyroidism, such as nephrolithiasis and osteopenia. The conventional surgical approach is bilateral neck exploration under general anesthesia. Minimally invasive adenomectomy guided by preoperative technetium-99-m sestamibi scanning or ultrasound plus spiral CT is an alternative to conventional neck exploration. With the minimally invasive approach, the solitary adenoma is excised through a small unilateral incision with the patient under local cervical block anesthesia.
- Percutaneous ethanol injection into the parathyroid gland should be considered in selected patients who have undergone a subtotal parathyroidectomy for multigland disease and have recurrent hyperparathyroidism as a result of remnant gland.

- Asymptomatic elderly patients can be followed conservatively with periodic monitoring of serum calcium level and review of symptoms. Serum creatinine and PTH levels should also be obtained at 6- to 12-mo intervals, bone density (cortical and trabecular) yearly. Criteria for medical monitoring of patients with asymptomatic primary hyperparathyroidism are as follows:
  1. Serum calcium level only mildly elevated
  2. Asymptomatic patient
  3. Normal bone status (no osteoporosis)
  4. Normal kidney function and no urolithiasis or nephrocalcinosis
  5. No previous episode of life-threatening hypercalcemia
- Nearly 25% of asymptomatic patients develop indications for surgery during observation.

ACUTE GENERAL Rx

Acute severe hypercalcemia (serum calcium >13 mg/dl) or symptomatic patients can be treated with the following:

- Vigorous IV hydration with NS followed by IV furosemide. Use NS with caution in patients with cardiac or renal insufficiency to avoid fluid overload.
- Calcitonin 4 IU/kg q12h is indicated when saline hydration and furosemide are ineffective or contraindicated.
- Biphosphonates (pamidronate, etidronate), mithramycin, and gallium nitrate are also effective for severe hypercalcemia.
- Cinacalcet (Sensipar) is an oral calcimimetic agent that directly lowers PTH levels by increasing the Calcium-sensing receptor to extracellular calcium. The reduction in PTH is associated with a concomitant decrease in serum calcium levels. It is indicated in treatment of secondary hyperparathyroidism in patients with chronic kidney disease on dialysis and hypercalcemia in parathyroid carcinoma. Initial dose is 30 mg po qd.

PEARLS & CONSIDERATIONS

COMMENTS

- Patients with hyperparathyroidism should undergo further evaluation for the presence of MEN I or II.
- Decreased bone mineral density and nephrolithiasis are the major sequelae of untreated hyperparathyroidism.
- An experienced endocrine surgeon cures more than 95% of patients undergoing bilateral neck exploration and incurs <1% perioperative mortality.
- In pregnant women it is preferable to perform parathyroidectomy after the first trimester.

SUGGESTED READINGS

Monchik JM et al: Minimally invasive parathyroid surgery in 103 patients with local/regional anesthesia, without exclusion criteria, *Surgery* 131:502, 2002.

Taniegra ED: Hyperparathyroidism, *Am Fam Physician* 69:333, 2004.

Udelsman R: Six hundred fifty-six consecutive explorations for primary hyperparathyroidism, *Ann Surg* 235:665, 2002.

AUTHOR: **FRED F. FERRI, M.D.**

BASIC INFORMATION

DEFINITION

Hypersensitivity pneumonitis (HP) is a group of pulmonary diseases. It is characterized by an immunologically induced inflammation of the lung parenchyma, which is due to intense or repeated inhalation of an organic agent or inorganic chemicals.

SYNONYMS

Extrinsic allergic alveolitis (EAA)
Some specific examples:
- Bird fancier's lung
- Farmer's lung
- Chemical worker's lung
- Humidifier lung
- Hot tub lung
- Sauna taker's lung

ICD-9CM CODES
495.9 Pneumonitis, hypersensitivity

EPIDEMIOLOGY & DEMOGRAPHICS

Anyone with exposure to an offending antigen is susceptible. The list of identified agents is extensive and can essentially be caused by microbes, animal or plant proteins, organic and inorganic chemicals. Most causative agents have been recognized in a wide variety of occupations. Therefore the disease is less common than 20 years ago. Now, the important exposures occur at home (birds, humidifiers, mold), and residential exposure is more difficult to diagnose.

PHYSICAL FINDINGS & CLINICAL PRESENTATION

Vary depending on frequency and intensity of antigen exposure.
- *Acute:* Fever, cough, and dyspnea 4 to 6 hr after an intense exposure, lasting 18 to 24 hr
- *Subacute:* Insidious onset of productive cough, dyspnea on exertion, anorexia, and weight loss, usually from a heavy, sustained exposure
- *Chronic:* Gradually progressive cough, dyspnea, malaise, and weight loss, usually from low-grade or recurrent exposure

Physical examination: cyanosis and "crepitant rales," possible fever

ETIOLOGY

- Nuerous environmental agents, often encountered in occupational settings
- Common sources of antigens: "moldy" hay, silage, grain, or vegetables; bird droppings or feathers; low-molecular-weight chemicals (i.e., isocyanates), pharmaceutical products

DIAGNOSIS

DIFFERENTIAL DIAGNOSIS

Acute stages:	Chronic stages:
Acute bronchopulmonary aspergillosis	IPF
Pulmonary embolism	Bronchiectasis
Asthma	Chronic bronchitis
Aspiration pneumonia	
Recurrent pneumonia	
BOOP	
Sarcoidosis	
Churg-Strauss syndrome	
Wegener's granulomatosis	

WORKUP

There is no single radiologic, physiologic, or immunologic test specific for the diagnosis of HP. HP must be suspect in any patient presenting with cough, dyspnea, fever, and malaise. A thorough history focusing on potential exposures is essential.

Major criteria:
1. History of symptoms compatible with HP that appear to worsen within hours after antigen exposure.
2. Confirmation of exposure to the offending agent by history, investigation of the environment, serum precipitin test, and/or BAL antibody.
3. Compatible changes on CXR or HRCT of the chest.
4. BAL fluid lymphocytosis (if performed).
5. Compatible histologic changes by lung bx (if performed).
6. Positive natural challenge (reproduction of symptoms and laboratory abnormalities after exposure to the suspected environment) or by controlled inhalation challenge.

Minor criteria:
1. Basilar crackles
2. Decreased diffusion capacity
3. Arterial hypoxemia (either at rest or with exercise)

LABORATORY TESTS

- Routine lab tests do not make the diagnosis, but typically the ESR, CRP, and leukocyte count are increased; the total IgG is elevated and RF is often positive; peripheral eosinophil count and serum IgE are generally normal
- Pulmonary function tests: Restrictive ventilatory patterns are typically seen. Decreased FEV1, decreased VC, decreased diffusing capacity, and decreased static compliance
- ABG: Mild hypoxemia
- Serum precipitin test: Sensitive but not specific for HP (asymptomatic patients may have IgG antibodies in serum)
- Skin testing: Unclear if helpful. However, some feel it to be a safe, effective, and rapid procedure in the diagnosis and follow-up of patients with HP. Sensitivity is similar to that of the precipitin test but the specificity is higher

IMAGING STUDIES

Chest x-ray: Nonspecific; may be normal in early stage.
- *Acute/subacute:* Bilateral interstitial and alveolar nodular infiltrates (Fig. 1-127) in a patchy or homogeneous distribution. Apices are often spared.

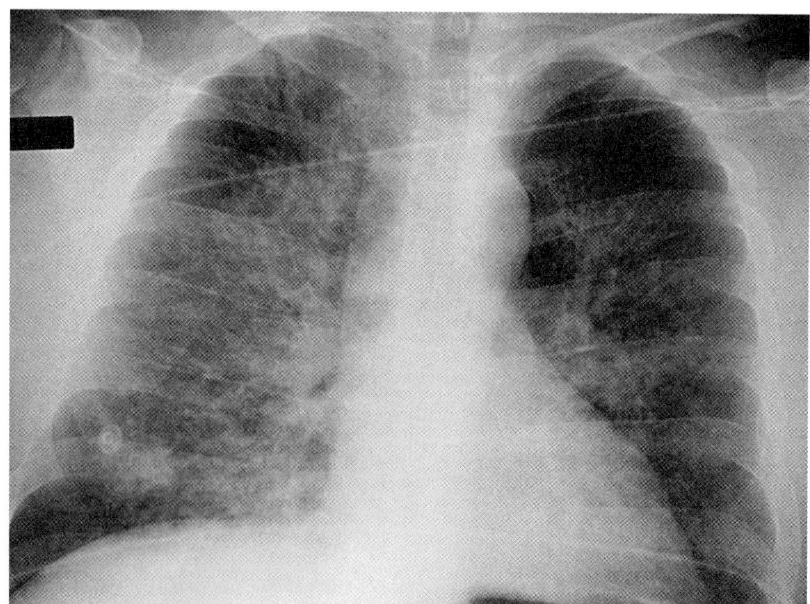

FIGURE 1-127 Chest radiograph of a patient with acute hypersensitivity pneumonitis. Bilateral interstitial infiltrates are evident, more on the right side than the left. Note the absence of pleural effusion, hilar adenopathy, and hyperinflation. (From Altman LV [ed]: *Allergy in primary care,* Philadelphia, 2000, WB Saunders.)

- *Chronic:* Diffuse reticulonodular infiltrates and fibrosis. Honeycombing may develop.

High-resolution chest CT scan: No pathognomonic features but demonstrates airspace and interstitial patterns in the acute and subacute stage. The chronic stage reveals honeycombing and bronchiectasis.

TREATMENT

NONPHARMACOLOGIC THERAPY

Early recognition and avoidance of the causative antigen

ACUTE GENERAL Rx

- Glucocorticoids accelerate initial lung recovery but may have no effect long term
- Prednisone 0.5-1mg/kg usually over 1-2 wk then tapered over 4 wk

DISPOSITION/PROGNOSIS

See Table 1-27.

REFERRAL

- Bronchoscopy: BAL provides useful supportive data in the diagnosis of HP. Usually reveals intense lymphocytosis of predominantly CD 8+ suppressor cells. In acute stages neutrophils predominate but as the disease progresses to chronic form the ratio of CD 4+ to CD 8+ cells increase. When fibrosis is present the number of neutrophils increase.
- Lung biopsy: The histopathologic features of HP are distinctive but not pathognomonic. Typically bronchiolitis and interstitial pneumonitis with granuloma formation is seen.
- Laboratory inhalation challenge: Testing to prove a direct relationship between a suspected antigen and disease; extract of antigen is inhaled via a nebulizer.

SUGGESTED READINGS

Ferran M, Roger A, Cruz MJ: Correspondence: usefulness of specific skin tests in the diagnosis of hypersensitivity pneumonitis.

Fraser et al: *Synopsis of diseases of the chest,* ed 2, 1994.

Patel AM, Ryu JH, Reed CE: Hypersensitivity pneumonitis: current concepts and further questions, *J Allergy Clin Immunol* 108:661, 2001.

Schuyler M, Cormier Y: The diagnosis of hypersensitivity pneumonitis, *Chest* 111:534, 1997.

AUTHOR: **CAROLYN J. O'CONNOR, M.D.**

TABLE 1-27 **Key Features of the Stages of Hypersensitivity Pneumonitis**

	Time frame	Clinical Features	HRCT Findings	Immunopath	Prognosis
Acute	4-48 hr	Fever, chills, cough, hypoxia, malaise	Ground-glass infiltrates	Alveolitis, immune complex	Good
Subacute	Weeks-4 mo	Dyspnea, cough, episodic flares	Micronodules, air trapping	Granulomas, bronchiolitis	Good
Chronic	4 mo-years	Dyspnea, cough, fatigue, weight loss	Fibrosis +/-, honeycombing, emphysema	Lymphocytic infiltration and fibrosis, neutrophil-mediated air space destruction	Poor

BASIC INFORMATION

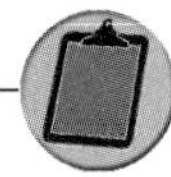

DEFINITION

Hypersplenism is a syndrome characterized by splenomegaly, cytopenia (decrease of one or more of the peripheral cell lines), and compensatory hyperplastic bone marrow.

ICD-9CM CODES
289.4 Hypersplenism

EPIDEMIOLOGY & DEMOGRAPHICS

Most often seen in patients with liver disease, hematologic malignancy, or infection.

PHYSICAL FINDINGS & CLINICAL PRESENTATION

- History: early satiety, abdominal discomfort/fullness, left upper quadrant pleuritic pain (abscess, infarction), episodes of acute left upper quadrant pain (sequestration crisis), referred pain to left shoulder
- Physical examination: splenomegaly, presence of a rub in left upper quadrant (suggestive of a splenic infarct), stigmata of cytopenias

ETIOLOGY

The spleen is an important component of cellular and humoral immunity. It is responsible for the modification and removal of old red blood cells, as well as the removal of bacteria from the circulation. The spleen's normal activities are augmented when it is enlarged.

- Splenomegaly increases the proportion of blood channeled through the red pulp, causing inappropriate splenic pooling of both normal and abnormal blood cells. The size of the spleen determines the amount of cell sequestration. Up to 90% of platelets may be pooled in an enlarged spleen.
- Splenomegaly leads to increased destruction of RBCs. Platelets and WBCs have about normal survival time even when sequestered and may be available if needed.
- Splenomegaly causes plasma volume expansion and thus exacerbates cytopenias by dilution.

DIAGNOSIS

DIFFERENTIAL DIAGNOSIS

Hypersplenism can be caused by splenomegaly of almost any cause.

- Splenic congestion: cirrhosis, CHF, portal, splenic or hepatic vein thrombosis
- Hematologic causes: hemolytic anemia, sickle cell anemia, thalassemia, spherocytosis, elliptocytosis, extramedullary hematopoiesis
- Infections: viral (hepatitis, infectious mononucleosis, CMV, HIV), bacterial (endocarditis, tuberculosis, brucellosis, lyme), parasitic (babesiosis, malaria, leishmaniasis, schistosomiasis, toxoplasmosis), fungal
- Malignancy: leukemia, lymphoma, polycythemia vera, myeloproliferative diseases, metastatic tumors
- Inflammatory diseases: Felty syndrome, SLE, sarcoidosis
- Infiltrative diseases: amyloidosis, Gaucher's disease, Niemann-Pick disease, glycogen storage disease

WORKUP

History (including travel), physical examination, laboratory tests, imaging studies

LABORATORY TESTS

- CBC with differential: neutrophilia (infection)
- Peripheral smear: abnormal cells (malignancy, RBC abnormalities), organisms (bacteria, malaria, babesiosis)
- Bone marrow biopsy: hyperplasia of corresponding cellular element: hematologic, infiltrative disorders
- Tests to diagnose suspected cause of splenomegaly: LFT, hepatitis serology, HIV, RF, ANA, etc.
- NOTE: Red cell mass may be used to assess severity of anemia. If considering splenectomy secondary to severe anemia, RBC mass measurement will differentiate true anemia (decrease in red cells) from dilutional anemia (plasma volume expansion).

IMAGING STUDIES

- Ultrasound to determine splenic size
- CT scan/MRI to obtain structural information; rule out cysts, tumors, infarcts
- Consider other studies as suggested by history and exam: CXR, cardiac echo, etc.

TREATMENT

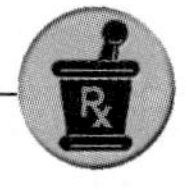

ACUTE GENERAL Rx

- Treat underlying disease
- Splenectomy is considered if
  1. Indicated for the management of the underlying cause
  2. Persistent symptomatic disease (severe cytopenia) not responding to therapy
  3. Necessary for diagnosis

Risks:

- Infections (especially encapsulated organisms): can be decreased with vaccination. Immunize with pneumococcal and meningococcal vaccines 3 wk prior to splenectomy and revaccinate with pneumococcal every 10 yr.
- Rapid increase in platelet count may cause thromboembolic complications
- Splenectomy should not be performed if the spleen is the main site of hematopoesis secondary to bone marrow failure (i.e., myelofibrosis)

DISPOSITION

- Thrombocytopenia is rarely of clinical consequence because of the ability to slowly mobilize platelets from the spleen if needed.
- Cytopenias are usually correctable with splenectomy, cell counts return to normal within a few weeks.
- Splenectomy may alleviate portal hypertension.
- Prognosis depends on the underlying disease.

REFERRAL

Hematology for bone marrow biopsy

SUGGESTED READING

Beutler E et al: *Williams hematology,* ed 6, New York, 2001, McGraw-Hill.

AUTHOR: **SUDEEP K. AULAKH, M.D., F.R.C.P.C.**

BASIC INFORMATION

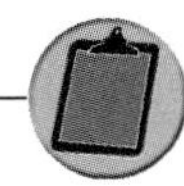

DEFINITION

The Joint National Committee on Prevention, Detection, Evaluation, and Treatment of High Blood Pressure (JNC 7) classifies normal blood pressure in adults as <120 mm Hg systolic and <80 mm Hg diastolic. "Prehypertension" is defined as systolic pressure 120-139 mm Hg or diastolic pressure 80-89 mm Hg. "Stage 1 hypertension" is systolic BP 140-159 mm Hg or diastolic BP 90-99 mm HG. "Stage 2 hypertension" is systolic BP ≥160 mm Hg or diastolic BP ≥100 mm Hg.

SYNONYMS

Essential hypertension
Idiopathic hypertension
High blood pressure

ICD-9CM CODES
401.1 Essential hypertension
401.0 Malignant hypertension caused by renal artery stenosis
642 Hypertension complicating pregnancy
405.01 Malignant hypertension secondary to renal artery stenosis
437.2 Hypertensive encephalopathy

EPIDEMIOLOGY & DEMOGRAPHICS

- Incidence of hypertension in adult population: 10% to 15%
- Increased incidence in males and in the elderly
- 50 million individuals in the U.S. and approximately 1 billion individuals worldwide meet the criteria for diagnosis of hypertension

PHYSICAL FINDINGS & CLINICAL PRESENTATION

Physical examination may be entirely within normal limits except for the presence of hypertension. A proper initial physical examination on a hypertensive patient should include the following:
- Measure height and weight.
- Evaluate skin for the presence of café-au-lait spots (neurofibromatosis), uremic appearance (CRF), striae (Cushing's syndrome).
- Perform careful funduscopic examination: check for papilledema, retinal exudates, hemorrhages, arterial narrowing, AV compression.
- Examine the neck for carotid bruits, distended neck veins, or enlarged thyroid gland.
- Perform extensive cardiopulmonary examination: check for loud aortic component of S_2, S_4, ventricular lift, murmurs, arrhythmias.
- Check abdomen for masses (pheochromocytoma, polycystic kidneys), presence of bruits over the renal artery (renal artery stenosis), dilation of the aorta.
- Obtain two or more BP measurements separated by 2 min with the patient either supine or seated and after standing for at least 2 min. Measure BP in both upper extremities (if values are discrepant, use the higher value).
- Examine arterial pulses (dilated or absent femoral pulses and BP greater in upper extremities than lower extremities suggest aortic coarctation).
- Note the presence of truncal obesity (Cushing's syndrome) and pedal edema (CHF, nephrosis).
- Perform full neurologic assessment.
- The clinical evaluation should help determine if the patient has primary or secondary (possibly reversible) hypertension, if there is target organ disease present, and if there are cardiovascular risk factors in addition to hypertension.

ETIOLOGY

- Essential (primary) hypertension (85%)
- Drug-induced or drug-related (5%)
- Renal hypertension (5%)
  1. Renal parenchymal disease (3%)
  2. Renovascular hypertension (<2%)
- Endocrine (4% to 5%)
  1. Oral contraceptives (4%)
  2. Primary aldosteronism (0.5%)
  3. Pheochromocytoma (0.2%)
  4. Cushing's syndrome and chronic steroid therapy (0.2%)
  5. Hyperparathyroidism or thyroid disease (0.2%)
- Coarctation of the aorta (0.2%)

DIAGNOSIS

WORKUP

Pertinent history:
- Age of onset of hypertension, previous antihypertensive therapy
- Family history of hypertension, stroke, cardiovascular disease
- Diet, salt intake, alcohol, drugs (e.g., oral contraceptives, NSAIDs, decongestants, steroids)
- Occupation, lifestyle, socioeconomic status, psychologic factors
- Other cardiovascular risk factors: hyperlipidemia, obesity, diabetes mellitus, carbohydrate intolerance
- Symptoms of secondary hypertension:
  1. Headache, palpitations, excessive perspiration (possible pheochromocytoma)
  2. Weakness, polyuria (consider hyperaldosteronism)
  3. Claudication of lower extremities (seen with coarctation of aorta)

LABORATORY TESTS

- Urinalysis: for evidence of renal disease.
- BUN, creatinine: to rule out renal disease. High-serum creatinine is a predictor of cardiovascular risk in essential hypertension.
- Serum electrolyte levels: low potassium is suggestive of primary aldosteronism, diuretic use.
- Screening for coexisting diseases that may adversely affect prognosis:
  1. Fasting serum glucose
  2. Serum lipid panel, uric acid, calcium
  3. If pheochromocytoma is suspected: 24-hr urine for VMA and metanephrines

IMAGING STUDIES

- ECG: check for presence of left ventricular hypertrophy (LVH) with strain pattern.
- MRA of the renal arteries: in suspected renovascular hypertension (renal artery stenosis).

TREATMENT

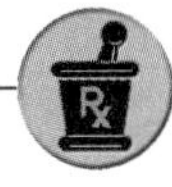

NONPHARMACOLOGIC THERAPY

Lifestyle modifications:
- Lose weight if overweight.
- Limit alcohol intake to ≤1 oz of ethanol per day in men or ≤0.5 oz in women.
- Exercise (aerobic) regularly (at least 30 min/day, most days).
- Reduce sodium intake to <100 mmol/day (<2.3 g of sodium).
- Maintain adequate dietary potassium (>3500 mg/day) intake.
- Stop smoking and reduce dietary saturated fat and cholesterol intake for overall cardiovascular health. Consume diet rich in fruits and vegetables.

ACUTE GENERAL Rx

According to the Seventh Report of the Joint National Committee on Detection, Evaluation, and Treatment of High Blood Pressure:
- Antihypertensive drug therapy should be initiated in patients with stage 1 hypertension. Diuretics or β-blockers are preferred for initial therapy because a reduction in morbidity and mortality has been demonstrated and because of their lower cost.
- ACE inhibitors, calcium antagonists, α-1 receptor blockers, and α-β blockers are also effective.
- Two-drug combination is necessary for most patients with stage 2 hypertension.

- When selecting drugs, also consider the cost of the medication, metabolic and subjective side effects, and drug-drug interactions.
- The major advantages and limitations of each class of drugs are described as follows:
  1. Diuretics
     a. Advantages: inexpensive, once per day dosing. Useful in edema states, CHF, chronic renal disease, elderly patients (decreased incidence of hip fractures in elderly patients)
     b. Disadvantages: significant adverse metabolic effects, increased risk of cardiac arrhythmias, sexual dysfunction, possible adverse effects on lipids and glucose levels
  2. β-Blockers
     a. Advantages: ideal in hypertensive patients with ischemic heart disease or post-MI. Favored in hyperkinetic, young patients (resting tachycardia, wide pulse pressure, hyperdynamic heart) and stable (Class II-III) CHF patients.
     b. Disadvantages: adverse effect on quality of life (increased incidence of fatigue, depression, impotence, bronchospasm, hypoglycemia, peripheral vascular disease, adverse effects on lipids, masking of signs and symptoms of hypoglycemia in diabetics).
  3. Calcium antagonists
     a. Advantages: helpful in hypertensive patients with ischemic heart disease. Generally favorable effect on quality of life; can be used in patients with bronchospastic disorders, renal disease, peripheral avascular disease, metabolic disorders, and salt sensitivity. Nondihydropyridine calcium channel blockers (verapamil, diltiazem) are useful in reducing proteinuria.
     b. Disadvantages: diltiazem and verapamil should be avoided in patients with CHF because of their chronotropic and inotropic effects; pedal edema may occur with nifedipine and amlodipine; constipation can be severe in elderly patients receiving verapamil.
  4. ACE inhibitors
     a. Advantages: well tolerated, favorable impact on quality of life; useful in hypertension complicated by CHF; helpful in prevention of diabetic renal disease; effective in decreasing LVH.
     b. Disadvantages: cough is a frequent side effect (5% to 20% of patients); hyperkalemia may occur in patients with diabetes or severe renal insufficiency; hypotension may occur in volume-depleted patients.
  5. Angiotensin II receptor blockers (ARB)
     a. Advantages: well tolerated, favorable impact on quality of life; useful in patients unable to tolerate ACE inhibitors because of persistent cough and in CHF and diabetic patients; single daily dose.
     b. Disadvantages: excessive cost; hypotension may occur in volume-depleted patients; contraindicated in pregnancy.
  6. α-Adrenergic blockers
     a. Advantages: no adverse effect on blood lipids or insulin sensitivity; helpful in BPH.
     b. Disadvantages: frequent postural hypotension; syncope can be avoided by giving an initial low dose at bedtime.

TREATMENT OF RENOVASCULAR HYPERTENSION (RVH): The therapeutic approach varies with the cause of the RVH.

1. Young patients with fibromuscular dysplasia can be treated with percutaneous transluminal renal angioplasty (PTRA).
2. Medical therapy is advisable in elderly patients with atheromatous renal vascular hypertension; useful agents are:
   a. β-Blockers: very effective in patients with elevated plasma renin.
   b. ACE inhibitors: very effective; however, should be avoided in patients with bilateral renal artery stenosis or in patients with solitary kidney and renal stenosis.
   c. Diuretics: often used in combination with ACE inhibitors.
3. Surgical revascularization is generally reserved for atheromatous RVH in patients responding poorly to medical therapy (uncontrolled hypertension, deteriorating renal function).

HYPERTENSION DURING PREGNANCY:

1. Hypertension complicates 5% to 12% of all pregnancies.
2. The American Obstetrical Committee defines blood pressure of 130/80 mm Hg as the upper limit of normal at any time during pregnancy.
3. A rise of 30 mm Hg systolic or 15 mm Hg diastolic is also considered abnormal regardless of the absolute values obtained.
4. Chronic hypertension (occurring before pregnancy) must be distinguished from preeclampsia, because the risk to mother and fetus is much greater in the latter.
5. Treatment of chronic hypertension during pregnancy is as follows:
   a. Initial treatment with conservative measures (proper nutrition, limited physical activity)
   b. When drug therapy is necessary, initiation of one of the following agents—methyldopa, hydralazine, labetalol, or atenolol—is preferred
   c. ACE inhibitors can cause fetal and neonatal complications; their use should be avoided in pregnancy
   d. The safety of calcium channel blockers remains unclear
   e. Diuretics should be used only if there is a specific reason for initiating and maintaining their use (e.g., hypertension associated with severe fluid overload or left ventricular dysfunction)

MALIGNANT HYPERTENSION, HYPERTENSIVE EMERGENCIES, AND HYPERTENSIVE URGENCIES:

- Definitions:

1. **Malignant hypertension** is a potentially life-threatening situation that is secondary to elevated BP.
   a. The rate of BP rise is a critical factor.
   b. The clinical manifestations are grade IV hypertensive retinopathy (exudates, hemorrhages, and papilledema), cardiovascular and/or renal compromise, and encephalopathy.
   c. It requires immediate BP reduction (not necessarily into normal ranges) to prevent or limit target organ disease.
2. **Hypertensive emergencies** are situations that require rapid (within 1 hr) lowering of BP to prevent end-organ damage.
3. **Hypertensive urgencies** are significant BP elevations that should be corrected within 24 hr of presentation.

- Therapy:

The choice of therapeutic agents in malignant hypertension varies with the cause.

1. Nitroprusside is the drug of choice in hypertensive encephalopathy, hypertension and intracranial bleeding, malignant hypertension, hypertension and heart failure, dissecting aortic aneurysm (used in combination with the propranolol); its onset of action is immediate.
2. Fenoldopam is a newer vasodilator agent useful for the short-term (up to 48 hr) management of severe hypertension when rapid but quickly reversible reduction of blood pressure is required.

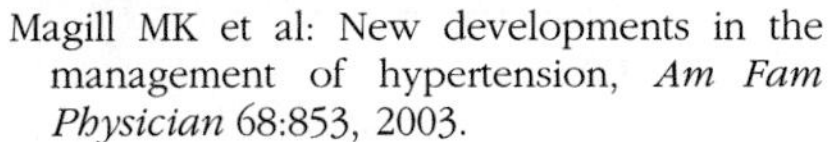
SECTION I

3. The following are important points to remember when treating hypertensive emergencies:
   a. Introduce a plan for long-term therapy at the time of the initial emergency treatment.
   b. Agents that reduce arterial pressure can cause the kidney to retain sodium and water; therefore the judicious administration of diuretics should accompany their use.
   c. The initial goal of antihypertensive therapy is not to achieve a normal BP, but rather to gradually reduce the BP; cerebral hyperperfusion may occur if the mean BP is lowered >40% in the initial 24 hr.
4. Hypertensive urgencies can be effectively treated with oral clonidine 0.1 mg q20min (to a maximum of 0.8 mg); sedation is common.

PEARLS & CONSIDERATIONS

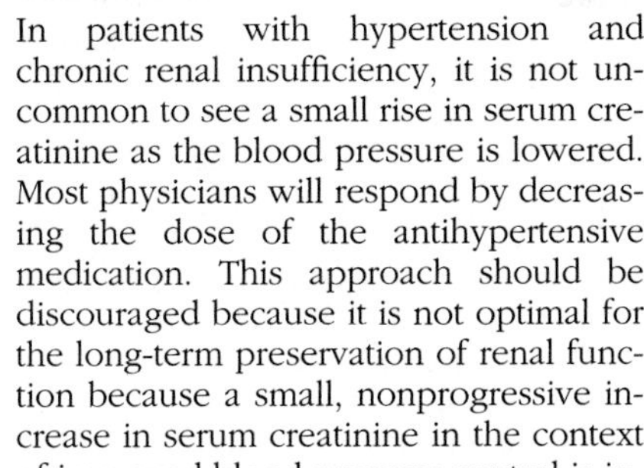

COMMENTS

In patients with hypertension and chronic renal insufficiency, it is not uncommon to see a small rise in serum creatinine as the blood pressure is lowered. Most physicians will respond by decreasing the dose of the antihypertensive medication. This approach should be discouraged because it is not optimal for the long-term preservation of renal function because a small, nonprogressive increase in serum creatinine in the context of improved blood pressure control is indicative of successful reduction of the intraglomerular pressure.

SUGGESTED READINGS

Magill MK et al: New developments in the management of hypertension, *Am Fam Physician* 68:853, 2003.

Murphy MB et al: Fenoldopam, a selective peripheral dopamine-receptor agonist for the treatment of severe hypertension, *N Engl J Med* 345:1548, 2001.

Oparil S et al: Pathogenesis of hypertension, *Ann Intern Med* 139:761, 2003.

Seventh Report of the Joint National Committee on Prevention, Detection, Evaluation, and Treatment of High Blood Pressure, *JAMA* 289:2560, 2003.

AUTHOR: **FRED F. FERRI, M.D.**

BASIC INFORMATION

DEFINITION

Hyperthyroidism is a hypermetabolic state resulting from excess thyroid hormone.

SYNONYMS

Thyrotoxicosis

ICD-9CM CODES
242.9 Hyperthyroidism
242.0 Hyperthyroidism with goiter
242.2 Hyperthyroidism, multinodular
242.3 Hyperthyroidism, uninodular

EPIDEMIOLOGY & DEMOGRAPHICS

INCIDENCE/PREVALENCE:

- Hyperthyroidism affects 2% of women and 0.2% of men in their lifetime.
- Toxic multinodular goiter usually occurs in women >55 yr old and is more common than Graves' disease in the elderly.

PHYSICAL FINDINGS & CLINICAL PRESENTATION

- Patients with hyperthyroidism generally present with the following clinical manifestations: tachycardia, tremor, hyperreflexia, anxiety, irritability, emotional lability, panic attacks, heat intolerance, sweating, increased appetite, diarrhea, weight loss, menstrual dysfunction (oligomenorrhea, amenorrhea); the presentation may be different in elderly patients (see third bullet).
- Patients with Graves' disease may present with exophthalmos, lid retraction (Fig. 1-128, *A*), lid lag (Graves' ophthalmopathy). The following signs and symptoms of ophthalmopathy may be present: blurring of vision, photophobia, increased lacrimation, double vision, deep orbital pressure. Clubbing of fingers associated with periosteal new bone formation in other skeletal areas (Graves' acropachy) and pretibial myxedema (Fig. 1-128, *B*) may also be noted.
- In the elderly the clinical signs of hyperthyroidism may be masked by manifestations of coexisting disease (e.g., new-onset atrial fibrillation, exacerbation of CHF).

ETIOLOGY

- Graves' disease (diffuse toxic goiter): 80% to 90% of all cases of hyperthyroidism
- Toxic multinodular goiter (Plummer's disease)
- Toxic adenoma
- Iatrogenic and factitious
- Transient hyperthyroidism (subacute thyroiditis, Hashimoto's thyroiditis)
- Rare causes: hypersecretion of TSH (e.g., pituitary neoplasms), struma ovarii, ingestion of large amount of iodine in a patient with preexisting thyroid hyperplasia or adenoma (Jod-Basedow phenomenon), hydatidiform mole, carcinoma of thyroid, amiodarone therapy

DIAGNOSIS

DIFFERENTIAL DIAGNOSIS

- Anxiety disorder
- Pheochromocytoma
- Metastatic neoplasm
- Diabetes mellitus
- Premenopausal state

WORKUP

Suspected hyperthyroidism requires laboratory confirmation and identification of its etiology, because treatment varies with its cause. A detailed medical history will often provide clues to the diagnosis and etiology of the hyperthyroidism.

LABORATORY TESTS

- Elevated free thyroxine (T_4)
- Elevated free triiodothyronine (T_3): generally not necessary for diagnosis
- Low TSH (unless hyperthyroidism is a result of the rare hypersecretion of TSH from a pituitary adenoma)
- Thyroid autoantibodies useful in selected cases to differentiate Graves' disease from toxic multinodular goiter (absent thyroid antibodies)

A
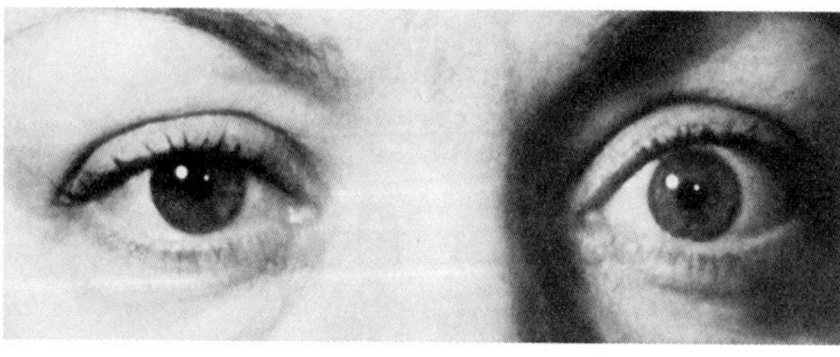

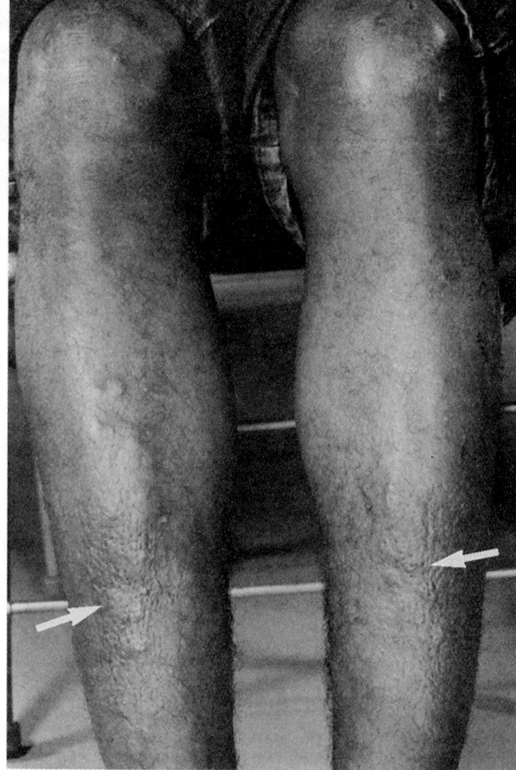
B

FIGURE 1-128 **A,** Unilateral (*left*) lid retraction in a patient with hyperthyroidism. **B,** Pretibial myxedema (*arrows*) in a patient with Graves' disease. (From Noble J [ed]: *Textbook of primary care medicine*, ed 2, St Louis, 1996, Mosby.)

IMAGING STUDIES

- 24-hr radioactive iodine uptake (RAIU) is useful to distinguish hyperthyroidism from iatrogenic thyroid hormone synthesis (thyrotoxicosis factitia) and from thyroiditis.
- An overactive thyroid shows increased uptake, whereas a normal underactive thyroid (iatrogenic thyroid ingestion, painless or subacute thyroiditis) shows normal or decreased uptake.
- The RAIU results also vary with the etiology of the hyperthyroidism: Graves' disease: increased homogeneous uptake.

Multinodular goiter: increased heterogeneous uptake.

Hot nodule: single focus of increased uptake.

- RAIU is also generally performed before the therapeutic administration of radioactive iodine to determine the appropriate dose.

TREATMENT

NONPHARMACOLOGIC THERAPY

Patient education regarding thyroid disease and discussion of the therapeutic options (medications, radioactive iodine, and thyroid surgery)

ACUTE GENERAL Rx

ANTITHYROID DRUGS (THIONAMIDES): Propylthiouracil (PTU) and methimazole (Tapazole) inhibit thyroid hormone synthesis by blocking production of thyroid peroxidase (PTU and methimazole) or inhibit peripheral conversion of T_4 to T_3 (PTU).

1. Dosage: PTU 50 to 100 mg PO q8h; methimazole 10 to 20 mg PO q8h or 30 to 60 mg/day given as a single dose.
2. Antithyroid drugs can be used as the primary form of treatment or as adjunctive therapy before radioactive therapy or surgery or afterward if the hyperthyroidism recurs.
3. Side effects: skin rash (3% to 5% of patients), arthralgias, myalgias, granulocytopenia (0.5%). Rare side effects are aplastic anemia, hepatic necrosis from PTU, cholestatic jaundice from methimazole.
4. When antithyroid drugs are used as primary therapy, they are usually given for 6 to 24 mo; prolonged therapy may cause hypothyroidism.
5. The use of antithyroid drugs before radioactive iodine therapy is best reserved for patients in whom exacerbation of hyperthyroidism after radioactive iodine therapy is hazardous (e.g., elderly patients with coronary artery disease or significant coexisting morbidity). In these patients the antithyroid drug can be stopped 2 days before radioactive iodine therapy, resumed 2 days later, and continued for 4 to 6 wk.

RADIOACTIVE IODINE (RAI; ^{131}I):

1. RAI is the treatment of choice for patients >21 yr of age and younger patients who have not achieved remission after 1 yr of antithyroid drug therapy. Radioiodine is also used in hyperthyroidism caused by toxic adenoma or toxic multinodular goiter.
2. Contraindicated during pregnancy (can cause fetal hypothyroidism) and lactation. Pregnancy should be excluded in women of childbearing age before radioactive iodine is administered.
3. A single dose of radioactive iodine is effective in inducing euthyroid state in nearly 80% of patients.
4. There is a high incidence of postradioactive iodine hypothyroidism (>50% within first year and 2%/yr thereafter); therefore these patients should be frequently evaluated for the onset of hypothyroidism (see Chronic Rx).

SURGICAL THERAPY (SUBTOTAL THYROIDECTOMY):

1. Indicated in obstructing goiters, in any patient who refuses radioactive iodine and cannot be adequately managed with antithyroid medications (e.g., patients with toxic adenoma or toxic multinodular goiter), and in pregnant patients who cannot be adequately managed with antithyroid medication or develop side effects to them.
2. Patients should be rendered euthyroid with antithyroid drugs before surgery.
3. Complications of surgery include hypothyroidism (28% to 43% after 10 yr), hypoparathyroidism, and vocal cord paralysis (1%).
4. Hyperthyroidism recurs after surgery in 10% to 15% of patients.

ADJUNCTIVE THERAPY: Propranolol alleviates the β-adrenergic symptoms of hyperthyroidism; initial dose is 20 to 40 mg PO q6h; dosage is gradually increased until symptoms are controlled; major contraindications to use of propranolol are CHF and bronchospasm. Diagnosis and treatment of "thyroid storm" are discussed elsewhere in Section I.

CHRONIC Rx

Patients undergoing treatment with antithyroid drugs should be seen every 1 to 3 mo until euthyroidism is achieved and every 3 to 4 mo while they remain on antithyroid therapy. After treatment is stopped, periodic monitoring of thyroid function tests with TSH every 3 mo for 1 yr, then every 6 mo for 1 yr, then annually is recommended.

DISPOSITION

Successful treatment of hyperthyroidism requires lifelong monitoring for the onset of hypothyroidism or the recurrence of thyrotoxicosis.

REFERRAL

- Endocrinology referral is recommended at the time of initial diagnosis and during treatment
- Surgical referral in selected patients (see Surgical Therapy)
- Hospitalization of all patients with thyroid storm

PEARLS & CONSIDERATIONS

COMMENTS

- Elderly hyperthyroid patients may have only subtle signs (weight loss, tachycardia, fine skin, brittle nails). This form is known as **apathetic hyperthyroidism** and manifests with lethargy rather than hyperkinetic activity. An enlarged thyroid gland may be absent. Coexisting medical disorders (most commonly cardiac disease) may also mask the symptoms. These patients often have unexplained CHF, worsening of angina, or new-onset atrial fibrillation resistant to treatment. See "Graves' Disease" in Section I for additional information on the diagnosis and treatment of Graves' disease.
- **Subclinical hyperthyroidism** is defined as a normal serum free thyroxine and free triiodothyronine levels with a thyroid-stimulating hormone level suppressed below the normal range and usually undetectable. These patients usually do not present with signs or symptoms of overt hyperthyroidism. Treatment options include observation or a therapeutic trial of low-dose antithyroid agents for 6 mo to attempt to induce remission.

SUGGESTED READINGS

Kearns AE, Thompson GB: Medical and surgical management of hyperthyroidism, *Mayo Clin Proc* 77:87, 2002.

Shrier DK et al: Subclinical hyperthyroidism: controversies in management, *Am Fam Physician* 65:431, 2002.

Toft AD: Subclinical hyperthyroidism, *N Engl J Med* 345:512, 2001.

AUTHOR: **FRED F. FERRI, M.D.**

BASIC INFORMATION

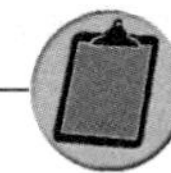

DEFINITION

Hypertrophic osteoarthropathy (HOA) is a syndrome of clubbing of the digits, periostitis of long bones, and arthritis. HOA may be primary or secondary to other underlying disease processes.

SYNONYMS

- Primary hypertrophic osteoarthropathy
  1. Pachydermoperiostosis
  2. Heredofamilial
  3. Idiopathic clubbing
  4. Touraine-Solente-Golé syndrome
- Secondary hypertrophic osteoarthropathy

ICD-9CM CODES
731.2 Hypertrophic osteoarthropathy

EPIDEMIOLOGY & DEMOGRAPHICS

- Primary HOA is familial autosomal dominant disease affecting young children between ages 1 and 20.
- Secondary HOA typically occurs in adults and is associated with other illnesses including:
  1. Pulmonary: Bronchogenic carcinoma, lung abscess, bronchiectasis, cystic fibrosis, pulmonary fibrosis, mesothelioma, sarcoidosis
  2. Gastrointestinal: Esophageal carcinoma, colon cancer, inflammatory bowel disease (Crohn's disease, ulcerative colitis), hepatocellular carcinoma, liver cirrhosis, amebiasis
  3. Cardiac: Infective endocarditis, right-to-left cardiac shunts, aortic aneurysm
  4. Thymoma
  5. Lymphoma
  6. Connective tissue diseases
  7. Thyroid acropachy

PHYSICAL FINDINGS & CLINICAL PRESENTATION

- Primary HOA typically presents with the insidious onset of clubbing of the hands and feet and is described as "spadelike." Other signs and symptoms include:
  1. Joint pain and swelling
  2. Decreased use of the fingers and hands
  3. Facial changes, coarse facial skin grooves
  4. Thickening of the arms and legs
  5. Oily skin, diaphoresis, gynecomastia, and acne
- Secondary HOA patients may present with clinical symptoms before the underlying disorder can be detected. Signs and symptoms are similar to the above mentioned in addition to findings related to the underlying disease (e.g., bronchogenic carcinoma, infective endocarditis).

ETIOLOGY

Unknown; immunologic, endocrine, and vascular etiologies have been suggested.

DIAGNOSIS

DIFFERENTIAL DIAGNOSIS

- Other causes of periostitis include Paget's disease, Reiter's syndrome, psoriasis, syphilis, osteoarthritis, rheumatoid arthritis, and osteomyelitis.
- Hypertrophic osteoarthropathy with the classic finding of clubbing of the digits warrants an investigation into any associated illnesses.

WORKUP

Primarily consists of blood tests, x-rays, and bone scans

LABORATORY TESTS

- CBC, electrolytes, and urine studies will typically be normal in both primary and secondary HOA.
- ESR will be elevated in secondary HOA.
- LFTs may be abnormal in patients with secondary HOA from GI pathology.
- Alkaline phosphatase may be elevated secondary to periostitis of long bones.
- Analysis of the synovial fluid from joint effusions reveals a low WBC count with normal viscosity, color, and complement levels.

IMAGING STUDIES

- X-rays of the long bones show periosteal new bone formation.
- A chest x-ray should be obtained to rule out underlying lung cancer.
- Bone scan with technetium-99m reveals uptake along the long bones, phalanxes, and periarticular joint spaces are common findings.

TREATMENT

ACUTE GENERAL Rx

- Treatment of primary HOA is symptomatic. Aspirin (acetylsalicylic acid) 325 mg PO q4-6 hr prn, salicylate 750 mg bid prn, ibuprofen 400 to 800 mg tid prn, naproxen 250 to 500 mg bid prn, indomethacin 25 to 50 mg qid prn will provide bone and joint pain relief.
- For secondary HOA the treatment of choice is to eradicate the underlying disease (e.g., antibiotics for infective endocarditis, surgery for bronchogenic carcinoma).

CHRONIC Rx

- In patients with secondary HOA refractory to NSAIDs and aspirin, vagotomy has been tried with some success. However, the definitive treatment is to treat the underlying disease.

DISPOSITION

- Patients with primary HOA typically will have symptoms of joint pains and swelling for the early part of their life, but thereafter the disease becomes quiescent.
- Prognosis and disease course in patients with secondary HOA will depend on the underlying cause. The insidious development of clubbing suggests infectious process, whereas the rapid progression of clubbing may suggest underlying malignancy.

REFERRAL

Referral should be made to rheumatology when the diagnosis of HOA is suspected and the cause remains unclear.

PEARLS & CONSIDERATIONS

COMMENTS

- HOA may be a marker for an underlying serious illness and a thorough investigation should be pursued. Infections and intrathoracic malignancies are the most common causes of secondary HOA.

SUGGESTED READINGS

Ramakrishnan S, Das SK, Mishra K: A current perspective on clubbing and hypertrophic osteoarthropathy, *J Assoc Physicians India* 49:1106, 2001.

Viola JC, Jaffe S, Brent LH: Primary hypertrophic osteoarthropathy, *J Rheumatol* 27(6):1562, 2000.

AUTHOR: **PETER PETROPOULOS M.D.**

BASIC INFORMATION

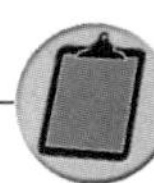

DEFINITION

Hypoaldosteronism is an aldosterone deficiency or impaired aldosterone function.

ICD-9CM CODES
255.4 Hypoadrenalism

EPIDEMIOLOGY AND DEMOGRAPHICS

Selective hypoaldosteronism accounts for as many as 10% of cases of unexplained hyperkalemia.

PHYSICAL FINDINGS & CLINICAL PRESENTATION

- Physical examination may be entirely within normal limits.
- Hypertension may be present in some patients.
- Profound muscle weakness and cardiac arrhythmias may be present.

ETIOLOGY

- Hyporeninemic hypoaldosteronism (renin-angiotensin dependent): decreased aldosterone production secondary to decreased renin production; the typical patient has renal disease secondary to various factors (e.g., diabetes mellitus, interstitial nephritis, multiple myeloma).
- Hyperreninemic hypoaldosteronism (renin-angiotensin independent): renin production by the kidneys is intact; the defect is in aldosterone biosynthesis or in the action of angiotensin II. Common causes of this form of hypoaldosteronism are medications (ACE inhibitors, heparin), lead poisoning, aldosterone enzyme defects, and severe illness.

DIAGNOSIS

DIFFERENTIAL DIAGNOSIS

Pseudohypoaldosteronism: renal unresponsiveness to aldosterone. In this condition, both renin and aldosterone levels are elevated. Pseudohypoaldosteronism can be caused by medications (spironolactone), chronic interstitial nephritis, systemic disorders (SLE, amyloidosis), or primary mineralocorticoid resistance.

WORKUP

Measurement of plasma renin activity following 4 hr of upright posture can differentiate hyporeninemic from hyperreninemic causes. Renin levels in the normal or low range identify cases that are renin-angiotensin dependent, whereas high renin levels identify cases that are renin-angiotensin independent. The diagnosis and etiology of hypoaldosteronism can be confirmed with the renin-aldosterone stimulation test:

- Hyporeninemic hypoaldosteronism: low stimulated renin and aldosterone levels
- End-organ refractoriness to aldosterone action: high stimulated renin and aldosterone levels
- Adrenal gland abnormality: high stimulated renin and low aldosterone levels

LABORATORY TESTS

- Increased potassium, normal or decreased sodium
- Hyperchloremic metabolic acidosis (caused by the absence of hydrogen-secreting action of aldosterone)
- Increased BUN and creatinine (secondary to renal disease)
- Hyperglycemia (diabetes mellitus is common in these patients)

TREATMENT

NONPHARMACOLOGIC THERAPY

- Low-potassium diet with liberal sodium intake (at least 4 g of sodium chloride per day)
- Avoidance of ACE inhibitors and potassium-sparing diuretics

ACUTE GENERAL Rx

- Judicious use of fludrocortisone (0.05 to 0.1 mg PO qam) in patients with aldosterone deficiency associated with deficiency of adrenal glucocorticoid hormones
- Furosemide 20 to 40 mg qd to correct hyperkalemia of hyporeninemic hypoaldosteronism

DISPOSITION

Prognosis varies with the etiology of hypoaldosteronism and presence of associated disorders.

REFERRAL

Endocrinology referral for renin-aldosterone stimulation test

PEARLS & CONSIDERATIONS

COMMENTS

Treatment of pseudohypoaldosteronism is the same as for hypoaldosteronism; however, effect is limited because of impaired renal sensitivity.

AUTHOR: **FRED F. FERRI, M.D.**

BASIC INFORMATION

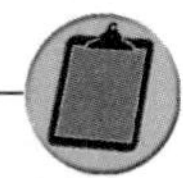

DEFINITION

Preoccupation with the fear of having, or the idea that one has, a serious disease. The fear is usually based on a misinterpretation of bodily signs or symptoms and persists despite medical reassurance, although the belief does not have the certainty or intensity of a delusion. The preoccupation causes clinically significant distress or impairment in social, occupational, or other important areas of functioning and lasts for at least 6 months.

SYNONYMS

None

ICD-9CM CODES
300.7 Hypochondriasis

EPIDEMIOLOGY & DEMOGRAPHICS

PREVALENCE (IN GENERAL POPULATION): 1%-5%, but it is thought to be higher in primary care outpatient settings where estimates range from 3%-10%.
PREDOMINANT SEX: None
PREDOMINANT AGE: Onset can occur at any age, but incidence is most common between 20 and 30 years of age.
GENETICS AND RISK FACTORS: No genetic component has been identified, and no socioeconomic factors appear to predispose people to this disorder. Patients with hypochondriasis are more likely than the general population to have Axis I disorders, such as anxiety and depression, as well as Axis II personality disorders.

CLINICAL PRESENTATION

- Presents with a complaint of a physical symptom or sign, bodily sensation, or pain, which leads, with further questioning, to concern about a serious disease.
- Childhood illnesses common in past medical history.
- No specific physical examination findings.

ETIOLOGY

Unknown etiology, but there are four competing psychiatric theories: (1) amplification of normal somatic sensations, with a tendency to attribute these sensations to a pathologic process; (2) psychodynamic interplay in which aggression toward others is transformed into physical complaints or in which feelings of guilt or low self-esteem lead to somatic pain as "punishment" for perceived wrongdoing; (3) learning and then reinforcement of the sick role; and (4) variant of another psychiatric condition such as depression.

DIAGNOSIS

DIFFERENTIAL DIAGNOSIS

- Underlying general medical condition, such as multiple sclerosis, hypothyroidism, or systemic lupus erythematosus
- Somatization disorder
- Body dysmorphic disorder
- Factitious disorder or malingering
- Generalized anxiety disorder with health concerns as one worry among many others
- Major depressive disorder with health concerns occurring only during depressive episodes
- Psychotic disorders, as may occur with depression and schizophrenia

WORKUP

- History and physical examination, laboratory and imaging tests as directed by history, as appropriate—there are no tests that diagnose this disorder.
- Evaluate for other psychiatric disorders that may be associated with hypochondriasis such as depression and anxiety disorders.

LABORATORY TESTS

None

IMAGING STUDIES

None

TREATMENT

NONPHARMACOLOGIC

- Reassurance and education, used sparingly and appropriately
- Brief and regularly scheduled appointments with the primary care physician
- Avoidance of laboratory tests, imaging studies, and diagnostic and surgical procedures unless clearly indicated
- Prohibition on reading medical texts or searching heath-related websites on the Internet
- Cognitive-behavioral therapy with techniques such as thought stopping, exposure to the feared situation with subsequent desensitization, mechanisms to control perceptions or to reprocess them, and restructuring of hypochondriacal beliefs
- Group therapy, both cognitive-behavioral or psychoeducational

ACUTE GENERAL Rx

None

CHRONIC Rx

- Pharmacologic treatment of comorbid psychiatric conditions, if present, such as depression, anxiety, or obsessive-compulsive disorder.
- SSRIs may also be helpful in patients without features of depression—fluoxetine, paroxetine, and fluvoxamine all studied in small, open-label trials; nefazodone also studied in small, open-label trial.

DISPOSITION

Waxing and waning course over decades, with relapses often triggered by psychosocial stressors. Good prognostic features include acute onset, absence of secondary gain, lack of comorbid psychiatric disorder, and high socioeconomic status.

REFERRAL

Attempts can be made to refer patients to a psychiatrist; however, patients will typically strongly resist referral as they believe their symptoms are due to an undiagnosed medical illness.

PEARLS & CONSIDERATIONS

COMMENTS

The onset of physical symptoms late in life is almost always the result of a medical disorder.

SUGGESTED READINGS

Barksy AJ, Ahern DK: Cognitive behavior therapy for hypochondriasis: a randomized controlled trial, *JAMA* 291(12):1464, 2004.

Fallon BA et al: An open trial of fluvoxamine for hypochondriasis, *Psychosomatics* 44(4):298, 2003.

Kjernisted KD et al: An open-label clinical trial of nefazodone in hypochondriasis, *Psychosomatics* 43(4):290, 2002.

Lidbeck J: Group therapy for somatization disorders in primary care: maintenance of treatment goals of short cognitive-behavioural treatment one-and-a-half-year follow-up, *Acta Psychiatrica Scandinavica* 107(6):449, 2003.

Lispitt DR: Hypochondriasis and body dysmorphic disorder. In Gabbard GO (ed): *Treatments of Psychiatric Disorders,* ed 3, Washington, DC, 2001, American Psychiatric Press.

Looper KJ, Kirmayer LJ: Behavioral approaches to somatoform disorders, *J Consult Clin Psychol* 70(3):810, 2002.

AUTHOR: **REBEKAH LESLIE GARDNER, M.D.**

BASIC INFORMATION

DEFINITION

Hypopituitarism is the partial or complete loss of secretion of one or more pituitary hormones resulting from diseases of the hypothalamus or pituitary gland.

SYNONYMS

Panhypopituitarism
Pituitary insufficiency

ICD-9CM CODES
253.2 Panhypopituitarism

EPIDEMIOLOGY & DEMOGRAPHICS

- Pituitary tumors are the most common causes of hypopituitarism with an incidence of 0.2 to 2.8 cases per 100,000.
- Increased incidence of vascular or cerebrovascular disease in patients with panhypopituitarism.
- Predisposing factors for pituitary apoplexy (another cause of panhypopituitarism) include diabetes mellitus, anticoagulant therapy, head trauma, pituitary tumors, and radiation.
- Empty sella syndrome, a third cause of panhypopituitarism, can occur in both adults and children.

PHYSICAL FINDINGS & CLINICAL PRESENTATION

The onset of hypopituitarism is usually gradual, and symptoms are related to the lack of one or more hormones and/or mass effect if a pituitary tumor is the cause. Specific symptoms depend on the hormones involved, the severity of the deficiencies, and the patient's age at onset.

- Mass effect of a pituitary tumor can cause headaches and visual disturbances
- Corticotropin deficiency:
  1. Fatigue and weakness, no appetite, abdominal pain, nausea, and vomiting
  2. Hypotension, hair loss, and change in mental status
- Thyrotropin deficiency:
  1. Fatigue and weakness, weight gain, cold intolerance, and constipation
  2. Bradycardia, hung-up reflexes, pretibial edema, and hair loss
- Gonadotropin deficiency:
  1. Loss of libido, erectile dysfunction, amenorrhea, hot flashes, dyspareunia, infertility
  2. Gynecomastia with lack of hair growth and decreased muscle mass
- Growth hormone deficiency:
  1. Growth retardation in children
  2. Easy fatigue, hypoglycemia
  3. Decreased muscle mass and obesity
- Hyperprolactinemia
  1. Galactorrhea
  2. Hypogonadism
- Vasopressin deficiency:
  1. Polyuria, polydipsia and nocturia
  2. Hypotension and dehydration

ETIOLOGY

Hypopituitarism is the result of destruction of pituitary cells caused by:

- Pituitary tumors
  1. Macroadenomas $>$10 mm
  2. Microadenomas $<$10 mm
- Pituitary apoplexy caused by hemorrhage or infarction of the pituitary gland
- Pituitary radiation therapy
- Pituitary surgery
- Empty sella syndrome with enlargement of the sella turcica and flattening of the pituitary gland caused by extension of the subarachnoid space and filling of cerebrospinal fluid into the sella turcica
- Infiltrative disease including sarcoidosis, hemochromatosis, histiocytosis X, Wegener's granulomatosis, and lymphocytic hypophysitis
- Infection (tuberculosis, mycosis, and syphilis)
- Head trauma
- Internal carotid artery aneurysm

DIAGNOSIS

The diagnosis of hypopituitarism is suspected by clinical history and physical findings and is established by endocrine stimulation testing.

DIFFERENTIAL DIAGNOSIS

The differential diagnosis is as outlined under Etiology. Other rare causes include postpartum necrosis (Sheehan's syndrome), hypopituitary tumors (e.g., craniopharyngiomas and meningioma), metastatic tumors (lung, colon, prostate, melanoma, plasmacytoma), and developmental abnormalities.

WORKUP

Includes basal determination of each anterior pituitary hormone followed by provocative stimulation tests and x-ray imaging

LABORATORY TESTS

- Corticotropin deficiency:
  1. Serum am cortisol level usually is low ($<$3 g/dl).
  2. Corticotropin stimulation test using 250 μg of corticotropin given IV and measuring serum cortisol before and 30 and 60 min after administration. A normal response is an increase in serum cortisol level $>$20 μg/dl.
  3. With pituitary disease, these tests may be indeterminate, and more dynamic testing such as an insulin-tolerance or metyrapone test may be necessary.
- Thyrotropin deficiency:
  1. TSH and free T_4 measurements
  2. Primary hypothyroidism shows elevated TSH with low free T_4. Secondary hypothyroidism shows normal or low TSH with low free T_4 and low T_3 resin uptake
- Gonadotropin deficiency:
  1. FSH, LH, estrogen, and testosterone measurements
  2. In men, hypogonadotropic hypogonadism is seen with low testosterone levels and normal or low FSH and LH levels
  3. In premenopausal women with amenorrhea, low estrogen with normal or low FSH and LH levels is typically seen
- Growth hormone deficiency:
  1. Insulin-induced hypoglycemia stimulation test using 0.1 to 0.15 unit/kg regular insulin given IV and measuring growth hormone 30, 60, and 120 min after administration. A normal response is a growth hormone level $>$10 μg/dl.
  2. Serum insulin-like growth factor I can also be measured after provocative testing.
- Hyperprolactinemia:
  1. Prolactin levels may be elevated in prolactin-secreting pituitary adenomas.
- Vasopressin deficiency:
  1. Urinalysis shows low specific gravity.
  2. Urine osmolality is low.
  3. Serum osmolality is high.
  4. Fluid deprivation test over 18 hr with inability to concentrate the urine.
  5. Serum vasopressin level is low.
  6. Electrolytes may show hyponatremia and exclude hyperglycemia.

IMAGING STUDIES

- When hypopituitarism has been established clinically and biochemically, imaging of the pituitary gland is necessary to identify the specific lesion.
- MRI is more sensitive than CT scan of the head in visualizing the pituitary fossa, sella turcica, optic chiasm, pituitary stalk, and cavernous sinuses. It is also more sensitive in detecting pituitary microadenomas.
- CT scan with coronal cuts through the sella turcica gives better images of bony structures.

TREATMENT

Hormone replacement therapy and either surgery, radiation, or medications in patients with pituitary tumors.

NONPHARMACOLOGIC THERAPY

- IV fluid resuscitation with normal saline to maintain hemodynamic stability may be needed in some circumstances
- Correction of electrolyte and metabolic abnormalities with potassium, bicarbonate, and oxygen therapy

ACUTE GENERAL Rx

Acute situations like adrenal crisis or myxedema coma can occur in untreated hypopituitarism and should be treated accordingly with IV corticosteroids (e.g., hydrocortisone 100 mg IV q6h for 24 hr) and levothyroxine (e.g., 5 to 8 μg/kg IV over 15 min, then 100 μg IV q24h).

CHRONIC Rx

Treatment is lifelong and requires the following hormone replacement therapy:

- Hydrocortisone 20 mg PO qam and 10 mg PO qpm or prednisone 5 mg PO qam and 2.5 mg PO qpm
- Testosterone enanthate or propionate 200 to 300 mg IM q2 to 3 wk or transdermal testosterone scrotal patches can be tried
- Conjugated estrogen 0.3 to 1.25 mg/day and held the last 5 to 7 days of each month with the addition of medroxyprogesterone 10 mg/day given during days 15 to 25 of the normal menstrual cycle.
- Levothyroxine 0.05 to 0.15 mg/day
- Growth hormone is not used in adults; however, can be given at 0.04 to 0.08 mg/kg/day subcutaneously in children
- Desmopressin (DDAVP) 10 to 20 μg via intranasal spray or 0.05 to 0.1 mg PO bid is used in patients with diabetes insipidus

DISPOSITION

- Hormone replacement therapy is adjusted according to serum hormone blood monitoring.
- Hypopituitarism if untreated can lead to adrenal crisis, severe hyponatremia and hypothyroidism, metabolic abnormalities, and death.
- The prognosis for patients with hypopituitarism is excellent, and life expectancy can be normal in patients with eradication of the pituitary disease and adequate hormone replacement therapy that is closely monitored in long-term follow-up.

REFERRAL

Anyone suspected of having hypopituitarism should have an endocrine consultation. For patients with pituitary tumors, a radiation oncologist and neurosurgeon consultation should be consulted.

PEARLS & CONSIDERATIONS

COMMENTS

- Hyperprolactinemia resulting in galactorrhea or hypogonadism may be associated with hypopituitarism in cases where the pituitary stalk is transected by tumor or trauma/surgery. In these cases, inhibitory dopaminergic effects on the prolactin-secreting cells of the anterior pituitary from neurons in the hypothalamus is disrupted.
- Thyroxine supplementation increases the rate of cortisol metabolism and can lead to adrenal crisis. It is therefore recommended to supplement corticosteroids first before administering thyroid hormone replacement therapy.
- All patients receiving glucocorticoid replacement therapy should wear proper identification stating the need for this therapy.
- Stress doses of corticosteroids are indicated before surgery or for any medical emergency (e.g., sepsis, acute myocardial infarction, etc.).
- Mineralocorticoid replacement is not necessary in secondary adrenal insufficiency because the rennin-angiotensin-aldosterone system is unaffected by pituitary failure.

SUGGESTED READINGS

Heshmann AM et al: Hypopituitarism caused by intracellular aneurysms, *Mayo Clin Proc* 76:789, 2001.

Lamberts SWJ, de Herder WW, van der Lely AJ: Pituitary insufficiency, *Lancet* 352:127, 1998.

Schmidt DN, Wallace K: How to diagnose hypopituitarism: Learning the features of secondary hormonal deficiencies, *Postgrad Med* 104(7):1, 1998.

Vance ML: Hypopituitarism, *N Engl J Med* 330(23):1651, 1994.

AUTHORS: **JASON IANNUCCILLI, M.D.,** and **PETER PETROPOULOS, M.D.**

BASIC INFORMATION

DEFINITION

Hypospadias is a developmental abnormality of the penis characterized by

- Abnormal ventral opening of the urethral meatus anywhere from the ventral aspect of the glans penis to the perineum
- Ventral curvature of the penis (chordee)
- Dorsal foreskin hood

ICD-9CM CODES
ICD-9CM: 752.61
Congenital Chordee: 752.63

ETIOLOGY

Multifactorial

- Endocrine factors
  1. Abnormal androgen production
  2. Limited androgen sensitivity in the target tissues
  3. Premature cessation of androgenic stimulation secondary to Leydig cell dysfunction
  4. Insufficient testosterone-dihydrotestosterone synthesis as a result of deficient 5-alpha reductase enzyme activity
- Arrested development

EPIDEMIOLOGY & DEMOGRAPHICS

- Prevalence: 1 in 250
- Pertinent familial aspects of hypospadias include the finding of hypospadias in 6.8% of fathers of affected boys and in 14% of male siblings
- An 8.5-fold higher rate of hypospadias is reported in monozygotic twins suggesting that there is insufficient production of human chorionic gonadotropin by the single placenta

PHYSICAL FINDINGS & CLINICAL PRESENTATION

- Genetics: normal karyotypes are seen with glandular hypospadias; abnormal karyotypes are noted in more severe forms of hypospadias
- Cryptorchidism: 8% to 9% occurrence
- Inguinal hernia: 9% to 10% occurrence
- Hydrocele: 9% to 16% occurrence

PENILE CURVATURE (CHORDEE)

Three theories

- Abnormal development of the urethral plate
- Abnormal fibrotic mesenchymal tissue at the urethral meatus
- Corporal disproportion

DIAGNOSIS

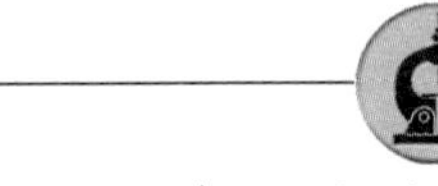

WORKUP

Made by observation and examination

LABORATORY TESTS

Intersex evaluation should be undertaken if there is associated cryptorchidism. The evaluation should include: ultrasound, genitographic studies, chromosomal, gonadal, biochemical, and molecular studies.

TREATMENT

ACUTE GENERAL Rx

DESIGNATION/CLASSIFICATION

Anterior: 33%
Middle: 25%
Posterior: 41%

SPECIAL CONSIDERATION

- The only reason for operating on any hypospadias patient is to correct deformities that interfere with the function of urination and procreation
- Other reasons for interventions: Cosmetic concerns
- The American Academy of Pediatrics recommends the best time for surgical intervention is 6 to 12 mo

HORMONAL MANIPULATION

- Controversial
- hCG administration is given before repair of proximal hypospadias
- The effect of the hCG administration is decreased hypospadias and chordee severity in all patients, increased vascularity and thickness of the proximal corpus spongiosum
- Application of topical testosterone increased mean penile circumference and length without any lasting side effects
- Prepubertal exogenous testosterone does not adversely effect ultimate penile growth

CHRONIC Rx

SURGICAL PROCEDURES

- Orthoplasty (correcting penile curvature)
- Urethroplasty
- Meatoplasty
- Glanuloplasty
- Skin coverage

There is no single universally acceptable applicable technique for hypospadias repair.

TYPES OF REPAIR

- Anterior hypospadias: MAGPI, Thiersch-Duplay urethroplasty, glans approximation procedure (GAP), tubularized incised plate (TIP) urethroplasty, Mathieu perimeatal flap, Mustarde technique, megameatus intact prepuce (MIP), pyramid procedure
- Midlevel hypospadias: TIP, Mathieu, onlay island flap (OIF), King procedure
- Posterior hypospadias:
  1. One-stage repair: OIF, double onlay preputial flap, pedicled preputial flap, transverse preputial island flap (TPIF)
  2. Two-stage repair: Orthoplasty to correct chordee followed 6 mo later or longer by Thiersch-Duplay, bladder and/or buccal mucosal hypospadias repair

COMPLICATIONS OF REPAIR

Hematoma, meatal stenosis, fistula, urethral stricture, urethral diverticulum, wound infection, impaired healing, balanitis xerotica obliterans, penile curvature

PEARLS & CONSIDERATIONS

- It must be kept in mind that apparent simple isolated hypospadias may be the only visible indication of an underlying abnormality.
- The dorsal hood of redundant foreskin is used in the repair of hypospadias, and the patient with hypospadias and a dorsal hood should not be circumcised.

SUGGESTED READINGS

American Academy of Pediatrics: Timing of elective surgery on the genitalia of male children with particular reference to the risks, benefits, and psychological effects of surgery and anesthesia, *Pediatrics* 97:590, 1996.

Belman AB: Hypospadias update, *Urology* 49:166, 1997.

Borer JG, Retik AB: Current trends in hypospadias repair, *Urol Clin North Am* 26:1:15, 1999.

Retik AB, Borer JG. In Walsh PC et al, eds: *Campbell's urology,* ed 8, Philadelphia, 2002, WB Saunders.

Zaontz MR, Packer MG: Abnormalities of the external genitalia. *Pediatr Clin North Am* 44:1267, 1997.

AUTHOR: **PHILIP J. ALIOTTA, M.D., M.S.H.A.**

BASIC INFORMATION

DEFINITION

Hypothermia is a rectal temperature <35° C (95.8° F). *Accidental hypothermia* is unintentionally induced decrease in core temperature in absence of preoptic anterior hypothalamic conditions.

ICD-9CM CODES
991.6 Accidental hypothermia
780.9 Hypothermia not associated with low environmental temperature

EPIDEMIOLOGY & DEMOGRAPHICS

Hypothermia occurs most frequently in the following groups: alcoholics, learning-impaired, patients with cardiovascular, cerebrovascular, or pituitary disorders, those using sedatives or tranquilizers, and elderly patients.

PHYSICAL FINDINGS & CLINICAL PRESENTATION

- The clinical presentation varies with the severity of hypothermia. Shivering may be absent if body temperature is <33.3° C (92° F) or in patients taking phenothiazines.
- Hypothermia may masquerade as CVA, ataxia, or slurred speech, or the patient may appear comatose or clinically dead.
- Physiologic stages of hypothermia:
  1. Mild hypothermia (32.2° to 35° C [90° to 95° F]): arrhythmias, ataxia
  2. Moderate hypothermia (28° to 32.2° C [82.4° to 90° F]):
     a. Progressive decrease of level of consciousness, pulse, cardiac output, and respiration
     b. Fibrillation, dysrhythmias (increased susceptibility to ventricular tachycardia)
     c. Elimination of shivering mechanism for thermogenesis
  3. Severe hypothermia (≤28° C [82.4° F]):
     a. Absence of reflexes or response to pain
     b. Decreased cerebral blood flow, decreased CO_2
     c. Increased risk of ventricular fibrillation or asystole

ETIOLOGY

Exposure to cold temperatures for a prolonged period

DIAGNOSIS

DIFFERENTIAL DIAGNOSIS

- CVA
- Myxedema coma
- Drug intoxication
- Hypoglycemia

LABORATORY TESTS

1. Metabolic and respiratory acidosis are usually present.
   a. When blood cools, the arterial pH increases, oxygen tension (Po_2) increases, and the Pco_2 falls:
      (1) pH ↑ 0.008 U/°F (or 0.015 U/°C), ↓ in temperature.
      (2) Pao_2 ↑ 3.3%/°F, ↓ in temperature.
      (3) $Paco_2$ ↓ 2.4%/°F, ↓ in temperature.
   b. Blood gas analyzers warm the blood to 37° C, increasing the partial pressure of dissolved gases, resulting in higher oxygen and carbon dioxide levels and a lower pH than the patient's actual values. Correction of ABGs for temperature is unnecessary as a guide to therapy. The use of uncorrected values also permits reference to the standard acid-base nomograms.
2. ↓ K^+ initially, then ↑ K^+ with increasing hypothermia; extreme hyperkalemia indicates a poor prognosis.
3. Hematocrit (Hct) ↑ (caused by hemoconcentration), ↓ leukocytes, ↓ platelets (caused by splenic sequestration).

Blood viscosity, ↑ clotting time

IMAGING STUDIES

- Chest x-ray: generally not helpful; may reveal evidence of aspiration (e.g., intoxicated patient with aspiration pneumonia).
- ECG: prolonged PR, QT, and QRS segments, depressed ST segments, inverted T waves, AV block, hypothermic J waves (Osborne waves) may appear at 25° to 30° C; characterized by notching of the junction of the QRS complex and ST segments (Fig. 1-129).

TREATMENT

NONPHARMACOLOGIC THERAPY

- Treatment of hypothermia varies with the following:
  1. Degree of hypothermia
  2. Existence of concomitant diseases (e.g., cardiovascular insufficiency)
  3. Patient's age and medical condition (e.g., elderly, debilitated patients vs. young, healthy patients)
- General measures:
  1. Secure an airway before warming all unconscious patients; precede endotracheal intubation with oxygenation (if possible) to minimize the risk of arrhythmias during the procedure.
  2. Peripheral vasoconstriction may impede placement of a peripheral intravenous catheter; consider femoral venous access as an alternative to the jugular or subclavian sites to avoid ventricular stimulation.

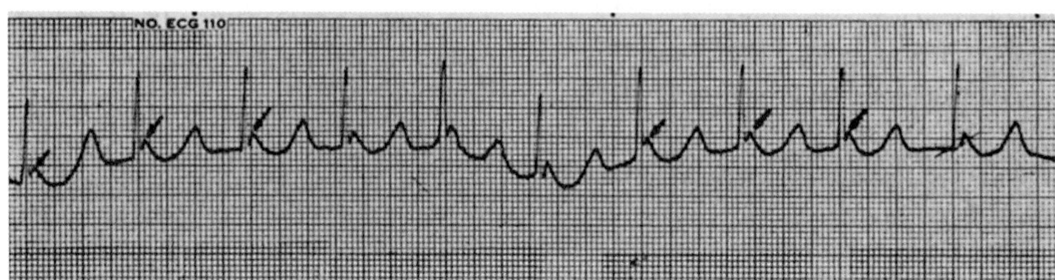

FIGURE 1-129 Osborne waves (*arrows*) in an 80-year-old man with core temperature of 86° F (30° C). These waves disappeared with rewarming. (From Morse CD, Rial WY: Emergency medicine. In Rakel RE [ed]: *Textbook of family practice*, ed 4, Philadelphia, 1990, WB Saunders.)

3. A Foley catheter should be inserted, and urinary output should be monitored and maintained above 0.5 to 1 ml/kg/hr with intravascular volume replacement.

ACUTE GENERAL Rx

- Continuous ECG monitoring of patients is recommended; ventricular arrhythmias can be treated with bretylium; lidocaine is generally ineffective, and procainamide is associated with an increased incidence of ventricular fibrillation in hypothermic patients.
- Correct severe acidosis and electrolyte abnormalities.
- Hypothyroidism, if present, should be promptly treated (refer to "Myxedema Coma").
- If clinical evidence suggests adrenal insufficiency, administer IV methylprednisolone.
- In patients unresponsive to verbal or noxious stimuli or with altered mental status, 100 mg of thiamine, 0.4 mg of naloxone, and 1 ampule of 50% dextrose may be given.
- Warm (104° to 113° F [40° to 45° C]), humidified oxygen should also be given if it is available.
- Specific treatment:

1. Mild hypothermia (rectal temperature <32.3° C [90° F]): passive external rewarming is indicated. Place the patient in a warm room (temperature >21° C [69.8° F]), and cover with insulating material after gently removing wet clothing; recommended rewarming rates vary between 0.5° and 20° C/hr but should not exceed 0.55° C/hr in elderly persons.
2. Moderate to severe hypothermia:
   a. Active core rewarming
      (1) Delivery of heat via fluids: warm GI irrigation (with saline enemas and via NG tube); IV fluids (usually D_5NS without potassium) warmed to 104° to 107.6° F (40° to 42° C), peritoneal dialysis with dialysate heated to 40.5° to 42.5° C.
      (2) Inhalation of heated humidified oxygen
   b. Active external rewarming: immersion in a bath of warm water (40° to 41° C); active external rewarming may produce shock because of excessive peripheral vasodilation. Ideal candidates are previously healthy, young patients with acute immersion hypothermia.
   c. Extracorporeal blood warming with cardiopulmonary bypass appears to be an efficacious rewarming technique in young, otherwise healthy persons.

AUTHOR: **FRED F. FERRI, M.D.**

BASIC INFORMATION

DEFINITION

Hypothyroidism is a disorder caused by the inadequate secretion of thyroid hormone.

SYNONYMS

Myxedema

ICD-9CM CODES
244 Acquired hypothyroidism
243 Congenital hypothyroidism
244.1 Surgical hypothyroidism
244.3 Iatrogenic hypothyroidism
244.8 Pituitary hypothyroidism
246.1 Sporadic goitrous hypothyroidism

EPIDEMIOLOGY & DEMOGRAPHICS

INCIDENCE/PREVALENCE: 1.5% to 2% of women and 0.2% of men

PREDOMINANT AGE: Incidence of hypothyroidism increases with age; among persons older than 60 yr, 6% of women and 2.5% of men have laboratory evidence of hypothyroidism (TSH > twice normal).

PHYSICAL FINDINGS & CLINICAL PRESENTATION

- Hypothyroid patients generally present with the following signs and symptoms: fatigue, lethargy, weakness, constipation, weight gain, cold intolerance, muscle weakness, slow speech, slow cerebration with poor memory.
- Skin: dry, coarse, thick, cool, sallow (yellow color caused by carotenemia); nonpitting edema in skin of eyelids and hands (myxedema) secondary to infiltration of subcutaneous tissues by a hydrophilic mucopolysaccharide substance.
- Hair: brittle and coarse; loss of outer one third of eyebrows.
- Facies: dulled expression, thickened tongue, thick slow-moving lips.
- Thyroid gland: may or may not be palpable (depending on the cause of the hypothyroidism).
- Heart sounds: distant, possible pericardial effusion.
- Pulse: bradycardia.
- Neurologic: delayed relaxation phase of the DTRs, cerebellar ataxia, hearing impairment, poor memory, peripheral neuropathies with paresthesia.
- Musculoskeletal: carpal tunnel syndrome, muscular stiffness, weakness.

ETIOLOGY

PRIMARY HYPOTHYROIDISM (THYROID GLAND DYSFUNCTION): The cause of >90% of the cases of hypothyroidism

- Hashimoto's thyroiditis is the most common cause of hypothyroidism after 8 yr of age
- Idiopathic myxedema (nongoitrous form of Hashimoto's thyroiditis)
- Previous treatment of hyperthyroidism (radioiodine therapy, subtotal thyroidectomy)
- Subacute thyroiditis
- Radiation therapy to the neck (usually for malignant disease)
- Iodine deficiency or excess
- Drugs (lithium, PAS, sulfonamides, phenylbutazone, amiodarone, thiourea)
- Congenital (approximately 1 case per 4000 live births)
- Prolonged treatment with iodides

SECONDARY HYPOTHYROIDISM: Pituitary dysfunction, postpartum necrosis, neoplasm, infiltrative disease causing deficiency of TSH

TERTIARY HYPOTHYROIDISM: Hypothalamic disease (granuloma, neoplasm, or irradiation causing deficiency of TRH)

TISSUE RESISTANCE TO THYROID HORMONE: Rare

DIAGNOSIS

DIFFERENTIAL DIAGNOSIS

- Depression
- Dementia from other causes
- Systemic disorders (e.g., nephrotic syndrome, CHF, amyloidosis)

LABORATORY TESTS

- Increased TSH: TSH may be normal if patient has secondary or tertiary hypothyroidism, is receiving dopamine or corticosteroids, or the level is obtained following severe illness
- Decreased free T_4
- Other common laboratory abnormalities: hyperlipidemia, hyponatremia, and anemia
- Increased antimicrosomal and antithyroglobulin antibody titers: useful when autoimmune thyroiditis is suspected as the cause of the hypothyroidism

TREATMENT

NONPHARMACOLOGIC THERAPY

Patients should be educated regarding hypothyroidism and its possible complications. Patients should also be instructed about the need for lifelong treatment and monitoring of their thyroid abnormality.

ACUTE GENERAL Rx

Start replacement therapy with levothyroxine (Synthroid, Levothroid) 25 to 100 μg/day, depending on the patient's age and the severity of the disease. The dose may be increased every 6 to 8 wk, depending on the clinical response and serum TSH level. Elderly patients and patients with coronary artery disease should be started with 12.5 to 25 μg/day (higher doses may precipitate angina). The average maintenance dose of levothyroxine is 1.7 μg/kg/day (100 to 150 μg/day in adults). The elderly may require <1 μg/kg/day, whereas children generally require higher doses (up to 3 to 4 μg/kg/day). Pregnant patients also have increased requirements. Estrogen therapy may also increase the need for thyroxine. Women with hypothyroidism should increase their levothyroxine dose by approximately 30% as soon as pregnancy is confirmed. Close monitoring of serum thyrotropin levels and adjustment of levothyroxine dose is recommended throughout pregnancy.

CHRONIC Rx

- Periodic monitoring of TSH level is an essential part of treatment. Patients should be evaluated initially with office visit and TSH levels every 6 to 8 wk until the patient is clinically euthyroid and the TSH level is normalized. The frequency of subsequent visits and TSH measurement can then be decreased to every 6 to 12 mo. Pregnant patients should be checked every trimester.
- For monitoring therapy in patients with central hypothyroidism, measurement of serum free thyroxine (free T_4 level) is appropriate and should be maintained in the upper half of the normal range.

REFERRAL

Admission to the hospital ICU is recommended in all patients with myxedema coma. Additional information on the diagnosis and treatment of this life-threatening complication of hypothyroidism is available in the topic "Myxedema Coma" in Section I.

PEARLS & CONSIDERATIONS

COMMENTS

Subclinical hypothyroidism occurs in as many as 15% of elderly patients and is characterized by an elevated serum TSH and a normal free T_4 level. Treatment is individualized. Generally, replacement therapy is recommended for all patients with serum TSH >10 mU/L and with presence of goiter or thyroid autoantibodies.

SUGGESTED READING

Alexander EK et al: Timing and magnitude of increases in levothyroxine requirements during pregnancy in women with hypothyroidism, *N Engl J Med* 351:241, 2004.

AUTHOR: **FRED F. FERRI, M.D.**

BASIC INFORMATION

DEFINITION

Idiopathic intracranial hypertension is a syndrome of increased intracranial pressure without underlying hydrocephalus or mass lesion, and with normal cerebrospinal fluid analysis.

SYNONYMS

Pseudotumor cerebri
IIH
Benign intracranial hypertension

ICD-9CM CODES
348.2 Pseudotumor cerebri

EPIDEMIOLOGY & DEMOGRAPHICS

1 case/100,000 women
19 cases/100,000 women ages 20 to 44 and more than 20% of ideal body weight
0.3-1.5 cases/100,000 men
Female:male ratio from 4.3:1 to 8:1
More than 90% of IIH patients are obese
Mean age at diagnosis is 30 years

CLINICAL PRESENTATION

Symptoms
- Headaches—generalized, throbbing, slowly progressive, worse with straining maneuvers, worse in the morning.
- Transient visual obscurations—described as a brief blurring of vision or scotomata. Lasting less than 30 sec. Frequently with Valsalva. May be monocular.
- Double vision—most often in the horizontal plane (due to pseudo-sixth nerve palsy).
- Pulsatile tinnitus—may be initial complaint.
- Photopsia—lights, sparkles in the eyes.
- Pain—mainly retro-orbital. Pain may also be located in the shoulders or neck. Could be present without a headache. May be associated with Lhermitte's sign.

Signs
- Papilledema—in virtually all cases. Bilateral, but may be asymmetric.
- Sixth nerve palsy—in approximately 10%-20% of patients.
- Reduced visual fields—enlarged physiologic blind spot, constricted visual fields.
- Loss of vision—end result of longstanding and untreated IIH.

ETIOLOGY

IIH may be explained on the basis of decreased CSF absorption and increased intracerebral blood volume.
- Decreased CSF absorption due to increased venous sinus pressure—this hypothesis is supported by direct retrograde venography studies and would explain higher incidence of IIH in patients with CHF, hypertension, and obesity.
- Increase in cerebral blood volume—supported by magnetic resonance imaging and positron emission topography, as well as the presence of edema on microscopic evaluation.

DIAGNOSIS

DIFFERENTIAL DIAGNOSIS

- The symptoms and signs of IIH are essentially those of raised intracranial pressure (ICP), and the differential diagnosis includes any condition that may be associated with raised ICP. Here we consider only those disease processes in which elevated ICP occurs in the context of normal CSF analysis and normal MRI. (Of note, venous sinus thrombosis [VST] was placed on this list despite associated MRI findings. VST should be excluded in all individuals with suspected IIH.)
- Medications—vitamin A, steroids (both use and withdrawal), oral contraceptives
- Autoimmune disorders—systemic lupus erythematosus, Behçet's disease
- Vascular disease—venous sinus thrombosis
- Other conditions—hypertension, CHF, pregnancy, obesity, uremia, obstructive sleep apnea

LABORATORY TESTS

- Cerebrospinal fluid analysis
  1. Shows elevated opening pressure
  2. Shows normal protein, glucose, and cell count
- Hypercoagulability workup if suspicion for venous sinus thrombosis

IMAGING STUDIES

- Magnetic resonance imaging of the brain to rule out underlying structural lesions
  1. "Empty sella sign" often associated with idiopathic intracranial hypertension but is not pathognomonic.
- Cerebral venography to evaluate venous flow
  1. Magnetic venography
  2. CT venography
  3. Conventional contrast venography

TREATMENT

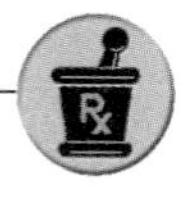

NONPHARMACOLOGIC THERAPY

- Weight loss in obese patients
- Continuous positive airway pressure—if obstructive sleep apnea is suspected

ACUTE GENERAL Rx

- Acetazolamide 250 mg to 4 g per day—reduces CSF production by inhibition of carbonic anhydrase, occasionally causing anorexia and resultant weight loss. Should be avoided in pregnant women because of possible teratogenic risk.
- Furosemide 40-120 mg per day in divided doses—apparent mechanism of action is via reduced sodium transport, leading to decreased total CSF volume.
- Topiramate 100-400 mg per day—antiepileptic medication, recently reported to be effective in treatment of IIH. Weak carbonic anhydrase inhibitor associated with weight loss as one of its primary side effects. May cause word-finding difficulties and renal stone formation.
- Serial lumbar punctures—attempted in patients with severe headaches resistant to medical therapy. Goal is to reduce spinal fluid pressure allowing for immediate reduction in headache severity. This treatment should be reserved only for most resistant cases, and should be used as a conduit to future surgical intervention.
- IIH presents a special dilemma in pregnant women. Acetazolamide has been shown teratogenic in animals and caloric restrictions are not advised in pregnancy. Symptomatic treatment of headache should be the mainstay of therapy. Recurrent lumbar punctures can be used to alleviate headache and delay the onset of visual loss.

CHRONIC Rx

Surgical intervention is indicated in cases of treatment failure and progressive visual loss.

- Optic nerve fenestration—preferred for patients with visual loss and easily controlled headaches. Proposed mechanism is decompression of the optic nerve. Highly effective; however, has been associated with significant number of failure rates.
- CSF shunting—neurosurgical procedure. Performed in patients with significant visual deterioration and difficult-to-control headaches. Provides rapid improvement in symptoms; however, reported to have significant rates of shunt revisions due to shunt malfunction.

DISPOSITION

- Idiopathic intracranial hypertension is a self-limiting disease with occasional periods of relapses. Each episode may last from 1 to several years.
- All patients with IIH should undergo MR or CT venography to rule out the possibility of VST.
- The major complication of IIH is visual loss, and treatment should be directed toward reducing intracranial pressure to prevent visual loss.

REFERRAL

- Neuro-ophthalmologist for serial evaluation of visual fields and fundus photographs
- Nutritionist for weight loss
- General neurologist for the initial workup and eventual treatment of raised intracranial pressure

PEARLS & CONSIDERATIONS

COMMENTS

- Idiopathic intracranial hypertension is a diagnosis of exclusion.
- IIH is a disease of young obese women.
- Ongoing treatment is essential to avoid progressive visual loss, which is the most significant complication of this disorder.

PREVENTION

Maintenance of ideal body weight is one of the best preventative mechanisms for avoidance of IIH. However, it does occur in patients with normal body weight. In these cases, there are no known preventable risk factors.

PATIENT/FAMILY EDUCATION

Combination of weight loss and medical therapy is highly effective in treatment of IIH. Given that most patients with IIH are often young and otherwise healthy, high success rates can be accomplished. Because IIH is a self-limiting condition, patients with IIH may expect to become both symptom- and medication-free after intracranial hypertension resolves.

SUGGESTED READINGS

Binder D et al: Idiopathic intracranial hypertension, *Neurosurgery* 54:538, 2004.

Friedman D, Jacobson D: Diagnostic criteria for idiopathic intracranial hypertension, *Neurology* 59:1492, 2002.

Mathews M, Sergott R, Savino P: Pseudotumor cerebri, *Curr Opin Ophthalmol* 14:364, 2003.

Miller N: Papilledema. In Miller N, Newman N (eds): *Clinical Neuro-Ophthalmology,* ed 5, Baltimore, 1998, Williams and Wilkins.

Wall M: Papilledema and idiopathic intracranial hypertension (pseudotumor cerebri). In Noseworthy J (ed): *Neurological Therapeutics Principles and Practice.* London and New York, 2003, Martin Dunitz.

AUTHOR: **GENNA GEKHT, M.D.**

BASIC INFORMATION

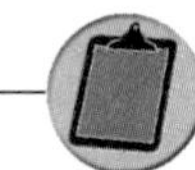

DEFINITION

Specific form of chronic fibrosing interstitial pneumonia with histopathology characteristic of usual interstitial pneumonia

SYNONYMS

Cryptogenetic fibrosing alveolitis
IPF

ICD-9CM CODES
516.3 Idiopathic pulmonary fibrosis

EPIDEMIOLOGY & DEMOGRAPHICS

- Presents in fifth and sixth decades and is more common in men than women
- 3% appear to cluster in families, but no clear evidence for a genetic basis
- No distinct geographic distribution, rural and urban, no prediction by race or ethnicity
- Cigarette smoking is strongly linked to idiopathic pulmonary fibrosis (IPF) and may be a cause (75% of patients with IPF have history of smoking)

PHYSICAL FINDINGS & CLINICAL PRESENTATION

- Initial presentation is consistent and insidious exertional dyspnea and nonproductive cough. Over many months dyspnea is the most prominent symptom
- Associated symptoms such as fever and myalgia may be present but are not common and suggest another diagnosis
- Tachypnea to compensate for stiff noncompliant lung
- Physical examination shows fine bibasilar inspiratory crackles in more than 80% of patients, with progression upward as the disease advances
- Clubbing is seen in 25% to 50% of patients
- Cyanosis, cor pulmonate, right ventricular heave, and peripheral edema may be seen
- Extrapulmonary involvement does not occur, but weight loss, malaise, and fatigue can

ETIOLOGY

- Unknown
- Numerous hypotheses, including contribution of environmental insults, such as metal and wood dust, infectious cause, chronic aspiration, or exposure to certain drugs (antidepressants)
- New research suggests little role for inflammation, abhorrent wound healing, and alveolar epithelial damage may be the major issues

DIAGNOSIS

DIFFERENTIAL DIAGNOSIS

- Sarcoidosis, drug-induced lung diseases, and connective tissue disease with similar clinical and pathologic presentations
- Other idiopathic interstitial pneumonias: desquamative interstitial pneumonia, respiratory bronchitis interstitial lung disease, acute interstitial pneumonia, nonspecific interstitial pneumonia, cryptogenic organizing pneumonia, bronchiolitis obliterans organizing pneumonia

It is very important to differentiate these from IPF pathologically because IPF responds better to treatment

- Occupational exposures (e.g., asbestos, silica) may cause pneumoconiosis that mimics IDF

WORKUP

- Almost all patients have abnormal chest radiographs at presentation with bilateral reticular opacities most prominent in the periphery and lower lobes. Peripheral honeycombing may be seen.
- High-resolution CT scan shows patchy peripheral reticular abnormalities with intralobular linear opacities, irregular septal thickening, subpleural honeycombing, and ground glass appearance.
- Pulmonary function tests show restrictive impairment with reduced vital capacity and total lung capacity. An obstructive picture only seen in smokers with IPF. Reduced DLCO.
- Laboratory abnormalities are mild and nonspecific. Mild anemia increases in ESR, LDH, CRP; low titers in ANA and RF are seen in up to 30% of patients.
- Limited role for bronchioalveolar lavage either in diagnosis or monitoring IPF. A lone increase in lymphocytes is uncommon, so if found, another diagnosis should be excluded.
- Gold standard for diagnosis is lung biopsy (open thoracotomy or video-assisted thorascopy), which shows hallmark features of a heterogeneous distribution of parenchymal fibrous against a background of mild inflammation (UIP-usual interstitial pneumonia).
- Transbronchial lung biopsies do not provide a large enough sample to make diagnosis.
- Among experienced clinicians the combination of the clinical and radiographic features are often enough to establish the diagnosis.
- Lung biopsies are often not done because of other medical problems, especially severe COPD; however, they are critical to evaluate for the potential of a more treatable disease, especially in patients with any atypical features.
- The diagnosis will be missed in one third of new-onset IPF cases despite evaluations by experts with clinical diagnosis alone.

TREATMENT

- There is no proven treatment for IPF.
- Much of the focus has been on antiinflammatory medications, especially steroids. Current thinking suggests fibrosis, not inflammation, is the major issue.
- Many studies that have evaluated treatment responses have grouped together several forms of idiopathic interstitial pneumonia under the IPF label.
- A trial of corticosteroids at 0.5 mg/kg × 4 wk, 0.25 mg/kg × 8 wk, then tapered down combined with azathioprine or cyclophosphamide for 3 to 6 mo is reasonable. 10% to 30% of patients may respond.
- Treatment is continued up to 18 months if the patient improves or is stable. Long-term treatment only with objective evidence of continued improvement or stabilization.
- Subjective improvement only may be a result of the mood-enhancing effects of the steroids.
- Complications of steroid use, especially infections, may be quite severe.
- Single lung transplantation should be considered, especially in younger, healthier patients.
- Treatment options include cytotoxic agents, antifibrotic agents (colchicine, pirfenidone, interferon gamma 16) alone or in combination with steroids.

PEARLS & CONSIDERATIONS

- Spontaneous remissions do not occur
- The course is progressive with increasing fibrosis
- Mean survival after the diagnosis of biopsy-confirmed IPF is 3 yr
- 40% of patients die of respiratory failure
- The incidence of bronchiogenic carcinoma is increased

SUGGESTED READINGS

Am J Med 110(4), 2002.

ATS Guidelines IPF: Diagnosis and Treatment, July 1999.

Chest 125(5), 2004.

Gross TJ, Hunninghake GW: Idiopathic pulmonary fibrosis, *N Engl J Med* 345(7):517, 2001.

AUTHOR: **LYNN BOWLBY, M.D.**

BASIC INFORMATION

DEFINITION

Immune thrombocytopenic purpura (ITP) is an autoimmune disorder characterized by a low platelet count and mucocutaneous bleeding.

SYNONYMS

ITP
Idiopathic thrombocytopenic purpura
Autoimmune thrombocytopenic purpura

ICD-9CM CODES
287.3 Idiopathic thrombocytopenic purpura (ITP)

EPIDEMIOLOGY & DEMOGRAPHICS

PREVALENCE: 5 to 10 cases/100,000 persons
INCIDENCE: 100 cases/1 million persons/yr
PREDOMINANT SEX: 72% of patients >10 yr old are female; in children, males = females
PREDOMINANT AGE: Children age 2 to 4 yr and young women (70% are <40 yr old)

PHYSICAL FINDINGS & CLINICAL PRESENTATION

The presentation of ITP is different in children and adults.

- Children generally present with sudden onset of bruising and petechiae from severe thrombocytopenia.
- In adults the presentation is insidious; a history of prolonged purpura may be present; many patients are diagnosed incidentally on the basis of automated laboratories that now routinely include platelet counts.
- The physical examination may be entirely normal.
- Patients with severe thrombocytopenia may have petechiae, purpura, epistaxis, or heme-positive stool from GI bleeding.
- Splenomegaly is unusual; its presence should alert to the possibility of other etiologies of thrombocytopenia.
- The presence of dysmorphic features (skeletal anomalies, auditory abnormalities) may indicate a congenital disorder as the etiology of the thrombocytopenia.

ETIOLOGY

Increased platelet destruction caused by autoantibodies to platelet-membrane antigens

DIAGNOSIS

DIFFERENTIAL DIAGNOSIS

- Falsely low platelet count (resulting from EDTA-dependent or cold-dependent agglutinins)
- Viral infections (e.g., HIV, mononucleosis, rubella)
- Drug-induced (e.g., heparin, quinidine, sulfonamides)
- Hypersplenism resulting from liver disease
- Myelodysplastic and lymphoproliferative disorders
- Pregnancy, hypothyroidism
- SLE, TTP, hemolytic-uremic syndrome
- Congenital thrombocytopenias (e.g., Fanconi's syndrome, May-Hegglin anomaly, Bernard-Soulier syndrome)

LABORATORY TESTS

- CBC, platelet count, and peripheral smear: platelets are decreased but are normal in size or may appear larger than normal. RBCs and WBCs have a normal morphology.
- Additional tests may be ordered to exclude other etiologies of the thrombocytopenia when clinically indicated (e.g., HIV, ANA, TSH, liver enzymes, bone marrow examination).
- The direct assay for the measurement of platelet-bound antibodies has an estimated positive predictive value of 80% to 83%. A negative test cannot be used to rule out the diagnosis.

IMAGING STUDIES

CT scan of abdomen in patients with splenomegaly to exclude other disorders causing thrombocytopenia

TREATMENT

NONPHARMACOLOGIC THERAPY

- Minimize activity to prevent injury or bruising (e.g., contact sports should be avoided).
- Avoid medications that increase the risk of bleeding (e.g., aspirin and other NSAIDs).

ACUTE GENERAL Rx

- Treatment varies with the platelet count, patient's age, and bleeding status.
- Observation and frequent monitoring of platelet count are needed in asymptomatic patients with platelet counts $>30,000/mm^3$.
- Methylprednisolone 30 mg/kg/day IV infused over a period of 20 to 30 min (max dose of 1 g/day for 2 or 3 days) plus IV immunoglobulin (1 g/kg/day for 2 or 3 days) and infusion of platelets should be given to patients with neurologic symptoms, internal bleeding, or those undergoing emergency surgery.
- Prednisone 1 to 2 mg/kg qd, continued until the platelet count is normalized then slowly tapered off, is indicated in adults with platelet counts $<20,000/mm^3$ and those who have counts $<50,000/mm^3$ and significant mucous membrane bleeding. Response rates range from 50% to 75%, and most responses occur within the first 3 wk.
- High-dose immunoglobulins (IgG 0.4 g/kg/day IV, infused on 3 to 5 consecutive days) or high-dose parenteral glucocorticoids (methylprednisolone 30 mg/kg/day) can be used in children with platelet count $<20,000/mm^3$ and significant bleeding or adults with severe thrombocytopenia or bleeding.
- Rituximab, a monoclonal antibody directed against the CD_{20} antigen, has been reported useful for ITP patients resistant to conventional treatment and may help prevent serious or fatal bleeding.
- Platelet transfusion is needed only in case of life-threatening hemorrhage.
- Splenectomy should be considered in adults with platelet count $<30,000/mm^3$ after 6 wk of medical treatment or after 6 mo if more than 10 to 20 mg of prednisone per day is required to maintain a platelet count $>30,000/mm^3$. In children, splenectomy is generally reserved for persistent thrombocytopenia (>1 yr) and clinically significant bleeding. Appropriate immunizations (pneumococcal vaccine in adults and children, *H. influenzae* vaccine, meningococcal vaccine in children) should be administered before splenectomy.

CHRONIC Rx

Frequent monitoring of platelet count and symptom review in patients with chronic ITP to detect and prevent significant bleeding. A regimen of cyclophosphamide, vincristine, and prednisone (CVP) has been partially effective in chronic ITP.

DISPOSITION

- More than 80% of children have a complete remission within a few weeks.
- In adults, the course of the disease is chronic and only 5% of adults have spontaneous remission.
- The principal cause of death from ITP is intracranial hemorrhage (1% of children, 5% of adults).

SUGGESTED READINGS

Cheng Y et al: Initial treatment of immune thrombocytopenic purpura with high dose dexamethasone, *N Engl J Med* 349:831, 2003.

Cines DB, Blanchette VS: Immune thrombocytopenic purpura, *N Engl J Med* 346:995, 2002.

Shanafelt TD et al: Rituximab for immune cytopenia in adults: idiopathic thrombocytopenic purpura, autoimmune hemolytic anemia, and Evans syndrome, *Mayo Clin Proc* 78:1340, 2003.

Zheng X et al: Remission of chronic TTP after treatment with cyclophosphamide and rituximab, *Ann Intern Med* 138:105, 2003.

AUTHOR: **FRED F. FERRI, M.D.**

BASIC INFORMATION

DEFINITION

Impetigo is a superficial skin infection generally secondary to *Staphylococcus aureus* and/or *Streptococcus* spp.
Common presentations are bullous impetigo (generally secondary to staphylococcal disease) and nonbullous impetigo (secondary to streptococcal infection and possible staphylococcal infection); the bullous form is caused by an epidermolytic toxin produced at the site of infection.

SYNONYMS

Impetigo vulgaris
Pyoderma

ICD-9CM CODES
684 Impetigo

EPIDEMIOLOGY & DEMOGRAPHICS

- Bullous impetigo is most common in infants and children. The nonbullous form is most common in children ages 2 to 5 yr with poor hygiene in warm climates.
- The overall incidence of acute nephritis with impetigo varies between 2% and 5%.

PHYSICAL FINDINGS & CLINICAL PRESENTATION

- Multiple lesions with golden yellow crusts and weeping areas often found on the skin around the nose, mouth, and limbs (nonbullous impetigo) (Fig. 1-130).
- Presence of vesicles that enlarge rapidly to form bullae with contents that vary from clear to cloudy; there is subsequent collapse of the center of the bullae; the peripheral areas may retain fluid, and a honey-colored crust may appear in the center; as the lesions enlarge and become contiguous with the others, a scaling border replaces the fluid-filled rim (bullous impetigo); there is minimal erythema surrounding the lesions.
- Regional lymphadenopathy is most common with nonbullous impetigo.
- Constitutional symptoms are generally absent.

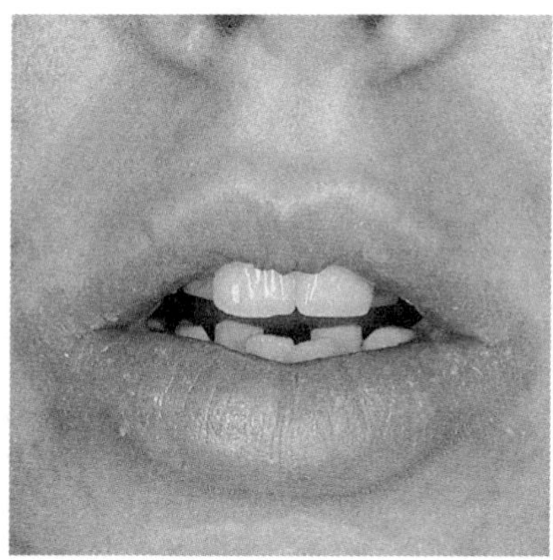

FIGURE 1-130 Impetigo. Serum and crust at the angle of the mouth is a common presentation for impetigo. (From Habif TB: *Clinical dermatology: a color guide to diagnosis and therapy,* ed 3, St Louis, 1996, Mosby.)

ETIOLOGY

- *S. aureus* coagulase positive is the dominant microorganism.
- *S. pyogenes* (group A β-hemolytic streptococci): M-T serotypes of this organism associated with acute nephritis are 2, 49, 55, 57, and 60.

DIAGNOSIS

DIFFERENTIAL DIAGNOSIS

- Acute allergic contact dermatitis
- Herpes simplex infection
- Ecthyma
- Folliculitis
- Eczema
- Insect bites
- Scabies
- Tinea corporis
- Pemphigus vulgaris and bullous pemphigoid
- Chickenpox

WORKUP

Diagnosis is clinical.

LABORATORY TESTS

- Generally not necessary
- Gram stain and C&S to confirm the diagnosis when the clinical presentation is unclear
- Sedimentation rate parallel to activity of the disease
- Increased anti-DNAse B and antihyaluronidase
- Urinalysis revealing hematuria with erythrocyte casts and proteinuria in patients with acute nephritis (most frequently occurring in children between 2 and 4 yr of age in the southern part of the U.S.)

TREATMENT

NONPHARMACOLOGIC THERAPY

Remove crusts by soaking with wet cloth compresses (crusts block the penetration of antibacterial creams).

GENERAL Rx

- Application of 2% mupirocin ointment (Bactroban) tid for 10 days to the affected area or until all lesions have cleared.
- Oral antibiotics are used in severe cases: commonly used agents are dicloxacillin 250 mg qid for 7 to 10 days, cephalexin 250 mg qid for 7 to 10 days, or azithromycin 500 mg on day 1, 250 mg on days 2 through 5.
- Impetigo can be prevented by prompt application of mupirocin or triple antibiotic ointment (bacitracin, Polysporin, and neomycin) to sites of skin trauma.
- Patients who are carriers of *S. aureus* in their nares should be treated with mupirocin ointment applied to their nares bid for 5 days.
- Fingernails should be kept short, and patients should be advised not to scratch any lesions to avoid spread of infection.

DISPOSITION

Most cases of impetigo resolve promptly with appropriate treatment. Both bullous and nonbullous forms of impetigo heal without scarring.

REFERRAL

Nephrology referral in patients with acute nephritis

PEARLS & CONSIDERATIONS

COMMENTS

- Patients should be instructed on use of antibacterial soaps and avoidance of sharing of towels and washcloths, because impetigo is extremely contagious.
- Children attending day care should be removed until 48 to 72 hr after initiation of antibiotic treatment.

AUTHOR: **FRED F. FERRI, M.D.**

BASIC INFORMATION

DEFINITION

Inappropriate secretion of antidiuretic hormone (SIADH) is a syndrome characterized by excessive secretion of ADH in absence of normal osmotic or physiologic stimuli (increased serum osmolarity, decreased plasma volume, hypotension).

SYNONYMS

SIADH

ICD-9CM CODES
276.9 Inappropriate secretion of antidiuretic hormone

EPIDEMIOLOGY & DEMOGRAPHICS

Nearly 50% of hyponatremia detected in the hospital setting is caused by SIADH.

PHYSICAL FINDINGS & CLINICAL PRESENTATION

- The patient is generally normovolemic or slightly hypervolemic; edema is absent.
- Delirium, lethargy, and seizures may be present if the hyponatremia is severe or of rapid onset.
- Manifestations of the underlying disease may be evident (e.g., fever from an infectious process or headaches and visual field defects from an intracranial mass).
- Diminished reflexes and extensor plantar responses may occur with severe hyponatremia.

ETIOLOGY

- Neoplasm: lung, duodenum, pancreas, brain, thymus, bladder, prostate, mesothelioma, lymphoma, Ewing's sarcoma
- Pulmonary disorders: pneumonia, TB, bronchiectasis, emphysema, status asthmaticus
- Intracranial pathology: trauma, neoplasms, infections (meningitis, encephalitis, brain abscess), hemorrhage, hydrocephalus
- Postoperative period: surgical stress, ventilators with positive pressure, anesthetic agents
- Drugs: chlorpropamide, thiazide diuretics, vasopressin, desmopressin, oxytocin, chemotherapeutic agents (vincristine, vinblastine, cyclophosphamide), carbamazepine, phenothiazines, MAO inhibitors, tricyclic antidepressants, narcotics, nicotine, clofibrate, haloperidol, SSRIs
- Other: acute intermittent porphyria, Guillain-Barré syndrome, myxedema, psychosis, delirium tremens, ACTH deficiency (hypopituitarism)

DIAGNOSIS

DIFFERENTIAL DIAGNOSIS

- Hyponatremia associated with hypervolemia (CHF, cirrhosis, nephrotic syndrome)
- Factitious hyponatremia (hyperglycemia, abnormal proteins, hyperlipidemia)
- Hypovolemia associated with hypovolemia (e.g., burns, GI fluid loss)

WORKUP

- Demonstration through laboratory evaluation (see Laboratory Tests) of excessive secretion of ADH in absence of appropriate osmotic or physiologic stimuli
- Demonstration of normal thyroid, adrenal, and cardiac function
- No recent or concurrent use of diuretics

LABORATORY TESTS

- Hyponatremia
- Urinary osmolarity > serum osmolarity
- Urinary sodium usually >30 mEq/L
- Normal BUN, creatinine (indicative of normal renal function and absence of dehydration)
- Decreased uric acid

IMAGING STUDIES

Chest x-ray to rule out neoplasm or infectious process

TREATMENT

NONPHARMACOLOGIC THERAPY

Fluid restriction to 500 to 800 ml/day

ACUTE GENERAL Rx

In emergency situations (seizures, coma) SIADH can be treated with combination of hypertonic saline solution (slow infusion of 250 ml of 3% NaCl) and furosemide; this increases the serum sodium by causing diuresis of urine that is more dilute than plasma; the rapidity of correction varies depending on the degree of hyponatremia and if the hyponatremia is acute or chronic; generally the serum sodium should be corrected only halfway to normal in the initial 24 hr and serum sodium should be increased by <0.5 mEq/L/hr.

CHRONIC Rx

- Depending on the underlying etiology, fluid restriction may be needed indefinitely. Monthly monitoring of electrolytes is recommended in patients with chronic SIADH.
- Demeclocycline (Declomycin) 300 to 600 mg PO bid may be useful in patients with chronic SIADH (e.g., secondary to neoplasm), but use with caution in patients with hepatic disease; its side effects include nephrogenic DI and photosensitivity. This medication is also very expensive.

DISPOSITION

- Prognosis varies depending on the cause. Generally prognosis is benign when SIADH is caused by an infectious process.
- Morbidity and mortality are high (>40%) when serum sodium concentration is <110 mEq/L.

REFERRAL

Hospital admission depending on severity of symptoms and degree of hyponatremia

PEARLS & CONSIDERATIONS

COMMENTS

- Use of hypertonic (3%) saline is contraindicated in patients with CHF, nephrotic syndrome, or cirrhosis.
- Too rapid correction of hyponatremia can cause demyelination and permanent CNS damage.

AUTHOR: **FRED F. FERRI, M.D.**

BASIC INFORMATION

DEFINITION

Inclusion body myositis (IBM) is an inflammatory myopathy with distinctive clinical and pathologic features.

ICD-9CM CODES
710.8 Other specified diffuse diseases of connective tissue

EPIDEMIOLOGY & DEMOGRAPHICS

INCIDENCE (IN U.S.): It is the third major form of idiopathic inflammatory myopathy (after polymyositis and dermatomyositis). It accounts for 15%-28% of inflammatory myopathies in the U.S. and Canada.
PREVALENCE (IN U.S.): 4-9 cases/ 1,000,000 persons
PREDOMINANT SEX: Male > female (3:1); more common in white than black population
PREDOMINANT AGE: >50 years of age; rare before the age of 30
PEAK INCIDENCE: Fifth decade
GENETICS:
- Two forms:
  1. Acquired sporadic: most cases (discussed here).
  2. Familial: differs from the acquired form by the age of onset (early childhood), distribution of muscle weakness (spares quadriceps), and biopsy findings (lack of inflammation and less amyloid deposits). It is linked to chromosome 9 and can be expressed in an autosomal dominant or recessive fashion.
- HLA types: DR_1*0301, DR_3*0101 (or DR_3*0202) and DQ_1*0201

PHYSICAL FINDINGS & CLINICAL PRESENTATION

- Insidious onset (>6 yr from the onset of symptoms to diagnosis).
- Steadily progressive asymmetric and painless muscle weakness and atrophy of the finger or wrist flexors (commonly the flexor pollicis longus), knee extensor (quadriceps), and foot dorsiflexion. Over time weakness spreads to involve other muscles.
- A common complaint is difficulty with ambulation and frequent falls (due to buckling of knees caused by knee extensor weakness).
- Fatigue and reduced tolerance of exertion are common.
- Dysphagia (up to 60%).
- Classic appearance is a scooped-out medial aspect of forearms and thin, atrophic quadriceps muscles.
- Facial and neck weakness can be seen.
- Early loss of patellar reflexes.
- Up to 15% of patients have other autoimmune diseases (systemic lupus erythematosus, Sjögren syndrome, scleroderma, interstitial pneumonitis, psoriasis, and sarcoidosis), diabetes, and mild polyneuropathy.
- Cardiovascular abnormalities have been documented in some reports.
- There is no documented association with malignancies.
- Diagnostic criteria of either definite or possible IBM based on muscle biopsy, clinical features, and laboratory findings have been published.

ETIOLOGY

- Not well understood
- Cell-mediated immune response: CD8 cytotoxic T-cell endomysial infiltration
- Abnormal protein processing: accumulation of Alzheimer-type proteins (prion protein, β amyloid protein, neuronal microtubule-associated protein, amyloid precursor protein, α-1-antichymotrypsin, phosphorylated tau, apolipoprotein E, ubiquitin, and presenilin) within the degenerating muscle fibers
- Deletion of mitochondrial DNA
- Nitric oxide induced oxidative stress
- Possible viral pathogenesis: filamentous inclusions resembling myxovirus nucleocapsids

DIAGNOSIS

DIFFERENTIAL DIAGNOSIS

- Amyotrophic lateral sclerosis
- Polymyositis
- Oculopharyngeal dystrophy
- Chronic atrophic sarcoid myopathy
- Myasthenia gravis
- Acid maltase deficiency
- Chronic inflammatory demyelinating polyradiculoneuropathy

WORKUP

- Good history and physical examination demonstrating the characteristic pattern of weakness in a male who is older than age 50.
- Electromyography: active myopathic changes (fibrillation potentials, positive sharp waves and short duration, low-amplitude, polyphasic motor unit action potentials). Mixed myopathic and neurogenic changes can also be seen.
- Nerve conduction studies: occasionally sensory nerve conduction studies are abnormal (if there is an associated neuropathy).
- Muscle biopsy: small angular atrophic and denervated fibers. CD8 cytotoxic T-cell endomysial infiltration. Intracytoplasmic rimmed vacuoles and cytoplasmic tubofilamentous inclusions on electromicroscopic examination of the affected muscle fiber.

LABORATORY TESTS

- CPK (normal to increased 3-5 times normal)
- Thyroid function test to rule out thyroid disease
- Antinuclear antigen (ANA), rheumatoid factor (RF), double-stranded DNA (ds-DNA), erythrocyte sedimentation rate (ESR), scl-70, anti-Ro, and anti-La to rule out other autoimmune diseases
- Standard serum studies (hemogram and electrolytes)

TREATMENT

NONPHARMACOLOGIC THERAPY

- Exercise therapy: isotonic training program of the weak muscles
- Nutritional assessment if dysphagia is present
- Braces/orthotics for weakness of tibialis anterior and/or quadriceps
- Routine follow-up visits

GENERAL Rx

- Resistant to treatment.
- Corticosteroids, cyclophosphamide, chlorambucil, azathioprine, cyclosporine, methotrexate, and IVIG have been used but without evidence of benefit.
- IVIG might provide some benefit for patients with dysphagia (Cherin P et al).
- β-Interferon has been used but further studies are needed (Chabot S et al, Toepfer M et al).
- Oxandrolone (a synthetic anabolic steroid) use resulted in muscle strength improvement but further studies are needed (Rutkove SB et al).
- Several months' trial of prednisone (0.6 mg/kg) is usually recommended (Lotz et al).
- Patients should be given a trial of immunosuppressive therapy if a connective tissue disease coexists.

DISPOSITION

- The progression of the disease is very slow.

- The rate of decline in strength (based on handheld myometry or manual muscle testing) is 0.66%-1.4% per mo.
- The rate of functional decline from the onset of symptoms to use of a walker varies depending on the age of onset of symptoms (17 yr and 3.2 yr for age of onset 40-49 and 70-79, respectively).
- Periods of stabilization (3-6 mo) can be seen in 25%-50% of patients.

REFERRAL

- Surgical evaluation for muscle biopsy
- A neurologist or a neuromuscular specialist

PEARLS & CONSIDERATIONS

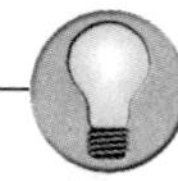

COMMENTS

- Risk of falls should be assessed by a physical therapist.
- Quantitative measures of muscle strength (myometry) should be used to assess response to treatment and disease activity.

SUGGESTED READINGS

Chabot S, Williams G, Yong VW: Microglial production of TNF-alpha is induced by activated T lymphocytes: involvement of VLA-4 and inhibition by interferon beta-1b, *J Clin Invest* 100:604, 1997.

Cherin P et al: Intravenous immunoglobulin for dysphagia of inclusion body myositis, *Neurology* 58:326, 2002.

Katirji B et al: *Neuromuscular Disorders in Clinical Practice.* Boston, 2002, Butterworth-Heinemann.

Lotz BP et al: Inclusion body myositis: observation in 40 patients, *Brain* 112:727, 1989.

Rutkove SB et al: A pilot randomized trial of oxandrolone in inclusion body myositis, *Neurology* 58:1081, 2002.

Tawil R, Griggs RC: Inclusion body myositis, *Curr Opin Rheumatol* 14:653, 2002.

Toepfer M et al: Expression of chemokines in normal muscle and inflammatory myopathies, *Neurology* 50:A413, 1998.

AUTHOR: **MUSTAFA A. HAMMAD, M.D.**

BASIC INFORMATION

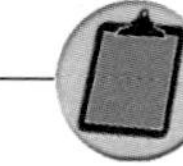

DEFINITION

Incontinence is the involuntary loss of urine.

ICD-9CM CODES
788.3 Incontinence
625.6 Stress incontinence
788.33 Mixed stress and urge incontinence
788.32 Male incontinence
788.39 Neurogenic incontinence
307.6 Nonorganic origin

EPIDEMIOLOGY & DEMOGRAPHICS

INCIDENCE AND PREVALENCE: In the general population between the ages of 15 and 64 yr, 1.5% to 5% of men and 10% to 25% of women will suffer from incontinence. In the nursing home population, 50% of the population suffers some degree of incontinence. Nearly 20% of children through the midteenage years have episodes of urinary incontinence.

CLINICAL, PSYCHOLOGIC, & SOCIAL IMPACT

Less than 50% of the individuals with incontinence living in the community consult health care providers, preferring to "suffer silently," turning to "home remedies," commercially available absorbent materials, and supportive aids. As their condition worsens, they become depressed, sacrifice their independence, suffer from recurrent urinary tract infection and its sequelae, limit their social interaction, refrain from sexual intimacy, and become homebound. In terms of costs, for all ages living in the community, it is estimated that $7 billion is spent for incontinence annually.

MAJOR TYPES OF INCONTINENCE

TRANSIENT INCONTINENCE: Incontinence occurring as a result or reaction to an acute medical problem affecting the lower urinary tract. Many of these problems can be reversed with treatment of the underlying problem.

URGE INCONTINENCE: Involuntary loss of urine associated with an abrupt and strong desire to void. It is usually associated with involuntary detrusor contractions on urodynamic investigation. In *neurologically impaired patients,* the involuntary detrusor contraction is referred to as *detrusor hyperreflexia*. In *neurologically normal patients* the involuntary contraction is called *detrusor instability*.

STRESS INCONTINENCE: The involuntary loss of urine with physical activities that increase abdominal pressure in the absence of a detrusor contraction or an overdistended bladder. Classification of stress incontinence:

Type 0: Complaint of incontinence without demonstration of leakage

Type I: Incontinence in response to stress but little descent of the bladder neck and urethra

Type II: Incontinence in response to stress with >2 cm descent of the bladder neck and urethra

Type III: Bladder neck and urethra wide open without bladder contraction; intrinsic sphincter deficiency; and denervation of the urethra. The most common causes: urethral hypermobility and displacement of the bladder neck with exertion, intrinsic sphincter deficiency from failed antiincontinence surgery, prostatectomy, radiation, cord lesions, epispadias, or myelomeningocele.

OVERFLOW INCONTINENCE: Loss of urine resulting from overdistention of the bladder with resultant "overflow" or "spilling" of the urine. Causes: hypotonic-to-atonic bladder resulting from drug effect, fecal impaction, or neurologic conditions such as diabetes, spinal cord injury, surgery, vitamin B_{12} deficiency. It is also caused by obstruction at the bladder neck and urethra. In this situation, prostatism, prostatic cancer, urethral stenosis, antiincontinence surgery, pelvic prolapse, and detrusor-sphincter dyssynergia cause the incontinence.

FUNCTIONAL INCONTINENCE: Involuntary loss of urine resulting from chronic impairments of physical and/or cognitive functioning. This is a diagnosis of exclusion. The condition can sometimes be improved or cured by improving the patient's functional status, treating comorbidities, changing medications, reducing environmental barriers, etc.

MIXED STRESS AND URGE INCONTINENCE

SENSORY URGENCY INCONTINENCE: Involuntary loss of urine as a result of decreased bladder compliance and increased intravesical pressures accompanied by severe urgency and bladder hypersensitivity without detrusor overactivity. This is seen with radiation cystitis, interstitial cystitis, eosinophilic cystitis, myelomeningocele, and radical pelvic surgery. Nephropathy can occur as a complication of this vesicoureteral reflux.

SPHINCTERIC INCONTINENCE:

Urethral Hypermobility: The basic abnormality is a weakness of pelvic floor support. Because of this weakness, during increases in abdominal pressure there is rotational descent of the vesical neck and proximal urethra. If the urethra opens concomitantly, stress urinary incontinence ensues. Urethral hypermobility is often present in women who are not incontinent. Its mere presence is not sufficient evidence to make the diagnosis of sphincteric abnormality unless incontinence is shown.

Intrinsic Sphincter Deficiency: There is an intrinsic malfunction of the sphincter itself. It is characterized by an open vesical neck at rest and a low leak point pressure (<65 cm water). Urethral hypermobility and intrinsic sphincter deficiency may coexist in the same patient. Causes of intrinsic sphincter deficiency are previous pelvic surgery, antiincontinence surgery, urethral diverticulectomy, radical hysterectomy, abdominoperineal resection of the rectum, urethrotomy, Y-V plasty of the vesical neck, myelodysplasia, anterior spinal artery syndrome, lumbo-sacral disease, aging, and hyperestrogenism.

DIAGNOSIS

HISTORY

- History of present illness, psychosocial factors, congenital disorders, access issues for the physically challenged, neurologic disorders, and disorders pertinent to the urologic tract
- Review of prescription and nonprescription medications
- Voiding diary to assess total voided volume, frequency of micturition, mean volume voided, largest single volume, diurnal distribution, nature and severity of incontinence

WORKUP

- Physical examination including general examination, gait of the patient (neuromuscular deficits), estrogen status, vaginal examination to include the periurethral region, evaluation for cystocele, rectocele, and enterocele
- Pelvic floor strength assessment
- Rectal examination to assess sphincter tone and bulbocavernosus reflex
- Neurologic examination
- Postvoid residual check using bladder scan or catheter

LABORATORY TESTS

Urinalysis, urine culture, urine cytology, BUN, and creatinine

IMAGING STUDIES

- KUB to assess bony skeleton
- IVP to rule out upper tract abnormalities, developmental anomalies, bladder configuration, and fistula
- Renal ultrasound if dye study is contraindicated

SPECIALIZED STUDIES

Simple cystometrogram, complex urodynamics including leak point pressures and uroflowmetry, endoscopic evaluation, and cystogram

TREATMENT

TRANSIENT INCONTINENCE

Treatment of underlying medical conditions and behavioral therapy to include habit training and timed voiding

URGE INCONTINENCE

Bladder relaxants (i.e., tolterodine [Detrol], oxybutynin [Ditropan], imipramine), trospium chloride, estrogen, biofeedback, Kegel exercises, and surgical removal of obstructing or other pathologic lesions

STRESS INCONTINENCE

- Pelvic floor exercises, Kegel exercises, α-adrenergic agonists (i.e., ephedrine), estrogen, biofeedback

CYSTOURETHROPEXY: Marshall-Marchetti-Krantz procedure, Burch procedure, Raz procedure, Stamey-Raz procedure, Gittes procedure, in situ transvaginal sling, pubovaginal sling with autologous or cadaver graft, laparoscopic Burch procedure, laparoscopic sling, tension-free vaginal tape (TVT)

- For intrinsic sphincter deficiency: bulking agents (e.g., collagen), sling, and artificial sphincter

OVERFLOW INCONTINENCE

Surgical removal of any obstructing lesions, clean intermittent catheterization, and indwelling catheter

FUNCTIONAL INCONTINENCE

Behavioral training to include habit training and timed voiding, incontinence undergarments and pads, external collecting devices, and environmental manipulation

MIXED URGENCY AND STRESS INCONTINENCE

Use of measures recommended in the management of stress and urge incontinence

SENSORY URGENCY

Bladder relaxants (e.g., anticholinergics, muscle relaxants, and tricyclic antidepressants), behavior therapy to include habit training and timed voiding, cystoscopy and hydrodilation

SPHINCTERIC DEFICIENCY

Urethral bulking agents, sling procedure, artificial sphincter, mechanical clamp, and external collection devices

PEARLS & CONSIDERATIONS

COMMENTS

Other forms of incontinence:

NOCTURNAL ENURESIS: (ICD-9CM Code: 788.3) Can be caused by sphincter abnormalities and detrusor overactivity; can occur as idiopathic, neurogenic, and with outlet obstruction

POSTVOID DRIBBLE: (ICD-9CM Code: 599.2) A postsphincteric collection of urine that is seen with urethral diverticulum and can be idiopathic

EXTRAURETHRAL INCONTINENCE: Enterovesical (ICD-9CM Codes: 596.1 and 596.2), Urethral (ICD-9CM Code: 599.1), also known as fistula

CONDITIONS THAT PREDISPOSE TO SURGICAL FAILURE: Advanced age, postmenopausal state, hysterectomy, prior failed incontinence surgery, concurrent detrusor instability, abnormal perineal electromyography, pelvic radiation

SUGGESTED READINGS

Burgio UL et al: Behavioral vs. drug treatment for urge urinary incontinence in older women: a randomized controlled trial, *JAMA* 280:1995, 1998.

Holroyd-Leduc J, Straus SE: Management of urinary incontinence in women, *JAMA* 291:996, 2004.

U.S. Department of Health and Human Services, Public Health Service, Agency for Health Care Policy and Research: *Clinical practice guideline: urinary incontinence in adults,* Rockville, Md, 1996, US Department of Health and Human Services.

AUTHOR: **PHILIP J. ALIOTTA, M.D., M.S.H.A.**

BASIC INFORMATION

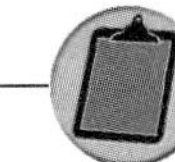

DEFINITION

Influenza is an acute febrile illness caused by infection with influenza type A or B virus.

SYNONYMS

Flu

ICD-9CM CODES
487.1 Influenza

EPIDEMIOLOGY & DEMOGRAPHICS

INCIDENCE (IN U.S.): Annual incidence of influenza-related deaths is approximately 20,000 deaths/yr
PREDOMINANT SEX: Male = female
PREDOMINANT AGE: Attack rates are higher among children than adults, although children are less prone to develop pulmonary complications
PEAK INCIDENCE: Winter outbreaks lasting 5 to 6 wk

PHYSICAL FINDINGS & CLINICAL PRESENTATION

- "Classic flu" is characterized by abrupt onset of fever, headache, myalgias, anorexia, and malaise after a 1- to 2-day incubation period.
- Clinical syndromes are similar to those produced by other respiratory viruses, including pharyngitis, common colds, tracheobronchitis, bronchiolitis, croup.
- Respiratory symptoms such as cough, sore throat, and nasal discharge are usually present at the onset of illness, but systemic symptoms predominate.
- Elderly patients may experience fever, weakness, and confusion without any respiratory complaints.
- Acute deterioration to status asthmaticus may occur in patients with asthma.
- Influenza pneumonia: rapidly progressive cough, dyspnea, and cyanosis may occur after typical flu onset.

ETIOLOGY

- Variation in the surface antigens of the influenza virus, hemagglutinin (HA) and neuraminidase (NA), leading to infection with variants to which resistance is inadequate in the population at risk
- Transmitted by small-particle aerosols and deposited on the respiratory tract epithelium

DIAGNOSIS

DIFFERENTIAL DIAGNOSIS

- Respiratory syncytial virus, adenovirus, parainfluenza virus infection
- Secondary bacterial pneumonia or mixed bacterial-viral pneumonia

WORKUP

- Virus isolation from nasal or throat swab or sputum specimens is the most rapid diagnostic method in the setting of acute illness.
- Specimens are placed into virus transport medium and processed by a reference laboratory.
- For serologic diagnosis:
  1. Paired serum specimens, acute and convalescent, the latter obtained 10 to 20 days later
  2. Fourfold rises or falls in the titer of antibodies (various techniques) considered diagnostic of recent infection

LABORATORY TESTS

Septic syndrome presentation: CBC, ABG analysis, blood cultures

IMAGING STUDIES

- Chest x-ray examination to demonstrate findings of viral pneumonia: peribronchial and patchy interstitial infiltrates in multiple lobes with atelectasis
- Possible progression to diffuse interstitial pneumonitis

TREATMENT

NONPHARMACOLOGIC THERAPY

- Bed rest
- Hydration

ACUTE GENERAL Rx

- Supportive care: antipyretics—*Avoid use of aspirin in children because of the association with Reye's syndrome*
- Antibiotics if bacterial pneumonia is proven or suspected
- Amantadine (100 mg PO bid for children >10 yr and adults <65 yr; once daily in patients >65 yr) and rimantadine (same dose schedule as amantadine)
  1. Further dose adjustments needed with renal insufficiency
  2. Fewer CNS side effects with rimantadine
- Neuraminidase inhibitors block release of virions from infected cells, resulting in shortened duration of symptoms and decrease in complications; effective against both influenza A and B
  1. Zanamivir, administered via inhaler, 10 mg bid
  2. Oseltamivir, administered orally
- Placebo-controlled studies have suggested that antiviral therapy with any of the above mentioned agents must be initiated within 1 to 2 days of the onset of symptoms and reduces the duration of illness by approximately 1 day

DISPOSITION

Patients are hospitalized if signs of pneumonia are present.

REFERRAL

Infectious disease and/or pulmonary consultation when influenza pneumonia is suspected

PEARLS & CONSIDERATIONS

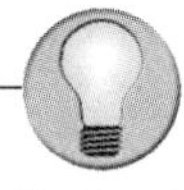

COMMENTS

- Prevention of influenza in patients at high risk is an important goal of primary care.
- Vaccines reduce the risk of infection and the severity of illness.
  1. Antigenic composition of the vaccine is updated annually.
  2. Vaccination should be given at the start of the flu season (October) for the following groups:
     a. Adults ≥65 yr
     b. Adults and children with chronic cardiac or pulmonary disease, including asthma
     c. Adults and children with illness requiring frequent follow-up (e.g., hemoglobinopathies, diabetes mellitus)
     d. Children receiving long-term aspirin therapy
     e. Immunocompromised patients
     f. Household contacts of persons in the previous groups
     g. Health-care workers
  3. Only contraindication to vaccination is hypersensitivity to hen's eggs.
  4. Special efforts should be made to vaccinate high-risk patients <65 yr, only 10% to 15% of whom are vaccinated each year.

- Chemoprophylaxis:
  1. Amantadine and rimantadine approved for prophylaxis against influenza A; they are ineffective against influenza B
  2. Consider:
     a. For high-risk patients in whom vaccination is contraindicated
     b. When the available vaccine is known not to include the circulating strain
     c. To provide added protection to immunosuppressed patients likely to have a diminished response to vaccination
     d. In the setting of an outbreak, when immediate protection of unvaccinated or recently vaccinated patients is desired
  3. Give for 2 wk in the case of late vaccination and for the duration of the flu season in all other patients

SUGGESTED READINGS

Colgan R et al: Antiviral drugs in the immunocompetent host: part II. Treatment of influenza and respiratory syncytial virus infections, *Am Fam Physician* 67(4):763, 2003.

Montalto NJ: An office-based approach to influenza: clinical diagnosis and laboratory testing, *Am Fam Physician* 67(1):111, 2003.

AUTHOR: **CLAUDIA L. DADE, M.D.**

Insemination, Therapeutic (Frozen Donor Semen)

BASIC INFORMATION

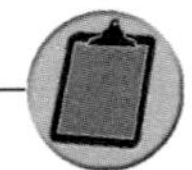

DEFINITION

Insemination is a therapeutic intervention designed to overcome defects preventing achieving proper concentration of functional sperm cells in the vicinity of the egg.

SYNONYMS

Artificial insemination

ICD-9CM CODES
606.0 Irreversible azoospermia
Husband's carrier status for genetic disease such as:
- 303.1 Tay-Sachs
- 286.0 Hemophilia
- 333.4 Huntington's disease
- 758.9 Chromosomal abnormalities
- 773.0 Severe Rh disease

608.89.1 Husband's sperm frozen before orchidectomy
606.8 Husband's sperm frozen before radiation or chemotherapy

ETIOLOGY

See ICD-9CM Codes.

DIAGNOSIS

DIFFERENTIAL DIAGNOSIS

See ICD-9CM Codes.

WORKUP

Male: refer to urologist; ascertain that azoospermia is indeed irreversible. Individuals who were considered intractable in the recent past can now produce pregnancies with intracytoplasmic sperm injections (ICSI), even with cells obtained by testicular biopsy. Such an option should be offered to the patient before recommending a donor.

LABORATORY TESTS

- Testing of both partners for hepatitis, HIV, and other STDs is recommended before donor inseminations.
- Female: as described in the topic "Therapeutic Insemination (Husband/Partner)" for general infertility workup.

IMAGING STUDIES

As described in the topic "Therapeutic Insemination (Husband/Partner)" for general infertility workup.

TREATMENT

NONPHARMACOLOGIC THERAPY

SPERM SOURCE: *Use of fresh donor semen is no longer acceptable.* Semen is obtained from state-certified "sperm banks" adhering to the proper routines of donor screening for genetic and infectious diseases, and quarantining the sperm for at least 6 mo. Sperm can be shipped from the bank in containers that will maintain the sample in a frozen state for 48 hr. After this time the sample has to be transferred to another liquid nitrogen storage tank.

SPERM PREPARATION: Sperm is removed from the liquid nitrogen and allowed to thaw at room temperature, or is thawed per sperm bank instructions. Refer to "Therapeutic Insemination (Husband/Partner)" in Section I for insemination techniques. If sperm supply is not limited and the woman's age is not a factor (<35 yr), simple applications of thawed semen to the external cervical os are usually undertaken first.

DISPOSITION

In healthy women <34 yr of age, fecundity of approximately 10% per cycle can be expected. Fertility is age dependent. After 12 cycles, expect 75% pregnancy for women <34 yr of age.

PEARLS & CONSIDERATIONS

COMMENTS

- Risks: infections with STDs, including AIDS, although rare, have been reported as a result of donor semen insemination.
- Caution: observe laws applicable in the state and obtain proper consents.
- Caution: before declaring the male azoospermic, centrifuge the semen and examine sediment; several sperm cells missed on "plain" microscopic examination may suffice for ICSI.

SUGGESTED READINGS

Guzick DS et al: Sperm morphology, motility, and concentration in fertile and infertile men, *N Engl J Med* 345:1388, 2001.

Hansen M et al: The risk of major birth defects after intracytoplasmic sperm injection and in vitro fertilization, *N Engl J Med* 346:725, 2002.

Schieve L et al: Low and very low birth weight in infants conceived with use of assisted reproductive technology, *N Engl J Med* 346:731, 2002.

Speroff L, Glass RH, Kase NG: *Clinical gynecologic endocrinology and infertility,* ed 6, Baltimore, 1999, Lippincott Williams & Wilkins.

AUTHOR: **JOHN M. WIECKOWSKI, M.D., PH.D.**

BASIC INFORMATION

DEFINITION

Insemination is a therapeutic intervention designed to overcome defects preventing achieving proper concentration of functional sperm cells in the vicinity of the egg.

SYNONYMS

Artificial insemination

ICD-9CM CODES
628.9 Infertility (female unspecified)
606.9 Infertility (male unspecified)
302.7 Sexual/erectile dysfunction
625.1 Vaginismus
752.6 Hypospadias
792.2 Asthenospermia
606.1 Oligospermia

EPIDEMIOLOGY & DEMOGRAPHICS

Approximately 15% of couples experience infertility.

ETIOLOGY

MALE:
- Hypospadias: congenital
- Sexual/erectile dysfunction: psychogenic, vascular, neurogenic
- Asthenospermia: idiopathic, varicocele, status post vasectomy reversal, environmental (toxins, heavy metals, heat exposure, trauma to testicles)
- Antisperm antibodies, unknown, trauma to testicles, vasectomy

FEMALE:
- Cervical mucus hostility: unknown, infection
- Antisperm antibodies: unknown
- Idiopathic infertility: unknown

DIAGNOSIS

DIFFERENTIAL DIAGNOSIS

- Diagnosis of infertility is established by a history of 1 yr of unprotected intercourse without conception.
- Establish male vs. female infertility, or combined.
- Male: rule out congenital abnormalities, varicocele, endocrine defects.
- Female: rule out ovulatory dysfunction, tubal factors, uterine defects, endometriosis.

WORKUP

- Male routine: urologic examination, semen analysis
- Specialized (if indicated): sonography, vasogram, Doppler studies, testicular biopsy
- Female routine: gynecologic examination, establish ovulatory pattern by basal body temperature or endometrial biopsy
- Postcoital test
- Specialized (if indicated): diagnostic/therapeutic laparoscopy

LABORATORY TESTS

- Male routine: semen analysis; specialized (if indicated): antisperm antibodies, endocrine studies, testicular biopsy
- Female routine: blood type, rubella immunity, hepatitis immunity
- Selectively (>35 yr or as indicated by history): day 3 of the cycle, test FSH, LH, and estradiol to rule out occult ovarian failure, polycystic ovarian syndrome (LH/FSH inversion); androgen levels if hirsutism present; prolactin level if galactorrhea; thyroid studies if clinically indicated; anti-*Chlamydia* antibodies if tubal damage suspected or history of IUD use

IMAGING STUDIES

- Hysterosalpingogram: rule out hydrosalpinx, salpingitis isthmica nodosa, intramural tubal polyps, intrauterine synechiae, or polyps
- Pelvic sonography: in midcycle to rule out myomas, endometrial polyps, endometrial hypoplasia, ovarian pathology (cysts, endometriomas), or confirm dominant follicle formation
- Pituitary MRI if tumor suspected

TREATMENT

NONPHARMACOLOGIC THERAPY

Type of insemination depends on the nature of the fertility defect and varies in depth to which the sperm cells are delivered into the female genital tract. The following types of inseminations may be done:
- Cervical and endocervical insemination
- Intrauterine insemination
- Intratubal insemination
- Cul-de-sac insemination
- Intrafollicular insemination
- In vitro fertilization (IVF)
- IVF with intracytoplasmic sperm injection (ICSI)

Only the cervical and intrauterine inseminations can be done in a primary care setting.

CERVICAL AND INTRACERVICAL INSEMINATION: This method is indicated when normal coital sperm delivery to the cervix is prevented (e.g., coital dysfunction and hypospadias).

Semen Preparation: None; whole semen is used.

Technique: Semen is delivered to the external os or endocervical canal using a syringe with soft-tipped cannula. Cervical cap, which prolongs the contact of semen with the cervix, can be used to overcome high semen viscosity.

INTRAUTERINE INSEMINATION (IUI): This method is used for the following reasons (listed in order of decreasing effectiveness):
- Cervical mucus hostility caused by poor mucus production or quality (idiopathic or iatrogenic, such as status postcervical conization, laser treatment, etc.)
- Antisperm antibodies
- Empirical treatment for unexplained infertility
- Mild male factor defects, such as oligospermia, high semen viscosity, high or low seminal volume

Semen Preparation: Seminal fluid should not be introduced into the uterine cavity. Sperm cells have to be separated from the seminal fluid by the process of sperm "washing," and resuspended in a protein-containing medium (5% to 10% serum or synthetic serum substitute), to endow the cells with proper motility. Method that can be used without the necessity of having incubator involves centrifugation of semen through a density gradient and resuspending the pellet in the protein-containing medium. Media for the previous procedures, with or without antibiotics, are commercially available from several sources.

Technique: Internal cervical os is negotiated with one of the various commercially available "insemination catheters" and the "washed" sperm suspension is delivered to the endometrial cavity. Timing: basal body temperature graphs, cervical mucus observation, testing of urine for LH surge, or serial sonography is often used for detecting ovulation. Cervical insemination should be performed within 24 hr before anticipated ovulation. Timing of IUI should be within a few hours of ovulation, preferably before it. It is usually performed at 40 hr after the ovulation-inducing hCG injection.

ACUTE GENERAL Rx:

- Clomiphene citrate (Clomid, Serophene) is commonly used to correct ovulatory defects. It is given in doses of 50 to 200 mg qd, on days 5 through 9 after the onset of progesterone withdrawal bleeding. The higher the dose of clomiphene necessary to induce ovulation, the lower the pregnancy chance. Prolonged use of clomiphene may adversely affect the endometrium and cervical mucus.
- Tamoxifen (Nolvadex) 10 to 20 mg qd given on days 5 through 9 as described previously is also a mild ovulation-inducing agent that improves endometrial formation and cervical mucus.

- Human chorionic gonadotropin (hCG, Pregnyl, Profasi, APL) can be used to trigger ovulation when the dominant follicle size reaches 20-mm diameter.
- Use of injectable FSH (Follistim, Gonal-F, Repronex) preparations is not advisable in primary care setting.

DISPOSITION: Majority of conceptions should occur within the first 6 mo of insemination. In healthy young women a 15% to 25% pregnancy rate per cycle can be expected. The great variety of results reported in the literature indicates that the practitioner's skill in performing ovarian stimulations and sperm preparation plays a significant role in the outcome.

REFERRAL: To specialist if:

- No result after six cycles of inseminations
- Ovulatory dysfunction does not promptly respond to a low dose (50 to 100 mg) of clomiphene citrate
- Woman's age >35 yr: efficiency of treatment becomes critical
- Poor semen parameters
- Pelvic pathology needs correction

PEARLS & CONSIDERATIONS

COMMENTS

- Risks of insemination: flare-up of unsuspected pelvic infection, ovarian overstimulation with gonadotropins, multifetal pregnancy.
- Caution: if sperm is in limited supply (semen frozen before orchidectomy) or woman's age is an issue, a thorough fertility evaluation is indicated to make sure that no valuable time or valuable semen is wasted. If fertility defects are found, they should be corrected, or IVF should be offered.
- IVF combined with ICSI is the ultimate insemination technique and delivers pregnancy rates of 20% to 40% per cycle.
- Results of several studies suggest that ICSI is associated with a slightly increased risk for chromosomal abnormalities.

SUGGESTED READINGS

Abulghar H et al: A prospective controlled study of karyotyping for 430 consecutive babies conceived through intracytoplasmic injection, *Fertil Steril* 76:249, 2001.

Ren D et al: A sperm ion channel required for sperm motility and male fertility, *Nature* 413:603, 2001.

Speroff L, Glass RH, Kase NG: *Clinical gynecologic endocrinology and infertility,* ed 6, Baltimore, 1999, Lippincott Williams & Wilkins.

AUTHOR: **JOHN M. WIECKOWSKI, M.D., PH.D.**

BASIC INFORMATION

DEFINITION

Insomnia is a disturbance of initiating or maintaining sleep. Restless, nonrestorative sleep may also be described as insomnia. The disturbance may be subjective without daytime sequela but still a cause of distress, or may be objectively measurable with poor sleep efficiency and daytime consequences of sleepiness and functional impairment.

SYNONYMS

Sleeplessness, sleep disorder, sleep disturbance, dysomnia. The terms sleep disorder, sleep disturbance, and dysomnia are generic and can refer to disorders of wakefulness (hypersomnia) or sleep-related behavior disorders (parasomnias).

ICD-9CM CODES
780.52 Insomnia
780.51 Insomnia with sleep apnea
307.41 Insomnia nonorganic origin
307.42 Insomnia persistent (primary)
307.41 Insomnia transient
307.49 Subjective complaint
DSM IV-TR Codes:
307.42 Primary insomnia
307.45 Circadian rhythm disorders
780.52 Insomnia due to a general medical condition
291.89 Substance-induced insomnia due to alcohol
292.89 Substance-induced insomnia due to other (i.e., caffeine, drug)

EPIDEMIOLOGY & DEMOGRAPHICS

INCIDENCE (IN U.S.): 30%-45% of adults experience insomnia per year.
PREVALENCE (IN U.S.): 1%-15% of all adults develop persistent insomnia, 25% of older adults.
PREDOMINANT SEX: More common in women.
PREDOMINANT AGE: Transient insomnia is common at any age, persistent insomnia is more common in those >60 yrs. Younger adults usually complain of sleep-onset insomnia, older adults usually have more sleep maintenance difficulty.
GENETICS: Both idiopathic primary insomnia and chronobiologic forms of insomnia run in families and may be genetically determined.

CLINICAL PRESENTATION

- Complain of difficulty falling asleep, difficulty staying asleep, early morning awakening, restless or nonrestorative sleep, or difficulty sleeping at desired times.
- May or may not complain of daytime sleepiness or fatigue.
- Symptoms may be acute and self-limited, chronic but intermittent, or chronic and frequent.

ETIOLOGY

- Transient insomnia:
  1. Stress
  2. Illness
  3. Travel
  4. Environmental disruptions (noise, heat, cold, poor bedding, unfamiliar surroundings, etc.)
- Persistent insomnia:
  1. Mood disorders (depression, hypomania/mania)
  2. Primary or psychophysiologic (with or without poor sleep hygiene)
  3. Sleep-related breathing disorders (e.g., obstructive apnea)
  4. Chronobiologic (a.k.a. circadian rhythm) disorder (delayed sleep phase, advanced sleep phase, shift work, free-running rhythm secondary to blindness)
  5. Drug and alcohol abuse
  6. Restless legs and periodic leg movements
  7. Neurodegenerative (Alzheimer's disease, Parkinson's disease, etc.)
  8. Medical (pain, GERD, nocturia, orthopnea, medications, etc.)

DIAGNOSIS

DIFFERENTIAL DIAGNOSIS

- Primary or psychophysiologic insomnia is diagnosed when other etiologies (see above) are ruled out.

WORKUP

- History (with bed partner interview, if possible)
- Sleep diary for 2 weeks to document severity, frequency, daytime function, and distress (sample sleep diary can be downloaded from the National Sleep Foundation website: http://www.sleepfoundation.org)
- Validated sleep-quality rating scale (optional)
  1. Pittsburgh Sleep Quality Index or similar questionnaire
  2. Epworth Sleepiness Scale (see Daytime Sleepiness Test at http://www.sleepfoundation.org)

LABORATORY TESTS

- Evaluate for anemia, uremia (for restless legs), thyroid function (if other signs present)
- Polysomnography (in home or in sleep lab) for symptoms suggesting something other than primary insomnia: daytime sleepiness (obstructive sleep apnea, narcolepsy), nonrestorative sleep (periodic leg movements), or sleep behavior suggesting parasomnia (somnambulism, REM sleep behavior)

IMAGING STUDIES

- Not generally helpful for insomnia
- Brain CT or MRI for severe daytime sleepiness of acute onset

TREATMENT

NONPHARMACOLOGIC THERAPY

- Sleep hygiene measures (see Box 1-9).
- Cognitive-behavioral therapy (CBT) to address anxiety and insomnia-perpetuating behaviors.
- Bright light exposure timed to correct a circadian phase disturbance can be helpful for insomnia secondary to delayed or advanced sleep phase, jet lag, or shift work.

ACUTE GENERAL Rx

- Benzodiazepine sedative-hypnotics (e.g., temazepam 7.5-30 mg, triazolam 0.125-0.25 mg).
  1. In critical care: lorazepam 0.25-0.5 mg PO, SL, or IV as needed for sleep.
- Benzodiazepine receptor agonists (e.g., zolpidem 5-10 mg for sleep-onset and maintenance insomnia, zaleplon 5-10 mg for sleep-onset insomnia).
- Avoid antihistamines except for occasional use.
- Optimize treatment of medical symptoms, especially pain.

CHRONIC Rx

- No medication has been proven to be safe and effective for prolonged use.
- Some evidence that benzodiazepines and benzodiazepine receptor agonists can be used for chronic insomnia on either intermittent or nightly use with moderate risk of tolerance and dependence but low risk of addiction.
- Sedating antidepressants (e.g., trazodone 25-150 mg, mirtazapine 7.5-30 mg, amitriptyline 25-50 mg) in widespread use but limited data on safety and efficacy for insomnia. Treatments of choice for comorbid depression or anxiety. Amitriptyline should be avoided if possible in older adults.
- Sedating antipsychotics (e.g., quetiapine 25-200 mg, olanzapine 2.5-10 mg) for severe mood or psychotic disorders associated with insomnia.

COMPLEMENTARY & ALTERNATIVE MEDICINE

Melatonin is the only substance that has been studied in larger controlled trials. It may shorten sleep-onset latency in some individuals. Melatonin can be very effective for insomnia due to circadian rhythm disturbances if scheduled to correct the underlying circadian phase disturbance.

DISPOSITION

- Transient insomnia: usually self-limited, but may require follow-up if stress- or illness-related because of risk of depression or persistent insomnia.
- Persistent insomnia: patients have a chronic and recurrent disorder and will need periodic follow-up to reinforce good sleep hygiene measures and to reassess need for pharmacologic and nonpharmacologic therapies.

REFERRAL

- Excessive daytime sleepiness not obviously due to insomnia (e.g., narcolepsy, sleep-related breathing disorder, etc.)
- Nighttime behavior suggestive of a parasomnia (e.g., somnambulism, REM behavior disorder, etc.)
- Severe insomnia not responsive to basic interventions

PEARLS & CONSIDERATIONS

COMMENTS

Treatment of insomnia should focus on reducing daytime sleepiness and improving daytime function, rather than trying to achieve the elusive goal of uninterrupted nighttime sleep.

PREVENTION

Not much is known about prevention of insomnia. Effective treatment of transient insomnia may reduce the risk of developing persistent insomnia.

PATIENT/FAMILY EDUCATION

The National Sleep Foundation (http://www.sleepfoundation.org) is a comprehensive resource for health care providers and patients.

SUGGESTED READINGS

Jacobs GD et al: Cognitive behavior therapy and pharmacotherapy for insomnia: a randomized controlled trial and direct comparison, *Arch Int Med* 164(17):1888, 2004.

Krystal AD: The changing perspective on chronic insomnia management, *J Clin Psychiatry* 65(Suppl 8):20, 2004.

Ringdahl EN, Pereira SL, Delzell JE: Treatment of primary insomnia, *J Am Board Fam Pract Behavioural Medicine in Primary Care: A Practical Guide,* ed 2, New York, 2003, Lange Medical Books/McGraw Hill.

Smith MT et al: Comparative meta-analysis of pharmacotherapy and behaviour therapy for persistent insomnia, *Am J Psychiatry* 159:5, 2002.

AUTHOR: **CLIFFORD MILO SINGER, M.D.**

BOX 1-9 Sleep Habits (Sleep Hygiene Measures) That May Improve Insomnia

1. Reduce caffeine, alcohol, or tobacco late in the day or evening.
2. Avoid heavy meals at night.
3. Increase daytime activity.
4. Increase daytime exposure to natural light.
5. Take warm bath as part of bedtime ritual.
6. Restrict bed to sleep and sex.
7. Get out of bed if not asleep after 30 minutes and return when drowsy.
8. Repeat above if awakened during the night.
9. Maintain regular sleep and wake times.
10. Go to bed with calm mind; resolve arguments or deal with problems earlier in day.

Insulinoma

BASIC INFORMATION

DEFINITION

Insulinoma is a pancreatic insulin-secreting tumor that causes symptoms associated with hypoglycemia.

ICD-9CM CODES
M8151/0 Insulinoma

EPIDEMIOLOGY & DEMOGRAPHICS

INCIDENCE: 1 case/250,000 persons/yr
DEMOGRAPHICS: Insulinomas occur in both sexes (approximately 60% in women) and at all ages. In the Mayo Clinic series, the median age at diagnosis was 50 yr in sporadic cases but 23 yr in patients with multiple endocrine neoplasia (MEN), type 1.

PHYSICAL FINDINGS & CLINICAL PRESENTATION

Symptoms occur typically in the morning before breakfast (i.e., fasting hypoglycemia as opposed to reactive hypoglycemia, which is not commonly associated with insulinoma)

Neuroglycopenic symptoms	**%**
Various combinations of diplopia, blurred vision, sweating, palpitations, or weakness	85
Confusion or abnormal behavior	80
Unconsciousness or amnesia	53
Grand mal seizures	12
Adrenergic symptoms	**%**
Sweating	43
Tremulousness	23
Hunger, nausea	12
Palpitations	10

ETIOLOGY, PATHOLOGY, PATHOPHYSIOLOGY

- Insulinomas are almost always solitary. Malignant insulinomas account for 5% of the total; they tend to be larger (6 cm). Metastases are usually to the liver (47%), regional lymph nodes (30%), or both.
- Insulinomas are evenly distributed in the head, body, and tail of the pancreas; ectopic insulinomas are rare (1% to 3%). Tumor size: 5% 0.5 cm or less, 34% 0.5 to 1 cm, 53% 1 to 5 cm, 8% >5 cm.
- Histologic classification includes insulinoma in 86% of patients, adenomatosis in 5% to 15%, nesidioblastosis in 4%, and hyperplasia in 1%. Adenomatosis consists of multiple macroadenomas or microadenomas and occurs especially in patients with MEN-1. Nesidioblastosis is also a diffuse lesion, in which islet cells form as buds on ductular structures.

DIAGNOSIS

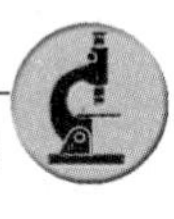

DIFFERENTIAL DIAGNOSIS (OF FASTING HYPOGLYCEMIA)

HYPERINSULINISM:
- Insulinoma
- Nonpancreatic tumors
- Severe congestive heart failure
- Severe renal insufficiency in non-insulin-dependent diabetes

HEPATIC ENZYME DEFICIENCIES OR DECREASED HEPATIC GLUCOSE OUTPUT (PRIMARILY IN INFANTS, CHILDREN):
- Glycogen storage diseases
- Endocrine hypofunction
- Hypopituitarism
- Addison's disease
- Liver failure
- Alcohol abuse
- Malnutrition

EXOGENOUS AGENTS:
- Sulfonylureas, biguanides
- Insulin
- Other drugs (aspirin, pentamidine)

FUNCTIONAL FASTING HYPOGLYCEMIA: Autoantibodies to insulin receptor or insulin

LABORATORY TESTS

- An overnight fasting blood sugar level combined with a simultaneous plasma insulin, proinsulin, and/or C peptide level will establish the existence of fasting organic hypoglycemia in 60% of patients.
- If single overnight fasting glucose and insulin levels are nondiagnostic, a 72-hr fast is usually done with blood glucose and insulin levels determined at 2- to 4-hr intervals: 75% of patients with insulinoma develop symptoms and a blood sugar level of less than 40 mg/dl by 24 hr, 92% to 98% develop these by 48 hr, and virtually all patients develop them by 72 hr. The test is considered positive for insulinoma if the plasma insulin/glucose ratio is more than 0.3. If, at any point, the patient becomes symptomatic, plasma insulin and glucose values should be obtained and intravenous glucose should be administered.
- Plasma proinsulin, C-peptide, antibodies to insulin, and plasma sulfonylurea levels may be used to rule out factitious use of insulin or hypoglycemic agents or autoantibodies against the insulin receptor or insulin.
- See Section III, Hypoglycemia, for a description of the diagnostic approach to patients with documented hypoglycemia and elevated insulin.

IMAGING STUDIES

- Abdominal CT scan or MRI detects half to two thirds of insulinomas (abdominal ultrasound is not effective). Should be done only after laboratory tests for insulinoma have confirmed the diagnosis.
- Intraoperative ultrasound
- Arteriography
- Octreotide scan

TREATMENT

SURGICAL TREATMENT

- Enucleation of single insulinoma
- Partial pancreatectomy for multiple adenomas

MEDICAL TREATMENT

- Carbohydrate administration
- Diazoxide directly inhibits insulin release and has an extrapancreatic, hyperglycemic effect that enhances glycogenolysis
- Lanreotide and octreotide (somatostatin analogs)
- Streptozotocin

REFERRAL

At some point in the workup the patient will probably be referred to an endocrinologist and then to a surgeon. A combination of fasting hypoglycemia and elevated insulin level is probably a good point at which to refer.

SUGGESTED READINGS

Axelrod L: Insulinoma: cost-effective care in patients with rare disease, *Ann Intern Med* 123:311, 1995.

Gerich JE: Hypoglycemia. In DeGroot LS, Jameson JL, eds, *Endocrinology,* ed 4, Philadelphia, 2001, WB Saunders.

Service FJ et al: Functioning insulinoma—incidence, recurrence and long-term survival of patients, *Mayo Clin Proc* 66:711, 1991.

AUTHOR: **TOM J. WACHTEL, M.D.**

BASIC INFORMATION

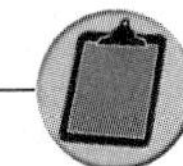

DEFINITION

Interstitial nephritis refers to a group of disorders primarily affecting the interstitium and renal tubules. Interstitial nephritis may be acute or chronic.

SYNONYMS

Acute interstitial nephritis (AIN)
Chronic interstitial nephritis (CIN)
Tubulointerstitial diseases

ICD-9CM CODES
583.9 Nephritis
580.89 Acute
582.89 Chronic

EPIDEMIOLOGY & DEMOGRAPHICS

- Approximately 1% of patients being evaluated for hematuria and proteinuria will have interstitial nephritis.
- Interstitial nephritis accounts for 25% of all cases of chronic renal failure.
- Up to 15% of all renal biopsies performed on patients with renal diseases have acute interstitial nephritis.
- Drug-induced AIN is more common in adults.
- Infection-induced AIN is more common in children.

PHYSICAL FINDINGS & CLINICAL PRESENTATION

Acute interstitial nephritis (AIN)
- Patients usually asymptomatic and found to have a sudden decrease in renal function
- Characteristically occurs over several days to weeks after an infection or initiation of a new medication
- Classic triad—fever, rash, and arthralgias
- Lumbar flank pain
- Gross hematuria
- Usually oliguric

Chronic interstitial nephritis (CIN)
- Usually present with symptoms related to the underlying cause (e.g., sarcoidosis, multiple myeloma, urate nephropathy)
- Symptoms of renal failure (e.g., weakness, nausea, pruritus)
- Hypertension

ETIOLOGY

- AIN is usually caused by drugs, infection, or is associated with immune or neoplastic disorders
- Common drugs include penicillin, methicillin, rifampin, cephalosporins, trimethoprim-sulfamethoxazole, ciprofloxacin, NSAIDs, thiazides, furosemide, triamterene, allopurinol, phenytoin, captopril, and cimetidine
- Infection (e.g., *Streptococcus, Legionella, Corynebacterium diphtheriae, Yersinia, Salmonella,* HIV, EBV, CMV, *Mycoplasma, Rickettsia,* and *Mycobacterium tuberculosis)*
- Autoimmune causes of AIN include Sjögren's syndrome, SLE, and Wegener's granulomatosis
- Common causes of CIN include polycystic kidney disease, urate nephropathy, analgesic nephropathy, sarcoidosis, multiple myeloma, lead nephropathy, hypercalcemia, and Balkan nephropathy

DIAGNOSIS

Renal biopsy is the only definitive method of establishing the diagnosis of interstitial nephritis. All other labs provide supportive evidence of interstitial nephritis.

DIFFERENTIAL DIAGNOSIS

The differential diagnosis includes the diseases listed under Etiology.

WORKUP

Any patient found to be in renal failure without evidence of prerenal or obstructive uropathy should be worked up for interstitial nephritis. Workup generally includes blood and urine studies, x-rays, and renal biopsy.

LABORATORY TESTS

- CBC showing anemia and eosinophilia
- BUN and creatinine are elevated and typically represent the first clue of interstitial nephritis
- Electrolytes, calcium, and phosphorus
- Uric acid
- Elevated IgE level
- Urinalysis reveals hematuria and pyuria
- Eosinophiluria by Hansen stain is suggestive of allergic interstitial nephritis
- Proteinuria <3 g/24 hr

IMAGING STUDIES

- Ultrasound of the kidneys shows normal size kidneys in AIN and small contracted kidneys in CIN.
- IVP findings are similar to ultrasound findings.
- Renal biopsy in AIN reveals infiltration of inflammatory cells into the interstitium with interstitial edema and sparing of the glomeruli. In CIN fibrotic scar tissue replaces the cellular infiltrate.

TREATMENT

NONPHARMACOLOGIC THERAPY

- Low-protein, low-potassium, low-sodium diet
- Correction of underlying electrolyte abnormalities
- IV hydration for hypercalcemia

ACUTE GENERAL Rx

- Corticosteroids 1 mg/kg/day are used in patients with drug-induced AIN not responding to withdrawal of the medication within 3 to 4 days. Therapy is continued for a total of 4 to 6 wk.
- Cyclophosphamide 2 mg/kg/day is added as a second agent for patients not responding to corticosteroids.
- Combined therapy is continued for 6 wk.

CHRONIC Rx

- Treatment of chronic interstitial nephritis is directed at the underlying cause (e.g., corticosteroids for sarcoidosis, EDTA in lead nephropathy).
- Other therapeutic measures include blood pressure control, reducing uric acid and calcium levels if indicated.

DISPOSITION

- Most cases of AIN resolve by withdrawing the offending drug or agent within several days.
- Dialysis is required in up to one third of patients with drug-induced AIN.
- By the time most patients with chronic interstitial nephritis present, their creatinine clearance is <50 ml/min.
- Chronic interstitial nephritis patients usually have progressive deterioration in their renal function.

REFERRAL

Patients with acute renal failure or chronic renal failure from interstitial nephritis should be referred to a nephrologist.

PEARLS & CONSIDERATIONS

COMMENTS

- There are no randomized controlled trials comparing treatment of AIN with corticosteroids versus other forms of therapy.
- If AIN has resulted from penicillin, the use of another penicillin or cephalosporins has led to recurrence.
- Patients with chronic interstitial nephritis usually have advanced renal disease with no specific therapy.

SUGGESTED READINGS

Kelly CJ, Neilson EG: Tubulointerstitial diseases. In Brenner BM, Rector FC (eds): Brenner & Rector's the kidney, ed 5, Philadelphia, 1996, WB Saunders.

Kodner CM, Kudrimoti A: Diagnosis and management of acute interstitial nephritis, Amer Acad of Fam Phys 67(12):2527, 2003.

AUTHOR: **PETER PETROPOULOS, M.D.**

BASIC INFORMATION

DEFINITION

Irritable bowel syndrome (IBS) is a chronic functional disorder manifested by alteration in bowel habits and recurrent abdominal pain and bloating.

SYNONYMS

Irritable colon
Spastic colon
IBS

ICD-9CM CODES
564.1 Irritable bowel syndrome

EPIDEMIOLOGY & DEMOGRAPHICS

- IBS occurs in 20% of population of industrialized countries and is responsible for >50% of GI referrals. Worldwide adult prevalence is 12%. Incidence increases during adolescence and peaks in third and fourth decade of life.
- Female:male ratio is 2:1.
- Nearly 50% of patients have psychiatric abnormalities, with anxiety disorders being most common.

PHYSICAL FINDINGS & CLINICAL PRESENTATION

- The clinical presentation of IBS consists of abdominal pain and abnormalities of defecation, which may include loose stools usually after meals and in the morning, alternating with episodes of constipation.
- Physical examination is generally normal.
- Nonspecific abdominal tenderness and distention may be present.

ETIOLOGY

- Unknown
- Associated pathophysiology includes altered GI motility and increased gut sensitivity
- Risk factors: anxiety, depression, personality disorders, history of childhood sexual abuse, and domestic abuse in women

DIAGNOSIS

DIFFERENTIAL DIAGNOSIS

- IBD
- Diverticulitis
- Colon malignancy
- Endometriosis
- PUD
- Biliary liver disease
- Chronic pancreatitis

WORKUP

Diagnostic workup is aimed primarily at excluding the conditions listed in the differential diagnoses. It is important to identify "red flags" of other diseases, such as weight loss, rectal bleeding, onset in patients 50 years of age, fever, nocturnal pain, family history of malignancy. The criteria for diagnosis of IBS are: more than 3 months of symptoms *including* abdominal pain that is relieved by a bowel movement, *or* pain accompanied by a change in bowel pattern, *and* abnormality in bowel movement 25% of the time, characterized by two of the following features:
- Abdominal distention
- Abnormal consistency
- Abnormal defecation (e.g., straining, sense of incomplete evacuation)
- Abnormal frequency
- Mucus with bowel movement

LABORATORY TESTS

- Blood work is generally normal. The presence of anemia should alert to the possibility of a colonic malignancy or IBD.
- Testing of stool for ova and parasites should be considered in patients with chronic diarrhea.

IMAGING STUDIES

- Small bowel series and barium enema are normal and not necessary for diagnosis.
- Lower endoscopy is generally normal except for the presence of some spasms.

TREATMENT

NONPHARMACOLOGIC THERAPY

- The patient should be encouraged to maintain a high-fiber diet and to eliminate foods that aggravate symptoms. Avoidance of dietary caffeine and dietary excesses is also helpful.
- Behavioral therapy is also recommended, particularly in younger patients because psychosocial stressors are important triggers of IBS.
- Importance of regular exercise and adequate fluid intake should be stressed.

GENERAL Rx

- The mainstay of treatment of IBS is high-fiber diet. Because symptoms are chronic, the use of laxatives should be avoided.
- Fiber supplementation with psyllium 1 tablespoon bid or calcium polycarbophil (FiberCon) 2 tablets one to four times daily followed by 8 oz of water may be necessary in some patients.
- Patients should be instructed that there might be some increased bloating on initiation of fiber supplementation, which should resolve within 2 to 3 wk. It is important that patients take these fiber products on a regular basis and not only prn.
- Antispasmodics-anticholinergics may be useful in refractory cases (e.g., dicyclomine [Bentyl] 10 to 20 mg up to three times daily).
- Patients who appear anxious can benefit from use of sedatives and anticholinergics such as chlordiazepoxide-clidinium (Librax) or SSRIs. Tricyclic antidepressants in low doses are also effective in some patients with IBS.
- Loperamide is effective for diarrhea. Alosetron (Lotronex), a serotonin type 3 receptor antagonist previously withdrawn because of severe constipation and ischemic colitis, has been reintroduced with limited availability. It is indicated only for women with severe chronic diarrhea-predominant IBS unresponsive to conventional therapy and not caused by anatomic or metabolic abnormality. Starting dose is 1 mg qd.

- Tegaserod (Zelnorm), a 5-HT_4 receptor partial agonist, increases GI motility and can be used to relieve symptoms in patients whose predominant symptom is constipation. Usual dose is 2 to 6 mg PO bid before meals. Tegaserod is contraindicated in patients with severe renal insufficiency, moderate to severe hepatic impairment, intestinal adhesions, or a history of bowel obstruction.

DISPOSITION

Greater than 60% of patients respond successfully to treatment over the initial 12 mo; however, IBS is a chronic relapsing condition and requires prolonged therapy.

REFERRAL

GI referral is recommended in patients with rectal bleeding, fever, nocturnal diarrhea, anemia, weight loss, or onset of symptoms after age 40 yr.

PEARLS & CONSIDERATIONS

COMMENTS

- Patients should be educated regarding maintenance of high-fiber diet and elimination of stressors, which can precipitate attacks of IBS. They should be reassured that their condition cannot lead to cancer.
- The modified ROME criteria define IBS as:
  A. The presence of ≥12 wk of continuous or recurrent abdominal pain or discomfort that cannot be explained by structural or biochemical abnormalities and
  B. The presence of at least two of the following three features:
    1. Pain is relieved with defecation
    2. Its onset is associated with a change in the frequency of bowel movement
    3. Its onset is associated with a change in the form of the stool.

SUGGESTED READINGS

Mertz HR: Irritable bowel syndrome, *N Engl J Med* 349:22, 2003.

Viera AJ et al: Management of irritable bowel syndrome, *Am Fam Physician* 66:1867, 2002.

AUTHOR: **FRED F. FERRI, M.D.**

BASIC INFORMATION

DEFINITION

Kaposi's sarcoma (KS) is a vascular neoplasm most frequently occurring in AIDS patients. It can be divided into the following four subsets:

1. *Classic Kaposi's sarcoma:* most frequently found in elderly Eastern European and Mediterranean males. It consists initially of violaceous macules and papules with subsequent development of plaques and red/purple nodules. Growth is slow, and most of the patients die of unrelated causes.
2. *Epidemic* or *AIDS-related Kaposi's sarcoma:* most frequently occurs in homosexual men. Lesions are generally multifocal and widespread. Lymphadenopathy may be associated.
3. *Endemic Kaposi's sarcoma:* usually affects African children and adults. An aggressive lymphadenopathic form affects African children in particular.
4. *Immunosuppression-associated,* or *transplantation-associated, Kaposi's sarcoma:* usually associated with chemotherapy.

SYNONYMS

KS

ICD-9CM CODES

173.9 Malignant neoplasm of the skin

EPIDEMIOLOGY & DEMOGRAPHICS

- AIDS-related KS affects >35% of AIDS cases.
- Highest incidence is in homosexual men.

PHYSICAL FINDINGS & CLINICAL PRESENTATION

- AIDS-related KS: multifocal and widespread red-purple or dark plaques and/or nodules on cutaneous or mucosal surfaces (Fig. 1-131).
- Generalized lymphadenopathy at the time of diagnosis is present in >50% of patients with AIDS-related KS; the initial lesions have a rust-colored appearance; subsequent progression to red or purple nodules or plaques occurs.
- Most frequently affected areas are the face, trunk, oral cavity, and upper and lower extremities.

ETIOLOGY

A herpesvirus (HHV-8, Kaposi's sarcoma-associated herpesvirus KSHV) has been isolated from patients with most forms of KS and is believed to be the causative agent. It can be transmitted sexually (homosexual, heterosexual activities) and by other forms of nonsexual contact such as maternal-infant transmission (common in African countries).

DIAGNOSIS

DIFFERENTIAL DIAGNOSIS

- Stasis dermatitis
- Pyogenic granuloma
- Capillary hemangiomas
- Granulation tissue
- Postinflammatory hyperpigmentation
- Cutaneous lymphoma
- Melanoma
- Dermatofibroma
- Hematoma
- Prurigo nodularis

The differential diagnosis of cutaneous lesions in patients with HIV infection is described in section III.

WORKUP

Diagnosis can generally be made on clinical appearance; tissue biopsy will confirm diagnosis.

LABORATORY TESTS

HIV in patients suspected of AIDS

TREATMENT

NONPHARMACOLOGIC THERAPY

Observation is a reasonable option in patients with slowly progressive disease.

GENERAL Rx

- Excisional biopsy often provides adequate treatment for single lesions and resected recurrences in classic Kaposi's sarcoma.
- Liquid nitrogen cryotherapy can result in complete response in 80% of lesions.
- Interlesional chemotherapy with vinblastine is useful for nodular lesions >1 cm in diameter. Intralesional injection of interferon alfa-2b has also been reported as effective and well tolerated.
- Radiation therapy is effective in non-AIDS KS and for large tumor masses that interfere with normal function.
- Systemic therapy with interferon is also effective in AIDS-related KS and is often used in combination with AZT.
- Systemic chemotherapy (vinblastine, bleomycin, doxorubicin, and dacarbazine) can be used for rapidly progressive disease and for classic and African endemic KS.
- Oral etoposide is also effective and has less myelosuppression than vinblastine.
- Paclitaxel is also effective in patients with advanced KS and represents an excellent second-line therapy.

DISPOSITION

- Prognosis is poor in AIDS-related KS. Death is often a result of other AIDS-defining illnesses.
- Prognosis is better in African cutaneous KS and classic sarcoma (patients usually die of unrelated causes).

PEARLS & CONSIDERATIONS

COMMENTS

Immunosuppression-associated Kaposi's sarcoma usually regresses with the cessation, reduction, or modification of immunosuppression therapy in most patients. Similarly in HIV patients, Kaposi's sarcoma responds concurrently with the decrease in serum HIV RNA and increase in the CD4 count.

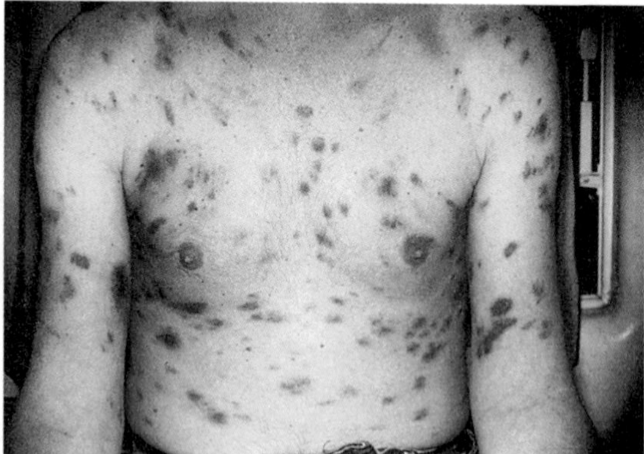

FIGURE 1-131 Kaposi's sarcoma. More advanced lesions. Note widespread hemorrhagic plaques and nodules. (From Noble J [ed]: *Textbook of primary care medicine,* ed 2, St Louis, 1995, Mosby.)

SUGGESTED READINGS

Grossma Z et al: Absence of Kaposi sarcoma among Ethiopian immigrants to Israel despite high seroprevalence of human herpesvirus 8, *Mayo Clin Proc* 77:905, 2002.

Sarid R et al: Virology, pathogenetic mechanisms, and associated diseases of Kaposi sarcoma-associated herpesvirus (human herpesvirus 8), *Mayo Clin Proc* 77:941, 2002.

Webster-Cyriaque J: Development of Kaposi's sarcoma in a surgical wound, *N Engl J Med* 346:1207, 2002.

AUTHOR: **FRED F. FERRI, M.D.**

BASIC INFORMATION

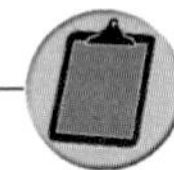

DEFINITION

Kawasaki disease (KD) refers to a generalized vasculitis of unknown etiology and characterized by cutaneous and mucous membrane edema, rash, lymphadenopathy, and involvement of multiple organs.

SYNONYMS

Mucocutaneous lymph node syndrome

ICD-9CM CODES
446.1 Kawasaki disease

EPIDEMIOLOGY & DEMOGRAPHICS

- KD is a leading cause of acquired heart disease in children.
- KD commonly occurs under the age of 5 (80%).
- KD is found more often in boys than in girls (1.5:1).
- In the United States the incidence of KD is 8.9 cases/100,000 children <5 years of age.
- Approximately 1900 new cases are diagnosed each year in the U.S.
- The incidence of KD in Japan is 80 to 90/100,000 under the age of 5.

PHYSICAL FINDINGS & CLINICAL PRESENTATION

A typical presentation is a young child with fever unresponsive to antibiotics for more than 5 days associated with:
- Bilateral conjunctivitis
- Erythema and edema of the hands and feet (Fig. 1-132, *B*)
- Periungual desquamation
- Fissuring of the lips
- Erythematous pharynx
- Strawberry tongue (Fig. 1-132, *A*)
- Cervical adenopathy
- Truncal scarlatiniform rash, usually nonvesicular
- Diarrhea
- Dyspnea
- Arthralgias and myalgia
- Sudden death from coronary artery involvement
- Myocardial infarction
- Congestive heart failure

ETIOLOGY

The cause of KD is not known although evidence substantiates an infectious etiology precipitating an immune-mediated reaction.

DIAGNOSIS

The diagnosis of Kawasaki disease is based on a fever lasting more than 5 days along with four of the following five features:
- Bilateral conjunctival swelling
- Inflammatory changes of the lip, tongue, and pharynx
- Skin changes of the limbs
- Rash over the trunk
- Cervical lymphadenopathy

DIFFERENTIAL DIAGNOSIS

- Scarlet fever
- Stevens-Johnson syndrome
- Drug eruption
- Henoch-Schönlein purpura
- Toxic shock syndrome
- Measles
- Rocky Mountain spotted fever
- Infectious mononucleosis

WORKUP

Clinical findings in addition to lab and imaging studies are useful in searching for organ system involvement and complications (e.g., cardiac, lung, liver).

LABORATORY TESTS

- CBC commonly shows a normochromic normocytic anemia, a left-shift in the white blood cell count, and an elevated platelet count
- ESR is elevated
- C-reactive protein is positive
- LFTs (e.g., elevated SGOT and SGPT)
- Urinalysis may show sterile pyuria

IMAGING STUDIES

- Chest x-ray may reveal pulmonary infiltrates
- Echocardiogram is very helpful and may show depressed left ventricular function with regional wall motion abnormalities, pericardial effusions (30%), and abnormal coronary artery aneurysms. The echocardiogram is also useful in the long-term follow-up of patients with KD
- Intravascular ultrasound looking for coronary artery lumen irregularities
- Exercise testing with myocardial perfusion studies can be done to assess for coronary blood flow
- Cardiac catheterization with coronary angiography in the proper clinical setting is done to rule out significant obstructive coronary disease

TREATMENT

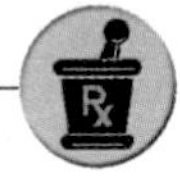

NONPHARMACOLOGIC THERAPY

- Oxygen in selected patients
- Salt restriction in patients with CHF

ACUTE GENERAL Rx

- Intravenous immunoglobulin (IVIG) 2 g/kg IV over 8 to 12 hr is the treatment of choice in children diagnosed with KD and ideally should be given within the first 10 days of the illness.
- Aspirin 30 to 100 mg/kg/day given in four divided doses until the patient is no longer febrile. Thereafter aspirin 3 to 5 mg/kg/day is continued until lab studies (e.g., sedimentation rate) return to normal, generally within 6 to 8 wk.

A

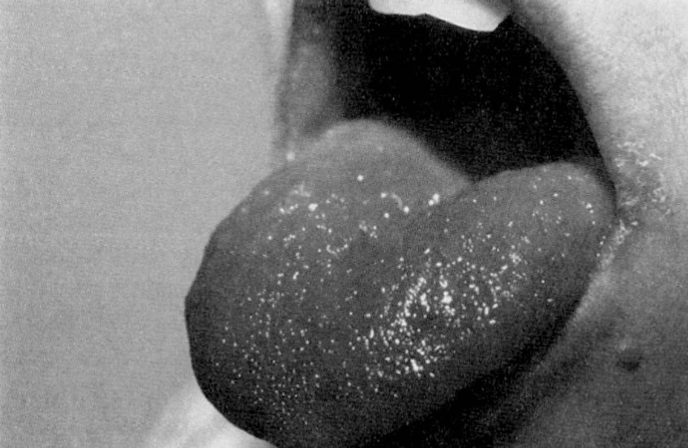

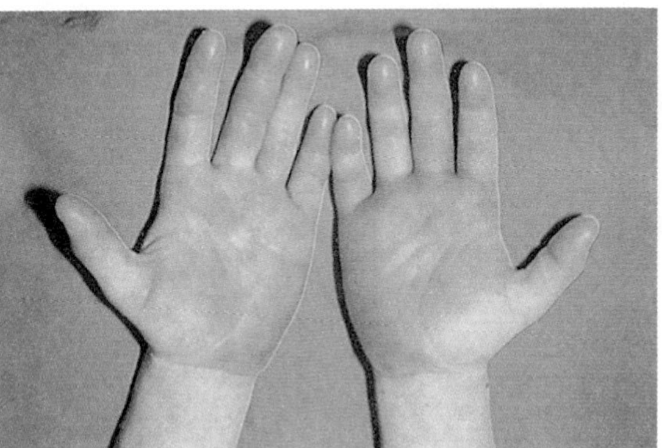

B

FIGURE 1-132 **A,** Strawberry tongue in a patient with Kawasaki syndrome. **B,** Erythema of the hands, to be followed by desquamation. (**A** Courtesy Marshall Guill, M.D. In Goldstein B [ed]: *Practical dermatology,* ed 2, St Louis, 1997, Mosby. **B** Courtesy Department of Dermatology, University of North Carolina at Chapel Hill. In Goldstein B [ed]: *Practical dermatology,* ed 2, St Louis, 1997, Mosby.)

- In patients that do not defervesce within 48 hr or have recrudescent fever after initial IVIG treatment, a second dose of IVIG 2 g/kg IV over 8 to 12 hr should be considered.
- Corticosteroids and NSAIDs are not effective in the treatment of KD.

CHRONIC Rx

Interventional and surgical procedures can be tried in children who have developed cardiac complications of KD.

- Percutaneous transluminal coronary angioplasty
- Coronary bypass graft surgery using the internal mammary artery or the gastroepiploic artery has met with greater patency success than saphenous vein grafts
- Cardiac transplantation is an option and is indicated in patients with:
  1. Severe left ventricular failure
  2. Malignant arrhythmias
  3. Multivessel distal coronary artery disease

DISPOSITION

- Mortality rate of children with KD is 0.5% to 2.8%, usually from coronary artery aneurysm, coronary thrombosis, myocarditis, and pancarditis.
- Death usually occurs in the third to fourth week of the illness.
- Before the use of IVIG, approximately 20% of all patients with KD develop coronary aneurysms.
- Treatment with IVIG has reduced the incidence of coronary aneurysms by 80%.
- IVIG has also been shown to improve left ventricular function during the acute stages of the disease.
- Risk factors for the development of coronary aneurysms or giant coronary aneurysms (>8 mm) are:
  1. Fever lasting >10 days
  2. Age <1 year
  3. Male
  4. Recurrence of fever
- Between 1% to 2% of patients have recurrences of KD.

REFERRAL

Multiple specialists may be consulted to assist in the diagnosis of KD including dermatology, rheumatology, and infectious disease. Cardiology consultation is recommended in any patient with cardiac involvement and in the long-term follow-up of patients with KD.

PEARLS & CONSIDERATIONS

COMMENTS

- KD was first described by Dr. Tomasaku Kawasaki in 1967 and published in the *Journal of Allergology*.
- Kawasaki disease is not transmitted from person to person.
- The mechanism of action of intravenous gamma-globulin therapy for KD remains unknown.

SUGGESTED READINGS

Barron KL et al: Report of the National Institutes of Health Workshop on Kawasaki Disease, *J Rheumatol* 26(1):170, 1999.

Freeman AF, Shulran ST: Recent developments in Kawasaki disease, *Curr Opin Infect Dis* 14(3):357, 2001.

Fulton DR, Newburger JW: Long-term cardiac sequelae of Kawasaki disease, *Curr Rheumatol Rep* 2(4):324, 2000.

Gardner-Medwin JM et al: Incidence of Henoch-Schönlein purpura, Kawasaki disease, and rare vasculitides in children of different ethnic origins, *Lancet* 360:1197, 2002.

Gedalia A: Kawasaki disease: an update, *Curr Rheumatol Rep* 4(1):259, 2002.

Sundel RP: Update on the treatment of Kawasaki disease in childhood, *Curr Rheumatol Rep* 4:474, 2002.

Taubert KA, Shulman ST: Kawasaki disease, *Am Fam Physician* 59(11):3093, 1999.

AUTHOR: **PETER PETROPOULOS, M.D.**

BASIC INFORMATION

DEFINITION

Klinefelter's syndrome is a congenital disorder in which a 47,XXY chromosome complement is associated with hypogonadism and infertility.

SYNONYMS

47,XXY Hypogonadism

ICD-9CM CODES
758.7 Klinefelter's syndrome

EPIDEMIOLOGY & DEMOGRAPHICS

INCIDENCE: 1 in 500 men (most common sex chromosome disorder)

GENETICS: The most common mosaic complement is 46,XY/47,XXY. 47,XXY karyotype and occasional 48,XXYY; 48,XXXY; or 49,XXXXY have been reported. The manifestations vary in severity in patients. It is this sex chromosome mosaicism that is thought to account for the variable presentation. Fertility, although very rare, has been reported in men with Klinefelter's syndrome.

PHYSICAL FINDINGS

CLASSIC TRIAD: Small firm testes, azoospermia, and gynecomastia

Prepubertal: Small testes, gonadal volume <1.5 ml is a result of loss of germ cells before puberty.

Postpubertal: Gynecomastia (periductal fat growth) with small, firm, pea-sized testes. Exaggerated growth of the lower extremities results in a decreased crown-to-pubis:pubis-to-floor ratio (Fig. 1-133). There are diminished strength, diminished ability to grow a full beard or mustache, infertility; decreased intellectual development and antisocial behavior are thought to occur with high frequency.

ETIOLOGY

- Several postulated mechanisms: nondisjunction during meiosis and mitosis and anaphase lag during mitosis or meiosis
- Reason: maternal age
  1. The incidence of Klinefelter's rises from 0.6% when the maternal age is 35 yr or less to 5.4% when the maternal age is in excess of 45 yr.
  2. It is of interest to note that the extra X chromosome has a paternal origin as often as a maternal origin.

DIAGNOSIS

- Markedly elevated FSH levels
- Total plasma testosterone are decreased in 50% to 60% of patients
- Free testosterone levels are decreased
- Plasma estradiol is increased stimulating the increase in levels of testosterone-binding globulin with resultant decrease in the testosterone-to-estradiol ratio, which is felt to be the cause of gynecomastia

LABORATORY TESTS

- Normal to low serum testosterone
- Elevated sex hormone binding globulin
- Increased sex hormone binding globin (acts to further suppress any available free testosterone)
- Normal to increased estradiol (a result of augmented peripheral conversion of testosterone to estradiol)
- Testis biopsy shows azoospermia, Leydig cell hyperplasia, hyalinization, and fibrosis of the seminiferous tubules. Mosaics may have focal areas of spermatogenesis, and, on rare occasions, a sperm may appear in the ejaculate. It is the extra X chromosome that is the pivotal factor controlling spermatogenesis as well as affecting neuronal function directly leading to the behavioral abnormalities related to decreased IQ
- Buccal smear: one sex chromatin body

PREPUBERTAL MALE: Gonadotropin levels are normal.

POSTPUBERTAL MALE: Gonadotropin levels are elevated even when the testosterone level is normal.

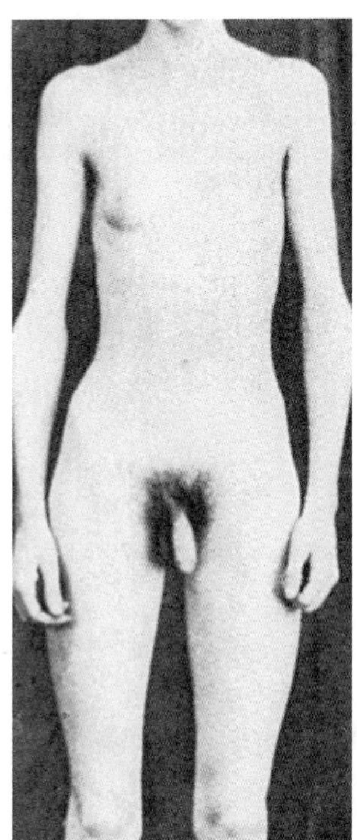

FIGURE 1-133 Klinefelter's syndrome. (From Harrison JH et al: *Campbell's urology,* ed 4, Philadelphia, 1979, WB Saunders.)

DISEASE ASSOCIATIONS:

Malignancies: Breast cancer (20 times greater than XY men and 20% the rate of occurrence in women), nonlymphocytic leukemia, lymphomas, marrow dysplastic syndromes, extragonadal germ cell neoplasms

Autoimmune Disorders: Chronic lymphocytic thyroiditis, Takayasu arteritis, taurodontism (enlarged molar teeth), mitral valve prolapse, varicose veins, asthma, bronchitis, osteoporosis, abnormal glucose tolerance testing, diabetes, varicose veins

TREATMENT

Revolves around three facets of Klinefelter's syndrome:

1. Hypogonadism: androgen replacement in the form of testosterone
2. Gynecomastia: cosmetic surgery
3. Psychosocial problems: androgen therapy and educational support
4. After extensive genetic counseling intracytoplasmic sperm insertion (ICSI) has been used to treat infertility with limited success

PEARLS & CONSIDERATIONS

COMMENTS

- Androgen therapy should not be used in the case of severe mental retardation.
- Also, rule out breast and prostate cancer before initiating or continuing androgen therapy.
- Furthermore, androgen therapy will not improve infertility; it may suppress any spermatogenesis that is taking place within the testes.
- Other causes of primary hypogonadism:
  1. Myotonic muscular dystrophy
  2. Sertoli-cell–only syndrome
  3. Kartagener's syndrome
  4. Anorchia
  5. Acquired hypogonadism
- A 50-fold higher risk of breast cancer is reported in this population.

SUGGESTED READINGS

Manning MA, Hoyme HE: Diagnosis and management of the adolescent boy with Klinefelter syndrome, *Adolescent Medicine State of the Art Reviews* 13(2):367, 2002.

Palermo GD et al: Births after intracytoplasmic sperm insertion of sperm obtained by testicular extraction from men with non-mosaic Klinefelter's syndrome, *N Engl J Med* 338:588, 1998.

Smyth CM, Bremner WJ: Klinefelter syndrome, *Arch Intern Med* 158:1309, 1998.

AUTHOR: **PHILIP J. ALIOTTA, M.D., M.S.H.A.**

Korsakoff's Psychosis

BASIC INFORMATION

DEFINITION

Korsakoff's psychosis is a disorder of learning and memory, out of proportion to other cognitive functions, associated with thiamine deficiency. It is classically seen in alcoholics and may follow the presentation of Wernicke's encephalopathy (see relevant entry).

SYNONYMS

Korsakoff's syndrome
Wernicke-Korsakoff syndrome
Alcoholic polyneuritic psychosis

ICD-9CM CODES
291.1 Alcohol amnestic syndrome

EPIDEMIOLOGY & DEMOGRAPHICS

- Formerly seen most commonly in alcoholics, but declining in recent years
- Slightly more common in males
- Age of onset evenly distributed between age 30 and 70

PHYSICAL FINDINGS & CLINICAL PRESENTATION

- Impairment of ability to remember new material
- Remote memory is said to be retained but is almost universally diminished on careful testing
- Confabulation may occur

ETIOLOGY

Thiamine deficiency, commonly in alcoholics or other malnourished populations, although it may be iatrogenic from prolonged infusion of dextrose-containing fluids without thiamine repletion.

DIAGNOSIS

DIFFERENTIAL DIAGNOSIS

- Stroke, trauma, or tumor affecting the temporal lobes or hippocampus
- Cerebral anoxia
- Transient Global Amnesia
- Dementing illness

WORKUP

A high index of suspicion should be maintained in all alcoholics and other malnourished states.

LABORATORY TESTS

- Serum pyruvate is elevated.
- Whole-blood or erythrocyte transketolase are decreased; rapid resolution to normal in 24 hours with thiamine repletion.

IMAGING STUDIES

MRI may show diencephalic and mesencephalic lesions acutely, but there is no definitive radiologic study for diagnosis.

TREATMENT

NONPHARMACOLOGIC THERAPY

A supervised environment may be required.

ACUTE GENERAL Rx

- Thiamine 100 mg IV or IM should be given immediately.
- Thiamine given acutely during Wernicke's phase (disorders of extraocular movements, confusion, and ataxia), may prevent the development of Korsakoff's psychosis.

CHRONIC Rx

- It is impossible to predict acutely the degree of recovery of an individual patient, although the vast majority will have lasting deficits. Decisions regarding long-term institutionalization should therefore be made cautiously.
- Chronic treatment with thiamine (typically 5 mg per day) is the rule.

DISPOSITION

Patient often must live in protected environment for rest of life.

REFERRAL

- A neurologist should assess the patient.
- Neuropsychologic testing may be helpful.

PEARLS & CONSIDERATIONS

COMMENTS

- This disease is probably underdiagnosed.
- Give thiamine if the disease is even suspected.
- A preventable cause is prolonged dextrose-containing IV fluids without supplemental thiamine.

SUGGESTED READINGS

Cook CC: Prevention and treatment of Wernicke-Korsakoff syndrome, *Alcohol Alcohol Suppl* 35(suppl):19, 2000.

Gallucci M et al: Wernicke encephalopathy: MR findings in five patients, *Am J Roentgenol* 155(6):1309, 1990.

Zubaran C, Fernandes JG, Rodnight R: Wernicke-Korsakoff syndrome, *Postgrad Med J* 78(855):27, 1997.

AUTHOR: **DANIEL MATTSON, M.D., M.SC. (MED.)**

BASIC INFORMATION

DEFINITION

Labyrinthitis is a peripheral vestibulopathy characterized by acute onset of vertigo usually associated with nausea and vomiting. It may or may not be associated with hearing loss.

SYNONYMS

Acute labyrinthitis
Acute vestibular neuronopathy
Vestibular neuronitis
Viral neurolabyrinthitis

ICD-9CM CODES
386.12 Vestibular neuronitis (active and recurrent)
386.3 Labyrinthitis

EPIDEMIOLOGY & DEMOGRAPHICS

INCIDENCE (IN U.S.): Most common cause of prolonged spontaneous vertigo associated with nausea at any age.
PREDOMINANT AGE: Any

CLINICAL PRESENTATION

- Vertigo, nausea and vomiting with onset over several hours
- Symptoms usually peak within 24 hr, then resolve gradually over several weeks
- During the first day the patient usually has difficulty focusing the eyes because of spontaneous nystagmus
- Usually has benign course, with complete recovery within 1 to 3 mo, although older patients may have intractable dizziness that persists for many months

PHYSICAL FINDINGS

- Nystagmus
- Nausea
- Vomiting
- Vertigo worsening with head movement
- Abnormal caloric tests
- Possible hearing loss in the affected ear
- Normal otoscopic examination typically
- Otherwise normal neurologic examination

ETIOLOGY

Often preceded 1-2 wk by a viral-like illness

DIAGNOSIS

DIFFERENTIAL DIAGNOSIS

- Acute labyrinthine ischemia (vascular insufficiency)
- Other forms of labyrinthitis (bacterial and syphilitic)
- Labyrinthine fistula
- Benign positional vertigo
- Meniere's syndrome
- Cholesteatoma
- Drug-induced
- Eighth nerve tumor
- Head trauma

WORKUP

- Otoscopic examination
- Neurologic examination, with close attention to cranial nerves
- Audiogram if symptoms accompanied by hearing loss
- Caloric test if presentation is atypical

LABORATORY TESTS

- Routine laboratory tests are generally not helpful.
- If history of significant emesis, check electrolytes, BUN, and creatinine.

IMAGING STUDIES

Usually not necessary, but enhancement of bony labyrinth may be seen by MRI after injection of contrast material. Head CT with fine cuts through temporal bones if history of trauma or suspect cholesteatoma. MRI of the brain with and without contrast with fine cuts through the internal auditory canal if abnormal cranial nerve examination or suspect eighth nerve tumor.

TREATMENT

NONPHARMACOLOGIC THERAPY

Reassurance. Initial bedrest, then encourage increase in activity as tolerated

ACUTE GENERAL Rx

- Phenergan or other antiemetics are effective
- Vestibular suppressant: Meclizine 12.5 to 25 mg qid often used. Scopolamine patch also effective
- Methylprednisolone 100 mg/day for 3 days, with slow taper over 3 wk.
- Valacyclovir has not been shown to be helpful.

CHRONIC Rx

Important to wean off vestibular suppressant therapy as soon as possible

DISPOSITION

Usually does not require hospital admission unless patient is unable to tolerate oral intake of liquids

REFERRAL

- If symptoms persist or neurologic abnormalities are present
- Consider vestibular rehabilitation, particularly in the elderly

PEARLS & CONSIDERATIONS

COMMENTS

Labyrinthitis is a term that usually implies peripheral vestibulopathy associated with hearing loss. The term "vestibular neuronitis" is typically used when hearing is not affected. Despite this technical distinction, many physicians use both of these terms interchangeably.

SUGGESTED READINGS

Baloh RW et al: Neurotology, *Continuum, Lifelong Learning in Neurology* 2(2):37, 1996.
Strupp M et al: Methylprednisolone, valacyclovir, or the combination for vestibular neuritis, *N Engl J Med* 351(4):322, 2004.

AUTHOR: **SHARON S. HARTMAN, M.D., PH.D.**

Lactose Intolerance 

BASIC INFORMATION

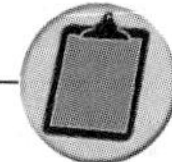

DEFINITION

Lactose intolerance is the insufficient concentration of lactase enzyme, leading to fermentation of malabsorbed lactose by intestinal bacteria with subsequent production of intestinal gas and various organic acids.

SYNONYMS

Lactase deficiency
Milk intolerance

ICD-9CM CODES
271.3 Lactose intolerance

EPIDEMIOLOGY & DEMOGRAPHICS

Nearly 50 million people in the U.S. have partial or complete lactose intolerance. There are racial differences, with <25% of white adults being lactose intolerant, whereas >85% of Asian Americans and >60% of blacks have some form of lactose intolerance.

PHYSICAL FINDINGS & CLINICAL PRESENTATION

- Abdominal tenderness and cramping, bloating, flatulence
- Diarrhea
- Symptoms are directly related to the osmotic pressure of substrate in the colon and occur about 2 hr after ingestion of lactose
- Physical examination: may be entirely within normal limits

ETIOLOGY

- Congenital lactase deficiency: common in premature infants; rare in full-term infants and generally inherited as a chromosomal recessive trait
- Secondary lactose intolerance: usually a result of injury of the intestinal mucosa (Crohn's disease, viral gastroenteritis, AIDS enteropathy, cryptosporidiosis, Whipple's disease, sprue)

DIAGNOSIS

DIFFERENTIAL DIAGNOSIS

- IBD
- IBS
- Pancreatic insufficiency
- Nontropical and tropical sprue
- Cystic fibrosis
- Diverticular disease
- Bowel neoplasm
- Laxative abuse
- Celiac disease
- Parasitic disease (e.g., giardiasis)
- Viral or bacterial infections

WORKUP

- The diagnosis can usually be made on the basis of the history and improvement with dietary manipulation.
- Diagnostic workup may include confirming the diagnosis with hydrogen breath test and excluding other conditions listed in the differential diagnosis that may also coexist with lactase deficiency.

LABORATORY TESTS

- Lactose breath hydrogen test: A rise in breath hydrogen >20 ppm within 90 min of ingestion of 50 g of lactose is positive for lactase deficiency. This test is positive in 90% of patients with lactose malabsorption. Common causes of false-negative results are recent use of oral antibiotics or recent high colonic enema.
- The lactose tolerance test is an older and less accurate testing modality (20% rate of false positive and negative results). The patient is administered an oral dose of 1 to 1.5 gm of lactose/kg body weight. Serial measurement of blood glucose level on an hourly basis for 3 hr is then performed. The test is considered positive if the patient develops intestinal symptoms and the blood glucose level rises <20 mg/dl above the fasting baseline level.
- Diarrhea associated with lactase deficiency is osmotic in nature with an osmotic gap and a pH below 6.5.

IMAGING STUDIES

Imaging studies are generally not indicated. A small bowel series may be useful in patients with significant malabsorption.

TREATMENT

NONPHARMACOLOGIC THERAPY

A lactose-free diet generally results in prompt resolution of symptoms. Lactose is primarily found in dairy products but may be present as an ingredient or component of common foods and beverages. Possible sources of lactose are breads, candies, cold cuts, dessert mixes, cream soups, bologna, commercial sauces and gravies, chocolate, drink mixes, salad dressings, and medications. Labels should be read carefully to identify sources of lactose.

ACUTE GENERAL Rx

- Addition of lactase enzyme supplement (Lactaid tablets, Dairy Ease) before the ingestion of milk products may prevent symptoms in some patients. However, it is not effective for all lactose-intolerant patients.
- Lactose-intolerant patients must ensure adequate calcium intake. Calcium supplementation is recommended to prevent osteoporosis.

CHRONIC Rx

Patient education regarding foods high in lactose, such as milk, cottage cheese, or ice cream, is recommended.

DISPOSITION

Clinical improvement with restriction or elimination of milk products

REFERRAL

GI referral for endoscopic procedures if concomitant GI disorders are suspected

PEARLS & CONSIDERATIONS

COMMENTS

- There is great variability in signs and symptoms in patients with lactose intolerance depending on the degree of lactase deficiency.
- Most patients with lactose intolerance can ingest up to 12 oz of milk daily without symptoms.
- Nondairy synthetic drinks (e.g., Coffee-Mate) and use of rice milk are well tolerated.

SUGGESTED READING

Swagerty DL et al: Lactose intolerance, *Am Fam Physician* 65:1845, 2002.

AUTHOR: **FRED F. FERRI, M.D.**

BASIC INFORMATION

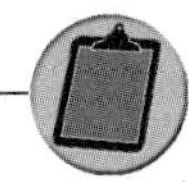

DEFINITION

Lambert-Eaton myasthenic syndrome (LEMS) is a disorder of neuromuscular transmission caused by antibodies directed against presynaptic voltage-gated P/Q calcium channels on motor and autonomic nerve terminals. There are two forms: paraneoplastic (most common) and nonparaneoplastic (autoimmune).

SYNONYMS

Eaton-Lambert syndrome

ICD-9CM CODES
199.1 Malignant neoplasm without specification of site, other

EPIDEMIOLOGY & DEMOGRAPHICS

INCIDENCE (IN U.S.): Uncertain; estimated at 5 cases/1 million persons/yr
PREVALENCE (IN U.S.): Uncertain; estimated at 1 per 100,000
PREDOMINANT SEX: Male > female in a 2:1 ratio.
PEAK INCIDENCE: Sixth decade

PHYSICAL FINDINGS & CLINICAL PRESENTATION

- Weakness with diminished or absent muscle stretch reflexes
- Proximal lower extremity muscles affected most
- Ocular and bulbar muscles less commonly affected
- Transient strength improvement with brief exercise
- Autonomic dysfunction common (dry mouth in 75%, sexual dysfunction, blurred vision, constipation, orthostasis, etc.)

ETIOLOGY

- Antibodies directed against presynaptic voltage-gated P/Q calcium channels are present in most patients. The reduction in calcium influx causes a reduction in acetylcholine release at motor and autonomic nerve terminals.
- Paraneoplastic forms, usually associated with small cell lung cancer (SCLC), are present in 50%-70% of patients. About 1%-3% of patients with SCLC develop LEMS.
- Autoimmune forms, usually in patients with other autoimmune diseases, occur in 10%-30%.

DIAGNOSIS

DIFFERENTIAL DIAGNOSIS

Include: Myasthenia gravis, polymyositis, primary myopathies, carcinomatous myopathies, polymyalgia rheumatica, botulism, Guillain-Barré syndrome.
Section II describes the differential diagnosis of muscle weakness.

WORKUP

Confirm diagnosis by characteristic electrodiagnostic (EMG/NCS) findings: Reduced motor amplitudes with normal sensory studies; >10% decrement in motor amplitudes on slow repetitive nerve stimulation (RNS) at 2-3Hz, with >100% increment on fast RNS (20-30 HZ) or immediately after 10 seconds of maximum exercise (postexercise facilitation).

LABORATORY TESTS

Check P/Q calcium channel antibody titers (commercially available).

IMAGING STUDIES

Screen for an underlying malignancy. Presentation with LEMS may precede diagnosis of SCLC by up to 5 yr. Chest x-ray/CT chest may be required every 6-12 mo for small cell lung cancer.

TREATMENT

NONPHARMACOLOGIC THERAPY

Symptomatic treatment for autonomic dysfunction.

ACUTE GENERAL Rx

- Anticholinesterase agents (pyridostigmine 30-60 mg q4-6h) may yield some improvement.
- Guanidine hydrochloride: start 5-10 mg/kg/day; up to 30 mg/kg/day in 3-day intervals.
- Plasma exchange (200-250 mL/kg over 10-14 days) or IV immunoglobulins (2 g/kg over 2 to 5 days) often produce significant, temporary improvement.
- Prednisone 1.0-1.5 mg/kg/day can be gradually tapered over months to minimal effective dose.
- Azathioprine can be given alone or in combination with prednisone. Give up to 2.5 mg/kg/day. If intolerant of this, can administer cyclosporine up to 3 mg/kg/day instead.
- 3,4-diaminopyridine 10-20 mg PO qid (max 100 mg/day) may improve muscle strength and reduce autonomic symptoms in up to 85% of patients in uncontrolled series. Available in Europe, but limited to research studies in the U.S.

CHRONIC Rx

Treat underlying malignancy if present.

DISPOSITION

- Gradually progressive weakness leading to impaired mobility if untreated
- Clinical remission may occur with chronic immunosuppressive therapy in 43% of cases
- Possible substantial improvement with successful treatment of underlying malignancy

REFERRAL

To a neurologist (recommended) because of infrequency of this disease and risks associated with some treatments. Referral to specialist centers for 3,4-DAP therapy may be warranted in the U.S. Surgical referral for tumor debulking in paraneoplastic forms.

PEARLS & CONSIDERATIONS

COMMENTS

- Prominent autonomic symptoms (dry eyes, dry mouth, impotence, orthostasis) are often the clue to the diagnosis in the appropriate clinical context.
- Many drugs may worsen weakness and should be used only if absolutely necessary. Included are succinylcholine, d-tubocurarine, quinine, quinidine, procainamide, aminoglycoside antibiotics, β-blockers, and calcium channel blockers.

SUGGESTED READINGS

Dropcho EJ: Remote neurologic manifestations of cancer, *Neurol Clin* 20:85, 2002.
Maddison P, Newsom-Davis J: Lambert-Eaton myasthenic syndrome. In: Katirji B et al (eds): *Neuromuscular disorders in clinical practice,* Boston, 2002, Butterworth-Heinemann.
Sanders DB: The Lambert-Eaton myasthenic syndrome diagnosis and treatment, *Ann N Y Acad Sci* 998:500, 2003.

AUTHOR: **EROBOGHENE E. UBOGU, M.D.**

Laryngeal Carcinoma (PTG)

BASIC INFORMATION

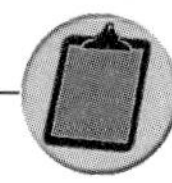

DEFINITION

Cancer of the larynx, including the vocal cords (glottis), supraglottis, and subglottis.

SYNONYMS

Laryngeal cancer
Head and neck cancer (subsite); other sites include oral cavity, pharynx, perinasal sinus, and salivary glands

ICD-9CM CODES
231.0 Carcinoma of larynx

EPIDEMIOLOGY & DEMOGRAPHICS

- 12,000 new cases per year in the U.S.
- 80% male predominance (current, with past and projected increase in female rates as a result of changing smoking habits)
- Peak incidence in sixth decade

PHYSICAL FINDINGS & CLINICAL PRESENTATION

Glottis
- Early diagnosis possible because of voice change (hoarseness). Any voice change of more than 2 wk duration should prompt a laryngeal examination.
- Supraglottis
  1. No early symptom
  2. Cervical lymphadenopathy
  3. Neck pain or ear pain
  4. Discomfort during swallowing
  5. Odynophagia
  6. Later: hoarseness, dysphagia, airway obstruction
- Subglottis

Even more subtle than supraglottic lesion; the same signs occur, only later in the course

ETIOLOGY

- Smoking (cigarette, cigar, or pipe)
- Alcohol intake/abuse
- Diet and nutritional deficiencies
- Gastroesophageal reflux
- Voice abuse
- Chronic laryngitis
- Exposure to wood dust
- Asbestosis
- Exposure to radiation
- Possible role of human papilloma virus

DIAGNOSIS

DIFFERENTIAL DIAGNOSIS

- Laryngitis
- Allergic and nonallergic rhinosinusitis
- Gastroesophageal reflux
- Voice abuse leading to hoarseness
- Laryngeal papilloma
- Vocal cord paralysis secondary to a neurologic condition or secondary to entrapment of the recurrent laryngeal nerve caused by mediastinal compression
- Tracheomalacia

STAGING:

Supraglottic

T1 Tumor limited to one subsite with normal cord mobility
T2 Tumor invades mucosa of more than one subsite (e.g., base of tongue, vallecula, pyriform sinus) without fixation of larynx
T3 Tumor limited to larynx with vocal cord fixation or invasion of postcricoid area or preepiglottis
T4 Tumor invades thyroid cartilage or extends into soft tissue of the neck, thyroid, or esophagus

Glottic

T1 Tumor limited to vocal cord with normal mobility
T1a Tumor limited to one vocal cord
T1b Tumor involves both vocal cords
T2 Tumor extends to supra or subglottis or impairs cord mobility
T3 Tumor limited to larynx with cord fixation
T4 Tumor invades through cartilage or other tissues beyond larynx

Stage grouping

Stage I: T1, N0, M0
Stage II: T2, N0, M0
Stage III: T3, N0, M0
T1, T2, T3, N1, M0
Stage IV: T4, N0, N1, M0
Any T, N2, N3, M0
Any T, any N or M >0

WORKUP

- Laboratory: none
- Endoscopic laryngeal inspection
- After (and only after) diagnosis of the malignancy, imaging with CT or MRI should be undertaken to stage the disease

HISTOLOGIC CLASSIFICATION:

Epithelial cancers
- Squamous cell carcinoma in situ
- Superficially invasive cancer
- Verrucous carcinoma
- Pseudosarcoma
- Anaplastic cancer
- Transitional cell carcinoma
- Lymphoepithelial cancer
- Adenocarcinoma
- Neuroendocrine tumors, including small cell and carcinoid

Sarcomas
Metastatic malignancies

TREATMENT

ACUTE GENERAL Rx

- Early Stage (T or T_2): two options
  1. Conservative surgery (partial laryngectomy) with neck dissection
  2. Primary radiation
- Intermediate Stage: four options
  1. Primary radiation alone
  2. Supraglottic laryngectomy with neck dissection
  3. Supraglottic laryngectomy with postoperative radiation
  4. Chemotherapy with radiation
- Advanced Stage

Chemotherapy and radiation with total laryngectomy reserved for treatment failure

Glottis
- Carcinoma in situ
  1. Microexcision
  2. Laser vaporization
  3. Radiation
- Early Stage (T or T_2): two options
  1. Voice conservation surgery
  2. Radiation
- Intermediate Stage (T_3)
  1. Combined radiation and chemotherapy (cisplatin and 5FU)
  2. Total laryngectomy for treatment failure
- Advanced Stage (T_4)
  1. Combined radiation and chemotherapy
  2. Total laryngectomy and neck dissection followed by postoperative radiation in unfavorable lesion or treatment failure

Subglottis
Total laryngectomy and approximate neck surgery to excise the tumor, followed by radiation

Unresected Cancers
- Induction chemotherapy and radiation followed by neck dissection in chemosensitive tumors, or by laryngectomy and neck dissection in chemoresistant tumors
- If hypopharyngeal involvement exists: laryngopharyngectomy, neck dissection, and postoperative radiation

DISPOSITION

Supraglottis 5-yr control
- T_1 95% to 100%
- T_2 80% to 90%
- T_3 65% to 85%
- T_4 40% to 55%

Glottis 5-yr control
- T_1 95% to 100%
- T_2 50% to 85%
- T_3 35% to 85%
- T_4 20% to 65%

SUGGESTED READING

Sessions RB, Harrison LB, Forastiere AA: Tumors of the larynx and hypopharynx. In *Cancer: principals and practice of oncology*, ed 6, Philadelphia, 2001, Lippincott Williams & Wilkins.

AUTHOR: **TOM J. WACHTEL, M.D.**

BASIC INFORMATION

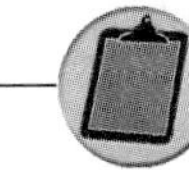

DEFINITION

Laryngitis is an acute or chronic inflammation of the laryngeal mucous membranes.

ICD-9CM CODES
464.0 Acute laryngitis
476.0 Chronic laryngitis

PHYSICAL FINDINGS AND CLINICAL PRESENTATION

ACUTE LARYNGITIS

- Clinical syndrome characterized by the onset of hoarseness, voice breaks, or episodes of aphonia. May also have accompanying sore throat, cough, nasal congestion, and rhinorrhea
- Usually associated with viral upper respiratory infection
- Larynx with diffuse erythema, edema, and vascular engorgement of the vocal folds, and occasionally mucosal ulceration
- In young children subglottis is often affected, resulting in airway narrowing with marked hoarseness, inspiratory stridor, dyspnea, and restlessness
- Respiratory compromise rare in adults

CHRONIC LARYNGITIS

Characterized by hoarseness or dysphonia persisting for longer than 2 wk

ETIOLOGY

ACUTE LARYNGITIS

- Most often caused by viruses so treatment consists of supportive measures as outlined in nonpharmacologic therapy section.
- Studies evaluating the use of antibiotics (erythromycin, penicillin) in acute laryngitis failed to show objective clinical benefit over placebo so they are not routinely recommended. Antibiotics and other antimicrobials may be indicated in cases where specific treatable pathogens are identified.
- Avoid decongestants secondary to their drying effect.
- Guaifenesin may be a useful adjunct as a mucolytic agent.
- In GERD-associated laryngitis use acid-suppressive therapy (H2 blockers, proton pump inhibitors) and nocturnal antireflux precautions.

CHRONIC LARYNGITIS

- Results from any of the following: tuberculosis, usually through bronchogenic spread; leprosy, from nasopharyngeal or oropharyngeal spread; syphilis, in secondary and tertiary stages; rhinoscleroma, extending from the nose and nasopharynx; actinomycosis; histoplasmosis; blastomycosis; paracoccidiomycosis; coccidiosis; candidiasis; aspergillosis; sporotrichosis; rhinosporidiosis; parasitic infections including leishmaniasis and Clinostomum infection following raw freshwater fish ingestion
- Noninfectious causes of both acute and chronic laryngitis include malignancy, voice abuse (singers), gastroesophageal reflux disease, and chemical or environmental irritants such as cigarettes and allergens. Other causes of inflammatory or granulomatous lesions of the larynx include relapsing polychondritis, Wegener's granulomatosis, and sarcoidosis

DIAGNOSIS

WORKUP

- History and physical examination: diagnosis is usually apparent.
- Laryngoscopy for severe or persistent cases.
- Laryngeal cultures should be performed if etiology other than acute viral infection is suspected.
- Imaging not indicated unless evidence of airway compromise. Obtain plain radiographs of neck, anteroposterior and lateral views, to differentiate laryngitis from acute laryngotracheobronchitis or supraglottitis.

DIFFERENTIAL DIAGNOSIS

Young children with signs of airway obstruction:

- Supraglottitis (epiglottitis)
- Laryngotracheobronchitis
- Tracheitis
- Foreign body aspiration

Adults with persistent hoarseness consider noninfectious causes of laryngitis as listed previously

TREATMENT

NONPHARMACOLOGIC THERAPY

- Rest the voice.
- Use an air humidifier.
- Adequate hydration. Avoid alcohol and caffeine because of diuretic effect.

ACUTE GENERAL Rx

- Antibiotics and other antimicrobials: indicated only when a specific pathogen is isolated
- Avoid decongestants secondary to their drying effect
- Guaifenesin may be a useful adjunct as a mucolytic agent
- In GERD-associated laryngitis use acid-suppressive therapy (H2 blockers, proton pump inhibitors) and nocturnal antireflux precautions

DISPOSITION

Uncomplicated laryngitis is usually benign, with gradual resolution of symptoms

REFERRAL

If symptoms persist for >2 wk, refer to otolaryngologist for laryngoscopy

Consider referral to gastroenterologist if GERD is suspected

SUGGESTED READINGS

Garrett CG, Osoff RH: Hoarseness, *Med Clin North Am* 83(1)115, 1999.

Nostrant TT: Gastroesophageal reflux and laryngitis: a skeptic's view, *Am J Med* 108(4A):149S, 2000.

AUTHORS: **JANE V. EASON, M.D.,** and **MARILYN FABBRI, M.D.**

Laryngotracheobronchitis, Acute (Croup)

BASIC INFORMATION

DEFINITION

Acute laryngotracheobronchitis is a viral infection of the upper and lower respiratory tract leading to erythema and edema of the tracheal walls and narrowing of the subglottic region.

SYNONYMS

Croup

ICD-9CM CODES
464.4 Croup

EPIDEMIOLOGY & DEMOGRAPHICS

- Croup is primarily a disease of children occurring between the ages of 1 and 6 yr.
- The peak incidence of croup is the second year of life (50 cases/1000 children).
- Most cases usually occur in the fall and represent parainfluenza type 1 viral infection.
- Winter outbreaks usually represent infection by influenza A and B viruses.
- Croup accounts for 10% to 15% of lower respiratory tract infections in young children.
- Boys are affected more often than girls.

PHYSICAL FINDINGS & CLINICAL PRESENTATION

- Most children with croup present with symptoms of an upper respiratory infection for several days
- Rhinorrhea
- Cough
- Low-grade fever
- Barking cough that usually occurs at night and wakes the child up
- Sore throat
- Stridor
- Apprehension
- Use of accessory muscles of respiration
- Tachypnea
- Tachycardia
- Wheezing

ETIOLOGY

- Parainfluenza viruses (types 1, 2, and 3) are the most common causes of croup in the U.S.
- Influenza A and B, although not a common cause of croup, does lead to more severe cases of the disease
- Adenovirus
- Respiratory syncytial virus
- *Mycoplasma pneumoniae* (rare)

DIAGNOSIS

The diagnosis of croup is usually based on the characteristic clinical presentation of a young child between the ages of 1 to 6 yr waking up with a barking cough ("seal's bark") and stridor.

DIFFERENTIAL DIAGNOSIS

Spasmodic croup, epiglottitis, bacterial tracheitis, angioneurotic edema, diphtheria, peritonsillar abscess, retropharyngeal abscess, smoke inhalation, foreign body

WORKUP

- The workup of a child with croup is to differentiate viral laryngotracheobronchitis from noninfectious causes of stridor and epiglottitis caused by *H. influenzae*.
- The clinical presentation and plain films of the soft tissues of the neck assist in differentiating viral from nonviral and noninfectious causes.

LABORATORY TESTS

- Laboratory tests are not often used to make the diagnosis of viral tracheobronchitis.
- CBC, viral serology, and tissue cultures can be ordered and may detect the infecting agent in up to 65% of cases.
- Pulse oximetry and arterial blood gas determination for patients with tachypnea and respiratory distress.

IMAGING STUDIES

- Plain (AP and lateral) films of the soft tissues of the neck may show the classic radiographic finding of subglottic stenosis or "steeple" sign.
- CT scan of the soft tissues of the neck may be performed in the cases where the differential between croup, epiglottitis, and noninfectious is more difficult.
- Direct visualization via laryngoscopy may be useful in some situations under a controlled setting.

TREATMENT

Treatment of croup focuses on airway management.

NONPHARMACOLOGIC THERAPY

- Oxygen
- Cool mist
- Hot steam

ACUTE GENERAL Rx

- Use of 0.25 to 0.75 ml of 2.25% racemic epinephrine every 20 min is used in children with severe respiratory symptoms, rest stridor, and impending intubation.
- Corticosteroids (e.g., dexamethasone 0.6 mg/kg IV or PO, prednisone 2 mg/kg/day) have been shown to be effective.
- Budesonide, a nebulized corticosteroid given at 4 mg, has been shown to improve symptoms in patients with moderate to severe croup.

CHRONIC Rx

Croup is an acute infectious disease with a short natural history; thus, chronic management is not usually an issue.

DISPOSITION

- Croup is usually benign and self-limited, resolving within 3 to 4 days.
- Complications include:
  1. Airway obstruction
  2. Otitis media
  3. Pneumonia
  4. Dehydration

REFERRAL

If intubation is needed (rarely), an emergency consultation with ENT and/or anesthesiology is recommended.

PEARLS & CONSIDERATIONS

COMMENTS

- Most patients with croup can be managed at home (e.g., patients without stridor and in no respiratory distress).
- Hospitalization and observation is required for children with moderate-to-severe croup (e.g., rest stridor, respiratory distress refractory to the above mentioned acute treatments).

SUGGESTED READINGS

Johnson DW, Jacobson S, Edney PC: A comparison of nebulized budesonide, intramuscular dexamethasone, and placebo for moderately severe croup, *N Engl J Med* 339(8):498, 1998.

Knutson D, Aring A: Viral croup, *Am Fam Physician* 69:535, 2004.

Rosekrans JA: Viral croup: current diagnosis and treatment, *Mayo Clin Proc* 73:1102, 1998.

AUTHOR: **DENNIS MIKOLICH, M.D.**

BASIC INFORMATION

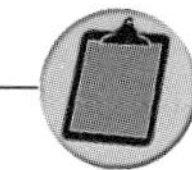

DEFINITION

Lead poisoning refers to multisystem abnormalities resulting from excessive lead exposure.

SYNONYMS

Plumbism

ICD-9CM CODES
984.0 Lead poisoning

EPIDEMIOLOGY & DEMOGRAPHICS

- Lead poisoning is most common in children ages 1 to 5 yr (17,000 cases/100,000 persons). The highest rates are among blacks, those with low income, and urban children.
- In 1991 the Centers for Disease Control and Prevention lowered the definition of a safe blood lead level to <10 μg/dl of whole blood (a blood lead level of 25 μg/dl was considered acceptable before 1991).
- It is estimated that >15% of preschoolers in the U.S. have a blood lead level >15 μg/dl.

PHYSICAL FINDINGS & CLINICAL PRESENTATION

- Findings vary with the degree of toxicity. Examination may be normal in patients with mild toxicity.
- Myalgias, irritability, headache, and general fatigue may be present initially.
- Abdominal cramping, constipation, weight loss, tremor, paresthesias and peripheral neuritis, seizures, and coma may occur with severe toxicity.
- Motor neuropathy is common in children with lead poisoning; learning disorders are also frequent.

ETIOLOGY

Chronic repeated exposure to paint containing lead, plumbing, storage of batteries, pottery, lead soldering

DIAGNOSIS

DIFFERENTIAL DIAGNOSIS

- Polyneuropathies from other sources
- Anxiety disorder, attention deficit disorder
- Malabsorption, acute abdomen
- Iron deficiency anemia

WORKUP

Laboratory screening: all U.S. children should be considered to be at risk for lead poisoning and should be screened routinely starting at 1 yr of age for low-risk children and 6 mo of age for high-risk ones.

LABORATORY TESTS

- Venous blood lead level: normal level: <10 μg/dl; levels of 50 to 70 μg/dl: indicative of moderate toxicity; levels >70 μg/dl: associated with severe poisoning
- Mild anemia with basophilic stippling on peripheral smear
- Elevated zinc protoporphyrin levels or free erythrocyte protoporphyrin level
- An increased body burden of lead with previous high-level exposure in patients with occupational lead poisoning can be demonstrated by measuring the excretion of lead in urine after premedication with calcium EDTA or another chelating agent

IMAGING STUDIES

- Imaging studies are generally not necessary.
- A plain abdominal film can visualize lead particles in the gut.
- "Lead lines" may be noted on x-ray films of long bones.

TREATMENT

NONPHARMACOLOGIC THERAPY

- Provide adequate amounts of calcium, iron, zinc, and protein in patient's diet
- Family education on sources of lead exposure and potential adverse health effects

ACUTE GENERAL Rx

- For children with blood levels of 10 to 19 μg/dl the CDC recommends nonpharmacologic interventions (see Nonpharmacologic Therapy).
- For children with blood levels between 20-44 μg/dl the CDC recommendations include case management by a qualified social worker, clinical management, environmental assessment, and lead hazard control. Chelation therapy should be considered in children with refractory blood lead levels.

Chelation therapy is indicated in children with blood lead levels 45 μg/dl:

- Succimer (DMSA) 10 mg/kg PO q8h for 5 days then q12h for 2 wk can be used in patients with levels between 45 and 70 μg/dl.
- Edetate calcium disodium (EDTA) and dimercaprol (BAL) are effective in patients with severe toxicity.
- Use of both EDTA and DMSA is indicated in children with blood levels >70 μg/dl.
- d-Penicillamine (Cuprimine) can also be used for lead poisoning, but it is not FDA approved for this condition.

CHRONIC Rx

- Reduce exposure, remove any potential lead sources.
- Correct iron deficiency and any other nutritional deficiencies.
- Recheck blood lead level 7 to 21 days after chelation therapy.

DISPOSITION

Patients with mild to moderate toxicity generally improve without any residual deficits. The presence of encephalopathy at diagnosis is a poor prognostic sign. Residual neurologic deficits may persist in these patients. Chelation therapy seems to slow the progression of renal insufficiency in patients with mildly elevated body lead burden.

REFERRAL

If exposure to lead is work related, it should be reported to the Office of the United States Occupational Safety and Health Administration (OSHA).

PEARLS & CONSIDERATIONS

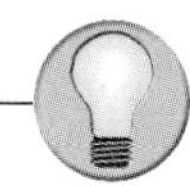

COMMENTS

- Even blood lead concentrations <10 mcg/DL are inversely associated with children's IQ scores at 3 and 5 yr of age.
- Screening of household members of affected individuals is recommended.
- In children with blood lead levels ≤45 mg/dl, treatment with succimer does not improve scores on tests of cognition, behavior, or neuropsychological function.
- Lead toxicity may delay growth and pubertal development in girls.
- Low-level environmental lead exposure may accelerate progressive renal insufficiency in patients without diabetes who have chronic renal disease. Repeated chelation therapy may improve renal function and slow the progression of renal failure.

SUGGESTED READINGS

Canfield RL et al: Intellectual impairment in children with blood lead concentrations below 10 mcg/deciliter, *N Engl J Med* 348:1517, 2003.

Lin JL et al: Environmental lead exposure and progression of chronic renal diseases in patients without diabetes, *N Engl J Med* 348:277, 2003.

Selevan SG et al: Blood lead concentration and delayed puberty in girls, *N Engl J Med* 348:1527, 2003.

AUTHOR: **FRED F. FERRI, M.D.**

BASIC INFORMATION

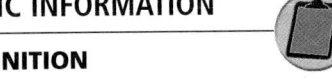

DEFINITION

Legg-Calvé-Perthes disease is a self-limited disorder of unknown etiology caused by ischemia of the immature femoral head that leads to bone necrosis and variable amounts of collapse during the reparative process.

SYNONYMS

Coxa plana
Capital femoral osteochondrosis

ICD-9CM CODES
732.1 Perthes' disease

EPIDEMIOLOGY & DEMOGRAPHICS

PREVALENCE: 1 case/1300 children
PREDOMINANT SEX: Male:female ratio of 4:1
PREDOMINANT AGE: 3 to 10 yr

PHYSICAL FINDINGS & CLINICAL PRESENTATION

- Initial complaint: usually a mildly painful limp
- Pain referred down the inner aspect of the thigh to the knee
- Moderate restriction of motion resulting from hip synovitis (abduction and internal rotation are especially limited)
- Pain at the extremes of movement and tenderness over anterior hip joint

ETIOLOGY

Unknown

DIAGNOSIS

DIFFERENTIAL DIAGNOSIS

- Toxic synovitis
- Low-grade septic arthritis
- JRA

WORKUP

Diagnosis is usually based on the physical findings and eventual radiographic findings.

IMAGING STUDIES

- Plain roentgenography to establish the diagnosis (Fig. 1-134)
- AP and frog-leg lateral radiographs
- Technetium bone scanning to assist in making the diagnosis in early cases

TREATMENT

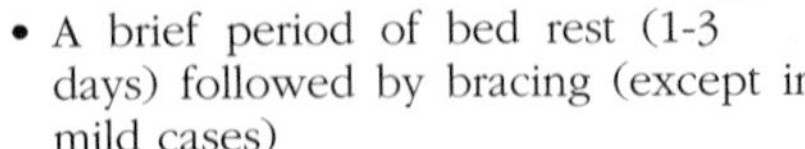

ACUTE GENERAL Rx

- A brief period of bed rest (1-3 days) followed by bracing (except in mild cases)
- Bracing possibly required for 2 to 3 yr in small percent of patients

DISPOSITION

- Prognosis depends on age of patient and degree of involvement of the femoral head at onset.
- Young patients (under 6 yr) with minimal involvement do well.
- Older patients (over 8 yr) often do poorly.
- A few patients eventually develop degenerative arthritis.

REFERRAL

For orthopedic consultation when diagnosis is suspected

PEARLS & CONSIDERATIONS

COMMENTS

There is great uncertainty regarding treatment and its effect on outcome. It may be that bracing has no effect whatsoever on the end result.

SUGGESTED READINGS

Gregorzewski A et al: Treatment of the collapsed femoral head by containment in Legg-Calvé-Perthes disease, *J Pediatr Orthop* 23:15, 2003.
Guerado E, Garces G: Perthes disease: a study of constitutional aspects in adulthood, *J Bone Joint Surg Br* 83(4):569, 2001.
Joseph B, Mulpuri K, Varghese G: Perthes' disease in the adolescent, *J Bone Joint Surg Br* 83(5):715, 2001.
Scherl SA: Lower extremity problems in children, *Pediatr Rev* 25:52, 2004.
Stevens DB, Tao SS, Glueck CJ: Recurrent Legg-Calvé-Perthes disease: case report and long term follow up, *Clin Orthop* 385:124, 2001.
Thompson GH et al: Legg-Calvé-Perthes disease: current concepts, *Instr Course Lect* 51:367, 2002.

AUTHOR: **LONNIE R. MERCIER, M.D.**

A
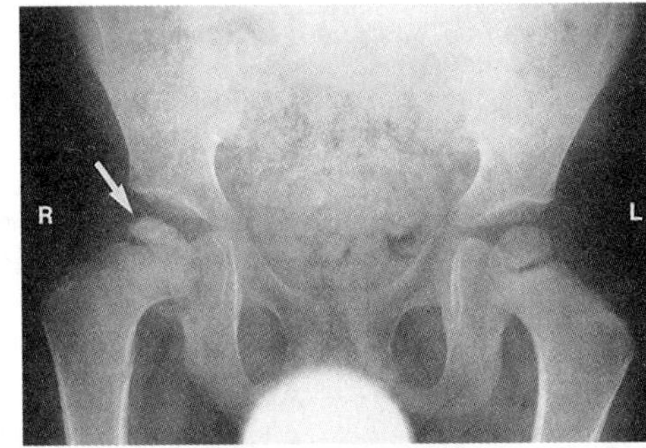

B
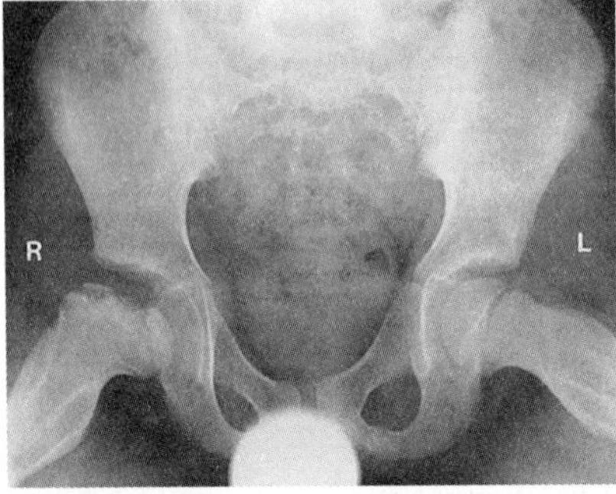

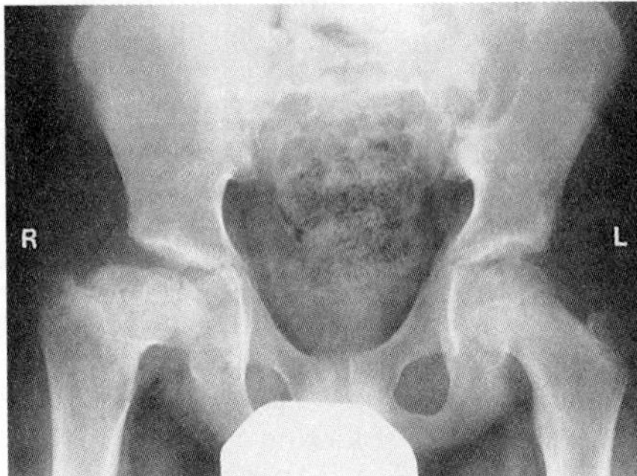

C

FIGURE 1-134 Legg-Calvé-Perthes disease. A, An anteroposterior view of the pelvis demonstrates fragmentation and sclerosis of the right femoral epiphysis (*arrow*) in this 6-year-old male. **B,** A follow-up film obtained 8 years later shows continuing deformity resulting from the osteonecrosis. The patient developed significant degenerative arthritis (**C**) by the age of 12 years. (From Mettler FA[ed]: *Primary care radiology,* Philadelphia, 2000, WB Saunders.)

BASIC INFORMATION

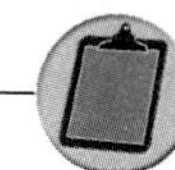

DEFINITION

Leishmaniasis is an infectious disease caused by a heterogeneous group of protozoan parasites belonging to the genus *Leishmania* and resulting in a variety of different clinical syndromes.

ICD-9CM CODES
085.9 Leishmaniasis

EPIDEMIOLOGY & DEMOGRAPHICS

INCIDENCE: Approximately 400,000 new cases occur each year with almost 400 million people at risk for the disease.

- Can be classified geographically into New World versus Old World disease
- Infection can be divided into cutaneous, mucocutaneous, visceral disease
- Incubation period: from 1 wk to many months for cutaneous and mucosal leishmaniasis; 2 to 6 mo (range is 10 days to years) for visceral leishmaniasis
- Mode of transmission: by the sandfly vector; can also be spread via shared needles, blood transfusions, vertically from the mother to fetus, or sexually

PHYSICAL FINDINGS & CLINICAL PRESENTATION

Cutaneous Syndrome

- Localized cutaneous leishmaniasis
- Mucosal leishmaniasis
- Leishmania recidivans
- Diffuse cutaneous leishmaniasis

Visceral Syndrome

- Viscerotrophic leishmaniasis: fever, chronic fatigue, malaise, cough, intermittent diarrhea, and abdominal pain. Signs include adenopathy, hepatosplenomegaly, hyperpigmentation of skin, petechiae, jaundice, edema, and ascites
- Post–kala-azar dermal leishmaniasis: generalized cutaneous rash that is often papular or nodular; severe forms with desquamation of skin and mucosa

ETIOLOGY

- Old-World parasite: *Leishmania tropica, L. major, L. aethiopica, L. donovani, L. infantum*
- New-World parasite: *L. braziliensis* and *L. mexicana complex, L. chagasi, L.b. guyanensis, L.b. panamensis*

DIAGNOSIS

DIFFERENTIAL DIAGNOSIS

- Malaria
- African trypanosomiasis
- Brucellosis
- Enteric fever
- Bacterial endocarditis
- Generalized histoplasmosis
- Chronic myelocytic leukemia
- Hodgkin's disease and other lymphomas
- Sarcoidosis
- Hepatic cirrhosis
- Tuberculosis

WORKUP

- CBC
- LFTs
- Renal panel
- Serology
- Biopsy for histology and culture
- PCR

LABORATORY TESTS

- CBC: anemia, neutropenia, thrombocytopenia, and eosinophilia
- LFTs: hypergammaglobulinemia, hypoalbuminemia, and hyperbilirubinemia
- Elevated BUN and creatinine
- Specific diagnosis confirmed by intracellular amastigote in Giemsa-stained impression smears or sectioned tissue or culture performed in NNN (Novy, MacNeal, Nicolle) or Schneider's medium
- Serologic diagnosis: ELISA, direct agglutination tests, K39 ELISA, PCR, and monoclonal antibody staining of tissue smears.
- Montenegro skin test

TREATMENT

- Nonspecific or supportive care
  1. Nutritional diet
  2. Antimicrobial agents for concurrent infections
  3. Blood transfusions
  4. Iron and vitamins
- Specific antileishmanial therapy
  1. Pentavalent antimonials: sodium stibogluconate and sodium antimonygluconate
  2. Amphotericin B
  3. Pentamidine
  4. Aminosidine
  5. Other agents: allopurinol, ketoconazole, paromomycin (combined with other regimens)
  6. Immunotherapy: IFN-γ
  7. New agent: Miltefosine
  8. Local or tropical treatments and physical therapy, including thermal treatments
  9. Plastic surgery

DISPOSITION

Follow-up examination is important for the early detection and treatment relapse.

REFERRAL

To infectious disease experts for accurate diagnosis and management

PEARLS & CONSIDERATIONS

COMMENTS

- Prevention by reservoir control-destruction of animal reservoir hosts, mass treatment of human in kala-azar–prevalent areas
- Prevention by vector control: insecticide spraying in domestic and peridomestic areas
- Vaccines are in various stages of development and clinical trials. None are licensed or commercially available at this time

SUGGESTED READINGS

Abdeen ZA et al: Epidemiology of visceral leishmaniasis in the Jenin District, West Bank 1989-1998, *Am J Trop Med Hyg* 66(4):329, 2002.

Berman JD: Human leishmaniasis: clinical, diagnostic, and chemotherapeutic developments in the last 10 years, *Clin Infect Dis* 24:684, 1997.

Royer MA, Crowe CO: American cutaneous leishmaniasis, *Arch Pathol Lab Med* 126(4):471, 2002.

Sundar S et al: Low-dose liposomal amphotericin B in refractory Indian visceral leishmaniasis: a multicenter study, *Am J Trop Med Hyg* 66(2):143, 2002.

Sundar S et al: Oral miltefosine for Indian visceral leishmaniasis, *N Engl J Med* 347:1739, 2002.

AUTHOR: **VASANTHI ARUMUGAM, M.D.**

BASIC INFORMATION

DEFINITION

Leprosy is a chronic granulomatous infection of humans that primarily affects the skin and peripheral nerves.

SYNONYMS

Hansen's disease

ICD-9CM CODES

030.9 Leprosy

EPIDEMIOLOGY & DEMOGRAPHICS

- The number of cases worldwide has fallen from more than 5 million cases in 1985 to less than 1 million cases in 1998.
- Nearly 75% of the cases of leprosy are found in India, Brazil, Bangladesh, Indonesia, and Myanmar.
- More than 85% of the cases diagnosed in the U.S. are found among immigrants.
- Worldwide incidence is 650,000 new cases per year.
- Annual incidence in the U.S. is 150 new cases per year.
- Leprosy is more common in men than women (2:1).
- Leprosy can occur at any age but usually is found in young children.

PHYSICAL FINDINGS & CLINICAL PRESENTATION

- A skin lesion: most common initial presentation
- Sensory loss
- Anhidrosis
- Neuritic pain
- Palpable peripheral nerves
- Nerve damage (most commonly affected nerves are ulnar, median, common peroneal, posterior tibial, radial cutaneous nerve of the wrist, facial, and posterior auricular)
- Muscle atrophy and weakness
- Foot drop
- Claw hand and claw toes
- Lagophthalmos, nasal septal perforation, collapse of bridge of nose (Fig. 1-135, *A*), loss of eyebrows resulting in "leonine" facies

Leprosy can present along a spectrum from simple cutaneous skin lesions with minimal sensory loss (Fig. 1-135, *B*) to severe extensive skin involvement, painful neuritis, muscle wasting and contractures, and multiple peripheral nerve damage.

ETIOLOGY

- Leprosy is caused by *Mycobacterium leprae,* an obligate intracellular acid-fast rod.
- The mode of transmission remains elusive. Spread in humans is thought to occur via the respiratory route or entry through broken skin.
- Zoonotic transmission from armadillos has not been proven.
- The majority of people exposed to patients with leprosy do not develop the disease because of their natural immunity.
- Incubation period is 3 to 5 yr.

DIAGNOSIS

- The diagnosis of leprosy relies on a detailed history and physical examination and is established by the demonstration of acid-fast bacilli in skin smears or skin biopsies of the affected sites.
- Leprosy has been classified according to the WHO system into:
  1. Paucibacillary leprosy defined as fewer than five skin lesions with no bacilli on skin smear.
  2. Multibacillary leprosy defined as six or more skin lesions and may be skin-smear positive.
- Leprosy has also been classified more specifically according to the type of skin lesions, sensory and motor deficits, and biopsy into:
  1. Indeterminate leprosy
  2. Tuberculoid leprosy

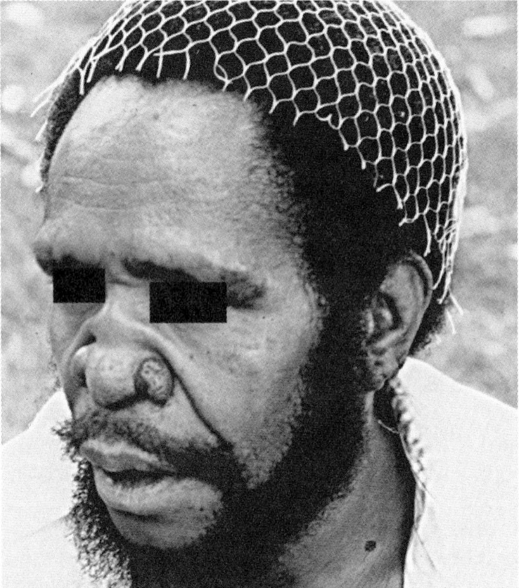

A

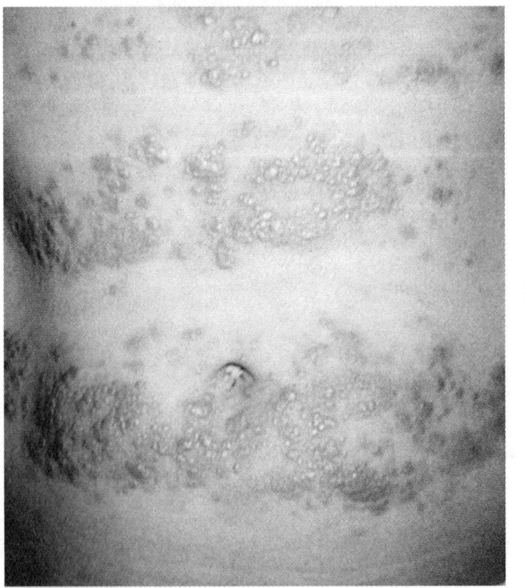

B

FIGURE 1-135 **A,** Advanced lepromatous leprosy with collapse of the nasal septum. **B,** Lepromatous leprosy characterized by extensive papule formation over abdomen. Minimal or no sensory loss is present in the affected areas. (**A** from Gorbach SL: *Infectious diseases,* ed 2, Philadelphia, 1998, WB Saunders; **B** from Mandell GL; *Mandell, Douglas, and Bennett's principles and practice of infectious diseases,* ed 5, New York, 2000, Churchill Livingstone.)

3. Borderline tuberculoid leprosy
4. Borderline lepromatous leprosy
5. Lepromatous leprosy

DIFFERENTIAL DIAGNOSIS

The differential diagnosis of leprosy includes: sarcoidosis, rheumatoid arthritis, systemic lupus erythematosus, lymphomatoid granulomatosis, carpal tunnel syndrome, cutaneous leishmaniasis, fungal infections and other causes of hypopigmented, hyperpigmented, and erythematous skin lesions.

WORKUP

Any patient who presents with skin lesions and a sensory or muscle deficit should have a workup for leprosy.

LABORATORY TESTS

- *Mycobacterium leprae* cannot be cultured on artificial media. The bacteria rapidly proliferate when injected into the footpads of mice or into armadillos and sometimes is used for drug-sensitivity testing.
- Serologic tests, including the antibody to phenolic glycolipid 1 (PGL-1), are available and used for diagnostic confirmation and research epidemiologic studies.
- Lepromin intradermal skin test is not diagnostic and not for commercial use.
- Skin smears are taken from active sites or most commonly from the earlobe, elbows, or knees and are stained for acid-fast bacilli.
- Skin biopsies of active sites are stained for acid-fast bacilli.
- Peripheral nerve biopsy can be done in patients with sensory loss and no skin lesions. Common nerves biopsied are the radial cutaneous nerve of the wrist and the sural nerve of the ankle.

IMAGING STUDIES

X-ray studies are usually of no benefit in the diagnosis or treatment of leprosy.

TREATMENT

NONPHARMACOLOGIC THERAPY

- Physical therapy for patients with upper and lower extremity deformities
- Proper foot care and footwear to prevent ulcer formation

ACUTE GENERAL Rx

For paucibacillary leprosy:

- Dapsone 100 mg PO qd for 6 mo in an unsupervised setting is the treatment of choice.
- Rifampin 600 mg PO qd for 6 mo in a supervised setting is the recommendation by WHO.
- Ofloxacin 400 mg qd or minocycline 100 mg qd are other alternatives.

For multibacillary leprosy:

- Rifampin 600 mg PO qd and clofazimine 300 mg PO qd for 24 mo in a supervised setting.
- Rifampin 100 mg PO qd and clofazimine 50 mg PO qd for 24 mo in an unsupervised setting.
- Dapsone 100 mg PO qd is sometimes added as triple therapy in this group of patients.
- Clofazimine 50 mg daily is usually used in combination with dapsone for better bacteriocidal effect.

CHRONIC Rx

- If relapse occurs, the patient is treated with the same medical regimen because resistance is low.
- If relapse is from paucibacillary to multibacillary, the medical regimen for multibacillary should be used for therapy.

DISPOSITION

- Relapse is $<1\%$ for multibacillary and just over 1% in paucibacillary cases.
- Patients are initially followed up monthly and when treatment is completed every 3 to 6 mo for the next 5 to 10 yr.
- Some patients develop reactions known as erythema nodosum leprosum and reversal reaction, usually during treatment.
  1. Erythema nodosum leprosum results in tender nodules and is treated with either prednisolone 40 to 60 mg qd until the reaction is controlled and tapered or thalidomide 300 to 400 mg qd and tapered to 100 mg qd with monthly attempts to wean down further.
  2. Reactive reaction results in the development of new skin lesions with swelling and erythema of existing lesions. Treatment is with either NSAIDs or prednisolone.

REFERRAL

- National Hansen's Disease Programs (NHDP) Center in Baton Rouge, Louisiana, and 15 outpatient clinics in the U.S. offer consultations and treatment. Telephone: 1-800-642-2477.
- Any suspected case of leprosy merits an infectious disease consultation. Consultation with orthopedic, podiatry, ophthalmology, physical therapy, plastic surgery, and psychology are all in order for any of the potential sequelae of the disease.

PEARLS & CONSIDERATIONS

COMMENTS

- The risk of transmission is low in patients with leprosy, and therefore no infection control precautions of patients hospitalized is needed.
- Family members and close contacts need to be examined frequently for the development of lesions.
- Dapsone or rifampin prophylaxis is not recommended in the prevention of leprosy.
- BCG vaccination has a 50% protective effect in the prevention of leprosy and may be considered.

SUGGESTED READINGS

Cambau E et al: Multidrug-resistance to dapsone, rifampicin, and ofloxacin in *Mycobacterium leprae, Lancet* 349:103, 1997.

Jacobsen RR, Krahenbuhl JL: Leprosy, *Lancet* 353:655, 1999.

Leprosy: global target attained, *Wkly Epidemiol Rec* 20:155, 2001.

Ramos-e-Silva M, Rebello PF: Leprosy: recognition and treatment, *Am J Clin Dermatol* 2(4):203, 2001.

AUTHORS: **PETER PETROPOULOS, M.D.,** and **DENNIS MIKOLICH, M.D.**

BASIC INFORMATION

DEFINITION

Leptospirosis is a zoonosis caused by the spirochete *Leptospira interrogans.*

SYNONYMS

Weil's disease

ICD-9CM CODES
100.9 Leptospirosis

EPIDEMIOLOGY & DEMOGRAPHICS

INCIDENCE (IN U.S.):
- 0.05 cases/100,000 persons
- Significant underestimation because of underreporting
- Hawaii consistently has the highest reported annual incidence rate in U.S.

PREDOMINANT SEX: Male (4:1)
PREDOMINANT AGE: Teenagers and young adults
PEAK INCIDENCE: Summer months, into the fall
GENETICS:
Neonatal Infection: Can occur

PHYSICAL FINDINGS & CLINICAL PRESENTATION

ANICTERIC FORM:
- Milder and more common presentation of disease
- A self-limited systemic illness with two stages:
  1. Septicemic stage: presents abruptly with fevers, headache, severe myalgias, rigors, prostration, and sometimes circulatory collapse; conjunctival suffusion is common; skin rash, pharyngitis, lymphadenopathy, hepatomegaly, splenomegaly, or muscle tenderness may occur; lasts about 1 wk with complete resolution usual.
  2. Immune stage: occurs a few days after first stage with similar symptoms; hallmark is aseptic meningitis.

ICTERIC LEPTOSPIROSIS (WEIL'S SYNDROME):
1. Denotes severe cases, with symptoms of hepatic, renal, and vascular dysfunction
2. Biphasic course: persistence of fever, jaundice, and azotemia
3. Complications: oliguria or anuria, hemorrhage, hypotension, vascular collapse

ETIOLOGY

Caused by a spirochete, *L. interrogans*
- Infects a variety of animals, including most mammals
- Specific serotypes associated with different hosts—*pomona* in livestock, *canicola* in dogs (Fig. 1-136), and *icterohaemorrhagiae* in rodents
- Exposure to animal urine or infected water method by which organism penetrates skin or mucous membranes; most cases related to recreational swimming and canoeing; outbreak occurred in participants of triathlons in Wisconsin and Illinois; recently described cases in inner-city residents are related to exposure to rat urine

DIAGNOSIS

DIFFERENTIAL DIAGNOSIS

- Bacterial meningitis
- Viral hepatitis
- Influenza
- Legionnaire's disease

WORKUP

Culture of blood, CSF, and urine:
- Organism can be isolated from blood or CSF during first 10 days of illness.
- Urine should be cultured after first week and for up to 30 days after onset of illness.

LABORATORY TESTS

- Normal or elevated WBCs, at times up to 70,000/mm^3
- Elevated transaminases or bilirubin
- Anemia, azotemia, hypoprothrombinemia in those with icteric illness
- Elevated CK in first phase
- Meningitis in both phases, but aseptic in second phase

IMAGING STUDIES

Chest radiographs to show bilateral nonlobar infiltrates

TREATMENT

NONPHARMACOLOGIC THERAPY

- Supportive
- Observation for dehydration, hypotension, renal failure, hemorrhage

ACUTE GENERAL Rx

- IV penicillin G 1 million U q4h
- Doxycycline 100 mg PO bid for 7 days
- Vitamin K administration if hypoprothrombinemia present
- Possible Jarisch-Herxheimer reaction when treated with penicillin

DISPOSITION

- Anicteric leptospirosis is self-limited, but administration of antibiotics can decrease severity and duration of symptoms.
- Icteric leptospirosis, even with supportive therapy, may have a mortality as high as 10%.

REFERRAL

- If more than mild disease
- If no response to treatment

PEARLS & CONSIDERATIONS

COMMENTS

Significantly underreported illness

SUGGESTED READINGS

Katz AR et al: Leptospirosis in Hawaii, 1974-1998: epidemiologic analysis of 353 laboratory-confirmed cases, *Am J Trop Med Hyg* 66:61, 2002.

Tunbridge AJ et al: A breathless triathlete, *Lancet* 359:130, 2002.

Vinetz JM: Leptospirosis, *Curr Opin Infect Dis* 14:527, 2001.

AUTHOR: **MAURICE POLICAR, M.D.**

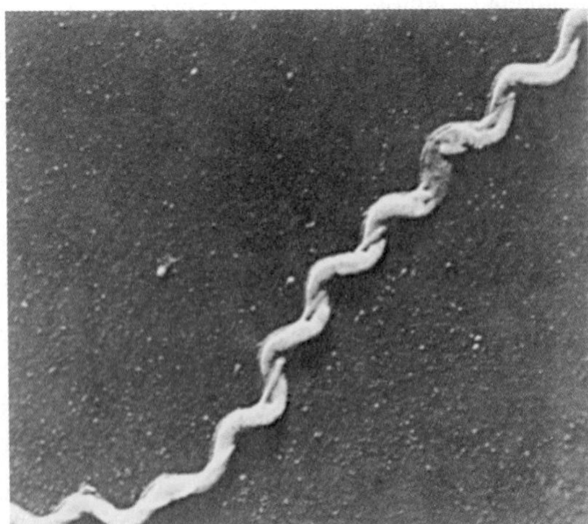

FIGURE 1-136 Electron micrograph of *Leptospira interrogans* (serovar *canicola*) showing the tightly coiled helicoids rod with the periplasmic axial filament. (Courtesy Armed Forces Institute of Pathology, AFIP No. 60-10941. In Gorbach SL: *Infectious diseases,* ed 2, Philadelphia, 1998, WB Saunders.)

BASIC INFORMATION

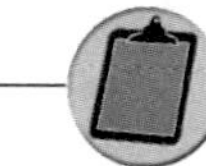

DEFINITION

Acute lymphoblastic leukemia (ALL) is characterized by uncontrolled proliferation of abnormal, immature lymphocytes and their progenitors, ultimately replacing normal bone marrow elements.

SYNONYMS

Lymphoid leukemia
ALL

ICD-9CM CODES

204.0 Acute lymphoblastic leukemia

EPIDEMIOLOGY & DEMOGRAPHICS

- ALL is primarily a disease of children (peak incidence at ages 2 to 10 yr).
- It is diagnosed in 3000 to 4000 persons in the U.S. each year; two thirds are children.

PHYSICAL FINDINGS & CLINICAL PRESENTATION

- Skin pallor, purpura, or easy bruising
- Lymphadenopathy or hepatosplenomegaly
- Fever, bone pain, oliguria, weakness, weight loss, mental status changes

ETIOLOGY

- Unknown; increased risk in patients with a previous use of antineoplastic agents (e.g., chemotherapy of NHL, Hodgkin's disease, ovarian cancer, myeloma)
- Environmental factors (e.g., ionizing radiation), toxins (e.g., benzene)

DIAGNOSIS

DIFFERENTIAL DIAGNOSIS

Acute myeloid leukemia (AML): the distinction between ALL and AML and the classification of the various subtypes are based on the following factors:

- Cell morphology
  1. Lymphoblasts: a high nucleus/cytoplasmic ratio; usually, cytoplasmic granules are not present.
  2. Myeloblasts: abundant cytoplasm; often, cytoplasmic granules (Auer rods) are present.
- Histochemical stains
  1. Peroxidase and Sudan black stains: negative in ALL; useful to distinguish nonlymphoid from lymphoid cells
  2. Chloroacetate esterase: a pink cytoplasmic reaction identifies granulocytes; useful to distinguish granulocytes from monocytes in patients with AML

Lymphoblastic lymphoma
Aplastic anemia
Infectious mononucleosis
Leukemoid reaction to infection
Multiple myeloma

WORKUP

- Laboratory evaluation
- Bone marrow examination (with biopsy, cytochemistry, immunophenotyping, and cytogenetics)
- Lumbar puncture and imaging studies

LABORATORY TESTS

- CBC reveals normochromic, normocytic anemia, thrombocytopenia.
- Peripheral smear will reveal lymphoblasts.
- Initial blood work should also include BUN, creatinine, serum electrolytes, uric acid, LDH.
- Special diagnostic tests include immunophenotyping, cytogenetics, and cytochemistry.
- The French, American, British (FAB) Cooperative Study Group has classified ALL into three groups (L1-L3) based on cell size, cytoplasmic appearance, nucleus shape, and chromatin pattern; the most common form is the L2 type.
- Immunologic classification is on the basis of expression of surface antigens by blast cells: T lineage and B lineage.

IMAGING STUDIES

- Chest radiograph to evaluate for the presence of mediastinal mass
- CT scan or ultrasound of abdomen to assess splenomegaly or leukemic infiltration of abdominal organs

TREATMENT

ACUTE GENERAL Rx

- Emergency treatment is indicated in patients with intracerebral leukostasis. It consists of one or more of the following:
  1. Cranial irradiation of the whole brain in one- or two-dose fractions
  2. Leukapheresis
  3. Oral hydroxyurea (requires 48 to 72 hr to significantly lower the circulating blast count)
- Urate nephropathy can be prevented by vigorous hydration and lowering uric acid level with allopurinol and urine alkalization with acetazolamide.
- Infections must be aggressively treated with broad-spectrum antibiotics.
  1. Any febrile or neutropenic patients must have cultures taken and be properly treated with IV antibiotics.
  2. If evidence of infection persists despite adequate treatment with antibiotics, amphotericin B may be added to provide coverage against fungal infections *(Candida, Aspergillus)*.
- Correct significant thrombocytopenia (platelet counts <20,000/mm^3) with platelet transfusion.
- Bleeding secondary to DIC is treated with heparin and replacement of clotting factors.
- Induction therapy is intensive chemotherapy to destroy a significant number of leukemic cells and achieve remission; it usually consists of a combination of vincristine (Oncovin), prednisone, and l-asparaginase (ELSPAR) in children or an anthracene in adults.
- Consolidation therapy consists of an aggressive course of chemotherapy with or without radiotherapy shortly after complete remission has been obtained. Its purpose is to prolong the remission period or cure. Commonly used agents are VM-26, VP-16, HiDAC.
- Meningeal prophylactic therapy with intrathecal methotrexate with or without cranial irradiation is indicated to prevent meningeal sequestration of leukemic cells.
- The goal of maintenance therapy is to maintain a state of remission. In patients with ALL, intermittent therapy is continued for at least 3 yr with a combination of methotrexate and 6-mercaptopurine (Purinethol).
- Bone marrow transplantation: patients should receive allograft in the first complete remission if they are between ages 20 and 50 yr and have matched a sibling donor.

DISPOSITION

- Prognosis is generally poorer in adult disease compared with childhood disease (40% adult cure rate versus 80% cure rate in children).
- Five-year leukemia-free survival is <40%.
- The presence of Philadelphia chromosome (Ph$^+$), monosomy 5 and 7, and abnormalities of 11q23 are bad prognostic signs.

REFERRAL

Referral to hematologist is indicated in all cases of actue lymphoblastic leukemia.

SUGGESTED READING

Chin-Hon P et al: Acute lymphoblastic leukemia, *N Engl J Med* 350:1535, 2004.

AUTHOR: **FRED F. FERRI, M.D.**

Leukemia, Acute Myelogenous

BASIC INFORMATION

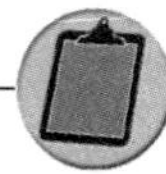

DEFINITION

Acute myelogenous leukemia (AML) is a disorder characterized by uncontrolled proliferation of primitive myeloid cells (blasts), ultimately replacing normal bone marrow elements frequently resulting in hematopoietic insufficiency (granulocytopenia, thrombocytopenia, or anemia) with or without leukocytosis.

SYNONYMS

Acute nonlymphoblastic leukemia (ANLL)
Acute nonlymphocytic leukemia
Acute myeloid leukemia (AML)

ICD-9CM CODES
205.0 Acute myelogenous leukemia

EPIDEMIOLOGY & DEMOGRAPHICS

- AML usually affects adults (most patients are 30 to 60 yr old; median age at presentation is 50 yr).
- Annual incidence is 2 to 4/100,000

PHYSICAL FINDINGS & CLINICAL PRESENTATION

Patients generally come to medical attention because of the effects of the cytopenias:

- Anemia manifests with weakness or fatigue.
- Thrombocytopenia can manifest with bleeding, petechiae, and ecchymosis.
- Neutropenia can result in infections and fever.
- Physical examination may reveal skin pallor, bruises, petechiae; abdominal examination may reveal hepatosplenomegaly; peripheral lymphadenopathy may also be present.
- Hyperleukocytosis can lead to symptoms of leukostasis, such as ocular and cerebrovascular dysfunction or bleeding.

ETIOLOGY

Risk factors are previous use of antineoplastic agents, chromosomal abnormalities, ionizing radiation, toxins, immunodeficiency states, and chronic myeloproliferative disorders.

DIAGNOSIS

DIFFERENTIAL DIAGNOSIS

- Acute lymphocytic leukemia
- Leukemoid reaction
- Myelodysplastic syndrome
- Infiltrative diseases of the bone marrow
- Epstein-Barr, other viral infection

LABORATORY TESTS

- CBC reveals anemia, thrombocytopenia. Peripheral WBC count varies from <5000/mm^3 to >100,000/mm^3.
- Additional laboratory findings may include elevated LDH and uric acid levels, decreased fibrinogen, and increased FDP secondary to DIC.
- Cytogenetic abnormalities are common (chromosome 8 is most frequently involved in AML).
- The distinction between ALL and AML and the classification of the various subtypes are based on the following factors:
  1. Cell morphology: myeloblasts reveal abundant cytoplasm; cytoplasmic granules are often present (Auer rods).
  2. Histochemical stains:
     a. Peroxidase and Sudan black stains are negative in ALL.
     b. Chloroacetate esterase: a pink cytoplasmic reaction identifies granulocytes; useful to distinguish granulocytes from monocytes in patients with AML.
- AML is diagnosed by the presence of at least 30% blast cells and positive peroxidase or Sudan black histochemical stain in the bone marrow aspirate.
- The French, American, British (FAB) Cooperative Study Group has classified AML into seven categories (M1-M7) based on the type and percentage of immature cells.

IMAGING STUDIES

- Chest x-ray is useful to evaluate for the presence of mediastinal masses.
- CT scan of the abdomen may reveal hepatosplenomegaly or leukemic involvement of other organs.

TREATMENT

ACUTE GENERAL Rx

- Emergency treatment consisting of one or more of the following is indicated in patients with intracerebral leukostasis:
  1. Cranial irradiation
  2. Leukapheresis
  3. Oral hydroxyurea
- Urate nephropathy can be prevented by vigorous hydration and lowering uric acid level with allopurinol and urine alkalinization with acetazolamide.
- Infections must be aggressively treated with broad-spectrum antibiotics.
- Correct significant thrombocytopenia with platelet transfusions.
- Bleeding secondary to DIC is treated with heparin and replacement of clotting factors.
- Intensive induction chemotherapy to destroy a significant number of leukemic cells and achieve remission usually consists of cytarabine (Cytosar) and daunorubicin. Alltransretinoic acid is effective for the induction of remission of AML M3 subtype (acute promyelocytic leukemia).
- High-dose cytarabine (ARA-C) (HiDAC) can be used in patients with refractory or relapsed AML. It usually takes 28 to 32 days from the start of therapy to achieve remission. The duration of remission is variable; the median duration of remission in an adult with AML is 1 yr.
- Consolidation therapy consists of an aggressive course of chemotherapy with or without radiation shortly after complete remission has been obtained; its purpose is to prolong the remission period or cure. Complications of consolidation therapy are usually secondary to severe bone marrow suppression (anemia, thrombocytopenia, granulocytopenia).
- Goal of therapy is to maintain a state of remission. A postinduction course of high-dose cytarabine can provide equivalent disease-free survival and somewhat better overall survival than autologous marrow transplantation in adults.
- Autologous bone marrow transplantation is indicated in patients <55 yr without a sibling donor. Allogeneic bone marrow transplantation is generally available to <20% of patients; usually performed only in patients <40 yr old because of higher incidence of GVHD with advancing age.

DISPOSITION

- Remission can be achieved in nearly 80% of patients <55 yr of age. Remission rates are highest in children.
- Cure for allogeneic bone marrow transplantation approaches 60%; cure rates with autologous transplantation are slightly lower.
- Favorable cytogenics are inv (16) (p13;q22) and t(8;21), t(15;17).

PEARLS & CONSIDERATIONS

COMMENTS

- The major complication of chemotherapy is profound marrow depression with pancytopenia lasting 3 to 4 wk. Treatment is aimed at RBC and platelet replacement and aggressive monitoring and treatment of suspected infections.
- Low doses of arsenic trioxide can induce complete remissions in patients with acute promyelocytic leukemia.

AUTHOR: **FRED F. FERRI, M.D.**

BASIC INFORMATION

DEFINITION

Chronic lymphocytic leukemia (CLL) is a lymphoproliferative disorder characterized by proliferation and accumulation of mature-appearing neoplastic lymphocytes.

SYNONYMS

CLL

ICD-9CM CODES
204.1 Leukemia, chronic lymphocytic

EPIDEMIOLOGY & DEMOGRAPHICS

- Most frequent form of leukemia in Western countries (10,000 new cases/yr in the U.S.)
- Generally occurs in middle-aged and elderly patients (median age of 65 yr)
- Male:female ratio of 2:1

PHYSICAL FINDINGS & CLINICAL PRESENTATION

- Lymphadenopathy, splenomegaly, and hepatomegaly in the majority of patients
- Variable clinical presentation according to stage of the disease
- Abnormal CBC: many cases are diagnosed on the basis of laboratory results obtained after routine physical examination
- Some patients come to medical attention because of weakness and fatigue (secondary to anemia) or lymphadenopathy

ETIOLOGY

Unknown

DIAGNOSIS

DIFFERENTIAL DIAGNOSIS

- Hairy cell leukemia
- Adult T cell lymphoma
- Proiymphocytic leukemia
- Viral infections
- Waldenström's macroglobulinemia

WORKUP

- Laboratory evaluation
- Bone marrow aspirate
- Chromosome analysis

LABORATORY TESTS

- Proliferative lymphocytosis (≥15,000/dl) of well-differentiated lymphocytes is the hallmark of CLL.
- There is monotonous replacement of the bone marrow by small lymphocytes (marrow contains ≥30% of well-differentiated lymphocytes).
- Hypogammaglobulinemia and elevated LDH may be present at the time of diagnosis.
- Anemia or thrombocytopenia, if present, indicates poor prognosis.
- Trisomy-12 is the most common chromosomal abnormality, followed by 14 q+, 13 q, and 11 q; these all indicate a poor prognosis.
- New laboratory techniques (CD 38, fluorescence in situ hybridization [FISH]) can identify patients with early-stage CLL at higher risk of rapid disease progression.

STAGING

- Rai et al divided CLL into five clinical stages:

Stage 0—Characterized by lymphocytosis only (≥15,000/mm^3 on peripheral smear, bone marrow aspirate ≥40% lymphocytes). The coexistence of lymphocytosis and other factors increases the clinical stage.

Stage 1—Lymphadenopathy

Stage 2—Lymphadenopathy/hepatomegaly

Stage 3—Anemia (Hgb <11 g/mm^3)

Stage 4—Thrombocytopenia (platelets <100,000/mm^3)

- Another well-known staging system developed by Binet divides chronic lymphocytic leukemia into three stages:

Stage A—Hgb ≥10 g/dl, platelets ≥100,000/mm^3, and fewer than three areas involved (the cervical, axillary, and inguinal lymph nodes [whether unilaterally or bilaterally]; the spleen; and the liver)

Stage B—Hgb ≥10 g/dl, platelets ≥100,000/mm^3, and three or more areas involved

Stage C—Hgb <10 g/dl, low platelets (<100,000/mm^3), or both (independent of the areas involved)

IMAGING STUDIES

CT scan of abdomen to evaluate for hepatomegaly and splenomegaly

TREATMENT

NONPHARMACOLOGIC THERAPY

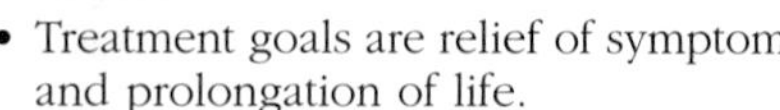

- Treatment goals are relief of symptoms and prolongation of life.
- Observation is appropriate for patients in Rai Stage 0 or Binet Stage A.

ACUTE GENERAL Rx

- Symptomatic patients in Rai Stage I and II or Binet Stage B: chlorambucil; local irradiation for isolated symptomatic lymphadenopathy and lymph nodes that interfere with vital organs
- Fludarabine is an effective treatment for CLL that does not respond to initial treatment with chlorambucil. Recent reports indicate that when used as the initial treatment for CLL, fludarabine yields higher response rates and a longer duration of remission and progression-free survival than chlorambucil; overall survival, however, is not enhanced.
- Rai Stages III and IV, Binet Stage C: chlorambucil chemotherapy with or without prednisone
  1. Fludarabine, CAP (cyclophosphamide, Adriamycin, prednisone), or cyclophosphamide, doxorubicin, vincristine, and prednisone (mini-CHOP) can be used in patients who respond poorly to chlorambucil.
  2. Splenic irradiation can be used in selected patients with advanced disease.

CHRONIC Rx

Treatment of systemic complications:

- Hypogammaglobulinemia is frequent in CLL and is the chief cause of infections. Immune globulin (250 mg/kg IV every 4 wk) may prevent infections but has no effect on survival. Infections should be treated with broad-spectrum antibiotics. Patients should be monitored for opportunistic infections.
- Recombinant hematopoietic cofactors (e.g., granulocyte-macrophage colony–stimulating factor and granulocyte colony–stimulating factor) may be useful to overcome neutropenia related to treatment.
- Erythropoietin may be useful to treat anemia that is unresponsive to other measures.

DISPOSITION

The patient's prognosis is directly related to the clinical stage (e.g., the average survival in patients in Rai Stage 0 or Binet Stage A is >120 mo, whereas for RAI Stage 4 or Binet Stage C it is approximately 30 mo). Overall 5-yr survival is 60%.

PEARLS & CONSIDERATIONS

COMMENTS

Long-term follow-up and frequency of follow-up are generally determined by the pace of the disease.

SUGGESTED READING

Shanafelt TD, Call TG: Current approach to diagnosis and management of chronic lymphocytic leukemia, *Mayo Clin Proc* 79:388, 2004.

AUTHOR: **FRED F. FERRI, M.D.**

BASIC INFORMATION

DEFINITION

Chronic myelogenous leukemia (CML) is a malignant clonal disorder of hemopoietic stem cells characterized by abnormal proliferation and accumulation of immature granulocytes. CML is characterized by a chronic phase lasting months to years, followed by an accelerated myeloproliferative phase manifested by poor response to therapy, worsening anemia, or decreased platelet count; the second phase then evolves into a terminal phase (acute transformation), characterized by elevated number of blast cells and numerous complications (e.g., sepsis, bleeding).

SYNONYMS

CML
Chronic granulocytic leukemia
Chronic myeloid leukemia

ICD-9CM CODES
201.1 Chronic myelogenous leukemia

EPIDEMIOLOGY & DEMOGRAPHICS

- CML usually affects middle-aged patients (median age at presentation is 53 yr) and accounts for 15% of adult leukemias
- 4300 new cases/yr in the U.S.

PHYSICAL FINDINGS & CLINICAL PRESENTATION

- The chronic phase usually reveals splenomegaly; hepatomegaly is not infrequent, but lymphadenopathy is very unusual and generally indicates the accelerated proliferative phase of the disease.
- Common complaints at the time of diagnosis are weakness or discomfort secondary to an enlarged spleen (abdominal discomfort or pain). Splenomegaly is present in up to 40% of patients at time of diagnosis.
- 40% of patients are asymptomatic and diagnosis is based solely on an abnormal blood count.

ETIOLOGY

Current evidence strongly implicates the chromosome translocation t (9;22) (q34;q11.2) as the cause of chronic granulocytic leukemia. This translocation is present in >95% of patients. The remaining patients have a complex or variant translocation involving additional chromosomes that have the same end result (fusion of the BCR [break point cluster region] gene on chromosome 22 to ABL [Ableson leukemia virus] gene on chromosome 9).

DIAGNOSIS

DIFFERENTIAL DIAGNOSIS

- Splenic lymphoma
- CLL
- Myelodysplastic syndrome

LABORATORY TESTS

- Elevated WBC count (generally >100,000/mm^3) with broad spectrum of granulocytic forms.
- Bone marrow demonstrates hypercellularity with granulocytic hyperplasia, increased ratio of myeloid cells to erythroid cells, and increased number of megakaryocytes. Blasts and promyelocytes constitute <10% of all cells.
- Philadelphia chromosome (which results from the reciprocal translocation between the long arms of chromosomes 9 and 22) is present in >95% of patients with CML; its presence (Ph^1) is a major prognostic factor because survival rate of patients with Philadelphia chromosome is approximately eight times better than that of those without it. Some believe that Ph$^+$ defines CML and that those who are Ph$^-$ have another disease.
- Leukocyte alkaline phosphatase (LAP) markedly decreased (used to distinguish CML from other myeloproliferative disorders).
- Anemia and thrombocytosis are often present.
- Additional laboratory results are elevated vitamin B_{12} levels (caused by increased transcobalamin 1 from granulocytes) and elevated blood histamine levels (because of increased basophils).

IMAGING STUDIES

Chest x-ray and CT scan of abdomen

TREATMENT

ACUTE GENERAL Rx

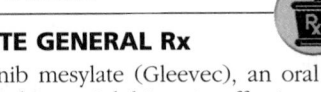

Imatinib mesylate (Gleevec), an oral tyrosine kinase inhibitor, is effective and indicated as first-line treatment for CML myeloid blast crisis, accelerated phase, or CML in its chronic phase. More than 60% of patients have major cytogenetic response (<35% Philadelphia chromosome-positive cells in the marrow) and more than 80% have progression-free survival after 24 mo. Complete hematologic response usually occurs in less than 1 mo.

- Symptomatic hyperleukocytosis (e.g., CNS symptoms) can be treated with leukapheresis and hydroxyurea; allopurinol should be started to prevent urate nephropathy following the rapid lysis of the leukemia cells.
- Cytotoxic chemotherapy with hydroxyurea has largely replaced busulfan as the standard cytotoxic drug.
- Allogeneic stem-cell transplantation (SCT) (following intense chemotherapy with busulfan and cyclophosphamide or combined chemotherapy with cyclophosphamide and fractionated total body irradiation to destroy residual leukemic cells) is the only curative treatment for CML in chronic phase unresponsive to imatinib. Generally only 20% of patients are candidates for SCT given the limitations of age or lack of HLA-matched related donors.
    1. It should be considered in "young" patients (increased survival in patients <55 yr) with compatible siblings.
    2. Early transplantation is also important for patient's survival.
- Transplantation of marrow from an HLA-matched, unrelated donor is also now recognized as safe and effective therapy for selected patients with chronic myelogenous leukemia.

SUGGESTED READINGS

Goldman JM, Melo JV: Chronic myeloid leukemia, advances in biology and new approaches to treatment, *N Engl J Med* 349:1451, 2003.

Hughes TP et al: Frequency of major molecular responses to imatinib or interferon alfa plus cytarabine in newly diagnosed chronic myeloid leukemia, *N Engl J Med* 349:1423, 2003.

Kantarjian H et al: Hematologic and cytogenetic responses to imatinib mesylate in chronic myelogenous leukemia, *N Engl J Med* 346:645, 2002.

AUTHOR: **FRED F. FERRI, M.D.**

BASIC INFORMATION

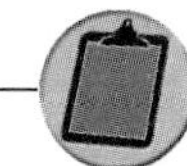

DEFINITION

Hairy cell leukemia is a lymphoid neoplasm characterized by the proliferation of mature B cells with prominent cytoplasmic projections (hairs).

SYNONYMS

Leukemic reticuloendotheliosis

ICD-9CM CODES
202.4 Hairy cell leukemia

EPIDEMIOLOGY & DEMOGRAPHICS

PREVALENCE: Occurs predominantly in men between 40 and 60 yr of age. About 2% of leukemia cases are of the hairy cell type.
PREDOMINANT SEX: Male:female ratio of 4:1

PHYSICAL FINDINGS & CLINICAL PRESENTATION

- Usually, splenomegaly (present in >90% of cases) secondary to tumor cell infiltration
- Pallor, ecchymosis, and evidence of infection if the pancytopenia is severe
- Weakness, lethargy, and fatigue
- Infections (resulting from impaired resistance secondary to neutropenia) and easy bruising (secondary to thrombocytopenia) also common

ETIOLOGY

Neoplastic disease of the lymphoreticular system of unknown etiology

DIAGNOSIS

DIFFERENTIAL DIAGNOSIS

- Other forms of leukemia
- Lymphoma
- Viral syndrome

WORKUP

Comprehensive history, physical examination, and laboratory evaluation to confirm the diagnosis

LABORATORY TESTS

- Pancytopenia involving erythrocytes, neutrophils, and platelets is common; anemia is usually present and varies from minimal to severe.
- Hairy cells (Fig. 1-137) can account for 5% to 80% of cells in the peripheral blood. The cytoplasmic projections on the cells are redundant plasma membranes.
- Leukemic cells stain positively for tartrate-resistant acid phosphatase (TRAP) stain.
- Bone marrow may result in a "dry tap" (because of increased marrow reticulin).

TREATMENT

NONPHARMACOLOGIC THERAPY

Approximately 8% to 10% of patients are asymptomatic and have minimal splenomegaly and minor cytopenia. They are usually detected on routine laboratory evaluation and do not require initial therapy. They should, however, be frequently monitored for progression of their disease.

ACUTE GENERAL Rx

- Drugs of choice are the purine analogues 2-Chloro-2 deoxyadenosine (Cladribine) or 2-deoxycoformycin (DCF, Pentostatin). They induce complete remissions in up to 85% of patients and partial responses in 5% to 25%.
- 2-Chloro-2 deoxyadenosine (CdA) 0.14 mg/kg qd for 7 days has minimal toxicity and is able to induce complete durable responses with a single course of therapy.

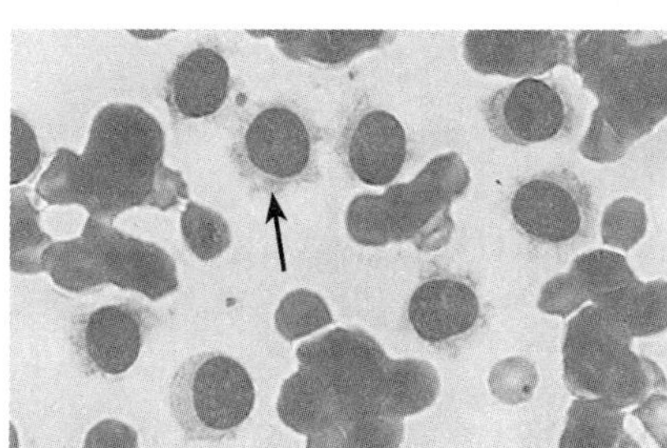

FIGURE 1-137 Hairy cell leukemia. Note the lymphocytes with hairlike cytoplasmic projections surrounding the nucleus. (From Rodak BF: *Diagnostic hematology,* Philadelphia, 1995, WB Saunders.)

- Interferon-α produces a partial remission in 30% to 70% of patients and complete remission, often of short duration, in 5% to 10% of patients.
- The anti-CD 22 recombinant immunotoxin BL 22 can induce complete remission in patients with hairy cell leukemia that is resistant to treatment with purine analogues.

CHRONIC Rx

Patients should be monitored with periodic examination and laboratory tests for progression of their disease.

DISPOSITION

Prognosis has become increasingly favorable with the newer agents. Approximately 90% of patients who are treated have a complete or partial response.

REFERRAL

Hematology consultation is recommended in all patients.

PEARLS & CONSIDERATIONS

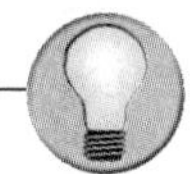

COMMENTS

The diagnosis of hairy cell leukemia is occasionally missed and subsequently made by the histopathologist following removal of the spleen for diagnostic purposes.

SUGGESTED READING

Kreitman RJ et al: Efficacy of the anti-CD 22 recombinant immunotoxin BL 22 in chemotherapy resistant hairy-cell leukemia, *N Engl J Med* 345:241, 2001.

AUTHOR: **FRED F. FERRI, M.D.**

BASIC INFORMATION

DEFINITION

Oral hairy leukoplakia (OHL) is a painless, white, nonremovable, plaquelike lesion typically located on the lateral aspect of the tongue.

ICD-9CM CODES
528.6 Oral hairy leukoplakia

ETIOLOGY

Epstein-Barr virus (EBV) is implicated in its etiology, and OHL is a result of replication EBV in the epithelium of keratinized cells.

EPIDEMIOLOGY & DEMOGRAPHICS

OHL is usually found in human immunodeficiency virus (HIV) seropositive individuals but may also be identified in other immunocompromised patients such as transplant recipients (particularly renal) and patients taking steroids. A diagnosis of OHL is an indication to institute a workup to evaluate and manage HIV disease. Despite a high incidence of EBV seroprevalence in HIV-seropositive individuals, OHL occurs in only 25% of these cases.

PHYSICAL FINDINGS & CLINICAL PRESENTATION

- Varying morphology and appearance
- May be unilateral or bilateral
- White and can be small with fine vertical corrugations on the lateral margin of the tongue (Fig. 1-138)
- Irregular surface; may have prominent folds or projection, occasionally markedly resembling hairs
- May spread to cover the entire dorsal surface or spread onto the ventral surface of the tongue where they usually appear flat
- Rarely lesions manifest on the soft palate, buccal mucosa, and in the posterior oropharynx
- Usually asymptomatic, but some have mouth pain, soreness, or a burning sensation, impaired taste, or difficulty eating; others complain of its unsightly appearance
- OHL may progress to oral squamous cell carcinoma, which has a poor prognosis

DIAGNOSIS

DIFFERENTIAL DIAGNOSIS

- *Candida albicans*
- Lichen planus
- Idiopathic leukoplakia
- White sponge nevus
- Dysplasia
- Squamous cell carcinoma

WORKUP

Requires physical examination and evaluation of HIV disease

LABORATORY TESTS

The *provisional* diagnosis is clinical and based on:
- Visual inspection
- Inability to scrape the lesion off the tongue with a blade
- Failure to respond to antifungal therapy

The *presumptive* diagnosis requires biopsy and histologic demonstration of:
- Epithelial hyperplasia with hairs
- Absence of inflammatory cell infiltrate

The *definitive* diagnosis requires:
- In situ hybridization of histologic or cytologic specimens revealing EBV DNA *or*
- Electron microscopy of specimens revealing herpeslike particles
- Measurement of the DNA content in cells of oral leukoplakia may be used to predict the risk of oral carcinoma.

NOTE: Specimens obtained from lesions may demonstrate hyphae of *Candida albicans,* which may coexist and potentiate EBV-induced OHL.

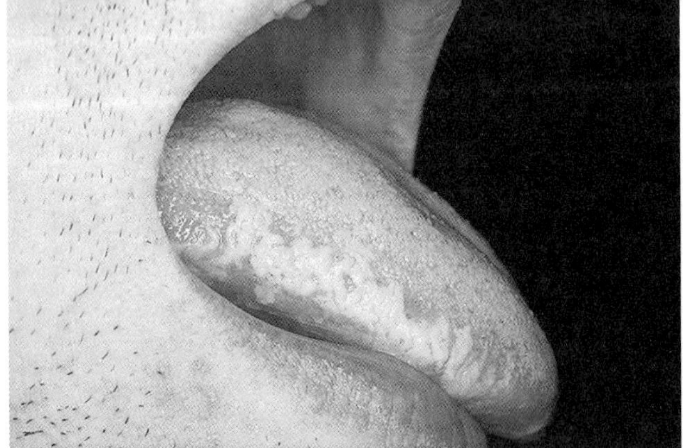

FIGURE 1-138 Oral hairy leukoplakia. Note white verrucoid plaques on the lateral border of the tongue. (From Noble J: *Primary care medicine,* ed 3, St Louis, 2001, Mosby.)

TREATMENT

NONPHARMACOLOGIC THERAPY

OHL is usually asymptomatic and requires no specific therapy. It may resolve spontaneously and has no known premalignant potential.

ACUTE GENERAL Rx

- Highly active antiretroviral (HAART) therapy has considerably changed the frequency of oral lesions caused by opportunistic infections in HIV-seropositive individuals.
- Topical retinoids (0.1% vitamin A) may improve the appearance of OHL-affected oral surfaces through their dekeratinizing and immunomodulation effects; however, they are expensive and prolonged use may result in a burning sensation over the treated area.
- Topical podophyllin resin 25% solution has been reported to induce resolution.
- Surgical excision and cryotherapy may help, but the lesions may recur.
- High-dose acyclovir or ganciclovir will cause lesions to resolve, but only temporarily.

SUGGESTED READING

Sudbo J et al: DNA content as a prognostic marker in patients with oral leukoplakia, *N Engl J Med* 344:1270, 2001.

AUTHOR: **SAJEEV HANDA, M.D.**

BASIC INFORMATION

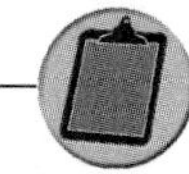

DEFINITION

Lichen planus refers to a papular skin eruption characteristically found over the flexor surfaces of the extremities, genitalia, and mucous membranes.

SYNONYMS

Lichen
Lichen planus et atrophicus

ICD-9CM CODES
697.0 Lichen planus

EPIDEMIOLOGY & DEMOGRAPHICS

- Incidence in the U.S.: 440/100,000
- Usually found in people between the ages of 30 to 60
- Found equally between males and females (1:1)
- Lichen planus associated with discoid lupus, SLE, pemphigus vulgaris, bullous pemphigoid, myasthenia gravis, and ulcerative colitis

PHYSICAL FINDINGS & CLINICAL PRESENTATION

History
- Usually starts on an extremity and may remain localized or it can spread to involve other areas over a 1- to 4-mo time period.
- Pruritic

Physical findings
- Anatomic distribution:
  1. Flexor surface of wrists, forearms, shins, and upper thighs
  2. Neck and back area
  3. Nails
  4. Scalp
  5. Oral mucosa, buccal mucosa, tongue, gingiva, and lips

Genital mucosa
- Lesion configuration:
  1. Linear
  2. Annular (more common)
  3. Reticular pattern noted on oral mucosa and genital area
- Lesion morphology:
  1. Papules (flat, smooth and shiny)—most common presentation
  2. Hypertrophic
  3. Follicular
  4. Vesicular
- Color:
  1. Dark red, bluish red, purplish-violaceous color is noted in cutaneous lichen planus
  2. Individual lesions characteristically have white lines visible (Wickham's striae)
  3. Oral and genital lichen planus have a reticular network of white lines that may be raised or annular in appearance
  4. Atrophic purplish violaceous color
- Scalp lesions may result in alopecia.

ETIOLOGY

- The cause of lichen planus is unknown. Leading theory is cell-mediated immune response.
- Lichenlike reactions can occur from drugs (e.g., tetracycline, quinacrine, chloroquine, penicillamine, and hydrochlorothiazide).

DIAGNOSIS

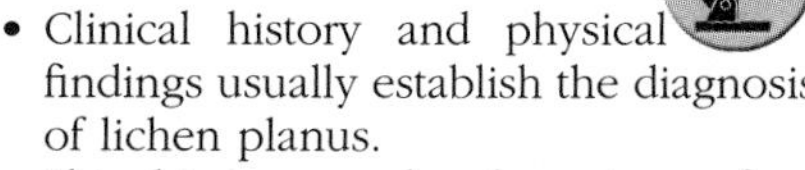

- Clinical history and physical findings usually establish the diagnosis of lichen planus.
- Skin biopsy can be done to confirm the diagnosis.

DIFFERENTIAL DIAGNOSIS

- Drug eruption
- Psoriasis
- Basal cell carcinoma
- Bowen's disease
- Leukoplakia
- Candidiasis
- Lupus rash
- Secondary syphilis
- Seborrheic dermatitis

WORKUP

No workup is necessary in patients with lichen planus. If the diagnosis is questionable, a skin biopsy is performed.

LABORATORY TESTS

Laboratory tests are not specific for the diagnosis of lichen planus.

IMAGING STUDIES

Imaging studies are not helpful in diagnosing lichen planus.

TREATMENT

There are no large, randomized trials published to date substantiating the benefit and effectiveness of treatment in lichen planus. Much of the therapeutic information is based on observational data and the personal preferences of experts.

NONPHARMACOLOGIC THERAPY

- Avoid scratching.
- Use mild soaps and emollients after bathing to prevent dryness.

ACUTE GENERAL Rx

For cutaneous lichen planus
- Topical steroids, triamcinolone acetonide 0.1% with occlusion
- Acitretin 30 mg/day PO for 8 wk can be used
- Systemic prednisone 30 to 60 mg/day as a starting dose and tapered to 15 to 20 mg/day maintenance for 6 wk has also been tried
- Intradermal steroid triamcinolone acetonide 5 mg/ml can be tried for thick hyperkeratotic lesions
- Hydroxyzine 25 mg PO q6h can be used for pruritus

For oral lichen planus
- Topical steroid fluocinonide in an adhesive base used six times/day for 9 wk
- Topical retinoids 0.1% retinoic acid in an adhesive base or gel can be used for oral or genital lesions
- Etretinate 75 mg/day for 2 mo can also be used for oral lesions

CHRONIC Rx

Refer to acute general treatment

DISPOSITION

- Spontaneous remissions of cutaneous lichen planus occur in over 65% of cases within the first year.
- Spontaneous remission of oral lichen planus usually occurs by 5 yr.
- Approximately 10% to 20% of patients will have recurrence.

REFERRAL

If the diagnosis of lichen planus is suspected, a dermatology consultation is recommended.

PEARLS & CONSIDERATIONS

COMMENTS

- Lichen planus can be remembered as purple, planar, pruritic, polygonal papules (5 Ps).
- Lesions can develop at the site of prior skin injury (Koebner's phenomenon).
- Although transformation to skin cancer has been seen in patients with lichen planus, it remains unclear if there is a true correlation.

SUGGESTED READINGS

Boyd AS, Neldner KH: Lichen planus, *J Am Acad Dermatol* 25:593, 1991.

Cribier B, Rances C, Chosidow O: Treatment of lichen planus: an evidence-based medicine analysis of efficacy, *Arch Dermatol* 134(12):1521, 1998.

Katta R: Lichen planus, *Am Fam Physician* 61(11):3319, 2000.

AUTHOR: **PETER PETROPOULOS, M.D.**

 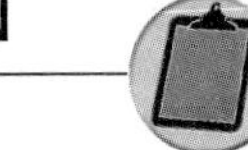

BASIC INFORMATION

DEFINITION

Chronic inflammatory condition of the skin usually affecting the vulva, perianal area, and groin

ICD-9CM CODES
701.0 Lichen sclerosus

EPIDEMIOLOGY & DEMOGRAPHICS

- Most common in postmenopausal women and men between ages 40 and 60 yr
- More common in females
- Can occur in children (usually prepubertal girls with involvement of the vulva and perineum)

PHYSICAL FINDINGS & CLINICAL PRESENTATION

- Erythema may be the only initial sign. A characteristic finding is the presence of ivory-white atrophic lesions on the involved area.
- Close inspection of the affected area will reveal the presence of white-to-brown follicular plugs on the surface (dells).
- When the genitals are involved, the white parchmentlike skin assumes an hourglass configuration around the introital and perianal area ("keyhole" distribution, see Fig. 1-139). Inflammation, subepithelial hemorrhages, and chronic ulceration may develop.
- Dyspareunia, genital bleeding, and anal bleeding are common.

ETIOLOGY

Unknown. There may be an autoimmune association and a genetic familial component.

DIAGNOSIS

DIFFERENTIAL DIAGNOSIS

- Localized scleroderma (morphea)
- Cutaneous discoid lupus erythematosus
- Atrophic lichen planus
- Psoriasis

WORKUP

Diagnosis is based on close examination of the lesions for the presence of ivory-white atrophic lesions and typical location.

LABORATORY TESTS

Punch or deep shave biopsy can be used to confirm the diagnosis when in doubt.

IMAGING STUDIES

Not indicated

TREATMENT

NONPHARMACOLOGIC THERAPY

Attention to hygiene and elimination of irritants or excessive bathing with harsh soaps

GENERAL Rx

- Application of clobetasol propionate 0.05% topically bid for up to 4 wk is usually effective. Repeat courses of corticosteroids may be necessary because of the chronic nature of this disorder. Continual application of topical steroids may lead to atrophy of the vulva.
- Use of topical testosterone (2%) has been found to be less effective than topical corticosteroids.
- Lubricants (e.g., Nutraplus cream) are useful to soothe dry tissues.
- Hydroxyzine 25 mg at hs is effective in decreasing nocturnal itching.
- Use of intralesional steroids, etretinate, and surgical management are usually reserved for refractory cases.

DISPOSITION

- The disease persists in approximately one third of patients.
- Most prepubertal girls improve spontaneously at menarche.
- Squamous cell carcinoma can develop within the lesions in 3% to 10% of older patients; therefore, periodic examination and biopsy of suspicious areas are indicated.

PEARLS & CONSIDERATIONS

COMMENTS

- Prepubertal lichen sclerosus may be confused with sexual abuse in prepubertal girls and may lead to false accusations and investigations.
- Lichen sclerosus of the vulva (kraurosis vulvae) usually occurs after menopause and is generally chronic. It can be painful and interfere with sexual activity.
- Lichen sclerosus of the penis (balanitis xerotica obliterans) is seen more commonly in uncircumcised males. It affects the glans and prepuce and may lead to stricture if it encroaches into the urinary meatus.

AUTHOR: **FRED F. FERRI, M.D.**

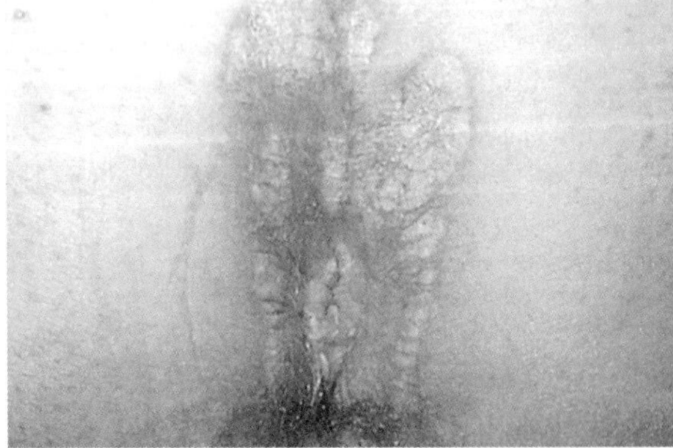

FIGURE 1-139 Lichen sclerosus. Perianal area is thinned and chalk white (keyhole distribution). (Courtesy Department of Dermatology, University of North Carolina at Chapel Hill. From Goldstein BG, Goldstein AO: *Practical dermatology,* ed 2, St Louis, 1997, Mosby.)

BASIC INFORMATION

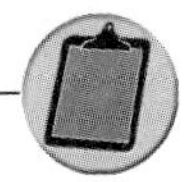

DEFINITION

Listeriosis is a systemic infection caused by the gram-positive aerobic bacterium *Listeria monocytogenes*.

ICD-9CM CODES
027.0 Listeriosis
771.2 Congenital listeriosis
771.2 Fetal listeriosis
665.4 Suspected fetal damage affecting management of pregnancy

EPIDEMIOLOGY & DEMOGRAPHICS

INCIDENCE (IN U.S.):

- Listeria meningitis: about 0.7 cases/100,000 persons (fourth most common cause of community-acquired bacterial meningitis in adults)
- Perinatal listeriosis: 8.6 cases/100,000 persons
- Nonperinatal listeriosis: 3 cases/1 million persons

PREDOMINANT SEX: Pregnant women are more susceptible to *Listeria* bacteremia, accounting for up to one third of reported cases.

PREDOMINANT AGE:

- Pregnant women
- Immunocompromised patients of any age

GENETICS

Congenital Infection:

- With transplacental transmission, syndrome termed *granulomatosis infantisepticum* in neonate
- Characterized by disseminated abscesses in multiple organs, skin lesions, conjunctivitis
- Mortality: 33% to 100%

Neonatal Infection:

- Infant becoming ill after 3 days of age; mother invariably asymptomatic
- Clinical picture of sepsis of unknown origin

PHYSICAL FINDINGS & CLINICAL PRESENTATION

- Infections in pregnancy
  1. More common in third trimester
  2. Usually present with fever and chills without localizing symptoms or signs of infection
- Meningoencephalitis
  1. More common in neonates and immunocompromised patients, but up to 30% of adults have no underlying condition
  2. In neonates: poor appetite with or without fever possibly the only presenting signs
  3. In adults: presentation often subacute, with low-grade fever and personality change as only signs
  4. Focal neurologic signs seen without demonstrable brain abscess on CT scan
- Cerebritis/thromboencephalitis:
  1. Headache and fever may be only presenting complaints
  2. Progressive cranial nerve palsies, hemiparesis, seizures, depressed level of consciousness, cerebellar signs, respiratory insufficiency may also be seen
- Focal infections
  1. Ocular infections (purulent conjunctivitis) and skin lesions (granulomatosis infantisepticum) as a result of inadvertent inoculation by laboratory and veterinary personnel
  2. Others: arthritis, prosthetic joint infections, peritonitis, osteomyelitis, organ abscesses, cholecystitis

ETIOLOGY

- Direct invasion of skin and eye has been documented, but mechanism of GI entry is unclear.
- Organism's intracellular life cycle explanatory of:
  1. Importance of cell-mediated immunity in host defense
  2. Increased incidence of infection in neonates, pregnant women, and immunocompromised hosts

DIAGNOSIS

DIFFERENTIAL DIAGNOSIS

- Meningitis caused by other bacteria, mycobacteria, or fungi
- CNS sarcoidosis
- Brain neoplasm or abscess
- Tuberculous and fungal (especially cryptococcal) meningitis
- Cerebral toxoplasmosis
- Lyme disease
- Sarcoidosis

WORKUP

Dictated by age, end-organ involvement, and immune status

LABORATORY TESTS

- Cultures of blood and other appropriate body fluids
- Variable CSF findings, but neutrophils usually predominate
- Organisms uncommonly seen on Gram stain and may be difficult to identify morphologically
- Monoclonal antibodies, polymerase chain reaction, and DNA probe techniques to detect *Listeria* in foods

IMAGING STUDIES

- If focal cerebral involvement suspected: CT scan or MRI
- MRI most sensitive for evaluation of brainstem and cerebellum

TREATMENT

Empiric therapy should be administered when diagnosis is suspected because overall mortality is 23%.

ACUTE GENERAL Rx

- Drugs of choice:
  1. IV ampicillin 8 to 12 g/day in divided doses
  2. IV penicillin 12 to 24 million U/day in divided doses
- Continuation of therapy for 2 wk
- Alternative: trimethoprim/sulfamethoxazole
- Gentamicin added to provide synergy

CHRONIC Rx

Relapses reported, especially in immunocompromised hosts, after 2 wk of therapy

DISPOSITION

Long-term follow-up of immunodeficiency state

REFERRAL

Infectious disease consultation for all patients

PEARLS & CONSIDERATIONS

COMMENTS

- Foodborne cases have been linked to various products: coleslaw, soft cheese, pasteurized milk, vegetables, undercooked chicken, hot dogs.
- Complete decontamination of food products is difficult because *Listeria* is resistant to pasteurization and refrigeration.

SUGGESTED READINGS

Mylonakis E et al: Listeriosis during pregnancy: a case series and review of 222 cases, *Medicine* 81:260, 2002.

Wing EJ, Gregory SH: Listeria monocytogenes: clinical and experimental update, *J Infect Dis* 185(Suppl 1):S18, 2002.

AUTHOR: **MAURICE POLICAR, M.D.**

Long QT Syndrome 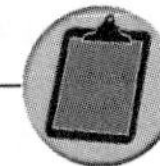

BASIC INFORMATION

DEFINITION

Long QT syndrome is an electrocardiographic abnormality characterized by a corrected QT interval longer than 0.44 sec and associated with an increased risk of developing life-threatening ventricular arrhythmias.

SYNONYMS

Congenital forms:
- Jervell and Lange-Nielsen syndrome (associated with deafness)
- Romano-Ward syndrome (associated with normal hearing)

Sporadic forms of long QT syndrome (nonfamilial)

ICD-9CM CODES
427.9 Unspecified cardiac dysrhythmia

EPIDEMIOLOGY & DEMOGRAPHICS

- Familial associated with deafness: autosomal recessive
- Familial associated with normal hearing: autosomal dominant (the incidence is unknown)

PHYSICAL FINDINGS & CLINICAL PRESENTATION

- Syncope caused by ventricular tachycardia
- Sudden death
- Abnormal ECG (prolonged QT) in asymptomatic relatives of known case. Bazett formula; QTc5QT/√RR. Calculated QTc should be <440 ms. If patient has atrial fibrillation, take the average of the longest and shortest QTc intervals.
- Routine (baseline) ECG finding.

ETIOLOGY

- Cardiac repolarization abnormality
- Congenital cause (chromosome 3 or chromosome 7 abnormality)
- Acquired causes:

Drugs (quinidine, procainamide, sotalol, amiodarone, disopyramide, phenothiazines, tricyclic antidepressants, quinolones, astemizole or cisapride given with ketoconazole or erythromycin, and antimalarials), particularly among patients with asthma or those using potassium-lowering medications

Hypokalemia, hypomagnesemia

Liquid protein diet

CNS lesions

Mitral valve prolapse

DIAGNOSIS

DIFFERENTIAL DIAGNOSIS

See "Syncope."

Diagnostic criteria for the congenital long QT syndrome

ECG criteria	
Corrected QT >480 ms	3 points
Corrected QT 460 to 480 ms	2 points
Corrected QT 450 to 460 ms (males)	1 point
Torsades de Pointe	2 points
T-wave alternans	1 point
Notched T wave in 3 leads	1 point
Bradycardia	0.5 points
History	
Syncope with stress	2 points
Syncope without stress	1 point
Congenital deafness	0.5 points
Definite family history of long QT	1 point
Unexplained cardiac death in first-degree relative under age 30	0.5 points

Total score $\geq$4: definite long QT syndrome

Total score 2 to 3: intermediate probability

Total score $\leq$1: low probability

WORKUP

In relatives of known patients with long QT syndrome or in young patients with syncope:
- Stress test may prolong the QT interval or cause T-wave alternans
- Valsalva maneuver: may prolong the QT interval or cause T-wave alternans
- Prolonged ECG monitoring with various stimulations aimed at increasing catecholamines (perform in a setting that can provide resuscitation)
- Epinephrine-induced prolongation of the 2T interval (Epinephrine infusion QT stress test)
- Genetic analysis

LQT1 locus of KCNQ1 potassium channel gene

LQT2 locus of KCNH2 potassium channel gene

LQT33 locus of SCN5A sodium channel gene

TREATMENT

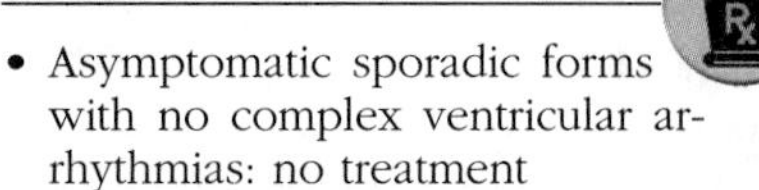

- Asymptomatic sporadic forms with no complex ventricular arrhythmias: no treatment
- Risk stratification

High risk (<50% of cardiac event): QTc >500 ms and LQT1 and LQT2 or male with LQT3

Moderate risk (30% to 50%): QTc >500 ms in female with LQT3 or L QTc <500 ms in male with LQT3 or in female with LQT2 or 3

Low risk (<30%): QTc <500 ms and LQT1 and or male OQT2

- General recommendations:

Avoid competitive sports

β-blocker at maximum tolerated dose

Cardiology referral is recommended for all cases. Pacemaker and implantable defibrillator may be advised

SUGGESTED READINGS

Ackerman MJ et al: Epinephrine-induced QT interval prolongation: a gene-specific paradoxical response in congenital long QT syndrome, *Mayo Clin Proc* 77:413, 2002.

Al-Khatib SM et al: What clinicians should know about the QT interval, *JAMA* 289:2120, 2003.

De Bruin ML, Hoes AW, Leufkens HGM: QTc-prolonging drugs and hospitalizations for cardiac arrhythmias, *Am J Cardiol* 91:59, 2003.

Montanez Aetal: Prolonged QTc interval and risks of total and cardiovascular mortality and sudden death in the general population, *Arch Intern Med* 164:943, 2004.

Nemec J et al: Catecholamine-induced T-wave lability in congenital long qt syndrome, *Mayo Clin Proc* 78:40, 2003.

Priori SG et al: Risk stratification in the long-QT syndrome, *N Engl J Med* 348:1866, 2003.

Roden DM: Drug-induced prolongation of the QT interval, *N Engl J Med* 350:1013, 2004.

Wehrens HXT: Novel insights in the congenital long QT syndrome, *Ann Intern Med* 137;981, 2002.

AUTHOR: **TOM J. WACHTEL, M.D.**

BASIC INFORMATION

DEFINITION

Lumbar disk syndromes are diseases resulting from disk disorder, either herniation or degenerative change (spondylosis). Massive disk protrusion may rarely lead to paralysis in the lower extremity, a condition termed *cauda equina syndrome.* Gradual narrowing of the spinal canal (lumbar stenosis), usually from spondylosis, may also cause lower extremity symptoms.

ICD-9CM CODES
722.10 Lumbar disk displacement
724.02 Lumbar stenosis
344.60 Cauda equina syndrome
721.3 Lumbar spondylosis

EPIDEMIOLOGY & DEMOGRAPHICS

PREVALENCE:
- Variable
- At least one episode in 80% of adults

PREVALENT AGE:
- Herniation: 20 to 40 yr
- Stenosis: >40 to 50 yr
- Disk symptoms: rare <20 yr

PREVALENT SEX: Approximately equal

PHYSICAL FINDINGS & CLINICAL PRESENTATION (TABLE 1-28)

- Overlapping clinical syndromes that may result:
  1. Mild herniation without nerve root compression
  2. Herniation with nerve root compression
  3. Cauda equina syndrome
  4. Chronic degenerative disease with or without leg symptoms
  5. Spinal stenosis
- Low back pain, often worsened by activity or coughing and sneezing
- Local lumbar or lumbosacral tenderness
- Paresthesias, usually unilateral
- Restricted low back motion
- Increased pain on bending toward affected side
- Weakness and reflex changes
- Sensory examination usually not helpful
- Lumbar stenosis that possibly produces symptoms (pseudoclaudication), which are often misinterpreted as being vascular
- Positive straight leg raising test if nerve root compression is present

ETIOLOGY

Unknown

DIAGNOSIS

DIFFERENTIAL DIAGNOSIS

- Soft-tissue strain/sprain
- Tumor
- Degenerative arthritis of hip
- Insufficiency fracture of hip or pelvis

Section II describes the differential diagnosis of common low back pain syndromes.

WORKUP

In most cases, the diagnosis can be established on a clinical basis alone.

IMAGING STUDIES

- Plain roentgenograms may be indicated within the first few weeks; they are usually normal in soft disk herniation, but with chronic degenerative disk disease, loss of height of the disk space and osteophyte formation can occur.
- Myelography, CT scanning, and MRI may be indicated in patients whose symptoms do not resolve or when other spinal pathology may be suspected.
- Electrodiagnostic studies may confirm the diagnosis or rule out peripheral nerve disorders.

TREATMENT

NONPHARMACOLOGIC THERAPY

- Short course (3 to 5 days) of bed rest for severe pain; prolonged rest for acute disk herniation with leg pain
- Physical therapy for modalities plus a careful gradual exercise program
- Lumbosacral corset brace during rehabilitation process in conjunction with exercise program
- Percutaneous electrical nerve stimulation (PENS) may be beneficial in selected patients with chronic back pain

PHARMACOLOGIC THERAPY

- NSAIDs
- Muscle relaxants for sedative effect
- Analgesics
- Epidural steroid injection for leg symptoms in selected patients

DISPOSITION

- Almost all lumbar disk syndromes improve with time.
- Recurrent episodes usually respond to medical management.
- Recovery from the rare paralytic event is often incomplete.

REFERRAL

- For orthopedic or neurosurgical consultation for intractable pain or significant neurologic deficit
- Emergency referral for cauda equina syndrome

PEARLS & CONSIDERATIONS

COMMENTS

- Surgery is most consistently helpful when leg pain (not back pain) predominates.
- A clinical algorithm for evaluation of back pain is described in Section III.

TABLE 1-28 Diagnosis of Lower Lumbar and Sacral Radiculopathy

	Pain	Weakness (Selected Muscles)	Sensory Loss	Reflex Loss
L4	Across thigh and medial leg to medial malleolus	Quadriceps, thigh adductors, tibialis anterior	Medial leg	Knee
L5	Posterior thigh and lateral calf, dorsum of foot	Extensor digitorum brevis and longus, peronei	Dorsum of foot	
S1	Buttock and posterior thigh, calf, and lateral foot	Extensor digitorum brevis, peronei, gastrocnemius, soleus	Sole or lateral border of foot	Ankle
S2-4	Posterior thigh, buttock, and genitalia	Gastrocnemius, soleus, abductor hallucis, abductor digiti quinti pedis, sphincter muscles	Buttocks, anal region, and genitalia	Bulbocavernosus, anal

From Goldman L, Bennett JC (eds): Cecil textbook of medicine, ed 21, Philadelphia, 2000, WB Saunders.

SUGGESTED READINGS

Biyani A, Andersson GB: Low back pain: Pathophysiology and management, *J Am Acad Orthop Surg* 12:106, 2004.

Brodke DS, Ritter SM: Nonoperative management of low back pain and lumbar disc degeneration, *J Bone Joint Surg* 86A:1810, 2004.

Buchner M, Schilotenwolf M: Cauda equina syndrome caused by intervertebral lumbar disc prolapse: mid-term results of 22 patients and literature review, *Orthopedics* 25:727, 2002.

Butterman GR: Treatment of lumbar disc herniation: epidural steroid infection compared with discectomy: a prospective, randomized study, *J Bone Joint Surg* 86A:670, 2004.

Dreyfuss P et al: Sacroiliac joint pain, *J Am Acad Orthop Surg* 12:255, 2004.

Kawaguchi Y et al: The association of lumbar disc disease with vitamin-D receptor gene polymorphism, *J Bone Joint Surg* 84(a):2022, 2002.

Paassilta P et al: Identification of a novel common genetic risk factor for lumbar disc disease, *JAMA* 285:1843, 2001.

Robinson LR: Role of neurophysiologic evaluation in diagnosis, *J Am Acad Orthop Surg* 8:190, 2000.

Silber JS et al: Advances in surgical management of lumbar degenerative disc disease, *Orthopedics* 25:767, 2002.

Simotas AC: Non-operative treatment for lumbar spinal stenosis, *Clin Orthop* 384:153, 2001.

Swenson R, Haldeman S: Spinal manipulation for low back pain, *J Am Acad Orthop Surg* 11:228, 2003.

Tribus CB: Degenerative lumbar scoliosis: evaluation and management, *J Am Acad Orthop Surg* 11:174, 2003.

Wetzel FT, McNally TA: Treatment of chronic discogenic low back pain with intradiskal electrothermal therapy, *J Am Acad Orthop Surg* 11:6, 2003.

Yoshihara K et al: Atrophy of the multifidus muscle in patients with lumbar disc herniation: histochemical and electromyographic study, *Orthopedics* 26:493, 2003.

AUTHOR: **LONNIE R. MERCIER, M.D.**

BASIC INFORMATION

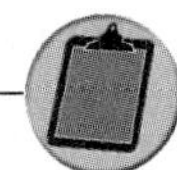

DEFINITION

A primary lung neoplasm is a malignancy arising from lung tissue. The World Health Organization distinguishes 12 types of pulmonary neoplasms. Among them, the major types are *squamous cell carcinoma, adenocarcinoma, small cell carcinoma,* and *large cell carcinoma.* However, the crucial difference in the diagnosis of lung cancer is between small cell and non–small cell types, because the therapeutic approach is different. Selective characteristics of lung carcinomas:

ADENOCARCINOMA: Represents 35% of lung carcinomas; frequently located in mid lung and periphery; initial metastases are to lymphatics, frequently associated with peripheral scars

SQUAMOUS CELL (EPIDERMOID): 20% to 30% of lung cancers; central location; metastasis by local invasion; frequent cavitation and obstructive phenomena

SMALL CELL (OAT CELL): 20% of lung carcinomas; central location; metastasis through lymphatics; associated with lesion of the short arm of chromosome 3; high cavitation rate

LARGE CELL: 15% to 20% of lung carcinomas; frequently located in the periphery; metastasis to CNS and mediastinum; rapid growth rate with early metastasis

BRONCHOALVEOLAR: 5% of lung carcinomas; frequently located in the periphery; may be bilateral; initial metastasis through lymphatic, hematogenous, and local invasion; no correlation with cigarette smoking; cavitation rare

SYNONYMS

Lung cancer

ICD-9CM CODES
162.9 Malignant neoplasm of bronchus and lung, unspecified

EPIDEMIOLOGY & DEMOGRAPHICS

- Lung cancer is responsible for >30% of cancer deaths in males and >25% of cancer deaths in females.
- Tobacco smoking is implicated in 85% of cases; second-hand smoke is responsible for approximately 20% of cases.
- There are >180,000 new cases of lung cancer yearly in the U.S., most occurring >age 50 yr (<4% in patients <40 yr of age).

PHYSICAL FINDINGS & CLINICAL PRESENTATION

- Weight loss, fatigue, fever, anorexia, dysphagia
- Cough, hemoptysis, dyspnea, wheezing
- Chest, shoulder, and bone pain
- Paraneoplastic syndromes:
  1. *Eaton-Lambert syndrome:* myopathy involving proximal muscle groups
  2. Endocrine manifestations: hypercalcemia, ectopic ACTH, SIADH
  3. Neurologic: subacute cerebellar degeneration, peripheral neuropathy, cortical degeneration
  4. Musculoskeletal: polymyositis, clubbing, hypertrophic pulmonary osteoarthropathy
  5. Hematologic or vascular: migratory thrombophlebitis, marantic thrombosis, anemia, thrombocytosis, or thrombocytopenia
  6. Cutaneous: acanthosis nigricans, dermatomyositis
- Pleural effusion (10% of patients), recurrent pneumonias (secondary to obstruction), localized wheezing
- *Superior vena cava syndrome:*
  1. Obstruction of venous return of the superior vena cava is most commonly caused by bronchogenic carcinoma or metastasis to paratracheal nodes.
  2. The patient usually complains of headache, nausea, dizziness, visual changes, syncope, and respiratory distress.
  3. Physical examination reveals distention of thoracic and neck veins, edema of face and upper extremities, facial plethora, and cyanosis.
- *Horner's syndrome:* constricted pupil, ptosis, facial anhidrosis caused by spinal cord damage between C8 and T1 secondary to a superior sulcus tumor (bronchogenic carcinoma of the extreme lung apex); a superior sulcus tumor associated with ipsilateral Horner's syndrome and shoulder pain is known as *"Pancoast" tumor.*

ETIOLOGY

- Tobacco abuse
- Environmental agents (e.g., radon) and industrial agents (e.g., ionizing radiation, asbestos, nickel, uranium, vinyl chloride, chromium, arsenic, coal dust)

DIAGNOSIS

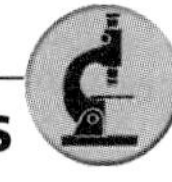

DIFFERENTIAL DIAGNOSIS

- Pneumonia
- TB
- Metastatic carcinoma to the lung
- Lung abscess
- Granulomatous disease
- Carcinoid tumor
- Mycobacterial and fungal diseases
- Sarcoidosis
- Viral pneumonitis
- Benign lesions that simulate thoracic malignancy:
  1. Lobar atelectasis: pneumonia, TB, chronic inflammatory disease, allergic bronchopulmonary aspergillosis
  2. Multiple pulmonary nodules: septic emboli, Wegener's granulomatosis, sarcoidosis, rheumatoid nodules, fungal disease, multiple pulmonary AV fistulas
  3. Mediastinal adenopathy: sarcoidosis, lymphoma, primary TB, fungal disease, silicosis, pneumoconiosis, drug-induced (e.g., phenytoin, trimethadione)
  4. Pleural effusion: CHF, pneumonia with parapneumonic effusion, TB, viral pneumonitis, ascites, pancreatitis, collagen-vascular disease

WORKUP

Workup generally includes chest x-ray, CT scan of chest, PET scan, and tissue biopsy.

LABORATORY TESTS

Obtain tissue diagnosis. Various modalities are available:

- Biopsy of any suspicious lymph nodes (e.g., supraclavicular node)
- Flexible fiberoptic bronchoscopy: brush and biopsy specimens are obtained from any visualized endobronchial lesions
- Transbronchial needle aspiration: done via a special needle passed through the bronchoscope; this technique is useful to sample mediastinal masses or paratracheal lymph nodes
- Transthoracic fine-needle aspiration biopsy with fluoroscopic or CT scan guidance to evaluate peripheral pulmonary nodules
- Mediastinoscopy and anteromedial sternotomy in suspected tumor involvement of the mediastinum
- Pleural biopsy in patients with pleural effusion
- Thoracentesis of pleural effusion and cytologic evaluation of the obtained fluid: may confirm diagnosis

IMAGING STUDIES

- Chest x-ray: The radiographic presentation often varies with the cell type. Pleural effusion, lobar atelectasis, and mediastinal adenopathy can accompany any cell types.
- CT scan of chest: to evaluate mediastinal and pleural extension of suspected lung neoplasms.
- Positron emission tomography (PET) with 18F-fluorodeoxyglucose (18 FDG-PET), a metabolic marker of malignant tissue, is superior to CT scan in detecting mediastinal and distant metastases in non–small cell lung cancer. It is useful for preoperative staging of non–small call lung cancer.

STAGING

- Following confirmation of diagnosis, patients should undergo staging:
  1. The international staging system is the most widely accepted staging system for non–small cell lung cancer. In this system, stage 1 (N0 [no lymph node involvement]), stage 2 (N1 [spread to ipsilateral bronchopulmonary or hilar lymph nodes]) include localized tumors for which surgical resection is the preferred treatment. Stage 3 is subdivided into 3A (potentially resectable) and 3B. The surgical management of stage IIIA disease (N2 [involvement of ipsilateral mediastinal nodes]) is controversial. Only 20% of N2 disease is considered minimal disease (involvement of only one node) and technically resectable. Stage 4 indicates metastatic disease. The pathologic staging system uses a tumor/nodal involvement/metastasis system.
  2. In patients with small cell lung cancer, a more practical accepted staging system is the one developed by the Veterans Administration Lung Cancer Study Group (VALG). This system contains two stages:
     a. Limited stage: disease confined to the regional lymph nodes and to one hemithorax (excluding pleural surfaces)
     b. Extensive stage: disease spread beyond the confines of limited stage disease
  3. Pretreatment staging procedures for lung cancer patients, in addition to complete history and physical examination, generally include the following tests:
     a. Chest x-ray (PA and lateral), ECG
     b. Laboratory evaluation: CBC, electrolytes, platelets, calcium, phosphorus, glucose, renal and liver function studies, ABGs, and skin tests for TB
     c. Pulmonary function studies
     d. CT scan of chest and PET scan: A recent Dutch trial revealed a 51% relative reduction in futile thoracotomies for patients with suspected non–small cell lung cancer who underwent preoperative assessment with PET with the tracer 18FDG-PET in addition to conventional workup
     e. Mediastinoscopy or anterior mediastinotomy in patients being considered for possible curative lung resection
     f. Biopsy of any accessible suspect lesions
     g. CT scan of liver and brain; radionuclide scans of bone in all patients with small cell carcinoma of the lung and patients with non–small cell lung neoplasms suspected of involving these organs
     h. Bone marrow aspiration and biopsy only in selected patients with small cell carcinoma of the lung. In the absence of an increased LDH or cytopenia, routine bone marrow examination is not recommended

TREATMENT

NONPHARMACOLOGIC THERAPY

- Nutritional support
- Avoidance of tobacco or other substances toxic to the lungs
- Supplemental O_2 prn

ACUTE GENERAL Rx

NON–SMALL CELL CARCINOMA:

- Surgery
  1. Surgical resection is indicated in patients with limited disease (not involving mediastinal nodes, ribs, pleura, or distant sites). This represents approximately 15% to 30% of diagnosed cases.
  2. Preoperative evaluation includes review of cardiac status (e.g., recent MI, major arrhythmias) and evaluation of pulmonary function (to determine if the patient can tolerate any loss of lung tissue). Pneumonectomy is possible if the patient has a preoperative $FEV_1 \geq 2$ L or if the MVV is >50% of predicted capacity.
  3. Preoperative chemotherapy should be considered in patients with more advanced disease (stage IIIA) who are being considered for surgery, because it increases the median survival time in patients with non–small cell lung cancer compared with the use of surgery alone.
- Treatment of unresectable non–small cell carcinoma of the lung:
  1. Radiotherapy can be used alone or in combination with chemotherapy; it is used primarily for treatment of CNS and skeletal metastases, superior vena cava syndrome, and obstructive atelectasis; although thoracic radiotherapy is generally considered standard therapy for stage 3 disease, it has limited effect on survival. Palliative radiotherapy should be delayed until symptoms occur since immediate therapy offers no advantage over delayed therapy and results in more adverse events from the radiotherapy.
  2. Chemotherapy: various combination regimens are available. Current drugs of choice are paclitaxel plus either carboplatin or cisplatin; cisplatin plus vinorelbine; gemcitabine plus cisplatin; carboplatin or cisplatin plus docetaxel. The overall results are disappointing, and none of the standard regimens for non–small cell lung cancer is clearly superior to the others. Gefitinib (Iressa), an inhibitor of epidermal growth factor receptor (EGFR) tyrosine kinase, is an oral preparation currently undergoing clinical trials for advanced non–small cell lung cancer.
  3. The addition of chemotherapy to radiotherapy improves survival in patients with locally advanced, unresectable non–small cell lung cancer. The absolute benefit is relatively small, however, and should be balanced against the increased toxicity associated with the addition of chemotherapy.

TREATMENT OF SMALL CELL LUNG CANCER:

- Limited stage disease: standard treatments include thoracic radiotherapy and chemotherapy (cisplatin and etoposide)
- Extensive stage disease: standard treatments include combination chemotherapy (cisplatin or carboplatin plus etoposide or combination of irinotecan and cisplatin)
- Prophylactic cranial irradiation for patients in complete remission to decrease the risk of CNS metastasis

DISPOSITION

- The 5-yr survival of patients with non–small cell carcinoma when the disease is resectable is approximately 30%.
- Median survival time in patients with limited stage disease and small cell lung cancer is 15 mo; in patients with extensive stage disease, it is 9 mo.

SUGGESTED READINGS

Kris MG et al: Efficacy of gefitinib, an inhibitor of the epidermal growth factor receptor tyrosine kinase, in symptomatic patients with non-small cell lung cancer, *JAMA* 290:2149, 2003.

Lardinois D et al: Staging of non-small cell lung cancer with integrated positron-emission tomography and computed tomography, *N Engl J Med* 348:2500, 2003.

Schiller JH et al: Comparison of four chemotherapy regimens for advanced non-small-cell lung cancer, *N Engl J Med* 346:92, 2002.

Spira A, Ettinger DS: Multidisciplinary management of lung cancer, *N Engl J Med* 350:379, 2004.

AUTHOR: **FRED F. FERRI, M.D.**

BASIC INFORMATION

DEFINITION

Lyme disease is a multisystem inflammatory disorder caused by the transmission of a spirochete, *Borrelia burgdorferi*. Lyme disease is spread by the bite of infected *Ixodes* ticks, taking 36 to 48 hr for a tick to feed and spread *B. burgdorferi*.

SYNONYMS

Bannworth's syndrome
Acrodermatitis chronica atrophicans

ICD-9CM CODES
088.8 Lyme disease

EPIDEMIOLOGY & DEMOGRAPHICS

INCIDENCE (IN U.S.): Geographic variation, 4.4 cases/100,000 persons; reported in 43 states and District of Columbia. Approximately 90% of cases in the U.S. are found in nine states: Massachusetts, Connecticut, Rhode Island, New York, New Jersey, Pennsylvania, Minnesota, Wisconsin, and California.
PREDOMINANT SEX: Male = female
PREDOMINANT AGE: Median age of 28 yr
PEAK INCIDENCE: May to November

PHYSICAL FINDINGS

Lyme disease may present in the following stages:
- *Early localized:* early Lyme disease, erythema chronicum migrans (ECM); skin rash, often at site of tick bite; possible fever, myalgias 3 to 32 days after tick bite
- *Early disseminated:* days to weeks later; multiorgan system involvement, including CNS, joints, cardiac; related to dissemination of spirochete
- *Late persistent:* months to years after tick exposure; affects central and peripheral nervous system, cardiac, joints

Common presenting signs and symptoms include:
- ECM (Fig. 1-140)
- Lymphadenopathy, neck pains, pharyngeal erythema, myalgias, hepatosplenomegaly often present early in the disease
- Patients will complain of malaise, fatigue, lethargy, headache, fever/chills, neck pain, myalgias, back pain

ETIOLOGY

B. burgdorferi transmitted from bite of an *Ixodes* tick (most commonly belonging to the species *Scapularis*)

DIAGNOSIS

Clinical presentation, exposure to ticks in endemic area, and diagnostic testing for antibody response to *B. burgdorferi*

DIFFERENTIAL DIAGNOSIS

- Chronic fatigue/fibromyalgia
- Acute viral illnesses
- Babesiosis
- Ehrlichiosis

WORKUP

- ELISA testing—Western blot
- Immunofluorescent assay
- Early disease often difficult to diagnose serologically secondary to slow immune response
- Culturing of skin lesions (ECM) and polymerase chain reaction (PCR) of skin biopsy and blood to give definitive diagnosis (available only in reference laboratories)

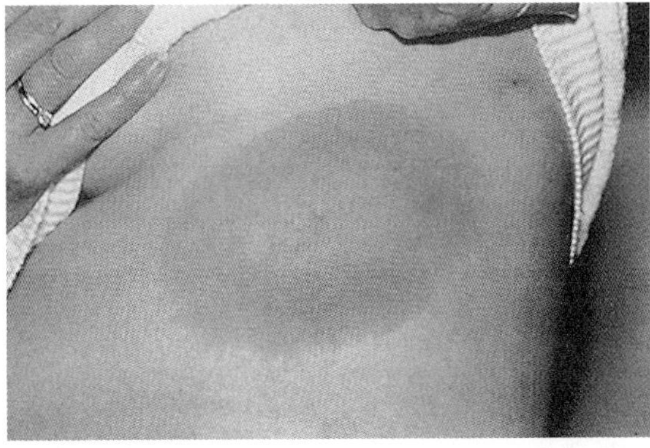

FIGURE 1-140 Erythema migrans. Note expanding erythematous lesion with central clearing on trunk. (Courtesy John Cook, M.D. From Goldstein B [ed]: *Practical dermatology,* ed 2, St Louis, 1997, Mosby.)

IMAGING STUDIES

- Echocardiogram if conduction abnormalities are present with cardiac involvement
- CT scan, MRI of head for CNS involvement

TREATMENT

- Early Lyme disease
  Doxycycline 100 mg bid or amoxicillin 500 mg qid for 10-14 days (doxycycline should be avoided in children/
  pregnant females)
  Alternative treatments: cefuroxime axetil 500 mg bid for 10-14 days, azithromycin 500 mg PO qd for 1 day followed by 250 mg qd for 6 days
- Early Disseminated and late persistent infection: 30 days of treatment necessary; doxycycline and ceftriaxone appear equally effective for acute disseminated Lyme disease
- Arthritis: 30 days of doxycycline or amoxicillin plus probenecid (repeated courses of therapy are often needed)
- Neurologic involvement requires
  Parenteral antibiotics
  Ceftriaxone 2 g/day for 21 to 28 days
  Alternative: cefotaxime 2 g q8h Alternative: penicillin G 5 million U qid
- Cardiac involvement: IV ceftriaxone or penicillin plus cardiac monitoring
- Evidence from recent study suggests that prolonged treatment with IV or PO antibiotic therapy for up to 90 days did not improve symptoms more than placebo

PEARLS & CONSIDERATIONS

- The U.S. Advisory Committee on immunization practices (ACIP) has recommended that "vaccination should be considered for patients 15 to 70 years of age who live, work, and recreate in high- or moderate-risk areas, and are exposed to ticks either frequently or for long periods of time."
- In some patients with Lyme disease, nonspecific complaints such as headache, fatigue, and arthralgia may persist for months after appropriate (and ultimately successful) antibiotic treatment. These patients undergo slow spontaneous resolution; further therapy for Lyme disease should not be given unless there are objective findings of active disease (including physical findings; abnormalities on cerebrospinal or synovial fluid analy-

sis; changes on formal neuropsychologic testing).

- A single dose of 200 mg doxycycline given within 72 hr of *Ixodes* tick bite can prevent development of Lyme disease.

SUGGESTED READINGS

Gomes-Solecki MCJ et al: A first tier rapid assay for the serodiagnosis of *Borrelia burgdorferi* infection, *Arch Intern Med* 161:2015, 2002.

Klempner MS et al: Two controlled trials of antibiotic treatment in patients with persistent symptoms and a history of Lyme disease, *N Engl J Med* 345:85, 2001.

Nadelman RB et al: Prophylaxis with single dose doxycycline for the prevention of Lyme disease after an *Ixodes scapularis* tick bite, *N Engl J Med* 345:79, 2001.

Poland GA: Prevention of Lyme disease: a review of the evidence, *Mayo Clin Proc* 76:713, 2001.

Shadick NA et al: The cost-effectiveness of vaccination against Lyme disease, *Arch Intern Med* 161:554, 2001.

Smith RP et al: Clinical characteristics and treatment outcome of early Lyme disease in patients with microbiologically confirmed erythema migrans, *Ann Intern Med* 136:421, 2002.

Steere AC: Lyme disease, *N Engl J Med* 345:115, 2001.

Wormer GP et al: Duration of antibiotic therapy for early Lyme disease. A randomized, double-blind, placebo-controlled trial, *Ann Intern Med* 138:697, 2003.

AUTHORS: **JOSEPH F. GRILLO, M.D.,** and **DENNIS J. MIKOLICH, M.D.**

BASIC INFORMATION

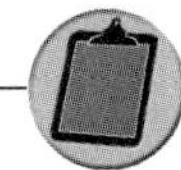

DEFINITION

Lymphangitis refers to the inflammation of lymphatic vessels.

SYNONYMS

Nodular lymphangitis
Sporotrichoid lymphangitis

ICD-9CM CODES
457.2 Lymphangitis

EPIDEMIOLOGY & DEMOGRAPHICS

Incidence (in U.S.): Several hundred cases/yr of sporotrichoid lymphangitis

PHYSICAL FINDINGS & CLINICAL PRESENTATION

ACUTE LYMPHANGITIS:

- Commonly associated with a bacterial cellulitis
- May or may not recognize site of skin trauma (i.e., laceration, puncture, ulcer)
- In hours to days, distal appearance of erythema, edema, and tenderness, with linear erythematous streaks extending proximally to regional lymph nodes
- Possible lymphadenitis and fever
- Predisposition to group A streptococcal infection of the skin in those with chronic lymphedema and superficial fungal infections (e.g., tinea pedis)

"SPOROTRICHOID" OR "NODULAR" LYMPHANGITIS:

- Includes subcutaneous nodules that develop along the path of involved lymphatics
- Most commonly results from inoculation of the skin of the hand
- Usually preceded by well-defined episode of cutaneous inoculation or trauma
- Lesions apparent from one to several weeks after inoculation
- Initially, nodular or papular lesion; may ulcerate
- May have frank pus or a serosanguineous discharge
- Systemic complaints uncommon, but infection with certain microorganisms associated with fever, chills, myalgias, and headache

ETIOLOGY

- Acute lymphangitis: usually associated with *Streptococcus pyogenes* (group A streptococcus), but staphylococcal organisms have been implicated
- Nodular lymphangitis caused by one of several organisms
  1. *Sporothrix schenckii*
     a. Most common recognized cause in the U.S., usually in the Midwest
     b. Found in soil and plant debris
  2. *Nocardia brasiliensis:* found in soil
  3. *Mycobacterium marinum:* associated with trauma related to water (e.g., aquariums, swimming pools, fish)
  4. *Leishmania brasiliensis*
     a. Protozoal parasite transmitted to humans by sandflies, mostly to travelers in endemic areas
     b. Small endemic focus in Texas
  5. *Francisella tularensis*
     a. Most often in Midwestern states
     b. Associated with contact with infected mammals (e.g., rabbits) or tick bites

DIAGNOSIS

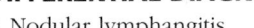

DIFFERENTIAL DIAGNOSIS

- Nodular lymphangitis
- Insect or snake bites
- Filariasis

WORKUP

- Acute lymphangitis: blood cultures
- Nodular lymphangitis: various stains and cultures of drainage or biopsy specimens of inoculation sites to make definitive diagnosis

LABORATORY TESTS

- WBCs possibly elevated with cellulitis
- Eosinophilia common with helminthic infections

TREATMENT

NONPHARMACOLOGIC THERAPY

Limb elevation

ACUTE GENERAL Rx

- Penicillin possibly sufficient, but 1 wk of dicloxacillin or cephalexin 500 mg PO qid commonly used to ensure antistaphylococcal coverage
- If allergic to penicillin:
  1. Clindamycin 300 mg PO qid for 7 days *or*
  2. Erythromycin 500 mg PO qid for 7 days
- Nodular lymphangitis: specific therapy directed at etiologic agent
- For superficial fungal infections: treatment may prevent recurrence of acute lymphangitis

DISPOSITION

- Acute lymphangitis: usually resolves with therapy
- Recurrent attacks: may lead to chronic lymphedema of limb, rarely resulting in elephantiasis nostras (nonfilarial elephantiasis)
- Nodular lymphangitis: usually responds to appropriate therapy

REFERRAL

- If acute lymphangitis is more than a mild disease or involves the face
- If nodular lymphangitis or filariasis is suspected

PEARLS & CONSIDERATIONS

COMMENTS

- Outside of the U.S., initial episodes of filariasis caused by *Brugia malayi* resemble acute lymphangitis.
- Chronic lymphedema or elephantiasis results from recurrent episodes.

SUGGESTED READING

Tobin EH, Jih WW: Sporotrichoid lymphocutaneous infections: etiology, diagnosis and therapy, *Am Fam Physician* 63:326, 2001.

AUTHOR: **MAURICE POLICAR, M.D.**

BASIC INFORMATION

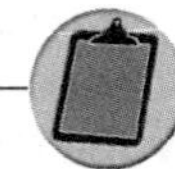

DEFINITION

Lymphedema refers to excessive accumulation of interstitial protein rich fluid typically resulting from impaired regional lymphatic drainage.

SYNONYMS

Elephantiasis

ICD-9CM CODES
457.1 Lymphedema: acquired (chronic), praecox, secondary
457.1 Elephantiasis (nonfilarial)

EPIDEMIOLOGY & DEMOGRAPHICS

PRIMARY LYMPHEDEMA:
- Found in 1.1/100,000 people <20 yr old.
- Females outnumber males 3.5:1.
- Incidence peaks between ages 12 to 16 yr old.

SECONDARY LYMPHEDEMA: See specific etiology (e.g., filariasis, breast cancer, prostate cancer)

PHYSICAL FINDINGS & CLINICAL PRESENTATION

Edema:
- Painless and progressive
  1. Initially, the edema is pitting and smooth; however, with advanced cases, the edema becomes nonpitting (this depends on the extent of fibrosis that has occurred).
  2. Elevation of the leg resolves the swelling in the early stages but not in the advanced stages.
- More often unilateral but depending on the etiology can be bilateral
- Not always restricted to the lower extremities but may involve the genitals, face, or upper extremities (e.g., arm swelling after mastectomy)
- Stemmer's sign (squaring of the toes caused by edema in the digits)
- "Buffalo hump" appearance of the dorsum of the foot
- Loss of the ankle contour, giving a "tree trunk" appearance of the leg

Skin:
- Hard, thick, leathery skin secondary to fibrosis induced by chronic stasis
- Occasional drainage of lymph
- Infections (cellulitis, lymphangitis, onychomycosis)

ETIOLOGY

Lymphedema is caused by a reduction in lymphatic transport and is classified into primary and secondary forms.

Primary idiopathic lymphedema is thought to result from developmental abnormalities such as lymphatic hypoplasia and functional insufficiency or absence of lymphatic valves. Subclasses of this type of lymphedema include:
- Congenital lymphedema
  1. Detected at birth or recognized within first 2 yr of life
  2. Involving one or both extremities, usually the entire leg
  3. May be familial (Milroy's disease)
- Lymphedema praecox
  1. Onset in teenage years
  2. Usually unilateral; occurring in the teenage years
  3. Most common form of primary lymphedema (up to 94% of cases)
  4. More common in females (10:1), suggesting estrogen plays a role in pathogenesis
  5. May be familial (Meige's disease)
- Lymphedema tarda
  1. Usually occurs after the age of 30 yr
  2. Uncommon, accounting for less than 10% of cases of primary lymphedema

Secondary lymphedema develops after disruption or obstruction of the lymphatic system as a consequence of:
- Surgery for malignant tumors (e.g., breast, prostate, lymphoma)
- Edema of the arm after axillary lymph node dissection is the most common cause of lymphedema in the U.S.
- Incidence of lymphedema is ~14% in patients s/p mastectomy with adjuvant radiation treatment
- Inflammation (streptococci, filariasis)
- Filariasis is the most common cause of lymphedema in the world
- Trauma
- Radiation with lymph node removal

DIAGNOSIS

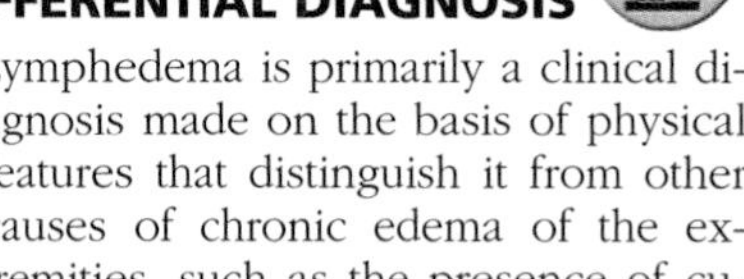

DIFFERENTIAL DIAGNOSIS

- Lymphedema is primarily a clinical diagnosis made on the basis of physical features that distinguish it from other causes of chronic edema of the extremities, such as the presence of cutaneous and subcutaneous fibrosis (peau d'orange) and the Stemmer sign.
- When physical examination is inconclusive, other available imaging tests can help make the diagnosis: isotopic lymphoscintigraphy, indirect and direct lymphography, lymphatic capillaroscopy, MRI, CT, or ultrasound.
- Isoptopic lymphoscintigraphy is currently considered the gold standard for diagnosis of lymphedema.

Exclude other causes of edema (e.g., cirrhosis, nephrosis, CHF, myxedema, hypoalbuminemia, chronic venous stasis, reflex sympathetic dystrophy, obstruction from abdominal or pelvic malignancy).

WORKUP

A detailed history and physical examination should help exclude most of the differential diagnosis.

LABORATORY TESTS

- BUN, Cr, liver function tests, albumin, urine analysis, TFTs are obtained to exclude possible systemic causes of edema.
- Noninvasive venous studies help exclude venous insufficiency.
- Genetic testing may be practical in defining a specific hereditary syndrome with a discrete gene mutation such as lymphedema-distichiasis (FOXC2) and some forms of Milroy disease (VEGFR-3).

IMAGING STUDIES

- Lymphoscintigraphy:
  1. Diagnostic image of choice
  2. Sensitivity and specificity of 100% in diagnosing lymphedema
- CT scan: to exclude malignancy leading to obstruction
- Duplex ultrasound to rule out venous obstruction as a cause for edema
- Lymphangiography:
  1. Available but rarely used
  2. May be requested by surgeons considering repair or excision of tissue for lymphedema
  3. Difficult to perform; most information can be obtained from the nuclear lymphoscintigram

TREATMENT

NONPHARMACOLOGIC THERAPY

Complex Decongestive Therapy (CDT) is backed by longstanding experience as the primary treatment of choice for lymphedema in both children and adults. It involves a two-stage treatment program:
1. Reduce leg swelling and size:
   - Leg elevation
   - Limb massage
   - Pneumatic leg compression

2. Maintain edema-free state:
   - Elastic support stockings that are properly fitted according to compression pressure and length are essential to prevent edema from returning.
   - Compression pressures are graduated; most of the pressure is distal with less and less pressure from the stockings, moving proximally.
   - Compression pressures range from 20 to 30 mm Hg, 30 to 40 mm Hg, 40 to 50 mm Hg, and 50 to 60 mm Hg. Most prefer 40 to 50 mm Hg for lymphedema.
   - The length should cover the edematous site. Choices include below the knee, thigh-high, and pantyhose lengths.

ACUTE GENERAL Rx

- Diuretics, including furosemide 40 to 80 mg qd, may aid in reducing leg swelling but should be used only temporarily. Hydrochlorothiazide 25 mg qd can also be used for reducing edema or preventing leg swelling.
- Treat infections, such as lymphangitis (usually caused by group A streptococcus), with penicillin VK 250 mg qid for 10 days or erythromycin 250 mg qid in penicillin-allergic patients. If recurrent episodes of infection occur, many consider prophylaxis with penicillin VK 250 mg qid for 10 days at the beginning of each month. Clotrimazole 1% cream should be applied qd to dried fissured areas in between toes to prevent fungal infections.
- In secondary lymphedema, treating the underlying cause is indicated (e.g., prostate cancer, breast cancer). If the etiology is filariasis caused by the parasites *Wuchereria bancrofti* or *Brugia malayi,* treatment is diethylcarbamazine citrate (DEC) 5 mg/kg in divided doses for 3 wk.
- Mesotherapy (hyaluronidase), immunological therapy (autologous lymphocyte injection), and fluid restriction all have uncertain benefit in the treatment of lymphedema.
- In children with chylous reflux syndromes, a diet low in long-chain triglycerides and high in short and medium-chain triglycerides has been shown to be of benefit in treatment.

CHRONIC Rx

Surgery for chronic lymphedema should act as an adjunct to CDT or as an alternative if CDT has proven unsuccessful. Operative treatment is considered if:
- Continued increase in leg size despite medical treatment
- Impaired leg function
- Recurrent infections
- Emotional lability secondary to the cosmetic appearance

Surgical procedures are divided into two types:
- Those performed to improve lymph node drainage (e.g., anastomoses of the lymph system with the venous system)
- Those performed to excise the subcutaneous tissue (e.g., Charles' procedure, Thompson's procedure, and the modified Homans' procedure)
- Liposuction in combination with long-term decongestive therapy has been shown to be mroe effective in reducing edema than long-term decongestive therapy alone.

DISPOSITION

- Lymphedema is a slowly progressive disorder that can lead to significant disfigurement of the extremities or other body parts.
- The extent of fibrotic change to the skin of the affected limb increases with the chronicity of lymphatic stasis.
- In many patients, the maximum girth of the affected limb is reached within the first year after onset, unless complications like recurrent cellulitis supervene.
- Patients with lymphedema commonly manifest psychiatric comorbidities as a result of their disease, such as anxiety, depression, adjustment problems, and difficulty in vocational, domestic, or social domains.
- Chronic lymphedema can be complicated by cellulitis or, in rare cases, development of lymphagiosarcomata or other cutaneous malignancies.

REFERRAL

- If the diagnosis of lymphedema is unclear or in need of better definition for prognostic considerations, consultation with a clinical lymphologist or referral to a lymphohologic center if accessible is recommended.
- Consultation with vascular surgeons should be made if medical therapy for leg size reduction fails or if recurrent infections occur.

PEARLS & CONSIDERATIONS

COMMENTS

- Lymphedema is a chronic, generally incurable ailment, and requires lifelong care and attention along with psychosocial support.
- It is important to remember that surgery is not a cure.
- Children and adolescents (along with parents and adults) should be encouraged to pursue a normal life, participating in school activities and sports (preferably noncontact, e.g., swimming).
- It should also be remembered that cases of lymphangiosarcomas have been associated, although rarely, with postmastectomy lymphedema.
- In the U.S., the leading cause of lymphedema of both upper and lower extremities is neoplastic disease and its related therapies. In a previously treated cancer patient with new or worsening edema, cancer recurrence leading to intrinsic or extrinsic lymphatic obstruction must be considered.

SUGGESTED READINGS

Caban ME: Trends in the evaluation of lymphedema, *Lymphology* 35(1):28, 2002.

International Society of Lymphology: The diagnosis and treatment of peripheral lymphedema: Consensus document of the International Society of Lymphology, *Lymphology* 36(2):84, 2003.

Neese PY: Management of lymphedema, *Lippincotts Prim Care Pract* 4(4):390, 2000.

Rockson SG: Lymphedema, *Am J Med* 110:288, 2001.

Rockson SG et al: American Cancer Society Lymphedema Workshop. Workgroup III: diagnosis and management of lymphedema, *Cancer* 83(12 suppl):2882, 1998.

AUTHORS: **JASON IANNUCCILLI, M.D.,** and **PETER PETROPOULOS, M.D.**

Lymphogranuloma Venereum (PTG)

BASIC INFORMATION

DEFINITION

Lymphogranuloma venereum (LGV) is a sexually transmitted, systemic disease caused by *Chlamydia trachomatis*.

SYNONYMS

Tropical bubo
Poradenitis inguinalis
LGV

ICD-9CM CODES
099.1 Lymphogranuloma venereum

EPIDEMIOLOGY & DEMOGRAPHICS

- Male:female ratio is 5:1
- LGV is rare in the U.S. (285 cases reported in 1993).
- LGV is endemic in Africa, India, parts of Southeast Asia, South America, and the Caribbean.

PHYSICAL FINDINGS & CLINICAL PRESENTATION

Primary stage:
- Primary lesion caused by multiplication of organism at site of infection
- Papule, shallow ulcer
- Herpetiform lesion at site of inoculation (most common)
- Incubation period of 3 to 21 days
- Most common site of lesion in women: posterior wall, fourchette, or vulva
- Spontaneous healing, without scarring

Second stage:
- Inguinal syndrome: characteristic inguinal adenopathy
- Begins 1 to 4 wk after primary lesion
- Syndrome is the most frequent clinical sign of the disease
- Unilateral inguinal adenopathy in 70% of cases
- Symptoms: painful, extensive adenitis (bubo) and suppuration may occur with numerous sinus tracts
- "Groove sign" signaling femoral and inguinal node involvement (20%); most often seen in men
- Involvement of deep iliac and retroperitoneal lymph nodes in women may present as a pelvic mass

Third stage (anogenital syndrome):
- Subacute: proctocolitis
- Late: tissue destruction or scarring, sinuses, abscesses, fistulas, strictures of perineum, elephantiasis

ETIOLOGY

Chlamydia trachomatis is the causative agent. There are three serotypes: L1, L2, and L3.

DIAGNOSIS

DIFFERENTIAL DIAGNOSIS

- Inguinal adenitis, suppurative adenitis, retroperitoneal adenitis, proctitis, schistosomiasis
- Section II describes the differential diagnosis of genital sores.

WORKUP

- Clinical manifestation
- Screening for other STDs
- A clinical algorithm for evaluation of genital ulcer disease is described in Section III, Genital Lesions.

LABORATORY TESTS

- Positive Frei test:
  1. Intradermal chlamydial antigen
  2. Nonspecific for all *Chlamydia*
  3. No longer available (historical significance only)
- Complement fixation test:
  1. Titer >1:64 in active infection
  2. Convalescent titers no difference
- Cell culture of *Chlamydia*—aspiration of fluctuant node yields highest rates of recovery
- CBC—mild leukocytosis with lymphocytosis or monocytosis
- Elevated sedimentation rate
- VDRL and HIV screening to rule out other STDs

IMAGING STUDIES

- Barium enema: may reveal elongated structure of LGV
- CT scan for retroperitoneal adenitis

TREATMENT

NONPHARMACOLOGIC THERAPY

- Avoid milk and milk products while taking medication.
- Practice sexual abstinence.
- Treat sexual partners.

ACUTE GENERAL Rx

- Doxycycline 100 mg PO bid × 21 days
- Erythromycin base 500 mg PO qid × 21 days
- Sulfisoxazole 500 mg PO qid × 21 days
- Surgical:
  1. Aspirate fluctuant nodes
  2. Incise and drain abscesses

CHRONIC Rx

- Longer course of therapy will be needed for chronic or relapsing cases, which may be caused by reinfection and/or inadequate treatment.
- A rectal stricture will require a colostomy.
- Surgery should be considered only after antibiotic treatment.

DISPOSITION

Good prognosis with early treatment, usually resulting in complete resolution of symptoms.

REFERRAL

Surgical consultation if patient develops obstruction, fistula, or rectal stricture. May need referral to plastic surgeon if patient has lymphatic obstruction.

PEARLS & CONSIDERATIONS

COMMENTS

- Pregnant and lactating women should be treated with erythromycin regimen.
- Congenital transmission does not occur, but infection may be acquired through an infected birth canal.
- Patient education materials may be obtained through local and state health clinics.

SUGGESTED READING

Centers for Disease Control and Prevention: 2002 sexually transmitted diseases treatment guidelines, *MMWR Morb Mortal Wkly Rep* 51(RR-6), 2002.

AUTHOR: **GEORGE T. DANAKAS, M.D.**

BASIC INFORMATION

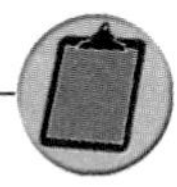

DEFINITION

Non-Hodgkin lymphoma is a heterogeneous group of malignancies of the lymphoreticular system.

SYNONYMS

NHL

ICD-9CM CODES
201.9 Lymphoma, non-Hodgkin

EPIDEMIOLOGY & DEMOGRAPHICS

- Median age at time of diagnosis: 50 yr
- Sixth most common neoplasm in the U.S. (56,000 new cases/yr)
- Increasing incidence with age

PHYSICAL FINDINGS & CLINICAL PRESENTATION

- Patients often present with asymptomatic lymphadenopathy.
- Approximately one third of NHL originates extranodally. Involvement of extranodal sites can result in unusual presentations (e.g., GI tract involvement can simulate PUD).
- NHL cases associated with HIV occur predominantly in the brain.
- Pruritus, fever, night sweats, weight loss are less common than in Hodgkin's disease.
- Hepatomegaly and splenomegaly may be present.

DIAGNOSIS

DIFFERENTIAL DIAGNOSIS

- Hodgkin's disease
- Viral infections
- Metastatic carcinoma
- A clinical algorithm for evaluation of lymphadenopathy is described in Section III
- The differential diagnosis of lymphadenopathy is described in Section II

WORKUP

Initial laboratory evaluation may reveal only mild anemia and elevated LDH and ESR. Proper staging of non-Hodgkin's lymphoma requires the following:

- A thorough history, physical examination, and adequate biopsy
- Routine laboratory evaluation (CBC, ESR, urinalysis, LDH, BUN, creatinine, serum calcium, uric acid, LFTs, serum protein electrophoresis)
- Chest x-ray examination (PA and lateral)
- Bone marrow evaluation (aspirate and full bone core biopsy)
- CT scan of abdomen and pelvis; CT scan of chest if chest x-ray films abnormal
- Bone scan (particularly in patients with histiocytic lymphoma)
- Depending on the histopathology, the results of the above studies and the planned therapy, some other tests may be performed: gallium scan (e.g., in patients with high-grade lymphomas), liver/spleen scan, PET scan, lymphangiography, lumbar puncture
- β-2 Microglobulin levels should be obtained initially (prognostic value) and serially in patients with low-grade lymphomas (useful to monitor therapeutic response of the tumor)
- Serum interleukin levels have prognostic value in diffuse large cell lymphoma

CLASSIFICATION: The Working Formulation of non-Hodgkin lymphoma for clinical usage subdivides lymphomas into low grade, intermediate grade, high grade, and miscellaneous (Table 1-29).

STAGING: The Ann Arbor classification is used to stage non-Hodgkin lymphomas (see "Hodgkin's Disease" in Section I). Histopathology has greater therapeutic implications in NHL than in Hodgkin's disease.

IMAGING STUDIES

See "Workup."

TREATMENT

ACUTE GENERAL Rx

The therapeutic regimen varies with the histologic type and pathologic stage. Following are the commonly used therapeutic modalities:

LOW-GRADE NHL (E.G., NODULAR, POORLY DIFFERENTIATED):

1. Local radiotherapy for symptomatic obstructive adenopathy
2. Deferment of therapy and careful observation in asymptomatic patients
3. Single-agent chemotherapy with cyclophosphamide or chlorambucil and glucocorticoids
4. Combination chemotherapy alone or with radiotherapy: generally indicated only when the lymphoma becomes more invasive, with poor response to less aggressive treatment; commonly used regimens: CVP, CHOP, CHOP-BLEO, COPP, BACOP; addition of recombinant alpha interferon at low doses to chemotherapy prolongs remission duration in patients with low-grade NHL
5. Monoclonal antibodies directed against B-cell surface antigens can also be used to treat follicular lymphomas that are resistant to conventional therapy. The anti-CD20 monoclonal antibody rituximab is a targeted, minimally toxic treatment effective against low-grade NHL in patients who have not received previous treatment
6. The addition of rituximab to CHOP is generally well tolerated; however, additional studies may be necessary to clarify the role of CHOP plus rituximab in patients with indolent NHL
7. Ibritumomab tiuxetan (Zevalin), an immunoconjugate that combines the linker-chelator tiuxetan with the monoclonal antibody ibritumomab, can be used as part of a two-step regimen for treatment of patients with relapsed or refractory low-grade, follicular, or transformed B-cell NHL refractory to rituximab
8. New purine analogs (FLAMP, 2CDA) can be used in salvage treatment of refractory lymphomas. They all have activity in follicular lymphomas

INTERMEDIATE- AND HIGH-GRADE LYMPHOMAS (E.G., DIFFUSE HISTIOCYTIC LYMPHOMA):
Combination chemotherapy regimens (e.g., CHOP, PRO-MACE-CYTABOM, MACOP-B, M-BACOD). An anthracycline-containing regimen (such as CHOP) given in standard doses and schedule is generally best for treatment of older patients with advanced stage, aggressive-histology lymphoma who do not have significant comorbid illness.

1. High-dose sequential therapy is superior to standard-dose MACOP-B for patients with diffuse large-cell lymphoma of the B-cell type.
2. Dose-modified chemotherapy should be considered for most HIV-infected patients with lymphoma. As compared with treatment with standard doses of cytotoxic chemotherapy (M-BACOD), reduced doses cause significantly fewer hematologic toxic effects yet have similar efficacy in patients with HIV-related lymphoma.
   - Three cycles of CHOP followed by involved-field radiotherapy may be superior to eight cycles of CHOP alone in patients with localized intermediate- and high-grade NHL.
   - The addition of rituximab against CD20 B-cell lymphoma to the CHOP regimen increases the complete response rate and prolongs event-free and overall survival in elderly patients with diffuse large B-cell lymphoma without a clini-

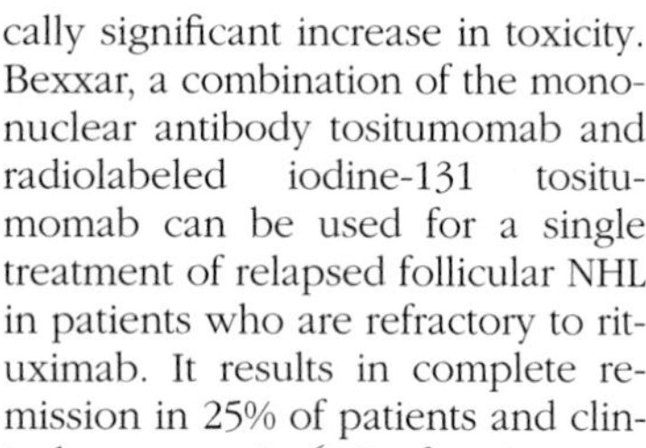

cally significant increase in toxicity. Bexxar, a combination of the mononuclear antibody tositumomab and radiolabeled iodine-131 tositumomab can be used for a single treatment of relapsed follicular NHL in patients who are refractory to rituximab. It results in complete remission in 25% of patients and clinical response in 60% of patients.
- Granulocyte-colony stimulating factor (G-CSF): may be effective in reducing the risk of infection in patients with aggressive lymphoma undergoing chemotherapy
- Radioimmunotherapy with (^{131}I) anti-B1 antibody therapy for NHL either by itself or in combination with other treatments
- Treatment with high-dose chemotherapy and autologous bone marrow transplant: as compared with conventional chemotherapy, increases event-free and overall survival in patients with chemotherapy-sensitive non-Hodgkin lymphoma in relapse

DISPOSITION

- Patients with low-grade lymphoma, despite their long-term survival (6 to 10 yr average), are rarely cured, and the great majority (if not all) eventually die of the lymphoma, whereas patients with a high-grade lymphoma may achieve a cure with aggressive chemotherapy.
- Complete remission occurs in 35% to 50% of patients with intermediate- and high-grade lymphoma. Prognostic factors include the histiologic subtype, age of patient, and bulk of disease.

AUTHOR: **FRED F. FERRI, M.D.**

TABLE 1-29 **Classification Systems for Grading Lymphomas**

Kiel Classification	Working Formulation	Revised European-American Classification
Low-grade malignancy	Low grade	B-cell lymphomas
Lymphocytic, CLL	A. Malignant lymphoma, small lymphocytic	
Lymphocytic, other	Consistent with chronic lymphocytic leukemia	B-CLL/SLL
Lymphoplasmacytoid		Lymphoplasmacytoid lymphoma
Centrocytic	B. Malignant lymphoma, follicular, predominantly small cleaved cell	Follicle center lymphomas
Centroblastic/Centrocytic		Marginal zone lymphomas (MALT)
Follicular without sclerosis	Diffuse areas	Mantle cell lymphoma
Follicular with sclerosis	Sclerosis	
Follicular and diffuse, without sclerosis	C. Malignant lymphoma, follicular mixed, small cleaved and large cell	
Follicular and diffuse, with sclerosis	Diffuse areas	Diffuse large B-cell lymphoma
Diffuse	Sclerosis	Primary mediastinal large B-cell lymphoma
Low-grade malignant lymphoma, unclassified	Intermediate grade	Burkitt's lymphoma
High-grade malignancy	D. Malignant lymphoma, follicular	T-cell lymphomas
Centroblastic	Diffuse areas	
Lymphoblastic, Burkitt's type	E. Malignant lymphoma, diffuse small cleaved cell	
Lymphoblastic, convoluted cell type		T-CLL
Lymphoblastic, other (unclassified) immunoblastic		Mycosis fungoides/Sézary syndrome
High-grade malignant lymphoma, unclassified	F. Malignant lymphoma, diffuse mixed, small and large cell sclerosis	
Malignant lymphoma unclassified (unable to specify high grade or low grade)	G. Malignant lymphoma diffuse	Peripheral T-cell lymphoma, unspecified
Composite lymphoma	Large cell	Angioimmunoblastic T-cell lymphoma
	Cleaved cell	Angiocentric lymphoma
	Noncleaved cell	Intestinal T-cell lymphoma
	Sclerosis	Adult T-cell lymphoma/leukemia
	High grade	Anaplastic large cell lymphoma
	H. Malignant lymphoma large cell, immunoblastic	Precursor T-lymphoid lymphoma/leukemia
	Plasmacytoid	
	Clear cell	
	Polymorphous	
	Epithelioid cell component	
	I. Malignant lymphoma lymphoblastic	
	Convoluted cell	
	Nonconvoluted cell	
	J. Malignant lymphoma small noncleaved cell	
	Burkitt's	
	Follicular areas	

From Abeloff MD: ***Clinical oncology,*** ed 2, New York, 2000, Churchill Livingstone.
B-CLL, B-cell chronic lymphoid leukemia; ***MALT,*** mucosa-associated lymphoid tumor; ***SLL,*** lymphoid leukemia; ***T-CLL,*** T-cell CLL.

BASIC INFORMATION

DEFINITION

Macular degeneration refers to a group of diseases associated with loss of central vision and damage to the macula. Degenerative changes occur in the pigment, neural, and vascular layers of the macula. The dry macular degeneration is usually ischemic in etiology, and a wet macular degeneration is associated with leakage of fluid from blood vessels, usually referred to as age-related macular degeneration (ARMD).

ICD-9CM CODES
362.5 Degeneration of macula and posterior pole

EPIDEMIOLOGY & DEMOGRAPHICS

INCIDENCE (IN U.S.):
- Main cause of blindness in the U.S. in 40 yr and older
- Increases with age
- 1.75 million individuals in the U.S. currently affected; 3 million by year 2020

PREVALENCE (IN U.S.): Varies, but approximately 5% of people <50 yr old have some signs of macular degeneration.

PREDOMINANT SEX: Male = female (15% of white women >80 have severe ARMD)

PREDOMINANT AGE: >50 yr

PEAK INCIDENCE:
- 75 to 80 yr old
- Dramatic increases in incidence and prevalence with age until approximately 80% of people 75 yr or older have senile macular degeneration.

GENETICS:
- Different syndrome: senile macular degeneration is age related.
- Several rare neurologic syndromes are associated with macular degeneration.
- Vascular disease closely related to macular degeneration.

PHYSICAL FINDINGS

- Decreased central vision
- Macular hemorrhage, pigmentation, edema, atrophy
- The most common abnormality seen in age-related macular degeneration (AMD) is the presence of drusen, or yellowish deposits deep to the retina; this may be early in course of disease

ETIOLOGY

- Subretinal neovascular membrane early
- Pigmentary and vascular changes with exudate, edema, and scar tissue development
- Early in course, possible subretinal neovascularization
- Dry type atrophy of macular pigment epithelium

DIAGNOSIS

DIFFERENTIAL DIAGNOSIS

- Diabetic retinopathy
- Hypertension
- Histoplasmosis
- Trauma with scar

WORKUP

- Complete eye examination, including visual field and fluorescein angiography
- Optical coherence tomography (OCT)

LABORATORY TESTS

Evaluate for diabetes and other metabolic problems, as well as vascular diseases.

IMAGING STUDIES

- Optical coherence tomography (OCT)
- Fluorescein angiography

TREATMENT

NONPHARMACOLOGIC THERAPY

- Laser treatment to stop progression of disease—photo dynamic treatment with verteporfin IV
- Laser (Argon)
- Diet, exercise
- Vitamins with zinc and antioxidants

ACUTE GENERAL Rx

Intravitral steroids, photodynamic treatment (PDT) with laser

CHRONIC Rx

- Repeated laser treatments
- Antioxidants and zinc may slow down progression of ARMD

DISPOSITION

- Follow closely by ophthalmologist.
- If vision deteriorates, refer urgently to an ophthalmologist.

REFERRAL

- To ophthalmologist early in the course of the disease if the sight is to be saved
- Immediate referral if any change in vision

PEARLS & CONSIDERATIONS

COMMENTS

- Sildenafil has no significant effect on macular degeneration.
- The vision of only 1 out of 10 people can be saved, but the disease is so devastating that vigorous therapy should be attempted.
- Statins plus aspirin may slow down progression.
- Vitamins with zinc and antioxidants may slow down progression of ARMD.

SUGGESTED READINGS

Friedman DS et al: Prevalence of age-related macular degeneration in the US, *Arch Ophthalmol* 122(4):564, 2004.

Gottlieb JL: Age-related macular degeneration, *JAMA* 288:2233, 2002.

Jonas, JB: Verteporfin theory of subfoveal chorordial neovascularization in age-related macular degeneration, *Am J Ophthalmol* 133(6):F57, 2002.

Liu M, Regillo CD: A review of treatments for macular degeneration: a synopsis of currently approved treatments and ongoing clinical trials, *Curr Opin Ophthalmol* 15(3):221, 2004.

Makenzie PJ, Chang TS: ETN assessment of vision-related emotion in patients with age related macular degeneration, *Ophthalmology* 109(4):720, 2002.

Ting TD et al: Decreased visual acuity associated with cystoid macular edema in neovascular or age-related macular degeneration, *Arch Ophthamol* 120(6):731, 2002.

AUTHOR: **MELVYN KOBY, M.D.**

BASIC INFORMATION

DEFINITION

Malaria is a protozoan disease caused by the genus *Plasmodium* and transmitted by female *Anopheles spp.* mosquitoes. It is characterized by hectic fever and often presents with classic malarial paroxysm. Four species of genus plasmodium usually infect humans
- *P. falciparum*
- *P. vivax*
- *P. malariae*
- *P. ovale*

ICD-9CM CODES
084.6 Malaria

EPIDEMIOLOGY & DEMOGRAPHICS

Global:
- 300 to 500 million cases/yr
- 1 to 3 million deaths/yr
- 41% of the world's population lives in endemic area

U.S.:
- Total 1544 cases reported by CDC in 1997
- 567 cases diagnosed as *P. falciparum*
- Most infections limited to
  1. Immigrant population
  2. Returned travelers or troops from endemic area
- Occasionally, transmission through exposure to infected blood product
- Congenital transmission is possible
- Local mosquito-borne transmission has been reported
- Competent mosquito vectors are present
  1. *A. albimanus* in eastern U.S.
  2. *A. freeborni* in western U.S.

Geographic distribution:
- *P. falciparum:* Sub-Saharan Africa, Papua New Guinea, Solomon Islands, Haiti, Indian subcontinent
- *P. vivax:* Central America, South America, North Africa, Middle East, Indian subcontinent
- *P. vivax* and *P. falciparum:* South America, Eastern Asia, Oceania
- *P. Ovale:* West Africa
- *P. malariae:* worldwide

Parasite life cycle (Fig. 1-141):
- Human infection begins when a female anopheline mosquito bites (only female anopheline mosquito takes blood meal) and inoculates plasmodial sporozoites into bloodstream
- The sporozoites then travel to liver and invade to hepatocytes
- In the hepatocytes, the sporozoites mature to tissue schizont or become dormant hypnozoites
- The tissue schizont amplify the infection by producing large number of merozoites (10,000 to 30,000)
- Each merozoite is capable of invading an RBC and can establish the asexual cycle of replication in RBC
- Asexual cycles produce and release 24 to 32 merozoites at the end of 48- or 72-hr *(P. malariae)* cycle
- The hypnozoites are only found in relapsing malaria *P. vivax* or *P. ovale* and may remain dormant up to 6 to 11 mo
- Eventually some intraerythrocytic parasites develop into gametocytes, the sexual form necessary to complete the life cycle in the anopheline mosquito vector
- The gametocytes, when taken up by a female anopheline mosquito with a blood meal, further differentiate to form male and female gametes
- They fertilize in the mosquito gut to produce a diploid zygote that matures to an ookinete
- The ookinete produce haploid sporozoites by meiotic division
- The sporozoites then migrate to the salivary gland of the mosquito, ready to infect the human

PHYSICAL FINDINGS & CLINICAL PRESENTATION

- Fever is the hallmark of malaria, known as malarial paroxysm, initially daily until synchronization of infection after several weeks, when fever may occur every other day (tertian) in *P. vivax, P. ovale,* or *P. falciparum* malaria or every third day (quartan) in *P. malarie* malaria.
- Classic malarial paroxysm characterized by
  1. Cold stage: abrupt onset of cold feeling associated with rigors, shakes
  2. Hot stage: high fever (~40° C) associated with restlessness
  3. Sweating stage: patient defervesces
- Nonspecific symptoms are
  1. Headache
  2. Cough
  3. Myalgia
  4. Vomiting
  5. Diarrhea
  6. Jaundice

P. Falciparum:
- Most pathogenic of the four species
- Rapidly progresses to high-level parasitemia
- Important cause of the fatal malaria
- Classic malarial paroxysm usually absent
- Incubation period after exposure is 12 days (range: 9 to 60 days)
- Cytoadherence and resetting of RBC play central role in pathogenesis
- The sequestration of RBC in vital organs leads to fatal complications
- Cerebral malaria is a feared complication
- Invades erythrocytes of all ages

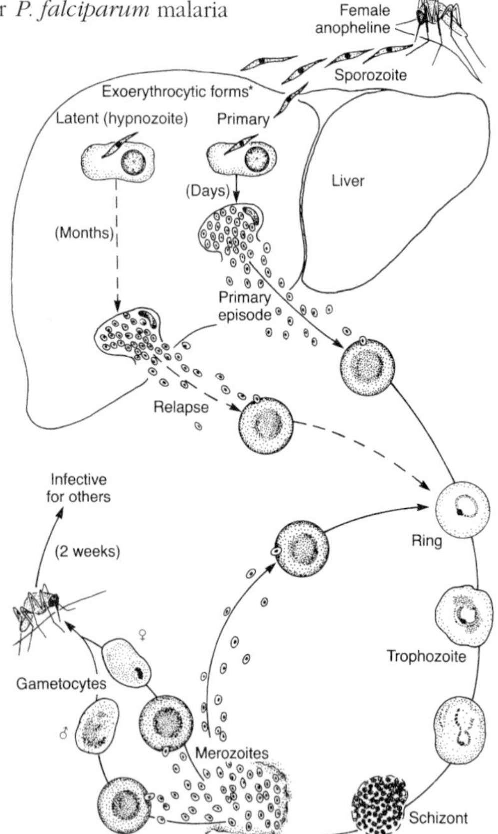

FIGURE 1-141 Life cycle of plasmodia in humans. *Exoerythrocytic forms are also called tissue schizonts. (From Gorbach SL: *Infectious diseases,* ed 2, Philadelphia, 1998, WB Saunders.)

- Lacks hypnozoites (intrahepatic stage), does not relapse
- Blood smear usually shows ring form only
- Pigment color is black
- Banana-shaped gametocytes; if seen in blood, smear is diagnostic
- Chloroquine resistance widely present

P. vivax:
- Known as tertian malaria: fever occurs every other day
- Duffy blood-group antigen FYA- or FYB-related receptor needed for attachment to RBC
- FyFy phenotype (most West African) individuals are resistant to *P. Vivax* malaria
- Incubation period after exposure is 14 days (range: 8 to 27 days)
- Hypnozoites may cause relapse of infection after years
- Infects mainly reticulocytes
- Irregularly shaped large rings and trophozoites, enlarged RBC, and Schüffner's dot are seen in peripheral blood smear (Fig. 1-142)
- Pigment color is yellow-brown
- *P. vivax* from Papua New Guinea have reduced sensitivity to chloroquine
- Primaquine needed to eradicate the hypnozoites

P. ovale:
- Also known as tertian malaria; fever occurs every other day
- Occurs mainly in tropical Africa
- Incubation period after exposure is 14 days (range: 8 to 27 days)
- Hypnozoits may cause relapse of infection
- Infects mainly reticulocytes
- Infected RBC seen as enlarged, oval shape containing large ring or trophozoites with Schüffner's dot
- Pigment color is dark brown
- Primaquine needed to eradicate the hypnozoites
- No chloroquine resistance encountered

P. malarie:
- Known as quartan malaria; fever occurs every third day
- Common cause of chronic malarial infection
- May persist 20 to 30 yr after leaving the endemic area
- Worldwide distribution
- Incubation period after exposure is 30 days (range: 16 to 60 days)
- Lacks hypnozoits (intrahepatic stage)
- May persist in blood for many years if treated inadequately
- Chronic infection may cause soluble immune-complex, resulting in nephritic syndrome
- Infects mainly mature RBC
- Band or rectangular forms of trophozoites are commonly seen in peripheral blood smear
- Pigment color is brown-black

Cerebral malaria:
- Feared complication of *P. falciparum* infection
- Mortality ~20%
- Pathogenesis is poorly understood
- Ischemia as a result of sequestration of parasites or cytokines induced by parasite toxin(s) is the key debate
- Seizure and altered mental status leading to coma are cardinal manifestation
- Hypoglycemia, lactic acidosis, and elevated circulating TNF-α may present
- CSF studies: no increase of WBC count or protein, raised lactate concentrate, and increased opening pressure, especially in children, may present

DIAGNOSIS

DIFFERENTIAL DIAGNOSIS OF MALARIA
- Typhoid fever
- Dengue fever
- Yellow fever
- Viral hepatitis
- Influenza
- Brucellosis
- UTI
- Leishmaniasis
- Trypanosomiasis
- Rickettsial diseases
- Leptospirosis

WORKUP
- Clinical diagnosis is notoriously inaccurate
- Demonstration of malarial parasites in blood smear is essential
- Newer molecular diagnostic techniques are promising

LABORATORY TESTS
- The thick and thin blood film is required to identify malarial parasites
- The thick smears are more sensitive and primarily used to detect the presence of parasites
- The thin smears are used for species differentiation and parasite density estimation
- Person suspected of having malaria but no parasite seen in blood smears should have blood smears repeated every 12 to 24 hr for 3 consecutive days

PREPARATION OF BLOOD SMEAR
- Must be prepared from fresh blood obtained by pricking the fingers
- The thin smear is fixed in methanol before staining
- The thick smear is stained unfixed
- The smear should be stained with a 3% Giemsa solution (pH of 7.2) for 30 to 45 min
- The parasite density should be estimated by counting the percentage of RBC infected, not the number of parasites, under an oil immersion lens on thin film

COMMON ERRORS IN READING MALARIAL SMEARS
- Platelets overlying an RBC
- Misreading artifacts as parasites
- Concern about missing a positive slide

MOLECULAR DIAGNOSIS OF MALARIA
- Polymerase chain reaction (PCR)
  1. It is useful in accurate species diagnosis
  2. It can detect the low-level parasitemias
  3. Is expensive and time-consuming
  4. It needs technical expertise
- Quantitative buffy cost (QBC)
  1. This test detects nuclear material of parasites using acridine orange stain
  2. It is unable to speciate the parasites accurately
  3. It cannot quantitate parasitemias
- Para Sight F and Malaria PF Test
  1. This test uses a monoclonal antibody to detect *P. falciparum*-specific, histidine-rich protein (HRP)-2
  2. It can detect *P. falciparum* only
  3. Past infection may confuse diagnosis
- OptiMal test
  1. This test detects lactage dehydrogenase (LDH) of parasites
  2. It can differentiate *falciparum* from *non-falciparum*

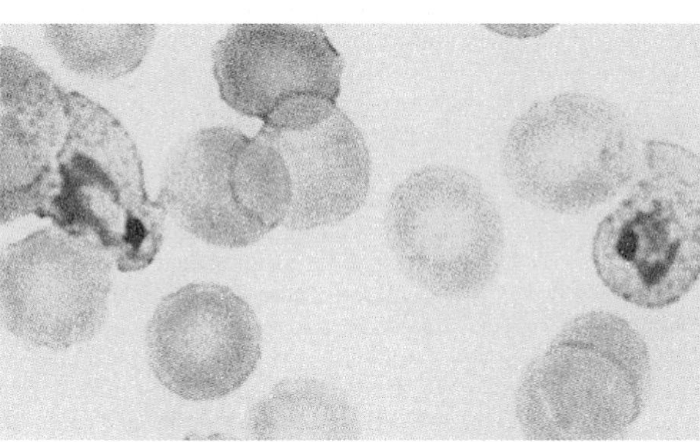

FIGURE 1-142 Giemsa-stained blood smear in Plasmodium vivax malaria. Asexual parasites. Note that the parasites are large and ameboid, the infected erythrocytes are the largest cells in the field (because they are reticulocytes), and the erythrocytes contain numerous pink dots (Schüffner's dots) (×2000). (From Klippel JH et al [eds]: *Internal medicine,* ed 5, St Louis, 1998, Mosby.)

TREATMENT

NONPHARMACOLOGIC THERAPY

- ANTIMOSQUITO MEASURES
  1. Eradication of mosquito breeding places by chemical spray
  2. Use of mosquito nets properly in the endemic areas
  3. Use of protective clothing
  4. Use of insect spray (permethrin), mosquito coils, or repellents (diethyltoluamide)

ACUTE GENERAL THERAPY

A definitive diagnosis of malaria is essential for specific antimalarial chemotherapy

NON-*FALCIPARUM* MALARIA:

- Chloroquine 600 mg base (1000 mg chloroquine phosphate) po loading dose, 6 hr later 300 mg base (500 mg salt), then 300 mg base (500 mg salt) daily for 2 days
- In the case of *P. vivax* and *P. ovale,* treatment with primaquine 15 mg daily for 14 days is needed to eradicate the exoerythrocytic forms, especially the hypnozoites responsible for relapses
- G6PD should be measured before primaquine is given
- Chloroquine-resistant *P. vivax* has been documented; in that case, quinine is given

***FALCIPARUM* MALARIA:**

- Chloroquine can be used cautiously for falciparum malaria acquired in chloroquine-sensitive areas (chloroquine is more rapidly effective than quinine)
- Mainstay of treatment is oral quinine sulfate 10 mg (salt)/kg (usually 650 mg) q8h for 3 to 7 days, followed by pyrimethamine with sulfadoxine (Fansider) 3 tablets (each tablets contains 500 mg sulfadoxine and 25 mg pyrimethamine) or doxycycline 200 mg loading dose, then 100 mg bid for 7 days to eradicate asexual forms of the parasite

ALTERNATIVES:

- Quinine followed by clindamycin 900 mg tid × 5 days, or
- Mefloquine 1250 mg as a single dose, or
- Halofantrine 500 mg q6 h × 3 doses, repeat a week later, or
- Atovaquone 1000 mg daily × 3 days plus proguanil 400 mg daily × 3 days, or
- Atovaquone 1000 mg daily × 3 days plus doxycycline 100 mg bid × 3 days, or
- Artesunate 4 mg/kg daily × 3 days plus mefloquine 1250 mg single dose

NOTE: Parasitemia may paradoxically rise in the first 24 to 36 hr and is not an indication of treatment failure.

SEVERE *FALCIPARUM* MALARIA:

- It is a medical emergency
- Intensive care is preferred
- Measurement of blood glucose, lactate, ABG is important
- Intravenous quinidine gluconate 10 mg salt/kg loading dose (maximum 600 mg) in NS infuse slowly over 1 to 2 hr, followed by continuous infusion of 0.02 mg/kg/min until patient can swallow
- Cardiac monitor needed for observation of QT interval
- Alternatively, artemether 3.2 mg/kg IM then 1.6 mg/kg daily × 3 days
- Plasmaparesis is an option for parasitemia >30% or in pregnant woman and in elderly with severe malaria

MULTIDRUG-RESISTANT MALARIA:

- Mefloquine 1250 mg as a single dose, or
- Halofantrine 500 mg every 6 hr for three doses, repeat same course after 1 wk
- Combination therapy usually preferred

DISPOSITION

RISK FACTOR FOR FATAL MALARIA:

- Failure to take chemoprophylaxis
- Delay in seeking medical care
- Misdiagnosis

COMPLICATIONS OF MALARIA:

- Anemia
- Acidosis
- Hypoglycemia
- Respiratory distress
- DIC
- Blackwater fever
- Renal failure
- Shock

PEARLS & CONSIDERATIONS

HOST RESPONSE:

- The specific immune response to malaria confers protection from high-level parasitemia and disease, but not from infection
- Asymptomatic parasitemia without illness (premunition) is common among adults in endemic area
- Immunity is specific for both the species and the strain of infecting malarial parasites
- Immunity to all strains is never achieved
- Normal spleen function is an important host factor because of immunologic as well as filtering functions of the spleen
- Both humoral and cellular immunity are necessary for protection
- Polyclonal increase in serum level of IgG, IgM, and IgA occur in immune individuals
- Antibody to antigenically variant protein PfEMP1 is important for protection in case of *P. falciparum* malaria
- Passively transferred IgG from immune individual has been shown protective
- Maternal antibody confers relative protection of infants from severe disease
- Genetic disorders (sickle cell disease, thalassemia, and G6PD deficiency) confer protection from death because parasites are unable to grow efficiently in low-oxygen tensions, thus preventing high-level parasitemias
- Individuals deficient of Duffy factor in RBC are resistant to infection by *P. vivax*
- Nonspecific defense mechanisms, cytokines (TNF-α, IL-1, 6, 8) also play an important role in protection; it causes fever (temperatures of 40° C damage mature parasites) and other pathologic effects

PREVENTION OF MALARIA:

Prophylaxis should be taken 1 wk before travel, continue weekly for the duration of stay and for 4 wk after leaving endemic area

NON-*FALCIPARUM* MALARIA:

Chloroquine 300 mg base (500 mg chloroquine phosphate) PO/wk

***FALCIPARUM* MALARIA:**

- Mefloquine 250 mg (228 mg base) PO/wk, or
- Doxycycline 100 mg PO/day, or
- Primaquine 0.5 mg base/kg/day, or
- Chloroquine (300 mg base) plus proguanil (200 mg) PO/day

SPECIAL CONSIDERATION:

- Long-term visitors or travelers
- Children <12 yr
- Immunocompromised host
- Pregnant women

VACCINATION:

- No effective and safe vaccine available yet
- A live, attenuated, whole sporozoite vaccine shown to work
- A synthetic peptide (SPf66) vaccine proved ineffective
- New DNA-based vaccines are in development

MALARIA INFORMATION:

- CDC Travelers' Health Hotline (877) 394-8747
- CDC Travelers' Health Fax (888) 232-3299
- CDC Malaria Epidemiology (770) 488-7788
- Internet: http://www.cdc.gov

SUGGESTED READINGS

Djmide A et al: A molecular marker for chloroquine-resistant falciparum malaria, *N Engl J Med* 344(4):257, 2001.

Malaria surveillance: 1996-97, *MMWR Morb Mortal Wkly Rep* 50, 2001.

White P: The treatment of malaria, *N Engl J Med* 335:800, 1996.

Winstanley P: Modern chemotherapeutic options for malaria, *Lancet Infect Dis* 1:242, 2001.

AUTHOR: **AMAR ASHRAF, M.D.**

BASIC INFORMATION

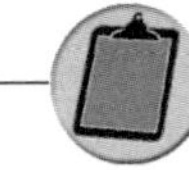

DEFINITION

A Mallory-Weiss tear is a longitudinal mucosal laceration in the region of the gastroesophageal junction.

SYNONYMS

Mallory-Weiss syndrome

ICD-9CM CODES
530.7 Gastroesophageal laceration-hemorrhage syndrome
530.82 Esophageal hemorrhage

EPIDEMIOLOGY & DEMOGRAPHICS

- Accounts for 5% to 15% of cases of upper GI bleeding
- Reported from early childhood to old age; the majority of patients are in their 40s to 60s
- More common in males
- Alcohol use is present in 30% to 60% of patients

PHYSICAL FINDINGS & CLINICAL PRESENTATION

- Vomiting, retching, or vigorous coughing will often, but not always, precede hematemesis.
- Patients may be clinically stable or present with tachycardia, hypotension, melena, or hematochezia.
- Bleeding may be self-limited or severe.
- Tears may be seen in association with other upper GI tract lesions, including hiatus hernia (present in as many as 90% of patients), ulcers, and esophageal varices, particularly in alcoholics.

ETIOLOGY

- An acute increase in intraabdominal pressure is transmitted to the esophagus, resulting in mucosal laceration.
- Vomiting may be associated with alcohol use, ketoacidosis, ulcer disease, uremia, pancreatitis, cholecystitis, pregnancy, or myocardial infarction.
- Tears may be iatrogenic, related to endoscopy (especially in struggling or retching patients), esophageal dilation, lower esophageal pneumatic disruption therapy for achalasia, transesophageal echocardiography, or in association with polyethylene glycol electrolyte colonic lavage preparation.

DIAGNOSIS

DIFFERENTIAL DIAGNOSIS

- Esophageal or gastric varices
- Esophagitis/esophageal ulcers (peptic or pill-induced)
- Gastric erosions
- Gastric or duodenal ulcer
- Dieulafoy lesion
- Arteriovenous malformations
- Neoplasms (usually gastric)

WORKUP

Endoscopy is the diagnostic method of choice.

LABORATORY TESTS

- Complete blood count, PT, PTT
- Lytes, BUN, creatinine, LFTs, pregnancy test, or others to evaluate for predisposing conditions

IMAGING STUDIES

Upper GI series are usually insensitive for the detection of Mallory-Weiss tears.

TREATMENT

NONPHARMACOLOGIC THERAPY

- Supportive care
- Aspirin, NSAIDs, and anticoagulants should be held

ACUTE GENERAL Rx

- Patients with active bleeding or hemodynamic instability require large-bore IVs, fluid resuscitation, and transfusion of blood products (red blood cells, FFP, and platelets) as appropriate
- NG decompression and antiemetics may be considered
- Endoscopic therapy for patients with active or ongoing hemorrhage, including electrocoagulation, injection (e.g., 1:10,000 epinephrine), sclerotherapy (for bleeding associated with esophageal varices), band ligation, or endoscopic hemoclips (therapies may be used alone or in combination)
- Arterial embolization is described in patients with active bleeding who are poor surgical candidates
- Laparotomy, with gastrotomy and oversewing of the tear, is required in a small percentage of patients with uncontrolled bleeding

CHRONIC Rx

- Healing will usually occur without specific therapy.
- H_2-blockers or proton pump inhibitors may be given to help facilitate healing, but should not be used chronically unless appropriate indications are present.
- Predisposing conditions should be identified and treated.

DISPOSITION

Prognosis is good, with spontaneous cessation of bleeding in upwards of 90% of patients. Endoscopic features can guide treatment. Delayed rebleeding is described. Death has been reported in 3% to 12% of patients, often with severe bleeding and underlying comorbid conditions, including coagulopathy, thrombocytopenia, alcohol use, and multisystem organ failure.

REFERRAL

- GI referral for endoscopy
- Surgical referral for bleeding unresponsive to endoscopic treatment, or in the setting of coexistent perforation

PEARLS & CONSIDERATIONS

COMMENTS

Detecting and treating predisposing conditions is as important as assessing and treating the bleeding itself.

SUGGESTED READING

Kortas DY et al: Mallory-Weiss tear: predisposing factors and predictors of a complicated course. *Am J Gastro* 96:2863, 2001.

AUTHOR: **HARLAN G. RICH, M.D.**

BASIC INFORMATION

DEFINITION

Marfan's syndrome is an inherited disorder of connective tissue involving skeleton, cardiovascular system, eyes, lungs, and central nervous system.

ICD-9CM CODES
759.82 Marfan's syndrome

EPIDEMIOLOGY & DEMOGRAPHICS

PREVALENCE: 1 case/10,000 persons

- Both sexes are affected equally by this autosomal dominant syndrome.
- Approximately 30% of cases are a new mutation.

PHYSICAL FINDINGS & CLINICAL PRESENTATION

Diagnostic criteria for Marfan's syndrome (Fig. 1-143):

- Skeleton
  Joint hypermobility, tall stature, pectus excavatum, reduced thoracic kyphosis, scoliosis, arachnodactyly, dolichostenomelia, pectus carinatum, and erosion of the lumbosacral vertebrae from dural ectasia†
- Eye
  Myopia, retinal detachment, elongated globe, ectopia lentis†
- Cardiovascular
  Mitral valve prolapse, endocarditis, arrhythmia, dilated mitral annulus, mitral regurgitation, tricuspid valve prolapse, aortic regurgitation, aortic dissection,† dilation of the aortic root†
- Pulmonary
  Apical blebs, spontaneous pneumothorax
- Skin and integument
  Inguinal hernias, incisional hernias, striae atrophicae
- Central nervous system
  Attention deficit disorder, hyperactivity, verbal-performance discrepancy, dural ectasia, anterior pelvic meningocele†

If the family history is positive for a close relative clearly affected by Marfan's syndrome, manifestations should be present in the skeleton and one of the other organ systems, and the diagnosis confirmed by linkage analysis or mutation detection.

If the family history is negative or unknown, the patient should have manifestations in the skeleton, the cardiovascular system, and one other system, and at least one of the manifestations indicated by †.

Manifestations are listed within each organ system in increasing specificity for Marfan's syndrome; although none is completely specific, those indicated by † are the most specific.

ETIOLOGY

Mutations in the gene that encodes fibrillin-1, the major constituent of microfibrils, which form the frame for elastic fibers. All the manifestations of Marfan's syndrome can be explained by the defective microfibrils.

DIAGNOSIS

DIFFERENTIAL DIAGNOSIS

Each of the clinical manifestations of the syndrome may have other causes; however, if the diagnostic criteria are met, the diagnosis is made.

WORKUP

- Echocardiography to establish:
  Mitral valve prolapse
  Mitral regurgitation
  Tricuspid valve prolapse
  Aortic regurgitation
  Dilation of the aortic root
- Chest x-ray
- Transesophageal echocardiography, chest CT scan, chest MRI, or aortography for suspected aortic dissection
- Chest x-ray for pulmonary apical bullae
- Ophthalmologic examination by ophthalmologist

TREATMENT

- Regular cardiac and aorta monitoring by physical examination and echocardiography
- Endocarditis prophylaxis
- Restriction of contact sports, weight lifting, and overexertion
- β-Blockers
- Early use of angiotensin-converting enzyme inhibitors in young patients with Marfan syndrome and valvular regurgitation may lessen the need for mitral valve surgery
- Genetic counseling
- Monitor aorta during pregnancy (because of increased risk of dissection)

SUGGESTED READINGS

Pyertiz ER: Marfan's syndrome. In Braunwald E (ed): *Heart disease: a textbook of cardiovascular medicine,* ed 6, Philadelphia, 2001, WB Saunders.

Yetman AT et al: Comparison of outcome of the Marfan syndrome in patients diagnosed at age 6 years versus those diagnosed at age >6 years of age, *Am J Cardiol* 91:102, 2003.

AUTHOR: **TOM J. WACHTEL, M.D.**

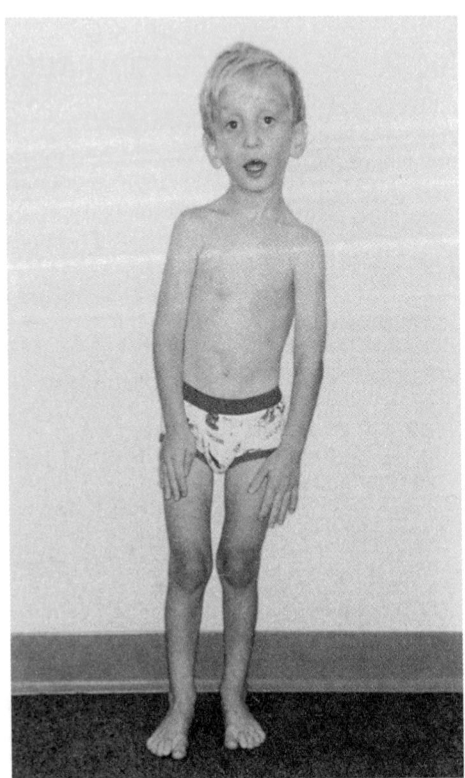

FIGURE 1-143 Marfan's syndrome. Note the elongated facies, droopy lids, apparent dolichostenomelia, and mild scoliosis. (From Behrman RE: *Nelson's textbook of pediatrics,* Philadelphia, 1996, WB Saunders.)

BASIC INFORMATION

DEFINITION

- Pain in the breast.
- Mastodynia is synonymous with mastalgia.
- This condition is usually cyclical, but may be noncyclical or extramammary.

ICD-9CM CODES
611.71 Mastodynia

EPIDEMIOLOGY & DEMOGRAPHICS

- Mastodynia will affect up to 70% of women at some time in their reproductive lives.
- Severe cyclical mastodynia lasting more than 5 days/mo and of sufficient intensity to interfere with sexual, physical, social, and work-related activities is reported among 30% of premenopausal women.
- Underlying fear of breast cancer is the reason most of these women seek medical consultation.
- One tenth of women with mastodynia require pain-relieving therapy.

PHYSICAL FINDINGS & CLINICAL PRESENTATION

- Usually, the breasts are normal bilaterally
- Full, tender breasts
- Generalized breast nodularity without discrete lumps
- Chest wall tenderness: extramammary breast pain
- Distinguishing mammary from extramammary pain can be difficult
- With the patient lying on her side so that the breast tissue falls away from the chest wall, tenderness can then be reproduced by direct pressure over the offending site
- Cyclical mastodynia presents in the luteal phase of the menstrual cycle
- Women with cyclical mastodynia tend to have abdominal bloating, leg swelling, and other symptoms of premenstrual syndrome
- Noncyclical mastodynia, on the other hand, is unrelated to the menstrual cycle
- Extramammary breast pain simulates noncyclical mastodynia

ETIOLOGY

- Hormonal imbalance
- Abnormal lipid metabolism
- Premenstrual syndrome (20%)
- Fibrocystic breast disease
- Emotional abuse and anxiety
- Excessive caffeine intake
- Breast cancer (10%)
- Tietze syndrome (idiopathic costochondritis)

DIAGNOSIS

DIFFERENTIAL DIAGNOSIS

- See Etiology.
- The majority of women with mastodynia have no underlying abnormality.
- Breast fullness and tenderness associated with hormonal changes fluctuate with menstrual cycle.
- Similarly, the breast nodularity, which may or may not be the result of fibrocystic breast disease, also fluctuate with the menstrual cycle.
- Discrete breast lump needs full evaluation to rule out malignancy.
- Tietze syndrome is usually unilateral and may be associated with chest wall swelling.

WORKUP

- Complete history and thorough clinical examination.
- Pain analogue cards may be helpful in establishing the pattern of symptomatology. In patients >35 years of age, mammography should be performed as part of the baseline investigations.
- Most women presenting with severe mastodynia are <35. This group has a lower risk of subclinical breast cancer, and their breasts have increased density. In this younger group, radiologic investigations are of limited value, unless a discrete breast lump is palpated.

LABORATORY TESTS

Although hormonal imbalance and abnormal lipid metabolism have been implicated in the etiopathogenesis of mastodynia, there is no good evidence to support any consistent pattern of serum hormonal or lipid profile in women with mastodynia. These tests are therefore not recommended.

IMAGING STUDIES

- Mammography should be part of the baseline investigations if the woman is >35 yr.
- Ultrasound can be performed as needed; it is particularly helpful in the assessment of cystic breast lesions.
- In women <35 yr, imaging investigations are not helpful unless a lump has been palpated clinically.
- There are no radiologic features associated with mastodynia: rather, radiologic investigations are performed to exclude the rare presence of a subclinical carcinoma.

TREATMENT

NONPHARMACOLOGIC THERAPY

- 85% of the women with mastodynia can be reassured after full clinical evaluation
- The remaining 15% will require some form of therapy in addition to reassurance
- Firm, supportive brassiere designed for postpartum use; this is particularly helpful if mastodynia is associated with breast swelling
- Low-fat, high-carbohydrate diet
- Reduction of caffeine intake

ACUTE GENERAL Rx

- Evening primrose oil (EPO), which contains gamma-linolenic acid, has been shown to have some effectiveness and is an acceptable treatment for mastodynia.
- Topical NSAID preparations may confer some benefit and can be prescribed for these women.
- Hormonal therapy is the mainstay of treatment.
- Danazol is the only drug approved by the FDA for the treatment of mastodynia. Danazol is an antigonadotrophin with some androgenic and peripheral antiestrogenic effects. Its efficacy is well established with significant relief of mastodynia in 70% to 93% of cases.
- Widespread use of danazol is limited because of its adverse side effects. These include menstrual irregularities, depression, acne, hirsutism, and, in severe cases, voice deepening. Women taking danazol should be advised to use effective nonhormonal contraception because of its potential adverse effects on the fetus.
- The side effects of danazol can be significantly reduced by using a low dose (100 mg daily) and confining treatment to the fortnight preceding menstruation.
- Tamoxifen, a synthetic antiestrogen, has also been shown to be effective in the treatment of mastodynia. Although effective in relieving symptoms, its use is extremely limited because of side effects. When used, it should be at a low dosage of 10 mg/day, and duration should be limited to 6 mo at a time. In the U.S., this agent has no approval for use in women with mastodynia.
- Bromocriptine is a dopamine-receptor agonist whose primary action is inhibition of prolactin release. It has been used extensively in the treatment of severe cyclical mastodynia and is effective. Again, side effects such as headache and dizziness have limited its use.

- Lisuride maleate was recently found to be effective by one study.
- Other hormonal agents that have been reported to be effective in small studies cannot be recommended. They either have unacceptable side effect profiles or their efficacy is not established. These agents include gestrinone, GnRH analogues, progesterone, and hormone replacement therapy.

CHRONIC Rx

- Long-standing cases of mastodynia can be managed with intermittent low-dose danazol therapy to limit side effects. In between these courses of hormone, nonpharmacologic and nonhormonal therapy can be used.
- Severe, unremitting mastodynia that fails to respond to medical treatment may require mastectomy; this is rare.

DISPOSITION

- Cyclical mastodynia resolves spontaneously in 20% to 30% of women.
- Up to 60% of women may develop recurrent symptoms 2 yr after treatment.
- Noncyclical mastodynia responds poorly to treatment, but may resolve spontaneously in up to 50% of women.

REFERRAL

- Detection of a breast lump or any other findings suggestive of neoplasm should be fully investigated. In addition, an immediate referral should be arranged.
- Women with chronic, unremitting mastodynia that fails to respond to pharmacologic therapy should be referred for possible mastectomy; this is rare.

PEARLS & CONSIDERATIONS

COMMENTS

- There is no good evidence to support the use of vitamin B_6, diuretics, and vitamin E. Mastodynia may represent a presenting symptom of other more generalized disorder (e.g., premenstrual syndrome, psychologic disturbance).
- In these cases, treating mastodynia in isolation will not work; the underlying conditions must be appropriately addressed.

SUGGESTED READINGS

Colgrave S, Holcombe C, Salmon P: Psychological characteristics of women presenting with breast pain, *J Psychosom Res* 50:303, 2001.

Fentiman IS, Hamed H: Assessment of breast problems, *Int J Clin Pract* 55:458, 2001.

Kaleli S et al: Symptomatic treatment of premenstrual mastalgia in premenopausal women with lisuride maleate: a double-blind placebo-controlled randomized study, *Fertility & Sterility* 75:718, 2001.

Marchant DJ: Benign breast disease, *Obstet Gynecol Clin North Am* 29:1-20, 2002.

Norlock FE: Benign breast pain in women: a practical approach to evaluation and treatment, *J Am Med Womens Assoc* 57:85, 2002.

AUTHOR: **ALEXANDER OLAWAIYE, M.D.**

BASIC INFORMATION

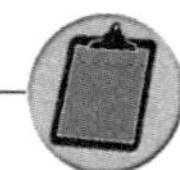

DEFINITION

Mastoiditis is inflammation of the mastoid process and air cells, a complication of acute otitis media.

ICD-9CM CODES
383.00 Mastoiditis, acute or subacute
383.1 Mastoiditis, chronic

EPIDEMIOLOGY & DEMOGRAPHICS

INCIDENCE (IN U.S.): Widespread use of broad-spectrum antibiotics has led to a marked decline in the incidence of acute mastoiditis.
PREDOMINANT SEX: More common in males
PREDOMINANT AGE: 2 mo to 18 yr
PEAK INCIDENCE: Early childhood

PHYSICAL FINDINGS & CLINICAL PRESENTATION

- Acute mastoiditis is usually a complication of acute otitis media.
- Most common presenting symptom: pain and tenderness in the postauricular region.
- Other signs or symptoms include:
  1. Fever
  2. Postauricular erythema and edema
  3. Protrusion of the pinna inferiorly and anteriorly
  4. Tympanic membrane usually intact with signs of acute otitis media (occasionally ruptured with otorrhea)
- Complications of acute mastoiditis include:
  1. Subperiosteal abscess (most common complication)
  2. Hearing loss
  3. Facial nerve palsy
  4. Labyrinthitis
  5. Intracranial complications such as hydrocephalus, meningitis, encephalitis, intracranial abscess, and lateral sinus thrombosis
- Chronic mastoiditis (which follows a long course of recurrent otitis media, treated but never controlled completely) is characterized by chronic otorrhea and chronic tympanic membrane perforation.

ETIOLOGY

- All patients with otitis media exhibit some degree of mastoid inflammation because of the continuity between the middle air space and the mastoid cavity.
- Initial hyperemia and edema of the mucosal lining of the air cells results in accumulation of purulent exudate.
- Dissolution of calcium from bony septae and osteoclastic activity in the inflamed periosteum lead to bone necrosis and coalescence of air cells. This process can result in the development of a subperiosteal abscess.
- Most common bacterial isolates:
  1. *Streptococcus pneumoniae*
  2. *Streptococcus pyogenes*
  3. *Haemophilus influenzae*
  4. *Moraxella catarrhalis*
  5. *Staphylococcus aureus*
- Often, multiple organisms in chronic mastoiditis, with predominance of anaerobes and gram-negative bacteria.
- *Mycobacterium tuberculosis,* as well as nontuberculous mycobacteria, has been isolated in cases of mastoiditis.
- Unusual organisms such as *Aspergillus* and *Rhodococcus equi* have been reported in cases of mastoiditis in severely immunocompromised individuals.

DIAGNOSIS

DIFFERENTIAL DIAGNOSIS

- Children
  1. Rhabdomyosarcoma
  2. Histiocytosis X
  3. Leukemia
  4. Kawasaki syndrome
- Adults
  1. Fulminant otitis externa
  2. Histiocytosis X
  3. Metastatic disease

WORKUP

Thorough history and physical examination are important in establishing diagnosis.

LABORATORY TESTS

- Fluid for Gram stain and culture may be obtained by myringotomy.
- If there is a perforation in the tympanic membrane with drainage, cultures of this may be taken after carefully cleaning the external canal.

IMAGING STUDIES

- Plain x-rays of the mastoid region may demonstrate clouding or opacification in areas of pneumatization resulting from inflammatory swelling of the air cells.
- CT scan is the best radiologic modality for evaluating inflammation in this region.
- CT scan can demonstrate early involvement of bone (mastoiditis with bone destruction).
- MRI is more sensitive than CT scan in evaluating soft tissue involvement and is useful in conjunction with CT scan to investigate other complications of mastoiditis.

TREATMENT

NONPHARMACOLOGIC THERAPY

Myringotomy, if the ear is not already draining

ACUTE GENERAL Rx

- Initiated with IV antibiotics directed against the common organisms *S. pneumoniae* and *H. influenzae.* If the disease in the mastoid has had a prolonged course, coverage for *Staphylococcus aureus* with gram-negative enteric bacilli may be considered for initial therapy until results of cultures become available.
- Continued until all signs of mastoiditis have resolved
- Directed against enteric gram-negative organisms and anaerobes in chronic mastoiditis
- Indications for mastoidectomy:
  1. Failure to improve after 24 to 72 hr of therapy
  2. Persistent fever
  3. Imminent or overt signs of intracranial complications
  4. Evidence of a subperiosteal abscess in the mastoid bone

DISPOSITION

Proceed with mastoidectomy when medical therapy fails.

REFERRAL

- To otorhinolaryngologist:
  1. If diagnosis in doubt
  2. If aural complications present
  3. To evaluate for surgical intervention
- To neurosurgeon if intratemporal orintracranial extension of infection suspected
  1. Aural complications: bone destruction, subperiosteal abscess, petrositis, facial paralysis, labyrinthitis
  2. Intracranial complications: extradural abscess, lateral sinus thrombophlebitis or thrombosis, subdural abscess, meningitis, brain abscess, otitic hydrocephalus

SUGGESTED READINGS

De S, Makura ZG, Clarke RW: Paediatric acute mastoiditis: the Alder Hey experience, *J Laryngol Otol* 116(6):440, 2002.

Vassbotn FS et al: Acute mastoiditis in a Norwegian population: a 20-year retrospective study, *Int J Pediatr Otorhinolaryngol* 62(3):237, 2002.

AUTHORS: **MARILYN FABBRI, M.D.,** and **JANE V. EASON, M.D.**

BASIC INFORMATION

DEFINITION

Measles is a childhood exanthem, caused by an RNA virus called *Morbillivirus,* belonging to the family *Paramyxoviridae.*

SYNONYMS

Rubeola

ICD-9CM CODES
055.9 Measles
055.0 Encephalitis
055.1 Pneumonia
V04.2 Vaccination

EPIDEMIOLOGY & DEMOGRAPHICS

- Before the introduction of an effective vaccine in 1963, measles was one of the most common childhood illnesses, and in developing countries, where it strikes mostly children under age 5 yr, it remains a leading cause of childhood mortality
- 30 million cases worldwide each year
- In developed countries, measles outbreaks occur occasionally in adolescents and young adults who have not been immunized (incidence 0 to 10/100,000 person-years)

PHYSICAL FINDINGS & CLINICAL PRESENTATION

- Incubation: 10 to 14 days (up to 3 wk in adults)
- Prodrome: 2 to 4 days; malaise, fever, rhinorrhea, conjunctivitis, cough
- Exanthem phase: 7 to 10 days
  The fever increases and peaks at 104° to 105° F together with the rash; it persists for 5 or 6 days. The patient's fever decreases over 24 hr.
  Rash: Erythematous maculopapular eruption begins behind the ears, progresses to the forehead and neck (Fig. 1-144), then spreads to face, trunk, upper extremities, buttocks, and lower extremities in that order. After 3 days the rash fades in the same sequence by becoming copper brown and then desquamates.
  Enanthem: Koplik spots are white papules of 1 to 2 mm in diameter on an erythematous base. They first appear on the buccal mucosa opposite the lower molar 2 days before the rash and spread over 24 hours to involve most of the buccal and lower labial mucosa. They fade after 3 days.
  Other symptoms and signs: malaise, anorexia, vomiting, diarrhea, abdominal pain, pharyngitis, lymphadenopathy, and occasional splenomegaly.
- Atypical measles (in vaccinated persons)
  Incubation: 10 to 14 days
  Prodrome: 1 to 3 days; high fever and headache
  Rash: maculopapular, urticarial, or petechial rash that begins peripherally and progresses centrally
- Modified measles applies to patients who have received immune serum globulin and develop a milder illness
- Complications (30% of cases):
  Otitis media
  Laryngitis, tracheitis
  Pneumonia (accounts for 90% of measles deaths)
  Encephalitis with lethargy, irritability, and seizures; 60% recover completely, 25% have neurologic sequelae (mental retardation, hemiplegia, paraplegia, epilepsy, deafness), and 15% die
  Myocarditis, pericarditis, and hepatitis
  Complications more common in immunocompromised hosts and persons with AIDS

ETIOLOGY & PATHOGENESIS

- The measles virus is transmitted through the respiratory tract by airborne droplets.
- It initially infects the respiratory epithelium; the patient becomes viremic during the prodromal phase and the virus is disseminated to skin, respiratory tract, and other organs.
- Viral clearance is achieved via cellular immunity.

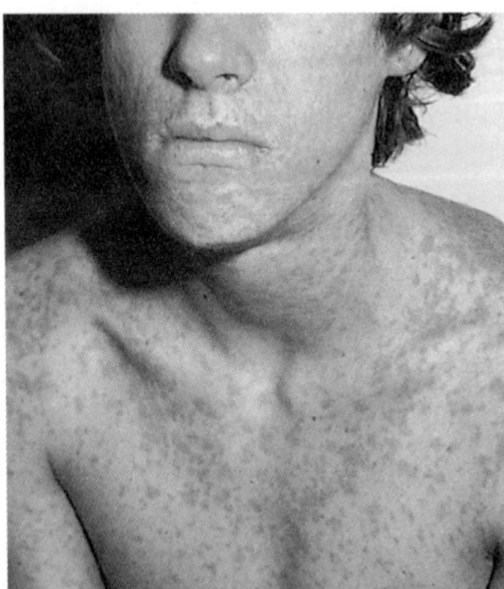

FIGURE 1-144 Rubeola. (From Zitelli BJ, Davis HW: *Atlas of pediatric physical diagnosis,* ed 3, St Louis, 1997, Mosby.)

DIAGNOSIS

DIFFERENTIAL DIAGNOSIS

- Other viral infections by enteroviruses, adenoviruses, human parvovirus B-19, rubella
- Scarlet fever
- Allergic reaction
- Kawasaki disease

WORKUP

Knowledge of outbreak, history and physical findings (Koplik spots are diagnostic), laboratory tests

LABORATORY TESTS

- CBC: leukopenia
- ELISA for measles antibodies, which appear shortly after the onset of the rash and peak 3 to 4 wk later
- CSF analysis in encephalitis may reveal a pleocytosis (lymphocytes) and an elevated protein

IMAGING STUDIES

Chest x-ray if pneumonia is suspected

TREATMENT

- Supportive
- Vitamin A
- Ribavirin for severe measles pneumonitis

PREVENTION

- Passive immunization: Human immunoglobulin 0.25 ml/kg IM within 6 days of exposure. Double the dose for immunocompromised persons.
- Active immunization (see Section V, Table 5-6).

SUGGESTED READINGS

Bernstein DI, Schiff GM: Measles. In Gorbach SL, Bartlett JG, Blacklow NR (eds): *Infectious diseases,* ed 2, Philadelphia, 1998, Saunders.

Epidemiology of measles—United States, *MMWR* 48:749, 1998.

Measles, *Clin Evid Concise* 7:55-56, 2002.

AUTHOR: **TOM J. WACHTEL, M.D.**

BASIC INFORMATION

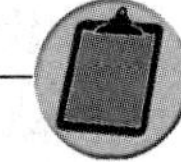

DEFINITION

Meckel's diverticulum is an ileal diverticulum located 100 cm proximal to the cecum. It results from failure of the omphalomesenteric duct to obliterate completely (as it should by the eighth week of gestation).

ICD-9CM CODES
751.0 Meckel's diverticulum

EPIDEMIOLOGY & DEMOGRAPHICS

Meckel's diverticulum, based on autopsy studies, occurs in 1% to 3% of the population. Complications occur more frequently in males.

PHYSICAL FINDINGS & CLINICAL PRESENTATION

- Painless lower GI bleeding (4%)
- Intestinal obstruction secondary to intussusception, volvulus, herniation, or entrapment of a loop of bowel through a defect in the diverticular mesentery (6%)
- Meckel's diverticulitis mimics acute appendicitis (5%)
- Rare primary tumor arising from diverticulum (carcinoid, sarcoma, leiomyoma, adenocarcinoma)
- Asymptomatic (80% to 95%)

ETIOLOGY & PATHOGENESIS

As a remnant of the omphalomesenteric duct, Meckel's diverticulum contains all layers of the intestinal wall and has its own mesentery and blood supply (branch of the superior mesenteric artery). The mucosa is usually ileal or gastric.

DIAGNOSIS

DIFFERENTIAL DIAGNOSIS

- Appendicitis
- Crohn's disease
- All causes of lower GI bleeding (polyp, colon cancer, AV malformation, diverticulosis, hemorrhoids)

Diagnosis is often made intraoperatively when the preoperative diagnosis is appendicitis. In the case of GI bleeding of unknown sources, a technetium scan will identify Meckel's diverticulum (sensitivity: 85% in children, 62% in adults; specificity: 95% in children, 9% in adults) (Fig. 1-145).

TREATMENT

Surgical resection

SUGGESTED READINGS

Keljo DJ, Squires RH: Meckel's diverticulum. In Feldman M, Scharschmidt BF, Sleisenger MH (eds): *Gastrointestinal and liver disease,* ed 6, Philadelphia, 1998, WB Saunders.

Martin JP et al: Meckel's diverticulum, *Am Fam Physician* 61:1037, 2000.

AUTHOR: **TOM J. WACHTEL, M.D.**

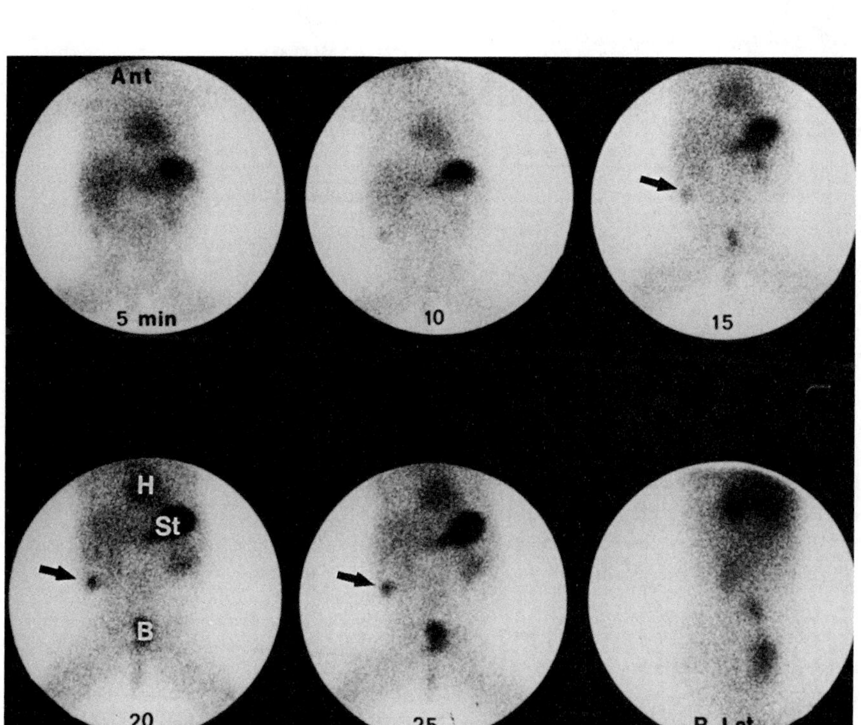

FIGURE 1-145 Meckel's diverticulum. In this 2-year-old child who had unexplained rectal bleeding, a nuclear medicine study was performed using radioactive material that concentrates in gastric mucosa (technetium-99m pertechnetate). Sequential 5-minute images of the abdomen are obtained. On the 20-minute image, the heart (*H*), stomach (*St*), and bladder (*B*) are clearly seen, in addition to an ectopic focus of activity (*arrow*) representing a Meckel diverticulum. (From Mettler FA [ed]: *Primary care radiology,* Philadelphia, 2000, WB Saunders.)

Meigs' Syndrome

BASIC INFORMATION

DEFINITION

Meigs' syndrome is characterized by the presence of a benign solid ovarian tumor associated with ascites and right hydrothorax that disappear after tumor removal.

ICD-9CM CODES
620.2 Ovarian mass (unspecified)
220.0 Benign ovarian lesion
789.5 Ascites
511.9 Pleural effusion

EPIDEMIOLOGY & DEMOGRAPHICS

- Occurs in <1% of ovarian fibromas (associated with approximately 0.004% of ovarian tumors)
- Most frequently encountered during middle age (average age, approximately 48 yr)

PHYSICAL FINDINGS & CLINICAL PRESENTATION

- Asymptomatic pelvic mass on bimanual examination
- Intermittent pelvic pain (intermittent torsion)
- Acute pelvic tenderness
- Acute abdominal tenderness
- Abdominal pelvic mass
- Abdominal bloating
- Fluid wave
- Shifting dullness
- "Puddle sign"
- Hyperresonance or flatness to chest percussion, absence of tactile and vocal fremitus
- Absent or loud bronchial breath sounds, rales, mediastinal displacement, tracheal shift
- Weight loss and emaciation

ETIOLOGY

- Not specifically known
- Usually associated with "edematous" fibromas (or other benign ovarian solid tumor) in excess of 10 cm
- Plausible that large fibroma with narrow stalk has inadequate lymphatic drainage; when coupled with intermittent torsion, results in back flow transudation into the peritoneal cavity; accumulated peritoneal ascites then passes to the right pleural cavity via lymphatics (overloaded thoracic duct) or via abdominal pleural commutation (i.e., foramen of Bochdalek)

DIAGNOSIS

DIFFERENTIAL DIAGNOSIS

- Abdominal ovarian malignancy
- Various gynecologic disorders:
  1. Uterus; endometrial tumor, sarcoma, leiomyoma ("pseudo-Meigs' syndrome")
  2. Fallopian tube: hydrosalpinx, granulomatous salpingitis, fallopian tube malignancy
  3. Ovary: benign, serous, mucinous, endometrioid, clear cell, Brenner tumor, granulosa, stromal, dysgerminoma, fibroma, metastatic tumor
- Nongynecologic (GI tract or GU tract tumor or pathology) causes of pelvic mass
  1. Ascites
  2. Portal vein obstruction
  3. IVC obstruction
  4. Hypoproteinemia
  5. Thoracic duct obstruction
  6. TB
  7. Amyloidosis
  8. Pancreatitis
  9. Neoplasm
  10. Ovarian hyperstimulation
  11. Pleural effusion
  12. CHF
  13. Malignancy
  14. Collagen-vascular disease
  15. Pancreatitis
  16. Cirrhosis

WORKUP

- Clinical condition characterized by ovarian mass, ascites, and right-sided pleural effusion
- Ovarian malignancy and the other causes (see "Differential Diagnosis") of pelvic mass, ascites, and pleural effusion to be considered
- History of early satiety, weight loss with increased abdominal girth, bloating, intermittent abdominal pain, dyspnea, nonproductive cough

LABORATORY TESTS

- CBC to rule out inflammatory process
- Tumor markers (CA-125, Hcg, AFP, CEA) to evaluate malignancy
- Chemical/LFT profile to evaluate metabolic or hepatic involvement

IMAGING STUDIES

- Pelvic sonography (color flow Doppler evaluation of adnexal mass) to evaluate pelvic pathology (CT scan or MRI if etiology indeterminate)
- Chest x-ray examination
- ABG if respiratory compromise

TREATMENT

NONPHARMACOLOGIC TREATMENT

- Informed consent and proper preparation of patient for possible staging laparotomy (TAHBSO, omentectomy, possible bowel resection, pelvic/periaortic lymphadenectomy)
- Bowel prep if considering pelvic malignancy

ACUTE GENERAL Rx

Depending on clinical presentation, size of pelvic mass, amount of ascites, and pleural effusion:

- If pelvic mass <10 cm, minimal ascites/pleural effusion: consider diagnostic open laparoscopy (possible exploratory laparotomy) and salpingo-oophorectomy with removal of ovarian fibroma (tumor).
- If pelvic mass >10 cm, moderate/large amount ascites/pleural effusion: consider pleurocentesis if respiratory compromise (cytology: AFB) and exploratory laparotomy with salpingo-oophorectomy and removal of ovarian fibroma (tumor).
- Treat pelvic malignancy, GI or GU tumor as indicated.

CHRONIC Rx

- Resolution of ascites and right-sided pleural effusion after removal of ovarian fibroma
- No long-term follow-up for benign ovarian fibroma

DISPOSITION

Excellent progress and complete survival are expected.

REFERRAL

To gynecologist or gynecologic oncologist for evaluation and treatment, especially if malignancy considered or encountered

SUGGESTED READINGS

Abramov Y et al: The role of inflammatory cytokines in Meigs' syndrome, *Obstet Gynecol* 99(5 Pt 2):917, 2002.

Buttin BM et al: Meigs' syndrome with an elevated CA 125 from benign Brenner tumors, *Obstet Gynecol* 98(5 Pt 2):980, 2001.

Meigs JV, Cass JW: Fibroma of the ovary with ascites and hydrothorax: with a report of seven cases, *Am J Obstet Gynecol* 33:249, 1937.

AUTHOR: **DENNIS M. WEPPNER, M.D.**

BASIC INFORMATION

DEFINITION

Melanoma is a skin neoplasm arising from the malignant degeneration of melanocytes. It is classically subdivided in four types:

- Superficial spreading melanoma (70%) (Fig. 1-146, *A*)
- Nodular melanoma (15% to 20%) (Fig. 1-146, *B*)
- Lentigo maligna melanoma (5% to 10%)
- Acral lentiginous melanoma (7% to 10%)

SYNONYMS

Malignant melanoma

ICD-9CM CODES
172.9 Melanoma of the skin, site unspecified

EPIDEMIOLOGY & DEMOGRAPHICS

- Annual incidence of melanoma is 13 cases/100,000 persons.
- Melanoma has doubled to tripled in incidence over the past 25 years.
- Melanoma is the most common cancer among women 20-29 yr of age.
- Lifetime risk of cutaneous melanoma for white Americans is 1/90.
- Melanoma is the leading cause of death from skin disease.
- Median age at diagnosis is 53 yr.
- Superficial spreading melanoma occurs most often in young adults on sun-exposed areas.
- Acral lentiginous melanoma is most often found in Asian Americans and African Americans and is not related to sun exposure.
- Death rate for white men with melanoma is 3/100,000.
- 8%-10% of melanomas arise in people with a family history of the disease.

PHYSICAL FINDINGS & CLINICAL PRESENTATION

Variable depending on the subtype of melanoma:

- *Superficial spreading melanoma* is most often found on the lower legs, arms, and upper back. It may have a combination of many colors or may be uniformly brown or black.
- *Nodular melanoma* can be found anywhere on the body, but it most frequently occurs on the trunk on sun-exposed areas. It has a dark-brown or red-brown appearance, can be dome shaped or pedunculated; they are frequently misdiagnosed because they may resemble a blood blister or hemangioma and may also be amelanotic.
- *Lentigo maligna melanoma* is generally found in older adults in areas continually exposed to the sun and frequently arising from lentigo maligna (Hutchinson's freckle) or melanoma in situ. It might have a complex pattern and variable shape; color is more uniform than in superficial spreading melanoma.
- *Acral lentiginous melanoma* frequently occurs in soles, subungual mucous membranes, and palms (sole of the foot is the most prevalent site). Unlike other types of melanoma, it has a similar incidence in all ethnic groups.
- The warning signs that the lesion may be a melanoma can be summarized with the ABCD rules:
  A: Asymmetry (e.g., lesion is bisected and halves are not identical)
  B: Border irregularity (uneven, ragged border)
  C: Color variegation (presence of various shades of pigmentation)
  D: Diameter enlargement (>6 mm)

ETIOLOGY

- UV light is the most important cause of malignant melanoma.
- There is a modest increase in melanoma risk in patients with small nondysplastic nevi and a much greater risk in those with dysplastic lesions.
- The CDKN2A gene, residing at the 9p21 locus, is often deleted in people with familial melanoma.

DIAGNOSIS

DIFFERENTIAL DIAGNOSIS

- Dysplastic nevi
- Solar lentigo
- Vascular lesions
- Blue nevus
- Basal cell carcinoma
- Seborrheic keratosis

WORKUP

- Perform excisional biopsy with elliptical excision that includes 1 to 2 mm of normal skin surrounding the lesion and extends to the subcutaneous tissue; incisional punch biopsy is sometimes necessary in surgically sensitive areas (e.g., digits, nose).
- The sentinel lymph node dissection (SLND) should be considered in patients with intermediate (1 to 4 mm) melanomas or high-risk skin tumors to obtain information regarding a patient's subclinical lymph node status with minimal morbidity. It involves the use of radiologic lymphoscintigraphy to map lymphatic drainage from the site of the primary melanoma to the first "sentinel" lymph node in the region. When properly performed, if the sentinel node is negative, the remaining lymph nodes in the region will not have metastases in more than 98% of cases.

A 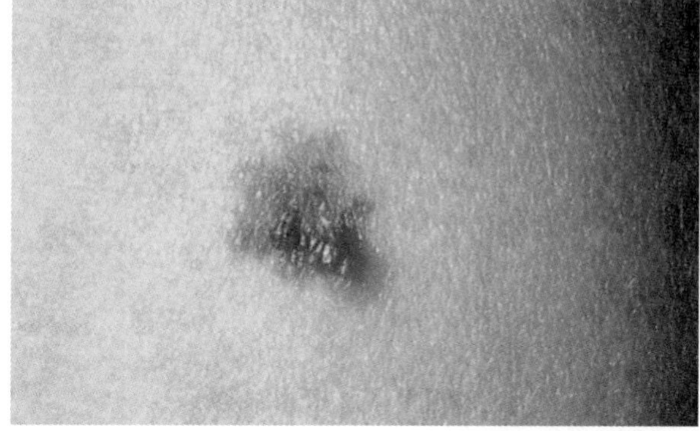

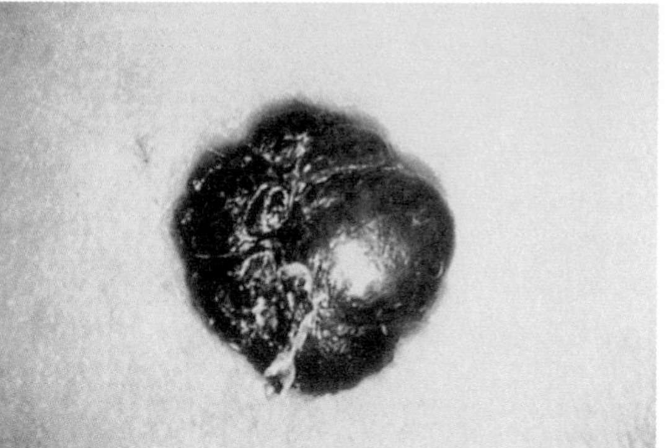 B

FIGURE 1-146 **A,** Superficial spreading melanoma. **B,** Nodular melanoma. (From Abeloff MD [ed]: *Clinical oncology,* ed 2, New York, 2000, Churchill Livingstone.)

- The staging system for melanoma adapted by the American Joint Committee on Cancer (AJCC) is as follows:

T*	Thickness of primary tumor
Tis	In situ
T1	≤1.0 mm
T2	1.01-2.0 mm
T3	2.01-4.0 mm
T4	>4.0 mm
N†	Number of positive lymph nodes
N0	0
N1	1
N2	2 or 3
N3	≥4 (or combination of in-transit metastases, satellite lesions, or an ulcerated primary lesion with any number of nodes)
M	Metastases
M0	0
M1	Distant subcutaneous or lymph node metastases
M2	Lung metastases
M3	All other visceral or any distant metastases or an elevated lactate dehydrogenase level not attributable to another cause
Clinical Stage	
0	(T0N0M0)
IA	(T1aN0M0)
IB	(T1bN0M0) (T2aN0M0)
IIA	(T2bN0M0) (T3aN0M0)
IIB	(T3bN0M0) (T4aN0M0)
IIC	(T4bN0M0)
IIIA	(T1-T4aN1bM0)
IIIB	T1-T4aN2bM0)
IIIC	(AnyT,N2c,M0) (Any T, N3, M0)
IV	(Any T, Any N, >M1)

*a, without ulceration; b, with ulceration

†a, micrometastasis; b, macrometastases; c, in-transit metastases with metastatic lymph nodes

LABORATORY TESTS

The pathology report should indicate the following:

- Tumor thickness (Breslow microstage)
- Tumor depth (Clark level)
- Mitotic rate
- Radial growth rates vs. vertical growth rate
- Tumor infiltrating lymphocyte
- Histologic regression
- Reverse transcriptase-polymerase chain reaction (RT-PCR) assay for tyrosine messenger RNA is a useful marker for the presence of melanoma cells. It is performed on sentinel lymph node biopsy and is useful for detection of submicroscopic metastases.

TREATMENT

NONPHARMACOLOGIC THERAPY

Avoid excessive sun exposure; liberal use of sunscreens with UBV and UVA protection (recent laboratory data suggest that melanoma is promoted by UVA; therefore UVB sunscreens may not be effective in preventing melanoma). Recent literature reports, however, reveal no association between melanoma and sunscreen use.

GENERAL Rx

- Initial excision of the melanoma
- Reexcision of the involved area after histologic diagnosis:
  1. The margins of reexcision depend on the thickness of the tumor.
  2. Low-risk or intermediate-risk tumors require excision of 1 to 3 cm.
  3. Melanomas of moderate thickness (0.9 to 2.0 mm) can be excised safely with 2-cm margins.
  4. A 1-cm margin of excision for melanoma with a poor prognosis (as defined by a tumor thickness of at least 2 mm) is associated with a significantly greater risk of regional recurrence than is a 3-cm margin, but with a similar overall survival rate.
- Lymph node dissection: recommended in all patients with enlarged lymph nodes.
  1. Elective lymph node dissection remains controversial.
  2. It is indicated with positive sentinel node. It may be considered in those with a primary melanoma that is between 1 and 4 mm thick (especially in patients <60 yr old).
- Adjuvant therapy with interferon alfa-2b (intron A) is considered controversial in patients with metastatic melanoma. It is approved by the FDA for AJCC stages IIb and III melanoma; however, its statistical benefit remains unclear.
- Dacarbazine (DTIC) and interleukin 2 (IL-2) can be used in metastatic melanoma. Results are generally poor, with median survival in patients with distant metastatic melanoma approximately 6 mo.
- Patients with a history of melanoma should be followed with skin examinations every 6 mo or sooner if patient detects any new lesions; the assessments usually consist of medical history, physical examination, chest x-ray examination, and laboratory evaluation.

DISPOSITION

- Prognosis varies with the stage of the melanoma. The 5-yr survival related to thickness is as follows: <0.76 mm, 99% survival; 0.6 to 1.49 mm, 85%; 1.5 to 2.49 mm, 84%; 2.5 to 3.9 mm, 70%; >4 mm, 44%.
- The 5-yr survival in patients with distant metastasis is <10%.
- Treatment of advanced disease consists (in addition to surgical excision and lymph node dissection) of chemotherapy, immunotherapy, and radiation therapy.

SUGGESTED READINGS

Balch CM et al: A new American Joint Committee on Cancer Staging System for cutaneous melanoma, *Cancer* 88:1484, 2000.

Dennis LK et al: Sunscreen use and the risk for melanoma: a quantitative review, *Ann Intern Med* 139:966, 2003.

Kanzler MH, Mraz-Gernhard S: Treatment of primary cutaneous melanoma, *JAMA* 285:1819, 2001.

Masci P, Borden EC: Malignant melanoma: treatment emerging, but early detection is still key, *Cleve Clin J Med* 69:529, 2002.

Thomas JM et al: Excision margins in high-risk malignant melanoma, *N Engl J Med* 350:757, 2004.

Tsao H et al: Management of cutaneous melanoma, *N Engl J Med* 351:998, 2004.

AUTHOR: **FRED F. FERRI, M.D.**

SECTION I

BASIC INFORMATION

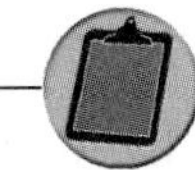

DEFINITION

Meniere's disease is a syndrome characterized by recurrent vertigo with fluctuating hearing loss, tinnitus, and fullness in the ear.

SYNONYMS

Endolymphatic hydrops
Lermoyez's syndrome
Meniere's syndrome

ICD-9CM CODES
386.01 Meniere's disease, cochleovestibular (active)

EPIDEMIOLOGY & DEMOGRAPHICS

INCIDENCE (IN U.S.): 15 cases/100,000 persons
PREVALENCE (IN U.S.): 100-200 cases/100,000 persons
PREDOMINANT SEX: Male = female
PREDOMINANT AGE: Adults
GENETICS: Not known to be genetic

PHYSICAL FINDINGS & CLINICAL PRESENTATION

- Hearing may be unilaterally decreased
- Pallor, sweating, and nausea may occur during a severe attack
- Usually the patient develops a sensation of fullness and pressure along with decreased hearing and tinnitus in a single ear
- The patient typically experiences severe vertigo, which peaks within minutes, then slowly subsides over hours
- Persistent sense of disequilibrium for days is typical after an acute episode

ETIOLOGY

- Unknown; viral and autoimmune etiologies have been suggested
- Associated with endolymphatic hydrops

DIAGNOSIS

DIFFERENTIAL DIAGNOSIS

- Acoustic neuroma
- Migrainous vertigo
- Multiple sclerosis
- Autoimmune inner ear syndrome
- Otitis media
- Vertebrobasilar disease
- Viral labyrinthitis

WORKUP

- Electronystagmography may show peripheral vestibular deficit.
- Electrocochleography and glycerol test used by some otoneurologists and ENT specialists.

LABORATORY TESTS

Audiogram may show sensorineural hearing loss, with lower frequencies primarily affected.

IMAGING STUDIES

MRI to rule out acoustic neuroma, especially if cerebellar or CNS dysfunction is present

TREATMENT

NONPHARMACOLOGIC THERAPY

Limit activity during attacks.

ACUTE GENERAL Rx

- Prochlorperazine 5 to 10 mg PO q6h or 25 mg PO bid
- Promethazine 12.5 to 25 mg PO q4-6h
- Diazepam 5 to 10 mg IV/PO for acute attack
- Meclizine 25 mg q6h
- Scopolamine patch

CHRONIC Rx

Diuretics such as hydrochlorothiazide or acetazolamide, salt restriction, and avoidance of caffeine are traditional.

DISPOSITION

- Usually followed by an otoneurologist or ENT specialist
- Usual course of disease consists of alternating attacks and remissions
- Majority of patients can be managed medically; fewer than 10% of patients will undergo surgical intervention for persistent incapacitating vertigo

REFERRAL

To an otolaryngologist for surgical intervention if attacks persist despite medical therapy

PEARLS & CONSIDERATIONS

COMMENTS

- Many variations of the classical clinical picture. The essential features for diagnosis are episodic vertigo and sensorineural hearing loss audiometrically documented on at least one occasion.
- In one-third of patients both ears are eventually involved.
- Some evidence that Meniere's disease and migraine may be pathophysiologically linked.

SUGGESTED READINGS

Baloh RW, Fife TD, Furman JM, Zee DS: Recurrent spontaneous attacks of vertigo, *Continuum Lifelong Learning in Neurology* 2(2):56, 1996.
Radtke A et al: Migraine and Meniere's disease: is there a link? *Neurology* 59(11):1700, 2002.
Thai-Von H, Bounaix MJ, Fraysse B: Meniere's disease: pathophysiology and treatment, *Drugs* 61(8):1089, 2001.
Weber PC, Adkins WY Jr: The differential diagnosis of Meniere's disease, *Otolaryngol Clin North Am* 30(6):977, 1997.

AUTHOR: **SHARON S. HARTMAN, M.D., Ph.D.**

BASIC INFORMATION

DEFINITION

A meningioma is an intracranial tumor arising from arachnoid cells.

ICD-9CM CODES
225.2 Cerebral meninges

EPIDEMIOLOGY & DEMOGRAPHICS

INCIDENCE (IN U.S.): 2.6/100,000 persons/yr. Accounts for approximately 20% of primary intracranial tumors.

PREDOMINANT SEX: Female:male ratio of 3:2 in adults; male > female in childhood and male = female among African Americans

PEAK INCIDENCE: Males: sixth decade, females: seventh decade; rare in childhood

GENETICS: Tumors associated with a missing sequence/loss of heterozygosity on chromosome 22.

ENVIRONMENTAL: Only known environmental risk factor is ionizing radiation; peak risk 10-20 yr after treatment.

PHYSICAL FINDINGS AND CLINICAL PRESENTATION

- Varies with location and size
- May be asymptomatic and present incidentally on a neuroimaging study or at autopsy
- Focal or generalized seizures and hemiparesis common, as are headache, personality change/confusion and visual impairment
- Children are more likely to present with signs of increased intracranial pressure without further localizing features

TYPICAL LOCATIONS

- Parasagittal
- Convexity
- Sphenoid wing
- Spinal canal
- Others: optic nerve sheath, choroid plexus, éctopic (intraventricular)

ETIOLOGY

- Abnormalities on chromosome 22 are found in >50% of meningiomas. This region also contains the gene for neurofibromatosis type 2, which is a tumor suppressor gene encoding a cytoskeletal protein called merlin.
- Cranial radiation may be responsible for some cases where the tumor occurs in the irradiated field following an appropriate latency period from the radiation.
- The link with sex hormones is suggested by the increase in growth rate during luteal phase of the menstrual cycle and during pregnancy, as well as with breast carcinomas.

DIAGNOSIS

IMAGING STUDIES

- Cranial CT scanning or MRI can detect and determine the extent of meningiomas (Fig. 1-147).
- Bone windows optimally identify bone involvement.
- On non-enhanced scans, meningiomas typically are isodense to slightly hyperdense to brain and are homogeneous in appearance. With the addition of contrast, meningiomas show homogeneous enhancement; gadolinium can facilitate imaging of smaller additional lesions that are missed on unenhanced images.

DIFFERENTIAL DIAGNOSIS

Other well-circumscribed intracranial tumors:

- Acoustic schwannoma (typically at the pontocerebellar junction)
- Ependymoma, lipoma, and metastases within the spinal cord

WORKUP

- Imaging studies with CT or MRI, followed by surgical removal with histologic confirmation if clinically indicated
- PET scanning may help to predict the aggressiveness and potential for recurrence.
- There are nine benign histologic variants and four variants associated with increased recurrence and rates of metastasis. Features suggesting increased rate of recurrence include brain invasion, high rate of mitosis, and highly anaplastic features

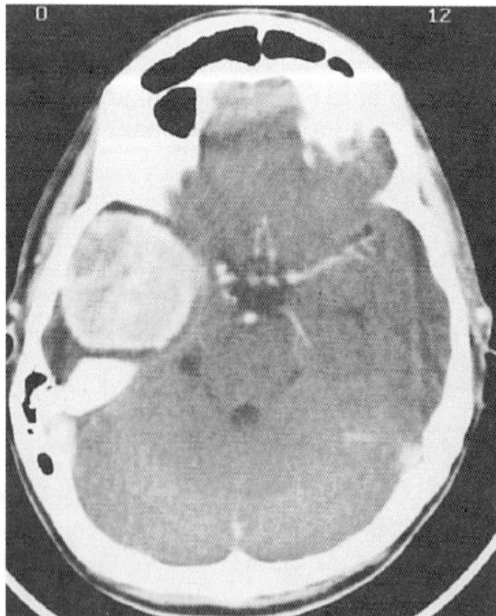

FIGURE 1-147 Contrast-enhanced CT scan demonstrates a large contrast-enhancing right sphenoid wing meningioma. (From Specht N [ed]: *Practical guide to diagnostic imaging,* St Louis, 1998, Mosby.)

TREATMENT

NONPHARMACOLOGIC THERAPY

The mainstay of treatment for meningiomas remains surgical removal if symptomatic

ACUTE GENERAL Rx

- Generally none. For lesions that cause significant mass effect, steroids (Decadron) are sometimes used to decrease brain edema
- Anticonvulsants to control seizures

CHRONIC Rx

- Radiation therapy is the only validated form of adjuvant therapy and may be beneficial in patients with incomplete resections or inoperable tumors.
- Sterotactic radiosurgery has increasingly been used to treat meningiomas.
- Little information is available on the efficacy of traditional antineoplastic agents.
- Hydroxyurea induces apoptosis and inhibits meningioma growth in culture.
- Hormonal treatments, such as the progesterone and glucocorticoid receptor antagonist mifepristone (RU486), are currently under investigation.

DISPOSITION

- Estimated surgical mortality is 7%.
- Long-term outcome is variable, based on histopathology, tumor grade location, and completeness of resection.
- Most incidentally discovered meningiomas remain asymptomatic. Calcified tumors may be less likely to progress than noncalcified ones.
- Significant morbidity and mortality can be observed in meningiomas with otherwise favorable pathology secondary to unfavorable location (e.g, skull base).

REFERRAL

Neurosurgical consultation for all cases

SUGGESTED READINGS

Gor S et al: The natural history of asymptomatic meningiomas in Olmsted County, Minnesota, *Neurology* 51:1718, 1998.

Grunberg SM: Treatment of unresectable meningiomas with the antiprogesterone agent mifepristone, *J Neurosurg* 74:861, 1991.

Kleihues P et al: The WHO classification of tumors of the nervous system, *J Neuropathol Exp Neurol* 61(3):215, 2002.

Mason WP: Stabilization of disease progression by hydroxyurea in patients with recurrent or unresectable meningioma, *J Neurosurg* 97:341, 2002.

Seizinger JP: Deletion mapping of a locus on human chromosome 22 involved in the oncogenesis of meningioma, *Proc Natl Acad Sci U S A* 84:5419, 1987.

Sekhar LN, Levine ZT, Sarma S: Grading of meningiomas, *J Clin Neurosci* 8(suppl 1):1, 2001.

AUTHOR: **NICOLE J. ULLRICH, M.D., PH.D.**

BASIC INFORMATION

DEFINITION

Bacterial meningitis is an inflammation of meninges with increased intracranial pressure, and pleocytosis or increased WBCs in CSF secondary to bacteria in the pia-subarachnoid space and ventricles, leading to neurologic sequelae and abnormalities.

ICD-9CM CODES
320 Bacterial meningitis

EPIDEMIOLOGY & DEMOGRAPHICS

INCIDENCE (IN U.S.): 3 cases/100,000 persons
PREDOMINANT SEX: Male = female
PREDOMINANT AGE: All ages, neonate to geriatric

PHYSICAL FINDINGS & CLINICAL PRESENTATION

- Fever
- Headache
- Neck stiffness, nuchal rigidity, meningismus
- Altered mental state, lethargy
- Vomiting, nausea
- Photophobia
- Seizures
- Coma; lethargy, stupor
- Rash: petechial associated with meningococcal infection
- Myalgia
- Cranial nerve abnormality (unilateral)
- Papilledema
- Dilated, nonreactive pupil(s)
- Posturing: decorticate/decerebrate
- Physical examination findings of Kernig's sign and Brudzinski's sign in adults with meningitis are often not helpful in determining meningeal inflammation

ETIOLOGY

Neisseria meningitidis is now more common than *Haemophilus influenzae* as a cause of bacterial meningitis in children as well as adults. *H. influenzae* is the cause of >30% of cases of meningitis (usually in infants and children <6 yr old). It is associated with sinusitis, otitis media.

- Neonates: group B streptococci, *Escherichia coli, Klebsiella* sp., *Listeria monocytogenes*
- Infants through adolescence:
  1. *N. meningitidis*
  2. *H. influenzae*
  3. *Streptococcus pneumoniae*
- Adults
  1. *N. meningitidis*
  2. *S. pneumoniae*
- Elderly
  1. *S. pneumoniae*
  2. *N. meningitidis*
  3. *L. monocytogenes*
  4. Gram-negative bacilli

DIAGNOSIS

Diagnostic approach is based on patient presentation and physical examination. Key elements to diagnosis are CSF evaluation and CT scan or MRI if the patient is in a coma or has focal neurologic deficits, pupillary abnormalities, or papilledema.

DIFFERENTIAL DIAGNOSIS

- Endocarditis, bacteremia
- Intracranial tumor
- Lyme disease
- Brain abscess
- Partially treated bacterial meningitis
- Medications
- SLE
- Seizures
- Acute mononucleosis
- Other infectious meningitides
- Neuroleptic malignant syndrome
- Subdural empyema
- Rocky Mountain spotted fever

WORKUP

CSF examination:

- Opening pressure >100 to 200 mm Hg
- WBC <5 to >100 mm^3
- Neutrophilic predominance: >80%
- Gram stain of CSF: positive in 60% to 90% patients
- CSF protein: >50 mg/dl
- CSF glucose: <40 mg/dl
- Culture: positive in 65% to 90% cases
- CSF bacterial antigen: 50% to 100% sensitivity
- E-test for susceptibility of pneumococcal isolates

LABORATORY TESTS

Blood culturing, WBC with differential, and CSF examination (see "Workup")

IMAGING STUDIES

- CT scan or MRI of head: necessary with increased intracranial pressure, coma, neurologic deficits
- Sinus CT: if sinusitis suspected

TREATMENT

- Empiric therapy is necessary with IV antibiotic treatment if patient has purulent CSF fluid at time of lumbar puncture, is asplenic, or has signs of DIC/sepsis pending Gram stain and culture results. Therapy after Gram stain pending cultures is recommended for the following age and patient risk groups:
  1. Neonates: ampicillin plus cefotaxime
  2. Infants/children: ampicillin or third-generation cephalosporin (plus chloramphenicol if purulent or patient compromised)
  3. Adults (18 to 50 yr): third-generation cephalosporin
  4. Older adults (>50 yr): ampicillin plus third-generation cephalosporin
- Penicillin-resistant pneumococcus: because of an increasing incidence of this organism, empiric treatment with ceftriaxone or cefotaxime plus vancomycin (60 mg/kg/day) has been recommended.
- Table 1-30 describes common pathogens of bacterial meningitis and their empiric treatment based on age.
- Table 1-31 describes specific antibiotic treatments for known pathogens.
- Steroids: dexamethasone 0.15 mg/kg q6h for first 4 days of therapy should be used in adults with bacterial meningitis and mental status changes or acute neurologic phenomenon. Decreased mortality and neurologic sequelae are seen with adjunct therapy.
- Dexamethasone also benefits children with Hib or pneumococcal meningitis and should be given within the first 2 days of illness.

PEARLS & CONSIDERATIONS

COMMENTS

- Prevention of meningitis can be achieved through chemoprophylaxis of close contacts (household members and anyone exposed to oral secretions).
- Effective medications are rifampin 10 mg/kg PO bid for 2 days or ceftriaxone 250 mg IM single dose in patients over age 12; 125 mg IM if age 12 and under.
- Ciprofloxacin 500 mg for prevention of Neisseria meningitis can be given to patients over the age of 18 yr who cannot tolerate rifampin to eradicate pharyngeal colonization.
- Vaccines with antibodies against serogroup A, C, Y, W-135 capsular polysaccharides are available for adults and children over the age of 2 yr.

SUGGESTED READINGS

Aronin SI, Peduzzi P, Quagliarello VJ: Community-acquired bacterial meningitis: risk stratification for adverse clinical outcome an effect of antibiotic timing, *Ann Int Med* 129:862, 1998.

Choi C: Bacterial meningitis in aging adults, *Clin Infect Dis* 33:1380, 2001.

Hasbun R et al: Computed tomography of the head before lumbar puncture in adults with suspected meningitis, *N Engl J Med* 345:1727, 2001.

Rosenstein NE et al: Meningococcal disease, *N Engl J Med* 344:1378, 2001.

Thomas KE et al: The diagnostic accuracy of Kernig's sign, Brudzinski's sign, and nuchal rigidity in adults with suspected meningitis, *Clin Infect Dis* 35:46, 2002.

AUTHORS: **GLENN G. FORT, M.D.**, and **DENNIS J. MIKOLICH, M.D.**

TABLE 1-30 Common Pathogens of Bacterial Meningitis and Their Empiric Treatment Based on Age

Age	Common Pathogens	Treatment*	Duration (days)
0-1 mo	Group B streptococcus *Listeria monocytogenes* *Escherichia coli*	Ampicillin + third-generation cephalosporin† or ampicillin + aminoglycoside	14-21 14-21 21
1-3 mo	Streptococcus pneumoniae Group B streptococcus, *E. coli, L. monocytogenes* *S. pneumoniae* *Neisseria meningitidis, Haemophilus influenzae*	Ampicillin + third-generation cephalosporin†	10-14 14-21 14-21 10-14 7-10
3 mo-18 yr	*H. influenzae, H. meningitidis, S. pneumoniae*	Third-generation cephalosporin† or meropenem or chloramphenicol	7-10 (*N. influenzae* and *N. meningitidis*) 10-14 *(S. pneumoniae)*
18-50 yr	*H. influenzae, N. meningitidis, S. pneumoniae*	Third-generation cephalosporin† or meropenem or ampicillin + chloramphenicol	Same as above
>50 yr	*S. pneumoniae, L. monocytogenes,* gram-negative bacilli	Ampicillin + third-generation cephalosporin† or ampicillin + fluoroquinolone‡ or meropenem	10-14 *(S. pneumoniae)* 14-21 *(L. monocytogenes)* 21 Gram-negative bacilli other than *H. influenzae*

From Rakel RE (ed): *Principles of family practice,* ed 6, Philadelphia, 2002, WB Saunders.
*Add vancomycin in areas where there is greater than 2% incidence of highly drug resistant *S. pneumoniae.*
†Ceftriaxone or cefotaxime.
‡Ciprofloxacin or levofloxacin.

TABLE 1-31 Specific Antibiotic Treatments for Known Pathogens

Pathogen	Primary Therapy	Alternative*
Group B streptococcus	Penicillin G or ampicillin	Vancomycin or third-generation cephalosporin†
Streptococcus pneumoniae (MIC < 0.1)	Third-generation cephalosporin†	Meropenem, penicillin
S. pneumoniae (MIC < 0.1)	Vancomycin + third-generation cephalosporin*	Substitute rifampin for vancomycin; or meropenem; or vancomycin as monotherapy if highly allergic to other alternatives
Haemophilus influenzae (β-lactamase-negative)	Ampicillin	Third-generation cephalosporin† or chloramphenicol or aztreonam
H. influenzae (β-lactamase-positive)	Third-generation cephalosporin†	Chloramphenicol or aztreonam or fluoroquinolones‡
Listeria monocytogenes	Ampicillin + gentamicin	Trimethoprim-sulfamethoxazole
Neisseria meningitidis	Penicillin G or ampicillin	Third-generation cephalosporin†
Enterobacteriaceae	Third-generation cephalosporin† 1 aminoglycoside	Trimethoprim-sulfamethoxazole or aztreonam or fluoroquinolones or antipseudomonal penicillin (or ampicillin) + aminoglycoside
Pseudomonas aeruginosa	Ceftazidine + aminoglycoside	Aminoglycoside + aztreonam or aminoglycoside + antipseudomonal penicillin§
Staphylococcus aureus (methicillin-sensitive)	Antistaphylococcal penicillin¶ 6 rifampin	Vancomycin + rifampin or trimethoprim-sulfamethoxazole + rifampin
S. aureus (methicillin-resistant)	Vancomycin + rifampin	
Staphylococcus epidermidis	Vancomycin + rifampin	

From Rakel RE (ed): *Principles of family practice,* ed 6, Philadelphia, 2002, WB Saunders.
MIC, Minimum inhibitory concentration.
*If patient is highly allergic or intolerant of primary therapy.
†Ceftriaxone or cefotaxime.
‡Ciprofloxacin or levofloxacin.
§Piperacillin, mezlocillin, or ticarcillin.
¶Nafcillin, oxacillin, or methicillin.

BASIC INFORMATION

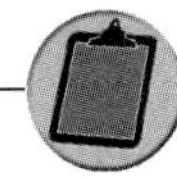

DEFINITION

Viral meningitis is an acute aseptic meningitis usually with lymphocytic pleocytosis and negative CSF stains and cultures.

SYNONYMS

Aseptic meningitis

ICD-9CM CODES
047.8 Meningitis, aseptic

EPIDEMIOLOGY & DEMOGRAPHICS (TABLE 1-32)

INCIDENCE (IN U.S.): 11 cases/100,000 persons
PREDOMINANT SEX: Male = female
GENETICS: Those with abnormal humoral immunity and agammaglobulinemia have associated difficulty with viral clearance.

PHYSICAL FINDINGS & CLINICAL PRESENTATION

- Fever
- Headache
- Nuchal rigidity
- Photophobia
- Myalgias
- Vomiting
- Rash
- Diarrhea
- Pharyngitis

ETIOLOGY

- Enterovirus
- Mumps virus
- Measles
- Enteroviruses
- Arboviruses
- Herpes (simplex and zoster)
- HIV
- Lymphocytic choriomeningitis virus
- Adenovirus
- CMV
- Arthropod-borne viruses
- West Nile virus

DIAGNOSIS

The diagnostic approach is similar to bacterial meningitis (see "Bacterial Meningitis"); the foremost need is to rule out bacterial meningitis with CSF evaluation. Presentation may be similar to that of meningitis with bacterial involvement.

DIFFERENTIAL DIAGNOSIS

- Bacterial meningitis
- Meningitis secondary to Lyme disease, TB, syphilis, amebiasis, leptospirosis
- Rickettsial illnesses: Rocky Mountain spotted fever
- Migraine headache
- Medications
- SLE
- Acute mononucleosis/Epstein-Barr virus
- Seizures
- Carcinomatous meningitis

WORKUP

CSF examination:
- Usually shows pleocytosis
- Lymphocytic predominance (polyps in early stages)
- Opening pressure: 200 to 250 mm Hg
- WBC: 100 to 1000 mm^3
- Increased CSF protein
- Decreased or normal CSF glucose
- Negative Gram stain, cultures, CIE, latex agglutination
- No viral cultures routinely available; if patient is suspected of having mumps, serologic testing may be diagnostic; complement fixation used
- PCR for HSV, West Nile or enterovirus (which could shorten duration of antibiotic treatment and hospitalization if bacterial meningitis was suspected)

LABORATORY TESTS

CBC with differential, blood culturing, and CSF examination (see Workup)

IMAGING STUDIES

CT scan or MRI: if cerebral edema, focal neurologic findings develop

TREATMENT

No specific antiviral therapy for enterovirus, arbovirus, mumps virus; lymphocytic choriomeningitis virus is available. Treatment is supportive unless HSV is detected, which would be treated with IV acyclovir.

SUGGESTED READINGS

Attia J et al: Does this adult patient have acute meningitis? *JAMA* 282:175, 1999.

Barton LL, Hyndman NJ: Lymphocyticchoriomengitis virus: reemerging central nervous system pathogen, *Pediatrics* 105:E351C, 2000.

Oostenbrink R et al: Children with meningeal signs: predicting who needs empiric antibiotic treatment, *Arch Pediatr Adolesc Med* 156(12):1189, 2002.

Ramers C et al: Impact of a diagnostic cerebrospinal fluid enterovirus polymerase chain reaction test on patient management, *JAMA* 283:2680, 2000.

AUTHORS: **GLENN G. FORT, M.D.,** and **DENNIS J. MIKOLICH, M.D.**

TABLE 1-32 Epidemiology of Acute Viral Meningitis

EPIDEMIOLOGIC FACTORS*

Season	Patient's Age (yr)	Patient's Sex	Risk Factor	Suggested Viral Agent
Summer-fall	Infant	—	Infected mother	Coxsackievirus B
	1-15	—	Swimming pools, closed communities	Enteroviruses
			Geographic area: California, southeastern United States	California serogroup virus
Winter	1-15	—	School exposure	Varicella virus, measles virus
		Male/female 3:1		Mumps virus
	16-21	—	College exposure	Measles virus
		Male/female 3:1		Mumps virus
		—		Epstein-Barr virus (mononucleosis)
	Any	—	Mice, rats, hamsters	Lymphocytic choriomeningitis virus
	Adults	—	Varicella-zoster	Varicella-zoster virus
Any	Any	—	Immunocompromise	Adenovirus
		—	Acquired immunodeficiency syndrome	Human immunodeficiency virus

From Gorbach SI: *Infectious diseases,* ed 2, Philadelphia, 1998, WB Saunders.
*Epidemiologic factors are suggestive but should not be used to exclude diagnoses in individual cases.

Meningomyelocele

BASIC INFORMATION

DEFINITION

Meningomyelocele is the most common type of spina bifida and is characterized by herniation of the spinal cord, nerves, or both through a bony defect of the spine.

SYNONYMS

Myelomeningocele
Spina bifida cystica

ICD-9CM CODES
741.9 Spina bifida without mention of hydrocephalus
741.9 Meningomyelocele

EPIDEMIOLOGY & DEMOGRAPHICS

INCIDENCE (IN U.S.): 4.6/10,000 births
PREDOMINANT SEX: Male = female
PREDOMINANT INCIDENCE: Newborn
GENETICS: Environmental and genetic factors have a joint role.

ETIOLOGY

- Failure of neural tube to close completely at about 4 wk gestation
- Associated with maternal valproate use

PHYSICAL FINDINGS & CLINICAL PRESENTATION

- Evident at birth—a sac protruding in the lumbar region (Fig. 1-148)
- Severity of neurologic deficits depends on the location of the lesion along the neuroaxis
- Motor dysfunction in the legs
- Lack of bladder or bowel control
- Often associated with Chiari II malformation and resulting obstructive hydrocephalus

DIAGNOSIS

- Prenatal diagnosis through ultrasound and MRI is being made more frequently.
- MR imaging can provide better definition of the defect.
- Coexisting hydrocephalus is detected by measurement of head size, ultrasonography, CT, or MRI.

DIFFERENTIAL DIAGNOSIS

- Teratoma
- Meningocele

WORKUP

- Evaluate for hydrocephalus.
- Evaluate for other congenital abnormalities, such as congenital heart disease, hydronephrosis, intestinal malformation, club foot, and skeletal deformities.

LABORATORY TESTS

Prenatal testing often reveals elevated alpha fetoprotein in amniotic fluid or maternal serum.

IMAGING STUDIES

- MRI of spine
- X-ray studies of skull exhibit craniolacuna, a honeycombed pattern associated with hydrocephalus
- CT or MRI of head may reveal hydrocephalus

TREATMENT

- Surgical closure of myelomeningocele is performed soon after birth
- Control of hydrocephalus (shunt)
- Management of urinary incontinence
- Counseling of parents

ACUTE GENERAL Rx

- Immediate goal after delivery is to close defect and prevent infection; surgery usually performed within 24 hr of birth
- Shunt placement for obstructive hydrocephalus
- Treatment of seizures, if present

CHRONIC Rx

- Follow closely for development of hydrocephalus
- Bladder catheterization
- Avoid use of latex-containing products to prevent development of latex allergy

DISPOSITION

Followed by a team of specialists including neurosurgeons, urologists, orthopedists, and myelodysplasia nurses

PEARLS & CONSIDERATIONS

All mothers of children with neural tube defects should be instructed on nutritional supplementation with folate for future pregnancies.

COMMENTS

- Intrauterine repair of meningomyelocele decreases the incidence of hindbrain herniation and shunt-dependent hydrocephalus in infants, but increases the incidence of premature delivery.
- U.S. Public Health Service recommends 400 micrograms of folate intake per day for all women capable of becoming pregnant for primary prevention of neural tube defects.

SUGGESTED READINGS

Adzick NS, Walsh DS: Myelomeningocele: prenatal diagnosis, pathophysiology and management, *Semin Pediatr Surg* 12(3):168. 2003.

Botto LD et al: Neural-tube defects, *N Engl J Med* 341(20):1509, 1999.

Jobe AH: Fetal surgery for myelomeningocele, *N Engl J Med* 347(4):230, 2002.

Kaufman BA: Neural tube defects, *Pediatr Clin North Am* 51(2):389, 2004.

Spina bifida incidence at birth—United States, 1983-1990, *MMWR Morb Mortal Wkly Rep* 41(27):497, 1992.

AUTHOR: **MAITREYI MAZUMDAR, M.D.**

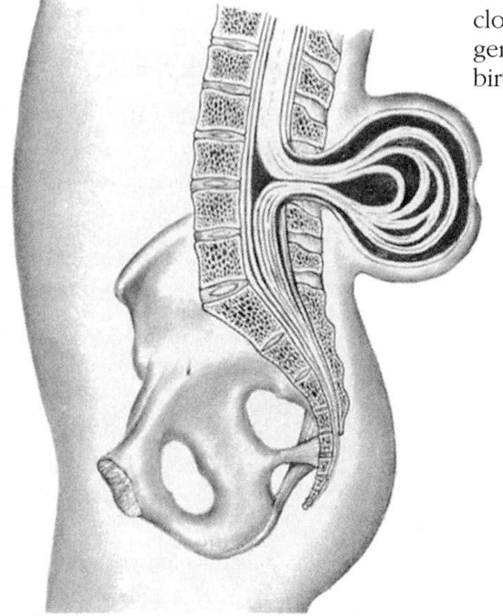

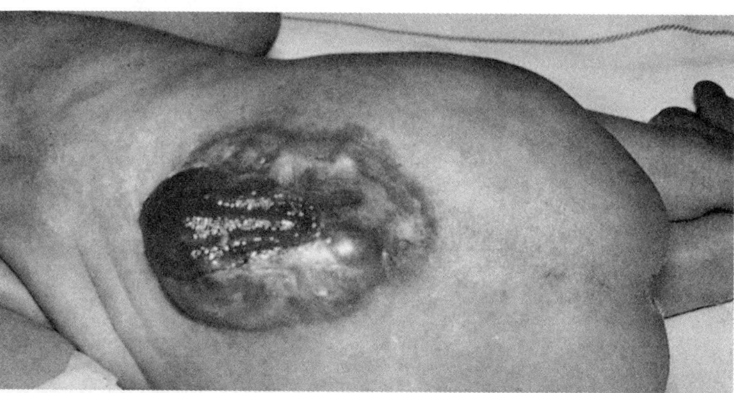

FIGURE 1-148 Meningomyelocele. (From Wong DL: *Whaley's and Wong's nursing care of infants and children,* ed 5, St Louis, 1995, Mosby.)

BASIC INFORMATION

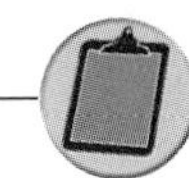

DEFINITION

Menopause is the occurrence of no menstrual periods for 1 yr after age 40 yr or permanent cessation of ovulation following lost ovarian activity. It is a climacteric reproductive stage of life marked by waxing and waning estrogen levels followed by decreasing ovarian function. Premature ovarian failure and no menstrual periods may also occur because of depletion of ovarian follicles before the age of 40 yr.

SYNONYMS

Change of life
Climacteric ovarian failure

ICD-9CM CODES
627 Premenopausal menorrhagia
627.2 Menopausal or female climacteric states
627.4 States associated with artificial menopause
716.3 Climacteric arthritis

EPIDEMIOLOGY & DEMOGRAPHICS

- Average age of menopause in the U.S. is 51 yr.
- Age at which menopause occurs is genetically determined.
- Smokers experience menopause an average of 1.5 yr earlier than nonsmokers.
- More than one third of a woman's life will be spent after menopause.
- Onset of perimenopause is usually in a woman's mid- to late-40s.
- Approximately 4000 women each day begin menopause.

PHYSICAL FINDINGS & CLINICAL PRESENTATION

- Atrophic vaginitis, which can cause burning, itching, bleeding, dyspareunia
- Either complete cessation of menses or a period of irregular cycles and diminished or heavier bleeding
- Osteoporosis
- Psychologic dysfunction:
  1. Anxiety
  2. Depression
  3. Insomnia
  4. Nervousness
  5. Irritability
  6. Inability to concentrate
- Sexual changes, decreased libido, dyspareunia
- Urinary incontinence
- Vasomotor symptoms (hot flashes, flushes), night sweats, cardiovascular disease, coronary artery disease, atherosclerosis, headaches, tiredness, and lethargy

ETIOLOGY

- The most common etiology: physiologic, caused by degenerating theca cells that fail to react to endogenous gonadotropins, producing less estrogen; decreased negative feedback in the hypothalamic pituitary access, increased follicle-stimulating hormone (FSH), and increased luteinizing hormone (LH), which leads to stromal cells that continue to produce androgens as a result of the LH stimulation
- Surgical castration
- Family history of early menopause, cigarette smoking, blindness, abnormal chromosomal karyotype (Turner's syndrome, gonadal dysgenesis), precocious puberty, and left-handedness

DIAGNOSIS

DIFFERENTIAL DIAGNOSIS

- Asherman's syndrome
- Hypothalamic dysfunction
- Hypothyroidism
- Pituitary tumors
- Adrenal abnormalities
- Ovarian abnormalities
- Polycystic ovarian syndrome
- Pregnancy
- Ovarian neoplasm
- TB

WORKUP

- If the clinical picture is highly suggestive of menopause, estrogen can be prescribed. If all symptoms resolve, then diagnosis has essentially been made. Before estrogen is prescribed, a complete history and physical examination are needed. If a patient has estrogen-dependent malignancy, unexplained abnormal uterine bleeding, history of thrombophlebitis, or acute liver disease, estrogen therapy is contraindicated.
- Progesterone challenge test: progesterone 100 mg is given IM to induce withdrawal bleeding. If no withdrawal bleeding is obtained, it would be safe to assume that a hypoestrogenic state is present.
- Physical examination, height, weight, blood pressure, breast examination, and pelvic examination are needed.
- Assess risk for coronary artery disease, osteoporosis, cigarette smoking, personal history, history of breast cancer, liver disease, active coagulation disorder, or any unexplained vaginal bleeding.

LABORATORY TESTS

- FSH, LH, and estrogen levels: if the FSH is markedly elevated and the estrogen level is markedly depressed, constitutes laboratory diagnosis of ovarian failure; LH only if polycystic ovarian disease is to be ruled out in a younger patient
- TSH to rule out thyroid dysfunction and prolactin level if patient has symptoms of galactorrhea and if suspicion of pituitary adenoma exists
- A general chemistry profile to check for any systemic diseases
- Pap smear, endometrial biopsy, or D&C in patients who have had irregular periods or intermenstrual or postmenopausal bleeding
- Mammogram

IMAGING STUDIES

- CT scan or MRI of head if pituitary tumor is suspected
- Bone density studies
- Pelvic ultrasound to check endometrial stripe

TREATMENT

NONPHARMACOLOGIC THERAPY

- A balanced diet: low in fat, with total fat intake being <30% of calories; total calories sufficient to maintain body weight or to produce weight loss if that is needed
- Avoidance of smoking, excessive alcohol or caffeine intake
- Exercise: weight-bearing exercise for osteoporosis prevention
- Kegel exercises for strengthening the pelvic floor
- Adequate calcium intake: 1500 mg qd is necessary to maintain zero calcium balance in postmenopausal women
- Change in the ambient temperature (may ameliorate hot flashes and reduce night sweats)
- Vitamin E
- Avoidance of caffeine, alcohol, and spicy foods if they trigger hot flashes
- Vaginal lubricants to help with the dyspareunia secondary to vaginal dryness (e.g., Replens, K-Y Jelly, or Gyne-Moistrin cream)

ACUTE GENERAL Rx

Estrogen replacement in symptomatic patients can be done in a variety of forms, including oral estrogen and transdermal estrogen patch.

- Examples of oral estrogen would include conjugated estrogens:
  1. Premarin: start with 0.625 mg qd and increase up to 1.25 mg qd, depending on symptoms. Cenestin (synthetic conjugated estrogens, A) available in 0.625-, 0.9-, and 1.25-mg doses.
  2. Estradiol (Estrace): start with 1 mg qd and increase to 2 mg qd; also available in 0.5 mg tablet for patients who experience side effects from the estrogen.
  3. Esterified estrogens (Estratab): start with 0.3 to 1.25 mg qd.

4. Estropipate (Ogen, Ortho-Est): start with 0.625 to 1.25 mg qd.
5. Esterified estrogen/testosterone combination: give 1.25 mg and methyltestosterone 2.5 mg (Estratest) and esterified estrogen 0.625 mg and methyltestosterone 1.25 mg (Estratest HS). May improve sexual enjoyment and libido.

- If the patient has had a hysterectomy for benign disease, estrogen alone is sufficient. However, if she still has her uterus, progestin should be added for its protective effect against endometrial cancer. Medroxyprogesterone acetate (Provera) is the most commonly prescribed progestin. It can be prescribed in a continual daily dose of 2.5 mg or of 5 mg if continual breakthrough bleeding is encountered. This can also be prescribed in a 5-mg cyclic fashion for the first 14 days of the month or as 10-mg tablets for the first 10 days of the month. Patients need to be advised that this generally will cause withdrawal bleeding but in a fairly regular fashion. Continuous hormone replacement therapy is preferred, because after a period of time the patient should be amenorrheic. Patients should be counseled that they may experience some irregular spotting for the first 6 to 9 mo after starting the hormone replacement therapy.
- Combination oral preparations Femhrt ⅕ (1 mg norethindrone acetate/5 μg ethinyl estradiol) one pill daily. Ortho—Prefest 1 mg 17β-estradiol (white pill) alternating with 1 mg 17β-estradiol and 0.9 mg norgestimate (pink pill) q3d Prempro 0.625 mg conjugated estrogen/2.5 mg medroxyprogesterone one pill daily Prempro 0.625 mg conjugated estrogen/5.0 mg medroxyprogesterone one pill daily Activella 1 mg estradiol and 0.5 mg norethindrone acetate Premphase 0.625 mg conjugated estrogen with 5 mg medroxyprogesterone last 14 days.
- Transdermal patches can be either estradiol (Estraderm, Vivelle, Fempatch) 0.025 to 0.1 mg applied twice weekly or Climara 0.025 to 0.1 mg used once a week. With these preparations, progesterone should be used in a similar fashion. Combipatch—apply twice weekly (combination estrogen and progesterone).
- Vaginal creams can be used, and these should be reserved for local therapy of atrophic vaginitis. Systemic absorption does occur; however, blood levels are unpredictable. Start with a loading dose of 2 to 4 g of estrogen-containing cream nightly for 1 to 2 wk. When symptoms improve, once to twice weekly is adequate maintenance.
- Vagifem estradiol vaginal tablets. Initial dosage: one Vagifem tablet, inserted vaginally, once daily for 2 wk. Maintenance dose: one Vagifem tablet, inserted vaginally, twice weekly.
- Femring vaginal ring delivering the equivalent of 50 micrograms per day inserted every 3 months.
- EstroGel 0.06% (estrodiol gel) One Pump (1.25 g/day) applied to one arm from wrist to shoulder.
- For women in whom estrogen is contraindicated or for those who do not wish to take estrogen, the following regimens can be used:
  1. Depo-Provera 150 mg IM every month (may be helpful in alleviating hot flashes)
  2. Clonidine 0.05 to 0.15 mg qd
  3. Bellergal-S
  4. Fosamax (alendronate sodium) or Actonel (risedronate) 5 mg qd or 35 mg weekly are approved for prophylactic prevention of osteoporosis. They should be taken on an empty stomach; wait at least 30 min before ingesting any substance, including liquids, because this decreases absorption into the body. They should be swallowed on arising for the day with a full glass of water, 6 to 8 oz, and patients should not lie down for at least 30 min and until after their first food of the day.
  5. Evista (Raloxifene) 60 mg daily PO has positive bone effect, a total cholesterol–lowering effect, and LDL cholesterol–lowering effect; it is a selective estrogen receptor agonist; it does not affect estrogen receptors in the breast or uterus. It does not ameliorate vasomotor symptoms or vaginal atrophy.
- Tibolone significantly improves vasomotor symptoms, libido, and vaginal lubrication.

CHRONIC Rx

Hormone replacement therapy should be used only for the short term unless benefits outweigh the risks of long-term use.

DISPOSITION

If treated, the patient should have resolution of her symptoms and reduced incidence of osteoporosis. Lifelong medical supervision is necessary to monitor adequacy of treatment and prevention of complications. This should include annual Pap smears, pelvic examinations, breast examinations, mammography, and endometrial sampling of any type of abnormal bleeding. If untreated, the vasomotor symptoms will eventually disappear; however, this takes many years, and some women who are in their 80s have experienced hot flashes. Urogenital atrophy will continue to worsen. Osteoporosis and coronary artery disease risks will increase with every passing year. Women using ERT for >10 yr may have increased risk of developing ovarian cancer.

REFERRAL

Most menopausal women are managed by their gynecologist. However, this condition can be managed adequately by the patient's primary care physician who has an interest in treating menopausal women.

PEARLS & CONSIDERATIONS

COMMENTS

- Short-term risks of HRT include an 18-fold increased rise for cholecystitis, 3.5-fold risk of a thrombocardiac event in the first year, and probably increased risk of stroke and MI.
- Results of the WHI study found that for every 10,000 women taking HRT for 1 yr (10,000 person-yr), 7 more would have coronary events, 8 more strokes, 8 more pulmonary emboli, and 8 more with early breast cancer than would 10,000 women taking placebo. Benefits of HRT were 6 fewer cases of colorectal cancer and 5 fewer hip fractures per 10,000 women.
- HRT should not be initiated or continued for the primary or secondary prevention of CHD.
- Patient education materials can be obtained through the American College of Obstetricians and Gynecologists, 409 12th Street SW, Washington, DC 20024, and *Menopause News,* 2074 Union Street, San Francisco, CA 94123; phone: 1-800-241-MENO. Multiple patient educational brochures are produced by pharmacologic companies.

SUGGESTED READINGS

Gambrell RD: The Women's Health Initiative Reports: critical review of the findings, the female patient, *Menopause* 29:(11):23, 2004.

Han KK et al: Benefits of soy isoflavone therapeutic regimen on menopausal symptoms, *Obstet Gynecol* 99:389, 2002.

Lacey JV et al: Menopausal hormone replacement therapy and risk of ovarian cancer, *JAMA* 288:334, 2002.

Nelson H et al: Postmenopausal hormone replacement therapy, *JAMA* 288:872, 2002.

Santoro N: The menopause transition: an update, *Human Reproduction Update* 8(2):155, 2002.

Speroff L: Efficacy and tolerability of a noval estradiol vaginal ring for relief of menopausal symptoms, *Obstet Gynecol* 102(4):823, 2003.

Writing Group for the Women's Health Initiative Investigators: Risks and benefits of estrogen plus progestin in healthy postmenopausal women, *JAMA* 288:321, 2002.

AUTHOR: **GEORGE T. DANAKAS, M.D.**

BASIC INFORMATION

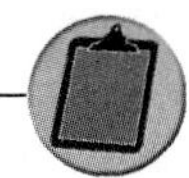

DEFINITION

Mesenteric adenitis is a painful enlargement of mesenteric lymph nodes.

ICD-9CM CODES
289.2 Mesenteric adenitis

EPIDEMIOLOGY & DEMOGRAPHICS

- Incidence unknown
- Affects mostly children (under age 18 yr) with no sex preference
- When *Yersinia* enterocolitis is the cause, boys are more frequently involved

PHYSICAL FINDINGS & CLINICAL PRESENTATION

- Abdominal pain of variable severity (mild ache to severe colic) beginning in upper abdomen or right lower quadrant, eventually localizes in right side but not in a precise location (unlike appendicitis)
- In *Yersinia* infection outbreaks, the symptoms include abdominal pain (84%), diarrhea (78%), fever (43%), anorexia (22%), nausea (13%), and vomiting (8%)
- Physical findings:
  Other lymphadenopathy (20% of cases)
  Right lower quadrant tenderness (site of maximum tenderness may vary from one examination to the next)
  Guarding (rare)
  Mild fever

ETIOLOGY & PATHOGENESIS

- Reactive hyperplasia of lymph nodes that drain the ileocecal region, similar to that seen in inflammatory or allergic conditions. One study reported that approximately two thirds of cases are secondary (reactive) and one third are primary (no demonstrable associated inflammatory process).
- *Yersinia enterocolitica, Yersinia pseudotuberculosis, Salmonella* species, *E. coli,* streptococci have been implicated with mesenteric adenitis.

DIAGNOSIS

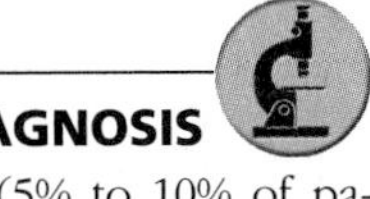

DIFFERENTIAL DIAGNOSIS

- Acute appendicitis (5% to 10% of patients admitted to hospitals with a diagnosis of appendicitis are discharged with a diagnosis of mesenteric adenitis)
- Crohn's disease

Section II describes the differential diagnosis of abdominal pain.

LABORATORY TESTS

- CBC may show leukocytosis
- Abdominal sonography and helical appendiceal CT scan may be useful
- Laparotomy if appendicitis is suspected

PROGNOSIS

Recurrent bouts are common; therefore if laparotomy is performed and a normal appendix is found, it should be removed.

SUGGESTED READINGS

Adam JT: Nonspecific mesenteric lymphadenitis. In Schwartz SE et al (eds): *Principles of surgery,* ed 6, New York, 1994, McGraw-Hill.

Macari M et al: Mesenteric adenitis: CT diagnosis of primary versus secondary causes, incidence, and clinical significance on pediatric and adult patients, *Am J Roentgenol* 178:853, 2002.

Pearson RD, Guerrant RL: Enteric fever and other causes of abdominal symptoms with fever. In Mandell GL (ed): *Mandell, Douglas, and Bennett's principles and practice of infectious diseases,* ed 5, New York, 2000, Churchill Livingstone.

AUTHOR: **TOM J. WACHTEL, M.D.**

SECTION I

Mesenteric Venous Thrombosis

BASIC INFORMATION

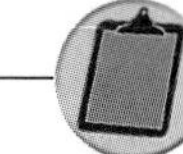

DEFINITION

Mesenteric venous thrombosis (MVT) is a thrombotic occlusion of the mesenteric venous system involving major trunks or smaller branches and leading to intestinal infarction in its acute form.

ICD-9CM CODES
557.0 Mesenteric venous thrombosis

EPIDEMIOLOGY & DEMOGRAPHICS

Between 5% and 15% of patients with acute mesenteric infarction have mesenteric venous thrombosis. MVT is slightly more common in men than women. The typical age of occurrence is 50 to 60 yr.

PHYSICAL FINDINGS & CLINICAL PRESENTATION

Acute MVT
- Symptoms: abdominal pain in 90% of patients, typically out of proportion to the physical findings. Nausea and vomiting occur in 50% and GI bleeding occurs in 50% (occult), 15% (gross).
- Physical findings:
  Early: abdominal tenderness, decreased bowel sounds, abdominal distention
  Later: guarding and rebound tenderness, fever, and septic shock

Subacute MVT
- Symptoms: nonspecific abdominal pain for weeks or months
- Physical findings: none

Chronic MVT
- Symptoms: upper GI hemorrhage from bleeding varices
- Physical findings: none other than signs of blood loss if significant

ETIOLOGY & PATHOGENESIS

Hypercoagulable states (see "Hypercoagulable States" in Section I)
- Peripheral deep venous thrombosis
- Neoplasms
- Antithrombin III, protein C, protein S deficiencies
- Lupus anticoagulant (antiphospholipid antibody)
- Oral contraceptive use, pregnancy
- Polycythemia vera
- Thrombocytosis
- Paroxysmal nocturnal hemoglobinuria

Portal hypertension
- Cirrhosis

Inflammation
- Pancreatitis
- Peritonitis (e.g., appendicitis, diverticulitis, perforated viscus)
- Inflammatory bowel disease
- Pelvic or intraabdominal abscess
- Intraabdominal cancer

Postoperative state or trauma
- Blunt abdominal trauma
- Postoperative states (abdominal surgery)

Thrombosis may begin in small mesenteric branches (e.g., in hypercoagulable states) and propagate to the major venous mesenteric trunks, or begin in large veins (e.g., in cirrhosis, intraabdominal cancer, surgery) and extend distally. If collateral drainage is inadequate, the intestine becomes congested, edematous, cyanotic, and hemorrhagic and eventually may infarct.

DIAGNOSIS

DIFFERENTIAL DIAGNOSIS

All other causes of abdominal pain (e.g., peritonitis, intestinal obstruction, pancreatitis, peptic ulcer disease, gastritis, inflammatory bowel disease, perforated viscus). Also to be considered in the differential diagnosis of GI hemorrhage

WORKUP

Laboratory tests and imaging studies

LABORATORY TESTS

- CBC: leukocytosis
- Electrolytes: metabolic acidosis (lactic) indicate bowel infarction
- Elevated amylase
- Tests for hypercoagulable status

IMAGING STUDIES

- Abdominal plain x-ray: ileus, ascites, bowel dilation, bowel wall thickening, loop separation, and thumbprinting
- Abdominal CT scan (diagnostic in 90%) bowel wall thickening, venous dilation, venous thrombus
- Arteriography if CT scan is not diagnostic

Occasionally the diagnosis is made by a laparotomy.

TREATMENT

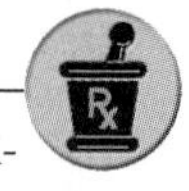

- Anticoagulation or thrombolytic therapy
- Laparotomy if intestinal infarction is suspected

Short ischemic segment: resection
Long ischemic segment:
1. Nonviable: resection or close
2. Viable: intraarterial papaverine, and/or thrombectomy followed by "second look" intervention

- The treatment of chronic MVT is the same as for portal hypertension

PROGNOSIS

- Mortality of acute mesenteric venous thrombosis: 20% to 50%
- Recurrence rate: 15% to 25%

SUGGESTED READINGS

Brandt LJ, Smithline AE: Ischemic lesions of the bowel. In Feldman M, Scharsachmidt BF, Sleisenger MH (eds): *Gastrointestinal and liver disease,* ed 6, Philadelphia, 1998, WB Saunders.

Kumar S, Sarr MG, Kemeth PS: Mesenteric venous thrombosis, *N Engl J Med* 345:1683, 2002.

AUTHOR: **TOM J. WACHTEL, M.D.**

BASIC INFORMATION

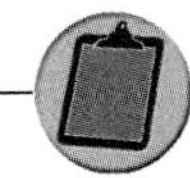

DEFINITION

Malignant mesothelioma is a rare neoplastic lesion associated with asbestos exposure. There are three major histologic subtypes: epithelial (most common), sarcomatous, and mixed (epithelial/sarcomatous).

ICD-9CM CODES
199.1 Malignant mesothelioma, site NOS

EPIDEMIOLOGY & DEMOGRAPHICS

- Associated with asbestos exposure (all fiber types)
- Over 3000 new cases diagnosed in U.S. annually
- More common in men as a result of asbestos exposure in the workplace
- Right-sided involvement is more common
- Incidence of mesothelioma increases with age; median age at presentation is >60 yr
- There are currently more than 8 million persons in the U.S. who are at risk for mesothelioma because of prior asbestos exposure

PHYSICAL FINDINGS & CLINICAL PRESENTATION

- Dyspnea
- Nonpleuritic chest pain
- Fever, weight loss, sweats, fatigue, loss of appetite
- Dysphagia, superior vena cava syndrome, Horner's syndrome in advanced stages
- Auscultation may reveal unilateral loss of breath sounds
- Dullness on percussion may be present

ETIOLOGY

- Asbestos exposure
- Other reported potentially causal factors include prior radiation therapy and extravasated thorotrast, zeolite, and erionite fibers

DIAGNOSIS

DIFFERENTIAL DIAGNOSIS

Metastatic adenocarcinomas (from lung, breast, ovary, kidney, stomach, prostate)

WORKUP

- Staging evaluation includes complete history (including occupational history), physical examination, and testing to determine potential operability (CT, bone scan, PFTs)
- Thoracoscopy, pleuroscopy, and open lung biopsy are useful in obtaining adequate tissue samples for diagnosis
- Pulmonary function tests
- Staging: the UICC staging uses the TNM categories to organize mesothelioma in stages I-IV in a manner similar to that used for non–small cell lung cancer

LABORATORY TESTS

- Diagnostic thoracentesis is generally insufficient for diagnosis because pleural effusions may only reveal atypical mesothelial cells
- Immunohistochemistry is useful to distinguish adenocarcinoma from epithelial malignant mesothelioma (mesotheliomas are generally CEA negative and cytokeratin positive)
- Thrombocytosis and anemia may be found on initial lab evaluation

IMAGING STUDIES

- Chest radiographs may reveal pleural plaques or calcifications in the diaphragm
- CT scan of the chest/abdomen and bone scan are used to assess the extent of disease

TREATMENT

GENERAL Rx

- Operable patient (epithelial type, no positive nodes, confined to pleura, adequate PFTs): the two surgical techniques for therapeutic intervention are decortication (pleurectomy) and extrapleural pneumonectomy. Postoperative chemotherapy with cisplatin, doxorubicin, and cyclophosphamide and subsequent external beam radiation are used in some centers with limited success.
- Inoperable patient (disease too extensive, sarcomatous or mixed histology type, poor PFTs): supportive care plus/minus radiation therapy for symptoms or supportive care plus chemotherapy. Combined modality therapies (surgery, radiation therapy, chemotherapy, and biologics) have also been used to reduce both local and distant recurrences. The combination of pemetrexed (an antimetabolite that inhibits enzymes involved in folate metabolism) and cisplatin is used for chemotherapy of unresectable malignant pleural mesothelioma.
- Intrapleural instillation of cisplatin or biologics (e.g., interferons, interleukin-2) is generally limited to very early disease because it can only penetrate a very limited depth of the tumor and there is a propensity of the pleural space to become progressively obliterated with advancing disease.
- The role of radiation therapy in the treatment of mesotheliomas remains uncertain. It is often used for palliation of local pain despite lack of trials to prove its utility.
- Obliteration of the pleural space (pleurodesis) with instillation of tetracycline, bleomycin, or biologic substances such as C. parvum into the pleural cavity is often tried in attempting to treat recurrent symptomatic pleural effusions.

DISPOSITION

Median survival for patients undergoing pleurectomy ranges from 6.7 to 21 mo, for extrapleural pneumonectomy 4 to 21 mo. Survival is better for patients with epithelial form.

PEARLS & CONSIDERATIONS

COMMENTS

- Patients with early disease should be referred to treatment centers specializing in mesothelioma treatment before attempts are made to obliterate the pleural space with pleurodesis.
- An approach to the evaluation and treatment of mesothelioma is described in Section III.

SUGGESTED READING

Abeloff MD: *Clinical oncology,* ed 2, New York, 2000, Churchill Livingstone.

AUTHOR: **FRED F. FERRI, M.D.**

BASIC INFORMATION

DEFINITION

Guidelines from the National Cholesterol Education Program define the metabolic syndrome as the presence of any three of the following:

- Abdominal obesity: waist circumference >102 cm (40 inches) in men and >88 cm (35 inches) in women
- Hypertriglyceridemia: ≥150 mg/dl (1.69 mmol/L)
- Low high-density lipoprotein cholesterol: <40 mg/dl (1.04 mmol/L) in men and <50 mg/dl (1.29 mmol/L) in women
- High blood pressure: ≥130/85 mm Hg
- High fasting glucose: ≥110 mg/dl (6.1 mmol/L)

SYNONYMS

Syndrome X
Insulin resistance syndrome
Obesity dyslipidemia syndrome

ICD-9CM CODES
277.7 Dysmetabolic syndrome X

EPIDEMIOLOGY & DEMOGRAPHICS

- 22% of U.S. adults
- Prevalence increases with age; impacts over 40% of individuals >60 yr
- Increased prevalence in women compared with men (2:1)
- Other risk factors include ethnic background such as Mexican American, low socioeconomic status, lack of physical activity, high carbohydrate diet, no alcohol intake, smoking, postmenopausal status high body mass index, and family history

CLINICAL PRESENTATION & PHYSICAL FINDINGS

- Hypertension, hyperglycemia and obesity as defined previously
- Patients with the metabolic syndrome are at markedly increased risk for coronary artery disease and diabetes
- Associated with several obesity-related disorders including fatty liver disease, chronic kidney disease, microalbuminuria, polycystic ovary syndrome, and obstructive sleep apnea

ETIOLOGY

- Abdominal obesity is associated with insulin resistance and hyperinsulinemia.
- Insulin may increase blood pressure through increased activity of the sympathetic nervous system, reduction in nitric oxide production, and upregulation of angiotensin II receptors.
- Androgens may play a role in abdominal obesity and insulin resistance.
- Genetic factors may predispose patients to develop the metabolic syndrome.
- Elevations in inflammatory markers and cytokines (i.e., IL-6 and CRP) have been associated with insulin resistance and metabolic syndrome.
- Deficiency of adiponectin plays a role in the development of insulin resistance.

DIAGNOSIS

DIFFERENTIAL DIAGNOSIS

- Other forms of obesity (i.e., Cushing's syndrome, hypothyroidism)
- Other forms of hyperlipidemia (i.e., familial combined hyperlipidemia, familial hypercholesterolemia, dysbetalipoproteinemia, hypothyroidism)
- Other forms of hypertension (i.e., pheochromocytoma, hyperaldosteronism, Cushing's syndrome)
- Other forms of diabetes (i.e., Type 1, pancreatic insufficiency)

WORKUP

- History with focus on symptoms of coronary artery disease (angina) and diabetes
- Complete physical examination, including height, weight, waist circumference, and blood pressure

LABORATORY TESTS

- Fasting lipid profile (total cholesterol, LDL cholesterol, HDL cholesterol, and triglyceride)
- Fasting glucose

TREATMENT

NONPHARMACOLOGIC THERAPY

- Dietary modifications aimed at weight loss
- Increase physical activity

PHARMACOLOGIC THERAPY

- Treat hypertension (see "Hypertension")
  1. Systolic BP of 120 to 139 mm Hg or a diastolic BP of 80 to 89 mm Hg: Recommend lifestyle modifications to prevent cardiovascular disease
  2. Systolic blood pressures above 130/80: Consider angiotensin converting-enzyme inhibitors or thiazide-type diuretics as first line
- Treat hyperlipidemia
  1. Serum LDL cholesterol of <100 mg/dL (2.6 mmol/L) is recommended for secondary prevention; however, recent studies suggest greater benefit with a more aggressive goal of <80 mg/dL (2.1 mmol/L). For primary prevention, an LDL goal <130 mg/dl (3.4 mmol/l) is recommended for individuals with greater than 2 coronary heart disease risk factors. HMG CoA reductase inhibitors (statins) commonly used as first-line agents.
  2. Patients with high triglycerides (>200 mg/dl) may benefit from the addition of a Fibrate. Must rule out hypothyroidism and normalize blood glucose.
- Treat diabetes
  1. Goal fasting blood glucose <130 mg/dl
  2. Metformin and thiazolidinediones used as first line to improve insulin sensitivity
- Treat cardiovascular risk factors
  1. Aspirin therapy in patients with CAD
  2. Risk can be lowered with weight loss, exercise, blood pressure control and treatment of hyperlipidemia

REFERRAL

- To nutritionist for diet counseling
- To weight-loss and exercise programs
- To endocrinologist if difficulty reaching therapeutic goals

SUGGESTED READINGS

Cannon CP et al: Intensive versus moderate lipid lowering with statins after acute coronary syndromes, *N Engl J Med* 350:1495, 2004.

Chobanian AV et al: The seventh report of the joint national committee on prevention, detection, evaluation, and treatment of high blood pressure: the JNC 7 report, *JAMA* 289:2560, 2003.

Executive summary of the third report of the national cholesterol education program (NCEP) expert panel on detection, evaluation, and treatment of high blood cholesterol in adults (adult treatment panel III), *JAMA* 287:2486, 2001.

Grundy SM et al: Definition of metabolic syndrome: report of the National Heart, Lung, and Blood Institute/American Heart Association conference on scientific issues related to definition, *Circulation* 109:433, 2004.

Pearson TA et al: AHA guidelines for primary prevention of cardiovascular disease and stroke: 2002 update: consensus panel guide to comprehensive risk reduction for adult patients without coronary or other atherosclerotic vascular diseases. American Heart Association Science Advisory and Coordinating Committee, *Circulation* 106:388, 2002.

AUTHORS: **MARK J. FAGAN, M.D.,** and **GEETA GOPALAKRISHNAN, M.D.**

SECTION I

BASIC INFORMATION

DEFINITION

Metatarsalgia refers to pain of the metatarsus, especially of the MTP articulation (Fig. 1-149). This is a nonspecific symptom usually involving the lesser toes.

ICD-9CM CODES
726.7 Metatarsalgia

PHYSICAL FINDINGS & CLINICAL PRESENTATION

- Pain beneath the metatarsal heads with ambulation
- Plantar callus formation beneath the metatarsal heads, usually involving one of the middle three toes
- Local tenderness
- Deformity
- Joint stiffness

ETIOLOGY

- Splayfoot
- Osteoarthritis, rheumatoid arthritis
- Freiberg's disease (avascular necrosis of second metatarsal head)
- Cavus foot (high arch)
- Bunion deformity
- Hallux rigidus
- MTP synovitis
- Morton's neuroma
- Often no obvious cause

DIAGNOSIS

DIFFERENTIAL DIAGNOSIS

See Etiology.

WORKUP

Underlying cause should always be sought.

LABORATORY TESTS

Rheumatoid factor may be required to rule out rheumatoid synovitis.

IMAGING STUDIES

Plain radiography to determine presence or absence of joint disease or deformity

TREATMENT

NONPHARMACOLOGIC THERAPY

- Metatarsal bar or pad proximal to heads to redistribute weight
- Extra-depth shoe for contracture or deformity, if present
- Soft orthotic or well-padded liner to diffuse pressure around metatarsal heads
- Relief pads for plantar keratoses
- Soaks and pumice stone abrasion to decrease callus volume
- Rocker bottom shoe for resistant cases

CHRONIC Rx

- NSAIDs
- Intraarticular injection in selected cases with joint involvement

DISPOSITION

Prognosis is variable, depending on etiology.

REFERRAL

Failure to respond to medical management

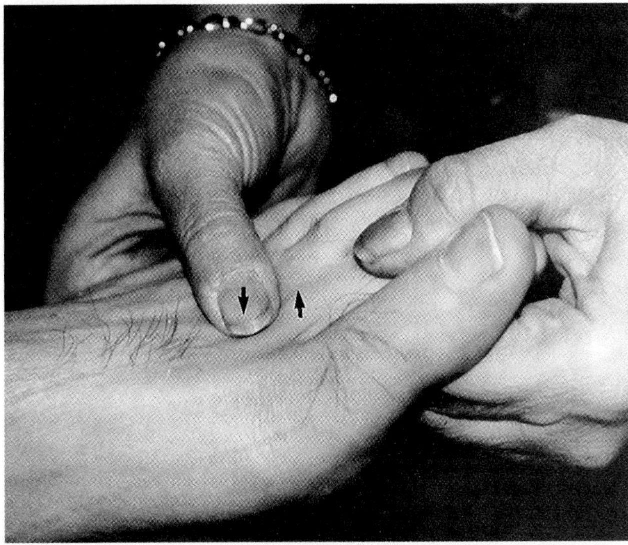

FIGURE 1-149 Vertical stress test for metatarsophalangeal stability. One of the examiner's hands stabilizes the metatarsal head, whereas the other grasps the proximal phalanx. Examiner attempts to displace the proximal phalanx dorsally. A positive test result is the ability to displace dorsally while reproducing symptoms. (From Scuderi G [ed]: *Sports medicine: principles of primary care St Louis,* 1997, Mosby.)

SUGGESTED READINGS

Chalmers AC et al: Metatarsalgia and rheumatoid arthritis—a randomized, single blind, sequential comparing 2 types of foot orthoses and supportive shoes, *J Rheumatol* 27(7):1643, 2000.

Gorter K et al: Variation in diagnosis and management of common foot problems by GPs, *Fam Pract* 18(6):569, 2001.

Jarboe NE, Quesada PM: The effects of cycling shoe stiffness on forefoot pressure, *Foot Ankle Int* 24:784, 2003.

Morscher E, Ulrich J, Dick W: Morton's intermetatarsal neuroma: morphology and histological substrate, *Foot Ankle Int* 21(7):558, 2000.

Sherry DD, Sapp LR: Enthesalgia in childhood, *J Rheumatol* 30:1335, 2003.

Waldecker U: Metatarsalgia in hallux valgus deformity: a pedographic analysis, *J Foot Ankle Surg* 41(5):300, 2002.

Yu JS, Tanner JR: Considerations in metatarsalgia and midfoot pain: an MR imaging perspective, *Semin Musculoskelet Radiol* 6(2):91, 2002.

AUTHOR: **LONNIE R. MERCIER, M.D.**

Milk-Alkali Syndrome

BASIC INFORMATION

DEFINITION

Consumption of large amounts of calcium and alkali resulting in the triad of hypercalcemia, metabolic alkalosis, and renal insufficiency.

ICD-9CM CODES
275.42 Milk-alkali syndrome

EPIDEMIOLOGY & DEMOGRAPHICS

In the early 20th century the milk-alkali syndrome was associated with an antacid regimen created by F.W. Sippy that included large amounts of calcium and bicarbonate. With the development of more effective and less toxic treatments, the syndrome virtually disappeared. Since the 1980s, however, there has been a small resurgence associated with exuberant use of calcium-containing products for the prevention of osteoporosis and the use of calcium bicarbonate rather than aluminum bicarbonate in patients with chronic renal failure.

PHYSICAL FINDINGS & CLINICAL PRESENTATION

Symptoms range from asymptomatic (diagnosis made by the incidental finding hypercalcemia and renal failure) to symptomatic hypercalcemia including nausea, vomiting, anorexia, fatigue, vague abdominal pain, nephrolithiasis and constipation. In more chronic cases, polyuria and polydipsia may be reported.

ETIOLOGY

Overconsumption of supplemental calcium bicarbonate with reported ranges of 2.5 to 20 g/day

DIAGNOSIS

DIFFERENTIAL DIAGNOSIS

Hypercalcemia secondary to hyperparathyroidism or malignancy

LABORATORY TESTS

- Elevated plasma calcium (wide variation reported)
- Renal insufficiency
- Elevated plasma bicarbonate and arterial pH
- PTH, usually suppressed, may be elevated, particularly if checked after treatment has begun
- Phosphate level is variable

TREATMENT

NONPHARMACOLOGIC THERAPY

Hemodialysis has been indicated for some patients with significant renal failure.

ACUTE GENERAL Rx

- Discontinuation of calcium bicarbonate supplements
- Hydration and furosemide if symptomatic hypercalcemia
- Monitor for rebound hypocalcemia as a result of elevation of PTH with treatment
- Patient education regarding appropriate calcium supplementation

PROGNOSIS

Hypercalcemia and symptoms resolve with withdrawal of excess calcium supplementation and treatment of hypercalcemia. Patients initially presenting with renal failure may have residual renal insufficiency.

REFERRAL

Differentiation from hyperparathyroidism can be difficult and may require the assistance of an endocrinologist. Referral to a nutritionist is generally not required as the excess calcium is from nutritional supplements rather than dietary factors.

PEARLS & CONSIDERATIONS

COMMENTS

Detailed history of dietary supplements and OTC medications can provide the most important clues.

SUGGESTED READINGS

Abreo K et al: The milk-alkali syndrome: a reversible form of acute renal failure, *Arch Intern Med* 153:1005, 1993.

Beall DP, Scofield RH: Milk-alkali syndrome associated with calcium carbonate consumption, *Medicine* 74:89, 1995.

Sippy BW: Gastric and duodenal ulcer: medical cure by an efficient removal of gastric juice corrosion, *JAMA* 64:1625, 1915.

AUTHOR: **MICHELLE A. STOZEK, M.D.**

BASIC INFORMATION

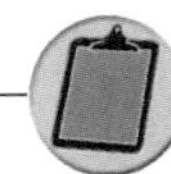

DEFINITION

Mitral regurgitation (MR) is retrograde blood flow through the left atrium secondary to an incompetent mitral valve. Eventually there is an increase in left atrial and pulmonary pressures, which may result in right ventricular failure.

SYNONYMS

Mitral insufficiency
MR

ICD-9CM CODES
424.0 Mitral regurgitation

EPIDEMIOLOGY & DEMOGRAPHICS

The incidence of MR has increased over the past 30 yr; however, this may be because of increasing availability of echocardiography rather than any real increases in this condition.

PHYSICAL FINDINGS & CLINICAL PRESENTATION

- Patients with MR generally present with the following symptoms:
  1. Fatigue, dyspnea, orthopnea, frank CHF
  2. Hemoptysis (caused by pulmonary hypertension)
  3. Possible systemic emboli in patients with left atrial mural thrombi associated with atrial fibrillation
- Hyperdynamic apex, often with palpable left ventricular lift and apical thrill
- Holosystolic murmur at apex with radiation to base or to left axilla; poor correlation between the intensity of the systolic murmur and the degree of regurgitation
- Apical early- to mid-diastolic rumble (rare)

ETIOLOGY

- Papillary muscle dysfunction (as a result of ischemic heart disease)
- Ruptured chordae tendineae
- Infective endocarditis
- Calcified mitral valve annulus
- Left ventricular dilation
- Rheumatic valvulitis
- Primary or secondary mitral valve prolapse
- Hypertrophic cardiomyopathy
- Idiopathic myxomatous degeneration of the mitral valve
- Myxoma
- SLE
- Fenfluramine, dexfenfluramine

DIAGNOSIS

DIFFERENTIAL DIAGNOSIS

- Hypertrophic cardiomyopathy
- Pulmonary regurgitation
- Tricuspid regurgitation
- VSD

WORKUP

Diagnostic workup consists of echocardiography, ECG, and chest x-ray.

IMAGING STUDIES

- Echocardiography: enlarged left atrium, hyperdynamic left ventricle (erratic motion of the leaflet is seen in patients with ruptured chordae tendineae); Doppler electrocardiography will show evidence of MR. The most important aspect of the echocardiographic examination is the quantification of left ventricular systolic performance.
- Chest x-ray study:
  1. Left atrial enlargement (usually more pronounced in mitral stenosis)
  2. Left ventricular enlargement
  3. Possible pulmonary congestion
- ECG:
  1. Left atrial enlargement
  2. Left ventricular hypertrophy
  3. Atrial fibrillation

TREATMENT

NONPHARMACOLOGIC THERAPY

Salt restriction

ACUTE GENERAL Rx

- Medical: Medical therapy is primarily directed toward treatment of complications (e.g., atrial fibrillation) and prevention of bacterial endocarditis.
  1. Consider digitalis for inotropic effect and to control ventricular response if atrial fibrillation with fast ventricular response is present
  2. Afterload reduction (to decrease the regurgitant fraction and to increase cardiac output): may be accomplished with nifedipine, hydralazine plus nitrates or ACE inhibitors
  3. Anticoagulants if atrial fibrillation occurs
  4. Antibiotic prophylaxis before dental and surgical procedures (see Section V)
- Surgery: Surgery is the only definitive treatment for MR. Transesophageal echocardiography allows accurate assessment of the feasibility of valve repair and is indicated before surgical intervention. The timing of surgical repair is controversial; generally surgery should be considered early in symptomatic patients despite optimal medical therapy and in patients with moderate to severe MR and minimal symptoms if there is echocardiographic evidence of rapidly progressive increase in left ventricular end-diastolic and end-systolic dimension (echocardiographic evidence of systolic failure includes end-systolic dimension >55 mm and fractional shortening <31%). Surgery is also indicated in asymptomatic patients with preserved ventricular function if there is a high likelihood of valve repair or if there is evidence of pulmonary hypertension or recent atrial fibrillation.

DISPOSITION

Prognosis is generally good unless there is significant impairment of left ventricle or significantly elevated pulmonary artery pressures. Most patients remain asymptomatic for many years (average interval from diagnosis to onset of symptoms is 16 yr).

REFERRAL

Surgical referral in selected patients (see "Acute General Rx"); emergency surgery may be necessary in patients with MR caused by ruptured chordae tendineae following MI.

PEARLS & CONSIDERATIONS

COMMENTS

Patients should be counseled regarding weight reduction (if obese), avoidance of tobacco, and maintenance of normal (nonstrenuous) activities.

SUGGESTED READING

Otto CM: Evaluation and management of chronic mitral regurgitation, *N Engl J Med* 345:740, 2001.

AUTHOR: **FRED F. FERRI, M.D.**

Mitral Stenosis (PTG)

BASIC INFORMATION

DEFINITION

Mitral stenosis is a narrowing of the mitral valve orifice. The cross section of a normal orifice measures 4 to 6 cm^2. A murmur becomes audible when the valve orifice becomes smaller than 2 cm^2. When the orifice approaches 1 cm^2, the condition becomes critical, and symptoms become more evident.

SYNONYMS

MS

ICD-9CM CODES
394.0 Mitral stenosis

EPIDEMIOLOGY & DEMOGRAPHICS

- The occurrence of mitral valve stenosis has decreased worldwide over the past 30 yr (particularly in developed countries) as a result of declining incidence of rheumatic fever.
- The incidence of mitral stenosis is higher in women.

PHYSICAL FINDINGS & CLINICAL PRESENTATION

- Exertional dyspnea initially, followed by orthopnea and PND
- Acute pulmonary edema (may develop after exertion)
- Systemic emboli (caused by stagnation of blood in the left atrium; may occur in patients with associated atrial fibrillation)
- Hemoptysis (may be present as a result of persistent pulmonary hypertension)
- Prominent jugular A waves are present in patients with normal sinus rhythm.
- Opening snap occurs in early diastole; a short (<0.07-second) A_2 to opening snap interval indicates severe mitral stenosis.
- Apical middiastolic or presystolic rumble that does not radiate is present.
- Accentuated S_1 (because of delayed and forceful closure of the valve) is present.
- If pulmonary hypertension is present, there may be an accentuated P_2 and/or a soft, early diastolic decrescendo murmur (Graham Steell murmur) caused by pulmonary regurgitation (it is best heard along the left sternal border and may be confused with aortic regurgitation).
- A palpable right ventricular heave may be present at the left sternal border.
- Patients with mitral stenosis usually have symptoms of left-sided heart failure: dyspnea on exertion, PND, orthopnea.
- Right ventricular dysfunction (in late stages) may be manifested by peripheral edema, enlarged and pulsatile liver, and ascites.

ETIOLOGY

- Progressive fibrosis, scarring, and calcification of the valve
- Rheumatic fever (still a common cause in underdeveloped countries); heart valves most frequently affected in rheumatic heart disease (in descending order of occurrence): mitral, aortic, tricuspid, and pulmonary
- Congenital defect (parachute valve)
- Rare causes: endomyocardial fibroelastosis, malignant carcinoid syndrome, SLE

DIAGNOSIS

DIFFERENTIAL DIAGNOSIS

- Left atrial myxoma
- Other valvular abnormalities (e.g., tricuspid stenosis, mitral regurgitation)
- Atrial septal defect

WORKUP

Physical examination and echocardiography

IMAGING STUDIES

- Echocardiography:
  1. The characteristic finding on echocardiogram is a markedly diminished E to F slope of the anterior mitral valve leaflet during diastole; there is also fusion of the commissures, resulting in anterior movement of the posterior mitral valve leaflet during diastole (calcification in the valve may also be noted).

  Two-dimensional echocardiogram can accurately establish valve area.
- Chest x-ray:
  1. Straightening of the left cardiac border caused by dilated left atrial appendage
  2. Left atrial enlargement on lateral chest x-ray (appearing as double density of PA chest x-ray)
  3. Prominence of pulmonary arteries
  4. Possible pulmonary congestion and edema (Kerley B lines)
- ECG:
  1. Right ventricular hypertrophy; right axis deviation caused by pulmonary hypertension
  2. Left atrial enlargement (broad notched P waves)
  3. Atrial fibrillation
- Cardiac catheterization to help establish the severity of mitral stenosis and diagnose associated valvular and coronary lesions. Findings on cardiac catheterization include:
  1. Normal left ventricular function
  2. Elevated left atrial and pulmonary pressures

TREATMENT

NONPHARMACOLOGIC THERAPY

Decrease level of activity in symptomatic patients.

ACUTE GENERAL Rx

- Medical:
  1. If the patient is in atrial fibrillation, control the rate response with diltiazem, digitalis, or esmolol. Although digitalis is the drug of choice for chronic heart rate control, IV diltiazem or esmolol may be acutely preferable when a rapid decrease in heart rate is required.
  2. If the patient has persistent atrial fibrillation (because of large left atrium), permanent anticoagulation is indicated to decrease the risk of serious thromboembolism.
  3. Treat CHF with diuretics and sodium restriction.
  4. Give antibiotic prophylaxis with dental and surgical procedures (see Section V).
- Surgical: valve replacement is indicated when the valve orifice is <0.7 to 0.8 cm^2 or if symptoms persist despite optimal medical therapy; commissurotomy may be possible if the mitral valve is noncalcified and if there is pure mitral stenosis without significant subvalvular disease.
- Percutaneous transvenous mitral valvotomy (PTMV) is becoming the therapy of choice for many patients with mitral stenosis responding poorly to medical therapy, particularly those who are poor surgical candidates and whose valve is not heavily calcified; balloon valvotomy gives excellent mechanical relief, usually resulting in prolonged benefit.

DISPOSITION

- Prognosis is generally good except in patients with chronic pulmonary hypertension.
- Operative mortality rates for mitral valve replacement are 1% to 5% in most institutions.

AUTHOR: **FRED F. FERRI, M.D.**

BASIC INFORMATION

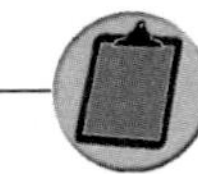

DEFINITION

Mitral valve prolapse (MVP) is the posterior bulging of interior and posterior leaflets in systole. Mitral valve prolapse syndrome refers to a constellation of MVP and associated symptoms (e.g., autonomic dysfunction, palpitations) or other physical abnormalities (e.g., pectus excavatum).

SYNONYMS

MVP
Mitral click murmur syndrome

ICD-9CM CODES
424.0 Mitral valve disorders
394.9 Other and unspecified mitral valve diseases

EPIDEMIOLOGY & DEMOGRAPHICS

- MVP can be found by 2-D echocardiogram in 4% of the general population (females > males).
- Increased incidence is seen with autoimmune thyroid disorders, Ehlers-Danlos syndrome, Marfan's syndrome, pseudoxanthoma elasticum, pectus excavatum, anorexia nervosa, and bulimia.

PHYSICAL FINDINGS & CLINICAL PRESENTATION

- Usually, young female patient with narrow AP chest diameter, low body weight, low blood pressure
- Mid to late click, heard best at the apex
- Crescendo mid to late diastolic murmur
- Findings accentuated in the standing position
- Most patients with MVP are asymptomatic; symptoms (if present) consist primarily of chest pain and palpitations
- Neurologic abnormalities (e.g., TIA or stroke) are rare
- Patients may also complain of anxiety, fatigue, and dyspnea

ETIOLOGY

- Myxomatous degeneration of connective tissue of mitral valve
- Congenital deformity of mitral valve and supportive structures
- Secondary to other disorders (e.g., Ehlers-Danlos, pseudoxanthoma elasticum)

DIAGNOSIS

DIFFERENTIAL DIAGNOSIS

- Other valvular abnormalities
- Constrictive pericarditis
- Ventricular aneurysm

WORKUP

- Medical history and physical examination
- Workup consists primarily of echocardiography in patients with a systolic click or murmur on careful auscultation

IMAGING STUDIES

Echocardiography shows the anterior and posterior leaflets bulging posteriorly in systole.

TREATMENT

NONPHARMACOLOGIC THERAPY

Avoidance of stimulants (e.g., caffeine, nicotine) in patients with palpitations

ACUTE GENERAL Rx

- The empiric use of antiarrhythmic drugs to prevent sudden death in patients with uncomplicated MVP is not advisable; β-blockers may be tried in symptomatic patients (e.g., palpitations, chest pain); they decrease the heart rate, thus decreasing the stretch on the prolapsing valve leaflets.
- Antibiotic prophylaxis for infective endocarditis when undergoing dental, GI, or GU procedures is indicated only in patients with MVP who have a systolic murmur and echocardiographic evidence of mitral regurgitation (see Section V).

CHRONIC Rx

Monitoring for complications:

- Bacterial endocarditis (risk is three to eight times that of the general population)
- TIA or stroke secondary to embolic phenomena (from fibrin and platelet thrombi); risk in young patients: <0.05%/yr
- Cardiac arrhythmias (usually supraventricular)
- Sudden death (rare occurrence, most often caused by ventricular arrhythmias)
- Mitral regurgitation (most common complication of MVP)

DISPOSITION

The incidence of complications of MVP is very low (<1%/yr) and generally associated with an increase in mitral leaflet thickness to ≥5 mm; young patients (age <45) with absence of mitral systolic murmur or mitral regurgitation on Doppler echocardiography are at low risk for any complications.

REFERRAL

Surgical referral may be necessary in patients who develop symptomatic progressive mitral regurgitation.

PEARLS & CONSIDERATIONS

COMMENTS

- Recent studies suggest that the prevalence of MVP and its propensity to cause symptoms and serious complications have been overestimated in the past.
- Asymptomatic patients with MVP and mild or no mitral regurgitation can be evaluated clinically every 3 to 5 yr. High-risk patients should undergo a follow-up examination once a year.

SUGGESTED READINGS

Bouknight DP, O'Rourke RA: Current management of mitral valve prolapse, *Am Fam Physician* 61:3343, 2000.
Freed LA: Prevalence and clinical outcome of mitral valve prolapse, *N Engl J Med* 341:1, 1999.
Gilon D et al: Lack of evidence of an association between MVP and stroke in young patients, *N Engl J Med* 341:8, 1999.

AUTHOR: **FRED F. FERRI, M.D.**

Mixed Connective Tissue Disease

BASIC INFORMATION

DEFINITION

The term *mixed connective tissue disease* describes a set of connective tissue symptoms that sometimes overlap with other known connective tissue diseases (SLE, progressive systemic sclerosis, polymyositis) but whose exact significance remains under debate. The disorder is sometimes referred to as an "overlap syndrome," but many prefer the term *undifferentiated connective tissue disease.*

ICD-9CM CODES
710.9 Diffuse connective tissue disease

EPIDEMIOLOGY & DEMOGRAPHICS

PREVALENCE: Approximately 10 to 15 cases/100,000 persons
PREDOMINANT SEX: Female:male ratio of 8:1
PREDOMINANT AGE: 4 to 80 yr

PHYSICAL FINDINGS & CLINICAL PRESENTATION

- Polyarthritis, polyarthralgia
- Raynaud's phenomenon, hand swelling, or sclerodactyly
- Esophageal hypomotility, myalgia, and muscle weakness
- Other: pericarditis, facial erythema, psychosis

ETIOLOGY

Autoimmune disorder

DIAGNOSIS

DIFFERENTIAL DIAGNOSIS

Other connective tissue disorders (SLE, progressive systemic sclerosis, polymyositis)

WORKUP

- Diagnosis is not well defined.
- Commonly used diagnostic tests are described in Laboratory Tests.

LABORATORY TESTS (BOX 1-10)

- Rheumatoid factor is often present in low titers.
- If myositis is present, muscle enzyme (CPK) levels increase.
- Positive ANA is often present with a speckled pattern.
- ESR is elevated.
- Anti-RNP antibodies may be present.

TREATMENT

- Except for pulmonary and scleroderma-like symptoms, response to corticosteroids is excellent in most cases.
- Rheumatoid symptoms may respond to NSAIDs, but other cases may not even respond to gold or penicillamine.
- Immunosuppressive agents are used on occasion, but the best therapeutic options remain uncertain.

DISPOSITION

- Initially, this disorder was thought to be a mild variant of SLE, sometimes called "benign lupus," with excellent prognosis.
- Further studies suggested, however, that this was not always the case and serious renal, vascular, and neurologic complications were noted.
- Pulmonary involvement is a common clinical manifestation that may even lead to pulmonary hypertension and sometimes death.
- Whether MCTD is a separate entity continues under debate as concepts about the disorder evolve.
- Long-term outcomes remain uncertain.

PEARLS & CONSIDERATIONS

COMMENTS

A clinical algorithm for evaluation of a positive ANA titer is described in Section III, Antinuclear Antibody Testing.

SUGGESTED READINGS

Bodolay E et al: Osteoporosis in mixed connective disease, *Clin Rheumatol* 22:213, 2003.

Chan AT, Wordsworth BP, McNally J: Overlap connective tissue disease, pulmonary fibrosis, and extensive soft tissue calcification, *Ann Rheum Dis* 62:690, 2003.

Kozaka T et al: Pulmonary involvement in mixed connective tissue disease: high-resolution CT findings in 41 patients, *J Thorac Imaging* 16:94, 2001.

Ling TC, Johnson BT: Esophageal investigations in connective tissue disease: which tests are most appropriate? *J Clin Gastroenterol* 32:33, 2001.

Lopez-Longo FJ et al: Does mixed connective tissue disease have a less favorable prognosis than systemic lupus erythematosis? *Arthritis Rheum* 44(suppl):119, 2001.

Lowe D, Kredich DW, Schanberg Durham LE: Thalidomide: an effective and safe agent for the treatment of pediatric mixed connective tissue disease, *Arthritis Rheum* 43(suppl): 117, 2000.

AUTHOR: **LONNIE R. MERCIER, M.D.**

BOX 1-10 Guidelines for Diagnosing Mixed Connective Tissue Disease

General

Clinical features of a diffuse connective tissue disorder

Serologic

1. Positive ANA, speckled pattern, titer >1:1000
2. Antibodies to U1 RNP
3. Absence of antibodies to dsDNA, histones, Sm, Scl-70, and other specificities
4. Commonly: Hypergammaglobulinemia and positive rheumatoid factor

Clinical

1. Sequential evolution of overlap features over course of several years, including Raynaud's phenomenon, serositis, gastrointestinal dysmotility, myositis, arthritis, sclerodactyly, skin rashes, and an abnormal DLco on pulmonary function tests
2. Absence of truncal scleroderma, severe renal disease, and severe central nervous system involvement
3. A nail fold capillary pattern identical to that seen in systemic sclerosis (dropout and dilated vessels)

From Bennett RM: Mixed connective tissue disease and other overlap syndromes. In Kelley WN et al (eds): *Textbook of rheumatology*, ed 3, Philadelphia, 1989, WB Saunders.
ANA, Antinuclear antibodies; *dsDNA*, double-stranded DNA; *MCTD*, mixed connective tissue disease; *RNP*, ribonucleoprotein.

BASIC INFORMATION

DEFINITION

Viral infection characterized by discrete skin lesions with central umbilication (Fig. 1-150).

ICD-9CM CODES
078.0 Molluscum contagiosum

EPIDEMIOLOGY & DEMOGRAPHICS

- Molluscum contagiosum spreads by autoinoculation, scratching or touching a lesion.
- It usually occurs in young children. It is also common in sexually active adults and patients with HIV infection.
- Incubation period varies between 4 and 8 wk.
- Spontaneous resolution in immunocompetent patients can occur after several months.

PHYSICAL FINDINGS & CLINICAL PRESENTATION

- The individual lesion appears initially as a flesh-colored, firm, smooth-surfaced papule with subsequent central umbilication. Lesions are frequently grouped. The size of each lesion generally varies from 2 to 6 mm in diameter.
- Typical distribution in children involves the face, extremities, and trunk. Mucous membranes are spared.
- Distribution in adults generally involves pubic and genital areas.
- Erythema and scaling at the periphery of the lesions may be present as a result of scratching or hypersensitivity reaction.
- Lesions are not present on the palms and soles.

ETIOLOGY

Viral infection of epithelial cells caused by a pox virus

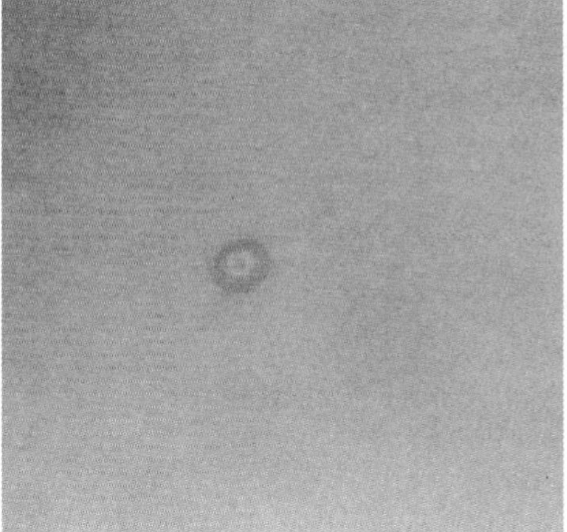

FIGURE 1-150 Molluscum contagiosum. (From Rakel RE: *Textbook of family practice, ed* 6, Philadelphia, 2002, WB Saunders.)

DIAGNOSIS

Diagnosis is usually established by the clinical appearance of the lesions (distribution and central umbilication). A magnifying lens can be used to observe the central umbilication. If necessary, the diagnosis can be confirmed by removing a typical lesion with a curette and examining the content on a slide after adding potassium hydroxide and gentle heating. Staining with toluidine blue will identify viral inclusions.

DIFFERENTIAL DIAGNOSIS

- Verruca plana (flat warts): no central umbilication, not dome shaped, irregular surface, can involve palms and soles
- Herpes simplex: lesions become rapidly umbilicated
- Varicella: blisters and vesicles are present
- Folliculitis: no central umbilication, presence of hair piercing the pustule or papule
- Cutaneous cryptococcosis in AIDS patients: budding yeasts will be present on cytologic examination of the lesions
- Basal cell carcinoma: multiple lesions are absent

WORKUP

Careful examination of the papules

LABORATORY TESTS

Generally not indicated in children. STD screening for other sexually transmitted diseases is recommended in all cases of genital molluscum contagiosum.

IMAGING STUDIES

Not indicated

TREATMENT

NONPHARMACOLOGIC THERAPY

Prevention of autoinoculation by scratching or touching lesions

GENERAL THERAPY

- Therapy is individualized depending on number of lesions, immune status, and patient's age and preference.
- Observation for spontaneous resolution is reasonable in patients with few, small, not irritated, and not-spreading lesions. Genital lesions should be treated in all sexually active patients.
- Curettage following pretreatment of the area with combination prilocaine 2.5% with lidocaine 2.5% cream (EMLA) for anesthesia is useful for treatment of few lesions. Curettage should be avoided in cosmetically sensitive areas because scarring may develop.
- Treatments with liquid nitrogen therapy in combination with curettage are effective in older patients who do not object to some discomfort.
- Application of cantharidin 0.7% to individual lesions covered with clear tape will result in blistering over 24 hr and possible clearing without scarring. This medication should be avoided on facial lesions.
- Other treatment measures include use of tretinoin 0.025% gel or 0.1% cream at hs, daily use of salicylic acid (Occlusal) at hs, and use of laser therapy.
- Trichloroacetic acid peel generally repeated every 2 wk for several weeks is useful in immunocompromised patients with extensive lesions.

DISPOSITION

Most patients respond well to the therapeutic modalities listed previously. Spontaneous resolution can occur after 6 to 9 mo in some immunocompetent patients.

REFERRAL

To dermatology when diagnosis is in doubt or in patients with extensive lesions

PEARLS & CONSIDERATIONS

COMMENTS

Genital molluscum contagiosum in children may be indicative of sexual abuse.

AUTHOR: **FRED F. FERRI, M.D.**

Mononucleosis

BASIC INFORMATION

DEFINITION

Mononucleosis is a symptomatic infection caused by Epstein-Barr virus.

SYNONYMS

Infectious mononucleosis (IM)

ICD-9CM CODES
075 Infectious mononucleosis

EPIDEMIOLOGY & DEMOGRAPHICS

INCIDENCE IN U.S.: 45 cases/100,000 persons/yr

PREDOMINANT SEX: Incidence is the same, but occurs earlier in females.

PREDOMINANT AGE: Most common between the ages of 15 and 24 yr.

PHYSICAL FINDINGS & CLINICAL PRESENTATION

- Following an incubation period of 1 to 2 mo, a prodrome may occur, with fever, chills, malaise, and anorexia for several days. This is followed by the classic triad, which includes pharyngitis, fever, and adenopathy. Although fatigue and malaise may be prominent, pharyngitis is usually the most severe symptom. Exudates are common.
- Lymphadenopathy is most prominent in the cervical region but may be diffuse.
- Splenomegaly may occur, most commonly during the second week of illness.
- Rash is uncommon, but will occur in nearly all patients who receive ampicillin.
- At times, IM can present as fever and adenopathy without pharyngitis. Although complications may be severe, they are uncommon, and tend to resolve completely. Involvement of the hematologic, pulmonary, cardiac, or nervous system may occur; splenic rupture is rare. IM is usually a self-limited illness, but symptoms of malaise and fatigue may last months before resolving.

ETIOLOGY

The cause of IM is primary infection with Epstein-Barr virus (EBV). Primary infection during childhood causes little or no symptoms. Infection during childhood is more common in lower socioeconomic groups. The frequency of IM in late adolescence is attributed to the onset of social contact between the sexes. Close personal contact is usually necessary for transmission, although EBV has occasionally been transmitted by blood transfusion. Transfer via saliva while kissing may be responsible for many cases.

DIAGNOSIS

DIFFERENTIAL DIAGNOSIS

- Heterophile-negative infectious mononucleosis caused by cytomegalovirus (CMV); although clinical presentation may be similar, CMV more frequently follows transfusion
- Bacterial and viral causes of pharyngitis
- Toxoplasmosis
- Acute retroviral syndrome of HIV, lymphoma

WORKUP

Heterophile antibody (monospot) and complete blood counts should be sent.

LABORATORY TESTS

- Increased WBC is common, with a relative lymphocytosis and neutropenia. Atypical lymphocytes are the hallmark of IM, but are not pathognomonic. Mild thrombocytopenia is common. A falling hematocrit may signal splenic rupture. Elevated hepatocellular enzymes and cryoglobulins occur in most cases. Heterophile antibody, as measured by the Monospot test, may be positive at presentation, or may appear later in the course of illness. A negative test should be repeated if clinical suspicion is high. If this test remains negative for 8 wk, other causes of IM are likely. The monospot usually remains positive for 3 to 6 mo, but can last for 1 yr.
- A positive test has been reported with primary HIV infection.
- In addition to the heterophile antibody, virus-specific antibodies may result in response to IM. Determination of these EBV-specific antibodies is rarely necessary to diagnose IM, although early diagnosis in monospot negative cases may be made by isolating IgM to the viral capsid antigen (VCA), which is usually positive during the acute illness.

IMAGING STUDIES

Chest radiograph may rarely show infiltrates. An elevated left hemidiaphragm may occur in cases of splenic rupture.

TREATMENT

NONPHARMACOLOGIC THERAPY

- Supportive rest is advocated by some, but impact on outcome is not clear
- Splenectomy if rupture occurs. Transfusions for severe anemia or thrombocytopenia

ACUTE GENERAL Rx

- Pharmacologic therapy is not indicated in uncomplicated illness.
- The use of steroids is suggested in patients who have severe thrombocytopenia or hemolytic anemia, or impending airway obstruction as a result of enlarged tonsils. Prednisone, 60-80 mg PO qd for 3 days, then tapered over 1 to 2 wk. There is no role for antiviral agents such as acyclovir in the management of IM.

CHRONIC Rx

An extremely rare, chronic form of IM with persistent fevers and other objective findings has been described. This should be differentiated from chronic fatigue syndrome, which is not related to EBV.

DISPOSITION

Eventual resolution of all symptoms is the rule.

REFERRAL

More than mild illness

PEARLS & CONSIDERATIONS

COMMENTS

Contact sports should be avoided during the first month of illness, because splenic rupture can occur, even in the absence of clinically detectable splenomegaly.

SUGGESTED READINGS

Auwaerter PG: Infectious mononucleosis: return to play, *Clin Sports Med* 23:485, 2004.

Crawford DH et al: Sexual history and Epstein-Barr virus infection, *J Infect Dis* 186:731, 2002.

Godshall SE, Kirchner JT: Infectious mononucleosis: complexities of a common syndrome, *Postgrad Med* 107:175, 2000.

Vidrih JA et al: Positive Epstein-Barr virus heterophile antibody tests in patients with primary immunodeficiency virus infection, *Am J Med* 111:192, 2001.

AUTHOR: **MAURICE POLICAR, M.D.**

BASIC INFORMATION

DEFINITION

Morton's neuroma refers to an inflammatory fibrosing process of the plantar digital nerve characterized by pain in the sole of the foot. Morton's neuroma is also described as an interdigital plantar neuropathy with or without plantar neuroma.

SYNONYMS

Morton's metatarsalgia
Morton's toe
Interdigital neuroma

ICD-9CM CODES
355.6 Morton's neuroma

EPIDEMIOLOGY & DEMOGRAPHICS

- Morton's neuroma most commonly involves the plantar digital nerve between the heads of the third and fourth metatarsals
- May also involve the second and third metatarsal and can involve both simultaneously
- Commonly occurs in people wearing tight-fitting shoes in toe region and high heels
- Morton's neuroma is usually unilateral
- Morton's neuroma is found more often in women than in men
- Can occur in both young and old

PHYSICAL FINDINGS & CLINICAL PRESENTATION

- Pain is usually located in a specific region, usually in the sole of the foot between the third and fourth metatarsal area and is unilateral in the majority of cases.
- Numbness may occur.
- Pain is exacerbated with exercise and relieved with rest and may radiate to the toes and to the ankle.
- Point tenderness is noted on examination, and palpation reveals fullness at the site of discomfort.
- An audible, painful click called "Murder's click" is noted in patients with Morton's neuroma after compressing and releasing the forefoot.
- Patients may have neuroma but silent lesions without symptoms.

ETIOLOGY

- Morton's neuroma is thought to be caused by nerve thickening from repeated injury.
- The typical finding is swelling of the plantar digital nerve that pathologically resembles other nerve entrapment syndromes (e.g., median nerve compression in carpal tunnel syndrome).

DIAGNOSIS

The diagnosis of Morton's neuroma is strictly made on clinical grounds alone as there are no laboratory tests or x-ray imaging studies that are specific for this disorder.

DIFFERENTIAL DIAGNOSIS

- Diabetic neuropathy
- Alcoholic neuropathy
- Nutritional neuropathy
- Toxic neuropathy
- Osteoarthritis
- Trauma (e.g., fracture)
- Gouty arthritis
- Rheumatoid arthritis

WORKUP

Exclude other causes as mentioned in the Differential Diagnosis.

LABORATORY TESTS

- Laboratory studies are not specific for the diagnosis of Morton's neuroma
- CBC and ESR are usually normal
- Blood glucose
- B_{12} and folic acid level

IMAGING STUDIES

- X-ray imaging is primarily done to exclude other causes of foot pain (e.g., fractures, ostearthritis, gouty arthritis).
- MRI can detect and localize a neuroma but is rarely needed to make the diagnosis. An MRI can also be performed in patients with recurrent pain after surgical excision of a Morton's neuroma.
- Ultrasound imaging is also being used to locate Morton's neuromas but is rarely needed to make the diagnosis.

TREATMENT

NONPHARMACOLOGIC THERAPY

- Changing the type of footwear is the first line of treatment.
- Use open footwear and custom shoe inserts and avoid weight-bearing activities.
- Metatarsal pad with arch support is helpful.
- Participate in ultrasound therapy.

ACUTE GENERAL Rx

- If conservative measures are unsuccessful, injection of the intermetatarsal bursa with hydrocortisone may help
- Nonsteroidal antiinflammatory agents (e.g., ibuprofen 400 to 800 mg PO tid or naproxen 250 to 500 mg bid)

CHRONIC Rx

- If nonpharmacologic and acute treatments do not give sufficient relief, surgical excision of the nerve has been successful in 95% of the cases.
- Surgery can be performed in the physician's office using local anesthesia.
- Numbness in the area where the nerve was excised is a common postoperative finding.

DISPOSITION

- Postoperative patients return to their normal activities by 3 to 6 wk.
- In cases where pain persists after surgery a "stump neuroma" may be present.
- Approximately 80% of patients who failed to have relief with the initial surgery did find relief with a second procedure.

REFERRAL

If surgery is being considered, a consultation with either a podiatrist or an orthopedic surgeon is indicated.

PEARLS & CONSIDERATIONS

COMMENTS

- Dr. Thomas G. Morton is given credit for describing this disorder in 1876.
- Morton's neuroma occurs just before the nerve bifurcates at the metatarsal area to innervate sides of two adjacent toes.

SUGGESTED READINGS

Bencardino J et al: Morton's neuroma: is it always symptomatic? *AJR Am J Roentgenol* 175(3):649, 2000.
Morscher E, Ulrich J, Dick W: Morton's intermetatarsal neuroma: morphology and histological substrate, *Foot Ankle Int* 21:558, 2000.
Wu J, Chin DT: Painful neuromas: a review of treatment modalities, *Ann Plast Surg* 43(6):661, 1999.
Wu KK: Morton's interdigital neuroma: a clinical review of its etiology, treatment and results, *J Foot Ankle Surg* 35(2):112, 1996.
Zanetti M et al: Morton neuroma: effect on MR imaging findings on diagnostic thinking and therapeutic decisions, *Radiology* 326:188, 1999.

AUTHOR: **DENNIS J. MIKOLICH, M.D.**

BASIC INFORMATION

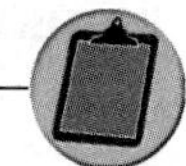

DEFINITION

Patients with motion sickness suffer perspiration, nausea, vomiting, increased salivation, and generalized malaise in response to movement.

SYNONYMS

Physiologic vertigo

ICD-9CM CODES
994.6 Motion sickness

EPIDEMIOLOGY & DEMOGRAPHICS

INCIDENCE (IN U.S.): Common
PREVALENCE (IN U.S.): Common
PREDOMINANT SEX: Male = female
PREDOMINANT AGE: Any age
PEAK INCIDENCE: Any age
GENETICS: Not known to be genetic

PHYSICAL FINDINGS & CLINICAL PRESENTATION

- Vomiting
- Sweating
- Pallor

ETIOLOGY

- Motion (e.g., amusement rides, rides in automobiles or planes)
- Exacerbated by anxiety, fumes (e.g., industrial pollutants), visual stimuli

DIAGNOSIS

DIFFERENTIAL DIAGNOSIS

- Acute labyrinthitis
- Gastroenteritis
- Metabolic disorders
- Viral syndrome

WORKUP

None necessary in routine case

LABORATORY TESTS

None necessary

IMAGING STUDIES

None necessary

TREATMENT

NONPHARMACOLOGIC THERAPY

- Fixate on far object.
- Cease motion.
- Avoid reading.
- Avoid alcohol.

ACUTE GENERAL Rx

- Scopolamine patch (Transderm Scop) is most effective. It should be applied to hairless area behind ear every 3 days prn. It should be applied >4 hr before antiemetic effect is required.
- Over-the-counter oral preparations (e.g., Dramamine) are less effective.
- Meclizine (Antivert) 12.5 to 25 mg q6h may be effective.

CHRONIC Rx

- Rarely chronic
- Symptoms generally resolve completely with cessation of motion exposure

DISPOSITION

Follow-up is not needed.

REFERRAL

If another diagnosis is suspected (e.g., purulent ear, fever, cranial nerve abnormalities)

PEARLS & CONSIDERATIONS

COMMENTS

- Many patients with migraine report having severe motion sickness as a child.
- Improved ventilation, avoidance of large meals before travel, semirecumbent sitting, and avoidance of reading while in motion will minimize the risk of motion sickness.

SUGGESTED READINGS

Koch KL: Illusory self-motion and motion sickness: a model for brain-gut interacting and nausea, *Dig Dis Sc:* 48(8 Suppl):53S, 1999.

Yates BJ, Miller AD, Lacot JB: Physiological basis and pharmacology of motion sickness: an update, *Brain Res Bull* 45(5):395, 1998.

AUTHOR: **FRED F. FERRI, M.D.**

BASIC INFORMATION

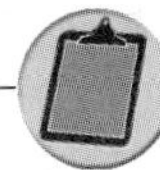

DEFINITION

Mucormycosis is a fungal infection by *Zygomycetes* fungi, which include *Mucorales* spp. *(Mucor, Rhizopus, Absidia, Cunninghamella, Mortierella, Saksenaea, Syncephalastrum, Apophysomyces,* and *Thamnidium)* and *Entomophthorales* spp. (*Conidiobolus* and *Basidiobolus).*

ICD-9CM CODES
117.7 Mucormycosis

EPIDEMIOLOGY & DEMOGRAPHICS

Infection by these ubiquitous organisms occurs in association with underlying conditions including diabetes mellitus, lymphoma, severe burns or trauma, prolonged postoperative course, multiple myeloma, hepatitis, cirrhosis, renal failure, steroid treatment, immunodeficiency states (e.g., AIDS), and use of contaminated Elastoplast bandages. Immunocompetent hosts may become infected in tropical climates.

PHYSICAL FINDINGS & CLINICAL PRESENTATION

- Rhinocerebral-rhinoorbital-paranasal syndrome may present with fever, facial and orbital pain, headache, diplopia, loss of vision, facial or orbital cellulitis, facial anesthesia, cranial nerve dysfunction, black nasal discharge, epistaxis, and seizure. Physical findings in this situation include proptosis, chemosis, nasal, palatal or pharyngeal necrotic ulcerations, and retinal infarction. Thrombosis of the cavernous sinus or internal carotid artery may occur.
- Pulmonary mucormycosis can present with pneumonia, lung abscess, pulmonary infarction, pleurisy, pleural effusion, hemoptysis, chills, and fever.
- Gastrointestinal zygomycosis presents with abdominal pain, diarrhea, GI hemorrhage, ulcers, peritonitis, and bowel infarction.
- Cutaneous zygomycosis presents as nodular lesions (hematogenous seeding) or a wound infection.
- Cardiac mucormycosis is a form of endocarditis.
- Septic arthritis and osteomyelitis.
- Brain abscess.
- Disseminated zygomycosis (rare but uniformly fatal).
- Physical findings depend on the location of the infection.

ETIOLOGY & PATHOGENESIS

The cause of mucormycosis is infection by a fungus of the *Zygomycetes* class (see Definition). Normal host defenses include leukocytes and pulmonary macrophages. Quantitative (e.g., neutropenia) or qualitative (e.g., diabetes mellitus or steroid treatment) disruption in the host defenses predisposes the patient to infection.

DIAGNOSIS

DIFFERENTIAL DIAGNOSIS

- Infection of the sites described previously by other organisms (bacterial [including TB and leprosy], viral, fungal, or protozoan)
- Noninfectious tissue necrosis (e.g., neoplasia, vasculitis, degenerative) of the sites described previously

WORKUP

- Biopsy of infected tissue with direct light microscopy examination establishes the diagnosis within minutes of the biopsy in the case of nasopharyngeal infection
- Bronchoalveolar lavage or bronchoscopy with biopsy for smear, culture, and histologic examination
- X-rays and other imaging studies of symptomatic sites may be required before infection is suspected and tissue specimens are obtained

TREATMENT

Amphotericin B given IV at a daily dose of 0.5 to 1.5 mg/kg infused over 2 to 4 hr for a total of 1 to 4 g. Adverse reactions may be managed as follows:

- Fever, chills, headache, myalgias, nausea, and vomiting: premedicate with aspirin (650 mg PO), acetaminophen (650 mg PO), diphenhydramine (25 to 50 mg IV), hydrocortisone (25 to 100 mg IV), or meperidine (25 to 50 mg IV).
- Hypokalemia and hypomagnesemia are treated with potassium and magnesium replacement.
- Nephrotoxicity and renal tubular acidosis can be mitigated to some extent with 500 ml of normal saline infusion 30 min before and after each dose of amphotericin. Amphotericin dose reduction may also be necessary.
- Renal function and electrolytes should be monitored twice a week during the entire course of amphotericin.
- Lipid preparations of amphotericin B may be less toxic (i.e., amphotericin B lipid complex, amphotericin B colloidal dispersion, and liposomal amphotericin B).
- The role of flucytosine, rifampin, and tetracycline is controversial.
- Surgical debridement or radical resection.

PROGNOSIS

- Sinus infection with no underlying disease: 75% survival.
- Sinus infection with diabetes: 60% survival.
- Sinus infection with renal disease: 25% survival.
- Surgery may increase survival by 5% to 20%.
- Early diagnosis improves survival as well as control of the underlying condition.

SUGGESTED READING

Meyers BR, Gurtman AC: Phycomycetes. In Gorbach SL, Bartlett JG, Blacklow NR (eds): *Infectious diseases,* ed 2, Philadelphia, 1998, WB Saunders.

AUTHOR: **TOM J. WACHTEL, M.D.**

BASIC INFORMATION

DEFINITION

Multifocal atrial tachycardia is a supraventricular, moderately rapid arrhythmia (rate 100 to 140 bpm) with P waves having at least three or more different morphologies.

SYNONYMS

Chaotic atrial rhythm; the term "wandering pacemaker" is used for a similar arrhythmia associated with a normal or slow heart rate.

ICD-9CM CODES
427.89 Multifocal atrial tachycardia

EPIDEMIOLOGY & DEMOGRAPHICS

Same as chronic lung disease (obstructive or restrictive), which the arrhythmia may complicate

PHYSICAL FINDINGS & CLINICAL PRESENTATION

Symptoms:
- Palpitation
- Lightheadedness
- Syncope
- Symptoms of the underlying pulmonary disease
- Physical findings associated with the underlying pulmonary disease

ETIOLOGY

- Exact mechanism unknown
- Associated abnormalities include hypoxia, hypercarbia, acidosis, electrolyte disturbances, digitalis toxicity

DIAGNOSIS

DIFFERENTIAL DIAGNOSIS

- Atrial fibrillation
- Atrial flutter
- Sinus tachycardia
- Paroxysmal atrial tachycardia
- Extrasystoles

WORKUP

- ECG (Fig. 1-151)
- Pulmonary function tests
- Electrolytes
- Arterial blood gases
- Digoxin level (if patient on digoxin)

TREATMENT

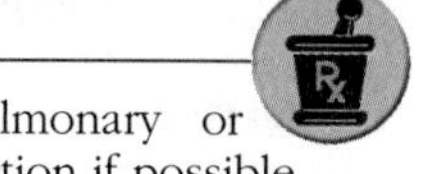

- Improve the pulmonary or metabolic dysfunction if possible
- Calcium blockers
- β-Blockers if not contraindicated by obstructive lung disease
- If the arrhythmia is asymptomatic, it can be left untreated

SUGGESTED READING

Myerburg RJ, Kloosterman EM, Castellanos A: Recognition, clinical assessment, and management of arrhythmias and conduction disturbances. In Fuster V et al (eds): *Hurst's: the heart, arteries, and veins,* ed 10, New York, 2001, McGraw-Hill.

AUTHOR: **TOM J. WACHTEL, M.D.**

MULTIFOCAL ATRIAL TACHYCARDIA

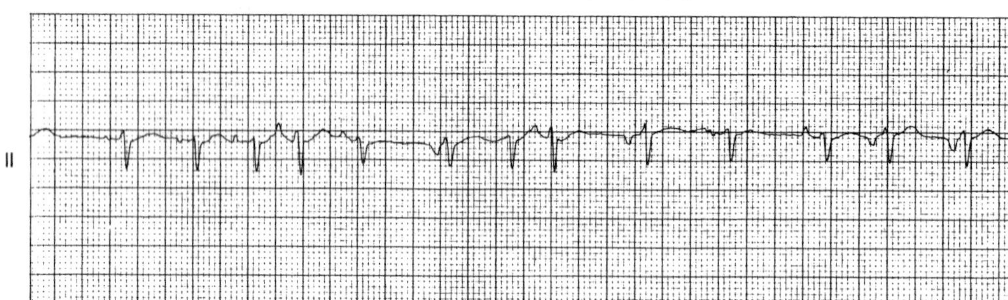

FIGURE 1-151 The P waves show variable shapes or variable PR intervals, or both. (From Goldberger AL: *Clinical electrocardiography,* ed 5, St Louis, 1994, Mosby.)

BASIC INFORMATION

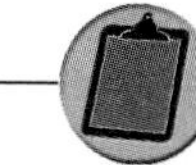

DEFINITION

Multiple myeloma is a malignancy of plasma cells characterized by overproduction of intact monoclonal immunoglobulin or free monoclonal kappa or lambda chains.

ICD-9CM CODES
203.0 Multiple myeloma

EPIDEMIOLOGY & DEMOGRAPHICS

ANNUAL INCIDENCE: 4 cases/100,000 persons (blacks affected twice as frequently as whites); multiple myeloma accounts for 10% of all hematologic cancers

PREDOMINANT AGE: Peak incidence in the seventh decade at a median age of 69 yr

PHYSICAL FINDINGS & CLINICAL PRESENTATION

The patient usually comes to medical attention because of one or more of the following:

- Bone pain (back, thorax) or pathologic fractures caused by osteolytic lesions
- Fatigue or weakness because of anemia secondary to bone marrow infiltration with plasma cells
- Recurrent infections as a result of impaired neutrophil function and deficiency of normal immunoglobulins
- Nausea and vomiting caused by constipation and uremia
- Delirium secondary to hypercalcemia
- Neurologic complications, such as spinal cord or nerve root compression, blurred vision from hyperviscosity
- Pallor and generalized weakness from anemia
- Purpura, epistaxis from thrombocytopenia
- Evidence of infections from impaired immune system
- Bone pain, weight loss
- Swelling on ribs, vertebrae, and other bones

DIAGNOSIS

DIFFERENTIAL DIAGNOSIS

- Metastatic carcinoma
- Lymphoma
- Bone neoplasms (e.g., sarcoma)
- Monoclonal gammopathy of undetermined significance (MGUS)

LABORATORY TESTS

- Normochromic, normocytic anemia; rouleaux formation on peripheral smear
- Hypercalcemia is present in 15% of patients at diagnosis
- Elevated BUN, creatinine, uric acid, and total protein
- Proteinuria secondary to overproduction and secretion of free monoclonal kappa or lambda chains (Bence Jones protein)
- Tall homogeneous monoclonal spike (M spike) on protein immunoelectrophoresis (IEP) in approximately 75% of patients; decreased levels of normal immunoglobulins
  1. The increased immunoglobulins are generally IgG (75%) or IgA (15%).
  2. Approximately 17% of patients have flat level of immunoglobulins but increased light chains in the urine by electrophoresis.
  3. A very small percentage (<2%) of patients have nonsecreting myeloma (no increase in immunoglobulins and no light chains in the urine) but have other evidence of the disease (e.g., positive bone marrow examination).
- Reduced ion gap resulting from the positive charge of the M proteins and the frequent presence of hyponatremia in myeloma patients
- Hyponatremia, serum hyperviscosity (more common with production of IgA)
- Bone marrow examination: usually demonstrates nests or sheets of plasma cells, which comprise >30% of the bone marrow, and ≥10% are immature
- Serum β-2 microglobulin has little diagnostic value; it is useful for prognosis because levels >8 mg/L indicate high tumor mass and aggressive disease
- Elevated serum levels of LDH at the time of diagnosis define a subgroup of myeloma patients with very poor prognosis
- Increased interleukin-6 in serum during active stage of myeloma
- The production of DKK1, an inhibitor of osteoblast differentiation, by myeloma cells is associated with the presence of lytic bone lesions in patients with multiple myeloma.

IMAGING STUDIES

X-ray films of painful areas may demonstrate punched-out lytic lesions or osteoporosis. Bone scans are not useful, because lesions are not blastic.

TREATMENT

NONPHARMACOLOGIC THERAPY

Prevention of renal failure with adequate hydration and avoidance of nephrotoxic agents and dye contrast studies

ACUTE GENERAL Rx

- Newly diagnosed patients with good performance status are best treated with autologous stem cell transplantation, resulting in improved survival. Useful guidelines (from the Hematology Disease Site Group of the Cancer Care Ontario Practice Guidelines Initiative) regarding the role of high-dose chemotherapy and stem-cell transplantation are as follows:
  1. Autologous transplantation is recommended for patients with stage II or III myeloma and good performance status.
  2. Allogenic transplantation is not recommended as routine therapy.
  3. Patients potentially eligible for transplantation should be referred for assessment early after diagnosis and should not be extensively exposed to alkylating agents before collection of stem cells.

4. Autologous peripheral stem cells should be harvested early in the patient's treatment course (best when performed as part of initial therapy).
5. A single transplant with high-dose melphalan, with or without total body irradiation, is suggested for patients undergoing transplantation outside a clinical trial.
6. At this time no conclusion can be reached about the role of interferon therapy after transplantation.

- Chemotherapeutic agents effective in multiple myeloma are:
  1. Melphalan and prednisone: the rates of response to this treatment range from 40% to 60%. Adding continuous low-dose interferon to standard melphalan-prednisone therapy does not improve response rate or survival; however, response duration and plateau phase duration are prolonged by maintenance therapy with interferon.
  2. Vincristine, doxorubicin (Adriamycin), and dexamethasone (VAD) can be used in patients not responding or relapsing after treatment with melphalan and prednisone; methylprednisolone is substituted for dexamethasone (VAMP) in some centers.
  3. High-dose chemotherapy (HDCT) with vincristine, melphalan, cyclophosphamide, and prednisone (VMCP) alternating with vincristine, carmustine, doxorubicin, and prednisone (BVAP) combined with bone marrow transplantation improves the response rate, event-free survival, and overall survival in patients with myeloma.
  4. Current HDCT regimen with autologous stem-cell support achieve complete response in approximately 20% to 30% of patients, with best results seen in good-risk patients, defined as young patients (<50 yr of age) with good performance status and a low tumor burden (β_2 microglobulin ≤ 2.5 mg/L).
  5. Thalidomide, an agent with antiangiogenic properties, is useful to induce responses in patients with multiple myeloma refractory to chemotherapy.
  6. Bortezomib (Velcade) is a newer protease inhibitor that is cytotoxic for multiple myeloma. It is indicated for treatment of refractory multiple myeloma. It is expensive, with an average course of treatment (5 cycles) costing >$20,000.

CHRONIC Rx

- Promptly diagnose and treat infections. Common bacterial agents are *Streptococcus pneumoniae* and *Haemophilus influenzae.* Prophylactic therapy against *Pneumocystic carinii* with trimethoprim sulfamethoxazole must be considered in patients receiving chemotherapy and high-dose corticosteroid regimens.
- Control hypercalcemia and hyperuricemia.
- Control pain with analgesics; radiation therapy and surgical stabilization may also be indicated.
- Treat anemia with epoetin alfa.
- Monthly infusions of the biphosphonate pamidronate provide significant protection against skeletal complications and improve the quality of life of patients with advanced multiple myeloma. Zoledronic acid (Zometa) can be infused over 15 min and is more effective than pamidronate for treatment of hypercalcemia of malignancy. Biphosphonates (pamidronate, zoledranate, and ibandronate) also appear to have an antitumor effect.

DISPOSITION

- Prognosis is better in asymptomatic patients with indolent or smoldering myeloma: median survival time is approximately 10 yr in persons with no lytic bone lesions and a serum myeloma protein concentration <3 g/dl.
- As compared with a single autologus stem-cell transplantation, double transplantation (two successive autologus stem-cell transplantations) improves survival among patients with myeloma, especially those who do not have a very good partial response after undergoing one transplantation.

SUGGESTED READINGS

Attal M et al: Single versus double autologus stem-cell transplantation for multiple myeloma, *N Engl J Med* 349:2495, 2003.

Imrie K et al: The role of high dose chemotherapy and stem-cell transplantation in patients with multiple myeloma: a practice guideline of the Cancer Care Ontario Practice Guidelines Initiative, *Ann Intern Med* 136:619, 2002.

Rajkumar SV et al: Current therapy for multiple myeloma, *Mayo Clin Proc* 77:813, 2002.

Tian E et al: The role of WNT-signaling antagonist DKK1 in the development of osteolytic lesions in multiple myeloma, *N Engl J Med* 349:2483, 2003.

AUTHOR: **FRED F. FERRI, M.D.**

BASIC INFORMATION

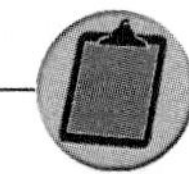

DEFINITION

Multiple sclerosis (MS) is a chronic inflammatory demyelinating disease of the central nervous system (CNS) characterized by demyelinating lesions separated in time and space. Subtypes include relapsing-remitting MS (RRMS), which later transitions to secondary progressive MS (SPMS), and primary progressive MS (PPMS). RRMS is most common.

ICD-9CM CODES
340 Multiple sclerosis

EPIDEMIOLOGY & DEMOGRAPHICS

PREVALENCE: Higher in northern latitudes and rare geographic clustering. 100 per 100,000 in the U.S.; <5 per 100,000 in Asia, Central America, and most of Africa.

GENETICS: Twin studies demonstrate the frequency of MS in dizygotic twins and siblings is 3%-5%; monozygotic twins 20%-40%. Associated with multiple haplotypes of the major histocompatibility complex, most commonly DR2, DR15, and DR4.

PREDOMINANT AGE & SEX: Most commonly a disease of young adults; however, can present in children and in the seventh decade. Mean ages of onset: overall 30, RRMS 28, SPMS 40, and PPMS 37 yr old. Female:male ratio is 1.5:1.

PHYSICAL FINDINGS & CLINICAL PRESENTATION

- Common symptoms: fatigue, blurred vision, diplopia, vertigo, hemiparesis, paraparesis, monoparesis, numbness, paresthesias, ataxia, cognitive and urinary dysfunction.
- Visual abnormalities:
  1. Internuclear ophthalmoplegia (INO)—paresis of the adducting eye on conjugate lateral gaze with horizontal nystagmus of the abducting eye.
  2. Optic neuritis (ON)—see topic "Optic Neuritis."
  3. Nystagmus.
- Upper motor neuron (UMN) signs: spasticity, increased deep tendon reflexes, positive Hoffmann's sign, extensor plantar responses, clonus and an UMN pattern of weakness (shoulder abduction, elbow, hand and finger extension, hip and knee flexion, foot dorsiflexion).
- Sensory loss: dermatomal loss of pain/temp, loss of vibration/position sense, thoracic band of sensory loss.
- Ataxia: intention tremor, heel-to-shin ataxia, inability to tandem.
- Bladder dysfunction: detrusor hyperreflexia (urge incontinence), flaccidity (neurogenic bladder), and dyssynergia (bladder contracts against a closed sphincter).
- Lhermitte's sign: flexion of the neck elicits an electrical sensation extending down the spine and occasionally into the extremities.

ETIOLOGY

The exact etiology of MS is unknown. It is thought to be a combination of multiple genes and environmental factors, possibly including exposure to certain viruses, vitamin D, and sun exposure.

DIAGNOSIS

- MS is primarily a clinical diagnosis based on a consistent clinical presentation with evidence of CNS demyelinating lesions disseminated in time and space not better explained by another disease.
- A history of two relapses and confirmation on neurologic examination may be sufficient if *both* support the presence of two demyelinating lesions separated in time and space. If, however, there is only evidence of one lesion on examination or clinical history of one relapse, MRI or paraclinical testing and/or positive CSF (positive oligoclonal bands or elevated IgG Index) may be used to make the diagnosis. Possibilities include:
  1. A new lesion on MRI (at least 6 mo after the initial MRI for a new MS-like T2 lesion or 3 mo for an enhancing lesion)
  2. At least two lesions consistent with MS plus positive CSF
  3. Specific MRI criteria—at least three of the following: (1) one enhancing lesion or nine T2 hyperintense lesions, (2) one infratentorial lesion, (3) one juxtacortical lesion, and (4) three periventricular lesions
- In relapsing-remitting MS (80% of patients), signs and symptoms evolve over a period of several days, stabilize, and then improve spontaneously or in response to corticosteroids. Most patients with relapsing-remitting MS eventually transition to secondary progressive MS. In secondary progressive MS, manifestations progressively worsen, with or without superimposed acute relapses. In primary progressive MS, manifestations gradually worsen from disease onset without relapses.

DIFFERENTIAL DIAGNOSIS

- Autoimmune: acute disseminated encephalomyelitis (ADEM), postvaccination encephalomyelitis.
- Degenerative: subacute combined degeneration (B_{12} deficiency), inherited spastic paraparesis.
- Infections: progressive multifocal leukoencephalopathy, Lyme, syphilis, HIV, HTLV-1, Whipple's, expanded differential in immunocompromised patients.
- Inflammatory: SLE, Sjögren's, Behçet's, vasculitis, sarcoidosis, celiac disease.
- Inherited metabolic disorders: leukodystrophies.
- Mitochondrial: Leber's hereditary optic neuropathy, mitochondrial encephalopathy lactic acidosis and strokelike episodes (MELAS).
- MS variants: recurrent optic neuropathy, neuromyelitis optica (Devic's disease), acute tumor-like lesion (Marburg variant), Baló's concentric sclerosis, myelinoclastic diffuse sclerosis (Schilder's disease).
- Neoplasms: metastases, CNS lymphoma.
- Vascular: subcortical infarcts, Binswanger's disease.

WORKUP

- Lumbar puncture is indicated for all first-time relapses and recommended for all evaluations when the diagnosis of MS is not definite. Possible CSF abnormalities include an increase in total protein and mononuclear WBCs (both usually only a mild elevation). An elevated CSF IgG Index and positive OCBs (both sent with paired serum samples) are present in 70% and 90% respectively of patients with clinically definite MS. False positives occur less often with other inflammatory conditions.
- Serum: recommend CBC, ESR, CHEM 7, LFTs, ANA, B12. Consider Lyme titer, ACE, infectious and collagen-vascular serologies, TFTs, very-long-chain fatty acids and arylsulfatase A.
- Consider paraclinical testing: evoked potentials (VEPs, BAERs, SSEPs) and urodynamic testing. Myelin loss will slow conduction velocities.

IMAGING STUDIES

MRI of the head with gadolinium is standard (see Fig. 1-152). MRI of the cervical spine is often recommended. MRIs can be used to assess disease load, activity, and progression. A normal MRI, however, cannot be used conclusively to exclude MS.

TREATMENT

NONPHARMACOLOGIC THERAPY

Patient education regarding the disease, treatment options, and prognosis

ACUTE GENERAL Rx

- Relapses: typically high-dose IV methylprednisolone (5 days of 1g/day can be used; an alternative dose is 15 mg/kg per day). A 7- to 10-day prednisone taper following IV treatment is often given.
- Disease-modifying therapy: includes interferon ß-1a (Avonex, Rebif), interferon ß-1b (Betaseron), and glatiramer acetate (Copaxone). All four drugs have been shown to slow progression of relapsing disease and reduce the annual relapse rate by 20%-40%. Preliminary studies suggest natalizumab (Antegran, a monoclonal antibody against β-4 integrin) reduces relapse rate by 50%.
- Cytotoxic: mitoxantrone and cyclophosphamide can be effective in rapidly relapsing and early secondary progressive MS. In these cases, refer to an MS specialist.

CHRONIC Rx

- Fatigue: options include amantadine 100 mg bid, modafinil (most effective for somnolence) and fluoxetine.
- Spasticity: options include baclofen, tizanidine, diazepam, lorazepam, botox, and an intrathecal baclofen pump.
- Pain: carbamazepine and gabapentin are most effective.
- Depression: frequent (20% of patients) and can be treated with antidepressants.
- Urinary urgency: oxybutynin or propantheline.
- Tremor: can generally be controlled with clonazepam 0.5 mg bid.

DISPOSITION

Most patients experience clinical improvement in weeks to months after the initial manifestations. The rate of disease progression is highly variable. Without disease-modifying therapy, 50% of patients are moderately disabled at 6 yr. With therapy, this is thought to be substantially reduced.

REFERRAL

- Initial neurology referral is recommended in all patients with MS.
- Referrals for therapy, a support group, PT/OT, urology, and psychiatry are often needed.

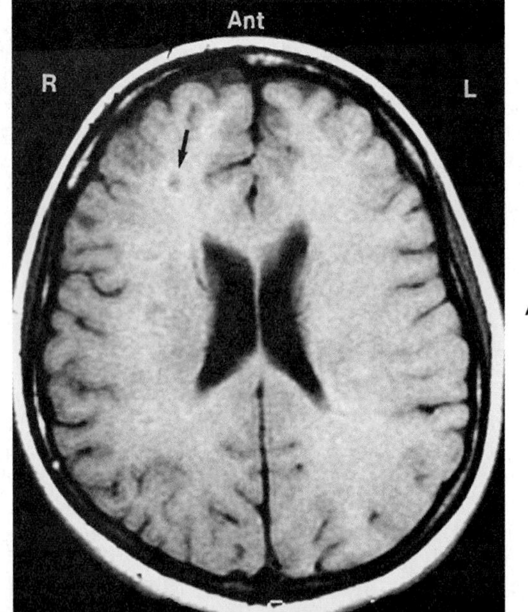

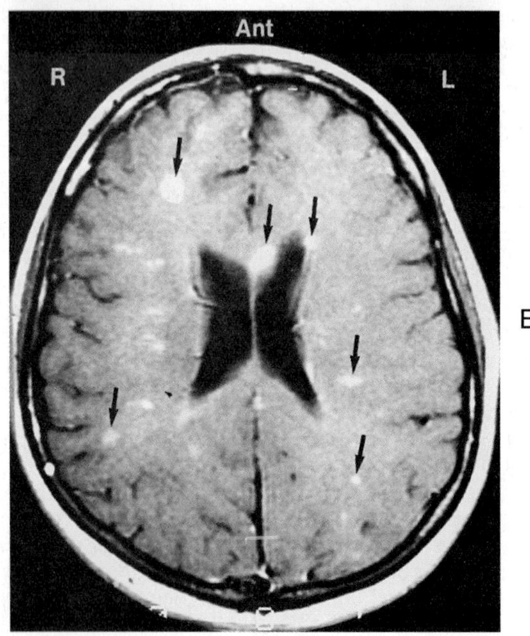

FIGURE 1-152 Multiple sclerosis. The noncontrasted T1-weighted magnetic resonance scan **(A)** shows one hypodensity (black hole) in the right frontal lobe (*arrow*). A gadolinium-enhanced scan **(B)** shows many enhancing lesions, only some of which are indicated (*arrows*). (From Mettler FA [ed]: *Primary care radiology,* Philadelphia, 2000, WB Saunders.)

SUGGESTED READINGS

CHAMPS Study Group: MRI predictors of early conversion to clinically definite MS in the CHAMPS placebo group, *Neurology* 59:998, 2002.

Compston A, McAlpine D (eds): *McAlpine's multiple sclerosis,* London, 1998, Churchill Livingstone.

Confravreux et al: Course and prognosis of multiple sclerosis assessed by the computerized data processing of 349 patients, *Brain* 103:281, 1980.

Ebers GC et al: A population-based study of multiple sclerosis in twins, *N Engl J Med* 315:1638, 1986.

Galetta SL et al: Immunomodulatory agents for the treatment of relapsing multiple sclerosis, *Arch Intern Med* 162:2161, 2002.

Jacobs LD et al: Intramuscular interferon beta-1a therapy, initiated during a first demyelinating event in multiple sclerosis, *N Engl J Med* 343:898, 2000.

Kurtzke JF: Geography in multiple sclerosis, *J Neurol* 215:1, 1977.

Miller DH et al: A controlled trial of natalizumab for relapsing multiple sclerosis, *N Engl J Med* 348:15, 2003

AUTHOR: **ALEXANDRA DEGENHARDT, M.D.**

BASIC INFORMATION

DEFINITION

Mumps is an acute generalized viral infection that is usually characterized by nonsuppurative swelling and tenderness of one or both parotid glands. It is caused by mumps virus, a paramyxovirus and member of the paramyxoviridae family.

ICD-9CM CODES
072.9 Mumps

EPIDEMIOLOGY & DEMOGRAPHICS

INCIDENCE (IN U.S.):
- About 1600 infections/yr
- More than 150,000 cases/yr before licensure of mumps vaccine in 1967

PREDOMINANT SEX: Males = females

PREDOMINANT AGE: 75% of disease in teenage yr

PEAK INCIDENCE: Late winter and early spring months

GENETICS:

Congenital Infection:
- First-trimester infection is associated with excessive fetal deaths.
- Second- and third-trimester infection is not associated with increased fetal mortality.

Neonatal Infection:
- Uncommon
- Uncommon in infants <1 yr because of passive immunity conferred by placental transfer of maternal antibody

PHYSICAL FINDINGS & CLINICAL PRESENTATION

- Prodromal period:
  1. Low-grade fever
  2. Malaise
  3. Anorexia
  4. Headache
- Parotid swelling and tenderness are often first signs of infection.
  1. Progresses over 2 to 3 days, then opposite side may become involved
  2. Unilateral parotitis in 25% of cases
  3. Considerable pain with parotid swelling, causing trismus and difficulty with mastication and pronunciation
  4. Pain exacerbated by eating or drinking citrus and other acidic foods
  5. Possible fever with parotid swelling, ranging up to 40° C
  6. Parotid swelling usually resolving within 1 wk
- CNS involvement:
  1. May occur from 1 wk before to 2 wk after the onset of parotitis or even in its absence
  2. Meningitis
     a. Occurs in 1% to 10% of persons with mumps parotitis
     b. Occur three times more often in males than females
     c. Symptoms: headache, fever, nuchal rigidity, and vomiting
     d. Full recovery with no sequelae
  3. Encephalitis
     a. May develop early, as a result of direct viral invasion of neurons, or late, around the second week after onset of parotitis, and is a postinfectious demyelinating process
     b. Mumps accounted for only 0.5% of viral meningitis
     c. Symptoms: fever, alterations in the level of consciousness, possible seizures, paresis or paralysis, and aphasia. Fever can be quite high (40° C-41° C)
     d. Cerebellitis and hydrocephalus are serious complications of mumps encephalitis
     e. May result in permanent sequelae or death
  4. Other rare neurologic complications
     a. Cerebellar ataxia
     b. Transverse myelitis
     c. Gullain-Barré syndrome
     d. Facial palsy
- Epididymoorchitis:
  1. Most common extra salivary gland complication of mumps in adult men
  2. Occurs in 38% of postpubertal males who have mumps
  3. Most often unilateral but is bilateral in 30% of males who develop this complication
  4. May precede development of parotitis
  5. May be only manifestation of mumps
  6. Two thirds of cases develop during first week of parotitis
  7. One quarter of cases develop in second week
  8. Symptoms
     a. Severe pain, swelling, and tenderness of the testes and scrotal erythema
     b. Fever and chills
  9. Some degree of testicular atrophy in 50% of cases, months to years later
  10. Sterility from bilateral orchitis is rare
- Involvement of pancreas and ovaries:
  1. Abdominal pain
  2. Fever
  3. Vomiting
  4. Oophoritis
     a. Occurs in 5% of postpubertal women with mumps
     b. Symptoms include fever, nausea, vomiting, and lower abdominal pain
     c. May rarely result in decreased fertility and premature menopause
- Transient renal impairment:
  1. Common
  2. Manifest by hematuria and polyuria
- Joint involvement:
  1. Migratory polyarthritis is most frequent
  2. Infrequently affects adults with mumps
  3. Rarely in children
  4. Self-limited, with complete resolution
- Pancreatitis
  1. Uncommon as a severe illness
  2. Milder degree of upper abdominal discomfort
- Deafness:
  1. Most often unilateral, involving high frequencies; may rarely cause bilateral involvement
  2. Most patients recover
  3. Permanent unilateral deafness reported in 1 in 20,000 cases
  4. Labrynthitis and end lymphatic hydrops also reported
- Myocardial involvement:
  1. Uncommon
  2. Rarely causes progressive and culminant fatal myocarditis with dilated cardiomyopathy
  3. Refractory arrhythmia and congestive heart failure
  4. Coronary artery involvement
- Eye involvement:
  1. Corneal endothelitis following mumps parotitis

ETIOLOGY

- Virus is spread via direct contact, droplet nuclei, fomites, or secretions through the nose and mouth
- Patients are contagious from 48 hr before to 9 days after parotid swelling

DIAGNOSIS

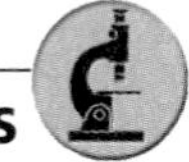

DIFFERENTIAL DIAGNOSIS

- Other viruses that may cause acute parotitis:
  1. Parainfluenza types 1 and 3
  2. Coxsackie viruses
  3. Influenza A
  4. Cytomegalovirus
- Suppurative parotitis:
  1. Most often caused by staphylococcal aureus

2. May be differentiated from mumps
   a. Extreme indurations, tenderness and erythema overlying the gland
   b. Ability to express pus from Stensen's duct or massage of parotid
- Other conditions that may occur with parotid enlargement or swelling
  1. Sjögren's syndrome
  2. Leukemia
  3. Diabetes mellitus
  4. Uremia
  5. Malnutrition
  6. Cirrhosis
- Drugs that cause parotid swelling:
  1. Phenothiazines
  2. Phenylbutazone
  3. Thiouracil
  4. Iodides
- Conditions that cause unilateral swelling:
  1. Tumors
  2. Cysts
  3. Stones causing obstruction
  4. Strictures causing obstruction

WORKUP

- Diagnosis based on history of exposure and physical finding of parotid tenderness with mild to moderate constitutional symptoms.
- Diagnosis is confirmed by a variety of serologic tests or isolation of the virus.

LABORATORY TESTS

- Diagnosis is confirmed by fourfold rise between acute and convalescent sera by CF, ELISA, or neutralization tests.
- Virus can be isolated from the saliva, usually from 2 to 3 days before to 4 to 5 days after the onset of parotitis.
- Virus can be isolated from CSF in patients with meningitis during the first 3 days of meningeal findings. More rapid confirmation of mumps in the CSF is IgM antibody capture Immunoassay and nested PCR assay.
- Virus can be detected in urine during the first 2 wk of infection.
- WBC
  1. May be normal
  2. Possible mild leucopenia with a relative lymphocytosis
  3. Leucocytosis with left shift with extra salivary gland involvement, such as meningitis, orchitis, or pancreatitis
- Serum amylase:
  1. Elevated in the presence of parititis
  2. May remain elevated for 2 to 3 wk
  3. May be differentiated from mumps and parotids by isoenzyme analysis or serum pancreatic lipase
- Mumps meningitis:
  1. CSF WBCs from 10 to 2000 WBC/mm3 with a predominance of lymphocytes
  2. In 20% to 25% of patients, predominance of polymorphonuclear cells
  3. CSF protein normal or mildly elevated
  4. CSF glucose low, >40mg/100ml, in 6% to 30% of patients

TREATMENT

NONPHARMACOLOGIC THERAPY

- Supportive treatment
- Adequate hydration and nutrition

ACUTE GENERAL Rx

- Analgesics and antipyretics to relieve pain and fever
- Narcotic analgesics, along with bed rest, ice packs, and a testicular bridge, to relieve pain associated with mumps orchitis
- IV fluids for patients with frequent vomiting associated with mumps pancreatitis or meningitis

DISPOSITION

Most patients recover without incident.

PEARLS & CONSIDERATIONS

COMMENTS

Prevention:
- Attenuated live mumps virus vaccine has been available since 1967.
  1. Usually given in combination with measles and rubella vaccines
  2. Should be given at 15 mo of age, and again at 5 to 12 yr
  3. Seroconversion in about 100% infants given the vaccine
  4. Contraindicated in pregnant women and immunocompromised patients
  5. Patients with asymptomatic HIV infection and patients with symptomatic HIV infection, in the absence of severe immunosuppression, can safely receive MMR vaccine
  6. Adverse events of vaccination include
     a. Local pain
     b. Indurations
     c. Thrompocypenic purpura
     d. Guillain-Barré syndrome
     e. Cerebellar ataxia
- Infected patients should be isolated until parotid swelling resolves
- Because virus may be shed before the onset of parotid swelling, isolation possibly not of great value in limiting spread of infection.

SUGGESTED READINGS

Centers for Disease Control and Prevention: Mumps surveillance—United States 1988-1993, *MMWR Morb Mortal Wkly Rep* 4A(No ss-3):1, 1995.

Gans H et al: Immune responses to measles and mumps vaccination of infants at 6, 9, 12 months, *J Infect Dis* 184(7):817, 2001.

Singh K, Sodhi PK: Mumps-induced corneal endothelitis, *Cornea* 23(4):400, 2004.

AUTHOR: **VASANTHI ARUMUGAM, M.D.**

BASIC INFORMATION

DEFINITION

Muscular dystrophy (MD) refers to a heterogeneous group of inherited disorders resulting in characteristic patterns of muscle weakness, some with cardiac involvement even in the absence of sekeletal muscle weakness. For the purposes of this section, only disorders with childhood or adult onset will be considered (i.e., excluding congenital myopathies).

ICD-9CM CODES
359 Muscular dystrophies and other myopathies
359.1 Hereditary progressive muscular dystrophy

EPIDEMIOLOGY & DEMOGRAPHICS

INCIDENCE:

- Most common childhood MD is Duchenne's muscular dystrophy with an incidence of 1/3500 male births
- Most common adult MD is myotonic dystrophy with an incidence as high as 1/8000

GENETICS:

- **Dystrophinopathies:** X-linked recessive defect in dystrophin gene resulting in either absence (Duchenne MD) or reduced/defective (Becker's MD) dystrophin.
- **Myotonic Dystrophy:** Autosomal dominant (AD) CTG trinucleotide repeat.
- **Limb-Girdle Muscular Dystrophy:** Autosomal recessive, also autosomal dominant forms with deficiency identified in multiple proteins (sarcoglycan, calpain, dysferlin, telethonin, lamin A/C, myotilin, and caveolin-3).
- **Emery-Dreifuss Muscular Dystrophy:** X-linked recessive defect in nuclear protein emerin or AR defect in inner nuclear lamina proteins lamin A/C.
- **Fascioscapulohumeral Muscular Dystrophy:** AD; genetic mutation causes deletion of 3.3 kb repeat.
- **Oculopharyngeal Muscular Dystrophy:** AD GCG trinucleotide repeat resulting in deficient mRNA transfer from nucleus.

PHYSICAL FINDINGS & CLINICAL PRESENTATION

- **Dystrophinopathies:** Proximal arm and leg weakness with hypertrophic calf muscles, delayed motor milestones, cognitive impairment, cardiac involvement, progressive course resulting in respiratory complications and respiratory failure
  Duchenne's (DMD) onset 2-3 yr old, typically wheelchair-bound by 12 yr
  Becker's (BMD) onset 5-15 yr old, ambulatory beyond age 15
- **Myotonic Dystrophy:** Variable age of onset and severity manifesting as predominately distal weakness with long face, percussion and grip myotonia, temporalis and masseter wasting, ptosis, hypersomnolence, cognitive impairment, and cardiac conduction defects. May be associated with frontal balding, cataracts, impaired glucose tolerance, male infertility.
- **Limb-Girdle Muscular Dystrophy:** Phenotypically and genetically heterogenous characterized by proximal hip and shoulder girdle weakness, some genotypes featuring cardiac involvement.
- **Emery-Dreifuss Muscular Dystrophy:** Early adulthood onset with predominately humeroperoneal weakness, early contractures, and cardiac conduction defects.
- **Fascoscapulohumeral Muscular Dystrophy:** Onset typically in late childhood or adolescence with weakness mostly in face and shoulder girdle musculature and possible later, mild involvement of lower extremities. Cardiac conduction defects and cognitive impairment may occur.
- **Oculopharyngeal Muscular Dystrophy:** Symptom onset typically in mid-adult life with ptosis, dysphagia, dysarthria, and proximal muscle weakness.

ETIOLOGY

Contingent upon genotype, see Genetics

DIAGNOSIS

DIFFERENTIAL DIAGNOSIS

Myasthenia gravis, inflammatory myopathy, metabolic myopathy, endocrine myopathy, toxic myopathy, mitochondrial myopathy

WORKUP

- Creatine kinase (CK)
- ECG, Holter monitor, formal cardiac electrophysiology or echocardiography to screen for cardiac conduction defects and cardiomyopathy
- EMG
- Muscle biopsy with histochemistry useful for diagnosis of dystrophinopathies and limb-girdle muscular dystrophy (sarcoglycanopathy, dysferlinopathy)
- DNA analysis helpful if clinical suspicion is for myotonic, Emery-Drefuss, facioscapulohumeral, and oculopharyngeal muscular dystrophies
- Assessment of respiratory parameters, including forced vital capacity (FVC)

TREATMENT

NONPHARMACOLOGIC THERAPY

- Genetic counseling
- Physical, occupational, respiratory, speech therapy as symptoms dictate
- Screening for sleep-disordered breathing with overnight polysomnogram (PSG) if daytime hypersomnolence, early morning headaches, disturbed sleep; the patient may benefit from noninvasive positive pressure ventilation
- Pacemaker placement may be necessary if cardiac conduction defect present

ACUTE GENERAL Rx

Prednisone may modestly prolong ambulation in Duchenne MD and may be recommended until loss of ambulatory function.

CHRONIC Rx

Vigilance to avoid cardiac and respiratory complications, joint contractures

DISPOSITION

Variable course as severity of phenotype contingent upon diagnosis as well as genotype.

REFERRAL

- Surgical referral for correction of scoliosis or contractures may be necessary
- Assessment and follow-up in a muscular dystrophy specialty clinic

PEARLS & CONSIDERATIONS

- Formal evaluation recommended by anesthetist before any operation with general anesthesia in patients with dystrophinopathy
- Gower's sign: difficulty in rising from a supine to a standing position as a result of truncal and hip-girdle weakness. Affected patients push themselves on all fours and then quickly grab their thighs and walk up the thighs to a standing position

COMMENTS

Muscular Dystrophy Association—USA National Headquarters, 3300 E. Sunrise Drive, Tucson, AZ 85718. Toll-free phone number: (800) 572-1717. Web address: www.mdausa.org/

SUGGESTED READINGS

Emery AE: Muscular dystrophy into the new millennium, *Neuromuscul Disord* 12(4):843, 2002.

Emery AE: The muscular dystrophies, *Lancet* 359(9307):687, 2002.

Saperstein DS, Amato AA, Barohn RJ: Clinical and genetic aspects of distal myopathies, *Muscle Nerve* 24(11):1440, 2001.

AUTHOR: **TAYLOR HARRISON, M.D.**

Mushroom Poisoning (PTG)

BASIC INFORMATION

DEFINITION

Mushroom poisoning is intoxication resulting from ingestion of poisonous mushrooms.

ICD-9CM CODES
988.1 Mushroom poisoning

EPIDEMIOLOGY & DEMOGRAPHICS

- Five percent of all mushrooms are poisonous. Distinction between poisonous and edible mushrooms may be difficult even by experienced persons.
- Common poisonous species include *Amanita, Russula, Gyromitra,* and *Omphalotus*.

PHYSICAL FINDINGS & CLINICAL PRESENTATION (TABLE 1-33)

- *Russula* causes confusion, delirium, visual disturbance, tachycardia, and diarrhea within a few hours of ingestion. Prognosis: spontaneous recovery (mortality <1%).
- *Amanita* and *Gyromitra* intoxication begins with symptoms of gastroenteritis (nausea, vomiting, diarrhea, abdominal cramps) approximately 10 hr following ingestion. *Amanita* then goes on to cause cardiomyopathy and hepatic and renal failure. *Gyromitra* produces jaundice and seizures. Both mushrooms are associated with a 50% mortality rate.
- *Omphalotus* causes symptoms of gastroenteritis that subside spontaneously within 24 hr.

PATHOPHYSIOLOGY

- *Amanita* contains cytotoxic substances and isoxazoles that are gamma-aminobutyric acid neurotransmitter analogs.
- *Gyromitra* contains a pyridoxine antagonist that disrupts the GI mucosa and causes hemolysis.
- *Russula* contains a cholinergic substance.

DIAGNOSIS

DIFFERENTIAL DIAGNOSIS

- Food poisoning
- Overdose of prescription or illegal drug
- Other intoxications
- See topic on specific organ failure (e.g., renal or hepatic failure) for differential diagnosis of those conditions

WORKUP

- History
- Inspection and identification of suspected mushrooms
- Mushroom or gastric content analysis (by thin-layer chromatography or radioimmunoassay)

TREATMENT

- Gastric lavage
- Repeated administration of activated charcoal
- Supportive care as needed (may require respiratory assistance, hemodialysis, or emergency liver transplantation)

SUGGESTED READING

Haubrich WS: Mushroom poisoning. In Haubrich WS, Schaffner F, Berk JE (eds): *Gastroenterology,* ed 5, Philadelphia, 1995, WB Saunders.

AUTHOR: **TOM J. WACHTEL, M.D.**

TABLE 1-33 **Mushroom Poisoning Syndromes**

Syndrome	Incubation Period (hr)	Species	Toxin
Confusion, restlessness, visual disturbances, lethargy	2	*Amanita muscaria* *Amanita pantherina*	Ibotenic acid, muscimol
Parasympathetic activity	2	*Inocybe* sp. *Clitocybe* sp.	Muscarine
Hallucinations	2	*Psilocybe* sp. *Panacolus* sp.	Psilocybin Psilocin
Disulfiram	2	*Coprinus atramentarius*	Disulfiram-like substances
Gastroenteritis	2	Many	Unknown
Hepatorenal failure	6-24	*Amanita phalloides* *Amanita virosa* *Amanita verna* *Galerina autumnalis* *Galerina marginata* *Galerina venenata*	Amatoxins Phallotoxins
Hepatic failure	6-24	*Gyromitra* sp.	Gyromitrin

From Gorbach SL: *Infectious diseases,* ed 2, Philadelphia, 1998, WB Saunders.

SECTION I

BASIC INFORMATION

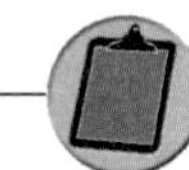

DEFINITION

Myasthenia gravis (MG) is an autoimmune disorder of postsynaptic neuromuscular transmission classically directed against the nicotinic acetylcholine receptor (AChR) of the neuromuscular junction, resulting in a decrease in functional postsynaptic ACh receptors and consequent weakness.

ICD-9CM CODES
358.0 Myasthenia gravis

EPIDEMIOLOGY & DEMOGRAPHICS

INCIDENCE (IN U.S.): 2 to 5 cases/yr/1,000,000 persons
PREVALENCE (IN U.S.): 1/20,000 persons
PREDOMINANT SEX: Female > male (3:2) in adults; female = male in elderly
PEAK INCIDENCE: Female: second-third decade; male: sixth-seventh decade
GENETICS: Increased frequency of HLA-B8, DR3
Congenital MG: Related to multiple identified genetic defects of neuromuscular transmission, not an autoimmune etiology and not to be treated with immunosuppressive drugs
Neonatal MG: Occurs in 15% to 20% of infants born to mothers with MG. This condition is only temporary and is caused by transplacental passage of AChR-ab. Spontaneous recovery often occurs within 1 mo.

PHYSICAL FINDINGS & CLINICAL PRESENTATION

- The hallmark of MG is fluctuating weakness worsened with exercise and improved with rest
- Generalized weakness involving proximal muscles, diaphragm, neck extensors in 85%
- Weakness confined to eyelids and extraocular muscles in about 15% of patients
- Bulbar symptoms of ptosis, diplopia, dysarthria, dysphagia common
- Normal reflexes, sensation, and coordination

ETIOLOGY

Antibody-mediated decrease in nicotinic acetylcholine receptors in the postsynaptic neuromuscular junction resulting in defective neuromuscular transmission and subsequent muscle weakness and fatigue

DIAGNOSIS

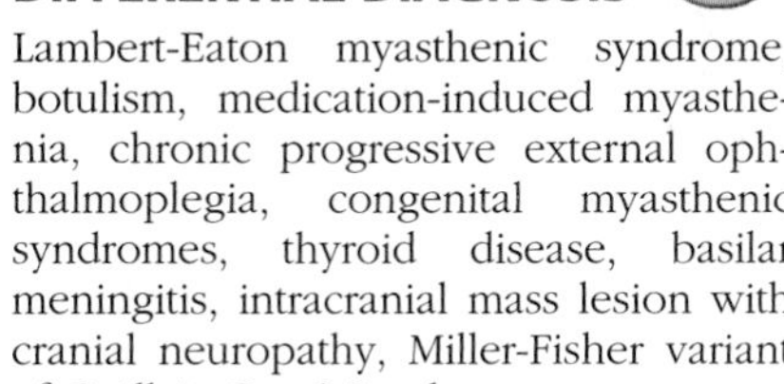

DIFFERENTIAL DIAGNOSIS

Lambert-Eaton myasthenic syndrome, botulism, medication-induced myasthenia, chronic progressive external ophthalmoplegia, congenital myasthenic syndromes, thyroid disease, basilar meningitis, intracranial mass lesion with cranial neuropathy, Miller-Fisher variant of Guillain-Barré Syndrome

WORKUP

Tensilon test: edrophonium chloride (Tensilon), 2 mg IV; useful in MG patients with ocular symptoms; it has rapid onset (30 sec) and short duration of action (5 min). Nonspecific.

Repetitive nerve stimulation (RNS): successive stimulation shows decrement of muscle action potential in clinically weak muscle, may be negative in up to 50%.

Single-fiber electromyography (SFEMG): highly sensitive, abnormal in up to 95% of myasthenics.

Serum AChR antibodies found in up to 80% of patients.

A subset of patients with seronegative MG may have muscle-specific tyrosine kinase (MuSK) antibodies.

ADDITIONAL TESTS

- Spirometry to document pulmonary function
- CT scan of anterior chest to rule out thymoma (found in 12% of patients with MG) or residual thymic tissue
- TSH, free T_4: to rule out thyroid disease (found in 5% to 15% of patients with MG)
- PPD, chest x-ray if immunosuppressive treatment considered

TREATMENT

NONPHARMACOLOGIC THERAPY

- Patient education to facilitate recognition of worsening symptoms and impress need for medical evaluation at onset of clinical deterioration
- Avoidance of selected drugs known to provoke exacerbations of MG (β-blockers, aminoglycoside and quinolone antibiotics, class I antiarrhythmics)
- Prompt treatment of infections, diet modification, and speech evaluation with dysphagia

ACUTE GENERAL Rx

- Symptomatic treatment with acetylcholinesterase inhibitors:
  1. Pyridostigmine 30 to 60 mg PO q4-6h initially; onset of effects is 30 min, duration 4 hr
  2. Mestinon timespan, 180 mg can be given qd or bid; however, absorption may be erratic
  3. Major side effects are GI upset and increased salivary and bronchial secretions, which may be treated with hyoscyamine or glycopyrrolate
- Immunosuppressive treatment with corticosteroids, azathioprine, mycophenolate mofetil, cyclosporine for chronic disease-modifying therapy
  1. Prednisone initiated at 15-20 mg qd titrate by 5 mg increments to effect or dose of 1 mg/kg per day with improvement in 2-4 wk and maximal response by 3-6 mo
  2. Azathioprine initiated at 50 mg qd titrated to 2-3 mg/kg/day with clinical effect in 6-12 mo
  3. Mycophenolate mofetil initiated at 500 mg bid and titrated to 2-3 g per day, clinical effect in 2 wk to 2 mo
  4. Cyclosporine initiated at 5 mg/kg/day with clinical effect within 1-2 mo
- Plasmapheresis and intravenous immunoglobulin are effective short-term options for immunotherapy
- Mechanical ventilation is lifesaving in setting of a myasthenic crisis, defined as neuromuscular respiratory failure related to diaphragm weakness. Consider elective intubation if forced vital capacity <155 cc/kg, maximal expiratory pressure (<40 cm H_2O), or negative inspiratory pressure (<25 cm H_2O)

SURGICAL Rx

- In thymomatous MG, thymectomy is indicated in all patients.
- For nonthymomatous autoimmune MG: thymectomy is an option in patients less than 40 yr of age to increase probability of remission or improvement; however, benefit not conclusively established.

DISPOSITION

Course of disease is highly variable, influenced by factors such as clinical features at onset, association with thymic pathology, age, duration of symptoms at time of diagnosis.

REFERRAL

Surgical referral for thymectomy in selected cases (see Surgical Rx)

SUGGESTED READINGS

Drachman DB: Medical progress: myasthenia gravis, *N Engl J Med* 330(25):1797, 1994.
Wittbrodt ET: Drugs and myasthenia gravis: an update, *Arch Int Med* 157(4):399, 1997.

AUTHOR: **TAYLOR HARRISON, M.D.**

BASIC INFORMATION

DEFINITION

Mycosis fungoides refers to a T-cell lymphoproliferative disorder with characteristic cutaneous skin lesions and with the potential to disseminate into lymph nodes and viscera (Fig. 1-153).

SYNONYMS

Cutaneous T-cell lymphoma

ICD-9CM CODES
202.1 Mycosis fungoides

EPIDEMIOLOGY & DEMOGRAPHICS

- Incidence of mycosis fungoides is 4/1 million.
- Approximately 1000 new cases are diagnosed annually in the U.S.
- More commonly affects males than females (2:1).
- Blacks > whites (2:1).
- Usually found in males 40 to 60 yr of age.

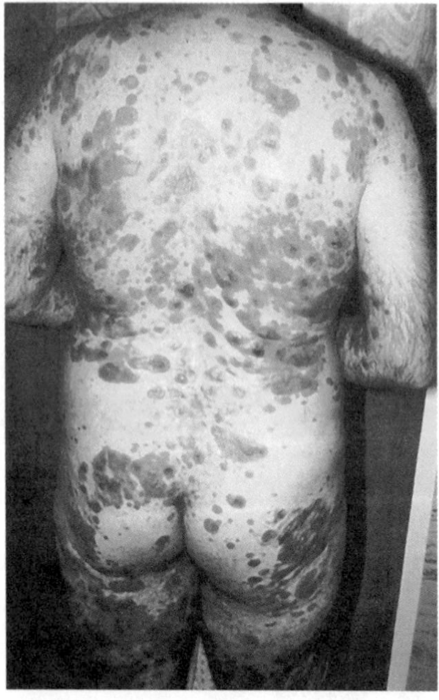

FIGURE 1-153 Cutaneous T-cell lymphoma (mycosis fungoides). Note patch, plaque, and tumor stages. (From Noble J [ed]: *Textbook of primary care medicine*, ed 2, St Louis, 1996, Mosby.)

PHYSICAL FINDINGS & CLINICAL PRESENTATION

Mycosis fungoides characteristically progresses through three phases:

- A premycotic phase featuring scaly, erythematous patches that can last from months to years. During this stage the diagnosis can only be suspected, because the histopathologic features are not definitive for mycosis fungoides. Lesions are pruritic and can appear anywhere but are usually found in sun-shielded areas. Parapsoriasis en plaques, poikilodermatous parapsoriasis, parapsoriasis lichenoides, and variegata are skin lesions suspicious of representing premycotic cutaneous T-cell lymphoma.
- The infiltrative plaque phase features raised, indurated erythematous palpable plaques that are pruritic and may be associated with alopecia.
  1. Stage IA disease is defined as a patch or plaque skin disease involving <10% of the skin surface area.
  2. Stage IB disease is defined as a patch or plaque skin disease involving ≥10% of the skin surface area.
- The tumor phase is characterized by large, lumpy nodules arising from a premycotic patch, plaque, or unaffected skin and represents systemic infiltration and spreading. The tumors can be pruritic and large (>10 cm) and ulceration can occur.
  1. Stage II disease is defined by the presence of tumors.
- In approximately 5% of cases of mycosis fungoides, the presentation may be a diffuse, painful, pruritive erythroderma known as Sézary syndrome.
  1. Stage III disease is defined by the presence of generalized erythroderma.
- Lymphadenopathy can occur during the plaque or tumor stages and may be regional or diffuse.
  1. Stage IVA disease is defined by a lymph node biopsy showing large clusters of atypical cells, more than six cells, or showing total effacerent by atypical cells.
- Infiltration of the liver, spleen, lungs, bone marrow, kidney, stomach, and brain can occur.
  1. Stage IVB disease is defined by the presence of visceral involvement.

ETIOLOGY

The specific cause of mycosis fungoides is not known. Infection with the retrovirus HTLV-1 has been suspected, given the association of HTLV-1 infected individuals and T-cell leukemia. Other considerations listed but unsubstantiated include environmental toxins (e.g., tobacco, pesticides, herbicides, and solvents) and genetic predisposition.

DIAGNOSIS

The diagnosis of mycosis fungoides is established by skin biopsy. This may be difficult to differentiate from other skin lesions in the early phases of the disease (e.g., premycotic patch or early plaque lesions) and therefore the diagnosis can only be suspected.

DIFFERENTIAL DIAGNOSIS

- Contact dermatitis
- Atopic dermatitis
- Nummular dermatitis
- Parapsoriases
- Superficial fungal infections
- Drug eruptions
- Psoriasis
- Photodermatitis
- Alopecia mucinosa
- Lymphomatoid papulosis

WORKUP

- Any patient who is suspected of having mycosis fungoides should have a staging workup done. Prognosis in patients with mycosis fungoides depends on the type of skin lesions and the extent of disease.
- The workup should focus on identifying:
  1. The type of skin lesion and the extent of skin involvement of the body (e.g., skin involvement is > or <10% of the skin surface)
  2. Presence of lymphadenopathy
  3. Visceral involvement (e.g., lungs, liver)
  4. Presence of Sézary cells in the blood
- A TNM staging classification has been proposed by the Cutaneous T-Cell Lymphoma Workshop in 1979 and continues to be used today in guiding therapy.

LABORATORY TESTS

- CBC with differential
- Total lymphocyte count
- Measure the percentage of Sézary cells present (normal <5%)
- BUN/creatinine
- Electrolytes, calcium, and phosphorus
- LFTs
- Multiple skin biopsies over suspected areas are done to confirm the diagnosis
- If lymph nodes are present, excisional lymph node biopsy is performed
- Bone marrow and liver biopsies can be done if initial laboratory screening suggests organ involvement

IMAGING STUDIES

- Chest x-ray to rule out pulmonary involvement
- Chest, abdominal, and pelvic CT-scan looking for mediastinal, abdominal, and pelvic lymphadenopathy

TREATMENT

Treatment is guided according to the stage of disease.

NONPHARMACOLOGIC THERAPY

- For dry cracking skin, emollients (e.g., lanolin and petrolatum) are applied bid.
- Moisturizing lotion (e.g., ammonium lactate) applied bid.
- Topical antibiotics (e.g., bacitracin) are used on ulcerative tumors.

ACUTE GENERAL Rx

- Treatment of patients with premycotic limited patch or plaque phase include:
  1. Psoralen ultraviolet light (PUVA) therapy where 0.6 mg/kg of 8-methoxypsoralen is ingested 1 to 2 hr before exposure of the skin to UV light (320 to 400 nm). This is done three times per week and tapered to two times per week until all the lesions have cleared. This is typically continued for 6 mo.
  2. Remissions can be retreated with PUVA.
- Treatment of patients with cutaneous patch and plaque lesions involving >10% of the skin surface includes:
  1. Topical chemotherapy using nitrogen mustard, carmustine, or mechlorethamine hydrochloride applied to the affected body areas.
  2. PUVA is an alternative treatment option.
- Treatment of patients with tumor phase disease includes:
  1. Total skin electron beam therapy in doses of 3000 to 3600 cGy given over 8 to 10 wk.
  2. Total skin electron beam therapy with PUVA is an alternative in recurrence tumor phase disease.

CHRONIC Rx

- In patients developing diffuse erythroderma (e.g., Sézary syndrome, extracorporeal photophoresis) in which 8-methoxypsoralen is ingested and peripheral blood is exposed to UVA through a membrane filter.
- Interferon and other systemic chemotherapeutic agents (e.g., methotrexate, cyclophosphamide, doxorubicin, vincristine, and prednisone) are considered in disseminated mycosis fungoides.

DISPOSITION

- The median survival in patients with early patch or plaque phase disease and no extradermal involvement is 12 yr.
- The median survival of patients with skin involvement, lymph node involvement, but no visceral involvement is approximately 5 yr.
- The median survival in patients with visceral involvement is 2.5 yr.

REFERRAL

Any patient with suspected mycosis fungoides should be referred to a dermatologist for definitive diagnosis and initial therapy. Oncology consultation is also indicated in patients with more advanced disease.

PEARLS & CONSIDERATIONS

COMMENTS

- Mycosis fungoides is thought to represent one class of the spectrum of cutaneous T-cell lymphomas. Sézary syndrome, reticulum-cell sarcoma, and histiocytic lymphoma are also classified as T-cell neoplasias.
- Alibert was the first to describe mycosis fungoides in 1806 and named it so because of its resemblance to mushrooms.

SUGGESTED READINGS

Apisarnthanarox N, Talpur R, Duvic M: Treatment of cutaneous T cell lymphoma: current status and future directions, *Am J Clin Dermatol* 3(3):195, 2002.

Kim YH, Hoppe RT: Mycosis fungoides and the Sézary syndrome, *Semin Oncol* 26(3):276, 1999.

Lorincz AL: Cutaneous T-cell lymphoma (mycosis fungoides), *Lancet* 347(9005):871, 1996.

Siegel RS, Kozel TM: Cutaneous T-cell lymphoma leukemia, *Curr Treat Options Oncol* 1(1):43, 2000.

AUTHOR: **PETER PETROPOULOS, M.D.**

BASIC INFORMATION

DEFINITION

Myelodysplastic syndromes (MDS) are a group of acquired clonal disorders affecting the hemopoietic stem cells and characterized by cytopenias with hypercellular bone marrow and various morphologic abnormalities in the hemopoietic cell lines. MDSs show abnormal (dysplastic) hemopoietic maturation. Marrow cellularity is increased, reflecting an effective hematopoiesis, but inadequate maturation results in peripheral cytopenias. Myelodysplasia encompasses several heterogenous syndromes. The French-American-British classification of myelodysplastic syndromes includes the following: refractory anemia, refractory anemia with ringed sideroblasts, refractory anemia with excess blasts, chronic myelomonocytic leukemia, and refractory anemia with excess blasts in transformation.

SYNONYMS

MDS
Preleukemia
Dysmyelopoietic syndrome

ICD-9CM CODES
238.7 Myelodysplastic syndrome

EPIDEMIOLOGY & DEMOGRAPHICS

INCIDENCE (IN U.S.): Approximately 82 cases/100,000 persons/yr
PREDOMINANT AGE: More common in elderly patients, with a median age of >65 yr

PHYSICAL FINDINGS & CLINICAL PRESENTATION

- Splenomegaly, skin pallor, mucosal bleeding, ecchymosis may be present.
- Patients often present with fatigue.
- Fever, infection, and dyspnea are common.

ETIOLOGY

Unknown. However, exposure to radiation, chemotherapeutic agents, benzene, or other organic compounds is associated with myelodysplasia.

DIAGNOSIS

DIFFERENTIAL DIAGNOSIS

- Hereditary dysplasias (e.g., Fanconi's anemia, Diamond-Blackfan syndrome)
- Vitamin B_{12}/folate deficiency
- Exposure to toxins (drugs, alcohol, chemotherapy)
- Renal failure
- Irradiation
- Autoimmune disease
- Infections (TB, viral infections)
- Paroxysmal nocturnal hemoglobinuria

WORKUP

- Diagnostic workup includes laboratory evaluation and bone marrow examination.
- An algorithmic approach to patients with suspected myelodysplastic syndromes is described in Section III.

LABORATORY TESTS

- Anemia with variable MCV (normal or increased)
- Reduced reticulocyte count (in relation to the degree of anemia)
- Hypogranular or agranular neutrophils
- Thrombocytopenia or normal platelet count
- Hypogranular platelets may be present
- Hypercellular bone marrow, with frequent clonal chromosomal abnormalities

IMAGING STUDIES

Abdominal CT scan may reveal hepatosplenomegaly.

TREATMENT

NONPHARMACOLOGIC THERAPY

RBC transfusions in patients with severe symptomatic anemia

ACUTE GENERAL Rx

- Results of chemotherapy are generally disappointing.
- The role of myeloid growth factors (granulocyte colony–stimulating factor, granulocyte-macrophage colony–stimulating factor) and immunotherapy is undefined. In a recent trial, 34% of patients treated with antithymocyte globulin (40 mg/kg for 4 days) became transfusion independent. Response was also associated with a statistically significantly longer survival.
- Allogeneic stem-cell transplantation should be considered in patients <60 yr old because this is the established procedure with cure potential.

CHRONIC Rx

Monitor for infections, bleeding, and complications of anemia.

DISPOSITION

- Cure rates in young patients with allogeneic bone marrow transplantations approach 30% to 50%.
- The risk of transformation to acute myelogenous leukemia varies with the percentage of blasts in the bone marrow.
- Advanced age, male sex, and deletion of chromosomes 5 and 7 are associated with a poor prognosis.
- According to the International Myelodysplastic Syndrome Risk Analysis Workshop, the most important variables in disease outcome are the specific cytogenetic abnormalities, the percentage of blasts in the bone marrow, and the number of hematopoietic lineages involved in the cytopenias.

REFERRAL

Hematology referral in all patients with MDS

PEARLS & CONSIDERATIONS

COMMENTS

- Erythropoietin (epoetin alfa) SC three times weekly may be effective in increasing the Hgb and reducing the RBC transfusion requirement in some patients.
- Lenalidomide, a novel analogue of thalidomide, has demonstrated hematologic activity in patients with low-rise myelodysplastic syndrome who have no response to erythropoietin or who are unlikely to benefit from conventional therapy.
- Patients with cytogenetic abnormalities associated with poor prognosis should be considered for aggressive treatment with high-dose chemotherapy and stem-cell transplantation.
- Nearly 50% of the deaths that result from myelodysplastic syndromes are the result of cytopenia associated with bone marrow failure.

SUGGESTED READINGS

List A et al: Efficacy of lenalidomide in myelodysplastic syndromes, *N Engl J Med* 352:549, 2005.
Molldrem JJ et al: Antithymocyte globulin for treatment of the bone marrow failure associated with myelodysplastic syndromes, *Ann Intern Med* 137:156, 2002.

AUTHOR: **FRED F. FERRI, M.D.**

BASIC INFORMATION

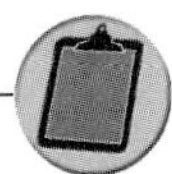

DEFINITION

Acute coronary syndromes are manifestations of ischemic heart disease and represent a broad clinical spectrum that includes unstable angina/non-ST elevation MI and ST-elevation MI.

1. **Myocardial infarction** is characterized by necrosis resulting from an insufficient supply of oxygenated blood to an area of the heart. According to the joint European Society of Cardiology/ American College of Cardiology, either one of the following criteria for acute evolving or recent MI satisfies the diagnosis:
   a. Typical rise and gradual fall (troponin) or more rapid rise and fall (CK-MB) of biochemical markers of myocardial necrosis with at least one of the following:
      i. Ischemic symptoms
      ii. Development of pathologic Q waves on ECG
      iii. ECG changes indicative of ischemia (ST-segment elevation or depression)
      iv. Coronary artery intervention (e.g., coronary angioplasty)
   b. Pathologic findings of acute MI
2. **ST elevation MI:** area of ischemic necrosis that penetrates the entire thickness of the ventricular wall and results in ST-segment elevation.
3. **Unstable angina:** coronary arterial plaque rupture with fragmentation and distal arterial embolization resulting in myocardial necrosis. Usually occurs without ST-elevation and is thus termed **non-ST elevation MI.**

SYNONYMS

MI
Non-ST elevation MI
ST-elevation MI
Heart attack
Coronary thrombosis
Coronary occlusion

ICD-9CM CODES
410.9 Acute myocardial infarction, unspecified site

EPIDEMIOLOGY & DEMOGRAPHICS

INCIDENCE/PREVALENCE (IN U.S.):

- >500 cases/100,000 persons.
- >500,000 MIs in the U.S. yearly.
- More prominent in males between the ages of 40 and 65 yr; no predominant sex after age 65 yr.
- Women experience more lethal and severe first acute MIs than men, regardless of comorbidity, previous angina, or age.
- At least one fourth of all myocardial infections are clinically unrecognized.

PHYSICAL FINDINGS & CLINICAL PRESENTATION

Clinical presentation:

- Crushing substernal chest pain usually lasts longer than 30 min.
- Pain is unrelieved by rest or sublingual nitroglycerin or is rapidly recurring.
- Pain radiates to the left or right arm, neck, jaw, back, shoulders, or abdomen and is not pleuritic in character.
- Pain may be associated with dyspnea, diaphoresis, nausea, or vomiting.
- There is no pain in approximately 20% of infarctions (usually in diabetic or elderly patients).

Physical findings:

- Skin may be diaphoretic, with pallor (because of decreased oxygen).
- Rales may be present at the bases of lungs (indicative of CHF).
- Cardiac auscultation may reveal an apical systolic murmur caused by mitral regurgitation secondary to papillary muscle dysfunction; S_3 or S_4 may also be present.
- Physical examination may be completely normal.

ETIOLOGY

- Coronary atherosclerosis
- Coronary artery spasm
- Coronary embolism (caused by infective endocarditis, rheumatic heart disease, intracavitary thrombus)
- Periarteritis and other coronary artery inflammatory diseases
- Dissection into coronary arteries (aneurysmal or iatrogenic)
- Congenital abnormalities of coronary circulation
- MI with normal coronaries (MINC syndrome): more frequent in younger patients and cocaine addicts. The risk of acute MI is increased by a factor of 24 during the 60 min after the use of cocaine in persons who are otherwise at relatively low risk. Most patients with cocaine-related MI are young, nonwhite, male cigarette smokers without other risk factors for ASHD who have a history of repeated cocaine use. Blood and urine toxicology screen for cocaine is recommended in all young patients who present with acute MI
- Hypercoagulable states, increased blood viscosity (polycythemia vera)

DIAGNOSIS

DIFFERENTIAL DIAGNOSIS

The various causes of myocardial ischemia are described in Section II along with the differential diagnosis of chest pain.

LABORATORY TESTS

- Cardiac troponin levels: cardiac-specific troponin T (cTnT) and cardiac-specific troponin I (cTnl) are highly specific for myocardial injury. Increases in serum levels of cTnT and cTnI may occur relatively early after muscle damage (3-12 hr), peak within 24 hr, and may be present for several days after MI (up to 7 days for cTnI and up to 10-14 days for cTnT). Troponin T tests can be falsely positive in patients with renal failure. The threshold level of troponin T considered positive for MI is 0.1 ng/ml in patients with normal renal function or 0.5 ng/ml in patients with renal impairment.
- Creatine kinase MB isoenzyme is a useful marker for MI. It is released in the circulation in amounts that correlate with the size of the infarct.
- Neither CK-MB nor troponin consistently appear in the blood within 6 hr after an ischemic event; therefore serial testing (e.g., on presentation and after 8 hr) is necessary to definitely rule out MI.
- ECG:

1. In ST-elevation MI, there is development of:
   a. Inverted T waves, indicating an area of ischemia
   b. Elevated ST segment, indicating an area of injury
   c. Q waves, indicating an area of infarction (usually develop over 12 to 36 hr)
2. In unstable angina/non-ST elevation MI, Q waves are absent, but the following indications are present:
   a. History and myocardial enzyme elevations are compatible with MI.
   b. ECG shows ST segment elevation, depression, or no change followed by T wave inversion.

IMAGING STUDIES

- Chest radiography is useful to evaluate for pulmonary congestion and exclude other causes of chest pain.
- Echocardiography can evaluate wall motion abnormalities and identify mural thrombus or mitral regurgitation, which can occur acutely after MI.

TREATMENT

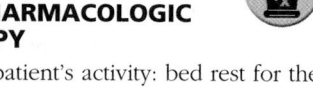

NONPHARMACOLOGIC THERAPY

- Limit patient's activity: bed rest for the initial 24 hr; if the patient remains stable, gradually increase activity.
- Diet: NPO until stable, then no added salt and a low-cholesterol diet.
- Patient education to decrease the risk of subsequent cardiac events (proper diet, cessation of smoking, regular exercise) should be initiated when the patient is medically stable.

ACUTE GENERAL Rx

- Any patient with suspected acute MI should immediately receive the following:
  1. Aspirin: give 160 to 325 mg PO unless true aspirin allergy is suspected. If the first dose is chewed, a blood level is achieved more rapidly than if it is swallowed. Clopidogrel may be substituted if true allergy is present.
  2. Nitrates: they increase the supply of oxygen by reducing coronary vasospasm and decrease consumption of oxygen by reducing ventricular preload. Sublingual nitroglycerin can be administered immediately on suspicion of MI (unless systolic blood pressure is <90 mm Hg or heart rate is <50 bpm or >100 bpm); IV nitroglycerin can be subsequently used. Nitroglycerin should be used with great caution in patients with inferior wall MI; nitrate usage can result in hypotension because these patients are sensitive to change in preload. It should also be avoided in patients suspected of having right ventricular infarction (increased risk of preload reduction) and if a patient has used sildenafil (Viagra), or vardenafil (Levitra) within the previous 24 hr or tadalafil (Cialis) in the previous 36 to 48 hr.
  3. Adequate analgesia: morphine sulfate 2 mg IV q5min PRN can be given for severe pain unrelieved by nitroglycerin. Hypotension secondary to morphine can be treated with careful IV hydration with saline solution. If sinus bradycardia accompanies hypotension, use atropine (0.5 to 1.0 mg IV q 5 min PRN to a total dose of 2.5 mg). Respiratory depression caused by morphine can be reversed with naloxone (Narcan) 0.8 mg.
  4. Nasal oxygen: administer at 2 to 4 L/min.
- If readily available without delay, percutaneous coronary intervention (PCI) with adjunctive glycoprotein IIb/IIIa is preferred over thrombolytic therapy. It is effective and generally results in more favorable outcomes than thrombolytic therapy. When PCI is performed, use of IV heparin is recommended. Coronary stents are useful to decrease ischemia, improve long-term patency, and lower the rate of restenosis of the infarct-related artery.
- Thrombolytic therapy: if the duration of pain has been <6 hr and primary angioplasty is not readily available, recanalization of the occluded arteries should be attempted with thrombolytic agents, possibly in combination with glycoprotein IIb/IIIa inhibition. Because the effectiveness of thrombolytics is time-dependent, ideally these agents should be administered either in the field or within 30 min of the patient's arrival in the emergency department. When tPA or rPA is used, IV heparin is given to increase the likelihood of patency in the infarct-related artery. In patients receiving streptokinase or APSAC, IV heparin is not indicated, because it does not offer any additional benefit and can result in increased bleeding complications. Tenecteplase and reteplase are comparable with accelerated infusion recombinant TPA in terms of efficacy and safety, but are more convenient because they are administered by bolus injection. Lanoplase and heparin bolus plus infusion is as effective as TPA with regard to mortality, but the rate of intracranial hemorrhage is significantly higher. Absolute contraindications to thrombolytic therapy include active internal bleeding, intracranial neoplasm or arteriovenous malformation, intracranial surgery in past 6 mo, stroke in past year, head trauma with loss of consciousness in past 6 mo, surgery in noncompressible location in past 6 wk, alteration in mental status, and infectious endocarditis.
- β-adrenergic blocking agents should be given to all patients with evolving acute MI, provided that there are no contraindications (see below). β-Blockers are useful to reduce myocardial oxygen consumption and prevent tachyarrhythmias. Early IV β-blockage (in the initial 24 hr) followed by institution of an oral maintenance regimen is also effective in reducing recurrent infarction and ischemia. Frequently used agents are:
  1. Metoprolol (Lopressor): IV 5 mg q2min × 3 doses, then PO 25 to 50 mg q6h, given 15 min after last IV dose, continued for 48 hr; maintenance dosage is 50 to 100 mg bid.
  2. Atenolol (Tenormin): IV 5 mg over 5 min, repeat in 10 min if initial dose is well tolerated, then start PO dose 10 min after the last IV dose; PO 50 mg qd, increasing to 100 mg as tolerated.

  Before using β-blockers, some of the contraindications and side effects (i.e., exacerbation of asthma, CNS effects, hypertension, bradycardia) must be carefully assessed.
- ACE inhibitors reduce left ventricular dysfunction and dilation and slow the progression of CHF during and after acute MI. They should be initiated within hours of hospitalization, provided that the patient does not have hypotension or a contraindication (bilateral renal stenosis, renal failure, or history of angioedema caused by previous treatment with ACE inhibitors).
  1. Commonly used agents are captopril 12.5 mg PO bid, enalapril 2.5 mg bid, or lisinopril 2.5 to 5 mg qd initially, with subsequent titration as needed.
  2. ACE inhibitors may be stopped in patients without complications and no evidence of left ventricular dysfunction after 6 to 8 wk.
  3. ACE inhibitors should be continued indefinitely in patients with impaired left ventricular function (ejection fraction <40%) or clinical CHF.
- Glycoprotein IIb receptor inhibitors (tirofiban, eptifibatide), when administered with heparin and aspirin, further reduce the incidence of ischemic events in patients with non-Q wave MI. The use of IV glycoprotein IIb/IIIa inhibitors (e.g., abciximab) before and during PTCA also reduces the risk of closure postangioplasty.
- Initiation of statin therapy before hospital discharge.

CHRONIC Rx

Discharge medications in all patients with UA/NSTEMI (unless contraindicated) should include antiischemic medications (e.g., nitroglycerin, β-blocker), lipid-lowering agents, and aspirin (81-325 mg/day), Clopidogrel (Plavix), 75 mg/day can be given in addition to aspirin for up to nine months or in place of aspirin in those who cannot tolerate aspirin. The addition of ACE inhibitors is also recommended in all patients with diabetes, CHF, and in those with EF <40%.

Evaluation of post-MI patients

- Submaximal (low level) treadmill test (can be done 1 to 3 wk after MI) in stable patients without any clinical evidence of significant left ventricular dysfunction or post-MI angina
  1. Useful to assess the patient's functional capacity and formulate an at-home exercise program
  2. Helpful to determine the patient's prognosis
- Radionuclide angiography or two-dimensional echocardiography
  1. To evaluate patient's left ventricular ejection fraction
  2. To evaluate ventricular size and segmental wall motion
  3. Echocardiography to rule out presence of mural thrombi in patients with anterior wall infarction; transesophageal echo is preferred if mural thrombosis is suspected
- A 24-hr Holter monitor study to evaluate patients who have demonstrated significant arrhythmias during their hospital stay; selected patients with complex ventricular ectopy may be candidates for programmed electrical stimulation studies and antiarrhythmic therapy and/or implanted defibrillator, depending on the results of these studies

DISPOSITION

The prognosis after MI depends on multiple factors:

- Use of β-blockers: the mortality of patients on a regular regimen of β-blockers is significantly decreased when compared with that of control groups. Discharge medication in patients with UA/NSTEMI should include a β-blocker in all patients without contraindications.
- Presence of arrhythmias, frequent ventricular ectopy (≥10/hr), or repetitive forms of ventricular ectopic beats (couplets, triplets) indicates an increased risk (two to three times greater) of sudden cardiac death. New bundle branch block, Mobitz II second-degree block, and third-degree heart block also adversely affect outcome.
- Size of infarct: the larger it is, the higher the post-MI mortality rate. Significant myocardial stunning with subsequent improvement of ventricular function occurs in most patients after anterior MI. A lower level of creatine kinase, an estimate of the extent of necrosis, is independently predictive of recovery of function.
- Site of infarct: inferior wall MI carries a better prognosis than anterior wall MI; however, patients with inferior wall MI and right ventricular involvement have a high risk for arrhythmic complications and cardiac shock.
- Ejection fraction after MI: the lower the left ventricular ejection fraction, the higher the mortality after MI.
- Presence of post-MI angina indicates a high mortality rate.
- Performance on low-level exercise test: the presence of ST segment changes during the test is a predictor of high mortality during the first year.
- Presence of pericarditis during the acute phase of MI increases mortality at 1 yr.
- Type A behavior (competitive drive, ambitiousness, hostility) is associated with a lower mortality rate after symptomatic MI.
- The Killip classification is an independent predictor of all-cause mortality in patients with non-ST elevation acute coronary syndromes.
- Self-reported moderate alcohol consumption in the year before acute MI is associated with reduced 1-yr mortality.
- Discharge medication in patients with UA/NSTEMI should include lipid-lowering agents in patients with hyperlipidemia unresponsive to exercise and dietary restrictions is beneficial. Statins may also lower vascular inflammation and damage by mechanisms other than reduction of LDL cholesterol. Early initiation of statin treatment in patients with acute MI is associated with reduced 1-yr mortality.
- Additional poor prognostic factors include the following: cigarette smoking, history of hypertension or prior MI, presence of ST segment depression in acute MI, increasing age, diabetes mellitus, and female sex (especially women >50 yr of age).

SUGGESTED READINGS

Andersen HR et al: A comparison of coronary angioplasty with fibrinolytic therapy in acute myocardial infarction, *N Engl J Med* 349:733, 2003.

Becker RC: Antithrombotic therapy after myocardial infarction, *N Engl J Med* 347:1019, 2002.

Birnbaum Y et al: Ventricular septal rupture after acute myocardial infarction, *N Engl J Med* 347:1426, 2002.

Brennan ML et al: Prognostic value of myeloperoxidase in patients with chest pain. N Engl J Med 349:1595, 2003

Cannon CP, Baim DS: Expanding the reach of primary percutaneous coronary intervention for the treatment of acute myocardial infarction, *J Am Coll Cardiol* 39:1720, 2002.

Cannon CP et al: Intensive versus moderate lipid lowering with statins after acute coronary syndromes, *N Eng L Med* 350:1495, 2004.

Dickstein K et al: Effects of losartan and captopril on mortality and morbidity in high-risk patients after acute myocardial infarction: the OPTIMAAL randomized trial, *Lancet* 360:752, 2002.

Hurlen et al: Warfarin, aspirin, or both after myocardial infarction, *N Engl J Med* 347:969, 2002.

Khot UN et al: Prognostic importance of physical examination for heart failure in Non-ST elevation acute coronary syndromes, *JAMA* 290:2174, 2003.

Meier MA et al: The new definition of myocardial infarction, *Arch Intern Med* 162: 1585, 2002.

Moss AJ et al: Prophylactic implantation of a defibrillator in patients with myocardial infarction and reduced ejection fraction, *N Engl J Med* 346:877, 2002.

Newby LK et al: Early statin initiation and outcomes in patients with acute coronary syndromes, *JAMA* 287:3087, 2002.

Stenestrand U, Wallentin L: Early revascularisation and 1-year survival in 14-day survivors of acute myocardial infarction: a prospective cohort study, *Lancet* 359:1805, 2002.

Stone GW et al: Comparison of angioplasty with stenting, with or without abciximab, in acute myocardial infarction, *N Engl J Med* 346:957, 2002.

Wiviott SD, Braunwauld E: Unstable Angina and Non-ST-Segment Elevation Myocardial Infarction, *Am Fam Physician* 70:525, 2004.

Zimetbaum PJ, Josephson ME: Use of electrocardiogram in acute myocardial infarction, *N Engl J Med* 348:933, 2003.

AUTHOR: **FRED F. FERRI, M.D.**

Myocarditis

BASIC INFORMATION

DEFINITION

Myocarditis is an inflammatory condition of the myocardium.

ICD-9CM CODES
429.0 Myocarditis, nonspecific
391.2 Myocarditis, rheumatic
422.91 Myocarditis, viral (except coxsackie)
074.23 Myocarditis, coxsackie
422.92 Myocarditis, bacterial

EPIDEMIOLOGY & DEMOGRAPHICS

- The incidence of focal myocarditis reported at autopsy is 1% to 7% in asymptomatic patients.
- Myocarditis is a major cause of sudden unexpected death (15% to 20% of cases) in adults <40 years of age.

PHYSICAL FINDINGS & CLINICAL PRESENTATION

- Persistent tachycardia out of proportion to fever
- Faint S_1, S_4 sound on auscultation
- Murmur of mitral regurgitation
- Pericardial friction rub if associated with pericarditis
- Signs of biventricular failure (hypotension, hepatomegaly, peripheral edema, distention of neck veins, S_3)
- Patients may present with a history of recent flulike syndrome (fever, arthralgias, malaise)

ETIOLOGY

- Infection
  1. Viral (coxsackie B virus, CMV, echovirus, polio virus, adenovirus, mumps, HIV, EBV)
  2. Bacterial (*Staphylococcus aureus, Clostridium perfringens,* diphtheria, and any severe bacterial infection)
  3. Mycoplasma
  4. Mycotic *(Candida, Mucor, Aspergillus)*
  5. Parasitic (*Trypanosoma cruzi, Trichinella, Echinococcus,* amoeba, *Toxoplasma*)
  6. *Rickettsia rickettsii*
  7. Spirochetal (*Borrelia burgdorferi*—Lyme carditis)
- Rheumatic fever
- Secondary to drugs (e.g., cocaine, emetine, doxorubicin, sulfonamides, isoniazid, methyldopa, amphotericin B, tetracycline, phenylbutazone, lithium, 5-FU, phenothiazines, interferon alfa, tricyclic antidepressants, cyclophosphamides)
- Toxins (carbon monoxide, ethanol, diphtheria toxin, lead, arsenicals)
- Collagen-vascular disease (SLE, scleroderma, sarcoidosis, Kawasaki syndrome)
- Sarcoidosis
- Radiation
- Postpartum

DIAGNOSIS

DIFFERENTIAL DIAGNOSIS

- Cardiomyopathy
- Acute myocardial infarction
- Valvulopathies

The differential diagnosis of chest pain is described in Section II

WORKUP

- Medical history: the clinical presentation of myocarditis is nonspecific and can consist of fatigue, palpitations, dyspnea, precordial discomfort, myalgias.
- Diagnostic workup includes chest x-ray examination, ECG, laboratory evaluation, echocardiogram, cardiac catheterization, and endomyocardial biopsy (selected patients).

LABORATORY TESTS

- Elevated cardiac troponin T (TnT) is suggestive of myocarditis in patients with clinically suspected myocarditis. A normal level does not rule out the diagnosis
- Increased CK (with elevated MB fraction, LDH), and AST secondary to myocardial necrosis
- Increased ESR (nonspecific but may be of value in following the progress of the disease and the response to therapy)
- Increased WBC (increased eosinophils if parasitic infection)
- Viral titers (acute and convalescent)
- Cold agglutinin titer, ASLO titer, blood cultures
- Lyme disease antibody titer

IMAGING STUDIES

- Chest x-ray: enlargement of cardiac silhouette
- ECG: sinus tachycardia with nonspecific ST-T wave changes; interventricular conduction defects and bundle branch block may be present
  1. Lyme disease and diphtheria cause all degrees of heart block.
  2. Changes of acute MI can occur with focal necrosis.
- Echocardiogram:
  1. Dilated and hypokinetic chambers
  2. Segmental wall motion abnormalities
- Cardiac catheterization and angiography:
  1. To rule out coronary artery disease and valvular disease.
  2. A right ventricular endomyocardial biopsy can confirm the diagnosis, although a negative biopsy result does not exclude myocarditis. Recent studies have shown that myocardial biopsy may be unnecessary, because immunosuppression therapy based on biopsy results is generally ineffective.

TREATMENT

NONPHARMACOLOGIC THERAPY

- Supportive care is the first line of therapy for patients with myocarditis.
- Restrict physical activity (to decrease cardiac work). Bed rest is advisable during viremia.

ACUTE GENERAL Rx

- Treat underlying cause (e.g., use specific antibiotics for bacterial infection).
- Treat CHF with diuretics, ACE inhibitors, and salt restriction. A β-blocker may be added once clinical stability has been achieved. Digoxin should be used with caution and only at low doses.
- If ventricular arrhythmias are present, treat with quinidine or procainamide.
- Provide anticoagulation to prevent thromboembolism.
- Use preload and afterload reducing agents for treating cardiac decompensation.
- Corticosteroid use is contraindicated in early infectious myocarditis; it may be justified in only selected patients with intractable CHF, severe systemic toxicity, and severe life-threatening arrhythmias.
- Immunosuppressive drugs (prednisone with cyclosporine or azathioprine) do not have any significant effect on the prognosis of myocarditis and should not be used in the routine treatment of patients with myocarditis. Immunosuppression may have a role in the treatment of myocarditis from systemic autoimmune disease (e.g., SLE, scleroderma) and in patients with idiopathic giant cell myocarditis.

DISPOSITION

Nearly 50% of patients with myocarditis will die within 5 yr of diagnosis. Prognosis is best for patients with "fulminant" lymphocytic myocarditis (severe hemodynamic compromise, rapid onset of symptoms, or high fever). These patients tend to have complete recovery with total resolution of myocarditis on repeat biopsy

REFERRAL

Consider heart transplant if patient develops intractable CHF.

SUGGESTED READING

Wu LA et al: Current role of endomyocardial biopsy in the management of dilated cardiomyopathy and myocarditis, *Mayo Clin Proc* 76:1030, 2001.

AUTHOR: **FRED F. FERRI, M.D.**

BASIC INFORMATION

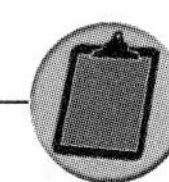

DEFINITION

Sudden, brief, involuntary jerks or contractions, either rhythmic or irregular, of single muscles or groups of muscles. It can occur at rest or in response to sensory stimulation (touch, auditory, visual) and can involve active muscle contraction (positive myoclonus) or inhibition of ongoing muscle activity (negative myoclonus). Myoclonus is not a disease entity, but rather a symptom that may result from a wide variety of disorders.

ICD-9CM CODES
333.2 Myoclonus

EPIDEMIOLOGY & DEMOGRAPHICS

INCIDENCE: 1.3 cases/100,000 person-years. Incidence increases with age.
LIFETIME PREVALENCE: 8.6/100,000 persons

CLINICAL PRESENTATION

- Careful history of any precipitating or alleviating factors—sensory stimuli, startle, alcohol (may alleviate essential myoclonus).
- History of accompanying neurologic symptoms (seizures, cognitive decline, family history) provide an important clue to diagnoses like myoclonic epilepsies versus essential myoclonus.
- Clinical features and natural history vary with the underlying disorder.
- Frequently normal physical examination.
- Myoclonic jerks may be seen on examination and persist during sleep.
- Spatial distribution of myoclonus (unilateral versus bilateral, focal versus generalized) may provide clues to the etiology.
- Try to determine whether myoclonus occurs spontaneously or with particular precipitants.
- Testing the patient with outstretched arms might reveal negative myoclonus (asterixis) in metabolic encephalopathy.

ETIOLOGY

Five major etiologic categories:
- Physiologic myoclonus—hiccups, hypnic jerks, anxiety induced, exercise induced, benign infantile.
- Essential myoclonus—autosomal dominant and sporadic varieties.
- Epileptic myoclonus—includes progressive degenerative disorders of the nervous system in which myoclonus may occur in association with dementia, ataxia, and multiple seizure types. Examples include myoclonic absence, infantile spasms, and Lennox-Gastaut syndrome.
- Symptomatic myoclonus in progressive myoclonic epilepsies—includes diseases where myoclonus is accompanied by other multisystem disturbances. Examples include mitochondrial and storage disease, such as sialidoses type I and II, Gaucher's type 3, GM2 gangliosidoses, MERRF (myoclonus epilepsy with ragged red fibers), ceroid lipofuscinoses, and Unverricht-Lundborg disease.
- Symptomatic myoclonus without prominent seizures—examples include posthypoxic, posttraumatic, myoclonic dementias (e.g., Creutzfeldt-Jakob disease); basal ganglia disorders such as Parkinson's, Huntington's, and Wilson's disease; drug-induced myoclonus; systemic metabolic disturbances such as uremia and liver failure; and viral infections.

DIAGNOSIS

DIFFERENTIAL DIAGNOSIS

- Tremor—usually rhythmic and oscillatory and significantly slower than myoclonus.
- Tics—often slower than myoclonus and are stereotyped and repetitive.
- Paroxysmal dyskinesias—episodic and sometimes triggered by voluntary movement.
- Dystonia—typically a sustained posture, but can sometimes have rapid clonic movements that mimic myoclonus.
- Psychogenic myoclonus—in patients with conversion disorder.

WORKUP

Given the large number of conditions in which myoclonus may occur, workup of myoclonus should be individualized.

LABORATORY TESTS

- General chemistry (sodium, magnesium, carbon dioxide, creatinine, liver function test, renal function, toxicology screen)
- HIV testing
- Lumbar puncture (for suspected viral encephalopathies, or CJD)
- Genetic testing (if diagnosis of progressive myoclonic epilepsy is entertained)
- EEG (to determine whether myoclonus is epileptic or not)

IMAGING STUDIES

MRI may show T1 hyperintensity in the putamen in hepatolenticular degeneration, or characteristic diffusion-weighted imaging abnormalities in CJD.

TREATMENT

NONPHARMACOLOGIC THERAPY

In cases where myoclonus is a consequence of an underlying metabolic abnormality, correction of the disturbance should be addressed.

ACUTE GENERAL Rx

- Most commonly used are clonazepam and valproic acid (VPA).

CHRONIC Rx

- Posthypoxic myoclonus (Lance-Adams syndrome): clonazepam, VPA, levetiracetam.
- Progressive myoclonic epilepsy: piracetam (not FDA approved), VPA, clonazepam; recent reports of zonisamide being very effective.
- Essential myoclonus: clonazepam; very responsive to small amounts of alcohol.
- Intractable hiccups: baclofen, amitriptyline, VPA.
- Palatal myoclonus: clonazepam, sumatriptan, botulinum toxin.
- Positive myoclonus often responds to treatment, whereas therapy for negative myoclonus is extremely limited.

DISPOSITION

Prognosis depends on the underlying neurologic disorder responsible for the myoclonus

REFERRAL

Neurologist with an interest in movement disorders.

PEARLS & CONSIDERATIONS

COMMENTS

- Myoclonus should be regarded as the "tip of the iceberg" of an underlying disorder; it is a symptom rather than a disease.
- Myoclonus may occur in a wide variety of conditions and at times may be disabling.
- Most current therapies rely on antiepileptics, with acceptable results.

SUGGESTED READINGS

Agarwal P et al: Myoclonus, *Curr Opin Neurol* 16:515, 2003.

Brashear A: Approach to the hyperkinetic patient. In Biller J (ed): *Practical Neurology*, Philadelphia, 2002, Lippincott Williams and Wilkins.

Fahn S et al: Definition and classification of myoclonus, *Adv Neurol* 143:1, 1986.

Frucht S: Myoclonus. In Noseworthy J (ed): *Neurological Therapeutics, Principle and Practice*, London, 2003, Martin Dunitz.

Myoclonus Research Foundation: http://www.myoclonus.com.

NINDS Myoclonus fact sheet: http://www.ninds.nih.gov/health_and_medical/pubs/myoclonus_doc.htm.

AUTHOR: **ACHRAF A. MAKKI, M.D., M.Sc.**

BASIC INFORMATION

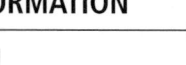

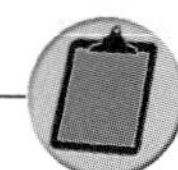

DEFINITION

Inflammatory myopathies are idiopathic diseases of muscle characterized clinically by muscle weakness and pathologically by inflammation and muscle fiber breakdown. The three most common are dermatomyositis, polymyositis, and inclusion body myositis. (See also, inclusion body myositis entry.)

SYNONYMS

See Definition.

ICD-9CM CODES
710.3 Dermatomyositis
710.4 Polymyositis
729.1: Myalgia and myositis unspecified

EPIDEMIOLOGY & DEMOGRAPHICS

Dermatomyositis (DM)

- Occurs in children and in adults.
- Incidence 1:100,000.
- Prevalence 1-10 cases/million in adults and 1-3.2 cases/million in children.
- More common in females than males (2:1).
- Average age at diagnosis is 40. The average age of onset in children is between 5 and 14 yr.
- Approximately 15%-20% of patients with DM over the age of 50 have associated malignancies.

Polymyositis (PM)

- Incidence: 5 cases/1 million annually.
- Age >18 yr.

Inclusion body myositis (IBM)

- Comprises about 15%-25% of inflammatory myopathies.
- Male:female ratio is 3:1.
- Most common myopathy above the age of 50.
- Some inherited forms, as opposed to DM and PM.

PHYSICAL FINDINGS & CLINICAL PRESENTATION

DM and PM:

- Most patients have a subacute onset, over weeks to months.
- Symmetrical proximal muscle weakness involving the neck flexors, shoulders, and pelvic girdle.
- Difficulty getting up from a chair, climbing stairs, reaching for objects above head, or combing hair.
- Distal muscle and ocular involvement is uncommon.
- Sensation and reflexes are preserved.
- Dysphagia and dysphonia result from pharyngeal muscle involvement.
- Esophageal dysmotility often occurs in DM.
- Rales, dyspnea, and respiratory failure from associated pulmonary fibrosis.
- Cardiac conduction abnormalities can be seen with DM.
- Systemic autoimmune disease occurs frequently in PM, and rarely in DM.
- Skin findings in DM:
  1. Heliotrope rash on the upper eyelids (Fig. 1-154)
  2. Erythematous rash on the face (see Fig. 1-154)
  3. Can also involve the back and shoulders (shawl sign), neck and chest (V-shape), knees and elbows
  4. Photosensitivity
  5. Gottron's papules (violaceous papules overlying dorsal interphalangeal or metacarpophalangeal areas, elbow or knee joints—Fig. 1-155)
  6. Nail cracking, thickening, and irregularity with periungual telangiectasia (see Fig. 1-155)
  7. Mechanic's hand: fissured, hyperpigmented, scaly, and hyperkeratotic; also associated with increased risk of interstitial lung disease

IBM:

- Asymmetric.
- Preferential weakness for quadriceps and wrist/finger flexors out of proportion to weakness in other muscles.
- Neck flexor weakness and paraspinal muscle weakness can be seen.
- Reflexes and sensation are preserved.
- Dysphagia is common.

ETIOLOGY:

- DM: humorally mediated microangiopathy
- PM: unknown
  1. Cell-mediated immune major histocompatibility-I (MHC-1) process directed against muscle fibers is likely, given biopsy features.
  2. A viral etiology has been proposed secondary to the presence of autoantibodies to histidyl transferase antibody, anti-Jo-1 antibody, and signal recognition particle.
- IBM: unknown in sporadic cases (majority). There is a rare, autosomal recessive form of IBM.

FIGURE 1-154 The facial rash of juvenile dermatomyositis. There is erythema over the bridge of the nose and malar areas, with violaceous (heliotropic) discoloration of the upper eyelids. (From Behrman RE: *Nelson textbook of pediatrics,* ed 16, Philadelphia, 2000, WB Saunders.)

DIAGNOSIS

- Characteristic pattern of muscle weakness for each type.
- EMG and nerve conduction studies should be consistent with myopathic features.
- Laboratory tests listed below.
- Biopsy required for diagnosis and should confirm inflammation *before* treatment started: myopathic features (variation in fiber size, fiber splitting, fatty replacement of muscle tissue, and increased endomysial connective tissue) should be seen in addition to the following:
  1. DM: perifascicular atrophy, MAC deposition along capillaries
  2. PM: endomysial infiltrates composed of CD8+ T cells and macrophages invading nonnecrotic muscle fibers that express MHC-I antigen.
  3. IBM: inclusion bodies and rimmed vacuoles—these features may not be seen despite a classic presentation, and patients may be erroneously diagnosed with PM.

DIFFERENTIAL DIAGNOSIS

- Muscular dystrophies
- Amyloid myoneuropathy
- Amyotrophic lateral sclerosis
- Myasthenia gravis
- Eaton-Lambert syndrome
- Drug-induced myopathies (e.g., quinidine, NSAIDs, penicillamine, HMG CoA-reductase inhibitors)
- Diabetic amyotrophy

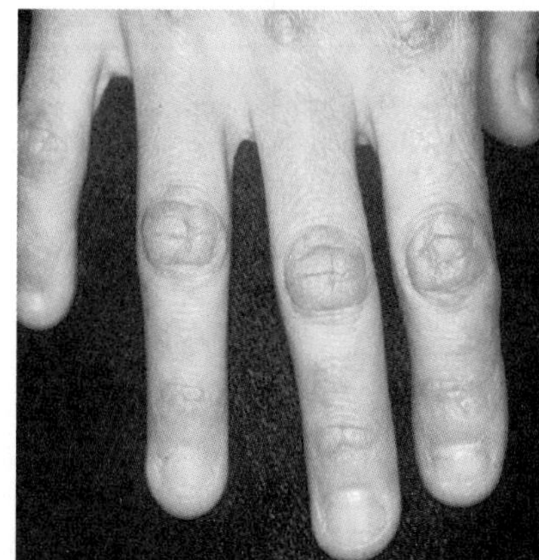

FIGURE 1-155 Dermatomyositis (Gottron's papules). Note erythematous papules over joints and periungual telangiectasias. (From Nobel J [ed]: *Textbook of primary care medicine,* ed 2, St Louis, 1996, Mosby.)

- Guillain-Barré syndrome
- Hyperthyroidism or hypothyroidism
- Lichen planus
- Amyopathic DM (rash without weakness)
- SLE
- Contact atopic or seborrheic dermatitis
- Psoriasis

LABORATORY TESTS

- Creatine kinase is the most sensitive muscle enzyme test for muscle breakdown and can be elevated as much as 50 times above normal in DM and PM. In IBM, it may be only slightly elevated.
- Aldolase, AST, ALT, alkaline phosphatase, and LDH can be elevated. ESR, although not specific, is elevated in the majority of cases of DM and PM.
- Anti-Jo-1 antibodies are seen in myositis with associated interstitial lung disease, but are not specific for either DM or PM.
- Electrolytes, TSH, Ca, and Mg should be requested to exclude other causes of weakness.
- ECG for cardiac involvement.

IMAGING STUDIES

- Chest x-ray to rule out pulmonary involvement. If suspicious for pulmonary interstitial disease, a high-resolution CT scan of the chest may be helpful.
- Video fluoroscopy or barium swallow to look for upper esophageal dysfunction in patients with dysphagia and DM.

TREATMENT

The therapeutic goal is to maintain function and prevent or minimize sequelae. There is no current pharmacologic treatment for IBM; treatment discussed below is for either DM or PM. In general, patients with DM seem to respond better than patients with PM.

NONPHARMACOLOGIC THERAPY

- Sun-blocking agents with SPF 15 or greater for skin protection in patients with DM.
- Physical therapy is beneficial for gait training and increasing muscle tone and strength.
- Occupational therapy to assist with activities of daily living.
- Speech therapy for dysphagia and swallowing problems.

ACUTE GENERAL Rx

- Prednisone 1-2 mg/kg per day up to 100 mg/day. The dose is continued until muscle strength improves and/or muscle enzymes have returned to normal for 4 weeks. Thereafter, taper by 10 mg/month until 60 mg/day, then taper by 5 mg/month. When the patient is stable, every-other-day prednisone treatment at same dose may decrease side effects.
- Immunosuppressive agents such as intravenous immunoglobulin (IVIg) or cyclophosphamide should be used if the patient fails to improve on prednisone or muscle enzymes begin rising when tapering off prednisone. See Chronic Rx for specific dosage.
- Hydroxychloroquine can be used to treat the cutaneous lesions of DM.

CHRONIC Rx

The goal is to maintain strength while sparing steroid use.

- Chronic prednisone therapy may be needed for years, but other immunosuppressive agents should be added early to decrease long-term steroid side effects.
- Azathioprine 2-3 mg/kg per day tapered to 1 mg/kg per day once steroid is tapered to 15 mg/day. Reduce dosage monthly by 25-mg intervals. Maintenance dosage is 50 mg/day.
- Methotrexate 7.5 to 10 mg PO/wk, increased by 2.5 mg/wk to total of 25 mg/wk.
- IVIg 2g/kg total dose over 2-5 days can be used before azathioprine/methotrexate use. If improvement occurred after initial dosing, this would need to be repeated if a clinical relapse was evident.
- IV cyclophosphamide 1 g/M^2 monthly x 6 is preferred to oral dosing for refractory cases. However, oral dosing of cyclophosphamide is 1-3 mg/kg per day PO or 2-4 mg/kg per day in conjunction with prednisone.
- Other drugs include mycophenolate mofetil, cyclosporine, and hydroxychloroquine.

DISPOSITION

- As treatment is initiated, the muscle enzymes should return to normal before symptoms improve.
- During exacerbations, enzymes may rise first before symptoms appear.
- Approximately 50% of the patients will go into remission and stop therapy within 5 yr. The remaining will have either active disease requiring ongoing treatment or inactive disease with permanent muscle atrophy and contractures.
- Poor prognostic indicators include:
  1. Delay in diagnosis
  2. Older age
  3. Recalcitrant disease
  4. Malignancy
  5. Interstitial pulmonary fibrosis
  6. Dysphagia
  7. Leukocytosis
  8. Fever
  9. Anorexia
  10. Infection, malignancy, and cardiac and pulmonary dysfunction are the most common causes of death

With early treatment, 5- and 8-yr survival rates of 80% and 73%, respectively, have been reported.

REFERRAL

- Neurology or rheumatology referral should be made to help establish the diagnosis and implement treatment.
- ENT referral for pharyngeal myotomy procedure should be considered before gastrostomy tube placement for patients with IBM.

PEARLS & CONSIDERATIONS

COMMENTS

- Do *not* implement treatment before muscle biopsy.
- When assessing response to treatment, it is best to follow clinical muscle strength over muscle enzyme tests.
- The concern of malignancies (ovary, lung, breast, GI) associated with myositis is legitimate and merits screening in patients older than age 40 at time of diagnosis and every 2-3 yr thereafter.
- There does not appear to be any association between juvenile dermatomyositis and malignancy.
- Overlap syndrome refers to patients with dermatomyositis who also meet criteria for other connective tissue disorder (e.g., rheumatoid arthritis, scleroderma, SLE).
- If patient is taking steroids chronically, be sure to monitor for development of:
  1. Diabetes (oral glucose tolerance test or hemoglobin A1C)
  2. Osteopenia/osteoporosis (DEXA scan q 6 months)
  3. Cataracts (yearly ophthalmologic appointment)
  4. Hypertension
  5. Psychiatric side effects including depression or psychosis
  6. Poor sleep (prescribe nighttime sleep aids if needed)
  7. Peptic ulcer disease (prescribe H2 antagonist or proton-pump inhibitor)

SUGGESTED READINGS

Amato AA, Griggs RC: Unicorns, dragons, polymyositis, and other mythological beasts, *Neurology* 61:288, 2003.

Callen JP: Dermatomyositis, *Lancet* 355(9197): 53, 2000.

Dalakas M: Controlled studies with high-dose intravenous immunoglobulin in the treatment of dermatomyositis, inclusion body myositis, and polymyositis, *Neurology* 51(6):S37, 1998.

http://www.neuro.wustl.edu/neuromuscular

Koler RA, Montemarano A: Dermatomyositis, *Am Fam Physician* 64(156):5, 2001.

AUTHOR: **GREGORY J. ESPER, M.D.**

BASIC INFORMATION

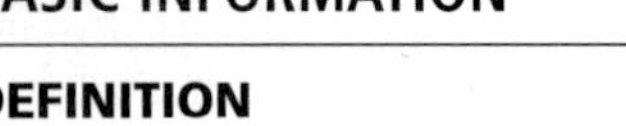

DEFINITION

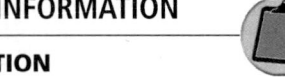

Myotonia is a type of muscular dystrophy in which relaxation of a muscle after contraction is delayed or prolonged. The most common type of muscular dystrophy with myotonia is myotonic dystrophy, which is described below.

SYNONYMS

Myotonic dystrophy

ICD-9CM CODES
359.2 Myotonic disorders
728.85 Muscle spasm

EPIDEMIOLOGY & DEMOGRAPHICS

PREVALENCE: 3 to 5 cases/100,000 persons

- Genetic disorder inherited as an autosomal dominant illness
- Symptoms usually manifest during adolescence or early adulthood. Cases of infantile myotonic dystrophy have been described.

PHYSICAL FINDINGS & CLINICAL PRESENTATION

- Usual first complaint is distal extremity weakness sometimes associated with muscle stiffness, cramps, or difficulty relaxing the grasp.
- Weakness spreads to eventually involve all muscle groups. Flexor neck muscle weakness and masseter and temporal wasting are often prominent features, as is dysarthria.
- Percussion of a muscle produces a slow contraction followed by prolonged relaxation. The "myotonic reflex" is best tested by percussing the thenar muscles and observing a slow flexion followed by slow relaxation of the thumb.
- As the disease progresses, generalized weakness becomes more pronounced and myotonia becomes less evident.
- Extramuscular involvement:
  Mental retardation of variable severity (may be absent)
  Frontal baldness (Fig. 1-156)
  Cataracts
  Diabetes mellitus
  Hypogonadism
  Adrenal failure
  Cardiomyopathy
- Infantile myotonic dystrophy presents as neonatal extreme hypotonia with "shark mouth" deformity (upper lip forming an inverted V).

ETIOLOGY & PATHOGENESIS

Genetic disorder encoded on chromosome 19 leading to sustained firing of the muscle membrane, causing prolonged muscle contraction

DIAGNOSIS

DIFFERENTIAL DIAGNOSIS

- Myotonia congenita (Thomsen's disease)
  May be autosomal dominant or recessive (two distinct varieties)
  The disease is limited to muscles and causes hypertrophy and stiffness after rest. Muscle function normalizes with exercise. There is no weakness. Symptoms are exacerbated by exposure to cold.
- Paramyotonia congenita

Autosomal dominant disease

Weakness and stiffness of facial muscles and distal upper extremities, especially or exclusively on cold exposure

- Muscular dystrophies
- Inflammatory myopathies (polymyositis)
- Metabolic muscle diseases
- Myasthenic syndromes
- Motor neuron disease

WORKUP

- History and physical examination usually sufficient
- Muscle enzymes usually abnormal (CPK, aldolase, AST)
- EMG: typical myotonic "dive bomber" bursts
- Muscle biopsy: type I fiber atrophy, ring fibers, and increased central nucleation

TREATMENT

- Phenytoin
- Quinine
- Quinidine
- Procainamide
- Acetazolamide
- Genetic counseling
- Assistive devices, orthotics

REFERRAL

To neurologist

SUGGESTED READING

Rose M, Griggs R: Inherited muscle, neuromuscular, and neuronal disorders. In Goetz CG (ed): *Textbook of clinical neurology,* Philadelphia, 1999, WB Saunders.

AUTHOR: **TOM J. WACHTEL, M.D.**

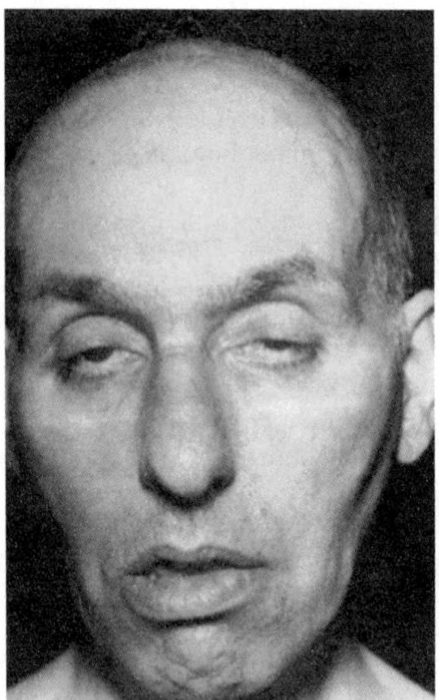

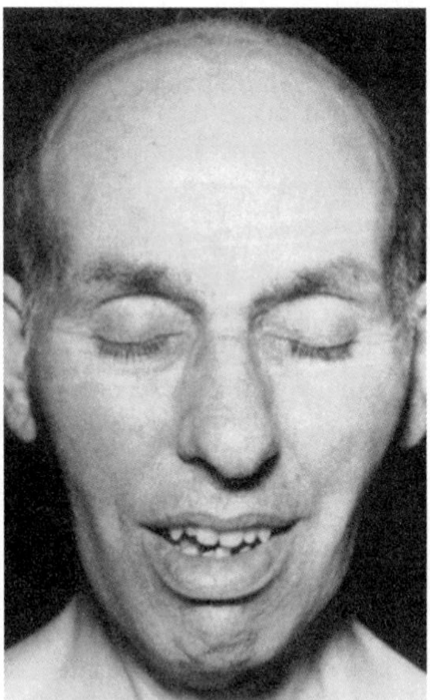

FIGURE 1-156 Myotonic dystrophy with typical myopathic facies, frontal balding, and sunken cheeks. (From Dubowitz V: *Muscle disorders in childhood,* London, 1995, WB Saunders.)

BASIC INFORMATION

DEFINITION

Myxedema coma is a life-threatening complication of hypothyroidism characterized by profound lethargy or coma and usually accompanied by hypothermia.

ICD-9CM CODES
244.8 Myxedema, pituitary
244.1 Myxedema, primary

PHYSICAL FINDINGS & CLINICAL PRESENTATION

- Profound lethargy or coma
- Hypothermia (rectal temperature <35° C [95° F]); often missed by using ordinary thermometers graduated only to 34.5° C or because the mercury is not shaken below 36° C
- Bradycardia, hypotension (secondary to circulatory collapse)
- Delayed relaxation phase of DTR, areflexia
- Myxedema facies (Fig. 1-157)
- Alopecia, macroglossia, ptosis, periorbital edema, nonpitting edema, doughy skin
- Bladder dystonia and distention

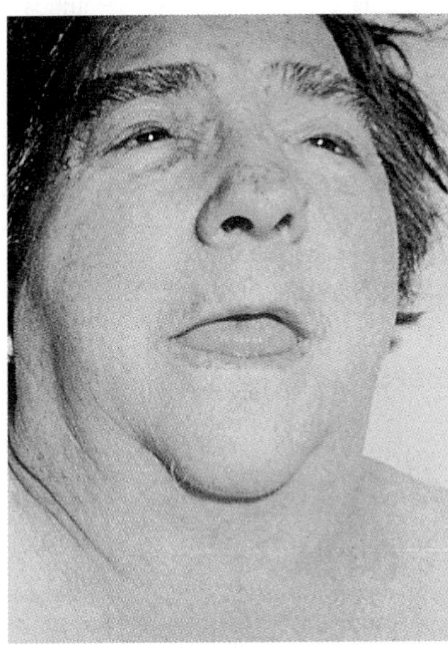

FIGURE 1-157 Myxedema facies. Note dull, puffy, yellowed skin, coarse, sparse hair; temporal loss of eyebrows; periorbital edema; prominent tongue. (Courtesy Paul W. Ladenson, M.D. The Johns Hopkins University and Hospital, Baltimore: In Seidel HM [ed]: *Mosby's guide to physical examination,* ed 4, St Louis, 1999, Mosby.)

ETIOLOGY

Decompensation of hypothyroidism secondary to:

- Sepsis
- Exposure to cold weather
- CNS depressants (sedatives, narcotics, antidepressants)
- Trauma, surgery

DIAGNOSIS

DIFFERENTIAL DIAGNOSIS

- Severe depression, primary psychosis
- Drug overdose
- CVA, liver failure, renal failure
- Hypoglycemia, CO_2 narcosis, encephalitis

WORKUP

Diagnosis of hypothyroidism and exclusion of contributing factors (e.g., sepsis, CVA) with laboratory and radiographic studies (see Laboratory Tests)

LABORATORY TESTS

- Markedly increased TSH (if primary hypothyroidism), decreased serum free T_4
- CBC with differential, urine and blood cultures to rule out infectious process
- Electrolytes, BUN, creatinine, LFTs, calcium, glucose
- ABGs to rule out hypoxemia and carbon dioxide retention
- Cortisol level to rule out adrenal insufficiency
- Elevated CPK
- Hyperlipidemia

IMAGING STUDIES

- CT scan of head in suspected CVA
- Chest x-ray to rule out infectious process

TREATMENT

NONPHARMACOLOGIC THERAPY

- Prevent further heat loss; cover the patient but avoid external rewarming because it may produce vascular collapse.
- Support respiratory function; intubation and mechanical ventilation may be required.
- Monitor patients in the ICU.

ACUTE GENERAL Rx

- Give levothyroxine 5 to 8 μg/kg (300 to 500 μg) IV infused over 15 min, then 100 μg IV q24h.
- Glucocorticoids should also be administered until coexistent adrenal insufficiency can be ruled out. Hydrocortisone hemisuccinate 100 mg IV bolus is initially given, followed by 50 mg IV q12h or 25 mg IV q6h until initial plasma cortisol level is confirmed normal.
- IV hydration with D_5NS is used to correct hypotension and hypoglycemia (if present); avoid overhydration and possible water intoxication because clearance of free water is impaired in these patients.
- Rule out and treat precipitating factors (e.g., antibiotics in suspected sepsis).

CHRONIC Rx

Refer to "Hypothyroidism" in Section I.

DISPOSITION

Mortality rate in myxedema coma is 20% to 50%.

REFERRAL

Endocrinology consultation is appropriate in patients with myxedema coma.

PEARLS & CONSIDERATIONS

COMMENTS

If the diagnosis is suspected, initiate treatment immediately without waiting for confirming laboratory results.

SUGGESTED READING

Wall CR: Myxedema coma: diagnosis and treatment, *Am Fam Physician* 62:2485, 2000.

AUTHOR: **FRED F. FERRI, M.D.**

Narcissistic Personality Disorder

BASIC INFORMATION

DEFINITION

Narcissistic personality disorder (NPD) is characterized by a pattern of grandiosity, need for admiration, and lack of empathy that begins by early adulthood and causes significant distress or impairment in multiple domains of functioning. The individual must meet five or more of the following criteria:

1. Grandiose sense of self-importance. For example, the person may exaggerate achievements and talents or expect recognition as superior without commensurate achievements.
2. Preoccupied with fantasies of unlimited success, power, brilliance, beauty, or ideal love.
3. Views self as "special" and unique and should only associate with other special or highly regarded people and institutions.
4. Requires excessive admiration.
5. Sense of entitlement. For example, unreasonable expectations of especially favorable treatment or automatic compliance with his or her expectations.
6. Interpersonally exploitative.
7. Lacks empathy—unwilling to recognize or identify with the feelings or needs of others.
8. Often envious of others or believes others envious of him or her.
9. Shows arrogant or haughty behaviors.

SYNONYMS

None

ICD-9CM CODES
301.81

EPIDEMIOLOGY & DEMOGRAPHICS

PREVALENCE: Less than 1% of the general population. Estimates range from 2%-16% in the clinical population.
PREDOMINANT SEX: More commonly diagnosed in males (up to 3:1).
PREDOMINANT AGE: 20s and 30s.

CLINICAL PRESENTATION

- Patients experience an underlying sense of inferiority and inadequacy that has its origins in early childhood.
- Often related to the failure of parents or parental surrogates to impart a sense of "self-worth."
- To avoid these beliefs and their associated painful affects, patients seek to convince self and others that they are special, the best, unusually talented. This leads to grandiosity in fantasy and behavior and an excessive need for admiration.
- Astutely aware of status, pecking order, whether they are in the "one-up" or "one-down" position.
- Vulnerability in self-esteem makes these patients exquisitely sensitive to "criticism," "defeat," or "perceived weakness," which in turn can lead to feeling humiliated, degraded, and empty.
- These patients react to perceived slights either with more intense grandiosity and admiration seeking or with disdain and rage. Either approach seeks to bolster their sense of self often by devaluing or criticizing the other person.
- Experiences of self-deflation lead to social withdrawal or depressed mood or to feigned humility that protects grandiosity.
- Interpersonal relationships typically shallow and limited because of problems derived from entitlement, the need for admiration, and relative disregard for feelings of others.
- Though ambition and confidence may lead to high achievement, vocational functioning may be disrupted because of intolerance for criticism.

ETIOLOGY

- At this point, limited knowledge about role of genetic loading and neurobiologic vulnerability in the etiology.
- Prevailing hypotheses focus on impaired development of self as "worthy" because of insufficient affirmation and warmth from parents or parental surrogates.

DIAGNOSIS

DIFFERENTIAL DIAGNOSIS

- Mania and hypomania, which are characterized by an episodic course and impairments.
- Dysthymia and major depressive episode, which causes depressed mood and feelings of worthlessness without criticism or perceived slight.
- Substance-induced euphoria, especially cocaine abuse.
- Histrionic, borderline, antisocial, and paranoid personality disorders share common features and are often comorbid.
- Personality changes due to a general medical condition, including CNS processes in the frontal-temporal regions of the brain.

WORKUP

- History—collateral information essential to establishing presence of longstanding interpersonal pattern in multiple domains of the patient's life.
- Physical examination.
- Mental status examination.

LABORATORY TESTS

Those tests necessary to rule out medical causes of personality changes

IMAGING STUDIES

Those necessary to rule out medical causes of personality changes

TREATMENT

NONPHARMACOLOGIC THERAPY

- No randomized trials assessing treatment.
- Cognitive behavioral therapy to help patients control rage, manage perceived criticism, and develop social skills.
- Psychodynamic psychotherapy to help patients develop stronger sense of self-worth.

ACUTE GENERAL Rx

Benzodiazepines or low-dose antipsychotics to control rage

CHRONIC Rx

- SSRIs if comorbid depression
- Mood stabilizers if comorbid bipolar
- Substance abuse treatment if comorbid dependence

COMPLEMENTARY & ALTERNATIVE MEDICINE

None

DISPOSITION

- Severity is variable and course is chronic. Most patients obtain greater functioning in fifth decade and beyond when pessimism replaces grandiosity. Often lifelong difficulty maintaining intimate relationships.
- At increased risk for major depressive disorder and substance abuse or dependence (especially cocaine).

REFERRAL

- If pharmacotherapy contemplated
- If patient's functioning impaired

PEARLS & CONSIDERATIONS

COMMENTS

- Illness threatens these patients' image of superiority.
- To defend against this threat, patients may minimize symptoms or deny presence of illness.
- As they seek to recapture idealized, admired status, patients will commonly demand special treatment from the most senior and well-known physicians.
- To defend against feeling inferior, these patients may devalue, criticize, or question the behavior or credentials of the treating physician.
- The patients' grandiosity and entitled behavior can be extremely irritating.
- Management guidelines:
  1. Be respectful and nonconfrontational about patient's sense of specialness.
  2. Help patient use self-perceived talents in service of his or her treatment.
  3. Do not personalize patient's devaluation, but understand criticalness as an attempt to manage his or her own intense insecurity.
  4. Appeal to the patient's narcissism. For example, explain the chosen course of action as the best possible care—the type of care such a patient deserves. In other words, agree with the patient that he or she is "entitled" to appropriate care.
  5. Validate patient's concerns about the illness and capacity to respond to the challenges.

SUGGESTED READINGS

Feder A, Robbins SW, Ostermeyer B: Personality disorders. In Feldman MD, Christensen JF (eds): *Behavioral medicine in primary care,* New York, 2003, McGraw Hill.

Shea MT et al: Associations in the course of personality disorders and Axis I disorders over time, *J Abnorm Psychol* 113(4):499, 2004.

Ward RK: Assessment and management of personality disorders, *Am Fam Physician* 70(8):1505, 2004.

AUTHORS: **JOHN Q. YOUNG, M.D., M.P.P.,** and **CRAIG VAN DYKE, M.D.**

Narcolepsy (PTG)

BASIC INFORMATION

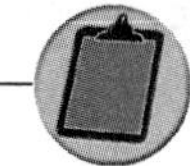

DEFINITION

Narcolepsy is a chronic neurologic disorder characterized by excessive daytime sleepiness and a dysregulation of rapid eye movement (REM) sleep features. Symptoms associated with the dysregulation of REM sleep include cataplexy, sleep paralysis, and hallucinations during the transition between sleep and wakefulness.

ICD-9CM CODES
347 Narcolepsy

EPIDEMIOLOGY & DEMOGRAPHICS

PREVALENCE: Approximately 1 in 2000 men and women in the U.S.

AGE OF ONSET: Peak 15-30 yr (range 10-55 yr)

GENETICS:

- Associated with specific human leukocyte antigen (HLA) subtypes (i.e., DQB1*0602)
- There is a 20-40 times higher risk of developing narcolepsy if there is an affected family member
- Monozygotic concordance rate is 17%-36%, indicating incomplete penetrance with an environmental contribution to the disease process

PHYSICAL FINDINGS & CLINICAL PRESENTATION

- Irresistible urges to sleep may occur during the day and lead to temporarily refreshing naps.
- Cataplexy occurs in 60%-100% of narcoleptics and is reported as a partial or total loss of voluntary muscle control with preserved consciousness that is precipitated by a strong emotion. This is the most specific symptom associated with narcolepsy.
- Sleep paralysis, which occurs in 60% to 80% of narcoleptics, is a loss of muscle tone during the transition between sleep and wakefulness. It may be associated with frightening or vivid hallucinations and can be interrupted by sensory stimuli.
- Hypnagogic (wake to sleep) or hypnopompic (sleep to wake) hallucinations may occur in 60%-80% of patients.
- Fragmented nighttime sleep is reported by 60%-90% of narcoleptics and may be mistaken for insomnia or other intrinsic sleep disorder.

ETIOLOGY

Narcolepsy is a complex disorder with no clear etiology. Research suggests that a deficient hypocretin/orexin system in the hypothalamus may be associated with the development of narcolepsy. Human cerebrospinal fluid levels of hypocretin-1 are low to undetectable in narcoleptics; however, this finding is not specific for narcolepsy.

DIAGNOSIS

DIFFERENTIAL DIAGNOSIS

Excessive daytime somnolence:

- Sleep apnea
- Inadequate sleep time
- Insomnia
- Hypothyroidism
- Drugs and alcohol
- Seizures
- Sleep fragmentation (multiple causes)

Cataplexy:

- Seizures
- Cardiovascular insufficiency
- Psychogenic (multiple causes)

WORKUP

- Medical history should include questions regarding sleep apnea, seizures, dissociated REM sleep features, and a detailed family history. Questions concerning other hypothalamic dysfunction such as unexplained weight gain, endocrinologic abnormalities, circadian dysrhythmias, and autonomic nervous system problems are also helpful.
- Overnight polysomnography followed by a multiple sleep latency test is the standard used for diagnosis. A clinical diagnosis of narcolepsy can be made with a clear history of cataplexy and excessive daytime somnolence. Without these features, the diagnosis depends upon the sleep laboratory testing.

LABORATORY TESTS

HLA subtyping and CSF hypocretin/orexin levels may be helpful in cases of suspected but unconfirmed narcolepsy; however, there is currently no clinical standard by which to interpret these results. Complicated cases should be referred to institutions with active narcolepsy protocols for further workup and data collection.

TREATMENT

NONPHARMACOLOGIC THERAPY

Scheduled daily naps can be used for symptoms of excessive daytime somnolence and to combat irresistible sleep urges.

CHRONIC Rx

For excessive daytime somnolence:

1. Modafinil (Provigil) 200-600 mg PO qam, or divided bid
2. Methylphenidate (Ritalin) 5-15 mg PO bid-tid
3. Methylphenidate SR (Concerta) 18-54 mg PO qam, or divided bid
4. Dextroamphetamine (Dexedrine) 10-60 mg PO qd
5. Sodium Oxybate (Xyrem); contact the Xyrem Success Program for prescription information

For cataplexy and REM-related symptoms:

1. Fluoxetine (Prozac) 20 mg PO qd initially
2. Venlafaxine (Effexor) 25 mg PO qd initially
3. Sertraline (Zoloft) 25 mg PO qd initially
4. Clomipramine (Anafranil) 25 mg/day initially
5. Protriptyline (Vivactil) 5 mg tid initially
6. Imipramine (Tofranil) 25 to 50 mg/day initially
7. Desipramine (Norpramine) 10 mg bid initially
8. Sodium Oxybate (Xyrem); contact the Xyrem Success Program for prescription information

DISPOSITION

This is a chronic sleep disorder without periods of remission.

REFERRAL

Because this disorder is under intense investigation, patients should be referred to programs with sleep specialists who study, manage, and implement new therapies as they arise.

PEARLS & CONSIDERATIONS

Most narcoleptics report the onset of symptoms beginning in childhood to early adulthood. Often the symptoms of narcolepsy begin with excessive daytime sleepiness and progress with time to include REM-dysregulation (e.g., cataplexy, sleep paralysis, hypnagogic hallucinations).

COMMENTS

True narcolepsy is a relatively rare cause of excessive daytime sleepiness. Except for cataplexy, symptoms of REM dysregulation are not specific for narcolepsy. Sleep paralysis, hyponogogic hallucinations, and sleep onset REM may occur as a result of sleep deprivation.

SUGGESTED READINGS

Brooks SN, Guilleminault C: New insights into the pathogenesis and treatment of narcolepsy, *Curr Opin Pulm Med* 7(6):407, 2001.

Greenhill LL et al: Practice parameter for the use of stimulant medications in the treatment of children, adolescents, and adults, *J Am Acad Child Adolesc Psychiatry* 41(2 suppl):26S, 2002.

Hublin C et al: Epidemiology of narcolepsy, *Sleep* 17:S7, 1994.

Mignot E: Genetic and familial aspects of narcolepsy, *Neuorology* 50:S16, 1998.

Mignot E et al: The role of cerebrospinal fluid hypocretin measurement in the diagnosis of narcolepsy and other hypersomnias, *Arch Neurol* 59:1553, 2002.

Overeem S et al: Narcolepsy: clinical features, new pathophysiologic insights, and future perspectives, *J Clin Neurophysiol* 18(2):78, 2001.

Scammell TE: The neurobiology, diagnosis, and treatment of narcolepsy, *Ann Neurol* 53:154, 2003.

Thorpy M: Current concepts in the etiology, diagnosis and treatment of narcolepsy, *Sleep Med* 2:5, 2001.

Xyrem multicenter study group: A 12-month, open-label, multicenter extension trial of orally administered sodium oxybate for the treatment of narcolepsy, *Sleep* 26:31, 2003.

AUTHOR: **JEFFREY S. DURMER, M.D., PH.D.**

Nephroblastoma

BASIC INFORMATION

DEFINITION

Malignant renal tumor derived from primitive metanephric blastome. Most tumors are unicentric, but some are multifocal in one or both kidneys. Associated anomalies may be present.

SYNONYM

Wilms' Tumor

ICD-9CM CODES
189.0 Nephroblastoma

EPIDEMIOLOGY & DEMOGRAPHICS

- Pediatric malignancy mean presentation is at 41.5 mo in boys and 46.9 mo in girls
- Slightly more frequent in girls
- Incidence rate is 7.9 cases/yr/million white children <15 yr (a little over 500 new cases/yr in the U.S.); the incidence is double in black children
- Associated syndromes:
  1. Cryptorchidism
  2. Hypospadias
  3. Hemihypertrophy with or without the Beckwith-Wiedemann syndrome, aniridia
  4. Denys-Drash syndrome (nephroblastoma, pseudohermaphrodism, glomerulonephritis)
  5. WAGR syndrome (Wilms' tumor, aniridia, genitourinary malformations, and mental retardation)
- Familial nephroblastoma occurs in 1.5% (with younger age at diagnosis and more frequent multifocal tumors)

PHYSICAL FINDINGS & CLINICAL PRESENTATION

- Wilms' tumor often is discovered when a parent notices a mass while bathing or dressing a child, most commonly a child who is about 3 yr old, or during a routine physical examination. The mass is unilateral, firm, and nontender and below the costal margin
- Abdominal swelling and/or pain
- Nausea
- Vomiting
- Constipation
- Loss of appetite
- Fever of unknown origin
- Night sweats
- Hematuria (less common than in adult renal malignancies)
- Malaise
- High blood pressure that is triggered when the tumor obstructs the renal artery
- Varicocele
- Signs of associated syndromes

PATHOLOGY

- Three cell types: blastomal, stromal, and epithelial may be present. Structural diversity is characteristic.
- Anaplasia is evidenced by the presence of gigantic polyploid nuclei. The term *focal anaplasia* is used to describe such findings when it is confined within the primary tumor in the kidney.
- Staging

Stage I: Tumor limited to the kidney whose capsule is intact. The tumor is completely excised.

Stage II: Tumor extends beyond the kidney but is completely excised. No peritoneal involvement.

Stage III: Residual tumor confined to the abdomen following surgery. No hematogenous metastases.

Stage IV: Hematogenous metastases present.

Stage V: Bilateral renal involvement at time of initial diagnosis.

DIAGNOSIS

DIFFERENTIAL DIAGNOSIS

- Other renal malignancies
  1. Hypernephroma
  2. Transitional cell carcinoma
  3. Lymphoma
  4. Clear cell sarcoma
  5. Rhabdoid tumor of the kidney
- Renal cyst
- Other intraabdominal or retroperitoneal tumors.

LABORATORY TESTS

- CBC
- Transaminases (ALT, AST)
- Alkaline phosphatase
- BUN and creatinine
- Serum calcium
- Urinalysis

IMAGING STUDIES

- Renal ultrasound to confirm existence of a solid mass in a kidney
- Abdominal CT scan with contrast (Fig. 1-158)
- Chest x-ray or CT scan

TREATMENT

- Surgical resection and surgical staging
  1. Stages I and II: surgery followed by chemotherapy
  2. Stages III and IV: surgery followed by radiation and chemotherapy
- Chemotherapeutic agents used in the treatment of Wilms' tumor include vincristine, dactinomycin, and doxorubicin

PROGNOSIS

- Stage I: 95% survival
- Stage II: 91% survival
- Stage III: 91% survival
- Stage IV: 81% survival
- Prognosis is better for patients whose age is <2 yr

SUGGESTED READING

Ebb DH et al: Solid tumors of childhood. In *Cancer, principles and practice of oncology*, ed 6, Philadelphia, 2001, Lippincott Williams & Wilkins.

AUTHOR: **TOM J. WACHTEL, M.D.**

A

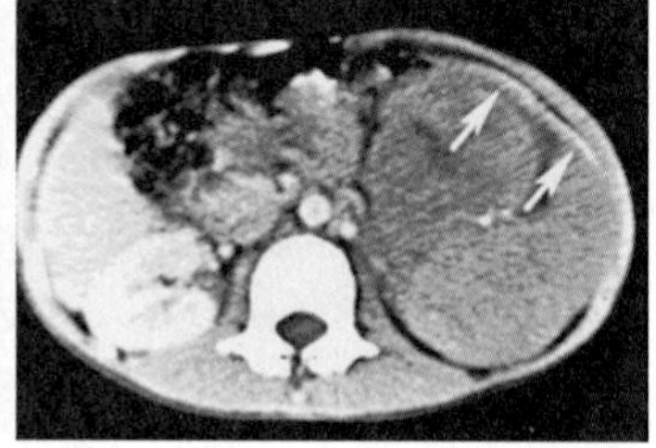

B

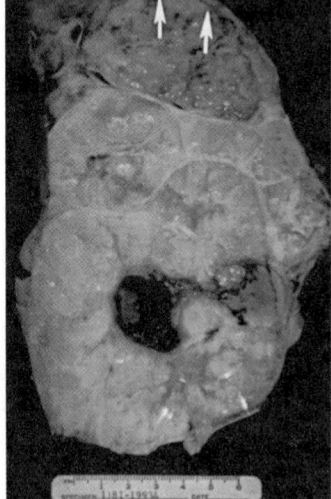

FIGURE 1-158 Wilms' tumor. A, Gross specimen shows a large mass compressing a small rim of normal renal tissue (*arrows*). **B,** CT scan of kidney. A rim of compressed normal tissue represents the residual normal renal parenchyma (*arrows*). (From Behrman RE: *Nelson textbook of pediatrics,* ed 16, Philadelphia, 2000, WB Saunders.)

BASIC INFORMATION

DEFINITION

Nephrotic syndrome is characterized by high urine protein excretion (>3.5g/1.73 m^3/24 hr), peripheral edema, and metabolic abnormalities (hypoalbuminemia, hypercholesterolemia).

ICD-9CM CODES
581.9 Nephrotic syndrome

EPIDEMIOLOGY & DEMOGRAPHICS

- Nephrotic syndrome occurs predominantly in children ages 2 to 6 yr (2 new cases/100,000 persons/yr) and in adults of all ages (3 to 4 new cases/100,000 persons/yr).
- Membranous glomerulonephritis is the most common cause of nephrotic syndrome.

PHYSICAL FINDINGS & CLINICAL PRESENTATION

- Peripheral edema
- Ascites, anasarca
- Hypertension
- Pleural effusion
- Typically patients present with severe peripheral edema, exertional dyspnea, and abdominal fullness secondary to ascites. There is a significant amount of weight gain in most patients

ETIOLOGY

- Idiopathic (may be secondary to the following glomerular diseases: minimal change disease [nil disease, lipoid nephrosis], focal segmental glomerular sclerosis, membranous nephropathy, membranoproliferative glomerular nephropathy)
- Associated with systemic diseases (diabetes mellitus, SLE, amyloidosis). Amyloidosis and dysproteinemias should be considered in patients older than 40 yr
- Majority of children with nephrotic syndrome have minimal change disease (this form also associated with allergy, nonsteroidals, and Hodgkin's disease)
- Focal glomerular disease: can be associated with HIV infection, heroin abuse. A more severe form of nephrotic syndrome associated with rapid progression to end-stage renal failure within months can also occur in HIV seropositive patients and is known as "collapsing glomerulopathy"
- Membranous nephropathy: can occur with Hodgkin's lymphoma, carcinomas, SLE, gold therapy
- Membranoproliferative glomerulonephropathy: often associated with upper respiratory infections

DIAGNOSIS

DIFFERENTIAL DIAGNOSIS

- Other edema states (CHF, cirrhosis)
- Primary renal disease (e.g., focal glomerulonephritis, membranoproliferative glomerulonephritis). Table 1-34 summarizes primary renal diseases that present as idiopathic nephrotic syndrome
- Carcinoma, infections
- Malignant hypertension
- Polyarteritis nodosa
- Serum sickness
- Toxemia of pregnancy

WORKUP

- Diagnostic workup consists of family history and history of drug use or toxin exposure and laboratory evaluation. Renal biopsy is generally performed in individuals with persistent proteinuria in whom the etiology of the proteinuria is unclear.

LABORATORY TESTS

- Urinalysis reveals proteinuria. The presence of hematuria, cellular casts, and pyuria is suggestive of nephritic syndrome. Oval fat bodies (tubular epithelial cells with cholesterol esters) are also found in the urine in patients with nephrotic syndrome.
- 24-hr urine protein excretion is >3.5 g/1.73 m^3/24 hr.
- Abnormalities of blood chemistries include serum albumin <3 g/dl, decreased total protein, elevated serum cholesterol, glucose, azotemia.
- Additional tests in patients with nephrotic syndromes depending on the history and physical examination are ANA, serum and urine immunoelectrophoresis, C3, C4, CH-50, LDH, liver enzymes, alkaline phosphatase, hepatitis B and C screening, and HIV.

IMAGING STUDIES

- Ultrasound of kidneys
- Chest x-ray

TREATMENT

NONPHARMACOLOGIC THERAPY

- Bed rest as tolerated, avoidance of nephrotoxic drugs, low-fat diet, fluid restriction in hyponatremic patients; normal protein intake unless urinary protein loss exceeds 10 g/24 hr (some patients may require additional dietary protein to prevent negative nitrogen balance and significant protein malnutrition)
- Improved urinary protein excretion and serum lipid changes have been observed with a low-fat soy protein diet providing 0.7 g of protein/kg/day. However, because of increased risk of malnutrition, many nephrologists recommend normal protein intake
- Strict sodium restriction to help manage peripheral edema
- Close monitoring of patients for development of peripheral venous thrombosis and renal vein thrombosis because of hypercoagulable state secondary to loss of antithrombin III and other proteins involved in the clotting mechanism

ACUTE GENERAL Rx

- Furosemide is useful for severe edema.
- Use of ACE inhibitors to reduce proteinuria is generally indicated even in normotensive patients.
- Anticoagulant therapy should be administered as long as patients have nephrotic proteinuria, an albumin level <20 g/L, or both.

The mainstay of therapy is treatment of the underlying disorder:

- Minimal change disease generally responds to prednisone 1 mg/kg/day. Relapses can occur when steroids are discontinued. In these individuals, cyclophosphamide and chlorambucil may be useful.
- Focal and segmental glomerulosclerosis: steroid therapy is also recommended. However, response rate is approximately 35% to 40%, and most patients progress to end-stage renal disease within 3 yr.
- Membranous glomerulonephritis: prednisone 2 mg/kg/day may be useful in inducing remission. Cytotoxic agents can be added if there is poor response to prednisone.
- Membranoproliferative glomerulonephritis: most patients are treated with steroid therapy and antiplatelet drugs. Despite treatment, the majority of patients will progress to end-stage renal disease within 5 yr.

CHRONIC Rx

- Patients should be monitored for azotemia and should be aggressively treated for hypertension and hyperlipidemia. Furosemide is useful for severe edema. Anticoagulants may be necessary for thromboembolic events. Prophylactic anticoagulation should be considered in patients with membranous glomerulonephritis.
- Oral vitamin D is useful in the treatment of hypocalcemia (because of vitamin D loss).

REFERRAL

Nephrology consultation is recommended in all cases of nephrotic syndrome.

AUTHOR: **FRED F. FERRI, M.D.**

TABLE 1-34 **Summary of Primary Renal Diseases that Present as Idiopathic Nephrotic Syndrome**

	Minimal-Change Nephrotic Syndrome (MCNS)	Focal Segmental Sclerosis	Membranous Nephropathy	MEMBRANOPROLIFERATIVE GLOMERULONEPHRITIS (MPGN) Type I	MEMBRANOPROLIFERATIVE GLOMERULONEPHRITIS (MPGN) Type II
Frequency*					
Children	75%	10%	<5%	10%	10%
Adults	15%	15%	50%	10%	10%
Clinical Manifestations					
Age (yr)	2-6, some adults	2-10, some adults	40-50	5-15	5-15
Sex	2:1 male	1.3:1 male	2:1 male	Male-female	Male-female
Nephrotic syndrome	100%	90%	80%	60%	60%
Asymptomatic proteinuria	0	10%	20%	40%	40%
Hematuria	10%-20%	60%-80%	60%	80%	80%
Hypertension	10%	20% early	Infrequent	35%	35%
Rate of progression to renal failure	Does not progress	10 years	50% in 10-20 yr	10-20 yr	5-15 yr
Associated conditions	Allergy? Hodgkin's disease, usually none	None	Renal vein thrombosis, cancer, SLE, hepatitis B	None	Partial lipodystrophy
Laboratory Findings	Manifestations of nephrotic syndrome ↑ BUN in 15%-30%	Manifestations of nephrotic syndrome ↑ BUN in 20%-40%	Manifestations of nephrotic syndrome	Low C1, C4, C3–C9	Normal C1, C4, low C3–C9 C3 nephritic factor
Immunogenetics	HLA-B8, B12 (3.5)†	Not established	HLA-DRW3 (12–32)†	Not established	Not established
Renal Pathology					
Light microscopy	Normal	Focal sclerotic lesions	Thickened GBM, spikes	Thickened GBM, proliferation	Lobulation
Immunofluorescence	Negative	IgM, C3 in lesions	Fine granular IgG, C3	Granular IgG, C3	C3 only
Electron microscopy	Foot process fusion	Foot process fusion	Subepithelial deposits	Mesangial and subendothelial deposits	Dense deposits
Response of Steroids	90%	15%-20%	May slow progression	Not established	Not established

Modified from Goldman L, Ausiello D (eds): *Cecil textbook of medicine,* ed 22, Philadelphia, 2004, WB Saunders.
*Approximate frequency as a cause of idiopathic nephrotic syndrome. About 10% of adult nephrotic syndrome is due to various diseases that usually present with acute glomerulonephritis.
†Relative risk.
↑, Elevated; *BUN,* blood urea nitrogen; *C,* complement; *GBM,* glomerular basement membrane; *hepatitis B,* hepatitis B virus; *HLA,* human leukocyte antigen; *Ig,* immunoglobulin; *SLE,* systemic lupus erythematosus.

BASIC INFORMATION

DEFINITION

Neuroblastomas are tumors of postganglionic sympathetic neurons that typically originate in the adrenal medulla or the sympathetic chain/ganglion. Often present at birth, but not diagnosed until later, when the child shows symptoms of the disease. Almost exclusively a disease of childhood.

ICD-9CM CODES
194.0 Neuroblastoma, unspecified site

EPIDEMIOLOGY & DEMOGRAPHICS

INCIDENCE (IN U.S.): 8%-10% of all solid tumors of childhood (third most common childhood cancer, after leukemia and brain tumors); 1/10,000 children <15 yr

PREDOMINANT SEX: Male:female ratio of 1:1.3

PEAK AGE: Mean age of onset is 18 mo; 75% onset by 5 yr; 97% by 10 yr

GENETICS: Chromosomal deletions (loss of heterozygosity) found in nearly half of tumors, most commonly localized to chromosomes 1p, 11q, and 14q. Deletion of 1p36 (leading to amplification and overexpression of N-myc protooncogene) associated with poor prognosis. There is a small subset with an autosomal dominant pattern of inhesitance.

PHYSICAL FINDINGS & CLINICAL PRESENTATION

- Mass in abdomen, neck, or chest. Approximately 2/3 arise in the abdomen; of these, 2/3 arise in the adrenal glands. 70%-80% of children have regional lymph node involvement or distant metastases at time of presentation
- Spinal cord/paraspinal: can present with back pain, signs of compression—paraplegia, stool/urine retention
- Horner's syndrome (ptosis, miosis, anhidrosis)
- Thoracic: difficulty breathing, dysphagia, infections, chronic cough
- Secondary symptoms referable to metastatic disease: chronic pain, pancytopenia, periorbital ecchymosis, proptosis, weight loss, fever, multiple subcutaneous bluish nodules, irritability

PARANEOPLASTIC SYNDROMES

- Opsoclonus-myoclonus syndrome → "dancing eyes, dancing feet," myoclonic jerks and chaotic eye movements in all directions; may be initial presentation before tumor diagnosis; present in 1%-3% of patients with neuroblastoma; of all patients with opsoclonus-myoclonus, 20%-50% have an underlying neuroblastoma.
- Progressive cerebellar ataxia
- Abnormal secretion of vasoactive intestinal peptide by the tumor, leading to distention of the abdomen and secretory diarrhea

DIAGNOSIS

DIFFERENTIAL DIAGNOSIS

- Other small, round, blue-cell childhood tumors, such as lymphoma and rhabdomyosarcoma, soft-tissue sarcoma, and primitive neuroectodermal tumors (PNETs)
- Wilms' tumor
- Hepatoblastoma

WORKUP

- Careful general physical examination
- Biopsy and resection of tumor when possible

LABORATORY TESTS

- 24-hour urine for catecholamines → homovanillic acid (HVA) and vanillymandelic acid (VMA) are secreted by 90%-95% of tumors
- Bone marrow biopsy and aspirate → karyotype, DNA index, N-myc copy number

IMAGING STUDIES

- Chest x-ray, abdominal x-ray, skeletal survey, abdominal ultrasound
- CT scan of the chest and abdomen
- Body scan with ^{131}I-MIBG (metaiodobenzylguanidine) → taken up by neuroblasts
- Bone scan Tc-99 MDP → visualize lytic bone lesions and metastases

STAGING (INTERNATIONAL NEUROBLASTOMA STAGING SYSTEM)

I. Confined to single organ
IIA. Localized tumor with incomplete gross resection; lymph nodes negative
IIB. Localized tumor with incomplete gross resection; ipsilateral lymph nodes positive
III. Extension across midline, with or without lymph node involvement
IV. Distant metastases to lymph nodes, bone, bone marrow, liver, skin
IVs. Localized primary tumor with dissemination limited to skin, liver, and/or bone marrow; limited to infants <1 yr of age

TREATMENT

NONPHARMACOLOGIC THERAPY

Assure patient that there is hope for recovery with aggressive treatment.

ACUTE GENERAL Rx

- Overall, treatment will be determined by several factors, including age at diagnosis, stage of disease, site of primary tumor and metastases and tumor histology
- Surgery, particularly for low-risk tumors
- Radiation therapy, often reserved for unresectable tumors or tumors that are not responsive to chemotherapy
- Multiagent chemotherapy is mainstay (e.g., cisplatinum, etoposide, adriamycin, cyclophosphamide, carboplatin)
- Autologous bone marrow transplantation following aggressive chemotherapy for stage IV disease or patients who are at highest risk based on presence of disseminated disease or unfavorable markers such as N-myc amplification
- Novel therapies include immunotherapy using monoclonal antibodies and vaccines that attempt to initiate an immune reaction against the disease and targeting of tumor cells with drugs that induce apoptosis or have antiangiogenic effect

DISPOSITION/PROGNOSIS

- Refer immediately to a multidisciplinary oncology team
- Overall survival is >40%. Children under the age of 1 yr have a cure rate as high as 90%
- Poor prognosis associated with stage IV disease (20% survival compared with >95% in stage I), age >1 yr at diagnosis, increased number of N-myc copies, adrenal tumor, chronic 1p deletion

SUGGESTED READINGS

Bown N: Neuroblastoma tumor genetics: clinical and biological aspects, *J Clin Path* 54(12):897, 2001.

Brodeur GM: Neuroblastoma. In Pizzo PA, Poplack DG (eds): *Principles and practice of pediatric oncology,* Philadelphia, 2002, Lippincott Williams Wilkins.

Marcus K et al: Primary tumor control in patients with stage 3/4 unfavorable neuroblastoma treated with tandem double autologous stem cell transplants, *J Pediatr Hematol Oncol* 25:934, 2003.

Russo C: Long-term neurologic outcome in children with oopsoclonus-myoclonus associated with neuroblastoma: a report from the Pediatric Oncology Group, *Med Pediatr Oncol* 28:284, 1997.

Schilling FH et al: Neuroblastoma screening at one year of age, *N Engl J Med* 346:1047, 2002.

Shimada H: International neuroblastoma pathology classification for prognostic evaluation of patients with peripheral neuroblastic tumors: a report from the Children's Cancer Group, *Cancer* 92:2451, 2001.

Woods WG et al: Screening of infants and mortality due to neuroblastoma, *N Engl J Med* 346:1041, 2002.

AUTHOR: **NICOLE J. ULLRICH, M.D., PH.D.**

Neurofibromatosis (PTG)

BASIC INFORMATION

DEFINITION

Neurofibromatosis (NF) is an autosomal dominant inherited neurocutaneous disorder. There are two types of neurofibromatosis disorders: NF type 1 (NF1) and NF type 2 (NF2).

SYNONYMS

- NF1 is also called von Recklinghausen disease
- NF2 is also called bilateral acoustic neurofibromatosis

ICD-9CM CODES
237.71 Type 1, von Recklinghausen's
237.72 Type 2, acoustic

EPIDEMIOLOGY & DEMOGRAPHICS

- Incidence of NF1 (1/3000), NF2 (1/33,000)
- Prevalence of NF1 (1/5000), NF2 (1/210,000)
- NF1 and NF2 are autosomal dominant, with approximately 50% of cases having no family history
- The two disorders affect approximately 100,000 people in the U.S.
- Equally affects males and females
- NF1 may be associated with optic gliomas, astrocytomas, spinal neurofibromas, pheochromocytomas, and chronic myeloid leukemia
- NF2 may be associated with meningiomas, spinal schwannomas, and cataracts

PHYSICAL FINDINGS & CLINICAL PRESENTATION

- Common features of NF1 include:
  1. Café-au-lait macules (100% of children by age 2)
     a. Hyperpigmented skin lesions occurring anywhere on the body except the face, palms, and soles
     b. Appear early in life and increase in size and number during puberty
     c. Focal or diffuse
  2. Axillary and inguinal freckling (70%)
  3. Multiple cutaneous and subcutaneous neurofibromas (95%) (Fig. 1-159)
     a. Firm, varying in size from mm to cm
     b. Vary in number from a few to thousands
     c. May be sessile, pedunculated, regular or irregular in shape
  4. Lisch nodule (small hamartoma of the iris) found in >90% of adult cases
  5. Visual defects possibly related to optic gliomas (2% to 5%)
  6. Neurodevelopment problems (30% to 40%)
- Common features of NF2 include:
  1. Hearing loss and tinnitus related to bilateral acoustic neuromas (>90% of adults)
  2. Cataracts (81%)
  3. Headache
  4. Unsteady gait
  5. Cutaneous neurofibromas but less than NF1
  6. Café-au-lait macules (1%)

ETIOLOGY

- NF1 is caused by DNA mutations located on the long arm of chromosome 17 responsible for encoding the protein neurofibromin.
- NF2 is caused by DNA mutations located in the middle of the long arm of chromosome 22 responsible for encoding the protein merlin.

DIAGNOSIS

- NF1 is diagnosed if the person has two or more of the following features:
  1. Six or more café-au-lait macules >5 mm in prepubertal patients and >15 mm in postpubertal patients
  2. Two or more neurofibromas of any type or one plexiform neurofibroma
  3. Axillary or inguinal freckling
  4. Optic glioma
  5. Two or more Lisch nodules (iris hamartomas)
  6. Sphenoid wing dysplasia or cortical thinning of long bones, with or without pseudarthrosis
  7. A first-degree relative (parent, sibling, or child) with NF1 based on the previous criteria
- NF2 is diagnosed if the person has either of the following two criteria:
  1. Bilateral eighth nerve masses seen by appropriate imaging studies
  2. A first-degree relative with NF2 and either a unilateral eighth nerve mass or two of the following: neurofibroma, meningioma, glioma, schwannoma, or juvenile posterior subcapsular lenticular opacity

WORKUP

The diagnosis of neurofibromatosis is usually self-evident. Workup is dictated by clinical symptoms in NF1 and usually includes MRI evaluation of the head and spine in NF2.

LABORATORY TESTS

- Genetic testing is possible in individuals who desire prenatal diagnosis for NF1. There is no single standard test and multiple tests are required. Results can only tell if an individual is affected but cannot predict the severity of the disease.
- In NF2, linkage analysis testing provides a >99% certainty the individual has NF2.

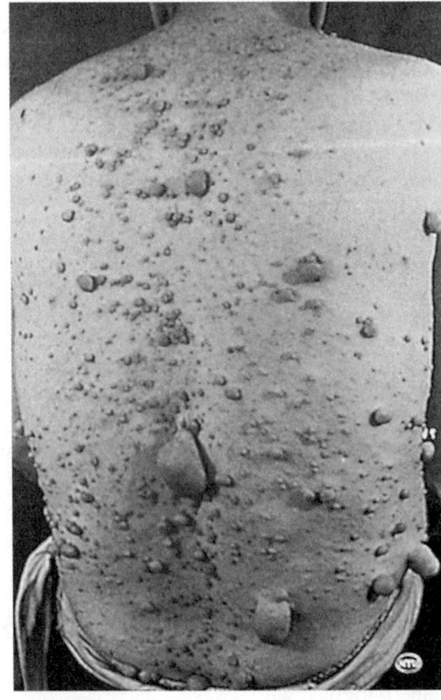

FIGURE 1-159 Nodules. Solid, large (>1 cm), deep-seated mass in dermal or subcutaneous tissues. These nodules are neurofibromas in a patient with neurofibromatosis. (From Goldman L, Ausiello D [eds]: *Cecil textbook of medicine,* ed 22, Philadelphia, 2004, WB Saunders.)

IMAGING STUDIES

- MRI with gadolinium is the imaging study of choice in both NF1 and NF2 patients. MRI increases detection of optic gliomas, tumors of the spine, acoustic neuromas, and "bright spots" thought to represent hamartomas.
- MRI of the spine is recommended in all patients diagnosed with NF2 to exclude intramedullary tumors.

TREATMENT

Treatment is directed primarily at symptoms and complications of NF1 and NF2.

NONPHARMACOLOGIC THERAPY

- Counseling addressing prognosis, genetic, psychologic, and social issues
- Slit-lamp examination by an ophthalmologist searching for cataracts and hamartomas
- Hearing testing and speech pathology evaluation

ACUTE GENERAL Rx

- Surgery is usually not done on skin tumors unless cosmetically requested or if suspicion of malignant transformation exists.
- Surgery may be indicated for spinal or cranial neurofibromas, gliomas, or meningiomas.
- Acoustic neuromas can be treated by surgical excision.

CHRONIC Rx

- Radiation may be indicated in NF1 patients with optic nerve gliomas.
- Stereotactic radiosurgery using gamma knife may be an alternative approach to surgery for acoustic neuromas.

DISPOSITION

- Prognosis varies according to the severity of involvement.
- There is no cure for neurofibromatosis.

REFERRAL

A multidisciplinary team of consultants is needed in patients with neurofibromatosis including neurosurgeon, otolaryngologist, dermatologist, neurologist, audiologist, speech pathologist, and neuropsychologist.

PEARLS & CONSIDERATIONS

COMMENTS

- Friedrich Daniel von Recklinghausen first reported his cases in 1882, although there had been similar accounts dating back to the 1600s.
- The first report in the literature of NF2 was by Wishart in 1822.
- For additional information refer to the National Neurofibromatosis Foundation (141 Fifth Avenue, Suite 7-S, New York, NY 10010, 800-322-7838) or Neurofibromatosis Inc. (3401 Woodbridge Court, Mitchellville, MD 20716, 301-577-8984).

SUGGESTED READINGS

Evans DG, Sainio M, Baser NE: Neurofibromatosis type 2, *J Med Genet* 37(12):897, 2000.

Gutmann DH et al: The diagnostic evaluation and multidisciplinary management of neurofibromatosis 1 and neurofibromatosis 2, *JAMA* 278(1):51, 1997.

Karnes PS: Neurofibromatosis: a common neurocutaneous disorder, *Mayo Clin Proc* 73(11):1071, 1998.

Korf BP: Diagnosis and management of neurofibronatosum type 1, *Curr Neurol Neurosci Rep* 1(2):162, 2001.

Lakkis MM, Tennekoon GI: Neurofibronatosin type 1: 1 general overview, *J Neurosci Res* 62(6):755, 2000.

Young H, Hyman S, North K: Neurofibromatosis 1: clinical review and exception to the rates, *J Child Neurol* 17(8):588, 2002.

AUTHOR: **PETER PETROPOULOS, M.D.**

Neuroleptic Malignant Syndrome

BASIC INFORMATION

DEFINITION

Neuroleptic malignant syndrome is a disorder characterized by hyperthermia, muscular rigidity, autonomic dysfunction, and depressed/fluctuating levels of arousal that evolve over 24-72 hours. This occurs as an idiosyncratic adverse reaction most commonly to dopamine-receptor antagonists (especially D2/4 receptor) or sudden withdrawal from a dopaminergic agent or agonist, such as antiparkinsonian medications.

ICD-9CM CODES
333.92 Neuroleptic malignant syndrome

EPIDEMIOLOGY & DEMOGRAPHICS

INCIDENCE (IN U.S.): 0.07%-0.15% annual incidence in psychiatric population. Incidence falling from as high as 1.4% to 12.2% in the 1980s because of better recognition of early signs, low threshold to discontinue typical neuroleptics, and more frequent use of atypical agents.

PREDOMINANT SEX: More than two thirds of patients are male.

PREDOMINANT AGE: Young and middle-aged adults

PREDISPOSING FACTORS:
- High-potency dopamine antagonists
- Long-acting depot preparations or multiple agents used
- Preexisting brain disease

PHYSICAL FINDINGS & CLINICAL PRESENTATION

- Muscle rigidity (hypertonia, cogwheeling, or "lead pipe" rigidity)
- Hyperthermia (38.6° to 42.3° C, usually <40° C)
- Autonomic symptoms: diaphoresis, sialorrhea, skin pallor, urinary incontinence
- Tachycardia, tachypnea
- Labile blood pressure (hypertension or postural hypotension)
- Mental status changes (agitation, catatonia, fluctuating consciousness, obtundation)

ETIOLOGY

- Unknown. Impaired thermoregulation in hypothalamus and limbic cortex may occur as a result of relative lack of dopamine activity (central dopamine-blockade hypothesis: most accepted)
- Neuroleptic drugs have different potencies for inducing NMS:
  1. Typical neuroleptics: High potency—haloperidol; medium potency—chlorpromazine, fluphenazine; low potency—levomepromazine, loxapine
  2. Atypical neuroleptics: Low potency—risperidone, olanzapine, clozapine, quetiapine

DIAGNOSIS

DIFFERENTIAL DIAGNOSIS

- Heatstroke, drug-induced states and overdose (ecstasy abuse, phencyclidine), thyrotoxicosis, pheochromocytoma, serotonin syndrome
- Malignant hyperthermia, catatonia, acute psychosis with agitation
- Central nervous system or systemic infections, including sepsis

WORKUP

Careful drug history

LABORATORY TESTS

- Elevated creatine phosphokinase (CPK) (in 71% of patients, with a mean value of 3700 U/L)
- Urinary myoglobin
- Leukocytosis, usually 10,000 to 40,000/mm^3
- Electrolytes and renal function
- Blood gases
- Drug levels

IMAGING STUDIES

None specific for this disease

TREATMENT

NONPHARMACOLOGIC THERAPY

- Stop all neuroleptic agents and reinstitute any recently discontinued dopaminergic agents
- Respiratory support; nutritional support in cases with dysphagia or comatose
- Careful fluid balance monitoring with adequate hydration (intravenous in severe cases)
- Active cooling (cooling blanket and antipyretics)
- Skilled nursing care to prevent decubitus ulcers in bed-confined patients

ACUTE GENERAL Rx

- Intravenous benzodiazepines (e.g., diazepam 2-10 mg, with total daily dose of 10-60 mg) to relax muscles and control agitation.
- Bromocriptine, a dopamine receptor agonist, is the mainstay of therapy for patients with neuroleptic malignant syndrome. Initial doses of 2.5 to 10 mg are given IV q8h and are increased by 5 mg/day until clinical improvement is seen. The drug should be continued for at least 10 days after the syndrome has been controlled and then tapered slowly.
- Amantadine, a NMDA receptor antagonist with possible dopaminergic properties, administered orally at doses of 100-200 mg PO bid, has been shown to reduce mortality in comparison to supportive therapy alone.
- Dantrolene therapy is also effective. Initially, patients can be given 0.25 mg/kg IV q6-12h, followed by a maintenance dose up to 3 mg/kg/day. After 2 to 3 days, patients may be given the drug orally (25 to 600 mg/day in divided doses). Oral dantrolene therapy (50-600 mg/day) may be continued for several days afterwards.
- Electroconvulsive therapy with neuromuscular blockage in pharmacologically refractory cases. Succinylcholine should not be used as it may cause hyperkalemia and cardiac arrhythmias in patients with rhabdomyolysis or dysautonomia.

CHRONIC Rx

- Mortality rate is currently 5%-10% despite previous therapeutic measures. Serious sequelae may occur in a further 20%. Complete recovery occurs in >70% of patients. Mortality rates have declined from 15%-25% because of earlier recognition and aggressive pharmacologic and supportive care.
- Factors adversely affecting mortality are development of renal failure and core temperature >104° F (40° C).
- Respiratory care, nutritional support, and physical therapy in more severe cases.

DISPOSITION

Monitor closely for future complications of pharmacologic therapy.

REFERRAL

If patient's condition is critical, patients are preferably treated in a medical/neurologic ICU.

PEARLS & CONSIDERATIONS

COMMENTS

Early detection and diagnosis lead to a more favorable outcome. Treatment is a medical emergency.

SUGGESTED READINGS

Buckley PF, Sajatovic M, Adityanjee. Neuroleptic malignant syndrome. In Katirji B et al: *Neuromuscular disorders in clinical practice.* Boston, 2002, Butterworth-Heinemann.

Chandran GJ, Mikler JR, Keegan DL: Neuroleptic malignant syndrome: case report and discussion, *CMAJ* 169:439, 2003.

Sueman VL: Clinical management of neuroleptic malignant syndrome, *Psychiatr Q* 72(4):825, 2001.

Ty EB, Rothner AD: Neuroleptic malignant syndrome in children and adolescents, *J Child Neurol* 16(3):157, 2001.

AUTHOR: **EROBOGHENE E. UBOGU, M.D.**

BASIC INFORMATION

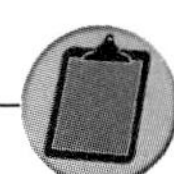

DEFINITION

Neuropathic pain is not a disease. It is a symptom, and at most, a syndrome. It may result from multiple illnesses, and it is not enough to define its presence without searching for its cause. It is defined as the sensation derived from the abnormal discharges of impaired or injured neural structures in either the peripheral or central nervous system, including receptors, axons, and cell bodies.

- Hyperalgesia: extreme sensitivity to painful stimuli, or reduced threshold to feel pain
- Hypalgesia: decreased sensibility to pain, or increased threshold to feel pain
- Hyperesthesia: abnormal acuteness of sensitivity to touch, pain, or other sensory stimuli
- Hypesthesia: diminished sensitivity to stimulation
- Allodynia: nonpainful stimulus is painful

ICD-9CM CODES
729.1 Pain, neuromuscular
729.2 Pain, nerve not elsewhere classified

EPIDEMIOLOGY

- Neuropathic pain affects 1.5% of the U.S. population, but this is likely an underestimate.
- Diagnosis and especially drug treatment contribute to rising costs in health care.
- Demographics vary widely depending upon etiology, for example:
  1. Postherpetic neuralgia: affects elderly, and pain seen in almost 100% of cases
  2. AIDS: 33% of patients affected
  3. Diabetes mellitus: 33% affected
  4. Fabry's disease: affects mostly children, pain in almost 90% of patients

PHYSICAL FINDINGS & CLINICAL PRESENATION

History: localize the disease with your questions.

- Type of pain: burning, lancinating, shooting, sharp, hot or cold pain, pins and needles, broken glass, stinging, and so on can occur in any part of the body (e.g., V1-V3 in trigeminal neuralgia).
- Identify if symptoms occur along a nerve distribution (i.e., superficial peroneal nerve) or plexus distribution (acute brachial neuritis or lumbosacral plexus in diabetic amyotrophy).
- Generalized small fiber neuropathy: dysesthesias without numbness common, but many etiologies (e.g., diabetes) cause both small and large fiber dysfunction.
- Large fiber neuropathy: coexisting numbness or weakness can be seen, usually worse distally than proximally.
- Nerve root: coexisting neck or low back pain that radiates along a specific dermatome; most common cause is structural compression.
- Spinal cord symptoms: spasticity, bowel or bladder involvement, sensory level.
- Past history of stroke in thalamic distribution.

Family history suggests genetic cause.
Examination: see Table 1-35 and Section III, Neuropathic Pain.

ETIOLOGY & LABORATORY EVALUATION (SEE TABLE 1-36)

Metabolic
- Diabetes mellitus—check fasting blood sugar and 2-hour glucose tolerance test.
- Porphyria—consider urine and stool protoporphyrins.
- Fabry's disease.
- Thiamine deficiency, commonly seen in malnutrition and alcoholism—consider vitamin B_1 level.
- Vitamin B_{12} deficiency—check vitamin B_{12} level, and if normal, consider confirming by serum methylmalonic acid and homocysteine levels.

Inflammatory
- Immune vasculitides (lupus, Sjögren's syndrome, polyarteritis nodosa, etc.)—consider serum ANA, SS-A and SS-B, and p-ANCA.
- Acute inflammatory demyelinating polyneuropathy (also classically presents with ascending weakness and/or numbness).
- Sarcoid—consider serum ACE level, though pathologic evidence on nerve biopsy is definitive.
- Multiple sclerosis (common cause of trigeminal neuralgia)—lumbar puncture for oligoclonal bands and CSF/Serum IgG index.
- Arachnoiditis—imaging.

Infiltrative
- Amyloidosis—nerve biopsy
- Paraproteinemias (e.g., MGUS)—SPEP, UPEP, immunofixation

Infectious
- Postviral (brachial neuritis)
- HIV/AIDS
- HSV—lumbar puncture with HSV PCR
- VZV—lumbar puncture with VZV PCR
- Lyme disease—serum and CSF Lyme antibody (IgM and IgG)
- Leprosy—thickened nerves and skin lesions, diagnosis by biopsy
- Syphilis—serum RPR or FTA-ABS; also consider CSF VDRL

Neoplastic and paraneoplastic
- Carcinomatous infiltration of nerve/nerve root—imaging.
- Anti-Hu—serum anti-Hu level. May be positive without evidence of lung cancer, and it can be seen in both small cell and non-small-cell lung cancer.

Drugs/Toxins: determined by history
- Alcohol
- Chemotherapeutic agents: paclitaxel, vincristine
- Isoniazid
- Metronidazole
- Gold
- Thallium

DIAGNOSIS

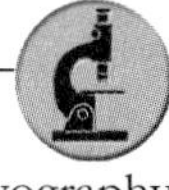

WORKUP

- Electrophysiology (electromyography with nerve conduction studies): normal in exclusively small fiber neuropathy, abnormal in large fiber neuropathy, normal in spinal cord disease
- Quantitative sensory testing: abnormal in small and large fiber neuropathy
- Epidermal nerve fiber biopsy: preferential diagnostic test for small fiber neuropathy when other studies are normal

IMAGING

MRI
- Of the brain to exclude thalamic pathology if symptoms and signs are consistent with thalamic lesion
- Of the spinal cord to exclude structural, inflammatory, neoplastic, or infectious causes
- Of the lumbar roots to evaluate for arachnoiditis

If MRI is not able to be performed, consider
- CT of the brain for thalamic pathology
- CT myelography of the spinal cord to evaluate for structural disease, but only if clinical signs of spinal compression or radiculopathy are present

TREATMENT

Nonpharmacologic
- Counseling: should be initiated at the beginning of therapy to address psychologic issues exacerbating physiologic pain
- Physical therapy: especially in cases of chronic neck and low back pain

Pharmacologic
- Antidepressants:
  1. Tricyclic antidepressants: nortriptyline before amitriptyline (less anticholinergic side effects). Begin 10 mg po qd in elderly, but 25 mg po qd in adults. Can increase by 25 mg every week until usual maximal effective dose of 150 mg/day.
  2. Paroxetine: begin 10 mg po qd, increase by 10 mg/week, max dose 60 mg po qd.

3. Buproprion: 100 mg po qd, increase by 100 mg/week, max 200-400 mg/day.
- Antiepileptics:
  1. Gabapentin: begin 300 mg po qd, advance to 300 mg po tid by the end of the first week. Effective dose: higher than 1600 mg/day. Max dose: 1500 mg po tid.
  2. Carbamazepine: especially for trigeminal neuralgia. Begin 400 mg po bid, increase to tid if necessary. Side effects and/or drug levels should determine safe increase in dosing. Risk: aplastic anemia.
  3. Oxcarbazepine: better tolerated than carbamazepine. Initiate 300 mg po bid and increase to 600 mg po bid if necessary.
  4. Topiramate: begin 25 mg po qd, increase by 25 mg/week until max effective dose 400-800 mg/day.
  5. Lamotrigine: begin 25 mg po bid, increase slowly (by 100 mg biweekly) until maximum effective dose of 200-300 mg po bid. Risk: Stevens-Johnson syndrome.
- Analgesics:
  1. Tramadol: 150 mg/day (50 mg tid), increase by 50 mg/week, max 200-400 mg/day.
  2. Morphine (oral): 15-30 mg q 8 hours, max 90-360 mg/day.
  3. Oxycodone: 20 mg q 12 hours, increase by 10 mg/week, max 40-160 mg/day.
- Topical anesthetics:
  1. 5% lidocaine patch, apply to area of pain, max three patches per 12 hours.
  2. Capsaicin is inconsistent in its ability to relieve pain and may exacerbate it. Use not recommended.

Procedural/Surgical: this option is considered mostly when the patient suffers from pain secondary to spinal cord or cauda equina injury. Studies are limited and benefit not completely established. Procedures should be considered only when all other therapeutic modalities have failed. In addition, the patient should be cautioned that surgical procedures may not result in pain relief and may be associated with significant morbidity and even mortality.
- Dorsal root rhizotomy
- Nerve blocks
- Spinal cord stimulator

PEARLS & CONSIDERATIONS

COMMENTS

Prognosis is dependent on multiple factors including:
- Etiology of pain
- Initiation of multiple therapeutic modalities
- Acceptance by patient of therapeutic modalities
- Initial response to pain management

Disposition: most care is accomplished in the outpatient setting, except when surgery is required.

REFERRALS

- Pain clinic
- Psychiatry
- Psychology
- Physiatry
- Anesthesiology (nerve blocks)
- Neurosurgery if considering surgical management

SUGGESTED READINGS

Chelimsky TC, Mehari E: Neuropathic pain. In Katirji B et al(eds): *Neuromuscular disorders in clinical practice,* Boston, 2002, Butterworth-Heinemann.

http://www.neuro.wustl.edu/neuromuscular.

Mendell JR, Sahenk Z: Painful sensory neuropathy, *N Engl J Med* 348(13):1243, 2003.

Sindou M, Mertens P: Neurosurgical management of neuropathic pain, *Stereotact Funct Neurosurg* 75(2-3):76, 2000.

Spaic M, Markovic N, Tadic R: Microsurgical DREZotomy for pain of spinal cord and Cauda equina injury origin: clinical characteristics of pain and implications for surgery in a series of 26 patients, *Acta Neurochir* 144(5):453, 2002.

AUTHOR: **GREGORY ESPER, M.D.**

TABLE 1-35 **Examination**

Exam Finding	Localization
Pinprick/temperature loss alone	Small fibers only
Pinprick/temperature loss + vibratory/proprioceptive loss	Small and large fibers
Sensory loss and motor dysfunction worse distally than proximal	Large fiber neuropathy
Sensory loss and motor dysfunction along single nerve distribution	Single nerve
Sensory loss and motor dysfunction along multiple single nerves	Multiple mononeuropathies (i.e., mononeuropathy multiplex)
Motor and sensory loss involving multiple nerves belonging to specific region of brachial or lumbar plexus	Plexopathy
Sensory loss along dermatome with multiple myotomal muscles affected	Nerve root lesion
Asymmetric sensory loss without weakness and pseudoathetosis	Dorsal root ganglion
Vibratory/proprioceptive loss without pinprick/temperature loss	Dorsal column dysfunction (from compressive lesion, B_{12} deficiency, or tabes dorsalis)
Sensory level with weakness below the level of lesion and long tract signs (spasticity/Babinski's sign)	Spinal cord lesion
Hemisensory hyperalgesia	Contralateral thalamus

TABLE 1-36 Clinical Presentation and Laboratory Findings

Neuropathy Type	Predisposition	Examination Findings	EMG/NCS	Laboratory Analysis
Idiopathic small fiber PN	Age >50	Strength: normal Reflexes: normal Pos/Vib: normal Pain/Temp: decreased distally	Normal	Serum studies: normal Skin biopsy: abnormal Sudomotor studies: abnormal
Diabetic PN	Long-standing disease Family history	Strength normal to reduced, sensation reduced distally	Abnormal	Elevated HbA1C Abnormal glucose tolerance High fasting glucose
Inherited PN	Family history	Pes cavus, hammer toes, reduced reflexes, sensation reduced distally	Abnormal	Genetic studies may be abnormal, other studies normal
Familial amyloid PN	Family history	Pain/temp loss Reduced reflexes Orthostasis	Abnormal if large fibers affected; also carpal tunnel syndrome	Transthyretin genetic study
Acquired amyloid PN	Monoclonal gammopathy	Pain/temp loss Reduced reflexes Orthostasis	Abnormal if large fibers affected; also carpal tunnel syndrome	SPEP, UPEP, Immunofixation abnormal
Fabry's disease	Age <20 Renal failure Strokes	Normal; possible reduced pain/temp sensation	Normal	α-galactosidase levels in cultured fibroblasts
PN + mixed connective tissue disease	History of lupus, rheumatoid arthritis, Sjögren's syndrome	Reduced reflexes and distal sensation	Abnormal	ANA, RF, SS-A/SS-B may be abnormal
Peripheral nerve vasculitis	Asymmetric disease	Multiple peripheral nerves involved	Abnormal	ANA, RF, SS-A/SS-B, ANCA, cryoglobulins may be abnormal
Paraneoplastic neuropathy	Lung cancer risk factors, chemical exposures	Asymmetric sensory loss, pseudoathetosis, relatively preserved strength	Abnormal	Anti-Hu
Sarcoidosis	Pulmonary sarcoid	Multiple mononeuropathies	Abnormal	Abnormal biopsy, elevated serum ACE, CXR abnormal
Arsenic	Pesticides, copper smelting	Reduced reflexes and distal sensation	Abnormal	Elevated arsenic in plasma, urine, and hair
HIV	Promiscuity, unprotected sex, IV drug abuse, blood transfusion	Variable, but most often reduced reflexes and distal sensation	Abnormal if large fibers involved	HIV antibody

ACE, Angiotensin-converting enzyme; *ANA,* antibody to nuclear antigens; *ANCA,* antineutrophil cytoplasmic antibodies; *CXR,* chest x-ray; *EMG,* electromyography; *HbA1C,* glycosylated hemoglobin; *HIV,* human immunodeficiency virus; *IV,* intravenous; *NCS,* nerve conduction studies; *PN,* polyneuropathy; *Pos,* position sensation; *RF,* rheumatoid factor; *SPEP,* serum protein electrophoresis; *SS-A,* Sjögren syndrome A; *SS-B,* Sjögren syndrome B; *Temp,* temperature sensation; *UPEP,* urine protein electrophoresis; *Vib,* vibration sensation.

(Adapted from Mendell JR, Sahenk Z: Painful sensory neuropathy, *N Engl J Med* 348(13):1243, 2003).

BASIC INFORMATION

DEFINITION

Any disorder affecting the peripheral nervous system, including nerve roots, plexuses, and individual peripheral nerves, that has a genetic basis of inheritance and has been or is capable of being transmitted along generations.

There are many different types of hereditary peripheral neuropathies, including Dejerine-Sottas disease, inherited metabolic neuropathies, hereditary sensory and autonomic neuropathies (HSANs), and hereditary motor neuropathies such as spinal muscular atrophy (SMA). Most disorders are diagnosed in infancy or childhood; as such, adult clinicians rarely see these patients. For this reason, this chapter discusses only the hereditary motor and sensory neuropathies that an adult clinician may encounter.

SYNONYMS

Charcot-Marie-Tooth (CMT) disease, a.k.a. hereditary motor-sensory neuropathy (HMSN)

Hereditary neuropathy with liability to recurrent pressure-sensitive palsies (HNPP)

ICD-9CM CODES
CMT: 356.1
HNPP: 689

EPIDEMIOLOGY & DEMOGRAPHICS

All CMT: approximately 30 per 100,000

- CMT type 1 (demyelinating pathophysiology): 1 in 2500
- CMT type 2 (axonal pathophysiology): 7 in 1000
- CMT type 4 and CMT-X: rare (either axonal or demyelinating pathophysiology)

HNPP: 2-5 per 100,000

PHYSICAL FINDINGS & CLINICAL PRESENATION

CMT: Highly variable

- Age at onset earlier for CMT-1 than CMT-2, but both may present from childhood to old age.
- CMT-1 manifestations are typically more severe than CMT-2.
- Severely affected patients have severe distal weakness and muscle atrophy with hand (prominently affecting interossei) and foot deformities (pes cavus, high arched feet, hammer toes).
- Mildly affected patients may have only foot deformity (pes cavus) with little or no weakness/sensory loss.
- Legs can be affected greater than arms, and patients will complain of gait abnormalities (steppage), which cause them to trip and fall.
- Sensory complaints (paresthesias, numbness, dysesthesia) are rare despite physical findings of impaired sensation.
- Decreased or absent reflexes.
- Some patients may have postural tremor of the upper limbs.

HNPP (a.k.a. tomaculous neuropathy):

- Age at onset is commonly adolescence.
- Disorder is characterized by recurrent peripheral mononeuropathies with accompanying signs and symptoms (paresthesias and/or weakness in anatomical distributions). Most common are:
  1. Median nerve at the wrist (carpal tunnel syndrome)
  2. Ulnar nerve at the elbow (cubital tunnel syndrome)
  3. Painless brachial plexopathies
  4. Lateral femoral cutaneous nerve (meralgia paresthetica)
  5. Peroneal nerve at the fibular head
- May be associated with a generalized polyneuropathy.

ETIOLOGY

CMT: more than 30 subgroups have been identified and have various chromosomal abnormalities.

- Most common mutation is PMP-22 mutations, giving rise to CMT 1A demyelinating phenotype.
- Other mutations include P0 (demyelinating) and neurofilament light chain mutations (demyelinating or axonal phenotype)—see below.
- Updated information available at http://www.neuro.wustl.edu/neuromuscular

HNPP: deletion of chromosome 17p11.2-12.

DIAGNOSIS

DIFFERENTIAL DIAGNOSIS

CMT: other genetic, metabolic, and multisystem disorders including:

- Spinocerebellar ataxias
- Friedreich's ataxia
- Leukodystrophies
- Refsum's disease (elevated serum phytanic acid)
- Distal spinal muscular atrophies and distal myopathies, which can present with pes cavus and other foot deformities
- Chronic inflammatory demyelinating polyneuropathy (CIDP)

HNPP:

- Hereditary neuralgic amyotrophy (HNA), which typically is painful rather than painless. In addition, in HNA, there is no evidence of generalized polyneuropathy.
- Multifocal motor neuropathy with conduction block (MMNCB—autoimmune mediated)
- Neuropathy associated with renal failure
- Lead neuropathy

EVALUATION

CMT

- History is very important (slow and gradual versus acute).
- Family history with PEDIGREE is essential. Consider examination of multiple family members.
- Environmental history should be taken for possible heavy metal exposure.
- History of dysesthesias is uncommon and should prompt search for acquired neuropathy or other inherited neuropathies (e.g., Fabry's disease).
- Laboratory tests are listed below.

HNPP: genetic testing after identification of multiple entrapment neuropathies on EMG and nerve conduction studies

LABORATORY TESTS

- Neurophysiology: electromyography (EMG) and nerve conduction studies (NCSs) must be done first to determine type of pathophysiology: demyelinating or axonal. This will guide genetic testing.
- NCSs in CMT-1 will reveal demyelinating physiology characterized by very slow conduction velocities around 15-30 m/s with prolonged distal latencies. Inherited demyelinating disorders can be distinguished from acquired demyelinating disorders (e.g., chronic inflammatory demyelinating polyneuropathy or CIDP) by the presence of conduction block in the latter.
- In HNPP, diffusely prolonged distal latencies with superimposed entrapment neuropathies at common sites will be seen on NCSs.
- EMG will reveal reinnervation characterized by long-duration, large-amplitude, polyphasic motor unit potentials (MUPs) with decreased MUP recruitment.
- Genetic tests are available for some CMT subtypes:
  1. CMT-1A: chromosome 17p11—PMP-22 duplication
  2. CMT-1B: chromosome 1q22—P0 mutation
  3. CMT-2E: chromosome 8p21—neurofilament light chain (NF-L) point mutation
  4. CMT-X: connexin 32
  5. HNPP: chromosome 17p11.2-12, which includes the PMP-22 gene
- Serum heavy metals.
- Anti-GM1 antibody (positive in MMNCB).
- Lumbar puncture may reveal elevated CSF protein in CIDP.

- Peripheral nerve biopsy:
  1. Demyelination with onion bulb pathology. Tomaculae, or focal thickening of myelin sheaths, seen in HNPP
  2. Generally not indicated secondary to use of electrodiagnostic and DNA testing

IMAGING STUDIES

- Spine plain films: for evaluation of scoliosis.
- MRI: indicated if dissociative sensory loss (dorsal column dysfunction with intact spinothalamic tract function) or if upper motor neuron findings (spasticity, Babinski's sign, clonus, increased tendon reflexes) are present.
- Exclusion of involvement of brain or spinal cord compressive lesions causing arm or leg weakness.
- Some inherited peripheral demyelinating disorders (i.e., CMT-X) are associated with intracerebral white matter abnormalities on MRI.
- Exclusion of structural, infectious, or inflammatory nerve root pathology.

TREATMENT

There is no known cure for any of these disorders. Management is supportive.

NONPHARMACOLOGIC THERAPY

- Physical therapy (PT) and occupational therapy (OT) to provide assistance with gait and coordination.
- PT and OT will also provide walking aids including ankle foot orthoses (AFO), canes, walkers, and possibly wheelchairs depending on the severity of the neuropathy.
- Wrist splints for superimposed carpal tunnel syndrome
- Elbow pads (Heelbo Pads) to cushion the ulnar nerve at the elbow.
- Heel-cord strengthening.
- Stretching exercises.
- Analgesics for pain associated with foot deformity.
- Surgical correction of foot deformities by orthopedic surgeons if indicated.

Vincristine may worsen existing neuropathy. Therefore if patients develop cancer and need to receive chemotherapy, they and covering physicians should be aware.

SURGICAL ISSUES:

- Patients with HNPP should probably not undergo surgical decompression of the median nerve at the wrist or the ulnar nerve at the elbow; these nerves are sensitive to manipulation. Poor results have been reported with ulnar nerve transposition.
- Anesthesiologists should be aware of HNPP diagnosis in patients undergoing surgery to prevent compression neuropathies from occurring during surgical procedures.

Genetic counseling: must be routinely done for patient and family when diagnosis is established. Many aspects of the patient and family's life are affected including:

- Future progeny of patient and/or patient's parents or children
- Psychosocial aspects including social functioning, marriage, employment
- Financial needs
- Medical and life insurability

PROGNOSIS

- CMT—slowly progressive, and patients tend to continue walking until late in life. Life expectancy is normal. Patients with respiratory involvement (i.e., phrenic nerve involvement with diaphragm paresis) may have shorter life expectancy.
- HNPP—benign prognosis.

DISPOSITION

- Outpatient care. Routine follow-up appointments should be done initially every 6 mo, and then every 1-2 yr.

REFERRAL

- Neurology and/or neuromuscular disease specialist
- Podiatry for recurrent feet problems, including appropriate arches

PEARLS & CONSIDERATIONS

PATIENT/FAMILY EDUCATION

Patients can benefit from use of Muscular Dystrophy Association (MDA) resources.

SUGGESTED READINGS

Chance PF, Shapiro BE: Charcot-Marie-Tooth disease and related disorders. In Katirji B et al (eds): *Neuromuscular Disorders in Clinical Practice,* Boston, 2002, Butterworth-Heinemann.

Neuromuscular Disease Center: http://www.neuro.wustl.edu/neuromuscular.

Nelis E et al: Estimation of the mutation frequencies in Charcot-Marie-Tooth disease type 1 and hereditary neuropathy with liability to pressure palsies: a European collaborative study, *Eur J Hum Genet* 4(1):25, 1996.

AUTHOR: **GREGORY ESPER, M.D.**

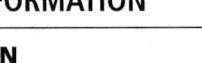

BASIC INFORMATION

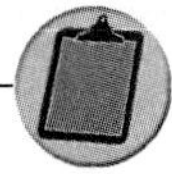

DEFINITION

Nocardiosis is an infection caused by aerobic actinomycetes found in soil and characterized by lung, soft tissue, or CNS involvement.

ICD-9CM CODES
039 Actinomycotic infections
039.9 Nocardiosis NOS, of unspecified site

EPIDEMIOLOGY & DEMOGRAPHICS

- *Nocardia* species are found worldwide in the soil.
- Nocardiosis is found most commonly in patients who are compromised (e.g., receiving steroids, immunosuppressive therapy, lymphoma, leukemia, lung cancer, and other pulmonary infections).
- Other underlying conditions associated with nocardiosis are pemphi-gus vulgaris, Whipple's disease, Goodpasture's syndrome, Cushing's disease, cirrhosis, ulcerative colitis, and rheumatoid arthritis.
- Use of steroids is an independent risk factor for developing nocardiosis.
- Between 500 to 1000 new cases are diagnosed each year in the United States.
- Approximately 2% of patients with AIDS develop nocardiosis.
- Occurs more commonly in men than in women (2:1).
- Adults > children.

PHYSICAL FINDINGS & CLINICAL PRESENTATION

- Inhalation of *Nocardia* organisms is the most common mode of entry, and pneumonia is the most common presentation, with 75% manifesting with fever, chills, dyspnea, and a productive cough (Fig. 1-160).
  1. Presentation can be acute, subacute, or chronic.
  2. Nocardiosis should be suspected if soft tissue abscesses or CNS tumors or abscesses form in conjunction with the pulmonary infection.
  3. Pulmonary infection may spread into the pericardium, mediastinum, and superior vena cava.
- Cutaneous disease usually occurs via direct inoculation of the organism as a result of skin puncture by a thorn or splinter, surgery, IV catheter use, or animal scratches or bites manifesting in:
  1. Cellulitis
  2. Lymphocutaneous nodules appearing along lymphatic sites draining the infected puncture wound
  3. Mycetoma (Madura foot), a chronic deep nodular infection usually involving the hands or feet that can cause skin breakdown, fistula formation, and spread along the fascial planes to infect surrounding skin, subcutaneous tissue, and bone
- The CNS system is infected in approximately one third of all cases. Brain abscesses is the most common pathologic finding.
- Dissemination of nocardiosis may infect other tissues and organs including kidney, heart, skin, and bone.

ETIOLOGY

- The most common *Nocardia* species leading to infection in humans are:
  1. *N. asteroides* (causing more than 80% of the cases of pulmonary nocardiosis)
  2. *N. brasiliensis* (most common cause of mycetoma)
  3. *N. otitidiscaviarum*
- *N. asteroides* has two subgroups
  1. *N. farcinica*
  2. *N. nova*

DIAGNOSIS

The diagnosis of nocardiosis requires a high index of suspicion in the proper clinical setting and is confirmed by bacteriologic staining and growth of the organism in culture.

DIFFERENTIAL DIAGNOSIS

- There are no pathognomonic findings separating nocardiosis pneumonia from other infectious etiologies of the lung. Diagnoses presenting in a similar manner and often confused for nocardiosis are:
  1. Tuberculosis
  2. Lung abscess
  3. Lung tumor
  4. Other causes of pneumonia
  5. Actinomycosis
  6. Mycosis
  7. Cellulitis
  8. Coccidioidomycosis
  9. Histoplasmosis
  10. Aspergillosis
  11. Kaposi's sarcoma

WORKUP

All patients with suspected nocardiosis need laboratory identification of the microorganism by obtaining sputum in the case of pneumonia, cultures of the infected skin lesions in mycetoma or lymphocutaneous disease, or the sampling of any purulent material (e.g., brain abscess, lung abscess, and pleural effusion).

LABORATORY TESTS

- Blood tests are not very sensitive in the diagnosis of nocardiosis.
- Gram stain shows gram-positive beaded filaments with multiple branches.

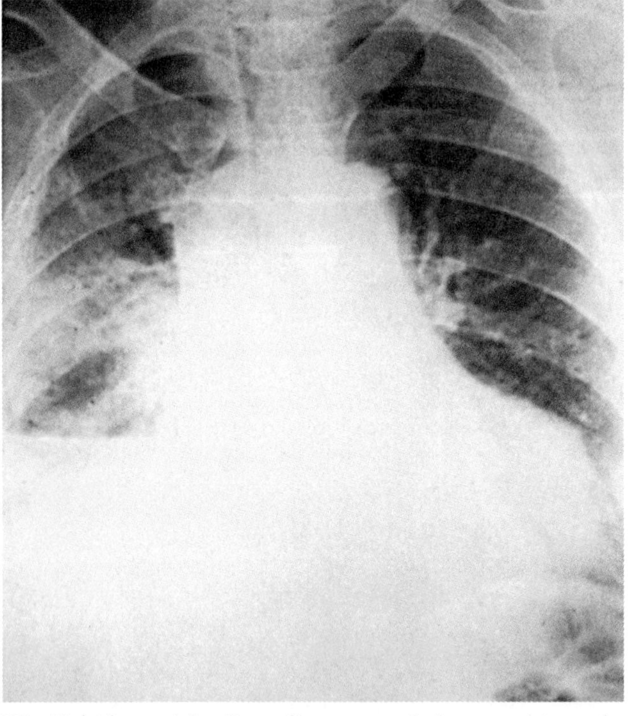

FIGURE 1-160 Right lower lobe *Nocardia* pneumonia in a renal transplant recipient. (From Gorbach SL: *Infectious diseases,* ed 2, Philadelphia, 1998, WB Saunders.)

- Gomori methenamine silver staining may detect the organism.
- *Nocardia* species are acid-fast on a modified Ziehl-Neelsen stain.
- *Nocardia* are slow-growing organisms and colony growth in cultures may take up to 2 to 3 wk.

IMAGING STUDIES

- Chest x-ray may demonstrate infiltrates, densities, nodules, cavitary masses, or multiple abscesses.
- CT scan of the brain is indicated in the appropriate clinical setting to exclude CNS brain abscesses.

TREATMENT

NONPHARMACOLOGIC THERAPY

- Supportive therapy with oxygen in patients with pneumonia
- Chest physiotherapy
- For any abscess formation, surgical drainage indicated (e.g., skin, lung, or brain)

ACUTE GENERAL Rx

- There are no prospective randomized trials to date highlighting the most effective treatment of nocardiosis. Nevertheless, sulfonamides are considered the treatment of choice. Sulfadiazine 6 to 10 g is given in 4 to 6 divided oral doses.
- Trimethoprim-sulfamethoxazole (160 mg/800 mg) given orally every 6 to 8 hr.
- Amikacin has been the IV antibiotic of choice.
- Alternative drug treatment includes:
  1. Minocycline 100 to 200 mg bid
  2. Erythromycin 500 mg qid and ampicillin 1 g qid for *N. nova* species
  3. Amoxicillin 500 mg and clavulanate 125 mg tid
  4. Ofloxacin 400 mg bid
  5. Clarithromycin 500 mg bid

CHRONIC Rx

- Although the optimal duration of therapy has not been determined, long-term therapy is generally recommended for all infections caused by *Nocardia*.
- Patients with cellulitis and lymphocutaneous syndrome are treated for 2 to 4 mo depending on whether there is bone involvement or not.
- Mycetomas are best treated with antibiotics for 6 to 12 mo but may require surgical drainage.
- Pulmonary and systemic nocardiosis excluding the CNS is treated for 6 to 12 mo.
- CNS involvement is treated with drainage and antibiotics for 12 mo.
- All immunosuppressed patients should receive 12 mo of antibiotic therapy.

DISPOSITION

- Patients with pulmonary nocardiosis have a mortality rate of 15% to 30%.
- CNS involvement carries a >40% mortality rate.
- Isolated skin lesions have a low mortality rate.

REFERRAL

Whenever the diagnosis of nocardiosis is suspected, consultation with infectious disease is indicated. Pulmonary evaluation and assistance may be needed in pulmonary nocardiosis. Neurosurgery consultation is indicated in patients with single or multiple brain abscesses.

PEARLS & CONSIDERATIONS

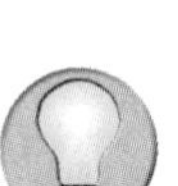

COMMENTS

- Tuberculosis and nocardiosis may coexist in the same patient.
- Nocardiosis does not spread from animal to animal.
- Nocardiosis is not transmitted from person to person.
- Nocardiosis is distinguished by its ability to disseminate to any organ and its tendency to relapse despite appropriate antibiotic therapy.

SUGGESTED READINGS

Boiron P et al: Nocardia, nocardiosis and mycetoma, *Med Mycol* 36(Suppl 1):26, 1998.

Lerner PI: Nocardiosis, *Clin Infect Dis* 22(6):891, 1996.

Torres HA et al: Nocardiosis in cancer patients, *Medicine* 81(5):388, 2002.

Wallace RJ et al: Taxonomy of *Nocardia* species, *Clin Infect Dis* 18:476, 1994.

AUTHOR: **PETER PETROPOULOS, M.D.**

Nonalcoholic Fatty Liver Disease 

BASIC INFORMATION

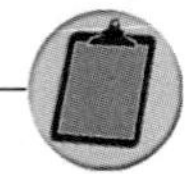

DEFINITION

Liver disease occurring in patients who do not abuse alcohol and manifested histologically by mononuclear cells and/or polymorphonuclear cells, hepatocyte ballooning, and spotty necrosis.

SYNONYMS

- Nonalcoholic steatohepatitis (NASH)
- Fatty liver hepatitis
- Diabetes hepatitis
- Alcohol-like liver disease
- Laënnec's disease

ICD-9CM CODES
571.8 Fatty liver

EPIDEMIOLOGY & DEMOGRAPHICS

- Nonalcoholic fatty liver disease affects 10% to 24% of general population
- Increased prevalence in obese persons (57% to 74%), type 2 diabetes mellitus, and hyperlipidemia (primarily hypertriglyceridemia)
- Most common cause of abnormal liver test results in adults in the U.S. (accounts for up to 90% of cases of asymptomatic ALT elevations)
- 30 million obese adults have steatosis, 8.6 million may have steatohepatitis

PHYSICAL FINDINGS & CLINICAL PRESENTATION

- Most patients are asymptomatic
- Patients may report a sensation of fullness or discomfort on the right side of the upper abdomen
- Nonspecific complaints of fatigue or malaise may be reported
- Hepatomegaly is generally the only positive finding on physical examination
- Acanthosis nigricans may be found in children

ETIOLOGY

- Insulin resistance is the most reproducible factor in the development of nonalcoholic fatty liver disease
- Risk factors are obesity (especially truncal obesity), diabetes mellitus, hyperlipidemia

DIAGNOSIS

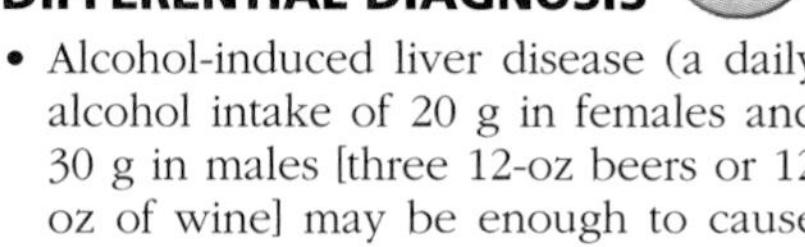

DIFFERENTIAL DIAGNOSIS

- Alcohol-induced liver disease (a daily alcohol intake of 20 g in females and 30 g in males [three 12-oz beers or 12 oz of wine] may be enough to cause alcohol-induced liver disease)
- Viral hepatitis
- Autoimmune hepatitis
- Toxin or drug-induced liver disease

WORKUP

Diagnosis is usually suspected on the basis of hepatomegaly, asymptomatic elevations of transaminases, or "fatty liver" on sonogram of abdomen in obese patients with little or no alcohol use. Liver biopsy will confirm diagnosis and provide prognostic information. It should be considered in patients with suspected advanced liver fibrosis (presence of obesity or type 2 diabetes, AST/ALT ratio 1, age 45 yr).

LABORATORY TESTS

- Elevated ALT, AST: AST/ALT ratio is usually <1, but can increase as fibrosis advances
- Negative serology for infectious hepatitis; generally normal GGTP, and serum alkaline phosphatase
- Hyperlipidemia (primarily hypertriglyceridemia) may be present
- Elevated glucose levels may be present
- Prolonged prothrombin time, hypoalbuminuria, and elevated bilirubin may be present in advanced stages
- Elevated serum ferritin and increased transferrin saturation may be found in up to 10% of patients; however, hepatic iron index and hepatic iron level are normal
- Liver biopsy may show a wide spectrum of liver damage, ranging from simple steatosis to advanced fibrosis and cirrhosis

IMAGING STUDIES

- Ultrasound generally reveals diffuse increase in echogenicity as compared with that of the kidneys; CT scan reveals diffuse low-density hepatic parenchyma.
- Occasionally patients may have focal rather than diffuse steatosis, which may be misinterpreted as a liver mass on ultrasound or CT; use of MRI in these cases will identify focal fatty infiltration.

TREATMENT

NONPHARMACOLOGIC THERAPY

Weight reduction in all obese patients (500 g per week in children and 1600 g per week in adults is preferred)

GENERAL THERAPY

- No medications have been proved to directly improve liver damage from nonalcoholic fatty liver disease.
- Medications to control hyperlipidemia (e.g., fenofibrates for elevated triglycerides) and hyperglycemia (e.g., metformin) can lead to improvement in abnormal liver test results.

DISPOSITION

- Patients with pure steatosis on liver biopsy generally have a relatively benign course.
- The presence of steatohepatitis or advanced fibrosis on liver biopsy is associated with a worse prognosis.

REFERRAL

Liver transplantation should be considered in patients with decompensated, end-stage disease; however, in these patients there may be a recurrence of nonalcoholic fatty liver disease posttransplantation.

SUGGESTED READINGS

Angulo P: Nonalcoholic fatty liver disease, *N Engl J Med* 346:1221, 2002.

Clark JM: Nonalcoholic fatty liver disease, *JAMA* 289:3000, 2003.

Dixon JB et al: Nonalcoholic fatty liver disease: predictors of nonalcoholic steatohepatitis and liver fibrosis in the severely obese, *Gastroenterology* 121:91, 2001.

AUTHOR: **FRED F. FERRI, M.D.**

BASIC INFORMATION

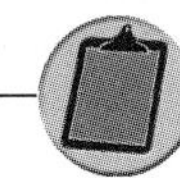

DEFINITION

Nosocomial infections (NI) are infections acquired as a result of hospitalization, generally after 48 hr of admission.

SYNONYMS

Hospital-acquired infections

EPIDEMIOLOGY & DEMOGRAPHICS

INCIDENCE (IN U.S.):

- Develop in at least 5% of hospitalized patients
- Account for 88,000 deaths/yr

In 1992 these infections were estimated to add $45 billion to the annual expenditures for health care in the U.S.

PREVALENCE (IN U.S.): 2 to 4 million cases/yr

PREDOMINANT SEX:

- Overall, approximately equal
- Elderly women: predominantly nosocomial urinary tract infections

PREDOMINANT AGE:

- Elderly patients (>60 yr old) at highest risk
- High-risk patients who may develop NI at any age:
  1. ICU
  2. Intubation
  3. Chronic lung disease
  4. Renal disease
  5. Comatose
  6. Chronic urethral or vascular catheterization
  7. Malnutrition
  8. Postoperative state

PEAK INCIDENCE: Varies widely with infection site

PHYSICAL FINDINGS & CLINICAL PRESENTATION

Vary with specific NI

ETIOLOGY

- Bacteria
- Fungi
- Viruses

SOURCES AND MODES OF TRANSMISSION:

1. Patient's own flora
   a. Comprises resistant organisms acquired during hospitalization
   b. Frequently maintained thereafter by persistent GI colonization
2. Unwashed hands of staff
   a. Physicians
   b. Nurses
3. Invasion of protective defenses (intact skin, respiratory cilia, urinary sphincters, and mucosa)
   a. IV lines
   b. Catheters
   c. Respiratory equipment
   d. Surgical wounds
   e. Scopes and other imaging devices
4. Failure to provide adequate negative pressure, high-volume air flow chambers for respiratory isolation of patients with TB
5. Failure to rapidly identify and provide appropriate care (with isolation or precautions) for patients with communicable diseases
6. Inanimate environment
7. Food
8. Fomites

RISKS AMPLIFIED:

1. Use of broad-spectrum antibiotics
   a. Select highly resistant bacteria
   b. Establish highly resistant bacteria as endemic flora in microenvironments within the hospital
2. Highly vulnerable patients with specific risk factors
   a. Immunosuppression (as a result of therapy, transplantation, AIDS)
   b. Old age
   c. Postsurgery
   d. Prolonged surgery
   e. Chronic lung disease
   f. Ventilator dependence
   g. Antacid therapy
   h. Vascular lines
   i. Hyperalimentation
   j. ICU stay
   k. Recent antibiotic therapy
3. Clustering of seriously ill patients
   a. Often with wounds or drainage of contaminated materials
   b. Intensifying probability of cross-infection

HAND WASHING BETWEEN ALL PATIENT CONTACTS: Single most important method of decreasing NI

1. Regular soap
2. Chlorhexidine for methicillin-resistant *Staphylococcus aureus* (MRSA) and other resistant gram-positive organisms
3. Iodophor for resistant gram-negative organisms
4. Purpose
   a. Degrease hand surfaces
   b. Wash away oils and associated bacteria
5. Procedure
   a. Lukewarm water
   b. Must include all surfaces
   c. Special attention to areas between fingers and to the dirtier dominant hand (most people reflexively wash their cleaner, nondominant hand more vigorously)

VANCOMYCIN-RESISTANT *ENTEROCOCCUS FAECIUM* (VREF):

1. The percentage of nosocomial infections caused by VREF increased more than 20-fold between 1989 and 1993, rising from 0% to 3% to 7% to 9%.
2. A high percentage of VREF isolated, 80% are also ampicillin resistant.
3. Factors predisposing to VREF colonization or infection include percentage of hospital days receiving antimicrobial therapy, use of IV, underlying disease, immunosuppression, and abdominal surgery.
4. Evidence suggests that vehicle is the hands of medical personnel.
5. Control measures
   a. Aggressive isolation of colonized and infected patients
   b. Restraint in using broad-spectrum antibiotics

CLOSTRIDIUM DIFFICILE:

1. Causes diarrhea as a result of pseudomembranous colitis
2. May be transmitted among hospitalized patients
3. Warrants stool (contact) precautions

SURVEILLANCE:

1. Crucial for early identification of infections
   a. Enabling immediate intervention
   b. Education
2. Prospective, concurrent, total hospital surveillance
   a. Provides most complete data
   b. Feasible with sophisticated computerized data collection and analysis
3. Daily plotting of all infections on comprehensive wall maps
   a. Including all beds on all wards
   b. Enhances immediate recognition of microclusters of infections by body site and by organism
   c. Facilitates proper early control of potential outbreaks

DIAGNOSIS

MOST COMMON NOSOCOMIAL INFECTIONS:

- Urinary tract infections (40% to 45%)
- Surgical wound and other soft tissue infections (25% to 30%)
- Pneumonia (15% to 20%)
- Bacteremia (5% to 12%)

NOSOCOMIAL URINARY TRACT INFECTIONS:

- General associations:
  1. Foley catheters
  2. Inappropriate catheter care (including opening catheter junctions)
  3. Female sex
  4. Absence of systemic antibiotics
- Physical findings:
  1. Fever
  2. Dysuria
  3. Leukocytosis
  4. Pyuria
  5. Flank or costovertebral angle tenderness
- Usual organisms:
  1. *E. coli*
  2. *Klebsiella*
  3. *Enterobacter*
  4. *Pseudomonas*
  5. *Enterococcus*

- Sepsis in 1% to 3% of nosocomial UTIs
- Prevention:
  1. Meticulous technique during insertion and daily perineal care
  2. Never open the catheter-collection tubing junction
  3. Obtain all specimens using sterile syringe
  4. Substitute intermittent catheterization for Foley catheters

NOSOCOMIAL BACTEREMIAS:
- General associations:
  1. IV lines
  2. Arterial lines
  3. CVP lines
  4. Phlebitis
  5. Hyperalimentation
- Fever possibly only presenting sign
- Exit site of all vascular lines carefully evaluated for:
  1. Erythema
  2. Induration
  3. Tenderness
  4. Purulent drainage
- Usual organism for device-associated bacteremia
  1. *S. aureus*
  2. *Staphylococcus epidermidis* for long-term IV lines
  3. *Enterobacter*
  4. *Klebsiella*
  5. *Candida* spp.
  6. *Pseudomonas aeruginosa* may come from a water source or reflect cutaneous bacteria
- Phlebitis in 1.3 million patients yearly
- Approximately 10,000 annual deaths from IV sepsis
- Prevention:
  1. Meticulous sterile technique during IV insertion
  2. Emphasis should be placed on attention to detail, including hand washing, adherence to guidelines for catheter insertion and maintenance, appropriate use of antiseptic solutions such as chlorhexidine or iodine to prepare the skin around the catheter insertion site, and use of sterile technique for central catheter insertion
  3. Modified catheter may reduce risk for endoluminal colonization and catheter-related sepsis in subclavian lines
  4. Decrease use of routine IVs (patients would rather drink)

NOSOCOMIAL PNEUMONIAS:
- More common in ICUs
- General associations:
  1. Aspiration
  2. Intubation
  3. Altered consciousness
  4. Old age
  5. Chronic lung disease
  6. Postsurgery
  7. Antacids
- Signs of pneumonia common among patients on general wards:
  1. Cough
  2. Sputum
  3. Fever
  4. Leukocytosis
  5. New infiltrate on chest x-ray examination
- Signs more subtle in ICUs, because many patients have purulent sputum because of chronic intubation
  1. Change in sputum character or volume
  2. Small changes on chest x-ray examination
- Usual organisms:
  1. *Klebsiella*
  2. *Acinetobacter*
  3. *Enterobacter*
  4. *Pseudomonas aeruginosa*
  5. *S. aureus*
- Less common organisms:
  1. MRSA
  2. *Legionella, Flavobacterium*
  3. Respiratory syncytial virus (infants)
  4. Adenovirus
- 1% of hospitalized patients affected
- Mortality rate high (40%)
- Prevention:
  1. Meticulous sterile technique during suctioning and handling airway
  2. Do not routinely change ventilator breathing circuits and components more frequently than q48h
  3. Drain respirator tubing without allowing fluid to return to respirator
  4. Hand washing routinely to prevent colonization of patients and transfer of organisms among patients

NOSOCOMIAL SOFT TISSUE INFECTIONS:
- Associations:
  1. Decubitus ulcers
  2. Surgical wound classification (contaminated or dirty-infected)
  3. Abdominal surgery
  4. Presence of drain
  5. Preoperative length of stay
  6. Duration of surgery >2 hr
  7. Surgeon
  8. Presence of other infection
- Physical findings:
  1. Decubitus ulcer with fluctuance at margin or under firm eschar
  2. Erythema extending >2 cm beyond margin of surgical wound
  3. Tenderness
  4. Induration
  5. Erythema
  6. Fluctuance
  7. Purulent drainage
  8. Dehiscence of sutures
- Usual organisms:
  1. *S. aureus*
  2. *Enterococcus*
  3. *Enterobacter*
  4. *Acinetobacter*
  5. *E. coli*
- Prevention:
  1. Careful skin care and frequent, proper positioning of patient to prevent decubitus ulcer
  2. Meticulous sterile surgical technique
  3. Hand washing to decrease colonization when handling postoperative wound
  4. Limit prophylactic antibiotics to 24 hr perioperatively
  5. Double-wrap contaminated dressings (hold in gloved hand and evert gloves over dressings) before disposal

LABORATORY TESTS

- Appropriate to specific NI and specific patient's condition
- Cultures generally indicated for proper confirmation of responsible pathogens
  1. Urine
  2. Blood
  3. Sputum
  4. Soft tissue infection
- Molecular analysis of nosocomial epidemics
  1. Plasmid fingerprinting
  2. Restriction endonuclease digestion (plasmid and genomic DNA)
  3. Peptide analysis by SDS-PAGE
  4. Immunoblotting
  5. Ribosomal (rRNA) typing
  6. DNA probes
  7. Multilocus enzyme electrophoresis
  8. Restriction fragment length polymorphism (RFLP)
  9. Polymerase chain reaction (PCR)
  10. Provide confirmation of point-source or common strains
  11. Offer occasionally indispensable corroboration of hypotheses reached utilizing classic epidemiology

IMAGING STUDIES

Rarely needed for diagnosis of NI

TREATMENT

ACUTE GENERAL Rx

- Appropriate to etiologic organism:
  1. Antibiotic
  2. Antifungal
  3. Antiviral
- Specific therapy determined after careful consideration of resident flora within the microenvironment in which the patient was hospitalized
  1. Empiric therapy
     a. Frequently difficult to fashion accurately
     b. Often undesirable, unless the patient's clinical condition requires urgent treatment

2. Consultation for expert advice regarding antibiotic selection in view of known epidemiologic risks within the hospital
   a. Nosocomial infection control nurses
   b. Hospital epidemiologist
- Avoid unnecessary treatment for organisms that are colonizing but not infecting patients
- Prevention of spread of communicable diseases often requiring Isolation or Precautions
  1. Classic Schema (Strict, Respiratory Isolation and Contact [Skin and Wound] Precautions) being replaced by more streamlined Revised Guidelines (Airborne, Droplet, Contact Isolation Precautions)
  2. Less careful response to some diseases (e.g., hemorrhagic fevers) inadvertently induced by removal of strict isolation category
  3. Universal/Standard Precautions and Body Substance Isolation continue within a new Standard Isolation Precautions Guideline
- Universal Precautions used for all patients during all contacts with blood, body fluids, or secretions
  1. Gloves
  2. Goggles
  3. Impermeable gowns if aerosol or splash is likely
- Consider aggressive isolation to restrict spread of resistant organisms and their plasmids
  1. MRSA
  2. VREF
  3. Highly resistant gram-negative organisms

REFERRAL

- To nosocomial infection control nurses
- To hospital epidemiologist

PEARLS & CONSIDERATIONS

COMMENTS

- Sharps and splash injuries to staff relatively are rare, but nearly all are preventable.
  1. Nurses incur most injuries.
  2. Usual causes:
     a. Needle sticks
     b. Scalpel and surgical needle injuries
     c. Blood splashes
  3. Prevention:
     a. Never recap needles
     b. Needle disposal only in rigid, impermeable plastic containers
     c. Clearly announce instrument passes in operating room or during procedures and use passing trays
     d. Gloves and goggles if aerosol or splash is likely
     e. Never leave needles or other sharp items in beds
     f. Never dispose of sharp items in regular trash bags
  4. Infection control staff should be consulted immediately after exposure to determine need for prophylaxis for hepatitis B or HIV.
  5. All staff should be immune to hepatitis B (natural or vaccine).
- Fungi previously considered to be contaminants now risks for patients with cancer and organ transplantation
  1. *Candida* spp.
     a. *C. guilliermondii*
     b. *C. krusei*
     c. *C. parapsilosis*
     d. *C. tropicalis*
  2. *Aspergillus* spp.
  3. *Curvularia* spp.
  4. *Bipolaris* spp.
  5. *Exserohilum* spp.
  6. *Alternaria* spp.
  7. *Fusarium* spp.
  8. *Scopulariopsis* spp.
  9. *Pseudallescheria boydii*
  10. *Trichosporon beigelii*
  11. *Malassezia furfur*
  12. *Hansenula* spp.
  13. *Microsporum canis*
- Focused, committed efforts by the entire health care staff continuously directed toward prevention
  1. Each NI addressed as an opportunity to improve the organization and delivery of care
  2. Essential that individual staff members understand that small risks applied to large populations result in a large number of total events (i.e., NI)

SUGGESTED READINGS

Goldmann DA: Blood-borne pathogens and nosocomial infections, *J Allergy Clin Immunol* S21-6, 2002.

Johanson WG, Dever LL: Nosocomial pneumonia, *Intensive Care Med* 29(1):23, 2003.

Rowin ME et al: Pediatric intensive care unit nosocomial infections: epidemiology, sources and solutions, *Crit Care Clin* 19(3):473, 2003.

AUTHOR: **ZEENA LOBO, M.D.**

BASIC INFORMATION

DEFINITION

Obesity refers to excess body fat defined as a body mass index (BMI) ≥30 kg/m^2. Overweight is defined as BMI of 25 to 29.9 kg/m^2. These conditions result from a problem of imbalance between energy intake and expenditure.

SYNONYMS

Overweight

ICD-9CM CODES
278.0 Obesity

EPIDEMIOLOGY & DEMOGRAPHICS

- Approximately 97 million adults in the U.S. and 310 million people worldwide are overweight or obese.
- The present costs of obestiy in the U.S. population are estimated to run at 5%-8% of total healthcare spending, which equates to $92.6-$99.2 billion annually (1998 data normalized to 2002 dollars).
- From 1960 to 1999, the prevalence of excess weight (BMI ≥25 kg/m^2) increased from 44% to 61% of the adult population, and the prevalence of obesity (BMI ≥30 kg/m^2) doubled, from 13% to 27%. Estimates in 2003 suggest that 31% of the U.S. population is now obese.
- In the U.S., the progression of obesity is 3-4 yr ahead of the problem in Europe.
- The Third National Health and Nutrition Examination Survey (NHANES III) estimated that 13.7% of children and 11.5% of adolescents are overweight.
- Overweight and obesity are defined as stated previously on the basis of epidemiologic data showing increased mortality with BMIs above 25 kg/m^2.
- For persons with a BMI of ≥30 kg/m^2, all-cause mortality is increased by 50% to 100% above that of persons with BMIs in the range of 20 to 25 kg/m^2.
- Obese individuals are at increased risk of morbidity/mortality from type 2 diabetes, hypertension, CVD, cancer (particularly breast cancer), sleep apnea, osteoarthritis, and skin disorders.
- The effects of obesity on health outcome appear to be reversible with weight loss.
- Obesity is more prevalent in black and Hispanic women compared with non-Hispanic white women and men. Approximately 50% of the black female population is estimated to be obese.
- People in the U.S. with low incomes or low education are 5% more likely to be obese than those of higher socioeconomic status.
- In 1993 the Deputy Assistant Secretary for Health (J. Michael McGinnis) and the former Director of the Centers for Disease Control and Prevention (CDC) (William Foege) coauthored a journal article, "Actual Causes of Death in the U.S." It concluded that a combination of dietary factors and sedentary activity patterns accounts for at least 300,000 deaths each year, and obesity is the second leading cause of preventable death in the United States.

PHYSICAL FINDINGS & CLINICAL PRESENTATION

- Obesity is self-evident on examination.
- Measuring the height in meters and weight in kilograms determines your BMI.
- Increased waist circumference (>40 inches in men and >35 inches in women) is apparent.
- Hypertension is related to obesity.
- Symptoms of diabetes (e.g., polyuria, polydipsia, retinopathy, and neuropathy) may be present.
- Joint pain and swelling are associated with osteoarthritis and obesity.
- Dyspnea may be present.

ETIOLOGY

- The cause of obesity is multifactorial, involving social, cultural, behavioral, physiologic, metabolic, and genetic factors.
- Supporting genetic factors come from identical twins reared apart and "obesity genes" encoding for the appetite-suppressant hormone leptin.
- Environmental factors are a major determinant of obesity with the underlying theme of excess calorie intake and lack of physical activity. In children, time spent sleeping or watching television has been directly correlated with prevalence of obesity.
- Genetics and environmental factors exert their effects on energy balance and obesity via effects on behavior and physiology. There is no direct link between genetics and body weight or obesity. Obesity develops as a result of excessive energy intake, inadequate energy expenditure, or both.
- Over the last 2 decades, fat consumption has declined in parallel with the increased prevalence of obesity in both the U.S. and Europe, and the decline is matched by a parallel increase in carbohydrate consumption, suggesting a role for excessive dietary carbohydrate in the development of obesity.

DIAGNOSIS

- Determination of the BMI establishes the diagnosis of obesity according to the previous definition and assesses the individual's risk for disease.
- BMI is defined as the weight in kilograms divided by the square of the height in meters (W÷H^2).
- Strict BMI measurements should be used with caution in making a diagnosis of obesity. Although BMI is commonly used to define obesity, it is not a very accurate indicator of body fat composition in children, who are undergoing rapid changes in height, or in bodybuilders or athletes who have large amounts of muscle tissue.

DIFFERENTIAL DIAGNOSIS

It is important to rule out specific causative medical disorders in obese patients. Hypothalamic disorders, hypothyroidism, Cushing's syndrome, insulinoma, and chronic corticosteroid use can cause obesity.

WORKUP

The workup of an obese patient typically requires laboratory work to assess for risks and complications as well as to rule out underlying causative medical conditions.

LABORATORY TESTS

- Laboratory tests are not specific in diagnosing obesity; however, they are used to identify diabetes and hyperlipidemia commonly related to excess weight.
- In the proper clinical setting, thyroid function studies (TSH, free T_4), AM cortisol level, and insulin level with C-peptide measurements will exclude hypothyroidism, Cushing's syndrome, and insulinoma as underlying causes of obesity.

IMAGING STUDIES

- X-ray imaging studies are not specific in the diagnosis of obesity.
- Several methods are available for determining or calculating total body fat but offer no significant advantage over the BMI.
  1. Total body water
  2. Total body potassium
  3. Bioelectrical impedance
  4. Dual-energy x-ray absorptiometry
  - Buoyancy testing is the most accurate method for determining total body fat composition.

TREATMENT

- Treatment is aimed at weight reduction and risk factor modification (e.g., diabetes, lipids, hypertension).
- Once a joint decision between patient and clinician has been made to lose weight, the expert panel recommends as an initial goal the loss of 10% of baseline weight, to be lost at a rate of 1 to 2 lb/wk over a 6- to 12-mo period followed by long-term maintenance of reduced weight.

NONPHARMACOLOGIC THERAPY

- The three major components of weight loss therapy are:
  1. Many studies demonstrate that obese adults can lose about 0.5 kg per wk by decreasing their daily intake to 500 to 1000 kcal below the caloric intake required for the maintenance of their current weight.
  2. Increased physical activity initially by walking 30 min 3 times/wk and gradually build up to intense walking 45 min 5 days/wk. The eventual goal is at least 30 min of moderate intense walking.
  3. Behavioral therapy is also necessary.

ACUTE GENERAL Rx

- Medications for the treatment of obesity are currently approved as an adjunct to diet and physical activity for patients with a BMI of ≥30 with no concomitant obesity-related risk factors or diseases, and for patients with a BMI ≥27 with concomitant obesity-related risk factors or diseases.
- Medications approved for the treatment of obesity include
  1. Sibutramine 5-15 mg/day
  2. Orlistat 120 mg 3 times/day with or within 1 hour after fat-containing meals, plus a daily vitamin.
  3. Benzphetamine 25-50 mg 1-3 times/day
  4. Phendimetrazine 17.5-70 mg 2-3 times/day or 105 mg sustained-release/day
  5. Phentermine 18.75-37.5 mg/day
  6. Phentermine resin 15-30 mg/day
  7. Diethylpropion 25 mg 3 times/day or 75 mg sustained-release/day
- Benzphetamine, phendimetrazine, phentermine and diethylpropion are approved for use of a few weeks generally presumed to be 12 wk or less. Only sibutramine and orlistat are approved for long-term use. The safety and efficacy of weight loss medications beyond 2 yr of use have not been established.
- Medications are divided into appetite suppressants (e.g., sibutramine) and those that decrease nutrient absorption (e.g., orlistat).
- In 1997 both dexfenfluramine and fenfluramine were withdrawn from the market secondary to side effects of valvular heart lesions and pulmonary hypertension.
- Contraindications using benzphetamine, phendimetrazine, phentermine, and diethylpropion include hypertension, advanced cardiovascular disease, hyperthyroidism, glaucoma, and history of substance abuse.
- Side effects of sibutramine include increases in blood pressure and pulse, dry mouth, headache, insomnia, and constipation. Side effects of orlistat include oily spotting, flatus with discharge, and fecal urgency.
- Other medications in clinical trials include bupropion (Wellbutrin), topiramate (Topamax), and metformin (Glucophage).

CHRONIC Rx

- Surgery is a consideration in clinically severe obesity (e.g., BMI ≥ 40 or ≥ 35 with comorbid conditions).
- Gastroplasty, gastric banding, gastric partitioning, and gastric bypass are the surgical procedures performed.

DISPOSITION

- Obesity increases the risk of developing hypertension, hyperlipidemia, type 2 diabetes, coronary artery disease, cerebrovascular disease, osteoarthritis, sleep apnea, and endometrial, breast, prostate, and colon cancers.
- Obesity accelerates the progression of coronary atherosclerosis in young men (age range 15 to 34 yr).
- All-cause mortality is increased in obese patients.

REFERRAL

Obesity is commonly seen in the primary care setting. If pharmacologic therapy is considered, consultation with physicians specializing in obesity and experienced with the use of the drug is recommended. In addition, consultation with nutritionists and behavioral therapists is helpful. A consultation with general surgery is indicated in patients being considered for surgical intervention.

PEARLS & CONSIDERATIONS

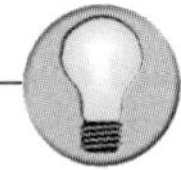

COMMENTS

- The National Heart, Lung, and Blood Institute's (NHLBI) Obesity Education Initiative in cooperation with the National Institute of Diabetes convened the Expert Panel on the Identification, Evaluation, and Treatment of Overweight and Obesity in Adults in May 1995 and have since published evidence-based clinical guidelines for treatment of obesity.
- Only about 20% of adult men and women actually restrict caloric intake and increase physical activity to consciously control body weight.
- As knowledge of the physiologic process governing maintenance of body weight increases, newer drug therapies are emerging, which will target lipid metabolic enzymes involved in digestion, absorption, synthesis, storage, and mobilization of fat within the human body

SUGGESTED READINGS

Blanck HM et al: Use of non-prescription weight loss products: results from a multistate survey, *JAMA* 286:930, 2001.

Clinical Guidelines on the Identification, Evaluation, and Treatment of Overweight and Obesity in Adults. The Evidence Report. National Institute of Health, National Heart, Lung, and Blood Institute. *www.nhlbi.nih.gov/guidelines/obesity/ob_gdlns.pdf*

Executive Summary of the Clinical Guidelines on the Identification, Evaluation, and Treatment of Overweight and Obesity in Adults, *Arch Intern Med* 158(17):1855, 1867, 1998.

Korner J, Aronne LJ: Pharmacological approaches to weight reduction: Therapeutic targets, *J Clin End Metab* 89(6)2616, 2004.

Lyznicki JM et al: Obesity: assessment and management in primary care, *Am Fam Physician* 63:2185, 2001.

McTigue KM et al: The natural history of the development of obesity in a cohort of young US adults between 1981 and 1988, *Ann Intern Med* 136:857, 2002.

McTigue KM et al: Screening and interventions for obesity in adults: summary of the evidence for the U.S. Preventive Services Task Force, *Ann Intern Med* 139:933, 2003.

Speakman JR: Obesity: the integrated roles of environment and genetics, *J Nutr* 134:2090S, 2004.

Weil E et al: Obesity among adults with disabling conditions, *JAMA* 288:1265, 2002.

Wilson PW et al: Overweight and obesity as determinants of cardiovascular risk, *Arch Intern Med* 162:1867, 2002.

Yanovski SZ, Yanovski JA: Obesity: drug therapy, *N Engl J Med* 346(8):591, 2002.

AUTHORS: **JASON IANNUCCILLI, M.D.,** and **PETER PETROPOULOS, M.D.**

 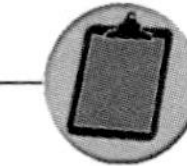

BASIC INFORMATION

DEFINITION

Obsessive-compulsive disorder (OCD) involves recurrent obsessions (intrusive and inappropriate thoughts, impulses, or images) and/or compulsions (behaviors or mental acts performed in response to obsessions or rigid application of rules) that consume >1 hr/day or cause marked impairment or distress. The symptoms are perceived as excessive and unreasonable.

ICD-9CM CODES
F42.8 Obsessive-compulsive disorder (DSM-IV 300.3)

EPIDEMIOLOGY & DEMOGRAPHICS

LIFETIME PREVALENCE (IN U.S.): 2.5% of adults

PREDOMINANT SEX: Approximately equal distribution between sexes.

PREDOMINANT AGE:
- Modal age of onset for females is between 20 and 29 yr.
- Modal age of onset for males is between 6 and 15 yr.

PEAK INCIDENCE: Mean age at onset is 19.6 yr.

DISEASE COURSE:
- Condition is chronic with waxing and waning.
- Symptoms typically worsen with stress.
- 15% show progressive deterioration while 5% show an episodic course with little impairment between episodes.

GENETICS:
- There is no clear genetic pattern.
- Rate of concordance is higher in monozygotic (33%) vs. dizygotic (7%) twins.
- Rate of disorder is also higher in first-degree relatives of individuals with OCD and Tourette's disorder than the general population.

PHYSICAL FINDINGS & CLINICAL PRESENTATION

- Persistent and recurrent intrusive and ego-dystonic obsessive ideas, thoughts, impulses, or images that are perceived as alien and beyond one's control.
- Frequent experiencing of obsessions related to contamination (e.g., when using the telephone), excessive doubt (e.g., was the door locked?), organization (the need for a particular order), violent impulses (e.g., to yell obscenities in church), or intrusive sexual imagery.
- Obsessions possibly leading to compulsive behaviors meant to temporarily ameliorate the anxiety caused by obsessions (e.g., repeated hand washing, checking, rearranging), or mental tasks (e.g., counting, repeating phrases).
- Obsessions and compulsions almost always accompanied with high anxiety and subjective distress. Both are seen as excessive and unreasonable.

ETIOLOGY

- Strong evidence of neurobiological etiology.
- OCD may have onset after infectious illness of CNS (e.g., Von Economo's encephalitis, Sydenham's chorea).
- OCD may follow head trauma or other premorbid neurological conditions including birth hypoxia and Tourette's syndrome.
- Serotoninergic pathways believed important in some ritualistic instinctual behaviors, with dysfunction of these pathways possibly giving rise to OCD.

DIAGNOSIS

DIFFERENTIAL DIAGNOSIS

- Obsessive-compulsive personality disorder (OCPD) is a maladaptive personality style defined by excessive rigidity, need for order/control, preoccupation with details, and excessive perfectionism. Unlike OCD, OCPD, is egosyntonic.
- Other psychiatric disorders in which obsessive or intrusive thoughts occur (e.g., body dysmorphic disorder phobias, posttraumatic stress disorder).
- Other conditions in which compulsive or impulse control behaviors are seen (e.g., trichotillomania, gambling, paraphilias).
- Major depression, hypochondriasis, and several anxiety disorders with predominant obsessions or compulsions; however, in these disorders the thoughts are not anxiety provoking or are extremes of normal concern.
- Delusions or psychosis, which may be mistaken for obsessive thoughts; unlike OCD, these individuals do not believe their obsessions are unreal and may likely meet criteria for another psychotic spectrum disorder that fully accounts for the obsessions (e.g., schizophrenia).
- Tics and stereotypic movements that appear compulsive but are not driven by the desire to neutralize an obsession.

WORKUP

- Careful history leading to diagnosis
- Neurologic examination to rule out concomitant Tourette's or other tic disorder
- In adolescents and children: psychologic testing to reveal learning disabilities

LABORATORY TESTS

No specific tests are indicated.

IMAGING STUDIES

- No specific studies are indicated.
- There have been research reports of reversible abnormalities on PET scans.

TREATMENT

NONPHARMACOLOGIC THERAPY

- Average delay between symptom onset and treatment is 17 yr.
- Initiation of treatment will help about 50% of patients achieve partial remission within the first 6 mo.
- Cognitive-behavioral therapy (especially exposure with response prevention) is successful in up to 70% of patients but nearly 25% drop out of treatment due to the initial anxiety the exposures create. Best results are found for contamination obsessions and washing compulsions.

PHARMACOLOGIC THERAPY

- Antidepressants with serotonergic reuptake blockade, including fluoxetine, clomipramine, fluvoxamine, paroxetine, sertraline, and citalopram; optimal dosages are typically at the high end of the prescription range
- No response in only 15% of patients
- Indefinite treatment
- Treatment augmentation.
- Combination cognitive-behavioral therapy and pharmacotherapy typically yields superior outcomes.
- Patients with comorbid psychosis and/or tic disorders may benefit from the addition of a neuroleptic.
- PRN clonazapam may be helpful in patients with extreme anxiety or those with a history of seizure disorder.
- Surgical interventions (e.g., cingulotomy) are available for the most extreme, refractory cases.

REFERRAL

- If distinction from other psychiatric conditions, particularly delusional disorder, is not clear
- If patient refractory to drug treatment and/or requests cognitive-behavioral therapy
- If treatment with antidepressants is problematic

SUGGESTED READINGS

Ackerman DL, Greenland S: Multivariate meta-analysis of controlled drug studies for obsessive-compulsive disorder, *J Clin Psychopharmacol* 22:309, 2002.

Goodman WK: Obsessive compulsive disorder: Diagnosis and treatment, *J Clin Psychiatry* 60(suppl 18):27, 1999.

McDonough M, Kennedy N: Pharmacological management of obsessive-compulsive disorder: a review for clinicians, *Harv Rev Psychiatry* 10:127, 2002.

AUTHORS: **JASON M. SATTERFIELD, PH.D.,** and **MITCHELL D. FELDMAN, M.D., M.PHIL.**

BASIC INFORMATION

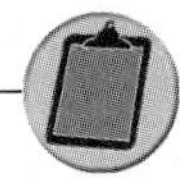

DEFINITION

The term *ocular foreign body* refers to a foreign body on the surface of the corneal epithelium.

ICD-9CM CODES
930 Foreign body in external eye

EPIDEMIOLOGY & DEMOGRAPHICS

INCIDENCE (IN U.S.): Universal, with a predominance in active people
PREDOMINANT SEX: Perhaps slightly more common in men
PREDOMINANT AGE: Childhood through active adult years
PEAK INCIDENCE: Childhood through active adult years

PHYSICAL FINDINGS & CLINICAL PRESENTATION

Pain is most common symptom
Most common foreign bodies:
- Grinding (Fig. 1-161)
- Drilling
- Auto mechanics
- Working beneath cars
- Airborne particles blown by fans and so forth

DIAGNOSIS

DIFFERENTIAL DIAGNOSIS

- History of corneal foreign body seen
- Hemorrhage, loss of vision
- Distorted anterior chamber, soft eye
- Corneal abrasion
- Corneal ulceration or laceration
- Glaucoma
- Herpes ulcers
- Infection
- Other keratitis
- Intraocular foreign body

WORKUP

- Fluorescein stain, slit lamp examination if no foreign body is found
- Ultrasound exam
- Plain x-Ray

LABORATORY TESTS

Intraocular pressure to make certain that eye has not been penetrated

IMAGING STUDIES

Occasionally, MRI of the orbits to identify foreign bodies not found by other means. Do not do MRI if suspect metallic foreign body. Plain x-ray and ultrasound are sufficient.

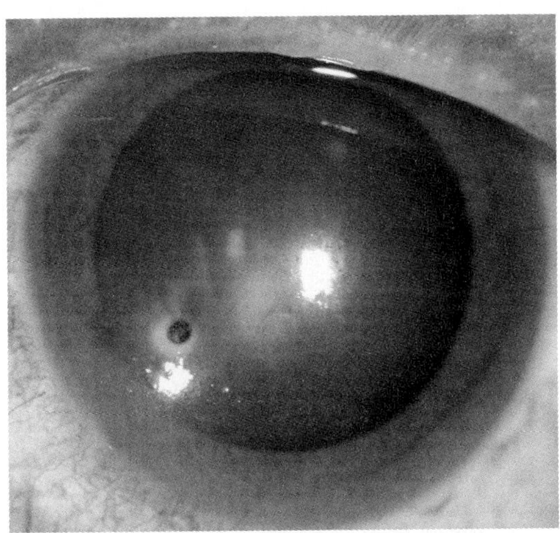

FIGURE 1-161 A small, iron foreign body may be seen on external examination. (Courtesy Department of Dermatology, University of North Carolina at Chapel Hill. In Goldstein GB, Goldstein AO: *Practical dermatology,* ed 2, St Louis, 1997, Mosby.)

TREATMENT

NONPHARMACOLOGIC THERAPY

- Remove foreign body
- Treat infection
- Repair eye if ruptured
- Treat corneal abrasion or injury

ACUTE GENERAL Rx

- Saline irrigation
- Removal of foreign body with moist cotton-tipped applicator after instillation of topical anesthetic drops
- Use Burr or more aggressive treatment if needed
- Cycloplegics, antibiotics, and pressure dressing after removal of foreign body
- Repair corneal laceration or damaged eye

DISPOSITION

If symptoms persist 24 hr after examination, refer to an ophthalmologist.

REFERRAL

To ophthalmology within 24 hr if patient not completely comfortable

PEARLS & CONSIDERATIONS

COMMENTS

- Make sure foreign body is not intraocular inside eye
- Alkaline or acidic chemical foreign bodies can be dangerous, and pH test must be performed if either of these is suspected (for all chemical foreign bodies).

SUGGESTED READING

Ta CN, Bowman RW: Hyphema caused by a metallic intraocular foreign body during magnetic resonance imaging, *Am J Ophthalmol* 129(4):533, 2000.

AUTHOR: **MELVYN KOBY, M.D.**

BASIC INFORMATION

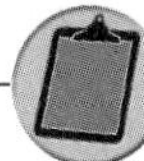

DEFINITION

Onychomycosis is defined as a persistent fungal infection affecting the toenails and fingernails.

SYNONYMS

Tinea unguium
Ringworm of the nails

ICD-9CM CODES
110.1 Onychomycosis

EPIDEMIOLOGY & DEMOGRAPHICS

- Onychomycosis is most commonly found in people between the ages of 40 to 60 yr.
- Onychomycosis rarely occurs before puberty.
- Incidence: 20 to 100 cases/1000 population.
- Toenail infection is four to six times more common than fingernail infections.
- Onychomycosis affects men more often than women.
- Occurs more frequently in patients with diabetes, peripheral vascular disease, and any conditions resulting in the suppression of the immune system.
- Occlusive footwear, physical exercise followed by communal showering, and incompletely drying the feet predisposes the individual to developing onychomycosis.

PHYSICAL FINDINGS & CLINICAL PRESENTATION

- Onychomycosis causes nails to become thick, brittle, hard, distorted, and discolored (yellow to brown color). Eventually, the nail may loosen, separate from the nail bed, and fall off (Fig. 1-162).
- Onychomycosis is frequently associated with tinea pedis (athlete's foot).

ETIOLOGY

- The most common causes of onychomycosis are dermatophyte, yeast, and nondermatophyte molds.
- The dermatophyte *Trichophyton rubrum* accounts for 80% of all nail infections caused by fungus.
- *Trichophyton interdigitale* and *Trichophyton mentagrophytes* are other fungi causing onychomycosis.
- The yeast *Candida albicans* is responsible for 5% of the cases of onychomycosis.
- Nondermatophyte molds *Scopulariopsis brevicaulis* and *Aspergillus niger,* although rare, can also cause onychomycosis.
- Onychomycosis is classified according to the clinical pattern of nail bed involvement. The main types are:
  1. Distal and lateral subungual onychomycosis (DLSO)
  2. Superficial onychomycosis
  3. Proximal subungual onychomycosis
  4. Endonyx onychomycosis
  5. Total dystrophic onychomycosis

DIAGNOSIS

The diagnosis of onychomycosis is based on the clinical nail findings and confirmed by direct microscopy and culture.

DIFFERENTIAL DIAGNOSIS

- Psoriasis
- Contact dermatitis
- Lichen planus
- Subungual keratosis
- Paronychia
- Infection (e.g., *Pseudomonas*)
- Trauma
- Peripheral vascular disease
- Yellow nail syndrome

WORKUP

The workup of suspected onychomycosis is directed at confirming the diagnosis of onychomycosis by visualizing hyphae under the microscope or by growing the organism in culture.

LABORATORY TESTS

- Blood tests are not specific in the diagnosis of onychomycosis
- KOH prep
- Fungal cultures on Sabouraud medium

IMAGING STUDIES

- Imaging studies are not very specific in making the diagnosis of onychomycosis.
- If an infection is present and osteomyelitis is a consideration, an x-ray of the specific area and a bone scan may help establish the diagnosis.

TREATMENT

NONPHARMACOLOGIC THERAPY

- Surgical removal of the nail plate is a treatment option; however, the relapse rate is high.
- Prevention of reinfection by wearing properly fitted shoes, avoiding public showers, and keeping feet and nails clean and dry.

ACUTE GENERAL Rx

- Topical antifungal creams are used for early superficial nail infections.
  1. Miconazole 2% cream applied over the nail plate bid
  2. Clotrimazole 1% cream bid
- Oral agents
  1. *Itraconazole*
     a. For toenails: 200 mg qd × 3 mo
     b. For fingernails: 200 mg PO bid × 7 days, followed by 3 wk of no medicine, for two pulses
  2. *Terbinafine*
     a. For toenails: 250 mg/day for 3 mo
     b. For fingernails: 250 mg/day for 6 wk

A

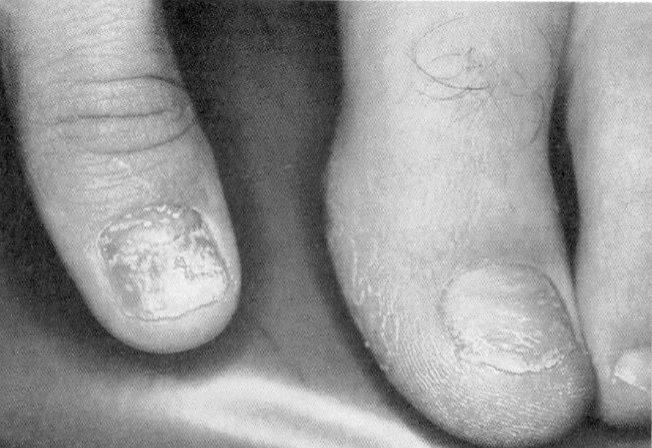

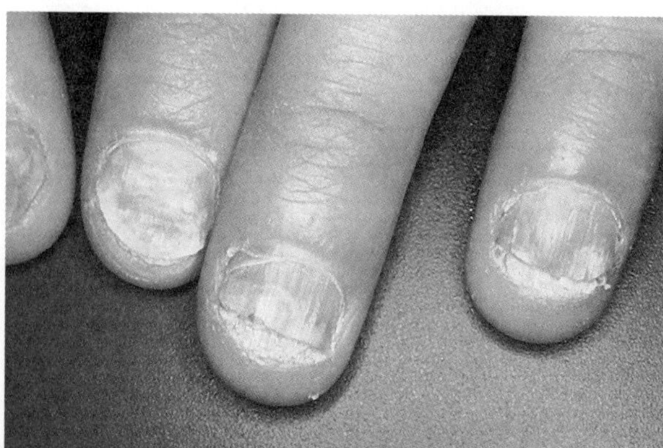

B

FIGURE 1-162 **A,** Superficial white onychomycosis. **B,** Distal subungual onychomycosis. (From Noble J [ed]: *Textbook of primary care medicine,* ed 3, St Louis, 2002, Mosby.)

3. *Fluconazole*
   a. For toenails: 150 to 300 mg once weekly, until infection clears
   b. For fingernails: 150 to 300 mg once weekly until infection clears

- All oral agents used for onychomycosis require periodic monitoring of liver function blood tests.
- Itraconazole is contraindicated in patients taking cisapride, astemizole, triazolam, midazolam, and terfenadine. Statins should be discontinued during itraconazole therapy.
- Fluconazole is contraindicated in patients taking cisapride and terfenadine.
- Oral antifungal agents should not be initiated during pregnancy.
- Ciclopirox, a topical nail lacquer antifungal agent, is FDA approved for treatment of mild to moderate disease not involving the lunula.

CHRONIC Rx

See under "Acute General Rx."

DISPOSITION

- Spontaneous remission of onychomycosis is rare.
- A disease-free toenail is reported to occur in approximately 25% to 50% of patients treated with the oral antifungal agents mentioned previously.

REFERRAL

- Podiatry consultation is indicated in diabetic patients for proper instruction in foot care, footwear, and nail debridement or surgical removal of the toenail.
- Dermatology consultation is indicated in patients refractory to treatment or if another diagnosis is considered (e.g., psoriasis).

PEARLS & CONSIDERATIONS

COMMENTS

- The growth of fungus on an infected nail typically begins at the end of the nail and spreads under the nail plate to infect the nail bed as well.
- Please review informational insert regarding drug-drug interactions and contraindications before initiating oral antifungal agents.

SUGGESTED READINGS

Elewski BE, Hay RJ: Update on the management of onychomycosis: highlights of the Third International Summit on Cutaneous Antifungal Therapy, *Clin Infect Dis* 23:305, 1996.

Epstein E: How often does oral treatment of toenail onychomycosis produce a disease-free nail? an analysis of published data, *Arch Dermatol* 134(12):1551, 1998.

Gupta AK: The new oral antifungal agents for onychomycosis of the toenails, *J Eur Acad Dermatol Venereol* 13(1):1, 1999.

Rodgers P, Bassler M: Treating onychomycosis, *Am Fam Physician* 63:663, 2001.

Scher RK, Coppa LM: Advances in the diagnosis and treatment of onychomycosis, *Hosp Med* 34(4):11, 1998.

AUTHOR: **DENNIS MIKOLICH, M.D.**

BASIC INFORMATION

DEFINITION

Optic atrophy refers to the degeneration of the axons of the optic nerve.
It is a symptom rather than a disease.

SYNONYMS

Unilateral/Bilateral optic atrophy

ICD-9CM CODES
377.10 Atrophy, optic nerve

EPIDEMIOLOGY & DEMOGRAPHICS

PREDOMINANT SEX: Unilateral optic atrophy in women is most commonly MS; may also occur after head injury (more commonly in men)
PREDOMINANT AGE: 21 to 40 yr
PEAK INCIDENCE: Varies depending on etiology

PHYSICAL FINDINGS & CLINICAL PRESENTATION

- Asymmetry of disc color is often first subtle finding
- Temporal part of optic disc is pale initially (Fig. 1-163); later the entire disc becomes pale/white
- Optic disc pallor occurs 4-6 wk after optic nerve injury
- Unilateral lesion produces a relative afferent pupillary defect (RAPD): swing flashlight eye to eye; abnormal pupil dilates to direct light
- Decreased visual acuity, blurred vision, visual field deficits (e.g., central scotoma), abnormal color vision (e.g., red desaturation)

ETIOLOGY

- Optic neuritis—multiple sclerosis, sarcoidosis, infections (syphilis, CMV, HIV)
- Vascular—ischemic optic neuropathy, central retinal artery occlusion, temporal arteritis
- Compression—glaucoma, pituitary tumor, meningioma, thyroid eye disease
- Hereditary—Leber's hereditary optic neuropathy
- Nutritional, toxic and metabolic—Amiodarone, Isoniazid, B_{12} deficiency, tobacco-alcohol
- Trauma

DIAGNOSIS

DIFFERENTIAL DIAGNOSIS

- Nutritional, toxic, and hereditary causes are usually bilateral.
- Unilateral optic atrophy in a young person is more commonly MS.
- Postviral atrophy may be seen in childhood.

WORKUP

- Depends on suspected etiology/clinical presentation. History including age of onset, risk factors, acuity of onset of symptoms, presence of pain, family history, and other associated neurologic findings should be considered.
- Visual field testing may help identify etiology (e.g., centrocecal field defects may occur with nutritional/toxic causes), but specificity is low.
- To differentiate between optic nerve vs. macular disease an Amsler chart and/or visual evoked responses may be helpful.
- If high clinical suspicion for MS, consider MRI of brain with contrast and LP with oligoclonal bands.
- Measure intraocular pressure (glaucoma).

LABORATORY TESTS

- Depends on suspected etiology: none for trauma, tumor, MS
- Serum B_{12}
- Autoimmune diseases: ESR, ANA, ACE

IMAGING STUDIES

- MRI brain with special (thin) cuts through orbits to identify compressive lesions
- MRI brain with contrast to evaluate for demyelinating plaques (MS)
- If sarcoid is suspected, order chest x-ray

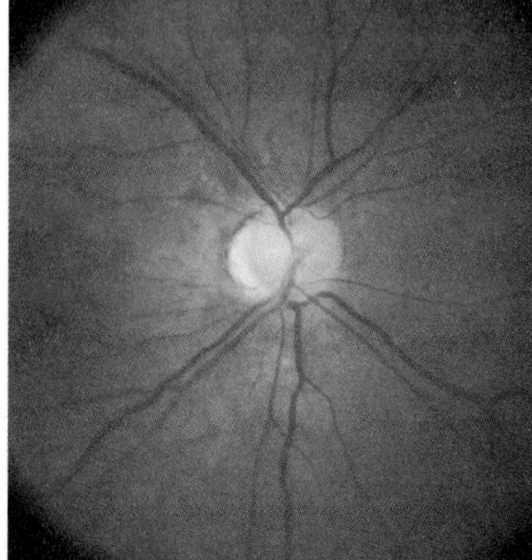

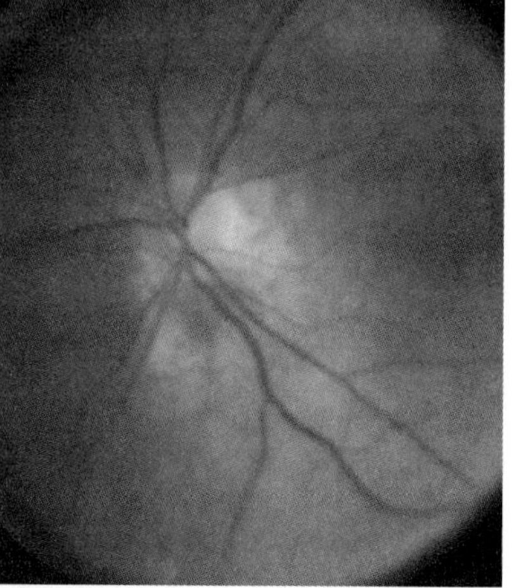

FIGURE 1-163 Optic atrophy. A, Patient's right eye shows atrophy. **B,** Left eye is unaffected. (Courtesy John W. Payne, M.D., The Wilmer Ophthalmological Institute, The Johns Hopkins University and Hospital, Baltimore. From Seidel HM [ed]: *Mosby's guide to physical examination,* ed 4, St Louis, 1999, Mosby.)

TREATMENT

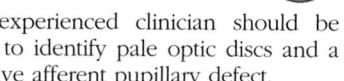

ACUTE GENERAL Rx

Treat the underlying cause—discontinue identifiable toxins, B_{12} replacement, neurosurgical intervention if tumor found; consider IV steroids if there is evidence for active demyelinating disease.

CHRONIC Rx

The optic nerve does not regenerate although symptoms often improve.

DISPOSITION

- Visual loss occurs over weeks to months
- Usually follow-up by neurologist or ophthalmologist

REFERRAL

If tumor or demyelinating lesions are found or if etiology is unknown

PEARLS & CONSIDERATIONS

COMMENTS

- An experienced clinician should be able to identify pale optic discs and a relative afferent pupillary defect.
- Pupillary dilation with mydriatic agents (e.g., Pilocarpine) may be necessary for a better funduscopic examination.
- Patient education material can be obtained from the National Eye Institute, Department of Health and Human Services, 9000 Rockville Pike, Bethesda, MD 20892.

SUGGESTED READING

Van Stavern GP, Newman NJ: Optic neuropathies. An overview, *Ophthalmol Clin North Am* 14(1):61, 2001.

AUTHOR: **RICHARD S. ISAACSON, M.D.**

SECTION I

BASIC INFORMATION

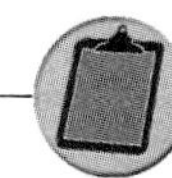

DEFINITION

Optic neuritis is an inflammation of the optic nerve resulting in a reduction of visual function.

SYNONYMS

Optic papillitis
Retrobulbar neuritis

ICD-9CM CODES
377.3 Optic neuritis

EPIDEMIOLOGY & DEMOGRAPHICS

INCIDENCE (IN U.S.): Relatively common, 1-5/100,000 per yr
PREVALENCE (IN U.S.): Common in patients with multiple sclerosis (MS)
PREDOMINANT SEX: Female
PEAK INCIDENCE: 20-49 yr
GENETICS: MS more common in patients with certain HLA blood types

PHYSICAL FINDINGS & CLINICAL PRESENTATION

- Presents with acute or subacute (days) visual loss and most often pain or tenderness with movement of affected eye
- Relative afferent papillary defect (RAPD) (swing flashlight eye to eye—pupil of affected eye dilates to direct light)
- Decreased visual acuity
- Visual field abnormalities, most commonly central scotoma
- Color desaturation, red most affected
- Normal orbit and fundus; occasionally there is disc edema acutely (see Fig. 1-164)
- After several months the optic disc may become pale

ETIOLOGY

An inflammatory response associated with an infection, mitochondrial disorder or autoimmune disease. Over 10 yr, clinically definite MS develops in about 22% of patients with no MRI lesions and 56% with one or more typical MRI lesions.

DIAGNOSIS

DIFFERENTIAL DIAGNOSIS

- Inflammatory: Sarcoidosis, SLE, Sjogren's, Behçet's, postinfectious, postvaccination
- Infectious: syphilis, TB, Lyme, Bartonella, HIV
- Ischemic: giant cell arteritis, anterior and posterior ischemic optic neuropathies, diabetic papillopathy, branch or central retinal artery or vein occlusion
- Mitochondrial: Leber's hereditary optic neuropathy
- Mass lesion: aneurysm, meningioma, glioma, metastases
- Retinal migraine
- Ocular: optic drusen, retinal detachment, vitreous hemorrhage, posterior scleritis, neuroretinitis, maculopathies and retinopathies
- Acute papilledema

WORKUP

The neurologic examination, with particular attention to the cranial nerves and the fundoscopic exam should otherwise be normal.

LABORATORY TESTS

- Recommend: CBC, ANA, ESR, RPR
- Consider HIV Ab, Lyme titer, sarcoidosis testing

IMAGING STUDIES

MRI of the brain and orbits with gadolinium is needed to rule out compressive or infiltrative etiologies. The risk to develop MS can also be assessed.

TREATMENT

NONPHARMACOLOGIC THERAPY

Assure patient that in most cases there is nearly complete recovery of vision.

ACUTE GENERAL Rx

Not shown to improve recovery of visual function. Methylprednisolone 250 mg IV every 6 hr for 3 days followed by an oral prednisone taper of 11 days hastens recovery and reduces the conversion rate to clinically definite MS over 2 yr. Methylprednisolone 1 g IV every day for 3 days followed by a prednisone taper is an alternate option.

CHRONIC Rx

None, unless at high risk to develop MS, then consider disease modifying therapy. See Section I, "Multiple Sclerosis."

DISPOSITION

90% regain near normal or normal vision by 6 months.

REFERRAL

- If patient has other neurologic signs, such as proptosis, ophthalmoplegia, or tender temporal artery
- If onset is gradual and if vision does not improve after several weeks
- If vision deteriorates as steroids are tapered

PEARLS & CONSIDERATIONS

COMMENTS

Bilateral ON, especially with poor recovery, suggests a diagnosis other than possible MS, such as Leber's hereditary optic neuropathy or toxic optic neuropathies. Acute bilateral loss with a severe headache or diplopia should raise concern for pituitary apoplexy.

SUGGESTED READINGS

Beck R et al: The effect of corticosteroids for acute optic neuritis on the subsequent development of multiple sclerosis, *N Engl J Med* 329:1764, 1993.

Beck R et al: High and low risk profiles for the development of MS within 10 years after optic neuritis, *Arch Ophthalmol* 121(7):944, 2003.

Eggenber ER: Inflammatory optic neuropathies, *Ophthalmol Clin North Am* 14(1):73, 2001.

Hickman S et al: Management of acute optic neuritis, *Lancet* 360:1953, 2002.

AUTHOR: **ALEXANDRA DEGENHARDT, M.D.**

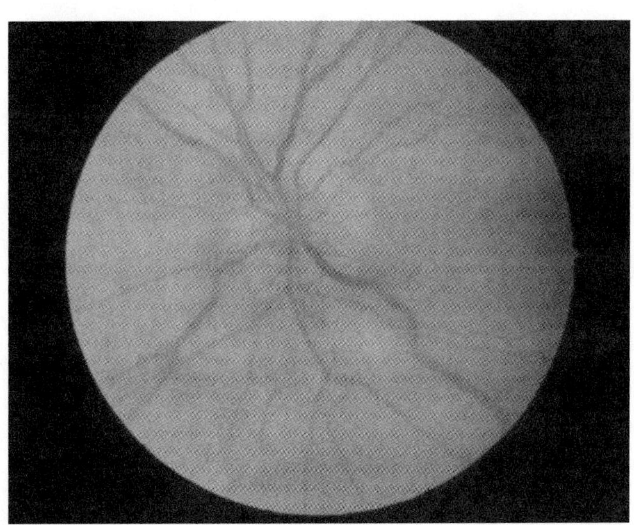

FIGURE 1-164 A case of optic neuritis. The optic disc edema seen here is often not present. Note the otherwise normal fundus. (Courtesy of J. Barton, M.D., Beth Israel Deaconess Medical Center, Boston.)

Orchitis

BASIC INFORMATION

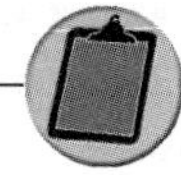

DEFINITION

Orchitis is an inflammatory process (usually infectious) involving the testicles. Infection may be viral or bacterial and can be associated with infection of other male sex organs (prostate, epididymis, bladder) or lower urogenital tract or sexually transmitted diseases often via hematogenous spread. Common causes are:

- Viral: Mumps—20% postpubertal; coxsackie B virus
- Bacterial: Pyogenic via spread from involving epididymis; bacteria include *Escherichia coli, Klebsiella pneumoniae, Staphylococcus, Streptococcus, P. aeruginosa, Rickettsia, Brucella*
- Other:
  HIV associated
  CMV
  Toxoplasmosis
  Fungi
  1. Cryptococcosis
  2. Histoplasmosis
  3. *Candida*
  4. Blastomycosis
  Mycobacteria

ICD-9CM CODES
0.72 Mumps
098.13 Acute gonococcal orchitis
095.8 Syphilitic orchitis
016.50 Tuberculous orchitis, unspecified

EPIDEMIOLOGY & DEMOGRAPHICS

PREDOMINANT SEX: Male

PREDOMINANT ORGANISM: The leading cause of viral orchitis is mumps. The mumps virus rarely causes orchitis in prepubertal males but involves one or both testicles in nearly 30% of postpubertal males.

PHYSICAL FINDINGS & CLINICAL PRESENTATION

- Testicular pain, swelling
- Unilateral or bilateral
- May have associated epididymitis, prostatitis, fever, scrotal edema, erythema cellulitis
- Inguinal lymphadenopathy
- Nausea, vomiting
- Acute hydrocele (bacterial)
- Rare development—abscess formation, pyocele of scrotum, testicular infarction
- Spermatic cord tenderness may be present

DIAGNOSIS

Clinical presentation as described previously with possible history of acute viral illness or concomitant epididymitis.

DIFFERENTIAL DIAGNOSIS

- Epididymoorchitis—gonococcal
- Autoimmune disease
- Vasculitis
- Epididymyosis
- Mumps—with or without parotitis
- Neoplasm
- Hematoma
- Spermatic cord torsion

LABORATORY TESTS

- CBC with differential
- Urinalysis
- Viral titer—mumps
- Urine culture
- Ultrasound of testicle to rule out abscess

IMAGING STUDIES

Ultrasound if abscess suspected

TREATMENT

- Dependent on etiology
- Viral (mumps)—observation
- Bacterial—empiric antibiotic treatment with parenteral antibiotic treatment for identified pathogen, including gram-negative rods, staphylococci, streptococci; treatment options are ceftriaxone (250 mg IM × 1) plus doxycycline (100 mg PO bid × 10 days), ofloxacin (300 mg PO bid × 10 days), ciprofloxacin (500 mg PO bid or 400 mg IV bid)
- Surgery for abscess, pyogenic process

SUGGESTED READING

Cook JL, Dewbury K: The changes seen on high-resolution ultrasound in orchitis, *Clin Radiol* 55(1):13, 2000.

AUTHOR: **DENNIS J. MIKOLICH, M.D.**

BASIC INFORMATION

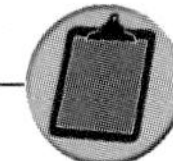

DEFINITION

Osgood-Schlatter disease is a painful swelling of the tibial tuberosity that occurs in adolescence.

ICD-9CM CODES
732.4 Osgood-Schlatter disease

EPIDEMIOLOGY & DEMOGRAPHICS

PREVALENCE: 4 cases/100 adolescents
PREDOMINANT AGE: 11 to 15 yr (bilateral in 20%)
PREDOMINANT SEX: Male:female ratio of 3:1

PHYSICAL FINDINGS & CLINICAL PRESENTATION

- Pain at the tibial tubercle that is aggravated by activity, especially stair-walking and squatting
- Tender swelling and enlargement of the tibial tubercle
- Increased pain with knee extension against resistance

ETIOLOGY

- Unknown
- May be traumatically induced inflammation

DIAGNOSIS

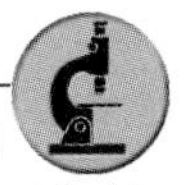

DIFFERENTIAL DIAGNOSIS

- Referred hip pain (any child with hip pain should have a thorough clinical hip examination)
- Patellar tendinitis

WORKUP

In most cases, the diagnosis is obvious on a clinical basis.

IMAGING STUDIES

- Lateral roentgenogram of the upper portion of the tibia with the leg slightly internally rotated may reveal variable degrees of separation and fragmentation of the upper tibial epiphysis (Fig. 1-165).
- Occasionally, fragmented area fails to unite to the tibia and persists into adulthood.

TREATMENT

ACUTE GENERAL Rx

- Ice, especially after exercise
- NSAIDs
- Gentle hamstring and quadriceps stretching exercises
- Abstinence from physical activity
- Temporary immobilization in a knee splint for 2 to 4 wk in resistant cases

DISPOSITION

- Prognosis for complete restoration of function and relief from pain is excellent.
- Condition usually heals when the epiphysis closes.
- Complications are rare.
- Symptoms in the adult:
  1. Although unusual, prominence of the tibial tubercle is usually permanent
  2. May be more susceptible to local irritation, especially when kneeling
  3. Rarely, nonunion of the epiphyseal fragment, but it is usually asymptomatic
  4. Surgery rarely required

REFERRAL

For orthopedic consultation when diagnosis is uncertain or when symptoms persist.

PEARLS & CONSIDERATIONS

COMMENTS

Larsen-Johansson disease is a similar disorder that can develop where either the quadriceps or patellar tendon inserts into the patella. Treatment and prognosis are the same as with Osgood-Schlatter disease.

SUGGESTED READINGS

Bloom OJ, Mackler L, Barbee J: What is the best treatment for Osgood-Schlatter disease? *J Fam Pract* 53(2):153, 2004.
Duri ZA, Patel DV, Aichroth PM: The immature athlete, *Clin Sports Med* 21(3):461, 2002.
Hirano A et al: Magnetic resonance imaging of Osgood-Schlatter disease: the course of the disease, *Skeletal Radiol* 31(6):334, 2002.
Ross MD, Villard D: Disability levels of college-aged men with history of Osgood-Schlatter disease, *J Strength Cond Res* 17(4)659, 2003.
Tyler W, McCarthy EF: Osteochondrosis of the superior pole of the patelia: two cases with histologic correlation, *Iowa Orthop J* 22:86, 2002.

AUTHOR: **LONNIE R. MERCIER, M.D.**

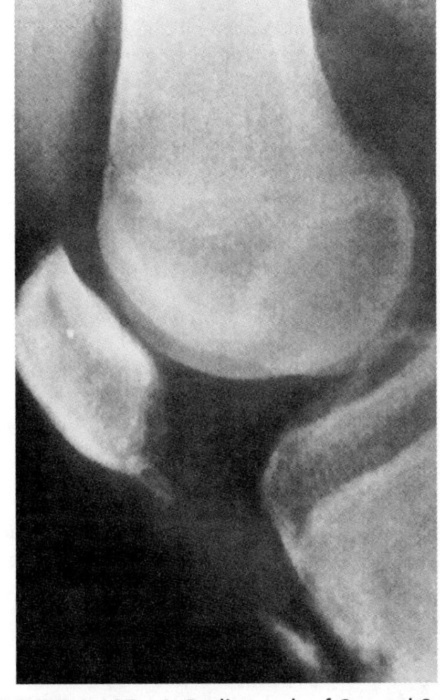

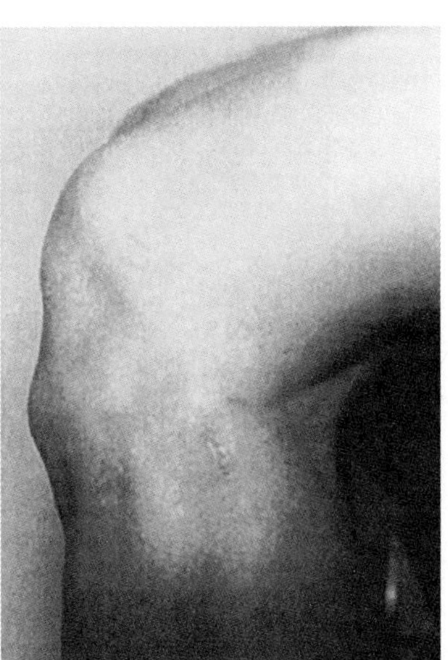

FIGURE 1-165 **A,** Radiograph of Osgood-Schlatter disease demonstrating thickening of patella tendon, fragmentation of the tibial tubercle, and soft tissue swelling. **B,** Clinical picture of bony prominence anteriorly at the tibial tubercle. (From Scuderi G [ed]: *Sports medicine: principles of primary care,* St Louis, 1997, Mosby.)

BASIC INFORMATION

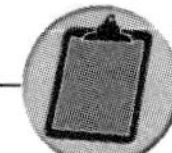

DEFINITION

Osteoarthritis is a joint condition in which degeneration and loss of articular cartilage occur, leading to pain and deformity. Two forms are usually recognized: primary (idiopathic) and secondary. The primary form may be localized or generalized.

SYNONYMS

Degenerative joint disease
Osteoarthrosis
Arthrosis

ICD-9CM CODES
715.0 Osteoarthrosis and allied disorders

EPIDEMIOLOGY & DEMOGRAPHICS

PREVALENCE: 2% to 6% of general population
PREDOMINANT SEX: Female = male
PREDOMINANT AGE: >50 yr

PHYSICAL FINDINGS & CLINICAL PRESENTATION

- Similar symptoms in most forms: stiffness, pain, and crepitus
- Joint tenderness, swelling
- Decreased range of motion
- Crepitus with motion
- Bony hypertrophy
- Pain with range of motion
- DIP joint involvement possibly leading to development of nodular swellings called Heberden's nodes (Fig. 1-166)
- PIP joint involvement possibly leading to development of nodular swellings called Bouchard's nodes

ETIOLOGY

Primary osteoarthritis is of unknown cause. Secondary osteoarthritis may result from a number of disorders including trauma, metabolic conditions, and other forms of arthritis.

DIAGNOSIS

DIFFERENTIAL DIAGNOSIS

- Bursitis, tendinitis
- Radicular spine pain
- Inflammatory arthritides
- Infectious arthritis

WORKUP

- No diagnostic test exists for degenerative joint disease.
- Laboratory evaluation is normal.
- Rheumatoid factor, ESR, CBC, and ANA tests may be required if inflammatory component is present.
- Synovial fluid examination is generally normal.

IMAGING STUDIES

- Roentgenographic evaluation reveals:
  1. Joint space narrowing
  2. Subchondral sclerosis
  3. New bone formation in the form of osteophytes
- When knee is involved, standing AP x-ray on any patient over 40.

TREATMENT

ACUTE GENERAL Rx

- Rest, restricted use or weight bearing, and heat
- Walking aids such as a cane (often helpful for weight-bearing joints)
- Suitable footwear
- Gentle range of motion and strengthening exercise
- Local creams and liniments to provide a counterirritant effect
- Education, reassurance

PHARMACOLOGIC THERAPY

- Mild analgesics for joint pain
- NSAIDs if inflammation is present
- Occasional local corticosteroid injections
- Mild antidepressants, especially at night, if depression is present
- Viscosupplementation (injection of hyaluronic acid products into the degenerative joint) is of uncertain benefit
- Nutritional supplements (glucosamine and chondroitin) are unproven

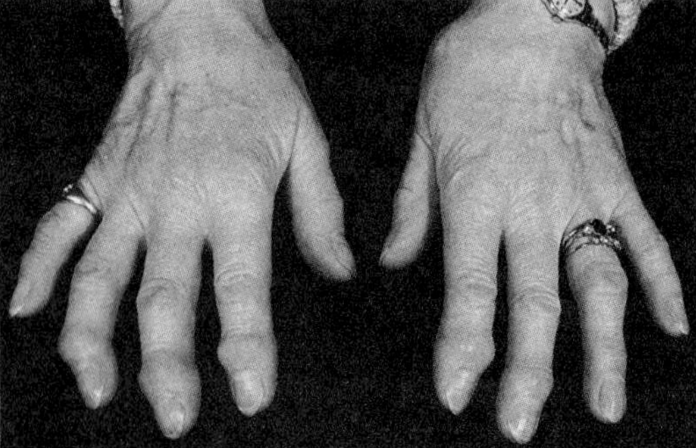

FIGURE 1-166 Osteoarthritis of the distal interphalangeal (DIP) joints. This patient has the typical clinical findings of advanced osteoarthritis of the DIP joints, including large, firm swellings (Heberden's nodes), some of which are tender and red because of associated inflammation of the periarticular tissues as well as of the joint. (From Klippel J, Dieppe P, Ferri F [eds]: *Primary care rheumatology,* London, 1999, Mosby.)

DISPOSITION

Progression is not always inevitable, and the prognosis is variable depending on the site and extent of the disease.

REFERRAL

Surgical consultation for patients not responding to medical management

PEARLS & CONSIDERATIONS

COMMENTS

Surgical intervention is generally helpful in degenerative joint disease. Arthroplasty, arthrodesis, and realignment osteotomy are the most common procedures performed. Arthroscopic debridement (of the knee) appears to be of only limited value.

SUGGESTED READINGS

Callahan JJ et al: Results of Charnley total hip arthroplasty at a minimum of thirty years, *J Bone Joint Surg* 86A:690, 2004.

Felson DT: Hyaluronate sodium injections for osteoarthritis: hope, hype and hard truths, *Arch Intern Med* 162:245, 2002.

Hartofilakidis G, Karachalios T: Idiopathic osteoarthritis of the hip: incidence, classification and natural history of 272 cases, *Orthopedics* 26:161, 2003.

Hinton R et al: Osteoarthritis: diagnosis and therapeutic considerations, *Am Fam Physician* 65:841, 2002.

Hunt SA, Jazrawi LM, Sherman OH: Arthroscopic management of osteoarthritis of the knee, *J Am Orthop Surg* 10:356, 2002.

Kelly MA et al: Osteoarthritis and beyond: a consensus on the past, present and future of hyaluronans in orthopedics, *Orthopedics* 26:1064, 2003.

Leopold S et al: Corticosteroid compared with hyaluronic acid injections for the treatment of osteoarthritis of the knee, *J Bone Joint Surg* 85:1197, 2003.

Lo HG: Intra-articular hyaluronic acid in treatment of knee osteoarthritis, *JAMA* 290:3115, 2003.

Moseley JB et al: A controlled trial of arthroscopic surgery for osteoarthritis of the knee, *N Engl J Med* 347:81, 2002.

Scott WN, Clarke HD: Early knee arthritis: the role of arthroscopy, *Orthopedics* 26:943, 2003.

Wai EK, Kreder HJ, Williams JI: Arthroscopic debridement of the knee for osteoarthritis in patients fifty years of age or older, *J Bone Joint Surg* 84(A):17, 2002.

Wang C et al: Therapeutic effects of hyaluronic acid in osteoasrthritis of the knee, *J Bone Joint Surg* 86A:538, 2004.

Wegman A et al: Nonsteroidal antiinflammatory drugs or acetominophen for osteoarthritis of the hip or knee? A systematic review of evidence adn guidelines, *J Rheumatol* 31:344, 2004.

AUTHOR: **LONNIE R. MERCIER, M.D.**

BASIC INFORMATION

DEFINITION

Osteochondritis dissecans is a disorder in which a portion of cartilage and underlying subchondral bone separates from a joint surface and may even become detached.

SYNONYMS

Osteochondrosis
Talar dome fracture: commonly used in describing the lesion of the talus
Panners disease (capitellum)

ICD-9CM CODES
732.7 Osteochondritis dissecans

EPIDEMIOLOGY & DEMOGRAPHICS

PREVALENCE: 0.3 cases/1000 persons
PREVALENT AGE: Onset at 10 to 30 yr
PREVALENT SEX: Male:female ratio of 3:1
The most common joint affected is the knee, with the lateral surface of the medial femoral condyle the most frequent area involved. The capitellum of the humerus, dome of the talus, shoulder, and hip may also be affected.

PHYSICAL FINDINGS & CLINICAL PRESENTATION

- Pain, stiffness, and swelling
- Intermittent locking if the fragment becomes detached
- Occasionally palpable loose body
- Tenderness at the site of the lesion
- When the knee is involved, positive Wilson's sign (pain with knee extension and internal rotation)
- Some asymptomatic cases

ETIOLOGY

Unknown

DIAGNOSIS

DIFFERENTIAL DIAGNOSIS

- Acute fracture
- Neoplasm

IMAGING STUDIES

- Plain roentgenography to confirm the diagnosis (Fig. 1-167)
- "Tunnel view" helpful in knee cases
- Typical finding: radiolucent, semilunar line outlining the oval fragment of bone (but findings variable, depending on the amount of healing and stability)
- MRI or bone scanning usually not necessary in establishing diagnosis but helpful in determining prognosis and management, especially with regards to the stability of the lesion

TREATMENT

ACUTE GENERAL Rx

- Observation every 4 to 6 mo for patients in whom the lesion is asymptomatic
- Symptomatic patients who are skeletally immature:
  1. Observation with an initial period of non–weight-bearing for 6 to 8 wk (in knee cases)
  2. When symptoms subside, gradual resumption of activities

DISPOSITION

- Juvenile cases with open epiphyses have a favorable prognosis.
- Cases developing after skeletal maturity are more likely to develop osteoarthritis.
- Large fragments, especially those in weight-bearing areas, have a more unfavorable prognosis, especially if they involve the lateral femoral condyle.
- Loose body formation and degenerative joint disease are more common when condition develops after age 20 yr.

REFERRAL

For orthopedic consultation:
- For most adults with unstable lesions
- If a loose body is present
- If symptomatic care has failed

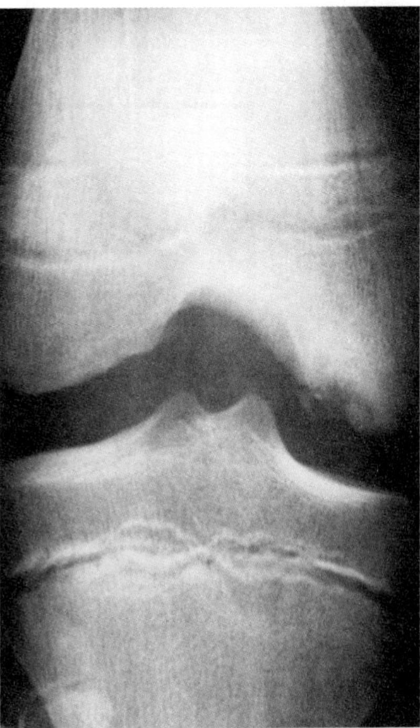

FIGURE 1-167 Osteochondritis dissecans of the knee. The "tunnel" view is often helpful in visualizing the defect. This fragment may become detached and form a loose body. This area should not be confused with the normal irregularity of the distal femoral epiphysis in young children.

PEARLS & CONSIDERATIONS

COMMENTS

- Although inflammation is suggested by the name, it has not been shown to be of significance in this disorder. "Osteochondral lesion" or "osteochondrosis dissecans" may be more appropriate terms to describe these disorders.
- Repetitive trauma with ischemic necrosis is the most likely cause.
- The condition is often bilateral, especially in the knee, which could suggest the possibility of an endocrine or genetic basis.
- This condition should always be considered in the patient whose "sprained ankle" does not improve over the usual course of treatment.

SUGGESTED READINGS

Bramer JA et al: Increased external tibial torsion and osteochondritis dissecans of the knee, *Clin Orthop* 422:175, 2004.

Cain EL, Clancy WG: Treatment algorithm for osteochondral injuries of the knee, *Clin Sports Med* 20:321, 2001.

Hixon AL, Gibbs LM: Osteochondritis dissecans: a diagnosis not to miss, *Am Fam Physician* 61:151, 2000.

Kobaynsh, K, Burton KJ et al: Lateral compression injuries in the pediatric elbow. Panner's disease and osteochondritis dissecans of the capitellum, *J Am Acad Orthop Surg* 12:246, 2004.

Peh WC: Osteochondritis dissecans, *am J Orthop* 33(1):46, 2004.

Sanders RK, Crim JR: Osteochondral injuries, *Semin Ultrasound CT MRI* 22:352, 2001.

AUTHOR: **LONNIE R. MERCIER, M.D.**

BASIC INFORMATION

DEFINITION

Osteomyelitis is an acute or chronic infection of the bone secondary to the hematogenous or contiguous source of infection or direct traumatic inoculation, which is usually bacterial.

SYNONYMS

Bone infection

ICD-9CM CODES
730.1 Chronic osteomyelitis
730.2 Acute or subacute osteomyelitis

EPIDEMIOLOGY & DEMOGRAPHICS

PREDOMINANT SEX: Male > female
PREDOMINANT AGE: All ages

PHYSICAL FINDINGS

HEMATOGENOUS OSTEOMYELITIS: Usually occurs in tibia/fibula (children).
- Localized inflammation: often secondary to trauma with accompanying hematoma or cellulitis
- Abrupt fever
- Lethargy
- Irritability
- Pain in involved bone

VERTEBRAL OSTEOMYELITIS: Usually hematogenous.
- Fever: 50%
- Localized pain/tenderness
- Neurologic defects: motor/sensory

CONTIGUOUS OSTEOMYELITIS: DIRECT INOCULATION.
- Associated with trauma, fractures, surgical fixation
- Chronic infection of skin/soft tissue
- Fever, drainage from surgical site

CHRONIC OSTEOMYELITIS:
- Bone pain
- Sinus tract drainage, nonhealing ulcer
- Chronic low-grade fever
- Chronic localized pain

ETIOLOGY

- *Staphylococcus aureus*
- *S. aureus* (methicillin-resistant)
- *Pseudomonas aeruginosa*
- Enterobacteriaceae
- *Streptococcus pyogenes*
- *Enterococcus*
- Mycobacteria
- Fungi
- Coagulase-negative staphylococci
- *Salmonella* (in sickle cell disease)

DIAGNOSIS

DIFFERENTIAL DIAGNOSIS

- Brodie's abscess
- Gaucher's disease
- Bone infarction
- Charcot's joint
- Gout
- Fracture

WORKUP

- ESR, C-reactive protein
- Blood culturing
- Bone culture
- Pathologic evaluation of bone biopsy for acute/chronic changes consistent with necrosis or acute inflammation

IMAGING STUDIES

- Bone x-ray examination
- Bone scan (Fig. 1-168)
- Gallium scan
- Indium scan
- MRI (most accurate imaging study)
- Doppler studies: useful in patients with peripheral vascular disease to determine vascular adequacy

TREATMENT

Surgical debridement in biopsy-positive cases will guide direction for antibiotic therapy. This will vary with type of osteomyelitis. Duration of therapy is usually 6 wk for acute osteomyelitis; chronic osteomyelitis may need a longer course of medication.

- *S. aureus:* cefazolin IV, nafcillin IV, vancomycin IV (in patient allergic to penicillin)
- *S. aureus* (methicillin resistant): vancomycin IV
- *Streptococcus* spp.: cefazolin or ceftriaxone
- *P. aeruginosa:* piperacillin plus aminoglycoside or ceftazidime plus aminoglycoside
- Enterobacteriaceae: ceftriaxone or fluoroquinolone
- Hyperbaric oxygen therapy: may be useful in treatment of chronic osteomyelitis, especially with associated wound healing
- Surgical debridement of all devitalized bone and tissue
- Immobilization of affected bone (plaster, traction) if bone is unstable
- Bone grafts using a vascularized or open graft may be necessary if the remaining bone is inadequate

SUGGESTED READINGS

Boutin RD et al: Update on imaging of orthopedic infections, *Orthop Clin North Am* 29:41, 1998.

Carek PJ et al: Diagnosis and management of osteomyelitis, *Am Fam Physician* 63:2413, 2001.

AUTHORS: **GLENN G. FORT, M.D.,** and **DENNIS J. MIKOLICH, M.D.**

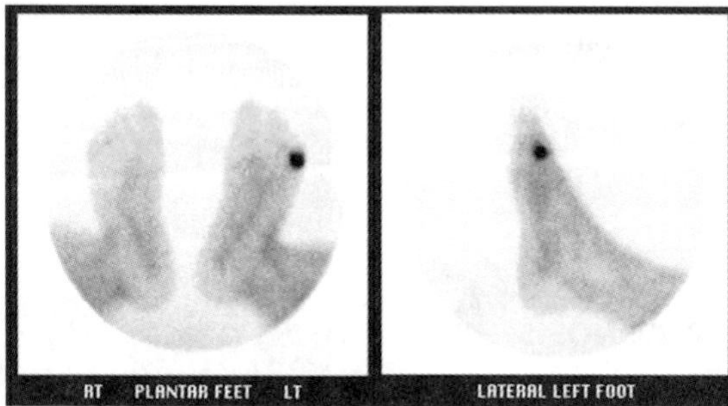

FIGURE 1-168 Osteomyelitis. Intense accumulation of Tc-99m WBC in proximal phalanx of fifth digit of left foot at 4 hours after injection. (From Specht N [ed]: *Practical guide to diagnostic imaging,* St Louis, 1998, Mosby.)

BASIC INFORMATION

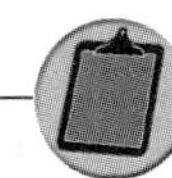

DEFINITION

Osteonecrosis refers to the death of bone marrow, cortex, and medullary bone caused by interruption of blood supply to the bone.

SYNONYMS

Aseptic necrosis
Avascular necrosis
Ischemic necrosis

ICD-9CM CODES
730.1 Osteonecrosis

EPIDEMIOLOGY & DEMOGRAPHICS

- Osteonecrosis accounts for 10% of all hip surgeries performed annually in the U.S.
- Osteonecrosis involves the femoral head most frequently, followed by the humeral head, femoral condyles, and distal femur.
- Between 5% to 25% of patients on chronic corticosteroid use develop osteonecrosis.
- Incidence of osteonecrosis in alcoholics is 2% to 5%.
- Osteonecrosis is found in 10% of patients with sickle cell anemia.

CLINICAL PRESENTATION & PHYSICAL FINDINGS

- May be clinically silent
- Pain in the affected bone (hip, knee, or shoulder)
- Pain at rest or with use
- Decreased range of motion of the affected joint
- Joint pain with passive motion

ETIOLOGY

The etiology of osteonecrosis can be divided into:

- Atraumatic
  1. Idiopathic
  2. Alcohol
  3. Hemoglobinopathy (e.g., sickle cell disease)
  4. Connective tissue disorders (SLE, rheumatoid arthritis, vasculitis, antiphospholipid syndrome)
  5. Corticosteroid use
  6. Pregnancy
  7. Estrogen use
  8. Gaucher's disease
  9. Dysbarism
  10. Radiation therapy
- Traumatic
  1. Femoral neck fracture
  2. Septic

DIAGNOSIS

The diagnosis of avascular necrosis should be suspected in any patient with focal bone pain on corticosteroids or with any of the above mentioned comorbid conditions.

DIFFERENTIAL DIAGNOSIS

The differential diagnosis of osteonecrosis is as stated under Etiology and includes hyperlipidemias, pancreatitis, renal transplantation, chronic liver disease, obesity, and chemotherapy.

WORKUP

Radiographic imaging is the mainstay for confirming the clinical suspicion of osteonecrosis.

LABORATORY TESTS

CBC, electrolytes, BUN, creatinine, LFTs, ESR, ANA, RF, lipid profile, and other serologic tests are used as adjuncts in supporting the diagnosis of avascular necrosis.

IMAGING STUDIES

- Plain films help define and classify the disease course. Staging systems have been developed for osteonecrosis of the femoral head:
  1. Stage I: Initial x-rays are normal, but bone scan is positive.
  2. Stage II: Abnormal radiolucency is noted.
  3. Stage III: Deformity with collapse and sclerosis.
  4. Stage IV: Early osteoarthritis.
- Bone scan reveals decreased uptake at the affected site with a "doughnut sign" and can detect avascular necrosis before the plain x-rays.
- MRI scan is more sensitive and specific than bone scan, especially when looking for osteonecrosis of the femoral head.
- If a MRI is not available, CT scan of the involved bone is efficacious.

TREATMENT

Treatment of osteonecrosis of the hip can be directed at three stages:

- Before bone collapse
- After bone collapse
- After arthritic formation

NONPHARMACOLOGIC THERAPY

- Immobilization
- Non–weight-bearing with the use of crutches
- Special muscle strengthening exercise

ACUTE GENERAL Rx

- NSAIDs, ibuprofen 800 mg PO tid, naproxen 500 mg bid, or acetaminophen 500 mg (2 tabs) PO q6h can be used for symptom relief.
- For displaced hip fractures, prompt surgical reduction is indicated in attempt to reperfuse the femoral head.

CHRONIC Rx

- For patients with stage I or II osteonecrosis (before bone collapse occurs), core decompression treatment is tried to prevent bone collapse.
- In stage III osteonecrosis (after bone collapse), a hemiarthroplasty or total joint replacement is required.
- In stage IV osteonecrosis (arthritis setting in after bone collapse), a total joint replacement is usually required.

DISPOSITION

- There is no therapy to prevent avascular necrosis from occurring in patients predisposed to getting the disease.
- Patients diagnosed with avascular necrosis have a slow progressive course.
- Patients with symptoms and diagnosed by x-ray imaging to be at stage I or II (pre-bone collapse) can expect within 18 to 36 mo to develop bone collapse of the affected site.

REFERRAL

Whenever the diagnosis of avascular necrosis is suspected clinically or detected radiographically, a rheumatology and/or orthopedic consultation should be made.

PEARLS & CONSIDERATIONS

COMMENTS

- The pathogenesis of osteonecrosis is secondary to decrease perfusion of the bone elements leading to necrosis. Interruption of blood supply can occur either by arterial or venous occlusion, traumatic vascular injury, or extravascular compression.
- How each specific cause (e.g., alcohol, corticosteroids, SLE) leads to vascular interruption remains elusive.
- In approximately 70% of all patients with displaced hip fractures, there is near total loss of blood supply to the femoral head.

SUGGESTED READINGS

Assouline-Dayan Y, Chang C: Pathogenesis and natural history of osteonecrosis, *Semin Arthritis Rheum* 32(2):94, 2002.
Koo K-H et al: Preventing collapse in early osteonecrosis of the femoral head, *J Bone Joint Surg* 77B:870, 1995.
Pavelka K: Osteonecrosis, *Baillieres Best Pract Res Clin Rheumatol* 14(2):399, 2000.

AUTHOR: **PETER PETROPOULOS, M.D.**

BASIC INFORMATION

DEFINITION

Osteoporosis is characterized by a progressive decrease in bone mass that results in increased bone fragility and a higher fracture risk. The various types are as follows:

PRIMARY OSTEOPOROSIS: 80% of women and 60% of men with osteoporosis

- Idiopathic osteoporosis: unknown pathogenesis; may occur in children and young adults
- Type I osteoporosis: may occur in postmenopausal women (age range: 51 to 75 yr); characterized by accelerated and disproportionate trabecular bone loss and associated with vertebral body and distal forearm fractures (estrogen withdrawal effect)
- Type II osteoporosis (involutional): occurs in both men and women >70 yr of age; characterized by both trabecular and cortical bone loss, and associated with fractures of the proximal humerus and tibia, femoral neck, and pelvis

SECONDARY OSTEOPOROSIS: 20% of women and 40% of men with osteoporosis; osteoporosis that exists as a common feature of another disease process, heritable disorder of connective tissue, or drug side effect (see "Differential Diagnosis")

ICD-9CM CODES
733.0 Osteoporosis

EPIDEMIOLOGY & DEMOGRAPHICS

PREVALENCE (IN U.S.):

- Approximately 25 million men and women
- Twice as common in women
- Results in 1.5 million fractures annually (70% women)
- Osteoporosis-related fractures in 50% women and 20% men >65 yr
- Results: institutionalization, mortality, and costs in excess of $10 billion annually

RISK FACTORS:

- Age: each decade after 40 yr associated with a fivefold increase risk
- Genetics:
  1. Ethnicity (white/Asian > black > Polynesian)
  2. Gender (female > male)
  3. Family history
- Environmental factors: poor nutrition, calcium deficiency, physical inactivity, medication (steroids/heparin), tobacco use, ETOH, traumatic injury
- Chronic disease states: estrogen deficiency, androgen deficiency, hyperthyroidism, hypercortisolism, cirrhosis, gastrectomy

PHYSICAL FINDINGS & CLINICAL PRESENTATION

- Most commonly silent with no signs and symptoms
- Insidious and progressive development of dorsal kyphosis (dowager's hump), loss of height, and skeletal pain typically associated with fracture, other physical findings related to other conditions with associated increased risk for osteoporosis (see "Risk Factors")

ETIOLOGY

- Primary osteoporosis; multifactorial resulting from a combination of factors including nutrition, peak bone mass, genetics, level of physical activity, age of menopause (spontaneous vs. surgical), and estrogen status
- Secondary osteoporosis: associated decrease in bone mass resulting from an identified cause, including endocrinopathies—hypogonadism, hyperthyroidism, hyperparathyroidism, Cushing's syndrome, hyperprolactinemia, acromegaly, diabetes mellitus, gastrointestinal disease, malabsorption, primary biliary cirrhosis, gastrectomy, malnutrition (including anorexia nervosa)

DIAGNOSIS

DIFFERENTIAL DIAGNOSIS

- Malignancy (multiple myeloma, lymphoma, leukemia, metastatic carcinoma)
- Primary hyperparathyroidism
- Osteomalacia
- Paget's disease
- Osteogenesis imperfecta: types I, III, and IV (see also "Epidemiology and Demographics" and "Etiology")

WORKUP

- History and physical examination (20% of women with type I osteoporosis have associated secondary cause), with appropriate evaluation for identified risk factors and secondary causes
- Diagnosis of osteoporosis made by bone mineral density (BMD) determination (BMD should ideally evaluate the hip, spine, and wrist):
  1. Dual-energy x-ray absorptiometry (DEXA)
  2. Single-energy x-ray
  3. Peripheral dual-energy x-ray
  4. Single-photon absorptiometry
  5. Dual-photon absorptiometry
  6. Quantitative CT scan
  7. Radiographic absorptiometry

LABORATORY TESTS

- Biochemical profile to evaluate renal and hepatic function, primary hyperparathyroidism, and malnutrition
- CBC for nutritional status and myeloma
- TSH to rule out the presence of hyperthyroidism
- Consideration of 24-hr urine collection for calcium (excess skeletal loss, vitamin D malabsorption/deficiency), creatinine, sodium, and free cortisol (to detect occult Cushing's disease); no need to measure calcitropic hormones (PTH, calcitriol, calcitonin) unless specifically indicated
- Biochemical markers of bone remodeling; may be useful to predict rate of bone loss and/or follow therapy response; specific biochemical markers followed (e.g., 3-mo interval) to document normalization as a response to therapy
  1. High turnover osteoporosis: high levels of resorption markers (lysyl pyridinoline [LP], deoxylysyl pyridinoline [DPD], n-telopeptide of collagen cross-links [NTX], C-telopeptide of collagen cross-links [PICP]) and formation markers (osteocalcin [OCN], bone-specific alkaline phosphatase [BSAP], carboxy-terminal extension peptide of type I procollagen [PICP]); accelerated bone loss responding best to antiresorptive therapy
  2. Low-normal turnover osteoporosis: normal or low levels of the markers of resorption and formation (see "high turnover osteoporosis" above); no accelerated bone loss; responds best to drugs that enhance bone formation

IMAGING STUDIES

- BMD determination (see "Workup") should be performed on all women with determined risk factors and/or associated secondary causes; accepted screening criteria are currently being investigated.
  1. Normal: BMD <1 SD of the young adult reference mean
  2. Osteopenia: BMD <1 to 2.5 SD below the young adult reference mean
  3. Osteoporosis: BMD >2.5 SD below the young adult reference mean
- For patient undergoing treatment: annual BMD to follow response to therapy
- X-ray examination of appropriate part of skeleton to evaluate clinical osteoporotic fracture only

TREATMENT

NONPHARMACOLOGIC THERAPY

Prevention:

- Identification and minimization of risk factors
- Appropriate diagnosis and treatment of secondary causes
- Behavioral modification: proper nutrition (dietary calcium >800 mg/day, vitamin D 400 to 800 U/day), physical activity, fracture prevention strategies

ACUTE GENERAL Rx

- Vitamin D supplement: 400 U/day
- Calcium supplement: 1000 to 1500 mg/day
- Estrogen (conjugated equine estrogen or equivalent): 0.3 to 0.625 mg/day
- Progestin: continuous (e.g., 2.5 mg medroxyprogesterone acetate/day or equivalent) or cyclic (e.g., 10 mg medroxyprogesterone acetate days 16 to 25 each month or equivalent) coadministered in nonhysterectomized women
- Alendronate (10 mg/day) or risedronate (5 mg/day) on awakening with 8 oz water on empty stomach with no oral intake for at least 30 min
- Alendronate: 70 mg once weekly for treatment of postmenopausal osteoporosis and a 35-mg tablet for the prevention of osteogenesis in postmenopausal women
- Synthetic salmon calcitonin: 100 U/day SC or 200 U/day intranasally
- Raloxifene: 60 mg qd
- Risedronate: 35 mg once weekly on awakening with 8 oz water or empty stomach with no oral intake for at least 30 min
- Other FDA-approved drugs (without osteoporosis indication) used to treat osteoporosis:
  1. Calcitriol
  2. Etidronate
  3. Thiazide
- Combination estrogen/alendronate or estrogen-progestin/alendronate may be considered in individualized patients on HRT with identified osteoporosis
- BMD baseline obtained before onset of therapy and at 1 yr; decrease of 2% or greater results in dosage adjustment or medication change
- Baseline biochemical markers of remodeling baseline considered; identified high turnover osteoporosis patients rescreened at 3 mo to document marker return to normal

CHRONIC Rx

- Lifelong disorder requiring lifelong attention to behavior modification issues (nutrition, physical activity, fracture prevention strategies) and compliance with pharmacologic intervention
- Continuing need to eliminate high-risk factors where possible and to diagnose and optimally manage secondary causes of osteoporosis

DISPOSITION

Goal for diagnosis and treatment: identification of women at risk, initiation of preventive measures for all women lifelong, institution of treatment modalities that will result in a decrease in fracture risk, and reduction of morbidity, mortality, and unnecessary institutionalization, thereby improving quality of independent life and productivity.

REFERRAL

- To reproductive endocrinologist, endocrinologist, gynecologist, or rheumatologist if unfamiliar with diagnosis and management of osteoporosis
- If multidisciplinary management is required, to other specialties depending on presence of acute fracture and/or secondary associated disorders

PEARLS & CONSIDERATIONS

COMMENTS

Patient information is available from American College of Obstetricians and Gynecologists.

SUGGESTED READINGS

Bone HG et al: Ten years' experience with alendronate for osteoporosis in postmenopausal women, *N Engl J Med* 350:12, 2004.

Fitzpatrick LA: Secondary causes of osteoporosis, *Mayo Clin Proc* 77:453, 2002.

Greenspan SL et al: Alendronate improves bone mineral density in elderly women with osteoporosis residing in long-term care facilities, *Ann Intern Med* 136:742, 2002.

Nelson H et al: Screening for postmenopausal osteoporosis: a review of the evidence for the US Preventive Task Force, *Ann Intern Med* 137:529, 2002.

NIH consensus development panel on osteoporosis prevention, diagnosis, and therapy, *JAMA* 285:785, 2001.

Peb WCG et al: Percutaneous vertebroplasty for severe osteoporotic vertebral body compression fractures, *Radiology* 223:121, 2002.

Reid IR et al: Intravenous zoledronic acid in postmenopausal women with low bone mineral density, *N Engl J Med* 346:653, 2002.

South-Paul JE: Osteoporosis: part I. Evaluation and assessment, *Am Fam Physician* 63(5):897, 2001.

South-Paul JE: Osteoporosis: part II. Nonpharmacologic and pharmacologic treatment, *Am Fam Physician* 63(6):1121, 2001.

U.S. Preventive Services Task Force: Screening for osteoporosis in postmenopausal women: recommendations and rationale, *Ann Intern Med* 137:526, 2002.

AUTHOR: **DENNIS M. WEPPNER, M.D.**

SECTION I

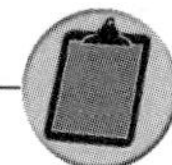

BASIC INFORMATION

DEFINITION

Otitis externa is a term encompassing a variety of conditions causing inflammation and/or infection of the external auditory canal (and/or auricle and tympanic membrane). There are six subgroups of otitis externa:

- Acute localized otitis externa (furunculosis)
- Acute diffuse bacterial otitis externa (swimmer's ear)
- Chronic otitis externa
- Eczematous otitis externa
- Fungal otitis externa (otomycosis)
- Invasive or necrotizing (malignant) otitis externa (See Fig. 1-169.)

SYNONYMS

See "Definition."

ICD-9CM CODES
38.10 Otitis externa

EPIDEMIOLOGY & DEMOGRAPHICS

INCIDENCE (IN U.S.)
- Among the most common disorders
- Affects 3% to 10% of patients seeking otologic care

PREVALENCE (IN U.S.)
- Diffuse otitis externa (swimmer's ear) is most often seen in swimmers and in hot, humid climates, conditions that lead to water retention in the ear canal.
- Necrotizing otitis externa is more common in elderly, diabetics, immunocompromised patients.

PREDOMINANT SEX: None
PREDOMINANT AGE:
- Occurs at all ages
- Necrotizing otitis externa: typically occurs in elderly: mean age >65 yr

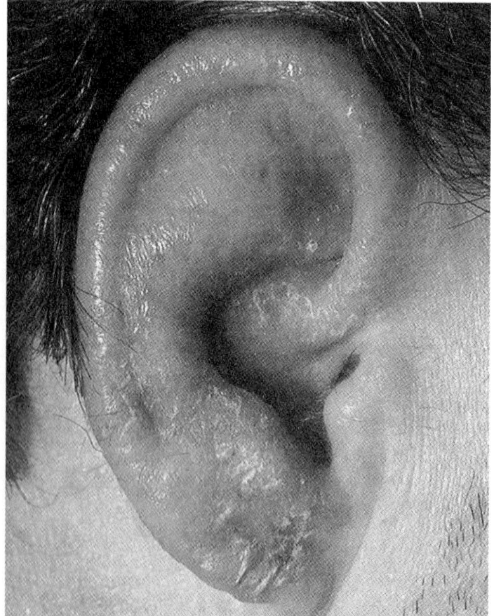

FIGURE 1-169 Malignant external otitis. Severe infection of the ear has occurred after months of chronic inflammation of the pinna. (From Habif TP: *Clinical dermatology: a color guide to diagnosis and therapy,* ed 3, St Louis, 1996, Mosby.)

PHYSICAL FINDINGS & CLINICAL PRESENTATION

The two most common symptoms are otalgia, ranging from pruritus to severe pain exacerbated by motion (e.g., chewing), and otorrhea. Patients may also experience aural fullness and hearing loss secondary to swelling with occlusion of the canal. More intense symptoms may occur with bacterial otitis externa, with or without fever, and lymphadenopathy (anterior to tragus). There are also findings unique to the various forms of the infection:

- Acute localized otitis externa (furunculosis):
  1. Occurs from infected hair follicles, usually in the outer third of the ear canal, forming pustules and furuncles
  2. Furuncles are superficial and pointing or deep and diffuse
- Impetigo:
  1. In contrast to furunculosis, this is a superficial spreading infection of the ear canal that may also involve the concha and the auricle
  2. Begins as a small blister that ruptures, releasing straw-colored fluid that dries as a golden crust
- Erysipelas:
  1. Caused by group A *Streptococcus*
  2. May involve the concha and canal
  3. May involve the dermis and deeper tissues
  4. Area of cellulitis, often with severe pain
  5. Fever chills, malaise
  6. Regional adenopathy
- Eczematous otitis externa:
  1. Stems from a variety of dermatologic problems that can involve the external auditory canal
  2. Severe itching, erythema, scaling, crusting, and fissuring possible
- Acute diffuse otitis externa (swimmer's ear):
  1. Begins with itching and a feeling of pressure and fullness in the ear that becomes increasingly tender and painful
  2. Mild erythema and edema of the external auditory canal, which may cause narrowing and occlusion of the canal, leading to hearing loss
  3. Minimal serous secretions, which may become profuse and purulent
  4. Tympanic membrane may appear dull and infected
  5. Usually absence of systemic symptoms such as fever, chills
- Otomycosis:
  1. Chronic superficial infection of the ear canal and tympanic membrane
  2. In primary fungal infection, major symptom is intense itching
  3. In secondary infection (fungal infection superimposed on bacterial infection), major symptom is pain
  4. Fungal growth of variety of colors
- Chronic otitis externa:
  1. Dry and atrophic canal
  2. Typically, lack of cerumen
  3. Itching, often severe, and mild discomfort rather than pain
  4. Occasionally, mucopurulent discharge
  5. With time, thickening of the walls of the canal, causing narrowing of the lumen
- Necrotizing otitis externa (also known as malignant otitis externa):
  1. Redness, swelling, and tenderness of the ear canal
  2. Classic finding of granulation tissue on the floor of the canal and the bone-cartilage junction
  3. Small ulceration of necrotic soft tissue at bone-cartilage junction
  4. Most common complaints: pain (often severe) and otorrhea
  5. Lessening of purulent drainage as infection advances
  6. Facial nerve palsy often the first and only cranial nerve defect
  7. Possible involvement of other cranial nerves

ETIOLOGY

- Acute localized otitis externa: *Staphylococcus aureus*
- Impetigo:
  1. *S. aureus*
  2. *Streptococcus pyogenes*
- Erysipelas: *S. pyogenes*
- Eczematous otitis externa:
  1. Seborrheic dermatitis
  2. Atopic dermatitis
  3. Psoriasis
  4. Neurodermatitis
  5. Lupus erythematosus
- Acute diffuse otitis externa:
  1. Swimming
  2. Hot, humid climates

3. Tightly fitting hearing aids
4. Use of ear plugs
5. *Pseudomonas aeruginosa*
6. *S. aureus*

- Otomycosis:
  1. Prolonged use of topical antibiotics and steroid preparations
  2. *Aspergillus* (80% to 90%)
  3. *Candida*
- Chronic otitis externa: persistent low-grade infection and inflammation
- Necrotizing otitis externa (NOE):
  1. Complication of persistent otitis externa
  2. Extends through Santorini's fissures, small apertures at the bone-cartilage junction of the canal, into the mastoid and along the base of the skull
  3. *P. aeruginosa*

DIAGNOSIS

DIFFERENTIAL DIAGNOSIS

- Acute otitis media
- Bullous myringitis
- Mastoiditis
- Foreign bodies
- Neoplasms

WORKUP

Thorough history and physical examination

LABORATORY TESTS

- Cultures from the canal are usually not necessary unless the patient is refractory to treatment.
- Leukocyte count normal or mildly elevated.
- ESR is often quite elevated in malignant otitis externa.

IMAGING STUDIES

- CT scan is the best technique for defining bone involvement and extent of disease in malignant otitis externa.
- MRI is slightly more sensitive in evaluation of soft tissue changes.
- Gallium scans are more specific than bone scans in diagnosing NOE.
- Follow-up scans are helpful in determining efficacy of treatment.

NOTE: Expert opinion supports history and physical examination as the best means of diagnosis. Persistent pain that is constant and severe should raise the question of NOE (particularly in elderly, diabetics, and immunocompromised).

TREATMENT

NONPHARMACOLOGIC THERAPY

- Cleansing and debridement of the ear canal with cotton swabs and hydrogen peroxide or other antiseptic solution allows for a more thorough examination of the ear.
- If the canal lumen is edematous and too narrow to allow adequate cleansing, a cotton wick or gauze strip inserted into the canal serves as a conduit for topical medications to be drawn into the canal. Usually remove wick after 2 days.
- Local heat is useful in treating deep furunculosis.
- Incision and drainage is indicated in treatment of superficial pointing furunculosis.

ACUTE GENERAL Rx

Topical medications:

- An acidifying agent, such as 2% acetic acid, inhibits growth of bacteria and fungi
- Topical antibiotics (in the form of otic or ophthalmic solutions) or antifungals, often in combination with an acidifying agent and a steroid preparation
- The following are some of the available preparations:
  1. Neomycin otic solutions and suspensions:
     a. with polymyxin-B-hydrocortisone (Corticosporin)
     b. with hydrocortisone-thonzonium (Coly-Mycin S)
  2. Polymyxin-B-hydrocortisone (Otobiotic)
  3. Quinolone otic solutions:
     a. Ofloxacin 0.3% solution (Floxin Otic)
     b. Ciprofloxacin 0.3% with hydrocortisone (Cipro HC)
  4. Quinolone ophthalmic solutions:
     a. Ofloxacin 0.3% (Ocuflox)
     b. Ciprofloxacin 0.3% (Ciloxan)
  5. Aminoglycoside ophthalmic solutions:
     a. Gentamicin sulfate 0.3% (Garamycin)
     b. Tobramycin sulfate 0.3% (Tobrex)
     c. Tobramycin 0.3% and dexamethasone 0.1% (TobraDex)
  6. Chloramphenicol 0.5% otic solution or 0.25% ophthalmic solution (Chloromycetin)
  7. Gentian violet (methylrosaniline chloride 1%, 2%)
  8. Antifungals:
     a. Amphotericin B 3% (Fungizone lotion)
     b. Clotrimazole 1% solution (Lotrimin)
     c. Tolnaftate 1% (Tinactin)
- Topical preparations should be applied qid (bid for quinolones, antifungals), generally for 3 days after cessation of symptoms (average 10 to 14 days total).

Systemic antibiotics:

- Reserved for severe cases, most often infections with *P. aeruginosa* or *S. aureus*
- Treatment usually for 10 days with ciprofloxacin 750 mg q12h or ofloxacin 400 mg q12h, or with antistaphylococcal agent (e.g., dicloxacillin or cephalexin 500 mg q6h)

Treatment for NOE:

- Requires prolonged therapy up to 3 mo. Whether to use oral parenteral therapy is based on clinical judgment
- Oral quinolones, ciprofloxacin 750 mg q12h or ofloxacin 400 mg q12h may be appropriate initial therapy or used to shorten the course of IV therapy
- Intravenous antipseudomonals with or without aminoglycosides are also appropriate
- Local debridement

Pain control:

- May require NSAIDs or opioids
- Topical corticosteroids to reduce swelling and inflammation

CHRONIC Rx

- Patients prone to recurrent infections should try to identify and avoid precipitants to infection.
- Swimmers should try tight-fitting ear plugs or tight-fitting bathing caps, and remove all excess water from the ears after swimming.
- Treat underlying systemic diseases and dermatologic conditions that predispose to infection.

DISPOSITION

Inadequate treatment of otitis externa may lead to NOE and mastoiditis.

REFERRAL

To an otolaryngologist:

- NOE
- Treatment failure
- Severe pain

SUGGESTED READINGS

Holten KB, Gick J: Management of the patient with otitis externa, *J Fam Practice* 50(4):353, 2001.

Sander R: Otitis externa: a practical guide to treatment and prevention, *Am Fam Physician* 63(5):927, 2001.

AUTHOR: **JANE V. EASON, M.D.**

BASIC INFORMATION

DEFINITION

Otitis media is the presence of fluid in the middle ear accompanied by signs and symptoms of infection.

SYNONYMS

Acute suppurative otitis media
Purulent otitis media

ICD-9CM CODES
382.9 Acute or chronic otitis media
382.10 381.00 Otitis media with effusion

EPIDEMIOLOGY & DEMOGRAPHICS

INCIDENCE (IN U.S.)

- Affects patients of all ages, but is largely a disease of infants and young children
- Occurs once in about 75% of all children
- Occurs three or more times in one third of all children by 3 yr of age
- The diagnosis of acute otitis media increased from 9.9 million in 1975 to 25.5 million in 1990
- From 1975 to 1990, office visits for acute otitis media increased threefold for children <2 yr, doubled for children ages 2 to 5, and almost doubled for children ages 6 to 10 yr

PREDOMINANT SEX: Males

PREDOMINANT AGE:

- 47% to 60% of all children have their first episode of OM during their first year of life, 60% to 70% by their fourth birthday
- Incidence of infection declines with age; seen infrequently in adults

PEAK INCIDENCE:

- Between 6 and 36 mo
- Second peak between ages 4 and 6 yr
- Fall, winter, early spring

GENETICS:

Familial Disposition:

- Native Americans
- Eskimos
- Australian aborigines
- Those with a strong family history

Congenital Infection: High incidence in children born with cleft palates and other craniofacial abnormalities

PHYSICAL FINDINGS & CLINICAL PRESENTATION

- Fluid in the middle ear along with signs and symptoms of local inflammation (Figs. 1-170 and 1-171).
  1. Erythema with diminished light reflex
- Erythema of the tympanic membrane without other abnormalities is not a diagnostic criterion for acute otitis media because it may occur with any inflammation of the upper respiratory tract, crying, or nose blowing.
- As infection progresses, middle ear exudation occurs (exudative phase); the exudate rapidly changes from serous to purulent (suppurative phase).
  1. Retraction and poor motility of the tympanic membrane, which then becomes bulging and convex
- At any time during the suppurative phase the tympanic membrane may rupture, releasing the middle ear contents.
- Symptoms:
  1. Otalgia, ranging from slight discomfort to severe, spreading to the temporal region
  2. Ear stuffiness and hearing loss may precede or follow otalgia
  3. Otorrhea
  4. Vertigo
  5. Nystagmus
  6. Tinnitus
  7. Fever
  8. Lethargy
  9. Irritability
  10. Nausea, vomiting
  11. Anorexia
- After an episode of acute otitis media:
  1. Persistence of effusion for weeks or months (called secretory, serous, or nonsuppurative otitis media)
  2. Fever and otalgia usually absent
  3. Hearing loss possible (10 to 50 dB, with predominant involvement of the low frequencies)

ETIOLOGY

- Most common etiologic factor is an upper respiratory tract infection (often viral), which causes inflammation and obstruction of the eustachian tube. Bacterial colonization of the nasopharynx in conjunction with eustachian tube dysfunction leads to infection.
- May occasionally develop as a result of hematogenous spread or via direct invasion from the nasopharynx.
- Most common bacterial pathogens:
  1. *Streptococcus pneumoniae* causes 40% to 50% of cases and is the least likely of the major pathogens to resolve without treatment
  2. *Haemophilus influenzae* causes 20% to 30% of cases
  3. *Moraxella catarrhalis* causes 10% to 15% of cases
  4. Of increasing importance, infection caused by penicillin-nonsusceptible *S. pneumoniae* (MIC 0.1 μg/ml), ranging from 8% to 34%. About 50% of PNSSP isolates are penicillin-intermediate (MIC 0.1 to 1.0 mg/ml)

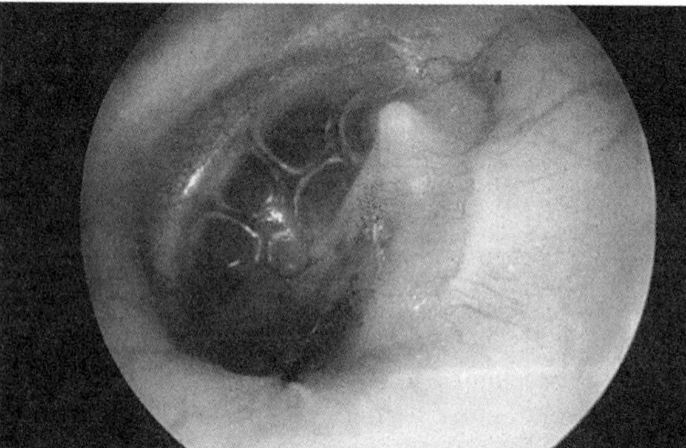

FIGURE 1-170 Otitis media with effusion of left ear. Retracted eardrum, prominent short process of malleus, and air bubbles seen anteriorly through the tympanic membrane. (From Behrman RE: *Nelson textbook of pediatrics,* ed 16, Philadelphia, 1996, WB Saunders.)

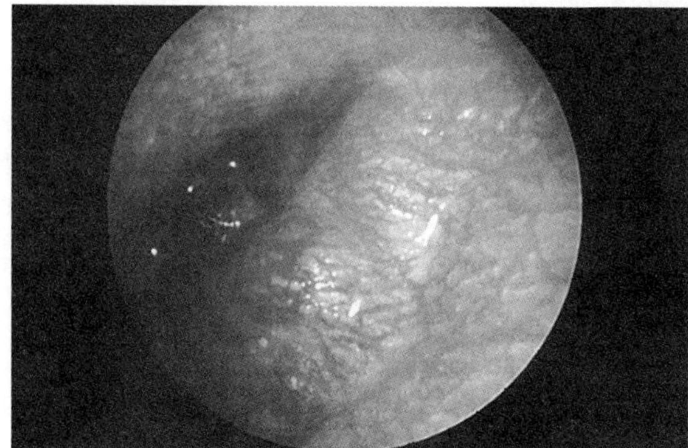

FIGURE 1-171 Acute left otitis media. (From Behrman RE: *Nelson textbook of pediatrics,* ed 16, Philadelphia, 1996, WB Saunders.)

- Viral pathogens:
  1. Respiratory syncytial virus
  2. Rhinovirus
  3. Adenovirus
  4. Influenza
- Others:
  1. *Mycoplasma pneumoniae*
  2. *Chlamydia trachomatis*

DIAGNOSIS

DIFFERENTIAL DIAGNOSIS

- Otitis externa
- Referred pain
  1. Mouth
  2. Nasopharynx
  3. Tonsils
  4. Other parts of the upper respiratory tract
- Section II describes the differential diagnosis of earache.

WORKUP

Thorough otoscopic examination; adequate visualization of the tympanic membrane requires removal of cerumen and debris.

- Tympanometry
  1. Measures compliance of the tympanic membrane and middle ear pressure
  2. Detects the presence of fluid
- Acoustic reflectometry
  1. Measures sound waves reflected from the middle ear
  2. Useful in infants >3 mo
  3. Increased reflected sound correlated with the presence of effusion

LABORATORY TESTS

- Tympanocentesis
  1. Not necessary in most cases as the microbiology of middle ear effusions has been shown to be quite consistent
  2. May be indicated in:
     a. Highly toxic patients
     b. Patients who fail to respond to treatment in 48 to 72 hr
     c. Immunocompromised patients
- Cultures of the nasopharynx: sensitive but not specific
- Blood counts: usually show a leukocytosis with polymorphonuclear elevation
- Plain mastoid radiographs: generally not indicated; will reveal haziness in the periantral cells that may extend to entire mastoid
- CT or MRI may be indicated if serious complications suspected (meningitis, brain abscess)

TREATMENT

ACUTE GENERAL Rx

Hydration, avoidance of irritants (e.g., tobacco smoke), nasal systemic decongestants, cool mist humidifier

Antimicrobials:

NOTE: Most uncomplicated cases of acute otitis media resolve spontaneously, without complications. Studies have demonstrated limited therapeutic benefit from antibiotic therapy. However, when opting to employ antibiotic therapy:

- Amoxicillin remains the drug of choice for first-line treatment of uncomplicated acute otitis media, despite increasing prevalence of drug-resistant *S. pneumoniae*.
- Treatment failure is defined by lack of clinical improvement of signs or symptoms after 3 days of therapy.
- With treatment failure, in the absence of an identified etiologic pathogen, therapy should be redirected to cover.
  1. Drug-resistant *S. pneumoniae*
  2. β-lactamase–producing strains of *H. influenzae* and *M. catarrhalis*
- Agents fulfilling these criteria include amoxicillin/clavulanate, second-generation cephalosporins (e.g., cefuroxime axetil, cefaclor); ceftriaxone (given IM). Cefaclor, cefixime, loracarbef and ceftibuten are active against *H. influenzae* and *M. catarrhalis,* but less active against *pneumococci,* especially drug resistant strains, than the agents listed previously.
- TMP/SMX and macrolides have been used as first- and second-line agents, but pneumococcal resistance to these agents is rising (up to 25% resistance to TMP/SMX, and up to 10% resistance to erythromycin).
- Cross-resistance between these drugs and the β-lactams exist; therefore patients who are treatment failures on amoxicillin are more likely to have infections resistant to TMP/SMX and macrolides.
- Newer fluoroquinolones (grepafloxacin, levofloxacin, sparfloxacin) have enhanced activity against *pneumococci* as compared with older agents (ciprofloxacin, ofloxacin).
- Treatment should be modified according to cultures and sensitivities.
- Generally treatment course is 10 to 14 days.
- Follow up approximately 4 wk after discontinuation of therapy to verify resolution of all symptoms, return to normal otoscopic findings, and restoration of normal hearing.

NOTE: Effusions may persist for 2 to 6 wk or longer in many cases of adequately treated otitis media.

SURGICAL Rx

- No evidence to support the routine of myringotomy, but in severe cases it provides prompt pain relief and accelerates resolution of infection.
- Purulent secretions retained in the middle ear lead to increased pressure that may lead to spread of infection to contiguous areas. Myringotomy to decompress the middle ear is necessary to avoid complications.
- Complications include mastoiditis, facial nerve paralysis, labyrinthitis, meningitis, brain abscess.
- Other procedures used for drainage of the middle ear include insertion of a ventilation tube and/or simple mastoidectomy.

CHRONIC Rx

- Myringotomy and tympanostomy tube placement for persistent middle ear effusion unresponsive to medical therapy for ≥3 mo if bilateral or ≥6 mo if unilateral.
- Adenoidectomy, with or without tonsillectomy, often advocated for treatment of recurrent otitis media, although indications for this procedure are controversial.
- Chronic complications include tympanic membrane perforations, cholesteatoma, tympanosclerosis, ossicular necrosis, toxic or suppurative labyrinthitis, and intracranial suppuration.

REFERRAL

- To otorhinolaryngologist if:
  1. Medical treatment failure
  2. Diagnosis uncertain: adults with ≥1 episode of otitis media should be referred for ENT evaluation to rule out underlying process (e.g., malignancy)
  3. Any of the above mentioned acute and chronic complications

PEARLS & CONSIDERATIONS

COMMENTS

Prevention:

- Multiple component conjugate vaccines hold promise for decreasing recurrent episodes of acute otitis media
- Breast-feeding, bottle-feeding infants in an upright position
- Avoidance of irritants (e.g., tobacco smoke)

SUGGESTED READINGS

American Academy of Pediatrics/American Academy of Family Physicians: Diagnosis and management of acute otitis media, *Pediatrics* 113(5):1451, 2004.

Rovers MM et al: Otitis media, *Lancet* 363(9407):465, 2004.

Zapalac JS et al: Suppurative complications of acute otitis media in the era of antibiotic resistance, *Arch Otolaryngol Head Neck Surg* 128(6):660, 2002.

AUTHORS: **JANE V. EASON, M.D.,** and **JOSEPH R. MASCI, M.D.**

Otosclerosis (Otospongiosis)

BASIC INFORMATION

DEFINITION

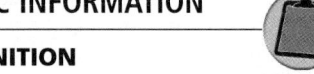

Otosclerosis is a conductive hearing loss secondary to fixation of the stapes resulting in gradual hearing loss. About 15% of cases affect only one ear.

ICD-9CM CODES
387.9 Otosclerosis

EPIDEMIOLOGY & DEMOGRAPHICS

INCIDENCE (IN U.S.): Most common cause of hearing loss in young adults
PREVALENCE (IN U.S.): 5 cases/1000 persons
PREDOMINANT SEX: Male:female ratio of 2:1
PREDOMINANT AGE: Symptoms start between 15 and 30 yr, with slowly progressive hearing loss.
PEAK INCIDENCE: Middle age
GENETICS: One half of cases are dominantly inherited.

PHYSICAL FINDINGS & CLINICAL PRESENTATION

- Tympanic membrane is normal in most cases (tested with tuning fork).
- Bone conduction is greater than air conduction.
- Weber localizes to affected ear.

ETIOLOGY

- A disease where vascular type of spongy bone is laid down
- Unknown

DIAGNOSIS

DIFFERENTIAL DIAGNOSIS

- Hearing loss from any cause: cochlear otosclerosis, polyps, granulomas, tumors, osteogenesis imperfecta, chronic ear infections, trauma
- A clinical algorithm for evaluation of hearing loss is described in Section III.
- Table 1-37 describes common types of conductive and sensorineural hearing loss.

WORKUP

Audiometry

LABORATORY TESTS

None, unless infection suspected

IMAGING STUDIES

MRI with specific cuts through inner ear

TREATMENT

NONPHARMACOLOGIC THERAPY

Hearing aid only of temporary use

CHRONIC Rx

Progresses to deafness without surgical intervention

DISPOSITION

Referral to ENT specialist

REFERRAL

To ENT specialist for surgery if moderate hearing loss suspected

PEARLS & CONSIDERATIONS

COMMENTS

A full ENT evaluation in a young or middle-aged person with hearing loss is mandatory unless cause is obvious (such as trauma or repeated infection).

SUGGESTED READING

Chole RA, McKenna M: Pathophysiology of otosclerosis, *Otol Neurotol* 22(2):249, 2001.

AUTHOR: **FRED F. FERRI, M.D.**

TABLE 1-37 Common Types of Conductive and Sensorineural Hearing Loss

Conductive Hearing Loss	Sensorineural Hearing Loss
Otitis media with effusion	Presbycusis (hearing loss with aging)
TM perforation	Ototoxicity
Tympanosclerosis	Meniere's disease
Retracted TM (eustachian tube dysfunction)	Idiopathic loss
Ossicular problems	Noise-induced loss
Otosclerosis	Perilymphatic fistula
Foreign body in ear canal	Hereditary (congenital) loss
Cerumen impaction	Multiple sclerosis
Tumor of the ear canal or middle ear	Diabetes
Cholesteatoma	Syphilis
	Acoustic neuroma

From Rakel RE (ed): *Principles of family practice,* ed 6, Philadelphia, 2002, WB Saunders.
TM, Tympanic membrane.

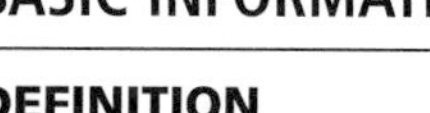

BASIC INFORMATION

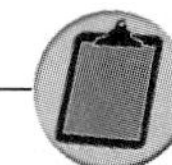

DEFINITION

Ovarian tumors can be benign, requiring operative intervention but not recurring or metastasizing; malignant, recurring, metastasizing, and having decreased survival; or borderline, having a small risk of recurrence or metastases but generally having a good prognosis.

SYNONYMS

Epithelial ovarian cancer
Germ cell tumor
Sex cord stromal tumor
Ovarian tumor of low malignant potential

ICD-9CM CODES
183.0 Malignant neoplasm of ovary

EPIDEMIOLOGY & DEMOGRAPHICS

INCIDENCE: 12.9 to 15.1 cases/100,000 persons; approximately 25,000 new cases annually
PREDOMINANCE: Median age of 61 yr, peaks at age 75 to 79 yr (54/100,000)
GENETICS: Familial susceptibility has been shown with the BRCA1 gene located on 17q12 to 21. This correlates with breast-ovarian cancer syndrome.
RISK FACTORS: Low parity, delayed childbearing, use of talc on the perineum, high-fat diet, fertility drugs (possibly), Lynch II syndrome (nonpolyposis colon cancer, endometrial cancer, breast cancer, and ovarian cancer clusters in first- and second-degree relatives), breast-ovarian familial cancer syndrome, site-specific familial ovarian cancer (NOTE: Use of oral contraceptives appears to have a protective effect.)

PHYSICAL FINDINGS & CLINICAL PRESENTATION

- 60% present with advanced disease
- Abdominal fullness, early satiety, dyspepsia
- Pelvic pain, back pain, constipation
- Pelvic or abdominal mass
- Lymphadenopathy (inguinal)
- Sister Mary Joseph nodule (umbilical mass)

ETIOLOGY

- Can be inherited as site-specific familial ovarian cancer (two or more first-degree relatives have ovarian cancer)
- Breast-ovarian cancer syndrome (clusters of breast and ovarian cancer among first- and second-degree relatives)
- Lynch syndrome
- No family history and unknown etiology in the majority of ovarian cancer cases

DIAGNOSIS

DIFFERENTIAL DIAGNOSIS

- Primary peritoneal cancer
- Benign ovarian tumor
- Functional ovarian cyst
- Endometriosis
- Ovarian torsion
- Pelvic kidney
- Pedunculated uterine fibroid
- Primary cancer from breast, GI tract, or other pelvic organ metastasized to the ovary

WORKUP

- Definitive diagnosis made at laparotomy
- Careful physical and history including family history
- Exclusion of nongynecologic etiologies
- Observation of small, cystic masses in premenopausal women for regression for 2 mo

LABORATORY TESTS

- CBC
- Chemistry profile
- CA-125 or lysophosphatidic acid level
- Consider: hCG, Inhibin, AFP, neuron-specific enolase (NSE), and LDH in patients at risk for germ cell tumors
- Osteopontin-Potential new biomarker for ovarian cancer

IMAGING STUDIES

- Ultrasound (has not been shown to be effective as a screening mechanism but is useful in the evaluation of a pelvic mass)
- Chest x-ray examination
- Mammogram
- CT scan to help evaluate extent of disease
- Other studies (BE, MRI, IVP, etc.) as clinically indicated

TREATMENT

NONPHARMACOLOGIC THERAPY

Virtually all cases of ovarian cancer involve surgical exploration. This includes:

- Abdominal cytology
- Total abdominal hysterectomy and bilateral salpingo-oophorectomy (except in early stages where fertility is an issue)
- Omentectomy
- Diaphragm sampling
- Selective lymphadenectomy (pelvis and paraaortic)
- Primary cytoreduction with a goal of residual tumor diameter <2 cm
- Bowel surgery, splenectomy if needed to obtain optimal (<2 cm) cytoreduction

ACUTE GENERAL Rx

- Optimal cytoreduction is generally followed by chemotherapy (except in some early-stage disease).
- Cisplatin-based combination chemotherapy is used for stage II or greater, 6 mo treatment.
- Chemotherapy regimens continue to change as research continues.
- Consider second-look surgery when chemotherapy is complete.

CHRONIC Rx

- If CA-125 have recurrent disease
- Physical and pelvic examinations every 3 mo for 2 yr, every 4 mo during third year, then every 6 mo
- CA-125 every visit
- Yearly Pap smear

DISPOSITION

- Overall 5-yr survival rates remain low because of the preponderance of late-stage disease:

Stage I and II 80% to 100%
Stage III 15% to 20%
Stage IV 5%

- Younger patients (<50 yr) in all stages have a considerably better 5-yr survival than older patients (40% vs. 15%).

REFERRAL

- Studies have shown that optimal cytoreduction is most likely to occur in the hands of a gynecologic oncologist.
- Have gynecologic/oncology backup available if suspicious of malignancy.
- Always refer advanced disease.

SUGGESTED READINGS

Haber D: Prophylactic oophorectomy to reduce the risk of ovarian and breast cancer in carriers of BRCA mutations, *N Engl J Med* 346:1660, 2002.
Kim JH et al: Osteopontin as a potential diagnostic biomarker for ovarian cancer, *JAMA* 287:1671, 2002.
Modan B et al: Parity, oral contraceptives and the risk of ovarian cancer among carriers and noncarriers of a brca1 or brca2 mutation, *N Engl J Med* 345:235, 2001.
Olson SH et al: Symptoms of ovarian cancer, *Obstet Gynecol* 98:212, 2001.

AUTHOR: **GIL FARKASH, M.D.**

Ovarian Tumor, Benign

BASIC INFORMATION

DEFINITION

Benign ovarian neoplasms are clinically indistinguishable from their malignant counterparts. Therefore all persistent adnexal masses must be considered malignant until proven otherwise. Nonneoplastic tumors are as follows:

- Germinal inclusion cyst
- Follicle cyst
- Corpus luteum cyst
- Pregnancy luteoma
- Theca lutein cysts
- Sclerocystic ovaries
- Endometrioma

Neoplastic tumors that are derived from coelomic epithelium are as follows:

- Cystic tumors: serous cystoma, mucinous cystoma, mixed forms
- Tumors with stromal overgrowth: fibroma, adenofibroma, Brenner tumor

Tumors derived from germ cells are dermoids (benign cystic teratomas).

ICD-9CM CODES
220 Benign neoplasm of ovary

EPIDEMIOLOGY & DEMOGRAPHICS

- Reproductive years:
  1. Most common benign ovarian neoplasms: serous cystadenoma and benign cystic teratoma
  2. Most common adnexal mass: functional cyst
- Risk of malignancy increases after age 40 yr.
- Infants: adnexal masses are usually follicular cysts secondary to maternal hormone stimulation that regress during first few months of life.
- Childhood:
  1. Adnexal masses are rare.
  2. 8% are malignant.
  3. Almost always dysgerminomas or teratomas (germ cell origin).
  4. Frequency of malignancy is inversely correlated with age.
- Adolescence:
  1. Most common adnexal mass is a functional cyst.
  2. Most common neoplastic ovarian tumor is a benign cystic teratoma.
  3. Solid/cystic adnexal tumors are rare and almost always dysgerminomas or malignant teratomas.

PHYSICAL FINDINGS & CLINICAL PRESENTATION

- Usually asymptomatic
- Pelvic pain/pressure
- Dyspareunia
- Abdominal pain ranging from mild to severe peritoneal irritation
- Increasing abdominal girth/distention
- Adnexal mass of pelvic examination
- Children: abdominal/rectal mass

ETIOLOGY

- Physiologic
- Endometriosis
- Unknown

DIAGNOSIS

DIFFERENTIAL DIAGNOSIS

- Ovarian torsion
- Malignancy: ovary, fallopian tube, colon
- Uterine fibroid
- Diverticular abscess/diverticulitis
- Appendiceal abscess/appendicitis (especially in children)
- Tuboovarian abscess
- Paraovarian cyst
- Distended bladder
- Pelvic kidney
- Ectopic pregnancy
- Retroperitoneal cyst/neoplasm

WORKUP

- Complete history and physical examination
- Pelvic examination/rectrovaginal examination to reveal firm, irregular, mobile mass
- Laparoscopy/laparotomy to establish diagnosis

LABORATORY TESTS

- Pregnancy test
- Serum tumor markers:
  1. Cancer antigen 125 (CA 125)
  2. α-Fetoprotein (AFP) (endodermal sinus tumor, immature teratoma)
  3. β-Human chorionic gonadotropin (hCG)
  4. Lactic dehydrogenase (LDH) (dysgerminoma)

IMAGING STUDIES

Ultrasound:

- May differentiate adnexal mass from other pelvic masses
- Features that increase risk of malignancy include solid component, papillae, multiple septations/solitary thick septa, ascites, matted bowel, bilaterality, irregular borders
- CT scan with contrast or IVP
- Colonoscopy/barium enema, if symptomatic

TREATMENT

NONPHARMACOLOGIC THERAPY

Repeat pelvic examination for premenopausal women in 4 to 6 wk.

ACUTE GENERAL Rx

Indications for surgery:

- Postmenopausal or premenarcheal palpable adnexal mass
- Adnexal mass with suspicious ultrasound features
- Premenopausal woman with persistent cyst >5 cm
- Any adnexal mass >10 cm
- Suspected torsion or rupture

CHRONIC Rx

- Depends on diagnosis
- Possible suppression of formation of new cysts by oral contraceptives

DISPOSITION

Depends on diagnosis

REFERRAL

- If malignancy suspected
- If surgery required

SUGGESTED READINGS

Copeland LJ, Jarrell JF: *Textbook of gynecology,* ed 2, Philadelphia, 1999, WB Saunders.

Dayal M, Barnhart KT: Noncontraceptive benefits and therapeutic uses of the oral contraceptive pill, *Semin Reprod Med* 19(4):295, 2001.

Doret M, Raudrant D: Functional ovarian cysts and the need to remove them, *Euro J Obstet Gynecol Reprod Biol* 100(1):1, 2001.

Kurjak A, Kupesic S, Simunic V: Ultrasonic assessment of the peri- and postmenopausal ovary, *Maturitas* 41(4):245, 2002.

AUTHOR: **GEORGE T. DANAKAS, M.D.**

BASIC INFORMATION

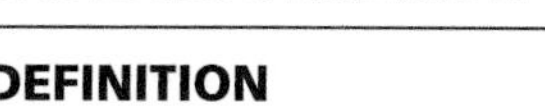

DEFINITION

Paget's disease of the bone is a nonmetabolic disease of bone characterized by repeated episodes of osteolysis and excessive attempts at repair that results in a weakened bone of increased mass. Monostotic (solitary lesion) and polyostotic (numerous lesions) disease are both described.

SYNONYMS

Osteitis deformans

ICD-9CM CODES
731.0 Paget's disease (osteitis deformans)

EPIDEMIOLOGY & DEMOGRAPHICS

PREVALENCE: Localized lesions in 3% of patients >50 yr
PREVALENT AGE: Rare before 40 yr
PREVALENT SEX: Male:female ratio of 2:1

PHYSICAL FINDINGS & CLINICAL PRESENTATION

- Many lesions are asymptomatic.
- Onset is variable.
- Symptoms result mainly from the effects of complications:
  1. Skeletal pain, especially hip and pelvis
  2. Bowing of long bones, sometimes leading to pathologic fracture
  3. Increased heat of extremity (resulting from increased vascularity)
  4. Skull enlargement and spinal involvement caused by characteristic bone enlargement, which can produce neurologic complications (vision, hearing loss, radicular pain, and cord compression)
  5. Thoracic kyphoscoliosis
  6. Secondary osteoarthritis, especially of hip
  7. Heart failure as a result of chest and spine deformity and blood shunting

ETIOLOGY

Unknown

DIAGNOSIS

DIFFERENTIAL DIAGNOSIS

- Fibrous dysplasia
- Skeletal neoplasm (primary or metastatic)
- Osteomyelitis
- Hyperparathyroidism
- Vertebral hemangioma

LABORATORY TESTS

- Increased serum alkaline phosphatase (SAP)
- Normal serum calcium and phosphorus levels
- Increased urinary excretion of pyridinoline cross-links, although test is expensive and not usually required in routine cases
- Other: bone biopsy only in uncertain cases or if sarcomatous degeneration is suspected

IMAGING STUDIES

- Appropriate radiographs reflect the characteristic radiolucency and opacity (Fig. 1-172).
- Bone scanning usually reflects the activity and extent of the disease.

TREATMENT

ACUTE GENERAL Rx

- Counseling regarding home environment to prevent falls
- Cane for balance and weight-bearing pain

PHARMACOLOGIC THERAPY

- Calcitonin
- Biphosphonates
- NSAIDs for pain relief
- General indications for treatment
  1. All symptomatic patients
  2. Asymptomatic patients with high level of metabolic activity or those at risk for deformity
  3. Preoperative, if surgery involves pagetic site

DISPOSITION

- Many monostotic lesions probably remain asymptomatic.
- Progression of the disease is common.
- Malignant degeneration occurs in <1% of patients and should be considered when there is a sudden increase in pain.
- Sarcomatous change carries a grave prognosis.

REFERRAL

- For dental evaluation if there is involvement of the mandible or maxilla
- For ENT evaluation if there is hearing loss
- For ophthalmologic evaluation if there is impaired vision
- For orthopedic consultation for assessment of pain in bone or joint

PEARLS & CONSIDERATIONS

COMMENTS

Surgical intervention is often required for neurologic complications or joint symptoms
- Often associated with profuse blood loss
- Elective cases: benefit from preoperative treatment to suppress bone activity and vascularity

SUGGESTED READINGS

Crandall C: Risedronate: a clinical review, *Arch Intern Med* 161:353, 2001.
Kotocvicz MA: Paget's disease of bone: Diagnosis and indications for treatment, *Aust Fam Physician* 33(3):127, 2004.
Langston AL, Ralston SH: Management of Paget's disease of bone, *Rheumatology* 43(8):955, 2004.
Lin JT, Lane JM; Bisphosphonates, *J Am Acad Orthop Surg* 11:1, 2003.
Roodman GD: Studies in Paget's disease and their relevance to oncology, *Semin Oncol* 28:15, 2001.
Schneider D et al: Diagnosis and treatment of Paget's disease of bone, *Am Fam Physician* 65:2069, 2002.

AUTHOR: **LONNIE R. MERCIER, M.D.**

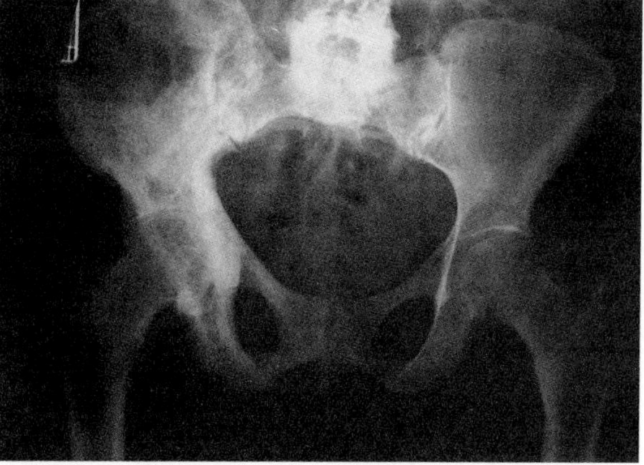

FIGURE 1-172 Frontal radiograph of the pelvis shows marked prominence to the trabeculae in the right ilium, ischium, and pubic bones with small lytic areas identified compatible with the later stages of Paget's disease. (From Specht N [ed]: *Practical guide to diagnostic imaging,* St Louis, 1998, Mosby.)

Paget's Disease of the Breast (PTG)

BASIC INFORMATION

DEFINITION

Paget's disease of the breast is a malignant disease that presents itself as a scaly, sore, eroding, bleeding ulcer of the nipple. Microscopically, typical large clear cells (Paget's cells) with pale and abundant cytoplasm and hyperchromatic nuclei with prominent nucleoli are found in the epidermal layer. Paget's disease is more often associated with primary invasive or in situ carcinoma of the breast.

ICD-9CM CODES
174.0 Malignant neoplasm of female breast, nipple, and areola

EPIDEMIOLOGY & DEMOGRAPHICS

- Not common
- Found in 1 in 100 to 200 breast cancer patients

PHYSICAL FINDINGS & CLINICAL PRESENTATION

- Variable
- Itching or burning nipple and/or reported lump
- Very minimal scaly lesion that may bleed when scales are lifted
- Typical ulcer located on nipple with serous fluid weeping or small amount of bleeding coming from it (Fig. 1-173)
- Palpable carcinoma in the breast of some patients

ETIOLOGY

- Exact origin unknown
- Possibly migration of either in situ or invasive carcinoma cells in breast to nipple skin to produce Paget's disease

DIAGNOSIS

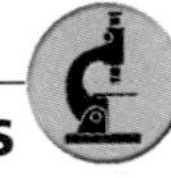

DIFFERENTIAL DIAGNOSIS

- Chronic dermatitis
- Florid papillomatosis of the nipple or nipple adenoma
- Eczema

WORKUP

- Clinically apparent
- Careful breast examination with diagnosis in mind
- Palpable mass or mammographic lesions in 60% to 70% of patients
- A clinical algorithm for the evaluation of nipple discharge is described in Section III, Breast, Nipple Discharge Evaluation.

LABORATORY TESTS

Biopsy of nipple lesion

IMAGING STUDIES

Mammograms to search for possible primary carcinoma

TREATMENT

NONPHARMACOLOGIC THERAPY

- Fewer patients:
  1. Paget's disease of nipple only finding when mammographically negative breast
  2. Consideration of wide excision of nipple with or without radiation
- Other patients: additional invasive or in situ carcinoma recognized
- Either modified mastectomy or breast conservation treatment
- Presence of underlying in situ or invasive carcinoma in mastectomy specimen of majority of patients

ACUTE GENERAL Rx

Systemic adjuvant therapy, depending on extent of invasive carcinoma found

DISPOSITION

- Parallel prognosis to that of breast cancer patient without Paget's disease
- Regular follow-up as in other invasive or in situ carcinoma patients

REFERRAL

At outset, all suspicious nipple lesions should be referred for evaluation and treatment.

SUGGESTED READINGS

Sakoratias GH et al: Paget's disease of the breast, *Canc Treat Rev* 27(1):9, 2001.

Sakoratias GH et al: Paget's disease of the breast: a clinical perspective, *Langenbecks Arch Surg* 386(6):444, 2001.

AUTHOR: **TAKUMA NEMOTO, M.D.**

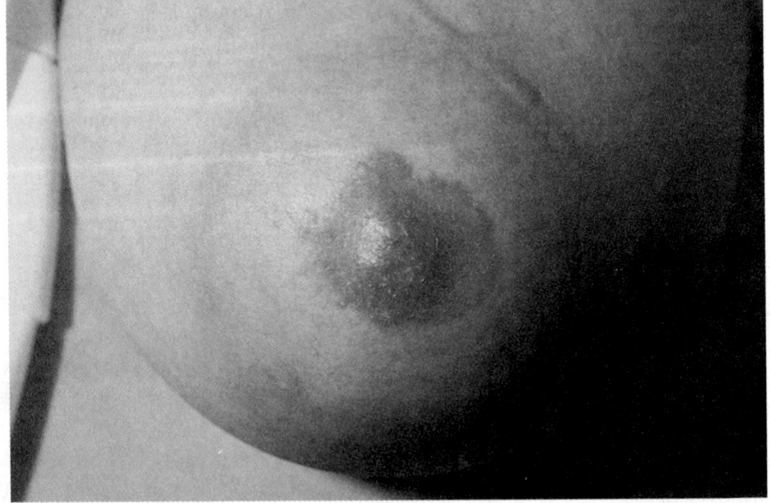

FIGURE 1-173 Paget's disease of the breast. The lesion has insidiously spread for 1 year to infiltrate the areola and surrounding skin. (From Habif TP: *Clinical dermatology: a color guide to diagnosis and therapy,* ed 3, St Louis, 1996, Mosby.)

BASIC INFORMATION

DEFINITION

Pancreatic cancer is an adenocarcinoma derived from the epithelium of the pancreatic duct.

ICD-9CM CODES
157.9 Pancreatic cancer
157.0 (head)
157.1 (body)
157.2 (tail)
157.3 (duct)
230.9 (in situ)

EPIDEMIOLOGY & DEMOGRAPHICS

INCIDENCE: 1 case/10,000 persons/yr
PEAK AGE: Seventh and eighth decades of life
PREDOMINANT SEX: Male:female ratio of 2:1

PHYSICAL FINDINGS & CLINICAL PRESENTATION

Presenting symptoms:
- Jaundice
- Abdominal pain
- Weight loss
- Anorexia/change in taste
- Nausea
- Uncommonly: depression, GI bleeding, acute pancreatitis, back pain

Physical findings:
- Icterus
- Cachexia
- Excoriations from scratching pruritic skin

ETIOLOGY

Unknown, but several conditions have been associated with pancreatic cancer:
- Smoking
- Alcoholism
- Gallstones
- Diabetes mellitus
- Chronic pancreatitis
- Diet rich in animal fat
- Occupational exposures: oil refining, paper manufacturing, chemical industry

DIAGNOSIS

DIFFERENTIAL DIAGNOSIS

- Common duct cholelithiasis
- Cholangiocarcinoma
- Common duct stricture
- Sclerosing cholangitis
- Primary biliary cirrhosis
- Drug-induced cholestasis (e.g., phenothiazines)
- Chronic hepatitis
- Sarcoidosis
- Other pancreatic tumors (islet cell tumor, cystadenocarcinoma, epidermoid carcinoma, sarcomas, lymphomas)

WORKUP

Routine laboratory tests	% abnormal
Alkaline phosphatase	80
Bilirubin	55
Total protein	15
Amylase	15
Hematocrit	60

IMAGING STUDIES

Noninvasive imaging	% abnormal
Abdominal ultrasonography	60
Abdominal CT scan (Fig. 1-174) (without or with contrast [IV or oral])	90
Abdominal MRI scan	90
Invasive imaging	
Endoscopic retrograde cholangiopancreatography (ERCP)	90
CT scan or ultrasonography-guided needle aspiration cytology	90-95

TREATMENT

- Surgery

Curative pancreatectomy (Whipple's procedure) appropriate for only 10% to 20% of patients whose lesion is <5 cm, solitary, and without metastases. Surgical mortality is 5%. Adjuvant chemotherapy may improve postoperative survival.

Palliative surgery (for biliary decompression/diversion)

Palliative therapeutic endoscopic retrograde cholangiopancreatography (ERCP) using stents

- Chemotherapy

The best combination chemotherapy using streptozotocin, mitomycin C, and 5-FU provides only a 19-wk median survival.

- Radiation

External beam radiation for palliation of pain.

- Combined chemotherapy and radiation provides a median survival of 11 mo.
- Celiac plexus block by an experienced anesthesiologist provides pain relief in 80% to 90% of cases.

DISPOSITION

Adjunct chemotherapy has a significant survival benefit in patients with resected pancreatic cancer, whereas adjuvant chemotherapy has a deleterious effect on survival.

SUGGESTED READINGS

Cello JP: Pancreatic cancer. In Feldman M, Scharschmidt BF, Sleisenger MH (eds): *Gastrointestinal and liver disease,* ed 6, Philadelphia, 1998, WB Saunders.

Michaud DS et al: Physical activity, obesity, height, and the risk of pancreatic cancer, *JAMA* 286:821, 2001.

Neoptolemos JP et al: A randomized trial of chemotherapy and radiochemotherapy after resection of pancreatic cancer, *N Engl J Med* 350:1200, 2004.

Wong GY: Effect of neurolytic celiac plexus block on pain relief, quality of life, and survival in patients with unresectable pancreatic cancer, *JAMA* 291:1092, 2004.

AUTHOR: **TOM J. WACHTEL, M.D.**

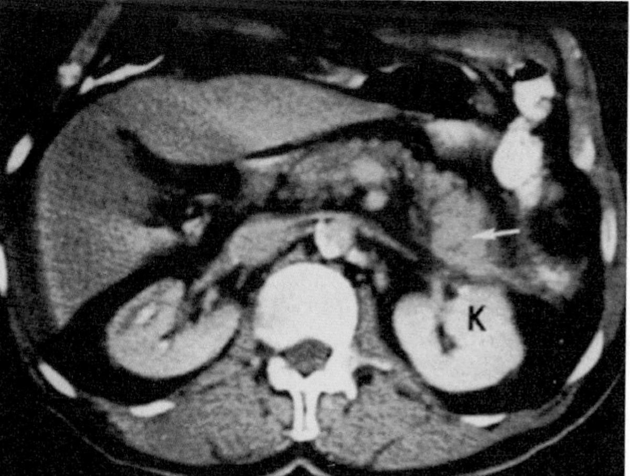

FIGURE 1-174 CT scan of a patient with adenocarcinoma of the body and tail of the pancreas. The tumor *(arrow)* is seen anterior and adjacent to the left kidney *(K)*. At operation, the tumor was invading Gerota's fascia. (From Sabiston D: *Textbook of surgery,* ed 15, Philadelphia, 1997, WB Saunders.)

BASIC INFORMATION

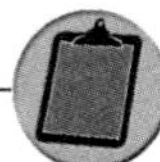

DEFINITION

Acute pancreatitis is an inflammatory process of the pancreas with intrapancreatic activation of enzymes that may also involve peripancreatic tissue and/or remote organ systems.

ICD-9CM CODES
577.0 Acute pancreatitis

EPIDEMIOLOGY & DEMOGRAPHICS

- Acute pancreatitis is most often secondary to biliary tract disease and alcohol.
- Incidence in urban areas is twice that of rural areas (20 cases/100,000 persons in urban areas).
- 20% of patients have necrotizing pancreatitis; the remainder have interstitial pancreatitis.

PHYSICAL FINDINGS & CLINICAL PRESENTATION

- Epigastric tenderness and guarding; pain usually developing suddenly, reaching peak intensity within 10 to 30 min, severe and lasting several hours without relief
- Hypoactive bowel sounds (secondary to ileus)
- Tachycardia, shock (secondary to decreased intravascular volume)
- Confusion (secondary to metabolic disturbances)
- Fever
- Tachycardia, decreased breath sounds (atelectasis, pleural effusions, ARDS)
- Jaundice (secondary to obstruction or compression of biliary tract)
- Ascites (secondary to tear in pancreatic duct, leaking pseudocyst)
- Palpable abdominal mass (pseudocyst, phlegmon, abscess, carcinoma)
- Evidence of hypocalcemia (Chvostek's sign, Trousseau's sign)
- Evidence of intraabdominal bleeding (hemorrhagic pancreatitis):
  1. Gray-bluish discoloration around the umbilicus (Cullen's sign)
  2. Bluish discoloration involving the flanks (Grey Turner's sign)
- Tender subcutaneous nodules (caused by subcutaneous fat necrosis)

ETIOLOGY

- In >90% of cases: biliary tract disease (calculi or sludge) or alcohol
- Drugs (e.g., thiazides, furosemide, corticosteroids, tetracycline, estrogens, valproic acid, metronidazole, azathioprine, methyldopa, pentamidine, ethacrynic acid, procainamide, sulindac, nitrofurantoin, ACE inhibitors, danazol, cimetidine, piroxicam, gold, ranitidine, sulfasalazine, isoniazid, acetaminophen, cisplatin, opiates, erythromycin)
- Abdominal trauma
- Surgery
- ERCP
- Infections (predominantly viral infections)
- Peptic ulcer (penetrating duodenal ulcer)
- Pancreas divisum (congenital failure to fuse of dorsal or ventral pancreas)
- Idiopathic
- Pregnancy
- Vascular (vasculitis, ischemic)
- Hypolipoproteinemia (types I, IV, and V)
- Hypercalcemia
- Pancreatic carcinoma (primary or metastatic)
- Renal failure
- Hereditary pancreatitis
- Occupational exposure to chemicals: methanol, cobalt, zinc, mercuric chloride, creosol, lead, organophosphates, chlorinated naphthalenes
- Others: scorpion bite, obstruction at ampulla region (neoplasm, duodenal diverticula, Crohn's disease), hypotensive shock

DIAGNOSIS

DIFFERENTIAL DIAGNOSIS

- PUD
- Acute cholangitis, biliary colic
- High intestinal obstruction
- Early acute appendicitis
- Mesenteric vascular obstruction
- DKA
- Pneumonia (basilar)
- Myocardial infarction (inferior wall)
- Renal colic
- Ruptured or dissecting aortic aneurysm

LABORATORY TESTS

Pancreatic enzymes
- Amylase is increased, usually elevated in the initial 3 to 5 days of acute pancreatitis. Isoamylase determinations (separation of pancreatic cell isoenzyme components of amylase) are useful in excluding occasional cases of salivary hyperamylasemia. The use of isoamylase rather than total serum amylase reduces the risk of erroneously diagnosing pancreatitis and is preferred by some as initial biochemical test in patients suspected of having acute pancreatitis.
- Urinary amylase determinations are useful to diagnose acute pancreatitis in patients with lipemic serum, to rule out elevated serum amylase secondary to macroamylasemia, and to diagnose acute pancreatitis in patients whose serum amylase is normal.
- Serum lipase levels are elevated in acute pancreatitis; the elevation is less transient than serum amylase; concomitant evaluation of serum amylase and lipase increases diagnostic accuracy of acute pancreatitis. An elevated lipase/amylase ratio is suggestive of alcoholic pancreatitis.
- Elevated serum trypsin levels are diagnostic of pancreatitis (in absence of renal failure); measurement is made by radioimmunoassay. Although not routinely available, the serum trypsin level is the most accurate laboratory indicator for pancreatitis.
- Rapid measurement of urinary trypsinogen-2 (if available) is useful in the ER as a screening test for acute pancreatitis in patients with abdominal pain; a negative dipstick test for urinary trypsinogen-2 rules out acute pancreatitis with a high degree of probability, whereas a positive test indicates need for further evaluation.

Additional tests:
- CBC: reveals leukocytosis; Hct may be initially increased secondary to hemoconcentration; decreased Hct may indicate hemorrhage or hemolysis.
- BUN is increased secondary to dehydration.
- Elevation of serum glucose in previously normal patient correlates with the degree of pancreatic malfunction and may be related to increased release of glycogen, catecholamines, and glucocorticoid release and decreased insulin release.
- Liver profile: AST and LDH are increased secondary to tissue necrosis; bilirubin and alkaline phosphatase may be increased secondary to common bile duct obstruction. A threefold or greater rise in serum ALT concentrations is an excellent indicator (95% probability) of biliary pancreatitis.
- Serum calcium is decreased secondary to saponification, precipitation, and decreased PTH response.
- ABGs: Pao_2 may be decreased secondary to ARDS, pleural effusion(s); pH may be decreased secondary to lactic acidosis, respiratory acidosis, and renal insufficiency.
- Serum electrolytes: potassium may be increased secondary to acidosis or renal insufficiency, sodium may be increased secondary to dehydration.

SECTION I

IMAGING STUDIES

- Abdominal plain film is useful initially to distinguish other conditions that may mimic pancreatitis (perforated viscus); it may reveal localized ileus (sentinel loop), pancreatic calcifications (chronic pancreatitis), blurring of left psoas shadow, dilation of transverse colon, calcified gallstones.
- Chest x-ray may reveal elevation of one or both diaphragms, pleural effusions, basilar infiltrates, platelike atelectasis.
- Abdominal ultrasonography is useful in detecting gallstones (sensitivity of 60% to 70% for detecting stones associated with pancreatitis). It is also useful for detecting pancreatic pseudocysts; its major limitation is the presence of distended bowel loops overlying the pancreas.
- CT scan is superior to ultrasonography in identifying pancreatitis and defining its extent, and it also plays a role in diagnosing pseudocysts (they appear as a well-defined area surrounded by a high-density capsule); GI fistulation or infection of a pseudocyst can also be identified by the presence of gas within the pseudocyst. Sequential contrast enhanced CT is useful for detection of pancreatic necrosis. The severity of pancreatitis can also be graded by CT scan.
- Magnetic resonance cholangiopancreatography (MRCP) is also a useful diagnostic modality if a surgical procedure is not anticipated.
- ERCP should not be performed during the acute stage of disease unless it is necessary to remove an impacted stone in the ampulla of Vater; patients with severe or worsening pancreatitis but without obstructive jaundice (biliary obstruction) do not benefit from early ERCP and papillotomy.

TREATMENT

NONPHARMACOLOGIC THERAPY

- Bowel rest with avoidance of PO liquids or solids during the acute illness
- Avoidance of alcohol and any drugs associated with pancreatitis

ACUTE GENERAL Rx

General measures:

- Maintain adequate intravascular volume with vigorous IV hydration.
- Patient should remain NPO until clinically improved, stable, and hungry.
- Nasogastric suction is useful in severe pancreatitis to decompress the abdomen in patients with ileus.
- Control pain: some analgesics may cause spasms of the sphincter of Oddi. Meperidine may produce less constriction than other analgesics; however, clear evidence regarding this claim is lacking and metabolites may cause significant neurotoxic effects such as seizures, myoclonus, or tremor).
- Correct metabolic abnormalities (e.g., replace calcium and magnesium as necessary).
- TPN may be necessary in prolonged pancreatitis.

Specific measures:

- IV antibiotics should not be used prophylactically; their use is justified if the patient has evidence of septicemia, pancreatic abscess, or pancreatitis secondary to biliary calculi. Appropriate empiric antibiotic therapy should cover:
  1. *B. fragilis* and other anaerobes (cefotetan, cefoxitin, metronidazole, or clindamycin plus aminoglycoside)
  2. *Enterococcus* (ampicillin)
- Surgical therapy has a limited role in acute pancreatitis; it is indicated in the following:
  1. Gallstone-induced pancreatitis: cholecystectomy when acute pancreatitis subsides
  2. Perforated peptic ulcer
  3. Excision or drainage of necrotic or infected foci
- Identification and treatment of complications:
  1. Pseudocyst: round or spheroid collection of fluid, tissue, pancreatic enzymes, and blood.
     a. Diagnosed by CT scan or sonography
     b. Treatment: CT scan or ultrasound-guided percutaneous drainage (with a pigtail catheter left in place for continuous drainage) can be used, but the recurrence rate is high; the conservative approach is to reevaluate the pseudocyst (with CT scan or sonography) after 6 to 7 wk and surgically drain it if the pseudocyst has not decreased in size. Generally pseudocysts <5 cm in diameter are reabsorbed without intervention whereas those >5 cm require surgical intervention after the wall has matured.
  2. Phlegmon: represents pancreatic edema. It can be diagnosed by CT scan or sonography. Treatment is supportive measures, because it usually resolves spontaneously.
  3. Pancreatic abscess: diagnosed by CT scan (presence of bubbles in the retroperitoneum); Gram staining and cultures of fluid obtained from guided percutaneous aspiration (GPA) usually identify bacterial organism. Therapy is surgical (or catheter) drainage and IV antibiotics (imipenem-cilastin [Primaxin] is the drug of choice).
  4. Pancreatic ascites: usually caused by leaking of pseudocyst or tear in pancreatic duct. Paracentesis reveals very high amylase and lipase levels in the pancreatic fluid; ERCP may demonstrate the lesion. Treatment is surgical correction if exudative ascites from severe pancreatitis does not resolve spontaneously.
  5. GI bleeding: caused by alcoholic gastritis, bleeding varices, stress ulceration, or DIC.
  6. Renal failure: caused by hypovolemia resulting in oliguria or anuria, cortical or tubular necrosis (shock, DIC), or thrombosis of renal artery or vein.
  7. Hypoxia: caused by ARDS, pleural effusion, or atelectasis.

DISPOSITION

Prognosis varies with the severity of pancreatitis; overall mortality in acute pancreatitis is 5% to 10%; poor prognostic signs are the following:

- Age >55 yr
- Fluid sequestration >6000 ml
- Laboratory abnormalities on admission: WBC >16,000, blood glucose >200 ml/dl, serum LDH >350 IU/L, AST >250 IU/L
- Laboratory abnormalities during the initial 48 hr: decreased Hct >10% with hydration or Hct <30%, BUN rise >5 mg/dl, serum calcium <8 mg/dl, arterial Po_2 <60 mm Hg, and base deficit >4 mEq/L

REFERRAL

- Hospitalization is indicated in moderate/severe cases of pancreatitis.
- Surgical consultation is needed in suspected gallstone pancreatitis, perforated peptic ulcer, or presence of necrotic or infected foci.

AUTHOR: **FRED F. FERRI, M.D.**

BASIC INFORMATION

DEFINITION

Chronic pancreatitis is a recurrent or persistent inflammatory process of the pancreas characterized by chronic pain and by pancreatic exocrine and/or endocrine insufficiency.

ICD-9CM CODES
577.1 Chronic pancreatitis

EPIDEMIOLOGY & DEMOGRAPHICS

- Chronic pancreatitis occurs in approximately 5 to 10/100,000 persons in industrialized countries.
- Male:female ratio is 5:1.

PHYSICAL FINDINGS & CLINICAL PRESENTATION

- Persistent or recurrent epigastric and LUQ pain, may radiate to the back
- Tenderness over the pancreas, muscle guarding
- Significant weight loss
- Bulky, foul-smelling stools, greasy in appearance
- Epigastric mass (10% of patients)
- Jaundice (5% to 10% of patients)

ETIOLOGY

- Chronic alcoholism
- Obstruction (ampullary stenosis, tumor, trauma, pancreas divisum, annular pancreas)
- Hereditary pancreatitis
- Severe malnutrition
- Idiopathic
- Untreated hyperparathyroidism (hypercalcemia)
- Mutations of the cystic fibrosis transmembrane conductance regulator (CFTR) gene and the TF genotype
- Sclerosing pancreatitis: A form of chronic pancreatitis characterized by infrequent attacks of abdominal pain, irregular narrowing of the pancreatic duct, and swelling of the pancreatic parenchyma; these patients have high levels of serum immunoglobins (IgG4)

DIAGNOSIS

DIFFERENTIAL DIAGNOSIS

- Pancreatic cancer
- PUD
- Cholelithiasis with biliary obstruction
- Malabsorption from other etiologies
- Recurrent acute pancreatitis

WORKUP

Medical history with focus on alcohol use, laboratory tests, diagnostic imaging

LABORATORY TESTS

- Serum amylase and lipase may be elevated (normal amylase levels, however, do not exclude the diagnosis).
- Hyperglycemia, glycosuria, hyperbilirubinemia, and elevated serum alkaline phosphatase may also be present.
- 72-hr fecal fat determination (rarely performed) reveals excess fecal fat.
- Bentiromide test or secretin stimulation test can confirm pancreatic insufficiency.
- Elevated levels of serum IgG4 are found in sclerosing pancreatitis, but not in other disorders of the pancreas.

IMAGING STUDIES

- Plain abdominal radiographs may reveal pancreatic calcifications (95% specific for chronic pancreatitis).
- Ultrasound of abdomen may reveal duct dilation, pseudocyst, calcification, and presence of ascites.
- CT scan of abdomen is useful for the detection of calcifications, to evaluate for ductal dilation, and for ruling out pancreatic cancer.
- ERCP can be used to evaluate for the presence of dilated ducts, strictures, pseudocysts, and intraductal stones.
- Use of fine needle aspiration (FNA) and endoscopic ultrasound (EUS) are newer diagnostic modalities.

TREATMENT

NONPHARMACOLOGIC THERAPY

- Avoidance of alcohol
- Frequent, small-volume, low-fat meals

ACUTE GENERAL Rx

- Avoidance of narcotics if possible (simple analgesics or NSAIDs can be used)
- Treatment of steatorrhea with pancreatic supplements (e.g., Pancrease, Creon, Pancrelipase titrated prn based on the amount of steatorrhea and patient's weight loss)
- Octreotide 200 μg SC tid may be useful for pain secondary to idiopathic chronic pancreatitis
- Treatment of complications (e.g., type 1 DM)
- Glucocorticoid therapy in patients with sclerosing pancreatitis can induce clinical remission and significantly decrease serum concentrations of IgG4, immune complexes, and the IgG4 subclass of immune complexes

CHRONIC Rx

- Surgical intervention may be necessary to eliminate biliary tract disease and improve flow of bile into the duodenum by eliminating obstruction of pancreatic duct.
- ERCP with endoscopic sphincterectomy and stone extraction is useful in selected patients.
- Transduodenal sphincteroplasty or pancreaticojejunostomy in selected patients. Surgery should also be considered in patients with intractable pain.

DISPOSITION

- Long-term survival is poor (50% of patients die within 10 hr from chronic pancreatitis or malignancy).
- Prognosis is best in patients with recurrent acute pancreatitis resulting from cholelithiasis, hyperparathyroidism, or stenosis of the sphincter of Oddi.

REFERRAL

GI referral for ERCP, surgical referral in selected patients (see "Chronic Rx").

SUGGESTED READINGS

Hamano H et al: High serum IgG4 concentrations in patients with sclerosing pancreatitis, *N Engl J Med* 344:732, 2001.

Hollerbach S et al: Endoscopic ultrasonography and fine needle aspiration cytology for diagnosis of chronic pancreatitis, *Endoscopy* 33:824, 2001.

AUTHOR: **FRED F. FERRI, M.D.**

BASIC INFORMATION

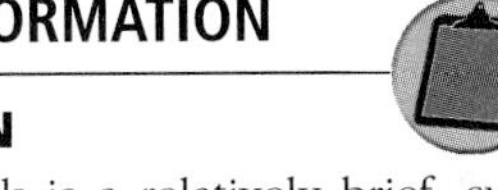

DEFINITION

A panic attack is a relatively brief, sudden episode of intense fear or apprehension, often associated with a sense of impending doom and various uncomfortable and disquieting physical symptoms. Panic attacks may be uncued ("out of the blue") or cued (i.e., triggered by a particular object or situation) and may be present in a variety of different anxiety-related disorders (e.g., phobias, social anxiety, OCD). Panic disorder is diagnosed after two uncued panic attacks have occurred followed by at least 1 month (or more) of significant concern about future attacks, worry about their implications, or a major change in behavior related to these attacks. Agoraphobia is anxiety about, and avoidance of, places or situations in which the ability to escape is limited or embarrassing or in which help might not be available in the event of having a panic attack.

SYNONYMS

Anxiety attacks
Fear attacks
Ataque de nervios

ICD-9CM CODES
F 41.0 Panic disorder without agoraphobia (DSM-IV: 300.01)
F 40.01 Panic disorder with agoraphobia (DSM-IV: 300.21)

EPIDEMIOLOGY & DEMOGRAPHICS

INCIDENCE (IN U.S.): 1% 1-mo incidence of panic attacks.

PREVALENCE (IN U.S.):
- 15% lifetime prevalence of panic attacks.
- Panic disorder much more uncommon, with a lifetime prevalence of 1.5%-3.5%; chronicity of condition reflected by a similar 1-yr prevalence rate of 1%-2%.
- Agoraphobia relatively rare; 0.3%-1% lifetime prevalence. 30%-50% of patients diagnosed with panic disorder also have agoraphobia.

PREDOMINANT SEX:
- Women more commonly affected (>85% of clinical population).
- Panic disorder twice as common in women.
- Panic disorder with agoraphobia three times as common in women.

PREDOMINANT AGE:
- Age of onset is typically late adolescence to mid-30s. Onset earlier in males (24 yr) than females (28 yr).
- Onset after age 45 yr rare and should raise suspicion of different etiology.

PEAK INCIDENCE:
- Chronic condition with a waxing and waning course.
- Bimodal incidence peaks noted, with the first peak between ages 15 and 24 yr and second peak between 35 and 44 yr.

GENETICS:
- Risk of developing panic disorder in first-degree relatives of individuals with panic disorder 4 to 7 times that of general population.
- Findings in twin studies: about 60% of contributing factors to panic are genetic.

PHYSICAL FINDINGS & CLINICAL PRESENTATION

Panic disorder
- Present either with a panic attack or with fear and anxiety related to anticipation of a future panic attack or its implications.
- Typical presentation: unexpected, untriggered periods of intense anxiety and fear with associated physiologic changes (e.g., palpitations, sweating, tremulousness, shortness of breath, chest pain, GI distress, faintness, derealization, paresthesia).
- Emergency or physician visits often occasioned by physical symptoms.

Agoraphobia
- Rare complaints to physician.
- Activities usually self-limited by avoiding public situations where the patient might experience a panic attack and would be unable to exit readily, such as the following:
  1. Crowded public areas (stores, public transportation, church)
  2. Individual interactions (hairdresser, neighborhood meetings)
- On exposure to or anticipation of exposure to such situations, significant anxiety occurs.

ETIOLOGY

Hypotheses (NOTE: There are sufficient data to support each model.)
1. Central dyscontrol of autonomic arousal (typically localized to the locus ceruleus); similar symptoms may be chemically induced with yohimbine, caffeine, or cholecystokinin (CKK).
2. Cognitive overreaction (i.e., "catastrophic misinterpretation") to relatively mild and/or benign physiologic cues that then triggers a genuine autonomic cascade.
3. Dysfunction of a central suffocation alarm mechanism; some signs of compensated respiratory alkalosis. Can be experimentally induced with sodium lactate or carbon dioxide.

DIAGNOSIS

DIFFERENTIAL DIAGNOSIS

Medical conditions
- Endocrinopathies
  1. Hyperthyroidism
  2. Hyperparathyroidism
  3. Pheochromocytoma
  4. Hypoglycemia
- Cardiac and respiratory diseases
  1. Arrhythmias
  2. Myocardial infarction
  3. COPD
  4. Asthma
- Seizure disorders
- Psychiatric disorders
  1. Phobias (e.g., specific phobia or social phobia)
  2. Obsessive-compulsive disorder (cued by exposure to the object of the obsession)
  3. Posttraumatic stress disorder (cued by recall of a stressor)

Therapeutic (theophylline, steroids) and recreational (cocaine, amphetamine, caffeine) drugs and drug withdrawal (alcohol, barbiturates, benzodiazepines)

WORKUP

- Emergency presentation: cardiac, respiratory, or neurologic symptoms
- History and physical examination to rule out a concomitant medical or substance-related condition

NOTE: Panic disorder and agoraphobia are not diagnoses of exclusion, but exclusion of other conditions is usually required.

LABORATORY TESTS

- Thyroid profile
- Electrolyte measures, including calcium
- Toxicology screen
- ECG
- Acute cases: possible monitoring and cardiac enzymes to rule out arrhythmia or ischemia

IMAGING STUDIES

- For temporal lobe dysfunction (e.g., temporal lesions or as ictal or interictal manifestation of temporal lobe seizures): brain CT scan or MRI and/or an EEG in some patients
- Holter monitor to rule out occult or episodic arrhythmias
- Chest x-ray examination, ABG, or pulmonary function tests if respiratory compromise suspected

TREATMENT

NONPHARMACOLOGIC THERAPY

- Cognitive-behavioral therapy (CBT) generally very effective with strongest results for cognitive restructuring (i.e., challenging catastrophic misinterpretations of somatic symptoms) and interoceptive exposures (i.e., recreation and management of feared somatic sensations). CBT effect sizes are larger than for pharmacotherapy, attrition rates are lower, and relapse rates are lower.

ACUTE GENERAL Rx

- Benzodiazepines, particularly alprazolam: very effective in acute setting.
- Low-dose alprazolam for patients with rare panic attacks and asymptomatic interattack periods (0.25-0.5 mg PO or sublingually prn).
- Start patient on selective serotonin reuptake inhibitor or similar agent and taper patient off of benzodiazepine by week 2-3.

CHRONIC Rx

- Preferred pharmacologic agents: antidepressants with a significant serotonin reuptake inhibitory action. Generally start at low dose and titrate upward. Minimum treatment duration is 6-8 months but many patients need to take medications indefinitely.
  1. Imipramine (100-300 mg/day)
  2. SSRIs; paroxetine (10-60 mg/day), sertraline (50-200 mg/day), citalopram (20-60 mg/day), and fluoxetine (5-80 mg/day)
- Combination CBT plus SSRI has shown good long-term effects but is not notably better than CBT alone. Combination CBT plus benzodiazepine does not provide any added benefit and may undermine CBT (interoceptive exposures are less effective if patient is on benzodiazepine).

DISPOSITION

- Typical course chronic but with significant waxing and waning (common to have long periods of remission).
- Presence of agoraphobia associated with a more chronic course.
- Findings with long-term follow-up studies: 6 to 10 yr after treatment some 30% in remission, 40% to 50% improved with residual symptoms, and the remainder either unchanged or worse.

REFERRAL

Referral needed if:

- Patients do not respond to a serotonin reuptake inhibitor
- Cognitive-behavioral therapy is the preferred treatment

SUGGESTED READINGS

American Psychiatric Association: *Diagnostic and statistical manual of mental disorders,* 4th ed. Washington DC, 1994, American Psychiatric Association Press.

American Psychiatric Association: Practice guideline for the treatment of patients with panic disorder. Work group on panic disorder. American Psychiatric Association, *Am J Psychiatry* 155(suppl5):1, 1998.

Gould RA et al: Meta-analysis of treatment outcome for panic disorder, *Clin Psychol Rev* 15(8):819, 1995.

Pollack MH: New advances in the management of anxiety disorders, *Psychopharmacol Bull* 36(4suppl3):79, 2002.

AUTHORS: **JASON M. SATTERFIELD, PH.D.,** and **MITCHELL D. FELDMAN, M.D., M.PHIL.**

BASIC INFORMATION

DEFINITION

Paranoid personality disorder (PPD) is characterized by a pattern of pervasive distrust and suspiciousness of others that leads the person to assign malevolence to the motives of others. PPD begins by early adulthood and causes significant distress or impairment in multiple domains of functioning. Individuals must meet four or more of the following criteria:

1. Suspect, without justification, that others are exploiting, harming, or deceiving them.
2. Preoccupied with unwarranted doubts about the loyalty or trustworthiness of friends or associates.
3. Reluctant to confide in others because of unjustified fear that the information will be used against them in a malicious fashion.
4. Infer demeaning or threatening statements from benign remarks or events.
5. Bear grudges for extended periods. For example, patients with PPDS are unforgiving of perceived or real insults and slights.
6. Perceive attacks on their character that are not apparent to others. Quick to react angrily or to counterattack.
7. Recurrent suspicions, without justification, regarding fidelity of spouse or partner.

SYNONYMS

None

ICD-9CM CODES
301.0

EPIDEMIOLOGY & DEMOGRAPHICS

PREVALENCE: 0.5%-4.4% in the general population, 10%-30% in inpatient psychiatric settings, and 2%-10% in outpatient mental health clinics.
PREDOMINANT SEX: more commonly diagnosed in males in clinical samples.
GENETICS: increased prevalence of PPD in relatives of probands with schizophrenia and delusional disorder, paranoid type.

CLINICAL PRESENTATION

- Signs of PPD in childhood include solitariness, poor peer relationships, social anxiety, underachievement in school, hypersensitivity, peculiar thoughts and language, and idiosyncratic fantasies.
- As children, these patients may have appeared "odd" or "eccentric" and attracted teasing.
- Their excessive suspiciousness often leads to either overt argumentativeness and recurrent complaining or quiet, hostile aloofness.
- These patients maintain interpersonal distance and may refuse to answer personal questions, saying the information is "nobody's business."
- Misinterpret benign actions by others as malicious assaults. Patients with PPDS may, for example, interpret an honest mistake as a deliberate attempt to harm, a casual humorous remark as a serious character attack, a compliment as a veiled criticism, and an offer of help as a judgment of failure.
- Close relationships are impaired by hypervigilance for threats and associated guardedness. May appear as "cold." Suspiciousness can lead to pathologic jealousy where patients with PPDS gather circumstantial evidence to support contention of betrayal.
- To protect themselves from the perceived malice of others, these patients often maintain a high degree of control over relationships and interactions, constantly questioning the whereabouts, intentions, or actions of the other.
- Often rigid and critical of others but have great difficulty accepting criticism themselves.
- Given their lack of trust of others, patients with PPDS have an excessive need for self-sufficiency and autonomy.
- Quick to counterattack and may be litigious.
- May join "cults" or groups who share their paranoid belief system.
- In response to stress, may experience very brief psychotic episodes (minutes to hours).

ETIOLOGY

- To date, limited knowledge about role of genetic loading and neurobiologic vulnerability.
- However, increased prevalence in families of probands with schizophrenia and delusional disorder, paranoid type, suggests possible genetic role.

DIAGNOSIS

DIFFERENTIAL DIAGNOSIS

- Schizophrenia, paranoid type, delusional disorder, paranoid type, and mood disorder with psychotic symptoms: require presence of persistent positive psychotic symptoms such as delusions and hallucinations. To give an additional diagnosis of PPD, the personality disorder must be present before the onset of psychotic symptoms and must persist when the psychotic symptoms are in remission.
- Substance-induced paranoia, especially in the context of cocaine or methamphetamine abuse or dependence.
- Personality changes due to a general medical condition that affects the central nervous system.
- Paranoid traits associated with a sensory disability. For example, hearing impairment.
- Increased risk for major depressive disorder, obsessive-compulsive disorder, agoraphobia, and substance abuse or dependence.
- The most common cooccurring personality disorders are schizotypal, schizoid, narcissistic, avoidant, and borderline:
  1. Schizotypal personality disorder includes magical thinking and unusual perceptual experiences.
  2. Schizoid and borderline personality disorders do not have prominent paranoid ideation.
  3. Avoidant personality disorder, which includes fear of embarrassment.
  4. Narcissistic personality disorder, which includes the fear that hidden "flaws" or "inferiority" may be revealed.

WORKUP

- History—collateral information essential to establishing presence of longstanding interpersonal pattern in multiple domains of the patient's life.
- Physical examination.
- Mental status examination.

LABORATORY TESTS

Those tests necessary to rule out medical causes of personality changes

IMAGING STUDIES

Those necessary to rule out medical causes of personality changes

TREATMENT

NONPHARMACOLOGIC THERAPY

- No randomized trials assessing treatment.
- Cognitive behavioral therapy to help patient control rage, manage perceived criticism, and develop social skills.
- Psychodynamic psychotherapy to help patient develop capacity to trust.

ACUTE GENERAL Rx

Benzodiazepines or low-dose antipsychotics to control hostility and paranoia

CHRONIC Rx

- Low-dose antipsychotic medication. Increase dose in small increments to minimize risk of side effects.
- SSRIs if comorbid depression, obsessive-compulsive disorder, or agoraphobia.
- Substance abuse treatment if comorbid dependence.

COMPLEMENTARY & ALTERNATIVE MEDICINE

None

DISPOSITION

- Severity is variable and course is chronic. Often lifelong difficulty maintaining intimate relationships.
- At increased risk for major depressive disorder, obsessive compulsive disorder, agoraphobia, and substance abuse or dependence.
- In some cases, PPD can be a prepsychotic antecedent of delusional disorder, paranoid type.

REFERRAL

- If pharmacotherapy or psychotherapy contemplated
- If patient's functioning impaired

PEARLS & CONSIDERATIONS

COMMENTS

- Illness exacerbates these patients' sense of vulnerability.
- Communicating personal information to the physician challenges the guarded, self-protective approach to others and will often heighten these patients' fear that the physician will harm them.
- The encounter with the physician intensifies hypervigilance. As a result, innocuous or even overtly helpful behaviors by the physician may be perceived as threatening.
- With the perceived threat, these patients will often confront and challenge the physician on their motives and their rationale for diagnosis and treatment. Conflict and argument are not uncommon.
- Thus, establishing an alliance with the patient can be challenging.
- Faced with such a patient, physicians may understandably react defensively to unfounded suspicion or distance and not respond to the patient's concerns. Both responses increase the patient's anxiety and paranoia.
- Management guidelines:
  1. Convey intent "to do no harm."
  2. Address the patient's fears and concerns, no matter how irrationally, in a clear, direct, and detailed manner.
  3. Remember that behind the patient's hostility lie fears that are real to him or her.
  4. Maintain a professional and neutral stance.
  5. Responding with too much warmth and friendliness will intensify paranoia.
  6. Give patient detailed and factual information about treatment plan.
  7. Give patient as much control as possible, including maximum participation at each decision node.
  8. Do not personalize patient's hostility and suspicion, but understand his or her distrust as an attempt to manage own intense fear.

SUGGESTED READINGS

Feder A, Robbins SW, Ostermeyer B: Personality disorders. In Feldman MD, Christensen JF (eds): *Behavioral medicine in primary care,* New York, 2003, McGraw Hill.

Shea MT et al: Associations in the course of personality disorders and Axis I disorders over time, *J Abnorm Psychol* 113(4):499, 2004.

Ward RK: Assessment and management of personality disorders, *Am Fam Physician* 70(8):1505, 2004.

AUTHORS: **JOHN Q. YOUNG, M.D., M.P.P.,** and **CRAIG VAN DYKE, M.D.**

BASIC INFORMATION

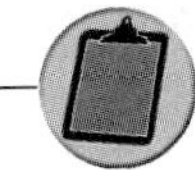

DEFINITION

Idiopathic Parkinson's disease is a progressive neurodegenerative disorder characterized clinically by rigidity, tremor, and bradykinesia. The major manifestations of the disease are due to loss of dopamine in the substantia nigra pars compacta. Its pathological hallmark is the Lewy body, which is a cytoplasmic eosinophilic inclusion body.

SYNONYMS

Paralysis agitans

ICD-9CM CODES
332.0 Idiopathic Parkinson's disease, primary
332.1 Parkinson's disease, secondary

EPIDEMIOLOGY & DEMOGRAPHICS

PREVALENCE:
- Affects over 1 million people in North America
- In age group, <40 yr, <5/100,000 are affected
- In those >70 yr, 700/100,000 are affected
- Highest incidence in whites, lowest incidence in Asians and black Africans

PHYSICAL FINDINGS & CLINICAL PRESENTATION

- Tremor—typically a resting tremor with a frequency of 4-6 Hz that is often first noted in the hand as a pill rolling tremor (thumb and forefinger). Can also involve the leg and lip. Tremor improves with purposeful movement. Usually starts asymmetrically but can eventually involve the other hemibody.
- Rigidity—increased muscle tone. This, too, is usually asymmetric in onset, involving the arm, leg or both. It is resistance that persists throughout the range of passive movement of a joint.
- Akinesia/Bradykinesia—slowness in initiating movement.
- Masked facies—face seems expressionless, giving the appearance of depression. Decreased blink, often there is excess drooling.
- Gait disturbance.
- Stooped posture, decreased arm swing.
- Difficulty initiating the first step; small shuffling steps that increase in speed (festinating gait) as if the patient is chasing his or her center of gravity (steps become progressively faster and shorter while the trunk inclines further forward).
- Other complaints and findings early on include micrographia—handwriting becomes smaller, and hypophonia—voice becomes softer.
- Postural instability—tested by "pull test." Ask patient to stand in place with back to examiner. Examiner pulls patient back by the shoulders, and proper response would be to take no steps back or very few steps back without falling. Retropulsion is a positive test as is falling straight back. This is not usually severe early on. If falls and postural reflexes are greatly impaired early on, then consider other disorders.

ETIOLOGY

- Unknown.
- Most cases are sporadic, with age being the most common risk factor, although there is probably a combination of both environmental and genetic factors contributing to disease expression. There are rare familial forms with at least five different genes identified. The two most well known are the parkin gene, which is a significant cause of early-onset autosomal recessive Parkinson's disease and isolated juvenile-onset Parkinson's' disease (at or before age 20), and alpha synuclein, which is responsible for autosomal dominant Parkinson's disease in isolated families.

DIAGNOSIS

A presumptive clinical diagnosis can be made based on a comprehensive history and physical examination. The combination of asymmetric signs, resting tremor, and good response to levodopa best differentiates idiopathic Parkinson's disease from other causes of parkinsonism (see "Differential Diagnosis").

DIFFERENTIAL DIAGNOSIS

- Multisystem atrophy—distinguishing features include autonomic dysfunction, (including urinary incontinence, orthostatic hypotension, and erectile dysfunction), parkinsonism, cerebellar signs, and normal cognition.
- Diffuse Lewy Body disease—parkinsonism with concomitant dementia. Patients often have early hallucinations and fluctuations in level of alertness and mental status.
- Corticobasal degeneration—often begins asymmetrically with apraxia, cortical sensory loss in one limb, and sometimes alien limb phenomenon.
- Progressive supranuclear palsy—tends to have axial rigidity greater than appendicular (limb) rigidity. These patients have early and severe postural instability. Hallmark is supranuclear gaze palsy that usually involves vertical gaze before horizontal.
- Essential tremor—bilateral postural and action tremor.
- Secondary (acquired) parkinsonism
  1. Postinfectious parkinsonism—von Economo's encephalitis
  2. Parkinson's pugilistica—after repeated head trauma
  3. Iatrogenic—any of the neuroleptics and antipsychotics. The high potency D_2-blocker neuroleptics are most likely to cause parkinsonism. Quetiapine is an atypical antipsychotic with a lower risk of causing parkinsonism. Clozaril does not cause parkinsonism.
  4. Toxins (e.g., MPTP, manganese, carbon monoxide)
- Cerebrovascular disease (basal ganglia infarcts)

WORKUP

Identification of clinical signs and symptoms associated with Parkinson's disease (see "Physical Findings") and elimination of conditions that may mimic it with a comprehensive history and physical examination

IMAGING STUDIES

CT scan has almost no role in investigations. MRI of the head may sometimes distinguish between idiopathic Parkinson's disease and other conditions that present with signs of parkinsonism (see "Differential Diagnosis").

TREATMENT

NONPHARMACOLOGIC THERAPY

- Physical therapy, patient education and reassurance, treatment of associated conditions (e.g., depression)
- Avoidance of drugs that can induce or worsen parkinsonism: neuroleptics (especially high potency), certain antiemetics (prochlorperazine, trimethobenzamide), metoclopramide, nonselective MAO inhibitors (may induce hypertensive crisis), reserpine, methyldopa

ACUTE GENERAL Rx

- There is persistent controversy whether L-dopa or dopamine agonists should be the initial treatment. In younger patients, agonists are usually the drug of choice; in patients >70 levodopa is the drug of choice.

- It is appropriate to initiate pharmacotherapy when required by symptoms; prior practice of waiting for limitation of ADLs is now outdated.
- Motor complications do develop during the course of the disease and likely reflect the combination of disease progression together with the side effects of dopaminergic medications.

CHRONIC Rx

- Levodopa therapy
  1. Cornerstone of symptomatic therapy—should be used with a peripheral dopa decarboxylase inhibitor (carbidopa) to minimize side effects (nausea, mood changes, postural hypotension). The combination of the two drugs is marketed under the trade name Sinemet.
  2. Usual starting dose is 25/100 mg (carbidopa/levodopa) tid 1 hr before meals.
  3. Controlled-release preparations (Sinemet CR [200 mg levodopa/50 mg of carbidopa, or 100 mg levodopa/25 mg carbidopa]) are available, but their use should be deferred to a neurologist.
- Dopamine receptor agonists (Ropinirole, Pramipexole, Pergolide, and Bromocriptine) are not as potent as levodopa, but they are often used as initial treatment in younger patients to attempt to delay the onset of complications (dyskinesias, motor fluctuations) associated with levodopa therapy. These medications are more expensive than levodopa. In general they cause more side effects than levodopa. These include nausea, vomiting, lightheadedness, peripheral edema, confusion, and somnolence.
  1. Ropinirole (Requip): initial dose is 0.25 mg tid
  2. Pramipexole (Mirapex): initial dose of 0.125 mg tid
  3. Pergolide (Permax): initial dose, 0.05 mg for first 2 days increased by 0.1 mg every third day over next 12 days. There have been cases of restrictive valvulopathy, most commonly in tricuspid valve, associated with Permax use. All patients on this medication need a good clinical cardiac examination, and if any concern, an echo
  4. Bromocriptine (Parlodel): initial dose, 1.25 mg qhs
- Selegiline (Eldepryl), an inhibitor of MAO B, can be used early as initial therapy in those with very mild disease or as adjunctive therapy. Selegiline was once advocated as early, first-line therapy because of proposed neuroprotective effects; however, those benefits are probably less robust than once thought. Usual dose, 5 mg bid with breakfast and lunch. It can be useful in treating the fatigue that is commonly associated with PD. Concurrent use of stimulants and sympathomimetics should be avoided.
- Amantadine (Symmetrel) is an antiviral agent that augments release and decreases reuptake of dopamine. It can be used alone early in the disease or in combination with levodopa; dosage is 100 mg tid (titrate q week from 100 mg qd). Must adjust for elderly and renal impairment. Most notable side effect, especially in elderly, is confusion.
- Anticholinergic agents are helpful in treating the tremor and drooling in patients with Parkinson's disease and can be used alone or in combination with levodopa; potential side effects include constipation, urinary retention, memory impairment, and hallucinations. They should be avoided in the elderly.
  1. Trihexyphenidyl (Artane): initial dose, 1 mg PO tid po
  2. Benztropine (Cogentin): usual dose, 0.5 to 1 mg qd or bid
- SURGICAL OPTIONS
  1. Pallidal (globus pallidus interna) and subthalamic deep brain stimulation are currently the surgical options of choice; Thalamic DBS may be useful for refractory tremor.
  2. Surgery is limited to patients with disabling, medically refractory problems, and patients must still have a good response to L-dopa to undergo surgery. DBS results in decreased dyskinesias, fluctuations, rigidity, and tremor.

DISPOSITION

Parkinson's disease usually follows a slowly progressive course leading to disability over the course of several years. However, every patient will progress individually and patients should be reassured that this diagnosis does not, by definition, result in being either wheelchair or bed bound.

REFERRAL

- Neurology consultation is recommended on initial diagnosis of Parkinson's disease.
- Participation in outpatient physical therapy program is recommended for patients with moderate to advanced disease. The most useful speech therapy method available is the Lee Silverman technique, which focuses on projection.

PEARLS & CONSIDERATIONS

- Asymmetry of symptoms at onset is very useful in distinguishing PD from other causes of parkinsonism.
- Although resting tremor is a common presenting symptom, up to one fourth of patients with idiopathic PD do not have classic resting tremor.

COMMENTS

Additional patient information on Parkinson's disease can be obtained from the Internet at www.parkinson.org and from the National Parkinson Foundation, Inc., 1501 Ninth Avenue NW, Miami, FL 33136; phone: (800) 327-4545.

SUGGESTED READINGS

Ahlskog, JE: Parkinson's disease: medical and surgical treatment, in Hurtig H, Stern M (eds): *Neurologic clinics: movement disorders* 19:3, 2001.

Lang AE et al: Parkinson's disease, *N Engl J Med* 339(15):1044,

Lang AE et al: Parkinson's disease, *N Engl J Med* 339(16):1130,

Siderowf, A: Parkinson's disease: clinical features, epidemiology, and genetics, in Hurtig H, Stern M (eds): *Neurologic clinics: movement disorders* 19:3, 2001.

AUTHOR: **CINDY ZADIKOFF, M.D.**

BASIC INFORMATION

DEFINITION

Paronychia is a localized superficial infection or abscess of the lateral and proximal nail fold. Paronychia may be acute or chronic.

ICD-9CM CODES
681.9 Paronychia

EPIDEMIOLOGY & DEMOGRAPHICS

- Acute paronychia affects males and females equally.
- Chronic paronychia more common in females than males (9:1).
- Acute paronychia most often occurs in children.
- Chronic paronychia usually presents in the fifth or sixth decade of life.
- Paronychia is the most common infection of the hand.

PHYSICAL FINDINGS & CLINICAL PRESENTATION

- Acute paronychia usually presents with the sudden onset of redness, swelling, and pain with abscess or cellulitis formation in the nail fold. Fluid with purulence is often present.
- Chronic paronychia is insidious, presenting with mild swelling and erythema of the nail folds.
- Acute paronychia usually involves only one finger.
- Chronic paronychia may involve more than one finger.
- Acute paronychia usually involves the thumb.
- Chronic paronychia commonly involves the middle finger.

ETIOLOGY

- Any disruption of the seal between the proximal nail fold and the nail plate can cause paronychial infections.
- Acute paronychia is almost always bacterial in origin (e.g., *Staphylococcus aureus* [most common], *Streptococcus pyogenes, Streptococcus faecalis, Proteus* and *Pseudomonas* species, and anaerobes).
- Chronic paronychia is commonly caused by *Candida albicans* (70%) with bacterial organisms accounting for the remaining 30%.
- Trauma, nail biting, hangnails, diabetes, and chronic exposure to water are common predisposing features of paronychia.

DIAGNOSIS

The diagnosis of paronychia is self-evident on physical examination.

DIFFERENTIAL DIAGNOSIS

- Herpetic whitlow
- Pyogenic granuloma
- Viral warts
- Ganglions
- Squamous cell carcinoma

WORKUP

A workup is usually not pursued unless there is treatment failure.

LABORATORY TESTS

- Gram stain and culture any purulent drainage.
- KOH mount may show pseudohyphae.

IMAGING STUDIES

X-ray the digit if concerned about osteomyelitis.

TREATMENT

NONPHARMACOLOGIC THERAPY

- For acute paronychia without purulent drainage, warm soaks tid or qid are helpful. If pus is present, surgical drainage is required.
- For chronic paronychia, avoid chronic immersion in water or exposure to moisture.

ACUTE GENERAL Rx

- First-generation cephalosporin (e.g., cephalexin 250 to 500 mg qid) or penicillinase-resistant penicillin (e.g., dicloxacillin 250 to 500 mg qid) are usually the antibiotics of choice for acute paronychia.
- Alternative antibiotic choices include clindamycin and amoxicillin-clavulanate potassium
- Surgical drainage is indicated if purulent discharge is noted.
- A No. 11 blade scalpel is used to lift the lateral perionychium and proximal eponychium off the nail, facilitating drainage.
- If the pus is located beneath the nail, the lateral edge of the nail can be lifted off the nail bed and excised.

CHRONIC Rx

- If no fungal organism is found, tincture of iodine (2 drops bid) helps keep the nail and skin dry.
- Chronic paronychia caused by *Candida albicans* is treated with topical antifungal agents (e.g., miconazole or ketoconazole applied tid).
- Unresponsive cases may be treated with itraconazole or fluconazole but should be done in consultation with dermatology and/or infectious disease.
- Surgery may be needed in refractory cases.

DISPOSITION

- Most acute paronychias with appropriate treatment resolve within 7 to 10 days.
- Osteomyelitis is a potential complication of paronychia.
- Untreated chronic paronychia leads to thickening and discoloration with eventual nail loss.

REFERRAL

Chronic paronychia refractory to topical medical therapy is best referred to dermatology and/or infectious disease. A hand surgeon is consulted if abscess drainage is needed or if surgery is being considered.

PEARLS & CONSIDERATIONS

COMMENTS

- Women with chronic paronychia caused by *Candida albicans* should also be examined for candidal vaginitis.
- The GI tract, including the mouth and bowel, were the usual sources of *Candida albicans* in chronic paronychia.

SUGGESTED READINGS

Rich P: Nail disorders: diagnosis and treatment of infectious, inflammatory, and neoplastic conditions, *Med Clin North Am* 82:1171, 1998.

Rockwell PG: Acute and chronic paronychia, *Am Fam Physician* 63:1113, 2001.

AUTHORS: **PETER PETROPOULOS, M.D.,** and **DENNIS MIKOLICH, M.D.**

Paroxysmal Atrial Tachycardia

BASIC INFORMATION

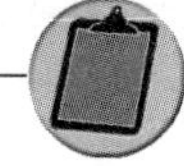

DEFINITION

Paroxysmal atrial tachycardia (PAT) is a group of arrhythmias that generally originate as reentrant rhythm from the AV node and are characterized by sudden onset and abrupt termination.

SYNONYMS

PAT
SVT
Supraventricular tachycardia

ICD-9CM CODES

427.0 Paroxysmal atrial tachycardia

PHYSICAL FINDINGS & CLINICAL PRESENTATION

- Patient is usually asymptomatic.
- Patient may be aware of "fast" heartbeat.
- Persistent tachycardia may precipitate CHF or hypotension during acute MI.

ETIOLOGY

- Preexcitation syndromes (Wolff-Parkinson-White [WPW] syndrome)
- Atrial septal defect
- Acute MI

DIAGNOSIS

WORKUP

ECG:

- Absolutely regular rhythm at rate of 150-220 bpm is present.
- P waves may or may not be seen (the presence of P waves depends on the relationship of atrial to ventricular depolarization).
- Wide QRS complex (>0.12 sec) with initial slurring (delta wave) during sinus rhythm and short PR (≤0.12 sec) is characteristic of WPW syndrome; this syndrome is a result of an accessory AV pathway (bundle of Kent) that preexcites the ventricular muscle earlier than would be expected if the impulse reached the ventricles by way of normal conduction system; arrhythmias associated with WPW are narrow-complex SVT, atrial fibrillation, and ventricular fibrillation; digoxin and verapamil use should be avoided because they can lead to arrhythmia acceleration through the accessory pathway. Radiofrequency catheter ablation of accessory pathways (performed in conjunction with diagnostic electrophysiology testing) is a safe and effective treatment of patients with WPW syndrome.

TREATMENT

NONPHARMACOLOGIC THERAPY

- Valsalva maneuver in the supine position is the most effective way to terminate SVT; carotid sinus massage (after excluding occlusive carotid disease) is also commonly used to elicit vagal efferent impulses.
- Synchronized DC shock is used if patient shows signs of cardiogenic shock, angina, or CHF.

ACUTE GENERAL Rx

- Adenosine (Adenocard), an endogenous nucleoside, is useful for treatment of paroxysmal SVT, particularly that associated with WPW; it is considered by many the first choice of therapy for treatment of almost all episodes of SVT unresponsive to vagal maneuvers; the dose is 6 mg given as a rapid IV bolus; tachycardia is usually terminated within a few seconds; if necessary, may repeat with 12 mg IV bolus. Contraindications are second- or third-degree AV block, sick sinus syndrome (SSS), atrial fibrillation, and ventricular tachycardia. Adenosine may cause bronchospasm in asthmatics. Patients receiving theophylline (a competitive antagonist of adenosine receptors) are usually refractory to treatment. Dipyridamole enhances the effect of adenosine; therefore patients receiving dipyridamole should be started at lower doses.
- Verapamil 5 to 10 mg IV is given over 5 min; if no effect, may repeat in 30 min.
  1. Verapamil should be used cautiously in patients with SVT associated with hypotension.
  2. Slow injection of calcium chloride (10 ml of a 10% solution given over 5 to 8 min before verapamil administration) decreases the hypotensive effect without compromising its antiarrhythmic effect.
- Repeat carotid massage after IV verapamil if SVT persists.
- Metoprolol (IV 5 mg/2 min up to 15 mg) or esmolol (500 μg/kg IV bolus, then 50 μg/kg/min) may be effective in the treatment of SVT.
- IV digitalization (0.75 to 1 mg slow IV loading) if other agents are not effective
  1. Repeat carotid massage 30 min later; if not successful, give additional 0.25 mg IV digoxin and repeat carotid sinus massage 1 hr later.
  2. Digoxin should be avoided in patients with WPW syndrome and narrow QRS tachycardia (increased risk of atrial fibrillation during AV reentrant tachycardia).

DISPOSITION

Most patients respond well with resolution of the paroxysmal atrial tachycardia with treatment (see "Acute General Rx").

REFERRAL

Radiofrequency ablation is the procedure of choice in patients with accessory pathways and recurrent symptomatic episodes.

PEARLS & CONSIDERATIONS

COMMENTS

Accessory pathways occur in 0.1% to 0.3% of the general population.

AUTHOR: **FRED F. FERRI, M.D.**

BASIC INFORMATION

DEFINITION

Paroxysmal cold hemoglobinuria is a rare disease characterized by episodic massive intravascular hemolysis after exposure to cold temperatures. The disease may occur in an idiopathic form in adults or, more commonly, after a respiratory illness in children.

SYNONYMS

PCH

ICD-9CM CODES
283.2 Hemoglobinuria caused by hemolysis from external causes

EPIDEMIOLOGY & DEMOGRAPHICS

- Accounts for up to 5% of adult cases of autoimmune hemolytic anemia
- Accounts for nearly 30% of childhood cases of autoimmune hemolytic anemia
- No race or sex predilection

PHYSICAL FINDINGS & CLINICAL PRESENTATION

- Occurs minutes to hours after exposure to cold.
- Associated with back, leg, and abdominal pain.
- Headaches, nausea, vomiting, and diarrhea common.
- Raynaud's phenomenon often present.
- Associated with cold urticaria.
- Transient splenomegaly and jaundice may occur.
- Symptoms and gross hemoglobinuria usually resolve after a few hours.

ETIOLOGY & PATHOGENESIS

- Donath-Landsteiner antibody (polyclonal IgG) binds to P antigen on RBCs when blood is exposed to cold temperatures. As blood warms to body temperature, complement-mediated hemolysis ensues.
- Has been seen in association with a variety of viral and bacterial illnesses including EBV, CMV, H. influenza, influenza A, varicella, syphilis, measles, mumps, and adenovirus.

DIAGNOSIS

DIFFERENTIAL DIAGNOSIS

- Cold agglutinin disease associated with hemoglobinuria

LABORATORY TESTS

- Clinical presentation of hemolysis after cold exposure.
- Elevated bilirubin and LDH.
- Abnormal RBC forms such as poikilocytosis, spherocytosis, and anisocytosis.
- Erythrophagocytosis by neutrophils and monocytes may be seen.
- D-L Ab detected by the Biphasic Donath-Landsteiner Test in which a patient's serum is incubated with donated RBCs at 4° C then warmed to 37° C. Lysis is observed in a positive test.

TREATMENT

- Avoidance of cold exposure.
- Testing and treatment for syphilis if present.
- Steroids generally are not found to be helpful.

PROGNOSIS

- Postinfectious varieties are self-limited.
- Adult idiopathic form is generally manageable by avoidance of environmental exposure.

SUGGESTED READINGS

Packman CH: Cryopathic hemolytic syndromes. In Beutler et al (eds): *Williams Hematology,* ed 6, New York, 2001, McGraw-Hill.

Thomas AT: Autoimmune hemolytic anemias. In Lee et al (eds): *Wintrobes' Clinical Hematology,* Philadelphia, 1999, Lippincott Williams & Wilkins.

AUTHOR: **MICHAEL MAHER, M.D.**

Paroxysmal Nocturnal Hemoglobinuria

BASIC INFORMATION

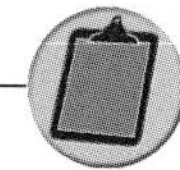

DEFINITION

Paroxysmal nocturnal hemoglobinuria (PNH) is a rare disease characterized by episodes of intravascular hemolysis and hemoglobinuria usually occurring at night. Thrombocytopenia, leukopenia, and recurrent venous thrombosis are also associated with PNH.

SYNONYMS

PNH

ICD-9CM CODES
283.2 Paroxysmal nocturnal hemoglobinuria

EPIDEMIOLOGY & DEMOGRAPHICS

- Affects patients of any age (reported spectrum 6 to 82 yr) but most common in patients aged 30 to 50 yr
- Affects both sexes (slight female predominance) and all races

PHYSICAL FINDINGS & CLINICAL PRESENTATION

Initial manifestations
- Anemia symptoms (35%)
- Hemoglobinuria (25%)
- Bleeding (20%)
- Aplastic anemia (15%)
- GI symptoms (10%)
- Hemolytic anemia (10%)
- Iron deficiency anemia (5%)
- Venous thrombosis (5%)
- Infections (5%)
- Neurologic symptoms

Hemoglobinuria
- Typically the first morning void reveals dark urine with progressive clearing during the day. The cause for the circadian rhythm is unknown.

Hemolysis
- In addition to the circadian hemolysis and resulting hemoglobinuria, episodes of hemolytic exacerbations can accompany infections, menstruation, transfusion, surgery, iron therapy, and vaccinations. Symptoms of severe hemolysis include chest, back, or abdominal pain, headache, fever, malaise, and fatigue.

Aplastic anemia
- Aplastic anemia may be the presenting manifestation of PNH (therefore PNH must be in the differential diagnosis of aplastic anemia) or may develop as a later complication of PNH.

Thrombosis
- Lower extremity DVT
- Subclavian thrombosis
- Portal or mesenteric vein thrombosis
- Hepatic vein thrombosis (Budd-Chiari syndrome)
- Cerebrovascular thromboses

Renal failure
- Acute renal failure associated with massive hemoglobinuria (acute tubular necrosis)
- Progressive renal failure associated with thrombosis within renal small veins

Dysphagia

Infections (associated with leukopenia or steroid treatment)

Physical findings include:
- Pallor (anemia)
- Jaundice (hemolysis)
- Splenomegaly
- Unilateral extremity swelling (DVT)
- Ascites (Budd-Chiari syndrome)

ETIOLOGY & PATHOGENESIS

- Complement-mediated hemolysis; the erythrocytes are abnormally sensitive to acidified serum.
- Patients have two populations of RBCs, some sensitive to hemolysis (PNH III cells) and others not (PNH I cells) in variable proportions (10% to 75% PNH III cells). About 20% PNH III are required for hemoglobinuria to be detectable.
- The RBC defects in PNH are in the membrane proteins as follows:
  Decay-accelerating factor deficiency
  Membrane inhibitor of reactive lysis deficiency
  C-8 binding protein deficiency
- These protein deficiencies are the result of an acquired mutation located in the X chromosome, which regulates glycosylphosphatidylinositol (GPI). GPI anchors the abovementioned proteins in the RBC membrane; GPI-deficient RBCs proliferate as an abnormal clone. Because women are affected least as frequently as men are, the mutation must be expressed as dominant gene. The mechanism whereby the mutant stem cells can dominate hematopoiesis in PNH is unknown.
- The pathophysiology of the relationship of PNH and aplastic anemia is unknown.

DIAGNOSIS

Clinical situations:
- Intravascular hemolysis
- Hemoglobinuria
- Pancytopenia associated with hemolysis
- Iron deficiency associated with hemolysis
- Recurrent venous thrombosis
- Recurrent episodes of abdominal pain, headache, or back pain associated with hemolysis

DIFFERENTIAL DIAGNOSIS

- See "Hemolytic Anemia" in Section I.
- See "Aplastic Anemia" in Section I.
- See "Anemia" algorithm in Section III.

LABORATORY TESTS

- CBC: anemia, leukopenia, thrombocytopenia
- Reticulocytosis
- RBC smear: spherocytes
- Negative Coombs' test
- Low leukocyte alkaline phosphatase
- Elevated LDH
- Low serum haptoglobin
- Low serum iron saturation, low ferritin
- Elevated urine hemoglobin
- Elevated urine urobilinogen
- Elevated urine hemosiderin
- Positive Ham test (acidified serum RBC lysis)
- Normoblastic hyperplasia on bone marrow aspirate or biopsy
- Identification of GPI-anchored protein deficiency on hematopoietic cells using monoclonal antibodies or flow cytometry
- Cytogenetic studies are not diagnostic

TREATMENT

- Androgenic steroids
- Prednisone (15 to 40 mg qod)
- Eculizumab, a humanized antibody that inhibits the activation of terminal complement components reduces intravascular hemolysis, hemoglobinuria, and need for transfusion in patients with PNH.
- Iron replacement
- Transfusions
- Treatment and prevention of thrombosis (heparin, coumarin)
- Avoidance of oral contraceptives
- Bone marrow transplantation

REFERRAL

To hematologist

PROGNOSIS

- 50% survival to 10 to 15 yr
- 25% survival to 25 yr
- If thrombosis at presentation, only 40% survival to 4 yr
- 1% incidence of leukemia
- 5% incidence of myelodysplastic syndrome

SUGGESTED READINGS

Hillmen P et al: Effect of eculizumab on hemolysis and transfusion requirements in patients with paroxysmal nocturial hemoglobinuria, *N Engl J Med* 350:6, 2004.

Parker CJ, Lee GR: Paroxysmal nocturnal hemoglobinuria. In Lee GR et al (eds): *Wintrobe's clinical hematology,* ed 10, Baltimore, 1999, Williams & Wilkins.

AUTHOR: **TOM J. WACHTEL, M.D.**

BASIC INFORMATION

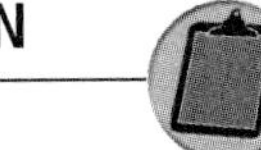

DEFINITION

Pediculosis is lice infestation. Humans can be infested with three kinds of lice: *Pediculus capitis* (head louse [Fig. 1-175]), *Pediculus corporis* (body louse), and *Phthirus pubis* (pubic, or crab, louse). Lice feed on human blood and deposit their eggs (nits) on the hair shafts (head lice and pubic lice) and along the seams of clothing (body lice). Nits generally hatch within 7 to 10 days. Lice are obligate human parasites and cannot survive away from their hosts for longer than 7 to 10 days.

SYNONYMS

Lice

ICD-9CM CODES
132.9 Pediculosis

EPIDEMIOLOGY & DEMOGRAPHICS

- There are 6 million to 12 million cases of head lice in the U.S. yearly.
- Lice infestation of the scalp is most common in children (girls > boys).
- Infestation of the eyelashes is most frequently seen in children and may indicate sexual abuse.
- The chance of acquiring pubic lice from one sexual exposure with an infested partner is >90% (most contagious STD known).
- Body lice is most common in conditions of poor hygiene.

PHYSICAL FINDINGS & CLINICAL PRESENTATION

- Pruritus with excoriation may be caused by hypersensitivity reaction, inflammation from saliva, and fecal material from the lice.
- Nits can be identified by examining hair shafts.
- The presence of nits on clothes is indicative of body lice.
- Lymphadenopathy may be present (cervical adenopathy with head lice, inguinal lymphadenopathy with pubic lice).
- Head lice is most frequently found in the back of the head and neck, behind the ears.
- Scratching can result in pustules and crusting.
- Pubic lice may affect the hair around the anus.

ETIOLOGY

Lice are transmitted by close personal contact or use of contaminated objects (e.g., combs, clothing, bed linen, hats).

DIAGNOSIS

DIFFERENTIAL DIAGNOSIS

- Seborrheic dermatitis
- Scabies
- Eczema
- Other: pilar casts, trichonodosis (knotted hair), monilethrix

WORKUP

Diagnosis is made by seeing the lice or their nits. Combing hair with a fine-toothed comb is recommended because visual inspection of the hair and scalp may miss more than 50% of infestations.

LABORATORY TESTS

Wood's light examination is useful to screen a large number of children: live nits fluoresce, empty nits have a gray fluorescence, nits with unborn louse reveal white fluorescence.

TREATMENT

NONPHARMACOLOGIC THERAPY

- Patients with body lice should discard infested clothes and improve their hygiene.
- Combing out nits is a widely recommended but unproven adjunctive therapy.
- Personal items such as combs and brushes should be soaked in hot water for 15 to 30 min.
- Close contacts and household members should also be examined for the presence of lice.

ACUTE GENERAL Rx

The following products are available for treatment of lice:

- Permethrin: available over the counter (1% permethrin [Nix]) or by prescription (5% permethrin [Elimite]); should be applied to the hair and scalp and rinsed out after 10 min. A repeat application is generally not necessary in patients with head lice.
- Lindane 1% (Kwell), pyrethrin S (Rid): available as shampoos or lotions; they are applied to the affected area and washed off in 5 min; treatment should be repeated in 7 to 10 days to destroy hatching nits.
- Malathion (Ovide) or organophosphate is effective in head lice. It is available by prescription. Use should be avoided in children ≤2 yr.
- Eyelash infestation can be treated with the application of petroleum jelly rubbed into the eyelashes three times a day for 5 to 7 days. The application of baby shampoo to the eyelashes and brows three or four times a day for 5 days is also effective. The use of fluorescein drops applied to the lids and eyelashes is also toxic to lice.
- In patients who have previously failed treatment or in whom resistance with 1% permethrin cream rinse occurs, a 10-day course of trimethoprim-sulfamethoxazole (TMP-SMX) 8 mg/kg/day of trimethoprim in divided doses is an effective treatment for head lice infestation.
- Ivermectin (Mectizan), an antiparasitic drug, given in a single oral dose of 200 μg/kg is effective for head lice resistant to other treatments (currently not FDA approved for pediculosis).

PEARLS & CONSIDERATIONS

COMMENTS

- Patients with pubic lice should notify their sexual contacts. Sex partners within the last month should be treated.
- Parents of patients should also be educated that head lice infestation (unlike body lice) does not indicate poor hygiene.

SUGGESTED READINGS

Flinders DC, DeSchweinitz P: Pediculosis and scabies, *Am Fam Physician* 69:341, 2004.

Meinking TL et al: An observer-blinded study of 1% permethrin crème rinse with and without adjunctive combing in patients with head lice, *J Pediatr* 141:665, 2002.

Roberts RJ: Head lice, *N Engl J Med* 346:1645, 2002.

AUTHOR: **FRED F. FERRI, M.D.**

FIGURE 1-175 ***Pediculus humanus* var. *capitis* (head louse).** (From Mandell GL [ed]: *Mandell, Douglas, and Bennett's principles and practice of infectious diseases,* ed 5, New York, 2000, Churchill Livingstone.)

BASIC INFORMATION

DEFINITION

Pedophilia is a sexual disorder that involves recurrent, intense, distressing sexual urges and/or fantasies involving prepubescent children. A person must be at least 16 yr of age and at least 5 yr older than the child affected. The behavior may range from looking, to fondling, masturbation, and various degrees of penetration and coercion.

SYNONYMS

Pedophilia erotica
Acts referred to as child sexual abuse or child molestation
One of the paraphilias

ICD-9CM CODES
302.2 Pedophilia

EPIDEMIOLOGY & DEMOGRAPHICS

PREVALENCE (IN U.S.): 12% of men and 17% of women report being sexually touched by an older person when they were children.

PREDOMINANT SEX:
- Majority of perpetrators are men: nearly 75% attracted to females exclusively; nearly 25% attracted to males exclusively; small minority attracted to both sexes
- Girls sexually abused 3 times more often than boys; children from the lowest-income families 18 times more likely to be sexually abused.

PREDOMINANT AGE: 1 of every 7 sexual assaults of juveniles occurs in children younger than 6 yr and one-third are younger than 12 yr.

PEAK INCIDENCE:
- Usually, onset in adolescence

GENETICS: No genetic factor has been identified.

PHYSICAL FINDINGS & CLINICAL PRESENTATION

- Often shy, passive, and with social and interpersonal difficulties
- Frequently, has experienced early abuse himself/herself
- Sexually excited by young children and adults with the build that resembles young children
- Do not all act on their sexual fantasies; may occasionally seek help before any sexual acts with children
- Some "belief" among those who actually molest children that their behavior is good for or welcomed by the child

ETIOLOGY

- Personal experience with early molestation may be important, but only a minority of molested children develop pedophilia.
- Influence of personality factors is cited by some experts (i.e., inadequate attachment style that is rooted in a dysfuncitonal family).
- Elevated plasma epinephrine and norepinephrine levels, and reduced cortisol responses to meta-chlorophenylpiperazine challenges have been identified in pedophilic cohorts.

DIAGNOSIS

DIFFERENTIAL DIAGNOSIS

- Psychosis: may present with unusual ideas or statements that may rarely be confused with pedophilia; but statements or behaviors of psychotic individuals are usually disorganized and relatively short lived.
- Incest: some is not based in pedophilia, but may instead reflect a dysfunctional family unit.
- Paraphilic sexual behavior in the setting of another condition such as mental retardation, brain injury, or drug intoxication.

WORKUP

- History is essential for diagnosis; however, most pedophiles are less than forthcoming even to direct questions by a physician.
- Children who have been sexually abused may display depression and aggressive behaviors, have an increased frequency of anxiety disorders, and have problems with age-appropriate sex roles and sexual functioning.
- Collateral information should be obtained from family members, suspected victims, or legal and social organizations; but even experienced interviewers may be unable to diagnose pedophilia consistently.

LABORATORY TESTS

- Hormone profile (total testosterone, free testosterone, luteinizing hormone, follicle-stimulating hormone, prolactin, and progesterone) is sometimes recommended.

IMAGING STUDIES

Useful only if pedophilic behavior is believed to be a consequence of CNS damage (e.g., head trauma or mental retardation), then a head CT scan or MRI may document extent of anatomic damage.

TREATMENT

NONPHARMACOLOGIC THERAPY

- Usually obtain treatment under legal coercion after child molestation charge.
- Behavioral approaches are centered on aversion conditioning in which an aversive stimulus is paired with the pedophilic fantasy; when outcome is measured by repeat child molestation charges, these methods are moderately successful.
- Outpatient group therapy sometimes combined with the administration of antiandrogenic medications.
- For incestuous adult-child relationships not based in pedophilia, intensive family systems investigation and therapy are needed.
- Pedophilia is considered a chronic disorder. Therefore, treatment should focus on stopping the behavior and achieving long-term behavioral change in the community.
- Any comorbid conditions, such as alcoholism and affective illness, also must be treated.

ACUTE GENERAL Rx & CHRONIC Rx

- Brief periods of inpatient hospitalizaiton may be required as a precaution during periods of heightened stress or risk.
- Chemical castration with antiandrogen compounds; although research into the optimal dosage and the efficacy of these compounds is ongoing, they are generally believed to be safe, effective, and reversible.
- Medroxyprogesterone acetate (Provera) can be administered PO (60 mg/day) or in a depot IM form (200 to 400 mg IM once weekly).
- Testosterone-lowering medications are Depo-Provera (medroxyprogesterone acetate) or Depo-Lupron (leuprolide acetate). Although these drugs suppress the intensity of libidinal drive, they generally allow erectile function.
- Some experts advocate the use of selective serotonin reuptake inhibitors to suppress sexual drive.

DISPOSITION

- Untreated, child molesters are highly likely to be repeat offenders.

REFERRAL

- Refer to specialty mental health for treatment.
- Physicians should be aware of reporting requirements in their jurisdiction.

SUGGESTED READINGS

Briken P, Hill A, Berner W: Pharmacotherapy of paraphilias with long-acting agonists of luteinizing hormone-releasing hormone: a systematic review, *J Clin Psychiatry* 64(8): 890, 2003.

Fagan PJ et al: Pedophilia, *JAMA* 288(19):2458, 2002.

Murray JB: Psychological profile of pedophiles and child molesters, *J Psychol* 134:211, 2000.

AUTHORS: **MITCHELL D. FELDMAN, M.D., M.PHIL.,** and **RIF S. EL-MALLAKH, M.D.**

BASIC INFORMATION

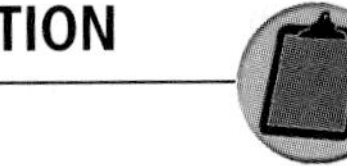

DEFINITION

Pelvic inflammatory disease (PID) is a spectrum of inflammatory disorders of the upper genital tract including a combination of any of the following:

- Endometritis, salpingitis, tuboovarian abscess, or pelvic peritonitis
- Resulting from an ascending lower genital tract infection
- Not related to obstetric or surgical intervention

SYNONYMS

Adnexitis
Pyosalpinx
Salpingitis
Tuboovarian abscess

ICD-9CM CODES
614.9 Unspecified inflammatory disease of female pelvic organs and tissue

EPIDEMIOLOGY & DEMOGRAPHICS

INCIDENCE/PREVALENCE:

- Estimated 600,000 to 1 million cases annually (U.S.)
- Diagnosed in 2% to 5% of women seen in STD clinics
- Most common cause of female infertility and ectopic pregnancy

RISK FACTORS:

- Adolescent sexually active in females <20 yr old (1:8)
- Previous episode of gonococcal PID
- Multiple sexual partners
- Vaginal douching
- Use of intrauterine device (threefold to fivefold increased risk of developing acute PID)

PHYSICAL FINDINGS & CLINICAL PRESENTATION

- Lower abdominal pain
- Abnormal vaginal discharge
- Abnormal uterine bleeding
- Dysuria
- Dyspareunia
- Nausea and vomiting (suggestive of peritonitis)
- Fever
- RUQ tenderness (perihepatitis): 5% of PID cases
- Cervical motion tenderness and adnexal tenderness
- Adnexal mass

ETIOLOGY

- *Chlamydia trachomatis*
- *Neisseria gonorrhoeae*
- Polymicrobial infection—*Bacteroides fragilis, Escherichia coli, Gardnerella vaginalis, Haemophilus influenzae, Mycoplasma hominis, U. urealyticum*
- *Mycobacterium tuberculosis* (an important cause in developing countries)
- Cytomegalovirus (CMV)

DIAGNOSIS

DIFFERENTIAL DIAGNOSIS

- Ectopic pregnancy
- Appendicitis
- Ruptured ovarian cyst
- Endometriosis
- Urinary tract infection (cystitis or pyelonephritis)
- Renal calculus
- Adnexal torsion
- Proctocolitis

WORKUP

DIAGNOSTIC CONSIDERATIONS:

- Clinical diagnosis is difficult and imprecise. A clinical algorithm for the evaluation of pelvic pain is described in Section III, "Pelvic Pain, Reproductive-Age Woman;" evaluation of vaginal discharge is described in Section III, "Vaginal Discharge."
- Clinical diagnosis of symptomatic PID has a positive predictive value of 65% to 90% when compared with laparoscopy as the standard.
- No single historical, physical, or laboratory finding is both sensitive and specific for the diagnosis of PID.

2002 CDC DIAGNOSTIC CRITERIA FOR PID:

- Empiric treatment is based on the presence of all of the following minimum criteria:
  1. Uterine tenderness
  2. Adnexal tenderness
  3. Cervical motion tenderness
- Additional criteria to increase the specificity of the diagnosis of PID in women with severe clinical signs:
  1. Oral temperature >38.3° C (101° F)
  2. Abnormal cervical or vaginal discharge
  3. Elevated ESR
  4. Elevated C-reactive protein
  5. Laboratory documentation of cervical infection with *N. gonorrhoeae* or *C. trachomatis*
- Definitive criteria for diagnosing PID, which are warranted in selected cases:
  1. Laparoscopic abnormalities consistent with PID
  2. Histopathologic evidence of endometritis on biopsy
  3. Transvaginal sonography or other imaging techniques showing thickened fluid-filled tubes with or without free pelvic fluid or tuboovarian complex

LABORATORY TESTS

- Leukocytosis
- Elevated acute phase reactants: ESR >15 mm/hr, C-reactive protein
- Gram stain of endocervical exudate: >30 PMNs per high-power field correlates with chlamydial or gonococcal infection
- Endocervical cultures for *N. gonorrhoeae* and *C. trachomatis*
- Fallopian tube aspirate or peritoneal exudate culture if laparoscopy performed
- hCG to rule out ectopic pregnancy

IMAGING STUDIES

- Transvaginal ultrasound to look for adnexal mass has sensitivity for PID of 81%, specificity 78%, accuracy 80%.
- MRI has sensitivity for PID of 95%, specificity 89%, accuracy 93%. It is useful not only for establishing the diagnosis of PID, but also for detecting other processes responsible for the symptoms. Disadvantages are its higher cost and unavailability in certain areas.

TREATMENT

NONPHARMACOLOGIC THERAPY

- Most patients are treated as outpatients.
- Criteria for hospitalization (2002 CDC) as follows:
  1. Surgical emergencies such as appendicitis cannot be excluded
  2. Tuboovarian abscess
  3. Pregnant patient
  4. Patient is immunodeficient
  5. Severe illness, nausea, or vomiting precluding outpatient management
  6. Patient unable to follow or tolerate outpatient regimens
  7. No clinical response to outpatient therapy

ACUTE GENERAL Rx

REGIMENS FOR TREATMENT OF PID RECOMMENDED BY THE CDC, 2002:

- Outpatient treatment: Regimen A:
  1. Ofloxacin 400 mg PO bid × 14 days or Levofloxacin 500 mg PO × 14 days plus metronidazole 500 mg PO bid × 14 days
- Outpatient treatment: Regimen B:
  1. Cefoxitin 2 g IM plus probenecid 1 g PO *or*
  2. Ceftriaxone 250 mg IM *or*
  3. Equivalent cephalosporin (ceftizoxime or cefotaxime) plus doxycycline 100 mg PO bid × 10 to 14 days
- Inpatient treatment: Regimen A:
  1. Cefoxitin 2 g IV q6h or cefotetan 2 g IV q12h plus doxycycline 100 mg IV or PO q12h
  2. Continuation of regimen for at least 24 hr after substantial clinical im-

provement, after which doxycycline 100 mg PO bid is continued for a total of 14 days

- Inpatient treatment: Regimen B:
  1. Clindamycin 900 mg IV q8h plus gentamicin loading dose IV or IM (2 mg/kg of body weight), followed by a maintenance dose (1.5 mg/kg) q8h
  2. Continuation of regimen for at least 24 hr after substantial clinical improvement, followed by doxycycline 100 mg PO bid or clindamycin 450 mg PO qid to complete a total of 14 days of therapy
- Alternative parental regimens:
  1. Ofloxacin 400 mg IV q12h or
  2. Levofloxacin 500 mg IV once daily with or without Metronidazole 500 mg IV q8h or
  3. Ampicillin/sulbactam 3 gm IV q6h plus doxycycline 100 mg PO or IV q12h

CHRONIC Rx

Hospitalized patients receiving IV therapy:

1. Significant clinical improvement is characterized by defervescence, decreased abdominal tenderness, and decreased uterine, adnexal, and cervical motion tenderness within 3 to 5 days.
2. If no clinical improvement occurs, further diagnostic workup is necessary, including possible surgical intervention.

DISPOSITION

- Long-term sequelae of PID: recurrent PID, chronic pelvic pain, ectopic pregnancy, infertility, Fitz-Hugh–Curtis syndrome (Fig. 1-176)
- Risk of tubal infertility related to episodes of PID: first episode, 8%; second episode, 20%; third episode, 40%
- Essential to evaluate and treat male sex partners

REFERRAL

If there is no clinical improvement with outpatient therapy observed within 72 hr, patient should be hospitalized and gynecology consult requested.

PEARLS & CONSIDERATIONS

COMMENTS

- Maintain a low threshold for the diagnosis of PID
- Patient education material is available from local and state health departments or from the American College of Obstetricians and Gynecologists.

SUGGESTED READINGS

Centers for Disease Control and Prevention: 2002 sexually transmitted diseases treatment guidelines, *MMWR Morb Mortal Wkly Rep* 51(RR-6), 2002.

Tukeva TA et al: MR imaging in pelvic inflammatory disease: comparison with laparoscopy and ultrasound, *Radiology* 210:209, 1999.

AUTHOR: **GEORGE T. DANAKAS, M.D.**

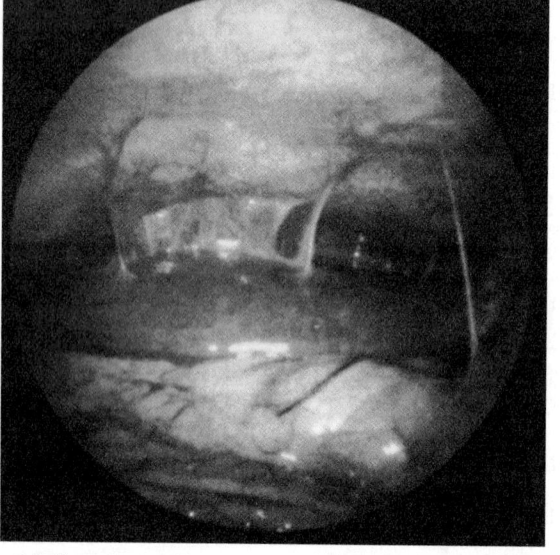

FIGURE 1-176 "Violin string" adhesions are visualized in this patient with Fitz-Hugh-Curtis syndrome. (From Copeland LJ: *Textbook of gynecology,* ed 2, Philadelphia, 2000, WB Saunders.)

BASIC INFORMATION

DEFINITION

- Pemphigus refers to a group of chronic, autoimmune diseases resulting in intraepidermal blister formation.
- Pemphigus has four subtypes:
  1. Pemphigus vulgaris (Fig. 1-177)
  2. Pemphigus vegetans
  3. Pemphigus foliaceus
  4. Pemphigus erythematosus
- Pemphigus vulgaris refers to an intraepidermal blistering skin disorder characterized by the formation of the flaccid blister.

SYNONYMS

Pemphigus

ICD-9CM CODES
694.4 Pemphigus

EPIDEMIOLOGY & DEMOGRAPHICS

- Incidence is 1/100,000
- More common in Ashkenazi Jews
- Typically occurs in the fourth and fifth decades of life
- Male = females
- Can occur in the young

PHYSICAL FINDINGS & CLINICAL PRESENTATION

- History
  1. Oral mucosa lesions typically occur first, followed by a generalized bullous eruption within a few months
  2. Lesions are fragile and rupture easily, leaving painful denuded lesions
  3. Usually not pruritic
- Physical findings
  1. Anatomic distribution
     a. Oral mucosa
     b. Can also involve the pharynx, larynx, vagina, penis, anus, and conjunctival mucosa
     c. Generalized cutaneous involvement
  2. Lesion configuration
     a. All stratified squamous epithelium can become involved.
  3. Lesion morphology
     a. Bullae
     b. Denuded crusting and erosion commonly occurs

ETIOLOGY

Pemphigus vulgaris, like all subtypes of pemphigus, is an autoimmune disease caused by autoantibodies binding to antigens within the epithelial layer of the skin.

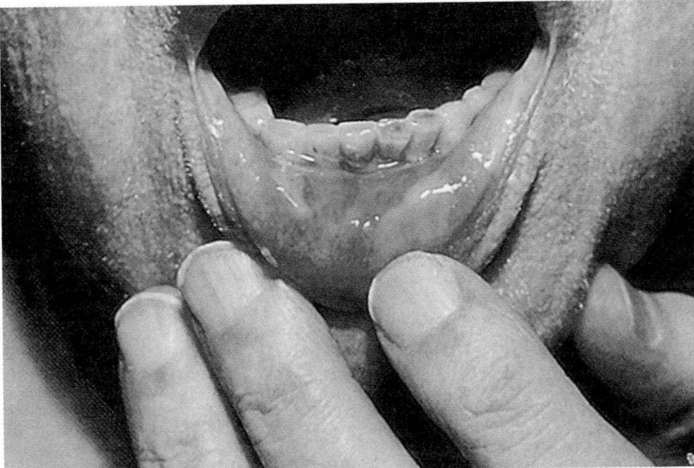

FIGURE 1-177 Pemphigus vulgaris with oral lesions and no intact bullae. (Courtesy Department of Dermatology, University of North Carolina at Chapel Hill. In Goldstein BG, Goldstein AO: *Practical dermatology,* ed 2, St Louis, 1997, Mosby.)

DIAGNOSIS

The diagnosis of pemphigus vulgaris should be suspected in patients with oral lesion and flaccid bullae on the skin.

DIFFERENTIAL DIAGNOSIS

- Bullous pemphigoid (see Table 1-38)
- Cicatricial pemphigoid
- Behçet's disease
- Erythema multiforme
- Systemic lupus erythematosus
- Aphthous stomatitis
- Dermatitis herpetiformis
- Drug eruptions

WORKUP

The workup for patients with suspected pemphigus vulgaris requires specific laboratory tests and special histology and immunofluorescence testing to establish the diagnosis.

LABORATORY TESTS

- Autoantibodies can be detected in the serum by indirect immunofluorescence assays.
- Skin biopsy reveals intraepidermal bulla formation, also called acantholysis (loss of cell adhesion between the epidermal cells).
- Direct and indirect immunofluorescence studies of the lesion show deposits of IgG and C3 in the epidermal layers of the skin.

IMAGING STUDIES

X-ray imaging is not useful in the diagnosis of pemphigus vulgaris.

TABLE 1-38 **Differentiation of Pemphigus Vulgaris and Bullous Pemphigoid**

Characteristics	Pemphigus Vulgaris	Bullous Pemphigoid
Age	≥50 years	≥60 years
Site	Oral mucosa, face, chest, groin	Flexural areas, groin, axilla, less often oral
Findings	Flaccid bullae, intraepidermal blisters, IgG autoantibodies	Intact bullae, subepidermal blisters, IgG and complement autoantibodies
Treatment	Prednisone 40-60 mg/day, immunosuppressant agents; often chronically steroid-dependent	Prednisone 1 mg/kg/day or higher initially; taper over months to years
Prognosis	>90% respond; steroid side effects significant	>90% respond; remissions and recurrences common

TREATMENT

NONPHARMACOLOGIC THERAPY

- Use mild soaps.
- Soak lesions with Burow's solution.
- Soft diet and viscous lidocaine can be used in patients with oral lesions.

ACUTE GENERAL Rx

- For mild cases, topical intralesional steroids using triamcinolone acetonide 5 to 10 mg/ml can be used for individual lesions.
- For more severe cases, systemic corticosteroids are indicated at high dosages:
  1. Prednisone 200 to 400 mg/day for 6 to 8 wk, tapered to 15 mg/day
  2. Alternative approaches include prednisone 80 to 120 mg PO qd increasing the dose rapidly by 50% every 7 days until no new lesions appear; then proceed with tapering over a 6-mo period

CHRONIC Rx

- Adjuvant therapy is tried in patients in an attempt to decrease the amount of steroids required.
  1. Azathioprine 100 to 150 mg qd given concurrently with prednisone
  2. Cyclophosphamide 1 to 3 mg/kg/day
  3. Dapsone 25 to 100 mg/day
  4. Nicotinamide 500 mg PO qd plus tetracycline 1.5 to 3 g/day
  5. Plasmapheresis

DISPOSITION

- Before the use of corticosteroids, approximately 75% of patients died of pemphigus.
- Combined corticosteroids and adjuvant therapy has decreased mortality rates to <10%.
- Pemphigus vulgaris patients usually die from sepsis or complications from therapy.

REFERRAL

A dermatology consult is recommended for any patient with pemphigus vulgaris.

PEARLS & CONSIDERATIONS

COMMENTS

- Pemphigus vulgaris, unlike bullous pemphigus, rarely occurs in the elderly population.
- It is important to diagnose pemphigus vulgaris early in its course.

SUGGESTED READINGS

Bickle K, Roark TR, Hsu S: Autoimmune bullous dermatoses: a review, *Am Fam Physician* 65(9):1861, 2002.

Brenner S, Sasson A, Sharon O: Pemphigus and infections, *Clin Dermatol* 20(2):114, 2002.

Stanley JR: Therapy of pemphigus vulgaris, Editorial, *Arch Dermatol* 135(1):76, 1999.

Toth GG, Jonkman MF: Therapy of pemphigus, *Clin Dermatol* 19(6):761, 2001.

AUTHOR: **PETER PETROPOULOS, M.D.**

BASIC INFORMATION

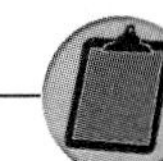

DEFINITION

Peptic ulcer disease (PUD) is an ulceration in the stomach or duodenum resulting from an imbalance between mucosal protective factors and various mucosal damaging mechanisms (see "Etiology").

SYNONYMS

PUD
Duodenal ulcer (DU)
Gastric ulcer (GU)

ICD-9CM CODES
536.8 Peptic ulcer disease
531.3 Peptic ulcer, stomach, acute
531.7 Peptic ulcer, stomach, chronic
532.3 Peptic ulcer, duodenum, acute
532.7 Peptic ulcer, duodenum, chronic

EPIDEMIOLOGY & DEMOGRAPHICS

- Incidence: 250,000 to 500,000 (200,000 to 400,000 DU; 50,000 to 100,000 GU) annually; duodenal ulcer:gastric ulcer ratio is 4:1.
- Anatomic location: >90% of DUs occur in the first portion of the duodenum; GU occurs most frequently in the lesser curvature near the incisura angularis.

PHYSICAL FINDINGS & CLINICAL PRESENTATION

- Physical examination is often unremarkable.
- Patient may have epigastric tenderness, tachycardia, pallor, hypotension (from acute or chronic blood loss), nausea and vomiting (if pyloric channel is obstructed), boardlike abdomen and rebound tenderness (if perforated), and hematemesis or melena (with a bleeding ulcer).

ETIOLOGY

Often multifactorial; the following are common mucosal damaging factors:

- *Helicobacter pylori* infection
- Medications (NSAIDs, glucocorticoids)
- Incompetent pylorus or LES
- Bile acids
- Impaired proximal duodenal bicarbonate secretion
- Decreased blood flow to gastric mucosa
- Acid secreted by parietal cells and pepsin secreted as pepsinogen by chief cells
- Cigarette smoking
- Alcohol

DIAGNOSIS

DIFFERENTIAL DIAGNOSIS

- GERD
- Cholelithiasis syndrome
- Pancreatitis
- Gastritis
- Nonulcer dyspepsia
- Neoplasm (gastric carcinoma, lymphoma, pancreatic carcinoma)
- Angina pectoris, MI, pericarditis
- Dissecting aneurysm
- Other: high small bowel obstruction, pneumonia, subphrenic abscess, early appendicitis

WORKUP

- Comprehensive history and physical examination to exclude other diagnoses. Diagnostic modalities include endoscopy or UGI series. Endoscopy is invasive and more expensive; however, it is preferred for the following reasons:
  1. Highest accuracy (approximately 90% to 95%)
  2. Useful to identify superficial or very small ulcerations
  3. Essential to diagnose gastric ulcers (1% to 4% of gastric ulcers diagnosed as benign by UGI series are eventually diagnosed as gastric carcinoma)
  4. Additional advantages over UGI series include:
     - Biopsy of suspicious looking ulcers
     - Electrocautery of bleeding ulcers
     - Measurement of gastric pH in suspected gastrinoma (e.g., patient with multiple ulcers)
     - Diagnosis of esophagitis, gastritis, duodenitis
     - Endoscopic biopsy for *H. pylori*

LABORATORY TESTS

- Routine laboratory evaluation is usually unremarkable.
- Anemia may be present in patients with significant GI bleeding.
- *H. pylori* testing via endoscopic biopsy, urea breath test, stool antigen test (*H. pylori* stool antigen), or specific antibody test is recommended:
  1. Serologic testing for antibodies to *H. pylori* is easy and inexpensive; however, the presence of antibodies demonstrates previous but not necessarily current infection. Antibodies to *H. pylori* can remain elevated for months to years after infection has cleared; therefore antibody levels must be interpreted in light of patient's symptoms and other test results (e.g., PUD seen on UGI series).
  2. The urea breath test documents active infection. The patient ingests a small amount of urea labeled with carbon 13 (^{13}C) or carbon 14. If urease is present (produced by the organism), the urea is hydrolyzed and the patient exhales labeled carbon dioxide that is then collected and measured. This test is more expensive and not as readily available. Use of proton pump inhibitors within 2 wk of the urea breath test may interfere with test results.
  3. Histologic evaluation of endoscopic biopsy samples is currently the gold standard for accurate diagnosis of *H. pylori* infection.
  4. Stool antigen test is as accurate as the urea breath test for follow-up evaluation of patients treated for *H. pylori*. This test detects the presence of infection by measuring the fecal excretion of *H. pylori* antigens. A negative result on the stool antigen test 8 wk after completion of therapy identifies patients in whom eradication of *H. pylori* was unsuccessful.
- Additional laboratory evaluation is indicated only in specific cases (e.g., amylase level in suspected pancreatitis, serum gastrin level in suspected Zollinger-Ellison [Z-E] syndrome).

IMAGING STUDIES

Conventional UGI barium studies identify approximately 70% to 80% of PUD; accuracy can be increased to approximately 90% by using double contrast.

TREATMENT

NONPHARMACOLOGIC THERAPY

- Stop cigarette smoking; cigarette smoking increases the risk of PUD, decreases the healing rate, and increases the frequency of recurrence.
- Avoid NSAIDs and alcohol.
- Special diets have been proved *unrelated* to ulcer development and healing; however, avoid foods that cause symptoms.

ACUTE GENERAL Rx

Eradication of *H. pylori*, when present, can be accomplished with various regimens:

1. Proton pump inhibitors (PPI) bid (e.g., omeprazole 20 mg bid or lansoprazole 30 mg bid) *plus* clarithromycin 500 mg bid *and* amoxicillin 1000 mg bid for 7 to 10 days
2. PPI bid *plus* amoxicillin 500 mg bid *plus* metronidazole 500 mg for 7 to 10 days

3. PPI bid *plus* clarithromycin 500 mg bid *and* metronidazole 500 mg bid for 7 days
4. Recent trials indicate that a 1-day quadruple therapy may be as effective as a 7-day triple therapy regimen. The 1-day quadruple therapy regimen consists of two tablets of 262 mg bismouth subsalicylate qid, one 500 mg metronidazole tablet qid, 2 g of amoxicillin suspension qid, and two capsules of 30 mg of lansoprazole.
5. Bismouth compound qid *plus* tetracycline 500 mg qid *and* metronidazole 500 mg qid for 14 days
6. A 5-day treatment with three antibiotics (amoxicillin 1 g bid, clarithromycin 250 mg bid, and metronidazole 400 mg bid) plus either lansoprazole 30 mg bid or ranitidine 300 mg bid is an efficacious cost-saving option for patients older than 55 yr with no prior history of PUD

PUD patients testing negative for *H. pylori* should be treated with antisecretory agents:

- Histamine-2 receptor antagonists (H_2RAs): cimetidine, ranitidine, famotidine, and nizatidine are all effective; they are usually given in split dose or at nighttime.
- Proton pump inhibitors (PPIs): can also induce rapid healing; they are usually given 30 min before meals.

Antacids and sucralfate are also effective agents for the treatment and prevention of PUD.

CHRONIC Rx

Maintenance therapy in duodenal ulcer patients is indicated in the following situations:

- Persistent smokers
- Recurrent ulcerations
- Chronic treatment with NSAIDs, glucocorticoids
- Elderly or debilitated patients
- Aggressive or complicated ulcer disease (e.g., perforation, hemorrhage)
- Asymptomatic bleeders

Misoprostol therapy (100 μg qid with food, increased to 200 μg qid if well tolerated) is useful for the prevention of NSAID-induced gastric ulcers in all patients on long-term NSAID therapy; it is contraindicated in women of childbearing age because of its abortifacient properties. Proton pump inhibitors are also effective at healing ulcers and maintaining remission in patients on long-term NSAIDs.

DISPOSITION

- The recurrence rate for untreated PUD is approximately 60% (>70% in smokers). Treatment decreases the recurrence rate by nearly 30%.
- Patients with recurrent ulcers should be retreated for an additional 8 wk and then placed on maintenance therapy with H_2RAs, PPIs, sucralfate, or antacids.
- An ulcer is considered refractory to treatment if healing is not evident after 8 wk for duodenal ulcers and 12 wk for gastric ulcers. In these patients maximum acid inhibition (e.g., Esomeprazole 40 mg BID) is preferred over continued therapy with standard antiulcer therapy.
- Eradication of *H. pylori* (when present) is indicated in all patients. A negative stool antigen test for *H. pylori* 6 weeks after treatment accurately confirms cure of *H. pylori* infection with reasonable sensitivity in initially seropositive healthy subjects.
- Screening for Zollinger-Ellison (Z-E) syndrome should also be considered in patients with multiple recurrent ulcers; in patients with Z-E, the serum gastrin level is >1000 pg/ml and the basal acid output is usually >15 mEq/hr.
- Surgery for refractory ulcers is now only rarely performed; it consists of highly selective vagotomy for duodenal ulcers or ulcer removal with antrectomy or hemigastrectomy without vagotomy for gastric ulcers.

REFERRAL

- GI referral for patients requiring endoscopy
- Surgical referral for patients with nonhealing ulcers despite appropriate medical therapy

PEARLS & CONSIDERATIONS

COMMENTS

- Patients with gastric ulcers should have repeat endoscopy after 4 to 6 wk of therapy to document healing and test exfoliative cytology for gastric carcinoma.
- After endoscopic treatment of bleeding peptic ulcers, bleeding recurs in up to 20% of patients. PPI administration intravenously by continuous infusion substantially reduces the risk of recurrent bleeding.

SUGGESTED READINGS

Graham DY et al: Ulcer prevention in long-term users of nonsteroidal anti-inflammatory drugs, *Arch Intern Med* 162:169, 2002.

Lai KC et al: Lansoprazole for the prevention of recurrences of ulcer complications from long-term low-dose aspirin use, *N Engl J Med* 346:2033, 2002.

Lara LF et al: One day quadruple therapy compared with 7-day triple therapy for helicobacter pylori infection, *Arch Intern Med* 163:2079, 2003.

AUTHOR: **FRED F. FERRI, M.D.**

BASIC INFORMATION

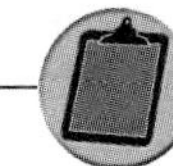

DEFINITION

Pericarditis is the inflammation (or infiltration) of the pericardium associated with a wide variety of causes (see "Etiology").

ICD-9CM CODES
420.91 Pericarditis

EPIDEMIOLOGY & DEMOGRAPHICS

- The incidence of acute pericarditis is 2% to 6%.
- Increased incidence in males and in adults compared with children.
- Most common cause (>40%) of constrictive pericarditis is idiopathic.
- The use of thrombolytic agents has greatly reduced the incidence of both early postinfarction pericarditis and Dressler's syndrome.

PHYSICAL FINDINGS & CLINICAL PRESENTATION

- Severe constant pain that localizes over the anterior chest and may radiate to arms and back; it can be differentiated from myocardial ischemia, because the pain intensifies with inspiration and is relieved by sitting up and leaning forward (the pain of myocardial ischemia is not pleuritic).
- Pericardial friction rub is best heard with patient upright and leaning forward and by pressing the stethoscope firmly against the chest; it consists of three short, scratchy sounds:
  1. Systolic component
  2. Diastolic component
  3. Late diastolic component (associated with atrial contraction)
- Cardiac tamponade may be occurring if the following are observed:
  1. Tachycardia
  2. Low blood pressure and pulse pressure
  3. Distended neck veins
  4. Paradoxical pulse

ETIOLOGY

- Idiopathic (possibly postviral)
- Infectious (viral, bacterial, tuberculous, fungal, amebic, toxoplasmosis)
- Collagen-vascular disease (SLE, rheumatoid arthritis, scleroderma, vasculitis, dermatomyositis)
- Drug-induced lupus syndrome (procainamide, hydralazine, phenytoin, isoniazid, rifampin, doxorubicin, mesalamine)
- Acute MI
- Trauma or posttraumatic
- After MI (Dressler's syndrome)
- After pericardiotomy
- After mediastinal radiation (e.g., patients with Hodgkin's disease)
- Uremia
- Sarcoidosis
- Neoplasm (primary or metastatic)
- Leakage of aortic aneurysm in pericardial sac
- Familial Mediterranean fever
- Rheumatic fever
- Leukemic infiltration
- Other: anticoagulants, amyloidosis, ITP

DIAGNOSIS

DIFFERENTIAL DIAGNOSIS

- Angina pectoris
- Pulmonary infarction
- Dissecting aneurysm
- GI abnormalities (e.g., hiatal hernia, esophageal rupture)
- Pneumothorax
- Hepatitis
- Cholecystitis
- Pneumonia with pleurisy

WORKUP

ECG, laboratory tests, and echocardiogram

LABORATORY TESTS

The following tests may be useful in absence of an obvious cause:

- CBC with differential
- Viral titers (acute and convalescent)
- ESR (not specific but may be of value in following the course of the disease and the response to therapy)
- ANA, rheumatoid factor
- PPD, ASLO titers
- BUN, creatinine
- Blood cultures
- Cardiac isoenzymes (usually normal, but mild elevations of CK-MB may occur because of associated epicarditis)

IMAGING STUDIES

- Echocardiogram to detect and determine amount of pericardial effusion; absence of effusion does not rule out the diagnosis of pericarditis. Divergence of right and left ventricular systolic pressures is present in cardiac tamponade and constrictive pericarditis.
- ECG: varies with the evolutionary stage of pericarditis
  1. Acute phase: diffuse ST-segment elevations (particularly evident in the precordial leads), which can be distinguished from acute MI by:
     a. Absence of reciprocal ST-segment depression in oppositely oriented leads (reciprocal ST-segment depression may be seen in aV_R and VI)
     b. Elevated ST segments concave upward
     c. Absence of Q waves
  2. Intermediate phase: return of ST segment to baseline, and T wave inversion in leads previously showing ST-segment elevation (Fig. 1-178)
  3. Late phase: resolution of the T wave changes
- Chest radiography
  1. Cardiac silhouette appears enlarged if more than 250 ml of fluid has accumulated
  2. Calcifications around the heart may be seen with constrictive pericarditis

TREATMENT

NONPHARMACOLOGIC THERAPY

- Limitation of activity until the pain abates
- Patient education regarding potential complications (e.g., cardiac tamponade, constrictive pericarditis)

ACUTE GENERAL Rx

- Antiinflammatory therapy (NSAIDs, [e.g., naproxen 500 mg bid, indomethacin 25 to 50 mg tid])
- Prednisone 30 mg bid for severe forms of acute pericarditis (before use of prednisone, tuberculous pericarditis must be excluded)
- Colchicine 0.6 mg bid may be used as an alternative in patients intolerant to NSAIDs and corticosteroids
- Consider ventricular rate control with verapamil or diltiazem because of the propensity for atrial fibrillation in these patients
- Close observation of patients for signs of cardiac tamponade
- Avoidance of anticoagulants (increased risk of hemopericardium)

TREATMENT OF UNDERLYING CAUSE:

1. Bacterial pericarditis
   a. Commonly caused by streptococci, meningococci, staphylococci, *Haemophilus*, gram-negative bacteria, anaerobic bacteria
   b. Therapy: systemic antibiotics and surgical drainage of pericardium
2. Fungal pericarditis
   a. Caused by histoplasmosis, coccidioidomycosis, candidiasis, blastomycosis, or aspergillosis
   b. Therapy: IV amphotericin B and drainage of pericardial space (if necessary)
3. Tuberculous endocarditis
   a. Therapy: antituberculous drugs for a minimum of 9 mo; concomitant corticosteroid therapy early in treatment may decrease inflammatory response and improve prognosis.
   b. Pericardiectomy may be necessary 2 to 4 wk after antituberculous drugs have been started.

4. Collagen vascular disease and idiopathic: NSAIDs, prednisone
5. Uremic: dialysis

POTENTIAL COMPLICATIONS FROM PERICARDITIS:

1. Pericardial effusion: the time required for pericardial effusion to develop is of critical importance; if the rate of accumulation is slow, the pericardium can gradually stretch and accommodate a large effusion (up to 1000 ml), whereas rapid accumulation can cause tamponade with as little as 200 ml of fluid.
2. Chronic constrictive pericarditis:
   a. Physical examination reveals jugular venous distention, Kussmaul's sign (increase in jugular venous distention during inspiration as a result of increased venous pulse), pericardial knock (early diastolic filling sound heard 0.06 to 0.1 sec after S_2), clear lungs, tender hepatomegaly, pedal edema, ascites
   b. Chest x-ray: clear lung fields, normal or slightly enlarged heart, pericardial calcification
   c. ECG: low-voltage QRS complex
   d. Echocardiography: may show pericardial thickening or may be normal
   e. Cardiac catheterization: M or W contour of the central venous pattern caused by both systolic (x) and diastolic (y) dips (this differs from cardiac tamponade, which does not display a prominent diastolic descent; in chronic constrictive pericarditis, there is also increased right ventricular and pulmonary arterial pressures)
   f. Therapy: surgical stripping or removal of both layers of the constricting pericardium
3. Cardiac tamponade:
   a. Signs and symptoms: dyspnea, orthopnea, interscapular pain.
   b. Physical examination: distended neck veins, distant heart sounds, decreased apical impulse, diaphoresis, tachypnea, tachycardia, Ewart's sign (an area of dullness at the angle of the left scapula caused by compression of the lungs by the pericardial effusion), pulsus paradoxus (decrease in systolic blood pressure >10 mm Hg during inspiration), hypotension, narrowed pulse pressure.
   c. Chest x-ray: cardiomegaly (water bottle configuration of the cardiac silhouette may be seen) with clear lungs; the chest x-ray film may be normal when acute tamponade occurs rapidly in the absence of prior pericardial effusion.
   d. ECG reveals decreased amplitude of the QRS complex, variation of the R wave amplitude from beat to beat (electrical alternans). This results from the heart's oscillating in the pericardial sac from beat to beat and frequently occurs with neoplastic effusions.
   e. Echocardiography: detects effusions as small as 30 ml; a paradoxical wall motion may also be seen.
   f. Cardiac catheterization: equalization of pressures within chambers of the heart, elevation of right atrial pressure with a prominent x but no significant y descent.
   g. MRI can also be used to diagnose pericardial effusions.
   h. Therapy for pericardial tamponade consists of immediate pericardiocentesis preferably by needle paracentesis with the use of echocardiography, fluoroscopy, or CT; in patients with recurrent effusions (e.g., neoplasms), placement of a percutaneous drainage catheter or pericardial window draining in the pleural cavity may be necessary. Aspirated fluid should be sent for analysis (protein, LDH, cytology, CBC, Gram stain, AFB stain) and cultures for AFB, fungi, and bacterial C&S.

DISPOSITION

- Complete resolution of pain and other signs and symptoms during the initial 3 wk of therapy
- Recurrence in 10% to 15% of patients within the initial 12 mo
- Recurrent pericarditis in 28% of patients
- Relapsing acute pericarditis and idiopathic chronic large pericardial effusion without tamponade may respond to treatment with colchicine
- Recurrence of large effusion after pericardiocentesis is common in patients with idiopathic chronic pericardial effusion. Pericardiectomy should be considered in these patients

SUGGESTED READINGS

Goyle K, Walling A: Diagnosing pericarditis, *Am Fam Physician* 66:1695, 2002.

Spodick DH: Acute cardiac tamponade, *N Engl J Med* 349:7, 2003.

AUTHOR: **FRED F. FERRI, M.D.**

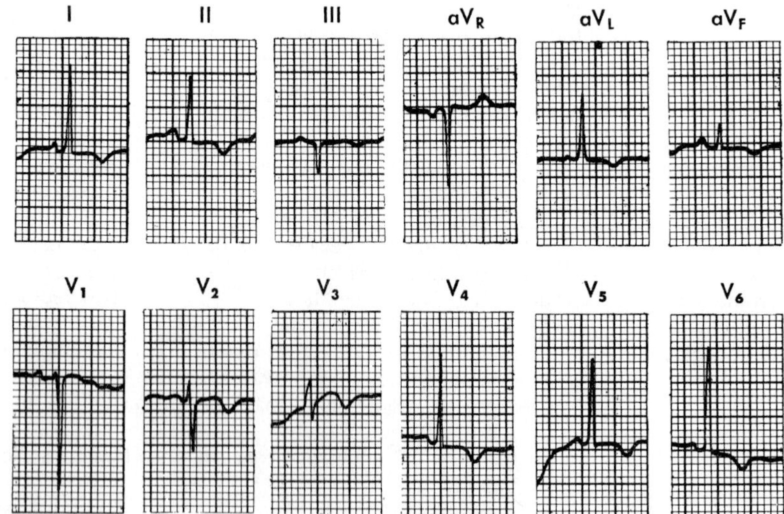

FIGURE 1-178 Notice the diffuse T wave inversions in leads I, II, III, aV_L, aV_F, and V_2 to V_6. (From Goldberg AL [ed]: *Clinical electrocardiography,* ed 5, St Louis, 1994, Mosby.)

BASIC INFORMATION

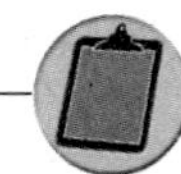

DEFINITION

Peripheral arterial disease (PAD) usually refers to atherosclerotic obstruction of the arteries to the lower extremity.

ICD-9CM CODES
443.9 Peripheral vascular disease

EPIDEMIOLOGY & DEMOGRAPHICS

- Age-adjusted prevalence of PAD is approximately 12%.
- PAD affects men and women equally.
- An estimated 27 million people in Europe and North America (or 16% of the population 55 yr of age and older) have PAD.
- African Americans and Hispanics with diabetes have a higher prevalence of PAD than whites.
- PAD is a marker for systemic vascular disease.
- Patients with newly diagnosed PAD are 6 times more likely to die within the next 10 yr when compared with patients without PAD.
- Risk factors associated with PAD are similar to coronary artery disease, including tobacco, diabetes, hyperlipidemia, hypertension, and advanced age.
- Smoking is the major determinant of disease progression.
- Other potential risk factors include elevated levels of C-reactive protein, fibrinogen, homocysteine, apolipoprotein (a), and plasma viscocity.
- An inverse relationship has been suggested between PAD and alcohol consumption.

PHYSICAL FINDINGS & CLINICAL PRESENTATION

- Nearly 50% of the patients with PAD experience no symptoms, making PAD an underdiagnosed and undertreated condition
- Approximately one third of patients with PAD present with intermittent claudication described as an aching or cramping leg pain brought on by exertion and relieved with rest that can progress with time; however, relying on the classic history of claudication alone will miss 85%-90% of patients with PAD
- Pain at rest occurring commonly at night when the patient is supine
- Diminished pulses
- Bruits heard over the distal aorta, iliac, or femoral arteries
- Rubor with prolonged capillary refill on dependency
- Cool skin temperature
- Trophic changes of hair loss and muscle atrophy
- Nonhealing ulcers, necrotic tissue, and gangrene possible

ETIOLOGY

The primary cause of peripheral arterial disease is atherosclerosis: atherosclerotic lesions of the arteries to the lower extremities subsequently leading to stenosis of peripheral vessels and inability to supply oxygenated blood to working limb muscles.

DIAGNOSIS

DIFFERENTIAL DIAGNOSIS

- Spinal stenosis
- Degenerative joint disease of the lumbar spine and hips
- Muscle cramps
- Compartment syndrome

WORKUP

- The initial workup in any patient suspected of having PAD includes measuring the ankle-brachial index (ABI). The ABI is calculated by dividing the highest ankle systolic pressure using either the dorsalis pedis or posterior tibial artery by the highest systolic pressure from either arm.
- A diagnosis of PAD is based on the presence of limb symptoms or an ABI
- The severity of PAD is based on the ABI at rest and during treadmill exercise (1 to 2 mph, 5 min, or symptom-limited) and is classified as follows:
  1. Mild: ABI at rest 0.71 to 0.90 or ABI during exercise >0.50
  2. Moderate: ABI at rest 0.41 to 0.70 or ABI during exercise >0.20
  3. Severe: ABI at rest <0.40 or ABI during exercise <0.20

LABORATORY TESTS

- Lipid profile
- Blood glucose
- HgbA1c levels in diabetic patients
- Homocysteine
- Fibrinogen

IMAGING STUDIES

- Duplex ultrasound can be used to locate the occluded areas and assess the patency of the distal arterial system or prior vein grafts.
- Rest or exercise pulse volume recordings. Pulse volume recordings measures volume of limb flow per pulse in different segments of the limb (e.g., thigh, calf, ankle, metatarsal, and toes). It helps to localize the site of the stenosis since the contour of the pulse wave changes distal to the occlusion.
- MRA can be used as a noninvasive approach to visualize the aorta and peripheral lower extremity arteries. A major advantage of MRA is that it does not require contrast agents.
- Angiography remains the gold standard for visualizing the arterial anatomy before revascularization.

TREATMENT

NONPHARMACOLOGIC THERAPY

- PAD patients with no prior history of a cardiac event are to be considered as a cardiovascular "equivalent" with risks of future cardiovascular events similar to patients with prior MIs
- Diet counseling (e.g., salt restriction in hypertension, ADA calorie diets in diabetics)
- Exercise training walking 30 to 60 min/day at about 2 mi/hr every day improves exercise capacity, walking distance, and quality of life
- Aggressive management of risk factors for PAD including:
  1. Tobacco counseling and smoke cessation programs are indispensable in decreasing the progression of disease as well as reducing the mortality rate from cardiovascular events in patients with PAD.
  2. Management of hypertension.
  3. Tight glycemic control (A1C <7%) in diabetic patients with PAD results in prevention of microvascular complications.
  4. Control of dyslipidemia reduces severity of claudication symptoms.

ACUTE GENERAL THERAPY

Most patients with PAD respond to conservative management mentioned previously. If this fails, medicines can be tried (see "Chronic Rx"). Surgical reconstitution has its specific indications reserved for patient with impending limb loss (see "Chronic Rx").

CHRONIC Rx

- Aspirin 81 mg to 325 mg daily is recommended for secondary disease prevention in patients with cardiovascular disease.
- Clopidogrel 75 mg daily also provides protection from cardiovascular and cerebrovascular events associated with PAD.
- Pentoxyphylline (Trental, Pentoxil) 400 mg tid may provide a small benefit in walking distance when compared with placebo.

- Cilostazol (Pletal) 100 mg bid has been shown to significantly increase the distance patients with claudication can walk when compared with placebo, but should not be given to patients with congestive heart failure and an ejection fraction <40.
- Surgical reconstruction is indicated in patients with refractory rest pain, limb ischemia, nonhealing ulcers, or gangrene, and in a select group of patients with functional disability. Common surgical procedures:
  1. Aortoiliofemoral reconstruction
  2. Infrainguinal bypass (e.g., femoropopliteal, femorotibial)
  3. Extraanatomic bypass (e.g., axillofemoral or femorofemoral bypass)
- Angioplasty is used on short, discrete stenotic lesions in the iliac or femoropopliteal artery.

DISPOSITION

Risk factor modification with aggressive pharmacotherapy in the treatment of hyperlipidemia, diabetes, hypertension, and smoking is essential in the prevention of progression, limb ischemia, and cardiovascular events in patients with PAD.

REFERRAL

Consultation with a vascular surgeon is recommended in patients with PAD and rest pain, functional disability from pain, ABI less than 0.50 at rest, any signs of limb ischemia, or gangrene.

PEARLS & CONSIDERATIONS

COMMENTS

- Asymptomatic PAD, similar to symptomatic PAD, is associated with an increased risk of atherothrombotic events (e.g., MI and CVA).
- Although the prevalence of PAD in Europe and North America is estimated at approximately 27 million people, PAD remains underdiagnosed and undertreated.

When PAD limits a patient's ability to walk and exercise, percutaneous revascularization can be considered. Data reveal excellent outcomes with angioplasty and stenting. Outcomes will likely be better as peripheral interventional technology and skills improve.

SUGGESTED READINGS

American Diabetes Association: peripheral arterial disease in people with diabetes, *Diabetes Care* 26:3333, 2003.

Belch JJ et al: Critical issues in peripheral arterial disease detection and management, *Arch Intern Med* 163;884, 2003

Burns P, Gaugh S, Bradbury AW: Management of peripheral arterial disease in primary care, *British Medical Journal* 326:584, 2003.

Hiatt WR: Medical treatment of peripheral arterial disease and claudication, *N Engl J Med* 344:21, 2001.

Hirsch AT et al: Peripheral arterial disease detection, awareness, and treatment in primary care, *JAMA* 286:ll, 2001.

Lesho E et al: Management of peripheral arterial disease, *Am Fam Physician* 69:525, 2004.

Mukheijee D, Yadav JS: Update on peripheral vascular diseases: from smoking cessation to stenting, *Cleve Clinic J Med* 68:8, 2001.

AUTHORS: **PRANAV M. PATEL, M.D.,** and **WEN-CHIH WU, M.D.**

BASIC INFORMATION

DEFINITION

Peritonitis refers to the acute onset of severe abdominal pain secondary to peritoneal inflammation.

Secondary peritonitis is a localized (abscess) or diffuse peritonitis originating from a defect in abdominal viscus.

SYNONYMS

Acute abdomen
Surgical abdomen

ICD-9CM CODES
567.2 Peritonitis

EPIDEMIOLOGY & DEMOGRAPHICS

Common presentation as a result of diverse etiologies; for example, 5% to 10% of the population have acute appendicitis at some point in their life.

PHYSICAL FINDINGS

- Acute abdominal pain
- Abdominal distention and ascites
- Abdominal rigidity, rebound, and guarding
- Fever, chills
- Exacerbation with movement
- Anorexia, nausea, and vomiting
- Constipation
- Decreased bowel sounds
- Hypotension and tachycardia
- Tachypnea, dyspnea

ETIOLOGY

- Microbiology: most common is gram-negative bacteria (*E. coli, enterobacter, klebsiella, proteus*), gram-positive bacteria (*enterococci, streptococci, staphylococci*), anerobic bacteria (*bacteroides, clostridium*), and fungi
- Acute perforation peritonitis: gastrointestinal perforation, intestinal ischemia, pelvic peritonitis and other forms
- Postoperative peritonitis: anastomotic leak, accidental perforation, and devascularization
- Posttraumatic peritonitis: after blunt or penetrating abdominal trauma

DIAGNOSIS

DIFFERENTIAL DIAGNOSIS

- Postoperative: abscess, sepsis, bowel obstruction, injury to internal organs
- Gastrointestinal: perforated viscus, appendicitis, IBD, infectious colitis, diverticulitis, acute cholecystitis, peptic ulcer perforation, pancreatitis, bowel obstruction
- Gynecologic: ruptured ectopic pregnancy, PID, ruptured hemorrhagic ovarian cyst, ovarian torsion, degenerating leiomyoma
- Urologic: nephrolithiasis, interstitial cystitis
- Miscellaneous: abdominal trauma, penetrating wounds, infections secondary to intraperitoneal dialysis

WORKUP

- Acute peritonitis is mainly a clinical diagnosis based on patient history and physical examination.
- Laboratory and imaging studies (see "Laboratory Tests") assist in determining the need for and type of intervention.
- If patient is hemodynamically unstable, immediate diagnostic laparotomy should be performed in lieu of adjuvant diagnostic studies.

LABORATORY TESTS

- CBC: leukocytosis, left shift, anemia
- SMA7: electrolyte imbalances, kidney dysfunction
- LFT: ascites secondary to liver disease, cholelithiasis
- Amylase: pancreatitis
- Blood cultures: bacteremia, sepsis
- Peritoneal cultures: infectious etiology
- Blood gas: respiratory vs. metabolic acidosis
- Ascitic fluid analysis: exudate vs. transudate
- Urinalysis and culture: urinary tract infection
- Cervical cultures for gonorrhea and *Chlamydia*
- Urine/serum hCG

IMAGING STUDIES

- Abdominal series: free air secondary to perforation, small or large bowel dilation secondary to obstruction, identification of fecalith
- Chest x-ray examination: elevated diaphragm, pneumonia
- Pelvic/abdominal ultrasound: abscess formation, abdominal mass, intrauterine vs. ectopic pregnancy, identify free fluid suggestive of hemorrhage or ascites
- CT: mass, ascites

TREATMENT

NONPHARMACOLOGIC THERAPY

- IV hydration to correct dehydration, hypovolemia
- Blood transfusion to correct anemia secondary to hemorrhage
- Nasogastric decompression, especially if obstruction is present
- Oxygen: intubation if necessary
- Bed rest

ACUTE GENERAL Rx

- Surgery to correct underlying pathology, such as controlling hemorrhage, correct perforation, drain abscess, and so forth.
- Broad-spectrum antibiotics:
  1. Single agent: ceftriaxone 1 to 2 g IV q24h, cefotaxime 1 to 2 g IV q4-6h
  2. Multiple agents:
     a. Ampicillin 2 g IV q4-6h; gentamicin 1.5 mg/kg/day; clindamycin 600 to 900 mg IV q8h
     b. Ampicillin 2 g IV q4-6h; gentamicin 1.5 mg/kg/day; metronidazole 500 mg IV q6-8h
- Pain control: morphine or meperidine as needed (hold until diagnosis confirmed)

DISPOSITION

Dependent on etiology of peritonitis, age of patient, coexisting medical disease, and duration of process before presentation

REFERRAL

Surgical consultation is required in all cases of acute peritonitis.

SUGGESTED READINGS

Bosscha K, van Vroonhover TJ, van der Werken C: Surgical management of severe secondary peritonitis, *Br J Surg* 86(11):1371, 1999.

Marshall JC, Innes M: Intensive care management of intra-abdominal infection, *Crit Care Med* 31(8):2228, 2003.

Wittmann DH, Schein M, Condon RE: Management of secondary peritonitis, *Ann Surg* 224(1):10, 1996.

AUTHOR: **ARUNDATHI G. PRASAD, M.D.**

Peritonitis, Spontaneous Bacterial

BASIC INFORMATION

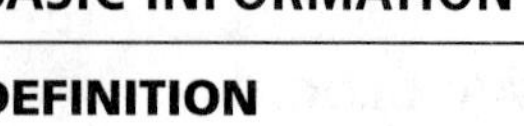

DEFINITION

Spontaneous bacterial peritonitis (SBP) is an inflammatory reaction of the peritoneum secondary to the presence of bacteria or other microorganisms. More specifically, SBP is defined as an ascitic fluid infection without an evident intraabdominal surgically treatable source occurring primarily in patients with advanced cirrhosis of the liver.

SYNONYMS

Primary peritonitis
SBP

ICD-9CM CODES
567.2 Peritonitis

EPIDEMIOLOGY & DEMOGRAPHICS

PREDOMINANT SEX: Male > female

PHYSICAL FINDINGS & CLINICAL PRESENTATION

- Acute fever with accompanying abdominal pain/ascites, nausea, vomiting, diarrhea
- In cirrhotic patients, presentation may be subtle when low-grade temperature (100° F) with or without abdominal abnormalities
- In patients with ascites, a heightened degree of awareness is necessary for detection
- Jaundice and encephalopathy
- Deterioration of mental status and/or renal function

ETIOLOGY

- *Escherichia coli*
- *Klebsiella pneumoniae*
- *Streptococcus pneumoniae*
- *Streptococcus* spp., including *Enterococcus*
- *Staphylococcus aureus*
- Anaerobic pathogens: *Bacteroides, Clostridium* organisms
- Other: fungal, mycobacterial, viral

DIAGNOSIS

The diagnosis of SBP is established by a positive ascitic fluid bacterial culture and an elevated ascitic fluid absolute polymorphonuclear leukocyte (PMN) count (> or = 250 cells/mm^3).

DIFFERENTIAL DIAGNOSIS

- Appendicitis (in children)
- Perforated peptic ulcer
- Secondary peritonitis
- Peritoneal abscess
- Splenic, hepatic, or pancreatic abscess
- Cholecystitis
- Cholangitis

WORKUP

Paracentesis and ascitic fluid analysis (see "Laboratory Tests") will confirm diagnosis.

LABORATORY TESTS

Ascitic fluid analysis reveals the following:

- Polymorphonuclear (PMN) cell count: >250/mm^3
- Presence of bacteria on Gram stain
- pH: <7.31
- Lactic acid: >32/dl
- Protein: <1 g/dl
- Glucose: >50 mg/dl
- LDH: <225 mU/ml
- Positive culture of peritoneal fluid
- Measurement of the serum-ascites albumin gradient: The serum-ascites albumin gradient indirectly measures portal pressure. The albumin concentration of ascitic fluid and serum must be obtained on the same day. The ascitic fluid value is subtracted from the serum value to obtain the gradient. If the difference (not a ratio) is >1.1 g/dL, the patient has portal hypertension, with 97% accuracy. If the difference is <1.1 g/dL, portal hypertension is not present. The vast majority of patients with SBP have portal hypertension secondary to cirrhosis.

IMAGING STUDIES

- Abdominal ultrasound: if there is clinical difficulty in performing paracentesis
- CT scan: to rule out secondary peritonitis (if indicated) and to exclude abscess, mass

TREATMENT

ACUTE GENERAL Rx

Cefotaxime 1 to 2 g IV q8h or ceftriaxone 2 g IV q24h in patients with normal renal function; duration of treatment is generally 7 to 10 days. Oral quinolone therapy (ofloxacin 400 to 800 mg/day) or ciprofloxacin may be an acceptable alternative in selected patients.

PROPHYLAXIS

Give double-strength trimethoprim/sulfamethoxazole qd 5 days/wk or ciprofloxacin 750 mg/wk PO. Both have been shown to decrease occurrence of SBP in patients with cirrhosis.

PEARLS & CONSIDERATIONS

COMMENTS

- Renal failure is a major cause of morbidity in cirrhotic patients with SBP. The use of IV albumin (1.5 g/kg at the time of diagnosis and 1 g/kg on day 3) may lower the rate of renal failure and mortality in patients with SBP.
- The criteria for the diagnosis of SBP require that abdominal paracentesis be performed and ascitic fluid be analyzed before a diagnosis of SBP can be made.
- Culturing ascitic fluid as if it were blood (with bedside inoculation of ascitic fluid into blood culture bottles) has been shown to significantly increase the culture-positivity of the ascitic fluid.
- Laparotomy may be life threatening in end-stage cirrhosis.
- Positive blood cultures in an individual with ascites require exclusion of a peritoneal source by paracentesis.

SUGGESTED READINGS

Garcia-Tsao G: Current management of the complications of cirrhosis and portal hypertension: variceal hemorrhage, ascites, and spontaneous bacterial peritonitis, *Gastroenterology* 120(3):726, 2001.

Navassa M et al: Randomized, comparative study of oral ofloxacin versus intravenous cefotoxin in spontaneous bacterial peritonitis, *Gastroenterology* 111:1011, 1996.

Runyon BA et al: The serum-ascites albumin gradient is superior to the exudates-transudate concept in the differential diagnosis of ascites, *Ann Intern Med* 117:215, 1992.

Sort P et al: Effects of intravenous albumin on renal impairment and mortality in patients with cirrhosis and SBP, *N Engl J Med* 341:403, 1999.

Such J, Runyon BA: Spontaneous bacterial peritonitis, *Clin Infect Disease* 27:669, 1998.

AUTHORS: **JOSEPH F. GRILLO, M.D.**, and **DENNIS J. MIKOLICH, M.D.**

BASIC INFORMATION

DEFINITION

Pertussis is a prolonged bacterial infection of the upper respiratory tract characterized by paroxysms of an intense cough.

SYNONYMS

Whooping cough

ICD-9CM CODES
033.9 Pertussis

EPIDEMIOLOGY

INCIDENCE (IN U.S.): Approximately 5000 new cases/yr (Fig. 1-179)

PREDOMINANT AGE:
- 50% in children <1 yr of age
- 20% in children >15 yr of age

PEAK INCIDENCE:
- Childhood
- Usually affects children <1 yr of age

PHYSICAL FINDINGS & CLINICAL PRESENTATION

- Usually begins with a 1- to 2-wk prodrome that resembles a common cold
- Following this initial phase, increased production of mucus is noted
- Increased mucus production is followed by an intense, paroxysmal cough, ending with gasps and an inspiratory whoop
- In some children, cyanosis and anoxia are noted
- When prolonged, frank exhaustion and even apnea occur
- Pertussis is characterized by the finding of intense cough with a marked lymphocytosis
- Improvement during the later stage is possible
- High fever may be an indication of secondary bacterial pneumonia, which may be a later complication of pertussis

ETIOLOGY

Gram-negative rod, *Bordetella pertussis,* which adheres to human cilia

DIAGNOSIS

DIFFERENTIAL DIAGNOSIS

- Croup
- Epiglottitis
- Foreign body aspiration
- Bacterial pneumonia

WORKUP

- Blood cultures
- Chest x-ray examination
- Culture of bacteria, usually from nasopharynx
- Immunofluorescent staining of nasopharyngeal secretions
- ELISA for detection of antibody to pertussis

LABORATORY TESTS

CBC, which usually demonstrates marked lymphocytosis:
1. Up to 18,000 WBCs
2. 70% to 80% lymphocytes

IMAGING STUDIES

Chest x-ray examination is of value if secondary bacterial pneumonia is suspected.

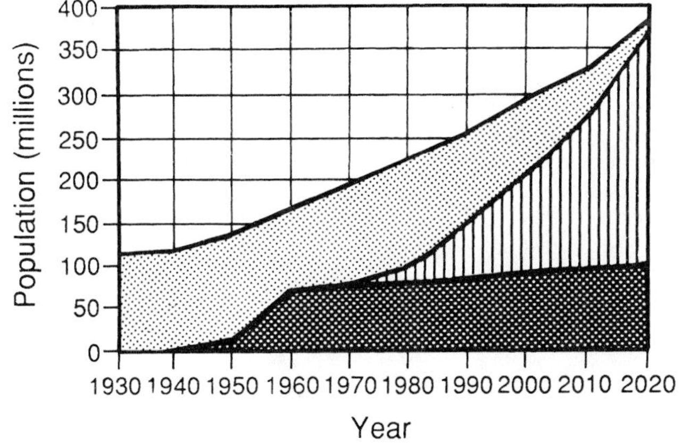

FIGURE 1-179 Projected pertussis epidemiology in the United States through the year 2020 with continued use of present-day whole-cell pertussis vaccines. (Modified from Bass JW, Stephenson SR: *Pediatr Infect Dis J 6:141,* 1987.)

TREATMENT

ACUTE GENERAL Rx

- Intensive supportive care:
  1. Adequate hydration
  2. Control of secretions
  3. Maintenance of airway
- Antibiotics are indicated even though their ability to alter the course of the disease is controversial.
  1. Erythromycin 50 mg/kg/day for 14 days. Recent literature reports indicate that a 7-day treatment regimen may be as effective as a 14-day course of erythromycin
  2. Although unproved, dexamethasone 1 mg/kg/day in 4 doses for severe, life-threatening paroxysms
  3. Ceftriaxone 75 mg/kg/day in 2 doses for broad coverage of secondary bacterial pneumonias
  4. Nafcillin or vancomycin when staphylococcal pneumonia is suspected
- Vaccination is successful in preventing the disease: universal vaccination is advised for all children <7 yr of age.
- Erythromycin is recommended for all close contacts in the household: TMP/SMX in two oral doses per day for those intolerant to erythromycin.
- Systemic steroids and nebulized steroids reduce length of hospital stay and improve symptoms.
- One small study showed nebulized epinephrine improves symptoms within 30 min, but found no difference after 2 hr.

DISPOSITION

Close attention to accepted vaccination schedules is the best prevention.

REFERRAL

To intensive care setting for life-threatening infections:
1. Pulmonologist
2. Infectious disease specialist

SUGGESTED READINGS

He Q et al: Whooping cough caused by *Bordetella pertussis* and *Bordetella para-pertussis* in an immunized population, *JAMA* 280:635, 1998.

MMWR: Pertussis—United States 1997-2000, *MMWR* 51-4, 73-75, 2002.

Tanaka M et al: Trends in pertussis among infants in the United States, 1980–1999, *JAMA* 290:2968, 2003.

Yaari E et al: Clinical manifestations of *Bordetella pertussis* infection in immunized children and young adults, *Chest* 115:1254, 1999.

AUTHOR: **JOSEPH J. LIEBER, M.D.**

Peutz-Jeghers Syndrome (PTG)

BASIC INFORMATION

DEFINITION

A hamartomatous polyp is a benign intestinal growth that may contain all components of the intestinal mucosa. In gastrointestinal polyposis, multiple such polyps coexist within the intestinal tract, and associated manifestations are usually also present.

Commonly recognized syndromes are Peutz-Jeghers syndrome, juvenile polyposis syndrome, Cowden's disease, Bannagan-Ruvalcaba-Riley syndrome, and Cronkhite-Canada syndrome. Other lesser known inherited hamartomatous polyposis syndromes are hereditary mixed polyposis syndrome, intestinal ganglioneuromatosis and neurofibromatosis (variant of Von Recklinghausen's syndrome), Devon family syndrome, basal cell nevus syndrome, and tuberous sclerosis (may involve GI tract).

ICD-9CM CODES
759.6 (Peutz-Jeghers syndrome)
211.3 (Cronkhite-Canada syndrome)

PHYSICAL FINDINGS & CLINICAL PRESENTATION

Peutz-Jeghers Syndrome:
- Transmission: autosomal dominant with incomplete penetrance
- Disease expression
  1. Stomach, small and large intestinal hamartomas with bands of smooth muscle in the lamina propria
  2. Pigmented lesions around mouth (lips and buccal mucosa), nose, hands, feet, genital, and perineal areas
  3. Ovarian tumors
  4. Sertoli cell testicular tumors
  5. Airway polyps
  6. Pancreatic cancer
  7. Breast cancer
  8. Urinary tract polyps
- Cumulative lifetime cancer risk
  1. Colon cancer: 39%
  2. Stomach cancer: 29%
  3. Small intestine cancer: 13%
  4. Pancreatic cancer: 36%
  5. Breast cancer: 54%
  6. Ovarian cancer: 10%
  7. Sertoli cell tumor: 9%
  8. Overall cancer risk: 93%
- Clinical manifestation
  1. Gastrointestinal, small bowel obstruction, intussusception, GI bleeding
  2. See chapters on relevant malignancies for their signs and symptoms.

Juvenile Polyposis Syndrome:
- Transmission: autosomal dominant
- Disease expression
  1. Solitary juvenile polyps numbering 10 or more in the rectum or throughout the gastrointestinal tract; the polyps are smooth and covered with normal epithelium
  2. Various congenital abnormalities coexist in 20%
- Cumulative cancer risk is increased (may be as high as 50%)
- Clinical manifestation
  1. Intestinal obstruction
  2. Intussusception
  3. GI bleeding

Cowden's Disease:
- Transmission: autosomal dominant, rare
- Disease expression
  1. Juvenile intestinal polyposis
  2. Orocutaneous hamartomas
  3. Fibrocystic breast disease and breast cancer
  4. Goiter and thyroid cancer
  5. Facial tricholemmomas (papules) in 83%
- Cumulative cancer risk
  1. GI: same as general population
  2. Thyroid: 3% to 10%
  3. Breast: 25% to 50%

Bannagan-Ruvalcaba-Riley Syndrome:
- Transmission: autosomal dominant, rare
- Disease expression
  1. Juvenile intestinal polyposis
  2. Macrocephaly
  3. Developmental delay
  4. Penile pigmented spots
  5. Cumulative cancer risk unknown

Cronkhite-Canada syndrome:
- Transmission: acquired
- Age of onset: midlife
- Disease expression
  1. Diffuse gastrointestinal juvenile polyposis (50%-95% of cases)
  2. Chronic diarrhea and protein-losing enteropathy (the entire intestinal mucosa may be inflamed), which leads to abdominal pain, weight loss, and various complications of malnutrition
  3. Dystrophic nails
  4. Alopecia
  5. Hyperpigmentation
- Cumulative cancer risk: same as the average population

DIAGNOSIS

Diagnosis is suggested in many cases by family history and confirmed by colonoscopy and physical findings described previously.

TREATMENT

GENERAL Rx

Peutz-Jeghers Syndrome:
- Colonoscopies with polypectomies
- Screening for breast cancer, testicular cancer, possibly ovarian cancer

Juvenile Polyposis Syndrome:
- Colonoscopies with polypectomies if few colon polyps
- Total colectomy if numerous polyps
- Esophagogastroscopies and polypectomies

Cowden's Disease: Rigorous breast cancer screening or prophylactic simple bilateral mastectomy with reconstruction

Cronkhite-Canada syndrome: Progressive malabsorption syndrome is the hallmark of this syndrome, and no specific treatment exists for it. Enteral or parenteral feeding is the cornerstone of management and can result in remission.

SUGGESTED READING

Itzkowitz SH: Colonic polyps and polyposis syndromes. In Feldman M, Friedman L, Sleisinger MH (eds): *Gastrointestinal and liver disease,* ed 7, Philadelphia, 2002, WB Saunders.

AUTHOR: **TOM J. WACHTEL, M.D.**

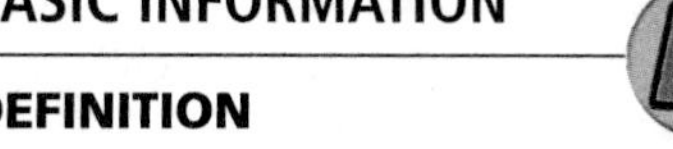

BASIC INFORMATION

DEFINITION

Peyronie's disease is an abnormal curvature and shortening of the penis during an erection (Fig. 1-180). This is caused by scarring of the tunica albuginea of the corpora cavernosa.

SYNONYMS

Plastic induration of the penis
Penile fibromatosis

ICD-9CM CODES
607.89 Peyronie's disease

EPIDEMIOLOGY & DEMOGRAPHICS

- Peyronie's disease occurs in approximately 1% of men (7:700).
- It is commonly seen between the ages of 45 to 60.
- A genetic predisposition has been suggested.
- There are no incidence and prevalence data available in the literature.

PHYSICAL FINDINGS & CLINICAL PRESENTATION

- Painful erections
- Tenderness over the scar tissue area
- Erectile dysfunction
- Curvature of the erected penis interfering with penetration
- Dupuytren's contracture is a commonly associated finding in patients with Peyronie's disease

ETIOLOGY

- The specific cause of the disease is not known. It is thought that scar tissue forms on either the dorsal or ventral midline surface of the penile shaft. The scar restricts expansion at the involved site, causing the penis to bend or curve in one direction.
- The precipitating factor appears to be trauma either from repetitive microvascular injury caused by vigorous sexual intercourse, accidents, or from prior surgeries (e.g., transurethral prostatectomy or radical prostatectomy, cystoscopy).

DIAGNOSIS

DIFFERENTIAL DIAGNOSIS

- The history differentiates congenital from acquired curvature of the penis.
- Other causes of erectile dysfunction must be excluded including metabolic, diabetes, thyroid, renal, hypogonadism, and hyperprolactinemia.

WORKUP

History and physical examination alone usually will establish the diagnosis of Peyronie's disease.

LABORATORY TESTS

There are no specific blood tests to diagnose Peyronie's disease. Electrolytes, BUN, creatinine, glucose, thyroid function tests (TSH, T_3U, T_4), testosterone, and prolactin level are blood tests to obtain to exclude other medical causes of erectile dysfunction.

IMAGING STUDIES

Imaging studies are not specific.

TREATMENT

NONPHARMACOLOGIC THERAPY

A conservative approach of reassurance and observation is taken at first because the disease process may be self-limiting.

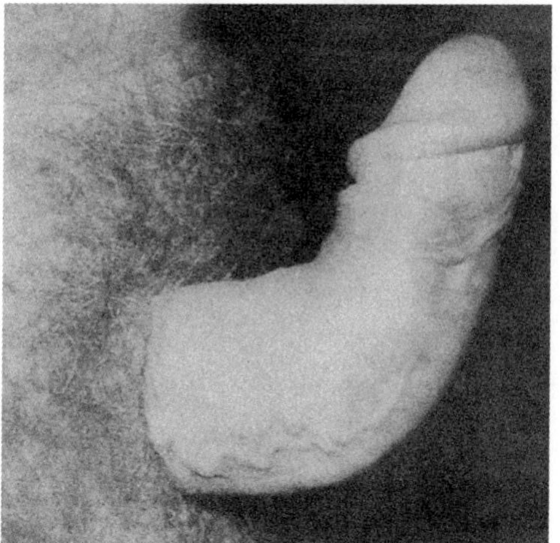

FIGURE 1-180 Peyronie's disease. (Courtesy Patrick C. Walsh, M.D., The Johns Hopkins University School of Medicine, Baltimore. In Seidel HM [ed]: *Mosby's guide to physical examination,* ed 4, St Louis, 1999, Mosby.)

ACUTE GENERAL Rx

Although not substantiated by direct randomized, controlled clinical trials, the following treatment modalities have been tried:

- Vitamin E 400 mg bid
- Paraaminobenzoic acid 12 g/day
- Colchicine 0.6 mg bid for 2 to 3 wk
- Fexofenadine 60 mg bid for 3 mo
- Steroid injection into the scar tissue
- Collagenase injection into the scar tissue
- Radiation to the scar tissue area

CHRONIC Rx

In patients who have progressed to intractable pain with erection or erectile dysfunction, surgical treatment with excision of the plaque and skin grafting may be indicated.

DISPOSITION

Peyronie's disease evolves slowly and in some cases can resolve on its own. Waiting for 1 yr before proceeding with surgical attempts is recommended.

REFERRAL

A urologic consultation is recommended in patients with progressive symptoms and erectile dysfunction.

PEARLS & CONSIDERATIONS

COMMENTS

- Peyronie's disease is not commonly seen in younger patients because they are able to sustain intracorporeal pressures high enough to stretch the scar tissue, preventing it from deforming the penis during erection.
- Trauma from buckling of the erected penis is thought to be the precipitant cause of scar formation and Peyronie's disease. It is found more often in men who are sexually very active and vigorous, having sexual intercourse daily or almost daily.
- Sexual positions with the women being on top or thrusting the penis into the anterior vaginal wall is thought to increase the chances of developing Peyronie's disease.

SUGGESTED READINGS

Gholami SS, Lue TF: Peyronie's disease, *Urol Clin North Am* 28(2):377, 2001.

Kadloglu A et al: A retrospective review of 307 men with Peyronie's disease, *J Urol* 168(3):1075, 2002.

Tunuguntla HS: Management of Peyronie's disease—a review, *World J Urol* 19(4):244, 2001.

AUTHOR: **PETER PETROPOULOS, M.D.**

BASIC INFORMATION

DEFINITION

Pharyngitis/tonsillitis is inflammation of the pharynx or tonsils.

SYNONYMS

Sore throat

ICD-9CM CODES
462 Pharyngitis

EPIDEMIOLOGY & DEMOGRAPHICS

PREDOMINANT SEX: Female = male
PREDOMINANT AGE:
- All ages affected
- Streptococcal pharyngitis most common among school-age children

PEAK INCIDENCE: Late winter/early spring (group A streptococcal infections)
GENETICS:
Neonatal Infection: Pharyngitis below the age of 3 yr is almost always of viral etiology.

PHYSICAL FINDINGS & CLINICAL PRESENTATION

- Pharynx:
  1. May appear normal to severely erythematous
  2. Tonsillar hypertrophy and exudates commonly seen but do not indicate etiology
- Viral infection:
  1. Rhinorrhea
  2. Conjunctivitis
  3. Cough
- Bacterial infection, especially group A *Streptococcus:*
  1. High fever
  2. Systemic signs of infection
- Herpes simplex or enterovirus infection: vesicles
- Streptococcal infection:
  1. Rare complications:
     a. Scarlet fever
     b. Rheumatic fever
     c. Acute glomerulonephritis
  2. Extension of infection: tonsillar, parapharyngeal, or retropharyngeal abscess presenting with severe pain, high fever, trismus

ETIOLOGY

- Viruses:
  1. Respiratory syncytial virus
  2. Influenza A and B
  3. Epstein-Barr virus
  4. Adenovirus
  5. Herpes simplex
- Bacteria:
  1. *Streptococcus pyogenes*
  2. *Neisseria gonorrhoeae*
  3. *Arcanobacterium haemolyticum*
- Other organisms:
  1. *Mycoplasma pneumoniae*
  2. *Chlamydia pneumoniae*

DIAGNOSIS

DIFFERENTIAL DIAGNOSIS

- Sore throat associated with granulocytopenia, thyroiditis
- Tonsillar hypertrophy associated with lymphoma
- Section II describes the differential diagnosis of sore throat.

WORKUP

- Throat swab for culture to exclude *S. pyogenes, N. gonorrhoeae* (requires specific transport medium)
- Rapid streptococcal antigen test (culture should be performed if rapid test negative)
- Monospot

LABORATORY TESTS

- CBC with differential
  1. May help support diagnosis of bacterial infection
  2. Streptococcal infection suggested by leukocytosis >15,000/mm^3
- Viral cultures, serologic studies rarely needed

IMAGING STUDIES

Seldom indicated

TREATMENT

NONPHARMACOLOGIC THERAPY

- Fluids
- Salt water gargles

ACUTE GENERAL Rx

- Aspirin (acetaminophen culture)
- If streptococcal infection proven or suspected:
  1. Penicillin V 500 mg PO bid for 10 days or benzathine penicillin 1.2 million U IM once (adults)
  2. Erythromycin 500 mg PO bid or 250 mg qid for 10 days if penicillin allergic
- If gonococcal infection proven or suspected: ceftriaxone 125 mg IM once

CHRONIC Rx

- Recurrent streptococcal infections are common and may represent reinfection from other household.
- There is no conclusive evidence from randomized clinical trials that tonsillectomy is superior to antibiotic therapy for recurrent tonsillitis in adults.

REFERRAL

- To otolaryngologist:
  1. If peritonsillar or other abscess is suspected
  2. If tonsillar hypertrophy persists
- To infectious diseases expert if unusual pathogen is suspected

PEARLS & CONSIDERATIONS

COMMENTS

Antibiotic therapy should be avoided unless bacterial etiology is suspected or proven, especially in adults.

SUGGESTED READINGS

Bisno AL: Acute pharyngitis, *N Engl J Med* 344:205, 2001.
McKerrow W: Tonsillectomy versus antibiotics, *Clin Evid Concise* 7:88, 2002.
Snow V et al: Principles of appropriate antibiotic use for acute pharyngitis in adults, *Ann Intern Med* 134:506, 2001.
Vincent M et al: Pharyngitis, *Am Fam Physician* 69:1465, 2004.

AUTHOR: **JOSEPH R. MASCI, M.D.**

BASIC INFORMATION

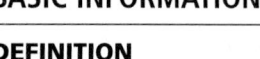

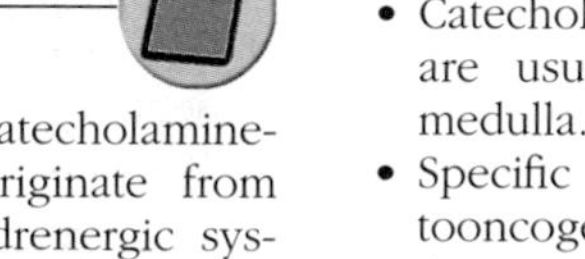

DEFINITION

Pheochromocytomas are catecholamine-producing tumors that originate from chromaffin cells of the adrenergic system. They generally secrete both norepinephrine and epinephrine, but norepinephrine is usually the predominant amine.

SYNONYMS

Paraganglioma

ICD-9CM CODES
194.0 Pheochromocytoma

EPIDEMIOLOGY & DEMOGRAPHICS

- Incidence: 0.05% of population; peak incidence in 30s and 40s.
- "Rough" rule of 10: 10% are extra-adrenal, 10% are malignant, 10% are familial, 10% occur in children, 10% involve both adrenals, 10% are multiple (other than bilateral adrenal).
- Approximately 25% of patients with apparently sporadic pheochromocytoma may be carriers of mutations.
- Pheochromocytoma is a feature of two disorders with autosomal dominant pattern of inheritance:
  1. Multiple endocrine neoplasia II
  2. Von Hippel-Lindau disease: angioma of the retina, hemangioblastoma of the CNS, renal cell carcinoma, pancreatic cysts, and epididymal cystoadenoma
- Pheochromocytomas occur in 5% of patients with neurofibromatosis type 1.

PHYSICAL FINDINGS & CLINICAL PRESENTATION

- Hypertension: can be sustained (55%) or paroxysmal (45%).
- Headache (80%): usually paroxysmal in nature and described as "pounding" and severe.
- Palpitations (70%): can be present with or without tachycardia.
- Hyperhidrosis (60%): most evident during paroxysmal attacks of hypertension.
- Physical examination may be entirely normal if done in a symptom-free interval; during a paroxysm the patient may demonstrate marked increase in both systolic and diastolic pressure, profuse sweating, visual disturbances (caused by hypertensive retinopathy), dilated pupils (secondary to catecholamine excess), paresthesias in the lower extremities (caused by severe vasoconstriction), tremor, tachycardia.

ETIOLOGY

- Catecholamine-producing tumors that are usually located in the adrenal medulla.
- Specific mutations of the RET protooncogene cause familial predisposition to pheochromocytoma in Men II.
- Mutations in the von Hippel-Lindau tumor suppressor gene (VHL gene) cause familial disposition to pheochromocytoma in von Hippel-Lindau disease.
- Recently identified genes for succinate dehydrogenase subunit D (SDHD) and succinate dehydrogenase subunit B (SDHB) predispose carriers to pheochromocytoma and globus tumors.

DIAGNOSIS

DIFFERENTIAL DIAGNOSIS

- Anxiety disorder
- Thyrotoxicosis
- Amphetamine or cocaine abuse
- Carcinoid
- Essential hypertension

WORKUP

Laboratory evaluation and imaging studies to locate the neoplasm.

LABORATORY TESTS

- Plasma-free metanephrines are the best test for excluding or confirming pheochromocytoma and should be the test of first choice for diagnosis of the tumor. Plasma concentrations of normetanephrines >2.5 pmol/ml or metanephrine levels >1.4 pmol/ml indicate a pheochromocytoma with 100% specificity.
- 24-hr urine collection for metanephrines (100% sensitive) will also show increased metanephrines; the accuracy of the 24-hr urinary levels for metanephrines can be improved by indexing urinary metanephrine levels by urine creatinine levels.
- The clonidine suppression test is useful for distinguishing between high levels of plasma norepinephrine caused by release from sympathetic nerves and those caused by release from a pheochromocytoma. A decrease <50% in plasma norepinephrine levels after clonidine administration is normal, whereas persistent elevations are indicative of pheochromocytoma.

IMAGING STUDIES

- Abdominal CT scan (88% sensitivity) is useful in locating pheochromocytomas >0.5 inch in diameter (90% to 95% accurate).
- MRI: pheochromocytomas demonstrate a distinctive MRI appearance (100% sensitivity); MRI may become the diagnostic imaging modality of choice.
- Scintigraphy with ^{131}I-MIBG (100% sensitivity): this norepinephrine analog localizes in adrenergic tissue; it is particularly useful in locating extraadrenal pheochromocytomas.
- 6 [^{18}F] Fluorodopamine positron emission tomography is reserved for cases in which clinical symptoms and signs suggest pheochromocytoma and results of biochemical tests are positive but conventional imaging studies cannot locate the tumor. An alternative approach is to use vena caval sampling for plasma catecholamines and metanephrines.

TREATMENT

ACUTE GENERAL Rx

Laparoscopic removal of the tumor (surgical resection for both benign and malignant disease):

1. Preoperative stabilization with combination of phenoxybenzamine, β blocker, metyrosine, and liberal fluid and salt intake starting 10 to 14 days before surgery.
   a. Volume expansion is done to prevent postoperative hypotension.
   b. α-Blockade to control hypertension: phenoxybenzamine (Dibenzyline) 5 mg PO bid initially, gradually increased to 10 mg q3d up to 50-100 mg bid; prazosin may be used when phenoxybenzamine therapy alone is not effective or not well tolerated.
   c. β-Blockade with propranolol 20 to 40 mg PO q6h (to be used only after α-blockade) is useful to prevent catecholamine-induced arrhythmias and tachycardia.
   d. Metyrosine reduces tumor stores of catecholamines, decreases need for intraoperative medication to control blood pressure, and lowers intraoperative fluid requirements.
2. Hypertensive crisis preoperatively and intraoperatively can be controlled with phentolamine (Regitine) 2 to 5 mg IV q1-2h prn or nitroprusside used in combination with β-adrenergic blockers.

3. Combination chemotherapy with cyclophosphamide, vincristine, and dacarbazine is useful for symptomatic advanced malignant pheochromocytoma.

DISPOSITION

- The 5-yr survival rate is approximately 95% with benign disease, 40% for malignant pheochromocytoma (malignancy is determined by metastasis).
- Pheochromocytomas are three times more likely to be malignant in women.
- Postoperative follow-up of patients with sporadic and familial forms should include plasma metanephrine levels after 6 wk, 6 mo, and then annually.

PEARLS & CONSIDERATIONS

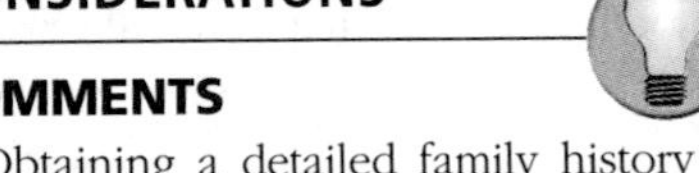

COMMENTS

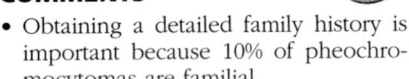

- Obtaining a detailed family history is important because 10% of pheochromocytomas are familial.
- Screening for pheochromocytoma should be considered in patients with any of the following:
  1. Malignant hypertension
  2. Poor response to antihypertensive therapy
  3. Paradoxical hypertensive response
  4. Hypertension during induction of anesthesia, parturition, surgery, or thyrotropin-releasing hormone testing
  5. Hypertension associated with imipramine or desipramine
  6. Neurofibromatosis (increased incidence of pheochromocytoma)
- All patients with pheochromocytoma should be screened for MEN-II and von Hippel-Lindau disease with pentagastrin test, serum PTH, ophthalmoscopy, MRI of the brain, CT scan of the kidneys and pancreas, and ultrasonography of the testes.
- In patients with pheochromocytoma, routine analysis for mutations of RET, VHL, SDHD, and SDHB is indicated to identify pheochromocytoma-associated syndromes.

SUGGESTED READINGS

Lenders JW et al: Biochemical diagnosis of pheochromocytoma, which test is best? *JAMA* 287:1427, 2002.

Neumann HP et al: Germ-line mutations in nonsyndromic pheochromocytoma, *N Engl J Med* 346:1459, 2002.

Pacak R: Recent advances in genetics, diagnosis, localization, and treatment of pheochromocytoma, *Ann Intern Med* 134:315, 2001.

AUTHOR: **FRED F. FERRI, M.D.**

BASIC INFORMATION

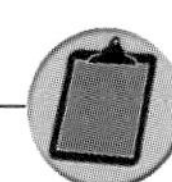

DEFINITION

Phobic anxiety disorders have at their core an extreme anxiety that is elicited by a specific object or situation that is usually perceived as more threatening than it really is and that often leads to avoidance behavior. The provoking stimuli may be social or performance situations (social phobia) or any other stimulus (specific phobia of animals, natural environments, blood, or situational).

SYNONYMS

Simple phobia (obsolete name for specific phobia)
Phobias named according to the inducing stimulus, for example, arachnophobia (fear of spiders), claustrophobia (fear of tight spaces)
Social anxiety disorder (obsolete name for social phobias)

ICD-9CM CODES
F40.2 Specific phobia (DSM-IV: 300.29)
F40.1 Social phobia (DMS-IV: 300.23)

EPIDEMIOLOGY & DEMOGRAPHICS

PREVALENCE (IN U.S.):

- Specific phobias affect 5%-10% of the general population.
- Social phobias affect about 3%.

PREDOMINANT SEX:

- Females with specific phobias outnumber males, though rates vary according to the phobia.
- More women are affected with social phobia; however, men are more likely to seek treatment.

PREDOMINANT AGE:

- Onset of most specific phobias is in childhood.
- Major exceptions: situational phobias have two peaks—the first in childhood and the second in the mid-20s.
- Once developed, fears are generally stable.
- Roots of social phobia may be in childhood, with described shyness or social inhibition, but onset usually in the midteens or into late adulthood; disorder is generally lifelong.

PEAK INCIDENCE:

- Specific phobias: often a lifelong condition, but phobias with onset in childhood (e.g., animal phobias) tend to remit spontaneously
- Social phobia: may alternate in mid-to-late adulthood

GENETICS: Both specific phobias and social phobias are more common in first-degree relatives than the general population

PHYSICAL FINDINGS & CLINICAL PRESENTATION

- Specific phobias: frequently occur with other anxiety disorders, particularly panic and agoraphobias.
- When approaching the phobic object the patient experiences extreme anxiety often accompanied by autonomic symptoms such as tachycardia, tremor, and diaphoresis. In addition, depersonalizaiton may occur. In blood phobias, however, these symptoms are often followed by a parasympathetic response consisting of hypotension and in some instances vaso-vagal syncope.
- Social phobias are distinguished from specific phobias in that what is feared is humiliation or embarrassment rather than the thing itself. Persons with social phobia usually have low self-esteem and fear of evaluation from others; avoid or are fearful of any situation in which others may assess or evaluate them directly or indirectly. Concurrent anxiety disorders are common.

ETIOLOGY

- Unknown. For some persons phobias may develop because of pairing of anxiety with a specific experience.

DIAGNOSIS

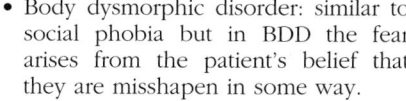

DIFFERENTIAL DIAGNOSIS

- Body dysmorphic disorder: similar to social phobia but in BDD the fear arises from the patient's belief that they are misshapen in some way.
- Panic attacks (+/− agorophobia): anxiety symptoms seen in specific phobia may resemble panic attacks, but the stimulus in specific phobias or social phobias is clear, whereas panic attacks are unexpected.
- Generalized anxiety disorder: difficult to distinguish from social phobia, but in social phobia the cognitive focus is fear of embarrassment or humiliation, whereas in generalized anxiety disorder the focus is more internal on the subjective sensations of discomfort.
- Avoidant personality disorder is often comorbid with social phobia.
- Psychotic disorders: fear of being in public arise from delusions.

WORKUP

- History: usually diagnostic
- Social phobia is a chronic condition. Individuals with social phobia often underachieve, drop out of school, avoid seeking work as a result of anxiety about interviews, refrain from dating and remain with family of origin, and are less likely to marry.
- Physical examination: to confirm absence of cardiovascular abnormalities (e.g., a chronic sinus arrhythmia)

LABORATORY TESTS

No specific laboratory tests are indicated.

IMAGING STUDIES

No specific imaging studies are recommended.

TREATMENT

NONPHARMACOLOGIC THERAPY

- Cognitive-behavioral therapy (CBT) and other psychotherapeutic approaches found to be effective in controlled trials.
- Behavioral treatment involves relaxation training, usually paired with visualization and progressive desensitization.
- Success rates are higher when the phobia is not complicated by other anxiety disorders.
- Social phobia is more problematic to treat because the psychologic difficulties are more pervasive, but cognitive-behavioral therapy and other psychotherapies are quite effective.

ACUTE GENERAL Rx

- Benzodiazepines: provide rapid relief of anxiety associated with exposure to fearful stimuli
- Alprazolam or lorazepam: both administered sublingually to increase rate of absorption
- β-Blockers: (e.g., propanolol) have been used to decrease autonomic hyperarousal and tremor associated with performance situations (e.g., before a public speech)

CHRONIC Rx

- If the phobic stimulus is rarely encountered, benzodiazepines as needed may be appropriate long-term treatment.
- SSRIs (particularly paroxetine and sertraline) are effective in reducing symptoms and improving function for persons with social phobia.

REFERRAL

Recommended to confirm diagnosis and to evaluate for psychotherapy.

SUGGESTED READINGS

Davidson JR, Foa EB, Huppert JD: Fluoxetine, comprehensive cognitive behavioral therapy, and placebo in generalized social phobia, *Arch Gen Psychiatry* 61:1005, 2004.
Kendler KS et al: The etiology of phobias: an evaluation of the stress-diathesis model, *Arch Gen Psychiatry* 59:242, 2002.

AUTHOR: **MITCHELL D. FELDMAN, M.D., M.PHIL.**

Pilonidal Disease

BASIC INFORMATION

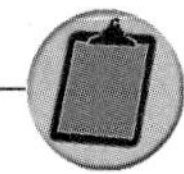

DEFINITION

From Latin: *pilus* = hair and *nidus* = nest. A *pilonidal sinus* is a short tract that extends from the skin surface, is most commonly found in the intergluteal fold sacrococcygeal region, additionally described in the interdigital area, umbilicus, chest wall, and scalp. It most likely represents a distended hair follicle. An *acute pilonidal abscess,* which consists of pus and a wall of edematous fat, results from rupture of an infected follicle into fat. A *chronic pilonidal abscess* results when an infected follicle ruptures directly into surrounding tissues; the wall of a chronic pilonidal abscess consists of fibrous tissue. A *pilonidal cyst* develops from a chronic abscess of long duration as a thin and flat lining of epithelium grows into the cavity from the skin surface.

SYNONYMS

Jeep disease

ICD-9CM CODES
685.1 Pilonidal cyst

EPIDEMIOLOGY & DEMOGRAPHICS

INCIDENCE: 26 cases/100,000 persons
PREDOMINANT SEX: Male > female (2.2:1)
AVERAGE AGE OF PRESENTATION: 21 yr
GENETICS: Theory of congenital origin is now disfavored.
RISK FACTORS:
- Male sex
- Caucasian race
- Family predisposition
- Obesity
- Sedentary lifestyle
- Occupation requiring prolonged sitting
- Local hirsutism
- Poor hygiene
- Increased sweat activity

PHYSICAL FINDINGS & CLINICAL PRESENTATION

- May manifest as asymptomatic pits or pores in the natal cleft
- Tenderness after physical activity or prolonged sitting
- Acute pilonidal abscess in 20% of patients with pilonidal disease
- Presents as a hot, tender, fluctuant swelling just lateral to the midline over the sacrum that may exude pus through the midline pit
- Chronic pilonidal abscess in 80% of patients with pilonidal disease
- Acute suppuration, tenderness, swelling, and heat
- Infrequently, systemic reaction: occasionally fever, leukocytosis, and malaise

ETIOLOGY

- Currently, thought to be acquired rather than congenital.
- Drilling of hair shed from the perineum or the head into sebaceous or hair follicles in the natal cleft.
- Drilling is facilitated by the friction of the natal cleft.
- Subsequent infection by skin organisms leads to pilonidal abscess.

DIAGNOSIS

DIFFERENTIAL DIAGNOSIS

- Perianal abscess arising from the posterior midline crypt
- Hidradenitis suppurativa
- Carbuncle
- Furuncle
- Osteomyelitis
- Anal fistula
- Coccygeal sinus

WORKUP

- Diagnosis is based on history and physical examination.
- Midline pits present behind the anus overlying the sacrum and coccyx.
- Broken hairs are often seen extruding from the midline pits.
- Insert probe in pilonidal sinus in path away from the anus.
- Complicated anal fistula may be angulating posteriorly before passing into a retrorectal abscess, but thorough examination of the anal cavity usually discloses point of origin.

LABORATORY TESTS

CBC

IMAGING STUDIES

CT scan in advanced recurrent cases

TREATMENT

NONPHARMACOLOGIC THERAPY

Prevention of exacerbations:
1. Local hygiene
2. Avoidance of prolonged sitting position
3. Weight reduction

ACUTE GENERAL Rx

- Procedure of choice for first-episode acute abscess: simple incision and drainage in an outpatient setting
- Cure rate of 76% after 18 mo
- Antibiotics: generally not indicated unless the patient has a medical condition such as rheumatic heart disease or is immunosuppressed

CHRONIC Rx

Elective treatment of pilonidal disease:
1. Minimal surgery
   a. Remove hair from midline pits and shave buttocks.
   b. May use a fine wire brush with local anesthesia to clear the pits and any lateral openings of granulation tissue and hair.
   c. Keep area clean.
2. Fistulotomy and curettage
   a. Used when minimal surgery does not control episodes of suppuration
   b. Pass probe to outline the pilonidal sinus and open tract surgically
   c. Curette granulation tissue at the base of the sinus and excise edges of the skin
   d. Keep open granulating wound meticulously clean and allow to heal
   e. If complete healing does not take place, use a skin graft or advancement flap to close the defect
3. Marsupialization
   a. This is the treatment of choice for chronic pilonidal disease.
   b. Wide excision of the pilonidal area is performed, including all affected skin and subcutaneous tissues down to the presacral fascia.
   c. Wound is left open, allowed to marsupialize, or closed as a primary procedure.
   d. Give antibiotics for 24 hr (particularly those directed against *Staphylococcus* and *Bacteroides* spp).
4. Other procedures
   a. Excision and closure
   b. Excision and skin grafting
   c. Bascom procedure (follicle removal & lateral drainage)
   d. Flaps: Z-palsty, V-Y advancement flap, rhomboid flap, gluteus maximus myocutaneous flap

DISPOSITION

- Recurrence rate for excision (most definitive procedure): 1% to 6%
- Incidence of squamous cell carcinoma in a chronic, recurrent pilonidal sinus is rare <1%

REFERRAL

- Emergency room for incision and drainage for an acute abscess
- To a surgeon for elective treatment or management of chronic or recurrent disease

PEARLS & CONSIDERATIONS

COMMENTS

Because of significant associated morbidity, the elective surgical procedures outlined are performed only after the potential risks vs. benefits are carefully weighed.

SUGGESTED READINGS

Church JM: Pilonidal cyst: cause and treatment, *Dis Colon Rectum* 43(8):1146, 2000.
Hull TL, Wu J: Pilonidal disease, *Surg Clin North Am* 82(6):1169, 2002.

AUTHOR: **ARUNDATHI G. PRASAD, M.D.**

BASIC INFORMATION

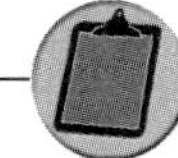

DEFINITION

Pinworms are a noninvasive infestation of the intestinal tract by *Enterobius vermicularis,* a helminth of the nematode family.

SYNONYMS

Enterobiasis

ICD-9CM CODES
127.4 Enterobiasis

EPIDEMIOLOGY & DEMOGRAPHICS

- Most common intestinal nematode with approximately 30,000 cases/yr in the U.S.
- Worldwide distribution, but most common in temperate climates.
- Highest infection rate in school-age children.
- Clusters are found in families, institutionalized persons, and homosexual men.

PHYSICAL FINDINGS & CLINICAL PRESENTATION

- Most infested persons are asymptomatic.
- Perianal itching is the most common reported symptom, with scratching leading to excoriation and sometimes secondary infection.
- Rarely insomnia, irritability, anorexia, and weight loss are described.
- Granulomas have been described in various organs resulting from worms wandering outside the intestines and dying there.

ETIOLOGY & PATHOGENESIS

Humans are the only host for this worm. Infestation is by fecal-oral route; ingested eggs hatch in the stomach and the larvae migrate to the colon where they mature. Gravid female worms migrate to the perianal skin at night, lay their eggs there, and die. The eggs cause itching; scratching causes egg deposition under fingernails, from which they can contaminate food or lead to autoreinfection.

DIAGNOSIS

DIFFERENTIAL DIAGNOSIS

- Perianal itching related to poor hygiene
- Hemorrhoidal disease and anal fissures
- Perineal yeast/fungal infections
- Section II describes the causes of pruritus ani

WORKUP

Identification of adult worms or eggs (Fig. 1-181) on transparent tape placed on the perianal skin upon awakening (NOTE: Five consecutive negative tests rule out the diagnosis.)

TREATMENT

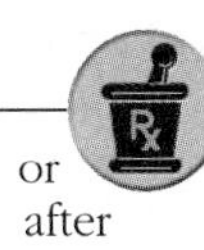

Single dose of mebendazole or pyrantel pamoate repeated after 2 to 3 wk

SUGGESTED READING

Hamer DH, Despommier DD: Intestinal nematodes. In Gorbach SL, Bartlett JG, Blacklow NR (eds): *Infectious diseases,* ed 2, Philadelphia, 1998, WB Saunders.

AUTHOR: **TOM J. WACHTEL, M.D.**

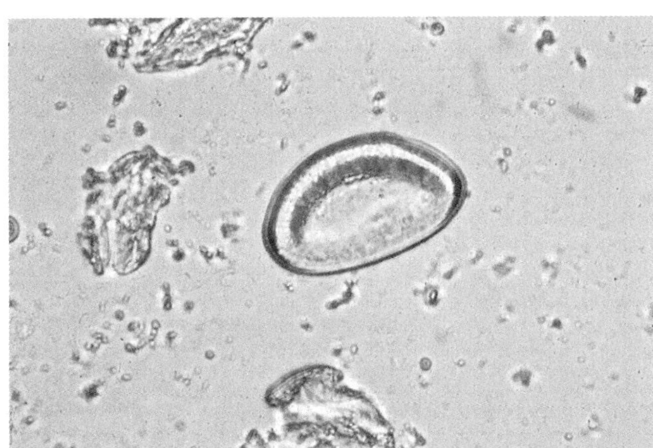

FIGURE 1-181 *Enterobius vermicularis* embryonated egg. Note larva inside (40 × 10 μm). (From Gorbach SL, Bartlett JG, Blacklow NR (eds): *Infectious diseases,* ed 2, Philadelphia, 1998, WB Saunders.)

BASIC INFORMATION

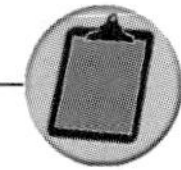

DEFINITION

Pituitary adenoma is a benign neoplasm of the anterior lobe of the pituitary that causes symptoms, either by excess secretion of hormones or by a local mass effect as the tumor impinges on other, nearby structures (e.g., optic chiasm, hypothalamus, pituitary stalk). Pituitary adenomas are classified by their size, function, and features that characterize their appearance. Microadenomas are <10 mm in size, and macroadenomas are >10 mm in size.

- *Acromegaly* is the disease state characterized by a pituitary adenoma that secretes growth hormone (GH).
- A *prolactinoma* secretes prolactin (PRL).
- *Cushing's disease* is a disease state in which there is hypersecretion of adrenocorticotropic hormone (ACTH).
- *Thyrotropin-secreting pituitary adenomas* secrete primarily thyroid-stimulating hormone (TSH).
- *Nonsecretory pituitary adenomas* are those in which the neoplasm is a space-occupying lesion whose secretory products do not cause a specific disease state.

ICD-9CM CODES
253 Pituitary adenoma
253.0 Acromegaly
253.1 Prolactinoma

EPIDEMIOLOGY & DEMOGRAPHICS

CLASSIFICATION (BY HORMONE SECRETED):
- PRL only ~35%
- No hormone ~30%
- GH only ~20%
- PRL and GH ~7%
- ACTH ~7%
- LF/FSH/TSH ~1%

PREVALENCE/INCIDENCE:
Pituitary Adenomas: Up to 10% to 15% of all intracranial neoplasms; 3% to 27% autopsy series
Prolactinomas: Up to 20% in women with unexplained primary or secondary amenorrhea
Growth Hormone–Secreting Pituitary Adenoma: 50 to 60 cases/1,000,000 persons
Thyrotropin-Secreting Pituitary Adenoma: 2.8% of pituitary adenomas with a slight female:male predominance of 1.7:1
Corticotropin-Secreting Pituitary Adenomas: Female:male predominance of 8:1

PHYSICAL FINDINGS

PROLACTINOMAS:
- Females:
  1. Galactorrhea
  2. Amenorrhea
  3. Oligomenorrhea with anovulation
  4. Infertility
  5. Estrogen deficiency leading to hirsutism
  6. Decreased vaginal lubrication
  7. Osteopenia
- Males:
  1. Large tumors more common secondary to delayed diagnosis
  2. Possible impotence or decreased libido or hypogonadism
  3. Galactorrhea rare because males lack the estrogen-dependent breast growth and differentiation

GROWTH HORMONE–SECRETING PITUITARY ADENOMA: Acromegaly
- Coarse facial features
- Oily skin
- Prognathism
- Carpal tunnel syndrome
- Osteoarthritis
- History of increased hat, glove, or shoe size
- Decreased exercise capacity
- Visual field deficits
- Diabetes mellitus

CORTICOTROPIN-SECRETING PITUITARY ADENOMA: Cushing's disease
- Usually present when the tumor is small (1 to 2 mm)
- 50% of the tumors <5 mm
- Other symptoms:
  1. Truncal obesity
  2. Round facies (moon face)
  3. Dorsocervical fat accumulation (buffalo hump)
  4. Hirsutism
  5. Acne
  6. Menstrual disorders
  7. Hypertension
  8. Striae
  9. Bruising
  10. Thin skin
  11. Hyperglycemia

THYROTROPIN-SECRETING PITUITARY ADENOMA:
- In males, larger, more invasive, and more rapidly growing tumors that present later in life
- Other symptoms: thyrotoxicosis, goiter, visual impairment

NONSECRETORY PITUITARY ADENOMAS (ENDOCRINE INACTIVE PITUITARY ADENOMA):
- Usually large at the time of diagnosis
- Symptoms:
  1. Bitemporal hemianopia secondary to compression of the optic chiasm
  2. Hypopituitarism secondary to compression of the pituitary gland
  3. Hypogonadism in men and in premenopausal women
  4. Cranial nerve deficits, secondary to extension into the cavernous sinus
  5. Hydrocephalus, secondary to extension into the third ventricle, compressing the foramen of Monro
  6. Diabetes insipidus, secondary to compression of the hypothalamus or pituitary stalk (a rare complication)

ETIOLOGY

Benign neoplasms of epithelial origin

DIAGNOSIS

DIFFERENTIAL DIAGNOSIS

PROLACTINOMA:
- Pregnancy
- Postpartum puerperium
- Primary hypothyroidism
- Breast disease
- Breast stimulation
- Drug ingestion (especially phenothiazines, antidepressants, haloperidol, methyldopa, reserpine, opiates, amphetamines, and cimetidine)
- Chronic renal failure
- Liver disease
- Polycystic ovarian disease
- Chest wall disorders
- Spinal cord lesions
- Previous cranial irradiation

ACROMEGALY: Ectopic production of growth hormone–releasing hormone from a carcinoid or other neuroendocrine tumor
CUSHING'S DISEASE:
- Diseases that cause ectopic sources of ACTH overproduction (including small cell carcinoma of the lung, bronchial carcinoid, intestinal carcinoid, pancreatic islet cell tumor, medullary thyroid carcinoma, or pheochromocytoma)
- Adrenal adenomas, adrenal carcinoma
- Nelson's syndrome

THYROTROPIN-SECRETNG PITUITARY ADENOMAS: Primary hypothyroidism
NONSECRETORY PITUITARY ADENOMA: Nonneoplastic mass lesions of various etiologies (e.g., infectious, granulomatous)

WORKUP (see Section III, "Pituitary Tumor")

PROLACTINOMA: First step: Measurement of basal PRL levels
- Elevated PRL levels are correlated with tumor size.
- Levels >200 ng/ml are diagnostic, with levels of 100 to 200 ng/ml being equivocal.
- Basal PRL levels between 20 and 100 suggest a microprolactinoma, as well as other conditions such as drug ingestion
- Basal level <20 is normal.

ACROMEGALY:
- First screening test is the measurement of the serum IGF-I level, post serum GH, TRH stimulation test.
- Follow with an oral glucose tolerance test.
- Failure to suppress serum GH to <2 ng/ml with an oral load of 100 g glucose is considered conclusive.
- A GHRH level >300 ng/ml is indicative of an ectopic source of GH.

CUSHING'S DISEASE:
- Normal or slightly elevated corticotropin levels ranging from 20 to 200 pg/ml; normal is 10 to 50 pg/ml.
- Levels <10 pg/ml usually indicate an autonomously secreting adrenal tumor.
- Levels >200 pg/ml suggest an ectopic corticotropin-secreting neoplasm.
- Cushing's disease is confirmed by demonstration of low-dose dexamethasone, which shows presence of abnormal cortisol suppressibility.
- 24-hr urine collection should demonstrate an increased level of cortisol excretion.

THYROTROPIN-SECRETING PITUITARY ADENOMA:
- Highly sensitive thyrotropin assays, which evaluate the presence of thyrotoxicosis, are one way to detect a thyrotropin-secreting tumor.
- Free alpha subunit is secreted by >80% of tumors with the ratio of the alpha subunit to thyrotropin >1.
- With central resistance to thyroid hormone, ratio is <1 and the sella is normal.
- Laboratory tests show elevated serum levels of both T_3 and T_4.

NONSECRETORY PITUITARY ADENOMA:
- Visual field testing
- Assessment of the pituitary and organ function to determine if there is hypopituitarism or hypersecretion of hormones (even if the effects of hypersecretion are subclinical)
- TRH to provoke secretion of FSH, LH, and LH-beta-subunit; will not elicit response in normal persons
- Exclusion of Klinefelter's syndrome in patient with long-standing primary hypogonadism, elevated gonadotropin levels, and enlargement of the sella

IMAGING STUDIES

- Study of choice: MRI of the pituitary and hypothalamus
  1. When evaluating Cushing's disease, small size at the onset of symptoms noted
- MRI, in this case, only 60% sensitive at best and may yield false positive results
- CT scan only when MRI is unavailable or is otherwise contraindicated

TREATMENT

NONPHARMACOLOGIC THERAPY

SURGERY:
- Selective transsphenoidal resection of the adenoma is the treatment of choice for prolactinoma, acromegaly, Cushing's disease, and thyrotropin-secreting pituitary adenomas, which all tend to be microadenomas at the time of onset of symptoms.
- Macroadenomas, such as the nonsecretory pituitary adenoma, may also be surgically removed, but risk of recurrence is greater with these tumors, and adjunctive therapy such as irradiation may also be necessary.
- Radiotherapy is reserved for patients who have failed surgical treatment and who still experience the symptoms of their adenoma.
- Bilateral adrenalectomy has been done in patients with Cushing's disease on failure of other therapies; complications requiring lifelong hormone replacement or Nelson's syndrome may occur.

RADIOTHERAPY:
- Generally reserved for patients who have failed surgical treatment
- Used with varying degrees of success in all of the different pituitary adenomas

PHARMACOLOGIC THERAPY

PROLACTINOMA:
- Bromocriptine, a dopamine analog, is generally given orally in divided doses of 1.5 to 10 mg.
- Side effects include orthostatic hypotension, nausea, and dizziness; avoided by beginning with low-dose therapy.
- Other compounds under investigation include pergolide mesylate, a long-acting ergot derivative with dopaminergic properties, as well as other nonergot derivatives.

ACROMEGALY:
- Octreotide, a somatostatin analog, 100 µg SC, is the medical therapy of choice but is limited by side effects such as biliary sludge and gallstones, nausea, cramps, steatorrhea, and its parenteral administration.
- Bromocriptine 10 to 20 mg PO tid-qid is less effective than octreotide, but has the advantage of oral administration.

CUSHING'S DISEASE:
- Ketoconazole, which inhibits the cytochrome P-450 enzymes involved in steroid biosynthesis, is effective in managing mild to moderate disease in daily oral dosages of 600 to 1200 mg.
- Metyrapone and aminoglutethimide can be used to control hypersecretion of cortisol but are generally used when preparing a patient for surgery or while waiting for a response to radiotherapy.

THYROTROPIN-SECRETING PITUITARY ADENOMA:
- Ablative therapy with either radioactive iodide or surgery is indicated.
- Treatment directed to the thyroid alone may accelerate growth of the pituitary adenoma.
- Octreotide has been shown to be effective in doses similar to those used for acromegaly.

NONSECRETORY PITUITARY ADENOMA:
- There is no role for medical therapy at this time
- Surgery and radiotherapy are indicated.

CHRONIC Rx

For all pituitary adenomas:
- Careful follow-up is important. Patients undergoing transsphenoidal microsurgical resection should be seen in 4 to 6 wk to ensure that the adenoma has been completely removed and that the endocrine hypersecretion is resolved.
- If there is good clinical response, patient should be monitored yearly for recurrence and to follow the level of the hypersecreted hormone.
- Patients who have undergone irradiation should have close follow-up with backup medical therapy because response to radiotherapy may be delayed; incidence of hypopituitarism also increases with time.

SUGGESTED READINGS

Davis AK, Farrell WE, Clayton RN: Pituitary tumors, *Reproduction* 121(3):363, 2001.

Kovacs K, Horvath E, Vidal S: Classification of pituitary adenomas, *J Neurooncol* 54(2): 121, 2001.

Shimon I, Melmed S: Management of pituitary tumors, *Ann Intern Med* 129:472, 1998.

AUTHOR: **BETH J. WUTZ, M.D.**

Pityriasis Rosea 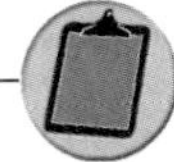

BASIC INFORMATION

DEFINITION

Pityriasis is a common self-limiting skin eruption of unknown etiology.

ICD-9CM CODES
696.3 Pityriasis rosea

EPIDEMIOLOGY & DEMOGRAPHICS

- Most cases of pityriasis rosea occur between ages 10 and 35 yr; mean age is 23 yr.
- The incidence of disease is highest in the fall and spring.
- Female:male ratio is 1.5:1.

PHYSICAL FINDINGS & CLINICAL PRESENTATION

- Initial lesion (herald patch) precedes the eruption by approximately 1 to 2 wk; typically measures 3 to 6 cm; it is round to oval in appearance and most frequently located on the trunk.
- Eruptive phase follows within 2 wk and peaks after 7 to 14 days.
- Lesions are most frequently located in the lower abdominal area. They have a salmon-pink appearance in whites and a hyperpigmented appearance in blacks.
- Most lesions are 4 to 5 mm in diameter; center has a "cigarette paper" appearance; border has a characteristic ring of scale (collarette).
- Lesions occur in a symmetric distribution and follow the cleavage lines of the trunk (Christmas tree pattern [Fig. 1-182]).
- The number of lesions varies from a few to hundreds.
- Most patients are asymptomatic; pruritus is the most common symptom.
- History of recent fatigue, headache, sore throat, and low-grade fever is present in approximately 25% of cases.

ETIOLOGY

Unknown, possibly viral (picornavirus)

DIAGNOSIS

DIFFERENTIAL DIAGNOSIS

- Tinea corporis (can be ruled out by potassium hydroxide examination)
- Secondary syphilis (absence of herald patch, positive serologic test for syphilis)
- Psoriasis
- Nummular eczema
- Drug eruption
- Viral exanthem
- Eczema
- Lichen planus
- Tinea versicolor (the lesions are more brown and the borders are not as ovoid)

WORKUP

Presence of herald lesion and characteristic rash are diagnostic. Skin biopsy is generally reserved for atypical cases.

LABORATORY TESTS

Generally not necessary; serologic test for syphilis if clinically indicated

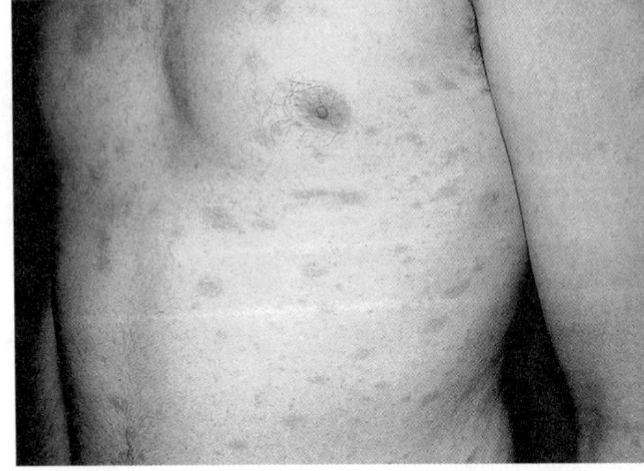

FIGURE 1-182 Scale (pityriasis rosea). Shows example of how unique scaling (collarette of fine scale within several lesions), distribution and shape of lesions (oval lesions with long axis paralleling natural skin cleavage lines), and color (salmon-pink) help in diagnosing skin disease. (From Noble J [ed]: *Textbook of primary care medicine,* ed 3, St Louis, 2001, Mosby.)

TREATMENT

NONPHARMACOLOGIC THERAPY

The disease is self-limited and generally does not require any therapeutic intervention.

ACUTE GENERAL Rx

- Use calamine lotion or oral antihistamines in patients with significant pruritus.
- Use prednisone tapered over 2 wk in patients with severe pruritus.
- Direct sun exposure or use of ultraviolet light within the first week of eruption is beneficial in decreasing the severity of disease.

DISPOSITION

- Spontaneous complete resolution of the rash within 4 to 8 wk
- Recurrence rare (<2% of cases)

PEARLS & CONSIDERATIONS

COMMENTS

Reassure patient that the disease is not contagious and its course is benign.

SUGGESTED READING

Stulberg D, Wolfrey J: Pityaris rosea, *Am Fam Physician,* 69:87, 2004.

AUTHOR: **FRED F. FERRI, M.D.**

BASIC INFORMATION

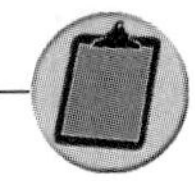

DEFINITION

Placenta previa is the implantation of the placenta over the internal os. Four degrees of this abnormality have been defined:

- Total placenta previa: the internal os is covered completely.
- Partial placenta previa: the internal os is partially covered.
- Marginal placenta previa: the edge of the placenta is at the margin of the internal os.
- Low-lying placenta: the placenta is implanted in the lower uterine segment, and although its edge does not reach the internal os, it is in close proximity to it.

See Fig. 1-183.

ICD-9CM CODES
641.1 Placenta previa

EPIDEMIOLOGY & DEMOGRAPHICS INCIDENCE

0.26% to 0.7% of pregnancies

RISK FACTORS

Previous cesarean delivery (after one such delivery, the risk is 1% to 4%; after four or more cesarean deliveries, the risk approaches 10%). Multiparity has also been associated with placenta previa.

PHYSICAL FINDINGS & CLINICAL PRESENTATION

The classic presentation of placenta previa is painless vaginal bleeding, usually in the second or third trimester. Uterine contractions may or may not be present. On physical examination, the uterus is soft and pain-free. The fetus is often in breech, transverse lie, or high. Fetal distress is usually not present.

ETIOLOGY

Uncertain

DIAGNOSIS

DIFFERENTIAL DIAGNOSIS

- Placenta accreta
- Placenta percreta
- Placenta increta
- Vasa previa
- Abruptio placentae
- Vaginal or cervical trauma
- Labor
- Local malignancy

WORKUP

- Do NOT perform a digital vaginal examination.
- The diagnosis of placenta previa can seldom be firmly established by physical examination alone. A speculum examination in a hospital setting to exclude any local bleeding may be performed.
- This diagnosis should not be dismissed until thorough evaluation, including sonography, has completely excluded its presence.

LABORATORY TESTS

- A complete blood count (CBC) can be used to monitor hemoglobin and hematocrit
- A Kleihauer-Betke preparation of maternal blood in all Rh-negative women and Rh-immune globulin when indicated

IMAGING STUDIES

- The simplest, most precise, and safest method of placental localization is transabdominal sonography with confirmatory imaging by transvaginal ultrasonography. Transperineal sonography has also proven effective in detection.
- Magnetic resonance imaging has also been effective in detecting placenta previa, although sonography remains the preferred method.

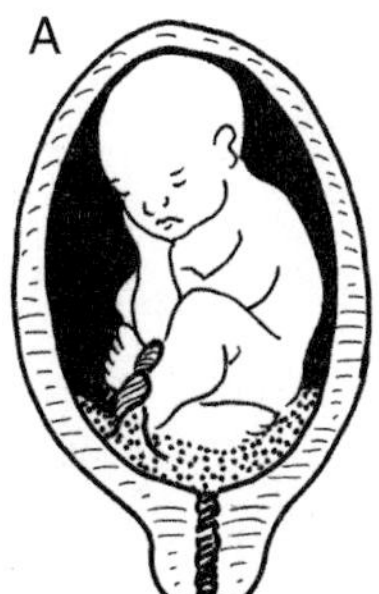

FIGURE 1-183 Various types of placenta previa. **A,** The cervical os is completely covered by placenta. **B,** The cervical os is partially covered by placenta. **C,** The placenta extends to the edge of the cervical os. (From Rakel RE: *Textbook of family practice,* ed 6, Philadelphia, 2002, WB Saunders.)

TREATMENT

NONPHARMACOLOGIC THERAPY

- In preterm pregnancies with no active bleeding, close observation and expectant management are indicated. In those with active bleeding, conservative management, including blood transfusions for severe bleeds, is appropriate. The woman should stay in the hospital for at least 48 hr after the bleeding has stopped.
- Bedrest, preferably in a hospital setting, should be prescribed.

ACUTE GENERAL Rx

- Initial assessment for signs of maternal hemodynamic compromise or hemorrhagic shock; large-bore intravenous access with crystalloid fluid resuscitation
- Assess fetal status and gestational age using sonogram and continuous fetal heart rate monitoring
- Cross-matched blood should be made available during bleeding episodes; if the hemorrhage is severe, cesarean delivery is indicated despite fetal immaturity
- Tocolytic therapy may be considered in those women in preterm labor, as well as the administration of corticosteroids to enhanced fetal lung maturity

CHRONIC Rx

- Cesarean delivery is necessary in nearly all cases of placenta previa.
- Uncontrollable hemorrhage after placental removal should be anticipated secondary to the poorly contractile nature of the lower uterine segment. The need for hysterectomy to control bleeding should be discussed with the patient before delivery, if possible.

DISPOSITION

Because of the unpredictable nature of placenta previa, not all women with placenta previa can be treated expectantly.

REFERRAL

Affected women and their families should be aware of all signs and symptoms that would necessitate immediate transport to the hospital. The possibility of hysterectomy should also be discussed early during pregnancy.

SUGGESTED READINGS

Baron F, Hill WC: Placenta previa, placenta abruptio, *Clin Obstet Gynecol* 41(3):527, 1998.

Faiz AS, Ananth CV: Etiology and risk factors for placenta previa: an overview and meta-analysis of observational studies, *J Matern Fetal Neonatal Med* 13(3):175, 2003.

AUTHOR: **SONYA S. ABDEL-RAZEQ, M.D**

Plantar Fasciitis

BASIC INFORMATION

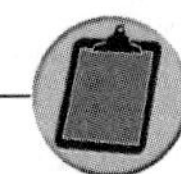

DEFINITION

Plantar fasciitis is a common, painful inflammation or degeneration of the plantar fascia, a tissue that extends from the calcaneus to the proximal phalanges of each toe.

SYNONYMS

Painful heel syndrome
Painful heel spur

ICD-9CM CODES
728.71 Plantar fasciitis
726.73 Calcaneal spur

EPIDEMIOLOGY & DEMOGRAPHICS

PREVALENT AGE: Middle age
PREVALENT SEX: Males = females
Bilateral in 10% to 20% of cases

PHYSICAL FINDINGS & CLINICAL PRESENTATION

- Pain is characteristically worse on arising and after periods of rest; "warming up" often lessens the pain
- Local tenderness at site involvement, usually the medial tubercle of the calcaneus, sometimes in the midfascia
- Pain sometimes elicited by passive dorsiflexion of toes and ankle, which stretches the plantar fascia
- A tight heel cord may be present

ETIOLOGY

- Uncertain
- Inflammation, microscopic tears, and/or degeneration
- The role of the calcaneal traction osteophyte (spur) is unclear
- May be associated with tight heel cord

DIAGNOSIS

DIFFERENTIAL DIAGNOSIS

- Other regional tendonitis
- Stress fracture
- Tarsal tunnel syndrome
- Tumor, infection

IMAGING STUDIES

Traction osteophyte or minor soft tissue calcification may be present on plain radiography. Other studies are usually not required.

TREATMENT

- Sensible activity restriction
- Gentle stretching exercises
- NSAIDS
- Local steroid/lidocaine injections (Fig. 1-184)
- Heel lift
- Night brace, daytime cast brace

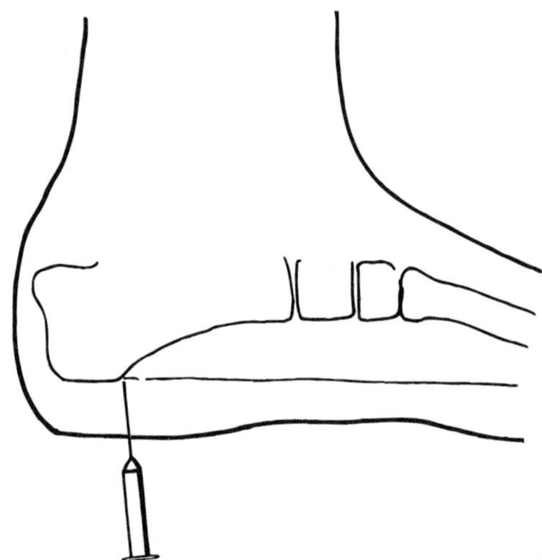

FIGURE 1-184 Injection site for plantar fasciitis. Injection should be through the sole into the area of maximum tenderness. A 25- or 27-gauge needle should be used and the medication injected slowly as some pain may occur. The total volume should be no greater than 1.5 ml. (From Mercier L: *Practical orthopedics,* ed 5, St Louis, 2002, Mosby.)

DISPOSITION

Disorder is usually self-limited, although full recovery may take 1 to 2 yr.

REFERRAL

- If symptoms fail to respond to medical management
- For surgical consideration (plantar fascia release, excision of osteophyte)

PEARLS & CONSIDERATIONS

COMMENTS

- Various cushions and heel cups are generally ineffective because stretching, not heel strikes, is probably cause of disorder.
- Surgical intervention is rarely necessary.
- Shock wave therapy is of unproven benefit.

SUGGESTED READINGS

Aldridge J: Diagnosing heel pain in adults, *Am Fam Physician* 70:332, 2004.

Bachbinder R et al: Ultrasound-guided extracorporeal shockwave therapy for plantar fasciitis, *JAMA* 288:1364, 2002.

Bachbinder R: Plantar fasciitis, *N Engl J Med* 350:2159, 2004.

DiGiovanni BF et al: Tissue specific plantar fascia stretching exercises enhances outcomes in patients with chronic heel pain, *J Bone Joint Surg* 85:1270, 2003.

Haake M et al: Extra-corporeal shockwave therapy for plantar fasciitis: randomized controlled multicentre trial, *Br Med J* 327:75, 2003.

Riddle DL et al: Risk factors for plantar fasciitis: a matched case-control study, *J Bone Joint Surg* 85:872, 2003.

Rompe JD et al: Evaluation of low-energy extracorporeal shockwave application for chronic plantar fasciitis, *J Bone Joint Surg* 84(A):335, 2002.

Young CC et al: Treatment of plantar fasciitis, *Am Fam Physician* 63:467, 2001.

AUTHOR: **LONNIE R. MERCIER, M.D.**

BASIC INFORMATION

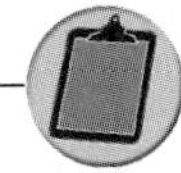

DEFINITION

Aspiration pneumonia is a lung infection caused by bacterial organisms aspirated from nasopharyngeal space.

ICD-9CM CODES
507.0 Aspiration pneumonia

EPIDEMIOLOGY & DEMOGRAPHICS

INCIDENCE (IN U.S.):
- Few reliable data
- 20% to 35% of all pneumonias
- 5% to 15% of all community acquired pneumonias

PREVALENCE (IN U.S.): Unreliable data
PREDOMINANT SEX: Equal
PREDOMINANT AGE: Elderly
PEAK INCIDENCE: Elderly patients in hospitals or nursing homes

PHYSICAL FINDINGS & CLINICAL PRESENTATION

- Shortness of breath, tachypnea, cough, sputum, fever after vomiting, or difficulty swallowing
- Rales, rhonchi, often diffusely throughout lung

ETIOLOGY

Complex interaction of etiologies, ranging from chemical (often acid) pneumonitis following aspiration of sterile gastric contents (generally not requiring antibiotic treatment) to bacterial aspiration

COMMUNITY-ACQUIRED ASPIRATION PNEUMONIA:
- Generally results from predominantly anaerobic mouth bacteria (anaerobic and microaerophilic streptococci, fusobacteria, gram-positive anaerobic non–spore-forming rods), *Bacteroides* species *(melaninogenicus, intermedius, oralis, ureolyticus), Haemophilus influenzae,* and *Streptococcus pneumoniae*
- Rarely caused by *Bacteroides fragilis* (of uncertain validity in published studies) or *Eikenella corrodens*
- High-risk groups: elderly, alcoholics, IV drug users, patients who are obtunded, those with esophageal disorders, seizures, poor dentition, stroke victims, or recent dental manipulations

HOSPITAL-ACQUIRED ASPIRATION PNEUMONIA:
- Often occurs among elderly patients and others with diminished gag reflex; those with nasogastric tubes, intestinal obstruction, or ventilator support; and especially those exposed to contaminated nebulizers or unsterile suctioning
- High-risk groups: seriously ill hospitalized patients (especially patients with coma, acidosis, alcoholism, uremia, diabetes mellitus, nasogastric intubation, or recent antimicrobial therapy, who are frequently colonized with aerobic gram-negative rods); patients undergoing anesthesia; those with strokes, dementia, swallowing disorders; the elderly; and those receiving antacids or H_2 blockers (but not sucralfate)
- Hypoxic patients receiving concentrated O_2 have diminished ciliary activity, encouraging aspiration
- Causative organisms:
  1. Anaerobes listed previously, although in many studies gram-negative aerobes (60%) and gram-positive aerobes (20%) predominate
  2. *E. coli, P. aeruginosa, S. aureus, Klebsiella, Enterobacter, Serratia,* and *Proteus* spp. *H. influenzae, S. pneumoniae, Legionella,* and *Acinetobacter* spp. (sporadic pneumonias) in two thirds of cases
  3. Fungi, including *Candida albicans,* in fewer than 1%

DIAGNOSIS

DIFFERENTIAL DIAGNOSIS

- Other necrotizing or cavitary pneumonias (especially tuberculosis, gram-negative pneumonias)
- See "Pulmonary Tuberculosis"

WORKUP

- Chest x-ray examination
- CBC, blood cultures
- Sputum Gram stain and culture
- Consideration of tracheal aspirate

LABORATORY TESTS

- CBC: leukocytosis often present
- Sputum Gram stain
  1. Often useful when carefully prepared immediately after obtaining suctioned or expectorated specimen, examined by experienced observer.
  2. Only specimens with multiple WBCs and rare or absent epithelial cells should be examined.
  3. Unlike nonaspiration pneumonias (e.g., pneumococcal), multiple organisms may be present.
  4. Long, slender rods suggest anaerobes.
  5. Sputum from pneumonia caused by acid aspiration may be devoid of organisms.
  6. Cultures should be interpreted in light of morphology of visualized organisms.

IMAGING STUDIES

- Chest x-ray examination often reveals bilateral, diffuse, patchy infiltrates, and posterior segment upper lobes.
- Aspiration pneumonias of several days' or longer duration may reveal necrosis (especially community-acquired anaerobic pneumonias) and even cavitation with air-fluid levels, indicating lung abscess.

TREATMENT

NONPHARMACOLOGIC THERAPY

- Airway management to prevent repeated aspiration
- Ventilatory support if necessary

ACUTE GENERAL Rx

Acute aspiration of acidic gastric contents without bacteria may not require antibiotic therapy; consult infectious diseases or pulmonary expert.

FOR COMMUNITY-ACQUIRED ANAEROBIC ASPIRATION PNEUMONIA:
- Levofloxacin 500 mg qd or ceftriaxone 1 to 2 g/day

NURSING HOME ASPIRATIONS:
- Levofloxacin 500 mg qd or piperacillin-tazobactam 3.375 g q6h or ceftazidime 2 g q8h

HOSPITAL-ACQUIRED ASPIRATION PNEUMONIA:
- Piperacillin-tazobactam 3.375 g IV q6h, or clindamycin 450-900 mg IV q8h, or cefoxitin 2 g IV q8h
- Knowledge of resident flora in the microenvironment of the aspiration within the hospital is crucial to intelligent antibiotic selection; consult infection control nurses or hospital epidemiologist.
- Confirmed *Pseudomonas* pneumonia should be treated with antipseudomonal β-lactam agent plus an aminoglycoside until antimicrobial sensitivities confirm that less toxic agents may replace aminoglycoside.
- Do not use metronidazole alone for anaerobes.

DISPOSITION

Repeat chest x-ray examination in 6 to 8 wk.

REFERRAL

For consultation with infectious disease and/or pulmonary experts for patients with respiratory distress, hypoxia, ventilatory support, pneumonia in more than one lobe, necrosis or cavitation on x-ray examination, or not responding to antibiotic therapy within 2 to 3 days

SUGGESTED READING

Marik PE: Aspiration pneumonitis and aspiration pneumonia, *N Engl J Med* 344:665, 2001.

AUTHOR: **BETH J. WUTZ, M.D.**

BASIC INFORMATION

DEFINITION

Bacterial pneumonia is an infection involving the lung parenchyma

ICD-9CM CODES
486.0 Pneumonia, acute
507.0 Pneumonia, aspiration
482.9 Pneumonia, bacterial
481 Pneumonia, pneumococcal
482.1 Pneumonia, *Pseudomonas*
482.4 Pneumonia, staphylococcal
428.0 Pneumonia, *Klebsiella*
482.2 Pneumonia, *Haemophilus influenzae*

EPIDEMIOLOGY & DEMOGRAPHICS

- Incidence of community-acquired pneumonia is 1/100 persons.
- Incidence of nosocomial pneumonia is 8 cases/1000 persons/yr.
- Primary care physicians see an average of 10 cases of pneumonia annually.
- Hospitalization rate for pneumonia is 15% to 20%.
- Most cases of pneumonia occur in the winter and in elderly patients.

PHYSICAL FINDINGS & CLINICAL PRESENTATION

- Fever, tachypnea, chills, tachycardia, cough
- Presentation varies with the cause of pneumonia, the patient's age, and the clinical situation:
  1. Patients with streptococcal pneumonia usually present with high fever, shaking chills, pleuritic chest pain, cough, and copious production of purulent sputum.
  2. Elderly or immunocompromised hosts may initially present with only minimal symptoms (e.g., low-grade fever, confusion); respiratory and nonrespiratory symptoms are less commonly reported by older patients with pneumonia.
  3. Generally, auscultation reveals crackles and diminished breath sounds.
  4. Percussion dullness is present if the patient has pleural effusion.

ETIOLOGY

- *Streptococcus pneumoniae*
- *Haemophilus influenzae*
- *Legionella pneumophila* (1% to 5% of adult pneumonias)
- *Klebsiella, Pseudomonas, E. coli*
- *Staphylococcus aureus*
- Pneumococcal infection is responsible for 50% to 75% of community-acquired pneumonias, whereas gram-negative organisms cause >80% of nosocomial pneumonias
- Predisposing factors are:
  1. COPD: *H. influenzae, S. pneumoniae, Legionella*
  2. Seizures: aspiration pneumonia
  3. Compromised hosts: *Legionella*, gram-negative organisms
  4. Alcoholism: *Klebsiella, S. pneumoniae, H. influenzae*
  5. HIV: *S. pneumoniae*
  6. IV drug addicts with right-sided bacterial endocarditis: *S. aureus*

DIAGNOSIS

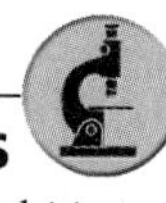

DIFFERENTIAL DIAGNOSIS

- Exacerbation of chronic bronchitis
- Pulmonary embolism or infarction
- Lung neoplasm
- Bronchiolitis
- Sarcoidosis
- Hypersensitivity pneumonitis
- Pulmonary edema
- Drug-induced lung injury
- Viral pneumonias
- Fungal pneumonias
- Parasitic pneumonias
- Atypical pneumonia
- Tuberculosis

WORKUP

Laboratory evaluation and chest x-ray examination

LABORATORY TESTS

- In hospitalized patients, attempt to obtain an adequate sputum specimen for Gram stain and cultures.
  1. An expectorated sputum sample is often inadequate because of many false positive results (secondary to contamination from oral flora) and many false negative results; a specimen may be considered adequate if the Gram stain shows >25 PMNs and <10 epithelial cells per low-power field.
  2. Aerosol induction with hypertonic saline solution (3% to 10%) may increase the diagnostic yield of sputum.
  3. The use of fiberoptic bronchoscopy to obtain a sputum sample is generally reserved for critically ill patients responding poorly to initial antimicrobial therapy.
  4. Gram stain of sputum may reveal the following:

  Lancet-shaped, gram-positive cocci indicate streptococcal pneumonia.

  Pleomorphic, small coccobacillary, gram-negative organisms indicate *H. influenzae*.

  Encapsulated gram-negative bacilli: *K. pneumoniae*
- WBC count is elevated, usually with left shift
- Blood cultures: positive in approximately 20% of cases of pneumococcal pneumonia
- Pulse oximetry or ABGs: hypoxemia with partial pressure of oxygen <60 mm Hg while the patient is breathing room air is a standard criterion for hospital admission
- Direct immunofluorescent examination of sputum when suspecting Legionella (e.g., direct fluorescent antibody [DFA] stain is a highly specific and rapid test for detecting legionellae in clinical specimen)
- Serologic testing for HIV in selected patients

IMAGING STUDIES

Chest x-ray: findings vary with the stage and type of pneumonia and the hydration of the patient (Fig. 1-185).

- Classically, pneumococcal pneumonia presents with a segmental lobe infiltrate.
- Diffuse infiltrates on chest x-ray can be seen with *L. pneumophila, M. pneumoniae*, viral pneumonias, *P. carinii*, miliary TB, aspiration, aspergillosis.
- An initial chest x-ray is also useful to rule out the presence of any complications (pneumothorax, empyema, abscesses).

TREATMENT

NONPHARMACOLOGIC THERAPY

- Avoidance of tobacco use
- Oxygen to maintain partial oxygen pressure in arterial blood >60 mm Hg
- IV hydration, correction of dehydration
- Assisted ventilation in patients with significant respiratory failure

ACUTE GENERAL Rx

- Initial antibiotic therapy should be based on clinical, radiographic, and laboratory evaluation.
- Macrolides (azithromycin or clarithromycin) or levofloxacin is recommended for empirical out-patient treatment of community-acquired pneumonia; cefotaxime or a beta-lactam/beta-lactamase inhibitor can be added in patients with more severe presentation who insist on out-patient therapy. Duration of treatment ranges from 7 to 14 days.
- In the hospital setting, patients admitted to the general ward can be treated empirically with a second- or third-generation cephalosporin (ceftriaxone, ceftizoxime, cefotaxime, or cefuroxime) plus a macrolide (azithromycin or clarithromycin) or doxycycline. An an-

tipseudomonal quinolone (levofloxacin, moxifloxacin, or gatifloxacin) may be substituted in place of the macrolide or doxycycline.
- In hospitalized patients at risk for *P. aeruginosa* infection, empirical treatment should consist of an antipseudomonal beta-lactam (cefepime or piperacillin-tazobactam) *plus* an aminoglycoside *plus* an antipseudomonal quinolone or macrolide.

CHRONIC Rx

Parapneumonic effusion-empyema can be managed with chest tube placement for drainage. Instillation of fibrinolytic agents (streptokinase, urokinase) via the chest tube may be necessary in resistant cases.

DISPOSITION

- Most patients respond well to antibiotic therapy.
- Indications for hospital admission are:
  1. Hypoxemia (oxygen saturation <90% while patient is breathing room air)
  2. Hemodynamic instability
  3. Inability to tolerate medications
  4. Active co-existing condition requiring hospitalization

PEARLS & CONSIDERATIONS

COMMENTS

Causes of slowly resolving or nonresolving pneumonia:
- Difficult to treat infections: viral pneumonia, *Legionella,* pneumococci, or staphylococci with impaired host response, TB, fungi
- Neoplasm: lung, lymphoma, metastasis
- CHF
- Pulmonary embolism
- Immunologic or idiopathic: Wegener's granulomatosis, pulmonary eosinophilic syndromes, SLE
- Drug toxicity (e.g., amiodarone)

SUGGESTED READINGS

Davidson R et al: Resistance to levofloxacin and failure of treatment of pneumococcal pneumonia, *N Engl J Med* 346:747, 2002.

Halm EA, Teirstein AS: Management of community-acquired pneumonia, *N Engl J Med* 347:2039, 2002.

AUTHOR: **FRED F. FERRI, M.D.**

A

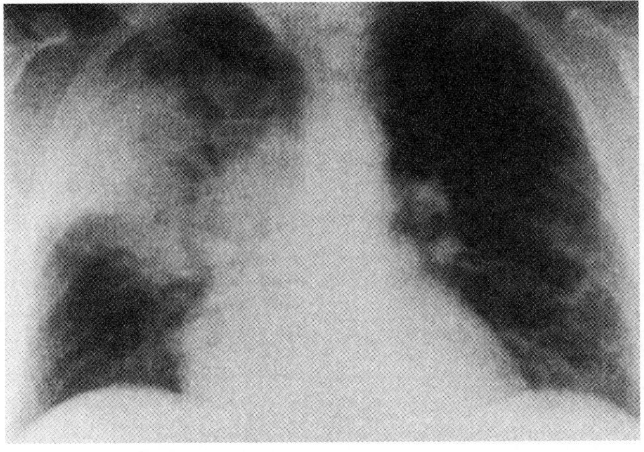

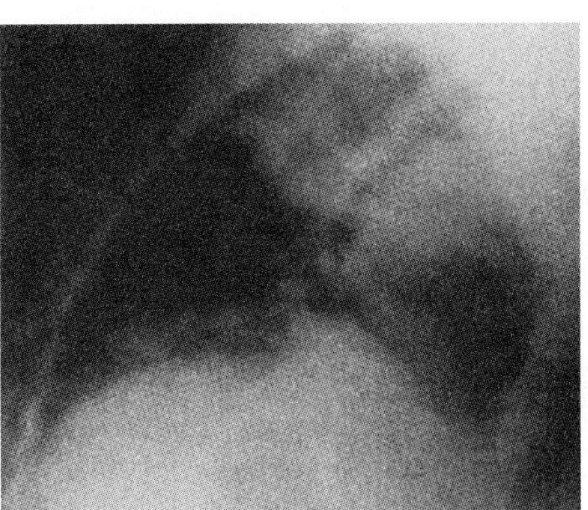

B

FIGURE 1-185 **A,** PA and, **B,** lateral chest radiographs reveal right upper lobe pneumonia and patchy left lower lobe infiltrate. A variety of organisms can produce this pattern, including *S. pneumoniae* and *H. influenzae.* (From Marx J [ed]: Rosen's *Emergency medicine,* ed 5, St Louis, 2003, Mosby.)

BASIC INFORMATION

DEFINITION

Mycoplasma pneumonia is an infection of the lung parenchyma caused by *Mycoplasma pneumoniae.*

SYNONYMS

Primary atypical pneumonia
Eaton's pneumonia
Walking pneumonia

ICD-9CM CODES
483 *Mycoplasma* pneumonia

EPIDEMIOLOGY & DEMOGRAPHICS

INCIDENCE (IN U.S.):
- Hard to determine incidence precisely because of difficulty in making the diagnosis, but it is a frequent cause of community-acquired pneumonia.
- Probably many cases resolve without coming to medical attention.
- Incidence is estimated at 1 case/1000 persons/yr.
- Incidence is estimated to at least triple every (approximately) 5 yr during epidemics.

PREVALENCE (IN U.S.):
- Estimated to be present in 1 of 5 patients hospitalized for pneumonia (generally a self-limited disease, so its true prevalence is unknown)
- Estimated to cause 7% of all pneumonias and about half in those age 5 to 20 yr

PREDOMINANT SEX: Equal distribution
PREDOMINANT AGE:
- Most commonly affected: school-age children and young adults (ages 5 to 20 yr)
- Occurs in older adults as well, especially with household exposure to a young child
- More severe infections in affected elderly patients

PEAK INCIDENCE:
- Some increased incidence in fall to early winter
- Seems more prevalent in temperate climates

GENETICS:
Familial Disposition:
- None known
- May be more severe in patients with sickle cell anemia

Neonatal Infection: Severe respiratory distress, sometimes requiring intubation, attributed to this disease in infants.

PHYSICAL FINDINGS & CLINICAL PRESENTATION

- Nonexudative pharyngitis (common)
- Rhonchi or rales, without evidence of consolidation (common) in lower lung zones
- Associated with bullous myringitis (perhaps no more frequently than in other pneumonias)
- Skin rashes in up to one fourth of patients
  1. Morbilliform
  2. Urticaria
  3. Erythema nodosum (unusual)
  4. Erythema multiforme (unusual)
  5. Stevens-Johnson syndrome (rare)
- Muscle tenderness (<50% of the patients)
- On examination (and confirmed with testing):
  1. Mononeuritis or polyneuritis
  2. Transverse myelitis
  3. Cranial nerve palsies
  4. Meningoencephalitis
- Lymphadenopathy and splenomegaly
- Conjunctivitis

ETIOLOGY

Infection is spread by droplet infection from respiratory tract secretions.

DIAGNOSIS

DIFFERENTIAL DIAGNOSIS

- *Chlamydia pneumoniae*
- *C. psittaci*
- *Legionella* spp.
- *Coxiella burnetii*
- Several viral agents
- Q fever
- *Pneumococcus pneumoniae*
- Pleuritic pain
- Pulmonary embolism/infarction

WORKUP

- Chest x-ray examination
- Thorough history and physical examination
- Laboratory tests
- Evaluation guided by symptoms and findings

LABORATORY TESTS

- WBC:
  1. WBC count >10,000/mm^3 in about a quarter of patients
  2. Differential count nonspecific
  3. Leukopenia rare
- Cold agglutinins:
  1. Detected in about half of the patients
  2. Also may be found in:
     a. Lymphoproliferative diseases
     b. Influenza
     c. Mononucleosis
     d. Adenovirus infections
     e. Occasionally, Legionnaires' disease
  3. Titers typically >1:64
     a. May be detectable with bedside testing
     b. Appear between days 5 and 10 of the illness (so may be demonstrable when patient is first examined) and disappear within about 1 mo
- Uncommonly, hemolysis
- Complement fixation testing of paired sera (fourfold rise) in patients with pneumonia and a compatible history:
  1. Considered diagnostic
  2. Not specific for the disease
- Culture of the organism from specimens
  1. Only truly specific test for infection
  2. Technically difficult and done reliably by few laboratories
  3. May require weeks to get results
- Sputum
  1. Often no sputum produced for laboratory testing
  2. When present, gram-stained specimens show polyps without organisms
- Infection occasionally complicated by pancreatitis or glomerulitis
- Disseminated intravascular coagulation is a rare complication.
- Electrocardiographic evidence of pericarditis or myocarditis may be present.

IMAGING STUDIES

- Predilection for lower lobe involvement (upper lobes involved in less than a fourth), with radiographic abnormalities frequently out of proportion to those on physical examination (Fig. 1-186)
- Small pleural effusions in about 30% of patients
- Large effusions: rare
- Infiltrates: patchy, unilateral, and with a segmental distribution, although multilobe involvement may be seen
- Evidence of hilar adenopathy on chest films in 20% to 25%
- Rare cases reported:
  1. Associated lung abscess
  2. Residual pneumatoceles
  3. Lobar collapse
  4. Hyperlucent lung syndrome

TREATMENT

ACUTE GENERAL Rx

- Therapy (10 to 14 days) with erythromycin (500 mg qid), azithromycin (500 mg daily), or clarithromycin (500 mg bid) is preferred to tetracycline, especially in young children or women of childbearing age.
- Therapy shortens the duration and severity of symptoms and may hasten radiographic clearing, but the disease is self-limiting.

CHRONIC Rx

- Effective antimicrobial therapy does not eliminate the organism from the respiratory secretions, which may be positive for weeks.
- Serum antibody response does not necessarily provide lifelong immunity.
- Chronic symptoms do not occur, although clinical relapses may occur 7 to 10 days following the initial response and may be associated with new areas of infiltration.

DISPOSITION

- Clinical improvement is almost universal within 10 days.
- Infiltrates generally clear within 5 to 8 wk.
- Rare deaths are likely attributable to underlying medical diseases.
- Person-to-person spread can be minimized by avoiding open coughing, especially in enclosed areas.

REFERRAL

- Not responding to treatment
- Severe infection
- Severe extrapulmonary manifestations
- Multilobe involvement accompanied by respiratory embarrassment (very rare)

PEARLS & CONSIDERATIONS

COMMENTS

X-ray resolution complete by 8 wk in about 90% of patients.

SUGGESTED READINGS

Falguera M et al: Nonsevere community-acquired pneumonia: correlation between cause and severity or comorbidity, *Arch Intern Med* 161(15):1866, 2001.

Hyde TB et al: Azithromycin prophylaxis during a hospital outbreak of *Mycoplasma pneumoniae* pneumonia, *J Infect Dis* 183(6):907, 2001.

Waites KG, Talkington DF: Mycoplasma pneumoniae and its role as a human pathogen, *Clin Microbiol Rev* 17(4):697, 2004.

AUTHOR: **HARVEY M. SHANIES, M.D., PH.D.**

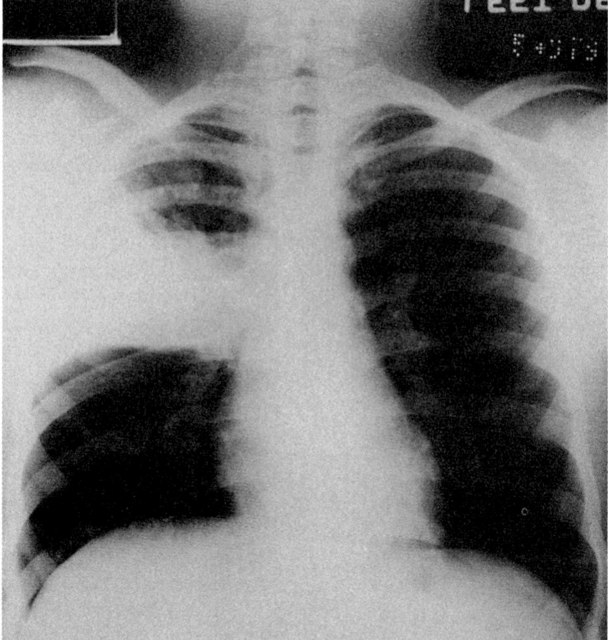

FIGURE 1-186 Localized airspace opacification secondary to *Mycoplasma pneumoniae*. (From Specht N [ed]: *Practical guide to diagnostic imaging,* St Louis, 1998, Mosby.)

SECTION I

BASIC INFORMATION

DEFINITION

Pneumocystis carinii pneumonia is a serious respiratory infection caused by the fungal or protozoal organism *Pneumocystis carinii.*

SYNONYMS

PCP

ICD-9CM CODES
136.3 *Pneumocystis carinii* pneumonia

EPIDEMIOLOGY & DEMOGRAPHICS

INCIDENCE (IN U.S.):

- Seen primarily in the setting of acquired immunodeficiency syndrome (AIDS)
- Approximately 11 cases/100 patient-years among HIV-infected patients with CD4 lymphocyte counts <100/mm^3

PREDOMINANT SEX: Equal incidence when corrected for HIV status

PREDOMINANT AGE:

- <2 yr
- 20 to 40 yr

PEAK INCIDENCE: 20 to 40 yr (parallel to AIDS epidemic)

GENETICS:

Neonatal Infection:

- Most frequent opportunistic infection among HIV-infected children, occurring in approximately 30%
- Neonatal occurrence unusual

PHYSICAL FINDINGS & CLINICAL PRESENTATION

- Fever, cough, shortness of breath present in almost all cases
- Lungs frequently clear to auscultation, although rales occasionally present
- Cyanosis and pronounced tachypnea in severe cases
- Hemoptysis unusual
- Spontaneous pneumothorax

ETIOLOGY

- *Pneumocystis carinii,* recently reclassified as a fungal organism
- Reactivation of dormant infection
- Extrapulmonary involvement rare

DIAGNOSIS

DIFFERENTIAL DIAGNOSIS

- Other opportunistic respiratory infections:
  1. Tuberculosis
  2. Histoplasmosis
  3. Cryptococcosis
- Nonopportunistic infections:
  1. Bacterial pneumonia
  2. Viral pneumonia
  3. Mycoplasmal pneumonia
  4. Legionellosis
- Occurs virtually exclusively in the setting of profound depression of cellular immunity

WORKUP

- Chest x-ray examination
- ABG
- Sputum examination for cysts of PCP and to exclude other pathogens
- Bronchoscopy with bronchoalveolar lavage or lung biopsy for diagnosis if sputum examination is negative or equivocal

LABORATORY TESTS

- ABG monitoring
- Elevated lactate dehydrogenase (LDH) in majority of cases
- HIV antibody test if cause of underlying immune deficiency state is unclear

IMAGING STUDIES

Diffuse uptake on gallium scanning of the lungs is suggestive but not diagnostic.

TREATMENT

NONPHARMACOLOGIC THERAPY

- Supplemental oxygen
- Ventilatory support if needed
- Prompt thoracotomy if pneumothorax develops

ACUTE GENERAL Rx

For confirmed or suspected PCP:

- Trimethoprim-sulfamethoxazole (20 mg/kg trimethoprim and 100 mg/kg sulfamethoxazole qd) PO or IV
- Pentamidine (4 mg/kg IV qd)
- Either regimen with prednisone (40 mg PO bid):
  1. If arterial oxygen pressure <70 mm Hg
  2. If arterial-alveolar oxygen pressure difference >35 mm Hg
  3. Dose tapered to 20 mg bid after 5 days and 20 mg qd after 10 days
- Therapy continued for 3 wk
- Alternative therapies available for patients unable to tolerate conventional therapy:
  1. Dapsone/trimethoprim
  2. Clindamycin/primaquine
  3. Atovaquone
- Alternative therapies should be given in consultation with a physician experienced in the management of PCP

CHRONIC Rx

- After completion of therapy, lifelong prophylaxis should be maintained with trimethoprim-sulfamethoxazole (one single-strength tablet PO qd or double-strength three times weekly).
- Patients intolerant of this therapy should be treated with dapsone (50 mg PO qd) plus pyrimethamine (50 mg PO weekly) plus leucovorin (25 mg PO weekly).
- Inhaled pentamidine (300 mg monthly by standardized nebulizer) is less effective and is reserved for patients intolerant to other forms of prophylaxis.
- Same approach taken to all HIV-infected patients with CD4 lymphocyte counts <200 to 250/mm^3 or <20% of the total lymphocyte count because of their high risk of PCP.

DISPOSITION

- Patients should be hospitalized unless infection mild.
- After completion of therapy, long-term ambulatory follow-up is mandatory to provide secondary prevention of PCP (see "Chronic Rx") and management of the underlying immunodeficiency syndrome.

REFERRAL

To pulmonologist for bronchoscopy if diagnosis cannot be confirmed by sputum examination

PEARLS & CONSIDERATIONS

COMMENTS

All patients, especially those with severe infection or intolerant of conventional therapy, should be followed by a physician experienced in the management of PCP and, if appropriate, in the long-term management of HIV infection or other underlying disease.

SUGGESTED READINGS

Al Soub H et al: *Pneumocystis carinii* pneumonia in a patient without a predisposing illness: case report and review, *Scand J Infect Dis* 36(8):618, 2004.

Kaplan JE et al: Epidemiology of human immunodeficiency virus: associated opportunistic infections in the United States in the era of highly active antiretroviral therapy, *Clin Infect Dis* 30(suppl 1):S5, 2000.

Kazanjian PH et al: Increase in prevalence of *Pneumocystis carinii* mutations in patients with AIDS and *P carinii* pneumonia, in the United States and China, *J Infect Dis* 189(9):1684, 2004.

Russian DA, Levine SJ: *Pneumocystis carinii* pneumonia in patients without HIV infection, *Am J Med Sci* 321(1):56, 2001.

AUTHOR: **JOSEPH R. MASCI, M.D.**

BASIC INFORMATION

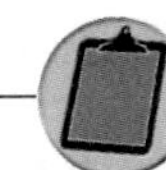

DEFINITION

Viral pneumonia is infection of the pulmonary parenchyma caused by any of a large number of viral agents. The most important viruses are discussed in the following sections.

SYNONYMS

Nonbacterial pneumonia
Atypical pneumonia

ICD-9CM CODES
480.9 Viral pneumonia

EPIDEMIOLOGY & DEMOGRAPHICS

INCIDENCE (IN U.S.):

- Influenza virus:
  1. 10% to 20% of population in temperate zones infected during 1- to 2-mo epidemics occurring yearly during winter months.
  2. Up to 50% infected during pandemics.
  3. Pneumonia develops in small percentage of infected persons.
- Incidence of other important viral pneumonias is not known precisely.

PREVALENCE (IN U.S.):

- Often related to immune status of the population or presence of an epidemic
- Normal hosts (estimates):
  1. 86% of cases of pneumonia resulting in hospitalization in American adults
  2. 16% of pediatric pneumonias managed as outpatients
  3. 49% of hospitalized infants with pneumonia
- Important problem in hosts with impaired immunity

PREDOMINANT SEX:

- None generally
- Male sex may predispose to more severe respiratory disease in respiratory syncytial virus (RSV) infection

PREDOMINANT AGE:

Influenza:

- Overall incidence greatest at age 5 yr
- Falls with increasing age
- The most serious sequelae in those with chronic medical illnesses, especially cardiopulmonary disease
- Hospitalizations greatest in infants and adults >64 yr of age

RSV:

- Young children (as the major cause of pneumonia)
- Occurs throughout life

Adenoviruses:

- Young children
- Adults, primarily military recruits

Varicella:

- About 16% of adults (not infected in childhood) who contract chickenpox
- Acute varicella during pregnancy more likely to be complicated by severe pneumonia
- 90% of reported varicella pneumonia cases are in adults (highest incidence 20 to 60 yr old)

Measles:

- Young adults and older children who received a single vaccination (5% failure rate)
- Measles during pregnancy more likely to be complicated by pneumonia
- Underlying cardiopulmonary diseases and immunosuppression predispose to serious pneumonia complicating measles
- Before availability of measles vaccine, 90% of pneumonias in those <10 yr
- Currently more than a third of U.S. patients >14 yr old
- 3% to 50% of measles cases are complicated by pneumonia

CMV:

- Neonatal through adult
- Immunosuppression is key predisposing factor

PEAK INCIDENCE:

Influenza:

- Winter months for influenza A
- Year round for influenza B
- Peak of pneumonia seen weeks into the outbreak of infection

RSV: Winter and spring
Adenovirus: Endemic (military)
Varicella: Spring in temperate zones
Measles: Year round
CMV: Year round

GENETICS:

Familial Disposition:

- Close contact, not genetics, is important in acquisition
- Congenital anomalies and immunosuppression worsen course of RSV pneumonia

Congenital Infection:

- CMV is the most common intrauterine infection in the U.S.
- Pneumonia occurs occasionally in infants with symptomatic congenital infection.

Neonatal Infection:

- Severe RSV pneumonia
- Adenovirus pneumonia
  1. 5% to 20% fatality rate
  2. Can lead to residual restrictive or obstructive functional abnormalities
- "Varicella neonatorum"
  1. Disseminated visceral disease including pneumonia
  2. May develop in neonates whose mothers develop peripartum chickenpox
- CMV pneumonia
  1. Generally fatal
  2. Associated with severe cerebral damage in this population

PHYSICAL FINDINGS & CLINICAL PRESENTATION

INFLUENZA:

- Fever
- Uncomfortable or lethargic appearance
- Prominent dry cough (rarely hemoptysis)
- Flushed integument and erythematous mucous membranes
- Rales or rhonchi

RSV:

- Fever
- Tachypnea
- Prolonged expiration
- Wheezes and rales

ADENOVIRUSES:

- Hoarseness
- Pharyngitis
- Tachypnea
- Cervical adenitis

MEASLES:

- Conjunctivitis
- Rhinorrhea
- Koplik's spots
- Exanthem
- Pneumonitis
  1. May occur as a complication in 3% to 4% of adolescents and young adults
  2. Coincident with rash
  3. May also develop following apparent recovery from measles
- Fever
- Dry cough

VARICELLA:

- Fever
- Maculopapular or vesicular rash
  1. Becomes encrusted
  2. Pneumonia typical 1 to 6 days after rash appears
  3. Pneumonia accompanied by cough, and occasionally hemoptysis
- Few auscultatory abnormalities noted on examination of the lungs

CMV:

- Fever
- Paroxysmal cough
- Occasional hemoptysis
- Diffuse adenopathy when pneumonia occurs after transfusion

ETIOLOGY

Viral infection can lead to pneumonia in both immunocompetent and immunocompromised hosts.

DIAGNOSIS

DIFFERENTIAL DIAGNOSIS

- Bacterial pneumonia, which frequently complicates (i.e., can follow or be simultaneous with) viral (especially influenza) pneumonia
- Other causes of atypical pneumonia:
  1. *Mycoplasma*
  2. *Chlamydia*
  3. *Coxiella*
  4. Legionnaires' disease

- ARDS
- Physical findings and associated hypoxemia confused with pulmonary emboli

WORKUP

- Information about the prevalent strain of influenza virus can be obtained from local health departments or from the Centers for Disease Control and Prevention.
- Viral diagnostic tests are usually not necessary once an outbreak has been defined.
- Influenza and other viruses can be cultured from respiratory secretions during the initial few days of the illness (special media and techniques necessary).
- Paired sera antibody titers are also useful.
- Monoclonal antibody tests are available for influenza and other respiratory viruses.
- Measles and adenovirus pneumonia are usually diagnosed clinically.
- Polymerase chain reaction may be able to rapidly detect and identify viral nucleic acid.
- Open lung biopsy is required for definite diagnosis of CMV pneumonia.

LABORATORY TESTS

- Sputum Gram stain (usually produced in scanty amounts) typically shows few polymorphonuclear leukocytes and few bacteria.
- WBC count may vary from leukopenic to modest elevation, usually without a leftward shift.
- Disseminated intravascular coagulation has occasionally complicated adenovirus type 7 pneumonia.
- Multinucleated giant cells on Tzanck preparation of an unroofed vesicular lesion are useful in diagnosing varicella in a patient with an infiltrate (also found in herpes simplex).
- Severe immunosuppression is associated with symptomatic CMV pneumonia (usually reactivation of latent infection, or in previously seronegative recipients from the donor).
- Hypoxemia may be profound.
- Cultures may be helpful in identifying superinfecting bacterial pathogens.
- When they occur, parapneumonic pleural effusions are exudative.

IMAGING STUDIES

- Chest x-ray examination may demonstrate a spectrum of findings from ill-defined, patchy, or generalized interstitial infiltrates, which can be associated with ARDS.
- A localized dense alveolar infiltrate suggests a superimposed bacterial pneumonia.
- Small calcified nodules may develop as a radiographic residual of varicella pneumonia (Fig. 1-187).

TREATMENT

NONPHARMACOLOGIC THERAPY

GENERAL:

- Measures to diminish person-to-person transmission
- Modified bed rest
- Maintenance of adequate hydration
- Possible ventilatory support for severe pneumonia or ARDS

INFLUENZA:

- Yearly prophylactic strain-specific influenza vaccination (only subvirion vaccine should be used in children <13 yr) can be given to prevent infection.
- Live, attenuated influenza vaccines administered by nose drops may be more effective than the injected inactivated viral vaccines now available (under investigation).

RSV:

- Isolation techniques are important in limiting spread of RSV infections.
- Immunoglobulins with a high RSV-neutralizing antibody titer are beneficial in treatment.

ADENOVIRUSES:

- Intestinal inoculation of respiratory adenoviruses has been used to successfully immunize military recruits.
- Although they produce no disease in recipients, the viruses may be shed chronically and may infect others at a later date.
- These vaccines are not available for civilian populations.

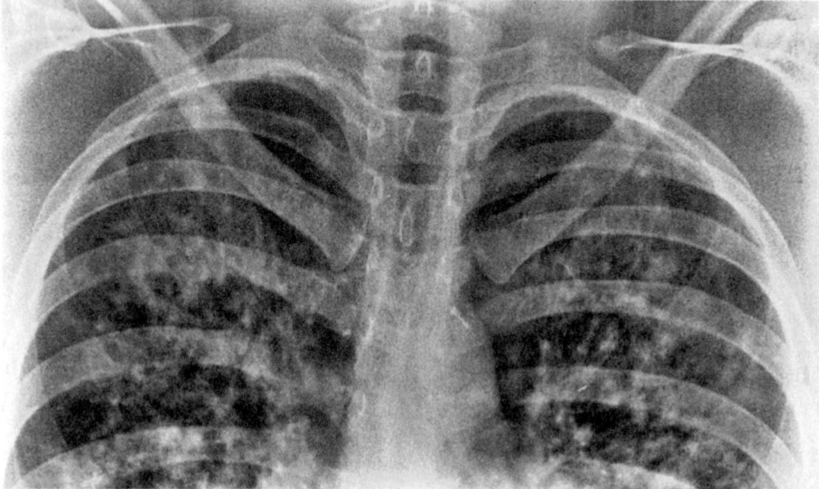

FIGURE 1-187 Chickenpox—varicella pneumonia. Coned-down view of the upper lobes shows multiple ill-defined nodules in both upper lobes. (From McLoud TC: *Thoracic radiology: the requisites,* St Louis, 1998, Mosby.)

VARICELLA:
- Live, attenuated varicella vaccine has been successfully used in clinical trials.
- Varicella-zoster immune globulin should be administered within 4 days of exposure to prevent or modify the disease in susceptible persons.
- Nonimmunized persons exposed to varicella are potentially infectious between 10 and 21 days after exposure.

MEASLES:
- Effective measles vaccine is available:
    1. The vaccine should be administered at 15 mo.
    2. A second dose should be administered at the time of school entry.
- Live, attenuated vaccine or γ-globulin can prevent measles in unvaccinated persons if administered early following exposure.
- Vitamin A given PO for 2 days reduces morbidity and mortality from measles in exposed children.
- SARS = associated coronaviruses:
    1. No vaccine currently available.
    2. Combination therapy with lopinavir/ritonavir and ribavirin may reduce viral load.

ACUTE GENERAL Rx

GENERAL: Administer appropriate antibiotics for bacterial superinfections.

INFLUENZA:
- Amantadine and rimantadine (not commercially available) for influenza A. Early use can speed recovery from small airways dysfunction, but whether it influences the development or course of pneumonia is uncertain.
- Amantadine is also effective prophylactically during the time it is administered.
- Aerosolized ribavirin or amantadine may have a role in severe influenza pneumonia but have not been approved for this indication.

RSV: Ribavirin aerosol is effective for severe RSV pneumonia.

ADENOVIRUSES: No effective antiadenovirus agent.

VARICELLA:
- Varicella pneumonia can be treated with IV acyclovir.
- Adults who develop chickenpox should be considered for acyclovir treatment, which may prevent the development of pneumonia.

MEASLES: No effective antimeasles agent.

CMV:
- Acyclovir can prevent CMV infection in renal transplant recipients.
- Ganciclovir and foscarnet, with or without CMV hyperimmune globulin, show promise in the treatment of serious CMV infection, including pneumonia, in compromised hosts.

DISPOSITION

- Supportive therapy is useful.
- Deaths are possible during acute illness.
- Residual functional abnormalities may be persistent, develop into, or predispose to chronic respiratory diseases in later life.
- Morbidity and mortality following most viral pneumonias are increased by bacterial superinfection.

REFERRAL

- Uncertainty about the diagnosis in a compromised host
- Symptoms or findings progressive
- Severe respiratory compromise, diffuse infiltrates, or the development of ARDS

PEARLS & CONSIDERATIONS

COMMENTS

- Influenza spreads by close contact and by small droplets transmitted by cough, which typifies the illness.
- RSV is effectively transmitted by fomites and by direct contact (little by aerosol).
- Varicella is transmitted by direct contact or by aerosol.
- Measles is transmitted by aerosol and possibly by fomites.

SUGGESTED READINGS

Cheng VC et al: Medical treatment of viral pneumonia including SARS in immunocompetent adults, *J Infect* 49(4):262, 2004.

De Roux A et al: Viral community-acquired pneumonia in nonimmunocompromised adults, *Chest* 125(4):1343, 2004.

AUTHORS: **HARVEY M. SHANIES, M.D., PH.D.,** and **JOSEPH R. MASCI, M.D.**

BASIC INFORMATION

DEFINITION

A spontaneous pneumothorax (SP) is defined as the accumulation of air into the pleural space, collapsing the lung (Fig. 1-188). This can be primary SP (i.e., without any obvious underlying lung disease) or secondary SP (i.e., with underlying lung disease).

SYNONYMS

Primary spontaneous pneumothorax
Secondary spontaneous pneumothorax

ICD-9CM CODES
512.0 Spontaneous tension pneumothorax
512.8 Other spontaneous pneumothorax

EPIDEMIOLOGY & DEMOGRAPHICS

- Primary SP occurs in healthy individuals whereas secondary SP occurs in patients who have underlying lung disease.
- Approximately 20,000 new cases of spontaneous pneumothoraces occur each year in the U.S.
- SP is more common in men than women (6:1).
- Incidence of primary SP is 7.4/100,000 in men and 1.2/100,000 in women.
- Incidence of secondary SP is 6.3/100,000 in men and 2.0/100,000 in women.
- SP is commonly seen in tall, thin young men 20 to 40 yr of age.
- Tobacco increases the risk of SP.

PHYSICAL FINDINGS & CLINICAL PRESENTATION

- Sudden onset of pleuritic chest pain (90%)
- Dyspnea (80%)
- Tachycardia
- Diminished breath sounds
- Decreased tactile fremitus
- Hyperresonance

ETIOLOGY

- In primary SP, rupture of small blebs usually located near the apex of the upper lobes is a common cause. Although rare, loud music has recently been documented as a new cause of primary SP.
- In secondary SP, COPD is the most common cause but can also be associated with pneumonia, bronchogenic carcinoma, mesothelioma, sarcoidosis, tuberculosis, cystic fibrosis, and many other lung diseases.

DIAGNOSIS

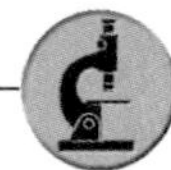

Established by the chest x-ray

DIFFERENTIAL DIAGNOSIS

- Pleurisy
- Pulmonary embolism
- Myocardial infarction
- Pericarditis
- Asthma
- Pneumonia

WORKUP

Includes arterial blood gases, chest x-ray, and in some cases, CT scan of the chest

LABORATORY TESTS

ABGs may show hypoxemia and hypocapnia secondary to hyperventilation.

IMAGING STUDIES

- Spontaneous pneumothorax is usually confirmed by chest x-ray. X-ray findings include:
  1. Pleural line with absence of vessel markings peripheral to this line
  2. Expiratory films are better at demarcating the pneumothorax pleural line
  3. Films should be done with patient standing and not supine
- CT scan can be done in suspected but difficult-to-visualize pneumothoraces.

TREATMENT

NONPHARMACOLOGIC THERAPY

- Supplemental oxygen increases the rate of pneumothorax absorption.
- Cautious observation in the asymptomatic patient with <15% pneumothorax can be done but requires close daily outpatient monitoring.

ACUTE GENERAL Rx

- Aspiration using a small IV catheter in the second intercostal space midclavicular line attached to a three-way stopcock and a large syringe. Air is aspirated until resistance, excess cough by the patient, or >2.5 L is taken out. Repeat films are done immediately after aspiration and again in 24 hr.
- Chest tube insertion has been recommended for patients with primary SP who failed observation and simple aspiration and for all patients with secondary SP.
- There is no firm conclusion on the optimal treatment (simple aspiration versus chest tube insertion) for a first episode of primary SP.

CHRONIC Rx

- Chest tube with pleurodesis has been used to prevent recurrence of both primary and secondary SP. Sclerosing agents commonly instilled through the chest tube into the pleural cavity are minocycline 5 mg/kg in 50 ml of normal saline or doxycycline 500 mg in 50 ml of normal saline.
- Talc has also been used as a sclerosing agent.
- Thoracoscopy or video-assisted thoracoscopy (VAT) is indicated in patients who have not responded to chest tube suctioning in 7 days, patients who have persistent bronchopleural fistula, and patients who have recurrent pneumothorax after chemical pleurodesis.
- Timing of VAT surgery in the prevention of primary SP recurrence remains controversial.
- Open thoracotomy is done in patients who fail VAT.

DISPOSITION

- Approximately 25% of patients with primary SP will have recurrence within 2 yr.
- The rates of recurrence after the second and third episode of spontaneous pneumothorax are 60% and 80%, respectively, with the majority of recurrences occurring on the same side as the first pneumothorax.
- Death from primary SP is uncommon. In patients with secondary SP and COPD, mortality ranges from 1% to 16%.
- The recurrence rate after open thoracotomy is <2%.

REFERRAL

A pulmonary specialist and general surgeon consultation is recommended.

PEARLS & CONSIDERATIONS

COMMENTS

- The rate of pleural air absorption is about 1.25%/day.
- Patients with AIDS and *Pneumocystis carinii* infection have a high incidence of SP. Treatment typically requires chest tube placement and either thoracoscopy or open thoracotomy.

SUGGESTED READINGS

Baumann MH et al: Pneumothorax, *Respirology* 9(2):137, 2004.

Baumann MH et al: Management of spontaneous pneumothorax: an American College of Chest Physicians Delphi consensus statement, *Chest* 119(2):590, 2001.

Deavanand A et al: Simple aspiration versus chest tube insertion in the management of primary spontaneous pneumothorax: a systematic review, *Respir Med* 98(7):579, 2004.

Morimoto T et al: Effects of timing of thoracoscopic surgery for primary spontaneous pneumothorax on prognosis and cost, *Am J Surg* 187(6):767, 2004.

Noppen M et al: Music: a new cause of primary spontaneous pneumothorax, *Thorax* 59(8):722, 2004.

Sahn SA, Heffner JE: Spontaneous pneumothorax, *N Engl J Med* 342(12)868, 2000.

AUTHOR: **HEMCHAND RAMBERAN, M.D.**

A

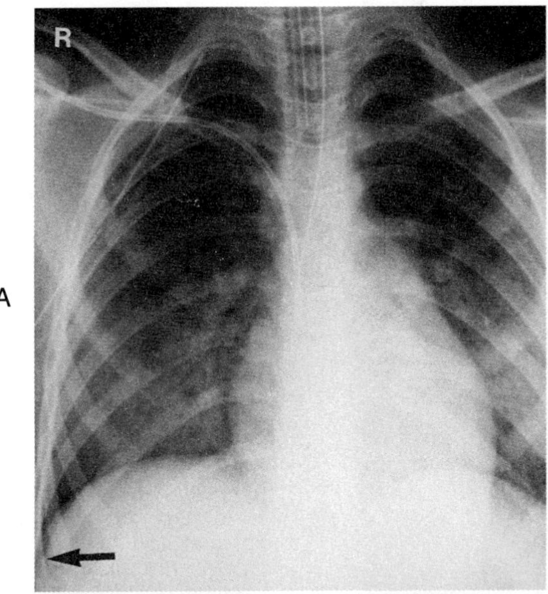

B

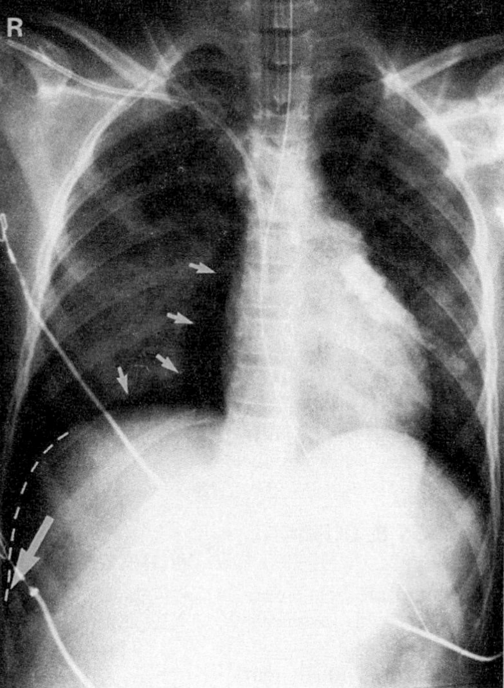

C

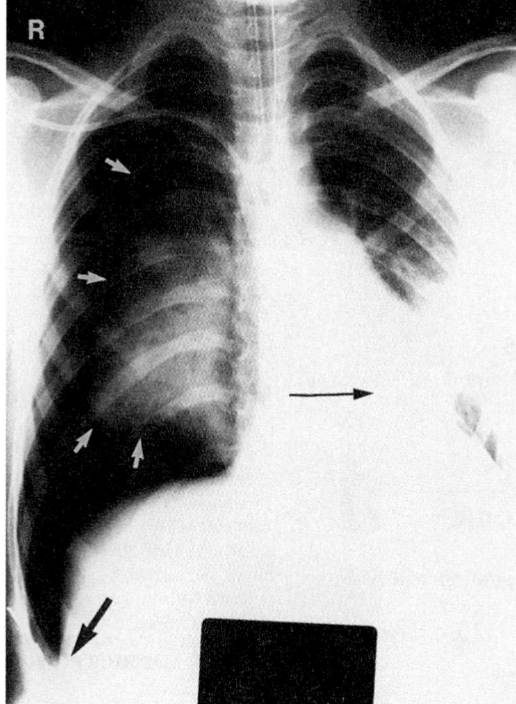

FIGURE 1-188 Deep sulcus sign of pneumothorax. On a PA chest radiograph **(A)** the costophrenic angle is normally acute (*arrow*). In a supine patient, a pneumothorax will often be anterior, medical, and basilar. On a subsequent supine film **(B)** the dark area along the right cardiac border and lung base angle became much deeper and more acute than normal (*large arrow*). These findings were not recognized, and as a result, the same patient developed a tension pneumothorax **(C)** with an extremely deep costophrenic angle (*large black arrow*) and almost completely collapsed right lung (*small white arrows*) and shift of the mediastinum to the left. (From Mettler FA [ed]: *Primary care radiology,* Philadelphia, 2000, WB Saunders.)

Poliomyelitis

BASIC INFORMATION

DEFINITION

Poliomyelitis is a symptomatic infection caused by poliovirus, which (on rare occasions) may result in paralysis.

SYNONYMS

Polio
Infantile paralysis

ICD-9CM CODES
045.9 Poliomyelitis

EPIDEMIOLOGY & DEMOGRAPHICS

INCIDENCE (IN U.S.):
- Approximately 8 cases/yr.
- All cases in the U.S. and Western Hemisphere are now vaccine associated (because of oral polio vaccine [OPV]).

PREDOMINANT AGE: Almost always infants or young children

GENETICS:

Neonatal Infection: Most cases occur in otherwise healthy infants who receive OPV, or their contacts.

PHYSICAL FINDINGS & CLINICAL PRESENTATION

- Exposure of a nonimmune host to poliovirus usually results in asymptomatic infection.
- A small percentage of individuals may have one of three presentations:
  1. Abortive poliomyelitis: a flulike illness
     a. Fever
     b. Malaise
     c. Headache
     d. Sore throat
  2. Nonparalytic poliomyelitis: an aseptic meningitis that correlates with invasion of the CNS
     a. Headache
     b. Neck stiffness
     c. Change in mental status
  3. Paralytic poliomyelitis
     a. Most commonly affects the lumbar or bulbar regions
     b. Following paralysis, a period of variable degrees of recovery, the majority of which occurs in 2 to 6 mo
     c. Paralysis from involvement of motor neurons in the spinal cord
     d. Flaccid paralysis without sensory defects
     e. Postpolio syndrome late sequela, which may occur many years after the acute illness
     f. Functional deterioration of muscle groups that had recovered from initial paralysis thought to result from failure of reinnervation, which initially was able to restore function to weakened or paralyzed areas

ETIOLOGY

- Virus of genus *Enterovirus*
- Classic endemic and epidemic disease caused by wild-type poliovirus
- All cases in the U.S. currently caused by a live, attenuated virus in the OPV
  1. Extremely rare complication that occurs in vaccine recipients or their contacts
  2. Paralysis from lower motor neuron damage caused by viral infection

DIAGNOSIS

DIFFERENTIAL DIAGNOSIS

- Guillain-Barré syndrome
- CVA
- Spinal cord compression
- Other enteroviruses:
  1. Aseptic meningitis
  2. Paralysis (rare)

WORKUP

- Isolation of virus:
  1. Stool or a rectal swab
  2. Throat swabs
  3. Rarely CSF
- Paired sera for antibody titer determinations

LABORATORY TESTS

CSF:
- Aseptic meningitis
- Elevated WBCs
- Elevated protein
- Normal glucose

IMAGING STUDIES

MRI may show involvement of anterior horn of the spinal cord.

TREATMENT

NONPHARMACOLOGIC THERAPY

- Maintenance of respiration and hydration
- Early mobilization and exercise once fever subsides

ACUTE GENERAL Rx

- Aimed at reduction of pain and muscle spasm
- No agent to alter the course of disease

CHRONIC Rx

Physical therapy

DISPOSITION

- In the abortive and nonparalytic forms, complete recovery
- Paralytic disease:
  1. Variable degrees of recovery
  2. 80% usually in the first 6 mo following illness

REFERRAL

Always refer to an infectious disease consultant. Cases should be reported to public health agencies.

PEARLS & CONSIDERATIONS

COMMENTS

- Risk of disease in recipients of OPV is approximately 1 in 2.5 million.
- Use of inactivated polio vaccine (IPV) is not associated with disease:
  1. Does not confer local (mucosal) immunity
  2. Will not immunize nonvaccinated contacts
  3. Requires boosters
  4. Is given by injection
- To decrease the incidence of vaccine-associated polio, the routine childhood vaccination schedule has been changed. A recent recommendation for use of a sequential IPV-OPV schedule has again been modified. Exclusive use of IPV is now recommended. OPV use is limited to unvaccinated persons with plans for imminent (<4 wk) travel to polio-endemic areas.

SUGGESTED READINGS

Centers for Disease Control and Prevention: Poliomyelitis prevention in the United States: updated recommendations of the Advisory Committee on Immunization Practices (ACIP), *MMWR Morb Mortal Wkly Rep* 49(RR-05):1, 2000.

Silver JK, Aiello DD: What internists need to know about postpolio syndrome, *Cleve Clin J Med* 69:704, 2002.

AUTHOR: **MAURICE POLICAR, M.D.**

BASIC INFORMATION

DEFINITION

Polyarteritis nodosa is a vasculitic syndrome involving medium-size to small arteries, characterized histologically by necrotizing inflammation of the arterial media and inflammatory cell infiltration.

SYNONYMS

Periarteritis nodosa
PAN
Necrotizing arteritis

ICD-9CM CODES
446.0 Polyarteritis nodosa

EPIDEMIOLOGY & DEMOGRAPHICS

- Incidence is 1:100,000 annually.
- Male:female ratio is 2:1.
- Increased incidence in patients with hepatitis B surface antigen, hepatitis C virus.

PHYSICAL FINDINGS & CLINICAL PRESENTATION

- Typical presentation is subacute, with the onset of constitutional symptoms over weeks to months
- Weight loss, nausea, vomiting
- Testicular pain or tenderness
- Myalgias, weakness, or leg tenderness
- Neuropathy (mononeuritis multiplex), foot drop
- Livedo reticularis, ulceration of digits, abdominal pain after meals, hematemesis, hematochezia, hypertension, asymmetric polyarthritis (tending to involve large joints of lower extremities); true synovitis occurs only in a minority of patients
- Fever may be present (polyarteritis nodosa is often a cause of fever of unknown origin) and can range from intermittent, low-grade fevers to high fevers with chills
- Tachycardia is common and often striking

ETIOLOGY

- Unknown
- Hepatitis B virus-associated PAN appears to be an immune complex-mediated disease

DIAGNOSIS

DIFFERENTIAL DIAGNOSIS

Cryoglobulinemia, SLE, infections (e.g., SBE, trichinosis, *Rickettsia*), lymphoma

WORKUP

- Laboratory evaluation, arteriography, and biopsy of small or medium-size arteries can confirm diagnosis. Clinical manifestations are variable and depend on the arteries involved and the organs affected (e.g., kidney involvement occurs in >80% of cases).
- The presence of any three of the following ten items allows the diagnosis of polyarteritis nodosa with a sensitivity of 82% and a specificity of 86%:
  1. Weight loss >4 kg
  2. Livedo reticularis
  3. Testicular pain or tenderness
  4. Myalgias, weakness, or leg tenderness
  5. Neuropathy
  6. Diastolic blood pressure >90 mm Hg
  7. Elevated BUN or creatinine
  8. Positive test for hepatitis B virus
  9. Arteriography revealing small or large aneurysms and focal constrictions between dilated segments
  10. Biopsy of small or medium-size artery containing WBC

LABORATORY TESTS

- Elevated BUN or creatinine, positive test for hepatitis B virus or hepatitis C
- Elevated ESR and C-reactive protein, anemia, elevated platelets, eosinophilia, proteinuria, hematuria
- Biopsy of small or medium-size artery of symptomatic sites (muscle, nerve) is >90% specific. Biopsy of the gastrocnemius muscle and sural nerve are commonly performed
- Assays for ANA and RF are negative; however, low, nonspecific titers may be detected

IMAGING STUDIES

Arteriography can be done in patients with negative biopsies or if there are no symptomatic sites. Visceral angiography will reveal aneurysmal dilation of the renal, mesenteric, or hepatic arteries.

TREATMENT

NONPHARMACOLOGIC THERAPY

Low-sodium diet in hypertensive patients

ACUTE GENERAL Rx

Prednisone 1 to 2 mg/kg/day; cyclophosphamide in refractory cases

CHRONIC Rx

Monitoring for infections and potential complications such as thrombosis, infarction, or organ necrosis

DISPOSITION

The 5-yr survival is <20% in untreated patients. Treatment with corticosteroids increases survival to approximately 50%. Usage of both corticosteroids and immunosuppressive drugs may increase 5-yr survival >80%. Poor prognostic signs are severe renal or GI involvement.

REFERRAL

Surgical referral for biopsy

SUGGESTED READING

Stone JH: Polyarteritis nodosa, *JAMA* 288: 1632, 2002.

AUTHOR: **FRED F. FERRI, M.D.**

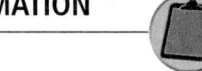

BASIC INFORMATION

DEFINITION

Polycystic kidney disease refers to a systemic hereditary disorder characterized by the formation of cysts in the cortex and medulla of both kidneys (Fig. 1-189).

SYNONYMS

Autosomal dominant polycystic kidney disease (ADPKD)

ICD-9CM CODES
753.1 Polycystic kidney, unspecified type
753.13 Polycystic kidney, autosomal dominant

EPIDEMIOLOGY & DEMOGRAPHICS

- Occurs in 1:400 to 1:1000 people
- Incidence: 6000 new cases per year
- Approximately 500,000 people with ADPKD in the U.S.
- Found in all ages
- Accounts for 10% of end-stage renal disease
- Associated with liver cysts (50% to 70%), pancreatic cysts (10%), splenic cysts (5%), and CNS arachnoid cysts (5%)
- Also associated with cerebral aneurysms (20%); 6% of patients with berry aneurysms have polycystic kidney disease
- Increased incidence of diverticular disease and mitral valve prolapse

PHYSICAL FINDINGS & CLINICAL PRESENTATION

- Usually presents in the third to fourth decade of life
- Pain (abdominal, flank, or back)
- Palpable flank mass
- Hypertension
- Headache
- Nocturia
- Hematuria
- Nephrolithiasis (20%)
- Urinary tract infection

ETIOLOGY

- Approximately 90% of cases are inherited as an autosomal dominant trait.
- Spontaneous mutations occur in 10% of cases.
- The abnormal gene in the majority of cases has been located to the short arm of chromosome 16. In the minority of cases the defect is located on chromosome 4.
- All cysts develop from preexisting renal tubules segments and only a small portion of the nephrons (1%) undergoes cystic formation.

DIAGNOSIS

A person is considered to have polycystic kidney disease if three or more cysts are noted in both kidneys and there is a positive family member with ADPKD.

FIGURE 1-189 Tomogram of autosomal dominant polycystic kidney disease. Kidney cysts. (From Stein JH [ed]: *Internal medicine*, ed 5, St Louis, 1998, Mosby.)

DIFFERENTIAL DIAGNOSIS

- Simple cysts
- Autosomal recessive polycystic kidney disease in children
- Tuberous sclerosis
- Von Hippel-Lindau syndrome
- Acquired cystic kidney disease

WORKUP

The workup to establish the diagnosis of ADPKD includes a detailed family history and either an ultrasound or a CT scan of the abdomen to visualize bilateral renal cysts.

LABORATORY TESTS

- Hemoglobin and hematocrit is elevated because of increased secretion of erythropoietin from functioning renal cysts. This also explains the relatively mild anemia found in patients with ADPKD and renal insufficiency.
- Electrolyte abnormalities commonly seen in any patients with renal insufficiency may be present.
- BUN and creatinine can be elevated.
- Urinalysis can show microscopic hematuria, WBC casts in pyelonephritis, or proteinuria (seldom >1 g/24 hr).
- Increased erythropoietin level.
- Patients with a strong positive family history of ADPKD and no cysts detected by imaging studies can undergo genetic linkage analysis.

IMAGING STUDIES

- Abdominal renal ultrasound is the easiest and more cost-efficient test for renal cysts. Renal ultrasound can detect cysts from 1 to 1.5 cm.
- Abdominal CT scan is more sensitive than ultrasound and can detect cysts as small as 0.5 cm.
- Both studies can detect associated hepatic, splenic, and pancreatic cysts.
- MRI is more sensitive than ultrasound and may help in distinguishing renal cell carcinomas from simple cysts.

TREATMENT

NONPHARMACOLOGIC THERAPY

- Nephrolithiasis is treated in a similar manner with either IV or PO hydration. If stones remain lodged, lithotripsy or percutaneous nephrostolithotomy can be done.
- Hypertension treatment is initiated with salt restriction, weight loss, and daily walking exercise.
- Avoidance of physical contact sports is advised.

ACUTE GENERAL Rx

- Kidney infections should be treated with antibiotics known to penetrate the cyst (e.g., trimethoprim-sulfamethoxazole 1 tablet PO bid or ciprofloxacin 250 mg PO bid).
- Angiotensin-converting enzyme inhibitors (e.g., captopril 25 mg bid or tid, lisinopril 10 mg PO qd, fosinopril 10 mg PO qd, or enalapril 10 mg qd) are effective in the treatment of hypertension associated with ADPKD.
- Calcium channel blockers (e.g., nifedipine 30 to 90 mg PO qd, amlodipine 5 to 10 mg PO qd, or felodipine 5 to 10 mg PO qd) can be used with or without ACE inhibitors in the treatment of hypertension.
- α-Blockers and diuretics can be added as adjunctive therapy for hypertension.
- Blood pressure <130/85 is the goal for patients with renal disease. If there is >1 g of urinary protein per 24 hr, the target blood pressure is <125/75 mm Hg.

CHRONIC Rx

- Dialysis for end-stage renal failure
- Renal transplantation
- Cystic decompression in patients with intractable pain caused by enlarging cysts

DISPOSITION

- Approximately half the patients with ADPKD will progress to renal failure.
- Gross hematuria is usually self-limited.
- Complications of ADPKD include:
  1. End-stage renal failure
  2. Infected cysts and urinary tract infections
  3. Pyelonephritis
  4. Nephrolithiasis
  5. Electrolyte abnormalities
  6. Cerebral aneurysm rupture
  7. Intractable pain from enlarging cysts

REFERRAL

Nephrology consultation should be made in patients with renal insufficiency, difficult-to-control hypertension, recurrent infections, or renal stones. Urology can also be consulted in patients with nephrolithiasis, recurrent episodes of gross hematuria, or consideration for nephrectomy before transplantation.

PEARLS & CONSIDERATIONS

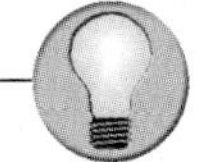

COMMENTS

- A cyst is considered to be present if it measures >2 mm in diameter.
- A positive family history of ADPKD is found in approximately 60% of the cases. Renal ultrasound performed on patient's parents reveals ADPKD in about 30% of the cases.
- Up to 25% of patients may not have cysts present before the age of 30.
- Screening patients with ADPKD for cerebral aneurysms is not recommended unless there is a positive family history of cerebral aneurysms or family member with ruptured cerebral aneurysm.

SUGGESTED READINGS

Beebe DK: Autosomal dominant polycystic kidney disease, *Am Fam Physician* 53(3):925, 1996.

Chapman AB, Johnson AM, Gabow PA: Intracranial aneurysms in patients with autosomal dominant polycystic kidney disease: how to diagnose and who to screen, *Am J Kidney Dis* 22:526, 1993.

Gabow PA: Autosomal dominant polycystic kidney disease, *N Engl J Med* 329(5):332, 1993.

Gibson P, Watson ML: Managing the patient with polycystic kidney disease, *Practitioner* 246(1638):450, 2002.

Welling LW, Grantham JJ: Cystic and developmental diseases of the kidney. In Brenner BM, Rector FC: *Brenner & Rector's the kidney,* ed 5, Philadelphia, 1996, WB Saunders.

Wilson PD: Polycystic kidney disease, *N Engl J Med* 350:2, 2004.

AUTHOR: **PETER PETROPOULOS, M.D.**

BASIC INFORMATION

DEFINITION

Polycystic ovary syndrome (PCOS) in its complete form associates polycystic ovaries, amenorrhea, hirsutism, and obesity.

SYNONYMS

Stein-Leventhal syndrome
PCOS

ICD-9CM CODES
256.4 Polycystic ovary syndrome

EPIDEMIOLOGY & DEMOGRAPHICS

PREVALENCE: 3% of adolescent and adult women.

- Symptoms usually begin around the time of menarche, and the diagnosis is often made during adolescence or young adulthood.
- Increased risk of endometrial and ovarian cancers.

PHYSICAL FINDINGS & CLINICAL PRESENTATION

- Oligomenorrhea or amenorrhea
- Dysfunctional uterine bleeding
- Infertility
- Hirsutism
- Acne
- Obesity (40% only)
- Insulin resistance (type 2 diabetes mellitus)

ETIOLOGY & PATHOGENESIS

- PCOS is probably a genetic disorder, but in most cases no family history is evident. Whether transmission is autosomal or X-linked is still unclear.
- Elevated serum LH concentrations and an increased serum LH:FSH ratio result either from an increased GnRH hypothalamic secretion or less likely from a primary pituitary abnormality. This results in dysregulation of androgen secretion and increased intraovarian androgen, the effect of which in the ovary is follicular atresia, maturation arrest, polycystic ovaries, and anovulation. Hyperinsulinemia is a contributing factor to ovarian hyperandrogenism, independent of LH excess. A role for insulin growth factor (IGF) receptors has been postulated for the association of PCOS and diabetes.

DIAGNOSIS

Clinical:

- PCOS is the most common cause of chronic anovulation with estrogen present. A positive progesterone withdrawal test establishes the presence of estrogen. Medroxyprogesterone (Provera) 10 mg qd is administered for 5 days and bleeding occurs if estrogen is present.
- The presence of oligomenorrhea, hirsutism, obesity, and documentation of polycystic ovaries establishes the diagnosis.

DIFFERENTIAL DIAGNOSIS

Causes of amenorrhea:

- Primary (unusual in PCOS)

Genetic disorder (Turner's syndrome)
Anatomic abnormality (e.g., imperforate hymen)

- Secondary

Pregnancy
Functional (cause unknown, anorexia nervosa, stress, excessive exercise, hyperthyroidism, less commonly hypothyroidism, adrenal dysfunction, pituitary dysfunction, severe systemic illness, drugs such as oral contraceptives, estrogens, or dopamine agonists)
Abnormalities of the genital tract (uterine tumor, endometrial scarring, ovarian tumor)

LABORATORY TESTS

Fasting blood glucose to rule out diabetes
Elevated LH/FSH ratio >2.5
Prolactin level elevation in 25%
Elevated androgens (testosterone, DHEA-S)

IMAGING STUDIES

Pelvic ultrasound (or CT scan) reveals the presence of twofold to fivefold ovarian enlargement with a thickened tunica albuginea, thecal hyperplasia, and 20 or more subcapsular follicles from 1 to 15 mm in diameter (Fig. 1-190).

TREATMENT

The goal is to interrupt the self-perpetuating abnormal hormone cycle:

- Reduction of ovarian androgen secretion by laparoscopic ovarian wedge resection
- Reduction of ovarian androgen secretion by using oral contraceptives or LHRH analogs
- Weight reduction for all obese women with PCOS
- FSH stimulation with clomiphene HMG, or pulsatile LHRH
- Urofollitropin (pure FSH) administration
- Glitazones may improve ovulation and hirsutism in the polycystic ovary syndrome

Choice of treatment:

- The management of hirsutism without risking pregnancy includes oral contraceptives, glucocorticoids, LHRH analogs, or spironolactone (an antiandrogen)
- Pregnancy can be achieved with clomiphene (alone or with glucocorticoids, hCG, or bromocriptine), HMG, urofollitropin, pulsatile LHRH, or ovarian wedge resection.

(Metformin may induce ovulation.)

REFERRAL

Gynecologist or endocrinologist

SUGGESTED READINGS

Azziz R et al: Troglitazone improves ovulation and hirsutism in the polycystic ovary syndrome: a multicenter, double blind, placebo-controlled trial, *J Clin Endocrinol Metab* 86:1626, 2001.

Lord JM et al: Metformin in polycystic ovary syndrome: Systematic review and meta-analysis, *Br Med J* 327:951, 2003.

Marx TL, Mehta AE: Polycystic ovary syndrome: pathogenesis and treatment over the short and long term, *Cleve Clin J Med* 70:31, 2003.

Richardson MR: Current perspectives in polycystic ovary syndrome, *Am Fam Physician* 68:697, 2003.

AUTHOR: **TOM J. WACHTEL, M.D.**

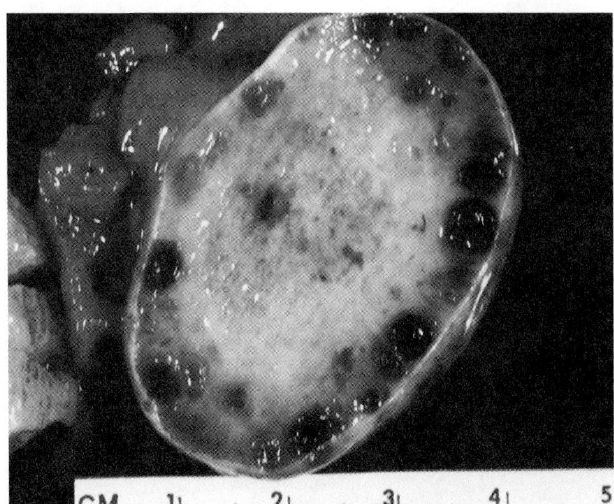

FIGURE 1-190 Sagittal section of a polycystic ovary illustrating large number of follicular cysts and thickened stroma. (From Mishell DR: *Comprehensive gynecology,* ed 3, St Louis, 1997, Mosby.)

BASIC INFORMATION

DEFINITION

Polycythemia vera is a chronic myeloproliferative disorder characterized mainly by erythrocytosis (increase in RBC mass).

SYNONYMS

Primary polycythemia
Vaquez disease

ICD-9CM CODES
238.4 Polycythemia vera

EPIDEMIOLOGY & DEMOGRAPHICS

INCIDENCE/PREVALENCE: 0.5 cases/100,000 persons; mean age at onset is 60 yr; men are more affected than women.

PHYSICAL FINDINGS & CLINICAL PRESENTATION

The patient generally comes to medical attention because of symptoms associated with increased blood volume and viscosity or impaired platelet function:

- Impaired cerebral circulation resulting in headache, vertigo, blurred vision, dizziness, TIA, CVA
- Fatigue, poor exercise tolerance
- Pruritus, particularly following bathing (caused by overproduction of histamine)
- Bleeding: epistaxis, UGI bleeding (increased incidence of PUD)
- Abdominal discomfort secondary to splenomegaly; hepatomegaly may be present
- Hyperuricemia may result in nephrolithiasis and gouty arthritis

The physical examination may reveal:
Facial plethora, congestion of oral mucosa, ruddy complexion
Enlargement and tortuosity of retinal veins
Splenomegaly (found in >75% of patients)

DIAGNOSIS

DIFFERENTIAL DIAGNOSIS

SMOKING:

- Polycythemia is secondary to increased carboxyhemoglobin, resulting in left shift in the Hgb dissociation curve.
- Laboratory evaluation shows increased Hct, RBC mass, erythropoietin level, and carboxyhemoglobin.
- Splenomegaly is not present on physical examination.

HYPOXEMIA (SECONDARY POLYCYTHEMIA): Living for prolonged periods at high altitudes, pulmonary fibrosis, congenital cardiac lesions with right-to-left shunts

- Laboratory evaluation shows decreased arterial oxygen saturation and elevated erythropoietin level.
- Splenomegaly is not present on physical examination.

ERYTHROPOIETIN-PRODUCING STATES: Renal cell carcinoma, hepatoma, cerebral hemangioma, uterine fibroids, polycystic kidneys

- The erythropoietin level is elevated in these patients; the arterial oxygen saturation is normal.
- Splenomegaly may be present with metastatic neoplasms.

STRESS POLYCYTHEMIA (GAISBÖCK'S SYNDROME, RELATIVE POLYCYTHEMIA):

- Laboratory evaluation demonstrates normal RBC mass, arterial oxygen saturation, and erythropoietin level; plasma volume is decreased.
- Splenomegaly is not present on physical examination.

HEMOGLOBINOPATHIES ASSOCIATED WITH HIGH OXYGEN AFFINITY: An abnormal oxyhemoglobin-dissociation curve (P50) is present.

WORKUP

Serum erythropoietin level is the best initial test for the diagnosis of polycythemia vera. A low serum erythropoietin level is highly suggestive of polycythemia vera. A normal level does not exclude the diagnosis. If the erythropoietin level is elevated, obtain abdominal and pelvic CT to rule out renal cercal carcinoma and other causes of polycythemia.

In patients with elevated erythropoietin level, evaluate for secondary erythrocytosis:

- Measure RBC mass by isotope dilution using ^{51}Cr-labeled autologous RBCs (expensive test); a high value eliminates stress polycythemia.
- Measure arterial saturation; a normal value eliminates polycythemia secondary to smoking.
- The diagnosis of hemoglobinopathy with high affinity is ruled out by a normal oxyhemoglobin dissociation curve.

LABORATORY TESTS

- Elevated RBC count (>6 million/mm^3), elevated Hgb (>18 g/dl in men, >16 g/dl in women), elevated Hct (>54% in men, >49% in women)
- Increased WBC (often with basophilia); thrombocytosis in the majority of patients
- Elevated leukocyte alkaline phosphatase, serum vitamin B$_{12}$, and uric acid levels
- Low serum erythropoietin level
- Bone marrow aspiration revealing RBC hyperplasia and absent iron stores

TREATMENT

NONPHARMACOLOGIC THERAPY

Phlebotomy to keep Hct <45% in men and <42% in women is the mainstay of therapy.

ACUTE GENERAL Rx

- Hydroxyurea can be used in conjunction with phlebotomy to decrease the incidence of thrombotic events.
- Interferon α-2b is also effective in controlling RBC values without significant side effects.
- Myelosuppressive therapy with chlorambucil is effective but not routinely used because of its leukemogenic potential.

CHRONIC Rx

- Patient education regarding need for lifelong monitoring and treatment
- Adjunctive therapy: treatment of pruritus with antihistamines, control of significant hyperuricemia with allopurinol, reduction of gastric hyperacidity with antacids of H$_2$ blockers, low-dose aspirin to treat vasomotor symptoms in patients without bleeding diathesis

DISPOSITION

- The median survival time without treatment is 6 to 18 mo following diagnosis; phlebotomy extends the average survival time to 12 yr.
- Prognosis is worse in patients >60 yr of age and those who have a history of thrombosis.

PEARLS & CONSIDERATIONS

COMMENTS

The diagnosis of polycythemia vera generally requires the following three major criteria or the first two major criteria plus two minor criteria:

- Major criteria
  1. Increased RBC mass (>36 ml/kg in men, >32 ml/kg in women)
  2. Normal arterial oxygen saturation (>92%)
  3. Splenomegaly
- Minor criteria
  1. Thrombocytosis (>400,000/mm^3)
  2. Leukocytosis (>12,000/mm^3)
  3. Elevated leukocyte alkaline phosphatase (>100)
  4. Elevated serum vitamin B$_{12}$ (>900 pg/ml) or vitamin B$_{12}$ binding protein (>2200 pg/ml)

SUGGESTED READING

Landolfi R et al: Efficacy and safety of lower-dose aspirin in polycythemia vera, *N Engl J Med* 350(2):114, 2004.

AUTHOR: **FRED F. FERRI, M.D.**

BASIC INFORMATION

DEFINITION

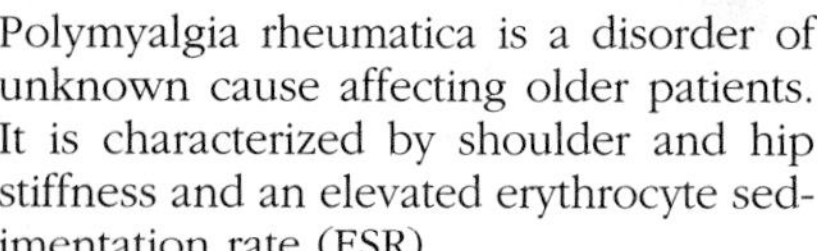

Polymyalgia rheumatica is a disorder of unknown cause affecting older patients. It is characterized by shoulder and hip stiffness and an elevated erythrocyte sedimentation rate (ESR).

SYNONYMS

Anarthritic rheumatoid syndrome

ICD-9CM CODES
725.0 Polymyalgia rheumatica

EPIDEMIOLOGY & DEMOGRAPHICS

PREVALENCE: 1 case/135 persons >50 yr old

PREDOMINANT SEX: Female:male ratio of 2:1

PREDOMINANT AGE: Rare under age 50 yr; average age at onset: 70 yr

PHYSICAL FINDINGS & CLINICAL PRESENTATION

- Symptoms are frequently of sudden onset but are often present for months before the diagnosis is made.
- Neck, shoulder, low back, and thigh pain are common complaints.
- Morning stiffness lasting 2 to 3 hr is typical, and patients often have difficulty getting out of bed.
- Malaise, weight loss, depression, and a low-grade fever are common constitutional symptoms and may suggest systemic inflammation.
- Physical findings are usually limited. Synovitis may be present in peripheral joints and may also be responsible for the proximal girdle symptoms in spite of the fact that they appear to be "muscular" in nature.
- Mild soft tissue tenderness may be present.
- Distal extremity manifestations (knee, wrist, metacarpophalangeal joints) may occur in 25% to 45% of patients.
- The temporal arteries should be carefully examined because of the strong relation of polymyalgia rheumatica with temporal or giant cell arteritis.

ETIOLOGY

Unknown

DIAGNOSIS

DIFFERENTIAL DIAGNOSIS (Table 1-39)

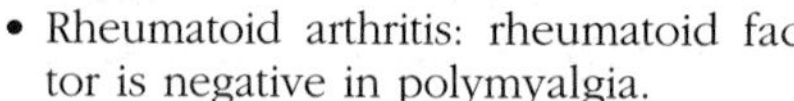

- Rheumatoid arthritis: rheumatoid factor is negative in polymyalgia.
- Polymyositis: enzyme studies are negative in polymyalgia.
- Fibromyalgia

WORKUP

The diagnosis of polymyalgia rheumatica is suggested by the following findings:

- Pain and stiffness of pectoral and pelvic musculature
- Patient >50 yr old
- Morning stiffness >1 hr
- Normal motor strength
- Symptoms for at least 4 to 6 wk
- Elevated ESR (>45)
- Rapid clinical response to low-dose corticosteroid therapy

LABORATORY TESTS

- CBC, ESR, and rheumatoid factor should be performed.
- Mild anemia may be present.

TREATMENT

ACUTE GENERAL Rx

- Prednisone 10 to 20 mg/day is given. The response is often so dramatic that it can be used to confirm the diagnosis. Improvement is usually noted within 24 to 48 hr. Generally, if the initial prednisone dose is 20 mg/day, reduce by 2.5 mg every wk to 10 mg/day, then by 1 mg/day every month if tolerated.
- Steroids are gradually tapered over the next few weeks as soon as symptoms permit, but small doses (5 mg/day) may be needed for 2 yr.
- NSAIDs may be tried in mild cases.
- Physical therapy is usually unnecessary.

PEARLS & CONSIDERATIONS

COMMENTS

The prognosis is generally favorable. Relapse occasionally occurs in several years, but again responds well to prednisone.

TABLE 1-39 Differential Features in Polymyalgia Rheumatica and Similar Disorders

Signs/Symptoms	Polymyalgia Rheumatica	Giant Cell Arteritis	Rheumatoid Arthritis	Dermatomyositis	Fibromyalgia
Morning stiffness >30 min	+	±	+*	±	Variable
Headache and/or scalp tenderness	0	+	0	0	Variable
Pain with active joint movement	+	0	+*	0	Inconstant
Tender joints	±	0	+*	0	Tender spots
Swollen joints	±	±	+	0	0
Muscle weakness	±†	0	+*	+	0
Normochromic anemia	+	+	+	0	0
Elevated erythrocyte sedimentation rate	+	+	+	±	0
Elevated serum creatine kinase	0	0	0	+	0
Serum rheumatoid factor	0	0	70%	0	0
Distinct electromyographic abnormality	0	0	0	+	0
Response to nonsteroidal antiinflammatory drug	±	0	+	0	0

From Goldman L, Ausiello D, (eds): *Cecil textbook of medicine,* ed 22, Philadelphia, 2004, WB Saunders.
0, Absent; +, present; ±, present in minority of cases.
*Associated with affected joints
†Pain inhibits movement. Disuse atrophy may occur.

SUGGESTED READINGS

Cimmino MA, Macchioni P et al: Pulse steroid treatment of polymyalgia rheumatica, *Clin Exp Rheumatol* 22(3):381, 2004.

Clough JD: Polymyalgia rheumatica: not well understood, but important to consider, *Cleve Clin J Med* 71(6):446, 2004.

Cohen MD, Abril A: Polymyalgia rheumatica revisited, *Bull Rheum Dis* 50:1, 2001.

De Jager JP: Polymyalgia rheumatica and giant cell arteritis: avoiding management traps, *Aust Fam Physician* 30:643, 2001.

Mandell BF: Polymyalgia rheumatica: clinical presentation is key to diagnosis and treatment, *Cleve Clin J Med* 71(6):489, 2004.

Marti J, Anton E: Polymyalgia rheumatica complication influenza vaccination, *J Am Geriatr Soc* 52(8):1412, 2004.

Meskimen S, Cook TD, Blake RL: Management of giant cell arteritis and polymyalgia rheumatica, *Am Fam Physician* 61:2061, 2000.

Salvarani C et al: Polymyalgia rheumatica and giant-cell arteritis, *N Engl J Med* 347:261, 2002.

AUTHOR: **LONNIE R. MERCIER, M.D.**

DEFINITION

Clinically significant portal hypertension is defined as a portal vein pressure >10 mm Hg.

ICD-9CM CODES
572.3 Portal hypertension

EPIDEMIOLOGY & DEMOGRAPHICS

- Incidence of portal hypertension is not known.
- Cirrhosis is the most common cause of portal hypertension in the U.S.
- More than 90% of patients with cirrhosis develop portal hypertension.
- Alcoholic and viral liver diseases are the most common causes of cirrhosis and portal hypertension in the U.S.
- Schistosomiasis is the main cause of portal hypertension outside of the U.S.
- Esophageal varices may appear when portal vein pressures rise above 10 mm Hg.
- Variceal hemorrhage is the most serious complication of portal hypertension and may occur when portal pressures rise above 12 mm Hg.

PHYSICAL FINDINGS & CLINICAL PRESENTATION

- Jaundice
- Ascites
- Spider angiomata
- Testicular atrophy
- Gynecomastia
- Palmar erythema
- Dupuytren's contracture
- Asterixis (with advanced liver failure)
- Irritability
- Splenomegaly
- Dilated veins in the anterior abdominal wall
- Venous pattern on the flanks
- Caput medusae (tortuous collateral veins around the umbilicus)
- Hemorrhoids
- Hematemesis
- Melena
- Pruritus

ETIOLOGY

- Pathophysiologically caused by:
  1. Conditions resulting in an increased resistance to flow
     a. Prehepatic (e.g., portal vein thrombosis, splenic vein thrombosis, congenital stenosis)
     b. Hepatic (e.g., cirrhosis, alcoholic liver disease, primary biliary cirrhosis, schistosomiasis)
     c. Posthepatic (e.g., Budd-Chiari syndrome, constrictive pericarditis, inferior vena cava obstruction)
  2. Conditions leading to increase portal blood flow
     a. Splanchnic arterial vasodilation accompanying portal hypertension, mediated by local release of nitric oxide.
     b. Arterial-portal venous fistulae

DIAGNOSIS

- The diagnosis of portal hypertension is made on clinical grounds after a comprehensive history and physical examination.
- Noninvasive and invasive procedures serve to confirm diagnosis and determine the severity of portal hypertension.

DIFFERENTIAL DIAGNOSIS

- Cirrhosis
- Portal vein obstruction
- Portal vein thrombosis
- Hepatic vein thrombosis (Budd-Chiari syndrome)
- Schistosomiasis
- Right-sided heart failure
- Tricuspid regurgitation
- Constrictive pericarditis

WORKUP

The workup of portal hypertension includes blood tests and noninvasive imaging studies to determine if the cause of portal hypertension is prehepatic, hepatic, or posthepatic in origin.

LABORATORY TESTS

- CBC
- Platelet count
- LFTs
- PT/PIT
- Albumin
- Hepatitis B surface antigen and antibody
- Hepatitis C antibody
- Iron, TIBC, and ferritin
- ANA
- Anti-smooth muscle antibodies (ASMA)
- Antimitochondrial antibody (AMA)
- Ceruloplasmin
- α-1 antitrypsin
- Ascitic fluid analysis: a serum-ascites albumin gradient (SAAG) > 1.1 mg/dL suggests portal hypertension

IMAGING STUDIES

- Duplex-Doppler ultrasound is effective in screening for portal hypertension.
- Liver spleen scan looking for a colloidal shift from liver to spleen or bone marrow is suggestive of portal hypertension.
- CT scan can be used in the diagnosis of portal hypertension when results from Duplex-Doppler are equivocal.
- MRI provides information when Duplex-Doppler is inconclusive.
- MRA aids in the detection of portal vein obstruction.
- Measuring hepatic venous pressure gradient, although invasive and not commonly done, can be performed to estimate portal venous pressures.
- Upper endoscopy is the most reliable test documenting the presence of esophageal varices.

TREATMENT

- The treatment of portal hypertension primarily focuses on three strategies in the treatment of its major complication, variceal bleeding:
  1. Prevention of first-time variceal bleeding
  2. Treating the acute variceal bleed
  3. Prevention of rebleeding from esophageal varices

NONPHARMACOLOGIC THERAPY

Treatment of acute variceal bleeding requires immediate volume resuscitation with fluids and blood products.

ACUTE GENERAL THERAPY

- For acute variceal bleeds:
  1. Octreotide acetate 50 to 100 µg IV bolus followed by an infusion at 25 to 50 µg/hr
  2. Terlipressin 2 mg IV q4h is used until bleeding stops for 24 hr and then continued at 1 mg IV q4h for 5 days
- Endoscopic sclerotherapy and elastic band ligation can be used if the aforementioned acute pharmacotherapy fails or in combination with pharmacotherapy.
- Transjugular intrahepatic portosystemic shunt (TIPS) or surgically placed shunts are used in patients failing medical and endoscopic therapy. Can be complicated by hepatic encephalopathy, as the shunt bypasses the liver and hepatic metabolism of portal blood.

CHRONIC Rx

- Nonselective β-blockers (propranolol and nadolol) in dosages sufficient to reduce the resting heart rate by 25% has been shown to be effective in primary prophylaxis for first-time variceal bleeding and for preventing recurrent variceal bleeding. Dosages are usually given bid and decreased if heart rate falls <55 beats/min or systolic BP <90 mm Hg.

- Combination therapy with-long acting nitroglycerine, isosorbide-5-mononitrate (ISMN) 20 mg q HS added to β-blockers has been shown to improve the therapeutic benefit in preventing recurrent variceal bleeding.
- Sclerotherapy using sclerosing agents, 5% ethanolamine, 1% to 2% polidocanol, or ethanol stimulates an inflammatory fibrous reaction and variceal thrombosis and eradicates esophageal varices in 70% of patients.
- Endoscopic banding ligation of varices can be used in preventing recurrent variceal bleeding.
- TIPS is an interventional radiology procedure that decompresses the portal vein and is used as a "rescue" therapy in patients who have failed medical management, usually as a bridge toward transplantation.

DISPOSITION

- The most common complication associated with portal hypertension is variceal bleeding.
- The risk of bleeding from varices is approximately 15% at 1 yr.
- Of those who have bled from esophageal varices, approximately 30% will die; among the survivors, the risk of rebleeding is 70%, with a similar third of these patients dying from this complication.

REFERRAL

Consultation with a gastroenterologist is recommended in patients with portal hypertension and variceal bleeding.

PEARLS & CONSIDERATIONS

COMMENTS

- The portal vein is formed from the convergence of the superior mesenteric vein and the splenic vein and serves as a gate into which the splanchnic circulatory system connects with the liver.
- The normal portal vein carries 1500 ml/min of blood from the stomach, spleen, and small and large intestine to the liver at a pressure of 5 to 10 mm Hg.
- Clinical complications of portal hypertension (e.g., bleeding from esophageal varices, ascites, and hepatic encephalopathy) can occur when portal vein pressures rise above 12 mm Hg.

SUGGESTED READINGS

De Franchis R: Updating consensus in portal hypertension: report of the Baveno III Consensus Workshop on definitions, methodology and therapeutic strategies in portal hypertension, *J Hepatol* 33:846, 2000.

Garcia-Pagan JC, Bosch J: Medical treatment of portal hypertension, *Bailliere's Clin Gastroenterol* 14(6):895, 2000.

Gines P et al: Current concepts: management of cirrhosis and ascites, *N Engl J Med* 350:1646, 2004.

Krige JEJ, Beckingham IJ: ABC of diseases of liver, pancreas, and biliary system: portal hypertension—1: varices, *BMJ* 322:348, 2001.

Wongcharatrawee S, Groszmann RJ: Diagnosing portal hypertension, *Bailliere's Clin Gastroenterol* 14(6):881, 2000.

AUTHOR: **MEL ANDERSON, M.D.**

BASIC INFORMATION

DEFINITION

Portal vein thrombosis is thrombotic occlusion of the portal vein.

SYNONYMS

Pylethrombosis

ICD-9CM CODES
452 Portal vein thrombosis
572.1 Septic portal vein thrombosis

EPIDEMIOLOGY & DEMOGRAPHICS

Occurs with equal frequency in children (peak age: 6 yr) and adults (peak age: 40 yr)

PHYSICAL FINDINGS & CLINICAL PRESENTATION

Upper GI hemorrhage (hematemesis and/or melena) caused by esophageal varices. If abdominal pain is present, mesenteric venous thrombosis should be suspected (see "Mesenteric Venous Thrombosis" in Section I).

ETIOLOGY AND PATHOPHYSIOLOGY

In children: umbilical sepsis (pathophysiology unknown)
In adults:
1. Hypercoagulable states
   - Antiphospholipid syndrome
   - Neoplasm (common cause)
   - Paroxysmal nocturnal hemoglobinuria
   - Myeloproliferative diseases
   - Oral contraceptives
   - Polycythemia vera
   - Pregnancy
   - Protein S or C deficiency
   - Sickle cell disease
   - Thrombocytosis
2. Inflammatory diseases
   - Crohn's disease
   - Pancreatitis
   - Ulcerative colitis
3. Complications of medical intervention
   - Ambulatory dialysis
   - Chemoembolization
   - Liver transplantation
   - Partial hepatectomy
   - Sclerotherapy
   - Splenectomy
   - Transjugular intrahepatic portosystemic shunt
4. Infections
   - Appendicitis
   - Diverticulitis
   - Cholecystitis
5. Miscellaneous
   - Cirrhosis (common cause)
   - Bladder cancer

Pathophysiology: portal vein thrombosis results in portal hypertension leading to esophageal and gastrointestinal varices. The liver sustained by the hepatic artery maintains normal function.

DIAGNOSIS

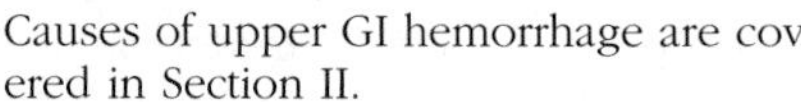

DIFFERENTIAL DIAGNOSIS

Causes of upper GI hemorrhage are covered in Section II.

WORKUP

- Esophagogastroscopy shows esophageal varices.
- Abdominal ultrasound (Fig. 1-191) or MRI may show the portal vein thrombosis.

TREATMENT

- Variceal sclerotherapy or banding
- Surgical mesocaval or splenorenal shunt

REFERRAL

To gastroenterologist, surgeon, or both

SUGGESTED READING

Schafter DF, Sorrell MF: Vascular diseases of the liver. In Feldman M et al (eds): *Gastrointestinal and liver disease,* ed 6, Philadelphia, 1998, WB Saunders.

AUTHOR: **TOM J. WACHTEL, M.D.**

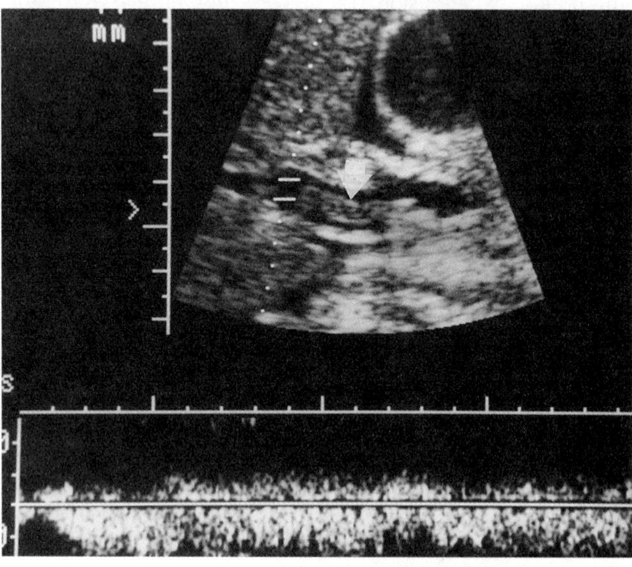

FIGURE 1-191 Thrombus in portal vein evident on pulsed Doppler ultrasonography. An echogenic thrombus (*arrow*) is within the lumen of the portal vein. Doppler tracing indicates flow within portal vein. (From Sabiston D: *Textbook of surgery,* ed 15, Philadelphia, 1997, WB Saunders.)

BASIC INFORMATION

DEFINITION

- Postconcussive syndrome (PCS) refers to persistent neurologic symptoms that result from mild traumatic brain injury or concussion.
- Concussion may be defined as an acute trauma-induced alteration of mental function lasting fewer than 24 hr, with or without preceding loss of consciousness.
- Concussion is graded by the Colorado Medicine Society (Table 1-40) as:
  1. Grade 1 concussion (mild): No loss of consciousness (LOC), no posttraumatic amnesia but with confusion.
  2. Grade 2 concussion (moderate): No LOC, but posttraumatic amnesia and confusion.
  3. Grade 3 concussion (severe): LOC of any duration along with posttraumatic amnesia and confusion.

ICD-9CM CODES
310.2 Postconcussive syndrome

EPIDEMIOLOGY & DEMOGRAPHICS

- PCS incidence is 27/100,000.
- Approximately 15% of patients with mild traumatic brain injury will have persistent neurologic symptoms 1 yr after the injury.
- More often seen in men than in women.
- Usually seen in the young 20 to 30 yr of age.

PHYSICAL FINDINGS & CLINICAL PRESENTATION

- PCS patients usually present with neurologic symptoms and no focal neurologic deficits on examination. Symptoms start within a few days after the head injury with 15% of patients having persistent symptoms 1 yr later.
- Symptoms include:
  1. Headache (migraine type)
  2. Neck pain
  3. Dizziness and vertigo
  4. Paresthesias
  5. Difficulty in concentrating and with memory
  6. Insomnia
  7. Irritability

ETIOLOGY

- PCS by definition is caused by traumatic brain injury from falls, motor vehicle accidents, contact sports, and so forth.
- Postmortem findings reveal diffuse axonal injury as the primary pathologic finding along with small petechial hemorrhages and local edema.
- Diffuse axon injury is thought to lead to altered neurotransmitters and possibly to clinical manifestations.

DIAGNOSIS

A careful history, a nonfocal neurologic examination, and normal neurologic testing usually will establish the diagnosis of postconcussive syndrome.

DIFFERENTIAL DIAGNOSIS

- Headache (vascular or tension)
- Epidural hematoma
- Subdural hematoma
- Skull fracture
- Cervical spine disk disease
- Whiplash
- Seizure
- Cerebrovascular accident
- Depression
- Anxiety

WORKUP

A patient presenting with PCS merits a workup to exclude other causes of neurologic symptoms following traumatic brain injury.

TABLE 1-40 Concussion Guidelines and Recommendations

Acute head injuries are usually divided into two categories:
1. Diffuse brain injuries—concussion and diffuse axonal injuries.
2. Focal brain injuries—all fractures and intracranial injuries.

It is not necessary to have loss of consciousness to have a concussion.* Several severity grading scales for concussion exist; one that is commonly used is the following:

COLORADO MEDICAL SOCIETY GUIDELINES

Grade	Confusion	Amnesia	Loss of Consciousness
I	+	–	–
II	+	+	–
III	+	+	+

Return-to-Play Criteria

Return-to-play criteria are based on prevention of the second impact syndrome. This syndrome is characterized by a loss of autoregulation of cerebral blood flow, manifest as a rapid increased intracranial pressure following a second head injury before full recovery from the initial head injury has occurred. Return to contact sports is based on the grade of the injury.

RECOMMENDATIONS FOR RETURN TO CONTACT SPORTS FOLLOWING A CONCUSSION†

Grade	Minimum Time to Return	Time Asymptomatic‡
I	20 min	When examined
II	1 wk	1 wk
III	1 mo	1 wk

RECOMMENDATIONS FOR RETURN TO CONTACT SPORTS FOLLOWING REPEATED CONCUSSIONS

Grade	Minimum Time to Return	Time Asymptomatic‡
I (second time)	2 wk	1 wk
II (second time)	1 mo	1 wk
I (3 3), II (3 2), III (3 2)	Season over	1 wk

From Behrman RE: *Nelson textbook of pediatrics,* ed 16, Philadelphia, 2000, WB Saunders.

*In animal studies, there is evidence that there are microscopic changes in the brain after a concussion. These may not be evident in imaging studies, so the clinician must rely on history and neuropsychologic examination to follow a patient's progress. In college football players who experienced their first concussion, the neuropsychologic testing normalized in 5 days and symptoms of headache and memory resolved in 10 days.

The chronic effects of repetitive boxing injuries include cortical atrophy and a cavum septum pellucidum (identified radiographically). Whether this occurs in other sports in which head injuries are common (football, ice hockey, wrestling) or in which the head is used as part of the game (soccer) is debatable. However, there appears to be no danger in the young soccer player occasionally heading the ball.

†Contact sports means any situation in which contact is possible, including practice.

‡A symptomatic athlete should not return to contact sports regardless of the initial diagnosis. Athletes with focal brain injuries are excluded from contact sports indefinitely. Patients with a neck injury can return to contact sports when they have full, pain-free range of motion, strength and sensation, and normal lordosis of the cervical spine.

LABORATORY TESTS

Blood tests are not very specific in diagnosing PCS.

IMAGING STUDIES

- CT scan of the head is normal.
- MRI of the head is often normal but may show petechial hemorrhages or cerebral contusions.
- EEG is normal.
- Evoked potentials are normal.
- Neuropsychologic testing may reveal difficulties in concentration, memory, and executive function but is not very specific for PCS.

TREATMENT

Postconcussive syndrome must be recognized as a physiologic and psychologic problem and treated accordingly.

NONPHARMACOLOGIC THERAPY

- Heat
- Physical therapy
- Avoidance of alcohol, narcotics, and sleep deprivation

ACUTE GENERAL Rx

- Headaches can be treated with NSAIDs, ibuprofen 800 mg tid or naproxen 500 mg bid.
- Neck pain can be treated in a similar fashion.

CHRONIC Rx

- Psychotherapy
- Behavioral therapy
- Vocational rehabilitation
- Depression can be treated with SSRIs but may not respond as well when compared with non-PCS patients with depression

DISPOSITION

- Most patients after mild traumatic brain injury improve without any residual deficits.
- Neuropsychologic testing may be abnormal but usually improves during the first 6 mo after injury.
- If related to contact sports, see Table 1-44.
- Predictors for the development of persistent postconcussive syndrome (>1 yr) include:
  1. Female
  2. Ongoing litigation
  3. Low socioeconomic status
  4. Prior headaches
  5. Prior mild traumatic brain injury
  6. Prior psychiatry illnesses

REFERRAL

Postconcussive syndrome patients may benefit from consultations with psychologists, psychiatrists, and neurologists.

PEARLS & CONSIDERATIONS

COMMENTS

- PCS syndrome starts within a few days after the injury. Recognizing depression and treating pain symptoms early in the course may help prevent the development of persistent postconcussive syndrome (>1 yr).
- The severity of the fall, duration of unconsciousness, and amnesia helps assess the severity of axonal injury.
- Attempts to determine how much of a role psychologic and neurologic factors play in the PCS are important but very difficult.

SUGGESTED READINGS

Alexander MP: Mild traumatic brain injury: pathophysiology, natural history, and clinical management, *Neurology* 45:1253, 1995.

Evans RW: The postconcussive syndrome: 130 years of controversy, *Semin Neurol* 14:32, 1994.

Koshner DS: Concussion in sports: minimizing the risk for complications, *Am Fam Physician* 64:1007, 2001.

Marguiles S: The postconcussion syndrome after mild head trauma: Is brain damage overdiagnosed? Part 1, *J Clin Neuroses* 7(5): 400, 2000.

Mittenberg S, Strauman S: Diagnosis of mild head injury and the postconcussion syndrome, *J Head Trauma Rehabil* 15(2):783, 2000.

AUTHOR: **PETER PETROPOULOS, M.D.**

BASIC INFORMATION

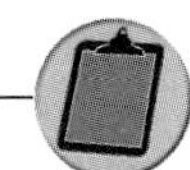

DEFINITION

Postpolio syndrome (PPS) is a lower motor neuron disease characterized by late-onset chronic progressive weakness, muscle cramps, joint pain, and fatigue (muscular fatigability or generalized) occurring several decades after recovering from an acute poliomyelitis infection.

SYNONYMS

Progressive postpoliomyelitis muscular atrophy

ICD-9CM CODES
138 Late effects of acute poliomyelitis

EPIDEMIOLOGY & DEMOGRAPHICS

INCIDENCE (IN U.S.): 250,000 to 640,000 people survived acute poliomyelitis from the 1940 and 1950 epidemics. Of those, 28.5% to 64% develop PPS.

PEAK INCIDENCE: Occurs 8 to 71 yr (mean 36 yr) from the time of the acute poliomyelitis infection

RISK FACTORS:
- Severe acute paralysis
- Adolescent and adult onset of the acute infection
- Less recovery and greater physical activity during the intervening years

PHYSICAL FINDINGS & CLINICAL PRESENTATION

- Polio "wall": generalized fatigue occurring with minimal activity
- A slow progressive asymmetric, proximal, distal, or patchy weakness and atrophy, mainly involving previously affected muscles by the acute infection
- Focal muscle fatigue (decreased endurance)
- Muscle tenderness on palpation, pain (aches and soreness), fasciculations, and cramps
- Bulbar muscle dysfunction (dysphasia, dysarthria, aphonia, and less commonly facial weakness)
- Cold intolerance and vasomotor instability
- Respiratory insufficiency, sleep apnea, and sleep disturbances
- Diagnostic criteria (set by the Post-Polio Task Force in 1997):
  1. A confirmed episode of acute poliomyelitis infection with residual motor neuron loss documented by a typical history, neurologic examination, and/or electromyographic studies
  2. Neurologic and functional stability after recovery from the acute episode for a period that is usually more than 15 yr
  3. Insidious onset of new muscle weakness, atrophy, or fatigue (muscle fatigability or generalized weakness)
  4. Exclusion of other conditions that can present like PPS

ETIOLOGY

- Controversial.
- Overwork of a weak muscle (most widely held hypothesis): many years of muscle overuse causes excessive metabolic stress on the remaining motor neurons that already have branched out to innervate denervated muscle fibers from the acute infection. This results in the gradual degeneration of those nerve terminals that are supplying the denervated muscles.
- Vulnerability of the anterior horns: due to the earlier acute infection or preexistent since birth.
- Scar tissue forming in the anterior horns: forms "a locus resistentiae minoris" (an area of little resistance) or "a latent inflammatory focus" that could produce new symptoms at any time.
- Chronic persistent poliovirus infection.
- Persistent immune-mediated mechanism: supported by the presence of oligoclonal bands in the CSF and lymphocytic infiltration of muscles and spinal cord of some patients.

DIAGNOSIS

DIFFERENTIAL DIAGNOSIS

- Amyotrophic lateral sclerosis
- Cervical and lumbosacral radiculopathy
- Adult spinal muscular atrophy
- Diabetic amyotrophy
- Multifocal motor neuropathy with conduction block
- Chronic inflammatory demyelinating polyneuropathy
- Entrapment neuropathies
- Inflammatory and metabolic myopathies
- Vasculitis
- Connective tissue disease associated myopathies

WORKUP

- A good history and physical examination demonstrating the characteristic pattern of weakness in an individual who has history of documented acute poliomyelitis illness.
- Electromyography: ongoing denervation and chronic reinnervation. Fibrillation potentials and fasciculations may be present in symptomatic muscles. Single fiber EMG may show increased jitter and blocking. However, those findings cannot separate PPS from an asymptomatic patient with previous poliomyelitis.
- Nerve conduction studies: decreased compound muscle action potential amplitudes with normal distal latencies and conduction velocities. Sensory nerve action potentials are normal.
- Muscle biopsy: fiber type grouping (remote denervation), myofiber atrophy (recent permanent loss of motor innervation), and neural cell adhesion molecule (N-CAM)-positive myofibers (denervation).
- Lumbar puncture: CSF might show a nonspecific protein elevation and oligoclonal bands.
- Imaging studies (MRI, CT, X-ray): to rule out spine disease, such as spondylosis or spinal stenosis or radiculopathy.

LABORATORY TESTS

- Creatine kinase (CPK) (mildly elevated in many patients).
- Thyroid function test to rule out thyroid disease causing myopathy.
- Antinuclear antigen (ANA), rheumatoid factor (RF), double-stranded DNA (ds-DNA), erythrocyte sedimentation rate (ESR), scl-70, anti-Ro, and anti-La to rule out other autoimmune diseases.
- Heavy metal screening should be considered.
- Standard serum studies (complete blood count and electrolytes).

TREATMENT

NONPHARMACOLOGIC THERAPY

- Treatment is supportive and focused on reducing physical exhaustion.
- Generalized fatigue:
  1. Energy conservation (pacing of physical activities combined with frequent rest periods and daytime naps), weight loss, and assistive devices (orthoses, canes, intermittent use of wheelchairs).
  2. Amantadine, pyridostigmine, amitriptyline, fluoxetine, and pemoline might be considered.
- New weakness: nonfatiguing aerobic exercise and isometric or isokinetic exercise (short intervals, frequent rest, and should be performed on alternate days). A physical therapist should be involved.

- Respiratory insufficiency: nighttime noninvasive positive-pressure ventilation. Some patients might require tracheostomy and permanent ventilation.
- Dysphagia: speech therapist to teach proper food and swallowing techniques.
- Musculoskeletal pain (joint or muscle pain) and joint instability: pacing activities and lifestyle changes, decreasing mechanical stress with bracing and wheelchairs. Nonsteroidals, heat, and massage might be used.
- Pneumonia and influenza vaccines should be given.
- Smoking cessation.

GENERAL Rx

- Anticholinesterases (pyridostigmine): an open trial reported improvement of fatigue with pyridostigmine (Trojan et al 1995). Preliminary data from a double-blinded, placebo-controlled crossover trial suggested subjective improvement of fatigue and strength in the upper extremities with the same drug (Seizert et al 1994).

DISPOSITION

- Slow progression with an average decline in strength of about 1% to 2% per yr

REFERRAL

- Surgical evaluation for muscle biopsy
- A neurologist or a neuromuscular specialist for neurophysiologic testing
- Physical and occupational therapists and a physiatrist

PEARLS & CONSIDERATIONS

COMMENTS

- Risk of falls should be assessed by a physical therapist.
- Interdisciplinary approach should be used in the management of those patients, including primary care physician; physiatrist; neurologist; pulmonologist; psychiatrist; physical, occupational, and respiratory therapists; nurse, and social worker.

SUGGESTED READINGS

Katirji B et al: *Neuromuscular Disorders in Clinical Practice*. Boston, 2002, Butterworth-Heinemann.

Nollet F, de Visser M: Postpolio syndrome, *Arch Neurol* 61(7):1142, 2004.

Seizert BP, Speier JL, Canine JK: Pyridostigmine effect on strength, endurance, and fatigue in post-polio patients (abstract), *Arch Phys Med Rehabil* 75:1049, 1994.

Trojan DA, Cashman NR: An open trial of pyridostigmine in post-poliomyelitis syndrome, *Can J Neurol Sci* 22(3):223, 1995.

AUTHOR: **MUSTAFA A. HAMMAD, M.D.**

BASIC INFORMATION

DEFINITION

Posttraumatic stress disorder (PTSD) is an anxiety disorder that arises when an individual has witnessed or experienced a potentially fatal or serious injurious condition during which he or she felt helpless or horrified. The individual continues to experience the event in the form of flashbacks (reliving the trauma), intrusive recollections, dreams, or physiologic reactivity or psychologic distress in response to cues symbolizing the event. These responses are associated with persistent hyperarousal (e.g., hypervigilance, exaggerated startle, sleep disturbance, irritability, and difficulty concentrating) and avoidance (both physically and cognitively) of stimuli associated with the traumatic event.

SYNONYMS

Soldier's heart
Effort syndrome
Shell shock
Irritable heart
Traumatic necrosis
Survivor syndrome
Concentration camp syndrome
Gross stress reaction (DSM-I, published in 1952)

ICD-9CM CODES
308.3 Posttraumatic stress syndrome, acute
309.81 Posttraumatic stress syndrome, chronic

EPIDEMIOLOGY & DEMOGRAPHICS

PREVALENCE (IN U.S.):

- PTSD is one of the most common psychiatric disorders, with an estimated lifetime prevalence of 7.8%.
- Prevalence estimates among high-risk populations (e.g., combat veterans or victims of violent crimes) range up to 58%.

PREDOMINANT SEX: 5% to 6% of men and 10% to 14% of women; more than 50% of cases in women are related to sexual assault.

PREDOMINANT AGE: No predisposing age factors have been identified.

PEAK INCIDENCE: PTSD cannot be diagnosed until at least 1 month after the traumatic event.

GENETICS: Twin studies have demonstrated the important role of genetic vulnerability in the development of PTSD related to combat. There are no comparable studies for civilian trauma.

PHYSICAL FINDINGS & CLINICAL PRESENTATION

- The reexperiencing of traumatic events in the form of dreams, flashbacks, and intrusive memories tends to be the most prominent of the diagnostic criteria.
- After severe life-threatening event, complaints of derealization, depersonalization, detachment, dissociation, or being dazed, in association with a marked increase in anxiety and arousal.
- Within 3 mo, signs of persistent hyperarousal, anxiety, and distressing memories or reexperiences of the traumatic event in most patients; symptoms may be disabling.

ETIOLOGY

- By definition, the patient must have been exposed to a traumatic event that involved actual or threatened death or serious injury. Events that involve interpersonal violence are more likely to give rise to PTSD than are events such as motor vehicle accidents and natural disasters.
- The likelihood of developing PTSD varies with severity, duration, and proximity of the experienced trauma.
- A personal or family history of psychiatric disorder and a prior history of traumatic experiences are associated with an increased risk of developing PTSD.
- The severity of the physical injury is a weaker predictor of the likelihood of developing PTSD than the psychologic distress; the duration of the stress is the most important factor.
- Human-made disasters cause more intense reactions than natural disasters.
- Symptoms are mediated, in part, by the autonomic nervous system and the hypothalamic-pituitary-adrenal (HPA) system. Research suggests that patients with PTSD have an exaggerated negative feedback inhibition of the HPA axis by glucocorticoids.

DIAGNOSIS

DIFFERENTIAL DIAGNOSIS

- Adjustment disorders are distinguished from PTSD in that the precipitating stress is less catastrophic and the psychologic reaction less specific.
- PTSD is associated with high rates of depression, anxiety disorders, and substance use. Overall, about 80% of persons with PTSD also have a comorbid psychiatric disorder.
- Acute stress reaction typically lasts <48 hr; acute stress disorder begins during or shortly after the precipitating event (within 4 wk) and must last at least 48 hr.
- Borderline personality disorder and dissociative identity disorder.

WORKUP

- Diagnosis of PTSD relies on a thorough history.
- There are numerous self-report questionnaires and structured diagnostic instruments; mainly useful in research settings.
- Laboratory and imaging not sufficiently validated or replicated to be clinically useful.

TREATMENT

NONPHARMACOLOGIC THERAPY

- In most cases, treatment of PTSD should be multidimensional, consisting of patient education and support, cognitive-behavioral therapy and psychopharmacotherapy.
- Cognitive-behavioral therapy is the nonpharmacologic treatment of choice.
- Group therapy is often helpful for many PTSD victims, particularly combat veterans.

ACUTE GENERAL Rx

- Symptomatic and generally aimed at alleviating distress.
- Benzodiazepines for reducing anxiety symptoms.
- Sedating antidepressants to treat initial insomnia and suppress nightmares; in low doses may also alleviate daytime anxiety.

CHRONIC Rx

- SSRIs are the pharmacologic treatment of choice for PTSD. Sertraline and paroxetine are notable for having been assessed in large, multisite, randomized double-blind controlled trials.
- Other antidepressants (TCAs and MAOs) also helpful in reducing symptoms associated with PTSD.
- Diagnose and treat comorbid substance use and other psychiatric problems.

Alternative approaches:

- Eye movement desensitization reprocessing (EMDR); results from controlled trials have shown mixed results.

- β-adrenergic antagonists and clonidine may be helpful for treating aggression and other psychophysiologic arousal symptoms.

DISPOSITION

- Recovery rates are highest in the first 12 mo after onset of symptoms.
- Average duration of symptoms is 36 mo for those who undergo treatment and 64 months for those never treated.
- Up to half of patients experience chronic symptoms.
- Predictors of chronic course:
  1. Premorbid psychiatric function
  2. Acute response to stress (e.g., individuals who experience an acute stress disorder immediately after the trauma do better in the long term)

REFERRAL

Because early intervention improves outcome, referral to psychotherapy as soon as diagnosis made.

SUGGESTED READINGS

Davidson J: Recognition and treatment of posttraumatic stress disorder, *JAMA* 286:584, 2001.

Grinage BD: Diagnosis and management of post-traumatic stress disorder, *Am Fam Physician* 68(12):2409, 2003.

Schoenfeld FB, Marmar CR, Neylan TC: Current concepts in pharmacotherapy for posttraumatic stress disorder, *Psychiatr Serv* 55(5):519, 2004.

Yehuda R: Post-traumatic stress disorder, *N Engl J Med* 346:108, 2002.

AUTHOR: **MITCHELL D. FELDMAN, M.D., M.PHIL.**

BASIC INFORMATION

DEFINITION

Precocious puberty is defined as sexual development occurring before 8 yr of age in males and 9 yr of age in females.

SYNONYMS

Pubertas praecox

ICD-9CM CODES
259.1 Precocious puberty

EPIDEMIOLOGY & DEMOGRAPHICS

INCIDENCE: Estimated to be between 1:5000 and 1:10,000

PREDOMINANT SEX: Females > males for the idiopathic variant; for other causes, dependent on the underlying etiology.

GENETICS: The genetics for some of the etiologies of precocious puberty are known.

PHYSICAL FINDINGS & CLINICAL PRESENTATION

- In females: breast development, pubic hair development, accelerated growth, and menarche
- In males: increase in testicular volume and penile length, pubic hair development, accelerated growth, muscular development, acne, change in voice, and penile erections

ETIOLOGY

- Idiopathic or true: diagnosis of exclusion
- CNS pathology: tumors, hydrocephalus, ventricular cysts, benign lesions
- Severe hypothyroidism
- Posttraumatic head injury
- Genetic disorders: neurofibromatosis, tuberous sclerosis, McCune-Albright syndrome, congenital adrenal hyperplasia
- Gonadal tumors
- Nongonadal tumors: hepatoblastoma
- Exposure to exogenous sex steroids

DIAGNOSIS

DIFFERENTIAL DIAGNOSIS

- Most common diagnoses to consider: premature thelarche and premature adrenarche
- Gonadotropin hormone–releasing hormone (GnRH)–dependent precocious puberty: idiopathic, CNS tumors, hypothalamic hamartomas, neurofibromatosis, tuberous sclerosis, hydrocephalus, post acute head injury, ventricular cysts, post CNS infection
- GnRH-independent precocious puberty: congenital adrenal hyperplasia, adrenocortical tumors (males), McCune-Albright syndrome (females), gonadal tumors, ectopic hCG-secreting tumors (chorioblastoma, hepatoblastoma), exposure to exogenous sex steroids, severe hypothyroidism

WORKUP

Thorough history and physical examination are essential to determine if the patient has true precocious puberty. Particular attention should be paid to growth, development, order of appearance of the secondary sexual characteristics, pubertal development in family members, medications, neurologic symptoms, Tanner staging, abdominal and neurologic examination. Section III, Puberty, Precocious describes a clinical approach to precocious puberty.

LABORATORY TESTS

- GnRH testing will help determine if dependent or independent cause
- Sex hormone studies: LH, FSH, hCG, testosterone (males), estrogen (females)
- T_4, TSH

IMAGING STUDIES

- CT scan or MRI of the brain to evaluate for CNS pathology
- Consideration of pelvic ultrasound in female patients to evaluate for cysts/tumors
- Abdominal imaging with CT scan if intraabdominal pathology suspected

TREATMENT

NONPHARMACOLOGIC THERAPY

- Good communication with the parents is essential to care.
- Psychologic support for the child may be needed with regard to self-image and problems with peer acceptance.

ACUTE GENERAL Rx

There is no acute therapy for precocious puberty.

CHRONIC Rx

Therapy depends on the etiology of precocious puberty:

- For true precocious puberty and some CNS lesions, the treatment of choice is leuprolide 0.25 to 0.3 mg/kg with a 7.5 mg minimum IM every 4 wk.
- For other CNS lesions and extragonadal tumors, therapy is dependent on the type of lesion, location of the lesion, and the overall prognosis of the underlying problem.
- For severe hypothyroidism, treatment with thyroid hormone will result in regression of the sexual development. The child will subsequently undergo appropriate pubertal development later in life.
- For familial male gonadotropin-independent precocious puberty, ketoconazole can be used at doses of 600 mg/day divided tid, or a combination of testolactone and spironolactone can be used.

DISPOSITION

- For true precocious puberty and some CNS lesions, long-term outcome is usually very good. When drug therapy is instituted, it is continued until a time when further pubertal development is appropriate. It is then discontinued, allowing the child to progress through puberty.
- For other cases, long-term outcomes are dependent on the prognosis of the underlying cause.

REFERRAL

- Initial workup can be instituted by the primary care provider.
- Referral to an endocrinologist is indicated for most children because they will need long-term management, monitoring, and treatment.

SUGGESTED READING

Root AW: Precocious puberty, *Pediatr Rev* 21(1):10, 2000.

AUTHOR: **BETH J. WUTZ, M.D.**

Preeclampsia

BASIC INFORMATION

DEFINITION

Preeclampsia involves a triad of hypertension, proteinuria, and edema that develops after the twentieth week of gestation. Mild preeclampsia is defined as a blood pressure of <140/90 mm Hg. Severe preeclampsia is associated with a blood pressure >160/110 mm Hg, proteinuria >5 g in a 24-hr urine collection, oliguria (<400 ml/24 hr), cerebral or visual disturbances, epigastric pain, pulmonary edema, thrombocytopenia, hepatic dysfunction, or severe intrauterine growth retardation.

SYNONYMS

Pregnancy-induced hypertension
Toxemia of pregnancy

ICD-9CM CODES
642.6 Preeclampsia

EPIDEMIOLOGY & DEMOGRAPHICS

INCIDENCE: 10% to 14% in primigravidas, 5.7% to 7.3% in multigravidas
RISK FACTORS: Increased incidence and severity with multiple gestations, renal or collagen-vascular diseases. Extremes of reproductive age, <20 or >35 yr of age, obesity, African Americans, thrombophilia, previous preeclampsia.
GENETICS: Positive correlation with maternal and paternal family history.

PHYSICAL FINDINGS & CLINICAL PRESENTATION

- Generalized swelling or nondependent edema, possibly manifested by rapid weight gain (>4 lb/wk) even in the absence of edema
- Auscultation of pulmonary rales
- RUQ pain (HELLP syndrome or subcapsular liver hematoma)
- Hyperreflexia or clonus
- Vaginal bleeding (placental abruption)
- Acute or chronic fetal compromise manifested by intrauterine growth restriction or fetal tachycardia with late decelerations, respectively
- Wide range of symptoms attributable to multiorgan system dysfunction, involving hepatic, hematologic, renal, pulmonary, and CNS
- Possibility of severe disease despite "normal" blood pressure readings, so a high index of suspicion must be maintained in high-risk situations

ETIOLOGY

- Exact etiology or toxic substance is unknown
- Theories
  1. Imbalance between thromboxane A_2 (vasoconstrictor and platelet aggregator) and prostacyclin (vasodilator)
  2. Abnormal trophoblastic invasion of spiral arteries
  3. Increased sensitivity to angiotensin II by the muscular walls of the arteries
  4. Excess circulating soluble fms-like tyrosine kinase 1 (SFlT-1), which binds placental growth factor (PlGF) and vascular endothelial growth factor (VEGF), may have a pathogenic role

DIAGNOSIS

DIFFERENTIAL DIAGNOSIS

- Acute fatty liver of pregnancy
- Appendicitis
- Diabetic ketoacidosis
- Gallbladder disease
- Gastroenteritis
- Glomerulonephritis
- Hemolytic-uremic syndrome
- Hepatic encephalopathy
- Hyperemesis gravidarum
- Idiopathic thrombocytopenia
- Thrombotic thrombocytopenic purpura
- Nephrolithiasis
- Pyelonephritis
- PUD
- SLE
- Viral hepatitis

WORKUP

- Two blood pressure measurements in lateral recumbent position 6 hr apart, with an absolute pressure >140/90 mm Hg or an increase of 30 mm Hg systolic or 15 mm Hg diastolic from baseline, an increase in the mean arterial pressure (MAP) of 20 mm Hg, or an absolute MAP >105 mm Hg
- Evaluation for proteinuria as defined by >0.1 g/L on urine dipstick or >300 mg protein on a 24-hr urine collection
- Evaluation of fetal status for evidence of intrauterine growth restriction, oligohydramnios, alteration in umbilical or uterine artery Doppler flow, or acute compromise, such as abruption
- Because of the insidious nature of the disease with potential for multiple organ involvement, complete evaluation for preeclampsia in any pregnant patient presenting with CNS derangement or GI complaints after 20 wk of gestation
- Evaluation for associated conditions such as disseminated intravascular coagulation, hepatic dysfunction, or subcapsular hematoma

LABORATORY TESTS

- High-risk patients: baseline assessment of renal function (24-hr urine collection for protein and creatinine clearance), platelets, BUN, creatinine, LFTs, and uric acid should be obtained at the first prenatal visit.
- CBC (Hgb, Hct, platelets) may show signs of volume contraction or HELLP syndrome.
- LFTs (AST, ALT, LDH) are useful in evaluation for HELLP syndrome or to exclude important differentials.
- Hyperuricemia or increased creatinine may indicate decreasing renal function.
- PT, PTT, and fibrinogen should be checked to rule out disseminated intravascular coagulation.
- Peripheral smear may demonstrate microangiopathic hemolytic anemia.
- Complement levels can be used to differentiate from an acute exacerbation of a collagen-vascular disease.
- Increased levels of SFlT-1 and reduced levels of PlGF predict subsequent development of preeclampsia.

IMAGING STUDIES

- CT scan of head if atypical presentation of eclampsia, possibility of intracerebral bleed, or prolonged postictal state
- Sonogram of fetus to evaluate for IUGR, amniotic fluid, placenta
- Sonogram of maternal liver if suspect subcapsular hematoma

TREATMENT

NONPHARMACOLOGIC THERAPY

Bed rest in left lateral decubitus position

ACUTE GENERAL Rx

Delivery is the treatment of choice and the only cure for the disease. This must be taken in the context of the gestational age of the fetus, severity of the preeclampsia, and the likelihood of a successful induction and reliability of patient.

- Administer magnesium sulfate 6 g IV loading dose, with 2 to 3 g maintenance or phenytoin at 10 to 15 mg/kg loading dose, then 200 mg IV q8h starting 12 hr after loading dose.
- Hydralazine 10 mg IV, labetalol hydrochloride 20 to 40 mg IV, nifedipine 20 mg SL can be used for acute blood pressure control.
- Continuous fetal monitoring is needed.
- Epidural is anesthesia of choice for pain management in labor or C-section.
- All patients undergoing induction of labor should receive antiseizure medications regardless of severity of disease.

CHRONIC Rx

- Mild preeclampsia <37 wk: close observation for worsening maternal or fetal condition, with delivery at ≥37 wk with favorable cervix or at 40 wk regardless of cervical status.
- Severe preeclampsia: delivery in the presence of maternal or fetal compromise, labor, or >34 wk; at 28 to 34 wk consider steroids with close monitoring, and at <24 wk consider termination of pregnancy.
- Methyldopa is drug of choice for chronic blood pressure control during pregnancy.

DISPOSITION

Preeclampsia is a progressive and unpredictable disease process; a course of expectancy should be managed with caution. Up to 20% of patients who have seizures are normotensive.

REFERRAL

Obstetric management is indicated because of the insidious nature of the disease, with transfer of all cases <34 wk to a facility with a level three nursery.

PEARLS & CONSIDERATIONS

COMMENTS

- Low-dose aspirin 81 mg qd and calcium supplementation 1500 mg qd can be considered in high-risk patients to decrease the risk of recurrence.
- Begin after first trimester.

SUGGESTED READINGS

Creasy RT, Resnik R: *Maternal-fetal medicine,* ed 4, Philadelphia, 1999, WB Saunders.

Duley L et al: Antiplatelet drugs for prevention of pre-eclampsia and its consequences: systematic review, *BMJ* 322:329, 2001.

Esplin MS et al: Paternal and maternal components of the predisposition to preeclampsia, *N Engl J Med* 344:867, 2001.

Lain KY, Roberts JM: Contemporary concepts of the pathogenesis and management of preeclampsia, *JAMA* 287:3183, 2002.

Levine RJ et al: Circulating angiogonic factors and risk of preeclampsia, *N Enl J Med* 350:672, 2004.

Skjaerven R et al: The interval between pregnancies and the risk of preeclampsia, *N Engl J Med* 346:33, 2002.

AUTHOR: **SCOTT J. ZUCCALA, D.O.**

Premenstrual Dysphoric Disorder

BASIC INFORMATION

DEFINITION

The Diagnostic and Statistical Manual of Mental Disorders, 4th edition, classifies premenstrual dysphoric disorder (PMDD) as a "depressive disorder not otherwise specified" and requires as criteria for definition the presence of five or more of the following symptoms in most menstrual cycles for the past year.

- The symptoms should be present most of the time during the last week of the luteal phase, with remission beginning within a few days after the onset of the follicular phase, and absent during the week after menses, with at least one of the symptoms being either (1), (2), (3), or (4):
  1. Marked depressed mood, feeling of hopelessness, or self-deprecating thoughts
  2. Marked anxiety, tension, feeling of being "keyed up" or "on edge"
  3. Marked affective lability (e.g., feeling suddenly sad or tearful or increased sensitivity to rejection)
  4. Persistent and marked anger or irritability or increased interpersonal conflicts
  5. Decreased interest in usual activities (e.g., work, school, friends, hobbies)
  6. Subjective sense of difficulty in concentrating
  7. Lethargy, easy fatigability, or marked lack of energy
  8. Marked change in appetite, overeating, or specific food cravings
  9. Hypersomnia or insomnia
  10. A subjective sense of being overwhelmed or out of control
  11. Other physical symptoms, such as breast tenderness or swelling, headaches, joint or muscle pain, a sensation of "bloating," or weight gain
- The disturbance markedly interferes with work or school or with usual social activities and relationships with others (e.g., avoidance of social activities, decreased production and efficiency at work or school).
- The disturbance is not merely an exacerbation of the symptoms of another disorder, such as major depressive disorder, panic disorder, dysthymic disorder, or a personality disorder (although it may be superimposed on any of these disorders).
- The first three criteria must be confirmed by prospective daily ratings during at least two consecutive symptomatic cycles (diagnosis may be made provisionally before such confirmation).

NOTE: In menstruating women, the luteal phase corresponds to the period between ovulation and the onset of menses, and the follicular phase begins with menses. In nonmenstruating women (e.g., women who have had a hysterectomy), determination of the timing of the luteal and follicular phases may require measurement of circulating reproductive hormones.

ICD-9CM CODES
625.4 Premenstrual dysphoric syndrome

EPIDEMIOLOGY & DEMOGRAPHICS

- PMDD affects 3%-10% of women of reproductive age.
- Genetic factors play a significant role (increased incidence in monozygotic twins and in women whose mothers had PMDD).
- 30%-76% of women with PMDD have a lifetime history of depression.

PHYSICAL FINDINGS & CLINICAL PRESENTATION

- Physical examination may be completely normal.
- Depressed mood, tachycardia, sweating from comorbid disorders (e.g., panic disorder, major depression) may be present.
- Symptoms occur during the last half of the menstrual cycle (the luteal phase) and are absent from the first day of menstruation until ovulation (follicular phase).

ETIOLOGY

Unknown. Serotonin deficiency and altered sensitivity in serotoninergic system in response to phasic hormone fluctuations in the menstrual cycle are believed to play a role.

DIAGNOSIS

DIFFERENTIAL DIAGNOSIS

- Premenstrual syndrome
- Dysthymic syndrome
- Personality disorder
- Panic disorder
- Major depressive disorder
- Hyperthyroidism
- Polycystic ovarian syndrome
- Drug or alcohol abuse
- Irritable bowel syndrome
- Endometriosis

WORKUP

- Diagnosis is based on obtaining a detailed history and ruling out the presence of physical or psychiatric disorders. No objective diagnostic tests exist.
- The diagnosis should be confirmed using a symptom checklist prospectively for two consecutive menstrual cycles. Commonly used diagnostic instruments include the Calendar of Premenstrual Experiences (see reference Mortola et al), the Premenstrual Syndrome Diary (see reference Endicott J).

LABORATORY TESTS

- None are usually necessary.
- A serum TSH to exclude thyroid problems, CBC to rule out anemia, and a chemistry profile to assess electrolytes may be ordered if diagnosis is unclear.

IMAGING STUDIES

- None

TREATMENT

NONPHARMACOLOGIC THERAPY

- Reduction in intake of caffeine, refined sugars, or sodium may be helpful in some patients.
- Increased aerobic exercise, smoking cessation, alcohol restriction, and regular sleep are often beneficial.
- Stress reduction and management will decrease severity of symptoms.

GENERAL THERAPY

- Selective serotonin reuptake inhibitors (SSRIs) are first-line agents for the treatment of PMDD. Commonly used agents and initial doses are fluoxetine 10 mg qd, sertraline 50 mg qd, paroxetine 10 mg qd, and citalopram 20 mg qd. Many patients will require titration to significantly higher doses to achieve therapeutic benefit. These medications can be administered continuously during the menstrual cycle or only when the patients experience symptoms. Luteal-phase or intermittent administration involves initiating medication at the time of ovulation and stopping it at the beginning of menses.

- Second-line agents are benzodiazepines (alprazolam 0.25 mg tid prn) and the tricyclic antidepressant (clomipramine 25 mg qd as starting dose).
- Hormonal intervention with monthly IM injections of leuprolide has been reported effective in some patients; however, it should be reserved only for patients unresponsive to first- and second-line agents.
- Nutritional supplementation (vitamin B_6 up to 100 mg/day, vitamin E up to 600 IU/day, calcium carbonate up to 1200 mg/day, and magnesium up to 500 mg/day) are also commonly used and effective in symptom reduction in some patients.
- Ovariectomy may be considered in severe refractory cases.

COMMENTS

Patients should complete a course of medication for at least a couple of menstrual cycles before switching to other therapeutic options.

SUGGESTED READINGS

American Psychiatric Association: *Diagnostic and statistical manual of mental disorders,* ed 4. Washington, DC, 1994, American Psychiatric Association.

Bhatia SC, Bhatia SK: Diagnosis and treatment of premenstrual dysphoric disorder, *Am Fam Physician* 66:1239, 2002.

Endicott J: Severe premenstrual dysphoria: differential diagnosis and treatment, *J Am Med Womens Assoc* 53(4):170, 1998.

Grady-Weliky TA: Premenstrual dysphoric disorder, *N Engl J Med* 348:433, 2003.

Kaur G, Gonsalves L, Thacker H: Premenstrual dysphoric disorder: a review for the treating practitioner, *Cleve Clin J Med* 71:303, 2004.

Mortola JF et al: Diagnosis of premenstrual syndrome by a simple, prospective, and reliable instrument: the calendar of premenstrual experiences, *Obstet Gynecol* 76:302, 1990.

AUTHOR: **FRED F. FERRI, M.D.**

Premenstrual Syndrome 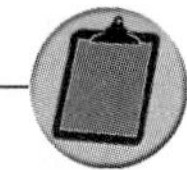

BASIC INFORMATION

DEFINITION

Premenstrual syndrome (PMS) is a cyclic recurrence during the luteal phase of the menstrual cycle of somatic, affective, and behavioral disturbances that are of sufficient severity to affect interpersonal relationships adversely or interfere with normal activities.

SYNONYMS

PMS
PMDD

ICD-9CM CODES
625.4 Premenstrual tension syndromes

EPIDEMIOLOGY & DEMOGRAPHICS

- PMS is thought to be extremely prevalent, intermittently affecting approximately one third of all premenopausal women.
- Severe cases occur in approximately 2%-10% of women with PMS.
- Those seeking treatment for PMS are usually in their 30s or 40s.
- The natural history of PMS has not been clearly elucidated.

PHYSICAL FINDINGS & CLINICAL PRESENTATION

- Diverse and potentially disabling symptoms
- Associated with >150 psychologic, physical, and behavioral symptoms
- Most frequent reason for seeking treatment: emotional symptoms
- Most common emotional symptoms: depression, irritability, anxiety, labile moods, anger, crying easily, sadness, overly sensitive, nervous tension
- Most common physical complaints: headache, bloating, cramps, breast tenderness, migraines, fatigue, weight gain, aches and pains, palpitations
- Most common behavior symptom: food cravings
- Other behavioral symptoms: increased appetite, increased alcohol intake, decreased motivation, decreased efficiency, avoidance of activities, staying home, sleep changes, libido changes, forgetfulness, decreased concentration

ETIOLOGY

- Etiology remains obscure.
- Because of multifactorial-multiorgan nature of PMS, a single etiologic cause is unlikely.

DIAGNOSIS

DIFFERENTIAL DIAGNOSIS

- A diagnosis of exclusion, so other medical or psychologic disorders should be ruled out
- Most common disorders: depression or anxiety, thyroid disease
- Section II describes the differential diagnosis of menstrual pain

WORKUP

- History
- Physical examination
- Laboratory studies to rule out alternative diagnosis
- If no alternative diagnosis confirms diagnosis of PMS, basal body temperature charting is used to determine if the patient is ovulating:
  1. If she is not ovulating, it is not PMS.
  2. If she is ovulating, symptoms should be charted for at least two cycles to determine if the symptoms occur in the luteal phase.
  3. If symptoms are not occurring in the luteal phase, it is not PMS, and further investigation is needed.
     a. If symptoms occur in the follicular phase, patient has premenstrual exacerbation of another condition.
     b. If symptoms do not occur in the follicular phase, diagnosis of PMS is confirmed.

LABORATORY TESTS

- None available to specifically confirm the diagnosis of PMS
- Thyroid function tests to rule out thyroid disease

TREATMENT

NONPHARMACOLOGIC THERAPY

- Individualization of the treatment plan to maximize therapeutic response
- Psychosocial intervention:
  1. Education
  2. Stress management
  3. Environmental changes
  4. Adequate rest and sleep
  5. Regular exercise
- Nutritional recommendations:
  1. Regularly eaten, well-balanced meals
  2. Adequate amounts of protein, fiber, and complex carbohydrates; low fat
  3. Avoidance of foods that are high in salt and simple sugars; may promote water retention, weight gain, and physical discomfort
  4. Avoidance of caffeine-containing beverages; stimulant effects of caffeine may worsen tension, irritability, and insomnia
  5. Avoidance of alcohol and illicit drugs; may worsen emotional lability
  6. Calcium supplementation (1000 mg/day for women 19-50 yr, 1300 mg/day for girls 14-18 yr) to reduce the physical and emotional symptoms
  7. Magnesium (360 mg/day) to reduce water retention and the negative effect associated with PMS.
  8. Pyridoxine (vitamin B_6) 50 mg bid to improve depression, fatigue, irritability and natural diuretic ability; neurotoxicity observed at higher dosages

ACUTE GENERAL Rx

SUPPRESSION OF OVULATION:

- Oral contraceptives—one pill per day
- Progestin-only oral contraceptive—one pill per day
- Oral micronized progesterone—100 mg qam and 200 mg qpm on days 17 through 28 of menstrual cycle
- Progestin suppository—200 to 400 mg bid on days 17 through 28 of menstrual cycle
- Oral contraceptive containing arosperenone/ethinyl estradiol—very effective in decreasing physical symptoms
- Medroxyprogesterone (depot)—150 mg IM every 3 mo
- Levonorgestrel implants—surgical insertion every 5 yr
- Transdermal estradiol—one or two 100-μg patches every 3 days
- Danazol—100 to 200 mg/day (ovulation not suppressed at this dose)
- Gonadotropin-releasing hormone (GnRH) agonists—daily by intranasal spray or monthly by depot injection

SUPPRESSION OF PHYSICAL SYMPTOMS:

- Spironolactone—25 to 50 mg bid on days 14 through 28 of menstrual cycle
- Mefenamic acid
  1. For fluid retention: 250 mg tid on days 24 through 28 of cycle
  2. For pain: 500 mg tid on days 19 through 28 of cycle

- Bromocriptine—5 mg/day on days 10 through 26 of cycle
- Danazol—200 mg/day on days 19 through 28 of cycle
- Naproxen (Anaprox)—550 mg bid on days 17 through 28 of cycle; Naprosyn—500 mg bid on days 17 through 28 of cycle.

SUPPRESSION OF PSYCHOLOGIC SYMPTOMS:

- Nortriptyline—50 to 125 mg/day
- Fluoxetine (Prozac)—20 mg/day or 90 mg weekly (this medication has indications for premenstrual dysphoric disorder)
- Buspirone—10 mg bid or tid on days 16 through 28 of cycle, then taper drug
- Alprazolam—25 mg tid on days 16 through 28 of cycle, then taper drug
- Clonidine—0.1 mg bid
- Naltrexone—0.25 mg/day on days 9 through 18 of cycle
- Atenolol—50 mg/day
- Paroxetine (Paxil)—20 mg/day
- Sertraline (Zoloft)—50 to 100 mg/day
- Nefazodone (Serzone)—Initial dosage 100 mg bid; after 1 wk increase to 150 mg bid
- Propranolol—20 to 40 mg bid
- Verapamil—100 to 320 mg qd

CHRONIC Rx

- Therapy is largely trial and error, with the goal of providing effective treatment with the safest and most simple therapy.
- For severe intractable PMS: hysterectomy with bilateral oophorectomy; give trial of GnRH therapy or danazol before surgery.
- Estrogen replacement therapy recommended postoperatively to reduce the risk of osteoporosis, heart disease, and genitourinary atrophy.

DISPOSITION

Improved symptoms in 90% of women over time.

REFERRAL

- For counseling with a psychologist or psychiatrist if underlying psychiatric disorder is discovered (cognitive behavioral therapy)
- To a gynecologist if surgical therapy is contemplated

PEARLS & CONSIDERATIONS

COMMENTS

Patient educational material is available through bookstores and pharmaceutical companies.

SUGGESTED READINGS

Brown C: A new monophasic oral contraceptive containing drospirenone: effect on premenstrual symptoms, *J Reprod Med* 47(1):14, 2002.

Dimmock PW et al: Efficacy of selective serotonin-reuptake inhibitors in premenstrual syndrome: a systematic review, *Lancet* 356:1131, 2000.

Miner C, Brown E: Weekly luteal-phase dosing with enteric-coated fluoxetine 90 mg in premenstrual dysphoric disorder: a randomized, double blind, placebo-controlled clinical trial, *Clin Therapeut* 24(3):417, 2002.

Pearlstein T: Selective serotonin reuptake inhibitors for premenstrual dysphoric disorder: the emerging gold standard? *Drugs* 62(13):1869, 2002.

Thys-Jacobs S et al: Calcium carbonate and the premenstrual syndrome: effects on premenstrual and menstrual symptoms, *Am J Obstet Gynecol* 179:444, 1998.

Wyatt K: Premenstrual syndrome, *Clin Evid* 7:338, 2002.

Wyatt KM et al: Efficacy of vitamin B-6 in the treatment of premenstrual syndrome: systematic review, *BMJ* 318:1375, 1999.

AUTHOR: **GEORGE T. DANAKAS, M.D.**

Priapism (PTG)

BASIC INFORMATION

DEFINITION

Priapism is the persistent, usually painful, erection associated or unassociated with sexual stimulation.

ICD-9CM CODES
607.3 Priapism

EPIDEMIOLOGY & DEMOGRAPHICS

- Incidence and prevalence unavailable because of relative rarity
- Can affect male of any age, including children

PHYSICAL FINDINGS & CLINICAL PRESENTATION

- In idiopathic priapism the initial erection is associated with prolonged sexual excitement. Previous transient episodes are frequently reported. The erection involves the corpora cavernosa alone. Detumescence does not occur spontaneously.
- In secondary priapism, sexual excitement need not be involved. Otherwise the clinical picture is the same as in idiopathic priapism.
- Table 1-41 compares normal erection and priapism.

ETIOLOGY

Idiopathic: prolonged sexual arousal
Secondary or associated causes:

- Sickle cell disease
- Diabetes
- Leukemia
- Solid tumor penile infiltration

Iatrogenic

- TPN, which includes a fat emulsion
- Anticoagulant therapy
- Phenothiazines
- Trazodone
- Intracorporeal injection therapy for impotence
- Sildenafil (Viagra)

PATHOPHYSIOLOGY

- Low-flow priapism: prolonged erection leads to edema of the cavernosal trabeculae, resulting in a sequence of statis, thrombosis, venous occlusion, fibrosis, scarring, and possibly impotence
- High-flow priapism: cavernosal artery rupture leading to an arteriocavernous fistula

DIAGNOSIS

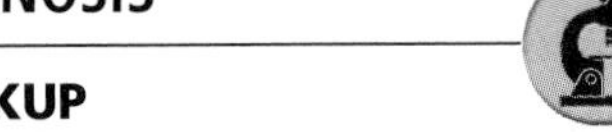

WORKUP

None if the associated underlying causes are known to be present. Otherwise they should be ruled out.

TREATMENT

Goal: achieve detumescence with preservation of potency

1. Medical therapies:
   - Ice packs
   - Ice water enemas
   - Hot water enemas
   - Pressure dressing
   - Sedatives
   - Analgesics
   - Antispasmodic/anticholinergic drugs
   - Estrogens
   - Anticoagulants
   - Procaine
   - Amyl nitrite
   - Local or general anesthesia
   - Ketamine (1 mg/lb)
2. In the patient with sickle cell disease: intravenous hydration, alkalinization, transfusion or exchange-transfusion, oxygen
3. Corpora cavernosa aspiration followed by injection of an α-adrenergic agonist (e.g., phenylephrine 50 μg)
4. Surgery
   - Cavernospongiosum shunt
   - Glans-cavernosum shunt
   - Cavernosaphenous shunt
   - In the less common situation of high-flow priapism (diagnosed by the finding of bright red arterial blood on aspiration), arterial embolization or surgical ligation is recommended

PROGNOSIS

Impotence is associated with the duration of priapism, with 36 hr being an important threshold.

REFERRAL

To urologist

SUGGESTED READING

Benson GS, Boileau MA: Priapism. In Gillenwater JY et al (eds): *Adult and pediatric urology,* St Louis, 1996, Mosby.

AUTHOR: **TOM J. WACHTEL, M.D.**

TABLE 1-41 Comparison of Normal Erection and Priapism

Factor	Normal Erection	Priapism
Portion of penis involved	Corpora cavernosa and corpus spongiosum and glans	Corpora cavernosa
Cause	Vasodilatation of penile arteries	Obstruction of venous outflow
		Disturbance of neuroarterial mechanism (imbalance between it and adrenergic activity)
		Increased viscosity
Sexual desire	Present	Absent
Pain	Absent	Present
Duration	Minutes to hours	Hours to days

From Nseyo UO (ed): *Urology for primary care physicians,* Philadelphia, 1999, WB Saunders.

BASIC INFORMATION

DEFINITION

Progressive supranuclear palsy (PSP) is a progressive degenerative disease of the central nervous system particularly affecting the brainstem and basal ganglia with core features of supranuclear ophthalmoplegia, rigidity, postural instability, and cognitive decline.

SYNONYMS

Steele-Richardson-Olszewski syndrome
Progressive supranuclear ophthalmoplegia

ICD-9CM CODES
333.0 Other degenerative diseases of the basal ganglia

EPIDEMIOLOGY & DEMOGRAPHICS

- Peak incidence is between ages 50-70.
- Onset is nearly always after age 40.
- Age-adjusted prevalence is 1.3-6.4 cases per 100,000.
- There is no gender predilection.

CLINICAL PRESENTATION

- Common early symptoms include slowness (bradykinesia) and stiffness, as well as falls.
- Differences from PD become more pronounced with progression. Tremor is present in only 5%-10% of patients.
- Hallmark on examination is supranuclear gaze palsy; impaired voluntary conjugate eye movements, primarily on attempted up-and-down gaze.
- Predominantly axial rigidity leading to typical neck extension. This plus low blink rate and facial muscle contraction gives a characteristic appearance of "sustained surprise" (see Fig. 1-192).
- Limb rigidity is typically proximal in contrast to the distal rigidity seen in idiopathic PD.
- Gait is slow and stiff, with marked postural instability leading to unheralded, often backward falls.
- Cognitive impairment is frequent and consists of mental slowness, irritability, and social withdrawal.

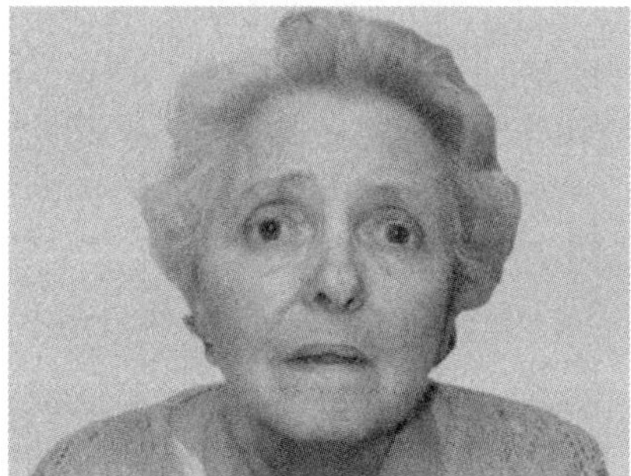

FIGURE 1-192 A patient with PSP, with staring expression, frontalis overactivity, and retrocolitis. She is wearing a neck sling for a fractured wrist, sustained in a fall. (From Burn D, Lees A: Progressive supranuclear palsy: where are we now? *Lancet Neurol* 1:359, 2002.)

ETIOLOGY

Pathogenesis is believed to be related to accumulation of hyperphosphorylated tau protein in neurons and glia in basal ganglia and brainstem nuclei.

DIAGNOSIS

DIFFERENTIAL DIAGNOSIS

- Parkinson's disease—differs from PSP in which early falls are prominent, tremor is unusual, and there is very little response to levodopa.
- Cortical basal ganglionic degeneration—differentiated from PSP by presence of cortical sensory signs and asymmetrical limb apraxia.
- Multiple systems atrophy—differs from PSP by the presence of prominent autonomic symptoms and/or cerebellar signs.
- Dementia with Lewy bodies (DLB)—in PSP visual hallucinations typically only occur if provoked by dopaminergic therapy, whereas in DLB there are prominent visual hallucinations that may be spontaneous or provoked.

WORKUP

- Diagnosis is largely clinical. National Institute of Neurologic Disorders and Stroke (NINDS) provides inclusion and exclusion criteria. Mandatory exclusion criteria include:
  1. Recent history of encephalitis
  2. Cortical sensory deficits
  3. Hallucinations or delusions unrelated to dopaminergic therapy
  4. Cortical dementia of Alzheimer type
- There are no diagnostic laboratory tests at present.

LABORATORY TESTS

If there is a question of recent encephalitis, spinal fluid analysis may be indicated.

IMAGING STUDIES

- If atypical features such as unilateral symptoms or signs are present, brain MRI may be helpful in ruling out structural lesions.
- Conventional neuroimaging is not useful to differentiate PSP from the major differential diagnoses. Functional neuroimaging such as PET and SPECT show promise, but are not yet routinely indicated or available.

TREATMENT

NONPHARMACOLOGIC THERAPY

- Physical, occupational, and speech/swallowing therapies can be helpful for both patients and caregivers.
- Patients with significant dysphagia may require a feeding gastrostomy.

ACUTE GENERAL Rx

None available.

CHRONIC Rx

- Levodopa may be mildly helpful with rigidity and bradykinesia early in the disease course, but typically loses effectiveness quickly. Dopamine receptor agonists are not typically effective.
- Cholinesterase inhibitors have not been shown to help with the cognitive impairment.

DISPOSITION

Median survival after diagnosis is <10 yr.

REFERRAL

Referral to a general neurologist or movement disorders center is appropriate.

PEARLS & CONSIDERATIONS

COMMENTS

- Unheralded, often backward falls is one of the most common initial presentations.
- Poor downgaze is an especially helpful examination finding because upgaze palsy is common in normal aging.
- Poor or unsustained response to levodopa therapy suggests a diagnosis other than idiopathic Parkinson's disease.

PREVENTION

None known.

PATIENT/FAMILY EDUCATION

Comprehensive movement disorders website with disease information as well as links to support and discussion groups: http://www.wemove.org

SUGGESTED READINGS

Burn D, Lees A: Progressive supranuclear palsy: where are we now? *Lancet Neurol* 1:359, 2002.

Margery M: Lumping and splitting the Parkinson plus syndromes, *Neurol Clin* 19:3, 2001.

Pastor P, Tolosa E: Progressive supranuclear palsy: clinical and genetic aspects, *Curr Opin Neurol* 15:429, 2002.

AUTHOR: **DAVID P. WILLIAMS, M.D.**

Prolactinoma (PTG)

BASIC INFORMATION

DEFINITION

Prolactinomas are monoclonal tumors that secrete prolactin.

ICD-9CM CODES
253.1 Forbes-Albright syndrome

EPIDEMIOLOGY & DEMOGRAPHICS

INCIDENCE: Most common pituitary tumor; nearly 30% of all pituitary adenomas secrete enough prolactin to cause hyperprolactinemia.
PREDOMINANT SEX: Microadenomas are more common in women; macroadenomas are more frequent in men.

PHYSICAL FINDINGS & CLINICAL PRESENTATION

MEN: Decreased facial and body hair, small testicles; may also have decreased libido, impotence, and delayed puberty (caused by decreased testosterone secondary to inhibition of gonadotropin secretion).
WOMEN: Physical examination may be normal; history may reveal amenorrhea, galactorrhea, oligomenorrhea, and anovulation.
BOTH SEXES: Visual field defects and headache may occur depending on size of tumor and its expansion.

ETIOLOGY

Prolactin-secreting pituitary adenomas: microadenomas (<10 mm diameter) or macroadenomas (>10 mm diameter)

DIAGNOSIS

DIFFERENTIAL DIAGNOSIS

Hyperprolactinemia may be caused by the following:

- Drugs: phenothiazines, methyldopa, reserpine, MAO inhibitors, androgens, progesterone, cimetidine, tricyclic antidepressants, haloperidol, meprobamate, chlordiazepoxide, estrogens, narcotics, metoclopramide, verapamil, amoxapine, cocaine, oral contraceptives
- Hepatic cirrhosis, renal failure, primary hypothyroidism
- Ectopic prolactin-secreting tumors (hypernephroma, bronchogenic carcinoma)
- Infiltrating diseases of the pituitary (sarcoidosis, histiocytosis)
- Head trauma, chest wall injury, spinal cord injury
- Polycystic ovary disease, pregnancy, nipple stimulation
- Idiopathic hyperprolactinemia, stress, exercise

WORKUP

- The diagnosis of prolactinoma is established by demonstration of an elevated serum prolactin level (after exclusion of other causes of hyperprolactinemia) and radiographic evidence of a pituitary adenoma.
  1. Normal mean prolactin levels are 8 ng/ml in women and 5 ng/ml in men.
  2. Levels >300 ng/ml are virtually diagnostic of prolactinomas.
  3. Prolactin levels can vary with time of day, stress, sleep cycle, and meals. More accurate measurements can be obtained 2 to 3 hr after awakening, preprandially, and when patient is not distressed.
  4. Serial measurements are recommended in patients with mild prolactin elevations.
- TRH stimulation test may be useful in equivocal cases. The normal response is an increase in serum prolactin levels by 100% within 1 hr of TRH infusion; failure to demonstrate an increase in prolactin level is suggestive of pituitary lesion.
- All patients with prolactinomas should undergo visual field testing. Serial evaluation is recommended, particularly during pregnancy in patients with macroadenomas.

IMAGING STUDIES

- MRI with gadolinium enhancement is the procedure of choice in the radiographic evaluation of pituitary disease.
- In absence of MRI, a radiographic diagnosis is best accomplished with a high-resolution CT scanner and special coronal cuts through the pituitary region.

TREATMENT

NONPHARMACOLOGIC THERAPY

Pregnancy and breast-feeding should be avoided, because they can encourage tumor growth.

ACUTE GENERAL Rx

- Management of prolactinomas depends on their size and encroachment on the optic chiasm and other vital structures, the presence or absence of gonadal dysfunction, and the patient's desires with respect to fertility.
- Medical therapy is preferred when fertility is an important consideration.
  1. Bromocriptine (Parlodel): Initial dose is 0.625 at hs for the first week. After 1 wk, add AM dose of 1.25 mg. Gradually increase dose by 1.25 mg/wk until dose of 5 to 10 mg/day is achieved; Bromocriptine decreases size of the tumor and generally lowers the prolactin level into the normal range when the initial serum prolactin is <500 ng/ml. Side effects of bromocriptine are nausea, constipation, dizziness, and nasal stuffiness. Bromocriptine appears to be safe during pregnancy.
  2. Cabergoline (Dostinex) is a longer-acting dopamine agonist that is more expensive but may be more effective and better tolerated than bromocriptine; initial dose is 0.25 mg twice weekly.
- Transsphenoidal resection: option in an infertile patient who cannot tolerate bromocriptine or cabergoline or when medical therapy is ineffective. The success rate depends on the location of the tumor (entirely intrasellar), experience of the neurosurgeon, and size of the tumor (<10 mm in diameter); the recurrence rate may reach 80% within 5 yr. Possible complications of transsphenoidal surgery include transient diabetes insipidus, hypopituitarism, CSF rhinorrhea, and infections (meningitis, wound infection).
- Pituitary irradiation is useful as adjunctive therapy of macroadenomas (>10 mm in diameter) and in patients with persistent hypersecretion following surgery. Potential complications include cranial nerve damage, radionecrosis, and cognitive abnormalities.
- Stereotactic radiosurgery (gamma knife) has become popular as a modality in the treatment of prolactinomas. A high dose of ionizing radiation is delivered to the tumor through multiple ports. Its advantage is minimal irradiation to surrounding tissues. Proximity of the tumor to the optic chiasm limits this therapeutic modality.

CHRONIC Rx

- Patients on medical therapy require periodic measurement of prolactin levels. An attempt to reduce the dose of bromocriptine or cabergoline can be made after the prolactin level has been normal for 2 yr. An MRI scan of the pituitary should be obtained to rule out tumor enlargement within 6 mo of initiation of tapering regimen.

- Evaluation and monitoring of pituitary function are recommended following transsphenoidal surgery.

DISPOSITION

- Transsphenoidal surgery will result in a cure in nearly 50% to 75% of patients with microadenomas and 10% to 20% of patients with macroadenomas.
- Nearly 20% of microprolactinomas resolve during long-term dopamine agonist treatment.

PEARLS & CONSIDERATIONS

COMMENTS

Patients must be monitored for several years after surgery, because up to 50% of microadenomas and nearly 90% of macroadenomas can recur.

SUGGESTED READINGS

Leung A, Pacaud D: Diagnosis and management of galactorrhea, *Am Fam Physician* 70:543, 2004.

Schlechte JA: Prolactinoma, *N Engl J Med* 349:2035, 2003.

AUTHOR: **FRED F. FERRI, M.D.**

Pronator Syndrome (PTG)

BASIC INFORMATION

DEFINITION

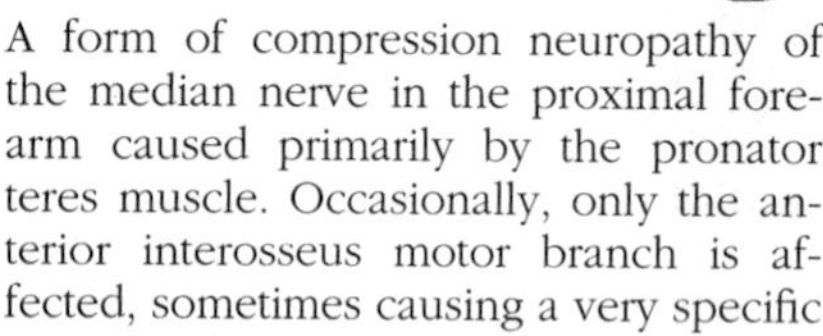

A form of compression neuropathy of the median nerve in the proximal forearm caused primarily by the pronator teres muscle. Occasionally, only the anterior interosseus motor branch is affected, sometimes causing a very specific separate clinical presentation.

SYNONYMS

Kiloh-Nevin syndrome (anterior interosseus syndrome)

ICD-9CM CODES
354.1 Median nerve entrapment
354.9 Mononeuritis of upper limb

EPIDEMIOLOGY & DEMOGRAPHICS

- Males = females
- Most common in dominant arm
- Rare (<1% median nerve entrapment disorders)

PHYSICAL FINDINGS & CLINICAL PRESENTATION

- Forearm discomfort and fatigue, often resulting from repetitive pronation
- Insidious onset
- Nocturnal paresthesias are not typical
- Vague numbness in hand, primarily in thumb and index finger, may be present
- Tenderness and enlargement of the pronator teres may be present
- Tinel's sign may be positive at the site of compression
- Although there are no reliable provocative tests, painful paresthesias may occasionally be elicited with forced pronation of the forearm against resistance
- Motor impairment is rare

Anterior interosseus nerve syndrome:

- Forearm pain and weakness
- Patient may be unable to form a circle when trying to pinch the index finger and thumb because of inability to flex distal phalanges of thumb and index finger
- Sensation to the hand is not affected

ETIOLOGY

- Localized anatomic compression
- Trauma
- Traumatic cut down or phlebotomy

DIAGNOSIS

DIFFERENTIAL DIAGNOSIS

- Carpal tunnel syndrome
- Cervical disc syndrome with radiculopathy
- Tendon rupture
- Tendinitis

WORKUP

- Electrodiagnostic studies may be helpful; they are indicated if symptoms persist longer than 4-6 wk or if motor weakness is suspected
- Plain radiography to rule out bony abnormalities causing compression

TREATMENT

- Rest, bracing of forearm, sling
- Stretching exercises, physical therapy
- NSAIDs

REFERRAL

Surgical referral in cases of failed medical management or when motor weakness is present

PEARLS & CONSIDERATIONS

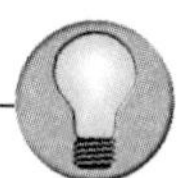

COMMENTS

Prognosis for recovery is good. When indicated, surgical intervention is most effective if the diagnosis can be firmly established by objective testing.

SUGGESTED READINGS

Cain EL et al: Elbow injuries in throwing athletes: a current concepts review, *Am J Sports Med* 31(4):621, 2003.

Rehak DC: Pronator syndrome, *Clin Sports Med* 20(3):531, 2001.

AUTHOR: **LONNIE R. MERCIER, M.D.**

BASIC INFORMATION

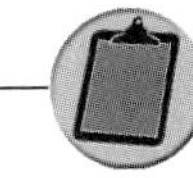

DEFINITION AND CLASSIFICATION

Prostate cancer is a neoplasm involving the prostate; various classifications have been developed to evaluate malignancy potential and prognosis:

- The degree of malignancy varies with the stage

Stage A: Confined to the prostate, no nodule palpable
Stage B: Palpable nodule confined to the gland
Stage C: Local extension
Stage D: Regional lymph nodes or distant metastases

- In the Gleason classification, two histologic patterns are independently assigned numbers 1 to 5 (best to least differentiated). These numbers are added to give a total tumor score:
  1. Prognosis is generally good if score is <5.
  2. Score 6 to 10 carries an intermediate prognosis.
  3. Score >10 correlates with anaplastic lesions with poor prognosis.
- Another commonly used classification is the Tumor-Node-Metastasis (TNM) classification of prostate cancer.

ICD-9CM CODES
185 Malignant neoplasm of prostate

EPIDEMIOLOGY & DEMOGRAPHICS

- Prostate cancer has surpassed lung cancer as the most common nonskin cancer in men.
- More than 100,000 cases are diagnosed yearly, and nearly 30,000 males die from prostate cancer each year (second leading cause of death from cancer in U.S. men).
- Incidence of prostate cancer increases with age: uncommon <50 yr; 80% of new cases are diagnosed in patients ≥65 yr.
- Average age at time of diagnosis is 72 yr.
- Blacks in the U.S. have the highest incidence of prostate cancer in the world (1 in every 9 males).
- Incidence is low in Asians.
- Approximately 9% of all prostate cancers may be familial.

PHYSICAL FINDINGS & CLINICAL PRESENTATION

- Generally silent disease until it reaches advanced stages.
- Bone pain and pathologic fractures may be initial symptoms of prostate cancer.
- Local growth can cause symptoms of outflow obstruction.
- Digital rectal examination (DRE) may reveal an area of increased firmness; 10% of patients will have a negative DRE.
- Prostate may be hard, fixed, with extension of tumor to the seminal vesicles in advanced stages.

DIAGNOSIS

DIFFERENTIAL DIAGNOSIS

- Benign prostatic hypertrophy
- Prostatitis
- Prostate stones

LABORATORY TESTS

- Measurement of PSA is useful in early diagnosis of prostate cancer and in monitoring efficacy of therapy. Normal PSA is found in >20% of patients with prostate cancer, whereas only 20% of men with PSA levels between 4 ng/ml and 10 ng/ml have prostate cancer. The American Cancer Society recommends offering the PSA test and digital rectal examination yearly to men 50 years or older who have a life expectancy of at least 10 years. Earlier testing, starting at age 45, is recommended for men at high risk (e.g., blacks, men with family history of prostate cancer). An isolated elevation in PSA level should be confirmed several weeks later before proceeding with further testing, including prostate biopsy.
- The use of serum-free PSA for prostate screening has been proposed by some urologists as a means to decrease unwarranted biopsies without missing a significant number of prostate cancers. This approach is based on the higher free PSA in men with benign prostatic hyperplasia and the higher protein-bound PSA levels in men with prostate cancer. For example, in men with total PSA levels of 4 to 10 ng/ml, the cancer probability is 0.25, but if the percent free PSA is ≤17%, the probability of cancer increases to 0.45.
- Prostatic acid phosphatase (PAP) can be used for evaluation of nonlocalized disease.
- Transrectal biopsy and fine-needle aspiration of prostate can confirm the diagnosis.

IMAGING STUDIES

- Bone scan is useful to evaluate bone metastasis (present or eventually develops in almost 80% of patients). However, according to the American Urological Association (AUA), the routine use of bone scanning is not required for staging of prostate cancer in asymptomatic men with clinically localized cancer if the PSA level is ≤20 ng/ml.
- CT scan, MRI, and transrectal ultrasonography may be useful in selected patients to assess extent of prostate cancer. High-resolution MRI with magnetic nanoparticles has been used for the detection of small and otherwise undetectable lymph-node metastases in patients with prostate cancer. However, according to the AUA, transrectal ultrasonography adds little to the combination of PSA and digital rectal examination. Similarly, CT and MRI imaging are generally not indicated for cancer staging in men with clinically localized cancer and PSA <25 ng/ml. With regard to pelvic lymph node dissection in staging, the AUA states that it may not be required in patients with PSA levels <10 ng/ml and when PSA level is <20 ng/ml and the Gleason score is <6.

TREATMENT

NONPHARMACOLOGIC THERAPY

Watchful waiting is reasonable in patients with early stage (T-IA) and projected life expectancy <10 yr or in patients with focal and moderately differentiated carcinoma.

ACUTE GENERAL Rx

- Therapeutic approach varies with the following:
  1. Stage of the tumor
  2. Patient's life expectancy
  3. General medical condition
  4. Patient's treatment preference (e.g., patient may be opposed to orchiectomy)

- The optimal treatment of clinically localized prostate cancer is unclear.
  1. Radical prostatectomy is generally performed in patients with localized prostate cancer and life expectancy >10 yr.
  2. Radiation therapy (external beam irradiation or implantation of radioactive pellets [seeds]) represents an alternative in patients with localized prostate cancer, especially poor surgical candidates or patients with a high-grade malignancy. Patients with localized prostate cancer and high risk for extraprostatic disease and disease recurrence (e.g., Gleason score ≥7 with multiple positive biopsy cores and clinical stage T1b-T2b) may benefit (increased overall survival) with the addition of 6 mo of androgen suppression therapy to radiation therapy.
  3. Watchful waiting is reasonable in patients who are too old or too ill to survive longer than 10 yr. If the cancer progresses to the point where it becomes symptomatic, palliation can be attempted with several methods.
- Patients with advanced disease and projected life expectancy <10 yr are candidates for radiation therapy and hormonal therapy (DES, LHRH analogs, antiandrogens, bilateral orchiectomy).
- Recommended treatment of patients with regional metastatic prostate cancer with projected life expectancy ≥10 yr includes radical prostatectomy, radiation therapy, hormonal therapy.
- Androgen-deprivation therapy with a gonadotropin-releasing hormone agonist is the mainstay of treatment for metastatic prostate cancer. Adjuvant treatment with GnRH agonists (goserelin leuprolide, or triptorelin) plus antiandrogens (flutamide, bicalutamide, or nilutamide), when started simultaneously with external irradiation, improves local control and survival in patients with locally advanced prostate cancer. Pamidronate inhibits osteoclast-mediated bone resorption and prevents bone loss in the hip and lumbar spine in men receiving treatment for prostate cancer with a GnRH.
- Abarelix (Plenaxis) is an injectable GnRH agonist useful to suppress testosterone in patients with prostate cancer who are not good candidates for LHRH agonists and refuse surgical castration.

CHRONIC Rx

- Patients should be monitored at 3- to 6-mo intervals with clinical examination, and PSA for the first year, then every 6 mo for the second year, then yearly if stable. For patients who have undergone radical prostatectomy, a rising PSA level suggests evidence of residual or recurrent prostate cancer. Salvage radiotherapy may potentially cure patients with disease recurrence after radical prostatectomy.
- Chest x-ray and bone scan should be performed yearly or sooner if patient develops symptoms.

DISPOSITION

- Prognosis varies with the stage of the disease (see "Definition") and the Gleason classification (see "Definition").
- The ploidy of the tumor also has prognostic value: prognosis is better with diploid tumor cells, worse with aneuploid tumor cells.
- For grade 1 tumors, the extended 10-yr, disease-specific survival is similar for patients with prostatectomy (94%), radiotherapy (90%), and conservative management (93%); survival rate is better with surgery than with radiotherapy or conservative management in patients with grade 2 or 3 localized prostate cancer.
- Expression of the gene EZH2 has been identified as an important factor in the determination of the aggressiveness of prostate cancer. A recent study revealed that expression of the EZH2 gene may be a better predictor of clinical failure than Gleason score, tumor stage, or surgical margin status. Testing for EZH2 protein in prostate cancer tissue may be useful to determine prognosis and direct treatment.
- PSA velocity (annual increase in PSA level) has prognostic significance. Men whose PSA level increases by >2.0 μg/ml during the year before the diagnosis of cancer may have a relatively high risk of death from prostate cancer despite undergoing radical prostatectomy.

SUGGESTED READINGS

D'Amico AV et al: Six month androgen suppression plus radiation therapy vs radiation therapy alone for patients with clinically localized prostate cancer, *JAMA* 292:821, 2004.

D'Amico AV et al: Preoperative PSA velocity and the risk of death from prostate cancer after radical prostatectomy, *N Engl J Med* 351:125, 2004.

Eastham JA et al: Variation of serum prostate specific antigen levels, *JAMA* 289:2695, 2003.

Gann PH et al: Strategies combining total and percent free prostate specific antigen for detecting prostate cancer: a perspective evaluation, *J Urol* 167:2427, 2002.

Harisinghani MG et al: Noninvasive detection of clinically occult lymph-node metastases in prostate cancer, *N Engl J Med* 348:2491, 2003.

Homberg L et al: A randomized trial comparing radical prostatectomy with watchful waiting in early prostate cancer, *N Engl J Med* 347:781, 2002.

Johansson JE et al: Natural history of early, localized prostate cancer, *JAMA* 291:2713, 2004.

Makinen T et al: Family history and prostate cancer screening with prostate specific antigen, *J Clin Oncol* 20:2658, 2002.

Nelson WG: Prostate cancer, *N Engl J Med* 349:366, 2003.

Rubin MA et al: α-Methylacyl coenzyme a racemase as a tissue biomarker for prostate cancer, *JAMA* 287:1662, 2002.

Steineck G et al: Quality of life after radical prostatectomy or watchful waiting, *N Engl J Med* 347:790, 2002.

Varambally S et al: The polycarb group protein EZH2 is involved in progression of prostate cancer, *Nature* 419:624, 2002.

AUTHOR: **FRED F. FERRI, M.D.**

BASIC INFORMATION

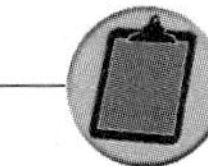

DEFINITION

Benign prostatic hyperplasia is the benign growth of the prostate, generally originating in the periureteral and transition zones, with subsequent obstructive and irritative voiding symptoms.

SYNONYMS

BPH
Prostatic hypertrophy

ICD-9CM CODES
600 Benign prostatic hyperplasia

EPIDEMIOLOGY & DEMOGRAPHICS

- 80% of men have evidence of benign prostatic hypertrophy by age 80 yr.
- Medical and surgical intervention for problems caused by BPH is required in >20% of males by age 75 yr.
- Transurethral resection of the prostate (TURP) is the tenth most common operative procedure (>400,000/yr in U.S.).
- 10% to 30% of men with BPH have occult prostate cancer.

PHYSICAL FINDINGS & CLINICAL PRESENTATION

- Digital rectal examination (DRE) reveals enlargement of the prostate.
- Focal enlargement may be indicative of malignancy.
- There is poor correlation between size of prostate and symptoms (BPH may be asymptomatic if it does not encroach on the urethral lumen).
- Most patients with BPH complain of difficulty in initiating urination (hesitancy), decrease in caliber and force of stream, incomplete emptying of bladder often resulting in double voiding (need to urinate again a few minutes after voiding), postvoid "dribbling," and nocturia.

ETIOLOGY

Multifactorial; a functioning testicle is necessary for development of BPH (as evidenced by the absence in males who were castrated before puberty).

DIAGNOSIS

DIFFERENTIAL DIAGNOSIS

- Prostatitis
- Prostate cancer
- Strictures (urethral)
- Medication interfering with the muscle fibers in the prostate and also with bladder function

WORKUP

Symptom assessment (use of American Urological Association [AUA] Symptom Index for BPH [Table 1-42]), laboratory tests, and imaging studies

LABORATORY TESTS

- Prostate specific antigen (PSA): protease secreted by epithelial cells of the prostate; elevated in 30% to 50% of patients with BPH. Testing for PSA increases detection rate for prostate cancer and tends to detect cancer at an earlier stage. However, the PSA test does not discriminate well between patients with symptomatic BPH and those with prostate cancer, particularly if the cancers are pathologically localized and curable. The test may also trigger additional evaluation, including

TABLE 1-42 **International Prostate Symptom Score (I-PSS)**

SCORE

Symptom	Not at all	Less than 1 time in 5	Less than half the time	About half the time	More than half the time	Almost always	Total score
Incomplete emptying: Over the past month, how often have you had a sensation of not emptying your bladder completely after you finished urinating?	0	1	2	3	4	5	
Frequency: Over the past month, how often have you had to urinate again <2 hr after you finished urinating?	0	1	2	3	4	5	
Intermittency: Over the past month, how often have you found you stopped and started again several times when you urinated?	0	1	2	3	4	5	
Urgency: Over the past month, how often have you found it difficult to postpone urination?	0	1	2	3	4	5	
Weak stream: Over the past month, how often have you had a weak urinary stream?	0	1	2	3	4	5	
Straining: Over the past month, how often have you had to push or strain to begin urination?	0	1	2	3	4	5	
	None	**1 Time**	**2 Times**	**3 Times**	**4 Times**	**5 or More Times**	
Nocturia: Over the past month, how many times did you most typically get up to urinate from the time you went to bed at night until the time you got up in the morning?	0	1	2	3	4	5	
Total I-PSS score =							

ultrasound biopsy of the prostate. Asymptomatic men with PSA levels <2 ng/ml do not need annual testing. According to the AUA, PSA testing and digital rectal examination should be offered to any asymptomatic man older than 50 yr of age with a life expectancy of 10 yr. PSA testing can also be offered at an earlier age in men at higher risk of prostatic cancer (e.g., first-degree relatives with prostate cancer; black men)

- Measurement of "free" PSA is useful to assess the probability of prostate cancer in patients with normal digital rectal examination and total PSA between 4 and 10 ng/ml. In these patients the global risk of prostate cancer is 25%; however, if the free PSA is >25%, the risk of prostate cancer decreases to 8%, whereas if the free PSA is <10%, the risk of cancer increases to 56%. Free PSA is also useful to evaluate the aggressiveness of prostate cancer. A low free PSA percentage generally indicates a high-grade cancer, whereas a high free PSA percentage is generally associated with a slower growing tumor
- Urinalysis, urine C&S to rule out infection (if suspected)
- BUN and creatinine to rule out postrenal insufficiency

IMAGING STUDIES

- Transrectal ultrasound may be indicated in patients with palpable nodules or significant elevation of PSA. It is also useful to estimate prostate size.
- Uroflowmetry may be used to determine relative impact of obstruction on urine flow. Urethral pressure profile is useful to predict prostatic hypertrophy within the urethral lumen.
- Pressure flow studies, although invasive, are particularly helpful in patients whose history and/or examination suggest primary bladder dysfunction as a cause of symptoms of prostatism. They are also useful in patients for whom a distinction between prostatic obstruction and impaired detrusor contractility may affect the choice of therapy. However, pressure flow studies may not be useful in the workup of the usual patient with symptoms of prostatism.
- Postvoid residual urine measurement has not been proved useful in predicting the need for or response to treatment; may be useful in monitoring the course of the disease in patients who elect nonsurgical treatment.
- Urethral cystoscopy is an option during later evaluation if invasive treatment is being planned.

TREATMENT

NONPHARMACOLOGIC THERAPY

- Avoidance of caffeine or any other foods that may exacerbate symptoms
- Avoidance of medications that may exacerbate symptoms (e.g., most cold and allergy remedies)

GENERAL Rx

- Asymptomatic patients with prostate enlargement caused by BPH generally do not require treatment. Patients with mild to moderate symptoms are candidates for pharmacologic treatment (see below). For those patients who have specific complications from BPH, prostate surgery is usually the most appropriate form of treatment. However, surgery may result in significant complications (e.g., incontinence, infection).
- TURP is the most commonly used surgical procedure for BPH. Transurethral incision of the prostate (TUIP), a procedure almost equivalent in efficacy, is limited to patients whose estimated resection tissue weight would be 30 g or less. TUIP can be performed in an ambulatory setting or during a 1-day hospitalization. Open prostatectomy is typically performed on patients with very large prostates.
- Laser therapy for BPH is a less invasive alternative to TURP; however, recent studies indicate that at least in the initial 7 mo after surgery, TURP is moderately more effective than laser therapy in relieving symptoms of BPH.
- Surgery need not be treatment of last resort for most patients; that is, patients need not undergo other treatments for BPH before they can have surgery. However, recommending surgery on the grounds that a patient's surgical risk will "only increase with age" is generally inappropriate.
- Balloon dilation of the prostatic urethra is less effective than surgery for relieving symptoms but is associated with fewer complications. It is a reasonable treatment option for patients with smaller prostates and no middle lobe enlargement.
- The dietary supplement saw palmetto is effective in relieving BPH symptoms in patients with mild obstruction.
- α-Blockers (e.g., tamsulosin [Flomax], alfuzosin [Uroxatral], doxazosin, prazosin, and terazosin) relax smooth muscle of the bladder neck and prostate and can increase peak urinary flow rate. They have no effect on the size of the prostate. α-1 blockers are useful in symptomatic patients to relieve symptoms of obstruction by causing relaxation of smooth muscle tone in the prostatic capsule and urethra and bladder neck.
- Hormonal manipulation with finasteride (Proscar), a 5α-reductase inhibitor that blocks conversion of testosterone to dihydrotestosterone, can reduce the size of the prostate. Usual dose is 5 mg qd. Treatment requires 6 mo or more for maximal effect.
- Dutasteride (Avodart) is also a 5 α-reductase inhibitor useful to decrease prostate size and improve urinary flow. In addition to inhibiting the isoform of 5-α reductase located in the prostate, the medication also inhibits a second isoform and reduces DHT formation in the skin and liver. Usual dose is 0.5 mg qd.

CHRONIC Rx

- Avoid medications and foods that exacerbate symptoms.
- Symptomatic improvement occurs in >70% of patients with proper treatment.

DISPOSITION

With appropriate therapy, symptoms improve or stabilize in >70% of patients with BPH.

REFERRAL

Urology referral for patients with severe or intolerable symptoms and for any patient suspected of having prostate cancer (10% to 30% of men with BPH).

PEARLS & CONSIDERATIONS

COMMENTS

- Emerging technologies for treating BPH include lasers, coils, stents, thermal therapy, and hyperthermia. Laser prostatectomy appears promising; however, long-term effectiveness has not yet been demonstrated.
- The increase in the use of pharmacologic management has resulted in more than 30% reduction in the total number of transurethral resections of the prostate.

SUGGESTED READING

Dull P et al: Managing benign prostatic hyperplasia, *Am Fam Physician* 66:77, 2002.

AUTHOR: **FRED F. FERRI, M.D.**

BASIC INFORMATION

DEFINITION

Prostatitis refers to inflammation of the prostate gland. There are four major categories:

- Acute bacterial prostatitis
- Chronic bacterial prostatitis
- Nonbacterial prostatitis
- Prostatodynia

ICD-9CM CODES
601.0 Prostatitis (acute)
601.1 Prostatitis (chronic)
099.54 Prostatitis (chlamydial)

EPIDEMIOLOGY & DEMOGRAPHICS

- 50% of men experience symptoms of prostatitis in their lifetime
- Acute bacterial prostatitis is uncommon
- The relative prevalence of the other three entities among men with inflammatory prostatic symptoms is:
  1. 5% to 10% chronic bacterial prostatitis
  2. 10% to 65% nonbacterial prostatitis
  3. 30% to 80% prostatodynia

The figures are imprecise because nonbacterial prostatitis and prostatodynia are very difficult to differentiate.

PHYSICAL FINDINGS & CLINICAL PRESENTATION

ACUTE BACTERIAL PROSTATITIS:

- Sudden or rapidly progressive onset of:
  1. Dysuria
  2. Frequency
  3. Urgency
  4. Nocturia
  5. Perineal pain that may radiate to the back, the rectum, or the penis
- Hematuria or a purulent urethral discharge may occur.
- Occasionally urinary retention complicates the course.
- Fever, chills, and signs of sepsis can also be part of the clinical picture.
- On rectal examination the prostate is typically tender.

CHRONIC BACTERIAL PROSTATITIS:

- May be asymptomatic when the infection is confined to the prostate
- May present as an increase in severity of baseline symptoms of benign prostatic hypertrophy
- When cystitis is also present, urinary frequency, urgency, and burning may be reported
- Hematuria may be a presenting complaint
- In elderly men, new onset of urinary incontinence may be noted

NONBACTERIAL PROSTATITIS AND PROSTATODYNIA:

- Present similarly with symptoms of bladder irritation (urinary frequency, urgency, dysuria, increase in nocturia episodes) and perineal discomfort
- The symptoms can be of variable severity, but tend to be more bothersome in prostatodynia

ETIOLOGY

ACUTE BACTERIAL PROSTATITIS:

- Acute usually gram-negative infection of the prostate gland
  1. Generally associated with cystitis
  2. Resulting from the ascent of bacteria in the urethra
- Occasionally the route of infection is hematogenous or a lymphatogenous spread of rectal bacteria
- The condition is seen in young or middle-aged men

CHRONIC BACTERIAL PROSTATITIS:

- Often asymptomatic
- Exacerbation of symptoms of benign prostatic hypertrophy caused by the same mechanism as in acute bacterial prostatitis

NONBACTERIAL PROSTATITIS:

- Refers to symptoms of prostatic inflammation associated with the presence of WBCs in prostatic secretions with no identifiable bacterial organism
- Chlamydia infection may be etiologically implicated in some cases

PROSTATODYNIA:

- Refers to symptoms of prostatic inflammation with no or few WBCs in the prostatic secretion
- Spasm in the bladder neck or urethra is felt to be the cause of symptoms

DIAGNOSIS

DIFFERENTIAL DIAGNOSIS

- Benign prostatic hypertrophy with lower urinary tract symptoms
- Prostate cancer
- Also see differential diagnosis of hematuria

WORKUP

- Rectal examination
  1. Tender prostate most suggestive of acute bacterial prostatitis
  2. Enlarged prostate common in chronic bacterial prostatitis
  3. Normal prostate is consistent with chronic bacterial and nonbacterial prostatitis and is typical in prostatodynia
- Expression of prostatic secretions (EPS) by prostate massage is contraindicated in acute bacterial prostatitis but is appropriate in the other three situations

LABORATORY TESTS

- Urinalysis
- Urine culture and sensitivity
- Bacterial localization studies can be performed but are cumbersome and impractical in most clinical settings
- Cell count and culture of expressed prostatic secretions
- The yield of a urine culture may be increased if the specimen is obtained after a prostatic massage
- PSA is not used to diagnose prostatitis; however, a rapid rise over baseline should raise the possibility of prostatitis even in the absence of symptoms. In such cases, a follow-up PSA after treatment of prostatitis is appropriate
- CBC and blood cultures if fever, chills, or signs of sepsis exist
- If hematuria is present, a workup to rule out a urologic malignancy should be considered if the hematuria does not clear after treatment of prostatitis

TREATMENT

ACUTE BACTERIAL PROSTATITIS:

Culture guided antibiotic therapy for 4 wk (beginning with a few days of intravenous antibiotics if the infection is serious or if the patient is bacteremic).

CHRONIC BACTERIAL PROSTATITIS:

- Trimethoprim-sulfamethoxazole is first-line choice for 4 wk if the organism is sensitive.
- Second-line choice for treatment failure or organisms resistant to TMP-SMX is with a fluoroquinolone.
- Patient with refractory infection or with multiple relapses may be offered long-term suppressive therapy.

NONBACTERIAL PROSTATITIS AND PROSTATODYNIA:

- No specific treatment
- Antibiotics are not effective
- A trial of treatment with an α-adrenergic blocker (terazosin, doxazosin, or tamsulosin) may be considered
- Any underlying bladder pathology should be ruled out by cystoscopy and treated if identified

SUGGESTED READINGS

Fowler JE: Prostatitis. In Gillenwater JY et al (eds): *Adult and pediatric urology,* St Louis, 1996, Mosby.

McNaughton Collins M, MacDonald R, Wilt TJ: Diagnosis and treatment of chronic abacterial prostatitis: a systemic review, *Ann Intern Med* 133:367, 2000.

AUTHOR: **TOM J. WACHTEL**

Pruritus Ani (PTG)

BASIC INFORMATION

DEFINITION

Pruritus ani refers to an intense chronic itching of the anus and perianal skin.

ICD-9CM CODES
698.0 Pruritus ani

EPIDEMIOLOGY & DEMOGRAPHICS

- Any age can be affected.
- Occurs in 1% to 5% of the population.
- Male to female predominance of 4:1.

PHYSICAL FINDINGS & CLINICAL PRESENTATION

- Anal itching
- Anal fissures
- Hemorrhoids
- Excoriations
- Pinworms
- Fecal incontinence

ETIOLOGY

ANORECTAL DISEASES AND FECAL CONTAMINATION:
- Diarrhea
- Anal incontinence
- Hemorrhoids
- Fissures
- Fistulae
- Rectal prolapse
- Malignancy: Bowen's disease, epidermoid cancer, perianal Paget's disease

INFECTIONS:
- Fungal: candidiasis, dermatophytes
- Parasitic: pinworms, scabies
- Bacterial: *Staphylococcus aureus*, erythrasma
- Lymphogranuloma venereal
- Granuloma
- Inguinale
- Chancroid
- Molluscum contagiosa
- Trichomoniasis
- Venereal: herpes, gonococcal syphilis, human papillomavirus

LOCAL IRRITANTS:
- Moisture, obesity, excessive perspiration
- Soaps, hygiene products
- Toilet paper: perfumed, dyed
- Underwear: irritating fabrics, detergents
- Anal creams, suppositories
- Dietary: coffee, beer, acidic foods
- Drugs: mineral oil, ascorbic acid, hydrocortisone sodium succinate, quinine, colchicine

DERMATOLOGIC DISEASES:
- Psoriasis
- Atopic dermatitis
- Seborrheic dermatitis

Section II also describes the various causes of pruritus ani.

DIAGNOSIS

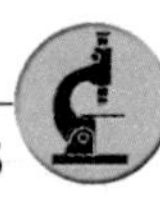

DIFFERENTIAL DIAGNOSIS

- Allergies
- Anxiety
- Dermatologic conditions
- Infections
- Parasites
- Diabetes mellitus
- Chronic liver disease
- Neoplasia
- Proctalgia fugax

WORKUP

- Detailed history regarding bowel habits, hygiene, use of perfumed products, and medical history
- Inspection of perianal area
- Possible biopsy to exclude neoplasia
- Microscopic inspection of scrapings
- Colposcopy of perineum

LABORATORY TESTS

- Chemistry profile
- Urinalysis
- Cultures
- Stool for ova and parasites
- Tape test
- Glucose tolerance test, if necessary

TREATMENT

NONPHARMACOLOGIC THERAPY

- Avoidance of tight, nonporous clothing and underclothing
- Discontinuation or curtailment of coffee, beer, citrus fruits, tomatoes, chocolate, and tea
- Cleansing of anal area after bowel movements with a premoistened pad or tissue and avoidance of perfumes and dyes present in toilet paper and soaps
- Avoidance of excessive perspiration
- Aggressive management of fecal leakage or incontinence to avoid soiling of perianal skin

ACUTE GENERAL Rx

- Minimization of frequent loose stools with antidiarrheals and fiber agents if appropriate
- Use of a 1% hydrocortisone cream sparingly bid during the acute phase of pruritus ani but not for >2 wk to avoid atrophy
- Treatment of predisposing factors, such as parasites, diabetes, liver disease, hemorrhoids, and other infections

CHRONIC Rx

- Possible complications: excoriation and secondary bacterial infection; must be treated aggressively
- Long-standing, intractable pruritus ani: good response to intracutaneous injections of methylene blue and other agents, steroid injection

DISPOSITION

- Usually good results with total resolution of symptoms
- In some, persistent and recurrent symptoms

REFERRAL

To colorectal specialist if conservative measures fail

SUGGESTED READINGS

Fardi A, Rath W: Infections of the perianal region, *Gynakoloe* 34(10):907, 2001.

Gerdom LE, Dixon D, DiPalma JA: Hemorrhoids, genital warts and other perianal complaints, *JAAPA* 14(9):37, 2001.

Pfenninger JL, Zainea GG: Common anorectal conditions: part I: symptoms and complaints, *Am Fam Physician* 63(12):2391, 2001.

Watson AJ, Loudon M: Diagnosing minor anorectal conditions, *Practitioner* 245(1627): 790, 2001.

Yamada T, Alpers DH, Laine L: *Textbook of gastroenterology*, ed 3, Baltimore, 1999, Lippincott Williams & Wilkins.

AUTHOR: **MARIA A. CORIGLIANO, M.D.**

BASIC INFORMATION

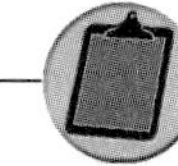

DEFINITION

Pruritus vulvae refers to intense itching of the female external genitalia.

SYNONYMS

Vulvodynia

ICD-9CM CODES

698.1 Pruritus of genital organs

EPIDEMIOLOGY & DEMOGRAPHICS

- A female disorder that can affect women at any age
- Young girls: infection is usually causative
- Postmenopausal women: frequently affected because of hypoestrogenic state

PHYSICAL FINDINGS & CLINICAL PRESENTATION

Constant intense itching or burning of the vulva

ETIOLOGY

- About 50% are caused by monilial infection or trichomoniasis.
- Other infectious causes are herpes simplex, condylomata acuminata, and molluscum contagiosum.
- Other causes:
  1. Infestations with scabies, pediculosis pubis, and pinworms
  2. Dermatoses such as hypertrophic dystrophy, lichen sclerosus, lichen planus, and psoriasis
  3. Neoplasms such as Bowen's disease, Paget's disease, and squamous cell carcinoma
  4. Allergic or chemical dermatitis caused by dyes in clothing or toilet paper, detergents, contraceptive gels, vaginal medications, douches, or soaps
  5. Vulva or vaginal atrophy
- Severe pruritus is probably caused by degeneration and inflammation of terminal nerve fibers.
- Most intense itching occurs with hyperplastic lesions.
- Children (75%) nonspecific pruritus, lichen sclerosus, bacterial infections, yeast infection, and pinworm infestation.

DIAGNOSIS

DIFFERENTIAL DIAGNOSIS

- Vulvitis
- Vaginitis
- Lichen sclerosus
- Squamous cell hyperplasia
- Pinworms
- Vulvar cancer
- Syringoma of the vulva

WORKUP

- Inspection of vulva, vagina, and perianal area looking for infection, fissures, ulcerations, induration, or thick plaques
- Must rule out trichomoniasis, candidiasis, allergy, vitamin deficiencies, diabetes

LABORATORY TESTS

- Wet prep of saline and KOH of vaginal discharge
- Tape test to look for pinworms
- Vaginal cultures
- Biopsy when needed

TREATMENT

NONPHARMACOLOGIC THERAPY

- Keep vulva clean and dry.
- Wear white cotton panties.
- Avoid perfumes and body creams over vulvar area because they can cause irritation.
- Reduce stress.
- Apply wet dressings with aluminum acetate (Burow's) solution frequently.
- Avoid coffee and caffeine-containing beverages, chocolate, tomatoes.
- Sitz baths may be helpful.

ACUTE GENERAL Rx

Need to treat underlying problem:

- Yeast infection: any of the vaginal creams or Diflucan 150-mg one-time dose
- Trichomoniasis or *Gardnerella vaginalis:* Flagyl 500 mg or 375 mg PO bid for 7 days
- Urinary tract infection: treatment of specific organism
- Estrogen replacement therapy if atrophy is the cause of pruritus
- Pinworms: mebendazole (Vermox) 100 mg one tablet at diagnosis and repeated in 1 to 2 wk; also treat other members in family >2 yr of age
- Squamous cell hyperplasia: local application of corticosteroids
  1. One of the high- or medium-potency corticosteroids (0.025% or 0.01% fluocinolone acetonide or 0.01% triamcinolone acetonide) can be used to relieve itching.
  2. Rub into vulva bid or tid for 4 to 6 wk.
  3. Once itching is controlled, fluorinated steroid can be discontinued and patient can be switched to hydrocortisone preparation.
- Lichen sclerosus: topical 2% testosterone in petrolatum massaged into the vulvar tissue bid or tid; Temovate (clobetasol propionate gel 0.05%) cream tid × 5 days is very effective
- Treatment with immune response modifiers

CHRONIC Rx

- If not relieved by topical measures: intradermal injection of triamcinolone (10 mg/ml diluted 2:1 saline) 0.1 ml of the suspension injected at 1-cm intervals and tissue gently massaged
- If symptoms still uncontrollable: SC injection of absolute alcohol 0.1 ml at 1-cm intervals

DISPOSITION

Usually controlled with conservative measures and topical steroids

REFERRAL

To a gynecologist for further workup if conservative measures do not give relief

SUGGESTED READINGS

Copeland L: *Textbook of gynecology,* ed 2, Philadelphia, 1999, WB Saunders.

Foster DC: Vulvar disease, *Obstet Gynecol* 100(1):145, 2002.

Gerdsen R et al: Periodic genital pruritus caused by syringoma of the vulva, *Acta Obstet Gynecol Scand Suppl* 81(4):369, 2002.

Mead P: *Protocols for infectious diseases in obstetrics and gynecology,* ed 2, Cambridge, Mass, 2000, Blackwell Science.

Palk SC, Merritt DF, Mallory SB: Pruritus vulvae in prepubertal children, *J Am Acad Dermatol* 44(5):795, 2001.

AUTHOR: **MARIA A. CORIGLIANO, M.D.**

BASIC INFORMATION

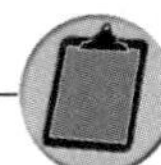

DEFINITION

Pseudogout is one of the clinical patterns associated with a crystal-induced synovitis resulting from the deposition of calcium pyrophosphate dehydrate (CPPD) crystals in joint hyaline and fibrocartilage. The cartilage deposition is termed *chondrocalcinosis*.

SYNONYMS

Calcium pyrophosphate dehydrate crystal deposition disease (CPDD)
Chondrocalcinosis
Pyrophosphate arthropathy

ICD-9CM CODES
275.4 Chondrocalcinosis

EPIDEMIOLOGY & DEMOGRAPHICS

PREVALENCE:
- Uncertain
- Probably similar to gout (3/1000 persons)
- Chondrocalcinosis is present in >20% of all people at age 80 yr, but most are asymptomatic

PREDOMINANT SEX: Female:male ratio of approximately 1.5:1
PREVALENT AGE: 60 to 70 yr at onset

PHYSICAL FINDINGS & CLINICAL PRESENTATION

- Symptoms are similar to those of gouty arthritis with acute attacks and chronic arthritis
- Knee joint is most commonly affected
- Swelling, stiffness, and increased heat in affected joint

ETIOLOGY

- Unknown
- Often associated with various medical conditions, including hyperparathyroidism and amyloidosis

DIAGNOSIS

DIFFERENTIAL DIAGNOSIS

- Gouty arthritis
- Rheumatoid arthritis
- Osteoarthritis
- Neuropathic joint

Section II describes the differential diagnosis of acute monoarticular and oligoarticular arthritis and crystal-induced arthritides. An algorithm for evaluation of arthralgia is described in Section III, "Arthralgia Limited to One or Few Joints."

WORKUP

- Variable clinical presentation
- Diagnosis dependent on the identification of CPPD crystals
- The American Rheumatism Association revised diagnostic criteria for CPPD crystal deposition disease (pseudogout) are often used:
  1. Criteria
     I. Demonstration of CPPD crystals (obtained by biopsy, necroscopy, or aspirated synovial fluid) by definitive means (e.g., characteristic "fingerprint" by x-ray diffraction powder pattern or by chemical analysis)
     II. (a) Identification of monoclinic and/or triclinic crystals showing either no or only a weakly positive birefringence by compensated polarized light microscopy
     (b) Presence of typical calcifications in roentgenograms
     III. (a) Acute arthritis, especially of knees or other large joints, with or without concomitant hyperuricemia
     (b) Chronic arthritis, especially of knees, hips, wrists, carpus, elbow, shoulder, and metacarpophalangeal joints, especially if accompanied by acute exacerbations; the following features are helpful in differentiating chronic arthritis from osteoarthritis:
       1. Uncommon site—for example, wrist, MCP, elbow, shoulder
       2. Appearance of lesion radiologically—for example, radiocarpal or patellofemoral joint space narrowing, especially if isolated (patella "wrapped around" the femur)
       3. Subchondral cyst formation
       4. Severity of degeneration—progressive, with subchondral bony collapse (microfractures), and fragmentation, with formation of intraarticular radiodense bodies
       5. Osteophyte formation—variable and inconstant
       6. Tendon calcifications, especially Achilles, triceps, obturators
  2. Categories
     Definite—Criteria I or II (a) plus (b) must be fulfilled.
     Probable—Criteria II(a) or II(b) must be fulfilled.
     Possible—Criteria III(a) or (b) should alert the clinician to the possibility of underlying CPPD deposition.

LABORATORY TESTS

Crystal analysis of the synovial fluid aspirate to reveal rhomboid calcium pyrophosphate crystals

IMAGING STUDIES

Plain radiographs to reveal the following:
- Stippled calcification in bands running parallel to the subchondral bone margins
- Crystal deposition in menisci, synovium, and ligament tissue; triangular wrist cartilage and symphysis pubis are often affected

TREATMENT

NONPHARMACOLOGIC THERAPY

General measures such as heat, rest, and elevation as needed

ACUTE GENERAL Rx

- NSAIDs (as for gout)
- Colchicine
- Aspiration/steroid injection

DISPOSITION

Structural joint damage may occasionally occur, requiring arthroplasty in rare cases.

REFERRAL

For orthopedic consultation for destructive joint changes

PEARLS & CONSIDERATIONS

COMMENTS

As with gout, acute attacks may be triggered by various surgical or medical events.

SUGGESTED READINGS

Agudelo CA, Wise CM: Crystal-associated arthritis in the elderly, *Rheum Dis Clin North Am* 26:527, 2000.

Canhao H et al: Cross-sectional study of 50 patients with calcium pyrophosphate dihydrate crystal arthropathy, *Clin Rheumatol* 20:119, 2001.

Halverson PB, Derfus BA: Calcium crystal-induced inflammation, *Curr Opin Rheumatol* 13:221, 2001.

Mader B: Calcium pyrophosphate dihydrate deposition disease of the wrist, *Clin Rheumatol* 23(1):95, 2004.

Rosenthal AK: Crystal arthropathies and other unpopular rheumatic diseases, *Curr Opin Rheumatol* 16(3):262, 2004.

Sagarin MJ: Pseudogout, *Emerg Med* 18:373, 2000.

AUTHOR: **LONNIE R. MERCIER, M.D.**

BASIC INFORMATION

DEFINITION

Pseudomembranous colitis is the occurrence of diarrhea and bowel inflammation associated with antibiotic use.

SYNONYMS

Antibiotic-induced colitis

ICD-9CM CODES

008.45 *Clostridium difficile,* pseudomembranous colitis

EPIDEMIOLOGY & DEMOGRAPHICS

- Cephalosporins are the most frequent offending agent in pseudomembranous colitis because of their high rates of use.
- The antibiotic with the highest incidence is clindamycin (10% incidence of pseudomembranous colitis with its use).
- *Clostridium difficile* causes more than 250,000 cases of diarrhea and colitis in the U.S. every year.

PHYSICAL FINDINGS & CLINICAL PRESENTATION

- Abdominal tenderness (generalized or lower abdominal)
- Fever
- In patients with prolonged diarrhea, poor skin turgor, dry mucous membranes, and other signs of dehydration may be present

ETIOLOGY

Risk factors for *C. difficile* (the major identifiable agent of antibiotic-induced diarrhea and colitis):

- Administration of antibiotics: can occur with any antibiotic, but occurs most frequently with clindamycin, ampicillin, and cephalosporins
- Prolonged hospitalization
- Advanced age
- Abdominal surgery
- Hospitalized, tube-fed patients are at risk for *C. difficile*–associated diarrhea. Clinicians should consider testing for *C. difficile* in tube-fed patients with diarrhea unrelated to the feeding solution

DIAGNOSIS

The clinical signs of pseudomembranous colitis generally include diarrhea, fever, and abdominal cramps following use of antibiotics.

DIFFERENTIAL DIAGNOSIS

- GI bacterial infections (e.g., *Salmonella, Shigella, Campylobacter, Yersinia*)
- Enteric parasites (e.g., *Cryptosporidium, Entamoeba histolytica*)
- IBD
- Celiac sprue
- Irritable bowel syndrome

WORKUP

- All patients with diarrhea accompanied by current or recent antibiotic use should be tested for *C. difficile* (see "Laboratory Tests").
- Sigmoidoscopy (without cleansing enema) may be necessary when the clinical and laboratory diagnosis is inconclusive and the diarrhea persists.
- In antibiotic-induced pseudomembranous colitis, the sigmoidoscopy often reveals raised white-yellow exudative plaques adherent to the colonic mucosa (Fig. 1-193).

LABORATORY TESTS

- *C. difficile* toxin can be detected by cytotoxin tissue-culture assay (gold standard for identifying *C. difficile* toxin in stool specimen) and by enzyme-linked immunoabsorbent assay (ELISA) for *C. difficile* toxins A and B. The latter is used most widely in the clinical setting. It has a sensitivity of 85% and a specificity of 100%.
- Fecal leukocytes (assessed by microscopy or lactoferrin assay) are generally present in stool samples.
- CBC usually reveals leukocytosis.

IMAGING STUDIES

Abdominal film (flat plate and upright) is useful in patients with abdominal pain or evidence of obstruction on physical examination.

TREATMENT

NONPHARMACOLOGIC THERAPY

- Discontinue offending antibiotic
- Fluid hydration and correct electrolyte abnormalities

ACUTE GENERAL Rx

- Metronidazole 250 mg PO qid for 10 to 14 days
- Vancomycin 125 mg PO qid for 10 to 14 days in cases resistant to metronidazole
- Cholestyramine 4 g PO qid for 10 days in addition to metronidazole to control severe diarrhea (avoid use with vancomycin)
- When parenteral therapy is necessary (e.g., patient with paralytic ileus), IV metronidazole 500 mg qid can be used. It can also be supplemented with vancomycin 500 mg via NG tube or enema

CHRONIC Rx

Judicious future use of antibiotics to prevent recurrences (e.g., avoid prolonged antibiotic therapy)

DISPOSITION

Most patients recover completely with appropriate therapy. Fever resolves within 48 hr and diarrhea within 4 to 5 days. Mortality exceeds 10% in untreated patients.

REFERRAL

Hospital admission and IV hydration in severe cases

PEARLS & CONSIDERATIONS

COMMENTS

Possible complications of pseudomembranous colitis include dehydration, bowel perforation, toxic megacolon, electrolyte imbalance, and reactive arthritis.

SUGGESTED READINGS

Bartlett JG: Antibiotic-associated diarrhea, *N Engl J Med* 346:334, 2002.

Hurley BW, Nguyen CC: The spectrum of pseudomembranous enterocolitis and antibiotic-associated diarrhea, *Arch Intern Med* 162:2177, 2002.

AUTHOR: **FRED F. FERRI, M.D.**

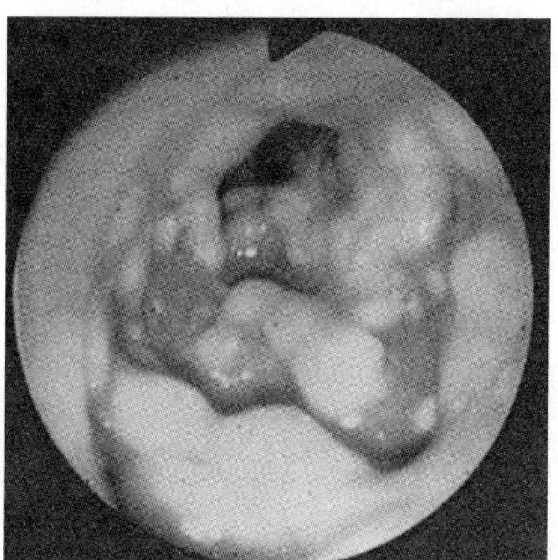

FIGURE 1-193 Pseudomembranous plaques seen with colonoscopy in a patient with *C. difficile*-associated PMC. (From Gorbach SL: *Infectious diseases,* ed 2, Philadelphia, 1998, WB Saunders.)

SECTION I

Psittacosis

BASIC INFORMATION

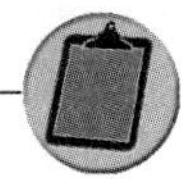

DEFINITION

Psittacosis is a systemic infection caused by *Chlamydia psittaci*.

SYNONYMS

Ornithosis

ICD-9CM CODES
073.9 Psittacosis

EPIDEMIOLOGY & DEMOGRAPHICS

INCIDENCE (IN U.S.):
- 45 cases reported in 1996
- True incidence possibly higher because infections may be subclinical
- Highest incidence among pet owners and people working in contact with birds

PREVALENCE (IN U.S.):
- Low among humans
- Organism carried in 5% to 8% of birds

PREDOMINANT SEX: Equal sex distribution

PREDOMINANT AGE: More common in adults

PEAK INCIDENCE: 30 to 60 yr of age

PHYSICAL FINDINGS & CLINICAL PRESENTATION

- Incubation period of 5 to 15 days
- Subclinical infection
- Onset abrupt or insidious
- Most common symptoms:
  1. Fever
  2. Myalgias
  3. Chills
  4. Cough
- Most common clinical syndrome: atypical pneumonia with fever, headache, dry cough, and a chest x-ray more dramatically abnormal than the physical examination
- Ranges from mild disease to respiratory failure and death, although this is extremely unusual
- Other clinical presentations:
  1. Mononucleosis-like syndrome
  2. Typhoidal form
- Most frequent physical findings:
  1. Fever
  2. Pharyngeal erythema
  3. Rales
  4. Hepatomegaly
- Less common findings:
  1. Somnolence
  2. Confusion
  3. Relative bradycardia
  4. Pleural rub
  5. Adenopathy
  6. Splenomegaly
  7. Horder's spots (pink blanching maculopapular rash)
- Besides the lungs, other specific end-organ involvement:
  1. Pericarditis
  2. Myocarditis
  3. Endocarditis
  4. Hepatitis
  5. Joints
  6. Kidneys (glomerulonephritis)
  7. CNS

ETIOLOGY

- *Chlamydia psittaci* is an obligate intracellular bacterium.
- Infection is usually spread by the respiratory route from infected birds.
- There is a history of exposure to birds in 85% of patients.
- Strains from turkeys and psittacine birds are most virulent for humans.
- Cows, goats, and sheep are occasionally implicated.

DIAGNOSIS

DIFFERENTIAL DIAGNOSIS

- *Legionella*
- *Mycoplasma*
- *Chlamydia pneumoniae* (TWAR)
- Viral respiratory infections
- Bacterial pneumonia
- Typhoid fever
- Viral hepatitis
- Aseptic meningitis
- Fever of unknown origin
- Mononucleosis

WORKUP

- CBC, renal and liver function tests
- *Chlamydia* serology
- Chest x-ray examination
- Special immunostaining of respiratory secretions

LABORATORY TESTS

- WBC count is normal or slightly elevated.
- Mild liver function abnormalities are common (50%).
- Blood cultures are almost always negative.
- Studies on respiratory secretions:
  1. Direct immunofluorescent antibody (DFA) of respiratory secretions with monoclonal antibodies to chlamydial antigens
  2. Chlamydial LPS (lipopolysaccharide) antigen by enzyme immunoassay (EIA)
  3. Polymerase chain reaction (PCR)
- Serologic studies:
  1. Complement-fixing antibodies
  2. Microimmunofluorescence
  3. Possible false-negative results and cross-reaction with other chlamydial species with both techniques

IMAGING STUDIES

- Chest x-ray examination is abnormal in 50% to 90% with a variety of patterns.
- Pleural effusions are common.

TREATMENT

NONPHARMACOLOGIC THERAPY

Oxygen supplementation as needed

ACUTE GENERAL Rx

- Tetracycline (500 mg PO qid) *or*
- Doxycycline (100 mg PO bid) *or*
- Erythromycin (500 mg PO qid): less effective

CHRONIC Rx

In the rare cases of endocarditis, combination of heart valve replacement and prolonged antibiotic course may be the treatment of choice.

DISPOSITION

- Mortality low (0.7%)
- Poor prognostic factors:
  1. Advanced age
  2. Leukopenia
  3. Severe hypoxemia
  4. Renal failure
  5. Confusion
  6. Multilobe pulmonary involvement
- Possible reinfection

REFERRAL

- To infectious disease expert:
  1. Complicated atypical pneumonia or other end-organ involvement
  2. Suspicion of an outbreak
- To pulmonologist for diagnostic bronchoscopy

PEARLS & CONSIDERATIONS

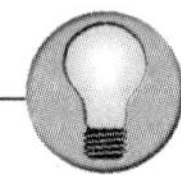

COMMENTS

- Hospitalized patients do not require specific isolation precautions.
- Any confirmed or suspected case of psittacosis should be reported to public health authorities.

SUGGESTED READINGS

Centers for Disease Control and Prevention: Compendium of measures to control *Chlamydia psittaci* and pet birds (avian chlamydiosis), 1998, *MMWR* 47(RR-10):1, 1998.

Elliott JH: Psittacosis: a flu-like syndrome, *Aust Fam Physician* 30(8):739, 2001.

AUTHOR: **MICHELE HALPERN, M.D.**

BASIC INFORMATION

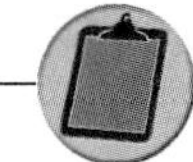

DEFINITION

Psoriasis is a chronic skin disorder characterized by excessive proliferation of keratinocytes, resulting in the formation of thickened scaly plaques, itching, and inflammatory changes of the epidermis and dermis. The various forms of psoriasis include guttate, pustular, and arthritis variants.

ICD-9CM CODES
696.0 Psoriasis, arthritis, arthropathic
696.1 Psoriasis, any type except arthropathic

EPIDEMIOLOGY & DEMOGRAPHICS

- Psoriasis affects 1% to 3% of the world's population. Most patients have limited psoriasis involving <5% of their body surface.
- There is a strong association between psoriasis and HLA B13, B17, and B27 (pustular psoriasis).
- Peak age of onset is bimodal (adolescents and at 60 yr of age).
- Men and women are equally affected.

PHYSICAL FINDINGS & CLINICAL PRESENTATION

- The primary psoriatic lesion is an erythematous papule topped by a loosely adherent scale. Scraping the scale results in several bleeding points (Auspitz sign).
- Chronic plaque psoriasis generally manifests with symmetric, sharply demarcated, erythromatous, silver-scaled patches affecting primarily the intergluteal folds, elbows, scalp, fingernails, toenails, and knees (Fig. 1-194, *A*). This form accounts for 80% of psoriasis cases.
- Psoriasis can also develop at the site of any physical trauma (sunburn, scratching). This is known as Koebner's phenomenon.
- Nail involvement is common (pitting of the nail plate), resulting in hyperkeratosis, onychodystrophy with onycholysis (Fig. 1-194, *B*).
- Pruritus is variable.
- Joint involvement can result in sacroiliitis and spondylitis.
- Guttate psoriasis is generally preceded by streptococcal pharyngitis and manifests with multiple droplike lesions on the extremities and the trunk (Fig. 1-194, *C*).

ETIOLOGY

- Unknown
- Familial clustering (genetic transmission with a dominant mode with variable penetrants)
- One third of persons affected have a positive family history

DIAGNOSIS

DIFFERENTIAL DIAGNOSIS

- Contact dermatitis
- Atopic dermatitis
- Stasis dermatitis
- Tinea
- Nummular dermatitis
- Candidiasis
- Mycosis fungoides
- Cutaneous SLE
- Secondary and tertiary syphilis
- Drug eruption

WORKUP

- Diagnosis is clinical.
- Skin biopsy is rarely necessary.

LABORATORY TESTS

Generally not necessary for diagnosis

TREATMENT

NONPHARMACOLOGIC THERAPY

- Sunbathing generally leads to improvement.
- Eliminate triggering factors (e.g., stress, certain medications [e.g., lithium, β-blockers, antimalarials]).
- Patients with psoriasis benefit from a daily bath in warm water followed by application of a cream or ointment moisturizer. Regular use or an emollient moisturizer limits evaporation of water from the skin and allows the stratum corneum to rehydrate itself.

GENERAL Rx

Therapeutic options vary according to the extent of disease.

- Patients with limited disease (<20% of the body) can be treated with the following:
  1. Topical steroids: disadvantages are brief remissions, expense, and decreased effect with continued use. Salicylic acid can be compounded by pharmacist in concentrations of 2% to 10% and used in combination with a corticosteroid to decrease amount of scale.
  2. Calcipotriene (Dovonex): a vitamin D analogue, is effective for moderate plaque psoriasis; adults should comb the hair, apply solution to the lesions, and rub it in, avoiding uninvolved skin; disadvantages are its cost and potential burning and skin irritation. It should not be used concurrently with salicylic acid because calcipotriene is inactivated by the acidic nature of salicylic acid.
  3. Tar products (Estar, LCD, psoriGel) can be used overnight and are most effective when combined with UVB light (Goeckerman regimen).
  4. Anthralin (Drithocreme): useful for chronic plaques, can result in purple/brown staining; best used with UVB light.
  5. Retinoids such as tazarotene 0.05%, 0.1% cream or gel, are effective in thinning plaques but are expensive and can produce irritation.
  6. Other useful measures include tape or occlusive dressing, UVB and lubricating agents, interlesional steroids.

A

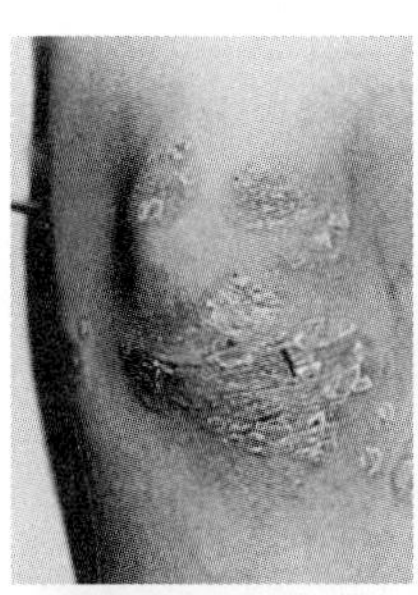

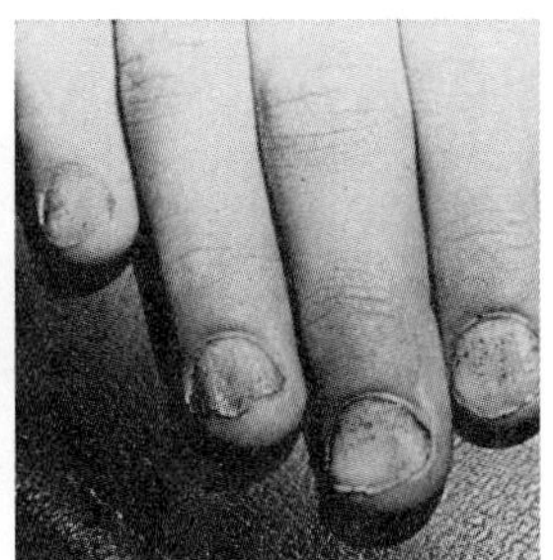

B

C

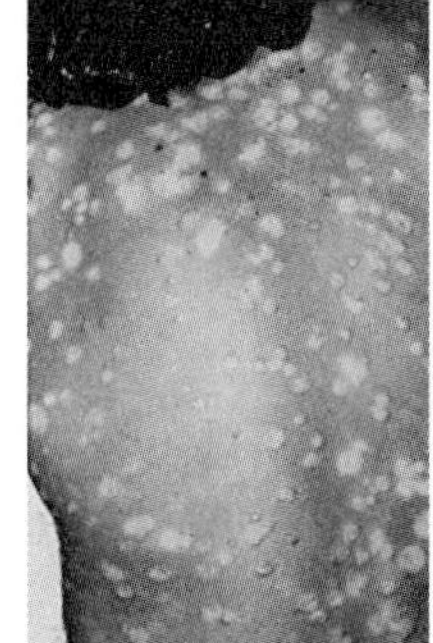

FIGURE 1-194
A, Chronic psoriatic plaques on the knee. **B,** Psoriatic nail changes of pitting and dystrophy. **C,** Guttate psoriasis in widespread distribution over the trunk. (From Behrman RE: *Nelson textbook of pediatrics,* ed 16, Philadelphia, 2000, WB Saunders.)

- Therapeutic options for persons with generalized disease (affecting >20% of the body):
  1. UVB light exposure three times a week
  2. Oral PUVA (psoralen plus ultraviolet A) administered two to three times weekly is effective for generalized disease. However, many treatments are required, necessitating frequent office visits, and it may be associated with phototoxicity, such as erythema and blistering, and increased risk of skin cancer
- Systemic treatments include methotrexate 25 mg every week for severe psoriasis. Etretinate (Tegison) (a synthetic retinoid) is most effective for palmar-plantar pustular psoriasis. Dose is 0.5 to 1 mg/kg/day. It can cause liver enzyme and lipid abnormalities and is teratogenic.
- Cyclosporine is also effective in severe psoriasis; however, relapses are common.
- Chronic plaque psoriasis may be treated with alefacept, a recombinant protein that selectively targets T lymphocytes. Treatment with alefacept for 12 wk (0.025, 0.075, or 0.150 mg/kg of body weight IV weekly) may result in significant improvement. Some patients also experience a sustained clinical response after the cessation of treatment. This medication is very expensive (a 12-wk course costs >$8,000). Treatment with etanercept, a tumor necrosis factor (TNF) antagonist, for 24 wk can also lead to a reduction in severity of plaque psoriasis. Efalizumab, a humanized monoclonal antibody that inhibits the activation of T cells, has also been reported to produce significant improvement in plaque psoriasis over a 24-wk treatment period.

DISPOSITION

The course of psoriasis is chronic, and the disease may be refractory to treatment.

REFERRAL

- Dermatology referral is recommended in all patients with generalized disease.
- Hospital admission may be necessary for severe diffuse or poorly responsive psoriasis. The Goeckerman regimen combines daily application of tar with UVB exposure and can result in prolonged remissions.

PEARLS & CONSIDERATIONS

COMMENTS

Psoriasis is more emotionally than physically disabling for most patients. Counseling may be indicated, particularly when it affects younger patients.

SUGGESTED READINGS

Gordon KB et al: Efalizumab for patients with moderate to severe plaque psoriasis, *JAMA* 290:3073, 2003.

Lebwohl M et al: A novel targeted T-cell modulator, efalizumab, for plaque psoriasis, *N Engl J Med* 349:2004, 2003.

Leonardi CL et al: Etanercept as monotherapy in patients with psoriasis, *N Engl J Med* 349:2014, 2003.

AUTHOR: **FRED F. FERRI, M.D.**

BASIC INFORMATION

DEFINITION

A state in which external reality is distorted by delusions and/or hallucinations (where a delusion is a fixed false belief, and a hallucination is a false auditory, visual, olfactory, tactile, or taste perception).

SYNONYMS

Psychosis is a key finding in many mental illnesses, such as brief psychotic disorder, delusional disorder, schizoaffective disorder, schizophrenia, schizophreniform disorder, or shared psychotic disorder.

EPIDEMIOLOGY & DEMOGRAPHICS

The demographics of psychosis depend on the underlying disorder.

CLINICAL PRESENTATION

History
- Past medical history of any of the etiologies
- Use of possible offending medications
- Use of illicit substances
- Impaired function
- ICU stay >5 days

Physical examination
- If associated with a mood disorder, delusions/hallucinations are usually consistent with mood (e.g., auditory hallucinations in a depressed patient may tell the patient what a terrible person he is).
- Altered, disorganized thought pattern, which is usually reflected in disorganized speech (including word salad, thought blocking, rhyming, clang).
- Lack insight into problems.
- Behavior is odd or unpredictable; patient may clearly be responding to internal stimuli.
- Signs of Parkinson's disease, dementia.

ETIOLOGY

- Pathophysiologically, an interaction among:
  1. Dopaminergic overactivity (particularly in the mesolimbic, nigrostriatal, and mesocortical systems)
  2. Environmental, social/childhood factors
  3. Genetic predisposition
- Underlying mental disorder:
  1. Schizophrenia
  2. Major depression
  3. Brief psychotic disorder
  4. Delusional disorder
  5. Schizoaffective disorder
  6. Schizophrenia
  7. Schizophreniform disorder
  8. Shared psychotic disorder
- Underlying personality disorder:
  1. Borderline
  2. Paranoid
  3. Schizoid
  4. Schizotypal
- Underlying medical condition:
  1. HIV/AIDS
  2. Parkinson's
  3. Huntington's
  4. Leprosy
  5. Malaria
  6. Sarcoidosis
  7. SLE
  8. Prion disease
  9. Hypoglycemia
  10. Postpartum state
  11. Cerebrovascular event
  12. Temporal lobe epilepsy
  13. Brain neoplasm
- Medications: systemic steroids, anticonvulsants, anti-Parkinsonian medications, some chemotherapy, scopolamine
- Underlying dementia: Alzheimer's, Lewy body dementia
- Illicit drugs (usually with chronic use; can be with intoxication or withdrawal):
  1. LSD
  2. PCP
  3. Cocaine
  4. GHB (withdrawal)
  5. Alcohol
  6. Amphetamines
  7. Marijuana
- Traumatic brain injury
- ICU stay: hypoxia, decreased cardiac output, infection, medications, sleep deprivation, alteration of diurnal cycle, sensory deprivation/overload, pain
- Emotional stress

DIAGNOSIS

WORKUP

Any workup would be to better assess etiology and would depend on the clinical situation.

LABORATORY TESTS

Consider checking glucose, HIV, RPR, TSH, toxicology screen, LP.

IMAGING STUDIES

Consider CXR (sarcoid), head CT/MRI.

TREATMENT

NONPHARMACOLOGIC THERAPY

- Cognitive behavioral therapy.
- Social/behavioral skills training.
- Training for self-management of disease.
- Aforementioned strategies favored over psychoanalytic techniques given the relative inability for abstract thought and lack of insight in psychotic patients.
- Family intervention, including education and strategies to reduce emotional expression.
- Counseling for substance abuse.

ACUTE GENERAL Rx

- Haldol (remember, it prolongs the QT interval).
- Ativan.
- Discontinue offending medication if present.

CHRONIC Rx

Atypical antipsychotics (have decreased incidence of tardive dyskinesias versus older antipsychotics); even shown to be effective in demented and Huntington's patients.

COMPLEMENTARY & ALTERNATIVE MEDICINE

Electroconvulsive therapy for acute psychosis only.

DISPOSITION

Prognosis varies according to etiology of psychosis. In general, the more severe and longer the psychotic episode, the worse the prognosis.

REFERRAL

Patient should be admitted for acute stabilization if actively psychotic to prevent harm to self and others, as well as to ensure administration of medications.

SUGGESTED READINGS

AllPsych Online: http://www.allpsych.com
Patkar AA, Mago R, Masand PS: Psychotic symptoms in patients with medical disorders, *Curr Psychiatry Rep* 6(3), 2004.

AUTHOR: **RACHAEL LUCATORTO, M.D.**

BASIC INFORMATION

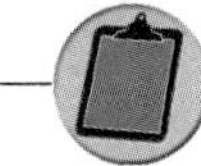

DEFINITION

Cardiogenic pulmonary edema is a life-threatening condition caused by severe left ventricular decompensation.

SYNONYMS

Cardiogenic pulmonary edema

ICD-9CM CODES
428.1 Acute pulmonary edema with heart disease

PHYSICAL FINDINGS & CLINICAL PRESENTATION

- Dyspnea with rapid, shallow breathing
- Diaphoresis, perioral and peripheral cyanosis
- Pink, frothy sputum
- Moist, bilateral pulmonary rales
- Increased pulmonary second sound, S_3 gallop (in association with tachycardia)
- Bulging neck veins

ETIOLOGY

Increased pulmonary capillary pressure secondary to:
- Acute myocardial infarction
- Exacerbation of CHF
- Valvular regurgitation
- Ventricular septal defect
- Severe myocardial ischemia
- Mitral stenosis
- Other: cardiac tamponade, endocarditis, myocarditis, arrhythmias, cardiomyopathy, hypertensive crisis

DIAGNOSIS

DIFFERENTIAL DIAGNOSIS

- Noncardiogenic pulmonary edema
- Pulmonary embolism
- Exacerbation of asthma
- Exacerbation of COPD
- Sarcoidosis
- Pulmonary fibrosis
- Viral pneumonitis and other pulmonary infections

LABORATORY TESTS

ABGs: respiratory and metabolic acidosis, decreased Pao_2, increased Pco_2, low pH.

NOTE: The patient may initially show respiratory alkalosis secondary to hyperventilation in attempts to maintain Pao_2.

IMAGING STUDIES

- Chest x-ray examination:
  1. Pulmonary congestion with Kerley B lines; fluffy perihilar infiltrates in the early stages; bilateral interstitial alveolar infiltrates
  2. Pleural effusions
- Echocardiogram:
  1. Useful to evaluate valvular abnormalities, diastolic vs. systolic dysfunction
  2. Can aid in differentiation of cardiogenic vs. noncardiogenic pulmonary edema
  3. Can also estimate pulmonary capillary wedge pressure and rule out presence of myxoma or atrial thrombus
- Right heart catheterization (selected patients): cardiac pressures and cardiogenic pulmonary edema reveal increased PADP and PCWP ≥25 mm Hg

TREATMENT

NONPHARMACOLOGIC THERAPY

Patients should be placed in a sitting position with legs off the side of the bed to improve breathing and decrease venous return.

ACUTE GENERAL Rx

All the following steps can be performed concomitantly:
- 100% oxygen by face mask. Both CPAP and BiPAP systems can improve oxygenation and lower carbon dioxide tensions. Check ABGs; if marked hypoxemia or severe respiratory acidosis, intubate the patient and place on a ventilator. Positive end-expiratory pressure (PEEP) increases functional capacity and improves oxygenation.
- Furosemide: 1 mg/kg IV bolus (typically 40 to 100 mg) to rapidly establish diuresis and decrease venous return through its venodilator action; may double the dose in 30 min if no effect.
- Vasodilator therapy:
  1. Nitrates: particularly useful if the patient has concomitant chest pain.
     a. Nitroglycerin: 150 to 600 μg SL or nitroglycerin spray (Nitrolingual) may be given immediately on arrival and repeated multiple times if the patient remains symptomatic and blood pressure remains stable.
     b. 2% nitroglycerin ointment: 1 to 3 inches out of the tube applied continuously; absorption may be erratic.
     c. IV nitroglycerin: 100 mg in 500 ml of D_5W solution; start at 6 μg/min (2 ml/hr).
  2. Nitroprusside: useful for afterload reduction in hypertensive patients with decreased cardiac index (CI).
     a. Increases the CI and decreases left ventricular filling pressure.
     b. Vasodilator and diuretic therapy should be tailored to achieve PCWP ≤18 mm Hg, RAP ≤8 mm Hg, systolic blood pressure >90 mm Hg, SVR >1200 dynes/sec/cm^{-5}. The use of nitroprusside in patients with acute MI is controversial because it may intensify ischemia by decreasing the blood flow to the ischemic left ventricular myocardium.
  3. Nesiritide (Natrecor) is a B-type natriuretic peptide has venous, arterial, and coronary vasodilatory properties that decrease preload and afterload and increase cardiac output without direct inotropic effects. It is effective in cardiogenic pulmonary edema.
  4. Morphine: 2 to 4 mg IV/SC/IM, may repeat q15min prn. It decreases venous return, anxiety, and systemic vascular resistance (naloxone should be available at bedside to reverse the effects of morphine if respiratory depression occurs). Morphine may induce hypotension in volume-depleted patients.
  5. Afterload reduction with ACE inhibitors. Captopril 25 mg PO tablet can be used for SL administration (placing a drop or two of water on the tablet and placing it under the tongue helps dissolve it), onset of action is <10 min, peak effect can be reached in 30 min. ACE inhibitors can also be given IV (e.g., enalaprilat 1 mg IV given q2h prn).
  6. Dobutamine: parenteral inotropic agent of choice in severe cases of cardiogenic pulmonary edema. It can be administered at a dosage of 2.5 to 10 μg/kg/min IV. IV phosphodiesterase inhibitors (amrinone, milrinone) may be useful in refractory cases.
  7. Aminophylline: useful *only* if patient has concomitant severe bronchospasm.
  8. Digitalis: limited use in acute pulmonary edema caused by MI and generally not recommended. May be useful in pulmonary edema resulting from atrial fibrillation or flutter with a fast ventricular response.
  9. Acute cardiogenic pulmonary edema caused by IHSS should be treated with IV normal saline solution and negative inotropic agents such as verapamil and β-blockers.

DISPOSITION

- Mortality for cardiogenic pulmonary edema is approximately 60% to 80%.

SUGGESTED READING

Gandhi SU et al: The pathogenesis of acute pulmonary edema associated with hypertension, *N Engl J Med* 344:17, 2001.

AUTHOR: **FRED F. FERRI, M.D.**

BASIC INFORMATION

DEFINITION

Pulmonary embolism (PE) refers to the lodging of a thrombus or other embolic material from a distant site in the pulmonary circulation.

SYNONYMS

Pulmonary thromboembolism
PE

ICD-9CM CODES
415.1 Pulmonary embolism and infarction

EPIDEMIOLOGY & DEMOGRAPHICS

- 650,000 cases of PE occur in the U.S. each year; 50,000 result in death (increased incidence in women and with advanced age).
- More than 90% of pulmonary emboli originate in the deep venous system of the lower extremities.
- Pulmonary thromboembolism is associated with >200,000 hospitalizations each year in the U.S.
- 8% to 10% of victims of PE die within the first hour.

PHYSICAL FINDINGS & CLINICAL PRESENTATION

- Most common symptom: dyspnea
- Chest pain: may be nonpleuritic or pleuritic (infarction)
- Syncope (massive PE)
- Fever, diaphoresis, apprehension
- Hemoptysis, cough
- Evidence of DVT may be present (e.g., swelling and tenderness of extremities)
- Cardiac examination: may reveal tachycardia, increased pulmonic component of S_2, murmur of tricuspid insufficiency, right ventricular heave, right-sided S_3
- Pulmonary examination: may demonstrate rales, localized wheezing, friction rub
- Most common physical finding: tachypnea

ETIOLOGY

- Thrombus, fat, or other foreign material
- Risk factors for PE:
  1. Prolonged immobilization
  2. Postoperative state
  3. Trauma to lower extremities
  4. Estrogen-containing birth control pills
  5. Prior history of DVT or PE
  6. CHF
  7. Pregnancy and early puerperium
  8. Visceral cancer (lung, pancreas, alimentary and genitourinary tracts)
  9. Trauma, burns
  10. Advanced age
  11. Obesity
  12. Hematologic disease (e.g., antithrombin III deficiency, protein C deficiency, protein S deficiency, lupus anticoagulant, polycythemia vera, dysfibrinogenemia, paroxysmal nocturnal hemoglobinuria, factor V Leiden mutation, G20210A prothrombin mutation)
  13. COPD, diabetes mellitus
  14. Prolonged air travel

DIAGNOSIS

DIFFERENTIAL DIAGNOSIS

- Myocardial infarction
- Pericarditis
- Pneumonia
- Pneumothorax
- Chest wall pain
- GI abnormalities (e.g., peptic ulcer, esophageal rupture, gastritis)
- CHF
- Pleuritis
- Anxiety disorder with hyperventilation
- Pericardial tamponade
- Dissection of aorta
- Asthma

WORKUP

- Clinical assessment alone is insufficient to diagnose or rule out PE. It is also important to remember that no single noninvasive test has both high sensitivity and high specificity for PE. Consequently, in addition to clinical assessment, most patients will require several noninvasive tests or pulmonary angiography to diagnose PE.
- Spiral CT of chest or lung scan may be diagnostic. Pulmonary angiogram (when indicated) will confirm the diagnosis.
- Serial compressive duplex ultrasonography of lower extremities can be used in patients with "low-probability" lung scan and high clinical suspicion (see "Imaging Studies"). It is useful if positive, negative results do not exclude pulmonary embolism.

LABORATORY TESTS

- ABGs generally reveal decreased Pao_2 and $Paco_2$ and increased pH; normal results do not rule out PE.
- Alveolar-arteriolar (A-a) oxygen gradient, a measure of the difference in oxygen concentration between alveoli and arterial blood, is a more sensitive indicator of the alteration in oxygenation than Pao_2; it can easily be calculated using the information from ABGs; a normal A-a gradient among patients without history of PE or DVT makes the diagnosis of PE unlikely.
- Plasma D-dimer measurement: D-dimer assays by ELISA detect the presence of plasmin-mediated degradation products of fibrin that contain cross-linked D fragments in the whole blood or plasma. A normal plasma D-dimer level is useful to exclude pulmonary embolism in patients with a nondiagnostic lung scan and a low pretest probability of PE. However, it cannot be used to "rule in" the diagnosis because it increases with many other disorders (e.g., metastatic cancer, trauma, sepsis, postoperative state). Plasma D-dimer can also be used in conjunction with lower-extremity compression ultrasonography in patients with indeterminate V/Q and spiral CT scans. Absence of DVT and presence of a normal D-dimer level in these settings generally rules out clinically significant pulmonary embolism.
- Elevated cardiac troponin levels also occur in patients with pulmonary embolism because of right ventricular dilation and myocardial injury; therefore, PE should be considered in the differential diagnosis of all patients presenting with chest pain or dyspnea and elevated cardiac troponin levels.
- ECG is abnormal in 85% of patients with acute PE. Frequent abnormalities are sinus tachycardia; nonspecific ST-segment or T wave changes; S-I, Q-III, T-III pattern (10% of patients); S-I, S-II, S-III pattern; T wave inversion in V_1 to V_6; acute RBBB; new-onset atrial fibrillation; ST segment depression in lead II; right ventricular strain.

IMAGING STUDIES

- Chest x-ray may be normal; suggestive findings include elevated diaphragm, pleural effusion, dilation of pulmonary artery, infiltrate or consolidation, abrupt vessel cut-off, or atelectasis. A wedge-shaped consolidation in the middle and lower lobes is suggestive of a pulmonary infarction and is known as "Hampton's hump."
- Lung scan (in patient with normal chest x-ray examination):
  1. A normal lung scan rules out PE.
  2. A ventilation-perfusion mismatch is suggestive of PE, and a lung scan interpretation of high probability is confirmatory.
  3. If the clinical suspicion of PE is high and the lung scan is interpreted as low probability, moderate probability, or indeterminate, a pulmonary arteriogram is diagnostic; a positive arteriogram confirms diagnosis; a positive compressive duplex ultrasonography for DVT obviates the need for an arteriogram, because treatment with IV anticoag-

ulants is indicated in these patients; the overall sensitivity of compressive ultrasonography for DVT in patients with PE is 29%, specificity 97%; adding ultrasonography in patients with a nondiagnostic lung scan prevents 9% of angiographies; however, this improvement in efficacy is achieved at the cost of unnecessary anticoagulant therapy in 26% of patients who have false-positive ultrasonography results.

- Spiral CT is an excellent modality for diagnosing PE. It may be used in place of the lung scan and is favored in patients with baseline lung abnormalities on initial chest x-ray. It has the added advantage of detecting other pulmonary pathology that can mimic pulmonary embolism.
- Angiography: pulmonary angiography is the gold standard; however, it is invasive, expensive, and not readily available in some clinical settings. False-positive pulmonary angiograms may result from mediastinal disorders such as radiation fibrosis and tumors. CT angiography is an accurate, noninvasive tool in the diagnosis of PE at the main, lobar, and segmental pulmonary artery levels. A major advantage of CT angiography over standard pulmonary angiography is its ability to diagnose intrathoracic disease other than PE that may account for the patient's clinical picture. It is also less invasive, less costly, and more widely available. Its major shortcoming is its poor sensitivity for subsegmental emboli. Gadolinium-enhanced magnetic resonance angiography of the pulmonary arteries has a moderate sensitivity and high specificity for the diagnosis of PE; MRA is best reserved for selected patients when CT scan and/or lung scan are inconclusive and the risk of pulmonary angiography is high.

TREATMENT

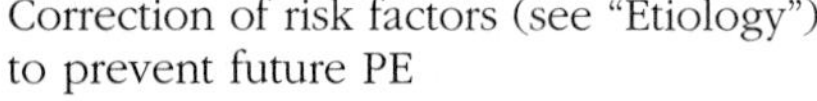

NONPHARMACOLOGIC THERAPY

Correction of risk factors (see "Etiology") to prevent future PE

ACUTE GENERAL Rx

- Heparin by continuous infusion for at least 5 days; many experts recommend a larger initial IV heparin bolus (15,000 to 20,000 U) to block platelet aggregation and thrombi and subsequent release of vasoconstrictive substances.
- Thrombolytic agents (urokinase, tPA, streptokinase): provide rapid resolution of clots; thrombolytic agents are the treatment of choice in patients with massive PE who are hemodynamically unstable and with no contraindication to their use. The use of thrombolytic agents in the treatment of hemodynamically stable patients with acute submassive pulmonary embolism remains controversial. Use of the thrombolytic agents alteplase (100 mg IV over a 2-hr period) in normotensive patients with moderate or severe right ventricular dysfunction identified by echocardiography has been advocated by some physicians. Use of alteplase in conjunction with heparin has been shown to improve the clinical course of stable patients who have acute submassive PE without internal bleeding. Additional studies are needed to confirm these findings before recommending routine use of this therapeutic approach.
- Long-term treatment is generally carried out with warfarin therapy started on day 1 or 2 and given in a dose to maintain the INR at 2 to 3.
- If thrombolytics and anticoagulants are contraindicated (e.g., GI bleeding, recent CNS surgery, recent trauma) or if the patient continues to have recurrent PE despite anticoagulation therapy, vena caval interruption is indicated by transvenous placement of a Greenfield vena caval filter.
- Acute pulmonary artery embolectomy may be indicated in a patient with massive pulmonary emboli and refractory hypotension.

CHRONIC Rx

Elimination of risk factors (see "Etiology") and monitoring of warfarin dose with INR on a routine basis

DISPOSITION

- Mortality can be reduced to <10% by rapid and effective treatment.
- Mortality from recurrent pulmonary emboli is 8% with effective treatment and >30% in patients with untreated pulmonary emboli.

PEARLS & CONSIDERATIONS

COMMENTS

- In hemodynamically stable patients with pulmonary embolism, initial treatment with once-daily SC administration of the synthetic antithrombotic agent fondaparinux without monitoring has been reported to be at least as safe and as effective as adjusted-dose IV unfractionated heparin. Several other trials have also demonstrated that fixed-dose low molecular weight heparin to be as effective and safe as dose-adjusted IV unfractionated heparin for the initial treatment of nonmassive PE.
- The duration of oral anticoagulant treatment is 6 mo in patients with reversible risk factors and indefinitely in patients with persistence of risk factors that caused the initial PE.
- For the diagnosis of PE, Wells et al have developed the following clinical prediction rules to determine the probability of PE, assigning a score to each finding:
  1. Clinical signs/symptoms of DVT (minimum of leg swelling and pain with palpation of the deep veins of the legs (score = 3.0)
  2. No alternate diagnosis likely or more likely than PE (score = 3.0)
  3. Heart rate >100/min (score = 1.5)
  4. Immobilization or surgery in last 4 wk (score = 1.5)
  5. Previous history of DVT or PE (score = 1.5)
  6. Hemoptysis (score = 1.0)
  7. Cancer actively treated within last 6 months (score = 1.0)
- Probability of PE is high if total score is >6, moderate if 2-6, and low if < 2

SUGGESTED READINGS

Agnelli G et al: Extended oral anticoagulant therapy after a first episode of pulmonary embolism, *Ann Intern Med* 139:19, 2003.

Fedullo PF, Tapson VF: The evaluation of suspected pulmonary embolism, *N Engl J Med* 349:1247, 2003.

Quinlan DJ et al: Low-molecular weight heparin compared with IV unfractionated heparin for treatment of pulmonary embolism, *Ann Intern Med* 140:175, 2004.

The Matisse Investigators: Subcutaneous fondaparinux versus IV unfractionated heparin in the initial treatment of pulmonary embolism, *N Engl J Med* 349:1695, 2003.

Wells PS et al: Use of a clinical model for safe management of patients with suspected PE, *Ann Intern Med* 129:997, 1998.

AUTHOR: **FRED F. FERRI, M.D.**

BASIC INFORMATION

DEFINITION

Pulmonary hypertension (PH) is abnormally elevated pressure in the arterial side of the pulmonary circulation, usually defined as mean pulmonary pressure >25 mm Hg at rest or greater than 30 mmHg with exercise. Sustained elevation in pulmonary arterial pressure due to increased pulmonary venous pressure, hypoxic pulmonary vasoconstriction, or increased flow is often referred to as secondary pulmonary hypertension.

SYNONYMS

Primary pulmonary hypertension (PPH)
Secondary pulmonary hypertension

ICD-9CM CODES
416.0 Primary pulmonary hypertension
416.8 Secondary pulmonary hypertension

EPIDEMIOLOGY & DEMOGRAPHICS

- Primary pulmonary hypertension (PPH) is rare, occurring in 2 cases per 1 million people per year, with an overall prevalence estimated at 1,300 per million.
- PPH is more common in women than men (1.7:1), usually presenting in the third to fourth decade of life.
- Secondary pulmonary hypertension is more common than PPH.
- Secondary pulmonary hypertension is the common pathophysiologic mechanism leading to cor pulmonale in patients with underlying pulmonary disease (e.g., COPD, pulmonary embolism).

PHYSICAL FINDINGS & CLINICAL PRESENTATION

Primary pulmonary hypertension:
- PPH is insidious and may go undetected for years.
- Exertional dyspnea is the most common presenting symptom (60%).
- Fatigue and weakness.
- Syncope.
- Chest pain.
- Loud P2 component of the second heart sound.
- Right-sided S4.
- Jugular venous distension.
- Abdominal distension/ascites.
- Prominent parasternal (RV) impulse.
- Holosystolic tricuspid regurgitation murmur heard best along the left fourth parasternal line that increases in intensity with inspiration.
- Peripheral edema.

Secondary pulmonary hypertension:
- Similar to PPH but depends on the underlying cause (e.g., left-sided CHF, mitral stenosis, COPD).

ETIOLOGY

- The etiology of PPH is unknown. Most cases are sporadic, but there is a 6% to 12% familial incidence.
- PPH is associated with several known risk factors: portal hypertension and liver cirrhosis, appetite-suppressant drugs (fenfluramine), and HIV disease.
- Several genetic abnormalities have been associated with the familial form of PPH, many of which are mutations in the genes that code for members of the TGF-_ family of receptors (BMPR-II, ALK-1) on chromosome 2q33.
- Familial PPH is an autosomal-dominant disease with variable penetrance, affecting only about 10% to 20% of carriers.
- Several factors have been identified that play a role in the pathogenesis of PPH, including a genetic predisposition, endothelial cell dysfunction, abnormalities in vasomotor control, thrombotic obliteration of the vascular lumen, and vascular remodeling through cell proliferation and matrix production. An emerging theory involves abnormal membrane potassium channels modulating calcium kinetics.
- Secondary pulmonary hypertension is primarily caused by underlying pulmonary and cardiac conditions including:
  1. Pulmonary thromboembolic disease
  2. Chronic obstructive pulmonary disease (COPD)

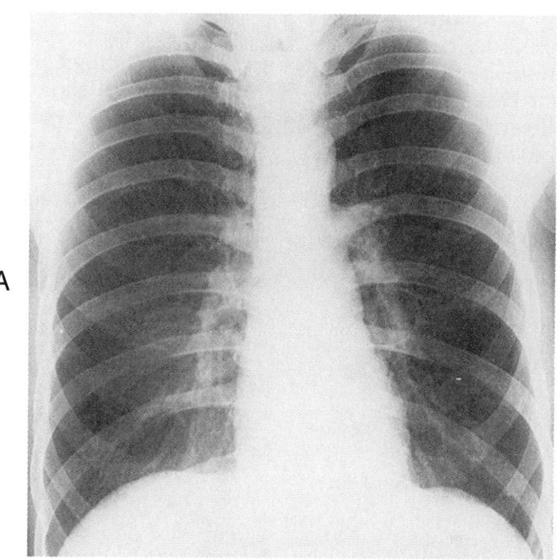

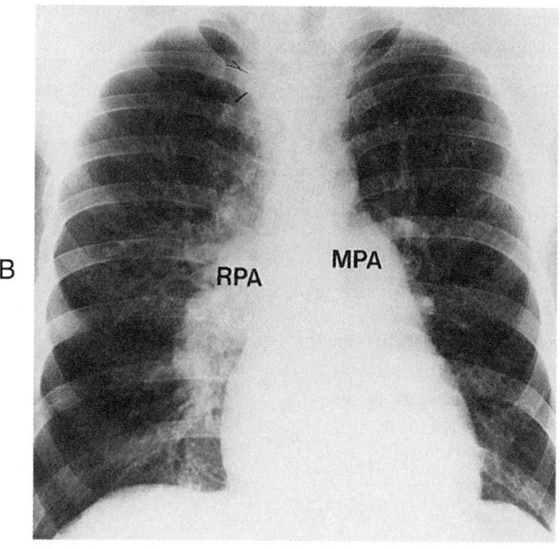

FIGURE 1-195 Progressive pulmonary arterial hypertension. This patient initially presented with a relatively normal chest radiograph **(A)**. However, several years later **(B)**, there is increasing heart size as well as marked dilation of the main pulmonary artery *(MPA)* and right pulmonary artery *(RPA)*. Rapid tapering of the arteries as they proceed peripherally is suggestive of pulmonary hypertension and is sometimes referred to as pruning. (From Mettler FA [ed]: *Primary care radiology,* Philadelphia, 2000, WB Saunders.)

3. Interstitial lung disease
4. Obstructive sleep disorder
5. Neuromuscular diseases causing hypoventilation (e.g., ALS)
6. Collagen-vascular disease (e.g., SLE, CREST, systemic sclerosis)
7. Pulmonary venous disease
8. Left ventricular failure resulting from hypertension, cad, aortic stenosis, and cardiomyopathy
9. Valvular heart disease (e.g., mitral stenosis, mitral regurgitation)
10. Congenital heart disease with left-to-right shunting (e.g., ASD)

DIAGNOSIS

- The normal pulmonary arterial systolic pressure ranges from 18 to 30 mm Hg and the diastolic pressure ranges from 4 to 12 mm Hg.
- PH is a hemodynamic diagnosis involving two stages: detection of elevated pressure in the pulmonary arteries, and characterization of this abnormality to determine its etiology by ruling out secondary causes.
- Right-heart catheterization must be performed in all patients suspected of having PH to establish the diagnosis and document pulmonary hemodynamics.
- Primary pulmonary hypertension is a diagnosis of exclusion; all secondary causes as mentioned under "Etiology" must be excluded.

DIFFERENTIAL DIAGNOSIS

The differential diagnosis is as listed under "Etiology."

WORKUP

- Screening for the presence of PH using Doppler echocardiography is warranted in individuals with a known predisposing genetic mutation or first-degree relative with idiopathic PPH, scleroderma, congenital heart disease with left-to-right shunt, or portal hypertension undergoing evaluation for orthotopic liver transplantation.
- The workup of a patient suspected of having PPH includes a detailed evaluation of the heart and lungs. Blood tests, chest x-ray, pulmonary function tests, CT scan of the chest, radionuclide studies of the heart and lungs, echocardiogram, electrocardiograms, pulmonary angiogram, and right- and left-heart catheterization are all required to exclude secondary causes of pulmonary hypertension.
- Once the diagnosis has been made, functional assessment should be undergone to determine disease prognosis and potential treatment options.
- The degree of functional impairment as assessed by the WHO classification system, and the 6-minute walk test is a useful way to monitor disease progression and assess response to treatment.

LABORATORY TESTS

- CBC is usually normal in PPH but may show secondary polycythemia.
- ABGs show low PO_2 and oxygen saturation.
- PFT is done to exclude obstructive or restrictive lung disease.
- Overnight oximetry and seep study to rule out sleep apnea/hypopnea.
- ECG may show evidence of both right atrial enlargement (tall P wave >2.5 mV in leads II, III, aVF) and right ventricular enlargement (right axis deviation >100 and R wave > S wave in lead V1).
- Other blood tests: ANA titer to screen for underlying connective tissue disease, HIV serology, liver function tests, and antiphospholipid antibodies.
- Assessment of exercise capacity is a key part of the evaluation of PH in characterizing the disease and determining prognosis and treatment options. The 6-minute walk test and cardiopulmonary exercise testing with gas exchange measurements are the most commonly used methods of assessment.

IMAGING STUDIES

- Chest x-ray shows enlargement of the main and hilar pulmonary arteries with rapid tapering of the distal vessels (Fig. 1-195). Right ventricular enlargement may be evident on lateral films.
- Lung perfusion scan (V/Q scan) aids in excluding chronic pulmonary embolism.
- Transthoracic Doppler echocardiogram including M-mode, 2 D, pulse, continuous and color Doppler assesses ventricular function, excludes significant valvular pathology, and visualizes abnormal shunting of blood between heart chambers if present. It also provides an estimate of pulmonary artery systolic pressure that has been shown by most studies to correlate well (0.57 to 0.93) with pressures measured by right-heart catheterization.
- Pulmonary angiogram is done in patients with suspicious V/Q scans.
- Cardiac catheterization is performed to directly measure pulmonary artery pressures and to detect any shunting of blood.

TREATMENT

NONPHARMACOLOGIC THERAPY

- Oxygen therapy to improve alveolar oxygen flow in both primary and secondary pulmonary hypertension
- Avoidance of vigorous exercise
- Chest physiotherapy

ACUTE GENERAL Rx

- PPH
  1. Diuretics (e.g., furosemide 40-80 mg qd) improve dyspnea and peripheral edema.
  2. Digoxin 0.25 mg qd has been used in patients with PPH.
  3. Vasodilator treatment is usually done with hemodynamic monitoring and includes IV adenosine, prostacyclin, or nitric oxide.
- Secondary pulmonary hypertension treatment is aimed at the underlying cause (see specific disease in text for treatment).

CHRONIC Rx

- Chronic anticoagulation with warfarin is recommended to prevent thromboses and has been shown to prolong life in patients with PPH.
- Calcium channel blockers may alleviate pulmonary vasoconstriction and prolong life in about 20% of patients with PPH.
- Continuous infusion of epoprostenol, or prostacyclin, a short-acting vasodilator and inhibitor of platelet aggregation, improves exercise capacity, quality of life, hemodynamics, and long-term survival in patients with WHO class III or IV function.
- Inhaled aerosolized prostacyclin, iloprost, 2.5 or 5.0 μg taken 6 to 9 times per day improves exercise capacity, NYHA class, and clinical deterioration in patients with primary pulmonary hypertension and selected forms of nonprimary pulmonary hypertension.
- The endothelin-receptor antagonist bosentan taken orally at a dose of 80-160 mg twice daily has been approved for the treatment of PPH and scleroderma pulmonary hypertension showing improvement in clinical class and exercise capacity. Newer selective and nonselective endothelin receptor antagonists are undergoing clinical trials.
- Combination therapy using inhaled iloprost taken 1 hour before oral sildenafil 12.5 or 50 mg causes pulmonary vasodilations and, pending future trials, may be consider treatment for pulmonary hypertension.

- Lung transplantation and heart-lung transplantation are other options in end-stage class IV patients.
- Lung transplant recipients with PPH had survival rates of 73% at 1 yr, 55% at 3 yr, and 45% at 5 yr.

DISPOSITION

- The 6-min walk test is predictive of survival in patients with idiopathic PPH. Desaturation >10% during the test increases mortality risk 2.9 times over a median follow-up of 26 mo.
- The actual 6-min walk distance on chronic epoprostenol treatment is more predictive of survival than the change in 6-min walk distance before and after treatment.
- WHO Class II and III patients with PPH have a mean survival of 3.5 yr.
- WHO Class IV patients have a mean survival of 6 mo.
- Logistic regression equations have been reported to predict survival or death within 1, 2, or 3 yr after diagnosis in patients with PPH.

REFERRAL

If the diagnosis of PPH is suspected, a consultation with a pulmonary specialist is recommended. Secondary causes of pulmonary hypertension may require consultations with rheumatology, neurology, and cardiology.

PEARLS & CONSIDERATIONS

COMMENTS

- The exertional dyspnea of PH is typically described by patients as being relentlessly progressive over several months to a year, often out of proportion to, or in the absence of, underlying heart or lung disease.
- Chest x-ray may reveal evidence of interstitial fluid within the lungs in cases of secondary pulmonary hypertension. PPH is not associated with infiltrates on CXR.
- Factors contributing to pulmonary arterial hypertension are:
  1. Alveolar hypoxia
  2. Acidosis
  3. Thromboemboli occluding arterial blood vessels (e.g., pulmonary embolism)
  4. Scarring or destruction of alveolar walls (e.g., COPD, infiltrative disease)
  5. Primary thickening of arterial walls as occurs in PPH
- RVSP as estimated by echocardiography is not a very good indicator of the presence of PH, because RVSP increases with age and BMI. Athletically conditioned men also have a higher resting RVSP, and thus these measurements can be misleading.
- Abrupt development of pulmonary edema during acute vasodilator testing suggests pulmonary veno-occlusive disease or pulmonary capillary hemangiomatosis and is a contraindication to chronic vasodilator treatment.

SUGGESTED READINGS

Barst RJ et al: Diagnosis and differential assessment of pulmonary arterial hypertension, *J Am Coll Cardiol* 43:40S, 2004.

Chatterjee K, De Marco T, Alpert JS: Pulmonary hypertension: hemodynamic diagnosis and management, *Arch Intern Med* 162:1925, 2002.

Ghofrani HA et al: Combination therapy with oral sildenafil and inhaled iloprost for severe pulmonary hypertension, *Ann Intern Med* 136:515, 2002.

Krowka MJ: Pulmonary hypertension: diagnosis and therapeutics, *Mayo Clin Proc* 75:625, 2000.

McLaughlin VV et al: Prognosis of pulmonary arterial hypertension: ACCP evidence-based clinical practice guidelines, *Chest* 1126:78S, 2004.

Nauser T, Stites S: Diagnosis and treatment of pulmonary hypertension, *Am Fam Physician* 63:1789, 2001.

Olschewski H et al: Inhaled iloprost for severe pulmonary hypertension, *N Engl J Med* 347:322, 2002.

Rubin LJ et al: Bosentan therapy for pulmonary arterial hypertension, *N Engl J Med* 346:896, 2002.

AUTHORS: **JASON IANNUCCILLI, M.D.,** and **PETER PETROPOULOS, M.D.**

Pyelonephritis 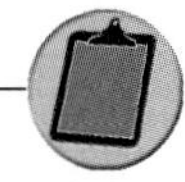

BASIC INFORMATION

DEFINITION

Pyelonephritis is an infection, usually bacterial in origin, of the upper urinary tract.

SYNONYMS

Acute pyelonephritis
Pyonephrosis
Renal carbuncle
Lobar nephronia
Acute bacterial nephritis

ICD-9CM CODES
590.81 Pyelonephritis
599.0 Urinary tract infection
595.9 Cystitis

EPIDEMIOLOGY & DEMOGRAPHICS

INCIDENCE (IN U.S.): Extremely common

PREDOMINANT SEX: Female

PREDOMINANT AGE:
- Sexually active years in women
- Usually >50 yr of age in men

PEAK INCIDENCE: See "Incidence."

GENETICS:

Congenital Infection: Congenital urologic structural disorders may predispose to infections at an early age.

PHYSICAL FINDINGS & CLINICAL PRESENTATION

- Fever
- Rigors
- Chills
- Flank pain
- Dysuria
- Polyuria
- Hematuria
- Toxic feeling and appearance
- Nausea and vomiting
- Headache
- Diarrhea
- Physical examination notable
  1. Costovertebral angle tenderness
  2. Exquisite flank pain

ETIOLOGY

- Gram-negative bacilli such as *E. coli* and *Klebsiella* spp. in more than 95% of cases
- Other, more unusual gram-negative organisms, especially if instrumentation of the urinary system has occurred
- Resistant gram-negative organisms or even fungi in hospitalized patients with indwelling catheters
- Gram-positive organisms such as enterococci
- *Staphylococcus aureus:* presence in urine indicates hematogenous origin
- Viruses: rarely, but these are usually limited to the lower tract

DIAGNOSIS

DIFFERENTIAL DIAGNOSIS

- Nephrolithiasis
- Appendicitis
- Ovarian cyst torsion or rupture
- Acute glomerulonephritis
- PID
- Endometritis
- Other causes of acute abdomen
- Perinephric abscess
- Hydronephrosis

WORKUP

- No workup in sexually active women
- Poorly responding infections, especially with azotemia and frank bacteremia
  1. Renal sonogram
  2. IVP
  3. To assess for underlying urologic pathology such as hydronephrosis
- Urologic imaging studies in all young men and boys
- Prostate assessment in older men

LABORATORY TESTS

- CBC with differential
- Renal panel
- Blood cultures
- Urine cultures
- Urinalysis
- Gram stain of urine
- Urgent renal sonography if obstruction or closed space infection suspected
- CT scans may better define the extent of collections of pus
- Helical CT scans excellent to detect calculi

TREATMENT

ACUTE GENERAL Rx

- Hospitalization for:
  1. Toxic patients
  2. Complicated infections
  3. Diabetes
  4. Suspected bacteremia
- Keep patients well hydrated.
- IV fluids are indicated for those unable to take adequate amounts of liquids.
- Give antipyretics such as acetaminophen when necessary.
- Antibiotic therapy should be initiated after cultures are obtained and guided by the results of culture and sensitivity testing.
  1. Oral TMP-SMX DS (bid for 10 days) or ciprofloxacin (500 mg orally bid for 10 days): adequate for stable patients who can tolerate oral medications with sensitive pathogens
  2. TMP-SMX or ciprofloxacin IV for more toxic patients
  3. Ceftazidime 1 g IV q6-8h
  4. Aminoglycosides such as gentamicin (2 mg/kg IV load followed by 1 mg/kg IV q8h adjusted for renal function) added but nephrotoxic especially in diabetics with azotemia
  5. Vancomycin 1 g IV q12h to cover gram-positive cocci such as enterococci or staphylococci
  6. Ampicillin 1 to 2 g IV q4-6h to cover enterococci, but an aminoglycoside is needed for synergy
  7. Oral ampicillin or amoxicillin: no longer adequate for therapy of gram-negative infections because of resistance
- Prompt drainage with nephrostomy tube placement for obstruction
- Surgical drainage of large collections of pus to control infection
- Diabetic patients, as well as those with indwelling catheters, are especially prone to complicated infections and abscess formation

CHRONIC Rx

- Repair underlying structural problems, especially when renal function is compromised.
  1. Reflux
  2. Obstruction
  3. Nephrolithiasis should be considered
- Patients with diabetes mellitus and indwelling urinary catheters are at particular risk of severe and complicated infections.
- When possible, remove catheters.

REFERRAL

- To surgeon: surgical correction of underlying urologic problems, such as reflux and hydronephrosis
- To pediatrician: in young children, prompt correction of reflux to avoid recurrent infections as well as loss of renal function
- To internist: aggressive metabolic as well as urologic evaluation and treatment for patients with nephrolithiasis

SUGGESTED READINGS

Benador D et al: Randomised controlled trial of three day versus 10 day intravenous antibiotics in acute pyelonephritis: effect on renal scarring, *Arch Dis Child* 84(3):241, 2001.

Foresman WH, Hulbert WC, Rabinowitz R: Does urinary tract ultrasonography at hospitalization for acute pyelonephritis predict vesicoureteral reflux? *J Urol* 165(6 pt 2):2232, 2001.

Vosti KL: Infections of the urinary tract in women: a prospective, longitudinal study of 235 women observed for 1-19 years, *Medicine* 81(5):369, 2002.

AUTHOR: **JOSEPH J. LIEBER, M.D.**

SECTION I

BASIC INFORMATION

DEFINITION

Pyogenic granuloma is a benign vascular lesion of the skin and mucus membranes. They are a result of capillary proliferation generally secondary to trauma.

ICD-9CM CODES
686.1 Pyogenic granuloma

EPIDEMIOLOGY & DEMOGRAPHICS

- Common in children and young adults
- Caused by trauma or surgery
- Occur more frequently during pregnancy

PHYSICAL FINDINGS & CLINICAL PRESENTATION

- Small (<1 cm), yellow-to-red, dome-shaped lesions (Fig 1-196)
- May have surrounding scale at base
- Most commonly found on the head, neck, and extremities
- Often found on the gingiva during pregnancy (called *epulis*)

ETIOLOGY

Trauma causing focal capillary growth

DIAGNOSIS

DIFFERENTIAL DIAGNOSIS

Amelanotic melanoma

WORKUP

Diagnosis is based on clinical history and appearance. Generally begins with trauma followed by the development of an erythematous papule. The lesion tends to bleed easily and develops over several days to weeks.

LABORATORY TESTS

Pathologic examination should be performed after excision to rule out melanoma

TREATMENT

ACUTE GENERAL Rx

- Excision: using 1% lidocaine for anesthesia, shave or curette at base and border. Follow with electrocauterization or cryotherapy.
- Pregnancy epulis generally resolve spontaneously following childbirth.

REFERRAL

Dermatology referral recommended if lesion recurs or multiple satellite lesions occur after excision.

PEARLS & CONSIDERATIONS

ACUTE GENERAL Rx

- Removal of entire lesion is essential because lesions may recur at the site of residual tissue.

AUTHOR: **JENNIFER R. SOUTHER, M.D.**

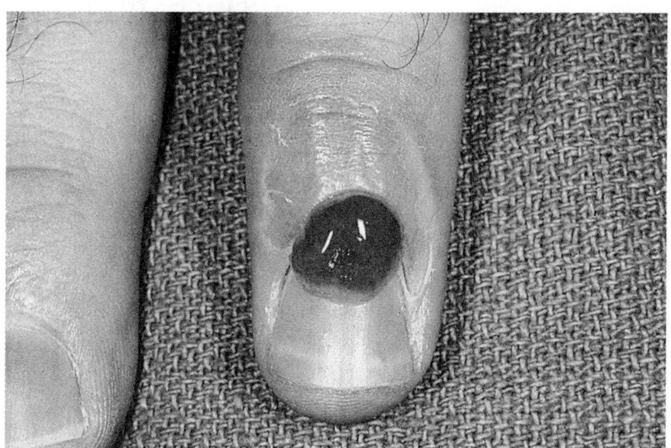

FIGURE 1-196 Pyogenic granuloma. Often the lesions have a collar or moat. (From Callen JP [ed]: *Color atlas of dermatology,* ed 2, Philadelphia, 2000, WB Saunders.)

BASIC INFORMATION

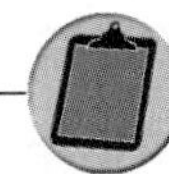

DEFINITION

Q fever is a systemic febrile illness caused by *Coxiella burnetii* that may be acute or chronic.

SYNONYMS

C. burnetii infection

ICD-9CM CODES
083.0 Q fever

EPIDEMIOLOGY & DEMOGRAPHICS

- *C. burnetii* is found worldwide.
- Common animal reservoirs are cattle, sheep, and goats.
- Most cases are found in individuals who have direct contact with infected animals (e.g., farmers, veterinarians) or who are exposed to contaminated animal urine, feces, milk, or placental tissues.
- Q fever is seen more in men than in women (3:1).

PHYSICAL FINDINGS & CLINICAL PRESENTATION

Acute Q fever presentation:
- Fever
- Pneumonia
- Hepatitis
- Meningoencephalitis

Chronic Q fever presentation:
- Endocarditis

Most common clinical symptoms:
- Chills
- Sweats
- Nausea
- Vomiting
- Cough, nonproductive
- Headache
- Fatigue

Most frequent physical findings:
- Fever
- Inspiratory rales
- Purpuric rash
- Hepatomegaly
- Splenomegaly

ETIOLOGY

- Q fever is caused by the rickettsial organism *C. burnetii.*
- *C. burnetii* is a gram-negative coccobacillus that is transmitted from arthropods to animals to humans.
- The disease is acquired most often via inhalation of aerosols. In the lungs, it proliferates in macrophases and then gains access to the blood, producing a transient bacteria. Thereafter it can invade many organs, but most commonly invades the lungs and liver.
- There is an incubation period between 3 to 30 days before systemic symptoms manifest.

DIAGNOSIS

DIFFERENTIAL DIAGNOSIS

Q fever can have various presentations and must be in the differential diagnosis of fever, hepatitis, pneumonia, endocarditis, and meningitis.

WORKUP

- CBC, ESR, and LFTs
- Urinalysis
- Serology
- Chest x-ray

LABORATORY TESTS

In acute Q fever:
- CBC and white blood cell count is usually normal.
- Thrombocytopenia can occur (25%).
- Elevation of hepatic transaminases (two to three times the abnormal range) may be seen.
- Complement fixation (CF) shows a fourfold rise in titer between acute and convalescent samples.

In chronic Q fever (almost always endocarditis):
- ESR is elevated
- Anemia is present
- Microscopic hematuria
- Blood cultures are almost always negative
- Complement fixation (CF) titer of >1:200 to phase I antigen is diagnostic

IMAGING STUDIES

- Chest x-ray examination is abnormal, showing segmental lobe consolidation
- Pleural effusions (35%)

TREATMENT

NONPHARMACOLOGIC THERAPY

Oxygen as needed in patients with pneumonia

ACUTE GENERAL Rx

- Acute Q fever can be treated with doxycycline (100 mg bid) for 14 to 21 days *or*
- Erythromycin (500 mg qid) for 14 days *or*
- Ofloxacin 200 mg PO q8h for 14 to 21 days
- Hydroxychloroquine plus doxycycline for endocarditis associated with Q fever
- Fluoroquinolones are recommended for suspected meningoencephalitis

CHRONIC Rx

- Chronic Q fever is treated with a combination of two antibiotics, doxycycline 100 mg bid and rifampin 300 mg qd *or*
- Doxycycline 100 mg bid and Ofloxacin 200 mg po q8h *or*
- Doxycycline 100 mg bid and hydroxychloroquine 200 mg PO tid
- Duration of treatment: 2 to 3 yr

DISPOSITION

- Patients with acute Q fever respond well with antibiotics, with rare deaths reported.
- Mortality rate in chronic Q fever endocarditis is high (24%). Most patients will come to valve replacement surgery.

REFERRAL

Referral to an infectious disease expert is recommended in any cases of suspected acute or chronic Q fever.

PEARLS & CONSIDERATIONS

COMMENTS

- No vaccines are available.
- Infected patients do not require specific isolation precautions.
- Q fever derived its name in 1935 from Derrick, who was suspicious of a new disease during a series of acute febrile illness in abattoir workers of Queensland, Australia, justifying the name of Q fever (for query).

REFERENCES

Caron F et al: Acute Q fever pneumonia: a review of 80 hospitalized patients, *Chest* 114(3):808, 1998.

Choi E: Tularemia and Q fever, *Med Clin North Am* 86(2):393, 2002.

Gami AS et al: Q fever ondocarditis in the United States, *Mayo Clin Proc* 79:253, 2004.

Raoult, D et al: Q fever 1985-1998. Clinical and epidemiologic features of 1,383 infections, *Medicine* 79:109, 2000.

AUTHORS: **PETER PETROPOULOS, M.D.,** and **DENNIS J. MIKOLICH, M.D.**

BASIC INFORMATION

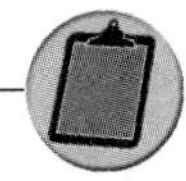

DEFINITION

Rabies is a fatal illness caused by the rabies virus and transmitted to humans by the bite of an infected animal.

SYNONYMS

Hydrophobia

ICD-9CM CODES
071 Rabies

EPIDEMIOLOGY & DEMOGRAPHICS

INCIDENCE (IN U.S.): Approximately 2 cases/yr
PREDOMINANT SEX: Men (70% of cases)
PREDOMINANT AGE: <16 yr and >55 yr

PHYSICAL FINDINGS & CLINICAL PRESENTATION

- Incubation period of 10 to 90 days
  1. Shorter with bites of the face
  2. Longer if extremities involved
- Prodrome
  1. Fever
  2. Headache
  3. Malaise
  4. Pain or anesthesia at exposure site
  5. Sore throat
  6. GI symptoms
  7. Psychiatric symptoms
- Acute neurologic period, with objective evidence of CNS involvement
  1. Extreme hyperactivity and bizarre behavior alternating with periods of relative calm
  2. Hallucinations
  3. Disorientation
  4. Seizures
  5. Paralysis may occur
  6. Spasm of the pharynx and larynx, accompanied by severe pain, caused by drinking
  7. Fear elicited by seeing water
  8. Paralysis
  9. Coma
- Possible death from respiratory arrest

ETIOLOGY

- Rabies virus
- Cases in U.S. are associated with:
  1. Bats
  2. Raccoons
  3. Foxes
  4. Skunks
- In 8 of the 32 cases occurring in the U.S. since 1980, there was a history of exposure to bats without an actual bite or scratch.
- Imported cases are usually associated with dogs.
- Unusual acquisition:
  1. Via organ transplantation
  2. Via aerosol transmission in laboratory workers and spelunkers

DIAGNOSIS

DIFFERENTIAL DIAGNOSIS

- Delirium tremens
- Tetanus
- Hysteria
- Psychiatric disorders
- Other viral encephalitides
- Guillain-Barré syndrome
- Poliomyelitis

WORKUP

- Rabies antibody
  1. Serum
  2. CSF
- Viral isolation
  1. Saliva
  2. CSF
  3. Serum
- Rabies fluorescent antibody: skin biopsy from the hair-covered area of the neck
- Characteristic eosinophilic inclusions (Negri bodies) in infected neurons

LABORATORY TESTS

See "Workup."

TREATMENT

NONPHARMACOLOGIC THERAPY

- Isolation of the patient to prevent transmission to others
- Supportive therapy (although this has not been shown to change outcome except in three cases in which the patients had received prophylaxis before onset of symptoms)

ACUTE GENERAL Rx

- No beneficial therapy
- Emphasis placed on prophylaxis of potentially exposed individuals as soon as possible following an exposure:
  1. Thorough wound cleansing
  2. Both active and passive immunization is most effective when used within 72 hr of exposure
- Vaccinations:
  1. Human diploid cell vaccine (HDCV) or rhesus monkey diploid cell vaccine (RVA), 1 ml IM (deltoid) on days 0, 3, 7, 14, and 28
  2. Human rabies hyperimmune globulin (RIG) 20 IU/kg, administered to persons not previously vaccinated. If anatomically feasible, the full dose should be infiltrated around the wounds and any remaining volume should be administered IM at an anatomically distant site from vaccine administration
- Preexposure prophylaxis using HDCV or RVA (1 ml IM days 0, 7, and 21 or 28) in individuals at high risk for acquisition:
  1. Veterinarians
  2. Laboratory workers working with rabies virus
  3. Spelunkers
  4. Visitors to endemic areas

DISPOSITION

Virtually always fatal

REFERRAL

- To infectious disease consultant
- To local health authorities

PEARLS & CONSIDERATIONS

COMMENTS

- Most cases in the U.S. are caused by:
  1. Wild animal bites (bats)
  2. Dog bites occurring outside the U.S.
  3. Some unknown exposure
- Rare cases can be transmitted by mucous membrane contact of aerosolized virus.

SUGGESTED READINGS

CDC: Investigation of rabies infections in organ donor and transplant recipients—Alabama, Arkansas, Oklahoma, and Texas, *MMWR* 53:586, 2004.

Hankins DG, Rosekrans JA: Overview, prevention, and treatment of rabies, *Mayo Clin Proc* 79:671, 2004.

National Association of State Public Health Veterinarians, Inc.: Compendium of animal rabies prevention and control, 2001, *MMWR* 50(RR-8):1, 2001.

Plotkin SA: Rabies, *Clin Infect Dis* 30:4, 2000.

AUTHOR: **MAURICE POLICAR, M.D.**

Radiation Exposure

BASIC INFORMATION

DEFINITION

Exposure to ionizing radiation has the potential for radiation injury. Radionuclides present a danger to humans through the particles emitted during radioactive decay. These particles can damage cellular structures and may result in mutation, cancer, or cell death.

PRINCIPLES OF RADIOACTIVITY, ADDITIONAL DEFINITIONS:

Particles of radiation

- Photons: massless particles that travel at the speed of light and produce electromagnetic radiation. Their wavelength determine their energy; the longer the wavelength the lower the energy. In order of increasing energy, they are called ultraviolet, visible light, infrared, microwave, gamma, and x-rays. X-rays consist of a spectrum of wavelengths while gamma rays have a fixed wavelength specific to the radioactive material that produces them. X-rays and gamma rays are highly penetrating.
- β particles are electrons. They may be emitted during decay of a radionuclide (atom) that disintegrates. Positrons (positively charged electrons) may also be produced during radioactive decay. β particles are less penetrating than x-rays and gamma rays, but can still pass through several centimeters of human tissue. Nonetheless, their main toxic effect is through inhalation.
- α particles are helium nuclei (2 protons and 2 neutrons) stripped of their electrons. They are stopped by clothing; therefore, they need to be "incorporated" to cause health problems.
- Neutrons are released during nuclear fission, not during natural radionuclide decay. They can cause a stable atom to become radioactive by collision (e.g., during nuclear fallout).
- Cosmic rays are streams of electrons, protons, and α particles that come from outer space. Most of their energy is dissipated by the earth's atmosphere.
- Ionizing radiation describes any radiation with sufficient energy to break up an atom or molecule with which it collides. This is the mechanism of radiation toxicity.
- Nonionizing radiation has insufficient energy to break up atoms; nonetheless sufficient energy in the form of heat may be produced to cause localized tissue damage.
- Radioactive decay: process of transformation of unstable nuclei into more stable ones via the emissions of various particles. Decay is described by half-life, which is a characteristic of every radioisotope.
- Radiation units of measure:
  1. Roentgen: amount of radiation to which an object is exposed.
  2. Rad (radiation absorbed dose) and Gray (Gy, the same concept in the international system): amount of radiation absorbed by tissue (1 Gy = 100 Rad).
  3. Rem (roentgen equivalent man) and Sievert (SV, the same concept in the International System): a measure that standardizes the amount of cellular damage produced by different types of radiation. One Rem (or 0.01 SV) is the dose of radiation that produces damage equivalent to one Rad of x-ray.

IRRADIATION, CONTAMINATION, AND INCORPORATION:

- Irradiation: exposure to ionizing radiation
- Contamination: an object or person covered with a radioactive substance
- Incorporation: exposure to a radionuclide by inhalation, ingestion, intravenous infusion, or percutaneously

STOCHASTIC EFFECTS OF IONIZING RADIATION:

Any dose of ionizing radiation can alter DNA, causing mutations or carcinogenic changes that may take years to be expressed. There is no dose threshold, and the effect is cumulative. The stochastic effects of radiation are mostly a concern with small but prolonged exposure to radiation.

DETERMINISTIC EFFECTS OF IONIZING RADIATION:

The dose of radiation is sufficient to kill cells; the higher the dose, the greater the number of killed cells and the greater the impact on an organ system. The deterministic effects of radiation are the consequence of a large whole-body exposure.

ICD-9CM CODE

990 Radiation exposure

PHYSICAL FINDINGS & ACUTE PRESENTATION

ACUTE RADIATION SYNDROME:

Follows a large, whole-body exposure of 2Sv or more (500 times the average annual exposure)

Sequence of events: four stages:

- Stage 1: nausea and vomiting begins within a few minutes to hours and lasts several hours to a few days depending on the dose.
- Stage 2: latent (asymptomatic), lasting several days to weeks, again depending on the dose.
- Stage 3: third to fifth week following exposure: abdominal pain, diarrhea, hair loss, bleeding, infection. During this stage, several subsyndromes may coexist, overlap, or occur in sequence.
  1. CNS syndrome: fever, ataxia, apathy, lethargy, and seizures
  2. Cardiovascular (CV) syndrome: arrhythmias, hypotension, myocardial injury
  3. GI syndrome: anorexia, nausea, vomiting, diarrhea, dehydration, superinfection, and sepsis
  4. Hematopoietic syndrome: pancytopenia with bleeding diathesis and sepsis
  5. Pneumonitis leading to pulmonary fibrosis
  6. Any of the syndromes has the potential to be lethal
- Stage 4: recovery, lasting weeks to months.

DOSE ESTIMATION AND PROGNOSIS:

Because radiation is often mixed and because body parts may be exposed to different amounts of radiation, the dose received is difficult to estimate in the field. Therefore, it is usually the acute radiation syndrome itself that allows prognosis. At a dose received under 3 Sv a lymphocyte count $>1200/mm^3$ at 48 hr confers a favorable prognosis; if the count is $<1200/mm^3$, a fatal dose is possible and more aggressive medical management is warranted. A drop in the number of granulocytes or platelets also portends a severe exposure. Patients exposed to less than 2 Sv will survive with no or minimal care. Patients exposed to 2 to 5 Sv are likely to survive with medical care. A dose of 5 to 20 Sv is survivable. A dose above 20 Sv is supralethal, and the patient will die within 24 to 48 hr from CNS or CV syndrome. At the Chernobyl nuclear reactor accident, mortality was 33% among those receiving 4 to 6 Sv and 95% among those receiving 6 to 16 Sv. When expressed in Gy units:

* Exposure <1 Gy: almost certain survival
* Exposure 1 to 2 Gy: 90% survival
* Exposure 2 to 3.5 Gy: probable survival
* Exposure 3.5 to 5.5 Gy: 50% survival
* Exposure 5.5 to 10 Gy: probable death
* Exposure >10 Gy: certain death

CARCINOGENESIS:
Leukemia, breast cancer, lung cancer, and thyroid cancer incidence increase following exposure to ionizing exposure. This is a stochastic effect that can occur with or without a history of acute radiation syndrome.

ETIOLOGY

SOURCE OF RADIATION:

* Natural
  1. Radon (domestic and mining industry)
  2. Cosmic
  3. Terrestrial
  4. Ingested (from food)
* Industrial
  1. X-ray diagnosis
  2. Nuclear medicine
  3. Consumer products
  4. Occupational (e.g., nuclear energy)
  5. Weapons

TREATMENT

* Decontamination
  1. Perform at site of exposure unless there is ongoing radiation
  2. Remove all clothing (and treat those as radioactive waste)
  3. Wash patient with soap and water. Dispose of the used water as radioactive waste
  4. Scrub any open wound
  5. Depending on the situation, the regional emergency response system should be called for additional measures such as evacuation
* Management of the acute radiation syndrome
  1. Establish IV access
  2. Manage the airway if needed
  3. Manage burns
  4. Identify and treat other injuries
  5. Provide analgesia
  6. Give antiemetics (e.g., ondansetron)
  7. Manage bleeding and transfuse if necessary
  8. Diagnose and treat sepsis
  9. Consider colony-stimulating factors
  10. Consider bone marrow transplantation

SUGGESTED READINGS

Rella J: Radiation. In Goldfrank LR et al (eds): *Toxicologic emergencies,* ed. 7, New York, 2002, McGraw-Hill.

Turai I et al: Medical response to radiation incidents and radionuclear threats, *Br Med J* 4:247, 2004.

Waselenko JK et al: Medical management of the acute radiation syndrome, *Ann Intern Med* 140:1037, 2004.

AUTHOR: **TOM J. WACHTEL, M.D.**

Ramsay Hunt Syndrome

BASIC INFORMATION

DEFINITION

Ramsay Hunt syndrome is a localized herpes zoster infection involving the seventh nerve and geniculate ganglia, resulting in hearing loss, vertigo, and facial nerve palsy.

SYNONYMS

Herpes zoster oticus
Geniculate herpes
Herpetic geniculate ganglionitis

ICD-9CM CODES
053.11 Ramsay Hunt syndrome

EPIDEMIOLOGY & DEMOGRAPHICS

PREDOMINANT SEX: Equal sex distribution

PREDOMINANT AGE:
- Increasingly common with advancing age
- Rare in childhood

PHYSICAL FINDINGS & CLINICAL PRESENTATION

- Characteristic vesicles:
  1. On pinna
  2. In external auditory canal
  3. In distribution of the facial nerve and, occasionally, adjacent cranial nerves
- Facial paralysis on the involved side

ETIOLOGY

Reactivation of dormant infection with varicella-zoster virus following primary varicella (usually in childhood)

DIAGNOSIS

- Usually made by recognition of the clinical features detailed previously
- Viral culture and/or microscopic examination of specimens taken from active vesicles

DIFFERENTIAL DIAGNOSIS

- Herpes simplex
- External otitis
- Impetigo
- Enteroviral infection
- Bell's palsy of other etiologies
- Acoustic neuroma (before appearance of skin lesions)
- The differential diagnosis of headache and facial pain is described in Section II.

WORKUP

If the diagnosis is in doubt, confirmation of varicella-zoster virus infection should be sought.

LABORATORY TESTS

- Viral culture of specimens of vesicular fluid and scrapings of the vesicle base
- Tzanck preparation, which may reveal multinucleated giant cells
- Direct immunofluorescent staining of scrapings

IMAGING STUDIES

MRI may demonstrate enhancement of the facial and vestibulocochlear nerves before appearance of vesicles.

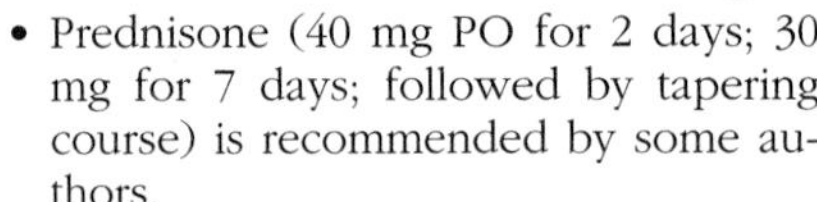

TREATMENT

ACUTE GENERAL Rx

- Prednisone (40 mg PO for 2 days; 30 mg for 7 days; followed by tapering course) is recommended by some authors.
- Acyclovir (800 mg PO five times qd for 10 days), famciclovir (500 mg tid for 7 days), or valacyclovir (1 g every 8 hr for 7 days) may hasten healing.
- Analgesics should be used as indicated.

CHRONIC Rx

- Amitriptyline is effective in some cases of postherpetic pain.
- Narcotic analgesics may occasionally be necessary.

DISPOSITION

Recurrences are unusual.

REFERRAL

To otolaryngologist: patients with persistent facial paralysis for potential surgical decompression of the facial nerve

PEARLS & CONSIDERATIONS

COMMENTS

Immunodeficiency states, particularly infection with the human immunodeficiency virus (HIV), should be considered in:
- Younger patients
- Severe cases
- Patients with a history of specific risk behavior

SUGGESTED READINGS

Furuta Y et al: Varicella-zoster virus DNA level and facial paralysis in Ramsay Hunt Syndrome, *Ann Otol Rhinol Laryngol* 113(9):700, 2004.

Hato N et al: Ramsay Hunt syndrome in children, *Ann Neurol* 48(2):254, 2000.

Ko JY, Sheen TS, Hsu MM: Herpes zoster oticus treated with acyclovir and prednisolone: clinical manifestations and analysis of prognostic factors, *Clin Otolaryngol* 25(2):139, 2000.

AUTHOR: **JOSEPH R. MASCI, M.D.**

BASIC INFORMATION

DEFINITION

Raynaud's phenomenon is a vasospastic disorder usually affecting the digital arteries precipitated by exposure to cold temperatures or emotional distress and manifesting in a triphasic discoloration of the fingers or toes.

SYNONYMS

Primary Raynaud's phenomenon or Raynaud's disease
Secondary Raynaud's phenomenon

ICD-9CM CODES
443.0 Raynaud's syndrome, Raynaud's disease, Raynaud's phenomenon (secondary)
785.4 If gangrene present

EPIDEMIOLOGY & DEMOGRAPHICS

- Raynaud's phenomenon (either primary [idiopathic] or secondary [see "Etiology"]) is found in 5% to 20% of the population.
- Primary Raynaud's phenomenon is more common than secondary Raynaud's in the U.S. and occurs in women more often than men (4:1) and in the young (<40 yr of age) more than the old.
- According to NIH, about 75% of causes occur in women aged 15-40 yr.
- Between 5% and 15% of patients thought to have primary Raynaud's will develop a secondary cause (commonly scleroderma or CREST syndrome).

PHYSICAL FINDINGS & CLINICAL PRESENTATION

- The classic manifestation is the triphasic color response to cold exposure, which may or may not be accompanied by pain (Fig. 1-197):
  1. Pallor of the digit resulting from vasospasm.
  2. Blue discoloration (cyanosis) secondary to desaturated venous blood.
  3. Red (rubor) with or without pain and paresthesia when vasospasm resolves and blood returns to the digit.
- Color changes are well delineated, symmetric, and usually bilateral involving the fingers and toes, but sparing the thumbs.
- Fingertips are most often involved, but feet, ears, and nose can be affected.
- Duration of attacks can range from seconds to hours.
- Chronic skin changes resulting from repeated attacks may include skin thickening and brittle nails. Ulcerations and rarely gangrene may occur.
- Secondary Raynaud's phenomenon may be associated with typical findings of the underlying disease (e.g., sclerodactyly and telangiectasia in CREST syndrome).

ETIOLOGY

- Primary Raynaud's phenomenon is generally referred to as Raynaud's disease when no cause can be found.
- Primary Raynaud's phenomenon has been shown to have a familial tendency, and 5 potential chromosomal regions have been identified that may be linked to its pathogenesis.
- Attacks are usually triggered by cold or emotional stimuli, but can also be triggered by vibration, caffeine, tobacco, pseudoephedrine, contact with polyvinylchloride (PVC), or frozen foods.
- Proposed mechanisms of pathogenesis include:
1. Up-regulation or sensitization of postsynaptic α-2-receptors in the digits.
2. Increased endothelin-1 (potent endothelium-derived vasoconstrictor), and decreased localized vasodilation medicated by CGRP.
- Secondary Raynaud's phenomenon has many causes:
  1. CREST syndrome (calcinosis, Raynaud's phenomenon, esophageal dysmotility, sclerodactyly, and telangiectasia)
  2. Scleroderma
  3. Mixed connective tissue disease, polymyositis, and dermatomyositis
  4. SLE
  5. Rheumatoid arthritis
  6. Thromboangiitis obliterans (Buerger's disease)
  7. Drug induced (β-blockers, ergotamine, methysergide, vinblastine, bleomycin, oral contraceptives)
  8. Polycythemia, cryoglobulinemia, and certain vasculitides
  9. Carpal tunnel syndrome
  10. Tools causing vibration
  11. Estrogen replacement therapy without progesterone

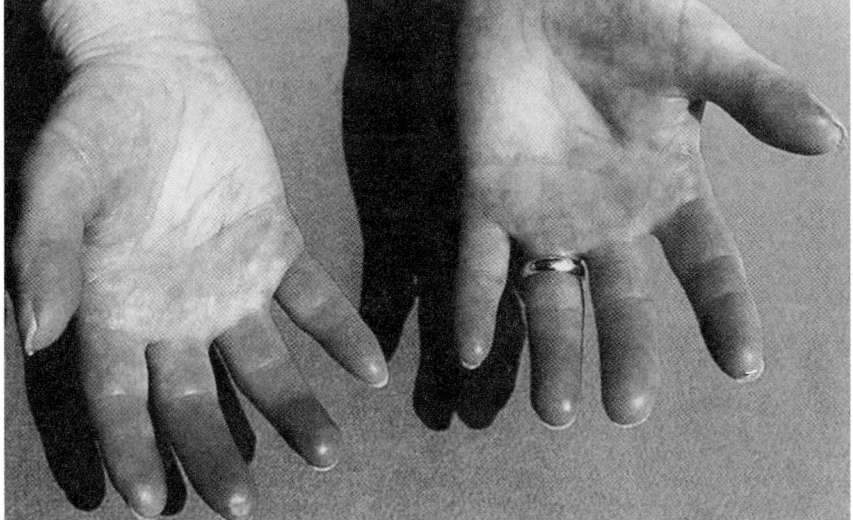

FIGURE 1-197 Raynaud's phenomenon. Sharply demarcated cyanosis of the fingers with proximal venular congestion (livedo reticularis) is seen. (From Klippel J, Dieppe P, Ferri F [eds]: *Primary care rheumatology*, London, 1999, Mosby.)

DIAGNOSIS

- The diagnosis of Raynaud's phenomenon can be made by a history of well-demarcated digit discoloration induced by cold exposure and a physical examination looking for possible secondary causes.
- Initial pallor is typically necessary for the diagnosis to be made.
- The triphasic color changes can sometimes be induced in the office by placing the hand in an ice bath.
- Color photos and questionnaires may be useful in assisting in the diagnosis.

DIFFERENTIAL DIAGNOSIS

See "Etiology."

WORKUP

- Once the diagnosis of Raynaud's phenomenon is established, differentiating primary from secondary is helpful in treatment and prognosis. History and physical examination usually make this distinction, whereas certain laboratory studies may predict secondary causes (see "Laboratory Tests").
- One test available but not commonly used is the nailfold microscopy. If positive, it may indicate the presence of underlying collagen-vascular disease

and would therefore suggest a diagnosis of secondary Raynaud's phenomenon.

LABORATORY TESTS

- CBC, electrolytes, BUN, Cr, ESR, ANA, VDRL, RF, and urinalysis should be included in the initial evaluation.
- If the history, physical examination, and initial laboratory tests suggest a possible secondary cause, specific serologic testing (e.g., anticentromere antibodies, anti-Scl 70, cryoglobulins, complement testing, and protein electrophoresis) may be indicated.

IMAGING STUDIES

- Chest x-ray examination may be helpful if a secondary cause, such as scleroderma, is suggested.
- Barium swallow may be helpful if CREST syndrome is suspected.
- Angiography is rarely needed for Raynaud's phenomenon but may be helpful in diagnosing Buerger's disease as a possible etiology.

TREATMENT

NONPHARMACOLOGIC THERAPY

- Avoid medications that may precipitate Raynaud's phenomenon (see "Etiology").
- Avoid cold exposure. Use warm gloves, hats, and garments during the winter months or before going into cold environments (e.g., air-conditioned rooms).
- Avoid stressful situations.
- Avoid nicotine, caffeine, and over-the-counter decongestants.

ACUTE GENERAL Rx

- Typically, patients with Raynaud's phenomenon respond well to nonpharmacologic measures.
- Medications should be used if the above mentioned treatment does not work.
- Goal is to prevent digital ulcers and gangrene.
- Medications commonly used are described in "Chronic Rx."

CHRONIC Rx

- Calcium channel blockers are the most effective treatment for Raynaud's phenomenon.
  1. Nifedipine is most often prescribed at a dose of 10 to 20 mg 30 min before going outside. If symptoms occur with long duration, nifedipine XL 30 to 90 mg PO qd is effective.
  2. If side effects occur with nifedipine, other calcium blockers can be used (e.g., diltiazem 30 mg qid and gradually increased to a maximum dose of 120 mg qid). Felodipine 2.5 mg qd up to 10 mg qd can also be used.
  3. Verapamil has not been shown to be effective with Raynaud's phenomenon.
- Prazosin 1 mg bid up to 4 mg bid has been effective with Raynaud's phenomenon.
- Reserpine and guanethidine, although effective, have a high side effect profile.
- Other agents that have been tried with limited results include aspirin, pentoxifylline, captopril, and topical nitrates.
- The prostaglandins, including inhaled iloprost, IV epoprostenol, and alprostadil, may be promising in severe Raynaud's phenomenon.
- Lower limb sympathectomy has been reported to be effective in relief of symptoms for very severe, refractory cases.

DISPOSITION

The prognosis of patients with Raynaud's phenomenon depends on the etiology.

- Primary Raynaud's phenomenon is fairly benign, usually remaining stable and controlled with nonpharmacologic medical treatment.
- Patients with secondary Raynaud's phenomenon, specifically those with scleroderma, CREST syndrome, and thromboangiitis obliterans, may develop severe ischemic digits with ulceration, gangrene, and autoamputation.

REFERRAL

- Rheumatology consult is indicated if secondary collagen-vascular disease is diagnosed.
- Vascular surgery consult is indicated if ulcers, gangrene, or threatened digit loss is noted.

PEARLS & CONSIDERATIONS

COMMENTS

Most patients with Raynaud's phenomenon can be managed by the primary care provider; however, it is important to differentiate primary from secondary forms. Secondary forms may become manifest as far out as 10 yr from the diagnosis of Raynaud's phenomenon. Periodic follow-up visits and reassessment to exclude secondary forms are important toward future treatment options and outcome.

SUGGESTED READINGS

Berlin AL, Pehr K: Coexistence of erythroelalgia and Raynaud's phenomenon, *J Am Acad Dermatol* 50:456, 2004.

O'Connor CM: Raynaud's phenomenon, *J Vasc Nurs* 19:87, 2001.

Spencer-Green G: Outcomes in primary Raynaud's phenomenon, *Arch Intern Med* 158:595, 1998.

Sturgill MG, Seibold JR: Rational use of calcium-channel antagonists in Raynaud's phenomenon, *Curr Opin Rheumatol* 10:584, 1998.

Wigley FM: Raynaud's phenomenon, *N Engl J Med* 347:1001, 2002.

AUTHOR: **PETER PETROPOULOS, M.D.**

BASIC INFORMATION

DEFINITION

Reflex sympathetic dystrophy (RSD) refers to a painful neuropathic symptom complex affecting an extremity following trauma, surgery, or nerve injury to that limb.

SYNONYMS

Causalgia
Shoulder-hand syndrome
Sudeck's atrophy
Posttraumatic pain syndrome

ICD-9CM CODES
337.20 Dystrophy sympathetic (posttraumatic) (reflex)

EPIDEMIOLOGY & DEMOGRAPHICS

- The incidence and prevalence of RSD is not known.
- RSD is usually initiated by trauma.
- RSD can occur in adults and children.
- RSD is often associated with psychiatric emotional lability, anxiety, and depression.

PHYSICAL FINDINGS & CLINICAL PRESENTATION

RSD is divided into three stages:

- Acute stage (occurring within hours to days after the injury)
  1. Burning or aching pain occurring over the injured extremity
  2. Hyperalgesia (exquisitely sensitive to touch)
  3. Edema
  4. Dysthermia
  5. Increased hair and nail growth
- Dystrophic stage (3 to 6 mo after the injury)
  1. Burning pain radiating both distal and proximally from the site of injury
  2. Brawny edema
  3. Hyperhidrosis
  4. Hypothermia and cyanosis
  5. Muscle tremors and spasms
  6. Increase muscle tone and reflexes
- Atrophic stage (6 mo after injury)
  1. Spread of pain proximally
  2. Cold, pale cyanotic skin
  3. Trophic skin changes with subcutaneous atrophy
  4. Fixed joints
  5. Contractures

ETIOLOGY

- The cause of RSD is unknown. It is thought to represent dysfunction of the sympathetic nervous system.
- Any injury can precipitate RSD including:
  1. Crush blunt trauma, burns, frostbite
  2. Surgery
  3. Parkinson's disease
  4. Cerebrovascular accident
  5. Myocardial infarction
  6. Osteoarthritis, cervical and lumbar disk disease
  7. Carpal tunnel and tarsal tunnel syndrome
  8. Diabetes
  9. Hyperthyroidism
  10. Isoniazid therapy

DIAGNOSIS

The diagnosis of RSD is primarily clinical, based on the patient's history and physical presentation.

DIFFERENTIAL DIAGNOSIS

The differential diagnosis includes all the causes mentioned under "Etiology."

WORKUP

In patients with RSD, no workup is needed because there are no specific diagnostic tests establishing the diagnosis.

LABORATORY TESTS

Blood tests are not specific in the diagnosis of RSD.

IMAGING STUDIES

- No imaging studies are diagnostic of RSD. Three-phase bone imaging may be helpful.
- Autonomic testing, although not commonly done, has been proposed.
  1. Measuring resting sweat output
  2. Measuring resting skin temperature
  3. Quantitative sudomotor axon reflex test
- X-ray studies of the affected limb may show osteoporosis from disuse.

TREATMENT

Treatment is aimed at relieving the pain and improving disuse atrophy with physical therapy.

NONPHARMACOLOGIC THERAPY

- Physical therapy
- Transcutaneous nerve stimulation

ACUTE GENERAL Rx

- The following has been tried for neuropathic pain relief:
- Amitriptyline 10 mg to 150 mg qd
- Phenytoin 300 mg qd
- Carbamazepine 100 mg bid
- Calcium channel blockers, nifedipine extended release 30 to 60 mg qd
- Prednisone 60 to 80 mg qd × 2 wk and then tapered over 1 to 2 wk to a maintenance dose of 5 mg qd for 2 to 3 mo.

CHRONIC Rx

- Stellate ganglion and lumbar sympathetic blocks can be tried
- IV qd α-adrenergic blockade with phentolamine is thought to be a good predictor of response to subsequent sympatholytic treatment
- Surgical sympathectomy

DISPOSITION

- Spontaneous remission can occur after several weeks to months.
- Patients with RSD variably will progress through all stages leading to atrophy and contractures.

REFERRAL

RSD is a very difficult diagnosis to make and referral to either rheumatology, neurology, orthopedic, or physiatry is recommended.

PEARLS & CONSIDERATIONS

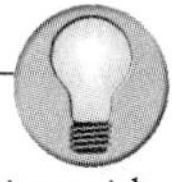

COMMENTS

- RSD is a common clinical entity without clear definition, pathophysiologic features, or treatment.
- Pain is the most disabling symptom for most patients with RSD and is usually out of proportion to the extent of the injury.

SUGGESTED READINGS

Ochoa JL: Reflex sympathetic dystrophy: a disease of medical understanding, *Clin J Pain* 8:363, 1992.
Raja SN, Grabow TS: Complex regional pain syndrome 1 (reflex sympathetic dystrophy), *Anesthesiology* 96(5):1254, 2002.
Schwartzman RJ: New treatments for reflex sympathetic dystrophy, *N Engl J Med* 343:654, 2000.
Schwartzman RJ, Maleki J: Postinjury neuropathic pain syndromes, *Med Clin North Am* 83(3):597, 1999.

AUTHOR: **PETER PETROPOULOS, M.D.**

Reiter's Syndrome (PTG)

BASIC INFORMATION

DEFINITION

Reiter's syndrome is one of the seronegative spondyloarthropathies, so called because serum rheumatoid factor is not present in these forms of inflammatory arthritis. Reiter's syndrome is an asymmetric polyarthritis that affects mainly the lower extremities and is associated with one or more of the following:

- Urethritis
- Cervicitis
- Dysentery
- Inflammatory eye disease
- Mucocutaneous lesions

SYNONYMS

Reiter's disease
Reactive arthritis
Seronegative spondyloarthropathy

ICD-9CM CODES
099.3 Reiter's syndrome

EPIDEMIOLOGY & DEMOGRAPHICS

INCIDENCE (IN U.S.): 0.0035% annually of men <50 yr
PREDOMINANT SEX: Male
PREDOMINANT AGE: 20 to 40 yr
PEAK INCIDENCE: Most common in the third decade
GENETICS:
Familial Disposition: Strongly associated with HLA-B27 (63% to 96%)

PHYSICAL FINDINGS & CLINICAL PRESENTATION

- Polyarthritis
  1. Affecting the knee and ankle
  2. Commonly asymmetric
- Heel pain and Achilles tendinitis, especially at the insertion of the Achilles tendon
- Plantar fasciitis
- Large effusions
- Dactylitis or "sausage toe"
- Urethritis
- Uveitis or conjunctivitis; uveitis can progress to blindness without treatment
- Keratoderma blennorrhagicum
  1. Hyperkeratotic lesions on soles of the feet, toes, penis, hands
  2. Closely resembles psoriasis
- Aortic regurgitation similar to that seen in ankylosing spondylitis

ETIOLOGY

- Epidemic Reiter's syndrome following outbreaks of dysentery has been well described.
- Genetically susceptible HLA-B27–positive individuals are at risk for developing Reiter's syndrome following infection with certain pathogens:
  1. *Salmonella*
  2. *Shigella*
  3. *Yersinia enterocolitica*
  4. *Chlamydia trachomatis*
  5. Molecular mimicry mechanism suspected
- Symptom complex indistinguishable from Reiter's syndrome has been described in association with HIV infection.

DIAGNOSIS

DIFFERENTIAL DIAGNOSIS

- Ankylosing spondylitis
- Psoriatic arthritis
- Rheumatoid arthritis
- Gonococcal arthritis-tenosynovitis
- Rheumatic fever

WORKUP

- X-ray examination of affected joints
- Synovial fluid examination and culture
- Careful examination of eyes and skin
- Cultures for gonococcus (urethral, cervical, stool)

LABORATORY TESTS

- Elevated but nonspecific ESR
- No specific laboratory tests to diagnose Reiter's syndrome

IMAGING STUDIES

Plain radiographs:

- Juxtaarticular osteopenia of affected joints
- Erosions and joint space narrowing in more advanced disease
- Periostitis and reactive new bone formation at the insertions of the Achilles tendon and the plantar fascia
- Sacroiliitis:
  1. Unilateral or bilateral
  2. Indistinguishable from ankylosing spondylitis
- Vertebral bridging osteophytes

TREATMENT

NONPHARMACOLOGIC THERAPY

Physical therapy to maintain range of motion of the back and other joints

ACUTE GENERAL Rx

Flares treated with NSAIDs such as indomethacin (25 to 50 mg PO tid)

- Enteric or urethral infection should be treated with appropriate antibiotic coverage.
- Uveitis should be treated with steroid eye drops in consultation with an ophthalmologist.
- Achilles tendinitis and plantar fasciitis should be treated with injections of methylprednisolone (40 to 80 mg).
- Sulfasalazine (2 to 3 g PO tid) may be effective.
- Careful monitoring for the following is essential:
  1. GI toxicity
  2. Hypersensitivity
  3. Bone marrow suppression
- Persistent and uncontrolled disease should be managed with cytotoxic drugs (methotrexate, azathioprine) in consultation with a rheumatologist.

CHRONIC Rx

Chronic disease is best managed by a team approach with the collaboration of a rheumatologist or other experienced physician and physical therapist.

DISPOSITION

- Recurrences are frequent, even with treatment.
- Long-term sequelae:
  1. Persistent polyarthritis
  2. Chronic back pain
  3. Heel pain
  4. Progressive iridocyclitis
  5. Aortic regurgitation

REFERRAL

- To ophthalmologist if uveitis is suspected
- To rheumatologist if arthritis and tendinitis fail to improve rapidly after a course of NSAIDs

PEARLS & CONSIDERATIONS

COMMENTS

- Infection with HIV is associated with particularly severe cases of Reiter's syndrome.
- HIV testing is recommended, especially if risk factors such as unprotected sexual activity or IV drug use are identified.

SUGGESTED READING

Al-Arfaj A: Profile of Reiter's disease in Saudi Arabia, *Clin Exp Rheumatol* 19(2):184, 2001.

AUTHOR: **DEBORAH L. SHAPIRO, M.D.**

BASIC INFORMATION

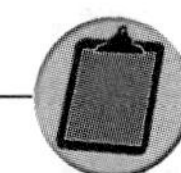

DEFINITION

Renal artery stenosis is the narrowing or occlusion of a renal artery, which can occur acutely (thrombosis or embolism) and cause renal infarction or progressively (e.g., atheroma or fibromuscular dysphasia) and cause renovascular hypertension and/or lead to ischemic nephropathy. In addition, renal atheroembolism caused by showers of cholesterol microemboli can lead to progressive renal failure if sustained or recurrent.

SYNONYMS

Acute:
Renal artery thrombosis
Renal artery embolism
Chronic:
Renovascular hypertension

ICD-9CM CODES
593.81 Renal artery occlusion
440.1 Renal artery stenosis
405.01 Renovascular hypertension, secondary
447.9 Renal artery hyperplasia

EPIDEMIOLOGY & DEMOGRAPHICS

- In acute renal artery occlusion, the epidemiology depends on the underlying cause (see below).
- Renovascular hypertension:

Prevalence of 0.2% to 5% of all hypertensive patients.

The prevalence is higher in patients with severe hypertension, reaching 43% of white patients and 7% of black patients with malignant hypertension.

- Approximately 1 in 6 patients with end-stage renal disease has ischemic nephropathy, and survival of patients with end-stage renal disease associated with ischemic nephropathy is half that of patients with end-stage renal disease from other causes.
- The demographics of atheromatous renal artery stenosis mirrors the pattern seen in other arteriosclerotic conditions (coronary artery disease, cerebrovascular disease, peripheral vascular disease) and is influenced by the usual risk factors (smoking, family history, diabetes, hyperlipidemia). For example, the prevalence of renal artery stenosis among hypertensive patients undergoing coronary catheterization is high (47%), with 19% having a stenosis of 50% or more. Fibromuscular dysplasia is most likely to be seen in young adult women. Takayasu's arteritis can involve the renal arteries and is also seen in young to middle-aged women.

PHYSICAL FINDINGS & CLINICAL PRESENTATION

Acute renal artery occlusion
- Flank or abdominal pain
- Fever
- Nausea or vomiting
- Leukocytosis
- Hematuria (microscopic or gross)
- Elevated AST, LDH, and alkaline phosphatase
- Oliguric renal failure if occlusion is bilateral; normal or near normal renal function in unilateral occlusion

Cholesterol emboli
- Multisystem manifestations resembling vasculitis (visual disturbance, painful distal extremities, abdominal pain, signs of organ or limb ischemia). Laboratory findings include eosinophiluria, proteinuria, renal failure, elevated ESR.

Progressive renal artery stenosis
- Hypertension in a young, white woman without a family history of such (fibromuscular dysplasia)
- Hypertension in a middle-aged man with other evidence of atheromatous disease
- Abdominal bruit (40% of cases)
- Renal failure
- Hypertensive retinopathy
- Pulmonary edema in a hypertensive patient
- Hypokalemia
- Renal failure following the administration of an angiotensin-converting enzyme inhibitor (if bilateral renal artery stenosis)

ETIOLOGY & PATHOGENESIS

Etiology of renal artery thrombosis
- Atherosclerosis
- Fibromuscular dysphasia
- Arteritis
- Aneurysm
- Arteriography
- Syphilis
- Hypercoagulable state
- Complication of renal transplantation (role of cyclosporine)

Etiology of renal artery embolism (cardiac conditions [90%])
- Myocardial infarction
- Atrial fibrillation
- Cardiomyopathy
- Endocarditis
- Paradoxical emboli from DVT in patient with cardiac septal defect
- Atheromatous plaques (cholesterol emboli)

PATHOGENESIS: Renal hypoperfusion or ischemia produces an increase in plasma renin that stimulates the conversion of angiotensin I to angiotensin II, causing vasoconstriction and aldosterone secretion, sodium retention, and potassium wasting. Hypertension results and can be self-sustaining after some time, even in the case of unilateral renal artery stenosis because of hypertensive damage to the other kidney.

DIAGNOSIS

WORKUP

- Documentation of hypertension
- Hypertensive workup (see "Hypertension" in Section I)

LABORATORY TESTS

- Creatinine
- Potassium level
- Urinalysis
- Peripheral plasma renin activity
- Captopril test (stimulation of excessive renin secretion)

IMAGING STUDIES

- Renal scan (70% sensitivity and 79% specificity)
- Captopril renal scan (92% sensitivity and 93% specificity)
- Hypertensive IVP (75% sensitivity and 85% specificity)
- Intravenous digital substraction angiography (88% sensitivity and 90% specificity)
- Magnetic resonance angiography
- Exercise renal scan (still being evaluated)
- Renal artery ultrasound (still being evaluated)

INVASIVE STUDIES

- Renal arteriography
- Selective renal vein renin measurements
- Renal biopsy for cholesterol emboli

TREATMENT

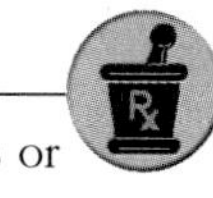

Acute renal artery thrombosis or embolism
- Thrombolytic therapy
- Anticoagulation
- Revascularization (surgery)
- Blood pressure control

Cholesterol emboli
- No treatment

Renal artery stenosis
- Blood pressure control (role of ACE inhibitors and angiotensin receptor blockers is controversial, but neither should be continued if renal function worsens)
- Angioplasty or revascularization should be reserved for patients whose blood pressure control with medication is difficult and for patients with progressive renal failure

NATURAL HISTORY

- Renal artery stenosis caused by fibromuscular dysplasia does not progress.
- Renal artery stenosis associated with atherosclerosis is progressive. Of patients with >60% stenosis, 5% progress to total occlusion in 1 yr and 11% progress in 2 yr.

SUGGESTED READINGS

Higashi Y et al: Endothelial function and oxidative stress in renovascular hypertension, *N Engl J Med* 346:1954, 2002.

Rihal CS et al: Incidental renal artery stenosis among a prospective cohort of hypertensive patients undergoing coronary angiography, *Mayo Clin Proc* 77:309, 2002.

AUTHOR: **TOM J. WACHTEL, M.D.**

Renal Cell Adenocarcinoma (PTG)

BASIC INFORMATION

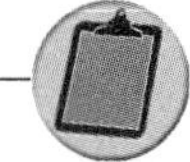

DEFINITION

Renal cell adenocarcinoma (RCA) is a primary adenocarcinoma originating in the renal parenchyma from the malignant transformation of proximal renal tubular epithelial cells.

SYNONYMS

Hypernephroma
Clear cell carcinoma of the kidney
Grawitz tumor

ICD-9CM CODES
189.0 Adenocarcinoma of kidney
189.1 (Renal pelvis)

EPIDEMIOLOGY & DEMOGRAPHICS

INCIDENCE: Approximately 1:10,000 persons/yr (3% of all adult malignancies)
AGE: Peak in age 50 to 70 yr
SEX: Male:female ratio of 2:1

PHYSICAL FINDINGS & CLINICAL PRESENTATION

Presenting findings in RCA patients:

Hematuria	50% to 60%
Elevated erythrocyte sedimentation rate	50% to 60%
Abdominal mass	25% to 45%
Anemia	20% to 40%
Flank pain	35% to 40%
Hypertension	20% to 40%
Weight loss	30% to 35%
Fever	5% to 15%
Hepatic dysfunction	10% to 15%
Classic triad (hematuria, abdominal mass, flank pain)	5% to 10%
Hypercalcemia	3% to 6%
Erythrocytosis	3% to 4%
Varicocele	2% to 3%

ETIOLOGY

Hereditary forms
- Familial renal carcinoma
- Renal carcinoma associated with von Hippel-Lindau disease
- Hereditary papillary renal cell carcinoma

Risk factors
- Cigarette smoking
- Obesity
- Use of diuretics
- Phenacetin-containing analgesics
- Asbestos exposure
- Gasoline and other petroleum products
- Lead
- Cadmium
- Thorotrast
- Role of the VHL gene located on chromosome 3

DIAGNOSIS

DIFFERENTIAL DIAGNOSIS

- Transitional cell carcinomas of the renal pelvis (8% of all renal cancers)
- Wilms' tumor
- Other rare primary renal carcinomas and sarcomas
- Renal cysts
- All causes of hematuria (see Section II)
- Retroperitoneal tumors

WORKUP

- Laboratory tests and imaging studies
- Section III, Renal Mass, describes the patients evaluation.

LABORATORY TESTS

- CBC: anemia or erythrocytosis
- Elevated sedimentation rate
- Nonmetastatic hepatic dysfunction with elevated alkaline phosphatase, prolonged prothrombin time, and hypoalbuminemia
- Hypercalcemia (secondary to parathyroid related protein)
- Other: elevated ferritin, elevated insulin and glucagon levels, elevated alpha-fetoprotein, and elevated beta-human chorionic gonadotropin

IMAGING STUDIES

- Intravenous pyelography (IVP)
- Renal ultrasound
- Abdominal CT scan with contrast (Fig. 1-198)
- MRI
- Renal arteriogram

STAGING

See Table 1-43.

COMMON SITES OF METASTASES

Lung	50% to 60%
Bone	30% to 40%
Regional nodes	15% to 30%
Main renal vein	15% to 20%
Perirenal fat	10% to 20%
Adrenal (ipsilateral)	10% to 15%
Vena cava	10% to 15%
Brain	10% to 15%
Adjacent organs (colon, pancreas)	10%
Kidney (contralateral)	2%

TREATMENT

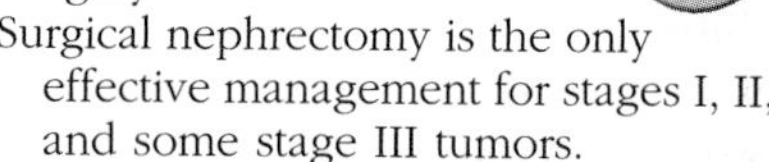

- Surgery
  Surgical nephrectomy is the only effective management for stages I, II, and some stage III tumors.
  Various forms of partial nephrectomy may be available for patients with bilateral cancers or with a solitary kidney.
  The role of nephrectomy in patients with metastatic renal cell carcinoma is controversial and should probably be reserved for patients who have a solitary metastasis amenable to surgical resection.
- Angioinfarction (for palliation)
- Radiotherapy (for palliation)
- Chemotherapy (only 5% response rate)
- Hormonal therapy (high-dose progesterone may achieve a 15% to 20% response rate)

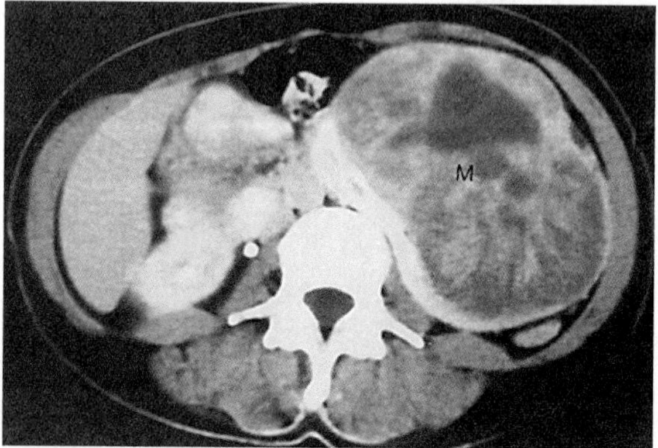

FIGURE 1-198 Large renal cell carcinoma. Large mass *(M)* containing areas of high enhancement, low enhancement, and necrosis. (From Stein JH [ed]: *Internal medicine*, ed 5, St Louis, 1998, Mosby.)

- Immunotherapy (interleukin-2 may achieve a 15% to 30% response rate; alpha, beta, and gamma interferons are somewhat less effective; for example, interferon alfa-2b increased postnephrectomy median survival by 30% in one recent trial)
- Antivascular endothelial growth factor antibody Bevacizumab slows disease progression in metastatic renal cancer.

PROGNOSIS

Prognosis of surgically treated patients

TNM stage	5-year survival (%)
I	95
II	88
III (renal vein or vena cava)	50 to 60
III (nodal involvement)	15 to 25
IV	5 to 20

REFERRAL

To urologist

SUGGESTED READINGS

Curti BD: Renal cell carcinoma, *JAMA* 292:97, 2004.

Flanigan RC et al: Nephrectomy followed by interferon alfa-2b compared with interferon alfa-2b alone for metastatic renal-cell cancer, *N Engl J Med* 345:1655, 2002.

Jennings SB, Linehan WM: Renal, perirenal, and ureteral neoplasms. In Gillenwater JY et al: *Adult and pediatric urology,* ed 3, St Louis, 1996, Mosby.

Yang CJ: A randomized trial of Bevacizumab, an anti-vascular endothelial growth factor antibody, for metastatic renal cancer, *N Engl J Med* 349:427, 2003.

AUTHOR: **TOM J. WACHTEL, M.D.**

TABLE 1-43 **Comparison of Conventional and TNM Staging Classification of RCC**

Robson Stage	T	N	M
I: Tumor confined by capsule	T_1 (tumor 2.5 cm or less)		
	T_2 (tumor >2.5 cm, limited to kidney)		
II: Tumor extension to perirenal fat or ipsilateral adrenal but confined by Gerota's fascia	T_3a (tumor invades adrenal gland or perinephric fat but not beyond Gerota's fascia)		
IIIa: Renal vein or inferior vena caval involvement	T_3b (renal vein or caval involvement below diaphragm)	N_0 (nodes negative)	M_0 (no distant metastases)
	T_3c (caval involvement above diaphragm)		
IIIb: Lymphatic involvement	T_{1-4}	N_1 (single lymph node 2 cm or less)	
		N_2 (single node between 2 and 5 cm, or multiple nodes <5 cm)	
		N3 (single or multiple nodes >5 cm)	
IIIc: Combination of IIIa and IIIb	$T_{3,4}$		
IVa: Spread to contiguous organs except ipsilateral adrenal	T_4 (tumor extends beyond Gerota's fascia)		
IVb: Distant metastases	T_{1-4}		M_1 (distant metastases)

BASIC INFORMATION

DEFINITION

Acute renal failure (ARF) is the rapid impairment in renal function resulting in retention of products in the blood that are normally excreted by the kidneys.

SYNONYMS

ARF

ICD-9CM CODES
584.9 Acute renal failure, unspecified

EPIDEMIOLOGY & DEMOGRAPHICS

- ARF requiring dialysis develops in 5/100,000 persons annually.
- >10% of ICU patients develop ARF.
- >40% of hospital ARF is iatrogenic.
- The most common cause of ARF in hospitalized patients is intrinsic renal failure caused by acute tubular necrosis (ATN).
- Acute renal failure occurs in 20% of patients with moderate sepsis and over 50% of patients with septic shock and positive blood cultures.

PHYSICAL FINDINGS & CLINICAL PRESENTATION

- The physical examination should focus on volume status. The physical findings noted below vary with the duration and rapidity of onset of renal failure
- Peripheral edema
- Skin pallor, ecchymoses
- Oliguria (however, patients can have nonoliguric renal failure), anuria
- Delirium, lethargy, myoclonus, seizures
- Back pain, fasciculations, muscle cramps
- Tachypnea, tachycardia
- Weakness, anorexia, generalized malaise, nausea

ETIOLOGY

- Prerenal: inadequate perfusion caused by hypovolemia, CHF, cirrhosis, sepsis. Sixty percent of community-acquired cases of ARF are due to prerenal conditions.
- Postrenal: outlet obstruction from prostatic enlargement, ureteral obstruction (stones), bilateral renal vein occlusion. Postrenal causes account for 5% to 15% of community-acquired ARF.
- Intrinsic renal: glomerulonephritis, acute tubular necrosis, drug toxicity, contrast nephropathy.
- Causes of acute renal failure are described in Section II.

DIAGNOSIS

DIFFERENTIAL DIAGNOSIS

Refer to "Etiology."

WORKUP

A thorough review of the patient's history is necessary to identify contributing factors (e.g., nephrotoxin exposure, hypertension, diabetes mellitus). Laboratory evaluation to quantify degree of abnormality; radiographic studies to exclude prerenal and postrenal factors. Categorization of renal failure into oliguric (urinary output <400 ml/day) or nonoliguric is important. Anuria is common in obstructive uropathy and acute cortical necrosis.

LABORATORY TESTS

- Elevated serum creatinine: the rate of rise of creatinine is approximately 1 mg/dl/day in complete renal failure.
- Elevated BUN: BUN/creatinine ratio is >20:1 in prerenal azotemia, postrenal azotemia, and acute glomerulonephritis; it is <20:1 in acute interstitial nephritis and acute tubular necrosis (Table 1-44).
- Electrolytes (potassium, phosphate) are elevated; bicarbonate level and calcium are decreased.
- CBC may reveal anemia because of decreased erythropoietin production, hemoconcentration, or hemolysis.
- Urinalysis may reveal the presence of hematuria (GN), proteinuria (nephrotic syndrome), casts (e.g., granular casts in ATN, RBC casts in acute GN, WBC casts in acute interstitial nephritis), eosinophiluria (acute interstitial nephritis).
- Urinary sodium and urinary creatinine should also be obtained to calculate the fractional excretion of sodium (FE_{Na}) (FE_{Na} = Urine sodium/plasma sodium × Plasma creatinine/urine creatinine × 100). The fractional excretion of sodium is <1 in prerenal failure, >1 in intrinsic renal failure in patients with urine output <400 ml/day.
- Urinary osmolarity is 250 to 300 mOsm/kg in ATN, <400 mOsm/kg in postrenal azotemia, and >500 mOsm/kg in prerenal azotemia and acute glomerulonephritis (Table 1-45).
- Additional useful studies are blood cultures for patients suspected of sepsis, LFTs, immunoglobulins, and protein electrophoresis in patients sus-

TABLE 1-44 Serum and Radiographic Abnormalities in Renal Failure

	Prerenal	Postrenal (Acute)	Intrinsic Renal (Acute)	Intrinsic Renal (Chronic)
BUN	↑10:1 > Cr	↑ 20-40/d	↑ 20-40/d	Stable, ↑ varies with protein intake
Serum creatinine	N/moderate ↑	↑ 2-4/d	↑ 2-4/d	Stable ↑ (production equals excretion)
Serum potassium	N/moderate ↑	↑ varies with urinary volume	↑↑ (particularly when patient is oliguric) ↑↑↑ with rhabdomyolysis	Normal until end stage, unless tubular dysfunction (type 4 RTA)
Serum phosphorus	N/moderate ↑	Moderate ↑ ↑↑ with rhabdomyolysis	↑ Poor correlation with duration of renal disease	Becomes significantly elevated when serum creatinine level surpasses 3 mg/dl
Serum calcium	N	N/↓ with PO_4^{-3} retention	↓ (poor correlation with duration of renal failure)	Usually ↓
Renal size				
By ultrasound	N/↑	↑ and dilated calyces	N/↑	↓ and with ↑ echogenicity
FE_{Na}*	<1	<1 → 1	>1	>1

From Kiss B: Renal failure. In Ferri FF (ed): *Practical guide to the care of the medical patient,* ed 6, St Louis, 2004, Mosby.
↑, Increase; ↓, decrease; ↑↑, large increase, *Cr,* creatinine; *N,* normal; *Na,* sodium; *P,* plasma; *RTA,* renal tubular acidosis; *U,* urine.
*$FE_{Na} = U_{Na}/P_{Na}U_{Cr}/P_{cr} \times 100$.

pected of myeloma, creatinine kinase in patients with suspected rhabdomyolysis.
- Renal biopsy may be indicated in patients with intrinsic renal failure when considering specific therapy; major uses of renal biopsy are differential diagnosis of nephrotic syndrome, separation of lupus vasculitis from other vasculitis and lupus membranous from idiopathic membranous, confirmation of hereditary nephropathies on the basis of the ultrastructure, diagnosis of rapidly progressing glomerulonephritis, separation of allergic interstitial nephritis from ATN, separation of primary glomerulonephritis syndromes. The biopsy may be performed percutaneously or by open method. The percutaneous approach is favored and generally yields adequate tissue in >90% of cases. Open biopsy is generally reserved for uncooperative patients, those with solitary kidney, and patients at risk for uncontrolled bleeding.

IMAGING STUDIES

- Chest x-ray is useful to evaluate for CHF and for pulmonary renal syndromes (Goodpasture's syndrome, Wegener's granulomatosis).
- Ultrasound of kidneys is used to evaluate for kidney size (useful to distinguish ARF from CRF), to evaluate for the presence of obstruction, and to evaluate renal vascular status (with Doppler evaluation).
- Anterograde and/or retrograde pyelogram can be used for ruling out obstruction; useful in patients at high risk of obstruction.

TREATMENT

NONPHARMACOLOGIC THERAPY

- Stop all nephrotoxic medications
- Dietary modification to supply adequate calories while minimizing accumulation of toxins; appropriate control of fluid balance. Physicians should recommend a nutrition program with an energy prescription of 120 to 150 KJ/kg per day and restriction of potassium (60 mEq/day), sodium (90 mEq/day), and phosphorus (800 mg/day). Ideal protein supplementation ranges from 0.6 to 1.4 g/kg depending on whether dialysis is required
- Daily weight
- Modifications of dosage of renally excreted drugs

ACUTE GENERAL Rx

Treatment is variable with etiology of ARF:
- Prerenal: IV volume expansion in hypovolemic patients
- Intrinsic renal: discontinuation of any potential toxins and treatment of condition causing the renal failure
- Postrenal: removal of obstruction

CHRONIC Rx

- Monitoring of renal function and electrolytes.
- Prevention of further insults to the kidneys with proper hydration, especially before contrast studies, and avoidance of nephrotoxic agents. Hydration with sodium bicarbonate (addition of 154 ml of 1000 mEq/L sodium bicarbonate to 846 mL of 5% dextrose in water) before contrast exposure is more effective than hydration with sodium chloride for prophylaxis of contrast-induced renal failure. After appropriate clinical evaluation and measurement of blood pressure, patients should receive an initial IV bolus of 3 mL/kg/hr for 1 hr immediately before radiocontrast injection and the same fluid at a rate of 1 mL/kg/hr during the contrast exposure and for 6 hr after the procedure.
- Refer to topic on chronic renal failure for indications for initiation of dialysis. Daily hemodialysis is superior to every-other-day hemodialysis in patients with acute tubular necrosis and ARF.

DISPOSITION

- Prognosis is variable depending on the etiology of the renal failure, degree of renal failure, multiorgan involvement, and patient's age.
- Renal function recovery (ability to discontinue dialysis) varies from 50% to 75% in survivors of ARF.

TABLE 1-45 **Urinary Abnormalities in Renal Failure**

	Prerenal	Postrenal (Acute)	Intrinsic Renal (Acute)	Intrinsic Renal (Chronic)
Urinary volume	↓	Absent-to-wide fluctuation	Oliguric or nonoliguric	1000 ml + until end stage
Urinary creatinine	↑ (U/P Cr ±40)	↓ (U/P Cr ±20)	↓ (U/P Cr <20)	↓ (U/P Cr <20)
Osmolarity	↑ (±400 mOsm/kg)	(<350 mOsm/kg)	(<350 mOsm/kg)	(<350 mOsm/kg)
Degree of proteinuria	Minimum	Absent	Varies with cause of renal failure: Modest with ATN; Nephrotic range common with acute glomerulopathies, usually <2 g/24 hr with interstitial disease*	Varies with cause of renal disease (from 1-2 g/d to nephrotic range)
Urinary sediment	Negative, or occasional hyaline cast	Negative or hematuria with stones or papillary necrosis; Pyuria with infectious prostatic disease	ATN: muddy brown; Interstitial nephritis: lymphocytes, eosinophils (in stained preparations), and WBC casts; RPGN: RBC casts; Nephrosis: oval fat bodies	Broad casts with variable renal "residual" acute findings

From Kiss B: Renal failure. In Ferri FF (ed): *Practical guide to the care of the medical patient,* ed 6, St Louis, 2004, Mosby.

↑, Increased; ↓, decreased; *ATN,* acute tubular necrosis; clearance = $\frac{\text{Urinary concentration} \times \text{Urinary volume}}{\text{Plasma concentration}}$ *Cr,* creatinine; *RBC,* red blood cell; *RPGN,* rapidly progressive glomerulonephritis; *U/P,* urine/plasma; *WBC,* white blood cell.

- Overall mortality rate in ARF is nearly 50%, varying from 60% in patients with ATN to 35% in patients with prerenal or postrenal ARF.
- The combination of acute renal failure and sepsis is associated with a 70% mortality rate.

REFERRAL

- Nephrology consultation is recommended in renal failure.
- General indications for initiation of dialysis are:
  1. Florid symptoms of uremia (encephalopathy, pericarditis)
  2. Severe volume overload
  3. Severe acid-base imbalance
  4. Significant derangement in electrolyte concentrations (e.g., hyperkalemia, hyponatremia)
- Surgical consult may be necessary in patients with obstruction.

PEARLS & CONSIDERATIONS

COMMENTS

- It is important for physicians to recognize the growing list of medications that can result in ARF.

SUGGESTED READINGS

Albright RC: Acute renal failure: a practical update, *Mayo Clin Proc* 76:67, 2001.

Kellum JA, Decker JM: Use of dopamine in acute renal failure: a meta analysis, *Crit Care Med* 29:1526, 2001.

Klassen PS et al: Association between pulse pressure and mortality in patients undergoing maintenance hemodialysis, *JAMA* 287: 1548, 2002.

Merten GJ et al: Prevention of contrast-induced nephropathy with sodium bicarbonate, *JAMA* 291:2328, 2004.

Nally JV: Acute renal failure in hospitalized patients, *Cleve Clin J Med* 69:569, 2002.

Schiffel H et al: Daily hemodialysis and the outcome of acute renal failure, *N Engl J Med* 346:305, 2002.

Schrier RW, Wang W: Acute renal failure and sepsis, *N Engl J Med* 351:159, 2004.

AUTHOR: **FRED F. FERRI, M.D.**

BASIC INFORMATION

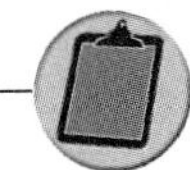

DEFINITION

Chronic renal failure (CRF) is a progressive decrease in renal function (CFR <60 ml/min for ≥3 mo) with subsequent accumulation of waste products in the blood, electrolyte abnormalities, and anemia.

SYNONYMS

CRF
End-stage renal disease

ICD-9CM CODES

585 Chronic renal failure

EPIDEMIOLOGY & DEMOGRAPHICS

- The number of patients with ESRD is increasing at the rate of 7% to 9%/yr in the U.S. Each year 2/10,000 persons develop end-stage CRF.
- In the U.S., >250,000/yr receive dialysis treatment for ESRD.

PHYSICAL FINDINGS & CLINICAL PRESENTATION

- Skin pallor, ecchymoses
- Edema
- Hypertension
- Emotional lability and depression
- The clinical presentation varies with the degree of renal failure and its underlying etiology. Common symptoms are generalized fatigue, nausea, anorexia, pruritus, insomnia, taste disturbances

ETIOLOGY

- Diabetes (37%), hypertension (30%), chronic glomerulonephritis (12%)
- Polycystic kidney disease
- Tubular interstitial nephritis (e.g., drug hypersensitivity, analgesic nephropathy), obstructive nephropathies (e.g., nephrolithiasis, prostatic disease)
- Vascular diseases (renal artery stenosis, hypertensive nephrosclerosis)

DIAGNOSIS

- CRF is primarily distinguished from ARF by the duration (progression over several months).
- Sonographic evaluation of the kidneys reveals smaller kidneys with increased echogenicity in CRF.

WORKUP

- Laboratory evaluation and imaging studies should be aimed at identifying reversible causes of acute decrements in GFR (e.g., volume depletion, urinary tract obstruction, CHF) superimposed on chronic renal disease
- Kidney biopsy: generally not performed in patients with small kidneys or with advanced disease
- The glomerular filtration rate is the best overall indicator of kidney function. It can be estimated using prediction equations that take into account the serum creatinine level and some or all of specific variables (body size, age, sex, race). GFR calculators are available on the National Kidney Foundation Web site (http://www.kidney.org/kls/professionals/gfr_calculator.cfm)

LABORATORY TESTS

- Elevated BUN, creatinine, creatinine clearance
- Urinalysis: may reveal proteinuria, RBC casts
- Serum chemistry: elevated BUN and creatinine, hyperkalemia, hyperuricemia, hypocalcemia, hyperphosphatemia, hyperglycemia, decreased bicarbonate
- Measure urinary protein excretion. The finding of a ratio of protein to creatinine of >1000 mg/g suggests the presence of glomerular disease
- Special studies: serum and urine immunoelectrophoresis (in suspected multiple myeloma), ANA (in suspected SLE)

IMAGING STUDIES

Ultrasound of kidneys to measure kidney size and to rule out obstruction

TREATMENT

NONPHARMACOLOGIC THERAPY

- Provide adequate nutrition and calories (147 to 168 kJ/kg/day in energy intake, chiefly from carbohydrate and polyunsaturated fats). Referral to a dietician for nutritional therapy for patients with GFR <50 ml/1.73 m^2 is recommended and is now a covered service by Medicare.
- Restrict sodium (approximately 100 mmol/day), potassium (≤60 mmol/day), and phosphate (<800 mg/day).
- Adjust drug doses to correct for prolonged half-lives.
- Restrict fluid if significant edema is present.
- Protein restriction (≤0.8 g/kg/day) may slow deterioration of renal function; however, recent studies have not confirmed this benefit. There is insufficient evidence to recommend or advise against routine restriction of protein intake
- Resistance exercise training can preserve lean body mass, nutritional status, and muscle function in patients with moderate chronic kidney disease.
- Avoid radiocontrast agents.
- Smoking cessation.
- Initiate hemodialysis or peritoneal dialysis (see "Acute General Rx").
- Prompt to nephrologist is essential. Late evaluation of patients with chronic renal disease is associated with greater burden and severity of comorbid disease and shorter survival.
- Kidney transplantation in selected patients.

GENERAL Rx

- ACE inhibitors, ARBs, and nondihydropyridine calcium channel blockers (diltiazem or verapamil) are useful in reducing proteinuria and slowing the progression of chronic renal disease, especially in hypertensive diabetic patients. A systolic blood pressure between 110 and 129 mm Hg may be beneficial in patients with urine protein excretion >1.0 g/day. Systolic BP <110 mm Hg may be associated with a higher risk for kidney disease progression.
- Initiation of dialysis
  1. Urgent indications: uremic pericarditis, neuropathy, neuromuscular abnormalities, CHF, hyperkalemia, seizures.
  2. Judgmental indications: creatinine clearance 10 to 15 ml/min; progressive anorexia, weight loss, reversal of sleep pattern, pruritus, uncontrolled fluid gain with hypertension and signs of CHF.
- Erythropoietin for anemia: 2000 to 3000 U three times a week IV/SC to maintain Hct 30% to 33%.
- Diuretics for significant fluid overload (loop diuretics are preferred).
- Correction of hypertension to at least 130/85 mm Hg with ACE inhibitors (avoid in patients with significant hyperkalemia), ARBs, and/or nondihydropyridene calcium channel blockers (verapamil, diltiazem) can be used in patients intolerant to ACE inhibitors or when other agents are needed to control blood pressure.
- Correction of electrolyte abnormalities (e.g., calcium chloride, glucose, sodium polystyrene sulfonate for hyperkalemia), sodium bicarbonate in patients with severe metabolic acidosis.
- Lipid-lowering agents in patients with dyslipidemia, target LDL cholesterol is <100 mg/dl.

- Control of renal osteodystrophy with calcium supplementation and vitamin D. Starting dose of calcium carbonate is 0.5 g with each meal, increased until the serum phosphorus concentration is normalized (most patients require 5 to 10 g/day). Calcitriol 0.125 to 0.25 μg/day PO is effective in increasing serum calcium concentration. Paricalcitol, a new vitamin-D analogue has been reported as more effective than calcitriol in lessening the elevations in serum calcium and phosphorus levels.
- Sevelamer (Renagel) is a useful phosphate binder to reduce serum phosphate levels.

DISPOSITION

- Prognosis is influenced by comorbidity of multisystem diseases.
- Kidney transplantation in selected patients improves survival. The 2-yr kidney graft survival rate for living related donor transplantations is >80%, whereas the 2-yr graft survival rate for cadaveric donor transplantation is approximately 70%.

SUGGESTED READINGS

Jafar TH et al: Progression of chronic kidney disease: the role of blood pressure control, proteinuria, and angiotensin-converting enzyme inhibition, *Ann Intern Med* 139:244, 2003.

Johnson CA et al: Clinical practice guidelines for chronic kidney disease in adults, *Am Fam Physician* 70:869, 2004.

Kinchen KS et al: The timing of specialist evaluation in chronic kidney disease and mortality, *Ann Intern Med* 137:479, 2003.

Levey AS: Nondiabetic kidney disease, *N Engl J Med* 347:1505, 2002.

Lewey AS et al: National Kidney Foundation practice guidelines for chronic kidney disease: evaluation, classification, and stratification, *Ann Intern Med* 139:137, 2003.

Lewinsky NG: Specialist evaluation in chronic kidney disease: too little too late, *Ann Intern Med* 137:542, 2002.

Remuzzi G et al: Chronic renal diseases: renoprotective benefits of renin-angiotensin system inhibition, *Ann Intern Med* 136:604, 2002.

Yu HT: Progression of chronic renal failure, *Arch Intern Med* 163:1417, 2003.

AUTHOR: **FRED F. FERRI, M.D.**

BASIC INFORMATION

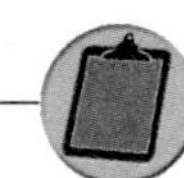

DEFINITION

Renal tubular acidosis (RTA) is a disorder characterized by inability to excrete H^+ or inadequate generation of new HCO_3^-. There are four types of renal tubular acidosis:

- Type I (classic, distal RTA): abnormality in distal hydrogen secretion resulting in hypokalemic hyperchloremic metabolic acidosis.
- Type II (proximal RTA): decreased proximal bicarbonate reabsorption resulting in hypokalemic hyperchloremic metabolic acidosis.
- Type III (RTA of glomerular insufficiency): normokalemic hyperchloremic metabolic acidosis as a result of impaired ability to generate sufficient NH_3 in the setting of decreased glomerular filtration rate (<30 ml/min). This type of RTA is described in older textbooks and is considered by many not to be a distinct entity.
- Type IV (hyporeninemic hypoaldosteronemic RTA): aldosterone deficiency or antagonism resulting in decreased distal acidification and decreased distal sodium reabsorption with subsequent hyperkalemic hyperchloremic acidosis.

SYNONYMS

RTA

ICD-9CM CODES
588.8 Renal tubular acidosis

EPIDEMIOLOGY & DEMOGRAPHICS

RTA type IV affects mostly adults, whereas RTA type I and II are more frequent in children.

PHYSICAL FINDINGS & CLINICAL PRESENTATION

- Examination may be normal.
- Poor skin turgor may be present from dehydration.
- Muscle weakness and muscle aches from hypokalemia may occur.
- Low back pain and bone pain may be present in patients with abnormalities of calcium metabolism (RTA II).
- There is failure to thrive in children (RTA II).

ETIOLOGY

- Type I RTA: primary biliary cirrhosis and other liver diseases, medications (amphotericin, nonsteroidals), SLE, Sjögren's syndrome
- Type II RTA: Fanconi's syndrome, primary hyperparathyroidism, multiple myeloma, medications (acetazolamide)
- Type IV RTA: diabetes mellitus, sickle cell disease, Addison's disease, urinary obstruction

DIAGNOSIS

DIFFERENTIAL DIAGNOSIS

- Diarrhea with significant bicarbonate loss
- Other causes of metabolic acidosis
- Respiratory acidosis

WORKUP

Detection of hyperchloremic metabolic acidosis with ABGs and serum electrolytes and evaluation of potential causes (see "Etiology")

LABORATORY TESTS

- ABGs reveal metabolic acidosis; serum potassium is low in RTA types I and II, normal in type III, and high in type IV.
- Minimal urine pH is >5.5 in RTA type I, <5.5 in types II, III, and IV.
- Urinary anion gap is 0 or positive in all types of RTA.
- Additional useful studies include serum calcium level and urine calcium.
- Anion gap is normal.
- PTH measurement is useful in patients suspected of primary hyperparathyroidism (may be associated with type II RTA).

IMAGING STUDIES

- Plain abdominal radiography is useful to evaluate for nephrocalcinosis
- Renal sonogram can be used to evaluate renal size or presence of stones
- IVP in patients with nephrocalcinosis or nephrolithiasis

TREATMENT

ACUTE GENERAL Rx

- Type I and type II are treated with oral sodium bicarbonate (1 to 2 mEq/kg/day in RTA 1, 2 to 4 mEq/kg/day in RTA type II) titrated to correct acidosis.
- Potassium supplementation is needed in hypokalemic patients.
- Type IV RTA can be treated with furosemide to lower elevated potassium levels and sodium bicarbonate to correct significant acidosis. Fludrocortisone 100 to 300 μg/day can be used to correct mineralocorticoid deficiency.

CHRONIC Rx

- Frequent monitoring of potassium levels in type IV RTA
- Monitoring for bone disease in RTA type II
- Monitoring for nephrocalcinosis and nephrolithiasis in RTA type I

DISPOSITION

- Prognosis varies with the presence of associated conditions (see "Etiology").
- Untreated distal RTA may result in hypercalcemia, hyperphosphaturia, nephrolithiasis, and nephrocalcinosis.

PEARLS & CONSIDERATIONS

COMMENTS

Patient education material can be obtained from the National Kidney and Urologic Diseases Information Clearinghouse, Box NKUDIC, Bethesda, MD 20893.

AUTHOR: **FRED F. FERRI, M.D.**

Renal Vein Thrombosis

BASIC INFORMATION

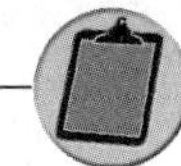

DEFINITION

Renal vein thrombosis is the thrombotic occlusion of one or both renal veins.

ICD-9CM CODES
453.3 Renal vein thrombosis

EPIDEMIOLOGY & DEMOGRAPHICS

- Incidence unknown, probably an underdiagnosed condition
- May occur at any age with no gender preference
- Epidemiology tied to the underlying cause

PHYSICAL FINDINGS & CLINICAL PRESENTATION

Acute bilateral renal vein thrombosis
- Back and bilateral flank pain
- Acute renal failure

Acute unilateral renal vein thrombosis
- Flank pain
- Decline in renal function
- Hematuria
- Increase in the amount of proteinuria if associated with nephrotic syndrome

Chronic unilateral renal vein thrombosis
- May be silent
- Pulmonary emboli and hemolysis
- Back pain
- DVT in lower extremities
- Edema
- Glycosuria
- Hyperchloremic acidosis
- Left varicocele (if the left renal vein is thrombosed)
- Dilated abdominal veins

ETIOLOGY & PATHOGENESIS

- Extrinsic compression by a tumor or retroperitoneal mass
- Invasion of the renal vein or inferior vena cava by tumor (almost always renal cell cancer)
- Trauma
- Hypercoagulable states
- Dehydration
- Glomerulopathies (membranous glomerulonephritis, crescenting glomerulonephritis, SLE, amyloidosis) especially in the presence of nephrotic syndrome when the serum albumin is lower than 2 g/dl
- NOTE: For unknown reasons, diabetic nephropathy is not commonly associated with renal vein thrombosis even if the nephrotic syndrome is present

A controversy has existed as to whether the renal vein thrombosis association with nephrotic syndrome is a complication of nephrotic syndrome or whether renal vein thrombosis occurring in the setting of increased renal vein pressure (e.g., with congestive heart failure, constrictive pericarditis, or extrinsic compression) can independently cause proteinuria. Current evidence is that renal vein thrombosis does not cause nephrotic syndrome.

DIAGNOSIS

DIFFERENTIAL DIAGNOSIS

The diagnosis of renal vein thrombosis does not include any differential consideration. The differential diagnosis is that of proteinuria. Renal vein thrombosis should be considered if proteinuria worsens or if renal function worsens in a patient with glomerulonephritis. Renal vein thrombosis should also be considered in patients with pulmonary emboli and no lower-extremity DVT.

WORKUP

Clinical suspicion (see "Differential Diagnosis") and imaging studies

IMAGING STUDIES

- Abdominal ultrasound
- Abdominal MRI
- Renal arteriography (delayed films during venous phase)
- Selective renal vein venography (inferior venacavogram images should be obtained before advancing the catheter in the vena cava because clots, if present, could be dislodged)
- Renal biopsy may be indicated if evidence of nephritis is present (e.g., active urinary sediment)

TREATMENT

- Anticoagulation in acute renal vein thrombosis to prevent pulmonary emboli and in attempt to improve renal function and decrease proteinuria
- Thrombolytic therapy or surgical thrombectomy has also been reported to be effective
- The value of anticoagulation in chronic renal vein thrombosis is dubious except in nephrotic patients with membranous glomerulonephritis with profound hypoalbuminemia where prolonged prophylactic anticoagulation may be of benefit even if renal vein thrombosis has not been documented

PROGNOSIS

Probable worsening of the underlying glomerulonephritis by acute renal vein thrombosis; the effect of chronic renal vein thrombosis is unclear.

SUGGESTED READING

Yudd M, Llach F: Renal vein thrombosis. In Brenner BM (ed): *The kidney,* ed 5, Philadelphia, 2000, WB Saunders.

AUTHOR: **TOM J. WACHTEL, M.D.**

BASIC INFORMATION

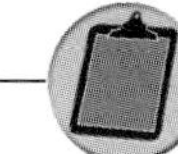

DEFINITION

Restless legs syndrome is a sensory-motor disorder with four cardinal features: (1) an uncomfortable sensation or urge to move the legs, (2) discomfort worse in the evening or night, (3) discomfort worse at rest, and (4) discomfort better with movement of the affected leg(s). There are two forms of RLS: primary (familial) and secondary (acquired). Most RLS sufferers (>85%) have periodic leg movements in sleep (PLMS), which also may disrupt sleep.

SYNONYMS

Restless limb syndrome
Growing pains
Night kicking
Night walker syndrome

ICD-9CM CODES
780.52-5 Restless legs syndrome

EPIDEMIOLOGY & DEMOGRAPHICS

PREVALENCE: 8% to 12%
DEMOGRAPHICS: Age 2 and up (youngest case—8 weeks old)
- <18: unknown.
- Age 18-29: 3%.
- Age 30-79: 10%.
- Age ≥80: 20%.
- Prevalence increases with age (likely because of increases in secondary RLS, which affects males and females equally).
- Symptoms may worsen with age and may spread to the arms.
- Prevalence data incomplete for ethnic or racial groups other than Caucasian.
- Primary RLS follows an autosomal-dominant mode of inheritance, shows genetic anticipation, and follows a female:male ratio of 6:4.

PHYSICAL FINDINGS & CLINICAL PRESENTATION

- Sensory complaints usually affecting one or both lower extremities during rest:
  1. "Worms" or "bugs" under the skin
  2. Sense of pressure under the skin
  3. Throbbing muscular ache or pain
  4. "Growing pains"
  5. Irresistible urge to move the symptomatic leg(s)
- Many other words used by patients to describe the leg symptoms: creeping, burning, searing, tugging, pulling, drawing, like water flowing, restless, and very often "indescribable."
- Temporary symptomatic relief or improvement with leg movement, rubbing, pressure, walking, or added warmth (bath or heating pad).
- Sleep disruption resulting from leg discomfort, PLMS, and urges to move or walk.
- Leg movements during sleep almost always occur and may be reported by a spouse or parent as kicking or constant movement during the night. These movements are stereotypic, and rhythmic ankle/leg shaking lasting <5 sec can cause arousals during sleep.
- Physical examination is normal in primary RLS, but may reveal subtle neuropathy, radiculopathy, or myelopathy in secondary RLS.
- Excessive daytime somnolence, insomnia, and occasional leg symptoms during the day while sedentary are common complaints.

ETIOLOGY

- One likely mechanism is related to dopaminergic dysregulation at the level of the spinal cord or higher in the central nervous system.
- Primary RLS (50%-60%).
- Secondary RLS associated with iron deficiency, pregnancy, renal failure, repetitive blood donation, neuropathy, radiculopathy, myelopathy, and rheumatologic conditions.
- Symptoms may be precipitated by medications (SSRIs and TCAs), caffeine, alcohol, and sleep deprivation.

DIAGNOSIS

DIFFERENTIAL DIAGNOSIS

- Periodic limb movement disorder (PLMD): repetitive limb movements (lower extremities > upper extremities) occurring during sleep; no sensory complaints or urges to move the limbs for comfort during periods of rest; associated with arousals in sleep and excessive daytime sleepiness; patient is typically unaware, but bed partner may report restlessness or kicking during sleep.
- Peripheral neuropathy, radiculopathy, myelopathy, or other CNS injury (i.e., stroke)
- Anxiety and mood disorders
- Narcolepsy
- REM behavior disorder
- Parasomnias (i.e., sleep-walking, confusional arousals, head-banging)
- Obstructive sleep apnea
- Iron deficiency
- Neuroleptic-induced akathisia
- Dyskinesias while awake
- Nocturnal leg cramps with or without peripheral arterial disease

WORKUP

- History is typically diagnostic, with sensitivity and specificity both >90%.
- Family history of RLS, growing pains, or "night walking."
- Polysomnography with arm and leg leads.
- Ambulatory recording of leg activity over several nights with sleep logs.
- Serum iron studies including TIBC, ferritin, and CBC.
- EMG for neuropathy, radiculopathy, or myelopathy, if suspected.
- Central nervous system MRI for myelopathy or stroke, if suspected.

TREATMENT

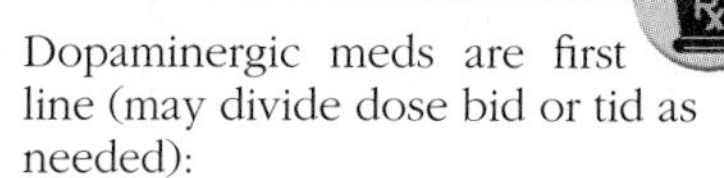

- Dopaminergic meds are first line (may divide dose bid or tid as needed):
  1. Requip (ropinirole): start 0.25 mg; avg dose 2 mg; max 12 mg/day.
  2. Mirapex (pramipexole): start 0.125 mg; avg dose 0.375 mg; max 5 mg/day.
  3. Permax (pergolide): start 0.05 mg; avg dose 0.5 mg; max 3 mg/day.
  4. Sinemet (levodopa/carbidopa): start 25/100; max 3-4 doses.
  5. Sinemet CR (continuous release): start 25/100; max 50/200.
- Antiepileptics:
  1. Neurontin (gabapentin): start 300mg; max 3600 mg/day.
  2. Carbatrol (carbamazepine): start 200 mg; max 1200 mg/day.
  3. Keppra (levetiracetam): start 250 mg; max 2000 mg/day.
  4. Topamax (topiramate): start 25 mg; max 200 mg/day.
- Opiates:
  1. Ultram (tramadol): start 25 mg; max 400 mg/day.
  2. Dilaudid (hydromorphone): start 2 mg; max 24 mg/day.
  3. Darvon (propoxyphene HCl): start 65 mg; max 195 mg/day.
  4. Oxycontin (oxycodone-XR): start 10 mg; max 30 mg/day.
  5. Roxicodone (oxycodone): start 5 mg; max 120 mg/day.
- Opiate/analgesic combinations:
  1. Vicodin/Lortab/ (hydrocodone/acetaminophen): start 5/500 mg; max 6 doses/day.
  2. Percocet (oxycodone/acetaminophen): start 10/325 mg; max 8 doses/day.
- Benzodiazepines:
  1. Restoril (temazepam): start 15 mg; max 30 mg/dose.
  2. Klonopin (clonazepam): start 0.25 mg; max 3 mg/dose.

SECTION I

- Iron supplementation:
  1. Hemocyte (oral ferrous fumarate): 324 mg qd (add vitamin C to enhance absorption)
  2. Iron sucrose or dextran (I.V. iron): follow published protocols

PROGNOSIS

Chronic and progressive

PEARLS & CONSIDERATIONS

- Up to 40% of adults with RLS report the onset of symptoms in childhood.
- In children with attention-deficit hyperactivity syndrome (ADHD), up to 40% may have undetected RLS and PLMS.
- Some patients may have more sensory symptoms than motor findings (PLMS) or vice versa.
- Short-acting dopamimetics (Sinemet) may cause symptoms to appear later at night or during the next day (augmentation). This may require additional doses or a change in medication.

SUGGESTED READINGS

Allen RP et al: Restless legs syndrome: diagnostic criteria, special considerations and epidemiology. A report from the restless legs syndrome diagnosis and epidemiology workshop at the National Institutes of Health, *Sleep Med* 4:101, 2003.

Allen RP, Earley CJ: Defining the phenotype of the restless legs syndrome (RLS) using age-of-symptom-onset, *Sleep Med* 1:11, 2000.

Earley CJ: Restless legs syndrome, *N Engl J Med* 348:2103, 2003.

Happe S, Trenkwalder C: Role of dopamine receptor agonists in the treatment of restless legs syndrome, *CNS Drugs* 18:27, 2004.

Phillips B et al: Epidemiology of restless legs symptoms in adults, *Arch Intern Med* 160:2137, 2000.

Walters AS et al: A questionnaire study of 138 patients with restless legs syndrome: the 'Night-Walkers' survey, *Neurology* 46:92, 1996.

Winkelmann J et al: Complex segregation analysis of restless legs syndrome provides evidence for an autosomal dominant mode of inheritance in early age at onset families, *Ann Neurol* 52:297, 2002.

AUTHOR: **J. S. DURMER, M.D., Ph.D.**

BASIC INFORMATION

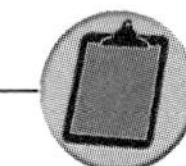

DEFINITION

Retinal detachment is a retinal separation where the inner or neural layer of the retina separates from the pigment epithelial layer and results from numerous causes.

SYNONYMS

Inflammatory lesions of choroid
Uveitis
Tumor
Vascular lesions
Congenital disorders

ICD-9CM CODES
361 Retinal detachment and defects

EPIDEMIOLOGY & DEMOGRAPHICS

INCIDENCE (IN U.S.):
- 0.02% of the population
- Particularly common in patients with high myopia of 5 diopters or more

PREVALENCE (IN U.S.): Busy ophthalmologist may see one or two acute retinal detachments per month
PREDOMINANT SEX: None
PREDOMINANT AGE:
- Congenital in younger patients
- Usually trauma in patients 30 to 40 yr and older
- High myopia a predisposition

PEAK INCIDENCE: Incidence increases with increasing age or increasing myopia.

PHYSICAL FINDINGS & CLINICAL PRESENTATION

Elevation of retina and vessels associated with tears in the retina, with fluid, and/or with hemorrhage beneath the retina and changes in the vitreous (Fig. 1-199).
Complaints of flashing lights and floaters

ETIOLOGY

- Trauma
- Tears in the retina
- Uveitis
- Fluid accumulation beneath the retina
- Tumors
- Scleritis
- Inflammatory disease
- Diabetes
- Collagen-vascular disease
- Vascular abnormalities

DIAGNOSIS

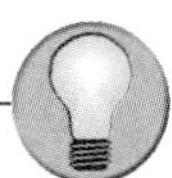

DIFFERENTIAL DIAGNOSIS

- Detachment
- Hemorrhage
- Tumors

WORKUP

- Full eye examination
- Fluorescein angiography
- Visual fields
- Ultrasonography to show the retinal detachment or tumors beneath it
- Medical workup only when inflammation or systemic disease considered

LABORATORY TESTS

Usually not necessary

IMAGING STUDIES

B scan of the eye

TREATMENT

NONPHARMACOLOGIC THERAPY

Immediate surgery

ACUTE GENERAL Rx

- Early surgery to repair the detachment
- Treatment of the underlying disorder

CHRONIC Rx

Occasionally, steroids or other treatment of underlying disease is indicated.

DISPOSITION

- Make an immediate referral to an ophthalmologist.
- Early intervention improves outcomes.

REFERRAL

Immediately

PEARLS & CONSIDERATIONS

COMMENTS

If treated early, most patients will recover a substantial portion of their vision.

SUGGESTED READINGS

Carpineto P et al: Retinal detachment prophylaxis, *Ophthalmology* 109(2):217, 2002.

Yazici B et al: Prediction of visual outcome after retinal detachment surgery using the Lotmar visometer, *Br J Ophthalmol* 86(3):278, 2002.

AUTHOR: **MELVYN KOBY, M.D.**

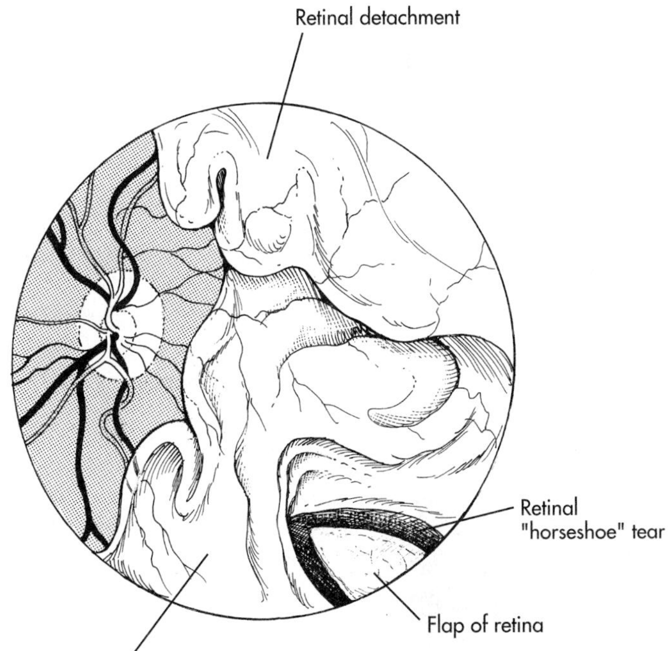

FIGURE 1-199 Retinal detachment. (From Scuderi G [ed]: *Sports medicine: principles of primary care,* St Louis, 1997, Mosby.)

BASIC INFORMATION

DEFINITION

In a retinal hemorrhage, blood accumulates in the retinal and subretinal areas as a result of multiple causes.

SYNONYMS

Pseudoxanthoma elasticum
Coats' disease
Retinal trauma
High-altitude retinopathy

ICD-9CM CODES
362.81 Retinal hemorrhage

EPIDEMIOLOGY & DEMOGRAPHICS

INCIDENCE (IN U.S.): Busy ophthalmologist sees one or two cases a month.
PREDOMINANT AGE: Degenerative disease in older patients
PEAK INCIDENCE:
- Children—associated primarily with trauma and hematologic disorders (must consider shaken baby syndrome)
- Associated with trauma, diabetes, vascular disease, macular degeneration, altitude changes (mountain climbing)

PHYSICAL FINDINGS & CLINICAL PRESENTATION

- Hemorrhage within the retina or subretinal area (Fig. 1-200)
- Evidence of retinal tears, tumors, and inflammation, macular degeneration, drugs, diabetes

ETIOLOGY

- Diabetes
- Hypertension
- Trauma
- Inflammation
- Tumors
- Subretinal neovascularization
- Associated with diabetes and aging
- Rapid changes in altitude (mountain climbing or scuba diving)

DIAGNOSIS

DIFFERENTIAL DIAGNOSIS

- Evaluate patients for local and systemic diseases.
- Trauma in children or adults.
- Either venous or arterial occlusion may cause retinal hemorrhage, and such occlusion is associated with atherosclerotic or heart disease, so look for these.
- Rule out malignant melanoma, trauma, hypertensive cardiovascular disease.

Section II describes the differential diagnosis of acute painless loss of vision. Look for systemic diseases and medication etiologies

WORKUP

Complete general physical examination, evaluate for trauma

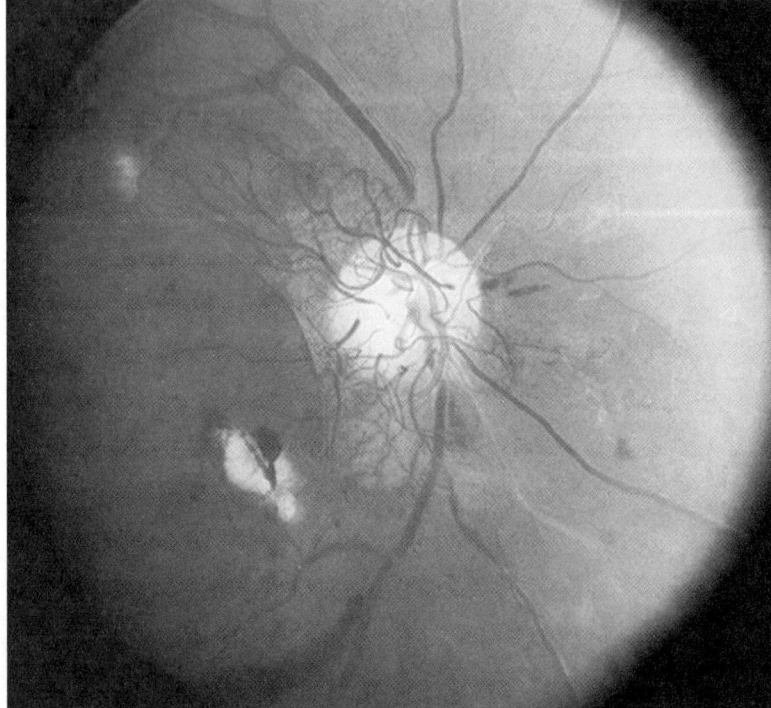

FIGURE 1-200 Fronds of neovascularization on the disc are present in this right eye. Temporally, two cotton-wool spots have adjacent intraretinal hemorrhage and preretinal hemorrhage. Native retinal arteries are narrowed and show evidence of sclerosis. (From Palay D [ed]: *Ophthalmology for the primary care physician,* St Louis, 1997, Mosby.)

LABORATORY TESTS

- Minimum: CBC, sedimentation rate, and complete blood chemistries
- Fluorescein
- Angiography
- Visual field testing

IMAGING STUDIES

- Usually not necessary
- Trauma—skull x-rays or head CT
- Ultrasound
- Fluorescein angiography

TREATMENT

NONPHARMACOLOGIC THERAPY

- Laser or treatment of underlying disorder
- Treat medical problems (ARMD, etc.)

ACUTE GENERAL Rx

- Laser is often indicated.
- Steroids may be indicated, with macular degeneration (intravitrial injection)
- Treat underlying disease.
- Repair damage if from trauma.

CHRONIC Rx

- Laser if hemorrhage is recurrent
- Vitamin therapy—high in zinc and antioxidants

DISPOSITION

Consider this an emergency.

REFERRAL

- Immediate referral to an ophthalmologist
- An emergency, with early treatment significantly affecting outcome

PEARLS & CONSIDERATIONS

COMMENTS

- Vision may return substantially.
- Complete recovery dependent on amount of scar tissue formed.
- Chronic situations have poor prognosis.

SUGGESTED READINGS

Duncan BB et al: Hypertensive retinopathy and incident coronary heart disease in high risk men, *Br J Ophth* 86(9):1002, 2002.

Gardner HB: Retinal hemorrhages in children, *Ophthalmology* 110(9):1863, 2003.

Lauritzen DB, Weiter JJ: Management of subretinal hemorrhage, *Int Ophthalmol Clin* 42(3):87, 2002.

Schloff S et al: Retinal findings in children with intracranial hemorrhage, *Ophthalmology* 109(8):1472, 2002.

AUTHOR: **MELVYN KOBY, M.D.**

BASIC INFORMATION

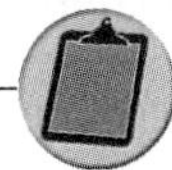

DEFINITION

Retinitis pigmentosa is a generalized retinal pigment degeneration associated with a variety of inheritance patterns resulting in decreased vision. A simple recessive pattern is most severe. It may be associated with some rare neurologic syndromes.

ICD-9CM CODES
362.74 Retinitis pigmentosa, pigmentary retinal dystrophy

EPIDEMIOLOGY & DEMOGRAPHICS

PREVALENCE (IN U.S.): 1 in 4000 people
PREDOMINANT SEX: Depends on inheritance
PREDOMINANT AGE: 60 yr
PEAK INCIDENCE:
- Recessive incidence: in the 20s
- Dominant form: in the 40s

GENETICS:
- 19% dominant
- 19% recessive
- 8% X-linked
- 46% not known to be genetically related (mutations)
- 8% undetermined cause

PHYSICAL FINDINGS & CLINICAL PRESENTATION

- Deposition of retinal pigment in midperiphery and centrally in the retina with a pale optic nerve and narrowing of blood vessels (Fig. 1-201)
- Possible cataracts and macular edema
- Decrease in night vision and peripheral vision

ETIOLOGY

Usually hereditary

DIAGNOSIS

DIFFERENTIAL DIAGNOSIS

- Syphilis
- Old inflammatory scars
- Old hemorrhage
- Diabetes
- Toxic retinopathies (phenothiazines, chloroquine)

WORKUP

- Electrophysiologic studies
- Dark adaptation studies
- Visual fields

LABORATORY TESTS

- Usually not necessary
- VDRL, glucose (selected patients)

IMAGING STUDIES

- Usually not necessary
- Rate of decline of vision for different groups cannot be accurately determined; decline rates are fastest with patients with mutations

TREATMENT

CHRONIC Rx

- No proven effective therapy
- Sometimes vitamin E or vitamin A may be helpful

DISPOSITION

Disease may be either mild or severe, but if the patient is expected to progress to total blindness, counseling and early education are important.

REFERRAL

To ophthalmologist to confirm diagnosis

PEARLS & CONSIDERATIONS

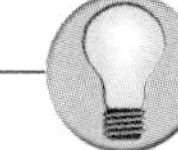

COMMENTS

- The spiderweb-like appearance of macular degeneration should not be confused with the extra pigments sometimes seen in dark-skinned individuals.
- Patient education material can be obtained from the Retinitis Pigmentosa Foundation Fighting Blindness, 1401 Mt. Royal Avenue, 4th Floor, Baltimore, MD 21217.
- Research in fetal retinal pigment transplantation and computer chip implantation are ongoing.

SUGGESTED READINGS

Berson E et al: Disease progression in patients with dominant retinitis pigmentosa and rhodopsin mutations, *Invest Ophthalmol Vis Sci* (43)9:3027, 2002.

Chow AY et al: The artificial silicon retina microchip for the treatment of vision loss from retinitis pigmentosa, *Arch Ophthalmol* 122(4):460, 2004.

Holopigiam K et al: Local cone and rod system function in patients with retinitis pigmentosa, *Invest Ophthal Vis Sci* 43(3):779, 2001.

Radtke ND et al: Vision change after sheet transplant of fetal retina with retinal pigment epithelium to a patient with retinitis pigmentosa, *Arch Ophthalmol* 122(8):1159, 2004.

AUTHOR: **MELVYN KOBY, M.D.**

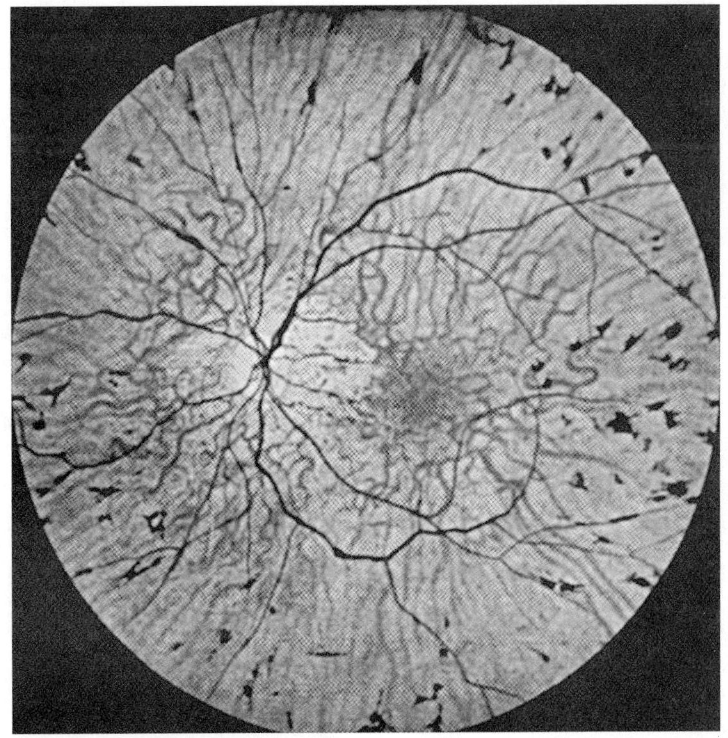

FIGURE 1-201 *Retinitis pigmentosa.* (From Behrman RE [ed]: *Nelson textbook of pediatrics,* Philadelphia, 1996, WB Saunders.)

 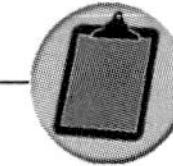

BASIC INFORMATION

DEFINITION

Retinoblastoma is an inherited, highly malignant congenital neoplasm arising from the neural layers of the retina.

ICD-9CM CODES
190.5 Retinoblastoma, malignant neoplasm of eyes, retina

EPIDEMIOLOGY & DEMOGRAPHICS

INCIDENCE (IN U.S.): 1 in every 23,000 to 34,000 births
PREDOMINANT AGE: 8 mo
PEAK INCIDENCE:
- 6 to 13 mo
- 72% diagnosed by 3 yr of age
- 90% diagnosed by 4 yr of age

GENETICS:
- Gene mutation or an autosomal dominant gene with 80% to 95% penetration
- 5% mutations

PHYSICAL FINDINGS & CLINICAL PRESENTATION

- White pupils (Fig. 1-202)
- White elevated retinal masses
- Strabismus
- Glaucoma
- Uveitis
- Vitrious masses and opacity

ETIOLOGY

Genetic

DIAGNOSIS

DIFFERENTIAL DIAGNOSIS

Examination of eye.
- Strabismus
- Retinal detachment
- Uveitis
- Other tumors
- Glaucoma
- Endophthalmitis
- Cataract
- Infectious

WORKUP

Ophthalmologic examination

IMAGING STUDIES

- MRI: may show calcifications in retina
- Ultrasonography: good delineation of mass

TREATMENT

NONPHARMACOLOGIC THERAPY

Treatment depends upon location and stage of tumor when diagnosed
- Enucleation of single eye
- External beam radiation
- Chemotherapy with local vitrious injections
- Radioactive plaque brachytherapy and cryotherapy
- Surgical enucleation of the eye
- Radiation and chemotherapy

DISPOSITION

Usually treated by an ophthalmologist/ oncologist

REFERRAL

To ophthalmologist/oncologist

PEARLS & CONSIDERATIONS

COMMENT

- With early aggressive treatment, many patients may survive.
- High incidence of second tumor in survivors compared to general population.
- High incidence of lung cancer, bladder, and other epithelial cancers.

SUGGESTED READINGS

Brichand B et al: Combined chemotherapy and local treatment in the management of intra ocular retinoblastoma, *Med Pediatr Oncol* 38(6):411, 2002.

Butros LJ et al: Delayed diagnosis of retinoblastoma analysis of degree, cause, and potential consequences, *Pediatric* 109(3):E45, 2002.

De Potter, P: Current treatment of retinoblastoma, *Curr Opin Ophthalmol* 13(5):331, 2002.

Lee V et al: Globe conserving treatment of the only eye in bilateral retinoblastoma, *Br J Ophthalmol* 87(11):1374, 2003.

Schouten-Van Meeteren AY et al: Overview: chemotherapy for retinoblastoma: an expanding area of clinical research, *Med Pediatr Oncol* 38(6):428, 2002.

Sussman DA et al: Comparison of retinoblastoma reduction for chemotherapy vs external beam radiotherapy, *Arch Ophthalmol* 121(7):979, 2003.

AUTHOR: **MELVYN KOBY, M.D.**

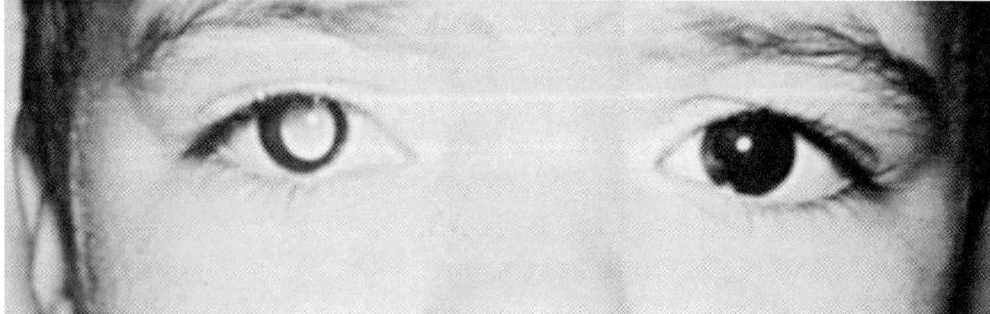

FIGURE 1-202 Leukocoria. White papillary reflex in a child with retinoblastoma. (From Behrman RE [ed]: *Nelson textbook of pediatrics,* Philadelphia, 1996, WB Saunders.)

BASIC INFORMATION

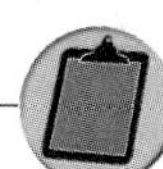

DEFINITION

Diabetic retinopathy is an eye abnormality of the retina associated with diabetes and consisting of microaneurysms, punctate hemorrhages, white and yellow exudates, flame hemorrhages, and neovascular vessel growth, and can ultimately end in blindness (Fig. 1-203).

SYNONYMS

NPDR—nonproliferative diabetic retinopathy
PDR—proliferative (advanced) diabetic retinopathy

ICD-9CM CODES
250.5 Diabetes with ophthalmic manifestations
362.1 Retinopathy, diabetic, background
362.02 Retinopathy, diabetic, proliferative

EPIDEMIOLOGY & DEMOGRAPHICS

INCIDENCE (IN U.S.):
- Affects 11 million persons
- A leading cause of blindness in people 20 to 70 yr old
- 5000 new cases annually

PREVALENCE (IN U.S.): Prevalence of retinopathy increases with duration of diabetes. Found in 18% of people diagnosed with diabetes for 3- to 4-yr duration and in up to 80% of diabetics with a diagnosis of 15 yr or more.

PREDOMINANT SEX: Male:female

PREDOMINANT AGE: 30 yr or older

PEAK INCIDENCE: Begins 10 yr after onset of diabetes

GENETICS: Diabetes is usually hereditary. Type I diabetes—80% have retinopathy before 30 yr old with 30% having vision-threatening retinopathy.

PHYSICAL FINDINGS & CLINICAL PRESENTATION

- See "Definition"
- Microaneurysms
- Hemorrhages
- Exudates
- Macular edema
- Neovascularization
- Retinal detachment
- Hemorrhages in the vitreous
- In early cases, patient may not complain of a visual disturbance

ETIOLOGY

Associated with diabetes mellitus

DIAGNOSIS

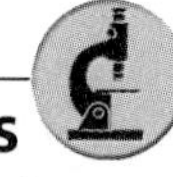

DIFFERENTIAL DIAGNOSIS

- Retinal exam—look for background retinopathy, microaneurysms, exudate, macular edema, retinal hemorrhage, proliferative neovascular growth on surface of retina
- Retinal inflammatory diseases
- Tumor
- Trauma
- Arteriosclerotic vascular disease
- Hypertension
- Vein or artery occlusion

WORKUP

- Fluorescein angiogram
- Frequent retinal examinations

LABORATORY TESTS

Those appropriate for diabetes mellitus

TREATMENT

NONPHARMACOLOGIC THERAPY

- Good control of diabetes, blood pressure, and other medical problems
- Laser Rx when indicated
- Laser treatment with proliferative disease or macular edema
- Photo coagulation of neovascular areas
- Exercise, diet, sugar control, and blood pressure control can slow down progression of background retinopathy, but has no effect on proliferative retinopathy

ACUTE GENERAL Rx

- Laser therapy
- Vitrectomy
- Repair of retinal detachment
- Medical control of disease and complications and associated diseases (hypertension, etc.)

CHRONIC Rx

- Repeated laser treatments may be necessary.
- Diet and exercise. Good control of disease medically.

DISPOSITION

- Retinal examination should be performed on all routine medical visits. Referral if abnormality seen.
- Routine annual eye examination in all patients with diabetes.
- Prognosis is improved with early diagnosis and treatment.

REFERRAL

Refer to ophthalmologist immediately on finding retinal abnormality to institute early treatment.

PEARLS & CONSIDERATIONS

COMMENTS

- Early laser treatment of severe, nonproliferative, and proliferative retinopathy may minimize complications and visual loss.
- Patient education information can be obtained from the American Academy of Ophthalmology (655 Beach Street, San Francisco, CA 94109-1336) and from the American Diabetes Association (1-800-232-3472).

SUGGESTED READINGS

Aiello LP et al: Systemic considerations in the management of diabetic retinopathy, *Am J Ophthal* 131(5):760, 2001.

Klein R et al: The association of atherosclerosis, vascular risk factors, and retinopathy in adults with diabetes, *Ophthalmology* 109(7):1225, 2002.

Raman V et al: Retinopathy screening in children and adolescents with diabetes, *Am NY Acad Sci* 958:387, 2002.

Roy MS, et al: The prevalence of diabetic retinopathy among adult type 1 diabetic persons in the US, *Arch Ophthalmol* 122(4):546, 2004.

Sjolie AK, Moller F: Medical management of diabetic retinopathy, *Diabet Med* 21(7):666, 2004.

AUTHOR: **MELVYN KOBY, M.D.**

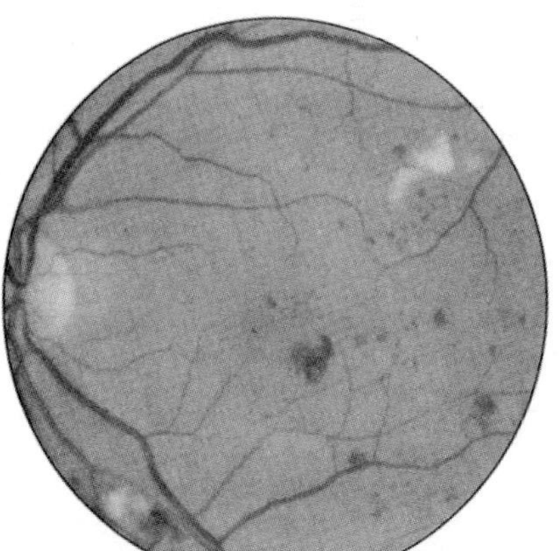

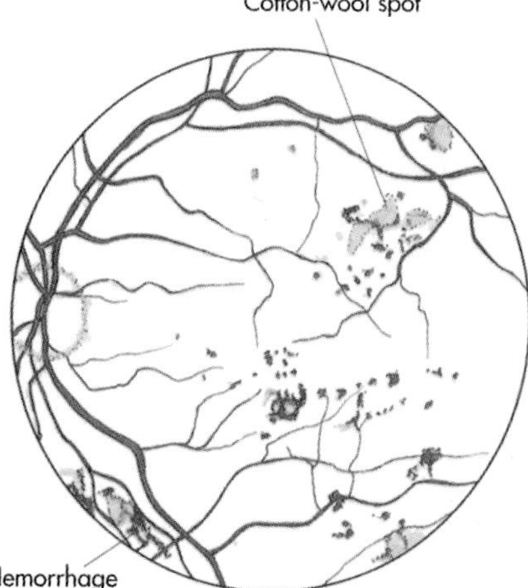

FIGURE 1-203 Background diabetic retinopathy. Note flame-shaped and dot-blot hemorrhages, cotton-wool spots, and microaneurysms. (From Barkaukas VH et al: *Health and physical assessment,* ed 2, St Louis, 1998, Mosby.)

BASIC INFORMATION

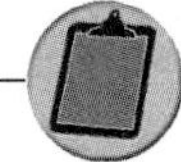

DEFINITION

Reye's syndrome is a postinfectious triad consisting of encephalopathy, fatty liver degeneration, and transaminase elevation.

ICD-9CM CODES
331.81 Reye's syndrome

EPIDEMIOLOGY & DEMOGRAPHICS

- During the 1970s, 300 to 600 cases were being reported yearly in the U.S
- Since the mid-1980s, following the understanding that aspirin is associated with Reye's syndrome, the yearly count has fallen to <20 cases
- Seasonal relation with influenza and varicella outbreaks
- Age: rare in persons over age 18 yr; peak age (in the U.S.) is 6 to 8 yr
- Case fatality rate: 25% to 50%

PHYSICAL FINDINGS & CLINICAL PRESENTATION

Shortly following recovery from a viral infection (flu or chicken pox) an afebrile child begins to vomit intractably. Hepatomegaly is often present. The vomiting can lead to dehydration. Occasionally, symptoms of hypoglycemia are present. After 2 days, symptoms of encephalopathy dominate the clinical picture (lethargy, confusion, stupor, coma, seizures, decorticate or decerebrate posture) (Table 1-46).

ETIOLOGY

- Temporal association with influenza and varicella infection
- Epidemiologic association with aspirin or other salicylate use to treat the viral infection
- Possible association with aflatoxin and pesticides
- Pathology

Liver: no inflammation; the striking finding is panlobular microvesicular hepatocyte infiltration on light microscopy and mitochondrial injury on electron microscopy.

Brain: no inflammation; there are cerebral edema and anoxic degeneration.

- Pathogenesis: not fully understood but mitochondrial dysfunction is clearly at the center stage

DIAGNOSIS

DIFFERENTIAL DIAGNOSIS

- Inborn errors of metabolism

Carnitine deficiency
Ornithine transcarbamylase deficiency
Others

- Salicylate or amiodarone intoxication
- Jamaican vomiting sickness
- Hepatic encephalopathy of any cause

WORKUP

According to the CDC's case definition, the following conditions must be met for consideration as a Reye's syndrome case:

- Acute noninflammatory encephalopathy documented by:

Alteration in the level of consciousness and, if available, a record of cerebrospinal fluid containing ≤8 leukocytes per mm^3 *or*

Histologic specimen demonstrating cerebral edema without perivascular or meningeal inflammation

- Hepatopathy documented either by a liver biopsy or autopsy considered to be diagnostic of Reye's syndrome or by a threefold or greater rise in the levels of serum aspartate aminotransferase, serum alanine aminotransferase, or serum ammonia *and*
- No more reasonable explanation for the cerebral and hepatic abnormalities

LABORATORY TESTS

- Elevated transaminase (ALT and AST)
- Elevated ammonia level
- Occasional elevation of CPK, LDH, and bilirubin and prolongation of prothrombin time
- Occasional hypoglycemia (in patients under the age of 4 yr)
- Cerebrospinal fluid is normal or contains <8 WBCs/ml
- Rarely a liver biopsy is indicated (in infants or in recurrent cases)

TREATMENT

- Supportive
- Mannitol, glycerol, or hyperventilation for cerebral edema if present
- Interferon alfa (experimental)
- Prevention

Influenza vaccine
Varicella vaccine
Avoidance of aspirin in children, especially during influenza and varicella outbreaks

SUGGESTED READINGS

Gellin BG, LaMontagne JR: Reye's syndrome. In Gorbach SL, Bartlett JG, Blacklow NR (eds): *Infectious diseases,* ed 2, Philadelphia, 1998, WB Saunders.

Reye syndrome—United States, 1985, *MMWR* 35:66, 1986.

AUTHOR: **TOM J. WACHTEL, M.D.**

TABLE 1-46 **Clinical Staging of Reye's Syndrome**

Grade	Symptoms at Time of Admission
I	Usually quiet, **lethargic** and sleepy, vomiting, laboratory evidence of liver dysfunction
II	Deep lethargy, **confusion,** delirium, combative, hyperventilation, hyperreflexic
III	Obtunded, **light coma,** seizures, decorticate rigidity, intact pupillary light reaction
IV	Seizures, deepening coma, **decerebrate rigidity,** loss of oculocephalic reflexes, fixed pupils
V	Coma, loss of deep tendon reflexes, respiratory arrest, fixed dilated pupils, **flaccidity/decerebrate** intermittent isoelectric electroencephalogram

From Behrman RE: Nelson textbook of pediatrics, ed 15, Philadelphia, 1996, WB Saunders.

BASIC INFORMATION

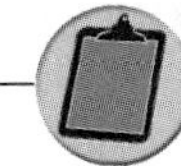

DEFINITION

Rh incompatibility occurs when an absence of the D antigen on maternal RBCs and its presence on fetal RBCs causes risk of Rh isoimmunization.

ICD-9CM CODES
656.1 Rh incompatibility

EPIDEMIOLOGY & DEMOGRAPHICS

INCIDENCE:

- The absence of the D antigen (Rh^- blood type) occurs in 15% of whites, 8% of blacks, and virtually no Asians or Native Americans. If the father's blood type is not known, the chance that an Rh^- pregnant woman is bearing an Rh^+ fetus is about 60%.
- Of those pregnancies complicated by Rh incompatibility, the risk of maternal isoimmunization to the D antigen is about 8% for each ABO compatible pregnancy *if no prophylaxis is given*.
- Maternal-fetal ABO incompatibility is somewhat protective against Rh isoimmunization.

GENETICS: Five major loci determine Rh status: C, D, E, c, e. The presence of the D antigen results in an Rh^+ individual. Its absence results in an Rh^- individual. Of Rh^+ fathers, 45% are homozygotes, 55% are heterozygotes. For homozygous Rh^+ fathers, the probability of an Rh^+ offspring is 100%. The probability for heterozygotes is about 50%.

RISK FACTORS FOR ISOIMMUNIZATION:

- Antepartum: fetal-to-maternal transfusion
- Intrapartum: fetal-to-maternal transfusion, spontaneous abortion, ectopic pregnancy, abruptio placentae, abdominal trauma, chorionic villus sampling, amniocentesis, percutaneous umbilical blood sampling (PUBS), external cephalic version, manual removal of the placenta, therapeutic abortion, autologous blood product administration

ETIOLOGY

The initial response to D antigen exposure is production of IgM (MW 900,000) that does not cross the placenta. With a repeated exposure, IgG (MW 160,000) is produced. IgG can cross the placenta and enter the fetal circulation, producing hemolysis in the fetus. This may produce erythroblastosis fetalis or hemolytic disease in the newborn, resulting in antepartum or neonatal death or neurologic damage to the fetus because of hyperbilirubinemia and kernicterus.

DIAGNOSIS

LABORATORY TESTS

ABO and Rh blood type and an antibody screen as part of the initial prenatal profile

- If antibody screen negative:
  1. Repeat antibody screen at 28 wk gestation.
  2. Obtain neonatal blood type after delivery.
  3. If Rh incompatibility is confirmed by the neonatal blood type, a Kleihauer-Betke or rosette test should be performed to determine the amount of fetomaternal transfusion in the following high-risk circumstances: abruptio placentae, placenta previa, cesarean delivery, intrauterine manipulation, manual removal of the placenta.
- If anti-D antibody screen is positive:
  1. Maternal indirect Coombs' test is needed to determine antibody titer.
  2. Determine paternal Rh status and zygosity.
  3. If father is heterozygous, PUBS or amniotic fluid is needed to determine fetal Rh status.

IMAGING STUDIES

Ultrasound evaluation can diagnose hydrops fetalis, but it cannot predict it.

TREATMENT

PREVENTION OF D ISOIMMUNIZATION

- Give 50 μg of D immunoglobulin: after spontaneous or induced abortion or ectopic pregnancy <13 wk gestation.
- Give 300 μg of D immunoglobulin (protects against 30 ml of fetal blood):
  1. After spontaneous or induced abortion >13 wk gestation, amniocentesis, CVS, PUBS, external cephalic version or other intrauterine manipulation.
  2. As antepartum prophylaxis at 28 wk gestation. Maternal anti-D prophylaxis does not cause hemolysis in the fetus or newborn.
  3. At delivery if the neonate is D- or Du-positive.
  4. If Kleihauer-Betke or rosette test confirms >30 ml of fetal red blood in maternal circulation, additional D immunoglobulin is indicated. Confirm adequacy of therapy by a maternal indirect Coombs' test 48 to 72 hr after Rh immune globulin is given.

MANAGEMENT OF D ISOIMMUNIZED PREGNANCIES

- Serial amniocentesis for assessment of OD_{450} after 25 wk gestation with interpretation of the Delta OD_{450} according to criteria established by Liley
- PUBS if ultrasonographic evidence of hydrops, rising zone II Delta OD_{450} values on amniocentesis, maternal history of a severely affected child
- Intrauterine exchange transfusion if severe anemia is documented remote from term
- Initiation of steroids for lung maturation at 28 wk in severely affected pregnancies with delivery at lung maturity
- Delivery as soon as lung maturation is achieved in mild to moderately affected pregnancies

DISPOSITION

Survival of nonhydropic infants is 90%. Of infants with hydrops, 82% survive.

REFERRAL

Refer all Rh isoimmunized pregnancies to a tertiary care center before 18 to 20 wk gestation.

SUGGESTED READING

Maayan-Metzger A et al: Maternal anti-D prophylaxis during pregnancy does not cause neonatal haemolysis, *Arch Dis Child* 84:60, 2001.

AUTHOR: **LAUREL M. WHITE, M.D.**

BASIC INFORMATION

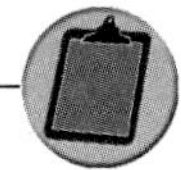

DEFINITION

Rhabdomyolysis is the dissolution or disintegration of muscle, which causes membrane lysis and leakage of muscle constituents, resulting in the excretion of myoglobin in the urine. Renal damage can occur as a result of tubular obstruction by myoglobin as well as hypovolemia.

ICD-9CM CODES
728.89 Rhabdomyolysis

EPIDEMIOLOGY & DEMOGRAPHICS

PREDOMINANT AGE: Rare in children

PHYSICAL FINDINGS & CLINICAL PRESENTATION

- Variable muscle tenderness
- Weakness
- Muscular rigidity
- Fever
- Altered consciousness
- Muscle swelling
- Malaise
- Dark urine

ETIOLOGY

- Exertion (exercise-induced)
- Electrical injury
- Drug-induced (statins, combination of statins with fibrates, amphetamines, haloperidol)
- Compartment syndrome
- Multiple trauma
- Malignant hyperthermia
- Limb ischemia
- Reperfusion after revascularization procedures for ischemia
- Extensive surgical (spinal) dissection
- Tourniquet ischemia
- Prolonged static positioning during surgery
- Infectious and inflammatory myositis
- Metabolic myopathies
- Hypovolemia and urinary acidification are important precipitating causes in the development of acute renal failure.
- Sickle cell trait is a predisposing condition.

DIAGNOSIS

DIFFERENTIAL DIAGNOSIS

Section III, "Creatine Kinase Elevation," describes a clinical algorithm for the evaluation of CPK elevation.

LABORATORY TESTS

- Screening for myoglobinuria with a simple urine dipstick test using ortho-toluidine or benzidine
- BUN, creatinine
- Increased CPK (Fig. 1-204)
- Hyperkalemia
- Hypocalcemia
- Hyperphosphatemia
- Increased urinary myoglobin
- Pigmented granular casts
- Hyperuricemia

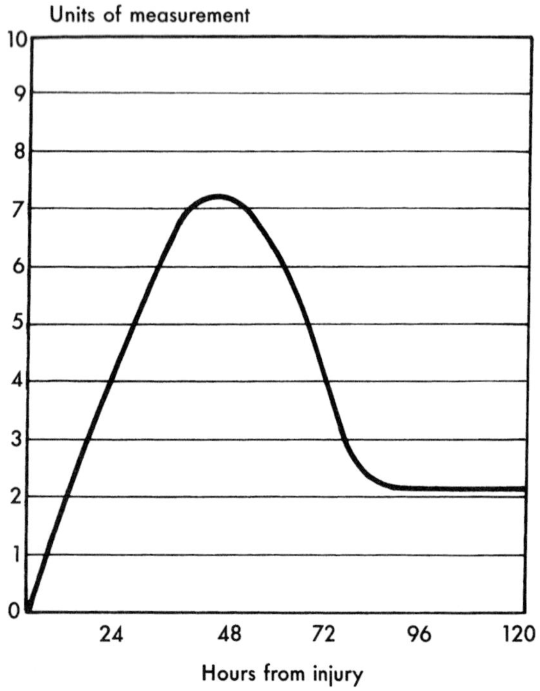

Units of measurement
0 1 2 3 4 5 6 7 8 9 10
24 48 72 96 120
Hours from injury

FIGURE 1-204 Typical CK elimination curve. (From Rosen P [ed]: *Emergency medicine,* ed 4, St Louis, 1998, Mosby.)

TREATMENT

ACUTE GENERAL Rx

- Early, aggressive high-volume IV fluid replacement with mannitol, to induce diuresis to prevent acute renal failure
- Treatment of electrolyte imbalances
- Alkalinization of urine is controversial but appears helpful in research models

DISPOSITION

The condition is easily treatable, but early diagnosis and management are necessary to avoid renal failure, which occurs in 30% of cases.

PEARLS & CONSIDERATIONS

COMMENTS

A clinical algorithm for the evaluation of muscle cramps and aches is described in Fig. 3-130.

SUGGESTED READINGS

Brown CV et al: Preventing renal failure in patients with rhabdomyolisis: do bicarbonate and mannitol make a difference? *J Trauma* 56(6):1191, 2004.

Garcia-Valdecasas-Campelo E et al: Acute rhabdomyolysis associated with cerivastatin therapy, *Arch Intern Med* 161:893, 2001.

Gunal AI et al: Early and vigorous fluid resuscitation prevents acute renal failure in the crush victims of catastrophic earthquakes, *J Am Soc Nephrol* 15(7):1862, 2004.

Halachanova V, Sansone RA, McDonald S: Delayed rhabdomyolysis after ecstasy use, *Mayo Clin Proc* 76:112, 2001.

Sauret JM et al: Rhabdomyolysis, *Am Fam Physician* 65:907, 2002.

Wappler F et al: Evidence for susceptibility to malignant hyperthermia in patients with exercise-induced rhabdomyolysis, *Anesthesiology* 94:95, 2001.

Wolfe SM: Dangers of rosuvastatin identified before and after FDA approval, *Lancet* 363(9427):2189, 2004.

AUTHOR: **LONNIE R. MERCIER, M.D.**

BASIC INFORMATION

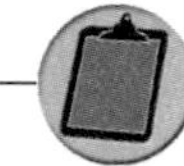

DEFINITION

Rheumatic fever is a multisystem inflammatory disease that occurs in the genetically susceptible host after a pharyngeal infection with group A streptococci.

SYNONYMS

Acute rheumatic fever
Rheumatic carditis

ICD-9CM CODES
390; 716.9 Rheumatic fever

EPIDEMIOLOGY & DEMOGRAPHICS

INCIDENCE (IN U.S.):

- 0.1% to 3% in patients with untreated streptococcal pharyngitis
- Higher incidence of streptococcal pharyngitis with:
  1. Crowding
  2. Poverty
  3. Young age

PREDOMINANT AGE:

- Age 5 to 15 yr for first attack
- Possible relapses later

PEAK INCIDENCE: School-age children

GENETICS:

Familial Disposition: Predisposition to the disease is likely to be genetically determined.

PHYSICAL FINDINGS & CLINICAL PRESENTATION

- Acute streptococcal pharyngitis, which may be subclinical and not reported by the patient
- After latent period of 1 to 5 wk (average, 19 days), acute rheumatic attack
- Patient is febrile, with a migratory polyarthritis of knees, ankles, wrists, elbows; typically severe for 1 wk, remits by 3 to 4 wk
- Carditis
  1. New heart murmur
     a. Mitral regurgitation
     b. Aortic insufficiency
     c. Diastolic mitral murmur
  2. Cardiomegaly
  3. CHF
  4. Pericardial friction rub or effusion
- Rarely, pancarditis is severe and fatal.
- Subcutaneous nodules can be palpated over extensor tendon surfaces or bony prominences, such as the skull.
- Chorea (Sydenham's chorea) is characterized by rapid involuntary movements affecting all muscles.
  1. Muscular weakness
  2. Emotional lability
  3. Rarely seen after adolescence and almost never in adult males
- Erythema marginatum
  1. Evanescent, pink, well-demarcated spreading to trunk and proximal extremities
  2. Not specific
- Arthralgias (joint pain without swelling)
- Abdominal pain

ETIOLOGY

- Group A streptococci not recovered from tissue lesions.
- It does not occur in the absence of a streptococcal antibody response.
- Immunologic cross-reactivity between certain streptococcal antigens and human tissue antigens suggests an autoimmune etiology.
- Both initial attacks and recurrences can be completely prevented by prompt treatment of streptococcal pharyngitis with penicillin.

DIAGNOSIS

DIFFERENTIAL DIAGNOSIS

- Rheumatoid arthritis
- Juvenile rheumatoid arthritis (Still's disease)
- Bacterial endocarditis
- Systemic lupus
- Viral infections
- Serum sickness

WORKUP

- "Jones Criteria (revised) for Guidance in the Diagnosis of Rheumatic Fever" published by the American Heart Association

One major and two minor criteria if supported by evidence of an antecedent group A streptococcal infection

- Major criteria
  1. Increased titer of antistreptococcal antibodies such as ASO
  2. Positive throat culture
  3. Recent scarlet fever
- Minor criteria
  1. Previous rheumatic fever or rheumatic heart disease
  2. Fever
  3. Arthralgia
  4. Increased acute-phase reactants
     a. ESR
     b. C-reactive protein
     c. Leukocytosis
  5. Prolonged P-R interval

LABORATORY TESTS

- Throat cultures are usually negative.
- Streptococcal antibody tests are more useful in establishing the diagnosis.
  1. Peak at the beginning of the attack
  2. Can document a recent streptococcal infection
- ASO (antistreptolysin O) titers peak:
  1. 4 to 5 wk after a streptococcal throat infection
  2. During the second or third week of illness
- Anti-DNase B (Streptozyme) is also commonly used but is less reliable.
- High-titer streptococcal antibodies:
  1. Are supportive of diagnosis, but not proof
  2. Should be interpreted in the context of clinical criteria

IMAGING STUDIES

- Chest x-ray to assess heart size
- Echocardiogram:
  1. To evaluate murmurs
  2. To rule out pericardial effusion

TREATMENT

ACUTE GENERAL Rx

- Course of penicillin to eradicate throat carriage of group A streptococci
- Arthralgia or arthritis without carditis: aspirin 40 mg/lb/day for 2 wk, followed by 20 mg/lb/day for 4 to 6 wk
- Carditis and heart failure:
  1. Prednisone 40 to 60 mg/day
  2. IV corticosteroids, such as methylprednisolone, 10 to 40 mg/day for severe carditis

CHRONIC Rx

Secondary prevention (prevention of recurrences):

- Monthly treatment with benzathine penicillin 1.2 million U IM
- Erythromycin in patients with penicillin allergy

DISPOSITION

- Damage of heart valves because of fibrosis
  1. Late sequela of recurrent attacks
  2. Frequent cause of valvular heart disease in developing countries
- May progress to heart failure

REFERRAL

To cardiologist for management of severe carditis

SUGGESTED READINGS

Carapetis JR, Currie BJ: Rheumatic fever in a high incidence population: the importance of monoarthritis and low grade fever, *Arch Dis Child* 85(30):223, 2001.

Figueroa FE et al: Prospective comparison of clinical and echocardiographic diagnosis of rheumatic carditis: long term follow up of patients with subclinical disease, *Heart* 85(40):407, 2001.

Guilherme L, Kalik J: Rheumatic fever: from sore throat to autoimmune heart lesions, *Int Arch Allergy Immunol* 134(1):56, 2004.

Kadir IS et al: Recurrent acute rheumatic fever: a forgotten diagnosis? *Ann Thorac Surg* 78(2):699, 2004.

Thatai D, Turi ZG: Current guidelines for the treatment of rheumatic fever, *Drugs* 57(4):545, 1999.

AUTHOR: **DEBORAH L. SHAPIRO, M.D.**

BASIC INFORMATION

DEFINITION

Allergic rhinitis is an IgE-mediated hypersensitivity response to nasally inhaled allergens that causes sneezing, rhinorrhea, nasal pruritus, and congestion.

SYNONYMS

Hay fever
IgE-mediated rhinitis

ICD-9CM CODES
477.9 Allergic rhinitis

EPIDEMIOLOGY & DEMOGRAPHICS

- Allergic rhinitis affects approximately 10% to 20% of the U.S. population.
- Mean age of onset is 8 to 12 yr.
- The prevalence of allergic rhinitis in patients presenting to their primary care provider with nasal symptoms is estimated to be 30%-60%.

PHYSICAL FINDINGS & CLINICAL FINDINGS

- Pale or violaceous mucosa of the turbinates caused by venous engorgement (this can distinguish it from erythema present in viral rhinitis)
- Nasal polyps
- Lymphoid hyperplasia in the posterior oropharynx with cobblestone appearance
- Erythema of the throat, conjunctival and scleral injection
- Clear nasal discharge
- Clinical presentation: usually consists of sneezing, nasal congestion, cough, postnasal drip, loss of or alteration of smell, and sensation of plugged ears

ETIOLOGY

- Pollens in the springtime, ragweed in fall, grasses in the summer
- Dust, mites, animal allergens
- Smoke or any irritants
- Perfumes, detergents, soaps
- Emotion, changes in atmospheric pressure or temperature

DIAGNOSIS

DIFFERENTIAL DIAGNOSIS

- Infections (sinusitis; viral, bacterial, or fungal rhinitis)
- Rhinitis medicamentosa (cocaine, sympathomimetic nasal drops)
- Vasomotor rhinitis (e.g., secondary to air pollutants)
- Septal obstruction (e.g., deviated septum), nasal polyps, nasal neoplasms
- Systemic diseases (e.g., Wegener's granulomatosis, hypothyroidism [rare])

WORKUP

- The initial strategy should be to determine whether patients should undergo diagnostic testing or receive empirical treatment.
- Workup is often unnecessary if the diagnosis is apparent. A detailed medical history is useful in identifying the culprit allergen.
- Selected patients with allergic rhinitis that is not controlled with standard therapy may benefit from allergy testing to target allergen avoidance measures or guide immunotherapy. Allergy testing can be performed using skin testing or radioallergosorbent (RAST) testing. In vitro tests also can assess serum levels of specific IgE antibodies. Overall, skin tests show greater sensitivity than serum assays. In vitro tests should be considered in rare patients who fear skin tests, must take medication that interferes with skin testing, or have generalized dermatographism.
- Examination of nasal smears for the presence of neutrophils to rule out infectious causes and the presence of eosinophils (suggestive of allergy) may be useful in selected patients.
- Peripheral blood eosinophil counts are not useful in allergy diagnosis.

TREATMENT

NONPHARMACOLOGIC THERAPY

- Maintain allergen-free environment by covering mattresses and pillows with allergen-proof casings, eliminating carpeting, eliminating animal products, and removing dust-collecting fixtures.
- Use of air purifiers and dust filters is helpful.
- Maintain humidity in the environment below 50% to prevent dust mites and mold.
- Use air conditioners, especially in the bedroom.
- Remove pets from homes of patients with suspected sensitivity to animal allergens.

ACUTE GENERAL Rx

- Determine if the patient is troubled by swollen turbinates (best treated with decongestants) or blockages secondary to mucus (effectively treated by antihistamines).
- Most first-generation antihistamines can cause considerable sedation and anticholinergic symptoms. The second-generation antihistamines (loratadine, fexofenadine, cetirizine, desloratadine) are preferred because they do not have any significant anticholinergic or sedative effects; however, they are more expensive.
- Montelukast (Singulair), a leukotriene receptor antagonist commonly used for asthma, is also effective for allergic rhinitis. Usual adult dose is 10 mg qd.
- Azelastine (Astelin) is an antihistamine nasal spray effective for seasonal allergic rhinitis.
- Topical nasal steroids are very effective and are preferred by many as first-line treatment for allergic rhinitis in adults. Patients should be instructed on proper use and informed that improvement might not occur for at least 1 wk after initiation of therapy. Commonly available inhalers are:
  1. Beclomethasone dipropionate (Beconase AQ): one to two sprays in each nostril bid
  2. Fluticasone (Flonase): initially two sprays in each nostril qd or one spray in each nostril bid, decreasing to one spray in each nostril qd based on response
  3. Flunisolide (Nasalide): initially two sprays in each nostril bid
  4. Budesonide (Rhinocort): two sprays in each nostril bid or four sprays in each nostril qam

CHRONIC Rx

- Cromolyn sodium (Nasalcrom): one spray to each nostril three to four times daily can be used for prophylaxis (mast cell stabilizer).
- Immunotherapy is generally reserved for patients responding poorly to the above treatments.

DISPOSITION

Most patients experience significant relief with avoidance of allergens and proper use of medications.

REFERRAL

Allergy testing in patients with severe symptoms that are unresponsive to therapy or when the diagnosis is uncertain

SUGGESTED READINGS

Gendo K, Larson EB: Evidence-based diagnostic strategies for evaluating suspected allergic rhinitis, *Ann Intern Med* 140:278, 2004.

Rinne J et al: Early treatment of perennial rhinitis with budesonide or cetirizine and its effect on long-term outcome, *J Allergy Clin Immunol* 109:426, 2002.

AUTHOR: **FRED F. FERRI, M.D.**

BASIC INFORMATION

DEFINITION

Rickets is a systemic disease of infancy and childhood in which mineralization of growing bone is deficient as a result of abnormal calcium, phosphorus, or vitamin D metabolism. *Osteomalacia* is the same condition in the adult. *Renal osteodystrophy* is a term used to describe a similar condition in patients with chronic kidney disease. Certain forms of the disorder may respond only to high doses of vitamin D and are referred to as vitamin D–resistant rickets (VDRR).

ICD-9CM CODES
268.0 Active rickets
275.3 Vitamin D–resistant rickets
588.0 Renal rickets (renal osteodystrophy)
268.2 Osteomalacia

PHYSICAL FINDINGS & CLINICAL PRESENTATION

The child with classic rickets usually develops a number of specific abnormalities:
- Softening of the skull bones (craniotabes) early in the disorder
- Enlargement of the ribs at the costochondral junctions, producing the "rachitic rosary"
- Limb deformities and epiphyseal swelling (Fig. 1-205)
- Height below normal range
- Irritability and easy fatigability
- Pigeon breast deformity and an indentation of the lower ribcage at the insertion of the diaphragm, sometimes referred to as Harrison's groove; possible decrease in thoracic volume, resulting in diminished pulmonary ventilation

Physical findings in the adult with osteomalacia are more subtle:
- Possible malaise and bone pain
- Many patients presumed to have osteoporosis but may also have osteomalacia

ETIOLOGY

- Deficiency states
  1. True classic VDDR is rare in Western society.
  2. Absorption of vitamin D, however, may be blocked in several GI disorders.
  3. Similar disorders may also prevent absorption of calcium and phosphorus, but in the absence of these other diseases, deficiencies of calcium and phosphorus are also rare.
- Acquired or inherited renal tubular abnormalities that cause resorptive defects and result in rickets and osteomalacia; syndromes include classical VDRR (probably the most common form of rickets seen in general practice)
- Chronic renal failure:
  1. Can produce renal rickets or renal osteodystrophy
  2. Results in the retention of phosphate

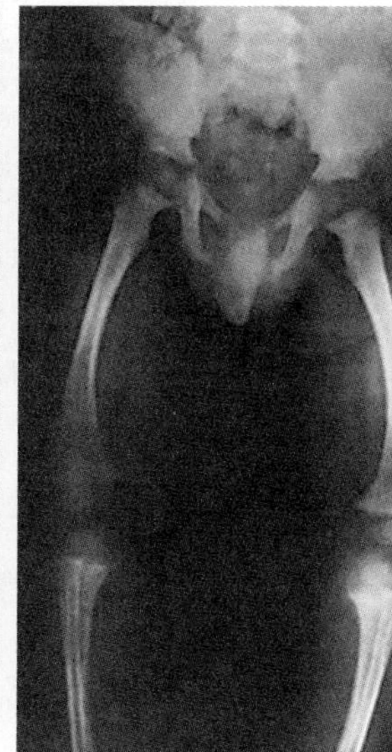

FIGURE 1-205 **A,** Clinical and, **B,** radiographic appearance of a young boy with X-linked hypophosphatemic rickets. Note the striking bowing of the legs, apparent in both femora and tibiae, with flaring of the ends of the bones at the knee. (Courtesy Dr. Sara B. Arnaud. From Bikle DB: Osteomalacia and rickets. In Wyngaarden JB, Smith LH Jr, Bennett JB [eds]: *Cecil textbook of medicine,* ed 19, Philadelphia, 1992, WB Saunders.)

DIAGNOSIS

DIFFERENTIAL DIAGNOSIS

- Osteoporosis
- Hyperparathyroidism
- Hyperthyroidism

LABORATORY TESTS

- Requires a high degree of interest because many of the conditions are so similar that only a complicated laboratory evaluation may establish the diagnosis
- BUN, creatinine, alkaline phosphatase, calcium, and phosphorus levels in any patient suspected of having metabolic bone disease

IMAGING STUDIES

- In rickets:
  1. Characteristic radiographic changes in the ends of growing long bones caused by the lack of calcification of the cartilage matrix
  2. Typically widening and irregularity of the epiphyseal plate
- Radiographs in the adult with osteomalacia:
  1. More subtle and often confused with osteoporosis
  2. Possible pseudofractures (Looser's zones) where major arteries cross bone
  3. Insufficiency compression deformities in the vertebral bodies

TREATMENT

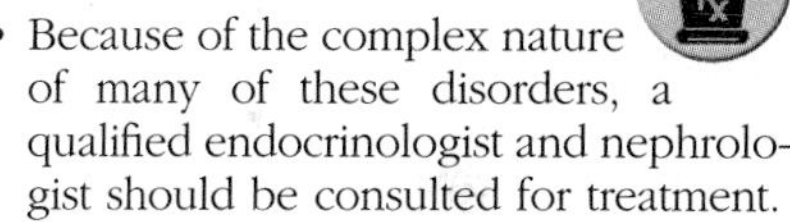

- Because of the complex nature of many of these disorders, a qualified endocrinologist and nephrologist should be consulted for treatment.
- The need for orthopedic intervention is rare.
- Surgical care is indicated for slipped capital femoral epiphysis, which is fairly common in renal rickets.
- Deformity may require bracing.

SUGGESTED READINGS

Abrams SA: Nutritional rickets: an old disease returns, *Nutr Rev* 60(4):111, 2002.

Allgrove J: Is nutritional rickets returning? *Arch Dis Child* 89(8):699, 2004.

Ashraf S, Mughal MZ: The prevalence of rickets among non-Caucasian children, *Arch Dis Child* 87(3):263, 2002.

Eliot MM: The control of rickets, *Am J Public Health* 94(8):1321, 2004.

Fulop M, Mackay M: Renal tubular acidosis, Sjogren Syndrome and bone disease, *Arch Intern Med* 164(8):905, 2004.

Joiner TA et al: Primary care pediatrician knowledge of nutritional rickets, *J Natl Med Assoc* 94(11):971, 2002.

Tortolani PJ, McCarthy EF, Sponseller PD: Bone mineral density deficiency in children, *J Am Acad Orthop Surg* 10(1):57, 2002.

AUTHOR: **LONNIE R. MERCIER, M.D.**

BASIC INFORMATION

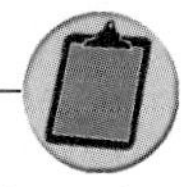

DEFINITION

Rocky Mountain spotted fever (RMSF) is a febrile illness caused by infection with *Rickettsia rickettsii.*

ICD-9CM CODES
082.0 Rocky Mountain spotted fever

EPIDEMIOLOGY & DEMOGRAPHICS

INCIDENCE: 0.18 to 0.32 cases/100,000 person-years

DEMOGRAPHICS: Affects both genders equally and occurs at any age, but more likely in children aged 5-14 yr

GEOGRAPHY: Most prevalent in the Southeast, followed by the South Central states, but seen anywhere

PHYSICAL FINDINGS & CLINICAL PRESENTATION

- Incubation: 3 to 12 days
- First symptoms: fever, headache, malaise, and myalgias

Common history, signs, or symptoms	%
Tick bite	65
Fever	100
Rash	90
Rash on palms and soles	80
Headache	90
Myalgia	75
Nausea or vomiting	60
Abdominal pain	40
Conjunctivitis	30
Edema	20
Pneumonitis	15
Any severe neurologic complication (including stupor, delirium, seizures, ataxia, papilledema, focal neurologic deficits, and coma)	30

Rash:
- Appears during first 3 days in 50%; by day 5, 80% have it. No rash in 10%.
- Initial appearance: blanching erythematous macules on wrists and ankles that then spread to trunk, palms, and soles.
- Lesions may evolve into papules and eventually become nonblanching (petechiae or palpable purpura).

Gastrointestinal symptoms:
- Nausea, vomiting, and abdominal pain are common
- Occasionally may mimic an "acute abdomen" (e.g., appendicitis, cholecystitis)
- Mild hepatitis

Cardiopulmonary involvement:
- Interstitial pneumonitis
- Myocarditis

Renal problems:
- Prerenal azotemia
- Interstitial nephritis
- Glomerulonephritis

Neurologic involvement:
- Encephalitis (confusion, lethargy, delirium)
- Ataxia
- Convulsion
- Cranial nerve palsy
- Speech impediment
- Hemiparesis or paraparesis
- Spasticity

Fulminant Rocky Mountain spotted fever
- Early, widespread vascular necrosis leading to multisystem illness and death

ETIOLOGY & PATHOGENESIS

- Infectious agent: *Rickettsia rickettsii* (an intracellular bacterium).
- Vector: dog tick and wood tick (vertical transmission exists in ticks, but horizontal transmission involving rodents represents an important reservoir for the agent).
- Pathogenesis: the spread of *R. rickettsii* is hematogenous with attachment to the vascular endothelium, causing a vasculitis. The manifestations of this illness are caused by increased vascular permeability.

DIAGNOSIS

DIFFERENTIAL DIAGNOSIS

Influenza A, enteroviral infection, typhoid fever, leptospirosis, infectious mononucleosis, viral hepatitis, sepsis, ehrlichiosis, gastroenteritis, acute abdomen, bronchitis, pneumonia, meningococcemia, disseminated gonococcal infection, secondary syphilis, bacterial endocarditis, toxic shock syndrome, scarlet fever, rheumatic fever, measles, rubella, typhus, rickettsialpox, Lyme disease, drug hypersensitivity reactions, idiopathic thrombocytopenic purpura, thrombotic thrombocytopenic purpura, Kawasaki disease, immune complex vasculitis, connective tissue disorders

WORKUP

Consider RMSF in any patient with an acute febrile illness with headache and myalgia, especially with an associated history of tick exposure. Absence of rash does not rule the diagnosis.

LABORATORY TESTS

Routine tests	%
White cell count	
<10,000/mm^3	72
>10% bands	69
Platelet count	
<150,000/mm^3	52
<99,000/mm^3	32
Serum sodium value <132 mEq/L	56
Aspartate aminotransferase ≥2× normal	62
Alanine aminotransferase ≥2× normal	39
Bilirubin value >1.4 mg/dl	30
Cerebrospinal fluid	
Opening pressure ≥250 mm H_2O	14
Glucose value ≤50 mg/dl	8
Protein value ≥50 mg/dl	35
White cell count ≥5/mm^3	38
Mononuclear cell predominance	46
Polymorphonuclear cell predominance	50

Etiologic tests
- Antibody titers to *R. rickettsii* (by indirect fluorescent antibody test). The diagnosis of RMSF requires a fourfold increase 2 wk apart and thus is not helpful in the care of the patients despite a sensitivity and specificity of near 100%.
- The only test that can provide a timely diagnosis is the immunohistologic demonstration of *R. rickettsii* in skin biopsy specimens.

TREATMENT

- Oral or intravenous doxycycline, 200 mg/day in two divided doses
- Oral tetracycline, 25-50 mg/kg/day in four divided doses
- Chloramphenicol, 50-75 mg/kg/day in four divided doses; therapy continued for at least 2 days after defervescence

PROGNOSIS

Fatality rate: 1%-4% (five times greater if treatment is initiated after day 5 of illness, which is more likely in absence of rash and during seasonal nonpeak tick activity). Long-term sequelae seen in patients who recover from severe RMSF: paraparesis, hearing loss; peripheral neuropathy; bladder and bowel incontinence; cerebellar, vestibular, and motor dysfunction; language disorders; limb amputation; and scrotal pain after cutaneous necrosis.

SUGGESTED READINGS

Dumler JS: Rocky Mountain spotted fever. In Gorbach SL, Bartlett JG, Blacklow NR (eds): *Infectious diseases,* ed 2, Philadelphia, 1998, WB Saunders.

Masters EJ: Rocky Mountain spotted fever, *Arch Intern Med* 163:769, 2003.

AUTHOR: **TOM J. WACHTEL, M.D.**

BASIC INFORMATION

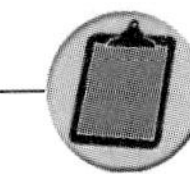

DEFINITION

Rosacea is a chronic skin disorder characterized by papules and pustules affecting the face and often associated with flushing and erythema.

SYNONYMS

Acne rosacea

ICD-9CM CODES
695.3 Rosacea

EPIDEMIOLOGY & DEMOGRAPHICS

- Rosacea occurs in 1 in 20 Americans
- Onset often between age 30 and 50 yr
- More common in people of Celtic origin; however, this disease may be overlooked in nonwhites because skin pigmentation results in atypical presentation
- Female:male ratio of 3:1

PHYSICAL FINDINGS & CLINICAL PRESENTATION

- Facial erythema, presence of papules, pustules, and telangiectasia.
- Excessive facial warmth and redness is the predominant presenting complaint.
- Itching is generally absent.
- Comedones are absent (unlike acne).
- Women are more likely to show symptoms on the chin and cheeks, whereas in men the nose is commonly involved.
- Ocular findings (conjunctival injection, burning, stinging, tearing, eyelid inflammation, swelling, and redness) are present in >20% of patients.

ETIOLOGY

- Unknown.
- Hot drinks, alcohol, and sun exposure may accentuate the erythema by causing vasodilation of the skin.
- Flare-ups may also result from reactions to medications (e.g., simvastatin, ACE inhibitors, vasodilators, fluorinated corticosteroids), stress, extreme heat or cold, spicy drinks.

DIAGNOSIS

DIFFERENTIAL DIAGNOSIS

- Drug eruption
- Acne vulgaris
- Contact dermatitis
- SLE
- Carcinoid flush
- Idiopathic facial flushing
- Seborrheic dermatitis
- Facial sarcoidosis
- Photodermatitis
- Mastocytosis

WORKUP

Diagnosis is based on clinical findings. Distinguishing features between acne and rosacea are the presence of telengiectasia and deep diffuse erythema and absence of comedones in rosacea.

LABORATORY TESTS

Not indicated

TREATMENT

NONPHARMACOLOGIC THERAPY

- Avoid alcohol, excessive sun exposure, and hot drinks of any type.
- Use of mild, nondrying soap is recommended; local skin irritants should be avoided.
- Reassure patient that rosacea is completely unrelated to poor hygiene.

GENERAL Rx

- Several classes of drugs are used in treatment of rosacea, including the metronidazole family, the tetracycline family, and azelic acid.
- Topical therapy with metronidazole aqueous gel (MetroGel) applied bid is effective as initial therapy for mild cases or following the use of oral antibiotics. A new 1% formulation of metronidazole (Noritate) applied qd may improve patient compliance. Clindamycin lotion (Cleocin) and sulfacetamide may also be effective.
- Systemic antibiotics: tetracycline 250 mg qid until symptoms diminish, then taper off; doxycycline 100 mg bid is also effective.
- Minocycline 50-100 mg qd should be used only in resistant cases, because this medication is expensive.
- Isotretinoin (Accutane) 0.5-1 mg/kg/day in two divided doses for 15-20 wk can be used for refractory papular and pustular rosacea; use of retinoids may however worsen erythema and telangiectasis.
- Laser treatment is an option for progressive telangiectasias or rhinophyma.
- Erythema and flushing may respond to low dose clonidine (0.05 mg bid).
- Another topical treatment modality for pustular and papular forms of rosacea is the use of azelaic acid (Finacea, Azelex). Azelex is available in a 20% cream base, Finacea as a 15% gel. Azelaic acid is as least as effective as topical metronidazole but may be more irritating.

DISPOSITION

- Rosacea is often resistant to initial treatment and recurrent. Periods of remission and relapse are common.
- The progression of rosacea is variable. Typical stages include:
  1. Facial flushing
  2. Erythema and/or edema and ocular symptoms
  3. Papules and pustules
  4. Rhinophyma

PEARLS & CONSIDERATIONS

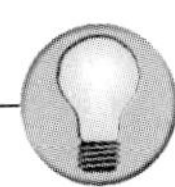

COMMENTS

- Patients with resistant cases may have *Demodex folliculorum* mite infestation or tinea infection (diagnosis can be confirmed with potassium hydroxide examination); the role of *D. folliculorum* in rosacea is unclear. These mites can sometimes be found in large numbers in the lesions; however, their numbers do not generally decline with treatment.
- Rosacea can result in emotional and social stigmas, especially because many people associate rosacea and rhinophyma with alcohol abuse.
- Early consultation with an ophthalmologist is recommended in patients with suspected ocular involvement.

SUGGESTED READING

Rosacea: a common, yet commonly overlooked condition, *Am Fam Physician* 66:435, 2002.

AUTHOR: **FRED F. FERRI, M.D.**

Roseola 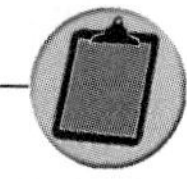

BASIC INFORMATION

DEFINITION

Roseola is a benign viral illness found in infants and is characterized by high fevers, followed by a rash.

SYNONYMS

Exanthem subitum
Sixth disease
Roseola infantum

ICD-9CM CODES

057.8 Roseola

EPIDEMIOLOGY & DEMOGRAPHICS

- Nearly one third of all infants develop roseola before the age of 2 yr.
- More than 90% of children older than 2 yr of age are seropositive for the virus causing roseola.
- Roseola is spread from person to person, but it is not known how.
- It is not known how contagious roseola is.
- There is no predilection for gender or time of year.

PHYSICAL FINDINGS & CLINICAL PRESENTATION

- Typically the child develops a high fever, usually up to 104° F (40° C) that lasts for 3-5 days
- Fever may be associated with a runny nose, irritability, and fatigue
- A rash appears within 48 hr of defervescence, mainly on the face, neck, trunk, arms, and legs
- The rash is a faint pink maculopapular rash that blanches when palpated
- The rash usually fades away within 48 hr
- Anorexia
- Seizures
- Cervical adenopathy

ETIOLOGY

- Roseola is caused by human herpesvirus-6 (HHV-6).
- The incubation period is between 5 and 15 days.

DIAGNOSIS

The diagnosis of roseola is usually made by the clinical presentation as stated previously.

DIFFERENTIAL DIAGNOSIS

- Measles
- Rubella
- Fifth disease
- Drug eruption
- Mononucleosis
- All causes of fever (e.g., otitis media, pneumonia, and urinary tract infection)
- Meningitis
- Other causes of seizures

WORKUP

- If unsure of the diagnosis of roseola in a febrile infant, a fever workup is done to rule out other infectious causes.
- The decision to proceed with a fever workup is a clinical judgment call.

LABORATORY TESTS

- CBC with differential
- Erythrocyte sedimentation rate (ESR)
- Blood cultures
- Urinalysis and urine cultures
- Stool cultures if diarrhea is present
- Lumbar puncture

IMAGING STUDIES

- Chest x-ray to rule out pneumonia

TREATMENT

NONPHARMACOLOGIC

- Supportive care
- Maintain hydration by drinking clear fluids: water, fruit juice, lemonade, and so forth
- Sponge bathe with lukewarm water if febrile

ACUTE GENERAL Rx

- Acetaminophen 10-15 mg/kg per dose at 4-hr intervals for fever
- Ibuprofen 5-10 mg/kg per dose at 6-hr intervals (maximal dose 600 mg)

CHRONIC Rx

Roseola is a viral disease that is short lasting; chronic treatment is usually not an issue.

DISPOSITION

- Roseola is generally a benign, self-limited disease that usually lasts approximately 1 wk.
- Complications, although rare, can occur and include:
  1. Febrile seizures
  2. Meningitis
  3. Encephalitis
  4. Pneumonitis
  5. Hepatitis

REFERRAL

Subspecialty consultation is made with the appropriate discipline if any of the above mentioned complications occur (e.g., neurology for seizures).

PEARLS & CONSIDERATIONS

COMMENTS

- A child with fever and rash should be excluded from daycare.
- Human herpesvirus 6 is named accordingly because it is the sixth herpesvirus discovered after herpes simplex 1 (HSV-1), HSV-2, cytomegalovirus (CMV), Epstein-Barr virus (EBV), and varicella-zoster virus (VZV).
- Roseola is called sixth disease because it represents one of six "exanthems" that occurs during childhood. The other five exanthems included in this old classification are measles, scarlet fever, rubella, Dukes disease, and erythema infectiosum (fifth disease).

SUGGESTED READINGS

Asano Y et al: Clinical features of infants with primary human herpesvirus 6 infection (exanthem subitum, roseola infantum), *Pediatrics* 93:104, 1994.

Dockrell DH, Smith TF, Paya C: Human herpesvirus 6, *Mayo Clin Proc* 74:163, 1999.

Stoeckle MY: The spectrum of human herpesvirus 6 infection: from roseola infantum to adult disease, *Annu Rev Med* 51:423, 2000.

AUTHOR: **DENNIS MIKOLICH, M.D.**

BASIC INFORMATION

DEFINITION

Rotator cuff syndrome refers to a spectrum of afflictions involving the tendons of the rotator cuff (primarily the supraspinatus), ranging from simple strains and tendinitis to complete rupture with cuff-tear arthropathy.

SYNONYMS

Impingement syndrome
Painful arc syndrome
Internal derangement of the subacromial joint
Supraspinatus syndrome

ICD-9CM CODES
726.10 Rotator cuff syndrome
727.61 Rotator cuff rupture

EPIDEMIOLOGY & DEMOGRAPHICS

PREVALENCE: 5% to 10% of the general population
PREDOMINANT AGE: Uncommon under 20 yr of age
PREDOMINANT SEX: More common in males than females

PHYSICAL FINDINGS & CLINICAL PRESENTATION

- Pain, often at night
- Rotator cuff tenderness
- Referred pain down deltoid, especially with abduction between 70 and 120 degrees ("the painful arc") (Fig. 1-206)
- Weakness in abduction or forward flexion
- Increased pain with overhead activities
- Atrophy in long-standing cases of complete tear
- Positive "drop-arm" test (weakness of abduction against downward pressure at 90°)

ETIOLOGY

- Microtrauma from repetitive use
- Abnormally shaped acromion
- Shoulder instability
- Worsening of process by the overhead throwing motion

DIAGNOSIS

DIFFERENTIAL DIAGNOSIS

- Shoulder instability
- Degenerative arthritis
- Cervical radiculopathy
- Avascular necrosis
- Suprascapular nerve entrapment

WORKUP

- In chronic tendinitis, clinical findings similar to those seen in partial rupture
- Even with complete rupture, may have full, active range of motion in shoulder

IMAGING STUDIES

- Plain radiography
- Ultrasonography may be useful but only in diagnosing moderately large tears
- MRI to evaluate full- or partial-thickness tears, chronic tendinitis, and other causes of shoulder pain
- Since MRI, arthrography is rarely used

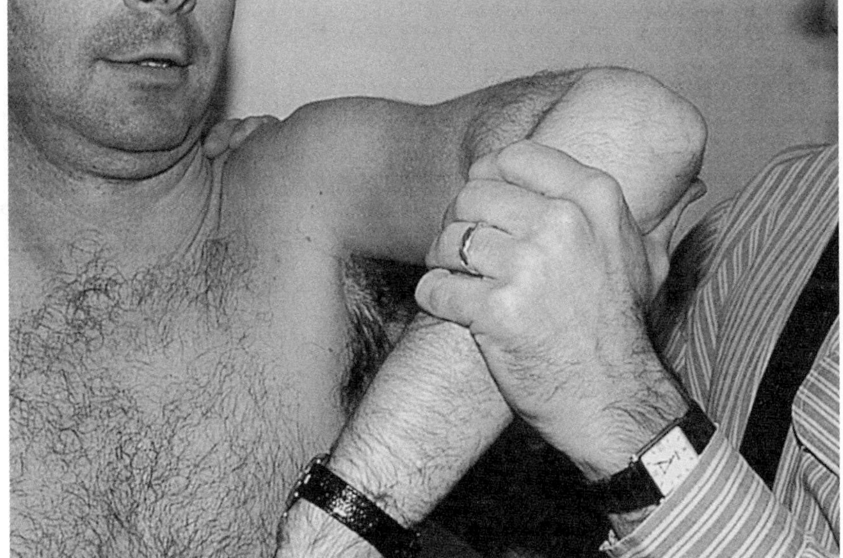

FIGURE 1-206 Rotator cuff lesions are often accompanied by painful impingement of the upwardly subluxating humerus onto the acromion. Evidence for this as a cause of pain is elicited by impingement tests, for example, by forced, passive, internal rotation and abduction of the shoulder, as shown here. (From Klippel J, Dieppe P, Ferri F [eds]: *Primary care rheumatology,* London, 1999, Mosby.)

TREATMENT

ACUTE GENERAL Rx

- Rest to avoid overhead activity
- Ice or heat for comfort
- Carefully supervised program of stretching and strengthening
- Medication: NSAIDs, subacromial corticosteroid injection (once or twice at 2 wk intervals)

DISPOSITION

- All forms are likely to respond to nonsurgical management.
- Even many complete rotator cuff tears have minimal pain and little loss of function.

REFERRAL

For orthopedic consultation in cases that fail to respond to medical management or in which rotator cuff tear is suspected

PEARLS & CONSIDERATIONS

COMMENTS

- There is considerable disagreement regarding the likelihood of recovery once a significant rotator cuff rupture has developed.
- Indications for surgery vary among surgeons.
- Injection is contraindicated in the presence of local infection.

SUGGESTED READINGS

Biberthaler P et al: Microcirculation associated with degenerative rotator cuff lesions, *J Bone Joint Surg* 85A:475, 2003.
Gorski JM, Schwartz LH: Shoulder impingement presenting as neck pain, *J Bone Joint Surg* 85:635, 2003.
Green A: Chronic massive rotator cuff tears: evaluation and management, *J Am Acad Orthop Surg* 11:321, 2003.
Tashjian RZ et al: The effect of comorbidity on self-assessed function in patients with chronic rotator cuff tears, *J Bone Joint Surg* 86A:355, 2004.
Teefey SA et al: Detection and quantification of rotator cuff tears, *J Bone Joint Surg* 86A:708, 2004.
Wendelboe AM et al: Associations between body mass index and surgery for rotator cuff tendinitis, *J Bone Joint Surg* 86A:743, 2004.

AUTHOR: **LONNIE R. MERCIER, M.D.**

Rubella (German Measles) 

BASIC INFORMATION

DEFINITION

Rubella is a mild illness caused by the rubella virus that can cause severe congenital problems via in vitro transmission to the fetus when a pregnant woman becomes infected.

SYNONYMS

German measles

ICD-9CM CODES
056.9 Rubella
771.0 (Congenital)
V04.3 (Vaccination)

EPIDEMIOLOGY & DEMOGRAPHICS

- Before vaccination (i.e., before 1969): 28 reported cases per 100,000 person-years, 8 of which were in persons over age 15 yr
  Four cases of congenital rubella syndrome per 100,000 live births
- After mass vaccination (i.e., after 1980) most cases have occurred in unimmunized people, with fewer than 1 case/100,000 person-years (acquired and congenital).
- Currently, 10%-20% of childbearing-age women are susceptible.
- The highest risk of developing long-term complications of congenital infection exists during the first trimester of gestation; both risk of congenital infection and long-term complications drop during the second trimester, and although the risk of congenital infection increases during the third trimester, there is no risk of long-term complication at that point.

PHYSICAL FINDINGS & CLINICAL PRESENTATION

Acquired infection
- Incubation: 14-21 days
- Prodrome: 1-5 days; low-grade fever, headache, malaise, anorexia, mild conjunctivitis, coryza, pharyngitis, cough, and cervical, suboccipital, and postauricular lymphadenopathy
- Rash: 1-5 days

Enanthema: palatal macules
Exanthema (rash): blotchy eruption beginning on face and neck and then spreading to trunk and limbs
- Occasional splenomegaly and hepatitis (during rash)
- Complications: arthritis (15%, mostly in adult women), thrombocytopenia, myocarditis, optic neuritis, encephalitis (all less than 0.1%)

Congenital infection
- Deafness: 85%
- Intrauterine growth retardation: 70%
- Cataracts: 35%
- Retinopathy: 35%
- Patent ductus arteriosus: 30%
- Pulmonary artery hypoplasia: 25%
- In utero death: 20%
- Mental retardation: 10% to 20%
- Meningoencephalitis: 10% to 20%
- Behavior disorder: 10% to 20%
- Hepatosplenomegaly: 10% to 20%
- Bone radiolucencies: 10% to 20%
- Diabetes mellitus (type 1): 10% to 20% by age 35 yr
- Other congenital heart defects: 2% to 5%

ETIOLOGY & PATHOGENESIS

Acquired infection
- Viral portal of entry is upper respiratory tract.
- Viral replication occurs in lymph nodes, then hematogenous dissemination occurs to many organs, including placenta if present.
- Immune complexes may be cause of rash and arthritis.

Congenital infection
- Fetus is infected via placenta during maternal acquired infection.
- Cellular damage in the fetus results from cytolysis of fetal cells, mostly via a fetal vasculitis or from an immune-mediated inflammation and damage.

DIAGNOSIS

DIFFERENTIAL DIAGNOSIS

Acquired rubella syndrome
- Other viral infections by enteroviruses, adenoviruses, human parvovirus B-19, measles
- Scarlet fever
- Allergic reaction
- Kawasaki disease

Congenital rubella syndrome
- Congenital syphilis, toxoplasmosis, herpes simplex, cytomegalovirus, and enterovirus can cause a similar set of problems.

WORKUP

Acquired infection
- Serologic test (hemagglutination inhibition, neutralization tests, complement fixation tests, passive agglutination, enzyme immunoassay [EIA], enzyme-linked immunosorbent assay [ELISA])
- IgM antibodies (by EIA) are detected early: second to fourth week
- IgG antibodies (by ELISA) can be measured as acute phase (7 days after rash onset) and convalescent phase (14 days later)

Congenital infection
- Viral culture (from nasopharynx)
- Serologic studies: IgM antirubella virus detection by EIA is the method of choice (after the newborn is 5 mo old)

IMMUNIZATION

Four existing vaccines provide persisting immunity in 92% of vaccinees. Indications:
- All children 12 mo or older (as part of the measles-mumps-rubella vaccine)
- Postpubertal women

Vaccinate if not known to be immunized (advise not to become pregnant within 3 mo of vaccination)
Premarital serologic screening for rubella immunity
Prenatal or antepartum serologic screening for rubella
Vaccinate susceptible women postpartum
Serologic screening for female workers likely to be exposed to rubella (e.g., teachers, child care employees, health care workers)
Contraindications
- Pregnancy
- Recent receipt of immune globulin or blood transfusion (2 wk before to 3 mo after)
- Immunodeficiency (except AIDS)

Adverse reaction
- Fever, rash, or lymphadenopathy: 5% to 15%
- Arthralgias: 0.5% in children; 25% in adult women
- Transient peripheral neuropathy (rare)

TREATMENT

- No known effective antiviral therapy
- Management of specific congenital problems as appropriate

SUGGESTED READINGS

Rakowsky A, Sever JL: Rubella. In Gorbach SL, Bartlett JG, Blacklow NR (eds): *Infectious diseases,* ed 2, Philadelphia, 1998, WB Saunders.

U.S. Department of Health: Control and prevention of rubella: evaluation and management of suspected outbreaks, rubella in pregnant women, and surveillance for congenital rubella syndrome, *MMWR* 50(RR-12):1, 2001.

AUTHOR: **TOM J. WACHTEL, M.D.**

BASIC INFORMATION

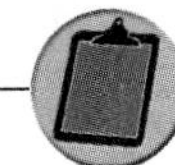

DEFINITION

Salivary gland neoplasms are benign or malignant tumors of a salivary gland (parotid, submandibular, or sublingual).

SYNONYMS

These tumors are often named according to their histologic type (see below).

ICD-9CM CODES
142.9 Salivary gland neoplasm
142.0 (Parotid)
142.1 (Submandibular)
142.2 (Sublingual)

EPIDEMIOLOGY & DEMOGRAPHICS

INCIDENCE: 1 to 2 cases/100,000 person-years (1% of all head and neck tumors)

DISTRIBUTION:
- Parotid gland 85% (80% are benign)
- Submandibular gland 10% (55% are benign)
- Sublingual and minor glands 5% (35% are benign)

PHYSICAL FINDINGS & CLINICAL PRESENTATION

- Parotid gland:
  1. Painless swelling overlying the masseter muscle (under the temporomandibular joint)
  2. Pain
  3. Facial nerve palsy
  4. Cervical lymph nodes
  5. Mass in oral cavity
- Submandibular gland: swelling under anterior portion of the mandible
- Sublingual gland: intraoral swelling under the tongue, medial to the mandible

DIAGNOSIS

PATHOLOGY

History

BENIGN TUMORS:
- Mixed tumor (usually parotid)
- Adenolymphoma (Warthin's tumor)
- Adenoma
- Hemangioma, lymphangioma (in children)
- Other

MALIGNANT TUMORS:
- Mucoepidermoid carcinoma
- Adenoid cystic carcinoma
- Adenocarcinoma
- Malignant mixed tumor
- Squamous cell carcinoma
- Other

Stage (TNM)

T_0 No evidence of primary tumor
T_1 Tumor <2 cm
T_2 Tumor 2 to 4 cm
T_3 Tumor 4 to 6 cm
T_4 Tumor >6 cm

All subdivided into
- Without local extension
- With local extension

N_0 No lymph node metastasis
N_1 Single ipsilateral node <3 cm
N_2 Ipsilateral, contralateral, or bilateral node <6 cm
N_3 Any node >6 cm
M_0 No distant metastasis
M_1 Distant metastasis

Stage I T_{1a} or $_{2a}N_0M_0$
Stage II $T_{1b,2b,3a}$ N_0M_0
Stage III $T_{3b,4a}$ N_0M_0 or any T except $_{4b}N_1M_0$
Stage IV T_{4b} any N any M or any T $N_{2,3}M_0$ or any T, any N_1M_1

WORKUP

- Fine-needle aspiration
- Imaging by CT scan or MRI
- Open biopsy (rarely indicated)

TREATMENT

Malignant tumors:
- Surgery is the mainstay of treatment; gland resection and neck dissection if lymph nodes are involved
- Postoperative radiation
- Chemotherapy

Benign tumors: surgery for tumor resection

PROGNOSIS OF MALIGNANT TUMORS

Five-year survival rates:
- Mucoepidermoid carcinoma: 75% to 95%
- Adenoid cystic carcinoma: 40% to 80%
- Adenocarcinoma: 20% to 75%
- Malignant mixed tumor: 35% to 75%
- Squamous cell carcinoma: 25% to 60%

SUGGESTED READING

Kaplan MJ, Johns ME: Malignant salivary neoplasms. In Cummings CW (ed): *Otolaryngology: head and neck surgery,* St Louis, 1992, Mosby.

AUTHOR: **TOM J. WACHTEL, M.D.**

BASIC INFORMATION

DEFINITION

Salmonellosis is an infection caused by one of several serotypes of *Salmonella.*

SYNONYMS

Typhoid
Typhoid fever
Enteric fever

ICD-9CM CODES
003.0 Salmonellosis

EPIDEMIOLOGY & DEMOGRAPHICS

INCIDENCE (IN U.S.):
- Estimated 1 million cases/yr of nontyphoidal salmonellosis
- Approximately 500 cases of *Salmonella typhi* infection reported each year
- Largest outbreak: 200,000 persons who ingested contaminated milk

PREDOMINANT AGE:
- <20 yr old
- >70 yr old
- Highest rates of infection in infants, especially neonates

PEAK INCIDENCE: Summer and fall
GENETICS:
Neonatal Infection: Highly susceptible to infection with nontyphoidal Salmonella

PHYSICAL FINDINGS & CLINICAL PRESENTATION

- Infections
  1. Localized to GI tract (gastroenteritis)
  2. Systemic (typhoid fever)
  3. Localized outside of GI tract
- Gastroenteritis
  1. Accounts for majority of disease in humans
  2. Incubation period: generally 12 to 48 hr
  3. Nausea
  4. Vomiting
  5. Diarrhea
  6. Abdominal cramps
  7. Fever
  8. Bacteremia
     a. Uncommon
     b. Occurs mostly in the immunocompromised host or those with underlying conditions
  9. Self-limited illness lasting 3 or 4 days
  10. Colonization of GI tract persistent for months, especially in those treated with antibiotics
- Typhoid fever
  1. Incubation period of few days to several months, usually several weeks
  2. Prolonged fever
  3. Myalgias
  4. Headache
  5. Cough
  6. Sore throat
  7. Malaise
  8. Anorexia
  9. Abdominal pain
  10. Hepatosplenomegaly
  11. Diarrhea or constipation early in the course of illness
  12. Rose spots (faint, maculopapular, blanching lesions) sometimes seen on chest or abdomen
- Untreated disease
  1. Fever lasting 1 to 2 mo
  2. Main complication of untreated disease: GI bleeding caused by perforation from ulceration of Peyer's patches in the ileum (Fig. 1-207)
  3. Rare complications:
     a. Mental status changes
     b. Shock
  4. Relapse rate of approximately 10%
- Infections outside GI tract
  1. Can occur in virtually any location
  2. Rare
  3. Usually occur in patients with underlying diseases
  4. Endovascular infections are caused by seeding of atherosclerotic plaques or aneurysms
  5. Endocarditis is a rare complication
  6. Hepatic or splenic abscesses in patients with underlying disease in these organs
  7. Urinary tract infections in patients with renal TB or schistosomiasis
  8. Salmonellae are a frequent cause of gram-negative meningitis in neonates
  9. Osteomyelitis in children with hemoglobinopathies may be caused by these organisms

ETIOLOGY

- More than 2000 serotypes of *Salmonella* exist, but only a few cause disease in humans.
- Some found only in humans are the cause of enteric fever.
  1. *S. typhi*
  2. *S. paratyphi*
- Some responsible for gastroenteritis and frequently isolated from raw meat and poultry and uncooked or undercooked eggs.
  1. *S. typhimurium*
  2. *S. enteritidis*
- *S. cholerae-suis* is a prototype organism that causes extraintestinal nontyphoidal disease.
- Transmission generally via ingestion of contaminated food or drink.

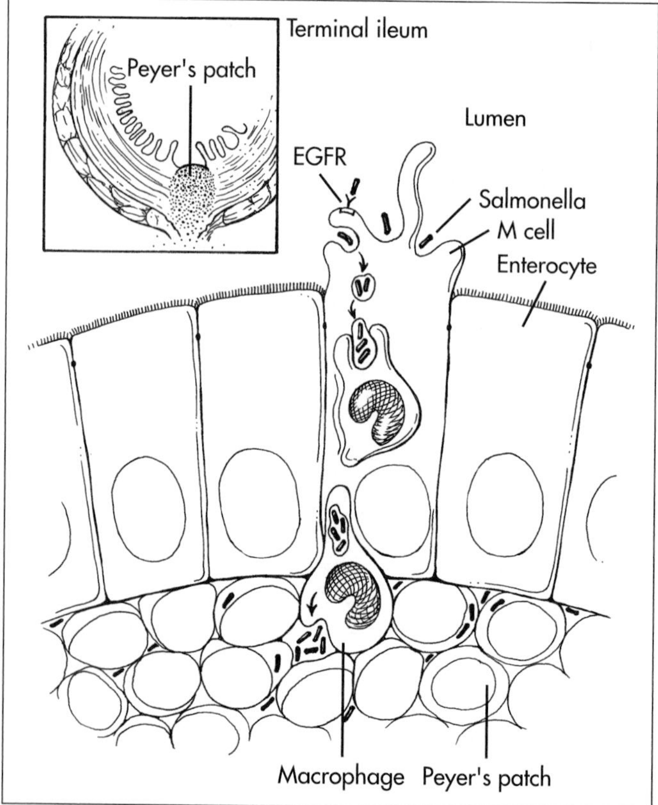

FIGURE 1-207 *Salmonella typhi* invade M cells through membrane ruffling and EGF receptor-dependent pathways. Macrophages originating from Peyer's patch take up *S. typhi* in close association with M cells. *S. typhi* replicate in Peyer's patches and then enter the lymphatic system, leading to bacteremia. Replication in Peyer's patches causes hypertrophy followed by necrosis, which can cause intestinal perforation. (From Stein JH [ed]: *Internal medicine,* ed 5, St Louis, 1998, Mosby.)

- Outbreaks of gastroenteritis related to contaminated poultry, meat, and dairy products.
- Typhoid fever is a systemic illness caused by serotypes exclusive to humans.
  1. Acquisition by ingestion of food or water contaminated by other humans
  2. Most cases in the U.S. are:
     a. Acquired during foreign travel
     b. Acquired by ingestion of food prepared by chronic carriers, many of whom have acquired the organism outside of the U.S.

DIAGNOSIS

DIFFERENTIAL DIAGNOSIS

- Other causes of prolonged fever:
  1. Malaria
  2. TB
  3. Brucellosis
  4. Amebic liver abscess
- Other causes of gastroenteritis:
  1. Bacterial: *Shigella, Yersinia, Campylobacter*
  2. Viral: Norwalk virus, rotavirus
  3. Parasitic: *Amoeba histolytica, Giardia lamblia*
  4. Toxic: enterotoxigenic *E. coli, Clostridium difficile*

WORKUP

- Typhoid fever
  1. Cultures of blood, stool, urine; repeat if initially negative.
  2. Blood cultures are more likely to be positive early in the course of illness.
  3. Stool and urine cultures are more commonly positive in the second and third week of illness.
  4. Highest yield with bone marrow biopsy cultures:
     a. 90% positive
     b. Usually not necessary
  5. Serology using Widal's test is helpful in retrospect, showing a fourfold increase in convalescent titers.
- Gastroenteritis: stool cultures
- Extraintestinal localized infection:
  1. Blood cultures
  2. Cultures from the site of infection

LABORATORY TESTS

- Neutropenia is common
- Transaminitis is possible
- Culture to grow organism: blood, body fluids, biopsy specimens

IMAGING STUDIES

- Radiographs of bone may be suggestive of osteomyelitis.
- CT scan or sonogram of abdomen:
  1. May reveal hepatic or splenic abscesses
  2. May reveal aortic aneurysm

TREATMENT

NONPHARMACOLOGIC THERAPY

Adequate hydration and electrolyte replacement in persons with diarrhea

ACUTE GENERAL Rx

- Typhoid fever:
  1. Ciprofloxacin 500 mg PO bid or 400 mg IV bid for 14 days
  2. Ceftriaxone 2 g IV qd for 14 days
  3. If sensitive, may switch therapy to TMP/SMX 1 to 2 DS tabs PO bid or amoxicillin 2 g PO q8h to complete 14 days
  4. Dexamethasone 3 mg IV initially, followed by 1 mg IV q6h for eight doses for patients with shock or mental status changes
- Gastroenteritis:
  1. Usually not indicated for gastroenteritis alone because this illness usually self-limited
  2. May prolong the carrier state
  3. Prophylactic treatment for patients who are at high risk of developing complications from bacteremia
     a. Neonates
     b. Patients with hemoglobinopathies
     c. Patients with atherosclerosis
     d. Patients with aneurysms
     e. Patients with prosthetic devices
     f. Immunocompromised patients
  4. Treatment can be oral or parenteral, with the same regimens used for typhoid, but only for 48 to 72 hr
- Intravascular infections require 6 wk of parenteral therapy.

CHRONIC Rx

- Carrier states are possible in those with typhoid fever.
- More common in persons >60 yr of age and in persons with gallstones.
- Usual site of colonization is the gallbladder.
- Treatment should be considered for those with persistently positive stool cultures and for food handlers.
- Suggested regimens for eradication of carrier state:
  1. Ciprofloxacin 500 mg PO bid for 4 wk
  2. SMX/TMP one to two DS tabs PO bid for 6 wk (if susceptible)
  3. Amoxicillin 2 g PO q8h for 6 wk (if susceptible)
- Cholecystectomy may be required in carriers with gallstones who fail medical therapy.
- Prolonged course of oral therapy or lifetime suppression for:
  1. Patients with AIDS who have chronic infection
  2. Patients with AIDS who relapse after therapy

DISPOSITION

- Typhoid fever
  1. Treated patients usually respond to therapy; small percentage of chronic carriers.
  2. Untreated patients may have serious complications.
- Gastroenteritis
  1. Usually self-limited
  2. May be recurrent or persistent in AIDS patients

REFERRAL

- If gastroenteritis is persistent or recurrent
- If there is evidence of extraintestinal infection
- For typhoid fever
- For chronic carriers

PEARLS & CONSIDERATIONS

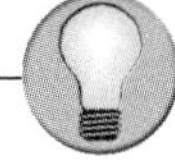

COMMENTS

- Quinolones should not be used in children or pregnant women.
- Infections should be reported to local health departments.

SUGGESTED READINGS

Benenson S et al: The risk of vascular infections in adult patients with nontyphi *Salmonella bacteremia, Am J Med* 110(1):60, 2001.

Outbreaks of multi-drug resistant *Salmonella typhimurium* associated with veterinary facilities. *MMWR* 50(33):701, 2001.

Soravia-Dunand VA et al: Aortitis due to Salmonella: report of 10 cases and comprehensive review of the literature, *Clin Infect Dis* 29:862, 1999.

AUTHOR: **MAURICE POLICAR, M.D.**

BASIC INFORMATION

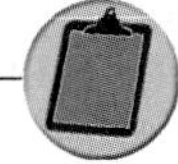

DEFINITION

Sarcoidosis is a chronic systemic granulomatous disease of unknown cause, characterized histologically by the presence of nonspecific, noncaseating granulomas.

SYNONYMS

Boeck's sarcoid

ICD-9CM CODES
135.0 Sarcoidosis

EPIDEMIOLOGY & DEMOGRAPHICS

- Incidence in U.S.: 10.9/100,000 whites, 35.5/100,000 blacks
- Increased incidence in females and patients 20 to 40 yr old
- Presents most commonly in the winter and early spring

PHYSICAL FINDINGS & CLINICAL PRESENTATION

- Clinical manifestations often vary with the stage of the disease and degree of organ involvement; patients may be asymptomatic, but a chest x-ray may demonstrate findings consistent with sarcoidosis (see "Imaging Studies"). Nearly 50% of patients with sarcoidosis are diagnosed by incidental findings on chest x-ray.
- Frequent manifestations:
  1. Pulmonary manifestations: dry, nonproductive cough, dyspnea, chest discomfort
  2. Constitutional symptoms: fatigue, weight loss, anorexia, malaise
  3. Visual disturbances: blurred vision, ocular discomfort, conjunctivitis, iritis, uveitis
  4. Dermatologic manifestations: erythema nodosum, macules, papules, subcutaneous nodules, hyperpigmentation, lupus pernio
  5. Myocardial disturbances: arrhythmias, cardiomyopathy
  6. Splenomegaly, hepatomegaly
  7. Rheumatologic manifestations: arthralgias have been reported in up to 40% of patients
  8. Neurologic and other manifestations: cranial nerve palsies, diabetes insipidus, meningeal involvement, parotid enlargement, hypothalamic and pituitary lesions, peripheral adenopathy

DIAGNOSIS

DIFFERENTIAL DIAGNOSIS

- TB
- Lymphoma
- Hodgkin's disease
- Metastases
- Pneumoconioses
- Enlarged pulmonary arteries
- Infectious mononucleosis
- Lymphangitic carcinomatosis
- Idiopathic hemosiderosis
- Alveolar cell carcinoma
- Pulmonary eosinophilia
- Hypersensitivity pneumonitis
- Fibrosing alveolitis
- Collagen disorders
- Parasitic infection

Section II describes the differential diagnosis of granulomatous lung disease and a classification of granulomatous disorders.

WORKUP

- Chest x-ray and biopsy. Initial lab evaluation should include CBC, serum chemistries, urinalysis, and tuberculin test. ECG should also be obtained in all patients with sarcoidosis.
- Biopsy should be done on accessible tissues suspected of sarcoid involvement (conjunctiva, skin, lymph nodes); bronchoscopy with transbronchial biopsy is the procedure of choice in patients without any readily accessible site.

LABORATORY TESTS

Laboratory abnormalities:

- Hypergammaglobulinemia, anemia, leukopenia
- LFT abnormalities
- Hypercalcemia, hypercalciuria (secondary to increased GI absorption, abnormal vitamin D metabolism, and increased calcitriol production by sarcoid granuloma)
- Cutaneous anergy to *Trichophyton, Candida,* mumps, and tuberculin
- Angiotensin-converting enzyme (ACE): elevated in approximately 60% of patients with sarcoidosis; nonspecific and generally not useful in following the course of the disease

IMAGING STUDIES

- Chest x-ray (Fig. 1-208): adenopathy of the hilar and paratracheal nodes is a frequent finding; parenchymal changes may also be present, depending on the stage of the disease (stage 0, normal x-ray; stage I, bilateral hilar adenopathy; stage II, stage I plus pulmonary infiltrate; stage III, pulmonary infiltrate without adenopathy); stage IV, advanced fibrosis with evidence of honey-combing, hilar retraction, bullae, cysts, and emphysema.
- PFTs (spirometry and diffusing capacity of the lung for carbon dioxide): may be normal or may reveal a restrictive pattern and/or obstructive pattern.
- Gallium-67 scan: will localize in areas of granulomatous infiltrates; however, it is not specific. The "panda" sign (localization in the lacrimal and salivary glands, giving a "panda" appearance to the face) is suggestive of sarcoidosis.

TREATMENT

GENERAL Rx

- Corticosteroids (Table 1-47) remain the mainstay of therapy when treatment is required (e.g., prednisone 40 mg qd for 8 to 12 wk with gradual tapering of the dose to 10 mg qod over 8 to 12 mo); corticosteroids should be considered in patients with severe symptoms (e.g., dyspnea, chest pain), hypercalcemia, ocular, CNS, or cardiac involvement, and progressive pulmonary disease. Patients with interstitial lung disease benefit from oral steroid therapy for 6-24 mo.
- Patients with progressive disease refractory to corticosteroids may be treated with methotrexate 7.5 to 15 mg once/week or azathioprine.
- Hydroxychloroquine is effective for chronic disfiguring skin lesions.
- NSAIDs are useful for musculoskeletal symptoms and erythema nodosum.
- Pulmonary rehabilitation in patients with significant respiratory insufficiency.

DISPOSITION

- The majority of patients with sarcoidosis have spontaneous remission within 2 yr and do not require treatment. Their course can be followed by periodic clinical evaluation, chest x-ray, and PFTs.
- Blacks have increased rates of pulmonary involvement, a worse long-term prognosis, and more frequent relapses.

- Adverse prognostic factors in sarcoidosis include age of onset >40 yr, cardiac involvement, neurosarcoidosis, progressive pulmonary fibrosis, chronic hypercalcemia, chronic uveitis, involvement of nasal mucosa, nephrocalcinosis, and presence of cystic bone lesions and lupus pernio.

REFERRAL

Ophthalmologic examination is indicated in all patients with suspected sarcoidosis, because ocular findings (iridocyclitis, uveitis, conjunctivitis, and keratopathy) are found in >25% of documented cases.

PEARLS & CONSIDERATIONS

COMMENTS

Approximately 15% to 20% of patients with lung involvement advance to irreversible lung impairment (bronchiectasis, cavitation, progressive fibrosis, pneumothorax, and respiratory failure). Death from pulmonary failure occurs in 5% to 7% of patients with sarcoidosis.

SUGGESTED READINGS

Paramothayan S, Jones PW: Corticosteroid therapy in pulmonary sarcoidosis, *JAMA* 287:1301, 2002.

Thomas KW, Hunninghake GW: Sarcoidosis, *JAMA* 289:3300, 2003.

Wu JJ, Schiff KR: Sarcoidosis, *Am Fam Physician* 70:312, 2004.

AUTHOR: **FRED F. FERRI, M.D.**

A

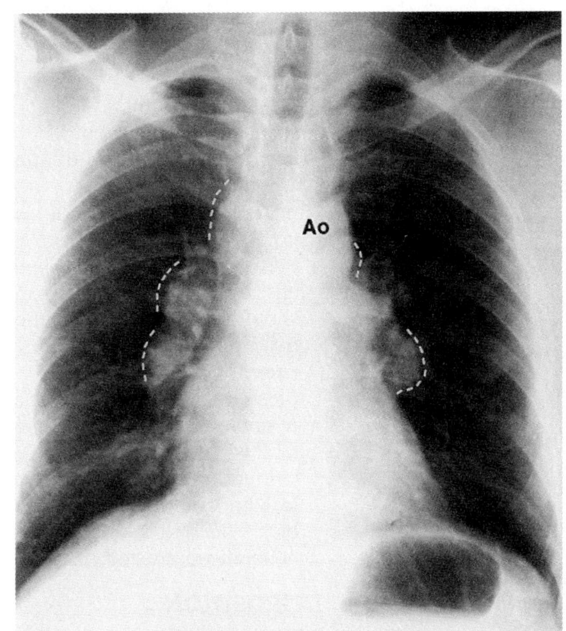

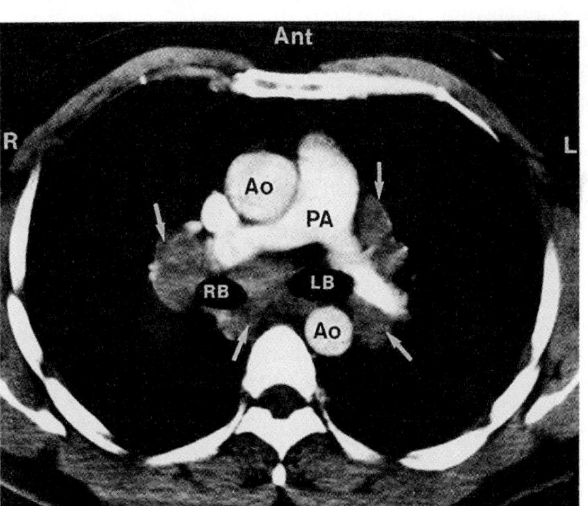

B

FIGURE 1-208 Sarcoid. Marked lymphadenopathy (*dotted lines*) is seen in the region of both hila in the right paratracheal region **(A)**. The transverse contrast-enhanced CT scan of the upper chest **(B)** clearly shows the ascending and descending aorta (*Ao*) as well as the pulmonary artery (*PA*) and superior vena cava. The right and left mainstem bronchus area is also seen. The arrows indicate the extensive lymphadenopathy. *LB,* Left bronchus; *RB,* right bronchus. (From Mettler FA [ed]: *Primary care radiology,* Philadelphia, 2000, WB Saunders.)

TABLE 1-47 **Indications for Use of Corticosteroids in Sarcoidosis**

Disorder	Treatment
Iridocyclitis	Corticosteroid eyedrops Local subjunctival deposit of cortisone
Posterior uveitis	Oral prednisone
Pulmonary involvement	Steroids rarely recommended for stage I; usually employed if infiltrate remains static or worsens over 3-mo period or the patient is symptomatic
Upper airway obstruction	Rare indication for intravenous steroids
Lupus pernio	Oral prednisone shrinks the disfiguring lesions
Hypercalcemia	Responds well to corticosteroids
Cardiac involvement	Corticosteroids usually recommended if patient has arrhythmias or conduction disturbances
CNS involvement	Response is best in patients with acute symptoms
Lacrimal/salivary gland involvement	Corticosteroids recommended for disordered function, not gland swelling
Bone cysts	Corticosteroids recommended if symptomatic

From Andreoli TE (ed): *Cecil essentials of medicine,* ed 5, Philadelphia, 2001, WB Saunders.
CNS, Central nervous system.

BASIC INFORMATION

DEFINITION

Scabies is a contagious disease caused by the mite *Sarcoptes scabiei.*

ICD-9CM CODES
133.0 Scabies

EPIDEMIOLOGY & DEMOGRAPHICS

- Scabies is generally acquired by sleeping with or in the bedding of infested individuals.
- It is generally associated with poor living conditions and is also common in hospitals and nursing homes.

PHYSICAL FINDINGS & CLINICAL PRESENTATION

- Primary lesions are caused when the female mite burrows within the stratum corneum, laying eggs within the tract she leaves behind; burrows (linear or serpiginous tracts) end with a minute papule or vesicle.
- Primary lesions are most commonly found in the web spaces of the hands, wrists, buttocks, scrotum, penis, breasts, axillae, and knees.
- Secondary lesions result from scratching or infection.
- Intense pruritus, especially nocturnal, is common; it is caused by an acquired sensitivity to the mite or fecal pellets and is usually noted 1 to 4 wk after the primary infestation.
- Examination of the skin may reveal burrows, tiny vesicles, excoriations, inflammatory papules.
- Widespread and crusted lesions (Norwegian or crusted scabies) may be seen in elderly and immunocompromised patients.

ETIOLOGY

Human scabies is caused by the mite *Sarcoptes scabiei,* var. *hominis* (Fig. 1-209).

DIAGNOSIS

DIFFERENTIAL DIAGNOSIS

- Pediculosis
- Atopic dermatitis
- Flea bites
- Seborrheic dermatitis
- Dermatitis herpetiformis
- Contact dermatitis
- Nummular eczema
- Syphilis
- Other insect infestation

WORKUP

Diagnosis is made on the clinical presentation and on the demonstration of mites, eggs, or mite feces.

LABORATORY TESTS

- Microscopic demonstration of the organism, feces, or eggs: a drop of mineral oil may be placed over the suspected lesion before removal; the scrapings are transferred directly to a glass slide; a drop of potassium hydroxide is added and a cover slip is applied.
- Skin biopsy is rarely necessary to make the diagnosis.

TREATMENT

NONPHARMACOLOGIC THERAPY

Clothing, underwear, and towels used in the 48 hr before treatment must be laundered.

ACUTE GENERAL Rx

- Following a warm bath or shower, Lindane (Kwell, Scabene) lotion should be applied to all skin surfaces below the neck (can be applied to the face if area is infested); it should be washed off 8-12 hr after application. Repeat application 1 wk later is usually sufficient to eradicate infestation.
- Pruritus generally abates 24-48 hr after treatment, but it can last up to 2 wk; oral antihistamines are effective in decreasing postscabietic pruritus.
- Topical corticosteroid creams may hasten the resolution of secondary eczematous dermatitis.
- If the patient is a resident of an extended care facility, it is important to educate the patients, staff, family, and frequent visitors about scabies and the need to have full cooperation in treatment. Scabicide should be applied to all patients, staff, and frequent visitors, whether symptomatic or not; symptomatic family members of staff and visitors should also receive treatment.
- Permethrin 5% cream (Elimite) is also effective with usually one treatment; it should be massaged into the skin from head to soles of feet; remove 8-14 hr later by washing. If living mites are present after 14 days, treat again.
- A single dose (150-200 mg/kg in 6-mg tablets) of ivermectin, an antihelminthic agent, is as effective as topical lindane for the treatment of scabies. It is the best treatment for generalized crusted scabies.

DISPOSITION

Refractory cases usually are seen with immunocompromised hosts or patients with underlying skin diseases.

PEARLS & CONSIDERATIONS

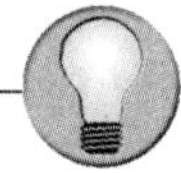

COMMENTS

- Lindane is potentially neurotoxic and should not be used for infants and pregnant women (permethrin is safe and effective in these situations).
- Sexual partners should be notified and treated.

SUGGESTED READINGS

Fawcett RS: Ivermectin use in scabies, *Am Fam Physician* 68:1089, 2003.

Flinders DC, DeSchweinitz P: Pediculosis and scabies, *Am Fam Physician* 341:8, 2004.

AUTHOR: **FRED F. FERRI, M.D.**

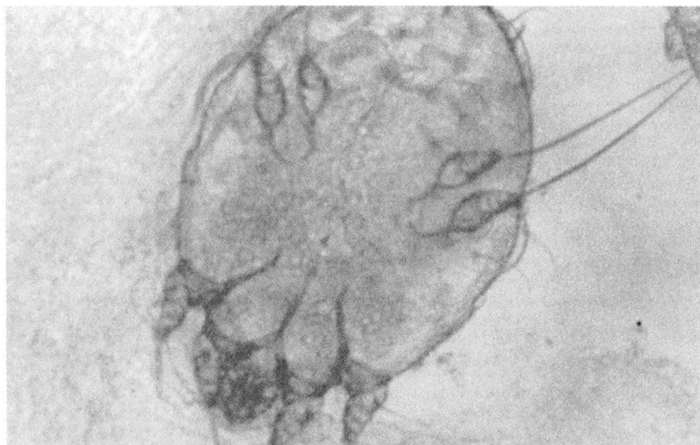

FIGURE 1-209 Scabies organism in a wet mount preparation. (From Mandell GL: *Mandell, Douglas, and Bennett's principles and practice of infectious diseases,* ed 5, New York, 2000, Churchill Livingstone.)

Scarlet Fever

BASIC INFORMATION

DEFINITION

Scarlet fever is a rash involving skin and tongue and complicating a streptococcal group A pharyngitis.

ICD-9CM CODES
034.1 Scarlet fever

EPIDEMIOLOGY & DEMOGRAPHICS

Same as streptococcal pharyngitis; namely, children aged 5-15 yr. May also complicate impetigo.

PHYSICAL FINDINGS & CLINICAL PRESENTATION

CLINICAL PRESENTATION:

- Febrile illness with headache, malaise, anorexia, and pharyngitis begins after a 2- to 4-day incubation period.
- Scarlatinal rash begins 1 or 2 days after the onset of pharyngitis (Fig. 1-210).

PHYSICAL FINDINGS:

- Diffuse erythema, beginning on face and spreading to neck, back, chest, rest of trunk, and extremities. Most intense on inner aspects of arms and thighs
- Erythema blanches, but nonblanching petechiae may be present or produced by a tourniquet
- Strawberry or raspberry tongue
- Rash lasts about 1 wk and then desquamates

ETIOLOGY

Caused by group A β-hemolytic *Streptococcus* infection, which produces one of three erythrogenic toxins (NOTE: Some streptococcal species have the ability to cause both scarlet fever and rheumatic fever)

DIAGNOSIS

DIFFERENTIAL DIAGNOSIS

- Viral exanthems (covered in Section II)
- Kawasaki disease
- Toxic shock syndrome
- Drug rashes

See differential diagnosis of Pharyngitis in Section I.

WORKUP

- Identification of group A *Streptococcus* by throat culture
- SLO antibody titers

TREATMENT

- Penicillin 250 mg PO qid for 10 days or erythromycin 250 mg PO qid for 10 days in penicillin-allergic patients
- Benzathine penicillin 1 to 2 million U IM once; may be used for a patient who cannot swallow

COMPLICATIONS (RARE)

- Peritonsillar abscess
- Mastoiditis
- Otitis media
- Pneumonia
- Sepsis and distant foci of infection
- Acute rheumatic fever
- Inability to swallow liquids or upper airway obstruction require hospitalization

NOTE: Failure to respond to penicillin should raise doubt about the diagnosis because *Streptococcus* may be carried in the pharynx without causing infection.

SUGGESTED READING

Stollerman GH: *Streptococcus pyogenes* (group A streptococci). In Gorbach SL, Bartlett JG, Blacklow NR (eds): *Infectious diseases,* ed 2, Philadelphia, 1998, WB Saunders.

AUTHOR: **TOM J. WACHTEL, M.D.**

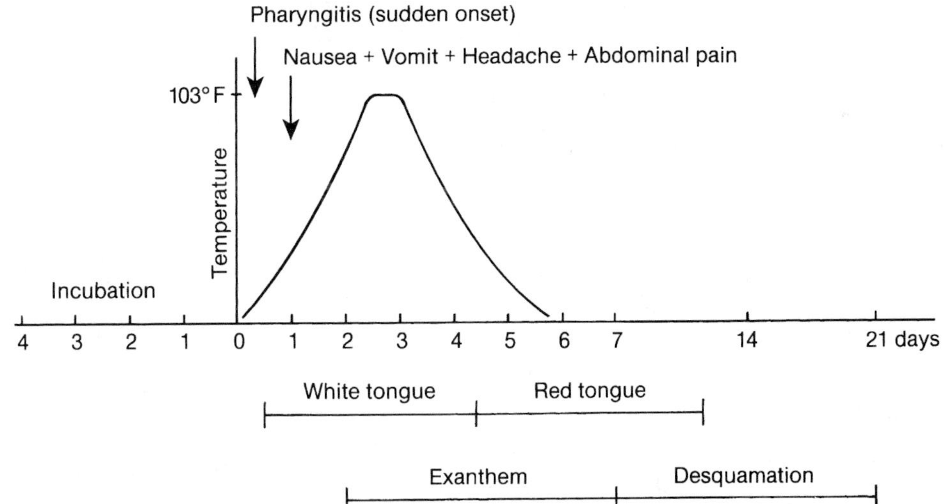

FIGURE 1-210 Scarlet fever. Evolution of signs and symptoms. (From Habif TP: *Clinical dermatology: a color guide to diagnosis and therapy,* ed 3, St Louis, 1996, Mosby.)

BASIC INFORMATION

DEFINITION

Schistosomiasis is caused by infection with parasite blood flukes known as schistosomes.

ICD-9CM CODES
120.9 Schistosomiasis

EPIDEMIOLOGY & DEMOGRAPHICS

INCIDENCE

- More than 200 million people worldwide and more than 200,000 deaths annually. In U.S., estimated to exceed 400,000 persons.
- Geographic distribution of schistosomiasis is confined to an area between 36° north and 34° south latitude, where fresh water temperatures averages 25° C to 30° C.

PREVALENCE

The greatest cercarial exposure usually occurs in boys aged 5-10 yr

DISTRIBUTION

- *S. mansoni* in tropical and subtropical areas of sub-Saharan Africa, the Middle East, South America, and the Caribbean
- *S. haematobium* in North Africa, sub-Saharan Africa, the Middle East, and India
- *S. japonicum* in Asia, particularly in China, the Philippines, Thailand, and Indonesia
- *S. intercalatum* in central and west Africa
- *S. mekonki* in Cambodia

ETIOLOGY

- Human infections are caused by *S. mansoni, S. haematobium, S. japonicum, S. mekonki,* and *S. intercalatum.*
- Acquisition of disease via contact with fresh water containing infectious free-living cercarial larvae.
- In U.S., most cases are acquired during foreign travel.

PATHOGENESIS

Human disease is primarily associated with the host's granulomatous response to eggs retained in the tissue.

PHYSICAL FINDINGS & CLINICAL PRESENTATION

ACUTE SYMPTOMS:

- Swimmers itch
- Katayama fever

CHRONIC SYMPTOMS:

- Intestinal schistosomiasis
  1. Abdominal pain
  2. Bloody diarrhea
  3. Iron deficiency anemia
  4. Intestinal polyp
  5. Bowel ulcer and strictures
- Hepatic schistosomiasis
  1. Hepatomegaly
  2. Splenomegaly
  3. Portal hypertension
  4. Esophageal varices
- Urinary schistosomiasis
  1. Hematuria
  2. Dysuria
  3. Urinary frequency
  4. Fibrosis of bladder and ureters
  5. Squamous cell ca of bladder
  6. Proteinuria
  7. Nephrotic syndrome

COMPLICATION:

- Neurologic complication
  1. Granuloma of spinal cord or brain
  2. Transverse myelitis
  3. Epilepsy or focal neurologic deficit
- Pulmonary complication
  1. Granulomatous pulmonary endarteritis
  2. Pulmonary hypertension
  3. Cor pulmonale
- Other complications include tubal obstruction and infertility
- Recurrent bacteremia and recurrent UTI

DIAGNOSIS

DIFFERENTIAL DIAGNOSIS

- Amebiasis
- Bacillary dysentery
- Bowel polyp
- Prostatic disease
- Genitourinary tract cancer
- Bacterial infections of the urinary tract

WORKUP

- Microscopy in urine or stool
- Tissue biopsy
- Serology
- CBC
- LFT
- US of abdomen
- CT scan of abdomen

LABORATORY TESTS

- CBC shows eosinophilia, anemia, thrombocytopenia
- LFT with mild increase in alkaline phosphatase and GGT
- Microscopy: stool and urine
- Serology: ELISA for detecting both schistosomal antibodies and antigen
- Rectal biopsy or bladder mucosal biopsy

IMAGING STUDIES

- X-ray of abdomen shows "fetal head" calcification.
- Sonography also documents a thickened bladder wall, hydronephrosis and hydroureter, and bladder polyps or calcification. It also demonstrates the thickened fibrosed portal tracts.
- Esophagoscopy documents esophageal varices.
- Liver biopsy may also demonstrate granuloma and clay pipestem fibrosis.

TREATMENT

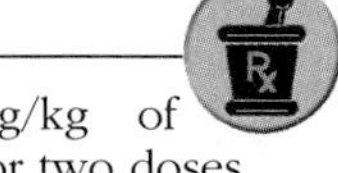

- Praziquantel 40 mg/kg of body weight in one or two doses
- Oxamniquine 15 mg/kg
- Metrifonate 7.5 to 10 mg/kg of body weight given in three doses at 2-wk intervals
- Amoscanate
- Oltipraz

DISPOSITION

Treated patients usually respond to therapy. Definitive cure has occurred only when there is total disappearance of viable eggs from the excreta for a total of 6 mo after treatment.

PEARLS & CONSIDERATIONS

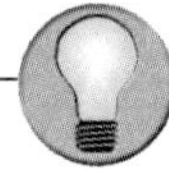

COMMENTS

Prevention:

- Chemotherapy
  1. Mass
  2. Targeted population
- Snail control
  1. Mollusciciding
  2. Environmental modification
  3. Biologic control
- Reduction of water contact and contamination
  1. Provision of domestic water supplies
  2. Provision for sanitary disposal of excreta
- Vaccination
  - Improved living standards

SUGGESTED READINGS

Ross A et al: Current concepts: schistosomiasis, *N Engl J Med* 346:1212, 2002.

Schwartz E et al: Schistosomiasis, *N Engl J Med* 347:766, 2002.

AUTHOR: **VASANTHI ARUMUGAM, M.D.**

BASIC INFORMATION

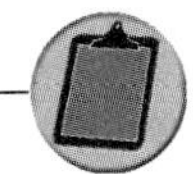

DEFINITION

Schizophrenia is a disorder that causes significant distortions in thinking, perception, speech, and behavior. Characteristics include psychosis, apathy and social withdrawal, and cognitive impairment, which result in significant social impairment.

SYNONYMS

Dementia praecox

ICD-9CM CODES
295.9 Schizophrenia

EPIDEMIOLOGY & DEMOGRAPHICS

PREVALENCE: 0.1%-0.5%, incidence 0.2-0.4 per 1000. Lifetime prevalence risk is 1%.

PREDOMINANT SEX: Males have a more severe illness with earlier onset; however, distribution is probably equal.

PREDOMINANT AGE:

- Age at onset of psychotic symptoms is in the early 20s for males and late 20s for females.
- Age of onset of the negative symptoms is usually earlier (midteenage years).

PEAK INCIDENCE: Ages 16-30

GENETICS:

- Accounts for 70% of risk, remaining 30% is biologic or psychosocial.
- First-degree relatives of schizophrenics have 10 times greater chance of becoming schizophrenic than the general population.
- Discordant rates among identical twins are higher than expected with simple inheritance pattern.
- Associations with several chromosomes have been described, but none have been replicated.
- Evidence exists that triplet nucleotide repeat expansion (such as seen with Huntington's disease) may play a role in inheritance of the disease.

PHYSICAL FINDINGS & CLINICAL PRESENTATION

- Best defined as a dementing illness beginning in early life and progressing slowly throughout the lifetime.
- Initial "negative" symptoms of adolescence—cognitive decline, social withdrawal and awkwardness, loss of motivation and pleasure, and loss of emotional expressiveness—begin after a period of normal development.
- In early adulthood, positive symptoms of psychosis and thought disturbance occur; psychotic symptoms then wax and wane throughout life; treatment ameliorates positive symptoms but generally does little for negative ones.
- It is also accompanied by cognitive impairment, including problems in attention and concentration, psychomotor speed, learning and memory, and executive functions (e.g., abstract thinking, problem solving).
- Social and occupational dysfunction can be profound.

ETIOLOGY

- Unknown.
- Basic distinction of whether this is a degenerative or a developmental condition is not settled.
- Frequent findings include enlargement of ventricular system and loss of brain volume and cortical gray matter.
- Major hypothesis: generation of the mesocortical pathways produce the hypofrontality and negative symptoms, along with a compensatory hyperactivation of the mesolimbic pathways, which produce the positive symptoms of psychosis.

DIAGNOSIS

DIFFERENTIAL DIAGNOSIS

- Schizophrenia is diagnosed when an individual has experienced at least 1 month of hallucinations, delusions, thought disorder, catatonia, or negative symptoms (avolition, anhedonia, social isolation, affective flattening).
- Any medical condition, medicine, or substance of abuse that can affect brain homeostasis and cause psychosis: distinguished from schizophrenia by their relatively brief course and the alteration in mental status that could suggest an underlying delirium.
- Other neurologic conditions (e.g., Huntington's) that have psychosis as the initial presentation.
- Other psychiatric disorders: source of greatest confusion.
- Mood disorders with psychosis: indistinguishable from schizophrenia cross-sectionally, but have a longitudinal course that includes full recovery.
- Delusional disorder: has nonbizarre delusions and lacks the thought disturbance, hallucinations, and negative symptoms of schizophrenia.
- Autism in the adult: has an early age at onset and lacks significant hallucinations or delusions.

WORKUP

- History and physical examination to aid in determining if psychosis is secondary or primary
- Neurologic examination to uncover soft neurologic signs (clumsy, cortical thumb, loss of fine motor movements) common in schizophrenia

LABORATORY TESTS

- No laboratory tests are specific for schizophrenia.
- Laboratory examinations (chemistry profile, blood count, sedimentation rate, toxicology screen, and urinalysis) are geared toward excluding a primary medical condition.

IMAGING STUDIES

- CT scan or MRI of brain during initial workup; repeated if the course of the illness varies from expected
- Sometimes EEG to reveal slowing when psychosis is secondary to an encephalopathy
- Chest x-ray examination during initial workup to rule out a primary medical condition

TREATMENT

NONPHARMACOLOGIC THERAPY

- Significant social support is required by most schizophrenic patients; available support services are grossly inadequate, and schizophrenia patients constitute nearly one third of all homeless individuals. They usually require help with basic social, occupational, and interactive skills.
- For schizophrenic patients who continue to live with their families, family stress can precipitate relapse and rehospitalization; family interventions can reduce morbidity.
- Cognitive behavioral therapy can reduce severity of both psychotic and negative symptoms.
- Illness management training for patients can increase medication adherence and reduce distress due to symptoms.

ACUTE GENERAL Rx

- Acute psychosis is usually adequately controlled by antipsychotic agents.
- Mainstay of therapy is the second-generation antipsychotics (risperidone, olanzapine, quetiapine, ziprasidone, aripiprazole, and clozapine). Traditional neuroleptic (e.g., haloperidol, perphenazine, fluphenazine, chlorpromazine) use is decreasing in part because of their propensity to cause a parkinsonian state and eventual tardive dyskinesia (rate of tardive dyskinesia 15%-30%). Antiparkinsonian drugs (benztropine, amantadine) are used to ameliorate the parkinsonism. Risperidone has been shown to be superior to haloperidol in preventing acute psychotic relapse.
- Sedatives (benzodiazepines, and to a lesser degree, barbiturates) can be used transiently if there is an agitated state.

CHRONIC Rx

- Relapse prevention is a major goal of treatment. Noncompliance is common and leads to high relapse rates. Antipsychotic agents usually must be continued at the same doses that controlled psychosis. For noncompliant patients, depot preparations that are given biweekly or monthly can be used.
- Antiparkinsonian agents may also need to be continued chronically.
- Tardive dyskinesia (choreoathetoid movements of the muscles of tongue, face, and occasionally other muscle groups) can occur in as many as 30% of patients with long-term use of the neuroleptics.
- The negative symptoms of schizophrenia can resemble depression. In addition, depressive disorders may occur in schizophrenic patients. Antidepressant treatment of the negative symptoms is usually without effect. However, antidepressants can improve the symptoms of a discrete comorbid depressive episode.
- Mood stabilizers, such as lithium, valproate, or carbamazepine, are of little use unless there is a comorbid impulse control disorder.
- Substance abuse is a major problem in more than one third of schizophrenics. Unfortunately, these patients do poorly in traditional substance abuse treatment programs. Specialized "dual diagnosis" programs with highly structured aftercare are required.
- Specific antipsychotics have been associated with weight gain and QT prolongation. Hyperlipidemia and diabetes mellitus are associated with second-generation antipsychotics, and hyperprolactinemia is associated with first-generation antipsychotics.

DISPOSITION

- The positive symptoms of as many as 20%-30% of schizophrenic patients do not respond to available treatments. A much higher fraction relapse as a result of poor compliance.
- The negative symptoms are responsible for the 50%-70% of cases in which deterioration in occupational and social function continues.
- Approximately 10% of patients will complete suicide.
- Course of illness most strongly predicted by level of social development attained at onset of psychosis.

REFERRAL

- If hospitalization is required
- If patient is noncompliant
- If patient is resistant to treatment

SUGGESTED READINGS

Csernansky JG et al: A comparison of risperidone and haloperidol for the prevention of relapse in patients with schizophrenia, *N Engl J Med* 346:16, 2002.

Freedman R: Schizophrenia, *N Engl J Med* 349:1738, 2003.

Marder SR et al: Physical health monitoring of patients with schizophrenia, *Am J Psychiatry* 161:1334, 2004.

Mueser KT, McGurk SR: Schizophrenia, *Lancet* 363:2063, 2004.

AUTHOR: **MICHAEL K. ONG, M.D., Ph.D.**

SECTION I

BASIC INFORMATION

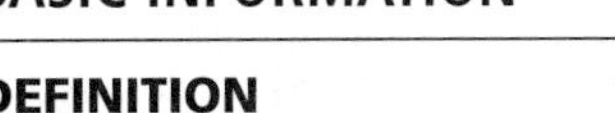

DEFINITION

Scleritis is inflammation of the sclera.

SYNONYMS

Anterior scleritis
Diffuse nodular, necrotizing scleritis
Scleromalacia perforans
Scleral melt syndrome

ICD-9CM CODES
379.0 Scleritis and episcleritis

EPIDEMIOLOGY & DEMOGRAPHICS

INCIDENCE (IN U.S.): Busy ophthalmologist may see one or two cases a year
PREVALENCE (IN U.S.): Relatively rare
PREDOMINANT SEX: 61% women
PREDOMINANT AGE: 52 yr
PEAK INCIDENCE: Increases with increasing age

PHYSICAL FINDINGS & CLINICAL PRESENTATION

- Deep, boring eye pain
- Photophobia
- Tearing
- Conjunctival injection (Fig. 1-211)
- Thinning of the sclera
- 44% of patients have associated medical conditions: 7% infections, 37% rheumatic disease. Most common infection is Herpes zoster. Most common rheumatic problem is rheumatoid arthritis. 4% have systemic vasculitis. Most patients with systemic disease are diagnosed before development of scleritis.

ETIOLOGY

- Inflammatory
- Allergic
- Toxic

DIAGNOSIS

DIFFERENTIAL DIAGNOSIS

- Most common causes are rheumatoid arthritis and collagen-vascular disease.
- Occasionally, there are allergic, infectious, or traumatic causes.
- Conjunctivitis, iritis, and episcleritis should be considered in the differential diagnosis.

WORKUP

- Fluorescein angiography
- Eye examination
- Visual field examination
- Workup for autoimmune disease
- Workup for vascuitis
- Collagen vascular workup

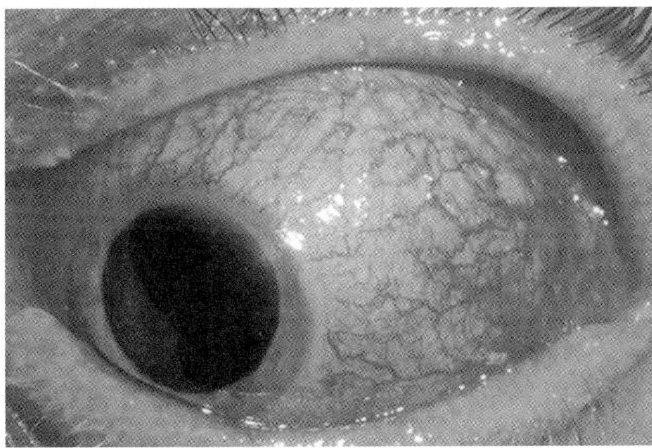

FIGURE 1-211 In diffuse anterior scleritis, widespread injection of the conjunctival and deep episcleral vessels occurs. (From Palay D [ed]: *Ophthalmology for the primary care physician,* St Louis, 1997, Mosby.)

LABORATORY TESTS

- RF, ANA, ESR may be useful
- For underlying etiology

IMAGING STUDIES

Usually not necessary; CT scan of orbit may be useful in selected patients for collagen vascular disease or vasculitis

TREATMENT

NONPHARMACOLOGIC THERAPY

- Patching
- Bandage lenses
- Surgery if thinning of the sclera is severe to prevent eye rupture
- Immunotherapy (with steroids and Imuran, etc.)

ACUTE GENERAL Rx

- Steroids (topical, periocular, and systemic)
- Cycloplegic drops
- NSAIDs (topical and systemic)
- Other immunosuppressive drugs

CHRONIC Rx

- Systemic steroids can be given for the underlying disease.
- Local steroids may be helpful.
- Control underlying disease.

DISPOSITION

Urgent referral to ophthalmologist

REFERRAL

If not referred to an ophthalmologist early, patients may develop uveitis and other complications.

PEARLS & CONSIDERATIONS

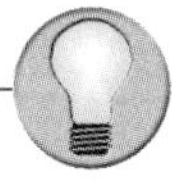

COMMENTS

An ominous diagnosis because these patients often have other severe underlying debilitating disease processes.

SUGGESTED READINGS

Akpek EK et al: Evaluation of patients with scleritis for systemic disease, *Ophthalmology* 111(3):501, 2004.
Paresio CG et al: Systemic disorders associated with episcleritis and scleritis, *Curr Opin Ophthalmal* 12(6):471, 2001.
Sainz de la Maza M et al: Ocular characteristics and disease associations in scleritis: associated peripheral keatopathy, *Arch Ophth* 120(1):15, 2002.
Thorne JE et al: Severe scleritis and urticarial lesions, *Am J Ophthalmol* 134(6):932, 2002.

AUTHOR: **MELVYN KOBY, M.D.**

BASIC INFORMATION

DEFINITION

Scleroderma is a connective tissue disorder characterized by thickening and fibrosis of the skin and variably severe involvement of diverse internal organs.

SYNONYMS

Systemic sclerosis; morphea applies to localized scleroderma affecting only the skin. Scleredema is a disease of the skin distinct from scleroderma.

ICD-9CM CODES
710.1 (Morphea: 701.0)

EPIDEMIOLOGY & DEMOGRAPHICS

INCIDENCE: 4 to 12 cases/million persons per year, but many mild cases go unrecognized
DEMOGRAPHICS: Female:male ratio of 4:1
PEAK AGE: 30 to 50 yr
DISTRIBUTION: Worldwide

PHYSICAL FINDINGS & CLINICAL PRESENTATION

CLINICAL PRESENTATION:
- Raynaud's phenomenon: initial complaint in 70% (NOTE: The prevalence of Raynaud's is 5% to 10% of the general population; most do not progress to scleroderma)
- Finger or hand swelling, sometimes associated with carpal tunnel syndrome
- Arthralgias/arthritis
- Internal organ involvement

PHYSICAL FINDINGS:

Skin
- Begins on hands, then face; skin is shiny, taut, sometimes red with loss of creases and hair
- Later skin tightening may limit movement
- Pigmentary changes occur
- Skin atrophy occurs in late stages

Musculoskeletal
- Symmetric inflammatory arthritis
- Myopathy

GI involvement
- Esophageal dysmotility with heartburn, dysphagia, odynophagia
- Delayed gastric emptying
- Small bowel dysmotility with abdominal cramps and diarrhea
- Colon dysmotility with constipation
- Primary biliary cirrhosis (see "Primary Biliary Cirrhosis" in Section I)

Pulmonary manifestations
- Pulmonary fibrosis with symptoms of dyspnea and nonproductive cough and fine inspiratory crackles on examination
- Pulmonary hypertension

Cardiac involvement
- Myocardial fibrosis leading to congestive heart failure

Renal involvement
- Malignant hypertension
- Rapidly progressive renal failure

Other organ involvement
- Hypothyroidism
- Erectile dysfunction
- Sjögren's syndrome
- Entrapment neuropathies

CREST syndrome
- Calcinosis, Raynaud's syndrome, esophageal dysmotility, sclerodactyly, telangiectasias (in CREST scleroderma is limited to distal extremities)

ETIOLOGY

Etiology is unknown. Unifying features exist in spite of heterogenous patterns of organ involvement and disease progression:
- Extracellular connective tissue activation
- Frequent immunologic abnormalities
- Inflammation
- Vasoconstriction

DIAGNOSIS

DIFFERENTIAL DIAGNOSIS

Dermatologic
- Mycosis fungoides
- Amyloidosis
- Porphyria cutanea tarda
- Eosinophilic fasciitis
- Reflex sympathetic dystrophy

Systemic
- Idiopathic pulmonary fibrosis
- Primary pulmonary hypertension
- Primary biliary cirrhosis
- Cardiomyopathies
- GI dysmotility problems
- SLE and overlap syndromes

WORKUP

Laboratory tests and imaging studies

LABORATORY TESTS

- Antinuclear antibodies (homogeneous, speckled, or nucleolar patterns)
- Negative antibody to native DNA
- Negative anti-Sm antibody
- Anti-nRNP positive in 20%
- Rheumatoid factor positive in 30%
- Anticentromere antibodies in fewer than 10% with systemic illness and in 50% to 95% with limited scleroderma (i.e., good prognosis if positive)
- Positive extractable nuclear antibody to SCL 70 in 30%
- Routine biochemistry tests may indicate specific organ involvement (e.g., liver, kidney, muscle)

IMAGING AND OTHER STUDIES

Arthritis: joint x-rays

GI
- Barium swallow
- Cine esophagography
- Endoscopy
- Esophageal manometry

Pulmonary
- Chest x-ray
- PFTs
- Chest CT scan
- Bronchoscopy with biopsy
- Gallium lung scan
- Bronchoalveolar lavage

Heart
- ECG
- Ambulatory (Holter) ECG monitoring
- Echocardiography
- Cardiac catheterization

Kidney: renal biopsy
Skin: skin biopsy

TREATMENT

D-penicillamine; recombinant human relaxin; supportive therapies used.

Raynaud's syndrome:
- Calcium channel blockers
- Peripheral α_1-adrenergic blockers

Arthralgias: NSAIDs
Skin: moisturizing agents
Esophageal reflux
- H_2-receptor blockers
- Proton pump inhibitors

Pulmonary hypertension and fibrosis
- Oxygen
- Lung transplant

Renal involvement
- Angiotensin-converting enzyme inhibitors
- Dialysis
- Renal transplantation

REFERRAL

To rheumatologist

SUGGESTED READINGS

Seibold JR: Scleroderma. In Kelley WN et al (eds): *Textbook of rheumatology,* ed 5, Philadelphia, 1997, WB Saunders.

Seibold JR, Koan JH, Simms R, et al: Recombinant human relaxin in the treatment of scleroderma, *Ann Intern Med* 132:871, 2000.

AUTHOR: **TOM J. WACHTEL, M.D.**

BASIC INFORMATION

DEFINITION

Scoliosis is a lateral curvature of the spine in the upright position, usually 10 degrees or greater. Scoliosis may be classified as either structural (fixed, nonflexible) or nonstructural (flexible, correctable).

ICD-9CM CODES
737.30 Idiopathic scoliosis
737.39 Paralytic scoliosis
754.2 Congenital scoliosis
724.3 Sciatic scoliosis
737.43 Associated with neurofibromatosis

EPIDEMIOLOGY & DEMOGRAPHICS (IDIOPATHIC FORM)

PREVALENCE: 4 cases/1000 persons

PREVALENT AGE:

- Onset is variable.
- Most curves are found in adolescents (age 11 yr and over).

PREDOMINANT SEX: Females > male (7:1)

PHYSICAL FINDINGS & CLINICAL PRESENTATION

- Record patient age (in years plus months) and height.
- Perform neurologic examination to rule out neuromuscular disease.
- Inspect the shoulders and iliac crests to determine if they are level.
- Palpate the spinous processes to determine their alignment.
- Have the patient bend forward symmetrically at the waist with the arms hanging free (Adams' position); observe from the back or front to detect abnormal spine rotation (Fig. 1-212).

ETIOLOGY

- 90% unknown, usually referred to as idiopathic (genetic)
- Congenital spine deformity
- Neuromuscular disease
- Leg length inequality
- Local inflammation or infection
- Acute pain (disk disease)
- Chronic degenerative disc disease with a symmetric disc narrowing

Curves of an idiopathic nature or those accompanying congenital deformity or neuromuscular disease are those associated with structural changes. The nonstructural types (leg length discrepancy, inflammation, or acute pain) disappear when the offending disorder is corrected.

DIAGNOSIS

WORKUP

- Curvatures associated with congenital spine abnormalities, neuromuscular disease, and the other less common forms of scoliosis can usually be identified by history or associated radiographic or physical findings.
- Section III, Scoliosis, describes an approach to scoliosis screening.

IMAGING STUDIES

- Diagnosis of idiopathic scoliosis is confirmed by a standing roentgenogram of the spine.
- Severity of the curve is measured in degrees, usually by the Cobb method.
- MRI is usually not indicated unless there is: (1) pain, (2) a neurologic deficit, or (3) a left thoracic curve (which is often associated with an underlying spinal disorder).

TREATMENT

ACUTE GENERAL Rx

- Treatment or correction of cause if curve is nonstructural
- Early detection is key in treating genetic curve
- Regular observation for curves <20 degrees
- Bracing for idiopathic curves of 20 to 40 degrees to prevent progression
- Surgery for idiopathic curves >40 to 50 degrees in immature patient

DISPOSITION

- The larger the curve at detection, the greater the chance of progression.
- Progression is more common in young children who are beginning their growth spurt.
- Curves in females are more likely to progress.
- Curves <20 degrees will improve spontaneously more than 50% of the time.
- Failure to diagnose and treat these curves may allow progressive deformity, pain, and cardiopulmonary compromise to develop.
- Spinal deformities >50 degrees in adults may progress and eventually become painful.
- There is no difference in the rate of back pain in the general population and patients with adolescent idiopathic scoliosis.

REFERRAL

For orthopedic consultation if structural curve is present

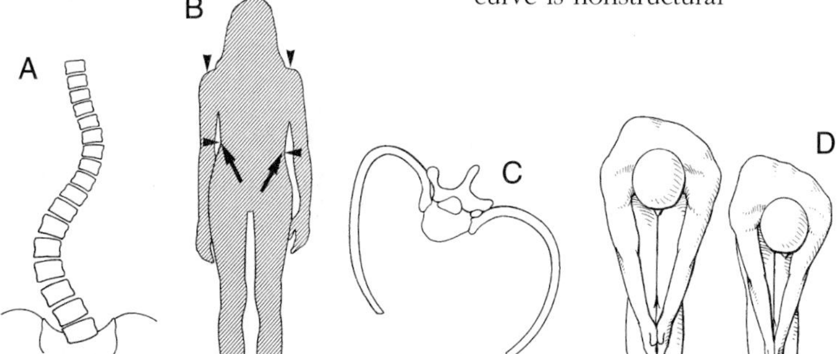

FIGURE 1-212 Structural changes in idiopathic scoliosis. A, As curvature increases, alterations in body configuration develop in both the primary and compensatory curve regions. **B,** Asymmetry of shoulder height, waistline, and the elbow-to-flank distance are common findings. **C,** Vertebral rotation and associated posterior displacement of the ribs on the convex side of the curve are responsible for the characteristic deformity of the chest wall in scoliosis patients. **D,** In the school screening examination for scoliosis, the patient bends forward at the waist. Rib asymmetry of even a small degree is obvious. (From Scoles PV: Spinal deformity in childhood and adolescence. In Behrman RE, Vaughn VC III [eds]: *Nelson textbook of pediatrics,* ed 5, Philadelphia, 1989, WB Saunders.)

PEARLS & CONSIDERATIONS

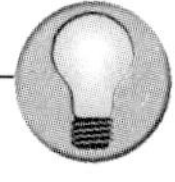

COMMENTS

Congenital scoliosis has a high incidence of cardiac and urinary tract abnormalities.

SUGGESTED READINGS

Greiner KA: Adolescent idiopathic scoliosis: radiologic decision-making, *Am Fam Physician* 65:1817, 2002.

Hedequist D, Emans J: Congenital scoliosis, *J Am Acad Orthop Surg* 12:266, 2004.

Lenke LG et al: Adolescent idiopathic scoliosis, *J Bone Joint Surg* 83(A):1169, 2001.

Mac-Thiong JM et al: Sagittal alignment of the spine and pelvis during growth, *Spine* 29:1642, 2004.

Mooney V, Brigham A: The role of measured resistance exercises in adolescent scoliosis, *Orthopedics* 26:167, 2003.

Reamy BV, Slakey JB: Adolescent idiopathic scoliosis: review and current concepts, *Am Fam Physician* 64:111, 2001.

Ugwonali OF et al: Effect of bracing on the quality of life of adolescents with idiopathic scoliosis, *Spine J* 4:254, 2004.

AUTHOR: **LONNIE R. MERCIER, M.D.**

BASIC INFORMATION

DEFINITION

Recurrent depressive episodes during autumn and winter alternating with nondepressive episodes during spring and summer. In the last 2 yr, two episodes of major depression have occurred that demonstrate the temporal seasonal relationships and there have been no nonseasonal episodes over this time period.

ICD-9CM CODES
296.30 Seasonal affective disorder

EPIDEMIOLOGY & DEMOGRAPHICS

- Climate, genetic vulnerability, and social-cultural factors all play a role. The risk of seasonal mood swings is clearly associated with northern latitudes. The prevalence of SAD is estimated to be 0.5%-1.5% in northern European populations, but up to 10%-20% of these populations report milder, recurrent episodes consistent with subsyndromal SAD. The average duration of the symptoms is 5 mo, generally commencing in November.
- As with other depressive disorders, women are affected disproportionate to men.

PHYSICAL FINDINGS & CLINICAL PRESENTATION

- The symptoms of seasonal affective disorder (SAD) can be identical to those of other depressive episodes, but tend to include those features associated with an atypical major depression, including low energy, irritability, weight gain, and overeating.
- The average duration of the symptoms is 5 mo, generally commencing in November.

ETIOLOGY

- Explanations for the phenomenon of SAD tend to focus on biologic models. The shorter photoperiod and decrease in sunlight exposure experienced by people living in temperate and higher latitudes during the winter is hypothesized to be the main trigger for SAD.
- Several neurotransmitters have been implicated in SAD, including dopamine, serotonin, and norepinephrine. Much current research is focused on the role of serotonin in the mediation of seasonal affective changes.

DIAGNOSIS

Diagnostic workup similar to that for major depression but with focus on the seasonal nature of the symptoms.

DIFFERENTIAL DIAGNOSIS

- Major depressive disorder
- Minor depression or adjustment disorder
- Bipolar affective disorder
- Evaluate for substance use (especially alcohol)
- Medical illness or medications that may contribute to depression (e.g., endocrine disorders, neurologic disease)

WORKUP

- As with major depression, consider medical etiologies and rule out as indicated by the presenting signs and symptoms. Consider endocrine evaluation, especially thyroid function; sleep studies, toxicology screen, might be considered.
- Structured Interview Guide for the Hamilton Depression Rating Scale-Seasonal Affective Disorders Version (SIGH-SAD) used in research settings.

LABORATORY TESTS

As directed by presenting complaints

IMAGING STUDIES

Generally not indicated.

TREATMENT

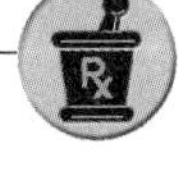

NONPHARMACOLOGIC THERAPY

- Phototherapy is based on the principle that the presentation of artificial light at a similar strength to natural sunlight will prevent the biologic changes that mediate SAD during the winter.
- There have been at least 20 randomized trials comparing light treatment with placebo in the treatment of SAD. Some of these trials have found a benefit, while others have been unable to demonstrate a benefit over placebo.
- Phototherapy for SAD tends to use 2500-10,000 lux delivered via a commercial light box or a portable head mounted unit. Phototherapy is recommended to commence within 2 wk of the start of symptoms and to continue through the winter months. Patients are instructed to sit approximately 18 inches away from the light box for 30 min up to several hours once or twice per day for a minimum of 1 wk.

ACUTE GENERAL Rx

None necessary unless patient is suicidal; immediate hospitalization may be necessary if suicidal ideation and intent is present.

CHRONIC Rx

There is no conclusive evidence from randomized trials to support the use of SSRIs in the treatment of SAD.

DISPOSITION

Psychiatric referral may be helpful to confirm diagnosis. Recommended for high-risk and suicidal patients.

PEARLS & CONSIDERATIONS

Patients with SAD may present with a complaint of overeating, particularly food high in carbohydrates.

SUGGESTED READINGS

Levitt AJ, Lam RW, Levitan R: A comparison of open treatment of seasonal major and minor depression with light therapy, *J Affect Dis* 71(1-3):243, 2002.

Magnussen A: An overview of epidemiological studies on seasonal affective disorder, *Acta Psychiatr Scand* 101(3):176, 2000.

Rosenthal NE: Diagnosis and treatment of seasonal affective disorder, *JAMA* 270(22):2717, 1995.

Wileman SM et al: Light therapy for seasonal affective disorder in primary care: randomised controlled trial, *Br J Psychiatry* 178:311, 2001.

AUTHOR: **MITCHELL D. FELDMAN, M.D., M.Phil.**

BASIC INFORMATION

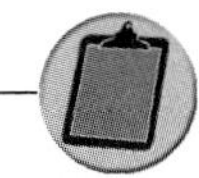

DEFINITION

Absence seizures are a type of generalized nonconvulsive seizure characterized by episodes of loss of awareness (typically ≤10 sec) associated with a 3 Hz generalized spike and slow wave EEG pattern, followed by abrupt return to full consciousness.

SYNONYMS

Petit mal seizures (obsolete)

ICD-9CM CODES
345.0 Generalized nonconvulsive epilepsy

EPIDEMIOLOGY & DEMOGRAPHICS

INCIDENCE (IN U.S.): 11 cases/100,000 persons from ages 1-10 yr, rare after age 14 yr
PREVALENCE (IN U.S.): Accounts for 2%-15% of the cases of childhood epilepsy
PREDOMINANT AGE: 4-8 yr
PEAK INCIDENCE: 6-7 yr
GENETICS: Clear genetic predisposition; undetermined mode of inheritance

PHYSICAL FINDINGS & CLINICAL PRESENTATION

- Findings are normal between seizures in children with typical absence epilepsy.
- During seizure, patient typically appears awake but abruptly ceases ongoing activity and does not respond to or recall stimuli.
- More prolonged episodes may be associated with automatisms and therefore mistaken for complex partial seizures.
- Tonic-clonic seizures can occur in approximately 40% of patients.

ETIOLOGY

- Idiopathic with a presumed genetic cause
- Absence seizures can also be seen with some types of generalized epilepsy syndromes such as juvenile absence epilepsy or juvenile myoclonic epilepsy
- Experimental data: seizures arise from impaired regulation of rhythmic thalamic discharges

DIAGNOSIS

DIFFERENTIAL DIAGNOSIS

- Complex partial seizures
- Daydreaming
- Psychogenic unresponsiveness

WORKUP

- EEG is the most powerful tool for identification of this seizure type.
- In the vast majority of untreated individuals, vigorous hyperventilation for 3-5 min provokes characteristic EEG finding.

IMAGING STUDIES

None needed for typical presentation

TREATMENT

NONPHARMACOLOGIC THERAPY

Avoid sleep deprivation and hyperventilation.

ACUTE GENERAL Rx

Not indicated for individual typical seizures

CHRONIC Rx

- Drug of choice is ethosuximide or sodium valproate.
- Ethosuximide does not suppress tonic-clonic seizures. Thus, sodium valproate is the drug of choice for patients with absence and tonic clonic seizures.
- The initial dose of ethosuximide in children is 10-15 mg/kg/day with maintenance dose of 15-40 mg/kg/day divided into a bid or tid dosing schedule. Can result in gastrointestinal side-effects so may be best to take with meals.
- Common pediatric doses for valproic acid are 15-60 mg/kg/day (bid-qid). Can result in hepatotoxity and blood dyscrasias.
- Lamotrigine is also effective, but is not FDA approved for the treatment of absence epilepsy.
- Because most patients will have spontaneous resolution of their seizures, one can consider withdrawing anticonvulsant therapy typically when the patient has been seizure-free for at least 2 yr.

DISPOSITION

- Favorable prognosis in typical childhood absence epilepsy without other seizure types
- Excellent response to medication
- Subsidence of seizures with advancing age in 70% to 90% of patients

REFERRAL

If uncertain about diagnosis or treatment

PEARLS & CONSIDERATIONS

COMMENTS

- Absence seizures may be mistakenly diagnosed as complex partial seizures based on clinical descriptions. The EEG is essential for making this distinction.
- Administering other anticonvulsants (particularly carbamazepine or phenytoin) to patients with typical absence epilepsy may exacerbate seizures.
- Patient education information can be obtained from the Epilepsy Foundation, 4351 Garden City Drive, Landover, MD 20785; phone: (800) 332-1000, web address: www.epilepsyfoundation.org.

SUGGESTED READINGS

Mattson RH: Overview: idiopathic generalized epilepsies, *Epilepsia* 44(2):2, 2003.
Panayiotopoulos CP: Treatment of typical absence seizures and related epileptic syndromes, *Paediatr Drugs* 3(5):379, 2001.

AUTHOR: **JOHN E. CROOM, M.D., Ph.D.**

BASIC INFORMATION

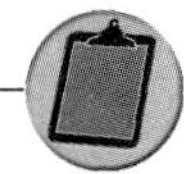

DEFINITION

Generalized tonic-clonic seizures (GTCS) are marked by paroxysmal hypersynchronous neuronal activity involving both cerebral hemispheres resulting in loss of consciousness with tonic muscle contraction followed by rhythmic clonic contractions. The seizure may start focally in one region or hemisphere of the brain with subsequent or secondary generalization.

SYNONYMS

Grand mal seizure (obsolete)

ICD-9CM CODES

345.1 Generalized convulsive epilepsy

EPIDEMIOLOGY & DEMOGRAPHICS

INCIDENCE (IN U.S.): 50-70 cases/100,000 persons/yr with highest rates during early childhood and those >65 yr of age

PREVALENCE (IN U.S.): Approximately 6.5 cases/1000 persons for all types of epilepsy

PREDOMINANT SEX: Males slightly higher than females

GENETICS: Genetic predisposition exists for the idiopathic generalized epilepsies; mode of transmission varies with the particular epilepsy syndrome.

PHYSICAL FINDINGS & CLINICAL PRESENTATION

- Generally normal neurologic examination. Focal deficits may be found in patients with an underlying lesion causing the seizures
- Sequence of motor events during the seizure typically includes widespread tonic muscle contraction evolving to clonic jerking
- Typically associated with postictal confusion lasting up to several hours
- May be associated with tongue, cheek, or lip biting and/or urinary incontinence

ETIOLOGY

- Seizures are a symptom of an underlying abnormality affecting the CNS, not a disease.
- Etiology of generalized tonic-clonic seizures can be divided into idiopathic, symptomatic, or cryptogenic causes.
- With idiopathic GTCS, there is a postulated inherited basis for the disorder. This includes some epilepsy syndromes such as juvenile myoclonic epilepsy and Lennox-Gastaut syndrome.
- Symptomatic GTCS result from an underlying cause such as inborn errors of metabolism, acquired metabolic or toxic abnormalities, CNS infection, tumor, or trauma.
- Cryptogenic seizures are those without a presumed genetic etiology or clear underlying cause.

DIAGNOSIS

DIFFERENTIAL DIAGNOSIS

- Syncope
- Psychogenic events
- Section II describes the differential diagnosis of epilepsy.

WORKUP

New-onset seizures: a detailed history and physical examination with the goal of determining the underlying etiology

LABORATORY TESTS

- Serum glucose and electrolytes
- Additional blood studies and lumbar puncture as indicated by history and physical examination
- EEG: most valuable diagnostic tool for identifying seizure type and predicting the likelihood of recurrence

IMAGING STUDIES

- Generally not necessary in well-documented cases of idiopathic GTCS
- MRI: modality of choice if history, examination, or EEG suggest partial (focal) onset

TREATMENT

NONPHARMACOLOGIC THERAPY

Avoid sleep deprivation or environmental precipitants (e.g., photosensitive epilepsy).

ACUTE GENERAL Rx

- Individual seizures lasting <5 min generally require no acute pharmacologic intervention.
- See "Status Epilepticus" in Section I for management of recurrent or prolonged seizures.

CHRONIC Rx

- A single seizure with an identifiable and easily correctable provoking factor (e.g., hyponatremia) does not warrant long-term use of anticonvulsants.
- If there is significant risk of recurrence (Table 1-48) or more than one unprovoked seizure, treatment is indicated.
- Sodium valproate phenytoin and carbamazepine are common first-line therapeutic agents in adults.
- Newer agents such as lamotrigine, topiramate, and levetiracetam may be better tolerated.
- For each patient, anticonvulsant choice is influenced by factors such as effectiveness, cost, adverse effects, ease of administration, and type of epilepsy syndrome if present.

DISPOSITION

- Varies with underlying etiology
- Excellent outcome for most patients with idiopathic generalized tonic-clonic seizures

REFERRAL

If uncertain about diagnosis or seizure type or if the seizures fail to respond to anticonvulsant treatment. Also, refer if the patient is considering pregnancy.

PEARLS & CONSIDERATIONS

CAUTION

EEG is normal in as many as 50% of patients; thus diagnosis is primarily by history. Usually, a single seizure is not treated with chronic anticonvulsants unless the patient has an epilepsy syndrome where the seizure recurrence is known to be high.

COMMENTS

Patient education information can be obtained from the Epilepsy Foundation, 4351 Garden City Drive, Landover, MD 20785; phone: (800) 332-1000; web address: www.epilepsyfoundation.org.

SUGGESTED READINGS

Browne TR, Holmes GL: Epilepsy, *N Engl J Med* 344:1145, 2001.

Chang BS, Lowenstein DH: Mechanisms of Disease: Epilepsy, *N Engl J Med* 349:1257, 2003.

AUTHOR: **JOHN E. CROOM, M.D., Ph.D.**

TABLE 1-48 **Risk of Recurrence After a First Tonic-Clonic Seizure**

High	Low
Abnormal neurologic findings	Febrile seizure in a child
Mental retardation	Febrile status epilepticus (child)
Abnormal EEG findings	Transient metabolic and toxic states
Myoclonic jerks, absences, or atonic seizures	Benign rolandic seizures
Structural brain lesions	Impact seizures in early nonsevere head trauma
Family history of epilepsy	
Elderly individuals	

From Johnson RT, Griffin JW: *Current therapy in neurologic disease,* ed 5, St Louis, 1997, Mosby.
EEG, Electroencephalogram.

Seizure Disorder, Partial (PTG)

BASIC INFORMATION

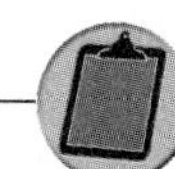

DEFINITION

In partial seizures, the onset of abnormal electrical activity originates in a focal region or lobe of the brain. Clinical manifestations may involve sensory, motor, autonomic, or psychic symptoms. Consciousness may be preserved (simple partial seizures) or impaired (complex partial seizures).

SYNONYMS

Localization-related seizures
Focal epilepsy
Obsolete terms include:
Minor motor seizures
Jacksonian seizures
Psychomotor seizures

ICD-9CM CODES
345.4 Partial epilepsy, with impairment of consciousness
345.5 Partial epilepsy, without impairment of consciousness

EPIDEMIOLOGY & DEMOGRAPHICS

INCIDENCE (IN U.S.): 20 cases/100,000 persons through age 65 yr, then rises sharply
PREVALENCE (IN U.S.): 6.5 cases/1000 persons for all types of epilepsy
PREDOMINANT SEX: Males slightly higher than females
GENETICS: Most acquired, but several distinct inherited syndromes have been identified.

PHYSICAL FINDINGS & CLINICAL PRESENTATION

- Range from normal to focal neurologic deficits, depending on underlying cause.
- Clinical presentation is varied and depends on the site of origin of the abnormal electrical discharges.
- Symptoms of simple partial seizures can include focal motor or sensory symptoms; language disturbance; olfactory, visual or auditory hallucinations; visceral sensations, or fear or panic.
- With complex partial seizures, there is a loss or reduction of awareness. This may be preceded by an aura (simple partial seizure). There may be associated automatisms or alterations in behavior.
- There may be a relatively quick "march" or progression of symptoms over seconds to minutes as the ictal focus spreads along the cortex.

ETIOLOGY

- Seizures are a symptom of an underlying abnormality affecting the CNS, not a disease.
- Partial-onset seizures may be caused by underlying disorders including stroke, tumor, infection, trauma, vascular malformations, or genetic factors.

DIAGNOSIS

DIFFERENTIAL DIAGNOSIS

- Migraine
- TIA
- Presyncope
- Psychogenic phenomena
- Section II describes the differential diagnosis of epilepsy

WORKUP

Because partial seizures are manifestations of an underlying focal CNS disturbance that must be identified if possible, imaging studies, preferably MRI, are essential.

LABORATORY TESTS

EEG is the most powerful tool for localization of the seizure focus.

IMAGING STUDIES

- MRI with contrast: modality of choice because of its high sensitivity for stroke, tumor, abscess, atrophy, and vascular malformations
- CT scan without contrast if hemorrhage is suspected

TREATMENT

NONPHARMACOLOGIC THERAPY

Avoid sleep deprivation.

ACUTE GENERAL Rx

- Individual seizures lasting <5 min generally require no acute pharmacologic intervention.
- For management of recurrent or prolonged seizures, see "Status Epilepticus" in Section I.

CHRONIC Rx

- Carbamazepine or phenytoin are common first-line therapeutic agents.
- Sodium valproate may also be effective.
- Newer agents such as lamotrigine, oxcarbazepine, levetiracetam, and topiramate may be better tolerated.
- For each patient, anticonvulsant choice is influenced by factors such as effectiveness, cost, adverse effects, and ease of administration.

DISPOSITION

- Determined by underlying cause
- Approximately 70% of patients are controlled with medication

REFERRAL

If uncertain about diagnosis or patient fails to respond to appropriate medication, refer to a neurologist or epilepsy specialist for further evaluation. In addition, some types of partial seizures, particularly temporal lobe epilepsy, are amenable to surgical resection.

PEARLS & CONSIDERATIONS

COMMENTS

- Patient education information can be obtained from the Epilepsy Foundation of America, 4351 Garden City Drive, Landover, MD 20785; phone: (800) 332-1000 web address: www.epilepsyfoundation.org.
- This is the most underdiagnosed, yet the most common, type of seizure in adults.

SUGGESTED READINGS

Chabolla DR: Characteristics of the epilepsies, *Mayo Clin Proc* 77:981, 2002.
Wiebe S et al: A randomized controlled trial of surgery for temporal-lobe epilepsy, *N Engl J Med* 345:311, 2001.

AUTHOR: **JOHN E. CROOM, M.D., Ph.D.**

BASIC INFORMATION

DEFINITION

A febrile seizure is a seizure in infancy or childhood, usually occurring between 3 mo and 5 yr of age, associated with fever but without evidence of intracranial infection or defined cause.

SYNONYMS

Benign febrile seizure

ICD-9CM CODES
780.3 Convulsions

EPIDEMIOLOGY & DEMOGRAPHICS

INCIDENCE (IN U.S.): Not reported
PREVALENCE (IN U.S.): 2% to 4% in children <5 yr of age
PREDOMINANT SEX: Male = female
PREDOMINANT AGE: 18-24 mo of age
GENETICS:
- Family history increases risk two- to threefold.
- Mode of inheritance is unknown.

PHYSICAL FINDINGS & CLINICAL PRESENTATION

- Typically occurs early in the course of an illness when temperature is rising.
- Most commonly associated with a viral upper respiratory or gastrointestinal infection.
- Febrile seizures can be either simple or complex.
- Simple febrile seizures are single events lacking focality and lasting less than 15 min. The children are neurologically normal and there are no persistent deficits following the seizure.
- Features of complex febrile seizures include: duration longer than 15 min, focal seizures, seizure recurrence within 24 hr, or abnormal neurologic examination. Children with complex febrile seizures are at greater risk of developing subsequent epilepsy.
- Physical and neurologic examination and developmental history may be normal especially with simple febrile seizures.

ETIOLOGY

Unknown

DIAGNOSIS

DIFFERENTIAL DIAGNOSIS

- Epilepsy
- Meningitis
- Encephalitis

WORKUP

- In children with simple febrile seizures, no further evaluation is usually required.
- In children with complex febrile seizures, more aggressive investigation is required.

LABORATORY TESTS

- Lumbar puncture is indicated in all children under 6 mo of age, in children with complex febrile seizures, or if signs or symptoms of meningitis are present.
- Complex febrile seizures may warrant EEG, toxicology screening, assessment of electrolytes, and so forth, depending on history and examination findings.

IMAGING STUDIES

- Not needed in simple febrile seizures
- Complex febrile seizures warrant head imaging studies

TREATMENT

NONPHARMACOLOGIC THERAPY

- Avoid excessive clothing.
- Encourage fluids.
- Apply tepid sponge bath to control fever.

ACUTE GENERAL Rx

- Antipyretics
- Possibly rectal diazepam in some instances of recurrent febrile seizures
- For prolonged seizures, can use parenteral diazepam or lorazepam.
- Febrile status epilepticus should be treated as a medical emergency (see "Status Epilepticus" in Section I).

CHRONIC Rx

- Prophylactic treatment with anticonvulsants is not indicated in children with typical simple febrile seizures.
- May consider anticonvulsant use in children with complex febrile seizures, but risks and benefits must be considered.

DISPOSITION

- Approximately one-third of patients will experience additional febrile seizures. Less than 6% of patients will suffer three or more febrile seizures.
- Independent predictors of febrile seizure recurrence include: (1) young age at onset (particularly less than 1 yr of age), (2) history of first degree-relatives with febrile seizures, (3) low degree of fever while in the emergency room, and (4) brief interval between fever onset and seizure presentation.
- Risk of subsequent epilepsy is estimated at 1%-2.5%. Risk of developing subsequent epilepsy is highest in children with complex febrile seizures and can be up to 13%-50%.
- Available data: there is no risk reduction with prophylactic anticonvulsants.

REFERRAL

If uncertain about diagnosis or with atypical presentation

SUGGESTED READINGS

Baumann RJ: Prevention and management of febrile seizures, *Paediatr Drugs* 3(8):585, 2001.

Berg AT et al: Predictors of recurrent febrile seizures: a prospective cohort study, *Arch Pediatr Adolesc Med* 151(4):371, 1997.

Knudsen FU: Febrile Seizures: Treatment and prognosis, *Epilepsia* 41(1):2, 2000.

Shinnar S, Glauser TA: Febrile seizures, *J Child Neurol* 17(Suppl 1):S44, 2002.

AUTHOR: **JOHN E. CROOM, M.D., Ph.D.**

BASIC INFORMATION

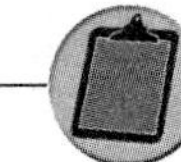

DEFINITION

Septicemia is a systemic illness caused by generalized bacterial infection and characterized by evidence of infection, fever or hypothermia, hypotension, and evidence of end-organ compromise.

SYNONYMS

Sepsis
Sepsis syndrome
Systemic inflammatory response syndrome
Septic shock

ICD-9CM CODES
038.9 Sepsis
038.40 Sepsis, gram-negative bacteremia
038.1 Sepsis, *Staphylococcus*

EPIDEMIOLOGY & DEMOGRAPHICS

INCIDENCE (IN U.S.):

- Exact incidence is unknown
- Approximately 300,000 cases of gram-negative bacteremia among hospitalized patients each year
- Complicates a minority of bacteremia cases and may occur in the absence of documented bacteremia

PREDOMINANT SEX: Male = female

PREDOMINANT AGE:

- Neonatal period
- Patients >70 yr of age

GENETICS:

Familial Disposition: A great variety of congenital immunodeficiency states and other inherited disorders may predispose to septicemia.

Neonatal Infection: Incidence is high in neonatal period.

PHYSICAL FINDINGS & CLINICAL PRESENTATION

- Fever or hypothermia
- Hypotension
- Tachycardia
- Tachypnea
- Altered mental status
- Bleeding diathesis
- Skin rashes
- Symptoms that reflect primary site of infection: urinary tract, GI tract, CNS, respiratory tract

ETIOLOGY

- Disseminated infection with a great variety of bacteria:
  1. Gram-negative bacteria
  2. *E. coli*
  3. *Klebsiella* spp.
  4. *Pseudomonas aeruginosa*
  5. *Proteus* spp.
  6. *Staphylococcus aureus*
  7. *Streptococcus* spp.
  8. *Neisseria meningitidis*
- Less common infections:
  1. Fungal
  2. Viral
  3. Rickettsial
  4. Parasitic
- Activation of coagulation, complement, and kinin cascades with release of a variety of vasoactive endogenous mediators
- Predisposing host factors:
  1. General medical condition
  2. Age
  3. Immunosuppressive therapy
  4. Recent surgery
  5. Granulocytopenia
  6. Hyposplenism
  7. Diabetes
  8. Instrumentation

DIAGNOSIS

DIFFERENTIAL DIAGNOSIS

- Cardiogenic shock
- Acute pancreatitis
- Pulmonary embolism
- Systemic vasculitis
- Toxic ingestion
- Exposure-induced hypothermia
- Fulminant hepatic failure
- Collagen-vascular diseases

WORKUP

- Evaluation should focus on identifying a specific pathogen and localizing the site of primary infection.
- Hemodynamic, metabolic, coagulation disorders should be carefully characterized.
- Intensive monitoring, including the use of central venous or Swan-Ganz catheters, may be necessary.

LABORATORY TESTS

- Cultures of blood and examination and culture of sputum, urine, wound drainage, stool, CSF
- CBC with differential, coagulation profile
- Routine chemistries, LFTs
- ABGs
- Urinalysis

IMAGING STUDIES

- Chest x-ray examination
- Other radiographic and radioisotope procedures according to suspected site of primary infection

TREATMENT

NONPHARMACOLOGIC THERAPY

- Tissue oxygenation: oxygen saturation maintained as high as possible; early mechanical ventilation
- Focal infection drained, if possible

ACUTE GENERAL Rx

- Blood pressure support
  1. IV hydration
  2. Therapy with pressors (e.g., dopamine) if mean blood pressure of 70 to 75 mm Hg cannot be maintained by hydration alone
- Correction of acidosis
  1. IV bicarbonate
  2. Mechanical ventilation
- Antibiotics
  1. Directed at the most likely sources of infection
  2. Should generally provide broad coverage of gram-positive and gram-negative bacteria
  3. Typical regimens:
     a. For hospital-acquired septicemia (pending culture results): vancomycin plus ceftazidime, imipenem, aztreonam, quinolones, or an aminoglycoside. Monotherapy with appropriate agents appears to be as effective as combination therapy in immunocompetent hosts.
     b. For community-acquired infection in the absence of granulocytopenia: above or single-drug therapy with third-generation cephalosporin.
     c. For infection in the granulocytopenic host: above or dual gram-negative coverage (e.g., cephalosporin and aminoglycoside).

4. Biological treatment Drotrecogin alfa (Xigris), a genetically engineered form of activated protein C, has recently been approved for use in patients with severe sepsis; when combined with conventional therapy, there may be a reduction in mortality.
5. The role of corticosteroids in the acute management of septicemia has long been debated. Although most well-constructed clinical trials have demonstrated no benefit, recent data suggest that patients with relative adrenal insufficiency may benefit from low-dose therapy with hydrocortisone (50 mg IV q6h) and fludrocortisone (50 mg daily PO) given together for 7 days. Recent data suggest that physiologic doses of corticosteroids with subsequent tapering may improve survival in some patients without proven adrenal insufficiency.

CHRONIC Rx

- Adjust antibiotic therapy on the basis of culture results.
- In general, continue therapy for a minimum of 2 wk.

DISPOSITION

All patients with suspected septicemia should be hospitalized and given access to intensive monitoring and nursing care.

REFERRAL

- To infectious diseases expert
- To physician experienced in critical care

PEARLS & CONSIDERATIONS

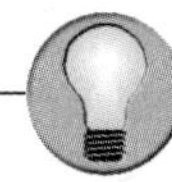

COMMENTS

Mortality rises quickly if antibiotic therapy is not instituted promptly and metabolic derangements are not treated aggressively.

SUGGESTED READINGS

Angus DC and Wax RS: Epidemiology of sepsis: an update, *Crit Care Med* 29(7 Suppl):S109, 2001.

Annane D et al: Effect of treatment with low doses of hydrocortisone and fludrocortisone on mortality in patients with septic shock, *JAMA* 288:862, 2002.

Balk RA: Severe sepsis and septic shock: definitions, epidemiology, and clinical manifestations, *Crit Care Clin* 16(2):179, 2000.

Minneci PC et al: Meta-analysis: the effect of steroids on survival and shock during sepsis depends on the dose, *Ann Intern Med* 141(1):47, 2004.

Paul M et al: Beta lactam monotherapy versus beta lactam-aminoglycoside combination therapy for sepsis in immunocompetent patients: systematic review and meta-analysis of randomized trials, *BMJ* 328(7441):668, 2004.

AUTHOR: **JOSEPH R. MASCI, M.D.**

BASIC INFORMATION

DEFINITION

Serotonin syndrome (SS) refers to a group of symptoms resulting from increased activity of serotonin (5-hydroxytryptamine) in the central nervous system. Serotonin syndrome is a drug-induced disorder that is characterized by a change in mental status and alteration in neuromuscular activity and autonomic function.

SYNONYMS

SS

ICD-9CM CODES
333.99 Syndrome serotonin

EPIDEMIOLOGY & DEMOGRAPHICS

- The incidence of serotonin syndrome is not known.
- Serotonin syndrome affects males and females from ages 20-70 yr.
- Serotonin syndrome commonly occurs in patients receiving two or more serotonergic drugs.
- Concomitant use of a selective serotonin reuptake inhibitor (SSRI) with a monoamine oxidase inhibitor (MAOI) poses the greatest risk of developing SS.
- Combination of SSRIs with other serotonergic drugs (e.g., tryptophan) or drugs with serotonin properties (e.g., lithium, meperidine) can also lead to SS.

PHYSICAL FINDINGS & CLINICAL PRESENTATION

- Symptoms usually start within minutes to hours after starting a new psychopharmacologic treatment or after administering a second serotonergic drug.
- Confusion, agitation, hypomania
- Fever, tachycardia, and tachypnea
- Nausea, vomiting, abdominal pain, and diaphoresis
- Diarrhea, tremors, shivering, and seizures
- Ataxia, myoclonus, and hyperreflexia

ETIOLOGY

- Hyperstimulation of the brainstem and spinal cord serotonin receptors because of blocking reuptake of serotonin and catecholamines is believed to be the underlying mechanism leading to the neuromuscular and autonomic symptoms seen in SS.
- Psychopharmacologic drugs, in particular, fluoxetine and sertraline coadministered with MAOI (e.g., tranylcypromine and phenelzine), have been cited in the literature as a common cause of SS.

DIAGNOSIS

The diagnosis of SS is made on clinical grounds. There are no specific laboratory tests for SS. A high index of suspicion along with a detailed medication history is the mainstay of diagnosis.

DIFFERENTIAL DIAGNOSIS

Neuroleptic malignant syndrome, substance abuse (e.g., cocaine, amphetamines), thyroid storm, infection, alcohol and opioid withdrawal

WORKUP

- Other causes described in the differential diagnosis must be excluded to make the diagnosis of SS. Thus all patients should have blood tests and diagnostic imaging studies to rule out infectious, toxic, and metabolic etiologies.
- Additional laboratory tests are performed to exclude complicating features of SS (e.g., renal failure secondary to rhabdomyolysis).

LABORATORY TESTS

- CBC with differential to rule out sepsis
- Electrolytes, BUN, and creatinine to rule out acidosis and renal failure
- Blood and urine toxicology screen
- Thyroid function tests
- CPK with isoenzymes
- Urine and blood cultures
- ECG, because ventricular rhythm disturbance is a potentially fatal complication

IMAGING STUDIES

Imaging studies are not very specific in the diagnosis of SS and are only ordered to exclude other causes with similar clinical presentations as SS.

TREATMENT

There is no specific antidote for excess serotonin.

NONPHARMACOLOGIC THERAPY

- Discontinuation of the drug is the mainstay of therapy
- Treatment is supportive: maintaining oxygenation and blood pressure and monitoring respiratory status
- Cooling blankets for patients with hyperthermia
- Mechanical intubation for patients unable to protect their airways as a result of mental status changes or seizures

ACUTE GENERAL Rx

- Cyproheptadine 4 mg tablet is given in 4- to 8-mg doses q1-4h (up to 32 mg for adults, 12 mg in children) until a therapeutic response is achieved.
- Benzodiazepines—lorazepam 1-2 mg IV q30min—has been used effectively in treating muscle rigidity, myoclonus, and seizure complications. Diazepam is an alternative choice.
- Methysergide has also been reported to be effective.
- Propranolol has serotonin-blocking properties and is given 1-3 mg q5min up to 0.1 mg/kg.

CHRONIC Rx

For patients not requiring hospital admission, cyproheptadine, lorazepam, or propranolol can be given in an oral dose on a prn basis with close follow-up.

DISPOSITION

- Serotonin syndrome is a potentially life-threatening condition if not recognized early.
- Prompt diagnosis and withdrawal of the medication results in improvement of symptoms within 24 hr.
- Seizures, rhabdomyolysis, hyperthermia, ventricular arrhythmia, respiratory arrest, and coma are all complicating features of SS.

REFERRAL

All cases of SS secondary to psychotropic medications should be referred to a psychiatrist.

PEARLS & CONSIDERATIONS

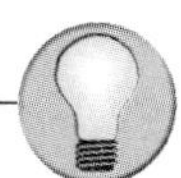

COMMENTS

- The use of SSRIs and MAOIs is contraindicated.
- The use of SSRIs and other serotonergic agents is not an absolute contraindication; however, prompt withdrawal of the medication is recommended if any symptoms suggesting SS occur.
- Serotonin syndrome is usually found in patients being treated for depression, bipolar disorders, obsessive-compulsive disorder, attention-deficit disorder, and Parkinson's disease.

SUGGESTED READINGS

Carbone JR: The neuroleptic malignant and serotonin syndromes, *Emerg Med Clin North Am* 18(2):317, 2000.

Gillman PK: The serotonin syndrome and its treatment, *J Psychopharmacol* 13(1):100, 1999.

Mason PJ, Morris VA, Balcezak TJ: Serotonin syndrome presentation of 2 cases and review of the literature, *Medicine* 79(4):201, 2000.

AUTHOR: **PETER PETROPOULOS, M.D.**

BASIC INFORMATION

DEFINITION

Severe acute respiratory syndrome (SARS) is a respiratory illness caused by a coronavirus called SARS-associated coronavirus (SARS-CoV).

CLINICAL CRITERIA:

A. Asymptomatic or mild respiratory illness
B. Moderate respiratory illness
   1. Temperature of >100.4°F (>38°C)*, and
   2. One or more clinical findings of respiratory illness (e.g., cough, shortness of breath, difficulty breathing, or hypoxia)
C. Severe respiratory illness
   1. Temperature of >100.4° F (>38°C)*, and
   2. One or more clinical findings of respiratory illness (e.g., cough, shortness of breath, difficulty breathing, or hypoxia), and
      a. Radiographic evidence of pneumonia, or
      b. Respiratory distress syndrome, or
      c. Autopsy findings consistent with pneumonia or respiratory distress syndrome without an identifiable cause

Epidemiologic criteria
- Travel (including transit in an airport) within 10 days of onset of symptoms to an area with current or previously documented or suspected community transmission of SARS, or
- Close contact† within 10 days of onset of symptoms with a person known or suspected to have SARS

Laboratory criteria
- Confirmed
  1. Detection of antibody to SARS-associated coronavirus (SARS-CoV) in a serum sample, or
  2. Detection of SARS-CoV RNA by RT-PCR confirmed by a second PCR assay, by using a second aliquot of the specimen and a different set of PCR primers, or
  3. Isolation of SARS-CoV
- Negative
  1. Absence of antibody to SARS-CoV in a convalescent-phase serum sample obtained >28 days after symptom onset‡
- Undetermined
  1. Laboratory testing either not performed or incomplete

Case classification§
- Probable case: meets the clinical criteria for severe respiratory illness of unknown etiology and epidemiologic criteria for exposure; laboratory criteria confirmed or undetermined.
- Suspect case: meets the clinical criteria for moderate respiratory illness of unknown etiology, and epidemiologic criteria for exposure; laboratory criteria confirmed or undetermined.

Exclusion criteria

A case may be excluded as a suspect or probable SARS case if:
- An alternative diagnosis can fully explain the illness.||
- The case has a convalescent-phase serum sample (i.e., obtained >28 days after symptom onset) that is negative for antibody to SARS-CoV.‡
- The case was reported on the basis of contact with an index case that was subsequently excluded as a case of SARS, provided other possible epidemiologic exposure criteria are not present.

SYNONYMS

SARS

ICD-9CM CODES
Not available

EPIDEMIOLOGY & DEMOGRAPHICS

- The disease was first recognized in Asia in February 2003, and over the next several months spread to more than 2 dozen countries in North and South America, Europe, and Asia affecting more than 8000 patients and resulting in more than 750 deaths. In July 2003, cases were no longer being reported, and SARS outbreaks worldwide were considered contained.
- Most reported cases of SARS in the United States were exposed through foreign travel to countries with community transmission of SARS, with only limited secondary spread to close contacts such as family members and health care workers.
- Incubation period is 2-10 days.
- Evidence of airborne transmission of the SARS virus and laboratory-acquired SARS has now been documented.

PHYSICAL FINDINGS & CLINICAL PRESENTATION

- Early manifestations: fever, myalgias and headache. Fever is often high and associated with chills or rigors. Fever may be absent in elderly patients.

---

* A measured documented temperature of >100.4° F (>38° C) is preferred. However, clinical judgment should be used when evaluating patients for whom a measured temperature of >100.4° F (>38° C) has not been documented. Factors that might be considered include patient self-report of fever, use of antipyretics, presence of immunocompromising conditions or therapies, lack of access to health care, or inability to obtain a measured temperature. Reporting authorities should consider these factors when classifying patients who do not strictly meet the clinical criteria for this case definition.

†Close contact is defined as having cared for or lived with a person known to have SARS or having a high likelihood of direct contact with respiratory secretions and/or body fluids of a patient known to have SARS. Examples of close contact include kissing or embracing, sharing eating or drinking utensils, close conversation (<3 ft), physical examination, and any other direct physical contact between persons. Close contact does not include activities such as walking by a person or sitting across a waiting room or office for a brief period.

‡ The WHO has specified that the surveillance period for China should begin on November 1; the first recognized cases in Hong Kong, Singapore, and Hanoi (Vietnam) had onset in February 2003. The date for Toronto is linked to the occurrence of a laboratory confirmed case of SARS in a U.S. resident who had traveled to Toronto; the date for Taiwan is linked to CDC's issuance of travel recommendations.

§ The last date for illness onset is 10 days (i.e., one incubation period) after removal of a CDC travel alert. The case patient's travel should have occurred on or before the last date the travel alert was in place.

Assays for the laboratory diagnosis of SARS-CoV infection include enzyme-linked immunosorbent assay, indirect fluorescent-antibody assay, and reverse transcription polymerase chain reaction (RT-PCR) assays of appropriately collected clinical specimens (Source: CDC. Guidelines for collection of specimens from potential cases of SARS. Available at http://www.cdc.gov/ncidod/sars/specimen_collection_sars2.htm). Absence of SARS-CoV antibody from serum obtained <28 days after illness onset,‡ a negative PCR test, or a negative viral culture does not exclude SARS-CoV infection and is not considered a definitive laboratory result. In these instances, a convalescent serum sample obtained >28 days after illness is needed to determine infection with SARS-CoV.‡ All SARS diagnostic assays are under evaluation.

‡Does not apply to serum samples collected before July 11, 2003. Testing results from serum samples collected before July 11, 2003, and between 22 and 28 days after symptom onset are acceptable and will not require collection of an additional sample >28 days after symptom onset.

§ Asymptomatic SARS-CoV infection or clinical manifestations other than respiratory illness might be identified as more is learned about SARS-CoV infection.

|| Factors that may be considered in assigning alternate diagnoses include the strength of the epidemiologic exposure criteria for SARS, the specificity of the diagnostic test, and the compatibility of the clinical presentation and course of illness for the alternative diagnosis.

- Dry nonproductive cough occurs within 2-4 days of onset of fever.
- Diarrhea may occur in up to 25% of cases.
- Dyspnea and hypoxemia follow the cough and may require intubation in nearly 20% of patients.
- A biphasic course of illness may occur with initial improvement followed by subsequent deterioration in some patients.

ETIOLOGY

SARS-associated coronavirus

DIAGNOSIS

DIFFERENTIAL DIAGNOSIS

- Legionella pneumonia
- Influenza A and B
- Respiratory syncytial virus
- Acute respiratory distress syndrome (ARDS)

WORKUP

- Initial diagnostic testing for suspected SARS patients should include chest radiograph, pulse oximetry, blood cultures, sputum Gram's stain and culture, and testing for viral respiratory pathogens, notably influenza A and B and respiratory syncytial virus. A specimen for Legionella and pneumococcal urinary antigen testing should also be considered.

LABORATORY TESTS

When to test for SARS:

- In the absence of documented SARS transmission, diagnostic testing for SARS-associated coronavirus (SARS-CoV) should *not* be considered unless the clinician and health department have a high index of suspicion for SARS (e.g., a hospitalized pneumonia patient has a possible SARS exposure during travel and no other explanation for their pneumonia).
- Respiratory specimens should be collected as soon as possible in the course of the illness. The likelihood of recovering most viruses diminishes markedly >72 hours after symptom onset.
- Three types of specimens may be collected for viral or bacterial isolation and PCR. These include (1) nasopharyngeal wash/aspirates, (2) nasopharyngeal swabs, or (3) oropharyngeal swabs. Nasopharyngeal aspirates are the specimen of choice for detection of respiratory viruses and are the preferred collection method among children aged <2 yr.
- Collection of bronchioalveolar lavage, tracheal aspirate, pleural tap: if these specimens have been obtained, half should be centrifuged and the cell-pellet fixed in formalin. Remaining unspun fluid should be placed in sterile vials with external caps and internal O-ring seals. If there are no internal O-ring seals, then cap securely and seal with parafilm.
- Acute serum specimens should be collected and submitted as soon as possible. If the patient meets the case definition, convalescent specimens should be collected and submitted no sooner than 29 days after the onset of fever.
- Laboratory assays for SARS-CoV are based on either the detection of the virus or virus products, or detection of an antibody response to viral infection.
- Isolation in Vero E6 cells and electron microscopy plays a critical role in the early identification of SARS-CoV; however, these methods are not suitable for routine diagnoses because they lack sensitivity and viral culture requires biosafety level III containment.
- Current detection methods for SARS-CoV include real-time reverse transcription polymerase chain reaction (RT-PCR) assay for detection of viral RNA and enzyme immunoassay (EIA) for detection of antibodies to SARS-CoV. The real-time RT-PCR assay is highly sensitive, detecting between 1 and 10 RNA transcript copies per reaction, and utilizes primer and probe sets to three independent sites along the SARS-CoV genome to assure specific detection of SARS CoV.
- Serology is the gold standard for diagnosis of SARS-CoV infection. The SARS EIA uses a lysate of SARS-CoV infected Vero E6 cells as antigen. Serosurveys with the SARS EIA have demonstrated low or undetectable levels of antibody to the SARS-CoV in the general population. No cross-reactivity has been observed in validation studies with serum specimens containing antibodies to other human coronaviruses.
- The CDC real-time RT-PCR assay has proven both sensitive and specific for detection of SARS-CoV. However, as with all PCR assays, there is potential for both false-positive and false-negative results. False-positive results can occur from contamination with previously amplified DNA during specimen processing or preparation of the amplification reaction. Cross-contamination between patient specimens can also occur during the course of collection, transport, storage, and processing.
- Detecting SARS-CoV antibodies by EIA is a less ambiguous approach to diagnosing SARS-CoV infection than is RT-PCR, but antibodies are often not detectable early in the course of illness or if the patient is immune suppressed and unable to mount a good antibody response. Seroconversion from negative to positive or a fourfold rise in antibody titer from acute to convalescent serum specimens confirms recent infection.
- When prior infection is exceedingly rare, a positive serology result is also considered indicative of acute infection with SARS-CoV in a patient with a SARS-like illness. Although many SARS patients develop antibodies to SARS-CoV within as few as 8-10 days, some patients do not test positive until more than 28 days after the onset of illness.
- For patients with a negative antibody test result with specimens collected <28 days after illness onset, an additional serum specimen collected >28 days after onset should be tested. A negative antibody test after 28 days from onset of illness can be used to rule out SARS-CoV infection.
- Laboratory testing on initial evaluation should also include CBC with differential, platelet count, liver enzymes, LDH, and CPK. Common laboratory abnormalities in SARS include thrombocytopenia, lymphopenia, elevated LDH, and elevated CPK, ALT, AST.

IMAGING STUDIES

- Chest x-ray: patchy focal infiltrates or consolidation with peripheral distribution.
- Chest x-ray may be normal in up to 25% of patients.
- Pleural effusions generally are not present.

TREATMENT

NONPHARMACOLOGIC THERAPY

- Supportive care.
- Nearly 25% of cases will require ventilator assistance.
- Nutritional support.

ACUTE GENERAL THERAPY

- There is no specific treatment currently available for SARS.
- Broad-spectrum antibiotics (quinolone or macrolide) are generally started pending laboratory testing.
- Use of corticosteroids (methylprednisolone 40 mg bid or doses up to 2 mg/kg/day) is controversial but may be beneficial in patients with significant hypoxemia and progressive pulmonary infiltrates.
- In a preliminary, uncontrolled study of patients with SARS, use of interferon alfacon-1 plus corticosteroids was beneficial.

DISPOSITION

- Case fatality rate is 3%-12%.
- Mortality rate is higher in elderly and immunocompromised patients and lower in pediatric age group.

REFERRAL

- Infectious disease consultation and pulmonary consultation is recommended in all cases.
- Notification of state Department of Health is mandatory.

PEARLS & CONSIDERATIONS

- Available information related to the spread of SARS suggests that only symptomatic patients transmit the virus to others. The following infection control measures are recommended for patients with suspected SARS in households or residential settings.
  1. SARS patients should limit interactions outside the home and should not go to work, school, out-of-home child care, or other public areas until 10 days after the resolution of fever, provided respiratory symptoms are absent or improving. During this time, infection control precautions should be used, as described below, to minimize the potential for transmission.
  2. All members of a household with a SARS patient should carefully follow recommendations for hand hygiene (e.g., frequent hand washing or use of alcohol-based hand rubs), particularly after contact with body fluids (e.g., respiratory secretions, urine, or feces).
  3. Use of disposable gloves should be considered for any direct contact with body fluids of a SARS patient. However, gloves are not intended to replace proper hand hygiene. Immediately after activities involving contact with body fluids, gloves should be removed and discarded and hands should be cleaned. Gloves must never be washed or reused.
  4. Each patient with SARS should be advised to cover his or her mouth and nose with a facial tissue when coughing or sneezing. If possible, a SARS patient should wear a surgical mask during close contact with uninfected persons to prevent spread of infectious droplets. When a SARS patient is unable to wear a surgical mask, household members should wear surgical masks when in close contact with the patient.
  5. Sharing of eating utensils, towels, and bedding between SARS patients and others should be avoided, although such items can be used by others after routine cleaning (e.g., washing with soap and hot water). Environmental surfaces soiled by body fluids should be cleaned with a household disinfectant according to manufacturer's instructions; gloves should be worn during this activity.
  6. Household waste soiled with body fluids of SARS patients, including facial tissues and surgical masks, may be discarded as normal waste.
  7. Household members and other close contacts of SARS patients should be actively monitored by the local health department for illness.
  8. Household members or other close contacts of SARS patients should be vigilant for fever (i.e., measure temperature twice daily) or respiratory symptoms and, if these develop, should immediately seek health care evaluation. In advance of evaluation, health care providers should be informed that the individual is a close contact of a SARS patient so arrangements can be made, as necessary, to prevent transmission to others in the health care setting. Household members or other close contacts with symptoms of SARS should follow the same precautions recommended for SARS patients.
  9. At this time, in the absence of fever or respiratory symptoms, household members or other close contacts of SARS patients need not limit their activities outside the home.

COMMENTS

- Persons who may have been exposed to SARS should be vigilant for fever (i.e., measure temperature twice daily) and respiratory symptoms over the 10 days after exposure. During this time, in the absence of both fever and respiratory symptoms, persons who may have been exposed to SARS patients need not limit their activities outside the home and should not be excluded from work, school, out-of-home child care, church, or other public areas.
- Exposed persons should notify their health care provider immediately if fever or respiratory symptoms develop.
- Symptomatic persons exposed to SARS should follow the following infection control precautions:
  1. If fever or respiratory symptoms develop, the person should limit interactions outside the home and not go to work, school, out-of-home child care, church, or other public areas. In addition, the person should use infection control precautions in the home to minimize the risk for transmission, and continue to measure temperature twice daily.
  2. If symptoms improve or resolve within 72 hr after first symptom onset, the person may be allowed, after consultation with local public health authorities, to return to work, school, out-of-home child care, church, or other public areas, and infection control precautions can be discontinued.
  3. For persons who meet or progress to meet the case definition for suspected SARS (e.g., develop fever and respiratory symptoms), infection control precautions should be continued until 10 days after the resolution of fever, provided respiratory symptoms are absent or improving.
  4. If the illness does not progress to meet the case definition, but the individual has persistent fever or unresolving respiratory symptoms, infection control precautions should be continued for an additional 72 hr, at the end of which time a clinical evaluation should be performed. If the illness progresses to meet the case definition, infection control precautions should be continued as described earlier. If case definition criteria are not met, infection control precautions can be discontinued after consultation with local public health authorities and the evaluating clinician.
- Persons who meet or progress to meet the case definition for suspected SARS (e.g., develop fever and respiratory symptoms) or whose illness does not meet the case definition, but who have persistent fever or unresolving respiratory symptoms over the 72 hr after onset of symptoms should be tested for SARS coronavirus infection.

SUGGESTED READINGS

Ksiazek TG et al: A novel coronavirus associated with severe acute respiratory syndrome, *N Engl J Med* 348:1953, 2003.

Lim PL et al: Laboratory-acquired SARS, *N Engl J Med* 350:1740, 2004.

Loutfy MR et al: Interferon alfacon-1 plus corticosteroids in severe acute respiratory syndrome, *JAMA* 290:3222, 2003.

MMRW: Severe acute respiratory syndrome—Taiwan, 2003, *MMWR* 52:20, 2003.

Peiris JS et al: The severe acute respiratory syndrome, *N Engl J Med* 349:2431, 2003.

Poutanen SM et al: Identification of severe acute respiratory syndrome in Canada, *N Engl J Med* 348:20, 2004.

Sampathkumar P et al: SARS: epidemiology, clinical presentation, management, and infection control measures, *Mayo Clin Proc* 78:882, 2003.

Yu, IT et al: Evidence of airborne transmission of SARS virus, *N Engl J Med* 350:1731, 2004.

AUTHOR: **FRED F. FERRI, M.D.**

BASIC INFORMATION

DEFINITION

Sheehan's syndrome is a state of hypopituitarism resulting from an infarct of the pituitary secondary to postpartum hemorrhage or shock, causing partial or complete loss of the anterior pituitary hormones (i.e., ACTH, FSH, LH, GH, PRL, TSH) and their target organ functions.

ICD-9CM CODES
253.2 Sheehan's syndrome

EPIDEMIOLOGY & DEMOGRAPHICS

INCIDENCE: 1 case/10,000 deliveries (perhaps more rare in the U.S.)
PREDOMINANT SEX: Affects only females
RISK FACTORS:
- Hypovolemic shock
- Type I (insulin-dependent) diabetes mellitus (secondary to microvascular disease)
- Sickle cell anemia (secondary to occlusion of the small vessels in the pituitary)

ONSET OF SYMPTOMS: Average delay of 5-7 yr between onset of symptoms and diagnosis of disease.

PHYSICAL FINDINGS & CLINICAL PRESENTATION

- Failure of lactation
- Infertility
- Failure to resume menses after delivery
- Failure to regrow shaved pubic or axillary hair
- Skin depigmentation (including areola)
- Rapid breast involution
- Superinvolution of the uterus
- Hypothyroidism
- Adrenal cortical insufficiency
- Diabetes insipidus (rare)

ETIOLOGY

- Compromise of the blood supply to the low-pressure pituitary sinusoidal system may occur with postpartum hemorrhage or shock, resulting in pituitary infarct and/or necrosis.
- It is hypothesized that locally released factors may mediate vascular spasm of the pituitary blood supply.
- Severity of postpartum hemorrhage does not always correlate with the presence of Sheehan's syndrome.

DIAGNOSIS

DIFFERENTIAL DIAGNOSIS

- Chronic infections
- HIV
- Sarcoidosis
- Amyloidosis
- Rheumatoid disease
- Hemachromatosis
- Metastatic carcinoma
- Lymphocytic hypophysitis

WORKUP

- Target gland deficiency should be investigated by measuring levels of ACTH, FSH, LH, TSH (which may be normal or low), and T_4. Cortisol and estradiol (which may be low) should also be measured.
- Provocative testing of pituitary hormone reserves (e.g., metyrapone test, insulin tolerance test, and cosyntropin test): normal, subnormal, or delayed responses may suggest the presence of islands of pituitary cells that no longer have the support of the hypothalamic-portal circulation.
- Measurement of IGF-I to screen for GH deficiency: subnormal levels suggest decreased GH.
- Impaired prolactin response to TRH or dopamine antagonist stimulation is frequently found.
- During pregnancy, adjustments must be made in interpreting both hormone levels and responses to various stimuli because of normal physiologic changes.

IMAGING STUDIES

- Study of choice: MRI of the pituitary
  1. Sella turcica partially or totally empty
  2. Rules out mass lesion
- CT scan of the pituitary when MRI is unavailable or contraindicated

TREATMENT

ACUTE GENERAL Rx

- Acute form can be lethal, presenting with hypotension, tachycardia, failure to lactate, and hypoglycemia.
- A high degree of suspicion is required with any woman who has undergone postpartum hemorrhage and shock.
- Intravenous corticosteroids and fluid replacement should be given initially.
- Diagnosis is confirmed with a full endocrinologic workup as noted previously.
- Thyroid hormone is replaced as l-thyroxin in doses of 0.1-0.2 mg qd.

CHRONIC Rx

- With late-onset disease (symptoms of general hypopituitarism, such as oligomenorrhea or amenorrhea, vaginal atrophic changes, and loss of libido): a full endocrinologic workup and replacement of the appropriate hormones are needed.
- With symptoms of adrenal insufficiency: corticosteroids should be given.
  1. A maintenance dose of cortisone acetate or prednisone may be given.
  2. Because adrenal production of cortisol is not entirely dependent on ACTH, replacement of mineralocorticoids is rarely necessary.
  3. Stress doses of glucocorticoids should be administered during surgery or during labor and delivery.

DISPOSITION

Patients who receive early diagnosis and adequate hormonal replacement may expect favorable outcomes, including subsequent pregnancy.

REFERRAL

Patients should have yearly examinations by endocrinologist.

SUGGESTED READINGS

Dejagter S et al: Sheehan's syndrome: differential diagnosis in the acute phase, *J Intern Med* 244(3):261, 1998.

Kovacs K: Sheehan's syndrome, *Lancet* 361(9356):520, 2003.

AUTHOR: **BETH J. WUTZ, M.D.**

Shigellosis (PTG)

BASIC INFORMATION

DEFINITION

Shigellosis is an inflammatory disease of the bowel caused by one of several species of *Shigella*. It is the most common cause of bacillary dysentery in the U.S.

SYNONYMS

Bacillary dysentery

ICD-9CM CODES
004.9 Shigellosis

EPIDEMIOLOGY & DEMOGRAPHICS

INCIDENCE (IN U.S.): Approximately 15,000 cases/yr
PREDOMINANT SEX: Male homosexuals at increased risk
PREDOMINANT AGE: Young children
PEAK INCIDENCE: Summer
GENETICS:
Neonatal Infection: Rare but severe

PHYSICAL FINDINGS & CLINICAL PRESENTATION

- Possibly asymptomatic
- Mild illness that is usually self-limited, resolving in a few days
- Fever
- Watery diarrhea
- Bloody diarrhea
- Dysentery (abdominal cramps, tenesmus, and numerous, small-volume stools with blood, mucus, and pus)
- Descending intestinal tract illness, reflecting infection of small bowel first and then the colon
- Severe disease is more common in children and elderly and outside of U.S.
- Complications of severe illness:
  1. Seizures
  2. Megacolon
  3. Intestinal perforation
  4. Death
- Extraintestinal manifestations are rare
- Bacteremia described in patients with AIDS
- Hemolytic-uremic syndrome: usually occurs as the initial illness seems to be resolving
- Reactive arthritis, sometimes as part of Reiter's syndrome

ETIOLOGY

- *Shigella*
  1. *S. flexneri*
  2. *S. dysenteriae*
  3. *S. sonnei*
  4. *S. boydii*
- *S. sonnei* is the most commonly isolated species in the U.S., and it usually causes a mild watery diarrhea.
- Direct person-to-person transmission is thought to be the most common route. Outbreaks among men who have sex with men have occurred because of direct or indirect oral-anal contact.
- Contaminated food or water may transmit disease.
- A recent outbreak occurred at a community wading pool frequented by toddlers.

DIAGNOSIS

DIFFERENTIAL DIAGNOSIS

- May mimic any bacterial or viral gastroenteritis
- Dysentery also caused by *Entamoeba histolytica*
- Bloody diarrhea may resemble disease caused by enterotoxigenic *E. coli*

LABORATORY TESTS

- Total WBCs may be low, normal, or high.
- Stool should be cultured from fresh samples, because the yield is increased by processing the specimen soon after passage.
- Serology is available but rarely useful.
- Polymerase chain reaction may be diagnostic.
- Fecal leukocyte preparation may show WBCs.

IMAGING STUDIES

Abdominal radiographs may suggest megacolon or perforation in rare, severe cases.

TREATMENT

NONPHARMACOLOGIC THERAPY

- Adequate hydration
- Electrolyte replacement

ACUTE GENERAL Rx

Antibiotics:
- To shorten course of illness
- To limit transmission of illness
- SMX/TMP, one DS tablet PO bid for 5 days
- Ciprofloxacin 500 mg PO bid for 5 days

DISPOSITION

- Most disease is self-limited.
- Severe illness may be fatal.

REFERRAL

For severe illness or complications

PEARLS & CONSIDERATIONS

COMMENTS

- *Shigella* is one cause of "gay bowel syndrome."
- Illness is worsened by agents that decrease intestinal motility.
- Food handlers, child-care providers, and health-care workers should have a negative stool culture documented following treatment.

SUGGESTED READINGS

Centers for Disease Control and Prevention: *Shigelia sonnei* outbreak among men who have sex with men, San Francisco, California, 200-2001, *MMWR,* 50:922, 2001.
Centers for Disease Control and Prevention, Shigellosis outbreak associated with an unchlorinated fill-and-drain wading pool, Iowa, 2001, *MMWR,* 50:797, 2001.
Rebarber A et al: Shigellosis complicating preterm premature rupture of membranes resulting in congenital infection and preterm delivery, *Obstet Gynecol* 100:1063, 2002.

AUTHOR: **MAURICE POLICAR, M.D.**

Short Bowel Syndrome

BASIC INFORMATION

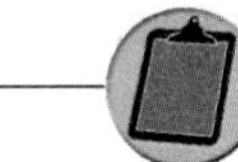

DEFINITION

Short bowel syndrome is a malabsorption syndrome that results from extensive small intestinal resection.

SYNONYMS

Short bowel

ICD-9CM CODES
579.3 (postsurgical malabsorption)

EPIDEMIOLOGY & DEMOGRAPHICS

- Parallels Crohn's disease (see "Crohn's Disease" in Section I), which is the most common cause of the syndrome in adults
- In children, two thirds of short bowels are related to congenital abnormalities (intestinal atresia, gastroschisis, volvulus, aganglionosis) and one third are related to necrotizing enterocolitis
- Prevalence: 10,000 to 20,000 cases are estimated to exist in the U.S.

PHYSICAL FINDINGS & CLINICAL PRESENTATION

- Diarrhea and steatorrhea
- Weight loss
- Anemia related to iron or vitamin B_{12} absorption
- Bleeding diathesis related to vitamin K malabsorption
- Osteoporosis/osteomalacia related to vitamin D and calcium malabsorption
- Hyponatremia, hypokalemia
- Hypovolemia
- Other macronutrient or micronutrient deficiency states

ETIOLOGY

- Extensive bowel resection for treatment of the conditions mentioned previously (see "Epidemiology").
- Pathogenesis (Fig. 1-213).

The human intestine is 3 to 8 m in length. Removal of up to one half of the small intestine produces no disruption in nutrient absorption, and most patients can maintain nutritional balance on oral feeding if they have more than 100 cm (3 ft) of jejunum. Similarly, 100 cm of intact jejunum can maintain a normal water, sodium, and potassium balance under normal circumstances. The presence of an intact colon can compensate for some small intestine loss.

Site-specific functions:

- Calcium, magnesium, phosphorus, iron, and vitamins are absorbed in the duodenum and proximal jejunum.
- Vitamin B_{12} and bile acids are absorbed in the ileum. The resection of more than 60 cm of ileum results in vitamin B_{12} malabsorption. The loss of more than 100 cm results in fat malabsorption (from the loss of bile acids).
- The loss of gastrointestinal endocrine hormones can affect intestinal motility.
- Intestinal bacterial overgrowth may also occur, especially if the ileocecal valve is lost.

DIAGNOSIS

Presence of macronutrient and/or micronutrient loss in a patient with a known history of bowel resection

DIFFERENTIAL DIAGNOSIS

Because the history of significant bowel resection is typically known, there is no differential diagnosis. If that history is not known, all causes of weight loss, malabsorption, and diarrhea must be considered (see respective chapters).

TREATMENT

Extensive small bowel resection with colectomy (<100 cm of jejunum)

- Rx: long-term parenteral nutrition (TPN). Some patients can switch to oral intake after 1 to 2 yr of TPN. In jejunostomy patients, excessive fluid loss can be reduced with H_2 blockers, proton pump inhibitors, or octreotide. Micronutrients are supplemented.

Extensive small bowel resection with partial colectomy (usually patients with Crohn's disease)

- Rx: oral intake alone is possible in all patients with >100 cm of jejunum. In addition to vitamin B_{12} deficiency, these patients often have diarrhea. Consider lactose malabsorption and bacterial overgrowth treated, respectively, with lactose restriction and antibiotics (tetracycline 250 mg tid or metronidazole 500 mg tid for 2 wk). Nonspecific antidiarrheal agents may also be indicated (e.g., Imodium or codeine). The patient must be monitored for micronutrient losses.

COMPLICATIONS

- Oxalate kidney stones
- Cholesterol gallstones
- D-Lactic acidosis

PROGNOSIS

Directly dependent on the extent of the bowel resection and in the case of Crohn's disease by the underlying illness

SUGGESTED READING

Westergaard H: Short bowel syndrome. In Feldman M, Scharschmidt BF, Sleisenger MH (eds): *Gastrointestinal and liver disease,* ed 6, Philadelphia, 1998, WB Saunders.

AUTHOR: **TOM J. WACHTEL, M.D.**

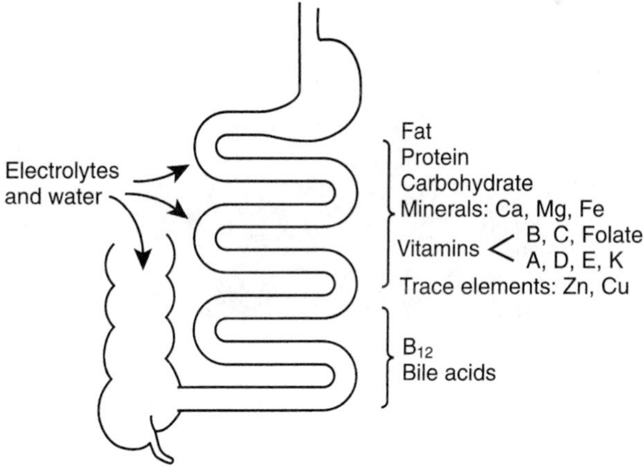

FIGURE 1-213 Specific areas of absorption of constituents of diet and secretions in the gastrointestinal tract. Macronutrients and micronutrients are predominantly absorbed in the proximal jejunum. Bile acids and vitamin B_{12} are only absorbed in the ileum. Electrolytes and water are absorbed in both the small and the large intestine. (From Feldman M, Scharschmidt BF, Sleisenger MH [eds]: *Sleisenger and Fordtran's gastrointestinal and liver disease: pathophysiology, diagnosis, and management,* ed 6, Philadelphia, 1998, WB Saunders.)

Sialadenitis (PTG)

BASIC INFORMATION

DEFINITION

Sialadenitis is an inflammation of the salivary glands.

ICD-9CM CODES
527.2 Sialadenitis

EPIDEMIOLOGY & DEMOGRAPHICS

Parotid or submandibular glands are most frequently affected (Fig. 1-214).

PHYSICAL FINDINGS & CLINICAL PRESENTATION

- Pain and swelling of the affected salivary gland
- Increased pain with meals
- Erythema, tenderness at the duct opening
- Purulent discharge from duct orifice
- Induration and pitting of the skin with involvement of the masseteric and submandibular spatial planes in severe cases

ETIOLOGY

- Ductal obstruction is generally secondary to a mucus plug caused by stasis of saliva with increased viscosity with subsequent stasis and infection.
- Most frequent infecting organisms are *Staphylococcus aureus, Pseudomonas, Enterobacter, Klebsiella, Enterococcus, Proteus,* and *Candida* spp.
- Sjögren's syndrome, trauma, radiation therapy, chemotherapy, dehydration, and chronic illness are predisposing factors.

DIAGNOSIS

DIFFERENTIAL DIAGNOSIS

- Salivary gland neoplasm
- Ductal stricture
- Sialolithiasis
- Decreased salivary secretion secondary to medications (e.g., amitriptyline, diphenhydramine, anticholinergics)

WORKUP

- Generally not necessary
- Ultrasound or CT scan in patients not responding to medical treatment (see "Imaging Studies")

LABORATORY TESTS

- Generally not indicated
- CBC with differential to possibly reveal leukocytosis with left shift

IMAGING STUDIES

- Ultrasound or CT scan may be needed in patients not responding to medical therapy.
- Sialography should not be performed during the acute phase.

TREATMENT

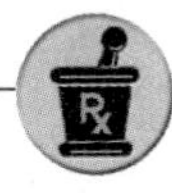

NONPHARMACOLOGIC THERAPY

- Massage of the gland: may express pus and relieve some of the pressure
- Rehydration
- Warm compresses
- Oral cavity irrigations

ACUTE GENERAL Rx

- Amoxicillin-clavulanate 500-875 mg or cefuroxime 250-500 mg bid should be given for 10 days. Clindamycin is an alternative choice in patients allergic to penicillin.
- IV antibiotics (e.g., cefoxitin, nafcillin) can be given in severe cases.

DISPOSITION

Complete recovery unless the patient has underlying obstruction (e.g., ductal stricture, tumor, or stone)

REFERRAL

- To ENT for nonresolving cases despite appropriate antibiotic therapy
- For salivary gland incision and drainage, which may be necessary in resistant cases

PEARLS & CONSIDERATIONS

COMMENTS

Prevention of dehydration will decrease the risk of sialadenitis.

AUTHOR: **FRED F. FERRI, M.D.**

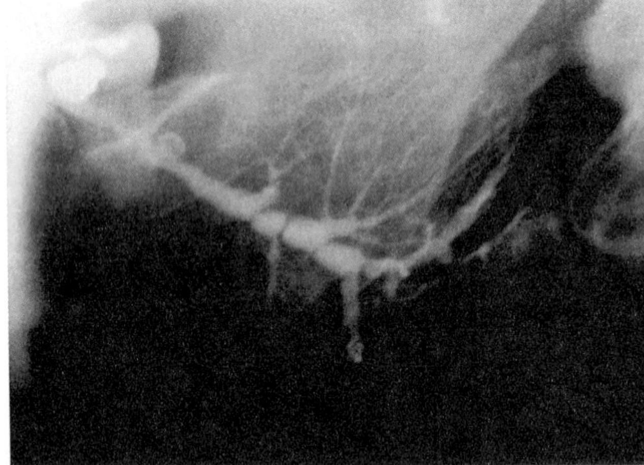

FIGURE 1-214 Sialogram of patient with chronic sialadenitis showing sausage link-like patterns and massive duct dilation. (From Blitzer CE, Lawson W, Reino A: Sialadenitis. In Johnson JT, Yu VL [eds]: *Infectious diseases and antimicrobial therapy of the ears, nose, and throat,* Philadelphia, 1997, WB Saunders.)

BASIC INFORMATION

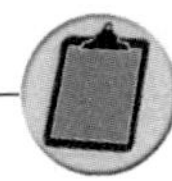

DEFINITION

Sialolithiasis is the existence of hardened intraluminal deposits in the ductal system of a salivary gland.

SYNONYMS

Salivary gland stone
Salivary calculus

ICD-9CM CODES
527.5 Sialolithiasis

EPIDEMIOLOGY & DEMOGRAPHICS

Affects patients mostly in their fifth to eighth decade and occurs most commonly in the submandibular gland (80%); only 14% are located in a parotid gland.

PHYSICAL FINDINGS & CLINICAL PRESENTATION

- Symptoms: colicky postprandial pain and swelling of a salivary gland. Tends to have a remitting/relapsing course.
- Signs: swelling and tenderness of a salivary gland. The stone may be felt by palpation of the floor of the mouth (Fig. 1-215).

ETIOLOGY

- The cause is unknown. Contributing factors include saliva stagnation, sialadenitis (inflammation of a salivary gland), ductal inflammation or injury.
- Salivary calculus composition is mainly calcium phosphate and carbonate, often combined with small proportions of magnesium, zinc, ammonium salts, and organic materials/debris.

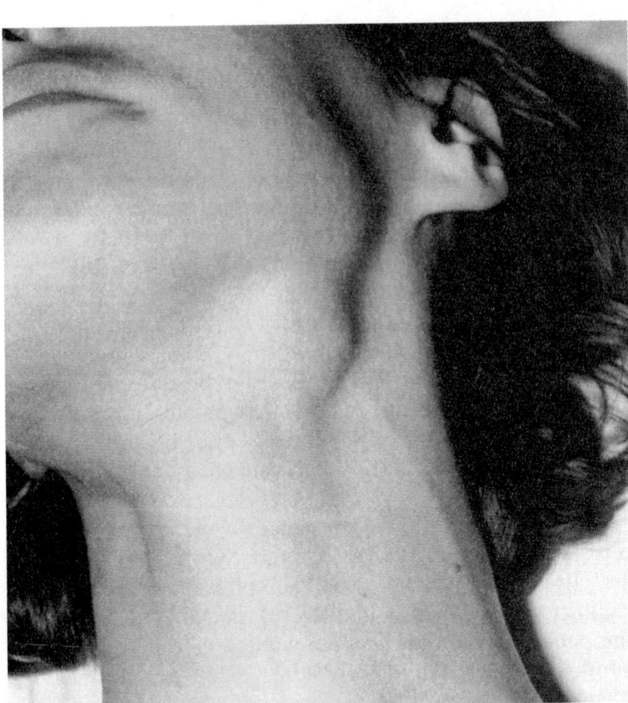

FIGURE 1-215 Patient with large calculus and obstruction of the left submandibular gland. (From Blitzer CE, Lawson W, Reino A: Sialadenitis. In Johnson JT, Yu VL [eds]: *Infectious diseases and antimicrobial therapy of the ears, nose, and throat,* Philadelphia, 1997, WB Saunders.)

DIAGNOSIS

DIFFERENTIAL DIAGNOSIS

- Lymphadenitis
- Salivary gland tumor
- Salivary gland bacterial (Staphylococcus or *Streptococcus),* viral (mumps), or fungal infection (sialadenitis)
- Noninfectious salivary gland inflammation (e.g., Sjögren's syndrome, sarcoidosis, lymphoma)
- Salivary duct stricture
- Dental abscess

IMAGING

- Plain x-ray
- Sialography

TREATMENT

- Warm soaks to area
- Antibiotics if associated bacterial sialadenitis is present
- Bland diet—avoid citrus fruit and spices
- Manual stone extraction sometimes associated with incisional enlargement of the ductal orifice
- Surgical salivary gland removal for retained hilar calculi

REFERRAL

To otorhinolaryngologist

SUGGESTED READING

Kane WJ, McCaffrey TV: Sialolithiasis. In Cummings CW (ed): *Otolaryngology: head and neck surgery,* ed 2, St Louis, 1992, Mosby.

AUTHOR: **TOM J. WACHTEL, M.D.**

SECTION I

BASIC INFORMATION

DEFINITION

Sick sinus syndrome is a group of cardiac rhythm disturbances characterized by abnormalities of the sinus node including (1) sinus bradycardia, (2) sinus arrest or exit block, (3) combinations of sinoatrial or atrioventricular conduction defects, and (4) supraventricular tachyarrhythmias. These abnormalities may coexist in a single patient so that a patient may have episodes of bradycardia and episodes of tachycardia.

SYNONYMS

Bradycardia-tachycardia syndrome

ICD-9CM CODES
427.81 Sick sinus syndrome

EPIDEMIOLOGY & DEMOGRAPHICS

- In children: associated with congenital heart disease
- In adults: typically associated with ischemic heart disease but may occur in the presence of a normal heart

PHYSICAL FINDINGS & CLINICAL PRESENTATION

- Lightheadedness, dizziness, syncope, palpitation
- Arterial embolization (e.g., stroke) associated with atrial fibrillation
- Physical examination may be normal or reveal abnormalities (e.g., heart murmurs or gallop sounds) associated with the underlying heart disease

ETIOLOGY

- Fibrosis or fatty infiltration involving the sinus node, atrioventricular node, the His bundle, or its branches
- In addition, inflammatory or degenerative changes of the nerves and ganglia surrounding the sinus nodes and other sclerodegenerative changes may be found

DIAGNOSIS

DIFFERENTIAL DIAGNOSIS

- Bradycardia: atrioventricular block
- Tachycardia: atrial fibrillation
- Atrial flutter
- Paroxysmal atrial tachycardia
- Sinus tachycardia
- Syncope (see "Syncope" in Section I)

WORKUP

- ECG
- Ambulatory cardiac rhythm monitoring
- 24-hour ambulatory ECG (Holter) (Fig. 1-216)
- Event recorder
- Electrophysiologic testing including sinus nodal recovery time and sino-atrial conduction time

TREATMENT

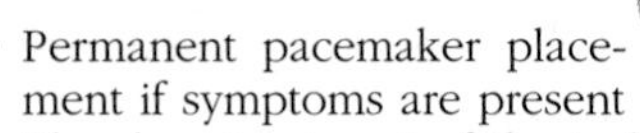

- Permanent pacemaker placement if symptoms are present
- The drug treatment of the tachycardia (e.g., with digitalis or calcium channel blockers) may worsen or bring out the bradycardia and become the reason for pacemaker requirement

REFERRAL

To cardiologist

SUGGESTED READING

Zipes DP, Olgin JE: Sick sinus syndrome. In Braunwald E (ed): *Heart disease: a textbook of cardiovascular medicine,* ed 6, Philadelphia, 2001, WB Saunders.

AUTHOR: **TOM J. WACHTEL, M.D.**

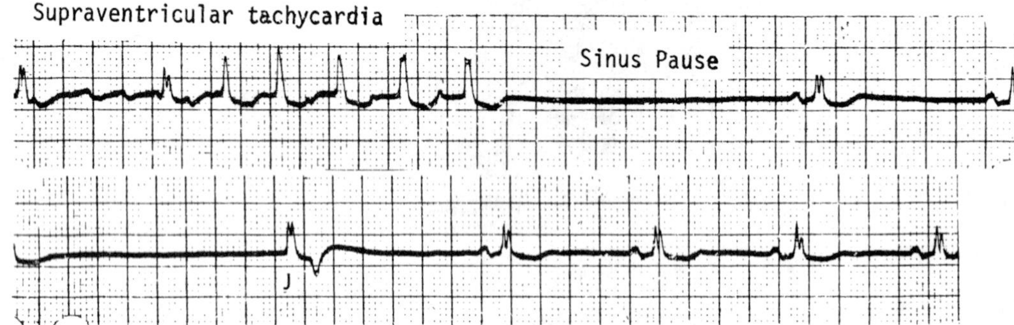

FIGURE 1-216 Brady-tachy (sick sinus) syndrome. This rhythm strip shows a narrow-complex tachycardia (probably atrial flutter) followed by a sinus pause, an AV junctional escape beat *(J),* and then sinus rhythm. (From Goldberger AL: *Clinical electrocardiography,* ed 5, St Louis, 1994, Mosby.)

BASIC INFORMATION

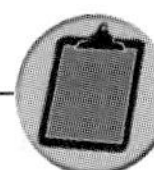

DEFINITION

Sickle cell disease is a hemoglobinopathy characterized by the production of hemoglobin S caused by substitution of the amino acid valine for glutamic acid in the sixth position of the γ-globin chain. When exposed to lower oxygen tension, RBCs assume a sickle shape resulting in stasis of RBCs in capillaries. Painful crises are caused by ischemic tissue injury resulting from obstruction of blood flow produced by sickled erythrocytes.

SYNONYMS

Sickle cell anemia
Hemoglobin S disease

ICD-9CM CODES
286.60 Sickle cell anemia

EPIDEMIOLOGY & DEMOGRAPHICS

- Sickle cell hemoglobin S is transmitted by an autosomal recessive gene. It is found mostly in blacks (1 in 400 black Americans).
- Sickle cell trait occurs in nearly 10% of black Americans.
- There is no predominant sex.

PHYSICAL FINDINGS & CLINICAL PRESENTATION

- Physical examination is variable depending on the degree of anemia and presence of acute vasoocclusive syndromes or neurologic, cardiovascular, GU, and musculoskeletal complications.
- There is no clinical laboratory finding that is pathognomonic of painful crisis of sickle cell disease. The diagnosis of a painful episode is made solely on the basis of the medical therapy and physical examination.
- Bones are the most common site of pain. Dactylitis, or hand-foot syndrome (acute, painful swelling of the hands and feet), is the first manifestation of sickle cell disease in many infants. Irritability and refusal to walk are other common symptoms. After infancy, musculoskeletal pain can be symmetric, asymmetric, or migratory, and it may or may not be associated with swelling, low-grade fever, redness, or warmth.
- In both children and adults, sickle vasoocclusive episodes are difficult to distinguish from osteomyelitis, septic arthritis, synovitis, rheumatic fever, or gout.
- When abdominal or visceral pain is present, care should be taken to exclude sequestration syndromes (spleen, liver) or the possibility of an acute condition such as appendicitis, pancreatitis, cholecystitis, urinary tract infection, PID, or malignancy.
- Pneumonia develops during the course of 20% of painful events and can present as chest and abdominal pain. In adults chest pain may be a result of vasoocclusion in the ribs and often precedes a pulmonary event. The lower back is also a frequent site of painful crisis in adults.
- The "acute chest syndrome" manifests with chest pain, fever, wheezing, tachypnea, and cough. Chest x-ray reveals pulmonary infiltrates. Common causes include infection (mycoplasma, chlamydia, viruses), infarction, and fat embolism.
- Musculoskeletal and skin abnormalities seen in sickle cell anemia include leg ulcers (particularly on the malleoli) and limb-girdle deformities caused by avascular necrosis of the femoral and humeral heads.
- Endocrine abnormalities include delayed sexual maturation and late physical maturation, especially evident in boys.
- Neurologic abnormalities on examination may include seizures and altered mental status.
- Infections, particularly involving *Salmonella, Mycoplasma,* and *Streptococcus,* are relatively common.
- Severe splenomegaly secondary to sequestration often occurs in children before splenic atrophy.

DIAGNOSIS

DIFFERENTIAL DIAGNOSIS

- Thalassemia
- Iron deficiency anemia, leukemia
- The differential diagnosis of patients presenting with a painful crisis is discussed in "Physical Findings."

WORKUP

- Screening of all newborns regardless of racial background is recommended. Screening can be performed with sodium metabisulfite reduction test (Sickledex test).
- Hemoglobin electrophoresis will also confirm the diagnosis and is useful to identify hemoglobin variants such as fetal hemoglobin and hemoglobin A2.

LABORATORY TESTS

- Anemia (resulting from chronic hemolysis), reticulocytosis, leukocytosis, and thrombocytosis are common.
- Elevations of bilirubin and LDH are also common.
- Peripheral blood smear may reveal sickle cells, target cells, poikilocytosis, and hypochromia (Fig. 1-217).
- Elevated BUN and creatinine may be present in patients with progressive renal insufficiency.
- Urinalysis may reveal hematuria and proteinuria.

IMAGING STUDIES

- Chest x-ray is useful in patients presenting with "chest syndrome." Cardiomegaly may be present on chest x-ray examination.

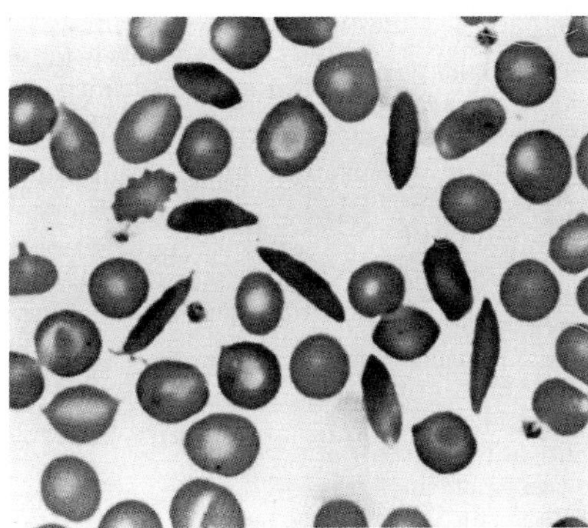

FIGURE 1-217 Photomicrograph of peripheral blood smear, sickle cells, typical of sickle cell anemia. (From Andreoli TE [ed]: *Cecil essential of medicine,* ed 4, Philadelphia, 1997, WB Saunders.)

- Bone scan is useful to rule out osteomyelitis (usually secondary to salmonella). MRI scan is also effective in diagnosing osteomyelitis.
- CT scan or MRI of brain is often needed in patients presenting with neurologic complications such as TIA, CVA, seizures, or altered mental status.
- Transcranial Doppler is a useful commodity to identify children with sickle cell anemia who are at risk for stroke.
- Doppler echocardiography can be used to diagnose pulmonary hypertension

TREATMENT

NONPHARMACOLOGIC THERAPY

- Patients should be instructed to avoid conditions that may precipitate sickling crisis, such as hypoxia, infections, acidosis, and dehydration.
- Maintain adequate hydration (PO or IV).
- Correct hypoxia.

ACUTE GENERAL Rx

- Aggressively diagnose and treat suspected infections (*Salmonella* osteomyelitis and pneumococcal infections occur more often in patients with sickle cell anemia because of splenic infarcts and atrophy). Combination therapy with a cephalosporin and erythromycin plus incentive spirometry and bronchodilators are useful in patients with acute chest syndrome.
- Provide pain relief during the vasoocclusive crisis. Medications should be administered on a fixed time schedule with a dosing interval that does not extend beyond the duration of the desired pharmacologic effect.
  1. Meperidine is contraindicated in patients with renal dysfunction or CNS disease because its metabolite, normeperidine (which is excreted by the kidneys) can cause seizures.
  2. Narcotics (e.g., morphine 0.1 mg/kg IV q 3-4 h or 0.3 mg/kg PO q 4 h) should be given on a fixed schedule (not prn for pain), with rescue dosing for breakthrough pain as needed.
  3. Except when contraindications exist, concomitant use of NSAIDs should be standard treatment.
  4. Nurses should be instructed not to give narcotics if the patient is heavily sedated or respirations are depressed.
  5. When the patient shows signs of improvement, narcotic drugs should be tapered gradually to prevent withdrawal syndrome. It is advisable to observe the patient on oral pain relief medications for 12-24 hr before discharge from the hospital.
  6. Analgesic medications should be used in combination with psychologic, behavioral, and physical modalities in the management of sickle cell disease.
- Aggressively diagnose and treat any potential complications (e.g., septic necrosis of the femoral head, priapism, bony infarcts, and acute "chest syndrome").
- Avoid "routine" transfusions but consider early transfusions for patients at high risk for complications. Indications for transfusion: aplastic crises, severe hemolytic crises (particularly during third trimester of pregnancy), acute chest syndrome, and high risk of stroke.
- Hydroxyurea (500-750 mg/day) increases hemoglobin F levels and reduces the incidence of vasoocclusive complications. It is generally well tolerated. Side effects consist primarily of mild reversible neutropenia.
- Replace folic acid (1 mg PO qd).

CHRONIC Rx

- Guidelines for prompt management of fever, infections, pain, and specific complications should be reviewed.
- Genetic counseling is recommended in all cases.
- Avoid unnecessary transfusions. Exchange transfusions may be necessary for patients with acute neurologic signs, in aplastic crisis, or undergoing surgery.
- Allogeneic stem cell transplantation can be curative in young patients with symptomatic sickle cell disease; however, the death rate from the procedure is nearly 10%, the marrow recipients are likely to be infertile, and there is an undefined risk of chemotherapy-induced malignancy.
- Penicillin V 125 mg PO bid should be administered by age 2 mo and increased to 250 mg bid by age 3. Penicillin prophylaxis can be discontinued after age 5 except in children who have had splenectomy.

REFERRAL

- Hospitalization is generally recommended for most crises and complications.
- Psychosocial counseling and support structures should be developed.

PEARLS & CONSIDERATIONS

COMMENTS

- Patients and their families should receive genetic counseling and should be made aware of the difference between sickle cell trait and sickle cell disease.
- Regular immunizations and pneumococcal vaccination are recommended. The prophylactic administration of penicillin soon after birth and the timely administration of pneumococcal and *H. influenzae* type b vaccines have resulted in a significant decline in the incidence of these infections. The heptavalent conjugated pneumococcal vaccine (Prevan) should be administered from 2 mo of age. The 23-valent unconjugated pneumococcal vaccine is given from age 2 and can be boosted once 3 yr later. Influenza vaccination can be given after 6 mo of age.
- Patients should be instructed on a well-balanced diet and appropriate folic acid supplementation.
- The presence of dactylitis, Hb 7, or leukocytosis in the absence of infection during the first 2 yr of life, indicates a higher risk of severe sickle cell disease later in life.
- Among patients with sickle cell disease, the acute chest syndrome is commonly precipitated by fat embolism and infection, especially community-acquired pneumonia. Among older patients and those with neurologic symptoms, the syndrome often progresses to respiratory failure.
- Poloxamer 188, a nonionic surfactant with hemorrheologic and antithrombotic properties, has been reported to produce a significant but relatively small decrease in the duration of painful episodes and an increase in the proportion of patients who achieved resolution of the symptoms. A more significant effect was observed in patients who received concomitant hydroxyurea.
- Pulmonary hypertension is a complication of chronic hemolysis and is associated with a high risk of death. It can be detected by Doppler echocardiography in over 30% of adult patients with sickle cell disease. Cardiac catheterization will confirm the diagnosis. It is resistant to hydroxyurea therapy.

SUGGESTED READINGS

Gladwin MT et al: Pulmonary hypertension as a risk factor for death in patients with sickle cell disease, *N Engl J Med* 350:886, 2004.

Orringer E et al: Purified poloxamer 188 for treatment of acute vaso-occlusive crisis of sickle cell disease, *JAMA* 286:2099, 2001.

Vichinski EP et al: Causes and outcomes of the acute chest syndrome in sickle cell disease, *N Engl J Med* 342:1855, 2000.

Wethers DL: Sickle cell disease in childhood, *Am Fam Physician* 62:1013, 2000.

AUTHOR: **FRED F. FERRI, M.D.**

BASIC INFORMATION

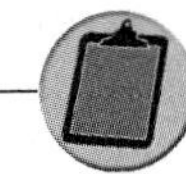

DEFINITION

Silicosis is a lung disease attributable to the inhalation of silica (silicon dioxide) in crystalline form (quartz) or in cristobalite or tridymite forms.

SYNONYMS

Pneumoconiosis caused by silica

ICD-9CM CODES
502 Silicosis, occupational
503 Pneumoconiosis caused by other inorganic dust

EPIDEMIOLOGY & DEMOGRAPHICS

- Occupational disease affecting men and women involved in gathering, milling, processing, or using silica-containing rock or sand
- An estimated 1 million Americans are exposed

PHYSICAL FINDINGS & CLINICAL PRESENTATION

- Dyspnea
- Cough
- Wheezing
- Abnormal chest x-ray in an asymptomatic person

PATHOGENESIS

- Silica particles are ingested by alveolar macrophages, which in turn release oxidants causing cell injury and cell death, attract fibroblasts, and activate lymphocytes, increasing immunoglobulins in the alveolar space.
- Hyperplasia of alveolar epithelial cells occurs.
- Collagen accumulates in the interstitium.
- Neutrophils also accumulate and secrete proteolytic enzymes, which leads to tissue destruction and emphysema.
- Silica dust may be carcinogenic (not proven).
- Exposure to silicosis predisposes to tuberculosis.
- Some patients develop rheumatoid silicotic pulmonary nodules and may have arthritic symptoms of rheumatoid arthritis (Caplan's syndrome). Scleroderma has also been associated with silicosis.

DIAGNOSIS

DIFFERENTIAL DIAGNOSIS

- Other pneumoconiosis, berylliosis, hard metal disease, asbestosis
- Sarcoidosis
- Tuberculosis
- Interstitial lung disease
- Hypersensitivity pneumonitis
- Lung cancer
- Langerhans' cell granulomatosis (histiocytosis X)
- Granulomatous pulmonary vasculitis

WORKUP

- History of occupational exposure
- Chest x-ray (Fig. 1-218)

Chronic silicosis

- Characteristic finding: small, rounded lung parenchymal opacities
- Hilar lymphadenopathy with "eggshell" calcifications
- Pleural plaques (uncommon)

Accelerated silicosis (progressive massive fibrosis)

- Large parenchymal lesions resulting from coalesced small nodules

Acute silicosis

- Ground-glass appearance of the lung fields
- Chest CT scan
- Pulmonary function tests

Combination of obstructive and restrictive changes with or without reduction in diffusing capacity

- Bronchoscopy with lung biopsy in uncertain cases

COURSE

CHRONIC SILICOSIS:

- May not progress with absence of further exposure
- Accelerated silicosis: progressive respiratory failure and cor pulmonale

ACUTE SILICOSIS: Fatal course from respiratory failure over several months to a few years

TREATMENT

- Prevention (industrial hygiene)
- Treatment of associated tuberculosis if present
- Supportive measures (oxygen, bronchodilators)
- Lung transplant

SUGGESTED READING

Becklake MR: Silicosis. In Murray JF, Nadel JA (eds): *Textbook of respiratory medicine,* ed 2, Philadelphia, 1994, WB Saunders.

AUTHOR: **TOM J. WACHTEL, M.D.**

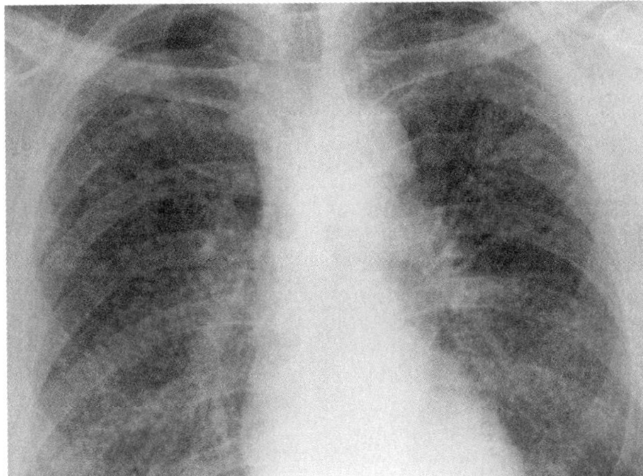

FIGURE 1-218 Simple silicosis. There are multiple small (2- to 4-mm) nodules distributed throughout the lungs, with an upper lobe predominance. (From McLoud TC: *Thoracic radiology: the requisites,* St Louis, 1998, Mosby.)

BASIC INFORMATION

DEFINITION

Sinusitis is inflammation of the mucous membranes lining one or more of the paranasal sinuses. The various presentations are:

- Acute sinusitis: infection lasting <30 days, with complete resolution of symptoms.
- Subacute infection: lasts from 30 to 90 days, with complete resolution of symptoms.
- Recurrent acute infection: episodes of acute infection lasting <30 days, with resolution of symptoms, which recur at intervals at least 10 days apart.
- Chronic sinusitis: inflammation lasting >90 days, with persistent upper respiratory symptoms.
- Acute bacterial sinusitis superimposed on chronic sinusitis: new symptoms that occur in patients with residual symptoms from prior infection(s). With treatment, the new symptoms resolve but the residual ones do not.

ICD-9CM CODES

473.9 Sinusitis (accessory) (nasal) (hyperplastic) (nonpurulent) (purulent) (chronic)

461.9 Acute sinusitis

SYNONYMS

Rhinosinusitis: Sinusitis is almost always accompanied by inflammation of the nasal mucosa; thus it is now the preferred term.

EPIDEMIOLOGY & DEMOGRAPHICS

INCIDENCE (IN U.S.): Seems to correlate with the incidence of upper respiratory tract infections

PEAK INCIDENCE: Fall, winter, spring: September through March

PHYSICAL FINDINGS & CLINICAL PRESENTATION

- Patients often give a history of a recent upper respiratory illness with some improvement, then a relapse
- Mucopurulent secretions in the nasal passage
  1. Purulent nasal and postnasal discharge lasting >7 to 10 days
  2. Facial tightness, pressure, or pain
  3. Nasal obstruction
  4. Headache
  5. Decreased sense of smell
  6. Purulent pharyngeal secretions, brought up with cough, often worse at night
- Erythema, swelling, and tenderness over the infected sinus in a small proportion of patients
  1. Diagnosis cannot be excluded by the absence of such findings.
  2. These findings are not common, and do not correlate with number of positive sinus aspirates.
- Intermittent low-grade fever in about half of adults with acute bacterial sinusitis
- Toothache is a common complaint when the maxillary sinus is involved
- Periorbital cellulitis and excessive tearing with ethmoid sinusitis
  1. Orbital extension of infection: chemosis, proptosis, impaired extraocular movements
- Characteristics of acute sinusitis in children with upper respiratory tract infections:
  1. Persistence of symptoms
  2. Cough
  3. Bad breath
- Symptoms of chronic sinusitis (may or may not be present)
  1. Nasal or postnasal discharge
  2. Fever
  3. Facial pain or pressure
  4. Headache
- Nosocomial sinusitis is typically seen in patients with nasogastric tubes or nasotracheal intubation.

ETIOLOGY

- Each of the four paranasal sinuses is connected to the nasal cavity by narrow tubes (ostia), 1 to 3 mm diameter; these drain directly into the nose through the turbinates. The sinuses are lined with a ciliated mucous membrane (mucoperiosteum).
- Acute viral infection
  1. Infection with the common cold or influenza
  2. Mucosal edema and sinus inflammation
  3. Decreased drainage of thick secretions/obstruction of the sinus ostia
  4. Subsequent entrapment of bacteria
     a. Multiplication of bacteria
     b. Secondary bacterial infection
- Other predisposing factors
  1. Tumors
  2. Polyps
  3. Foreign bodies
  4. Congenital choanal atresia
  5. Other entities that cause obstruction of sinus drainage
  6. Allergies
  7. Asthma
- Dental infections lead to maxillary sinusitis
- Viruses recovered alone or in combination with bacteria (in 16% of cases):
  1. Rhinovirus
  2. Coronavirus
  3. Adenovirus
  4. Parainfluenza virus
  5. Respiratory syncytial virus
- The principal bacterial pathogens in sinusitis are *Streptococcus pneumoniae,* nontypeable *Haemophilus influenzae,* and *Moraxella catarrhalis.*
- In the remainder of cases find *Streptococcus pyogenes, Staphylococcus aureus,* α-hemolytic streptococci, and mixed anaerobic infections *(Peptostreptococcus, Fusobacterium, Bacteroides, Prevotella).*
- Infection is polymicrobial in about one third of cases.
- Anaerobic infections seen more often in cases of chronic sinusitis and in cases associated with dental infection; anaerobes are unlikely pathogens in sinusitis in children.
- Fungal pathogens are isolated with increasing frequency in immunocompromised patients:
  1. *Aspergillus*
  2. *Pseudallescheria*
  3. *Sporothrix*
  4. Phaeohyphomycoses
  5. Hyalohyphomycoses
  6. Zygomycetes
- Nosocomial infections: occur in patients with nasogastric tubes, nasotracheal intubation, cystic fibrosis, immunocompromised
  1. *S. aureus*
  2. *Pseudomonas aeruginosa*
  3. *Klebsiella pneumoniae*
  4. *Enterobacter spp.*
  5. *Proteus mirabilis*
- Organisms typically isolated in chronic sinusitis:
  1. *S. aureus*
  2. *S. pneumoniae*
  3. *H. influenzae*
  4. *P. aeruginosa*
  5. Anaerobes

DIAGNOSIS

DIFFERENTIAL DIAGNOSIS

- Temporomandibular joint disease
- Migraine headache
- Cluster headache
- Dental infection
- Trigeminal neuralgia

WORKUP

- In the normal healthy host the paranasal sinuses should be sterile. Although the contiguous structures are colonized with bacteria and likely contaminate the sinuses, the mucociliary lining functions to remove these bacteria.
- Gold standard for diagnosis: recovery of bacteria in high density ($\geq 10^4$ colony-forming units/ml) from a paranasal sinus, in the setting of a patient with history of upper respiratory infection and symptoms persisting 7 to

10 days. Sinus aspiration is the best method for obtaining cultures; however, it must be performed by an otorhinolaryngologist and is not practical for the primary care practitioner. Therefore most diagnoses are based on the clinical history and presentation, possibly supported by radiologic evaluations.

1. Standard four-view sinus radiographs
   a. Complete opacification and air-fluid levels are most specific findings (average 85% and 80%, respectively)
   b. Mucosal thickening has low specificity (40% to 50%)
   c. Absence of all three of the previous findings has estimated sensitivity of 90%
   d. Overall, standard radiographs are of limited use in diagnosis, although negative films are strong evidence against the diagnosis
2. CT scans:
   a. Much more sensitive than plain radiographs in detecting acute changes and disease in the sinuses
   b. Recommended for patients requiring surgical intervention, including sinus aspiration; it is a useful adjunct to guide therapy
3. Transillumination:
   a. Used for diagnosis of frontal and maxillary sinusitis
   b. Place transilluminator in the mouth or against cheek to assess maxillary sinuses, under medial aspect of the supraorbital ridge to assess frontal sinuses
   c. Absence of light transmission indicates that sinus is filled with fluid
   d. Dullness (decreased light transmission) is less helpful in diagnosing infection
4. Endoscopy:
   a. Used to visualize secretions coming from the ostia of infected sinuses
   b. Culture collection via endoscopy often contaminated by nasal flora; not nearly as good as sinus puncture
5. Sinus puncture:
   a. Gold standard for collecting sinus cultures
   b. Generally reserved for treatment failures, suspected intracranial extension, and nosocomial sinusitis

TREATMENT

NONPHARMACOLOGIC THERAPY

To help promote sinus drainage:

- Air humidification with vaporizers (for steam) or humidifiers (for a cool mist)
- Application of hot, wet towel over the face
- Sipping hot beverages
- Hydration

ACUTE GENERAL Rx

- Sinus drainage:
  1. Nasal vasoconstrictors, such as phenylephrine nose drops, 0.25% or 0.5%
  2. Topical decongestants should not be used for more than a few days because of the risk of rebound congestion
  3. Systemic decongestants
  4. Nasal or systemic corticosteroids, such as nasal beclomethasone, short course oral prednisone
  5. Nasal irrigation, with hypertonic or normal saline (saline may act as a mild vasoconstrictor of nasal blood flow)
  6. Use of antihistamines has no proven benefit, and the drying effect on the mucous membranes may cause crusting, which blocks the ostia, thus interfering with sinus drainage
- Analgesics, antipyretics

Antimicrobial therapy:

- Most cases of acute sinusitis have a viral etiology and will resolve within 2 wk without antibiotics.
- Current treatment recommendations favor symptomatic treatment for those with mild symptoms.
- Antibiotics should be reserved for those with moderate to severe symptoms who meet the criteria for diagnosis of sinusitis.
- Antibiotic therapy is usually empiric, targeting the common pathogens:
  1. First-line antibiotics include amoxicillin, erythromycin, TMP/SMX.
  2. Second-line antibiotics include the newer macrolides: clarithromycin, azithromycin, amoxicillin/clavulanate, cefuroxime axetil, cefprozil, cefaclor, loracarbef, ciprofloxacin, levofloxacin, clindamycin, metronidazole, others.
  3. For patients with uncomplicated acute sinusitis, the less expensive first-line agents appear to be as effective as the costlier second-line agents.
- Hospitalization and IV antibiotics may be required for more severe infection and those with suspected intracranial complications. Broader-spectrum antibiotic coverage may be indicated in severe cases, to cover for MRSA, *Pseudomonas,* and fungal pathogens.

Duration of therapy generally 10 to 14 days, although some have success with much shorter regimens

Surgery:

- Surgical drainage indicated
  1. If intracranial or orbital complications suspected
  2. Many cases of frontal and sphenoid sinusitis
  3. Chronic sinusitis recalcitrant to medical therapy
- Surgical debridement imperative in the treatment of fungal sinusitis

Complications:

- Untreated, sinusitis may lead to a number of serious, life-threatening complications.
- Intracranial complications include meningitis, brain abscess, epidural and subdural empyema.
- Intracranial sequelae are more common with frontal and ethmoid infections.
- Extracranial complications include orbital cellulitis, blindness, orbital abscess, osteomyelitis.
- Extracranial sequelae are more commonly seen with ethmoid sinusitis.

CHRONIC Rx

- Broad-spectrum antibiotics that cover both aerobes and anaerobes
- Duration of therapy not clearly established: range 3 to 6 wk
- Adjunctive therapy: one or more of the various options listed previously
- Surgical intervention may be necessary in nonresponders

DISPOSITION

Appropriate diagnosis and treatment necessary to avoid the various sequelae that can occur without proper therapy

REFERRAL

- To infectious disease specialist if failure to respond to initial therapy
- To otorhinolaryngologist for:
  1. Failure to respond to therapy
  2. Fungal infection suspected
  3. Intracranial or orbital complications suspected

SUGGESTED READINGS

Brook I: Bacteriology of acute and chronic frontal sinusitis, *Arch Otolaryngol Head Neck Surg* 128(5):583, 2002.

Jiang RS, Lin JF, Hsu CY: Correlation between bacteriology of the middle meatus and ethmoid sinus in chronic sinusitis, *J Laryngol Otol* 116(6):443, 2002.

AUTHOR: **JANE V. EASON, M.D.**

BASIC INFORMATION

DEFINITION

Sjögren's syndrome (SS) is an autoimmune disorder characterized by lymphocytic and plasma cell infiltration and destruction of salivary and lacrimal glands with subsequent diminished lacrimal and salivary gland secretions.

- *Primary:* dry mouth (xerostomia) and dry eyes (xerophthalmia) develop as isolated entities.
- *Secondary:* associated with other disorders.

SYNONYMS

SS
Sicca syndrome

ICD-9CM CODES
710.2 Sjögren's syndrome

EPIDEMIOLOGY & DEMOGRAPHICS

INCIDENCE/PREVALENCE: 1 case/2500 persons; secondary SS is just as common and can affect up to one third of SLE patients and nearly 20% of RA patients.
PREDOMINANT AGE: Peak incidence is in the sixth decade.
PREDOMINANT SEX: Female > male

PHYSICAL FINDINGS & CLINICAL PRESENTATION

- Dry mouth with dry lips (cheilosis), erythema of tongue (Fig. 1-219), and other mucosal surfaces, carious teeth
- Dry eyes (conjunctival injection, decreased luster, and irregularity of the corneal light reflex)
- Possible salivary gland enlargement and dysfunction with subsequent difficulty in chewing and swallowing food and in speaking without frequent water intake
- Purpura (nonthrombocytopenic, hyperglobulinemic, vasculitic) may be present
- Evidence of associated conditions (e.g., RA or other connective disease, lymphoma, hypothyroidism, COPD, trigeminal neuropathy, chronic liver disease, polymyopathy)

ETIOLOGY

Autoimmune disorder

DIAGNOSIS

DIFFERENTIAL DIAGNOSIS

- Medication-related dryness (e.g., anticholinergics)
- Age-related exocrine gland dysfunction
- Mouth breathing
- Anxiety
- Other: sarcoidosis, primary salivary hypofunction, radiation injury, amyloidosis

WORKUP

Workup involves the demonstration of the following criteria for diagnosis of primary and secondary Sjögren's syndrome:

PRIMARY:

- Symptoms and objective signs of ocular dryness:
  1. Schirmer's test: <8 mm wetting per 5 min
  2. Positive rose bengal or fluorescein staining of cornea and conjunctiva to demonstrate keratoconjunctivitis sicca
- Symptoms and objective signs of dry mouth:
  1. Decreased parotid flow using Lashley cups or other methods
  2. Abnormal biopsy result of minor salivary gland (focus score >2 based on average of four assessable lobules)
- Evidence of systemic autoimmune disorder:
  1. Elevated titer of rheumatoid factor >1:320
  2. Elevated titer of ANA >1:320
  3. Presence of anti-SS A (Ro) or anti-SS B (La) antibodies

SECONDARY:

- Characteristic signs and symptoms of SS (described in "Physical Findings")
- Clinical features sufficient to allow a diagnosis of RA, SLE, polymyositis, or scleroderma

LABORATORY TESTS

- Positive ANA (>60% of patients) with autoantibodies anti-SS A and anti-SS B may be present.
- Additional laboratory abnormalities may include elevated ESR, anemia (normochromic, normocytic), abnormal liver function studies, elevated serum β_2 microglobulin levels, rheumatoid factor.
- A definite diagnosis SS can be made with a salivary gland biopsy.

TREATMENT

NONPHARMACOLOGIC THERAPY

- Adequate fluid replacement
- Proper oral hygiene to reduce the incidence of caries

ACUTE GENERAL Rx

- Use artificial tears frequently.
- Pilocarpine 5 mg PO qid is useful to improve dryness. A cyclosporine 0.05% ophthalmic emulsion (Restasis) may also be useful for dry eyes. Recommended dose is one drop bid in both eyes.
- Cevimeline (Evoxac), a cholinergic agent with muscarinic agonist activity, 30 mg PO tid is effective for the treatment of dry mouth in patients with Sjögren's syndrome.

CHRONIC Rx

Periodic dental and ophthalmology evaluations to screen for complications

PEARLS & CONSIDERATIONS

COMMENTS

Unusual presentations of SS may occur in association with polymyalgia rheumatica, chronic fatigue syndrome, FUO, and inflammatory myositis.

SUGGESTED READING

Kassan SS, Moutsopoulos HM: Clinical manifestations and early diagnosis of Sjogren syndrome, *Arch Intern Med* 164:1275, 2004.

AUTHOR: **FRED F. FERRI, M.D.**

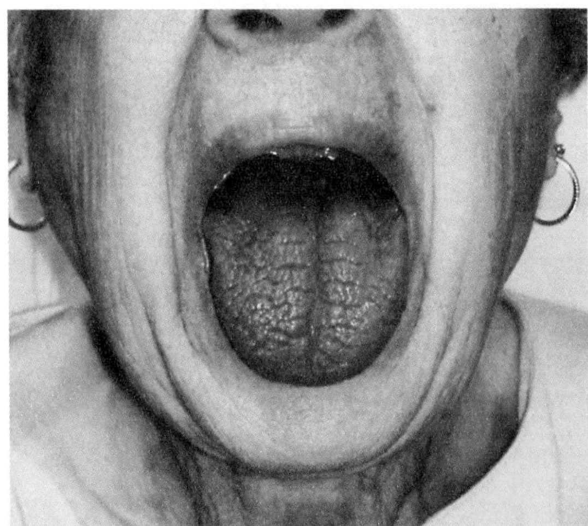

FIGURE 1-219 "Crocodile tongue" in SS patient. (From Noble J: *Primary care medicine,* ed 3, St Louis, 2001, Mosby.)

BASIC INFORMATION

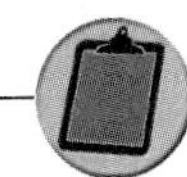

DEFINITION

The American Academy of Sleep Disorders defines obstructive sleep apnea as "characterized by repetitive episodes of upper airway obstruction that occur during sleep, usually associated with a reduction in blood oxygen saturation."

SYNONYMS

Sleep apnea syndrome
Obstructive sleep apnea-hypopnea syndrome

ICD-9CM CODE
780.53 Obstructive sleep apnea syndrome

EPIDEMIOLOGY & DEMOGRAPHICS

Obstructive sleep apnea (OSA) occurs most frequently in 40- to 65-year-old men (4%) and women (2%). The prevalence is higher in obese and hypertensive individuals. Pediatric OSA most frequently occurs in preschool-aged children (2%) and is associated with hypertrophy of the tonsils and adenoids.

PHYSICAL FINDINGS & CLINICAL PRESENTATION

- Systemic hypertension
- History of snoring, witnessed apneas and excessive daytime somnolence
- Obesity with body mass index >27 kg/m^2, neck circumference >43 cm (17″) in men
- Working memory impairment, inability to concentrate, short tempered
- Examination of oropharynx may reveal erythema caused by snoring and narrowing secondary to large tonsils, pendulous uvula, excessive soft tissue, prominent tongue and retrognathia
- Patient's bed partner may report loud, snoring, episodic choking sounds, disrupted sleep with repetitive arousals, thrashing movements of extremities during sleep
- Decreased libido, mood swings, and depression

ETIOLOGY

Narrowing of upper airway secondary to:
- Obesity
- Macroglossia
- Tonsillar and adenoid hypertrophy
- Micrognathia
- Muscular weakness
- Use of alcohol or sedatives at bedtime

DIAGNOSIS

DIFFERENTIAL DIAGNOSIS

- Excessive Daytime Somnolence
  Inadequate sleep time
  Pulmonary disease
  Parkinsonism
  Sleep-related epilepsy
  Narcolepsy
  Hypothyroidism
- Sleep Fragmentation
  Sleep-related asthma
  Sleep-related GERD
  Periodic limb movement disorder
  Parasomnias
  Psychophysiologic insomnia
  Panic disorder
  Narcolepsy

WORKUP

- Medical history should include questions about snoring, witnessed apneas, and excessive daytime sleepiness. Additional history concerning morning headaches, alcohol intake, weight gain, and mood/personality changes also may help to implicate apnea.
- Sleep apnea can be confirmed by overnight polysomnography (gold standard). Testing is performed during the patient's habitual sleep hours and ideally includes all stages of sleep and body positions. Patients with sleep apnea have >5 apneic/hypopneic episodes per hour (termed respiratory disturbance index, or RDI) with desaturations of at least 4% by oximetry or coincidental arousals. Overnight oximetry tests can suggest the presence of sleep apnea but are not sufficient to rule out sleep apnea.
- Portable monitors that measure RDI are available but they lack the EEG, EMG, and technical observations necessary to diagnose sleep apnea with reliable accuracy. The use of such devices is usually related to limited availability of polysomnography.

LABORATORY TESTS

- TSH level is indicated in suspected hypothyroidism.
- CBC (with iron studies) is indicated for detecting anemia.
- Pulmonary function tests are indicated for detecting related pulmonary disorders.
- ECG is indicated for detecting related heart disease.

IMAGING STUDIES

Radiography of soft tissues in the neck in patients with suspected anatomic abnormalities

TREATMENT

NONPHARMACOLOGIC THERAPY

- Weight loss in overweight patients including bariatric surgery
- Avoidance of sedating medications and alcohol
- Sleep hygiene training
- Elimination of the supine sleeping position
- For mild obstructive sleep apnea in select patient populations (e.g., retrognathia) an oral appliance (constructed by a qualified dentist) may be useful to push the mandible forward
- Uvulopalatopharyngoplasty (UPPP, both standard and laser-assisted [LAUP]) in patients with significant obstruction of retropalatal airway
- Nasal septoplasty in patients with nasoseptal deformity

ACUTE GENERAL Rx

- Nighttime treatment with continuous positive airway pressure (CPAP) provides immediate resolution of sleep apnea. Symptoms of excessive daytime somnolence may linger and necessitate further investigation or medical therapy
- Tracheostomy: reserved for life-threatening cases that are unresponsive to other treatments
- Nasal steroids in allergy or sinusitis patients

CHRONIC Rx

- CPAP therapy
- Weight loss

DISPOSITION

- Most patients improve with weight loss and CPAP.
- Overall success rate for UPPP is about 40% for snoring; likely less effective for apnea.
- Weight loss over time may reduce the need for CPAP pressure or obviate its use entirely.

REFERRAL

- Sleep physician for proper study type(s) and/or complex symptoms
- Surgical referral for patients unresponsive to weight loss and CPAP
- Dental referral for oral devices

PEARLS & CONSIDERATIONS

- In a primary care setting, patients with high risk of sleep apnea are those who meet two of the following three criteria: (1) snoring, (2) persistent daytime sleepiness or drowsiness while driving, (3) obesity or hypertension.
- Children with OSA may have symptoms of excessive daytime somnolence, hyperactivity, insomnia, inattention, declining academic performance, and a history of recurrent ear or throat infections.
- Some patients with sleep apnea experience nocturnal dysrhythmias (bradycardia, paroxysmal tachyarrhythmias). In cardiac patients, trials using atrial overdrive pacing have demonstrated a significant reduction in the number of episodes of sleep apnea without reduction in the total sleep time.
- The use of vagal nerve stimulators (VNS) in epilepsy patients has been associated with an increase in apneas and hypopneas. VNS-related respiratory events may be reduced by altering VNS stimulation parameters or by initiating CPAP.

SUGGESTED READINGS

American Academy of Pediatrics: Clinical practice guideline: diagnosis and management of childhood obstructive sleep apnea syndrome, *Pediatrics* 109:704, 2002.

Arens, R: Obstructive sleep apnea in childhood, clinical features. In Loughlin G, Carroll J, Marcus C (eds): *Sleep and breathing in children,* New York, 2000, Marcel Dekker.

Chervin RD et al: Inattention, hyperactivity and symptoms of sleep-disordered breathing, *Pediatrics* 109:449, 2002.

Flemons WW: Obstructive sleep apnea, *N Engl J Med* 347:498, 2002.

Garrigue A et al: Benefit of atrial pacing in sleep apnea syndrome, *N Engl J Med* 346:404, 2002.

Marzec M et al: Effects of vagal nerve stimulation on sleep-related breathing in epilepsy patients, *Epilepsia* 44:930, 2003.

Partinen M, Hublin C: Epidemiology of sleep disorders. In Kryger M, Roth T, Dement W (eds): *Principles and practice of sleep medicine,* ed 3, Philadelphia, 2000, WB Saunders.

Schroeder BM: Obstructive sleep apnea syndrome in children, *Am Fam Physician* 66:1338, 2002.

The International Classification of Sleep Disorders Revised, Diagnostic and Coding Manual. American Academy of Sleep Medicine, 2000.

AUTHOR: **J.S. DURMER, M.D., Ph.D.**

BASIC INFORMATION

DEFINITION

Smallpox infection is due to the variola virus, a DNA virus member of the genus *Orthopoxvirus*. It is a human virus with no known nonhuman reservoir of disease. Natural infection occurs following implantation of the virus on the oropharyngeal or respiratory mucosa.

ICD-9CM CODES
050.9 Smallpox NOS
V01.3 Smallpox exposure
050.0 Smallpox, hemorrhagic (pustular)
050.1 Variola minor (alastrim)
050.0 Variola major

EPIDEMIOLOGY & DEMOGRAPHICS

- Smallpox infection was eliminated from the world in 1977. The last cases of smallpox, from laboratory exposure, occurred in 1978. The threat of bioterrorism has brought on renewed interest in smallpox virus.
- Routine vaccination against smallpox ended in 1972.
- Smallpox is spread from one person to another by infected saliva droplets that expose a susceptible person who has face-to-face contact with the ill person.
- Persons with smallpox are most infectious during the first wk of illness, when the largest amount of virus is present in saliva; however, some risk of transmission lasts until all scabs have fallen off.
- The incubation period is about 12 days (range: 7-17 days) following exposure.
- Contaminated clothing or bed linen could also spread the virus. Special precautions need to be taken to ensure that all bedding and clothing of patients are cleaned appropriately with bleach and hot water. Disinfectants such as bleach and quaternary ammonia can be used for cleaning contaminated surfaces.

PHYSICAL FINDINGS & CLINICAL PRESENTATION

- Initial symptoms include high fever, fatigue, and headaches and back aches. A characteristic rash, most prominent on the face, arms, and legs, follows in 2-3 days (Fig. 1-220).
- The rash starts with flat red lesions that evolve at the same rate. The rash follows a centrifugal pattern.
- Lesions are firm to the touch, domed, or umbilicated. They become pus-filled and begin to crust early in the second wk.
- Scabs develop and then separate and fall off after about 3-4 wk. Depigmentation persists at the base of the skin lesions for 3 to 6 mo after illness. Scarring is usually most extensive on the face.
- Associated with the rash may be fever, headache, generalized malaise, vomiting, and colicky abdominal pain.
- Variola major may produce a rapidly fatal toxemia in some patients.
- Complications of smallpox include dehydration, pneumonia, blepharitis, conjunctivitis, and corneal ulcerations.

ETIOLOGY

Smallpox is caused by the variola virus. There are at least two strains of the virus, the most virulent known as *variola major* and a less virulent strain known as *variola minor* (elastrim).

DIAGNOSIS

DIFFERENTIAL DIAGNOSIS

- Rash from other viral illnesses (e.g., hemorrhagic chicken pox, measles, coxsackievirus)
- Abdominal pain may mimic appendicitis
- Meningococcemia
- Insect bites
- Impetigo
- Dermatitis herpetiformis
- Pemphigus
- Papular urticaria

WORKUP & LABORATORY TESTS

- Laboratory examination requires high-containment (BL-4) facilities.
- Electron microscopy of vesicular scrapings can be used to distinguish poxvirus particles from varicella-zoster virus or herpes simplex. To obtain vesicular or pustular fluid it may be necessary to open lesions with the blunt edge of a scalpel. A cotton swab may be used to harvest the fluid.
- In absence of electron microscopy, light microscopy can be used to visualize variola viral particles (Guarnieri bodies) following Giemsa staining.
- Polymerase chain reaction (PCR) techniques and restriction fragment-length polymorphisms can rapidly identify variola.

IMAGING STUDIES

Chest x-ray in patients with suspected pneumonia

TREATMENT

NONPHARMACOLOGIC THERAPY

- Supportive therapy
- IV hydration in severe cases
- A suspect case of smallpox should be placed in strict respiratory and contact isolation

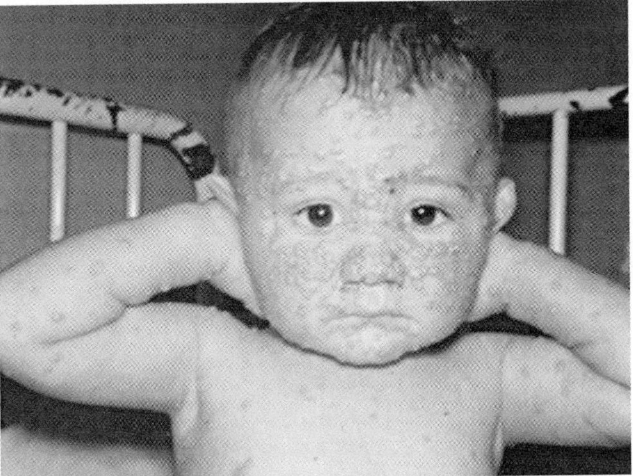

FIGURE 1-220 Appearance of the rash of smallpox on day 6 to 7. All of the lesions are in the same stage of development. (From Gorbach SL: *Infectious diseases,* ed 2, Philadelphia, 1998, WB Saunders.)

ACUTE GENERAL Rx

- There is no proven treatment for smallpox. Vaccination administered within 3-4 days may prevent or significantly ameliorate subsequent illness. Vaccinia immune globulin can be used for treatment of vaccine complications and for administration with vaccine to those for whom vaccine is otherwise contraindicated.
- Patients can benefit from supportive therapy (e.g., IV fluids, acetaminophen for pain or fever).
- Antibiotics are indicated only if secondary bacterial infections occur. Penicillase-resistant antimicrobial agents should be used if smallpox lesions are secondarily infected.
- Topical idoxuridine should be considered for corneal lesions.

DISPOSITION

- Mortality for variola major is 20%-50%. Variola minor has a mortality rate of 1%.
- After severe smallpox, pitted lesions (most commonly on the face) are seen in up to 80% of survivors.
- Panophthalmitis and blindness from viral keratitis or secondary eye infection occur in 1% of patients.
- Arthritis caused by viral infection of the metaphysis of growing bones occurs in 2% of children.

REFERRAL

- ID consultation and notification of local health authorities is mandatory in all cases of smallpox.

PEARLS & CONSIDERATIONS

- The smallpox virus is fragile and in the event of an aerosol release of smallpox, all viruses will be inactivated or dissipated within 1-2 days. Buildings exposed to the initial aerosol release of the virus do not need to be decontaminated. By the time the first cases are identified, typically 2 wk after release, the virus in the building will be gone. Infected patients, however, will be capable of spreading the virus and possibly contaminating surfaces while they are sick. Standard hospital-grade disinfectants such as quaternary ammonias are effective in killing the virus on surfaces and should be used for disinfecting hospitalized patients' rooms or other contaminated surfaces. In the hospital setting, patients' linens should be autoclaved or washed in hot water with bleach added. Infectious waste should be placed in biohazard bags and autoclaved before incineration.
- Symptomatic patients with suspected or confirmed smallpox are capable of spreading the virus. Patients should be placed in medical isolation to avoid spread of the virus. In addition, people who have come into close contact with smallpox patients should be vaccinated immediately and closely watched for symptoms of smallpox.

COMMENTS

- In people exposed to smallpox, the vaccine can lessen the severity of or even prevent illness if given within 4 days of exposure.
- Vaccine against smallpox contains another live virus called vaccinia. The vaccine does not contain smallpox virus.
- Primary vaccination confers full immunity to smallpox in more than 95% of persons for up to 10 yr.

SUGGESTED READINGS

Breman JG, Henderson DA: Diagnosis and management of smallpox, *N Engl J Med* 346:1300, 2002.

Frey SE et al: Clinical responses to undiluted and diluted smallpox vaccine, *N Engl J Med* 346:1265, 2002.

Henderson DA et al: Smallpox as a biological weapon, *JAMA* 281:2127, 1999. www.bt.cdc.gov/Agent/Smallpox/SmallpoxGen.asp

AUTHOR: **FRED F. FERRI, M.D.**

BASIC INFORMATION

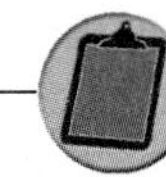

DEFINITION

Somatization disorder refers to a pattern of recurring multiple somatic complaints that begin before the age of 30 yr and persist over several years. Patients complain of multiple sites of pain (a minimum of four), GI symptoms (a minimum of two), a sexual or reproductive symptom, and a pseudoneurologic symptom. These cannot be explained by a medical condition or are in excess to expected disability from a coexisting medical condition.

SYNONYMS

Briquet's syndrome
Nonorganic physical symptoms
Medically unexplained symptoms
Functional somatic symptoms

ICD-9CM CODES
300.81 Somatization disorder

EPIDEMIOLOGY & DEMOGRAPHICS

PREVALENCE (IN U.S.): Lifetime rates of 0.25%-2% in women, <0.2% in men

PREDOMINANT SEX:
- Women are more commonly affected in the U.S. by 10:1 ratio
- Males of other cultures (e.g., Greece and Puerto Rico) are more commonly affected.

PREDOMINANT AGE: Onset occurs before age 30 yr and usually in adolescence.

PEAK INCIDENCE: Typically before age 25 yr

GENETICS:
- Genetic and environmental factors may be involved.
- There is a high risk of associated substance abuse or antisocial personality disorder.

PHYSICAL FINDINGS & CLINICAL PRESENTATION

- Most commonly patients are from lower socioeconomic groups.
- Onset is frequently in the teens; course is marked by frequent, unexplained, and frequently disabling pain and physical complaints.
- Patient frequently undergoes multiple procedures and seeks treatment from multiple physicians. Symptom focus rotates periodically with new physicians sought for new complaints.
- Patient often has a comorbid psychiatric disorder, most commonly generalized anxiety, panic disorder, or depression.

ETIOLOGY

- Believed to be the physical expression of psychologic distress; there appears to be a biological predisposition.
- May be more common in individuals without sufficient verbal or intellectual capacity to communicate psychologic distress, individuals with alexithymia (inability to describe emotional states), or individuals from cultural backgrounds that consider emotional distress as an undesirable weakness
- Some aspects of somatization behavior possibly learned from somatizing parents

DIAGNOSIS

DIFFERENTIAL DIAGNOSIS

- Undifferentiated somatoform disorder (ICD-10 F45.1, DMS-IV 300.81): one or more physical complaints that cannot be explained by a medical condition are present for at least 6 mo (NOTE: Somatization is more severe and less common).
- Conversion disorder: there is an alteration or loss of voluntary motor or sensory function without demonstrable physical cause and related to a psychologic stress or a conflict (NOTE: With multiple complaints, the diagnosis of conversion is not made).
- Pain disorder: distinguished from somatization disorder by the latter featuring multiple nonpain symptoms.
- Munchausen's (factitious disorder) and malingering: the psychologic basis of the complaints in somatization disorder is not conscious as in factitious disorder (Munchausen's) where the goal is to be in the patient role and malingering, in which symptoms are also produced consciously for some secondary gain.

WORKUP

- Rule out a general medical condition.
- If somatization is suspected on the basis of a history of repeated, multiple, unexplained complaints, restraint in ordering tests is recommended.

LABORATORY TESTS

No specific laboratory tests are required.

IMAGING STUDIES

No specific imaging studies are required.

TREATMENT

NONPHARMACOLOGIC THERAPY

- Legitimize patient's complaints; when this is not done, there is frequently an increase in complaints and associated disability.
- Minimize diagnostic investigation and symptomatic treatment. Only do invasive testing or procedures when there are clear-cut signs.
- Set attainable treatment goals. Patients may benefit from realizing that even though they cannot be cured, that they will be cared for.
- Treat coexisting psychiatric conditions such as depression and anxiety.

ACUTE GENERAL Rx

- At each visit do a brief physical examination focusing on the area of complaint.
- Gently praise increased functioning rather than focusing on symptoms.
- Explore recent life events and ask how the patient is handling these.
- Convey empathy with the patient's suffering and psychosocial difficulties.
- No specific pharmacologic therapy has been clearly proven effective, although a number of agents including gabapentin and St. John's wort have been useful in some studies.
- Antidepressants may be useful for coexisting anxiety and depression.

CHRONIC Rx

- Provide one primary care practitioner to manage care.
- Avoid confronting the patient regarding the psychological origin of symptoms.
- Ensure follow-up visits at regular (e.g., 2- to 4-wk intervals that are not symptom-contingent; i.e., maintain the regularity even if the symptoms improve so that the patient does not have to have new symptoms to keep the relationship with the physician).
- Avoid invasive or expensive diagnostic procedures unless there are clear signs of new illness, not just symptoms.
- Diagnose and treat mood or anxiety disorders.
- Cognitive behavior therapy groups have been helpful for patients with unexplained somatic symptoms and can dramatically improve functioning.

DISPOSITION

A chronic condition with frequent exacerbations

REFERRAL

If the patient is open to discussing psychological issues a referral for psychotherapy can be made. Often, however, the individual sees no need for this because they are focused on the somatic symptoms.

SUGGESTED READINGS

De Gucht V, Fischler B: Somatization: A critical review of conceptual and methodological issues, *Psychosomatics* 43:1, 2002.

Kroenke K, Swindle R: Cognitive-behavioral therapy for somatization and symptom syndromes: a critical review of controlled clinical trials, *Psychother Psychosom* 69:205, 2000.

Muller T et al: Treatment of somatoform disorders with St. John's wort: a randomized, double-blind and placebo-controlled trial, *Psychosom Med* 66(4):538, 2004.

AUTHOR: **STUART J. EISENDRATH, M.D.**

Spinal Cord Compression

BASIC INFORMATION

DEFINITION

Spinal cord compression is the neurologic loss of spine function. Lesions may be complete or incomplete and develop gradually or acutely. Incomplete lesions often present as distinct syndromes, as follows:

- Central cord syndrome
- Anterior cord syndrome
- Brown-Séquard syndrome
- Conus medullaris syndrome
- Cauda equina syndrome

ICD-9CM CODES
344.89 Brown-Séquard syndrome
344.60 Cauda equina syndrome
336.8 Conus medullaris syndrome
Other lesions listed by site

PHYSICAL FINDINGS & CLINICAL PRESENTATION

Clinical features reflect the amount of spinal cord involvement:

- Motor loss and sensory abnormalities
- Babinski testing usually positive
- Clonus
- Gradual compression, often manifested by progressive difficulty walking, clonus with weight bearing, and involuntary spasm; development of sensory symptoms; bladder dysfunction (late)
- Central cord syndrome: results in a variable quadriparesis with the upper extremities more severely involved than the lower extremities; some sensory sparing
- Anterior cord syndrome: results in motor, pain, and temperature loss below the lesion
- Brown-Séquard syndrome:
  1. Spinal cord syndrome caused by injury to either half of the spinal cord and resulting in the loss of motor function, position, vibration, and light touch on the affected side
  2. Pain and temperature sense lost on the opposite side
- Conus medullaris syndrome: results in variable motor loss in the lower extremities with loss of bowel and bladder function
- Cauda equina syndrome: typical low back pain, weakness in both lower extremities, saddle anesthesia, and loss of voluntary bladder and bowel control

ETIOLOGY

- Trauma
- Tumor
- Infection
- Inflammatory processes
- Degenerative disk conditions with spinal stenosis
- Acute disk herniation
- Cystic abnormalities

DIAGNOSIS

DIFFERENTIAL DIAGNOSIS

- See "Etiology."
- Section II describes the differential diagnosis of paraplegia.

WORKUP

- Spinal cord compression: requires an immediate referral for radiographic and neurologic assessment
- Laboratory results usually unremarkable unless infectious or inflammatory causes suspected

IMAGING STUDIES

- Depend on the suspected etiology
- MRI usually required

TREATMENT

Urgent surgical decompression is usually indicated as soon as the etiology is established.

DISPOSITION

Important indicators regarding prognosis (Leventhal):

- The greater the distal motor and sensory sparing, the greater the expected recovery.
- When a plateau of recovery is reached, no further improvement is expected.
- The quicker the recovery, the greater the recovery

REFERRAL

Immediate referral for radiographic and neurologic evaluation and treatment in all suspected cases of spinal cord compression

SUGGESTED READINGS

Baines MJ: Spinal cord compression—a personal and palliative care perspective, *Clin Oncol (R Coll Radiol)* 14(2):135, 2002.

Banerjee R, Stanley J, Palumbo M: Spinal Epidural Hematoma induced by leukemia, *Orthopedics* 27:864, 2004.

Benjamin R: Neurologic complications of prostate cancer, *Am Fam Physician* 65(9):1834, 2002.

Buchner M, Schiltenwolf M: Cauda equina syndrome caused by intervertebral lumbar disc prolapse: mid-term results of 22 patients and literature review, *Orthopedics* 25:727, 2002.

Carlson GD et al: Sustained spinal cord compression. Part I: time-dependent effect on long-term pathophysiology, *J Bone Joint Surg* 85:86, 2003.

Carlson GD et al: Sustained spinal cord compression. Part II: effect of methylprednisolone on regional blood flow and recovery of somatosensory evoked potentials, *J Bone Joint Surg* 85:95, 2003.

Casey AT et al: Rheumatoid arthritis of the cervical spine: current techniques for management, *Orthop Clin North Am* 33(2):291, 2002.

Kadanka Z et al: Approaches to spondylotic cervical myelopathy: conservative versus surgical in a 3-year follow-up study, *Spine* 27(20):2205, 2002.

Malcolm GP: Surgical disorders of the cervical spine: presentation and management of common disorders, *J Neurosurg Psychiatry* 73(Suppl 1):134, 2002.

Matsunaga S et al: Trauma-induced myelopathy in patients with ossification of the posterior longitudinal ligament, *J Neurosurg* 97(2 Suppl):172, 2002.

Mohanty SP, Venkatram N: Does neurological recovery in thoracolumbar and lumbar burst fractures depend on the extent of canal compromise? *Spinal Cord* 40(6):295, 2002.

Tang HJ et al: Spinal epidural abscess—experience with 46 patients and evaluation of prognostic factors, *J Infect* 45(2):76, 2002.

AUTHOR: **LONNIE R. MERCIER, M.D.**

Spinal Epidural Abscess

BASIC INFORMATION

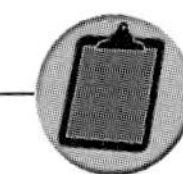

DEFINITION

A spinal epidural abscess (SEA) is a focal suppurative infection occurring in the spinal epidural space.

ICD-9CM CODES
324.1 Spinal epidural abscess

EPIDEMIOLOGY & DEMOGRAPHICS

INCIDENCE IN U.S.:

- 2 to 25 cases/100,000 hospitalized patients/yr
- May be increasing over the past three decades

PREDOMINANT AGE:

- Median age of onset approximately 50 yr (35 yr in intravenous drug users)
- Peak incidence in seventh and eighth decades of life

PHYSICAL FINDINGS

The presentation of SEA can be nonspecific. Fever, malaise, and back pain are the most consistent early symptoms. Pain is often focal. It may initially be mild but can progress to become severe. As the disease progresses, root pain can occur, followed by motor weakness, sensory changes, bladder and bowel dysfunction, and paralysis. Physical findings may be limited to fever or spinal tenderness. The evolution to neurologic deficits can occur as quickly as a few hours, or over weeks to months. Once paralysis occurs, it may quickly become irreversible without the appropriate intervention.

ETIOLOGY

- Bacteria account for the majority of cases in the U.S. Immigrants from tuberculosis-endemic areas may present with tuberculous SEAs. Fungi and parasites can also cause this condition. The most common causative organism is *Staphylococcus aureus*. Most posterior EAs thought to originate from distant focus (e.g., skin and soft tissue infections), while anterior EAs commonly associated with diskitis or vertebral osteomyelitis. No source found in approximately one third of cases.
- Associated predisposing conditions include a compromised immune system such as occurs in patients with diabetes mellitus, alcoholism, cancer, AIDS, and chronic renal failure, or following epidural anesthesia, spinal surgery or trauma, or intravenous drug use. No predisposing condition can be found in approximately 20% of patients.
- Damage to the spinal cord can be caused by direct compression of the spinal cord, vascular compromise, bacterial toxins, and inflammation.

DIAGNOSIS

DIFFERENTIAL DIAGNOSIS

- Herniated disc
- Vertebral osteomyelitis and diskitis
- Metastic tumors
- Meningitis

LABORATORY TESTS

- WBC may be normal or elevated.
- ESR usually elevated over 30 mm/hr.
- Blood cultures are positive in approximately 60% of patients with SEA.
- CSF cultures positive in 19%, but lumbar puncture unnecessary, and may be contraindicated.
- Once imaging is done, CT-guided aspiration or open biopsy should be done to determine causative organism. Abscess content culture positive in 90%

IMAGING STUDIES

- MRI with gadolinium is the imaging modality of choice; CT scan with contrast may show the abscess.
- CT with myelography is more sensitive for cord compression.

TREATMENT

NONPHARMACOLOGIC THERAPY

- Surgical decompression is the mainstay of treatment. Decompression within the first 24 hr has been related to an improved prognosis.
- Nonsurgical treatment is effective in some patients, but failure rate may be excessive. This approach should not be considered in most patients.

ACUTE GENERAL Rx

- In addition to surgery, antibiotics directed at the most likely organism should be initiated.
- If the organism is unknown, broad coverage against staphylococci, streptococci and gram-negative bacilli should be initiated. The regimen can be adjusted according to culture results. Therapy should continue for at least 4-6 wk.

CHRONIC Rx

Neurologic deficits may remain despite aggressive treatment.

DISPOSITION

Irreversible paralysis and death can occur in up to 25% of patients.

REFERRAL

All cases should be referred to a neurosurgeon and an infectious diseases specialist.

SUGGESTED READINGS

Chao D, Nanda A: Spinal epidural abscess: a diagnostic challenge, *Am Fam Physician* 65:1341, 2002.

Hooten WM, Kinney MO, Huntoon MA: Epidural abscess and meningitis after epidural corticosteroid injection, *Mayo Clin Proc* 79:682, 2004.

AUTHOR: **MAURICE POLICAR, M.D.**

Spinal Stenosis, Lumbar

BASIC INFORMATION

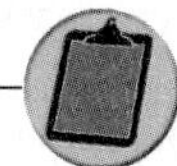

DEFINITION

Spinal stenosis is the pathologic condition compressing or narrowing the spinal canal, nerve root canal, or intervertebral foramina.

SYNONYMS

Central spinal stenosis
Lateral spinal stenosis
Spondylosis

ICD-9CM CODES
724.02 Spinal stenosis lumbar, lumbosacral

EPIDEMIOLOGY & DEMOGRAPHICS

- More common in the elderly >65 yr
- More than 30,000 patients underwent surgery for spinal stenosis in 1994

CLINICAL PRESENTATION & PHYSICAL FINDINGS

- Neurogenic claudication: leg, buttock, or back pain precipitated by walking and relieved by sitting
- Radicular leg pain
- Paresthesias
- Difficulty standing or lying in an erect position
- Decreased lumbar extension
- Normal peripheral pulses
- Positive Romberg
- Wide-based gait
- Reduced knee and ankle reflex
- Urine incontinence

ETIOLOGY

Spinal stenosis may be primary or secondary

- Primary stenosis (congenital or developmental narrowing)
  1. Idiopathic
  2. Achondroplasia
  3. Morquio-Ullrich syndrome
- Secondary stenosis (acquired)
  1. Degenerative (hypertrophy of the articular processes, disk degeneration, ligamentum flavum hypertrophy, spondylolisthesis)
  2. Fracture/trauma
  3. Postoperative (postlaminectomy)
  4. Paget's disease
  5. Ankylosing spondylitis
  6. Tumors
  7. Acromegaly

DIAGNOSIS

DIFFERENTIAL DIAGNOSIS

Spinal stenosis must be differentiated from other common causes of back and leg pain; osteoarthritis of the knee or hip, osteomyelitis, epidural abscess, metastatic tumors, multiple myeloma, intermittent claudication secondary to peripheral vascular disease, neuropathy, scoliosis, herniated nucleus pulposus, spondylolisthesis, acute cauda equina syndrome, ankylosing spondylitis, Reiter's syndrome, fibromyalgia.

WORKUP

The workup of spinal stenosis consists of a detailed history, physical examination, and specific imaging studies.

IMAGING STUDIES

- Lumbar spine film
- CT scan of the lumbosacral spine: sensitivity (75-85%), specificity (80%)
- MRI of the lumbosacral spine: sensitivity (80%-90%), specificity (95%)
- Myelogram: sensitivity (77%), specificity (72%). Absolute stenosis is defined as the anterior-posterior (AP) diameter of the spinal canal <10 mm. Relative stenosis: 10-12 mm AP diameter
- CT and MRI can visualize both the central and lateral canals

Electromyography (EMG) and nerve conduction velocity (NCV) are additional studies particularly useful in differentiating peripheral neuropathy from lumbar spinal stenosis.

TREATMENT

NONPHARMACOLOGIC THERAPY

- Physiotherapy
- Lumbar corsets
- Back exercises
- Abdominal muscle strengthening
- Aquatic exercises

ACUTE GENERAL Rx

- Surgery is indicated in patients with significant compression of nerve roots as determined by MRI or CT and incapacitating symptoms limiting activities of daily living or bladder and bowel incontinence.
- Surgical procedures include decompressive laminectomy, arthrodesis, hemilaminectomy, and medial facetectomy.

CHRONIC Rx

- Conservative therapy with NSAIDs, (ibuprofen 800 mg PO tid, naproxen 500 mg PO bid) may be tried for symptomatic relief in addition to acetaminophen 1 g PO qid.
- Epidural steroid injections may provide temporary relief.

DISPOSITION

- Approximately 20% of patients having surgery require repeat surgery within 10 yr. Nearly a third of the patients continue to experience pain.
- The natural history of spinal stenosis is one of slow progression. In some cases symptoms improve. Although not very common, cord compression with resultant bowel and bladder incontinence and paresis can occur.

REFERRAL

- Patients who have spinal stenosis should be referred to an orthopedic surgeon specializing in back surgery or to a neurosurgeon.
- Pain clinic referrals should be made if surgery is contraindicated or if the patient does not want surgery.

PEARLS & CONSIDERATIONS

COMMENTS

Approximately a third of the patients with neurogenic claudication have coexisting peripheral vascular disease.

Spinal stenosis not only is found in the elderly but also can be a common cause of chronic low back pain in the young and merits an evaluation.

SUGGESTED READINGS

Fritz JM et al: Lumbar spinal stenosis: a review of current concepts in evaluation, management, and outcome measurements, *Arch Phys Med Rehabil* 79:700, 1998.

Schonstrom N, Willen J: Imaging lumbar spinal stenosis, *Radiol Clin North Am* 39(1):31, 2001.

Sheehan JM, Shaffrey CI, Jane JA: Degenerative lumbar stenosis: the neurosurgical perspective, *Clin Orthop* 384:61, 2001.

AUTHOR: **PETER PETROPOULOS, M.D.**

BASIC INFORMATION

DEFINITION

A heterogenous group of autosomal dominantly inherited diseases with core features of progressive ataxia and spasticity. Current nomenclature (e.g., SCA1, SCA6) is based on genotyping of mutations.

SYNONYMS

Autosomal dominant spinocerebellar ataxia (ADCA)

- Machado-Joseph disease (MJD) is a subset, the most common type (SCA3).

ICD-9CM CODES
334.2 Primary cerebellar degeneration

EPIDEMIOLOGY & DEMOGRAPHICS

Epidemiology has not been well studied outside of isolated geographic regions. A conservative estimate of prevalence is 3 cases per 100,000 people. The most common subtypes worldwide are SCA3 (30%-50%) and SCA1, SCA2, SCA3, SCA6, SCA7, SCA8.

CLINICAL PRESENTATION

A. Chronic, slowly progressive ataxia is the hallmark of all of these diseases. Ataxia refers to incoordination or clumsiness of movements. Cerebellar ataxia is defined as lack of accuracy or coordination that is not due to weakness, alteration in tone, sensory loss, or the presence of involuntary movements.

B. Most often the SCAs present in adulthood (see later). Many of the diseases show the phenomenon of genetic anticipation (e.g., within a family). Successive generations will be affected at earlier ages.

C. Within a family, there can be significant phenotypic variability.

D. Although the nomenclature of these diseases is moving toward that based on genotyping, an older clinical classification still provides a useful framework (note that because of phenotypic variability within a genotype, some mutations can fit into more than one of the clinical groups):

1. Autosomal dominant cerebellar ataxia (ADCA) type I:
   a. Progressive cerebellar ataxia variably associated with other extracerebellar neurologic features, such as ophthalmoplegia, neuropathy, optic atrophy, pyramidal or extrapyramidal signs.
   b. The largest clinical subtype.
   c. Symptoms typically appear in third or fourth decades, but range from first to seventh.
   d. Gait is usually affected first, followed by arms, speech.
   e. Genetically heterogenous, includes most patients with SCA1, SCA2, SCA3, SCA4, SCA8, SCA10, SCA12.
2. ADCA type II:
   a. Progressive cerebellar ataxia invariably associated with pigmentary retinopathy. Other neurologic features may also be present, the most common of which is supranuclear ophthalmoplegia.
   b. Symptoms typically appear in third or fourth decades, but range from first to seventh.
   c. Onset may occur with either ataxia or vision loss.
   d. Early retinal changes subtle and only visible with indirect ophthalmoscopy.
   e. Genetically homogenous, most patients have SCA7.
3. ADCA type III:
   a. Progressive cerebellar ataxia without prominent visual or extracerebellar neurologic symptoms.
   b. Symptoms typically appear in third or fourth decades, but range from first to seventh.
   c. Genetically heterogenous, includes most patients with SCA5, SCA6, SCA11, SCA15, SCA16.

ETIOLOGY

Many of the currently identified mutations in the SCA genes are expansion of exonic CAG repeats. As in other diseases of this type (Huntington's chorea), the severity/age of onset of the disease is proportional to the number of CAG repeats in an individual's gene.

DIAGNOSIS

DIFFERENTIAL DIAGNOSIS

- Friedrich's ataxia (FA)—differs from the SCAs in that inheritance is autosomal recessive, that it almost always begins in childhood or adolescence, and that it is associated with early lower-limb areflexia.
- Sensory ataxias—differ from the SCAs in that the primary defect is not one of cerebellar function but of sensory inputs into the cerebellum. Can be the result of peripheral neuropathies or spinal cord disease that involves the posterior columns.
- Posterior fossa mass lesions.
- Acquired vitamin E deficiency—differs from SCAs in that patients almost always have clinically evident disorder of fat malabsorption.
- Chronic toxin exposure (alcohol, phenytoin, organic mercury).
- Multiple sclerosis, other CNS inflammatory diseases—differ from SCAs in that ataxia, when present, usually presents acutely to subacutely.
- Antigliadin antibodies—present in most patients with gluten enteropathy (celiac sprue); however, they can also be found in some ataxia patients without clinically evident celiac disease (this association remains controversial).
- Paraneoplastic cerebellar degeneration—differs from SCAs in that the ataxia progresses relatively rapidly.
- Creutzfeldt-Jakob disease—differs from the SCAs in that the ataxia progresses relatively rapidly, and is accompanied by dementia and myoclonus.
- Wilson's disease—differs from the SCAs in that there is often accompanying parkinsonism, psychiatric manifestations, and hepatic dysfunction.
- Superficial siderosis—differs from the SCAs in that it also often produces sensorineural hearing loss, anosmia, dementia, and bladder disturbance.
- Mitochondrial encephalomyopathies.
- Multiple systems atrophy—differs from the SCAs in that age of onset is usually later, and that there are often parkinsonism, long-tract signs, or orthostatic hypotension present.

LABORATORY TESTS

- Genetic testing:
  1. Available commercially for many of the SCAs. Given the number of available tests and significant expense for each, referral to a specialist is probably prudent before testing.
  2. In patients with a positive family history, this is an appropriate first step.
  3. In patients without a positive family history, testing for acquired/potentially reversible causes should be done first.
  4. There are significant ethical issues involved when testing presymptomatic individuals at risk within a family. Genetic and psychologic counseling is appropriate for these patients before testing is performed.
- Anti-Purkinje cell antibodies (anti-Yo, less commonly anti-Hu)—present in approximately half of patients with paraneoplastic cerebellar degeneration.
- Antigliadin antibodies (serum and spinal fluid).
- Serum vitamin E levels.

- If Wilson's disease is a consideration: serum transaminases and ceruloplasmin, 24-hr urine copper, ophthalmologic evaluation for Kayser-Fleischer rings.
- If Creutzfeldt-Jakob disease is a consideration: EEG, spinal fluid analysis for 14-3-3 protein.
- Testing for organic mercury poisoning is beyond the scope of this article but note that urinary mercury testing will not detect it.

IMAGING STUDIES

- MRI of the brain with and without contrast is the preferred imaging modality, mostly as a means of eliminating other differential diagnoses.
- Cerebellar atrophy, with or without brainstem atrophy is the typical picture seen in the SCAs. This finding on MRI is not terribly sensitive or specific for the SCAs, however.

TREATMENT

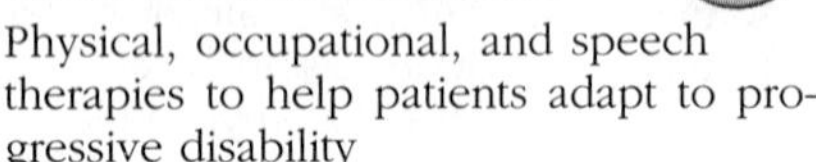

NONPHARMACOLOGIC

Physical, occupational, and speech therapies to help patients adapt to progressive disability

ACUTE GENERAL Rx

None available.

CHRONIC Rx

There are currently no disease-modifying treatments available. Symptomatic treatment of specific symptoms can be of benefit (e.g., treatment of spasticity with antispasticity agents, treatment of tremor with benzodiazepines or β-adrenergic blockers).

DISPOSITION

Variable life expectancies, roughly inversely related to age of onset.

REFERRAL

Referral to a general neurologist or movement disorders center is appropriate.

PEARLS & CONSIDERATIONS

COMMENTS

- In symptomatic patients with a family history of dominantly inherited ataxia, the diagnostic process is relatively straightforward. Genetic testing, directed toward likely mutations by phenotype and ethnic origin, should be the first step.
- In patients with subacute to chronic onset of cerebellar ataxia without a clear family history, the initial step in diagnosis should be brain MRI to look for structural lesions. If negative, or only showing atrophy, one should proceed with serologic/spinal fluid evaluation.

PREVENTION

None available.

PATIENT/FAMILY EDUCATION

Patient educational materials as well as contact information for support groups and advocacy available at the website for the National Ataxia Foundation: http://www.ataxia.org.

SUGGESTED READINGS

Paulson H, Ammache Z: Ataxia and hereditary disorders, *Neurol Clin* 19(3):759, 2001.

Schols L et al: Autosomal dominant cerebellar ataxias: clinical features, genetics, and pathogenesis, *Lancet Neurol* 3:291, 2004.

Wood N, Harding A: Cerebellar and spinocerebellar disorders. In Bradley W et al (eds): *Neurology in Clinical Practice,* ed 3, Boston, 2000, Butterworth-Heinemann.

AUTHOR: **DAVID P. WILLIAMS, M.D.**

BASIC INFORMATION

DEFINITION

Spontaneous miscarriage is fetal loss before wk 20 of pregnancy, calculated from the patient's last menstrual period or the delivery of a fetus weighing <500 g. *Early loss* is before menstrual wk 12, while *late loss* refers to losses from 12 to 20 wk.

Miscarriage can also be classified as *incomplete* (partial passage of fetal tissue through partially dilated cervix), *complete* (spontaneous passage of all fetal tissue), *threatened* (uterine bleeding without cervical dilation or passage of tissue), *inevitable* (bleeding with cervical dilation without passage of fetal tissue), or *missed abortion* (intrauterine fetal demise without passage of tissue).

Recurrent miscarriage involves three or more spontaneous pregnancy losses before wk 20.

ICD-9CM CODES
634.0 Spontaneous abortion

SYNONYMS

Abortion

EPIDEMIOLOGY & DEMOGRAPHICS

INCIDENCE: 15%-20% of clinically recognized pregnancies, with 80% of miscarriages occurring in the first trimester

RISK FACTORS: Prior pregnancy history (risk after live birth = 5%, prior pregnancy aborted = 20% subsequent risk) is the most significant risk factor. Vaginal bleeding, especially >3 days, carries with it a 15%-20% chance of miscarriage.

GENETICS:

- Distribution of abnormal karyotypes: autosomal trisomy (50%), monosomy 45,X (20%), triploidy (15%), tetraploidy (10%), structural chromosomal abnormalities (5%).
- With two or more spontaneous miscarriages, a karyotype should be performed to evaluate for balanced translocation, which has 80% risk for abortion, and, if the pregnancy is carried to term, has 3%-5% risk for unbalanced karyotype.
- After 9 wk, the later in gestation, the greater the chance of a normal karyotype.

PHYSICAL FINDINGS & CLINICAL PRESENTATION

- Profuse bleeding and cramping has a higher association with miscarriage than bleeding without cramping, which is more consistent with a threatened miscarriage.
- Cervical dilation with history or finding of fetal tissue at cervical os may be present.
- In cases of missed abortion, uterine size may be smaller than menstrual dating, in contrast to molar gestation, where size may be greater than dates.

ETIOLOGY

- In a general overview the etiology can be classified in terms of maternal (environmental) and fetal (genetic) factors, with the majority of miscarriages being related to genetic or chromosomal causes
- Causes: uterine anomalies (unicornuate uterus risk = 50%, bicornuate or septate uterus risk = 25%-30%), incompetent cervix (iatrogenic or congenital, associated with 20% of midtrimester losses), diethylstilbestrol exposure in utero (T-shaped uterus), submucous leiomyomas, intrauterine adhesions or synechiae, luteal phase or progesterone deficiency, autoimmune disease such as anticardiolipin antibodies, uncontrolled diabetes mellitus, HLA associations between mother and father, infections such as TB, *Chlamydia, Ureaplasma,* smoking and alcohol use, irradiation, and environmental toxins

DIAGNOSIS

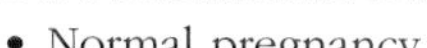

DIFFERENTIAL DIAGNOSIS

- Normal pregnancy
- Hydatidiform molar gestation
- Ectopic pregnancy
- Dysfunctional uterine bleeding
- Pathologic endometrial or cervical lesions

WORKUP

- Because of the potential for morbid maternal sequelae, all patients with bleeding in the first trimester should have an evaluation for possible ectopic pregnancy.
- Prior pregnancy history guides the workup, such that if there are three early, prior pregnancy losses a workup and treatment for recurrent miscarriage should begin before next conception, or if there is a strong history for second-trimester loss, consideration for cerclage should be given.
- Many of the treatments require preconceptual therapy, including control of disease processes, such as diabetes, and thus a careful workup can begin after the prior pregnancy loss but before conception.

LABORATORY TESTS

- Type and antibody screen is used to evaluate for the need for Rh immune globulin.
- In circumstances in which an ectopic gestation is considered, quantitative serum hCG can be used with transvaginal sonogram to assign a level of risk; 2000 mIU/ml (third reference standard) is the discriminatory zone above which an intrauterine gestational sac should be demonstrated.
- During the preconception period, Hgb A1C, anticardiolipin antibody, lupus anticoagulant, karyotyping, endometrial biopsy with progesterone level, and cervical cultures or serum antibodies can be checked for suspected disease processes.
- Progesterone level <5 mg/dl indicates nonviable gestation vs. >25 mg/dl, which confers a good prognosis.

IMAGING STUDIES

Transabdominal or transvaginal sonogram can be used in combination with menstrual dating and serum quantitative hCG to document pregnancy location, fetal heart presence, gestational sac size, and adnexal pathology and, if used serially, can help confirm a missed abortion.

TREATMENT

NONPHARMACOLOGIC THERAPY

Depending on the patient's clinical status, desire to continue the pregnancy, and certainty of the diagnosis, expectancy can be considered. In pregnancies <6 wk or >14 wk, complete expulsion of fetal tissue occurs and surgical intervention such as dilation and curettage (D&C) can be avoided.

ACUTE GENERAL Rx

- *Incomplete miscarriage* between 6 and 14 wk can be associated with large amounts of blood loss, and thus these patients should undergo D&C.
- In cases of *missed abortion,* if fetal demise has occurred >6 wk before or gestational age is >14 wk, there is an increased risk of hypofibrinogenemia with disseminated intravascular coagulation, and thus D&C should be performed early in the disease course. Can consider use of misoprostol (Cytotec) 200 mg po q6h × 4 doses
- *Threatened abortions* may be managed expectantly, watching for signs of cervical dilation or sonographic evidence of missed abortion. Hormonal therapy, such as progesterone, is contraindicated during this time because it may increase the chance of missed abortion.
- If surgical intervention is required, preoperative use of 40 U of oxytocin (Pitocin) in 1000 ml lactated Ringer's solution may be used to decrease the amount of bleeding and shorten the operative time.
- Postoperatively all patients undergoing a D&C should receive antibiotics (doxycycline 100 mg bid for 7 days), methylergonovine (Methergine) 0.2 mg q6h for four doses, and Motrin or NSAIDs prn for pain.
- Preoperative laminaria is useful in cases of nondilated or primigravida cervices.
- In all cases of first- or second-trimester bleeding in Rh-negative patients, Rh immune globulin 300 μg should be given to prevent Rh sensitization.

CHRONIC Rx

Expectancy may be considered for those pregnancies <6 menstrual weeks depending on the clinical situation and the patient's desire.

DISPOSITION

In most cases it is important to document the resolution of the pregnancy, in terms of either a pathology specimen from a D&C or documentation of decreasing quantitative hCGs. If the pathology report does not confirm a miscarriage or the quantitative hCG value plateaus or rises after evacuation, the diagnosis of ectopic or molar gestation must be examined.

REFERRAL

In cases of ectopic gestation, incomplete or missed abortion, surgical evacuation of the uterus and possible laparoscopic evaluation of the adnexa should be undertaken by qualified personnel.

SUGGESTED READINGS

Luise C et al: Outcome of expectant management of spontaneous first trimester miscarriage, *BMJ* 324:873, 2002.

Ness RB et al: Cocaine and tobacco use and the risks of spontaneous abortion, *N Engl J Med* 340:333, 1999.

AUTHOR: **SCOTT J. ZUCCALA, D.O.**

BASIC INFORMATION

DEFINITION

Sporotrichosis is a granulomatous disease caused by *Sporothrix schenckii.*

ICD-9CM CODES
117.1 Sporotrichosis

EPIDEMIOLOGY & DEMOGRAPHICS

PREDOMINANT SEX: The most common form, lymphocutaneous sporotrichosis, occurs equally in both sexes. Males predominate in both pulmonary and osteoarticular sporotrichosis.

PREDOMINANT AGE: Generally, lymphocutaneous sporotrichosis occurs in persons 35 yr of age or younger, and pulmonary sporotrichosis occurs in persons between the ages of 30 to 60 yr.

GENETICS:

Neonatal Infection: At least one case of transmission from the cheek lesion of the mother to the skin of the infant has been reported.

PHYSICAL FINDINGS & CLINICAL PRESENTATION

- Cutaneous disease
  1. Arises at the site of inoculation
  2. Initial lesion usually located on the distal part of an extremity, although any area may be affected, including the face
  3. Variable incubation period of approximately 3 wk once introduced into the skin
  4. Granulomatous reaction provoked
  5. Lesion becomes papulonodular, erythematous, elastic, variable in size
  6. Subsequently, nodule becomes fluctuant, undergoes central necrosis, breaks down, discharges mucoid pus from which fungus may be isolated
  7. Indolent ulcer with raised erythematous or violaceous borders
  8. Secondary lesions:
     a. Develop along superficial lymphatic channels
     b. Evolve in the same manner as the primary lesion, with subsequent inflammation, induration, and suppuration
- Fixed, or plaque form
  1. Erythematous verrucous, ulcerated, or crusted lesions
  2. Does not spread locally
  3. Does not involve lymphatic vessels
  4. Rarely undergoes spontaneous resolution
  5. More often persists for years without systemic symptoms and within a setting of normal laboratory examinations
- Osteoarticular involvement
  1. Most common extracutaneous form
  2. Usually presents as monoarticular arthritis
  3. Left untreated, may progress to:
     a. Synovitis
     b. Osteitis
     c. Periostitis
     d. All involving elbows, knees, wrists, and ankles
  4. Joint inflamed
     a. Associated with an effusion
     b. Painful on motion
- Early pulmonary disease
  1. Usually associated with a paucity of clinical findings
     a. Low-grade fever
     b. Cough
     c. Fatigue
     d. Malaise
     e. Weight loss
  2. Untreated
     a. Cavitary pulmonary disease
     b. Frank pulmonary dysfunction
  3. Meningitis uncommon
     a. Except perhaps in the immunocompromised patient
     b. Presents with few signs or symptoms of neurologic involvement
  4. Few reported cases
     a. Infection of the ocular adnexa
     b. Endophthalmitis without antecedent trauma
     c. Infection of the testes and epididymis

ETIOLOGY

- *Sporothrix schenckii*
  1. Global in distribution
  2. Often isolated from soil, plants, and plant products
  3. Majority of case reports from tropical and subtropical regions of the Americas
- Occupational or recreational exposure
  1. Hay
  2. Straw
  3. Sphagnum moss
  4. Timber
  5. Thorny plants (e.g., roses and barberry bushes)
- Animal contact
  1. Armadillos
  2. Cats
  3. Squirrels
- Human-to-human transmission
- Tattooing

DIAGNOSIS

DIFFERENTIAL DIAGNOSIS

- Fixed, or plaque, sporotrichosis
  1. Bacterial pyoderma
  2. Foreign body granuloma
  3. Tularemia
  4. Anthrax
  5. Other mycoses: blastomycosis, chromoblastomycosis
- Lymphocutaneous sporotrichosis
  1. *Nocardia brasiliensis*
  2. *Leishmania braziliensis*
  3. Atypical mycobacterial disease: *M. marinum, M. kansasii*
- Pulmonary sporotrichosis
  1. Pulmonary TB
  2. Histoplasmosis
  3. Coccidioidomycoses
- Osteoarticular sporotrichosis
  1. Pigmented villonodular synovitis
  2. Gout
  3. Rheumatoid arthritis
  4. Infection with *M. tuberculosis*
  5. Atypical mycobacteria: *M. marinum, M. kansasii, M. avium-intracellulare*
- Meningitis
  1. Histoplasmosis
  2. Cryptococcosis
  3. TB

WORKUP

- The diagnosis should be considered in individuals who are occupationally exposed to soil, decaying plant matter, and thorny plants (gardeners, horticulturists, farmers) who present with chronic nonhealing ulcers or lesions with or without associated arthritis or pulmonary symptoms.
- Diagnosis is made by culture:
  1. Pus
  2. Joint fluid
  3. Sputum
  4. Blood
  5. Skin biopsy
- Isolation of the fungus from any site is considered diagnostic of infection.
- Saprophytic colonization of the respiratory tract has been described.
- A positive blood culture may indicate infection in an immunocompromised host.
- Increasingly sensitive laboratory culturing systems may detect the fungus in the normal host.
- Biopsy specimens are diagnostic if characteristic cigar-shaped, round, oval, or budding yeast forms are seen.
- Despite special staining, the yeast may remain difficult to detect unless multiple sections are examined.
- No standard method of serologic testing is available.
- Previously described techniques have been hampered by the presence of antibody in the absence of infection.

LABORATORY TESTS

- CBCs and serum chemistries are generally normal.
- Elevated ESR is seen with extracutaneous disease.
- CSF analysis in meningeal disease reveals:
  1. Lymphocytic pleocytosis
  2. Elevated protein
  3. Hypoglycorrhachia

- Nested PCR assays represent future clinical modality to rapidly detect *Sporothrix schenckii.*

IMAGING STUDIES

- Chest x-ray examination: unilateral or bilateral upper lobe cavitary or noncavitary lesions
- Radiographic findings of affected joints:
  1. Loss of articular cartilage
  2. Periosteal reaction
  3. Periarticular osteopenia
  4. Cystic changes

TREATMENT

NONPHARMACOLOGIC THERAPY

Local heat and prevention of bacterial superinfection in cutaneous or plaque form

ACUTE GENERAL Rx

CUTANEOUS AND LYMPHOCUTANEOUS SPOROTRICHOSIS:

- Itraconazole at doses of 100-200 mg/day is the drug of choice and should be given for 3-6 mo.
- Use saturated solution of potassium iodide (SSKI) 5-10 drops PO tid or 1.5 ml PO tid, gradually increasing to 40-50 drops PO tid or 3 ml PO tid after meals.
- Maximum tolerated dose should be continued until cutaneous lesions have resolved, approximately 6-12 wk.
- Adjunctive therapy with heat is useful and occasionally curative.
- Side effects:
  1. Nausea
  2. Anorexia
  3. Diarrhea
  4. Parotid or lacrimal gland hypertrophy
  5. Acneiform rash

DEEP-SEATED MYCOSES (E.G., OSTEOARTICULAR, NONCAVITARY PULMONARY DISEASE)

- Itraconazole
  1. Appropriate initial chemotherapy
  2. Probably as effective as amphotericin B
  3. Less toxic than amphotericin B
  4. Better tolerated than ketoconazole
  5. 100-200 mg bid for 1-2 yr with continued lifelong suppressive therapy in selected patients
  6. Absence of relapses from 40 to 68 mo has been documented when at least 200 mg/day administered for 24 mo
  7. Insufficient data for use in disseminated disease (e.g., fungemia and meningitis)
- Parenteral amphotericin B, total course of 2-2.5 g or more, results in cure in approximately two thirds of cases
  1. Relapses are common.
  2. Amphotericin B–resistant isolates of *Sporothrix schenckii* have been reported.
  3. Remains the drug of choice for severely ill patients with disseminated disease.
  4. In cavitary pulmonary disease, given perioperatively as an adjunct to surgical resection.
  5. In meningitis, amphotericin B may be used alone or in combination with 5-fluorocytosine.
- Fluconazole
  1. Less effective than itraconazole
  2. Requires daily doses of 400 mg/day for lymphocutaneous disease and 800 mg/day for visceral or osteoarticular disease

CHRONIC Rx

For lymphocutaneous and visceral disease, therapy with itraconazole 200 mg/day for periods of 24 mo or greater

DISPOSITION

- Prognosis for cutaneous disease is good.
- Prognosis is less satisfactory for extracutaneous disease, especially if associated with abnormal immunologic states or other underlying systemic diseases.

REFERRAL

To surgeon; with an established diagnosis of pulmonary sporotrichosis, cavitary lesions require resection of involved tissue

PEARLS & CONSIDERATIONS

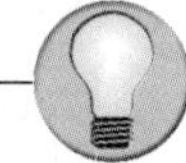

COMMENTS

- In patients with underlying immunosuppression (e.g., hematologic malignancy or infection with HIV), progression of the initial infection may develop into multifocal extracutaneous sporotrichosis.
- In this subset of patients, dissemination of cutaneous lesions is accompanied by hematogenous spread to lungs, bone, mucous membranes, CNS.
- Osteoarticular and pulmonary manifestations predominate with the development of polyarticular arthritis and osteolytic bone lesions.
- In the absence of therapy, the infection is ultimately fatal.
- Patients with underlying immunosuppressive states should be carefully evaluated even when presenting with single cutaneous lesions.
- Diagnostic modalities should include:
  1. Radiographic examination of chest
  2. Technetium pyrophosphate bone scan
  3. Culture of synovial fluid, blood, skin lesion(s)
- In patients with AIDS, itraconazole appears to be the drug of choice, although meningitis and pulmonary disease may warrant the use of amphotericin B.
- In patients with AIDS, lifetime suppressive therapy with itraconazole should follow initial therapy given the potential for relapse and dissemination.

SUGGESTED READINGS

Curi AL et al: Retinal granuloma caused by *Sporothrix schenckii, Am J Ophthalmol* 136(1):205, 2003.

de Lima Barros MB et al: Sporotrichosis with widespread cutaneous lesions: report of 24 cases related to transmission by domestic cats in Rio de Janeiro, Brazil, *Int J Dermatol* 42(9):677, 2003.

Gottlieb GS et al: Disseminated sporotrichosis associated with treatment with immunosuppressants and tumor necrosis factor-alpha antagonists, *Clin Infect Dis* 37(6):838, 2003.

Hu S et al: Detection of *Sporothrix schenckii* in clinical samples by a nested PCR assay, *J Clin Microbiol* 41(4):1414, 2003.

Queiroz-Telles F et al: Subcutaneous mycoses, *Infect Dis Clin North Am* 17(1):59, 2003.

Zhou CH et al: Laryngeal and respiratory tract sporotrichosis and steroid inhaler use, *Arch Pathol Lab Med* 127(7):893, 2003.

AUTHOR: **GEORGE O. ALONSO, M.D.**

BASIC INFORMATION

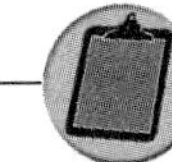

DEFINITION

Squamous cell carcinoma (SCC) is a malignant tumor of the skin arising in the epithelium.

SYNONYMS

SCC
Skin cancer

ICD-9CM CODES
173.9 Skin neoplasm, site unspecified

EPIDEMIOLOGY & DEMOGRAPHICS

- SCC is the second most common cutaneous malignancy, comprising 20% of all cases of nonmelanoma skin cancer.
- Incidence is highest in lower latitudes (e.g., southern U.S., Australia).
- Male:female ratio of 2:1.
- Incidence increases with age and sun exposure.
- Average age at diagnosis is 66 yr.

PHYSICAL FINDINGS & CLINICAL PRESENTATION

- SCC commonly affects scalp, neck region, back of hands, superior surface of the pinna, and the lip.
- The lesion may have a scaly, erythematous macule or plaque.
- Telangiectasia, central ulceration may also be present (Fig. 1-221).
- Most SCC present as exophytic lesions that grow over a period of months.

ETIOLOGY

Risk factors include UVB radiation and immunosuppression (renal transplant recipients have a threefold increased risk).

DIAGNOSIS

DIFFERENTIAL DIAGNOSIS

- Keratoacanthomas
- Actinic keratosis
- Amelanotic melanoma
- Basal cell carcinoma
- Benign tumors
- Healing traumatic wounds
- Spindle cell tumors
- Warts

WORKUP

Diagnosis is made with full-thickness skin biopsy (incisional or excisional).

TREATMENT

ACUTE GENERAL Rx

- Electrodesiccation and curettage for small SCCs (<2 cm in diameter), superficial tumors and lesions located in extremity and trunk.
- Tumors thinner than 4 mm can be managed by simple local removal.
- Lesions between 4 and 8 mm thick or those with deep dermal invasion should be excised.
- Tumors penetrating the dermis can be treated with several modalities, including excision and Mohs' surgery, radiation therapy, and chemotherapy.
- Metastatic SCC can be treated with cryotherapy and combination of chemotherapy using 13-*cis*-retinoic acid and interferon α-2A.

DISPOSITION

- Survival is related to size, location, degree of differentiation, immunologic status of the patient, depth of invasion, and presence of metastases. Risk factors for metastasis include lesions on the lip or ear, increasing lesion depth, and poor cell differentiation.
- Patients whose tumors penetrate through the dermis or exceed 8 mm in thickness are at risk of tumor recurrence.
- The most common metastatic locations are regional lymph nodes, liver, and lung.
- Tumors on the scalp, forehead, ears, nose, and lips also carry a higher risk.
- SCCs originating in the lip and pinna metastasize in 10% to 20% of cases.
- Five-year survival for metastatic squamous cell carcinoma is 34%.

REFERRAL

Oncology referral for metastatic SCC

PEARLS & CONSIDERATIONS

COMMENTS

SCC arising in areas of prior radiation, thermal injury, and areas of chronic ulcers or chronic draining sinuses are more aggressive and have a higher frequency of metastases than those originating in actinic damaged skin.

AUTHOR: **FRED F. FERRI, M.D.**

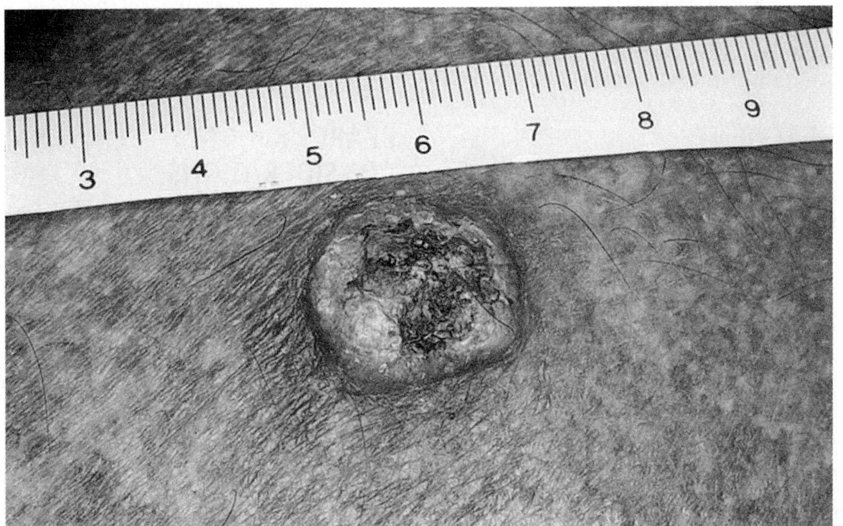

FIGURE 1-221 Squamous cell carcinoma. Nodular hyperkeratotic lesion with central erosion. (From Noble J et al: *Textbook of primary care medicine,* ed 3, St Louis, 2001, Mosby.)

BASIC INFORMATION

DEFINITION

Stasis dermatitis refers to an inflammatory skin disease of the lower extremities, commonly seen in patients with chronic venous insufficiency. (Fig. 1-222)

ICD-9CM CODES
459.81 Stasis dermatitis

EPIDEMIOLOGY & DEMOGRAPHICS

- Stasis dermatitis occurs more frequently in the elderly
- Rarely seen before the age of 50 yr
- Estimated to occur in up to 6% to 7% of the patients >50 yr
- Occurs in woman more often than men, perhaps related to lower extremity venous impairment aggravated through pregnancy

PHYSICAL FINDINGS & CLINICAL PRESENTATION

- Insidious onset
- Pruritus
- Chronic edema usually described as "brawny" edema as stasis dermatitis pathologically is associated with dermal fibrosis
- Erythema
- Scaly
- Eczematous patches
- Commonly located over the medial malleolus
- Progressive pigment changes can occur as a result of extravasation of red blood cells and hemosiderin deposition within the cutaneous tissue.
- Secondary infections can occur

ETIOLOGY

- Stasis dermatitis is thought to occur as a direct result from any insult or injury of the lower extremity venous system leading to venous insufficiency including:
  1. Deep vein thrombosis
  2. Trauma
  3. Pregnancy
  4. Vein stripping
  5. Vein harvesting in patients requiring coronary artery bypass grafting (CABG)
- Venous insufficiency subsequently results in venous hypertension, causing skin inflammation and the aforementioned physical findings and clinical presentation.

DIAGNOSIS

The diagnosis of stasis dermatitis is primarily made by a detailed history and physical examination.

DIFFERENTIAL DIAGNOSIS

- Contact dermatitis
- Atopic dermatitis
- Cellulitis
- Tinea dermatophyte infection
- Pretibial myxedema
- Nummular eczema
- Lichen simplex chronicus
- Xerosis
- Asteatotic eczema
- Deep vein thrombosis

WORKUP

The workup of a patient with stasis dermatitis is directed at excluding potential life-threatening causes (e.g., deep vein thrombosis) and complications (e.g., cellulites and sepsis).

LABORATORY TESTS

Blood tests are generally not very helpful unless a secondary infection is present.

IMAGING STUDIES

- X-rays, CT scans, and MRIs are generally not very helpful.
- Doppler studies are indicated in any patient suspected of having a deep vein thrombosis.

TREATMENT

NONPHARMACOLOGIC THERAPY

- Leg elevation
- Compression stocking with a gradient of at least 30-40 mm Hg
- For weeping skin lesions, wet to dry dressing changes are helpful

ACUTE GENERAL Rx

- In patients with acute stasis dermatitis, a compression (Unna) boot can be applied. An Unna boot consists of a roll of gauze that is saturated with zinc oxide ointment supported with an elastic wrap.
- Topical corticosteroid creams or ointments (e.g., triamcinolone 0.1% bid) are used frequently to help reduce inflammation and itching.
- Secondary infections should be treated with appropriate antibiotics. Most secondary infections are the result of *Staphylococcus* or *Streptococcus* organisms.

CHRONIC Rx

- Patients with chronic stasis dermatitis can be treated with topical emollients (e.g., white petrolatum, lanolin, Eucerin).
- Topical dressings (e.g., DuoDerm) are effective in the treatment of chronic venous stasis ulcers.

DISPOSITION

- The mainstay of treatment of stasis dermatitis is to control leg edema and prevent venous stasis ulcers from developing.
- Chronic venous stasis ulcers may take months to heal and may require skin grafting.

REFERRAL

- Dermatology referral is made if the diagnosis is unclear.
- Vascular surgery referral is made for assistance in the management of chronic venous insufficiency and chronic venous stasis ulcers.

PEARLS & CONSIDERATIONS

COMMENTS

Inflammatory skin changes from stasis dermatitis are thought to result from poor oxygen perfusion to the lower-extremity skin tissue. Various theories, including venous pooling, arteriovenous shunting, increased venous hydrostatic pressure affecting microcirculation, fibrin barriers preventing oxygen diffusion, and leukocyte trapping with resultant microvascular damage, have all been hypothesized as causes of stasis dermatitis.

SUGGESTED READINGS

Flugman SL et al: Stasis dermatitis, www.emedicine.com.

Yuwono HS: Diagnosis and treatment in the management of chronic venous insufficiency, *Clin Hemorheol Microcirc* 23(2-4):233, 2000.

AUTHOR: **PETER PETROPOULOS, M.D.**

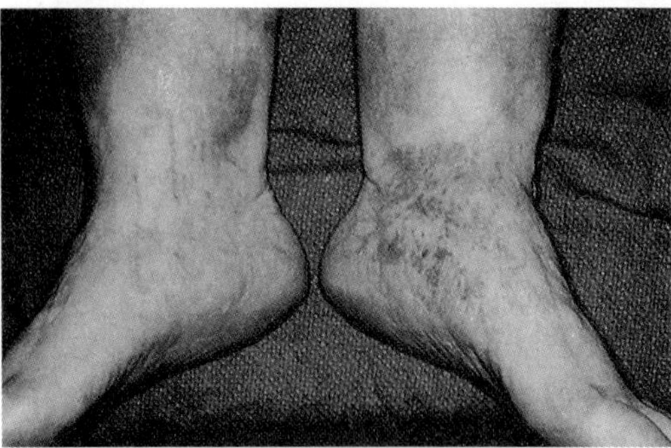

FIGURE 1-222 Moderate stasis dermatitis with hyperpigmentation and bilateral venous insufficiency. (Courtesy Department of Dermatology, University of North Carolina at Chapel Hill. From Goldstein BG, Goldstein AO: *Practical dermatology,* ed 2, St Louis, 1997, Mosby.)

BASIC INFORMATION

DEFINITION

The term *status epilepticus* refers to continuous seizure activity lasting at least 5 min, or two or more discrete seizures between which there is incomplete recovery of consciousness.

ICD-9CM CODES
345.3 Grand mal status

EPIDEMIOLOGY & DEMOGRAPHICS

INCIDENCE (IN U.S.): 100,000 to 152,000 cases per year
PREDOMINANT SEX: Male = female
GENETICS: Familial predisposition is rare.

PHYSICAL FINDINGS & CLINICAL PRESENTATION

- Patients are typically unresponsive and usually have obvious tonic, clonic, or tonic-clonic movements of the extremities (convulsive status epilepticus).
- Some patients are unresponsive or have an altered level of consciousness with no clear observable repetitive motor activity (nonconvulsive status epilepticus).
- Clinical manifestations can evolve and can become subtle with only small amplitude twitching movements of the face, limbs, or eyes.

ETIOLOGY

- Preexisting epilepsy with breakthrough seizures or low anticonvulsant drug levels
- CNS infection or tumor
- Drug toxicity or metabolic disturbance
- Hypoxia
- Head trauma
- Stroke

DIAGNOSIS

DIFFERENTIAL DIAGNOSIS

- Coma
- Encephalopathic states
- Psychogenic unresponsiveness

WORKUP

Because convulsive status epilepticus is an emergency with substantial morbidity and mortality, treatment must be early and aggressive, not postponed until an etiology is determined.

LABORATORY TESTS

- While treatment is being initiated: glucose, electrolytes, BUN, ABG, drug levels, CBC, UA, toxicology screen
- Lumbar puncture in children with fever and adults suspected to have meningitis

IMAGING STUDIES

Unless the etiology is known, CT or MRI of the brain is recommended as soon as possible after seizures have been controlled.

TREATMENT

NONPHARMACOLOGIC THERAPY

- Give oxygen by nasal cannula or nonrebreathing mask.
- Maintain blood pressure.
- Maintain body temperature.
- Monitor ECG.
- Obtain IV access.

ACUTE GENERAL Rx

- Thiamine 100 mg IV and glucose 50 mg D_{50} by IV push (2 ml/kg D_{25} in children) unless hyperglycemic
- Lorazepam 0.1 mg/kg IV at 2 mg/min
- If seizures persist, phosphenytoin 20 mg/kg IV at 150 mg/min (if not available, use phenytoin 20 mg/kg IV at up to 50 mg/min as tolerated)
- If seizures persist, phenobarbital 20 mg/kg IV at 50-75 mg/min; will likely require intubation
- If seizures persist, emergency neurologic consultation for management of additional doses of phenobarbital and/or general anesthesia with midazolam, propofol, or pentobarbital

CHRONIC Rx

Chronic treatment with anticonvulsants is indicated if there is significant risk of recurrence (i.e., known epilepsy, brain lesion, epileptiform EEG abnormalities).

DISPOSITION

- Favorable if status is treated promptly and there is no underlying acute symptomatic cause such as an underlying CNS lesion or systemic metabolic insult.
- Overall mortality is 22%; higher in the elderly (38%) and substantially lower in children (2.5%). Difference in mortality is mainly because status epilepticus in the elderly is more often the result of an acute symptomatic cause.

REFERRAL

If seizures do not respond to initial management as outlined, or if the patient is in nonconvulsive status epilepticus, because there is debate regarding the need for aggressive management

PEARLS & CONSIDERATIONS

COMMENTS

- Because of varied clinical presentations of status epilepticus, there is no clinical basis for being certain that seizures have stopped unless the patient regains full consciousness.
- EEG provides definitive information about seizure cessation. If available, use of EEG in the management of status epilepticus is recommended highly.

SUGGESTED READINGS

Logroscino G et al: Long-term mortality after a first episode of status epilepticus, *Neurology* 58:537, 2002.
Lowenstein DH, Alldredge B: Status epilepticus, *N Engl J Med* 338:970, 1998.
Treiman DM et al: A comparison of four treatments for generalized convulsive status epilepticus, *N Engl J Med* 339:792, 1998.

AUTHOR: **JOHN E. CROOM, M.D., Ph.D.**

BASIC INFORMATION

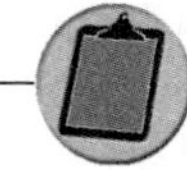

DEFINITION

Stevens-Johnson syndrome (SJS) is a severe vesiculobullous form of erythema multiforme affecting skin, mouth, eyes, and genitalia.

SYNONYMS

SJS
Herpes iris
Febrile mucocutaneous syndrome

ICD-9CM CODES
695.1 Stevens-Johnson syndrome

EPIDEMIOLOGY & DEMOGRAPHICS

- SJS affects predominantly children and young adults.
- Male:female ratio of 2:1.

PHYSICAL FINDINGS & CLINICAL PRESENTATION

- The cutaneous eruption is generally preceded by vague, nonspecific symptoms of low-grade fever and fatigue occurring 1-14 days before the skin lesions. Cough is often present. Fever may be high during the active stages.
- Bullae generally occur on the conjunctiva, mucous membranes of the mouth, nares, and genital regions.
- Corneal ulcerations may result in blindness.
- Ulcerative stomatitis results in hemorrhagic crusting.
- Flat, atypical target lesions or purpuric maculae may be distributed on the trunk or be widespread (Fig. 1-223).
- The pain from oral lesions may compromise fluid intake and result in dehydration.
- Thick, mucopurulent sputum and oral lesions may interfere with breathing.

ETIOLOGY

- Drugs (e.g., phenytoin, penicillins, phenobarbital, sulfonamides) are the most common cause.
- Upper respiratory tract infections (e.g., *Mycoplasma pneumoniae*) and herpes simplex viral infections have also been implicated in SJS.

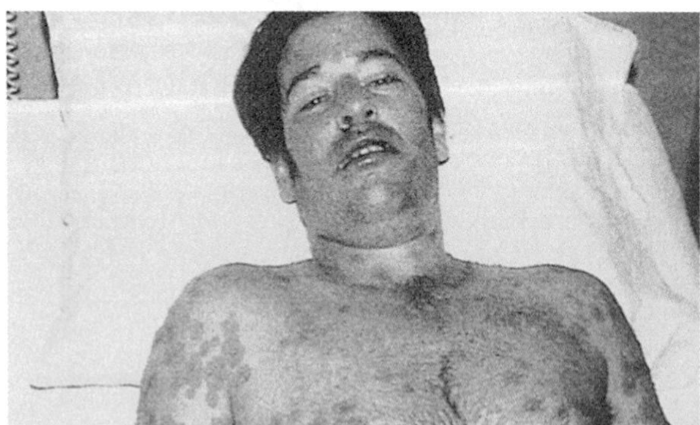

FIGURE 1-223 Stevens-Johnson syndrome. (From Stein JH: *Internal medicine,* ed 5, St Louis, 1998, Mosby.)

DIAGNOSIS

DIFFERENTIAL DIAGNOSIS

- Toxic erythema (drugs or infection)
- Pemphigus
- Pemphigoid
- Urticaria
- Hemorrhagic fevers
- Serum sickness
- *Staphylococcus* scalded-skin syndrome
- Behçet's syndrome

WORKUP

- Diagnosis is generally based on clinical presentation and characteristic appearance of the lesions.
- Skin biopsy is generally reserved for when classic lesions are absent and diagnosis is uncertain.

LABORATORY TESTS

CBC with differential, cultures in cases of suspected infection

IMAGING STUDIES

Chest x-ray may show patchy changes in patients with pulmonary involvement.

TREATMENT

NONPHARMACOLOGIC THERAPY

- Withdrawal of any potential drug precipitants
- Careful skin nursing to prevent secondary infection

ACUTE GENERAL Rx

- Treatment of associated conditions, (e.g., acyclovir for herpes simplex virus infection, erythromycin for mycoplasma infection)
- Antihistamines for pruritus
- Treatment of the cutaneous blisters with cool, wet Burow's compresses
- Relief of oral symptoms by frequent rinsing with lidocaine (Xylocaine Viscous)
- Liquid or soft diet with plenty of fluids to ensure proper hydration
- Treatment of secondary infections with antibiotics
- Corticosteroids: use remains controversial; when used, prednisone 20 to 30 mg bid until new lesions no longer appear, then rapidly tapered
- Topical steroids: may use to treat papules and plaques; however, should not be applied to eroded areas
- Vitamin A: may be used for lacrimal hyposecretion

DISPOSITION

- Prognosis varies with severity of disease. It is generally good in patients with limited disease; however, mortality may approach 10% in patients with extensive involvement.
- Oral lesions may continue for several months.
- Scarring and corneal abnormalities may occur in 20% of patients.

REFERRAL

- Hospital admission in a unit used for burn care is recommended in severe cases.
- Urethral involvement may necessitate catheterization.
- Ocular involvement should be monitored by an ophthalmologist.

PEARLS & CONSIDERATIONS

COMMENTS

Risk of recurrence of SJS is 30% to 40%.

AUTHOR: **FRED F. FERRI, M.D.**

BASIC INFORMATION

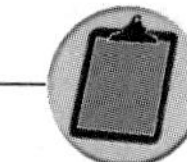

DEFINITION

Stomatitis is inflammation involving the oral mucous membranes.

SYNONYMS

Heterogeneous grouping of unrelated illnesses, each with their own designation(s)

ICD-9CM CODES
528.0 Stomatitis
054.2 (herpetic)
528.2 (aphthous)
112.0 (monilial)

CLASSIFICATION

WHITE LESIONS: Candidiasis (thrush) Caused by yeast infection *(Candida albicans)*

Examination: white, curdlike material that when wiped off leaves a raw bleeding surface

Epidemiology: seen in the very young and the very old, those with immunodeficiency (AIDS, cancer), persons with diabetes, and patients treated with antibacterial agents

Other

- Leukoedema: filmy opalescent-appearing mucosa, which can be reverted to normal appearance by stretching. This condition is benign.
- White sponge nevus: thick, white corrugated folds involving the buccal mucosa. Appears in childhood as an autosomal dominant trait. Benign condition.
- Darier's disease (keratosis follicularis): white papules on the gingivae, alveolar mucosa, and dorsal tongue. Skin lesions also present (erythematous papules). Inherited as an autosomal dominant trait.
- Chemical injury: white sloughing mucosa.
- Nicotine stomatitis: whitened palate with red papules.
- Lichen planus: linear, reticular, slightly raised striae on buccal mucosa. Skin is involved by pruritic violaceous papules on forearms and inner thighs.
- Discoid lupus erythematosus: lesion resembles lichen planus.
- Leukoplakia: white lesions that cannot be scraped off; 20% are premalignant epithelial dysplasia or squamous cell carcinoma.
- Hairy leukoplakia: shaggy white surface that cannot be wiped off; seen in HIV infection, caused by EBV.

RED LESIONS:

- Candidiasis may present with red instead of the more frequent white lesion (see "White Lesions"). Median rhomboid glossitis is a chronic variant.
- Benign migratory glossitis (geographic tongue): area of atrophic depapillated mucosa surrounded by a keratotic border. Benign lesion, no treatment required.
- Hemangiomas.
- Histoplasmosis: ill-defined irregular patch with a granulomatous surface, sometimes ulcerated.
- Allergy.
- Anemia: atrophic reddened glossal mucosa seen with pernicious anemia.
- Erythroplakia: red patch usually caused by epithelial dysplasia or squamous cell carcinoma.
- Burning tongue (glossopyrosis): normal examination; sometimes associated with denture trauma, anemia, diabetes, vitamin B_{12} deficiency, psychogenic problems.

DARK LESIONS (BROWN, BLUE, BLACK):

- Coated tongue: accumulation of keratin; harmless condition that can be treated by scraping
- Melanotic lesions: freckles, lentigines, lentigo, melanoma, Peutz-Jeghers syndrome, Addison's disease
- Varices
- Kaposi's sarcoma: red or purple macules that enlarge to form tumors; seen in patients with AIDS

RAISED LESIONS:

- Papilloma
- Verruca vulgaris
- Condyloma acuminatum
- Fibroma
- Epulis
- Pyogenic granuloma
- Mucocele
- Retention cyst

BLISTERS:

- Primary herpetic gingivostomatitis

Caused by herpes simplex virus type 1 or less frequently type 2

Course: day 1—malaise, fever, headache, sore throat, cervical lymphadenopathy; days 2 and 3—appearance of vesicles that develop into painful ulcers of 2-4 mm in diameter; duration of up to 2 wk

Recurrent intraoral herpes: rare, recurrences typically involve only the keratinized epithelium (lips)

- Pemphigus and pemphigoid
- Hand-foot-mouth disease: caused by coxsackievirus group A
- Erythema multiforme
- Herpangina: caused by echovirus
- Traumatic ulcer
- Primary syphilis
- Perlèche (or angular cheilitis)
- Recurrent aphthous stomatitis (canker sores)
- Behçet's syndrome (aphthous ulcers, uveitis, genital ulcerations, arthritis, and aseptic meningitis)
- Reiter's syndrome (conjunctivitis, urethritis, and arthritis with occasional oral ulcerations)
- Unknown cause

Course: solitary or multiple painful ulcers may develop simultaneously and heal over 10 to 14 days. The size of the lesions and the frequency of recurrences are variable.

DIAGNOSIS

WHITE LESIONS: Candidiasis (thrush) diagnosis: ovoid yeast and hyphae seen in scrapings treated with KOH culture

BLISTERS:

- Exfoliative cytology
- Viral culture
- Immunofluorescence for herpes antigen

TREATMENT

WHITE LESIONS: Candidiasis (thrush) treatment:

- Topical with nystatin or clotrimazole
- Systemic with ketoconazole or fluconazole

BLISTERS:

- Supportive
- Consider acyclovir

RECURRENT INTRAORAL HERPES: Topical corticosteroids or systemic steroids for severe cases

SUGGESTED READING

Allen CM, Blozis GG: Oral mucosal lesions. In Cummings CW (ed): *Otolaryngology: head and neck surgery,* ed 2, St Louis, 1992, Mosby.

AUTHOR: **TOM J. WACHTEL, M.D.**

Strabismus

BASIC INFORMATION

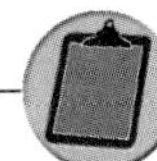

DEFINITION

Strabismus is a condition of the eyes in which the visual axes of the eyes are not straight in the primary position or in which the eyes do not follow each other in the different positions of gaze.

SYNONYMS

Esotropia
Exotropia
Restrictive eye movement

ICD-9CM CODES
378.9 Strabismus

EPIDEMIOLOGY & DEMOGRAPHICS

INCIDENCE (IN U.S.): 2% of all children
PREDOMINANT SEX: None
PREDOMINANT AGE: Birth to 5 yr of age
PEAK INCIDENCE: Childhood
GENETICS: None known

PHYSICAL FINDINGS & CLINICAL PRESENTATION

- Conjugate gaze loss in both eyes with the eyes focusing independently (Fig. 1-224)
- Amblyopia

ETIOLOGY

- Many cases are congenital.
- Accomodative cases occur later with focusing.
- Rarely, there is neurologic disease or severe refractive errors.
- Hereditary common, with hyperopia (far-sightedness) most common.

DIAGNOSIS

DIFFERENTIAL DIAGNOSIS

- Measuring eye position and movement
- Vision testing
- Refractive errors
- CNS tumors
- Orbital tumors
- Brain and CNS dysfunction

WORKUP

- Eye examination
- Visual field
- MRI to rule out tumors when develops later with no apparent cause

LABORATORY TESTS

Generally not needed

IMAGING STUDIES

Necessary only if other neurologic findings are found

TREATMENT

NONPHARMACOLOGIC THERAPY

- Glasses
- Patching—best between 3-7 yr old; vision most improved by 3-6 mo
- Prisms
- Atropine—same as patching most of time although patching may give better results in resistant cases

CHRONIC Rx

- Glasses
- Alternate eye patching
- Surgery
- Prisms

DISPOSITION

- The earlier the condition is treated, the more likely it is that the child will have normal vision in both eyes.
- After age 7 yr, visual loss is usually permanent from amblyopia.

REFERRAL

- Early for full rehabilitation of eye cosmetically and functionally
- To an ophthalmologist for management (usually)

PEARLS & CONSIDERATIONS

COMMENTS

- Children with strasbismus develop lower self-esteem and are generally treated differently by other children and adults. Early treatment is best for young children.
- If properly treated, this easily recognizable and treatable condition results in normal vision.
- If not treated, this condition can result in decrease in vision in one eye (amblyopia).

SUGGESTED READINGS

Kushmer BJ: Recently acquired diploxin in adults with long-standing strabismus, *Arch Ophth* 119(12):1795, 2001.

Mims JL: Strabology report of the 30th annual meeting of the Am Assoc for Ped Ophthalmol and Strabismus, Washington, DC, March 27-31, 2004, *Binocul Vis Strabismus Q* 19(2):98, 2004.

Rubin SE: Management of strabismus in the first year of life, *Pediatr Ann* 30(8):474, 2001.

Ziakas NG: A study of heredity as a risk factor in strabismus eye, 16(5):519, 2002.

AUTHOR: **MELVYN KOBY, M.D.**

A

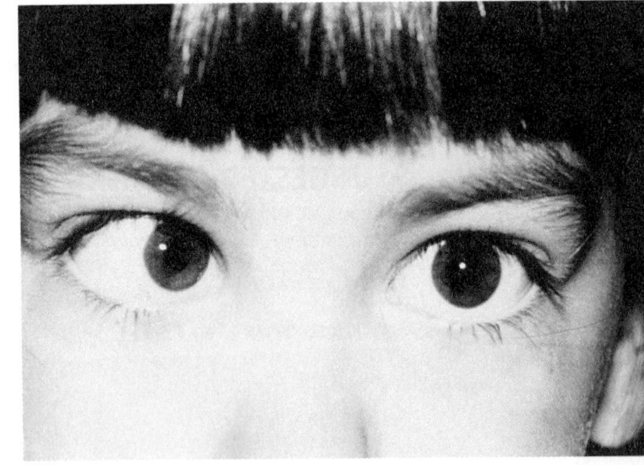

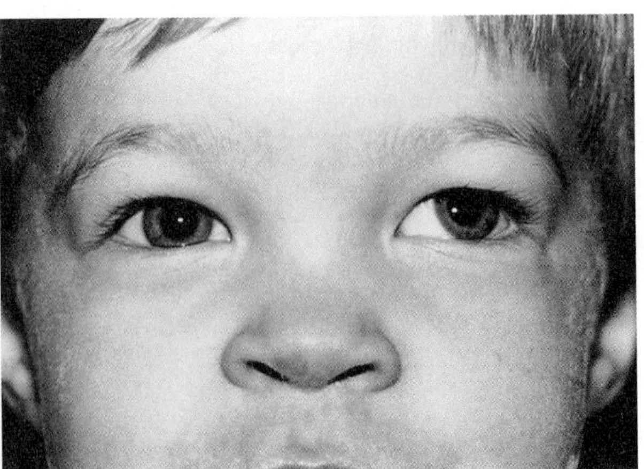

B

FIGURE 1-224 **A,** Note the nasal deviation of the right eye with the corneal light reflection temporally displaced on the right eye and centered in the left pupil, indicating an esotropia. **B,** Divergent strabismus of the left eye, defining an exotropia. (From Hodkelman [ed]: *Primary pediatric care,* ed 3, St Louis, 1997, Mosby.)

BASIC INFORMATION

DEFINITION

Stroke describes acute brain injury caused by decreased blood supply or hemorrhage.

SYNONYMS

Cerebrovascular accident (CVA)

ICD-9CM CODES
436 Acute stroke

EPIDEMIOLOGY & DEMOGRAPHICS

INCIDENCE (IN U.S.):
- Occurs in 5 to 10/100,000 persons <40 yr of age
- Occurs in 10 to 20/100,000 persons >65 yr of age

PREVALENCE (IN U.S.): Estimated at 2 million persons
PREDOMINANT SEX: Incidence is 30% higher in males
PREDOMINANT AGE: 60+ yr
PEAK INCIDENCE: 80-84 yr

PHYSICAL FINDINGS & CLINICAL PRESENTATION

Motor and/or sensory and/or cognitive deficits, depending on distribution and extent of involved vascular territory. More common manifestations include contralateral motor weakness or sensory loss, as well as language difficulties (aphasia; predominantly left-sided lesions) and visuospatial/neglect phenomena (predominantly right-sided lesions). Onset is usually sudden; however, this depends on specific etiology.

ETIOLOGY

- 70%-80% are caused by ischemic infarcts; 20%-30% are hemorrhagic.
- 80% of ischemic infarcts are from occlusion of large or small vessels caused by atherosclerotic vascular disease (due to hypertension, hyperlipidemia, tobacco abuse), 15% are caused by cardiac embolism, 5% are from other causes, including hypercoagulable states and vasculitis.
- Small vessel occlusion is most often caused by lipohyalinosis precipitated by chronic hypertension.
- Risk factors for ischemic stroke are described in Box 1-11.

DIAGNOSIS

DIFFERENTIAL DIAGNOSIS

- TIA (Transient ischemic attack, traditionally defined as focal neurologic deficits lasting <24 hr [usually lasting <60 min])
- Migraine
- Seizure
- Mass lesion

WORKUP

- Thorough history and physical examination, including detailed neurologic and cardiovascular evaluation to identify vascular territory and likely etiology (Table 1-49). Infectious, toxic, and metabolic causes should be excluded because each may cause clinical deterioration of old stroke symptoms.
- Cardiac: mandatory ECG, telemetry, consider serial cardiac enzymes; transthoracic and/or transesophageal echocardiography Holter monitor, should be seriously considered especially in setting of suspected embolic etiology. Carotid Doppler should be performed in cases of embolic stroke to anterior or middle cerebral artery territory.

LABORATORY TESTS

- CBC
- Platelet count
- PT (INR)
- PTT
- BUN, creatinine
- Lipid panel
- Glucose
- Electrolytes
- Urinalysis
- Additional tests, depending on suspected etiology (in younger patients; e.g., coagulopathies)

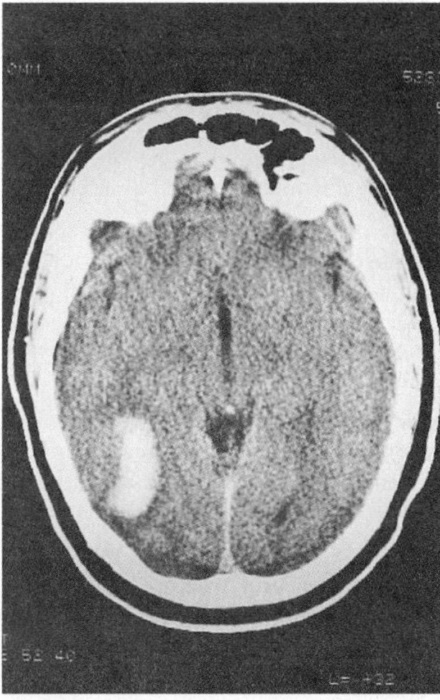

FIGURE 1-225 Intracerebral hemorrhage. Noncontrast CT scan demonstrates an intracerebral hemorrhage in the right occipital lobe. (From Specht N [ed]: *Practical guide to diagnostic imaging,* St Louis, 1998, Mosby.)

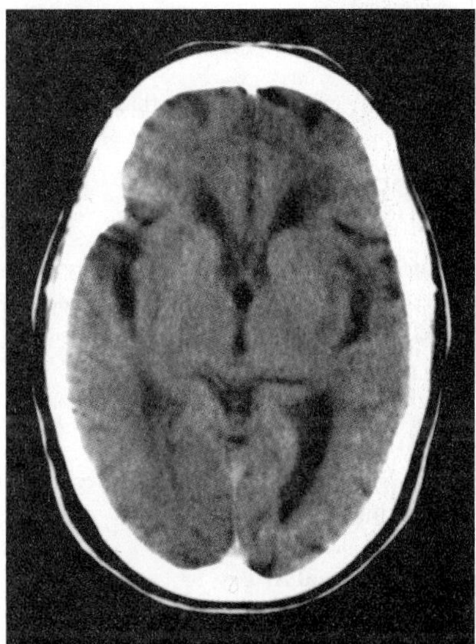

FIGURE 1-226 Occipital lobe infarct (posterior cerebral artery territory). Note the large right occipital hypodensity with mass effect caused by infarction and subsequent edema. (From Cwinn AA, Grahovac SZ [eds]: *Emergency CT scans of the head: a practical atlas,* St Louis, 1998, Mosby.)

BOX 1-11 Risk Factors for Ischemic Stroke

Diabetes
Hypertension
Smoking
Family history of premature vascular disease
Hyperlipidemia
Atrial fibrillation
History of transient ischemic attack (TIA)
History of recent myocardial infarction
History of congestive heart failure (left ventricular [LV] ejection fraction ,25%)
Drugs (sympathomimetics, oral contraceptive pill, cocaine)

From Andreoli TE (ed): *Cecil essentials of medicine,* ed 5, Philadelphia, 2001, WB Saunders.

TABLE 1-49 **Neurologic Signs Associated with Cerebrovascular Accident by Location**

Artery Affected	Neurologic Signs
Internal Carotid Artery	
(Supplies the cerebral hemispheres and diencephalon by the ophthalmic and ipsilateral hemisphere arteries)	Occasional unilateral blindness Severe contralateral hemiplegia, hemianesthesia, and hemianopia Profound aphasia if left hemisphere involved
Middle Cerebral Artery	
(Supplies structures of higher cerebral processes of communication; language interpretation; perception and interpretation of space, sensation, form, and voluntary movement)	Alterations in communication, cognition, mobility, and sensation Homonymous hemianopia Contralateral hemiplegia or hemiparesis
Anterior Cerebral Artery	
(Supplies medial surfaces and upper convexities of frontal and parietal lobes and medial surface of hemisphere, which includes motor and somesthetic cortex serving the legs)	Emotional lability Confusion, amnesia, personality changes Urinary incontinence Impaired mobility, with weakness greater in lower extremities than in upper
Posterior Cerebral Artery	
(Supplies medial and inferior temporal lobes, medial occipital lobe, thalamus, posterior hypothalamus, and visual receptive area)	Homonymous hemianopia Hemianesthesia Cortical blindness Memory deficits
Vertebral or Basilar Arteries	
(Supply the brainstem and cerebellum) Incomplete occlusion	Drop attacks Unilateral and bilateral weakness of extremities Diplopia, homonymous hemianopia Nausea, vertigo, tinnitus, and syncope Dysphagia Dysarthria Sometimes confusion and drowsiness
Anterior portion of pons	"Locked-in" syndrome—no movement except eyelids; sensation and consciousness preserved
Complete occlusion or hemorrhage	Coma Miotic pupils Decerebrate rigidity Respiratory and circulatory abnormalities Death
Posterior Inferior Cerebellar Artery	
(Supplies the lateral and posterior portion of the medulla)	Wallenberg syndrome Dysphagia, dysphonia Ipsilateral anesthesia of face and cornea for pain and temperature (touch preserved) Ipsilateral Horner syndrome Contralateral loss of pain and temperature sensation in trunk and extremities Ipsilateral decompensation of movement (cerebellar signs)
Anterior Inferior and Superior Cerebellar Arteries	
(Supply the cerebellum)	Difficulty in articulation, swallowing, gross movements of limbs; nystagmus (cerebellar signs)
Anterior Spinal Artery	
(Supplies the anterior spinal cord)	Flaccid paralysis, below level of lesion Loss of pain, touch, temperature sensation (proprioception preserved, sensory level)
Posterior Spinal Artery	
(Supplies the posterior spinal cord)	Sensory loss, particularly proprioception, vibration, touch, and pressure (movement preserved)

Adapted from Seidel HM (ed): *Mosby's guide to physical examination,* ed 4, St Louis, 1999, Mosby.

IMAGING STUDIES

- CT scan without contrast to distinguish hemorrhage from infarct (Figs. 1-225 and 1-226)
- An MRI is superior to CT in identifying abnormalities in the posterior fossa and, in particular, lacunar (small vessel) infarcts. Diffusion weighted imaging (DWI) is best to determine hyperacute ischemia (positive within 15-30 min of symptom onset). MRA is recommended to help identify vascular pathology (e.g., extent of intracranial atherosclerosis or vascular distribution of ischemia)
- In select cases (e.g., hemorrhagic stroke), conventional angiography may identify aneurysms or other vascular malformations

TREATMENT

NONPHARMACOLOGIC THERAPY

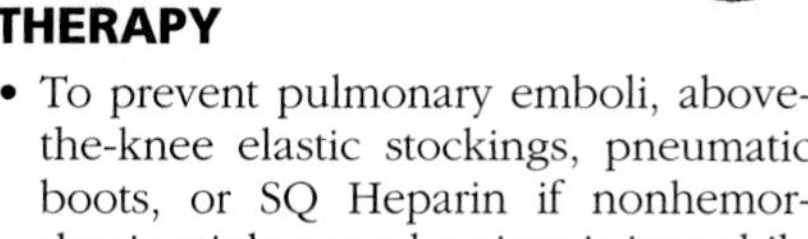

- To prevent pulmonary emboli, above-the-knee elastic stockings, pneumatic boots, or SQ Heparin if nonhemorrhagic etiology and patient is immobile in bed

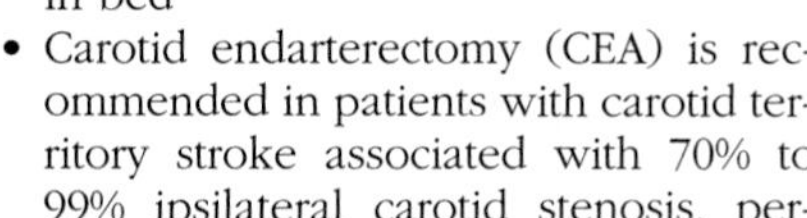

- Carotid endarterectomy (CEA) is recommended in patients with carotid territory stroke associated with 70% to 99% ipsilateral carotid stenosis, performed by an experienced surgeon who has demonstrated low morbidity and mortality
- Modification of risk factors (e.g., smoking cessation, exercise, diet)

ACUTE GENERAL Rx

- Box 1-12 describes initial considerations for patients with stroke.
- Judicious control of blood pressure; patients with chronic hypertension may extend the area of infarction if the blood pressure is lowered into the "normal" range. It is best not to lower blood pressure too aggressively in the acute setting unless it is very markedly elevated. Adequate hydration and bed rest (e.g., head of bed down in pressure dependent ischemia vs. head of bed up if patient is aspiration risk). Tight glycemic control is also recommended (e.g., sliding scale insulin).
- Patients presenting <3 hr after onset of a nonhemorrhagic stroke, thrombolytic therapy in a specialized stroke center is beneficial in selected populations.

ACUTE SPECIFIC Rx

- Depends on several factors, including etiology, vascular territory involved, risk factors, and elapsed time from symptom onset to arrival at hospital.
- Box 1-13 describes criteria for thrombolytic therapy in patients with thromboembolic stroke (IV tPA inclusion criteria includes clearly defined symptom onset within 3 hr of onset of treatment, measurable deficit with NIH Stroke Scale >4, and no evidence for bleed on neuroimaging).
- If atrial fibrillation and/or a cardiac mural thrombus is found on echocardiography, heparin may be considered.
- If a subarachnoid or intracerebral hemorrhage is found on CT, MR angiography and/or cerebral angiography may be indicated to identify aneurysm. If no aneurysm is found and clot is expanding, neurosurgical evacuation of clot may be attempted, but outcomes are generally poor.
- In select cases of patients presenting >3 hr but <6 hr, an *interventional* neuroradiologist or neurosurgeon may be able to offer either direct injection of a clot-busting agent (such as intraarterial tPA) or direct extraction of the clot (e.g., FDA approved Merci Retrieval System). However, this remains investigational and has yet to be well studied in the setting of a controlled trial. Intracranial angioplasty/stenting may also be a consideration.

BOX 1-12 Initial Considerations for Patients with Strokes

Initial care
- Stabilize the patient, secure the airway, and provide adequate oxygenation
- Assess level of consciousness, language, visual fields, eye movements, and pupillary movements
- Obtain history and perform physical examination
- Perform CT of head without contrast
- Obtain CBC with platelets and differential, electrolytes, creatinine, BUN, glucose, PT/PTT, arterial blood gas, or oxygen saturation
- Consider a toxicology screen
- Consider special coagulation studies such as antiphospholipid antibodies, factor V Leiden assay, protein C and protein S, antithrombin III, ANA, fibrinogen, RPR, homocysteine, serum protein electrophoresis

Consider acute intervention with t-PA if symptoms for less than 3 hr

Consider the following with admission orders
- Transthoracic echocardiogram (consider transesophageal echocardiogram if transthoracic echocardiogram is equivocal or there is a high suspicion of cardiogenic thromboembolism)
- Carotid duplex ultrasonography
- Telemetry
- Supplemental oxygen and appropriate oxygen saturation monitoring
- Antiplatelet therapy
- Fluid restriction if infarct is large, to reduce cerebral edema
- Close monitoring of intake and output
- Regular determinations of blood glucose levels to avoid hyperglycemia
- NPO if there are concerns about the pharyngeal reflex pending swallowing evaluation
- Elevate the head of the bed 20-30 degrees to reduce cerebral edema
- Bed rest for the first 24 hr with fall precautions, then advance as appropriate
- Vital signs and neurologic checks every 2 hr times four until stable
- Prophylaxis for DVT if immobile (elastic stockings at a minimum)
- Speech therapy consultation to evaluate swallowing
- Neurology, physical therapy, occupational therapy, nutrition, and social services consultations

From Rakel RE (ed): *Principles of family practice*, ed 6, Philadelphia, 2002, WB Saunders.

ANA, Antinuclear antibodies; *BUN,* blood urea nitrogen; *CBC,* complete blood count; *CT,* computed tomography; *DVT,* deep vein thrombosis; *NPO,* nothing by mouth; *PT/PTT,* prothrombin time/partial thromboplastin time; *RPR,* rapid plasma reagin; *t-PA,* tissue plasminogen activator.

CHRONIC Rx

- Antiplatelet therapy (aspirin, dipyridamole/aspirin [Aggrenox], clopidogrel [Plavix], or ticlopidine) reduces the risk of subsequent stroke.
- If patient presents with first TIA/stroke and was on no prior antiplatelet agent, aspirin (325 mg vs. 81 mg each day) is usually chosen initially. If a TIA occurs while on aspirin, the patient should be switched to dipyridamole/aspirin or clopidogrel (aspirin and clopidogrel should not be used in combination).
- Warafin is usually reserved for patients with cardioembolic stroke as well as for patients with atrial fibrillation.

DISPOSITION

Prognosis depends on severity of deficits, etiology, and other concurrent medical/surgical illness. A polymodality physical medicine and rehabilitative approach is an integral part of poststroke recovery. This includes physical, occupational, and speech therapy individualized depending on deficits.

REFERRAL

- Neurology/neurosurgical referral depending on etiology and resources available; depending on time of symptom onset, transfer of patient to institution able to provide more specific acute treatment is recommended.
- Vascular surgery if patient is candidate for CEA. If not a surgical candidate and endovascular treatment is available, refer to interventional neuroradiologist for carotid stenting.

SUGGESTED READINGS

American Heart Association Scientific Statement: Primary prevention of ischemic stroke: a statement for health care professionals from the stroke council of the American Heart Association, *Circulation* 103:167, 2001.

Barnett HJM: A modern approach to posterior circulation ischemic stroke, *Arch Neurol* 59:359, 2002.

Benevante D, Hart RG: Stroke: management of acute ischemic stroke, *Am Fam Physician* 59:2828, 1999.

Caplan LR: Stroke treatment: promising but still struggling, *JAMA* 279:1304, 1998.

Diener HC et al: Aspirin and clopidogrel compared with clopidogrel alone after recent ischaemic stroke or transient ischaemic attack in high-risk patients (MATCH): randomised, double-blind, placebo-controlled trial, *Lancet* 364(9431):331, 2004.

Endovascular versus surgical treatment in patients with carotid stenosis in the Carotid and Vertebral Artery Transluminal Angioplasty Study (CAVATAS): a randomised trial, *Lancet* 357(9270):1729, 2001.

Green DM et al: Serum potassium level and dietary potassium intake as risk factors for stroke, *Neurology* 59:314, 2002.

Halperin JL, Fuster V: Patent foramen ovale and recurrent stroke: another paradoxical twist, *Circulation* 105:2580, 2002.

Meschia JF et al: Thrombolytic treatment of acute ischemic stroke, *Mayo Clin Proc* 77:542, 2002.

Qureshi A et al: Spontaneous intracranial hemorrhage, *N Engl J Med* 344:1450, 2001.

Sacco RL et al: High-density lipoprotein cholesterol and ischemic stroke in the elderly, *JAMA* 285:2729, 2001.

Straus SE et al: New evidence for stroke prevention, clinical applications and scientific review, *JAMA* 288:1388, 2002.

AUTHOR: **RICHARD S. ISAACSON, M.D.**

BOX 1-13 Criteria for Tissue Plasminogen Activator (alteplase [Activase]) Use in Patients with Thromboembolic Stroke

Criteria for considering t-PA as a treatment option
- Age ≥18 yr
- Noncontrast CT without evidence of hemorrhage
- Time since onset of symptoms clearly <3 hr before t-PA administration would begin

Criteria for excluding t-PA as a treatment option

Historical and clinical findings
- Clinical presentation suggests subarachnoid hemorrhage, even if CT is normal
  - Sudden, severe headache, often with loss of consciousness at onset
  - Vomiting common
- Active internal bleeding, increased risk of bleeding, or known bleeding diathesis, including:
  - Recent use of warfarin with a prolonged international normalized ratio (INR)—some would add current use of warfarin regard less of INR
  - Use of heparin within 48 hr with a prolonged aPTT
  - Platelet count <100,000/mm3
  - History of intracranial hemorrhage
  - Known arteriovenous malformation or aneurysm
  - GI or GU bleeding within the past 21 days
  - Arterial puncture within the past 7 days
- Recent lumbar puncture
- Stroke, intracranial surgery, or head trauma within the previous 3 mo
- Major surgery or serious trauma within the preceding 14 days
- Persistent systolic blood pressure >185 mm Hg or diastolic blood pressure >110 mm Hg
- Seizure at stroke onset
- Rapidly improving neurologic signs
- Isolated, mild neurologic deficits
- Acute myocardial infarction
- Post–myocardial infarction pericarditis
- Blood glucose >50 mg/dl or <400 mg/dl
- Patient pregnant or lactating

CT findings
- Evidence of intracranial hemorrhage
- Hypodensity or effacement of the sulci in 1/3 of the territory of the middle cerebral artery

From Rakel RE (ed): *Principles of family practice,* ed 6, Philadelphia, 2002, WB Saunders.
aPTT, Activated partial thromboplastin time; *CT,* computed tomography; *GI,* gastrointestinal; *GU,* genitourinary; *t-PA,* tissue plasminogen activator.

BASIC INFORMATION

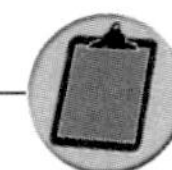

DEFINITION

Subarachnoid hemorrhage is the presence of active bleeding into the subarachnoid space usually secondary to a spontaneous ruptured aneurysm or after head trauma.

ICD-9CM CODES
430 Subarachnoid hemorrhage

EPIDEMIOLOGY & DEMOGRAPHICS

INCIDENCE (IN U.S.): 6 to 28 cases/100,000 persons/yr
PREDOMINANT SEX: Males > females in persons <40 yr of age; then female:male ratio of 3:2 in persons >40 yr old
PREDOMINANT AGE: >50 yr
PEAK INCIDENCE: 50-60 yr
GENETICS:
- First-degree relatives have a 4%-9% risk of intracranial aneurysms (as compared with about 2% in the general population) and these may tend to rupture at a younger age and at a smaller size than sporadic ones. Recommendations on screening unaffected family members depend on the number of relatives with aneurysms. There may also be a familial predisposition to multiple aneurysms.
- Increased incidence in some inherited systemic diseases (e.g., autosomal dominant polycystic kidney disease and connective tissue diseases such as Ehlers-Danlos syndrome).

PHYSICAL FINDINGS & CLINICAL PRESENTATION

- Patients typically present with sudden onset of a severe headache with maximal intensity at onset. Classically described by the patient as "the worst headache of my life," however, this is not always the case. Additional findings may include nuchal rigidity, nausea, and vomiting.
- Transient loss of consciousness occurs in 45% of patients.
- Focal neurologic deficits may be present.
- Funduscopic examination may reveal subhyaloid hemorrhage.

ETIOLOGY

- Key distinction is aneurysmal (nontraumatic etiology in >60% of cases, most commonly after rupture of saccular "berry" aneurysms) vs. nonaneurysmal (traumatic) SAH
- Others: Arteriovenous malformation (AVM), angioma, fusiform or mycotic aneurysm, dissecting and tumor-related aneurysms

DIAGNOSIS

DIFFERENTIAL DIAGNOSIS

- Intraparenchymal hemorrhage
- Subarachnoid extension of an extracranial arterial dissection or intracerebral hemorrhage
- Meningoencephalitis (e.g., hemorrhagic meningoencephalitis caused by HSV)
- Headache associated with sexual activity (e.g., coital/postcoital headache; usually acute onset of severe headache around time of orgasm)

WORKUP

- CT scan without contrast is initial test of choice, with a sensitivity of about 90% in the first 24 hr. If CT is negative and there is a high clinical suspicion for SAH, lumbar puncture must be considered as there is an approximately 7% (or 1 in 14) chance of having a SAH. Spinal fluid is considered positive if there is xanthochromia and if there is a constant amount of red cells in each LP tube. LP performed <2 hr after onset of headache may be falsely negative for xanthochromia.
- If CT scan is unavailable, transfer patient immediately to a facility that has one.
- ECG (nonspecific ST-and T-wave changes, "cerebral T-waves").

LABORATORY TESTS

PT, PTT, platelet count at a minimum for clotting abnormality

IMAGING STUDIES

CT scan (Fig. 1-227) followed by cerebral angiography if hemorrhage is confirmed. May also use Transcranial Doppler (TCD) as a baseline to later more adequately assess for vasospasm

TREATMENT

NONPHARMACOLOGIC THERAPY

- Intubation as necessary
- Bed rest, isotonic fluids

ACUTE GENERAL Rx

- Short-acting analgesics (e.g., morphine 1-4 mg IV) and sedation (e.g., midazolam 1-5 mg IV); avoid oversedation and watch neurologic examination closely
- Seizure prophylaxis controversial (consider phenytoin 15-20 mg/kg IV load, 100 mg TID maintenance)
- Vasospasm prophylaxis (nimodipine 60 mg PO q4h); see "Chronic Rx"
- BP control (e.g., labetalol 10-40 mg IV q30min); lower BP for unprotected aneurysms vs. higher BP if protected (post coiling/clipping)
- Stool softeners
- Neurosurgical or interventional neuroradiologic referral mandatory if aneurysm or arteriovenous malformation demonstrated by angiography; also, invasive ICP monitoring and/or ventriculostomy may be required on an emergent basis (e.g., deteriorating level of consciousness and/or development of hydrocephalus); elevated ICP is associated with a worse patient outcome, particularly if ICP does not respond to treatment

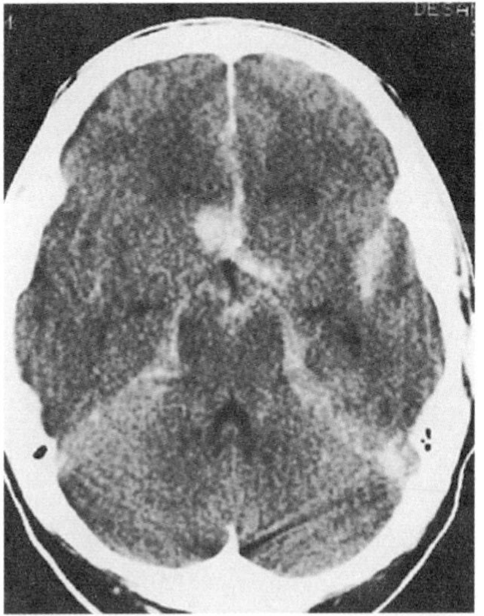

FIGURE 1-227 Noncontrast CT demonstrates diffuse subarachnoid hemorrhage. The rounded area of hyperdensity anterior to the suprasellar cistern represents an aneurysm of the anterior communicating artery. (From Specht N [ed]: *Practical guide to diagnostic imaging,* St Louis, 1998, Mosby.)

- Hypertonic saline (HS) solutions have been used in various concentrations (e.g., 7.5%, 10%, 23.5%) to treat elevated ICP and augment cerebral blood flow (CBF); in one study, HS 23.5% bolus (2 mL/kg IV x 1) exerted an early CBF-augmenting effect which lasted for up to 7.5 hr; despite this evidence, there are limited studies in this area and the exact recommended doses have yet to be determined; neurosurgical consultation is mandatory for persistently elevated ICP management

CHRONIC Rx

Vasospasm occurs in 20%-30% of patients and peaks at about 1 wk; monitor closely for this. Consider TCD monitoring in high-risk patients. "Triple H" therapy for prevention of vasospasm includes hemodilution, hypertension (consider pressors), and hypervolemia. Intraarterial papaverine and/or balloon angioplasty may be necessary in some cases.

DISPOSITION

Approximately 35% early mortality, 45% at 1 mo

REFERRAL

Transfer as soon as possible to a facility with neurosurgical care.

PEARLS & CONSIDERATIONS

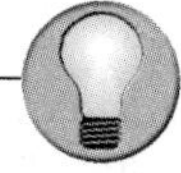

COMMENTS

About 20% of patients experience warning signs within 3 mo before aneurysm rupture, including moderate or severe headache ("sentinel headache"), dizziness, nausea and vomiting, transient motor or sensory deficits, loss of consciousness, or visual disturbances.

SUGGESTED READINGS

Bederson JB et al: Recommendations for the management of patients with unruptured intracranial aneurysms: a statement for healthcare professionals from the Stroke Council of the American Heart Association, *Circulation* 102(18):2300, 2000.

Edlow JA, Caplan LR: Avoiding pitfalls in the diagnosis of subarachnoid hemorrhage, *N Engl J Med* 342:29, 2000.

Edlow JA, Wyer PC: How good is a negative cranial computed tomographic scan result in excluding subarachnoid hemorrhage? *Ann Emerg Med* 36:507, 2000.

Heuer GG et al: Relationship between intracranial pressure and other clinical variables in patients with aneurysmal subarachnoid hemorrhage, *J Neurosurg* 101(3):408, 2004.

Morgenstern LB et al: Worst headache and subarachnoid hemorrhage: prospective modern computed tomography and spinal fluid analysis, *Ann Emerg Med* 32:297, 1998.

Raaymakers TW, and the MARS Study Group: Aneurysms in relatives of patients with subarachnoid hemorrhage. Frequency and risk factors, *Neurology* 53:982, 1999.

Suarez JI: Editorial comment: salting the brain to improve CBF in SAH patients, *Stroke* 34:1396, 2003.

Treggiari, MM et al: Systematic review of the prevention of delayed ischemic neurological deficits with hypertension, hypervolemia, and hemodilution therapy following subarachnoid hemorrhage, *J Neurosurg* 98:978, 2003.

Tseng MY et al: Effect of hypertonic saline on cerebral blood flow in poor-grade patients with subarachnoid hemorrhage, *Stroke* 34:1389, 2003.

Qureshi AI, Suarez JI: Use of hypertonic saline solutions in treatment of cerebral edema and intracranial hypertension, *Crit Care Med* 28(9):3301, 2000.

AUTHOR: **RICHARD S. ISAACSON, M.D.**

BASIC INFORMATION

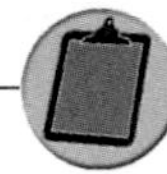

DEFINITION

Subclavian steal syndrome is an occlusion or severe stenosis of the proximal subclavian artery leading to decreased antegrade flow or retrograde flow in the ipsilateral vertebral artery and neurologic symptoms referable to the posterior circulation.

SYNONYMS

Proximal subclavian (or innominate) artery stenosis or occlusion

ICD-9CM CODES
435.2 Subclavian steal syndrome

EPIDEMIOLOGY & DEMOGRAPHICS

- Similar to that of other manifestations of atherosclerosis (coronary artery disease, cerebrovascular disease, or peripheral vascular disease)
- Affects middle-aged persons (men somewhat younger than women on average) with arteriosclerotic risk factors including family history, smoking, diabetes mellitus, hyperlipidemia, hypertension, sedentary lifestyle

PHYSICAL FINDINGS & CLINICAL PRESENTATION

Symptoms:
- Many patients are asymptomatic.
- Upper extremity ischemic symptoms: fatigue, exercise-related aching, coolness, numbness of the involved upper extremity.
- Neurologic symptoms are reported by 25% of patients with known unilateral subclavian steal. These include brief spells of:
  1. Vertigo
  2. Diplopia
  3. Decreased vision
  4. Oscillopsia
  5. Gait unsteadiness

These spells are only occasionally provoked by exercising the ischemic upper extremity (classic subclavian steal). Left subclavian steal is more common than right, but the latter is more serious.
- Posterior circulation stroke related to subclavian steal is rare.
- Innominate artery stenosis can cause decreased right carotid artery flow and cerebrovascular symptoms of the anterior cerebral circulation, but this is uncommon.

Physical findings:
- Delayed and smaller volume pulse (wrist or antecubital) in the affected upper extremity
- Lower blood pressure in the affected upper extremity
- Supraclavicular bruit

NOTE: Inflating a blood pressure cuff will increase the bruit if it originates from a vertebral artery stenosis and decrease the bruit if it originates from a subclavian artery stenosis.

ETIOLOGY & PATHOGENESIS

Etiology:
- Atherosclerosis
- Arteritis (Takayasu's disease and temporal arteritis)
- Embolism to the subclavian or innominate artery
- Cervical rib
- Chronic use of a crutch
- Occupational (baseball pitchers and cricket bowlers)

Pathogenesis: The vertebral artery originates from the subclavian artery. For subclavian steal to occur, the occlusion must be proximal to the takeoff of the vertebral artery. On the right side, only a small distance separates the bifurcation of the innominate artery and the takeoff of the vertebral artery, explaining why the condition occurs less commonly on the right side. Occlusion of the innominate artery must affect right carotid artery flow.

DIAGNOSIS

- See "History," "Physical Findings," and "Imaging Studies."
- The carotid arteries should be evaluated at least noninvasively in all cases.

DIFFERENTIAL DIAGNOSIS

- Posterior circulation TIA (and stroke)
- Upper extremity ischemia
  1. Distal subclavian artery stenosis/occlusion
  2. Raynaud's syndrome
  3. Thoracic outlet syndrome

IMAGING STUDIES

- Noninvasive upper extremity arterial flow studies
- Doppler sonography of the vertebral, subclavian, and innominate arteries
- Arteriography

TREATMENT

- In most patients the disease is benign and requires no treatment other than atherosclerosis risk factor modification and aspirin. Symptoms tend to improve over time as collateral circulation develops.
- Vascular surgical reconstruction requires a thoracotomy; it may be indicated in innominate artery stenosis or when upper extremity ischemia is incapacitating.

SUGGESTED READING

Caplan LR: Large-vessel occlusive disease of the posterior circulation. In Caplan LR (ed): *Stroke: a clinical approach,* ed 2, New York, 1993, Butterworth-Heinemann.

AUTHOR: **TOM J. WACHTEL, M.D.**

BASIC INFORMATION

DEFINITION

A subdural hematoma is bleeding into the subdural space, caused by rupture of bridging veins between the brain and venous sinuses.

ICD-9CM CODES
432.1 Subdural hematoma

EPIDEMIOLOGY & DEMOGRAPHICS

Nearly all cases are caused by trauma, although the trauma may be quite trivial and easily overlooked. Victims are commonly at the extremes of age. Coagulation abnormalities, especially use of anticoagulation in the elderly, is a significant risk factor.

PHYSICAL FINDINGS & CLINICAL PRESENTATION

- Vague headache, often worse in morning than evening.
- Some apathy, confusion, and clouding of consciousness is common, although frank coma may complicate late cases. Chronic subdural hematomas may cause a dementia picture.
- Neurologic symptoms may be transient, simulating TIA.
- Almost any sign of cortical dysfunction may occur, including hemiparesis, sensory deficits, or language abnormalities, depending on which part of the cortex the hematoma presses on.
- New-onset seizures should raise the index of suspicion.

ETIOLOGY

Traumatic rupture of cortical bridging veins, especially where stretched by underlying cerebral atrophy.

DIAGNOSIS

DIFFERENTIAL DIAGNOSIS

- Epidural hematoma
- Subarachnoid hemorrhage
- Mass lesion (e.g., tumor)
- Ischemic stroke
- Intraparenchymal hemorrhage

WORKUP

- CT scan is sensitive for diagnosis and should be performed in a timely fashion (Fig. 1-228).
- Hematocrit, platelet count, PTT, and PT/INR should be routinely checked.

TREATMENT

NONPHARMACOLOGIC THERAPY

Small subdural hematomas may be left untreated and the patient observed, but if there is an underlying cause, such as anticoagulation, this should be rapidly corrected to prevent further accumulation of blood.

ACUTE THERAPY

- Neurosurgical drainage of blood from subdural space via burr hole is the definitive procedure, although it is common for the hematoma to reaccumulate.
- There is an increased risk of seizures, which should be treated appropriately if they arise.

DISPOSITION

Referral to neurosurgery for possible evacuation

PEARLS & CONSIDERATIONS

- The very young and very old are particularly susceptible to subdural hematomas.
- Relatively minor trauma may cause a subdural hematoma.
- Caution should be taken in interpreting CT findings in the subacute stage, where blood appears as isodense to brain, and therefore the distance from the cortical sulci to the skull needs to be evaluated.

SUGGESTED READINGS

Chen JC, Levy ML: Causes, epidemiology, and risk factors of chronic subdural hematoma, *Neurosurg Clin N Am* 11(3):399, 2000.

Voelker JL: Nonoperative treatment of chronic subdural hematoma, *Neurosurg Clin N Am* 11(3):507, 2000.

AUTHOR: **DANIEL MATTSON, M.D., M.Sc.(MED.)**

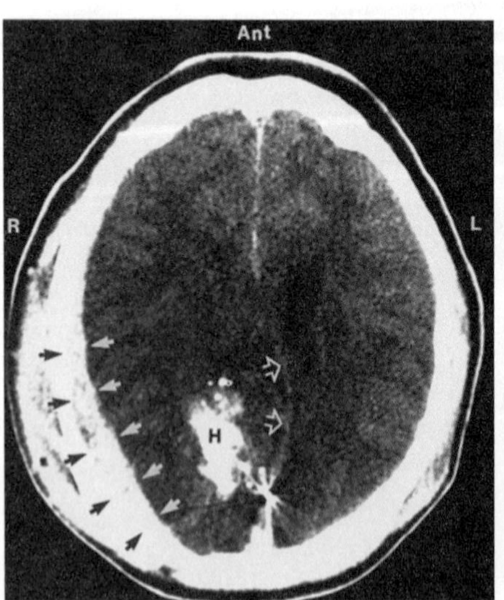

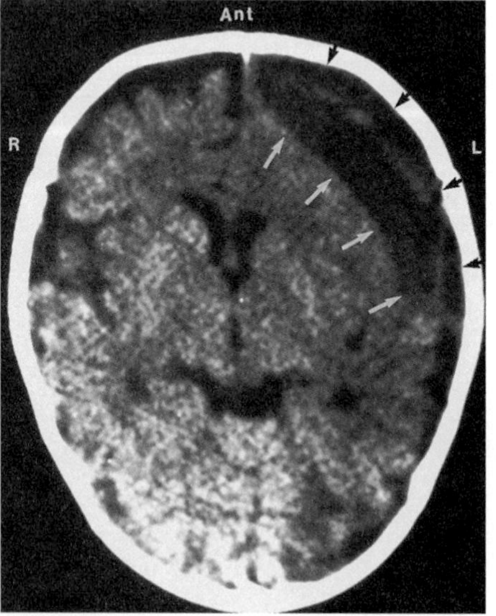

FIGURE 1-228 Subdural hematomas. A noncontrasted computed tomography scan of an acute subdural hematoma **(A)** shows a crescentic area of increased density in the right posterior parietal region between the brain and the skull (*black and white arrows*). An area of intraparenchymal hemorrhage *(H)* is also seen; a chronic subdural hematoma for a different patient is shown in **(B)**. There is an area of decreased density in the left frontoparietal region *(arrows)* effacing the sulci, compressing the anterior horn of the left lateral ventricle, and shifting the midline somewhat to the right. (From Mettler FA [ed]: *Primary care radiology,* Philadelphia, 2000, WB Saunders.)

BASIC INFORMATION

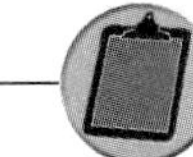

DEFINITION

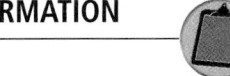

Suicide refers to successful and unsuccessful attempts to kill oneself.

SYNONYMS

Self-murder

ICD-9CM CODES
Categorized by method (e.g., poisoning)

EPIDEMIOLOGY & DEMOGRAPHICS

INCIDENCE (IN U.S.):
Suicide is the 11th leading cause of death and the 7th leading cause of years of potential life lost in the U.S.

- 10.42 cases/100,000 persons; 1.4% of total deaths
- 18.7/100,000 men
- 4.4/100,000 women

PREDOMINANT AGE:

- Increases with age (e.g., 13.1 cases/100,000 persons aged 15-24 yr, 16.9 cases/100,000 persons aged 65-74 yr, and 23.5 cases/100,000 persons aged 75-84 yr)
- Elderly people have a higher risk of completed suicide than any other age groups worldwide. White men >85 yr of age have an especially high rate.
- It is the third leading cause of death among persons 15-24 yr of age

PEAK INCIDENCE: >65 yr of age

GENETICS:

- Biologic factors may increase the risk of suicide directly (e.g., by increasing impulsivity) or indirectly (e.g., by predisposing to a mental illness).
- Family history of suicide is associated with suicidal behavior.
- Pediatric trials suggest that SSRIs are associated with an increased risk of suicidal behavior.

PHYSICAL FINDINGS & CLINICAL PRESENTATION

Methods used in attempted (unsuccessful) suicides differ from those used in completed suicides.

- Overdose used in >70% of attempted suicides. Cutting of wrists or other parts of the body is the second most common form.
- About 60% of completed suicides are accomplished with firearms. Hanging is the second most common method for completed suicides. Suffocation (e.g., carbon monoxide) and overdose are also relatively common forms of completing suicide.
- Several risk factors are usually present concurrently, including a psychiatric illness such as depression or anxiety, middle age or advanced age, white race, male gender, a recent divorce or separation, comorbid substance abuse (particularly when intoxicated), previous history of suicide attempts, fatal plan (e.g., firearms or hanging), history of violence, and family history of suicide. Concurrent chronic physical illness increases the risk for suicide greatly (e.g., the risk for suicide among AIDS or renal dialysis patients is nearly 30 times that of the general population).

ETIOLOGY

- Individuals with a mental disorder or substance abuse are responsible for >90% of all suicides.
- The concurrence of more than one condition (e.g., depression and alcohol abuse) greatly increases the risk of suicide.
- Pediatric trials suggest that SSRIs are associated with an increased risk of suicidal behavior.
- Hopelessness is a strong predictor of suicide potential.

DIAGNOSIS

DIFFERENTIAL DIAGNOSIS

- Some disorders are associated with self-injurious behavior that is not suicidal. Borderline personality disorder, for example, manifests with self-mutilation without active suicidal intent. Eating disorders are harmful and may be fatal, but death is rarely the goal.
- Some suicidal behavior is intended as a "call for help." In these situations individuals usually design the suicide so that they will be discovered before significant damage has been done.

WORKUP

- The physician must directly inquire into the presence of suicidal ideation. Approximately one half to two thirds of individuals who commit suicide visit physicians within 1 mo of taking their lives.
- Explicit suicidal intent, hopelessness, and a well formulated plan indicate high risk. Clinicians can use the mnemonic SAL: Is the method Specific? Is it Available? Is it Lethal?
- The concurrence of multiple psychiatric problems, substance abuse, and multiple physical problems increases the risk.
- Covert suicidal ideation occurs in patients primarily with multiple vague physical complaints, depression, anxiety, or substance abuse.

TREATMENT

NONPHARMACOLOGIC THERAPY

- Major immediate intervention: placement of the patient in a safe environment (usually hospitalization in a psychiatric unit or a medical unit with continuous observation)
- Long-term: psychotherapy aimed at factors that underlie the decision to pursue suicide or at the risk factors contributing to suicidal behavior
- Substance abuse treatment (e.g., AA, NA) when substance abuse is present

ACUTE GENERAL Rx

- Benzodiazepines are useful in reducing the extreme anxiety and dysphoria in a suicidal patient; however, these agents are depressive and should be used only when patient is in safe environment.
- Antipsychotics can be used if psychosis is present (e.g., voices telling patient to hurt self).
- Mood stabilizers and antidepressants should be started in the acute setting but may have up to a 2-wk latency period.

CHRONIC Rx

- Therapy should be aimed at the underlying condition (e.g., antidepressants for depression, anxiolytics or antidepressants for anxiety, ongoing substance abuse treatment for substance abuse history, or psychotherapy for chronic low self-esteem, hopelessness).
- In elderly, loneliness and medical disability are major reasons for suicide and therefore major targets for intervention.

DISPOSITION

- Prior suicide attempt is the best predictor for completed suicides (i.e., patients who attempt suicide once are at high risk for completing suicide in the future).
- Conditions associated with suicide (e.g., depression, physical ailments) are usually chronic and recurring.

REFERRAL

Patients with active suicidal ideation and intent should be referred to specialty mental health.

SUGGESTED READINGS

Gaynes BN et al: U.S. Preventive Services Task Force. Screening for suicide risk in adults: a summary of the evidence for the U.S. Preventive Services Task Force, *Ann Intern Med* 140(10):822, 2004.

Gunnell D, Ashby D: Antidepressants and suicide: what is the balance of benefit and harm? *BMJ* 329(7456):34, 2004.

Mann JJ: A current perspective of suicide and attempted suicide, *Ann Intern Med* 136:302, 2002.

AUTHOR: **MITCHELL D. FELDMAN, M.D., M.Phil.**

Superior Vena Cava Syndrome

BASIC INFORMATION

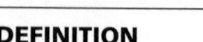

DEFINITION

Superior vena cava syndrome is a set of symptoms that results when a mediastinal mass compresses the superior vena cava (SVC) or the veins that drain into it.

ICD-9CM CODES
453.2 (vena cava thrombosis)

EPIDEMIOLOGY & DEMOGRAPHICS

Mirrors lung cancer (especially small cell carcinoma) and lymphoma: see "Lung Neoplasm" and "Lymphoma" in Section I

PHYSICAL FINDINGS & CLINICAL PRESENTATION

Symptoms:
- Shortness of breath
- Chest pain
- Cough
- Dysphagia
- Headache
- Syncope
- Visual trouble

Signs:
- Chest wall vein distention
- Neck vein distention
- Facial edema
- Upper extremity swelling
- Cyanosis

ETIOLOGY

- Lung cancer (80% of all cases, of which half are small cell lung cancer)
- Lymphoma (15%)
- Tuberculosis
- Goiter
- Aortic aneurysm (arteriosclerotic or syphilitic)
- SVC thrombosis
  1. Primary: associated with a central venous catheter
  2. Secondary: as a complication of SVC syndrome associated with one of the above mentioned causes

DIAGNOSIS

DIFFERENTIAL DIAGNOSIS

The syndrome is characteristic enough to exclude other diagnoses. The differential diagnosis concerns the underlying etiologies listed previously.

WORKUP

- Chest x-ray
- Venography
- Chest CT scan or MRI
- Ultrasonography
- Sputum cytology
- Bronchoscopy
- Mediastinoscopy
- Thoracotomy

TREATMENT

Although invasive procedures such as mediastinoscopy or thoracotomy are associated with higher than usual risk of bleeding, a tissue diagnosis is usually needed before commencing therapy.

Emergency empiric radiation is indicated in critical situations such as respiratory failure or central nervous system signs associated with increased intracranial pressure.

- Treatment of the underlying malignancy
  1. Radiation
  2. Chemotherapy
- Anticoagulant or fibrinolytic therapy in patients who do not respond to cancer treatment within a week or if an obstructing thrombus has been documented
- Diuretics
- Steroids

REFERRAL

To a thoracic surgeon, pulmonary specialist, and/or oncologist

SUGGESTED READING

Markman M: Diagnosis and management of superior vena cava syndrome, *Cleveland Clin J Med* 66:59, 1999.

AUTHOR: **TOM J. WACHTEL, M.D.**

BASIC INFORMATION

DEFINITION

Syncope is the temporary loss of consciousness resulting from an acute global reduction in cerebral blood flow.

ICD-9CM CODES
720.2 Syncope

EPIDEMIOLOGY & DEMOGRAPHICS

- Syncope accounts for 3% to 5% of emergency room visits.
- 30% of the adult population will experience at least one syncopal episode during their lifetime.
- Incidence of syncope is highest in elderly men and young women.

PHYSICAL FINDINGS & CLINICAL PRESENTATION

- Blood pressure: if low, consider orthostatic hypotension; if unequal in both arms (difference >20 mm Hg), consider subclavian steal or dissecting aneurysm. (NOTE: Blood pressure and heart rate should be recorded in the supine and standing positions.) If there is drop in BP but no change in HR, the patient may be on a beta blocker or may have an autonomic neuropathy.
- Pulse: if patient has tachycardia, bradycardia, or irregular rhythm, consider arrhythmia.
- Heart: if there are murmurs present suggestive of AS or IHSS, consider syncope secondary to left ventricular outflow obstruction; if there are JVD and distal heart sounds, consider cardiac tamponade.
- Carotid sinus pressure: can be diagnostic if it reproduces symptoms and other causes are excluded; a pause >3 sec or a systolic BP drop >50 mm Hg without symptoms or <30 mm Hg with symptoms when sinus pressure is applied separately on each side for <5 sec is considered abnormal. This test should be avoided in patients with carotid bruits or cerebrovascular disease; ECG monitoring, IV access, and bedside atropine should be available when carotid sinus pressure is applied.

ETIOLOGY

- Neurally mediated syncope
  1. Psychophysiologic (emotional upset, panic disorders, hysteria)
  2. Visceral reflex (micturition, defecation, food ingestion, coughing, ventricular contraction; glossopharyngeal neuralgia)
  3. Carotid sinus pressure
  4. Reduction of venous return caused by Valsalva maneuver
- Orthostatic hypotension
  1. Hypovolemia
  2. Vasodilator medications
  3. Autonomic neuropathy (diabetes, amyloid, Parkinson's disease, multisystem atrophy)
  4. Pheochromocytoma
  5. Carcinoid syndrome
- Cardiac
  1. Reduced cardiac output
     a. Left ventricular outflow obstruction (aortic stenosis, hypertrophic cardiomyopathy)
     b. Obstruction to pulmonary flow (pulmonary embolism, pulmonic stenosis, primary pulmonary hypertension)
     c. MI with pump failure
     d. Cardiac tamponade
     e. Mitral stenosis
     f. Reduction of venous return (atrial myxoma, valve thrombus)
     g. β-blockers
  2. Arrhythmias or asystole
     a. Extreme tachycardia (>160 to 180 bpm)
     b. Severe bradycardia (<30 to 40 bpm)
     c. Sick sinus syndrome
     d. AV block (second- or third-degree)
     e. Ventricular tachycardia or fibrillation
     f. Long QT syndrome
     g. Pacemaker malfunction
     h. Psychotropic medications and beta blockers
  3. Other causes
     a. Hypoxia
     b. Hypoglycemia
     c. Anemia
     d. Hyperventilation

DIAGNOSIS

DIFFERENTIAL DIAGNOSIS

1. Seizure (see "Workup")
2. Vertebrobasilar TIA usually manifests as diplopia, vertigo, ataxia but not loss of consciousness. Isolated syncopal episodes without accompanying neurologic symptoms are unlikely to be a TIA
3. Recreational drugs/alcohol
4. Psychologic stress

WORKUP

The history is crucial to diagnosing the cause of syncope and may suggest a diagnosis that can be evaluated with directed testing:

- Sudden loss of consciousness: consider cardiac arrhythmias.
- Gradual loss of consciousness: consider orthostatic hypotension, vasodepressor syncope, hypoglycemia.
- History of aura before loss of consciousness (LOC) or prolonged confusion (>1min), amnesia or lethargy after LOC suggests seizure rather than syncope.
- Patient's activity at the time of syncope:
  1. Micturition, coughing, defecation: consider syncope secondary to decreased venous return.
  2. Turning head or while shaving: consider carotid sinus syndrome.
  3. Physical exertion in a patient with murmur: consider aortic stenosis.
  4. Arm exercise: consider subclavian steal syndrome.
  5. Assuming an upright position: consider orthostatic hypotension.
- Associated events:
  1. Chest pain: consider MI, pulmonary embolism.
  2. Palpitations: consider arrhythmias.
  3. Incontinence (urine or fecal) and tongue biting are associated with seizure or syncope.
  4. Brief, transient shaking after LOC may represent myoclonus from global cerebral hypoperfusion and not seizures. However, sustained tonic/clonic muscle action is more suggestive of seizure.
  5. Focal neurologic symptoms or signs point to a neurologic event such as a seizure with residual deficits (e.g. Todd's paralysis) or cerebral ischemic injury.
  6. Psychologic stress: syncope may be vasovagal.
- Review current medications, particularly antihypertensive and psychotropic drugs.

LABORATORY TESTS

Routine blood tests rarely yield diagnostically useful information and should be done only if they are specifically suggested by the results of the history and physical examination. The following are commonly ordered tests.

- Pregnancy test should be considered in women of childbearing age
- CBC to rule out anemia, infection
- Electrolytes, BUN, creatinine, magnesium, calcium to rule out electrolyte abnormalities and evaluate fluid status
- Serum glucose level
- Cardiac isoenzymes should be obtained if the patient gives a history of chest pain before the syncopal episode
- ABGs to rule out pulmonary embolus, hyperventilation (when suspected)
- Evaluate drug and alcohol levels when suspecting toxicity

IMAGING STUDIES

- Echocardiogram is useful in patients with a heart murmur to rule out AS, IHSS, or atrial myxoma.
- If seizure is suspected, CT scan and/or MRI of the head and EEG may be useful.
- If head trauma or neurologic signs on examination, CT or MRI may be helpful.

- If pulmonary embolism is suspected, ventilation-perfusion scan should be done.
- If arrhythmias are suspected, a 24-hr Holter monitor and admission to a telemetry unit is appropriate. Generally, Holter monitoring is rarely useful, revealing a cause for syncope in <3% of cases. Loop recorders that can be activated after syncopal episode to retrieve information about the cardiac rhythm during the preceding 4 min add considerable diagnostic yield in patients with unexplained syncope.
- Implantable cardiac monitors that function as permanent loop recorders or implantable cardioverter-defibrillators, which are placed subcutaneously in the pectoral region with the patient under local anesthesia, are useful in patients with cardiac syncope.
- Electrophysiologic studies may be indicated in patients with structural heart disease and/or recurrent syncope.
- ECG to rule out arrhythmias; may be diagnostic in 5% to 10% of patients.

TILT-TABLE TESTING

- Useful to support a diagnosis of neurally mediated syncope. Patients older than age 50 should have stress testing before tilt-table testing. Positive results would preclude tilt-table testing.
- Indicated in patients with recurrent episodes of unexplained syncope as well as for patients in high-risk occupations (e.g., pilots, bus drivers) (Fig. 1-229). The test is also useful for identifying patients with prominent bradycardic response who may benefit from implantation of a permanent pacemaker.
- It is performed by keeping the patient in an upright posture on a tilt table with footboard support. The angle of the tilt table varies from 60 to 80 degrees. The duration of upright posture during tilt-table testing varies from 25 to 45 min.
- The hallmark of neurally mediated syncope is severe hypotension associated with a paradoxical bradycardia triggered by a specific stimulus. The diagnosis of neurally mediated syncope is likely if upright tilt testing reproduces these hemodynamic changes in <15 min and causes presyncope or syncope.

PSYCHIATRIC EVALUATION

- May be indicated in young patients without heart disease who have frequently recurring syncope and other somatic symptoms.
- Generalized anxiety disorder, pain disorder, and major depression predispose patients to neurally mediated reactions and may result in syncope.
- Alcohol and drug dependence can also lead to syncope.

TREATMENT

NONPHARMACOLOGIC THERAPY

- Ensure proper hydration; consider TED stockings and salt tablets.
- Eliminate medications that may induce hypotension.

ACUTE GENERAL Rx

- Varies with the underlying etiology of syncope (e.g., pacemaker in patients with syncope secondary to complete heart block)
- Syncope caused by orthostatic hypotension is treated with volume replacement in patients with intravascular volume depletion. Also consider midodrine to promote venous return via adrenergic-mediated vasoconstriction and Florinef for its mineralocorticoid effects to increase intravascular volume

DISPOSITION

Prognosis varies with the age of the patient and the etiology of the syncope. Generally:

- Benign prognosis (very low 1-yr morbidity) in patients:
  1. Age <30 yr and having noncardiac syncope
  2. Age <70 yr and having vasovagal/psychogenic syncope or syncope of unknown cause
- Poor prognosis (high mortality and morbidity) in patients with cardiac syncope
- Patients with the following risk factors have a higher 1-yr mortality: abnormal ECG, history of ventricular arrhythmia, history of CHF

REFERRAL

Hospital admission in elderly patients without prior history of syncope or unknown etiology of their syncope and in any patients suspected of having cardiac syncope.

PEARLS & CONSIDERATIONS

COMMENTS

- Section III, Syncope, describes an algorithmic approach to the patient.
- The etiology of syncope is identified in <50% of cases during the initial evaluation.
- A thorough history and physical examination are the most productive means of establishing a diagnosis in patients with syncope.

SUGGESTED READINGS

Fenton AM et al: Vasovagal syncope, *Ann Intern Med* 133:722, 2000.

Kapoor WN: Syncope, *N Engl J Med* 343:1856, 2000.

Menozzi C et al: Mechanism of syncope in patients with heart disease and negative electrophysiologic test, *Circulation* 105:2741, 2002.

Soteriades ES et al: Incidence and prognosis of syncope, *N Engl J Med* 347:878, 2002.

AUTHOR: **SEAN I. SAVITZ, M.D.**

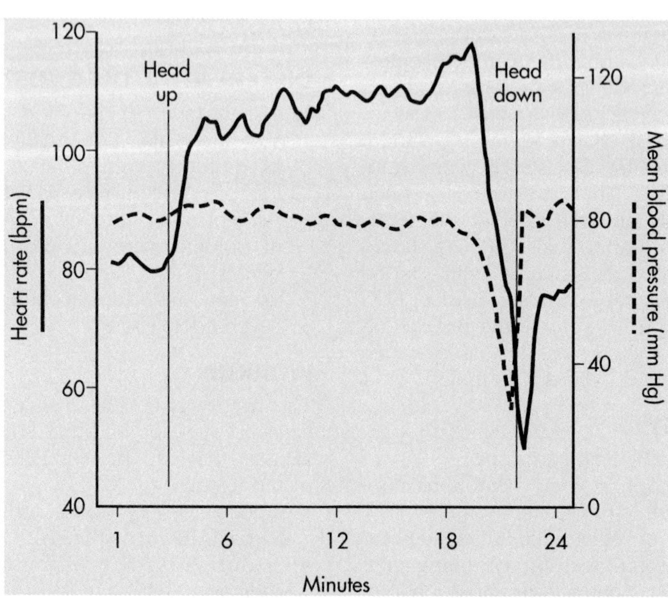

FIGURE 1-229 Head-up tilt test performed on an 18-year-old woman with a history of syncope associated with pain, preceded by a prodrome of dizziness, graying vision, and diaphoresis. A similar prodrome preceded syncope during the test. Note the precipitous, nearly simultaneous, decline of heart rate and blood pressure after an initial rise in heart rate. Vital signs returned to normal rapidly after the head was lowered. (Courtesy Robert F. Sprung, University of Utah. In Goldman L, Ausiello D [eds]: *Cecil textbook of medicine*, ed 22, Philadelphia, 2004, WB Saunders.)

BASIC INFORMATION

DEFINITION

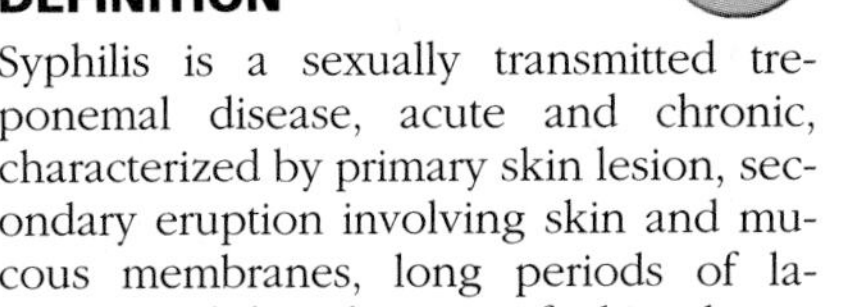

Syphilis is a sexually transmitted treponemal disease, acute and chronic, characterized by primary skin lesion, secondary eruption involving skin and mucous membranes, long periods of latency, and late lesions of skin, bone, viscera, CNS, and cardiovascular system.

SYNONYMS

Lues

ICD-9CM CODES
097.9 Syphilis, acquired unspecified

EPIDEMIOLOGY & DEMOGRAPHICS

- Widespread, primarily involving ages 20-35 yr. Racial differences in incidence are related to social factors. Usually more prevalent in urban areas. Estimated annual incidence of 90,000 cases in the U.S. Increase in incidence in the late 1980s to 1990s, likely related to illicit drug use and prostitution. Increase occurred primarily in lower socioeconomic groups.
- Communicability is indefinite and variable. Communicable during primary, secondary, and latent mucocutaneous lesions in up to first 4 yr of latency. Most probable congenital transmission occurs in early maternal syphilis. Adequate penicillin treatment ends infectivity within 24-48 hr.

PHYSICAL FINDINGS & CLINICAL PRESENTATION

PRIMARY SYPHILIS: Characteristic lesion is a painless chancre on genitalia, mouth, or anus; atypical primary lesions may occur. Usually appears 3 wk after exposure and may spontaneously involute.

SECONDARY SYPHILIS:
- Localized or diffuse mucocutaneous lesions and generalized lymphadenopathy. Common to have constitutional symptoms, flulike symptoms. May begin about 4 to 6 wk after appearance of primary lesion. Manifestations may resolve in 1 wk to 12 mo.
- 60%-80% of patients have maculopapular lesions on their palms and soles.
- Condylomata lata intertriginous papules form at areas of friction and moisture, such as the vulva.
- 21%-58% have mucocutaneous or mucosal lesions (pharyngitis, tonsillitis, "mucous patch" lesion on oral and genital mucosa).

EARLY LATENT (<1 YR): Generally asymptomatic

LATE LATENT (>1 YR):
- Characterized by gummas (nodular, ulcerative lesions) that can involve the skin, mucous membranes, skeletal system, and viscera.
- Manifestations of cardiovascular syphilis include aortitis, aneurysm, or aortic regurgitation.
- Neurosyphilis may be asymptomatic or symptomatic. Tabes dorsalis, meningovascular syphilis, general paralysis, or insanity may occur. Iritis, choroidoretinitis, and leukoplakia may also occur.

ETIOLOGY

- *Treponema pallidum,* a spirochete
- Spread by sexual intercourse or by intrauterine transfer

DIAGNOSIS

DIFFERENTIAL DIAGNOSIS

- Other genitoulcerative diseases such as herpes, chancroid (see Section II)
- See Section III for a clinical algorithm for the evaluation of genital ulcer disease

WORKUP

Confirmation is primarily through laboratory diagnosis.

LABORATORY TESTS

- Dark-field microscopy of fluid from lesion to look for treponeme
- Serologic testing, both nontreponemal (VDRL, RPR) and treponemal (FTA, MHA)
- Lumbar puncture for CSF VDRL in patients with evidence of latent syphilis

TREATMENT

ACUTE GENERAL Rx

- Early (primary, secondary, early latent): penicillin G benzathine 2.4 million U IM × 1 or doxycycline 100 mg PO bid × 14 days
- Late (late latent, cardiovascular, gumma): penicillin G benzathine 2.4 million U IM qwk × 3 wk or doxycycline 100 mg PO bid × 4 wk
- Neurosyphilis: aqueous crystalline penicillin G 18-24 million U/day, administered as 3-4 million U IV q4h × 10-14 days or procaine penicillin 2.4 million U IM/day plus probenecid 500 mg PO qid, both for 10-14 days
- Congenital syphilis: aqueous crystalline penicillin G 50,000 U/kg/dose IV q12h × first 7 days of life and q8h after that for total of 10 days or procaine penicillin G 50,000 U/kg/dose IM/day × 10 days
- Penicillin-allergic patients with primary or secondary syphilis: doxycycline 100 mg PO bid × 14 days, or tetracycline 500 mg PO qid × 14 days, or ceftriaxone 1 g IM or IV × 8 to 10 days, or azithromycin 2 g PO stat (preliminary data only)
- Latent syphilis in penicillin-allergic patient: doxycycline 100 mg PO bid or tetracycline 500 mg qid for 28 days
- Tetracyclines are contraindicated in pregnancy. If pregnant and penicillin allergic, must be desensitized

DISPOSITION

- Repeat quantitative nontreponemal tests at 3, 6, and 12 mo. Pregnancy requires monthly tests until delivery.
- If a fourfold increase in titer occurs, if initial high titer fails to drop by fourfold within a year, or persistent signs, retreatment may be indicated. Use treatment regimen for late syphilis.
- Pregnant women without a fourfold drop in titer in a 3-mo period need to be retreated.
- Cases should be reported to local or state health department for referral, follow-up, and partner notification.

REFERRAL

- Pregnant and possible congenital syphilis
- Pregnant and allergic to penicillin, with need to be desensitized
- Late latent syphilis with serious CNS, cardiovascular, or other organ system compromise

PEARLS & CONSIDERATIONS

COMMENTS

- Jarisch-Herxheimer reaction (fever, myalgia, tachycardia, hypotension) may occur within 24 hr of treatment.
- One third of untreated patients develop CNS and/or cardiovascular sequelae.
- Up to 80% of those treated during late stages remain seropositive indefinitely.
- Treponemal tests remain positive even after adequate therapy.

SUGGESTED READINGS

Centers for Disease Control and Prevention: Primary and secondary syphilis—United States, 1999, *MMWR Morb Mortal Wkly Rep* 50(7):113, 2001.

Centers for Disease Control and Prevention: 2002 sexually transmitted diseases treatment guidelines, *MMWR Morb Mortal Wkly Rep* 51(RR-6), 2002.

Golden MR, Marra CM, Holmes KK: Update on syphilis: resurgence of an old problem, *JAMA* 290(11):1510, 2003.

AUTHOR: **MARIA A. CORIGLIANO, M.D.**

BASIC INFORMATION

DEFINITION

Syringomyelia is a disease of the spine characterized by the formation of fluid-filled cavities within the spinal cord, sometimes extending into the brainstem.

ICD-9CM CODES
336.0 Syringomyelia

EPIDEMIOLOGY & CLINICAL PRESENTATION

- Often a history of birth injury exists.
- Onset is usually insidious, with symptoms often not beginning until the third or fourth decade.
- Cervical spine is the most commonly affected area.
  1. Intrinsic hand atrophy, weakness, and anesthetic sensory loss may develop.
  2. The latter may lead to unnoticed burns or other injuries in the hand.
  3. Loss of pain and temperature sensation may occur, but tactile sense in the upper extremity is preserved.
  4. Sharp testing elicits no pain, but patient often perceives the sharpness of the object.
  5. A Charcot joint in the shoulder or elbow may develop.
- Reflexes are absent in the upper extremity.
- Spasticity and hyperreflexia are present in the lower extremity.
- Scoliosis is common.
- Nystagmus and Horner's syndrome may also occur.
- Trophic skin changes eventually develop in many cases.

ETIOLOGY

- Cause is unknown, but condition is thought to result from obstruction of the outlet of the fourth ventricle, often associated with a Chiari I malformation, which causes fluid to be diverted down the central cord.
- Syringes later in life may be the result of trauma or an intramedullary tumor.

DIAGNOSIS

DIFFERENTIAL DIAGNOSIS

- ALS
- MS
- Spinal cord tumor
- Tabes dorsalis
- Progressive spinal muscular atrophy

IMAGING STUDIES

- Plain radiographs usually reveal widening of the bony canal in the region of involvement.
- Bony anomalies are often present at the base of the skull and at the C1-C2 spinal segments.
- Myelography, MRI (Fig. 1-230), and other imaging studies are recommended.

TREATMENT

Drainage and operative repair of any bony anomalies are undertaken, often with decompression laminectomy of C1 and C2.

DISPOSITION

- Condition is slowly progressive in most cases, but course may be quite variable, ranging from death in a few months to slow incapacitation over several years: progression may halt at any time.
- Surgical intervention often stops progression but frequently does not lead to improvement in neurologic findings.

REFERRAL

For neurosurgical consultation when diagnosis is suspected

SUGGESTED READINGS

Kimura R et al: Syringomyelia caused be cervical spondylosis, *Acta Neurochir* 146:175, 2004.

Klekamp J: The pathophysiology of syringomyelia: historical overview and current concepts, *Acta Neurochir* 144(7):649, 2002.

Riente L, Frigelli S, Delle SA: Neuropathic shoulder arthropathy associated with syringomyelia and Arnold-Chiari malformation (type I), *J Rheumatol* 29(3):638, 2002.

Silber JS, Vaccaro AR, Green B: Summary statement: chronic long-term sequelae after spinal cord injury: post-traumatic spinal deformity and post-traumatic myelopathy associated with syringomyelia, *Spine* 26(24 Suppl):S128, 2001.

Vannemreddy SS, Rowed DW, Bharatwal N: Posttraumatic syringomyelia: predisposing factors, *Br J Neurosurg* 16(3):276, 2002.

AUTHOR: **LONNIE R. MERCIER, M.D.**

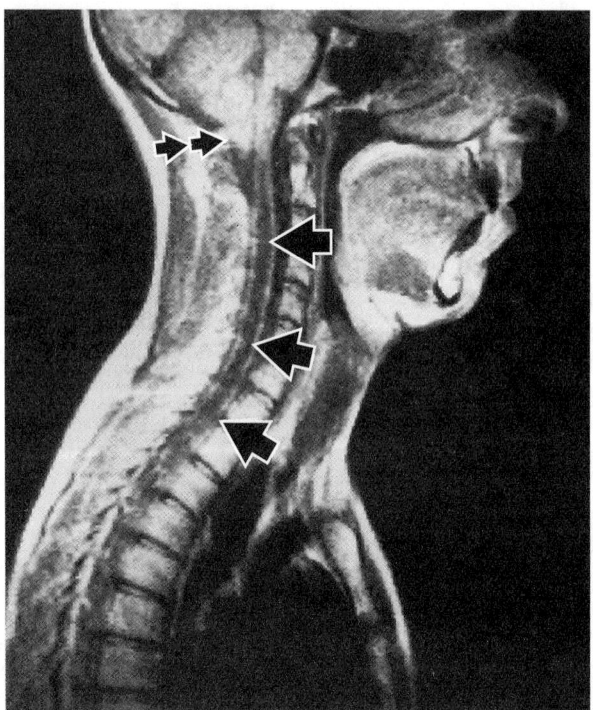

FIGURE 1-230 Midsagittal magnetic resonance image of Arnold-Chiari malformation *(small black arrows)* and syringomyelia *(three large black arrows)* in a 31-year-old man. Note the cerebellar tonsils extending below the posterior rim of the foramen magnum *(dark structure immediately above the black arrow)*. The syrinx extends from the medulla well into the thoracic cord. (From Andreoli TE [ed]: *Cecil essentials of medicine,* ed 4, Philadelphia, 1997, WB Saunders.)

BASIC INFORMATION

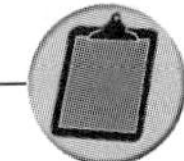

DEFINITION

Systemic lupus erythematosus (SLE) is a chronic multisystemic disease characterized by production of autoantibodies and protean clinical manifestations.

SYNONYMS

SLE

ICD-9CM CODES
710.0 Systemic lupus erythematosus

EPIDEMIOLOGY & DEMOGRAPHICS

PREVALENCE: 20 cases/100,000 persons
PREDOMINANT SEX: Female:male ratio of 7:1
PREDOMINANT AGE: 20-45 yr (childbearing years)

PHYSICAL FINDINGS & CLINICAL PRESENTATION

- Skin: erythematous rash over the malar eminences (Fig. 1-231), generally with sparing of the nasolabial folds (butterfly rash); alopecia; raised erythematous patches with subsequent edematous plaques and adherent scales (discoid lupus); leg, nasal, or oropharyngeal ulcerations; livedo reticularis; pallor (from anemia); petechiae (from thrombocytopenia)
- Joints: tenderness, swelling, or effusion, generally involving peripheral joints
- Cardiac: pericardial rub (in patients with pericarditis), heart murmurs (if endocarditis or valvular thickening or dysfunction)
- Other: fever, conjunctivitis, dry eyes, dry mouth (sicca syndrome), oral ulcers, abdominal tenderness, decreased breath sounds (pleural effusions)

ETIOLOGY

Unknown. Autoantibodies are typically present many years before the diagnosis of SLE.

DIAGNOSIS

DIFFERENTIAL DIAGNOSIS

- Other connective tissue disorders (e.g., RA, MCTD, progressive systemic sclerosis)
- Metastatic neoplasm
- Infection

WORKUP

The diagnosis of SLE can be made by demonstrating the presence of any four or more of the following criteria of the American Rheumatism Association:

1. Butterfly rash
2. Discoid rash
3. Photosensitivity (particularly leg ulcerations)
4. Oral ulcers
5. Arthritis
6. Serositis (pleuritis, pericarditis)
7. Renal disorder (persistent proteinuria >0.5 g/day or 3+ if quantitation not performed, cellular casts)
8. Neurologic disorder (seizures, psychosis [in absence of offending drugs or metabolic derangement])
9. Hematologic disorder:
   a. Hemolytic anemia with reticulocytosis
   b. Leukopenia (<4000/mm^3 total on two or more occasions)
   c. Lymphopenia (<1500/mm^3 on two or more occasions)
   d. Thrombocytopenia (<100,000/mm^3 in the absence of offending drugs)
10. Immunologic disorder:
    a. Positive SLE cell preparation
    b. Anti-DNA (presence of antibody to native DNA in abnormal titer)
    c. Anti-Sm (presence of antibody to Smith nuclear antigen)
    d. False-positive STS known to be positive for at least 6 mo and confirmed by negative TPI or FTA tests
11. ANA: an abnormal titer of ANA by immunofluorescence or equivalent assay at any time in the absence of drugs known to be associated with "drug-induced lupus" syndrome

LABORATORY TESTS

Suggested initial laboratory evaluation of suspected SLE:

- Immunologic evaluation: ANA, anti-DNA antibody, anti-Sm antibody
- Other laboratory tests: CBC with differential, platelet count (Coombs' test if anemia detected), urinalysis (24-hr urine collection for protein if proteinuria is detected), PTT and anticardiolipin antibodies in patients with thrombotic events, BUN, creatinine to evaluate renal function

IMAGING STUDIES

- Chest x-ray for evaluation of pulmonary involvement (e.g., pleural effusions, pulmonary infiltrates)
- Echocardiogram to screen for significant valvular heart disease (present in 18% of patients with SLE); echocardiography can identify a subset of lesions (valvular thickening and dysfunction) other than verrucous (Libman-Sacks) endocarditis that are prone to hemodynamic deterioration

TREATMENT

NONPHARMACOLOGIC THERAPY

Patients with photosensitivity should avoid sunlight and use high-factor sunscreen.

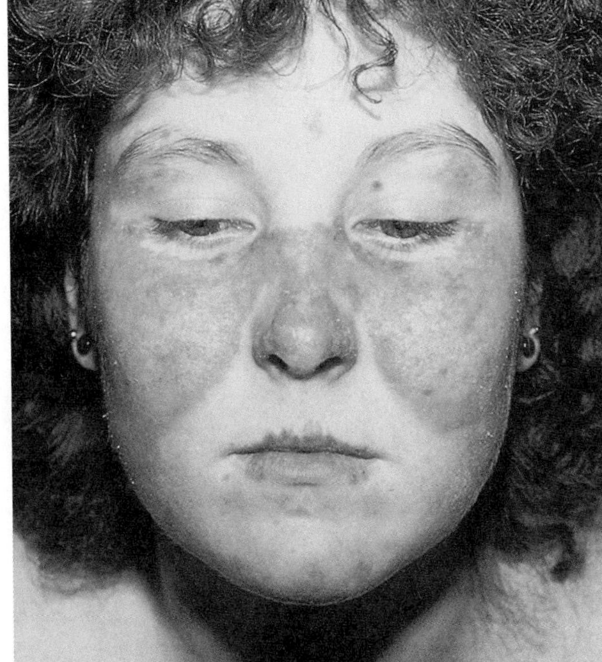

FIGURE 1-231 Acute cutaneous LE (systemic LE). The classic butterfly rash occurs in 10% to 50% of patients with acute LE. (From Habif TP: *Clinical dermatology: a color guide to diagnosis and therapy,* ed 3, St Louis, 1996, Mosby.)

GENERAL Rx

- Joint pain and mild serositis are generally well controlled with NSAIDs; antimalarials are also effective (e.g., hydroxychloroquine [Plaquenil]).
- Cutaneous manifestations are treated with the following:
  1. Topical corticosteroids; intradermal corticosteroids are helpful for individual discoid lesions, especially in the scalp
  2. Antimalarials (e.g., hydroxychloroquine [Plaquenil] and quinacrine)
  3. Sunscreens that block ultraviolet (UV) A and UVB radiation
  4. Immunosuppressive drugs (methotrexate or azathioprine) are used as steroid-sparing drugs
- Renal disease
  1. The use of high-pulsed doses of cyclophosphamide given at monthly intervals is more effective in preserving renal function than is treatment with glucocorticoids alone. The combination of methylprednisolone and cyclophosphamide is superior to bolus therapy with methylprednisolone or cyclophosphamide alone in patients with lupus nephritis. For patients with proliferative lupus nephritis, short-term therapy with IV cyclophosphamide followed by maintenance therapy with mycophenolate mofetil or azathioprine appears to be more efficacious and safer than long-term therapy with IV cyclophosphamide.
  2. The use of plasmapheresis in combination with immunosuppressive agents (to prevent the rebound phenomenon of antibody levels after plasmapheresis) is generally reserved for rapidly progressive renal failure or life-threatening systemic vasculitis.
- CNS involvement: treatment generally consists of corticosteroid therapy; however, its efficacy is uncertain, and it is generally reserved for organic brain syndrome. Anticonvulsants and antipsychotics are also indicated in selected cases; headaches are treated symptomatically.
- Hemolytic anemia: treatment of Coombs'-positive hemolytic anemia consists of high doses of corticosteroids; nonhemolytic anemia (secondary to chronic disease) does not require specific therapy.
- Thrombocytopenia
  1. Initial treatment consists of corticosteroids.
  2. In patients with poor response to steroids, encouraging results have been reported with the use of danazol, vincristine, and immunoglobulins. Combination chemotherapy with cyclophosphamide and prednisone combined with vincristine, vincristine and procarbazine, or etoposide may be useful in patients with severe refractory idiopathic thrombocytopenic purpura.
  3. Splenectomy generally does not cure the thrombocytopenia of SLE, but it may be necessary as an adjunct in managing selected cases.
- Infections are common because of compromised immune function secondary to SLE and the use of corticosteroid, cytotoxic, and antimetabolite drugs; pneumococcal bacteremia is associated with high mortality rate.
- Close monitoring for exacerbation of the disease and for potential side effects from medications (corticosteroids, cytotoxic agents) with frequent laboratory evaluation and office visits is necessary in all patients with SLE.
- Valvular heart disease is present in 18% of patients with SLE. The prevalence of infective endocarditis is approximately 1% (similar to the prevalence after prosthetic valve surgery, but greater than that following rheumatic valvulitis). Valvular heart disease in patients with SLE frequently changes over time (e.g., vegetations can appear unexpectedly for the first time, resolve, or change in size or appearance). These frequent changes are temporarily unrelated to other clinical features of SLE and can be associated with substantial morbidity and mortality.

DISPOSITION

- Most patients with lupus experience remissions and exacerbations.
- The leading cause of death in SLE is infection (one third of all deaths); active nephritis causes approximately 18% of deaths, and CNS disease causes 7% of deaths; the survival rate is 75% over the first 10 yr. Blacks and Hispanics generally have a worse prognosis.
- Symptomatic pericarditis occurs in one fourth of patients with SLE at some point during the course of the disease. Asymptomatic involvement is estimated to be more than 60% based on autopsy reports.
- Renal histologic studies and evaluation of renal function are useful in determining disease activity and predicting disease outcome (e.g., serum creatinine levels >3 mg/dl or evidence of diffuse proliferative involvement on renal biopsy are poor prognostic factors).
- Atherosclerosis occurs prematurely in patients with SLE and is independent of traditional risk factors for cardiovascular disease.

REFERRAL

- Rheumatology consultation in all patients with SLE
- Hematology consultation in patients with significant hematologic abnormalities (e.g., severe hemolytic anemia or thrombocytopenia)
- Nephrology consultation in patients with significant renal involvement

SUGGESTED READINGS

Arbuckle MR et al: Development of autoantibodies before the clinical onset of systemic lupus erythematosus, *N Engl J Med* 349:1526, 2003.

Contreras G et al: Sequential therapies for proliferative lupus nephritis, *N Engl J Med* 350:971, 2004.

Gill JM et al: Diagnosis of systemic lupus erythematosus, *Am Fam Phys* 68:2179, 2003.

Illei GG et al: Combination therapy with pulse cyclophosphamide plus methylprednisolone improves long-term renal outcome without adding toxicity in patients with lupus nephritis, *Ann Intern Med* 135:248, 2001.

Roman MJ et al: Prevalence and correlates of accelerated atherosclerosis in SLE, *N Engl J Med* 349:2399, 2003.

AUTHOR: **FRED F. FERRI, M.D.**

BASIC INFORMATION

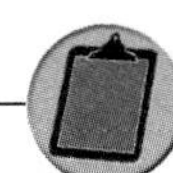

DEFINITION

Tabes dorsalis is a form of tertiary neurosyphilis affecting the dorsal columns of the spinal cord and peripheral nerves, characterized by paroxysmal pain, particularly in the abdomen and legs; sensory ataxia; normal strength; autonomic dysfunction, and Argyll-Robertson pupils.

SYNONYMS

Posterior spinal sclerosis
Tabetic neurosyphilis
Syphilitic myeloneuropathy

ICD-9CM CODES
094.0 Tabes dorsalis, ataxia, locomotor

EPIDEMIOLOGY & DEMOGRAPHICS

INCIDENCE (IN U.S.): Rare, but increasing with HIV/AIDS
PREVALENCE (IN U.S.): Rare; more common with HIV/AIDS epidemic. 10% of untreated cases of syphilis develop neurosyphilis, of which 2%-5% may develop tabes dorsalis. Relative prevalence of tabes dorsalis is reduced in comparison to the preantibiotic era.
PREDOMINANT SEX: Male
PEAK INCIDENCE: 15-20 yr after initial infection

PHYSICAL FINDINGS & CLINICAL PRESENTATION

- Argyll-Robertson pupil in 50% (pupil reacts poorly to light but well to accommodation)
- Loss of position and vibration at ankles (wide-based gait; inability to walk in the dark: sensory ataxia)
- Loss of deep pain sensation, resulting in deep foot ulcers
- Degenerative joint disease, especially in knees caused by severe neuropathy (Charcot joints)
- Normal strength with areflexia in the legs
- Lightning pains in the legs
- Severe intermittent visceral pains, such as gastrointestinal, laryngeal (visceral crises)
- Autonomic dysfunction (urinary and fecal incontinence)

ETIOLOGY

Infectious *(Treponema pallidum)*

DIAGNOSIS

DIFFERENTIAL DIAGNOSIS

- Vitamin B_{12} deficiency (subacute combined degeneration of the spinal cord)
- Vitamin E deficiency
- Chronic nitrous oxide abuse
- Spinal cord neoplasm (involving conus medullaris)
- Lyme disease

WORKUP

Thorough neurologic history and examination

LABORATORY TESTS

- Lumbar puncture for elevated VDRL and FTA-ABS titers. False-positive CSF VDRL titers may occur with traumatic tap. CSF mononuclear pleocytosis (>5 white cells/microL) with increased protein support the diagnosis.
- Serum venereal disease research laboratory test (VDRL). This may be normal in 25%-30% of patients. Serum microhemagglutination-Treponema Pallidum (MHA-TP) or Fluorescent Treponemal Antigen-Antibody test (FTA-ABS) is necessary if clinical suspicion high.
- False-positive serum VDRL may occur in Lyme disease, nonvenereal treponematoses, genital herpes simplex, pregnancy, SLE, alcoholic cirrhosis, scleroderma, and mixed connective tissue disease.

IMAGING STUDIES

Not necessary if diagnosis confirmed

TREATMENT

ACUTE GENERAL Rx

Procaine penicillin 2-4 million U IM qd, along with probenecid 500 mg PO qid, for 14 days, or aqueous penicillin G 3-4 million U IV q4h for 10-14 days.
If penicillin allergic, doxycycline 200 mg PO bid for 4 wk.
Many of the symptoms—degenerative neuropathic joint disease, lightning pains—persist after treatment.

CHRONIC Rx

- Physical therapy
- Analgesics, carbamazepine, gabapentin, or steroids may help "lightning" pain
- Supportive care (wheelchair, toileting issues, etc.)

DISPOSITION

Close follow-up required. Repeat lumbar puncture every 6 mo until CSF pleocytosis normalizes. If pleocytosis does not normalize in 6 mo or CSF is still abnormal in 2 yr, repeat treatment.
Further indication for retreatment: if there is a fourfold increase in titers or a failure of titers >1:32 to decrease at least fourfold by 12-24 mo.

REFERRAL

Joint replacement in moderate cases

SUGGESTED READINGS

Centers for Disease Control and Prevention: 2002 sexually transmitted diseases treatment guidelines, *MMWR Morb Mortal Wkly Rep* 51(RR-6), 2002.
Conde-Sendin MA et al: Current clinical spectrum of neurosyphilis in immunocompetent patients, *Eur Neurol* 52:29, 2004.
Solbrig MV, Healy JF, Jay CA: Infections of the nervous system. In Bradley WG, Daroff RB, Fenichel GM, Marsden CD: *Neurology in clinical practice. The neurological disorders. Vol II,* Boston, 2000, Butterworth-Heinemann.

AUTHOR: **EROBOGHENE E. UBOGU, M.D.**

BASIC INFORMATION

DEFINITION

Takayasu's arteritis refers to a chronic systemic granulomatous vasculitis primarily affecting large arteries (aorta and its branches).

SYNONYMS

Pulseless disease
Aortitis syndrome
Aortic arch arteritis

ICD-9CM CODES
446.7 Takayasu disease or syndrome

EPIDEMIOLOGY & DEMOGRAPHICS

- Most cases have been reported from Japan, China, India, and Mexico
- Exact incidence and prevalence is not known
- Incidence in the U.S. 2.6/1 million
- Females > males 9:1
- Seen predominantly in patients <30 yr old

PHYSICAL FINDINGS & CLINICAL PRESENTATION

Takayasu's arteritis most frequently involves the aortic arch and its branches and can manifest as:

- Arm claudication, weakness, and numbness
- Amaurosis fugax, diplopia, headache, and postural dizziness
- Systemic symptoms
  1. Low-grade fever
  2. Malaise
  3. Weight loss
  4. Fatigue
  5. Arthralgia and myalgia
- Vascular bruits of the carotid artery, subclavian artery, and aorta
- Discrepancy of blood pressures between the upper extremities
- Absent pulses
- Hypertension
- Retinopathy
- Aortic insufficiency murmur

ETIOLOGY

- The cause of Takayasu's arteritis is unknown. A delayed hypersensitivity to mycobacteria and spirochetes is a theory but remains to be substantiated.
- Infiltration of inflammatory cells into the vasa vasorum and media of large elastic arteries leads to thickening and narrowing or obliteration.

DIAGNOSIS

Criteria have been established for the diagnosis of Takayasu's arteritis by the American College of Rheumatology in 1990 and include:

- Age of disease <40 yr
- Claudication of extremities
- Decreased brachial artery pulse
- BP difference >10 mm Hg
- Bruit over subclavian arteries or aorta
- Abnormal arteriogram
- Takayasu's arteritis is diagnosed if at least three of the six criteria are present, giving a sensitivity of 90% and a specificity of 98%

DIFFERENTIAL DIAGNOSIS

Other causes of inflammatory aortitis must be excluded: giant cell arteritis, syphilis, tuberculosis, SLE, rheumatoid arthritis, Buerger's disease, Behçet's disease, Cogan's syndrome, Kawasaki disease, and spondyloarthropathies.

WORKUP

Any young patient with findings of absence pulses and loud bruits merits a workup for Takayasu's arteritis. The workup generally includes blood testing to look for signs of inflammation and imaging studies with the angiogram being the diagnostic gold standard.

LABORATORY TESTS

- CBC may reveal an elevated WBC count
- ESR is elevated in active disease

IMAGING STUDIES

- Ultrasound: Carotid, thoracic, and abdominal ultrasound are useful adjunctive imaging studies in diagnosing occlusive disease resulting from Takayasu's arteritis (Fig. 1-232).
- Doppler and noninvasive upper and lower extremity studies are helpful in assessing blood flow and absent pulses.
- CT scan is used to assess the thickness of the aorta.
- Angiogram can show narrowing of the aorta and/or branches of the aorta, aneurysm formation, and poststenotic dilation. Angiographic findings are classified as four types:
  1. Type I: Lesions involve only the aortic arch and its branches.
  2. Type II: Lesions only involving the abdominal aorta and its branches.
  3. Type III: Lesions involving the aorta above and below the diaphragm.
  4. Type IV: Lesions involving the pulmonary artery.

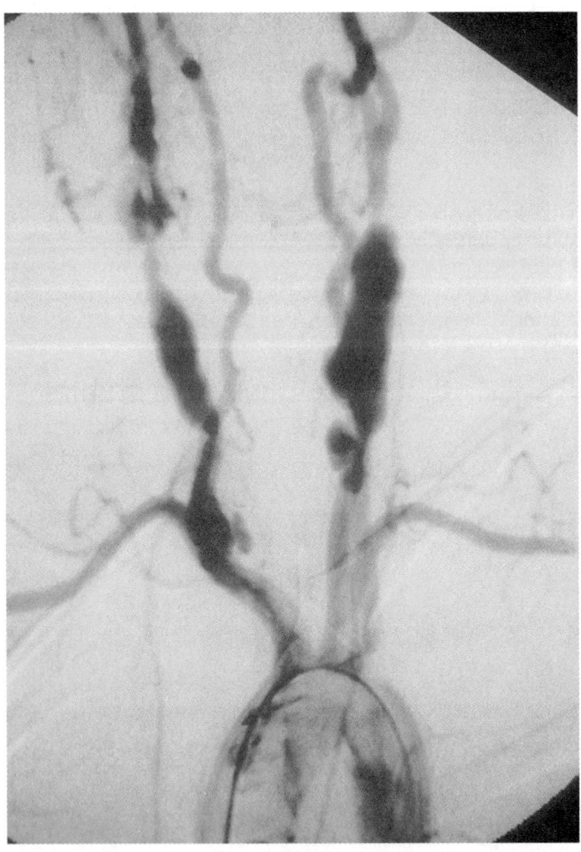

FIGURE 1-232 Angiogram of a child with Takayasu's arteritis showing massive bilateral carotid dilation, stenosis, and poststenotic dilation. (From Behrman RE: *Nelson textbook of pediatrics,* ed 16, Philadelphia, 2000, WB Saunders.)

TREATMENT

ACUTE GENERAL Rx

- Corticosteroids are the treatment of choice. Prednisone 40-60 mg PO qd or 1 mg/kg/day is used for 3 mo.
- Patients are monitored for symptoms and by following the ESR. If symptoms have resolved and the ESR is normal, attempts to taper prednisone are made.

CHRONIC Rx

- Patients who cannot be tapered off the corticosteroids or who have relapse of the disease are given methotrexate 0.15-0.35 mg/kg or approximately 15 mg/wk.
- Cyclophosphamide 1 to 2 mg/kg/day can be given with glucocorticoids as adjunctive therapy in relapse or treatment-resistant patients.

DISPOSITION

- Treatment improves symptoms within days with relief of ischemic claudication, return of pulses on examination, and reversal of lumen narrowing on angiograms. However, some patients may continue to have progression of arterial lesions despite therapy.
- With the addition of a second agent in patients with treatment resistance or relapse, 50% remission has been seen.
- Mortality results are mixed, showing high rates in reports from Asia and lower rates in studies done in the U.S. (2%).
- Death can occur suddenly from ruptured aneurysm, myocardial infarction, and stroke.

REFERRAL

Whenever the diagnosis of vasculitis is suspected, a rheumatology consult is appropriate. Vascular surgery and cardiology consultations are recommended for any evidence of carotid, peripheral, and coronary artery disease or if a large abdominal aneurysm is found.

PEARLS & CONSIDERATIONS

COMMENTS

The long-term prognosis of treated patients with Takayasu's disease is good, with >90% of patients surviving more than 15 yr.

SUGGESTED READINGS

Arend WP et al: American College of Rheumatology 1990 criteria for the classification of Takayasu's arteritis, *Arthr Rheum* 33:1129, 1990.

Fraga A, Medina F: Takayasu's arteritis, *Curr Rheumatol Rep* 4(1):30, 2002.

Giordano JM: Surgical treatment of Takayasu's disease, *Clev Clin J Med* 69(Suppl 2):S11, 2002.

Kerr GS et al: Takayasu arteritis, *Ann Intern Med* 120:919, 1994.

Weyend CM, Goronzy JJ: Mechanisms of disease: medium and large vessel vasculitis, *N Engl J Med* 349:160, 2003.

AUTHOR: **MEL ANDERSON, M.D.**

Tapeworm Infestation (PTG)

BASIC INFORMATION

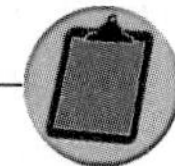

DEFINITION

Four species of adult tapeworm may infect humans as the definitive host: *Taenia saginata* (beef tapeworm), *Taenia solium* (pork tapeworm), *Diphyllobothrium latum* (fish tapeworm), and *Hymenolepis nana*. In addition, *T. solium* may infect humans in its larval form (cysticercosis), and several animal tapeworms (see "Echinococcosis" in Section I) may cause infection in an analogous manner.

SYNONYMS

Cysticercosis (larval infection by *T. solium*)

ICD-9CM CODES
123.9 Tapeworm infestation

EPIDEMIOLOGY & DEMOGRAPHICS

INCIDENCE (IN U.S.):
- Diagnosed primarily in immigrants
- Varies widely by country of origin and dietary practices

PREVALENCE (IN U.S.):
- *T. saginata:* <0.1%
- *D. latum:* <0.05%
- *T. solium:* <0.1%
- *H. nana:* sporadic, often in setting of outbreak

PREDOMINANT SEX: Equal sex distribution

PREDOMINANT AGE:
- *T. saginata, T. solium, D. latum:* 20 to 39 yr of age
- *H. nana* in setting of institution outbreaks: children

PHYSICAL FINDINGS & CLINICAL PRESENTATION

- Adult worms
  1. Attach to bowel mucosa
  2. Feed and grow
  3. Cause minimal or no symptoms or sequelae
- Cysticercosis
  1. Mass lesions of brain (neurocysticercosis), soft tissue, viscera
  2. Neurocysticercosis may cause seizures, hydrocephalus
- Prolonged infection with *D. latum*
  1. Vitamin B_{12} deficiency
  2. Megaloblastic anemia

ETIOLOGY

TAPEWORM
- Adult worm resides in small or large bowel; proglottids and eggs passed in stool.
- Eggs are ingested by the animal intermediate host.
- Eggs hatch into larvae.
- Larvae disseminate largely in skeletal muscle, brain, viscera.
- Humans eat infected beef *(T. saginata)*, infected pork *(T. solium)*, or infected fish *(D. latum)*.
- Larvae mature into adults within the GI lumen.
- *H. nana* infection is acquired by ingesting eggs in human or rodent feces.

CYSTICERCOSIS
- Humans ingest eggs of *T. solium* in food contaminated with human feces that contain the eggs.
- Eggs hatch into larvae in gut.
- Larvae disseminate widely through tissues (particularly soft tissue and CNS) forming cystic lesions containing either viable or nonviable larvae.

DIAGNOSIS

DIFFERENTIAL DIAGNOSIS

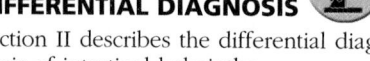

Section II describes the differential diagnosis of intestinal helminths.

WORKUP

- Stool examination for eggs or proglottids (tapeworm)
- Cerebral CT scan (neurocysticercosis)
- Serum antibody (neurocysticercosis)

IMAGING STUDIES

- Tapeworm: incidental finding on upper GI series
- Neurocysticercosis:
  1. Cerebral cysts are readily demonstrated by CT scan or MRI.
  2. Calcified lesions are an incidental finding.

TREATMENT

ACUTE GENERAL Rx

- All patients with intestinal tapeworm infections should be treated with a single oral dose of praziquantel.
  1. *T. solium:* 5 mg/kg
  2. *T. saginata:* 20 mg/kg
  3. *D. latum:* 10 mg/kg
  4. *H. nana:* 25 mg/kg
- Therapy that may be considered for symptomatic cysticercosis:
  1. May regress spontaneously
  2. Surgery
  3. Albendazole 15 mg/kg PO qd in three doses for 28 days
  4. Praziquantel 50 mg/kg PO qd in three doses for 15 days
- Therapy contraindicated with:
  1. Ocular infections
  2. Cerebral infections in which local inflammation caused by destruction of the parasite may cause significant damage

CHRONIC Rx

- Retreatment if required
- Avoidance of undercooked pork, meat, or fish
- Cysticercosis: proper hand washing, proper disposal of human waste

DISPOSITION

- Neurologic follow-up for patients with neurocysticercosis
- Ophthalmologic follow-up for patients with ocular involvement

REFERRAL

Patients treated for neurocysticercosis should be evaluated by a physician experienced in managing this infection, if possible.

PEARLS & CONSIDERATIONS

COMMENTS

T. solium is the most dangerous of the tapeworms because of the potential for cysticercosis by means of autoinfection.

SUGGESTED READINGS

Chandrasekhar MR, Nagesha CN: Intestinal helminthic infestation in children, *Indian J Pathol Microbiol* 46(3):492, 2003.

Garcia HH, Del Brutto OH: *Taenia solium* cysticercosis, *Infect Dis Clin North Am* 14(1):97, 2000.

Olson PD et al: Lethal invasive cestodiasis in immunosuppressed patients, *J Infect Dis* 187(12):1962, 2003.

AUTHOR: **JOSEPH R. MASCI, M.D.**

Tardive Dyskinesia

BASIC INFORMATION

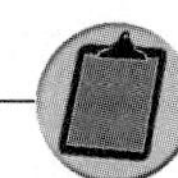

DEFINITION

Tardive dyskinesia (TD) is a syndrome of involuntary movements associated with the long-term use of antipsychotic medication, particularly dopamine-blocking neuroleptics. Patients usually exhibit rapid, repetitive, stereotypic movements mostly involving the oral, buccal, and lingual areas.

ICD-9CM CODES
333.82 Tardive dyskinesia

EPIDEMIOLOGY & DEMOGRAPHICS

- The disorder is caused by dopamine-blocking neuroleptics (e.g., Haldol).

The incidence is declining with the use of newer generation antipsychotics.

- At least 20% of patients treated with standard neuroleptic drugs are affected with TD, and approximately 5% are expected to develop TD with each year of neuroleptic treatment.
- The risk is greatest in the early years of exposure.
- Higher incidence and lower remission rates are seen in older persons.

PHYSICAL FINDINGS & CLINICAL PRESENTATION

- Typically appears with the reduction or withdrawal of the antipsychotics
- Characterized by:
  1. TD primarily involves the tongue, lips, and jaw. A combination of tongue twisting and protrusion, lip smacking and puckering, and chewing movements in a repetitive and stereotypic fashion is often observed.
  2. Slow, writhing movements of the arms and legs
  3. Symptoms subside when the antipsychotic is reintroduced
  4. The involuntary mouth movements in TD may be voluntarily suppressed by patients. They are also suppressed by voluntary actions such as putting food in the mouth or talking.

ETIOLOGY

Tardive dyskinesia results from chronic exposure to dopamine receptor blocking agents—drugs primarily used to treat psychosis. TD has not been reported with dopamine depleters (such as reserpine) and are seldom reported with atypical antipsychotic drugs such as clozapine. Some drugs for nausea (such as metoclopramide and prochlorperazine) and depression (such as amoxapine) can also cause TD.

DIAGNOSIS

DIFFERENTIAL DIAGNOSIS

- Huntington's chorea
- Excessive treatment with L-dopa

WORKUP

- Complete neuropsychiatric history (including medication history) and examination.
- If presentation atypical, consider evaluation with CBC, serum electrolytes, thyroid funciton tests, serum ceruloplasmin, and connective tissue disease screen.

IMAGING STUDIES

Brain imaging normal in TD.

TREATMENT

NONPHARMACOLOGIC THERAPY

None

PHARMACOLOGIC THERAPY

- Treatment predicated on prevention—limiting the indications for neuroleptics and using the lowest effective dose adn withdrawn when feasible.
- Use atypical antipsychotics if possible. Clozapine and quetiapine have the lowest reported incidence of TD.

CHRONIC Rx

- Benzodiazapines and vitamin E may be helpful but controlled trial evidence is weak.
- Clozapine, Olanzapine and amisulpride may be of symptomatic help, but long-term efficacy is unproven.

REFERRAL

Movement disorder specialist if symptoms are severe

PEARLS & CONSIDERATIONS

Only as a last resort, for persistent, disabling, and treatment-resistant TD, should neuroleptics be resumed to treat TD in the absence of active psychosis.

SUGGESTED READINGS

Casey DE: Pathophysiology of antipsychotic drug-induced movement disorders, *J Clin Psychiatry* 65(suppl9):25, 2004.

Fernandez HH, Friedman JH: Classification and treatment of tardive syndromes, *Neurologist* 9(1):16, 2003.

McGrath JJ, Soares KV: Miscellaneous treatments for neuroleptic-induced tardive dyskinesia, *Cochrane Database Syst Rev* (2):CD000208, 2003.

AUTHOR: **MITCHELL D. FELDMAN, M.D., M.PHIL.**

BASIC INFORMATION

DEFINITION

Tarsal tunnel syndrome is a rare entrapment neuropathy that develops as a result of compression of the posterior tibial nerve in the tunnel formed by the flexor retinaculum behind the medial malleolus of the ankle (Fig. 1-233).

ICD-9CM CODES
355.5 Tarsal tunnel syndrome

EPIDEMIOLOGY & DEMOGRAPHICS

PREVALENCE: Unknown
PREDOMINANT SEX: Female = male

PHYSICAL FINDINGS & CLINICAL PRESENTATION

- Neuritic symptoms along the course of the posterior tibial nerve in the sole and heel
- Swelling over tarsal tunnel
- Possible positive Tinel's sign
- Possible reproduction of symptoms with sustained eversion of hindfoot or digital compression of tunnel
- Sensory and motor changes unusual

ETIOLOGY

Space-occupying lesions (ganglia, varicosities, lipomas, synovial hypertrophy)

DIAGNOSIS

DIFFERENTIAL DIAGNOSIS

- Plantar fasciitis
- Peripheral neuropathy
- Proximal radiculopathy
- Local tendinitis
- Peripheral vascular disease
- Morton's neuroma

ELECTRICAL STUDIES

Electrodiagnostic testing is often inconclusive. Delayed sensory conduction or increased motor latency may be seen.

TREATMENT

- NSAIDs
- Immobilization for 4-6 wk with ankle orthosis or fracture cast boot
- Medial heel wedge or orthotic to minimize heel eversion
- Local steroid injection into tunnel (avoiding the posterior tibial nerve) if symptoms persist

REFERRAL

For surgical decompression if needed. Results of surgery are mixed unless an obvious compressive lesion is found.

SUGGESTED READINGS

Aldridge T: Diagnosing heel pain in adults, *Am Fam Physician* 70:332, 2004.

Gorter K et al: Variation in diagnosis and management of common foot problems by GPs, *Fam Pract* 18(6):569, 2001.

Labib SA et al: Heel pain triad (HPT): the combination of plantar fasciitis, posterior tibial tendon dysfunction and tarsal tunnel syndrome, *Foot Ankle Int* 23(3):212, 2002.

Mizel MS et al: Evaluation and treatment of chronic ankle pain, *Instr Course Lect* 53:311, 2004.

Mondelli M, Morana P, Padua L: Anelectrophysiological severity scale in tarsal tunnel syndrome, *Acta Neurol Scand* 109:284, 2004.

Pecina M: Diagnostic tests for tarsal tunnel syndrome, *J Bone Joint Surg Am* 84-A(9):1714, 2002.

AUTHOR: **LONNIE R. MERCIER, M.D.**

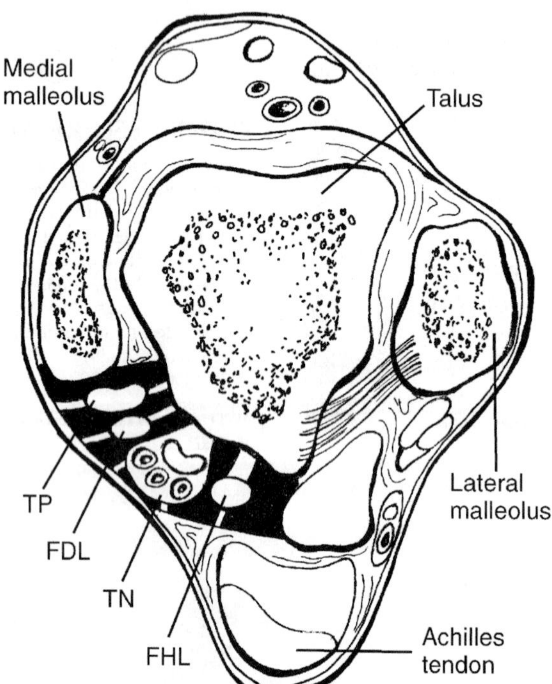

FIGURE 1-233 Anatomy of tarsal tunnel syndrome. Transverse view of ankle. *FDL,* Flexor digitorum longus; *FHL,* flexor hallucis longus tendon; *TN,* tibial nerve (single contour), posterior tibial artery, veins; *TP,* tibialis posterior tendon. Tendons and neurovascular elements are included into individual fibrous septa that connect periosteum with the deep fascia. (From Canoso J: *Rheumatology in primary care,* Philadelphia, 1997, WB Saunders.)

BASIC INFORMATION

DEFINITION

Temporomandibular joint (TMJ) syndrome refers to a group of disorders leading to symptoms of the temporomandibular joint.

SYNONYMS

Temporomandibular dysfunction
Painful temporomandibular joint

ICD-9CM CODES
524.60 Temporomandibular joint pain-dysfunction syndrome

EPIDEMIOLOGY & DEMOGRAPHICS

- 15% of the population have TMJ disorders
- Females > males 4:1
- Occurs between the second and fourth decades of life
- Usually unilateral, affecting either side with equal frequency

PHYSICAL FINDINGS & CLINICAL PRESENTATION

- Otalgia
- Odontalgia
- Headaches (frontal, temporal, retroorbital)
- Tinnitus
- Dizziness
- Clicking or popping sounds with movement of the TMJ
- Joint locking
- Tender to palpation
- Limited range of motion of the TMJ

ETIOLOGY

Causes of TMJ syndrome are multifactorial, encompassing local anatomic anomalies to familiar disease processes that can involve the TMJ.

- Myofascial pain-dysfunction syndrome (MPD): the most common cause of TMJ syndrome and results from teeth grinding and clenching the jaw (bruxism)
- Internal TMJ derangement: abnormal connection of the articular disk to the mandibular condyle
- Degenerative joint disease
- Rheumatoid arthritis
- Gouty arthritis
- Pseudogout
- Ankylosing spondylitis
- Trauma
- Prior surgery (orthodontic, intraarticular steroid injection)
- Tumors

DIAGNOSIS

DIFFERENTIAL DIAGNOSIS

The differential diagnosis of TMJ syndrome is thought of in terms of etiology and includes the list as mentioned previously under Etiology. Myofascial pain-dysfunction syndrome, internal TMJ derangement, and degenerative joint disease represent >90% of all causes of TMJ syndrome.

WORKUP

Includes a detailed history and physical examination, followed by radiographic imaging evaluation.

LABORATORY TESTS

Laboratory examination is not very helpful in the diagnosis of TMJ syndrome.

IMAGING STUDIES

- Plain x-rays: The most common x-rays are the panoramic, transorbital, and transpharyngeal views in both opened and closed positions.
- Arthrography is helpful in looking for meniscus involvement.
- CT scan is very accurate in diagnosing meniscal and osseous derangements of the TMJ.
- MRI can better visualize soft tissue inflammation, if present.

TREATMENT

NONPHARMACOLOGIC THERAPY

- Soft diet to rest the muscles of mastication
- Heat 15-20 min four to six times per day
- Massage of the masseter and temporalis muscles
- Formed splints or bite appliances
- Range-of-motion exercises

ACUTE GENERAL Rx

- Nonsteroidal antiinflammatory drugs (NSAIDs): ibuprofen 800 PO mg tid prn, naproxen 500 PO mg bid prn, titrated to relieve symptoms
- Muscle relaxants: diazepam 2.5-5 mg PO tid prn
- In degenerative joint disease of the TMJ, intraarticular steroid injection can be tried

CHRONIC Rx

- Most of the above mentioned treatment is used for myofascial pain- dysfunction syndrome; however, it can be applied to other causes of TMJ syndrome. Surgery is usually a measure of last resort in patients who are refractory to nonpharmacologic and acute general treatment.
- Surgical procedures include:
  1. Meniscoplasty
  2. Meniscectomy
  3. Subcondylar osteotomy
  4. TMJ reconstruction

DISPOSITION

The course depends on the underlying etiology; however, a lengthy course with exacerbations of symptoms can be expected.

REFERRAL

All patients with TMJ syndrome refractory to conservative nonpharmacologic and acute therapy should be referred to a periodontist, oral maxillofacial surgeon, or ENT surgeon.

PEARLS & CONSIDERATIONS

COMMENTS

- Patients with rheumatoid arthritis involving the TMJ usually will have bilateral involvement.
- Frequently emotional stress initiates the myofascial pain-dysfunction, which accounts for 85% of all cases of TMJ syndrome.

SUGGESTED READINGS

Baba K, Tsukiyama Y et al: A review of temporomandibular disorder diagnostic techniques, *J Prosthet Dent* 86(2):184, 2001.

Blank LW: Clinical guidelines for managing mandibular dysfunction, *Gen Dentist* 46(6):592, 1998.

Dierks EJ: Temporomandibular disorders and facial pain syndromes. In Kelly WN et al: *Textbook of rheumatology*, ed 5, Philadelphia, 1997, WB Saunders.

Pankhurst CL: Controversies in the aetiology of temporomandibular disorders. Part I. Temporomandibular disorders: all in the mind? *Prim Dent Care* 4(1):25, 1997.

AUTHOR: **PETER PETROPOULOS, M.D.**

BASIC INFORMATION

DEFINITION

Testicular neoplasms are primary cancers originating in a testis.

SYNONYMS

Testis tumor
Testicular cancer

ICD-9CM CODES
186.9 Testicular neoplasm
M906/3 (seminoma)
M9101/3 (embryonal carcinoma or teratoma)
M9100/3 (choriocarcinoma)

EPIDEMIOLOGY & DEMOGRAPHICS

- Incidence: 2-3 cases/100,000 men/yr
- 1%-2% of all cancers in males
- Age: can occur in any age but most common in young adults; average age for embryonal cell carcinoma: 30 yr; average age for seminoma: 36 yr

PHYSICAL FINDINGS & CLINICAL PRESENTATION

- Any mass within the testicle should be considered cancer until proven otherwise. It may be found by the patient who brings it to the attention of a physician or it may be found by a physician on a routine examination.
- Symptoms other than scrotal or testicular swelling are typically absent unless the cancer has metastasized. Occasionally a patient may complain of scrotal fullness or heaviness.
- Testicular palpation should be performed with two hands. Transillumination may distinguish a solid mass (e.g., cancer) and a fluid-filled lesion (e.g., hydrocele or spermatocele). The mass is nontender, indeed less sensitive than a normal testicle.

ETIOLOGY & PATHOLOGY

- Cryptorchidism (undescended testes) even if corrected by orchiopexy
- Pathology

Cell type	Frequency %
Seminoma	42
Embryonal cell carcinoma	26
Teratocarcinoma	26
Teratoma	5
Choriocarcinoma	1

Other rare types:
Yolk sac carcinoma
Mixed germ cell tumors
Carcinoid tumor
Sertoli cell tumors
Leydig cell tumors
Lymphoma
Metastatic cancer to the testes

- TNM staging system for testicular cancer

T_0 No apparent primary
T_1 Testis only (excludes rete testis)
T_2 Beyond the tunica albuginea
T_3 Rete testis or epididymal involvement
T_4 Spermatic cord
1. Spermatic cord
2. Scrotum

N_0 No nodal involvement
N_1 Ipsilateral regional nodal involvement
N_2 Contralateral or bilateral abdominal or groin nodes
N_3 Palpable abdominal nodes or fixed groin nodes
N_4 Juxtaregional nodes
M_0 No distant metastases
M_1 Distant metastases present

The clinical stages consist of stage A, with tumor confined to the testis and cord structures; stage B, with tumor confined to the retroperitoneal lymph nodes; and stage C, with tumor involving the abdominal viscera or disease above the diaphragm.

DIAGNOSIS

DIFFERENTIAL DIAGNOSIS

- Spermatocele
- Varicocele
- Hydrocele
- Epididymitis
- Epidermoid cyst of the testicle
- Epididymis tumors

WORKUP

Physical examination, laboratory tests, and imaging studies (Section III, "Testicular Mass")

LABORATORY TESTS

- Serum human chorionic gonadotropin (hCG)
- Serum alpha-fetoprotein (AFP)

One or both of these tumor markers will be elevated in 70% of cases of testicular cancer.

- Testicular biopsy is contraindicated.

IMAGING STUDIES

- Ultrasound
- CT scan or MRI of pelvis and abdomen
- Chest x-ray

TREATMENT

- Surgical exploration of the testicle through an inguinal incision with a noncrushing clamp placed on the cord before direct testicular examination. If a mass is confined within the body of the testicle, an orchiectomy is performed
- Retroperitoneal lymph node dissection for clinical stage A and low stage B (lymph nodes under 6 cm in greatest diameter) provides cure in 70%
- Chemotherapy: cisplatin, vinblastine, and bleomycin
  1. Not indicated in clinical stage A
  2. Controversial in low stage B
  3. Cornerstone of treatment in high stage B or stage C
- Radiation therapy for stage A and low stage B seminoma provides cure in 85%
- Posttreatment surveillance for testicular cancer survivors (annually)
  1. General maintenance
  2. Fertility assessment
  3. Sexuality status
  4. Skin examination (increased risk of dysplastic nivi)
  5. Testicular examination (3% to 4% risk of second testicular cancer)
  6. Serum tumor markers (hCG, AFP)
  7. Chest x-ray (for late relapse)
  8. Complications of cisplatin: hypertension, hyperlipidemia, renal failure, hypomagnesemia, hearing loss, tinnitus, peripheral neuropathy, and infertility

REFERRAL

To urologist

SUGGESTED READINGS

Rowland RG, Foster RS, Donohue JP: Testis tumors. In Gillenwater JY et al (eds): *Adult and pediatric urology,* vol 2, ed 3, St Louis, 1998, Mosby.
Vaughn D et al: Long-term medical care of testicular cancer survivors, *Ann Intern Med* 136:463, 2002.

AUTHOR: **TOM J. WACHTEL, M.D.**

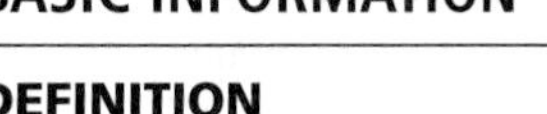

BASIC INFORMATION

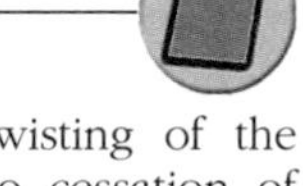

DEFINITION

Testicular torsion is a twisting of the spermatic cord leading to cessation of testicular blood flow, ischemia, and infarction if left untreated (Fig. 1-234).

SYNONYMS

Spermatic cord torsion

ICD-9CM CODES
608.2 Testicular torsion

EPIDEMIOLOGY & DEMOGRAPHICS

- Affects 1:4000 males
- Two thirds of all cases occur between the ages of 12 and 18 yr, but may occur at any age, including antenatally

PHYSICAL FINDINGS & CLINICAL PRESENTATION

- Typical sequence is sudden onset of hemiscrotal pain, then swelling, nausea, and vomiting without fever or urinary symptoms.
- Painless testicular swelling occurs in 10%.
- One out of three patients reports previous episodes of spontaneously remitting scrotal pain.
- In the neonate, testicular torsion should be presumed in patients with a painless, discolored hemiscrotal swelling.
- In rare cases, torsion may involve an undescended testicle. In such situations an empty hemiscrotum is palpated together with a tender lump in the inguinal area.

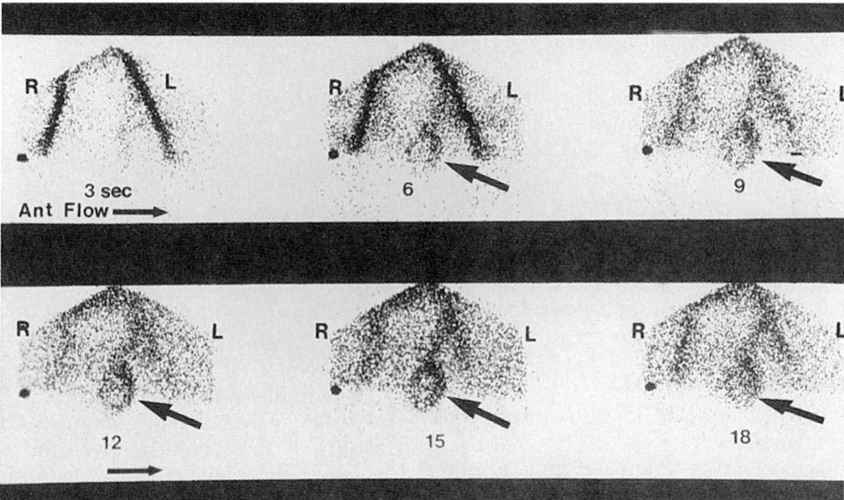

FIGURE 1-234 Testicular torsion. Evaluation of blood flow to the testicle has been done by giving an intravenous bolus of radioactive material. The right and left iliac vessels are clearly identified, and sequential images are obtained every 3 sec. Here, increased flow is seen to the rim of the left testicle *(arrows),* and there is no blood flow centrally. This is the appearance of a testicular torsion in which the torsion has been present for more than approximately 24 hr. (From Mettler FA [ed]: *Primary care radiology,* Philadelphia, 2000, WB Saunders.)

ETIOLOGY

Testicular torsion may occur without any underlying abnormality but is more likely when the tunica vaginalis extends high on the spermatic cord (bell-clapper deformity).

DIAGNOSIS

DIFFERENTIAL DIAGNOSIS (SEE ALSO SECTION II)

- Torsion of the testicular appendages
- Testicular tumor
- Epididymitis
- Incarcerated inguinoscrotal hernia
- Orchitis
- Spermatocele
- Hydrocele

WORKUP

The diagnosis is usually based on history and physical examination.

IMAGING STUDIES

- Radionuclide scrotal scanning (technetium-99m): cold testicle
- Doppler ultrasonic stethoscope (Doppler flowmetry)

TREATMENT

Surgical derotation of the spermatic cord followed by bilateral testicular fixation with nonabsorbable sutures

PROGNOSIS

- There is an 80% testicular salvage rate if detorsion occurs within 12 hr of onset.
- After 24 hr, irreversible testicular infarction is expected.
- Because the contralateral testes can be affected (immunologic process), when treatment is delayed and return of blood flow does not occur after detorsion, some recommend orchiectomy of the infarcted testicle.

REFERRAL

To urologist

SUGGESTED READING

Kogan S et al: Spermatic cord torsion. In Gillenwater JY et al (eds): *Adult and pediatric urology,* ed 3, St Louis, 1996, Mosby.

AUTHOR: **TOM J. WACHTEL, M.D.**

Tetanus (PTG)

BASIC INFORMATION

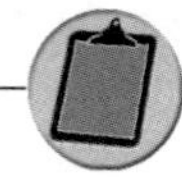

DEFINITION

Tetanus is a life-threatening illness manifested by muscle rigidity and spasms; it is caused by a neurotoxin (tetanospasmin) produced by *Clostridium tetani.*

ICD-9CM CODES
037 Tetanus

EPIDEMIOLOGY & DEMOGRAPHICS

INCIDENCE (IN U.S.): 48 to 64 cases reported annually since 1986
PREDOMINANT AGE: >60 yr of age
GENETICS:
Neonatal Infection:
- Rare in U.S.
- Among the leading causes of neonatal mortality in many parts of the world (caused by infection of the umbilical cord stump)

PHYSICAL FINDINGS & CLINICAL PRESENTATION

- Trismus ("lockjaw")
- Risus sardonicus (peculiar grin), characteristic grimace that results from contraction of the facial muscles
- Generalized muscle spasms causing severe pain and, at times, respiratory compromise and death
- Rigid abdominal muscles, flexed arms, and extended legs
- Autonomic dysfunction several days after onset of illness
- Leading cause of death: fluctuations in heart rate and blood pressure
- Usually, absence of fever
- Localized tetanus
  1. Rigidity of muscles near the injury
  2. Weakness as a result of lower motor neuron injury
  3. May be self-limited and resolve spontaneously
  4. More often progresses to generalized tetanus
  5. Cephalic tetanus:
     a. May occur with head injuries
     b. Can manifest as cranial nerve dysfunction

ETIOLOGY

- *C. tetani* is a gram-positive, spore-forming bacillus that resides primarily in the soil.
- Majority of cases are caused by punctures and lacerations.
- Toxin is elaborated from organisms in a contaminated wound.
- Local symptoms are caused by inhibition of neurotransmitter at presynaptic sites.
  1. Over the next 2 to 14 days, the toxin travels up the neurons to the CNS, where it acts on inhibitory neurons to prevent neurotransmitter release.
  2. Unopposed motor activity results in tonic contractions of muscles.

DIAGNOSIS

DIFFERENTIAL DIAGNOSIS

- Strychnine poisoning
- Dystonic reaction caused by neuroleptic agents
- Local infection (dental or masseter muscle) causing trismus
- Severe hypocalcemia
- Hysteria

WORKUP

- Positive wound culture is not helpful in diagnosis.
- Isolation of organism is possible in patients without the illness.

LABORATORY TESTS

- Usually, normal blood counts and chemistries
- Toxicology of serum and urine to rule out strychnine poisoning

TREATMENT

NONPHARMACOLOGIC THERAPY

- Monitoring in a hospital ICU: keep surroundings dark and quiet
- Intubation or tracheostomy for severe laryngospasm
- Debridement of wound

ACUTE GENERAL Rx

- Human tetanus immunoglobulin (HTIg) 500 U via IM injection
- Tetanus toxoid (Td) 0.5 ml by IM injection at a different site
- Metronidazole 500 mg IV q6h, or penicillin G 1 million U IV q4h for 10 days
- IV diazepam to control muscle spasms
- Neuromuscular blockade if necessary

CHRONIC Rx

- Supportive care
- Possible mechanical ventilation
- Minimal external stimuli
- Control of heart rate and blood pressure:
  1. Labetalol for sympathetic hyperactivity
  2. Pacemaker for sustained bradycardia
- Physical therapy once spasms subside

DISPOSITION

Full recovery over weeks to months if complications can be avoided

REFERRAL

- To emergency department
- To infectious disease specialist

PEARLS & CONSIDERATIONS

COMMENTS

- Illness is preventable.
- Boosters of Td should be given every 10 yr to maintain immune status.
- Passive as well as active immunization (HTIg + Td) should be given for patients with tetanus-prone wounds who have not been adequately immunized in the previous 5 yr.
- A recent U.S. study showed that only 72% of people >6 yr had protective levels of antibody.

SUGGESTED READINGS

Hsu SS et al: Tetanus in the emergency department: a current review, *J Emerg Med* 20(4):357, 2001.

McQuillam GM et al: Serologic immunity to diphtheria and tetanus in the United States, *Ann Intern Med* 136:660, 2002.

AUTHOR: **MAURICE POLICAR, M.D.**

BASIC INFORMATION

DEFINITION

Tetralogy of Fallot (TOF) is a congenital heart deformity consisting of the following four features:

- Ventricular septal defect (VSD)
- Infundibular stenosis leading to obstruction to the right ventricular (RV) outflow tract
- Overriding aorta
- Right ventricular hypertrophy (RVH)

See Fig. 1-235.

ICD-9CM CODES
745.2 Tetralogy of Fallot

EPIDEMIOLOGY & DEMOGRAPHICS

- TOF is the most common cyanotic congenital heart malformation diagnosed after age 1 yr.
- TOF accounts for nearly 10% of all congenital heart disease.
- TOF occurs in approximately 3000 newborns/yr.

PHYSICAL FINDINGS & CLINICAL PRESENTATION

- Of the four major features of TOF, infundibular stenosis leading to right ventricular outflow tract obstruction and VSD are the primary defects leading to:
  1. Right-to-left shunting and hypoxemia
  2. Altered RV hemodynamics
  3. Decreased pulmonary blood flow
- The aforementioned pathophysiologic concepts subsequently result in common manifestations of TOF, including:
  1. Cyanosis secondary to increased RV pressures from infundibular stenosis resulting in the shunting of deoxygenated blood from the RV through the VSD into the left ventricle, thus bypassing the lungs
  2. Dyspnea on exertion
  3. Clubbing
  4. Child assuming a squatting position after exercise increasing systemic vascular resistance, thereby decreasing right-to-left shunting
  5. Low birth weight and growth rate
  6. Palpable RV impulse
  7. Systolic thrill along the left sternal border
  8. Single second heart sound, inaudible P2 component
  9. Systolic ejection murmur resulting from RV outflow tract obstruction

ETIOLOGY

Unknown

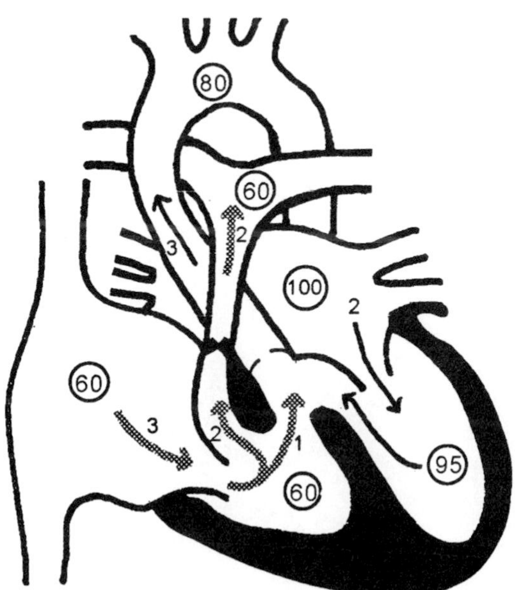

FIGURE 1-235 Physiology of tetralogy of Fallot (TOF). The circled numbers represent oxygen saturations. The numbers next to the arrows represent volumes of blood flow (in L/min/m^2). The atrial (mixed venous) oxygen saturation is decreased secondary to the systemic hypoxemia. Three L/min/m^2 of desaturated blood enter the right atrium and traverse the tricuspid valve. Two liters flow through the right ventricular outflow tract into the lungs, whereas 1 L shunts right to left through the VSD into the ascending aorta. Thus the pulmonary blood flow is two-thirds normal (Qp:Qs of 0.7:1). Blood returning to the left atrium is fully saturated. Only 2 L of blood flow across the mitral valve. The oxygen saturation in the left ventricle may be slightly decreased owing to right-to-left shunting across the VSD. Two liters of saturated left ventricular blood, mixing with 1 L of desaturated right ventricular blood, are ejected into the ascending aorta. The aortic saturation is decreased, and the cardiac output is normal. (From Behrman RE: *Nelson textbook of pediatrics,* ed 16, Philadelphia, 2000, WB Saunders.)

DIAGNOSIS

The diagnosis of TOF is suspected in any neonate, infant, or child presenting with cyanosis and a heart murmur.

DIFFERENTIAL DIAGNOSIS

- Asthma
- Isolated VSD
- Pulmonary atresia
- Patent ductus arteriosus
- Aortic stenosis
- Pneumothorax

WORKUP

The initial workup of TOF like any cardiac disease requires a detailed history and physical examination along with an echocardiography, chest x-ray, ECG, and simple laboratory tests.

LABORATORY TESTS

- CBC with polycythemia resulting from longstanding cyanosis
- ABGs with hypoxemia, normal pH, and pCO_2
- Pulse oximetry
- ECG commonly demonstrating RVH defined as right axis deviation >90 degrees with an R wave greater than S wave in lead V1. Right atrial enlargement with peaked p wave amplitude >2.5 mm in the inferior leads or initial portion of the p wave >1.5 mm in lead V1

IMAGING STUDIES

- CXR revealing boot-shaped heart commonly described as "coeur en sabot"; prominent RV with decreased pulmonary vascularity
- Echocardiography demonstrating VSD with a stenotic RV outflow tract and an overriding aorta
- Cardiac catheterization and angiography aid in the determination of the severity of right-to-left shunting, localization of the VSD, and anatomic assessment of the RV outflow tract, pulmonary artery, and coronary artery anatomy

TREATMENT

NONPHARMACOLOGIC THERAPY

- Oxygen
- Knee-chest position in hypoxemic spells helps reduce venous return and increase systemic vascular resistance, thus decreasing right-to-left shunting

ACUTE GENERAL THERAPY

Acute treatment of any infant or child with TOF who is cyanotic with respiratory distress is aimed at increasing systemic vascular resistance and decreasing right-to-left shunting (e.g., phenylephrine 0.1-0.5 μg/kg/min IV). Intravenous β-blockers (e.g., propranolol 0.15-0.25 mg/kg slow IV push) are used to decrease RV outflow tract contractility and subcutaneous morphine can be used to decrease venous return.

CHRONIC Rx

- Palliative repair includes procedures increasing pulmonary blood flow, thus reducing right-to-left shunting. Examples of palliative procedures include the Blalock-Taussig shunt whereby a shunt is made between the subclavian artery and the pulmonary artery, the Waterston shunt attaching the ascending aorta to right pulmonary artery, and the Potts shunt attaching the descending aorta to left pulmonary artery.
- Complete surgical repair has good success and involves closing the VSD with a Dacron patch and relieving the RV outflow tract obstruction. It is recommended for nearly every patient with TOF.

DISPOSITION

- Almost all TOF patients will have had either palliative or complete surgical repair before reaching adulthood.
- Less than 3% of patients with TOF reach 40 yr of age without having surgery.
- Survival after complete operative repair for TOF is excellent provided the RV outflow tract obstruction has been relieved and the VSD has been closed. Most adults lead unrestricted lives and are asymptomatic.
- 85% of patients who have operative repair of TOF survive >36 yr.
- Early and late postoperative complications can occur and generally manifest in arrhythmias from atrial and ventricular tachycardias and diminished exercise tolerance from RV failure. The latter is usually secondary to chronic pulmonary regurgitation and/or residual RV outflow tract obstruction.

REFERRAL

- Infants and children with cyanotic heart disease should be referred to a pediatric cardiologist for further diagnostic evaluation. On diagnosing TOF, patients should be referred to centers experienced in palliative and complete surgical repair.
- Adult patients with repaired TOF should be comanaged with cardiology.

PEARLS & CONSIDERATIONS

- Tetralogy of Fallot was first described and published by the French physician Etienne Fallot in 1888.
- The first surgical treatment for TOF was performed by Dr. Alfred Blalock at Johns Hopkins University in 1945.

COMMENTS

- The severity of right ventricular outflow tract obstruction is the primary determinant of clinical symptoms and outcome.
- Coexisting cardiac abnormalities occur in nearly 40% of patients with TOF, including patent ductus arteriosus, atrial septal defect (ASD), multiple VSDs, absence of a pulmonary artery, and complete AV septal defects.
- Children with TOF require SBE prophylaxis before any dental work or surgery on the bowel or bladder.

SUGGESTED READINGS

Braunwald *Heart disease: a textbook of cardiovascular medicine,* ed 6, Philadelphia, 2001, WB Saunders.

Hirsch JC, Mosca RS, Bove EL: Complete repair of tetralogy of Fallot in the neonate: results in the modern era, *Ann Surg* 232(4), 2000.

Nollert G et al: Long-term survival in patients with repair of tetralogy of Fallot: 36-year follow-up of 490 survivors of the first year after surgical repair, *J Am Coll Cardiol* 30:1374, 1997.

Therrien J, Marx GR, Gatzoulis MA: Late-problems in tetralogy of Fallot—recognition, management and prevention, *Cardiol Clin* 20(3), 2002.

AUTHORS: **GAURAV CHOUDHARY, M.D.,** and **WEN-CHIH WU, M.D.**

BASIC INFORMATION

DEFINITION

Thalassemias are a heterogeneous group of disorders of hemoglobin synthesis that have in common a deficient synthesis of one or more of the polypeptide chains of the normal human hemoglobin, resulting in a quantitative abnormality of the hemoglobin thus produced. There are no qualitative changes such as those encountered in the hemoglobinopathies (e.g., sickle cell disease).

SYNONYMS

Mediterranean anemia
Cooley's anemia

ICD-9CM CODES
282.4 Thalassemia

EPIDEMIOLOGY & DEMOGRAPHICS

- Thalassemia is the most common genetic disorder worldwide.
- The highest concentration of alpha-thalassemia is found in Southeast Asia and the African west coast. For example, in Thailand the prevalence is 5%-10%. It is also common among blacks, with a prevalence of approximately 5%.
- The worldwide prevalence of beta-thalassemia is approximately 3%; in certain regions of Italy and Greece the prevalence reaches 15%-30%. This high prevalence can be found in Americans of Italian or Greek descent.
- The distribution of thalassemia in Europe and Africa parallels that of malaria, suggesting that thalassemic persons are more resistant to the parasite, thus permitting evolutionary survival advantage.

CLASSIFICATION

BETA THALASSEMIA:
- Beta (+) thalassemia (suboptimal beta-globin synthesis)
- Beta (o) thalassemia (total absence of beta-globin synthesis)
- Delta-beta thalassemia (total absence of both delta-globin and beta-globin synthesis)
- Lepore hemoglobin (synthesis of small amounts of fused delta-beta-globin and total absence of delta- and beta-globin)
- Hereditary persistence of fetal hemoglobin (HPHF) (increased hemoglobin F synthesis and reduced or absence of delta- and beta-globin)

ALPHA THALASSEMIA:
- Silent carrier (three alpha-globin genes present)
- Alpha thalassemia trait (two alpha-globin genes present)
- Hemoglobin H disease (one alpha-globin gene present)
- Hydrops fetalis (no alpha-globin gene)
- Hemoglobin Constant Sprint (elongated alpha-globin chain)

THALASSEMIC HEMOGLOBINOPATHIES: Hb Terre Haute, Hb Quong Sze, HbE, Hb Knossos

PHYSICAL FINDINGS & CLINICAL PRESENTATION

BETA THALASSEMIA:
- Heterozygous beta thalassemia (thalassemia minor): no or mild anemia, microcytosis and hypochromia, mild hemolysis manifested by slight reticulocytosis and splenomegaly
- Homozygous beta thalassemia (thalassemia major): intense hemolytic anemia; transfusion dependency; bone deformities (skull and long bones); hepatomegaly; splenomegaly; iron overload leading to cardiomyopathy, diabetes mellitus, and hypogonadism; growth retardation; pigment gallstones; susceptibility to infection
- Thalassemia intermedia caused by combination of beta and alpha thalassemia or beta thalassemia and Hb Lepore: resembles thalassemia major but is milder

ALPHA THALASSEMIA:
- Silent carrier: no symptoms.
- Alpha thalassemia trait: microcytosis only.
- Hemoglobin H disease: moderately severe hemolysis with microcytosis and splenomegaly.
- The loss of all four alpha-globin genes is incompatible with life (stillbirth of hydropic fetus). NOTE: Pregnancies with hydrops fetalis are associated with a high incidence of toxemia.

PATHOGENESIS

- Beta thalassemia: The reduction of beta-globin synthesis results in redundant alpha-globin chains (Heinz bodies), which are cytotoxic and cause intramedullary hemolysis and ineffective erythropoiesis. More than 100 mutations have been identified. Fetal hemoglobin may be increased.
- Alpha thalassemia: Several mutations can result in insufficient amounts of alpha globin available for combination with non–alpha globins.

DIAGNOSIS

DIFFERENTIAL DIAGNOSIS

Usually the diagnosis is straightforward; iron deficiency must be ruled out in the presence of microcytosis; if iron deficiency is not present, the cause of microcytosis is probably thalassemia.

LABORATORY TESTS

BETA THALASSEMIA:
- Microcytosis (MCV: 55-80 FL)
- Normal RDW (RBC distribution width)
- Smear: nucleated RBCs, anisocytosis, poikilocytosis, polychromatophilia, Pappenheimer and Howell-Jolly bodies
- Hemoglobin electrophoresis: absent or reduced hemoglobin A, increased fetal hemoglobin, variable increase in the amount of hemoglobin A_2
- Markers of hemolysis: elevated indirect bilirubin and LDH, decreased haptoglobin

ALPHA THALASSEMIA:
- Microcytosis in the absence of iron deficiency
- Hemoglobin electrophoresis is normal, except for the presence of hemoglobin H in hemoglobin H disease

TREATMENT

- Thalassemia minor: no treatment but avoid iron administration for incorrect diagnosis of iron deficiency
- Beta thalassemia major (and hemoglobin H disease)
  1. Transfusion as required together with chelation of iron with desferrioxamine (by intravenous or subcutaneous administration, 8-12 hr nightly, 5-6 days a week at a dose of 2-6 g/day using a portable infusion pump)
  2. Splenectomy for hypersplenism if present
  3. Bone marrow transplantation
  4. Hydroxyurea may increase the level of hemoglobin F

REFERRAL

To hematologist

SUGGESTED READING

Olivieri NF: The beta-thalassemias, *N Engl J Med* 341:99, 1999.

AUTHOR: **TOM J. WACHTEL, M.D.**

BASIC INFORMATION

DEFINITION

Thoracic outlet syndrome is the term used to describe a condition producing upper extremity symptoms thought to result from neurovascular compression at the thoracic outlet. Three types are described based on the point of compression: (1) cervical rib and scalenus syndrome, in which abnormal scalene muscles or the presence of a cervical rib may cause compression; (2) costoclavicular syndrome, in which compression may occur under the clavicle; and (3) hyperabduction syndrome, in which compression may occur in the subcoracoid area.

ICD-9CM CODES
353.0 Thoracic outlet syndrome

EPIDEMIOLOGY & DEMOGRAPHICS

PREVALENCE: Varies from source to source; presence of cervical ribs in 0.5%-1% of population (50% bilateral), but most are asymptomatic

PREDOMINANT AGE: Rare under 20 yr of age

PREDOMINANT SEX: Female > male (3.5:1)

PHYSICAL FINDINGS & CLINICAL PRESENTATION

- Symptoms and signs are related to the degree of involvement of each of the various structures at the level of the first rib.
- True venous or arterial involvement is rare.
- Diagnosis is most often used in the consideration of neural pain affecting the arm, which would suggest involvement of the brachial plexus.
  1. *Arterial compression:* pallor, paresthesias, diminished pulses, coolness, digital gangrene, and a supraclavicular bruit or mass
  2. *Venous compression:* edema and pain; thrombosis causing superficial venous dilation about the shoulder
  3. *"True" neural compression:* lower trunk (C8, T1) findings with intrinsic weakness and diminished sensation to the finger and small fingers and ulnar aspect of the forearm
  4. Possible supraclavicular tenderness
  5. Provocative tests (Adson's, Wright's): may reproduce pain but are of disputed usefulness

ETIOLOGY

- Congenital cervical rib or fibrous extension of cervical rib (Fig. 1-236)
- Abnormal scalene muscle insertion
- Drooping of shoulder girdle resulting from generalized hypotonia or trauma
- Narrowed costoclavicular interval as a result of downward and backward pressure on shoulder (sometimes seen in individuals who carry heavy backpacks)
- Acute venous thrombosis with exercise (effort thrombosis)
- Bony abnormalities of first rib
- Abnormal fibromuscular bands
- Malunion of clavicle fracture

DIAGNOSIS

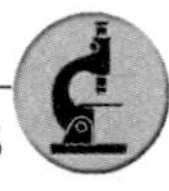

DIFFERENTIAL DIAGNOSIS

- Carpal tunnel syndrome
- Cervical radiculopathy
- Brachial neuritis
- Ulnar nerve compression
- Reflex sympathetic dystrophy
- Superior sulcus tumor

WORKUP

Except for venous or arterial pathology, no ancillary diagnostic tests are reliable for diagnostic confirmation.

IMAGING STUDIES

- Arteriography or venography when vascular pathology is strongly suspected clinically
- Cervical spine radiographs to rule out cervical disk disease
- Chest film to rule out lung tumor
- EMG, NCV studies to rule out carpal tunnel syndrome, cervical radiculopathy

TREATMENT

ACUTE GENERAL Rx

- Sling for pain relief
- Physical therapy modalities plus shoulder girdle–strengthening exercises
- Postural reeducation
- NSAIDs

DISPOSITION

- Surgery: generally successful for vascular disorders
- Nonsurgical treatment: often successful for patients with pain as the primary symptom

REFERRAL

For vascular surgery consultation when venous or arterial impairment is present

PEARLS & CONSIDERATIONS

COMMENTS

- True thoracic outlet syndrome is probably an uncommon condition.
- Diagnosis is often used to describe a wide variety of clinical symptoms.
- Considerable disagreement exists regarding the frequency of this disorder.

SUGGESTED READINGS

Kaymak B, Ozcakar L: Complex regional pain syndrome in thoracic outlet syndrome, *Br J Sports Med* 38:364, 2004.

Pascarelli EF, Hsu YP: Understanding work-related upper extremity disorders: clinical findings in 485 computer users, musicians and others, *J Occup Rehab* 11:1, 2001.

Sheth RN, Belzberg AJ: Diagnosis and treatment of thoracic outlet syndrome, *Neurosurg Clin North Am* 12:295, 2001.

Wehbe MA, Leinberry CF: Current trends in treatment of thoracic outlet syndrome, *Hand Clin* 20:119, 2004.

AUTHOR: **LONNIE R. MERCIER, M.D.**

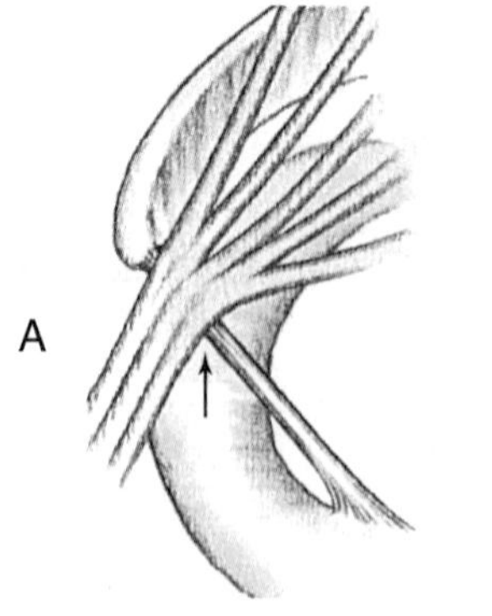

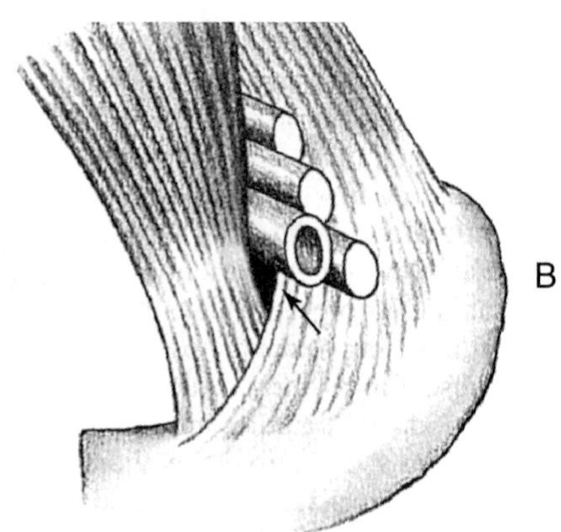

FIGURE 1-236 **A,** Compression caused by a cervical rib *(arrow).* **B,** Abnormal scalene muscle insertions that may cause compression at the cervicobrachial region *(arrow).* (From Mercier LR: *Practical orthopedics,* ed 5, St Louis, 2000, Mosby.)

BASIC INFORMATION

DEFINITION

Thromboangiitis obliterans (Buerger's disease) is an occlusive inflammatory disease of the small- to medium-size arteries of the upper and lower extremities.

SYNONYMS

Buerger's disease
Presenile gangrene

ICD-9CM CODES
443.1 Thromboangiitis obliterans (Buerger's disease)

EPIDEMIOLOGY & DEMOGRAPHICS

- Since 1950, the incidence of thromboangiitis obliterans has fallen significantly.
- The prevalence of thromboangiitis obliterans is higher in Japan, India, and Southeast Asia when compared with the U.S.
- Thromboangiitis obliterans is rare in women.
- The disease typically occurs before the age of 50 yr and is found predominantly in men who smoke.

PHYSICAL FINDINGS & CLINICAL PRESENTATION

- Paresthesias, coldness, skin ulcers, gangrene, along with pain at rest or with walking (claudication)
- Prolonged capillary refill with dependent rubor
- Necrotic skin ulcers at the tips of the digits
- Pathognomonic migratory thrombophlebitis

ETIOLOGY

- Unknown.
- The remarkable feature is the close association between tobacco smoking and disease exacerbation. If abstinence from tobacco is adhered to, thromboangiitis obliterans takes a favorable course. If smoking is continued, the disease progresses, leading to gangrene and small-digit amputations.
- There is some thought of a genetic predisposition because the prevalence is higher in the Far East.

DIAGNOSIS

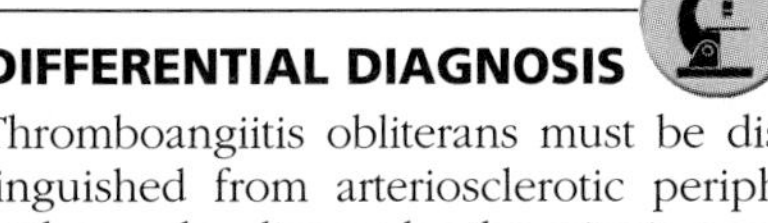

DIFFERENTIAL DIAGNOSIS

Thromboangiitis obliterans must be distinguished from arteriosclerotic peripheral vascular disease by the criteria mentioned in "Workup."

WORKUP

The diagnosis of thromboangiitis obliterans is made on:

- Clinical criteria
  1. Peripheral vascular disease occurring predominantly in men before the age of 50 yr
  2. Typically, affects the arms and the legs and not just the lower extremities as arteriosclerosis does
  3. Found solely in tobacco smokers, with improvement in those who abstain
  4. Associated with migratory thrombophlebitis
  5. No other atherosclerotic risk factors (e.g., diabetes, cholesterol, or hypertension)
- Angiographic criteria (see "Imaging Studies")
- Pathologic criteria: fresh inflammatory thrombus within both small- and medium-size arteries and veins, along with giant cells around the thrombus

IMAGING STUDIES

- Noninvasive vascular studies help differentiate proximal occlusive disease characteristic of arteriosclerosis from distal disease typical of thromboangiitis obliterans.
- Angiography findings in thromboangiitis obliterans include:
  1. Involvement of distal small- and medium-size vessels
  2. Occlusions are segmental, multiple, smooth, and tapered
  3. Collateral circulation gives a "tree root" or "spider leg" appearance
  4. Both upper and lower extremities are involved

TREATMENT

NONPHARMACOLOGIC THERAPY

Abstaining from smoking is the only way to stop the progression of the disease. Medical and surgical treatments will prove to be futile if the patient continues to smoke. Exacerbation of ischemic ulcers is directly related to tobacco use.

ACUTE GENERAL Rx

- The goal of medical treatment is to provide relief of ischemic pain and healing of ischemic ulcers. If the patient does not completely abstain from tobacco, medical measures will not be helpful.
- Prostaglandin vasodilator therapy given IV or intraarterially provides some relief of pain but does not change the course of the disease.
- Epidural anesthesia and hyperbaric oxygen have a vasodilator effect and have been shown to aid in pain relief from ischemic ulcers.

CHRONIC Rx

- Surgical bypass procedures and sympathectomy, as with medical treatment, will not be efficacious unless the patient stops smoking.
- Surgical bypass may be difficult because the occlusions of thromboangiitis obliterans are distal. Nevertheless, if successfully done, this can lead to rapid healing of ischemic ulcers.
- Sympathectomy leads to increased flow by decreasing the vasoconstriction of distal vessels and also has been shown to aid in the healing and relief of pain from ischemic ulcers.
- Debridement must be done on necrotic ulcers if needed.
- Amputation is frequently required for gangrenous digits; however, below-knee or above-knee amputations are rarely necessary.

DISPOSITION

The course of thromboangiitis obliterans can be dramatically changed by the cessation of tobacco smoking. If the patient continues to smoke, recurrent exacerbation of ischemic ulcers, necrosis, and gangrene leading to small digit amputations will be inevitable.

REFERRAL

Vascular surgical consultation is recommended in any young smoker with claudication and ischemic ulcers, especially if both the upper and lower extremities are involved.

PEARLS & CONSIDERATIONS

COMMENTS

Smoking cessation is mandatory. In individuals who quit smoking, prognosis is markedly improved.

SUGGESTED READING

Olin JW: Thromboangiitis obliterans (Buerger's disease), *N Engl J Med* 343(12):864, 2000.

AUTHOR: **PETER PETROPOULOS, M.D.**

Thrombophlebitis, Superficial

BASIC INFORMATION

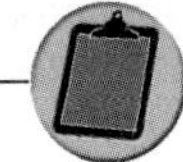

DEFINITION

Superficial thrombophlebitis is inflammatory thrombosis in subcutaneous veins.

SYNONYMS

Phlebitis

ICD-9CM CODES
451.0 Thrombophlebitis, superficial

EPIDEMIOLOGY & DEMOGRAPHICS

- 20% of superficial thrombophlebitis cases are associated with occult DVT.
- Catheter-related thrombophlebitis incidence is 100:100,000.

PHYSICAL FINDINGS & CLINICAL PRESENTATION

- Subcutaneous vein is palpable, tender; tender cord is present with erythema and edema of the overlying skin and subcutaneous tissue.
- Induration, redness, and tenderness are localized along the course of the vein. This linear appearance rather than circular appearance is useful to distinguish thrombophlebitis from other conditions (cellulitis, erythema nodosum).
- There is no significant swelling of the limb (superficial thrombophlebitis generally does not produce swelling of the limb).
- Low-grade fever may be present. High fever and chills are suggestive of septic phlebitis.

ETIOLOGY

- Trauma to preexisting varices
- Intravenous cannulation of veins (most common cause)
- Abdominal cancer (e.g., carcinoma of pancreas)
- Infection (*Staphylococcus* is the most common pathogen)
- Hypercoagulable state
- DVT

DIAGNOSIS

DIFFERENTIAL DIAGNOSIS

- Lymphangitis
- Cellulitis
- Erythema nodosum
- Panniculitis
- Kaposi's sarcoma

WORKUP

Laboratory evaluation to exclude infectious etiology and imaging studies to rule out DVT in suspected cases

LABORATORY TESTS

CBC with differential, blood cultures, culture of IV catheter tip (when secondary to intravenous cannulation)

IMAGING STUDIES

- Serial ultrasound or venography in patients with suspected DVT
- CT scan of abdomen in patients with suspected malignancy (Trousseau's syndrome: recurrent migratory thrombophlebitis)

TREATMENT

NONPHARMACOLOGIC THERAPY

- Warm, moist compresses
- It is not necessary to restrict activity; however, if there is extensive thrombophlebitis, bed rest with the leg elevated will limit the thrombosis and improve symptoms.

ACUTE GENERAL Rx

- NSAIDs to relieve symptoms
- Treatment of septic thrombophlebitis with antibiotics with adequate coverage of *Staphylococcus*
- Ligation and division of the superficial vein at the junction to avoid propagation of the clot in the deep venous system when the thrombophlebitis progresses toward the junction of the involved superficial vein with deep veins

DISPOSITION

Clinical improvement within 7-10 days

REFERRAL

Surgical referral in selected cases (see "Acute General Rx")

PEARLS & CONSIDERATIONS

COMMENTS

- Patients with positive cultures should be evaluated and treated for endocarditis.
- Septic thrombophlebitis is more common in IV drug addicts.

AUTHOR: **FRED F. FERRI, M.D.**

BASIC INFORMATION

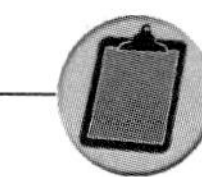

DEFINITION

Deep vein thrombosis (DVT) is the development of thrombi in the deep veins of the extremities or pelvis.

SYNONYMS

DVT
Deep venous thrombophlebitis

ICD-9CM CODES
451.1 Thrombosis of deep vessels of lower extremities
451.83 Thrombosis of deep veins of upper extremities
541.9 Deep vein thrombosis of unspecified site

EPIDEMIOLOGY & DEMOGRAPHICS

- Annual incidence in urban population is 1.6 cases/1000 persons.
- The risk of recurrent thromboembolism is higher among men than women.

PHYSICAL FINDINGS & CLINICAL PRESENTATION

- Pain and swelling of the affected extremity
- In lower extremity DVT, leg pain on dorsiflexion of the foot (Homans' sign)
- Physical examination may be unremarkable

ETIOLOGY

The etiology is often multifactorial (prolonged stasis, coagulation abnormalities, vessel wall trauma). The following are risk factors for DVT:

- Prolonged immobilization (≥3 days)
- Postoperative state
- Trauma to pelvis and lower extremities
- Birth control pills, high-dose estrogen therapy; conjugated equine estrogen but not esterified estrogen is associated wtih increased risk of DVT; estrogen plus progestin is associated with doubling the risk of venous thrombosis
- Visceral cancer (lung, pancreas, alimentary tract, GU tract)
- Age >60 yr
- History of thromboembolic disease
- Hematologic disorders (e.g., antithrombin III deficiency, protein C deficiency, protein S deficiency, heparin cofactor II deficiency, sticky platelet syndrome, G20210A prothrombin mutation, lupus anticoagulant, dysfibrinogenemias, anticardiolipin antibody, hyperhomocystinemia, concurrent homocystinuria, high levels of factors VIII, XI, and factor V Leiden mutation)
- Pregnancy and early puerperium
- Obesity, CHF
- Surgery, fracture, or injury involving lower leg or pelvis
- Surgery requiring >30 min of anesthesia
- Gynecologic surgery (particularly gynecologic cancer surgery)
- Recent travel (within 2 wk, lasting >4 hr)
- Smoking and abdominal obesity
- Central venous catheter or pacemaker insertion
- Superficial vein thrombosis, varicose veins

DIAGNOSIS

DIFFERENTIAL DIAGNOSIS

- Postphlebitic syndrome
- Superficial thrombophlebitis
- Ruptured Baker's cyst
- Cellulitis, lymphangitis, Achilles tendinitis
- Hematoma
- Muscle or soft tissue injury, stress fracture
- Varicose veins, lymphedema
- Arterial insufficiency
- Abscess
- Claudication
- Venous stasis

WORKUP

The clinical diagnosis of DVT is inaccurate. Pain, tenderness, swelling, or color changes are not specific for DVT. Compression ultrasonography is preferred as the initial study to diagnose DVT. An initial negative test should be repeated after 5 days (if the clinical suspicion of DVT persists) to detect propagation of any thrombosis to the proximal veins. Comprehensive ultrasonography is a more extensive test, which examines the deep veins from the inguinal ligament to the level of the malleolus. Recent literature reports indicate that it may be safe to withhold anticoagulation after negative results on comprehensive duplex ultrasonography in nonpregnant patients with a suspected first episode of symptomatic DVT of the leg.

LABORATORY TESTS

- Laboratory tests are not specific for DVT. Baseline PT (INR), PTT, and platelet count should be obtained on all patients before starting anticoagulation.
- Use of D-dimer assay by ELISA may be useful in the management of suspected DVT. The combination of a normal D-dimer study on presentation together with a normal compression venous ultrasound is useful to exclude DVT and generally eliminate the need to do repeat ultrasound at 5-7 days. Recent trials indicate that DVT can be ruled out in patients who are clinically unlikely to have DVT and who have a negative D-dimer test. Compressive ultrasonography can be safely omitted in such patients.
- Laboratory evaluation of young patients with DVT, patients with recurrent thrombosis without obvious causes, and those with a family history of thrombosis should include protein S, protein C, fibrinogen, antithrombin III level, lupus anticoagulant, anticardiolipin antibodies, factor V Leiden, factor VIII, factor IX, and plasma homocysteine levels.

IMAGING STUDIES

- Compression ultrasonography is generally preferred as the initial study because it is noninvasive and can be repeated serially (useful to monitor suspected acute DVT); it offers good sensitivity for detecting proximal vein thrombosis (in the popliteal or femoral vein). Its disadvantages are poor visualization of deep iliac and pelvic veins and poor sensitivity in isolated or nonocclusive calf vein thrombi.
- Contrast venography is the gold standard for evaluation of DVT of the lower extremity. It is, however, invasive and painful. Additional disadvantages are the increased risk of phlebitis, new thrombosis, renal failure, and hypersensitivity reaction to contrast media; it also gives poor visualization of deep femoral vein in the thigh and internal iliac vein and its tributaries.
- Magnetic resonance direct thrombus imaging (MRDTI) is an accurate noninvasive test for diagnosis of DVT. Current limitations are its cost and lack of widespread availability.

TREATMENT

NONPHARMACOLOGIC THERAPY

- Initial bed rest for 1-4 days followed by gradual resumption of normal activity
- Patient education on anticoagulant therapy and associated risks

ACUTE GENERAL Rx

- Traditional treatment consists of IV unfractionated heparin for 4 to 7 days followed by warfarin therapy. Low–molecular-weight heparin enoxaparin (Lovenox) is also effective for initial management of DVT and allows outpatient treatment. Recommended dose is 1 mg/kg q12h SC and continued for a minimum of 5 days and until a therapeutic INR (2-3) has been achieved with warfarin. Once-daily fondaparinux (Arixtra), a synthetic analog of heparin, is also as effective and safe as twice daily enoxaparin in the initial treatment of patients with symptomatic DVT. Warfarin therapy should be initiated when appropriate (usually within 72 hr of initiation of heparin). A 5 mg loading dose of warfarin is recommended in inpatients because it produces less excess anticoagulation than does a 10 mg dose; the smaller dose also avoids the development of a potential hypercoagulable state caused by precipitous decreases in levels of protein C during the first 36 hr of warfarin therapy. In the outpatient setting, a warfarin nomogram using 10 mg loading doses may be more effective in reaching a therapeutic INR.

- Low–molecular-weight heparin, when used, should be overlapped with warfarin for at least 5 days and until the INR has exceeded 2 for 2 consecutive days.
- Exclusions from outpatient treatment of DVT include patients with potential high complication risk (e.g., Hemoglobin <7, platelet count <75,000, guaiac-positive stool, recent CVA or noncutaneous surgery, noncompliance).
- Insertion of an inferior vena cava filter to prevent pulmonary embolism is recommended in patients with contraindications to anticoagulation.
- Thrombolytic therapy (streptokinase) can be used in rare cases (unless contraindicated) in patients with extensive iliofemoral venous thrombosis and a low risk of bleeding.

CHRONIC Rx

- Conventional-intensity warfarin therapy is more effective than low-intensity warfarin therapy for the long term prevention of recurrent DVT. The low-intensity warfarin regimen does not reduce the risk of clinically important bleeding.
- The optimal duration of anticoagulant therapy varies with the cause of DVT and the patient's risk factors:

1. Therapy for 3-6 mo is generally satisfactory in patients with reversible risk factors (low-risk group).
2. Anticoagulation for at least 6 mo is recommended for patients with idiopathic venous thrombosis or medical risk factors for DVT (intermediate-risk group)
3. Indefinite anticoagulation is necessary in patients with DVT associated with active cancer; long-term anticoagulation is also indicated in patients with inherited thrombophilia (e.g., deficiency of protein C or S antibody), antiphospholipid, and those with recurrent episodes of idiopathic DVT (high-risk group).

- Measurement of D-dimer after withdrawal of oral anticoagulation may be useful to estimate the risk of recurrence. Patients with a first spontaneous DVT and a D-dimer level <250 μg/mL after withdrawal of oral anticoagulation have a low risk of DVT recurrence.

PEARLS & CONSIDERATIONS

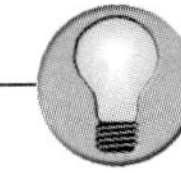

COMMENTS

- When using heparin, there is a risk of heparin-induced thrombocytopenia (with unfractionated more so than with LMWH). Platelet count should be obtained initially and repeated every 3 days while on heparin.
- Prophylaxis of DVT is recommended in all patients at risk (e.g., low—molecular-weight heparin [enoxaparin 30 mg SC bid] after major trauma, post surgery of hip and knee; enoxaparin 40 mg SC qd post–abdominal surgery in patients with moderate to high DVT risk; gradient elastic stockings alone or in combination with intermittent pneumatic compression [IPC] boots following neurosurgery).
- Ximelagatran is an oral direct thrombin inhibitor. For prophylaxis of venous thromboembolism, ximelagatran 24 mg PO bid started the morning after total knee arthroplasty is well tolerated and at least as effective as warfarin, but it does not require coagulation monitoring or dose adjustment.
- Fondaparinux (Arixtra), a synthetic analog of heparin, can also be used for prevention of DVT after hip fracture surgery, hip replacement, or knee replacement. Initial dose is 2.5 mg SC given 6 to 8 hr postoperatively and continued daily. Its bleeding risk is similar to enoxaparin; however, it is more effective in preventing DVT.
- The risk of recurrent venous thromboembolism in heterozygous carriers of factor V Leiden and a first spontaneous venous thromboembolism is similar to that of noncarriers of factor V Leiden; therefore heterozygous patients should receive secondary thromboprophylaxis for a similar length of time as patients without factor V Leiden.
- Approximately 20%-50% of patients with DVT develop postthrombotic syndrome characterized by leg edema, pain, venous ectasia, skin unduraiton, and ulceration.
- Exercise following DVT is reasonable because it improves flexibility of the affected leg and does not increase symptoms in patients with postthrombotic syndrome.

SUGGESTED READINGS

Baarslag et al: Prospective study of color duplex ultrasonography compared with contrast venography in patients suspected of having deep venous thrombosis of the upper extremities, *Ann Intern Med* 136:865, 2002.

Bates SM, Ginsberg JS: Treatment of deep-vein thrombosis, *N Engl J Med* 351:268, 2004.

Berquist D et al: Duration of prophylaxis against venous thromboembolism with enoxaparin after surgery for cancer, *N Engl J Med* 346:975, 2002.

Eichinger S et al: D-Dimer levels and risk of recurrent venous thromboembolism, *JAMA* 290:1071, 2003.

Francis CW et al: Ximelagatran versus warfarin for the prevention of venous thromboembolism after total knee arthroplasty, *Ann Intern Med* 137:648, 2002.

Fraser DG et al: Diagnosis of lower-limb deep venous thrombosis: a prospective blinded study of magnetic resonance direct thrombus imaging, *Ann Intern Med* 136:89, 2002.

Kahn SR et al: Acute effects of exercise in patients with previous DVT: impact of the post-thrombotic syndrome, *Chest* 123:399, 2003.

Kelly et al: Plasma D-Dimers in the diagnosis of venous thromboembolism, *Arch Intern Med* 162:747, 2002.

Kovacs MJ et al: Comparison of 10-mg and 5mg warfarin initiation nomograms together with low-molecular-weight heparin for outpatient treatment of acute venous thromboembolism. A randomized, double-blind, controlled trial, *Ann Intern Med* 138:714, 2003.

Kraaijenhagen RA et al: Simplification of the diagnostic management of suspected deep vein thrombosis, *Arch Intern Med* 162:907, 2002.

Meyer G et al: Comparison of low-molecular-weight heparin and warfarin for the secondary prevention of venous thromboembolism in patients with cancer, *Arch Intern Med* 162:1729, 2002.

Schulman S et al: Secondary prevention of venous thromboembolism with the oral direct thrombin inhibitor ximelagran, *N Engl J Med* 349:1713, 2003.

Stevens SM et al: Withholding anticoagulation after a negative result on duplex ultrasonography for suspected symptomatic deep venous thrombosis, *Ann Intern Med* 140:985, 2004.

Wells PS et al: Evaluation of d-dimer in the diagnosis of suspected deep vein thrombosis, *N Engl J Med* 349:1227, 2003.

AUTHOR: **FRED F. FERRI, M.D.**

Thrombotic Thrombocytopenic Purpura

BASIC INFORMATION

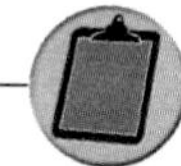

DEFINITION

Thrombotic thrombocytopenic purpura (TTP) is a rare disorder characterized by thrombocytopenia (often accompanied by purpura) and microangiopathic hemolytic anemia; neurologic impairment, renal dysfunction, and fever may also be present.

SYNONYMS

TTP

ICD-9CM CODES
446.6 Thrombotic thrombocytopenic purpura

EPIDEMIOLOGY & DEMOGRAPHICS

- TTP primarily affects females between 10 and 50 yr of age.
- Frequency is 3.7 cases/yr/1 million persons.

PHYSICAL FINDINGS & CLINICAL PRESENTATION

- Purpura (secondary to thrombocytopenia)
- Jaundice, pallor (secondary to hemolysis)
- Mucosal bleeding
- Fever
- Fluctuating levels of consciousness (secondary to thrombotic occlusion of the cerebral vessels)

ETIOLOGY

- The exact cause of TTP remains unknown. Recent studies reveal that there is platelet aggregation as a result of abnormalities in circulating von Willebrand factor caused by endothelial injury.
- Many drugs, including clopidogrel, penicillin, antineoplastic agents, oral contraceptives, quinine, and ticlopidine, have been associated with TTP. Other precipitating causes include infectious agents, pregnancy, malignancies, allogenic bone marrow transplantation, and neurologic disorders.

DIAGNOSIS

DIFFERENTIAL DIAGNOSIS

- DIC
- Malignant hypertension
- Vasculitis
- Eclampsia or preeclampsia
- Hemolytic-uremic syndrome (typically encountered in children, often following a viral infection)
- Gastroenteritis as a result of a serotoxin-producing serotype of *Escherichia coli*
- Medications: clopidogrel, ticlopidine, penicillin, antineoplastic chemotherapeutic agents, oral contraceptives

WORKUP

- A comprehensive history, physical examination, and laboratory evaluation usually confirms the diagnosis.
- The disease often begins as a flulike illness ultimately followed by clinical and laboratory abnormalities.

LABORATORY TESTS

- Severe anemia and thrombocytopenia
- Elevated BUN and creatinine
- Evidence of hemolysis: elevated reticulocyte count, indirect bilirubin, LDH, decreased haptoglobin
- Urinalysis: hematuria (red cells and red cell casts in urine sediment) and proteinuria
- Peripheral smear: severely fragmented RBCs (schistocytes)
- No laboratory evidence of DIC (normal FDP, fibrinogen)

TREATMENT

ACUTE GENERAL Rx

- Discontinue potential offending agents.
- Plasmapheresis with fresh frozen plasma (FFP) replacement; cryosupernatant may be substituted for FFP in patients who fail to respond to this treatment. Daily plasma exchange is generally performed until hemolysis has ceased and the platelet count has normalized.
- Corticosteroids (prednisone 1-2 mg/kg/day) may be effective alone in patients with mild disease or may be administered concomitantly with plasmapheresis plus plasma exchange with FFP.
- Vincristine has been used in patients refractory to plasmapheresis.
- Use of antiplatelet agents (ASA, dipyridamole) is controversial.
- Platelet transfusions are contraindicated except in severely thrombocytopenic patients with documented bleeding.
- Splenectomy is performed in refractory cases.

CHRONIC Rx

- Relapsing TTP may be treated with plasma exchange.
- Remission of chronic TTP that is unresponsive to conventional therapy has been reported after treatment with cyclophosphamide and the monoclonal antibody rituximab.
- Splenectomy done while the patients are in remission has been used in some centers to decrease the frequency of relapse in TTP.

DISPOSITION

- Survival of patients with TTP currently exceeds 80% with plasma exchange therapy.
- Relapse occurs in 20%-40% of patients who have TTP in remission.

REFERRAL

Surgical referral for splenectomy in selected patients (see "Acute General Rx" and "Chronic Rx")

PEARLS & CONSIDERATIONS

COMMENTS

Thrombotic microangiopathy can also be associated with administration of cyclosporine and mitomycin C, and with HIV infection.

SUGGESTED READINGS

Bennett CL et al: Thrombotic thrombocytopenic purpura associated with clopidogrel, *N Engl J Med* 342:1773, 2000.

Chen DK et al: Thrombotic thrombocytopenic purpura associated with ticlopidine use, *Arch Intern Med* 159:311, 1999.

Elliot MA, Nichols WL: Thrombotic thrombocytopenic purpura and hemolytic uremic syndrome, *Mayo Clin Proc* 76:1154, 2001.

Kojouri K et al: Quinine-associated thrombotic thrombocytopenic purpura-hemolytic uremic syndrome: frequency, clinical features, and long-term outcomes, *Ann Intern Med* 135:1047, 2001.

AUTHOR: **FRED F. FERRI, M.D.**

Thyroid Carcinoma 

BASIC INFORMATION

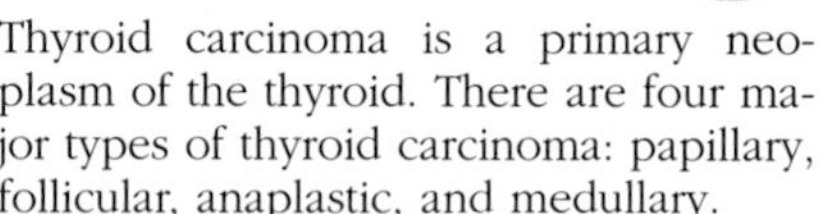

DEFINITION

Thyroid carcinoma is a primary neoplasm of the thyroid. There are four major types of thyroid carcinoma: papillary, follicular, anaplastic, and medullary.

SYNONYMS

Papillary carcinoma of thyroid
Follicular carcinoma of thyroid
Anaplastic carcinoma of thyroid
Medullary carcinoma of thyroid

ICD-9CM CODES
193 Malignant neoplasm of thyroid

EPIDEMIOLOGY & DEMOGRAPHICS

- Thyroid cancer is the most common endocrine cancer, with an annual incidence of 14,000 new cases in the U.S. and about 1100 deaths.
- Female:male ratio of 3:1.
- Most common type (50% to 60%) is papillary carcinoma.
- Median age at diagnosis: 45-50 yr.

PHYSICAL FINDINGS & CLINICAL PRESENTATION

- Presence of thyroid nodule
- Hoarseness and cervical lymphadenopathy
- Painless swelling in the region of the thyroid

ETIOLOGY

- Risk factors: prior neck irradiation
- Multiple endocrine neoplasia II (medullary carcinoma)

DIAGNOSIS

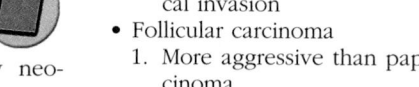

DIFFERENTIAL DIAGNOSIS

- Multinodular goiter
- Lymphocytic thyroiditis
- Ectopic thyroid

WORKUP

The workup of thyroid carcinoma includes laboratory evaluation and diagnostic imaging. However, diagnosis is confirmed with fine-needle aspiration (FNA) or surgical biopsy. The characteristics of thyroid carcinoma vary with the type:

- Papillary carcinoma
  1. Most frequently occurs in women during second or third decades
  2. Histologically, psammoma bodies (calcific bodies present in papillary projections) are pathognomonic; they are found in 35%-45% of papillary thyroid carcinomas
  3. Majority are not papillary lesions but mixed papillary follicular carcinomas
  4. Spread is via lymphatics and by local invasion
- Follicular carcinoma
  1. More aggressive than papillary carcinoma
  2. Incidence increases with age
  3. Tends to metastasize hematogenously to bone, producing pathologic fractures
  4. Tends to concentrate iodine (useful for radiation therapy)
- Anaplastic carcinoma
  1. Very aggressive neoplasm
  2. Two major histologic types: small cell (less aggressive, 5-yr survival approximately 20%) and giant cell (death usually within 6 mo of diagnosis)
- Medullary carcinoma
  1. Unifocal lesion: found sporadically in elderly patients
  2. Bilateral lesions: associated with pheochromocytoma and hyperparathyroidism; this combination is known as MEN-II and is inherited as an autosomal dominant disorder

LABORATORY TESTS

- Thyroid function studies are generally normal. TSH, T_4, and serum thyroglobulin levels should be obtained before thyroidectomy in patients with confirmed thyroid carcinoma
- Increased plasma calcitonin assay in patients with medullary carcinoma (tumors produce thyrocalcitonin)

IMAGING STUDIES

- Thyroid scanning with iodine-123 or technetium-99m can identify hypofunctioning (cold) nodules, which are more likely to be malignant. However, warm nodules can also be malignant.
- Thyroid ultrasound can detect solitary solid nodules that have a high risk of malignancy. However, a negative ultrasound does not exclude diagnosis of thyroid carcinoma.
- FNA biopsy is the best method to assess a thyroid nodule (refer to "Thyroid Nodule" in Section I).

TREATMENT

ACUTE GENERAL Rx

- Papillary carcinoma
  1. Total thyroidectomy is indicated if the patient has:
     a. Extrapyramidal extension of carcinoma
     b. Papillary carcinoma limited to thyroid but a positive history of irradiation to the neck
     c. Lesion >2 cm
  2. Lobectomy with isthmectomy may be considered in patients with intrathyroid papillary carcinoma <2 cm and no history of neck or head irradiation; most follow surgery with suppressive therapy with thyroid hormone because these tumors are TSH responsive. The accepted practice is to suppress serum TSH concentrations to <0.1 μU/ml.
  3. Radiotherapy with iodine-131 (after total thyroidectomy), followed by thyroid suppression therapy with triiodothyronine, can be used in metastatic papillary carcinoma.
- Follicular carcinoma
  1. Total thyroidectomy followed by TSH suppression as noted previously
  2. Radiotherapy with iodine-131 followed by thyroid suppression therapy with triiodothyronine is useful in patients with metastasis
- Anaplastic carcinoma
  1. At diagnosis, this neoplasm is rarely operable; palliative surgery is indicated for extremely large tumor compressing the trachea.
  2. Management is usually restricted to radiation therapy or chemotherapy (combination of doxorubicin, cisplatin, and other antineoplastic agents); these measures rarely provide significant palliation.
- Medullary carcinoma
  1. Thyroidectomy should be performed.
  2. Patients and their families should be screened for pheochromocytoma and hyperparathyroidism.

DISPOSITION

Prognosis varies with the type of thyroid carcinoma: 5-yr survival approaches 80% for follicular carcinoma and is approximately 5% with anaplastic carcinoma.

PEARLS & CONSIDERATIONS

COMMENTS

Family members of patients with medullary carcinoma should be screened; DNA analysis for the detection of mutations in the RET gene structure permits the identification of MEN IIA gene carriers.

AUTHOR: **FRED F. FERRI, M.D.**

SECTION I

BASIC INFORMATION

DEFINITION

A thyroid nodule is an abnormality found on physical examination of the thyroid gland; nodules can be benign (70%) or malignant.

ICD-9CM CODES
241.0 Nodule, thyroid

EPIDEMIOLOGY & DEMOGRAPHICS

- Palpable thyroid nodules occur in 4%-7% of the population.
- Thyroid nodules can be found in 50% of autopsies; however, only 1 in 10 is palpable.
- Malignancy is present in 5%-30% of palpable nodules.
- Incidence of thyroid nodules increases after 45 yr of age. They are found more frequently in women.
- History of prior head and neck irradiation increases the risk of thyroid cancer.
- Increased likelihood that nodule is malignant: nodule increasing in size or >2 cm, regional lymphadenopathy, fixation to adjacent tissues, age <40 yr, symptoms of local invasion (dysphagia, hoarseness, neck pain, male sex, family history of thyroid cancer or polyposis [Gardner syndrome]).

PHYSICAL FINDINGS & CLINICAL PRESENTATION

- Palpable, firm, and nontender nodule in the thyroid area should prompt suspicion of carcinoma. Signs of metastasis are regional lymphadenopathy, inspiratory stridor.
- Signs and symptoms of thyrotoxicosis can be found in functioning nodules.

ETIOLOGY

- History of prior head and neck irradiation
- Family history of pheochromocytoma, carcinoma of the thyroid, and hyperparathyroidism (medullary carcinoma of the thyroid is a component of MEN-II)

DIAGNOSIS

DIFFERENTIAL DIAGNOSIS

- Thyroid carcinoma
- Multinodular goiter
- Thyroglossal duct cyst
- Epidermoid cyst
- Laryngocele
- Nonthyroid neck neoplasm
- Branchial cleft cyst

WORKUP

- Fine-needle aspiration (FNA) biopsy is the best diagnostic study; the accuracy can be >90%, but it is directly related to the level of experience of the physician and the cytopathologist interpreting the aspirate.
- FNA biopsy is less reliable with thyroid cystic lesions; surgical excision should be considered for most thyroid cysts not abolished by aspiration.
- A diagnostic approach to thyroid nodule is described in Section III.

LABORATORY TESTS

- TSH, T_4, and serum thyroglobulin levels should be obtained before thyroidectomy in patients with confirmed thyroid carcinoma on FNA biopsy.
- Serum calcitonin at random or after pentagastrin stimulation is useful when suspecting medullary carcinoma of the thyroid and in anyone with a family history of medullary thyroid carcinoma.
- Serum thyroid autoantibodies (see "Thyroiditis" in Section I) are useful when suspecting thyroiditis.

IMAGING STUDIES

- Thyroid ultrasound is done in some patients to evaluate the size of the thyroid and the number, composition (solid vs. cystic), and dimensions of the thyroid nodule; solid thyroid nodules have a higher incidence of malignancy, but cystic nodules can also be malignant.
- The introduction of high-resolution ultrasonography has made it possible to detect many nonpalpable nodules (incidentalomas) in the thyroid (found at autopsy in 30%-60% of cadavers). Most of these lesions are benign. For most patients with nonpalpable nodules that are incidentally detected by thyroid imaging, simple follow-up neck palpation is sufficient.
- Thyroid scan with technetium-99m pertechnetate:
  1. Classifies nodules as hyperfunctioning (hot), normally functioning (warm), or nonfunctioning (cold); cold nodules have a higher incidence of malignancy.
  2. Scan has difficulty evaluating nodules near the thyroid isthmus or at the periphery of the gland.
  3. Normal tissue over a nonfunctioning nodule might mask the nodule as "warm" or normally functioning.
- Both thyroid scan and ultrasound provide information about the risk of malignant neoplasia based on the characteristics of the thyroid nodule, but their value in the initial evaluation of a thyroid nodule is limited because neither provides a definite tissue diagnosis.

TREATMENT

GENERAL Rx

- Evaluation of results of FNA
  1. Normal cells: may repeat biopsy during present evaluation or reevaluate patient after 3-6 mo of suppressive therapy (l-thyroxine, prescribed in doses to suppress the TSH level to 0.1-0.5)
     a. Failure to regress indicates increased likelihood of malignancy.
     b. Reliance on repeat needle biopsy is preferable to routine surgery for nodules not responding to thyroxine.
  2. Malignant cells: surgery
  3. Hypercellularity: thyroid scan
     a. Hot nodule: ^{131}I therapy if the patient is hyperthyroid
     b. Warm or cold nodule: surgery (rule out follicular adenoma vs. carcinoma)

DISPOSITION

Variable with results of FNA biopsy. Refer to "Thyroid Carcinoma" in Section I for prognosis in patients with malignant nodules diagnosed with biopsy.

REFERRAL

Surgical referral for FNA biopsy

PEARLS & CONSIDERATIONS

COMMENTS

- Most solid, benign nodules grow, therefore an increase in nodule volume alone is not a reliable predictor of malignancy.
- Surgery is indicated in hard or fixed nodule, presence of dysphagia or hoarseness, and rapidly growing solid masses regardless of "benign" results on FNA.
- Suppressive therapy of malignant thyroid nodules postoperatively with thyroxine is indicated. The use of suppressive therapy for benign solitary nodules is controversial.

SUGGESTED READINGS

Alexander EK et al: Natural history of benign solid and cystic thyroid nodules, *Ann Intern Med* 138:315, 2003.

Welker MJ, Orlov D: Thyroid nodules, *Am Fam Physician* 67:559, 2003.

AUTHOR: **FRED F. FERRI, M.D.**

Thyroiditis (PTG)

BASIC INFORMATION

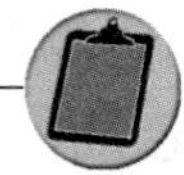

DEFINITION

Thyroiditis is an inflammatory disease of the thyroid. It is a multifaceted disease with varying etiology, different clinical characteristics (depending on the stage), and distinct histopathology. Thyroiditis can be subdivided into three common types (Hashimoto's, painful, painless) and two rare forms (suppurative, Riedel's). To add to the confusion, there are various synonyms for each form, and there is no internationally accepted classification of autoimmune thyroid disease.

SYNONYMS

Hashimoto's thyroiditis: *chronic lymphocytic thyroiditis, chronic autoimmune thyroiditis, lymphadenoid goiter*
Painful subacute thyroiditis: subacute thyroiditis, *giant cell thyroiditis, de Quervain's thyroiditis, subacute granulomatous thyroiditis, pseudogranulomatous thyroiditis*
Painless postpartum thyroiditis: *subacute lymphocytic thyroiditis, postpartum thyroiditis*
Painless sporadic thyroiditis: *silent sporadic thyroiditis, subacute lymphocytic thyroiditis*
Suppurative thyroiditis: *acute suppurative thyroiditis, bacterial thyroiditis microbial inflammatory thyroiditis, pyogenic thyroiditis*
Riedel's thyroiditis: *fibrous thyroiditis*

ICD-9CM CODES
245.2 Hashimoto's thyroiditis
245.1 Subacute thyroiditis
245.9 Silent thyroiditis
245.0 Suppurative thyroiditis
245.3 Riedel's thyroiditis

PHYSICAL FINDINGS & CLINICAL PRESENTATION

- Hashimoto's: patients may have signs of hyperthyroidism (tachycardia, diaphoresis, palpitations, weight loss) or hypothyroidism (fatigue, weight gain, delayed reflexes) depending on the stage of the disease. Usually there is diffuse, firm enlargement of the thyroid gland; thyroid gland may also be of normal size (atrophic form with clinically manifested hypothyroidism).
- Painful subacute: exquisitely tender, enlarged thyroid, fever; signs of hyperthyroidism are initially present; signs of hypothyroidism can subsequently develop.
- Painless thyroiditis: clinical features are similar to subacute thyroiditis except for the absence of tenderness of the thyroid gland.
- Suppurative: patient is febrile with severe neck pain, focal tenderness of the involved portion of the thyroid, erythema of the overlying skin.
- Riedel's: slowly enlarging hard mass in the anterior neck; often mistaken for thyroid cancer; signs of hypothyroidism occur in advanced stages.

ETIOLOGY

- Hashimoto's: autoimmune disorder that begins with the activation of CD4 (helper) T-lymphocytes specific for thyroid antigens. The etiologic factor for the activation of these cells is unknown.
- Painful subacute: possibly postviral; usually follows a respiratory illness; it is not considered to be a form of autoimmune thyroiditis.
- Painless thyroiditis: it frequently occurs postpartum.
- Suppurative: infectious etiology, generally bacterial, although fungi and parasites have also been implicated; it often occurs in immunocompromised hosts or following a penetrating neck injury.
- Riedel's: fibrous infiltration of the thyroid; etiology is unknown.
- Drug induced: lithium, interferon alfa, amiodarone, interleukin-2.

DIAGNOSIS

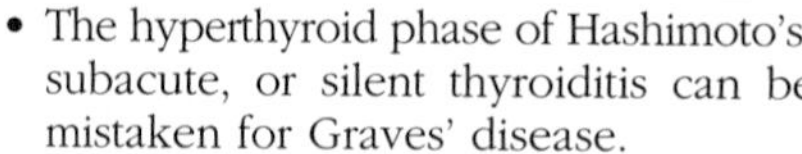

DIFFERENTIAL DIAGNOSIS

- The hyperthyroid phase of Hashimoto's, subacute, or silent thyroiditis can be mistaken for Graves' disease.
- Riedel's thyroiditis can be mistaken for carcinoma of the thyroid.
- Painful subacute thyroiditis can be mistaken for infections of the oropharynx and trachea or for suppurative thyroiditis.
- Factitious hyperthyroidism can mimic silent thyroiditis.

WORKUP

- The diagnostic workup includes laboratory and radiologic evaluation to rule out other conditions that may mimic thyroiditis (see "Differential Diagnosis") and to differentiate the various forms of thyroiditis.
- The patient's medical history may be helpful in differentiating the various types of thyroiditis (e.g., presentation following childbirth is suggestive of silent [postpartum, painless] thyroiditis; occurrence following a viral respiratory infection suggests subacute thyroiditis; history of penetrating injury to the neck indicates suppurative thyroiditis).

LABORATORY TESTS

- TSH, free T_4: may be normal, or indicative of hypo- or hyperthyroidism depending on the stage of the thyroiditis.
- WBC with differential: increased WBC with "shift to the left" occurs with subacute and suppurative thyroiditis.
- Antimicrosomal antibodies: detected in >90% of patients with Hashimoto's thyroiditis and 50% to 80% of patients with silent thyroiditis.
- Serum thyroglobulin levels are elevated in patients with subacute and silent thyroiditis; this test is nonspecific but may be useful in monitoring the course of subacute thyroiditis and distinguishing silent thyroiditis from factitious hyperthyroidism (low or absent serum thyroglobulin level).

IMAGING STUDIES

24-hr radioactive iodine uptake (RAIU) is useful to distinguish Graves' disease (increased RAIU) from thyroiditis (normal or low RAIU).

TREATMENT

ACUTE GENERAL Rx

- Treat hypothyroid phase with levothyroxine 25-50 μg/day initially and monitor serum TSH initially every 6-8 wk.
- Control symptoms of hyperthyroidism with β-blockers (e.g., propranolol 20-40 mg PO q6h).
- Control pain in patients with subacute thyroiditis with NSAIDs. Prednisone 20-40 mg qd may be used if NSAIDs are insufficient, but it should be gradually tapered off over several weeks.
- Use IV antibiotics and drain abscess (if present) in patients with suppurative thyroiditis.

DISPOSITION

- Hashimoto's thyroiditis: long-term prognosis is favorable; most patients recover their thyroid function.
- Painful subacute thyroiditis: permanent hypothyroidism occurs in 10% of patients.
- Painless thyroiditis: 6% of patients have permanent hypothyroidism.
- Suppurative thyroiditis: there is usually full recovery following treatment.
- Riedel's thyroiditis: hypothyroidism occurs when fibrous infiltration involves the entire thyroid.

REFERRAL

Surgical referral in patients with compression of adjacent neck structures and in some patients with suppurative thyroiditis

SUGGESTED READING

Pearce EN et al: Thyroiditis, *N Engl J Med* 348:2646, 2003.

AUTHOR: **FRED F. FERRI, M.D.**

BASIC INFORMATION

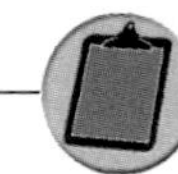

DEFINITION

Thyrotoxic storm is the abrupt and severe exacerbation of thyrotoxicosis.

ICD-9CM CODES
242.9 Thyrotoxic storm
242.0 With goiter
242.2 Multinodular
242.3 Adenomatous
242.8 Thyrotoxicosis factitia

PHYSICAL FINDINGS & CLINICAL PRESENTATION

- Goiter
- Tremor, tachycardia, fever
- Warm, moist skin
- Lid lag, lid retraction, proptosis
- Altered mental status (psychosis, coma, seizures)
- Other: evidence of precipitating factors (infection, trauma)

ETIOLOGY

- Major stress (e.g., infection, MI, DKA) in an undiagnosed hyperthyroid patient
- Inadequate therapy in a hyperthyroid patient

DIAGNOSIS

The clinical presentation is variable. The patient may present with the following signs and symptoms:

- Fever
- Marked anxiety and agitation, psychosis
- Hyperhidrosis, heat intolerance
- Marked weakness and muscle wasting
- Tachyarrhythmias, palpitations
- Diarrhea, nausea, vomiting
- Elderly patients may have a combination of tachycardia, CHF, and mental status changes

DIFFERENTIAL DIAGNOSIS

- Psychiatric disorders
- Alcohol or other drug withdrawal
- Pheochromocytoma
- Metastatic neoplasm

WORKUP

- Laboratory evaluation to confirm hyperthyroidism (elevated free T_4, decreased TSH)
- Evaluation for precipitating factors (e.g., ECG and cardiac enzymes in suspected MI, blood and urine cultures to rule out sepsis)
- Elimination of disorders noted in the differential diagnosis (e.g., psychiatric history, evidence of drug and alcohol abuse)

LABORATORY TESTS

- Free T_4, TSH
- CBC with differential
- Blood and urine cultures
- Glucose
- Liver enzymes
- BUN, creatinine
- Serum calcium
- CPK

IMAGING STUDIES

Chest x-ray to exclude infectious process, neoplasm, CHF in suspected cases

TREATMENT

NONPHARMACOLOGIC THERAPY

- Nutritional care: replace fluid deficit aggressively (daily fluid requirement may reach 6 L); use solutions containing glucose and add multivitamins to the hydrating solution.
- Monitor for fluid overload and CHF in the elderly and in those with underlying cardiovascular or renal disease.
- Treat significant hyperthermia with cooling blankets.

ACUTE GENERAL Rx

- Inhibition of thyroid hormone synthesis
  1. Administer propylthiouracil (PTU) 300-600 mg initially (PO or via NG tube), then 150-300 mg q6h.
  2. If the patient is allergic to PTU, use methimazole (Tapazole) 80-100 mg PO or PR followed by 30 mg PR q8h.
- Inhibition of stored thyroid hormone
  1. Iodide can be administered as sodium iodine 250 mg IV q6h, potassium iodide (SSKI) 5 gtt PO q8h, or Lugol's solution, 10 gtt q8h. It is important to administer PTU or methimazole 1 hr *before* the iodide to prevent the oxidation of iodide to iodine and its incorporation in the synthesis of additional thyroid hormone.
  2. Corticosteroids: dexamethasone 2 mg IV q6h or hydrocortisone 100 mg IV q6h for approximately 48 hr is useful to inhibit thyroid hormone release, impair peripheral conversion of T_3 from T_4, and provide additional adrenocortical hormone to correct deficiency (if present).
- Suppression of peripheral effects of thyroid hormone
  1. β-Adrenergic blockers: Administer propranolol 80-120 mg PO q4-6h. Propranolol may also be given IV 1 mg/min for 2-10 min under continuous ECG and blood pressure monitoring. β-Adrenergic blockers must be used with caution in patients with severe CHF or bronchospasm. Cardioselective β-blockers (e.g., esmolol or metoprolol) may be more appropriate for patients with bronchospasm, but these patients must be closely monitored for exacerbation of bronchospasm because these agents lose their cardioselectivity at high doses.
- Control of fever with acetaminophen 325-650 mg q4h; avoidance of aspirin because it displaces thyroid hormone from its binding protein
- Consider digitalization of patients with CHF and atrial fibrillation (these patients may require higher than usual digoxin doses)
- Treatment of any precipitating factors (e.g., antibiotics if infection is strongly suspected)

DISPOSITION

Patients with thyrotoxic crisis should be treated and appropriately monitored in the ICU.

REFERRAL

Endocrinology referral is appropriate in patients with thyrotoxic crisis.

PEARLS & CONSIDERATIONS

COMMENTS

If the diagnosis is strongly suspected, therapy should be started immediately without waiting for laboratory confirmation.

AUTHOR: **FRED F. FERRI, M.D.**

BASIC INFORMATION

DEFINITION

Tinea corporis is a dermatophyte fungal infection caused by the genera *Trichophyton* or *Microsporum.*

SYNONYMS

Ringworm
Body ringworm
Tinea circinata

ICD-9CM CODES
110.5 Tinea corporis

EPIDEMIOLOGY & DEMOGRAPHICS

- The disease is more common in warm climates.
- There is no predominant age or sex.

PHYSICAL FINDINGS & CLINICAL PRESENTATION

- Typically appears as single or multiple annular lesions with an advancing scaly border; the margin is slightly raised, reddened, and may be pustular.
- The central area becomes hypopigmented and less scaly as the active border progresses outward (Fig. 1-237).
- The trunk and legs are primarily involved.
- Pruritus is variable.
- It is important to remember that recent topical corticosteroid use can significantly alter the appearance of the lesions.

ETIOLOGY

Trichophyton rubrum is the most common pathogen.

DIAGNOSIS

DIFFERENTIAL DIAGNOSIS

- Pityriasis rosea
- Erythema multiforme
- Psoriasis
- SLE
- Syphilis
- Nummular eczema
- Eczema
- Granuloma annulare
- Lyme disease
- Tinea versicolor
- Contact dermatitis

WORKUP

Diagnosis is usually made on clinical grounds. It can be confirmed by direct visualization under the microscope of a small fragment of the scale using wet mount preparation and potassium hydroxide solution; dermatophytes appear as translucent branching filaments (hyphae) with lines of separation appearing at irregular intervals.

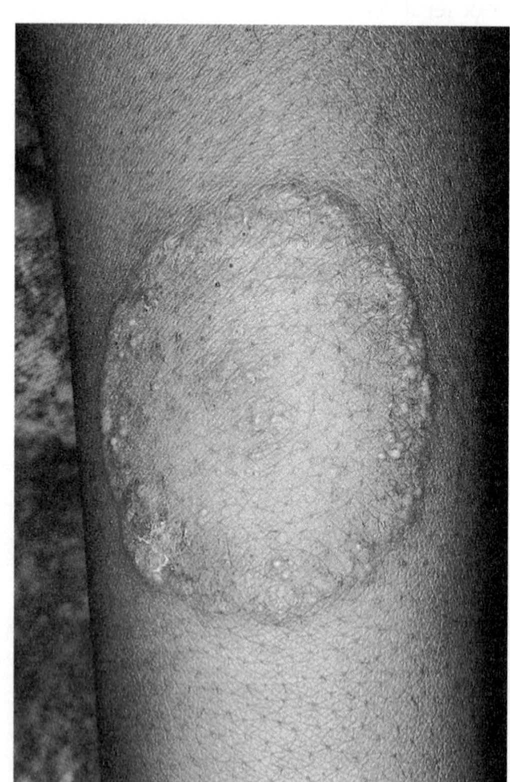

FIGURE 1-237 Annular lesion (tinea corporis). Note raised erythematous scaling border and central clearing. (From Noble J et al: *Textbook of primary care medicine,* ed 3, St Louis, 2001, Mosby.)

LABORATORY TESTS

- Microscopic examination of hyphae
- Mycotic culture is usually not necessary
- Biopsy is indicated only when the diagnosis is uncertain and the patient has failed to respond to treatment

TREATMENT

NONPHARMACOLOGIC THERAPY

Affected areas should be kept clean and dry.

ACUTE GENERAL Rx

- Various creams are effective; the application area should include normal skin about 2 cm beyond the affected area:
  1. Miconazole 2% cream (Monistat-Derm) applied bid for 2 wk
  2. Clotrimazole 1% cream (Mycelex) applied and gently massaged into the affected areas and surrounding areas bid for up to 4 wk
  3. Naftifine 1% cream (Naftin) applied qd
  4. Econazole 1% (Spectazole) applied qd
- Systemic therapy is reserved for severe cases and is usually given up to 4 wk; commonly used agents:
  1. Ketoconazole (Nizoral), 200 mg qd
  2. Fluconazole (Diflucan), 200 mg qd
  3. Terbinafine (Lamisil), 250 mg qd

DISPOSITION

Majority of cases resolve without sequelae within 3-4 wk of therapy.

REFERRAL

Dermatology referral in patients with persistent or recurrent infections

SUGGESTED READINGS

Friedlander SF et al: Terbinafine in the treatment of trichophytin tinea capitis, *Pediatrics* 109:602, 2002.

Hainer BL: Dermatophyte infections, *Am Fam Physician* 67:101, 2003.

Weinstein A, Berman B: Topical treatment of common superficial tinea infections, *Am Fam Physician* 65:2095, 2002.

AUTHOR: **FRED F. FERRI, M.D.**

BASIC INFORMATION

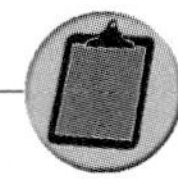

DEFINITION

Tinea cruris is a dermatophyte infection of the groin.

SYNONYMS

Jock itch
Ringworm

ICD-9CM CODES
110.3 Tinea cruris

EPIDEMIOLOGY & DEMOGRAPHICS

- Most common during the summer
- Men are affected more frequently than women

PHYSICAL FINDINGS & CLINICAL PRESENTATION

- Erythematous plaques have a half-moon shape and a scaling border.
- The acute inflammation tends to move down the inner thigh and usually spares the scrotum; in severe cases the fungus may spread onto the buttocks.
- Itching may be severe.
- Red papules and pustules may be present.
- An important diagnostic sign is the advancing well-defined border with a tendency toward central clearing (Fig. 1-238).

ETIOLOGY

- Dermatophytes of the genera *Trichophyton, Epidermophyton,* and *Microsporum. T. rubrum* and *E. floccosum* are the most common causes.
- Transmission from direct contact (e.g., infected persons, animals). The patient's feet should be evaluated as a source of infection because tinea cruris is often associated with tinea pedis.

DIAGNOSIS

DIFFERENTIAL DIAGNOSIS

- Intertrigo
- Psoriasis
- Seborrheic dermatitis
- Erythrasma
- Candidiasis
- Tinea versicolor

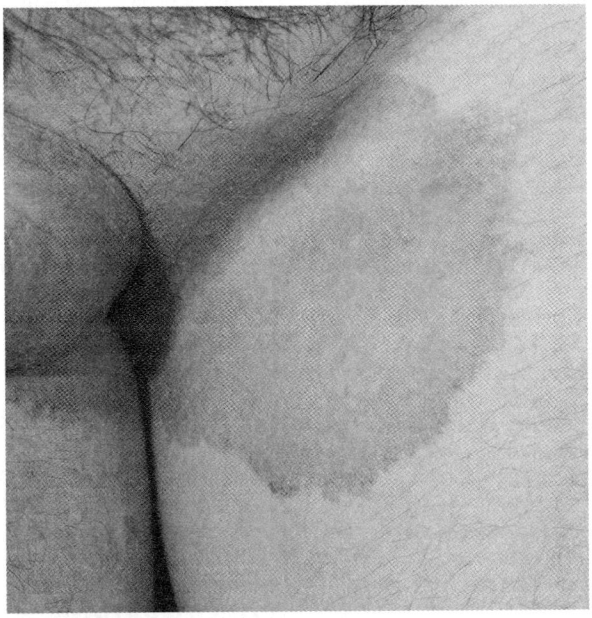

WORKUP

Diagnosis is based on clinical presentation and demonstration of hyphae microscopically using potassium hydroxide.

LABORATORY TESTS

- Microscopic examination
- Cultures are generally not necessary

TREATMENT

NONPHARMACOLOGIC THERAPY

- Keep infected area clean and dry.
- Use of boxer shorts is preferred to regular underwear.

ACUTE GENERAL Rx

- Drying powders (e.g., Miconazole nitrate [Zeasorb AF]) may be useful in patients with excessive perspiration.
- Various topical antifungal agents are available: miconazole (Lotrimin), terbinafine (Lamisil), sulconazole nitrate (Exelderm), betamethasone dipropionate/clotrimazole (Lotrisone).
- Oral antifungal therapy is generally reserved for cases unresponsive to topical agents. Effective medications are itraconazole (Sporonax) 100 mg/day for 2-4 wk, ketoconazole (Nizoral) 200 mg qd, fluconazole (Diflucan) 200 mg qd, and terbinafine (Lamisil) 250 mg qd.

DISPOSITION

Most cases respond promptly to therapy with complete resolution within 2-3 wk.

SUGGESTED READING

Hainer BL: Dermatophyte infections, *Am Fam Physician* 67:101, 2003.

AUTHOR: **FRED F. FERRI, M.D.**

FIGURE 1-238 Tinea cruris. A halfmoon-shaped plaque has a well-defined, scaling border. (From Habif TB: *Clinical dermatology: a color guide to diagnosis and therapy,* ed 3, St Louis, 1996, Mosby.)

BASIC INFORMATION

DEFINITION

Tinea pedis is a dermatophyte infection of the feet.

SYNONYMS

Athlete's foot

ICD-CM CODES
110.4 Tinea pedis

EPIDEMIOLOGY & DEMOGRAPHICS

- Most common dermatophyte infection
- Increased incidence in hot humid weather. Occlusive footwear is a contributing factor
- Occurrence is rare before adolescence
- More common in adult males

PHYSICAL FINDINGS & CLINICAL PRESENTATION

- Typical presentation is variable and ranges from erythematous scaling plaques (see Fig. 1-239) and isolated blisters to interdigital maceration.
- The infection usually starts in the interdigital spaces of the foot. Most infections are found in the toe webs or in the soles.
- Fourth or fifth toes are most commonly involved.
- Pruritus is common and is most intense following removal of shoes and socks.
- Infection with *tinea rubrum* often manifests with a moccasin distribution affecting the soles and lateral feet.

ETIOLOGY

Dermatophyte infection caused by *T. rubrum, T. mentagrophytes,* or less commonly *E. floccosum*

DIAGNOSIS

DIFFERENTIAL DIAGNOSIS

- Contact dermatitis
- Toe web infection
- Eczema
- Psoriasis
- Keratolysis exfoliativa
- Juvenile plantar dermatosis

WORKUP

- Diagnosis is usually made by clinical observation.
- Laboratory testing, when performed, generally consists of a simple potassium hydroxide (KOH) preparation with mycologic examination under a light microscope to confirm the presence of dermatophytes.

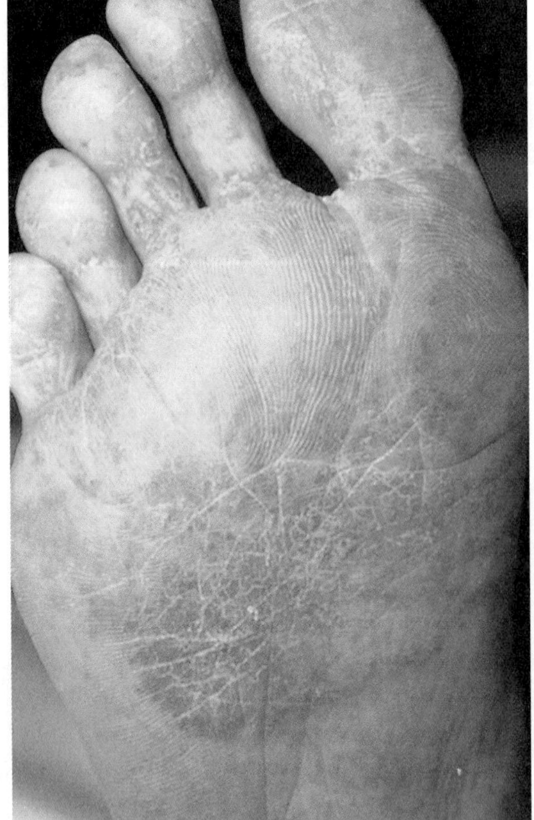

FIGURE 1-239 Tinea pedis. (From Goldstein BG, Goldstein AO: *Practical dermatology,* ed 2, St Louis, 1997, Mosby.)

LABORATORY TESTS

- Microscopic examination of a scale or the roof of a blister with 10% KOH under low or medium power will reveal hyphae.
- Mycologic culture is rarely indicated in the diagnosis of tinea pedis.
- Biopsy is reserved for when the diagnosis remains in question after testing or failure to respond to treatment.

IMAGING STUDIES

None

TREATMENT

NONPHARMACOLOGIC THERAPY

- Keep infected area clean and dry. Aerate feet by using sandals when possible.
- Use 100% cotton socks rather than nylon socks to reduce moisture.
- Areas likely to become infected should be dried completely before being covered with clothes.

ACUTE GENERAL THERAPY

- Butenafine Hcl 1% (Mentax) cream applied bid for 1 wk or qd for 4 wk is effective in interdigital tinea pedis.
- Ciclopirox 0.77 % (Loprox) cream applied bid for 4 wk is also effective.
- Clotrimazole 1% (Lotrimin AF) cream is an OTC treatment. It should be applied to affected and surrounding area bid for up to 4 wk.
- Naftifine (Naftin) 1 % cream applied qd or gel applied bid for 4 wk also produces a significantly high cure rate.
- When using topical preparations, the application area should include normal skin about 2 cm beyond the affected area.
- Areas of maceration can be treated with Burow's solution soaks for 10-20 min bid followed by foot elevation.
- Oral agents (fluconazole 150 mg once/wk for 4 wk) can be used in combination with topical agents in resistant cases.

PEARLS & CONSIDERATIONS

Combination therapy of antifungal and corticosteroid (clotrimazole/betamethasone [Lotrisone]) should only be used when the diagnosis of fungal infection is confirmed and inflammation is a significant issue.

SUGGESTED READING

Weinstein A, Berman B: Topical treatment of common superficial tinea infections, *Am Fam Physician* 65:2095, 2002.

AUTHOR: **FRED F. FERRI, M.D.**

BASIC INFORMATION

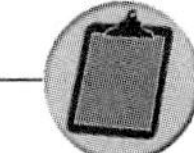

DEFINITION

Tinea versicolor is a fungal infection of the skin caused by the yeast *Pityrosporum orbiculare (Malassezia furfur)*.

SYNONYMS

Pityriasis versicolor

ICD-9CM CODES
111.0 Tinea versicolor

EPIDEMIOLOGY & DEMOGRAPHICS

- Increased incidence in adolescence and young adulthood
- More common during the summer (hypopigmented lesions are more evident when the skin is tanned)

PHYSICAL FINDINGS & CLINICAL PRESENTATION

- Most lesions begin as multiple small, circular macules of various colors.
- The macules may be darker or lighter than the surrounding normal skin and will scale with scraping.
- Most frequent site of distribution is trunk.
- Facial lesions are more common in children (forehead is most common facial site).
- Eruption is generally of insidious onset and asymptomatic.
- Lesions may be hyperpigmented in blacks.
- Lesions may be inconspicuous in fair-complexioned individuals, especially during the winter.
- Most patients become aware of the eruption when the involved areas do not tan (Fig. 1-240).

ETIOLOGY

The infection is caused by the lipophilic yeast *P. orbiculare* (round form) and *P. ovale* (oval form); these organisms are normal inhabitants of the skin flora; factors that favor their proliferation are pregnancy, malnutrition, immunosuppression, oral contraceptives, and excess heat and humidity.

DIAGNOSIS

DIFFERENTIAL DIAGNOSIS

- Vitiligo
- Pityriasis alba
- Secondary syphilis
- Pityriasis rosea
- Seborrheic dermatitis

WORKUP

Diagnosis is based on clinical appearance; identification of hyphae and budding spores (spaghetti and meatballs appearance) with microscopy confirms diagnosis.

LABORATORY TESTS

Microscopic examination using potassium hydroxide confirms diagnosis when in doubt.

TREATMENT

NONPHARMACOLOGIC THERAPY

Sunlight accelerates repigmentation of hypopigmented areas.

ACUTE GENERAL Rx

- Topical treatment: selenium sulfide 2.5% suspension (Selsun or Exsel) applied daily for 10 min for 7 consecutive days results in a cure rate of 80% to 90%.
- Antifungal topical agents (e.g., miconazole, ciclopirox, clotrimazole) are also effective but generally expensive.
- Oral treatment is generally reserved for resistant cases. Effective agents are ketoconazole (Nizoral) 200 mg qd for 5 days, or single 400-mg dose (cure rate >80%), fluconazole (Diflucan) 400 mg given as a single dose (cure rate >70% at 3 wk after treatment), or itraconazole 200 mg/day for 5 days.

DISPOSITION

The prognosis is good, with death of the fungus usually occurring within 3-4 wk of treatment; however, recurrence is common.

PEARLS & CONSIDERATIONS

COMMENTS

Patients should be informed that the hypopigmented areas will not disappear immediately after treatment and that several months may be necessary for the hypopigmented areas to regain their pigmentation.

AUTHOR: **FRED F. FERRI, M.D.**

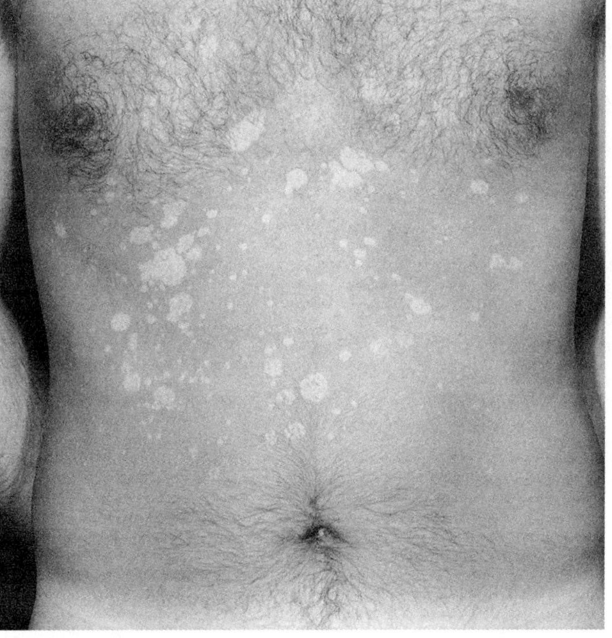

FIGURE 1-240 The classic presentation of tinea versicolor with white, oval, or circular patches on tan skin. (From Habif TB: *Clinical dermatology: a color guide to diagnosis and therapy,* ed 3, St Louis, 1996, Mosby.)

Tinnitus

BASIC INFORMATION

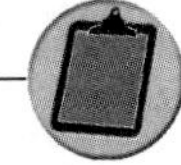

DEFINITION

Tinnitus is the false perception of sound in the absence of an acoustic stimulus.

SYNONYM

Ringing in the ear(s)

ICD-9CM CODES
388.30 Tinnitus

EPIDEMIOLOGY & DEMOGRAPHICS

- Prevalence: <45 yr: <1% in men and women; 45-65 yr old: 7% in men, 4% in women; above age 65: 10% in men, 5% in women
- More common in whites than in blacks
- More common in the southern U.S.
- Frequent association with hearing loss

SYMPTOMS (ALWAYS SUBJECTIVE)

- Ringing (35.5%)
- Buzzing (11.2%)
- Cricket-like (8.5%)
- Hissing (7.8%)
- Whistling (6.6%)
- Humming (5.3%)
- The pitch is high in most cases
- Tinnitus is reported to be unilateral (34%), bilateral with lateral dominance (44%), or equal in both ears (22%)
- Patients typically wait for several years before seeking medical attention
- Most patients report that the tinnitus is much louder subjectively than it is when matched with audible sounds

ETIOLOGY

OTOLOGIC:

- Noise-induced hearing loss
- Presbycusis
- Otosclerosis
- Otitis
- Ceruminosis
- Meniere's disease

NEUROLOGIC:

- Head and neck injury
- Multiple sclerosis
- Acoustic neuroma
- Other brain tumors

INFECTIONS:

- Otitis media
- Meningitis
- Lyme disease
- Syphilis

TOXIC (DRUGS):

- Aspirin
- NSAIDs
- Aminoglycosides
- Loop diuretics
- Vincristine

OTHER:

- Facial and dental disorders

DIAGNOSIS

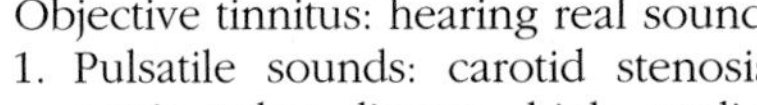

DIFFERENTIAL DIAGNOSIS

- Objective tinnitus: hearing real sounds
  1. Pulsatile sounds: carotid stenosis, aortic valve disease, high cardiac output, arteriovenous malformations
  2. Muscular sounds: palatal myoclonus, spasm of stapedius or tensor tympani muscle
  3. Spontaneous autoacoustic emissions auditory hallucinations

WORKUP

- Description of the sound
  1. Constant or episodic
  2. Unilateral or bilateral
  3. Gradual or sudden onset
  4. Duration
  5. Hearing loss present or not
  6. Vertigo present or not
  7. Precipitating factors (e.g., background noise, alcohol, stress, sleep)
  8. Impact in daily life

PHYSICAL EXAMINATION

- Focus on head and neck
- Vital signs
- Signs of associated illnesses

LABORATORY

- CBC, FBS, creatinine, ALT, Alk Phos, TSH, lipids, ESR, Lyme titer
- Comprehensive audiologic evaluation
- In selected cases: brain magnetic resonance imaging with contrast

TREATMENT

- Prevent (further) hearing loss with appropriate ear protection and avoidance of noise exposure.
- Treat any identified etiologic factor and avoid ototoxic drugs
- Medications:
  1. Antiarrhythmic drugs (lidocaine, tocainide, flecainide) probably ineffective
  2. Benzodiazepines may help, but tinnitus recurs upon cessation of therapy
  3. Carbamazepine and other anticonvulsants are ineffective
  4. Antidepressants may be helpful and are worth a trial (most studies involve tricyclics)
  5. Gingko biloba may be helpful
- Acupuncture is ineffective
- Tinnitus retraining (habituation) may lead to improvement in as many as 75% of patients. Programs include counseling combined with low-level broadband noise exposure and usually take 1.5 years to complete
- Masking devices that cover up the unwanted sounds may be helpful in selected patients
- Surgical treatment is controversial
- Self-help groups (e.g., the American Tinnitus Association) provide useful information and support
- Patient education and reassurance

REFERRAL

ENT

SUGGESTED READINGS

Lockwood AH, Salvi RJ, Burkard RF: Tinnitus, *N Engl J Med* 347:904, 2002.

Noell CA, Meyeroff WL: Tinnitus: diagnosis and treatment of this elusive symptom, *Geriatrics* 58:28, 2003.

AUTHOR: **TOM J. WACHTEL, M.D.**

SECTION I

BASIC INFORMATION

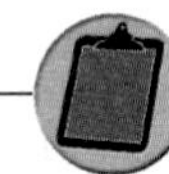

DEFINITION

Torticollis is a contraction or contracture of the muscles of the neck that causes the head to be tilted to one side. It is usually accompanied by rotation of the chin to the opposite side with flexion (Fig 1-241). Usually it is a symptom of some underlying disorder. This term is often used incorrectly in cases when the torticollis may simply be positional.

SYNONYMS

Twisted neck
"Wry neck"

ICD-9CM CODES
723.5 Spastic (intermittent) torticollis
754.1 Congenital muscular (sternocleidomastoid)
300.11 Hysterical
714.0 Rheumatoid
333.83 Spasmodic

PHYSICAL FINDINGS & CLINICAL PRESENTATION

- Congenital muscular torticollis:
  1. Palpable soft tissue "mass" in the sternocleidomastoid shortly after birth
  2. Mass gradually subsides, leaving a shortened, contracted sternocleidomastoid muscle
  3. Head characteristically tilted toward the side of the mass and rotated in the opposite direction
  4. Facial asymmetry and other secondary changes persisting into adulthood
- Spasmodic torticollis:
  1. "Spasms" in the cervical musculature; may be bilateral and uncontrollable
  2. Head often tilted toward the affected side
- Findings in other cases depend on etiology.

ETIOLOGY

Torticollis has been attributed to more than 50 different causes:

- Localized fibrous shortening of unknown cause involving the sternocleidomastoid, leading to the condition termed *congenital muscular torticollis*
- Spasmodic torticollis: of uncertain etiology, possibly a variant of dystonia musculorum deformans
- Infection, specifically pharyngitis, tonsillitis, retropharyngeal abscess
- Miscellaneous rare causes: congenital musculoskeletal deformities, trauma, inflammation from rheumatoid arthritis, vestibular disturbances, posterior fossa tumor, syringomyelia, neuritis of spinal accessory nerve, and drug reactions

DIAGNOSIS

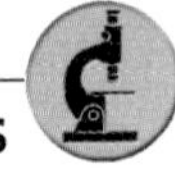

DIFFERENTIAL DIAGNOSIS

- Usually involves separating each disorder from the others
- Acquired positional disorders (e.g., ocular disturbances, acute disk herniation)

WORKUP

- Workup is dependent on the clinical situation.
- Laboratory studies are usually not helpful unless infection or rheumatoid disease is suspected.
- Section II describes a differential diagnosis for the evaluation and therapy of neck pain.
- Any child with a gradually increasing torticollis should have a complete eye examination.

IMAGING STUDIES

- Plain radiographs in cases of trauma or to rule out congenital abnormalities
- MRI in appropriate cases
- Electrodiagnostic studies: only rarely indicated to rule out neurologic causes

TREATMENT

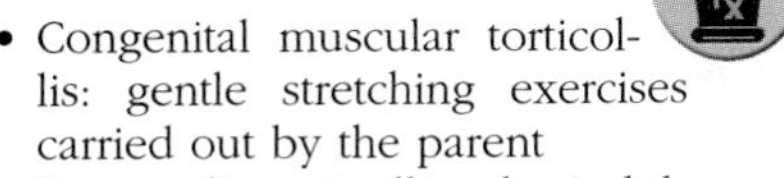

- Congenital muscular torticollis: gentle stretching exercises carried out by the parent
- Spasmodic torticollis: physical therapy, psychotherapy, cervical braces, biofeedback, and pain control
- Other forms: treated according to etiology

DISPOSITION

- Most patients with congenital muscular torticollis respond well to conservative treatment.
- Spasmodic torticollis is often resistant to normal conservative treatment.
- Prognosis of other forms of torticollis is dependent on etiology.

REFERRAL

- Torticollis often requires a multidisciplinary approach unless the etiology is obvious.
- Children usually do not require any specific studies; however, an orthopedic consultation is recommended.

SUGGESTED READINGS

Braun V, Richter HP: Selective peripheral denervation for spasmodic torticollis: 13 year experience with 155 patients, *J Neurosurg* 97:207, 2002.

Konrad C, Vollmer-Haase J et al: Orthopedic and neurologic complications of cervical dystonia-review of the literature, *Acto Neurol Scand* 109:369, 2004.

McGuire KJ et al: Torticollis in children: can dynamic computed tomography determine severity and treatment, *J Pediatr Orthop* 22:766, 2002.

Parikh SN, Crawford AH, Choudhary S: Magnetic resonance imaging in the evaluation of infantile torticollis, *Orthopedics* 27:509, 2004.

AUTHOR: **LONNIE R. MERCIER, M.D.**

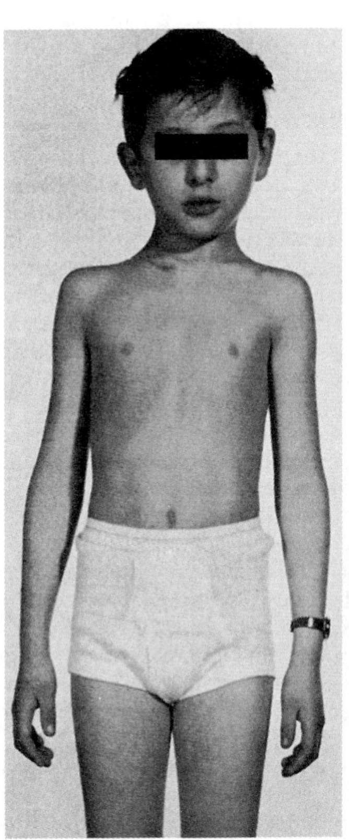

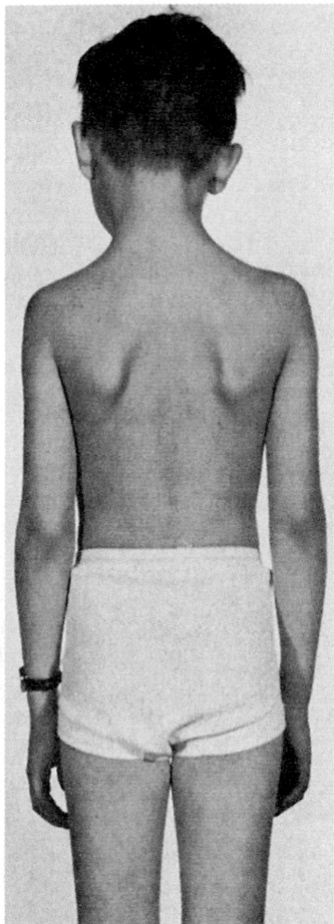

FIGURE 1-241 Torticollis. In this child, the right sternocleidomastoid muscle is contracted. (From Brinker MR, Miller MD: *Fundamentals of orthopaedics,* Philadelphia, 1999, WB Saunders.)

Tourette's Syndrome

BASIC INFORMATION

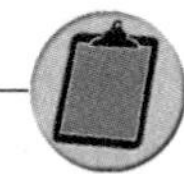

DEFINITION

Tics are sudden, brief, intermittent involuntary or semivoluntary movements (motor tics) or sounds (phonic or vocal tics) that mimic fragments of normal behavior.

Tourette's syndrome is an inherited neuropsychiatric disorder characterized by multiple motor and vocal tics that change during the course of the illness. Onset is before age 18.

SYNONYMS

Gilles de la Tourette syndrome
Motor-verbal tic disorder

ICD-9CM CODES
307.23 Gilles de la Tourette disorder

EPIDEMIOLOGY & DEMOGRAPHICS

PREVALENCE (IN U.S.): Unknown. Estimates range from 0.7% to 5%.
SEX: Male:female ratio of 3:1
AGE: Typical age of onset is between 2-15 yr. Mean is 5-7 yr.

PHYSICAL FINDINGS & CLINICAL PRESENTATION

Neurologic examination is normal.

- Vocal tics (clearing of throat, repetitive short phrases, e.g., "You bet," swearing [coprolalia]).
- Motor tics can be simple (e.g., blinking, grimacing, head jerking) or complex (e.g., gesturing). Tics wax, wane, and change over time. Often they can be suppressed for short periods. Commonly they are preceded by an urge to perform the tic.
- Often TS is associated with a variety of behavioral symptoms, most commonly ADHD and OCD. Incidence of OCD in TS patients is >30% and reaches its peak as tics are beginning to recede. 50%-75% of TS patients meet the criteria for ADHD and often this is what brings the patient to a doctor's attention.

ETIOLOGY

TS is at least in part genetic. There is a strong family history of OCD and/or TS in patients with tics, and twin studies provide evidence for importance of genetic factors. However, no candidate genes have been identified thus far. Based on beneficial effects of dopamine antagonists, dopamine is thought to be one of the major neurotransmitters involved.

DIAGNOSIS

DIFFERENTIAL DIAGNOSIS

- Sydenham's chorea—occurs after infection with group A streptococcus
- PANDAS—pediatric autoimmune neurolopsychiatric disorder associated with streptococcal infection
- Sporadic tic disorders—these tend to be motor or vocal but not both
- Head trauma
- Drug intoxication—there are many drugs that are known to induce or exacerbate tic disorder, including methylphenidate, amphetamines, pemoline, anticholinergics, and antihistamines
- Postinfectious encephalitis
- Inherited disorders—these include Huntington's disease, Hallervorden Spatz, and neuroacanthocytosis. All of these should have other abnormalities on neurologic examination

WORKUP

Clinical observation and history to confirm diagnosis

LABORATORY TESTS

No definitive laboratory tests

IMAGING STUDIES

CT scan and MRI of brain are normal and unnecessary in the absence of abnormal neurologic examination.

TREATMENT

NONPHARMACOLOGIC THERAPY

Multidisciplinary: parents, teachers, psychologists, school nurses

ACUTE GENERAL Rx

Dopamine-blocking agents may be used to reduce severity of tics acutely (e.g., haloperidol 0.25 mg PO qhs initially).

CHRONIC Rx

Tics only require treatment when they interfere with psychosocial, educational, and occupational functioning of a person.

TREATMENT OF TICS:

- Clonidine—many choose to use this as first-line agent because of fewer long-term side effects. Start at 0.05 mg and slowly titrate to about 0.45 mg daily (needs tid/qid dosing). May also help with symptoms of ADHD.
- Guanfacine (Tenex), another alpha agonist similar to clonidine but can be administered once daily. Typical starting dose is 0.5 mg titrating to 1-3 mg qd.
- Tetrabenazine—dopamine-depleting agent that is not currently available in the U.S. Avoids many of the typical side effects of the neuroleptics.
- Atypical antipsychotics such as Ziprasidone (Geodon) and Olanzapine (Zyprexa). These have fewer side effects than typical neuroleptics.
- Dopamine-blocking agents—neuroleptics. These should be avoided until other options have been exhausted. Many physicians use Pimozide before Haldol because it is thought to have fewer side effects. It can prolong the QT interval and so requires close monitoring of the ECG. Usual starting dose 0.5-1 mg qhs titrating to 2-4 mg/daily. Other agents include Fluphenazine (Prolixin).

TREATMENT OF ADHD:
Often treatment of this is needed before treatment of tics. Some of these stimulants can increase the frequency and intensity of tics and they may need to be combined with dopamine-depleting agents.

- Dextroamphetamine
- Methylphenidate

TREATMENT OF OCD:
SSRIs, such as fluoxetine, are the most effective.

DISPOSITION

- In the later teen years, intensity and frequency of tics diminish.
- One third of patients will achieve significant remission. Though complete, lifelong remission is rare.
- One third will have mild, persistent, but "unimpairing" tics.

REFERRAL

To neurologist to confirm initial diagnosis

PEARLS & CONSIDERATIONS

- Must emphasize that tics do not need treatment unless they interfere with an individual's ability to function.
- Coprolalia, one of the most recognizable and distressing symptoms, is present in less than half of patients with Tourette's and typically appears a few years after disease onset.

COMMENTS

Patient education may be obtained from the Tourette's Syndrome Association (TSA), 4240 Bell Blvd., Bayside, NY, 11361-2864; phone: (800) 237-0717, (718) 224-2999. www.tsa-usa.org.

SUGGESTED READINGS

Jankovic J: Tourette's syndrome, *N Engl J Med* 345:1184, 2001.

Jankovic J: Tics and Tourette's syndrome. In Jankovic J, Tolosa E (eds): *Parkinson's disease and movement disorders,* Philadelphia, 2002, Lippincott Williams & Wilkins.

Jimenez-Jimenez FJ, Garcia-Ruiz DJ: Pharmacological options for the treatment of Tourette's disorder, *Drugs* 61(15):2007, 2001.

Marcus D, Kurlan R: Tics and its disorders. In Hurtig H, Stern M (eds): *Neurologic clinics: movement disorders,* 19:3, 2001.

AUTHOR: **CINDY ZADIKOFF, M.D.**

BASIC INFORMATION

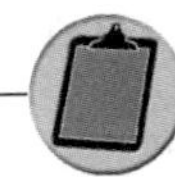

DEFINITION

Toxic shock syndrome is an acute febrile illness resulting in multiple organ system dysfunction caused most commonly by a bacterial exotoxin. Disease characteristics also include hypotension, vomiting, myalgia, watery diarrhea, vascular collapse, and an erythematous sunburnlike cutaneous rash that desquamates during recovery.

ICD-9CM CODES
040.89 Toxic shock syndrome

EPIDEMIOLOGY & DEMOGRAPHICS

- Case reported incidence peak: 14 cases/100,000 menstruating women/yr in 1980; has since fallen to 1 case/100,000 persons
- Occurs most commonly between ages 10 and 30 yr in healthy, young menstruating white females
- Case fatality ratio of 3%

ETIOLOGY

- Menstrually associated TSS: 45% of cases associated with tampons, diaphragm, or vaginal sponge use
- Nonmenstruating associated TSS: 55% of cases associated with puerperal sepsis, post–cesarean section endometritis, mastitis, wound or skin infection, insect bite, pelvic inflammatory disease, and postoperative fever
- Causative agent: *S. aureus* infection of a susceptible individual (10% of population lacking sufficient levels of antitoxin antibodies), which liberates the disease mediator TSST-1 (exotoxin)
- Other causative agents: coagulase-negative streptococci producing enterotoxins B or C, and exotoxin A producing group A β-hemolytic streptococci

PHYSICAL FINDINGS & CLINICAL PRESENTATION

- Fever (≥38.9° C)
- Diffuse macular erythrodermatous rash that desquamates 1-2 wk after disease onset in survivors
- Orthostatic hypotension
- GI symptoms: vomiting, diarrhea, abdominal tenderness
- Constitutional symptoms: myalgia, headache, photophobia, rigors, altered sensorium, conjunctivitis, arthralgia
- Respiratory symptoms: dysphagia, pharyngeal hyperemia, strawberry tongue
- Genitourinary symptoms: vaginal discharge, vaginal hyperemia, adnexal tenderness
- End-organ failure
- Severe hypotension and acute renal failure
- Hepatic failure
- Cardiovascular symptoms: DIC, pulmonary edema, ARDS, endomyocarditis, heart block

DIAGNOSIS

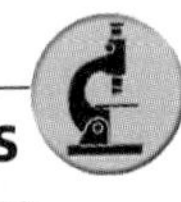

DIFFERENTIAL DIAGNOSIS

- Staphylococcal food poisoning
- Septic shock
- Mucocutaneous lymph node syndrome
- Scarlet fever
- Rocky Mountain spotted fever
- Meningococcemia
- Toxic epidermal necrolysis
- Kawasaki's syndrome
- Leptospirosis
- Legionnaires' disease
- Hemolytic-uremic syndrome
- Stevens-Johnson syndrome
- Scalded skin syndrome
- Erythema multiforme
- Acute rheumatic fever

WORKUP

Broad-spectrum syndrome with multiorgan system involvement and variable but acute clinical presentation, including the following:

1. Fever ≥38.1° C
2. Classic desquamating (1-2 wk) rash
3. Hypotension/orthostatic SBP 90 or less
4. Syncope
5. Negative throat/CSF cultures
6. Negative serologic test for Rocky Mountain spotted fever, rubeola, and leptospirosis
7. Clinical involvement of three or more of the following:
   a. Cardiopulmonary: ARDS, pulmonary edema, endomyocarditis, second- or third-degree AV block
   b. CNS: altered sensorium without focal neurologic findings
   c. Hematologic: thrombocytopenia (PLT <100 k)
   d. Liver: elevated LFT results
   e. Renal: >5/HPF, negative urine cultures, azotemia, and increased creatinine double normal
   f. Mucous membrane involvement: vagina, oropharynx, conjunctiva
   g. Musculoskeletal: myalgia, CPK twice normal
   h. GI: vomiting, diarrhea

LABORATORY TESTS

- Pan culture (cervix/vagina, throat, nasal passages, urine, blood, CSF, wound) for *Staphylococcus, Streptococcus,* or other pathogenic organisms
- Electrolytes to detect hypokalemia, hyponatremia
- CBC with differential and clotting profile for anemia (normocytic/ normochromic), thrombocytopenia, leukocytosis, coagulopathy, and bacteremia
- Chemistry profile to detect decreased protein, increased AST, increased ALT, hypocalcemia, elevated BUN/creatinine, hypophosphatemia, increased LDH, increased CPK
- Urinalysis to detect WBC (>5/HPF), proteinemia, microhematuria
- ABGs to assess respiratory function and acid-base status
- Serologic tests considered for Rocky Mountain spotted fever, rubeola, and leptospirosis

IMAGING STUDIES

- Chest x-ray examination to evaluate pulmonary edema
- ECG to evaluate arrhythmia
- Sonography/CT scan/MRI considered if pelvic abscess or TOA suspected

TREATMENT

NONPHARMACOLOGIC THERAPY

- For optimal outcome: high index of suspicion and early and aggressive supportive management in an ICU setting
- Aggressive fluid resuscitation (maintenance of circulating volume, CO, SBP)
- Thorough search for a localized infection or nidus: incision and drainage, debridement, removal of tampon or vaginal sponge
- Central hemodynamic monitoring, Swan-Ganz catheter and arterial line for surveillance of hemodynamic status and response to therapy
- Foley catheter to monitor hourly urine output
- Possible MAST trousers as temporary measure
- Acute ventilator management if severe respiratory compromise
- Renal dialysis for severe renal impairment
- Surgical intervention for indicated conditions (i.e., ruptured TOA, wound abscess, mastitis)

ACUTE GENERAL Rx

- Isotonic crystalloid (normal saline solution) for volume replacement following "7-3" rule
- Electrolyte replacement (K^+, Ca^+)
- PRBC/coagulation factor replacement/FFP to treat anemia or D&C
- Vasopressor therapy for hypotension refractory to fluid volume replacement (i.e., dopamine beginning at 2-5 μg/kg/min)
- Naloxone infusion (i.e., 0.5 mg/kg/hr) to improve SBP by blocking endogenous endorphin effects
- Parenteral antibiotic therapy; β-lactamase resistant antibiotic (methicillin, nafcillin, or oxacillin) initiated early
- Broad-spectrum antibiotic added if concurrent sepsis suspected
- Tetracycline added if considering Rocky Mountain spotted fever

CHRONIC Rx

- Severely ill patient: may require prolonged hospitalization and supportive management with gradual recovery and/or sequelae from severe end-organ involvement (ARDS or renal failure requiring dialysis)
- Majority of patients: complete recovery
- Early late-onset complications (within 2 wk):
  1. Skin desquamation
  2. Impaired digit sensation
  3. Denuded tongue
  4. Vocal cord paralysis
  5. ATN
  6. ARDS
- Late-onset complications (after 8 wk):
  1. Nail splitting/loss
  2. Alopecia
  3. CNS sequelae
  4. Renal impairment
  5. Cardiac dysfunction
- Recurrent TSS:
  1. More common in menstrually related cases
  2. Less common in patient treated with β-lactamase–resistant antistaphylococcal antibiotics
  3. Patients with history of TSS: if suspect signs and symptoms occur, should have high index of suspicion and low threshold for evaluation and treatment

PREVENTION

- Avoidance of tampons or use of low-absorbency tampons only (<4 hr in situ) and alternate with napkins
- Education for patients concerning signs and symptoms of TSS
- Avoidance of tampons for patients with history of TSS

DISPOSITION

- Complete recovery for most patients
- Long-term management of early- and late-onset complications for minority of patients

REFERRAL

- For multidisciplinary management, involving primary physician, gynecologist, internist, infectious disease specialist, and other supportive care specialists
- To tertiary level hospital

PEARLS & CONSIDERATIONS

COMMENTS

Patient information available from American College of Gynecologists and Obstetricians.

SUGGESTED READINGS

Davis D et al: Toxic shock syndrome: case report of a postpartum female and a literature review, *J Emerg Med* 16(4):607, 1998.

Hajjeh RA et al: Toxic shock syndrome in the United States: surveillance update, 1979-1996, *Emerg Infect Dis J* 5(6), 1999.

Issa NC et al: Staphylococcal toxic shock syndrome: suspicion and prevention are keys to control, *Postgrad Med* 110(4):55, 2001.

Miche CA, Shah V: Managing toxic shock syndrome. *Nursing Times* 99(5):26, 2003.

AUTHOR: **DENNIS M. WEPPNER, M.D.**

BASIC INFORMATION

DEFINITION

Toxoplasmosis is an infection caused by the protozoal parasite *Toxoplasma gondii.*

ICD-9CM CODES
130.9 Toxoplasmosis

EPIDEMIOLOGY & DEMOGRAPHICS

INCIDENCE (IN U.S.):
- Increases with age
- Increases with certain activities
  1. Slaughterhouse workers
  2. Cat owners
- Increases with certain geographic locations: high prevalence of cats

INCIDENCE (IN U.S.): 3%-70% of healthy adults

PREDOMINANT SEX: Equal gender distribution

PREDOMINANT AGE:
- Infancy (congenital infection)
- Prevalence increases with age

PEAK INCIDENCE: Temperate climates

GENETICS:

Congenital Infection:
- Incidence and severity vary with the trimester of gestation during which the mother acquired infection.
  1. 10%-25% (first trimester)
  2. 30%-54% (second trimester)
  3. 60%-65% (third trimester)
- Congenital infection occurring in the first trimester is the most severe.
- 89%-100% of infections in the third trimester are asymptomatic.
- Risk to the fetus is not correlated with symptoms in the mother.

PHYSICAL FINDINGS & CLINICAL PRESENTATION

- Acquired (immunocompetent host)
  1. 80%-90% asymptomatic
  2. Adenopathy (usually cervical)
  3. Fever
  4. Myalgias
  5. Malaise
  6. Sore throat
  7. Maculopapular rash
  8. Hepatosplenomegaly
  9. Chorioretinitis rare
- Acquired (in patients with AIDS)
  1. 89% of symptomatic cases
     a. Encephalitis
     b. Intracerebral mass lesions
  2. Pneumonitis
  3. Chorioretinitis
  4. Other end organ
- Acquired (immunocompromised patients)
  1. Encephalitis
  2. Myocarditis (especially in heart transplant patients)
  3. Pneumonitis
- Ocular infection in the immunocompetent host
  1. Congenital infection
  2. Blurred vision
  3. Photophobia
  4. Pain
  5. Loss of central vision if macula involved
  6. Focal necrotizing retinitis
  7. Typically presents in second or third decade
- Congenital
  1. Results from acute infection acquired by the mother within 6 to 8 wk before conception or during gestation
  2. Usually, asymptomatic mother
  3. No sign of disease
  4. Chorioretinitis
  5. Blindness
  6. Epilepsy
  7. Psychomotor or mental retardation
  8. Intracranial calcifications
  9. Hydrocephalus
  10. Microcephaly
  11. Encephalitis
  12. Anemia
  13. Thrombocytopenia
  14. Hepatosplenomegaly
  15. Lymphadenopathy
  16. Jaundice
  17. Rash
  18. Pneumonitis
  19. Most infected infants are asymptomatic at birth

ETIOLOGY

- *Toxoplasma gondii*
  1. Ubiquitous intracellular protozoan
  2. Present worldwide
  3. Cat is definitive host
- Human infection
  1. Ingestion of oocysts shed by cats
  2. Ingestion of meat containing tissue cysts
  3. Vertical transmission

DIAGNOSIS

DIFFERENTIAL DIAGNOSIS

- Lymphadenopathy
  1. Infectious mononucleosis
  2. CMV mononucleosis
  3. Cat-scratch disease
  4. Sarcoidosis
  5. Tuberculosis
  6. Lymphoma
  7. Metastatic cancer
- Cerebral mass lesions in immunocompromised host
  1. Lymphoma
  2. Tuberculosis
  3. Bacterial abscess
- Pneumonitis in immunocompromised host
  1. *Pneumocystis carinii* pneumonia
  2. Tuberculosis
  3. Fungal infection
- Chorioretinitis
  1. Syphilis
  2. Tuberculosis
  3. Histoplasmosis (competent host)
  4. CMV
  5. Syphilis
  6. Herpes simplex
  7. Fungal infection
  8. Tuberculosis (AIDS patient)
- Myocarditis
  1. Organ rejection in heart transplant recipients
- Congenital infection
  1. Rubella
  2. CMV
  3. Herpes simplex
  4. Syphilis
  5. Listeriosis
  6. Erythroblastosis fetalis
  7. Sepsis

WORKUP

- Acute infection, immunocompetent host
  1. CBC
  2. *Toxoplasma* serology (IgG, Ig) in serial blood specimens 3 wk apart
  3. Lymph node biopsy if diagnosis uncertain
- Immunocompromised host
  1. CNS symptoms
     a. Cerebral CT scan or MRI if CNS symptoms present
     b. Spinal tap, if safe
     c. Brain biopsy if no response to empiric therapy
  2. Ocular symptoms
     a. Funduscopic examination
     b. Serologic studies
     c. Rarely, vitreous tap
  3. Pulmonary symptoms
     a. Chest x-ray examination
     b. Bronchoalveolar lavage
     c. Transbronchial or open lung biopsy
  4. Myocarditis
     a. Cardiac enzymes
     b. Electrocardiogram
     c. Endomyocardial biopsy for definitive diagnosis
- Toxoplasmosis in pregnancy
  1. Initial maternal screening with IgM and IgG
     a. If negative, mother at risk of acute infection and should be retested monthly
     b. If both IgG and IgM positive, obtain IgA and IgE ELISA, AC/HS test
     c. IgA and IgE ELISA, AC/HS test elevated in acute infection
     d. Ig high for 1 yr or more
     e. IgG repeated 3 to 4 wk later to determine if titer is stable
  2. Acute maternal infection not excluded or documented
     a. Fetal blood sampling (for culture, Ig, IgA, IgE)
     b. Amniotic fluid PCR

3. Fetal ultrasound every other week if maternal infection documented
- Congenital toxoplasmosis
  1. Placental histology
  2. Specific IgM or IgA in infant's blood

LABORATORY TESTS

- Antibody studies
  1. More than one test necessary to establish diagnosis of acute toxoplasmosis
  2. IgM antibody
     a. Appears 5 days into infection
     b. Peaks at 2 wk
     c. Falls to low level or disappears within 2 mo
     d. May persist at low levels for 1 yr or more
  3. Antibody not measurable
     a. Ocular toxoplasmosis
     b. Reactivation
     c. Immunocompromised hosts
  4. IgA ELISA, IgE ELISA, and IgE ASAGA
     a. More sensitive tests
     b. Disappear more rapidly than Ig, establishing diagnosis of acute infection
  5. IgG antibody
     a. Appears 1-2 wk after infection
     b. Peaks at 6-8 wk
     c. Gradually declines over months to years

IMAGING STUDIES

- Chest x-ray examination if pulmonary involvement suspected
- Cerebral CT scan or MRI if encephalitis suspected

TREATMENT

NONPHARMACOLOGIC THERAPY

- Selected cases of ocular infection
  1. Photocoagulation
  2. Vitrectomy
  3. Lentectomy
- Selected cases of congenital cerebral infection
  1. Ventricular shunting

ACUTE GENERAL Rx

- Acute infection, immunocompetent host
  1. No treatment, unless severe and persistent symptoms or vital organ damage
- Acute infection, immunocompromised host, non-AIDS
  1. Treat even if asymptomatic
  2. Duration
     a. Until 4-6 wk after resolution of all signs and symptoms
     b. Usually 6 mo or longer
- Reactivated infection, immunocompromised host, non-AIDS
  1. Treat if symptomatic
- Acute or reactivated infection, AIDS
  1. Treat in all cases
  2. Induction course
     a. 3 to 6 wk
     b. Maintenance therapy continued for life
  3. Empiric therapy
     a. AIDS with positive IgG
     b. Multiple ring-enhancing lesions on cerebral CT scan or MRI
     c. Response seen by day 7 in 71% and day 14 in 91%
- Ocular infection
  1. Treat in all cases
  2. Therapy continued for 1 mo or longer if needed
  3. Response seen in 70% within 10 days
  4. Retreat as needed
  5. Steroids may be indicated
  6. Surgical treatment in selected cases
- Treatment regimens
  1. Pyrimethamine 100-200 mg loading dose once PO, then 25 mg PO qd (50-75 mg in AIDS) *plus*
  2. Leucovorin 10-20 mg PO qd *plus*
  3. Sulfadiazine 1-1.5 g PO q6h
- Acute infection in pregnancy
  1. Treat immediately
  2. Risk of fetal infection reduced by 60% with treatment
     a. First trimester
        i. Spiramycin 3 g PO qd in two to four divided doses
        ii. Sulfadiazine 4 g PO qd in four divided doses
     b. Second and third trimester
        i. Sulfadiazine as above *plus*
        ii. Pyrimethamine 25 mg PO qd *plus*
        iii. Leucovorin 5 to 15 mg PO qd
        iv. Spiramycin as above
- Congenital infection
  1. Sulfadiazine 50 mg/kg PO bid *plus*
  2. Pyrimethamine 2 mg/kg PO for 2 days, then 1 mg/kg PO, three times weekly *plus*
  3. Leucovorin 5-20 mg PO three times weekly
  4. Minimum duration of treatment: 12 mo

CHRONIC Rx

- Maintenance therapy in AIDS patients because of the high risk (80%) of relapse
  1. Pyrimethamine 25 mg PO qd
  2. Sulfadiazine 500 mg PO qid
  3. Leucovorin 10-20 mg PO qd

DISPOSITION

- Prognosis
  1. Excellent in the immunocompetent host
  2. Good in ocular infection (although relapses are common)
- Treatment of acute infection in pregnancy
  1. Reduces incidence and severity of congenital toxoplasmosis
- Treatment of congenital infection
  1. Improvement in intellectual function
  2. Regression of retinal lesions
- AIDS
  1. 70% to 95% response to therapy

REFERRAL

- To infectious disease expert:
  1. Immunocompromised hosts
  2. Pregnant women
  3. Difficulty in making a diagnosis or deciding on treatment
- To pediatric infectious disease expert:
  1. Congenital infection
- To obstetrician:
  1. Pregnant seronegative mother
  2. Acute seroconversion
- To ophthalmologist:
  1. Congenital infection
  2. Any case of ocular infection

PEARLS & CONSIDERATIONS

COMMENTS

- Prevention of toxoplasmosis is most important in seronegative pregnant women and immunocompromised hosts.
- Patient instructions:
  1. Cook meat to 66° C.
  2. Cook eggs.
  3. Do not drink unpasteurized milk.
  4. Wash hands thoroughly after handling raw meat.
  5. Wash kitchen surfaces that come in contact with raw meat.
  6. Wash fruits and vegetables.
  7. Avoid contact with materials potentially contaminated with cat feces.

SUGGESTED READINGS

Beazley DM, Egerman RS: Toxoplasmosis, *Semin Perinatol* 22(4):332, 1998.

Boyer KM: Diagnostic testing for congenital toxoplasmosis, *Pediatr Infect Dis J* 20(1):59, 2001.

Jones JL et al: Congenital toxoplasmosis: a review, *Obstet Gynecol Surv* 56(50):296, 2001.

Montoya JG, Liesenfeld O: Toxoplasmosis, *Lancet* 363(9425):1965, 2004.

AUTHOR: **MICHELE HALPERN, M.D.**

BASIC INFORMATION

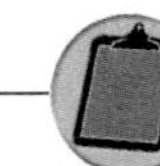

DEFINITION

Bacterial tracheitis is an acute infectious disease affecting the trachea and large conducting airways. Tracheal inflammation may be caused by a large number of inhaled stimuli, but bacterial infection is a life-threatening illness associated with viscous purulent secretions and subglottic edema.

SYNONYMS

Bacterial tracheobronchitis
Pseudomembranous croup
Membranous laryngotracheobronchitis

ICD-9CM CODES
464.10 Tracheitis

EPIDEMIOLOGY & DEMOGRAPHICS

INCIDENCE (IN U.S.):
- Uncommon
- May be the most common cause of acute upper airway obstruction requiring admission to pediatric ICUs

PREDOMINANT SEX: Boys > girls in one series

PREDOMINANT AGE:
- 1 mo to 8 yr
- Almost all <13 yr (most <3 yr)

PEAK INCIDENCE: Three fourths of cases reported in winter

GENETICS: Down syndrome is a possible predisposing factor.

Congenital Infection: Some cases found in those with anatomic abnormalities of the upper airways.

PHYSICAL FINDINGS & CLINICAL PRESENTATION

- Croupy or "brassy" cough
- Inspiratory stridor (frequent)
- Wheezing (unusual)
- Fever (often >102° F)
- Thick, purulent secretions expectorated
  1. Minority of patients expectorate "rice-like" pellets.
  2. Most patients are unable to mobilize secretions.
     a. Become inspissated
     b. Form pseudomembranes

ETIOLOGY

- *Staphylococcus aureus*
- *Haemophilus influenzae*
- β-Hemolytic streptococcal infection
- Secondary to viral infections of the respiratory tract
  1. Primary influenza
  2. RSV
  3. Parainfluenza
- Many cases follow measles
  1. Especially when accompanied by chest radiographic infiltrates
  2. Sometimes fatal outcome
  3. Associated with prolonged endotracheal intubation

DIAGNOSIS

DIFFERENTIAL DIAGNOSIS

- Viral croup
- Epiglottitis
- Diphtheria
- Necrotizing herpes simplex infection in the elderly
- CMV in immunocompromised patients
- Invasive *Aspergillosis* in immunocompromised patients

WORKUP

- Direct laryngoscopy
  1. Typical secretions
     a. May form pseudomembranes
     b. Airway obstruction
  2. Normal epiglottis rules out epiglottitis
  3. Possible subglottic edema

LABORATORY TESTS

- WBC is sometimes elevated.
- On differential, left shift is almost universal.
- Gram stain and culture of tracheal secretions confirm diagnosis.
- Blood cultures are positive in a minority.

IMAGING STUDIES

- Lateral x-ray examination of neck
  1. Normal epiglottis
  2. Vague density or a "dripping candle" appearance of tracheal mucosa
     a. Secretions
     b. Pseudomembranes
- Films
  1. Not diagnostic
  2. Should not be performed on patients in acute respiratory distress, because severe or fatal upper airway obstruction can develop suddenly
- Pneumonic infiltrates frequent
- Atelectasis
  1. Unusual
  2. May involve an entire lung

TREATMENT

NONPHARMACOLOGIC THERAPY

- Aggressive maintenance of a patent airway
  1. Laryngoscopy or bronchoscopy used diagnostically and therapeutically to strip away pseudomembranes
  2. Voluminous and tenacious secretions suctioned from the underlying friable mucosa
     a. May extend from between the vocal cords to the main carina
     b. Larger channels of rigid instruments for more effective suctioning
- Prevention of complete large airway obstruction
  1. Nasotracheal intubation
  2. Humidification of inspired gas
  3. Frequent saline instillation and suctioning
  4. Intubation with general anesthesia, performed in the operating room, is preferred by some
- Ventilatory support necessary
- Initial management in ICU

ACUTE GENERAL Rx

- Antibiotic therapy
  1. Start immediately
  2. Continue for 2 wk
- Initial therapy
  1. β-Lactamase–producing *H. influenzae*
  2. β-Lactamase–producing staphylococci
- Oral therapy is usually sufficient after 5 or 6 days of IV administration

DISPOSITION

- Most patients are extubated in 5 to 6 days after initiating antibiotic therapy.
- Anoxic encephalopathy is reported in 7% of survivors.

REFERRAL

Suspected diagnosis

PEARLS & CONSIDERATIONS

COMMENTS

- Infants are at increased risk of airway obstruction because of the small transverse area of the upper airway.
- Presence of pneumonia and a staphylococcal etiology are thought to worsen prognosis.
- Reported complications:
  1. Toxic shock syndrome
  2. Persistent postextubation stridor
  3. Pneumothorax
  4. Volutrauma

SUGGESTED READINGS

Ahmed QA, Niederman MS: Respiratory infection in the chronically critically ill patient, *Clin Chest Med* 22(10):71, 2001.

Bernstein T, Brilli R, Jacobs B: Is bacterial tracheitis changing? A 14-month experience in a pediatric intensive care unit, *Clin Infect Dis* 27:458, 1998.

Stroud RH, Friedman NR: An update on inflammatory disorders of the pediatric airway: epiglottitis, croup and tracheitis, *Am J Otolaryngol* 22(40):268, 2001.

Stuchell B, Chinnis A, Davis S: Case report: bacterial tracheitis in an adult female, *WV Med J* 99(4):154, 2003.

Takanami I: Life-threatening stridor due to membranous tracheitis as a rare complication of endotracheal intubation: report of a case, *Surg Today* 33(4):285, 2003.

AUTHOR: **HARVEY M. SHANIES, M.D., PH.D.**, and **JOSEPH R. MASCI, M.D.**

BASIC INFORMATION

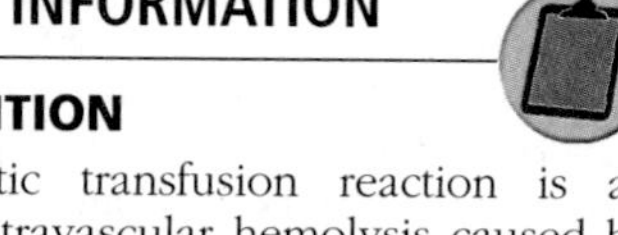

DEFINITION

Hemolytic transfusion reaction is an acute intravascular hemolysis caused by mismatches in the ABO system. It is caused by complement-fixing Ig and IgG antibodies to group A and B RBCs. Hemolytic transfusion reactions can also be caused by minor antigen systems; however, they are usually less severe. In delayed serologic transfusion reactions, hemolysis with hemoglobinemia is unusual; in these delayed reactions the only manifestations may be the development of a newly positive Coombs' test and fever.

ICD-9CM CODES
999.8 Other transfusion reaction

EPIDEMIOLOGY & DEMOGRAPHICS

Acute intravascular hemolysis occurs in <1 in 50,000 transfusions.

PHYSICAL FINDINGS & CLINICAL PRESENTATION (TABLE 1-50)

- Hypotension
- Pain at the infusion site
- Fever, tachycardia, chest or back pain, dyspnea
- Often, severe reactions occur in surgical patients under anesthesia who are unable to give any warning signs

ETIOLOGY

Most fatal hemolytic reactions are caused by clerical errors and mislabeled specimens.

DIAGNOSIS

DIFFERENTIAL DIAGNOSIS

- Bacterial contamination of blood
- Hemoglobinopathies

WORKUP

The transfusion must be stopped immediately. The blood bank must be notified, and the donor transfusion bag must be returned to the blood bank along with a freshly drawn posttransfusion specimen.

LABORATORY TESTS

- Positive Coombs' test, elevated BUN, creatinine, and bilirubin
- Hemoglobinuria (wine-colored urine), hemoglobinemia (pink plasma)
- Decreased Hct, decreased serum haptoglobin

TREATMENT

NONPHARMACOLOGIC THERAPY

- Stop transfusion immediately. Test anticoagulated blood from the recipient for the presence of free Hgb in the plasma.
- Monitor vital signs.

ACUTE GENERAL Rx

- Vigorous IV hydration to maintain urine flow at >100 ml/hr until hypotension is corrected and hemoglobinuria clears. IV furosemide may be necessary to maintain adequate renal flow.
- The addition of mannitol may prevent renal damage (controversial).
- Monitor for the presence of DIC.
- Use of IV steroids is controversial.

DISPOSITION

Mortality exceeds 50% in severe transfusion reactions.

PEARLS & CONSIDERATIONS

COMMENTS

Hemolysis caused by minor antigen systems is generally less severe and may be delayed 5-10 days after transfusion.

AUTHOR: **FRED F. FERRI, M.D.**

TABLE 1-50 Signs and Symptoms of Acute Adverse Reactions to Blood Transfusion

Reaction	Fever	Chills/ Rigors	Nausea/ Vomiting	Chest Discomfort/ Pain	Facial Flushing	Wheezing/ Dyspnea	Back/ Lumbar Pain	Discomfort at Infusion Site	Hypotension
Acute hemolytic	X	X	X	X	X	X	X	X	X
Febrile nonhemolytic	X	X		X	X				
Nonimmune hemolysis									
Acute lung injury	X			X		X			X
Allergic									
Massive transfusion complications									
Anaphylaxis	X	X	X	X	X	X	X	X	X
Passive cytokine infusion	X	X	X						
Hypervolemia						X			
Bacterial sepsis	X	X	X				X	X	X
Air embolus				X		X			

From Goldman L, Bennett JC (eds): *Cecil textbook of medicine*, ed 21, Philadelphia, 2000, WB Saunders.

BASIC INFORMATION

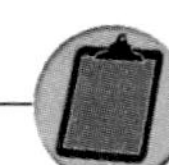

DEFINITION

Transient ischemic attack (TIA) refers to a transient neurologic dysfunction caused by focal brain or retinal ischemia with symptoms typically lasting less than 60 min but always less than 24 hr and is followed by a full recovery of function. Acute brain ischemia is a medical emergency requiring prompt neurologic evaluation and potential intervention.

SYNONYMS

TIA

ICD-9CM CODES
435.9 Unspecified transient cerebral ischemia

EPIDEMIOLOGY & DEMOGRAPHICS

INCIDENCE (IN U.S.): 49 cases/100,000 persons/yr
PREDOMINANT SEX: Males > females
PEAK INCIDENCE: >60 yr

PHYSICAL FINDINGS & CLINICAL PRESENTATION

- During an episode, neurologic abnormalities are confined to discrete vascular territory.
- Typical carotid territory symptoms are ipsilateral monocular visual disturbance, contralateral homonymous hemianopsia, contralateral hemimotor or sensory dysfunction, and language dysfunction (dominant hemisphere) alone or in combination.
- Typical vertebrobasilar territory symptoms are binocular visual disturbance, vertigo, diplopia, dysphagia, dysarthria, and motor or sensory dysfunction involving the ipsilateral face and contralateral body.

ETIOLOGY

- Cardioembolic
- Large vessel atherothrombotic disease
- Lacunar disease
- Hypoperfusion with fixed arterial stenosis
- Hypercoagulable states

DIAGNOSIS

DIFFERENTIAL DIAGNOSIS

- Hypoglycemia
- Seizures
- Migraine
- Subdural hemorrhage
- Mass lesions
- Vestibular disease
- Section II describes the differential diagnosis of neurologic deficits, focal and multifocal.

WORKUP

- Thorough history and physical examination
- Ancillary investigations including neuroimaging aimed at identifying the etiology quickly

LABORATORY TESTS

- CBC with platelets
- PT (INR) and PTT
- Glucose
- Lipid profile
- ESR (if clinical suspicion for infectious or inflammatory process)
- Urinalysis
- Chest x-ray
- ECG and consider cycling cardiac enzymes
- Other tests as dictated by suspected etiology

IMAGING STUDIES

- Head CT scan to exclude hemorrhage including a subdural hemorrhage
- MRI and MRA. (In several studies, MRI with diffusion-weighted imaging has identified early ischemic brain injury in up to 50% of patients with TIA). MRA of the brain and neck can identify large vessel intracranial and extracranial stenoses, arteriovenous malformations, and aneurysms
- Carotid Doppler studies identify carotid stenosis; neck ultrasound can also visualize stenoses of the vertebrobasilar arteries
- Echocardiography if cardiac source is suspected
- Telemetry for hospitalized patients for at least 24 hr. May consider 24-hr Holter if patient is being discharged
- Four-vessel cerebral angiogram if considering carotid endarterectomy or carotid stent

TREATMENT

NONPHARMACOLOGIC THERAPY

- Carotid endarterectomy for carotid territory TIA associated with an ipsilateral stenosis of 70%-99%: should be done by a surgeon who is experienced with and performs this procedure frequently. Carotid stenting is also being performed in patients who are not surgical candidates. Trials are comparing stenting versus surgery for carotid disease.
- Modification of risk factors including smoking cessation.

ACUTE GENERAL Rx

- Depends on etiology
- If the time of the onset of symptoms is clear, and there are significant deficits on neurologic examination, and brain hemorrhage has been ruled out, then the patient may be a candidate for thrombolytic therapy, but this should be discussed with a neurologist or a specialist in cerebrovascular disease.
- Acute anticoagulation: no data supporting benefits in the acute setting. Heparin is considered for new-onset atrial fibrillation and atherothrombotic carotid disease causing recurrent transient neurologic symptoms especially in the setting before carotid endarterectomy or carotid stenting. Also considered for basilar artery thrombosis given concern for progression to brainstem stroke with high morbidity and mortality.
- Section III, Transient Ischemic Attacks, describes a treatment algorithm.

CHRONIC Rx

- No data supporting the use of long-term anticoagulation in the management of TIA, although stroke patients with atrial fibrillation or demonstrated cardiac thrombi have been shown to benefit from long-term warfarin therapy.
- First line of treatment has traditionally been aspirin. No significant benefit of high-dose aspirin (up to 1500 mg/day) has been conclusively found over lower doses (75 mg to 325 mg/day). A baby aspirin (81 mg/day) is therefore appropriate.
- Also consider aspirin/dipyridamole extended-release capsules (Aggrenox, 1 capsule po bid) or plavix as a first-line therapy. In a study of patients with TIA or stroke, Aggrenox reduced subsequent cerebrovascular events to a greater extent than either drug alone. Plavix is equally effective to aspirin in secondary prevention but the combination of aspirin and plavix for patients with TIA or stroke causes more life threatening bleeding than plavix alone. Recommend Aggrenox or oral anticoagulation for patients who continue to have TIAs while on aspirin (aspirin failures), but there are no data to support this recommendation.
- In patients with cerebrovascular disease, HMG-CoA reductase inhibitors (statins) have been shown to provide significant protection against subsequent vascular events such as MI and stroke even for LDLs <100. Consider starting a statin agent unless LDL is <70.

DISPOSITION

- According to one study, 10% to 20% of patients have a stroke in the next 90 days, and in 50% of these patients, stroke occurs in the first day or two after the TIA.
- Another study showed a stroke risk of 4.4% in the first month and 11.6% in the first year.
- The annual risk of myocardial infarction is 2.4%.
- One-year and 3-yr survival rates are 98% and 94%, respectively.

REFERRAL

Recommend referring all patients with TIA for an urgent neurologic evaluation and management.

PEARLS & CONSIDERATIONS

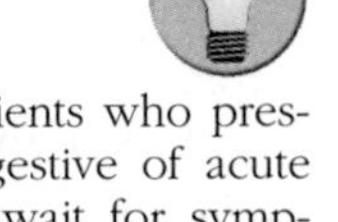

CAVEAT

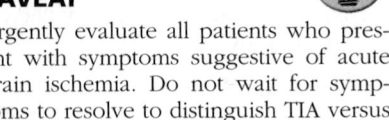

Urgently evaluate all patients who present with symptoms suggestive of acute brain ischemia. Do not wait for symptoms to resolve to distinguish TIA versus stroke.

SUGGESTED READINGS

Alamowitch S et al: Risk, causes, and prevention of ischaemic stroke in elderly patients with symptomatic internal-carotid-artery stenosis, *Lancet* 357:1154, 2001.

Albers GW: A review of published TIA treatment recommendations, *Neurology* 62:S26, 2004.

Albers GW et al: Transient ischemic attack—proposal for a new definition, *N Engl J Med* 347:1713, 2002.

Albers GW et al: Antithrombotic and thrombolytic therapy for ischemic stroke, *Chest* 119:300S, 2001.

Algra A et al: Oral anticoagulants versus antiplatelet therapy for preventing further vascular events after transient ischaemic attack or minor stroke of presumed arterial origin, *Stroke* 34:234, 2003.

Diener HC et al: Aspirin and clopidogrel compared with clopidogrel alone after recent ischemic stroke or transient ischaemic attack in high risk patients (MATCH): randomized, double-blind, placebo-controlled trial, *Lancet* 364:331, 2004.

Gorelick PB et al: Prevention of a first stroke, *JAMA* 281:1112, 1999.

Heart Protection Study Collaborative Group: MRC/BHF heart protection study of cholesterol lowering with simvastatin in 20,536 high-risk individuals: a randomized placebo-controlled trial, *Lancet* 360:7, 2002.

Johnston SC: Clinical practice. Transient ischemic attack, *N Engl J Med* 347:1687, 2002.

Sarasin FP, Gaspoz JM, Bounameaux H: Cost-effectiveness of new antiplatelet regimens used as secondary prevention of stroke or transient ischemic attack, *Arch Intern Med* 160(18):2773, 2000.

AUTHOR: **SEAN I. SAVITZ, M.D.**

BASIC INFORMATION

DEFINITION

Trichinosis is an infection by one of various species of *Trichinella*.

ICD-9CM CODES
124 Trichinosis

EPIDEMIOLOGY & DEMOGRAPHICS

INCIDENCE (IN U.S.): <100 cases/yr
GENETICS:
Congenital Infection:
- Abrupt delivery of stillbirths in infected pregnant women
- Vertical infection of the fetus

PHYSICAL FINDINGS

- Symptoms
  1. May vary widely depending on the time from ingestion of contaminated meat and on worm burden
  2. Most persons asymptomatic
- Enteral phase
  1. Correlates with penetration of ingested larvae into the intestinal mucosa
  2. May last from 2 to 6 wk
  3. Mild, transient diarrhea and nausea
  4. Abdominal pain
  5. Diarrhea or constipation
  6. Vomiting
  7. Malaise
  8. Low-grade fevers
- Migratory or parenteral phase
  1. In the intestine, maturation and mating
  2. Newborn larvae
     a. Penetrate into lymphatic and blood vessels
     b. Migrate to muscles where they penetrate into muscle cells, enlarge, coil, and develop a cyst wall
  3. Patients may present with
     a. Fever
     b. Myalgias
     c. Periorbital or facial edema
     d. Headache
     e. Skin rash
     f. Other symptoms caused by the penetration of tissues by the newborn migrating larvae
  4. Peak in symptoms 2-3 wk after infection, then slowly subside
- Severe complications
  1. Brain damage by granulomatous inflammation or occlusion of arteries
  2. Cardiac involvement
  3. Can lead to death

ETIOLOGY

- The nematode responsible for this illness is an obligate intracellular parasite belonging to the genus *Trichinella*.
- It is one of the most ubiquitous parasites in the world and may be found in virtually all warm-blooded animals.
- Infection in humans occurs by the ingestion of contaminated animal meat that is raw or partially cooked and contains viable cysts.
- Most cases are now related to the consumption of poorly processed pork or wild game (bear, wild boar, cougar, and walrus).

DIAGNOSIS

DIFFERENTIAL DIAGNOSIS

- Different presentations have different differential diagnoses.
- Early illness may resemble gastroenteritis.
- Later symptoms may be confused with:
  1. Measles
  2. Dermatomyositis
  3. Glomerulonephritis
- The differential diagnosis of nematode tissue infections is described in Section II.

WORKUP

- Antibody assay of serum is usually positive by approximately 2 wk after infection.
- Muscle biopsy is used to detect the larva in muscle tissue if diagnosis unclear; best done by placing the tissue between two slides.

LABORATORY TESTS

- CBC: leukocytosis with prominent eosinophilia
- ESR: usually normal
- Elevation of muscle enzymes common (i.e., CPK, aldolase)

IMAGING STUDIES

Soft-tissue radiographs may show calcified cyst walls.

TREATMENT

NONPHARMACOLOGIC THERAPY

Bed rest for myalgias

ACUTE GENERAL Rx

- Thiabendazole to treat persons within 24 hr of ingesting contaminated meat, at the dose of 25 mg/kg/day for 1 wk
- Salicylates to decrease muscle discomfort
- Steroids in critically ill patients
- A recent study showed clinical improvement of myositis significantly more often in patients treated with thiabendazole or mebendazole versus those treated with fluconazole or placebo

DISPOSITION

- Most symptoms subside over time.
- Reports of long-term sequelae:
  1. Myalgias
  2. Headaches
- Occasionally, death occurs.

REFERRAL

Diagnosis uncertain

PEARLS & CONSIDERATIONS

COMMENTS

- Prevention by thorough cooking of meats
- Inadequate to smoke, cure, or dry meats
- Freezing at specified temperatures kills *T. spiralis* larvae in pork
- *T. nativa* is a freeze-resistant species that remains viable after freezing, even for months or years—has been associated with infection from ingestion of bear meat

SUGGESTED READINGS

Centers for Disease Control and Prevention (CDC): Trichinellosis associated with bear meat—New York and Tennessee, *MMWR* 53(27):606, 2004.
Moorhead A et al: Trichinellosis in the United States, 1991-1996: declining but not gone, *Am J Trop Med Hyg* 60:66, 1999.
Watt G et al: Blinded, placebo-controlled trial of antiparasitic drugs for trichinosis myositis, *J Infect Dis* 182:371, 2000.

AUTHOR: **MAURICE POLICAR, M.D.**

SECTION I

BASIC INFORMATION

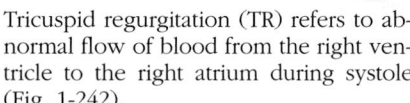

DEFINITION

Tricuspid regurgitation (TR) refers to abnormal flow of blood from the right ventricle to the right atrium during systole (Fig. 1-242).

SYNONYMS

Tricuspid insufficiency

ICD-9CM CODES
397.0 Disease of the tricuspid valve
424.2 Tricuspid valve insufficiency (nonrheumatic)

EPIDEMIOLOGY & DEMOGRAPHICS

- Isolated TR is more common than tricuspid stenosis (TS).
- In patients with rheumatic heart disease, TR rarely occurs alone and is usually associated with mitral and/or aortic valve disease.
- Trivial TR is frequently detected by echocardiogram and is considered a normal variant.

PHYSICAL FINDINGS & CLINICAL PRESENTATION

- Symptoms of TR are determined by the underlying cause (e.g., pulmonary hypertension, left ventricular failure, and mitral stenosis)
- Dyspnea
- Orthopnea
- Paroxysmal nocturnal dyspnea
- Signs of right-sided heart failure:
  1. Elevated jugular venous distention with large V waves
  2. Right ventricular lift
  3. Right-sided S_3
  4. Holosystolic murmur heard best along the left parasternal line and fourth intercostal space and is louder during inspiration
  5. Pulsatile liver
  6. Hepatomegaly
  7. Ascites
  8. Edema

ETIOLOGY

- TR is usually functional rather than structural.
- Functional TR refers to conditions leading to dilation of the tricuspid annulus and/or right ventricle and includes:
  1. Any cause of pulmonary hypertension (e.g., COPD, pulmonary embolism, restrictive lung disease, collagen vascular disease, and primary pulmonary hypertension)
  2. Coronary artery disease with right ventricular infarction
  3. Left-sided congestive heart failure leading to right-sided heart failure
  4. Dilated cardiomyopathy (e.g., alcohol, idiopathic)
- Structural TR refers to conditions directly affecting the tricuspid valve and includes:
  1. Rheumatic fever
  2. Infective endocarditis
  3. Congenital (e.g., Ebstein's anomaly)
  4. Carcinoid
  5. Marfan's syndrome
  6. Tricuspid valve prolapse
  7. Traumatic (e.g., pacemaker insertion)
  8. Right atrial myxoma
  9. Collagen-vascular disease (e.g., SLE)
  10. Radiation

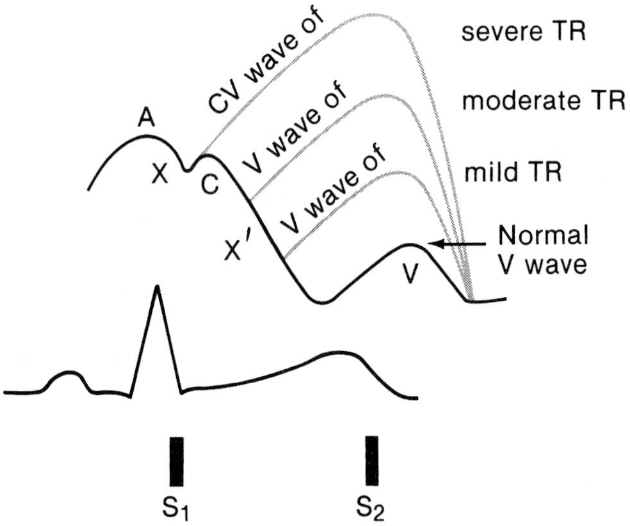

FIGURE 1-242 The jugular venous pulse in tricuspid regurgitation. The jugular venous pulse wave normally drops during ventricular systole. As TR becomes more severe, the CV wave becomes more obvious during ventricular systole. (From Conn R: *Current diagnosis,* ed 9, Philadelphia, 1997, WB Saunders.)

DIAGNOSIS

The diagnosis of TR is made by clinical history, physical examination, and adjunctive studies including ECG, chest x-ray, echocardiography, and rarely, right-sided heart catheterization.

DIFFERENTIAL DIAGNOSIS

The differential diagnosis of TR is as stated under "Etiology."

WORKUP

- Any patient suspected of having significant TR should undergo the following:
  1. Chest x-ray
  2. Electrocardiogram
  3. Echocardiogram (confirmatory)
  4. Right-sided cardiac catheterization

LABORATORY TESTS

- Blood tests are not very specific in diagnosing TR.
- ECG may show evidence of:
  1. Right atrial enlargement (e.g., P-wave height in leads II, III, aVF >2.5 mV)
  2. Right ventricular enlargement/hypertrophy (e.g., R wave > S wave in lead V_1)
  3. Right axis deviation >100 degrees
  4. Atrial fibrillation

IMAGING STUDIES

- Chest x-ray can show:
  1. Evidence of COPD with flattened diaphragms, barrel chest, dilated pulmonary arteries, and increased retrosternal air space
  2. Enlarged right atrium
  3. Enlarged right ventricle
- Echocardiogram, M-mode, 2-D with continuous wave, pulse wave, and color Doppler will:
  1. Detect TR
  2. Estimate the severity of TR
  3. Estimate the pulmonary artery pressure
  4. Exclude vegetation, mass, or prolapse
  5. Assess overall ventricular function
- Right-sided catheterization shows:
  1. Elevated right atrial and right ventricular end-diastolic pressures
  2. Large V waves

TREATMENT

Treatment of TR is directed at the underlying cause.

NONPHARMACOLOGIC THERAPY

Oxygen therapy is beneficial in patients with functional TR secondary to underlying pulmonary hypertension provoked by alveolar hypoxia.

ACUTE GENERAL Rx

- Functional TR caused by left-sided heart failure is treated in similar fashion with preload and afterload reduction with or without inotrope therapy:
  1. Digoxin 0.25 mg PO qd
  2. Furosemide 40-80 mg PO qd for edema
  3. Angiotensin-converting enzyme inhibitors (e.g., lisinopril 10-40 mg PO qd, fosinopril 10-40 mg PO qd, enalapril 10 mg PO bid, and captopril 50 mg PO tid).
- Structural TR treatment depends on the underlying cause (e.g., antibiotics for infective endocarditis).

CHRONIC Rx

- Tricuspid valve surgery is considered in patients with severe TR from rheumatic mitral stenosis and pulmonary hypertension, structural valve damage from carcinoid, congenital anomalies, or infective endocarditis.
- Surgical procedures may include:
  1. Total valve replacement
  2. Annuloplasty
  3. Converting the tricuspid valve from three leaflets to two leaflets

DISPOSITION

- The natural history of TR will depend on the underlying etiology.
- Patients with rheumatic valve disease requiring replacement of both the mitral and tricuspid valve have a high 30-day morbidity/mortality rate of 15%-20%.

REFERRAL

For patients with significant symptomatic TR, a cardiology consultation is recommended.

PEARLS & CONSIDERATIONS

COMMENTS

- Antibiotic prophylaxis for dental, GI, or GU procedures is recommended in patients with structural tricuspid valve abnormalities.
- TR secondary to tricuspid valve prolapse may also be associated with mitral valve prolapse.

SUGGESTED READINGS

Frater R: Tricuspid insufficiency, *J Thorac Cardiovasc Surg* 122(3):427, 2001.

Raman SV et al: Tricuspid valve disease: tricuspid valve complex perspective, *Curr Prob Cardiol* 27(3):103, 2002.

Trichon BH, O'Connor CM: Secondary mitral and tricuspid regurgitation accompanying left ventricular systolic function: is it important, and how is it treated? *Am Heart J* 144(3):373, 2002.

Waller BF et al: Pathology of tricuspid valve stenosis and pure tricuspid regurgitation—Part I, *Clin Cardiol* 18(2):97, 1995.

Waller BF et al: Pathology of tricuspid valve stenosis and pure tricuspid regurgitation—Part II, *Clin Cardiol* 18(3):167, 1995.

AUTHOR: **WEN-CHIH WU, M.D.**

BASIC INFORMATION

DEFINITION

Tricuspid stenosis (TS) is narrowing of the orifice of the tricuspid valve restricting right atrial emptying, resulting in a diastolic pressure gradient between the right atrium and right ventricle.

SYNONYMS

Tricuspid valve stenosis
TS

ICD-9CM CODES

397.0 Disease of the tricuspid valve

EPIDEMIOLOGY & DEMOGRAPHICS

- TS is more common in women than in men and is seen in patients between the ages of 20 to 60.
- TS is more common in India than in the U.S.
- In patients who have rheumatic heart disease, TS is present at autopsy in 15%, but was clinically significant in only 5%.
- Rheumatic TS very seldom occurs alone; it is usually associated with mitral and/or aortic valve disease.

PHYSICAL FINDINGS & CLINICAL PRESENTATION

- Patients with severe symptomatic TS usually present with symptoms of fatigue, abdominal swelling, and anasarca. They may complain of right upper quadrant abdominal pain secondary to passive congestive hepatomegaly from elevated systemic venous pressures.
- Jugular venous distention with a prominent a wave is noted along with a palpable hepatic pulsation.
- Right atrial pulsation may be palpated to the right of the sternum and a diastolic thrill may be felt over the left sternal edge that is increased with inspiration.
- An opening snap and diastolic murmur is best heard along the left sternal border of the fourth intercostal space and is augmented by inspiration.

ETIOLOGY

Rheumatic heart disease is the primary cause of TS, resulting in scarring of the valve leaflets and fusion of the commissures. This, along with shortening of the chordae tendineae and immobility of the valve leaflets, results in narrowing of the tricuspid valve orifice. Other causes of TS are congenital TS, right atrial myxoma, metastatic tumor (e.g., lymphoma), carcinoid syndrome, systemic lupus endocarditis, and tricuspid valve bacterial endocarditis.

DIAGNOSIS

DIFFERENTIAL DIAGNOSIS

- Congenital tricuspid atresia
- Endomyocardial fibrosis
- Right atrial thrombi
- Constrictive pericarditis

WORKUP

- Echocardiography (first choice)
- Chest x-ray examination
- ECG
- Cardiac angiography in selected patients

IMAGING STUDIES

- Echocardiography reveals doming of the anterior tricuspid leaflet with restriction of movement of the leaflet tip along with reduced excursion of the posterior and septal leaflets. Doppler is used to calculate the diastolic gradient across the tricuspid.
- Chest x-ray reveals an enlarged right atrium and pulmonary oligemia.
- ECG in many cases will show atrial fibrillation secondary to an enlarged right atrium. However, in patients who are in normal sinus rhythm, the ECG will show criteria for right atrial enlargement (tall peaked P waves >2.5 mm in height in leads II, III, or aVF).
- Cardiac catheterization will measure simultaneous pressures in the right atrium and right ventricle giving the gradient across the valve (normal gradient <1 mm Hg). Tricuspid valve area can also be determined (severe: <1 cm^2).

TREATMENT

NONPHARMACOLOGIC THERAPY

Most patients with severe TS will have peripheral edema and therefore salt restriction is essential.

ACUTE GENERAL Rx

- Furosemide 40 mg qd; gradually increased according to symptoms and edema.
- Digoxin 0.25 mg qd and warfarin (maintaining the INR between 2 to 3) is used in patients who develop atrial fibrillation.

CHRONIC Rx

- Balloon dilation of the stenosed tricuspid valve has been described in both rheumatic and congenital TS with some success, but experience is limited and complications may occur (e.g., advanced heart block, significant tricuspid regurgitation).
- It must be remembered that rheumatic TS is usually associated with mitral disease. The decision to proceed with surgery for TS typically occurs in the setting of significant symptomatic mitral valve disease requiring surgery and there is a mean diastolic gradient across the tricuspid valve of >5 mm Hg with a tricuspid valve area of <2 cm^2.
- Surgical procedures for significant tricuspid stenosis include closed commissurotomy, open commissurotomy, and tricuspid valve replacement. This is usually determined during surgery.
- Tricuspid valve replacement carries a high 30-day operative morbidity/mortality of 15%-20% in addition to the high risk of thrombus formation.

DISPOSITION

The natural course of severe TS is not very well known.

REFERRAL

TS is difficult to diagnose and therefore consultation with a cardiology specialist is recommended.

PEARLS & CONSIDERATIONS

COMMENTS

- Rheumatic TS almost always occurs in association with either mitral valve disease and/or aortic valve disease.
- Unlike mitral stenosis patients, TS patients typically do not complain of dyspnea, orthopnea, or paroxysmal nocturnal dyspnea.

SUGGESTED READINGS

Chrissos D et al: One-year follow-up of a patient with reversible tricuspid valve stenosis due to lymphomatic mass into the right atrioventriuclar wall, *Echocardiography* 19(7 pt 1):565, 2002.

Krishnamoorthy KM: Balloon dilatation of isolated congenital tricuspid stenosis, *Int J Cardiol* 89(1):119, 2003.

Mehra MR et al: Difficult cases in heart failure: isolated tricuspid stenosis and heart failure: a focus on carcinoid heart disease, *Congest Heart Fail* 9(5):294, 2003.

Raman SV et al: Tricuspid valve disease: tricuspid valve complex perspective, *Curr Prob Cardiol* 27(3):103, 2002.

Roguin A et al: Long-term follow-up of patients with severe rheumatic tricuspid stenosis, *Am Heart J* 136(1):103, 1998.

Waller BF et al: Pathology of tricuspid valve stenosis and pure tricuspid regurgitation—Part I, *Clin Cardiol* 18(2):97, 1995.

Waller BF et al: Pathology of tricuspid valve stenosis and pure tricuspid regurgitation—Part II, *Clin Cardiol* 18(3):167, 1995.

AUTHORS: **GAURAV CHOUDHARY, M.D.,** and **WEN-CHIH WU, M.D.**

BASIC INFORMATION

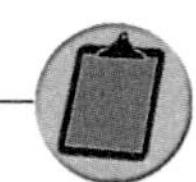

DEFINITION

Tricyclic antidepressants (TCAs) are secondary or tertiary amines that have variable abilities to inhibit reuptake of neurotransmitters (norepinephrine, dopamine, and serotonin) and to be anticholinergic, antihistaminic, and sedating. These properties are important to consider when prescribing these agents and when managing an intentional or accidental overdose.

SYNONYMS

Tricyclic antidepressant intoxication or poisoning
TCA OD

ICD-9CM CODES
969.0

EPIDEMIOLOGY & DEMOGRAPHICS

- TCAs are the most common cause of death resulting from prescription drug overdose in the U.S.
- Available TCAs: amitriptyline, imipramine, desipramine, nortriptyline, doxepin, amoxapine, clomipramine, protriptyline, and others

PHYSICAL FINDINGS & CLINICAL PRESENTATION

Cardiovascular
- Intraventricular conduction delay (QRS prolongation)
- Sinus tachycardia
- Atrioventricular block
- Prolongation of the QT interval
- Ventricular tachycardia
- Wide complex tachycardia without P waves
- Refractory hypotension (the most common cause of death from TCA OD)
- Late arrhythmias or sudden death (in addition to the previous, which occur during the first 24-48 hr: late problems can occur up to 5 days after the OD)

Central nervous system
- Coma
- Delirium
- Myoclonus
- Seizures

Other
- Hyperthermia
- Ileus
- Urinary retention
- Pulmonary complications (e.g., aspiration pneumonitis)
- Life-threatening overdose exists with the ingestion of more than 1 g of TCA. Among patients who reach a hospital, most deaths occur within the first 24 hr; lack of initial symptoms can be deceptive

PATHOGENESIS

Mechanisms of tricyclic antidepressant cardiovascular toxicity (Table 1-51)
CNS toxicity
- Cholinergic blockade is believed to cause hyperthermia, ileus, urinary retention, pupillary dilation, delirium, and coma.
- The mechanism of myoclonus and seizures is not fully understood.

DIAGNOSIS

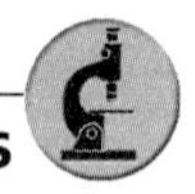

DIFFERENTIAL DIAGNOSIS

Cardiotoxicity from TCA can be confused with intoxication by drugs that cause QRS prolongation. These include class Ia antiarrhythmic agents (disopyramide, procainamide, quinidine), class Ic antiarrhythmic agents (encainide, flecainide, propafenone), cocaine, propranolol, quinine, chloroquine, neuroleptics, propoxyphene, and digoxin. Other causes of QRS prolongation include hyperkalemia, ischemic heart disease, cardiomyopathy, and cardiac conduction system dysfunction.

WORKUP

- Clinical presentation
- Knowledge of the overdose
- Serum drug levels (TCA concentration >1 μg/ml is life threatening and TCA concentration >3 μg/ml is often fatal)
- Baseline CBC, prothrombin time, BUN, creatinine, and electrolytes

TREATMENT

MANAGEMENT

Initial measures
- Hospitalization with cardiac monitoring as well as monitoring of vital signs and temperature
- Initiate intravenous access
- Administer activated charcoal with sorbitol
- Large-bore tube gastric lavage is of unproven benefit
- Ipecac is contraindicated
- 12-Lead ECG
- If no evidence of cardiotoxicity has been noted during the first 6 hr of observation, further monitoring is not necessary; if there is evidence of cardiotoxicity, monitoring should continue for 24 hr after all signs of toxicity have resolved

Treatment of specific complications of TCA toxicity: See Table 1-52
When the patient is medically stable, psychiatric evaluation should be obtained.

SUGGESTED READINGS

Glauser J: Tricyclic antidepressant poisoning, *Cleve Clin J Med* 67:704, 2000.

Pentel PR, Keyler DE, Haddad LM: Tricyclic antidepressants. In Haddad LM, Shannon MW, Winchester JF (eds): *Clinical management of poisoning and drug overdose*, ed 3, Philadelphia, 1998, WB Saunders.

AUTHOR: **TOM J. WACHTEL, M.D.**

TABLE 1-51 Mechanism of Tricyclic Antidepressant Cardiovascular Toxicity

Toxic Effect	Mechanism
Conduction Delays, Arrhythmias	
QRS prolongation atrioventricular block	Cardiac sodium channel → slowed depolarization in atrioventricular node, His-Purkinje fibers, and ventricular myocardium
Sinus tachycardia	Cholinergic blockade, inhibition of norepinephrine reuptake
Ventricular tachycardia	
Monomorphic	Cardiac sodium channel inhibition → reentry
Torsades de pointes	Cardiac potassium channel inhibition → prolonged repolarization
Ventricular bradycardia	Impaired cardiac automaticity
Hypotension	
Vasodilation	Vascular a-adrenergic receptor blockade
Decreased cardiac contractility	Cardiac sodium channel inhibition → impaired excitation-contraction coupling

TABLE 1-52 Treatment of Complications of Tricyclic Antidepressant Toxicity

Toxic effect	Treatment
Cardiovascular	
QRS prolongation	Hypertonic $NaHCO_3$ if QRS prolongation is marked or progressing; not clear if treatment is needed in the absence of hypotension or arrhythmias
Hypotension	Intravascular volume expansion, $NaHCO_3$ Vasopressors (norepinephrine) or inotropic agents (dopamine) Correct hyperthermia, acidosis, seizures Consider mechanical support
Ventricular tachycardia	$NaHCO_3$, lidocaine, overdrive, pacing Correct hypotension, hypothermia, acidosis, seizures
Torsades de pointes	Overdrive pacing
Ventricular bradycardia	Chronotropic agent (epinephrine), pacemaker
Sinus tachycardia	Treatment rarely needed
Atrioventricular block type II second or third degree	Pacemaker
Hypertension	Rapidly titratable antihypertensive agent (nitroprusside)
Central Nervous System	
Delirium	Restraints, benzodiazepine Neuromuscular blockade for hyperthermia, acidosis
Seizures	Benzodiazepine Neuromuscular blockade for hyperthermia, acidosis
Coma	Intubation, ventilation if needed
Other	
Hyperthermia	Control seizures, agitation Cooling measures
Acidosis	$NaHCO_3$ Correct hypotension, hypoventilation

BASIC INFORMATION

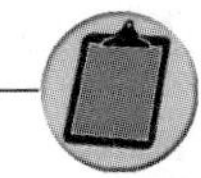

DEFINITION

Trigeminal neuralgia is a syndrome characterized by recurrent excruciating paroxysms of lancinating pain in the distribution of one or more divisions of the trigeminal (fifth) nerve.

SYNONYMS

Tic douloureux

ICD-9CM CODES
350.1 Trigeminal neuralgia

EPIDEMIOLOGY & DEMOGRAPHICS

INCIDENCE (IN U.S.): 3-5/100,000
PREVALENCE (IN U.S.): 155/1 million persons
PREDOMINANT SEX: Slight predominance of females to males
PEAK INCIDENCE: Median age 67 years
GENETICS: Uncommonly familial and possibly caused by underlying genetic etiology (see below in "Etiology" under "Rare causes")

PHYSICAL FINDINGS & CLINICAL PRESENTATION

- Each attack lasts only seconds but may cluster.
- Often, attacks are brought on by mild stimulation of trigger zones, located in the affected division of the fifth nerve. These triggers include light touching, eating, drinking, shaving and draught of air.

ETIOLOGY

- It is thought that 80%-90% of cases are due to compression of the trigeminal nerve root at the cerebellopontine angle by an aberrant loop of artery or vein, and rarely a saccular aneurysm or arteriovenous malformation
- Compressive lesions such as schwannomas, epidermoid cysts and meningiomas, also typically at the cerebellopontine angle
- Bony compression of the fifth nerve (e.g., from an osteoma or deformity resulting from osteogenesis imperfecta)
- Primary demyelinating disorders: multiple sclerosis (2%-4% of patients) and rarely Charcot-Marie-Tooth disease. In multiple sclerosis, usually there is a plaque of demyelination at the root entry zone of the fifth nerve in the pons
- Rare causes: (a) infiltrative disorders such as carcinomatous or amyloid deposits in the fifth nerve root, nerve proper, or ganglion; (b) familial occurrence has been reported in Charcot-Marie-Tooth disease

DIAGNOSIS

DIFFERENTIAL DIAGNOSIS

- Dental pathology
- The differential diagnosis of headache and facial pain is described in Section II.

WORKUP

MRI scans (CT scan with thin posterior fossa cuts if MRI not available) for all patients to exclude mass lesions or evidence of central demyelination as in multiple sclerosis

IMAGING STUDIES

See "Workup."

TREATMENT

NONPHARMACOLOGIC THERAPY

- In refractory cases, surgical options, including percutaneous radiofrequency gangliolysis and microvascular decompression
- Gamma-knife radiosurgery is an increasingly popular alternative to conventional surgery for trigeminal neuralgia

ACUTE GENERAL Rx

None, episodes are too brief

CHRONIC Rx

- Carbamazepine is the treatment of choice, providing relief to at least 75% of patients. Begin with 100 mg bid and increase gradually as tolerated using a tid regimen.
- If carbamazepine is not tolerated or effective, use gabapentin, 400 mg PO tid. Doses as high as 3600 mg/day are easily tolerated. Topiramate (Topamax) 25 mg qhs gradually titrated up to 100 mg bid is also effective.

DISPOSITION

Spontaneous remissions occur after months to years.

REFERRAL

If uncertain about diagnosis or if surgical treatment is necessary

PEARLS & CONSIDERATIONS

Even in patients with multiple sclerosis, a vascular compression may be the source of symptoms and thus may benefit from intervention such as surgery.

COMMENTS

Because prolonged remission may occur, drug tapering at yearly intervals is recommended.

SUGGESTED READINGS

Elias WJ and Burchiel KJ: Trigeminal neuralgia and other neuropathic pain syndromes of the head and face, *Curr Pain Headache Rep* 6(2):115, 2002.

Kitt CA et al. Trigeminal neuralgia: opportunities for research and treatment, *Pain* 85: 3, 2000

Loeser JD: Tic douloureux, *Pain Res Manag* 6(3):156, 2001.

Love S, Coakham HB: Trigeminal neuralgia: pathology and pathogenesis, *Brain* 124(Pt 12):2347, 2001.

Maesawa S et al: Clinical outcomes after stereotactic radiosurgery for idiopathic trigeminal neuralgia, *J Neurosurg* 94:16, 2001.

AUTHOR: **U. SHIVRAJ SOHUR, M.D., PH.D.**

BASIC INFORMATION

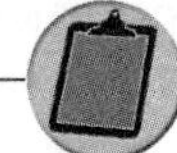

DEFINITION

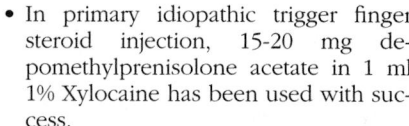

Digital stenosing tenosynovitis refers to an inflammatory process of the digital flexor tendon sheath.

SYNONYMS

Trigger finger

ICD-9CM CODES
727.03 Trigger finger (acquired)

EPIDEMIOLOGY & DEMOGRAPHICS

- Trigger finger can be found in all age groups but is commonly found in patients older than 45 yr
- More frequently affects females (4:1)
- Occupational risk groups: meat cutters, seamstress, tailors, and dentists
- In adults the middle finger is most often affected (Fig. 1-243)
- In children the thumb is most often affected

PHYSICAL FINDINGS & CLINICAL PRESENTATION

- Hand pain
- Painful triggering or snapping with flexion and extension of the affected digit
- Locking or loss of active digital extension is the most common symptom
- The digit possibly fixed in flexion (trapped or incarcerated)
- Usually affects one digit
- If more digits are involved, a systemic cause most likely present (e.g., diabetes, rheumatoid arthritis)
- A palpable tender nodule noted at the MCP joint of the affected digit
- Pain over the flexor tendon with resisted flexion
- Pain with passive stretching

ETIOLOGY

Trigger finger is described as being primary or secondary:

- Primary (idiopathic)
- Secondary
  1. Diabetes
  2. Rheumatoid arthritis
  3. Hypothyroidism
  4. Histiocytosis
  5. Amyloidosis
  6. Gout

DIAGNOSIS

The diagnosis of trigger finger is usually made by the clinical historical presentation and by physical examination.

DIFFERENTIAL DIAGNOSIS

- Dupuytren's contracture
- De Quervain's tenosynovitis
- Acute digital tenosynovitis
- Proliferative tenosynovitis
- Carpal tunnel syndrome
- Flexion tendon rupture
- Trauma

WORKUP

If a secondary cause of trigger finger is suspected, a workup should be pursued.

LABORATORY TESTS

- CBC with differential
- Electrolytes, BUN, and creatinine
- Blood glucose
- Thyroid function tests
- Uric acid
- Rheumatoid factor

IMAGING STUDIES

X-ray studies are not very helpful unless a secondary cause has affected other organs (e.g., rheumatoid lung).

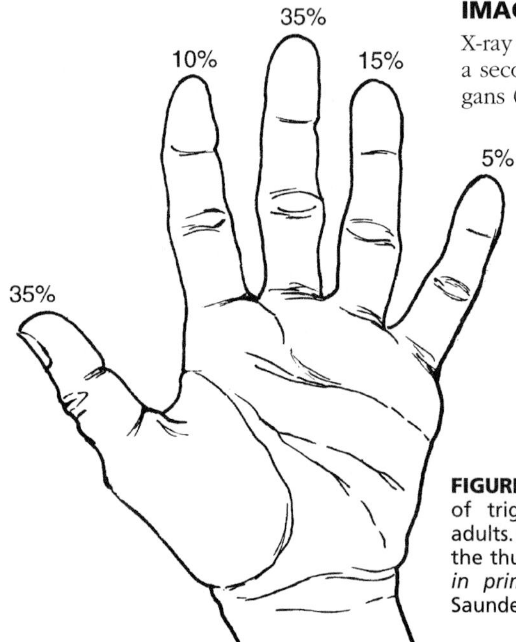

FIGURE 1-243 Trigger finger. Frequency of trigger finger according to digit in adults. In children, virtually all cases occur in the thumb. (From Canoso J: *Rheumatology in primary care,* Philadelphia, 1997, WB Saunders.)

TREATMENT

NONPHARMACOLOGIC THERAPY

Splinting can be tried early in the course but has been very successful.

ACUTE GENERAL Rx

- In primary idiopathic trigger finger steroid injection, 15-20 mg depomethylprenisolone acetate in 1 ml 1% Xylocaine has been used with success.
- Triamcinolone 10 mg with 1 ml of 1% Xylocaine is an alternative steroid choice to be used in patients who do not respond to the first injection.
- If symptoms do not resolve in 3 wk, a repeat injection can be tried.

CHRONIC Rx

- Surgical release is indicated in patients with refractory symptoms (e.g., locked digits) despite nonpharmacologic and acute treatment.
- Surgery is also indicated in patients with recurrent symptoms despite steroid injection therapy.

DISPOSITION

- Following steroid injection, symptoms usually resolve in 3-5 days, and locking resolves in 60% of the cases in 2-3 wk.
- If symptoms recur, a repeat steroid injection improves the symptoms in >80% of patients.
- Diabetic patients do not have the same success rate with steroid injections as the primary idiopathic group.

REFERRAL

If steroid injection therapy is considered, a rheumatology consult is requested.

PEARLS & CONSIDERATIONS

COMMENTS

If more than one digit is involved, a workup for a secondary systemic cause is in order.

SUGGESTED READINGS

Canoso JJ: Trigger finger. In *Rheumatology in primary care,* Philadelphia, 1997, Saunders.

Chin DH, Jones NF: Repetitive motion hand disorder, *J Calif Dent Assoc* 30(2):49, 2002.

Moore JS: Flexor tendon entrapment of the digits (trigger finger and trigger thumb), *J Occup Environ Med* 42(5):526, 2000.

Saldana MJ: Trigger digits: diagnosis and treatment, *J Am Acad Orthop Surg* 9(4):246, 2001.

AUTHOR: **PETER PETROPOULOS, M.D.**

BASIC INFORMATION

DEFINITION

Trochanteric bursitis is a presumed inflammation or irritation of the gluteus maximus bursa or the bursa separating the greater trochanter from the gluteus medius and gluteus minimus (Fig. 1-244).

SYNONYMS

Greater trochanteric pain syndrome

ICD-9CM CODES
726.5 Bursitis trochanteric area

EPIDEMIOLOGY & DEMOGRAPHICS

- Trochanteric bursitis is commonly associated with other conditions:
  1. Osteoarthritis of the hip
  2. Lumbar spinal degenerative joint disease
  3. Rheumatoid arthritis
- Incidence peaks between the fourth and sixth decades of life but can occur at any age group
- Occurs in females > males (4:1)

PHYSICAL FINDINGS & CLINICAL PRESENTATION

- Hip pain is the most common complaint. The pain is chronic, intermittent, and located over the lateral thigh.
- Numbness can be present.
- Pain is precipitated with prolonged lying or standing on the affected side.
- Walking, climbing, and running exacerbate the pain.
- Point tenderness over the greater trochanter is noted.
- Pain is reproduced with resisted hip abduction.

ETIOLOGY

- The specific cause of trochanteric bursitis is not known although repetitive high-intensity use of the hip joint, trauma, infection (tuberculosis and bacterial), and crystal deposition can precipitate the disease.
- Trochanteric bursitis can occur when other conditions such as osteoarthritis of the knee and hip and bunions of the feet cause changes in the patient's gait, placing varus stress on the hip joint.

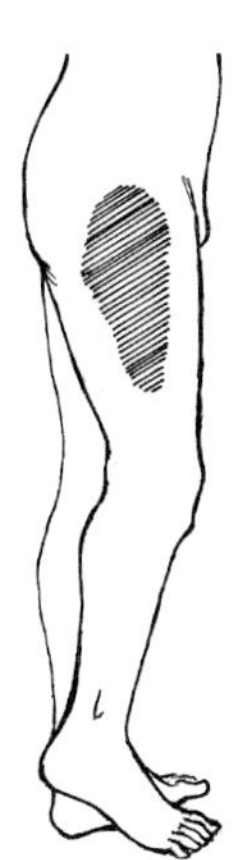

FIGURE 1-244 Typical location of pain in trochanteric bursitis syndrome. This is also a frequent pain radiation site for lumbar spine lesion, various nerve compression syndromes, and hip disease, particularly in osteonecrosis of the femoral head. (From Canoso J: *Rhematology in primary care,* Philadelphia, 1997, WB Saunders.)

DIAGNOSIS

A detailed physical examination and clinical presentation usually make the diagnosis of trochanteric bursitis. Laboratory tests and x-ray images are helpful adjunctive studies used to exclude other conditions either associated with or mimicking trochanteric bursitis.

DIFFERENTIAL DIAGNOSIS

- Osteoarthritis of the hip
- Osteonecrosis of the hip
- Stress fracture of the hip
- Osteoarthritis of the lumbar spine
- Fibromyalgia
- Iliopsoas bursitis
- Trochanteric tendonitis
- Gout
- Pseudogout
- Trauma
- Neuropathy

WORKUP

A workup is indicated if suspected associated conditions exist; otherwise treatment can be started on clinical grounds alone.

LABORATORY TESTS

CBC with differential may show elevated white count if infection is present.
ESR is elevated in an infectious process.
Uric acid may be elevated in patients with gout.

IMAGING STUDIES

- Plain x-rays of the hip are not very helpful in diagnosing trochanteric bursitis. Sometimes calcifications may be seen around the greater trochanter.
- Bone scan can be done but is usually not necessary.
- CT and MRI may show bursitis but are usually not warranted because it will not alter treatment.

TREATMENT

NONPHARMACOLOGIC THERAPY

- Heat 15-20 min four to six times per day
- Ultrasound therapy
- Rest
- Partial weight bearing
- Physical therapy to strengthen back, hip, and knee muscles

ACUTE GENERAL Rx

- NSAIDs, ibuprofen 800 mg PO tid, or naproxen 500 mg PO bid is used for pain relief.
- Acetaminophen 500-mg tablet, 1-2 tablets PO q6h prn can be used with NSAIDs or alternating with NSAIDs.
- Corticosteroid injection (30-40 mg depomethylprednisolone acetate mixed with 3 ml 1% Xylocaine)

CHRONIC Rx

Although rarely done, surgical removal of the bursa is possible for patients with refractory symptoms or infection.

DISPOSITION

- Most patients respond to NSAIDs and/or nonpharmacologic therapy.
- If steroid injection is used, approximately 70% of patients respond after the first injection and more than 90% respond to two injections.
- 25% of patients receiving steroid injection may develop a relapse.

REFERRAL

A rheumatology or orthopedics referral is made if steroid injection therapy is needed or if the etiology is thought to be infectious.

PEARLS & CONSIDERATIONS

COMMENTS

- The absence of pain with flexion and extension differentiates trochanteric bursitis from degenerative joint disease of the hip.
- Localization of pain over the lateral thigh differentiates trochanteric bursitis from pain caused by meralgia paresthetica located over the anterolateral thigh and pain from osteoarthritis located over the inner thigh groin area.

SUGGESTED READINGS

Adkins SB, Figler RA: Hip pain in athletes, *Am Fam Physician* 61(7):2109, 2000.
Canoso JJ: Hip pain. In Canoso JJ, Kersey R (eds): *Rheumatology in primary care.* Philadelphia, 1997, WB Saunders.

AUTHOR: **MEL ANDERSON, M.D.**

Tropical Sprue

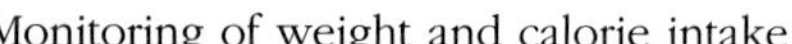

BASIC INFORMATION

DEFINITION

Tropical sprue is a malabsorption syndrome occurring primarily in tropical regions, including Puerto Rico, India, and Southeast Asia.

SYNONYMS

"Tropical enteropathy" refers to a subclinical form of tropical sprue.

ICD-9CM CODES
579.1 Tropical sprue

EPIDEMIOLOGY & DEMOGRAPHICS

Tropical sprue is endemic in tropical regions, the Middle East, the Far East, the Caribbean, and India.

PHYSICAL FINDINGS & CLINICAL PRESENTATION

- Diffuse, nonspecific abdominal tenderness and distention
- Low-grade fever
- Glossitis, cheilosis, hyperkeratosis, hyperpigmentation
- Diarrhea

ETIOLOGY

- Unknown
- Associated with overgrowth of predominantly coliform bacteria in the small intestine

DIAGNOSIS

The clinical features of tropical sprue include anorexia, diarrhea, weight loss, abdominal pain, and steatorrhea; these symptoms can develop in expatriates even several months after immigrating to temperate regions.

DIFFERENTIAL DIAGNOSIS

- Celiac disease
- Parasitic infestation
- Inflammatory bowel disease
- Other causes of malabsorption (e.g., Whipple's disease)

WORKUP

Diagnostic workup includes a comprehensive history (especially travel history), physical examination, laboratory evidence of malabsorption (see "Laboratory Tests"), and jejunal biopsy; the biopsy results are nonspecific, with blunting, atrophy, and even disappearance of the villi and subepithelial lymphocytic infiltration.

LABORATORY TESTS

- Megaloblastic anemia (>50% of cases)
- Vitamin B_{12} deficiency, folate deficiency
- Steatorrhea, abnormal D-xylose absorption

IMAGING STUDIES

GI series with small bowel follow-through may reveal coarsening of the jejunal folds.

TREATMENT

NONPHARMACOLOGIC THERAPY

Monitoring of weight and calorie intake

ACUTE GENERAL Rx

- Folic acid therapy (5 mg bid for 2 wk followed by a maintenance dose of 1 mg tid) will improve anemia and malabsorption in more than two thirds of patients
- Tetracycline 250 mg qid for 4-6 wk in individuals who have returned to temperate zones, up to 6 mo in patients in endemic areas; ampicillin 500 mg bid for at least 4 wk in patients intolerant to tetracycline
- Correction of vitamin B_{12} deficiency: vitamin B_{12} 1000 μg IM weekly for 4 wk, then monthly for 3-6 mo
- Correction of other nutritional deficiencies (e.g., calcium, iron)

DISPOSITION

Complete recovery with appropriate therapy

REFERRAL

GI referral for jejunal biopsy

PEARLS & CONSIDERATIONS

COMMENTS

Additional patient education information can be obtained from National Digestive Diseases Information Clearinghouse, Box NDDIC, Bethesda, MD 20892; phone: (301) 654-3810.

AUTHOR: **FRED F. FERRI, M.D.**

BASIC INFORMATION

DEFINITION

Miliary tuberculosis (TB) is an infection of disseminated hematogenous disease, caused by the bacterium *Mycobacterium tuberculosis,* and is often characterized as resembling millet seeds on examination. Extrapulmonary disease may occur in virtually every organ site.

SYNONYMS

Disseminated TB

ICD-9CM CODES
018.94 Miliary tuberculosis

EPIDEMIOLOGY & DEMOGRAPHICS

INCIDENCE (IN U.S.): >38% of AIDS patients with TB have disseminated disease, often with concurrent pulmonary and extrapulmonary active sites. (See "Pulmonary Tuberculosis" in Section I.)

PREVALENCE (IN U.S.):
- Undetermined
- Highest prevalence
  1. AIDS patients
  2. Minorities
  3. Children
  4. Foreign-born persons
  5. Elderly

PREDOMINANT SEX:
- No specific predilection
- Male predominance in AIDS, shelters, and prisons reflected in disproportionate male TB incidence

PREDOMINANT AGE: Predominantly among 24- to 45-yr-olds

PEAK INCIDENCE: HIV-positive patients, regardless of age

PHYSICAL FINDINGS & CLINICAL PRESENTATION

- See also "Etiology"
- Common symptoms
  1. High intermittent fever
  2. Night sweats
  3. Weight loss
- Symptoms referable to individual organ systems may predominate
  1. Meninges
  2. Pericardium
  3. Liver
  4. Kidney
  5. Bone
  6. GI tract
  7. Lymph nodes
  8. Serous spaces
     a. Pleural
     b. Pericardial
     c. Peritoneal
     d. Joint
  9. Skin
  10. Lung: cough, shortness of breath
- Adrenal insufficiency possible caused by infection of adrenal gland
- Pancytopenia
  1. With fever and weight loss *or*
  2. Without other localizing symptoms or signs *or*
  3. With only splenomegaly
- TB hepatitis
  1. Tender liver
  2. Obstructive enzymes (alkaline phosphatase) elevated out of proportion to minimal hepatocellular enzymes (SGOT, SGPT) and bilirubin
- TB meningitis
  1. Gradual-onset headache
  2. Minimal meningeal signs
  3. Malaise
  4. Low-grade fever (may be absent)
  5. Sudden stupor or coma
  6. Cranial nerve VI palsy
- TB pericarditis
  1. Effusions resembling TB pleurisy
  2. Cardiac tamponade
- Skeletal TB
  1. Large joint arthritis (with effusions resembling TB pericarditis)
  2. Bone lesions (especially ribs)
  3. Pott's disease
     a. TB spondylitis, especially of lower thoracic spine
     b. Paraspinous TB abscess
     c. Possible psoas abscess
     d. Frequent cord compression (often relieved by steroids)
- Genitourinary TB
  1. Renal TB
     a. Papillary necrosis
     b. Destruction of renal pelvis
     c. Strictures of upper third of ureters
     d. Hematuria
     e. Pyuria with misleading bacterial cultures
     f. Preserved renal function
  2. TB orchitis or epididymitis
     a. Scrotal mass
     b. Draining abscess
  3. Chronic prostatic TB
- Gastrointestinal TB
  1. Diarrhea
  2. Pain
  3. Obstruction
  4. Bleeding
  5. Especially common with AIDS
  6. Bowel lesions
     a. Circumferential ulcers
     b. Short strictures
     c. Calcified granulomas
     d. TB mesenteric caseous adenitis
     e. Abscess, but rare fistula formation
     f. Often difficult to distinguish from granulomatous bowel disease (Crohn's disease)
- TB peritonitis
  1. Fluid resembles TB pleurisy
  2. PPD often negative
  3. Tender abdomen
  4. Doughy peritoneal consistency, often with ascites
  5. Peritoneal biopsy indicated for diagnosis
- TB lymphadenitis (scrofula)
  1. May involve all node groups
  2. Common adenopathies
     a. Cervical
     b. Supraclavicular
     c. Axillary
     d. Retroperitoneal
  3. Biopsy generally needed for diagnosis
  4. Surgical resection of nodes may be necessary
  5. Especially common with AIDS
- Cutaneous TB
  1. Skin infection from autoinoculation or dissemination
  2. Nodules or abscesses
  3. Tuberculids (possibly allergic reactions)
  4. Erythema nodosum
- Miscellaneous presentations
  1. TB laryngitis
  2. TB otitis
  3. Ocular TB
     a. Choroidal tubercles
     b. Iritis
     c. Uveitis
     d. Episcleritis
  4. Adrenal TB
  5. Breast TB

ETIOLOGY

- See also "Pulmonary Tuberculosis" in Section I
- *Mycobacterium tuberculosis* (Mtb), a slow growing, aerobic, non–spore-forming, nonmotile bacillus
- Humans are the only reservoir for Mtb
- Pathogenesis:
  1. AFB (Mtb) are ingested by macrophages in alveoli, then transported to regional lymph nodes where spread is contained.
  2. Some AFB reach the bloodstream and disseminate widely.
  3. Immediate active disseminated disease may ensue or a latent period may develop.
  4. During latent period, T-cell immune mechanisms contain infection in granulomas until later reactivation occurs as a result of immunosuppression or other undefined factors in conjunction with reactivated pulmonary TB or alone.
- Miliary TB may occur as a consequence of the following:
  1. Primary infection: inability to contain primary infection leads to a hematogenous spread and progressive disseminated disease.

2. In late chronic TB and in those with advanced age or poor immunity, a continuous seeding of the blood may develop and lead to disseminated disease.

DIAGNOSIS

DIFFERENTIAL DIAGNOSIS

- Widespread sites of possible dissemination associated with myriad differential diagnostic possibilities
- Lymphoma
- Typhoid fever
- Brucellosis
- Other tumors
- Collagen-vascular disease

WORKUP

- Prompt evaluation is essential
- Sputum for AFB stain and culture
- Chest x-ray examination
- PPD
- Fluid analysis and culture wherever available
  1. Sputum
  2. Blood: particularly helpful in patients with AIDS
  3. Urine
  4. CSF
  5. Pleural
  6. Pericardial
  7. Peritoneal
  8. Gastric aspirates
- Biopsy of any involved tissue is advisable to make immediate diagnosis
  1. Transbronchial biopsy preferred and easily accessible
  2. Bone marrow
  3. Lymph node
  4. Scrotal mass if present
  5. Any other involved site
  6. Positive granuloma or AFB on biopsy specimen is diagnostic
- Imaging studies as needed

LABORATORY TESTS

- Culture and fluid analysis as described previously
- Smear-negative sputum often is positive weeks later on culture
- CBC is usually normal
- ESR is usually elevated

IMAGING STUDIES

- Chest x-ray examination (may or may not be positive) (See "Pulmonary Tuberculosis" in Section I)
- CT scan or MRI of brain
  1. Tuberculoma
  2. Basilar arachnoiditis
- Barium studies of bowel

TREATMENT

NONPHARMACOLOGIC THERAPY

- Bed rest during acute phase of treatment
- High-calorie, high-protein diet to reverse malnutrition and enhance immune response to TB
- Isolation in negative-pressure rooms with high-volume air replacement and circulation (with health care provider wearing proper protective 0.5- to 1-micron filter respirators)
  1. Until three consecutive sputum AFB smears are negative, if pulmonary disease coexists
  2. Isolation not required for closed-space TB infections

ACUTE GENERAL Rx

- See "Pulmonary Tuberculosis" in Section I.
- Therapy should be initiated immediately. Do not wait for definitive diagnosis.
- More rapid response to chemotherapy by disseminated TB foci than cavitary pulmonary TB.
- Treatment for 6 mo with INH plus rifampin plus PZA.
  1. Treatment for 12 mo often required for bone and renal TB.
  2. Prolonged treatment often required for CNS and pericardial.
  3. Prolonged treatment often required for all disseminated TB in infants.
- Compliance (rigid adherence to treatment regimen) is the chief determinant of success.
  1. Supervised DOT is recommended for all patients.
  2. Supervised DOT is mandatory for unreliable patients.
- Steroids are often helpful additions in fulminant miliary disease with the hypoxemia and DIC.

CHRONIC Rx

- Generally not indicated beyond treatment described previously
- Prolonged treatment supervised by ID expert required in a few complicated infections caused by resistant organisms

DISPOSITION

- Monthly follow-up by physician experienced in TB treatment
- Confirm sensitivity testing, and alter treatment appropriately (see "Pulmonary Tuberculosis" in Section I)

REFERRAL

- To infectious disease expert for:
  1. HIV-positive patient
  2. Patient with suspected drug-resistant TB
  3. Patients previously treated for TB
  4. Patients whose fever has not decreased and sputum (if positive) has not converted to negative in 2-4 wk
  5. Patients with overwhelming pulmonary or extrapulmonary tuberculosis
- To pulmonary, orthopedic, or GI physicians for examinations or biopsy

PEARLS & CONSIDERATIONS

COMMENTS

- All contacts (especially close household contacts and infants) should be properly tested for PPD conversions >3 mo following exposure.
- Those with positive PPD should be evaluated for active TB and properly treated or given prophylaxis.

SUGGESTED READINGS

American Thoracic Society: Diagnostic standards and classification of tuberculosis in adults and children, *Am J Respir Crit Care Med* 161:1376, 2000.

Del-Giudice P et al: Unusual cutaneous manifestations of miliary tuberculosis, *Clin Infect Dis* 30(1):201, 2000.

Goto S et al: A successfully treated case of disseminated tuberculosis-associated hemophagocytic syndrome and multiple organ dysfunction syndrome, *Am J Kidney Dis* 38(4):E19, 2001.

High WA et al: Cutaneous miliary tuberculosis in two patients with HIV infection, *J Am Acad Dermatol* 50(suppl5):S110, 2004.

Kuo PH et al: Severe immune hemolytic anemia in disseminated tuberculosis with response to antituberculosis therapy, *Chest* 119(6):1961, 2001.

Mert A et al: Spontaneous pneumothorax: a rare complication of miliary tuberculosis, *Ann Thorac Cardiovasc Surg* 7(1):45, 2001.

Small P, Fujiwara P: Management of tuberculosis in the United States, *N Engl J Med* 345:189, 2001.

Van den Bos F et al: Tuberculosis meningitis and miliary tuberculosis in young children, *Trop Med Int Health* 9(2):309, 2004.

AUTHOR: **GEORGE O. ALONSO, M.D.**

BASIC INFORMATION

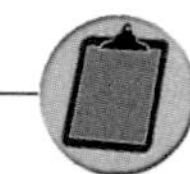

DEFINITION

Pulmonary tuberculosis (TB) is an infection of the lung and, occasionally, surrounding structures, caused by the bacterium *Mycobacterium tuberculosis.*

SYNONYMS

TB

ICD-9CM CODES
011.9 Pulmonary tuberculosis

EPIDEMIOLOGY & DEMOGRAPHICS

INCIDENCE (IN U.S.):

- Approximately 7 cases/100,000 persons—lowest in reported history
- >90% of new cases each year from reactivated prior infections
- 9% newly infected
- Only 10% of patients with PPD conversions (higher [8%/yr] in HIV-positive patients) will develop TB, most within 1-2 yr
- Two thirds of all new cases in racial and ethnic minorities
- 80% of new cases in children in racial and ethnic minorities
- Occurs most frequently in geographic areas and among populations with highest AIDS prevalence
  1. Urban blacks and Hispanics between 25 and 45 yr old
  2. Poor, crowded urban communities
- Nearly 36% of new cases from new immigrants

PREVALENCE (IN U.S.):

- Estimated 10 million people infected
- Varies widely among population groups

PREDOMINANT SEX:

- No specific predilection
- Male predominance in AIDS, shelters, and prisons reflected in disproportionate male incidence

PREDOMINANT AGE:

- 24-45 yr old
- Childhood cases common among minorities
- Nursing home outbreaks among elderly

PEAK INCIDENCE:

- Infancy
- Teenage years
- Pregnancy
- Elderly
- HIV-positive patients, regardless of age, at highest risk

GENETICS:

- Populations with widespread low native resistance have been intensely infected when initially exposed to TB.
- Following elimination of those with least native resistance, incidence and prevalence of TB tend to decline.

PHYSICAL FINDINGS & CLINICAL PRESENTATION

- See "Etiology"
- Primary pulmonary TB infection generally asymptomatic
- Reactivation pulmonary TB
  1. Fever
  2. Night sweats
  3. Cough
  4. Hemoptysis
  5. Scanty nonpurulent sputum
  6. Weight loss
- Progressive primary pulmonary TB disease: same as reactivation pulmonary TB
- TB pleurisy
  1. Pleuritic chest pain
  2. Fever
  3. Shortness of breath
- Rare massive, suffocating, fatal hemoptysis secondary to erosion of pulmonary artery within a cavity (Rasmussen's aneurysm)
- Chest examination
  1. Not specific
  2. Usually underestimates extent of disease
  3. Rales accentuated following a cough (posttussive rales)

ETIOLOGY

- *Mycobacterium tuberculosis* (Mtb), a slow-growing, aerobic, non–spore-forming, nonmotile bacillus, with a lipid-rich cell wall
  1. Lacks pigment
  2. Produces niacin
  3. Reduces nitrate
  4. Produces heat-labile catalase
  5. Mtb staining, acid-fast and acid-alcohol fast by Ziehl-Neelsen method, appearing as red, slightly bent, beaded rods 2-4 microns long (acid-fast bacilli [AFB]), against a blue background
  6. Polymerase chain reaction (PCR) to detect <10 organisms/ml in sputum (compared with the requisite 10,000 organisms/ml for AFB smear detection)
  7. Culture
     a. Growth on solid media (Löwenstein-Jensen; Middlebrook 7H11) in 2-6 wk
     b. Growth in liquid media (BACTEC, using a radioactive carbon source for early growth detection) often in 9-16 days
     c. Enhanced in a 5%-10% carbon dioxide atmosphere
  8. DNA fingerprinting (based on restriction fragment length polymorphism [RFLP])
     a. Facilitates immediate identification of Mtb strains in early growing cultures
     b. False-negatives possible if growth suboptimal
  9. Humans are the only reservoir for Mtb
  10. Transmission
     a. Facilitated by close exposure to high-velocity cough (unprotected by proper mask or respirators) from patient with AFB-positive sputum and cavitary lesions, producing aerosolized droplets containing AFB, which are inhaled directly into alveoli
     b. Occurs within prisons, nursing homes, and hospitals
- Pathogenesis
  1. AFB (Mtb) ingested by macrophages in alveoli, then transported to regional lymph nodes where spread is contained
  2. Some AFB may reach bloodstream and disseminate widely
  3. Primary TB (asymptomatic, minimal pneumonitis in lower or midlung fields, with hilar lymphadenopathy) essentially an intracellular infection, with multiplication of organisms continuing for 2-12 wk after primary exposure, until cell-mediated hypersensitivity (detected by positive skin test reaction to tuberculin purified protein derivative [PPD]) matures, with subsequent containment of infection
  4. Local and disseminated AFB thus contained by T-cell–mediated immune responses
     a. Recruitment of monocytes
     b. Transformation of lymphocytes with secretion of lymphokines
     c. Activation of macrophages and histiocytes
     d. Organization into granulomas, where organisms may survive within macrophages (Langhans' giant cells), but within which multiplication essentially ceases (95%) and from which spread is prohibited
  5. Progressive primary pulmonary disease
     a. May immediately follow the asymptomatic phase
     b. Necrotizing pulmonary infiltrates
     c. Tuberculous bronchopneumonia
     d. Endobronchial TB
     e. Interstitial TB
     f. Widespread miliary lung lesions
  6. Postprimary TB pleurisy with pleural effusion
     a. Develops after early primary infection, although often before conversion to positive PPD
     b. Results from pleural seeding from a peripheral lung lesion or rupture of lymph node into pleural space

c. May produce a large (sometimes hemorrhagic) exudative effusion (with polymorphonuclear cells early, rapidly replaced by lymphocytes), frequently without pulmonary infiltrates
d. Generally resolves without treatment
e. Portends a high risk of subsequent clinical disease, and therefore must be diagnosed and treated early (pleural biopsy and culture) to prevent future catastrophic TB illness
f. May result in disseminated extrapulmonary infection

7. Reactivation pulmonary TB
   a. Occurs months to years following primary TB
   b. Preferentially involves the apical posterior segments of the upper lobes and superior segments of the lower lobes
   c. Associated with necrosis and cavitation of involved lung, hemoptysis, chronic fever, night sweats, weight loss
   d. Spread within lung occurs via cough and inhalation
8. Reinfection TB
   a. May mimic reactivation TB
   b. Ruptured caseous foci and cavities, which may produce endobronchial spread
9. Mtb in both progressive primary and reactivation pulmonary TB
   a. Intracellular (macrophage) lesions (undergoing slow multiplication)
   b. Closed caseous lesions (undergoing slow multiplication)
   c. Extracellular, open cavities (undergoing rapid multiplication)
   d. INH and rifampin are cidal in all three sites
   e. PZA especially active within acidic macrophage environment
   f. Extrapulmonary reactivation disease also possible
10. Rapid local progression and dissemination in infants with devastating illness before PPD conversion occurs
11. Most symptoms (fever, weight loss, anorexia) and tissue destruction (caseous necrosis) from cytokines and cell-mediated immune responses
12. Mtb has no important endotoxins or exotoxins
13. Granuloma formation related to tumor necrosis factor (TNF) secreted by activated macrophages

DIAGNOSIS

DIFFERENTIAL DIAGNOSIS

- Necrotizing pneumonia (anaerobic, gram-negative)
- Histoplasmosis
- Coccidioidomycosis
- Melioidosis
- Interstitial lung diseases (rarely)
- Cancer
- Sarcoidosis
- Silicosis
- Paragonimiasis
- Rare pneumonias
  1. *Rhodococcus equi* (cavitation)
  2. *Bacillus cereus* (50% hemoptysis)
  3. *Eikenella corrodens* (cavitation)

WORKUP

- Sputum for AFB stains
- Chest x-ray examination
- PPD
  1. Recent conversion from negative to positive within 3 mo of exposure is highly suggestive of recent infection.
  2. Single positive PPD is not helpful diagnostically.
  3. Negative PPD never rules out acute TB.
  4. Be certain that positive PPD does not reflect "booster phenomenon" (prior positive PPD may become negative after several years and return to positive only after second repeated PPD; repeat second PPD within 1 wk), which thus may mimic skin test conversion.
  5. Positive PPD reaction is determined as follows:
     a. Induration after 72 hr of intradermal injection of 0.1 ml of 5 TU-PPD
     b. 5-mm induration if HIV-positive, close contact of active TB, fibrotic chest lesions
     c. 10-mm induration if in high–medical risk groups (immunosuppressive disease or therapy, renal failure, gastrectomy, silicosis, diabetes), foreign-born high-risk group (Southeast Asia, Latin America, Africa, India), low socioeconomic groups, IV drug addict, prisoner, health care worker
     d. 15-mm induration if low risk
  6. Anergy antigen testing (using mumps, *Candida,* tetanus toxoid) may identify patients who are truly anergic to PPD and these antigens, but results are often confusing. Not recommended.
  7. Patients with TB may be selectively anergic only to PPD.
  8. Positive PPD indicates prior infection but does not itself confirm active disease.

LABORATORY TESTS

- Sputum for AFB stains and culture
  1. Induced sputum if patient not coughing productively
- Sputum from bronchoscopy if high suspicion of TB with negative expectorated induced sputum for AFB
  1. Positive AFB smear is essential before or shortly after treatment to ensure subsequent growth for definitive diagnosis and sensitivity testing
  2. Consider lung biopsy if sputum negative, especially if infiltrates are predominantly interstitial
- AFB stain-negative sputum may grow Mtb subsequently
- Gastric aspirates reliable, especially in HIV-negative patients
- CBC
  1. Variable values
     a. WBCs: low, normal, or elevated (including leukemoid reaction: >50,000)
     b. Normocytic, normochromic anemia often
  2. Rarely helpful diagnostically
- ESR usually elevated
- Thoracentesis
  1. Exudative effusion
     a. Elevated protein
     b. Decreased glucose
     c. Elevated WBCs (polymorphonuclear leukocytes early, replaced later by lymphocytes)
     d. May be hemorrhagic
  2. Pleural fluid usually AFB-negative
  3. Pleural biopsy often diagnostic—may need to be repeated for diagnosis
  4. Culture pleural biopsy tissue for AFB
- Bone marrow biopsy is often diagnostic in difficult-to-diagnose cases, especially miliary tuberculosis

IMAGING STUDIES

- Chest x-ray examination
  1. Primary infection reflected by calcified peripheral lung nodule with calcified hilar lymph node
  2. Reactivation pulmonary TB
     a. Necrosis
     b. Cavitation (especially on apical lordotic views)
     c. Fibrosis and hilar retraction
     d. Bronchopneumonia
     e. Interstitial infiltrates
     f. Miliary pattern
     g. Many of previous may also accompany progressive primary TB
  3. TB pleurisy
     a. Pleural effusion, often rapidly accumulating and massive

4. TB activity not established by single chest x-ray examination
5. Serial chest x-ray examinations are excellent indicators of progression or regression

TREATMENT

NONPHARMACOLOGIC THERAPY

- Bed rest during acute phase of treatment
- High-calorie, high-protein diet to reverse malnutrition and enhance immune response to TB
- Isolation in negative-pressure rooms with high-volume air replacement and circulation, with health care provider wearing proper protective 0.5- to 1-micron filter respirators, until three consecutive sputum AFB smears are negative

ACUTE GENERAL Rx

- Compliance (rigid adherence to treatment regimen) chief determinant of success
  1. Supervised directly observed therapy (DOT) recommended for all patients and mandatory for unreliable patients
- Preferred adult regimen: DOT
  1. Isoniazid (INH) 15 mg/kg (max 900 mg) + rifampin 600 mg + ethambutol (EMB) 30 mg/kg (max 2500 mg) + pyrazinamide (PZA) (2 g [<50 kg]; 2.5 g [51 to 74 kg]; 3 g [>75 kg]) thrice weekly for 6 mo
  2. Alternative, more complicated DOT regimens
- Rifapentine, a rifampin derivative with a much longer serum half-life, was shown to be as effective when administered weekly (with weekly isoniazid) as conventional regimens for drug-sensitive pulmonary tuberculosis in non-HIV-infected patients.
- Short-course daily therapy: adult
  1. HIV-negative patient: 6 mo total therapy (2 mo INH 300 mg + rifampin 600 mg + EMB 15 mg/kg [max 2500 mg]) + PZA (1.5 g [<50 kg]; 2 g [51 to 74 kg]; 2.5 g [>75 kg]) daily and until smear negative and sensitivity confirmed; then INH + rifampin daily × 4 mo
  2. HIV-positive patient: 9 mo total therapy (2 mo INH + rifampin + EMB + PZA daily until smear negative and sensitivity confirmed; then INH + rifampin qd × 7 mo)
  3. Continue treatment at least 3 mo following conversion to negative cultures
- Drug resistance (often multiple drug resistance [MDRTB]) increased by:
  1. Prior treatment
  2. Acquisition of TB in developing countries
  3. Homelessness
  4. AIDS
  5. Prisoners
  6. IV drug addicts
  7. Known contact with MDRTB
- Never add single drug to failing regimen
- Never treat TB with fewer than two to three drugs or two to three new additional drugs
- Monitor for clinical toxicity (especially hepatitis)
  1. Patient and physician awareness that anorexia, nausea, RUQ pain, and unexplained malaise require immediate cessation of treatment
  2. Evaluation of LFTs
     a. Minimal SGOT/SGPT elevations without symptoms generally transient and not clinically significant
- Preventive treatment for PPD conversion only (infection without disease)
  1. Must be certain that chest x-ray examination is negative and patient has no symptoms of TB
  2. INH 300 mg daily for 6-12 mo; at least 12 mo if HIV-positive
  3. Most important groups:
     a. HIV-positive
     b. Close contact of active TB
     c. Recent converter
     d. Old TB on chest x-ray examination
     e. IV drug addict
     f. Medical risk factor
     g. High-risk foreign country
     h. Homeless
- Infants generally given prophylaxis immediately if recent contact of active TB (even if infant PPD negative), then retested with PPD in 3 mo (continuing INH if PPD becomes positive and stopping INH if PPD remains negative)
- Chronic, stable PPD (several years) given INH prophylaxis generally only if patient is <35 yr old
  1. INH toxicity may outweigh benefit
  2. Individualize decision
- Preventive therapy for suspected INH-resistant organisms is unclear

CHRONIC Rx

- Generally not indicated beyond treatment described previously
- Prolonged treatment, supervised by infectious disease expert, in a few very complicated infections caused by resistant organisms

DISPOSITION

- Monthly follow-up by physician experienced in TB treatment
- Confirm sensitivity testing and alter treatment appropriately
- Frequent sputum samples until culture is negative
- Confirm chest x-ray regression at 2 to 3 mo

REFERRAL

- To infectious disease expert for:
  1. HIV-positive patient
  2. Patient with suspected drug-resistant TB
  3. Patients previously treated for TB
  4. Patients whose fever has not decreased and sputum has not converted to negative in 2-4 wk
  5. Patients with overwhelming pulmonary or extrapulmonary tuberculosis
- To pulmonologist for bronchoscopy or pleural biopsy

PEARLS & CONSIDERATIONS

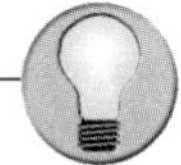

COMMENTS

- All contacts (especially close household contacts and infants) should be properly tested for PPD conversions during 3 mo following exposure.
- Those with positive PPD should be evaluated for active TB and properly treated or given prophylaxis.

SUGGESTED READINGS

Benator D et al: Rifapentine and isoniazid once a week versus rifampicin and isoniazid twice a week for treatment of drug susceptible pulmonary tuberculosis in HIV-negative patients: a randomized clinical trial, *Lancet* 360(9332):528, 2002.

Espinal MA et al: Infectiousness of mycobacterium tuberculosis in HIV-1-infected patients with tuberculosis: a prospective study, *Lancet* 355(9200):275, 2000.

Kanaya AM, Glidden DV, Chambers HF: Identifying pulmonary tuberculosis in patients with negative sputum smear results, *Chest* 120(2):349, 2001.

Karcic AA et al: An elderly woman with chronic knee pain and abnormal chest radiography, *Postgrad Med* 77(911):600, 2001.

Mulder K: Tuberculosis: a case history, *Lancet* 358(9283):776, 2001.

Salazar GE et al: Pulmonary tuberculosis in children in a developing country, *Pediatrics* 108(2):448, 2001.

Small P, Fujiwara P: Management of tuberculosis in the United States, *N Engl J Med* 345:189, 2001.

Tudo G et al: Detection of unsuspected cases of nosocomial transmission of tuberculosis by use of a molecular typing method, *Clin Infect Dis* 33(4):453, 2001.

AUTHOR: **GEORGE O. ALONSO, M.D.**

Tularemia (PTG)

BASIC INFORMATION

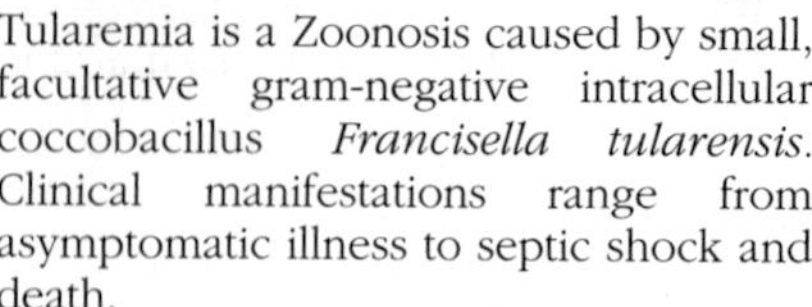

DEFINITION

Tularemia is a Zoonosis caused by small, facultative gram-negative intracellular coccobacillus *Francisella tularensis.* Clinical manifestations range from asymptomatic illness to septic shock and death.

ICD-9CM CODES
021.9 Tularemia

EPIDEMIOLOGY & DEMOGRAPHICS

INCIDENCE (IN U.S.): Highest overall incidence in Arkansas, Missouri, and Okalahoma. It also found in Canada, Mexico, and European countries, Turkey, Israel, China and Japan.
PREDOMINANT SEX: Male
PREDOMINANT AGE: Occurs at any age
PEAK INCIDENCE: June through August and in December
PHYSICAL FINDINGS:

- Incubation period is 3-5 days but may range from 1-21 days.
- Most common initial signs and symptoms:
  1. Fever
  2. Chills
  3. Headache
  4. Malaise
  5. Anorexia
  6. Fatigue
  7. Cough
  8. Myalgias
  9. Chest discomfort
  10. Vomiting
  11. Abdominal pain
  12. Diarrhea
  13. Conjunctivitis
  14. Lymphadenitis

CLINICAL SYNDROME OF TULAREMIA

1. Ulcer glandular and glandular: Account for 75%-80% of cases. Fever and a single erythematous papuloulcerative lesion with a central Escher accompanied by tender lymphadenopathy.
2. Oculoglandular: Accounts for 1%-2% of cases. Painful inflamed conjunctiva with numerous yellowish nodules and pinpoint ulcers. Purulent conjunctivitis with regional lymphadenopathy. Corneal perforation may occur.
3. Oropharyngeal and gastrointestinal: Account for 1%-4% of cases. Acute exudative membranes pharyngitis associated with cervical lymphadenopathy. Ulcerative intestinal lesion associated with mesenteric lymphadepathy, diarrhea, abdominal pain, nausea, vomiting and GI bleeding.
4. Pulmonary tularemia: Occurs often in the elderly and has a higher mortality. Symptoms include nonproductive cough, dysnoea, or pleuritic chest pain.
5. Typhoidal tularemia: 10% of all cases of tularemia. Rare in U.S. Symptoms include high continuous fever, signs of endotoxemia, and severe headache. Mortality can approach 30%.

COMPLICATIONS

1. Intravascular coagulation
2. Renal failure
3. Rhabitomyolysis
4. Jaundice
5. Hepatitis
6. Meningitis
7. Encephalitis
8. Percarditis
9. Peritonitis
10. Osteomyelitis
11. Spleenic rupture
12. Thrombophlebitis
13. Myositis and septicemia

ETIOLOGY

1. Caused by infection with *F. tularensis.*
2. Two main biovars of *F. tularensis:* Type A and Type B. Type A produces severe disease in humans. Type B produces milder subclinical infection.
3. Transmitted by ticks, tabanid flies, and mosquitoes. Also acquired by inhalation and ingestion.
4. Cases also occur after exposure to animals (wild rabbit, squirrels, birds, sheep, beavers, muskrats, and domestic dogs and cats) or animal products.
5. Laboratory acquisition is possible.
6. Pathogenesis: After inoculation into the skin the organism multiplies locally with in 2-5 days, then it produces erythematous tender or pruritic papule. The papule rapidly enlarges and forms an ulcer with a black base. The bacteria spread to the regional lymph nodes producing lymphadenopathy, and with bacremia may spread to distant organs.

DIAGNOSIS

DIFFERENTIAL DIAGNOSIS

1. Rickettsial infections
2. Meningococcal infections
3. Cat-scratch disease
4. Infectious mononucleosis
5. Atypical pneumonia
6. Group A strep pharyngitis
7. Typhoid fever
8. Fungal infection—sporotrichosis
9. Anthrax
10. Bacterial skin infections

WORKUP

1. CBC
2. Chest x-ray examination
3. Cultures of blood, lymph node, pleural fluid, wounds, sputum, and gastric aspirate
4. Antigen detection in urine
5. PCR
6. Serology

LABORATORY TESTS

1. WBC count and ESR normal or elevated
2. Rarely seen on Gram-stained smears or tissue biopsies
3. Antibodies to *F. tularensis* demonstrated by tube agglutination, micro agglutination, heme agglutination, and ELISA; definitive serologic diagnosis requires a fourfold or greater rise in titer between acute and convalescent specimens
4. Polymerase chain reaction (PCR) to facilitate early diagnosis

IMAGING STUDIES

Chest x-ray examination to show bilateral patchy infiltrate, lobar parenchymal infiltrate, cavitory lesion, pleural effusion, or emphysema

TREATMENT

ACUTE GENERAL Rx

Immediate therapy to limit extent of acute illness and complication

- Streptomycin 10 mg/kg IM q12h (daily dose should not exceed 2 g) or Gentamicin 3-5 mg/kg q8h
- Tetracycline 500 mg PO qid or Doxycycline 100 mg PO bid or Chloramphenicol 25-60 mg/kg q6h (do not exceed 6 g)
- Quinolones offer new options for the treatment of tularemia
- Combination antibiotics required for tularemic meningitis—Chloramphenicol plus Streptomycin

Surgical therapies are limited to drainage of abscessed lymph nodes and chest tube drainage of empyemas

PROGNOSIS

The mortality rate of severe untreated infection (tularemic pneumonia and typhoidal tularemia) can be as high as 30%. Overall mortality associated with tularemia is 2%-4% with appropriate treatment. Lifelong immunity usually follows tularemia.

DISPOSITION

Follow-up as outpatient

PREVENTION

1. Educate the public to prevent sick or dead animals.
2. Use insect repellants.
3. Remove ticks promptly.
4. Drink only portable water.
5. Adequately cook wild meats.
6. Tularemia vaccine has been developed but is not commercially available in U.S.; however, it is available from the Centers for Disease Control and Prevention (CDC). Vaccination of high-risk individuals working with large quantities of cultured organism is recommended.
7. Avoid skinning wild animals, especially rabbits; wear gloves while handling animal carcasses.
8. Do not use wells or other water that are contaminated by dead animals.
9. Hospitalized patients with tularemia do not need special isolation. Standard universal precautions for contaminated secretion are adequate when handling drainage from wounds.
10. Laboratory personnel should be notified of potential danger.

REFERRAL

For consultation with infectious diseases specialist in suspected cases

PEARLS & CONSIDERATIONS

- Alert the microbiology laboratory to the possibility of tularemia.
- Do not use doxycyclin or tetracyclin in children or pregnant women.
- Because of its highly contagious nature with low inoculums, tularemia is considered an agent that could be used by terrorists. It is classified as a category A critical biologic agent by the CDC.

SUGGESTED READINGS

Chocarro A, Gonzalez A, Garcia I: Treatment of tularemia with ciprofloxacin, *Clin Infect Dis* 31:623, 2000.

Cronquist SD: Tularemia: the disease and weapon, *Dermatol Clin* 22(3):313, 2004.

Jensen WA, Kirsch CM: Tularemia, *Semina Respir Infect* 18(3):146, 2003.

AUTHOR: **VASANTHI ARUMUGAM, M.D.**

BASIC INFORMATION

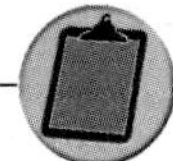

DEFINITION

Turner's syndrome refers to a pattern of malformation characterized by short stature, ovarian hypofunction, loose nuchal skin, and cubitus valgus as described by Turner in 1938. An associated 45,X chromosome constitution was recognized by Ford et al in 1959.

SYNONYMS

All obsolete:
Ullrich-Turner syndrome
Bonnevie-Ullrich-Turner syndrome

ICD-9CM CODES
758.6 Syndrome, Turner's

EPIDEMIOLOGY & DEMOGRAPHICS

INCIDENCE: 1 case out of every 2500 to 5000 live births

PHYSICAL FINDINGS & CLINICAL PRESENTATION

- Turner's phenotype is recognizable at any point on the developmental spectrum.
- In spontaneous abortuses the most common sex chromosome abnormality detected (45,X chromosome constitution) is found in 75% of affected individuals and accounts for 20% of such cases.
- In fetuses, it is suspected because of such ultrasonographic manifestations as thickening of the nuchal folds, frank nuchal cystic hygromas, or mild shortness of the femora at midtrimester.
- In infants:
  1. At birth may display loose nuchal skin (pterygium colli) and edema on the dorsa of hands and feet
  2. Canthal folds reflecting midface hypoplasia and redundant skin in the periorbital region
  3. Nipples appearing widely spaced
  4. Heart and cardiovascular system: murmur of aortic stenosis or bicuspid aortic valve or diminished femoral pulses suggestive of aortic coarctation
  5. Renal ultrasonography: renal ectopia such as pelvic kidney or horseshoe kidneys
- In older children:
  1. Slow linear growth
  2. Short stature—may be improved with growth hormone therapy (Fig. 1-245)
  3. Delayed or absent menses— secondary sex characteristics possibly normalized with estrogen replacement therapy
  4. Intelligence is often normal, but delays in spatial perception or visual motor integration are commonly observed; frank mental retardation is rare

ETIOLOGY

- Phenotype caused by absence of the second sex chromosome, whether X or Y
- 45,X chromosome constitution in about 50% of affected individuals
- Other chromosome aberrations (40% of cases): isochromosome Xq (46,X,i[Xq]) or mosaicism (XX/X)
- With deletions involving the short (or "p") arm of the X chromosome: short stature but little ovarian hypofunction
- Deletions involving Xq13-q27: ovarian failure
- Usually a deficiency of paternal contribution of sex chromosome, reflecting paternal nondisjunction

DIAGNOSIS

DIFFERENTIAL DIAGNOSIS

- Noonan syndrome, an autosomally dominant inherited disorder also characterized by loose nuchal skin, midface hypoplasia, canthal folds, and stenotic cardiac valvular defects and affecting males and females equally; also have normal chromosome constitutions
- Other conditions in the differential diagnosis of loose skin, whether or not associated with edema:
  1. Fetal hydantoin syndrome (loose nuchal skin, midface hypoplasia, distal digital hypoplasia)
  2. Disorders of chromosome constitution (trisomy 21, tetrasomy 12p mosaicism)
  3. Congenital lymphedema (Milroy edema)

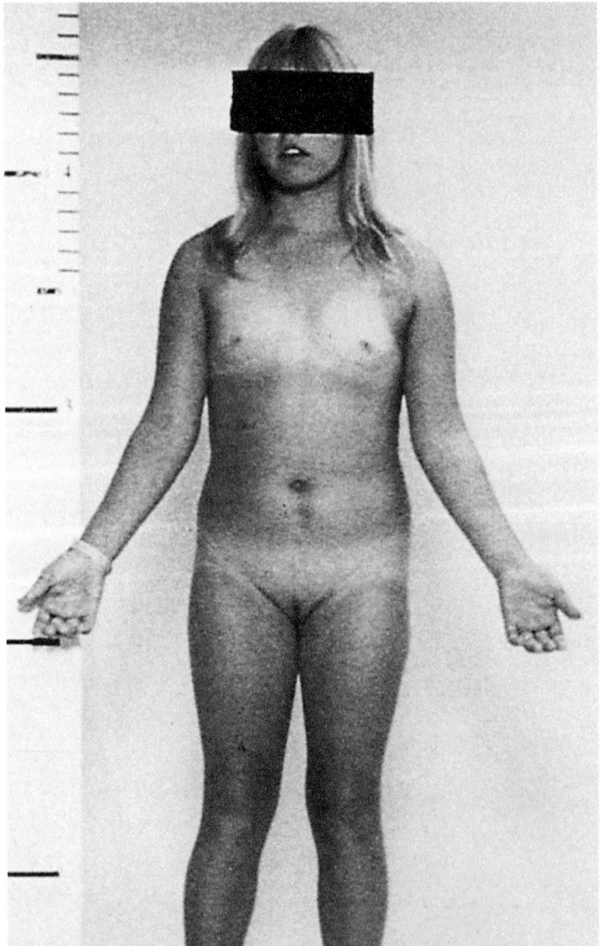

FIGURE 1-245 A 17-year-old patient with Turner's syndrome demonstrating short stature, poor sexual development, and increased carrying angles at elbows. Patient also has webbing of the neck. (From Mishell D [ed]: *Comprehensive gynecology,* ed 3, St Louis, 1997, Mosby.)

WORKUP

- Giemsa banded karyotype to confirm clinical diagnosis
- Once diagnosis is established: cardiologic consultation for evaluation for cardiac valvular abnormalities or aortic coarctation
- Renal ultrasonography
- Endocrine evaluations in older patients with short stature or amenorrhea
- Psychometrics to document known or suspected learning disabilities

LABORATORY TESTS

- As noted, routine Giemsa banded karyotype on peripheral lymphocytes to confirm the clinical impression in all suspected cases of Turner's syndrome
- Recognition of associated medical problems, such as hypergonadotropic hypogonadism or autoimmune thyroiditis prompting periodic evaluation of these potential areas

IMAGING STUDIES

- Echocardiogram
- Renal ultrasonography
- Abdominal ultrasonography for evaluation of ovarian and uterine size and morphology
- MRI of brain (especially in cases with known or suspected neurologic impairment)
- Radiographs (for evaluation of carpal/metacarpal abnormalities, radioulnar synostosis)
- Bone age (for evaluation of short stature)

TREATMENT

Recognition of the multisystem involvement of Turner's syndrome necessitates multiple medical specialists working in concert with the primary care provider to maximize and improve outcome while minimizing unnecessary or redundant testing.

NONPHARMACOLOGIC THERAPY

General medical care guided by normal medical standards with special attention paid to identifying such age-related problems as developmental delays, learning disabilities, slow growth, or amenorrhea.

ACUTE GENERAL Rx

Specific treatment geared to the specific medical problem (e.g., cardiac or renal dysfunction)

CHRONIC Rx

- Estrogen replacement therapy in early adolescence
- Some benefit from recombinant human growth hormone therapy

REFERRAL

- To geneticist: clinical diagnosis, differential diagnosis, recurrence risk counseling, cytogenetic tests
- To endocrinologist (pediatric): evaluation of short stature, estrogen or growth hormone replacement therapy
- To cardiologist

PEARLS & CONSIDERATIONS

COMMENTS

- Although newer studies are optimistic regarding outcomes, previous reports suffered from retrospective observations, case reports, and ascertainment bias, contributing to a generally poor interaction between physician and patient.
- Affected individuals and families often benefit from the contemporary experiences and expertise of members of genetic support groups. The Turner Syndrome Association (phone: 612-379-3607 or 800-365-9944; Internet: http://www.turner-syndrome-us.org) and the Alliance of Genetic Support Groups (phone: 800-336-4363; Internet: http://medhelp.org/www/agsg.htm) are valuable resources.

SUGGESTED READINGS

Conniff C: Turner's syndrome, *Adolesc Med* 13(2):359, 2002.

Elsheikh M et al: Turner's syndrome in adulthood, *Endocr Rev* 23(1):120, 2002.

AUTHOR: **LUTHER K. ROBINSON, M.D.**

Typhoid Fever 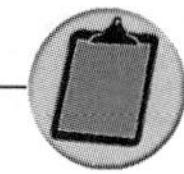

BASIC INFORMATION

DEFINITION

Typhoid fever is a systemic infection caused by *Salmonella typhi.*

SYNONYMS

Typhoid
Enteric fever

ICD-9CM CODES
002.0 Typhoid fever

EPIDEMIOLOGY & DEMOGRAPHICS

INCIDENCE (IN U.S.): Approximately 500 cases of *S. typhi* infections are reported annually.

PHYSICAL FINDINGS & CLINICAL PRESENTATION

- Incubation period of a few days to several weeks.
- Usual manifestations:
  1. Prolonged fever
  2. Myalgias
  3. Headache
  4. Cough
  5. Sore throat
  6. Malaise
  7. Anorexia, at times with abdominal pain and hepatosplenomegaly
  8. Diarrhea or constipation may occur early in the course of illness
  9. Rose spots, which are faint, maculopapular, blanching lesions, may sometimes be seen on the chest or abdomen
- In the untreated patient, fever may last 1-2 mo. The main complication of untreated disease is GI bleeding as a result of perforation from ulceration of Peyer's patches in the ileum. Mental status changes and shock are rare complications. The relapse rate is approximately 10%.

ETIOLOGY

- *Salmonella typhi*
- *S. paratyphi*
- *S. typhi* or *S. paratyphi* found only in humans
- Acquisition of disease by ingestion of food or water contaminated by other humans
- In the U.S. most cases are acquired either during foreign travel or by ingestion of food prepared by chronic carriers, many of whom acquired the organism outside of the U.S.

DIAGNOSIS

DIFFERENTIAL DIAGNOSIS

- Malaria
- Tuberculosis
- Brucellosis
- Amebic liver abscess

WORKUP

- Blood, stool, and urine cultures are helpful.
- Cultures should be repeated if initially negative.
- Blood cultures are more likely to be positive early in the course of illness.
- Stool and urine cultures are more commonly positive in the second and third weeks of illness.
- Bone marrow biopsy cultures are 90% positive, although this procedure is usually not necessary.
- Serology using Widal test is helpful in retrospect, showing a fourfold increase in convalescent titers.

LABORATORY TESTS

- Neutropenia is common.
- Transaminitis is possible.
- Culture:
  1. Blood
  2. Body fluids
  3. Biopsy specimens

TREATMENT

ACUTE GENERAL Rx

- Ciprofloxacin 500 mg PO bid or 400 mg IV bid for 14 days
- Ceftriaxone 2 g IV qd for 14 days
- If organism sensitive
  1. SMX/TMP, 1-2 DS tabs PO bid *or*
  2. Amoxicillin, 2 g PO q8h to complete 14 days
- Dexamethasone, 3 mg IV initially, followed by 1 mg IV q6h for 8 doses for patients with shock or mental status changes

CHRONIC Rx

- Carrier states possible
- More common in age >60 yr and in persons with gallstones
- Usual site of colonization: gallbladder
- Treatment in those with persistently positive stool cultures and in food-handlers
- Suggested regimens for eradication of carrier state
  1. Ciprofloxacin 500 mg PO bid for 4 wk
  2. SMX/TMP 1-2 tabs PO bid for 6 wk (if susceptible)
  3. Amoxicillin, 2 g PO q8h for 6 wk (if susceptible)
- Cholecystectomy possibly required in carriers with gallstones who fail medical therapy

DISPOSITION

- Treated patients usually respond to therapy, with a small percentage becoming chronic carriers.
- The relapse rate is approximately 10%.
- Untreated patients may have serious complications.

REFERRAL

- Failure of therapy
- Chronic carrier

PEARLS & CONSIDERATIONS

COMMENTS

- Oral and parenteral vaccines are available for travelers to areas of high risk.
- Vaccines are about 70% effective.
- Immunity wanes after several years.
- Parenteral preparations are accompanied by frequent side effects:
  1. Pain at injection site
  2. Fever
  3. Malaise
  4. Headaches

SUGGESTED READINGS

Ackers ML et al: Laboratory-based surveillance of *Salmonella* serotype *typhi* infections in the United States: antimicrobial resistance on the rise, *JAMA* 283(20):2668, 2000.

Hoffer RJ et al: Emergency department presentations of typhoid fever, *J Emerg Med* 19(4):317, 2000.

Yoon J, Segal-Maurer S, Rahal JJ: An outbreak of domestically acquired typhoid fever in Queens, NY, *Arch Intern Med* 164:565, 2004.

Zaidi AK, Hasan R, Bhutta ZA: Typhoid fever, *N Engl J Med* 347:1770, 2002.

AUTHOR: **MAURICE POLICAR, M.D.**

BASIC INFORMATION

DEFINITION

Ulcerative colitis is a chronic inflammatory bowel disease of undetermined etiology.

SYNONYMS

Inflammatory bowel disease (IBD)
Idiopathic proctocolitis

ICD-9CM CODES
556.9 Ulcerative colitis

EPIDEMIOLOGY & DEMOGRAPHICS

INCIDENCE:

- 50-150 cases/100,000 persons; most common between age 14 and 38 yr.
- Appendectomy for an inflammatory condition (appendicitis or lymphadenitis) but not for nonspecific abdominal pain is associated with a low risk of subsequent ulcerative colitis. This inverse relation is limited to patients who undergo surgery before the age of 20 yr.

PHYSICAL FINDINGS & CLINICAL PRESENTATION

- Patients with ulcerative colitis often present with bloody diarrhea accompanied by tenesmus, fever, dehydration, weight loss, anorexia, nausea, and abdominal pain.
- Abdominal distention and tenderness
- Bloody diarrhea
- Fever, evidence of dehydration
- Evidence of extraintestinal manifestations may be present: liver disease, sclerosing cholangitis, iritis, uveitis, episcleritis, arthritis, erythema nodosum, pyoderma gangrenosum, aphthous stomatitis

DIAGNOSIS

DIFFERENTIAL DIAGNOSIS

- Crohn's disease
- Bacterial infections
  1. Acute: *Campylobacter, Yersinia, Salmonella, Shigella, Chlamydia, Escherichia coli, Clostridium difficile,* gonococcal proctitis
  2. Chronic: Whipple's disease, TB, enterocolitis
- Irritable bowel syndrome
- Protozoal and parasitic infections (amebiasis, giardiasis, cryptosporidiosis)
- Neoplasm (intestinal lymphoma, carcinoma of colon)
- Ischemic bowel disease
- Diverticulitis
- Celiac sprue, collagenous colitis, radiation enteritis, endometriosis, gay bowel syndrome

WORKUP

Diagnostic workup includes:

- Comprehensive history, physical examination
- Laboratory tests (see below)
- Colonoscopy to establish the presence of mucosal inflammation: typical endoscopic findings in ulcerative colitis are friable mucosa, diffuse, uniform erythema replacing the usual mucosal vascular pattern, and pseudopolyps; rectal involvement is invariably present if the disease is active

LABORATORY TESTS

- Anemia, high sedimentation rate (in severe colitis) are common.
- Potassium, magnesium, calcium, albumin may be decreased.
- Antineutrophil cytoplasmic antibodies (ANCA) with a perinuclear staining pattern (pANCA) can be found in >45% of patients; there is an increased frequency in treatment-resistant left-sided colitis, suggesting a possible association between these antibodies and a relative resistance to medical therapy in patients with ulcerative colitis.

IMAGING STUDIES

Image studies are generally not indicated. Air-contrast barium enema, when used, may reveal continuous involvement (including the rectum), pseudopolyps, decreased mucosal pattern, and fine superficial ulcerations.

TREATMENT

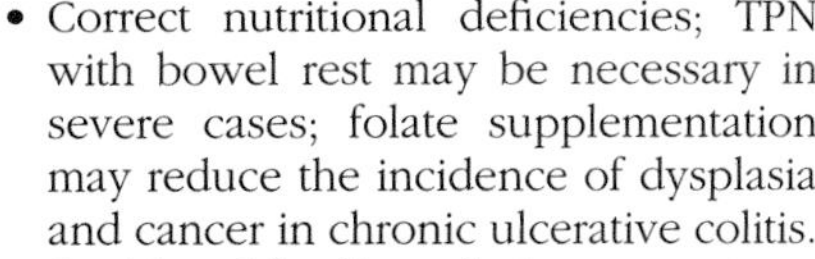

NONPHARMACOLOGIC THERAPY

- Correct nutritional deficiencies; TPN with bowel rest may be necessary in severe cases; folate supplementation may reduce the incidence of dysplasia and cancer in chronic ulcerative colitis.
- Avoid oral feedings during acute exacerbation to decrease colonic activity; a low-roughage diet may be helpful in *early* relapse.
- Psychotherapy is useful in most patients. Referral to self-help groups is also important because of the chronicity of the disease and the young age of the patients.

ACUTE GENERAL Rx

The therapeutic options vary with the degree of disease (mild, severe, fulminant) and areas of involvement (distal, extensive):

- Mild or moderate disease can be treated with mesalamine (Rowasa). It can be administered as an enema (40 mg once daily at bedtime for 3 to 6 wk) or suppository (500 mg bid) for patients with distal colonic disease. Oral forms in which the 5-ASA is in a slow-release or pH-dependent matrix (Pentasa 1 g qid, Asacol 800 mg PO tid) can deliver therapeutic concentrations to the more proximal small bowel or distal ileum.
- Olsalazine (Dipentum) is often useful for maintenance of remission of ulcerative colitis in patients intolerant to sulfasalazine. Usual dose is 500 mg bid taken with food.
- Balsalazide (Colazal) is indicated for mild to moderately active ulcerative colitis. Usual dose is three 750 mg capsules tid.
- Severe disease usually responds to oral corticosteroids (e.g., prednisone 40-60 mg/day); corticosteroid suppositories or enemas are also useful for distal colitis.
- Fulminant disease generally requires hospital admission and parenteral corticosteroids (e.g., IV hydrocortisone 100 mg q6h); when bowel movements have returned to normal and the patient is able to eat normally, oral prednisone is resumed. IV cyclosporine can also be used in severe refractory cases; renal toxicity is a potential complication.
- Surgery is indicated in patients who fail to respond to intensive medical therapy. Colectomy is usually curative in these patients and also eliminates the high risk of developing adenocarcinoma of the colon (10%-20% of patients develop it after 10 yr with the disease); newer surgical techniques allow for the preservation of the sphincter.

CHRONIC Rx

- Colonoscopic surveillance and multiple biopsies should be instituted approximately 10 yr after diagnosis because of the increased risk of colon carcinoma.
- Erythropoietin is useful in patients with anemia refractory to treatment with iron and vitamins.

DISPOSITION

The clinical course is variable; 15%-20% of patients will eventually require colectomy; >75% of patients treated medically will experience relapse.

REFERRAL

- GI consultation for initial diagnostic sigmoidoscopy/colonoscopy in suspected cases
- Surgical referral for patients with severe disease unresponsive to medical therapy

AUTHOR: **FRED F. FERRI, M.D.**

Urethritis, Gonococcal (PTG)

BASIC INFORMATION

DEFINITION

Urethritis is a well-defined clinical syndrome manifested by dysuria, a urethral discharge, or both.

ICD-9CM CODES
597.80 Urethritis, unspecified
098.20 Gonococcal

EPIDEMIOLOGY & DEMOGRAPHICS

- The major single specific etiology of acute urethritis is *Neisseria gonorrhoeae,* producing GCU. Urethritis of all other etiologies is called *nongonococcal urethritis* (NGU).
- NGU is twice as common as GCU in the U.S. NGU is the most common STD syndrome occurring in men, accounting for 6 million office visits annually. NGU is more frequently encountered in higher socioeconomic groups. GCU is more common in homosexual males than heterosexual males with acute urethritis.
- The gonococcus is a gram-negative, kidney-shaped diplococcus with flattened opposed margins. The urethra is the most common site of infection in all men. In heterosexual men, the pharynx is infected in 7%, and in homosexual men, the pharynx is infected in 40% and the rectum in 25%. A single episode of intercourse with an infected partner carries a transmission risk of 20% for males; female partners of an infected male will contract the disease 80% of the time.

PHYSICAL FINDINGS & CLINICAL PRESENTATION

SYMPTOMS OF GONOCOCCAL URETHRITIS: Urethral discharge and dysuria are the most common symptoms. There is complaint of urethral itching. Prostatic involvement can cause frequency, urgency, and nocturia. It can involve the epididymis through spreading down the vas deferens, causing acute epididymitis.
INCUBATION PERIOD: 3-10 days. Without treatment urethritis persists for 3-7 wk, with 95% of men becoming asymptomatic after 3 mo. GCU is asymptomatic in up to 60% of contacts.

SIGNS OF GONOCOCCAL URETHRITIS: Yellow-brown discharge, meatal edema, urethral tenderness to palpation. Rectal bleeding with pus is seen with gonococcal proctitis. Periurethritis leading to urethral stenosis can occur. Disseminated infection can occur. Tenosynovitis and arthritis can occur. Rarely, hepatitis, myocarditis, endocarditis, and meningitis can occur.

DIAGNOSIS

DIFFERENTIAL DIAGNOSIS

- NGU
- Herpes simplex virus

LABORATORY TESTS

- Calcium alginate or rayon swab on a metal shaft (*not* cotton-tipped swabs, which are bactericidal) of the urethra should be done anywhere from 2 to 4 hr after voiding to prevent bacterial washout with voiding.
- Cultures of the pharynx and rectum when indicated.
- Gram staining should be done. Modified Thayer-Martin media is used.
- On examination of the urethral smear, the presence of small numbers of PMNs provides objective evidence of urethritis. The complete absence of PMNs on a urethral smear argues against urethritis. If in addition to the PMNs there are gram-negative, intracellular diplococci, the diagnosis of gonorrhea is established.

TREATMENT

NONPHARMACOLOGIC THERAPY

BEHAVIORAL MANAGEMENT: Avoid intercourse until cure has been attained and sexual partners have been evaluated and treated.

ACUTE GENERAL Rx

FOR UNCOMPLICATED URETHRAL, CERVICAL, AND RECTAL GCU: Ceftriaxone 125 mg IM + doxycycline 100 mg bid × 7 days. Alternative therapy: ciprofloxacin 500 mg PO × 1 day; ofloxacin 400 mg PO × 1 day (all of these to be followed by 7 days of doxycycline 100 mg PO bid).

- In uncomplicated gonococcal infections, single-drug regimens using selected fluoroquinolones, selected cephalosporins, or spectinomycin are highly effective and safe.
- Resistance to penicillins, sulphonamides, and tetracyclines is now widespread.
- Dual treatment for gonococcal and chlamydial infections is based on theory and expert opinion rather than on evidence from clinical trials.

FOR EPIDIDYMITIS: Ceftriaxone 250 mg IM followed by doxycycline 100 mg PO bid × 10 days. Alternative therapy: ofloxacin 300 mg PO bid × 10 days.

CHRONIC Rx

POSTGONOCOCCAL URETHRITIS (PGU): Reinfection is the most common cause of recurrence. Repeat swab and culture of the urethra, pharynx, and rectum (where applicable) are mandatory. Persistence of PMNs with the absence of gram-negative intracellular diplococci suggests a diagnosis of postgonococcal urethritis. This occurs when GCU is treated with a regimen that is ineffective against coincident chlamydial infection; it represents NGU following GCU. The syndrome should be treated as NGU. Persistence of *N. gonorrhoeae* by smear or culture requires treatment for *N. gonorrhoeae.*

PEARLS & CONSIDERATIONS

COMMENTS

- CAUTION: Tetracyclines and fluoroquinolones are *contraindicated* in pregnancy. *Chlamydia* infection in pregnancy can be treated with amoxicillin 500 mg PO tid for 7 days or with clindamycin 450 mg PO tid for 10 days.
- *Posttreatment cultures are required.*

SUGGESTED READING

Centers for Disease Control and Prevention: 2002 sexually transmitted diseases treatment guidelines, *MMWR Morb Mortal Wkly Rep* 51(RR-6), 2002.

AUTHOR: **PHILIP J. ALIOTTA, M.D., M.S.H.A.**

BASIC INFORMATION

DEFINITION

Nongonococcal urethritis is urethral inflammation caused by any of several organisms.

SYNONYMS

NGU

ICD-9CM CODES
099.40 Nongonococcal
099.41 Chlamydial

EPIDEMIOLOGY & DEMOGRAPHICS

- Occurrence is 50% in STD clinics.
- NGU most commonly affects men in higher socioeconomic class, affecting heterosexual men more frequently than homosexual men.
- NGU carries a greater morbidity than GCU.

ETIOLOGY

- Most common agent is *Chlamydia* spp., an obligate intracellular parasite possessing both DNA and RNA, replicating by binary fission. It causes 20%-50% of NGU cases. Two species exist:
  1. *Chlamydia psittaci*
  2. *Chlamydia trachomatis* with its 15 serotypes
     a. Serotypes A-C cause hyperendemic blinding trachoma.
     b. Serotypes D-K cause genital tract infection.
     c. Serotypes L1-L3 cause lymphogranuloma venereum.
- Other causes of NGU: *Ureaplasma urealyticum* causing 15%-30% of the cases of NGU, *Trichomonas vaginalis,* and herpes simplex virus. The cause of 20% of the cases of NGU has not been identified.
- Asymptomatic infection occurs in 28% of the contacts of women with chlamydial cervical infection.

INCUBATION PERIOD: 2-35 days

SYMPTOMS: Dysuria, whitish-to-clear urethral discharge, and urethral itching. The onset of symptoms in NGU is less acute than GCU.

SIGNS: Whitish-to-clear urethral discharge, meatal edema, and erythema. Infected women manifest pyuria, and the disease can present as acute urethral syndrome.

COMPLICATIONS: Epididymitis in heterosexual men may be linked to nonbacterial prostatitis, proctitis in homosexual men, and Reiter's syndrome.

DIAGNOSIS

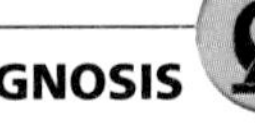

DIFFERENTIAL DIAGNOSIS

- GCU
- Herpes simplex virus
- Trichomoniasis

LABORATORY TESTS

- Requires demonstration of urethritis and exclusion of infection with *N. gonorrhoeae.*
- The appearance of PMNs on urethral smear confirms the diagnosis of urethritis. Because *Chlamydia* is an intracellular parasite of the columnar epithelium, the best specimen for culture is an endourethral swab taken from an area 2-4 cm inside the urethra. The organism can only be grown in tissue culture, which is expensive.
- New techniques have been developed and are useful in making the diagnosis: nucleic acid hybridization, enzyme-linked immunosorbent assay (ELISA), and direct immunofluorescence.
- For culture, a Dacron-tipped swab is used; avoid calcium alginate or cotton swabs.

TREATMENT

Because it is impossible to differentiate among the common etiologies of NGU, the condition is treated syndromically, including in the initial treatment regimen those drugs effective against the common causative agents.

- Recommended: doxycycline 100 mg PO bid for 7 days
- Other drugs: tetracycline 500 mg PO qid for 7 days
- Alternative regimens: azithromycin 1000 mg as a single dose, erythromycin 500 mg PO qid for 7 days, ofloxacin 300 mg PO bid for 7 days

In pregnant women:

- Both amoxicillin and erythromycin are likely effective in achieving microbiologic cure.
- Clindamycin and erythromycin have a similar effect on cure rates.
- A single dose of azithromycin is more effective in achieving microbiologic cure of *C. trachomatis* than a 7-day course of erythromycin.

In men and nonpregnant women:

- Multiple-dose regimens of tetracyclines and macrolides achieve microbiologic cure in at least 95% of patients.
- Erythromycin daily dose of 2 g is likely beneficial.
- Ciprofloxacin is less effective in the treatment of *C. trachomatis* infection when compared with doxycycline.
- A single dose of azithromycin is as successful at curing *C. trachomatis* as a 7-day course of doxycycline.

PEARLS & CONSIDERATIONS

COMMENTS

- CAUTION: Tetracyclines and fluoroquinolones are *contraindicated* in pregnancy. *Chlamydia* infection in pregnancy can be treated with amoxicillin 500 mg PO tid for 7 days or with clindamycin 450 mg PO tid for 10 days.
- *Posttreatment cultures are required.*

SUGGESTED READINGS

Centers for Disease Control and Prevention: 2002 sexually transmitted diseases treatment guidelines, *MMWR Morb Mortal Wkly Rep* 51(RR-6), 2002.

Gaydos CA et al: *Chlamydia trachomatis* infections in female military recruits, *N Engl J Med* 339:739, 1998.

AUTHOR: **PHILIP J. ALIOTTA, M.D., M.S.H.A.**

BASIC INFORMATION

DEFINITION

Urinary tract infection (UTI) is a term that encompasses a broad range of clinical entities that have in common a positive urine culture. A conventional threshold is growth of >100,000 colony-forming units per ml from a midstream-catch urine sample. In symptomatic patients, a smaller number of bacteria (between 100 and 10,000 colony-forming units per ml of midstream urine) is recognized as an infection.

SYNONYMS

UTI

ICD-9CM CODES
595.0 Acute cystitis
595.3 Trigonitis
595.2 Chronic cystitis
590.1 Acute pyelonephritis
590.0 Chronic pyelonephritis
590.8 Nonspecific pyelonephritis

CLASSIFICATION

FIRST INFECTION: The first documented UTI; tends to be uncomplicated and is easily treated.

UNRESOLVED BACTERIURIA: UTI in which the urinary tract is not sterilized during therapy. Main causes are bacterial resistance, patient noncompliance with medication, resistance, mixed bacterial infection, rapid reinfection, azotemia, infected stones, Munchausen's, and papillary necrosis.

BACTERIAL PERSISTENCE: UTI in which the urine cultures become sterile during therapy, but a persistent source of infection from a site within the urinary tract that was excluded from the high urinary concentrations gives rise to reinfection by the same organism. Causes: infected stone, chronic bacterial prostatitis, atrophic infected kidney, vesicovaginal or enterovesical fistulas, obstructive uropathy, infected pyelocalyceal diverticula, infected ureteral stump following nephrectomy, infected necrotic papillae from papillary necrosis, infected urachal cysts, infected medullary sponge kidney, urethral diverticula, and foreign bodies.

REINFECTION: UTI in which a new infection occurs with new pathogens at variable intervals after a previous infection has been eradicated.

Relapse: The less common form of recurrent infection; occurs within 2 wk of treatment when the same organism reappears in the same site as the previous infection. Relapsing infections of the urinary tract most commonly occur in pyelonephritis, kidney obstruction from a stone, and prostatitis.

EPIDEMIOLOGY & DEMOGRAPHICS

INCIDENCE:

In Neonates: More common in boys as a result of anatomic abnormalities.

In Preschool Children: More common in girls (4.5% vs. 0.5% for boys).

In Adulthood: More common in women, with a 1% to 3% prevalence in nonpregnant women. In pregnancy at 12 wk, the incidence of asymptomatic bacteriuria is similar to nonpregnant women, at 2% to 10%. However, 70% to 80% of women with asymptomatic bacteriuria develop acute pyelonephritis, especially in the second and third trimesters, and suffer a pyelonephritic recurrence rate of 10%. In adults, 65 yr and older, at least 10% of men and 20% of women have bacteriuria.

PATHOGENESIS:

- Four major pathways:
  1. Ascending from the urethra
  2. Lymphatic
  3. Hematogenous
  4. Direct extension from another organ system
- Other risk factors: neurologic diseases, renal failure, diabetes; anatomic abnormalities: bladder outlet obstruction, urethral stricture, vesicoureteral reflux, fistula, urinary diversion, megacystis, and infected stones; age; pregnancy; instrumentation, poor patient compliance, poor hygiene, infrequent voider, diaphragm contraceptives, tampon use, douches, and catheters

Catheters: All patients who require a long-term Foley catheter eventually develop significant levels of bacteriuria. Treatment is reserved for those individuals who become symptomatic (i.e., leukocytosis, fever, chills, malaise, loss of appetite, etc.) Using prophylactic antibiotics to treat patients who have chronic catheters is to be discouraged because of the risk of acquiring bacteria that are resistant to antibiotic therapy.

- Once bacteria reach the urinary tract, three factors determine whether the infection occurs (Box 1-14):
  1. Virulence of the microorganism
  2. Inoculum size
  3. Adequacy of the host defense mechanisms
- These factors also determine the anatomic level of the UTI.

Urinary Pathogens: In >95% of UTIs the infecting organism is a member of the Enterobacteriaceae, *Pseudomonas aeruginosa,* enterococci, or, in young women, *Staphylococcus saprophyticus.* In contrast, the organisms that commonly colonize the distal urethra and skin of both men and women and the vagina of women are *Staphylococcus epidermidis,* diphtheroids, lactobacilli, *Gardnerella vaginalis,* and a variety of anaerobes that rarely cause UTI. Generally, the isolation of two or more bacterial species from a urine culture signifies a contaminated specimen, unless the patient is being managed with an indwelling catheter or urinary diversion or has a chronic complicated infection.

Defense Mechanisms Against Cystitis: Low pH and high osmolarity, mucopolysaccharide glycosaminoglycan protective layer, normal bladder that empties completely and has no incontinence, and the presence of estrogen

PHYSICAL FINDINGS

- UTI presentation is inconsistent and cannot be relied upon to diagnose UTI accurately or to localize the site of infection. Patients complain of:
  1. Urinary frequency, urgency
  2. Dysuria
  3. Urge incontinence

BOX 1-14 Bacterial Factors

1. The size of the inoculum
2. The virulence of the infecting organism:
   a. Virulence factors:
      i. P-fimbriae facilitate the adherence of bacteria to biologic surfaces.
      ii. K-antigens facilitate adherence and protect the organisms from the host-immune response.
      iii. O-antigens are an important source of the systemic reactions, such as fever and shock, that occur with bacterial infections.
      iv. H antigens are associated with flagella and are related to bacterial locomotion.
      v. Hemolysin may potentiate tissue damage and facilitate local bacterial growth.
      vi. Urease alkalinizes the urine and facilitates stone formation, thus potentiating infection.
   b. Biofilms harbor bacteria on prosthetic devices and may be a source of recurrent infections.
   c. The presence of sialosyl galactosyl globoside (SGG) on the surface of kidney cells. This compound is a highly powerful receptor for E. coli bacteria.
   d. Women with a deficiency in human beta-defensin-1 (HBD-1) are at greater risk for urinary tract infection.
3. Adequacy of host defense mechanisms

4. Suprapubic pain
5. Gross or microscopic hematuria

- When negative cultures are associated with significant pyuria, vaginal discharge, or hematuria, infections with *Chlamydia trachomatis, Neisseria gonorrhoeae,* and *Trichomonas vaginalis* should be considered.
- Acute pyelonephritis (PN) presents with fever, flank or abdominal pain, chills, malaise, vomiting, and diarrhea. It is these systemic symptoms that distinguish pyelonephritis from cystitis. Complications of acute pyelonephritis are renal abscess, perinephric abscess, emphysematous pyelonephritis, and pyonephrosis.

DIAGNOSIS

DIFFERENTIAL DIAGNOSIS

- Interstitial cystitis
- Vaginitis
- Urethritis (gonococcal, nongonococcal, *Trichomonas*)
- Frequency-urgency syndrome, prostatitis (acute and chronic)
- Obstructive uropathy
- Infected stones
- Fistulas
- Papillary necrosis
- Vesicoureteral reflux

LABORATORY TESTS

- Urinalysis with microscopic evaluation of clean-catch urine for bacteria and pyuria
- Urine C&S
- CBC with differential (shows leukocytosis)
- Antibody-coated bacteria are seen with pyelonephritis

IMAGING STUDIES

- Warranted only if renal infection or genitourinary abnormality is suspected
- KUB, VCUG, renal sonogram, IVP, CT scan, and nuclear scan
- Specialty examination: cystoscopy with occasional retrograde pyelography to rule out obstructive uropathy; stenting the obstruction possibly required

TREATMENT

NONPHARMACOLOGIC THERAPY

- Hot sitz baths, anticholinergics, urinary analgesics
- For pyelonephritis: bed rest, analgesics, antipyretics, and IV hydration

ACUTE GENERAL Rx

- Conventional therapy of 7 days; short-term therapy of 1, 3, or 5 days.
- Agents of choice: amoxicillin/clavulanate, cephalosporins, fluoroquinolones, nitrofurantoin, and trimethoprim with sulfonamide.
- For pyelonephritis: hospitalization until afebrile and stable, then at home via home care agency with IV antibiotic composed of aminoglycoside plus cephalosporin × 1 wk followed by oral agents (based on sensitivity) for 2 wk. Moderate forms of pyelonephritis have been successfully treated with fluoroquinolone therapy for 21 days, without requiring hospitalization. Most important, complicating factors such as obstructive uropathy or infected stones must be identified and treated.
- Section III, "Urinary Tract Infection," describes an approach to the management of UTI.

PEARLS & CONSIDERATIONS

COMMENTS

- *Asymptomatic bacteriuria:* occurs in both anatomically normal and abnormal urinary tracts. This can clear spontaneously, persist, or lead to symptomatic kidney infection. Treatment is recommended in patients with vesicoureteral reflux, stones, obstructive uropathy, parenchymal renal disease, diabetes mellitus, and pregnant or immunocompromised patients.
- *Pregnancy:* 20%-40% of pregnant women with untreated bacteriuria develop pyelonephritis. This is associated with prematurity and low-birth-weight infants. Confirmed significant bacteriuria should be treated with an aminopenicillin and cephalosporin.
- *Recurrent UTI:* caused by an unresolved infection, vaginal colonization of the originally infecting organism, or reinfection with a new strain. Management of recurrent UTI includes continuous antibiotic prophylaxis, intermittent self-treatment, and postcoital prophylaxis. Prophylaxis is recommended for women who experience two or more symptomatic UTIs over a 6-mo period or three or more episodes over a 12-mo period.
  1. Changes after menopause: lower levels of lactobacilli, decreased estrogen, senile atrophy of the genitalia, and loss of bladder elasticity (compliance).
  2. Biologic factors altering defense systems: the presence of sialosyl galactosyl globoside (SGG) on the surface of the kidney acts as a powerful receptor for *E. coli* and increases the risk for UTI; the presence of the blood group P1 causes increased binding of *E. coli* that is resistant to normal infection-fighting mechanisms in the body and it is believed that some individuals are deficient in a compound called *human beta-defensin-1* (HBD-1), a naturally occurring antibiotic that fights *E. coli* within the urinary tract.

Resistance:

- Because of the overuse of antibiotics, organisms once sensitive to a number of agents are now increasingly more resistant, making effective management of UTI and pyelonephritis more difficult and potentially more dangerous. Most important has been the increasing resistance to TMP-SMX, the current primary care provider drug of choice for acute uncomplicated UTI in women.
- Facts about bacterial resistance:
  1. Given enough antibiotic and time, resistance will develop
  2. Organisms that are resistant to one antibiotic will likely become resistant to others
  3. Resistance is progressive, moving from low to intermediate to high levels
  4. Once selected, drug resistance will not disappear; because of poorly reversible genetic and environmental factors, it may decline slowly
  5. When antibiotics are used by any patient, this use affects other people by changing the immediate and extended environment
  6. No counterselective steps against resistant bacteria now exist
- When choosing a treatment regimen physicians should consider such factors as:
  1. In-vitro susceptibility
  2. Adverse effects
  3. Cost effectiveness
  4. Resistance rates in the respective communities

SUGGESTED READINGS

Bent S et al: Does this woman have an acute uncomplicated urinary tract infection? *JAMA* 287:2701, 2002.

Gomolin IH et al: Efficacy and safety of ciprofloxacin oral suspension versus trimethoprim-sulfamethoxazole oral suspension for treatment of older women with acute urinary tract infection, *J Am Geriatr Soc* 49:1606, 2001.

Gupta K et al: Increasing antimicrobial resistance and the management of uncomplicated community-acquired urinary tract infections, *Ann Int Med* 135:41, 2001.

Levy SB: Multidrug resistance—a sign of the times, *N Engl J Med* 338:1376, 1998 [editorial].

McIsaac WJ et al: The impact of empirical management of acute cystitis on unnecessary antibiotic use, *Arch Int Med* 161:600, 2002.

Saint S et al: The effectiveness of a clinical practical guideline for the management of presumed uncomplicated UTI in women, *Am J Med* 106:636, 1999.

AUTHOR: **PHILIP J. ALIOTTA, M.D., M.S.H.A.**

BASIC INFORMATION

DEFINITION

Urolithiasis is the presence of calculi within the urinary tract. The five major types of urinary stones are calcium oxalate (>50%), calcium phosphate (10% to 20%), uric acid (8%), struvite (15%), and cystine (3%).

SYNONYMS

Nephrolithiasis
Renal colic

ICD-9CM CODES
592.9 Urinary calculus

EPIDEMIOLOGY & DEMOGRAPHICS

- Urinary stone disease afflicts 250,000 to 750,000 Americans/yr.
- Male:female ratio is 4:1. After the sixth decade, the ratio is 1.5:1.
- Incidence of symptomatic nephrolithiasis is greatest during the summer (resulting from increased humidity and temperatures with increased risk of dehydration and concentrated urine).
- Calcium oxalate or mixed calcium oxalate/calcium phosphate stones account for 70% of urolithiasis.

PHYSICAL FINDINGS & CLINICAL PRESENTATION

Stones may be asymptomatic or may cause the following signs and symptoms from obstruction:

- Sudden onset of flank tenderness
- Nausea and vomiting
- Patient in constant movement, attempting to lessen the pain (patients with an acute abdomen are usually still because movement exacerbates the pain)
- Pain may be referred to the testes or labium (progression of stone down the urinary ureter)
- Fever and chills accompanying the acute colic if there is superimposed infection
- Pain may radiate anteriorly over to the abdomen and result in intestinal ileus

ETIOLOGY

- Increased absorption of calcium in the small bowel: type I absorptive hypercalciuria (independent of calcium intake)
- Idiopathic hypercalciuria nephrolithiasis is the most common diagnosis for patients with calcium stones; the diagnosis is made only if there is no hypercalcemia and no known cause for hypercalciuria
- Increased vitamin D synthesis (e.g., secondary to renal phosphate loss: type III absorptive hypercalciuria)
- Renal tubular malfunction with inadequate reabsorption of calcium and resulting hypercalciuria
- Heterozygous mutations in the NPT2a gene result in hypophosphatemia and urinary phosphate loss
- Hyperparathyroidism with resulting hypercalcemia
- Elevated uric acid level (metabolic defects, dietary excess)
- Chronic diarrhea (e.g., inflammatory bowel disease) with increased oxalate absorption
- Type I (distal tubule) renal tubular acidosis (<1% of calcium stones)
- Chronic hydrochlorothiazide treatment
- Chronic infections with urease-producing organisms (e.g., *Proteus, Providencia, Pseudomonas, Klebsiella*). Struvite, or magnesium ammonium phosphate crystals, are produced when the urinary tract is colonized by bacteria, producing elevated concentrations of ammonia
- Abnormal excretion of cystine
- Chemotherapy for malignancies

DIAGNOSIS

DIFFERENTIAL DIAGNOSIS

- Urinary tract infection
- Pyelonephritis
- Diverticulitis
- PID
- Ovarian pathology
- Factitious (drug addicts)
- Appendicitis
- Small bowel obstruction
- Ectopic pregnancy
- The differential diagnosis of obstructive uropathy is described in Section II

WORKUP

- Laboratory and imaging studies. Stone analysis should be performed on recovered stones.
- A clinical algorithm for evaluation of nephrolithiasis is described in Section III.
- Box 1-15 describes past medical history significant for urolithiasis.

LABORATORY TESTS

- Urinalysis: hematuria may be present; however, its absence does not exclude urinary stones. Evaluation of urinary pH is of value in identification of type of stone (pH >7.5 is associated with struvite stones, whereas pH <5 generally is seen with uric acid or with cystine stones).
- Urine C&S should be obtained for all patients.
- Serum chemistries should include calcium, electrolytes, phosphate, and uric acid.
- Additional tests: 24-hr urine collection for calcium, uric acid, phosphate, oxalate, and citrate excretion is generally reserved for patients with recurrent stones.

BOX 1-15 Past Medical History Significant for Urolithiasis

Diseases associated with disturbances of calcium metabolism: primary hyperparathyroidism, Wilson's disease, medullary sponge kidney, osteoporosis, immobilization, sarcoidosis, osteolytic metastases, plasmacytoma, neuroendocrine tumors, Paget's disease
Dietary history: purine gluttony, calcium excess, milk alkali, oxalate excess, sodium excess, low citrus fruit intake
Medications: uricosurics, diuretics, analgesics, vitamins C and D, antacids (especially phosphorus-binding agents), acetazolamide, calcium channel blockers, triamterene, theophylline, protease inhibitors (indinavir), sulfonamides
Diseases associated with disturbances of oxalate metabolism: primary hyperoxaluria types I and II, Crohn's disease, ulcerative colitis, intestinal bypass surgery (especially jejunoileal bypass), ileal resection
Diseases associated with disturbances of purine metabolism
Intrinsic metabolic disorders—anemia, neoplastic disorders (especially leukemias), intoxication, myocardial infarction, irradiation, cytotoxic chemotherapy
Enzyme deficiency—primary gout, Lesch-Nyhan syndrome
Altered excretion—renal insufficiency, metabolic acidosis
Infectious history: organisms (particularly Proteus and Klebsiella), febrile upper tract involvement and dates if hospitalized.

From Nseyo UO (ed): *Urology for primary care physicians*, Philadelphia, 1999, WB Saunders.

SECTION I

IMAGING STUDIES

- Plain films of the abdomen can identify radioopaque stones (calcium, uric acid stones).
- Renal sonogram may be helpful.
- IVP demonstrates the size and location of the stone, as well as degree of obstruction.
- Unenhanced (noncontrast) helical CT scan does not require contrast media and can visualize the calculus (identified by the "rim sign" or "halo" representing the edematous ureteral wall around the stone). It is fast, accurate (sensitivity 15%-100%, specificity 94%-96%), and readily identifies all stone types in all locations. This modality is being used increasingly in the initial assessment of renal colic.

TREATMENT

NONPHARMACOLOGIC THERAPY

- Increase in water or other fluid intake (doubling of previous fluid intake unless patient has a history of CHF or fluid overload)
- Normal dietary calcium intake. If one does not consume enough calcium, less is available to bind to dietary oxalate; as a result, more oxalate reaches the colon, is absorbed into the bloodstream, and is excreted as calcium oxalate, setting the stage for calcium urolithiasis
- Sodium restriction (to decrease calcium excretion), decreased protein intake to 1 g/kg/day (to decrease uric acid, calcium, and oxalate excretion)
- Increase in bran (may decrease bowel transit time with increased binding of calcium and subsequent decrease in urinary calcium)

ACUTE GENERAL Rx

- Pain control (use of narcotics is generally indicated because of the severity of pain)
- Specific therapy tailored to the stone type:
  1. Uric acid calculi: control of hyperuricosuria with allopurinol 100-300 mg/day; increase urinary pH with potassium citrate, 10-mEq tablets tid
  2. Calcium stones:
     a. HCTZ 25-50 mg qd in patients with type I absorptive hypercalciuria
     b. Decrease bowel absorption of calcium with cellulose phosphate 10 g/day in patients with type I absorptive hypercalciuria
     c. Orthophosphates to inhibit vitamin B synthesis in patients with type III absorptive hypercalciuria
     d. Potassium citrate supplementation in patients with hypocitraturic calcium nephrolithiasis
     e. Purine dietary restrictions or allopurinol in patients with hyperuricosuric calcium nephrolithiasis
  3. Struvite stones:
     a. Most of the stones are large and cause obstruction and bleeding.
     b. ESWL and percutaneous nephrolithotomy are generally necessary.
     c. Prolonged use of antibiotics directed against the predominant urinary tract organism may be beneficial to prevent recurrence.
  4. Cystine stones: Hydration and alkalization of the urine to pH >6.5, penicillamine, and tiopronin can also be used to reduce the formation of cystine; captopril is also beneficial and causes fewer side effects
- Surgical treatment in patients with severe pain unresponsive to medication and patients with persistent fever or nausea or significant impediment of urine flow:
  a. Ureteroscopic stone extraction
  b. Extracorporeal shock wave lithotripsy (ESWL) for most renal stones
- In 1997 the American Urological Association issued the following guidelines for the treatment of ureteral stones:
  1. Proximal ureteral stones <1 cm in diameter: options are ESWL, percutaneous nephroureterolithotomy, and ureteroscopy
  2. Proximal ureteral stones >1 cm in diameter: options are ESWL, percutaneous nephroureterolithotomy, and ureteroscopy. Placement of a ureteral stent should be considered if the stone is causing high-grade obstruction
  3. Distal ureteral stones <1 cm in diameter: most of these pass spontaneously. ESWL and ureteroscopy are two accepted modes of therapy
  4. Distal ureteral stones >1 cm in diameter: watchful waiting, ESWL, ureteroscopy (following stone fragmentation)
- Section III describes an approach to the management of ureteral calculi.

CHRONIC Rx

Maintenance of proper hydration and dietary restrictions (see "Acute General Rx")

DISPOSITION

- >50% of patients will pass the stone within 48 hr.
- Stones will recur in approximately 50% of patients within 5 yr if no medical treatment is provided.

REFERRAL

Urology referral in complicated or recurrent urolithiasis; most patients with small uncomplicated ureteral or renal calculi can be followed as outpatient, whereas patients with persistent vomiting, suspected UTI, pain unresponsive to oral analgesics, or obstructing calculus associated with solitary kidney should be admitted

PEARLS & CONSIDERATIONS

COMMENTS

- Early identification and aggressive treatment of urinary tract infections is indicated in all patients with struvite stones.
- Alkalinization of urine (pH >7.5 with penicillamine) is useful in patients with recurrent cystine stones.
- An algorithmic approach to the management of ureteral calculi is described in Section III.

SUGGESTED READINGS

Borghi L et al: Comparison of two diets for the prevention of recurrent stones in idiopathic hypercalciuria, *N Engl J Med* 346:77, 2002.

Prie D et al: Nephrolithiasis and osteoporosis associated with hypophosphatemia caused by mutations in the type 2a sodium-phosphate cotransporter, *N Engl J Med* 347:983, 2002.

Worster A et al: The accuracy of noncontrast helical computed tomography versus intravenous pyelography in the diagnosis of suspected acute urolithiasis: a meta-analysis, *Ann Intern Med* 40:280, 2002.

AUTHOR: **FRED F. FERRI, M.D.**

Urticaria

BASIC INFORMATION

DEFINITION

Urticaria is a pruritic rash involving the epidermis and the upper portions of the dermis, resulting from localized capillary vasodilation and followed by transudation of protein-rich fluid in the surrounding tissue and manifesting clinically with the presence of hives.

SYNONYMS

Hives
Wheals

ICD-9CM CODES
708.8 Other unspecified urticaria

EPIDEMIOLOGY & DEMOGRAPHICS

- At least 20% of the population will have one episode of hives during their lifetime.
- Incidence is increased in atopic patients.
- The etiology of chronic urticaria (hives lasting longer than 6 wk) is determined in only 5%-20% of cases.

PHYSICAL FINDINGS & CLINICAL PRESENTATION

- Presence of elevated, erythematous, or white nonpitting plaques that change in size and shape over time; they generally last a few hours and disappear without a trace.
- Annular configuration with central pallor (Fig. 1-246).

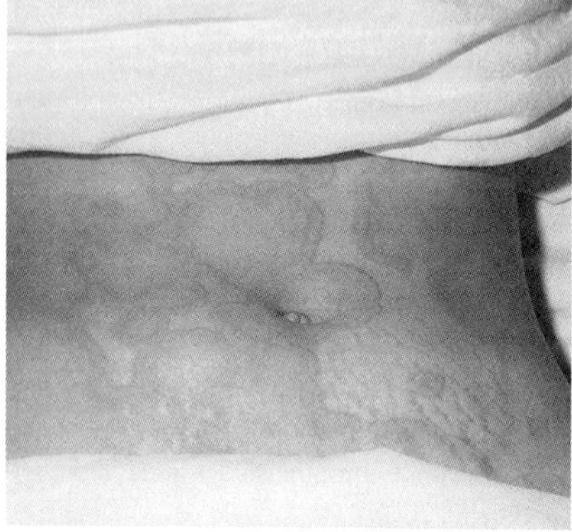

FIGURE 1-246 Wheal (urticaria). Note central cleaning, giving annular configuration. (From Noble J et al: *Textbook of primary care medicine*, ed 3, St Louis, 2001, Mosby.)

ETIOLOGY

- Foods (e.g., shellfish, eggs, strawberries, nuts)
- Drugs (e.g., penicillin, aspirin, sulfonamides)
- Systemic diseases (e.g., SLE, serum sickness, autoimmune thyroid disease, polycythemia vera)
- Food additives (e.g., salicylates, benzoates, sulfites)
- Infections (viral infections, fungal infections, chronic bacterial infections)
- Physical stimuli (e.g., pressure urticaria, exercise-induced, solar urticaria, cold urticaria)
- Inhalants (e.g., mold spores, animal danders, pollens)
- Contact (nonimmunologic) urticaria (e.g., caterpillars, plants)
- Other: hereditary angioedema, urticaria pigmentosa, pregnancy, cold urticaria, hair bleaches, chemicals, saliva, cosmetics, perfumes, pemphigoid, emotional stress

DIAGNOSIS

DIFFERENTIAL DIAGNOSIS

- Erythema multiforme
- Erythema marginatum
- Erythema infectiosum
- Urticarial vasculitis
- Herpes gestationis
- Drug eruption
- Multiple insect bites
- Bullous pemphigoid

WORKUP

- It is useful to determine whether hives are acute or chronic; a medical history focused on various etiologic factors is necessary before embarking on extensive laboratory testing.
- A diagnostic approach to chronic urticaria is described in Section III.

LABORATORY TESTS

- CBC with differential
- Stool for ova and parasites in patients with suspected parasitic infestations
- ANA, ESR, TSH, LFTs, eosinophil count are indicated only in selected patients
- Measurement of C_4 in patients who present with angioedema alone
- Skin biopsy is helpful in patients with fever, arthralgias, and elevated ESR

TREATMENT

NONPHARMACOLOGIC THERAPY

- Remove suspected etiologic agents (e.g., stop aspirin and all nonessential drugs), restrict diet (e.g., elimination of tomatoes, nuts, eggs, shellfish).
- Elimination of yeast should be attempted in patients with chronic urticaria (*Candida albicans* sensitivity may be a factor in patients with chronic urticaria).

ACUTE GENERAL Rx

- Oral antihistamines: use of nonsedating antihistamines (e.g., loratadine [Claritin] 10 mg qd or cetirizine [Zyrtec] 10 mg qd) is preferred over first-generation antihistamines (e.g., hydroxyzine, diphenhydramine).
- Doxepin (a tricyclic antidepressant) that blocks both H_1 and H_2 receptors 25-75 mg qhs may be effective in patients with chronic urticaria.
- Oral corticosteroids should be reserved for refractory cases (e.g., prednisone 20 mg qd or 20 mg bid).
- H_2 receptor antagonists (cimetidine, ranitidine, famotidine) can be added to H_1 antagonists in refractory cases.

CHRONIC Rx

- Use of nonsedating antihistamines, doxepin, and/or oral corticosteroids (see "Acute General Rx")
- Low dose of the immunosuppressant cyclosporine (2.5-3 mg/kg body weight/day) has been shown to be effective and corticosteroid sparing in chronic urticaria
- There is insufficient data to support use of leukotriene antagonists (zafirlukast, montelukast) in patients with chronic urticaria

DISPOSITION

- Most cases of urticaria resolve within 6 wk.
- Only 25% of patients with a history of chronic urticaria are completely cured after 5 yr.

PEARLS & CONSIDERATIONS

COMMENTS

Local treatment (e.g., starch baths or Aveeno baths) may be helpful in selected patients; however, local treatment is generally not rewarding.

SUGGESTED READINGS

Kaplan AP: Chronic urticaria and angioedema, *N Engl J Med* 346:157, 2002.
Miller BA: Urticaria and angioedema: A practical approach, *Am Fam Physician* 69:1123, 2004.

AUTHOR: **FRED F. FERRI, M.D.**

BASIC INFORMATION

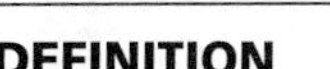

DEFINITION

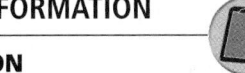

Uterine malignancy includes tumors from the endometrium (discussed elsewhere in this text) and sarcomas. Uterine sarcoma is an abnormal proliferation of cells originating from the mesenchymal, or connective tissue, elements of the uterine wall.

SYNONYMS

Leiomyosarcomas
Endometrial stromal sarcoma
Malignant mixed mullerian tumors
Adenosarcomas

ICD-9CM CODES
182.0 Malignant neoplasm of body of uterus (corpus uteri), except isthmus
182.1 Malignant neoplasm of body of uterus, isthmus
182.8 Malignant neoplasm of body of uterus, other specified sites of body of uterus

EPIDEMIOLOGY & DEMOGRAPHICS

PREVALENCE: Uterine sarcoma accounts for 4.3% of all cancers of the uterine corpus and is the most lethal gynecologic malignancy.
INCIDENCE: 17.1 cases/1 million females
MEAN AGE AT DIAGNOSIS: The age at diagnosis is variable. Mean age at diagnosis is 52 yr.
RISK FACTORS: Similar to endometrial carcinoma

PHYSICAL FINDINGS & CLINICAL PRESENTATION

- Abnormal vaginal bleeding is the most common symptom
- May also present as pelvic pain or pressure and pelvic mass on examination
- May appear as tumor protruding through the cervix
- Vaginal discharge may also be a presenting symptom
- Rapidly enlarging uterus

ETIOLOGY

- The exact etiology is unknown.
- Prior pelvic radiation is a risk factor for sarcoma.
- Black women may be at higher risk.

DIAGNOSIS

DIFFERENTIAL DIAGNOSIS

Leiomyoma

WORKUP

Diagnosis is made histologically by biopsy for abnormal bleeding.

LABORATORY TESTS

Chest radiography, CT scans, and MRI are used to evaluate spread.

IMAGING STUDIES

- Chest radiography is usually done as routine preoperative testing.
- CT scans and MRI are good for assessing tumor spread once diagnosis is made.

TREATMENT

NONPHARMACOLOGIC THERAPY

- Surgery excision is the mainstay of treatment.
- Grade and stage of tumor affect prognosis (Fig. 1-247).
- Adjuvant radiotherapy may improve pelvic disease control, but it does not improve survival.
- Chemotherapeutic agents have produced only partial and short-term responses.

DISPOSITION

- Survival varies with each type of sarcoma but is generally very poor.
- Five-year survival for leiomyosarcoma ranges from 48% for stage I to 0% for stage IV.
- Five-year survival for malignant mixed mesodermal tumor ranges from 36% for stage I to 6% for stage IV.

REFERRAL

Uterine sarcoma should be managed by a gynecologic oncologist and radiation oncologist.

SUGGESTED READINGS

Elima Y et al: Para-aortic lymph node metastasis in relation to serum CA 125 levels and nuclear grade in endometrial carcinoma, *Acta Obstet Gynecol Scond* 81(5):458, 2002.

Pitsm G et al: Stage II endometrial carcinoma: prognostic factors and risk classification in 170 patients, *Intern J Radiat Oncol Biol Physics* 53(4):862, 2002.

AUTHOR: **GIL FARKASH, M.D.**

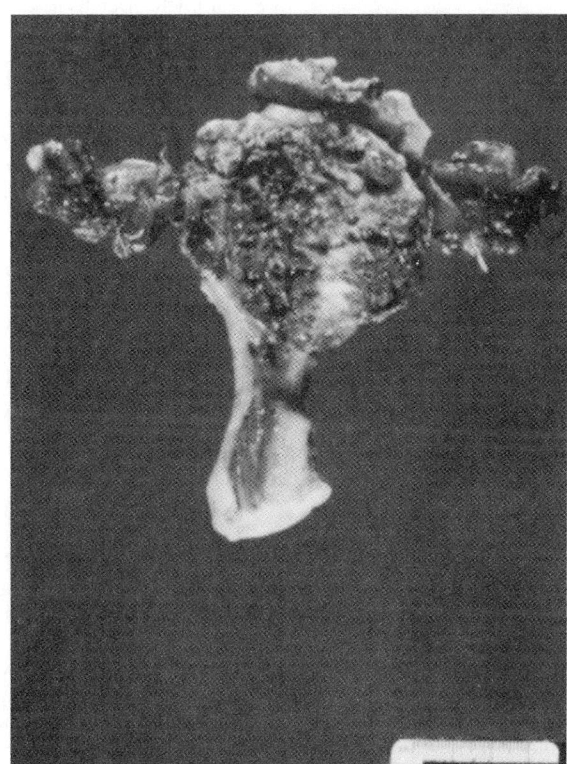

FIGURE 1-247 This grade 3 adenocarcinoma demonstrates extensive myometrial invasion. The tumor has penetrated the uterine serosa and extends onto the fundus and into the upper left broad ligament. (From Copeland LJ: *Textbook of gynecology,* ed 2, Philadelphia, 2000, WB Saunders.)

Uterine Myomas (PTG)

BASIC INFORMATION

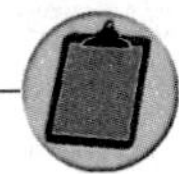

DEFINITION

Uterine myomas are benign tumors of muscle cell origin. They are discrete nodular tumors that vary in size and number and that may be found subserosal, intramucosal, or submucosal within the uterus or may be found in the cervix or broad ligament or on a pedicle.

SYNONYMS

Leiomyomas, fibroids

ICD-9CM CODES
218.9 Leiomyomas, fibroids

EPIDEMIOLOGY & DEMOGRAPHICS

- Estimated presence in at least 20% of all reproductive age women
- The most common benign uterine tumor
- More common in black than in white women
- Asymptomatic fibroids may be present in 40% to 50% of women >40 yr of age
- May occur singly but are often multiple
- Fewer than half of all fibroids are estimated to produce symptoms
- Frequently diagnosed incidentally on pelvic examination
- There is increased familial incidence
- Potential to enlarge during pregnancy, as well as to regress after menopause
- Infrequent primary cause of infertility in <3% of infertile patients
- Symptomatic myomas are the primary indication for approximately 30% of all hysterectomies.

PHYSICAL FINDINGS & CLINICAL PRESENTATION

- Enlarged, irregular uterus on pelvic examination.
- Presenting symptoms:
  1. Menorrhagia (most common)
  2. Chronic pelvic pain (dysmenorrhea, dyspareunia, pelvic pressure)
  3. Acute pain (torsion of pedunculated myoma, infarction, and degeneration)
  4. Urinary symptoms (frequency from bladder pressure, partial ureteral obstruction, complete ureteral obstruction)
  5. Rectosigmoid compression with constipation or intestinal obstruction
  6. Prolapse through cervix of pedunculated submucosal tumor
  7. Venous stasis of lower extremities
  8. Polycythemia
  9. Ascites

ETIOLOGY

Incompletely understood. It is suggested that myomas arise from an original single smooth muscle cell in the myometrium. Each individual myoma is monoclonal. All the cells are derived from one progenitor myocyte. Malignant degeneration of preexisting leiomyoma is extremely uncommon (<0.5%).

DIAGNOSIS

DIFFERENTIAL DIAGNOSIS

Leiomyosarcoma, ovarian mass (neoplastic, nonneoplastic, endometrioma), inflammatory mass, pregnancy

WORKUP

- Complete pelvic examination, rectovaginal examination, Pap test
- Estimation of size of mass in centimeters
- Endometrial sampling may be indicated (biopsy or D&C) when abnormal bleeding and pelvic mass are present
- If urinary symptoms are prominent, cystometry, cystoscopy to rule out bladder lesions, IVP to rule out impingement on urinary system

LABORATORY TESTS

- Pregnancy test
- Pap smear
- CBC, ESR
- Fecal occult blood

IMAGING STUDIES

- Pelvic ultrasound (transvaginal may have higher diagnostic accuracy) is useful.
- CT scan is helpful in planning treatment if malignancy is strongly suspected.
- Hysteroscopy may provide direct evidence of intrauterine pathology or submucosal leiomyoma that distorts uterine cavity.

TREATMENT

Management should be based on primary symptoms and may include observation with close follow-up, temporizing surgical therapies, medical management, or definitive surgical procedures.

NONSURGICAL Rx

- Patient observation and follow-up with periodic repeat pelvic examinations to ensure that tumors are not growing rapidly.
- GnRH agonist use results in 40% to 60% reduction in uterine volume. Hypoestrogenism, reversible bone loss, hot flushes associated with use. Limit to short-term use and consider low-dose hormonal replacement to minimize hypoestrogenic effects.
- Regrowth occurs in about 50% of women treated a few months after cessation.
- Indications for GnRH:
  1. Fertility preservation in women with large myomas before attempting conception or preoperative myectomy treatment
  2. Anemia treatment to normalize hemoglobin before surgery
  3. Women approaching menopause to avoid surgery
  4. Preoperative for large myomas to make vaginal hysterectomy, hysteroscopic resection/ablation, or laparoscopic destruction more feasible
  5. Women with medical contraindications for surgery
  6. Personal or medical indications for delaying surgery
- Progestational agents may also result in decrease in uterine size and amenorrhea, allowing iron therapy to treat anemia with limited success.
- Other drugs used and under investigation:
  1. Danazol: androgen and multienzyme inhibitor of steroidogenesis.
  2. Mifepristone: antiprogestagen, shown to reduce the fibroid volume of 40%-50% with amenorrhea.
  3. Raloxifene: SERM, either alone or with a GnRHa, shown to reduce the fibroid volume 70% up to 1 yr but only in postmenopausal women.
  4. Fadrozole: aromatase inhibitor, reported to have produced a 71% reduction in volume.

SURGICAL Rx

- Indications
  1. Abnormal uterine bleeding with anemia, refractory to hormonal therapy
  2. Chronic pain with severe dysmenorrhea, dyspareunia, or lower abdominal pressure/pain
  3. Acute pain, torsion, or prolapsing submucosal fibroid
  4. Urinary symptoms or signs such as hydronephrosis
  5. Rapid uterine enlargement premenopausal or any growth after menopause
  6. Infertility or recurrent pregnancy loss with leiomyoma as only finding
  7. Enlarged uterus with compression symptoms or discomfort
- Procedures
  1. Hysterectomy (definitive procedure)
  2. Abdominal myomectomy (to preserve fertility)
  3. Vaginal myomectomy for prolapsed pedunculated submucous fibroid
  4. Hysteroscopic resection
  5. Laparoscopic myomectomy
  6. Uterine fibroid embolization

COMPLICATIONS

- Red degeneration
- Leiomyosarcoma ($<0.1\%$)

REFERRAL

Consultation with gynecologic oncologist if suspicion of malignancy

SUGGESTED READINGS

DeWaay DJ et al: Natural history of uterine polyps and leiomyomata, *Obstet Gynecol* 100:3, 2002.

Olive DL, Lindheim SR, Pritts EA: Non-surgical management of leiomyoma, *Curr Opin Obstet Gynecol* 16(3):239, 2004.

AUTHOR: **ARUNDATHI G. PRASAD, M.D.**

SECTION I

BASIC INFORMATION

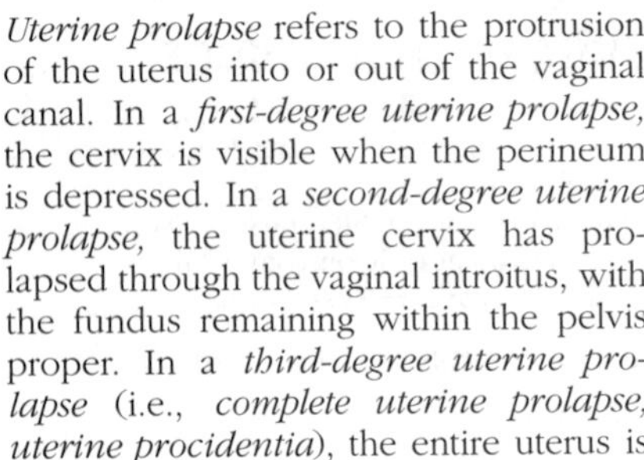

DEFINITION

Uterine prolapse refers to the protrusion of the uterus into or out of the vaginal canal. In a *first-degree uterine prolapse,* the cervix is visible when the perineum is depressed. In a *second-degree uterine prolapse,* the uterine cervix has prolapsed through the vaginal introitus, with the fundus remaining within the pelvis proper. In a *third-degree uterine prolapse* (i.e., *complete uterine prolapse, uterine procidentia*), the entire uterus is outside the introitus.

SYNONYMS

Genital prolapse
Uterine descensus
Pelvic organ prolapse

ICD-9CM CODES
618.8 Genital prolapse
618.1 Uterine descensus
618.8 Pelvic organ prolapse

EPIDEMIOLOGY & DEMOGRAPHICS

Most prevalent in postmenopausal multiparous women.

RISK FACTORS;
- Pregnancy
- Labor
- Vaginal childbirth
- Obesity
- Chronic coughing
- Constipation
- Pelvic tumors
- Ascites
- Strenuous physical exertion
- Caucasian race

GENETICS: Increased incidence in women with spina bifida occulta.

PHYSICAL FINDINGS & CLINICAL PRESENTATION

- Pelvic pressure
- Bearing-down sensation
- Bilateral groin pain
- Sacral backache
- Coital difficulty
- Protrusion from vagina
- Spotting
- Ulceration
- Bleeding
- Examination of patient in lithotomy, sitting, and standing positions and before, during, and after a maximum Valsalva effort
- Erosion or ulceration of the cervix possible in the most dependent area of the protrusion

ETIOLOGY

- Vaginal childbirth and chronic increases in intraabdominal pressure leading to detachments, lacerations, and denervations of the vaginal support system
- Further weakening of pelvic support system by hypoestrogenic atrophy
- Some cases from congenital or inherited weaknesses within the pelvic support system
- Neonatal uterine prolapse mostly coexistent with congenital spinal defects

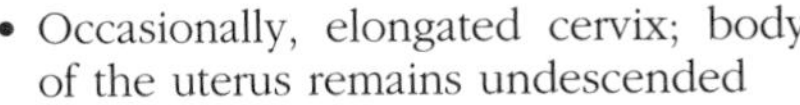

DIAGNOSIS

DIFFERENTIAL DIAGNOSIS

- Occasionally, elongated cervix; body of the uterus remains undescended
- Diagnosis is based on history and physical examination. Currently there is only one genital tract prolapse classification system that has attained international acceptance & recognition, the Patient pelvic organ prolapse quantification (POPQ). See Boxes 1-16 and 1-17.

WORKUP

- If erosion or ulceration of the cervix is present, a Pap smear followed by a cervical biopsy should be performed if indicated.
- If urinary symptoms are significant, further urodynamic workup is indicated, looking for concurrent cystourethrocele, cystocele, enterocele, or rectocele.

LABORATORY TESTS

Urine culture

IMAGING STUDIES

Ultrasound if concurrent fibroids need further evaluation

TREATMENT

NONPHARMACOLOGIC THERAPY

- Prophylactic measures
  1. Diagnosis and treatment of chronic respiratory and metabolic disorders
  2. Correction of constipation
  3. Weight control, nutrition, and smoking cessation counseling
  4. Teaching of pelvic muscle exercises

BOX 1-16 Staging of Pelvic Organ Prolapse Based on POP-Q Examination

Stage 0	No prolapse.
Stage I	Most distal prolapse more than 1 cm above hymenal ring.
Stage II	Most distal point is 1 cm or less above hymenal ring.
Stage III	Most distal point is more than 1 cm below the hymenal ring but not further than 2 cm less the total vaginal length i.e. $> +1$ cm but $< +$ (TVL-2) cm.
Stage IV	Complete vaginal eversion.

From Pemberton J (ed): *The pelvic floor,* Philadelphia, 2002, WB Saunders.

BOX 1-17 Points of Reference for POP-Q

Point A Three cm above the hymen on anterior vaginal wall (Aa) or posterior vaginal wall (Ap). Point Aa roughly corresponds with the urethrovesical junction. These points can range from −3 cm (no prolapse) to +3 cm (maximal prolapse.)
Point B The lowest extent of the segment of vagina between point A and the apex of the vagina. Unlike points A they are not fixed but will be the same as A if point A is the most protruding point. In maximal prolapse it will be the same as point C.
Point C The most distal part of the cervix or vaginal vault.
Point D The posterior fornix, which is thus omitted in women with prior hysterectomy.
Genital hiatus From midline external urethral meatus to inferior hymenal ring.
Perineal body From inferior hymenal ring to middle of anal orifice.
Vaginal length This should be measured without undue stretching of the vagina.

From Pemberton J (ed): *The pelvic floor,* Philadelphia, 2002, WB Saunders.

- Supportive pessary therapy
  1. Ring-type pessary useful for first- or second-degree prolapse
  2. Gellhorn pessary preferred for more advanced prolapse
  3. Use of pessaries in conjunction with continuous hormone replacement therapy, unless contraindicated
  4. Perineorrhaphy under local anesthesia possibly needed to support the pessary if the vaginal outlet is very relaxed

ACUTE GENERAL Rx

- Patients who are only infrequently symptomatic: insertion of a tampon or diaphragm for temporary relief when prolonged standing is anticipated
- Neonatal uterine prolapse: simple digital reduction or the use of a small pessary

CHRONIC Rx

- Hormone replacement therapy at the time of menopause helps preserve tissue strength, maintain elasticity of the vagina, and promote the durability of surgical repairs.
- Gold standard for therapy is vaginal hysterectomy.
- Vaginal apex should be well suspended, but a prophylactic sacrospinous ligament fixation is not routinely required.
- If occult enterocele present, McCall culdoplasty is performed.
- If vaginal approach to hysterectomy is contraindicated, abdominal hysterectomy is performed; vaginal apex likewise well supported.
- Colpocleisis is considered for the elderly patient who is sexually inactive and is a high-risk patient from a surgical point of view; can be done rapidly under local anesthesia with mild sedation if necessary.
- For symptomatic women who desire childbearing: management with pessaries or pelvic muscle exercises is recommended; if surgical correction is required, transvaginal sacrospinous fixation is the preferred method.
- Other surgical options are sling operations and sacral cervicopexy.

DISPOSITION

If untreated, uterine prolapse progressively worsens.

REFERRAL

To a gynecologist/urologist if pessary fitting or surgical intervention is needed

PEARLS & CONSIDERATIONS

COMMENTS

Surgery contraindicated in mild or asymptomatic uterine prolapse because the patient will seldom benefit from the operation although exposed to its risks.

SUGGESTED READINGS

Glass RH, Curtis MG, Hopkins MP: *Glass' office gynecology,* ed 5, Baltimore, 1999, Lippincott Williams & Wilkins.

Thaker R: Management of uterine prolapse, *BMJ* 324:1258, 2002.

AUTHOR: **ARUNDATHI G. PRASAD, M.D.**

SECTION I

BASIC INFORMATION

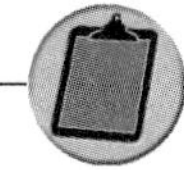

DEFINITION

Uveitis is inflammation of the uveal tract, including the iris, ciliary body, and choroid. It may also involve other closed structures such as the sclera, retina, and vitreous humor.

SYNONYMS

Anterior uveitis
Posterior uveitis
Acute or chronic uveitis
Granulomatous or nongranulomatous uveitis

ICD-9CM CODES
364.3 Unspecified iridocyclitis, uveitis

EPIDEMIOLOGY & DEMOGRAPHICS

INCIDENCE (IN U.S.): Common; busy ophthalmologist will see two or more cases per week
PREVALENCE (IN U.S.): 17 cases/100,000 persons
PREDOMINANT SEX: None
PREDOMINANT AGE: 38 yr
PEAK INCIDENCE: Middle age or older; uveitis in childhood rare; equal in boys and girls; 25% idiopathic and 75% related to toxoplasmosis, juvenile rheumatoid arthritis, pars planitis, toxicaris canis, or Behcet's disease

PHYSICAL FINDINGS & CLINICAL PRESENTATION

- Photophobia
- Blurred visual acuity
- Irregular pupil
- Hazy cornea
- Abnormal cells and flare in anterior chamber or vitreous humor
- Retinal hemorrhage, vascular sheathing (Fig. 1-248)
- Conjunctival injection
- Ciliary flush
- Keratitic precipitates (precipitates on the cornea)
- Hazy vitreous
- Retinal inflammation
- Iris nodules
- Glaucoma
- Rheumatoid arthritis
- Scleritis
- Systemic symptoms related to etiology

DIAGNOSIS

DIFFERENTIAL DIAGNOSIS

- Glaucoma
- Conjunctivitis
- Retinal detachment
- Retinopathy
- Keratitis
- Scleritis
- Episcleritis

WORKUP

- Associated with arthritis, syphilis, tuberculosis, granulomatous disease, collagen-vascular disease, allergies, AIDS, sarcoid, Behçet's disease, histoplasmosis, toxoplasmosis, and toxicaris canis
- Slit lamp examination, indirect ophthalmoscopy

LABORATORY TESTS

- CBC
- Laboratory tests for specific inflammatory causes cited previously in "Workup" (e.g., ANA, ESR, VDRL, HLA-B27 PPD, Lyme titer)
- Visual field testing

IMAGING STUDIES

- Chest x-ray examination in suspected sarcoidosis, TB, histoplasmosis
- Sacroiliac x-ray examination in suspected ankylosing spondylitis

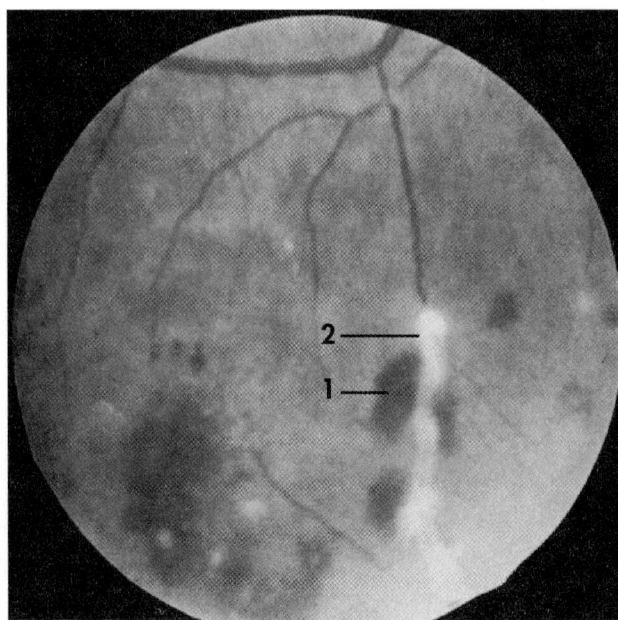

FIGURE 1-248 Sarcoid posterior uveitis showing retinal hemorrhage (*1*) and vascular sheating (*2*). (Palay D [ed]: *Ophthalmology for the primary care physician,* St Louis, 1997, Mosby.)

TREATMENT

NONPHARMACOLOGIC THERAPY

- Treat the underlying disease.
- Treat photophobia and local pain.

ACUTE GENERAL Rx

- Cycloplegic drops (cyclopentolate [Cyclogyl]) or cycloplegic agents (homatropine hydrobromide [Optic] 1gtt q3-4h while awake) and topical steroids (prednisone acetate 1% 1 gtt qh during day, prn at night until favorable response, then q4-6h); avoid topical corticosteroids in infectious uveitis
- Antibiotics when infection is suspected
- Systemic steroids if appropriate for the underlying disease
- Antimetabolites when indicated

CHRONIC Rx

- Topical steroids and cycloplegics
- Treat underlying cause

DISPOSITION

Urgent referral to ophthalmologist for diagnosis and treatment.

REFERRAL

- Eye problem should be followed early on by an ophthalmologist.
- Underlying medical disease should be treated by the primary care physician.

PEARLS & CONSIDERATIONS

COMMENTS

- In 90% of cases, the condition is idiopathic.
- Associated causes are found approximately 10% of the time, usually chronic and recurrent.
- Chronic glaucoma, cataracts, retinal degeneration, and other severe eye problems occur with the disease and the treatment.

SUGGESTED READINGS

Chang JH, Wakefield D: Uveitis: a global perspective, *Ocul Immunol Inflamm* 80(6):672, 2002.
Gardiner AM et al: Correlation between visual function and visual ability in patients with uveitis, *Br J Ophthmol* 86(9):993, 2002.
Kadayifcilar S, Eldem B, Tumer B: Uveitis in childhood, *J Pediatr Ophthalmol Strabismus* 40(6):335, 2003.

AUTHOR: **MELVYN KOBY, M.D.**

BASIC INFORMATION

DEFINITION

Bleeding per vagina at any time during pregnancy must be regarded as abnormal and is associated with an increased likelihood of pregnancy complications.

SYNONYMS

Hemorrhage

ICD-9CM CODES
634.9 Spontaneous abortion
633.9 Ectopic pregnancy
630/631 Molar pregnancy
622.7 Cervical polyps
180.9/180.0/180.8 Cervical dysplasia/cancer
616.0 Cervicitis
616.10 Vulvovaginitis
184.0 Vaginal cancer
644.2 Premature labor term labor
641.1 Placenta previa
641.2 Placental abruption

EPIDEMIOLOGY & DEMOGRAPHICS

- Common in U.S.; 20%-25% of patients have vaginal spotting/bleeding in first trimester; of those, miscarriage occurs in 50%.
- Occurs in women of childbearing age.
- Between 1% and 2% of all pregnancies in the U.S. are ectopic.
- After one ectopic pregnancy, the chance of another is 7%-15%.
- Ectopic pregnancy is the leading cause of maternal mortality in the first trimester.
- Average reported frequency for placental abruption is about 1 in 150 deliveries (0.3%).
- Incidence of placenta previa is <1 in 200 deliveries (0.5%).

PHYSICAL FINDINGS & CLINICAL PRESENTATION

- Bleeding: ranges from scant to life-threatening with hemodynamic instability
- Color: brown to bright red
- Can be painless or painful (cramps, back pain, severe abdominal pain)
- Fetal compromise: ranges from none to fetal demise

ETIOLOGY

- Influenced by gestational age
- Vaginal
- Cervical
- Uterine

DIAGNOSIS

DIFFERENTIAL DIAGNOSIS

- Any gestational age:
  1. Cervical lesions: polyps, decidual reaction, neoplasia
  2. Vaginal trauma
  3. Cervicitis/vulvovaginitis
  4. Postcoital trauma
  5. Bleeding dyscrasias
- Gestation <20 wk:
  1. Spontaneous abortion
  2. Presence of intrauterine device
  3. Ectopic pregnancy
  4. Molar pregnancy
  5. Implantation bleeding
  6. Low-lying placenta
- Gestation >20 wk:
  1. Molar pregnancy
  2. Placenta previa
  3. Placental abruption
  4. Vasa previa
  5. Marginal separation of the placenta
  6. Bloody show at term
  7. Preterm labor
- Section II describes the differential diagnosis of vaginal bleeding in pregnancy.

WORKUP

- Gestation <20 wk (Section III, "Bleeding, Early Pregnancy")
  1. Pelvic examination
  2. Culdocentesis
  3. Laparoscopy
  4. Laparotomy
- Gestation >20 wk:
  1. Ultrasound to locate placenta before pelvic examination
  2. If placenta previa, no speculum or bimanual examination
  3. If preterm labor, appropriate evaluation done

LABORATORY TESTS

- Urine pregnancy test: if positive, get quantitative β human chorionic gonadotropin (hCG)
  1. Early pregnancy: follow serially every 48 hr
  2. Normal pregnancy: hCG doubles approximately every 48 hr
  3. Spontaneous abortion: hCG levels will fall
  4. Ectopic pregnancy: hCG level will rise inappropriately
  5. Molar pregnancy: hCG level is extremely high
- CBC
- Blood type and screen (Rh-negative patients need RhoGAM)
- Coagulation profile (useful in missed abortion and abruption)
- Cervical cultures/wet mount
- Pap smear for cervical malignancy; caution with biopsy, because cervix can bleed extensively

IMAGING STUDIES

Ultrasound:
- 5-6 wk: gestational sac (transvaginally); hCG >2500 mIU/ml (third IS) or >1000 mIU/ml (second IS)
- 8-9 wk: fetal cardiac activity
- Molar pregnancy: characteristic cluster of cysts
- Location of placenta
- Degree of placental separation: difficult to assess

TREATMENT

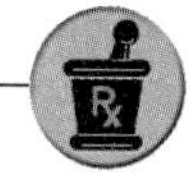

NONPHARMACOLOGIC THERAPY

- Pelvic rest: no coitus, douching, or tampons
- Bed rest, if >20 wk
- Counseling: genetic, bereavement

ACUTE GENERAL Rx

- Hemodynamic stabilization
- Emergency D&C, laparotomy, or cesarean section as necessary

CHRONIC Rx

Depends on diagnosis

DISPOSITION

Depends on diagnosis

REFERRAL

- If patient is unstable and needs emergency ob/gyn management and/or surgery
- If patient has diagnosis of ectopic or molar pregnancy, because immediate surgical treatment is indicated
- Perinatal consultation for high-risk pregnancy

SUGGESTED READINGS

Alexander JD, Schneider FD: Vaginal bleeding associated with pregnancy primary care; clinic in office, *Practice* 27(1):137, 2000.

Coppola PT, Coppola M: Vaginal bleeding in the first 20 weeks of pregnancy, *Emerg Med Clin North Am* 21(3):667, 2003.

AUTHOR: **GEORGE T. DANAKAS, M.D.**

BASIC INFORMATION

DEFINITION

Vaginal malignancy is an abnormal proliferation of vaginal epithelium demonstrating malignant cells below the basement membrane.

SYNONYMS

Squamous cell carcinoma of the vagina
Adenocarcinoma of the vagina
Melanoma of the vagina
Sarcoma of the vagina
Endodermal sinus tumor

ICD-9CM CODES
184.0 Vagina, vaginal neoplasm

EPIDEMIOLOGY & DEMOGRAPHICS

PREVALENCE: Vaginal cancer is the second rarest gynecologic cancer. It comprises 2% of malignancies of the female genital tract.

INCIDENCE: 0.42 cases/100,000 persons

MEAN AGE AT DIAGNOSIS: Predominantly a disease of menopause. Mean age at diagnosis is 60 yr old.

PHYSICAL FINDINGS & CLINICAL PRESENTATION

- Majority of cases are asymptomatic
- Postmenopausal vaginal bleeding and/or vaginal discharge are the most common symptoms
- May also present as pelvic pain or pressure, dyspareunia, dysuria, malodor, or postcoital bleeding
- May present as a vaginal lesion or abnormal Pap smear

ETIOLOGY

- The exact etiology is unknown.
- Vaginal intraepithelial neoplasia is thought to be a precursor for squamous cell carcinoma of the vagina.
- Chronic pessary use has been associated with vaginal malignancy.
- Prior pelvic radiation may be a risk factor.
- Clear-cell adenocarcinoma is related to in utero diethylstilbestrol exposure.

DIAGNOSIS

DIFFERENTIAL DIAGNOSIS

- Extension from other primary carcinoma; more common than primary vaginal cancer
- Vaginitis

WORKUP

- Diagnosis is made histologically by biopsy.
- Colposcopy and biopsy should follow suspicious Pap smear.
- Cystoscopy, proctosigmoidoscopy, chest radiography, IV urography, and barium enema may be used for clinical staging.
- CT scan and MRI are being used to evaluate spread.
- Staging I-IV (Fig. 1-249).

IMAGING STUDIES

- Chest radiography, IV urography, and barium enema are used for staging.
- CT scan and MRI are good for assessing tumor spread.

TREATMENT

NONPHARMACOLOGIC THERAPY

- Radiation therapy is the mainstay of treatment.
- Stage I tumors that are small and confined to the posterior, upper third of the vagina may be treated with radical surgery.
- Other stages require a whole-pelvis, interstitial, and/or intracavitary radiation therapy.
- Chemotherapy is used in conjunction with radiotherapy in rare select cases.

DISPOSITION

Five-year survival ranges from 80% for stage I to 17% for stage IV.

REFERRAL

Vaginal cancer should be managed by a gynecologic oncologist and radiation oncologist.

SUGGESTED READINGS

Kim H et al: Case report: magnetic resonance imaging of vaginal malignant melanoma, *J Comput Assist Tomogr* 27(3):357, 2003.

Stryker JA: Radiotherapy for vaginal carcinoma: a 23-year review, *Br J Radiol* 73 (875):1200, 2000.

AUTHOR: **GIL FARKASH, M.D.**

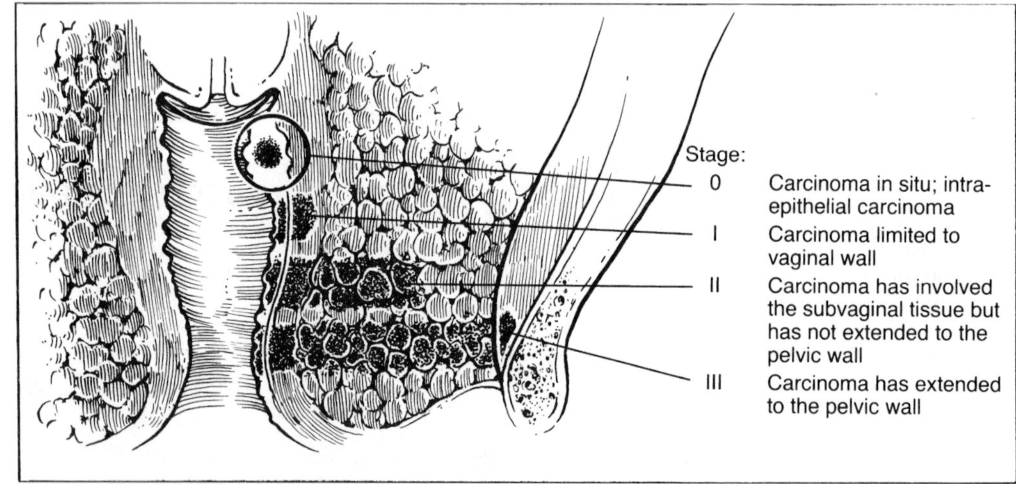

Stage:
0
Carcinoma in situ; intra-epithelial carcinoma
I
Carcinoma limited to vaginal wall
II
Carcinoma has involved the subvaginal tissue but has not extended to the pelvic wall
III
Carcinoma has extended to the pelvic wall

FIGURE 1-249 Staging system for vaginal cancer. Metastatic disease that involves the bladder or rectum is stage IV-a. Metastatic disease beyond the pelvis is stage IV-b. (From Copeland LJ: *Textbook of gynecology,* ed 2, Philadelphia, 2000, WB Saunders.)

BASIC INFORMATION

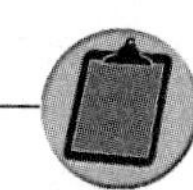

DEFINITION

Vaginismus refers to the involuntary spasm of the vaginal, introital, and/or levator ani muscles, preventing penetration or causing painful intercourse.

ICD-9CM CODES
300.11 Hysterical vaginismus
306.51 Psychogenic or functional vaginismus
625.1 Reflex vaginismus

EPIDEMIOLOGY & DEMOGRAPHICS

PREVALENCE: Affects approximately 1:200 women
INCIDENCE: Estimated at about 11.7%-42% of women presenting to sexual dysfunction clinics
RISK FACTORS: Any previous sexual trauma, including incest or rape
PREDOMINANT SEX: Affects only females

PHYSICAL FINDINGS & CLINICAL PRESENTATION

- Fear of pain with coitus
- Dyspareunia
- Orgasmic dysfunction

ETIOLOGY

- Learned conditioned response to real or imagined painful vaginal experience (e.g., traumatic speculum examination, incest, rape)
- Vaginitis
- PID
- Endometriosis
- Anatomic anomalies
- Atrophic vaginitis
- Mucosal tears
- Inadequate lubrication
- Focal vulvitis
- Painful hymenal tags
- Scarring secondary to episiotomy
- Skin disorders
- Topical allergies
- Postherpetic neuralgia

DIAGNOSIS

WORKUP

- Thorough history (including sexual history)
- Careful pelvic examination
- Behavioral therapy

TREATMENT

NONPHARMACOLOGIC THERAPY

- Deconditioning the response by systematic self-administered progressive dilation techniques using fingers or dilators
- Behavioral and/or psychosexual therapy

ACUTE GENERAL Rx

- Botulinum toxin therapy given locally has been shown to relieve the perineal muscle spasms associated with vaginismus, allowing resumption of intercourse.
  1. Acts by preventing neuromuscular transmission, causing muscle weakness
  2. Considered experimental treatment for vaginismus at this time
- Cause should be determined by history and explained to the patient so that she understands the mechanics of the muscle spasms.
- Patient must be motivated to desire painless vaginal insertion for such reasons as pleasurable coitus, tampon insertion, or gynecologic examination.
- Patient (and her partner) must be willing to patiently undergo the process of systematic desensitization and counseling.

DISPOSITION

A high percentage of successfully treated patients

REFERRAL

To a gynecologist or sex therapist

PEARLS & CONSIDERATIONS

COMMENTS

- May uncover early sexual abuse or an aversion to sexuality in general.
- To American Association of Sex Educators, Counselors and Therapists, 11 Dupont Circle, NW, Washington, DC, 20036.
- To Sex Information and Education Council of the U.S. (SIECUS), 85th Avenue, New York, NY 10022.

SUGGESTED READINGS

Brin MF, Vapnek JM: Treatment of vaginismus with botulinum toxin injections, *Lancet* 349:252, 1997.

Heim LJ: Evaluation and differential diagnosis of dyspareunia, *Am Fam Physician* 63(8):1535, 2001.

McGuire H, Hawton K: Interventions for vaginismus. [update of Cochrane Database Syst Rev. 2001;(2):CD001760; PMID:11406006]. Cochrane Database of Systematic Reveiws (1):CD001760, 2003.

Phillips NA: Female sexual dysfunction evaluation and treatment, *Am Fam Physician* 62(1):127, 2000.

AUTHOR: **BETH J. WUTZ, M.D.**

BASIC INFORMATION

DEFINITION

Bacterial vaginosis (BV) is a thin, gray, homogenous, malodorous vaginal discharge that results from a shift in the vaginal flora from a predominance of lactobacilli to high concentrations of anaerobic bacteria.

PREVIOUS NAMES

Before 1955: nonspecific vaginitis
1955: *Haemophilus vaginalis* vaginitis
1963: *Corynebacterium vaginalis* vaginitis
1980: *Gardnerella vaginalis* vaginitis
1990: Bacterial vaginosis

ICD-9CM CODES
616.10 Vaginitis, bacterial

EPIDEMIOLOGY & DEMOGRAPHICS

- Most common vaginal infection
- Studies by Thomason et al report that BV is present in:
  1. 16% of private patients
  2. 10%-25% of obstetric clinic patients
  3. 38%-64% of STD clinic patients
- *Gardnerella, Mycoplasma,* and *Mobiluncus* are harbored in the urethra of male partners; however,
  1. Male partners are asymptomatic.
  2. There is no improved cure rate or lower reinfection rate if the infected patient's male partner is treated.
  3. Abstinence from intercourse or condom use while the patient completes her treatment regimen may improve cure rates and lessen recurrences.

PHYSICAL FINDINGS & CLINICAL PRESENTATION

- 50% of patients are asymptomatic
- A thin, dark, or dull gray homogenous discharge that adheres to the vaginal walls
- An offensive, "fishy" odor that is accentuated after intercourse or menses
- Pruritus (only in 13%)

ETIOLOGY & PATHOGENESIS

- *Gardnerella vaginalis* is detected in 40%-50% of vaginal secretions.
  1. Increase in vaginal pH caused by decrease in hydrogen peroxide–producing lactobacilli
  2. Anaerobes predominate and produce amines
- Amines, when alkalinized by semen, menstrual blood, the use of alkaline douches, or the addition of 10% KOH, volatilize and cause the unpleasant "fishy" odor.
- In BV:
  1. *Bacteroides* (anaerobes) species are increased 1000× the usual concentration.
  2. *G. vaginalis* are 100× normal.
  3. *Peptostreptococcus* are 10× normal.
  4. *Mycoplasma hominis* and Enterobacteriacea members are present in increased concentrations.

ASSOCIATIONS WITH OTHER DISORDERS

Bacterial vaginosis has been associated with PID, cystitis, posthysterectomy vaginal cuff cellulitis, postabortal infection, preterm delivery, premature rupture of membranes (PROM), amnionitis, chorioamnionitis, and postpartum endometritis. New evidence also shows BV increases women's risk of acquiring HIV.

DIAGNOSIS

Seattle Group Criteria:
- Detecting three of the four following signs will diagnose 90% correctly, with <10% false positives:
  1. Thin, gray, homogenous, malodorous discharge that adheres to the vaginal walls
  2. Elevated pH >4.5
  3. Positive KOH whiff test
  4. Clue cells present on wet mount
- Cultures are unnecessary.
- Pap smear will not identify *G. vaginalis.*
- Gram stain of vaginal secretions will reveal clue cells and abnormal mixed bacteria (Fig. 1-250).

TREATMENT

RECOMMENDED REGIMENS (EQUAL EFFICACY)

1. Metronidazole 500 mg PO bid for 7 days
2. 0.75% metronidazole gel in vagina bid for 5 days
3. 2% clindamycin cream qd for 7 days

ALTERNATE REGIMENS (LOWER EFFICACY FOR BV)

1. Clindamycin ovules 100 g intravaginally qhs for 3 days
2. Clindamycin 300 mg PO bid for 7 days (increased incidence of diarrhea)
3. Metronidazole ER 750 mg PO qd for 7 days
4. Metronidazole 2 g PO single dose (higher relapse rate)

Patients should be advised to avoid alcohol while taking metronidazole and for 24 hr thereafter.

TREATMENT IN PREGNANCY

All pregnant patients proven to have BV should be treated because of its association with preterm labor, chorioamnionitis, and PROM.

RECOMMENDED REGIMENS

1. Metronidazole 250 mg PO tid for 7 days
2. Clindamycin 300 mg PO bid for 7 days

- Existing data do not support the use of topical agents during pregnancy.
- Multiple studies and meta-analysis have not demonstrated associations between metronidazole use during pregnancy and teratogenic effects in newborns.

RECURRENT BV:
- Condom use may help reduce the risk of recurrence.
- Concurrent treatment of male partner is controversial. Consider treating the male partner if there is recurrent vaginitis or any suspicion of associated upper genital tract infection.

SUGGESTED READINGS

Koumans EH, Kendrick JS, CDC Bacterial Vaginosis Working Group: Preventing adverse sequelae of bacterial vaginosis: A public health program and research agenda, *Sex Transm Dis* 28(5):292, 2001.
Mitchell H: Vaginal discharge-causes, diagnosis, and treatment, *BMJ* 328(7451):1306, 2004.

AUTHOR: **ARUNDATHI G. PRASAD, M.D.**

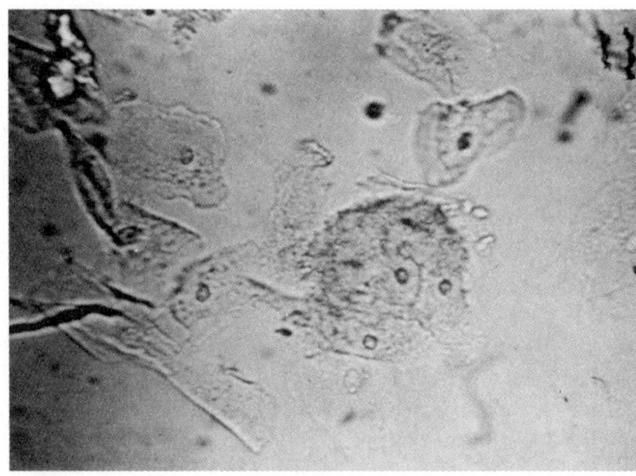

FIGURE 1-250 Clue cells characteristic of bacterial vaginosis, squamous epithelial cells whose borders are obscured by bacteria. (From Carlson K [ed]: *Primary care of women,* St Louis, 1995, Mosby.)

BASIC INFORMATION

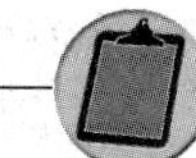

DEFINITION

Varicose veins are dilated networks of the subcutaneous venous system that result from valvular incompetence.

SYNONYMS

Chronic venous insufficiency
Stasis skin changes

ICD-9CM CODES
454.9 Varicose veins

EPIDEMIOLOGY & DEMOGRAPHICS

PREVALENCE:
- Approximately 30% of adults, with increasing incidence with age
- Increased incidence during pregnancy, especially with advanced maternal age

GENETICS:
- Familial tendency
- Evidence for dominant, recessive, and multifactorial types of inheritance

PREDOMINANT SEX: Female > male

RISK FACTORS:
- Advancing age
- Prolonged standing
- Pregnancy
- Obesity
- Use of oral contraceptives

PHYSICAL FINDINGS & CLINICAL PRESENTATION

- Visible tortuous veins in the territory of either the long saphenous vein (most common), short saphenous vein, or both.
- Dull ache, burning, or cramping in leg muscles
- Worsening discomfort with standing, warm temperatures, or menses
- Blowouts-localized dilatations
- Tortuous dilation of superficial veins
- Dermatitis, hyper/hypopigmentation, edema, eczema
- Varicose ulcer, sometimes with superficial infection

ETIOLOGY

- Normally, blood flow directed from the superficial venous system to the deep venous system via communication of perforating vessels
- Best thought of as "venous hypertension"
- Valvular incompetence in perforator veins of lower extremity leading to reverse flow of fluid from high-pressure deep venous system to low-pressure superficial venous system, resulting in dilation of superficial veins, leg edema, and pain
- Rarely associated with deep vein thrombophlebitis
- Exacerbated by restrictive clothing

DIAGNOSIS

DIFFERENTIAL DIAGNOSIS

Conditions that can lead to superficial venous stasis other than primary valvular insufficiency include:
- Arterial occlusive disease
- Diabetes
- Deep vein thrombophlebitis
- Peripheral neuropathies
- Unusual infections
- Carcinoma

WORKUP

- Mainly a clinical diagnosis—trendelenburg test
- Arterial studies to rule out arterial insufficiency before initiating therapy for venous insufficiency

LABORATORY TESTS

Not useful

IMAGING STUDIES

Duplex ultrasound
- Gold standard for evaluation of varicose veins
- Quantitation of flow through venous valves under direct visualization
- Allows precise anatomic identification of source of venous reflux
- Rarely ascending venography and varicography for unusually sited varices and recurrence after surgical treatment.

TREATMENT

NONPHARMACOLOGIC THERAPY

- Leg elevation and rest
- Graded compression stockings: used early in morning before edema accumulates and removed before going to bed
- Weight loss
- Avoidance of occlusive clothing

ACUTE GENERAL Rx

- For associated stasis dermatitis: topical corticosteroids
- Treatment of secondary infection with appropriate antibiotics

CHRONIC Rx

- Compression sclerotherapy: injection of 1%-3% solution of sodium tetradecyl sulfate or 5% ethanolamine oleate
- Surgery: indications include the following:
  1. Persistent varicosities with conservative treatment
  2. Failed sclerotherapy
  3. Previous or impending bleeding from ulcerated varicosities
  4. Disabling pain
  5. Cosmetic concerns
- Surgical methods include (must be combined with compressive therapy):
  1. Saphenous vein ligation
  2. Ligation of incompetent perforating veins
  3. Saphenous vein stripping with or without avulsion of varicosities
  4. Ambulatory "miniphlebectomies": avulsion of superficial varicosities with saphenous vein stripping
  5. New treatments: endovenous obliteration using radiofrequency (diathermy) or laser as an alternative to traditional stripping of the long saphenous vein and powered phlebectomy for avulsing calf varicosities.

COMPLICATIONS:
- Hemorrhage
- Thrombophlebitis
- Atrophie blanche
- Varicose eczema
- Lipodermatosclerosis
- Venous ulceration

DISPOSITION

A chronic condition in which a combination of compressive and surgical therapy can adequately control varicosities

REFERRAL

- To dermatologist for dermatitis complications
- To surgeon for failed conservative management or varicose veins with complications

SUGGESTED READINGS

Bradbury A et al: What are the symptoms of varicose veins? Edinburgh Vein Study cross sectional population survey, *BMJ* 318:353, 1999.

Crane J, Cheshire N: Recent developments in vascular surgery, *BMJ* 327(7420):911, 2003.

Hagen MD, Johnson ED: What treatments are effective for varicose veins? *J Fam Pract* 52(4):329, 2003.

AUTHOR: **ARUNDATHI G. PRASAD, M.D.**

BASIC INFORMATION

DEFINITION

- Ventricular septal defect (VSD) refers to an abnormal hole or opening in the septum separating the right and left ventricles.
- VSDs may be large or small, single or multiple.
- VSDs are located at various anatomic regions of the septum and classified as:
  1. Membranous (75%-80%): Most common defect that can extend into the vascular septum.
  2. Canal or inlet defects (8%): Commonly lie beneath the septal leaflet of the tricuspid valve and often seen in patients with Down syndrome.
  3. Muscular or trabecular defects (5%-20%): Can be single or multiple, small or large.
  4. Subarterial defect (5%-7%): Least common and also called outlet, infundibular, or supracristal defect. Commonly found beneath the aortic valve, leading to aortic valve prolapse and regurgitation.

SYNONYMS

VSD

ICD-9CM CODES
745.4 Ventricular septal defect

EPIDEMIOLOGY & DEMOGRAPHICS

- Isolated VSD is the most common congenital heart abnormality found at birth (excluding bicuspid aortic valve and mitral valve prolapse) and accounts for 30% of all congenital cardiac defects.
- Prevalence is 1.17 per 1000 live births and at 0.5 per 1000 adults.
- Found equally in males and females.
- VSD accounts for about 25% of all congenital heart defects in children and 10% in adults.
- VSDs may be associated with:
  1. Atrial septal defect (35%)
  2. Patent ductus arteriosus (22%)
  3. Coarctation of the aorta (17%)
  4. Subvalvular aortic stenosis (4%)
  5. Subpulmonic stenosis
- Multiple VSDs are more prevalent in patients with tetralogy of Fallot and double outlet right ventricular defects.

PHYSICAL FINDINGS & CLINICAL PRESENTATION

- Clinical presentation is dictated by the size of the defect and the direction and volume of the VSD shunt along with the ratio of the pulmonary to systemic vascular resistance.
- Infants at birth may be asymptomatic because of elevated pulmonary artery pressure and resistance. Over the next few weeks, pulmonary arterial resistance decreases, allowing more blood shunting through the VSD into the right ventricle, with subsequent increased flow into the lungs, left atrium, and left ventricle, causing LV volume overload. Tachypnea, failure to thrive, and congestive heart failure ensue.
- In adults with VSD, the shunt is left to right in the absence of pulmonary stenosis and pulmonary hypertension, and patients typically manifest with symptoms of heart failure (e.g., shortness of breath, orthopnea, and dyspnea on exertion).
- A spectrum of physical findings may be seen including:
  1. Polysystolic murmur heard best along the left sternal border
  2. Systolic thrill
  3. Mid-diastolic rumble heard at the apex
  4. S_3
  5. Rales
- With the development of pulmonary hypertension:
  1. Augmented pulmonic component of S_2
  2. Cyanosis, clubbing, right ventricular heave, and signs of right heart failure (seen in Eisenmenger's complex with reversal of the shunt in a right to left direction)

ETIOLOGY

- Usually congenital (focus of our review), but may occur postmyocardial infarction
- After acute myocardial infarction (MI): Rupture of the intraventricular septum typically occurs within 3-5 days after acture MI and occurs in up to 2% of MIs

DIAGNOSIS

The diagnosis of VSD is suspected by physical examination. Imaging studies, particularly transthoracic echocardiography, establishes the diagnosis.

DIFFERENTIAL DIAGNOSIS

Based on physical examination, the diagnosis of VSD may be confused with other causes of systolic murmurs such as mitral regurgitation, aortic stenosis, asymmetric septal hypertrophy, and pulmonary stenosis.

WORKUP

Any person that is suspected of having a VSD should have an ECG, a chest x-ray, and an echocardiogram and be considered for a cardiac catheterization and angiography.

LABORATORY TESTS

- Laboratory tests are not specific but may offer insight into the severity of the disease
- CBC may show polycythemia, especially in patients with Eisenmenger's complex
- Arterial blood gases showing hypoxemia

IMAGING STUDIES

- Chest x-ray findings in patients with VSD include:
  1. Cardiomegaly resulting from volume overload directly related to the magnitude of the shunt.
  2. Enlargement of the proximal pulmonary arteries along with redistribution and pruning of the distal pulmonary vessels resulting from sustained pulmonary hypertension (Fig. 1-251, *A*).
- ECG findings vary according to the size of the VSD and whether pulmonary hypertension is present or not. In large VSDs with pulmonary hypertension, right axis deviation is seen along with evidence of right ventricular hypertrophy.
- Echocardiography is the noninvasive procedure of choice in the diagnosis of VSD.
  1. Two-dimensional echo and color Doppler displays the size and location of the VSD (Fig. 1-251, *B*).
  2. Continuous wave Doppler not only approximates the gradient between the left and right ventricle but also estimates the pulmonary artery pressure.
- Cardiac catheterization measures right heart pressures and detects and estimates the size of the shunt by the calculation of the pulmonary to systemic flow ratio.
- Angiography also locates the VSD.

TREATMENT

The decision to treat a VSD depends on its type, size, shunt severity, pulmonary vascular resistance, functional capacity, and associated valvular abnormalities.

NONPHARMACOLOGIC THERAPY

- In young children, small asymptomatic VSDs with a pulmonary to systemic blood flow ratio of ≤1.5:1 and no evidence of pulmonary hypertension can be observed.

- Oxygen and low-salt diet is recommended in patients with congestive heart failure.

ACUTE GENERAL Rx

Surgery is indicated in:

- Infants with congestive heart failure
- Children between the ages of 1-6 with persistent VSD and apulmonary to systemic blood flow ratios >2:1
- Adults with VSD and flow ratios >1.5:1

Percutaneous transcatheter closure by umbrella or clamshell occluder devices are currently under investigation with anecdotal success.

CHRONIC Rx

See "Acute General Rx."

DISPOSITION

- The natural history of isolated VSD depends on the type of defect, its size, and associated abnormalities.
- Approximately 75%-80% of small VSDs close spontaneously by age 10 yr.
- In patients with large VSDs, only 10%-15% will close spontaneously.
- Large VSDs left untreated may lead to arrhythmias, congestive heart failure, pulmonary hypertension, and Eisenmenger's complex.
- Eisenmenger's complex carries a poor prognosis, with most patients dying before the age of 40 yr.

REFERRAL

All infants and children diagnosed with VSD should be referred to a pediatric cardiologist. Adults with VSD should be referred to a cardiologist. Cardiothoracic surgeons experienced in congenital heart disease surgery should be consulted if surgery is indicated.

PEARLS & CONSIDERATIONS

COMMENTS

- A loud murmur does not imply a large VSD. Small, hemodynamically insignificant VSDs can cause loud murmurs.
- In Eisenmenger's syndrome the right-to-left shunting across the VSD is usually not associated with an audible murmur.
- Ventricular septal defect was first described by Dalrymple in 1847.
- Risk of patients with VSD developing infective endocarditis is 4%. The risk is higher if aortic insufficiency is present.
- Bacterial endocarditis prophylaxis is recommended in all patients with VSD.
- Postoperatively, if no shunt remains, endocarditis prophylaxis is not indicated after 6 mo.

SUGGESTED READINGS

Ammash NM, Warnes CA: Ventricular septal defects in adults, *Ann Intern Med* 135:812, 2001.

Braunwald: *Heart disease: a textbook of cardiovascular medicine,* ed 6, Philadelphia, 2001, WB Saunders.

Congenital heart disease and vascular interventions, *Am J Cardiol* 88(Suppl 5A):118G, 2001.

Interventional approaches to septal defects, valve disease, and hypertrophic cardiomyopathy, *Am J Cardiol* 92(6A): 160L, 2003.

McDaniel NL: Ventricular and atrial septal defects, *Pediatr Rev* 22(8):265, 2001.

Merrick AF et al: Management of ventricular septal defect: a survey of practice in the United Kingdom, *Ann Thorac Surg* 68(3):983, 1999.

Turner SW, Hunter S, Wyllie JP: The natural history of ventricular septal defects, *Arch Dis Child* 81(5):413, 1999.

AUTHOR: **GAURAV CHOUDHARY, M.D.,** and **WEN-CHIH WU, M.D.**

A

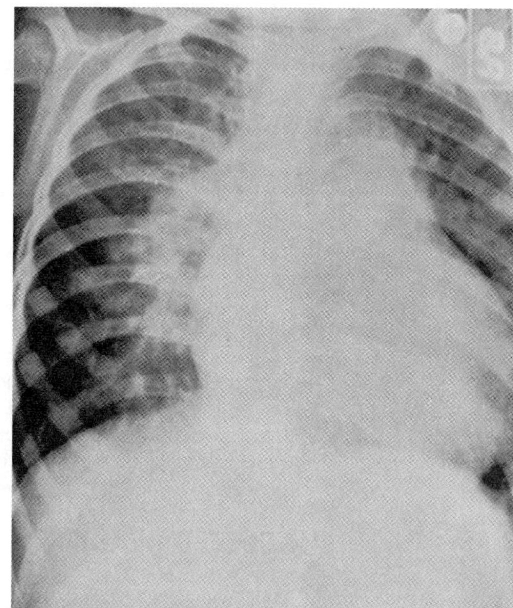

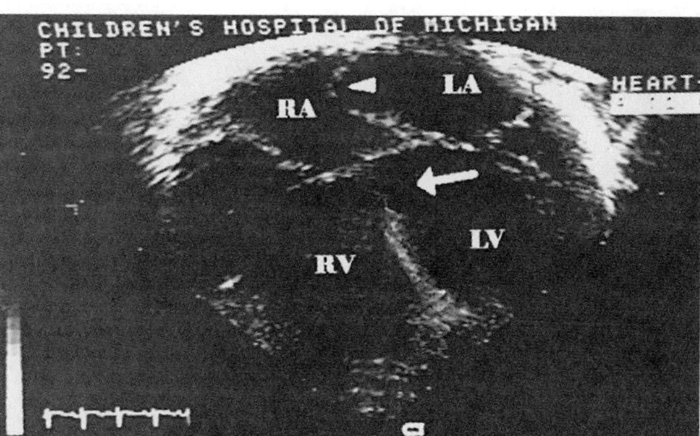

B

FIGURE 1-251 **A,** Chest roentgenogram of a child with a large VSD, large pulmonary blood flow, and pulmonary hypertension, but only mild elevation of PVR. This is reflected in the evidence of left and right ventricular enlargement, enlargement of the main pulmonary artery, and marked increase in pulmonary blood flow. **B,** Apical four-chamber echocardiographic view of ventricular septal defect *(large arrow).* Small arrow points to interatrial septum. *RA,* Right atrium; *LA,* left atrium; *RV,* right ventricle; *LV,* left ventricle. (**A** From Pacifico AD, Kirklin JW, Kirklin JK: Surgical treatment of ventricular septal defect. In Sabiston DC, Jr, spencer FC [eds]: *Surgery of the chest,* ed 5, Philadelphia, 1990, WB Saunders. **B** Courtesty Richard Humes, M.D., Associate Professor of Pediatrics, Director of Echocardiography Laboratory, Children's Hospital of Michigan, Detroit.)

BASIC INFORMATION

DEFINITION

Vitiligo is the acquired loss of epidermal pigmentation characterized histologically by the absence of epidermal melanocytes.

ICD-9CM CODES
709.1 Vitiligo

EPIDEMIOLOGY & DEMOGRAPHICS

- Prevalence: 1% of the population
- Positive family history in 25%-30%
- Can begin at any age, but age at onset is under 20 yr for half the patients

CLINICAL PRESENTATION & PHYSICAL FINDINGS

- Hypopigmented and depigmented lesions (Fig. 1-252) favor sun-exposed regions, intertriginous areas, genitalia, and sites over bony prominences (type A vitiligo).
- Areas around body orifices are also frequently involved.
- The lesions tend to be symmetric.
- Occasionally the lesions are linear or pseudodermatomal (type B vitiligo).
- Vitiligo lesions may occur at trauma sites (Koebner's phenomenon).
- The hair in affected areas may be white.
- The margins of the lesions are usually well demarcated, and when a ring of hyperpigmentation is seen, the term *trichrome vitiligo* is used.
- The term *marginal inflammatory vitiligo* is used to describe lesions with raised borders.
- Initially the disease is limited, but the lesions tend to become more extensive over the years.
- Type B vitiligo is more common in children.
- Vitiligo may begin around pigmented nevi, producing a halo (Sutton's nevus); in such cases the central nevus often regresses and disappears over time.

ETIOLOGY & PATHOGENESIS

Three pathophysiologic theories:
- Autoimmune theory (autoantibodies against melanocytes)
- Neural theory (neurochemical mediator selectively destroys melanocytes)
- Self-destructive process whereby melanocytes fail to protect themselves against cytotoxic melanin precursors

Although vitiligo is considered to be an acquired disease, 25%-30% is familial; the mode of transmission is unknown (polygenic or autosomal dominant with incomplete penetrance and variable expression).

Associated disorders:
- Alopecia areata
- Type 1 diabetes mellitus
- Adrenal insufficiency
- Hyper- and hypothyroidism
- Mucocutaneous candidiasis
- Pernicious anemia
- Polyglandular autoimmune syndromes
- Melanoma

DIAGNOSIS

DIFFERENTIAL DIAGNOSIS (OTHER HYPOPIGMENTATION DISORDERS)

Acquired:
- Chemical-induced
- Halo nevus
- Idiopathic guttate hypomelanosis
- Leprosy
- Leukoderma associated with melanoma
- Pityriasis alba
- Postinflammatory hypopigmentation
- Tinea versicolor
- Vogt-Koyanagi syndrome (vitiligo, uveitis, and deafness)

Congenital:
- Albinism, partial (piebaldism)
- Albinism, total
- Nevus anemicus
- Nevus depigmentosus
- Tuberous sclerosis

WORKUP

- Physical examination
- Wood's light examination may enhance lesions in light-skinned individuals

TREATMENT

- Treatment indicated primarily for cosmetic purposes when depigmentation causes emotional or social distress. Depigmentation is more noticeable in darker complexions.
- Cosmetic masking agents (Dermablend, Covermark) or stains (Dy-O-Derm, Vita-Dye).
- Sunless tanning lotions (dihydroxyacetone).
- Repigmentation (achieved by activation and migration of melanocytes from hair follicles; therefore skin with little or no hair responds poorly to treatment).
- PUVA (psoralen phototherapy): oral or topical psoralen administration followed by phototherapy with UVA (150-200 treatments required over 1-2 yr).
- Psoralens and sunlight (Puvasol).
- Topical midpotency steroids (e.g., triamcinolone 0.1% or desonide 0.05% cream qd for 3-4 mo).
- Intralesional steroid injection.
- Systemic steroids (betamethasone 5 mg qd on two consecutive days per wk for 2-4 mo).
- Total depigmentation (in cases of extensive vitiligo) with 20% monobenzyl ether or hydroquinone. This is a permanent procedure, and patients will require lifelong protection from sun exposure.

SUGGESTED READING

Habif TP: Vitiligo. In Habif TP (ed): *Clinical dermatology,* ed 3, St Louis, 1996, Mosby.

AUTHOR: **TOM J. WACHTEL, M.D.**

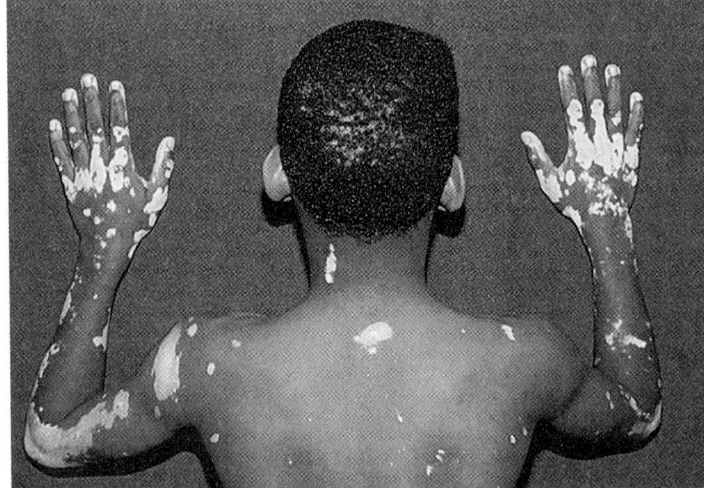

FIGURE 1-252 Multiple, sharply demarcated, symmetric, depigmented areas of vitiligo. (From Behrman RE: *Nelson textbook of pediatrics,* Philadelphia, 1996, WB Saunders.)

BASIC INFORMATION

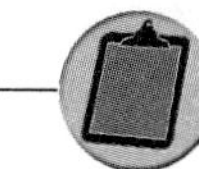

DEFINITION

Von Hippel-Lindau disease (VHL) is an autosomal dominant inherited disease characterized by the formation of hemangioblastomas, cysts, and malignancies involving multiple organs and systems.

SYNONYMS

Hippel-Lindau syndrome
Cerebelloretinal hemangioblastomatosis
Retinocerebellar angiomatosis

ICD-9CM CODE
759.6 von Hippel-Lindau disease

EPIDEMIOLOGY & DEMOGRAPHICS

- The incidence of VHL is 1 case/36,000 people.
- Age of onset varies but usually presents between the ages of 25-40 yr.
- In the U.S. approximately 7000 people are affected.
- Affected individuals are at risk of developing renal cell carcinoma, pheochromocytoma, pancreatic islet cell tumor, endolymphatic sac tumor, and hemangioblastomas of the cerebellum and retina.

PHYSICAL FINDINGS & CLINICAL PRESENTATION

- Retinal angiomas (59%)
  1. Most common presentation usually occurs by age 25
  2. Multiple angiomas
  3. Detached retina
  4. Glaucoma
  5. Blindness
- CNS hemangioblastomas (59%)
  1. Cerebellum is the most common site followed by the spine and medulla
  2. Usually multiple and occurs by the age of 30
  3. Headache, ataxia, slurred speech, nystagmus, vertigo, nausea, and vomiting
- Renal cysts (~60%) and clear cell renal cell carcinoma (25%-45%)
  1. Usually occurs by the age of 40
  2. May be asymptomatic or cause abdominal and flank pain
  3. Renal cell carcinoma is bilateral in 75% of patients
- Pancreatic cysts
  1. Usually asymptomatic
  2. Large cysts can cause biliary obstructive symptoms
  3. Diarrhea and diabetes may develop if enough of the pancreas is replaced by cysts
- Pheochromocytoma (7%-18%)
  1. Bilateral in 50%-80% of cases
  2. Hypertension, palpitations, sweating, and headache
  3. Commonly occurs with pancreatic islet cell tumors
- Papillary cystadenoma of the epididymis (10%-25% of men with VHL)
  1. Palpable scrotal mass
  2. May be unilateral or bilateral
- Endolymphatic sac tumors
  1. Ataxia
  2. Loss of hearing
  3. Facial paralysis

ETIOLOGY

VHL disease is primarily caused by a mutation of the von Hippel-Lindau gene located on chromosome 3. The VHL disease gene codes for a cytoplasmic protein that functions in tumor suppression.

DIAGNOSIS

- The diagnosis of VHL disease is established if in the presence of a positive family history, a single retinal or cerebellar hemangioblastoma is noted or a visceral lesion is found (e.g., renal cell carcinoma, pheochromocytoma, pancreatic cysts or tumor).
- If no clear family history is present, two or more hemangioblastomas or one hemangioblastoma with a visceral lesion are required to make the diagnosis.
- Screening family members is essential in the early detection of VHL disease.

WORKUP

All patients with VHL disease or patients at risk for the disease should have screening laboratory, ophthalmoscopic, and imaging studies performed to look for sites of involvement.

LABORATORY TESTS

- CBC may reveal erythrocytosis requiring periodic phlebotomies
- Electrolytes, BUN, and creatinine
- Urine for norepinephrine, epinephrine, and vanillylmandelic acid looking for pheochromocytoma

IMAGING STUDIES

- Indirect and direct ophthalmoscopy, fluorescein angioscopy, and tonometry are studies used in screening for retinal angiomas and glaucoma.
- CT scan of the abdomen is used in the screening, detection, and monitoring of patients with renal cysts renal tumors, pheochromocytomas, pancreatic cysts, and tumors.
  1. Renal cysts grow on average 0.5 cm/yr.
  2. Renal tumors grow on average 1.5 cm/yr.
  3. CT scans are done every 6 mo for the first 2 yr and every year for life in patients who have had surgery for renal cell carcinoma.
- MRI with gadolinium is used for screening and evaluation of CNS and spinal hemangioblastomas, endolymphatic sac tumors, and pheochromocytomas.
- Angiography may be done before CNS surgery.

TREATMENT

NONPHARMACOLOGIC THERAPY

Genetic counseling

ACUTE GENERAL Rx

- Laser photocoagulation and cryotherapy is used in patients with retinal angiomas to prevent blindness.
- For cerebellar hemangioblastomas the treatment is surgical removal. External-beam radiation and stereotaxic radiosurgery can also be done.
- For renal tumors, surgery is delayed until one of the renal tumors reaches 3 cm in diameter. Nephron-sparing surgery is the preferred surgical approach.
- Nephrectomy is indicated in patients with end-stage renal disease requiring dialysis because of the malignant potential of the disease.
- Pancreatic islet cell tumors usually require surgical removal.
- Adrenalectomy for pheochromocytoma.

CHRONIC Rx

- Dialysis has been delayed in many patients because of nephron-sparing surgery.
- Renal transplantation is usually delayed for 1 yr after bilateral nephrectomy for renal tumors so as to ensure that no metastases occur.

DISPOSITION

- Median life expectancy is 49 yr of age.
- The most common cause of death in VHL disease is from renal cell carcinoma.

REFERRAL

Geneticist, neurosurgeon, urologist, nephrologist, ophthalmologist, otolaryngologist, neurologist, endocrinologist, and radiation oncologist.

PEARLS & CONSIDERATIONS

COMMENTS

Patients interested in learning more von Hippel-Lindau Family Alliance (171 Clinton Road, Brookline, MA 02146. Tel: 1-800-767-4VHL).

SUGGESTED READINGS

Couch V et al: von Hippel-Lindau Disease, *Mayo Clin Proc* 75:265, 2000.
Zbar B et al: Third International meeting on von Hippel-Lindau disease, *Cancer Res* 59:2251, 1999.

AUTHOR: **PETER PETROPOULOS, M.D.**

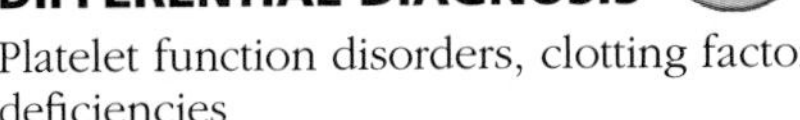

BASIC INFORMATION

DEFINITION

Von Willebrand's disease is a congenital disorder of hemostasis characterized by defective or deficient von Willebrand factor (vWF). There are several subtypes of von Willebrand's disease. The most common type (80% of cases) is type I, which is caused by a quantitative decrease in von Willebrand factor; type IIA and type IIB are results of qualitative protein abnormalities; type III is a rare autosomal recessive disorder characterized by a near complete quantitative deficiency of vWF. *Acquired von Willebrand's disease (AvWD)* is a rare disorder that usually occurs in elderly patients and usually presents with mucocutaneous bleeding abnormalities and no clinically meaningful family history. It is often accompanied by a hematoproliferative or autoimmune disorder. Successful treatment of the associated illness can reverse the clinical and laboratory manifestations.

SYNONYMS

Pseudohemophilia

ICD-9CM CODES
286.4 von Willebrand's disease

EPIDEMIOLOGY & DEMOGRAPHICS

- Autosomal dominant disorder
- Most common inherited bleeding disorder
- Occurs in >100/1 million persons

PHYSICAL FINDINGS & CLINICAL PRESENTATION

- Generally normal physical examination
- Mucosal bleeding (gingival bleeding, epistaxis) and GI bleeding may occur
- Easy bruising
- Postpartum bleeding, bleeding after surgery or dental extraction, menorrhagia

ETIOLOGY

Quantitative or qualitative deficiency of vWF (see "Definition")

DIAGNOSIS

DIFFERENTIAL DIAGNOSIS

Platelet function disorders, clotting factor deficiencies

WORKUP

- Laboratory evaluation (see "Laboratory Tests")
- Initial testing includes PTT (increased), platelet count (normal), and bleeding time (prolonged)
- Subsequent tests include vWF level (decreased), factor VIII:C (decreased), and ristocetin agglutination (increased in type II B) (Table 1-53)

LABORATORY TESTS

- Normal platelet number and morphology
- Prolonged bleeding time
- Decreased factor VIII coagulant activity
- Decreased von Willebrand factor antigen or ristocetin cofactor
- Normal platelet aggregation studies
- Type II A von Willebrand can be distinguished from type I by absence of ristocetin cofactor activity and abnormal multimer
- Type IIB von Willebrand is distinguished from type I by abnormal multimer

TREATMENT

NONPHARMACOLOGIC THERAPY

- Avoidance of aspirin and other NSAIDs.
- Evaluation for likelihood of bleeding (with measurement of bleeding time) before surgical procedures. When a patient undergoes surgery or receives repeated therapeutic doses of concentrates, factor VIII activity should be assayed every 12 hr on the day a dose is administered and every 24 hr thereafter.

GENERAL Rx

- The mainstay of treatment in von Willebrand's disease is the replacement of the deficient protein at the time of spontaneous bleeding, or before invasive procedures are performed.
- Desmopressin acetate (DDAVP) is useful to release stored vWF from endothelial cells. It is used to cover minor procedures and traumatic bleeding in mild type I von Willebrand's disease. Dose is 0.3 μg/kg in 100 ml of normal saline solution IV infused >20 min. DDAVP is also available as a nasal spray (dose of 150 μg spray administered to each nostril) as a preparation for minor surgery and management of minor bleeding episodes. DDAVP is not effective in type IIA von Willebrand's disease and is potentially dangerous in type IIB (increased risk of bleeding and thrombocytopenia).
- In patients with severe disease, replacement therapy in the form of cryoprecipitate is the method of choice. The standard dose is 1 bag of cryoprecipitate per 10 kg of body weight.
- Factor VIII concentrate rich in vWF (Humate-P, Armour) is useful to correct bleeding abnormalities.
- Life-threatening hemorrhage unresponsive to therapy with cryoprecipitate or factor VIII concentrate may require transfusion of normal platelets.

DISPOSITION

Prognosis is very good; most patients have minor bleeding complications and are able to lead a normal life.

SUGGESTED READINGS

Kumar S et al: Acquired von Willebrand disease, *Mayo Clin Proc* 77:181, 2002.
Mannucci PM: Treatment of von Willebrand's disease, *N Engl J Med* 351:683, 2004.

AUTHOR: **FRED F. FERRI, M.D.**

TABLE 1-53 **Genetic and Laboratory Findings in von Willebrand's Disease**

PARAMETER							
Type	BT	VIII-c	vw-Ag	R-cof	Ripa	Multimer Structure	Mode of Inheritance
I (classic)	P	R	R	R	R	N	AD
II							
A	P	N/R	N/R	R	R	Abn	AD
B	P	N/R	N/R	N/R	I	Abn	AD
III	P	R	R	R	R	Variable	AR

From Behrman RE: *Nelson textbook of pediatrics,* ed 15, Philadelphia, 1996, WB Saunders.
Abn, abnormal; *AD,* autosomal dominant; *AR,* autosomal recessive; *BT,* bleeding time; *I,* increased; *N,* normal; *N/R,* normal or reduced; *P,* prolonged; *R,* reduced; *R-Cof,* ristocetin cofactor; *RIPA,* ristocetin-induced platelet aggregation (agglutination); *vW-Ag,* von Willebrand antigen (protein); *VIII-C,* factor VIII coagulant activity.

BASIC INFORMATION

DEFINITION

Vulvar cancer is an abnormal cell proliferation arising on the vulva and exhibiting malignant potential. The majority are of squamous cell origin; however, other types include adenocarcinoma, basal cell carcinoma, sarcoma, and melanoma (Fig. 1-253).

SYNONYMS

Squamous cell carcinoma of the vulva (90%)
Basal cell carcinoma of the vulva
Adenocarcinoma of the vulva
Melanoma of the vulva
Bartholin gland carcinoma
Verrucous carcinoma of the vulva
Vulvar sarcoma

ICD-9CM CODES
184.4 Vulvar neoplasm

EPIDEMIOLOGY & DEMOGRAPHICS

PREVALENCE: Vulvar cancer is uncommon. It comprises 4% of malignancies of the female genital tract. It is the fourth most common gynecologic malignancy.
INCIDENCE: 1.8 cases/100,000 persons

MEAN AGE AT DIAGNOSIS: Predominantly a disease of menopause. Mean age at diagnosis is 65 yr.

PHYSICAL FINDINGS & CLINICAL PRESENTATION

- Vulvar pruritus or pain is present.
- May produce a malodor or discharge or present as bleeding.
- Raised lesion, may have fleshy, ulcerated, leukoplakic, or warty appearance; may have multifocal lesions.
- Lesions are usually located on labia majora, but may be seen on labia minora, clitoris, and perineum.
- The lymph nodes of groin may be palpable.

ETIOLOGY

- The exact etiology is unknown.
- Vulvar intraepithelial neoplasia has been reported in 20%-30% of invasive squamous cell carcinoma of the vulva, but the malignant potential is unknown.
- Human papillomavirus is found in 30%-50% of vulvar carcinoma, but its exact role is unclear.
- Chronic pruritus, wetness, industrial wastes, arsenicals, hygienic agents, and vulvar dystrophies have been implicated as causative agents.

A

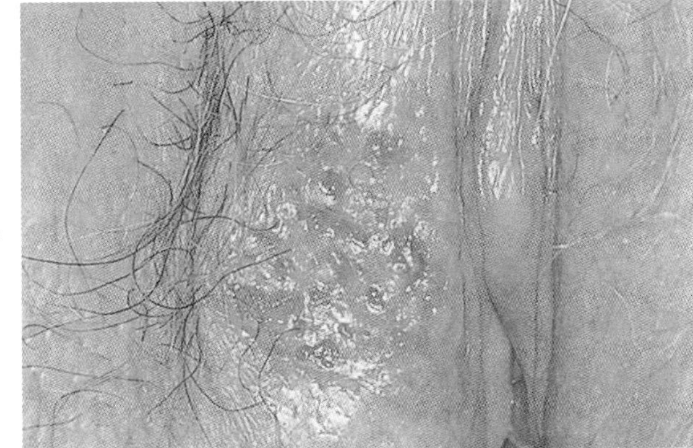

B

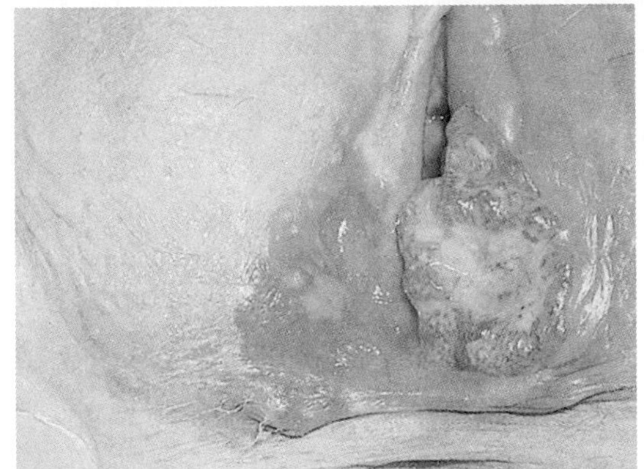

FIGURE 1-253 A, Basal cell carcinoma of the vulva. **B,** Ulcerative squamous cell carcinoma of the vulva. (From Symonds EM, Macpherson MBA: *Color atlas of obstetrics and gynecology,* St Louis, 1994, Mosby.)

DIAGNOSIS

DIFFERENTIAL DIAGNOSIS

- Lymphogranuloma inguinale
- Tuberculosis
- Vulvar dystrophies
- Vulvar atrophy
- Paget's disease

WORKUP

- Diagnosis is made histologically by biopsy
- Thorough examination of the lesion and assessment of spread
- Possible colposcopy of adjacent areas
- Cytologic smear of vagina and cervix
- Cystoscopy and proctosigmoidoscopy may be necessary

IMAGING STUDIES

- Chest radiography
- CT scan and MRI for assessing local tumor spread

TREATMENT

NONPHARMACOLOGIC THERAPY

- Treatment is individualized depending on the stage of the tumor.
- Stage I tumors with <1 mm stromal invasion are treated with complete local excision without groin node dissection.
- Stage I tumors with >1 mm stromal invasion are treated with complete local excision with groin node dissection.
- Stage II tumors require radical vulvectomy with bilateral groin node dissection.
- Advanced-stage disease may require the addition of radiation and chemotherapy to the surgical regimen.
- Section III describes a treatment algorithm for management of vulvar cancer.

DISPOSITION

Five-year survival ranges from 90% for stage I to 15% for stage IV.

REFERRAL

Vulvar cancer should be managed by a gynecologic oncologist and radiation oncologist.

SUGGESTED READINGS

Canavan TP, Cohen D: Vulvar cancer, *Am Fam Physician* 66(7):1269, 2002.
Coleman RL, Santoso JT: Vulvar carcinoma, *Curr Treat Opt Oncol* 1(2):177, 2000.
Grandys EC Jr, Aroris JV: Innovations in the management of vulvar carcinoma, *Curr Opin Obstet Gynecol* 12(1):15, 2000.

AUTHOR: **GIL FARKASH, M.D.**

 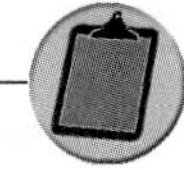

BASIC INFORMATION

DEFINITION

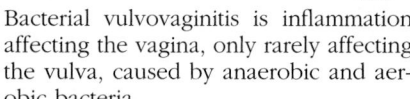

Bacterial vulvovaginitis is inflammation affecting the vagina, only rarely affecting the vulva, caused by anaerobic and aerobic bacteria.

SYNONYMS

Bacterial vaginosis
Gardnerella vaginalis
Haemophilus vaginalis
Corynebacterium vaginalis

ICD-9CM CODES
616.10 Vulvovaginitis

EPIDEMIOLOGY & DEMOGRAPHICS

- Most prevalent form of vaginal infection of reproductive age women in the U.S.
- 32%-64% in patients visiting STD clinics
- 12%-25% in other clinic populations
- 10%-26% in patients visiting obstetric clinics
- May be associated with adverse pregnancy outcomes: premature rupture of membranes, preterm labor, preterm birth
- Organisms frequently found in postpartum or postcesarean endometritis

PHYSICAL FINDINGS & CLINICAL PRESENTATION

- >50% of all women may be without symptoms.
- Unpleasant, fishy, or musty vaginal odor in about 50%-70% of all patients. Odor exacerbated immediately after intercourse or during menstruation.
- Vaginal discharge is increased.
- Vaginal itching and irritation occur.

ETIOLOGY

- Synergistic polymicrobial infection characterized by an overgrowth of bacteria normally found in the vagina
- Anaerobics: *Bacteroides* spp., *Peptostreptococcus* spp., *Mobiluncus* spp.
- Facultative anaerobes: *G. vaginalis, Mycoplasma hominis*
- Concentration of anaerobic bacteria increased to 100 to 1000 times normal
- Lactobacilli are absent or greatly reduced

DIAGNOSIS

DIFFERENTIAL DIAGNOSIS

- Fungal vaginitis
- *Trichomonas* vaginitis
- Atrophic vaginitis
- Cervicitis

WORKUP

- Pelvic examination
- Speculum examination
- Normal saline and 10% KOH slide of discharge
- Amsel criteria for diagnosis (three of four should be present):
  1. pH >4.5
  2. Clue cells (epithelial cells covered with bacteria) on saline solution slide
  3. Positive whiff test on 10% KOH
  4. Homogeneous, white, adherent discharge
- Section III, "Vaginal Discharge," describes the evaluation of discharge.

TREATMENT

ACUTE GENERAL Rx

- Metronidazole 500 mg PO bid × 7 days, >90% cure rate
- Metronidazole 2 g PO × 1 day, 67% to 92% cure rate
- Metronidazole gel 5 g, intravaginal bid × 5 days
- Clindamycin 2% cream 5 g, intravaginal qd × 7 days
- Clindamycin 300 mg PO bid × 7 days in pregnancy

CHRONIC Rx

Clindamycin 300 mg PO bid × 7 days; cure rate similar to those achieved with metronidazole
Related to adverse pregnancy outcomes
- Metronidazole 250 mg PO bid × 7 days
- Metronidazole zympoxidase
- Clindamycin 300 mg PO bid × 7 days
- Good hygiene: avoidance of douching, harsh shower gels, bubble baths; cotton underwear

DISPOSITION

- Reevaluate if not cured with treatment
- Recurrence fairly common

REFERRAL

Refer to obstetrician/gynecologist for recurrence or pregnant patient with bacterial vaginosis

PEARLS & CONSIDERATIONS

COMMENTS

Treating sexual partners has failed to demonstrate a benefit.

SUGGESTED READINGS

Centers for Disease Control and Prevention: 2002 Guidelines for treatment of sexually transmitted diseases, *MMWR, Morb Mortal Wkly Rep,* 51 (RR-6), 2002.

Mead P, Hager WD, Faro S: *Protocols for infectious diseases in obstetrics and gynecology,* ed 2, New York, 2000, Blackwell Science.

AUTHOR: **JULIE ANNE SZUMIGALA, M.D.**

BASIC INFORMATION

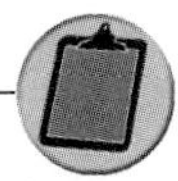

DEFINITION

Estrogen-deficient vulvovaginitis is the irritation and/or inflammation of the vulva and vagina because of progressive thinning and atrophic changes secondary to estrogen deficiency (Fig. 1-254).

SYNONYMS

Atrophic vaginitis

ICD-9CM CODES
616.10 Vulvovaginitis

EPIDEMIOLOGY & DEMOGRAPHICS

- Seen most often in postmenopausal women
- Average age of menopause is 52 yr
- In 1990, there were 36 million women 50 yr of age or older

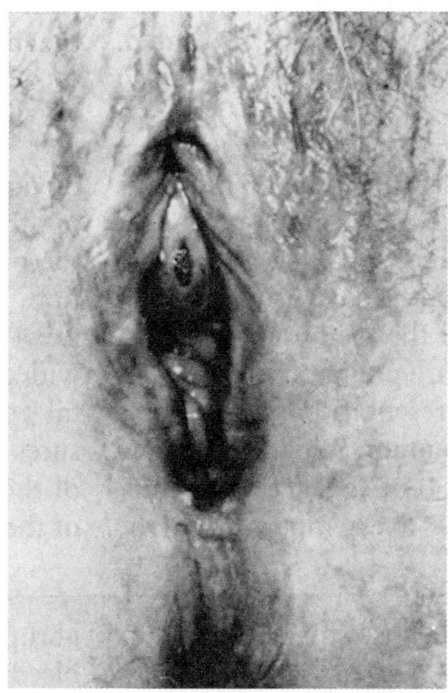

FIGURE 1-254 Advanced postmenopausal atrophy of the vulva in a 72-year-old woman. (From Symonds EM, Macpherson MBA: *Color atlas of obstetrics and gynecology,* St Louis, 1994, Mosby.)

PHYSICAL FINDINGS & CLINICAL PRESENTATION

- Thinning of pubic hair, labia minora and majora
- Decreased secretions from the vestibular glands, with vaginal dryness
- Regression of subcutaneous fat
- Vulvar and vaginal itching
- Dyspareunia
- Dysuria and urinary frequency
- Vaginal spotting

ETIOLOGY

Estrogen deficiency

DIAGNOSIS

DIFFERENTIAL DIAGNOSIS

- Infectious vulvovaginitis
- Squamous cell hyperplasia
- Lichen sclerosus
- Vulva malignancy
- Vaginal malignancy
- Cervical and endometrial malignancy

WORKUP

- Pelvic examination
- Speculum examination
- Pap smear
- Possible endometrial biopsy if bleeding

LABORATORY TESTS

FSH and estradiol: generally after menopause, estradiol <15 pg and FSH >40 mIU/ml

TREATMENT

ACUTE GENERAL Rx

- Premarin 0.625 mg PO qd
- Estraderm patch 0.05 mg × 2 per week
- If uterus present:
  1. Estrogen + 2.5 mg PO Provera qd
     or
  2. Estrogen + 10 mg PO Provera × 10 days each mo
- Conjugated estrogen vaginal cream intravaginally. Estradiol vaginal cream 0.01%
  2 to 4 g/day × 2 wk then
  1 to 2 g/day × 2 wk then
  1 to 2 g × 3 days/wk
- Vagifen (estradial vaginal tablets) 25 mg inserted intravaginally daily for 2 wk then twice weekly. May take up to 12 wk to feel the full benefits of the medication.
- Conjugated estrogen vaginal cream: 2-4 g qd (3 wk on, 1 wk off) for 3-5 mo.

CHRONIC Rx

See "Acute General Rx." May discontinue vaginal estrogen cream once symptoms alleviate.

DISPOSITION

The symptoms should be improved with the therapy. Caution for vaginal bleeding if uterus present

REFERRAL

To obstetrician/gynecologist if vaginal bleeding

SUGGESTED READING

Bornstein J et al: The classic approach to diagnosis of vulvovaginitis: a critical analysis, *Infect Dis Obstet Gynecol* 9(2):105, 2001.

AUTHOR: **JULIE ANNE SZUMIGALA, M.D.**

BASIC INFORMATION

DEFINITION

Fungal vulvovaginitis is the inflammation of vulva and vagina caused by *Candida* spp.

SYNONYMS

Monilial vulvovaginitis

ICD-9CM CODES
112.1 Vulvovaginitis, monilial

EPIDEMIOLOGY & DEMOGRAPHICS

- Second most common cause of vaginal infection.
- Approximately 13 million people were affected in 1990.
- 75% of women will have at least one episode during their childbearing years, and approximately 40%-50% of these will experience a second attack.
- No symptoms in 20%-40% of women who have positive cultures.

PHYSICAL FINDINGS & CLINICAL PRESENTATION

- Intense vulvar and vaginal pruritus
- Edema and erythema of vulva
- Thick, curdlike vaginal discharge
- Adherent, dry, white, curdy patches attached to vaginal mucosa

ETIOLOGY

- *Candida albicans* is responsible for 80%-95% of vaginal fungal infections.
- *Candida tropicalis* and *Torulopsis glabrata (Candida glabrata)* are the most common nonalbicans *Candida* species that can induce vaginitis.

PREDISPOSING HOST FACTORS

- Pregnancy
- Oral contraceptives (high-estrogen)
- Diabetes mellitus
- Antibiotics
- Immunosuppression
- Tight, poorly ventilated, nylon underclothing, with increased local perineal moisture and temperature

DIAGNOSIS

DIFFERENTIAL DIAGNOSIS

- Bacterial vaginosis
- *Trichomonas* vaginitis
- Atrophic vaginitis
- Section II describes the differential diagnosis of vaginal discharges and infections

WORKUP

- Pelvic examination
- Speculum examination
- Hyphae or budding spores on 10% KOH preparation (positive in 50%-70% of individuals with yeast infection)
- Section III, "Vaginal Discharge," describes the evaluation of discharge

LABORATORY TESTS

Culture, especially recurrence for identification

TREATMENT

ACUTE GENERAL Rx

- Cure rate of the various azole derivatives 85%-90%; little evidence of superiority of one azole agent over another
- No significant differences in persistent symptoms with oral or vaginal treatment
- Fluconazole (oral) associated with increased frequency of mild nausea, headache, abdominal pain
- Cure rate of polyene (Nystatin) cream and suppositories, 75%-80%
- Miconazole 200-mg suppository (Monistat 3), one suppository × 3 or 2% vaginal cream (Monistat 7), one applicator full intravaginally qhs × 7
- Clotrimazole 200-mg vaginal tablet, one tablet intravaginally qhs × 3 or 100-mg vaginal tablet (Gyne-Lotrimin, Mycelex-G) one tablet intravaginally qhs × 7, or 1% vaginal cream intravaginally qhs × 7
- Butoconazole 2% cream (Femstat) one applicator intravaginally qhs × 3
- Terconazole 80-mg suppository or 0.8% vaginal cream (Terazol 3), one suppository or one applicator intravaginally qhs × 3 or 0.4% vaginal cream (Terazol 7), one applicator intravaginally qhs × 7
- Gynecazole-1 vaginal cream one applicator intravaginally × 1
- Tioconazole 6.5% ointment (Vagi-stat), one applicator intravaginally × 1
- Fluconazole (Diflucan) 150 mg PO × 1

CHRONIC Rx (FOUR OR MORE SYMPTOMATIC EPISODES/YR)

- Resistance or recurrence
  1. 14- to 21-day course of 7-day regimens mentioned in "Acute General Rx"
  2. Fluconazole (Diflucan) 150 mg PO × 1
  3. Ketoconazole (Nizoral) 200 mg PO bid × 5-14 days
  4. Itraconazole (Sporanox) 200 mg PO qd × 3 days
  5. Boric acid 600-mg capsule intravaginally bid × 14 days
- Prophylactic regimens
  1. Clotrimazole one 500-mg vaginal tablet each month
  2. Ketoconazole 200 mg PO bid × 5 days each month
  3. Fluconazole 150 mg PO × 1 each month
  4. Miconazole 100-mg vaginal tablet × 2 weekly

DISPOSITION

- Approximately 40% of adult women experience more than one lifetime episode of fungal vulvovaginitis.
- If symptoms do not resolve completely with treatment, or if they recur within a 2- to 3-mo period, further evaluation is indicated.
- Reexamination and possibly culture are necessary.
- Positive culture in absence of symptoms should not lead to treatment. Approximately 30% of women harbor *Candida* spp. and other species in the vagina.

REFERRAL

To obstetrician/gynecologist for recurrence

PEARLS & CONSIDERATIONS

COMMENTS

- Treatment of sexual partner is not recommended.
- No evidence that treating a woman's male sexual partner significantly improves woman's infection or reduced their rate of relapse.

SUGGESTED READINGS

Marazzo J: Vulvovaginal candidiasis, *Clin Concise* 7:346, 2002.

Nyirjesy P: Chronic vulvovaginal candidiasis, *Am Fam Physician* 63:687, 2001.

Spinius A et al: Effect of antibiotic use on the prevalence of symptomatic vulvovaginal candidiasis, *Am J Obstet Gynecol* 180:14, 1999.

AUTHOR: **JULIE ANNE SZUMIGALA, M.D.**

BASIC INFORMATION

DEFINITION

Prepubescent vulvovaginitis is an inflammatory condition of vulva and vagina.

ICD-9CM CODES
616.10 Vulvovaginitis

EPIDEMIOLOGY & DEMOGRAPHICS

- Most common gynecologic problem of the premenarcheal female.
- Prepubertal girl is susceptible to irritation and trauma because of the absence of protective hair and labial fat pads and the lack of estrogenization with atrophic vaginal mucosa.
- Symptoms of vulvovaginitis and introital irritation and discharge account for 80%-90% of gynecologic visits.
- Nonspecific etiology in approximately 75% of children with vulvovaginitis.
- Majority of vulvovaginitis in children involves a primary irritation of the vulva with secondary involvement of the lower one third of the vagina.

PHYSICAL FINDINGS & CLINICAL PRESENTATION

- Vulvar pain, dysuria, pruritus
  1. Discharge is not a primary symptom.
  2. If present, vaginal discharge may be foul smelling or bloody.

ETIOLOGY

- Infections
  1. Bacterial
  2. Protozoal
  3. Mycotic
  4. Viral
- Endocrine disorders
- Labial adhesions
- Poor hygiene
- Sexual abuse
- Allergic substance
- Trauma
- Foreign body
- Masturbation
- Constipation
- Section II describes the differential diagnosis of vaginal discharge in prepubertal girls.

DIAGNOSIS

DIFFERENTIAL DIAGNOSIS

- Physiologic leukorrhea
- Foreign body
- Bacterial vaginosis
- Gonorrhea
- Fungal vulvovaginitis
- *Trichomonas* vulvovaginitis
- Sexual abuse
- Pinworms

WORKUP

- Pelvic, genital examination
- Speculum examination
- Rectal examination
- KOH and normal saline preparation of discharge
- Section III, "Vaginal Discharge," describes the evaluation of discharge

LABORATORY TESTS

- Urinalysis to rule out UTI and diabetes
- Cultures including STDs

TREATMENT

NONPHARMACOLOGIC THERAPY

- Avoid tight clothing
- Perineal hygiene
- Avoid irritant chemicals
- Reassurance

ACUTE GENERAL Rx

- Group A β *Streptococcus* and *Streptococcus pneumoniae:* penicillin V potassium 125-250 mg PO qid × 10 days
- *Chlamydia trachomatis:* erythromycin 50 mg/kg/day PO × 10 days
  1. Children >8 yr of age, doxycycline 100 mg bid PO × 7 days
- *Neisseria gonorrhoeae:* ceftriaxone 125 mg IM × 1 day
  1. Children >8 yr of age should also be given doxycycline 100 mg bid PO × 7 days
- *Staphylococcus aureus:* amoxicillin-clavulanate 20-40 mg/kg/day PO × 7 to 10 days
- *Haemophilus influenzae:* amoxicillin 20-40 mg/kg/day PO × 7 days
- *Trichomonas:* metronidazole 125 mg (15 mg/kg/day) tid PO × 7-10 days
- Pinworms: mebendazole 100-mg tablet chewable, repeat in 2 wk
- Labial agglutination: spontaneous resolution or topical estrogen cream for 7-10 days

CHRONIC Rx

See "Referral."

DISPOSITION

Further education:
- Young child: hygiene
- Adolescent: pregnancy prevention and "safe sex"

REFERRAL

- To obstetrician/gynecologist
- To pediatrician

SUGGESTED READING

Van Neer PA, Korver CR: Constipation presenting as recurrent vulvovaginitis in prepubertal children, *J Am Acad Dermatol* 43(4):718, 2000.

AUTHOR: **JULIE ANNE SZUMIGALA, M.D.**

BASIC INFORMATION

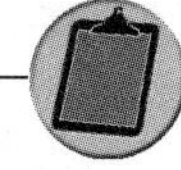

DEFINITION

Trichomonas vulvovaginitis is the inflammation of vulva and vagina caused by *Trichomonas* spp.

SYNONYMS

Trichomonas *vaginalis*

ICD-9CM CODES
131.01 Vulvovaginitis, trichomonal

EPIDEMIOLOGY & DEMOGRAPHICS

- Acquired through sexual contact
- Diagnosed in:
  1. 50%-75% of prostitutes
  2. 5%-15% of women visiting gynecology clinics
  3. 7%-32% of women in STD clinics
  4. 5% of women in family planning clinics

PHYSICAL FINDINGS & CLINICAL PRESENTATION

- Profuse, yellow, malodorous vaginal discharge and severe vaginal itching
- Vulvar itching
- Dysuria
- Dyspareunia
- Intense erythema of the vaginal mucosa
- Cervical petechiae ("strawberry cervix")
- Asymptomatic in approximately 50% of women and 90% of men

ETIOLOGY

Single-cell parasite known as *trichomonad*

RISK FACTORS

- Multiple sexual partners
- History of previous STDs

DIAGNOSIS

DIFFERENTIAL DIAGNOSIS (TABLE 1-54)

- Bacterial vaginosis
- Fungal vulvovaginitis
- Cervicitis
- Atrophic vulvovaginitis

WORKUP

- Pelvic examination
- Speculum examination
- Mobile trichomonads seen on normal saline preparation: 70% sensitivity
- Elevated pH (>5) of vaginal discharge
- Culture is most sensitive commercially available method
- A large number of inflammatory cells on normal saline preparation
- Section III describes the evaluation of vaginal discharge

LABORATORY TESTS

- Culture (modified Diamond media): 90% sensitivity
- Direct enzyme immunoassay
- Fluorescein-conjugated monoclonal antibody test
- Pap test 40% detected

TREATMENT

NONPHARMACOLOGIC THERAPY

Condom use

PHARMACOLOGIC THERAPY

Tindamax (tinidazole) single 2 grams oral dose in both sexes

ACUTE GENERAL Rx

Metronidazole (Flagyl) 2 g PO × 1 or 500 mg PO bid × 7 days

CHRONIC Rx

- Metronidazole gel: less likely to achieve therapeutic levels; therefore not recommended
- Metronidazole (retreat): 500 mg PO bid × 7 days
- Treatment of future recurrences: Metronidazole 2 g PO qd × 3-5 days
- Allergy, intolerance, or adverse reactions: Alternatives to metronidazole are not available. Patients who are allergic to metronidazole can be managed by desensitization
- Pregnancy
  1. Associated with adverse outcomes (i.e., PROM)
  2. Metronidazole 2 g PO × 1 day

DISPOSITION

Trichomonas infection is considered an STD; therefore treatment of the sexual partner is necessary.

REFERRAL

To obstetrician/gynecologist for recurrence and pregnancy

SUGGESTED READING

Workowski KA, Levine WC: Sexually transmitted diseases treatment guidelines, *MMWR Recomm Rep* 51:1, 2002.

AUTHOR: **JULIE ANNE SZUMIGALA, M.D.**

TABLE 1-54 Differential Diagnosis of Vaginitis

Characteristics of Vaginal Discharge	*C. Albicans* Vaginitis	*T. Vaginalis* Vaginitis	Bacterial Vaginosis
pH	4.5	>5.0	>5.0
White curd	Usually	No	No
Odor with KOH	No	Yes	Yes
Clue cells	No	No	Usually
Motile trichomonads	No	Usually	No
Yeast cells3	Yes	No	No

From Goldman L, Ausiello D (eds): *Cecil textbook of medicine,* ed 22, Philadelphia, 2004, WB Saunders.

BASIC INFORMATION

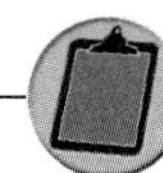

DEFINITION

Waldenström's macroglobulinemia (WM) is a plasma cell dyscrasia characterized by the presence of IgM monoclonal macroglobulins.

SYNONYMS

WM
Monoclonal macroglobulinemia

ICD-9CM CODES
273.3 Waldenström's macroglobulinemia

EPIDEMIOLOGY & DEMOGRAPHICS

- Accounts for 2% of all hematologic cancers
- 1500 people diagnosed each year in the U.S.
- Incidence: 0.61/100,000 in men; 0.36/100,000 in women
- Usually occurs in people over age 65 but can occur in younger people
- More common among men than women and among whites than blacks

PHYSICAL FINDINGS & CLINICAL PRESENTATION

- Weakness
- Fatigue
- Weight loss
- Headache, dizziness, vertigo, deafness, and seizures (hyperviscosity syndrome)
- Easy bleeding (e.g., epistaxis)
- Retinal vein link sausage shaped
- Lymphadenopathy (15%)
- Hepatomegaly (20%)
- Splenomegaly (15%)
- Purpura
- Peripheral neuropathy (5%)

ETIOLOGY

- The exact cause of WM is not known.
- Genetic predisposition, radiation exposure, occupational chemicals, and chronic inflammatory stimulation have been suggested but there is insufficient evidence to substantiate these hypotheses.

DIAGNOSIS

The diagnosis of WM is usually established by laboratory blood tests and by bone marrow biopsy.

DIFFERENTIAL DIAGNOSIS

- Monoclonal gammopathy of unknown significance (MGUS)
- Multiple myeloma
- Chronic lymphocytic leukemia
- Hairy-cell leukemia
- Lymphoma

WORKUP

In any patient suspected of having WM, specific blood tests (CBC, ESR, SPEP, IPEP, UPEP, IgM level, serum viscosity) and bone marrow biopsy will confirm the diagnosis.

LABORATORY TESTS

- CBC with differential:
  1. Anemia is a common finding, with a median hemoglobin value of approximately 10 g/dl. WBC count is usually normal; thrombocytopenia can occur.
  2. Peripheral smear may reveal malignant lymphoid cells in terminal patients.
- Elevated ESR
- Serum protein electrophoresis (SPEP): homogeneous M spike
- Immunoelectrophoresis: proves IgM
- Urine immunoelectrophoresis: monoclonal light chain usually kappa chains. Bence Jones protein can be seen but is not the typical finding in WM
- IgM levels are high, generally >3 g/dl
- Serum viscosity: symptoms usually occur when the serum viscosity is four times the viscosity of normal serum
- Cryoglobulins, rheumatoid factor, or cold agglutinins may be present
- Bone marrow biopsy: characteristically reveals lymphoplasmacytoid cells that have infiltrated the bone marrow

IMAGING STUDIES

Chest x-ray can be obtained to rule out pulmonary involvement.

TREATMENT

NONPHARMACOLOGIC THERAPY

Asymptomatic patients do not require treatment, and these patients should be monitored periodically for the onset of symptoms or changes in blood tests (e.g., worsening anemia, thrombocytopenia, rising IgM, and serum viscosity).

ACUTE GENERAL Rx

Symptomatic patients with WM usually receive chemotherapy.

- Chlorambucil and prednisone are given daily for 10 days and repeated at 6-wk intervals until a response is seen in the IgM concentration. Approximately 60% of patients respond to chemotherapy as defined by a 75% reduction in IgM concentration.
- Combination melphalan, cyclophosphamide, and prednisone chemotherapy given for 7 days at 4- to 6-wk intervals for 12 courses followed by continuous therapy with chlorambucil and prednisone until relapse has shown promising results.

CHRONIC Rx

- Refractory patients can be tried on fludarabine or 2-CdA (2-chlorodeoxyadenosine).
- New investigational treatment includes administration of rituximab, a monoclonal anti-CD 20 antibody.

DISPOSITION

- The onset of WM is slow and insidious. Most patients die from progression of the disease with hyperviscosity, hemorrhage, and infection, or from congestive heart failure.
- Some patients develop acute myelogenous leukemia, immunoblastic sarcoma, or chronic myelogenous leukemia as a preterminal event.
- Median survival in patients with WM is about 4 yr.
- Approximately 10% of patients will achieve complete remission with prognosis being more favorable (median survival 11 yr).

REFERRAL

If WM is suspected, a hematology consultation is helpful in guiding future workup, treatment, and monitoring.

PEARLS & CONSIDERATIONS

COMMENTS

- Waldenström's macroglobulinemia was first described in 1944 by the Swedish physician Jan Gosta Waldenström.
- Patients with MGUS carry a higher risk of developing WM.
- Amyloidosis is rare, occurring in 5% of patients with WM.

SUGGESTED READINGS

Dimopoulos MA, Galani E, Matsouka C: Waldenström's macroglobulinemia, *Hematol Oncol Clin North Am* 13(6):1351, 1999.

Gertz MA, Fonseca R, Rajkuma SV: Waldenstrom's macroglobulinemia, *Oncologist* 5(1):63, 2000.

Owen RG, Johnson SA, Morgan GJ: Waldenström's macroglobulinemia: laboratory diagnosis and treatment, *Hematol Oncol* 18(2):41, 2000.

AUTHOR: **PETER PETROPOULOS, M.D.**

BASIC INFORMATION

DEFINITION

Warts are benign epidermal neoplasms caused by human papillomavirus (HPV).

SYNONYMS

Verruca vulgaris (common warts)
Verruca plana (flat warts)
Condyloma acuminatum (venereal warts)
Verruca plantaris (plantar warts)
Mosaic warts (cluster of many warts)

ICD-9CM CODES
0.78.10 Viral warts
0.79.19 Venereal wart (external genital organs)

EPIDEMIOLOGY & DEMOGRAPHICS

- Common warts occur most frequently in children and young adults.
- Anogenital warts are most common in young, sexually active patients. Genital warts are the most common viral STD in the U.S., with up to 24 million Americans carrying the virus that causes them.
- Common warts are longer lasting and more frequent in immunocompromised patients (e.g., lymphoma, AIDS, immunosuppressive drugs).
- Plantar warts occur most frequently at points of maximal pressure (over the heads of the metatarsal bones or on the heels).

PHYSICAL FINDINGS & CLINICAL PRESENTATION

- Common warts (Fig. 1-255) have an initial appearance of a flesh-colored papule with a rough surface; they subsequently develop a hyperkeratotic appearance with black dots on the surface (thrombosed capillaries); they may be single or multiple and are most common on the hands.
- Warts obscure normal skin lines (important diagnostic feature). Cylindrical projections from the wart may become fused, forming a mosaic pattern.
- Flat warts generally are pink or light yellow, slightly elevated, and often found on the forehead, back of hands, mouth, and beard area; they often occur in lines corresponding to trauma (e.g., a scratch); are often misdiagnosed (particularly when present on the face) and inappropriately treated with topical corticosteroids.
- Filiform warts have a fingerlike appearance with various projections; they are generally found near the mouth, beard, or periorbital and paranasal regions.
- Plantar warts are slightly raised and have a roughened surface; they may cause pain when walking; as they involute, small hemorrhages (caused by thrombosed capillaries) may be noted.
- Genital warts are generally pale pink with several projections and a broad base. They may coalesce in the perineal area to form masses with a cauliflower-like appearance.
- Genital warts on the cervical epithelium can produce subclinical changes that may be noted on Pap smear or colposcopy.

ETIOLOGY

- Human papillomavirus (HPV) infection; >60 types of viral DNA have been identified. Transmission of warts is by direct contact.
- Genital warts are usually caused by HPV types 6 or 11.

DIAGNOSIS

DIFFERENTIAL DIAGNOSIS

- Molluscum contagiosum
- Condyloma latum
- Acrochordon (skin tags) or seborrheic keratosis
- Epidermal nevi
- Hypertrophic actinic keratosis
- Squamous cell carcinomas
- Acquired digital fibrokeratoma
- Varicella zoster virus in patients with AIDS
- Recurrent infantile digital fibroma
- Plantar corns (may be mistaken for plantar warts)

WORKUP

- Diagnosis is generally based on clinical findings.
- Suspect lesions should be biopsied.

LABORATORY TESTS

Colposcopy with biopsy of patients with cervical squamous cell changes

TREATMENT

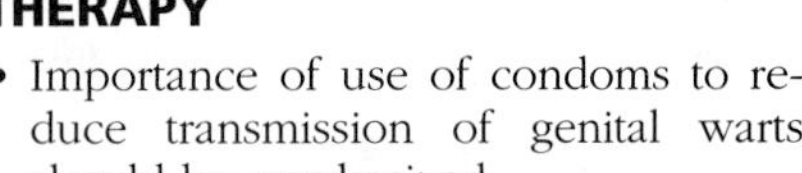

NONPHARMACOLOGIC THERAPY

- Importance of use of condoms to reduce transmission of genital warts should be emphasized.
- Watchful waiting is an acceptable option in the treatment of warts, because many warts will disappear without intervention over time.
- Plantar warts that are not painful do not need treatment.

GENERAL Rx

- Common warts:
  1. Application of topical salicylic acid 17% (e.g., Duofilm). Soak area for 5 min in warm water and dry. Apply thin layer once or twice daily for up to 12 wk, avoiding normal skin. Bandage.
  2. Liquid nitrogen, electrocautery are also common methods of removal.
  3. Blunt dissection can be used in large lesions or resistant lesions.

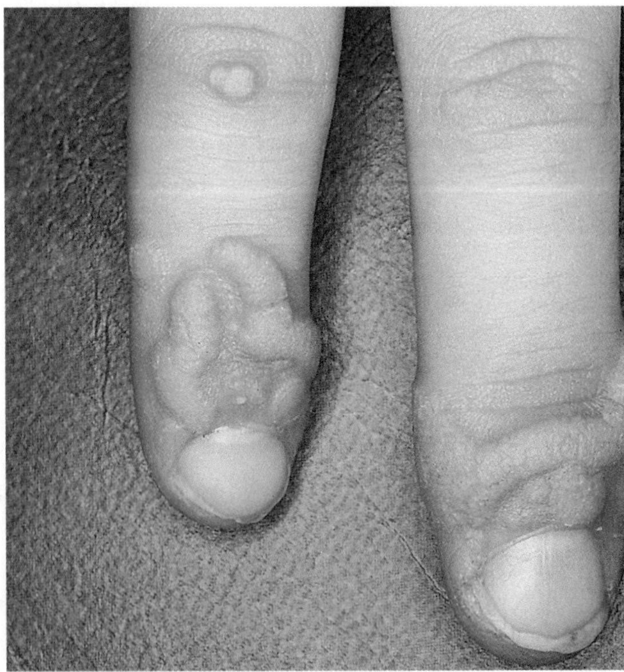

FIGURE 1-255 Verruca vulgaris or common viral warts. These papules often have verrucous surface changes. (From Callen JP: *Color atlas of dermatology,* ed 2, Philadelphia, 2000, WB Saunders.)

4. Duct tape occlusion is also effective for treating common warts. It is cut to cover warts and left in place for 6 days. It is removed after 6 days and the warts are soaked in water and then filed with pumice stones. New tape is applied 12 hr later. This treatment can be repeated until warts resolve.

- Filiform warts: surgical removal is necessary.
- Flat warts: generally more difficult to treat.
  1. Tretinoin cream applied at hs over the involved area for several weeks may be effective
  2. Application of liquid nitrogen
  3. Electrocautery
  4. 5-Fluorouracil cream (Efudex 5%) applied once or twice a day for 3-5 wk is also effective. Persistent hyperpigmentation may occur following Efudex use
- Plantar warts:
  1. Salicylic acid therapy (e.g., Occlusal-HP). Soak wart in warm water for 5 min, remove loose tissue, dry. Apply to area, allow to dry, reapply. Use once or twice daily; maximum 12 wk. Use of 40% salicylic acid plasters (Mediplast) is also a safe, nonscarring treatment; it is particularly useful in treating mosaic warts covering a large area.
  2. Blunt dissection is also a fast and effective treatment modality.
  3. Laser therapy can be used for plantar warts and recurrent warts; however, it leaves open wounds that require 4-6 wk to fill with granulation tissue.
  4. Interlesional bleomycin is also effective but generally used when all other treatments fail.
- Genital warts:
  1. Can be effectively treated with 20% podophyllin resin in compound tincture of benzoin applied with a cotton tip applicator by the treating physician and allowed to air dry. The treatment can be repeated weekly if necessary.
  2. Podofilox (Condylox 0.5% gel) is now available for application by the patient. Local adverse effects include pain, burning, and inflammation at the site.
  3. Cryosurgery with liquid nitrogen delivered with a probe or as a spray is effective for treating smaller genital warts.
  4. Carbon dioxide laser can also be used for treating primary or recurrent genital warts (cure rate >90%).
  5. Imiquimod (Aldara) cream, 5% is a patient-applied immune response modifier effective in the treatment of external genital and perianal warts (complete clearing of genital warts in >70% of females and >30% of males in 4-16 wk). Sexual contact should be avoided while the cream is on the skin. It is applied three times/wk before normal sleeping hours and is left on the skin for 6-10 hr.
- Application of trichloroacetic acid (TCA) or bichloracetic acid (BCA) 80%-90% is also effective for external genital warts. A small amount should be applied only to warts and allowed to dry, at which time a white "frosting" develops. This treatment can be repeated weekly if necessary.

DISPOSITION

- Warts can be effectively treated with the previous modalities, with complete resolution in the majority of patients; however, recurrence rate is high.
- Cervical carcinomas and precancerous lesions in women are associated with genital papillomavirus infection.
- Squamous cell anal cancer is also associated with a history of genital warts.

REFERRAL

- Dermatology referral for warts resistant to conservative therapy
- Surgical referral in selected cases
- STD counseling for patients with anogenital warts

PEARLS & CONSIDERATIONS

COMMENTS

- Subungual and periungual warts are generally more resistant to treatment. Dermatology referral for cryosurgery is recommended in resistant cases.
- Examination of sex partners is not necessary for the management of genital warts because no data indicate that reinfection plays a role.

SUGGESTED READINGS

Focht DR III et al: The efficacy of duct tape vs cryotherapy in the treatment of verruca vulgaris, *Arch Pediatr Adolesc Med* 156:971, 2002.

Gibbs S et al: Local treatment for cutaneous warts: systematic review, *BMJ* 325:461, 2002.

AUTHOR: **FRED F. FERRI, M.D.**

Wegener's Granulomatosis

BASIC INFORMATION

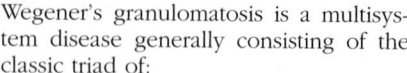

DEFINITION

Wegener's granulomatosis is a multisystem disease generally consisting of the classic triad of:

1. Necrotizing granulomatous lesions in the upper or lower respiratory tractis
2. Generalized focal necrotizing vasculitis involving both arteries and veins
3. Focal glomerulonephritis of the kidneys

"Limited forms" of the disease can also occur and may evolve into the classic triad; Wegener's granulomatosis can be classified using the "ELK" classification, which identifies the three major sites of involvement: *E,* ears, nose, and throat or respiratory tract; *L,* lungs; *K,* kidneys.

ICD-9CM CODES
446.4 Wegener's granulomatosis

EPIDEMIOLOGY & DEMOGRAPHICS

- The incidence of Wegener's granulomatosis is 0.5/100,000 persons.
- Mean age at onset is 40 yr.

PHYSICAL FINDINGS & CLINICAL PRESENTATION

- Clinical manifestations often vary with the stage of the disease and degree of organ involvement.
- Frequent manifestations are:
  1. Upper respiratory tract: chronic sinusitis, chronic otitis media, mastoiditis, nasal crusting, obstruction and epistaxis, nasal septal perforation, nasal lacrimal duct stenosis, saddle nose deformities (resulting from cartilage destruction)
  2. Lung: hemoptysis, multiple nodules, diffuse alveolar pattern
  3. Kidney: renal insufficiency, glomerulonephritis
  4. Skin: necrotizing skin lesions
  5. Nervous system: mononeuritis multiplex, cranial nerve involvement
  6. Joints: monarthritis or polyarthritis (nondeforming), usually affecting large joints
  7. Mouth: chronic ulcerative lesions of the oral mucosa, "mulberry" gingivitis
  8. Eye: proptosis, uveitis, episcleritis, retinal and optic nerve vasculitis

ETIOLOGY

Unknown

DIAGNOSIS

DIFFERENTIAL DIAGNOSIS

- Other granulomatous lung diseases (e.g., lymphomatoid granulomatosis, Churg-Strauss syndrome, necrotizing sarcoid granulomatosis, bronchocentric granulomatosis, sarcoidosis); the differential diagnosis of granulomatous lung disease is described in Section II
- Neoplasms
- Goodpasture's syndrome
- Bacterial or fungal sinusitis
- Midline granuloma
- Viral infections

WORKUP

Chest x-ray examination, laboratory evaluation, PFTs, and tissue biopsy

LABORATORY TESTS

- Positive test for cytoplasmic pattern of ANCA (c-ANCA)
- Anemia, leukocytosis
- Urinalysis: may reveal hematuria, RBC casts, and proteinuria
- Elevated serum creatinine, decreased creatinine clearance
- Increased ESR, positive rheumatoid factor, and elevated C-reactive protein may be found.

IMAGING STUDIES

- Chest x-ray: may reveal bilateral multiple nodules, cavitated mass lesions, pleural effusion (20%).
- PFTs: useful in detecting stenosis of the airways.
- Biopsy of one or more affected organs should be attempted; the most reliable source for tissue diagnosis is the lung. Lesions in the nasopharynx (if present) can be easily biopsied.

TREATMENT

NONPHARMACOLOGIC THERAPY

- Ensure proper airway drainage.
- Give nutritional counseling.

ACUTE GENERAL Rx

- Prednisone 60-80 mg/day and cyclophosphamide 2 mg/kg are generally effective and are used to control clinical manifestations; once the disease comes under control, prednisone is tapered and cyclophosphamide is continued.
- TMP-SMX therapy may represent a useful alternative in patients with lesions limited to the upper and/or lower respiratory tracts in absence of vasculitis or nephritis. Treatment with TMP-SMX (160 mg/800 mg bid) also reduces the incidence of relapses in patients with Wegener's granulomatosis in remission.

DISPOSITION

Five-year survival with aggressive treatment is approximately 80%; without treatment 2-yr survival is $<20\%$.

REFERRAL

Surgical referral for biopsy

PEARLS & CONSIDERATIONS

COMMENTS

- Methotrexate (20 mg/wk) represents an alternative to cyclophosphamide in patients who do not have immediately life-threatening disease.
- C-ANCA levels should not dictate changes in therapy, because they correlate erratically with disease activity.

AUTHOR: **FRED F. FERRI, M.D.**

BASIC INFORMATION

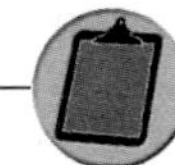

DEFINITION

Wernicke's encephalopathy is the syndrome of acute extraocular muscle dysfunction, confusion, and ataxia, resulting from thiamine deficiency.

SYNONYMS

Korsakoff's syndrome
Wernicke-Korsakoff syndrome
Alcoholic polyneuritic psychosis

ICD-9CM CODES
265.1 Wernicke's encephalopathy, disease, or syndrome

EPIDEMIOLOGY & DEMOGRAPHICS

- Most commonly seen in alcoholics
- Slightly more common in males
- Age of onset evenly distributed between age 30 and 70

PHYSICAL FINDINGS & CLINICAL PRESENTATION

- Disturbance of extraocular motility, including nystagmus, abducens nerve palsy, and disorders of conjugate gaze
- Encephalopathy
- Ataxia of gait
- Peripheral neuropathy may be seen in addition to the typical findings described previously

ETIOLOGY

Thiamine deficiency from alcohol abuse or other malnourished state

DIAGNOSIS

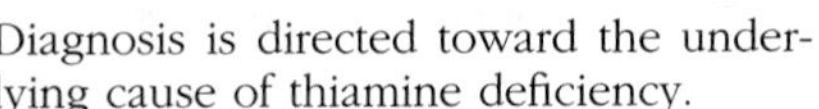

DIFFERENTIAL DIAGNOSIS

Diagnosis is directed toward the underlying cause of thiamine deficiency.

WORKUP

When suspected, treat immediately.

LABORATORY TESTS

- CBC
- Serum chemistries
- Serum pyruvate is elevated
- Whole-blood or erythrocyte transketolase are decreased; rapid resolution to normal in 24 hr with thiamine repletion

IMAGING STUDIES

- MRI may show diencephalic and mesencephalic lesions acutely, but there is no definitive radiologic study for diagnosis.
- CT scan may show cerebral atrophy from chronic alcoholism.

TREATMENT

NONPHARMACOLOGIC THERAPY

Alcoholics Anonymous

ACUTE GENERAL Rx

- 100 mg thiamine IV or IM immediately; typically thiamine IV for 3-5 days, then oral
- Avoid dextrose containing fluids until thiamine repleted
- Prophylactic treatment for delirium tremens if alcoholic

CHRONIC Rx

- Attempt to treat alcoholism or underlying malnourished state.
- Chronic oral thiamine repletion; typical dose 5 mg/day.
- Case reports suggest Donepezil may help chronic memory problems.
- Inadequately treated disease may progress to Korsakoff's psychosis (see relevant entry).

DISPOSITION

Enter substance abuse program after acute phase.

REFERRAL

Referral to a neurologist if symptoms do not resolve after thiamine therapy.

PEARLS & CONSIDERATIONS

COMMENTS

- Give thiamine if the disease is even suspected.
- Prognosis is generally poor, with 10%-20% mortality even with treatment. Most patients will be left with impaired learning and memory, which may be subtle.
- A preventable cause is prolonged dextrose-containing IV fluids without supplemental thiamine.

SUGGESTED READINGS

Cook CC: Prevention and treatment of Wernicke-Korsakoff syndrome, *Alcohol Alcohol Suppl* 35(suppl1):19, 2000.
Zubaran C, Fernandes JG, Rodnight R: Wernicke-Korsakoff syndrome, *Postgrad Med J* 73(855):27, 1997.

AUTHOR: **DANIEL MATTSON, M.D., M.SC.(MED.)**

West Nile Virus Infection

BASIC INFORMATION

DEFINITION

West Nile virus infection is an illness affecting the central nervous system (CNS) caused by the mosquito-borne West Nile virus.

ICD-9CM CODES
066.4 West Nile virus infection

EPIDEMIOLOGY & DEMOGRAPHICS

- Before 1999, West Nile virus infection was confined to areas in the Middle East, with occasional outbreaks in Europe. For the past 4 yr, the infection has been diagnosed for the first time in the Western hemisphere. First seen in the northeast and mid-Atlantic states, West Nile virus infection has spread steadily, each year, to new regions of the U.S. In the year 2002, a record number of cases were reported from the U.S. through November 2002, 3949 proven cases, 254 of which were fatal, were reported from 40 states. Hardest hit were Illinois, Ohio, Michigan, and Louisiana, each reporting more than 300 cases.
- The virus is carried by a number of species of birds, as well as horses and several other animals. It is transmitted to humans through the bite of an infected mosquito. For this reason, West Nile virus infection is seen primarily from mid-summer to mid-autumn, the period of maximum mosquito intensity.
- The majority of severe cases have been reported among individuals >50 yr of age. There is no gender predilection.

PHYSICAL FINDINGS & CLINICAL PRESENTATION

- Only 20% of infected individuals develop symptomatic disease. The initial phase of illness is nonspecific, with abrupt onset of fever accompanied by malaise, eye pain, anorexia, headache, and, occasionally, rash and lymphadenopathy. Less commonly, myocarditis, hepatitis, or pancreatitis may occur.
- In approximately 1 in 150 cases, especially among elderly patients, severe neurologic sequelae will occur. Most common among these are ataxia, cranial nerve palsies, optic neuritis, seizures, myelitis, and polyradiculitis.

ETIOLOGY

The West Nile virus is a member of the flavivirus group, along with the yellow fever, dengue, St. Louis, and Japanese encephalitis viruses. It has a large reservoir in nature, infecting many species of birds, as well as certain mammals, and is thought to be spread to humans exclusively by various species of mosquito. Neurologic disease is caused by direct invasion of the CNS.

DIAGNOSIS

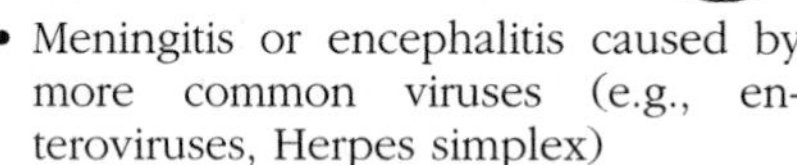

DIFFERENTIAL DIAGNOSIS

- Meningitis or encephalitis caused by more common viruses (e.g., enteroviruses, Herpes simplex)
- Bacterial meningitis
- Vasculitis
- Fungal meningitis (e.g., cryptococcal infection)
- Tuberculous meningitis

LABORATORY TESTS

- CBC, electrolytes (hyponatremia common)
- Spinal tap and CSF examination: typically demonstrates lymphocytic pleocytosis with normal level of glucose and elevated level of protein
- CSF West Nile virus IgM antibody level: rare false-positive results in persons recently vaccinated to Japanese encephalitis or yellow fever viruses

IMAGING STUDIES

CT or MRI studies of the brain to exclude mass lesions; cerebral edema

TREATMENT

NONPHARMACOLOGIC THERAPY

Hospitalization, intravenous hydration, ventilator support may be necessary.

ACUTE GENERAL Rx

No specific therapy has been established in clinical trials. Ribavirin and interferon alpha-2b have been shown to have in vitro activity against the virus.

CHRONIC Rx

Chronic rehabilitation therapy usually necessary for patients with severe neurologic impairment.

DISPOSITION

Chronic rehabilitation as needed following recovery from acute infection

REFERRAL

- Infectious disease consultant
- Public health authorities

PEARLS & CONSIDERATIONS

COMMENTS

- Diagnosis requires a high index of suspicion, because disease course may be nonspecific and may mimic other, more common disorders.
- Specific laboratory diagnostic studies are available only through public health laboratories.
- Best means of prevention is reduction in mosquito population by draining of stagnant water deposits and, if necessary, insecticide spraying.
- Individuals may reduce risk by covering arms and legs in areas where mosquitoes are likely to be found and using insect repellent.

SUGGESTED READINGS

Centers for Disease Control and Prevention: www.cdc.gov/ncidod/dvbid/westnile/surv&control.htm.

Kahler SC: APHIS: West Nile virus vaccine safe for use, *J Am Vet Med Assoc* 223(4):416, 2003.

Petersen LR, Marfin AA: West Nile virus: a primer for the clinician, *Ann Intern Med* 137:173, 2002.

AUTHOR: **JOSEPH R. MASCI, M.D.**

BASIC INFORMATION

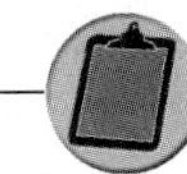

DEFINITION

Whiplash refers to a hyperextension injury to the neck, often the result of being struck from behind by a fast-moving vehicle. It is an acceleration-deceleration injury to the neck.

SYNONYMS

- Cervical strain
- Soft tissue cervical hyperextension injury
- Acceleration flexion-extension neck injury

ICD-9CM CODES
847.0 Whiplash injury or syndrome

EPIDEMIOLOGY & DEMOGRAPHICS

- Whiplash occurs in more than 1 million people each year.
- Most injuries (40%) are the result of rear-end motor vehicle accidents.
- Whiplash occurs at all ages, in both sexes, and at all socioeconomic levels.
- Incidence is 4 per 1000 persons and is higher in women than men.
- Nearly 50% of patients with whiplash seek legal advice.
- Whiplash is also seen in shaken baby syndrome.

PHYSICAL FINDINGS & CLINICAL PRESENTATION

- Most present with a history of being involved in a motor vehicle accident and rear-ended by another vehicle
- Pain not present initially but usually develops hours to a few days later
- Neck tightness and stiffness
- Occipital headache
- Shoulder, arm, and back pain
- Numbness in the arms
- Tinnitus
- TMJ pain
- Dysphagia (retropharyngeal hematoma)
- Decreased range of motion of the neck

ETIOLOGY

- The mechanism of injury is due to the sudden acceleration of the body forward, forcing the neck to hyperextend backward, causing injury to ligaments, muscles, bone, and/or intervertebral disk. At the end of the accident the head is thrust forward in a flexion position, sometimes causing injury to C5-C6-C7.
- Motor vehicle accidents, trauma from falls, contact sports, physical abuse, and altercations are all possible causes of whiplash.

DIAGNOSIS

The clinical presentation and physical examination determine both the diagnosis and clinical classification of whiplash-associated disorders.

DIFFERENTIAL DIAGNOSIS

The differential diagnosis of cervical strain is:

- Osteoarthritis
- Cervical disk disease
- Fibrositis
- Neuritis
- Torticollis
- Spinal cord tumor
- TMJ syndrome
- Tension headache
- Migraine headache

WORKUP

Any patient who presents with symptoms of whiplash and musculoskeletal or neurologic signs merits a workup to exclude cervical spine fractures or herniated disk disease.

LABORATORY TESTS

Laboratory studies are not helpful in the diagnosis of whiplash or in excluding complications of acute neck injuries.

IMAGING STUDIES

- Plain C-spine films (AP, lateral, and odontoid views) to exclude cervical spine fractures
- Flexion/extension x-rays looking for C-spine instability
- CT scan to exclude fracture if suspected by plain films
- MRI to look for cervical disk bulging or herniation

TREATMENT

NONPHARMACOLOGIC THERAPY

- Bed rest
- Soft cervical collar for no longer than 72 hr
- Moist heat 15-20 min four to six times per day

ACUTE GENERAL Rx

- Analgesics
  1. Ibuprofen 800 mg PO tid
  2. Naproxen 500 mg PO bid
  3. Acetaminophen 1 g PO qid
- Muscle relaxants (short-term use)
  1. Cyclobenzaprine 10 mg PO tid
  2. Methocarbamol 1 g PO qid
  3. Carisoprodol 350 mg PO qid

CHRONIC Rx

- NSAIDs as described previously can be used long term.
- Intraarticular corticosteroids have been tried in the past; however, recently they were found not to be effective for pain relief in patients with chronic whiplash syndrome.

DISPOSITION

- Most patients recover from the acute whiplash injury within weeks.
- 20%-40% may develop chronic whiplash syndrome (symptoms of headache, neck pain, and psychiatric complaints that persist for 6 mo).

REFERRAL

If symptoms are not relieved with conservative nonpharmacologic and acute treatments within 1-2 mo, a referral to orthopedic or rheumatology may be helpful.

PEARLS & CONSIDERATIONS

COMMENTS

- The entity of chronic whiplash syndrome remains elusive. Some authorities argue that financial motivation is a factor leading to persistent neck symptoms. Other studies do not substantiate this, countering a true chronic injury to the soft tissues of the neck.
- Nearly one third of all personal injury cases involve cervical injuries.

SUGGESTED READINGS

Eck JC, Hodges SD, Humphreys SC: Whiplash: a review of a commonly misunderstood injury, *Am J Med* 110(8):651, 2001.

Young WF: The enigma of whiplash injury: current management strategies and controversies, *Postgrad Med* 93(10):526, 2000.

AUTHOR: **PETER PETROPOULOS, M.D.**

Whipple's Disease (PTG)

BASIC INFORMATION

DEFINITION

Whipple's disease is a multisystem illness characterized by malabsorption and its consequences, lymphadenopathy, arthritis, cardiac involvement, ocular symptoms and neurologic problems, caused by the gram-positive bacillus *Tropheryma whippelii.*

SYNONYMS

Intestinal lipodystrophy (name used by Dr. Whipple in 1907)

ICD-9CM CODES
040.2 Whipple's disease

EPIDEMIOLOGY & DEMOGRAPHICS

- Uncommon illness
- Peak age: 30-60 yr of age
- More frequent in men than women

PHYSICAL FINDINGS & CLINICAL PRESENTATION

PRESENTATION: The disease may present with extraintestinal symptoms (e.g., arthralgia), but few clinicians will suspect the diagnosis unless or until GI symptoms are present.

The GI manifestations are those seen in malabsorption of any cause:
- Diarrhea: 5-10 semiformed, malodorous steatorrheic stools per day
- Abdominal bloating and cramps
- Anorexia

Extraintestinal manifestations of malabsorption:
- Weight loss, fatigue
- Anemia
- Bleeding diathesis
- Edema and ascites
- Osteomalacia

Extraintestinal involvement:
- Arthritis (intermittent, migratory, affecting small, large, and axial joints)
- Pleuritic chest pain and cough
- Pericarditis, endocarditis
- Dementia, ophthalmoplegia, myoclonus, and many other symptoms, because any portion of the central nervous system may be a disease site
- Fever

PHYSICAL FINDINGS:
- Abdominal distention, sometimes with tenderness and less commonly fullness or mass, which represents enlarged mesenteric lymph nodes
- Signs of weight loss, cachexia
- Clubbing
- Lymphadenopathy
- Inflamed joints
- Heart murmur or rub
- Sensory loss or motor weakness related to peripheral neuropathy
- Abnormal mental status examination
- Pallor

ETIOLOGY & PATHOGENESIS

- Infectious disease caused by *Tropheryma whippelii,* an actinobacter.
- The bacillus has never been cultured, nor has direct transmission from patient to patient ever been documented; however, the agent can be seen in tissue samples by electron microscopy and identified by polymerase chain reaction (PCR).
- Predictable response to appropriate antibiotic therapy confirms the pathogenic role of the infection.
- Tissue infiltration by macrophages is believed to be the mechanism of specific organ dysfunction and symptoms.

DIAGNOSIS

DIFFERENTIAL DIAGNOSIS

Malabsorption/maldigestion:
- Celiac disease
- *Mycobacterium avium-intracellulare* intestinal infection in patients with AIDS
- Intestinal lymphoma
- Abetalipoproteinemia
- Amyloidosis
- Systemic mastocytosis
- Radiation enteritis
- Crohn's disease
- Short bowel syndrome
- Pancreatic insufficiency
- Intestinal bacterial overgrowth
- Lactose deficiency
- Postgastrectomy syndrome
- Other cause of diarrhea (see Section III, Diarrhea, Acute and Diarrhea, Chronic)
- Seronegative inflammatory arthritis (see Section II for differential diagnosis)
- Pericarditis and pleuritis
- Lymphadenitis
- Neurologic disorders

WORKUP

Laboratory tests and imaging studies

LABORATORY TESTS

- Anemia (iron, folate, and/or vitamin B_{12} deficiency)
- Hypokalemia
- Hypocalcemia
- Hypomagnesemia
- Hypoalbuminemia
- Prolonged prothrombin time
- Low serum carotene
- Low cholesterol
- Leukocytosis
- Steatorrhea demonstrated by a Sudan fecal fat stain
- 72-Hr stool collection demonstrating more than 7 g/24 hr of fat in the stool is impractical to perform, especially in ambulatory patients
- Defective D-xylose absorption

IMAGING STUDIES

Small bowel x-rays after barium ingestion often show thickening of mucosal folds.

BIOPSY

Infiltration of the intestinal lamina propria by PAS-positive macrophages containing gram-positive, acid-fast negative bacilli, associated with lymphatic dilation (diagnostic); PCR of the involved tissue in uncertain cases

TREATMENT

- Antibiotics: TMP/SMX DS bid for 6-12 mo
- Alternative antibiotics: penicillin alone, penicillin plus streptomycin, ampicillin, tetracycline, chloramphenicol, ceftriaxone
- Treat specific vitamin, mineral, and nutrient deficiencies

SUGGESTED READINGS

Malwald M et al: *Tropheryma whippelii* DNA is rare in the intestinal mucosa of patients without other evidence of Whipple disease, *Ann Intern Med* 136:115, 2001.

Trier JS: Whipple's disease. In Feldman M, Scharschmidt BF, Sleisenger MH (eds): *Sleisenger and Fordtran's gastrointestinal and liver disease,* ed 6, Philadelphia, 1998, WB Saunders.

AUTHOR: **TOM J. WACHTEL, M.D.**

BASIC INFORMATION

DEFINITION

Wilson's disease is a disorder of copper transport with inadequate biliary copper excretion, leading to an accumulation of the metal in liver, brain, kidneys, and corneas.

ICD-9CM CODES
275.1 Wilson's disease

EPIDEMIOLOGY & DEMOGRAPHICS

- Prevalence: 1 in 30,000
- Affects men and women equally (autosomal recessive gene)
- Onset of symptoms: 3-40 yr of age

CLINICAL PRESENTATION & PHYSICAL FINDINGS

Hepatic presentation:
- Acute hepatitis with malaise, anorexia, nausea, jaundice, elevated transaminase, prolonged prothrombin time; rarely fulminant hepatic failure
- Chronic active (or autoimmune) hepatitis with fatigue, malaise, rashes, arthralgia, elevated transaminase, elevated serum IgG, positive ANA and anti–smooth muscle antibody
- Chronic liver disease/cirrhosis with hepatosplenomegaly, ascites, low serum albumin, prolonged prothrombin time, portal hypertension

Neurologic presentation:
- Movement disorder: tremors, ataxia
- Spastic dystonia: masklike facies, rigidity, gait disturbance, dysarthria, drooling, dysphagia

Psychiatric presentation:
- Depression, obsessive-compulsive disorder, psychopathic behaviors

Other organs:
- Hemolytic anemia
- Renal disease (i.e., Fanconi's syndrome with hematuria, phosphaturia, renal tubular acidosis, vitamin D–resistant rickets)
- Cardiomyopathy
- Arthritis
- Hypoparathyroidism
- Hypogonadism

PHYSICAL FINDINGS:
- Ocular: the Kayser-Fleischer ring is a gold-yellow ring seen at the periphery of the iris (Fig. 1-256)
- Stigmata of acute or chronic liver disease
- Neurologic abnormalities: see previous

ETIOLOGY & PATHOGENESIS

- Dietary copper is transported from the intestine to the liver where normally it is metabolized into ceruloplasmin. In Wilson's disease, defective incorporation of copper into ceruloplasmin and a decrease of biliary copper excretion lead to accumulation of this mineral.
- The gene for Wilson's disease is located in chromosome 13.

DIAGNOSIS

DIFFERENTIAL DIAGNOSIS

- Hereditary hypoceruloplasminemia
- Menkes' disease
- Consider the diagnosis of Wilson's disease in all cases of acute or chronic liver disease where another cause has not been established
- Consider Wilson's disease in patients with movement disorders or dystonia even without symptomatic liver disease

LABORATORY TESTS

- Abnormal LFTs (note that AST may be higher than ALT)
- Low serum ceruloplasmin level (<200 mg/L)
- Low serum copper (<65 μg/L)
- 24-hr urinary copper excretion greater than 100 μg (normal <30 μg); increases to greater than 1200 μg/24 hr after 500 mg of d-penicillamine (normal <500 μg/24 hr)
- Low serum uric acid and phosphorus
- Abnormal urinalysis (hematuria)

BIOPSY

- Early:
  Steatosis, focal necrosis, glycogenated hepatocyte nuclei
  May reveal inflammation and piecemeal necrosis
- Late: cirrhosis
- Hepatic copper content (>250 μg/g of dry weight) (normal is 20-50 μg)

TREATMENT

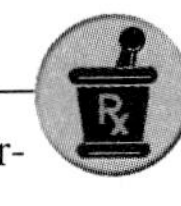

- Penicillamine: (chelator therapy)
  0.75-1.5 g/day divided bid (with pyridoxine 25 mg/day)
  Monitor CBC and urinalysis weekly
- Trientine: (triethylene tetramine) (chelator therapy)
  1-2 g/day divided tid
  Monitor CBC
- Zinc: (inhibits intestinal copper absorption)
  50 mg tid
  Monitor zinc level
- Ammonium tetrathiomolybdate for neurologic symptoms
- Antioxidants
- Liver transplant (for severe hepatic failure unresponsive to chelation)

PROGNOSIS

Good with early chelation treatment

REFERRAL

To gastroenterologist

SUGGESTED READINGS

Cox DW, Roberts EA: Wilson's disease. In Feldman M, Scharschmidt BF, Sleisenger MH (eds): *Sleisenger & Fordtran's gastrointestinal and liver disease,* ed 6, Philadelphia, 1998, WB Saunders.

El-Youssef M: Wilson's disease, *Mayo Clin Proc* 78:1126, 2003.

AUTHOR: **TOM J. WACHTEL, M.D.**

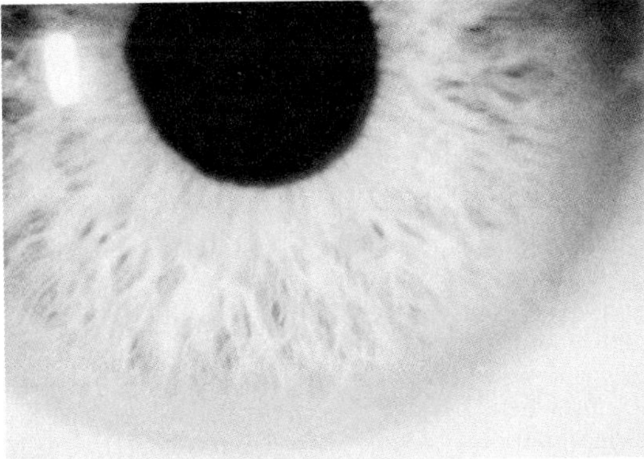

FIGURE 1-256 Wilson's disease. A Kayser-Fleisher ring, which is a gold-yellow ring, extends to the limbus without a clear interval. (From Palay D [ed]: *Ophthalmology for the primary care physician,* St Louis, 1997, Mosby.)

Wolff-Parkinson-White Syndrome (PTG)

BASIC INFORMATION

DEFINITION

Wolff-Parkinson-White syndrome is an electrocardiographic abnormality associated with earlier than normal ventricular depolarization following the atrial impulse and predisposing the affected person to tachyarrhythmias.

SYNONYMS

Preexcitation syndrome

ICD-9CM CODES

426.7 Wolff-Parkinson-White syndrome
426.81 Lown-Ganong-Levine syndrome

EPIDEMIOLOGY & DEMOGRAPHICS

- Prevalence: 1.5 cases/1000 persons
- Prevalence higher in males and decreases with age
- Most patients with WPW syndrome have normal hearts, but associations with mitral valve prolapse, cardiomyopathies, and Ebstein's anomaly have been reported

PHYSICAL FINDINGS & CLINICAL PRESENTATION

Paroxysmal tachycardias
- 10% of WPW patients aged 20-40 yr
- 35% of WPW patients aged >60 yr

The type of tachycardia is:
- Reciprocating tachycardia at 150-250 beats per minute (80%)
- Atrial fibrillation (15%)
- Atrial flutter (5%)
- Ventricular tachycardia: rare
- Sudden death is rare (<1/1000 cases)

PATHOPHYSIOLOGY

- Existence of accessory pathways (Kent bundles)
- If the accessory pathway is capable of anterograde conduction, two parallel routes of AV conduction are possible, one subject to delay through the AV mode, the other without delay through the accessory pathway. The resulting QRS complex is a fusion beat with the "delta" wave representing ventricular activation through the accessory pathway (Fig. 1-257).
- Tachycardias occur when, because of different refractory periods, conduction is anterograde in one pathway (usually the normal AV pathway) and retrograde in the other (usually the accessory pathway). Some patients (5% to 10%) with WPW syndrome have multiple accessory pathways.

DIAGNOSIS

Three basic features characterize the ECG abnormalities in WPW syndrome (Fig. 1-258):
- PR interval <120 msec
- QRS complex >120 msec with a slurred, slowly rising onset of QRS in some lead (delta wave)
- ST-T wave changes

Variants
- Lown-Ganong-Levine syndrome: atriohisian pathway with short PR interval and normal QRS complex on ECG (no delta wave)
- Atriofascicular accessory pathways: duplication of the AV node, with normal baseline ECG

TREATMENT

- No treatment in the absence of tachyarrhythmias.
- Symptomatic tachyarrhythmias.
- Acute episode: adenosine, verapamil, or diltiazem can be used to terminate an episode of reciprocal tachycardia.
- Digitalis should not be used because it can reduce refractoriness in the accessory pathway and accelerate the tachycardia. Cardioversion should be used in the presence of hemodynamic impairment.
- Prevention:
  Empiric trials or serial electrophysiologic drug testing of:
  1. Quinidine and propranolol
  2. Procainamide and verapamil
  3. Amiodarone
  4. Sotalol

  Electrical or surgical ablation of the accessory pathway

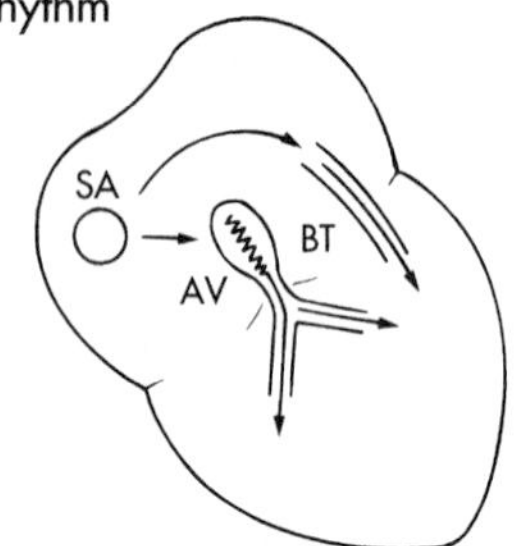

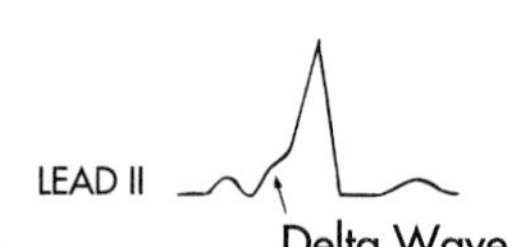

FIGURE 1-257 With Wolff-Parkinson-White syndrome an abnormal accessory conduction pathway called a bypass tract (BT) connects the atria and ventricles. (From Goldberger AL [ed]: *Clinical electrocardiography: a simplified approach,* ed 6, St Louis, 1999, Mosby.)

SUGGESTED READINGS

Gollob MH et al: Identification of a gene responsible for familial Wolff- Parkinson-White syndrome, *N Engl J Med* 366:1823, 2001.

Olgin JE, Zipes DP: Preexcitation syndrome. In Braunwald E (ed): *Heart disease: a textbook of cardiovascular medicine,* ed 6, vol 2, Philadelphia, 2001, WB Saunders.

Pappone C et al: A randomized study of prophylactic catheter ablation in asymptomatic patients with the WPW syndrome, *N Engl J Med* 349:1803, 2003.

AUTHOR: **TOM J. WACHTEL, M.D.**

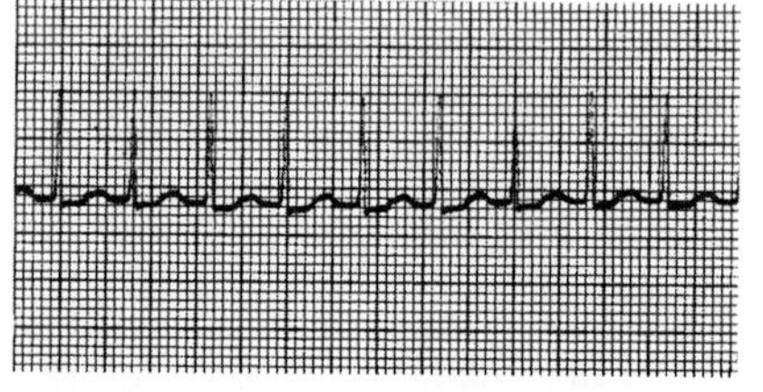

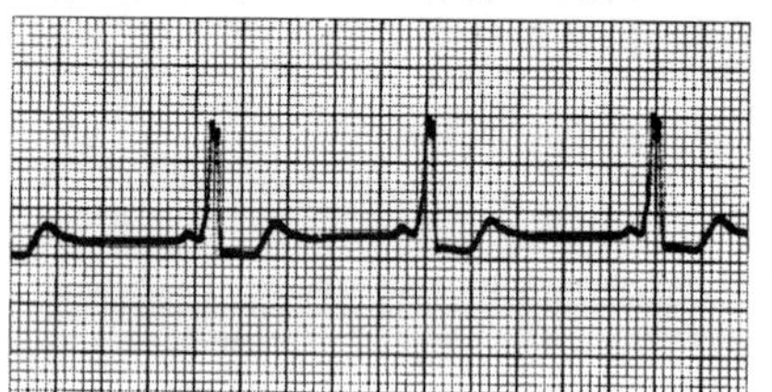

FIGURE 1-258 A, SVT in a child with Wolff-Parkinson-White (WPW) syndrome. Note the normal QRS complexes during the tachycardia. **B,** Later the typical features of WPW syndrome are apparent (short P-R interval, delta wave, and wide QRS). (From Behrman RE: *Nelson textbook of pediatrics,* ed 16, Philadelphia, 2000, WB Saunders.)

BASIC INFORMATION

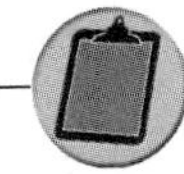

DEFINITION

Yellow fever is an infection, primarily of the liver, with systemic manifestations caused by the yellow fever virus (YFV). The clinical spectrum can range from asymptomatic infection to life-threatening disease with fever, jaundice, renal failure, and hemorrhage.

ICD-9CM CODES
060.9 Yellow fever

EPIDEMIOLOGY & DEMOGRAPHICS

GEOGRAPHIC DISTRIBUTION

- South America and Africa, in countries between +15 and −15 degrees latitude.
- From 1985 to 1999, more than 20,000 cases and 7000 deaths were reported to the World Health Organization, with more than 90% of cases in Africa.

INCIDENCE: Approximate attack rates of 3% in Africa and Amazon.

PREVALENCE: Endemic areas: 20% of population.

PREDOMINANT SEX: In Africa and Amazon, male agricultural workers.

PHYSICAL FINDINGS & CLINICAL PRESENTATION

- Most subclinical
- Onset sudden after incubation period of 3-6 days
- Viremic (early) phase
  1. Fever, chills
  2. Severe headache
  3. Lumbosacral pain
  4. Myalgias
  5. Nausea
  6. Severe malaise
  7. Conjunctivitis
  8. Relative bradycardia (Faget's sign)
- After brief recovery, toxic phase:
  1. Jaundice
  2. Oliguria
  3. Albuminuria
  4. Hemorrhage
  5. Encephalopathy
  6. Shock
  7. Acidosis
- Case fatality rate 25%-50% in patients with hemorrhages, jaundice, and renal disease.

ETIOLOGY

- Yellow fever virus *(L. flavus)*
  1. Prototype flavivirus.
  2. Infects primarily hepatic cells.
  3. Replication:
     a. Exclusively intracellular and intracytoplasmic
     b. Primarily in the endoplasmic reticulum
  4. Late in infection, cytopathic effects (antibody- and cell-mediated) produce pathology.
- Vector
  1. Aedes aegypti (urban).
  2. Aedes spp., Haemagogus (especially in Amazon) mosquitos (sylvan).
  3. Primary hosts humans and simian species.
  4. Exists in nature in two transmission cycles:
     a. Sylvatic or jungle cycle involving mosquitos and nonhuman primates.
     b. Urban cycle involving mosquitos and humans.
     c. Virus maintained in mosquito ova during dry season.
     d. Sylvan cycle interrupted by humans; agriculture, forest cleaning.

PATHOGENESIS & PATHOLOGY

- Virus replication begins at site of mosquito bite, spreading to lymphatic channels and regional lymph nodes. Viremic spread to other organs, especially liver, spleen, and bone marrow.
- Shock and fatal illness result from direct damage to myocardium, kidneys, and other organs as well as from effects of vasoactive cytokines.
- Viral antigen found in hepatocytes, kidneys, and myocardium.
- Midzone of liver lobules primarily affected, sparing hepatocytes around central vein and portal triad.
- Renal and myocardial damage characterized by degenerative and fatty changes.
- Hemorrhages of mucosal surfaces of gastrointestinal tract.

DIAGNOSIS

DIFFERENTIAL DIAGNOSIS

- Viral hepatitis
- Leptospirosis
- Malaria
- Typhoid fever
  1. Typhus
  2. Relapsing fever
- Hemorrhagic fevers (HF) with jaundice
  1. Dengue (HF)
  2. Rift Valley fever
  3. Crimean-Congo (HF)

WORKUP

- CBC
- Liver function tests
- Serum for serology (YFV, viral isolation)
- Coagulation studies
- Liver biopsy contraindicated (death from bleeding)

LABORATORY TESTS

- CBC
  1. Mild leukopenia
  2. Thrombocytopenia
  3. Anemia
- LFTs
  1. AST levels exceed ALT levels.
  2. Alkaline phosphatase normal or slightly elevated.
  3. Elevated bilirubin levels.
- Elevated BUN and creatinine
- Proteinuria
- Coagulation studies
  1. Demonstrate abnormal prothrombin time *or*
  2. Reveal DIC
- Terminal hypoglycemia
- CSF
  1. Pleocytosis
  2. Elevated protein count
- Specific diagnosis confirmed by:
  1. Viral isolation from blood
  2. Viral antigen in serum (ELISA)
  3. Viral RNA by PCR
  4. IgM-capture ELISA
     a. Preferred serologic test.
     b. Appears within 5-7 days.
     c. Rising Ab confirmed by paired sera.
     d. Cross-reactivity with other flavivirus infections.
  5. Immunohistochemical staining of postmortem liver biopsy specimens

TREATMENT

ACUTE GENERAL Rx

- Treatment symptomatic
- Acetaminophen (headache and fever)
- Antacids, cimetidine (GI bleeding)
- Blood transfusion, volume replacement for hemorrhage and shock
- Dialysis for renal failure
- Avoidance of sedatives and drugs dependent on hepatic metabolism
- Treatment of secondary bacterial infections

DISPOSITION

Follow-up until hepatic, renal, CNS disease resolved

REFERRAL

To infectious diseases expert for accurate diagnosis and management

PEARLS & CONSIDERATIONS

PREVENTION

- Yellow fever is preventable.
- Recovery from yellow fever confers lasting immunity.
- Live, attenuated yellow fever vaccine provides protective immunity in 95% of vaccinees within 10 days of vaccination.
- Reimmunization at 10-yr intervals is required for travel.
- Vaccine contraindicated in:
  1. Infants <6 months (postvaccinal encephalitis)
  2. Immunosuppressed patients
  3. Pregnant women and nursing mothers
  4. Patients with egg hypersensitivity
- Adverse effects of vaccine:
  1. General
     a. Mild headaches, myalgias, low-grade fevers (25% vaccinees in clinical trials).
     b. Immediate hypersensitivity reaction (history of egg allergy).
  2. Vaccine-associated neurotropic disease (postvaccine encephalitis)
     a. Primarily among infants.
     b. Adult cases only in first-time vaccine recipients.
  3. Vaccine-associated viscerotropic disease
     a. Disease syndrome resembling wild-type yellow fever, often fatal.
     b. All cases in first-time vaccinees.
     c. Health care providers should provide vaccine only to persons planning to travel to areas reporting yellow fever activity or areas in the yellow fever endemic zone.

SUGGESTED READINGS

Adverse events associated with 17D—derived yellow fever vaccination—United States, *Morb Mortal Wkly Rep* 51:989, 2002.

Monath TP: Yellow fever: an update, *Lancet* 1:11, 2001.

AUTHOR: **MARILYN FABBRI, M.D.**

BASIC INFORMATION

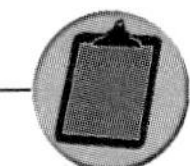

DEFINITION

Zenker's (hypopharyngeal) diverticulum refers to the acquired physiologic obstruction of the esophageal introitus that results from mucosal herniation (false diverticulum) posteriorly between the cricopharyngeus muscle and the inferior pharyngeal constrictor muscle (Fig. 1-259).

SYNONYMS

- Pharyngoesophageal diverticulum
- Pulsion diverticulum

ICD-9CM CODES
530.6 Zenker's diverticulum (esophagus)

EPIDEMIOLOGY & DEMOGRAPHICS

- Rare disease: <1% of all barium swallows
- Commonly seen in people over 50 yr of age (most common in women and elderly)
- Peak incidence is seventh to ninth decades
- Associated with GERD and hiatal hernia

PHYSICAL FINDINGS & CLINICAL PRESENTATION

Small Zenker's diverticulum may be asymptomatic. As they become larger, symptoms include:

- Dysphagia to solids and liquids
- Regurgitation of undigested food
- Sensation of globus or fullness in the neck
- Cough
- Halitosis
- Aspiration pneumonia
- Weight loss
- Voice changes

ETIOLOGY

The specific cause of Zenker's diverticulum is not known; however, the leading hypothesis suggests the following:

- During swallowing there is raised intraluminal pressure secondary to the incomplete opening of the cricopharyngeus muscle (improperly timed relaxation) before the bolus of food can be driven forward into the stomach.
- Discordination of the swallowing mechanism leads to increased pressure on the mucosa of the hypopharynx resulting in the slow progressive distention of the mucosa in the weakest area of the esophagus, namely the posterior wall. The end result being the formation of a false diverticulum where food elements and secretions may be lodged, causing the symptoms listed previously.

DIAGNOSIS

Clinical presentation and barium swallow typically make the diagnosis of Zenker's diverticulum.

DIFFERENTIAL DIAGNOSIS

The differential diagnosis is similar to anyone presenting with dysphagia:

- Achalasia
- Esophageal spasm
- Esophageal carcinoma
- Esophageal webs
- Peptic stricture
- Lower esophageal (Schatzki) ring
- Foreign bodies
- CNS disorders (stroke, Parkinson's disease, ALS, multiple sclerosis, myasthenia gravis, muscular dystrophies)
- Dermatomyositis
- Infection

WORKUP

The workup for suspected Zenker's diverticulum should include a barium swallow. Upper endoscopy runs the risk of perforation. Manometry motility studies are usually not indicated because they will not change the course of treatment.

LABORATORY TESTS

There are no specific laboratory tests to diagnose Zenker's diverticulum.

IMAGING STUDIES

- Barium swallow is the diagnostic procedure of choice. Radiographically Zenker's diverticulum is easily demonstrated with a barium contrast study (Fig. 1-260).
- Endoscopy is indicated if barium studies show mucosal irregularities to rule out neoplasia.
- Oropharyngeal-esophageal scintigraphy has recently been shown to be an effective, sensitive, and simple diagnostic study for both qualitative and quantitative analyses.
- Barium swallow characteristically demonstrates a herniated sac with a narrow diverticular neck that typically originates just proximal to the cricopharyngeus at the level of C5-C6.
- A chest x-ray is performed in cases of suspected aspiration pneumonia.

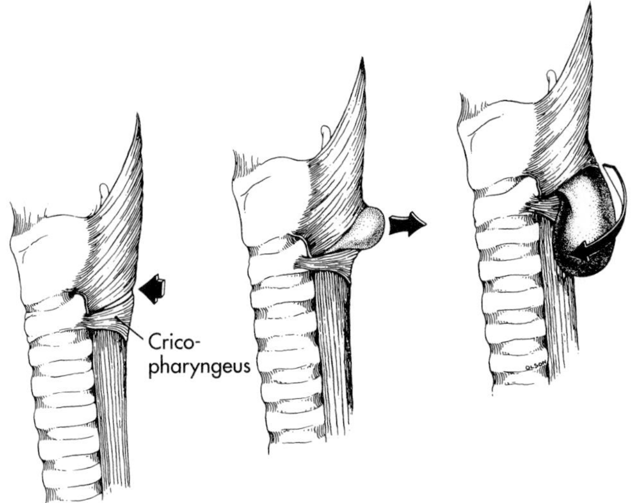

FIGURE 1-259 Formation of pharyngoesophageal (Zenker's) diverticulum. *Left,* Herniation of the pharyngeal mucosa and submucosa occurs at the point of transition *(arrow)* between the oblique fibers of the thyropharyngeus muscle and the more horizontal fibers of the cricopharyngeus muscle. *Center and right,* As the diverticulum enlarges, it dissects toward the left side and downward into the superior mediastinum in the prevertebral space. (From Sabiston D: *Textbook of surgery,* ed 15, Philadelphia, 1997, WB Saunders.)

TREATMENT

NONPHARMACOLOGIC THERAPY

- Soft mechanical diet can be tried in patients with symptoms of dysphagia.
- Avoid seeds, skins, and nuts.

ACUTE GENERAL Rx

- Endoscopic techniques (esophagodiverticulostomy) have largely replaced conventional treatment by open surgery; these include:
  1. Endoscopic stapler diverticulotomy (some recommend it as the initial treatment of choice)
  2. Microendoscopic carbon dioxide laser surgical diverticulotomy
- Surgery is the recommended treatment for symptomatic patients with Zenker's diverticulum.

- Surgical treatment relieves symptoms (dysphagia, cough, aspiration) in nearly all patients with Zenker's diverticulum.
- Surgical procedures include:
  1. Cervical diverticulectomy with cricopharyngeal myotomy (most common approach)
  2. Diverticulopexy or diverticular inversion with cricopharyngeal myotomy
  3. Diverticulectomy alone
  4. Cricopharyngeal myotomy alone
- Surgical mortality <1.5%.

CHRONIC Rx

In patients not having surgery, treatment is directed toward any complications that may occur:

- Antibiotics for aspiration pneumonia
- H_2 antagonists for ulcerations that can develop within the diverticulum
- Botulinum toxin is considered for temporary relief of dysphagia

DISPOSITION

- The natural history of Zenker's diverticulum if left untreated is one of progressive enlargement of the diverticulum.
- As the diverticulum enlarges, the risk of complications, including aspiration pneumonia, increases.
- Recurrence of Zenker's diverticulum (4%) postoperatively can occur; however, patients are usually not symptomatic.

REFERRAL

Any patient with dysphagia requires a gastroenterology consultation. A thoracic surgical, ENT, or head and neck surgeon may be consulted if surgery is considered for Zenker's diverticulum.

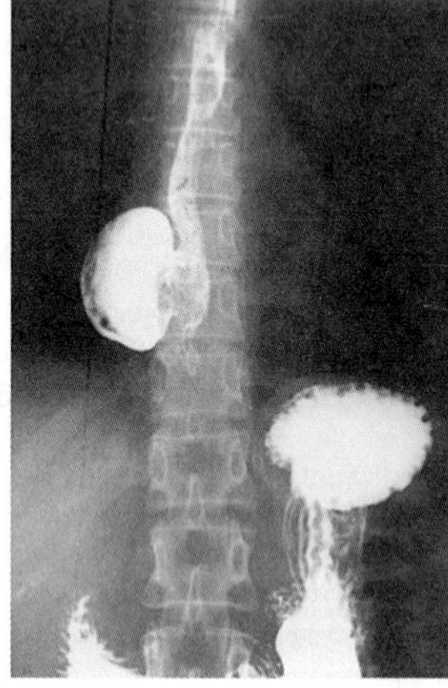
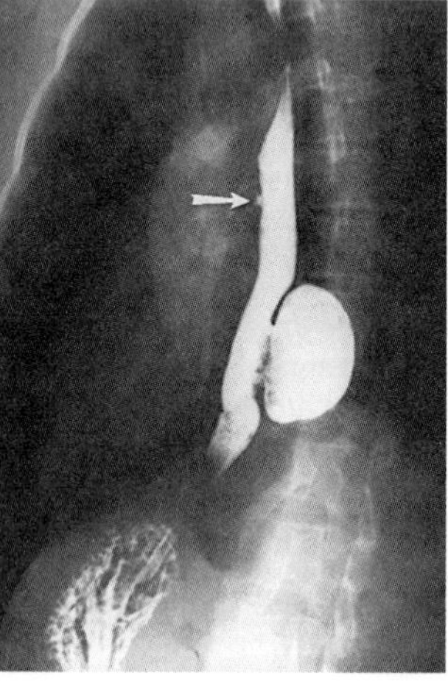

FIGURE 1-260 Posteroanterior *(left)* and oblique *(right)* views from barium esophagogram showing both a typical diverticulum of the junction of the mid- and distal esophagus and a small traction diverticulum *(arrow)* of the mid-esophagus. (From Sabiston D: *Textbook of surgery,* ed 15, Philadelphia, 1997, Saunders.)

PEARLS & CONSIDERATIONS

COMMENTS

- The association of cancer with Zenker's diverticulum is rare (0.4%).
- Zenker's diverticulum forms in "Killian's triangle," the point between the oblique fibers of the inferior pharyngeal muscle and the horizontal fibers of the cricopharyngeus muscle.

SUGGESTED READINGS

Achkar E: Zenker's diverticulum, *Dig Dis* 16(3):144, 1998.

Blitzer A, Brin MF: Use of botulinum toxin for diagnosis and management of cricopharyngeal achalasia, *Otolaryngol Head Neck Surg* 116(3):328, 1997.

Bremner CG: Zenker's diverticulum, *Arch Surg* 133(10):1131, 1998.

Bremmer CG, DeMeester TR: Endoscopic treatment of Zenker's diverticulum, *Gastrointestl Endosc* 49(1):126, 1999.

Chang W et al: Carbon dioxide laser endoscopic diverticulotomy versus open diverticulotomy for Zenker's Diverticulum, *Laryngoscope* 114(3):519, 2004.

Gustantini M et al: Esophageal diverticula, *Best Pract Res Clin Gastroenterology* 18(1):3, 2004.

Manni J et al: The endoscopic stapler diverticulotomy for Zenker's Diverticulum, *Eur Arch Otorhinolaryngol* 261(2):68, 2004.

Richtsmeire WJ: Endoscopic management of Zenker diverticulum: a staple assisted approach, *Am J Med* 3A:175S, 2003.

Siddiq MA, Sood S, Strachan D: Pharyngeal pouch (Zenker's diculum), *Postgrad Med J* 77(910):506, 2001.

Valenza V et al: Scintigraphic evaluation of Zenker's Diverticulum, *Eur J Nucl Med Mol Imaging* 30(12):1657, 2003.

AUTHOR: **HEMCHAND RAMBERAN, M.D.**

BASIC INFORMATION

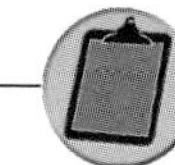

DEFINITION

Zollinger-Ellison (ZE) syndrome is a hypergastrinemic state caused by a pancreatic or extrapancreatic non–beta islet cell tumor (gastrinoma) and resulting in peptic acid disease.

SYNONYMS

Gastrinoma

ICD-9CM CODES

251.5 Zollinger-Ellison syndrome

EPIDEMIOLOGY & DEMOGRAPHICS

- Incidence is unknown, but 0.1% of all duodenal ulcers are believed to be caused by ZE.
- Occurs in both genders and at any age (most common in 30-50 yr of age).
- Two thirds of gastrinomas are sporadic, and one third are associated with multiple endocrine neoplasia type 1 (MEN-1), an autosomal dominant genetic disorder that also includes hyperparathyroidism and pituitary tumors.
- About 60% of gastrinomas are malignant.

PHYSICAL FINDINGS & CLINICAL PRESENTATION

- The vast majority of patients (95%) present with symptoms of peptic ulcer (see Section I).
- 60% of patients have symptoms related to gastroesophageal reflux disease (see Section I).
- One third of patients with ZE have diarrhea and, less commonly, steatorrhea.

The following circumstances warrant suspicion of ZE syndrome:

- Ulcers distal to the first portion of the duodenum
- Multiple peptic ulcers
- Ineffective treatment for peptic ulcer disease with the usual drug doses and schedules
- Peptic ulcer and diarrhea
- Familial history of peptic ulcer
- Patients with a personal or family history suggesting parathyroid or pituitary tumors of dysfunction
- Peptic ulcer and urinary tract calculi
- Patients with peptic ulcer who are negative for *H. pylori* and do not have a history of NSAID use

ETIOLOGY

- The pathophysiologic manifestations of ZE syndrome are related to the effects of hypergastrinemia. Gastrin stimulates gastric acid secretion, which in turn is responsible for the development of duodenal ulcers and diarrhea. Gastrin also promotes gastric mucosal epithelial cell growth and resulting parietal cell hyperplasia.
- Gastrinomas are usually small (0.1-2 cm) but sometimes large (>20 cm) tumors.
- 60% of gastrinomas are malignant, with liver and regional lymph nodes the most common site of metastases. Histology is not a good predictor of the biology of gastrinomas.
- 60% of patients with MEN-1 have gastrinomas.
- 10% of patients with ZE syndrome have islet cell hyperplasia rather than gastrinomas; in 10%-20% of patients with gastrinoma the tumors cannot be located because of small size.

DIAGNOSIS

DIFFERENTIAL DIAGNOSIS

- Peptic ulcer disease (see Section I)
- Gastroesophageal reflux disease (see Section I)

Diarrhea (see Section III, "Diarrhea, Acute" and "Diarrhea, Chronic")

WORKUP

- Diagnosis of peptic ulcer
  - UGI series (may also show prominent gastric rugal folds)
  - Endoscopy
- Gastric acid secretion
- Serum gastrin level (fasting) >150 pg/ml (causes of false-positive: pernicious anemia, renal failure, retained gastric antrum syndrome, diabetes mellitus, rheumatoid arthritis)
- Provocative gastrin level tests
  - Secretin stimulation
  - Calcium stimulation
  - Standard test meal stimulation
- Gastrinoma localization
  - Arteriography
  - Abdominal sonography
  - Abdominal CT scan
  - Abdominal MRI
  - Selective portal vein branch gastrin level
  - Octreotide scan

TREATMENT

- Surgical resection of the gastrinoma (NOTE: 90% of gastrinomas can be located, resulting in a 40% overall cure rate)
- Total gastrectomy or vagotomy (palliative in some patients)
- Medical treatment
  - Proton pump inhibitors (e.g., omeprazole or lansoprazole)
  - Somatostatin or octreotide
  - Chemotherapy for metastatic gastrinoma with streptozotocin, 5-FU, and doxorubicin

PROGNOSIS

Five-year survival:

- Two thirds of all patients
- 20% with liver metastases
- 90% without liver metastases

REFERRAL

To gastroenterologist

SUGGESTED READINGS

McGuigan JE: Zollinger-Ellison syndrome. In Feldman M, Scharschmidt BF, Sleisenger MH (eds): *Sleisenger & Fordtran's gastrointestinal and liver disease,* ed 6, St Louis, 1998, WB Saunders.

Norten JA et al: Surgery to cure Zollinger-Ellison syndrome, *N Engl J Med* 341:635, 1999.

AUTHOR: **TOM J. WACHTEL, M.D.**

SECTION II

Differential Diagnosis

ABDOMINAL DISTENTION

ICD-9CM # 787.3

NONMECHANICAL OBSTRUCTION

Excessive intraluminal gas.
Intraabdominal infection.
Trauma.
Retroperitoneal irritation (renal colic, neoplasms, infections, hemorrhage).
Vascular insufficiency (thrombosis, embolism).
Mechanical ventilation.
Extraabdominal infection (sepsis, pneumonia, empyema, osteomyelitis of spine).
Metabolic/toxic abnormalities (hypokalemia, uremia, lead poisoning).
Chemical irritation (perforated ulcer, bile, pancreatitis).
Peritoneal inflammation.
Severe pain, pain medications.

MECHANICAL OBSTRUCTION

Neoplasm (intraluminal, extraluminal).
Adhesions, endometriosis.
Infection (intraabdominal abscess, diverticulitis).
Gallstones.
Foreign body, bezoars.
Pregnancy.
Hernias.
Volvulus.
Stenosis at surgical anastomosis, radiation stenosis.
Fecaliths.
Inflammatory bowel disease.
Gastric outlet obstruction.
Hematoma.
Other: parasites, superior mesenteric artery (SMA) syndrome, pneumatosis intestinalis, annular pancreas, Hirschsprung's disease, intussusception, meconium.

ABDOMINAL PAIN, ADOLESCENCE[23]

ICD-9CM # 789.67

Acute gastroenteritis.
Appendicitis.
Inflammatory bowel disease.
Peptic ulcer disease.
Cholecystitis.
Neoplasm.
Other.
Functional abdominal pain.
Pelvic inflammatory disease.
Pregnancy.
Pyelonephritis.
Renal stone.
Trauma.

ABDOMINAL PAIN, CHILDHOOD[23]

ICD-9CM # 789.67

Acute gastroenteritis.
Appendicitis.
Constipation.
Cholecystitis, acute.
Intestinal obstruction.
Pancreatitis.
Neoplasm.
Inflammatory bowel disease.
Other:
 Functional abdominal pain.
 Pyelonephritis.
 Pneumonia.
 Diabetic ketoacidosis.
 Heavy metal poisoning.
 Sickle cell crisis.
 Trauma.

ABDOMINAL PAIN, DIFFUSE

ICD-9CM # 789.67

Early appendicitis.
Aortic aneurysm.
Gastroenteritis.
Intestinal obstruction.
Diverticulitis.
Peritonitis.
Mesenteric insufficiency or infarction.
Pancreatitis.
Inflammatory bowel disease.
Irritable bowel.
Mesenteric adenitis.
Metabolic: toxins, lead poisoning, uremia, drug overdose, diabetic ketoacidosis (DKA), heavy metal poisoning.
Sickle cell crisis.
Pneumonia (rare).
Trauma.
Urinary tract infection, pelvic inflammatory disease (PID).
Other: acute intermittent porphyria, tabes dorsalis, periarteritis nodosa, Henoch-Schönlein purpura, adrenal insufficiency.

ABDOMINAL PAIN, EPIGASTRIC

ICD-9CM # 789.66

Gastric: peptic ulcer disease (PUD), gastric outlet obstruction, gastric ulcer.
Duodenal: PUD, duodenitis.
Biliary: cholecystitis, cholangitis.
Hepatic: hepatitis.
Pancreatic: pancreatitis.
Intestinal: high small bowel obstruction, early appendicitis.
Cardiac: angina, MI, pericarditis.
Pulmonary: pneumonia, pleurisy, pneumothorax.
Subphrenic abscess.
Vascular: dissecting aneurysm, mesenteric ischemia.

ABDOMINAL PAIN, INFANCY[23]

ICD-9CM # 789.67

Acute gastroenteritis.
Appendicitis.
Intussusception.
Volvulus.
Meckel's diverticulum.
Other:
 Colic.
 Trauma.

ABDOMINAL PAIN, LEFT LOWER QUADRANT

ICD-9CM # 789.64

Intestinal: diverticulitis, intestinal obstruction, perforated ulcer, inflammatory bowel disease, perforated descending colon, inguinal hernia, neoplasm, appendicitis.
Reproductive: ectopic pregnancy, ovarian cyst, torsion of ovarian cyst, tuboovarian abscess, mittelschmerz, endometriosis, seminal vesiculitis.
Renal: renal or ureteral calculi, pyelonephritis, neoplasm.

SECTION II

Vascular: leaking aortic aneurysm.
Psoas abscess.
Trauma.

ABDOMINAL PAIN, LEFT UPPER QUADRANT

ICD-9CM # 789.32

Gastric: PUD, gastritis, pyloric stenosis, hiatal hernia.
Pancreatic: pancreatitis, neoplasm, stone in pancreatic duct or ampulla.
Cardiac: MI, angina pectoris.
Splenic: splenomegaly, ruptured spleen, splenic abscess, splenic infarction.
Renal: calculi, pyelonephritis, neoplasm.
Pulmonary: pneumonia, empyema, pulmonary infarction.
Vascular: ruptured aortic aneurysm.
Cutaneous: herpes zoster.
Trauma.
Intestinal: high fecal impaction, perforated colon, diverticulitis.

ABDOMINAL PAIN, PERIUMBILICAL

ICD-9CM # 789.65

Intestinal: small bowel obstruction or gangrene, early appendicitis.
Vascular: mesenteric thrombosis, dissecting aortic aneurysm.
Pancreatic: pancreatitis.
Metabolic: uremia, DKA.
Trauma.

ABDOMINAL PAIN, POORLY LOCALIZED[23]

ICD-9CM # 789.60

EXTRAABDOMINAL

Metabolic

DKA, acute intermittent porphyria, hyperthyroidism, hypothyroidism, hypercalcemia, hypokalemia, uremia, hyperlipidemia, hyperparathyroidism.

Hematologic

Sickle cell crisis, leukemia or lymphoma, Henoch-Schönlein purpura.

Infectious

Infectious mononucleosis, Rocky Mountain spotted fever, acquired immunodeficiency syndrome (AIDS), streptococcal pharyngitis (in children), herpes zoster.

Drugs and toxins

Heavy metal poisoning, black widow spider bites, withdrawal syndromes, mushroom ingestion.

Referred pain

Pulmonary: pneumonia, pulmonary embolism, pneumothorax.
Cardiac: angina, myocardial infarction, pericarditis, myocarditis.
Genitourinary: prostatitis, epididymitis, orchitis, testicular torsion.
Musculoskeletal: rectus sheath hematoma.

Functional

Somatization disorder, malingering, hypochondriasis, Munchausen syndrome.

INTRAABDOMINAL

Early appendicitis, gastroenteritis, peritonitis, pancreatitis, abdominal aortic aneurysm, mesenteric insufficiency or infarction, intestinal obstruction, volvulus, ulcerative colitis.

ABDOMINAL PAIN, PREGNANCY[23]

ICD-9CM # 789.67

GYNECOLOGIC (GESTATIONAL AGE IN PARENTHESES)

Miscarriage	(<20 wk; 80% <12 wk)
Septic abortion	(<20 wk)
Ectopic pregnancy	(<14 wk)
Corpus luteum cyst rupture	(<12 wk)
Ovarian torsion	(Especially <24 wk)
Pelvic inflammatory disease	(<12 wk)
Chorioamnionitis	(>16 wk)
Abruptio placentae	(>16 wk)

NONGYNECOLOGIC

Appendicitis	(Throughout)
Cholecystitis	(Throughout)
Hepatitis	(Throughout)
Pyelonephritis	(Throughout)
Preeclampsia	(>20 wk)

ABDOMINAL PAIN, RIGHT LOWER QUADRANT

ICD-9CM # 789.63

Intestinal: acute appendicitis, regional enteritis, incarcerated hernia, cecal diverticulitis, intestinal obstruction, perforated ulcer, perforated cecum, Meckel's diverticulitis.
Reproductive: ectopic pregnancy, ovarian cyst, torsion of ovarian cyst, salpingitis, tuboovarian abscess, mittelschmerz, endometriosis, seminal vesiculitis.
Renal: renal and ureteral calculi, neoplasms, pyelonephritis.
Vascular: leaking aortic aneurysm.
Psoas abscess.
Trauma.
Cholecystitis.

ABDOMINAL PAIN, RIGHT UPPER QUADRANT

ICD-9CM # 789.61

Biliary: calculi, infection, inflammation, neoplasm.
Hepatic: hepatitis, abscess, hepatic congestion, neoplasm, trauma.
Gastric: PUD, pyloric stenosis, neoplasm, alcoholic gastritis, hiatal hernia.
Pancreatic: pancreatitis, neoplasm, stone in pancreatic duct or ampulla.
Renal: calculi, infection, inflammation, neoplasm, rupture of kidney.
Pulmonary: pneumonia, pulmonary infarction, right-sided pleurisy.
Intestinal: retrocecal appendicitis, intestinal obstruction, high fecal impaction, diverticulitis.
Cardiac: myocardial ischemia (particularly involving the inferior wall), pericarditis.
Cutaneous: herpes zoster.
Trauma.
Fitz-Hugh-Curtis syndrome (perihepatitis).

ABDOMINAL PAIN, SUPRAPUBIC

ICD-9CM # 789.85

Intestinal: colon obstruction or gangrene, diverticulitis, appendicitis.
Reproductive system: ectopic pregnancy, mittelschmerz, torsion of ovarian cyst, PID, salpingitis, endometriosis, rupture of endometrioma.
Cystitis, rupture of urinary bladder.

ABORTION, RECURRENT

ICD-9CM # 761.8

Congenital anatomic abnormalities.
Adhesions (uterine synechiae).
Uterine fibroids.
Endometriosis.
Endocrine abnormalities (luteal phase insufficiency, hypothyroidism, uncontrolled diabetes mellitus).
Parenteral chromosome abnormalities.
Maternal infections (cervical mycoplasma, ureaplasma, chlamydia).
DES exposure, heavy metal exposure.
Thrombocytosis.
Allogenic immunity, autoimmunity, lupus anticoagulant.

ACHES AND PAINS, DIFFUSE[21]

ICD-9CM # 719.49

Postviral arthralgias/myalgias.
Bilateral soft tissue rheumatism.
Overuse syndromes.
Fibrositis.
Hypothyroidism.
Metabolic bone disease.
Paraneoplastic syndrome.
Myopathy (polymyositis, dermatomyositis).
RA.
Sjögren's syndrome.
Polymyalgia rheumatica.
Hypermobility.
Benign arthralgias/myalgias.
Chronic fatigue syndrome.
Hypophosphatemia.

ACIDOSIS, LACTIC

ICD-9CM # 276.2

TISSUE HYPOXIA

Shock (hypovolemic, cardiogenic, endotoxic).
Respiratory failure (asphyxia).
Severe CHF.
Severe anemia.
Carbon monoxide or cyanide poisoning.

ASSOCIATED WITH SYSTEMIC DISORDERS

Neoplastic diseases (e.g., leukemia, lymphoma).
Liver or renal failure.
Sepsis.
Diabetes mellitus.
Seizure activity.
Abnormal intestinal flora.
Alkalosis.
HIV.

SECONDARY TO DRUGS OR TOXINS

Salicylates.
Ethanol, methanol, ethylene glycol.
Fructose or sorbitol.
Biguanides (phenformin, metformin [usually occurring in patients with renal insufficiency]).
Isoniazid.
Streptozocin.
Nucleoside reverse transcriptase inhibitors (zidovudine, didanosine, stavudine).

HEREDITARY DISORDERS

G6PD deficiency and others.

ACIDOSIS, METABOLIC

ICD-9CM # 276.2

METABOLIC ACIDOSIS WITH INCREASED AG (AG ACIDOSIS)

Lactic acidosis.
Ketoacidosis (diabetes mellitus, alcoholic ketoacidosis).
Uremia (chronic renal failure).
Ingestion of toxins (paraldehyde, methanol, salicylate, ethylene glycol).
High-fat diet (mild acidosis).

METABOLIC ACIDOSIS WITH NORMAL AG (HYPERCHLOREMIC ACIDOSIS)

Renal tubular acidosis (including acidosis of aldosterone deficiency).
Intestinal loss of HCO_3^- (diarrhea, pancreatic fistula).
Carbonic anhydrase inhibitors (e.g., acetazolamide).
Dilutional acidosis (as a result of rapid infusion of bicarbonate-free isotonic saline).
Ingestion of exogenous acids (ammonium chloride, methionine, cystine, calcium chloride).
Ileostomy.
Ureterosigmoidostomy.
Drugs: amiloride, triamterene, spironolactone, β-blockers.

ACIDOSIS RESPIRATORY

ICD-9CM # 276.2

Pulmonary disease (COPD, severe pneumonia, pulmonary edema, interstitial fibrosis).
Airway obstruction (foreign body, severe bronchospasm, laryngospasm).
Thoracic cage disorders (pneumothorax, flail chest, kyphoscoliosis).
Defects in muscles of respiration (myasthenia gravis, hypokalemia, muscular dystrophy).
Defects in peripheral nervous system (amyotrophic lateral sclerosis, poliomyelitis, Guillain-Barré syndrome, botulism, tetanus, organophosphate poisoning, spinal cord injury).
Depression of respiratory center (anesthesia, narcotics, sedatives, vertebral artery embolism or thrombosis, increased intracranial pressure).
Failure of mechanical ventilator.

ACUTE SCROTUM

ICD-9CM # 608.9

Testicular torsion.
Epididymitis.
Testicular neoplasm.
Orchitis.

ADNEXAL MASS[23]

ICD-9CM # VARIES WITH SPECIFIC DISORDER

Ovary (neoplasm, endometriosis, functional cyst).
Fallopian tube (ectopic pregnancy, neoplasm, tuboovarian abscess, hydrosalpinx, paratubal cyst).
Uterus (fibroid, neoplasm).
Retroperitoneum (neoplasm, abdominal wall hematoma or abscess).
Urinary tract (pelvic kidney, distended bladder, urachal cyst).
Inflammatory bowel disease.
GI tract neoplasm.
Diverticular disease.
Appendicitis.
Bowel loop with feces.

ADRENAL MASSES[33]

ICD-9CM # 194.0 ADRENOCORTICAL CARCINOMA
255.8 ADRENAL HYPERPLASIA

UNILATERAL ADRENAL MASSES

Functional lesions
Adrenal adenoma.
Adrenal carcinoma.
Pheochromocytoma.
Primary aldosteronism, adenomatous type.
Nonfunctional lesions
Incidentaloma of adrenal.
Ganglioneuroma.
Myelolipoma.
Hematoma.
Adenolipoma.
Metastasis.

BILATERAL ADRENAL MASSES

Functional lesions:
ACTH-dependent Cushing's syndrome.
Congenital adrenal hyperplasia.
Pheochromocytoma.
Conn's syndrome, hyperplastic variety.
Micronodular adrenal disease.
Idiopathic bilateral adrenal hypertrophy.
Nonfunctional lesions:
Infection (tuberculosis, fungi).
Infiltration (leukemia, lymphoma).
Replacement (amyloidosis).
Hemorrhage.
Bilateral metastases.

ADYNAMIC ILEUS[23]

ICD-9CM # 560.1

Abdominal trauma.
Infection (retroperitoneal, pelvic, intrathoracic).
Laparotomy.
Metabolic disease (hypokalemia).
Renal colic.
Skeletal injury (rib fracture, vertebral fracture).
Medications (e.g., narcotics).

AEROPHAGIA (BELCHING, ERUCTATION)

ICD-9CM # 787.3

Anxiety disorders.
Rapid food ingestion.
Carbonated beverages.
Nursing infants (especially when nursing in horizontal position).
Eating or drinking in supine position.
Gum chewing.
Poorly fitting dentures, orthodontic appliances.
Hiatal hernia, gastritis, nonulcer dyspepsia.
Cholelithiasis, cholecystitis.
Ingestion of legumes, onions, peppers.

AIRWAY OBSTRUCTION, PEDIATRIC AGE[17]

ICD-9CM # 496 OBSTRUCTION DUE TO BRONCHOSPASM
934.9 OBSTRUCTION DUE TO FOREIGN BODY
478.75 OBSTRUCTION DUE TO LARYNGOSPASM
506.9 OBSTRUCTION DUE TO INHALATION OF FUMES OR VAPORS

CONGENITAL CAUSES

Craniofacial dysmorphism.
Hemangioma.
Laryngeal cleft/web.
Laryngoceles, cysts.
Laryngomalacia.
Macroglossia.
Tracheal stenosis.
Vascular ring.
Vocal cord paralysis.

ACQUIRED INFECTIOUS CAUSES

Acute laryngotracheobronchitis.
Epiglottitis.
Laryngeal papillomatosis.
Membranous croup (bacterial tracheitis).
Mononucleosis.
Retropharyngeal abscess.
Spasmodic croup.
Diphtheria.

ACQUIRED NONINFECTIOUS CAUSES

Anaphylaxis.
Foreign body aspiration.
Supraglottic hypotonia.
Thermal/chemical burn.
Trauma.
Vocal cord paralysis.
Angioneurotic edema.

AKINETIC/RIGID SYNDROME[1]

ICD-9CM # NOT AVAILABLE

Parkinsonism (idiopathic, drug-induced).
Catatonia (psychosis).
Progressive supranuclear palsy.
Multisystem atrophy (Shy-Drager syndrome, olivopontocerebellar atrophy).
Diffuse Lewy-body disease.
Toxins (MPTP, manganese, carbon monoxide).
Huntington's disease and other hereditary neurodegenerative disorders.

ALKALOSIS, METABOLIC

ICD-9CM # 276.3

CHLORIDE-RESPONSIVE

Vomiting.
Nasogastric (NG) suction.
Diuretics.
Posthypercapnic alkalosis.
Stool losses (laxative abuse, cystic fibrosis, villous adenoma).
Massive blood transfusion.
Exogenous alkali administration.

CHLORIDE-RESISTANT

Hyperadrenocorticoid states (Cushing's syndrome, primary hyperaldosteronism, secondary mineralocorticoidism [licorice, chewing tobacco]).
Hypomagnesemia.
Hypokalemia.
Bartter's syndrome.

ALKALOSIS, RESPIRATORY

ICD-9CM # 276.3

Hypoxemia (pneumonia, pulmonary embolism, atelectasis, high-altitude living).
Drugs (salicylates, xanthenes, progesterone, epinephrine, thyroxine, nicotine).
Central nervous system (CNS) disorders (tumor, cerebrovascular accident [CVA], trauma, infections).
Psychogenic hyperventilation (anxiety, hysteria).
Hepatic encephalopathy.
Gram-negative sepsis.
Hyponatremia.
Sudden recovery from metabolic acidosis.
Assisted ventilation.

ALOPECIA[12,25]

ICD-9CM # 704.00 ALOPECIA NOS
704.01 ALOPECIA, ANDROGENIC
704.01 ALOPECIA AREATA
757.4 ALOPECIA, CONGENITAL
316 ALOPECIA, PSYCHOGENIC

SCARRING ALOPECIA

Congenital (aplasia cutis).
Tinea capitis with inflammation (kerion).
Bacterial folliculitis.
Discoid lupus erythematosus.
Lichen planopilaris.
Folliculitis decalvans.
Neoplasm.
Trauma.

NONSCARRING ALOPECIA

Cosmetic treatment.
Tinea capitis.
Structural hair shaft disease.
Trichotillomania (hair pulling).
Anagen arrest.
Telogen arrest.
Alopecia areata.
Androgenetic alopecia.

ALVEOLAR CONSOLIDATION

ICD-9CM # 514

Infection.
Neoplasm (bronchoalveolar carcinoma, lymphoma).
Aspiration.
Trauma.
Hemorrhage (Wegener's Goodpasture, bleeding diathesis).
ARDS.
CHF.
Renal failure.
Eosinophilic pneumonia.
Bronchiolitis obliterans.
Pulmonary alveolar proteinosis.

ALVEOLAR HEMORRHAGE[25]

ICD-9CM # 770.3

Hematologic disorders (coagulopathies, thrombocytopenia).
Goodpasture syndrome (antibasement-membrane antibody disease).
Wegener's vasculitis.
Immune complex-mediated vasculitis.
Idiopathic pulmonary hemosiderosis.
Drugs (penicillamine).
Lymphangiogram contrast.
Mitral stenosis.

AMENORRHEA

ICD-9CM # 626.0

PREGNANCY

EARLY MENOPAUSE

HYPOTHALAMIC DYSFUNCTION: defective synthesis or release of LHRH, anorexia nervosa, stress, exercise.
PITUITARY DYSFUNCTION: neoplasm, postpartum hemorrhage, surgery, radiotherapy.
OVARIAN DYSFUNCTION: gonadal dysgenesis, 17-a-hydroxylase deficiency, premature ovarian failure, polycystic ovarian disease, gonadal stromal tumors.

UTEROVAGINAL ABNORMALITIES

Congenital: imperforate hymen, imperforate cervix, imperforate or absent vagina, müllerian agenesis.
Acquired: destruction of endometrium with curettage (Asherman's syndrome), closure of cervix or vagina caused by traumatic injury, hysterectomy.

OTHER

Metabolic diseases (liver, kidney), malnutrition, rapid weight loss, exogenous obesity, endocrine abnormalities (Cushing's syndrome, Graves' disease, hypothyroidism).

AMNESIA

ICD-9CM # 292.83 DRUG INDUCED
300.12 HYSTERICAL
780.9 RETROGRADE
437.7 TRANSIENT GLOBAL

Degenerative diseases (e.g., Alzheimer's, Huntington's disease).
CVA (especially when involving thalamus, basal forebrain, and hippocampus).
Head trauma.
Postsurgical (e.g., mammillary body surgery, bilateral temporal lobectomy).
Infections (herpes simplex encephalitis, meningitis).
Wernicke-Korsakoff syndrome.
Cerebral hypoxia.
Hypoglycemia.
CNS neoplasms.
Creutzfeldt-Jakob disease.
Medications (e.g., midazolam and other benzodiazepines).
Psychosis.
Malingering.

ANAL INCONTINENCE[23]

ICD-9CM # 787.6

TRAUMATIC

Nerve injured in surgery.
Spinal cord injury.

Obstetric trauma.
Sphincter injury.

NEUROLOGIC

Spinal cord lesions.
Dementia.
Autonomic neuropathy (e.g., diabetes mellitus).
Obstetrics: pudendal nerve stretched during surgery.
Hirschsprung's disease.

MASS EFFECT

Carcinoma of anal canal.
Carcinoma of rectum.
Foreign body.
Fecal impaction.
Hemorrhoids.

MEDICAL

Procidentia.
Inflammatory disease.
Diarrhea.
Laxative abuse.

PEDIATRIC

Congenital.
Meningocele.
Myelomeningocele.
Spina bifida.
After corrective surgery for imperforate anus.
Sexual abuse.
Encopresis.

ANAPHYLAXIS[18]

ICD-9CM # 995.0

PULMONARY

Laryngeal edema.
Epiglottitis.
Foreign body aspiration.
Pulmonary embolus.
Asphyxiation.
Hyperventilation.

CARDIOVASCULAR

Myocardial infarction.
Arrhythmia.
Hypovolemic shock.
Cardiac arrest.

CNS

Vasovagal reaction.
CVA.
Seizure disorder.
Drug overdose.

ENDOCRINE

Hypoglycemia.
Pheochromocytoma.
Carcinoid syndrome.
Catamenial (progesterone-induced anaphylaxis).

PSYCHIATRIC

Vocal cord dysfunction syndrome.
Munchausen's disease.
Panic attack/globus hystericus.

OTHER

Hereditary angioedema.
Cord urticaria.
Idiopathic urticaria.
Mastocytosis.
Serum sickness.
Idiopathic capillary leak syndrome.
Sulfite exposure.
Scombroid poisoning (tuna, blue fish, mackerel).

ANEMIA, DRUG-INDUCED[15]

ICD-9CM # 283.0

DRUGS THAT MAY INTERFERE WITH RED CELL PRODUCTION BY INDUCING MARROW SUPPRESSION OR APLASIA

Alcohol.
Antineoplastic drugs.
Antithyroid drugs.
Antibiotics.
Oral hypoglycemic agents.
Phenylbutazone.
Azidothymidine (AZT).

DRUGS THAT INTERFERE WITH VITAMIN B_{12}, FOLATE, OR IRON ABSORPTION OR UTILIZATION

Nitrous oxide.
Anticonvulsant drugs.
Antineoplastic drugs.
Isoniazid, cycloserine A.

DRUGS CAPABLE OF PROMOTING HEMOLYSIS

Immune Mediated
Penicillins.
Quinine.
Alpha-methyldopa.
Procainamide.
Mitomycin C.
Oxidative Stress
Antimalarials.
Sulfonamide drugs.
Nalidixic acid.

DRUGS THAT MAY PRODUCE OR PROMOTE BLOOD LOSS

Aspirin.
Alcohol.
Nonsteroidal antiinflammatory agents.
Corticosteroids.
Anticoagulants.

ANEMIA, LOW RETICYLOCYTE COUNT[1]

ICD-9CM # 285.9

MICROCYTIC ANEMIA (MCV <80)

Iron deficiency.
Thalassemia minor.
Sideroblastic anemia.
Lead poisoning.

MACROCYTIC ANEMIA (MCV >100)

Megaloblastic anemias.
Folate deficiency.
Vitamin B_{12} deficiency.
Drug-induced megaloblastic anemia.
Nonmegaloblastic macrocytosis.
Liver disease.
Hypothyroidism.

NORMOCYTIC ANEMIA (MCV 80-100)

Early iron deficiency.
Aplastic anemia.
Myelophthisic disorders.
Endocrinopathies.
Anemia of chronic disease.
Uremia.
Mixed nutritional deficiency.

ANEMIA, MEGALOBLASTIC[33]

ICD-9CM # 281.0 PERNICIOUS ANEMIA
281.1 B_{12} DEFICIENCY
281.2 FOLATE DEFICIENCY
281.3 B_{12} WITH FOLATE DEFICIENCY
281.4 PROTEIN OR AMINO ACID DEFICIENCY
281.8 NUTRITIONAL
281.9 NOS

COBALAMIN (CBL) DEFICIENCY

Nutritional Cbl deficiency (insufficient Cbl intake): vegetarians, vegans, breast-fed infants of mothers with pernicious anemia.
Abnormal intragastric events (inadequate proteolysis of food Cbl): atrophic gastritis, partial gastrectomy with hypochlorhydria.
Loss/atrophy of gastric oxyntic mucosa (deficient IF molecules): total or partial gastrectomy, pernicious anemia (PA), caustic destruction (lye).
Abnormal events in small bowel lumen:
Inadequate pancreatic protease (R-Cbl not degraded, Cbl not transferred to IF).
- Insufficiency of pancreatic protease—pancreatic insufficiency.
- Inactivation of pancreatic protease—Zollinger-Ellison syndrome.

Usurping of luminal Cbl (inadequate Cbl binding to IF).
- By bacteria—stasis syndromes (blind loops, pouches of diverticulosis, strictures, fistulas, anastomoses); impaired bowel motility (scleroderma, pseudoobstruction), hypogammaglobulinemia.
- By *Diphyllobothrium latum*.

Disorders of ileal mucosa/IF receptors (IF-Cbl not bound to IF receptors):
Diminished or absent IF receptors—ileal bypass/resection/fistula.
Abnormal mucosal architecture/function—tropical/nontropical sprue, Crohn's disease, TB ileitis, infiltration by lymphomas, amyloidosis.
IF-/post IF-receptor defects—Imerslund-Graesbeck syndrome, TC II deficiency.
Drug-induced effects (slow K, biguanides, cholestyramine, colchicine, neomycin, PAS).
DISORDERS OF PLASMA CBL TRANSPORT (TC II-CBL NOT DELIVERED TO TC II RECEPTORS)
Congenital TC II deficiency, defective binding of TC II-Cbl to TC II receptors (rare).
METABOLIC DISORDERS (CBL NOT UTILIZED BY CELL)
Inborn enzyme errors (rare).
Acquired disorders: (Cbl oxidized to cob[III]alamin)—N_2O inhalation.

FOLATE DEFICIENCY

Nutritional causes
Decreased dietary intake—poverty and famine (associated with kwashiorkor, marasmus), institutionalized individuals (psychiatric/nursing homes), chronic debilitating disease/goats' milk (low in folate), special diets (slimming), cultural/ethnic cooking techniques (food folate destroyed) or habits (folate-rich foods not consumed).
Decreased diet and increased requirements:
- Physiologic: pregnancy and lactation, prematurity, infancy
- Pathologic: intrinsic hematologic disease (autoimmune hemolytic disease), drugs, malaria; hemoglobinopathies (SS, thalassemia), RBC membrane defects (hereditary spherocytosis, paroxysmal nocturnal hemoglobinopathy); abnormal hematopoiesis (leukemia/lymphoma, myelodysplastic syndrome, agnogenic myeloid metaplasia with myelofibrosis); infiltration with malignant disease; dermatologic (psoriasis).

Folate malabsorption
With normal intestinal mucosa:
- Some drugs (controversial).
- Congenital folate malabsorption (rare).

With mucosal abnormalities—tropical and nontropical sprue, regional enteritis.
Defective cellular folate uptake—familial aplastic anemia (rare)
Inadequate cellular utilization
Folate antagonists (methotrexate).
Hereditary enzyme deficiencies involving folate.
Drugs (multiple effects on folate metabolism)
Alcohol, sulfasalazine, triamterine, pyrimethamine, trimethoprim-sulfamethoxazole, diphenylhydantoin, barbiturates.

MISCELLANEOUS MEGALOBLASTIC ANEMIAS (NOT CAUSED BY CBL OR FOLATE DEFICIENCY)

Congenital disorders of DNA synthesis (rare)
Orotic aciduria, Lesch-Nyhan syndrome, congenital dyserythropoietic anemia.
Acquired disorders of DNA synthesis
Thiamine-responsive megaloblastosis (rare).
Malignancy—erythroleukemia—refractory sideroblastic anemias—all antineoplastic drugs that inhibit DNA synthesis.
Toxic—alcohol.

ANERGY, CUTANEOUS[33]

ICD-9CM # 279.9

IMMUNOLOGIC

Acquired (AIDS, acute leukemia, carcinoma, CLL, Hodgkin's lymphoma, NHL).
Congenital (ataxia-telangiectasia, Di George's syndrome, severe combined immunodeficiency, Wiskott-Aldrich syndrome).

INFECTIONS

Bacterial (bacterial pneumonia, brucellosis).
Disseminated mycotic infections.
Mycobacterial (lepromatous leprosy, TB).
Viral (varicella, hepatitis, influenza, mononucleosis, measles, mumps).

IMMUNOSUPPRESSIVE MEDICATIONS

Systemic corticosteroids.
Methotrexate, cyclophosphamide.
Rifampin.

OTHER

Alcoholic cirrhosis, biliary cirrhosis, sarcoidosis, rheumatic disease.
Diabetes, Crohn's disease, uremia.
Anemia, pyridoxine deficiency, sickle cell anemia.
Burns, malnutrition, pregnancy, old age, surgery.

ANEURYSMS, THORACIC AORTA

ICD-9CM # 441.2

Trauma.
Infection.
Inflammatory (syphilis, Takayasu disease).
Collagen vascular disease (rheumatoid arthritis, ankylosing spondylitis).
Annuloaortic ectasia (Marfan's syndrome, Ehlers-Danlos syndrome).
Congenital.
Coarctation.
Cystic medial necrosis.

ANION GAP INCREASE

ICD-9CM # 276.9

Uremia.
Ketoacidosis (diabetic, starvation, alcoholic).
Lactic acidosis.
Ethylene glycol poisoning.
Salicylate overdose.
Methanol poisoning.

ANISOCORIA

ICD-9CM # 379.41

Mydriatic or miotic drugs.
Prosthetic eye.
Inflammation (keratitis, iridocyclitis).
Infections (herpes zoster, syphilis, meningitis, encephalitis, TB, diphtheria, botulism).
Subdural hemorrhage.
Cavernous sinus thrombosis.
Intracranial neoplasm.
Cerebral aneurysm.
Glaucoma.
CNS degenerative diseases.
Internal carotid ischemia.
Toxic polyneuritis (alcohol, lead).
Adie's syndrome.
Horner's syndrome.
Diabetes mellitus (DM).
Trauma.
Congenital.

ANOVULATION

ICD-9CM # 628.0

Anorexia and bulimia.
Strenuous exercise.
Weight loss/malnutrition.
Empty sella syndrome.
Pituitary disorders (infarction, infection, trauma, irradiation, surgery, microadenomas, macroadenomas).
Idiopathic hypopituitarism.
Drug induced.
Thyroid dysfunction (hypothyroidism, hyperthyroidism).
Systemic diseases (e.g., liver disease).
Adrenal hyperfunction (Cushing's syndrome, congenital adrenal hyperplasia).
Polycystic ovarian syndrome.
Isolated gonadotropin deficiency.

APPETITE LOSS IN INFANTS AND CHILDREN[17]

ICD-9CM # 783.0 APPETITE LOSS
307.59 APPETITE LOSS, PSYCHOGENIC ORIGIN

ORGANIC DISEASE

Infection (acute or chronic)
Neurologic
Congenital degenerative disease.
Hypothalamic lesion.
Increased intracranial pressure (including a brain tumor).
Swallowing disorders (neuromuscular).
Gastrointestinal
Oral lesions (e.g., thrush or herpes simplex).
Gastroesophageal reflux.
Obstruction (especially with gastric or intestinal distention).
Inflammatory bowel disease.
Celiac disease.
Constipation.
Cardiac
Congestive heart failure (especially associated with cyanotic lesions).
Metabolic
Renal failure and/or renal tubule acidosis.
Liver failure.
Congenital metabolic disease.
Lead poisoning.
Nutritional
Marasmus.
Iron deficiency.
Zinc deficiency.
Fever
Rheumatoid arthritis.
Rheumatic fever.
Drugs
Morphine.
Digitalis.
Antimetabolites.
Methylphenidate.
Amphetamines.
Miscellaneous
Prolonged restriction of oral feedings, beginning in the neonatal period.
Systemic lupus erythematosus.
Tumor.

PSYCHOLOGIC FACTORS

Anxiety, fear, depression, mania (limbic influence on the hypothalamus).
Avoidance of symptoms associated with meals (abdominal pain, diarrhea, bloating, urgency, dumping syndrome).
Anorexia nervosa.
Excessive weight loss and food aversion in athletes, simulating anorexia nervosa.

ARTERIAL OCCLUSION[13]

ICD-9CM # 444.22 ARTERIAL OCCLUSION, LOWER EXTREMITIES
444.21 ARTERIAL OCCLUSION, UPPER EXTREMITIES

Thromboembolism (post-MI, mitral stenosis, rheumatic valve disease, atrial fibrillation, atrial myxoma, marantic endocarditis, bacterial endocarditis, Libman-Sacks endocarditis).
Atheroembolism (microemboli composed of cholesterol, calcium, and platelets from proximal atherosclerotic plaques).
Arterial thrombosis (endothelial injury, altered arterial blood flow, trauma, severe atherosclerosis, acute vasculitis).

Vasospasm.
Trauma.
Hypercoagulable states.
Miscellaneous (irradiation, drugs, infections, necrotizing).

ARTHRITIS AND EYE LESIONS[6]

ICD-9CM # CODE VARIES WITH SPECIFIC DIAGNOSIS

SLE.
Sjögren's syndrome.
Behçet's syndrome.
Sarcoidosis.
SBE.
Lyme disease.
Wegener's granulomatosis.
Giant cell arteritis.
Takayasu arteritis.
Rheumatoid arthritis, JRA.
Scleroderma.
Inflammatory bowel disease.
Whipple's disease.
Ankylosing spondylitis.
Reactive arthritis.
Psoriatic arthritis.

ARTHRITIS AND HEART MURMUR[6]

ICD-9CM # CODE VARIES WITH SPECIFIC DIAGNOSIS

Subacute bacterial endocarditis (SBE).
Cardiac myxoma.
Ankylosing spondylitis.
Reactive arthritis.
Acute rheumatic fever.
Rheumatoid arthritis (RA).
SLE with Libman-Sacks endocarditis.
Relapsing polychondritis.

ARTHRITIS AND MUSCLE WEAKNESS[8]

ICD-9CM # CODE VARIES WITH SPECIFIC DIAGNOSIS

RA.
Ankylosing spondylitis.
Polymyositis.
Dermatomyositis.
SLE, scleroderma, mixed connective tissue disease.
Sarcoidosis.
HIV-associated arthritis.
Whipple's disease.

ARTHRITIS AND RASH[6]

ICD-9CM # CODE VARIES WITH SPECIFIC DIAGNOSIS

Chronic urticaria.
Vasculitic urticaria.
SLE.
Dermatomyositis.
Polymyositis.
Psoriatic arthritis.
Reactive arthritis.
Chronic sarcoidosis.
Serum sickness.
Sweet's syndrome.
Leprosy.

ARTHRITIS AND SUBCUTANEOUS NODULES[6]

ICD-9CM # CODE VARIES WITH SPECIFIC DIAGNOSIS

RA.
Gout.
Pseudogout (rare).
Sarcoidosis.
Light chain (LA) amyloidosis (primary, multiple myeloma).
Acute rheumatic fever (ARF).
Hemochromatosis.
Whipple's disease.
Multicentric reticulohistiocytosis.

ARTHRITIS AND WEIGHT LOSS[6]

ICD-9CM # CODE VARIES WITH SPECIFIC DIAGNOSIS

Severe RA.
RA with vasculitis.
Reactive arthritis.
RA or psoriatic arthritis or ankylosing spondylitis with amyloidosis.
Cancer.
Enteropathic arthritis (Crohn's, ulcerative colitis).
HIV infection.
Whipple's disease.
Blind loop syndrome.
Scleroderma with intestinal bacterial overgrowth.

ARTHRITIS, AXIAL SKELETON

ICD-9CM # 720.0 ARTHRITIS, RHEUMATOID, SPINE
696.0 ARTHRITIS, PSORIATIC
715.9 ARTHRITIS, DEGENERATIVE, NOS
720.0 ANKYLOSING SPONDYLITIS

RA.
Psoriatic arthritis.
Reiter's syndrome.
Ankylosing spondylitis.
Juvenile RA.
Degenerative disease of the nucleus pulposus.
Spondylosis deformans.
Diffuse idiopathic skeletal hyperostosis (DISH).
Alkaptonuria.
Infection.

ARTHRITIS, FEVER, AND RASH[6]

ICD-9CM # CODE VARIES WITH SPECIFIC DIAGNOSIS

Rubella, parvovirus B-19.
Gonococcemia, meningococcemia.
Secondary syphilis, Lyme borreliosis.
Adult acute rheumatic fever, adult Still's disease, adult Kawasaki disease.
Vasculitic urticaria.
Acute sarcoidosis.
Familial Mediterranean fever.
Hyperimmunoglobulinemia D and periodic fever syndrome.

ARTHRITIS, MONOARTICULAR AND OLIGOARTICULAR[2]

ICD-9CM # 715.3 OSTEOARTHRITIS, LOCALIZED
711.9 INFECTIOUS ARTHRITIS
716.6 MONOARTICULAR ARTHRITIS
5TH DIGIT TO BE ADDED TO THE ABOVE DEPENDING ON SITE OF ARTHRITIS
0. SITE UNSPECIFIED
1. SHOULDER REGION
2. UPPER ARM
3. FOREARM
4. HAND
5. PELVIC REGION AND THIGH
6. LOWER LEG
7. ANKLE AND/OR FOOT
8. OTHER SPECIFIED EXCEPT SPINE

Septic arthritis (*S. aureus, Neisseria gonorrhea, Meningococci, Streptococci, S. pneumoniae, enteric gram-neg bacilli).*
Crystalline-induced arthritis (gout, pseudogout, calcium oxalate, hydroxyapatite and other basic calcium/phosphate crystals).
Traumatic joint injury.
Hemarthrosis.
Monoarticular or oligoarticular flare of an inflammatory polyarticular rheumatic disease (RA, psoriatic arthritis, Reiter's syndrome, SLE).

ARTHRITIS, PEDIATRIC AGE[17]

ICD-9CM # 711.9 INFECTIOUS ARTHRITIS
714.30 JUVENILE CHRONIC OR UNSPECIFIED
714.31 JUVENILE RHEUMATOID POLYARTICULAR ACUTE
714.32 JUVENILE RHEUMATOID PAUCIARTICULAR
714.33 JUVENILE RHEUMATOID MONOARTICULAR

RHEUMATIC DISEASES OF CHILDHOOD

Acute rheumatic fever.
Systemic lupus erythematosus.
Juvenile ankylosing spondylitis.
Polymyositis and dermatomyositis.
Vasculitis.
Scleroderma.
Psoriatic arthritis.
Mixed connective tissue disease and overlap syndromes.
Kawasaki disease.
Behçet's syndrome.
Familial Mediterranean fever.
Reiter's syndrome.
Reflex sympathetic dystrophy.
Fibromyalgia (fibrositis).

INFECTIOUS DISEASES

Bacterial arthritis.
Viral or postviral arthritis.
Fungal arthritis.
Osteomyelitis.
Reactive arthritis.

NEOPLASTIC DISEASES

Leukemia.
Lymphoma.
Neuroblastoma.
Primary bone tumors.

NONINFLAMMATORY DISORDERS

Trauma.
Avascular necrosis syndromes.
Osteochondroses.
Slipped capital femoral epiphysis.
Diskitis.
Patellofemoral dysfunction (chondromalacia patellae).
Toxic synovitis of the hip.
Overuse syndromes.

GENETIC OR CONGENITAL SYNDROMES

HEMATOLOGIC DISORDERS

Sickle cell disease.
Hemophilia.

INFLAMMATORY BOWEL DISEASE

MISCELLANEOUS

Growing pains.
Psychogenic arthralgias (conversion reactions).
Hypermobility syndrome.
Villonodular synovitis.
Foreign body arthritis.

ARTHRITIS, POLYARTICULAR

ICD-9CM # 715.09 GENERALIZED OSTEOARTHRITIS, MULTIPLE SITES
716.89 ARTHRITIS, MULTIPLE SITES
714.31 JUVENILE RHEUMATOID, POLYARTICULAR, ACUTE

RA, juvenile (rheumatoid) polyarthritis.
SLE, other connective tissue diseases, erythema nodosum, palindromic rheumatism, relapsing polychondritis.
Psoriatic arthritis, ankylosing spondylitis.
Sarcoidosis.
Lyme arthritis, bacterial endocarditis, *Neisseria gonorrhoeae* infection, rheumatic fever, Reiter's disease.
Crystal deposition disease.
Hypersensitivity to serum or drugs.
Hepatitis B, HIV, rubella, mumps.
Other: serum sickness, leukemias, lymphomas, enteropathic arthropathy, Whipple's disease, Behçet's syndrome, Henoch-Schönlein purpura, familial Mediterranean fever, hypertrophic pulmonary osteoarthropathy.

ASCITES

ICD-9CM # 789.5 ASCITES NOS
197.6 ASCITES, CANCEROUS (MALIGNANT)
457.8 ASCITES, CHYLOUS

Hypoalbuminemia: nephrotic syndrome, protein-losing gastroenteropathy, starvation.
Cirrhosis.
Hepatic congestion: CHF, constrictive pericarditis, tricuspid insufficiency, hepatic vein obstruction (Budd-Chiari syndrome), inferior vena cava or portal vein obstruction.
Peritoneal infections: TB and other bacterial infections, fungal diseases, parasites.
Neoplasms: primary hepatic neoplasms, metastases to liver or peritoneum, lymphomas, leukemias, myeloid metaplasia.
Lymphatic obstruction: mediastinal tumors, trauma to the thoracic duct, filariasis.
Ovarian disease: Meigs' syndrome, struma ovarii.
Chronic pancreatitis or pseudocyst: pancreatic ascites.
Leakage of bile: bile ascites.

Urinary obstruction or trauma: urine ascites.
Myxedema.
Chylous ascites.

ASTHMA, CHILDHOOD[4]

ICD-9CM # 493.0 USE 5TH DIGIT
0. WITHOUT MENTION OF STATUS ASTHMATICUS
1. WITH STATUS ASTHMATICUS

INFECTIONS

Bronchiolitis (RSV).
Pneumonia.
Croup.
Tuberculosis, histoplasmosis.
Bronchiectasis.
Bronchiolitis obliterans.
Bronchitis.
Sinusitis.

ANATOMIC, CONGENITAL

Cystic fibrosis.
Vascular rings.
Ciliary dyskinesia.
B lymphocyte immune defect.
Congestive heart failure.
Laryngotracheomalacia.
Tumor, lymphoma.
H-type tracheoesophageal fistula.
Repaired tracheoesophageal fistula.
Gastroesophageal reflux.

VASCULITIS, HYPERSENSITIVITY

Allergic bronchopulmonary aspergillosis.
Allergic alveolitis, hypersensitivity pneumonitis.
Churg-Strauss syndrome.
Periarteritis nodosa.

OTHER

Foreign body aspiration.
Pulmonary thromboembolism.
Psychogenic cough.
Sarcoidosis.
Bronchopulmonary dysplasia.
Vocal cord dysfunction.

ATAXIA

ICD-9CM # 781.3 ATAXIA NOS
303.0 ALCOHOLIC, ACUTE
303.9 ALCOHOLIC, CHRONIC
334.3 CEREBELLAR
331.89 CEREBRAL
334.0 FRIEDREICH'S
300.11 HYSTERICAL

Vertebral-basilar artery ischemia.
Diabetic neuropathy.
Tabes dorsalis.
Vitamin B_{12} deficiency.
Multiple sclerosis and other demyelinating diseases.
Meningomyelopathy.
Cerebellar neoplasms, hemorrhage, abscess, infarct.
Nutritional (Wernicke's encephalopathy).
Paraneoplastic syndromes.
Parainfectious: Guillain-Barré syndrome, acute ataxia of childhood and young adults.
Toxins: phenytoin, alcohol, sedatives, organophosphates.
Wilson's disease (hepatolenticular degeneration).
Hypothyroidism.
Myopathy.
Cerebellar and spinocerebellar degeneration: ataxia/telangiectasia, Friedreich's ataxia.
Frontal lobe lesions: tumors, thrombosis of anterior cerebral artery, hydrocephalus.
Labyrinthine destruction: neoplasm, injury, inflammation, compression.
Hysteria.
AIDS.

ATELECTASIS

ICD-9CM # 518.0

Lung neoplasm (primary or metastatic).
Infection (pneumonia, TB, fungal, histoplasmosis).
Postoperative (lower lobes).
Sarcoidosis.
Mucoid impaction.
Foreign body.
Postinflammatory (middle lobe syndrome).
Pneumothorax.
Pleural effusion.
Pneumoconiosis.
Interstitial fibrosis.
Bulla.
Mediastinal or adjacent mass.

AV NODAL BLOCK[13]

ICD-9CM # 426.10 AV BLOCK (INCOMPLETE, PARTIAL)
426.0 AV BLOCK, COMPLETE

Idiopathic fibrosis (Lenegre's disease).
Sclerodegenerative processes (e.g., Lev's disease with calcification of the mitral and aortic annuli).
AV node radiofrequency ablation procedure.
Medications (e.g., digoxin, beta blockers, calcium channel blockers, class III antiarrhythmics).
Acute inferior wall MI.
Myocarditis.
Infections (endocarditis, Lyme disease).
Infiltrative diseases (e.g., hemochromatosis, sarcoidosis, amyloidosis).
Trauma (including cardiac surgical procedures).
Collagen vascular diseases.
Aortic root diseases (e.g., spondylitis).
Electrolyte abnormalities (e.g., hyperkalemia).

BACK PAIN

ICD-9CM # 724.5 BACK PAIN (POSTURAL)
724.2 LOW BACK PAIN
307.89 BACK PAIN PSYCHOGENIC
724.8 STIFF BACK
847.9 BACK STRAIN
724.6 BACKACHE, SACROILIAC

Trauma: injury to bone, joint, or ligament.
Mechanical: pregnancy, obesity, fatigue, scoliosis.
Degenerative: osteoarthritis.
Infections: osteomyelitis, subarachnoid or spinal abscess, TB, meningitis, basilar pneumonia.
Metabolic: osteoporosis, osteomalacia.
Vascular: leaking aortic aneurysm, subarachnoid or spinal hemorrhage/infarction.
Neoplastic: myeloma, Hodgkin's disease, carcinoma of pancreas, metastatic neoplasm from breast, prostate, lung.
GI: penetrating ulcer, pancreatitis, cholelithiasis, inflammatory bowel disease.

Renal: hydronephrosis, calculus, neoplasm, renal infarction, pyelonephritis.
Hematologic: sickle cell crisis, acute hemolysis.
Gynecologic: neoplasm of uterus or ovary, dysmenorrhea, salpingitis, uterine prolapse.
Inflammatory: ankylosing spondylitis, psoriatic arthritis, Reiter's syndrome.
Lumbosacral strain.
Psychogenic: malingering, hysteria, anxiety.
Endocrine: adrenal hemorrhage or infarction.

BLEEDING, LOWER GI

ICD-9CM # 578.9

(ORIGINATING BELOW THE LIGAMENT OF TREITZ)

Small Intestine
Ischemic bowel disease (mesenteric thrombosis, embolism, vasculitis, trauma).
Small bowel neoplasm: leiomyomas, carcinoids.
Hereditary hemorrhagic telangiectasia (Rendu-Osler-Weber syndrome).
Meckel's diverticulum and other small intestine diverticula.
Aortoenteric fistula.
Intestinal hemangiomas: blue rubber-bleb nevi, intestinal hemangiomas, cutaneous vascular nevi.
Hamartomatous polyps: Peutz-Jeghers syndrome (intestinal polyps, mucocutaneous pigmentation).
Infections of small bowel: tuberculous enteritis, enteritis necroticans.
Volvulus.
Intussusception.
Lymphoma of small bowel, sarcoma, Kaposi's sarcoma.
Irradiation ileitis.
AV malformation of small intestine.
Inflammatory bowel disease.
Polyarteritis nodosa.
Other: pancreatoenteric fistulas, Henoch-Schönlein purpura, Ehlers-Danlos syndrome, systemic lupus erythematosus, amyloidosis, metastatic melanoma.
Colon
Carcinoma (particularly left colon).
Diverticular disease.
Inflammatory bowel disease.
Ischemic colitis.
Colonic polyps.
Vascular abnormalities: angiodysplasia, vascular ectasia.
Radiation colitis.
Infectious colitis.
Uremic colitis.
Aortoenteric fistula.
Lymphoma of large bowel.
Hemorrhoids.
Anal fissure.
Trauma, foreign body.
Solitary rectal/cecal ulcers.
Long-distance running.

BLEEDING, LOWER GI, PEDIATRIC[2]

ICD-9CM # 578.9

<3 MONTHS

Swallowed maternal blood.
Infectious colitis.
Milk allergy.
Bleeding diathesis.
Intussusception.
Midgut volvulus.
Meckel's diverticulum.
Necrotizing enterocolitis.

<2 YEARS OLD

Anal fissure.
Infectious colitis.
Milk allergy.
Colitis.
Intussusception.
Meckel's diverticulum.
Polyp.
Duplication.
Hemolytic uremic syndrome.
Inflammatory bowel disease.
Pseudomembranous enterocolitis.

<5 YEARS OLD

Infectious colitis.
Anal fissure.
Polyp.
Intussusception.
Meckel's diverticulum.
Henoch-Schönlein purpura.
Hemolytic uremic syndrome.
Inflammatory bowel disease.
Pseudomembranous enterocolitis.

5-18 YEARS

Infectious colitis.
Inflammatory bowel disease.
Pseudomembranous enterocolitis.
Polyp.
Hemolytic-uremic syndrome.
Hemorrhoid.

BLEEDING, UPPER GI

ICD-9CM # 578.9

(ORIGINATING ABOVE THE LIGAMENT OF TREITZ)

Oral or pharyngeal lesions: swallowed blood from nose or oropharynx.
Swallowed hemoptysis
Esophageal: varices, ulceration, esophagitis, Mallory-Weiss tear, carcinoma, trauma.
Gastric: peptic ulcer (including Cushing and Curling's ulcers), gastritis, angiodysplasia, gastric neoplasms, hiatal hernia, gastric diverticulum, pseudoxanthoma elasticum, Rendu-Osler-Weber syndrome.
Duodenal: peptic ulcer, duodenitis, angiodysplasia, aortoduodenal fistula, duodenal diverticulum, duodenal tumors, carcinoma of ampulla of Vater, parasites (e.g., hookworm), Crohn's disease.
Biliary: hematobilia (e.g., penetrating injury to liver, hepatobiliary malignancy, endoscopic papillotomy).

BLEEDING, UPPER GI, PEDIATRIC[2]

ICD-9CM # 578.9

<3 MONTHS OLD

Swallowed maternal blood.
Gastritis.
Ulcer, stress.
Bleeding diathesis.
Foreign body (NG tube).
Vascular malformation.
Duplication.

<2 YEARS OLD

Esophagitis.
Gastritis.
Ulcer.
Pyloric stenosis.
Mallory-Weiss syndrome.
Vascular malformation.
Duplication.

<5 YEARS OLD

Esophagitis.
Gastritis.
Ulcer.
Esophageal varices.
Foreign body.
Mallory-Weiss syndrome.
Hemophilia.
Vascular malformations.

5-18 YEARS OLD

Esophagitis.
Gastritis.
Ulcer.
Esophageal varices.
Mallory-Weiss syndrome.
Inflammatory bowel disease.
Hemophilia.
Vascular malformation.

BLINDNESS, GERIATRIC AGE

ICD-9CM # 369.4

Cataracts.
Glaucoma.
Diabetic retinopathy.
Macular degeneration.
Trauma.
CVA.
Corneal scarring.

BLINDNESS, PEDIATRIC AGE[20]

ICD-9CM # VARIES WITH SPECIFIC DISORDER

CONGENITAL

Optic nerve hypoplasia or aplasia.
Optic coloboma.
Congenital hydrocephalus.
Hydranencephaly.
Porencephaly.
Micrencephaly.
Encephalocele, particularly occipital type.
Morning glory disc.
Aniridia.
Anterior microphthalmia.
Peter's anomaly.
Persistent pupillary membrane.
Glaucoma.
Cataracts.
Persistent hyperplastic primary vitreous.

PHAKOMATOSES

Tuberous sclerosis.
Neurofibromatosis (special association with optic glioma).
Sturge-Weber syndrome.
von Hippel–Lindau disease.

TUMORS

Retinoblastoma.
Optic glioma.
Perioptic meningioma.
Craniopharyngioma.
Cerebral glioma.
Posterior and intraventricular tumors when complicated by hydrocephalus.
Pseudotumor cerebri.

NEURODEGENERATIVE DISEASES

Cerebral storage disease.
Gangliosidoses, particularly Tay-Sachs disease (infantile amaurotic familial idiocy), Sandhoff's variant, generalized gangliosidosis.
Other lipidoses and ceroid lipofuscinoses, particularly the late-onset amaurotic familial idiocies such as those of Jansky-Bielschowsky and of Batten-Mayou-Spielmeyer-Vogt.
Mucopolysaccharidoses, particularly Hurler's syndrome and Hunter's syndrome.
Leukodystrophies (dysmyelination disorders), particularly metachromatic leukodystrophy and Canavan's disease.
Demyelinating sclerosis (myelinoclastic diseases), especially Schilder's disease and Devic's neuromyelitis optica.
Special types: Dawson's disease, Leigh's disease, Bassen-Kornzweig syndrome, Refsum's disease.
Retinal degenerations: retinitis pigmentosa and its variants, Leber's congenital type.
Optic atrophies: congenital autosomal recessive type, infantile and congenital autosomal dominant types, Leber's disease, and atrophies associated with hereditary ataxias—the types of Behr, of Marie, and of Sanger-Brown.

INFECTIOUS PROCESSES

Encephalitis, especially in the prenatal infection syndromes caused by Toxoplasma gondii, cytomegalovirus, rubella virus, *Treponema pallidum,* herpes simplex.
Meningitis; arachnoiditis.
Chorioretinitis.
Endophthalmitis.
Keratitis.

HEMATOLOGIC DISORDERS

Leukemia with central nervous system involvement.

VASCULAR AND CIRCULATORY DISORDERS

Collagen vascular diseases.
Arteriovenous malformations—intracerebral hemorrhage, subarachnoid hemorrhage.
Central retinal occlusion.

TRAUMA

Contusion or avulsion of optic nerves, chiasm, globe, cornea.
Cerebral contusion or laceration.
Intracerebral, subarachnoid, or subdural hemorrhage.

DRUGS AND TOXINS

OTHER

Retinopathy of prematurity.
Sclerocornea.
Conversion reaction.
Optic neuritis.
Osteopetrosis.

BLISTERS, SUBEPIDERMAL

ICD-9CM # 919.2

Burns.
Porphyria cutanea tarda.
Bullous pemphigoid.
Bullous drug reaction.
Arthropod bite reaction.
Toxic epidermal necrosis.
Dermatitis herpetiformis.
Polymorphous light eruption.
Variegate porphyria.
Lupus erythematosus.
Epidermolysis bullosa.
Pseudoporphyria.
Acute graft-versus-host reaction.
Linear IgA disease.
Leukocytoclastic vasculitis.
Pressure necrosis.
Urticaria pigmentosa.
Amyloidosis.

BONE LESIONS, PREFERENTIAL SITE OF ORIGIN[32]

ICD-9CM # 170.0 SKULL AND FACE
170.1 MANDIBLE
170.2 VERTEBRAL COLUMN
170.3 RIBS, STERNUM, CLAVICLE
170.4 SCAPULA, LONG BONES UPPER LIMB
170.5 SHORT BONES AND UPPER LIMB
170.6 PELVIC BONES, SACRUM COCCYX
170.7 LONG BONES LOWER LIMB
170.8 SHORT BONES LOWER LIMB
170.9 BONE CANCER NOS
198.5 BONE CANCER, METASTATIC

EPIPHYSIS

Chondroblastoma.
Giant-cell tumor—after fusion of growth plate.
Langerhans' cell histiocytosis.
Clear cell chondrosarcoma.
Osteosarcoma.

METAPHYSIS

Parosteal sarcoma.
Chondrosarcoma.
Fibrosarcoma.
Nonossifying fibroma.
Giant-cell tumor—before fusion of growth plate.
Unicameral bone cyst.
Aneurysmal bone cyst.

DIAPHYSIS

Myeloma.
Ewing's tumor.
Reticulum cell sarcoma.

METADIAPHYSEAL

Fibrosarcoma.
Fibrous dysplasia.
Enchondroma.
Osteoid osteoma.
Chondromyofibroma.

BONE MARROW FIBROSIS[12]

ICD-9CM # 289.9

MYELOID DISORDERS

Myelofibrosis with myeloid metaplasia.
Metastatic cancer.
Chronic myeloid leukemia.
Myelodysplastic syndrome.
Atypical myeloid disorder.
Acute megakaryocytic leukemia.
Other acute myeloid leukemias.
Gray platelet syndrome.

LYMPHOID DISORDERS

Hairy cell leukemia.
Multiple myeloma.
Lymphoma.

NONHEMATOLOGIC DISORDERS

Connective tissue disorder.
Infections (tuberculosis, kala-azar).
Vitamin D-deficiency rickets.
Renal osteodystrophy.

BONE PAIN

ICD-9CM # NOT AVAILABLE

Trauma.
Neoplasm (primary or metastatic).
Osteoporosis with compression fracture.
Paget's disease of bone.
Infection (osteomyelitis, septic arthritis).
Osteomalacia.
Viral syndrome.
Sickle cell disease.
Anxiety.

BONE RESORPTION[32]

ICD-9CM # 733.90 BONE DISORDER

DISTAL CLAVICLE

Hyperparathyroidism.
Rheumatoid arthritis.
Scleroderma.
Posttraumatic osteolysis.
Progeria.
Pycnodysostosis.
Cleidocranial dysplasia.

INFERIOR ASPECT OF RIBS

Vascular impression, associated with but not limited to coarctation of the aorta.
Hyperparathyroidism.
Neurofibromatosis.

TERMINAL PHALANGEAL TUFTS

Scleroderma.
Raynaud's phenomenon.
Vascular disease.
Frostbite, electrical burns.
Psoriasis.
Tabes dorsalis.
Hyperparathyroidism.

GENERALIZED RESORPTION

Paraplegia.
Myositis ossificans.
Osteoporosis.

BRADYCARDIA, SINUS[13]

ICD-9CM # 427.89

Idiopathic.
Degenerative processes (e.g., Lev's disease, Lenegre's disease).
Medications
Beta blockers.
Some calcium channel blockers (diltiazem, verapamil).
Digoxin (when vagal tone is high).
Class I antiarrhythmic agents (e.g., procainamide).
Class III antiarrhythmic agents (amiodarone, sotalol).
Clonidine.
Lithium carbonate.
Acute myocardial ischemia and infarction
Right or left circumflex coronary artery occlusion or spasm.
High vagal tone (e.g., athletes).

BREAST INFLAMMATORY LESION[10]

ICD-9CM # 611.0 ACUTE MASTITIS
610.1 CHRONIC CYSTIC MASTITIS
771.5 NEONATAL INFECTIVE MASTITIS
778.7 NEONATAL NONINFECTIVE MASTITIS

Mastitis *(S. aureus, Beta-hemolytic Strep).*
Trauma.
Foreign body (sutures, breast implants).
Granuloma (TB, fungal).
Fat necrosis post biopsy.
Necrosis or infarction (anticoagulant therapy, pregnancy).
Breast malignancy.

BREAST MASS

ICD-9CM # 611.72

Fibrocystic breasts.
Benign tumors (fibroadenoma, papilloma).
Mastitis (acute bacterial mastitis, chronic mastitis).
Malignant neoplasm.
Fat necrosis.
Hematoma.
Duct ectasia.
Mammary adenosis.

BREATH ODOR[31]

ICD-9CM # 784.9 HALITOSIS

Sweet, fruity: DKA, starvation ketosis.
Fishy, stale: uremia (trimethylamines).
Ammonia-like: uremia (ammonia).
Musty fish, clover: fetor hepaticus (hepatic failure).
Foul, feculent: intestinal obstruction/diverticulum.
Foul, putrid: nasal/sinus pathology (infection, foreign body, cancer), respiratory infections (empyema, lung abscess, bronchiectasis).
Halitosis: tonsillitis, gingivitis, respiratory infections, Vincent's angina, gastroesophageal reflux, achalasia.
Cinnamon: pulmonary TB.

BREATHING, NOISY[31]

ICD-9CM # 786.09 BREATHING, LABORED
789.09 SNORING, WHEEZING
786.1 STRIDOR

Infection: upper respiratory infection, peritonsillar abscess, retropharyngeal abscess, epiglottitis, laryngitis, tracheitis, bronchitis, bronchiolitis.
Irritants and allergens: hyperactive airway, asthma (reactive airway disease), rhinitis, angioneurotic edema.
Compression from outside of the airway: esophageal cysts or foreign body, neoplasms, lymphadenopathy.
Congenital malformation and abnormality: vascular rings, laryngeal webs, laryngomalacia, tracheomalacia, hemangiomas within the upper airway, stenoses within the upper airway, cystic fibrosis.
Acquired abnormality (at every level of the airway): nasal polyps, hypertrophied adenoids and/or tonsils, foreign body, intraluminal tumors, bronchiectasis.
Neurogenic disorder: vocal cord paralysis.

BULLOUS DISEASES

ICD-9CM # 694.9 BULLOUS DERMATOSES
694.5 BULLOUS PEMPHIGOID
694.4 PEMPHIGUS VULGARIS
694.4 PEMPHIGUS FOLIACEUS

Bullous pemphigoid.
Pemphigus vulgaris.
Pemphigus foliaceus.
Paraneoplastic pemphigus.
Cicatricial pemphigoid.
Erythema multiforme.
Dermatitis herpetiformis.
Herpes gestationis.
Impetigo.
Erosive lichen planus.
Linear IgA bullous dermatosis.
Epidermolysis bullosa acquisita.

CALCIFICATION ON CHEST X-RAY

ICD-9CM # 722.92

Lung neoplasm (primary or metastatic).
Silicosis.
Idiopathic pulmonary fibrosis.
Tuberculosis.
Histoplasmosis.
Disseminated varicella infection.
Mitral stenosis (end-stage).
Secondary hyperparathyroidism.

CARDIAC ARREST, NONTRAUMATIC[23]

ICD-9CM # 427.5 CARDIAC ARREST NOS

Cardiac (coronary artery disease, cardiomyopathies, structural abnormalities, valve dysfunction, arrhythmias).
Respiratory (upper airway obstruction, hypoventilation, pulmonary embolism, asthma, COPD exacerbation, pulmonary edema).
Circulatory (tension pneumothorax, pericardial tamponade, PE, hemorrhage, sepsis).
Electrolyte abnormalities (hypokalemia or hyperkalemia, hypomagnesemia or hypermagnesemia, hypocalcemia).
Medications (tricyclic antidepressants, digoxin, theophylline, calcium channel blockers).
Drug abuse (cocaine, heroin, amphetamines).
Toxins (carbon monoxide, cyanide).
Environmental (drowning/near-drowning, electrocution, lightning, hypothermia or hyperthermia, venomous snakes).

CARDIAC ENLARGEMENT[13]

ICD-9CM # 429.3 CARDIOMEGALY, IDIOPATHIC
746.89 CARDIOMEGALY, CONGENITAL
402.0 CARDIOMEGALY, MALIGNANT
402.1 CARDIOMEGALY, BENIGN

CARDIAC CHAMBER ENLARGEMENT

Chronic volume overload
Mitral or aortic regurgitation.
Left-to-right shunt (PDA, VSD, AV fistula).
Cardiomyopathy
Ischemic.
Nonischemic.
Decompensated pressure overload
Aortic stenosis.
Hypertension.
High-output states
Severe anemia.
Thyrotoxicosis.
Bradycardia
Severe sinus bradycardia.
Complete heart block.

LEFT ATRIUM

LV failure of any cause.
Mitral valve disease.
Myxoma.

RIGHT VENTRICLE

Chronic volume overload.
Tricuspid or pulmonic regurgitation.
Left-to-right shunt (ASD).
Decompensated pressure overload:
- Pulmonic stenosis.
- Pulmonary artery hypertension:
  - Primary.
  - Secondary (PE, COPD).
- Pulmonary venoocclusive disease.

RIGHT ATRIUM

RV failure of any cause.
Tricuspid valve disease.
Myxoma.
Ebstein's anomaly.

MULTICHAMBER ENLARGEMENT

Hypertrophic cardiomyopathy.
Acromegaly.
Severe obesity.

PERICARDIAL DISEASE

Pericardial effusion with or without tamponade.
Effusive constrictive disease.
Pericardial cyst, loculated effusion.

PSEUDOCARDIOMEGALY

Epicardial fat.
Chest wall deformity (pectus excavatum, straight back syndrome).
Low lung volumes.
AP chest x-ray.
Mediastinal tumor, cyst.

CARDIAC MURMURS

ICD-9CM # CODE VARIES WITH SPECIFIC DISORDER

SYSTOLIC

Mitral regurgitation (MR).
Tricuspid regurgitation (TR).
Ventricular septal defect (VSD).
Aortic stenosis (AS).
Idiopathic hypertrophic subaortic stenosis (IHSS).
Pulmonic stenosis (PS).
Innocent murmur of childhood.
Coarctation of aorta.
Mitral valve prolapse (MVP).

DIASTOLIC

Aortic regurgitation (AR).
Atrial myxoma.
Mitral stenosis (MS).
Pulmonary artery branch stenosis.
Tricuspid stenosis (TS).
Graham Steell murmur (diastolic decrescendo murmur heard in severe pulmonary hypertension).
Pulmonic regurgitation (PR).
Severe mitral regurgitation (MR).
Austin Flint murmur (diastolic rumble heard in severe AR).
Severe VSD and patent ductus arteriosus.

CONTINUOUS

Patent ductus arteriosus.
Pulmonary AV fistula.

CARDIOGENIC SHOCK

ICD-9CM # 785.51

Myocardial infarction.
Arrhythmias.
Pericardial effusion/tamponade.
Chest trauma.
Valvular heart disease.
Myocarditis.
Cardiomyopathy.
CHF, end-stage.

CAVITARY LESION ON CHEST X-RAY[14]

ICD-9CM # 793.1 CHEST X-RAY LUNG SHADOW

NECROTIZING INFECTIONS

Bacteria: anaerobes, *Staphylococcus aureus,* enteric gram-negative bacteria, *Pseudomonas aeruginosa, Legionella* species, *Haemophilus influenzae, Streptococcus pyogenes, Streptococcus pneumoniae* (?), *Rhodococcus, Actinomyces.*
Mycobacteria: *Mycobacterium tuberculosis, Mycobacterium kansasii,* MAI.
Bacteria-like: *Nocardia* species.
Fungi: *Coccidioides immitis, Histoplasma capsulatum, Blastomyces hominis, Aspergillus* species, *Mucor* species.
Parasitic: *Entamoeba histolytica, Echinococcus, Paragonimus westermani.*

CAVITARY INFARCTION

Bland infarction (with or without superimposed infection).
Lung contusion.

SEPTIC EMBOLISM

S. aureus, anaerobes, others.

VASCULITIS

Wegener's granulomatosis, periarteritis.

NEOPLASMS

Bronchogenic carcinoma, metastatic carcinoma, lymphoma.

MISCELLANEOUS LESIONS

Cysts, blebs, bullae, or pneumatocele with or without fluid collections.
Sequestration.
Empyema with air-fluid level.
Bronchiectasis.

CEREBROVASCULAR DISEASE, ISCHEMIC[35]

ICD-9CM # 437.9

VASCULAR DISORDERS

Large-vessel atherothrombotic disease.
Lacunar disease.
Arterial-to-arterial embolization.
Carotid or vertebral artery dissection.
Fibromuscular dysplasia.
Migraine.
Venous thrombosis.
Radiation.
Complications of arteriography.
Multiple, progressive intracranial arterial occlusions.

INFLAMMATORY DISORDERS

Giant cell arteritis.
Polyarteritis nodosa.
Systemic lupus erythematosus.
Granulomatous angiitis.
Takayasu's disease.
Arteritis associated with amphetamine, cocaine, or phenylpropanolamine.
Syphilis, mucormycosis.
Sjögren syndrome.
Behçet's syndrome.

CARDIAC DISORDERS

Rheumatic heart disease.
Mural thrombus.
Arrhythmias.
Mitral valve prolapse.
Prosthetic heart valve.
Endocarditis.
Myxoma.
Paradoxical embolus.

HEMATOLOGIC DISORDERS

Thrombotic thrombocytopenic purpura.
Sickle cell disease.
Hypercoagulable states.
Polycythemia.
Thrombocytosis.
Leukocytosis.
Lupus anticoagulant.

CHEST PAIN, CHILDREN[4]

ICD-9CM # 786.50 CHEST PAIN NOS
786.59 CHEST PRESSURE
786.52 CHEST PAIN, PLEURITIC

MUSCULOSKELETAL (COMMON)

Trauma (accidental, abuse).
Exercise, overuse injury (strain, bursitis).
Costochondritis (Tietze's syndrome).
Herpes zoster (cutaneous).
Pleurodynia.
Fibrositis.
Slipping rib.
Sickle cell anemia vaso-occlusive crisis.
Osteomyelitis (rare).
Primary or metastatic tumor (rare).

PULMONARY (COMMON)

Pneumonia.
Pleurisy.
Asthma.
Chronic cough.
Pneumothorax.
Infarction (sickle cell anemia).
Foreign body.
Embolism (rare).
Pulmonary hypertension (rare).
Tumor (rare).

GASTROINTESTINAL (LESS COMMON)

Esophagitis (gastroesophageal reflux).
Esophageal foreign body.
Esophageal spasm.
Cholecystitis.
Subdiaphragmatic abscess.
Perihepatitis (Fitz-Hugh-Curtis syndrome).
Peptic ulcer disease.

CARDIAC (LESS COMMON)

Pericarditis.
Postpericardiotomy syndrome.
Endocarditis.
Mitral valve prolapse.
Aortic or subaortic stenosis.
Arrhythmias.
Marfan's syndrome (dissecting aortic aneurysm).
Anomalous coronary artery.
Kawasaki disease.
Cocaine, sympathomimetic ingestion.
Angina (familial hypercholesterolemia).

IDIOPATHIC (COMMON)

Anxiety, hyperventilation.
Panic disorder.

OTHER (LESS COMMON)

Spinal cord or nerve root compression.
Breast-related pathologic condition.
Castleman's disease (lymph node neoplasm).

CHEST PAIN (NONPLEURITIC)[8]

ICD-9CM # 786.50 CHEST PAIN NOS
786.59 CHEST DISCOMFORT

Cardiac: myocardial ischemia/infarction, myocarditis.
Esophageal: spasm, esophagitis, ulceration, neoplasm, achalasia, diverticula, foreign body.
Referred pain from subdiaphragmatic GI structures.
Gastric and duodenal: hiatal hernia, neoplasm, PUD.
Gallbladder and biliary: cholecystitis, cholelithiasis, impacted stone, neoplasm.
Pancreatic: pancreatitis, neoplasm.
Dissecting aortic aneurysm.
Pain originating from skin, breasts, and musculoskeletal structures: herpes zoster, mastitis, cervical spondylosis.
Mediastinal tumors: lymphoma, thymoma.

Pulmonary: neoplasm, pneumonia, pulmonary embolism/infarction.
Psychoneurosis.
Chest pain associated with mitral valve prolapse.

CHEST PAIN (PLEURITIC)

ICD-9CM #786.52 CHEST PAIN, PLEURITIC

Cardiac: pericarditis, postpericardiotomy/Dressler's syndrome.
Pulmonary: pneumothorax, hemothorax, embolism/infarction, pneumonia, empyema, neoplasm, bronchiectasis, pneumomediastinum, TB, carcinomatous effusion.
GI: liver abscess, pancreatitis, esophageal rupture, Whipple's disease with associated pericarditis or pleuritis.
Subdiaphragmatic abscess.
Pain originating from skin and musculoskeletal tissues: costochondritis, chest wall trauma, fractured rib, interstitial fibrositis, myositis, strain of pectoralis muscle, herpes zoster, soft tissue and bone tumors.
Collagen vascular diseases with pleuritis.
Psychoneurosis.
Familial Mediterranean fever.

CHOLESTASIS[12]

ICD-9CM # 574.71

EXTRAHEPATIC

Choledocholithiasis.
Bile duct stricture.
Cholangiocarcinoma.
Pancreatic carcinoma.
Chronic pancreatitis.
Papillary stenosis.
Ampullary cancer.
Primary sclerosing cholangitis.
Choledochal cysts.
Parasites (e.g., ascaris, clonorchis).
AIDS.
Cholangiography.
Biliary atresia.
Portal lymphadenopathy.
Mirizzi's syndrome.

INTRAHEPATIC

Viral hepatitis.
Alcoholic hepatitis.
Drug induced.
Ductopenia syndromes.
Primary biliary cirrhosis.
Benign recurrent intrahepatic cholestasis.
Byler's disease.
Primary sclerosing cholangitis.
Alagille's syndrome.
Sarcoid.
Lymphoma.
Postoperative.
Total parenteral nutrition.
Alpha-1-antitrypsin deficiency.

CHOREOATHETOSIS[25]

ICD-9CM # 275.1 CHOREOATHETOSIS-AGITANS SYNDROME
33.5 CHOREOATHETOSIS PAROXYSMAL

SYSTEMIC DISEASES

Systemic lupus erythematosus.
Polycythemia.
Thyrotoxicosis.
Rheumatic fever.
Cirrhosis of the liver (acquired hepatocerebral degeneration).
Diabetes mellitus.
Wilson's disease.

PRIMARY DEGENERATIVE BRAIN DISEASES

Huntington's chorea.
Olivopontocerebellar atrophies.
Neuroacanthocytosis.

FOCAL BRAIN DISEASES

Hemichorea.
Stroke.
Tumor.
Arteriovenous malformation.

DRUG-INDUCED CHOREOATHETOSIS

Parkinson's disease drugs
Levodopa.
Epilepsy drugs
Phenytoin.
Carbamazepine.
Phenobarbital.
Gabapentin.
Valproate.
Psychostimulant drugs
Cocaine.
Amphetamine.
Methamphetamine.
Dextroamphetamine.
Methylphenidate.
Pemoline.
Psychotropic drugs
Lithium.
Tricyclic antidepressant drugs.
Oral contraceptive drugs
Cimetidine.

CLUBBING

ICD-9CM # 781.5 CLUBBING FINGER

Pulmonary neoplasm (lung, pleura).
Other neoplasm (GI, liver, Hodgkin's, thymus, osteogenic sarcoma).
Pulmonary infectious process (empyema, abscess, bronchiectasis, TB, chronic pneumonitis).
Extrapulmonary infectious process (subacute bacterial endocarditis, intestinal TB, bacterial or amebic dysentery, arterial graft sepsis).
Pneumoconiosis.
Cystic fibrosis.
Sarcoidosis.
Cyanotic congenital heart disease.
Endocrine (Graves' disease, hyperparathyroidism).
Inflammatory bowel disease.
Celiac disease.
Chronic liver disease, cirrhosis (particularly biliary and juvenile).
Pulmonary AV malformations.
Idiopathic.
Thyroid acropachy.
Hereditary (pachydermoperiostosis).
Chronic trauma (jackhammer operators, machine workers).

COLOR CHANGES, CUTANEOUS[31]

ICD-9CM # 709.00 PIGMENTATION ANOMALY

BROWN

Generalized: pituitary, adrenal, liver disease, ACTH-producing tumor (e.g., oat cell lung carcinoma)
Localized: nevi, neurofibromatosis.

WHITE

Generalized: albinism.
Localized: vitiligo, Raynaud's syndrome.

RED (ERYTHEMA)

Generalized: fever, polycythemia, urticaria, viral exanthems.
Localized: inflammation, infection, Raynaud's syndrome.

YELLOW

Generalized: liver disease, chronic renal disease, anemia.
Generalized (except sclera): hypothyroidism, increased intake of vegetables containing carotene.
Localized: resolving hematoma, infection, peripheral vascular insufficiency.

BLUE

Lips, mouth, nail beds: cardiovascular and pulmonary diseases, Raynaud's.

COMA

ICD-9CM # 780.01

Vascular: hemorrhage, thrombosis, embolism.
CNS infections: meningitis, encephalitis, cerebral abscess.
Cerebral neoplasms with herniation.
Head injury: subdural hematoma, cerebral concussion, cerebral contusion.
Drugs: narcotics, sedatives, hypnotics.
Ingestion or inhalation of toxins: CO, alcohol, lead.
Metabolic disturbances.
Hypoxia.
Acid-base disorders.
Hypoglycemia, hyperglycemia.
Hepatic failure.
Electrolyte disorders.
Uremia.
Hypothyroidism.
Hypothermia, hyperthermia.
Hypotension, malignant hypertension.
Postictal.

COMA, NORMAL COMPUTED TOMOGRAPHY[1]

ICD-9CM # 780.01

MENINGEAL DISORDERS

Subarachnoid hemorrhage (uncommon).
Bacterial meningitis.
Encephalitis.
Subdural empyema.

EXOGENOUS TOXINS

Sedative drugs and barbiturates.
Anesthetics and γ-hydroxybutyrate.*
Alcohols.
Stimulants:
  Phencyclidine.†
  Cocaine and amphetamine.‡
Psychotropic drugs:
  Cyclic antidepressants.
  Phenothiazines.
  Lithium.
Anticonvulsants.
Opioids.
Clonidine.§
Penicillins.
Salicylates.
Anticholinergics.
Carbon monoxide, cyanide, and methemoglobinemia.

ENDOGENOUS TOXINS/DEFICIENCIES/DERANGEMENTS

Hypoxia and ischemia.
Hypoglycemia.
Hypercalcemia.
Osmolar:
  Hyperglycemia.
  Hyponatremia.
  Hypernatremia.
Organ system failure.
  Hepatic encephalopathy.
  Uremic encephalopathy.
  Pulmonary insufficiency (carbon dioxide narcosis).

SEIZURES

Prolonged postictal state.
Spike-wave stupor.

HYPOTHERMIA OR HYPERTHERMIA

Brainstem ischemia.
Basilar artery stroke.
Brainstem or cerebellar hemorrhage.
Conversion or malingering.

*General anesthetic, similar to γ-aminobutyric acid; recreational drug and body building aid. Rapid onset, rapid recovery often with myoclonic jerking and confusion. Deep coma (2-3 hr; Glasgow Coma Scale = 3) with maintenance of vital signs.

† Coma associated with cholinergic signs: lacrimation, salivation, bronchorrhea, and hyperthermia.

‡ Coma after seizures or status (i.e., a prolonged postictal state).

§ An antihypertensive agent active through the opiate receptor system; frequent overdose when used to treat narcotic withdrawal.

COMA, PEDIATRIC POPULATION[28]

ICD-9CM # 780.01

ANOXIA

Birth asphyxia.
Carbon monoxide poisoning.
Croup/epiglottitis.
Meconium aspiration.

INFECTION

Hemolysis.
Blood loss.
Hydrops fetalis.
Infection.
Meningoencephalitis.
Sepsis.
Postimmunization encephalitis.

SECTION II

INCREASED INTRACRANIAL PRESSURE

Anoxia.
Inborn metabolic errors.
Toxic encephalopathy.
Reye's syndrome.
Head trauma/intracranial bleed.
Hydrocephalus.
Posterior fossa tumors.

HYPERTENSIVE ENCEPHALOPATHY

Coarctation of aorta.
Nephritis.
Vasculitis.
Pheochromocytoma.

ISCHEMIA

Hypoplastic left heart.
Shunting lesions.
Aortic stenosis.
Cardiovascular collapse (any cause).

PURPURIC CAUSES

Disseminated intravascular coagulation.
Hemolytic-uremic syndrome.
Leukemia.
Thrombotic purpura.

HYPERCAPNIA

Cystic fibrosis.
Bronchopulmonary dysplasia.
Congenital lung anomalies.

NEOPLASM

Medulloblastoma.
Glioma of brainstem.
Posterior fossa tumors.

DRUGS/TOXINS

Maternal sedation.
Alcohol.
Any drug.
Lead.
Salicylism.
Arsenic.
Pesticides.

ELECTROLYTE ABNORMALITIES

Hypernatremia (diarrhea, dehydration, salt poisoning).
Hyponatremia (SIADH, androgenital syndrome, gastroenteritis).
Hyperkalemia (renal failure, salicylism, androgenitalism).
Hypokalemia (diarrhea, hyperaldosteronism, salicylism, DKA).
Hypocalcemia (vitamin D deficiency, hyperparathyroidism).
Severe acidosis (sepsis, cold injury, salicylism, DKA).

HYPOGLYCEMIA

Birth injury or stress.
Diabetes.
Alcohol.
Salicylism.
Hyperinsulinemia.
Iatrogenic.

POSTSEIZURE

Renal causes
Nephritis.
Hypoplastic kidneys.
Hepatic causes
Acute hepatitis.
Fulminant hepatic failure.
Inborn metabolic errors.
Bile duct atresia.

CONSTIPATION

ICD-9CM # 564.0

Intestinal obstruction:
Fecal impaction.
Diverticular disease.
GI neoplasm.
Strangulated femoral hernia.
Gallstone ileus.
Tuberculous stricture.
Adhesions.
Ameboma.
Volvulus.
Intussusception.
Inflammatory bowel disease.
Hematoma of bowel wall, secondary to trauma or anticoagulants.
Poor dietary habits: insufficient bulk in diet, inadequate fluid intake.
Change from daily routine: travel, hospital admission, physical inactivity.
Acute abdominal conditions: renal colic, salpingitis, biliary colic, appendicitis, ischemia.
Hypercalcemia or hypokalemia, uremia.
Irritable bowel syndrome, pregnancy, anorexia nervosa, depression.
Painful anal conditions: hemorrhoids, fissure, stricture.
Decreased intestinal peristalsis: old age, spinal cord injuries, myxedema, diabetes, multiple sclerosis, parkinsonism and other neurologic diseases.
Drugs: codeine, morphine, antacids with aluminum, verapamil, anticonvulsants, anticholinergics, disopyramide, cholestyramine, alosetron, iron supplements.
Hirschsprung's disease, meconium ileus, congenital atresia in infants.

COUGH

ICD-9CM # 786.2

Infectious process (viral, bacterial).
Postinfectious.
"Smoker's cough."
Rhinitis (allergic, vasomotor, postinfectious).
Asthma.
Exposure to irritants (noxious fumes, smoke, cold air).
Drug-induced (especially ACE inhibitors, β-blockers).
GERD.
Interstitial lung disease.
Lung neoplasms.
Lymphomas, mediastinal neoplasms.
Bronchiectasis.
Cardiac (CHF, pulmonary edema, mitral stenosis, pericardial inflammation).
Recurrent aspiration.
Inflammation of larynx, pleura, diaphragm, mediastinum.
Cystic fibrosis.
Anxiety.
Other: pulmonary embolism, foreign body inhalation, aortic aneurysm, Zenker's diverticulum, osteophytes, substernal thyroid, thyroiditis, PMR.

CYANOSIS

ICD-9CM # 782.5 CYANOSIS NOS
770.8 CYANOSIS, NEWBORN

Congenital heart disease with right-to-left shunt.
Pulmonary embolism.
Hypoxia.
Pulmonary edema.
Pulmonary disease (oxygen diffusion and alveolar ventilation abnormalities).
Hemoglobinopathies.
Decreased cardiac output.
Vasospasm.
Arterial obstruction.
Pulmonary AV fistulas.
Elevated hemidiaphragm.
Neoplasm (bronchogenic carcinoma, mediastinal neoplasm, intrahepatic lesion).
Substernal thyroid.
Infectious process (pneumonia, empyema, TB, subphrenic abscess, hepatic abscess).
Atelectasis.
Idiopathic.
Eventration.
Phrenic nerve dysfunction (myelitis, myotonia, herpes zoster).
Trauma to phrenic nerve or diaphragm (e.g., surgery).
Aortic aneurysm.
Intraabdominal mass.
Pulmonary infarction.
Pleurisy.
Radiation therapy.
Rib fracture.
Superior vena cava syndrome.

DELIRIUM[23]

ICD-9CM # 780.09 DELIRIUM NOS
293.0 ACUTE DELIRIUM

PHARMACOLOGIC AGENTS

Anxiolytics (benzodiazepines).
Antidepressants (e.g., amitriptyline, doxepin, imipramine).
Cardiovascular agents (e.g., methyldopa, digitalis, reserpine, propranolol, procainamide, captopril, disopyramide).
Antihistamine.
Cimetidine.
Corticosteroids.
Antineoplastics.
Drugs of abuse (alcohol, cannabis, amphetamines, cocaine, hallucinogens, opioids, sedative-hypnotics, phencyclidine).

METABOLIC DISORDERS

Hypercalcemia.
Hypercarbia.
Hypoglycemia.
Hyponatremia.
Hypoxia.

INFLAMMATORY DISORDERS

Sarcoidosis.
SLE.
Giant cell arteritis.

ORGAN FAILURE

Hepatic encephalopathy.
Uremia.

NEUROLOGIC DISORDERS

Alzheimer's disease.
CVA.
Encephalitis (including HIV).
Encephalopathies.
Epilepsy.
Huntington's disease.
Multiple sclerosis.
Neoplasms.
Normal pressure hydrocephalus.
Parkinson's disease.
Pick's disease.
Wilson's disease.

ENDOCRINE DISORDERS

Addison's disease.
Cushing's disease.
Panhypopituitarism.
Parathyroid disease.
Postpartum psychosis.
Recurrent menstrual psychosis.
Sydenham's chorea.
Thyroid disease.

DEFICIENCY STATES

Niacin.
Thiamine, Vitamin B_{12}, and folate.

DELIRIUM, DIALYSIS PATIENT[23]

ICD-9CM # 293.0 ACUTE DELIRIUM
293.9 ENCEPHALOPATHY FROM DIALYSIS

STRUCTURAL

Cerebrovascular accident (particularly hemorrhage).
Subdural hematoma.
Intracerebral abscess.
Brain tumor.

METABOLIC

Disequilibrium syndrome.
Uremia.
Drug effects.
Meningitis.
Hypertensive encephalopathy.
Hypotension.
Postictal state.
Hypernatremia or hyponatremia.
Hypercalcemia.
Hypermagnesemia.
Hypoglycemia.
Severe hyperglycemia.
Hypoxemia.
Dialysis dementia.

DEMYELINATING DISEASES[35]

ICD-9CM # 341.9

MULTIPLE SCLEROSIS

Relapsing and chronic progressive forms.
Acute multiple sclerosis.
Neuromyelitis optica (Devic's disease).

DIFFUSE CEREBRAL SCLEROSIS

Schilder's encephalitis periaxialis diffusa.
Baló's concentric sclerosis.

ACUTE DISSEMINATED ENCEPHALOMYELITIS

After measles, chickenpox, rubella, influenza, mumps.
After rabies or smallpox vaccination.

NECROTIZING HEMORRHAGIC ENCEPHALITIS

Hemorrhagic leukoencephalitis.

LEUKODYSTROPHIES

Krabbe's globoid leukodystrophy.
Metachromatic leukodystrophy.
Adrenoleukodystrophy.
Adrenomyeloneuropathy.
Pelizaeus-Merzbacher leukodystrophy.
Canavan's disease.
Alexander's disease.

DIARRHEA, TUBE-FED PATIENT[12]

ICD-9CM # 564.4

COMMON CAUSES UNRELATED TO TUBE FEEDING

Elixir medications containing sorbitol.
Magnesium-containing antacids.
Antibiotic-induced sterile gut.
Pseudomembranous colitis.

POSSIBLE CAUSES RELATED TO TUBE FEEDING

Inadequate fiber to form stool bulk.
High fat content of formula (in the presence of fat malabsorption syndrome).
Bacterial contamination of enteral products and delivery systems (causal association with diarrhea not documented).
Rapid advancement in rate (after the GI tract is unused for prolonged periods).

UNLIKELY CAUSES RELATED TO TUBE FEEDING

Formula hyperosmolality (proven not to be the cause of diarrhea).
Lactose (absent from nearly all enteral feeding formulas).

DIPLOPIA, BINOCULAR

ICD-9CM # 368.2

Cranial nerve palsy (3rd, 4th, 6th).
Thyroid eye disease.
Myasthenia gravis.
Decompensated strabismus.
Orbital trauma with blow-out fracture.
Orbital pseudotumor.
Cavernous sinus thrombosis.

DRY EYE

ICD-9CM # 375.15

Contacts.
Medications (antihistamines, clonidine, beta blockers, ibuprofen, scopolamine).
Keratoconjunctivitis sicca.
Trauma.
Environmental causes (air conditioning in patient with contacts).

DYSPAREUNIA[10]

ICD-9CM # 625.0 DYSPAREUNIA
608.89 DYSPAREUNIA, MALE
302.76 DYSPAREUNIA, PSYCHOGENIC

INTROITAL

Vaginismus.
Intact or rigid hymen.
Clitoral problems.
Vulvovaginitis.
Vaginal atrophy: hypoestrogen.
Vulvar dystrophy.
Bartholin or Skene gland infection.
Inadequate lubrication.
Operative scarring.

MIDVAGINAL

Urethritis.
Trigonitis.
Cystitis.
Short vagina.
Operative scarring.
Inadequate lubrication.

DEEP

Endometriosis.
Pelvic infection.
Uterine retroversion.
Ovarian pathology.
Gastrointestinal.
Orthopedic.
Abnormal penile size or shape.

DYSPHAGIA

ICD-9CM # 787.2

Esophageal obstruction: neoplasm, foreign body, achalasia, stricture, spasm, esophageal web, diverticulum, Schatzki's ring.
Peptic esophagitis with stricture, Barrett's stricture.
External esophageal compression: neoplasms (thyroid neoplasm, lymphoma, mediastinal tumors), thyroid enlargement, aortic aneurysm, vertebral spurs, aberrant right subclavian artery (dysphagia lusoria).
Hiatal hernia, GERD.
Oropharyngeal lesions: pharyngitis, glossitis, stomatitis, neoplasms.
Hysteria: globus hystericus.
Neurologic and/or neuromuscular disturbances: bulbar paralysis, myasthenia gravis, ALS, multiple sclerosis, parkinsonism, CVA, diabetic neuropathy.
Toxins: poisoning, botulism, tetanus, postdiphtheritic dysphagia.
Systemic diseases: scleroderma, amyloidosis, dermatomyositis.
Candida and herpes esophagitis.
Presbyesophagus.

DYSPNEA

ICD-9CM # 786.00

Upper airway obstruction: trauma, neoplasm, epiglottitis, laryngeal edema, tongue retraction, laryngospasm, abductor paralysis of vocal cords, aspiration of foreign body.
Lower airway obstruction: neoplasm, COPD, asthma, aspiration of foreign body.
Pulmonary infection: pneumonia, abscess, empyema, TB, bronchiectasis.

Pulmonary hypertension.
Pulmonary embolism/infarction.
Parenchymal lung disease.
Pulmonary vascular congestion.
Cardiac disease: ASHD, valvular lesions, cardiac dysrhythmias, cardiomyopathy, pericardial effusion, cardiac shunts.
Space-occupying lesions: neoplasm, large hiatal hernia, pleural effusions.
Disease of chest wall: severe kyphoscoliosis, fractured ribs, sternal compression, morbid obesity.
Neurologic dysfunction: Guillain-Barré syndrome, botulism, polio, spinal cord injury.
Interstitial pulmonary disease: sarcoidosis, collagen vascular diseases, DIP, Hamman-Rich pneumonitis, etc.
Pneumoconioses: silicosis, berylliosis, etc.
Mesothelioma.
Pneumothorax, hemothorax, pleural effusion.
Inhalation of toxins.
Cholinergic drug intoxication.
Carcinoid syndrome.
Hematologic: anemia, polycythemia, hemoglobinopathies.
Thyrotoxicosis, myxedema.
Diaphragmatic compression caused by abdominal distention, subphrenic abscess, ascites.
Lung resection.
Metabolic abnormalities: uremia, hepatic coma, DKA.
Sepsis.
Atelectasis.
Psychoneurosis.
Diaphragmatic paralysis.
Pregnancy.

DYSURIA

ICD-9CM # 788.1 DYSURIA
306.53 DYSURIA, PSYCHOGENIC

Urinary tract infection.
Estrogen deficiency (in postmenopausal female).
Vaginitis.
Genital infection (e.g., herpes, condyloma).
Interstitial cystitis.
Chemical irritation (e.g., deodorant aerosols, douches).
Meatal stenosis or stricture.
Reiter's syndrome.
Bladder neoplasm.
GI etiology (diverticulitis, Crohn's disease).
Impaired bladder or sphincter action.
Urethral carbuncle.
Chronic fibrosis posttrauma.
Radiation therapy.
Prostatitis.
Urethritis (gonococcal, *Chlamydiae*).
Behçet's syndrome.
Stevens-Johnson syndrome.

EARACHE[30]

ICD-9CM # 388.70 EARACHE
388.72 EAR PAIN, REFERRED

Otitis media.
Serous otitis media.
Eustachitis.
Otitis externa.
Otitic barotrauma.
Mastoiditis.
Foreign body.
Impacted cerumen.
Referred otalgia, as with TMJ dysfunction, dental problems, and tumors.

ECTOPIC ACTH SECRETION[12]

ICD-9CM # 255.0

Small cell carcinoma of lung.
Endocrine tumors of foregut origin.
 Thymic carcinoid.
 Islet cell tumor.
 Medullary carcinoid, thyroid.
 Bronchial carcinoid.
Pheochromocytoma.
Ovarian tumors.

EDEMA, CHILDREN[17]

ICD-9CM # 782.3 EDEMA NOS

CARDIOVASCULAR

Congestive heart failure.
Acute thrombi or emboli.
Vasculitis of many types.

RENAL

Nephrotic syndrome.
Glomerulonephritis of many types.
End-stage renal failure.

ENDOCRINE OR METABOLIC

Thyroid disease.
Starvation.
Hereditary angioedema.

IATROGENIC

Drugs (diuretics and steroids).
Water or salt overload.

HEMATOLOGIC

Hemolytic disease of the newborn.

GASTROINTESTINAL

Hepatic cirrhosis.
Protein-losing enteritis.
Lymphangiectasis.
Cystic fibrosis.
Celiac disease.
Enteritis of many types.

LYMPHATIC ABNORMALITIES

Congenital (gonadal dysgenesis).
Acquired.

EDEMA, GENERALIZED

ICD-9CM # 782.3 EDEMA NOS

Congestive heart failure (CHF).
Cirrhosis.
Nephrotic syndrome.
Pregnancy.
Idiopathic.
Acute nephritic syndrome.
Myxedema.
Medications (NSAIDs, estrogens, vasodilators).

EDEMA, LEG, UNILATERAL[23]

ICD-9CM # 782.3

WITH PAIN

DVT.
Postphlebitic syndrome.

Popliteal cyst rupture.
Gastrocnemius rupture.
Cellulitis.
Psoas or other abscess.

WITHOUT PAIN

DVT.
Postphlebitic syndrome.
Other venous insufficiency (after saphenous vein harvest, varicosities).
Lymphatic obstruction/lymphedema (carcinoma, lymphoma, sarcoidosis, filariasis, retroperitoneal fibrosis).

EDEMA OF LOWER EXTREMITIES

ICD-9CM # 782.3

CHF (right-sided).
Hepatic cirrhosis.
Nephrosis.
Myxedema.
Lymphedema.
Pregnancy.
Abdominal mass: neoplasm, cyst.
Venous compression from abdominal aneurysm.
Varicose veins.
Bilateral cellulitis.
Bilateral thrombophlebitis.
Vena cava thrombosis, venous thrombosis.
Retroperitoneal fibrosis.

ELEVATED HEMIDIAPHRAGM

ICD-9CM # 519.4 DIAPHRAGM DISORDER
519.4 DIAPHRAGM PARALYSIS
756.6 DIAPHRAGM EVENTRATION, CONGENITAL

Neoplasm (bronchogenic carcinoma, mediastinal neoplasm, intrahepatic lesion).
Substernal thyroid.
Infectious process (pneumonia, empyema, TB, subphrenic abscess, hepatic abscess).
Atelectasis.
Idiopathic.
Eventration.
Phrenic nerve dysfunction (myelitis, myotonia, herpes zoster).
Trauma to phrenic nerve or diaphragm (e.g., surgery).
Aortic aneurysm.
Intraabdominal mass.
Pulmonary infarction.
Pleurisy.
Radiation therapy.
Rib fracture.

EMBOLI, ARTERIAL[23]

ICD-9CM # 444.22 EMBOLISM, ARTERY, LOWER EXTREMITY
444.21 EMBOLISM, ARTERY, UPPER EXTREMITY

Myocardial infarction with mural thrombi.
Atrial fibrillation.
Cardiomyopathies.
Prosthetic heart valves.
CHF.
Endocarditis.
Left ventricular aneurysm.
Left atrial myxoma.
Sick sinus syndrome.
Paradoxical embolus from venous thrombosis.
Aneurysms of large blood vessels.
Atheromatous ulcers of large blood vessels.

EMESIS, PEDIATRIC AGE[17]

ICD-9CM # 787.03

INFANCY

Gastrointestinal tract

Congenital:

Regurgitation—chalasia, gastroesophageal reflux.
Atresia—stenosis (tracheoesophageal fistula, prepyloric diaphragm, intestinal atresia).
Duplication.
Volvulus (errors in rotation and fixation, Meckel's diverticulum).
Congenital bands.
Hirschsprung's disease.
Meconium ileus (cystic fibrosis), meconium plug.

Acquired:

Acute infectious gastroenteritis, food poisoning (staphylococcal, clostridial).
Pyloric stenosis.
Gastritis, duodenitis.
Intussusception.
Incarcerated hernia—inguinal, internal secondary to old adhesions.
Cow's milk protein intolerance, food allergy, eosinophilic gastroenteritis.
Disaccharidase deficiency.
Celiac disease—presents after introduction of gluten in diet; inherited risk.
Adynamic ileus—the mediator for many nongastrointestinal causes.
Neonatal necrotizing enterocolitis.
Chronic granulomatous disease with gastric outlet obstruction.

Nongastrointestinal tract

Infectious—otitis, urinary tract infection, pneumonia, upper respiratory tract infection, sepsis, meningitis.
Metabolic—aminoaciduria and organic aciduria, galactosemia, fructosemia, adrenogenital syndrome, renal tubular acidosis, diabetic ketoacidosis, Reye's syndrome.
Central nervous system—trauma, tumor, infection, diencephalic syndrome, rumination, autonomic responses (pain, shock).
Medications—anticholinergics, aspirin, alcohol, idiosyncratic reaction (e.g., codeine).

CHILDHOOD

Gastrointestinal tract

Peptic ulcer—vomiting is a common presentation in children younger than 6 yr old.
Trauma—duodenal hematoma, traumatic pancreatitis, perforated bowel.
Pancreatitis—mumps, trauma, cystic fibrosis, hyperparathyroidism, hyperlipidemia, organic acidemias.
Crohn's disease.
Idiopathic intestinal pseudoobstruction.
Superior mesenteric artery syndrome.

Nongastrointestinal tract

Central nervous system—cyclic vomiting, migraine, anorexia nervosa, bulimia.

ENCEPHALOPATHY, METABOLIC[33]

ICD-9CM # 291.2 ALCOHOLIC ENCEPHALOPATHY
572.2 HEPATIC ENCEPHALOPATHY
251.2 HYPOGLYCEMIC ENCEPHALOPATHY
349.82 TOXIC ENCEPHALOPATHY
984.9 LEAD ENCEPHALOPATHY
293.9 ENCEPHALOPATHY

Substrate deficiency: hypoxia/ischemia, carbon monoxide poisoning, hypoglycemia.
Cofactor deficiency: thiamine, Vitamin B_{12}, pyridoxine (INH administration).
Electrolyte disorders: hyponatremia, hypercalcemia, carbon dioxide narcosis, dialysis, hypermagnesemia, disequilibrium syndrome.
Endocrinopathies: DKA, hyperosmolar coma, hypothyroidism, hyperadrenocorticism, hyperparathyroidism.
Endogenous toxins: liver disease, uremia, porphyria.
Exogenous toxins: drug overdose (sedative/hypnotics, ethanol, narcotics, salicylates, tricyclic antidepressants), drug withdrawal, toxicity of therapeutic medications, industrial toxins (e.g., organophosphates, heavy metals), sepsis.
Heat stroke.
Epilepsy (postictal).

ENTHESOPATHY

ICD-9CM # CODE NOT AVAILABLE

Viremia or bacteremia.
Ankylosing spondylitis.
Psoriatic arthritis.
Drug-induced (quinolones, etretinate).
Reactive arthritis.
Disseminated idiopathic skeletal hyperostosis (DISH).
Reiter's syndrome.

EPILEPSY

ICD-9CM # 345.9 EPILEPSY NOS

Psychogenic spells.
Transient ischemic attack.
Hypoglycemia.
Syncope.
Narcolepsy.
Migraine.
Paroxysmal vertigo.
Arrhythmias.
Drug reaction.

EPISTAXIS

ICD-9CM # 784.7

Trauma.
Medications (nasal sprays, NSAIDs, anticoagulants, antiplatelets).
Nasal polyps.
Cocaine use.
Coagulopathy (hemophilia, liver disease, DIC, thrombocytopenia).
Systemic disorders (hypertension, uremia).
Infections.
Anatomic malformations.
Rhinitis.
Nasal polyps.
Local neoplasms (benign and malignant).
Desiccation.
Foreign body.

ERECTILE DYSFUNCTION, ORGANIC[28]

ICD-9CM # 607.84

Neurogenic abnormalities: Somatic nerve neuropathy, central nervous system abnormalities.
Psychogenic causes: Depression, performance anxiety, marital conflict.
Endocrine causes: Hyperprolactinemia, hypogonadotropic hypogonadism, testicular failure, estrogen excess.
Trauma: Pelvic fracture, prostate surgery, penile fracture.
Systemic disease: Diabetes mellitus, renal failure, hepatic cirrhosis.
Medications: Diuretics, antidepressants, H2 blockers, exogenous hormones, alcohol, antihypertensives, nicotine abuse, finasteride, etc.
Structural abnormalities: Peyronie's disease.

ESOPHAGEAL PERFORATION[23]

ICD-9CM # 530.4 PERFORATION, NONTRAUMATIC
862.22 INJURY, TRAUMATIC

Trauma.
Caustic burns.
Iatrogenic.
Foreign bodies.
Spontaneous rupture (Boerhaave's syndrome).
Postoperative breakdown of anastomosis.

EXANTHEMS[25]

ICD-9CM # 782.1

Measles.
Rubella.
Erythema infectiosum (fifth disease).
Roseola exanthema.
Varicella.
Enterovirus.
Adenovirus.
Epstein-Barr virus.
Kawasaki disease.
Staphylococcal scalded skin.
Scarlet fever.
Meningococcemia.
Rocky Mountain spotted fever.

EYE PAIN

ICD-9CM # 379.91

Foreign body.
Herpes zoster.
Trauma.
Conjunctivitis.
Iritis.
Iridocyclitis.
Uveitis.
Blepharitis.
Ingrown lashes.
Orbital or periorbital cellulitis/abscess.
Sinusitis.
Headache.
Glaucoma.
Inflammation of lacrimal gland.
Tic douloureux.
Cerebral aneurysm.
Cerebral neoplasm.
Entropion.
Retrobulbar neuritis.

UV light.
Dry eyes.
Irritation or inflammation from eye drops, dust, cosmetics, etc.

FACIAL PAIN

ICD-9CM # 784.0

Infection, abscess.
Postherpetic neuralgia.
Trauma, posttraumatic neuralgia.
Tic douloureux.
Cluster headache, "lower-half headache."
Geniculate neuralgia.
Anxiety, somatization syndrome.
Glossopharyngeal neuralgia.
Carotidynia.

FACIAL PARALYSIS[25]

ICD-9CM # 351.0 FACIAL (7TH NERVE) PALSY

INFECTION

Bacterial: otitis media, mastoiditis, meningitis, Lyme disease.
Viral: herpes zoster, mononucleosis, varicella, rubella, mumps, Bell's palsy.
Mycobacterial: TB, meningitis, leprosy.
Miscellaneous: syphilis, malaria.

TRAUMA

Temporal bone fracture, facial laceration.
Surgery.

NEOPLASM

Malignant: squamous cell carcinoma, basal cell and adenocystic tumors, leukemia, parotid neoplasms, metastic tumors.
Benign: facial nerve neuroma, vestibular schwannoma, congenital cholesteatoma.

IMMUNOLOGIC

Guillain-Barré syndrome, periarteritis nodosa.
Reaction to tetanus antiserum.

METABOLIC

Pregnancy.
Hypothyroidism.
DM.

FAILURE TO THRIVE

ICD-9CM # 783.4

MALABSORPTION

Cow's milk protein allergy.
Cystic fibrosis.
Celiac disease.
Biliary atresia.

INSUFFICIENT CALORIC INTAKE

Parental neglect.
Feeding difficulties (CNS lesion, severe reflux, oromotor abnormalities).
Use of diluted formula preparation.
Food shortage (poverty).

INCREASED NEEDS

Hyperthyroidism.
Congenital heart defects.
Malignancy.
Renal or hepatic disease.
HIV.

IMPROPER UTILIZATION

Storage disorders.
Amino acid disorders.
Trisomy 13, 21, 18.

FATIGUE

ICD-9CM # 780.7 FATIGUE NOS
300.5 FATIGUE PSYCHOGENIC
780.7 CHRONIC FATIGUE SYNDROME

Depression.
Anxiety, emotional stress.
Inadequate sleep.
Prolonged physical activity.
Pregnancy and postpartum period.
Anemia.
Hypothyroidism.
Medications (β-blockers, anxiolytics, antidepressants, sedating antihistamines, clonidine, methyldopa).
Viral or bacterial infections.
Sleep apnea syndrome.
Dieting.
Renal failure, CHF, COPD, liver disease.

FATTY LIVER

ICD-9CM # 571.8

Obesity.
Alcohol abuse.
Diabetes mellitus.
Acute fatty liver of pregnancy.
Medications (tetracycline, valproic acidglucocorticoids, amiodarone, estrogen, methotrexate).
Reye's syndrome.
Wilson's disease.
Nonalcoholic steatosis.

FEVER AND JAUNDICE

ICD-9CM # 789.6 FEVER
782.4 JAUNDICE

Cholecystitis.
Hepatic abscess (pyogenic, amebic).
Ascending cholangitis.
Pancreatitis.
Malaria.
Neoplasm (hepatic pancreatic, biliary tract, metastatic).
Mononucleosis.
Viral hepatitis.
Sepsis.
Babesiosis.
HIV (cryptosporidium).
Biliary ascariasis.
Toxic shock syndrome.
Yersinia infection, leptospirosis, Yellow fever, Dengue fever, relapsing fever.

FEVER AND RASH

ICD-9CM # 782.1 EXANTHEM
57.9 EXANTHEM VIRAL
789.6 FEVER

Drug hypersensitivity: penicillin, sulfonamides, thiazides, anticonvulsants, allopurinol.

Viral infection: measles, rubella, varicella, erythema infectiosum, roseola, enterovirus infection, viral hepatitis, infectious mononucleosis, acute HIV.
Other infections: meningococcemia, staphylococcemia, scarlet fever, typhoid fever, Pseudomonas bacteremia, Rocky Mountain spotted fever, Lyme disease, secondary syphilis, bacterial endocarditis, babesiosis, brucellosis, listeriosis.
Serum sickness.
Erythema multiforme.
Erythema marginatum.
Erythema nodosum.
SLE.
Dermatomyositis.
Allergic vasculitis.
Pityriasis rosea.
Herpes zoster.

FEVER IN RETURNING TRAVELERS AND IMMIGRANTS[25]

ICD-9CM # CODE VARIES WITH SPECIFIC DISORDER

Differential Diagnosis of Some Selected Systemic Febrile Illnesses to Consider in Returned Travelers and Immigrants.*

COMMON

Acute respiratory tract infection (worldwide).
Gastroenteritis (worldwide) [foodborne, waterborne, fecal-oral].
Enteric fever, including typhoid (worldwide) [food, water].
Urinary tract infection (worldwide) [sexual contact].
Drug reactions [antibiotics, prophylactic agents, other] {rash frequent}.
Malaria (tropics, limited areas of temperate zones) [mosquitoes].
Arboviruses (Africa; tropics) [mosquitoes, ticks, mites].
Dengue (Asia, Caribbean, Africa) [mosquitoes].
Viral hepatitis (worldwide).
Hepatitis A (worldwide) [food, fecal-oral].
Hepatitis B (worldwide, especially Asia, sub-Saharan Africa) [sexual contact] {long incubation period}.
Hepatitis C (worldwide) [blood or sexual contact].
Hepatitis E (Asia, North Africa, Mexico, ?others) [food, water].
Tuberculosis (worldwide) [airborne, milk] {long period to symptomatic infection}.
Sexually transmitted diseases (worldwide) [sexual contact].

LESS COMMON

Filariasis (Asia, Africa, South America) [biting insects] {long incubation period, eosinophilia}.
Measles (developing world) [airborne] {in susceptible individual}.
Amebic abscess (worldwide) [food].
Brucellosis (worldwide) [milk, cheese, food, animal contact].
Listeriosis (worldwide) [foodborne] {meningitis}.
Leptospirosis (worldwide) [animal contact, open fresh water] {jaundice, meningitis}.
Strongyloidiasis (warm and tropical areas) [soil contact] {eosinophilia}.
Toxoplasmosis (worldwide) [undercooked meat].

RARE

Relapsing fever (western Americas, Asia, northern Africa) [ticks lice].
Hemorrhagic fevers (worldwide) [arthropod and nonarthropod transmitted].
Yellow fever (tropics) [mosquitoes] {hepatitis}.
Hemorrhagic fever with renal syndrome (Europe, Asia, North America) [rodent urine] {renal impairment}.
Hantavirus pulmonary syndrome (western North America, ?other) [rodent urine] {respiratory distress syndrome}.
Lassa fever (Africa) [rodent excreta, person to person] {high mortality rate}
Other—chikungunya, Rift Valley, Ebola-Marburg, etc. (various) [insect bites, rodent excreta, aerosols, person to person] {often severe}.
Rickettsial infections {Rashes and eschars}.
Leishmaniasis, visceral (Middle East, Mediterranean, Africa, Asia, South America) [biting flies] {long incubation period}.
Acute schistosomiasis (Africa, Asia, South America, Caribbean) [fresh water].
Chagas' disease (South and Central America) [reduviid bug bites] {often asymptomatic}.
African trypanosomiasis (Africa) [tsetse fly bite] {neurologic syndromes, sleeping sickness}.
Bartonellosis (South America) [sandfly bite; cb] {skin nodules}.
HIV infection/AIDS (worldwide) [sexual and blood contact].
Trichinosis (worldwide) [undercooked meat] {eosinophilia}.
Plague (temperate and tropical plains) [animal exposures and fleas].
Tularemia (worldwide) [animal contact, fleas, aerosols] {ulcers, lymph nodes}.
Anthrax (worldwide) [animal, animal product contact] {ulcers}.
Lyme disease (North America, Europe) [tick bites] {arthritis, meningitis, cardiac abnormalities}.

*Diagnoses for which particular symptoms are indicative are in italics. Exposure to regions of the world that are most likely to be significant to the diagnosis are presented in (parentheses). Vectors, risk behaviors, and sources associated with acquisition are presented in [brackets]. Special clinical characteristics are listed within {braces}.

FLATULENCE AND BLOATING[30]

ICD-9CM # 787.3

Ingestion of nonabsorbable carbohydrates.
Ingestion of carbonated beverages.
Malabsorption: pancreatic insufficiency, biliary disease, celiac disease, bacterial overgrowth in small intestine.
Lactase deficiency.
Irritable bowel syndrome.
Anxiety disorders.
Food poisoning, giardiasis.

FLUSHING[24]

ICD-9CM # 782.62

Physiologic flushing: menopause, ingestion of monosodium glutamate (Chinese restaurant syndrome), ingestion of hot drinks.
Drugs: alcohol (with or without disulfiram, metronidazole, or chlorpropamide), nicotinic acid, diltiazem, nifedipine, levodopa, bromocriptine, vancomycin, amyl nitrate.
Neoplastic disorders: carcinoid syndrome, Vipoma syndrome, medullary carcinoma of thyroid, systemic mastocytosis, basophilic chronic myelocytic leukemia, renal cell carcinoma.
Anxiety.
Agnogenic flushing.

FOOT PAIN

ICD-9CM # CODE VARIES WITH SPECIFIC DIAGNOSIS

Trauma (fractures, musculoskeletal and ligamentous strain).
Inflammation (Plantar fasciitis, Achilles tendonitis or bursitis, calcaneal apophysitis).

Arterial insufficiency, Raynaud's phenomenon, thromboangiitis obliterans.
Gout, pseudogout.
Calcaneal spur.
Infection (cellulitis, abscess, lymphangitis, gangrene).
Decubitus ulcer.
Paronychia, ingrown toenail.
Thrombophlebitis, postphlebitic syndrome.

FOREARM AND HAND PAIN

ICD-9CM # 959.3 FOREARM INJURY
959.4 HAND INJURY

Epicondylitis.
Tenosynovitis.
Osteoarthritis.
Cubital tunnel syndrome.
Carpal tunnel syndrome.
Trauma.
Herpes zoster.
Peripheral vascular insufficiency.
Infection (cellulitis, abscess).

GAIT ABNORMALITY

ICD-9CM # 781.2 GAIT ABNORMALITY

Parkinsonism.
Degenerative joint disease (hips, back, knees).
Multiple sclerosis.
Trauma, foot pain.
CVA.
Cerebellar lesions.
Infections (tabes, encephalitis, meningitis).
Sensory ataxia.
Dystonia, cerebral palsy, neuromuscular disorders.
Metabolic abnormalities.

GALACTORRHEA[25]

ICD-9CM # 611.6

Prolonged suckling.
Drugs (INH, phenothiazines, reserpine derivatives, amphetamines, spironolactone and tricyclic antidepressants).
Major stressors (surgery, trauma).
Hypothyroidism.
Pituitary tumors.

GASTRIC EMPTYING, DELAYED[1]

ICD-9CM # 536.8 GASTRIC MOTILITY DISORDER

MECHANICAL OBSTRUCTION

Duodenal or pyloric channel ulcer.
Pyloric stricture.
Tumor of the distal stomach.

FUNCTIONAL OBSTRUCTION (GASTROPARESIS)

Drugs: anticholinergics, beta-adrenergics, opiates.
Electrolyte imbalance: hypokalemia, hypocalcemia, hypomagnesemia.
Metabolic disorders: DM, hypoparathyroidism, hypothyroidism, pregnancy.
Vagotomy.
Viral infections.
Neuromuscular disorders (myotonic dystrophy, autonomic neuropathy, scleroderma, polymyositis).
Gastric pacemaker (i.e., tachygastria).
Brainstem tumors.
GERD.
Psychiatric disorders: anorexia nervosa, psychogenic vomiting.
Idiopathic.

GASTRIC EMPTYING, RAPID

ICD-9CM # 536.8 GASTRIC MOTILITY DISORDER

Pancreatic insufficiency.
Dumping syndrome.
Peptic ulcer.
Celiac disease.
Promotility agents.
Zollinger-Ellison disease.

GENITAL DISCHARGE, FEMALE[10]

ICD-9CM # 629.9

Physiologic discharge: cervical mucus, vaginal transudation, bacteria, squamous epithelial cells.
Individual variation.
Pregnancy.
Sexual response.
Menstrual cycle variation.
Infection.
Foreign body: tampon, cervical cap, other.
Neoplasm.
Fistula.
IUD.
Cervical ectropion.
Spermicide.
Nongenital causes: urinary incontinence, urinary tract fistula, Crohn's disease, rectovaginal fistula.

GENITAL SORES[1]

ICD-9CM # 054.10 GENITAL HERPES
91.0 GENITAL SYPHILIS
078.11 CONDYLOMA ACUMINATUM
099.0 CHANCROID
099.2 GRANULOMA INGUINALE
099.1 LYMPHOGRANULOMA VENEREUM
629.8 ULCER, GENITAL SITE, FEMALE
608.89 ULCER, GENITAL SITE, MALE

Herpes genitalis.
Syphilis.
Chancroid.
Lymphogranuloma venereum.
Granuloma inguinale.
Condyloma acuminatum.
Neoplastic lesion.
Trauma.

GLUCOCORTICOID DEFICIENCY[12]

ICD-9CM # 255.4

ACTH-independent causes.
TB.
Autoimmune (idiopathic).
Other rare causes:
- Fungal infection.
- Adrenal hemorrhage.
- Metastases.
- Sarcoidosis.
- Amyloidosis.
- Adrenoleukodystrophy.

Adrenomyeloneuropathy.
HIV infection.
Congenital adrenal hyperplasia.
Medications (e.g., ketoconazole).
ACTH-dependent causes:
Hypothalamic-pituitary-adrenal suppression.
Exogenous.
Glucocorticoid.
ACTH.
Endogenous—cure of Cushing's syndrome.
Hypothalamic-pituitary lesions.
Neoplasm.
Primary pituitary tumor.
Metastatic tumor.
Craniopharyngioma.
Infection.
Tuberculosis.
Actinomycosis.
Nocardiosis.
Sarcoid.
Head trauma.
Isolated ACTH deficiency.

GOITER

ICD-9CM # 240.9 GOITER, UNSPECIFIED
241.9 GOITER, ADENOMATOUS
246.1 GOITER, CONGENITAL
240.9 GOITER, NONTOXIC DIFFUSE
241.1 GOITER, NONTOXIC MULTINODULAR
240.0 SIMPLE GOITER
242.1 THYROTOXIC GOITER

Thyroiditis.
Toxic multinodular goiter.
Graves' disease.
Medications (PTU, methimazole, sulfonamides, sulfonylureas, ethionamide, amiodarone, lithium, etc.).
Iodine deficiency.
Sarcoidosis, amyloidosis.
Defective thyroid hormone synthesis.
Resistance to thyroid hormone.

GRANULOMATOUS DISORDERS[29]

ICD-9CM # 446.4 GRANULOMATOSIS
288.1 GRANULOMATOUS DISEASE

INFECTIONS

Fungi
Histoplasma.
Coccidioides.
Blastomyces.
Sporothrix.
Aspergillus.
Cryptococcus.
Protozoa
Toxoplasma.
Leishmania.
Metazoa
Toxocara.
Schistosoma.
Spirochetes
Treponema pallidum.
T. pertenue.
T. carateum.
Mycobacteria
M. tuberculosis.
M. leprae.
M. kansasii.
M. marinum.
M. avian.
Bacille Calmette-Guérin (BCG) vaccine.
Bacteria
Brucella.
Yersinia.
Other Infections
Cat scratch.
Lymphogranuloma.

NEOPLASIA

Carcinoma.
Reticulosis.
Pinealoma.
Dysgerminoma.
Seminoma.
Reticulum cell sarcoma.
Malignant nasal granuloma.

CHEMICALS

Beryllium.
Zirconium.
Silica.
Starch.

IMMUNOLOGIC ABERRATIONS

Sarcoidosis.
Crohn's disease.
Primary biliary cirrhosis.
Wegener's granulomatosis.
Giant-cell arteritis.
Peyronie's disease.
Hypogammaglobulinemia.
Systemic lupus erythematosus.
Lymphomatoid granulomatosis.
Histiocytosis X.
Hepatic granulomatous disease.
Immune complex disease.
Rosenthal-Melkersson syndrome.
Churg-Strauss allergic granulomatosis.

LEUKOCYTE OXIDASE DEFECT

Chronic granulomatous disease of childhood.

EXTRINSIC ALLERGIC ALVEOLITIS

Farmer's lung.
Bird fancier's.
Mushroom worker's.
Suberosis (cork dust).
Bagassosis.
Maple bark stripper's.
Paprika splitter's.
Coffee bean.
Spatlese lung.

OTHER DISORDERS

Whipple's disease.
Pyrexia of unknown origin.
Radiotherapy.
Cancer chemotherapy.
Panniculitis.
Chalazion.
Sebaceous cyst.
Dermoid.
Sea urchin spine injury.

GRANULOMATOUS LIVER DISEASE

ICD-9CM # 572.8

Sarcoidosis.
Wegener's granulomatosis.
Vasculitis.
Inflammatory bowel disease.
Allergic granulomatosis.
Erythema nodosum.
Infections (fungal, viral, parasitic).
Primary biliary cirrhosis.
Lymphoma.
Hodgkin's disease.
Drugs (e.g., allopurinol, hydralazine, sulfonamides, penicillins).
Toxins (copper sulfate, beryllium).

GROIN PAIN, ACTIVE PATIENT[34]

ICD-9CM # 959.1 GROIN INJURY
848.8 GROIN PAIN

MUSCULOSKELETAL

Avascular necrosis of the femoral head.
Avulsion fracture (lesser trochanter, anterior superior iliac spine, anterior inferior iliac spine).
Bursitis (iliopectineal, trochanteric).
Entrapment of the ilioinguinal or iliofemoral nerve.
Gracilis syndrome.
Muscle tear (adductors, iliopsoas, rectus abdominis, gracilis, sartorius, rectus femoris).
Myositis ossificans of the hip muscles.
Osteitis pubis.
Osteoarthritis of the femoral head.
Slipped capital femoral epiphysis.
Stress fracture of the femoral head or neck and pubis.
Synovitis.

HERNIA-RELATED

Avulsion of the internal oblique muscle in the conjoined tendon.
Defect at the insertion of the rectus abdominis muscle.
Direct inguinal hernia.
Femoral ring hernia.
Indirect inguinal hernia.
Inguinal canal weakness.

UROLOGIC

Epididymitis.
Fracture of the testis.
Hydrocele.
Kidney stone.
Posterior urethritis.
Prostatis.
Testicular cancer.
Torsion of the testis.
Urinary tract infection.
Varicocele.

GYNECOLOGIC

Ectopic pregnancy.
Ovarian cyst.
Pelvic inflammatory disease.
Torsion of the ovary.
Vaginitis.

LYMPHATIC ENLARGEMENT IN GROIN

GYNECOMASTIA

ICD-9CM # 611.1 GYNECOMASTIA, NONPUERPERAL

Physiologic (puberty, newborns, aging).
Drugs (estrogen and estrogen precursors, digitalis, testosterone and exogenous androgens, clomiphene, cimetidine, spironolactone, ketoconazole, amiodarone, ACE inhibitors, isoniazid, phenytoin, methyldopa, metoclopramide, phenothiazine).
Increased prolactin level (prolactinoma).
Liver disease.
Adrenal disease.
Thyrotoxicosis.
Increased estrogen production (hCG-producing tumor, testicular tumor, bronchogenic carcinoma).
Secondary hypogonadism.
Primary gonadal failure (trauma, castration, viral orchitis, granulomatous disease).
Defects in androgen synthesis.
Testosterone deficiency.
Klinefelter's syndrome.

HALITOSIS

ICD-9CM # 784.9

Tobacco use.
Alcohol use.
Dry mouth (mouth breathing, inadequate fluid intake).
Foods (onion, garlic, meats, nuts).
Disease of mouth or nose (infections, cancer, inflammation).
Medications (antihistamines, antidepressants).
Systemic disorders (diabetes, uremia).
GI disorders (esophageal diverticula, hiatal hernia, GERD, achalasia).
Sinusitis.
Pulmonary disorders (bronchiectasis, pneumonia, neoplasms, TB).

HAND PAIN AND SWELLING[6]

ICD-9CM # CODE VARIES WITH SPECIFIC DIAGNOSIS

Trauma.
Gout.
Pseudogout.
Cellulitis.
Lymphangitis.
DVT of upper extremity.
Thrombophlebitis.
Rheumatoid arthritis.
Remitting seronegative symmetrical synovitis with pitting edema (RS3PE).
Polymyalgia rheumatica.
Mixed connective tissue disease.
Scleroderma.
Rupture of the olecranon bursa.
Metzger's syndrome (neoplasia).
The puffy hand of drug addiction.
Reflex sympathetic dystrophy.
Eosinophilic fasciitis.
Sickle cell (hand-foot syndrome).
Leprosy.
Factitial (the rubber band syndrome).

HEADACHE[11]

ICD-9CM # 784.0 HEADACHE NOS
307.81 HEADACHE, TENSION
346.2 HEADACHE, CLUSTER
346.9 HEADACHE, MIGRAINE
784.0 HEADACHE, VASCULAR

Vascular: migraine, cluster headaches, temporal arteritis, hypertension, cavernous sinus thrombosis.
Musculoskeletal: neck and shoulder muscle contraction, strain of extraocular and/or intraocular muscles, cervical spondylosis, temporomandibular arthritis.
Infections: meningitis, encephalitis, brain abscess, sepsis, sinusitis, osteomyelitis, parotitis, mastoiditis.
Cerebral neoplasm.
Subdural hematoma.
Cerebral hemorrhage/infarct.
Pseudotumor cerebri.
Normal pressure hydrocephalus (NPH).
Postlumbar puncture.
Cerebral aneurysm, arteriovenous malformations.
Posttrauma.
Dental problems: abscess, periodontitis, poorly fitting dentures.
Trigeminal neuralgia, glossopharyngeal neuralgia.
Otitis and other ear diseases.
Glaucoma and other eye diseases.
Metabolic: uremia, carbon monoxide inhalation, hypoxia.
Pheochromocytoma, hypoglycemia, hypothyroidism.
Effort induced: benign exertional headache, cough, headache, coital cephalalgia.
Drugs: alcohol, nitrates, histamine antagonists.
Paget's disease of the skull.
Emotional, psychiatric.

HEADACHE AND FACIAL PAIN[33]

ICD-9CM # 784.0 HEADACHE NOS
784.0 FACIAL PAIN

VASCULAR HEADACHES

Migraine

Migraine with headaches and inconspicuous neurologic features:
-Migraine without aura ("common migraine").
Migraine with headaches and conspicuous neurologic features:
-With transient neurologic symptoms:
Migraine with typical aura ("classic migraine").
Sensory, basilar, and *hemiplegic migraine.*
-With prolonged or permanent neurologic features ("complicated migraine"):
Ophthalmoplegic migraine.
Migrainous infarction.
Migraine without headaches but with conspicuous neurologic features ("migraine equivalents"):
-Abdominal migraine.
-Benign paroxysmal vertigo of childhood.
-Migraine aura without headache ("isolated auras," transient migrainous accompaniments).

Cluster headaches

Episodic cluster headache ("cyclic cluster headaches").
Chronic cluster headaches.
Chronic paroxysmal hemicrania.

Other vascular headaches

Headaches of reactive vasodilation (fever, drug-induced, postictal, hypoglycemia, hypoxia, hypercarbia, hyperthyroidism).
Headaches associated with arterial hypertension:
-Chronic severe hypertension (diastolic .120 mm Hg).
-Paroxysmal severe hypertension (pheochromocytoma, some coital headaches).
Headaches caused by cranial arteritis:
-Giant cell arteritis ("temporal arteritis").
-Other vasculitides.

HEADACHES ASSOCIATED WITH DEMONSTRABLE MUSCLE SPASM

Headache caused by posturally induced or perilesional muscle spasm:
-Headaches of sustained or impaired posture (e.g., prolonged close work, driving).
-Headaches associated with cervical spondylosis and other diseases of cervical spine.
-Myofascial pain dysfunction syndrome (headache or facial pain associated with disorders of teeth, jaws, and related structures, or "TMJ syndrome").
Headaches caused by psychophysiologic muscular contraction ("muscle contraction headaches," or tension-type headache associated with disorder of pericranial muscles).

HEADACHES AND FACIAL PAIN WITHOUT DEMONSTRABLE PHYSICAL SUBSTRATE

Headaches of uncertain etiology:
-"Tension headaches" (tension-type headache unassociated with disorder of pericranial muscles).
-Some forms of posttraumatic headache.
Psychogenic headaches (e.g., hypochondriacal, conversional, delusional, malingered).
Facial pain of uncertain etiology ("atypical facial pain").

COMBINED TENSION-MIGRAINE HEADACHES

Episodic migraine superimposed on chronic tension headaches.
Chronic daily headaches:
-Associated with analgesic and/or ergotamine overuse ("rebound headaches").
-Not associated with drug overuse.

HEADACHES AND HEAD PAINS CAUSED BY DISEASES OF EYES, EARS, NOSE, SINUSES, TEETH, OR SKULL

HEADACHES CAUSED BY MENINGEAL INFLAMMATION

Subarachnoid hemorrhage.
Meningitis and meningoencephalitis.
Others (e.g., meningeal carcinomatosis).

HEADACHES ASSOCIATED WITH ALTERED INTRACRANIAL PRESSURE ("TRACTION HEADACHES")

Increased intracranial pressure

Intracranial mass lesions (neoplasm, hematoma, abscess, etc.).
Hydrocephalus.
Benign intracranial hypertension.
Venous sinus thrombosis.

Decreased intracranial pressure

Post–lumbar puncture headaches.
Spontaneous hypoliquorrheic headaches.

HEADACHES AND HEAD PAINS CAUSED BY CRANIAL NEURALGIAS

Presumed irritation of superficial nerves

Occipital neuralgia.
Supraorbital neuralgia.

Presumed irritation of intracranial nerves

Trigeminal neuralgia ("tic douloureux").
Glossopharyngeal neuralgia.

HEARING LOSS, ACUTE[23]

ICD-9CM # 388.2

Infectious: mumps, measles, influenza, herpes simplex, herpes zoster, CMV, mononucleosis, syphilis.
Vascular: macroglobulinemia, sickle cell disease, Berger's disease, leukemia, polycythemia, fat emboli, hypercoagulable states.
Metabolic: diabetes, pregnancy, hyperlipoproteinemia.
Conductive: cerumen impaction, foreign bodies, otitis media, otitis externa, barotrauma, trauma.
Medications: aminoglycosides, loop diuretics, antineoplastics, salicylates, vancomycin.
Neoplasm: acoustic neuroma, metastatic neoplasm.

HEARTBURN AND INDIGESTION[30]

ICD-9CM # 787.1 HEARTBURN
536.8 INDIGESTION

Reflux esophagitis.
Gastritis.
Nonulcer dyspepsia.
Functional GI disorder (anxiety disorder, social/environmental stresses).
Excessive intestinal gas (ingestion of flatulogenic foods, GI stasis, constipation).
Gas entrapment (hepatitis or splenic flexure syndrome).
Neoplasm (adenocarcinoma of stomach or esophagus, lymphoma).
Gallbladder disease.

HEEL PAIN, PLANTAR[21]

ICD-9CM # 729.5

SKIN

Keratoses.
Verruca.
Ulcer.
Fissure.

CONNECTIVE TISSUE

Fat
Atrophy.
Panniculitis.
Dense Connective Tissue
Inflammatory fasciitis.
Fibromatosis.
Enthesopathy.
Bursitis.
Bone (Calcaneus)
Stress fracture.
Paget's disease.
Benign bone cyst/tumor.
Malignant bone tumor.
Metabolic bone disease (osteopenia).
Nerve
Tarsal tunnel.
Plantar nerve entrapment.
S1 nerve root radiculopathy.
Painful peripheral neuropathy.

INFECTION

Dermatomycoses.
Acute osteomyelitis.
Plantar abscess.

MISCELLANEOUS

Foreign body.
Nonunion calcaneus fracture.
Psychogenic.
Idiopathic.

HEMARTHROSIS

ICD-9CM # 848.9 HEMARTHROSIS (SPRAIN) NOS

Trauma.
Anticoagulant therapy.
Thrombocytopenia, thrombocytosis.
Bleeding disorders (e.g., von Willebrand's disease).
Charcot's joint.
Idiopathic.
Other: pigmented villonodular synovitis, hemangioma, synovioma, AV fistula, ruptured aneurysm.

HEMATURIA

ICD-9CM # 599.7 HEMATURIA, BENIGN (ESSENTIAL)

Use the mnemonic TICS:
T (trauma): blow to kidney, insertion of Foley catheter or foreign body in urethra, prolonged and severe exercise, very rapid emptying of overdistended bladder.
(tumor): hypernephroma, Wilms' tumor, papillary carcinoma of the bladder, prostatic and urethral neoplasms.
(toxins): turpentine, phenols, sulfonamides and other antibiotics, cyclophosphamide, NSAIDs.
I (infections): glomerulonephritis, TB, cystitis, prostatitis, urethritis, Schistosoma haematobium, yellow fever, blackwater fever.
(inflammatory processes): Goodpasture's syndrome, periarteritis, postirradiation.
C (calculi): renal, ureteral, bladder, urethra.
(cysts): simple cysts, polycystic disease.
(congenital anomalies): hemangiomas, aneurysms, AVM.
S (surgery): invasive procedures, prostatic resection, cystoscopy.
(sickle cell disease and other hematologic disturbances): hemophilia, thrombocytopenia, anticoagulants.
(somewhere else): bleeding genitals, factitious (drug addicts).

HEMATURIA, CAUSED BY AGE AND SEX

ICD-9CM # 599.7 HEMATURIA BENIGN (ESSENTIAL)
OTHER CODES FOR HEMATURIA VARY WITH CAUSE OF HEMATURIA

0-20 YR

Acute urinary tract infections.
Acute glomerulonephritis.
Congenital urinary tract anomalies with obstruction.
Trauma to genitals.

20-40 YR

Acute urinary tract infection.
Trauma to genitals.
Urolithiasis.
Bladder cancer.

40-60 YR (WOMEN)

Acute urinary tract infection.
Bladder cancer.
Urolithiasis.

40-60 YR (MEN)

Acute urinary tract infection.
Bladder cancer.
Urolithiasis.

60 YR AND OLDER (WOMEN)

Acute urinary tract infection.
Bladder cancer.
Vaginal trauma or irritation.
Urolithiasis.

60 YR AND OLDER (MEN)

Acute urinary tract infection.
Benign prostatic hyperplasia.
Bladder cancer.
Urolithiasis.
Trauma.

HEMIPARESIS/HEMIPLEGIA

ICD-9CM # 436.0 ACQUIRED DUE TO ACUTE CVA, FLACCID
436.1 ACQUIRED DUE TO CVA, ACUTE, SPASTIC

CVA.
Transient ischemic attack.
Cerebral neoplasm.
Multiple sclerosis or other demyelinating disorder.
CNS infection.
Migraine.
Hypoglycemia
Subdural hematoma.
Vasculitis.
Todd's paralysis.
Epidural hematoma.
Metabolic (hyperosmolar state, electrolyte imbalance).
Psychiatric disorders.
Congenital disorders.
Leukodystrophies.

HEMOLYSIS AND HEMOGLOBINURIA

ICD-9CM # 773.2 HEMOLYSIS
791.2 HEMOGLOBINURIA

Erythrocyte trauma (prosthetic cardiac valves, marching and severe trauma, extensive burns).
Infections (malaria, *Bartonella, Clostridium Welchii*).
Brown recluse spider bite.
Incompatible blood transfusions.
Hemolytic uremic syndrome.
Thrombotic thrombocytopenic purpura (TTP).
Paroxysmal nocturnal hemoglobinuria (PNH).
Drugs (penicillins, quinidine, methyldopa, sulfonamides, nitrofurantoin).
Erythrocyte enzyme deficiencies (e.g., exposure to fava beans in patients with glucose-6-phosphate dehydrogenase deficiency).

HEMOLYSIS, INTRAVASCULAR

ICD-9CM # 283.2

Infections.
Exertional hemolysis (e.g., prolonged march).
Valve hemolysis.
Microangiopathic hemolytic anemia.
Osmotic and chemical agents.
Thermal injury.
Cold agglutinins.
Venoms (snakes, spiders).
Paroxysmal nocturnal hemoglobinuria (PNH).

HEMOPTYSIS

ICD-9CM # 786.3

CARDIOVASCULAR

Pulmonary embolism/infarction.
Left ventricular failure.
Mitral stenosis.
AV fistula.
Severe hypertension.
Erosion of aortic aneurysm.

PULMONARY

Neoplasm (primary or metastatic).
Infection.
Pneumonia: *Streptococcus pneumoniae, Klebsiella pneumoniae, Staphylococcus aureus, Legionella* pneumophila.
Bronchiectasis.
Abscess.
TB.
Bronchitis.
Fungal infections (aspergillosis, coccidioidomycosis).
Parasitic infections (amebiasis, ascariasis, paragonimiasis).
Vasculitis: Wegener's granulomatosis, Churg-Strauss syndrome, Henoch-Schönlein purpura.
Goodpasture's syndrome.
Trauma (needle biopsy, foreign body, right-sided heart catheterization, prolonged and severe cough).
Cystic fibrosis, bullous emphysema.
Pulmonary sequestration.
Pulmonary AV fistula.
SLE.
Idiopathic pulmonary hemosiderosis.
Drugs: aspirin, anticoagulants, penicillamine.
Pulmonary hypertension.
Mediastinal fibrosis.

OTHER

Epistaxis, trauma.
Laryngeal bleeding (laryngitis, laryngeal neoplasm).
Hematologic disorders (clotting abnormalities, DIC, thrombocytopenia).

HEPATIC CYSTS[33]

ICD-9CM # 751.62 HEPATIC CYST, CONGENITAL
122.8 ECHINOCOCCUS INFECTION, LIVER

CONGENITAL HEPATIC CYSTS

Parenchymal: solitary cyst, polycystic disease.
Ductal: localized dilatation, multiple cystic dilatations of intrahepatic ducts (Caroli's disease).

ACQUIRED HEPATIC CYSTS

Inflammatory cysts: retention cysts, echinococcal cyst, amebic cyst.
Neoplastic cyst.
Peliosis hepatis.

HEPATIC GRANULOMAS[1]

ICD-9CM # 572.8

INFECTIONS

Bacterial, spirochetal: TB and atypical mycobacterial infections, tularemia, brucellosis, leprosy, syphilis, Whipple's disease, listeriosis.
Viral: mononucleosis, CMV.
Rickettsial: Q fever.

Fungal: coccidioidomycosis, histoplasmosis, cryptococcal infections, actinomycosis, aspergillosis, nocardiosis.
Parasitic: schistosomiasis, clonorchiasis, toxocariasis, ascariasis, toxoplasmosis, amebiasis.

HEPATOBILIARY DISORDERS

Primary biliary cirrhosis, granulomatous hepatitis, jejunoileal bypass.

SYSTEMIC DISORDERS

Sarcoidosis, Wegener's granulomatosis, inflammatory bowel disease, Hodgkin's disease, lymphoma.

DRUGS/TOXINS

Beryllium, parenteral foreign material (starch, talc, silicone, etc.), phenylbutazone, a-methyldopa, procainamide, allopurinol, phenytoin, nitrofurantoin, hydralazine.

HEPATITIS, CHRONIC[22]

ICD-9CM # 571.40 HEPATITIS, NONINFECTIOUS, CHRONIC
072.22 HEPATITIS B, CHRONIC
070.44 HEPATITIS C, CHRONIC

Chronic viral hepatitis:
- Hepatitis B.
- Hepatitis C.
- Hepatitis D.

Autoimmune hepatitis and variant syndromes.
Hereditary hemochromatosis.
Wilson's disease.
α-Antitrypsin deficiency.
Fatty liver and nonalcoholic steatohepatitis.
Alcoholic liver disease.
Drug-induced liver disease.
Hepatic granulomas:
- Infectious.
- Drug induced.
- Neoplastic.
- Idiopathic.

HEPATOMEGALY

ICD-9CM # 789.1

FREQUENT JAUNDICE

Infectious hepatitis.
Toxic hepatitis.
Carcinoma: liver, pancreas, bile ducts, metastatic neoplasm to liver.
Cirrhosis.
Obstruction of common bile duct.
Alcoholic hepatitis.
Biliary cirrhosis.
Cholangitis.
Hemochromatosis with cirrhosis.

INFREQUENT JAUNDICE

CHF.
Amyloidosis.
Liver abscess.
Sarcoidosis.
Infectious mononucleosis.
Alcoholic fatty infiltration.
Nonalcoholic steatohepatitis
Lymphoma.
Leukemia.
Budd-Chiari syndrome.
Myelofibrosis with myeloid metaplasia.
Familial hyperlipoproteinemia type 1.
Other: amebiasis, hydatid disease of liver, schistosomiasis, kala-azar *(Leishmania donovani),* Hurler's syndrome, Gaucher's disease, kwashiorkor.

HERMAPHRODITISM[4]

ICD-9CM # 752.7 HERMAPHRODITISM, CONGENITAL

FEMALE PSEUDOHERMAPHRODITISM

Androgen exposure:
- Fetal source:
  - 21-Hydroxylase (P450 c21) deficiency.
  - 11β-Hydroxylase (P450 c11) deficiency.
  - 3β-Hydroxysteroid dehydrogenase II (3β-HSD II) deficiency.
  - Aromatase (P450arom) deficiency.
- Maternal source.
- Virilizing ovarian tumor.
- Virilizing adrenal tumor.
- Androgenic drugs.

Undetermined origin:
- Associated with genitourinary and gastrointestinal tract defects.

MALE PSEUDOHERMAPHRODITISM

Defects in testicular differentiation:
- Denys-Drash syndrome (mutation in WT1 gene).
- WAGR syndrome (*W*ilms tumor, *a*niridia, *g*enitourinary malformation, *r*etardation).
- Deletion of 11p13.
- Camptomelic syndrome (autosomal gene at 17q24.3- q25.1) and SOX 9 mutation.
- XY pure gonadal dysgenesis (Swyer syndrome).
  - Mutation in SRY gene.
  - Unknown cause.
- XY gonadal agenesis.

Deficiency of testicular hormones:
- Leydig cell aplasia.
- Mutation in LH receptor.
- Lipoid adrenal hyperplasia (P450 scc) deficiency; mutation in StAR (steroidogenic acute regulatory protein).
- 3b-HSDII deficiency.
- 17-Hydroxylase/17, 20-lyase (P450 c17) deficiency.
- Persistent müllerian duct syndrome.
  - Gene mutations, müllerian-inhibiting substance (MIS).
  - Receptor defects for mis.

Defect in androgen action:
- 5α-Reductase II mutations.
- Androgen receptor defects:
  - Complete androgen insensitivity syndrome.
  - Partial androgen insensitivity syndrome.
  - (Reifenstein and other syndromes).
  - Smith-Lemli-Opitz syndrome.
    - Defect in conversion of 7-dehydrocholesterol to cholesterol.

TRUE HERMAPHRODITISM

XX.
XY.
XX/XY chimeras.

HICCUPS[18]

ICD-9CM # 786.8

TRANSIENT HICCUPS

Sudden excitement, emotion.
Gastric distention.

Esophageal obstruction.
Alcohol ingestion.
Sudden change in temperature.

PERSISTENT OR CHRONIC HICCUPS

Toxic/metabolic: uremia, DM, hyperventilation, hypocalcemia, hypokalemia, hyponatremia, gout, fever.
Drugs: benzodiazepines, steroids, a-methyldopa, barbiturates.
Surgery/general anesthesia.
Thoracic/diaphragmatic disorders: pneumonia, lung cancer, asthma, pleuritis, pericarditis, myocardial infarction, aortic aneurysm, esophagitis, esophageal obstruction, diaphragmatic hernia or irritation.
Abdominal disorders: gastric ulcer or cancer, hepatobiliary or pancreatic disease, IBD, bowel obstruction, intraabdominal or subphrenic abscess, prostatic infection or cancer.
Central nervous system disorders: traumatic, infectious, vascular, structural.
Ear, nose, and throat disorders: pharyngitis, laryngitis, tumor, irritation of auditory canal.
Psychogenic disorders.
Idiopathic disorders.

HIP PAIN, CHILDREN[23]

ICD-9CM # 959.6 HIP INJURY
719.95 HIP JOINT DISORDER
843.9 HIP STRAIN

TRAUMA

Hip or pelvis fractures.
Overuse injuries.

INFECTION

Septic arthritis.
Osteomyelitis.

INFLAMMATION

Transient synovitis.
Juvenile rheumatoid arthritis.
Rheumatic fever.

NEOPLASM

Leukemia.
Osteogenic or Ewing's sarcoma.
Metastatic disease.

HEMATOLOGIC DISORDERS

Hemophilia.
Sickle cell anemia.

MISCELLANEOUS

Legg-Calvé-Perthes disease.
Slipped capital femoral epiphysis.

HIRSUTISM

ICD-9CM # 704.1

Idiopathic: familial, possibly increased sensitivity to androgens.
Menopause.
Polycystic ovarian syndrome.
Drugs: androgens, anabolic steroids, methyltestosterone, minoxidil, diazoxide, phenytoin, glucocorticoids, cyclosporine.
Congenital adrenal hyperplasia.
Adrenal virilizing tumor.
Ovarian virilizing tumor: arrhenoblastoma, hilus cell tumor.
Pituitary adenoma.
Cushing's syndrome.
Hypothyroidism (congenital and juvenile).
Acromegaly.
Testicular feminization.

HIV INFECTION, ANORECTAL LESIONS[23]

ICD-9CM # 042 HIV INFECTION, SYMPTOMATIC
V08 HIV INFECTION, ASYMPTOMATIC

COMMON CONDITIONS

Anal fissure.
Abscess and fistula.
Hemorrhoids.
Pruritus ani.
Pilonidal disease.

COMMON STDS

Gonorrhea.
Chlamydia.
Herpes.
Chancroid.
Syphilis.
Condylomata acuminata.

ATYPICAL CONDITIONS

Infectious: TB, CMV, actinomycosis, cryptococcus.
Neoplastic: lymphoma, Kaposi's sarcoma, squamous cell carcinoma.
Other: idiopathic and ulcer.

HIV INFECTION, CHEST RADIOGRAPHIC ABNORMALITIES[23]

ICD-9CM # 042 HIV INFECTION, SYMPTOMATIC
V08 HIV INFECTION, ASYMPTOMATIC

DIFFUSE INTERSTITIAL INFILTRATION

Pneumocystis carinii.
Cytomegalovirus.
Mycobacterium tuberculosis.
Mycobacterium avium complex.
Histoplasmosis.
Coccidioidomycosis.
Lymphoid interstitial pneumonitis.

FOCAL CONSOLIDATION

Bacterial pneumonia.
Mycoplasma pneumoniae.
Pneumocystis carinii.
Mycobacterium tuberculosis.
Mycobacterium avium complex.

NODULAR LESIONS

Kaposi's sarcoma.
Mycobacterium tuberculosis.
Mycobacterium avium complex.
Fungal lesions.
Toxoplasmosis.

CAVITARY LESIONS

Pneumocystis carinii.
Mycobacterium tuberculosis.
Bacterial infection.

PLEURAL EFFUSION

Kaposi's sarcoma.
(Small effusion may be associated with any infection).

ADENOPATHY

Kaposi's sarcoma.
Lymphoma.
Mycobacterium tuberculosis.
Cryptococcus.

PNEUMOTHORAX

Kaposi's sarcoma.

HIV INFECTION, COGNITIVE IMPAIRMENT[22]

ICD-9CM # 042 HIV INFECTION, SYMPTOMATIC

EARLY TO MID-STAGE HIV DISEASE

Depression.
Alcohol and substance abuse.
Medication-induced cognitive impairment.
Metabolic encephalopathies.
HIV-related cognitive impairment.

ADVANCED HIV DISEASE (CD4$^+$ <100/MM^3)

Opportunistic infection of CNS.
Neurosyphilis.
CNS lymphoma.
Progressive multifocal leukoencephalopathy.
Depression.
Metabolic encephalopathies.
Medication-induced cognitive impairment.
Stroke.
HIV dementia.

HIV INFECTION, CUTANEOUS MANIFESTATIONS[18]

ICD-9CM # 042 HIV INFECTION, SYMPTOMATIC
V08 HIV INFECTION, ASYMPTOMATIC

BACTERIAL INFECTION

Bacillary angiomatosis: Numerous angiomatous nodules associated with fever, chills, weight loss.
Staphylococcus aureus: Folliculitis, ecthyma, impetigo, bullous impetigo, furuncles, carbuncles.
Syphilis: May occur in different forms (primary, secondary, tertiary); chancre may become painful because of secondary infection.

FUNGAL INFECTION

Candidiasis: Mucous membranes (oral, vulvovaginal), less commonly candida intertrigo or paronychia.
Cryptococcoses: Papules or nodules that strongly resemble molluscum contagiosum; other forms include pustules, purpuric papules, and vegetating plaques.
Seborrheic dermatitis: Scaling and erythema in the hair-bearing areas (eyebrows, scalp, chest, and pubic area).

ARTHROPOD INFESTATIONS

Scabies: Pruritus with or without rash, usually generalized but can be limited to a single digit.

VIRAL INFECTION

Herpes simplex: Vesicular lesion in clusters; perianal, genital, orofacial, or digital; can be disseminated.
Herpes zoster: Painful dermatomal vesicles that may ulcerate or disseminate.
HIV: Discrete erythematous macules and papules on the upper trunk, palms, and soles are the most
characteristic cutaneous finding of acute HIV infection.
Human papillomavirus: Genital warts (may become unusually extensive).
Kaposi's sarcoma (herpesvirus): Erythematous macules or papules; enlarge at varying rates; violaceous nodules or plaques; occasionally painful.
Molluscum contagiosum: Discrete umbilicated papules commonly on the face, neck, and intertriginous sites (axilla, groin, or buttocks).

NONINFECTIOUS

Drug reactions: More frequent and severe in HIV patients.
Nutritional deficiencies: Mainly seen in children and patients with chronic diarrhea; diffuse skin manifestations, depending upon the deficiency.
Psoriasis: Scaly lesions; diffuse or localized; can be associated with arthritis.
Vasculitis: Palpable purpuric eruption (can resemble septic emboli).

HIV INFECTION, ESOPHAGEAL DISEASE

ICD-9CM # CODE VARIES WITH SPECIFIC DIAGNOSIS

Candida infection.
Cytomegalovirus infection.
Aphthous ulcer.
Herpes simplex.

HIV INFECTION, HEPATIC DISEASE[22]

ICD-9CM # 042 HIV INFECTION, SYMPTOMATIC

VIRUSES

Hepatitis A.
Hepatitis B.
Hepatitis C.
Hepatitis D (with HBV).
Epstein-Barr virus.
Cytomegalovirus.
Herpes simplex virus.
Adenovirus.
Varicella-zoster virus.

MYCOBACTERIA

Mycobacterium avium complex.
Mycobacterium tuberculosis.

FUNGI

Histoplasma capsulatum.
Cryptococcus neoformans.
Coccidioides immitis.
Candida albicans.
Pneumocystis carinii.
Penicillium marneffei.

PROTOZOA

Toxoplasma gondii.
Cryptosporidium parvum.
Microsporida spp.
Schistosoma.

BACTERIA

Bartonella henselae (peliosis hepatis).

MALIGNANCY

Kaposi's sarcoma (HHV-8).
Non-Hodgkin's lymphoma.
Hepatocellular carcinoma.

MEDICATIONS

Zidovudine.
Didanosine.

Ritonavir.
Other HIV-1 protease inhibitors.
Fluconazole.
Macrolide antibiotics.
Isoniazid.
Rifampin.
Trimethoprim-sulfamethoxazole.

HIV INFECTION, LOWER GI TRACT DISEASE[22]

ICD-9CM # 042 HIV INFECTION, SYMPTOMATIC

CAUSES OF ENTEROCOLITIS

Bacteria
Campylobacter jejuni and other spp.
Salmonella spp.
Shigella flexneri.
Aeromonas hydrophila.
Plesiomonas shigelloides.
Yersinia enterocolitica.
Vibrio spp.
Mycobacterium avium complex.
Mycobacterium tuberculosis.
Escherichia coli (enterotoxigenic, enteroadherent).
Bacterial overgrowth.
Clostridium difficile (toxin).
Parasites
Cryptosporidium parvum.
Microsporida *(Enterocytozoon bieneusi, Septata intestinalis).*
Isospora belli.
Entamoeba histolytica.
Giardia lamblia.
Cyclospora cayetanensis.
Viruses
Cytomegalovirus.
Adenovirus.
Calicivirus.
Astrovirus.
Picobirnavirus.
Human immunodeficiency virus.
Fungi
Histoplasma capsulatum.

CAUSES OF PROCTITIS

Bacteria
Chlamydia trachomatis.
Neisseria gonorrhoeae.
Treponema pallidum.
Viruses
Herpes simplex.
Cytomegalovirus.

HIV INFECTION, OCULAR MANIFESTATIONS[33]

ICD-9CM # 042 HIV INFECTION, SYMPTOMATIC
V08 HIV INFECTION, ASYMPTOMATIC

EYELIDS

Molluscum contagiosum.
Kaposi's sarcoma.

CORNEA/CONJUNCTIVA

Keratoconjunctivitis sicca.
Bacterial/fungal ulcerative keratitis.
Herpes simplex.
Herpes zoster ophthalmicus.
Conjunctival microvasculopathy.
Kaposi's sarcoma.

RETINA, CHOROID, AND VITREOUS

Microvasculopathy.
Endophthalmitis.
Cytomegalovirus retinitis.
Acute retinal necrosis.
Syphilis.
Toxoplasmosis.
Pneumocystis choroidopathy.
Cryptococcosis.
Mycobacterial infection.
Intraocular lymphoma.
Candidiasis.
Histoplasmosis.

DRUGS ASSOCIATED WITH OCULAR TOXICITY

Rifabutin.
Didanosine.

NEUROOPHTHALMIC

Disc edema.
Primary or secondary optic neuropathy.
Cranial nerve palsies.

ORBITAL

Lymphoma.
Infection.
Pseudotumor.

HIV INFECTION, PULMONARY DISEASE[22]

ICD-9CM # 042 HIV INFECTION, SYMPTOMATIC

MYCOBACTERIAL

M. tuberculosis.
M. kansasii.
M. avium complex.
Other nontuberculous mycobacteria.

OTHER BACTERIAL

Streptococcus pneumoniae.
Staphylococcus aureus.
Haemophilus influenzae.
Enterobacteriaceae.
Pseudomonas aeruginosa.
Moraxella catarrhalis.
Group A *Streptococcus.*
Nocardia species.
Rhodococcus equi.
Chlamydia pneumoniae.

FUNGAL

Pneumocystis carinii.
Cryptococcus neoformans.
Histoplasma capsulatum.
Coccidioides immitis.
Aspergillus species.
Blastomyces dermatitidis.
Penicillium marneffei.

VIRAL

Cytomegalovirus.
Herpes simplex virus.
Adenovirus.
Respiratory syncytial virus.
Influenza viruses.
Parainfluenza virus.

OTHER

Toxoplasma gondii.
Strongyloides stercoralis.
Kaposi's sarcoma.
Lymphoma.
Lung cancer.
Lymphocytic interstitial pneumonitis.
Nonspecific interstitial pneumonitis.
Bronchiolitis obliterans with organizing pneumonia.
Pulmonary hypertension.
Emphysema-like or bullous disease.
Pneumothorax.
Congestive heart failure.
Diffuse alveolar damage.
Pulmonary embolus.

HOARSENESS

ICD-9CM # 784.49

Allergic rhinitis.
Infections (laryngitis, epiglottitis, tracheitis, croup).
Vocal cord polyps.
Voice strain.
Irritants (tobacco smoke).
Vocal cord trauma (intubation, surgery).
Neoplastic involvement of vocal cord (primary or metastatic).
Neurologic abnormalities (multiple sclerosis, ALS, parkinsonism).
Endocrine abnormalities (puberty, menopause, hypothyroidism).
Other (laryngeal webs or cysts, psychogenic, muscle tension abnormalities).

HYDROCEPHALUS

ICD-9CM # 331.4

Head trauma.
Brain neoplasm (primary or metastatic).
Spinal cord tumor.
Cerebellar infarction.
Exudative or granulomatous meningitis.
Cerebellar hemorrhage.
Subarachnoid hemorrhage.
Aqueductal stenosis.
Third ventricle colloid cyst.
Hindbrain malformation.
Viral encephalitis.
Metastases to leptomeninges.

HYPERCALCEMIA

ICD-9CM # 275.42 HYPERCALCEMIA DISORDER

Malignancy: increased bone resorption via osteoclast-activating factors, secretion of PTH-like substances, prostaglandin E2, direct erosion by tumor cells, transforming growth factors, colony-stimulating activity. Hypercalcemia is common in the following neoplasms:
Solid tumors: breast, lung, pancreas, kidneys, ovary.
Hematologic cancers: myeloma, lymphosarcoma, adult T-cell lymphoma, Burkitt's lymphoma.
Hyperparathyroidism: increased bone resorption, GI absorption, and renal absorption; etiology:
Parathyroid hyperplasia, adenoma.
Hyperparathyroidism or renal failure with secondary hyperparathyroidism.
Granulomatous disorders: increased GI absorption (e.g., sarcoidosis).
Paget's disease: increased bone resorption, seen only during periods of immobilization.
Vitamin D intoxication, milk-alkali syndrome; increased GI absorption.
Thiazides: increased renal absorption.
Other causes: familial hypocalciuric hypercalcemia, thyrotoxicosis, adrenal insufficiency, prolonged immobilization, vitamin A intoxication, recovery from acute renal failure, lithium administration, pheochromocytoma, disseminated SLE.

HYPERCAPNIA, PERSISTENT[33]

ICD-9CM # 786.09

Hypercapnia with normal lungs: CNS disturbances (CVA, parkinsonism, encephalitis), metabolic alkalosis, myxedema, primary alveolar hypoventilation, spinal cord lesions.
Diseases of the chest wall (e.g., kyphoscoliosis, ankylosing spondylitis).
Neuromuscular disorders (e.g., myasthenia gravis, Guillain-Barré syndrome, amyotrophic lateral sclerosis, muscular dystrophy, poliomyelitis).
COPD.

HYPERHIDROSIS[4]

ICD-9CM # 780.8 HYPERHIDROSIS

CORTICAL

Emotional.
Familial dysautonomia.
Congenital ichthyosiform erythroderma.
Epidermolysis bullosa.
Nail-patella syndrome.
Jadassohn-Lewandowsky syndrome.
Pachyonychia congenita.
Palmoplantar keratoderma.

HYPOTHALAMIC

Drugs
Antipyretics.
Emetics.
Insulin.
Meperidine.
Exercise
Infection
Defervescence.
Chronic illness.
Metabolic
Debility.
Diabetes mellitus.
Hyperpituitarism.
Hyperthyroidism.
Hypoglycemia.
Obesity.
Porphyria.
Pregnancy.
Rickets.
Infantile scurvy.
Cardiovascular
Heart failure.
Shock.
Vasomotor
Cold injury.
Raynaud phenomenon.
Rheumatoid arthritis.
Neurologic
Abscess.
Familial dysautonomia.
Postencephalitic.
Tumor.

Miscellaneous
Chédiak-Higashi syndrome.
Compensatory.
Phenylketonuria.
Pheochromocytoma.
Vitiligo.
Medullary
Physiologic gustatory sweating.
Encephalitis.
Granulosis rubra nasi.
Syringomyelia.
Thoracic sympathetic trunk injury.
Spinal
Cord transection.
Syringomyelia.
Changes in blood flow
Mallucci syndrome.
Arteriovenous fistula.
Klippel-Trenaunay syndrome.
Glomus tumor.
Blue rubber bleb nevus syndrome.

HYPERKALEMIA

ICD-9CM # 276.7

Pseudohyperkalemia.
- Hemolyzed specimen.
- Severe thrombocytosis (platelet count .106 ml).
- Severe leukocytosis (white blood cell count .105 ml).
- Fist clenching during phlebotomy.

Excessive potassium intake (often in setting of impaired excretion).
- Potassium replacement therapy.
- High-potassium diet.
- Salt substitutes with potassium.
- Potassium salts of antibiotics.

Decreased renal excretion.
- Potassium-sparing diuretics (e.g., spironolactone, triamterene, amiloride).
- Renal insufficiency.
- Mineralocorticoid deficiency.
- Hyporeninemic hypoaldosteronism (DM).
- Tubular unresponsiveness to aldosterone (e.g., SLE, multiple myeloma, sickle cell disease).
- Type 4 RTA.
- ACE inhibitors.
- Heparin administration.
- NSAIDs.
- Trimethoprim-sulfamethoxazole.
- β-Blockers.
- Pentamidine.

Redistribution (excessive cellular release).
- Acidemia (each 0.1 decrease in pH increases the serum potassium by 0.4 to 0.6 mEq/L). Lactic acidosis and ketoacidosis cause minimal redistribution.
- Insulin deficiency.
- Drugs (e.g., succinylcholine, markedly increased digitalis level, arginine, β-adrenergic blockers).
- Hypertonicity.
- Hemolysis.
- Tissue necrosis, rhabdomyolysis, burns.
- Hyperkalemic periodic paralysis.

HYPERKINETIC MOVEMENT DISORDERS[27]

ICD-9CM # 314.8 HYPERKINETIC SYNDROME
275.1 CHOREOATHETOSIS
335.5 HEMIBALLISM
333.7 DYSTONIA DUE TO DRUGS
333.6 DYSTONIA, IDIOPATHIC

Chorea, choreoathetosis: drug-induced, Huntington's chorea, Sydenham's chorea.
Tardive dyskinesia (e.g., phenothiazines).
Hemiballismus (lacunar CVA near subthalamic nuclei in basal ganglia, metastatic lesions, toxoplasmosis [in AIDS]).
Dystonia (idiopathic, familial, drug-induced [prochlorperazine, metoclopramide]), Wilson's disease.
Liver failure.
Thyrotoxicosis.
SLE, polycythemia.

HYPERMAGNESEMIA

ICD-9CM # 275.2

Renal failure (decreased GFR).
Decreased renal excretion secondary to salt depletion.
Abuse of antacids and laxatives containing magnesium in patients with renal insufficiency.
Endocrinopathies (deficiency of mineralocorticoid or thyroid hormone).
Increased tissue breakdown (rhabdomyolysis).
Redistribution: acute DKA, pheochromocytoma.
Other: lithium, volume depletion, familial hypocalciuric hypercalcemia.

HYPERPHOSPHATEMIA

ICD-9CM # 275.3

Excessive phosphate administration.
Excessive oral intake or IV administration.
Laxatives containing phosphate (phosphate tablets, phosphate enemas).
Decreased renal phosphate excretion.
Acute or chronic renal failure.
Hypoparathyroidism or pseudohypoparathyroidism.
Acromegaly, thyrotoxicosis.
Biphosphonate therapy.
Tumor calcinosis.
Sickle cell anemia.
Transcellular shift out of cells.
Chemotherapy of lymphoma or leukemia, tumor lysis syndrome, hemolysis.
Acidosis.
Rhabdomyolysis, malignant hyperthermia.
Artifact: in vitro hemolysis.
Pseudohyperphosphatemia: hyperlipidemia, paraproteinemia, hyperbilirubinemia.

HYPERPIGMENTATION[5]

ICD-9CM # 709.00

Addison's disease.*
Arsenic ingestion.
ACTH or MSH producing tumors (e.g., oat cell carcinoma of the lung).*
Drug induced (i.e., antimalarials, some cytotoxic agents).
Hemochromatosis ("bronze" diabetes).
Malabsorption syndrome (Whipple's disease and celiac sprue).
Melanoma.
Melanotropic hormone injection.*

Pheochromocytoma.
Porphyrias (porphyria cutanea tarda and variegate porphyria).
Pregnancy.
Progressive systemic sclerosis and related conditions.
PUVA therapy (psoralen administration) for psoriasis and vitiligo.*

(*ACTH,* Adrenocorticotropic hormone; *MSH,* melanocyte-stimulating hormone; *PUVA,* psoralen plus ultraviolet A.)
*Accentuation on sun-exposed surfaces.

HYPERTRICHOSIS[7]

ICD-9CM # 704.1 HYPERTRICHOSIS NOS
757.4 HYPERTRICHOSIS, CONGENITAL

DRUGS

Dilantin.
Streptomycin.
Hexachlorobenzene.
Penicillamine.
Diazoxide.
Minoxidil.
Cyclosporine.

SYSTEMIC ILLNESS

Hypothyroidism.
Anorexia nervosa.
Malnutrition.
Porphyria.
Dermatomyositis.

IDIOPATHIC

HYPERVENTILATION, PERSISTENT[33]

ICD-9CM # 786.01

Fibrotic lung disease.
Metabolic acidosis (e.g., diabetes, uremia).
CNS disorders (midbrain and pontine lesions).
Hepatic coma.
Salicylate intoxication.
Fever.
Sepsis.
Psychogenic (e.g., anxiety).

HYPOCALCEMIA

ICD-9CM # 275.41

Renal insufficiency: hypocalcemia caused by:
- Increased calcium deposits in bone and soft tissue secondary to increased serum PO423 level.
- Decreased production of 1,25-dihydroxyvitamin D.
- Excessive loss of 25-OHD (nephrotic syndrome).

Hypoalbuminemia: each decrease in serum albumin (g/L) will decrease serum calcium by 0.8 mg/dl but will not change free (ionized) calcium.
Vitamin D deficiency:
- Malabsorption (most common cause).
- Inadequate intake.
- Decreased production of 1,25-dihydroxyvitamin D (vitamin D-dependent rickets, renal failure).
- Decreased production of 25-OHD (parenchymal liver disease).
- Accelerated 25-OHD catabolism (phenytoin, phenobarbital).
- End-organ resistance to 1,25-dihydroxyvitamin D.

Hypomagnesemia: hypocalcemia caused by:
- Decreased PTH secretion.
- Inhibition of PTH effect on bone.

Pancreatitis, hyperphosphatemia, osteoblastic metastases: hypocalcemia is secondary to increased calcium deposits (bone, abdomen).
Pseudohypoparathyroidism (PHP): autosomal recessive disorder characterized by short stature, shortening of metacarpal bones, obesity, and mental retardation; the hypocalcemia is secondary to congenital end-organ resistance to PTH.
Idiopathic hypoparathyroidism, surgical removal of parathyroids (e.g., neck surgery).
"Hungry bones syndrome": rapid transfer of calcium from plasma into bones after removal of a parathyroid tumor.
Sepsis.
Massive blood transfusion (as a result of EDTA in blood).

HYPOCAPNIA

ICD-9CM # 786.01

Hyperventilation.
Pneumonia, pneumonitis.
Fever, sepsis.
Medications (salicylates, β-adrenergic agonists, progesterone, methylxanthines).
Pulmonary disease (asthma, interstitial fibrosis).
Pulmonary embolism.
Hepatic failure.
Metabolic acidosis.
High altitude.
CHF.
Pregnancy.
Pain.
CNS lesions.

HYPOGONADISM

ICD-9CM # 256.3 FEMALE
257.2 MALE
256.3 OVARIAN
253.4 PITUITARY
257.2 TESTICULAR

HYPERGONADOTROPIC HYPOGONADISM

Hormone resistance (androgen, LH insensitivity).
Gonadal defects (e.g., Klinefelter's syndrome, myotonic dystrophy).
Drug induced (e.g., spironolactone, cytotoxins).
Alcoholism, radiation-induced.
Mumps orchitis.
Anatomic defects, castration.

HYPOGONADOTROPIC HYPOGONADISM

Pituitary lesions (neoplasms, granulomas, infarction, hemochromatosis, vasculitis).
Drug-induced (e.g., glucocorticoids).
Hyperprolactinemia.
Genetic disorders (Laurence-Moon-Biedl syndrome, Prader-Willi).
Delayed puberty.
Other: chronic disease, nutritional deficiency, Kallmann's syndrome, idiopathic isolated LH or FSH deficiency.

HYPOKALEMIA

ICD-9CM # 276.8

Cellular shift (redistribution) and undetermined mechanisms.
Alkalosis (each 0.1 increase in pH decreases serum potassium by 0.4 to 0.6 mEq/L).
Insulin administration.
Vitamin B_{12} therapy for megaloblastic anemias, acute leukemias.

Hypokalemic periodic paralysis: rare familial disorder manifested by recurrent attacks of flaccid paralysis and hypokalemia.
β-Adrenergic agonists (e.g., terbutaline), decongestants, bronchodilators, theophylline, caffeine.
Barium poisoning, toluene intoxication, verapamil intoxication, chloroquine intoxication.
Correction of digoxin intoxication with digoxin antibody fragments (Digibind).
Increased renal excretion.
  Drugs:
    Diuretics, including carbonic anhydrase inhibitors (e.g., acetazolamide).
    Amphotericin B.
    High-dose sodium penicillin, nafcillin, ampicillin, or carbenicillin.
    Cisplatin.
    Aminoglycosides.
    Corticosteroids, mineralocorticoids.
    Foscarnet sodium.
  RTA: distal (type 1) or proximal (type 2).
    Diabetic ketoacidosis (DKA), ureteroenterostomy.
    Magnesium deficiency.
    Postobstruction diuresis, diuretic phase of ATN.
    Osmotic diuresis (e.g., mannitol).
    Bartter's syndrome: hyperplasia of juxtaglomerular cells leading to increased renin and aldosterone, metabolic alkalosis, hypokalemia, muscle weakness, and tetany (seen in young adults).
    Increased mineralocorticoid activity (primary or secondary aldosteronism), Cushing's syndrome.
    Chronic metabolic alkalosis from loss of gastric fluid (increased renal potassium secretion).
GI loss.
  Vomiting, nasogastric suction.
    Diarrhea.
    Laxative abuse.
    Villous adenoma.
    Fistulas.
    Inadequate dietary intake (e.g., anorexia nervosa).
    Cutaneous loss (excessive sweating).
    High dietary sodium intake, excessive use of licorice.

HYPOMAGNESEMIA

ICD-9CM # 275.2

GI and nutritional
Defective GI absorption (malabsorption).
Inadequate dietary intake (e.g., alcoholics).
Parenteral therapy without magnesium.
Chronic diarrhea, villous adenoma, prolonged nasogastric suction, fistulas (small bowel, biliary).
Excessive renal losses
Diuretics.
RTA.
Diuretic phase of ATN.
Endocrine disturbances (DKA, hyperaldosteronism, hyperthyroidism, hyperparathyroidism), SIADH, Bartter's syndrome, hypercalciuria, hypokalemia.
Cisplatin, alcohol, cyclosporine, digoxin, pentamidine, mannitol, amphotericin B, foscarnet, methotrexate.
Antibiotics (gentamicin, ticarcillin, carbenicillin).
Redistribution: hypoalbuminemia, cirrhosis, administration of insulin and glucose, theophylline, epinephrine, acute pancreatitis, cardiopulmonary bypass.
Miscellaneous: sweating, burns, prolonged exercise, lactation, "hungry-bones" syndrome.

HYPOPHOSPHATEMIA

ICD-9CM # 275.3

Decreased intake (prolonged starvation [alcoholics], hyperalimentation, or IV infusion without phosphate).
Malabsorption.
Phosphate-binding antacids.
Renal loss:
  RTA.
  Fanconi syndrome, vitamin D-resistant rickets.
  ATN (diuretic phase).
  Hyperparathyroidism (primary or secondary).
  Familial hypophosphatemia.
  Hypokalemia, hypomagnesemia.
  Acute volume expansion.
  Glycosuria, idiopathic hypercalciuria.
  Acetazolamide.
Transcellular shift into cells:
  Alcohol withdrawal.
  DKA (recovery phase).
  Glucose-insulin or catecholamine infusion.
  Anabolic steroids.
  Total parenteral nutrition.
  Theophylline overdose.
  Severe hyperthermia; recovery from hypothermia.
  "Hungry bones" syndrome.

HYPOPIGMENTATION

ICD-9CM # 709.00

Vitiligo.
Tinea versicolor.
Atopic dermatitis.
Chemical leukoderma.
Idiopathic hypomelanosis.
Sarcoidosis.
SLE.
Scleroderma.
Oculocutaneous albinism.
Phenylketonuria.
Nevoid hypopigmentation.

HYPOTENSION, POSTURAL

ICD-9CM # 458.0

Antihypertensive medications (especially α-blockers, diuretics, ACE inhibitors).
Volume depletion (hemorrhage, dehydration).
Impaired cardiac output (constrictive pericarditis, aortic stenosis).
Peripheral autonomic dysfunction (DM, Guillain Barré).
Idiopathic orthostatic hypotension.
Central autonomic dysfunction (Shy-Grager syndrome).
Peripheral venous disease.
Adrenal insufficiency.

IMPOTENCE[24]

ICD-9CM # 302.72 PSYCHOSEXUAL
607.84 ORGANIC
997.99 ORGANIC POSTPROSTATECTOMY

Psychogenic.
Endocrine: hyperprolactinemia, DM, Cushing's syndrome, hypothyroidism or hyperthyroidism, abnormality of hypothalamic-pituitary-testicular axis.
Vascular: arterial insufficiency, venous leakage, AV malformation, local trauma.

SECTION II

Medications.
Neurogenic: autonomic or sensory neuropathy, spinal cord trauma or tumor, CVA, multiple sclerosis, temporal lobe epilepsy.
Systemic illness: renal failure, COPD, cirrhosis of liver, myotonic dystrophy.
Peyronie's disease.
Prostatectomy.

INFERTILITY, FEMALE[12]

ICD-9CM # 628.9

FALLOPIAN TUBE PATHOLOGY

PID or puerperal infection.
Congenital anomalies.
Endometriosis.
Secondary to past peritonitis of nongenital origin.
Amenorrhea and anovulation.
Minor anovulatory disturbances.

CERVICAL AND UTERINE FACTORS

Leiomyomas and polyps.
Uterine anomalies.
Intrauterine synechiae (Asherman's syndrome).
Destroyed endocervical glands (postsurgery or postinfection).

VAGINAL FACTORS

Congenital absence of vagina.
Imperforate hymen.
Vaginismus.
Vaginitis.

IMMUNOLOGIC FACTORS

Sperm-immobilizing antibodies.
Sperm-agglutinating antibodies.

NUTRITIONAL AND METABOLIC FACTORS

Thyroid disorders.
Diabetes mellitus.
Severe nutritional disturbances.

INFERTILITY, MALE[12]

ICD-9CM # 606.9

DECREASED PRODUCTION OF SPERMATOZOA

Varicocele.
Testicular failure.
Endocrine disorders.
Cryptorchidism.
Stress, smoking, caffeine, nicotine, recreational drugs.

DUCTAL OBSTRUCTION

Epididymal (postinfection).
Congenital absence of vas deferens.
Ejaculatory duct (postinfection).
Postvasectomy.

INABILITY TO DELIVER SPERM INTO VAGINA

Ejaculatory disturbances.
Hypospadias.
Sexual problems (i.e., impotence), medical or psychological.

ABNORMAL SEMEN

Infection.
Abnormal volume.
Abnormal viscosity.
Abnormal sperm motion.

IMMUNOLOGIC FACTORS

Sperm-immobilizing antibodies.
Sperm-agglutinating antibodies.

INSOMNIA[30]

ICD-9CM # 780.52 INSOMNIA NOS
307.42 INSOMNIA, CHRONIC ASSOCIATED WITH ANXIETY OR DEPRESSION
780.51 INSOMNIA WITH SLEEP APNEA

Anxiety disorder, psychophysiologic insomnia.
Depression.
Drugs (e.g., caffeine, amphetamines, cocaine), hypnotic-dependent sleep disorder.
Pain, fibromyalgia.
Inadequate sleep hygiene.
Restless leg syndrome.
Obstructive sleep apnea.
Sleep bruxism.
Medical illness (e.g., GERD, sleep-related asthma, parkinsonism and movement disorders).
Narcolepsy.
Other: periodic leg movement of sleep, central sleep apnea, REM behavioral disorder.

INTESTINAL PSEUDOOBSTRUCTION[33]

ICD-9CM # 560.1 ADYNAMIC INTESTINAL OBSTRUCTION
564.9 INTESTINAL DISORDER, FUNCTIONAL

"PRIMARY" (IDIOPATHIC INTESTINAL PSEUDOOBSTRUCTION)

Hollow visceral myopathy:
- Familial.
- Sporadic.

Neuropathic:
- Abnormal myenteric plexus.
- Normal myenteric plexus.

SECONDARY

Scleroderma.
Myxedema.
Amyloidosis.
Muscular dystrophy.
Hypokalemia.
Chronic renal failure.
Diabetes mellitus.
Drug toxicity caused by:
- Anticholinergics.
- Opiate narcotics.

Ogilvie's syndrome.

INTRACRANIAL LESION

ICD-9CM # 348.8

Tumor (primary or metastatic).
Abscess.
Stroke.
Intracranial hemorrhage.
Angioma.
Multiple sclerosis (initial single lesion).
Granuloma.
Herpes encephalitis.
Artifact.

IRON OVERLOAD

ICD-9CM # 790.6 IRON, ABNORMAL BLOOD LEVEL
275, IRON, METABOLISM DISORDER

Hereditary hemochromatosis.
Chronic iron supplementation (PO, IM, transfusions).
Nonalcoholic steatohepatitis.
Chronic viral hepatitis.
Alcoholic liver disease.
Chronic anemias (e.g., sideroblastic anemia, thalassemia major).
Porphyria cutanea tarda.

ISCHEMIC COLITIS, NONOCCLUSIVE[18]

ICD-9CM # 557.1

ACUTE DIMINUTION OF COLONIC INTRAMURAL BLOOD FLOW

Small vessel obstruction
Collagen-vascular disease.
Vasculitis, diabetes.
Oral contraceptives.
Nonocclusive hypoperfusion
Hemorrhage.
CHF, MI, Arrhythmias.
Sepsis.
Vasoconstricting agents: vasopressin, ergot.
Increased viscosity: polycythemia, sickle cell disease, thrombocytosis.

INCREASED DEMAND ON MARGINAL BLOOD FLOW

Increased motility
Mass lesion, stricture.
Constipation.
Increased intraluminal pressure
Bowel obstruction.
Colonoscopy.
Barium enema.

ISCHEMIC NECROSIS OF CARTILAGE AND BONE[12]

ICD-9CM # 733.90

ENDOCRINE/METABOLIC

Ethanol abuse.
Glucocorticoid therapy.
Cushing's disease.
Diabetes mellitus.
Hyperuricemia.
Osteomalacia.
Hyperlipidemia.

STORAGE DISEASES (E.G., GAUCHER'S DISEASE)

Hemoglobinopathies (e.g., sickle cell disease).
Trauma (e.g., dislocation, fracture).
HIV infection.
Dysbaric conditions (e.g., caisson disease).
Collagen-vascular disorders.
Irradiation.
Pancreatitis.
Organ transplantation.
Hemodialysis.
Burns.
Intravascular coagulation.
Idiopathic, familial.

JAUNDICE

ICD-9CM # 782.4 JAUNDICE NOS
576.8 JAUNDICE, OBSTRUCTIVE
277.4 BILIRUBIN EXCRETION DISORDERS

PREDOMINANCE OF DIRECT (CONJUGATED) BILIRUBIN

Extrahepatic obstruction.
Common duct abnormalities: calculi, neoplasm, stricture, cyst, sclerosing cholangitis.
Metastatic carcinoma.
Pancreatic carcinoma, pseudocyst.
Ampullary carcinoma.
Hepatocellular disease: hepatitis, cirrhosis.
Drugs: estrogens, phenothiazines, captopril, methyltestosterone, labetalol.
Cholestatic jaundice of pregnancy.
Hereditary disorders: Dubin-Johnson syndrome, Rotor's syndrome.
Recurrent benign intrahepatic cholestasis.

PREDOMINANCE OF INDIRECT (UNCONJUGATED) BILIRUBIN

Hemolysis: hereditary and acquired hemolytic anemias.
Inefficient marrow production.
Impaired hepatic conjugation: chloramphenicol.
Neonatal jaundice.
Hereditary disorders: Gilbert's syndrome, Crigler-Najjar syndrome.

JOINT PAIN, ANTERIOR HIP, MEDIAL THIGH, KNEE[25]

ICD-9CM # 719.4 ADD 5TH DIGIT
0 SITE NOS
1 SHOULDER REGION
2 UPPER ARM (ELBOW, HUMERUS)
3 FOREARM (RADIUS, WRIST, ULNA)
4 HAND
5 PELVIC REGION AND THIGH
6 LOWER LEG (FIBULA, PATELLA, TIBIA)
7 ANKLE AND/OR FOOT

ACUTE

Acute rheumatic fever.
Adductor muscle strain.
Avascular necrosis.
Crystal arthritis.
Femoral artery (pseudo) aneurysm.
Fracture (femoral neck or intertrochanteric).
Hemarthrosis.
Hernia.
Herpes zoster.
Iliopectineal bursitis.
Iliopsoas tendinitis.
Inguinal lymphadenitis.
Osteomalacia.
Painful transient osteoporosis of hip.
Septic arthritis.

SUBACUTE AND CHRONIC

Adductory muscle strain.
Amyloidosis.
Acute rheumatic fever.
Femoral artery aneurysm.
Hernia (inguinal or femoral).
Iliopectineal bursitis.
Iliopsoas tendinitis.

Inguinal lymphadenopathy.
Osteochondromatosis.
Osteomyelitis.
Osteitis deformans (Paget's disease).
Osteomalacia (pseudofracture).
Postherpetic neuralgia.
Sterile synovitis (e.g., rheumatoid arthritis, psoriatic, systemic lupus erythematosus).

JOINT PAIN, HIP, LATERAL THIGH[25]

ICD-9CM # 959.6 HIP INJURY
719.95 HIP JOINT DISORDER
843.9 HIP STRAIN

ACUTE

Herpes zoster.
Iliotibial tendinitis.
Impacted fracture of femoral neck.
Lateral femoral cutaneous neuropathy (meralgia paresthetica).
Radiculopathy: L4-5.
Trochanteric avulsion fracture (greater trochanter).
Trochanteric bursitis.
Trochanteric fracture.

SUBACUTE AND CHRONIC

Lateral femoral cutaneous neuropathy (meralgia paresthetica).
Osteomyelitis.
Postherpetic neuralgia.
Radiculopathy: L4-5.
Tumors.

JOINT PAIN, POSTERIOR HIPS, THIGH, BUTTOCKS[25]

ICD-9CM # 719.4 ADD 5TH DIGIT
0 SITE NOS
1 SHOULDER REGION
2 UPPER ARM (ELBOW, HUMERUS)
3 FOREARM (RADIUS, WRIST, ULNA)
4 HAND
5 PELVIC REGION AND THIGH
6 LOWER LEG (FIBULA, PATELLA, TIBIA)
7 ANKLE AND/OR FOOT

ACUTE

Gluteal muscle strain.
Herpes zoster.
Ischial bursitis.
Ischial or sacral fracture.
Osteomalacia (pseudofracture).
Sciatic neuropathy.
Radiculopathy: L5-S1.

SUBACUTE AND CHRONIC

Gluteal muscle strain.
Ischial bursitis.
Lumbar spinal stenosis.
Osteoarthritis of hip.
Osteitis deformans (Paget's disease).
Osteomyelitis.
Osteochondromatosis.
Osteomalacia (pseudofracture).
Postherpetic neuralgia.
Radiculopathy: L5-S1.
Tumors.

JOINT SWELLING

ICD-9CM # 719.0 ADD 5TH DIGIT
0 SITE NOS
1 SHOULDER REGION
2 UPPER ARM (ELBOW, HUMERUS)
3 FOREARM (RADIUS, WRIST, ULNA)
4 HAND
5 PELVIC REGION AND THIGH
6 LOWER LEG (FIBULA, PATELLA, TIBIA)
7 ANKLE AND/OR FOOT

Trauma.
Osteoarthritis.
Gout.
Pyogenic arthritis.
Pseudogout.
Rheumatoid arthritis.
Viral syndrome.

JUGULAR VENOUS DISTENTION

ICD-9CM # 459.89 INCREASED VENOUS PRESSURE

Right-sided heart failure.
Cardiac tamponade.
Constrictive pericarditis.
Goiter.
Tension pneumothorax.
Pulmonary hypertension.
Cardiomyopathy (restrictive).
Superior vena cava syndrome.
Valsalva maneuver.
Right atrial myxoma.
COPD.

KNEE PAIN[25]

ICD-9CM # 844.1 COLLATERAL LIGAMENT SPRAIN, MEDIAL
844.2 CRUCIATE LIGAMENT SPRAIN
716.96 KNEE INFLAMMATION
959.7 KNEE INJURY
718.86 KNEE INSTABILITY
836.1 LATERAL MENISCUS TEAR
836.0 MEDIAL MENISCUS TEAR
844.8 PATELLAR SPRAIN
719.56 KNEE STIFFNESS
719.06 KNEE SWELLING

DIFFUSE

Articular.
Anterior.
Prepatellar bursitis.
Patellar tendon enthesopathy.
Chondromalacia patellae.
Patellofemoral osteoarthritis.
Cruciate ligament injury.
Medial plica syndrome.

MEDIAL

Anserine bursitis.
Spontaneous osteonecrosis.
Osteoarthritis.
Medial meniscal tear.
Medial collateral ligament bursitis.
Referred pain from hip and L3.
Fibromyalgia.

LATERAL

Iliotibial band syndrome.
Meniscal cyst.
Lateral meniscal tear.
Collateral ligament.
Peroneal tenosynovitis.

POSTERIOR

Popliteal cyst (Baker's cyst).
Tendinitis.
Aneurysms, ganglions, sarcoma.

LEFT AXIS DEVIATION[19]

ICD-9CM # 426.3 LEFT BUNDLE BRANCH BLOCK
426.2 LEFT BUNDLE BRANCH HEMIBLOCK
429.3 LEFT VENTRICULAR HYPERTROPHY

Normal variation.
Left anterior fascicular block (hemiblock).
Left bundle branch block.
Left ventricular hypertrophy.
Mechanical shifts causing a horizontal heart, high diaphragm, pregnancy, ascites.
Some forms of ventricular tachycardia.
Endocardial cushion defects and other congenital heart disease.

LEFT BUNDLE BRANCH BLOCK

ICD-9CM # 426.3

Ischemic heart disease.
Electrolyte abnormalities (e.g., hyperkalemia).
Cardiomyopathy.
Idiopathic.
LVH.
Pulmonary embolism.
Cardiac trauma.
Bacterial endocarditis.

LEG CRAMPS, NOCTURNAL

ICD-9CM # 729.82 MUSCLE CRAMPS

Diabetic neuropathy.
Medications.
Electrolyte abnormalities (hypokalemia, hyponatremia, hypocalcemia, hyperkalemia, hypophosphatemia).
Respiratory alkalosis.
Uremia.
Hemodialysis.
Peripheral nerve injury.
ALS.
Alcohol use.
Heat cramps.
Vitamin B_{12} deficiency.
Hyperthyroidism.
Contractures.
DVT.
Hypoglycemia.
Peripheral vascular insufficiency.
Baker cyst.

LEG LENGTH DISCREPANCIES[20]

ICD-9CM # 736.81 LEG LENGTH DISCREPANCY, ACQUIRED
755.30 LEG LENGTH DISCREPANCY, CONGENITAL

CONGENITAL

Proximal femoral local deficiency.
Coxa vara.
Hemiatrophy-hemihypertrophy (anisomelia).
Development dysplasia of the hip.

DEVELOPMENTAL

Legg-Calvé-Perthes disease.

NEUROMUSCULAR

Polio.
Cerebral palsy (hemiplegia).

INFECTIOUS

Pyogenic osteomyelitis with physeal damage.

TRAUMA

Physeal injury with premature closure.
Overgrowth.
Malunion (shortening).

TUMOR

Physeal destruction.
Radiation-induced physeal injury.
Overgrowth.

LEG PAIN WITH EXERCISE

ICD-9CM # 729.82 MUSCLE CRAMPS

Shin splints.
Arteriosclerosis obliterans.
Neurogenic (spinal cord compression or ischemia).
Venous claudication.
Popliteal cyst.
DVT.
Thromboangiitis obliterans.
Adventitial cysts.
Popliteal artery entrapment syndrome.
McArdle syndrome.

LEG ULCERS[25]

ICD-9CM # 440.23 LOWER LIMB, ARTERIOSCLEROTIC
707.1 LOWER LIMB, CHRONIC
707.1 LOWER LIMB, NEUROGENIC
250.70 LOWER LIMB, CHRONIC DIABETES MELLITUS TYPE II
250.71 LOWER LIMB, CHRONIC, DIABETES MELLITUS TYPE I

VASCULAR

Arterial: arteriosclerosis, thromboangiitis obliterans, AV malformation, cholesterol emboli.
Venous: superficial varicosities, incompetent perforators, DVT, lymphatic abnormalities.

VASCULITIS HEMATOLOGIC

Sickle cell anemia, thalassemia, polycythemia vera, leukemia, cold agglutinin disease.
Macroglobulinemia, protein C and protein S deficiency, cryoglobulinemia, lupus anticoagulant, antiphospholipid syndrome.

INFECTIOUS

Fungus: Blastomycosis, coccidioidomycosis, histoplasmosis, sporotrichosis.
Bacterial: Furuncle, ecthyma, septic emboli.
Protozoal: leishmaniasis.

METABOLIC

Necrobiosis lipoidica diabeticorum.
Localized bullous pemphigoid.
Gout, calcinosis cutis, Gaucher's disease.

TUMORS

Basal cell carcinoma, squamous cell carcinoma, melanoma.
Mycosis fungoides, Kaposi's sarcoma, metastatic neoplasms.

TRAUMA

Burns, cold injury, radiation dermatitis.
Insect bites.
Factitial, excessive pressure.

NEUROPATHIC

Diabetic trophic ulcers.
Tabes dorsalis, syringomyelia.

DRUGS

Warfarin, IV colchicine extravasation, methotrexate, halogens, ergotism, hydroxyurea.

PANNICULITIS

Weber-Christian disease.
Pancreatic fat necrosis, alpha-antitrypsinase deficiency.

LEUKOCORIA

ICD-9CM # 379.90

Cataract.
Retinal detachment.
Retinoblastoma.
Retinal telangiectasia.
Retrolenticular vascularized membrane.
Familial exudative vitreoretinopathy.

LIMP

ICD-9CM # 781.2 GAIT ABNORMALITY
719.75 GAIT DISORDER DUE TO JOINT ABNORMALITY IN HIP, BUTTOCK, OR FEMUR
719.76 GAIT DISORDER DUE TO JOINT ABNORMALITY IN LOWER LEG
719.77 GAIT DISORDER DUE TO JOINT ABNORMALITY IN ANKLE AND/OR FOOT
300.11 HYSTERICAL GAIT DISORDER

Degenerative joint disease, osteochondritis dissecans, chondromalacia patellae.
Trauma to extremities, vertebral disc, hips.
Poorly fitting shoes, foreign body in shoe, unequal leg length.
Splinter in foot.
Joint infection (septic arthritis, osteomyelitis), viral arthritis.
Abdominal pain (e.g., appendicitis, incarcerated hernia), testicular torsion.
Polio, neuromuscular disorders, Guillain-Barré syndrome, multiple sclerosis.
Osgood-Schlatter disease.
Legg-Calvé-Perthes disease.
Factitious, somatization syndrome.
Neoplasm (local or metastatic).
Other: diskitis, periostitis, sickle cell disease, hemophilia.

LIMPING, PEDIATRIC AGE[20]

ICD-9CM # 781.2 GAIT ABNORMALITY

TODDLER (1-3 YR)

Infection:
- Septic arthritis:
  - -Hip.
  - -Knee.
- Osteomyelitis.
- Diskitis.

Occult trauma:
- Toddler's fracture.

Neoplasia.

CHILDHOOD (4-10 YR)

Infection:
- Septic arthritis:
  - -Hip.
  - -Knee.
- Osteomyelitis.
- Diskitis.
- Transient synovitis, hip.

LCPD.
Tarsal coalition.
Rheumatologic disorder:
- JRA.

Trauma.
Neoplasia.

ADOLESCENCE (11+ YR)

SCFE.
Rheumatologic disorder:
- JRA.

Trauma.
Tarsal coalition.
Hip dislocation (DDH).
Neoplasia.

(*DDH,* Developmental dysplasia of the hip; *JRA,* juvenile rheumatoid arthritis; *LCPD,* Legg-Calvé-Perthes disease; *SCFE,* slipped capital femoral epiphysis.)

LIVEDO RETICULITIS

ICD-9CM # CODE NOT AVAILABLE

Emboli (SBE, left atrial myxoma, cholesterol emboli).
Thrombocythemia or polycythemia.
Antiphospholipid antibody syndrome.
Cryoglobulinemia, cryofibrinogenemia.
Leukocytoclastic vasculitis.
SLE, rheumatoid arthritis, dermatomyositis.
Pancreatitis.
Drugs (quinine, quinidine, amantadine, catecholamines).
Physiologic (cutis marmorata).
Congenital.

LOW-VOLTAGE ECG

ICD-9CM # 794.31

Hypothyroidism.
Obesity.
Pericardial effusion.
Anasarca.

Pleural effusion.
Pneumothorax.
Amyloidosis.
Aortic stenosis.

LYMPHADENOPATHY[12]

ICD-9CM # 785.6

GENERALIZED

AIDS.
Lymphoma: Hodgkin's disease, non-Hodgkin's lymphoma.
Leukemias, reticuloendotheliosis.
Infectious mononucleosis, CMV, and other viral infections.
Diffuse skin infection: generalized furunculosis, multiple tick bites.
Parasitic infections: toxoplasmosis, filariasis, leishmaniasis, chagas' disease.
Serum sickness.
Collagen vascular diseases (RA, SLE).
Dengue (arbovirus infection).
Sarcoidosis and other granulomatous diseases.
Drugs: INH, hydantoin derivatives, antithyroid and antileprosy drugs.
Secondary syphilis.
Hyperthyroidism, lipid-storage diseases.

LOCALIZED

Cervical nodes
Infections of the head, neck, ears, sinuses, scalp, pharynx.
Mononucleosis.
Lymphoma.
TB.
Malignancy of head and neck.
Rubella.
Scalene/supraclavicular nodes
Lymphoma.
Lung neoplasm.
Bacterial or fungal infection of thorax or retroperitoneum.
GI malignancy.
Axillary nodes
Infections of hands and arms.
Cat-scratch disease.
Neoplasm (lymphoma, melanoma, breast carcinoma).
Brucellosis.
Epitrochlear nodes
Infections of the hand.
Lymphoma.
Tularemia.
Sarcoidosis, secondary syphilis (usually bilateral).
Inguinal nodes
Infections of leg or foot, folliculitis (pubic hair).
LGV, syphilis.
Lymphoma.
Pelvic malignancy.
Pasteurella pestis.
Hilar nodes
Sarcoidosis.
TB.
Lung carcinoma.
Fungal infections, systemic.
Mediastinal nodes
Sarcoidosis.
Lymphoma.
Lung neoplasm.
TB.
Mononucleosis.
Histoplasmosis.
Abdominal/retroperitoneal nodes
Lymphoma.
TB.
Neoplasm (ovary, testes, prostate and other malignancies).

MEDIASTINAL MASSES OR WIDENING ON CHEST X-RAY

ICD-9CM # 785.6 ADENOPATHY
519.3 DISEASE NEC
793.2 SHIFT (CXR)

Lymphoma: Hodgkin's disease and non-Hodgkin's lymphoma.
Sarcoidosis.
Vascular: aortic aneurysm, ectasia or tortuosity of aorta or bronchocephalic vessels.
Carcinoma: lungs, esophagus.
Esophageal diverticula.
Hiatal hernia.
Achalasia.
Prominent pulmonary outflow tract: pulmonary hypertension, pulmonary embolism, right-to-left shunts.
Trauma: mediastinal hemorrhage.
Pneumomediastinum.
Lymphadenopathy caused by silicosis and other pneumoconioses.
Leukemias.
Infections: TB, viral (rare), Mycoplasma (rare), fungal, tularemia.
Substernal thyroid.
Thymoma.
Teratoma.
Bronchogenic cyst.
Pericardial cyst.
Neurofibroma, neurosarcoma, ganglioneuroma.

MENINGITIS, CHRONIC[23]

ICD-9CM # 322.2

TB.
Fungal CNS infection.
Tertiary syphilis.
CNS neoplasm.
Metabolic encephalopathies.
Multiple sclerosis.
Chronic subdural hematoma.
SLE cerebritis.
Encephalitides.
Sarcoidosis.
NSAIDs.
Behçet's syndrome.
Anatomic defects (traumatic, congenital, postoperative).
Granulomatous angiitis.

MESENTERIC ISCHEMIA, NONOCCLUSIVE[23]

ICD-9CM # 557.0 MESENTERIC ARTERY EMBOLISM OR INFARCTION
557.1 MESENTERIC ARTERY INSUFFICIENCY, CHRONIC
902.39 MESENTERIC VEIN INJURY

Cardiovascular disease resulting in low-flow states (CHF, cardiogenic shock, post cardiopulmonary bypass, dysrhythmias).
Septic shock.
Drug induced (cocaine, vasopressors, ergot alkaloid poisoning).

SECTION II

MESENTERIC VENOUS THROMBOSIS[23]

ICD-9CM # 557.0

Hypercoagulable states (protein C or S deficiency, antithrombin III deficiency, Factor V Leyden, malignancy, P. Vera, Sickle cell disease, homocystinemia, lupus anticoagulant, cardiolipin antibody).
Trauma (operative venous injury, abdominal trauma, post-splenectomy).
Inflammatory conditions (pancreatitis, diverticulitis, appendicitis, cholangitis).
Other: CHF, renal failure, portal hypertension, decompression sickness.

METASTATIC NEOPLASMS

ICD-9CM # 198.5 BONE AND BONE MARROW
198.3 BRAIN AND SPINAL CORD
197.7 LIVER
197.0 LUNG

To: Bone	To: Brain	To: Liver	To: Lung
Breast	Lung	Colon	Breast
Lung	Breast	Stomach	Colon
Prostate	Melanoma	Pancreas	Kidney
Thyroid	GU tract	Breast	Testis
Kidney	Colon	Lymphomas	Stomach
Bladder	Sinuses	Bronchus	Thyroid
Endometrium	Sarcoma	Lung	Melanoma
Cervix	Skin	Sarcoma	
Melanoma	Thyroid	Choriocarcinoma	
		Kidney	

MICROCEPHALY[4]

ICD-9CM # 742.1 MICROCEPHALUS

PRIMARY (GENETIC)

Familial (autosomal recessive).
Autosomal dominant.
Syndromes:
- Down (21-trisomy).
- Edward (18-trisomy).
- Cri-du-chat (5 p-).
- Cornelia de Lange.
- Rubinstein-Taybi.
- Smith-Lemli-Opitz.

SECONDARY (NONGENETIC)

Radiation.
Congenital infections:
- Cytomegalovirus.
- Rubella.
- Toxoplasmosis.

Drugs:
- Fetal alcohol.
- Fetal hydantoin.

Meningitis/encephalitis.
Malnutrition.
Metabolic.
Hyperthermia.
Hypoxic-ischemic encephalopathy.

MICROPENIS[24]

ICD-9CM # 752.69 PENILE AGENESIS OR ATRESIA
607.89 PENILE ATROPHY
752.64 MICROPENIS (CONGENITAL)

HYPOGONADOTROPIC HYPOGONADISM (HYPOTHALAMIC OR PITUITARY DEFICIENCIES)

Kallmann's syndrome: autosomal dominant; associated with hyposmia.
Prader-Willi syndrome: hypotonia, mental retardation, obesity, small hands and feet.
Rud syndrome: hyposomia, ichthyosis, mental retardation.
De Morsier's syndrome (septooptic dysplasia): hypopituitarism, hypoplastic optic discs, absent septum pellucidum.

HYPERGONADOTROPIC HYPOGONADISM

Primary testicular defect: disorders of testicular differentiation or inborn errors of testosterone synthesis.
Klinefelter syndrome.
Other X polysomies (i.e., XXXXY, XXXY).
Robinow's syndrome: brachymesomelic dwarfism, dysmorphic facies.

PARTIAL ANDROGEN INSENSITIVITY

IDIOPATHIC

Defective morphogenesis of the penis.

MIOSIS

ICD-9CM # 379.42 MIOSIS PERSISTENT NOT DUE TO MIOTICS

Medications (e.g., morphine, pilocarpine).
Neurosyphilis.
Congenital.
Iritis.
CNS pontine lesion.
CNS infections.
Cavernous sinus thrombosis.
Inflammation/irritation of cornea or conjunctiva.

MONONEUROPATHY

ICD-9CM # 355.9

Herpes zoster.
Herpes simplex.
Vasculitis.
Trauma, compression.
Diabetes.
Postinfectious or inflammatory.

MUSCLE WEAKNESS

ICD-9CM # 728.9

Physical deconditioning.
Impaired cardiac output (e.g., mitral stenosis, mitral regurgitation).
Uremia, liver failure.
Electrolyte abnormalities (hypokalemia, hyperkalemia, hypophosphatemia, hypercalcemia), hypoglycemia.
Drug-induced (e.g., statin myopathy).
Muscular dystrophies.
Steroid myopathy.
Alcoholic myopathy.
Myasthenia gravis, Lambert-Eaton syndrome.

Infections (polio, botulism, HIV, hepatitis, diphtheria, tick paralysis, neurosyphilis, brucellosis, TB, trichinosis).
Pernicious anemia, other anemias, beriberi.
Psychiatric illness (depression, somatization syndrome).
Organophosphate or arsenic poisoning.
Inflammatory myopathies (e.g., collagen vascular disease, RA, sarcoidosis).
Endocrinopathies (e.g., adrenal insufficiency, hypothyroidism), diabetic neuropathy.
Other: motor neuron disease, mitochondrial myopathy,
L-tryptophan (eosinophilia-myalgia), rhabdomyolysis, glycogen storage disease, lipid storage disease.

MUSCLE WEAKNESS, LOWER MOTOR NEURON VERSUS UPPER MOTOR NEURON[35]

ICD-9CM # 728.9

LOWER MOTOR NEURON

Weakness, usually severe.
Marked muscle atrophy.
Fasciculations.
Decreased muscle stretch reflexes.
Clonus not present.
Flaccidity.
No Babinski sign.
Asymmetric and may involve one limb only in the beginning to become generalized as the disease progresses.

UPPER MOTOR NEURON

Weakness, usually less severe.
Minimal disuse muscle atrophy.
No fasciculations.
Increased muscle stretch reflexes.
Clonus may be present.
Spasticity.
Babinski sign.
Often initial impairment of only skilled movements.
In the limbs the following muscles may be the only ones weak or weaker than the others: triceps; wrist and finger extensors; interossei; iliopsoas; hamstrings; and foot dorsiflexors, inverters and extroverters.

MYDRIASIS

ICD-9CM # 379.43 MYDRIASIS PERSISTENT NOT DUE TO MYDRIATICS

Coma.
Medications (cocaine, atropine, epinephrine, etc.).
Glaucoma.
Cerebral aneurysm.
Ocular trauma.
Head trauma.
Optic atrophy.
Cerebral neoplasm.
Iridocyclitis.

MYELOPATHY AND MYELITIS[33]

ICD-9CM # 722.70 MYELOPATHY, DISCOGENIC INTERVERTEBRAL NOS
336.9 MYELOPATHY, NONDISCOGENIC UNSPECIFIED

INFLAMMATORY

Infectious: spirochetal TB, zoster, rabies, HIV, polio, rickettsial, fungal, parasitic.
Noninfectious: idiopathic transverse myelitis, multiple sclerosis.

TOXIC/METABOLIC

DM, pernicious anemia, chronic liver disease, pellagra, arsenic.

TRAUMA COMPRESSION

Spinal neoplasm, cervical spondylosis, epidural abscess, epidural hematoma.

VASCULAR

AV malformation, SLE, periarteritis nodosa, dissecting aortic aneurysm.

PHYSICAL AGENTS

Electrical injury, irradiation.

NEOPLASTIC

Spinal cord tumors, paraneoplastic myelopathy.

MYOCARDIAL ISCHEMIA[33]

ICD-9CM # 414.8 ISCHEMIA (CHRONIC)
411.89 ISCHEMIA, ACUTE WITHOUT MI

Atherosclerotic obstructive coronary artery disease.
Nonatherosclerotic coronary artery disease:
- Coronary artery spasm.
- Congenital coronary artery anomalies:
  - -Anomalous origin of coronary artery from pulmonary artery.
  - -Aberrant origin of coronary artery from aorta or another coronary artery.
  - -Coronary arteriovenous fistula.
  - -Coronary artery aneurysm.

Acquired disorders of coronary arteries:
- Coronary artery embolism.
- Dissection:
  - -Surgica.
  - -During percutaneous coronary angioplasty.
  - -Aortic dissection.
  - -Spontaneous (e.g., during pregnancy).
- Extrinsic compression:
  - -Tumors.
  - -Granulomas.
  - -Amyloidosis.
- Collagen-vascular disease:
  - -Polyarteritis nodosa.
  - -Temporal arteritis.
  - -Rheumatoid arthritis.
  - -Systemic lupus erythematosus.
  - -Scleroderma.
- Miscellaneous disorders:
  - -Irradiation.
  - -Trauma.
  - -Kawasaki disease.
- Syphilis.

Hereditary disorders:
- Pseudoxanthoma elasticum.
- Gargoylism.
- Progeria.
- Homocystinuria.
- Primary oxaluria.

"Functional" causes of myocardial ischemia in absence of anatomic coronary artery disease:
- Syndrome X.
- Hypertrophic cardiomyopathy.
- Dilated cardiomyopathy.
- Muscle bridge.
- Hypertensive heart disease.
- Pulmonary hypertension.
- Valvular heart disease; aortic stenosis, aortic regurgitation.

SECTION II

MYOPATHIES, INFECTIOUS

ICD-9CM # 359.8

HIV.
Viral myositis.
Trichinosis
Toxoplasmosis.
Cysticercosis.

MYOPATHIES, INFLAMMATORY

ICD-9CM # 359.9

SLE, rheumatoid arthritis.
Sarcoidosis.
Paraneoplastic syndrome.
Polymyositis, dermatomyositis.
Polyarteritis nodosa.
Mixed connective tissue disease.
Scleroderma.
Inclusion body myositis.
Sjögren's syndrome.
Cimetidine, D-penicillamine.

MYOPATHIES, TOXIC[1]

ICD-9CM # 359.4

Inflammatory: cimetidine, D-penicillamine.
Noninflammatory necrotizing or vacuolar: cholesterol-lowering agents, chloroquine, colchicine.
Acute muscle necrosis and myoglobinuria: cholesterol-lowering drugs, alcohol, cocaine.
Malignant hyperthermia: halothane, ethylene, others; succinylcholine.
Mitochondrial: zidovudine.
Myosin loss: nondepolarizing neuromuscular blocking agents; glucocorticoids.

MYOSITIS, INFLAMMATORY[1]

ICD-9CM # 729.1

INFECTIOUS

Viral myositis:
  Retroviruses (HIV, HTLV-I).
  Enteroviruses (echovirus, Coxsackievirus).
  Other viruses (influenza, hepatitis A and B, Epstein-Barr virus).
Bacterial: pyomyositis.
Parasites: trichinosis, cysticercosis.
Fungi: candidiasis.

IDIOPATHIC

Granulomatous myositis (sarcoid, giant cell).
Eosinophilic myositis.
Eosinophilia-myalgia syndrome.

ENDOCRINE/METABOLIC DISORDERS

Hypothyroidism.
Hyperthyroidism.
Hypercortisolism.
Hyperparathyroidism.
Hypoparathyroidism.
Hypocalcemia.
Hypokalemia.

METABOLIC MYOPATHIES

Myophosphorylase deficiency (McArdle's disease).
Phosphofructokinase deficiency.
Myoadenylate deaminase deficiency.
Acid maltase deficiency.
Lipid storage diseases.
Acute rhabdomyolysis.

DRUG-INDUCED MYOPATHIES

Alcohol.
D-Penicillamine.
Zidovudine.
Colchicine.
Chloroquine, hydroxychloroquine.
Lipid-lowering agents.
Cyclosporine.
Cocaine, heroin, barbiturates.
Corticosteroids.

NEUROLOGIC DISORDERS

Muscular dystrophies.
Congenital myopathies.
Motor neuron disease.
Guillain-Barré syndrome.
Myasthenia gravis.

NAIL CLUBBING

ICD-9CM # 703.9

COPD.
Pulmonary malignancy.
Cirrhosis.
Inflammatory bowel disease.
Chronic bronchitis.
Congenital heart disease.
Endocarditis.
AV malformations.
Asbestosis.
Trauma.
Idiopathic.

NAIL, HORIZONTAL WHITE LINES (BEAU'S LINES)

ICD-9CM # 703.8

Malnutrition.
Idiopathic.
Trauma.
Prolonged systemic illnesses.
Pemphigus.
Raynaud's disease.

NAIL KOILONYCHIA

ICD-9CM # 703.8

Trauma.
Iron deficiency.
SLE.
Hemochromatosis.
Raynaud's disease.
Nail-patella syndrome.
Idiopathic.

NAIL ONYCHOLYSIS

ICD-9CM # 703.8

Infection.
Trauma.
Psoriasis.
Connective tissue disorders.
Sarcoidosis.

Hyperthyroidism.
Amyloidosis.
Nutritional deficiencies.

NAIL PITTING

ICD-9CM # 703.8

Psoriasis.
Alopecia areata.
Reiter's syndrome.
Trauma.
Idiopathic.

NAIL SPLINTER HEMORRHAGE

ICD-9CM # 703.8

SBE.
Trauma.
Malignancies.
Oral contraceptives.
Pregnancy.
SLE.
Antiphospholipid syndrome.
Psoriasis.
Rheumatoid arthritis.
Peptic ulcer disease.

NAIL STRIATIONS

ICD-9CM # 703.8

Psoriasis.
Alopecia areata.
Trauma.
Atopic dermatitis.
Vitiligo.

NAIL TELANGIECTASIA

ICD-9CM # 703.8

Rheumatoid arthritis.
Scleroderma.
Trauma.
SLE.
Dermatomyositis.

NAIL WHITENING (TERRY'S NAILS)

ICD-9CM # 703.8

Malnutrition.
Trauma.
Liver disease (cirrhosis, hepatic failure).
Diabetes mellitus.
Hyperthyroidism.
Idiopathic.

NAIL YELLOWING

ICD-9CM # 703.8

Tobacco abuse.
Nephrotic syndrome.
Chronic infections (TB, sinusitis).
Bronchiectasis.
Lymphedema.
Raynaud's disease.
Rheumatoid arthritis.
Pleural effusions.
Thyroiditis.
Immunodeficiency.

NAUSEA AND VOMITING

ICD-9CM # 787.01

Infections (viral, bacterial).
Intestinal obstruction.
Metabolic (uremia, electrolyte abnormalities, DKA, acidosis, etc.).
Severe pain.
Anxiety, fear.
Psychiatric disorders (bulimia, anorexia nervosa).
Pregnancy.
Medications (NSAIDs, erythromycin, morphine, codeine, aminophylline, chemotherapeutic agents, etc.).
Withdrawal from substance abuse (drugs, alcohol).
Head trauma.
Vestibular or middle ear disease.
Migraine headache.
CNS neoplasms.
Radiation sickness.
PUD.
Carcinoma of GI tract.
Reye's syndrome.
Eye disorders.
Abdominal trauma.

NECK AND ARM PAIN

ICD-9CM # 723.1 NECK PAIN
847.0 NECK STRAIN
959.09 NECK INJURY
959.2 ARM INJURY
840.9 ARM STRAIN

Cervical disc syndrome.
Trauma, musculoskeletal strain.
Rotator cuff syndrome.
Bicipital tendonitis.
Glenohumeral arthritis.
Acromioclavicular arthritis.
Thoracic outlet syndrome.
Pancoast tumor.
Infection (cellulitis, abscess).
Angina pectoris.

NECK MASS[25]

ICD-9CM # 784.2

CONGENITAL ANOMALIES

Thyroglossal duct cyst.
Bronchial apparatus anomalies.
Teratomas.
Ranula.
Dermoid cysts.
Hemangioma.
Laryngoceles.
Cystic hygroma.

NONNEOPLASTIC INFLAMMATORY ETIOLOGIES

Folliculitis.
Adenopathy secondary to peritonsillar abscess.
Retropharyngeal or parapharyngeal abscess.
Salivary gland infections.
Viral infections (mononucleosis, HIV, CMV).
TB.
Cat-scratch disease.

Toxoplasmosis.
Actinomyces.
Atypical mycobacterium.
Jugular vein thrombus.

NEOPLASM (PRIMARY OR METASTATIC)

Lipoma

NECK PAIN[25]

ICD-9CM # 723.1 NECK PAIN (NONDISCOGENIC)
959.09 NECK INJURY

INFLAMMATORY DISEASES

Rheumatoid arthritis (RA).
Spondyloarthropathies.
Juvenile RA.

NONINFLAMMATORY DISEASE

Cervical osteoarthritis.
Diskogenic neck pain.
Diffuse idiopathic skeletal hyperostosis.
Fibromyalgia or myofascial pain.

INFECTIOUS CAUSES

Meningitis.
Osteomyelitis.
Infectious diskitis.

NEOPLASMS

Primary.
Metastatic.

REFERRED PAIN

Temporomandibular joint pain.
Cardiac pain.
Diaphragmatic irritation.
Gastrointestinal sources (gastric ulcer, gallbladder, pancreas).

NEPHRITIC SYNDROME, ACUTE[1]

ICD-9CM # 580.89

LOW SERUM COMPLEMENT LEVEL

Acute postinfectious glomerulonephritis.
Membranoproliferative glomerulonephritis.
SLE.
Subacute bacterial endocarditis.
Visceral abscess "shunt" nephritis.
Cryoglobulinemia.

NORMAL SERUM COMPLEMENT LEVEL

IgA nephropathy.
Idiopathic rapidly progressive glomerulonephritis.
Antiglomerular basement membrane disease.
Polyarteritis nodosa.
Wegener's glomerulonephritis.
Henoch-Schönlein purpura.
Goodpasture syndrome.

NEUROGENIC BLADDER[26]

ICD-9CM # 396.54

SUPRATENTORIAL

CVA.
Parkinson's disease.
Alzheimer's disease.
Cerebral palsy.

SPINAL CORD

Spinal cord injury.
Spinal stenosis.
Central cord syndrome.
ALS.
Multiple sclerosis.
Myelodysplasia.

PERIPHERAL NEUROPATHY

Diabetes.
Alcohol.
Shingles.
Syphilis.

NEUROLOGIC DEFICIT, FOCAL[23]

ICD-9CM # 436 CVA
435.9 TIA

TRAUMATIC: INTRACRANIAL, INTRASPINAL

Subdural hematoma.
Intraparenchymal hemorrhage.
Epidural hematoma.
Traumatic hemorrhagic necrosis.

INFECTIOUS

Brain abscess.
Epidural and subdural abscesses.
Meningitis.

NEOPLASTIC

Primary central nervous system tumors.
Metastatic tumors.
Syringomyelia.
Vascular.
Thrombosis.
Embolism.
Spontaneous hemorrhage: arteriovenous malformation, aneurysm, hypertensive.

METABOLIC

Hypoglycemia.
B_{12} deficiency.
Postseizure.
Hyperosmolar nonketotic.

OTHER

Migraine.
Bell's palsy.
Psychogenic.

NEUROLOGIC DEFICIT, MULTIFOCAL[23]

ICD-9CM # 436 CVA
435.9 TIA

Acute disseminated encephalomyelitis: Postviral or postimmunization.
Infectious encephalomyelitis: Poliovirus, enteroviruses, arbovirus, herpes zoster, Epstein-Barr virus.
Granulomatous encephalomyelitis: Sarcoid.
Autoimmune: Systemic lupus erythematosus.
Other: Familial spinocerebellar degenerations.

NEUROPATHIES, PAINFUL[35]

ICD-9CM # 355.9 NEUROPATHY NOS
357.5 ALCOHOLIC
357.8 CHRONIC PROGRESSIVE OR RELAPSING
356.2 CONGENITAL SENSORY
356.0 DEJERINE-SOTTAS
356.60 DIABETIC POLYNEUROPATHY, TYPE II
356.61 DIABETIC POLYNEUROPATHY TYPE I

MONONEUROPATHIES

Compressive neuropathy (carpal tunnel, meralgia paresthetica).
Trigeminal neuralgia.
Ischemic neuropathy.
Polyarteritis nodosa.
Diabetic mononeuropathy.
Herpes zoster.
Idiopathic and familial brachial plexopathy.

POLYNEUROPATHIES

Diabetes mellitus.
Paraneoplastic sensory neuropathy.
Nutritional neuropathy.
Multiple myeloma.
Amyloid.
Dominantly inherited sensory neuropathy.
Toxic (arsenic, thallium, metronidazole).
AIDS-associated neuropathy.
Tangier disease.
Fabry disease.

NYSTAGMUS

ICD-9CM # 379.50 NYSTAGMUS NOS
386.11 BENIGN POSITIONAL
386.2 CENTRAL POSITIONAL
379.59 CONGENITAL

Medications (meperidine, barbiturates, phenytoin, phenothiazines, etc.).
Multiple sclerosis.
Congenital.
Neoplasm (cerebellar, brainstem, cerebral).
Labyrinthine or vestibular lesions.
CNS infections.
Optic atrophy.
Other: Arnold-Chiari malformation, syringobulbia, chorioretinitis, meningeal cysts.

OPHTHALMOPLEGIA[1]

ICD-9CM # 378.9 OPHTHALMOPLEGIA NOS
378.52 CEREBELLAR ATAXIA SYNDROME
376.22 EXOPHTHALMIC

BILATERAL

Botulism.
Myasthenia gravis.
Wernicke's encephalopathy.
Acute cranial polyneuropathy.
Brainstem stroke.

UNILATERAL

Carotid-posterior (3rd cranial nerve, pupil involved communicating aneurysm).
Diabetic-idiopathic (3rd or 6th cranial nerve, pupil spared).
Myasthenia gravis.
Brainstem stroke.

ORAL MUCOSA, ERYTHEMATOUS LESIONS[8]

ICD-9CM # 528.3 ORAL ABSCESS
528.9 ORAL DISEASE (SOFT TISSUE)
528.8 HYPERPLASIA (TONGUE)

Allergy.
Erythroplakia.
Candidiasis.
Geographic tongue.
Stomatitis areata migrans.
Plasma cell gingivitis.
Pemphigus vulgaris.

ORAL MUCOSA, PIGMENTED LESIONS[8]

ICD-9CM # 528.3 ORAL ABSCESS
528.9 ORAL DISEASE (SOFT TISSUE)
528.8 HYPERPLASIA (TONGUE)

Racial pigmentation.
Oral melanotic macule.
Peutz-Jeghers syndrome.
Neurofibromatosis.
Albright's syndrome.
Addison's disease.
Chloasma.
Drug reaction: quinacrine, Minocin, chlorpromazine, Myleran.
Amalgam tattoo.
Lead line.
Smoker's melanosis.
Nevi.
Melanoma.

ORAL MUCOSA, PUNCTATE EROSIVE LESIONS[8]

ICD-9CM # 528.3 ORAL ABSCESS
528.9 ORAL DISEASE (SOFT TISSUE)
528.8 HYPERPLASIA (TONGUE)

Viral lesion: Herpes simplex, coxsackievirus (A, B, A16), herpes zoster.
Aphthous stomatitis.
Sutton's disease (giant aphthae).
Behçet's syndrome.
Reiter's syndrome.
Neutropenia.
Acute necrotizing ulcerative gingivostomatitis (ANUG).
Drug reaction.
Inflammatory bowel disease.
Contact allergy.

ORAL MUCOSA, WHITE LESIONS[8]

ICD-9CM # 528.3 ORAL ABSCESS
528.9 ORAL DISEASE (SOFT TISSUE)
528.8 HYPERPLASIA (TONGUE)

Leukoplakia.
White, hairy leukoplakia.
Squamous cell carcinoma.
Lichen planus.
Stomatitis nicotinica.
Benign intraepithelial dyskeratosis.
White spongy nevus.
Leukoedema.
Darier-White disease.
Pachyonychia congenital.
Candidiasis.
Allergy.
SLE.

ORAL VESICLES AND ULCERS[1]

ICD-9CM # 528.9

Aphthous stomatitis.
Primary herpes simplex infection.
Vincent's stomatitis.
Syphilis.
Coxsackievirus A (herpangina).
Fungi (histoplasmosis).
Behçet's syndrome.
Systemic lupus erythematosus.
Reiter's syndrome.
Crohn's disease.
Erythema multiforme.
Pemphigus.
Pemphigoid.

ORGASM DYSFUNCTION[10]

ICD-9CM # 302.73 ORGASM INHIBITED FEMALE PSYCHOSEXUAL
302.74 ORGASM INHIBITED MALE PSYCHOSEXUAL

Anorgasmia: inadequate stimulation or learning.
Spinal cord lesion or injury.
Multiple sclerosis.
Alcoholic neuropathy.
Amyotrophic lateral sclerosis.
Spinal cord accident.
Spinal cord trauma.
Peripheral nerve damage.
Radical pelvic surgery.
Herniated lumbar disk.
Hypothyroidism.
Addison's disease.
Cushing's disease.
Acromegaly.
Hypopituitarism.
Pharmacologic agents (e.g., SSRIs, β-blockers).
Psychogenic.

OVULATORY DYSFUNCTION[18]

ICD-9CM # 628.0 ANOVULATORY CYCLE
626.5 OVULATION PAIN

HYPERANDROGENIC ANOVULATION

Polycystic ovarian syndrome.
Late-onset congenital adrenal hyperplasias.
Ovarian hyperthecosis.
Androgen-producing ovarian tumors.
Androgen-producing adrenal tumors.
Cushing's syndrome.

HYPOESTROGENIC ANOVULATION (HYPOTHALAMIC OR PITUITARY ETIOLOGY)

Hypogonadotropic hypoestrogenic states

Reversible:
Functional hypothalamic amenorrheas:
  Eating disorders (anorexia nervosa, excessive weight loss).
  Excessive athletic training.
Neoplastic:
  Craniopharyngioma.
  Pituitary stalk compression.
Infiltrative diseases:
  Histiocytosis-X.
  Sarcoidosis.
Hypophysitis.
Pituitary adenomas:
  Hyperprolactinemia.
  Euprolactinemic galactorrhea.
Endocrinopathies:
  Hypothyroidism/hyperthyroidism.
  Cushing's disease.
Irreversible:
  Kallmann's syndrome.
  Isolated gonadotropin deficiency (hypothalamic or pituitary origin).
  Panhypopituitarism/pituitary insufficiency:
    -Sheehan's syndrome, pituitary apoplexy.
    -Pituitary irradiation or ablation.

Hypergonadotropic hypoestrogenic states

Physiologic states:
  Menopause.
  Perimenopause.
Premature ovarian failure.
Immune-related:
  Radiation/chemotherapy-induced.
Ovarian dysgenesis.
Turner's syndrome.
46XX with mutations of X.
Androgen insensitivity syndrome.

MISCELLANEOUS

Endometriosis.
Luteal phase defect.

PAIN, MIDFOOT

ICD-9CM # 719.47

MEDIAL ASPECT

Tendonitis of posterior tibialis.
Tendonitis of flexor digitorum longus.
Tendonitis of flexor hallucis longus.
Infection (osteomyelitis, septic arthritis, cellulitis) of foot.
Peripheral vascular insufficiency.
Fracture.
Osteoarthritis.
Gout, pseudogout.
Neuropathy.
Tumor.

LATERAL ASPECT

Peroneus longus tendonitis.
Peroneus brevis tendonitis.
Infection (osteomyelitis, septic arthritis, cellulitis) of foot.
Peripheral vascular insufficiency.
Fracture.
Osteoarthritis.
Gout, pseudogout.
Neuropathy.
Tumor.

PAIN, PLANTAR ASPECT, HEEL

ICD-9CM # 719.47

Plantar fasciitis.
Tarsal tunnel syndrome.
Neuroma.
Infection (osteomyelitis, septic arthritis, cellulitis) of foot.
Peripheral vascular insufficiency.
Fracture.
Bone cyst.
Osteoarthritis.
Gout, pseudogout.

Neuropathy.
Tumor.
Heel pad atrophy.
Plantar fascia rupture.

PAIN, POSTERIOR HEEL

ICD-9CM # 729.5

Achilles tendonitis.
Retrocalcaneal bursitis.
Retroachilles bursitis.
Infection (osteomyelitis, septic arthritis, cellulitis) of foot.
Peripheral vascular insufficiency.
Fracture.
Osteoarthritis.
Gout, pseudogout.
Neuropathy.
Tumor.

PALINDROMIC RHEUMATISM[6]

ICD-9CM # 719.3 USE 5TH DIGIT
0. SITE UNSPECIFIED
1. SHOULDER REGION
2. UPPER ARM (ELBOW, HUMERUS)
3. FOREARM (RADIUS, WRIST, ULNA)
4. HAND (CARPAL, METACARPAL, FINGERS)
5. PELVIC REGION AND THIGH
6. LOWER LEG
7. ANKLE AND FOOT
8. OTHER
9. MULTIPLE

Palindromic rheumatoid arthritis.
Essential palindromic rheumatism.
Crystal synovitis (gout, CPPD, pseudogout, calcific periarthritis).
Lyme borreliosis, stages 2 and 3.
Sarcoidosis.
Whipple's disease.
Acute rheumatic fever.
Reactive arthritis (rare).

PALPITATIONS[30]

ICD-9CM # 785.1 PALPITATIONS

Anxiety.
Electrolyte abnormalities (hypokalemia, hypomagnesemia).
Exercise.
Hyperthyroidism.
Ischemic heart disease.
Ingestion of stimulant drugs (cocaine, amphetamines, caffeine).
Medications (digoxin, β-blockers, calcium channel antagonists, hydralazines, diuretics, minoxidil).
Hypoglycemia in type 1 DM.
Mitral valve prolapse.
Wolff-Parkinson-White (WPW) syndrome.
Sick sinus syndrome.

PANCYTOPENIA[33]

ICD-9CM # 284.8

PANCYTOPENIA WITH HYPOCELLULAR BONE MARROW

Acquired aplastic anemia.
Constitutional aplastic anemia.
Exposure to chemical or physical agents, including ionizing irradiation and chemotherapeutic agents.
Some hematologic malignancies, including myelodysplasia and aleukemic leukemia.

PANCYTOPENIA WITH NORMAL OR INCREASED CELLULARITY OF HEMATOPOIETIC ORIGIN

Some hematologic malignancies, including myelodysplasia, and some leukemias, lymphomas, and myelomas.
Paroxysmal nocturnal hemoglobinuria.
Hypersplenism.
Vitamin B_{12}, folate deficiencies.
Overwhelming infection.

PANCYTOPENIA WITH BONE MARROW REPLACEMENT

Tumor metastatic to marrow.
Metabolic storage diseases.
Osteopetrosis.
Myelofibrosis.

PAPILLEDEMA

ICD-9CM # 377.00 PAPILLEDEMA NOS
377.02 WITH DECREASED OCULAR PRESSURE
377.01 WITH INCREASED INTRACRANIAL PRESSURE
377.03 WITH RETINAL DISORDER

CNS infections (viral, bacterial, fungal).
Medications (lithium, cisplatin, corticosteroids, tetracycline, etc.).
Head trauma.
CNS neoplasm (primary or metastatic).
Pseudotumor cerebri.
Cavernous sinus thrombosis.
SLE.
Sarcoidosis.
Subarachnoid hemorrhage.
Carbon dioxide retention.
Arnold-Chiari malformation and other developmental or congenital malformations.
Orbital lesions.
Central retinal vein occlusion.
Hypertensive encephalopathy.
Metabolic abnormalities.

PAPULOSQUAMOUS DISEASES[12]

ICD-9CM # 709.8

Psoriasis.
Pityriasis rubra pilaris.
Pityriasis rosea.
Lichen planus.
Lichen nitidus.
Secondary syphilis.
Pityriasis lichenoides.
Parapsoriasis.
Mycosis fungoides.
Dermatophytosis.
Tinea versicolor.

PARANEOPLASTIC SYNDROMES, ENDOCRINE[33]

ICD-9CM # CODE VARIES WITH SPECIFIC DISORDER

Hypercalcemia.
Syndrome of inappropriate secretion of antidiuretic hormone.
Hypoglycemia.
Zollinger-Ellison syndrome.

Ectopic secretion of human chorionic gonadotropin.
Cushing's syndrome.

PARANEOPLASTIC SYNDROMES, NONENDOCRINE[33]

ICD-9CM # CODE VARIES WITH SPECIFIC DISORDER

CUTANEOUS

Dermatomyositis.
Acanthosis nigricans.
Sweet's syndrome.
Erythema gyratum repens.
Systemic nodular panniculitis (Weber-Christian disease).

RENAL

Nephrotic syndrome.
Nephrogenic diabetes insipidus.

NEUROLOGIC

Subacute cerebellar degeneration.
Progressive multifocal leukoencephalopathy.
Subacute motor neuropathy.
Sensory neuropathy.
Ascending acute polyneuropathy (Guillain-Barré syndrome).
Myasthenic syndrome (Eaton-Lambert syndrome).

HEMATOLOGIC

Microangiopathic hemolytic anemia.
Migratory thrombophlebitis (Trousseau's syndrome).
Anemia of chronic disease.

RHEUMATOLOGIC

Polymyalgia rheumatica.
Hypertrophic pulmonary osteoarthropathy.

PARAPLEGIA

ICD-9CM # 344.1 PARAPLEGIA, ACQUIRED
343.0 PARAPLEGIA, CONGENITAL
438.50 PARAPLEGIA, LATE EFFECT OF CVA

Trauma: penetrating wounds to motor cortex, fracture-dislocation of vertebral column with compression of spinal cord or cauda equina, prolapsed disk, electrical injuries.
Neoplasm: parasagittal region, vertebrae, meninges, spinal cord, cauda equina, Hodgkin's disease, NHL, leukemic deposits, pelvic neoplasms.
Multiple sclerosis and other demyelinating disorders.
Mechanical compression of spinal cord, cauda equina, or lumbosacral plexus: Paget's disease, kyphoscoliosis, herniation of intervertebral disk, spondylosis, ankylosing spondylitis, RA, aortic aneurysm.
Infections: spinal abscess, syphilis, TB, poliomyelitis, leprosy.
Thrombosis of superior sagittal sinus.
Polyneuritis: Guillain-Barré syndrome, diabetes, alcohol, beriberi, heavy metals.
Heredofamilial muscular dystrophies.
ALS.
Congenital and familial conditions: syringomyelia, myelomeningocele, myelodysplasia.
Hysteria.

PARESTHESIAS

ICD-9CM # 782.0

Multiple sclerosis.
Nutritional deficiencies (thiamin, vitamin B_{12}, folic acid).
Compression of spinal cord or peripheral nerves.
Medications (e.g., INH, lithium, nitrofurantoin, gold, cisplatin, hydralazine, amitriptyline, sulfonamides, amiodarone, metronidazole, dapsone, disulfiram, chloramphenicol).
Toxic chemicals (e.g., lead, arsenic, cyanide, mercury, organophosphates).
DM.
Myxedema.
Alcohol.
Sarcoidosis.
Neoplasms.
Infections (HIV, Lyme disease, herpes zoster, leprosy, diphtheria).
Charcot-Marie-Tooth syndrome and other hereditary neuropathies.
Guillain-Barré neuropathy.

PAROTID SWELLING[3]

ICD-9CM # 527.2 ALLERGIC PAROTITIS
72.9 INFECTIOUS PAROTITIS
527.8 SALIVARY GLAND OBSTRUCTION
527.5 SALIVARY GLAND OBSTRUCTION WITH CALCULUS
527.8 SALIVARY GLAND STRICTURE
527.3 SALIVARY GLAND ABSCESS
235.1 SALIVARY GLAND NEOPLASM

INFECTIOUS

Mumps.
Parainfluenza.
Influenza.
Cytomegalovirus infection.
Coxsackievirus infection.
Lymphocytic choriomeningitis.
Echovirus infection.
Suppuration (bacterial).
Actinomyces infection.
Mycobacterial infection.
Cat-scratch disease.

NONINFECTIOUS

Drug hypersensitivity (thiouracil, phenothiazines, thiocyanate, iodides, copper, isoprenaline, lead, mercury, phenylbutazone).
Sarcoidosis.
Tumors, mixed.
Hemangioma, lymphangioma.
Sialectasis.
Sjögren syndrome.
Mikulicz syndrome (scleroderma, mixed connective tissue disease, systemic lupus erythematosus).
Recurrent idiopathic parotitis.
Pneumoparotitis.
Trauma.
Sialolithiasis.
Foreign body.
Cystic fibrosis.
Malnutrition (marasmus, alcohol cirrhosis).
Dehydration.
Diabetes mellitus.
Waldenström macroglobulinemia.
Reiter syndrome.
Amyloidosis.

NONPAROTID SWELLING

Hypertrophy of masseter muscle.
Lymphadenopathy.
Rheumatoid mandibular joint swelling.
Tumors of jaw.
Infantile cortical hyperostosis.

PELVIC MASS

ICD-9CM # 789.39

Hemorrhagic ovarian cyst.
Simple ovarian cyst (follicle or corpus luteum).
Ovarian carcinoma, carcinoma of fallopian tube, colorectal carcinoma, metastatic carcinoma, prostate carcinoma, bladder carcinoma, lymphoma, Hodgkin's disease.
Cystadenoma, teratoma, endometrioma.
Leiomyoma.
Leiomyosarcoma.
Diverticulitis, diverticular abscess.
Appendiceal abscess, tuboovarian abscess.
Ectopic pregnancy, intrauterine pregnancy.
Paraovarian cyst.
Hydrosalpinx.

PELVIC PAIN, CHRONIC[7]

ICD-9CM # 625.9 PELVIC PAIN, FEMALE
789.09 PELVIC PAIN, MALE

GYNECOLOGIC DISORDERS

Primary dysmenorrhea.
Endometriosis.
Adenomyosis.
Adhesions.
Fibroids.
Retained ovary syndrome after hysterectomy.
Previous tubal ligation.
Chronic pelvic infection.

MUSCULOSKELETAL DISORDERS

Myofascial pain syndrome.

GASTROINTESTINAL DISORDERS

Irritable bowel syndrome.
Inflammatory bowel disease.

URINARY TRACT DISORDERS

Interstitial cystitis.
Nonbacterial urethritis.

PELVIC PAIN, GENITAL ORIGIN[23]

ICD-9CM # 625.9 PELVIC PAIN, FEMALE
789.09 PELVIC PAIN, MALE

PERITONEAL IRRITATION

Ruptured ectopic pregnancy.
Ovarian cyst rupture.
Ruptured tuboovarian abscess.
Uterine perforation.

TORSION

Ovarian cyst or tumor.
Pedunculated fibroid.

INTRATUMOR HEMORRHAGE OR INFARCTION

Ovarian cyst.
Solid ovarian tumor.
Uterine leiomyoma.

INFECTION

Endometritis.
Pelvic inflammatory disease.
Trichomonas cervicitis or vaginitis.
Tuboovarian abscess.

PREGNANCY-RELATED

First Trimester
Ectopic pregnancy.
Abortion.
Corpus luteum hematoma.
Late Pregnancy
Placental problems.
Preeclampsia.
Premature labor.

MISCELLANEOUS

Endometriosis.
Foreign objects.
Pelvic adhesions.
Pelvic neoplasm.
Primary dysmenorrhea.

PERICARDIAL EFFUSION

ICD-9CM # 420.90

Pericarditis.
Uremia.
Myxedema.
Neoplasm (leukemia, lymphoma, metastatic).
Hemorrhage (trauma, leakage of thoracic aneurysm).
SLE, Rheumatoid disease.
Myocardial infarction.

PERIODIC PARALYSIS, HYPERKALEMIC

ICD-9CM # 344.9

Chronic renal failure.
Renal insufficiency with excessive potassium supplementation.
Potassium-sparing diuretics.
Endocrinopathies (hypoaldosteronism, adrenal insufficiency).

PERIODIC PARALYSIS, HYPOKALEMIC

ICD-9CM # 344.9

Chronic diarrhea (laxative abuse, sprue, villous adenoma).
Potassium depleting diuretics.
Medications (amphotericin B, corticosteroids).
Chronic licorice ingestion.
Thyrotoxicosis.
Renal tubular acidosis.
Conn's syndrome.
Barter's syndrome
Barium intoxication.

PERITONEAL CARCINONOMATOSIS[12]

ICD-9CM # 197.6

PRIMARY DISORDERS OF THE PERITONEUM: MESOTHELIOMA

METASTATIC SPREAD FROM
Stomach.
Colon.
Pancreas.
Carcinoid.
OTHER INTRAABDOMINAL ORGANS
Ovary.
Pseudomyxoma peritonei.
EXTRAABDOMINAL PRIMARY TUMORS
Breast.
Lung.
HEMATOLOGIC MALIGNANCY
Lymphoma.

PERITONEAL EFFUSION[16]

ICD-9CM # 792.9

TRANSUDATES

Increased hydrostatic pressure or decreased plasma oncotic pressure.
Congestive heart failure.
Hepatic cirrhosis.
Hypoproteinemia.

EXUDATES

Increased capillary permeability or decreased lymphatic resorption.
Infections (TB, spontaneous bacterial peritonitis, secondary bacterial peritonitis).
Neoplasms (hepatoma, metastatic carcinoma, lymphoma, mesothelioma).
Trauma.
Pancreatitis.
Bile peritonitis (e.g., ruptured gallbladder).

CHYLOUS EFFUSION

Damage or obstruction to thoracic duct.
Trauma.
Lymphoma.
Carcinoma.
Tuberculosis.
Parasitic infection.

PHOTODERMATOSES[12]

ICD-9CM # 692.72

Polymorphous light eruption.
Chronic actinic dermatitis.
Solar urticaria.
Phototoxicity and photoallergy.
Porphyrias.

PHOTOSENSITIVITY

ICD-9CM # 692.72

Solar urticaria.
Photoallergic reaction.
Phototoxic reaction.
Polymorphous light eruption.
Porphyria cutanea tarda.
SLE.
Drug-induced (e.g., tetracyclines).

PLEURAL EFFUSIONS

ICD-9CM # 511.9 PLEURAL EFFUSION, UNSPECIFIED

EXUDATIVE

Neoplasm: bronchogenic carcinoma, breast carcinoma, mesothelioma, lymphoma, ovarian carcinoma, multiple myeloma, leukemia, Meigs' syndrome.
Infections: viral pneumonia, bacterial pneumonia, *Mycoplasma,* TB, fungal and parasitic diseases, extension from subphrenic abscess.
Trauma.
Collagen vascular diseases: SLE, RA, scleroderma, polyarteritis, Wegener's granulomatosis.
Pulmonary infarction.
Pancreatitis.
Postcardiotomy/Dressler's syndrome.
Drug-induced lupus erythematosus (hydralazine, procainamide).
Postabdominal surgery.
Ruptured esophagus.
Chronic effusion secondary to congestive failure.

TRANSUDATIVE

CHF.
Hepatic cirrhosis.
Nephrotic syndrome.
Hypoproteinemia from any cause.
Meigs' syndrome.

PNEUMONIA, RECURRENT

ICD-9CM # 482.9 BACTERIAL PNEUMONIA
480.9 VIRAL PNEUMONIA
484.1 FUNGAL PNEUMONIA
485 SEGMENTAL PNEUMONIA

Mechanical obstruction from neoplasm.
Chronic aspiration (tube feeding, alcoholism, CVA, neuromuscular disorders, seizure disorder, inability to cough).
Bronchiectasis.
Kyphoscoliosis.
COPD, CHF, asthma, silicosis, pulmonary fibrosis, cystic fibrosis.
Pulmonary TB, chronic sinusitis.
Immunosuppression (HIV, corticosteroids, leukemia, chemotherapy, splenectomy).

POLYNEUROPATHY[35]

ICD-9CM # 357.9

PREDOMINANTLY MOTOR

Guillain-Barré syndrome.
Porphyria.
Diphtheria.
Lead.
Hereditary sensorimotor neuropathy, types I and II.
Paraneoplastic neuropathy.

PREDOMINANTLY SENSORY

Diabetes.
Amyloidosis.
Leprosy.
Lyme disease.
Paraneoplastic neuropathy.
Vitamin B_{12} deficiency.
Hereditary sensory neuropathy, types I-IV.

PREDOMINANTLY AUTONOMIC

Diabetes.
Amyloidosis.
Alcoholic neuropathy.
Familial dysautonomias.

MIXED SENSORIMOTOR

Systemic diseases: Renal failure, hypothyroidism, acromegaly, rheumatoid arthritis, periarteritis nodosa, systemic lupus erythematosus, multiple myeloma, macroglobulinemia, remote effect of malignancy.
Medications: Isoniazid, nitrofurantoin, ethambutol, chloramphenicol, chloroquine, vincristine, vinblastine, dapsone, disulfiram, diphenylhydantoin, cisplatin, 1-tryptophan.
Environmental toxins: *N*-hexane, methyl *N*-butyl ketone, acrylamide, carbon disulfide, carbon monoxide, hexachlorophene, organophosphates.
Deficiency disorders: Malabsorption, alcoholism, vitamin B_1 deficiency, Refsum's disease, metachromatic leukodystrophy.

POLYNEUROPATHY, DRUG-INDUCED[35]

ICD-9CM # 357.6

DRUGS IN ONCOLOGY

Vincristine.
Procarbazine.
Cisplatin.
Misonidazole.
Metronidazole (Flagyl).
Taxol.

DRUGS IN INFECTIOUS DISEASES

Isoniazid.
Nitrofurantoin.
Dapsone.
ddC (dideoxycytidine).
ddI (dideoxyinosine).

DRUGS IN CARDIOLOGY

Hydralazine.
Perhexiline maleate.
Procainamide.
Disopyramide.

DRUGS IN RHEUMATOLOGY

Gold salts.
Chloroquine.

DRUGS IN NEUROLOGY AND PSYCHIATRY

Diphenylhydantoin.
Glutethimide.
Methaqualone.

MISCELLANEOUS

Disulfiram (Antabuse).
Vitamin: pyridoxine (megadoses).

POLYNEUROPATHY, SYMMETRIC[35]

ICD-9CM # 357.9

ACQUIRED NEUROPATHIES

Toxic:
- Drugs.
- Industrial toxins.
- Heavy metals.
- Abused substances.

Metabolic/endocrine:
- Diabetes.
- Chronic renal failure.
- Hypothyroidism.
- Polyneuropathy of critical illness.

Nutritional deficiency:
- Vitamin B12 deficiency.
- Alcoholism.
- Vitamin E deficiency.

Paraneoplastic:
- Carcinoma.
- Lymphoma.

Plasma cell dyscrasia:
- Myeloma, typical, atypical, and solitary forms.
- Primary systemic amyloidosis.

Idiopathic chronic inflammatory demyelinating polyneuropathies.
Polyneuropathies associated with peripheral nerve autoantibodies.
Acquired immunodeficiency syndrome.

INHERITED NEUROPATHIES

Neuropathies with biochemical markers
Refsum's disease.
Bassen-Kornzweig disease.
Tangier disease.
Metachromatic leukodystrophy.
Krabbe's disease.
Adrenomyeloneuropathy.
Fabry's disease.
Neuropathies without biochemical markers or systemic involvement
Hereditary motor neuropathy.
Hereditary sensory neuropathy.
Hereditary sensorimotor neuropathy.

POLYURIA

ICD-9CM # 788.42

DM.
Diabetes insipidus.
Primary polydipsia (compulsive water drinking).
Hypercalcemia.
Hypokalemia.
Postobstructive uropathy.
Diuretic phase of renal failure.
Drugs: diuretics, caffeine, alcohol, lithium.
Sickle cell trait or disease, chronic pyelonephritis (failure to concentrate urine).
Anxiety, cold weather.

POPLITEAL SWELLING

ICD-9CM # 459.2 VENOUS OBSTRUCTION
747.4 VEIN ANOMALY, LOWER LIMB VESSEL
442.3 ARTERY ANEURYSM
904.41 ARTERY INJURY
447.8 ENTRAPMENT SYNDROME
727.51 BAKER'S CYST
451.2 PHLEBITIS, LOWER EXTREMITY
727.67 RUPTURE OF ACHILLES TENDON

Phlebitis (superficial).
Lymphadenitis.
Trauma: fractured tibia or fibula, contusion, traumatic neuroma.
DVT.
Ruptured varicose vein.
Baker's cyst.
Popliteal abscess.
Osteomyelitis.
Ruptured tendon.
Aneurysm of popliteal artery.
Neoplasm: lipoma, osteogenic sarcoma, neurofibroma, fibrosarcoma.

PORTAL HYPERTENSION[1]

ICD-9CM # 572.3

INCREASED RESISTANCE TO FLOW

Presinusoidal
Portal or splenic vein occlusion (thrombosis, tumor).
Schistosomiasis.
Congenital hepatic fibrosis.
Sarcoidosis.
Sinusoidal
Cirrhosis (all causes).
Alcoholic hepatitis.

Postsinusoidal
Venoocclusive disease.
Budd-Chiari syndrome.
Constrictive pericarditis.

INCREASED PORTAL BLOOD FLOW

Splenomegaly not caused by liver disease.
Arterioportal fistula.

POSTMENOPAUSAL BLEEDING

ICD-9CM # 627.1

Hormone replacement therapy.
Neoplasm (uterine, ovarian, cervical, vaginal, vulvar).
Atrophic vaginitis.
Vaginal infection.
Polyp.
Extragenital (GI, urinary).
Tamoxifen.
Trauma.

PROPTOSIS[27]

ICD-9CM # 376.30

Thyrotoxicosis.
Orbital pseudotumor.
Optic nerve tumor.
Cavernous sinus AV fistula, cavernous sinus thrombosis.
Cellulitis.
Metastatic tumor to orbit

PROTEINURIA

ICD-9CM # 791.0

Nephrotic syndrome as a result of primary renal diseases.
Malignant hypertension.
Malignancies: multiple myeloma, leukemias, Hodgkin's disease.
CHF.
DM.
SLE, RA.
Sickle cell disease.
Goodpasture's syndrome.
Malaria.
Amyloidosis, sarcoidosis.
Tubular lesions: cystinosis.
Functional (after heavy exercise).
Pyelonephritis.
Pregnancy.
Constrictive pericarditis.
Renal vein thrombosis.
Toxic nephropathies: heavy metals, drugs.
Radiation nephritis.
Orthostatic (postural) proteinuria.
Benign proteinuria: fever, heat, or cold exposure.

PRURITUS

ICD-9CM # 698.9 PRURITUS NOS
697.0 PRURITUS ANI
698.1 PRURITUS, GENITAL ORGANS

Dry skin.
Drug-induced eruption, fiberglass exposure.
Scabies.
Skin diseases.
Myeloproliferative disorders: mycosis fungoides, Hodgkin's lymphoma, multiple myeloma, polycythemia vera.
Cholestatic liver disease.
Endocrine disorders: DM, thyroid disease, carcinoid, pregnancy.
Carcinoma: breast, lung, gastric.
Chronic renal failure.
Iron deficiency.
AIDS.
Neurosis.
Sjögren's syndrome.

PRURITUS ANI[23]

ICD-9CM # 697.0

FECAL IRRITATION

Poor hygiene.
Anorectal conditions (fissure, fistula, hemorrhoids, skin tags, perianal clefts).
Spicy foods, citrus foods, caffeine, colchicine, quinidine.

CONTACT DERMATITIS

Anesthetic agents, topical corticosteroids, perfumed soap.

DERMATOLOGIC DISORDERS

Psoriasis, seborrhea, lichen simplex or sclerosus.

SYSTEMIC DISORDERS

Chronic renal failure, myxedema, DM, thyrotoxicosis, polycythemia vera, Hodgkin's disease.

SEXUALLY TRANSMITTED DISEASES

Syphilis, herpes simplex virus, human papillomavirus.

OTHER INFECTIOUS AGENTS

Pinworms.
Scabies.
Bacterial infection, viral infection.

PSEUDOINFARCTION[19]

ICD-9CM # CODE NOT AVAILABLE

Cardiac tumors, primary and secondary.
Cardiomyopathy (particularly hypertrophic and dilated).
Chagas disease.
Chest deformity.
COPD (particularly emphysema).
HIV infection.
Hyperkalemia.
Left anterior fascicular block.
Left bundle branch block.
Left ventricular hypertrophy.
Myocarditis and pericarditis.
Normal variant.
Pneumothorax.
Poor R wave progression, rotational changes, and lead placement.
Pulmonary embolism.
Trauma to chest (nonpenetrating).
Wolff-Parkinson-White syndrome.
Rare causes: pancreatitis, amyloidosis, sarcoidosis, scleroderma.

PSYCHOSIS[25]

ICD-9CM # 298.9 PSYCHOSIS NOS
298.90 PSYCHOSIS, AFFECTIVE
291.0 PSYCHOSIS, ALCOHOLIC
290.41 PSYCHOSIS, ACUTE ARTERIOSCLEROTIC

PRIMARY

Schizophrenia related.*
Major depression.
Dementia.
Bipolar disorder.

SECONDARY

Drug use.†
Drug withdrawal.‡
Drug toxicity.§
Charles Bonnet syndrome.
Infections (pneumonia).
Electrolyte imbalance.
Syphilis.
Congestive heart failure.
Parkinson's disease.
Trauma to temporal lobe.
Postpartum psychosis.
Hypothyroidism/hyperthyroidism.
Hypomagnesemia.
Epilepsy.
Meningitis.
Encephalitis.
Brain abscess.
Herpes encephalopathy.
Hypoxia.
Hypercarbia.
Hypoglycemia.
Thiamine deficiency.
Postoperative states.

*Includes schizophrenia, schizophreniaform disorder, brief reactive psychosis.
†Includes hypnotics, glucocorticoids, marijuana, phencyclidine, atropine, dopaminergic agents (e.g., amantadine, bromocriptine, l-dopa), immunosuppressants.
‡Includes alcohol, barbiturates, benzodiazepines.
§Includes digitalis, theophylline, cimetidine, anticholinergics, glucocorticoids, catecholaminergic agents.

PTOSIS

ICD-9CM # 374.30 PTOSIS NOS
743.61 CONGENITAL
374.33 MECHANICAL
374.32 MYOGENIC
374.31 PARALYTIC

Third nerve palsy.
Myasthenia gravis.
Horner's syndrome.
Senile ptosis.

PUBERTY, DELAYED[24]

ICD-9CM # 259.0

NORMAL OR LOW SERUM GONADOTROPIN LEVELS

Constitutional delay in growth and development.
Hypothalamic and/or pituitary disorders:
- Isolated deficiency of growth hormone.
- Isolated deficiency on Gn-RH.
- Isolated deficiency of LH and/or FSH.
- Multiple anterior pituitary hormone deficiencies.
- Associated with congenital anomalies: Kallmann's syndrome; Prader-Willi syndrome; Laurence-Moon-Biedl syndrome; Friedreich's ataxia.
- Trauma.
- Postinfection.
- Hyperprolactinemia.
- Postirradiation.
- Infiltrative disease (histiocytosis).
- Tumor.
- Autoimmune hypophysitis.
- Idiopathic.

Functional:
- Chronic endocrinologic or systemic disorders.
- Emotional disorders.
- Drugs: cannabis.

INCREASED SERUM GONADOTROPIN LEVELS

Gonadal abnormalities:
- Congenital:
  - Gonadal dysgenesis.
  - Klinefelter's syndrome.
  - Bilateral anorchism.
  - Resistant ovary syndrome.
  - Myotonic dystrophy in males.
  - 17-Hydroxylase deficiency in females.
  - Galactosemia.
- Acquired:
  - Bilateral gonadal failure resulting from trauma or infection or after surgery, irradiation, or chemotherapy.
  - Oophoritis: isolated or with other autoimmune disorders.

Uterine or vaginal disorders:
- Absence of uterus and/or vagina.
- Testicular feminization: complete or incomplete androgen insensitivity.

PULMONARY CRACKLES

ICD-9CM # NOT AVAILABLE

Pneumonia.
Left ventricular failure.
Asbestosis, silicosis, interstitial lung disease.
Chronic bronchitis.
Alveolitis (allergic, fibrosing).
Neoplasm.

PULMONARY LESIONS

ICD-9CM # 518.3 PULMONARY INFILTRATE
518.89 PULMONARY NODULE
508.9 PULMONARY DISORDER DUE TO UNSPECIFIED EXTERNAL AGENT
861.20 PULMONARY INJURY NOS

TB.
Legionella pneumonia.
Mycoplasma pneumonia.
Viral pneumonia.
Pneumocystis carinii.
Hypersensitivity pneumonitis.
Aspiration pneumonia.
Fungal disease (aspergillosis, histoplasmosis).
ARDS associated with pneumonia.
Psittacosis.
Sarcoidosis.
Septic emboli.
Metastatic cancer.
Multiple pulmonary emboli.
Rheumatoid nodules.

PULMONARY NODULE, SOLITARY

ICD-9CM # 518.89

Bronchogenic carcinoma.
Granuloma from histoplasmosis.
TB granuloma.
Granuloma from coccidioidomycosis.
Metastatic carcinoma.
Bronchial adenoma.
Bronchogenic cyst.
Hamartoma.
AV malformation.
Other: fibroma, intrapulmonary lymph node, sclerosing hemangioma, bronchopulmonary sequestration.

PULSELESS ELECTRICAL ACTIVITY

ICD-9CM # CODE NOT AVAILABLE

Hypovolemia.
Hypoxia.
Hyperkalemia.
Acidosis.
Cardiac tamponade.
Tension pneumothorax.
Pulmonary embolus.
Drug overdose.
Hypothermia.

PURPURA

ICD-9CM # 287.2 PURPURA NOS
287.0 AUTOIMMUNE
287.0 HENOCH-SCHÖNLEIN
287.3 IDIOPATHIC THROMBOCYTOPENIC
446.6 THROMBOCYTOPENIC

THROMBOTIC

Trauma.
Septic emboli, atheromatous emboli.
DIC.
Thrombocytopenia.
Meningococcemia.
Rocky Mountain spotted fever.
Hemolytic-uremic syndrome.
Viral infection: echo, coxsackie.
Scurvy.
Other: left atrial myxoma, cryoglobulinemia, vasculitis, hyperglobulinemic purpura.

QT INTERVAL PROLONGATION[19]

ICD-9CM # 794.31

Drugs:
- Class I antiarrhythmics (e.g., disopyramide, procainamide, quinidine).
- Class III antiarrhythmics.
- Tricyclic antidepressants.
- Phenothiazines.
- Astemizole.
- Terfenadine.
- Adenosine.
- Antibiotics (e.g., erythromycin and other macrolides).
- Antifungal agents.
- Pentamidine, chloroquine.

Ischemic heart disease.
Cerebrovascular disease.
Rheumatic fever.
Myocarditis.
Mitral valve prolapse.
Electrolyte abnormalities.
Hypocalcemia.
Hypothyroidism.
Liquid protein diets.
Organophosphate insecticides.
Congenital prolonged QT syndrome.

RECTAL PAIN

ICD-9CM # 569.42

Anal fissure.
Thrombosed hemorrhoid.
Anorectal abscess.
Foreign bodies.
Fecal impaction.
Endometriosis.
Neoplasms (primary or metastatic).
Pelvic inflammatory disease.
Inflammation of sacral nerves.
Compression of sacral nerves.
Prostatitis.
Other: proctalgia fugax, uterine abnormalities, myopathies, coccygodynia.

RED EYE

ICD-9CM # 379.93

Infectious conjunctivitis (bacterial, viral).
Allergic conjunctivitis.
Acute glaucoma.
Keratitis (bacterial, viral).
Iritis.
Trauma.

RENAL ARTERY OCCLUSION, CAUSES

ICD-9CM # 593.81

Atrial fibrillation.
Angiography or stent placement.
Abdominal aortic surgery.
Trauma.
Renal artery aneurysm/dissection.
Vasculitis.
Thrombosis in patient with fibromuscular dysplasia.
Atherosclerosis.
Septic embolism.
Mural thrombus thromboembolism.
Atrial myxoma thromboembolism.
Mitral stenosis thromboembolism.
Prosthetic valve thromboembolism.
Renal cell carcinoma.

RENAL FAILURE, INTRINSIC OR PARENCHYMAL CAUSES[33]

ICD-9CM # 584. ACUTE, USE 4TH DIGIT
5. WITH ACUTE TUBULAR NECROSIS
6. WITH CORTICAL NECROSIS
7. WITH MEDULLARY NECROSIS
8. WITH OTHER UNSPECIFIED PATHOLOGIC CONDITION IN KIDNEY
9. RENAL FAILURE UNSPECIFIED
585 RENAL FAILURE, CHRONIC

ABNORMALITIES OF THE VASCULATURE

Renal arteries: atherosclerosis, thromboembolism, arteritis.
Renal veins: thrombosis.
Microvasculature: vasculitis, thrombotic microangiopathy.

ABNORMALITIES OF GLOMERULI (ACUTE GLOMERULONEPHRITIS)

Antiglomerular membrane disease (Goodpasture syndrome).
Immune complex glomerulonephritis: SLE, postinfectious, idiopathic, membranoproliferative.

ABNORMALITIES OF INTERSTITIUM (ACUTE INTERSTITIAL NEPHRITIS)

Drugs (e.g., antibiotics, NSAIDs, diuretics, anticonvulsants, allopurinol).
Infectious pyelonephritis.
Infiltrative: lymphoma, leukemia, sarcoidosis.

ABNORMALITIES OF TUBULES

Physical obstruction (uric acid, oxalate, light chains).
Acute tubular necrosis:
- Ischemic.
- Toxic (antibiotics, chemotherapy, immunosuppressives, radiocontrast dyes, heavy metals, myoglobin, hemolysed RBCs).

RENAL FAILURE, POSTRENAL CAUSES[33]

ICD-9CM # 584. ACUTE, USE 4TH DIGIT
5. WITH ACUTE TUBULAR NECROSIS
6. WITH CORTICAL NECROSIS
7. WITH MEDULLARY NECROSIS
8. WITH OTHER UNSPECIFIED PATHOLOGIC CONDITION IN KIDNEY
9. RENAL FAILURE UNSPECIFIED
585 RENAL FAILURE, CHRONIC

URETER AND RENAL PELVIS

Intrinsic obstruction:
- Blood clots.
- Stones.
- Sloughed papillae: diabetes, sickle cell disease, analgesic nephropathy.
- Inflammatory: fungus ball.

Extrinsic obstruction:
- Malignancy.
- Retroperitoneal fibrosis.
- Iatrogenic: inadvertent ligation of ureters.

BLADDER

Prostatic hypertrophy or malignancy.
Neuropathic bladder.
Blood clots.
Bladder cancer.
Stones.

URETHRAL

Strictures.
Congenital valves.

RENAL FAILURE, PRERENAL CAUSES[33]

ICD-9CM # 584. ACUTE, USE 4TH DIGIT
5. WITH ACUTE TUBULAR NECROSIS
6. WITH CORTICAL NECROSIS
7. WITH MEDULLARY NECROSIS
8. WITH OTHER UNSPECIFIED PATHOLOGIC CONDITION IN KIDNEY
9. RENAL FAILURE UNSPECIFIED
585 RENAL FAILURE, CHRONIC

DECREASED CARDIAC OUTPUT

CHF.
Arrhythmias.
Pericardial constriction or tamponade.
Pulmonary embolism.

HYPOVOLEMIA

GI tract loss (vomiting, diarrhea, nasogastric suction).
Blood losses (trauma, GI tract surgery).
Renal losses (diuretics, mineralocorticoid deficiency, postobstructive diuresis).
Skin losses (burns).

VOLUME REDISTRIBUTION (DECREASE IN EFFECTIVE BLOOD VOLUME)

Hypoalbuminemic states (cirrhosis, nephrosis).
Sequestration of fluid in "third" space (ischemic bowel, peritonitis, pancreatitis).
Peripheral vasodilation (sepsis, vasodilators, anaphylaxis).

ALTERED RENAL VASCULAR RESISTANCE

Increase in afferent vascular resistance (NSAIDs, liver disease, sepsis, hypercalcemia, cyclosporine).
Decrease in efferent arteriolar tone (ACE inhibitors).

RENAL VEIN THROMBOSIS, CAUSES

ICD-9CM # 453.3

Nephrotic syndrome.
Renal cell carcinoma.
Aortic aneurysm causing compression.
Lymphadenopathy.
Retroperitoneal fibrosis.
Estrogen therapy.
Pregnancy.
Renal cell carcinoma with vein invasion.
Severe dehydration.

RESPIRATORY FAILURE, HYPOVENTILATORY[25]

ICD-9CM # 518.81 RESPIRATORY FAILURE

ABNORMAL RESPIRATORY CAPACITY (NORMAL RESPIRATORY WORKLOADS)

Acute depression of central nervous system:
- Various causes.

Chronic central hypoventilation syndromes:
- Obesity-hypoventilation syndrome.
- Sleep apnea syndrome.
- Hypothyroidism.
- Shy-Drager syndrome (multisystem atrophy syndrome).

Acute toxic paralysis syndromes:
- Botulism.
- Tetanus.
- Toxic ingestion or bites.
- Organophosphate poisoning.

Neuromuscular disorders (acute and chronic):
- Myasthenia gravis.
- Guillain-Barré syndrome.
- Drugs.
- Amyotrophic lateral sclerosis.
- Muscular dystrophies.
- Polymyositis.
- Spinal cord injury.
- Traumatic phrenic nerve paralysis.

ABNORMAL PULMONARY WORKLOADS

Chronic obstructive pulmonary disease:
- Chronic bronchitis.
- Asthmatic bronchitis.
- Emphysema.

Asthma and acute bronchial hyperreactivity syndromes.
Upper airway obstruction.
Interstitial lung diseases.

ABNORMAL EXTRAPULMONARY WORKLOADS

Chronic thoracic cage disorders:
- Severe kyphoscoliosis.
- After thoracoplasty.
- After thoracic cage injury.

Acute thoracic cage trauma and burns.
Pneumothorax.
Pleural fibrosis and effusions.
Abdominal processes.

RIGHT AXIS DEVATION[19]

ICD-9CM # CODE VARIES WITH SPECIFIC DIAGNOSIS

Normal variation.
Right ventricular hypertrophy.
Left posterior fascicular block.
Lateral myocardial infarction.
Pulmonary embolism.
Dextrocardia.
Mechanical shifts or emphysema causing a vertical heart.

SALIVARY GLAND ENLARGEMENT

ICD-9CM # 527.1

Neoplasm.
Sialolithiasis.
Infection (mumps, bacterial infection, HIV, TB).
Sarcoidosis.
Idiopathic.
Acromegaly.
Anorexia/bulimia.
Chronic pancreatitis.
Medications (e.g., phenylbutazone).
Cirrhosis.
Diabetes mellitus.

SALIVARY GLAND SECRETION, DECREASED

ICD-9CM # 527.7

Medications (antihistamines, antidepressants, neuroleptics, antihypertensives).
Dehydration.
Anxiety.
Sjögren's syndrome.
Sarcoidosis.
Mumps.
Amyloidosis.
CNS disorders.
Head and neck radiation.

SCROTAL PAIN[25]

ICD-9CM # 878.2 SCROTAL INJURY, TRAUMATIC
608.9 SCROTAL DISORDER NOS
608.4 SCROTAL CELLULITIS
608.83 SCROTAL HEMORRHAGE, NONTRAUMATIC
608.4 SCROTAL NODULE, INFLAMMATORY

Torsion:
- Appendages.
- Spermatic cord.

Infection:
- Orchitis.
- Abscess.
- Epididymitis.

Neoplasia:
- Benign.
- Malignant.

Incarcerated hernia.
Trauma.
Hydrocele.
Spermatocele.
Varicocele.

SCROTAL SWELLING

ICD-9CM # 608.86

Hydrocele.
Varicocele.
Neoplasm.
Acute epididymitis.
Orchitis.
Trauma.
Hernia.
Torsion of spermatic cord.
Torsion of epididymis.
Torsion of testis.
Insect bite.
Folliculitis.
Sebaceous cyst.
Thrombosis of spermatic vein.
Other: lymphedema, dermatitis, fat necrosis, Henoch-Schönlein purpura, idiopathic scrotal edema.

SEIZURE

ICD-9CM # 780.39

Syncope.
Alcohol abuse/withdrawal.
TIA.
Hemiparetic migraine.
Psychiatric disorders.
Carotid sinus hypersensitivity.
Hyperventilation, prolonged breath holding.
Hypoglycemia.
Narcolepsy.
Movement disorders (tics, hemiballismus).
Hyponatremia.
Brain tumor (primary or metastatic).
Tetanus.
Strychnine, phencyclidine poisoning.

SEIZURE, PEDIATRIC[2]

ICD-9CM # 780.39 INFANTILE SEIZURES
779.0 SEIZURES, NEWBORN

FIRST MONTH OF LIFE

First Day
Hypoxia.
Drugs.
Trauma.
Infection.
Hyperglycemia.
Hypoglycemia.
Pyridoxine deficiency.
Day 2-3
Infection.
Drug withdrawal.
Hypoglycemia.
Hypocalcemia.
Developmental malformation.
Intracranial hemorrhage.
Inborn error of metabolism.
Hyponatremia or hypernatremia.
Day >4
Infection.
Hypocalcemia.
Hyperphosphatemia.
Hyponatremia.
Developmental malformation.
Drug withdrawal.
Inborn error of metabolism.
1 TO 6 MONTHS
As above.

6 MONTHS TO 3 YEARS

Febrile seizures.
Birth injury.
Infection.
Toxin.
Trauma.
Metabolic disorder.
Cerebral degenerative disease.

>3 YEARS

Idiopathic.
Infection.
Trauma.
Cerebral degenerative disease.

SEXUAL PRECOCITY[36]

ICD-9CM # 259.1

TRUE PRECOCIOUS PUBERTY

Premature reactivation of LHRH pulse generator.

INCOMPLETE SEXUAL PRECOCITY

(Pituitary Gonadotropin Independent).
Males
Chorionic gonadotropin-secreting tumor.
Leydig cell tumor.
Familial testotoxicosis.
Virilizing congenital adrenal hyperplasia.
Virilizing adrenal tumor.
Premature adrenarche.
Females
Granulosa cell tumor (follicular cysts may be manifested similarly).
Follicular cyst.
Feminizing adrenal tumor.
Premature thelarche.
Premature adrenarche.
Late-onset virilizing congenital adrenal hyperplasia.
In both sexes
McCune-Albright syndrome.
Primary hypothyroidism.

SEXUALLY TRANSMITTED DISEASES, ANORECTAL REGION[23]

ICD-9CM # 569.49 INFECTION AND REGION

ULCERATIVE

Lymphogranuloma venereum.
Herpes simplex virus.
Early (primary) syphilis.
Chancroid (Haemophilus ducreyi).
Cytomegalovirus.
Idiopathic (usually HIV positive).

NONULCERATIVE

Condyloma acuminatum.
Gonorrhea.
Chlamydia (Chlamydia trachomitis).
Syphilis.

SHOULDER PAIN

ICD-9CM # 952.2 SHOULDER INJURY
718.81 SHOULDER INSTABILITY
726.19 SHOULDER LIGAMENT OR MUSCLE INSTABILITY
840.9 SHOULDER STRAIN, SITE UNSPECIFIED

WITH LOCAL FINDINGS IN SHOULDER

Trauma: contusion, fracture, muscle strain, trauma to spinal cord.
Arthrosis, arthritis, RA, ankylosing spondylitis.
Bursitis, synovitis, tendinitis, tenosynovitis.
Aseptic (avascular) necrosis.
Local infection: septic arthritis, osteomyelitis, abscess, herpes zoster, TB.

WITHOUT LOCAL FINDINGS IN SHOULDER

Cardiovascular disorders: ischemic heart disease, pericarditis, aortic aneurysm.
Subdiaphragmatic abscess, liver abscess.
Cholelithiasis, cholecystitis.
Pulmonary lesions: apical bronchial carcinoma, pleurisy, pneumothorax, pneumonia.
GI lesions: PUD, gastric neoplasm, peptic esophagitis.
Pancreatic lesions: carcinoma, calculi, pancreatitis.
CNS abnormalities: neoplasm, vascular abnormalities.
Multiple sclerosis.
Syringomyelia.
Polymyositis/dermatomyositis.
Psychogenic.
Polymyalgia rheumatica.
Ectopic pregnancy.

SHOULDER PAIN BY LOCATION

ICD-9CM # 952.2 SHOULDER INJURY
726.19 SHOULDER LIGAMENT OR MUSCLE INSTABILITY
840.8 SHOULDER SEPARATION

TOP OF SHOULDER (C4)

Cervical source.
Acromioclavicular.
Sternoclavicular.
Diaphragmatic.

SUPEROLATERAL (C5)

Rotator cuff tendinitis.
Impingement.
Adhesive capsulitis.
Glenohumeral arthritis.

ANTERIOR

Bicipital tendinitis and rupture.
Glenoid labral tear.
Adhesive capsulitis.
Glenohumeral arthritis.
Osteonecrosis.

AXILLARY

Neoplasm (Pancoast's, mediastinal).
Herpes zoster.

SMALL BOWEL OBSTRUCTION[23]

ICD-9CM # 751.1 SMALL INTESTINE OBSTRUCTION, CONGENITAL
560.81 SMALL INTESTINE OBSTRUCTION DUE TO ADHESION

INTRINSIC

Congenital (atresia, stenosis).
Inflammatory (Crohn's, radiation enteritis).
Neoplasms (metastatic or primary).
Intussusception.
Traumatic (hematoma).

EXTRINSIC

Hernias (internal and external).
Adhesions.
Volvulus.
Compressing masses (tumors, abscesses, hematomas).

INTRALUMINAL

Foreign body.
Gallstones.
Bezoars.
Barium.
Ascaris infestation.

SORE THROAT[30]

ICD-9CM # 426 PHARYNGITIS
075 MONONUCLEOSIS
472.1 CHRONIC PHARYNGITIS
487.1 PHARYNGITIS, INFLUENZAL
074.0 COXSACKIE VIRUS PHARYNGITIS

WITHOUT PHARYNGEAL ULCERS

Viral pharyngitis.
Allergic pharyngitis.
Infectious mononucleosis.
Streptococcal pharyngitis.
Gonococcal pharyngitis.
Sinusitis with postnasal drip.

WITH PHARYNGEAL ULCERS

Herpangina.
Herpes simplex.
Candidiasis.
Fusospirochetal infection (Vincent's angina).

SPASTIC PARAPLEGIAS

ICD-9CM # 344.1

Cervical spondylosis.
Friedreich's ataxia.
Multiple sclerosis.
Spinal cord tumor.
HIV.
Tertiary syphilis.
Vitamin B_{12} deficiency.
Spinocerebellar ataxias.
Syringomyelia.
Spinal cord AV malformations.
Adrenoleukodystrophy.

SPINAL CORD DYSFUNCTION

ICD-9CM # 336.9 SPINAL CORD COMPRESSION
336.9 SPINAL CORD DISEASE NOS
742.9 SPINAL CORD DISEASE, CONGENITAL
281.1 SPINAL CORD DEGENERATION, B_{12} DEFICIENCY ANEMIA
336.8 SPINAL CORD ATROPHY, ACUTE
336.10 SPINAL CORD ATROPHY, ADULT

Trauma.
Multiple sclerosis.
Transverse myelitis.
Neoplasm (primary, metastatic).
Syringomyelia.
Spinal epidural abscess.
HIV myelopathy.
Diskitis.
Spinal epidural hematoma.
Spinal cord infarction.
Spinal AV malformation.
Subarachnoid hemorrhage.

SPINAL TUMORS[12]

ICD-9CM # 299.7

EXTRADURAL

Metastases.
Primary bone tumors arising in spine.

INTRADURAL EXTRAMEDULLARY

Meningiomas.
Neurofibromas.
Schwannomas.
Lipomas.
Arachnoid cysts.
Epidermoid cysts.
Metastasis.

INTRAMEDULLARY

Ependymoma.
Glioma.
Hemangioblastoma.
Lipoma.
Metastases.

SPLENOMEGALY

ICD-9CM # 789.2 SPLENOMEGALY UNSPECIFIED
289.51 CHRONIC CONGESTIVE
759.0 CONGENITAL
789.2 UNKNOWN ORIGIN

Hepatic cirrhosis.
Neoplastic involvement: CML, CLL, lymphoma, multiple myeloma.
Bacterial infections: TB, infectious endocarditis, typhoid fever, splenic abscess.
Viral infections: infectious mononucleosis, viral hepatitis, HIV.
Gaucher's disease and other lipid storage diseases.
Sarcoidosis.
Parasitic infections (malaria, kala-azar, histoplasmosis).
Hereditary and acquired hemolytic anemias.
Idiopathic thrombocytopenic purpura (ITP).
Collagen vascular disorders: SLE, RA (Felty's syndrome), polyarteritis nodosa.
Serum sickness, drug hypersensitivity reaction.
Splenic cysts and benign tumors: hemangioma, lymphangioma.
Thrombosis of splenic or portal vein.
Polycythemia vera, myeloid metaplasia.

STEATOHEPATITIS

ICD-9CM # 571.8

Alcohol abuse.
Obesity.
Diabetes mellitus.
Parenteral nutrition.
Medications (high-dose estrogen, amiodarone, corticosteroids, methotrexate, nifedipine).
Jejunoileal bypass.
Abetalipoproteinemia.
Wilson's disease, Weber-Christian disease.

STOMATITIS, BULLOUS

ICD-9CM # 528.0

Erythema multiforme.
Erosive lichen planus.
Bullous pemphigoid.
SLE.
Pemphigus vulgaris.
Mucous membrane pemphigoid.

STRIDOR, PEDIATRIC AGE[4]

ICD-9CM # 786.1 STRIDOR
748.3 STRIDOR LARYNGEAL CONGENITAL

RECURRENT

Allergic (spasmodic) croup.
Respiratory infections in a child with otherwise asymptomatic anatomic narrowing of the large airways.
Laryngomalacia.

PERSISTENT

Laryngeal obstruction:
- Laryngomalacia.
- Papillomas, other tumors.
- Cysts and laryngoceles.
- Laryngeal webs.
- Bilateral abductor paralysis of the cords.
- Foreign body.

Tracheobronchial disease:
- Tracheomalacia.
- Subglottic tracheal webs.

Endotracheal, endobronchial tumors.
Subglottic tracheal stenosis.
Congenital.
Acquired.
Extrinsic masses.
Mediastinal masses.
Vascular ring.
Lobar emphysema.
Bronchogenic cysts.
Thyroid enlargement.
Esophageal foreign body.
Tracheoesophageal fistulas.
Other.
Gastroesophageal reflux.
Macroglossia, Pierre Robin syndrome.
Cri du chat syndrome.
Hysterical stridor.
Hypocalcemia.

STROKE[33]

ICD-9CM # 436 ACUTE STROKE

Hypoglycemia.
Drug overdose or intoxication.
Hysterical conversion reaction.
Hyperventilation.
Metabolic encephalopathy.
Migraine.
Syncope.
Transient global amnesia.
Seizures.
Vestibular vertigo.

STROKE, PEDIATRIC AGE[20]

ICD-9CM # 436 STROKE, ACUTE

CARDIAC DISEASE

Congenital:
- Aortic stenosis.
- Mitral stenosis; mitral prolapse.
- Ventricular septal defects.
- Patent ductus arteriosus.
- Cyanotic congenital heart disease involving right-to-left shunt.

Acquired:
- Endocarditis (bacterial, SLE).
- Kawasaki disease.
- Cardiomyopathy.
- Atrial myxoma.
- Arrhythmia.
- Paradoxical emboli through patent foramen ovale.
- Rheumatic fever.
- Prosthetic heart valve.

HEMATOLOGIC ABNORMALITIES

Hemoglobinopathies:
- Sickle cell (SS) disease.
- Sickle (SC) disease.

Polycythemia.
Leukemia/lymphoma.
Thrombocytopenia.
Thrombocytosis.
Disorders of coagulation:
- Protein C deficiency.
- Protein S deficiency.

SECTION II

Factor V Leiden.
Antithrombin III deficiency.
Lupus anticoagulant.
Oral contraceptive pill use.
Pregnancy and the postpartum state.
Disseminated intravascular coagulation.
Paroxysmal nocturnal hemoglobinuria.
Inflammatory bowel disease (thrombosis).

INFLAMMATORY DISORDERS

Meningitis:
Viral.
Bacterial.
Tuberculosis.
Systemic infection:
Viremia.
Bacteremia.
Local head and neck infections.
Drug-induced inflammation:
Amphetamine.
Cocaine.
Autoimmune disease:
Systemic lupus erythematosus.
Juvenile rheumatoid arthritis.
Takayasu arteritis.
Mixed connective tissue disease.
Polyarteritis nodosum.
Primary CNS vasculitis.
Sarcoidosis.
Behçet's syndrome.
Wegener granulomatosis.

METABOLIC DISEASE ASSOCIATED WITH STROKE

Homocystinuria.
Pseudoxanthoma elasticum.
Fabry disease.
Sulfite oxidase deficiency.
Mitochondrial disorders:
MELAS.
Leigh syndrome.
Ornithine transcarbamylase deficiency.

INTRACEREBRAL VASCULAR PROCESSES

Ruptured aneurysm.
Arteriovenous malformation.
Fibromuscular dysplasia.
Moyamoya disease.
Migraine headache.
Postsubarachnoid hemorrhage vasospasm.
Hereditary hemorrhagic telangiectasia.
Sturge-Weber syndrome.
Carotid artery dissection.
Postvaricella.

TRAUMA AND OTHER EXTERNAL CAUSES

Child abuse.
Head trauma/neck trauma.
Oral trauma.
Placental embolism.
ECMO therapy.
(*CNS,* Central nervous system; *ECMO,* extracorporeal membrane oxygenation; *MELAS,* mitochondrial encephalomyopathy, lactic acidosis, and stroke.)

STROKE, YOUNG ADULT, CAUSES[1]

ICD-9CM # 436

Cardiac factors (ASD, MVP, patent foramen ovale).
Inflammatory factors (SLE, polyarteritis nodosa).
Infections (endocarditis, neurosyphilis).
Drugs (cocaine, heroin, oral contraceptives, decongestants).
Arterial dissection.
Hematolic factors (DIC, TTP, deficiency of protein S, protein C, antithrombin III).
Migraine.
Postpartum angiopathy.
Others: premature atherosclerosis, fibromuscular dysplasia.

ST SEGMENT ELEVATIONS, NONISCHEMIC

ICD-9CM #794.31

Early repolarization.
Acute pericarditis.
LVH.
Normal pattern variant.
LBBB.
Pulmonary embolism.
Hyperkalemia.
Postcardioversion.

SUDDEN DEATH, YOUNG ATHLETE

ICD-9CM # CODE VARIES WITH SPECIFIC DIAGNOSIS

Hyperthrophic cardiomyopathy.
Coronary artery anomalies.
Myocarditis.
Ruptured aortic aneurysm (Marfan's syndrome).
Arrhythmias.
Aortic valve stenosis.
Asthma.
Trauma (cerebral, cardiac).
Drug and alcohol abuse.
Heat stroke.
Cardiac sarcoidosis.
Atherosclerotic coronary artery disease.
Dilated cardiomyopathy.

SUDDEN DEATH, PEDIATRIC AGE[4]

ICD-9CM # CODE VARIES WITH SPECIFIC DISORDER

SIDS AND SIDS "MIMICS"

SIDS.
Long Q-T syndromes.
Inborn errors of metabolism.
Child abuse.
Myocarditis.
Duct-dependent congenital heart disease.

CORRECTED OR UNOPERATED CONGENITAL HEART DISEASE

Aortic stenosis.
Tetralogy of Fallot.
Transposition of great vessels (postoperative atrial switch).
Mitral valve prolapse.
Hypoplastic left heart syndrome.
Eisenmenger's syndrome.

CORONARY ARTERIAL DISEASE

Anomalous origin.
Anomalous tract.
Kawasaki disease.
Periarteritis.
Arterial dissection.
Marfan's syndrome.
Myocardial infarction.

MYOCARDIAL DISEASE

Myocarditis.
Hypertrophic cardiomyopathy.
Dilated cardiomyopathy.
Arrhythmogenic right ventricular dysplasia.

CONDUCTION SYSTEM ABNORMALITY/ARRHYTHMIA

Long Q-T syndromes.
Proarrhythmic drugs.
Preexcitation syndromes.
Heart block.
Commotio cordis.
Idiopathic ventricular fibrillation.
Heart tumor.

MISCELLANEOUS

Pulmonary hypertension.
Pulmonary embolism.
Heat stroke.
Cocaine.
Anorexia nervosa.
Electrolyte disturbances.
SIDS, Sudden infant death syndrome.

SWOLLEN LIMB

ICD-9CM # 729.81 SWOLLEN ARM OR HAND
729.81 SWOLLEN LEG OR FOOT

Trauma.
Insect bite.
Abscess.
Lymphedema.
Thrombophlebitis.
Lipoma.
Neurofibroma.
Postphlebitic syndrome.
Myositis ossificans.
Nephrosis, cirrhosis, CHF.
Hypoalbuminemia.
Varicose veins.

TALL STATURE[24]

ICD-9CM # 253.0 GROWTH HORMONE OVERPRODUCTION, GIGANTISM

CONSTITUTIONAL (FAMILIAL OR GENETIC)—MOST COMMON CAUSE

ENDOCRINE CAUSES

Growth hormone excess—gigantism.
Sexual precocity (tall as children, short as adults):
  True sexual precocity.
  Pseudosexual precocity.
Androgen deficiency:
  Klinefelter's syndrome.
  Bilateral anorchism.

GENETIC CAUSES

Klinefelter's syndrome.
Syndromes of XYY, XXYY.

MISCELLANEOUS SYNDROMES AND DISORDERS

Cerebral gigantism or Sotos' syndrome: prominent forehead, hypertelorism, high arched palate, dolichocephaly, mental retardation, large hands and feet, and premature eruption of teeth. Large at birth, with most rapid growth in first 4 years of life.
Marfan's syndrome: disorder of mesodermal tissues, subluxation of the lenses, arachnodactyly, and aortic aneurysm.
Homocystinuria: same phenotype as Marfan's syndrome.
Obesity: tall as infants, children, and adolescents.
Total lipodystrophy: large hands and feet, generalized loss of subcutaneous fat, insulin-resistant diabetes mellitus, and hepatomegaly.
Beckwith-Wiedemann syndrome: neonatal tallness, omphalocele, macroglossia, and neonatal hypoglycemia.
Weaver-Smith syndrome: excessive intrauterine growth, mental retardation, megalocephaly, widened bifrontal diameter, hypertelorism, large ears, micrognathia, camptodactyly, broad thumbs, and limited extension of elbows and knees.
Marshall-Smith syndrome: excessive intrauterine growth, mental retardation, blue sclerae, failure to thrive, and early death.

TARDIVE DYSKINESIA[11]

ICD-9CM # 781.3 DYSKINESIA
300.11 HYSTERICAL DYSKINESIA
333.82 OROFACIAL DYSKINESIA
307.9 PSYCHOGENIC DYSKINESIA

DIFFERENTIAL DIAGNOSIS:

Medications (antidepressants, anticholinergics, amphetamines, lithium, l-dopa, phenytoin).
Brain neoplasms.
Ill-fitting dentures.
Huntington's disease.
Idiopathic dystonias (tics, blepharospasm, aging).
Wilson's disease.
Extrapyramidal syndrome (postanoxic or postencephalitic).
Torsion dystonia.

TASTE AND SMELL LOSS[1]

ICD-9CM # 781.1 SMELL AND TASTE DISTURBANCE OF SENSATION

TASTE

Local: radiation therapy.
Systemic: cancer, renal failure, hepatic failure, nutritional deficiency (vitamin B_{12}, zinc), Cushing's syndrome, hypothyroidism, DM, infection (influenza), drugs (antirheumatic and antiproliferative).
Neurologic: Bell's palsy, familial dysautonomia, multiple sclerosis.

SMELL

Local: allergic rhinitis, sinusitis, nasal polyposis, bronchial asthma.
Systemic: renal failure, hepatic failure, nutritional deficiency (vitamin B_{12}), Cushing's syndrome, hypothyroidism, DM, infection (viral hepatitis, influenza), drugs (nasal sprays, antibiotics).
Neurologic: head trauma, multiple sclerosis, Parkinson's disease, frontal brain tumor.

TELANGIECTASIA

ICD-9CM # 448.9

Oral contraceptive agents.
Pregnancy.
Rosacea.
Varicose veins.
Trauma.
Drug induced (corticosteroids, systemic or topical).
Spider telangiectases.
Hepatic cirrhosis.
Mastocytosis.
SLE, dermatomyositis, systemic sclerosis.

TENDINOPATHY[23]

ICD-9CM # 727.9

INTRINSIC FACTORS

Anatomic factors
Malalignment.
Muscle weakness or imbalance.
Muscle inflexibility.
Decreased vascularity.
Systemic factors
Inflammatory conditions (e.g., SLE).
Pregnancy.
Quinolone-induced tendinopathy.
Age-related factors
Tendon degeneration.
Increased tendon stiffness.
Tendon calcification.
Decreased vascularity.

EXTRINSIC FACTORS

Repetitive mechanical load
Excessive duration.
Excessive frequency.
Excessive intensity.
Poor technique.
Workplace factors.
Equipment problems
Footwear.
Athletic field surface.
Equipment factors (e.g., racquet size).
Protective gear.

TESTICULAR FAILURE[9]

ICD-9CM # 257.1 TESTICULAR FAILURE

PRIMARY

Klinefelter's syndrome (XXY).
XYY.
Vanishing testes syndrome (in utero or early postnatal torsion).
Noonan's syndrome.
Varicocele.
Myotonic dystrophy.
Orchitis (mumps, gonorrhea).
Cryptorchidism.
Chemical exposure.
Irradiation to testes.
Spinal cord injury.
Polyglandular failure.
Idiopathic oligospermia or azoospermia.
Germinal cell aplasia (Sertoli cell–only syndrome).
Idiopathic testicular failure.
Testicular torsion.
Testicular trauma.
Diethylstilbestrol (maternal use during pregnancy resulting in in utero estrogen exposure).
Testicular tumor with subsequent irradiation therapy, chemotherapy, or surgery (retroperitoneal lymph node dissection or orchiectomy).

SECONDARY

Delayed puberty.
Kallmann's syndrome.
Isolated gonadotropin deficiency.
Prader-Labhart-Willi syndrome.
Lawrence-Moon-Biedl syndrome.
Central nervous system irradiation.
Prepubertal panhypopituitarism.
Postpubertal panhypopituitarism.
Hypogonadism secondary to hyperprolactinemia.
Adrenogenital syndrome.
Chronic liver disease.
Chronic renal failure/uremia.
Hemochromatosis.
Cushing's syndrome.
Malnutrition.
Massive obesity.
Sickle cell anemia.
Hyper/hypothyroidism.
Anabolic steroid use.

TESTICULAR PAIN

ICD-9CM # 608.9

Testicular torsion.
Trauma.
Epididymitis.
Orchitis.
Neoplasm.
Urolithiasis.
Inguinal hernia.
Infection (cellulitis, abscess, folliculitis).
Anxiety.

TESTICULAR SIZE VARIATIONS[9]

ICD-9CM # 608.3 TESTICULAR ATROPHY
608.89 TESTICULAR MASS
257.2 HYPOGONADISM

SMALL TESTES

Hypothalamic-pituitary dysfunction.
Gonadotropin deficiency.
Growth hormone deficiency.
Normal variant.
Primary hypogonadism.
Autoimmune destruction, chemotherapy, cryptorchidism, irradiation, Klinefelter's syndrome, orchiditis, testicular regression syndrome, torsion, trauma.

LARGE TESTES

Adrenal rest tissue.
Compensatory.
Fragile X syndrome.
Idiopathic.
Tumor.

TETANUS[23]

ICD-9CM # 037

Acute abdomen.
Black widow spider bite.
Dental abscess.
Dislocated mandible.
Dystonic reaction.
Encephalitis.
Head trauma.
Hyperventilation syndrome.
Hypocalcemia.
Meningitis.
Peritonsillar abscess.
Progressive fluctuating muscular rigidity (stiff-man syndrome).
Psychogenic.
Rabies.
Sepsis.
Subarachnoid hemorrhage.
Status epilepticus.

Strychnine poisoning.
Temporomandibular joint syndrome.

THROMBOCYTOPENIA

ICD-9CM # 287.3 CONGENITAL OR PRIMARY
287.4 SECONDARY
287.5 THROMBOCYTOPENIA NOS

INCREASED DESTRUCTION

Immunologic

Drugs: quinine, quinidine, digitalis, procainamide, thiazide diuretics, sulfonamides, phenytoin, aspirin, penicillin, heparin, gold, meprobamate, sulfa drugs, phenylbutazone, nonsteroidal antiinflammatory drugs (NSAIDs), methyldopa, cimetidine, furosemide, INH, cephalosporins, chlorpropamide, organic arsenicals, chloroquine, platelet glycoprotein IIb/IIIa receptor inhibitors, ranitidine, indomethacin, carboplatin, ticlopidine, clopidogrel.
Idiopathic thrombocytopenic purpura (ITP).
Transfusion reaction: transfusion of platelets with plasminogen activator (PLA) in recipients without PLA-1.
Fetal/maternal incompatibility.
Collagen vascular diseases (e.g., systemic lupus erythematosus [SLE]).
Autoimmune hemolytic anemia.
Lymphoreticular disorders (e.g., CLL).

Nonimmunologic

Prosthetic heart valves.
Thrombotic thrombocytopenic purpura (TTP).
Sepsis.
DIC.
Hemolytic-uremic syndrome (HUS).
Giant cavernous hemangioma.

DECREASED PRODUCTION

Abnormal marrow.
Marrow infiltration (e.g., leukemia, lymphoma, fibrosis).
Marrow suppression (e.g., chemotherapy, alcohol, radiation).
Hereditary disorders.
Wiskott-Aldrich syndrome: X-linked disorder characterized by thrombocytopenia, eczema, and repeated infections.
May-Hegglin anomaly: increased megakaryocytes but ineffective thrombopoiesis.
Vitamin deficiencies (e.g., vitamin B_{12}, folic acid).

SPLENIC SEQUESTRATION, HYPERSPLENISM

DILUTIONAL, AS A RESULT OF MASSIVE TRANSFUSION

THROMBOCYTOSIS

ICD-9CM # 289.9 THROMBOCYTOSIS, ESSENTIAL

Iron deficiency.
Posthemorrhage.
Neoplasms (GI tract).
CML.
Polycythemia vera.
Myelofibrosis with myeloid metaplasia.
Infections.
After splenectomy.
Postpartum.
Hemophilia.
Pancreatitis.
Cirrhosis.
Idiopathic.

TICK-RELATED INFECTIONS

ICD-9CM # 082.0 ROCKY MOUNTAIN SPOTTED FEVER
066.1 COLORADO TICK FEVER
088.82 BABESIOSIS
082.8 EHRLICHIOSIS
088.81 LYME DISEASE

Lyme disease.
Rocky Mountain spotted fever.
Babesiosis.
Tularemia.
Q Fever.
Colorado tick fever.
Ehrlichiosis.
Relapsing fever.

TORSADES DE POINTES[19]

ICD-9CM # CODE NOT AVAILABLE

Antiarrhythmics known to increase the QT interval (e.g., quinidine, procainamide, amiodarone, disopyramide, sotalol).
Tricyclic antidepressants and phenothiazines.
Histamine (H1) antagonists (e.g., astemizole, terfenadine).
Antiviral and antifungal agents and antibiotics.
Hypokinemia.
Hypomagnesemia.
Insecticide poisoning.
Bradyarrhythmias.
Congenital long QT syndrome.
Subarachnoid hemorrhage.
Chloroquinine, pentamidine.
Cocaine abuse.

TREMOR

ICD-9CM # 781.0 TREMOR NOS
333.1 BENIGN ESSENTIAL TREMOR
333.1 FAMILIAL TREMOR

TREMOR PRESENT AT REST

Parkinsonism.
CNS neoplasms.
Tardive dyskinesia.

POSTURAL TREMOR (PRESENT DURING MAINTENANCE OF A POSTURE)

Essential senile tremor.

ACTION TREMOR (PRESENT WITH MOVEMENT)

Anxiety.
Medications (bronchodilators, caffeine, corticosteroids, lithium, etc.).
Endocrine disorders (hyperthyroidism, pheochromocytoma, carcinoid).
Withdrawal from substance abuse.

TUBULOINTERSTITIAL DISEASE, ACUTE[12]

ICD-9CM # 584.5

DRUGS

Antibiotics, penicillins, cephalosporins, rifampin.
Sulfonamides: cotrimoxazole, sulfamethoxazole.
NSAIDs: propionic acid derivatives.
Miscellaneous: phenytoin, thiazides, allopurinol, cimetidine, ifosfamide.

INFECTIONS

Invasion of renal parenchyma.
Reaction to systemic infections: streptococcal, diphtheria, hantavirus.

SYSTEMIC DISEASES

Immune mediated: lupus, transplanted kidney, cryoglobulinemias.
Metabolic: urate, oxalate.
Neoplastic: lymphoproliferative diseases.

IDIOPATHIC

TUBULOINTERSTITIAL KIDNEY DISEASE[12]

ICD-9CM # 584.5

Ischemic and toxic acute tubular necrosis.
Allergic interstitial nephritis.
Interstitial nephritis secondary to immune complex-related collagen vascular disease (e.g., SLE, Sjögren's).
Granulomatous diseases (sarcoidosis, uveitis).
Pigment related tubular injury (myoglobinuria, hemoglobinuria).
Hypercalcemia with nephrocalcinosis.
Tubular obstruction (drugs such as indinavir, uric acid in tumor lysis syndrome).
Myeloma kidney or cast nephropathy.
Infection-related interstitial nephritis: *legionella, leptospira.*
Infiltrative diseases (e.g., lymphoma).

URETHRAL DISCHARGE AND DYSURIA

ICD-9CM # 788.7 URETHRAL DISCHARGE
599.9 URETHRAL DISCHARGE BLOODY
788.1 DYSURIA

Urethritis (gonococcal, chlamydial, trichomonal).
Cystitis.
Prostatitis.
Vaginitis (candidiasis, chemical).
Meatal stenosis.
Interstitial cystitis.
Trauma (foreign body, masturbation, horseback or bike riding).

URINARY RETENTION, ACUTE

ICD-9CM # 788.20

Mechanical obstruction: urethral stone, foreign body, urethral stricture, BPH, prostate carcinoma, prostatitis, trauma with hematoma formation).
Neurogenic bladder.
Neurologic disease (MS, parkinsonism, tabes dorsalis, CVA).
Spinal cord injury.
CNS neoplasm (primary or metastatic).
Spinal anesthesia.
Lower urinary tract instrumentation.
Medications (antihistamines, antidepressants, narcotics, anticholinergics).
Abdominal or pelvic surgery.
Alcohol toxicity.
Pregnancy.
Anxiety.
Encephalitis.
Postoperative pain.
Encephalitis.
Spina bifida occulta.

URINE, RED[26]

ICD-9CM # CODE VARIES WITH SPECIFIC DIAGNOSIS

WITH A POSITIVE DIPSTICK

Hematuria.
Hemoglobinuria: negative urinalysis.
Myoglobinuria: negative urinalysis.

WITH A NEGATIVE DIPSTICK

Drugs
Aminosalicylic acid.
Deferoxamine mesylate.
Ibuprofen.
Phenacetin.
Phenolphthalein.
Phensuximide.
Rifampin.
Anthraquinone laxatives.
Doxorubicin.
Methyldopa.
Phenazopyridine.
Phenothiazine.
Phenytoin.
Dyes
Azo dyes.
Eosin.
Foods
Beets, berries, maize.
Rhodamine B.
Metabolic
Porphyrins.
Serratia marcescens (red diaper syndrome).
Urate crystalluria.

UROPATHY, OBSTRUCTIVE[33]

ICD-9CM # 599.6

INTRINSIC CAUSES

Intraluminal
Intratubular deposition of crystals (uric acid, sulfas).
Stones.
Papillary tissue.
Blood clots.
Intramural
Functional.
Ureter (ureteropelvic or ureterovesical dysfunction).
Bladder (neurogenic): spinal cord defect or trauma, diabetes, multiple sclerosis, Parkinson's disease, cerebrovascular accidents.
Bladder neck dysfunction.
Anatomic
Tumors.
Infection, granuloma.
Strictures.

EXTRINSIC CAUSES

Originating in the reproductive system
Prostate: benign hypertrophy or cancer.
Uterus: pregnancy, tumors, prolapse, endometriosis.
Ovary: abscess, tumor, cysts.
Originating in the vascular system
Aneurysms (aorta, iliac vessels).
Aberrant arteries (ureteropelvic junction).
Venous (ovarian veins, retrocaval ureter).
Originating in the gastrointestinal tract: Crohn's disease, pancreatitis, appendicitis, tumors
Originating in the retroperitoneal space
Inflammations.

Fibrosis.
Tumor, hematomas.

UTERINE BLEEDING, ABNORMAL[10]

ICD-9CM # 626.9

PREGNANCY

Threatened abortion.
Incomplete abortion.
Complete abortion.
Molar pregnancy.
Ectopic pregnancy.
Retained products of conception.

OVULATORY

Vulva: infection, laceration, tumor.
Vagina: infection, laceration, tumor, foreign body.
Cervix: polyps, cervical erosion, cervicitis, carcinoma.
Uterus: fibroids (submucous fibroids most likely to cause abnormal bleeding), polyps, adenomyosis, endometritis, intrauterine device, atrophic endometrium.
Pregnancy complications: ectopic pregnancy; threatened, incomplete, complete abortion; retained products of conception.
Abnormality of clotting system.
Midcycle bleeding.
Halban's disease (persistent corpus luteum).
Menorrhagia.
Pelvic inflammatory disease.

ANOVULATORY

Physiologic causes:
- Puberty.
- Perimenopausal.

Pathologic causes:
- Ovarian failure (FSH over 40 IU/ml).
- Hyperandrogenism.
- Hyperprolactinemia.
- Obesity.
- Hypothalamic dysfunction (polycystic ovaries); LH/FSH ratio greater than 2 to 1.
- Hyperplasia.
- Endometrial carcinoma.
- Estrogen-producing tumors.
- Hypothyroidism.

VAGINAL BLEEDING, PREGNANCY[7]

ICD-9CM # 626.6 IRREGULAR VAGINAL BLEEDING

FIRST TRIMESTER

Implantation bleeding.
Abortion.
Threatened.
Complete.
Incomplete.
Missed.
Ectopic pregnancy.
Neoplasia.
Hydatidiform mole.
Cervix.

THIRD TRIMESTER

Placenta previa.
Placental abruption.
Premature labor.
Choriocarcinoma.

VAGINAL DISCHARGE, PREPUBERTAL GIRLS[17]

ICD-9CM # 623.5 VAGINAL DISCHARGE

Irritative (bubble baths, sand).
Poor perineal hygiene.
Foreign body.
Associated systemic illness (group A streptococci, chickenpox).
Infections.
Escherichia coli with foreign body.
Shigella organisms.
Yersinia organisms.
Infections (consider sexual abuse).
Chlamydia trachomatis.
Neisseria gonorrhoeae.
Trichomonas vaginalis.
Tumor (rare).

VASCULITIS, CLASSIFICATION[23]

ICD-9CM # 447.6

LARGE VESSEL DISEASE

Arteritis
Giant cell arteritis.
Takayasu's arteritis.
Arteritis associated with Reiter's syndrome, ankylosing spondylitis.

MEDIUM AND SMALL VESSEL DISEASE

Polyarteritis nodosa
Primary (idiopathic).
Associated with viruses (Hepatitis B or C, CMV, HIV, herpes zoster).
Associated with malignancy (hairy cell leukemia).
Familial Mediterranean fever.
Granulomatous vasculitis
Wegener's granulomatosis.
Lymphomatoid granulomatosis.
Behçet's disease
Kawasaki disease (mucocutaneous lymph node syndrome)

PREDOMINANTLY SMALL VESSEL DISEASE

Hypersensitivity vasculitis (leukocytoclastic vasculitis)
Henoch-Schönlein purpura.
Mixed cryoglobulinemia.
Serum sickness.
Vasculitis associated with connective tissue diseases (SLE, Sjögren's syndrome).
Vasculitis associated with specific syndromes:
- Primary biliary cirrhosis.
- Lyme disease.
- Chronic active hepatitis.
- Drug-induced vasculitis.

Churg-Strauss syndrome
Goodpasture syndrome
Erythema nodosum
Panniculitis
Buerger's disease (thrombophlebitis obliterans)

VASCULITIS[25]

DISEASES THAT MIMIC VASCULITIS

ICD-9CM # VARIES WITH SPECIFIC DISEASE

EMBOLIC DISEASE

Infectious or marantic endocarditis.
Cardiac mural thrombus.
Atrial myxoma.
Cholesterol embolization syndrome.

NONINFLAMMATORY VESSEL WALL DISRUPTION

Atherosclerosis.
Arterial fibromuscular dysplasia.
Drug effects (vasoconstrictors, anticoagulants).
Radiation.
Genetic disease (neurofibromatosis, Ehlers-Danlos syndrome).
Amyloidosis.
Intravascular malignant lymphoma.

DIFFUSE COAGULATION

Disseminated intravascular coagulation.
Thrombotic thrombocytopenic purpura.
Hemolytic-uremic syndrome.
Protein C and S deficiencies, factor V/Leiden mutation.
Antiphospholipid syndrome.

VENTRICULAR FAILURE

ICD-9CM # 429.9 VENTRICULAR DYSFUNCTION

LEFT VENTRICULAR FAILURE

Systemic hypertension.
Valvular heart disease (AS, AR, MR).
Cardiomyopathy, myocarditis.
Bacterial endocarditis.
Myocardial infarction.
Idiopathic hypertrophic subaortic stenosis.

RIGHT VENTRICULAR FAILURE

Valvular heart disease (mitral stenosis).
Pulmonary hypertension.
Bacterial endocarditis (right-sided).
Right ventricular infarction.

BIVENTRICULAR FAILURE

Left ventricular failure.
Cardiomyopathy.
Myocarditis
Arrhythmias.
Anemia.
Thyrotoxicosis.
Arteriovenous fistula.
Paget's disease.
Beri-beri.

VERTIGO

ICD-9CM # 780.4 VERTIGO NOS
386.11 BENIGN PAROXYSMAL POSITIONAL
386.2 CENTRAL ORIGIN
386.10 PERIPHERAL
386.12 VESTIBULAR (NEURONITIS)

PERIPHERAL

Otitis media.
Acute labyrinthitis.
Vestibular neuronitis.
Benign positional vertigo.
Meniere's disease.
Ototoxic drugs: streptomycin, gentamicin.
Lesions of the eighth nerve: acoustic neuroma, meningioma, mononeuropathy, metastatic carcinoma.
Mastoiditis.

CNS OR SYSTEMIC

Vertebrobasilar artery insufficiency.
Posterior fossa tumor or other brain tumors.
Infarction/hemorrhage of cerebral cortex, cerebellum, or brainstem.
Basilar migraine.
Metabolic: drugs, hypoxia, anemia, fever.
Hypotension/severe hypertension.
Multiple sclerosis.
CNS infections: viral, bacterial.
Temporal lobe epilepsy.
Arnold-Chiari malformation, syringobulbia.
Psychogenic: ventilation, hysteria.

VESICULOBULLOUS DISEASES[12]

ICD-9CM # 709.8

IMMUNOLOGICALLY MEDIATED DISEASES

Bullous pemphigoid.
Herpes gestationis.
Mucous membrane pemphigoid.
Epidermolysis bullosa acquisita.
Dermatitis herpetiformis.
Pemphigus (vulgaris, foliaceus, paraneoplastic).

HYPERSENSITIVITY DISEASES

Erythema multiforme minor.
Erythema multiforme major (Stevens-Johnson syndrome).
Toxic epidermal necrolysis.

METABOLIC DISEASES

Porphyria cutanea tarda.
Pseudoporphyria.
Diabetic blisters.

INHERITED GENETIC DISORDERS

Epidermolysis bullosa.
- Simplex.
- Junctional.
- Dystrophic.

INFECTIOUS DISEASES

Impetigo.
Staphylococcal scalded skin syndrome.
Herpes simplex.
Varicella.
Herpes zoster.

VISION LOSS, ACUTE, PAINFUL

ICD-9CM # 368.11 VISION LOSS, SUDDEN

Acute angle-closure glaucoma.
Corneal ulcer.
Uveitis.
Endophthalmitis.
Factitious.
Somatization syndrome.
Trauma.

VISION LOSS, ACUTE, PAINLESS

ICD-9CM # 368.11 VISION LOSS, SUDDEN

Retinal artery occlusion.
Optic neuritis.
Retinal vein occlusion.
Vitreous hemorrhage.
Retinal detachment.
Exudative macular degeneration.
CVA.
Ischemic optic neuropathy.
Factitious.
Somatization syndrome, anxiety reaction.

VISION LOSS, CHRONIC, PROGRESSIVE

ICD-9CM # 369.9 VISION LOSS NOS

Cataract.
Macular degeneration.
Cerebral neoplasm.
Refractive error.
Open-angle glaucoma.

VISION LOSS, MONOCULAR, TRANSIENT

ICD-9CM # 369.9

Thromboembolism.
Vasculitis.
Migraine (vasospasm).
Anxiety reaction.
CNS tumor.
Temporal arteritis.
Multiple sclerosis.

VOCAL CORD PARALYSIS

ICD-9CM # 478.30 UNSPECIFIED
478.31 UNILATERAL PARTIAL
478.32 UNILATERAL COMPLETE
478.33 BILATERAL PARTIAL
478.34 BILATERAL COMPLETE

Neoplasm: primary or metastatic (e.g., lung, thyroid, parathyroid, mediastinum).
Neck surgery (parathyroid, thyroid, carotid endarterectomy, cervical spine).
Idiopathic.
Viral, bacterial, or fungal infection.
Trauma (intubation, penetrating neck injury).
Cardiac surgery.
Rheumatoid arthritis.
Multiple sclerosis.
Parkinsonism.
Toxic neuropathy.
CVA.
CNS abnormalities: hydrocephalus, Arnold-Chiari malformation, meningomyelocele.

VOLUME DEPLETION[1]

ICD-9CM # 276.5

Gastrointestinal losses:
Upper: bleeding, nasogastric suction, vomiting.
Lower: bleeding, diarrhea, enteric or pancreatic fistula, tube drainage.
Renal losses:
Salt and water: diuretics, osmotic diuresis, postobstructive diuresis, acute tubular necrosis (recovery phase), salt-
losing nephropathy, adrenal insufficiency, renal tubular acidosis.
Water loss: diabetes insipidus.
Skin and respiratory losses:
Sweat, burns, insensible losses.
Sequestration without external fluid loss:
Intestinal obstruction, peritonitis, pancreatitis, rhabdomyolysis, internal bleeding.

VOLUME EXCESS[1]

ICD-9CM # CODE VARIES WITH SPECIFIC DIAGNOSIS

PRIMARY RENAL SODIUM RETENTION (INCREASED EFFECTIVE CIRCULATING VOLUME)

Renal failure, nephritic syndrome, acute glomerulonephritis.
Primary hyperaldosteronism.
Cushing syndrome.
Liver disease.

SECONDARY RENAL SODIUM RETENTION (DECREASED EFFECTIVE CIRCULATING VOLUME)

Heart failure.
Liver disease.
Nephrotic syndrome (minimal change disease).
Pregnancy.

VOMITING

ICD-9CM # 787.03

GI disturbances:
Obstruction: esophageal, pyloric, intestinal.
Infections: viral or bacterial enteritis, viral hepatitis, food poisoning, gastroenteritis.
Pancreatitis.
Appendicitis.
Biliary colic.
Peritonitis.
Perforated bowel.
Diabetic gastroparesis.
Other: gastritis, PUD, IBD, GI tract neoplasms.
Drugs: morphine, digitalis, cytotoxic agents, bromocriptine.
Severe pain: MI, renal colic.
Metabolic disorders: uremia, acidosis/alkalosis, hyperglycemia, DKA, thyrotoxicosis.
Trauma: blows to the testicles, epigastrium.
Vertigo.
Reye's syndrome.
Increased intracranial pressure.
CNS disturbances: trauma, hemorrhage, infarction, neoplasm, infection, hypertensive encephalopathy, migraine.
Radiation sickness.
Nausea and vomiting of pregnancy, hyperemesis gravidarum.
Motion sickness.
Bulimia, anorexia nervosa.
Psychogenic: emotional disturbances, offensive sights or smells.
Severe coughing.
Pyelonephritis.
Boerhaave's syndrome.
Carbon monoxide poisoning.

VULVAR LESIONS[10]

ICD-9CM # 625.8 VULVAR MASS
098.0 VULVAR ULCER, GONOCOCCAL
091.0 VULVAR ULCER, SYPHILITIC
616.51 BEHÇET'S
624.0 LEUKOPLAKIA
624.8 DYSPLASIA
233.3 CARCINOMA
616.9 INFLAMMATORY LESION
624.4 VULVAR SCAR (OLD)
624.1 VULVAR ATROPHY

RED LESION

Infection/infestation

Fungal infection:
- Candida.
- Tinea cruris.
- Intertrigo.
- Pityriasis versicolor.

Sarcoptes scabiei.
Erythrasma: *Corynebacterium minutissimum.*
Granuloma inguinale: *Calymmatobacterium granulomatis.*
Folliculitis: *Staphylococcus aureus.*
Hidradenitis suppurativa.
Behçet's syndrome.

Inflammation

Reactive vulvitis.
Chemical irritation:
- Detergent.
- Dyes.
- Perfume.
- Spermicide.
- Lubricants.
- Hygiene sprays.
- Podophyllum.
- Topical 5-FU.
- Saliva.
- Gentian violet.
- Semen.

Mechanical trauma: scratching.
Vestibular adenitis.
Essential vulvodynia.
Psoriasis.
Seborrheic dermatitis.

Neoplasm

Vulvar intraepithelial neoplasia (VIN):
- Mild dysplasia.
- Moderate dysplasia.
- Severe dysplasia.
- Carcinoma-in-situ.

Vulvar dystrophy.
Bowen's disease.
Invasive cancer:
- Squamous cell carcinoma.
- Malignant melanoma.
- Sarcoma.
- Basal cell carcinoma.
- Adenocarcinoma.
- Paget's disease.
- Undifferentiated.

WHITE LESION

Vulvar dystrophy:
- Lichen sclerosus.
- Vulvar dystrophy.
- Vulvar hyperplasia.
- Mixed dystrophy.

VIN.
Vitiligo.
Partial albinism.
Intertrigo.
Radiation treatment.

DARK LESION

Lentigo.
Nevi (mole).
Neoplasm (see Neoplasm, Vulvar, below).
Reactive hyperpigmentation.
Seborrheic keratosis.
Pubic lice.

ULCERATIVE LESION

Infection

Herpes simplex.
Vaccinia.
Treponema pallidum.
Granuloma inguinale.
Pyoderma.
Tuberculosis.

Noninfection

Behçet's disease.
Crohn's disease.
Pemphigus.
Pemphigoid.
Hidradenitis suppurativa (see Neoplasm, Vulvar, below).

Neoplasm

Basal cell carcinoma.
Squamous cell carcinoma.
Vulvar tumor <1 cm:
- Condyloma acuminatum.
- Molluscum contagiosum.
- Epidermal inclusion.
- Vestibular cyst.
- Mesenephric duct.
- VIN.
- Hemangioma.
- Hidradenoma.
- Neurofibroma.
- Syringoma.
- Accessory breast tissue.
- Acrochordon.
- Endometriosis.
- Fox-Fordyce disease.
- Pilonidal sinus.

Vulvar tumor >1 cm:
- Bartholin cyst or abscess.
- Lymphogranuloma venereum.
- Fibroma.
- Lipoma.
- Verrucous carcinoma.
- Squamous cell carcinoma.
- Hernia.
- Edema.
- Hematoma.
- Acrochordon.
- Epidermal cysts.
- Neurofibromatosis.
- Accessory breast tissue.

WEAKNESS, ACUTE, EMERGENT[23]

ICD-9CM # 780.7

Demyelinating disorders (Guillain-Barré, chronic inflammatory demyelinating polyneuropathy [CIDP]).
Myasthenia gravis.
Infectious (poliomyelitis, diphtheria).

Toxic (botulism, tick paralysis, paralytic shellfish toxin, puffer fish, newts).
Metabolic (acquired or familial hypokalemia, hypophosphatemia, hypermagnesemia).
Metals poisoning (arsenic, thallium).
Porphyria.

WEAKNESS, GRADUAL ONSET

ICD-9CM # 780.7

Depression.
Malingering.
Anemia.
Hypothyroidism.
Medications (e.g., sedatives, antidepressants, narcotics).
CHF.
Renal failure.
Liver failure.
Respiratory insufficiency.
Alcoholism.
Nutritional deficiencies.
Disorders of motor unit.
Basal ganglia disorders.
Upper motor neuron lesions.

WEIGHT GAIN

ICD-9CM # 783.1 ABNORMAL WEIGHT GAIN
278.00 OBESITY

Sedentary lifestyle.
Fluid overload.
Discontinuation of tobacco abuse.
Endocrine disorders (hypothyroidism, hyperinsulinism associated with maturity-onset DM, Cushing's syndrome, hypogonadism, insulinoma, hyperprolactinemia, acromegaly).
Medications (nutritional supplements, oral contraceptives, glucocorticoids, etc.).
Anxiety disorders with compulsive eating.
Laurence-Moon-Biedl syndrome, Prader-Willi syndrome, other congenital diseases.
Hypothalamic injury (rare; <100 cases reported in medical literature).

WEIGHT LOSS

ICD-9CM # 783.2 ABNORMAL WEIGHT LOSS

Malignancy.
Psychiatric disorders (depression, anorexia nervosa).
New-onset DM.
Malabsorption.
COPD.
AIDS.
Uremia, liver disease.
Thyrotoxicosis, pheochromocytoma, carcinoid syndrome.
Addison's disease.
Intestinal parasites.
Peptic ulcer disease.
Inflammatory bowel disease.
Food faddism.
Postgastrectomy syndrome.

WHEEZING

ICD-9CM # 786.09

Asthma.
COPD.
Interstitial lung disease.
Infections (pneumonia, bronchitis, bronchiolitis, epiglottitis).
Cardiac asthma.
GERD with aspiration.
Foreign body aspiration.
Pulmonary embolism.
Anaphylaxis.
Obstruction airway (neoplasm, goiter, edema or hemorrhage from trauma, aneurysm, congenital abnormalities, strictures, spasm).
Carcinoid syndrome.

WHEEZING, PEDIATRIC AGE[4]

ICD-9CM # 786.09 WHEEZING

Reactive airways disease.
Atopic asthma.
Infection-associated airway reactivity.
Exercise-induced asthma.
Salicylate-induced asthma and nasal polyposis.
Asthmatic bronchitis.
Other hypersensitivity reactions:
  Hypersensitivity pneumonitis.
  Tropical eosinophilia.
  Visceral larva migrans.
  Allergic bronchopulmonary aspergillosis.
Aspiration:
  Foreign body.
  Food, saliva, gastric contents.
  Laryngotracheoesophageal cleft.
  Tracheoesophageal fistula, H-type.
  Pharyngeal incoordination or neuromuscular weakness.
Cystic fibrosis.
Primary ciliary dyskinesia.
Cardiac failure.
Bronchiolitis obliterans.
Extrinsic compression of airways:
  Vascular ring.
  Enlarged lymph node.
  Mediastinal tumor.
  Lung cysts.
Tracheobronchomalacia.
Endobronchial masses.
Gastroesophageal reflux.
Pulmonary hemosiderosis.
Sequelae of bronchopulmonary dysplasia.
"Hysterical" glottic closure.
Cigarette smoke, other environmental insults.

XEROPHTHALMIA[25]

ICD-9CM # 372.53 XEROPHTHALMIA

Medications
Tricyclic antidepressants: amitriptyline (Elavil), doxepin (Sinequan).
Antihistamines: diphenhydramine (Benadryl), chlorpheniramine (Chlor-Trimeton), promethazine (Phenergan), and many cold and decongestant preparations.
Anticholinergic agents: antiemetics such as scopolamine, antispasmodic agents such as oxybutynin chloride (Ditropan).
Abnormalities of eyelid function
Neuromuscular disorders.
Aging.
Thyrotoxicosis.
Abnormalities of tear production
Hypovitaminosis A.
Stevens-Johnson syndrome.
Familial diseases affecting sebaceous secretions.

Abnormalities of corneal surfaces
Scarring from past injuries and herpes simplex infection.

XEROSTOMIA[25]

ICD-9CM # 527.7

Medications
Tricyclic antidepressants: amitriptyline (Elavil), doxepin (Sinequan).
Antihistamines: diphenhydramine (Benadryl), chlorpheniramine (Chlor-Trimeton), promethazine (Phenergan), and many cold and decongestant preparations.
Anticholinergic agents: antiemetics such as scopolamine, antispasmodic agents such as oxybutynin chloride (Ditropan).
Dehydration
Debility.
Fever.
Polyuria
Alcohol intake.
Arrhythmia.
Diabetes.
Previous head and neck irradiation
Systemic diseases
Sjögren's syndrome.
Sarcoidosis.
Amyloidosis.
Human immunodeficiency virus (HIV) infection.
Graft-vs.-host disease.

REFERENCES

1. Andreoli TE, editor: *Cecil essentials of medicine,* ed 5, Philadelphia, 2001, WB Saunders.
2. Barkin RM, Rosen P: *Emergency pediatrics: a guide to ambulatory care,* ed 5, St Louis, 1998, Mosby.
3. Baude AI: *Infectious diseases and medical microbiology,* ed 2, Philadelphia, 1986, WB Saunders.
4. Behrman RE: *Nelson textbook of pediatrics,* ed 16, Philadelphia, 2000, WB Saunders.
5. Callen JP: *Color atlas of dermatology,* ed 2, Philadelphia, 2000, WB Saunders.
6. Canoso J: *Rheumatology in primary care,* Philadelphia, 1997, WB Saunders.
7. Carlson KJ: *Primary care of women,* ed 2, St Louis, 2000, Mosby.
8. Conn R: *Current diagnosis,* ed 9, Philadelphia, 1997, WB Saunders.
9. Copeland LJ: *Textbook of gynecology,* ed 2, Philadelphia, 2000, WB Saunders.
10. Danakas G, editor: *Practical guide to the care of the gynecologic/obstetric patient,* St Louis, 1997, Mosby.
11. Goldberg RJ: *The care of the psychiatric patient,* ed 22, St Louis, 1998, Mosby.
12. Goldman L, Ausiello D: *Cecil textbook of medicine,* ed 21, Philadelphia, 2004, WB Saunders.
13. Goldman L, Braunwauld E, editors: *Primary cardiology,* Philadelphia, 1998, WB Saunders.
14. Gorbach SL: *Infectious diseases,* ed 2, Philadelphia, 1998, WB Saunders.
15. Harrington J: *Consultation in internal medicine,* ed 2, St Louis, 1997, Mosby.
16. Henry JB: *Clinical diagnosis and management by laboratory methods,* ed 20, Philadelphia, 2001, WB Saunders.
17. Hoekelman R: *Primary pediatric care,* ed 3, St Louis, 1997, Mosby.
18. Kassirer J, editor: *Current therapy in adult medicine,* ed 4, St Louis, 1998, Mosby.
19. Khan MG: *Rapid ECG interpretation,* Philadelphia, 2003, WB Saunders.
20. Kliegman R: *Practical strategies in pediatric diagnosis and therapy,* Philadelphia, 1996, WB Saunders.
21. Klippel J, editor: *Practical rheumatology,* London, 1995, Mosby.
22. Mandell GL: *Mandell, Douglas, and Bennett's principles and practice of infectious diseases,* ed 5, New York, 2000, Churchill Livingstone.
23. Marx J, editor: *Rosen's emergency medicine: concepts and clinical practice,* ed. 5, St Louis, 2002, Mosby.
24. Moore WT, Eastman RC: *Diagnostic endocrinology,* ed 2, St Louis, 1996, Mosby.
25. Noble J, editor: *Primary care medicine,* ed 3, St Louis, 2001, Mosby.
26. Nseyo UO: *Urology for primary care physicians,* Philadelphia, 1999, WB Saunders.
27. Palay D, editor: *Ophthalmology for the primary care physician,* St Louis, 1997, Mosby.
28. Rakel RE: *Principles of family practice,* ed 6, Philadelphia, 2002, WB Saunders.
29. Schwarz MI: *Interstitial lung disease,* ed 2, St Louis, 1993, Mosby.
30. Seller RH: *Differential diagnosis of common complaints,* ed 4, Philadelphia, 2000,WB Saunders.
31. Siedel HM, editor: *Mosby's guide to physical examination,* ed 4, St Louis, 1999, Mosby.
32. Specht N: *Practical guide to diagnostic imaging,* St Louis, 1998, Mosby.
33. Stein JH, editor: *Internal medicine,* ed 5, St Louis, 1998, Mosby.
34. Swain R, Snodgrass: *Phys Sportmed* 23:56, 1995.
35. Wiederholt WC: *Neurology for non-neurologists,* ed 4, Philadelphia, 2000, WB Saunders.
36. Wilson JD: *Williams textbook of endocrinology,* ed 9, Philadelphia, 1998, WB Saunders.

SECTION III

Clinical Algorithms

PLEASE NOTE: These algorithms are designed to assist clinicians in the evaluation and treatment of patients. They may not apply to all patients with a particular condition and are not intended to replace a clinician's individual judgment.

ABUSE, CHILD

ICD-9CM # 995.5 Child maltreatment syndrome

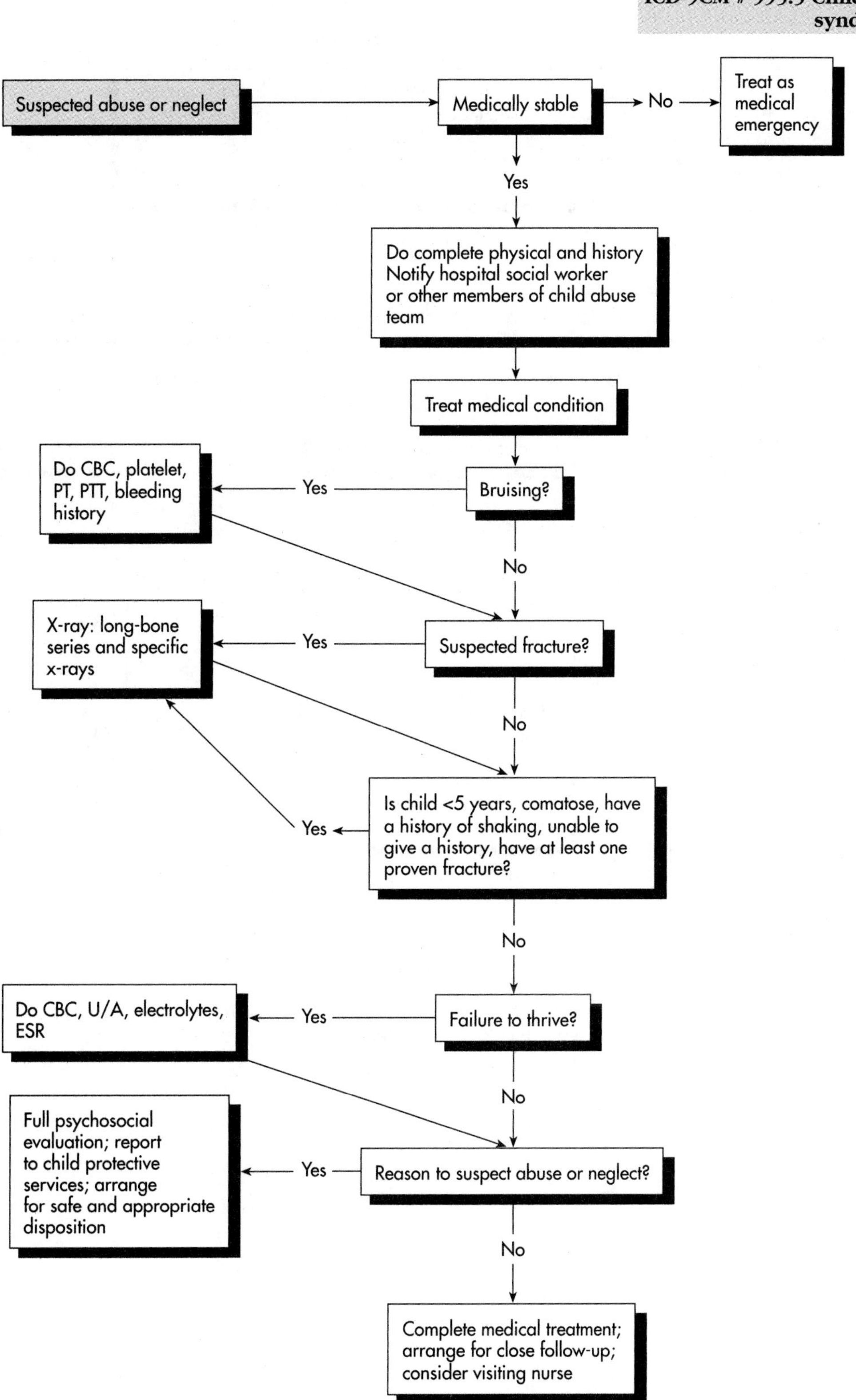

FIGURE 3-1 Management of suspected child abuse. *CBC,* Complete blood count; *ESR,* erythrocyte sedimentation rate; *PT,* prothrombin time; *PTT,* partial thromboplastin time; *U/A,* urinalysis. (From Marx J [ed]: *Rosen's emergency medicine,* ed 5, St Louis, 2002, Mosby.)

ABUSE, GERIATRIC

ICD-9CM # 995.81

Management of Geriatric abuse

- Assessment of general quality of care and relationships in household or institution
- Assessment of patient on their own, including assessment of mental capacity
- Assessment of suspected abuser or *their* problems
- Liaison with other professionals wherever possible, subject to confidentiality
- Full documentation

Victim is capable of making necessary decisions

Victim is **not** capable of making necessary decisions

Victim is **not** willing to accept help

- Educate/provide information about abuse, rights, and local services
- Provide written information about getting help in an emergency
- Assure victim of support and help if requested
- Develop a safety plan
- Develop a follow-up plan preferably to involve monitoring of the situation
- Legal intervention may be necessary where a criminal offence has been committed, or the victim's life or health are in danger

Victim is willing to accept help

In conjunction with other professionals

- Establish victim's needs
- Implement safety plan
- Educate/provide information about abuse, rights, and local services
- Provide services to victim, abuser, or both, that focus on preventing further abuse
- Assist with legal interventions
- Make sure that situation is monitored by someone

Victim is **not** willing to accept help

- Ensure protection for the victim either in terms of physical safety and/or proper financial arrangements
- Provide relevant help to the abuser
- Liaise with police if serious crime has been committed
- Make sure that situation is monitored by someone

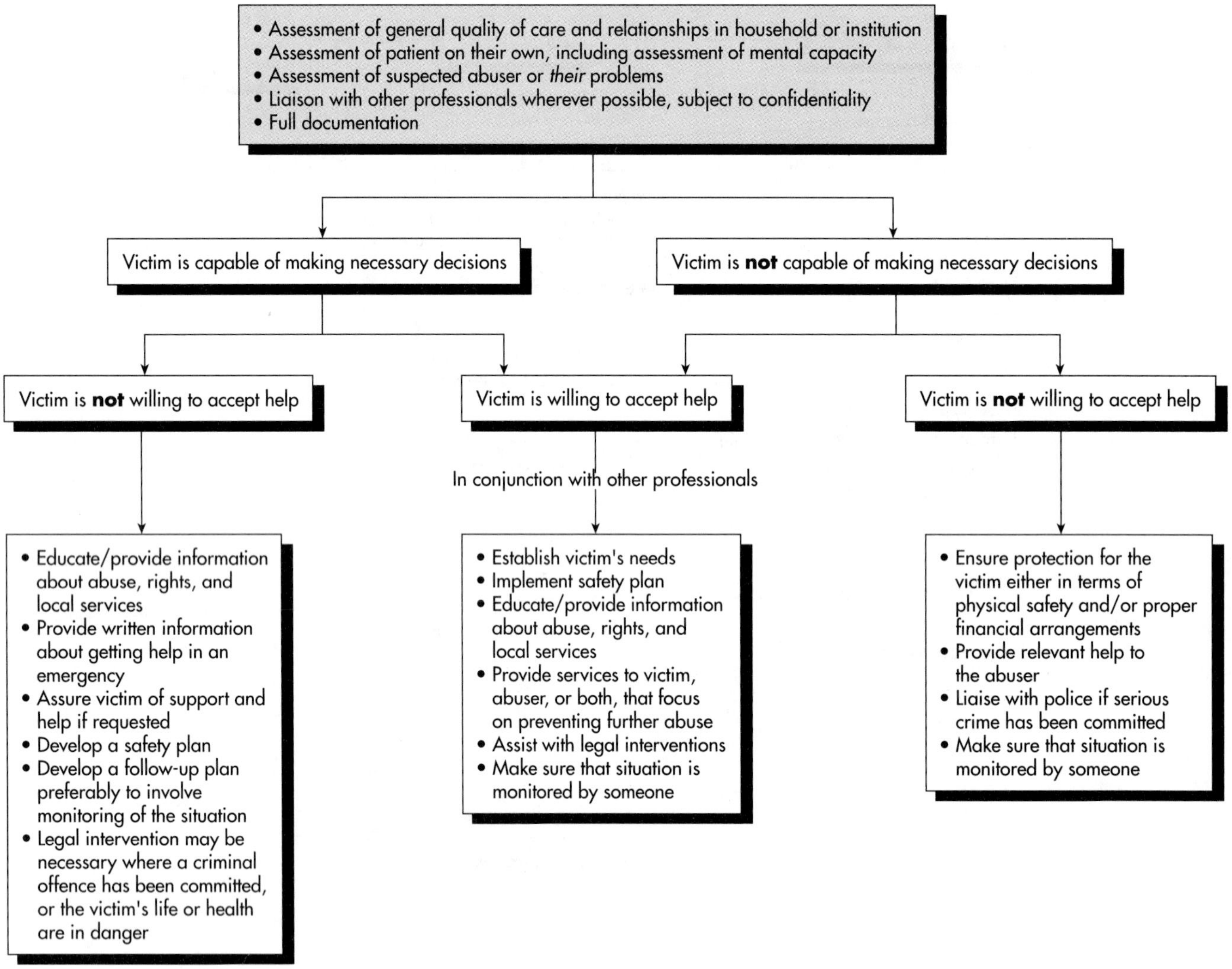

FIGURE 3-2 Management of Geriatric Abuse. (From Tallis RC, Fillit HM [eds]: *Brocklehurst's textbook of geriatric medicine and gerontology,* ed 6, London, 2003, Churchill Livingstone.)

ACETAMINOPHEN INGESTION

ICD-9CM # 965.4 Acetaminophen poisoning

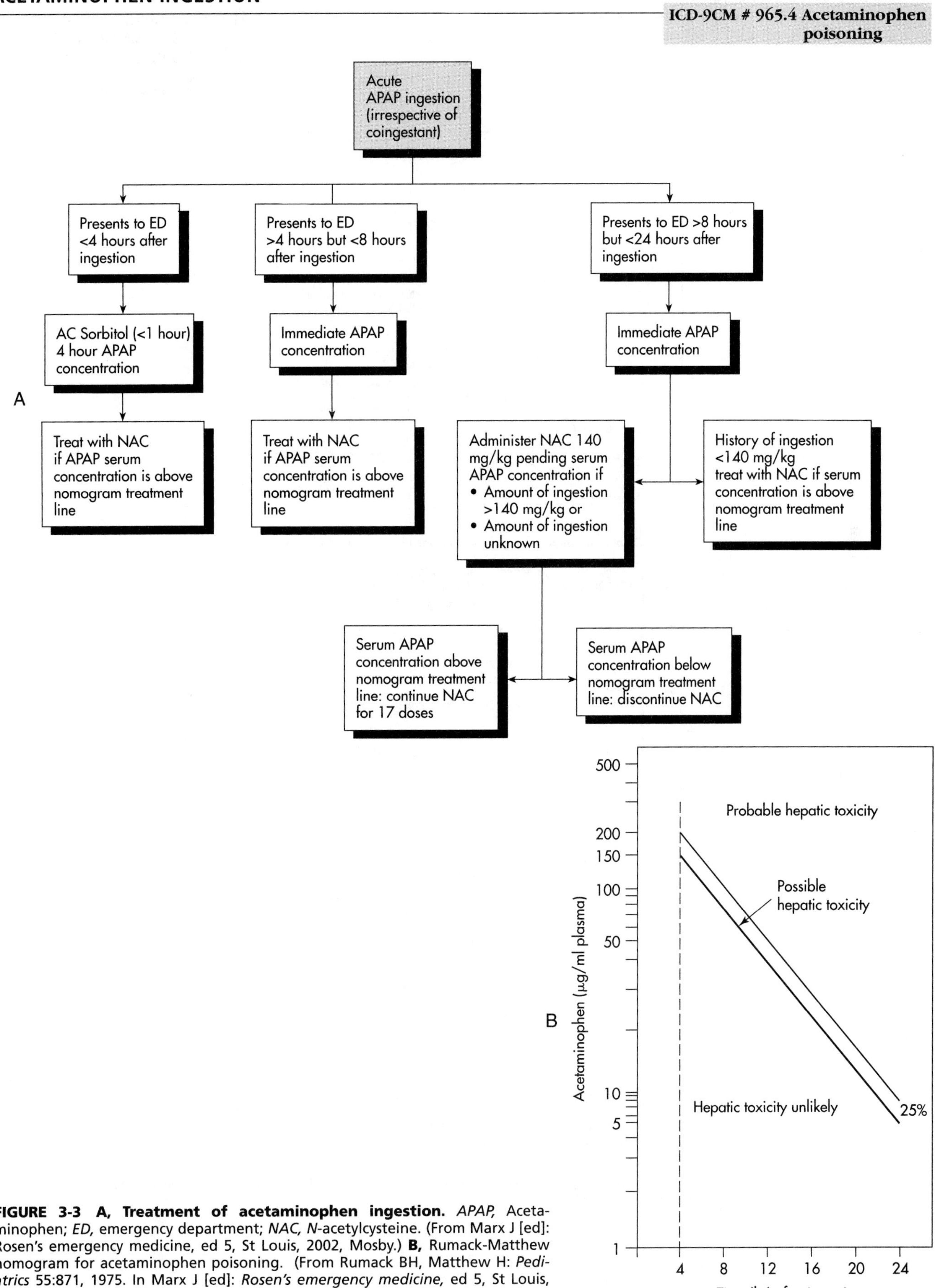

FIGURE 3-3 A, Treatment of acetaminophen ingestion. *APAP,* Acetaminophen; *ED,* emergency department; *NAC, N*-acetylcysteine. (From Marx J [ed]: Rosen's emergency medicine, ed 5, St Louis, 2002, Mosby.) **B,** Rumack-Matthew nomogram for acetaminophen poisoning. (From Rumack BH, Matthew H: *Pediatrics* 55:871, 1975. In Marx J [ed]: *Rosen's emergency medicine,* ed 5, St Louis, 2002, Mosby.)

ACID-BASE HOMEOSTASIS

ICD-9CM # 276.2 Lactic acidosis
276.2 Metabolic acidosis
276.2 Respiratory acidosis
276.3 Respiratory alkalosis
276.3 Metabolic alkalosis

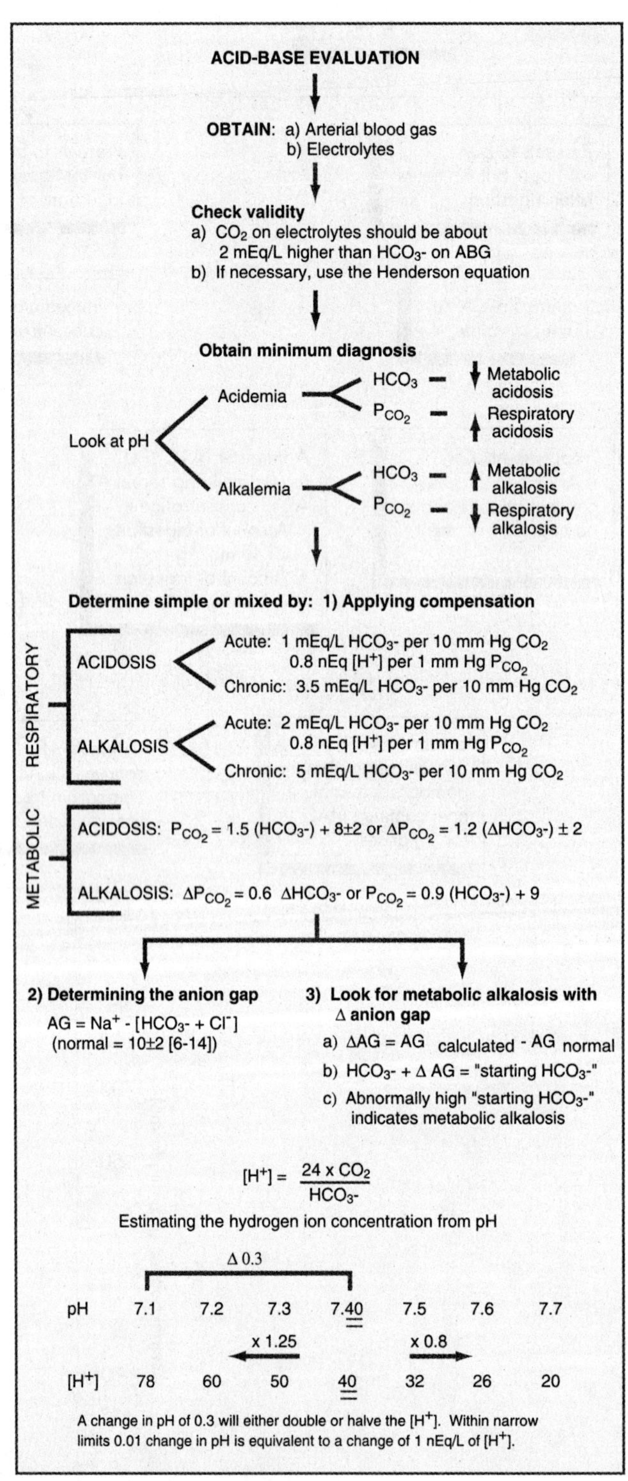

FIGURE 3-4 Scheme for assessing acid-base homeostasis. (From Andreoli TE [ed]: *Cecil essentials of medicine,* ed 4, Philadelphia, 1997, WB Saunders.)

ACIDOSIS, METABOLIC

ICD-9CM # 276.2

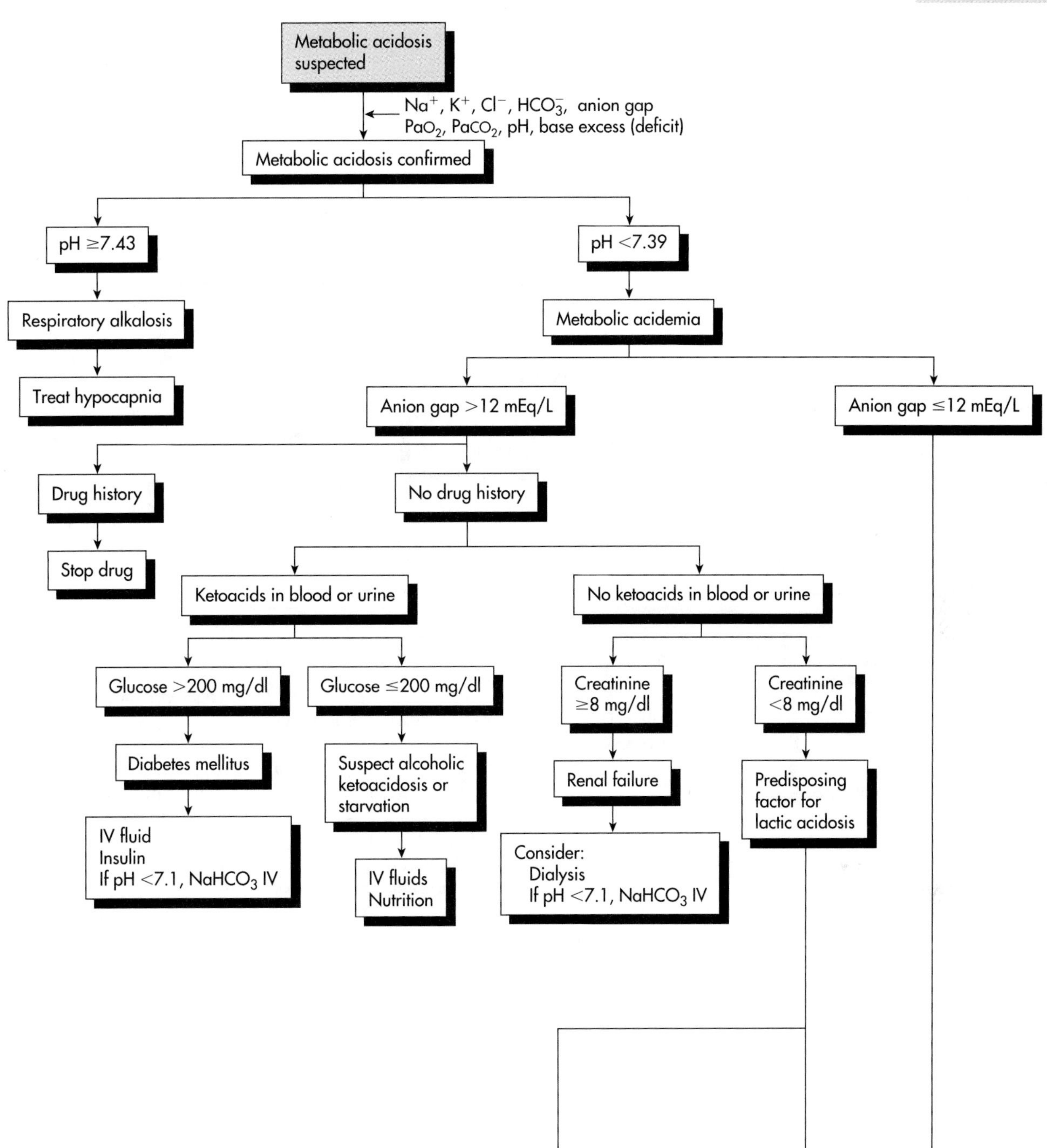

FIGURE 3-5 Suspected metabolic acidosis. (From Greene HL, Johnson WP, Lemke D [eds]: *Decision making in medicine,* ed 2, St Louis, 1998, Mosby.)

Continued

SECTION III

ACIDOSIS, METABOLIC—cont'd

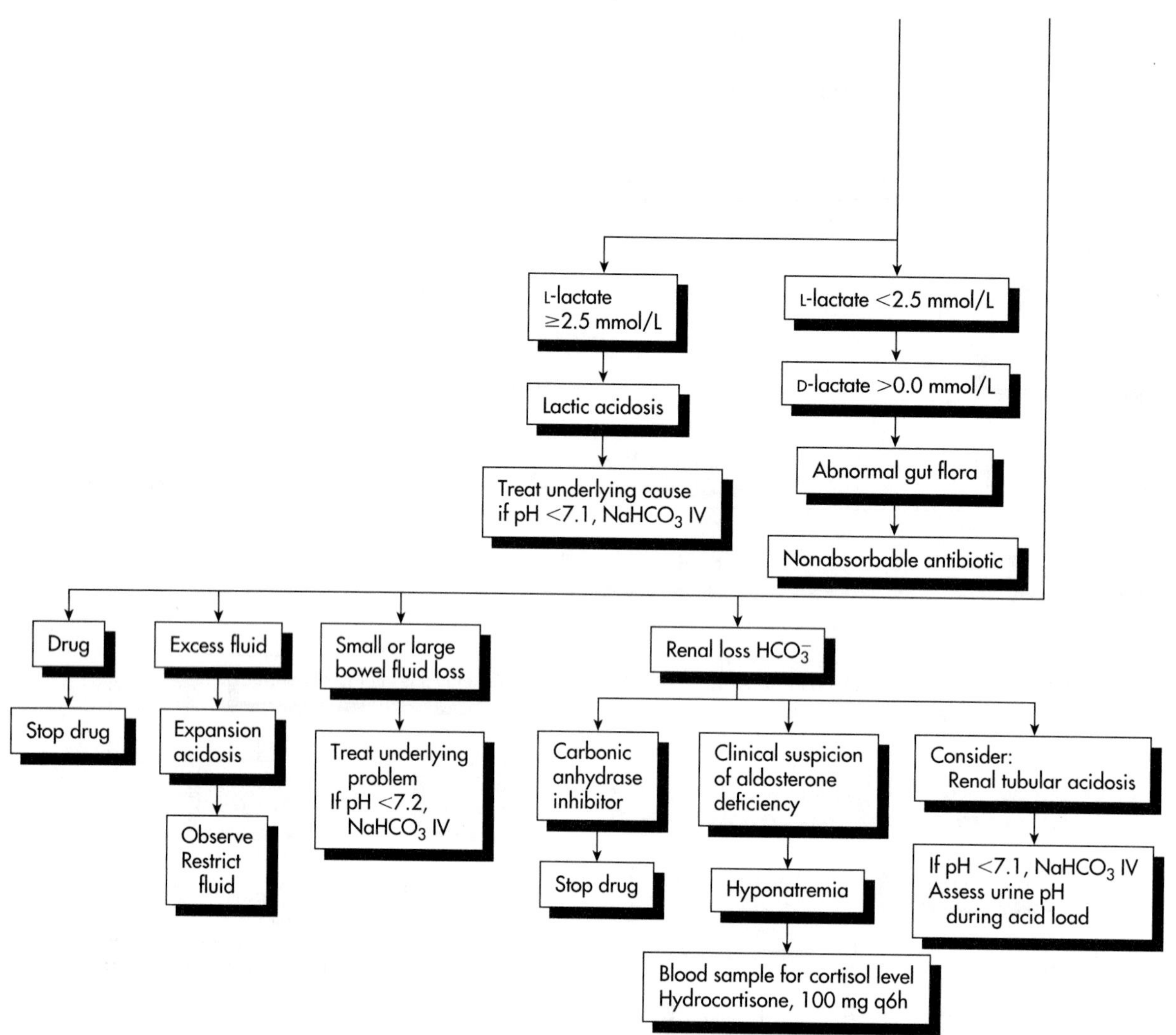

FIGURE 3-5, cont'd Suspected metabolic acidosis. (From Greene HL, Johnson WP, Lemke D [eds]: *Decision making in medicine,* ed 2, St Louis, 1998, Mosby.)

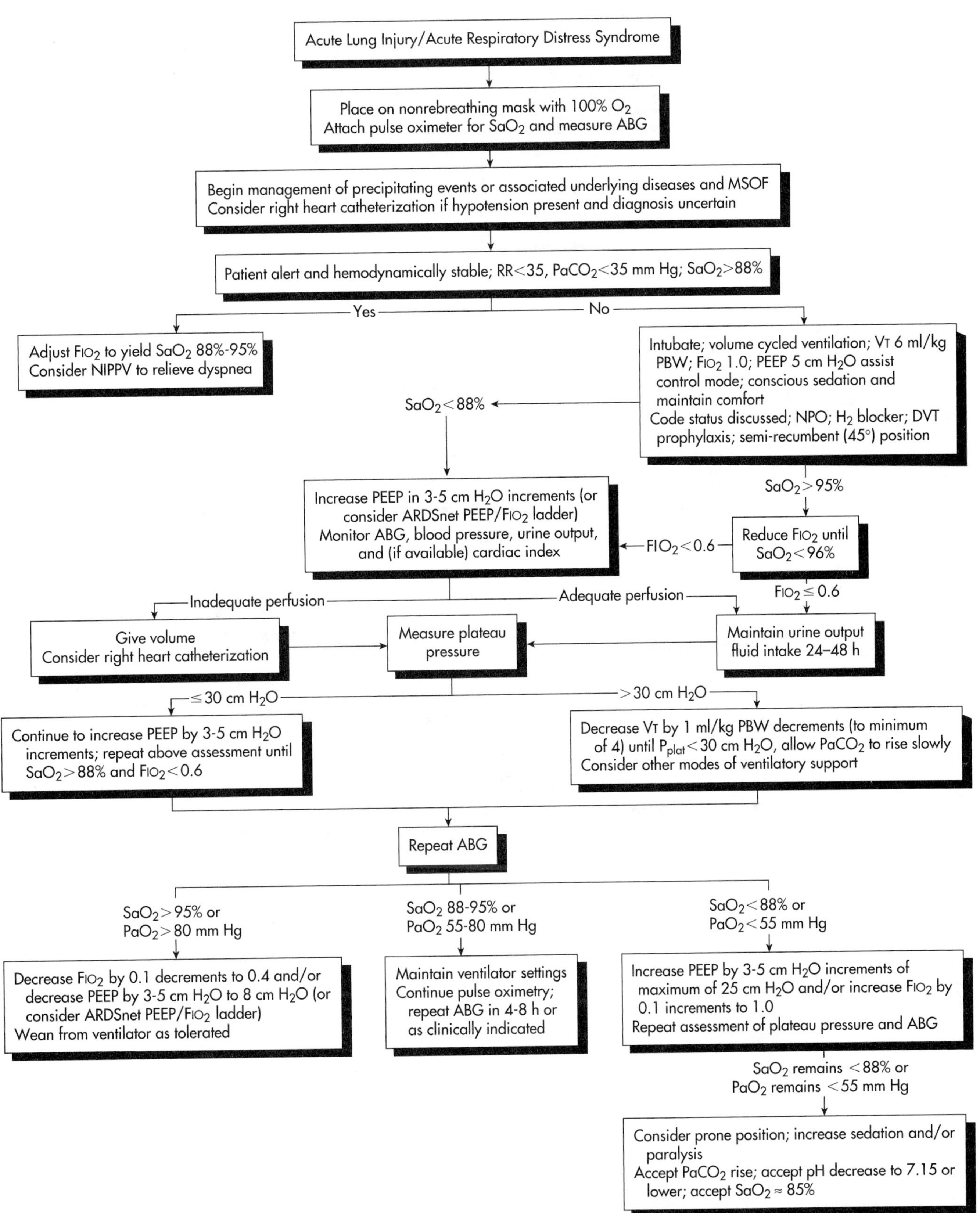

FIGURE 3-6 An algorithm for the initial management of acute respiratory distress syndrome. *ABG,* Arterial blood gas analysis; *CO,* carbon dioxide; *DVT,* deep venous thrombosis; *FiO_2,* inspired oxygen concentration; *MSOF,* multisystem organ failure; *NIPPV,* noninvasive intermittent positive pressure ventilation; *O_2,* oxygen; *$PaCO_2$,* arterial partial pressure of carbon dioxide; *PaO_2,* arterial partial pressure of oxygen; *PBW,* predicted body weight; *PEEP,* positive end-expiratory pressure; *P_{plat},* plateau pressure; *RR,* respiratory rate; *SaO_2,* arterial oxygen saturation; *VT,* tidal volume. (From Goldman L, Ausiello D [eds]: *Cecil textbook of medicine,* ed 22, Philadephia, 2004, WB Saunders.)

ADRENAL INCIDENTALOMA

ICD-9CM # 255.9

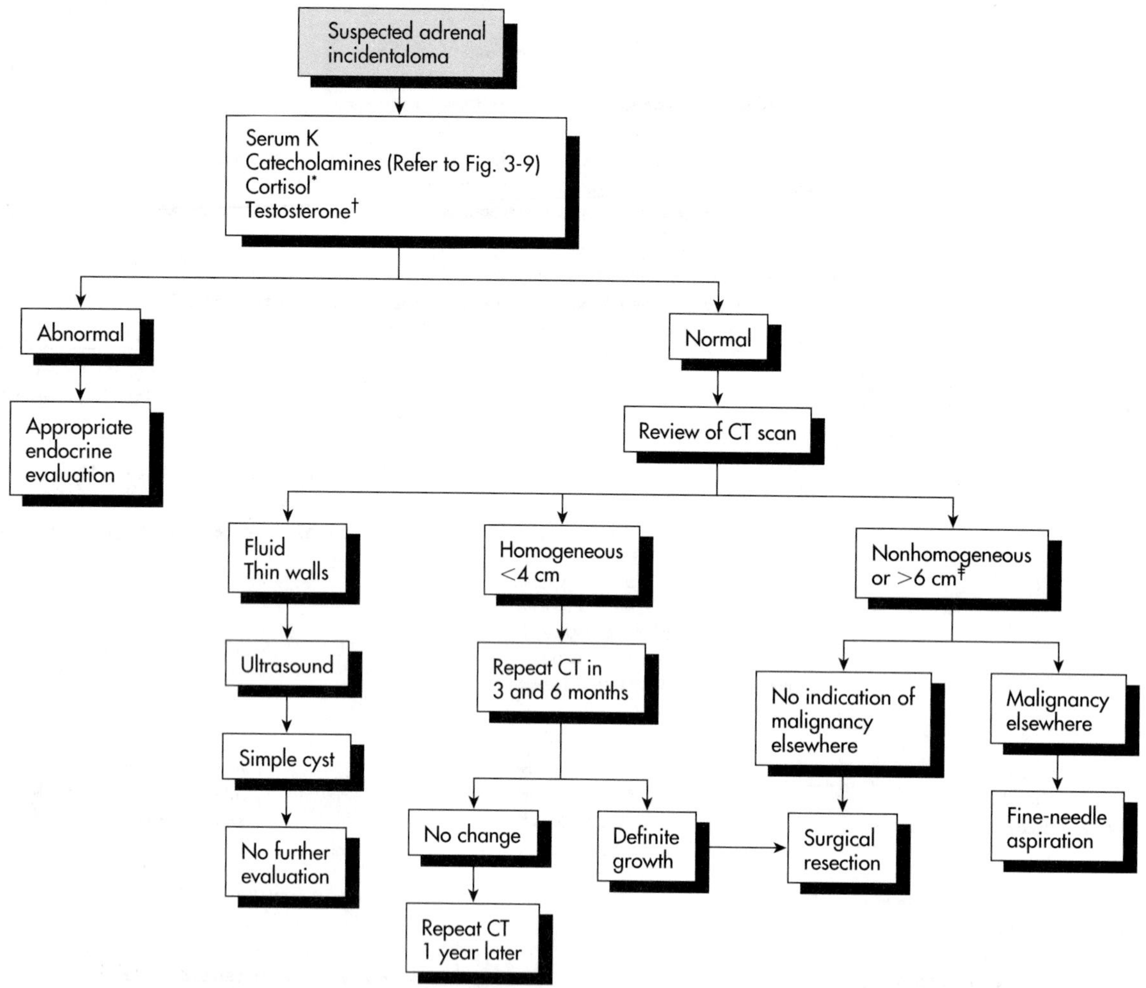

FIGURE 3-7 Algorithm for evaluation of an adrenal incidentaloma. *CT,* Computed tomography. *Only if there are clinical indications of excess cortisol. †Only in women with hirsutism. ‡Measure dehydroepiandrosterone sulfate, a marker of primary adrenal carcinoma. (From Nseyo UO [ed]: *Urology for primary care physicians,* Philadelphia, 1999, WB Saunders.)

ADRENAL INSUFFICIENCY

ICD-9CM # 255.4 Addison's disease

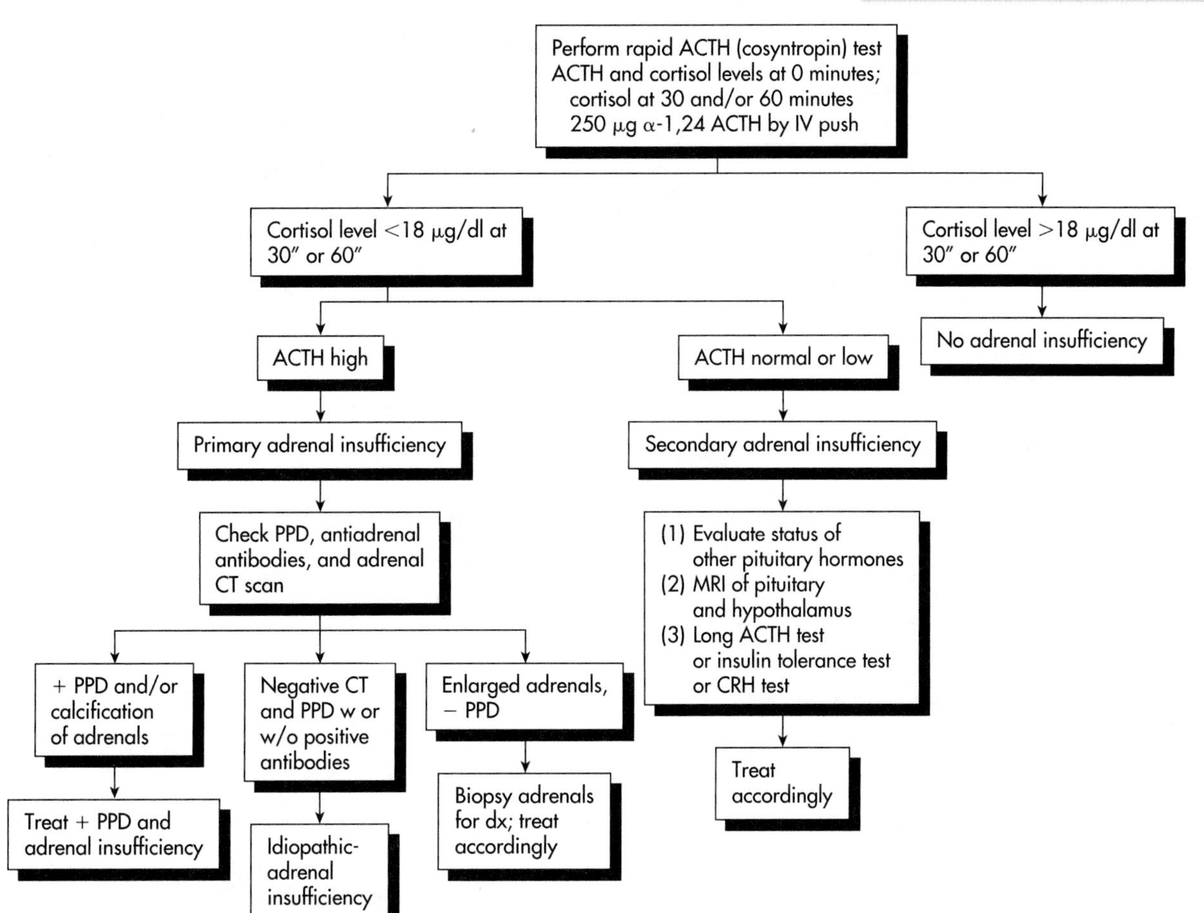

FIGURE 3-8 Evaluation of adrenal insufficiency. *ACTH,* Adrenocorticotropic hormone; *CRH,* corticotropin-releasing hormone; *CT,* computed tomography; *MRI,* magnetic resonance imaging; *PPD,* purified protein derivative. (From Noble J: *Primary care medicine,* ed 3, St Louis, 2001, Mosby.)

ICD-9CM # 194.0 Adrenal cortical carcinoma site NOS M8370/3
255.8 Adrenal hyperplasia

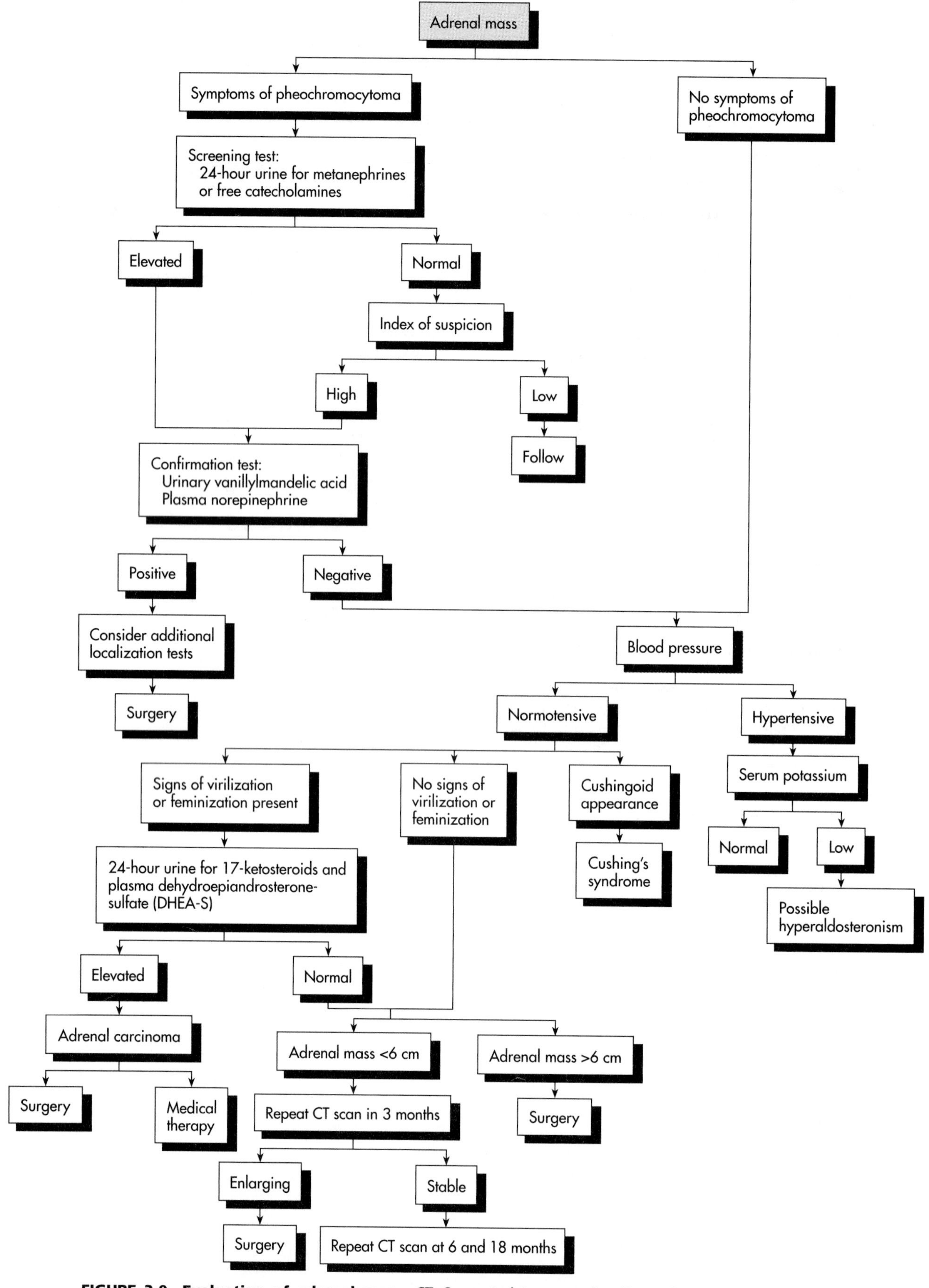

FIGURE 3-9 Evaluation of adrenal mass. *CT,* Computed tomography. (From Greene HL, Johnson WP, Lemcke D [eds]: *Decision making in medicine,* ed 2, St Louis, 1998, Mosby.)

ALCOHOLISM

ICD-9CM # 303.9

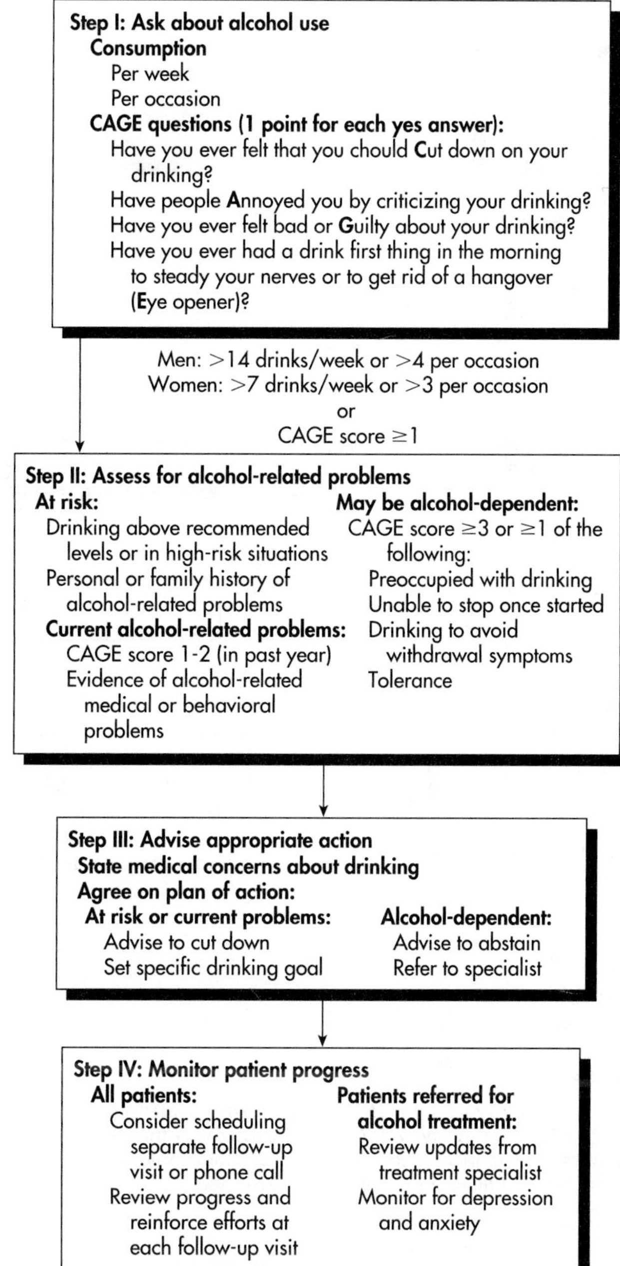

Step I: Ask about alcohol use
Consumption
Per week
Per occasion
CAGE questions (1 point for each yes answer):
Have you ever felt that you chould Cut down on your drinking?
Have people Annoyed you by criticizing your drinking?
Have you ever felt bad or Guilty about your drinking?
Have you ever had a drink first thing in the morning to steady your nerves or to get rid of a hangover (Eye opener)?
Men: >14 drinks/week or >4 per occasion
Women: >7 drinks/week or >3 per occasion
or
CAGE score ≥1
Step II: Assess for alcohol-related problems
At risk:
Drinking above recommended levels or in high-risk situations
Personal or family history of alcohol-related problems
Current alcohol-related problems:
CAGE score 1-2 (in past year)
Evidence of alcohol-related medical or behavioral problems
May be alcohol-dependent:
CAGE score ≥3 or ≥1 of the following:
Preoccupied with drinking
Unable to stop once started
Drinking to avoid withdrawal symptoms
Tolerance
Step III: Advise appropriate action
State medical concerns about drinking
Agree on plan of action:
At risk or current problems:
Advise to cut down
Set specific drinking goal
Alcohol-dependent:
Advise to abstain
Refer to specialist
Step IV: Monitor patient progress
All patients:
Consider scheduling separate follow-up visit or phone call
Review progress and reinforce efforts at each follow-up visit
Patients referred for alcohol treatment:
Review updates from treatment specialist
Monitor for depression and anxiety

FIGURE 3-10 Screening and brief intervention for alcohol problems in clinical practice. (From Goldman L, Ausiello D [eds]: *Cecil textbook of medicine,* ed 22, Philadelphia, 2004, WB Saunders.)

ALKALINE PHOSPHATASE ELEVATION

ICD-9CM # 790.4

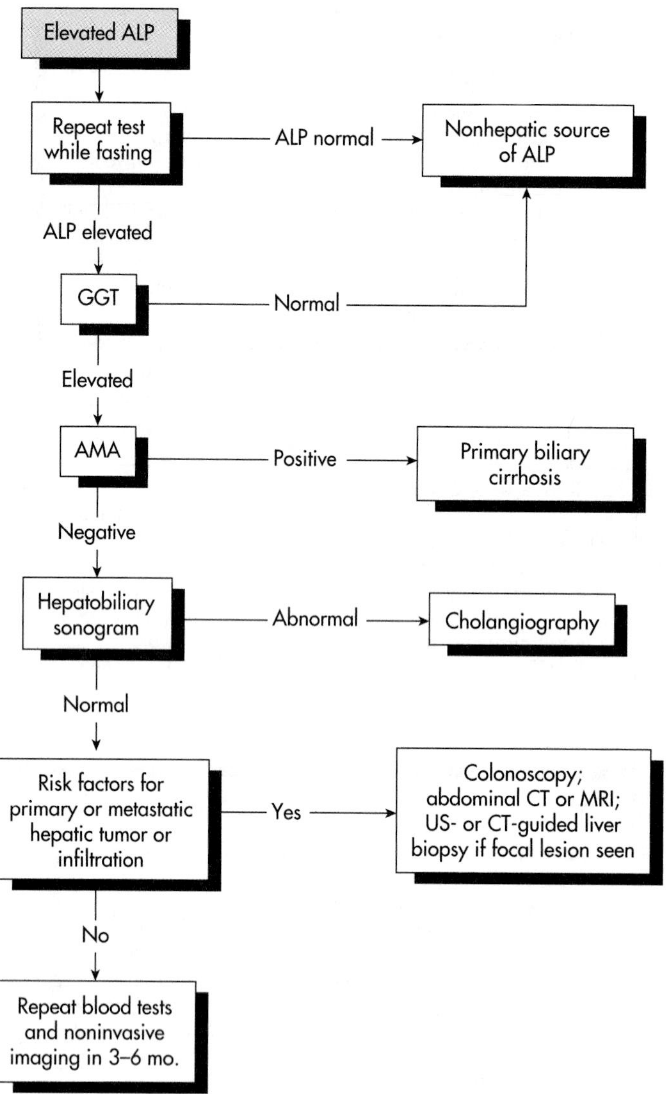

FIGURE 3-11 Approach to the asymptomatic patient with isolated elevated levels of serum alkaline phosphatase (ALP). *AMA,* Antimitochondrial antibody; *CT,* computed tomography; *GGT,* γ-glutayml transpeptidase; *MRI,* magnetic resonance imaging; *US,* ultrasonography. (From Goldman L, Ausiello D [eds]: *Cecil textbook of medicine,* ed 22, Philadelphia, 2004, WB Saunders.)

ALKALOSIS, METABOLIC

ICD-9CM # 273.6

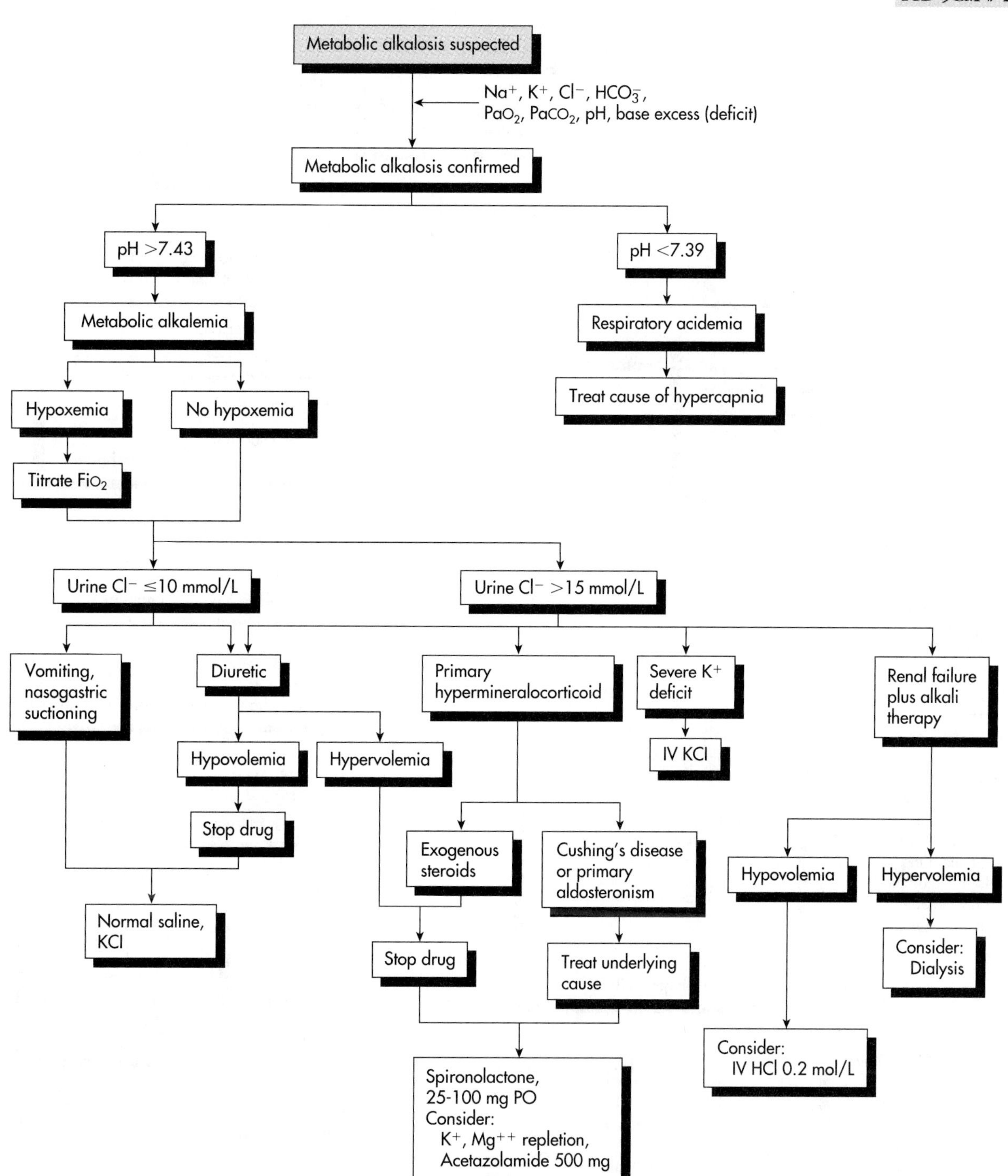

FIGURE 3-12 Suspected metabolic alkalosis. (From Greene HL, Johnson WP, Lemke D [eds]: *Decision making in medicine*, ed 2, St Louis, 1998, Mosby.)

ALOPECIA

"My hair is falling out in large amounts"
"I am afraid to wash or brush my hair"
"I am going bald"

Acquired diffuse scalp hair thinning →

May bring doctor bag of shed hair

→ Less common
Anagen effluvium
Hypothyroidism
Iron deficiency
Renal and hepatic failure
Nutritional disturbances
(e.g., hypervitaminosis A)
Systemic diseases

→ Common causes
Acute telogen effluvium
Chronic telogen effluvium
Drugs and other chemicals
Hair thinning as part of the aging process
50s, 60s, 70s

Child birth, acute illness, fever, chronic systemic disease, emotional stress, heparin, drugs, hypothyroidism, surgical operations, anesthesia, crash diets →

Acute telogen effluvium
Thinning 1-3 months after event
Lasts < 6 months
Diffuse thinning entire scalp
Hair shedding by roots
No miniaturized hairs
Positive telogen pull test

Idiopathic →

Chronic telogen effluvium
(middle aged women)
? Due to shortened anagen
Women aged 30-60 yr
Increased shedding
Thinning—abrupt onset
Long fluctuating course > 6 mo
Diffuse mild thinning
Bitemporal recession
Hair shedding by roots
No miniaturized hairs
Positive telogen pull test

Pull test (20-40 hairs)
Normal 1-4 hairs
CTE 2-8 hairs
ATE > 4 hairs
AGA Normal

Scalp biopsy
Two 4 mm punches
Horizontal sections
Vertical sections

Chronic telogen effluvium
Terminal/vellus like ratio 9:1
Anagen/telogen % 89:11
(normal or slightly increased)

Androgenetic alopecia
Terminal/vellus like ratio 2:1
Anagen/telogen % 83:17

Frontoparietal thinning →

Androgenetic alopecia

Onset—Teens, 20s, 30s, 40s
50% of women < age 50 have androgenetic alopecia
two thirds of all hair loss in women

History →

1. Gradual diffuse thinning
2. No increased shedding
3. Family history maybe +
4. Patient cuts hair shorter
5. Not taking drugs that cause hair loss

Scalp exam →

1. Increased spacing between hairs
2. Thinning in frontal or parietal areas
3. Rim of hair along the frontal hairline is retained
4. May have mild bitemporal recession
5. "Central part" looks wider in front
6. Pony tail is thinner
7. Pull test normal
8. Miniaturized hairs of varying diameter and length

History and PE for signs of androgen excess

No signs → Usually no laboratory studies required → Rx → Minoxidil (Rogaine)

Irregular menses
Infertility
Hirsutism
Severe cystic acne
Virilization
Galactorrhea

→ Total testosterone
DHEAS
Prolactin
?TSH

Heavy or long lasting menses
Iron
Iron-binding capacity
Ferritin

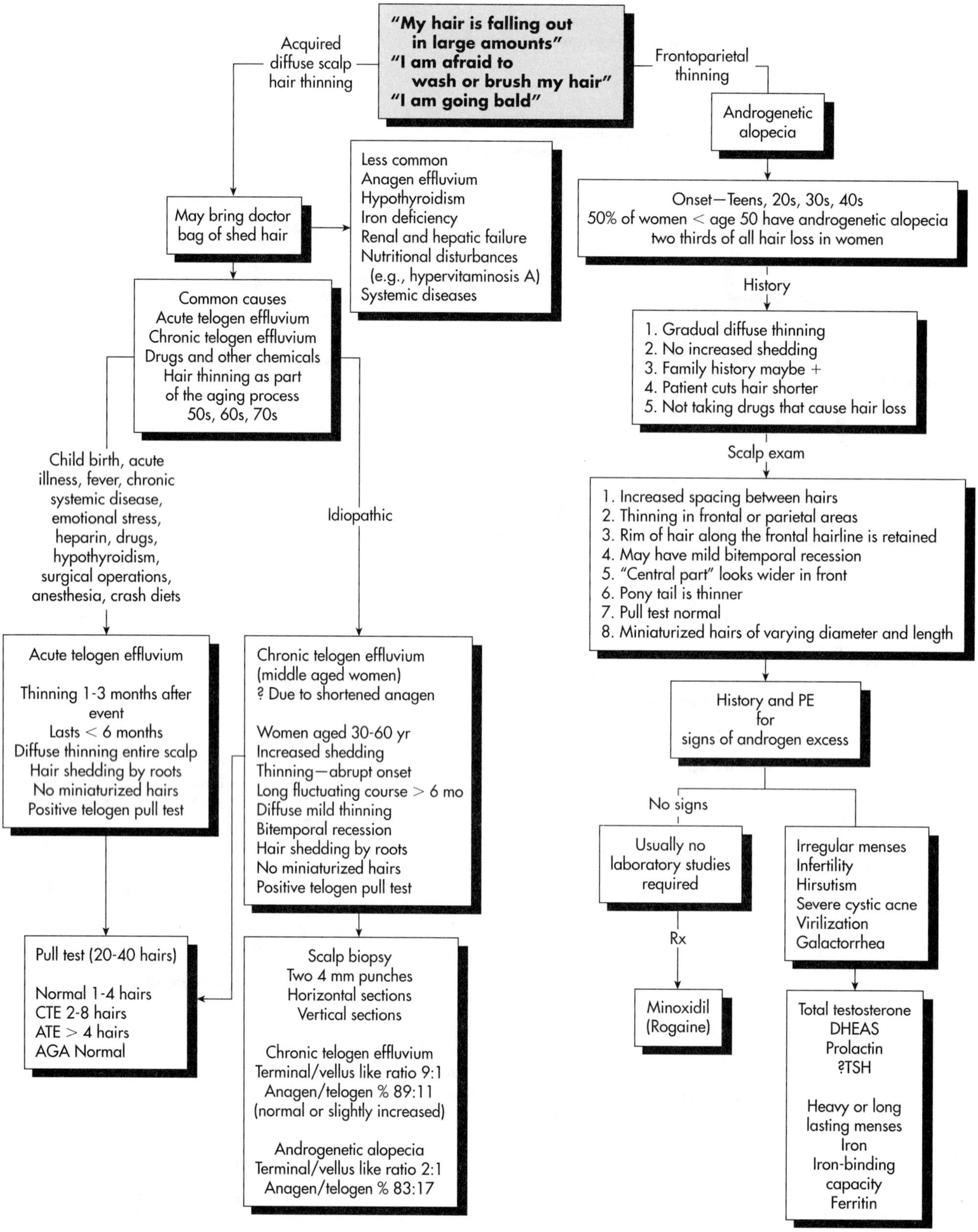

FIGURE 3-13 Evaluation and treatment of alopecia. *CTE,* Chronic telogen effluvium; *AGA,* androgenetic alopecia; *ATE,* acute telogen effluvium. (From Habif TA: *Clinical dermatology,* ed 4, St Louis, 2004, Mosby.)

ALT/AST ELEVATION

ICD-9CM # 573.9

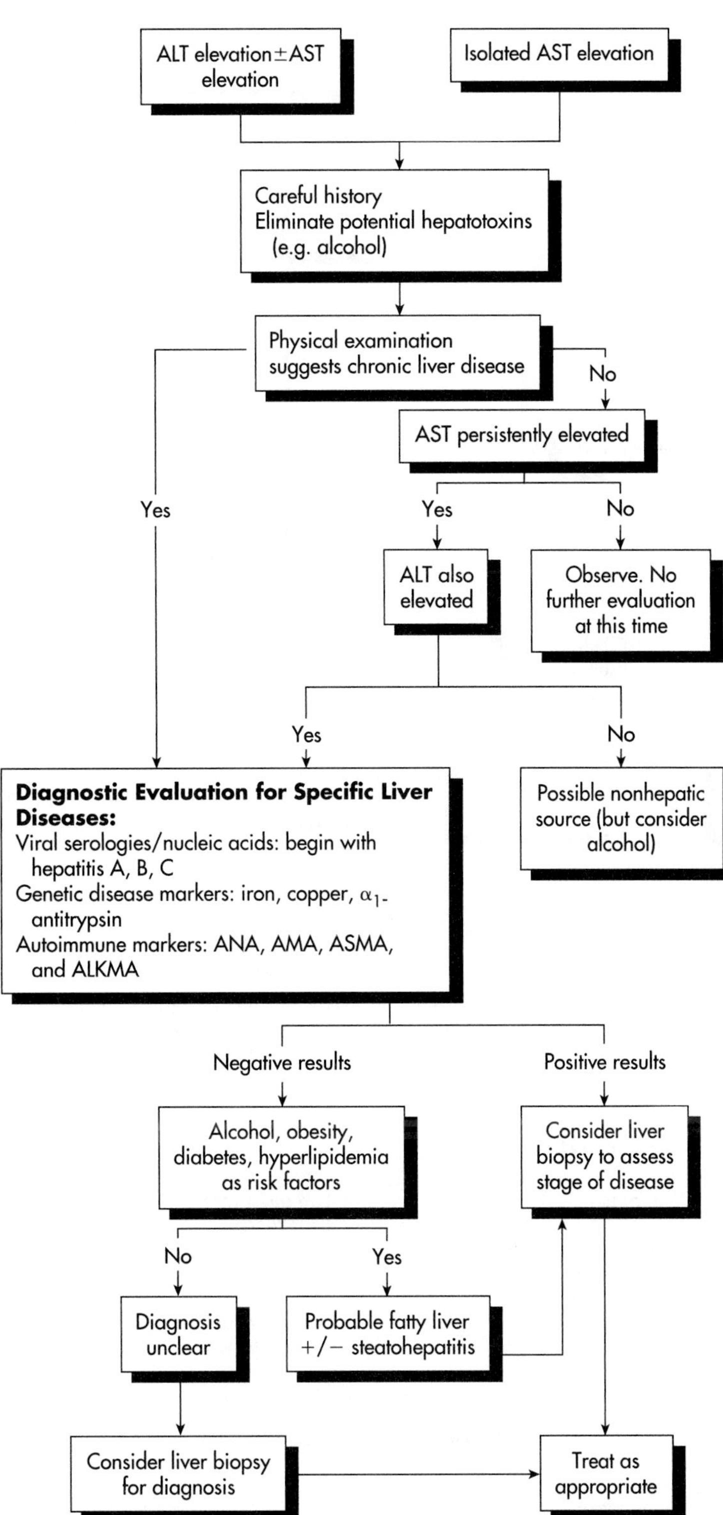

FIGURE 3-14 Approach to the evaluation of isolated elevated levels of serum alanine aminotransferase (ALT) and/or aspartate aminotransferase (AST) in the asymptomatic patient. *ALKMA,* anti–liver/kidney microsomal antibody; *AMA,* antimitochondrial antibody; *ANA,* antinuclear antibody; *ASMA,* anti–smooth muscle antibody. (From Goldman L, Ausiello D [eds]: *Cecil textbook of medicine,* ed 22, Philadelphia, 2004, WB Saunders.)

AMENORRHEA, PRIMARY

ICD-9CM # 626.0

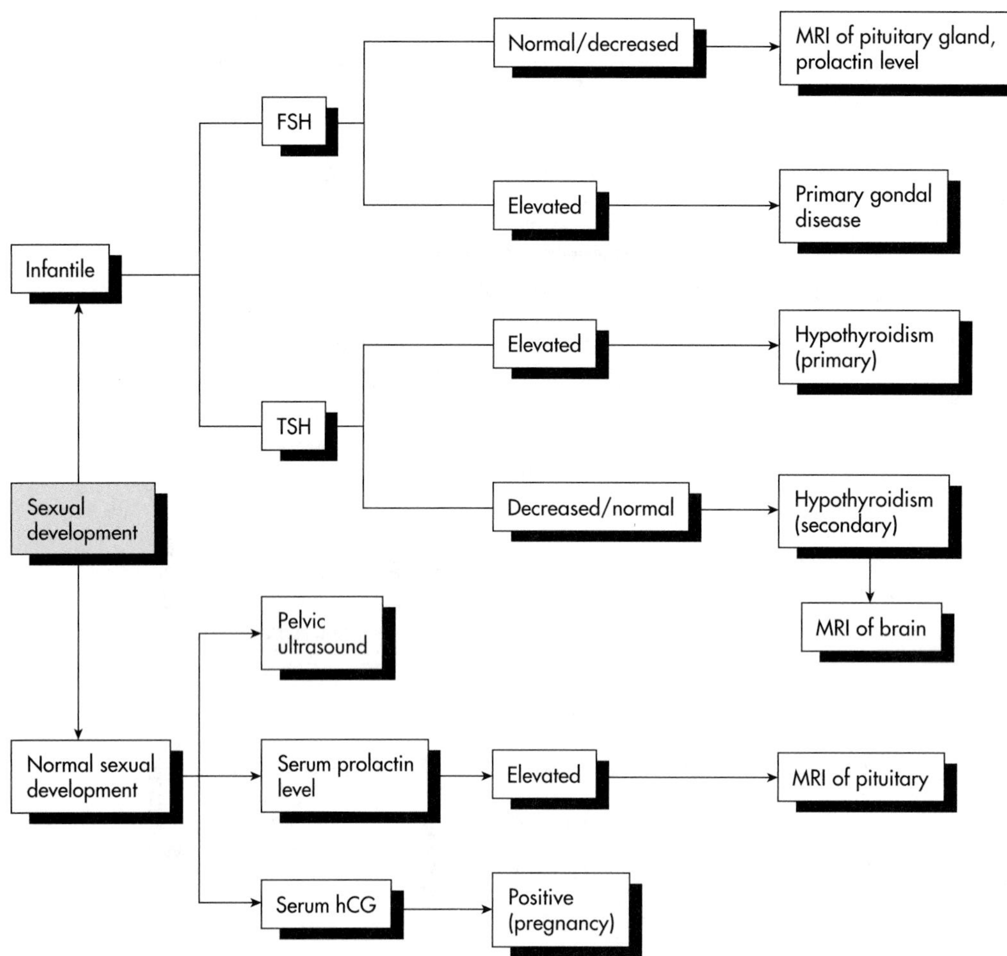

FIGURE 3-15 Evaluation of primary amenorrhea. *FSH,* Follicle-stimulation hormone; *MRI,* magnetic resonance imaging; *TSH,* thyroid stimulating hormone. (From Ferri FF: *Ferri's best test: a practical guide to clinical laboratory medicine and diagnostic imaging,* Philadelphia, 2004, Elsevier Mosby.)

BOX 3-1 Amenorrhea, Primary

Diagnostic imaging	Lab evaluation
Best test	***Best tests***
MRI of pituitary/hypothalamus with gadolinium when hypothalamic/pituitary lesion is suspected	FSH Prolactin TSH
Ancillary tests	***Ancillary tests***
Pelvic ultrasound	Serum hCG

From Ferri FF: *Ferri's best test: a practical guide to clinical laboratory medicine and diagnostic imaging,* Philadelphia, 2004, Elsevier Mosby.

FSH, Follicle-stimulating hormone, *MRI,* magnetic resonance imaging; *TSH,* thyroid-stimulating hormone.

AMENORRHEA, SECONDARY

ICD-9CM # 626.0

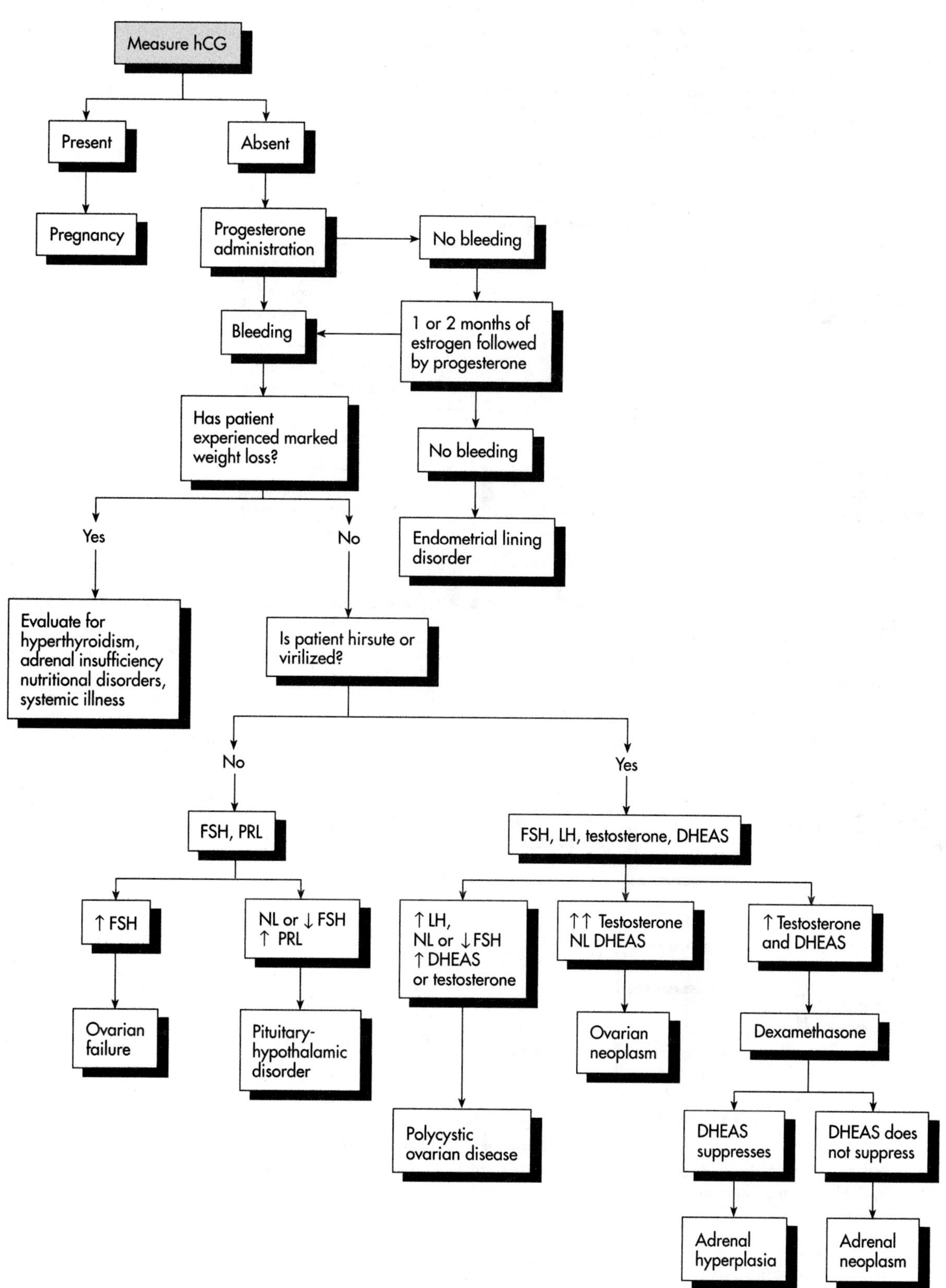

FIGURE 3-16 Evaluation of secondary amenorrhea. *DHEAS,* Dehydroepiandrosterone-sulfate; *FSH,* follicle-stimulating hormone; *hCG,* human chorionic gonadotropin; *LH,* luteinizing hormone; *NL,* normal; *PRL,* prolactin; ↑, increased; ↑↑, markedly increased; ↓, decreased. (From Andreoli TE [ed]: *Cecil essentials of medicine,* ed 5, Philadelphia, 2001, WB Saunders.)

AMYLOIDOSIS

ICD-9CM # 277.3

FIGURE 3-17 Approach to the patient with possible systemic amyloidosis. *IEP,* immunoelectrophoresis; *SPEP,* serum protein electrophoresis. (From Goldman L, Ausiello D [eds]: *Cecil textbook of medicine,* ed 22, Philadelphia, 2004, WB Saunders.)

ANEMIA

ICD-9CM # 285.9 Anemia NOS

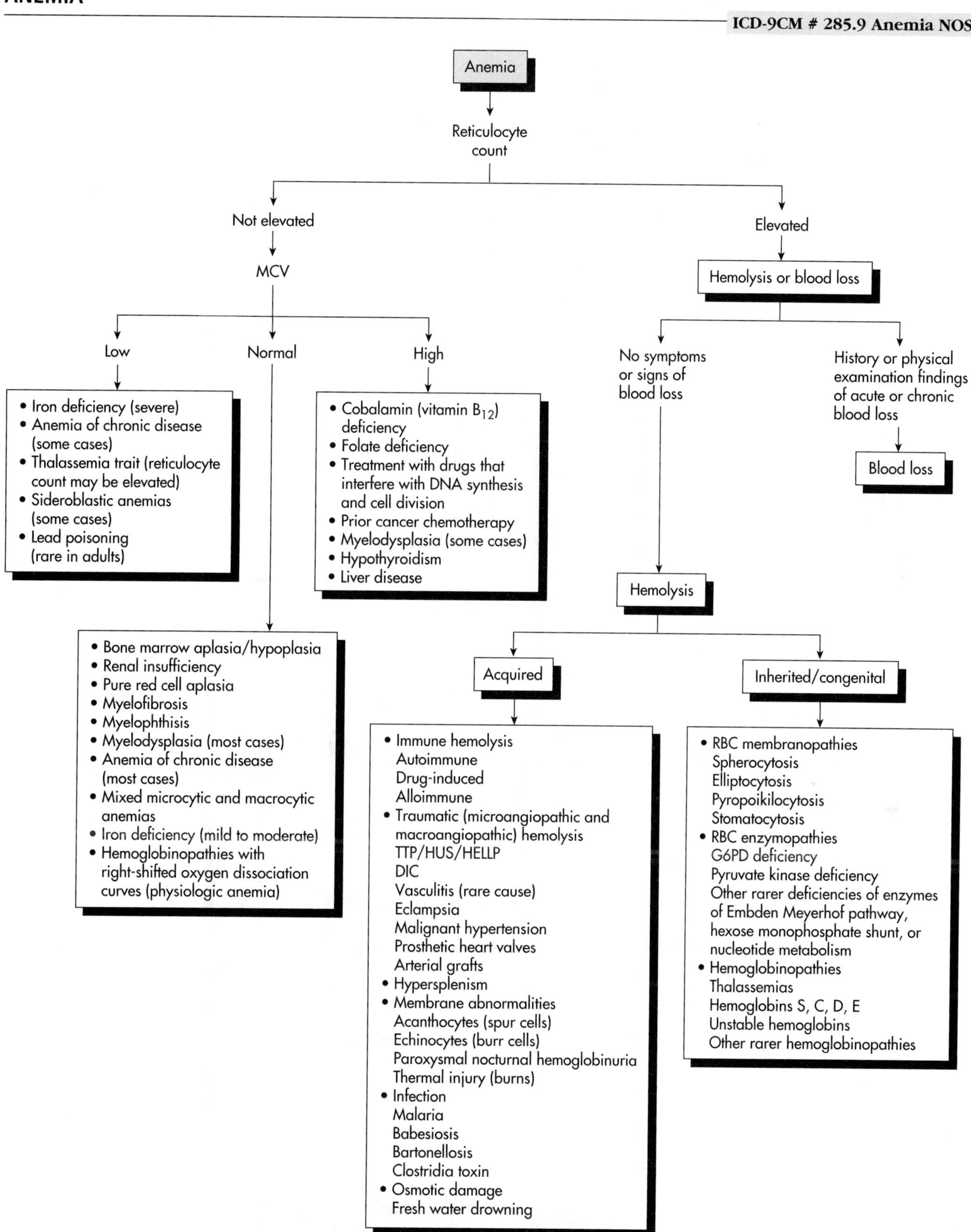

FIGURE 3-18 Algorithm for diagnosis of anemias. *DIC,* Disseminated intravascular coagulation; *HELLP,* hepatomegaly-elevated *l*iver (function tests)-*low p*latelets; *HUS,* hemolytic-uremic syndrome; *MCV,* mean corpuscular volume; *RBC,* red blood cell; *TTP,* thrombotic thrombocytopenic purpura. (From Goldman L, Ausiello D [eds]: *Cecil textbook of medicine,* ed 22, Philadelphia, 2004, WB Saunders.)

SECTION III

ANEMIA, MACROCYTIC

ICD-9CM # 281.9

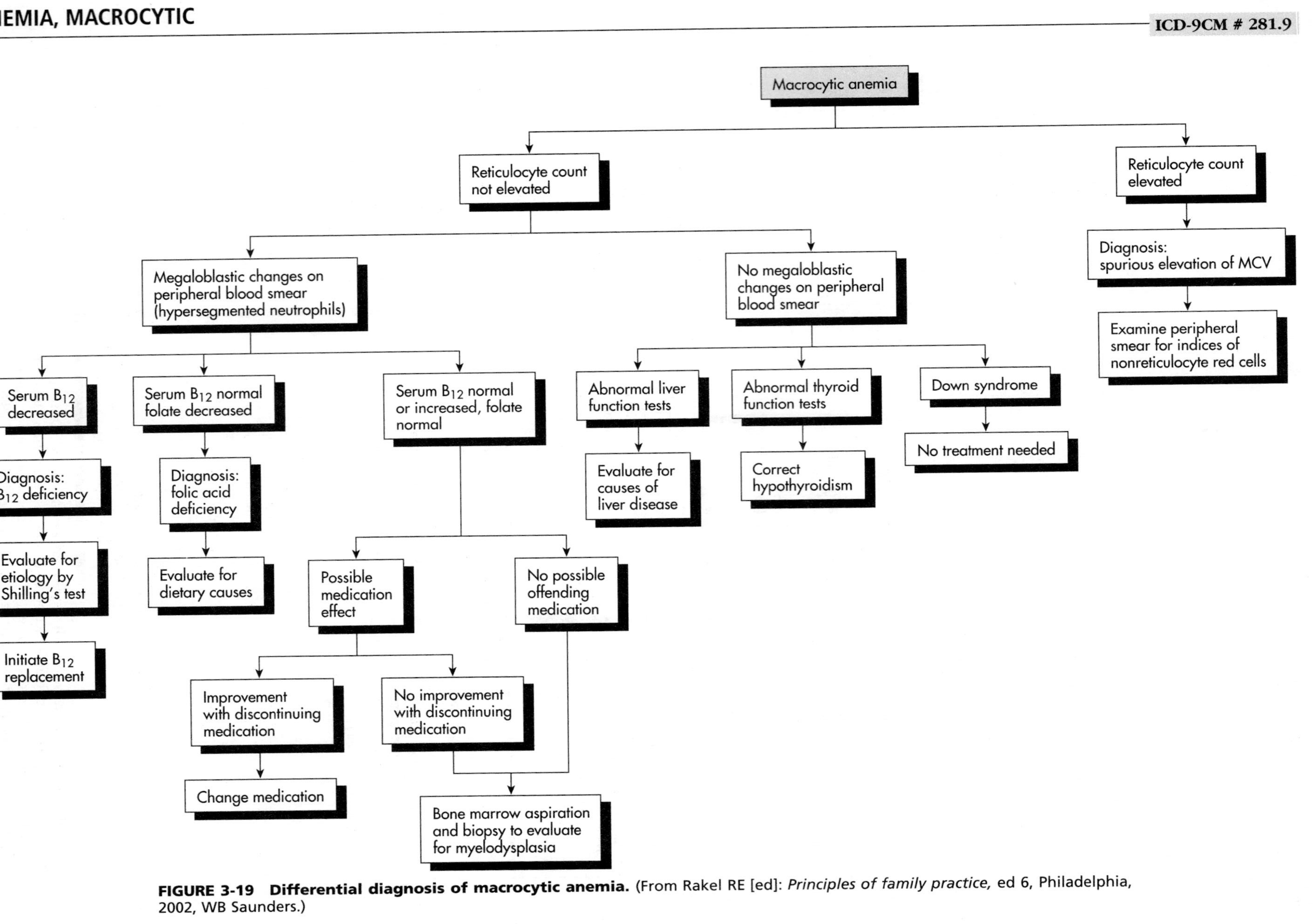

FIGURE 3-19 Differential diagnosis of macrocytic anemia. (From Rakel RE [ed]: *Principles of family practice,* ed 6, Philadelphia, 2002, WB Saunders.)

ANEMIA, MICROCYTIC

ICD-9CM # 282.4

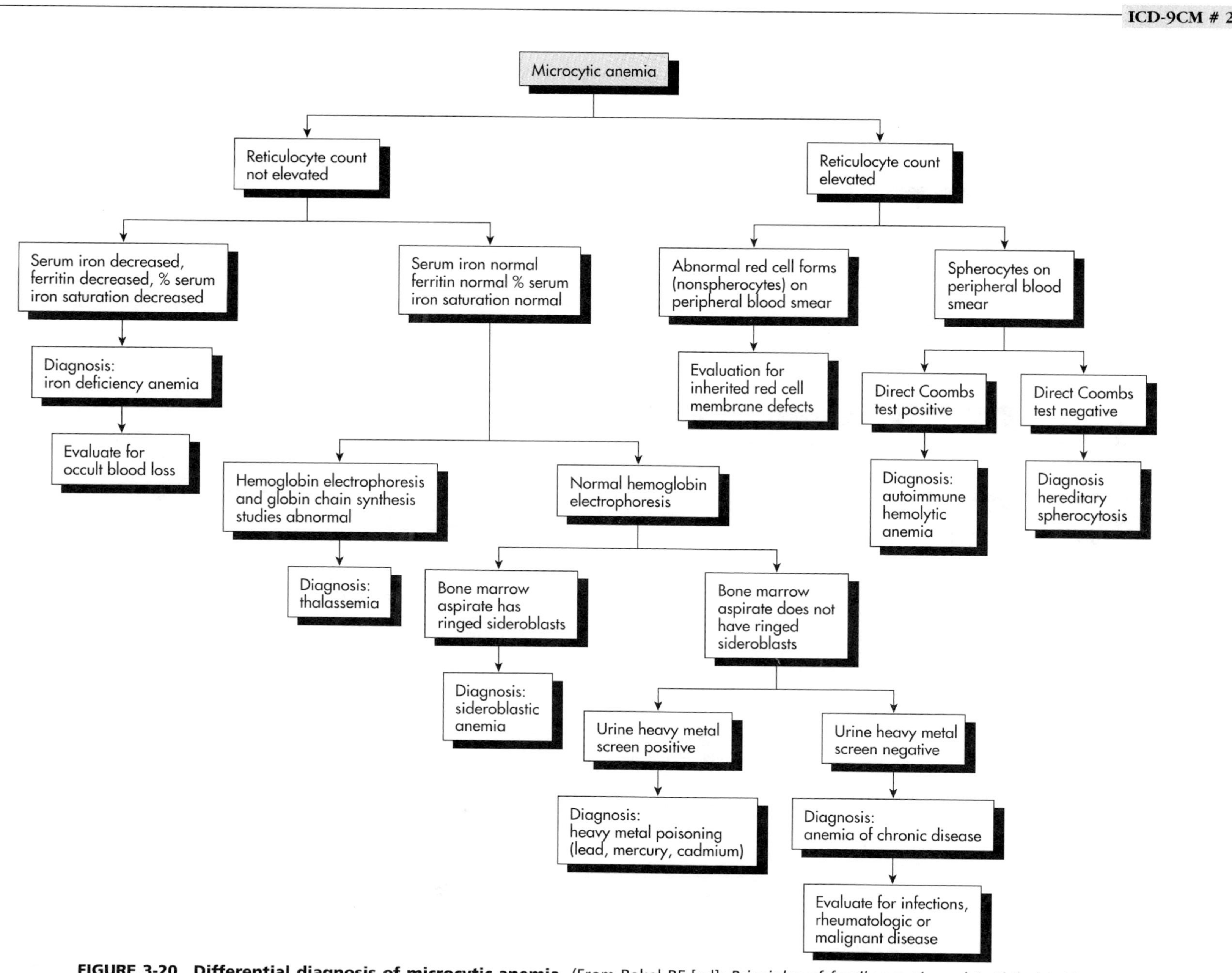

FIGURE 3-20 Differential diagnosis of microcytic anemia. (From Rakel RE [ed]: *Principles of family practice,* ed 6, Philadelphia, 2002, WB Saunders.)

ANEMIA, WITH RETICULOCYTOSIS

ICD-9CM # 790.99

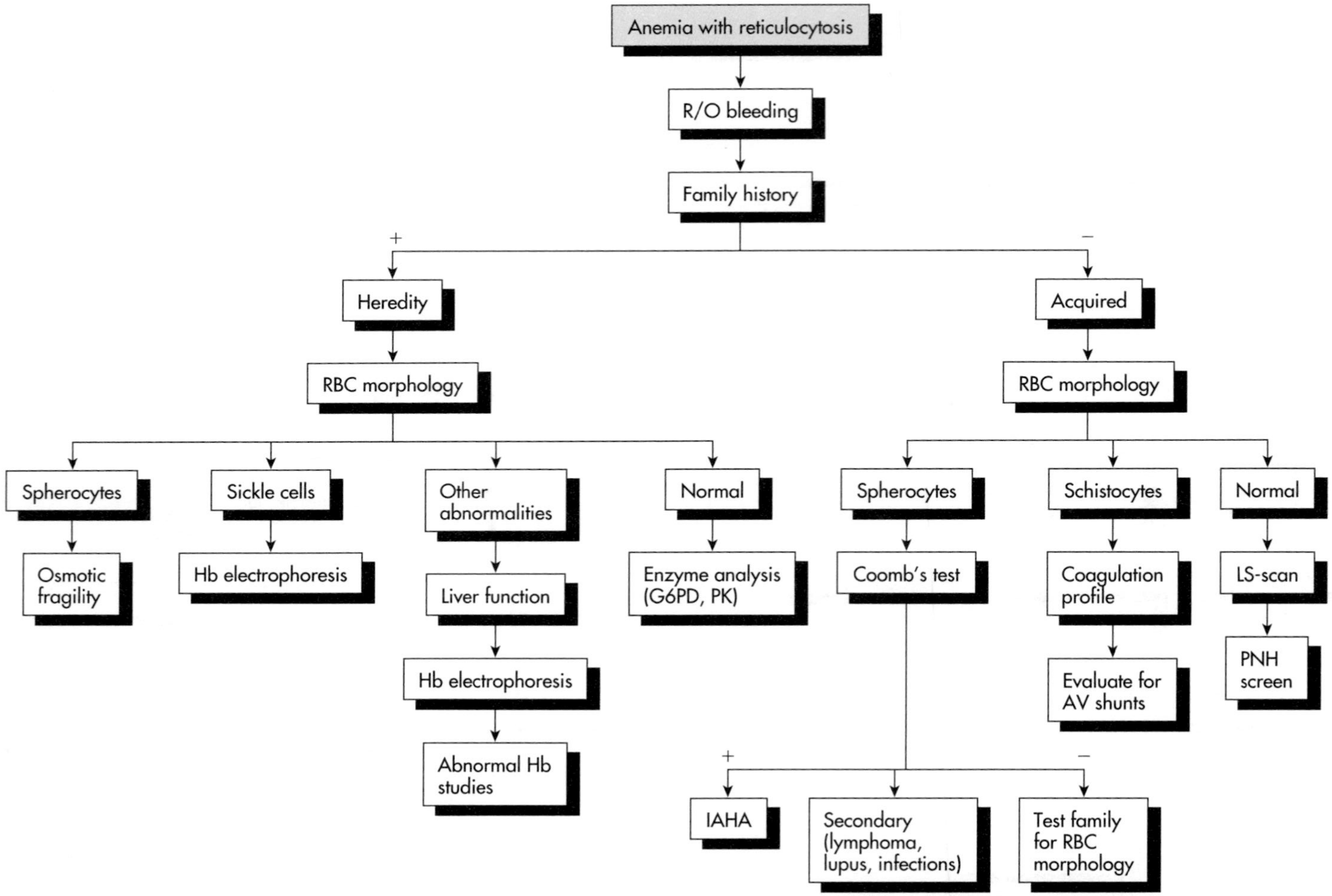

FIGURE 3-21 Evaluations of patients with hemolytic anemia. *AV,* Arteriovenous; *Hb,* hemoglobin; *IAHA,* idiopathic autoimmune hemolytic anemia; *LS,* liver spleen; *PK,* pyruvate kinase; *PNH,* paroxysmal nocturnal hemoglobinuria; *RBC,* red blood cell. (From Stein JH: *Internal medicine,* ed 5, St Louis, 1997, Mosby.)

ANISOCORIA

ICD-9CM # 379.41

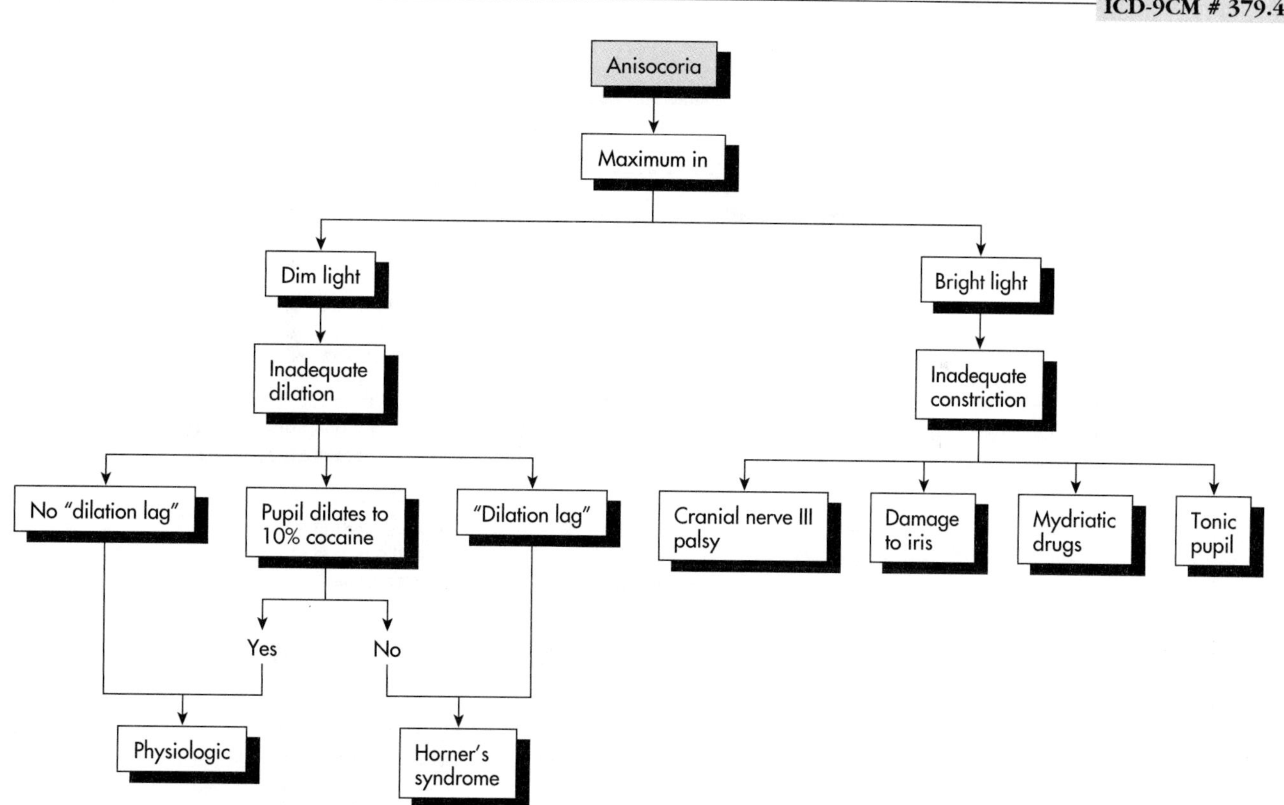

FIGURE 3-22 Algorithm for the approach to unequal pupils (anisocoria). (From Andreoli TE [ed]: *Cecil essentials of medicine,* ed 5, Philadelphia, 2001, WB Saunders.)

ANOREXIA

ICD-9CM # 783.0

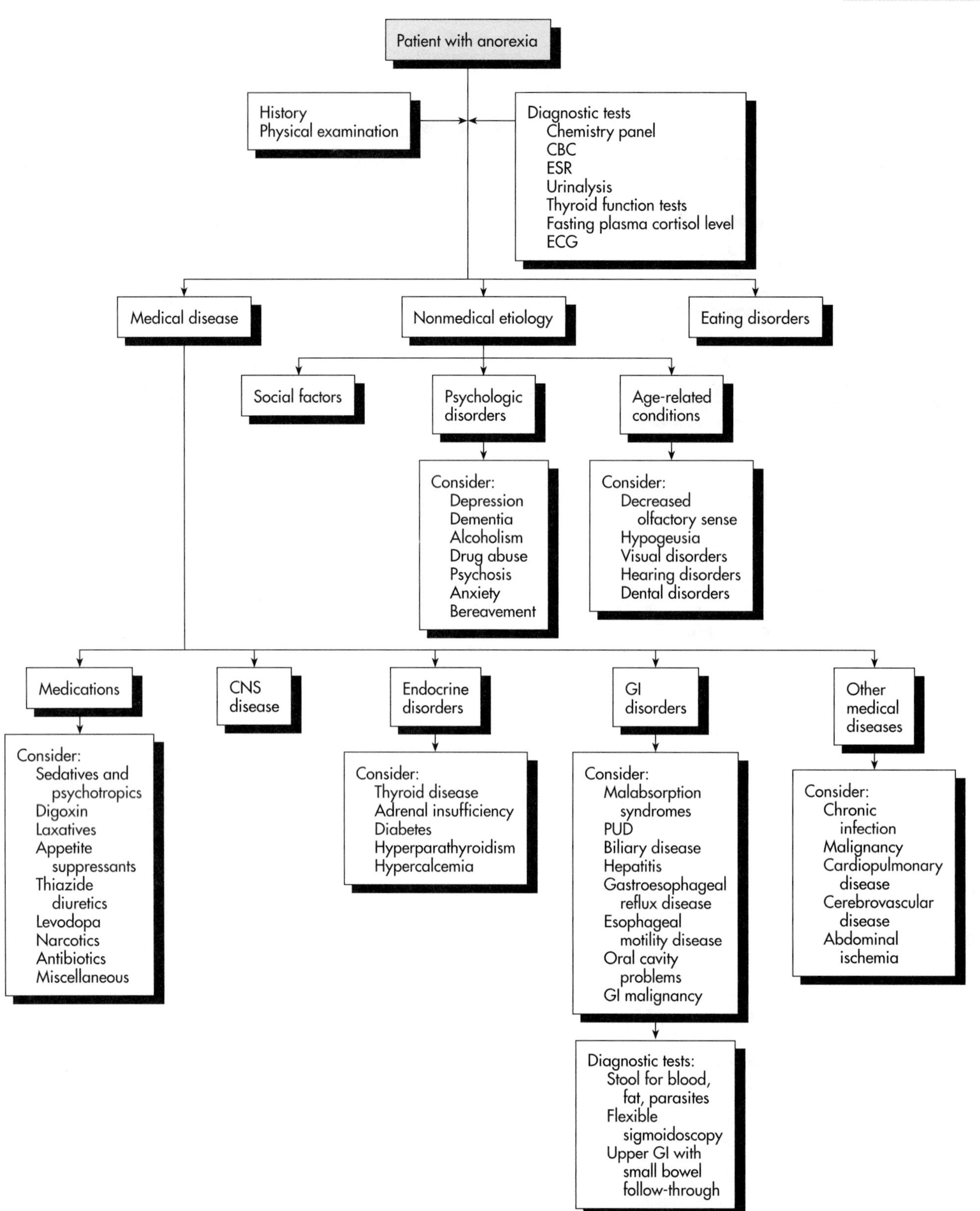

FIGURE 3-23 Evaluation of anorexia. *CBC,* Complete blood count; *CNS,* central nervous system; *ECG,* electrocardiogram; *ESR,* erythrocyte sedimentation rate; *GI,* gastrointestinal; *PUD,* peptic ulcer disease. (From Greene HL, Johnson WP, Lemcke D [eds]: *Decision making in medicine,* ed 2, St Louis, 1998, Mosby.)

ANTINUCLEAR ANTIBODY TESTING

ICD-9CM # 795.79

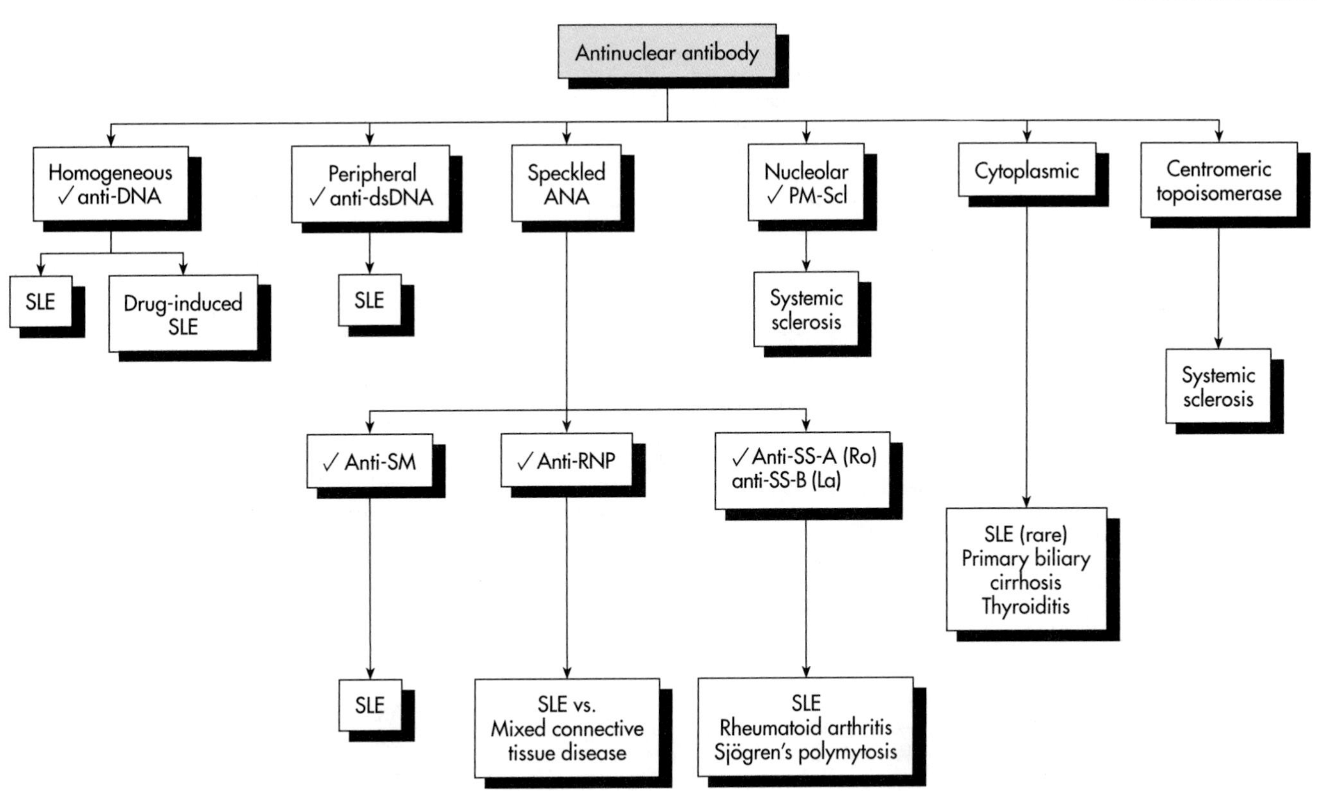

FIGURE 3-24 Diagnostic tests and diagnoses to consider from antinuclear antibody pattern. *ANA,* Antinuclear antibody; *SLE,* systemic lupus erythematosus. (From Carlson KJ et al: *Primary care of women,* ed 2, St Louis, 2002, Mosby.)

AORTIC DISSECTION

ICD-9CM # 441.00

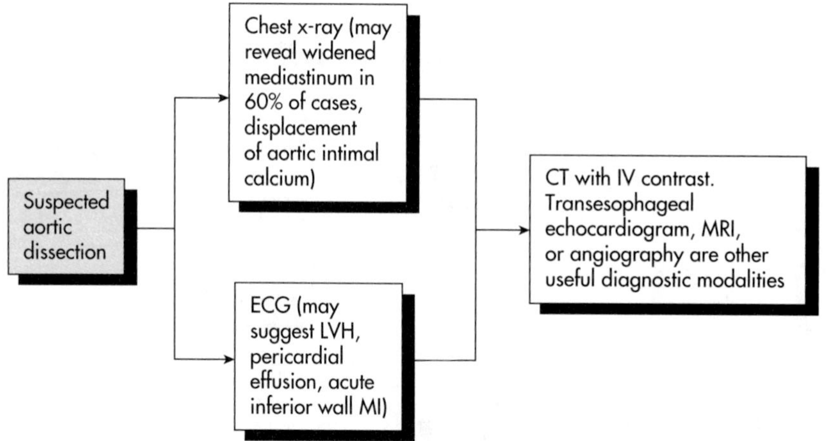

FIGURE 3-25 Aortic dissection. *CT,* Computed tomography; *IV,* intravenous; *LVH,* left ventricular hypertrophy; *MI,* myocardial infarction; *MRI,* magnetic resonance imaging. (From Ferri FF: *Ferri's best test: a practical guide to clinical laboratory medicine and diagnostic imaging,* Philadelphia, 2004, Elsevier Mosby.)

BOX 3-2 **Aortic Dissection**

Diagnostic imaging
Best test
CT (sensitivity 83% to 100%; CT of aorta is generally readily available and performed as the initial diagnostic modality in suspected aortic dissection)
Ancillary tests
MRI (sensitivity 90% to 100%; difficult test for unstable, intubated patient)
Transesophageal echocardiogram (sensitivity 97% to 100%; can also detect aortic insufficiency and pericardial effusion)
Aortography (sensitivity 80% to 90%; involves IV contrast; allows visualization of coronary arteries)
Lab evaluation
Best test
None
Ancillary tests
CBC
BUN, creatinine

From Ferri FF: *Ferri's best test: a practical guide to clinical laboratory medicine and diagnostic imaging,* Philadelphia, 2004, Elsevier Mosby.
BUN, Blood urea nitrogen; *CBC,* complete blood count; *CT,* computed tomography; *MRI,* magnetic resonance imaging.

ARTHRALGIA LIMITED TO ONE OR FEW JOINTS

ICD-9CM # 719.40 Arthralgia site NOS
719.41 Arthralgia, shoulder region
719.42 Arthralgia, upper arm
719.43 Arthralgia, forearm
719.44 Arthralgia, hand
719.45 Arthralgia, pelvic region and thigh
719.46 Arthralgia, lower leg
719.47 Arthralgia, ankle and/or foot

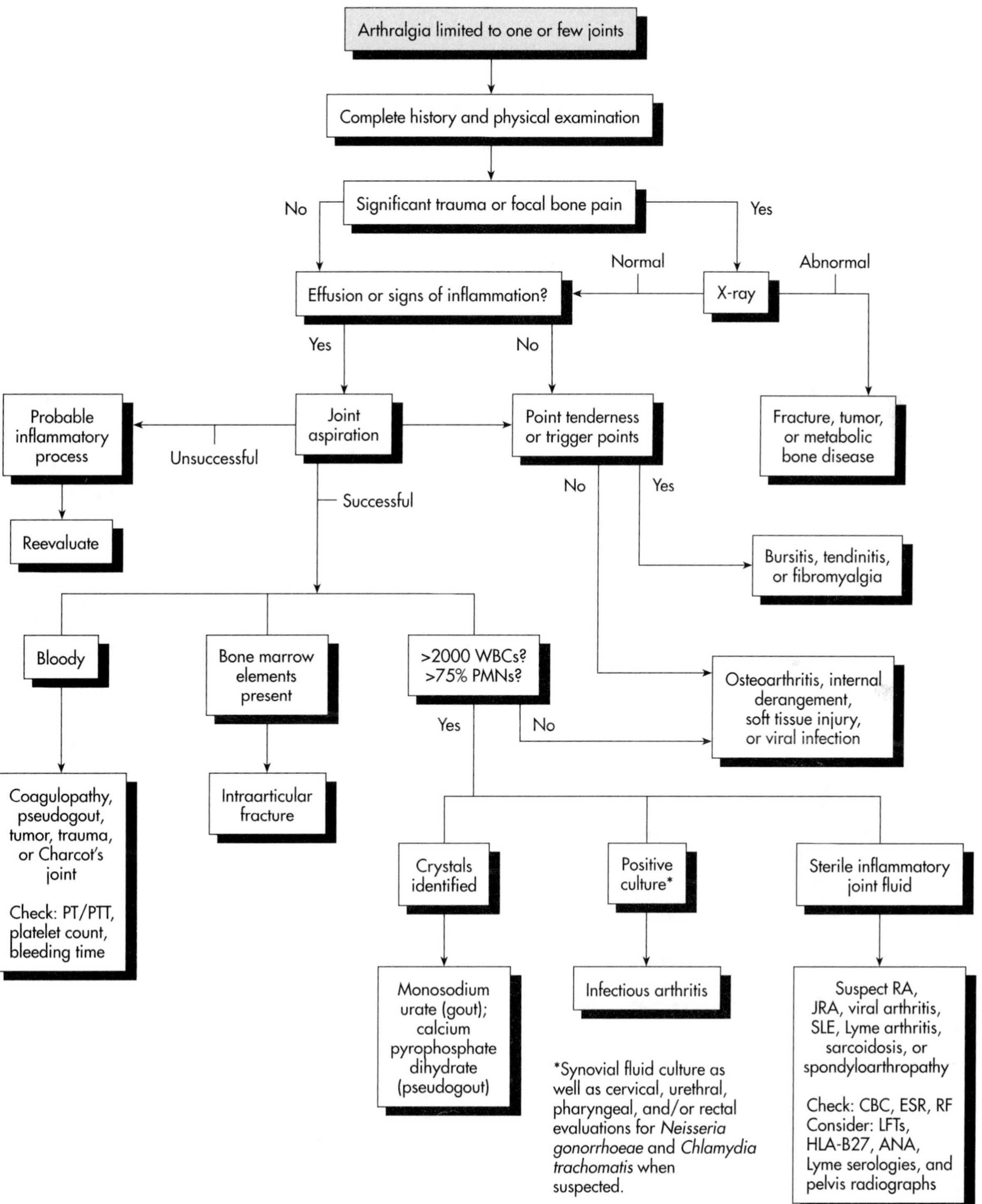

FIGURE 3-26 A diagnostic approach to arthralgia in a few joints. *ANA,* Antinuclear antibodies; *CBC,* complete blood count; *ESR,* erythrocyte sedimentation rate; *JRA,* juvenile rheumatoid arthritis; *LFTs,* liver function tests; *PMNs,* polymorphonuclear neutrophils; *PT,* prothrombin time; *PTT,* partial thromboplastin time; *RA,* rheumatoid arthritis; *RF,* rheumatoid factor; *SLE,* systemic lupus erythematosus; *WBCs,* white blood cells. (Modified from American College of Rheumatology Ad Hoc Committee on Clinical Guidelines: *Arthritis Rheum* 39:1, 1996.)

ASCITES

ICD-9CM # 789.5 Ascites NOS
197.6 Ascites, cancerous (malignant) M8000/6
457.8 Chylous
014.0 Tuberculous

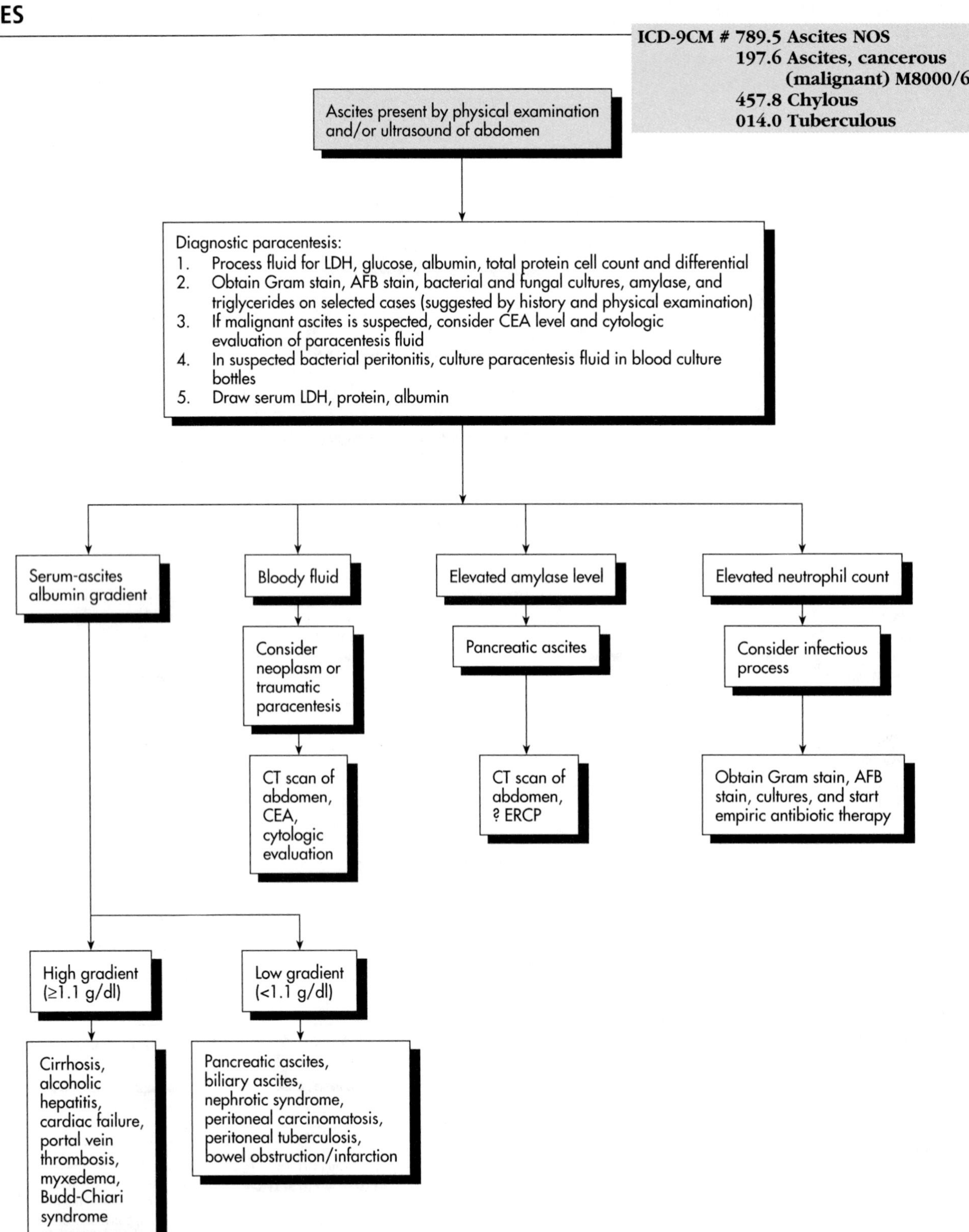

FIGURE 3-27 Evaluation of ascites. *AFB,* Acid-fast bacillus; *CEA,* carcinoembryonic antigen; *CT,* computed tomography; *ERCP,* endoscopic retrograde cholangiopancreatography; *LDH,* lactate dehydrogenase.

ASPIRATION, GASTRIC CONTENTS

ICD-9CM # 507.0

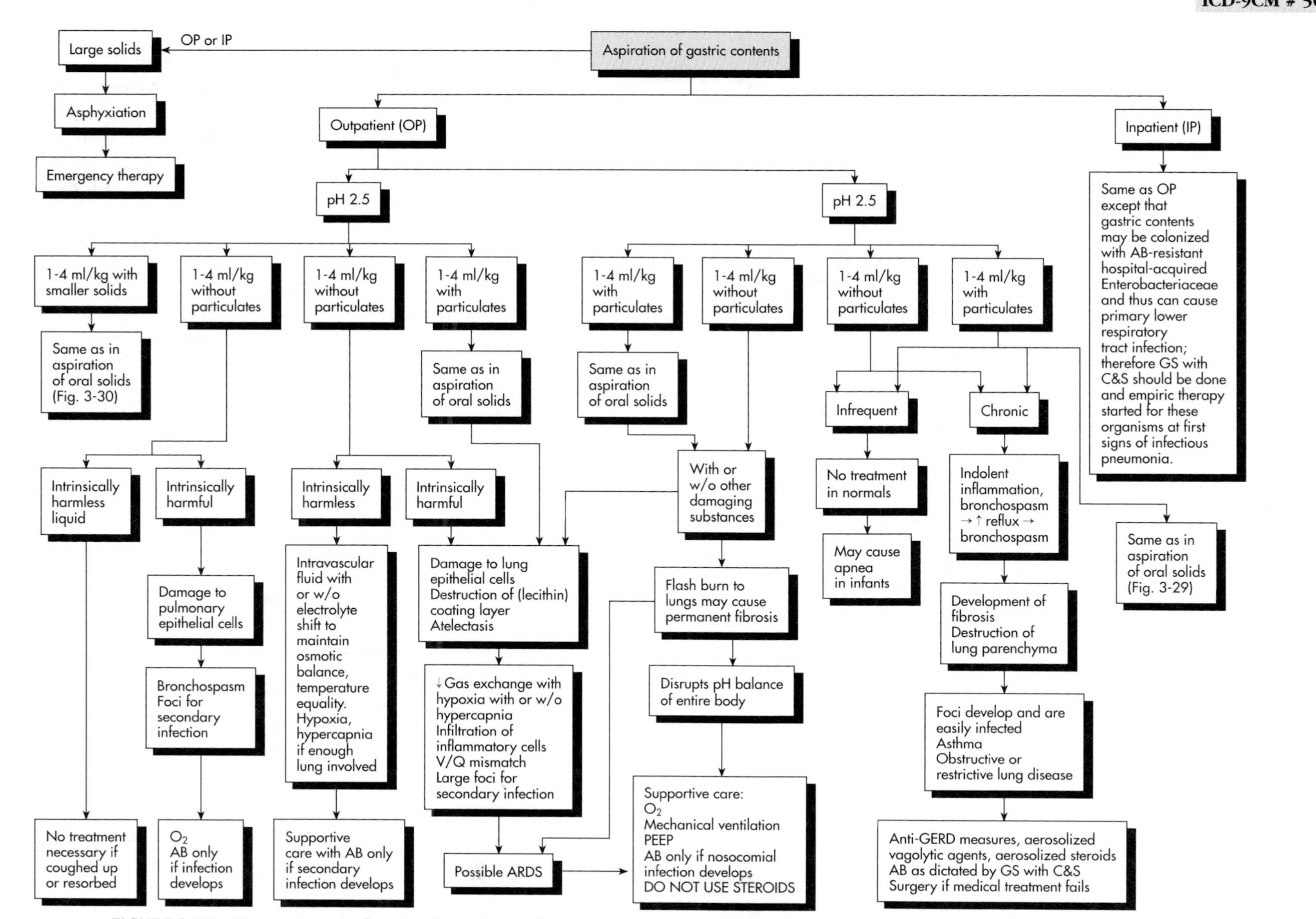

FIGURE 3-28 Management of aspiration of gastric contents. *AB,* Antibiotics; *ARDS,* acute respiratory distress syndrome; *C&S,* culture and sensitivity; *GERD,* gastroesophageal reflux disease; *GS,* Gram's stain; *PEEP,* positive end-expiratory pressure; *V/Q,* ventilation-perfusion. (From Kassirer J [ed]: *Current therapy in adult medicine,* ed 4, St Louis, 1998, Mosby.)

ASPIRATION, ORAL CONTENTS

ICD-9CM # 507.0

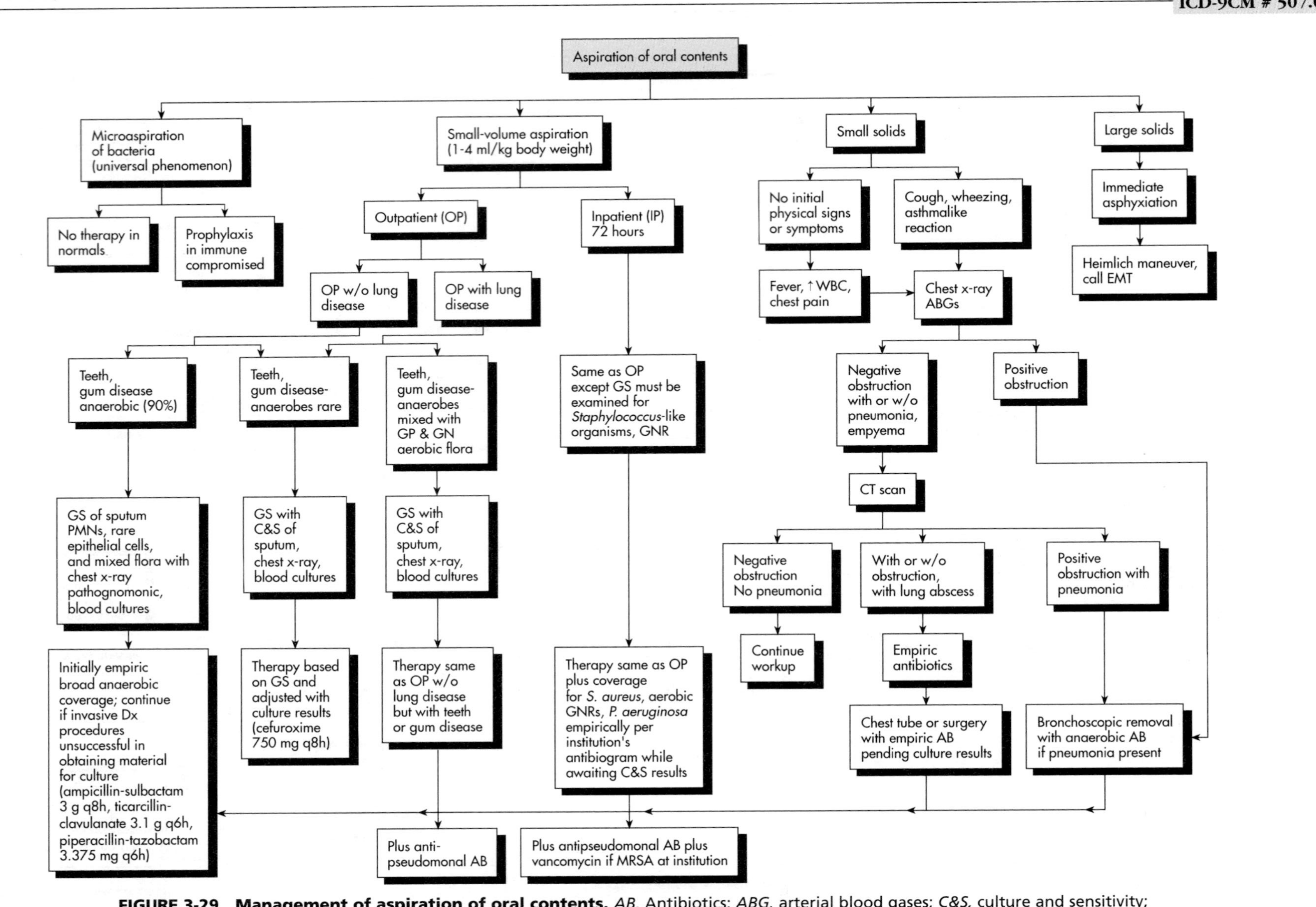

FIGURE 3-29 Management of aspiration of oral contents. *AB,* Antibiotics; *ABG,* arterial blood gases; *C&S,* culture and sensitivity; *CT,* computed tomography; *Dx,* diagnostic; *EMT,* emergency medical technician; *GN,* gram-negative; *GNRs,* gram-negative rods; *GP,* gram-positive; *GS,* Gram stain; *MRSA,* methicillin-resistant *Staphylococcus aureus; PMNs,* polymorphonuclear leukocytes; *WBC,* white blood cells. (From Kassirer J [ed]: *Current therapy in adult medicine,* ed 4, St Louis, 1998, Mosby.)

ICD-9CM # 493.9 Asthma, unspecified
493.1 Intrinsic asthma
493.0 Extrinsic asthma

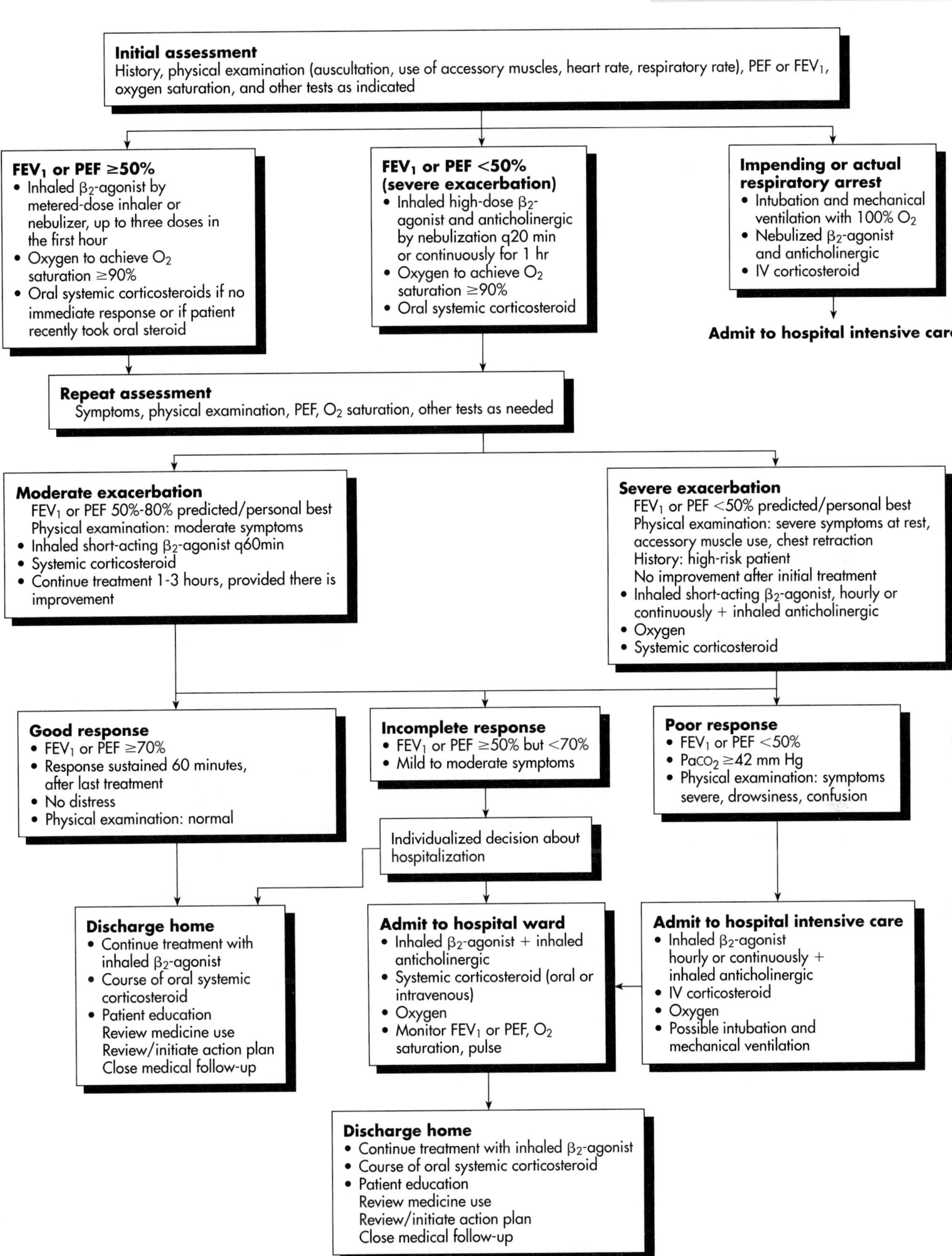

Initial assessment
History, physical examination (auscultation, use of accessory muscles, heart rate, respiratory rate), PEF or FEV_1, oxygen saturation, and other tests as indicated
FEV_1 or PEF ≥50%
• Inhaled β_2-agonist by metered-dose inhaler or nebulizer, up to three doses in the first hour
• Oxygen to achieve O_2 saturation ≥90%
• Oral systemic corticosteroids if no immediate response or if patient recently took oral steroid
FEV_1 or PEF <50% (severe exacerbation)
• Inhaled high-dose β_2-agonist and anticholinergic by nebulization q20 min or continuously for 1 hr
• Oxygen to achieve O_2 saturation ≥90%
• Oral systemic corticosteroid
Impending or actual respiratory arrest
• Intubation and mechanical ventilation with 100% O_2
• Nebulized β_2-agonist and anticholinergic
• IV corticosteroid
Admit to hospital intensive care
Repeat assessment
Symptoms, physical examination, PEF, O_2 saturation, other tests as needed
Moderate exacerbation
FEV_1 or PEF 50%-80% predicted/personal best
Physical examination: moderate symptoms
• Inhaled short-acting β_2-agonist q60min
• Systemic corticosteroid
• Continue treatment 1-3 hours, provided there is improvement
Severe exacerbation
FEV_1 or PEF <50% predicted/personal best
Physical examination: severe symptoms at rest, accessory muscle use, chest retraction
History: high-risk patient
No improvement after initial treatment
• Inhaled short-acting β_2-agonist, hourly or continuously + inhaled anticholinergic
• Oxygen
• Systemic corticosteroid
Good response
• FEV_1 or PEF ≥70%
• Response sustained 60 minutes, after last treatment
• No distress
• Physical examination: normal
Incomplete response
• FEV_1 or PEF ≥50% but <70%
• Mild to moderate symptoms
Poor response
• FEV_1 or PEF <50%
• $PaCO_2$ ≥42 mm Hg
• Physical examination: symptoms severe, drowsiness, confusion
Individualized decision about hospitalization
Discharge home
• Continue treatment with inhaled β_2-agonist
• Course of oral systemic corticosteroid
• Patient education
Review medicine use
Review/initiate action plan
Close medical follow-up
Admit to hospital ward
• Inhaled β_2-agonist + inhaled anticholinergic
• Systemic corticosteroid (oral or intravenous)
• Oxygen
• Monitor FEV_1 or PEF, O_2 saturation, pulse
Admit to hospital intensive care
• Inhaled β_2-agonist hourly or continuously + inhaled anticholinergic
• IV corticosteroid
• Oxygen
• Possible intubation and mechanical ventilation
Discharge home
• Continue treatment with inhaled β_2-agonist
• Course of oral systemic corticosteroid
• Patient education
Review medicine use
Review/initiate action plan
Close medical follow-up

FIGURE 3-30 Management of asthma exacerbations: emergency department and hospital-based care. *FEV_1*, Forced expiratory volume in 1 second; *PEF*, peak expiratory flow. (From National Asthma Education and Prevention Program: *Guidelines for the diagnosis and management of asthma*, NIH Pub No 97-4051A, Bethesda, Md, 1997, National Institutes of Health, National Heart, Lung, and Blood Institute.)

ASTHMA, HOME MANAGEMENT

ICD-9CM # 493.9 Asthma, unspecified
493.1 Intrinsic asthma
493.0 Extrinsic asthma

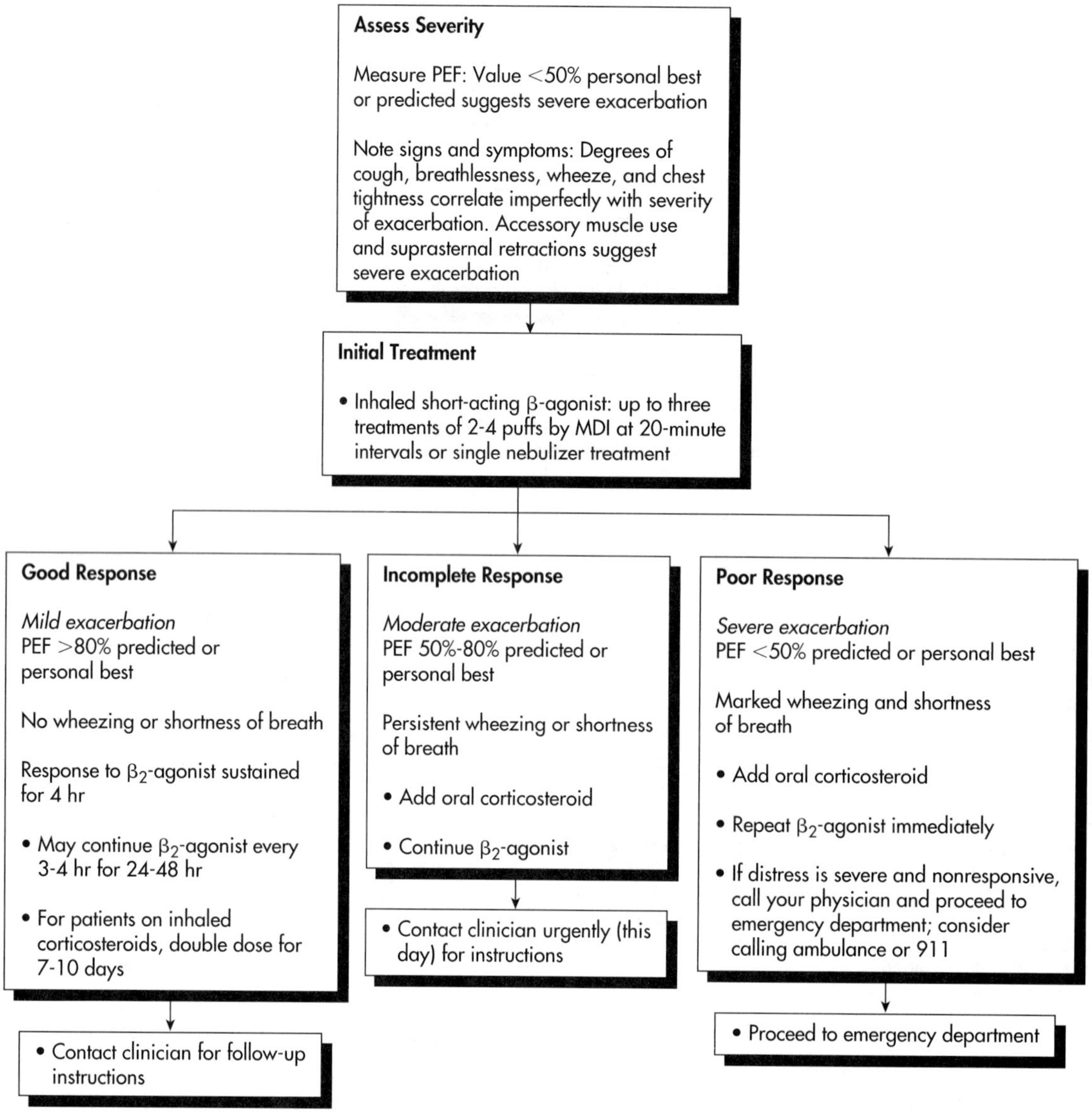

Assess Severity

Measure PEF: Value <50% personal best or predicted suggests severe exacerbation

Note signs and symptoms: Degrees of cough, breathlessness, wheeze, and chest tightness correlate imperfectly with severity of exacerbation. Accessory muscle use and suprasternal retractions suggest severe exacerbation

↓

Initial Treatment

- Inhaled short-acting β-agonist: up to three treatments of 2-4 puffs by MDI at 20-minute intervals or single nebulizer treatment

↓

Good Response

Mild exacerbation
PEF >80% predicted or personal best

No wheezing or shortness of breath

Response to β_2-agonist sustained for 4 hr

- May continue β_2-agonist every 3-4 hr for 24-48 hr
- For patients on inhaled corticosteroids, double dose for 7-10 days

↓

- Contact clinician for follow-up instructions

Incomplete Response

Moderate exacerbation
PEF 50%-80% predicted or personal best

Persistent wheezing or shortness of breath

- Add oral corticosteroid
- Continue β_2-agonist

↓

- Contact clinician urgently (this day) for instructions

Poor Response

Severe exacerbation
PEF <50% predicted or personal best

Marked wheezing and shortness of breath

- Add oral corticosteroid
- Repeat β_2-agonist immediately
- If distress is severe and nonresponsive, call your physician and proceed to emergency department; consider calling ambulance or 911

↓

- Proceed to emergency department

FIGURE 3-31 Home management of acute asthma. *MDI,* Metered-dose inhaler; *PEF,* peak expiratory flow rate. (Modified from National Asthma Education and Prevention Program, National Heart, Lung, and Blood Institute, Expert Panel Report 2: *Guidelines for the diagnosis and management of asthma,* NIH Pub No 97-4051, July 1997.)

BACK PAIN

ICD-9CM # 847.9

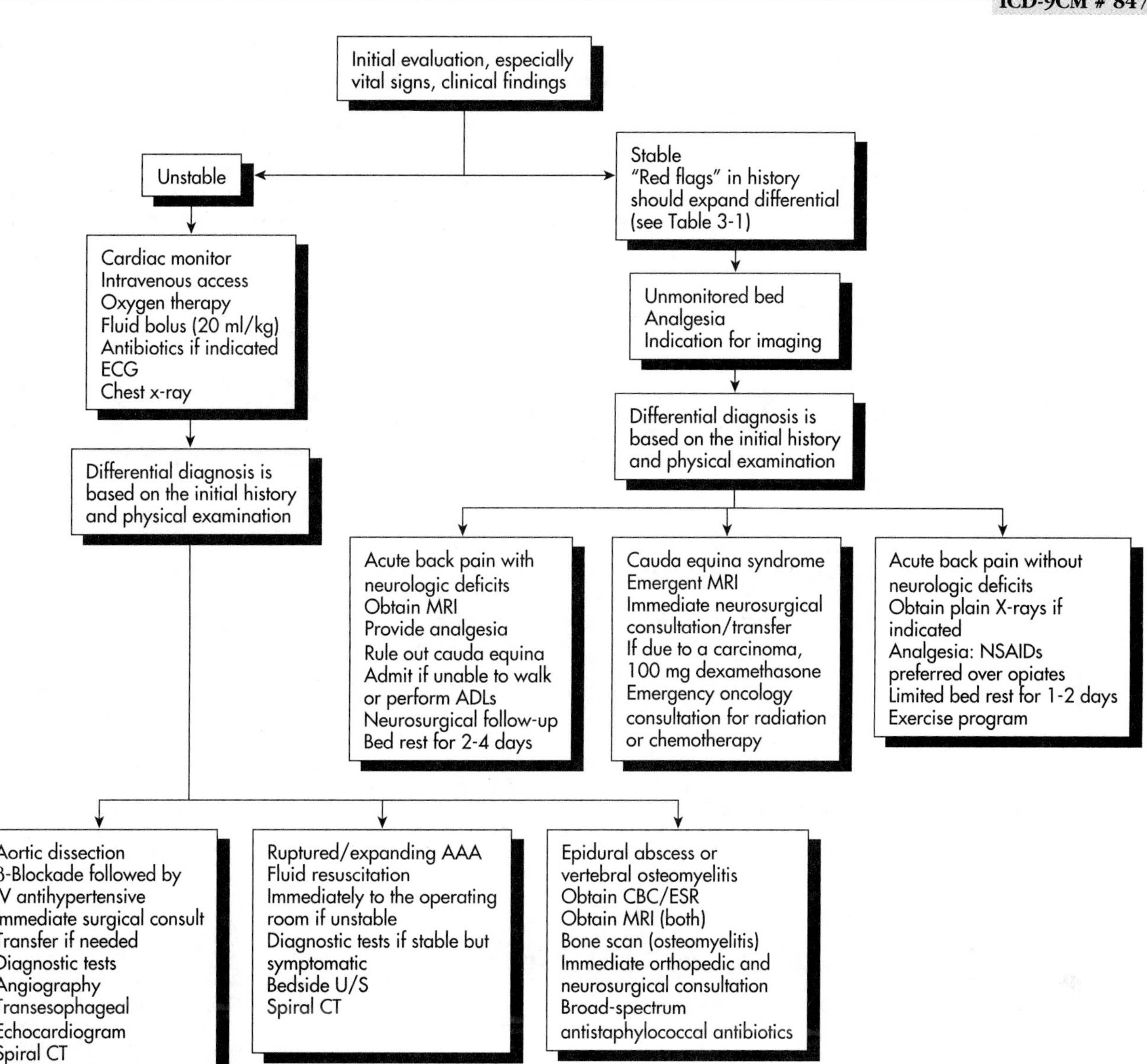

FIGURE 3-32 Management of acute low back pain. *AAA,* Abdominal aortic aneurysm; *ADL,* activities of daily living; *CBC,* complete blood count; *CT,* computed tomography; *ECG,* electrocardiogram; *ESR,* erythrocyte sedimentation rate; *IV,* intravenous; *NSAIDs,* nonsteroidal antiinflammatory drugs. (From Marx JA [ed]: *Rosen's emergency medicine,* ed 5, St Louis 2002, Mosby.)

TABLE 3-1 **Red Flags for Potentially Serious Conditions**

Possible Fracture	Possible Tumor or Infection	Possible Cauda Equina Syndrome
From Medical History		
Major trauma, such as vehicle accident or fall from height	Age over 50 or under 20 yr	Saddle anesthesia
Minor trauma or even strenuous lifting (in older or potentially osteoporotic patient)	History of cancer	Recent onset of bladder dysfunction, such as urinary retention, increased frequency, or overflow incontinence
	Constitutional symptoms, such as recent fever or chills or unexplained weight loss	Severe or progressive neurologic deficit in the lower extremity
	Risk factors for spinal infection: recent bacterial infection (e.g., urinary tract infection); intravenous drug abuse; or immune suppression (from steroids, transplant, or human immunodeficiency virus)	
	Pain that worsens when supine; severe nighttime pain	

SECTION III

BILIRUBIN ELEVATION

ICD-9CM # 782.4

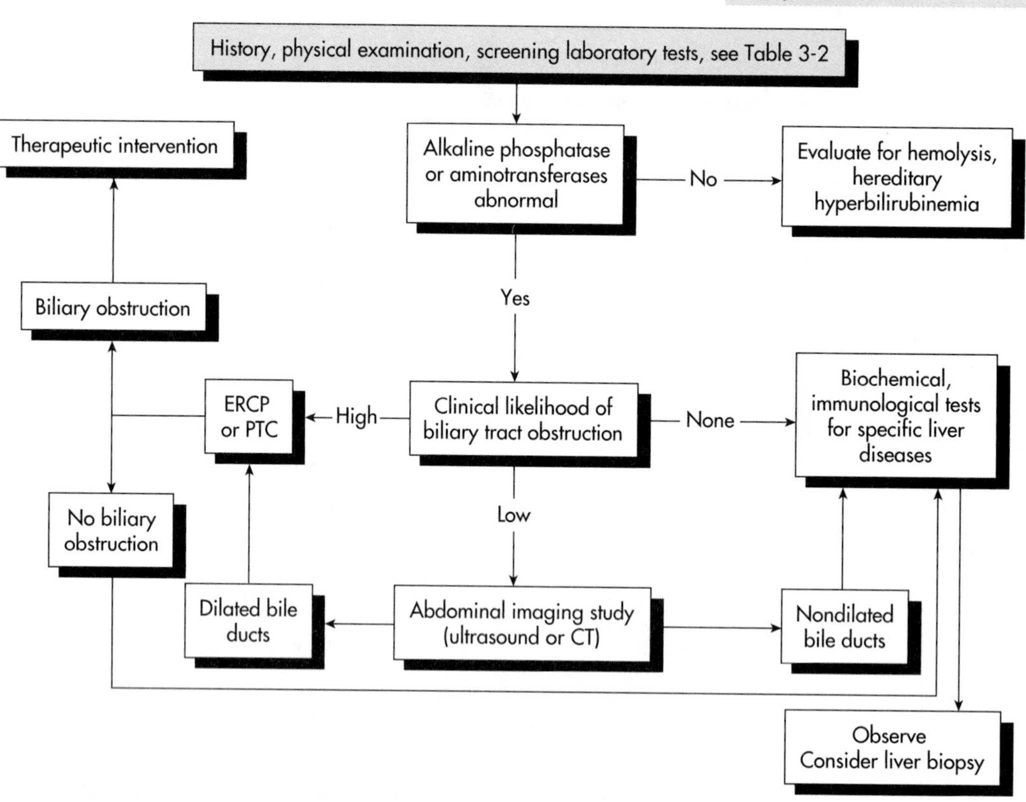

FIGURE 3-33 Diagnosis algorithm for the evaluation of hyperbilirubinemia and other liver test abnormalities and/or signs and symptoms suggestive of liver disease. *CT,* Computed tomography; *ERCP,* endoscopic retrograde cholangiopancreatography; *PTC,* percutaneous cholangiogram. (From Goldman L, Ausiello D [eds]: *Cecil textbook of medicine,* ed 22, Philadelphia, 2004, WB Saunders. Modified from Lidofsky SD, Scharschmidt BF: Jaundice, *in* Feldman M, Scharschmidt BF, Sleisenger MH [eds] *Gastrointestinal and liver disease,* ed 6, Philadelphia, 1998, WB Saunders.)

TABLE 3-2 Obstructive Jaundice Versus Cholestatic Liver Disease

Feature	Suggests Obstructive Jaundice	Suggests Parenchymal Liver Disease
History	Abdominal pain Fever, rigors Prior biliary surgery Older age Acholic stools	Anorexia, malaise, myalgias, suggestive of viral prodrome Known infectious exposure Receipt of blood products, use of intravenous drugs Exposure to known hepatotoxin Family history of jaundice
Physical examination	High fever Abdominal tenderness Palpable abdominal mass Abdominal scar	Ascites Other stigmata of liver disease (e.g., prominent abdominal veins, gynecomastia, spider angiomata, asterixis, encephalopathy, Kayser-Fleischer rings)
Laboratory studies	Predominant elevation of serum bilirubin and alkaline phosphatase Prothrombin time that is normal or normalizes with vitamin K administration Elevated serum amylase	Predominant elevation of serum aminotransferases Prolonged prothrombin time that does not correct with vitamin K administration Blood tests indicative of specific liver disease

From Goldman L, Ausiello D (eds): *Cecil textbook of medicine,* ed 22, Philadelphia, 2004, WB Saunders.

BLEEDING, CONGENITAL DISORDER

ICD-9CM # 286.9

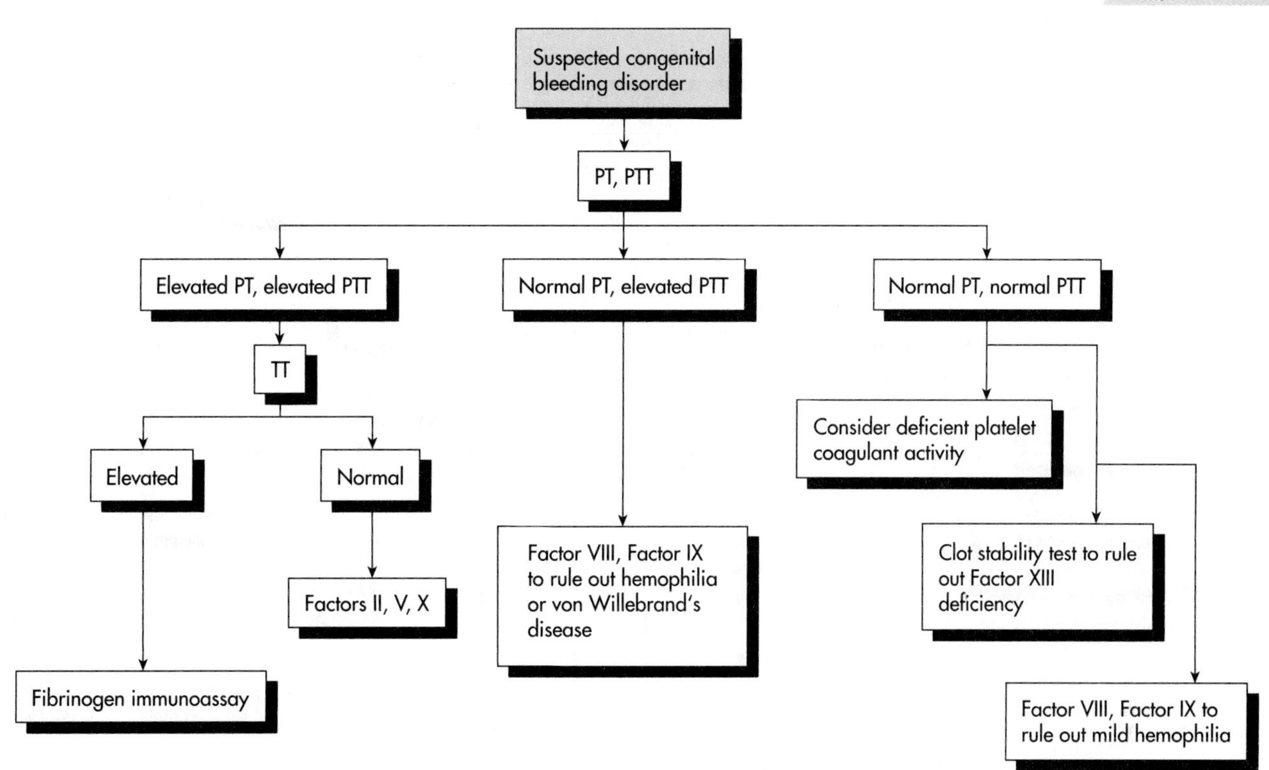

FIGURE 3-34 Bleeding, congenital disorder. *PT,* Prothrombin time; *PTT,* partial thromboplastin time; *TT,* thrombin time.

BLEEDING, EARLY PREGNANCY

ICD-9CM # 641.9 Vaginal bleeding NOS in pregnancy

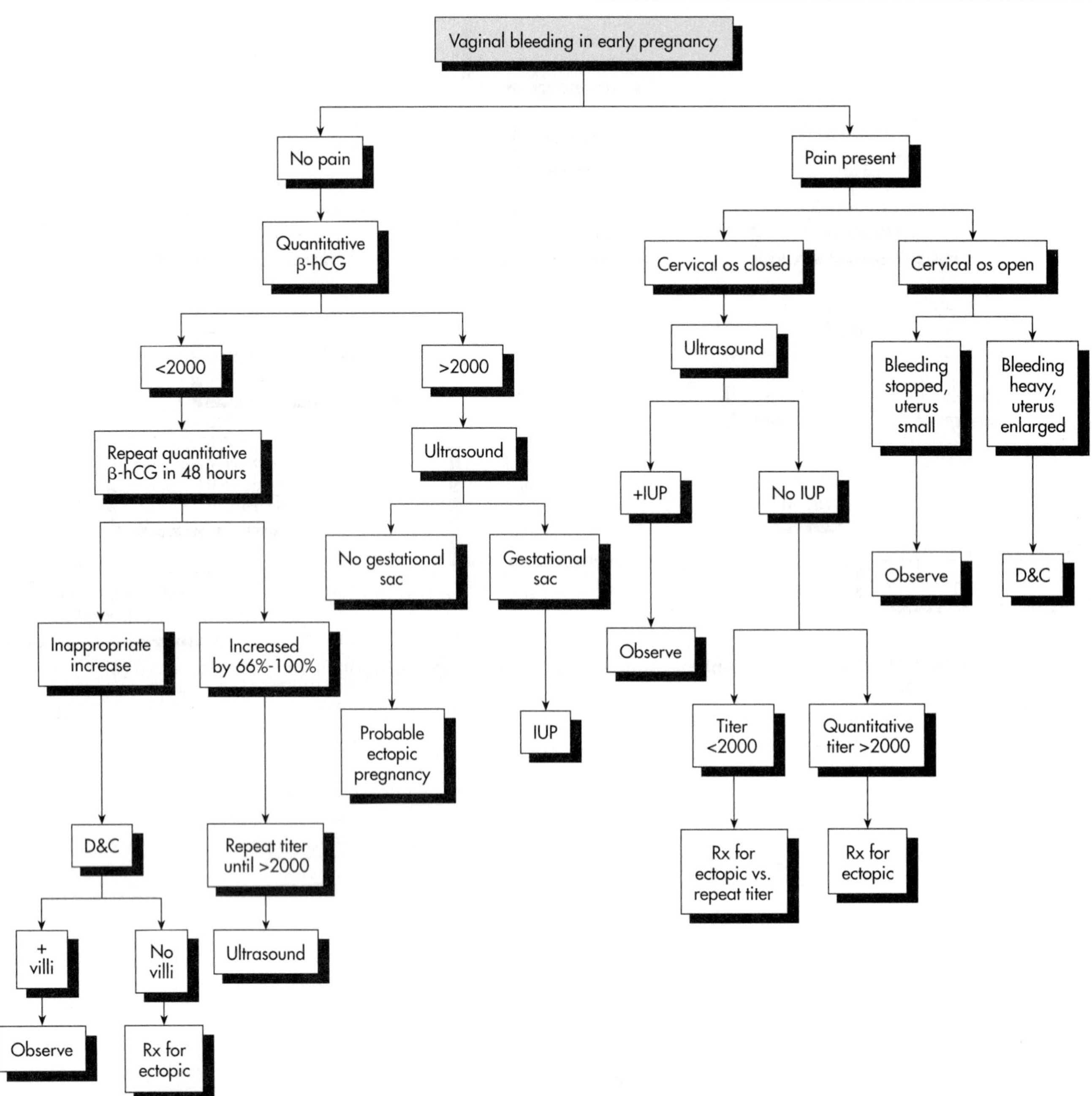

FIGURE 3-35 Diagnosis of vaginal bleeding in early pregnancy. *D&C,* Dilation and curettage; *β-hCG,* β-human chorionic gonadotropin; *IUP,* intrauterine pregnancy. (From Carlson KJ et al: *Primary care of women,* ed 2, St Louis, 2002, Mosby.)

BLEEDING, GASTROINTESTINAL

ICD-9CM # 578.9

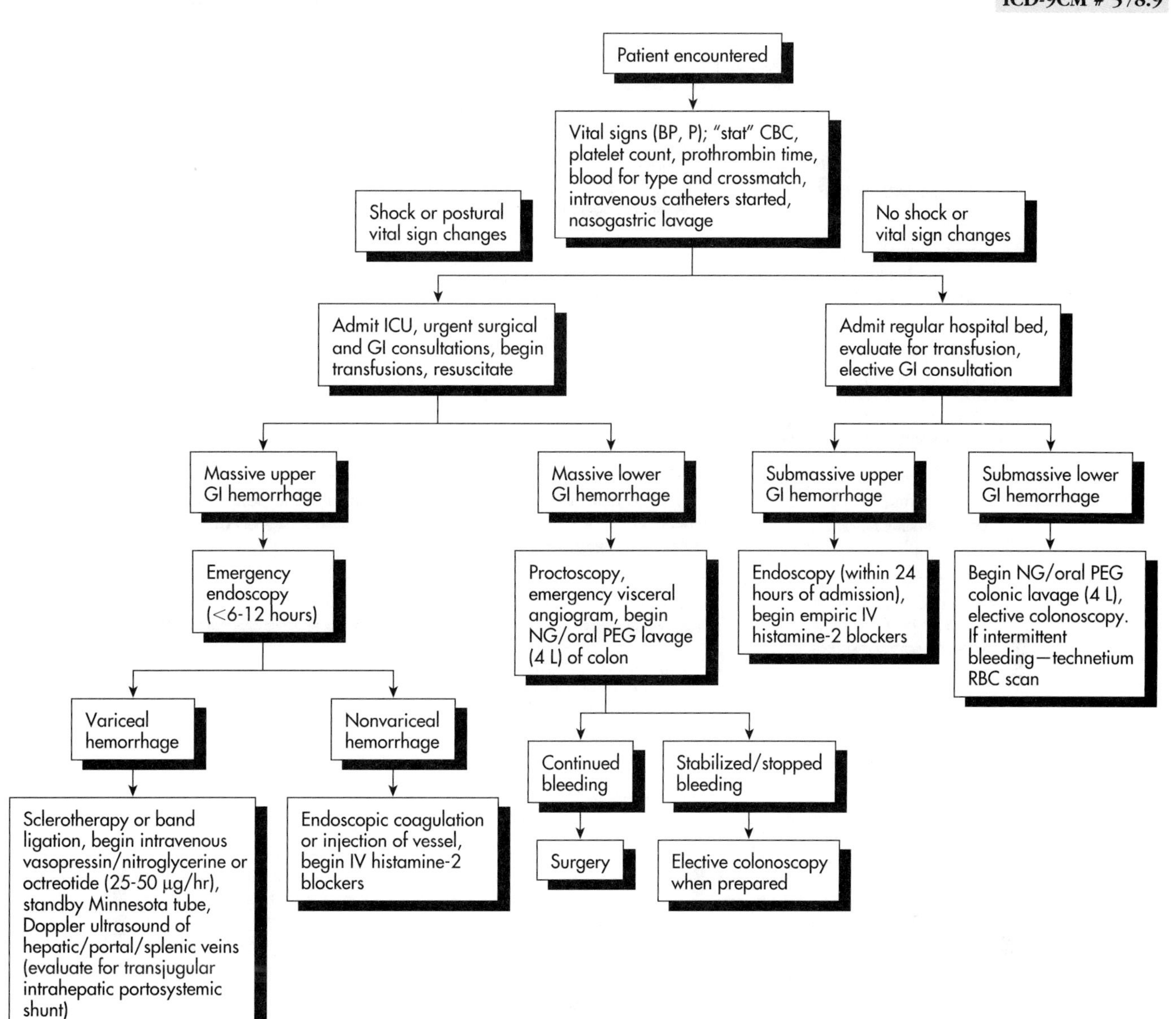

FIGURE 3-36 Approach to the patient with gastrointestinal hemorrhage. *BP,* Blood pressure; *CBC,* complete blood count; *GI,* gastrointestinal; *ICU,* intensive care unit; *IV,* intravenous; *NG,* nasogastric; *P,* weight; *PEG,* percutaneous endoscopic gastrostomy; *RBC,* red blood cell. (From Goldman L, Ausiello D [eds]: *Cecil textbook of medicine,* ed 22, Philadelphia, 2004, WB Saunders.)

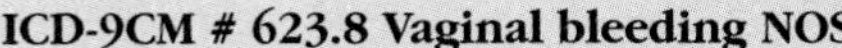

BLEEDING, VAGINAL

ICD-9CM # 623.8 Vaginal bleeding NOS

A

Determine bleeding pattern

- Ovulatory bleeding
  - Heavy bleeding (menorrhagia)
    - Evaluate for anemia, coagulopathy, hypothyroidism, medication use, structural lesions (fibroids)
      - No abnormalities → Reassure or treat with OCs or NSAIDs
      - Iron deficiency, otherwise normal evaluation → Treat with OCs or NSAIDs → No response → Refer to a gynecologist
      - Structural lesion, severe anemia → Refer to a gynecologist
- Intermenstrual bleeding (see Fig. 3-37, *B*)
- Anovulatory bleeding (see Fig. 3-37, *C*)

B

Pregnancy test

- Negative
  - Patient using OCs → Advise additional contraception; encourage compliance; ask about use of medications associated with breakthrough bleeding → No response → Consider changing OC formulation → No response; consider referral to a gynecologist
  - Patient not using OCs → Evaluate for structural lesions: cervicitis, cervical polyps, cervical CA, vaginal lacerations, and fibroids → No obvious cause; refer for hysteroscopy, endometrial sampling
- Positive (possible threatened abortion, ectopic pregnancy)

FIGURE 3-37 A, Evaluation of ovulatory bleeding. B, Evaluation of intermenstrual bleeding. *NSAIDs,* nonsteroidal antiinflammatory drugs; *OCs,* oral contraceptives. (From Appleby J, Henderson M, Wathen PI: *Intern Med* Sept:17, 1996.)

BLEEDING, VAGINAL—cont'd

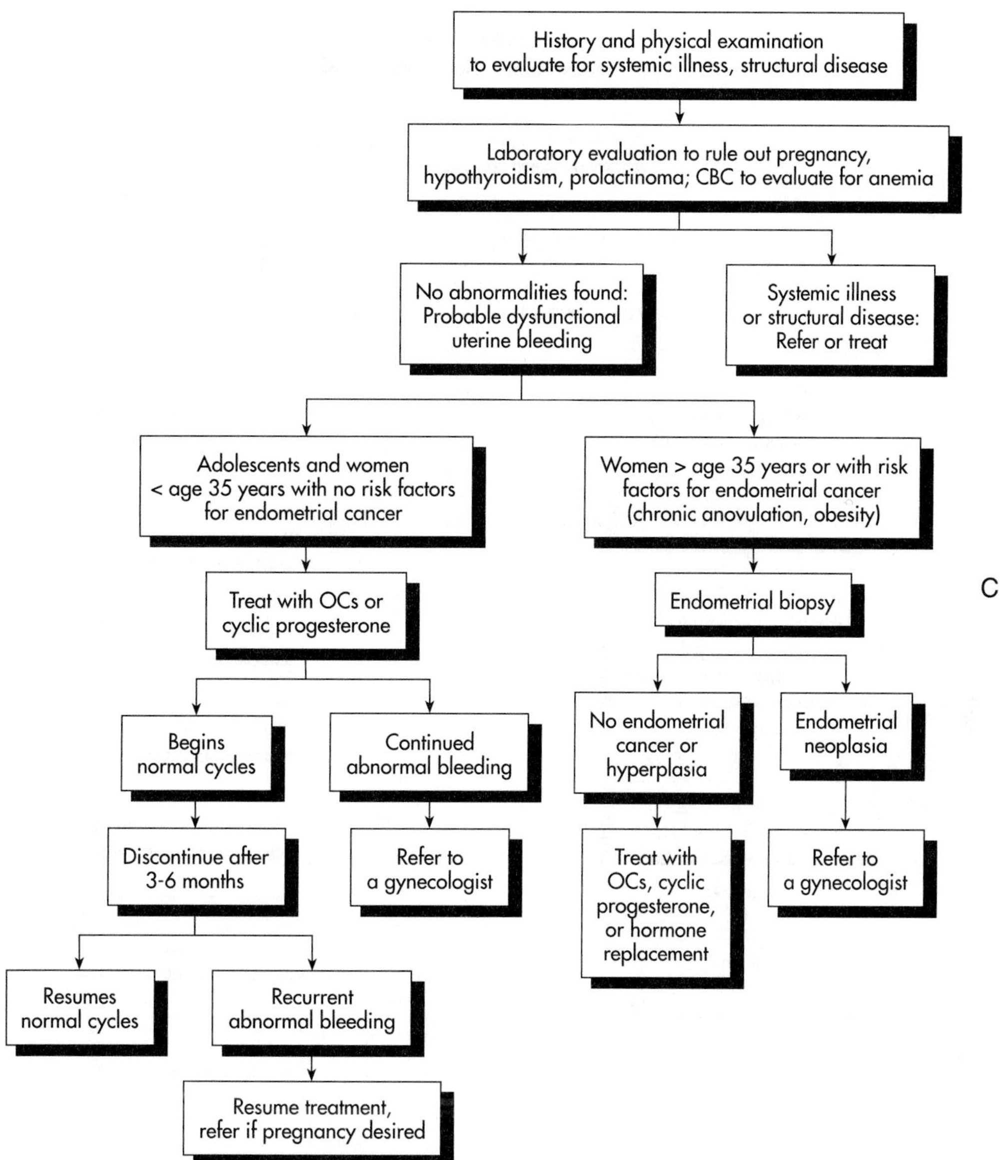

FIGURE 3-37 cont'd C, Evaluation of anovulatory bleeding. *CBC,* Complete blood count; *OCs,* oral contraceptives. (From Appleby J, Henderson M, Wathen PI: *Intern Med* Sept:17, 1996.)

BLEEDING, VARICEAL

ICD-9CM # 456.0

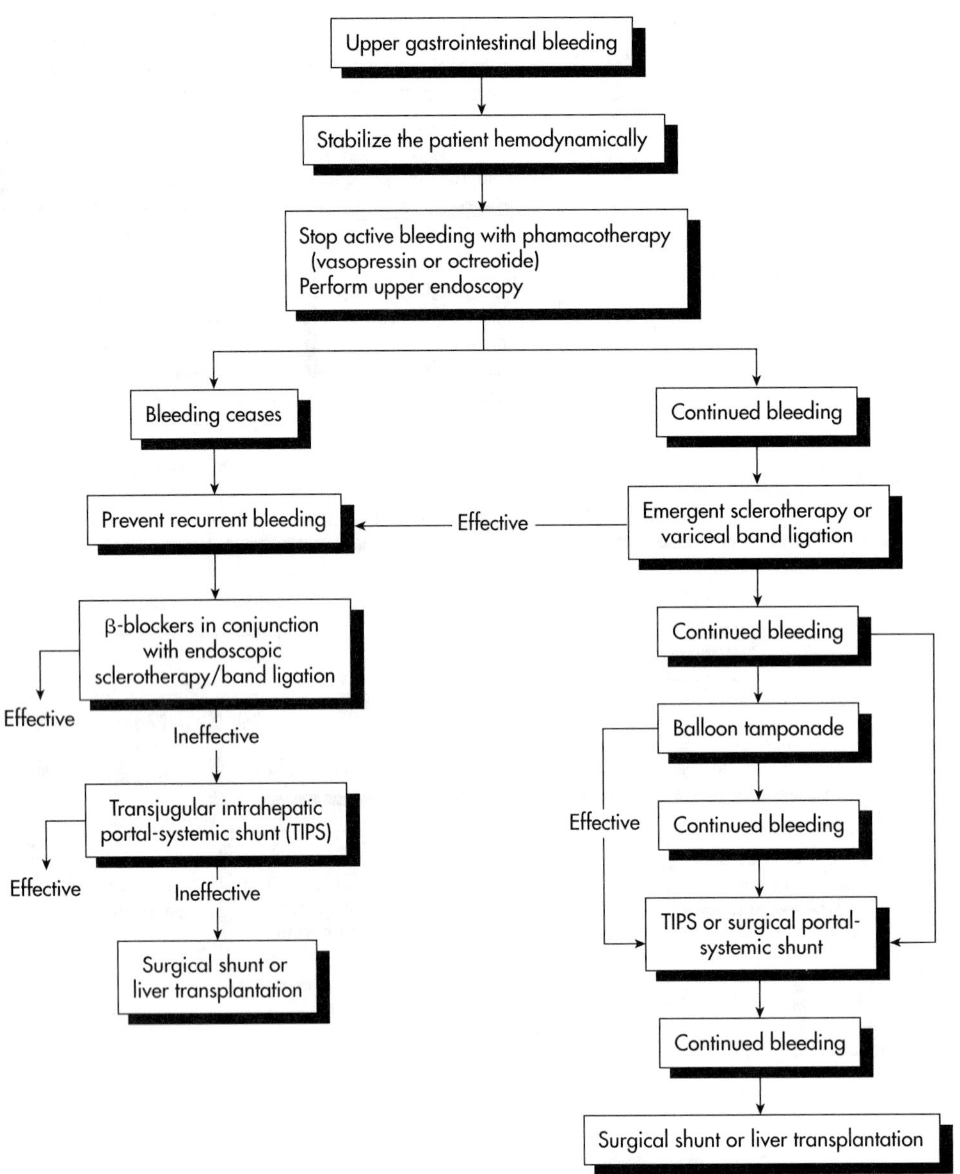

FIGURE 3-38 Management algorithm for variceal bleeding. (From Goldman L, Ausiello D [eds]: *Cecil textbook of medicine,* ed 22, Philadelphia, 2004, WB Saunders.)

BLEEDING DISORDER, CONGENITAL

ICD-9CM # 286.9

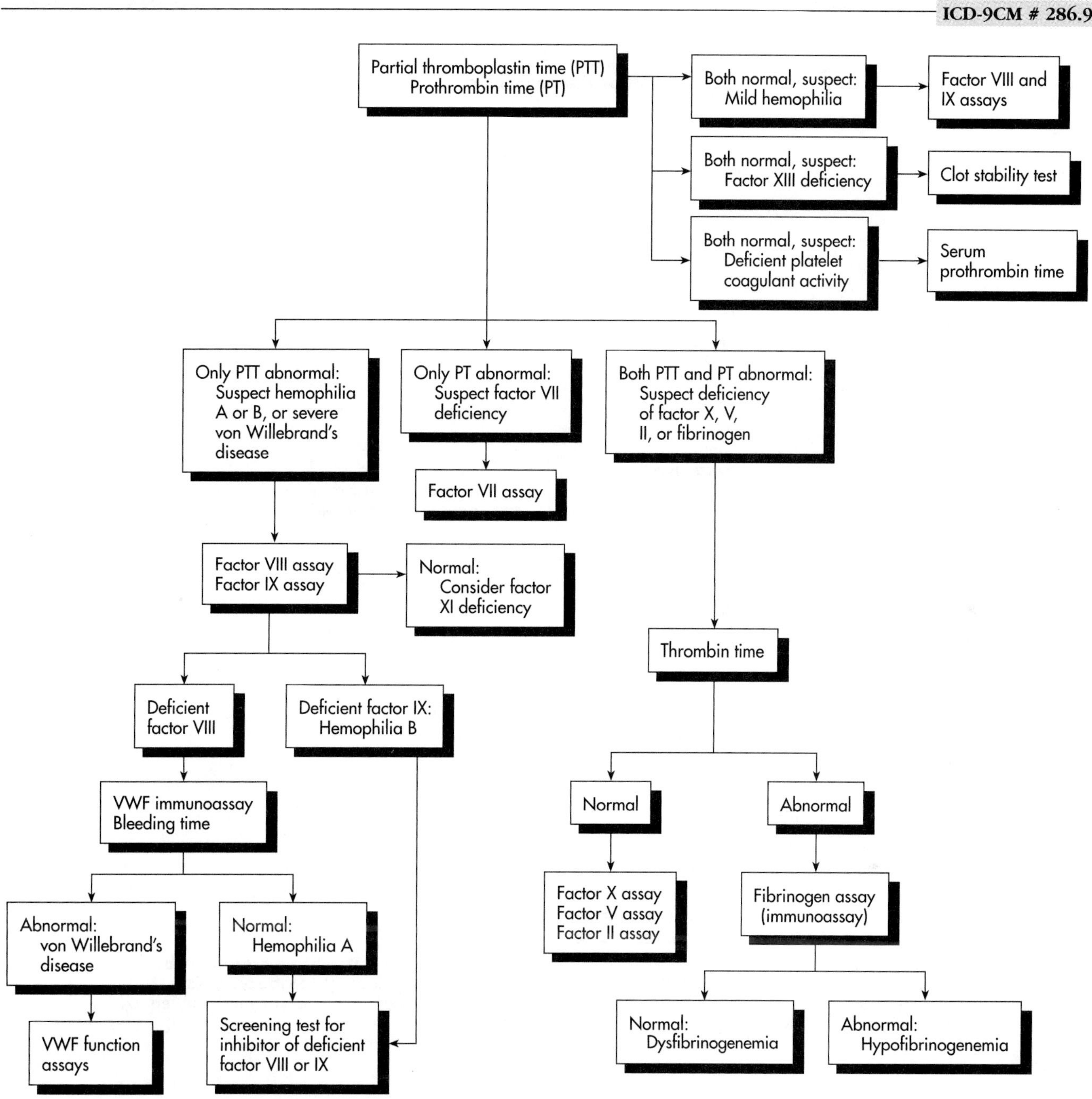

FIGURE 3-39 Laboratory evaluation of a patient with a bleeding disorder in whom the history and physical examination suggest a congenital coagulation disorder. *VWF,* von Willebrand factor. (From Stein JH [ed]: *Internal medicine,* ed 5, St Louis, 1998, Mosby.)

BLEEDING TIME PROLONGATION

ICD-9CM # 790.92

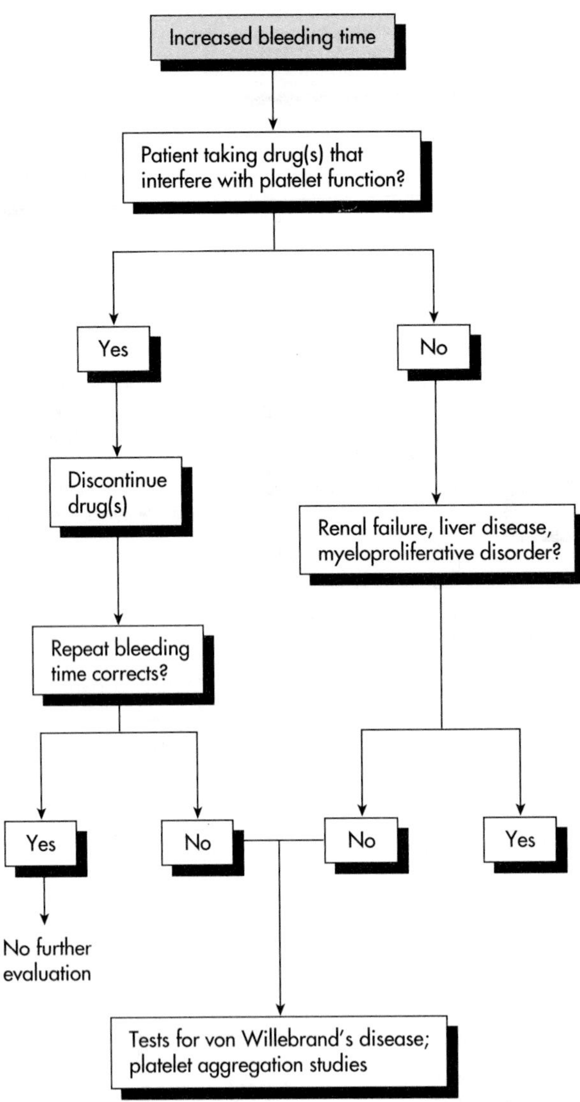

FIGURE 3-40 An algorithm for diagnostic decisions in evaluating patients with a prolonged bleeding time. The scheme assumes that the platelet count is normal, because thrombocytopenia itself can prolong the bleeding time. (From Goldman L, Ausiello D [eds]: *Cecil textbook of medicine,* ed 22, Philadelphia, 2004, WB Saunders.)

BRADYCARDIA

ICD-9CM # 427.89 Unspecified bradycardia
427.81 Chronic bradycardia
770.8 Newborn bradycardia
427.89 Postoperative bradycardia
337 Reflex bradycardia
427.89 Sinus bradycardia

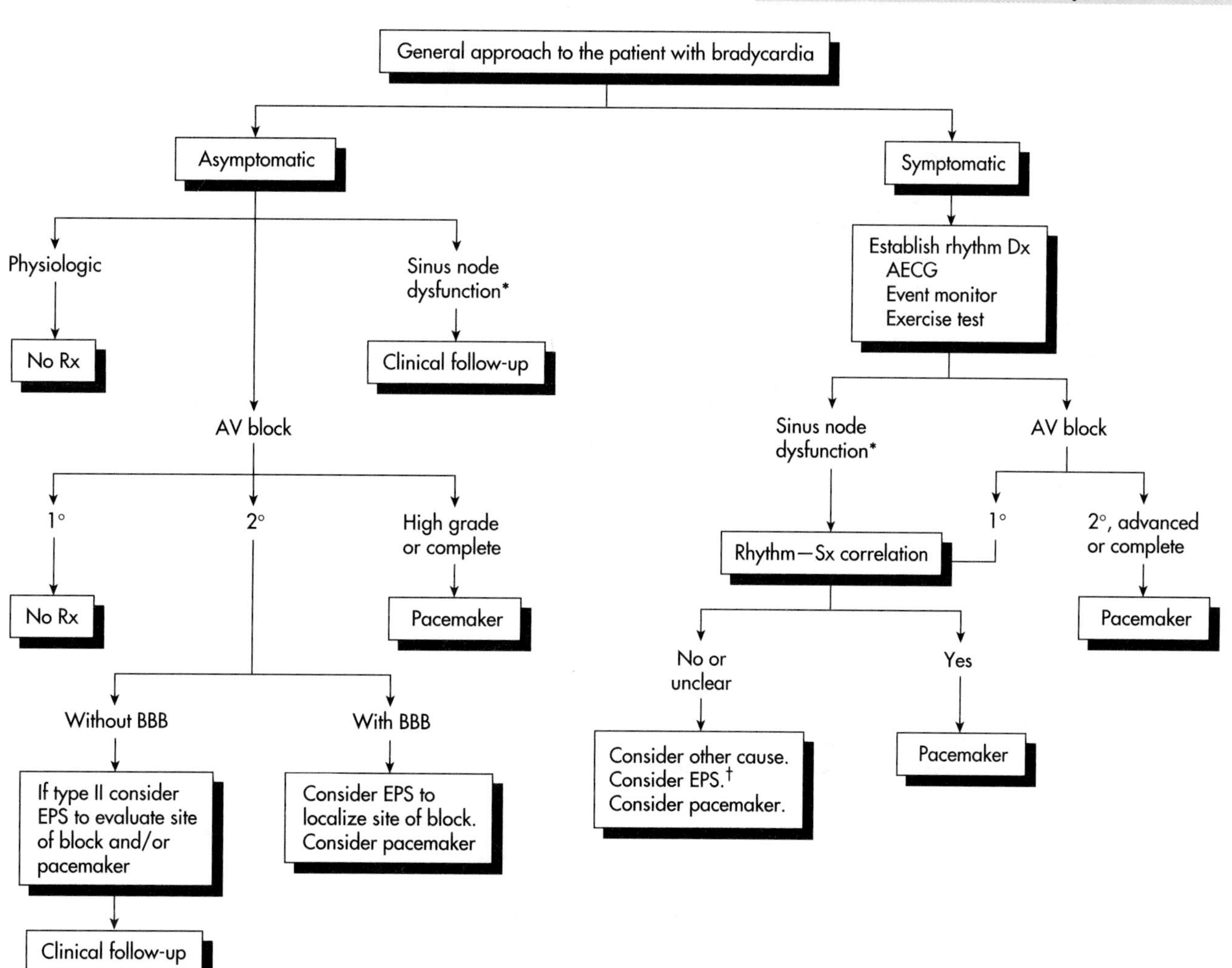

*Includes bradycardia-tachycardia syndrome.
†EPS includes sinus node function and ventricular arrhythmia induction studies.

FIGURE 3-41 General approach to the patient with bradycardia. *AECG,* Ambulatory electrocardiography; *AV,* atrioventricular; *BBB,* bundle branch block; *Dx,* diagnostic; *EPS,* electrophysiologic study; *Rx,* treatment; *Sx,* symptoms; 1°, first-degree; 2°, second-degree. (From Goldman L, Braunwald E [eds]: *Primary cardiology,* Philadelphia, 1998, WB Saunders.)

BREAST, NIPPLE DISCHARGE EVALUATION*

ICD-9CM # 611.79

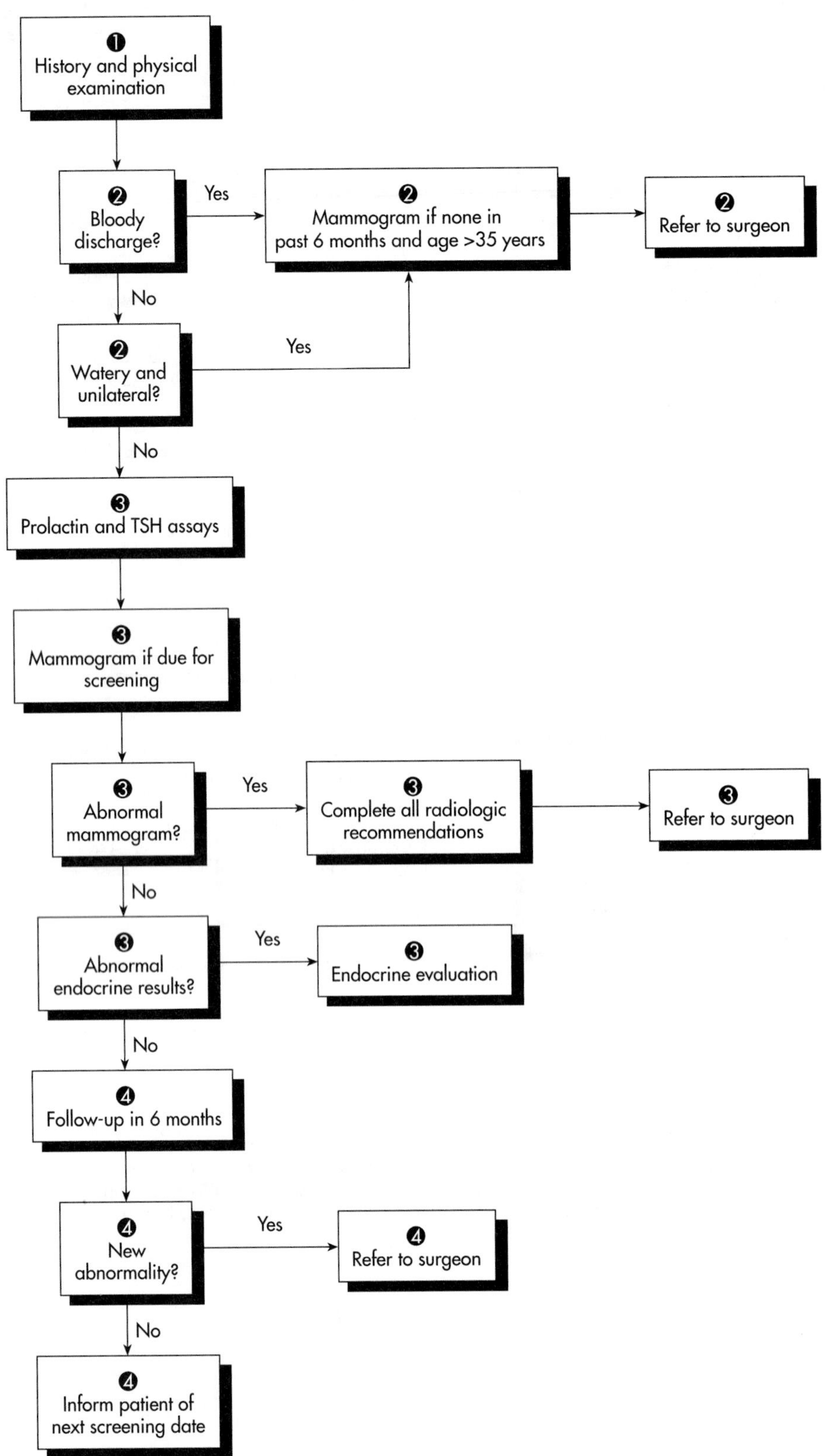

*Without palpable mass.

FIGURE 3-42 Breast cancer screening and evaluation. (From Institute for Clinical Systems Integration, Minneapolis: *Postgrad Med* 100:182, 1996.)

Fig. 3-42, cont'd

1. **HISTORY AND PHYSICAL EXAMINATION.*** Patients who present with a complaint of nipple discharge should be evaluated with breast-related history taking and a physical examination. History taking is aimed at uncovering and characterizing any other breast-related symptom. A risk assessment should also be undertaken for identified risk factors, including patient age over 50 years, any past personal history of breast cancer, history of hyperplasia on previous breast biopsies, and family history of breast cancer in first-degree relatives (mother, sister, daughter). Physical examination should include inspection of the breast for any evidence of ulceration or contour changes and inspection of the nipple for Paget's disease. Palpation should be performed with the patient in both the upright and the supine positions to determine the presence of any palpable mass.
2. **Bloody discharge?** If the discharge appears frankly bloody, the patient should be referred to a surgeon for evaluation. At the time of referral, a mammogram of the involved breast should be obtained if the patient is over 35 years of age and has not had a mammogram within the preceding 6 months. Similarly, patients with a watery, unilateral discharge should be referred to a surgeon for evaluation and possible biopsy.
3. **Endocrine tests. Mammogram.** If the discharge appears frankly milky or is bilateral, serum prolactin and serum thyroid-stimulating hormone (TSH) assays should be performed to rule out the presence of an endocrinologic basis for the symptoms. At the time of that visit, a mammogram should also be performed if the patient is due for routine mammographic screening according to the recommended intervals. A patient with an abnormal mammogram should be further evaluated radiologically to better characterize the lesion and then be referred to a surgeon if appropriate. Make certain that all recommended additional views, ultrasound examinations, and follow-up studies have been obtained before referral to a surgeon. Should the mammogram appear normal, results of the assays for TSH and prolactin should be reviewed. If the results are abnormal the patient should undergo appropriate evaluation for etiology, either by a primary care physician or by an endocrinologist.
4. **Six-month follow-up results.** If results of the mammogram and the endocrinologic screening studies are normal, the patient should return for a follow-up visit in 6 months to ensure that there has been no specific change in the character of the discharge, such as development of frank bleeding or Paget's disease, that would warrant surgical evaluation. If the evaluation at that follow-up visit fails to reveal any palpable or visible abnormalities, the patient should be returned to the routine screening process with studies performed at the recommended intervals.

---

*ICSI healthcare guidelines are designed to assist clinicians by providing an analytic framework for the evaluation and treatment of patients. They are not intended either to replace a clinician's judgment or to establish a protocol for all patients with a particular condition. A guideline will rarely establish the only approach to a problem. In addition, guidelines are "living documents" that are expected to be imperfect and are subject to annual review and revision.

ICSI is a nonprofit organization that provides healthcare quality improvement services to 20 medical groups affiliated with HealthPartners in central and southern Minnesota and western Wisconsin. The guidelines are developed through a process that involves physicians, nurses, and other healthcare professionals from beginning to end, and healthcare purchasers are included in decision making. To order any of the more than 40 guidelines ICSI has developed, contact the ICSI Publications Fulfillment Center, in care of the ARDEL Group, 6518 Walker St., Suite 150, Minneapolis, MN 55426; 612-927-6707.

BREAST, RADIOLOGIC EVALUATION

ICD-9CM # V76.10

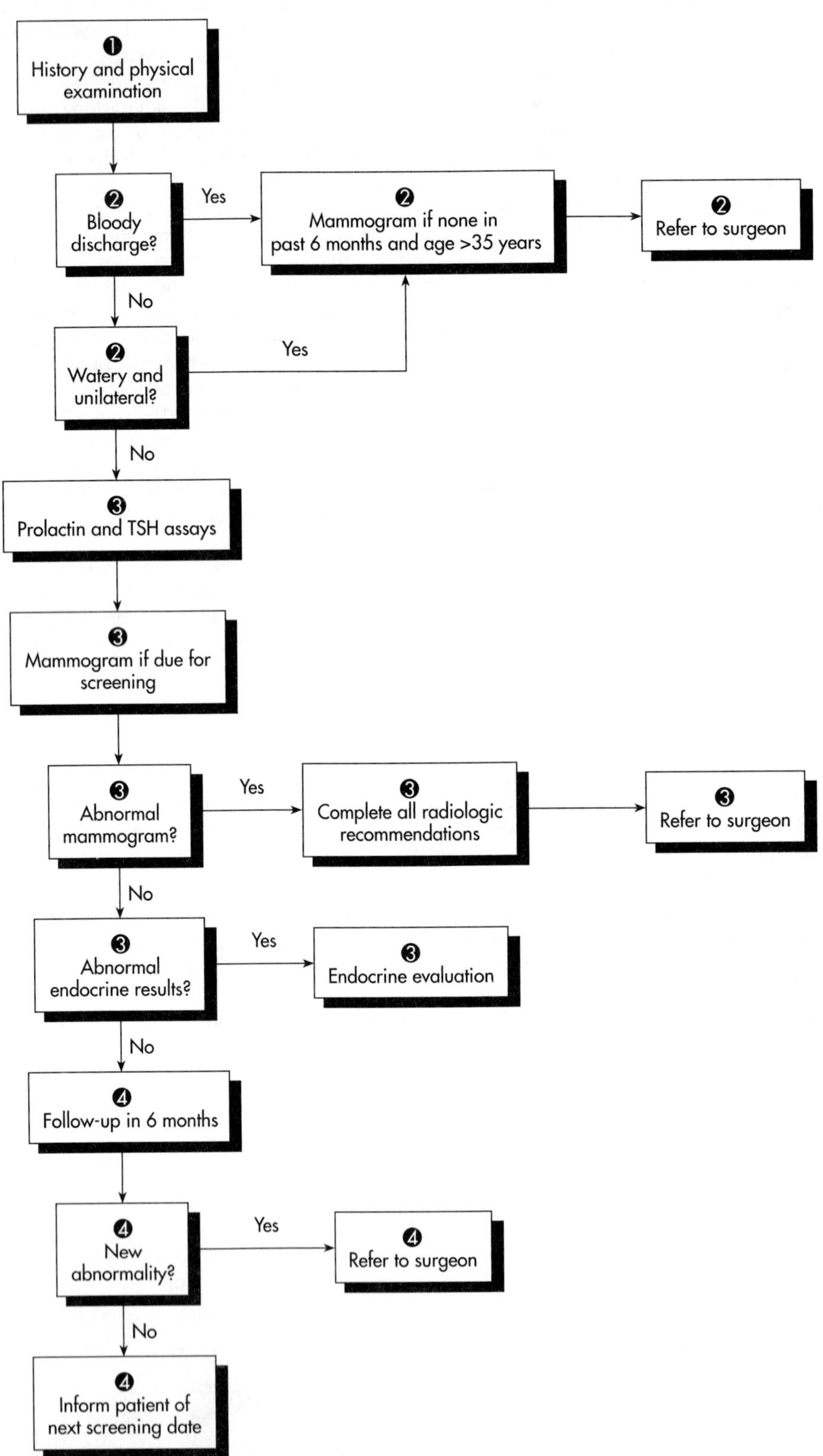

FIGURE 3-43 Breast cancer screening and evaluation. (From Institute for Clinical Systems Integration, Minneapolis: *Postgrad Med* 100:182-187, 1996.)

Fig. 3-43, cont'd

1. **Screening mammogram.*** Patients are most commonly referred to a radiologist for screening mammography. Occasionally, however, patients are referred for diagnostic mammography based on symptoms or findings on breast exam. In the event of an abnormal finding on the mammogram, complete evaluation under the direction of a radiologist is recommended. It is the responsibility of the radiologist to complete the radiologic assessment so that the best possible characterization of the abnormality can be provided in an expeditious fashion to the primary care physician who ordered the original study. Any recommendations for referral to a surgeon for possible biopsy should be made directly to the primary care physician. The ultimate responsibility to make the referral will rest with the primary care physician.
2. **Abnormal mammogram. Sorting abnormalities. Suspicious for cancer?** On obtaining an abnormal finding on a mammogram, the radiologist determines whether further mammographic images are required for completion of the evaluation process. This may include a repeated image of the involved breast at 6 months to document stability of a low-risk, probably benign lesion. Alternatively, spot compression, magnification, or both may be necessary to obtain further characterization of indeterminate breast lesions. These additional studies should be done with the radiologist present to reduce the risk of patient recall for further studies necessary to evaluate the same lesion.
   On completion of these views, each and every abnormality uncovered for each independent lesion of the breast studied should be sorted according to the nature of the abnormality. The radiologist should classify the lesion as representing either suspicious microcalcifications, architectural distortion, or a soft-tissue mass. For any lesions identified as demonstrating microcalcifications that suggest cancer, biopsy will be recommended. It is up to the primary care physician to make the referral to a surgeon for biopsy. If a soft-tissue mass is identified on the mammogram, it should be studied further to determine its relative risk for malignancy. Any suspect lesions identified as having associated microcalcifications, architectural distortion, or interval growth when compared with the previous mammogram should likewise be referred to a surgeon for possible biopsy.
3. **Ultrasound results.** When the mass is not immediately suggestive of cancer, an ultrasound should be performed to determine whether the lesion is solid. A solid mass should be further characterized for its level of benignity according to three criteria:
   - Size less than 15 mm
   - Three or fewer lobulations
   - More than 50% of the margin of the lesion appearing well circumscribed in any view

   Patients who have lesions that fit all three criteria may be observed and then evaluated with a 6-month follow-up study. Any lesion that does not fit all three criteria for benignity should be characterized as indeterminate, and biopsy should be considered. Likewise, any solid mass that is palpable should be referred to a surgeon for possible open biopsy. Finally, any lesion that appears to be new since the last screening mammogram should be considered for biopsy.
4. **Aspiration and results.** If the ultrasound of the soft-tissue mass demonstrates that it is a cystic lesion, the cyst should be further categorized by the criteria listed in the algorithm: irregular wall, as seen on ultrasonography; internal echoes; complex, septated appearance; and palpability within the region of the ultrasound-proven cyst. A positive finding for any of these criteria would be an indication for ultrasound-directed aspiration of the cyst. Aspiration should also be offered if the patient requests it.
   After cyst aspiration, a single-view mammogram should be obtained to demonstrate complete resolution of the lesion. If the lesion is sufficiently complex, a cyst pneumogram may be performed. Should any residual mass be present or if the cyst pneumogram findings are abnormal, biopsy should be recommended. If, on the other hand, the mass is a simple cyst that does not fit any of the previously listed criteria, the patient should be returned to the screening process, and completion of this evaluation should be reported to the ordering health care provider.

---

*ICSI healthcare guidelines are designed to assist clinicians by providing an analytic framework for the evaluation and treatment of patients. They are not intended either to replace a clinician's judgment or to establish a protocol for all patients with a particular condition. A guideline will rarely establish the only approach to a problem. In addition, guidelines are "living documents" that are expected to be imperfect and are subject to annual review and revision.

ICSI is a nonprofit organization that provides healthcare quality improvement services to 20 medical groups affiliated with HealthPartners in central and southern Minnesota and western Wisconsin. The guidelines are developed through a process that involves physicians, nurses, and other healthcare professionals from beginning to end, and healthcare purchasers are included in decision making. To order any of the more than 40 guidelines ICSI has developed, contact the ICSI Publications Fulfillment Center, in care of the ARDEL Group, 6518 Walker St., Suite 150, Minneapolis, MN 55426; 612-927-6707.

BREAST, ROUTINE SCREEN OR PALPABLE MASS EVALUATION

ICD-9CM # 611.72 Breast mass or lump, nonpuerperal

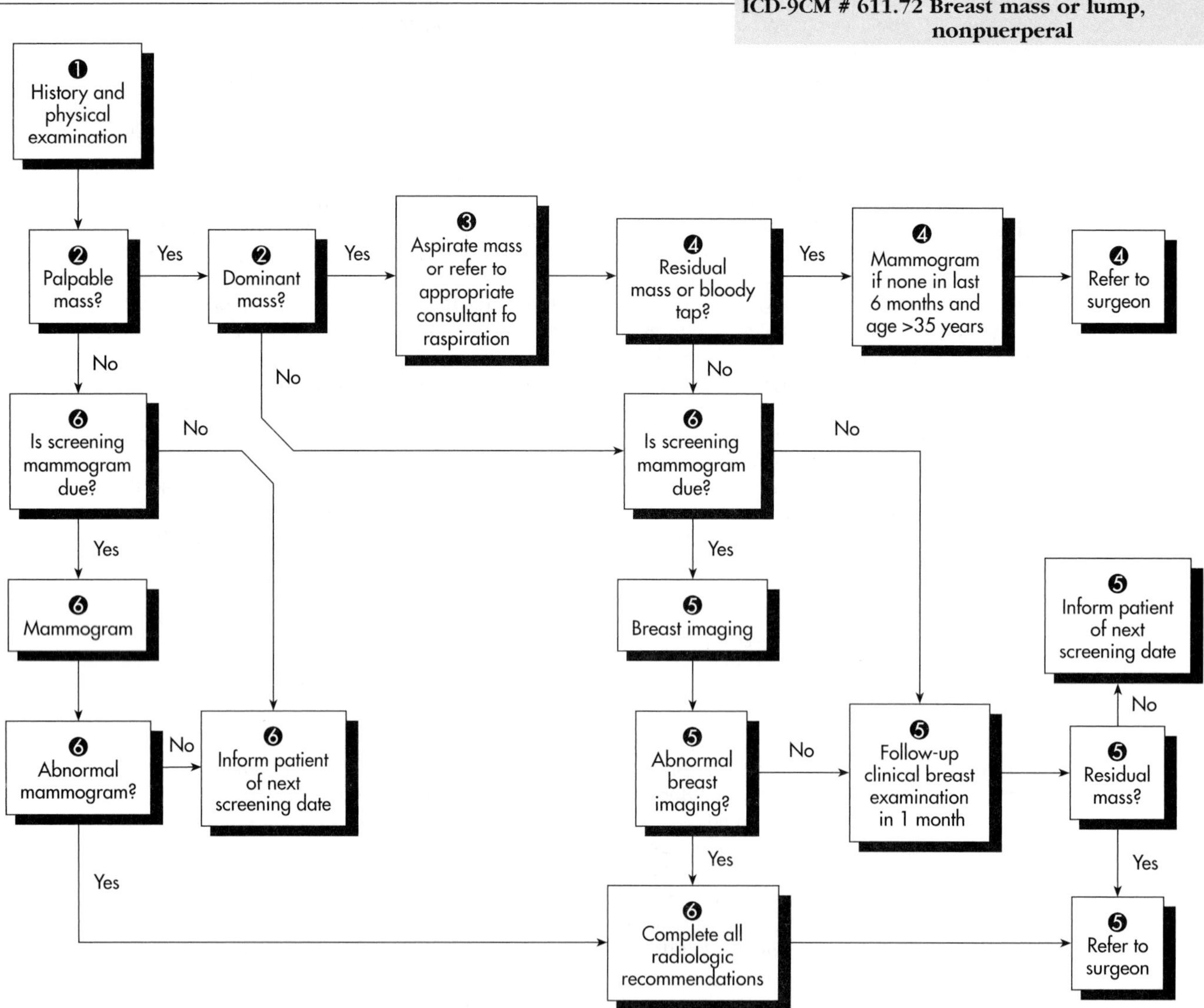

FIGURE 3-44 Breast cancer screening and evaluation. (From Institute for Clinical Systems Integration, Minneapolis: *Postgrad Med* 100:182, 1996.)

1. **History and physical examination.*** Primary care evaluation is initiated with history taking aimed at uncovering and characterizing any breast-related symptom. A risk assessment should also be undertaken for identified risk factors, including patient age over 50 years, any past personal history of breast cancer, history of hyperplasia on previous breast biopsies, and family history of breast cancer in first-degree relatives (mother, sister, daughter). Physical examination should include inspection of the breast for any evidence of ulceration or contour changes and inspection of the nipple for Paget's disease. Palpation should be performed with the patient in both the upright and supine positions to determine the presence of any palpable mass.
2. **Palpable mass? Dominant mass?** A dominant mass is a palpable finding that is discrete and clearly different from the surrounding parenchyma. If a palpable mass is identified, it should be determined whether it represents a dominant (i.e., discrete) mass, which requires immediate evaluation. The primary care physician or appropriate consultant should attempt to aspirate any dominant mass because a simple cyst may be uncovered, in which case aspiration completes the evaluation process.
3. **Aspirate mass or refer for aspiration.** Aspiration of a dominant palpable mass should be performed by the primary care physician or by the appropriate consultant. The breast skin is prepped with alcohol. Then, with the lesion immobilized by the nonoperating hand, an 18- to 25-gauge needle mounted on a 10-ml syringe is directed to the central portion of the mass for a single attempt at aspiration. Successful aspiration of a simple cyst would yield a nonbloody fluid with complete resolution of the dominant mass. Typical watery fluid may be discarded. However, cyst fluid that is bloody or unusually tenacious should be examined cytologically.

Fig. 3-44, cont'd

4. **Residual mass or bloody tap? Mammogram if none in past 6 months. Refer to surgeon.** Should the mass remain after the attempt at aspiration or should frank blood be aspirated during the process, the presence of a malignant process cannot be ruled out. Patients with a residual mass or bloody tap should be referred to a surgeon for possible biopsy. Before the referral, a mammogram should be obtained for any patient over age 35 years who has not had a mammogram within the preceding 6 months. In patients 35 years and under, obtaining any other breast-imaging studies should be left to the discretion of the surgeon or radiologist.
5. **Is screening mammogram due? Breast imaging. Follow-up clinical breast examination. Refer to surgeon.** Should physical examination demonstrate a palpable mass that is not clearly a discrete and dominant mass, its size, location, and character should be documented in anticipation of a follow-up examination. A screening mammogram should be obtained if one has not been done within the recommended interval. If no mammogram is required or if a required mammogram demonstrates no abnormality, a follow-up examination in 1 month is indicated. Should any residual mass be identified, the patient should be referred to a surgeon for possible biopsy. Patients with a persisting nondominant palpable mass that does not resolve within 1 month and those with any recurring cystic mass should be referred for surgical evaluation. If no mass is apparent at the time of the follow-up examination, the patient should then be informed of the appropriate date for her next screening examination, according to the recommended intervals.
6. **Screening mammogram and results.** After completion of the physical examination, the appropriateness of a routine screening mammogram should be determined. If a mammogram is done, the radiologist should provide the results to the primary care physician for reporting to the patient. Should any abnormalities be uncovered, it will be the responsibility of the radiologist to complete any additional imaging studies required for the complete radiographic characterization of the lesion. The radiologist should make certain that all recommended additional views, follow-up studies, and ultrasound examinations have been completed before referral to a surgeon. However, it is important that the primary care physician who ordered the mammogram review the results of these studies to understand fully the opinion of the radiologist and to ensure that all recommendations of the radiologist have been completed. Should the radiologist recommend that surgical consultation is warranted, it will be the responsibility of the primary care physician to establish this referral.

   NOTE: *The importance of communication between the surgical consultant and the primary care physician cannot be overstated. Biopsy results should be reported both to the surgeon and to the primary care physician. More important, patients who do not require biopsy after surgical consultation should be returned to the routine screening process. This process is under the supervision of the primary care physician. Therefore it is absolutely necessary for the primary care physician to know when the patient reenters the routine screening population. In the event that new symptoms arise during the screening interval, the patient should be evaluated by the primary care physician using the primary care evaluation process of this guideline.*

---

*ICSI healthcare guidelines are designed to assist clinicians by providing an analytic framework for the evaluation and treatment of patients. They are not intended either to replace a clinician's judgment or to establish a protocol for all patients with a particular condition. A guideline will rarely establish the only approach to a problem. In addition, guidelines are "living documents" that are expected to be imperfect and are subject to annual review and revision.

ICSI is a nonprofit organization that provides healthcare quality improvement services to 20 medical groups affiliated with HealthPartners in central and southern Minnesota and western Wisconsin. The guidelines are developed through a process that involves physicians, nurses, and other healthcare professionals from beginning to end, and healthcare purchasers are included in decision making. To order any of the more than 40 guidelines ICSI has developed, contact the ICSI Publications Fulfillment Center, in care of the ARDEL Group, 6518 Walker St., Suite 150, Minneapolis, MN 55426; 612-927-6707.

BREASTFEEDING DIFFICULTIES

ICD-9CM # 676.8

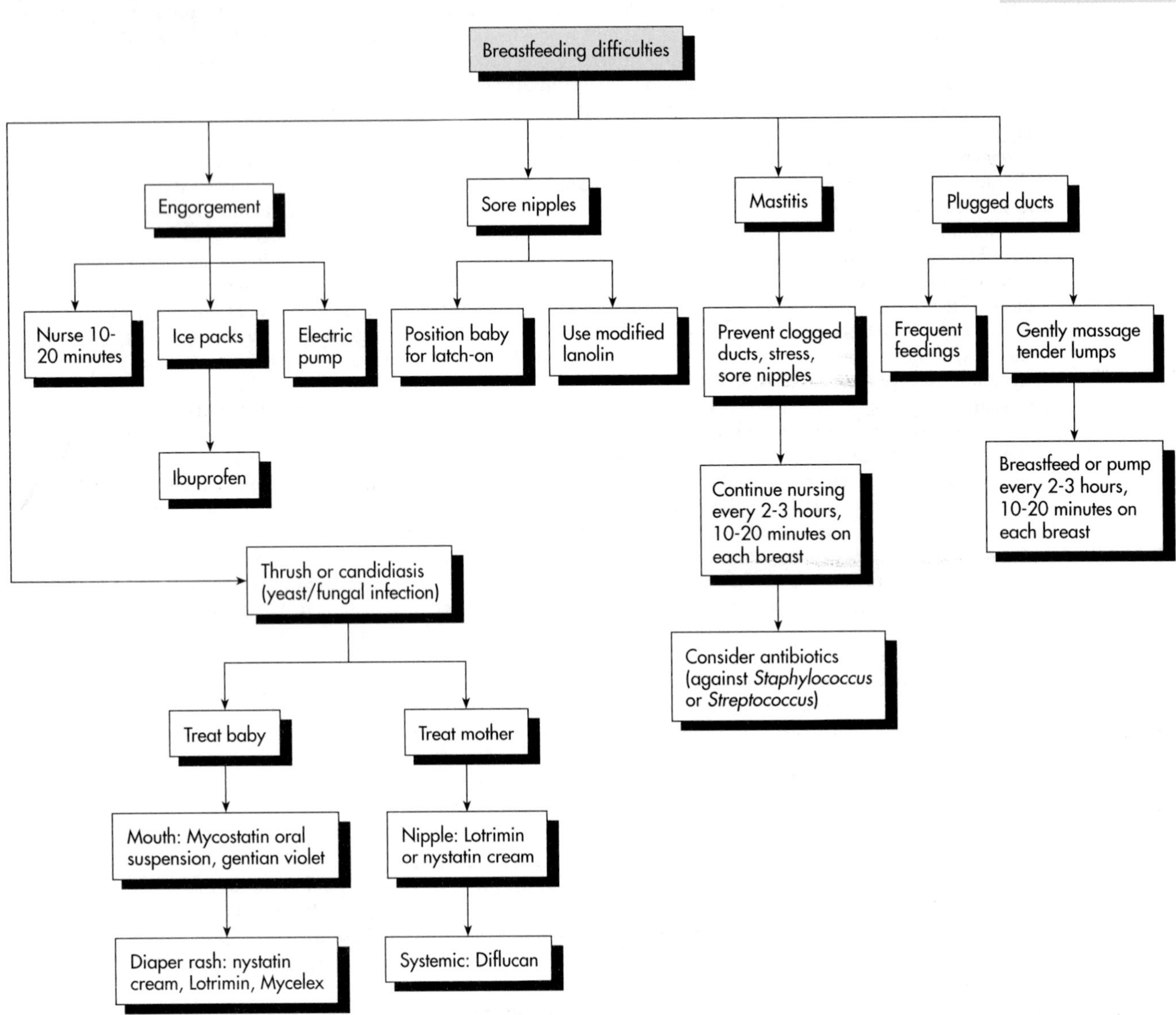

FIGURE 3-45 Management of breastfeeding difficulties. (From Zuspan FP [ed]: *Handbook of obstetrics, gynecology, and primary care,* St Louis, 1998, Mosby.)

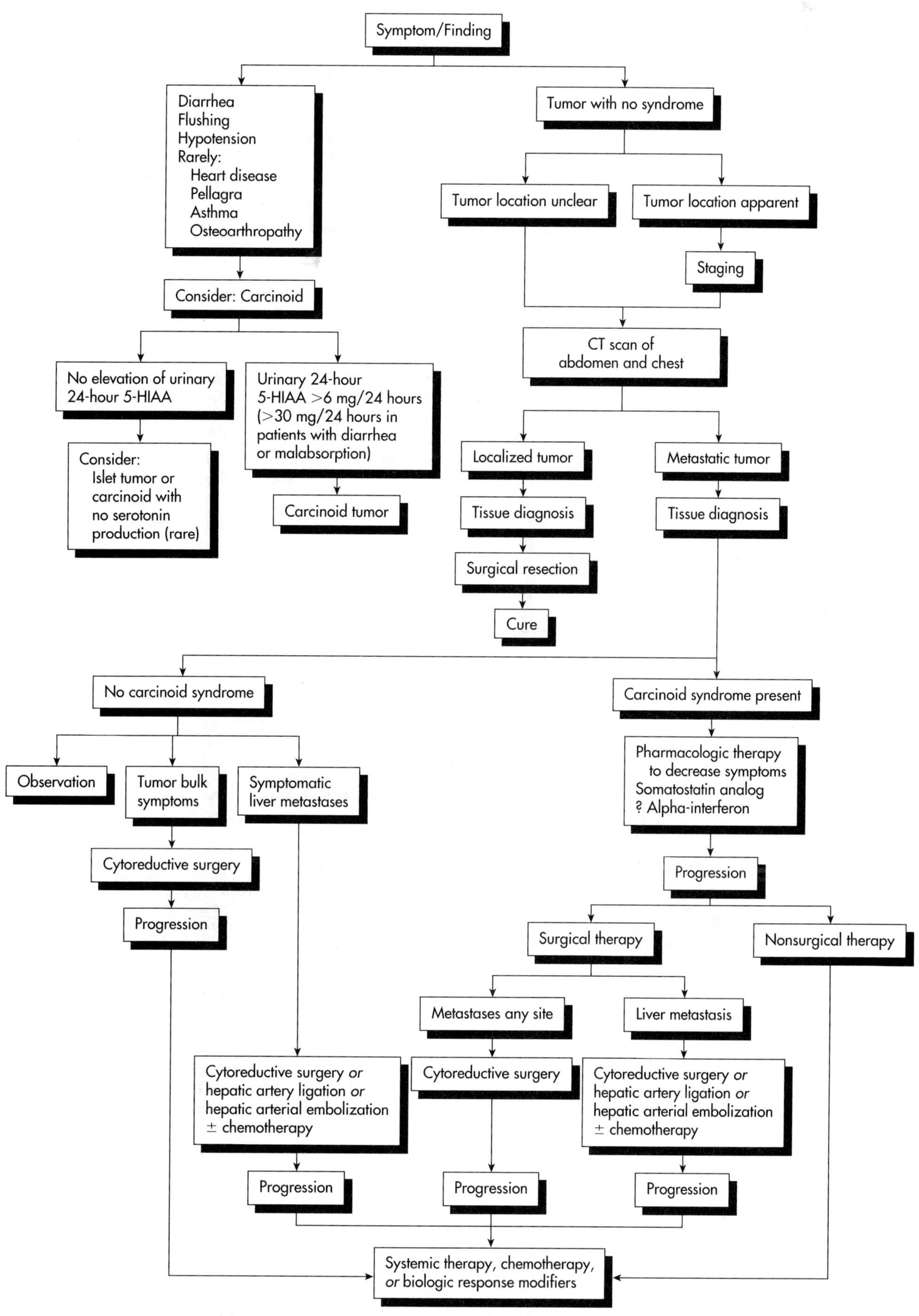

FIGURE 3-46 Diagnosis and treatment of carcinoid tumors. *5-HIAA,* 5-Hydroxyindoleacetic acid. (From Abeloff MD: *Clinical oncology,* ed 2, New York, 2000, Churchill Livingstone.)

CARDIOMEGALY ON CHEST X-RAY

ICD-9CM # 429.3 Idiopathic cardiomegaly
746.89 Congenital cardiomegaly
402.0 Hypertensive cardiomegaly, malignant
402.1 Hypertensive cardiomegaly, benign
402.11 Hypertensive cardiomegaly with congestive heart failure

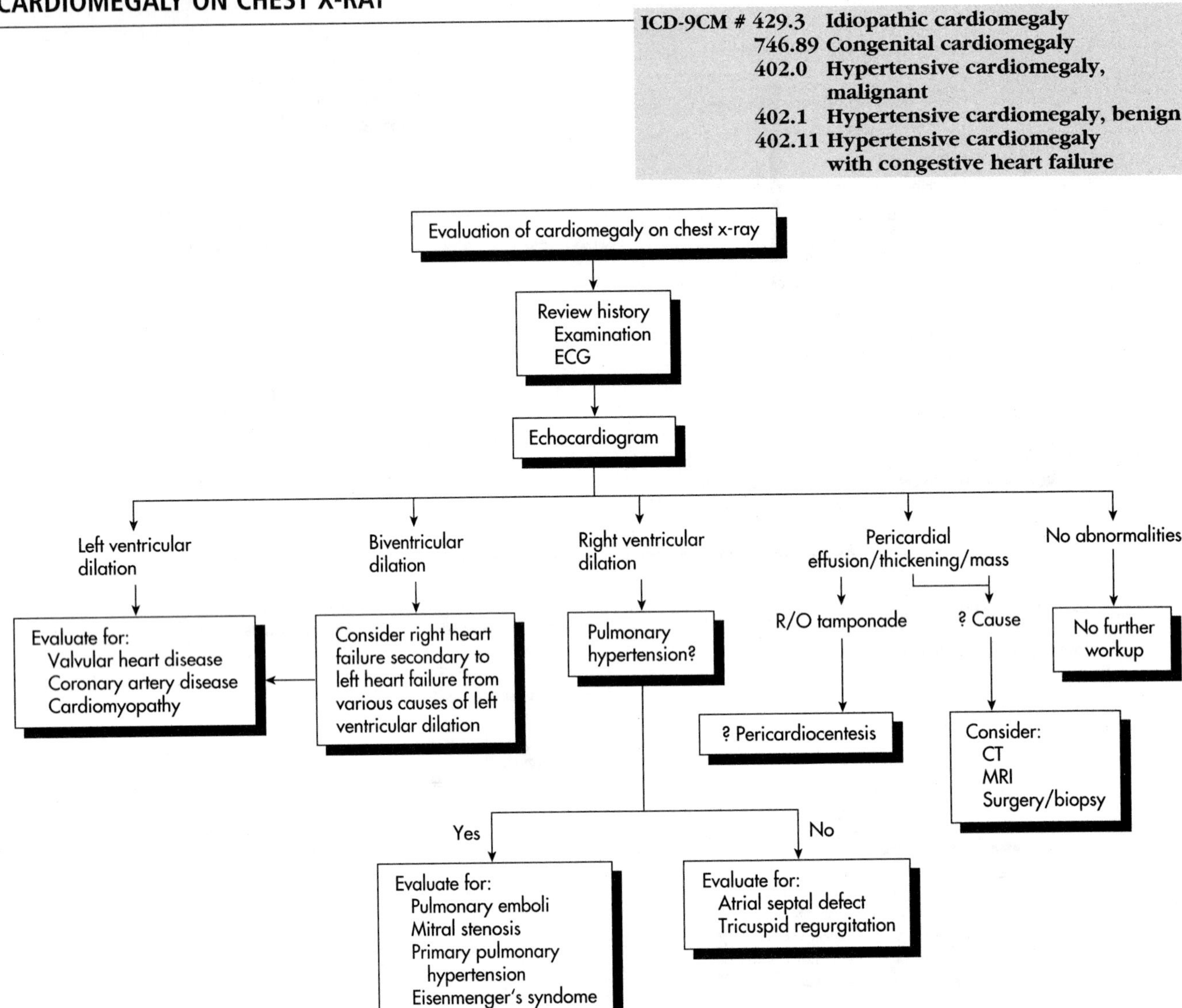

FIGURE 3-47 Approach to the patient with cardiomegaly. When cardiomegaly is found on the chest radiograph, the history and physical examination should be reviewed and an electrocardiogram (ECG) performed before obtaining a two-dimensional Doppler echocardiographic study. Cardiomegaly may be explained by left ventricular dilation, biventricular dilation, right ventricular dilation, or pericardial abnormalities, or it may be found to be spurious on the echocardiogram. Rarely, isolated abnormalities of the atrium, particularly the left atrium, may cause abnormalities on the chest radiograph but will not cause true cardiomegaly. Depending on the echocardiographic findings, further tests can help elucidate the cause of echocardiographically confirmed cardiomegaly. *CT,* Computer tomography; *MRI,* magnetic resonance imaging; *R/O,* rule out. (From Goldman L, Branwald E [eds]: *Primary cardiology,* Philadelphia, 1998, WB Saunders.)

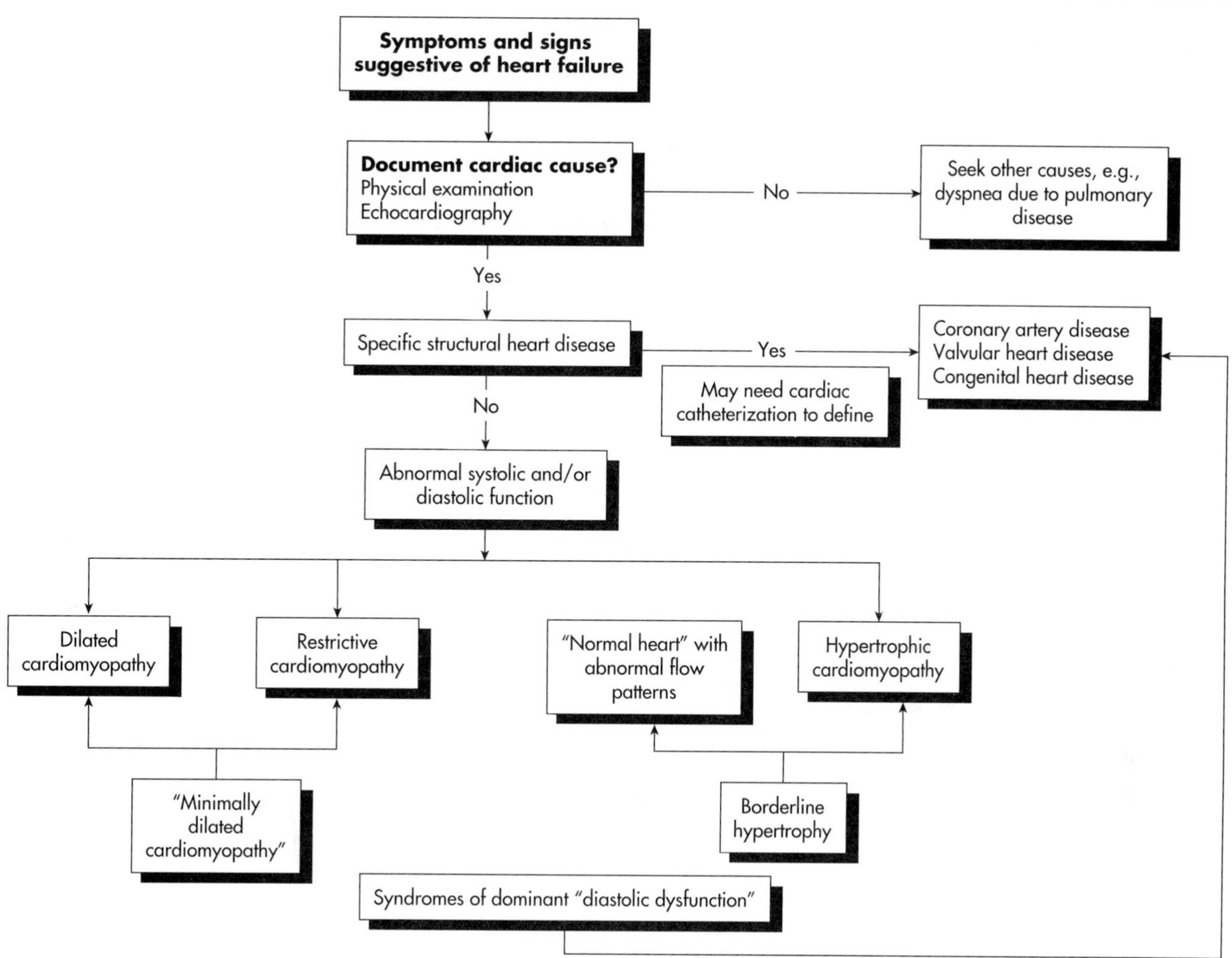

FIGURE 3-48 Initial approach to classification of cardiomyopathy. The evaluation of symptoms or signs consistent with heart failure first includes confirmation that they can be attributed to a cardiac cause. Although this conclusion is often apparent from routine physical examination, echocardiography serves to confirm cardiac disease and provides clues to the presence of other cardiac disease, such as focal abnormalities, suggesting primary valve disease or congenital heart disease. Having excluded these conditions, cardiomyopathy is generally considered to be dilated, restrictive, or hypertrophic. Patients with apparently normal cardiac structure and contraction are occasionally found to demonstrate abnormal intracardiac flow patterns consistent with diastolic dysfunction but should also be evaluated carefully for other causes of their symptoms. Most patients with so-called diastolic dysfunction also demonstrate at least borderline criteria for left ventricular hypertrophy, frequently in the setting of chronic hypertension and diabetes. A moderately decreased ejection fraction without marked dilation or a pattern of restrictive cardiomyopathy is sometimes referred to as "minimally dilated cardiomyopathy" which may represent either a distinct entity or a transition between acute and chronic disease. (From Goldman L, Ausiello D [eds]: *Cecil textbook of medicine,* ed 22, Philadelphia, 2004, WB Saunders.)

TABLE 3-3 **Profiles of Symptomatic Cardiomyopathy**

	Dilated	Restrictive	Hypertrophic
Ejection fraction (normal >55%)	<30%	25-50%	>60%
Left ventricular diastolic dimension (normal <55 mm)	≥60 mm	<60 mm	Often decreased
Left ventricular wall thickness	Decreased	Normal or increased	Markedly increased
Atrial size	Increased	Increased; may be massive	Increased
Valvular regurgitation	Mitral first during decompensation; tricuspid regurgitation in late stages	Frequent mitral and tricuspid regurgitation, rarely severe	Mitral regurgitation
Common first symptoms*	Exertional intolerance	Exertional intolerance, fluid retention	Exertional intolerance; may have chest pain
Congestive symptoms*	Left before right, except right prominent in young adults	Right often exceeds left	Primary exertional dyspnea
Risk for arrhythmia	Ventricular tachyarrhythmias; conduction block in Chagas' disease, giant cell myocarditis, and some families; atrial fibrillation	Ventricular tachyarrhythmias uncommon except in sarcoidosis; conduction block in sarcoidosis and amyloidosis, atrial fibrillation	Ventricular tachyarrhythmias, atrial fibrillation

From Goldman L, Ausiello D [eds]: *Cecil textbook of medicine,* ed 22, Philadelphia, 2004, WB Saunders.

*Left-sided symptoms of pulmonary congestion: dyspnea on exertion, orthopnea, paroxysmal nocturnal dyspnea. Right-sided symptoms of systemic venous congestion: discomfort on bending, hepatic and abdominal distention, peripheral edema.

CEREBRAL ISCHEMIA

ICD-9CM # 437.1 Cerebral ischemia (chronic)
435.9 Cerebral ischemia intermittent (transient)

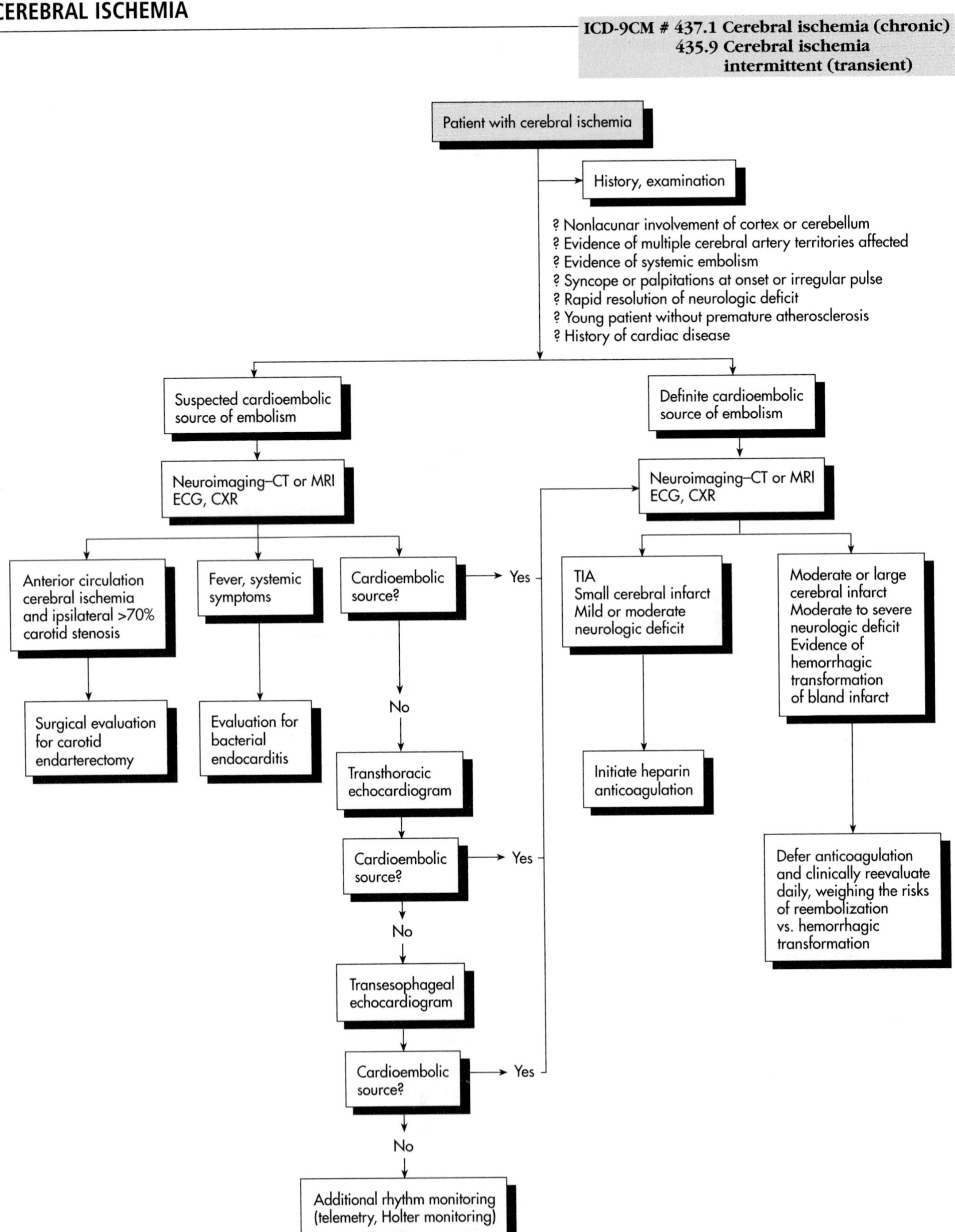

FIGURE 3-49 Evaluation of patients with cerebral ischemia for a cardioembolic source. *CT,* computed tomography; *CXR,* chest radiograph; *ECG,* electrocardiogram; *MRI,* magnetic resonance imaging; *TIA,* transient ischemic attack. (From Johnson R [ed]: *Current therapy in neurologic disease,* ed 5, St Louis, 1997, Mosby.)

CERVICAL DISK SYNDROME

ICD-9CM # 722.4 Degenerative intervertebral cervical disk
722.71 Degenerative cervical disk with myelopathy

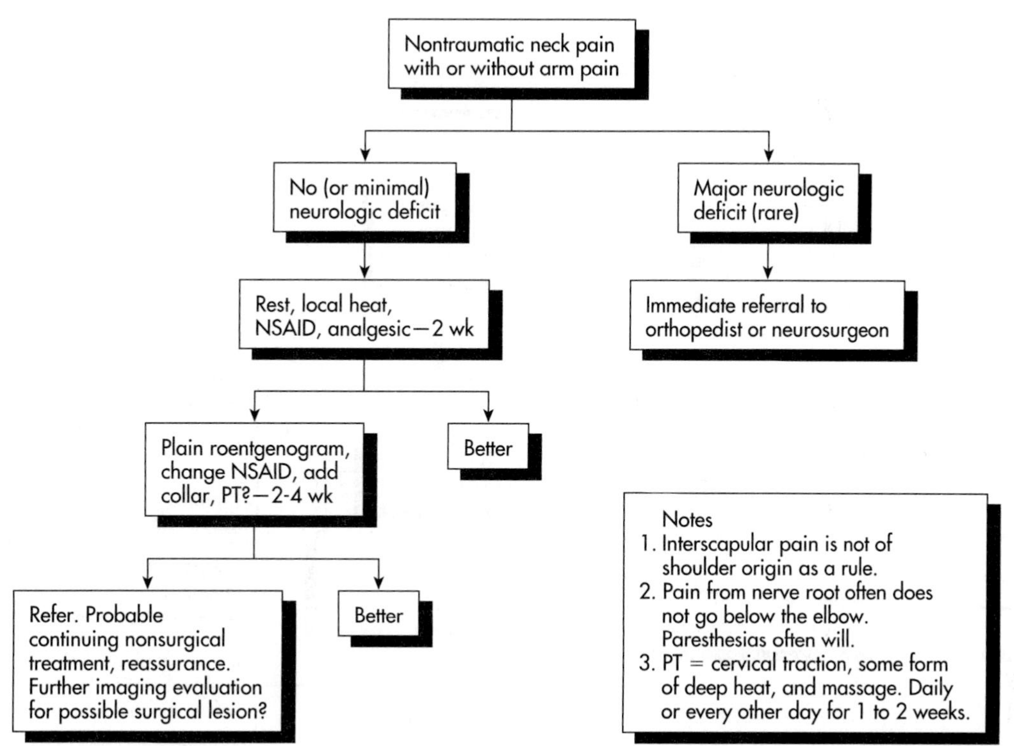

FIGURE 3-50 Algorithm for suspected cervical disk syndrome. *NSAID,* Nonsteroidal antiinflammatory drug; *PT,* physical therapy. (From Mercier LR [ed]: *Practical orthopaedics,* ed 4, St Louis, 1995, Mosby.)

CHRONIC OBSTRUCTIVE PULMONARY DISEASE

ICD-9CM # 496 COPD
492.8 Emphysema

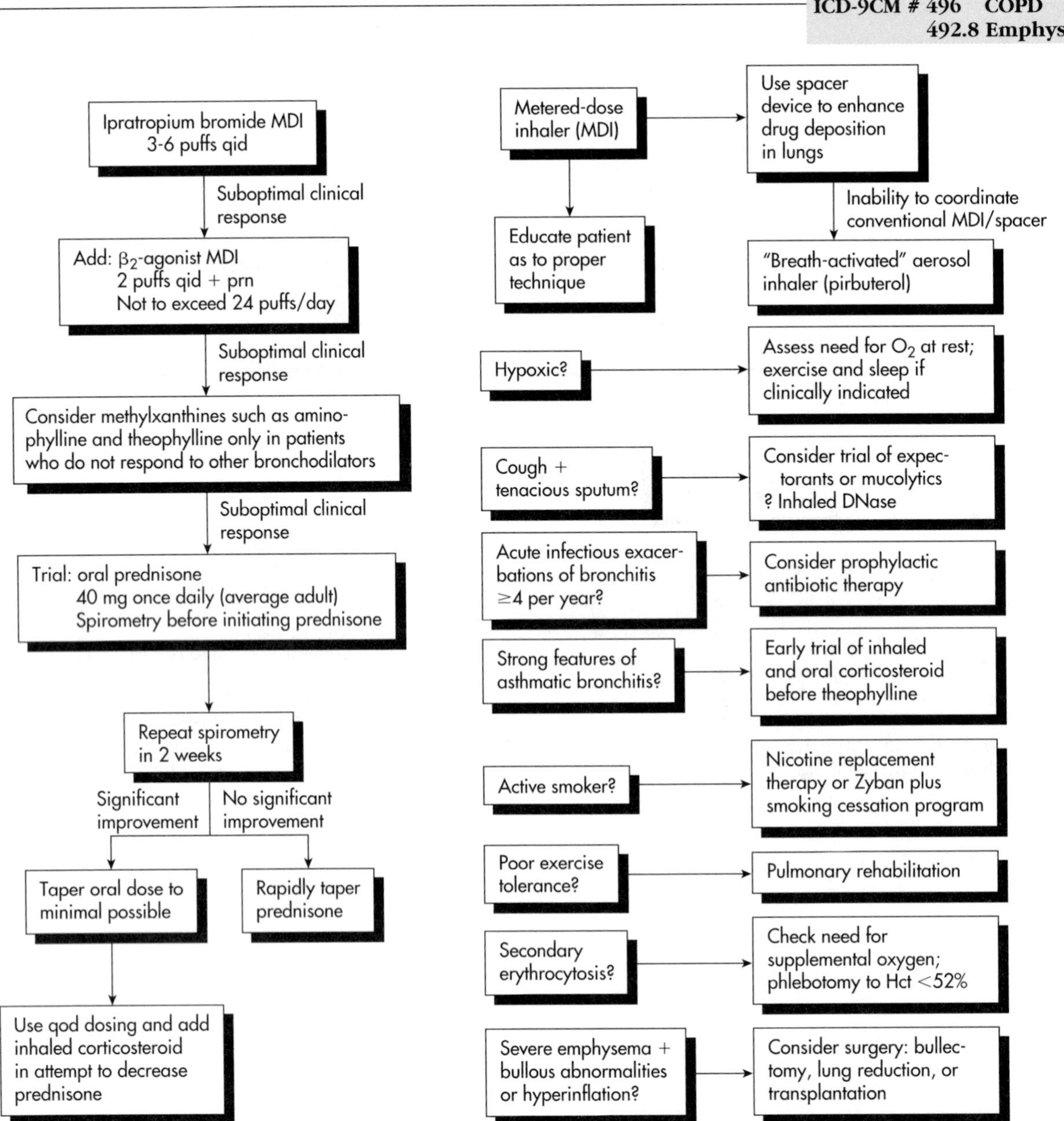

FIGURE 3-51 Managed care guide: pharmacotherapy and general management approaches for chronic obstructive pulmonary disease (COPD). *DNase,* Deoxyribonuclease; *Hct,* hematocrit; *prn,* as needed; *qid,* four times a day; *qod,* every other day. (Modified from Noble J: *Primary care medicine,* ed 3, St Louis, 2001, Mosby.)

CONSTIPATION

ICD-9CM # 564.0

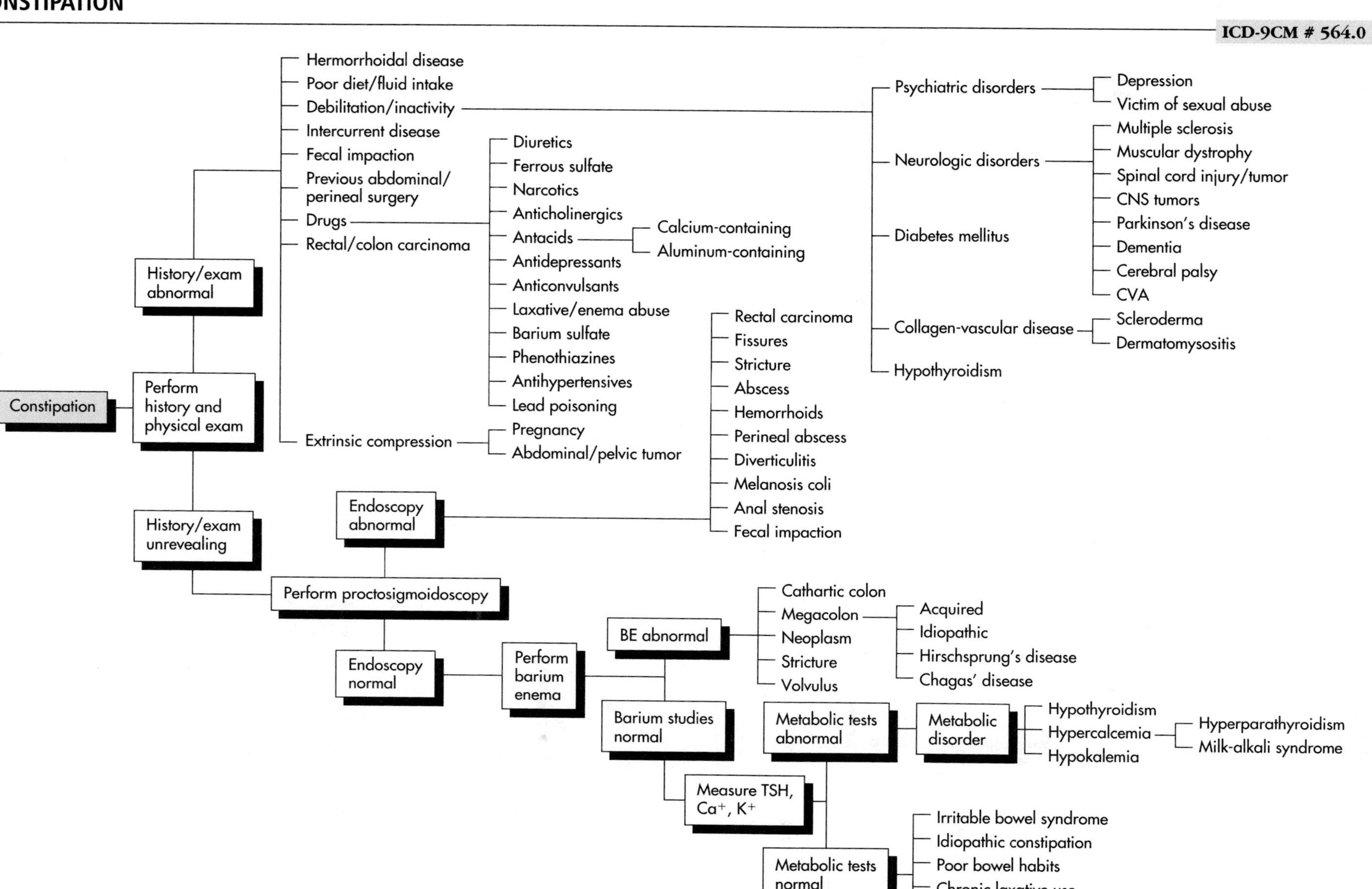

FIGURE 3-52 Constipation. *BE,* Barium enema; *CNS,* central nervous system; *CVA,* cerebral vascular accident; *TSH,* thyroid-stimulating hormone. (From Healey PM: *Common medical diagnosis: an algorithmic approach,* ed 3, Philadelphia, 2000, WB Saunders.)

CONTRACEPTIVE METHOD SELECTION

ICD-9CM # V25.09

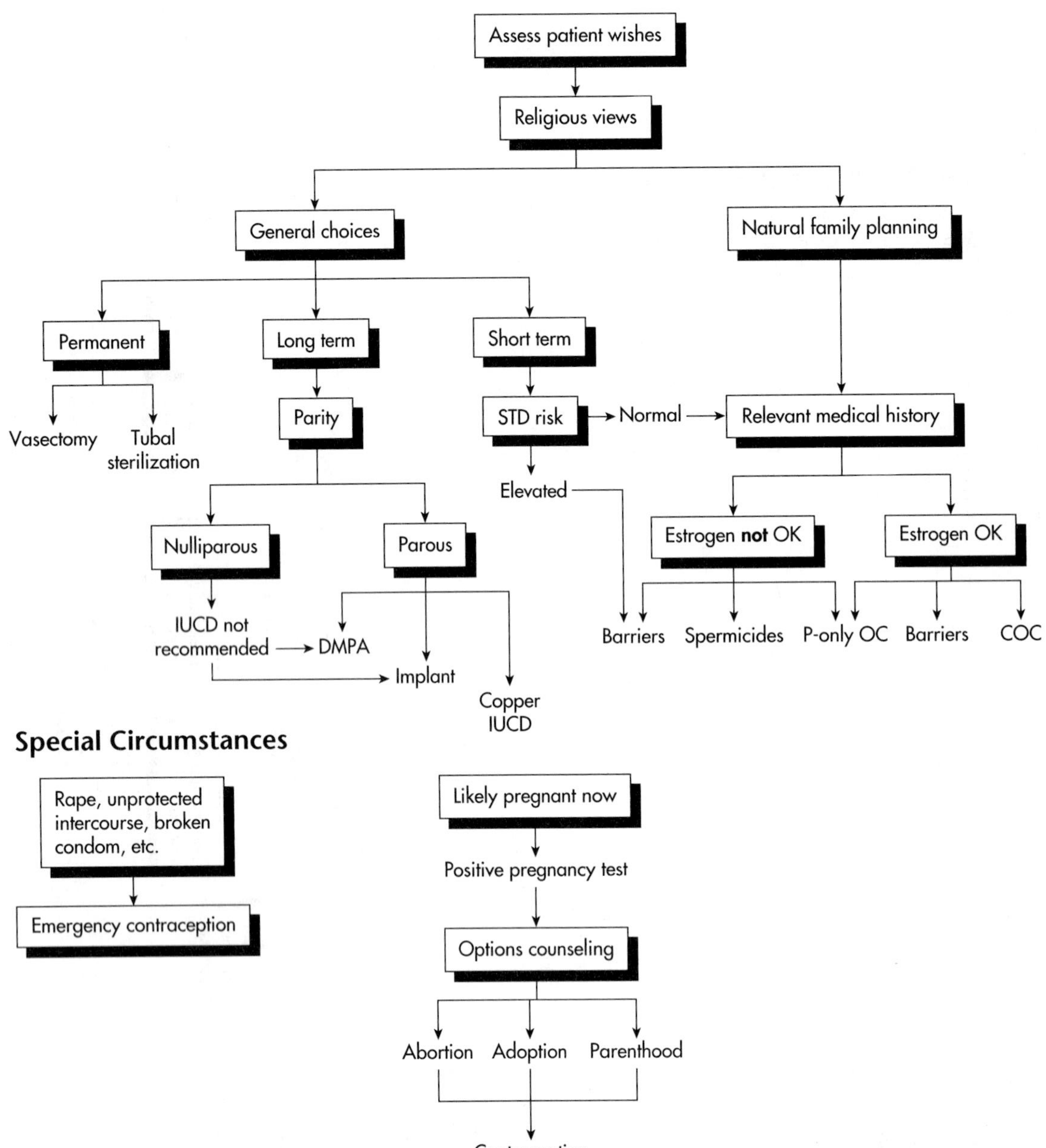

FIGURE 3-53 Helping couples select a contraceptive method. *COC,* Combination estrogen-progestin oral contraceptive; *DMPA,* depot medroxyprogesterone acetate; *IUCD,* intrauterine contraceptive device; *P-only OC,* progestin-only oral contraceptive; *STD,* sexually transmitted disease. (From Copeland LJ: *Textbook of gynecology,* ed 2, Philadelphia, 2000, WB Saunders.)

CONTRACEPTIVE USE, ORAL

ICD-9CM # V25.01 Prescription or use, oral contraceptive

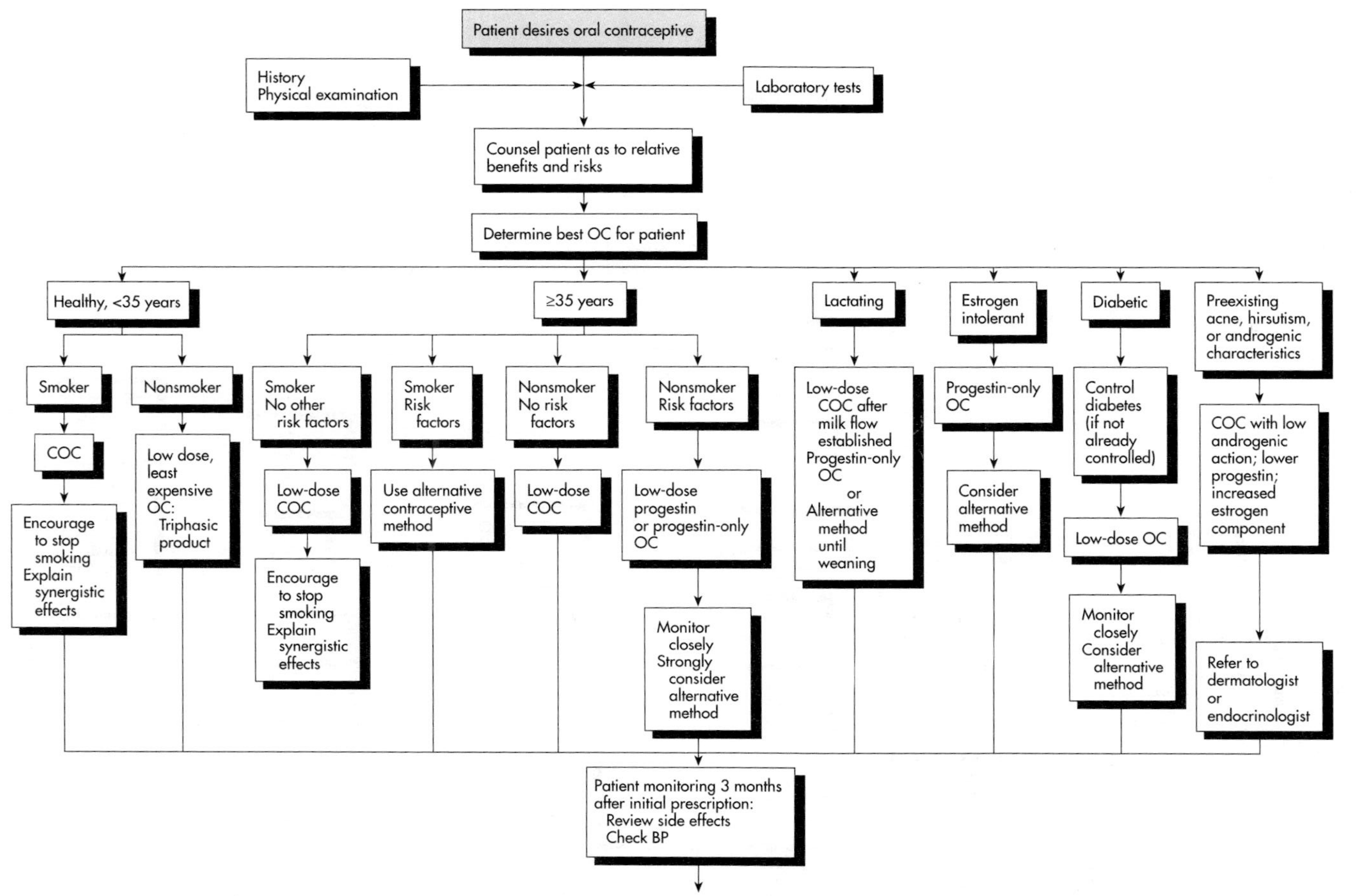

FIGURE 3-54 Contraceptive use. *BP,* Blood pressure; *BTB,* breakthrough bleeding; *COC,* combination oral contraceptives; *CVA,* cerebrovascular accident; *OC,* oral contraceptive. (From Robles TA: Use of oral contraceptives. In Greene HL, Johnson WP, Lemcke D [eds]: *Decision making in medicine,* ed 2, St Louis, 1998, Mosby.)

Continued

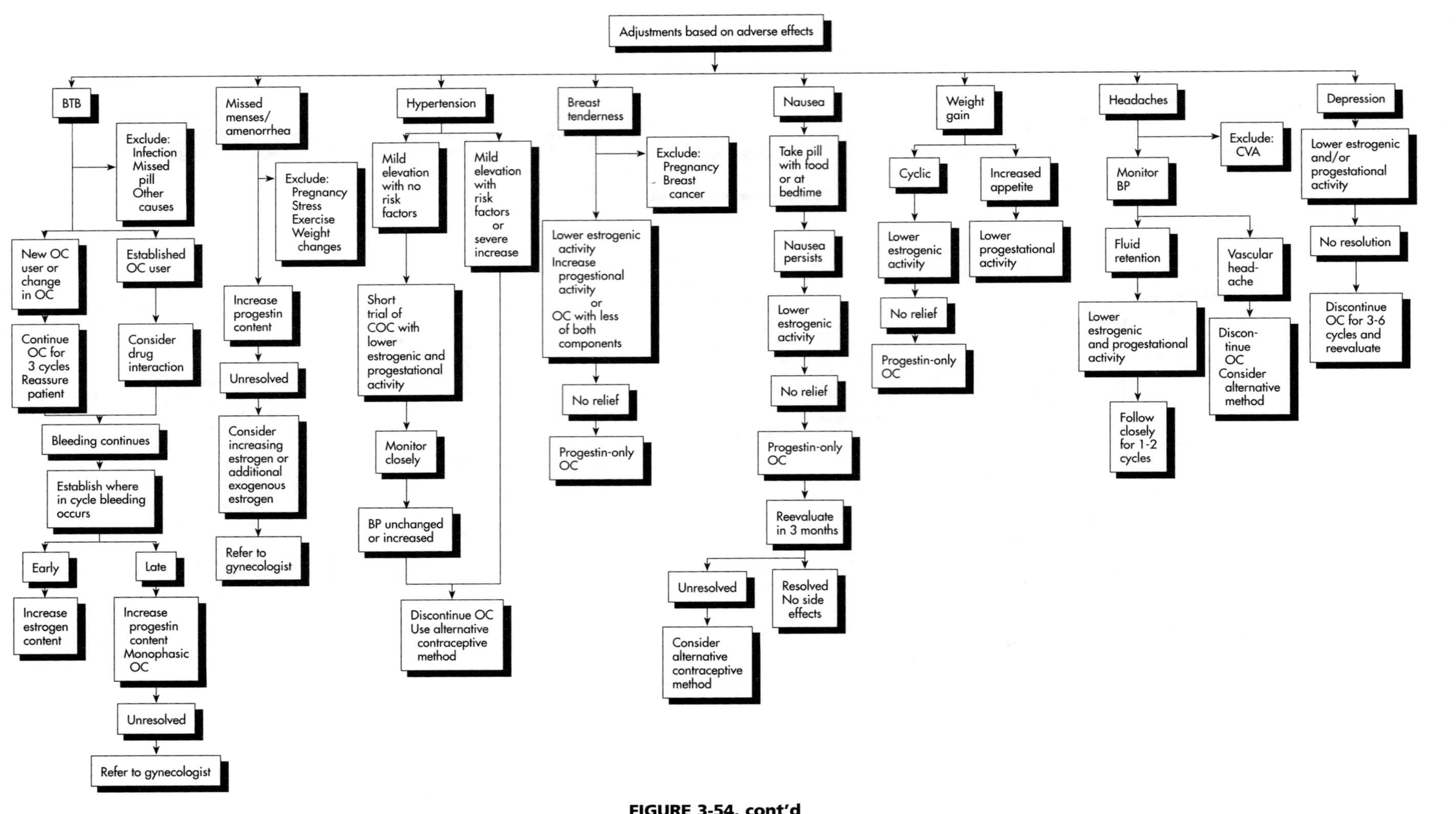

FIGURE 3-54, cont'd

CONVULSIVE DISORDER, PEDIATRIC AGE

ICD-9CM # 780.39

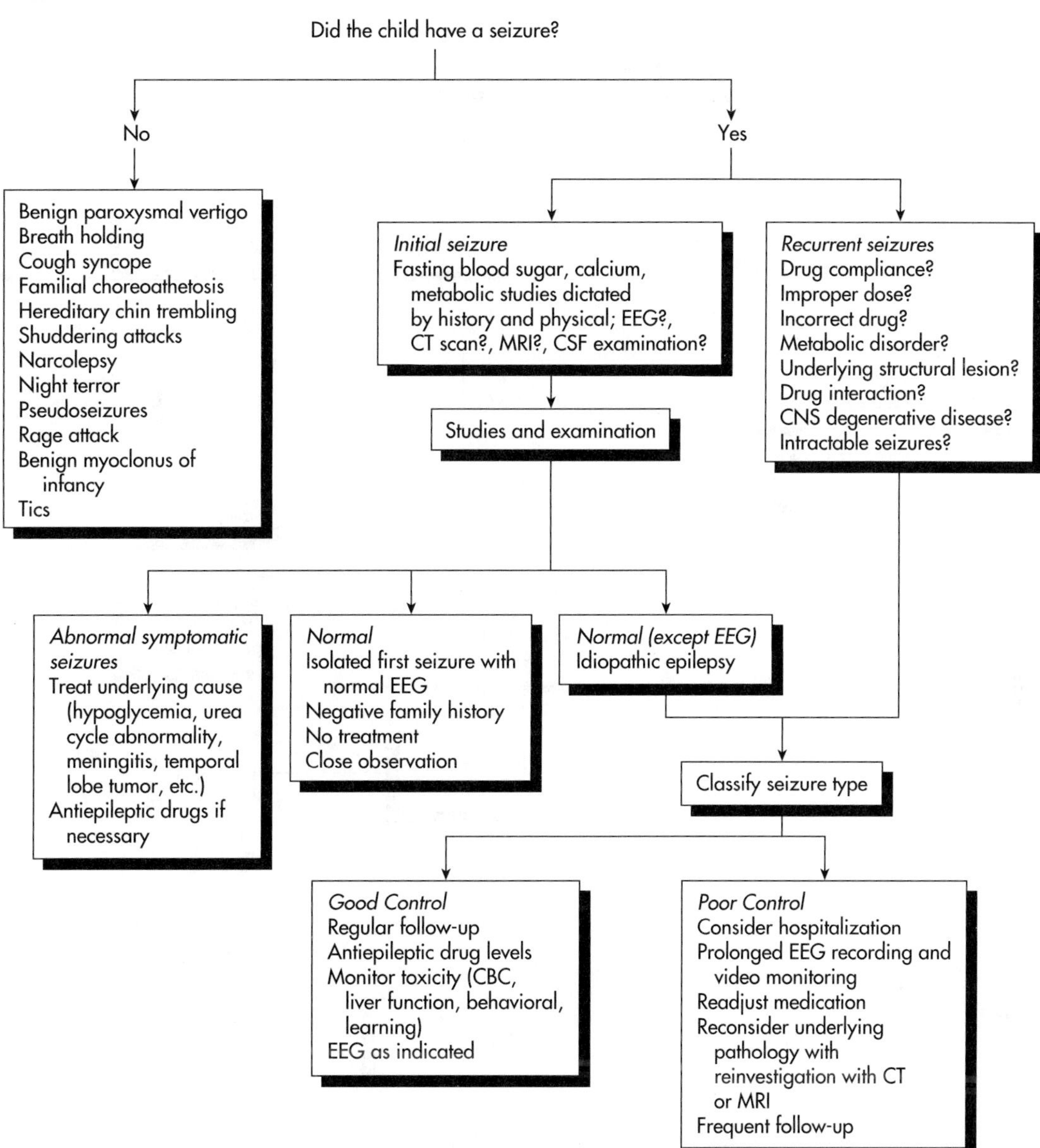

FIGURE 3-55 An approach to the child with a suspected convulsive disorder. *CBC,* Complete blood count; *CNS,* central nervous system; *CSF,* cerebrospinal fluid; *CT,* computed tomography; *EEG,* electroencephalogram; *MRI,* magnetic resonance imaging. (From Behrman RE: *Nelson textbook of pediatrics,* ed 16, Philadelphia, 2000, WB Saunders.)

CORNEAL DISORDERS

ICD-9CM # 918.1 Corneal abrasion
743.9 Corneal anomalies NOS

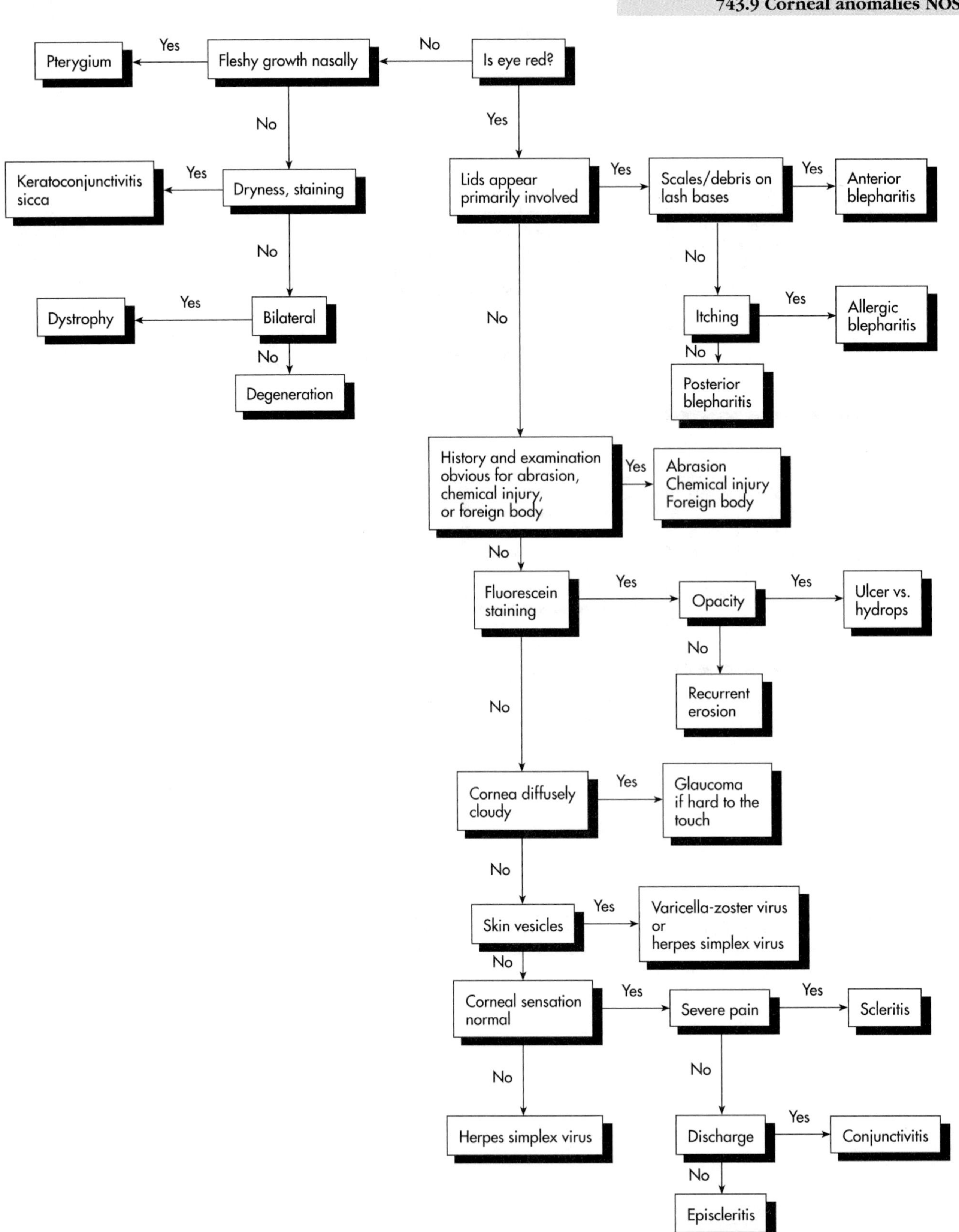

FIGURE 3-56 Approach to the patient with corneal disorders. (From Noble J [ed]: *Primary care medicine,* ed 3, St Louis, 2001, Mosby.)

COUGH, CHRONIC

ICD-9CM # 786.2

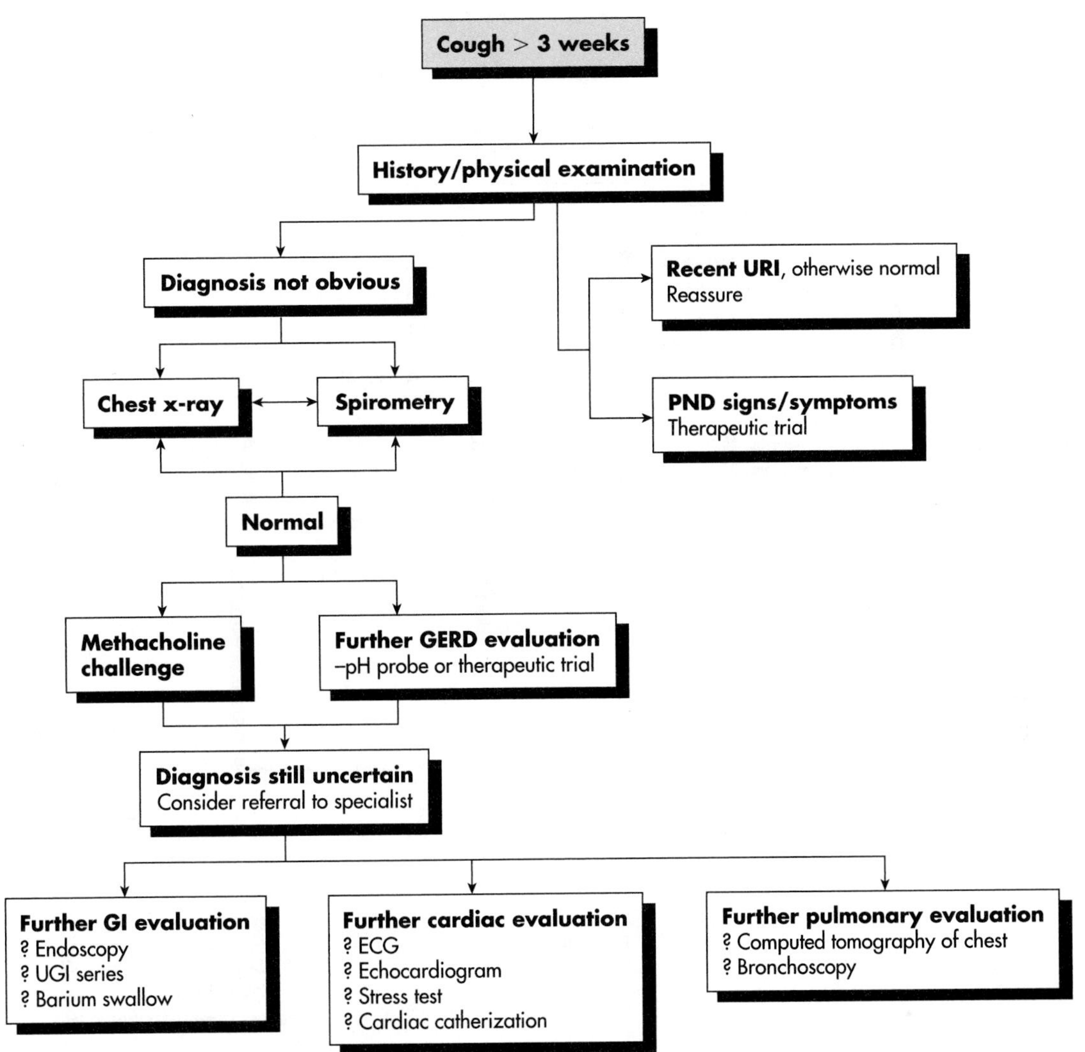

FIGURE 3-57 Diagnostic approach to chronic cough. *ECG,* Electrocardiogram; *GERD,* gastroesophageal reflux disease; *PND,* paroxysmal nocturnal dyspnea; *UGI,* upper gastrointestinal tract; *URI,* upper respiratory infection. (From Carlson KJ et al: *Primary care of women,* ed 2, St Louis, 2002, Mosby.)

CREATINE KINASE ELEVATION

ICD-9CM # V72.6

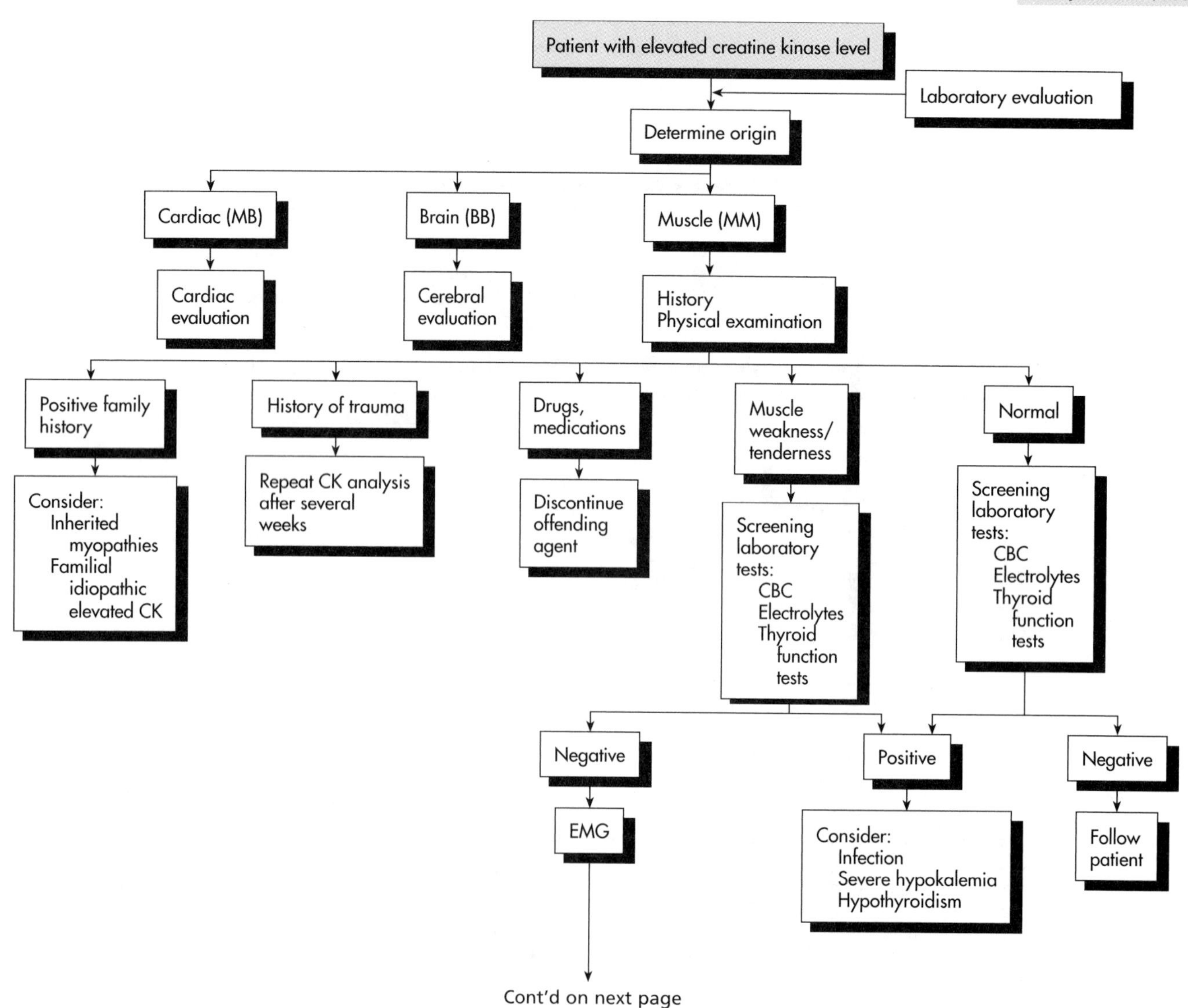

Cont'd on next page

FIGURE 3-58 Evaluation of creatine kinase elevation. *CBC,* Complete blood count; *CK,* creatine kinase; *EMG,* electromyography. (From Greene HL, Johnson WP, Lemcke D [eds]: *Decision making in medicine,* ed 2, St Louis, 1998, Mosby.)

Continued

CREATINE KINASE ELEVATION—cont'd

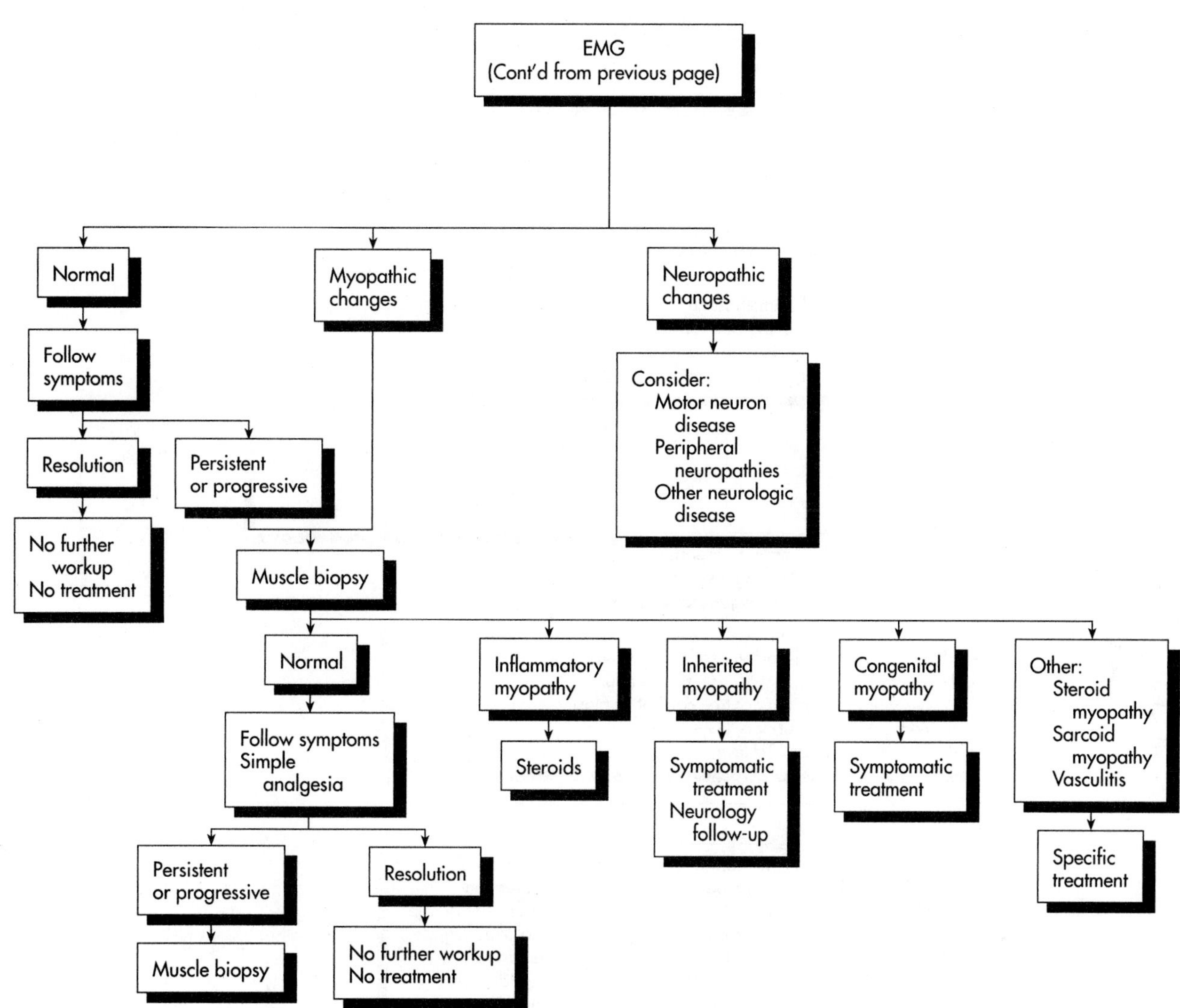

FIGURE 3-58, cont'd

CUSHING'S SYNDROME

ICD-9CM # 255.0

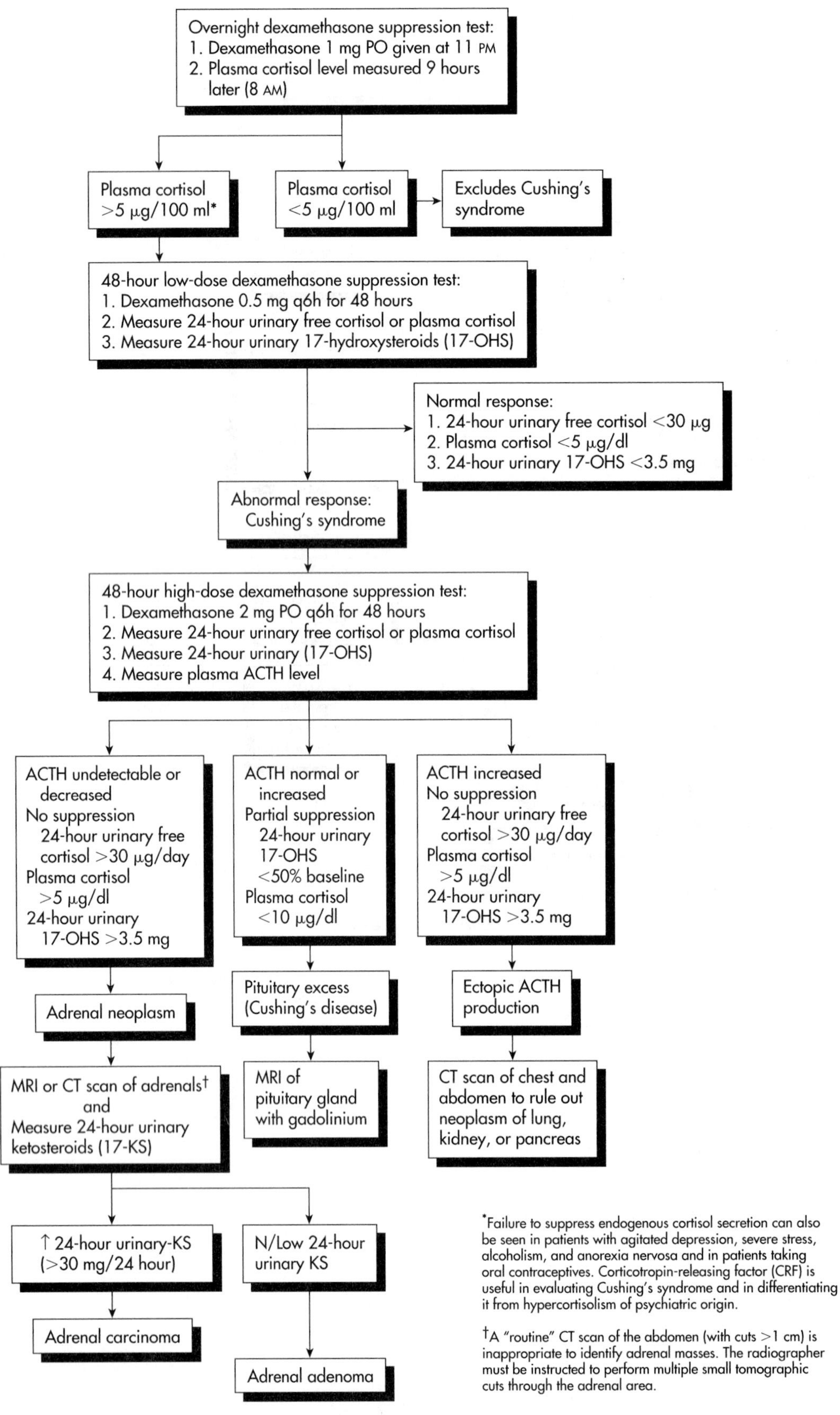

*Failure to suppress endogenous cortisol secretion can also be seen in patients with agitated depression, severe stress, alcoholism, and anorexia nervosa and in patients taking oral contraceptives. Corticotropin-releasing factor (CRF) is useful in evaluating Cushing's syndrome and in differentiating it from hypercortisolism of psychiatric origin.

†A "routine" CT scan of the abdomen (with cuts >1 cm) is inappropriate to identify adrenal masses. The radiographer must be instructed to perform multiple small tomographic cuts through the adrenal area.

FIGURE 3-59 Cushing's syndrome. *ACTH,* Adrenocorticotropic hormone; *CT,* computed tomography; *MRI,* magnetic resonance imaging; *PO,* by mouth. (From Ferri F: *Practical guide to the care of the medical patient,* ed 6, St Louis, 2004, Mosby.)

CYANOSIS

ICD-9CM # 782.5 Cyanosis NOS

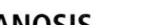

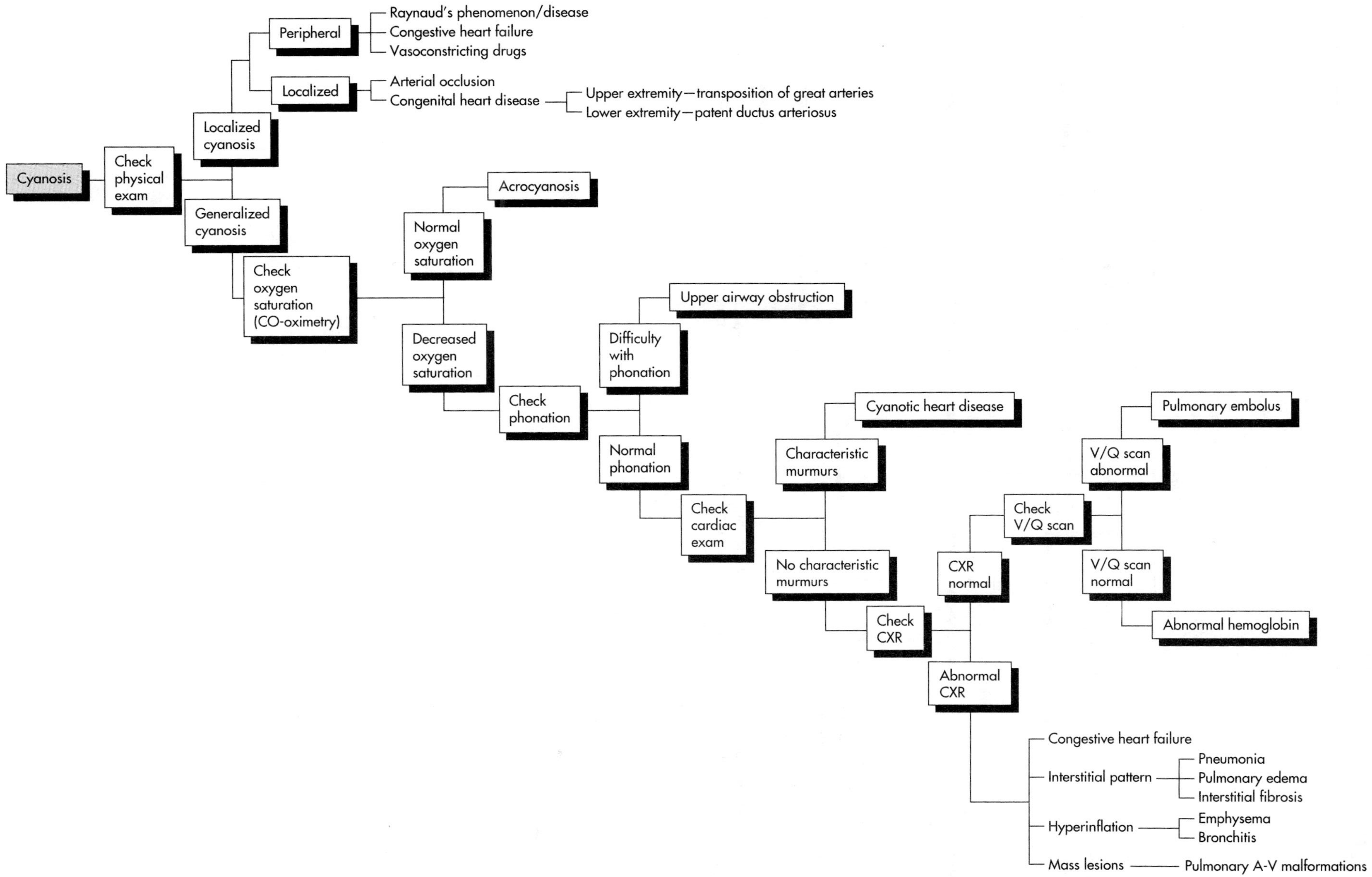

- Cyanosis
  - Check physical exam
    - Localized cyanosis
      - Peripheral
        - Raynaud's phenomenon/disease
        - Congestive heart failure
        - Vasoconstricting drugs
      - Localized
        - Arterial occlusion
        - Congenital heart disease
          - Upper extremity—transposition of great arteries
          - Lower extremity—patent ductus arteriosus
    - Generalized cyanosis
      - Check oxygen saturation (CO-oximetry)
        - Normal oxygen saturation
          - Acrocyanosis
        - Decreased oxygen saturation
          - Check phonation
            - Difficulty with phonation
              - Upper airway obstruction
            - Normal phonation
              - Check cardiac exam
                - Characteristic murmurs
                  - Cyanotic heart disease
                - No characteristic murmurs
                  - Check CXR
                    - CXR normal
                      - Check V/Q scan
                        - V/Q scan abnormal
                          - Pulmonary embolus
                        - V/Q scan normal
                          - Abnormal hemoglobin
                    - Abnormal CXR
                      - Congestive heart failure
                      - Interstitial pattern
                        - Pneumonia
                        - Pulmonary edema
                        - Interstitial fibrosis
                      - Hyperinflation
                        - Emphysema
                        - Bronchitis
                      - Mass lesions
                        - Pulmonary A-V malformations

FIGURE 3-60 Cyanosis. *A-V,* Arteriovenous; *CXR,* chest x-ray; *V/Q,* ventilation-perfusion. (From Healey PM: *Common medical diagnosis: an algorithmic approach,* ed 3, Philadelphia, 2000, WB Saunders.)

DELIRIUM

ICD-9CM # 293.0

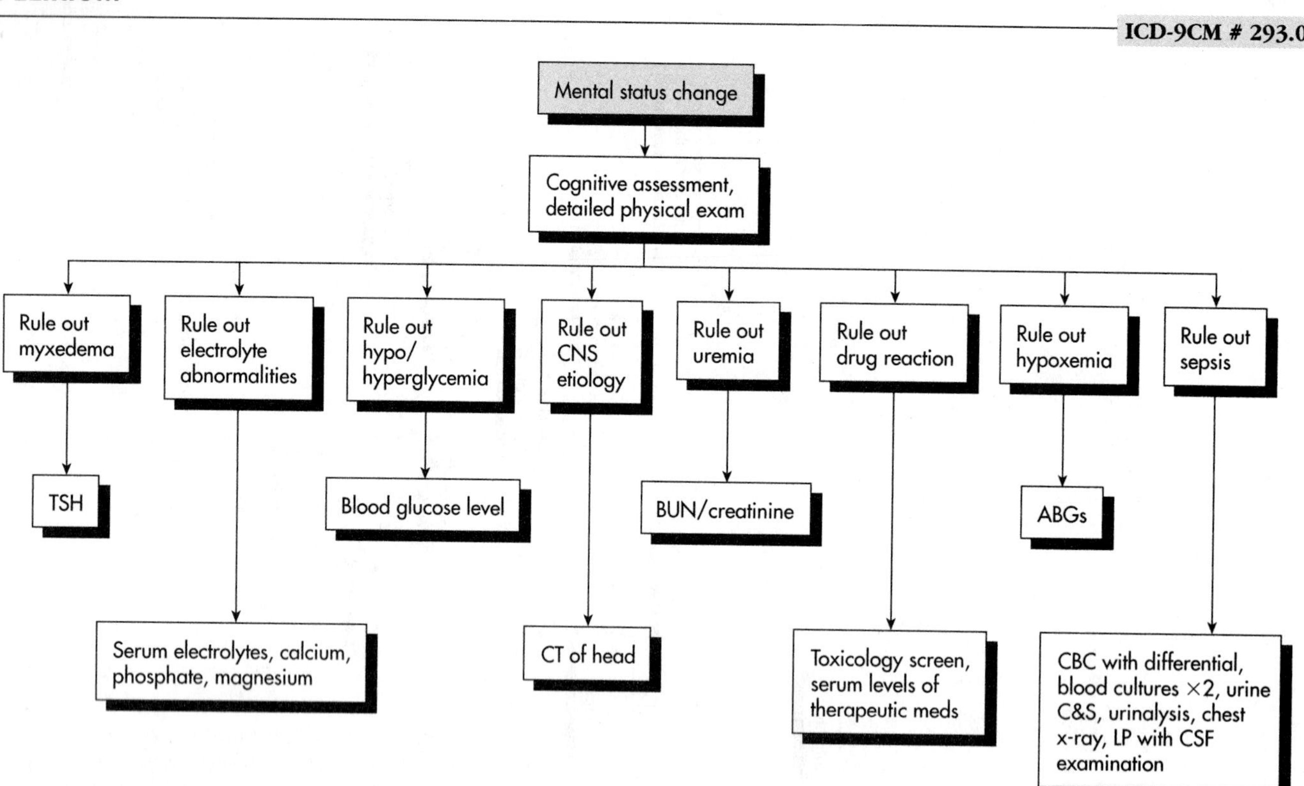

FIGURE 3-61 Delirium. *ABG,* Arterial blood gas; *BUN,* blood urea nitrogen; *CBC,* complete blood count; *CNS,* central nervous system; *C&S,* culture and sensitivity; *CSF,* cerebrospinal fluid; *CT,* computed tomography; *TSH,* thyroid-stimulating hormone.

DELIRIUM, GERIATRIC PATIENT

ICD-9CM # 293.0 Delirium, acute
292.81 Delirium, drug induced
293.1 Delirium, subacute
293.81 Delirium, transient organic with delusions
293.82 Delirium, transient organic with hallucinations

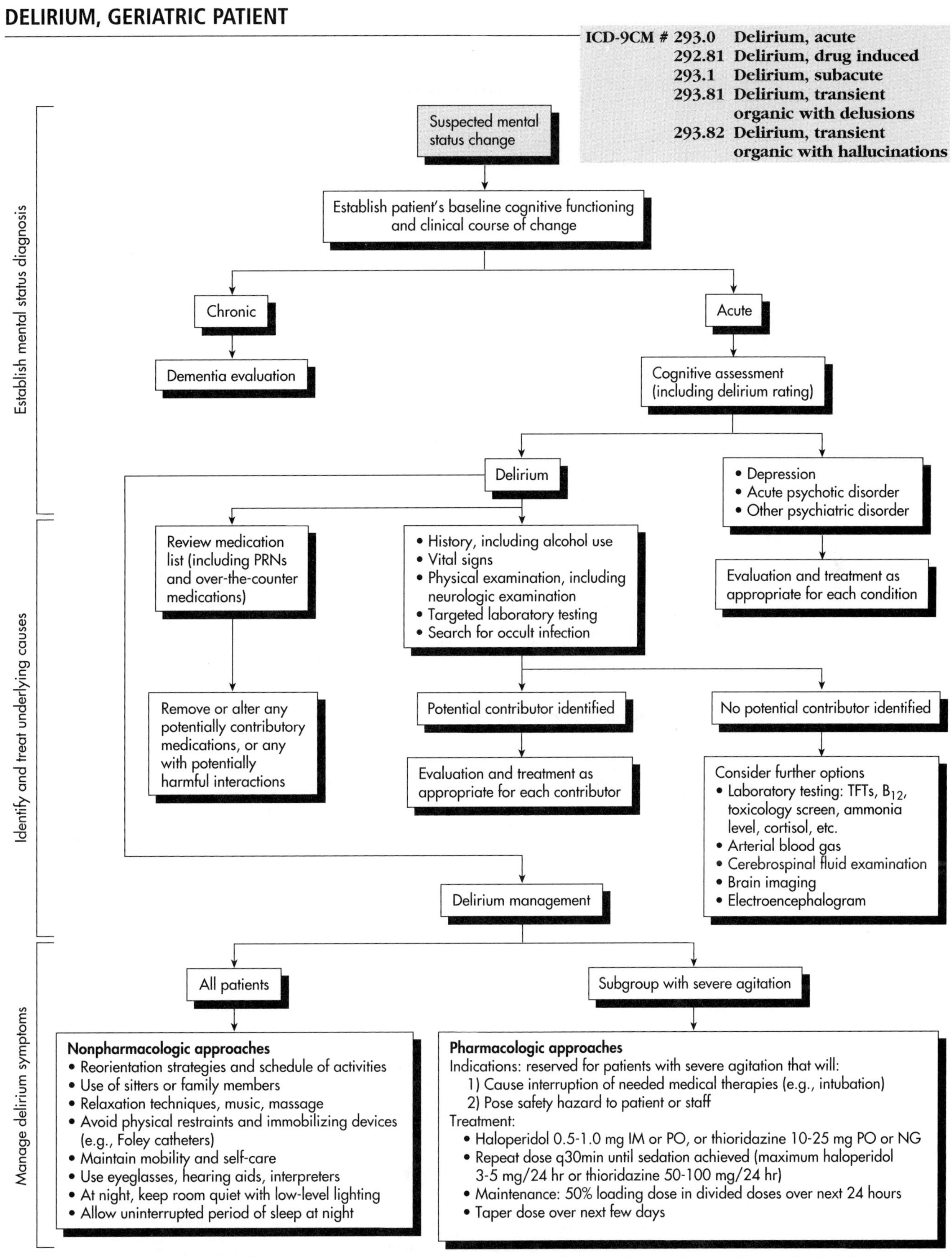

FIGURE 3-62 Algorithm for evaluation of suspected mental status change in an older patient. *IM,* Intramuscular; *NG,* nasogastric; *PO,* by mouth; *PRNs,* as needed; *TFTs,* thyroid function tests. (From Goldman L, Ausiello D [eds]: *Cecil textbook of medicine,* ed 22, Philadelphia, 2004, WB Saunders.)

SECTION III

ICD-9CM # 290.10 Dementia, presenile
290.0 Dementia, senile
437.0 Dementia, arteriosclerotic

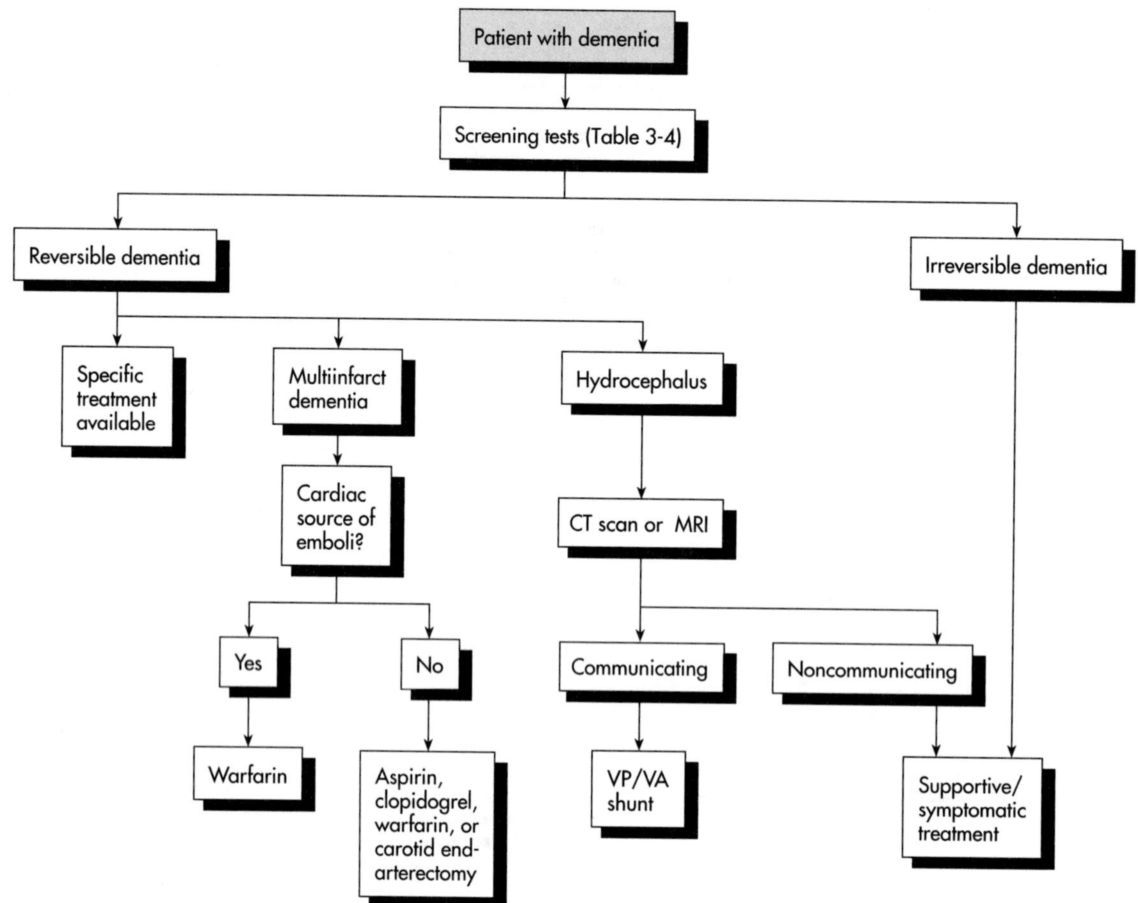

FIGURE 3-63 Management of dementia. *VA,* ventriculoatrial; *VP,* ventriculoperitoneal.

TABLE 3-4 **Screening Tests for Diagnosis of Dementia**

Test	Rationale	Remarks
Blood Test		
Complete blood count	Assess general nutritional status	
Serum B_{12} level	Exclude vitamin B_{12} deficiency	Consider Schilling's test if B_{12} level is low
TSH + free T4 *or* TSH + FTI	Exclude primary and secondary hypothyroidism	
HIV serology	Exclude HIV infection	Perform only if indicated; consent from patient required
Cerebrospinal Fluid		
Cell count/protein level	Exclude chronic meningitis	Perform only if indicated
Cytology	Exclude carcinomatous meningitis	Perform only if indicated
VDRL	Exclude neurosyphilis	Perform only if indicated; check serum TPHA and HIV serology if CSF VDRL is positive
CT Scan/MRI of the Brain	Identify infarcts and white matter changes; exclude presence of neoplasm, demyelinating disease, and hydrocephalus; location of atrophy may suggest the diagnosis (e.g., parahippocampal atrophy in Alzheimer's disease, frontotemporal atrophy in Pick's disease)	
Electroencephalogram	Exclude metabolic encephalopathies; useful if Creutzfeldt-Jakob disease or status epilepticus is suspected	Perform only if indicated
Neuropsychologic Evaluation	Help to characterize pattern of cognitive impairment, which may aid in the classification of dementia; rule out pseudodementia from depression	

From Johnson RT, Griffin JW: *Current therapy in neurologic disease,* ed 5, St Louis, 1997, Mosby.
CSF, Cerebrospinal fluid; *CT,* computed tomography; *FTI,* free thyroxine index; *HIV,* human immunodeficiency virus; *MRI,* magnetic resonance imaging; T_4, thyroxine; *TPHA,* Treponema pallidum hemagglutination assay; *TSH,* thyroid-stimulating hormone; *VDRL,* Venereal Disease Research Laboratory test.

DEPRESSION

ICD-9CM # 296.2 Major depressive disorder, single episode

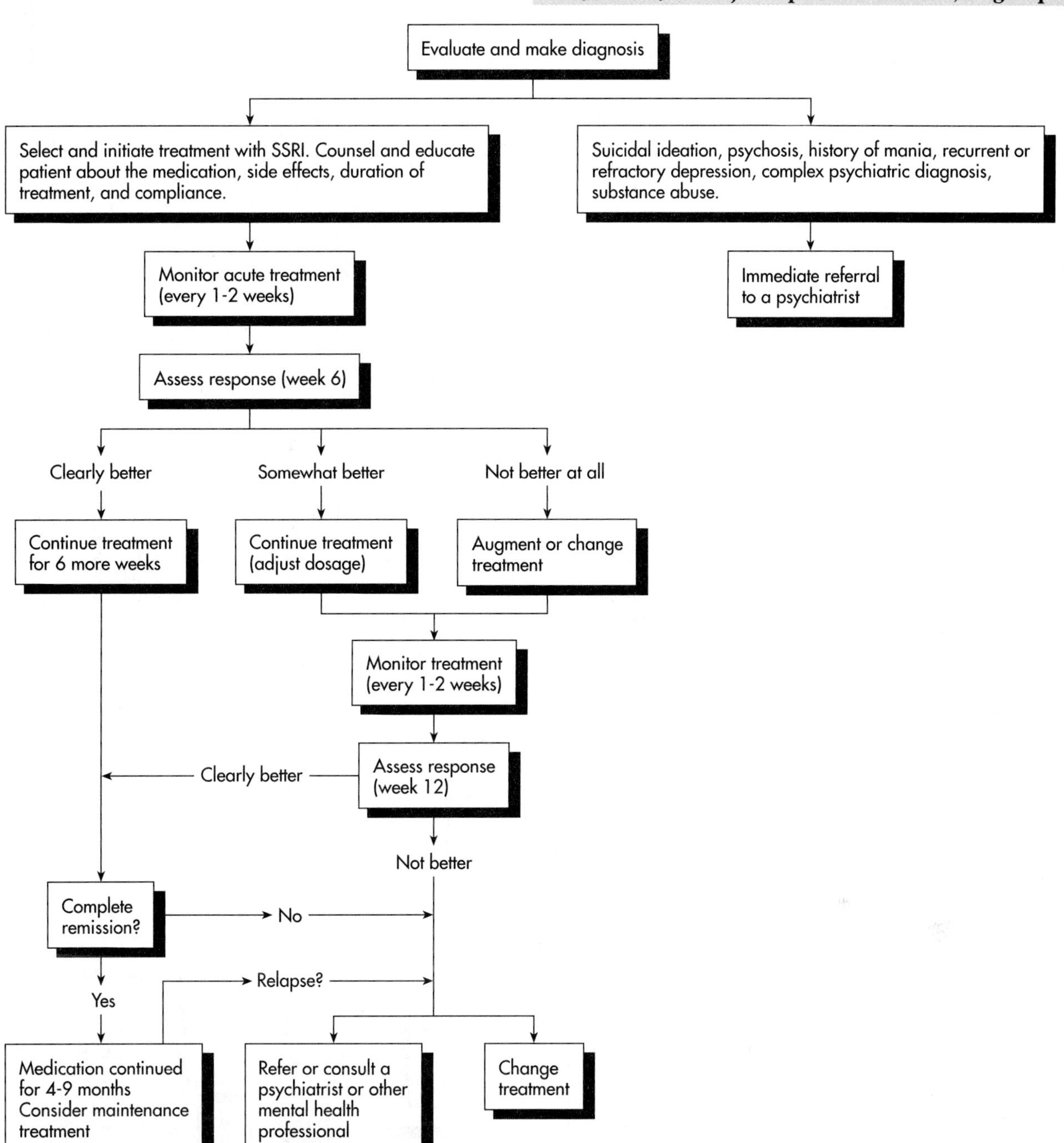

FIGURE 3-64 Guidelines for the treatment of depression in the primary care setting. *SSRI,* Selective serotonin reuptake inhibitor. NOTE: Time of assessment (weeks 6 and 12) rests on very modest data. It may be necessary to revise the treatment plan earlier for patients who fail to respond. (From AHCPR Quick Reference Guide of Clinicians, No. 5: Depression in primary care: *Detection, diagnosis and treatment,* 1993; and American Psychiatric Association: *Diagnostic and statistical manual of mental disorders,* ed 4, Washington, DC, 1994, American Psychiatric Association.)

DEVELOPMENTAL DELAY

ICD-9CM # 783.4 Developmental delay, physiological

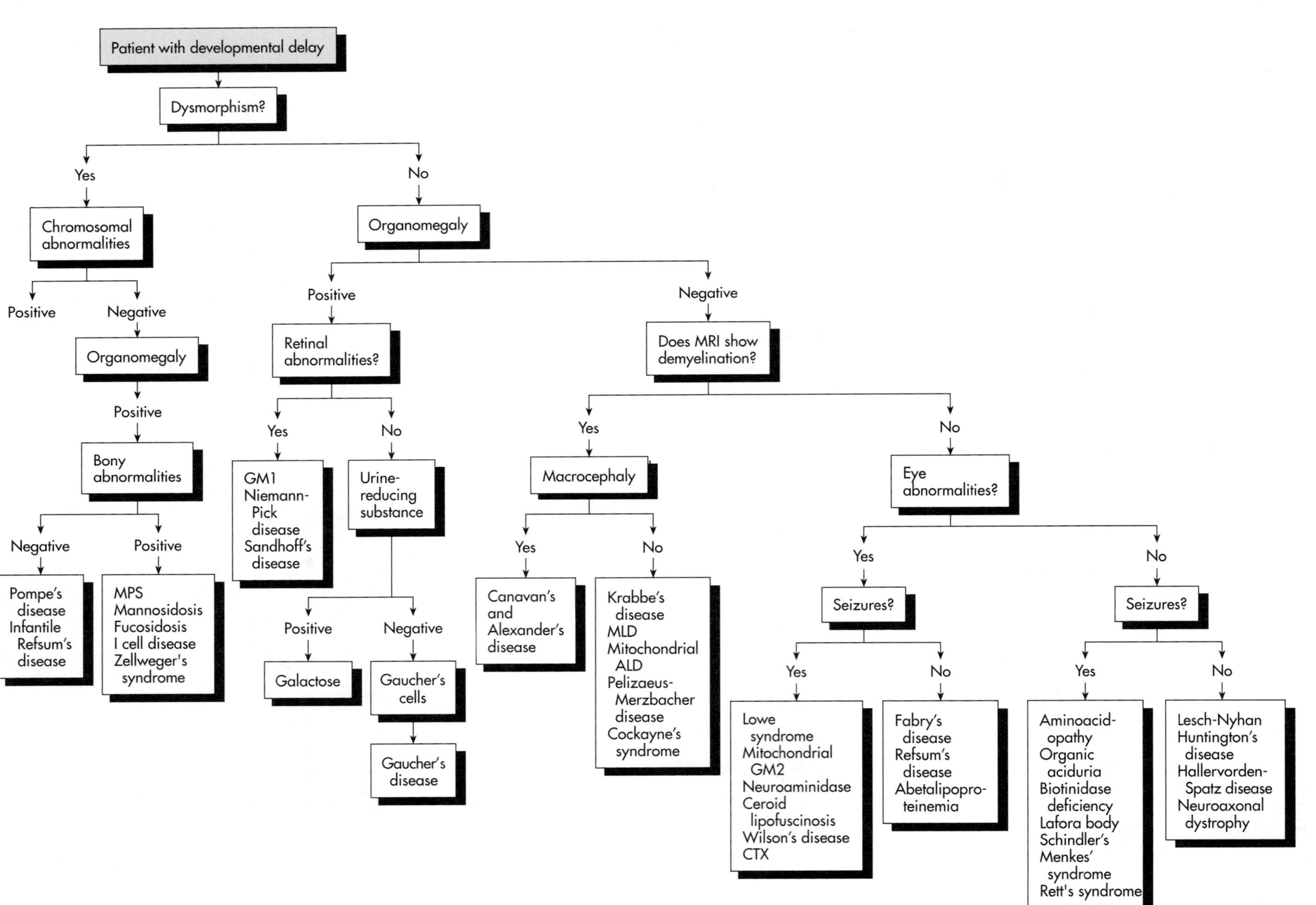

FIGURE 3-65 Workup for developmental delay. *ALD,* Adrenoleukodystrophy; *CTX,* cerebrotendinous xanthomatosis; *MLD,* metachromatic leukodystrophy; *MPS,* mucopolysaccharidosis; *MRI,* magnetic resonance imaging. (From Johnson RT, Griffin JW: *Current therapy in neurologic disease,* ed 5, St Louis, 1997, Mosby.)

DIABETES INSIPIDUS

ICD-9CM # 253.5

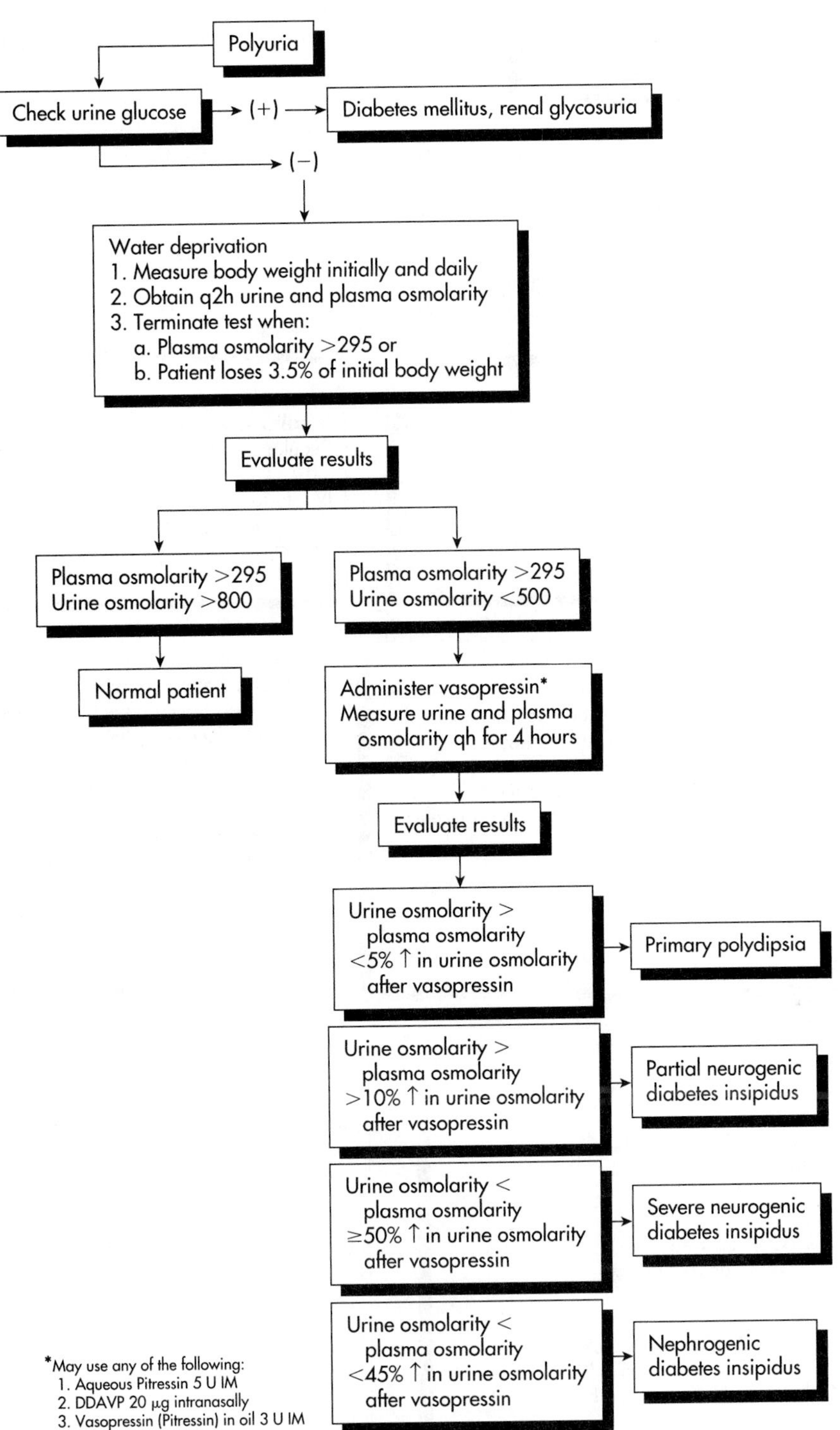

FIGURE 3-66 Diagnostic flowchart for diabetes insipidus. (From Ferri F: *Practical guide to the care of the medical patient,* ed 6, St Louis, 2004, Mosby.)

DIABETIC KETOACIDOSIS/HYPEROSMOLAR HYPERGLYCEMIC STATE

ICD-9CM # 250.1 Diabetic ketoacidosis
250.2 Hyperosmolar hyperglycemic state

Adult patient with DKA or HHS

Complete initial evaluation, including (but not limited to):
Medical history and physical examination
Complete blood count with differential
Fingerstick blood glucose
Serum chemistries ("Chem-10" plus serum ketones)
Urine for urinalysis and ketones
Cultures as indicated (wound, blood, urine, etc.)
Chest±Abdominal X-ray
12-lead electrocardiogram

Concurrently, begin empiric fluid resuscitation with 0.9% NaCl at 1000 mL/hr
Consider volume expanders if hypovolemic shock is present
Continue fluid resuscitation until volume status and cardiovascular parameters (pulse, blood pressure) have been restored

IV Fluids
Based on corrected serum sodium*
If high/normal, use 0.45% NaCl
If low/normal, use 0.9% NaCl
Continue IV fluids at 250-1000 mL/hr, depending on volume status, cardiovascular history, and cardiovascular status (pulse, BP)

Insulin Therapy
Regular insulin bolus, 0.15 U/kg
IV infusion, 0.10 U/kg hr
Check serum glucose hourly—should fall by 50-80 mg/dL/hr.
If serum glucose falling too rapidly, back off on insulin infusion
If serum glucose rising or falling too slowly, increase insulin infusion rate by 50-100%

When Serum Glucose Reaches 250–300 mg/dL:
Add dextrose to IV fluids. Continue IV fluids at 150-250 mL/hr, and adjust insulin infusion to maintain serum glucose of 200-250 mg/dL until metabolic control is achieved:
For DKA, continue until anion gap has closed and acidosis has resolved
For HHS, continue until plasma osmolality drops below 310 mOsm/kg
Begin more exhaustive search for precipitant of metabolic decompensation

Continuing Management:
Follow and replete serum electrolytes (including divalent cations) q2-4h until stable
After resolution of hyperglycemic state, follow blood glucose q4h and initiate sliding scale regular insulin coverage.
Convert IV insulin to subcutaneous injections (or resumption of prior therapy), ensuring adequate overlap if treating patients without endogenous insulin secretion.
Begin clear liquid diet and advance as tolerated. Encourage resumption of ambulation and activity
Review and update diabetes education, with special attention to prevention of further hyperglycemic crises

Potassium (K^+) Repletion
Obtain baseline serum potassium
Obtain 12-lead ECG

- $[K^+] \geq 5.5$ mEq/L → Hold K^+ therapy → Treat hyperkalemia if ECG changes present → Recheck $[K^+]$ in 2 hr
- $[K^+] < 5.5$ mEq/L and adequate urine output → Add K^+ to IV fluids (Use KCl and/or KPhos)
  - $[K^+] = 4.5$-5.4: add 20 mEq/L IVF
  - $[K^+] = 3.5$-4.4: add 30 mEq/L IVF
  - $[K^+] < 3.5$: add 40 mEq/L IVF

Follow serum $[K^+]$ every 2-4 hours until stable: anticipate rapid drop of serum $[K^+]$ during therapy, due to dilution and intracelular shifting
Ensure adequate urine output to avoid over-repletion and hyperkalemia
Continue K^+ repletion until serum $[K^+]$ is stable at between 4-5 mEq/L
If refractory hypokalemia, ensure concurrent magnesium repletion
Repletion may need to be continued for several days, as total body losses may reach up to 500 mEq

Bicarbonate Therapy
Obtain ABG
Obtain baseline serum bicarbonate

- pH<6.9 → 88 mEq/L (2 amps) $NaHCO_3$ over 2 hr
- 6.9≤pH<7.0 → 44 mEq/L (1 amp) $NaHCO_3$ over 1 hr
- pH≥7.0 → Assess need for bicarbonate

Repeat ABG after bicarbonate administration
Repeat $NaHCO_3$ therapy until pH≥7.0, then discontinue therapy
Follow serum bicarbonate q4h until stable

*Sodium correction: Serum sodium should be corrected for hyperglycemia. For every 100 mg/dL of glucose elevation above 100 mg/dL, add 1.6 mEq/L to the measured sodium value; this will yield the correction serum sodium concentration.

FIGURE 3-67 Management of diabetic ketoacidosis (DKA) and hyperosmolar hyperglycemic state (HHS). *ABG,* Arterial blood gas; *DKA,* diabetic ketoacidosis; *ECG,* electrocardiograph; *HHS,* hyperosmolar hyperglycemic state. (From Goldman L, Ausiello D [eds]: *Cecil textbook of medicine,* ed 22, Philadelphia, 2004, WB Saunders.)

DIARRHEA, ACUTE

ICD-9CM # 787.91

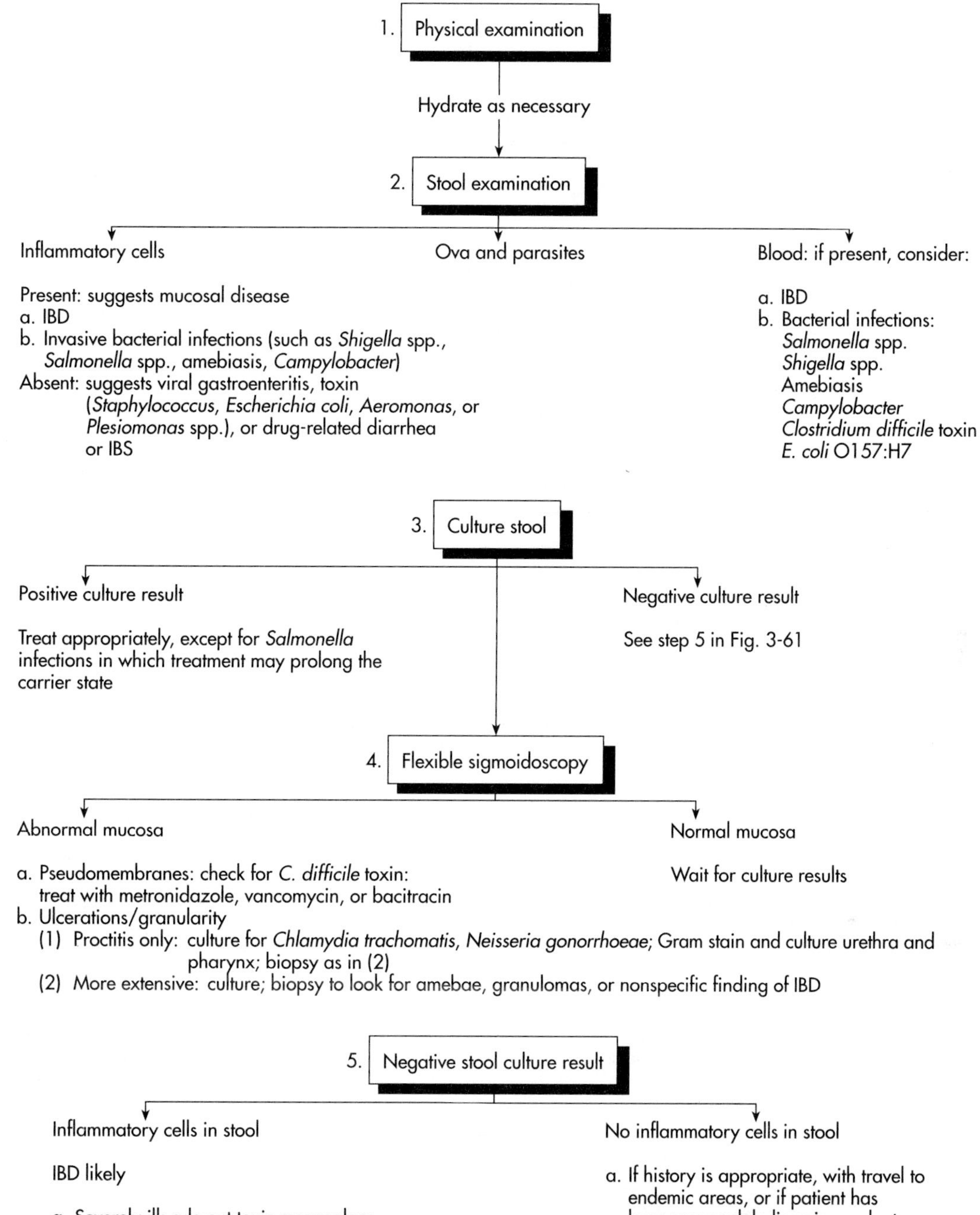
1. Physical examination
Hydrate as necessary
2. Stool examination
Inflammatory cells
Ova and parasites
Blood: if present, consider:
Present: suggests mucosal disease
a. IBD
b. Invasive bacterial infections (such as *Shigella* spp., *Salmonella* spp., amebiasis, *Campylobacter*)
Absent: suggests viral gastroenteritis, toxin (*Staphylococcus*, *Escherichia coli*, *Aeromonas*, or *Plesiomonas* spp.), or drug-related diarrhea or IBS
a. IBD
b. Bacterial infections:
Salmonella spp.
Shigella spp.
Amebiasis
Campylobacter
Clostridium difficile toxin
E. coli O157:H7
3. Culture stool
Positive culture result
Treat appropriately, except for *Salmonella* infections in which treatment may prolong the carrier state
Negative culture result
See step 5 in Fig. 3-61
4. Flexible sigmoidoscopy
Abnormal mucosa
a. Pseudomembranes: check for *C. difficile* toxin: treat with metronidazole, vancomycin, or bacitracin
b. Ulcerations/granularity
(1) Proctitis only: culture for *Chlamydia trachomatis*, *Neisseria gonorrhoeae*; Gram stain and culture urethra and pharynx; biopsy as in (2)
(2) More extensive: culture; biopsy to look for amebae, granulomas, or nonspecific finding of IBD
Normal mucosa
Wait for culture results
5. Negative stool culture result
Inflammatory cells in stool
IBD likely
a. Severely ill: rule out toxic megacolon; analyze blood cultures; abdominal x-ray; treat as IBD
b. Not severely ill: barium studies or colonoscopy after careful and gentle preparation
No inflammatory cells in stool
a. If history is appropriate, with travel to endemic areas, or if patient has hypogammaglobulinemia, evaluate duodenal aspirate for *Giardia*
b. Stop all drugs, stop milk products, rule out malabsorption, observe, and treat symptomatically; if symptoms persist or recur, perform barium studies or colonoscopy

FIGURE 3-68 Diagnostic steps in the assessment of acute diarrhea. *IBD,* Inflammatory bowel disease; *IBS,* irritable bowel syndrome. (From Stein JH [ed]: *Internal medicine*, ed 5, St Louis, 1998, Mosby.)

DIARRHEA, CHRONIC

ICD-9CM # 787.91

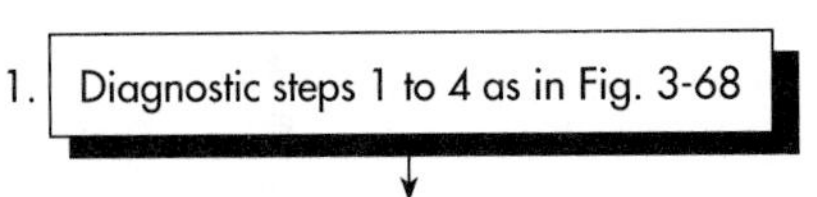

1. Diagnostic steps 1 to 4 as in Fig. 3-68

a. Results diagnostic for infectious diarrhea (uncommon in chronic diarrhea except for *Clostridium difficile* after antibiotics), inflammatory bowel disease, or overt drug-induced diarrhea
b. Results nondiagnostic; usually without inflammatory cells in stool

2. Stool volume

a. Small volume: usually seen in infectious diarrhea or inflammatory bowel disease (consider colonoscopy), but can also be seen in malabsorption syndromes and irritable bowel syndrome
b. Large volume: suggests malabsorption syndromes, secretory diarrhea, or laxative abuse

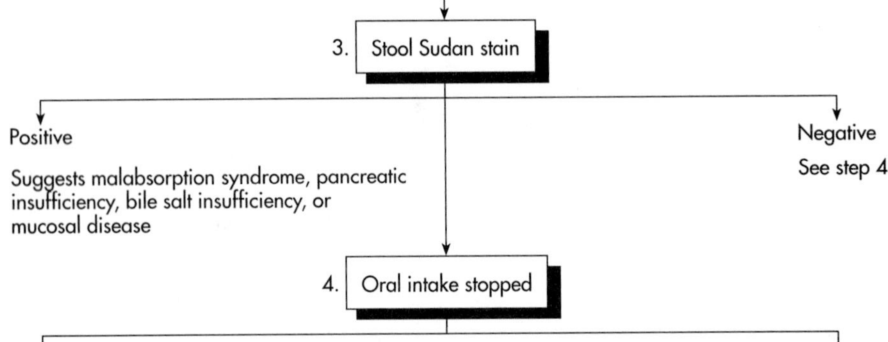

3. Stool Sudan stain

Positive

Suggests malabsorption syndrome, pancreatic insufficiency, bile salt insufficiency, or mucosal disease

Negative

See step 4

4. Oral intake stopped

Diarrhea continues

a. Secretory diarrhea: stool osmolality = stool $(Na^+ + K^+) \times 2$
b. Nasogastric suction
   (1) Diarrhea stops
      (a) Zollinger-Ellison syndrome: gastric analysis, gastrin, secretin stimulation
      (b) Laxative abuse: see step 5
   (2) Diarrhea continues
      (a) Secretory diarrhea: plasma VIP, calcitonin, urinary 5-HIAA abdominal ultrasound, computed tomography and/or selective mesenteric angiogram to identify tumor
      (b) Laxative abuse: see step 5

Diarrhea stops

a. Malabsorption syndromes: stool osmolality > plasma osmolality
b. Laxative ingestion: see step 5
c. Congenital chloridorrhea
   (1) Stool electrolytes: chloride concentration greater than the sum of sodium and potassium concentrations in stool water
   (2) No fecal osmotic gap

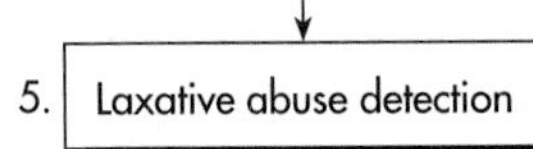

5. Laxative abuse detection

a. Screening tests
   (1) Detailed history
   (2) Sigmoidoscopy and biopsy for melanosis coli
   (3) Barium enema: dilated, hypomotile "cathartic colon"
b. Specific tests
   (1) Urine screening test for senna
   (2) Chromatographic test for bisacodyl
   (3) Stool test for fecal sulfate and phosphate
   (4) Magnesium concentration in fecal water (atomic absorption spectrophotometry)

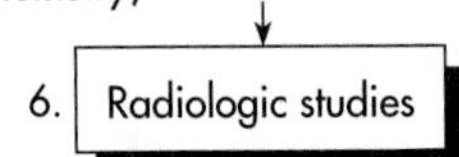

6. Radiologic studies

Perform barium studies only after stool examination, culture, and studies requiring quantitative measurements of the stool have been completed.

FIGURE 3-69 Diagnostic approach to the patient with chronic diarrhea. *5-HIAA,* 5-Hydroxyindoleacetic acid; *VIP,* vasoactive intestinal polypeptide. (Modified from Stein JH [ed]: *Internal medicine,* ed 5, St Louis, 1998, Mosby.)

DIARRHEA, CHRONIC, IN PATIENTS WITH HIV INFECTION

ICD-9CM # 787.1 Diarrhea, chronic

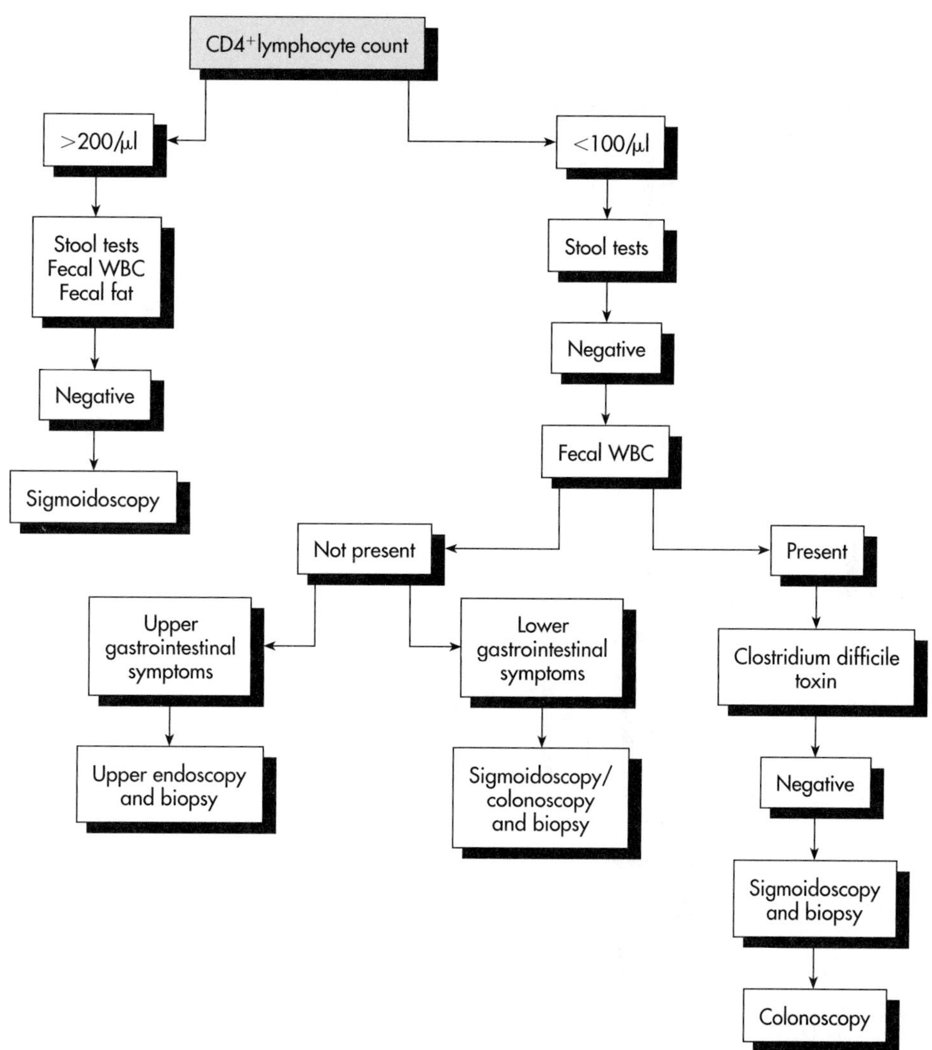

FIGURE 3-70 Approach to evaluating chronic diarrhea in patients with HIV infection. *WBC,* White blood cell count. (From Wilcox CM: *Gastrointest Dis Today* 5:9, 1996.)

TABLE 3-5 **Common Gastrointestinal Pathogens Associated with HIV Infection**

Pathogen	CD4+ Cells/µl	Stool Volume and Frequency	Abdominal Pain	Weight Loss	Fever	Fecal Leukocytes
Cytomegalovirus*	<100	Mild to moderate	++	++	++	+
Cryptosporidiosis	<100	Moderate to severe	−	++	−	−
Microsporidiosis	<100	Mild to moderate	−	+	−	−
Mycobacterium avium complex†	<100	Mild to moderate	+	+++	+++	−

From Wilcox CM: *Gastrointest Dis Today* 5:9, 1996.
*Can have proctitis symptoms when involving the distal colon.
†Typical presentation is fever and wasting; diarrhea is usually secondary.
+++, Very common; ++, frequent; +, can occur; −, absent.

SECTION III

DILATED PUPIL

ICD-9CM # 379.43 Pupil dilation

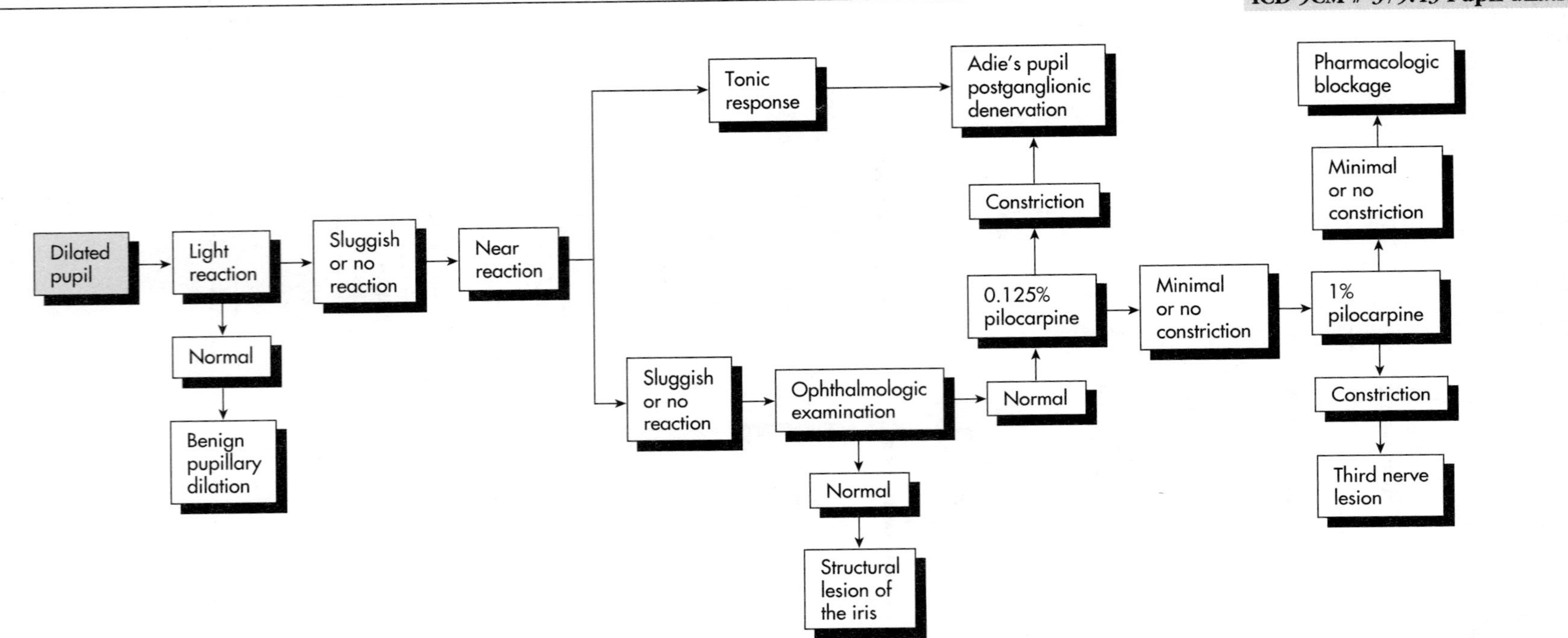

FIGURE 3-71 Use of pilocarpine to help differentiate between different causes of a dilated pupil. (From Goldman L, Ausiello D [eds]: *Cecil textbook of medicine,* ed 22, Philadephia, 2004, WB Saunders.)

DYSPEPSIA

ICD-9CM # 563.3 Dyspepsia atonic
536.8 Dyspepsia disorders other unspecified function of stomach
306.4 Dyspepsia, psychogenic

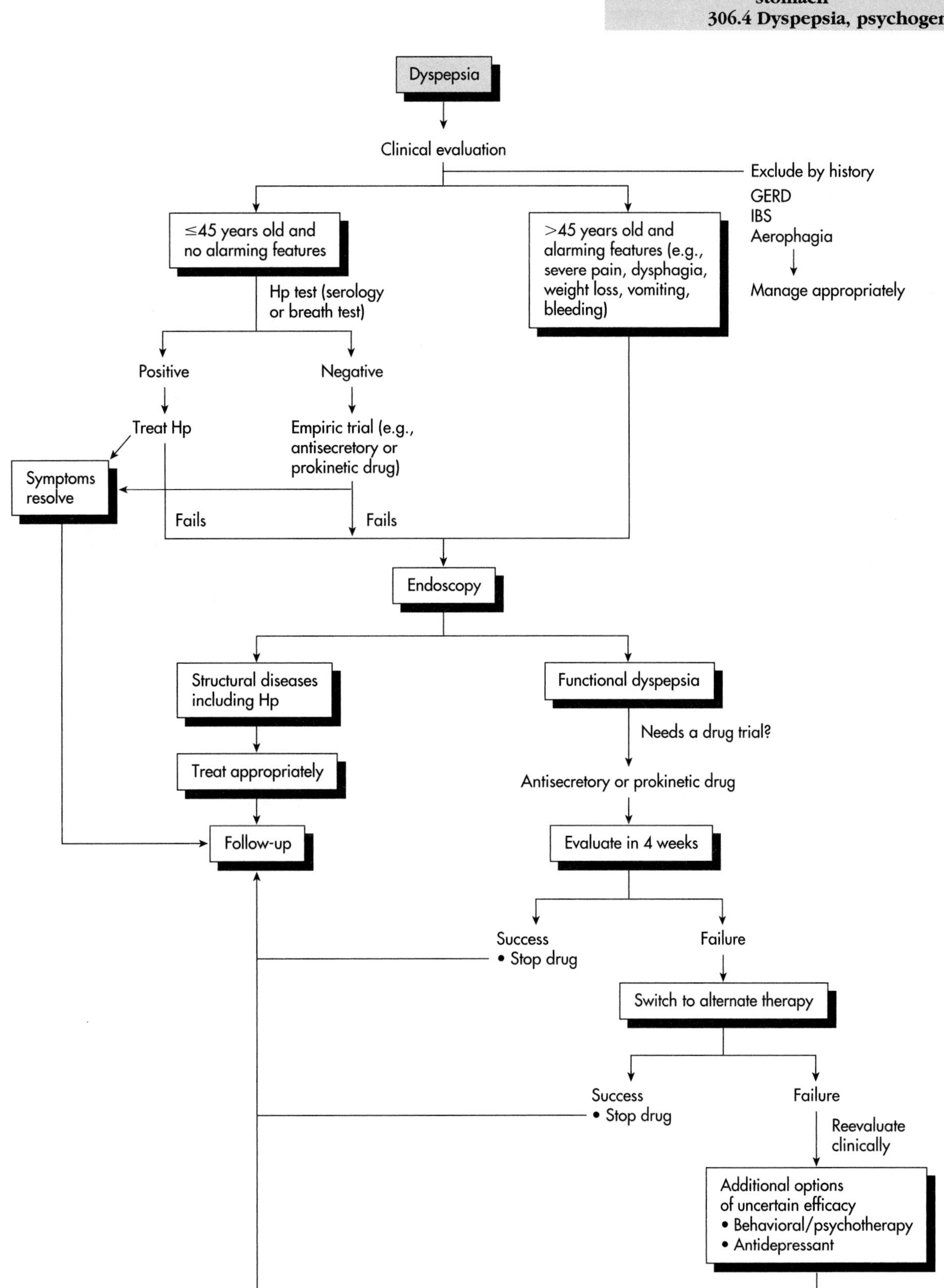

FIGURE 3-72 Algorithm for the evaluation of dyspepsia. *GERD,* Symptomatic gastroesophageal reflux disease; *Hp, Helicobacter pylori; IBS,* irritable bowel syndrome. (From goldman L, Ausiello D [eds]: *Cecil textbook of medicine,* ed 22, Philadelphia, 2004, WB Saunders.)

SECTION III

DYSPHAGIA

ICD-9CM # 787.2

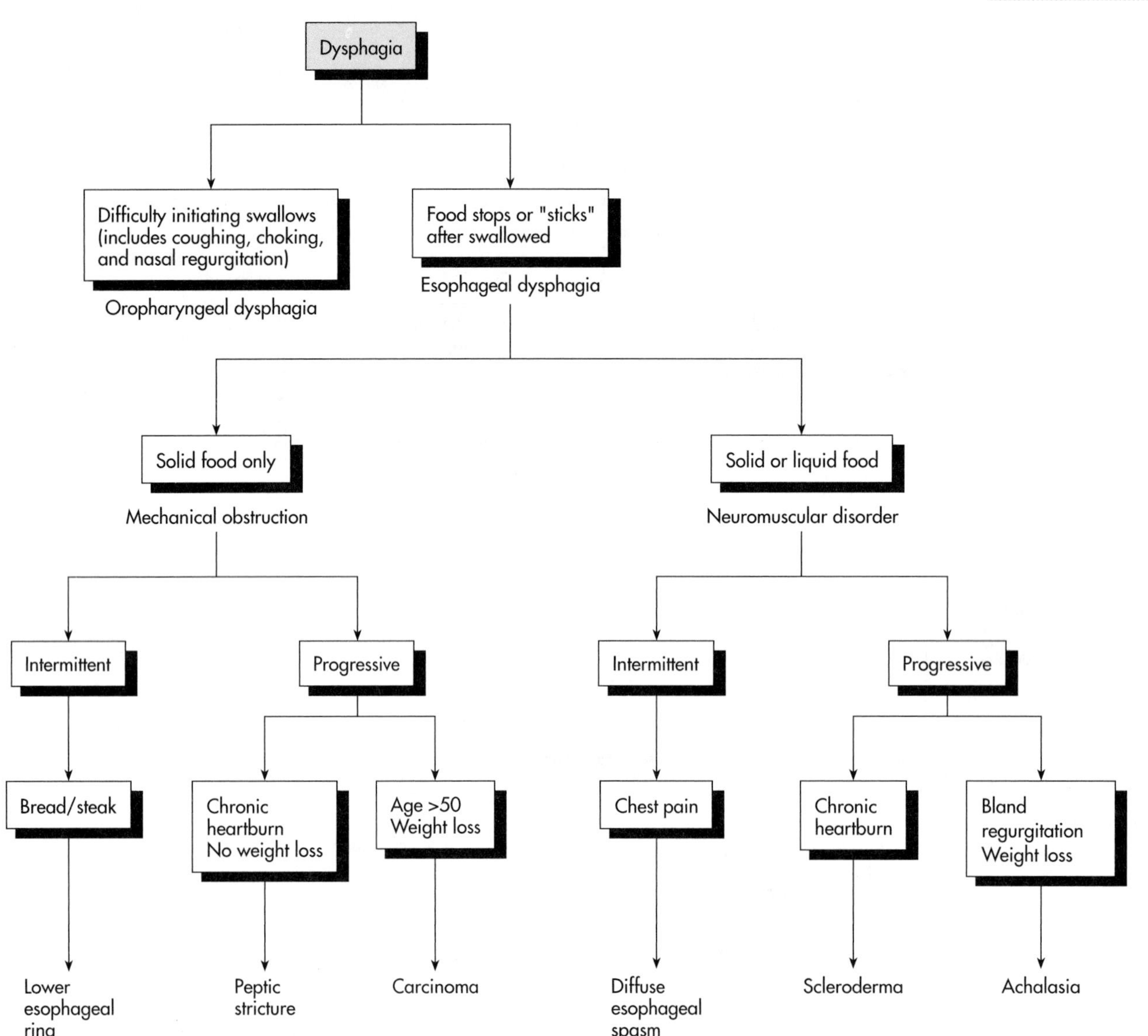

FIGURE 3-73 Differential diagnosis of dysphagia. (From Andreoli TE [ed]: *Cecil essentials of medicine,* ed 5, Philadelphia, 2001, WB Saunders.)

DYSPNEA, ACUTE

ICD-9CM # 786.00

What is the duration of dyspnea?
Acute (emergent)
Chronic (subacute)
Follow algorithm for acute dyspnea
Follow algorithm for chronic dyspnea (Fig. 3-75)

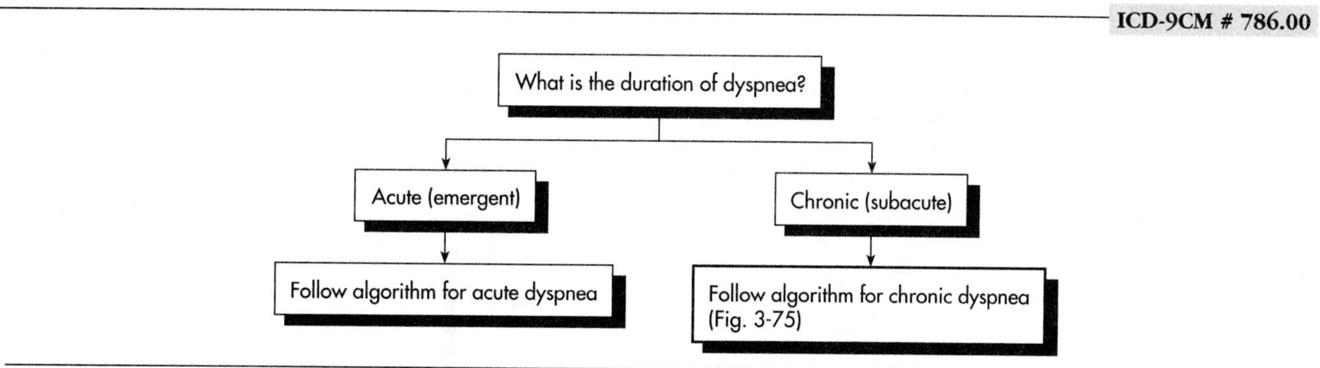

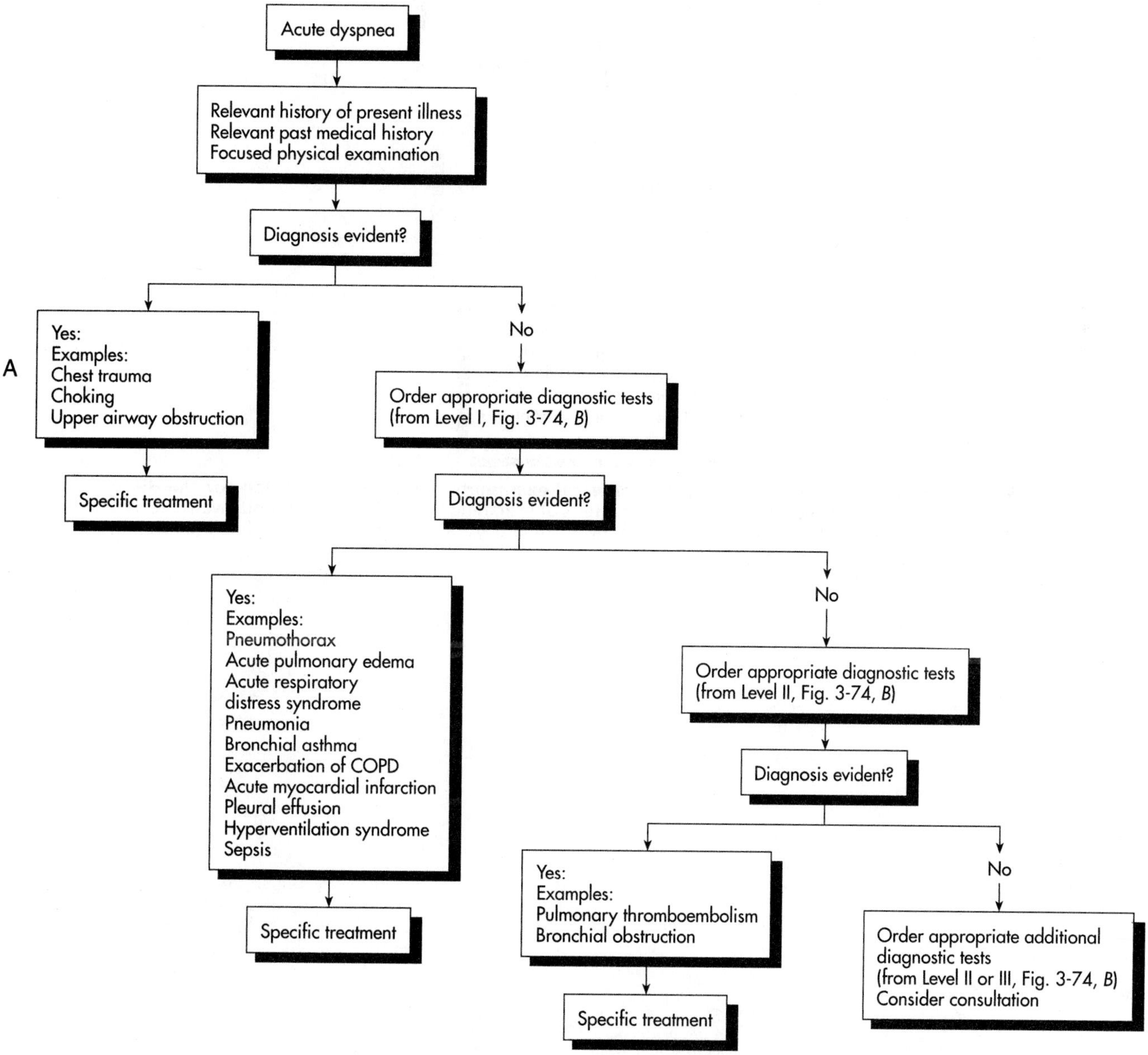

A
Acute dyspnea
Relevant history of present illness
Relevant past medical history
Focused physical examination
Diagnosis evident?
Yes:
Examples:
Chest trauma
Choking
Upper airway obstruction
Specific treatment
No
Order appropriate diagnostic tests (from Level I, Fig. 3-74, B)
Diagnosis evident?
Yes:
Examples:
Pneumothorax
Acute pulmonary edema
Acute respiratory distress syndrome
Pneumonia
Bronchial asthma
Exacerbation of COPD
Acute myocardial infarction
Pleural effusion
Hyperventilation syndrome
Sepsis
Specific treatment
No
Order appropriate diagnostic tests (from Level II, Fig. 3-74, B)
Diagnosis evident?
Yes:
Examples:
Pulmonary thromboembolism
Bronchial obstruction
Specific treatment
No
Order appropriate additional diagnostic tests
(from Level II or III, Fig. 3-74, B)
Consider consultation

FIGURE 3-74 A, Evaluation of the patient with dyspnea. *COPD,* Chronic obstructive pulmonary disease. (From Stein J [ed]: *Internal medicine,* ed 5, St Louis, 1998, Mosby.)

Continued

DYSPNEA, ACUTE—cont'd

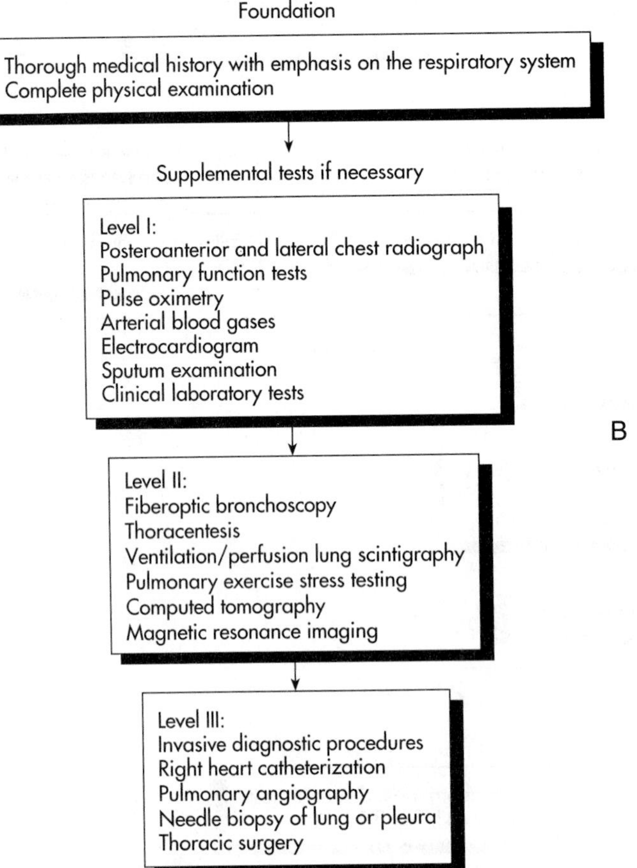

FIGURE 3-74, cont'd B, Medical history and physical examination are the foundation for the diagnosis of respiratory system disease. Diagnostic tests of increasing levels of complexity and invasiveness are performed if necessary to supplement the initial history and physical examination. (From Stein J [ed]: *Internal medicine,* ed 5, St Louis, 1998, Mosby.)

DYSPNEA, CHRONIC

ICD-9CM # 786.00

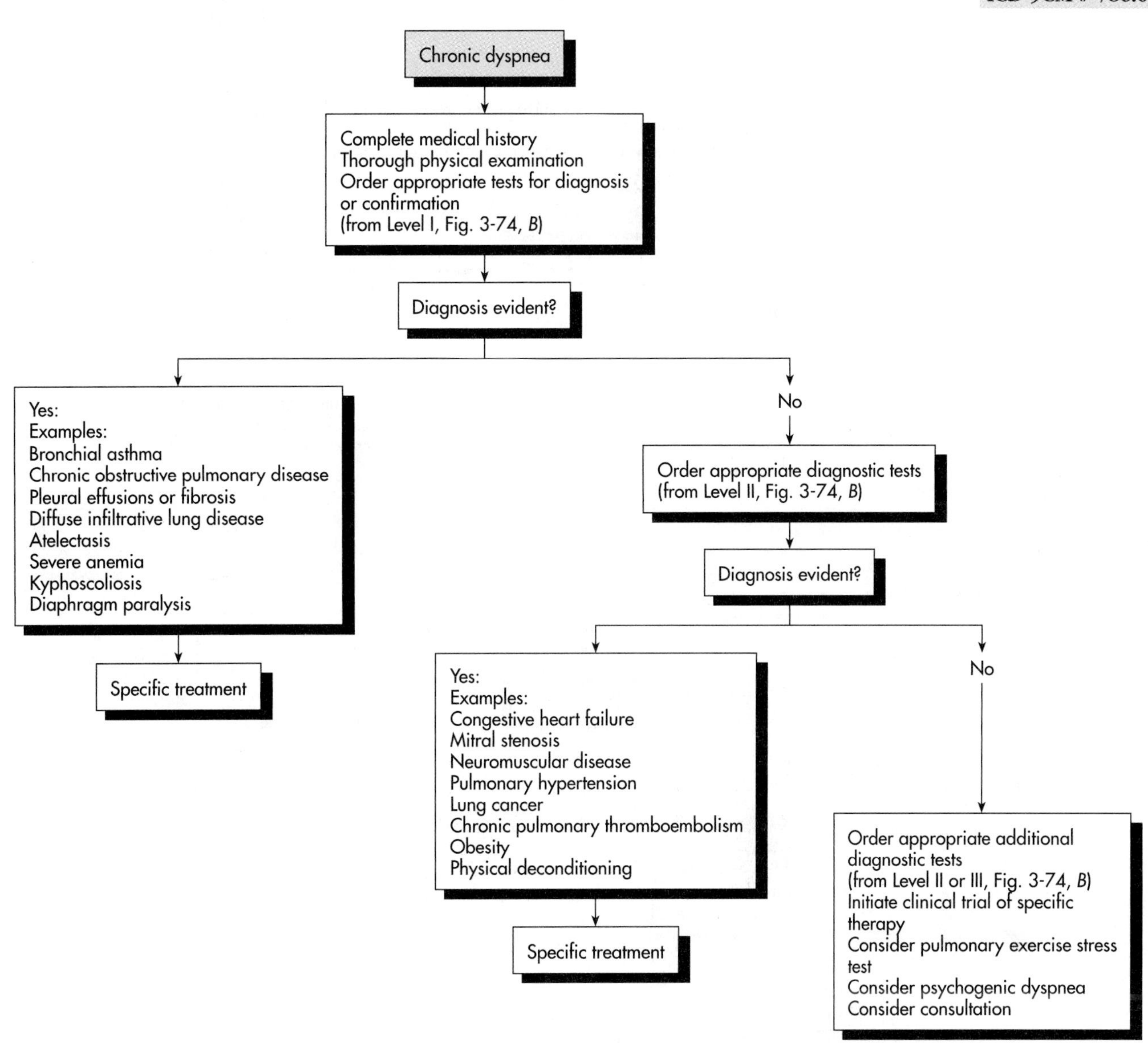

FIGURE 3-75 Chronic dyspnea. (From Stein J [ed]: *Internal medicine,* ed 5, St Louis, 1998, Mosby.)

DYSURIA AND/OR URETHRAL/VAGINAL DISCHARGE

ICD-9CM # 788.1 Dysuria
788.7 Urethral discharge
623.5 Vaginal discharge

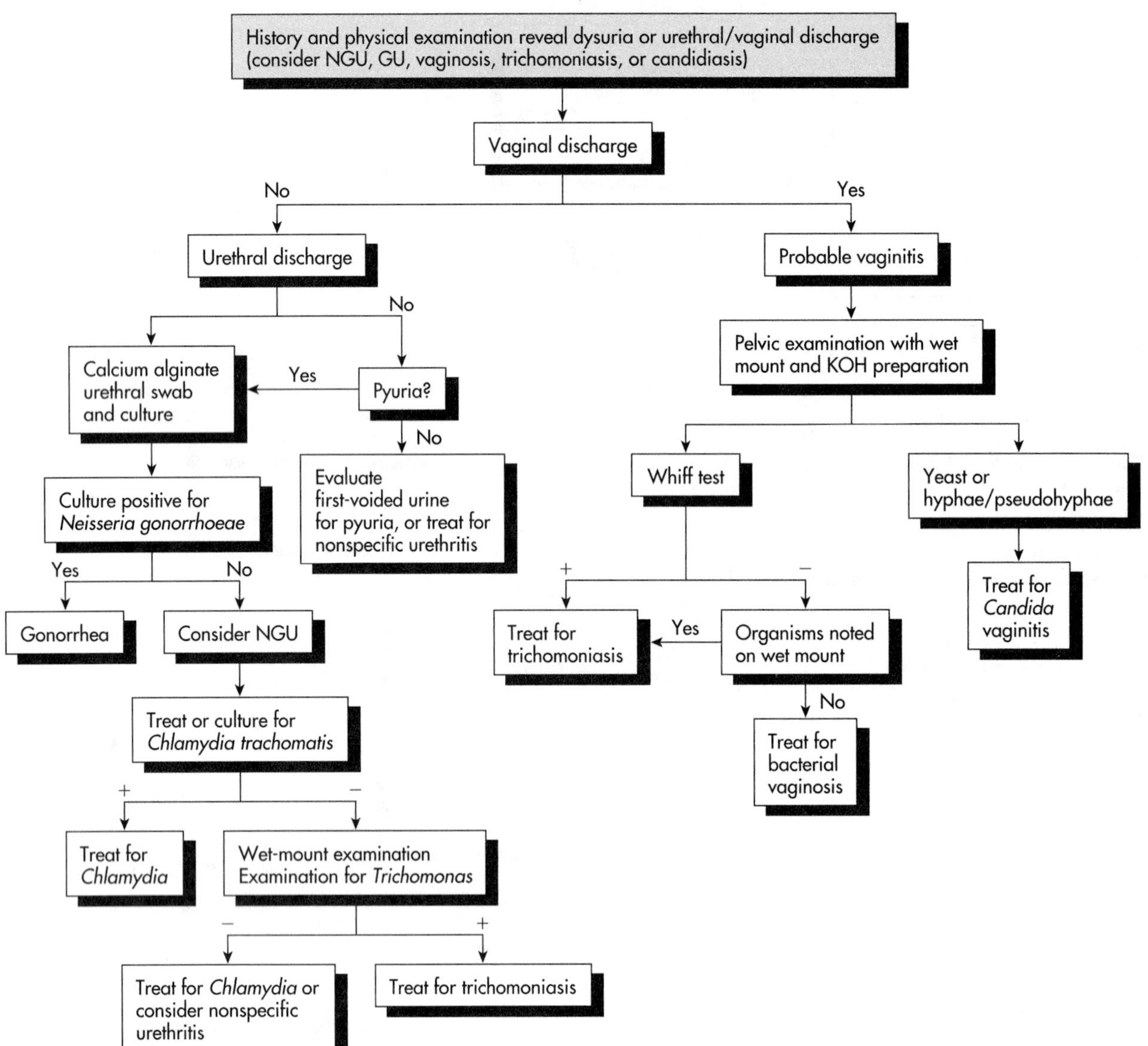

FIGURE 3-76 Evaluation of patients with dysuria and/or urethral/vaginal discharge. *GU,* Gonococcal urethritis; *KOH,* potassium hydroxide; *NGU,* nongonococcal urethritis. (From Nseyo UO [ed]: *Urology for primary care physicians,* Philadelphia, 1999, WB Saunders.)

ECTOPIC PREGNANCY

ICD-9CM # 633.01

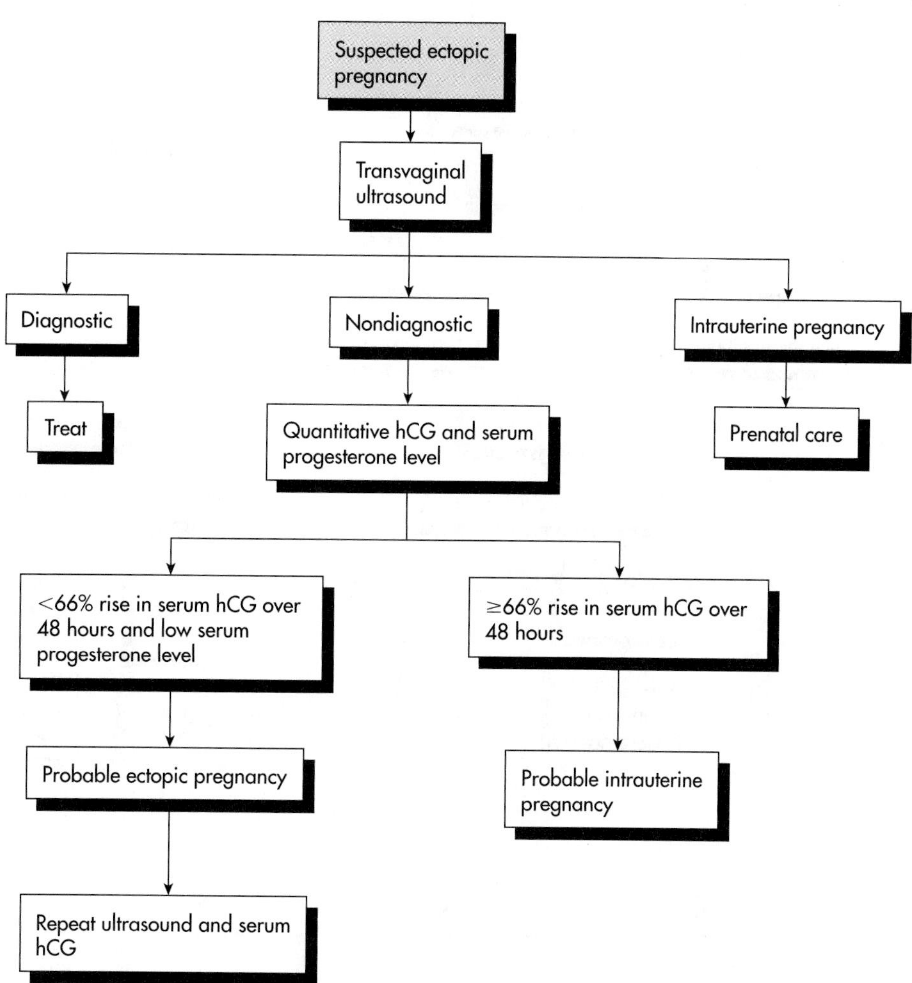

FIGURE 3-77 Ectopic pregnancy. *hCG,* Human chorionic gonadotropin.

ICD-9CM # 782.3 Edema NOS
782.3 Edema, lower extremities

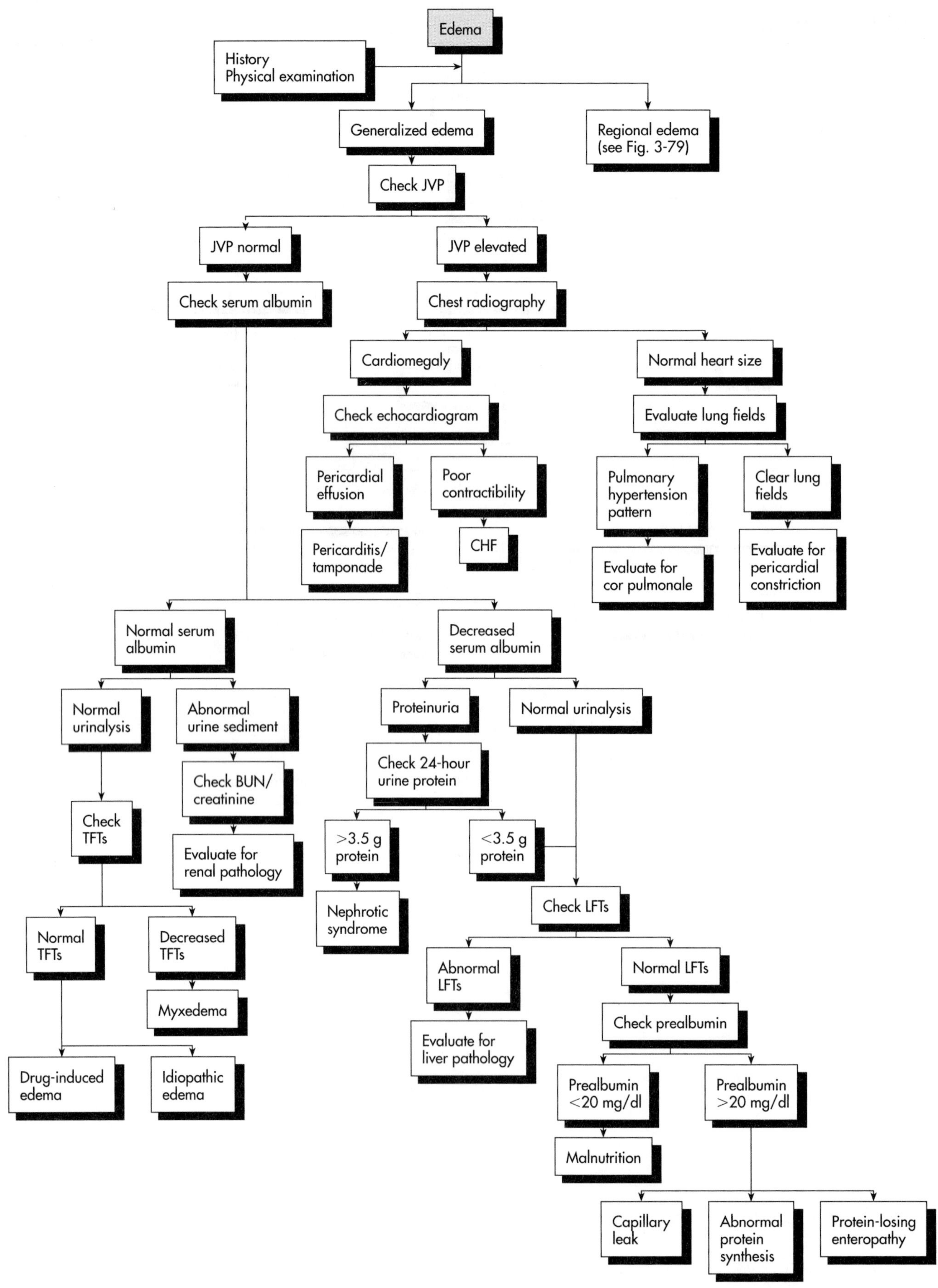

FIGURE 3-78 Evaluation of generalized edema. *BUN,* Blood urea nitrogen; *CHF,* congestive heart failure; *JVP,* jugular venous pressure; *LFT,* liver function tests; *TFT,* thyroid function tests. (From Greene HL, Johnson WP, Lemcke D [eds]: *Decision making in medicine,* ed 2, St Louis, 1998, Mosby.)

EDEMA, REGIONAL

ICD-9CM #	
782.3	Edema, lower extremities
629.8	Edema, genitalia, female
608.86	Edema, genitalia, male
376.33	Edema, orbital
518.4	Edema, pulmonary, acute
514	Edema, pulmonary, chronic
782.3	Edema, unknown etiology

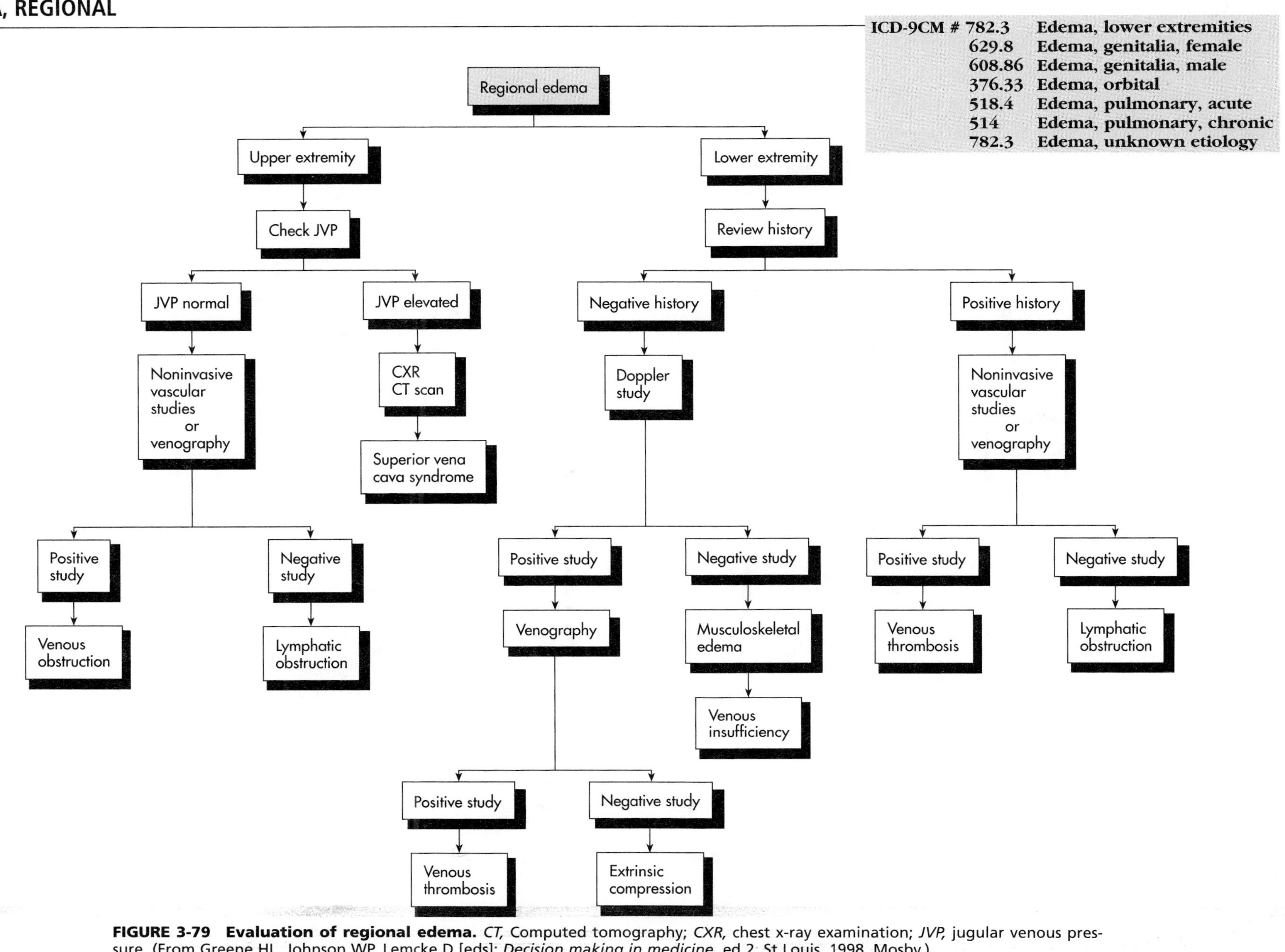

FIGURE 3-79 Evaluation of regional edema. *CT,* Computed tomography; *CXR,* chest x-ray examination; *JVP,* jugular venous pressure. (From Greene HL, Johnson WP, Lemcke D [eds]: *Decision making in medicine,* ed 2, St Louis, 1998, Mosby.)

ENDOCARDITIS, INFECTIVE

ICD-9CM # 421.0 Infective endocarditis
996.61 Prosthetic valve endocarditis

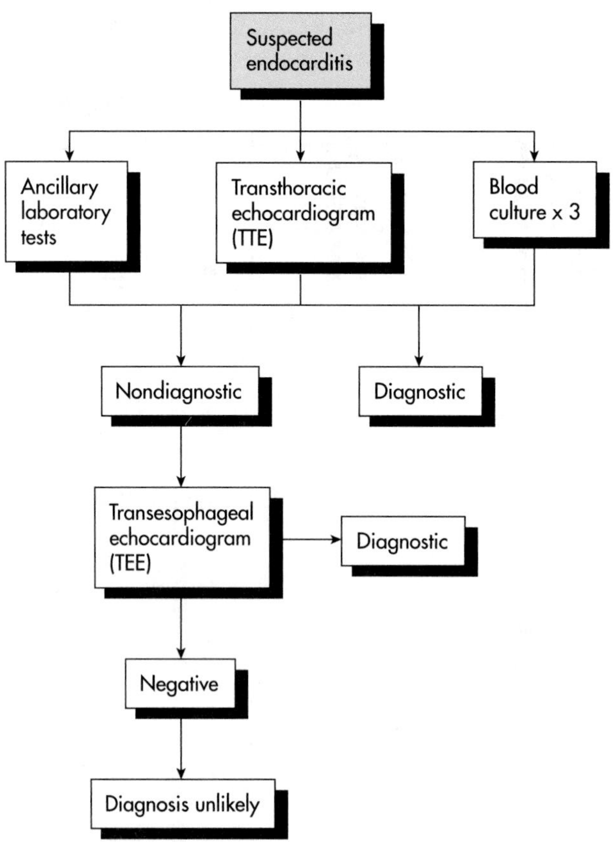

FIGURE 3-80 Evaluation of infective endocarditis. (From Ferri FF: *Ferri's best test: a practical guide to clinical laboratory medicine and diagnostic imaging,* Philadelphia, 2004, Elsevier Mosby.)

BOX 3-3 **Endocarditis, Infective**

Diagnostic imaging
Best test
- Transesophageal echocardiogram (TEE)

Ancillary tests
- Transthoracic echocardiography if TEE is not readily available or patient is uncooperative

Lab evaluation
Best test
- Blood culture × 3

Ancillary tests
- CBC with differential
- ESR (nonspecific)
- Urinalysis

ENURESIS AND VOIDING DYSFUNCTION, PEDIATRIC

ICD-9CM # 788.30

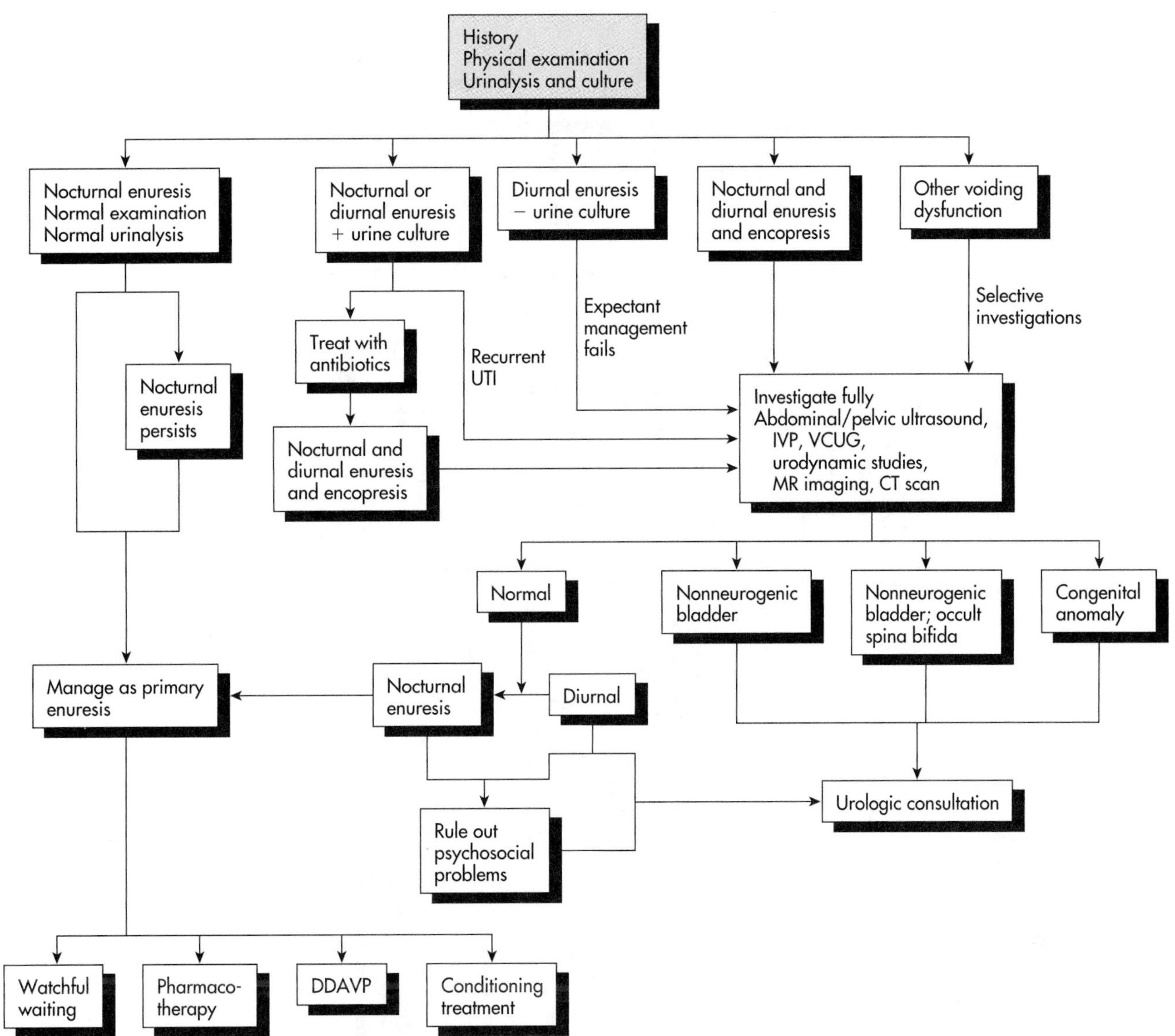

FIGURE 3-81 Algorithm of management of pediatric enuresis and voiding dysfunction. *CT,* Computed tomography; *DDAVP,* desmopressin acetate; *IVP,* intravenous pyelogram; *MR,* magnetic resonance; *UTI,* urinary tract infection; *VCUG,* voiding cystourethrogram. (From Nseyo UO [ed]: *Urology for primary care physicians,* Philadelphia, 1999, WB Saunders.)

ENVENOMATION, MARINE

ICD-9CM # 989.5

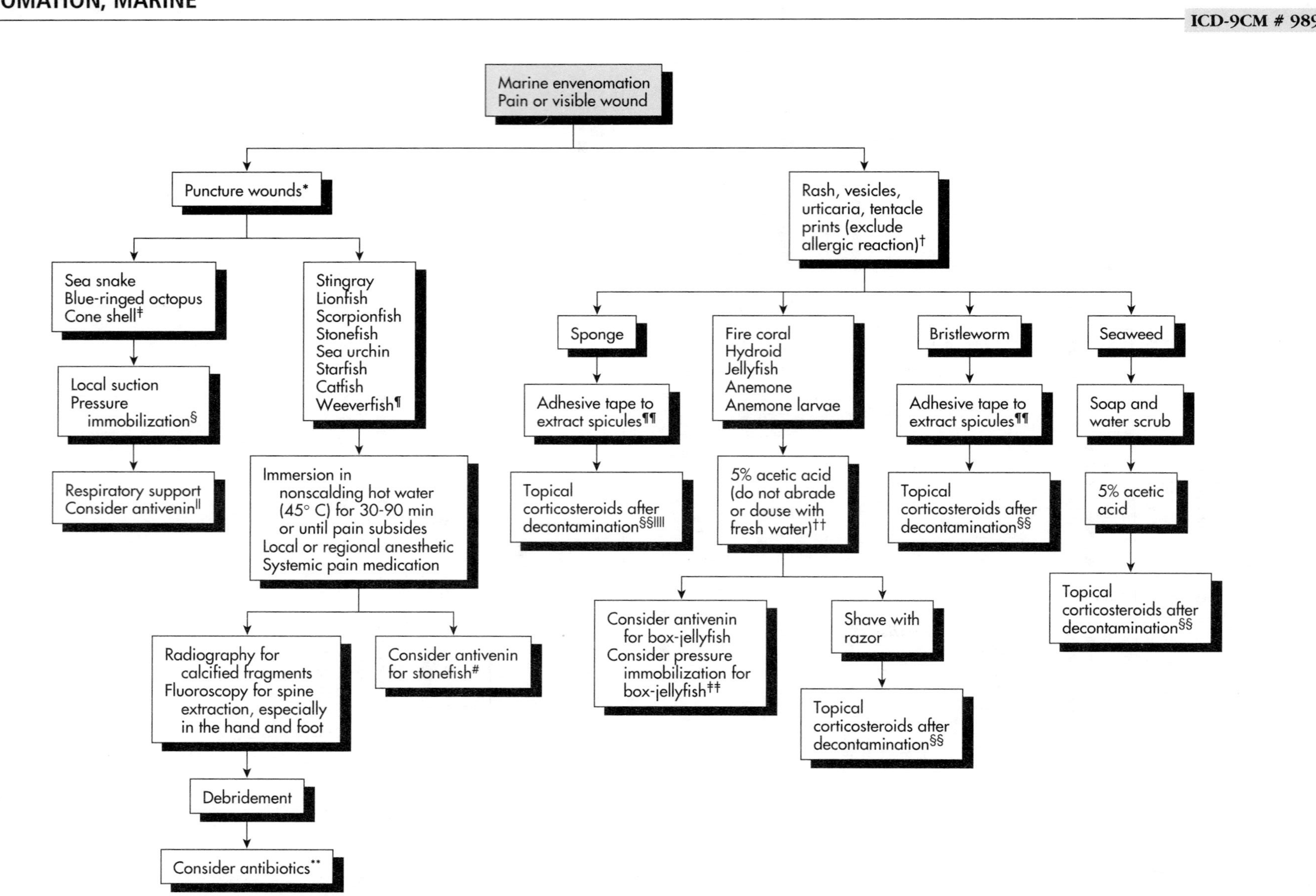

FIGURE 3-82 Algorithmic approach to marine envenomation. (From Auerbach PS: *Wilderness medicine,* ed 4, St Louis, 2001, Mosby.)

[*]A gaping laceration, particularly of the lower extremity, with cyanotic edges suggests a stingray wound. Multiple punctures in an erratic pattern with or without purple discoloration or retained fragments are typical of a sea urchin sting. One to eight (usually two) fang marks are usually present after a sea snake bite. A single ischemic puncture wound with an erythematous halo and rapid swelling suggests scorpionfish envenomation. Blisters often accompany a lionfish sting. Painless punctures with paralysis suggest the bite of a blue-ringed octopus; the site of a cone shell sting is punctate, painful, and ischemic in appearance.
[†]Wheal and flare reactions are nonspecific. Rapid (within 24 hours) onset of skin necrosis suggests an anemone sting. “Tentacle prints” with cross-hatching or a frosted appearance are pathognomonic for box-jellyfish (*Chironex fleckeri*) envenomation. Ocular or intraoral lesions may be caused by fragmented hydroids or coelenterate tentacles. An allergic reaction must be treated promptly.
[‡]Sea snake venom causes weakness, respiratory paralysis, myoglobinuria, myalgias, blurred vision, vomiting, and dysphagia. The blue-ringed octopus injects tetrodotoxin, which causes rapid neuromuscular paralysis.
[§]If *immediately* available (which is rarely the case), local suction can be applied without incision using a plunger device, such as The Extractor (Sawyer Products, Safety Harbor, Fla.). As soon as possible, venom should be sequestered locally with a proximal venous-lymphatic occlusive band of constriction or (preferably) the pressure immobilization technique, in which a cloth pad is compressed directly over the wound by an elastic wrap that should encompass the entire extremity at a pressure of 9.33 kPa (70 mm Hg) or less. Incision and suction are not recommended.
[||]Early ventilatory support has the greatest influence on outcome. The minimal initial dose of sea snake antivenin is 1 to 3 vials; up to 10 vials may be required.
[¶]The wounds range from large lacerations (stingrays) to minute punctures (stonefish). Persistent pain after immersion in hot water suggests a stonefish sting or a retained fragment of spine. The puncture site can be identified by forcefully injecting 1% to 2% lidocaine or another local anesthetic agent without epinephrine near the wound and observing the egress of fluid. Do not attempt to crush the spines of sea urchins if they are present in the wound. Spine dye from already-extracted sea urchin spines will disappear (be absorbed) in 24 to 36 hours.
[#]The initial dose of stonefish antivenin is one vial per two puncture wounds.
[**]The antibiotics chosen should cover *Staphylococcus*, *Streptococcus*, and microbes of marine origin, such as *Vibrio*.
[††]Acetic acid 5% (vinegar) is a good all-purpose decontaminant and is mandated for the sting from a box-jellyfish. Alternatives, depending on the geographic region and indigenous jellyfish species, include isopropyl alcohol, bicarbonate (baking soda), ammonia, papain, and preparations containing these agents.
[‡‡]The initial dose of box-jellyfish antivenin is one ampule intravenously or three ampules intramuscularly.
[§§]If inflammation is severe, steroids should be given systematically (beginning with at least 60 to 100 mg of prednisone or its equivalent) and the dose tapered over a period of 10 to 14 days.
[||||]An alternative is to apply and remove commercial facial peel materials.
[¶¶]An alternative is to apply and remove commercial facial peel materials followed by topical soaks of 30 ml of 5% acetic acid (vinegar) diluted in 1 L of water for 15 to 30 minutes several times a day until the lesions begin to resolve. Anticipate surface desquamation in 3 to 6 weeks.

EPIGLOTTITIS

ICD-9CM # 464.30

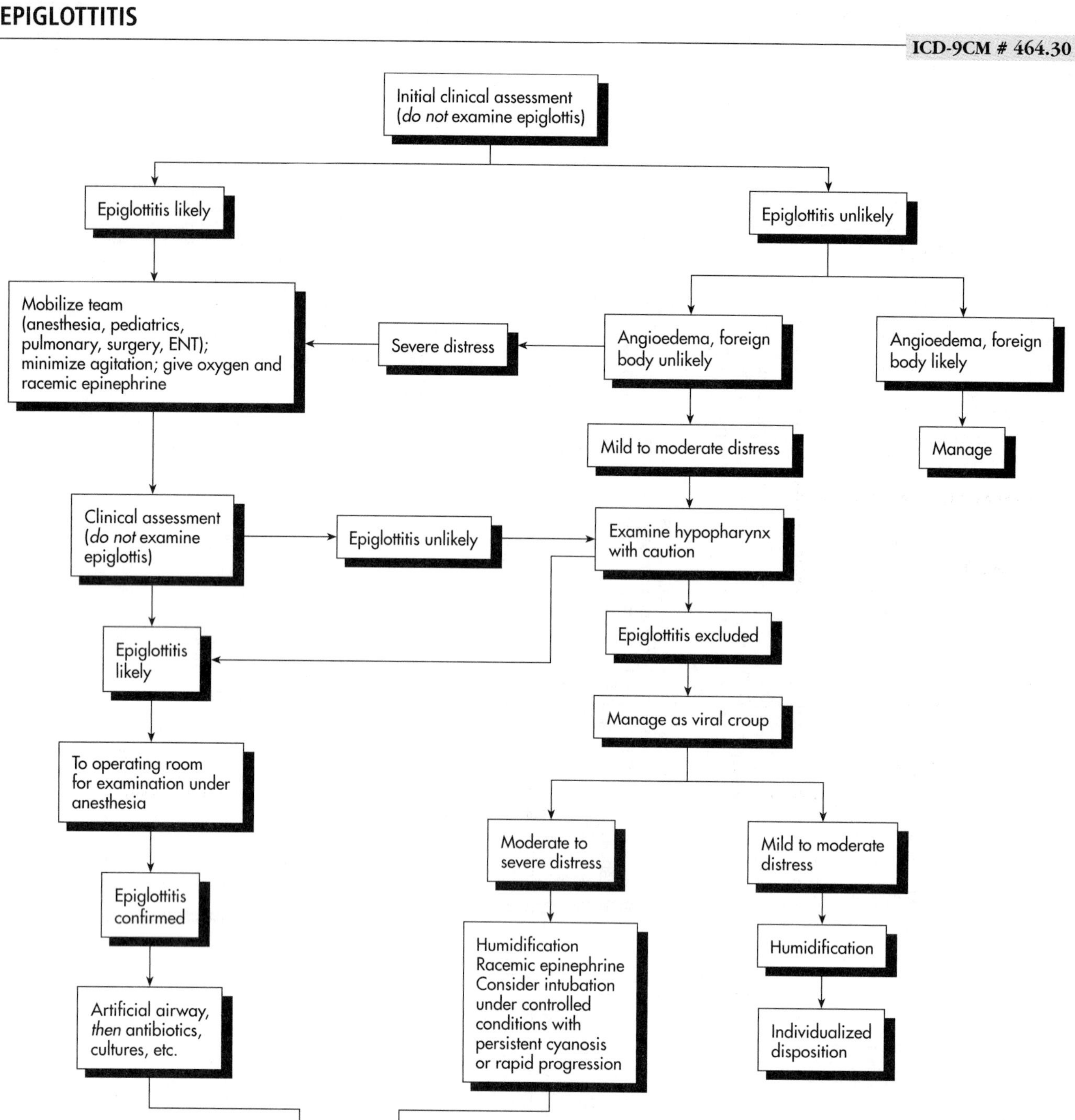

FIGURE 3-83 Optimal assessment and management of upper airway obstruction caused by epiglottitis or severe croup. Care must be individualized to reflect resources and logistic issues within a given institution. *ENT,* Ear, nose, throat. (From Barkin RM, Rosen P: *Emergency pediatrics,* St Louis, 1999, Mosby.)

ERYTHROCYTOSIS, ACQUIRED

ICD-9CM # 289.0 Polycythemia, acquired

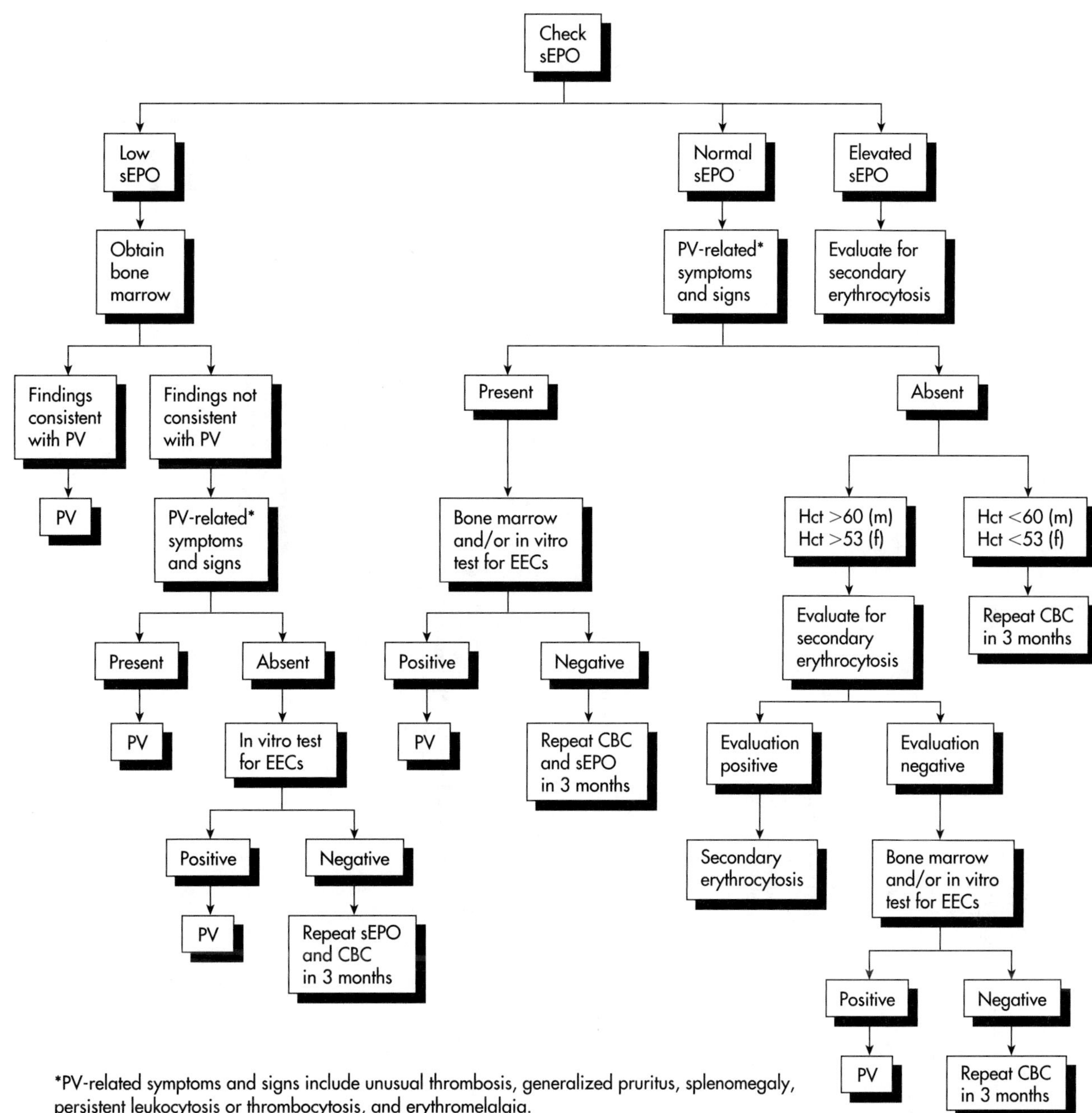

*PV-related symptoms and signs include unusual thrombosis, generalized pruritus, splenomegaly, persistent leukocytosis or thrombocytosis, and erythromelalgia.

FIGURE 3-84 A diagnostic approach to acquired erythrocytosis. *CBC,* Complete blood cell count; *EEC,* endogenous (spontaneous) erythroid colonies; *f,* female; *Hct,* hematocrit; *m,* male; PV, polycythemia vera; sEPO, serum erythropoietin level. (From Goldman L, Ausiello D [eds]: *Cecil textbook of medicine,* ed 22, Philadelphia, 2004, WB Saunders.)

SECTION III

FATIGUE

ICD-9CM # 780.7 Fatigue, general

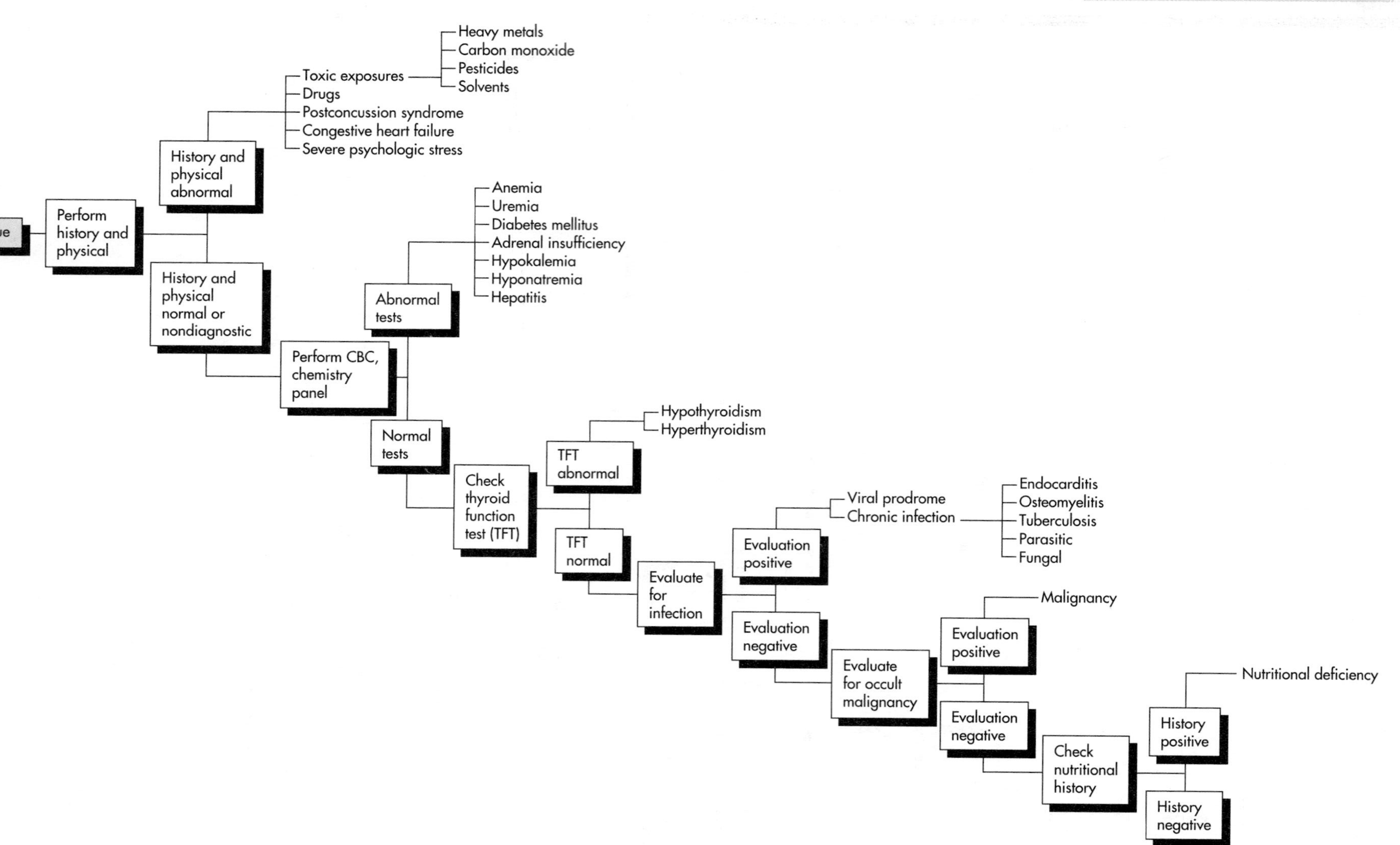

FIGURE 3-85 Evaluation of fatigue. *CBC,* Complete blood count. (From Healey PM: *Common medical diagnosis: an algorithmic approach,* ed 3, Philadelphia, 2000, WB Saunders.)

FECAL INCONTINENCE

ICD-9CM # 787.6

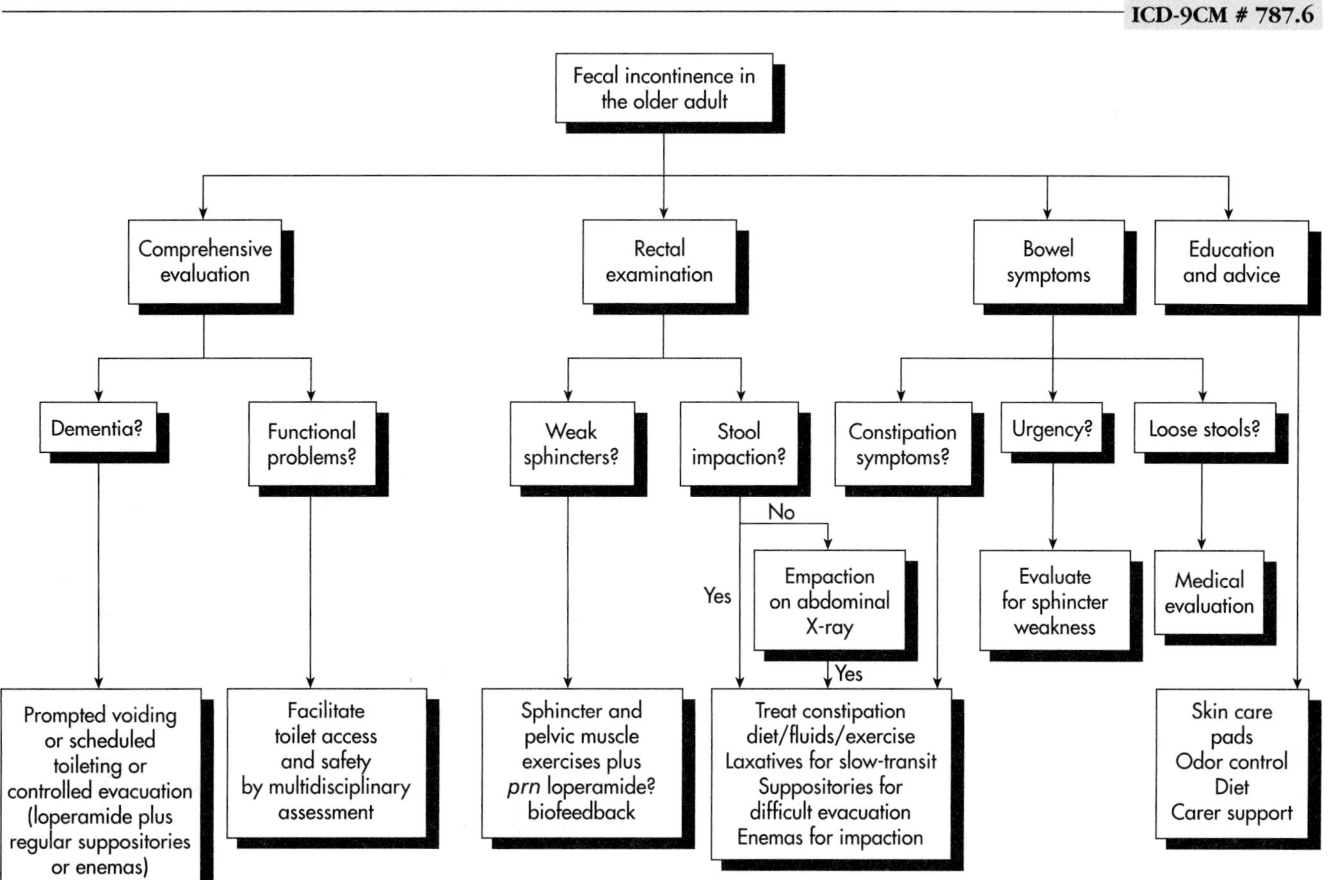

FIGURE 3-86 Evaluation of fecal incontinence. (From Tallis RC, Fillit HM [eds]: *Brocklehurst's textbook of geriatric medicine and gerontology,* ed 6, London, 2003, Churchill Livingstone.)

BOX 3-4 Clinical Assessment of Fecal Incontinence in Older People

Emphasis in older people is on a *structured clinical approach* to identify all contributing factors for fecal incontinence

History
- Duration of fecal incontinence
- Frequency of episodes
- Type (constant soiling, small amounts, complete bowel movement)
- Stool consistency (diarrhea, hard stool)
- Unconscious leakage or symptoms of urgency
- Constipation symptoms/current laxative use
- Systemic illness (confusion, depression, weight loss, anemia)
- Antibiotic use

General examination
- Cognitive and mood assessment
- Neurological profile (stroke, autonomic neuropathy, Parkinson's disease)

Toilet access
- Evaluate ability to use toilet based on muscle strength coordination, vision, limb function, and cognition
- Place in context of current living environment

Specific examination
Abdominal inspection for distension and tenderness
- Perineal inspection for skin breakdown, dermatitis, surgical scars
- Perianal sensation/cutaneous anal reflex
- Observe for excessive downward motion of the pelvic floor when asking patient to bear down in the lateral lying position
- Digital examination for stool impaction
- Digital examination for evaluation of impaired sphincter tone
  - Anal gaping, and/or easy insertion of finger (internal sphincter)
  - Reduced squeeze pressure (external sphincter)
- Ask patient to strain while sitting on commode and observe for rectal prolapse

From Tallis RC, Fillit HM (eds): *Brocklehurst's textbook of geriatric medicine and gerontology,* ed 6, London, 2003, Churchill Livingstone.

FEVER OF UNDETERMINED ORIGIN

ICD-9CM # 780.6 Pyrexia of undetermined origin

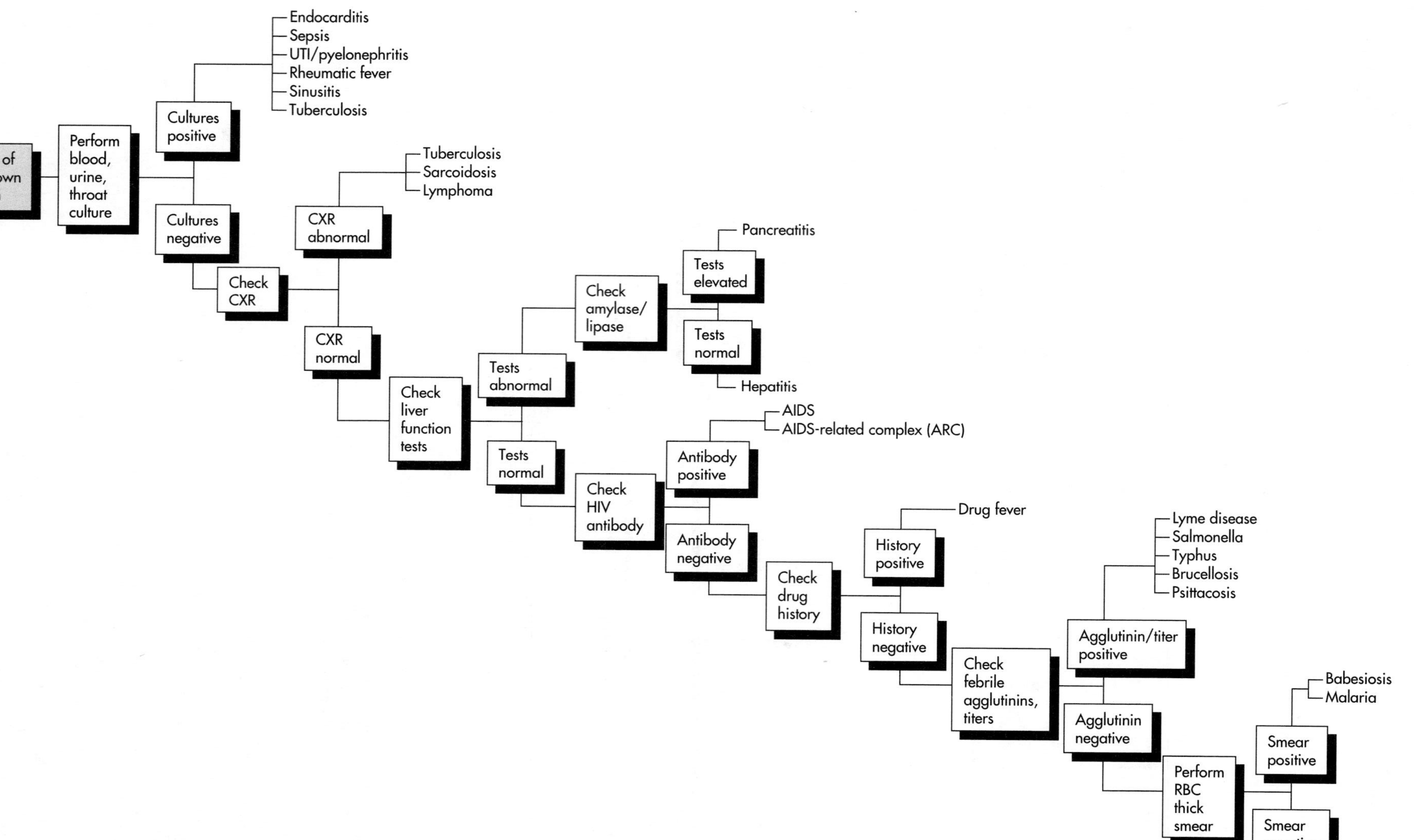

FIGURE 3-87 Approach to the patient with fever of undetermined origin. *AIDS,* Acquired immunodeficiency syndrome; *ANA,* antinuclear antibody; *CT,* computed tomography; *CSR,* chest x-ray; *ESR,* erythrocyte sedimentation rate; *GI,* gastrointestinal; *HIV,* human immunodeficiency virus; *RBC,* red blood cell; *UTI,* urinary tract infection. (From Healey PM: *Common medical diagnosis: an algorithmic approach,* ed 3, Philadelphia, 2000, WB Saunders.)

FEVER OF UNDETERMINED ORIGIN—cont'd

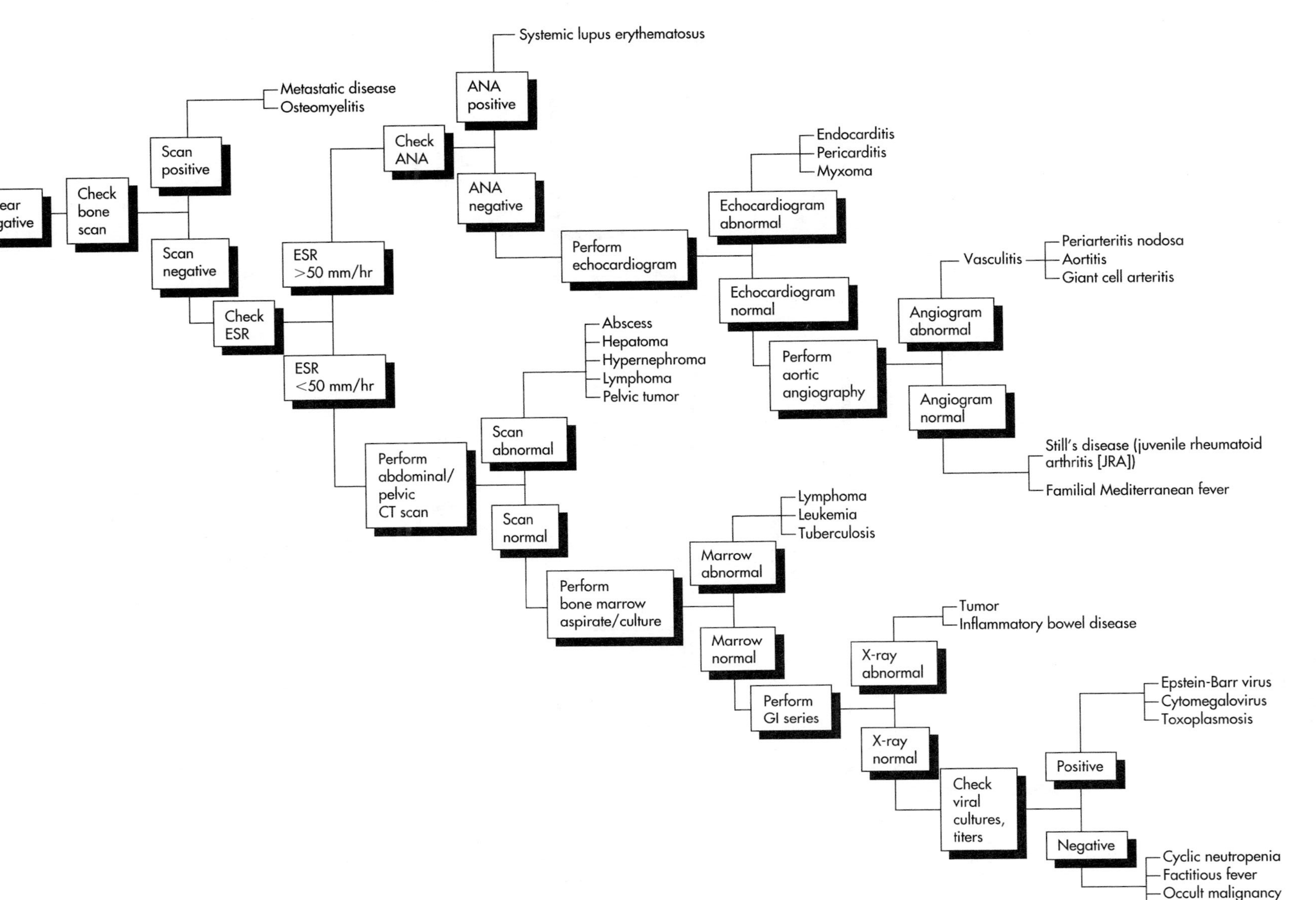

FIGURE 3-87, cont'd *AIDS,* Acquired immunodeficiency syndrome; *ANA,* antinuclear antibody; *CT,* computed tomography; *CSR,* chest x-ray; *ESR,* erythrocyte sedimentation rate; *GI,* gastrointestinal; *HIV,* human immunodeficiency virus; *RBC,* red blood cell; *UTI,* urinary tract infection. (From Healey PM: *Common medical diagnosis: an algorithmic approach,* ed 3, Philadelphia, 2000, WB Saunders.)

ICD-9CM # 829.0 Fracture bone(s) NOS closed
829.1 Fracture bone(s) NOS open

FIGURE 3-88 Bone fracture. *CT,* Computed tomography; *ESR,* erythrocyte sedimentation rate; *MRI,* magnetic resonance imaging; *SPEP,* serum protein electrophoresis; *UEP,* urine electrophoresis. (From Greene HL, Johnson WP, Lemcke D [eds]: *Decision making in medicine,* ed 2, St Louis, 1998, Mosby.)

FRACTURE, BONE—cont'd

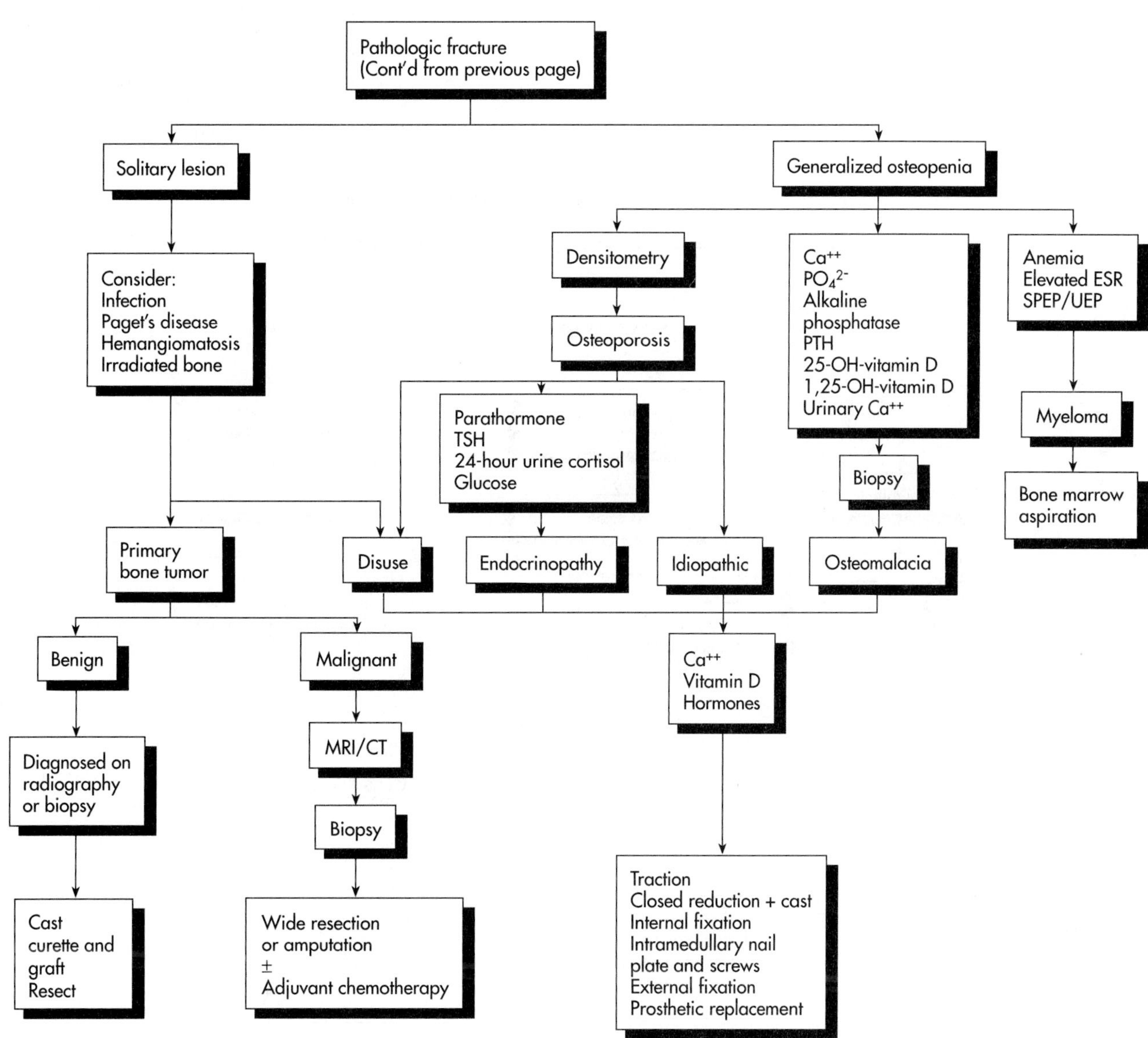

FIGURE 3-88, cont'd

GENITAL LESIONS OR ULCERS

ICD-9CM #	
054.10	Genital herpes
91.0	Genital syphilis
078.11	Condyloma acuminatum
099.0	Chancroid
099.2	Granuloma inguinale
099.1	Lymphogranuloma venereum
629.8	Ulcer, genital site, female
608.89	Ulcer, genital site, male

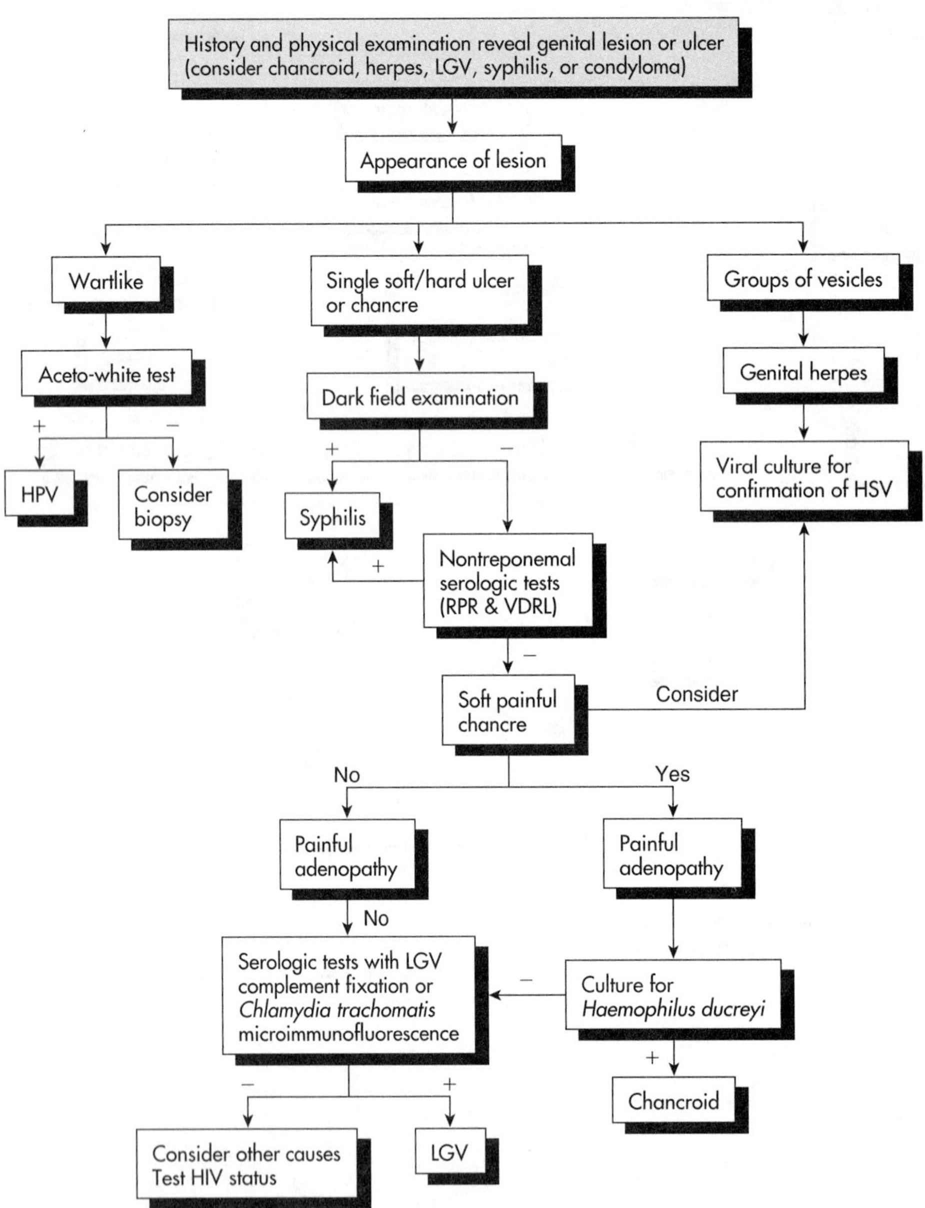

FIGURE 3-89 Evaluation of patients with genital lesions or ulcers. *HIV,* Human immunodeficiency virus; *HPV,* human papillomavirus; *HSV,* herpes simplex virus; *LGV,* lymphogranuloma venereum; *RPR,* rapid plasma reagin; *VDRL,* Venereal Disease Research Laboratory. (From Nseyo UO [ed]: *Urology for primary care physicians,* Philadelphia, 1999, WB Saunders.)

GOITER EVALUATION AND MANAGEMENT

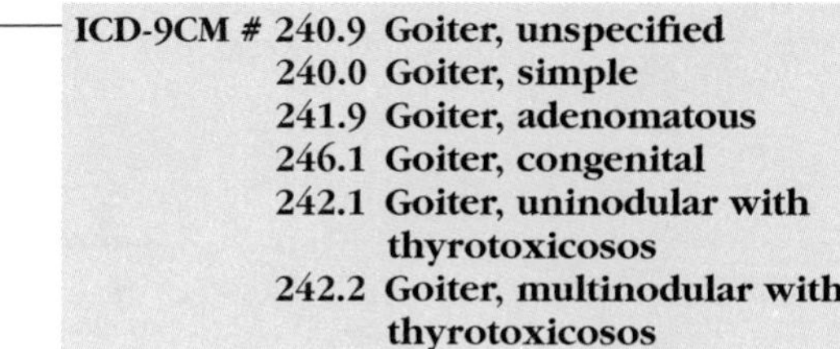

ICD-9CM # 240.9 Goiter, unspecified
240.0 Goiter, simple
241.9 Goiter, adenomatous
246.1 Goiter, congenital
242.1 Goiter, uninodular with thyrotoxicosos
242.2 Goiter, multinodular with thyrotoxicosos

History, physical examination (PE)
Goiter identified
Diffuse or nodular

Free T_4, TSH
Ultrasonography (if size and extension unclear)

Free T_4↑, TSH↓
Hyperthyroid

Therapy: antithyroid drugs, RAI, surgery

TSH elevated
Euthyroid or hypothyroid

T_4 therapy
Follow free T_4, TSH
Goiter size by PE

Free T_4, TSH normal

Diffuse goiter
No obstructive signs

T_4 therapy
Follow T_4, TSH
Goiter size by PE

Multinodular goiter, TSH low-normal
No obstruction, no dominant nodule

Free T_4, TSH, PE every 6-12 months
No T_4 therapy

Multinodular goiter
TSH mid-normal

Minimal obstructive signs

T_4 suppression trial limited to 6 months
Frequently no improvement
Stop T_4 if no size decrease

Significant obstructive signs
CT or MRI to determine size and confirm obstruction

Surgery

No obstructive signs
Dominant nodule

Biopsy nodule

Benign: T_4 suppression limited to 6-12 months
Frequently no size decrease
Rebiopsy nodule

Malignant

Surgery

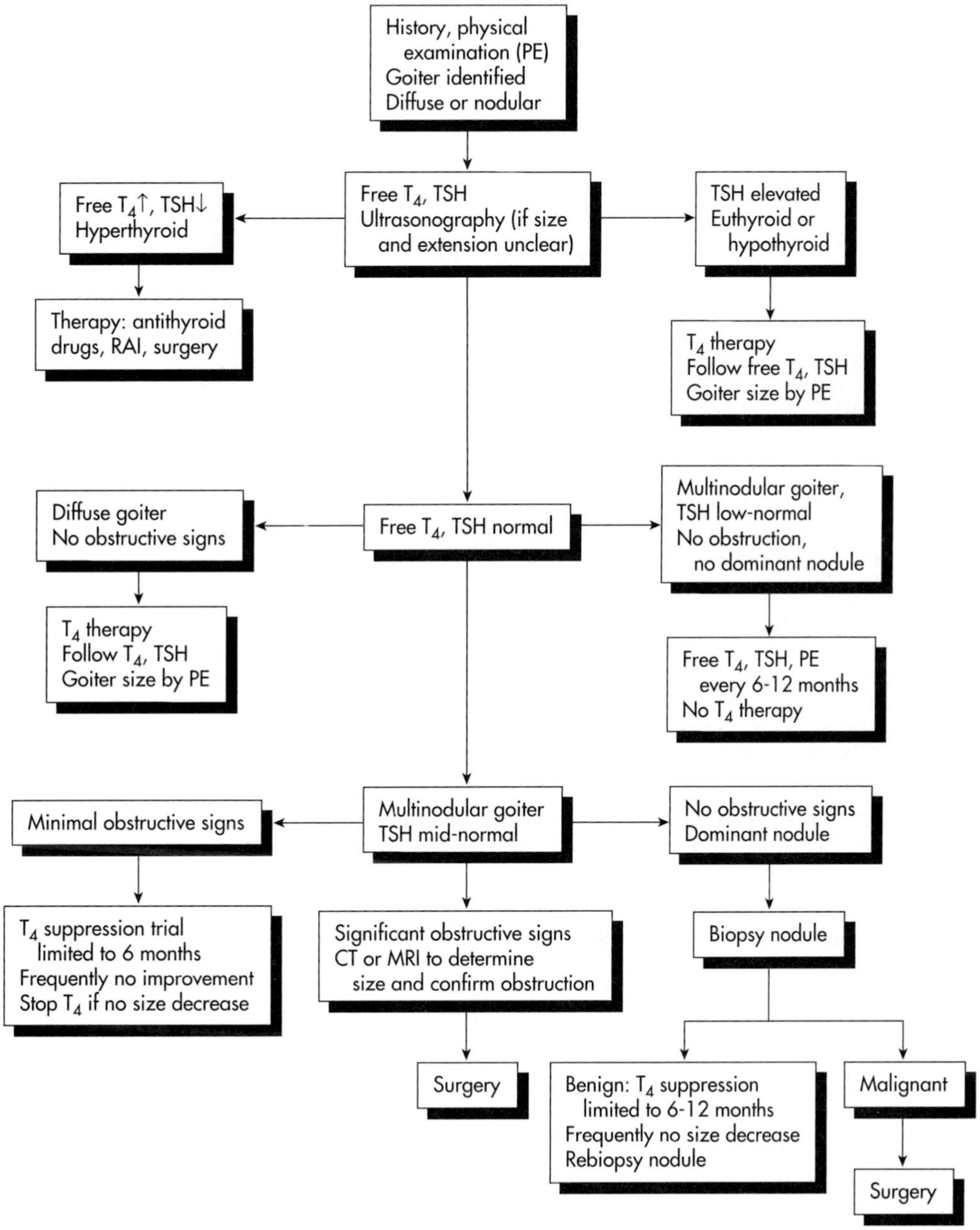

FIGURE 3-90 Evaluation and management of patients with nontoxic diffuse and nodular goiter and undetermined thyroid status. *CT,* Computed tomography; *MRI,* magnetic resonance imaging; *RAI,* radioactive iodine; *TSH,* thyroid-stimulating hormone. (From Goldman L, Ausiello D [eds]: *Cecil textbook of medicine,* ed 22, Philadelphia, 2004, WB Saunders.)

GOUT

ICD-9CM # 274.9

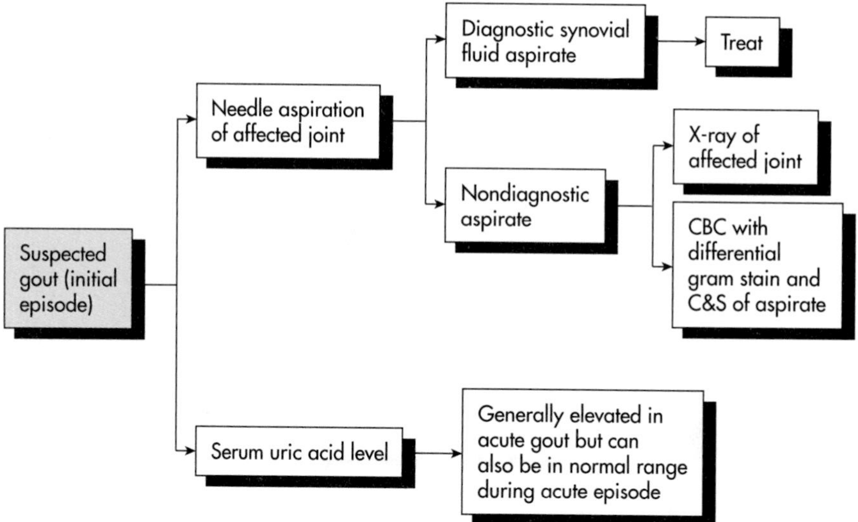

FIGURE 3-91 Evaluation of suspected gout. *CBC,* Complete blood count; *C&S,* culture and sensitivity. (From Ferri FF: *Ferri's best test: a practical guide to clinical laboratory medicine and diagnostic imaging,* Philadelphia, 2004, Elsevier Mosby.)

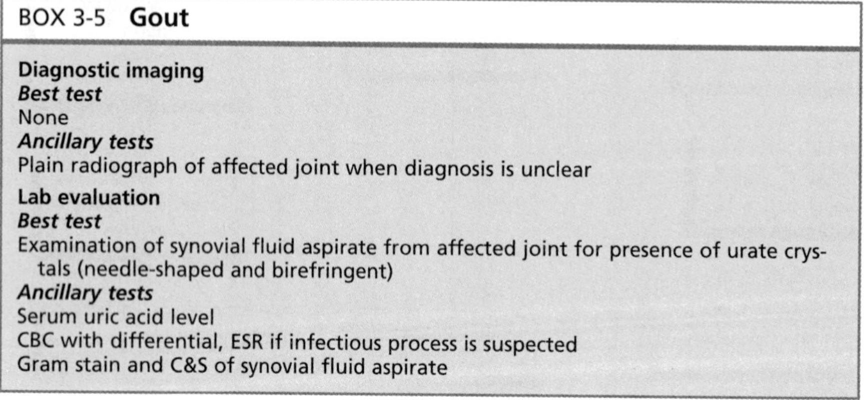
BOX 3-5 **Gout**

Diagnostic imaging
Best test
None
Ancillary tests
Plain radiograph of affected joint when diagnosis is unclear

Lab evaluation
Best test
Examination of synovial fluid aspirate from affected joint for presence of urate crystals (needle-shaped and birefringent)
Ancillary tests
Serum uric acid level
CBC with differential, ESR if infectious process is suspected
Gram stain and C&S of synovial fluid aspirate

From Ferri FF: *Ferri's best test: a practical guide to clinical laboratory medicine and diagnostic imaging,* Philadelphia, 2004, Elsevier Mosby.
CBC, Complete blood count; *C&S,* culture and sensitivity; *ESR,* erythrocyte sedimentation rate.

GYNECOMASTIA

ICD-9CM # 611.1 Gynecomastia nonpuerperal

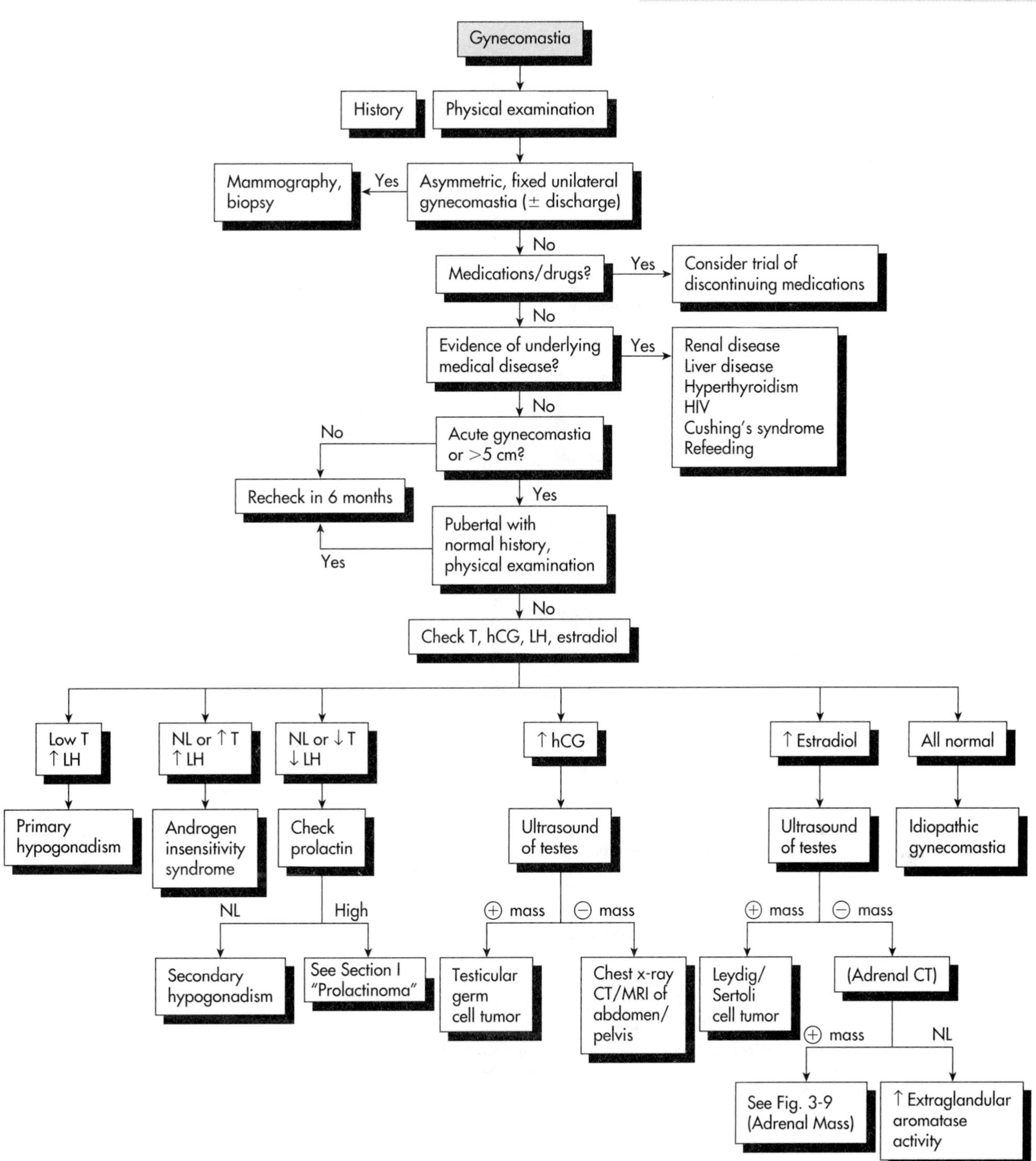

FIGURE 3-92 Evaluation of gynecomastia. *CT,* Computed tomography; *hCG,* human chorionic gonadotropin; *HIV,* human immunodeficiency syndrome; *LH,* luteinizing hormone; *MRI,* magnetic resonance imaging; *NL,* normal limits; *T,* testosterone. (From Noble J: *Primary care medicine,* ed 3, St Louis, 2001, Mosby.)

HEARING LOSS

ICD-9CM # 389.00 Hearing loss, conductive
389.10 Hearing loss, sensorineural

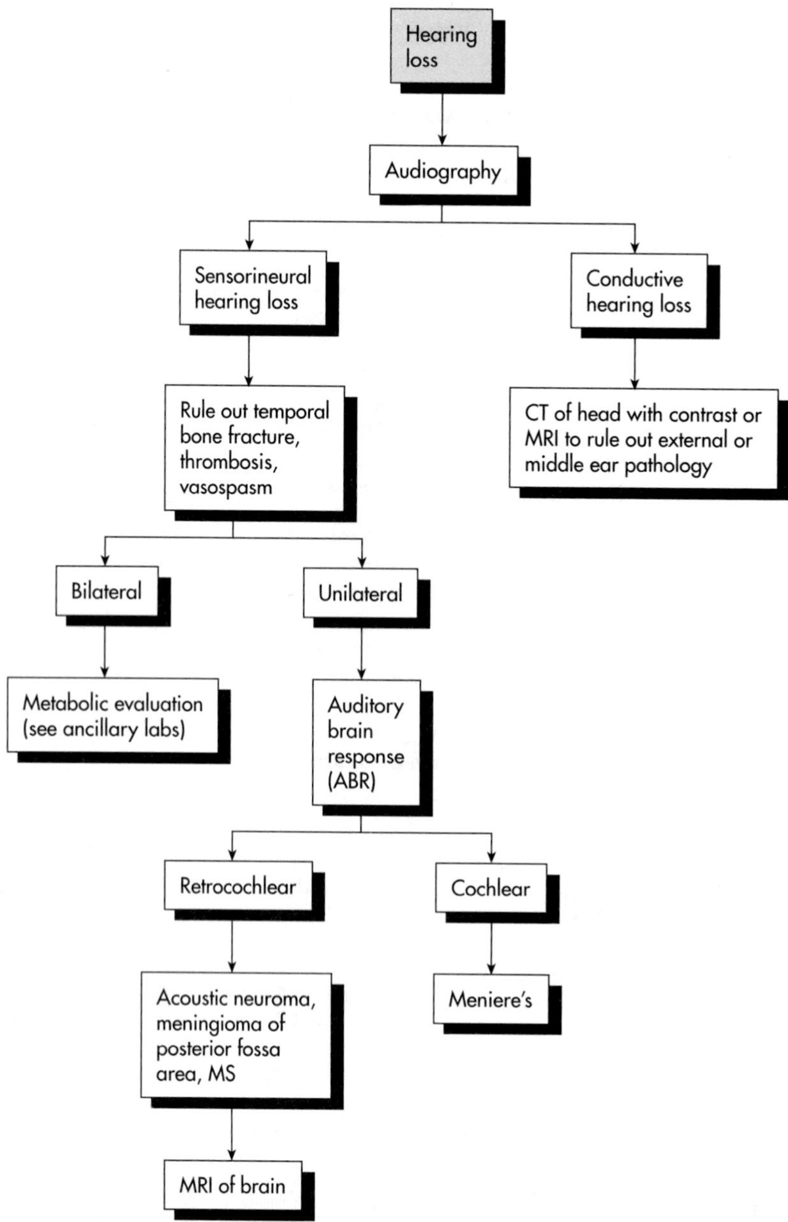

FIGURE 3-93 Evaluation of hearing loss. *CT,* Computed tomography; *MRI,* magnetic resonance imaging. (From Ferri FF: *Ferri's best test: a practical guide to clinical laboratory medicine and diagnostic imaging,* Philadelphia, 2004, Elsevier Mosby.)

BOX 3-6 Hearing Loss

Diagnostic imaging	Lab evaluation
Best test	***Best test***
None	None
Ancillary tests	***Ancillary tests***
CT of head with contrast or MRI with contrast	CBC
CT of temporal bone without contrast	ALT, AST
	ANA, VDRL
	TSH

From Ferri FF: *Ferri's best test: a practical guide to clinical laboratory medicine and diagnostic imaging.* *ALT,* Alanine aminotransferase; *ANA,* antibody to nuclear antigens; *AST,* angiotension sensitivity test; *CBC,* complete blood count; *CT,* computed tomography; *TSH,* thyroid-stimulating hormone; *VDRL,* Venereal Disease Research Laboratory test.

HEARTBURN

ICD-9CM # 787.1

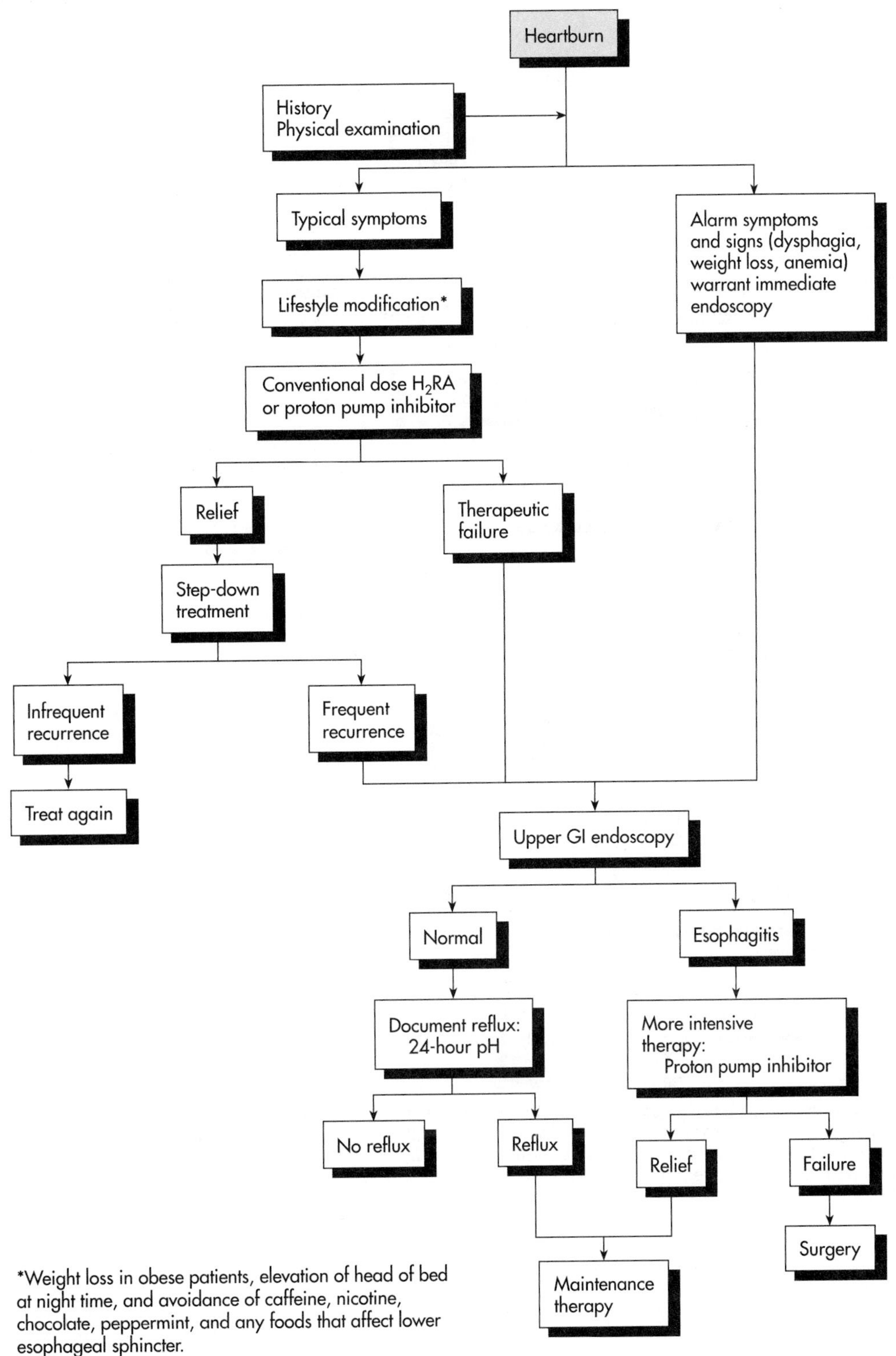

FIGURE 3-94 Treatment of a patient with heartburn. *GI,* Gastrointestinal; *H_2RA,* H_2 receptor antagonist. (Modified from Sampliner RE: Heartburn. In Greene HL, Johnson WP, Lemcke D [eds]: *Decision making in medicine,* ed 2, St Louis, 1998, Mosby.)

HEMATURIA, ASYMPTOMATIC

ICD-9CM # 599.7

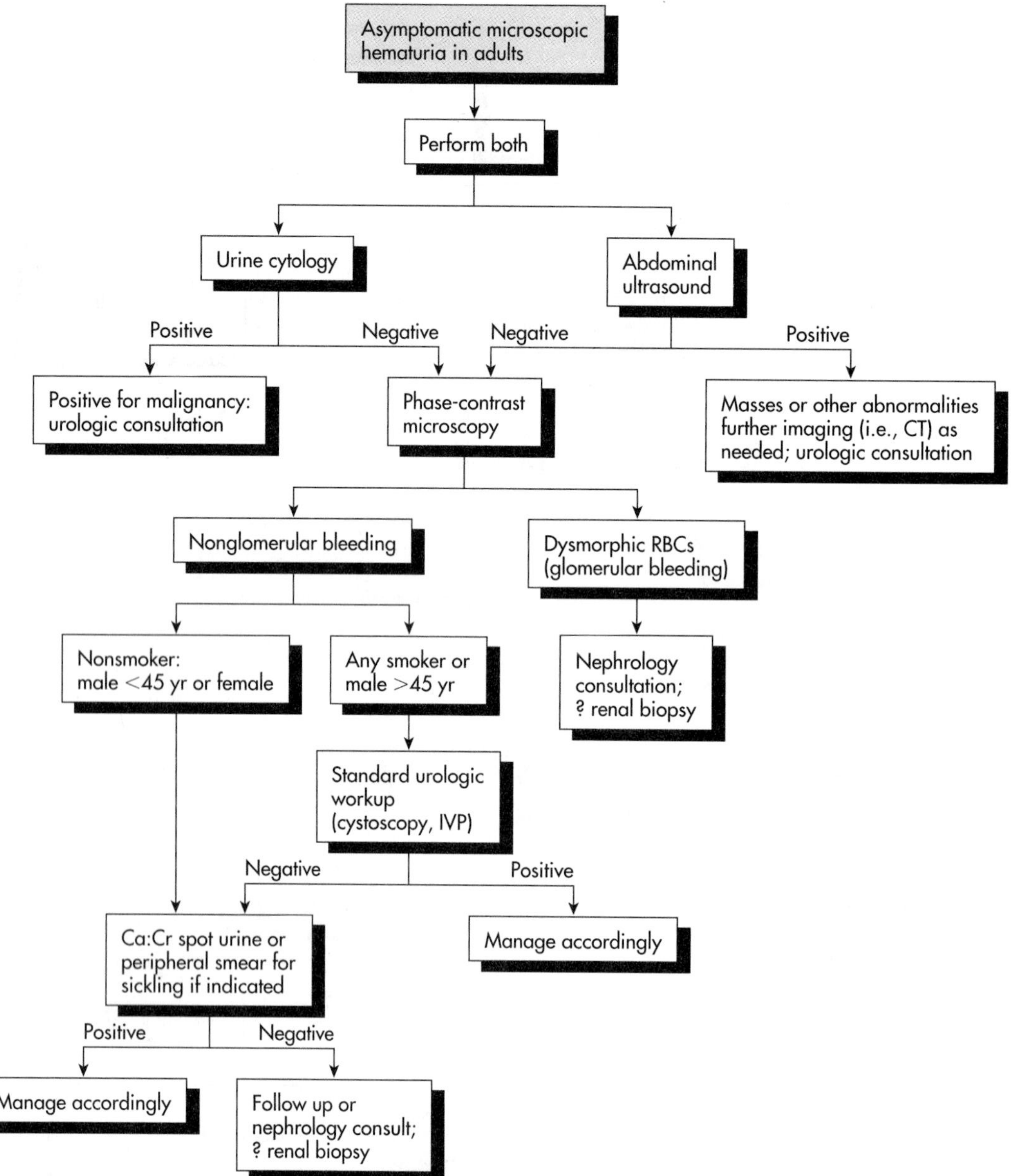

FIGURE 3-95 Suggested algorithm for the evaluation of adult asymptomatic microscopic hematuria. These patients must have no symptoms referable to the hematuria and a negative urinalysis except for red blood cells (RBCs). Adults with gross hematuria require a full urologic evaluation. *Ca:Cr,* Calcium:creatinine ratio; *IVP,* intravenous pyelogram. (From Nseyo UO [ed]: *Urology for primary care physicians,* Philadelphia, 1999, WB Saunders.)

HEMOCHROMATOSIS

ICD-9CM # 275.0

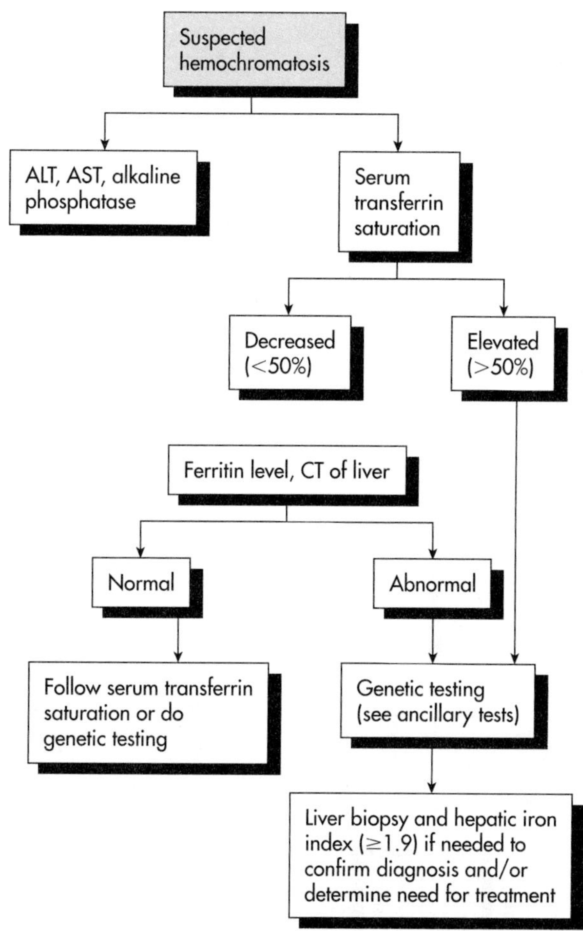

FIGURE 3-96 Evaluation of possible hemochromotosis. *ALT,* Alanine aminotransferase; *AST,* aspartate aminotransferase; *CT,* computed tomography. (From Ferri FF: *Ferri's best test: a practical guide to clinical laboratory medicine and diagnostic imagine,* Philadelphia, 2004, Elsevier Mosby.)

BOX 3-7 Hemochromatosis

Diagnostic imaging
Best test
None
Ancillary tests
Noncontrast CT or MRI of liver is useful for excluding other causes of elevated liver enzymes. Imaging of liver may reveal increased density of liver tissue and is also useful in screening for hepatoma (increased risk in patients with cirrhosis)

Lab evaluation
Best tests
Plasma transferring saturation is best screening test
Plasma ferritin is also a good indicator of total body iron stores but may be elevated in many other conditions (e.g., inflammation, malignancy)
Measurement of hepatic iron index (hepatic iron concentration/age) in liver biopsy specimen can confirm diagnosis
Ancillary tests
ALT, AST, alkaline phosphatase
Genetic testing (HFE phenotyping for C282Y and H63D mutations)

From Ferri FF: *Ferri's best test: a practical guide to clinical laboratory medicine and diagnostic imaging,* Philadelphia, 2004, Elsevier Mosby.
ALT, Alanine aminotransferase; *AST,* aspartate aminotransferase; *CT,* computed tomography; *MRI,* magnetic resonance imaging.

HEMOPTYSIS

ICD-9CM # 786.3

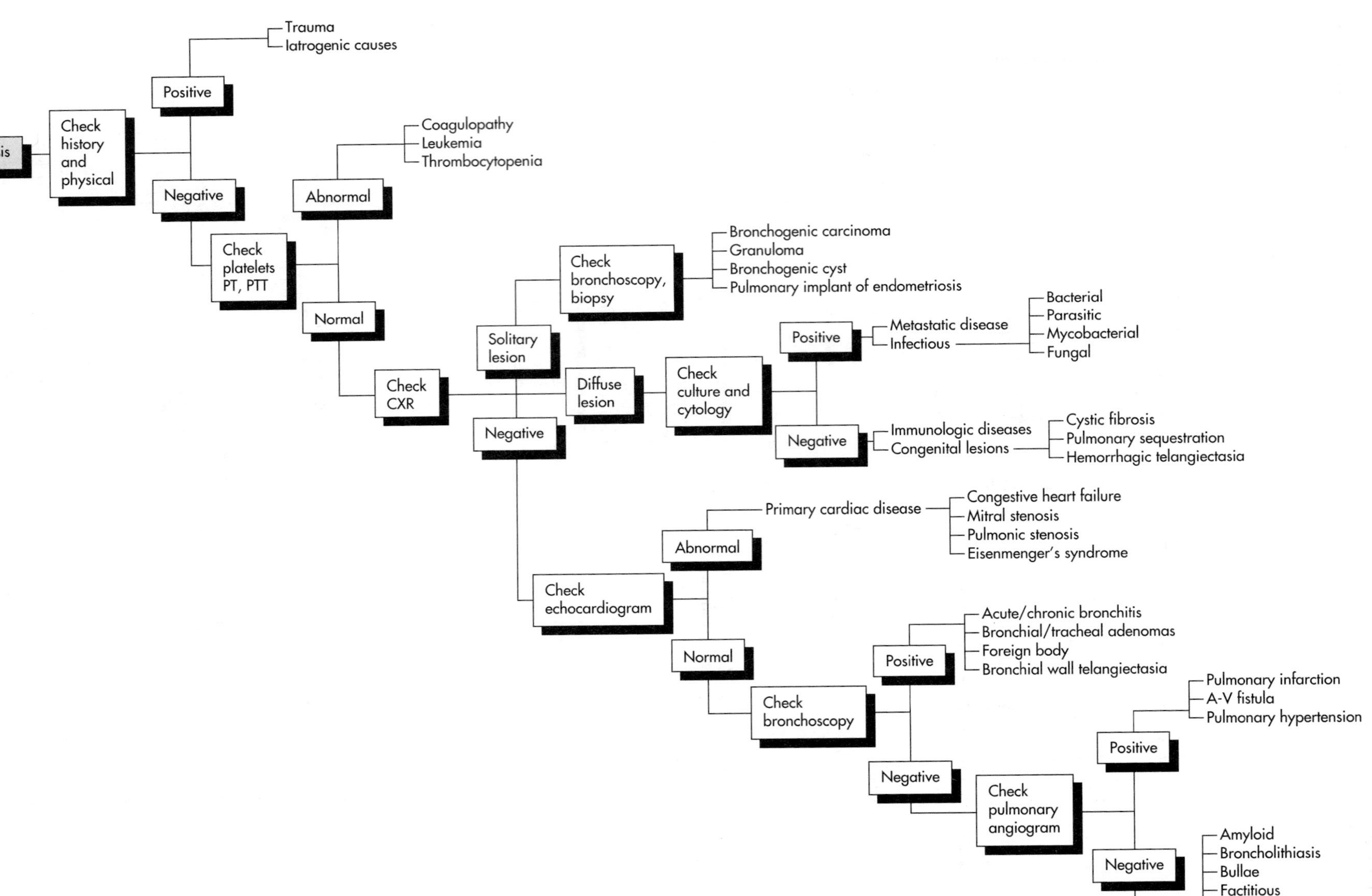

FIGURE 3-97 Evaluation of hemoptysis. *A-V,* Arteriovenous; *CXR,* chest x-ray; *PT,* prothrombin time; *PTT,* partial thromboplastin time. (From Healey PM: *Common medical diagnosis: an algorithmic approach,* ed 3, Philadelphia, 2000, WB Saunders.)

HEPATIC LESION

ICD-9CM # 751.60

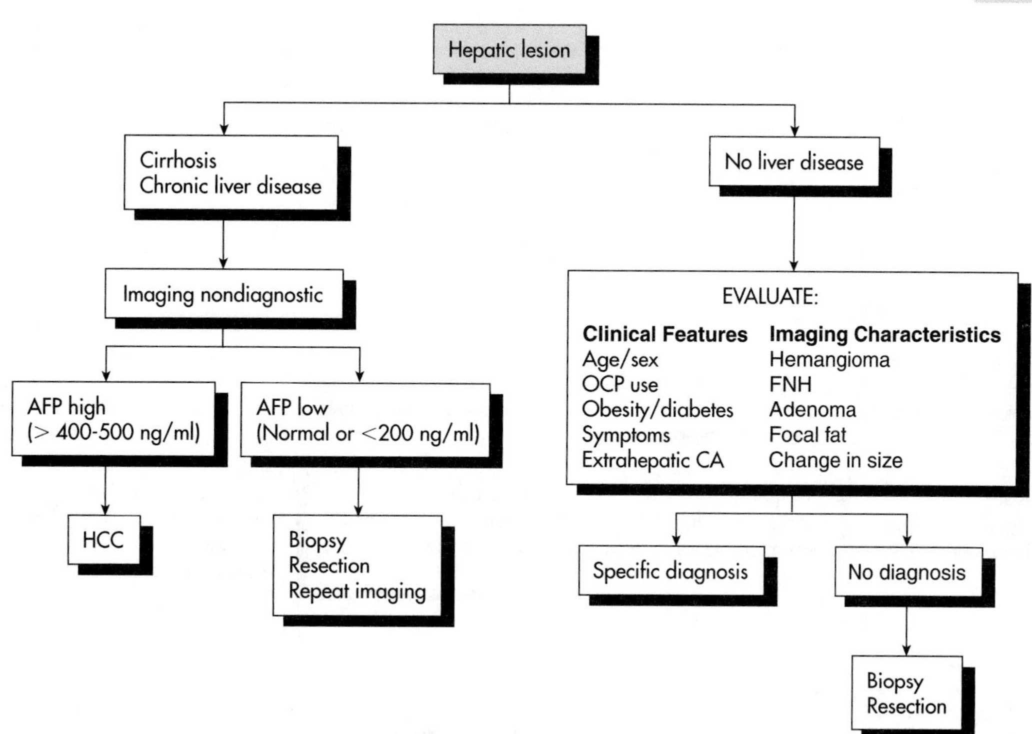

FIGURE 3-98 Diagnostic approach to space occupying lesions of the liver. *AFP,* α-Fetoprotein; *CA,* cancer antigen; *FNH,* focal nodular hyperplasia; *HCC,* hepatocellular carcinoma; *OCP,* oral contraceptives. (From Goldman L, Ausiello D [eds]: *Cecil textbook of medicine,* ed 22, Philadelphia, 2004, WB Saunders.)

HEPATITIS, VIRAL

ICD-9CM # 070.9

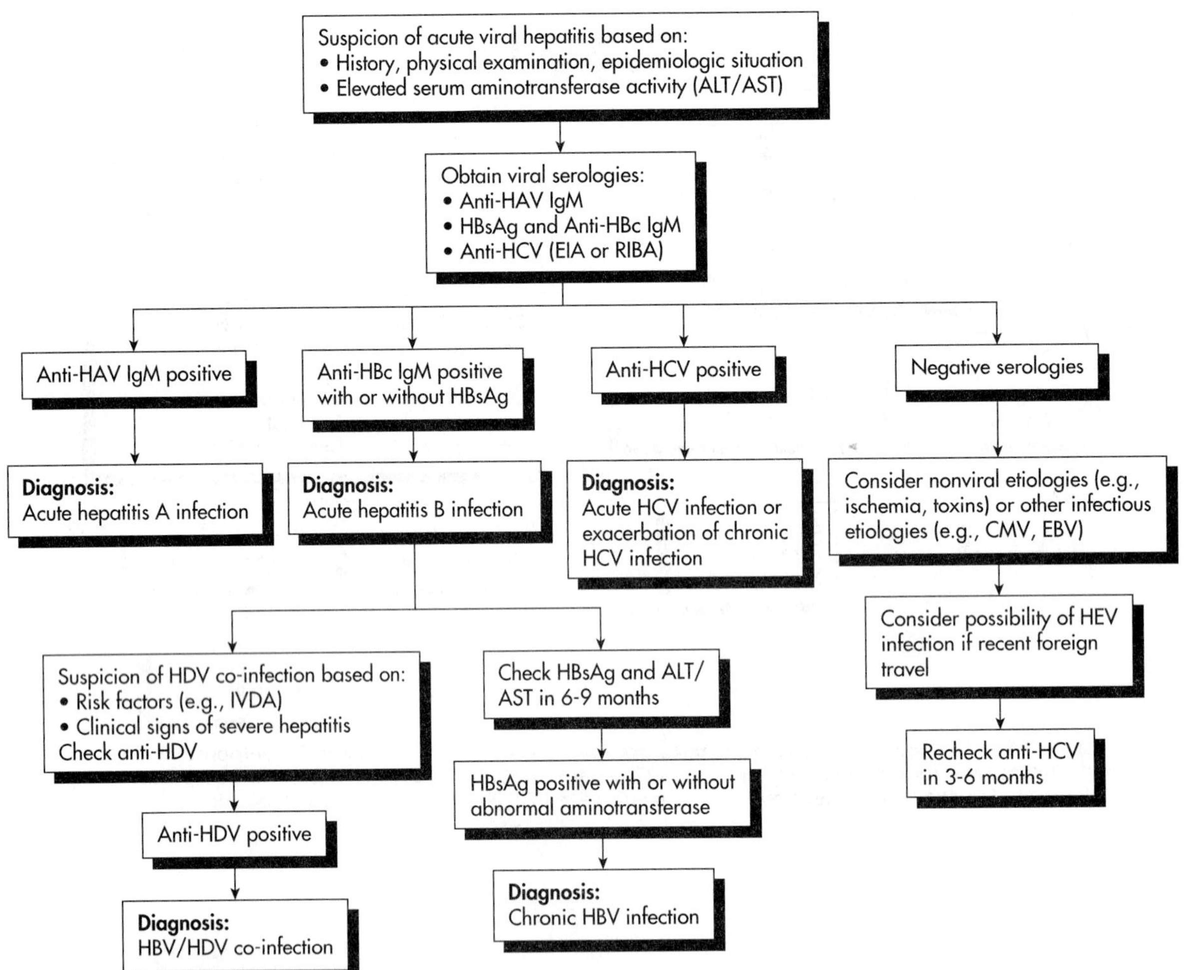

FIGURE 3-99 A flow diagram showing the use of specific serologic tests for the diagnosis of acute viral hepatitis in relation to the clinical and epidemiologic setting. Co-infections and superinfections of chronic hepatitis B or C patients should always be considered in cases that do not fit well with the clinical or serologic picture. *CMV,* Cytomegalovirus; *EBV,* Epstein-Barr virus; *EIA,* enzyme immunoassay; *HBV,* hepatitis B virus; *HCV,* hepatitis C virus; *HDV,* hepatitis D virus; *HEV,* hepatoencephalomyelitis virus; *IVDA,* intravenous drug abuse; *RIBA,* recombinant immunoblot assay. (From Mandell GL: *Mandell, Douglas, and Bennett's principles and practice of infectious diseases,* ed 5, New York, 2000, Churchill Livingstone.)

HEPATOMEGALY

ICD-9CM # 789.1

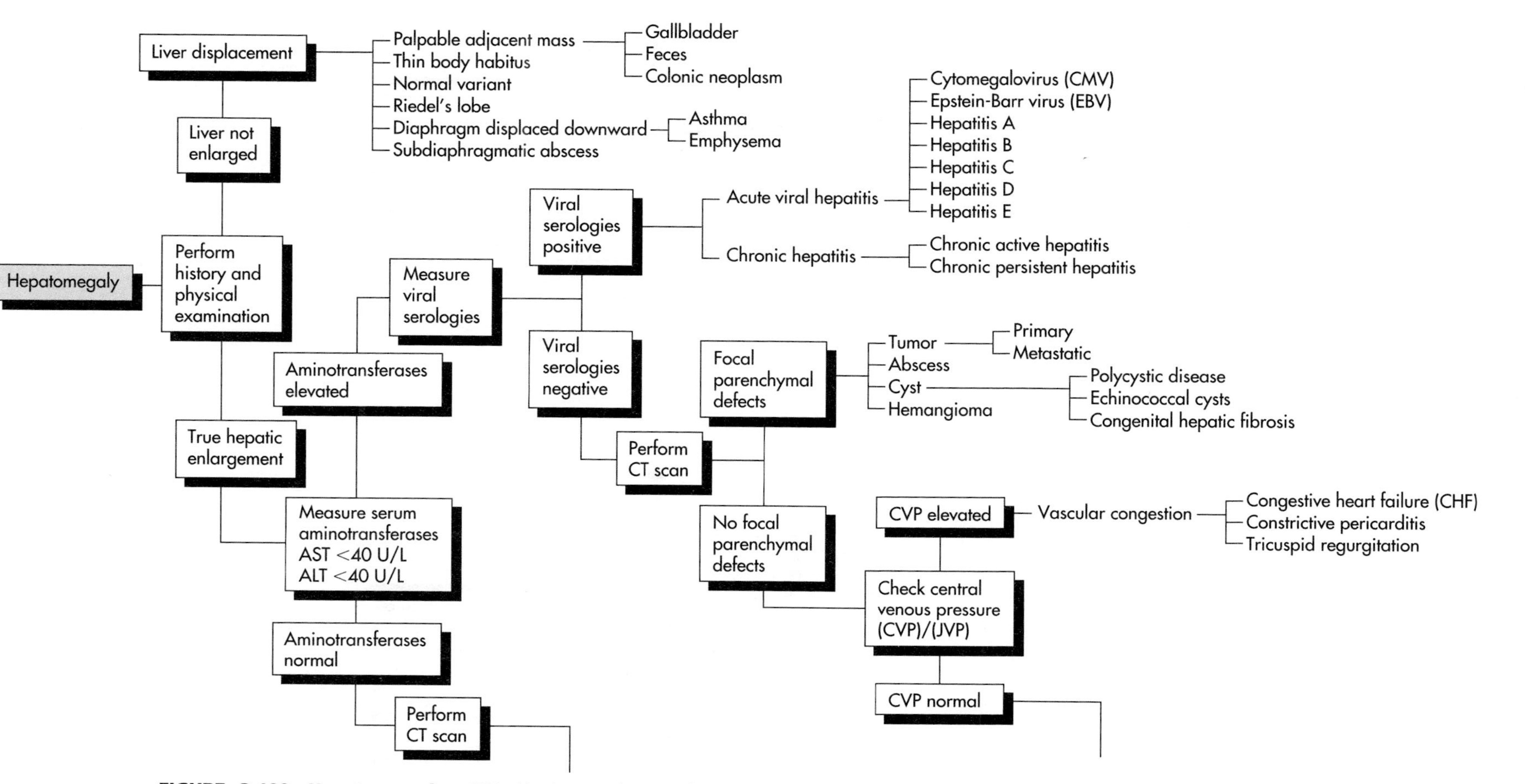

FIGURE 3-100 Hepatomegaly. *ALT,* Alanine aminotransferase; *AST,* aspartate aminotransferase; *CT,* computed tomography; *JVP,* jugular venous pressure. (From Healey PM: *Common medical diagnosis: an algorithmic approach,* ed 3, Philadelphia, 2000, WB Saunders.)

Continued

HEPATOMEGALY—cont'd

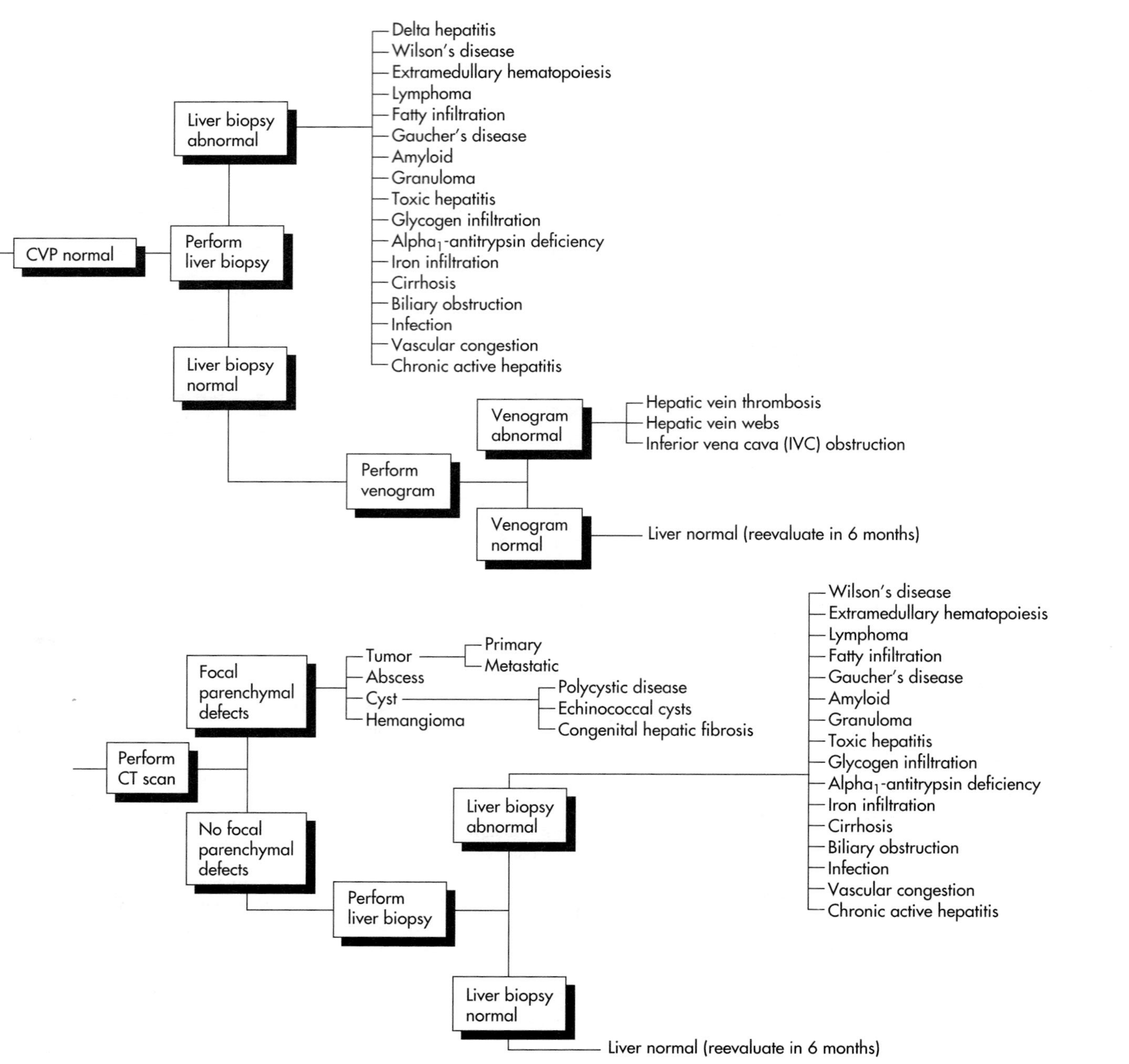

FIGURE 3-100, cont'd

HERPES ZOSTER/POSTHERPETIC NEURALGIA

ICD-9CM # 053.9

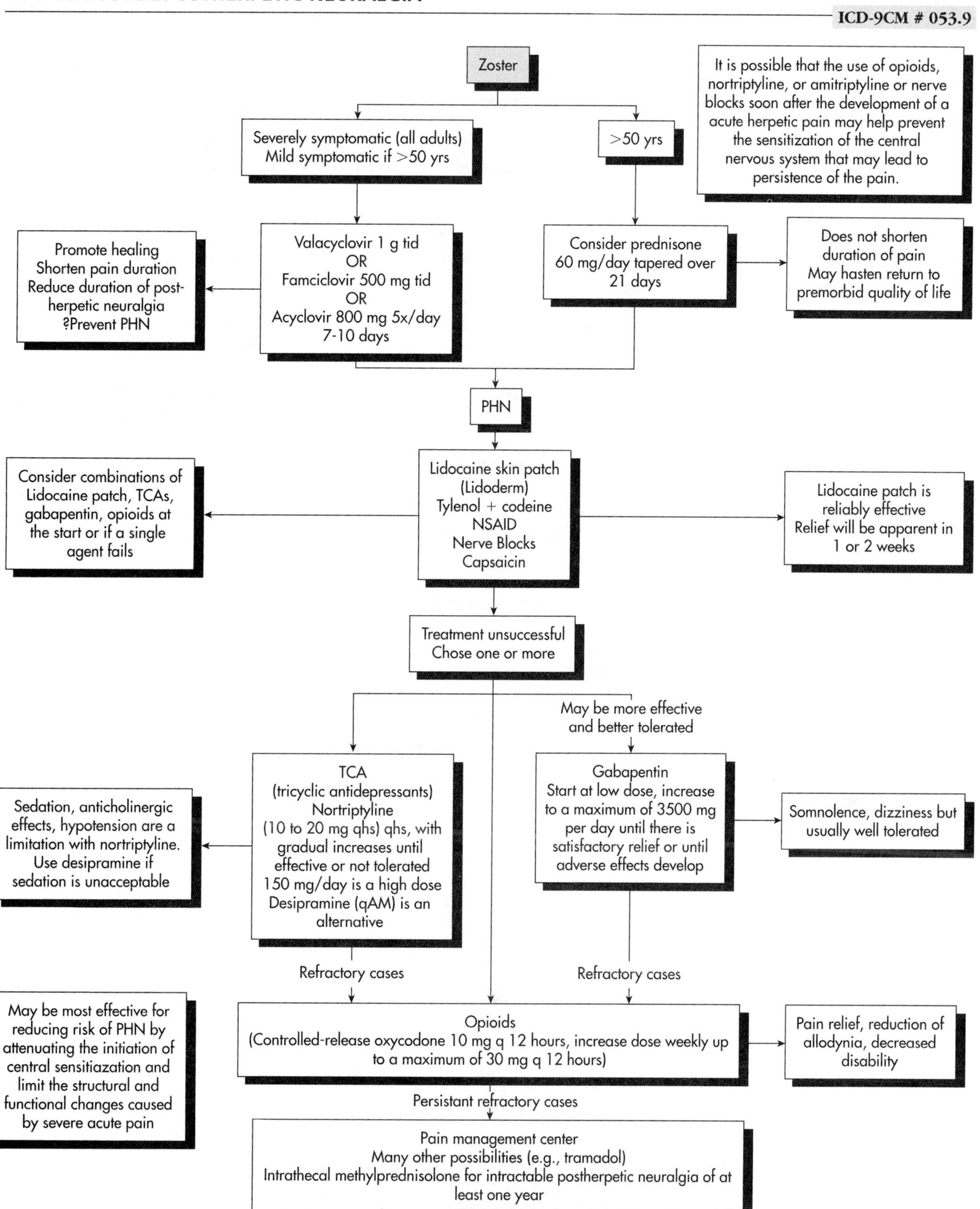

FIGURE 3-101 Treatment of herpes zoster and postherpetic neuralgia. PHN, postherpetic neuralgia; TCA, tricyclic antidepressant; NSAID, nonsteroidal antiinflammatory drug. (From Habif TA: *Clinical dermatology,* ed 4, St Louis, 2004, Mosby.)

SECTION III

HIGH-ALTITUDE PULMONARY EDEMA

ICD-9CM # 289 Mountain sickness, acute
993.2 High altitude, effects

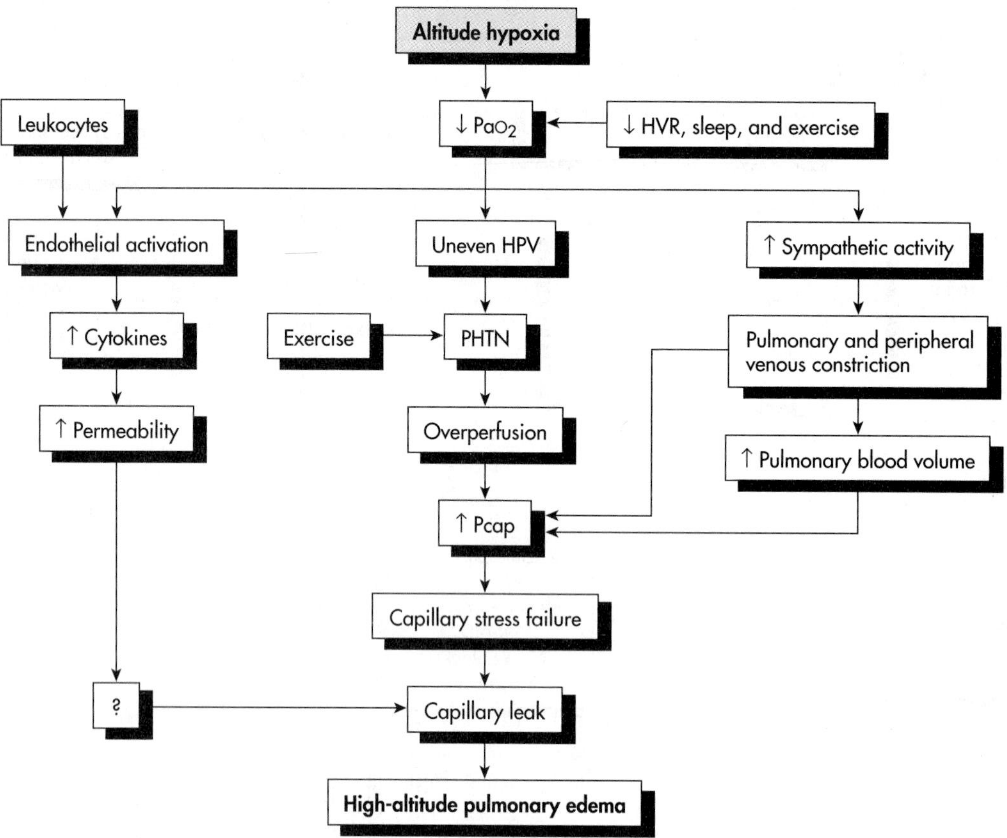

FIGURE 3-102 Proposed pathophysiology of high-altitude pulmonary edema. *HPV,* Hypoxic pulmonary vasoconstriction; *HVR,* hypoxic ventilatory response; *Pcap,* capillary pressure; *PHTN,* pulmonary hypertension. (From Auerbach PS: *Wilderness medicine,* ed 4, St Louis, 2001, Mosby.)

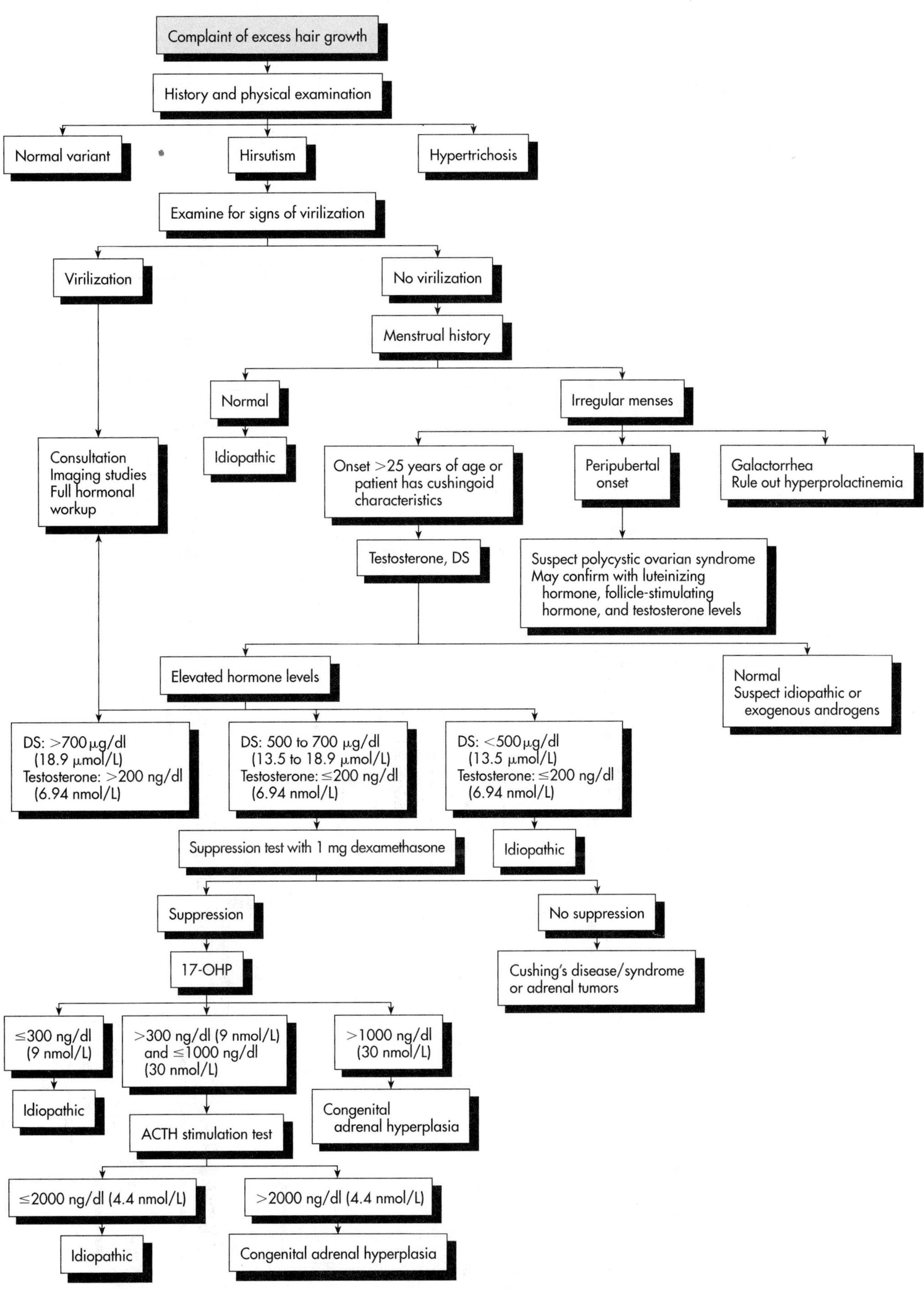

FIGURE 3-103 Algorithm showing the evaluation and treatment of hirsutism. *ACTH,* Adrenocorticotropic hormone; *DS,* dehydroepiandrosterone; *17-OHP,* 17-hydroxyprogesterone. (From Gilchrist VJ, Hecht BR: *Am Fam Physician* 52:1837, 1995.)

HIV-INFECTED PATIENT, ACUTELY ILL

ICD-9CM # 789.1

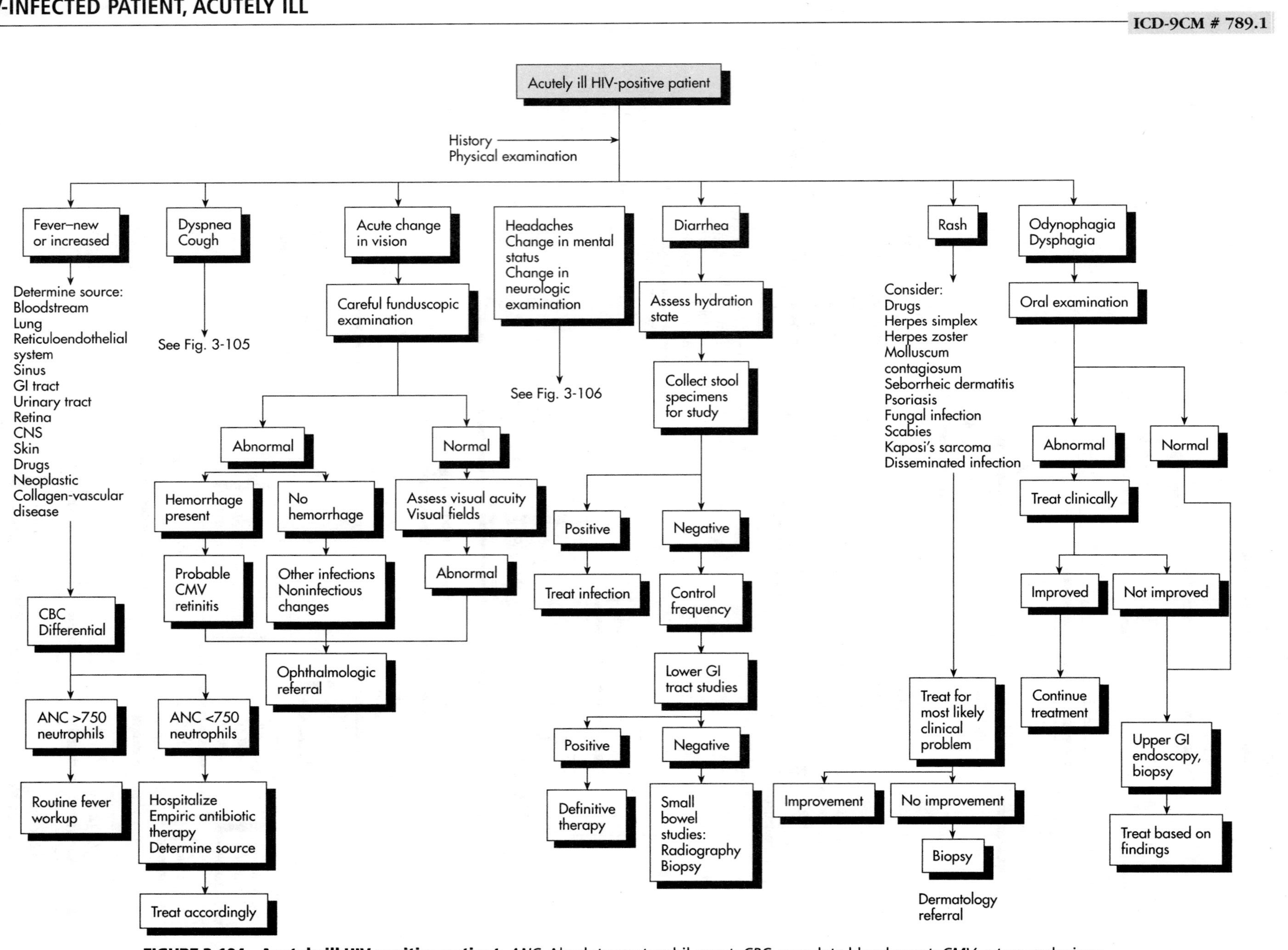

FIGURE 3-104 Acutely ill HIV-positive patient. *ANC,* Absolute neutrophil count; *CBC,* complete blood count; *CMV,* cytomegalovirus; *CNS,* central nervous system; *GI,* gastrointestinal. (From Greene HL, Johnson WP, Lemcke D [eds]: *Decision making in medicine,* ed 2, St Louis, 1998, Mosby.)

HIV-INFECTED PATIENT WITH RESPIRATORY COMPLAINTS

ICD-9CM # 042 HIV infection, symptomatic

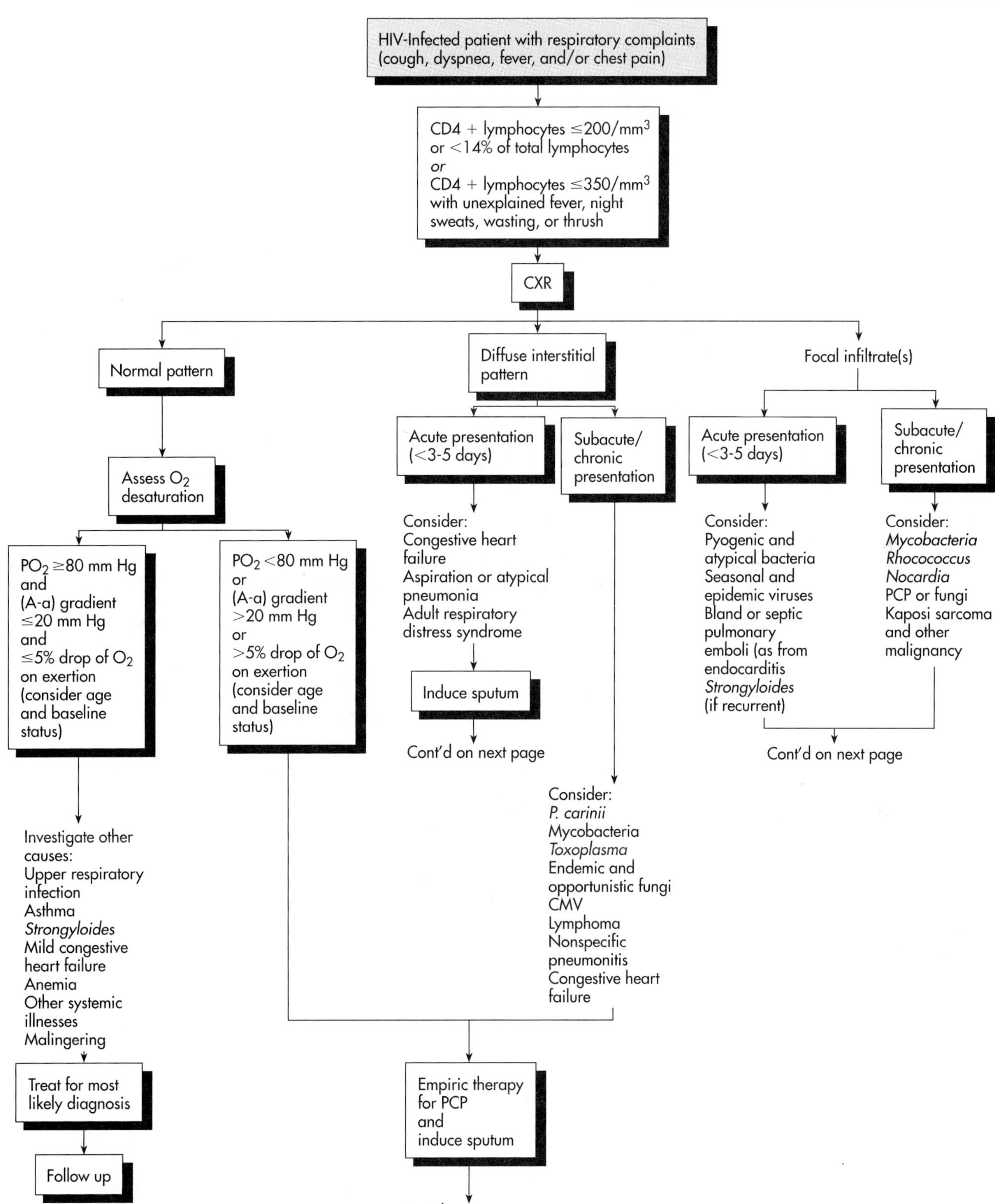

FIGURE 3-105 HIV-infected patient with respiratory complaints. *BAL,* Bronchoalveolar lavage; *CMV,* cytomegalovirus; *CXR,* chest x-ray examination; *PCP, Pneumocystis carinii* pneumonia; *TBB,* transbronchial biopsy. (From Greene HL, Johnson WP, Lemcke D [eds]: *Decision making in medicine,* 2, St Louis, 1998, Mosby.)

Continued

SECTION III

HIV-INFECTED PATIENT WITH RESPIRATORY COMPLAINTS—cont'd

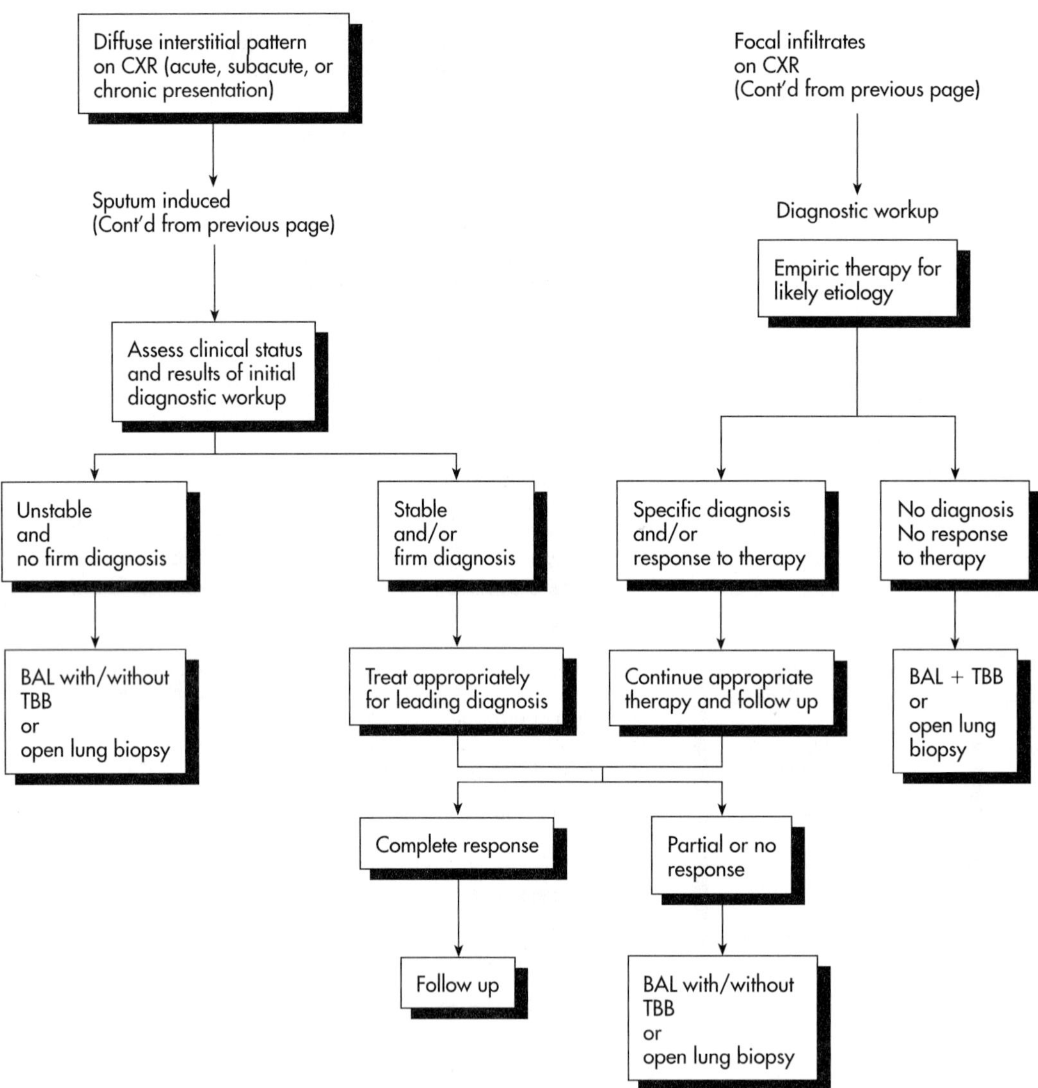

FIGURE 3-105, cont'd

HIV-INFECTED PATIENT WITH SUSPECTED CENTRAL NERVOUS SYSTEM INFECTION

ICD-9CM # 042 HIV infection, symptomatic

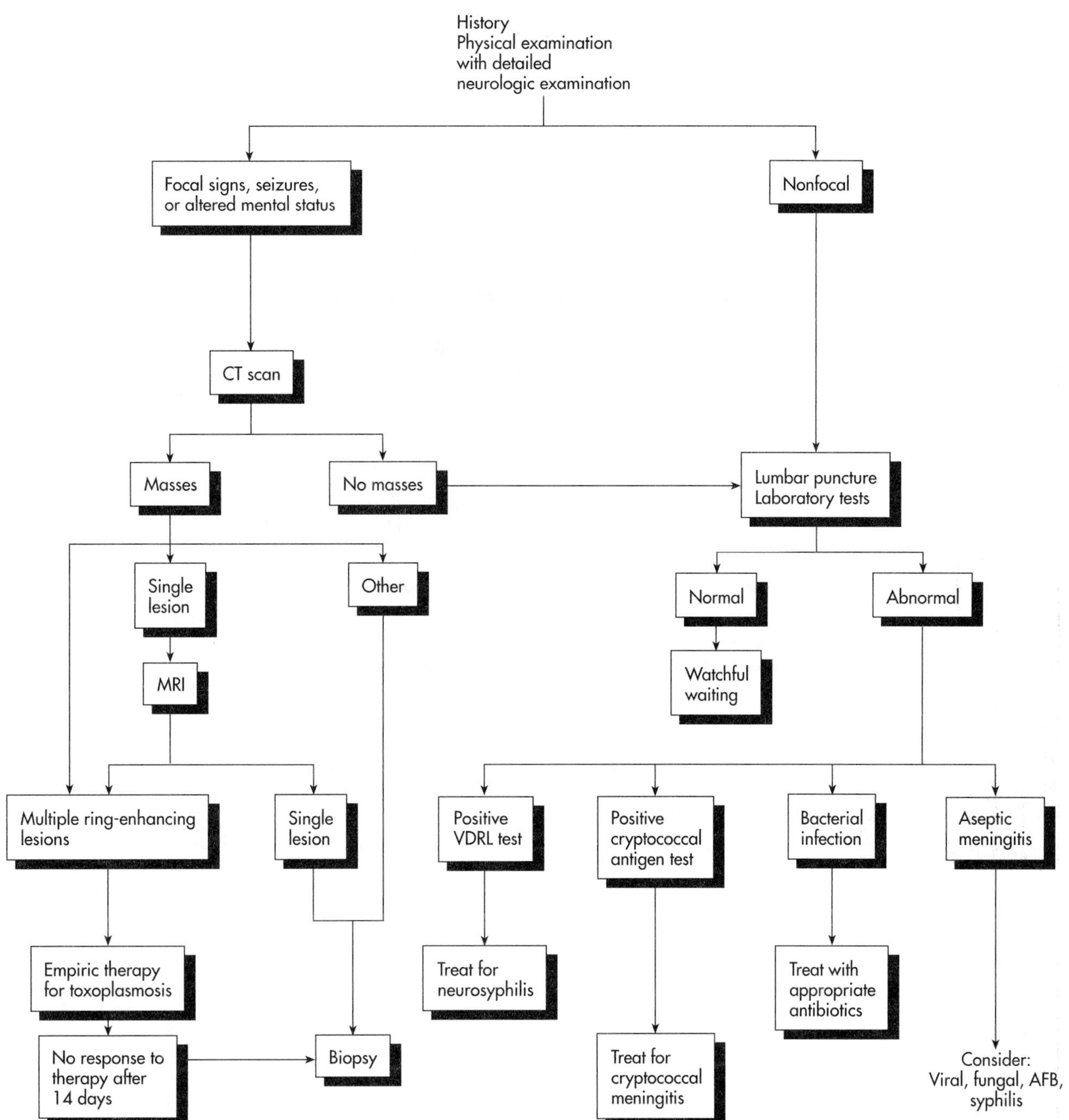

FIGURE 3-106 HIV-positive patient with suspected central nervous system infection. *AFB,* Acid-fast bacilli; *CNS,* central nervous system; *CT,* computed tomography; *MRI,* magnetic resonance imaging; *VDRL,* Venereal Disease Research Laboratory. (From Greene HL, Johnson WP, Lemcke D [eds]: *Decision making in medicine,* ed 2, St Louis, 1998, Mosby.)

HYPERALDOSTERONISM

ICD-9CM # 255.1 Primary aldosteronism

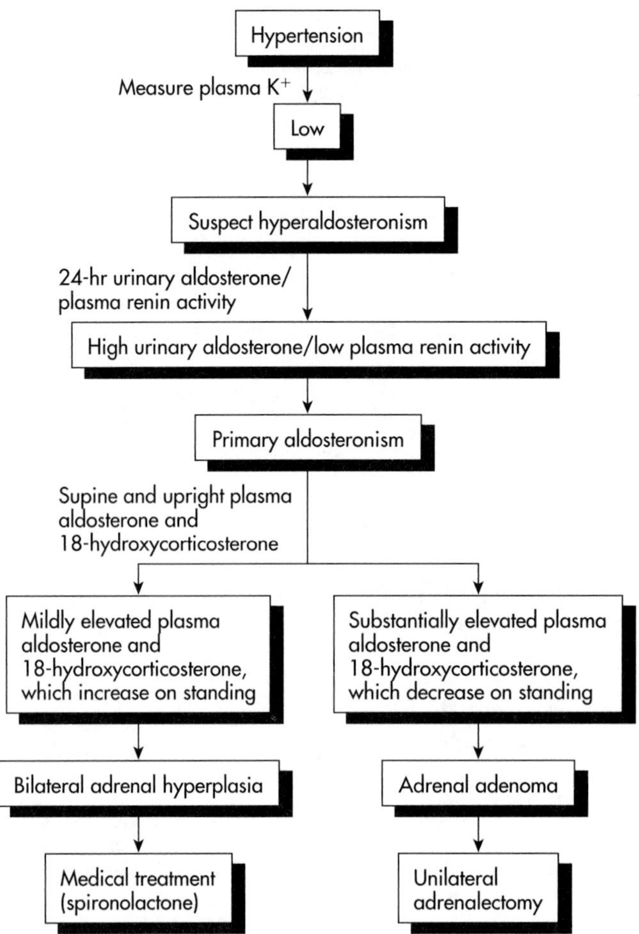

FIGURE 3-107 Flow chart for evaluating a patient with suspected primary hyperaldosteronism. (From Andreoli TE [ed]: *Cecil essentials of medicine,* ed 5, Philadelphia, 2001, WB Saunders.)

HYPERCALCEMIA

ICD-9CM # 275.24

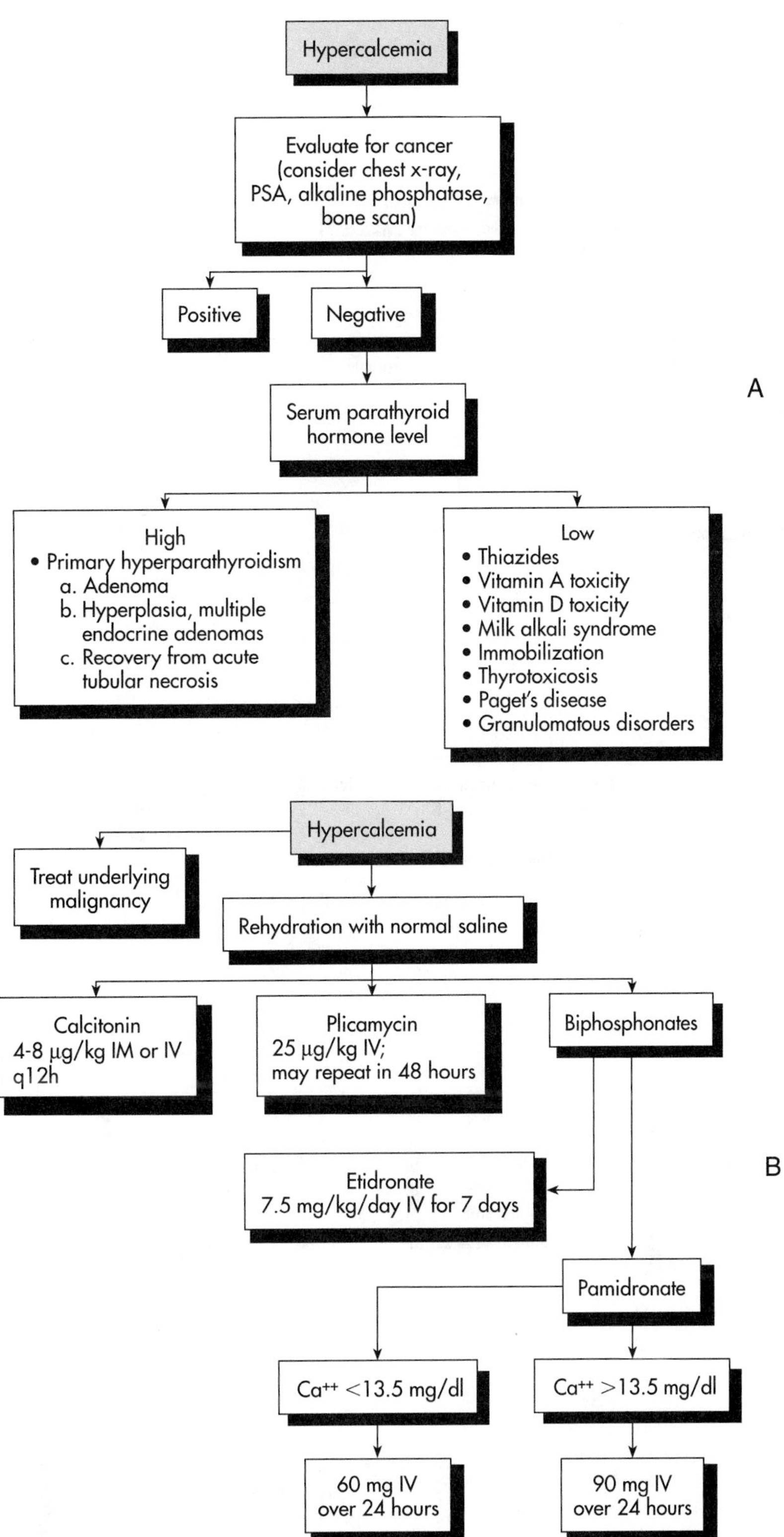

FIGURE 3-108 A, Evaluation of hypercalcemia. *PSA,* Prostate-specific antigen. **B, Therapy for hypercalcemia.** *IM,* Intramuscularly; *IV,* intravenously. (From Noble J [ed]: *Primary care medicine,* ed 3, St Louis, 2001, Mosby.) (From Wachtel TJ, Stein MD: *Practical guide to the care of the ambulatory patient,* ed 2, St Louis, 2000, Mosby.)

HYPERKALEMIA, DIAGNOSTIC APPROACH

ICD-9CM # 276.7

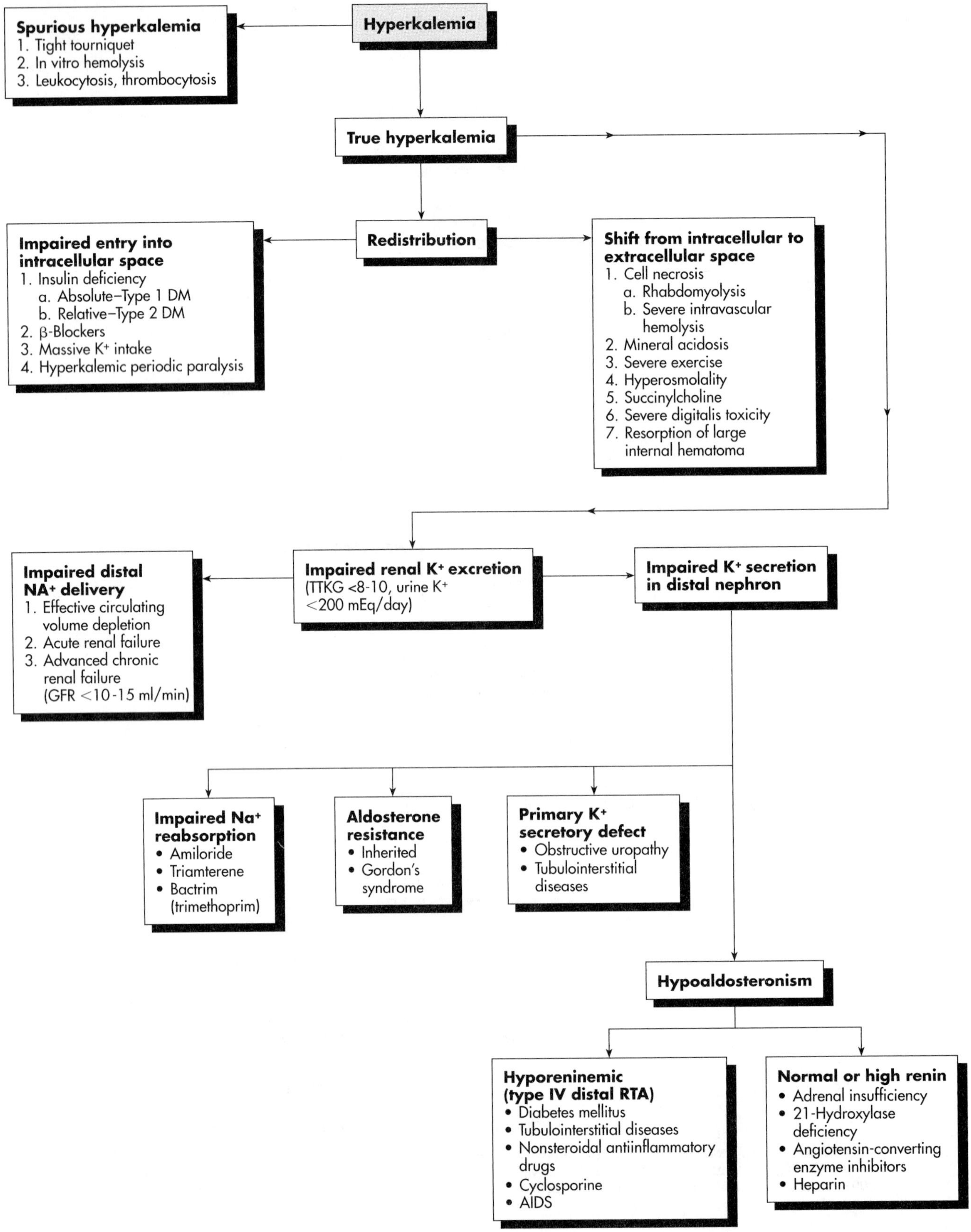

Hyperkalemia

Spurious hyperkalemia
1. Tight tourniquet
2. In vitro hemolysis
3. Leukocytosis, thrombocytosis

True hyperkalemia

Redistribution

Impaired entry into intracellular space
1. Insulin deficiency
   a. Absolute–Type 1 DM
   b. Relative–Type 2 DM
2. β-Blockers
3. Massive K^+ intake
4. Hyperkalemic periodic paralysis

Shift from intracellular to extracellular space
1. Cell necrosis
   a. Rhabdomyolysis
   b. Severe intravascular hemolysis
2. Mineral acidosis
3. Severe exercise
4. Hyperosmolality
5. Succinylcholine
6. Severe digitalis toxicity
7. Resorption of large internal hematoma

Impaired renal K^+ excretion
(TTKG <8-10, urine K^+ <200 mEq/day)

Impaired distal NA^+ delivery
1. Effective circulating volume depletion
2. Acute renal failure
3. Advanced chronic renal failure (GFR <10-15 ml/min)

Impaired K^+ secretion in distal nephron

Impaired Na^+ reabsorption
- Amiloride
- Triamterene
- Bactrim (trimethoprim)

Aldosterone resistance
- Inherited
- Gordon's syndrome

Primary K^+ secretory defect
- Obstructive uropathy
- Tubulointerstitial diseases

Hypoaldosteronism

Hyporeninemic (type IV distal RTA)
- Diabetes mellitus
- Tubulointerstitial diseases
- Nonsteroidal antiinflammatory drugs
- Cyclosporine
- AIDS

Normal or high renin
- Adrenal insufficiency
- 21-Hydroxylase deficiency
- Angiotensin-converting enzyme inhibitors
- Heparin

FIGURE 3-109 Diagnostic approach to hyperkalemia. *AIDS,* Acquired immunodeficiency syndrome; *DM,* diabetes mellitus; *GFR,* glomerular filtration rate; *RTA,* renal tubular acidosis; *TTKG,* transtubular potassium gradient. (From Andreoli TE [ed]: *Cecil essentials of medicine,* ed 4, Philadelphia, 1997, WB Saunders.)

HYPERKALEMIA, EVALUATION AND TREATMENT

ICD-9CM # 276.7

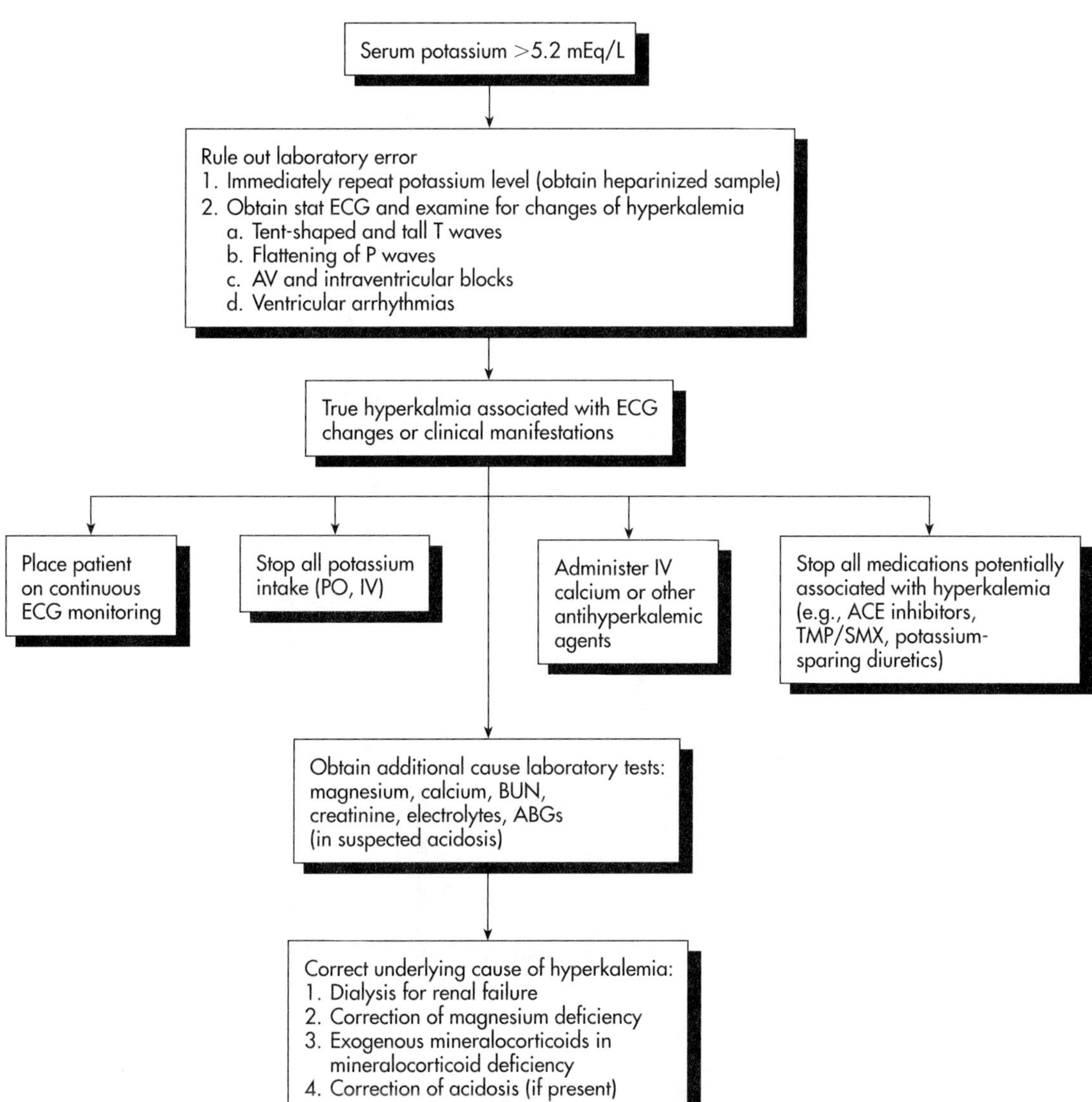

FIGURE 3-110 Evaluation and treatment of hyperkalemia. *ABGS,* Arterial blood gases; *ACE,* angiotensin-converting enzyme; *AV,* atrioventricular; *BUN,* blood urea nitrogen; *ECG,* electrocardiogram; *IV,* intravenous; *PO,* oral; *TMP/SMX,* trimethoprim-sulfamethoxazole. (From Ferri F: *Practical guide to the care of the medical patient,* ed 6, St Louis, 2004, Mosby.)

SECTION III

HYPERMAGNESEMIA

ICD-9CM # 275.2

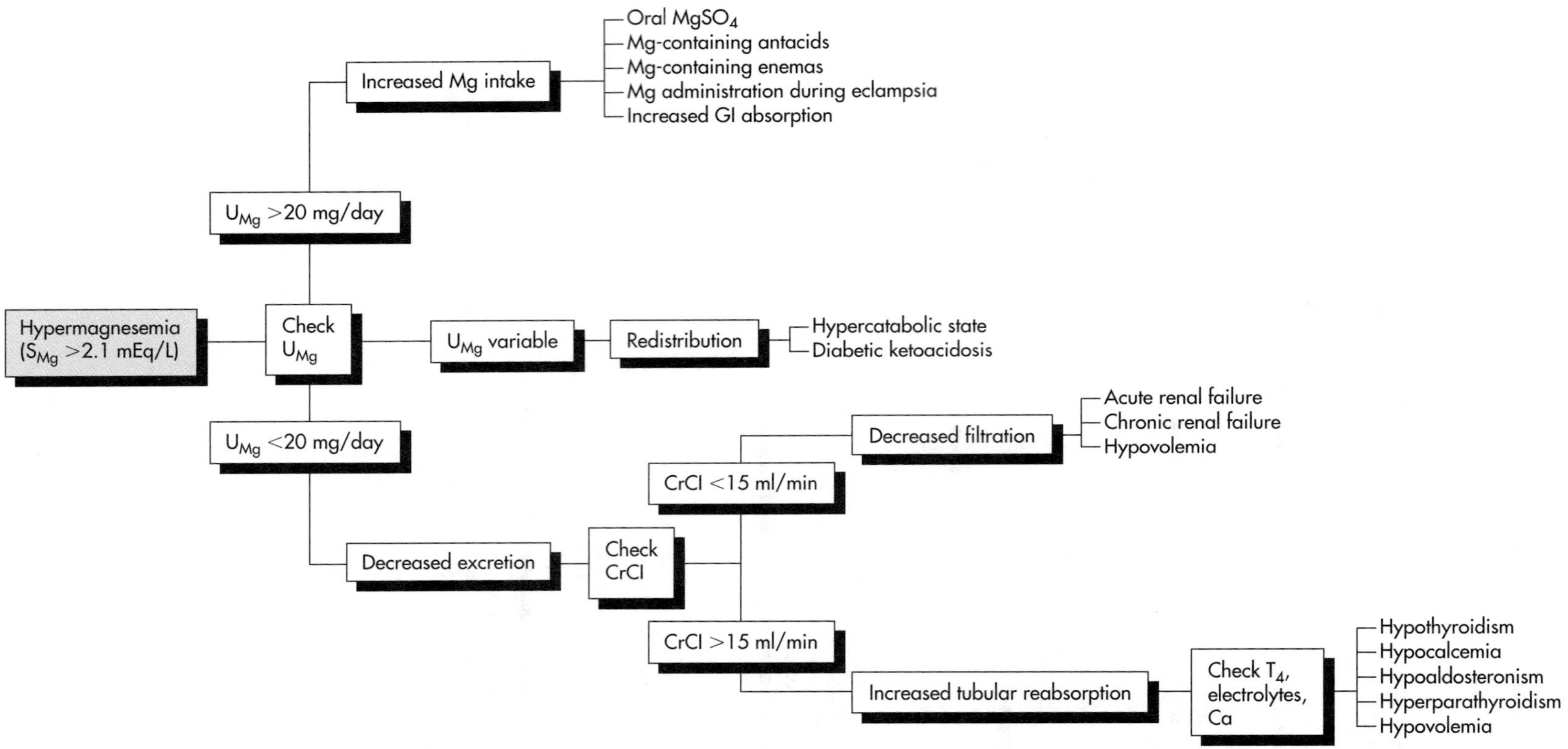

- Hypermagnesemia (S_{Mg} >2.1 mEq/L) → Check U_{Mg}
  - U_{Mg} >20 mg/day → Increased Mg intake
    - Oral $MgSO_4$
    - Mg-containing antacids
    - Mg-containing enemas
    - Mg administration during eclampsia
    - Increased GI absorption
  - U_{Mg} variable → Redistribution
    - Hypercatabolic state
    - Diabetic ketoacidosis
  - U_{Mg} <20 mg/day → Decreased excretion → Check CrCl
    - CrCl <15 ml/min → Decreased filtration
      - Acute renal failure
      - Chronic renal failure
      - Hypovolemia
    - CrCl >15 ml/min → Increased tubular reabsorption → Check T_4, electrolytes, Ca
      - Hypothyroidism
      - Hypocalcemia
      - Hypoaldosteronism
      - Hyperparathyroidism
      - Hypovolemia

FIGURE 3-111 Hypermagnesemia. *CrCl,* Creatinine clearance; *GI,* gastrointestinal; *MgSO,* magnesium sulfate. (From Healey PM: *Common medical diagnosis: an algorithmic approach,* ed 3, Philadelphia, 2000, WB Saunders.)

HYPERNATREMIA

ICD-9CM # 276.0

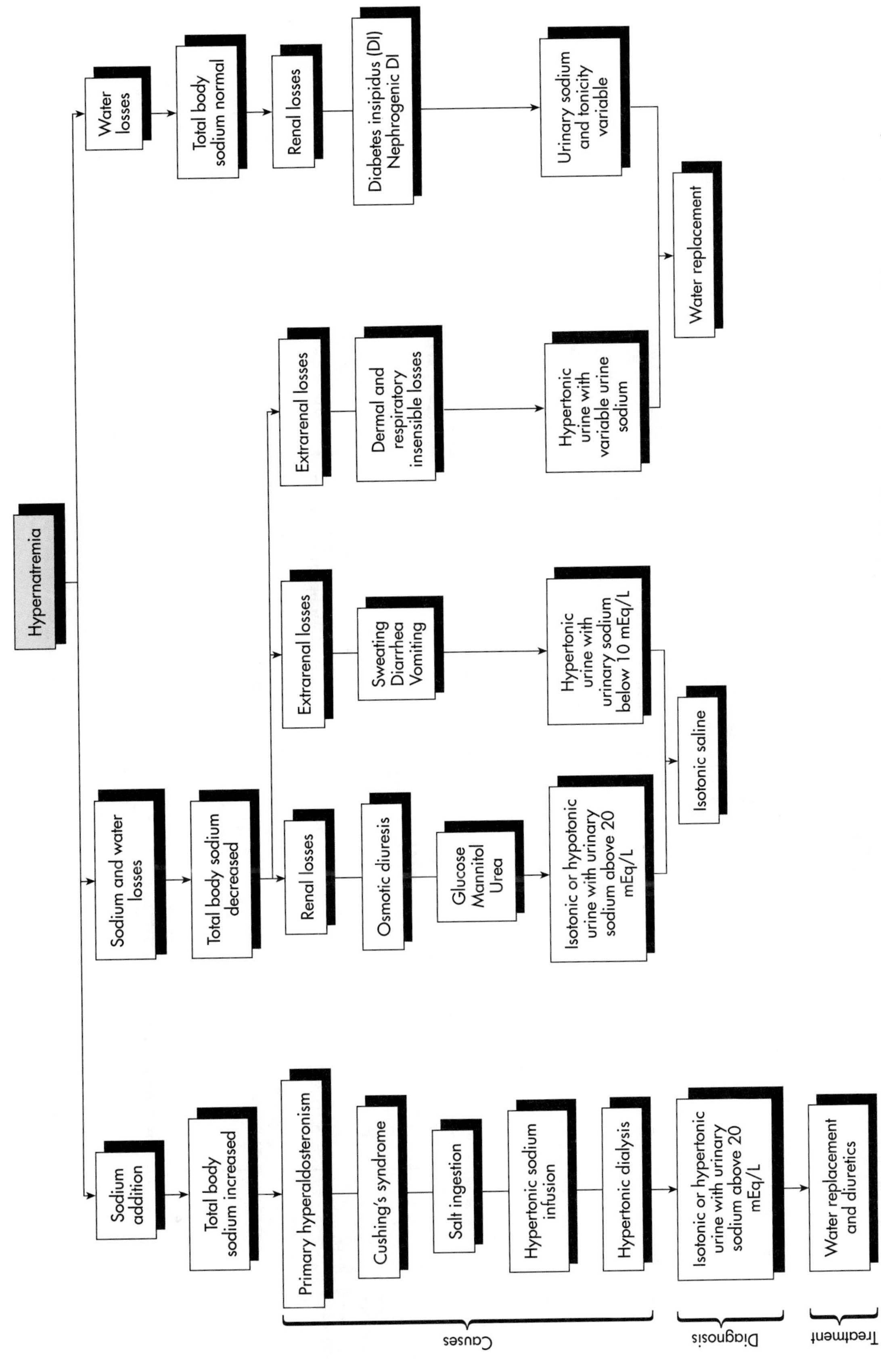

Hypernatremia

- Sodium addition → Total body sodium increased
  - Causes: Primary hyperaldosteronism; Cushing's syndrome; Salt ingestion; Hypertonic sodium infusion; Hypertonic dialysis
  - Diagnosis: Isotonic or hypertonic urine with urinary sodium above 20 mEq/L
  - Treatment: Water replacement and diuretics
- Sodium and water losses → Total body sodium decreased
  - Renal losses → Osmotic diuresis → Glucose, Mannitol, Urea → Isotonic or hypotonic urine with urinary sodium above 20 mEq/L → Isotonic saline
  - Extrarenal losses → Sweating, Diarrhea, Vomiting → Hypertonic urine with urinary sodium below 10 mEq/L → Isotonic saline
  - Extrarenal losses → Dermal and respiratory insensible losses → Hypertonic urine with variable urine sodium → Water replacement
- Water losses → Total body sodium normal → Renal losses → Diabetes insipidus (DI), Nephrogenic DI → Urinary sodium and tonicity variable → Water replacement

FIGURE 3-112 Evaluation and treatment of hypernatremia. (From Marx J et al [eds]: *Rosen's emergency medicine: concepts and clinical practice,* ed 6, St Louis, 2004, Mosby.)

HYPERPHOSPHATEMIA

ICD-9CM # 275.3

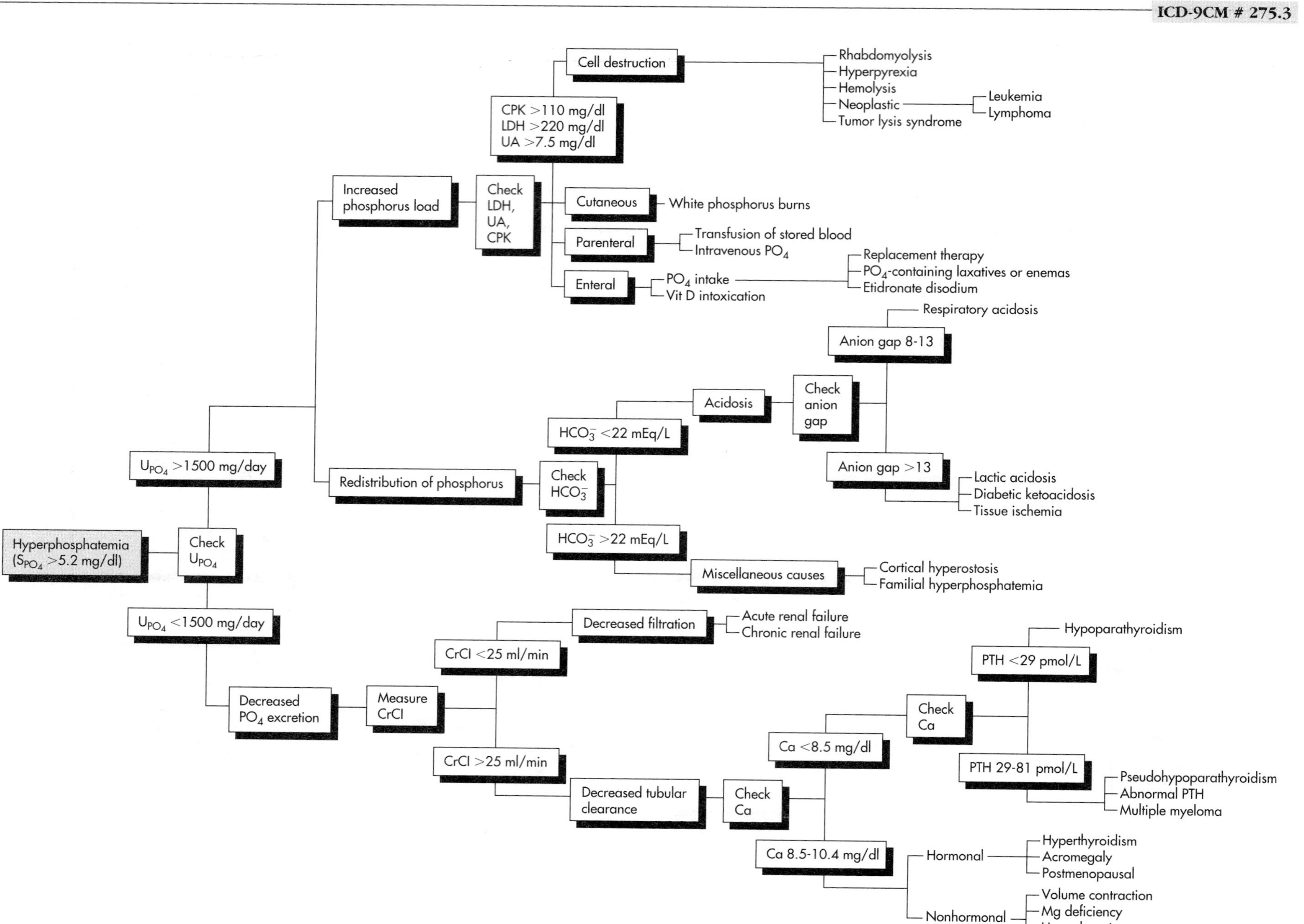

FIGURE 3-113 Approach to hyperphosphatemia. *CT,* Computerized tomography; *MRI,* magnetic resonance imaging; *T,* thyroxine; *TSH,* thyroid-stimulating hormone. (From Healey PM: *Common medical diagnosis: An algorithmic ...* [illegible]

HYPERPROLACTINEMIA

ICD-9CM # 253.1

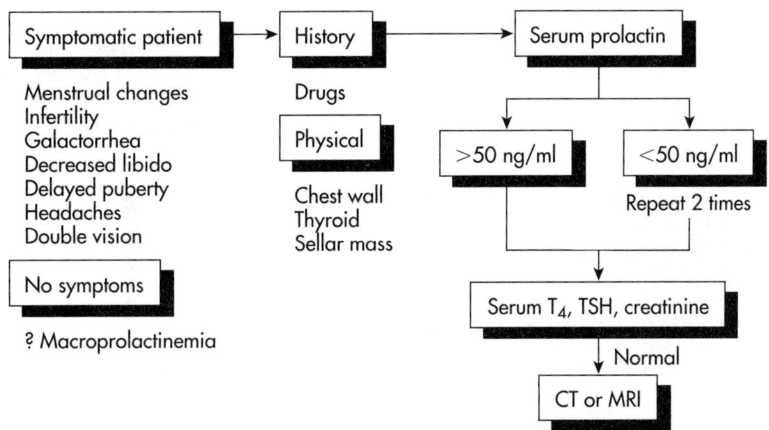

1. Normal: idiopathic hyperprolactinemia
2. Microprolactinoma
3. Mass >1 cm, prolactin >200 μg/L: macroprolactinoma
4. Mass >1 cm, prolactin <100 μg/L: pseudoprolactinoma
5. Suprasellar mass or infiltrate

FIGURE 3-114 Approach to hyperprolactinemia. *CT,* Computed tomography; *MRI,* magnetic resonance imaging; *T,* thyroxine; *TSH,* thyroid-stimulating hormone. (From Copeland LJ: *Textbook of gynecology,* ed 2, Philadelphia, 2000, WB Saunders.)

HYPERTENSION, SECONDARY CAUSES

ICD-9CM #		
	401.1	Essential hypertension
	401.0	Malignant hypertension due to renal artery stenosis
	642	Hypertension complicating pregnancy
	405.01	Malignant hypertension secondary to renal artery stenosis
	437.2	Hypertensive encephalopathy

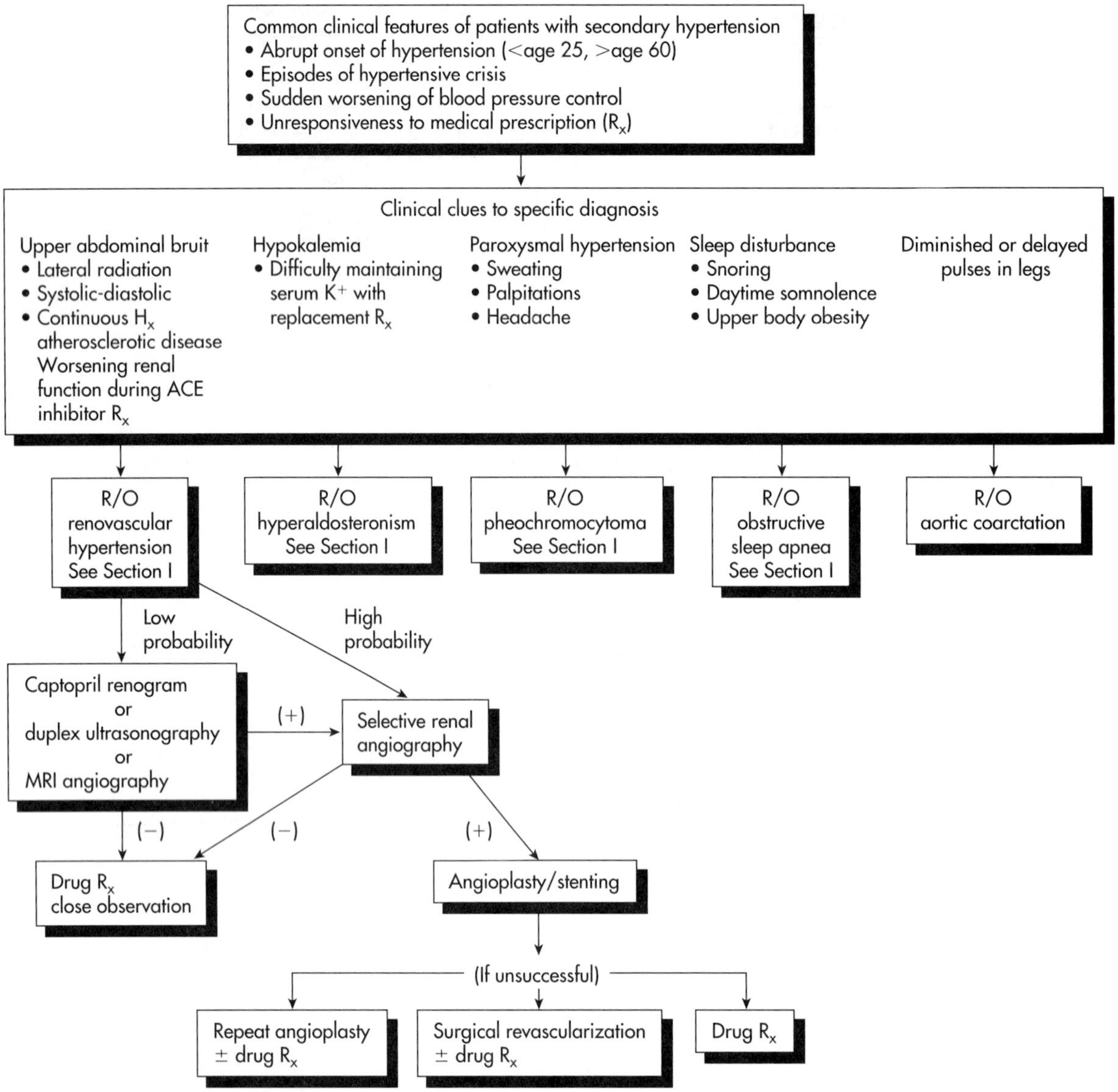

Common clinical features of patients with secondary hypertension
- Abrupt onset of hypertension (<age 25, >age 60)
- Episodes of hypertensive crisis
- Sudden worsening of blood pressure control
- Unresponsiveness to medical prescription (R_x)

Clinical clues to specific diagnosis

Upper abdominal bruit
- Lateral radiation
- Systolic-diastolic
- Continuous H_x atherosclerotic disease Worsening renal function during ACE inhibitor R_x

Hypokalemia
- Difficulty maintaining serum K^+ with replacement R_x

Paroxysmal hypertension
- Sweating
- Palpitations
- Headache

Sleep disturbance
- Snoring
- Daytime somnolence
- Upper body obesity

Diminished or delayed pulses in legs

R/O renovascular hypertension See Section I

R/O hyperaldosteronism See Section I

R/O pheochromocytoma See Section I

R/O obstructive sleep apnea See Section I

R/O aortic coarctation

Low probability → Captopril renogram or duplex ultrasonography or MRI angiography

High probability → Selective renal angiography

Captopril renogram or duplex ultrasonography or MRI angiography: (+) → Selective renal angiography; (−) → Drug R_x close observation

Selective renal angiography: (−) → Drug R_x close observation; (+) → Angioplasty/stenting

Angioplasty/stenting → (If unsuccessful) → Repeat angioplasty ± drug R_x / Surgical revascularization ± drug R_x / Drug R_x

FIGURE 3-115 Algorithm for identifying patients for evaluation of secondary causes of hypertension. *ACE,* Angiotension-converting enzyme; *Hx,* history; *K⁺,* potassium; *R/O,* rule out. (From Goldman L, Ausiello D [eds]: *Cecil textbook of medicine,* ed 22, Philadelphia, 2004, WB Saunders.)

HYPERTHYROIDISM

ICD-9CM # 242.9

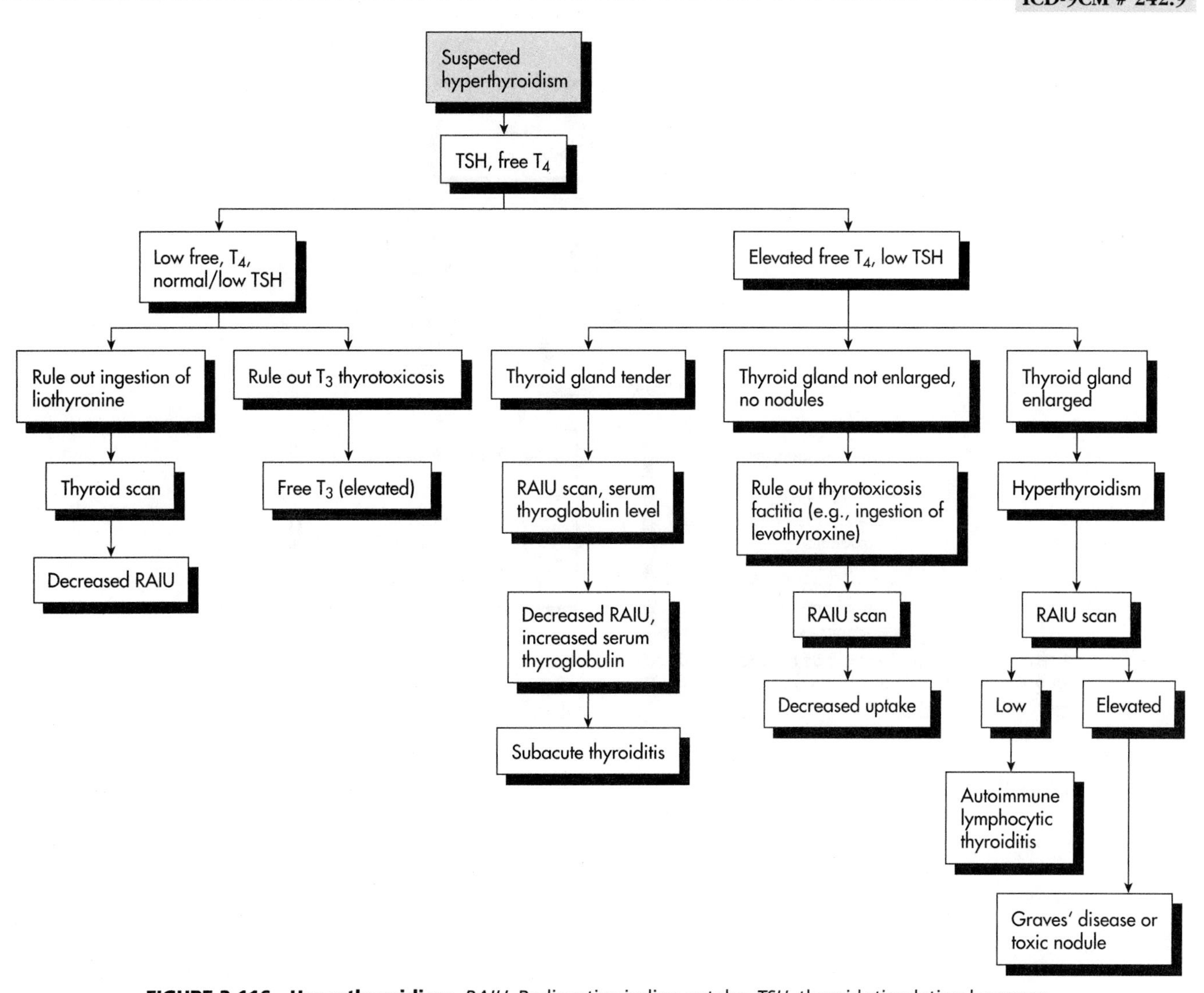

FIGURE 3-116 Hyperthyroidism. *RAIU,* Radioactive iodine uptake; *TSH,* thyroid-stimulating hormone.

HYPOCALCEMIA

ICD-9CM # 275.41

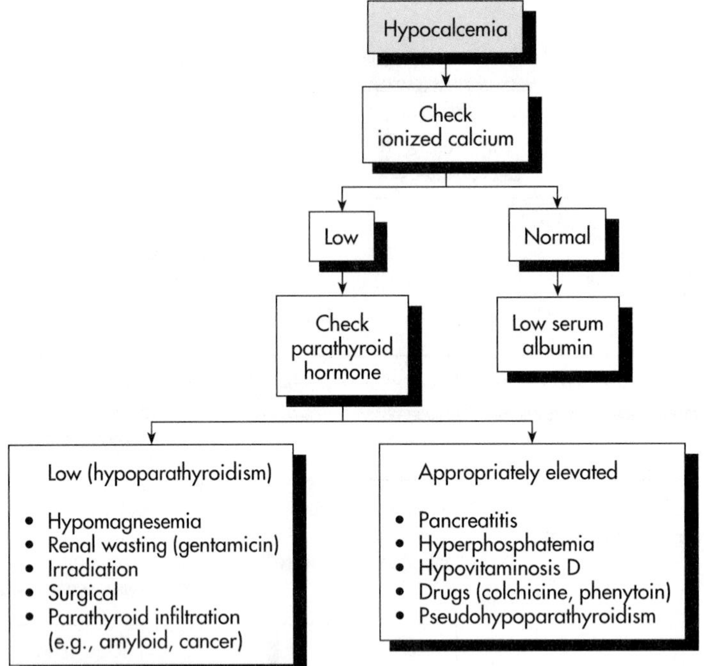

FIGURE 3-117 Evaluation of hypocalcemia. (From Wachtel TJ, Stein MD: *Practical guide to the care of the ambulatory patient,* ed 2, St Louis, 2000, Mosby.)

HYPOGLYCEMIA

ICD-9CM # 251.2

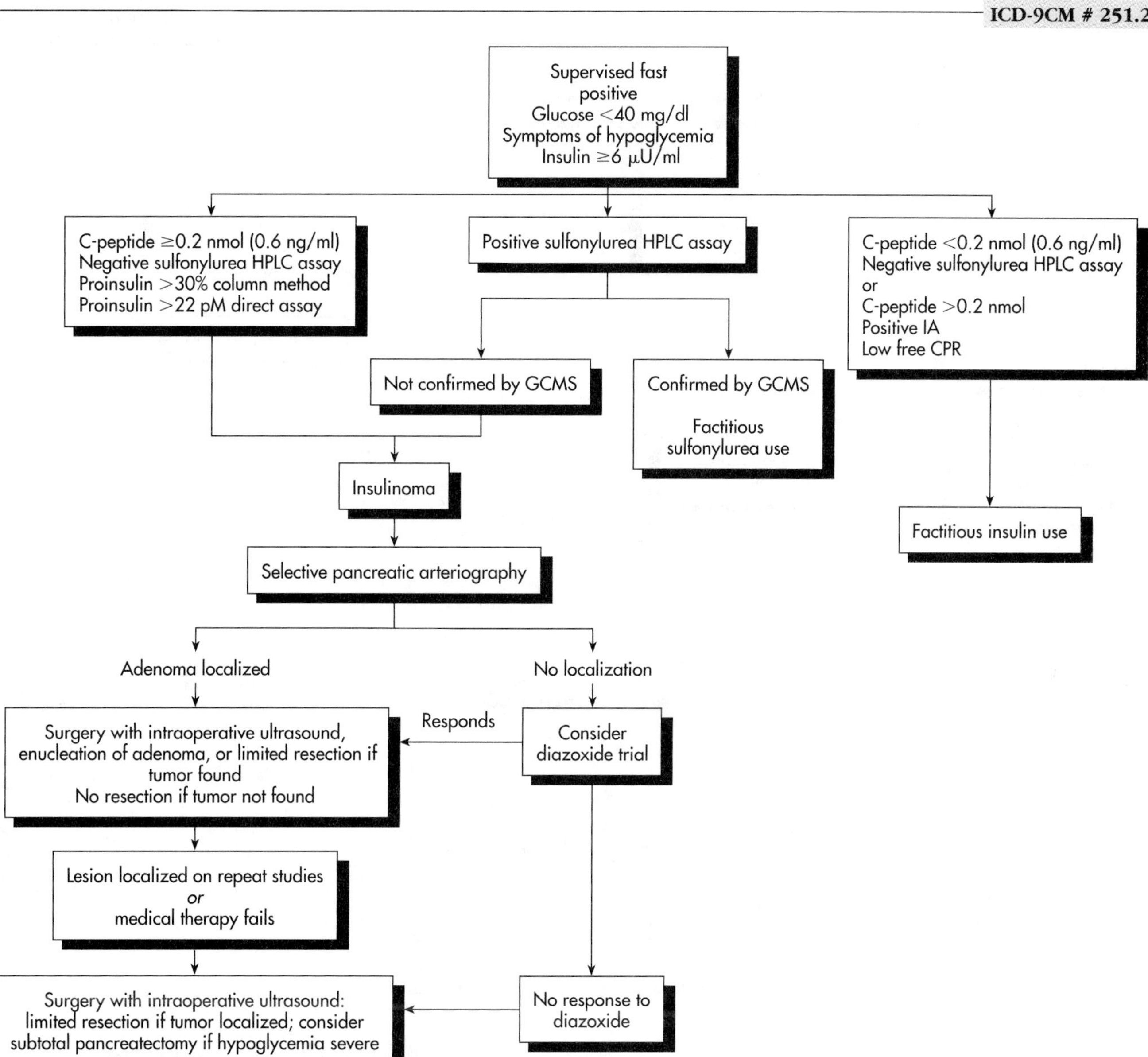

FIGURE 3-118 Diagnostic evaluation of patients with documented hypoglycemia and elevated insulin. *CPR,* C-peptide immunoreactivity; *GCMS,* gas chromatography mass spectrometry; *HPLC,* high-pressure liquid chromatography; *IA,* insulin antibodies. (From Moore WT, Eastman RC: *Diagnostic endocrinology,* ed 2, St Louis, 1996, Mosby.)

HYPOGONADISM

ICD-9CM # 256.3 Hypogonadism, female
257.2 Hypogonadism, male

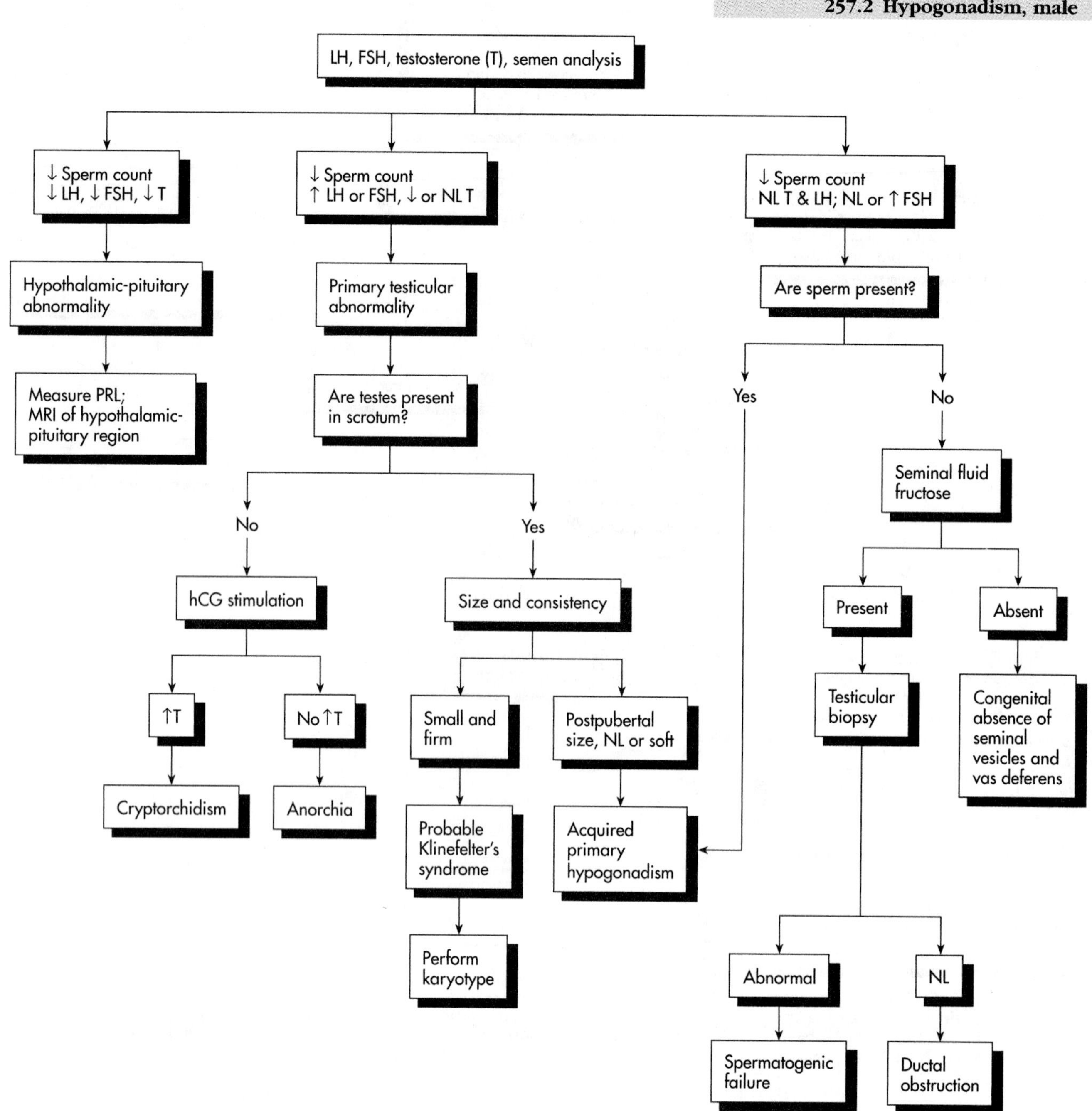

FIGURE 3-119 Laboratory evaluation of hypogonadism. *FSH,* Follicle-stimulating hormone; *hCG,* human chorionic gonadotropin; *LH,* luteinizing hormone; *MRI,* magnetic resonance imaging; *NL,* normal; *PRL,* prolactin; ↑, elevated; ↓, decreased or low. (From Andreoli TE [ed]: *Cecil essentials of medicine,* ed 5, Philadelphia, 2001, WB Saunders.)

HYPOKALEMIA

ICD-9CM # 276.8

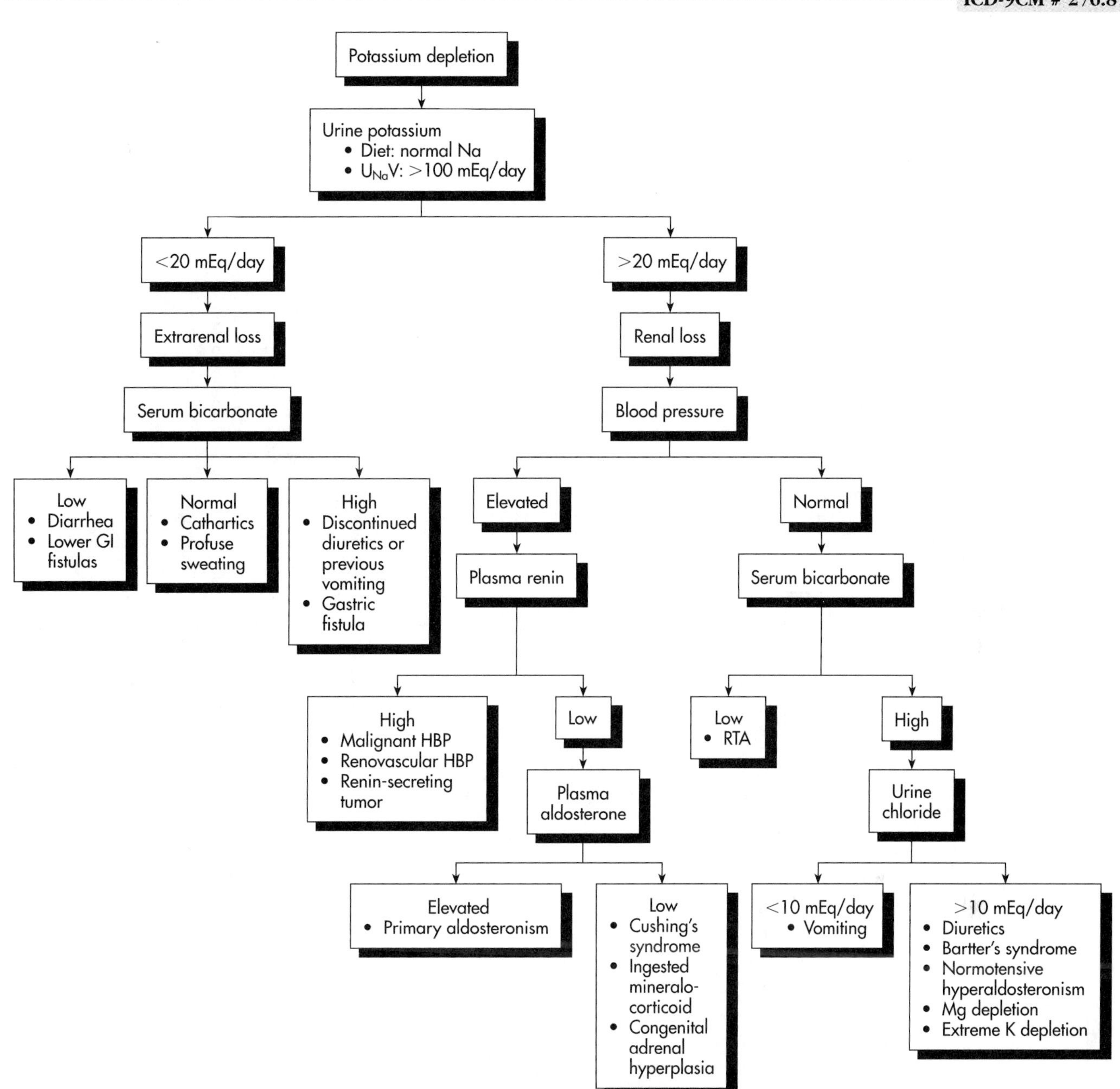

FIGURE 3-120 Diagnostic approach to hypokalemia. Because renal potassium wasting may improve during sodium restriction, diminished potassium excretion is indicative of extrarenal loss only when the diet (and therefore the urine) is rich in sodium. *GI,* Gastrointestinal; *HBP,* high blood pressure; *RTA,* renal tubular acidosis; $U_{NA}V$, urinary sodium volume. (From Stein JH [ed]: *Internal medicine,* ed 5, St Louis, 1998, Mosby.)

HYPOMAGNESEMIA

ICD-9CM # 275.2

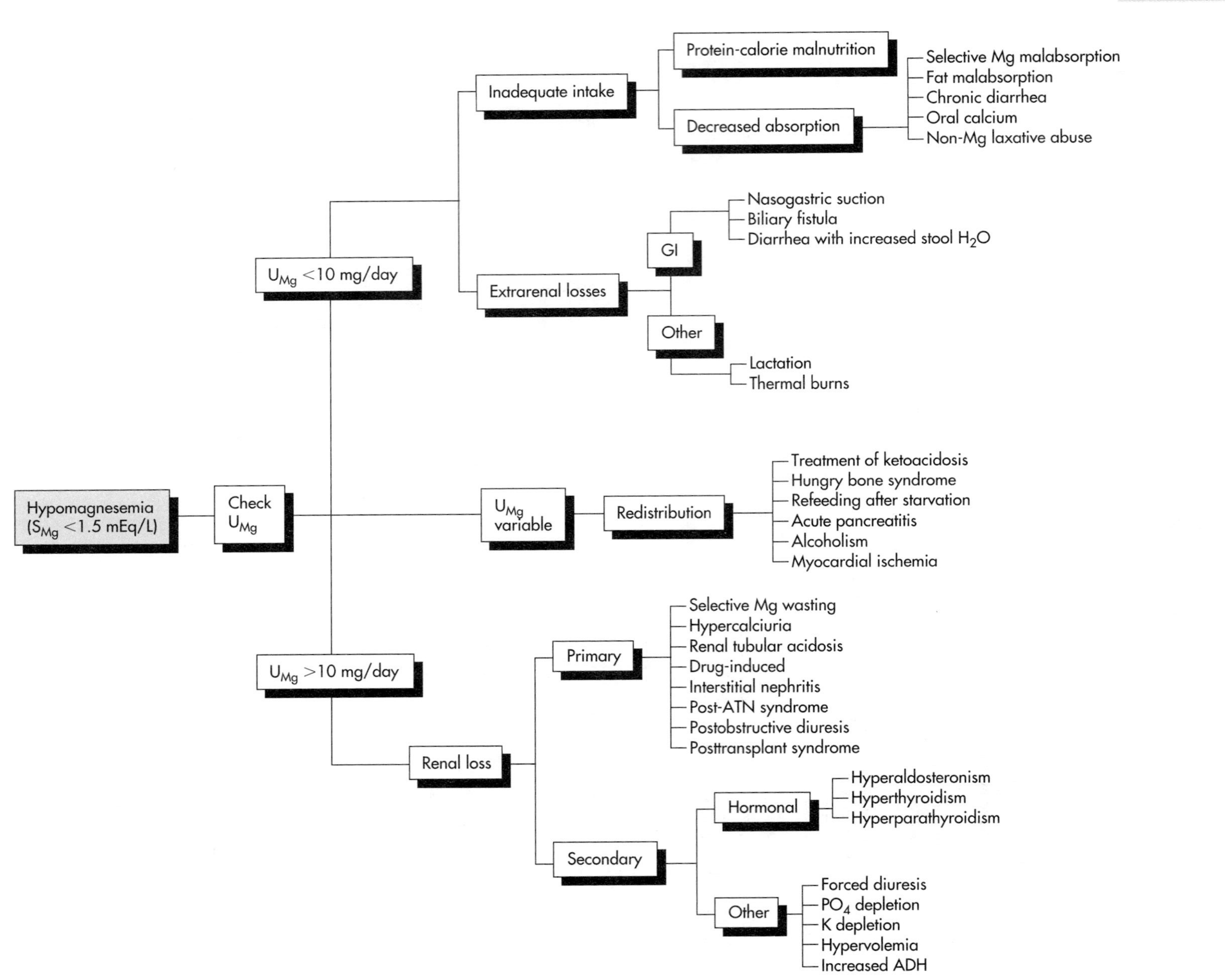

FIGURE 3-121 Hypomagnesemia. *ADH,* Antidiuretic hormone; *GI,* gastrointestinal; *post-ATN,* post acute tubular necrosis. (From Healy PM: *Common medical diagnosis: an algorithmic approach,* ed 3, Philadelphia, 2000, WB Saunders.)

HYPONATREMIA

ICD-9CM # 276.1

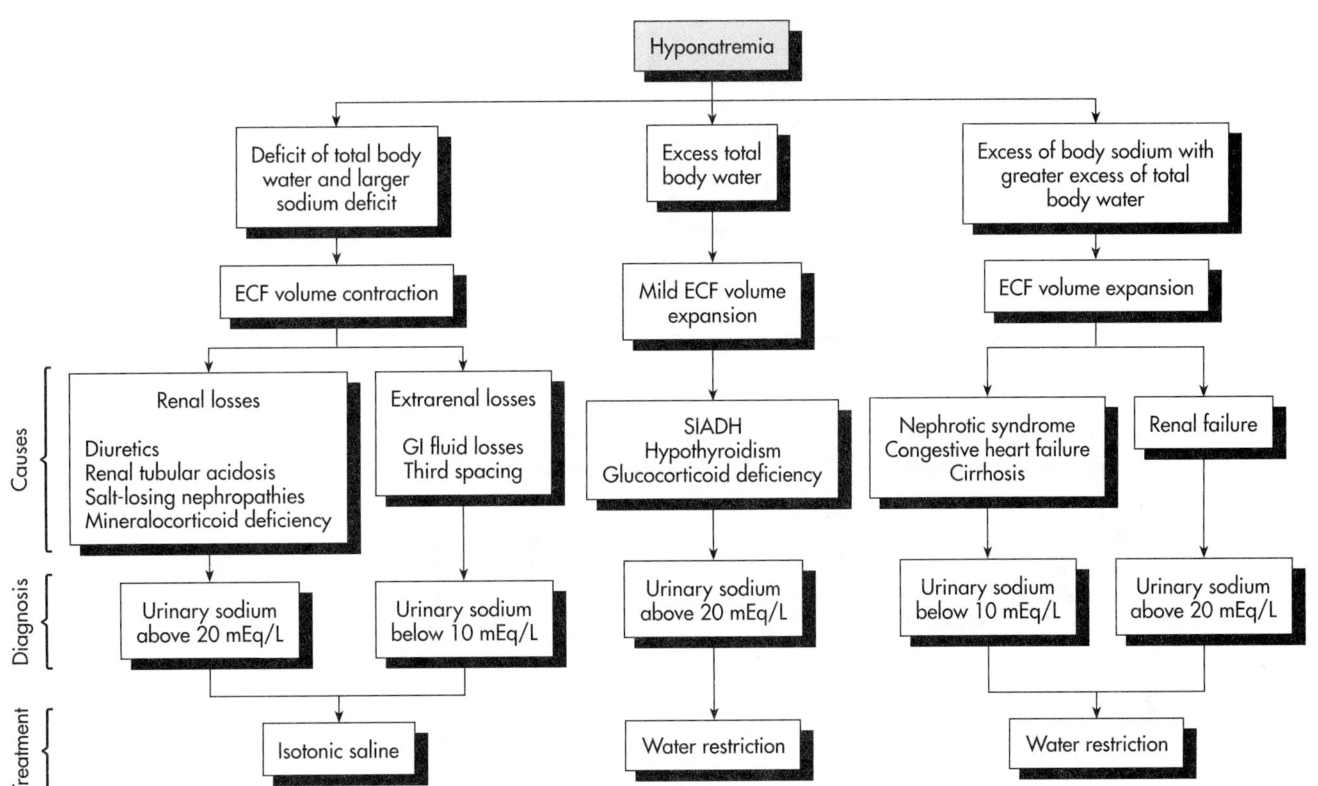

FIGURE 3-122 Evaluation and treatment of asymptomatic, mild hyponatremia. *ECF,* Extracellular fluid; *GI,* gastrointestinal; *SIADH,* syndrome of inappropriate secretion of antidiuretic hormone. (From Marx J et al [eds]: *Rosen's emergency medicine: concepts and clinical practice,* ed 5, St Louis, 2002, Mosby.)

HYPOPHOSPHATEMIA

ICD-9CM # 275.3

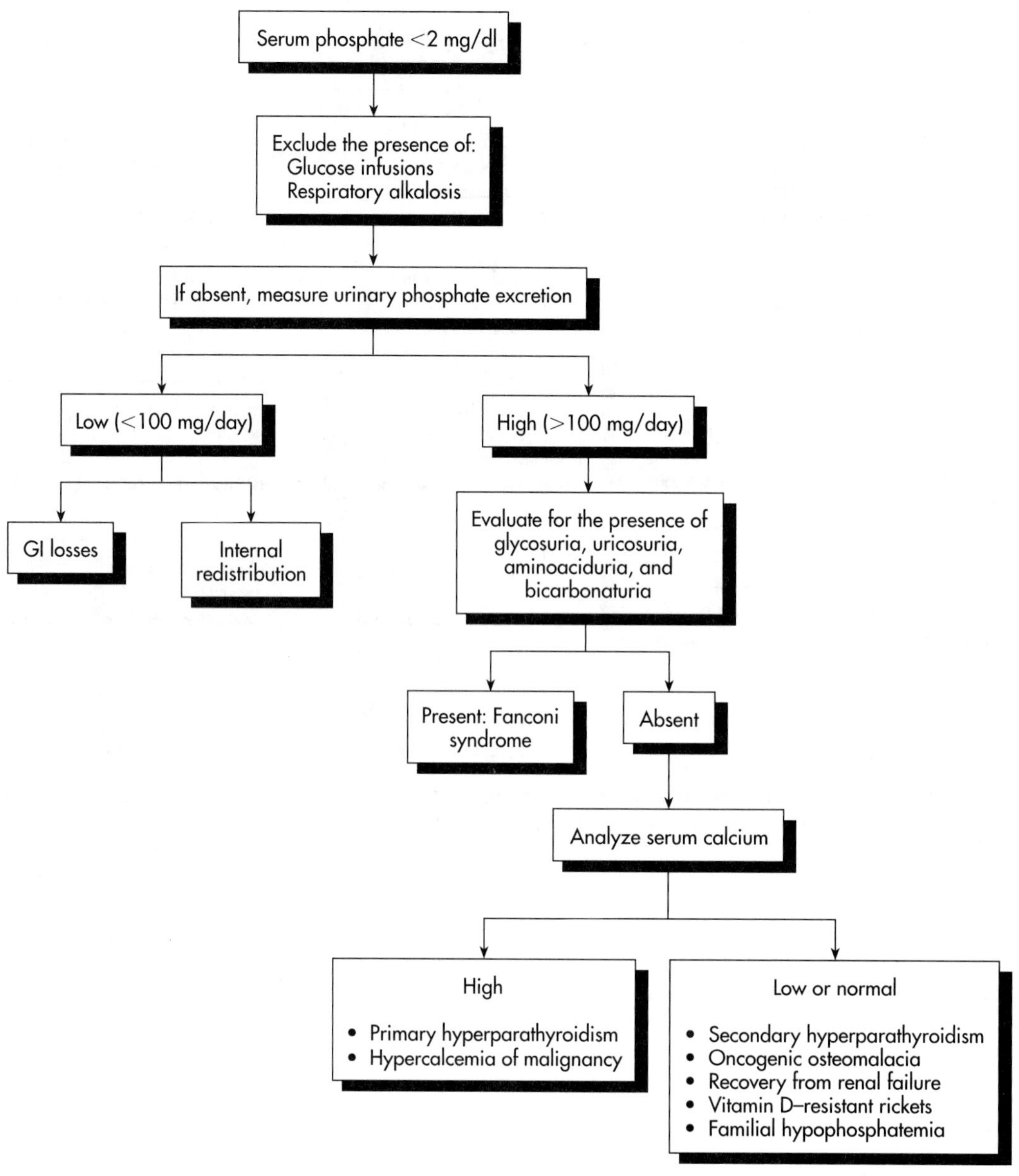

FIGURE 3-123 Diagnostic workup of hypophosphatemia. *GI,* Gastrointestinal. (From Stein JH [ed]: *Internal medicine,* ed 5, St Louis, 1998, Mosby.)

HYPOTENSION

ICD-9CM # 458.9 Hypotension, NOS
458.1 Hypotension, chronic
458.2 Hypotension, iatrogenic
458.0 Hypotension, orthostatic or postural

- Hypotension
  - Check for orthostatic changes
    - Orthostatic hypotension only
      - Check intravascular volume
        - Decreased volume
          - Blood loss
          - Dehydration
          - Third spacing of fluid
            - Ascites
            - Pleural effusions
            - Edema
          - Adrenal insufficiency
        - Normal volume
          - Check drug history
            - Drug history positive
              - Antihypertensives
              - Nitrates
              - Phenothiazines
              - Minor tranquilizers
              - Tricyclic antidepressants
            - Drug history negative
              - Autonomic dysfunction
                - Idiopathic postural hypotension
                - Shy-Drager syndrome
                - Spinal cord lesions
                - Peripheral neuropathy
    - Nonorthostatic hypotension
      - Check tissue perfusion
        - Perfusion normal
          - Vasovagal hypotension
        - Decreased perfusion
          - Check intravascular volume
            - Decreased volume
              - Toxic shock syndrome
              - Hypovolemia
              - Sepsis
              - Neuropathic
              - Anaphylactic
              - Drug-induced
              - Addisonian crisis
              - Metabolic acidosis
            - Volume normal or increased
              - Cardiovascular hypotension
                - Heart failure
                - Valvular dysfunction
                - Pericardial tamponade
                - Arrhythmia
                - Pulmonary embolus

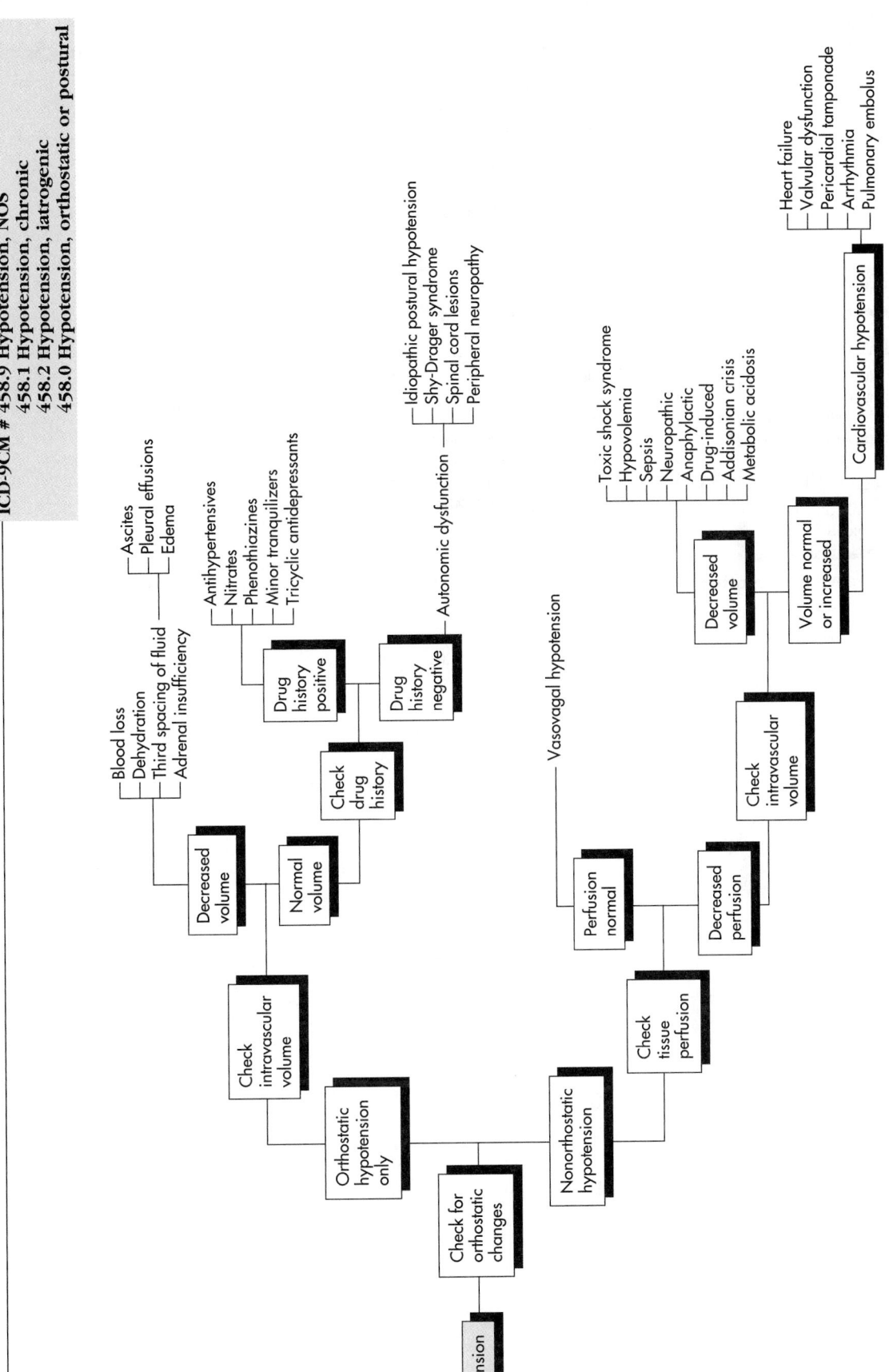

FIGURE 3-124 Hypotension. (From Healey PM: *Common medical diagnosis: an algorithmic approach,* ed 3, Philadelphia, 2000, WB Saunders.)

HYPOTHYROIDISM

ICD-9CM # 244

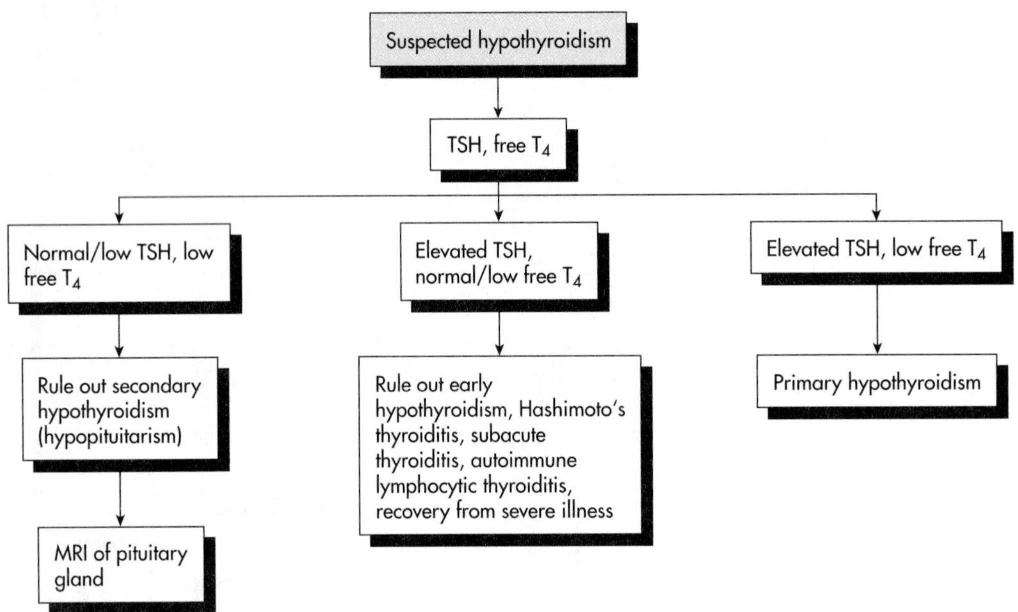

FIGURE 3-125 Hypothyroidism. *MRI,* Magnetic resonance imaging; *TSH,* thyroid-stimulating hormone.

IMMUNODEFICIENCY DISEASES, PRIMARY

ICD-9CM # 279.9

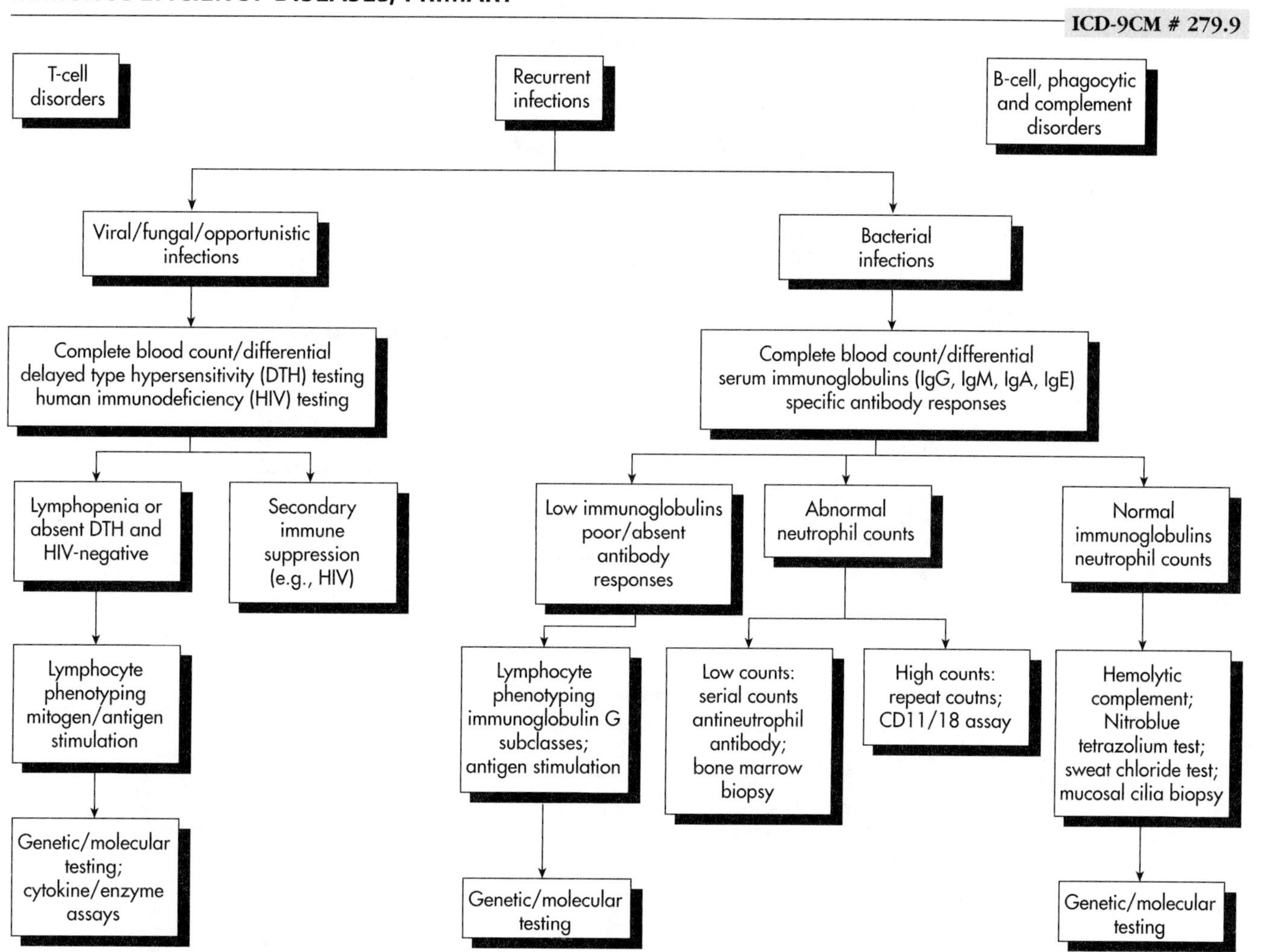

FIGURE 3-126 A diagnostic testing algorithm for primary immunodeficiency diseases. (From MMWR 53(RR-1), 2004.)

INFERTILITY

ICD-9CM # 628.9 Infertility, female, unspecified
606.9 Infertility, male, unspecified

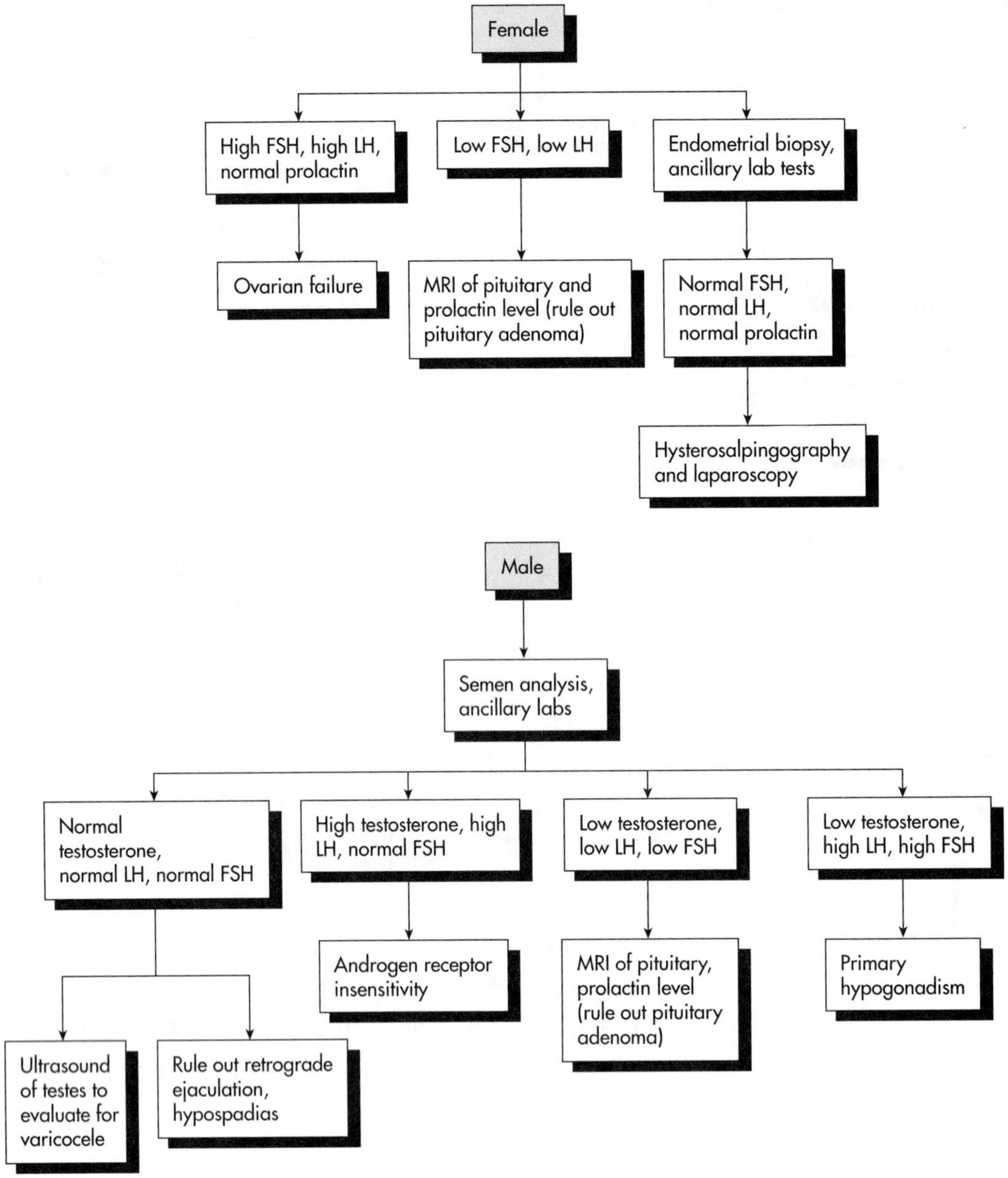

Female
- High FSH, high LH, normal prolactin → Ovarian failure
- Low FSH, low LH → MRI of pituitary and prolactin level (rule out pituitary adenoma)
- Endometrial biopsy, ancillary lab tests → Normal FSH, normal LH, normal prolactin → Hysterosalpingography and laparoscopy

Male → Semen analysis, ancillary labs
- Normal testosterone, normal LH, normal FSH → Ultrasound of testes to evaluate for varicocele; Rule out retrograde ejaculation, hypospadias
- High testosterone, high LH, normal FSH → Androgen receptor insensitivity
- Low testosterone, low LH, low FSH → MRI of pituitary, prolactin level (rule out pituitary adenoma)
- Low testosterone, high LH, high FSH → Primary hypogonadism

FIGURE 3-127 Approach to infertility diagnosis and management. FSH, Follicle-stimulating hormone; LH, luteinizing hormone; MRI, magnetic resonance imaging. (From Ferri FF: *Ferri's best test: a practical guide to clinical laboratory medicine and diagnostic imaging,* Philadelphia, 2004, Elsevier Mosby.)

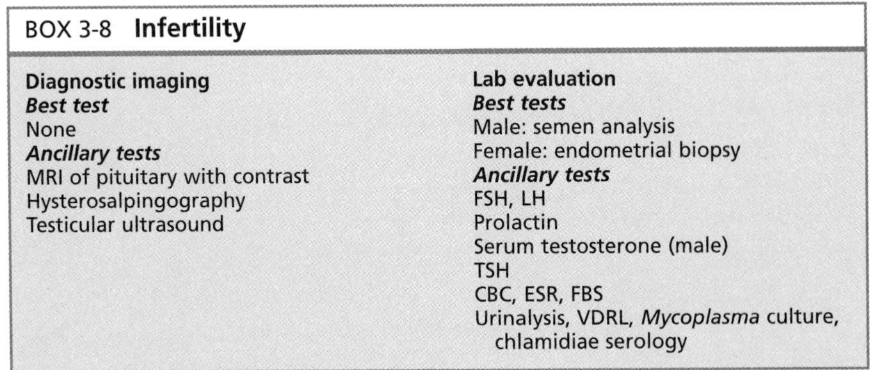

BOX 3-8 **Infertility**

Diagnostic imaging	Lab evaluation
Best test	***Best tests***
None	Male: semen analysis
Ancillary tests	Female: endometrial biopsy
MRI of pituitary with contrast	***Ancillary tests***
Hysterosalpingography	FSH, LH
Testicular ultrasound	Prolactin
	Serum testosterone (male)
	TSH
	CBC, ESR, FBS
	Urinalysis, VDRL, *Mycoplasma* culture, chlamidiae serology

Ferri FF: *Ferri's best test: a practical guide to clinical laboratory medicine and diagnostic imaging,* Philadelphia, 2004, Elsevier Mosby.

CBC, Complete blood count; *ESR,* erythrocyte sedimentation rate; *FBS,* fasting blood sugar; *FSH,* follicle-stimulating hormone; *LH,* luteinizing hormone; *MRI,* magnetic resonance imaging; *VDRL,* Venereal Disease Research Laboratory (test).

IRRITABLE BOWEL SYNDROME

ICD-9CM # 564.1

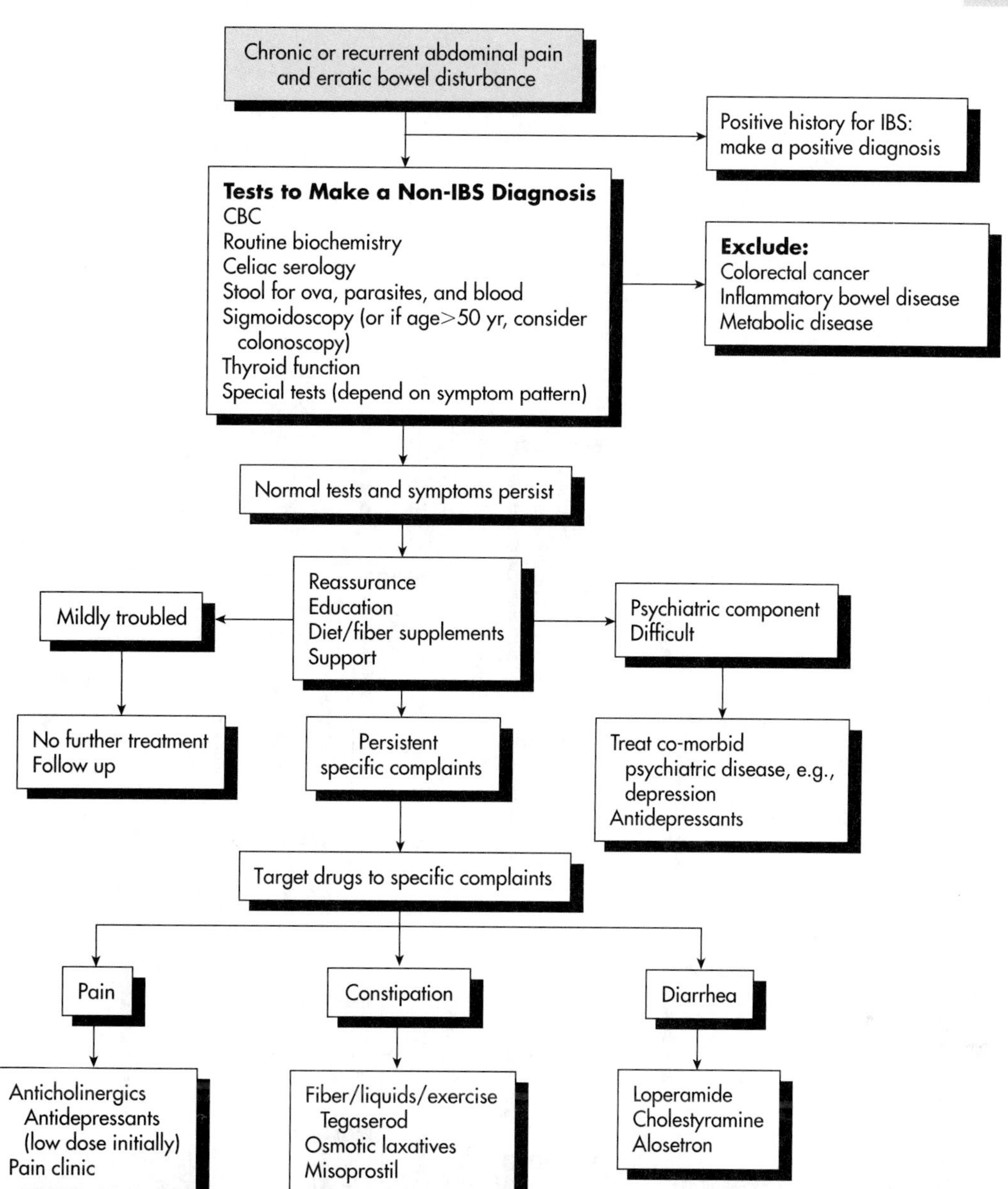

FIGURE 3-128 Evaluation of suspected irritable bowel syndrome (IBS). *CBC,* complete blood count. (From Goldman L, Ausiello D [eds]: *Cecil textbook of medicine,* ed 22, Philadelphia, 2004, WB Saunders.)

JAUNDICE AND HEPATOBILIARY DISEASE

ICD-9CM # 782.4 Jaundice NOS
277.4 Bilirubin excretion disorders
576.8 Jaundice, obstructive

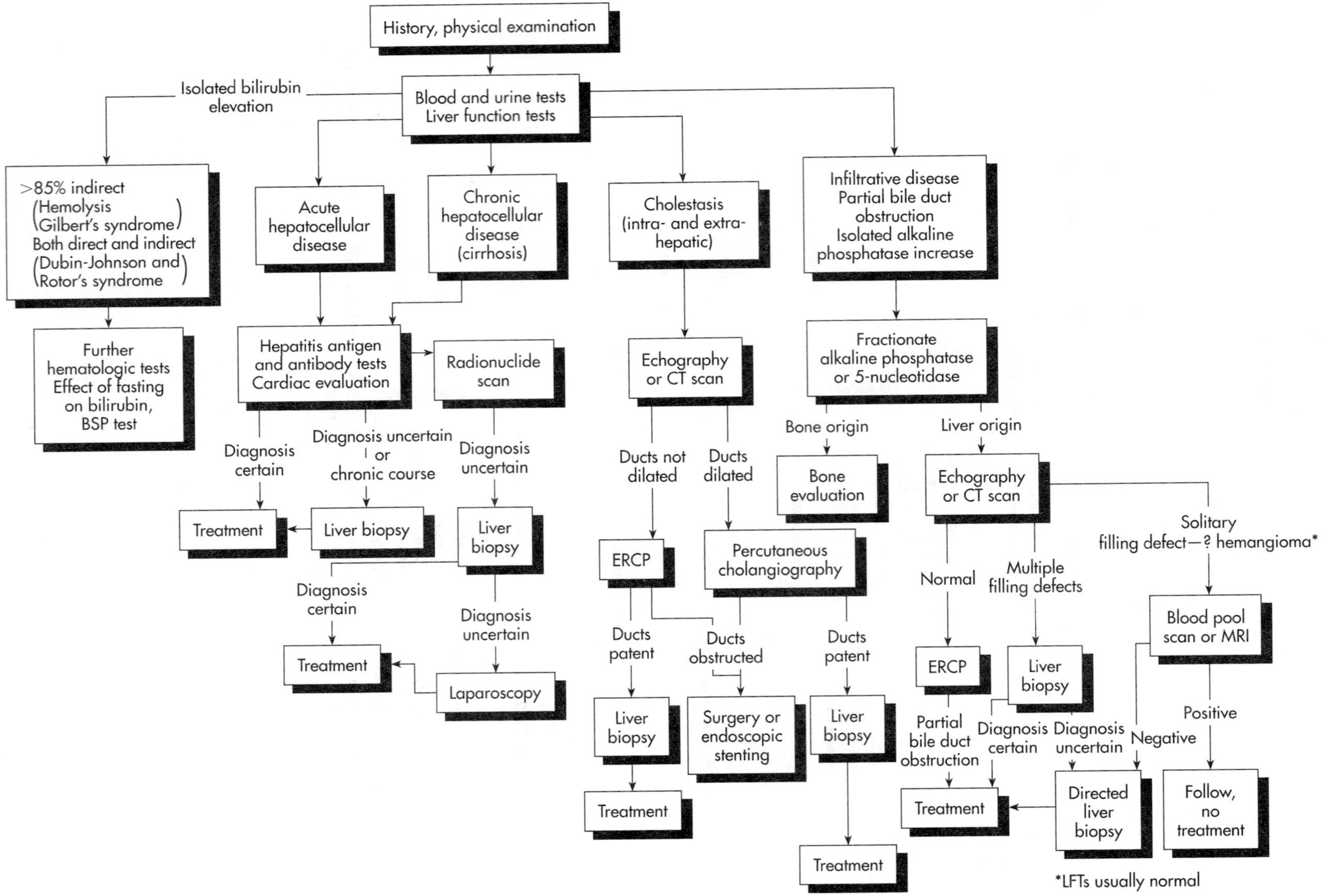

History, physical examination
Blood and urine tests
Liver function tests

Isolated bilirubin elevation
>85% indirect (Hemolysis, Gilbert's syndrome)
Both direct and indirect (Dubin-Johnson and Rotor's syndrome)
Further hematologic tests
Effect of fasting on bilirubin,
BSP test

Acute hepatocellular disease
Chronic hepatocellular disease (cirrhosis)
Hepatitis antigen and antibody tests
Cardiac evaluation
Diagnosis certain
Treatment
Diagnosis uncertain or chronic course
Liver biopsy
Radionuclide scan
Diagnosis uncertain
Liver biopsy
Diagnosis certain
Treatment
Diagnosis uncertain
Laparoscopy

Cholestasis (intra- and extra-hepatic)
Echography or CT scan
Ducts not dilated
ERCP
Ducts patent
Liver biopsy
Treatment
Ducts dilated
Percutaneous cholangiography
Ducts obstructed
Surgery or endoscopic stenting
Ducts patent
Liver biopsy
Treatment

Infiltrative disease
Partial bile duct obstruction
Isolated alkaline phosphatase increase
Fractionate alkaline phosphatase or 5-nucleotidase
Bone origin
Bone evaluation
Liver origin
Echography or CT scan
Normal
ERCP
Partial bile duct obstruction
Treatment
Multiple filling defects
Liver biopsy
Diagnosis certain
Diagnosis uncertain
Directed liver biopsy
Solitary filling defect—? hemangioma*
Blood pool scan or MRI
Positive
Follow, no treatment
Negative

*LFTs usually normal

FIGURE 3-129 Evaluation of jaundice and hepatobiliary disease. *BSP,* Bromsulphalein; *CT,* computed tomography; *ERCP,* endoscopic retrograde cholangiopancreatography; *LFTs,* liver function tests; *MRI,* magnetic resonance imaging. (From Stein JH [ed]: *Internal medicine*, ed 5, St Louis, 1998, Mosby.)

JAUNDICE, NEONATAL

ICD-9CM # 774.6 Jaundice neonatal, NOS
773.1 ABO reaction perinatal
774.1 Hemolytic perinatal
773.0 RH reaction perinatal
751.61 Bile duct obstruction, congenital

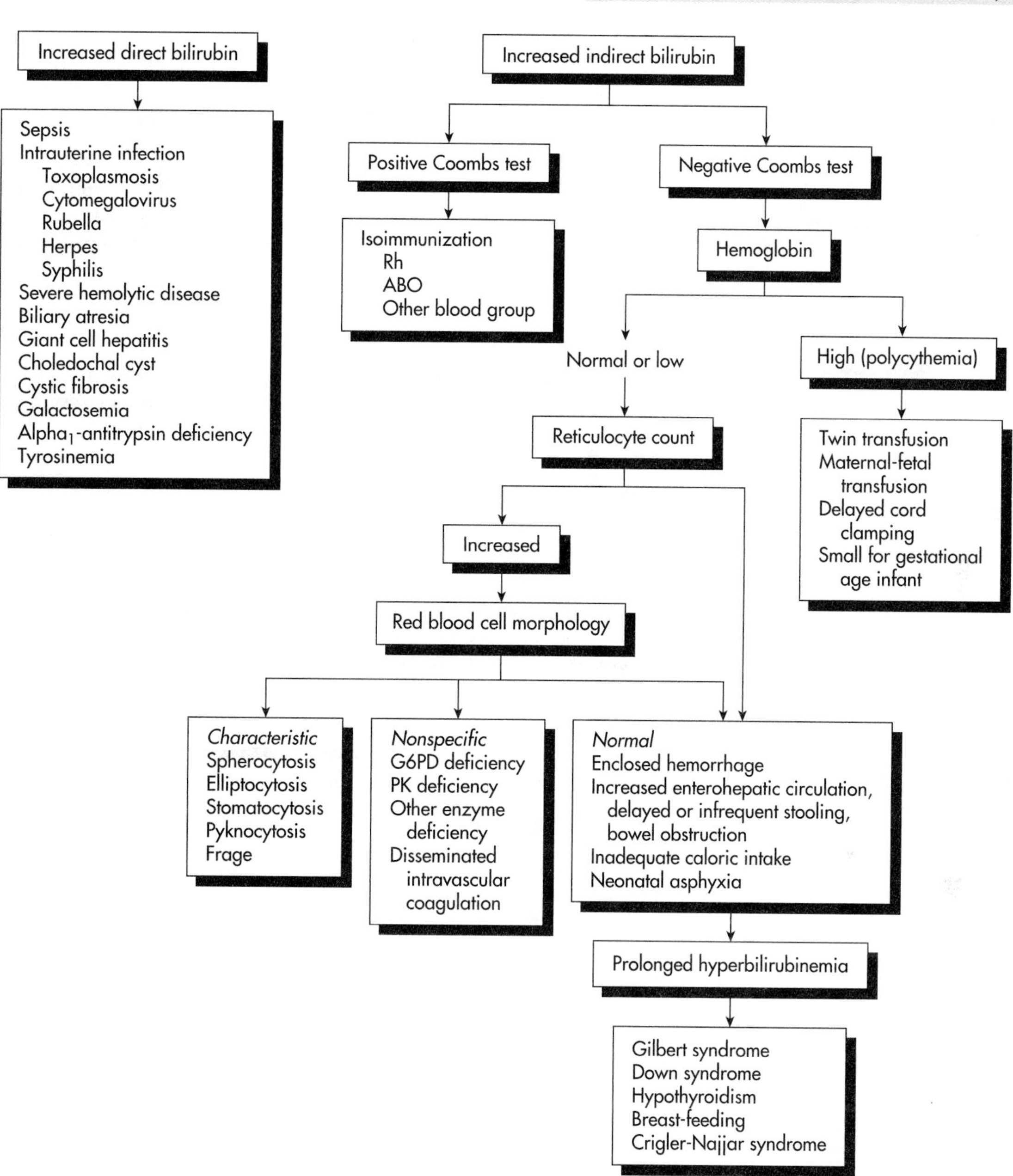

FIGURE 3-130 Schematic approach to the diagnosis of neonatal jaundice. *G6PD,* Glucose-6-phosphate dehydrogenase; *PK,* pyruvate kinase. (From Oski FA: Differential diagnosis of jaundice. In Taeusch HW, Ballard RA, Avery MA [eds]: *Schaffer and Avery's diseases of the newborn,* ed 6, Philadelphia, 1991, WB Saunders.)

SECTION III

JOINT EFFUSION

ICD-9CM # 719.0

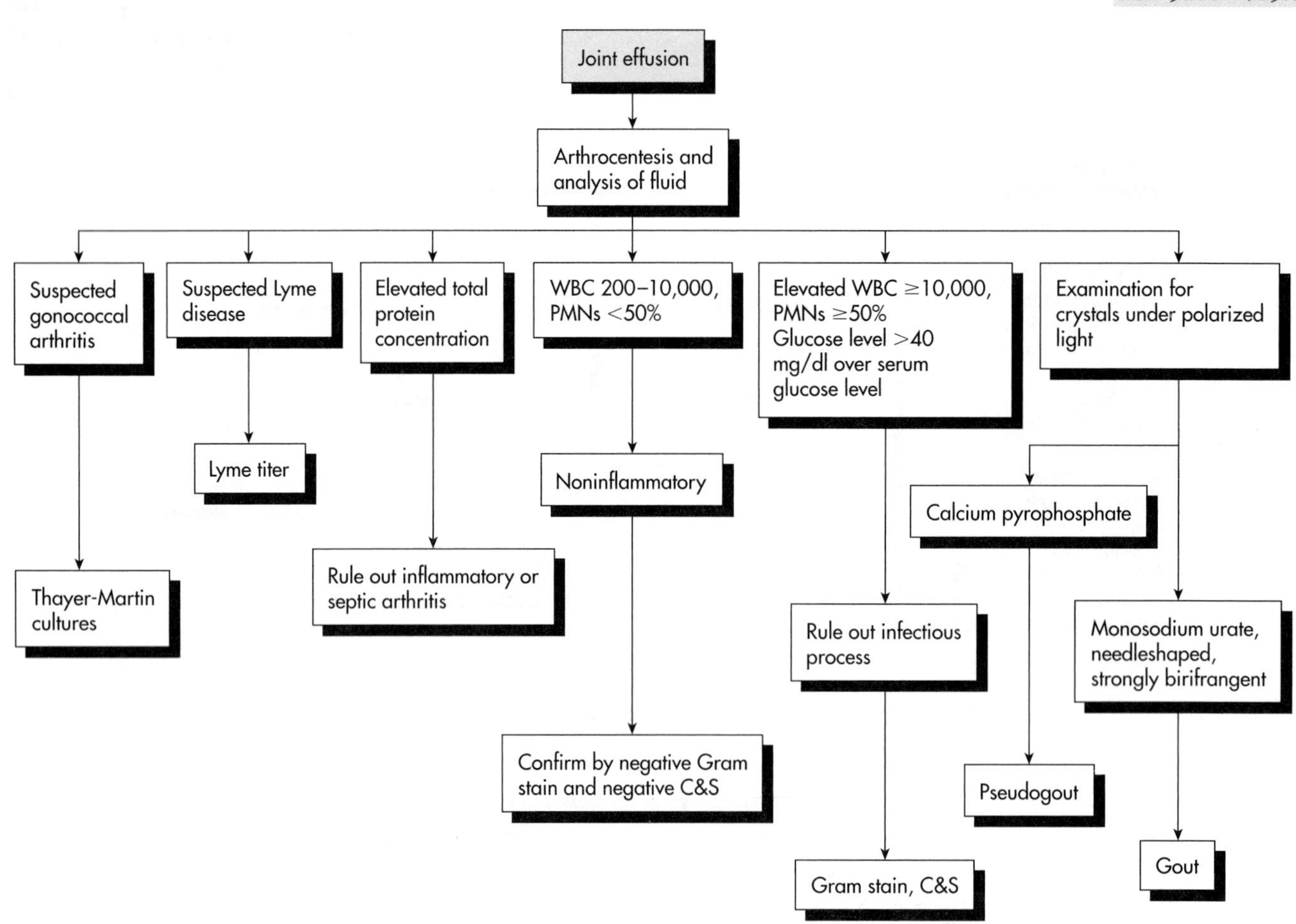

FIGURE 3-131 Joint effusion. *C&S,* Culture and sensitivity; *WBC,* white blood cell count.

JOINT SWELLING

ICD-9CM # 719.00

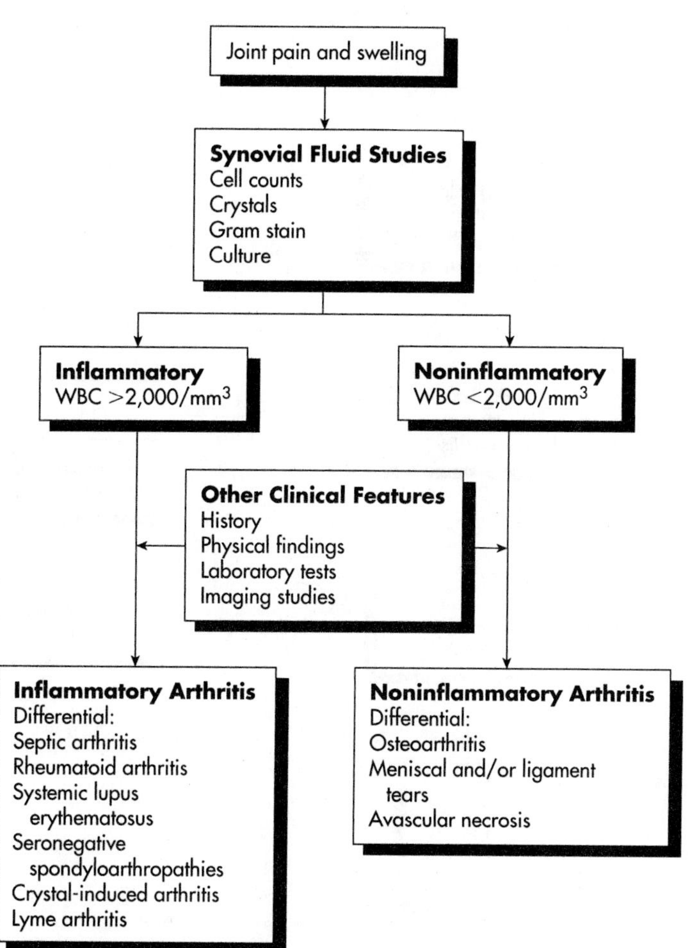

FIGURE 3-132 Diagnostic approach for swollen joints. *WBC,* White blood cell count. (From Goldman L, Ausiello D [eds]: *Cecil textbook of medicine,* ed 22, Philadelphia, 2004, WB Saunders.)

KNEE PAIN, ANTERIOR

ICD-9CM # 716.96 Knee inflammation
959.7 Knee injury
719.56 Knee stiffness
719.06 Knee swelling

FIGURE 3-133 Evaluation and management of knee extensor mechanism pain. Focused treatment based on specific etiology will prevent recurrence. *AP,* Anteroposterior; *NSAIDs,* nonsteroidal antiinflammatory drugs; *VMO,* vastus medialis obliquus muscle. (From Scudieri G [ed]: *Sports medicine, principles of primary care,* St Louis, 1997, Mosby.)

LEG ULCER

ICD-9CM #	
440.23	Ulcer, lower limb, arteriosclerotic
707.1	Ulcer, lower limb, chronic
707.1	Ulcer, lower limb, neurogenic
707.9	Ulcer, non-healing
707.0	Pressure ulcer

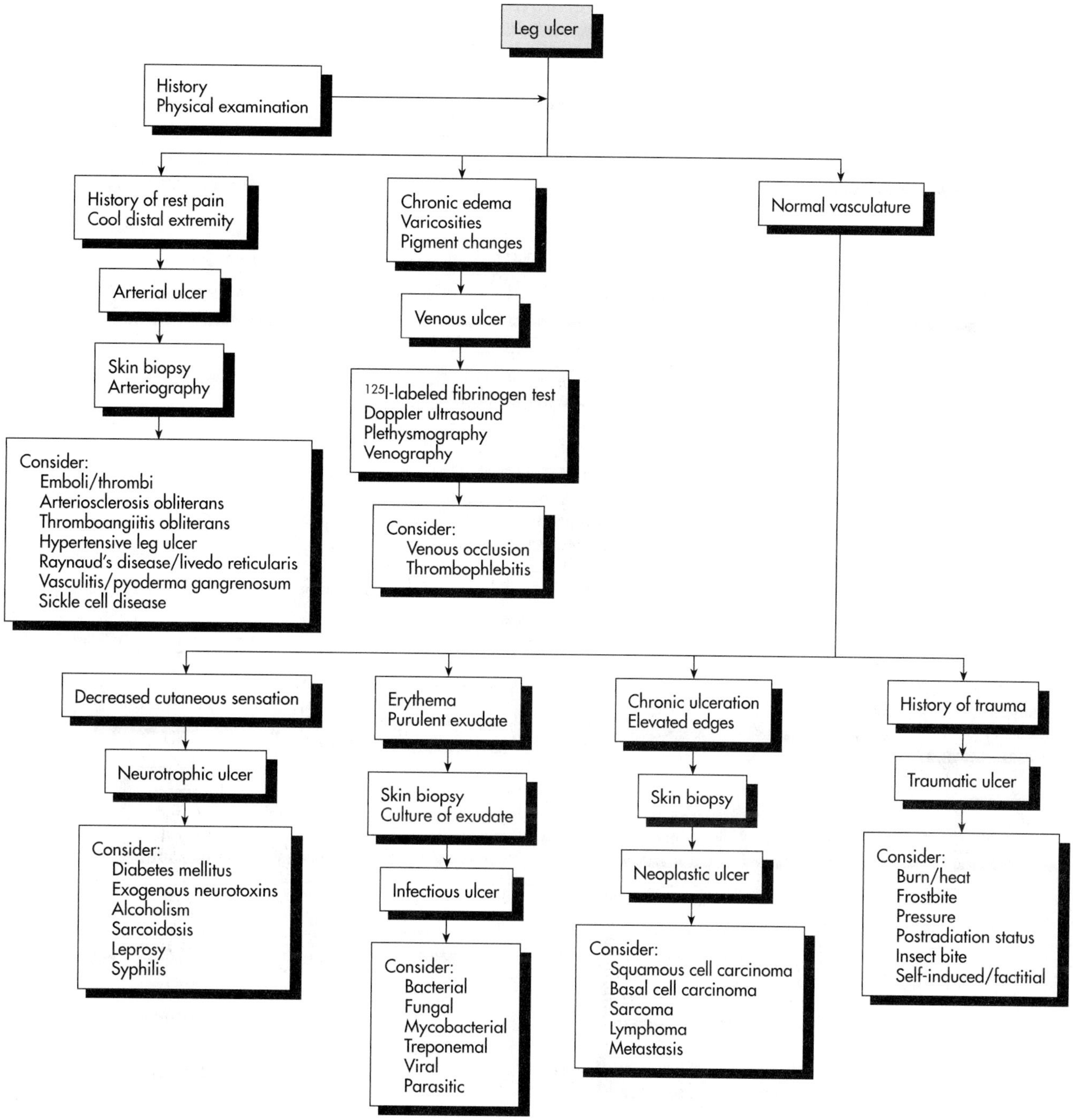

Leg ulcer

History
Physical examination

History of rest pain
Cool distal extremity

Arterial ulcer

Skin biopsy
Arteriography

Consider:
Emboli/thrombi
Arteriosclerosis obliterans
Thromboangiitis obliterans
Hypertensive leg ulcer
Raynaud's disease/livedo reticularis
Vasculitis/pyoderma gangrenosum
Sickle cell disease

Chronic edema
Varicosities
Pigment changes

Venous ulcer

^{125}I-labeled fibrinogen test
Doppler ultrasound
Plethysmography
Venography

Consider:
Venous occlusion
Thrombophlebitis

Normal vasculature

Decreased cutaneous sensation

Neurotrophic ulcer

Consider:
Diabetes mellitus
Exogenous neurotoxins
Alcoholism
Sarcoidosis
Leprosy
Syphilis

Erythema
Purulent exudate

Skin biopsy
Culture of exudate

Infectious ulcer

Consider:
Bacterial
Fungal
Mycobacterial
Treponemal
Viral
Parasitic

Chronic ulceration
Elevated edges

Skin biopsy

Neoplastic ulcer

Consider:
Squamous cell carcinoma
Basal cell carcinoma
Sarcoma
Lymphoma
Metastasis

History of trauma

Traumatic ulcer

Consider:
Burn/heat
Frostbite
Pressure
Postradiation status
Insect bite
Self-induced/factitial

FIGURE 3-134 Leg ulcer. (From Greene HL, Johnson WP, Lemcke D [eds]: *Decision making in medicine*, ed 2, St Louis, 1998, Mosby.)

SECTION III

LIVER FUNCTION TEST ELEVATIONS

ICD-9CM # 573.9

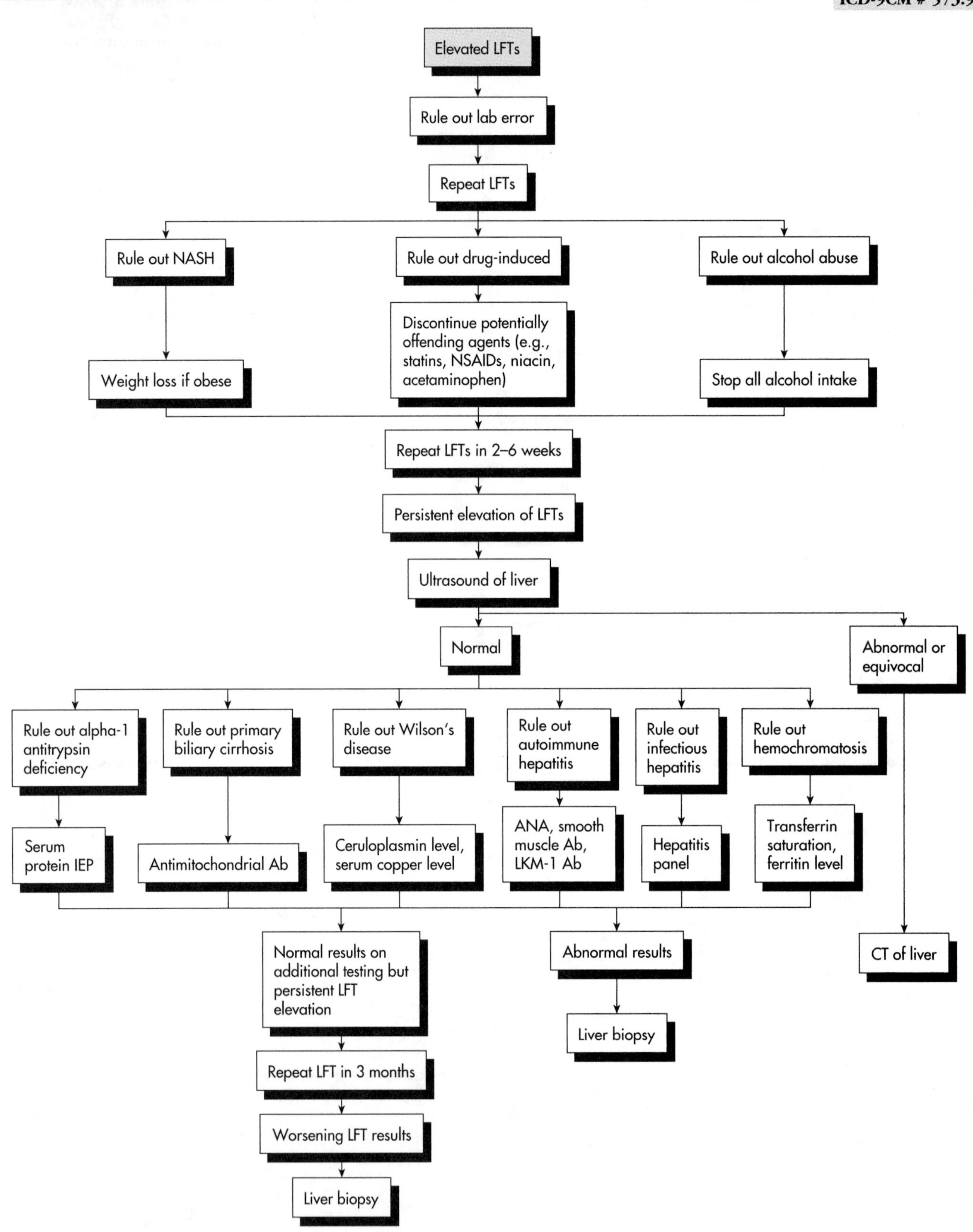

FIGURE 3-135 Liver function test elevations. *Ab,* Antibody; *ANA,* antibody to nuclear antigens; *CT,* computed tomography; *IEP,* immuno-electrophoresis; *LFT,* liver function test; *LKM,* liver-kidney microsome; *NSAIDs,* nonsteroidal antiinflammatory drugs.

LOW BACK AND/OR LEG PAIN

ICD-9CM # 724.2

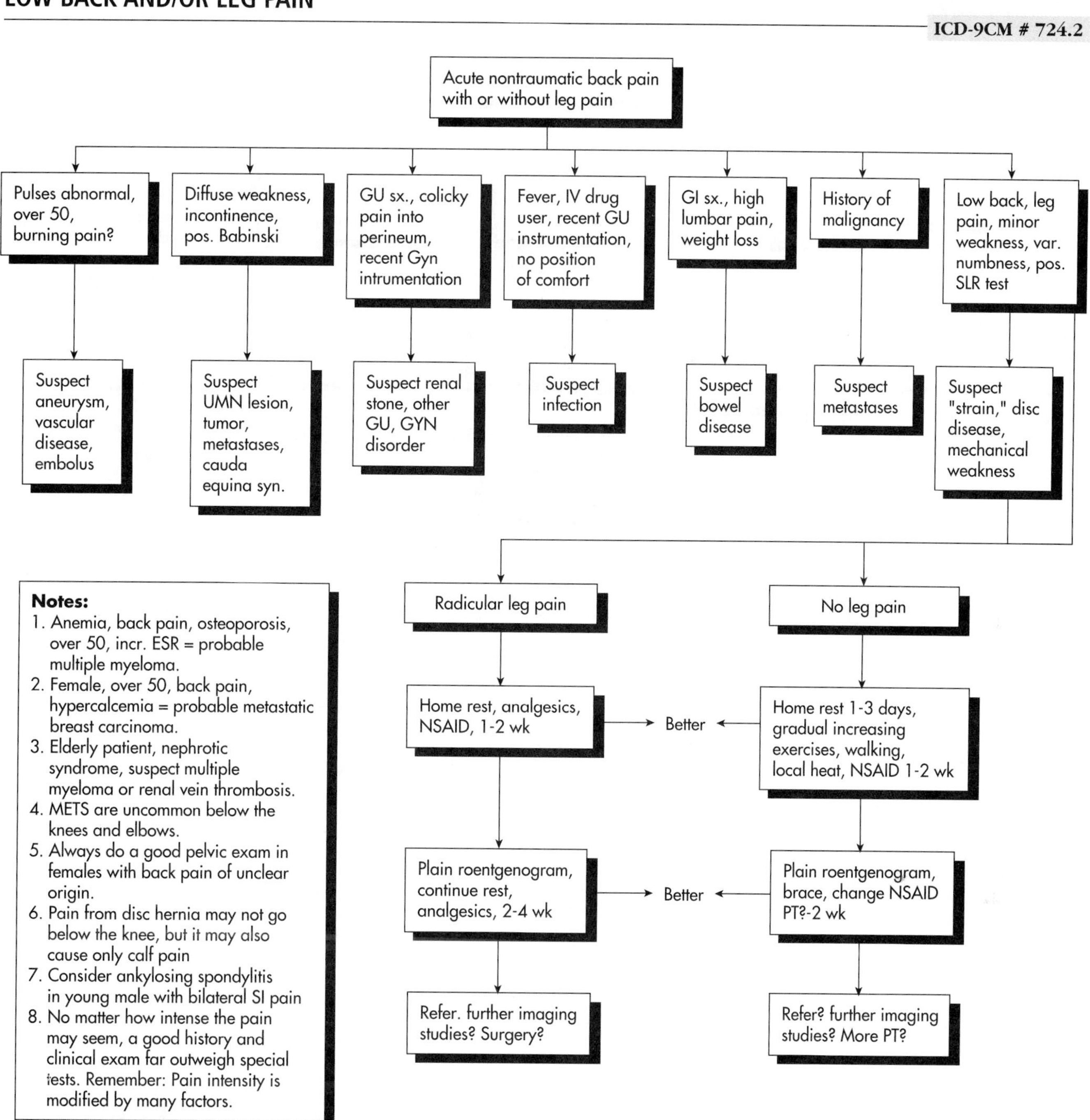

FIGURE 3-136 Algorithm for low back and/or leg pain. *GI,* Gastrointestinal; *GU,* genitourinary; *IV,* intravenous; *METS,* metabolic equivalents; *NSAID,* nonsteroidal anti-inflammatory drug; *PT,* physical therapy; *SLR,* straight-leg raising; *UMN,* upper motor neuron. (From Mercier LR: *Practical orthopedics,* St Louis, 2000, Mosby.)

LYMPHADENOPATHY, AXILLARY

ICD-9CM # 785.6

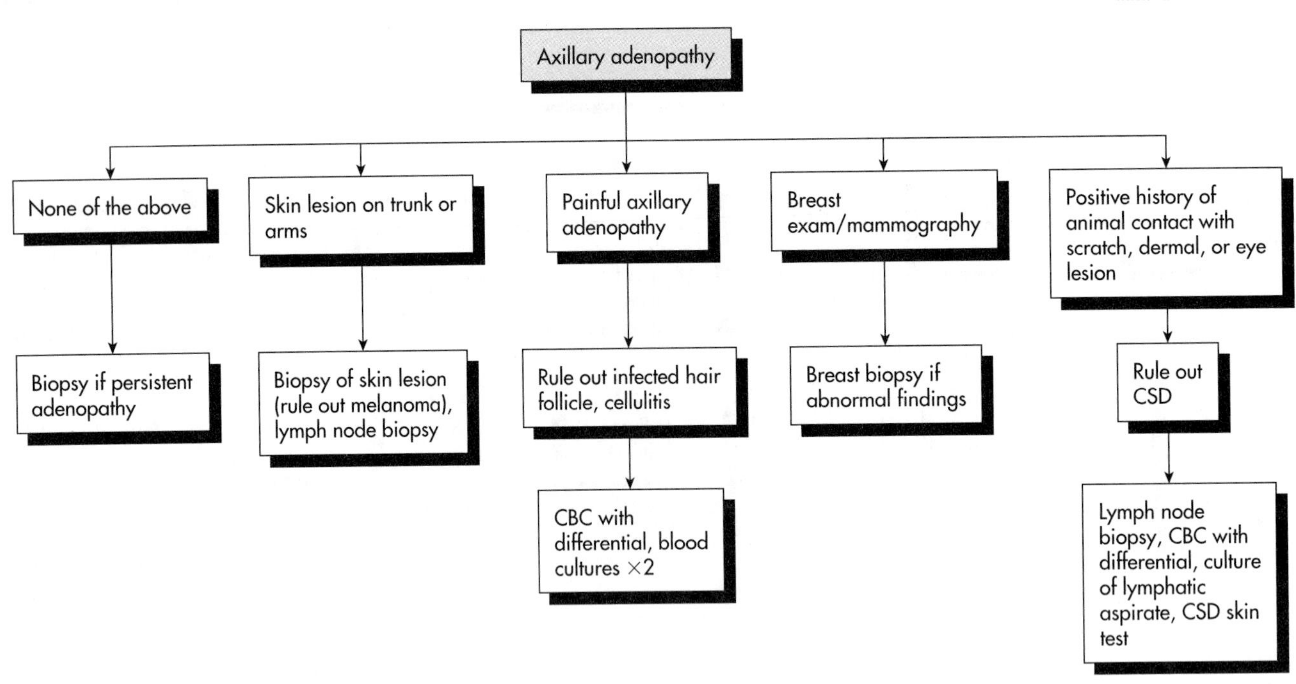

FIGURE 3-137 Lymphadenopathy, axillary. *CBC,* Complete blood count; *CSD,* cat-scratch disease.

LYMPHADENOPATHY, CERVICAL

ICD-9CM # 785.6

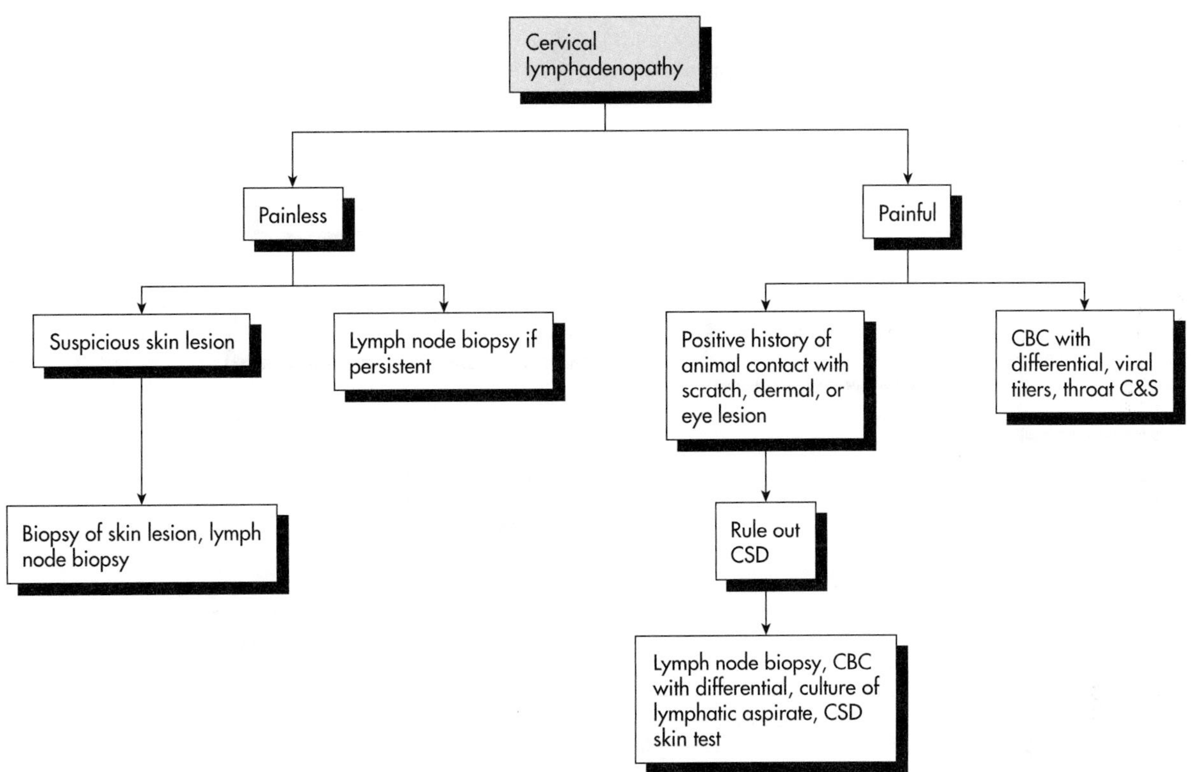

FIGURE 3-138 Lymphadenopathy, cervical. *CBC,* Complete blood count; *C&S,* culture and sensitivity; *CSD,* cat-scratch disease.

LYMPHADENOPATHY, EPITROCHLEAR

ICD-9CM # 785.6

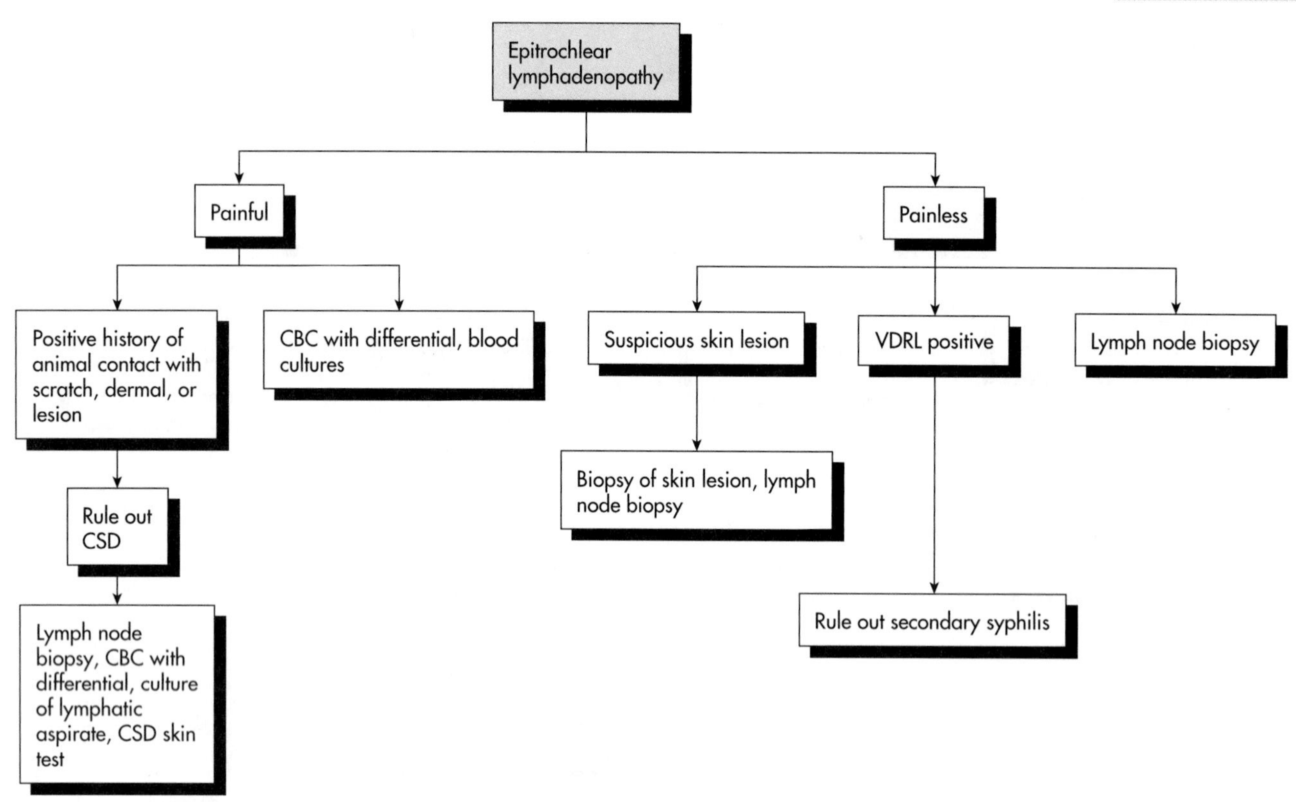

FIGURE 3-139 Lymphadenopathy, epitrochlear. *CBC,* Complete blood count; *CSD,* cat-scratch disease; *VDRL,* Venereal Disease Research Laboratory.

LYMPHADENOPATHY, GENERALIZED

ICD-9CM # 785.6 Lymphadenopathy, unknown etiology

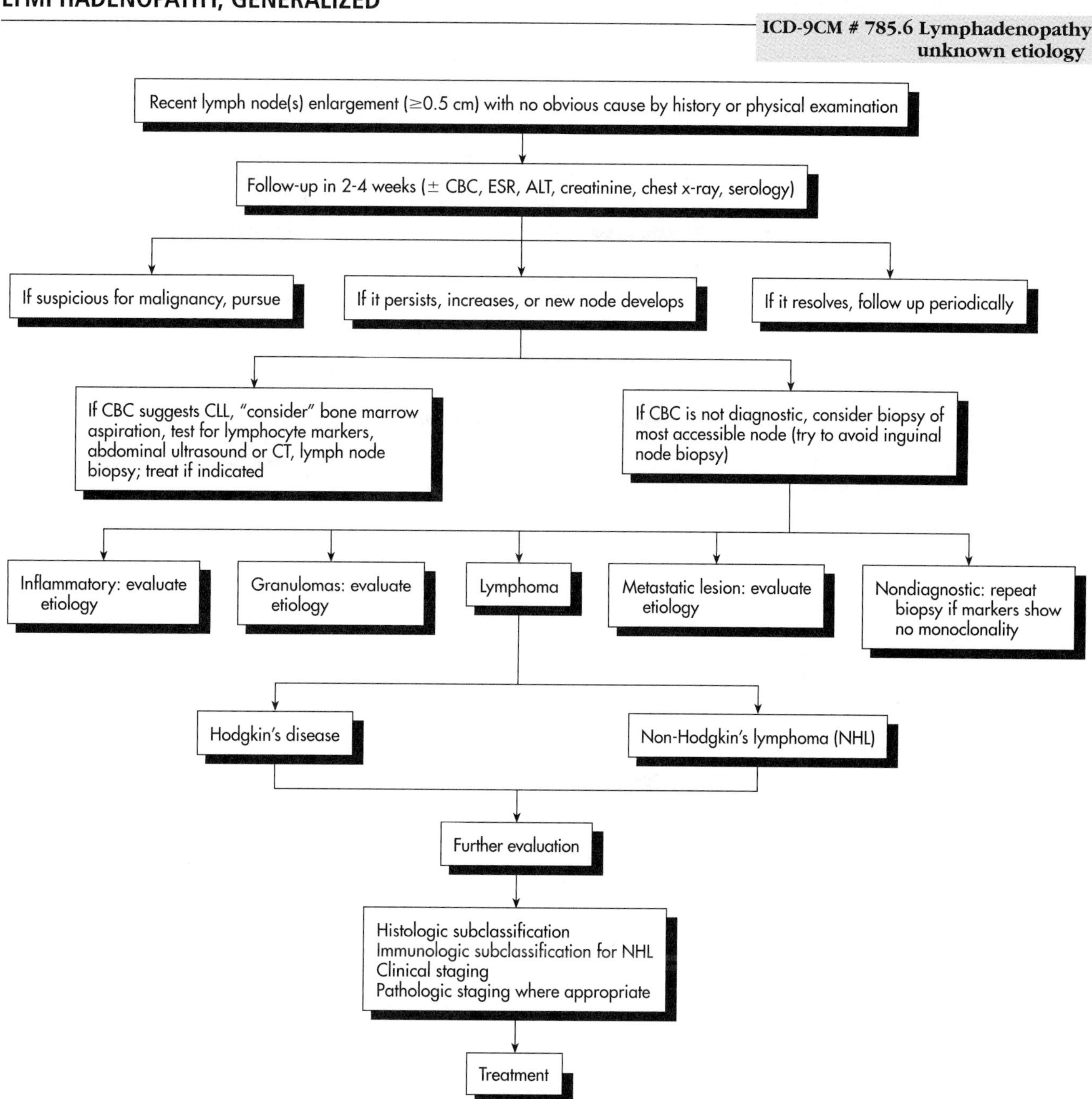
Recent lymph node(s) enlargement (≥0.5 cm) with no obvious cause by history or physical examination
Follow-up in 2-4 weeks (± CBC, ESR, ALT, creatinine, chest x-ray, serology)
If suspicious for malignancy, pursue
If it persists, increases, or new node develops
If it resolves, follow up periodically
If CBC suggests CLL, "consider" bone marrow aspiration, test for lymphocyte markers, abdominal ultrasound or CT, lymph node biopsy; treat if indicated
If CBC is not diagnostic, consider biopsy of most accessible node (try to avoid inguinal node biopsy)
Inflammatory: evaluate etiology
Granulomas: evaluate etiology
Lymphoma
Metastatic lesion: evaluate etiology
Nondiagnostic: repeat biopsy if markers show no monoclonality
Hodgkin's disease
Non-Hodgkin's lymphoma (NHL)
Further evaluation
Histologic subclassification
Immunologic subclassification for NHL
Clinical staging
Pathologic staging where appropriate
Treatment

FIGURE 3-140 Workup of lymphadenopathy. *ALT,* Alanine aminotransferase; *CBC,* complete blood count; *CLL,* chronic lymphocytic leukemia; *CT,* computed tomography; *ESR,* erythrocyte sedimentation rate. (Modified from Noble J [ed]: *Primary care medicine*, ed 3, St Louis, 2001, Mosby.)

LYMPHADENOPATHY, INGUINAL

ICD-9CM # 785.6

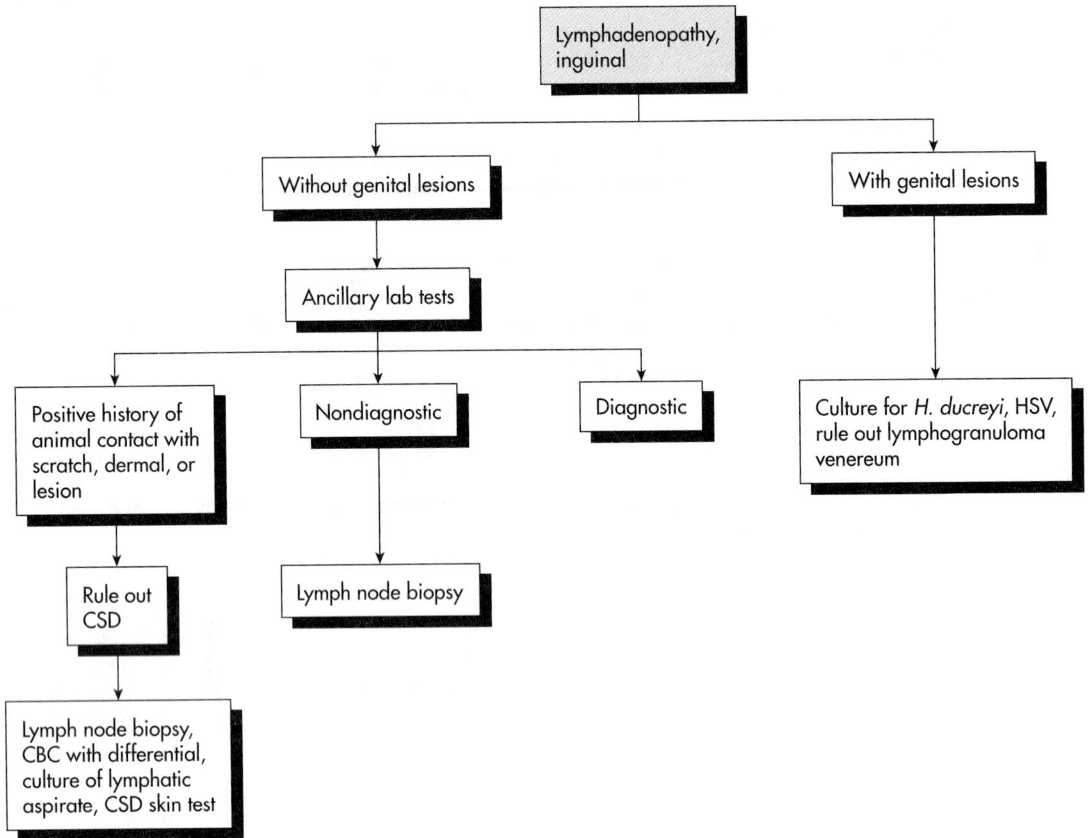

FIGURE 3-141 Lymphadenopathy, inguinal. *CBC,* Complete blood count; *CSD,* cat-scratch disease; *HSV,* herpes simplex virus.

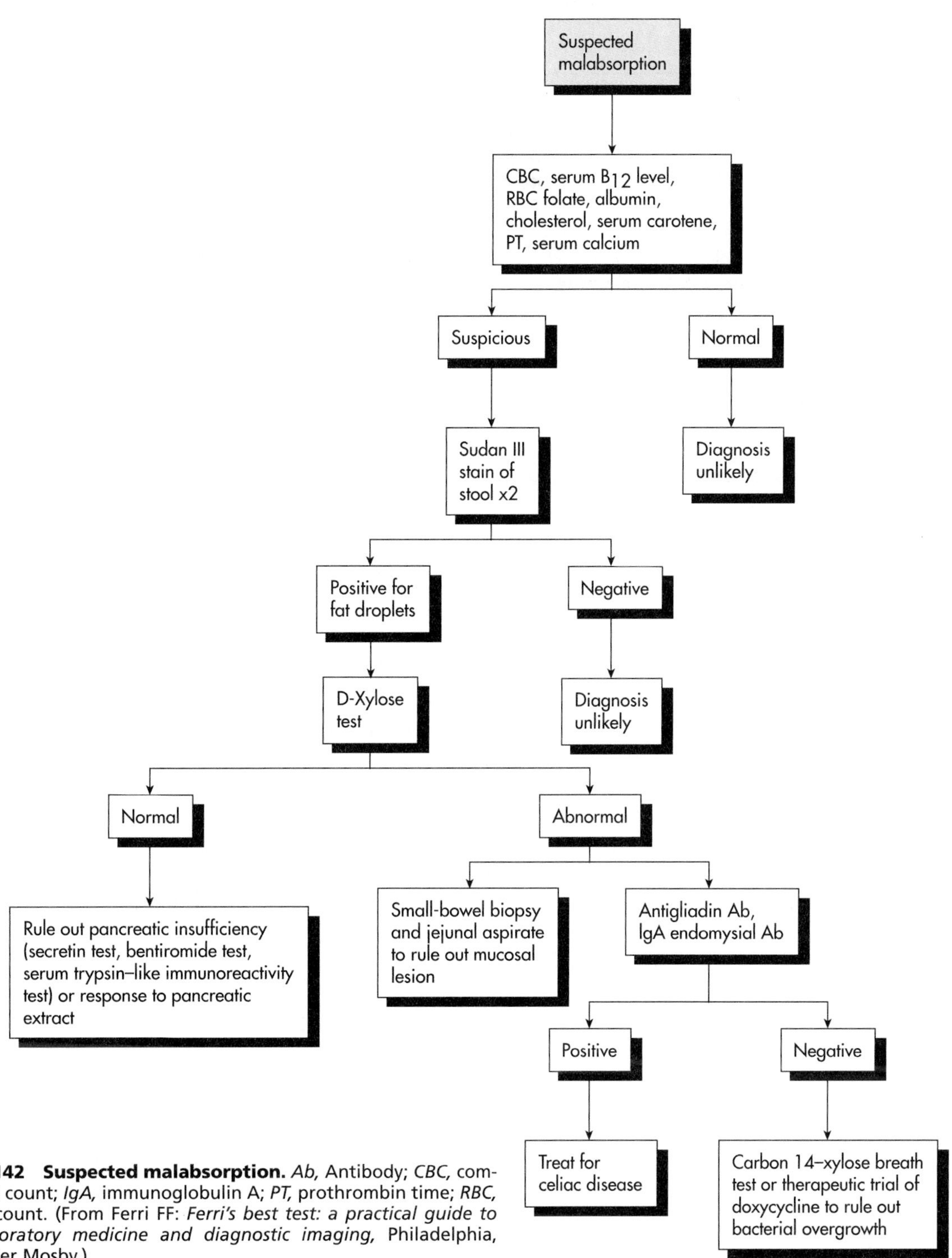

FIGURE 3-142 Suspected malabsorption. *Ab,* Antibody; *CBC,* complete blood count; *IgA,* immunoglobulin A; *PT,* prothrombin time; *RBC,* red blood count. (From Ferri FF: *Ferri's best test: a practical guide to clinical laboratory medicine and diagnostic imaging,* Philadelphia, 2004, Elsevier Mosby.)

BOX 3-9 **Malabsorption, Suspected**

Diagnostic imaging
Best test
Small-bowel series
Ancillary test
CT of pancreas with IV contrast

Lab evaluation
Best test
Biopsy of small bowel

Ancillary tests
Albumin, total protein
ALT, AST, PT
Serum lytes, BUN, creatinine
Sudan III stain of stool for fecal leukocytes
CBC, RBC folate, serum iron, serum carotene, cholesterol, serum calcium
Hydrogen 14-C xylose breath test
D-Xylose test, secretin test
Quantitative fecal test
Antigliadin antibody, IgA endomysial antibody

From Ferri FF: *Ferri's best test: a practical guide to clinical laboratory medicine and diagnostic imaging,* Philadelphia, 2004, Elsevier Mosby.
ALT, Alanine aminotransferase; *AST,* aspartate aminotransferase; *BUN,* blood urea nitrogen; *CBC,* complete blood count; *CT,* computed tomography; *IgA,* immunoglobulin A; *IV,* intravenous; *PT,* prothrombin time; *RBC,* red blood count.

MENINGITIS

ICD-9CM # 320 Bacterial meningitis
047.8 Meningitis, aseptic

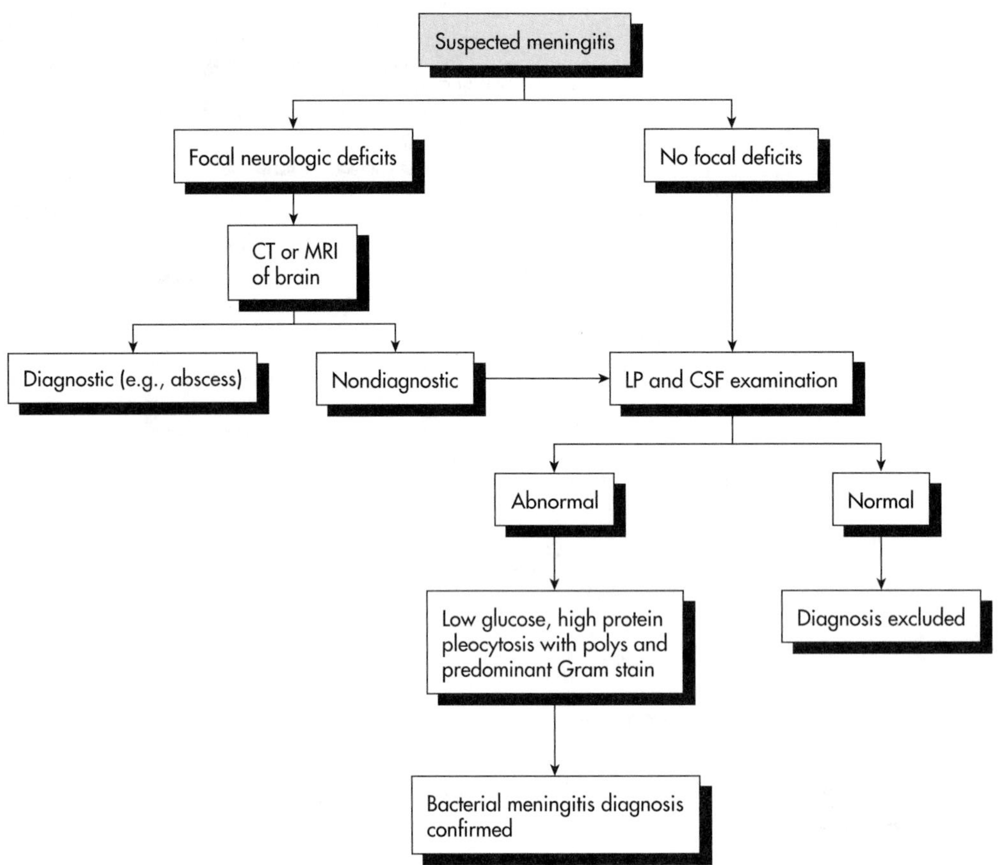

FIGURE 3-143 Meningitis. *CSF,* Cat-scratch fever; *CT,* computed tomography; *LP,* lumbar puncture.

MESOTHELIOMA

ICD-9CM # 199.1 Malignant mesothelioma, site Nos

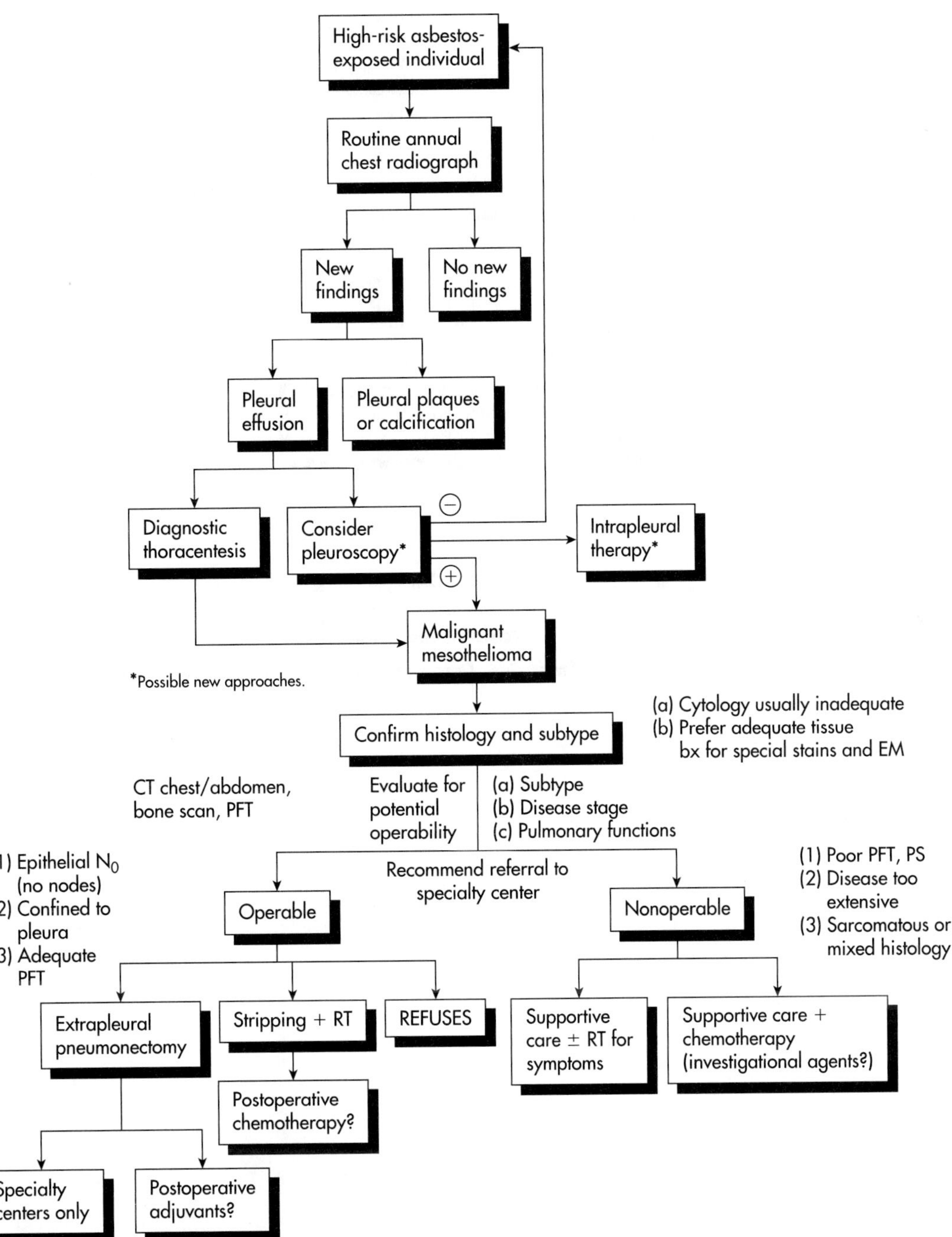

FIGURE 3-144 Evaluation and treatment of mesothelioma. *bx,* Biopsy; *CT,* computed tomography; *EM,* electron microscopy; *PFT,* pulmonary function test; *PS,* pleural sclerosis; *RT,* respiratory therapy. (From Abeloff MD: *Clinical oncology,* ed 2, New York, 2000, Churchill Livingstone.)

MULTIPLE MYELOMA

ICD-9CM # 203.0

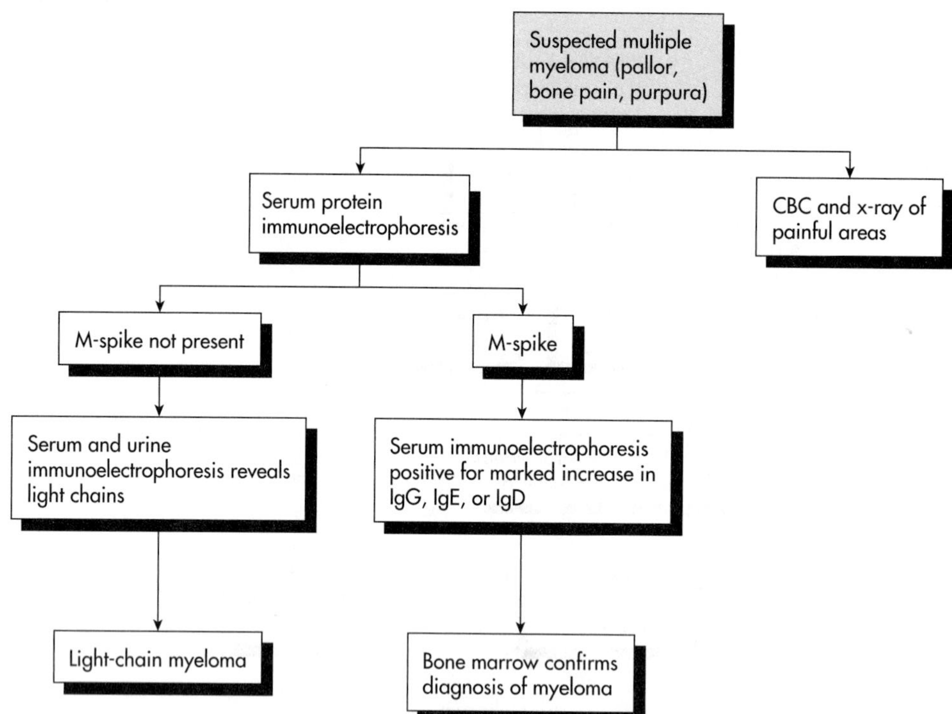

FIGURE 3-145 Multiple myeloma. *CBC,* Complete blood count; *Ig,* immunoglobulin.

MURMUR, DIASTOLIC

ICD-9CM # 785.2 Murmur heart

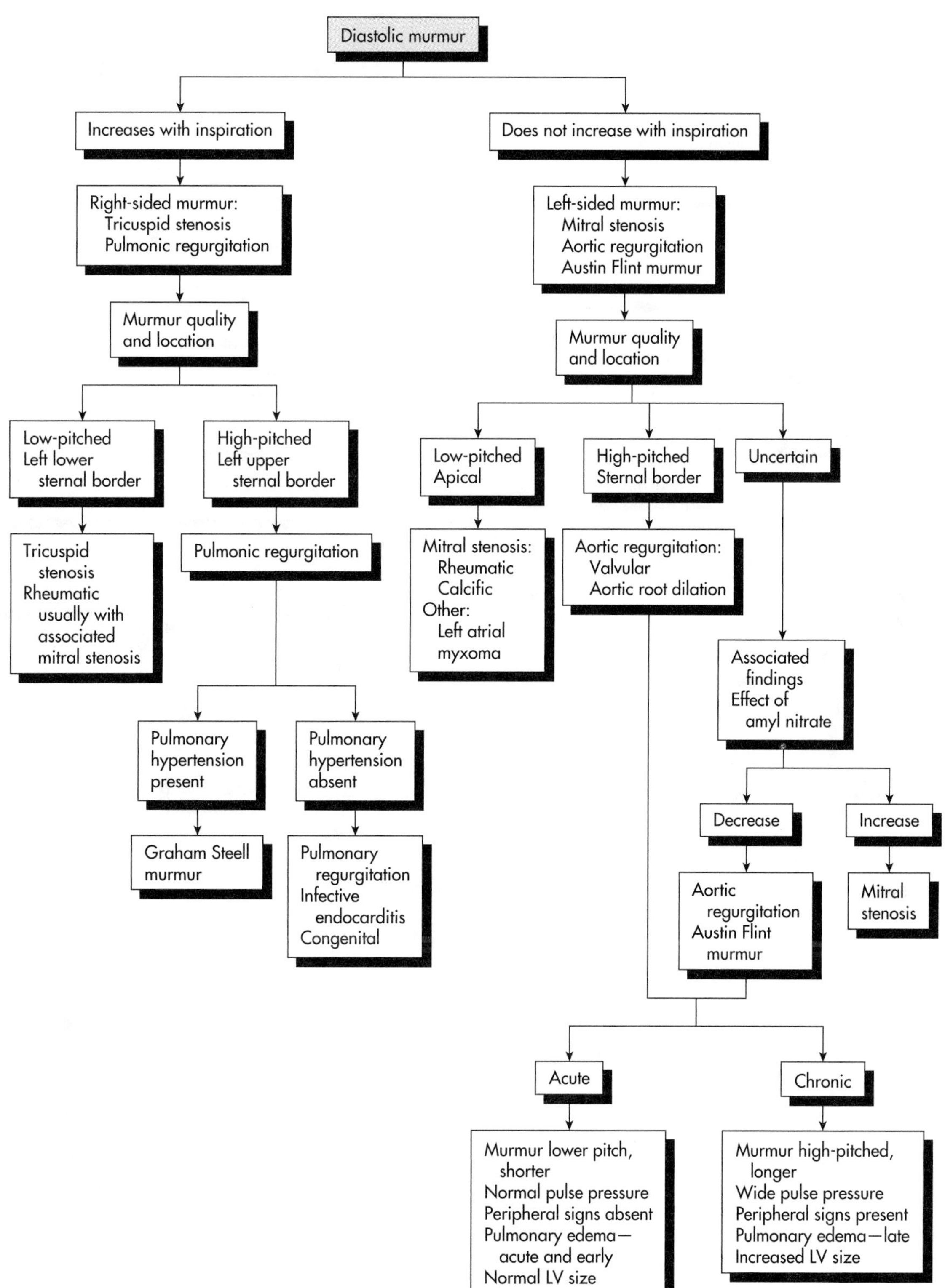

FIGURE 3-146 Diastolic murmur. *LV,* Left ventricle. (From Greene HL, Johnson WP, Lemke D [eds]: *Decision making in medicine,* ed 2, St Louis, 1998, Mosby.)

SECTION III

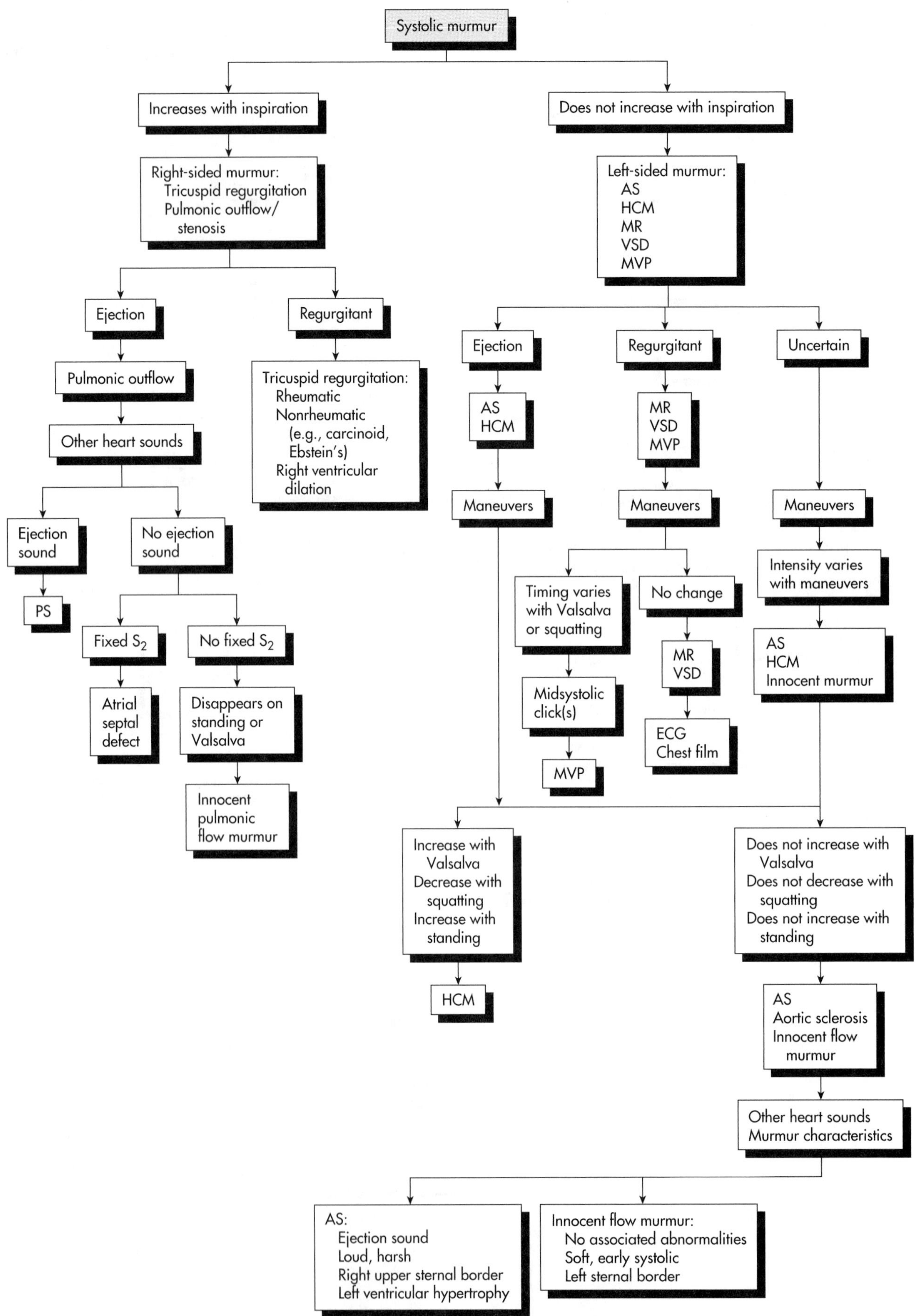

FIGURE 3-147 Systolic murmur. *AS,* Aortic stenosis; *ECG,* electrocardiogram; *HCM,* hypertrophic cardiomyopathy; *MR,* mitral regurgitation; *MVP,* mitral valve prolapse; *PS,* pulmonary stenosis; *VSD,* ventricular septal defect. (From Greene HL, Johnson WP, Lemke D [eds]: *Decision making in medicine,* ed 2, St Louis, 1998, Mosby.)

MUSCLE CRAMPS AND ACHES

ICD-9CM # 729.82

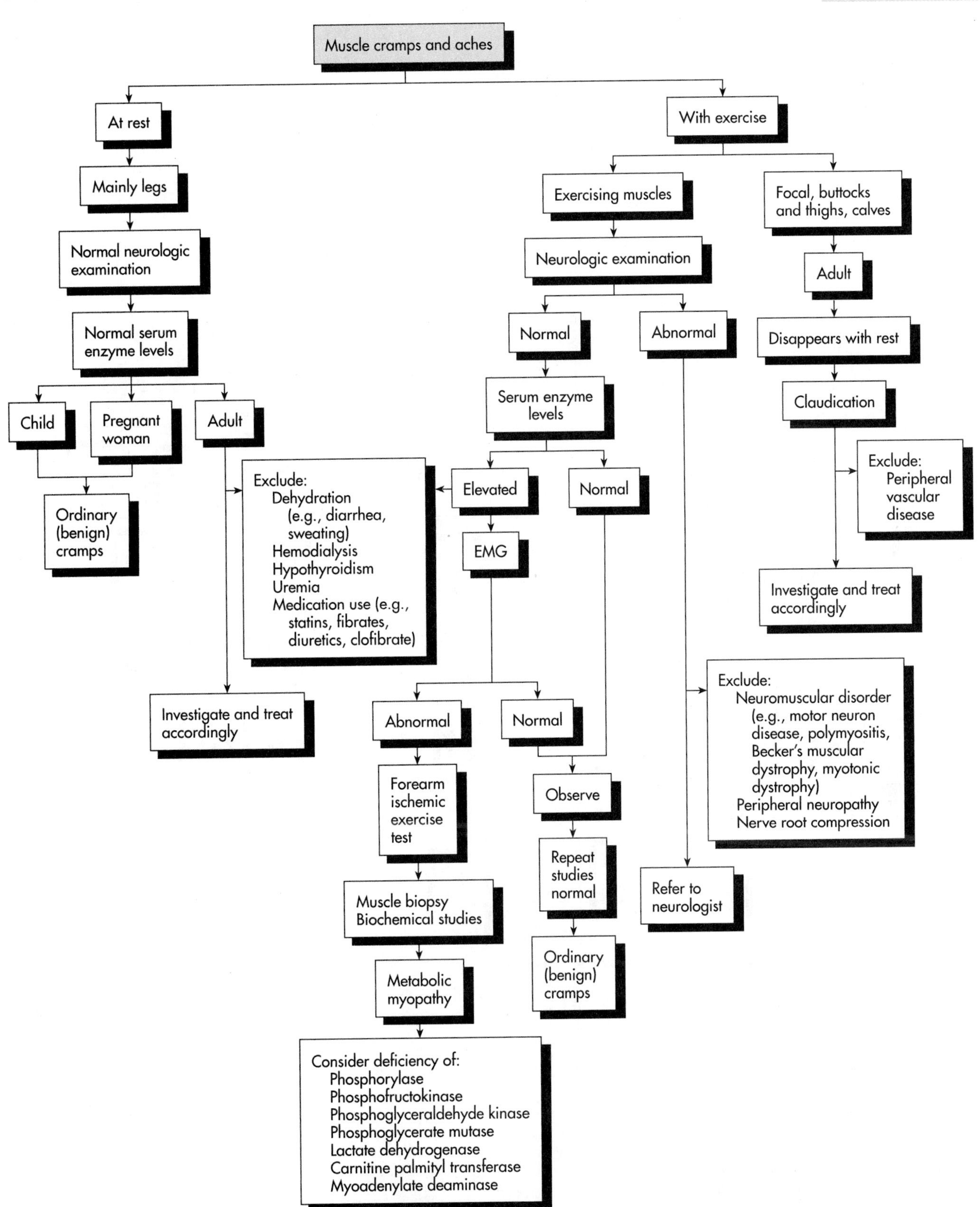

FIGURE 3-148 Evaluation of muscle cramps and aches. *EMG,* Electromyography. (From Greene HL, Johnson WP, Lemcke D [eds]: *Decision making in medicine,* ed 2, St Louis, 1998, Mosby.)

MUSCLE WEAKNESS

ICD-9CM # 782.9

- Muscle weakness
  - Perform history and physical, including neurologic exam
    - Neurologic exam abnormal
      - Neurogenic myopathy
        - Guillain-Barré syndrome
        - Porphyria
        - Myasthenia gravis
        - Eaton-Lambert syndrome
        - Amyotrophic lateral sclerosis
    - Neurologic exam normal
      - Primary myopathy
        - Check for systemic symptoms, fever
          - Systemic symptoms and fever present
            - Infection
              - Viral
                - Poliomyelitis
                - Rabies
                - Coxsackievirus
                - Influenza
                - Rubella
                - HIV (AIDS)
                - Epstein-Barr virus (EBV)
              - Bacterial
                - Staphylococcal
                - Streptococcal
                - Salmonella
                - Clostridial
                - *Mycobacterium leprae*
              - Parasitic
          - Systemic symptoms absent
            - Check serum glucose, electrolytes, Ca^{++}, Mg^{+}, phosphate, FT_4I, TSH level, and myoglobinuria
              - Tests abnormal
                - Metabolic abnormality
                  - Familial periodic paralysis
                  - Diabetes mellitus
                  - Hypo/hyperthyroidism
                  - Hypo/hyperkalemia
                  - Hypercalcemia
                  - Hypermagnesemia
                  - Hypophosphatemia
                  - Hyperparathyroidism
                  - Vitamin D deficiency
                  - Renal tubular acidosis
                  - Cushing's syndrome
                  - Rhabdomyolysis
                    - Progressive myopathy
                    - Seizures
                    - Hyperthermia
                    - Crush injury
                    - Extreme exertion
                    - Alcoholic myopathy
                  - McArdle's syndrome
                  - Familial myoglobinuria
              - Tests normal
                - Measure serum creatine kinase (CK) and aldolase
                  - CK/aldolase elevated
                    - Perform electromyography (EMG)
                      - EMG abnormal
                        - Polymyositis
                        - Dermatomyositis
                      - EMG normal
                        - Perform muscle biopsy
                          - Muscle biopsy abnormal
                            - Muscular dystrophy
                            - Sarcoidosis
                          - Muscle biopsy normal
                            - Exercise-induced
                            - Sampling error
                  - CK/aldolase normal
                    - Measure sedimentation rate (M <5 mm/hr; F <12 mm/hr)
                      - Sed rate elevated
                        - Perform electromyography (EMG)
                          - EMG abnormal
                            - Rheumatoid arthritis
                            - Systemic lupus erythematosus
                            - Polyarteritis nodosa
                            - Dermatomyositis/polymyositis
                            - Amyloidosis
                            - Sarcoidosis
                          - EMG normal
                            - Polymyalgia rheumatica (PMR)
                      - Sed rate normal
                        - Review drug history
                          - Positive drug history
                            - Corticosteroids (steroid myopathy)
                            - D-penicillamine
                            - Colchicine
                            - Chloroquine
                            - Clofibrate
                            - Cimetidine
                            - Statins
                          - Negative drug history
                            - Perform electromyography (EMG)
                              - EMG abnormal
                                - Muscular dystrophies
                                - Congenital myopathies
                                - Amyloidosis
                                - Metabolic storage disease
                                  - Adult acid maltase deficiency
                                  - Carnitine deficiency
                              - EMG normal
                                - Endogenous depressive psychosis

FIGURE 3-149 Muscle weakness. *AIDS,* Acquired immunodeficiency syndrome; *EBV,* Epstein-Barr virus; *F,* female; *HIV,* human immunodeficiency virus; *M,* male. (From Healey PM: *Common medical diagnosis: an algorithmic approach,* ed 3, Philadelphia, 2000, WB Saunders.)

MYELODYSPLASTIC SYNDROMES

ICD-9CM # 238.7

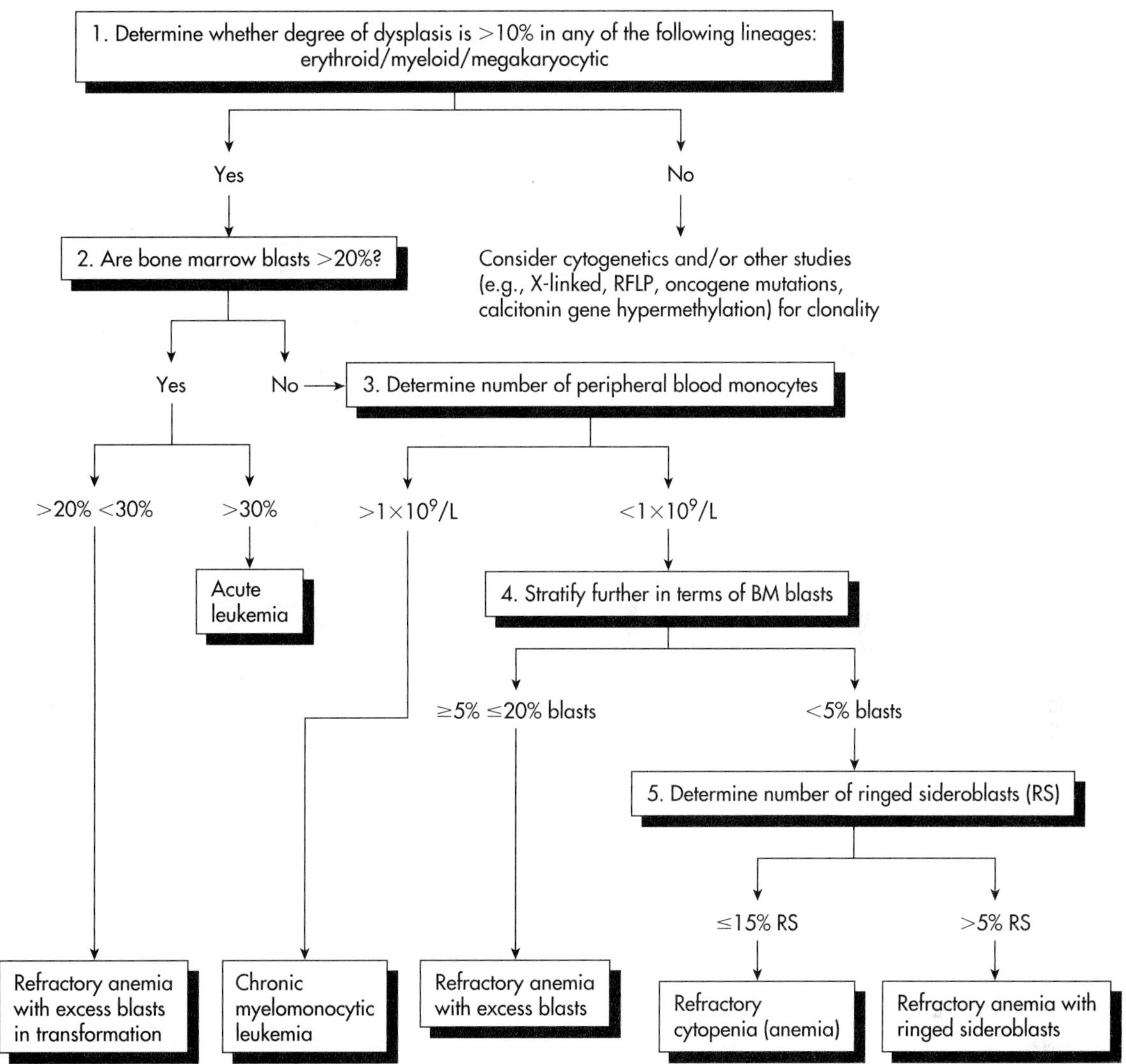

FIGURE 3-150 Myelodysplastic syndromes. *BM blasts,* Bone marrow blastocyst; *RFLP,* restriction fragment length polymorphism. (From Abeloff MD: *Clinical oncology,* ed 2, New York, 2000, Churchill Livingstone.)

SECTION III

MYOCARDIAL ISCHEMIA, SUSPECTED

ICD-9CM # 290.10 Dementia, presenile
290.0 Dementia, senile
437.0 Dementia, arteriosclerotic

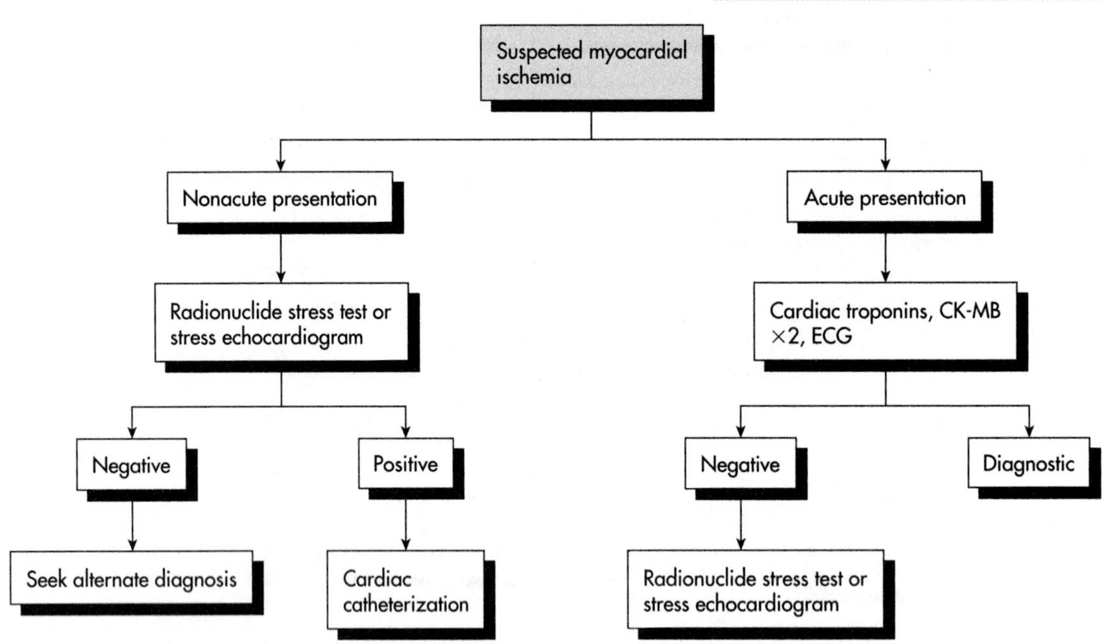

FIGURE 3-151 Myocardial ischemia, suspected. *CK-MB,* Myocardial muscle creatine kinase isoenzyme; *ECG,* electrocardiogram.

NECK MASS

ICD-9CM # 784.2

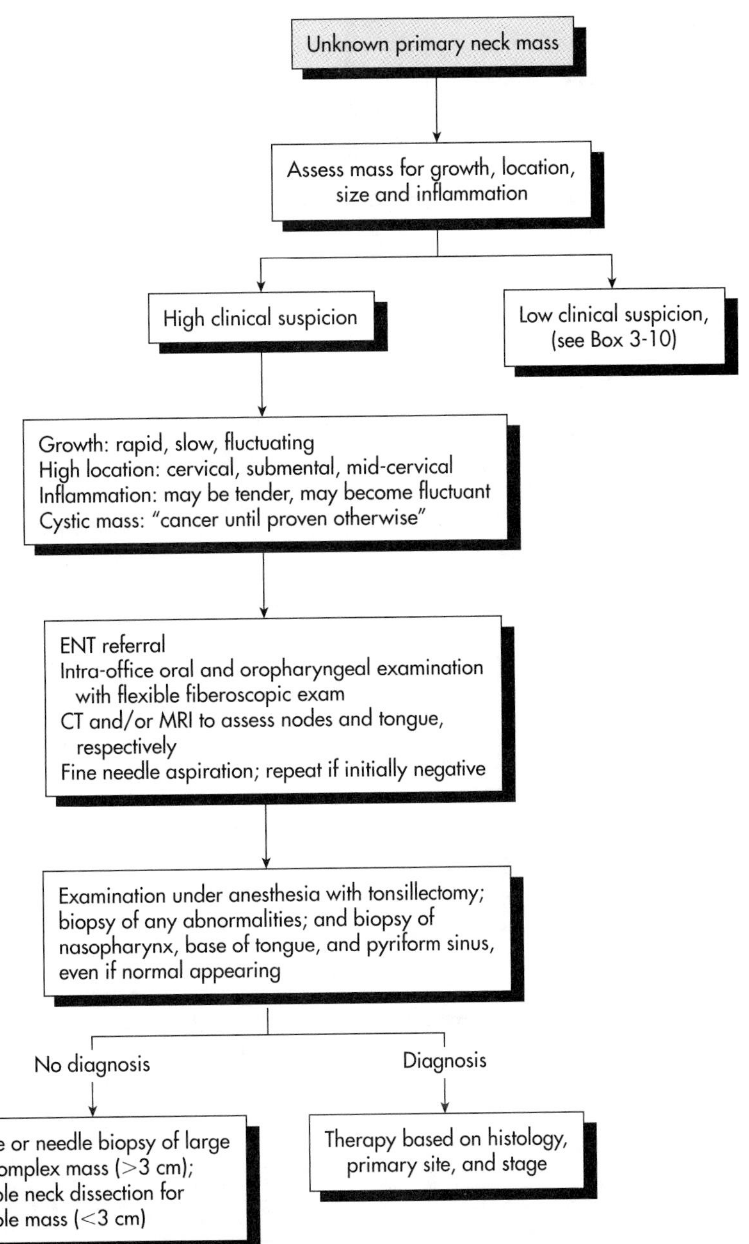

FIGURE 3-152 Evaluation of an unknown primary neck mass. *CT,* Computed tomography; *ENT,* ear, nose, and throat; *MRI,* magnetic resonance imaging. (From Goldman L, Ausiello D [eds]: *Cecil textbook of medicine,* ed 22, Philadelphia, 2004. WB Saunders.)

BOX 3-10 An Approach to the Patient with Lymphadenopathy

1. Does the patient have a known illness that causes lymphadenopathy? Treat and monitor for resolution.
2. Is there an obvious infection to explain the lymphadenopathy (e.g. infectious mononucleosis)? Treat and monitor for resolution.
3. Are the nodes very large and/or very firm and thus suggestive of malignancy? Perform a biopsy.
4. Is the patient very concerned about malignancy and unable to be reassured that malignancy is unlikely? Perform a biopsy.
5. If none of the preceding are true, perform a complete blood cell count and if it is unrevealing, monitor for a predetermined period (usually 2 to 6 weeks). If the nodes do not regress or if they increase in size, perform a biopsy.

From Goldman L, Ausiello D (eds): *Cecil textbook of medicine,* ed 22, Philadelphia, 2004, WB Saunders.

NEPHROLITHIASIS

ICD-9CM # 592.9 Urinary calculus

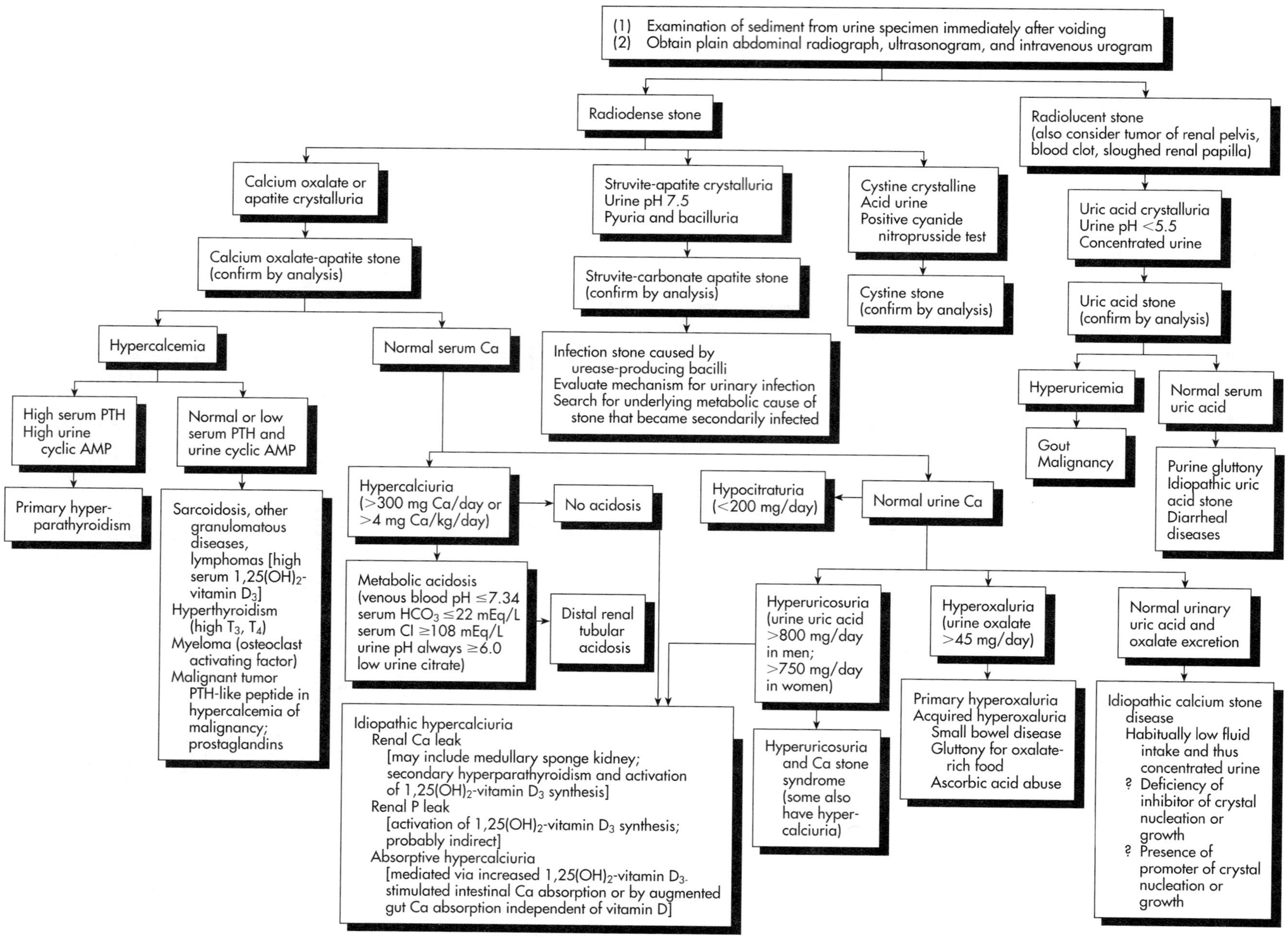

(1) Examination of sediment from urine specimen immediately after voiding
(2) Obtain plain abdominal radiograph, ultrasonogram, and intravenous urogram

Radiodense stone

Calcium oxalate or apatite crystalluria

Calcium oxalate-apatite stone (confirm by analysis)

Hypercalcemia

High serum PTH
High urine cyclic AMP

Primary hyperparathyroidism

Normal or low serum PTH and urine cyclic AMP

Sarcoidosis, other granulomatous diseases, lymphomas [high serum 1,25$(OH)_2$-vitamin D_3]
Hyperthyroidism (high T_3, T_4)
Myeloma (osteoclast activating factor)
Malignant tumor PTH-like peptide in hypercalcemia of malignancy; prostaglandins

Normal serum Ca

Hypercalciuria
(>300 mg Ca/day or >4 mg Ca/kg/day)

No acidosis

Metabolic acidosis
(venous blood pH ≤7.34
serum HCO_3 ≤22 mEq/L
serum Cl ≥108 mEq/L
urine pH always ≥6.0
low urine citrate)

Distal renal tubular acidosis

Idiopathic hypercalciuria
Renal Ca leak
[may include medullary sponge kidney; secondary hyperparathyroidism and activation of 1,25$(OH)_2$-vitamin D_3 synthesis]
Renal P leak
[activation of 1,25$(OH)_2$-vitamin D_3 synthesis; probably indirect]
Absorptive hypercalciuria
[mediated via increased 1,25$(OH)_2$-vitamin D_3-stimulated intestinal Ca absorption or by augmented gut Ca absorption independent of vitamin D]

Normal urine Ca

Hypocitraturia
(<200 mg/day)

Hyperuricosuria
(urine uric acid >800 mg/day in men; >750 mg/day in women)

Hyperuricosuria and Ca stone syndrome (some also have hypercalciuria)

Hyperoxaluria
(urine oxalate >45 mg/day)

Primary hyperoxaluria
Acquired hyperoxaluria
Small bowel disease
Gluttony for oxalate-rich food
Ascorbic acid abuse

Normal urinary uric acid and oxalate excretion

Idiopathic calcium stone disease
Habitually low fluid intake and thus concentrated urine
? Deficiency of inhibitor of crystal nucleation or growth
? Presence of promoter of crystal nucleation or growth

Struvite-apatite crystalluria
Urine pH 7.5
Pyuria and bacilluria

Struvite-carbonate apatite stone (confirm by analysis)

Infection stone caused by urease-producing bacilli
Evaluate mechanism for urinary infection
Search for underlying metabolic cause of stone that became secondarily infected

Cystine crystalline
Acid urine
Positive cyanide nitroprusside test

Cystine stone (confirm by analysis)

Radiolucent stone
(also consider tumor of renal pelvis, blood clot, sloughed renal papilla)

Uric acid crystalluria
Urine pH <5.5
Concentrated urine

Uric acid stone (confirm by analysis)

Hyperuricemia

Gout
Malignancy

Normal serum uric acid

Purine gluttony
Idiopathic uric acid stone
Diarrheal diseases

FIGURE 3-153 Evaluation of patients with suspected nephrolithiasis (flank pain, ureteral colic, hematuria, fever). *AMP,* Adenosine monophosphate; *PTH,* parathyroid hormone. (From Stein JH [ed]; *Internal medicine,* ed 5, St Louis, 1998, Mosby.)

NEUROPATHIC PAIN

ICD-9CM # 729.2

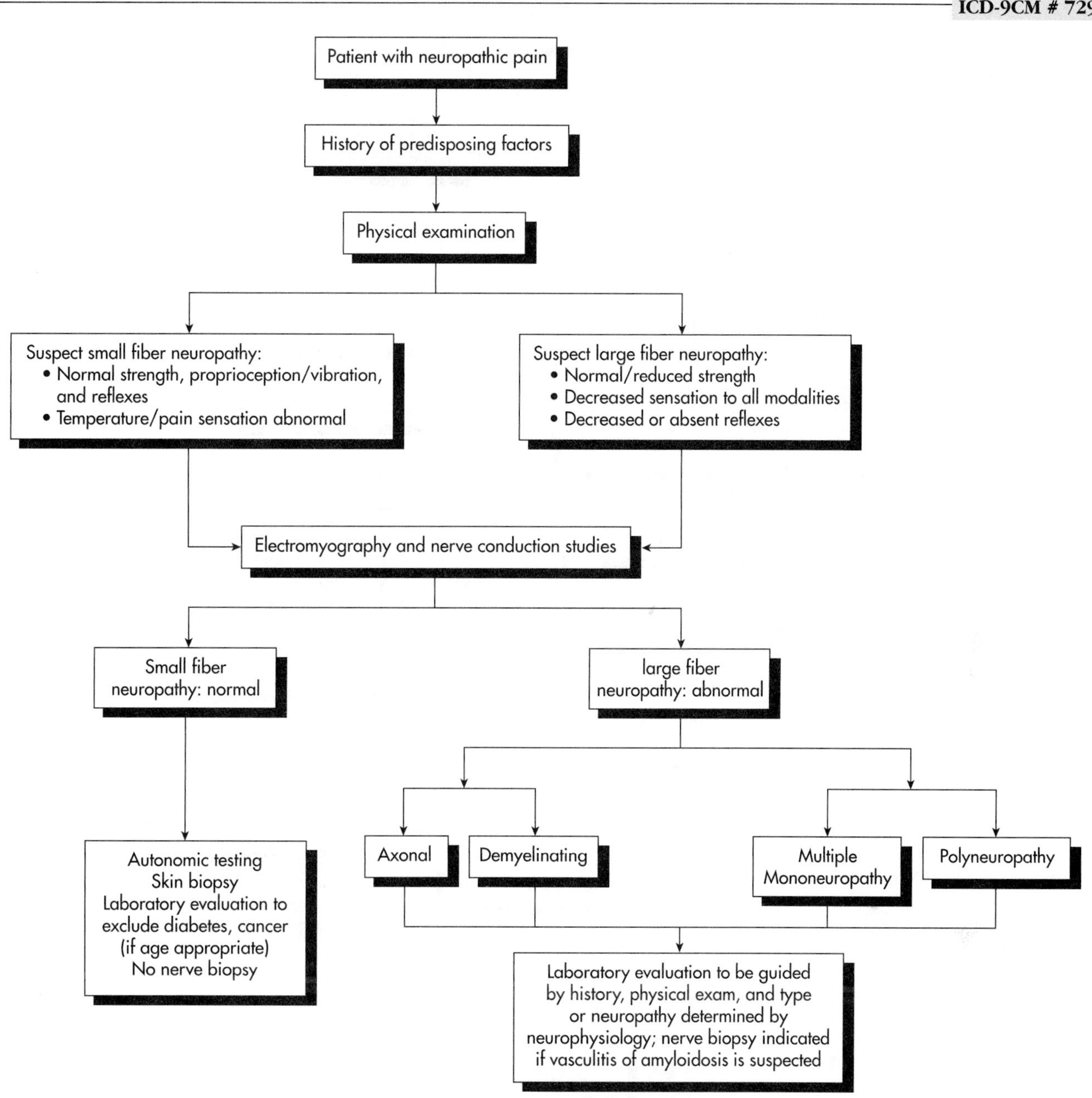

FIGURE 3-154 Neuropathic pain.

NEUTROPENIA

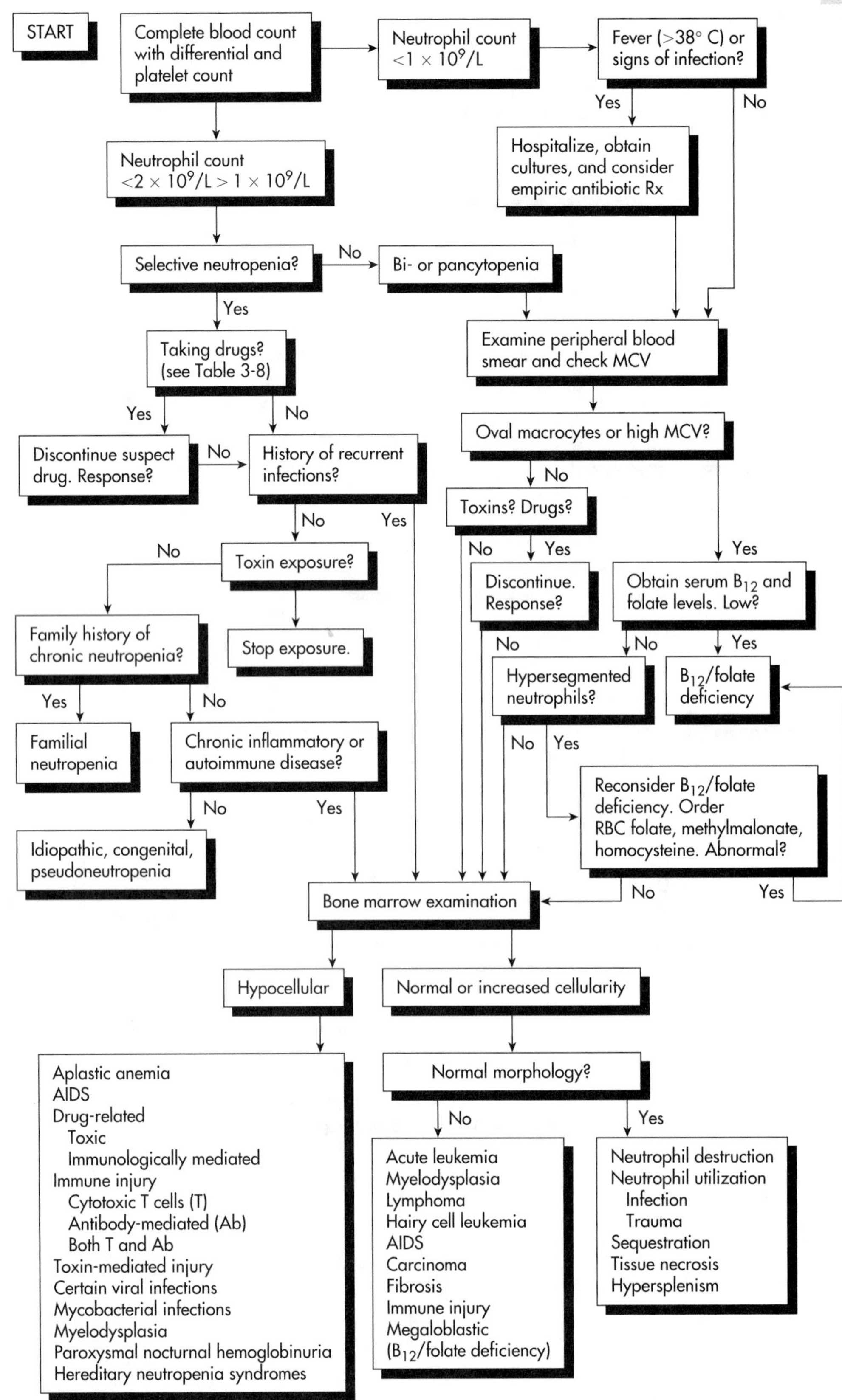

FIGURE 3-155 A practical algorithm for the evaluation of patients with neutropenia. The fundamental diagnostic principle is that for patients with severe neutropenia or for those with bicytopenia or pancytopenia, bone marrow examination will likely be necessary unless the following diagnoses are made: (1) a nutritional (folate or vitamin B_{12}) deficiency or (2) drug- or toxin-induced neutropenia in a patient whose neutropenia resolves after discontinuation of the offending agent. *AIDS,* Acquired immunodeficiency syndrome; *MCV,* mean corpuscular volume; *RBC,* red blood cell. (From Goldman L, Ausiello D [eds]: *Cecil textbook of medicine,* ed 22, Philadelphia, 2004, WB Saunders.)

NUTRITIONAL SUPPORT

ICD-9CM # 269.9

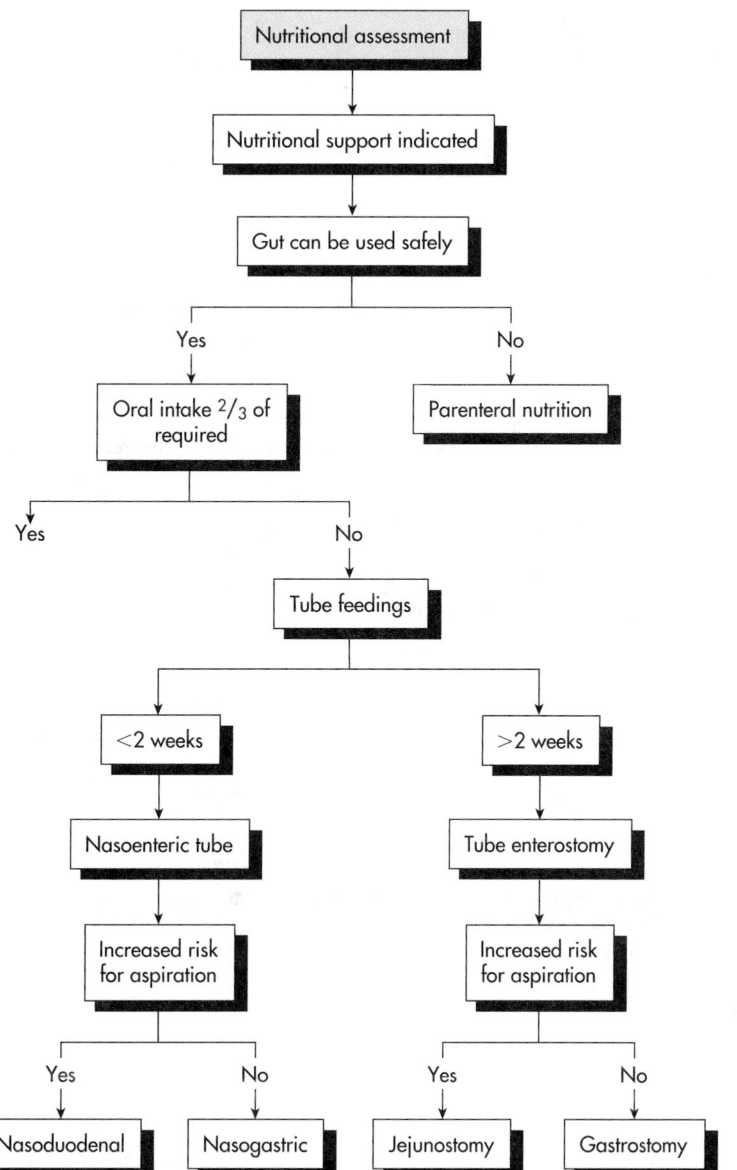

FIGURE 3-156 Decision approach for the type and route of nutritional support. (From Goldman L, Ausiello D [eds]: *Cecil textbook of medicine,* ed 22, Philadelphia, 2004, WB Saunders.)

BOX 3-11 **Indications for the Use of Enteral Nutrition in Adult Medical Patients**
Protein-energy malnutrition with anticipated significantly decreased oral intake for at least 7 days Anticipated significantly decreased oral intake for 10 days Severe dysphagia Massive small bowel resection (used in combination with total parenteral nutrition) Low-output (<500 mL/day) enterocutaneous fistula

From Goldman L, Ausiello D (eds): *Cecil textbook of medicine,* ed 22, Philadelphia, 2004, WB Saunders.

OCCUPATIONAL INTERSTITIAL LUNG DISEASE

ICD-9CM # 515

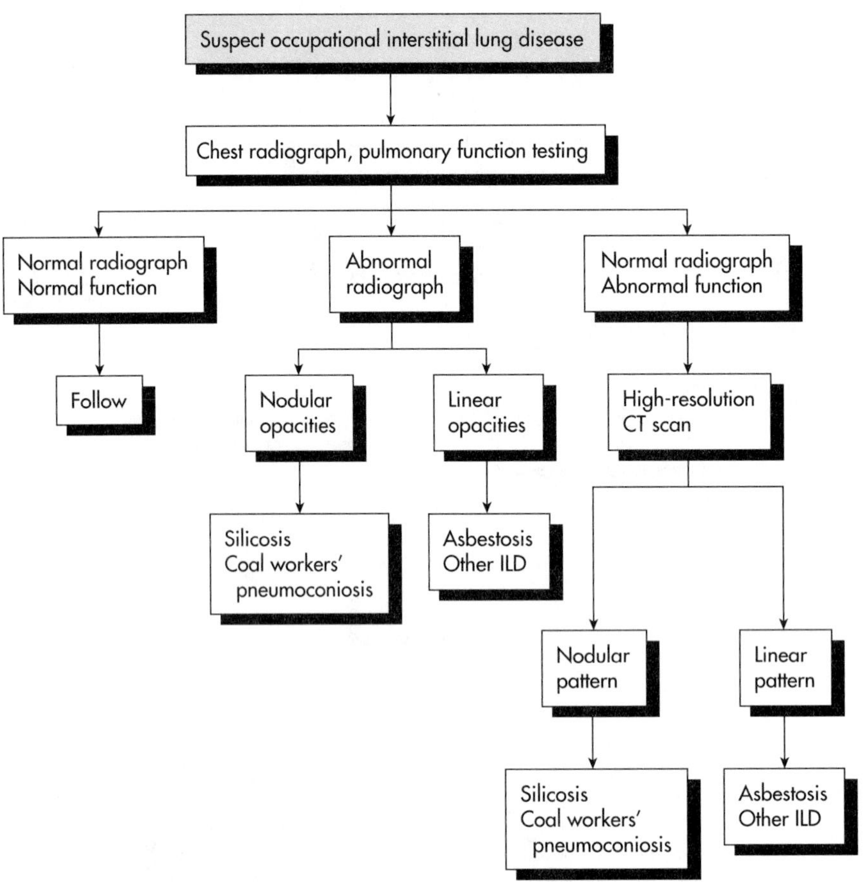

FIGURE 3-157 Diagnostic approach to occupational interstitial lung disease (ILD). *CT,* Computed tomography. (From Goldman L, Ausiello D [eds]): *Cecil textbook of medicine,* ed 22, Philadelphia, 2004, WB Saunders.)

OLIGURIA

ICD-9CM # 788.5

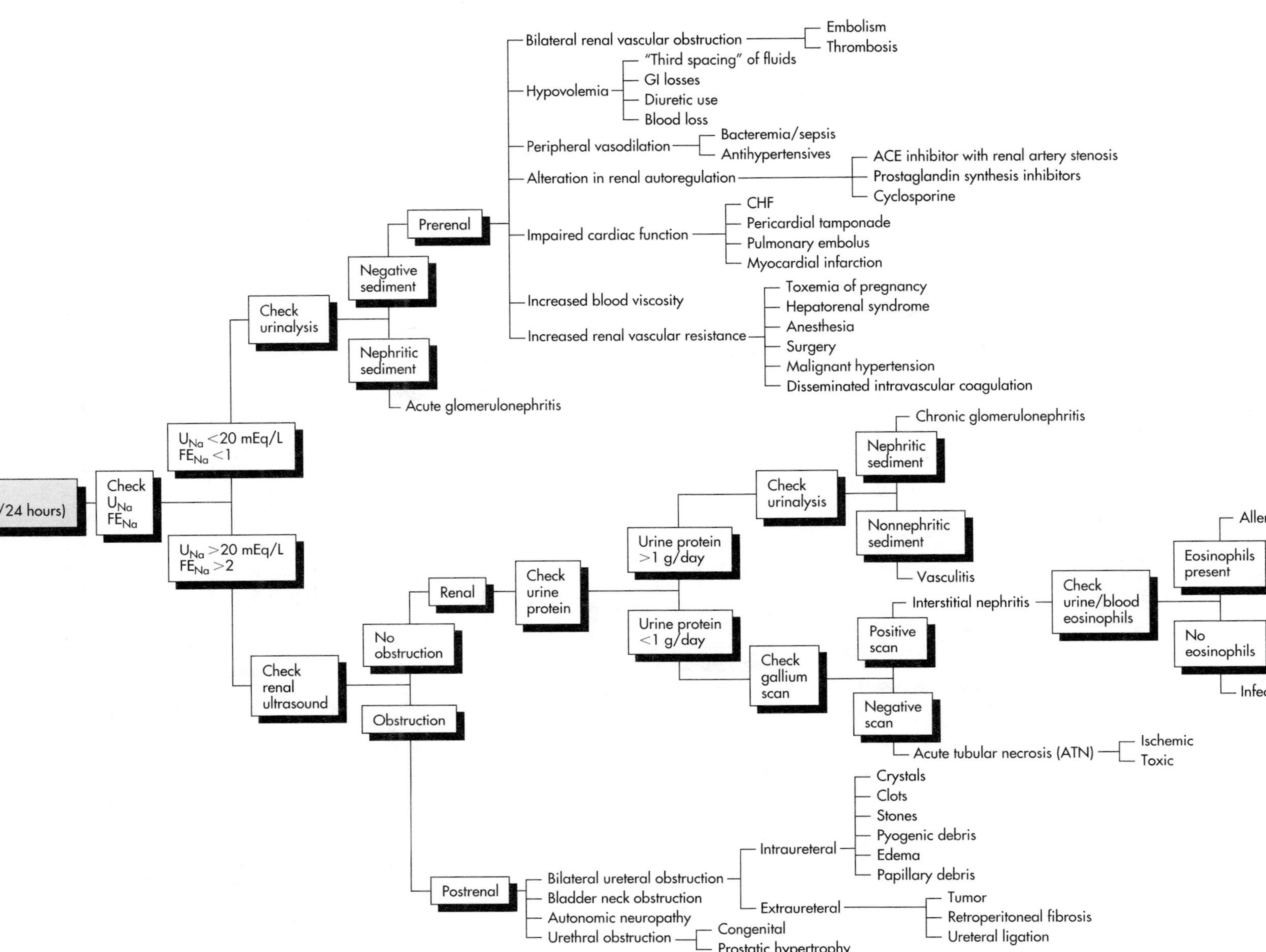

FIGURE 3-158 Evaluation of oliguria. *ACE,* Angiotensin-converting enzyme; *CHF,* congestive heart failure; *GI,* gastrointestinal. (From Healey PM: *Common medical diagnosis: an algorithmic approach,* ed 3, Philadelphia, 2000, WB Saunders.)

PAIN CONTROL

ICD-9CM # not available

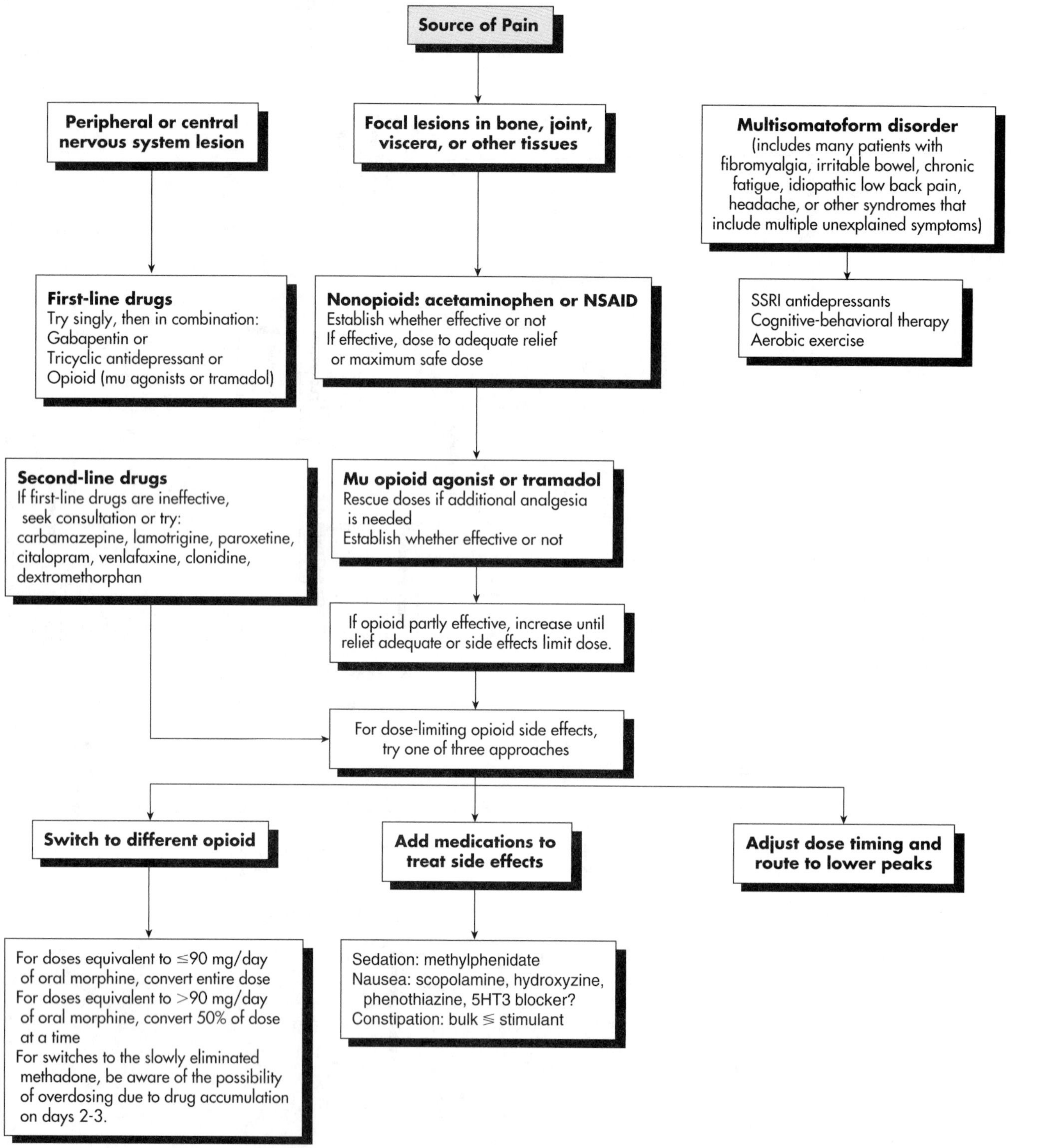

Source of Pain

Peripheral or central nervous system lesion

Focal lesions in bone, joint, viscera, or other tissues

Multisomatoform disorder
(includes many patients with fibromyalgia, irritable bowel, chronic fatigue, idiopathic low back pain, headache, or other syndromes that include multiple unexplained symptoms)

First-line drugs
Try singly, then in combination:
Gabapentin or
Tricyclic antidepressant or
Opioid (mu agonists or tramadol)

Nonopioid: acetaminophen or NSAID
Establish whether effective or not
If effective, dose to adequate relief or maximum safe dose

SSRI antidepressants
Cognitive-behavioral therapy
Aerobic exercise

Second-line drugs
If first-line drugs are ineffective, seek consultation or try:
carbamazepine, lamotrigine, paroxetine, citalopram, venlafaxine, clonidine, dextromethorphan

Mu opioid agonist or tramadol
Rescue doses if additional analgesia is needed
Establish whether effective or not

If opioid partly effective, increase until relief adequate or side effects limit dose.

For dose-limiting opioid side effects, try one of three approaches

Switch to different opioid

Add medications to treat side effects

Adjust dose timing and route to lower peaks

For doses equivalent to ≤90 mg/day of oral morphine, convert entire dose
For doses equivalent to >90 mg/day of oral morphine, convert 50% of dose at a time
For switches to the slowly eliminated methadone, be aware of the possibility of overdosing due to drug accumulation on days 2-3.

Sedation: methylphenidate
Nausea: scopolamine, hydroxyzine, phenothiazine, 5HT3 blocker?
Constipation: bulk ≤ stimulant

FIGURE 3-159 Algorithm for the treatment of pain. *COX,* Cyclooxygenese; *NSAID,* nonsteroidal anti-inflammatory drug; *SSRI,* selective serotonin reuptake inhibitor. (From Goldman L, Ausiello D [eds]: *Cecil textbook of medicine,* ed 22, Philadelphia, 2004, WB Saunders.)

PANCREATIC ISLET CELL TUMORS

ICD-9CM # 211.7

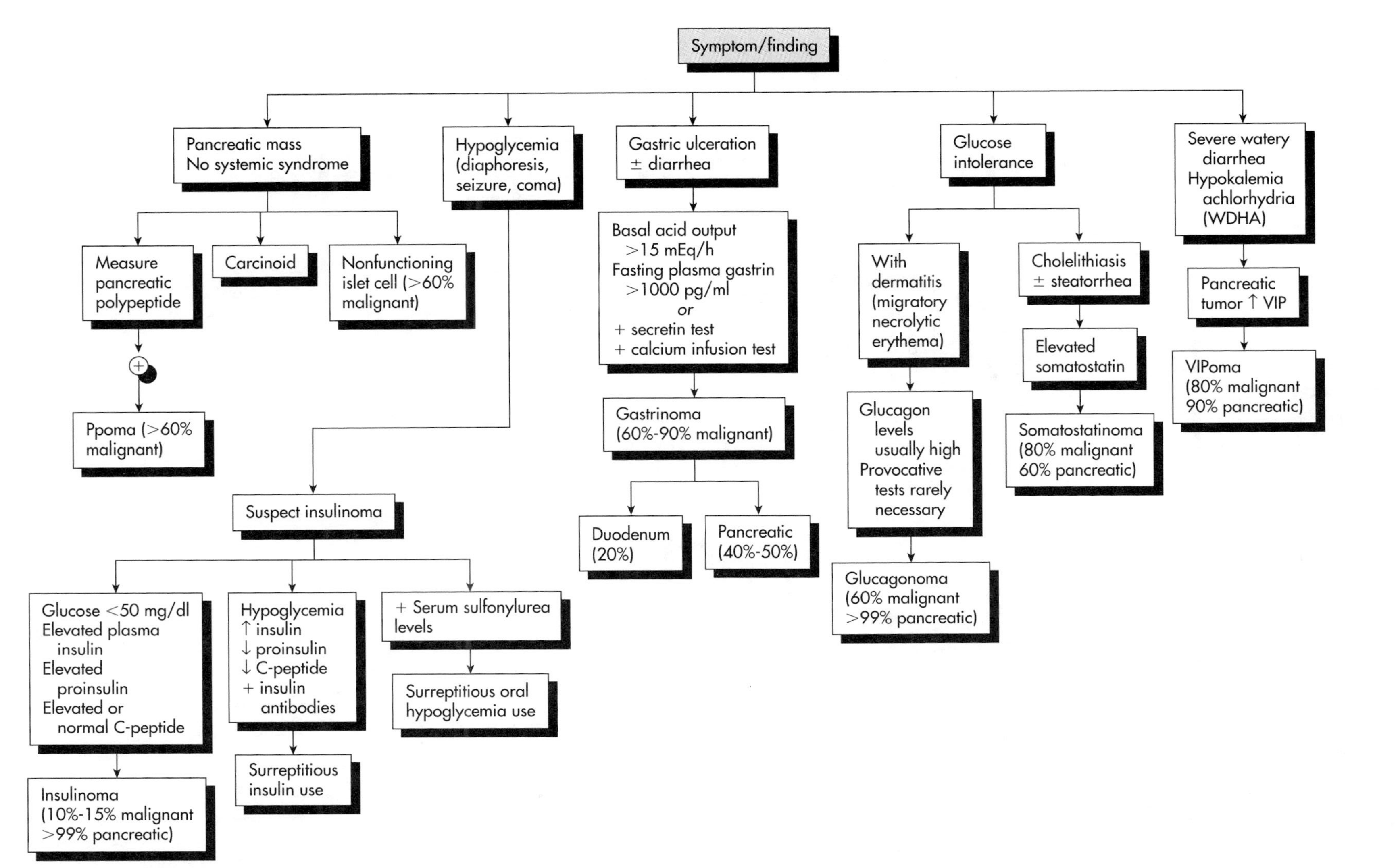

FIGURE 3-160 Diagnosis of pancreatic islet cell tumors. *Ppoma,* Islet cell tumor secreting pancreatic polypeptide; *VIP,* vasoactive intestinal peptide; *VIPoma,* islet cell tumor secreting vasoactive intestinal peptide. (From Abeloff MD: *Clinical oncology,* ed 2, New York, 2000, Churchill Livingston.)

PANCREATIC MASS

ICD-9CM # 789.36

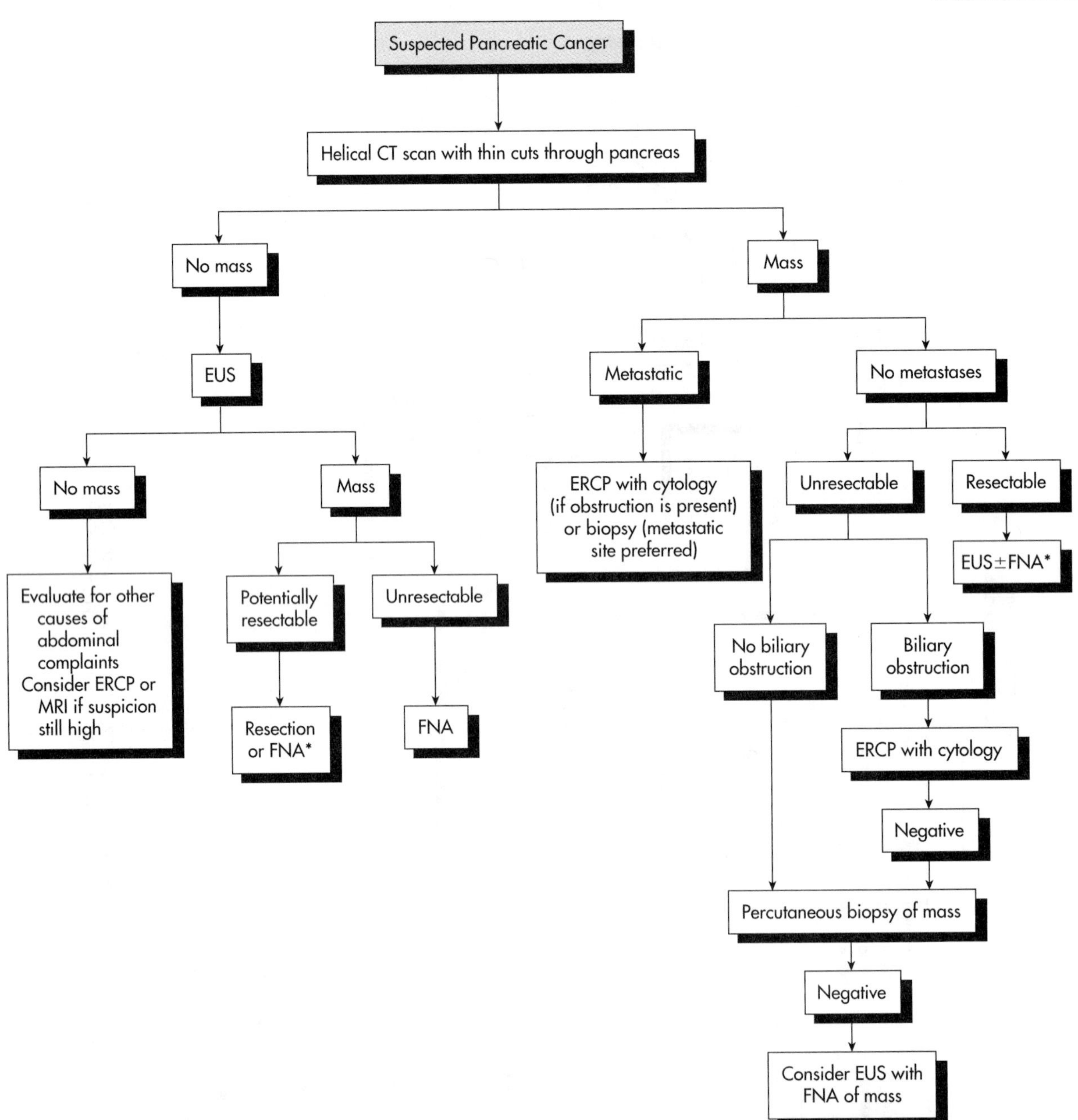

FIGURE 3-161 Diagnostic algorithm for pancreatic cancer. Intraoperative fine-needle aspiration (FNA) if found inoperable during surgery. *CT,* Computed tomographic scan; *ERCP,* endoscopic retrograde cholangiopancreatography; *EUS,* endoscopic ultrasonography; *MRI,* magnetic resonance imaging. (From Goldman L, Ausiello D [eds]: *Cecil textbook of medicine,* ed 22, Philadelphia, 2004, WB Saunders.)

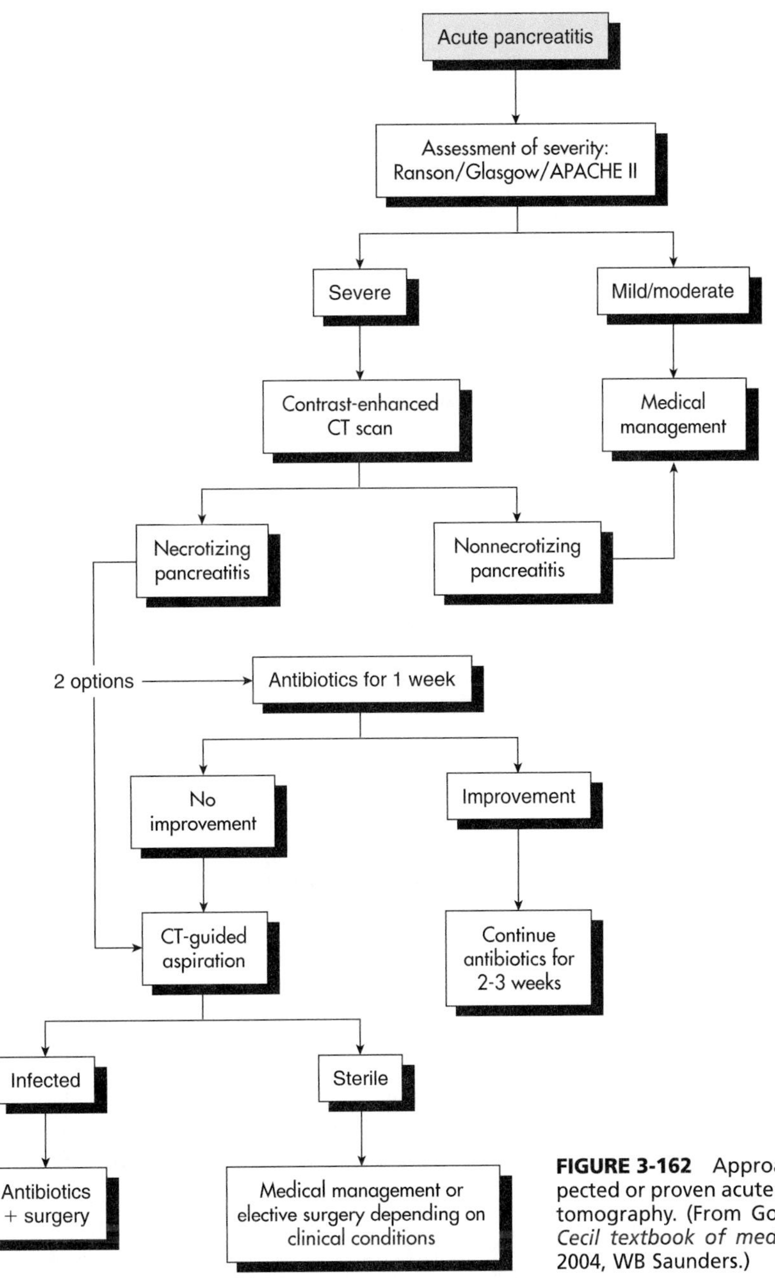

FIGURE 3-162 Approach to the patient with suspected or proven acute pancreatitis. *CT,* Computed tomography. (From Goldman L, Ausiello D [eds]: *Cecil textbook of medicine,* ed 22, Philadelphia, 2004, WB Saunders.)

SECTION III

TABLE 3-6 **Prognostic Criteria for Acute Pancreatitis**

Ranson Criteria*	Simplified Glasgow Criteria†	Computed Tomography Criteria‡
On admission	Within 48 hr of admission	Normal
Age >55 yr	Age >55 yr	Enlargement
WBC >16,000/μL	WBC >15,000/μL	Pancreatic inflammation
AST >250 U/L	LDH >600 U/L	Single fluid collection
LDH >350 U/L	Glucose >180 mg/dL	Multiple fluid collection
Glucose >200 mg/dL	Albumin <3.2 g/dL	
48 hr after admission	Ca^{2+} <8 mg/dL	
hematocrit	Arterial Po_2 <60 mm Hg	
decrease by >10%	BUN >45 mg/dL	
BUN increase by >5 mg/dL		
Ca^{2+} <8 mg/dL		
Arterial Po_2 <60 mm Hg		
Base deficit >4 mEq/L		
Fluid sequestration >6 L		

From Goldman L, Ausiello D (eds): *Cecil textbook of medicine,* ed 22, Philadelphia, 2004, WB Saunders.

AST, Aspartate aminotransferase; *BUN,* blood urea nitrogen; *LDH,* lactate dehydrogenase; *WBC,* white blood cells.

*Three or more Ranson's criteria predict a complicated clinical course. Data from Ranson JH, Rifkind KM, Turner JW: Prognostic signs and nonoperative peritoneal lavage in acute pancreatitis. Surg Gynecol Obstet 1976:143:209-219.

†Data from Blamey SL et al: Prognostic factors in acute pancreatitis, *Gut* 25:1340, 1984.

‡Grades A and B represent mild disease with no risk of infection or death. Grade C represents moderately severe disease with a minimal likelihood of infection and essentially no risk of mortality. Grades D and E represent severe pancreatitis with an infection rate of 30 to 50% and mortality rate of 15%. Data from Balthazar EJ et al: Acute pancreatitis value of CT in establishing prognosis, *Radiology* 174:331, 1990.

PANCREATITIS, CHRONIC

ICD-9CM # 577.1

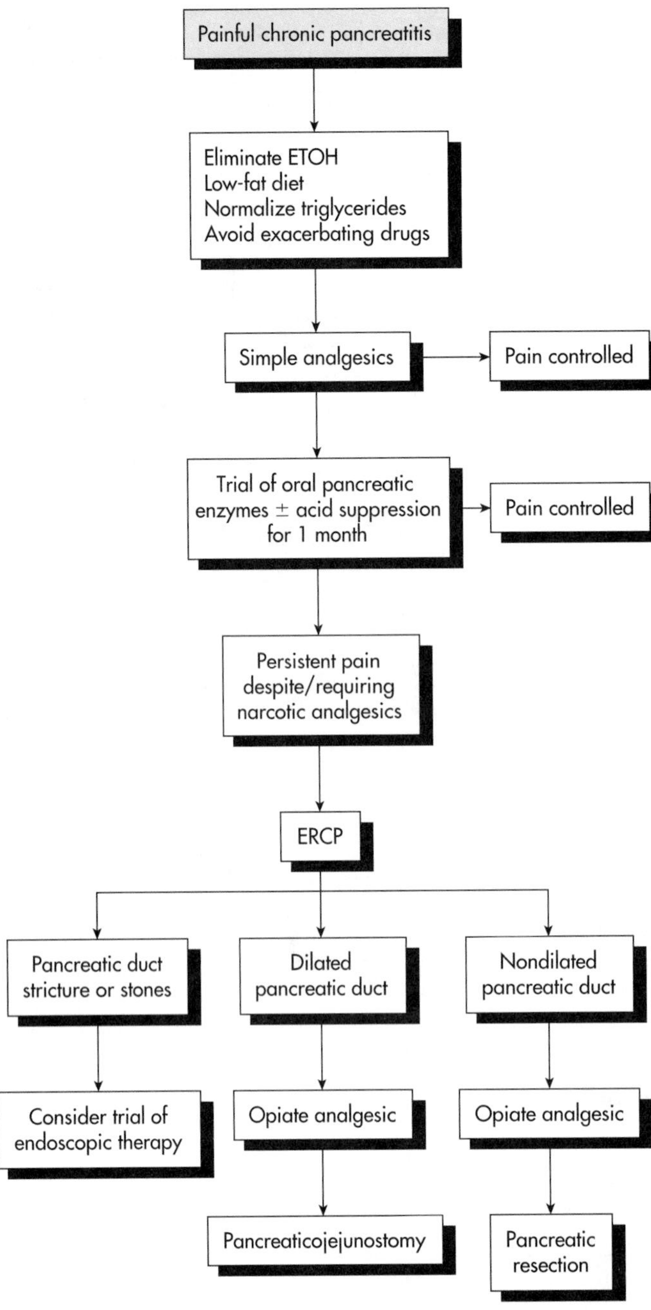

FIGURE 3-163 Approach to the patient with painful chronic pancreatitis. *ERCP,* Endoscopic retrograde cholangiopancreatography; *ETOH,* alcohol. (From Goldman L, Ausiello D [eds]: *Cecil textbook of medicine,* ed 22, Philadelphia, 2004, WB Saunders.)

PARKINSON'S DISEASE

ICD-9CM # 332.0 Idiopathic Parkinson's disease
332.1 Parkinson's disease, secondary

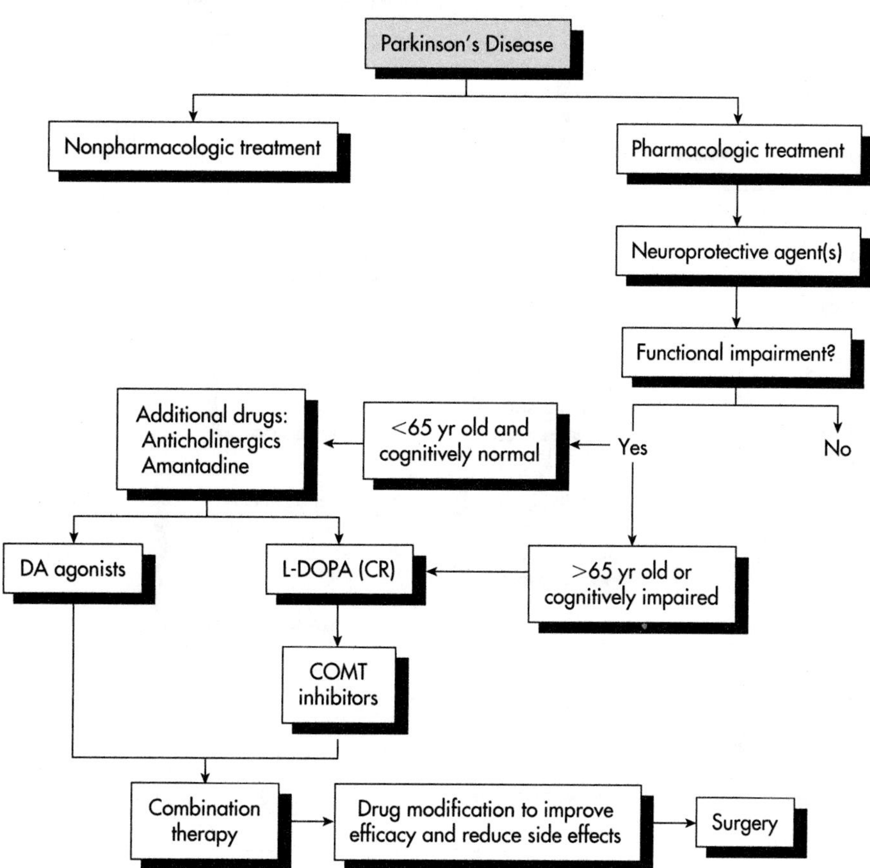

FIGURE 3-164 Diagrammatic representation of a therapeutic approach to patients with parkinsonism. *COMT,* Catechol-O-methyl transferase; *CR,* controlled release; *DA,* dopamine. (From Goldman L, Ausiello D [eds]: *Cecil textbook of medicine,* ed 22, Philadelphia, 2004, WB Saunders.)

ICD-9CM # 301.9 Personality disorder NOS
301.51 Munchausen syndrome

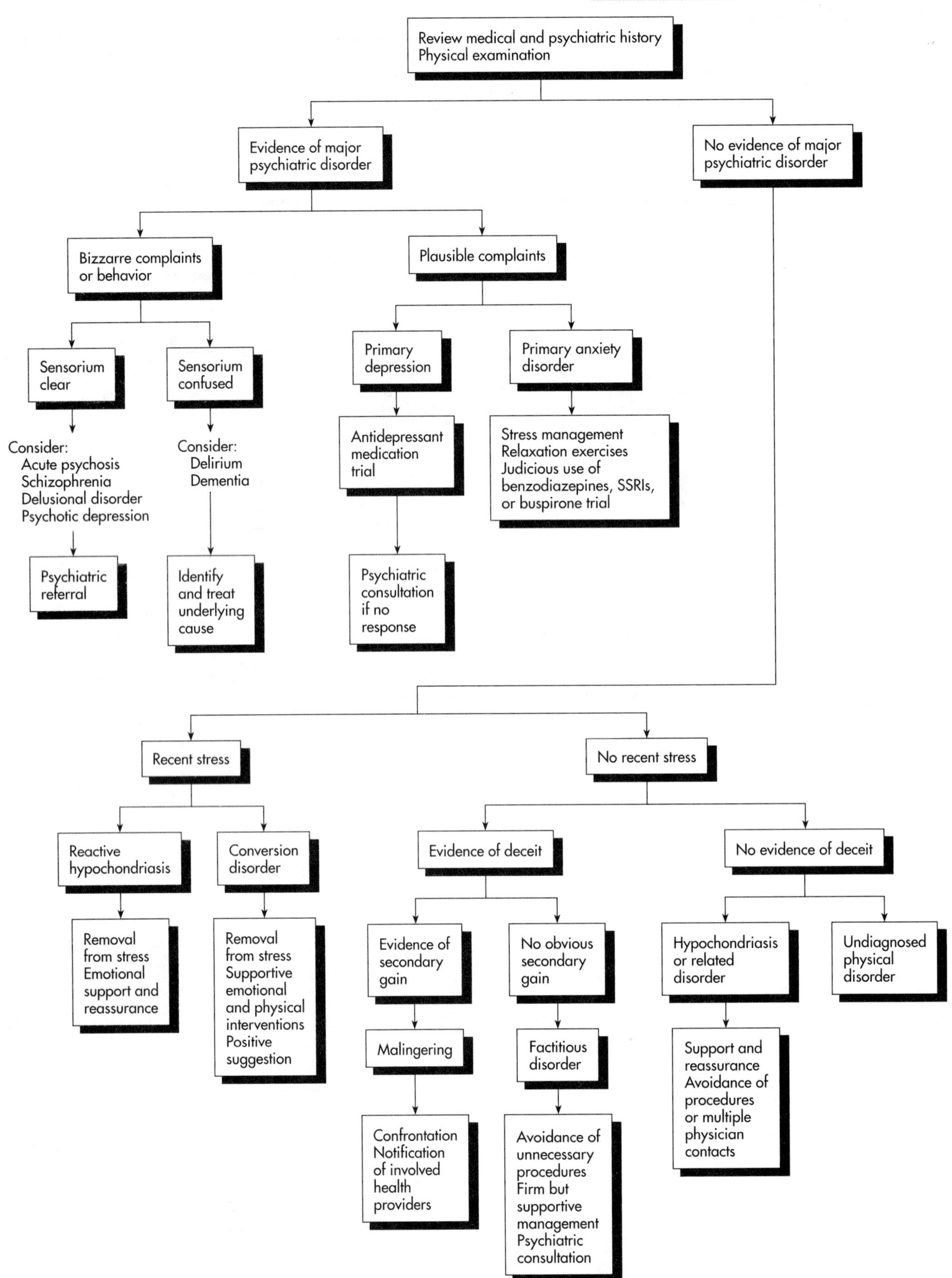

FIGURE 3-165 Patient with ill-defined physical complaints. Previous or recent evaluations are noncontributory. *SSRIs,* Selective serotonin reuptake inhibitors. (From Greene H, Johnson WP, Lemcke D [eds]: *Decision making in medicine,* ed 2, St Louis, 1998, Mosby.)

PELVIC MASS

ICD-9CM # 789.39

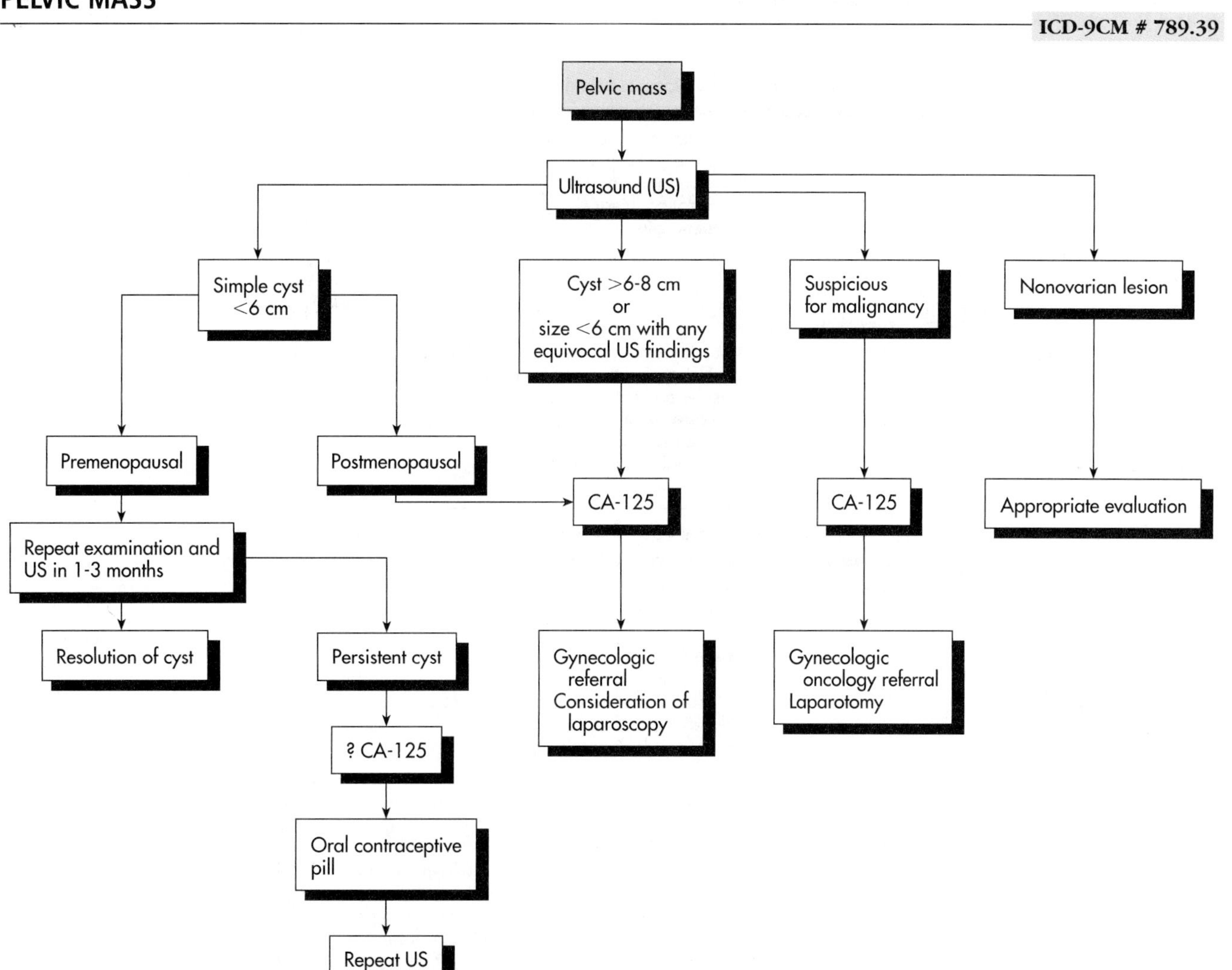

FIGURE 3-166 Approach to the patient with a pelvic mass. *US,* Ultrasound. (From Carlson KJ et al: *Primary care of women,* ed 2, St Louis, 2002, Mosby.)

PELVIC PAIN, REPRODUCTIVE-AGE WOMAN

ICD-9CM # 625.9

1. Rapid history and external abdominal examination

- **If surgical abdomen**: consider early ob/gyn/surgery consultation
  - Rupture (ectopic, cyst, abscess)
  - Torsion (adnexal, fibroid)
  - Perforation (uterine)
  - Appendicitis

2. Vital signs

- **If unstable**: Establish venous access and administer fluid bolus
  Spin Hct, type and crossmatch blood as needed
  Consider early ob/gyn/surgery consult without ultrasound
  - Rupture (ectopic, cyst)
  - Septic (abortion, abscess)
  - Placental (previa, abruptio)

3. Complete history and physical examination, and perform pelvic examination

- **If obvious abortion**: consult obstetrician and consider ultrasound
  - Abortion (incomplete, septic)
- **If late pregnancy**: forego pelvic exam
  Check for fetal heart tones
  Consider ultrasound followed by ob/gyn consultation
  - Placenta previa or abruptio
  - Premature labor contractions

4. Laboratory diagnostic workup (pregnancy test, CBC, UA/micro)

- **If pregnant**: consider ultrasound followed by ob/gyn consultation
  - R/I viable intrauterine gestation
  - R/O ectopic pregnancy, abortion, placental problems
  - R/O free intraperitoneal fluid, abscess formation
- **If not pregnant**: consider ultrasound and ob/gyn/surgery consultation
  - R/O gynecologic surgical problems
  - Ovarian cyst rupture, hemorrhage
  - Tubo-ovarian abscess rupture
  - Adnexal or fibroid torsion
  - Uterine perforation

  - Consider nonsurgical gynecologic problems
  - PID, pelvic adhesions, endometriosis, neoplasm, menstrual

  - R/O general surgery problems
  - Appendicitis and complications
  - Other, GI, GU, vascular, orthopedic surgery problems

  - Consider nonsurgical nongynecologic problems
  - Systemic illnesses

FIGURE 3-167 Evaluation and management of reproductive-age women with acute pelvic pain. *CBC,* Complete blood count; *GI,* gastrointestinal; *GU,* genitourinary; *Hct,* hematocrit; *PID,* pelvic inflammatory disease; *UA/micro,* urinalysis with microscopy. (From Marx JA (ed): *Rosen's emergency medicine,* ed 5, St Louis, 2002, Mosby.)

PERIPHERAL NEUROPATHY

ICD-9CM # 356.9 Peripheral nerve neuropathy
355.10 Lower extremity neuropathy
354.11 Upper extremity neuropathy

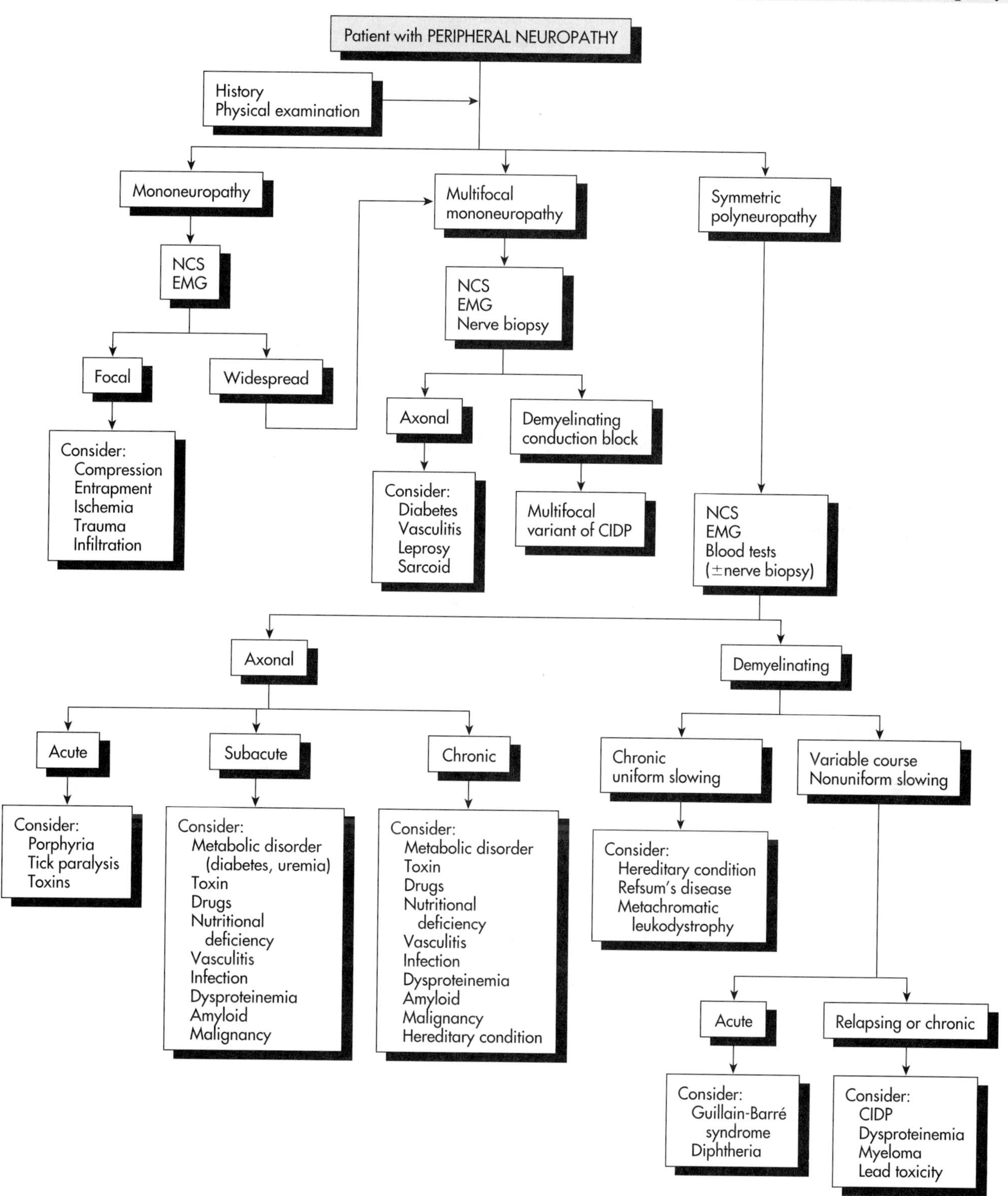

FIGURE 3-168 Approach to the patient with peripheral neuropathy. *CIDP,* Chronic inflammatory demyelinating polyradioneuropathy; *EMG,* electromyogram; *NCS,* nerve conduction studies. (From Greene HL, Johnson WP, Lemcke DL: *Decision making in medicine,* ed 2, St Louis, 1988, Mosby.)

SECTION III

PHEOCHROMOCYTOMA

ICD-9CM # 194.0

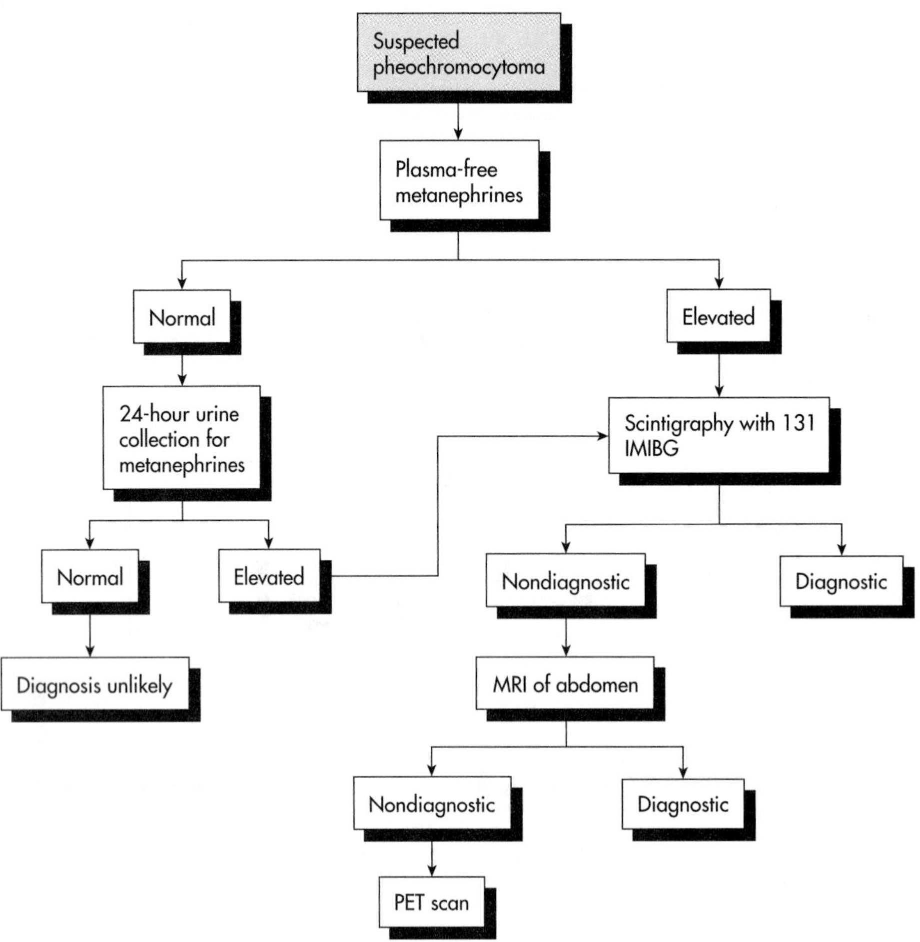

FIGURE 3-169 Pheochromocytoma. *IMIBG,* Iodine metaiodobenzyl guanidine; *MRI,* magnetic resonance imaging; *PET,* positron emission tomography.

PITUITARY TUMOR

ICD-9CM # 253 Pituitary adenoma
253.0 Acromegaly
253.1 Prolactinoma

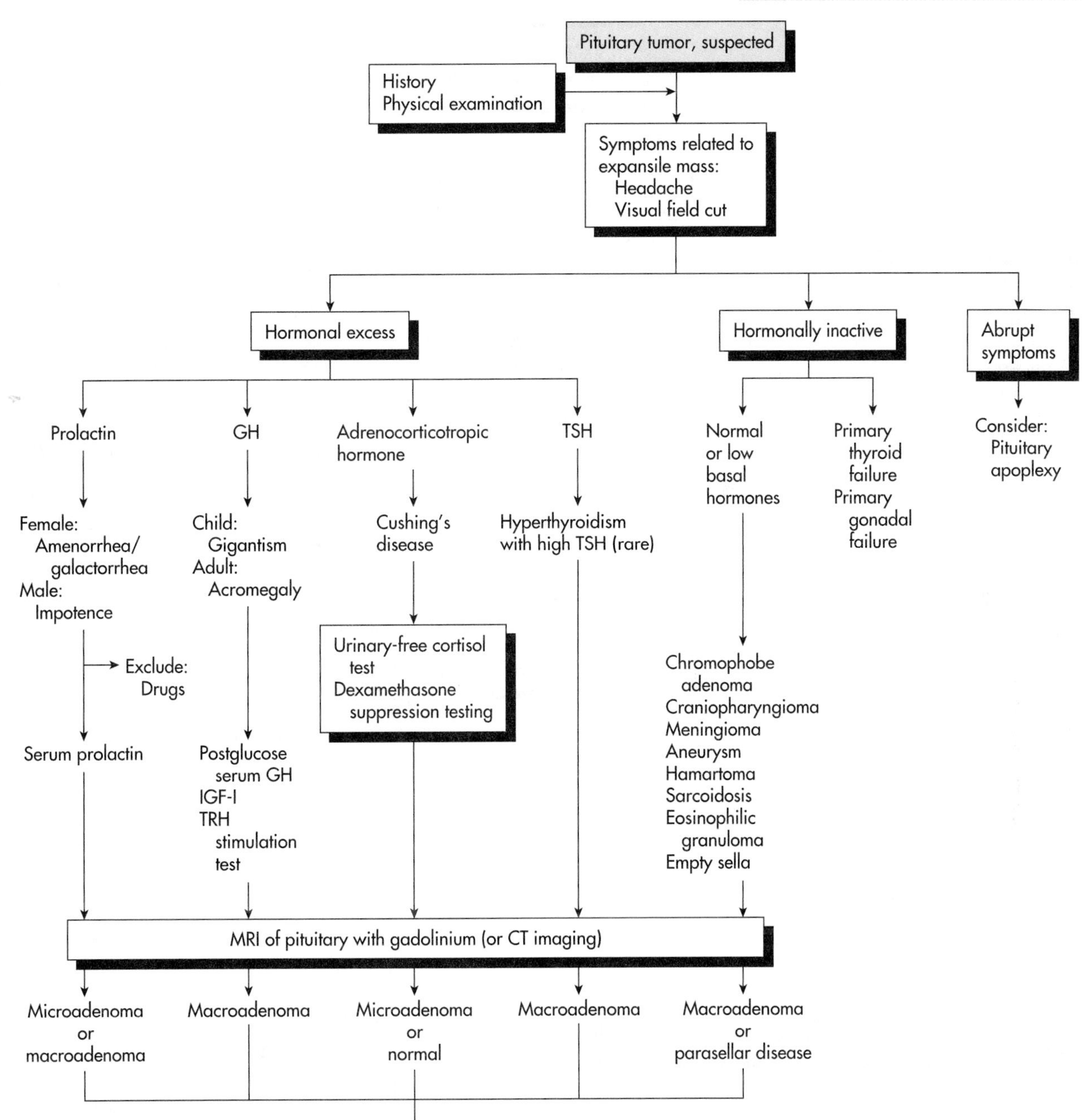

FIGURE 3-170 Evaluation of suspected pituitary tumor. *CT,* Computed tomography; *GH,* growth hormone; *IGF-I,* one of the insulin-like growth factors; *MRI,* magnetic resonance imaging; *TRH,* thyrotropin-releasing hormone; *TSH,* thyroid-stimulating hormone. (From Greene HL, Johnson WP, Lemcke D: *Decision making in medicine,* ed 2, St Louis, 1998, Mosby.)

PLEURAL SPACE FLUID

ICD-9CM # 511.9 Pleural effusion, unspecified

FIGURE 3-171 Evaluation, common etiologies, and management of pleural effusion and empyema. *LDH,* Lactate dehydrogenase; *RBC,* red blood cells; *SLE,* systemic lupus erythematosus; *WBC,* white blood cells. (From Kassirer J [ed]: *Current therapy in adult medicine,* ed 4, St Louis, 1998, Mosby.)

POISONING, ACUTE

ICD-9CM # 977.9

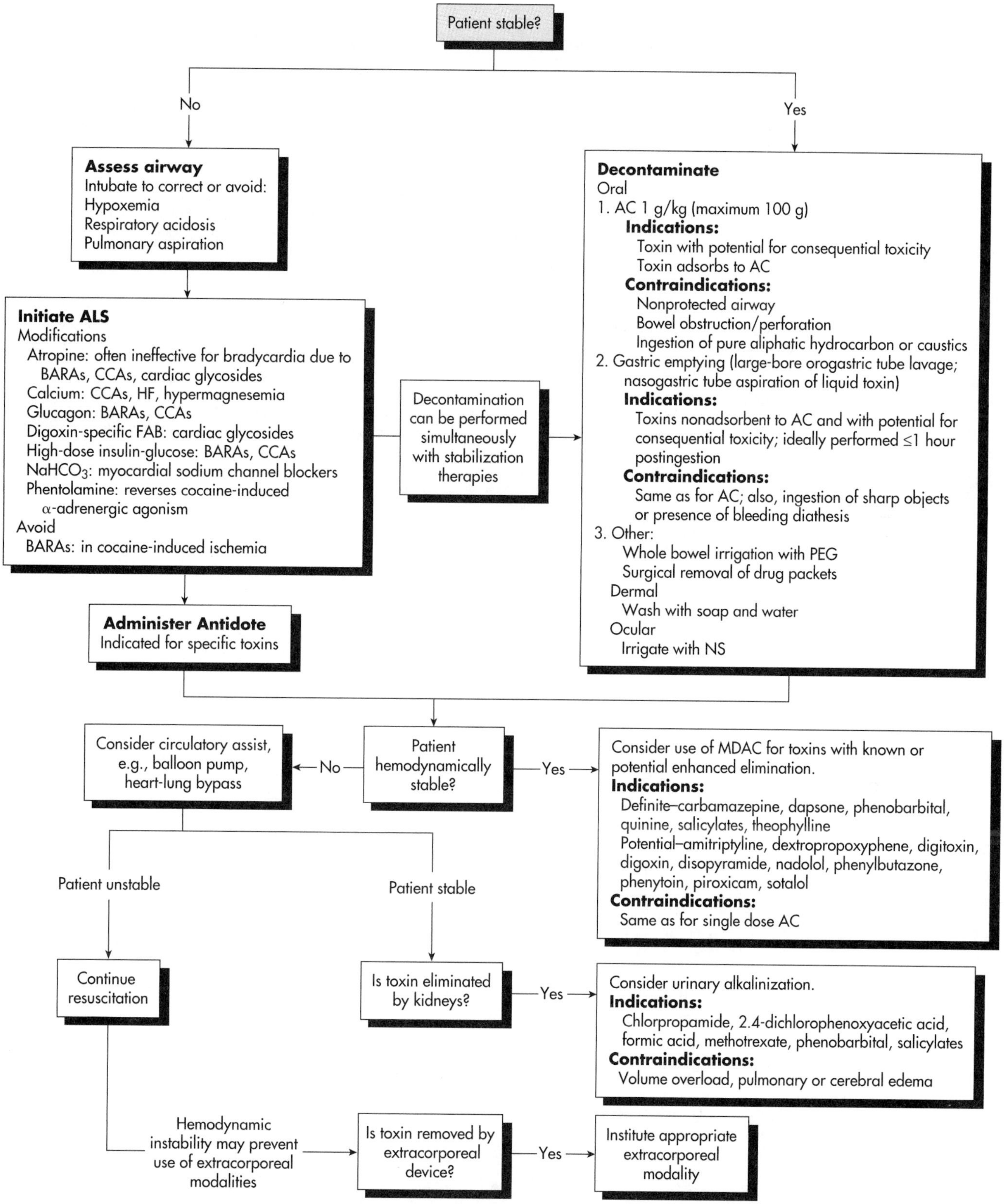

Patient stable?

No

Assess airway
Intubate to correct or avoid:
Hypoxemia
Respiratory acidosis
Pulmonary aspiration

Initiate ALS
Modifications
Atropine: often ineffective for bradycardia due to BARAs, CCAs, cardiac glycosides
Calcium: CCAs, HF, hypermagnesemia
Glucagon: BARAs, CCAs
Digoxin-specific FAB: cardiac glycosides
High-dose insulin-glucose: BARAs, CCAs
$NaHCO_3$: myocardial sodium channel blockers
Phentolamine: reverses cocaine-induced α-adrenergic agonism
Avoid
BARAs: in cocaine-induced ischemia

Decontamination can be performed simultaneously with stabilization therapies

Administer Antidote
Indicated for specific toxins

Yes

Decontaminate
Oral
1. AC 1 g/kg (maximum 100 g)
   Indications:
   Toxin with potential for consequential toxicity
   Toxin adsorbs to AC
   Contraindications:
   Nonprotected airway
   Bowel obstruction/perforation
   Ingestion of pure aliphatic hydrocarbon or caustics
2. Gastric emptying (large-bore orogastric tube lavage; nasogastric tube aspiration of liquid toxin)
   Indications:
   Toxins nonadsorbent to AC and with potential for consequential toxicity; ideally performed ≤1 hour postingestion
   Contraindications:
   Same as for AC; also, ingestion of sharp objects or presence of bleeding diathesis
3. Other:
   Whole bowel irrigation with PEG
   Surgical removal of drug packets

Dermal
Wash with soap and water
Ocular
Irrigate with NS

Patient hemodynamically stable?

No → Consider circulatory assist, e.g., balloon pump, heart-lung bypass

- Patient unstable → Continue resuscitation → Hemodynamic instability may prevent use of extracorporeal modalities → Is toxin removed by extracorporeal device?
- Patient stable → Is toxin eliminated by kidneys?

Yes → Consider use of MDAC for toxins with known or potential enhanced elimination.
Indications:
Definite–carbamazepine, dapsone, phenobarbital, quinine, salicylates, theophylline
Potential–amitriptyline, dextropropoxyphene, digitoxin, digoxin, disopyramide, nadolol, phenylbutazone, phenytoin, piroxicam, sotalol
Contraindications:
Same as for single dose AC

Is toxin eliminated by kidneys? — Yes → Consider urinary alkalinization.
Indications:
Chlorpropamide, 2.4-dichlorophenoxyacetic acid, formic acid, methotrexate, phenobarbital, salicylates
Contraindications:
Volume overload, pulmonary or cerebral edema

Is toxin removed by extracorporeal device? — Yes → Institute appropriate extracorporeal modality

FIGURE 3-172 Algorithm for the management of acute poisoning. See also Table 3-7. *AC,* activated charcoal; *BARAs,* beta-adrenergic receptor antagonists; *CCAs,* L-type calcium channel antagonists; *HF,* hydrolfuoric acid; *MDAC,* multidose activated charcoal; *NS,* 0.9% saline solution; *PEG,* nonabsorbable polyethylene glycol solution. (From Goldman L, Ausiello D [eds]: *Cecil textbook of medicine,* ed 22, Philadelphia, 2004, WB Saunders.)

Continued

POISONING, ACUTE—cont'd

TABLE 3-7 Common Toxicants Removed by Hemodialysis/Hemoperfusion

Toxicant	Indications	Technique	Comments
Ethylene glycol	Serum level ≥50 mL/dL, or lower levels with concomitant metabolic acidosis and evidence of end-organ toxicity	HD	May not be required in patient with normal creatinine clearance and acid-base status who is receiving fomepizole
Lithium*	Clinical indications	HD	Clinical indication is CNS toxicity (e.g., decreased mental status, ataxia, coma, seizures)
Methanol	Serum level ≥50 mL/dL, or lower levels with concomitant metabolic acidosis and evidence of end-organ toxicity	HD	Usually required owing to slow elimination half-life in presence of fomepizole or ethanol (30.3 to 54.4 hr), even in patients with no metabolic acidosis or evidence of end-organ toxicity
Phenobarbital	Clinical indications	HP/HD	Rarely necessary except when the patient is hemodynamically unstable despite aggressive support; clearance rates are better with HD than HP
Salicylates	*Acute toxicity:* serum level ≥100 mL/dL or <100 mg/dL in the presence of a clinical indication *Chronic toxicity:* any clinical indication	HD	Serum protein binding decreases with increasing toxic levels, increasing amount of free salicylate available for HD removal; clinical indications are one or more of the following: altered mental status, seizures, pulmonary edema, intractable acidosis, renal failure
Theophylline	*Acute toxicity:* serum level ≥90 μg/mL or <90 μg/mL plus any clinical indication *Chronic toxicity:* serum level ≥40 μg/dL and not declining despite MDAC; any clinical indication	HP/HD	Clinical indications: seizures, hypotension, ventricular arrhythmias; clearance rates better with HD than HP

From Goldman L, Ausiello D [eds]: *Cecil textbook of medicine,* ed 22, Philadelphia, 2004, WB Saunders.
CNS, Central nervous system; *HD,* hemodialysis; *HP,* hemoperfusion; *MDAC,* multidose activated charcoal.
*Hemodiafiltration removes lithium; clinical benefit with this technique is unknown.

PREOPERATIVE EVALUATION, PATIENT WITH CORONARY HEART DISEASE

ICD-9CM # 411.89 Coronary insufficiency, acute
411.8 Coronary insufficiency, chronic
411.1 Coronary insufficiency or intermediate syndrome

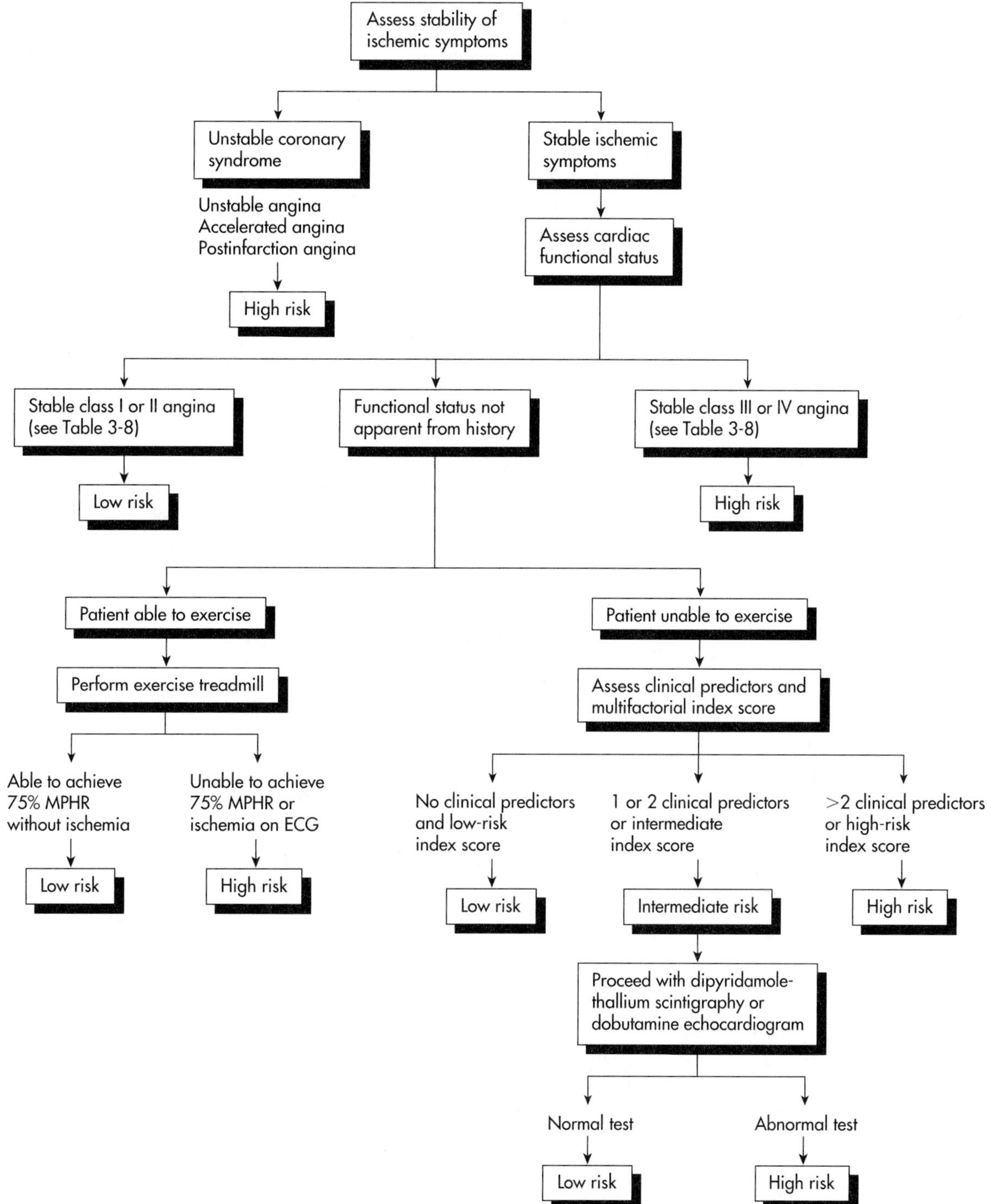

FIGURE 3-173 Preoperative evaluation of patients with known or suspected coronary artery disease. (From Goldman L, Braunwald E [eds]: *Primary cardiology*, Philadelphia, 1998, WB Saunders.)

TABLE 3-8 **New York Heart Association Functional Classification**

Class I	No limitation	Ordinary physical activity does not cause symptoms
Class II	Slight limitation	Comfortable at rest Ordinary physical activity causes symptoms
Class III	Marked limitation	Comfortable at rest Less than ordinary activity causes symptoms
Class IV	Inability to carry on any physical activity	Symptoms present at rest

SECTION III

PROSTATE CANCER

ICD-9CM # 185

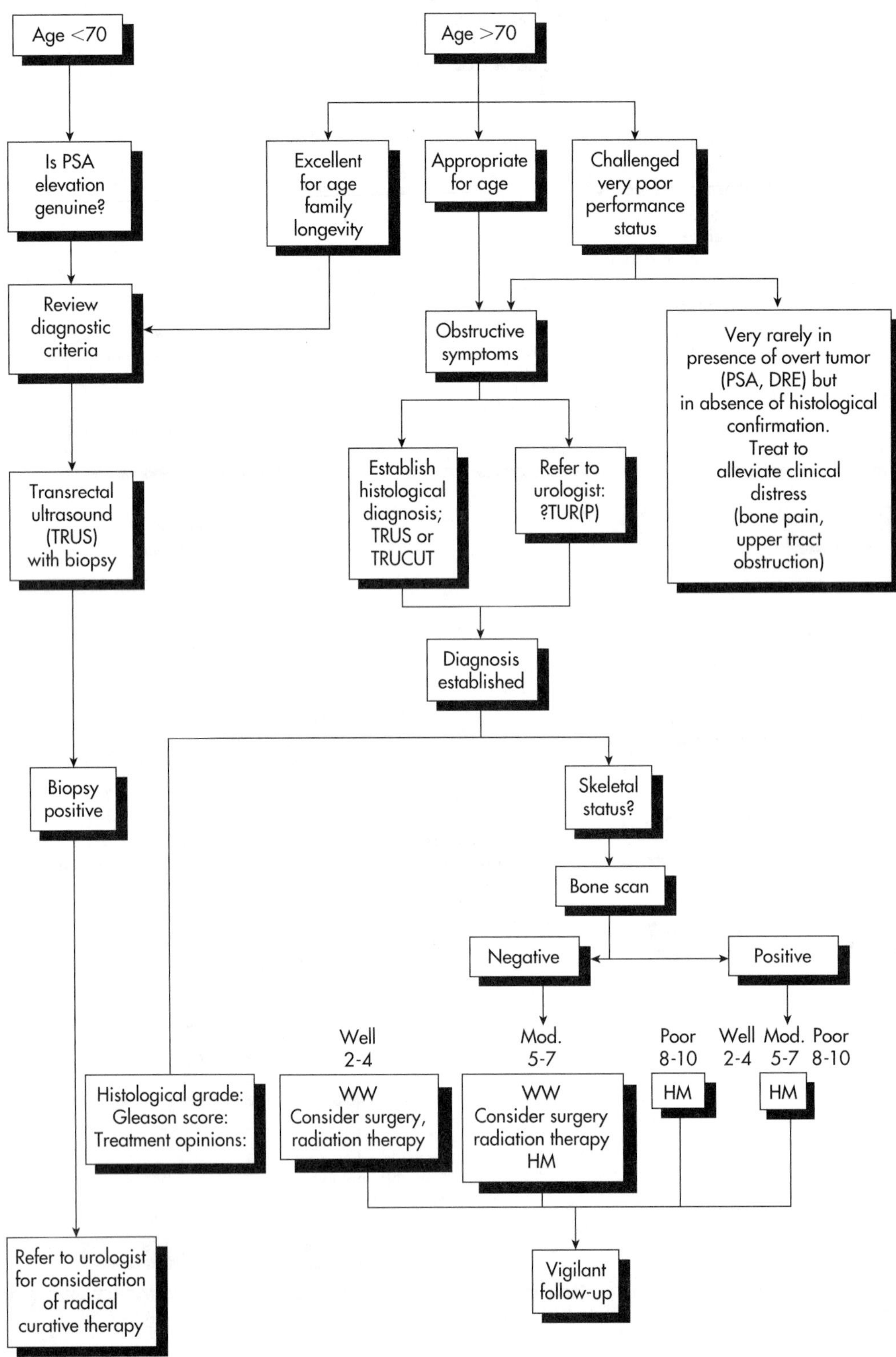

FIGURE 3-174 Assessment and treatment of a patient with prostate cancer suspected on the grounds of a digital rectal exam and PSA. *WW,* Watchful waiting; *HM,* hormonal manipulation; *PSA,* prostate specific antigen. (Modified from Tallis RC, Fillit HM [eds]: *Brocklehurst's textbook of geriatric medicine and gerontology,* ed 6, London, 2003, Churchill Livingstone.)

PROSTATIC HYPERPLASIA, BENIGN

ICD-9CM # 600 Benign prostatic hyperplasia

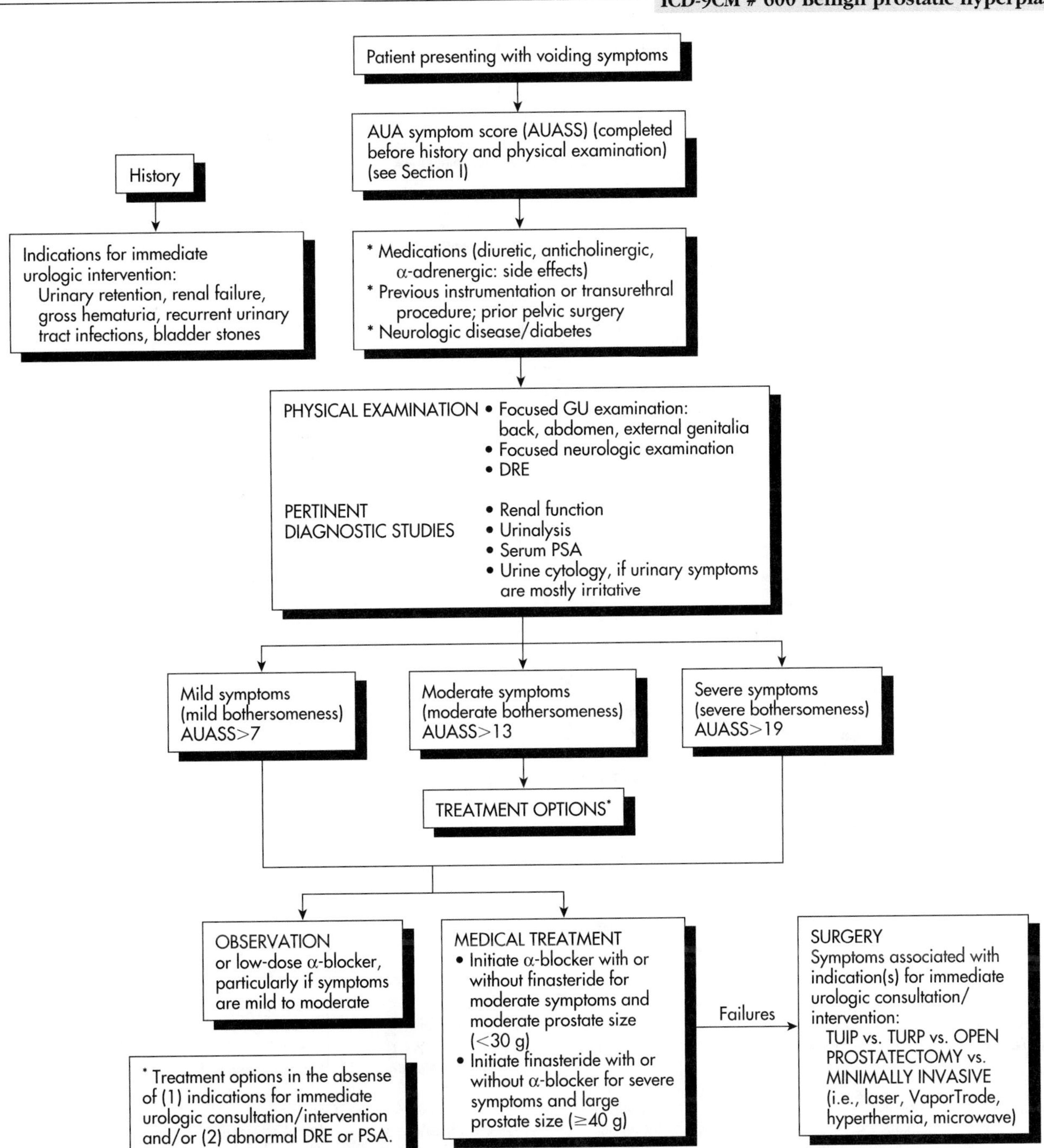

FIGURE 3-175 Critical pathway for patients with benign prostatic hypertrophy. *AUA,* American Urological Association; *DRE,* digital rectal examination; *GU,* genitourinary; *PSA,* prostate-specific antigen; *TUIP,* transurethral incision of the prostate; *TURP,* transurethral resection of the prostate. (From Nseyo UO [ed]: *Urology for primary care physicians,* Philadelphia, 1999, WB Saunders.)

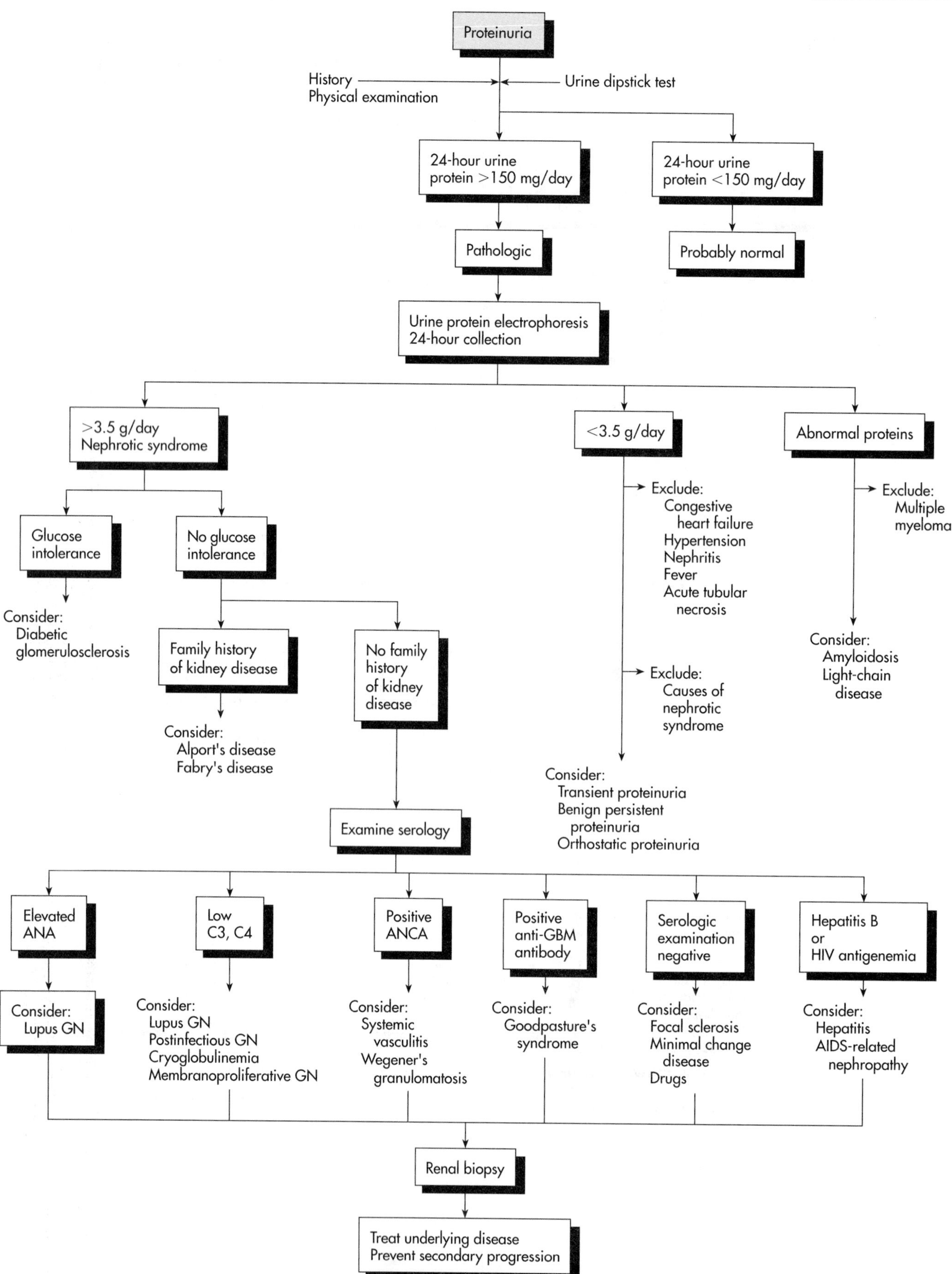

FIGURE 3-176 Proteinuria. *AIDS,* Acquired immunodeficiency syndrome; *ANA,* antinuclear antibody; *ANCA,* antineutrophil cytoplasmic autoantibody; *anti-GBM,* anti–glomerular basement membrane; *GN,* glomerulonephritis. (From Greene HL, Johnson WP, Lemcke D [eds]: *Decision making in medicine,* ed 2, St Louis, 1998, Mosby.)

PRURITUS, GENERALIZED

ICD-9CM # 698.9 Pruritus NOS

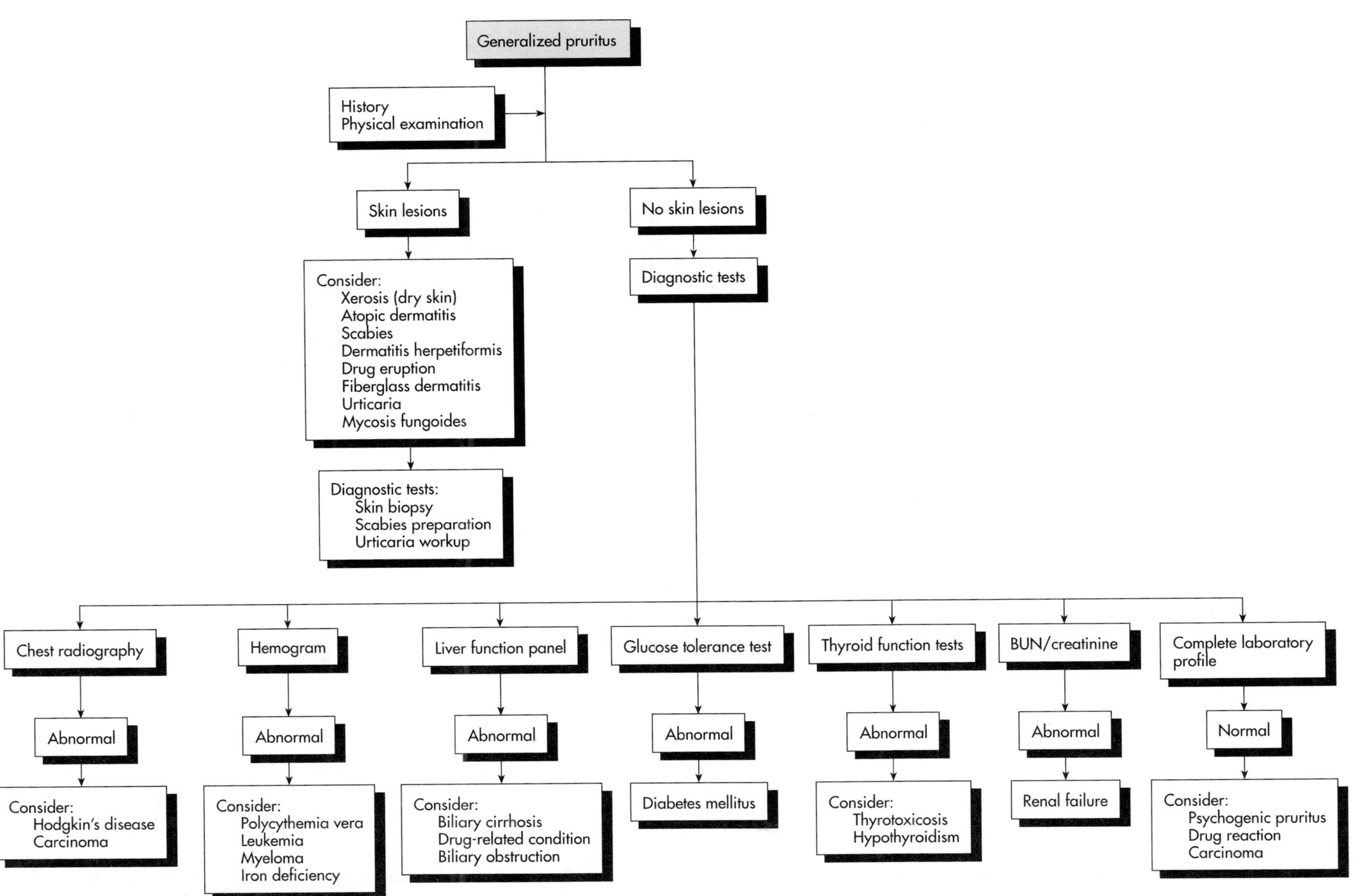

FIGURE 3-177 Evaluation of generalized pruritus. *BUN,* Blood urea nitrogen. (From Greene HL, Johnson WP, Lemcke D [eds]: *Decision making in medicine*, ed 2, St Louis, 1998, Mosby.)

ICD-9CM # 301.9 Psychosomatic personality disorder

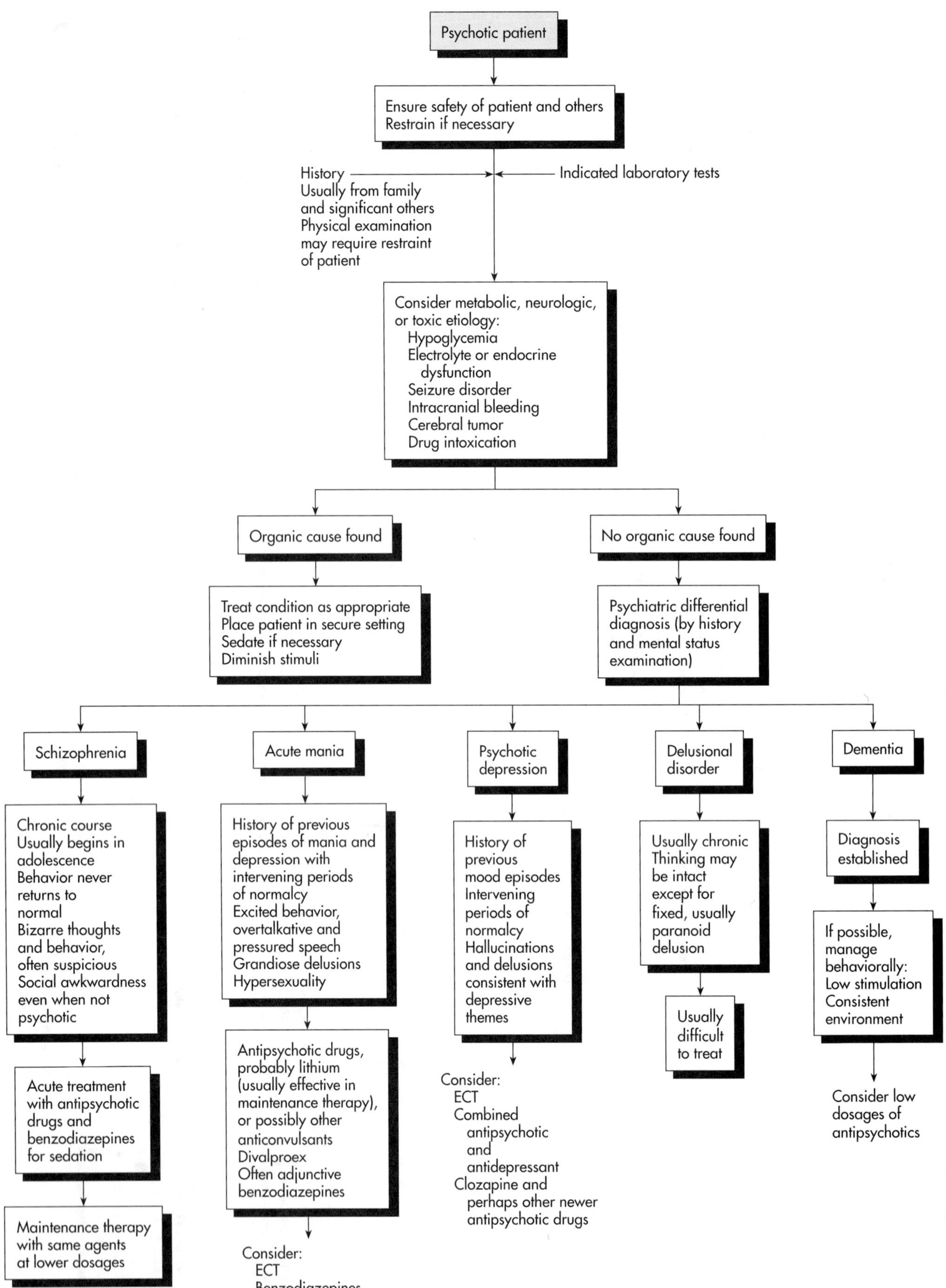

FIGURE 3-178 Evaluation of psychotic patient. *ECT,* Electroconvulsive therapy. (From Greene HL, Johnson WP, Lemcke D [eds]: *Decision making in medicine,* ed 2, St Louis, 1998, Mosby.)

PUBERTY, DELAYED

ICD-9CM # 259.0

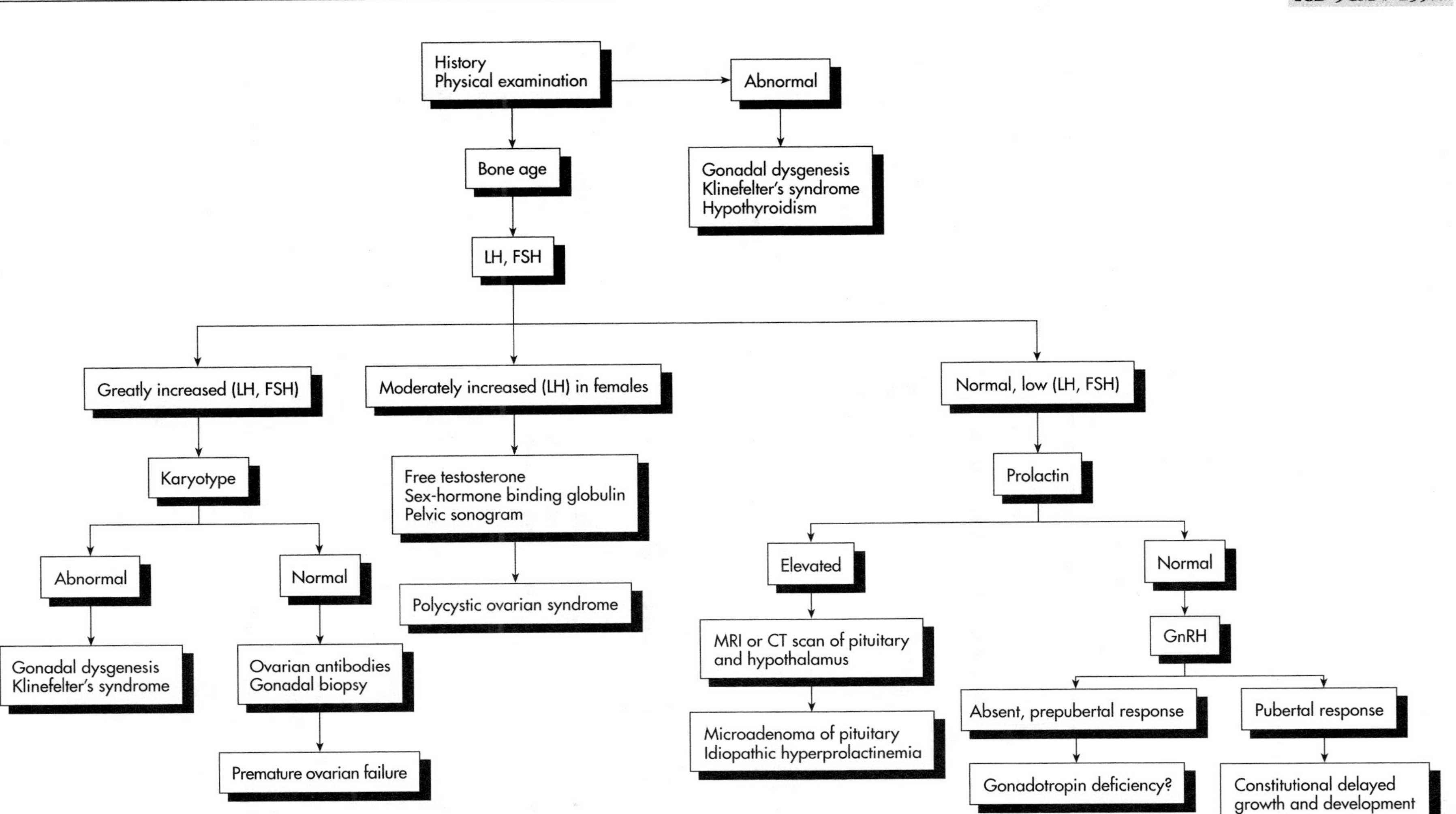

FIGURE 3-179 Evaluation of patient with delayed puberty. *CT,* Computed tomography; *FSH,* follicle-stimulating hormone; *GnRH,* gonadotropin-releasing hormone; *LH,* luteinizing hormone; *MRI,* magnetic resonance imaging. (From Moore WT, Eastman RC: *Diagnostic endocrinology,* ed 2, St Louis, 1996, Mosby.)

PUBERTY, PRECOCIOUS

ICD-9CM # 259.1 Puberty precocious NOS

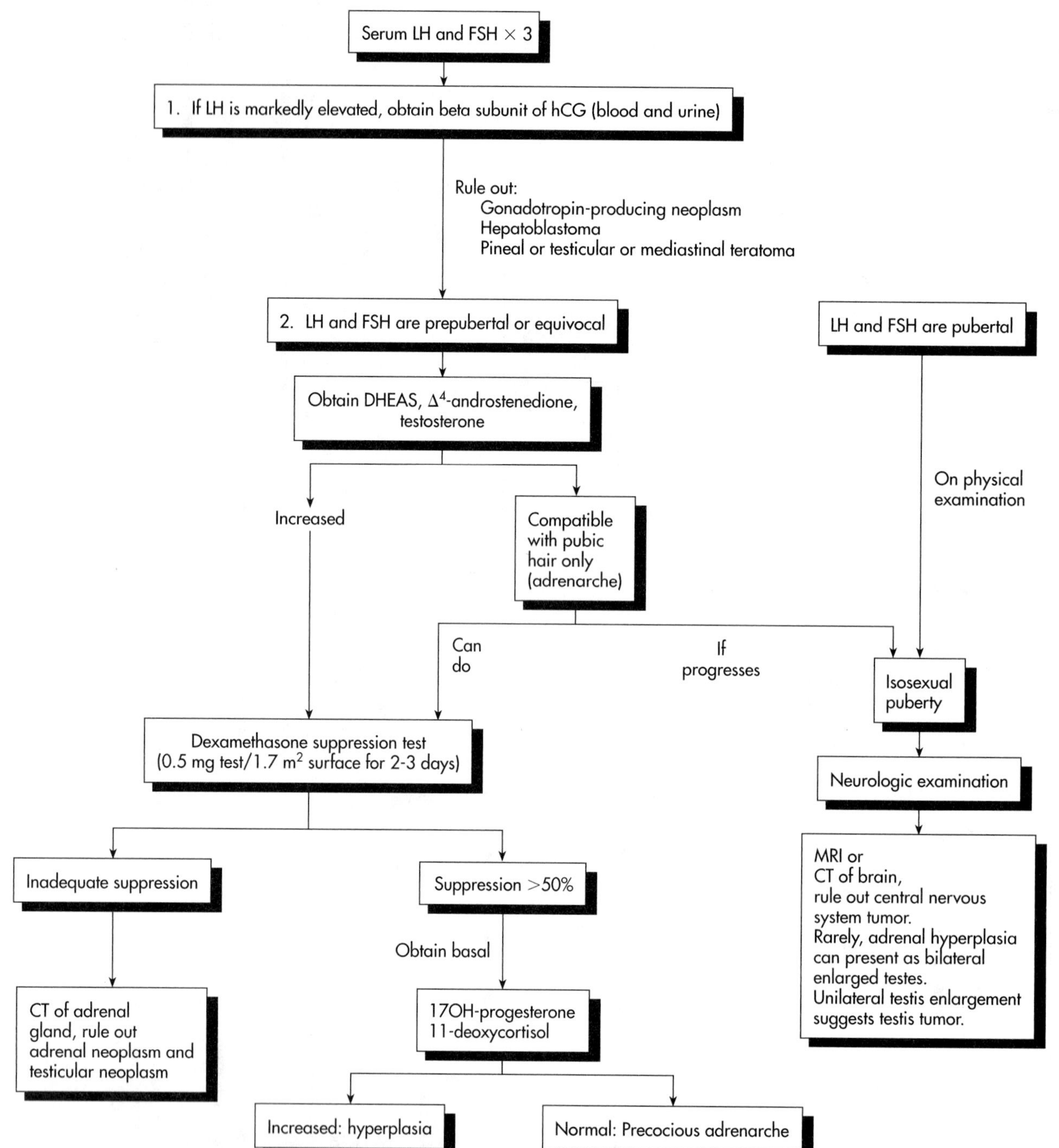

FIGURE 3-180 Evaluation of precocious puberty, excluding factitious and iatrogenic causes. *CT,* Computed tomography; *DHEAS,* dehydroepiandrosterone sulfate; *FSH,* follicle-stimulating hormone; *hCG,* human chorionic gonadotropin; *LH,* luteinizing hormone; *MRI,* magnetic resonance imaging. (Modified from Odell WD: The physiology of puberty: disorders of the pubertal process. In DeGroot LJ et al [eds]: *Endocrinology,* vol 3, New York, 1979, Grune & Stratton.)

PULMONARY EMBOLISM

ICD-9CM # 415.1

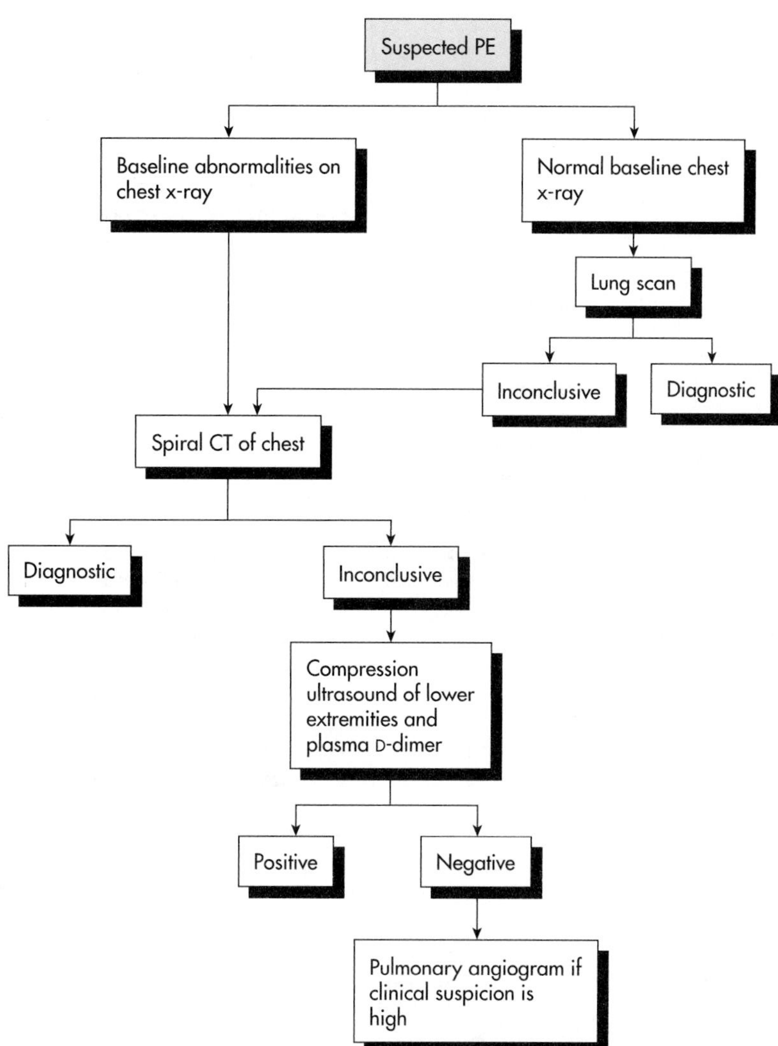

FIGURE 3-181 Pulmonary embolism. *CT,* Computed tomography; *PE,* pulmonary embolism.

PULMONARY NODULE

ICD-9CM # 518.89

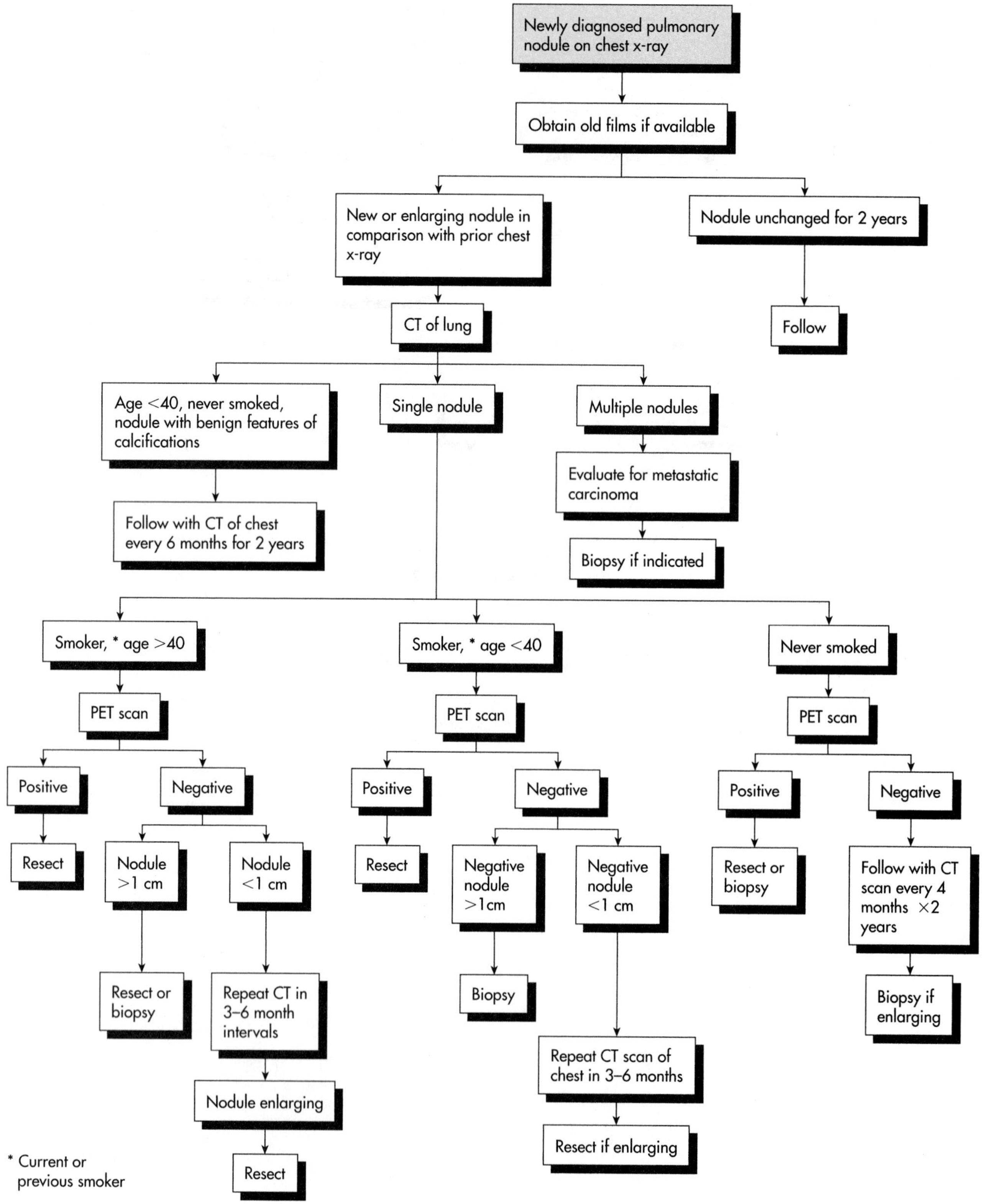

- Newly diagnosed pulmonary nodule on chest x-ray
  - Obtain old films if available
    - New or enlarging nodule in comparison with prior chest x-ray
      - CT of lung
        - Age <40, never smoked, nodule with benign features of calcifications
          - Follow with CT of chest every 6 months for 2 years
        - Single nodule
          - Smoker,* age >40
            - PET scan
              - Positive
                - Resect
              - Negative
                - Nodule >1 cm
                  - Resect or biopsy
                - Nodule <1 cm
                  - Repeat CT in 3–6 month intervals
                    - Nodule enlarging
                      - Resect
          - Smoker,* age <40
            - PET scan
              - Positive
                - Resect
              - Negative
                - Negative nodule >1cm
                  - Biopsy
                - Negative nodule <1 cm
                  - Repeat CT scan of chest in 3–6 months
                    - Resect if enlarging
          - Never smoked
            - PET scan
              - Positive
                - Resect or biopsy
              - Negative
                - Follow with CT scan every 4 months ×2 years
                  - Biopsy if enlarging
        - Multiple nodules
          - Evaluate for metastatic carcinoma
            - Biopsy if indicated
    - Nodule unchanged for 2 years
      - Follow

* Current or previous smoker

FIGURE 3-182 Pulmonary nodule. *CT,* Computed tomography; *PET,* positron emission tomography.

PURPURA, PALPABLE

ICD-9CM # 287.2 Purpura, NOS

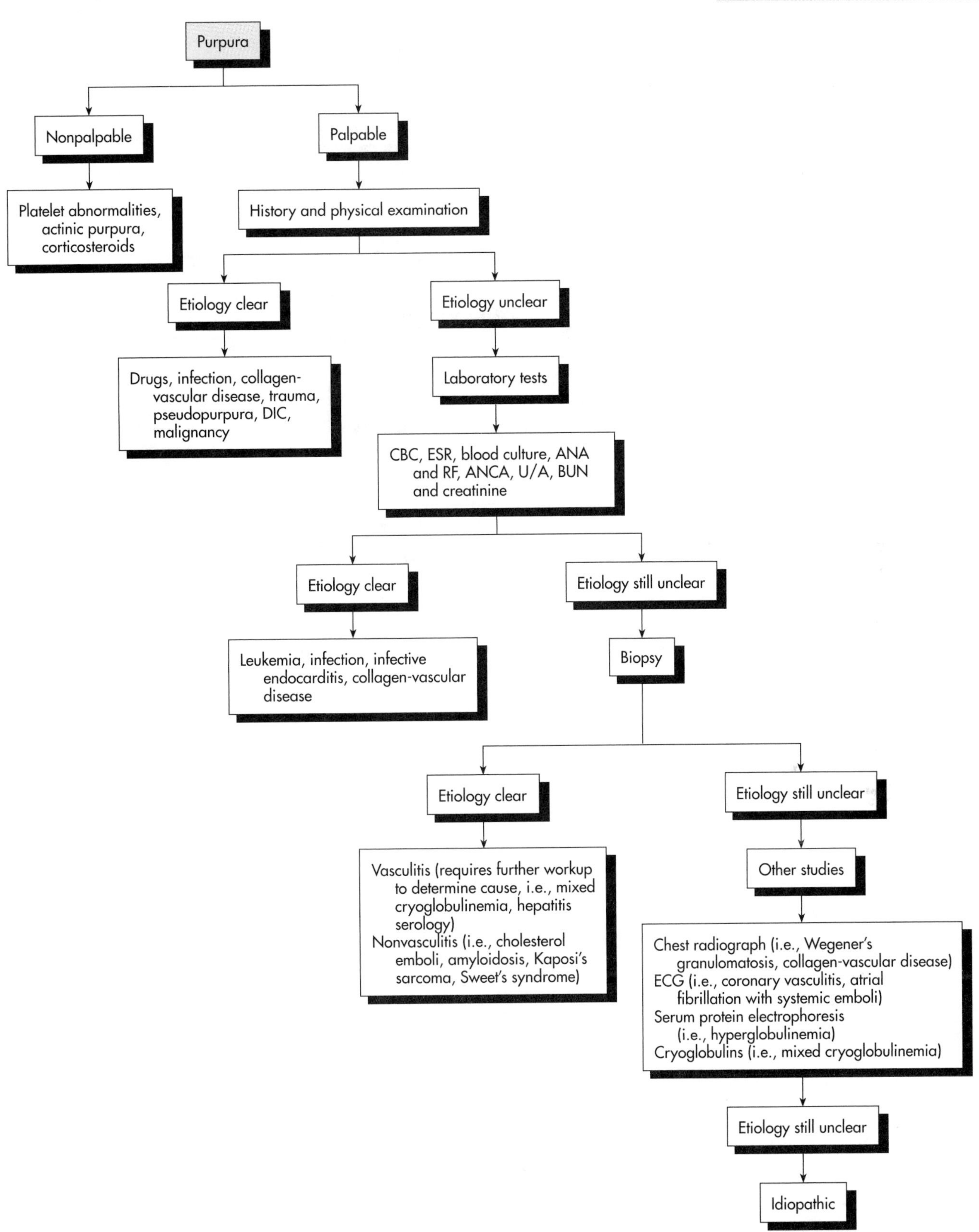

FIGURE 3-183 Diagnostic algorithm for palpable purpura. *AIDS,* Acquired immunodeficiency syndrome; *ANA,* antinuclear antibody; *ANCA,* antineutrophil cytoplasmic antibody test; *BUN,* blood urea nitrogen; *CBC,* complete blood cell count; *DIC,* disseminated intravascular coagulation; *ECG,* electrocardiogram; *ESR,* erythrocyte sedimentation rate; *MCV,* mean corpuscular volume; *RF,* rheumatoid factor; *U/A,* urinalysis. (From Stevens GL, Adelman HM, Wallach PM: *Am Fam Physician* 52:1355, 1995.)

RED EYE, ACUTE

ICD-9CM # 379.93

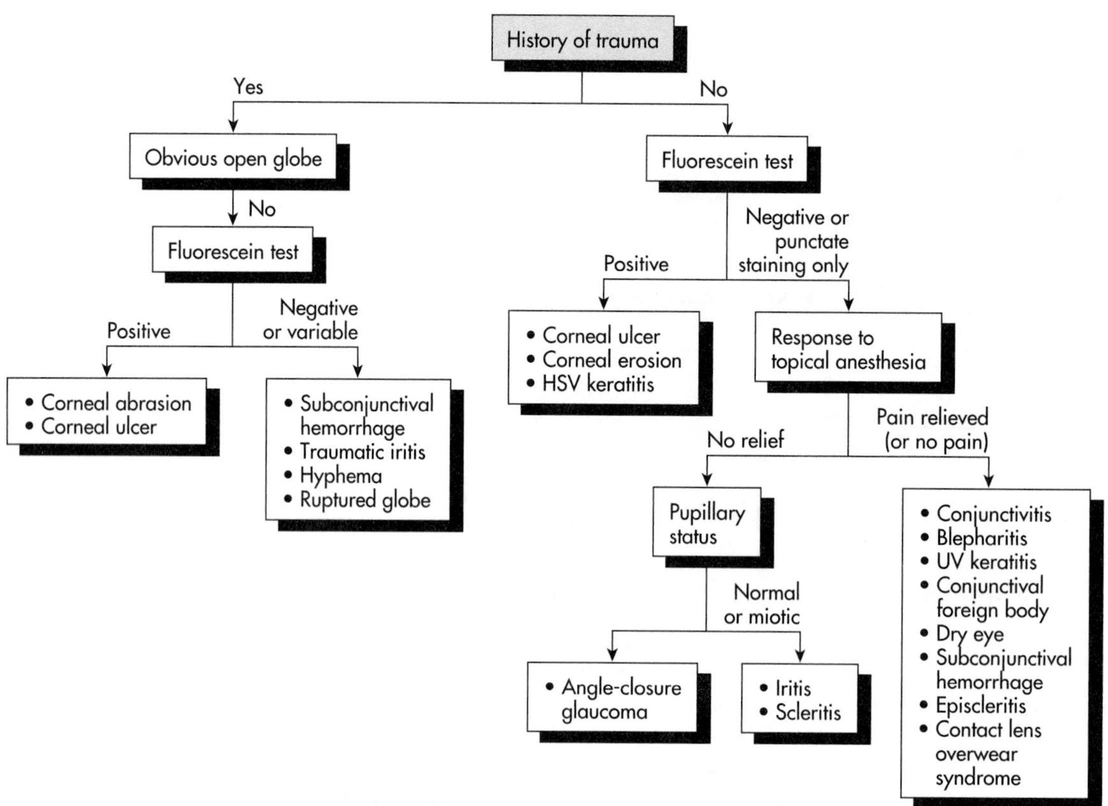

FIGURE 3-184 Algorithm showing diagnostic procedure for the acute red eye. *HSV,* Herpes simplex virus; *UV,* ultraviolet. (From Auerbach PS: *Wilderness medicine,* ed 4, St Louis, 2001, Mosby.)

RENAL FAILURE, ACUTE

ICD-9CM # 584.9 Acute renal failure, unspecified

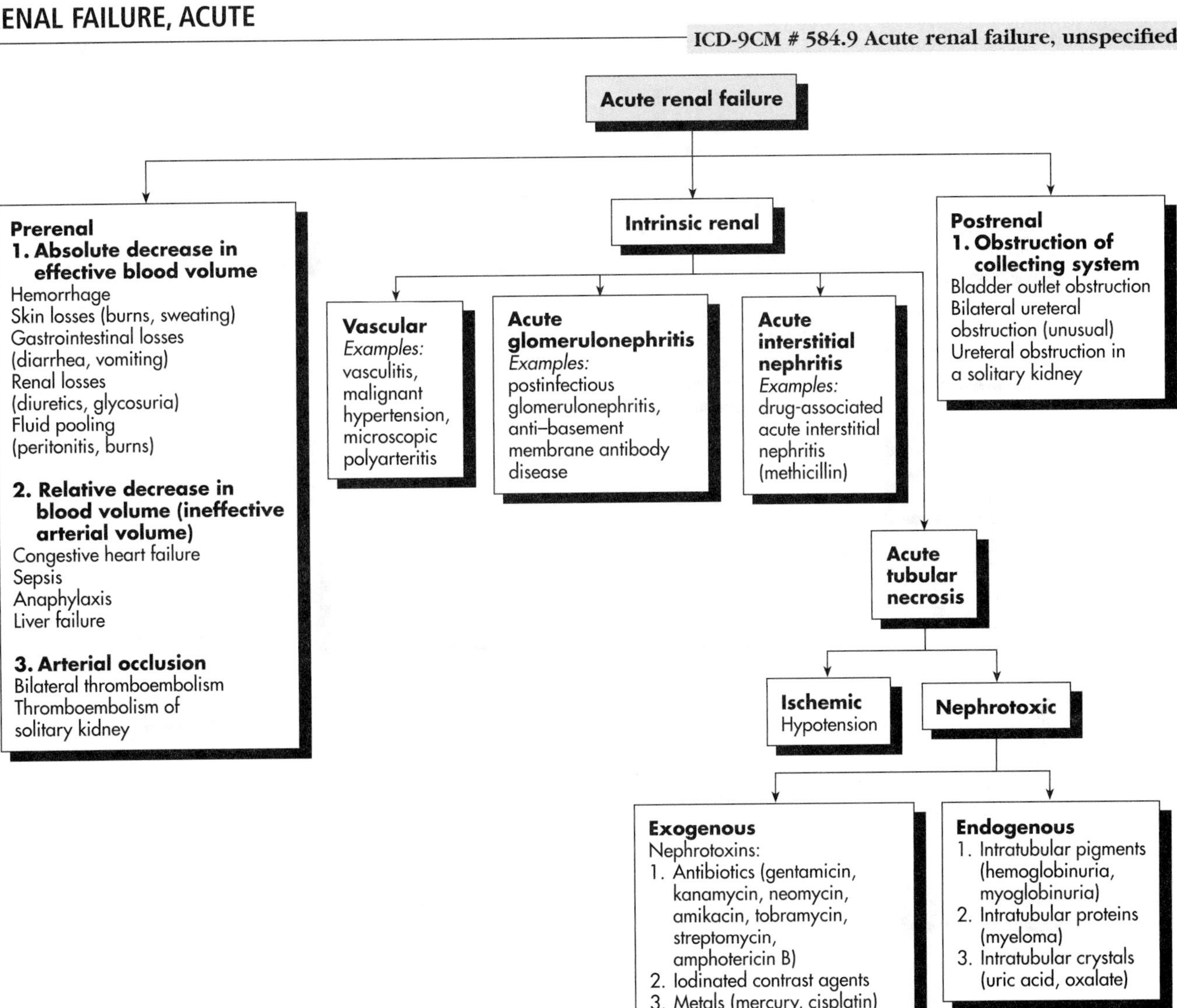

FIGURE 3-185 Causes of acute renal failure. (From Andreoli TE [ed]: *Cecil essentials of medicine,* ed 4, Philadelphia, 1997, WB Saunders.)

RENAL MASS

ICD-9CM # 593.9

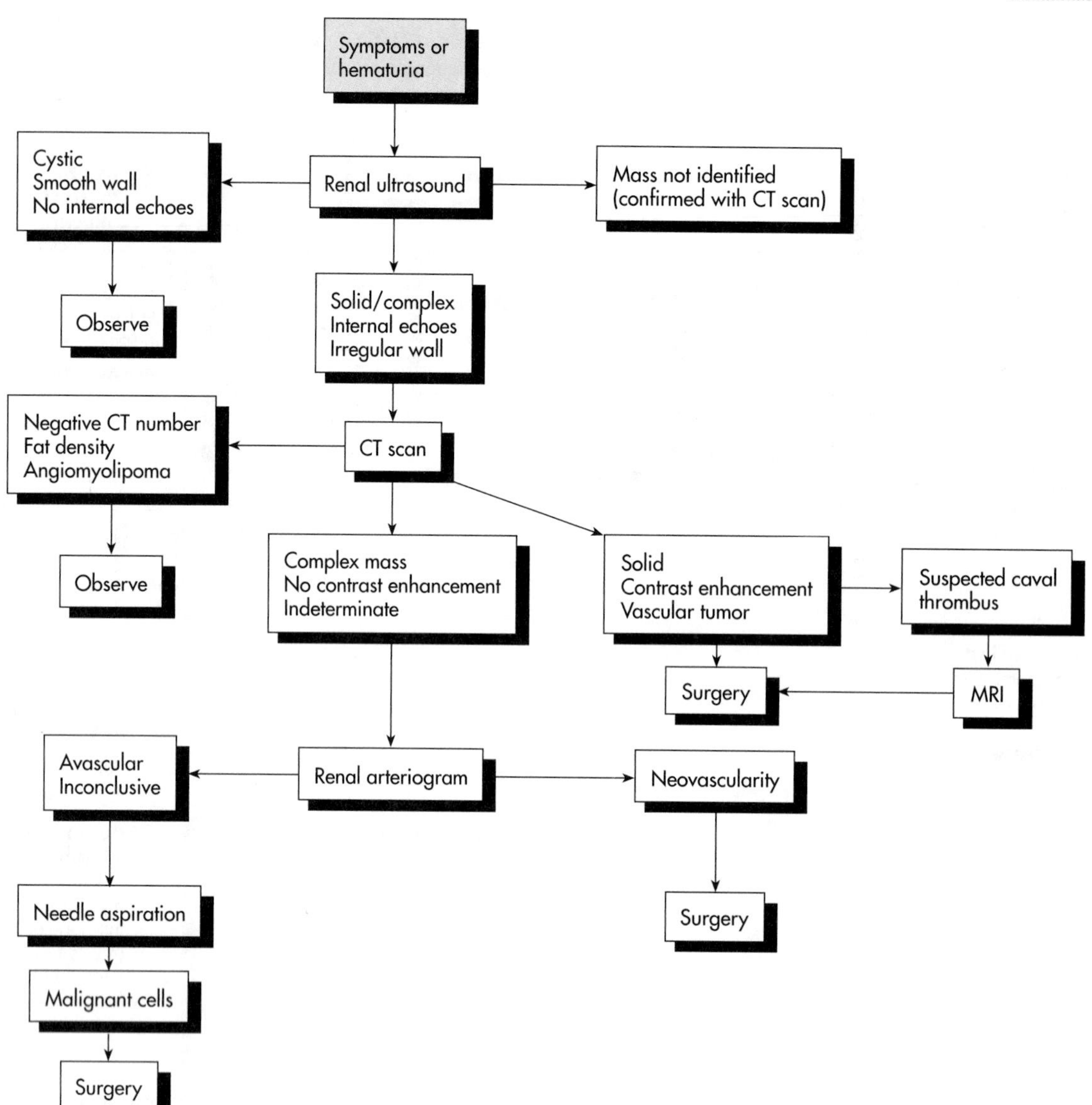

FIGURE 3-186 Evaluation of a patient with a renal mass. *CT,* Computed tomography; *MRI,* magnetic resonance imaging. (Modified from Williams RD: Tumors of the kidney, ureter, and bladder. In Goldman L, Ausiello D [eds]: *Cecil textbook of medicine,* ed 22, Philadelphia, 2004, WB Saunders.)

RESPIRATORY, DISTRESS

ICD-9CM # 786.09 Respiratory distress NOS
518.82 Respiratory distress, acute

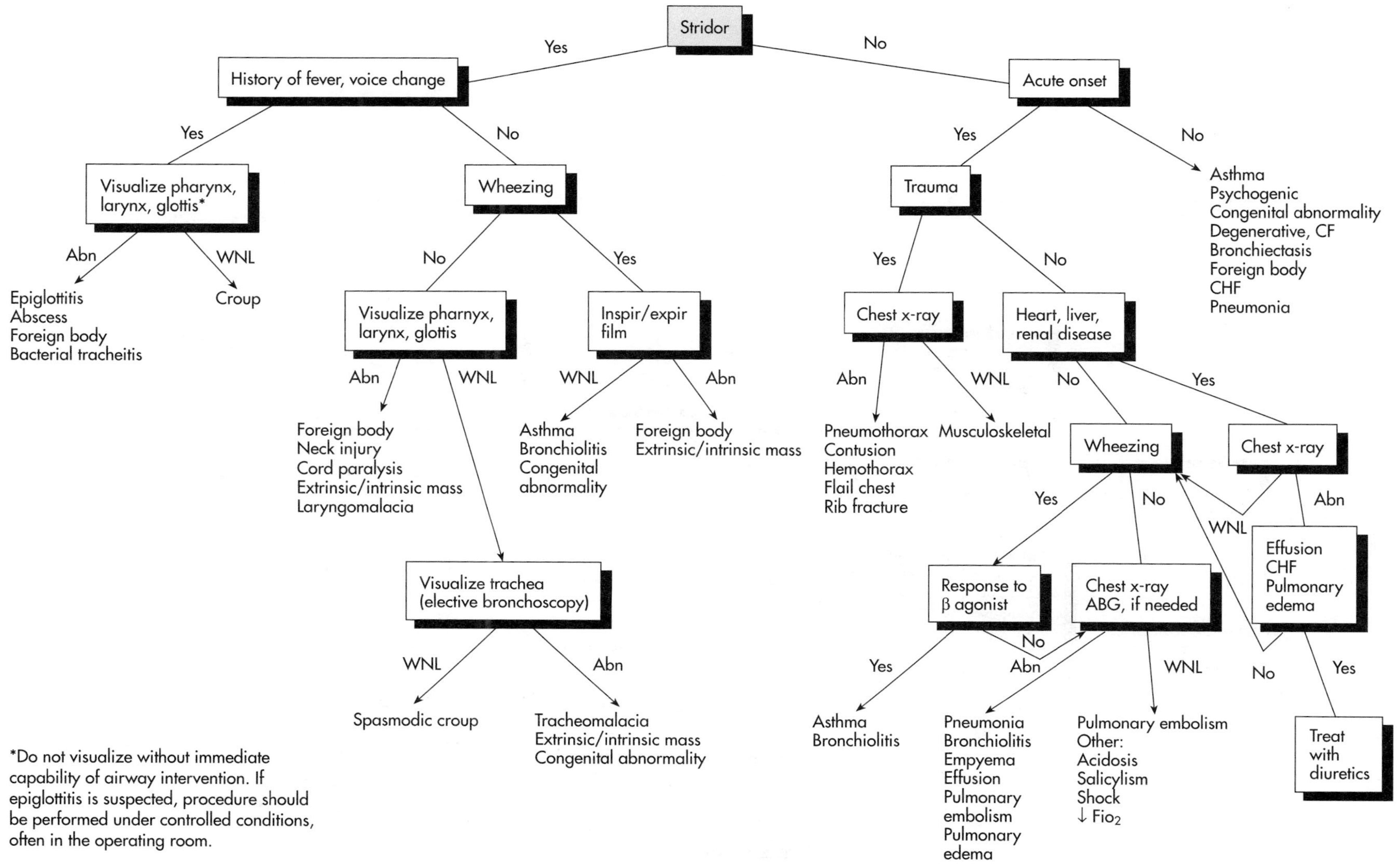

- **Stridor**
  - Yes → **History of fever, voice change**
    - Yes → **Visualize pharynx, larynx, glottis***
      - Abn → Epiglottitis, Abscess, Foreign body, Bacterial tracheitis
      - WNL → Croup
    - No → **Wheezing**
      - No → **Visualize pharynx, larynx, glottis**
        - Abn → Foreign body, Neck injury, Cord paralysis, Extrinsic/intrinsic mass, Laryngomalacia
        - WNL → **Visualize trachea (elective bronchoscopy)**
          - WNL → Spasmodic croup
          - Abn → Tracheomalacia, Extrinsic/intrinsic mass, Congenital abnormality
      - Yes → **Inspir/expir film**
        - WNL → Asthma, Bronchiolitis, Congenital abnormality
        - Abn → Foreign body, Extrinsic/intrinsic mass
  - No → **Acute onset**
    - Yes → **Trauma**
      - Yes → **Chest x-ray**
        - Abn → Pneumothorax, Contusion, Hemothorax, Flail chest, Rib fracture
        - WNL → Musculoskeletal
      - No → **Heart, liver, renal disease**
        - No → **Wheezing**
          - Yes → **Response to β agonist**
            - Yes → Asthma, Bronchiolitis
            - No/Abn → **Chest x-ray, ABG, if needed**
          - No → **Chest x-ray, ABG, if needed**
            - Abn → Pneumonia, Bronchiolitis, Empyema, Effusion, Pulmonary embolism, Pulmonary edema
            - WNL → Pulmonary embolism; Other: Acidosis, Salicylism, Shock, ↓ Fio_2
        - Yes → **Chest x-ray**
          - WNL → **Wheezing**
          - Abn → **Effusion, CHF, Pulmonary edema**
            - Yes → **Treat with diuretics**
            - No → **Wheezing**
    - No → Asthma, Psychogenic, Congenital abnormality, Degenerative, CF, Bronchiectasis, Foreign body, CHF, Pneumonia

*Do not visualize without immediate capability of airway intervention. If epiglottitis is suspected, procedure should be performed under controlled conditions, often in the operating room.

FIGURE 3-187 Respiratory distress. *ABG,* Arterial blood gas; *Abn,* abnormal; *CF,* cystic fibrosis; *CHF,* congestive heart failure; *WNL,* within normal limits. (From Barkin RM, Rosen P: *Emergency pediatrics,* St Louis, 1999, Mosby.)

RETICULOCYTE COUNT, ELEVATED

ICD-9CM # 790.99

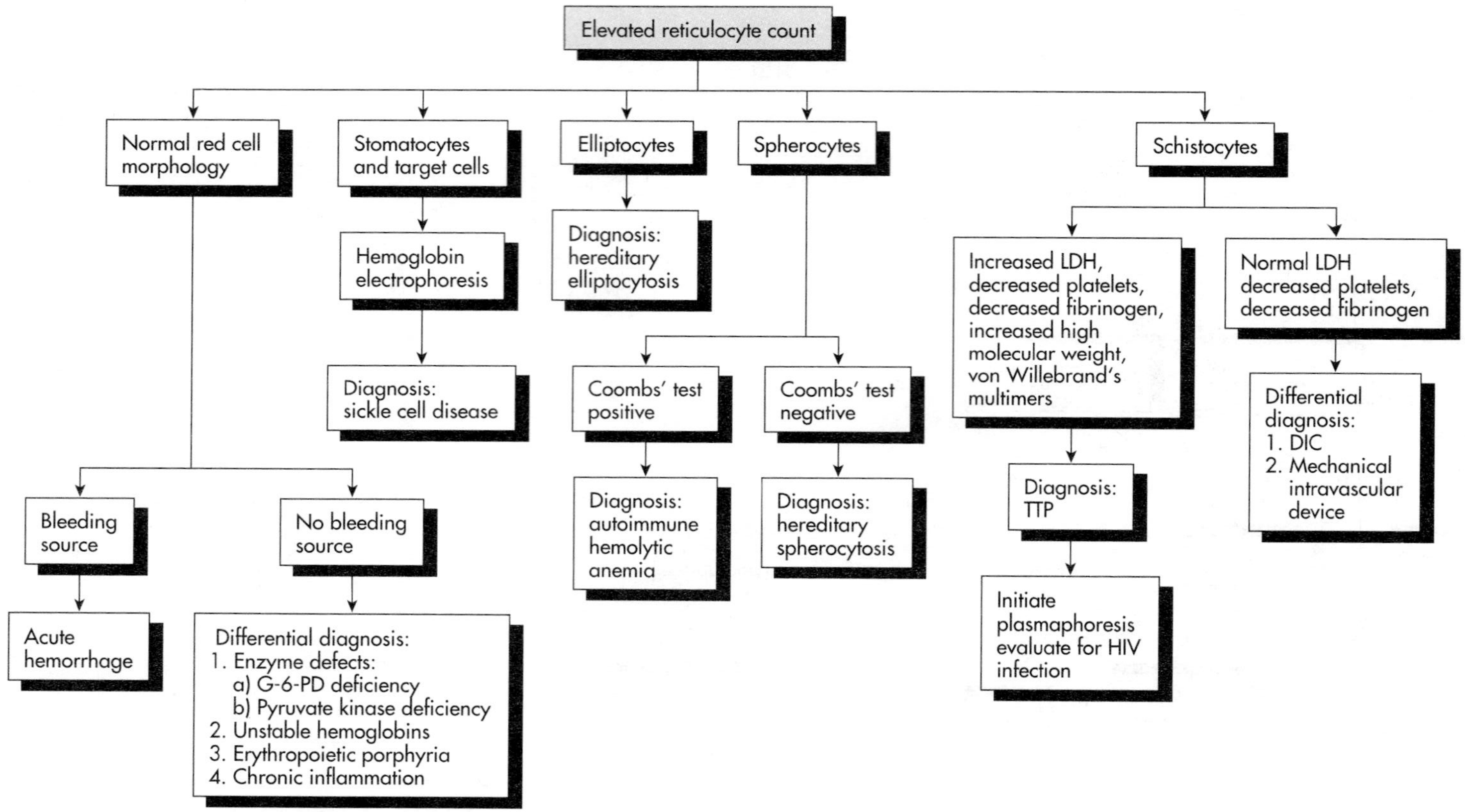

- Elevated reticulocyte count
  - Normal red cell morphology
    - Bleeding source → Acute hemorrhage
    - No bleeding source → Differential diagnosis:
      1. Enzyme defects:
         a) G-6-PD deficiency
         b) Pyruvate kinase deficiency
      2. Unstable hemoglobins
      3. Erythropoietic porphyria
      4. Chronic inflammation
  - Stomatocytes and target cells → Hemoglobin electrophoresis → Diagnosis: sickle cell disease
  - Elliptocytes → Diagnosis: hereditary elliptocytosis
  - Spherocytes
    - Coombs' test positive → Diagnosis: autoimmune hemolytic anemia
    - Coombs' test negative → Diagnosis: hereditary spherocytosis
  - Schistocytes
    - Increased LDH, decreased platelets, decreased fibrinogen, increased high molecular weight, von Willebrand's multimers → Diagnosis: TTP → Initiate plasmaphoresis evaluate for HIV infection
    - Normal LDH decreased platelets, decreased fibrinogen → Differential diagnosis:
      1. DIC
      2. Mechanical intravascular device

FIGURE 3-188 Differential diagnosis of elevated reticulocyte count. *DIC,* Disseminated intravascular coagulation; *G6PD,* glucose-6-phosphate dehydrogenase; *HIV,* human immunodeficiency virus; *LDH,* lactic dehydrogenase; *TTP,* thrombotic thrombocytopenic purpura. (From Rakel RE [ed]: *Principles of family practice,* ed 6, Philadelphia, 2002, WB Saunders.)

RHINORRHEA

ICD-9CM # 478.1

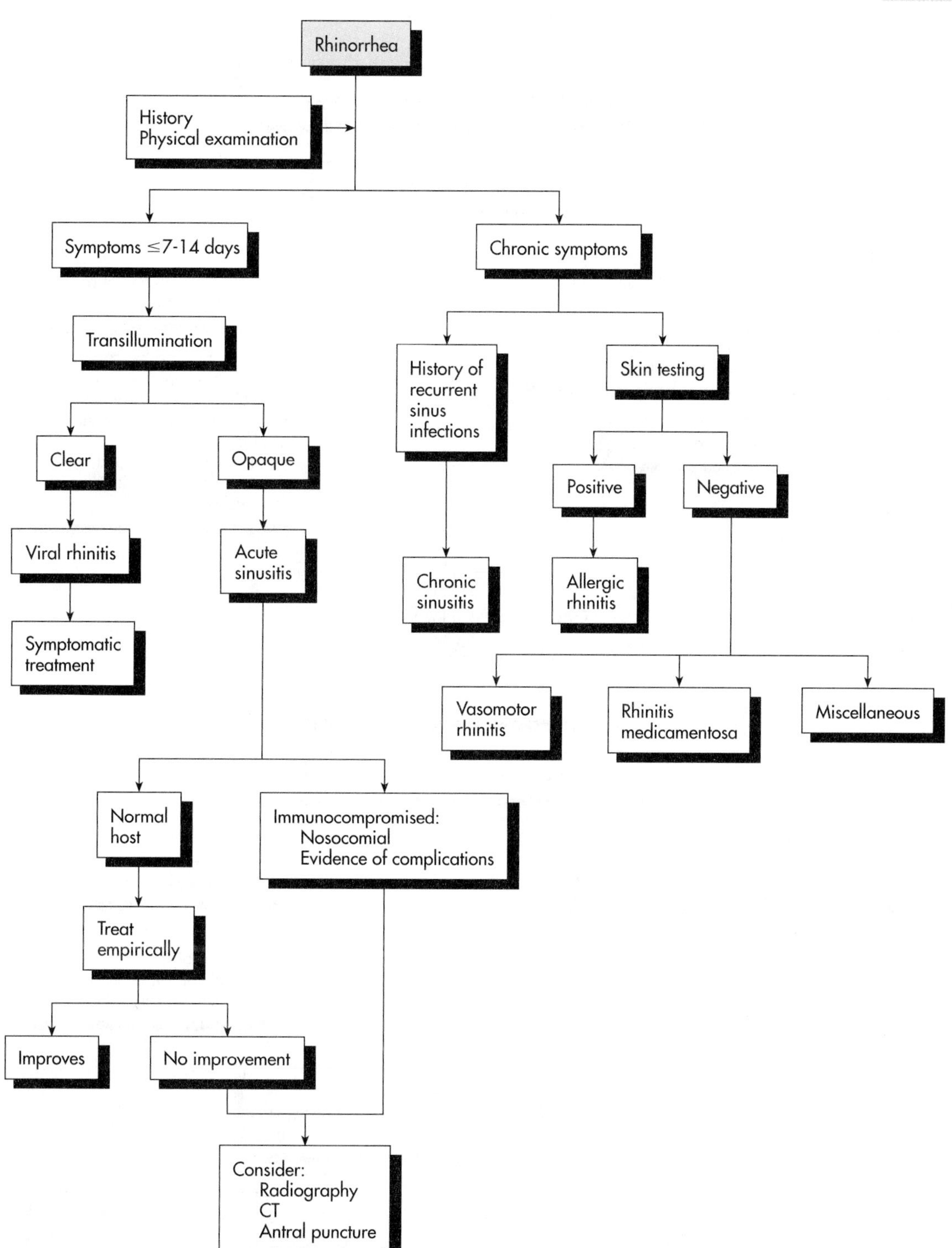

FIGURE 3-189 Approach to a patient with rhinorrhea. *CT,* Computed tomography. (From Noble J [ed]: *Primary care medicine,* ed 3, St Louis, 2001, Mosby.)

SCHILLING TEST

ICD-9CM # 281.0

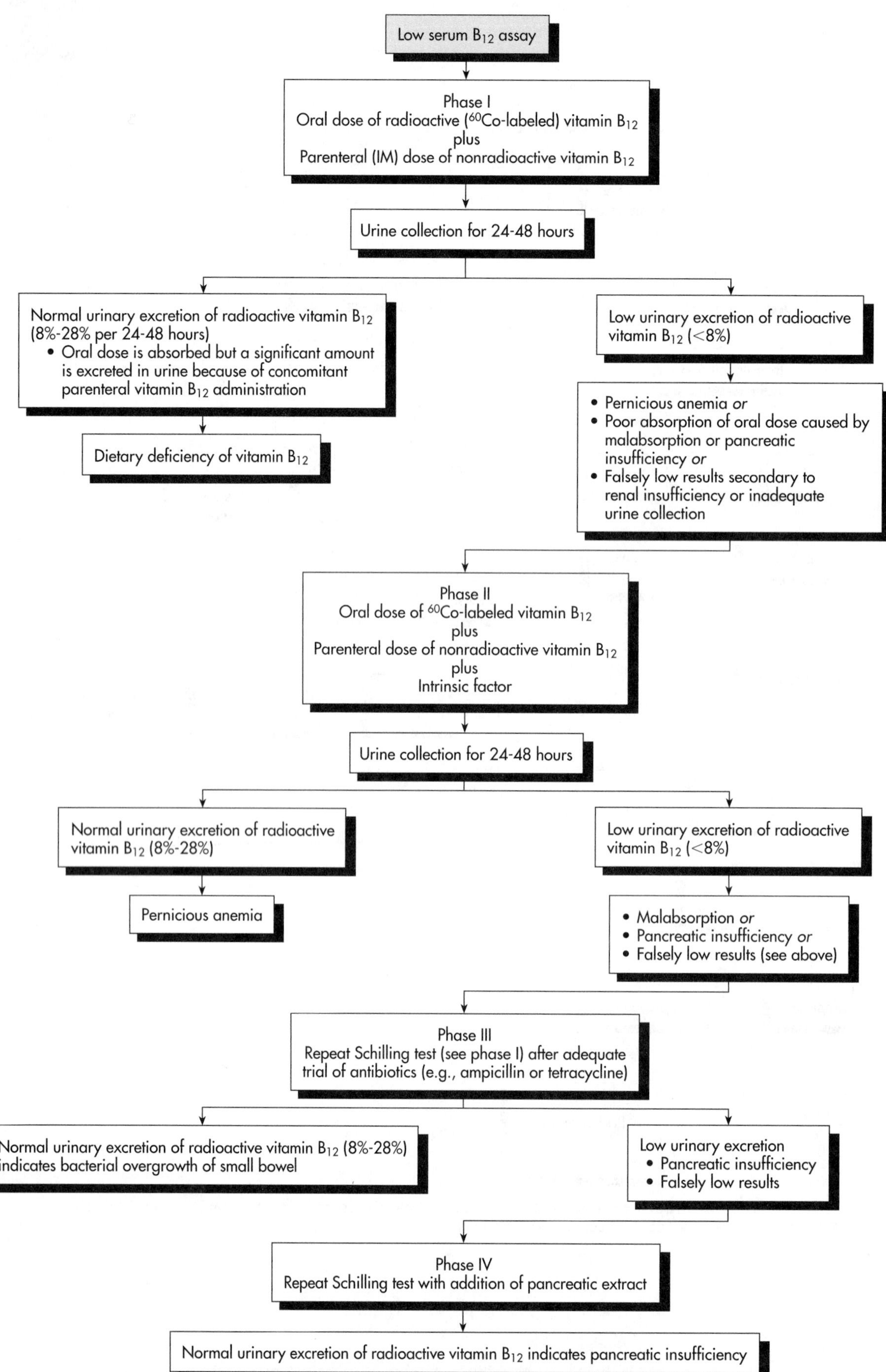

FIGURE 3-190 Schilling test. *IM,* Intramuscular. (From Ferri FF: *Practical guide to the care of the medical patient,* ed 6, St Louis, 2004, Mosby.)

SCOLIOSIS

ICD-9CM # 737.30 Idiopathic scoliosis
737.39 Paralytic scoliosis
754.2 Congenital scoliosis
724.3 Sciatic scoliosis
737.43 Associated with neurofibromatosis

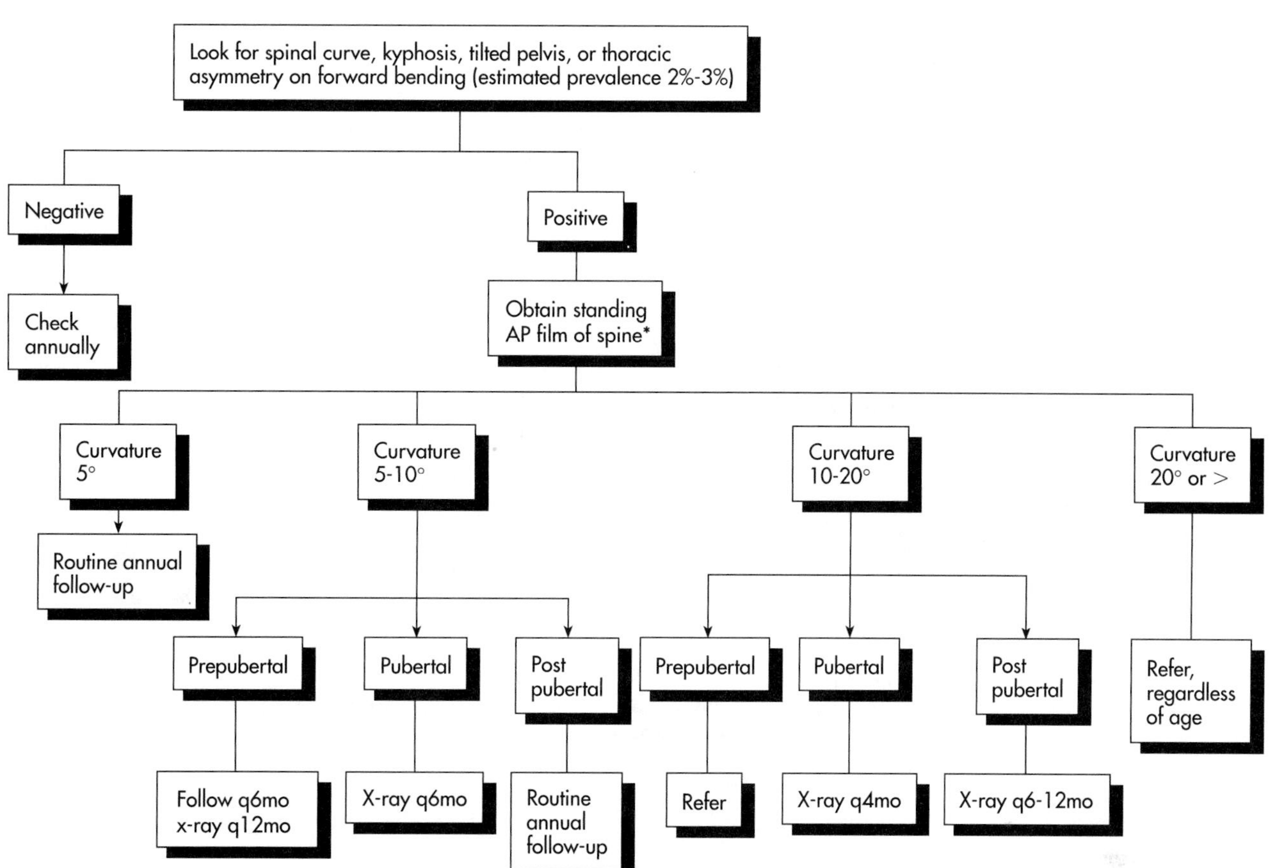

*Cobb method of angle measurement

1. Find the lowest vertebra whose bottom tilts toward concavity of curve.
2. Erect a perpendicular line from extension of bottom surface.
3. Find highest vertebra as in #1 and erect perpendicular from extension of top surface.
4. Measure intersecting angle = angle of scoliosis.

FIGURE 3-191 Scoliosis screening and follow-up. *AP,* Anteroposterior. (From Driscoll C [ed]: *The family practice desk reference,* ed 3, St Louis, 1996, Mosby.)

SCROTAL MASS

ICD-9CM # 608.89

FIGURE 3-192 Evaluation of scrotal mass. (From Greene HL, Johnson WP, Lemcke D [eds]: *Decision making in medicine,* ed 2, St Louis, 1998, Mosby.)

SEPSIS AND SEPTIC SHOCK

ICD-9CM # 038.9

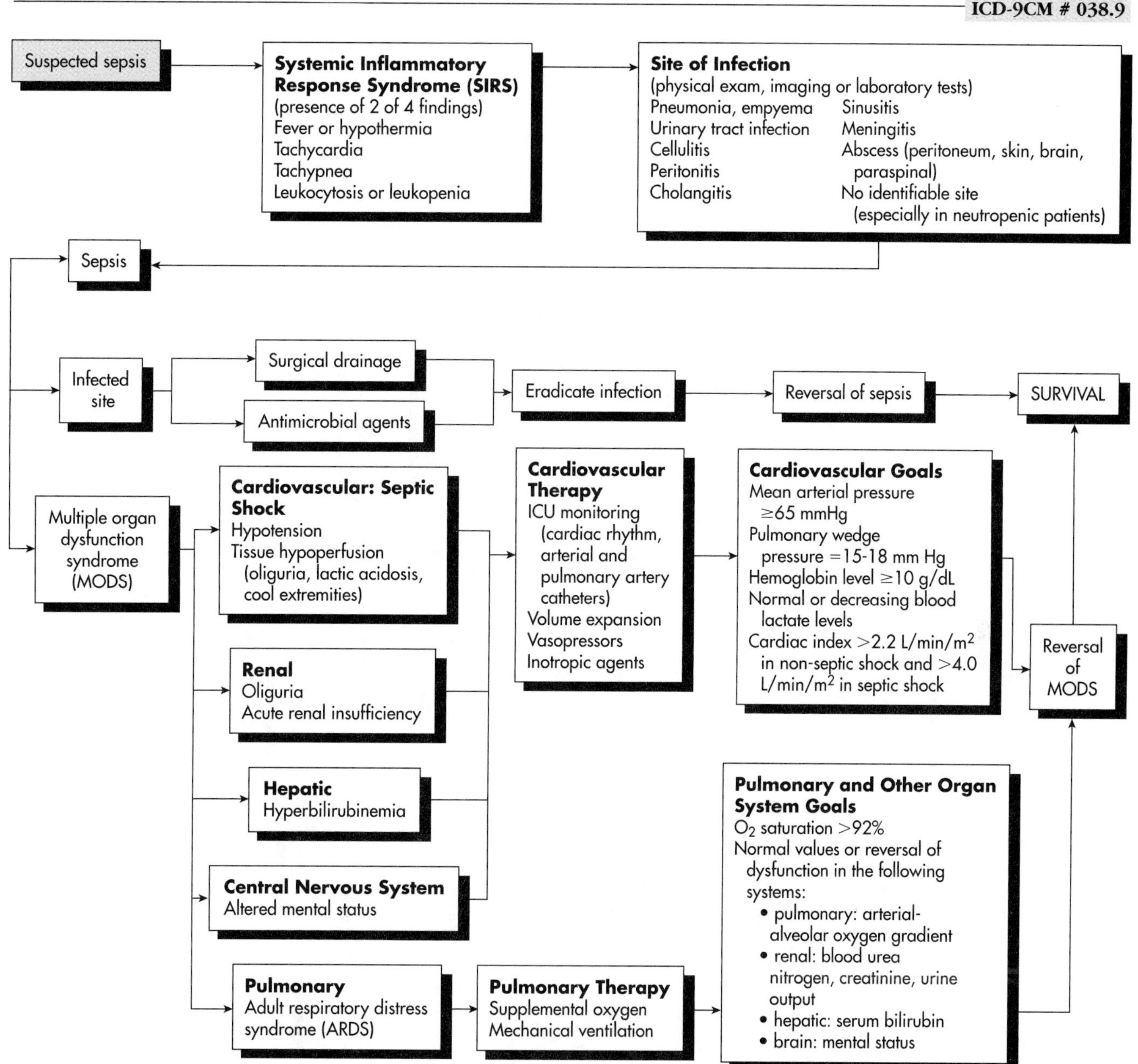

FIGURE 3-193 Diagnostic evaluation and management of sepsis and septic shock. (From Goldman L, Ausiello D [eds]: *Cecil textbook of medicine,* ed 22, Phiadeldelphia, 2004, WB Saunders.)

SEXUAL DYSFUNCTION

ICD-9CM # 309.2 Sexual disorder (psychosexual)
V41.7 Sexual function problem

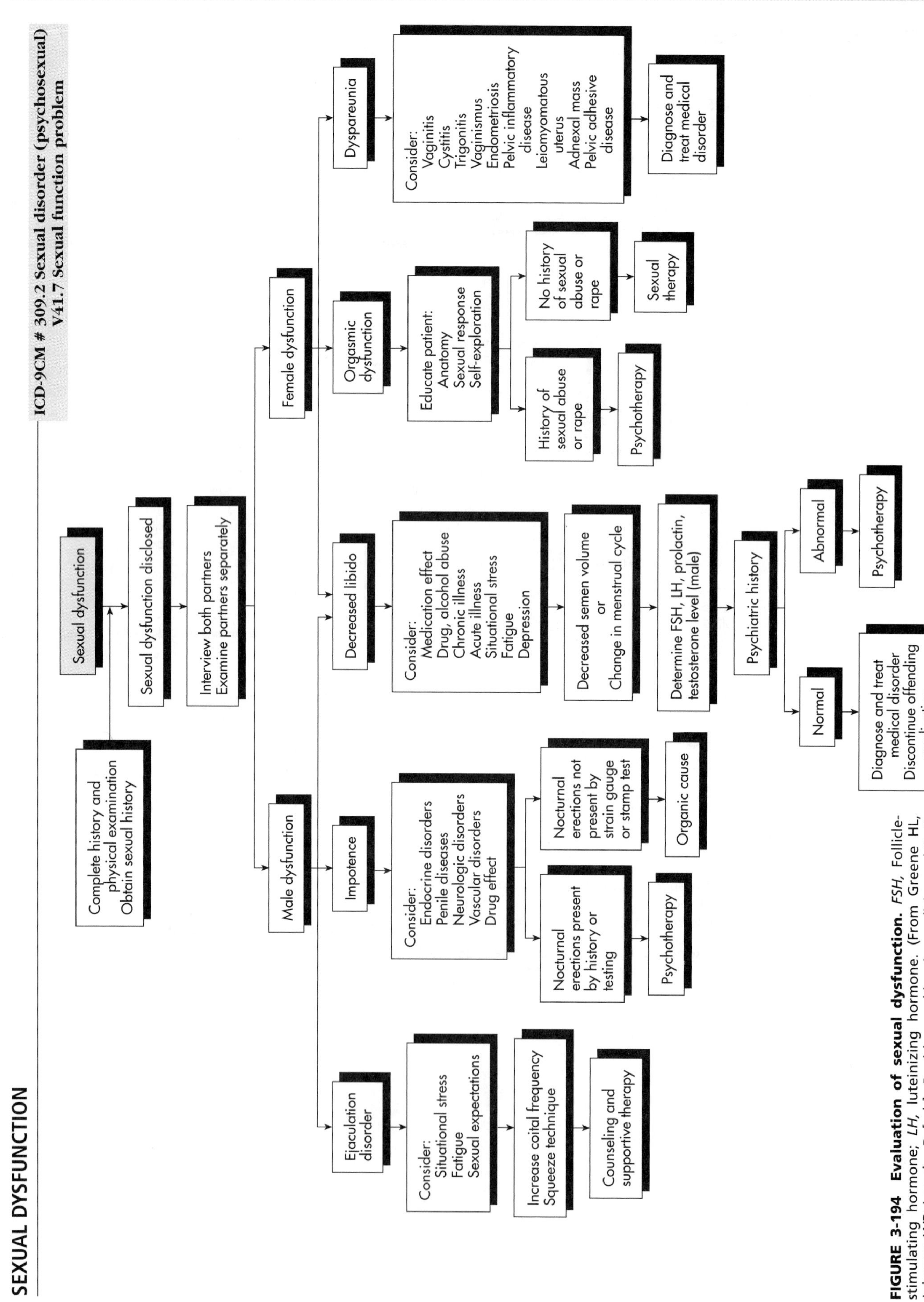

FIGURE 3-194 Evaluation of sexual dysfunction. *FSH,* Follicle-stimulating hormone; *LH,* luteinizing hormone. (From Greene HL, Johnson WP, Lemcke D [eds]: *Decision making in medicine,* ed 2, St Louis, 1998, Mosby.)

SHIN SPLINTS

ICD-9CM # 844.9

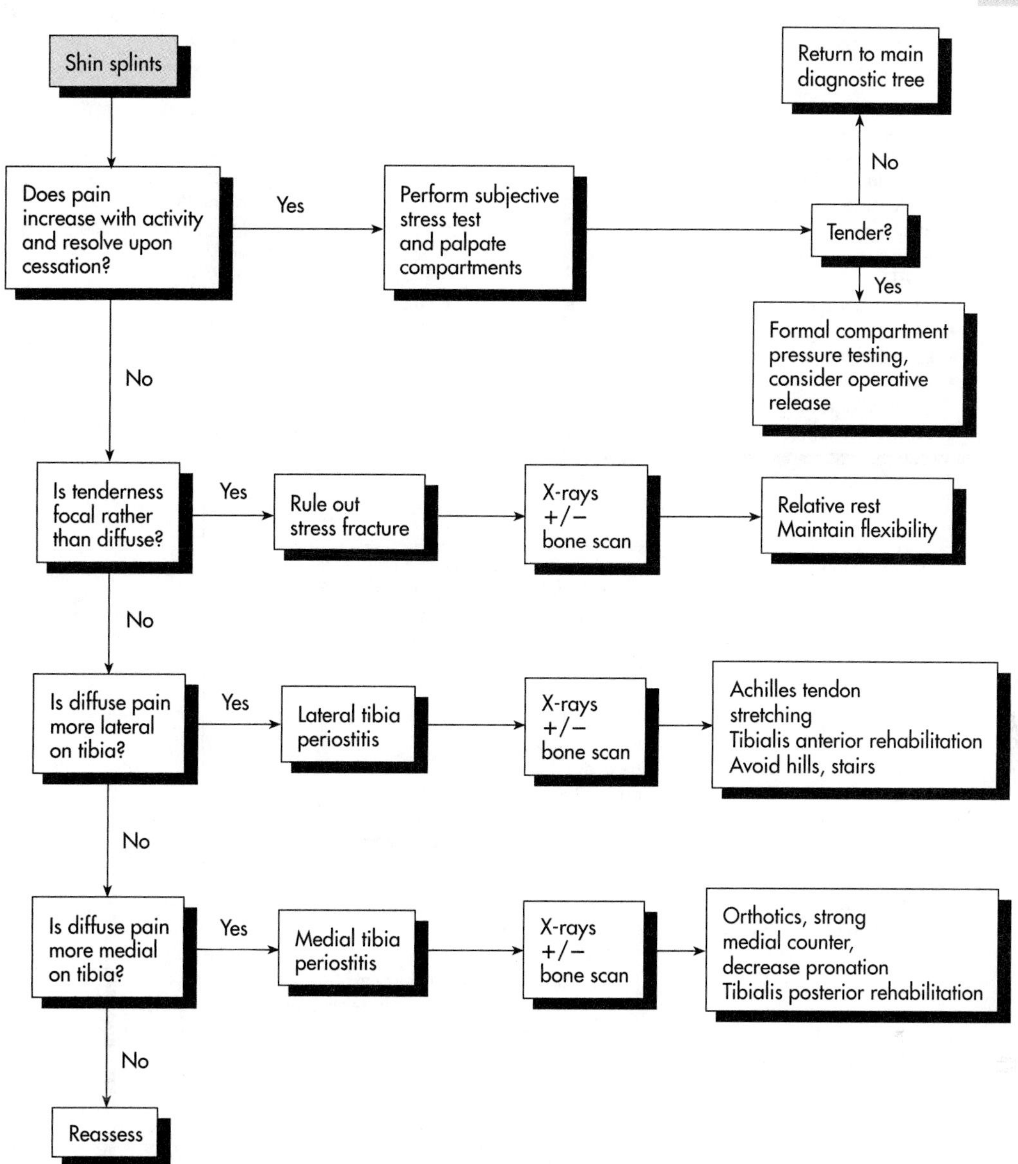

FIGURE 3-195 Evaluation and management of shin splints. (From Scudieri G [ed]: *Sports medicine, principles of primary care,* St Louis, 1997, Mosby.)

ICD-9CM # 785.50 Shock NOS
995.0 Shock anaphylactic
785.51 Shock cardiogenic
785.59 Shock septic
958.4 Shock traumatic
977.9 Shock due to drug, medicine incorrectly administered

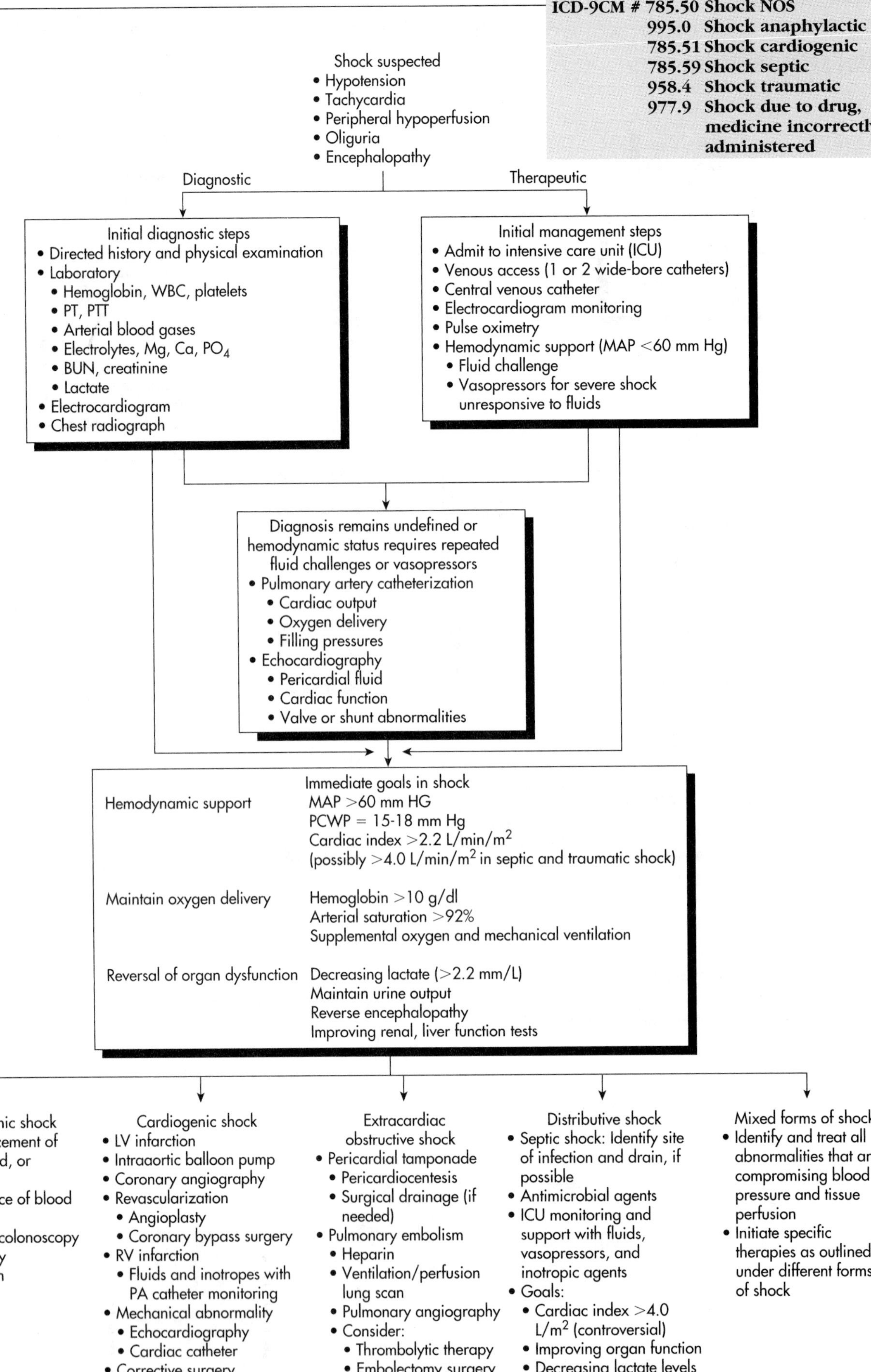

FIGURE 3-196 An approach to the diagnosis and treatment of shock. *BUN,* Blood urea nitrogen; *CT,* computed tomography; *LV,* left ventricular; *MAP,* mean arterial pressure; *MRI,* magnetic resonance imaging; *PA,* pulmonary arterial; *PCWP,* pulmonary capillary wedge pressure, *PT,* prothrombin time; *PTT,* partial thromboplastin time; *RV,* right ventricular; *WBC,* white blood cell count. (From Goldman L, Ausiello D [eds]: *Cecil textbook of medicine,* ed 22, Philadelphia, 2004, WB Saunders.)

SJOGREN'S SYNDROME

ICD-9CM # 710.2

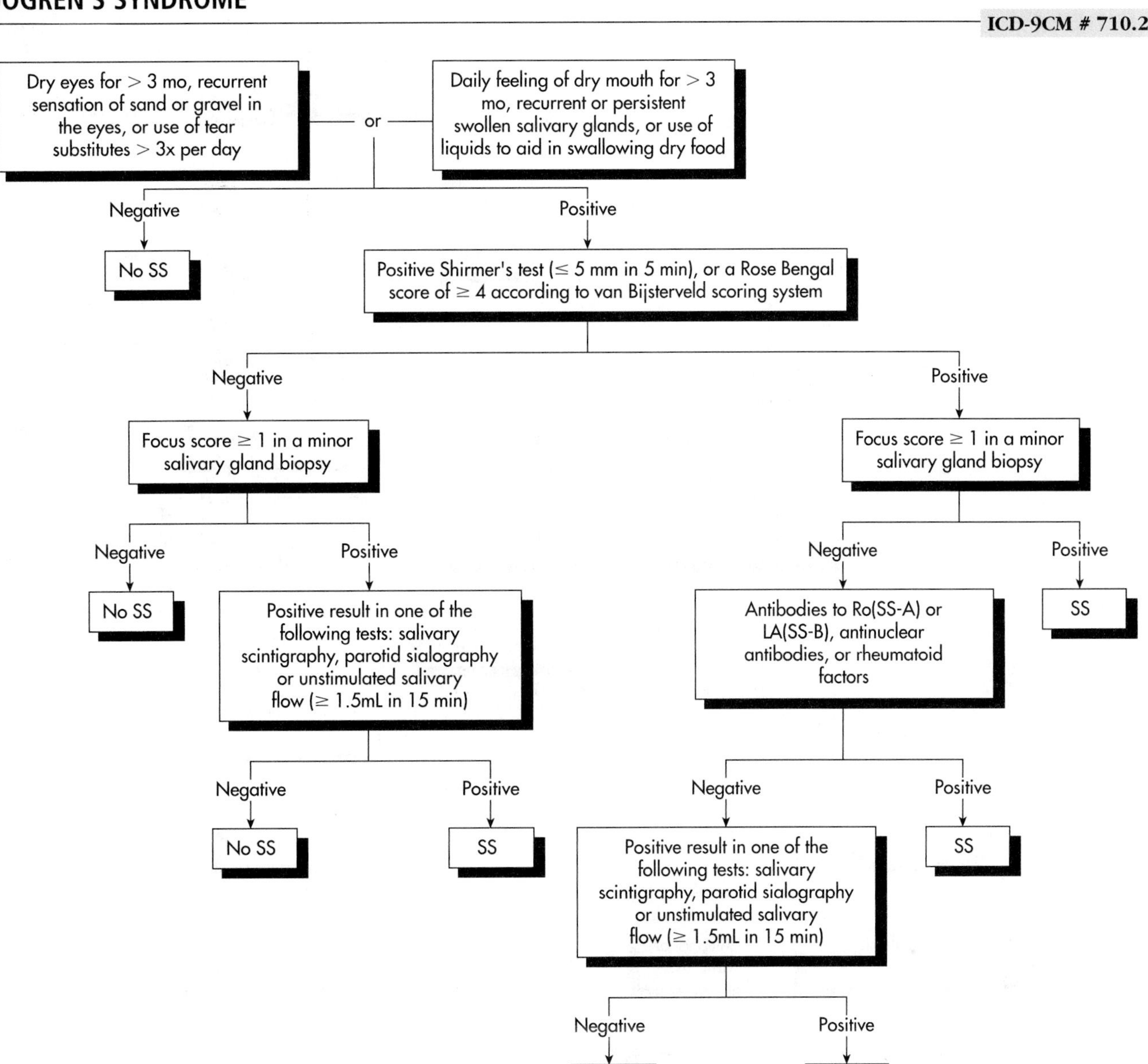

FIGURE 3-197 Algorithm for the diagnosis of Sjogren's syndrome. (From Tzoufas AG, Moutsopoulos HM: Sjogren's syndrome. In Klippel JH, Dieppe P [eds]: *Rheumatology,* ed 2, London, 1998, Mosby, with permission.

SLEEP DISORDERS

ICD-9CM # 780.50 Sleep disorder, unspecified cause

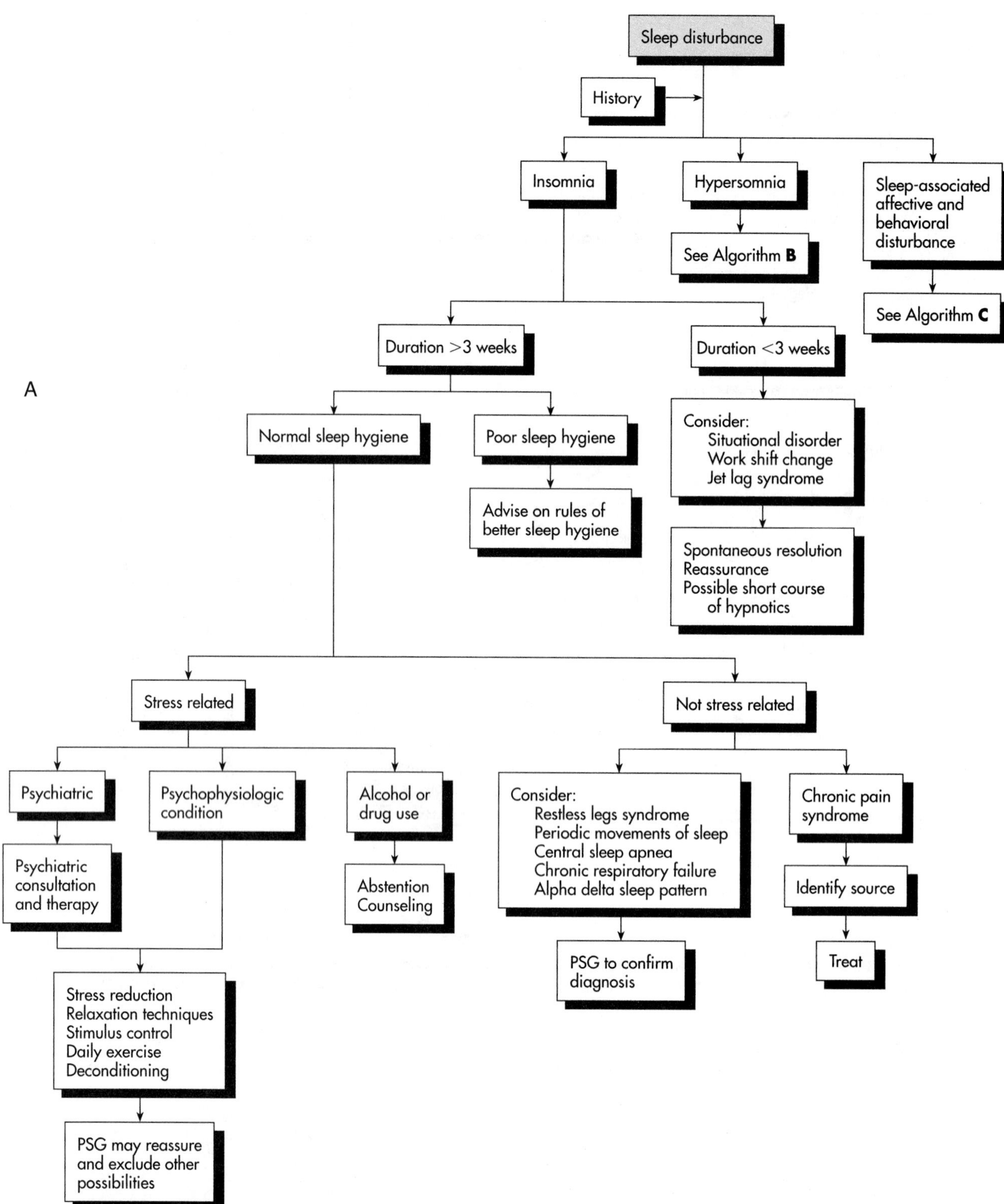

FIGURE 3-198 A, Patient with sleep disturbance. *MSLT,* Multiple sleep latency tests; *PSG,* polysomnography. (From Greene HL, Johnson WP, Lemcke D [eds]: *Decision making in medicine,* ed 2, St Louis, 1998, Mosby.)

Continued

SLEEP DISORDERS—cont'd

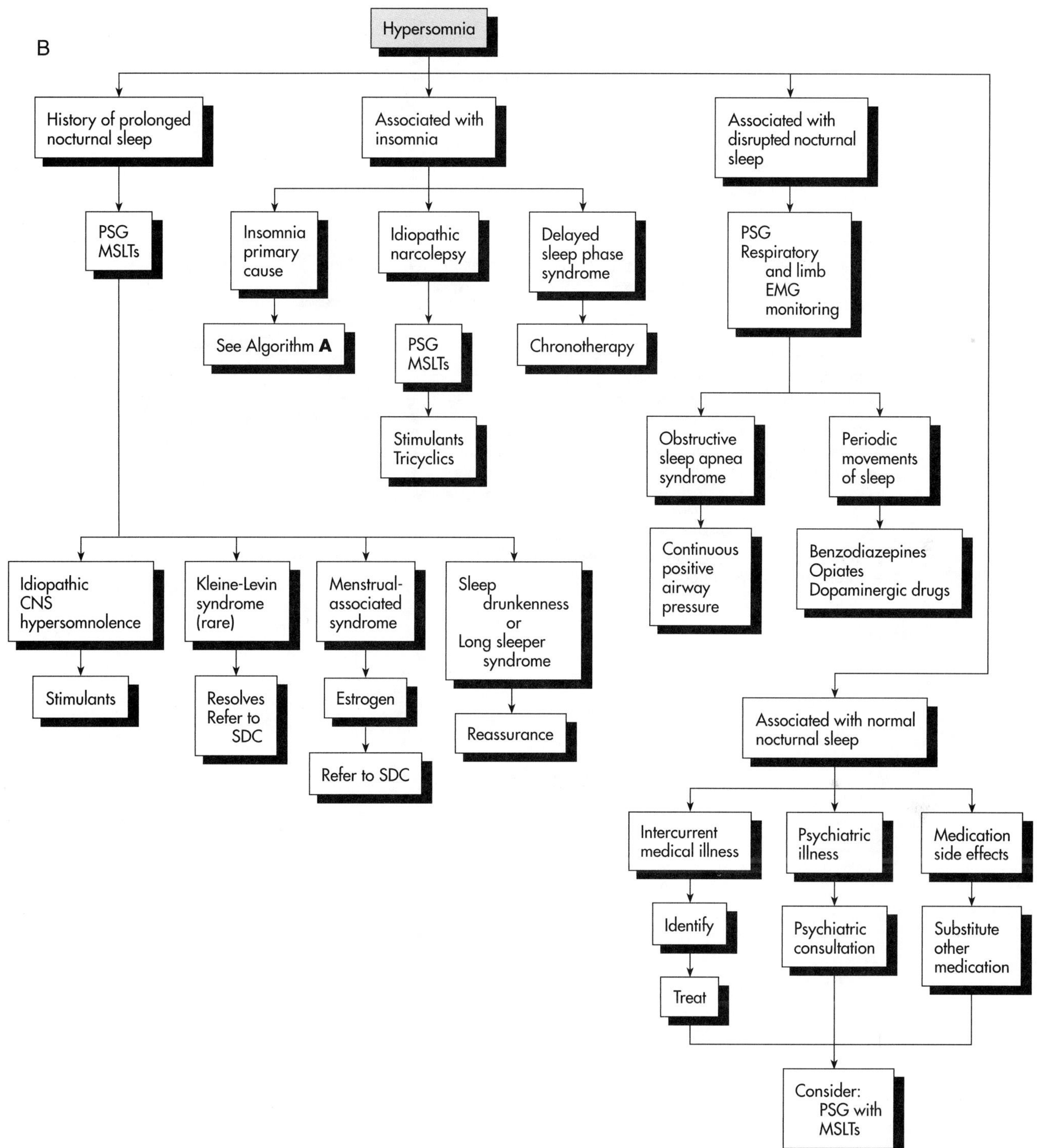

FIGURE 3-198, cont'd B, Hypersomnia. *CNS,* Central nervous system; *EMG,* electromyelogram; *MSLTs,* multiple sleep latency tests; *PSG,* polysomnography; *SDC,* sleep disorders clinic.

Continued

SLEEP DISORDERS—cont'd

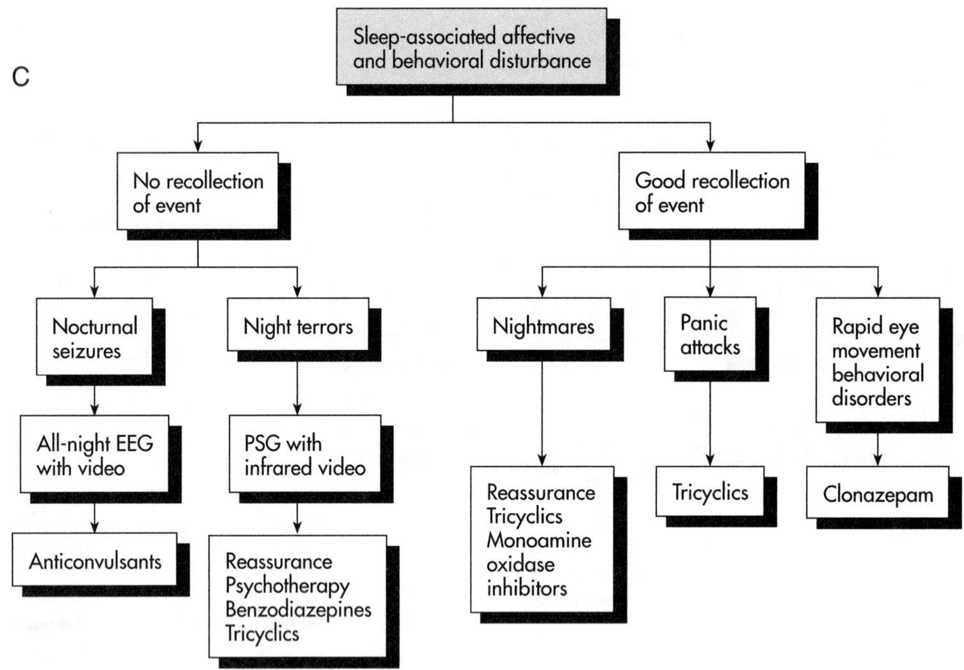

FIGURE 3-198, cont'd C, Sleep-associated affective and behavioral disturbance. *EEG,* Electroencephalogram; *PSG,* polysomnography.

SPLENOMEGALY

ICD-9CM #	
789.2	Splenomegaly, unspecified
289.51	Splenomegaly, chronic congestive
759.0	Splenomegaly, congenital
789.2	Splenomegaly, unknown etiology

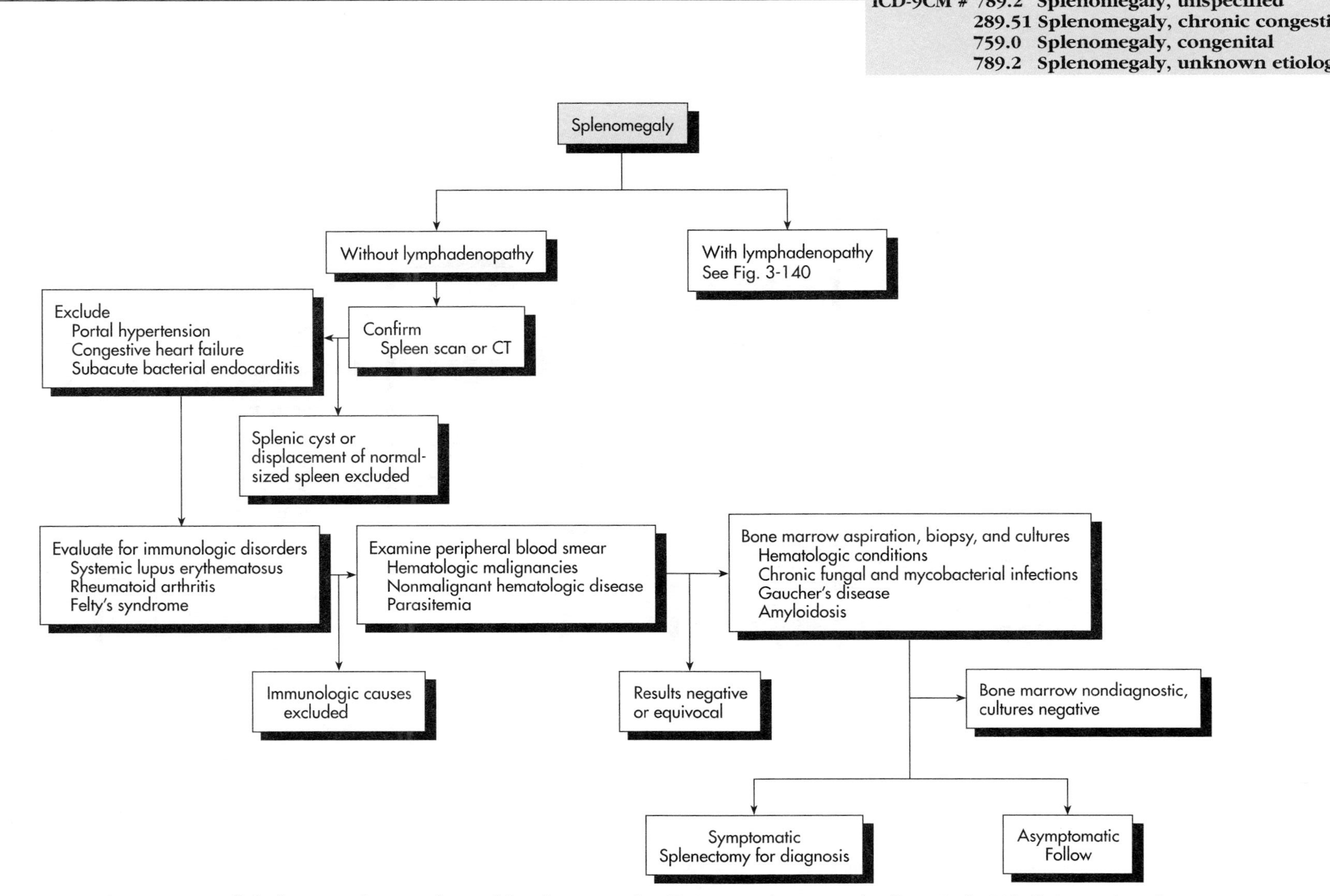

FIGURE 3-199 Clinical approach to patient with splenomegaly. *CT,* Computed tomography. (From Stein JH [ed]: *Internal medicine,* ed 5, St Louis, 1998, Mosby.)

SPONDYLOARTHROPATHY, DIAGNOSIS

ICD-9CM # 720.7

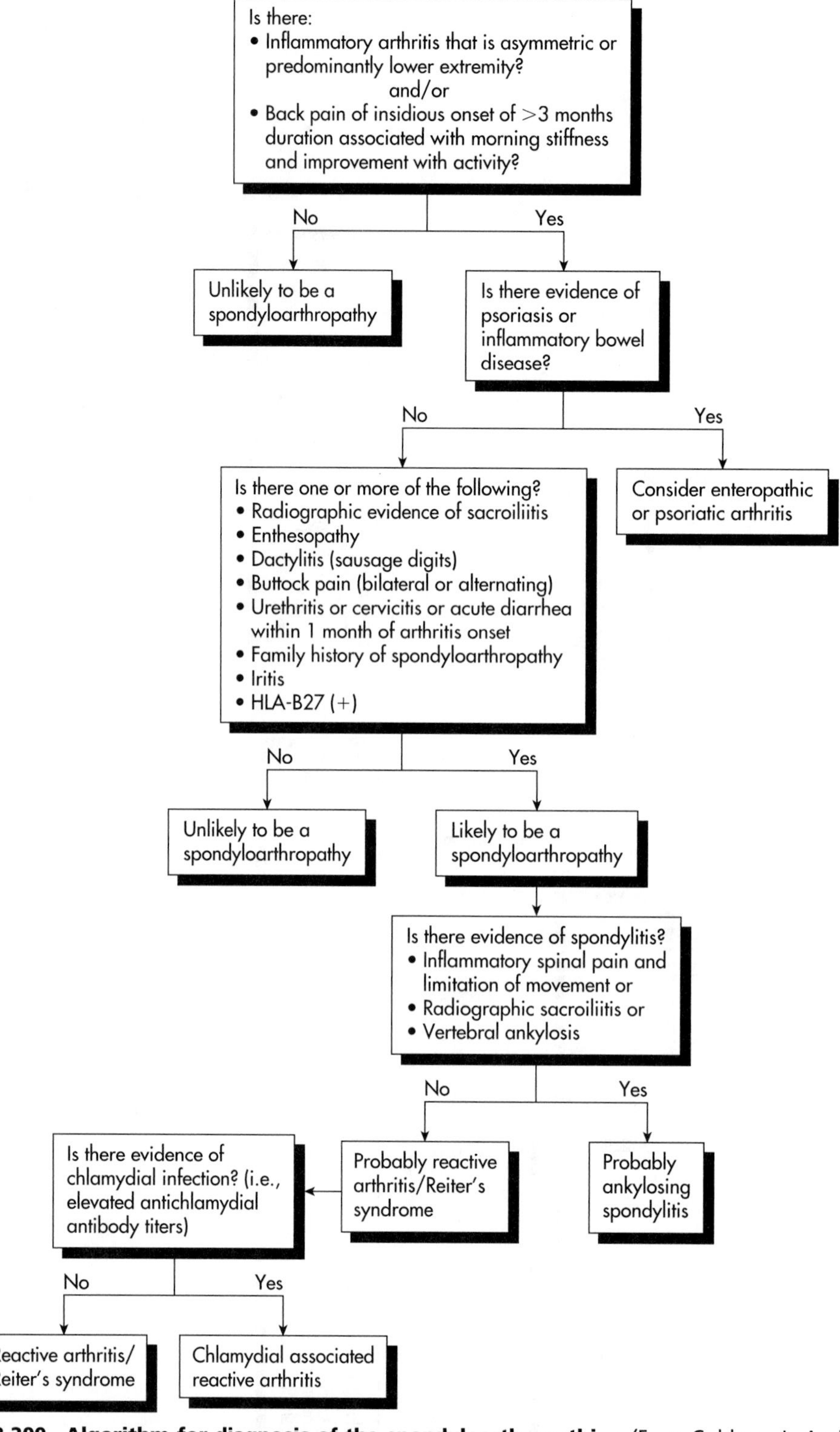

FIGURE 3-200 Algorithm for diagnosis of the spondyloarthropathies. (From Goldman L, Ausiello D: *Cecil textbook of medicine*, ed 22, Philadelphia, 2004, WB Saunders.)

SPONDYLOARTHROPATHY, TREATMENT

ICD-9CM # 720.7

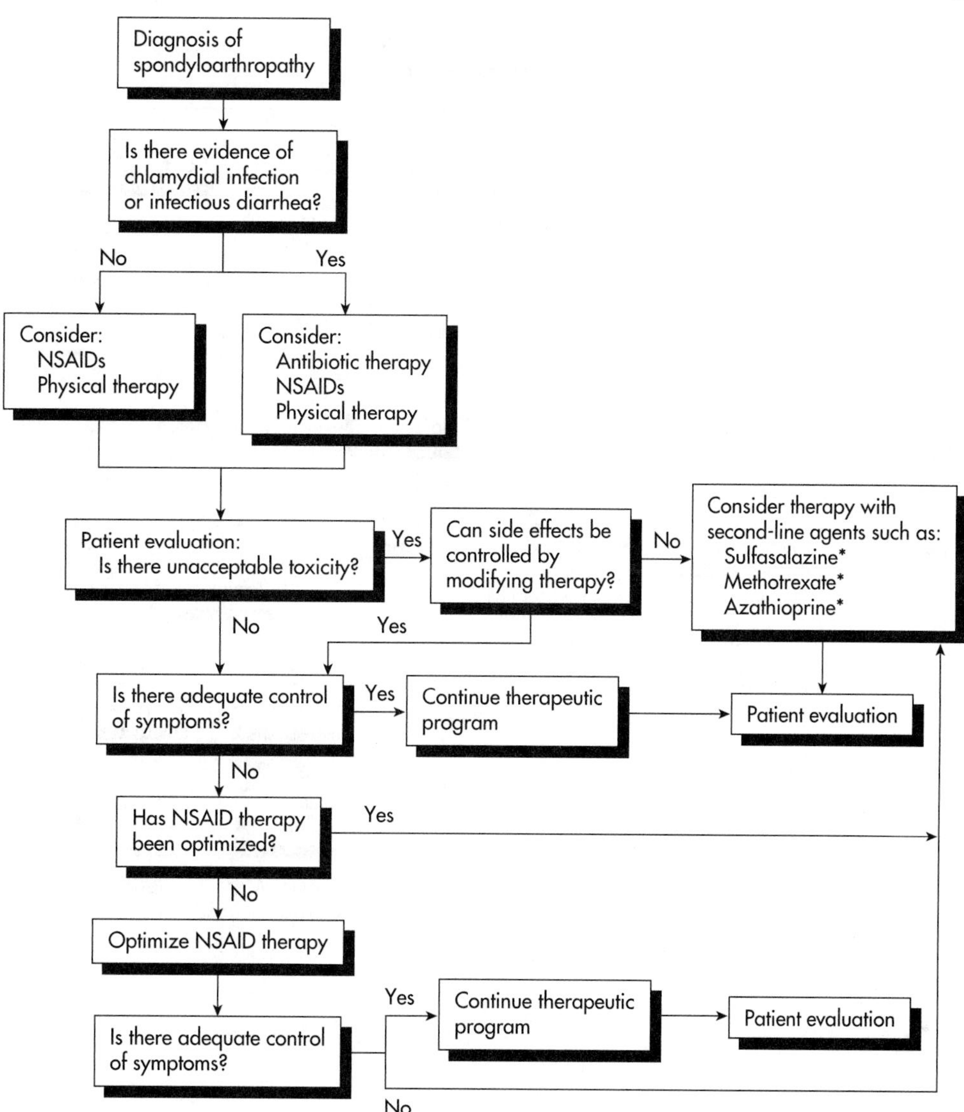

*Not approved by the FDA for treatment of spondyloarthropathies.

FIGURE 3-201 Treatment algorithm for patients with a spondyloarthropathy. *FDA,* Food and Drug Administration; *NSAID,* nonsteroidal antiinflammatory drug. (From Goldman L, Ausiello D: *Cecil textbook of medicine,* ed 22, Philadelphia, 2004, WB Saunders.)

SPONDYLOSIS, CERVICAL

ICD-9CM # 721.0

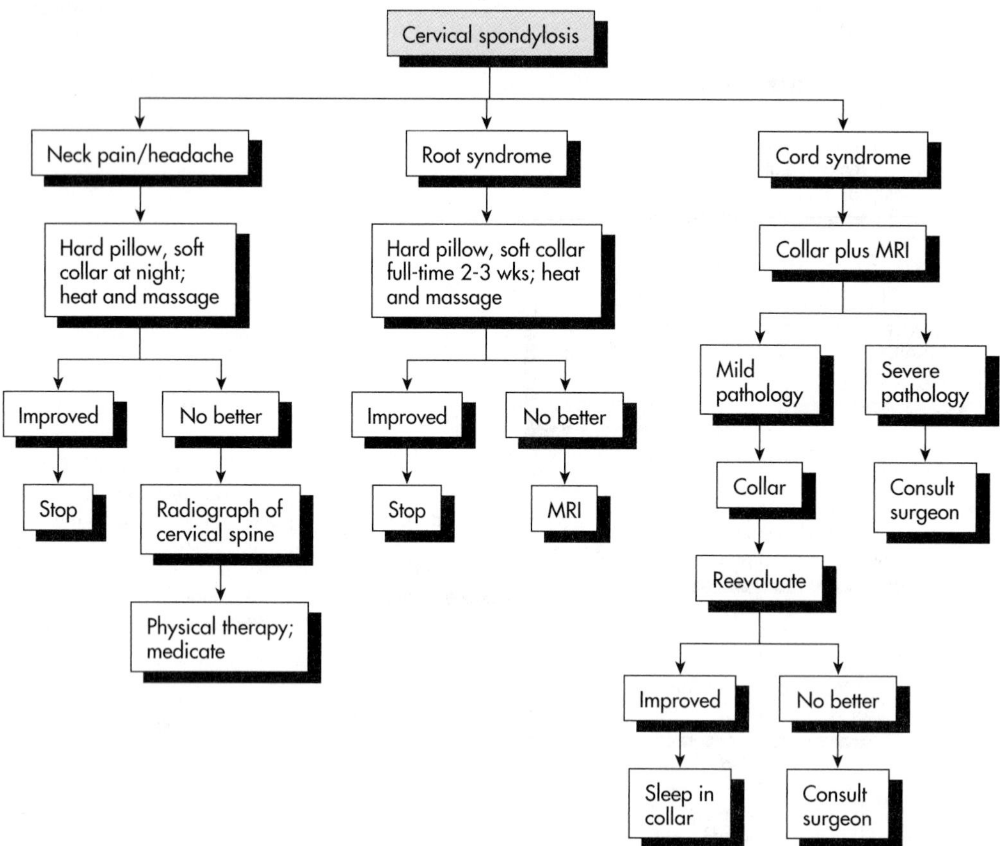

FIGURE 3-202 Algorithm for the treatment of cervical spondylosis. *MRI,* Magnetic resonance imaging. (From Ronthal M, Rachlin JR: Cervical spondylosis. In Johnson RT, Griffin JW [eds]: *Current therapy in neurologic disease,* ed 5, St Louis, 1997, Mosby.)

STRASBISMUS

ICD-9CM # 378.9

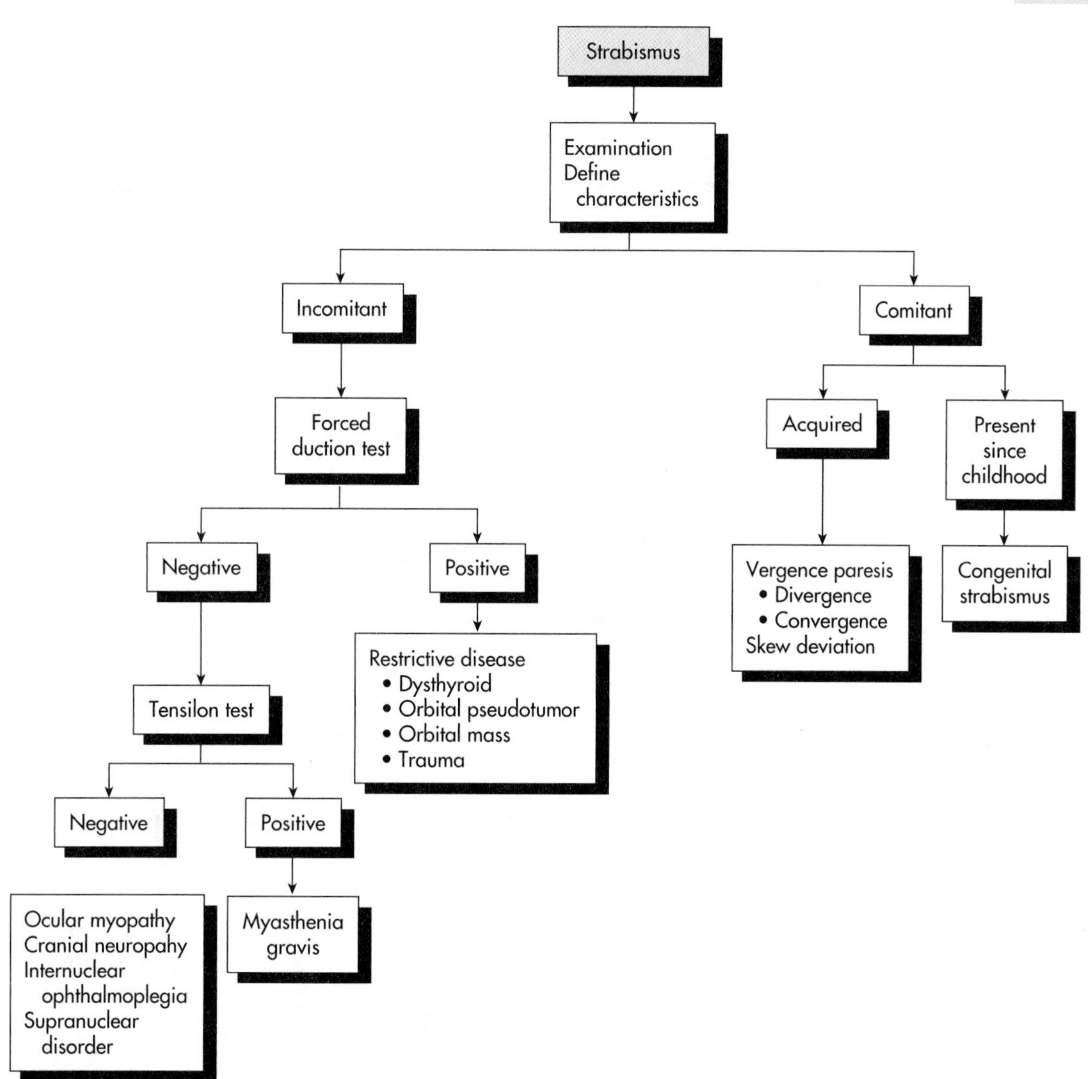

FIGURE 3-203 Diagnostic tests that help differentiate between common causes of strabismus. (From Goldman L, Ausiello D [eds]: *Cecil textbook of medicine,* ed 22, Philadelphia, 2004, WB Saunders.)

STROKE

ICD-9CM # 436

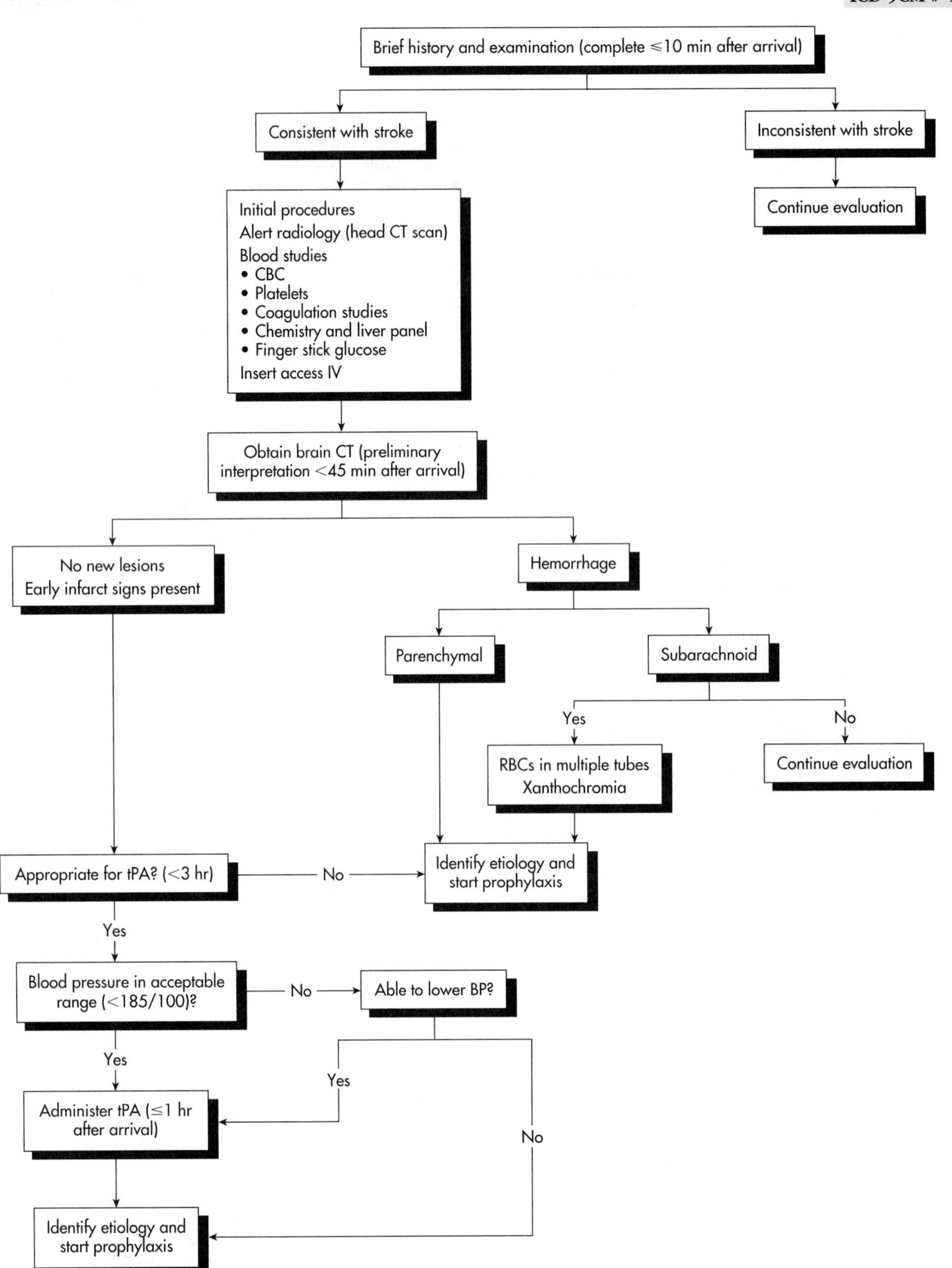

FIGURE 3-204 Algorithm for the emergency evaluation of a patient with suspected stroke. *BP,* Blood pressure; *CBC,* complete blood count; *CT,* computed tomography; *RBCs,* red blood cells; *tPA,* tissue plasminogen activator. (From Goldman L, Ausiello D [eds]: *Cecil textbook of medicine,* ed 22, Philadelphia, 2004, WB Saunders.)

SYNCOPE

ICD-9CM # 720.2

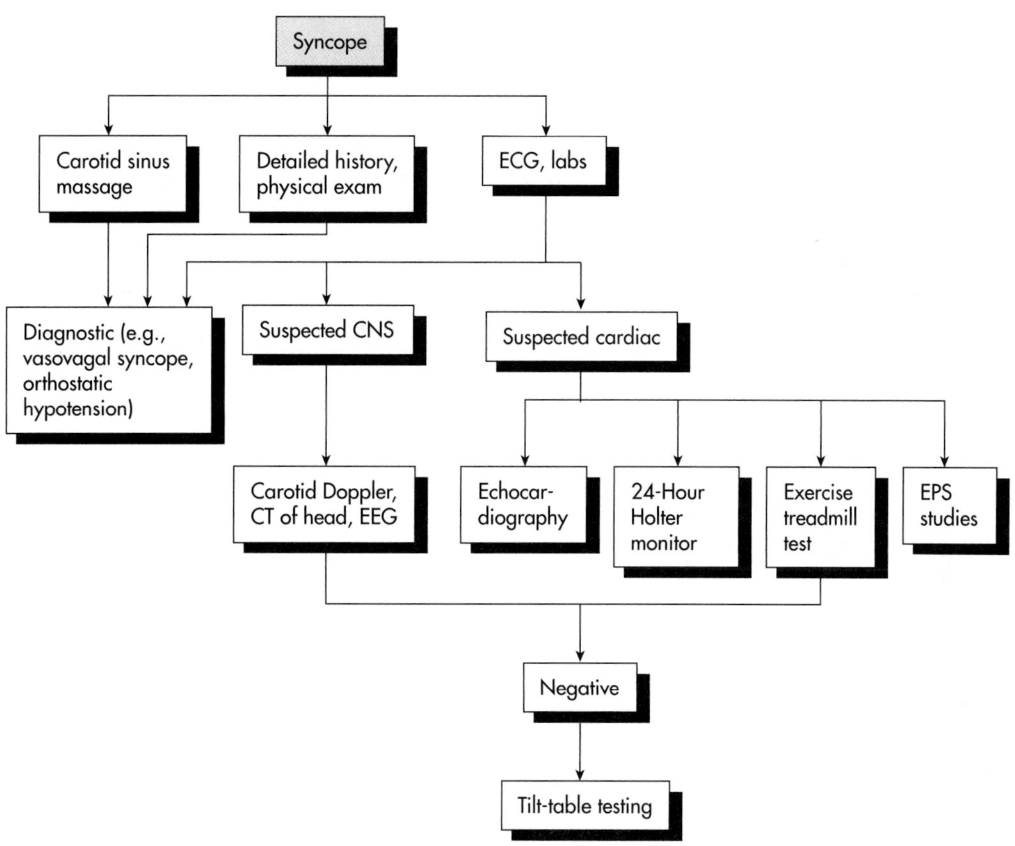

FIGURE 3-205 Syncope evaluation. *CNS,* Central nervous system; *CT,* computed tomography; *ECG,* electrocardiograph; *EEG,* electroencephalograph; *EPS,* electrophysiologic. (From Ferri FF: *Ferri's best test: a practical guide to clinical laboratory medicine and diagnostic imaging,* Philadelphia, 2004, Elsevier Mosby.)

BOX 3-12 Syncope

Diagnostic imaging

Best test

None. Diagnostic imaging should be guided by history and physical exam

Ancillary tests

Echocardiography is useful in patients with a heart murmur to r/o aortic stenosis, hypertrophic cardiomyopathy, or atrial myxoma

If seizure is suspected, CT of head and EEG are indicated

Spiral CT of chest or ventilation/perfusion scan if PE is suspected

Lab evaluation

Best test

None

Ancillary tests

Routine blood tests rarely yield diagnostically useful information and should be done only when specifically suggested by history and physical exam

Serum pregnancy test should be considered in women of childbearing age

CBC, lytes, BUN, creatinine

Serum calcium, magnesium

ABGs

ECG

Cardiac troponins, isoenzymes if history of chest pain before syncope

Toxicology screen in selected patients

Cardiac stress test

Electrophysiologic (EPS) studies

From Ferri FF: *Ferri's best test: a practical guide to clinical laboratory medicine and diagnostic imaging,* Philadelphia, 2004, Elsevier Mosby.

ABG, Arterial blood gas; *BUN,* blood urea nitrogen; *CBC,* complete blood count; *CT,* computed tomography; *ECG,* electrocardiograph; *EEG,* electroencephalograph.

SYPHILIS TESTING

ICD-9CM # 097.9

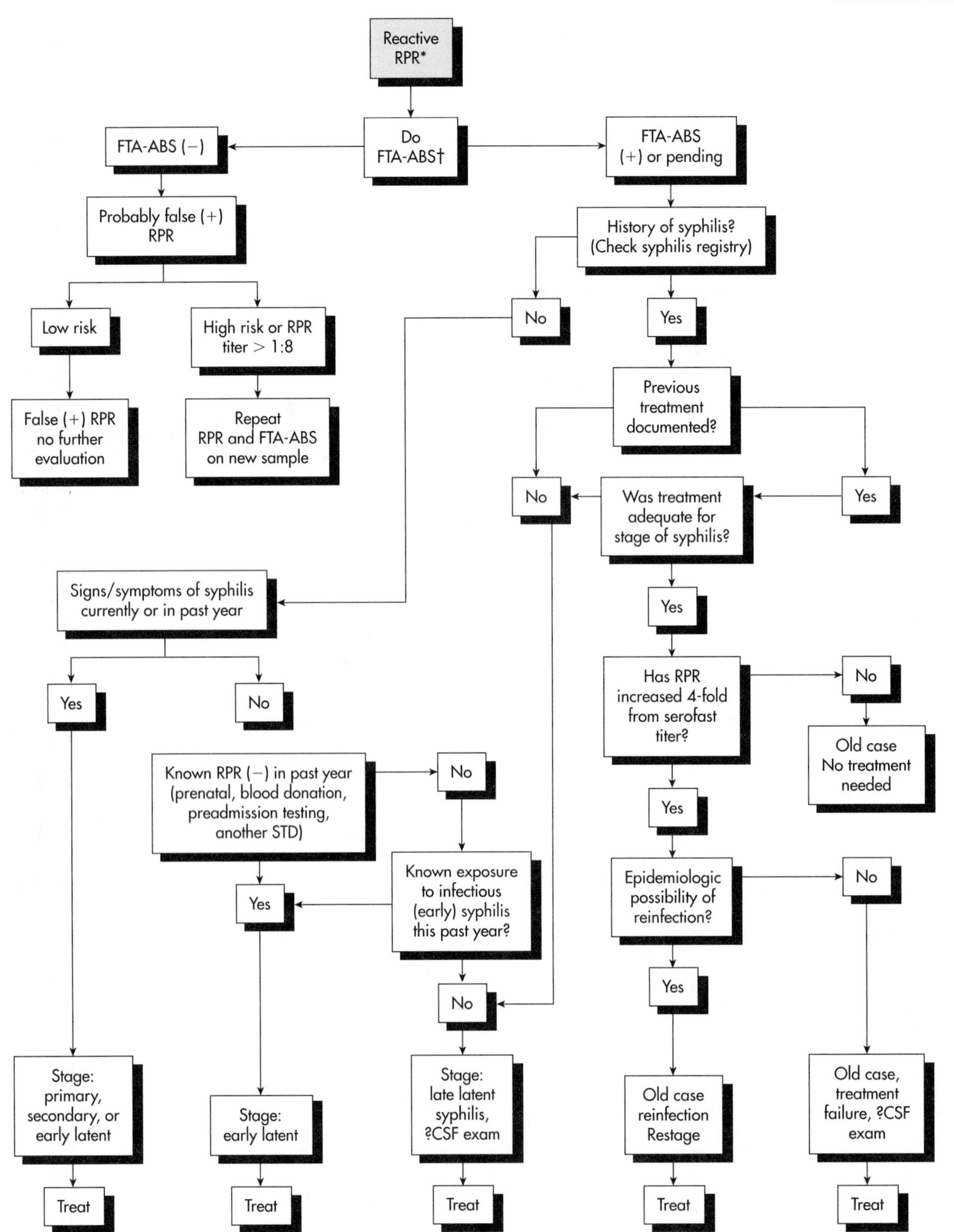

FIGURE 3-206 Interpretation of reactive serologic tests for syphilis. *CSF,* cerebrospinal fluid; *FTA-ABS,* fluorescent treponemal antibody absorption; *RPR,* rapid plasma reagent; *STD,* sexually transmitted disease. (From Habif TA: *Clinical dermatology,* ed 4, St Louis, 2004, Mosby.)

TACHYCARDIA, NARROW COMPLEX

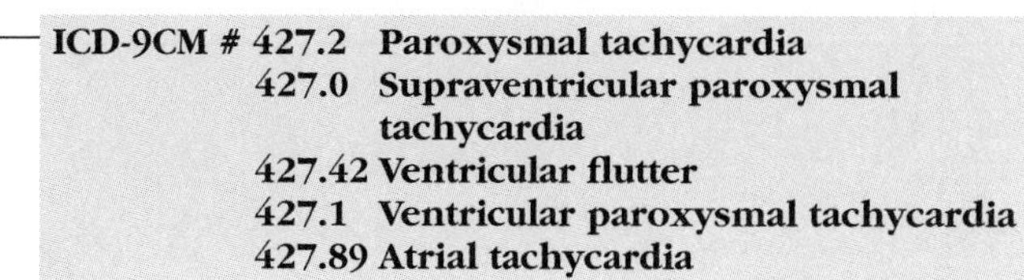
ICD-9CM # 427.2 Paroxysmal tachycardia
427.0 Supraventricular paroxysmal tachycardia
427.42 Ventricular flutter
427.1 Ventricular paroxysmal tachycardia
427.89 Atrial tachycardia

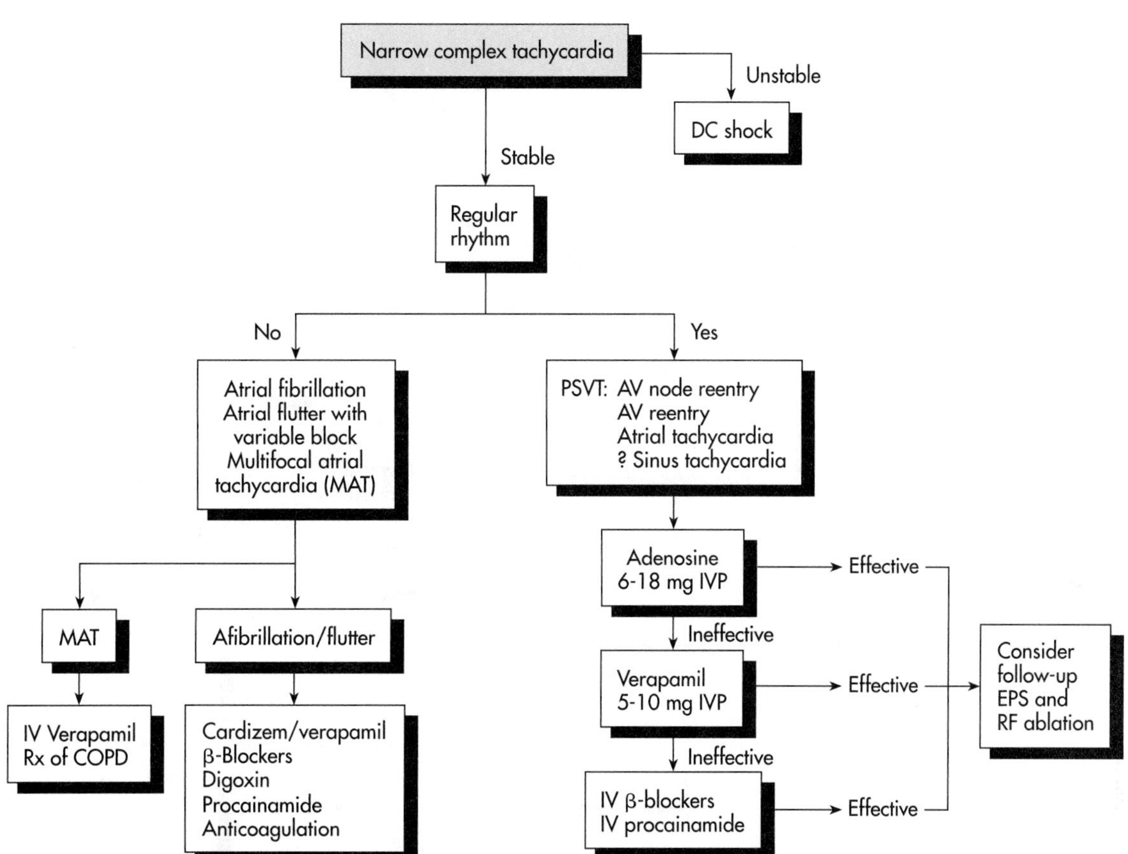

FIGURE 3-207 Evaluation and management of narrow complex tachycardia. *AV,* Atrioventricular; *COPD,* chronic obstructive pulmonary disease; *EPS,* electrophysiologic studies; *IV,* intravenous; *IVP,* intravenous push; *PSVT,* paroxysmal supraventricular tachycardia; *RF,* radiofrequency. (From Driscoll CE et al: *The family practice desk reference,* ed 3, St Louis, 1996, Mosby.)

TACHYCARDIA, WIDE COMPLEX

ICD-9CM # 427.2 Paroxysmal tachycardia
427.0 Supraventricular paroxysmal tachycardia
427.42 Ventricular flutter
427.1 Ventricular paroxysmal tachycardia
427.89 Atrial tachycardia

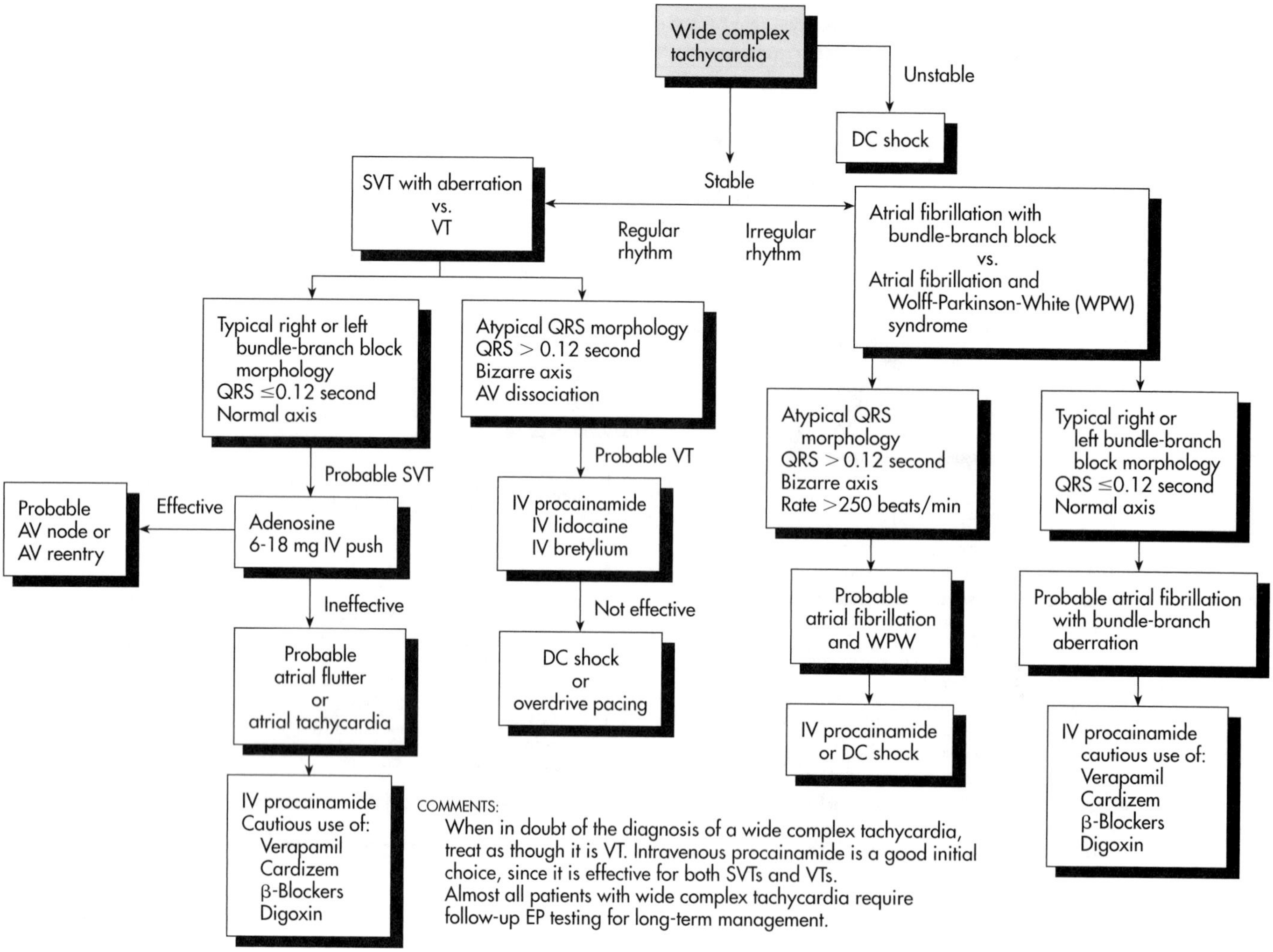

FIGURE 3-208 Evaluation and management of wide complex tachycardia. *AV,* Atrioventricular; *EP,* electrophysiologic; *IV,* intravenous; *SVT,* supraventricular tachycardia; *VT,* ventricular tachycardia. (From Driscoll CE et al: *The family practice desk reference,* ed 3, St Louis, 1996, Mosby.)

TESTICULAR MASS

ICD-9CM # 186.9 Testicular neoplasm
M906/3 (seminoma)
M9101/3 (embryonal carcinoma or teratoma)
M9100/3 (choriocarcinoma)

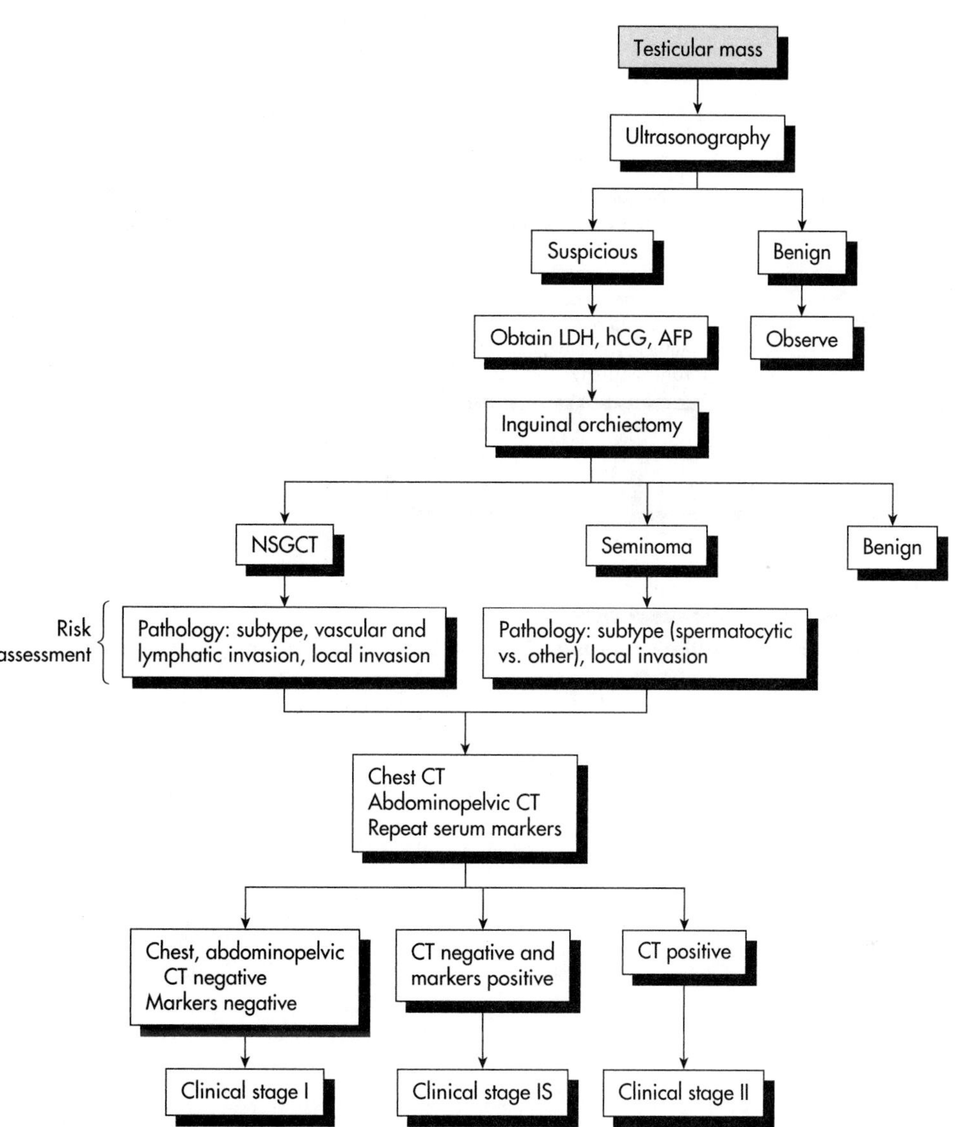

FIGURE 3-209 Diagnosis, staging, and risk assessment of patients with testicular germ cell tumor. *AFP,* Alpha-fetoprotein; *CT,* computed tomography; *hCG,* human chorionic gonadotropin; *LDH,* lactic dehydrogenase; *NSGCT,* nonseminoma germ cell tumor. (From Abeloff MD: *Clinical oncology,* ed 2, New York, 2000, Churchill Livingstone.)

THORACIC OUTLET SYNDROME

ICD-9CM # 353.0

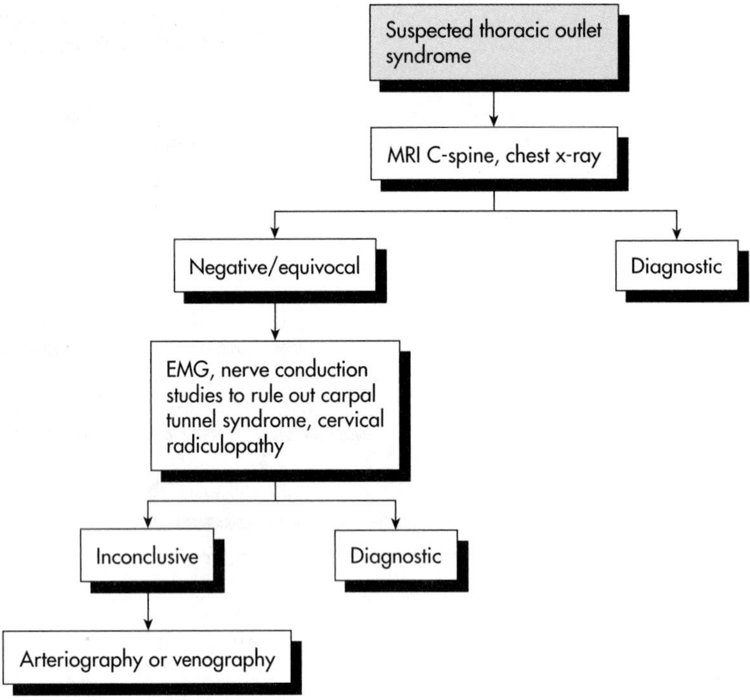

FIGURE 3-210 Thoracic outlet syndrome. *EMG,* Electromyogram; *MRI,* magnetic resonance imaging.

THROMBOCYTOPENIA

ICD-9CM # 287.3 Congenital or primary
287.4 Secondary
287.5 Thrombocytopenia NOS

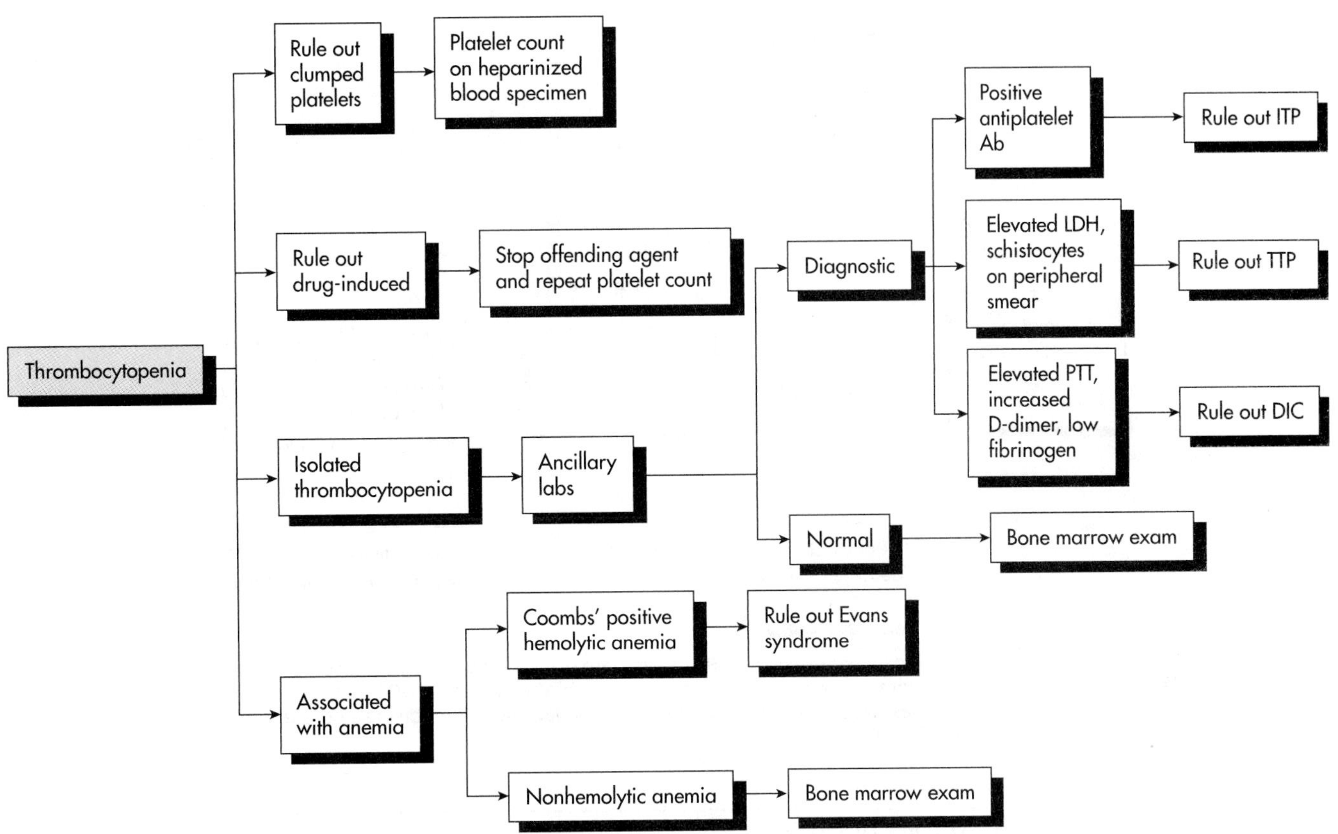

FIGURE 3-211 Evaluation of thrombocytopenia. *DIC,* Disseminated intravascular coagulation; *ITP,* idiopathic thrombocytopenic purpura; *LDH,* lactic dehydrogenase; *PPT,* partial thromboplastin time; *TTP,* thrombotic thrombocytopenic purpura. (From Ferri FF: *Ferri's best test: a practical guide to clinical laboratory medicine and diagnostic imaging,* Philadelphia, 2004, Elsevier Mosby.)

BOX 3-13 **Thrombocytopenia**

Diagnostic imaging
Best Test
None
Ancillary test
CT of abdomen if splenomegaly is present

Lab evaluation
Best Test
Bone marrow exam
Ancillary tests
CBC, PT, PTT
LDH
HIV, ANA
Antiplatelet Ab
D-dimer
Coombs' tests

From Ferri FF: *Ferri's best test: a practical guide to clinical laboratory medicine and diagnostic imaging,* Philadelphia, 2004, Elsevier Mosby.

ANA, Antibody to nuclear antigens; *CBC,* complete blood count; *CT,* computed tomography; *HIV,* human immunodeficiency virus; *LDH,* lactic dehydrogenase; *PT,* prothrombin time; *PTT,* partial thromboplastin time.

THROMBOCYTOSIS

ICD-9CM # 289.9

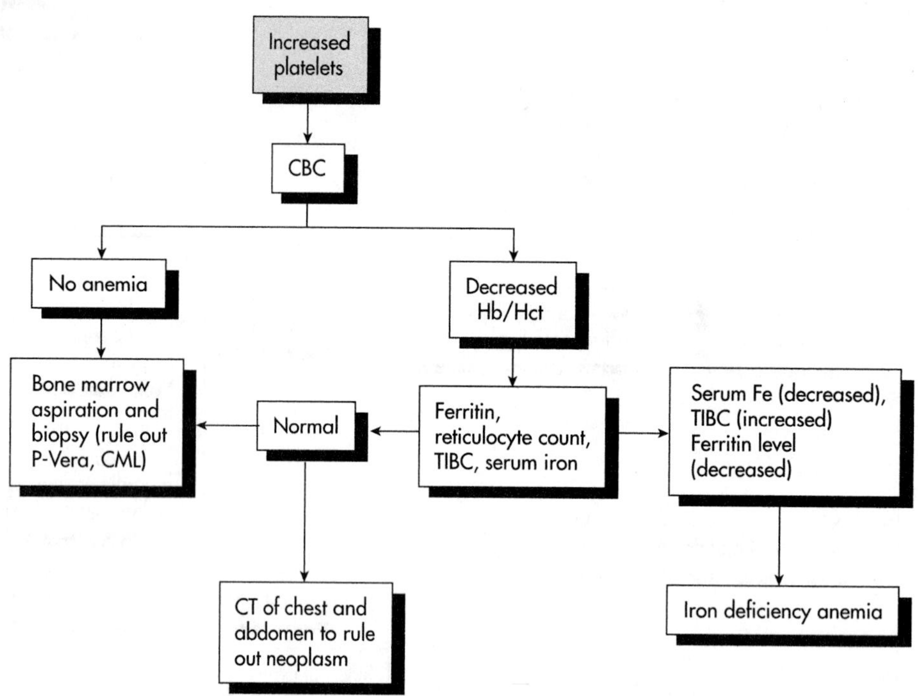

FIGURE 3-212 Thrombocytosis diagnosis. *CBC,* Complete blood count; *CML,* chronic myelogenous leukemia; *CT,* computed tomography; *Fe,* iron; *Hb/Hct,* hemoglobin/hematocrit; *TIBC,* total iron-binding capacity. (From Ferri FF: *Ferri's best test: a practical guide to clinical laboratory medicine and diagnostic imaging,* Philadelphia, 2004, Elsevier Mosby.)

BOX 3-14 Thrombocytosis

Diagnostic imaging	Lab evaluation
Best Test	***Best Test***
None	Bone marrow exam
Ancillary test	***Ancillary tests***
CT of chest and abdomen	CBC
	Reticulocyte count
	Stool for OB ×3
	Serum ferritin, TIBC, iron

Ferri FF: *Ferri's best test: a practical guide to clinical laboratory medicine and diagnostic imaging,* Philadelphia, 2004, Elsevier Mosby.

CBC, Complete blood count; *CT,* computed tomography; *OB,* occult blood; *TIBC,* total iron-binding capacity.

ICD-9CM # 245.0 Acute thyroiditis

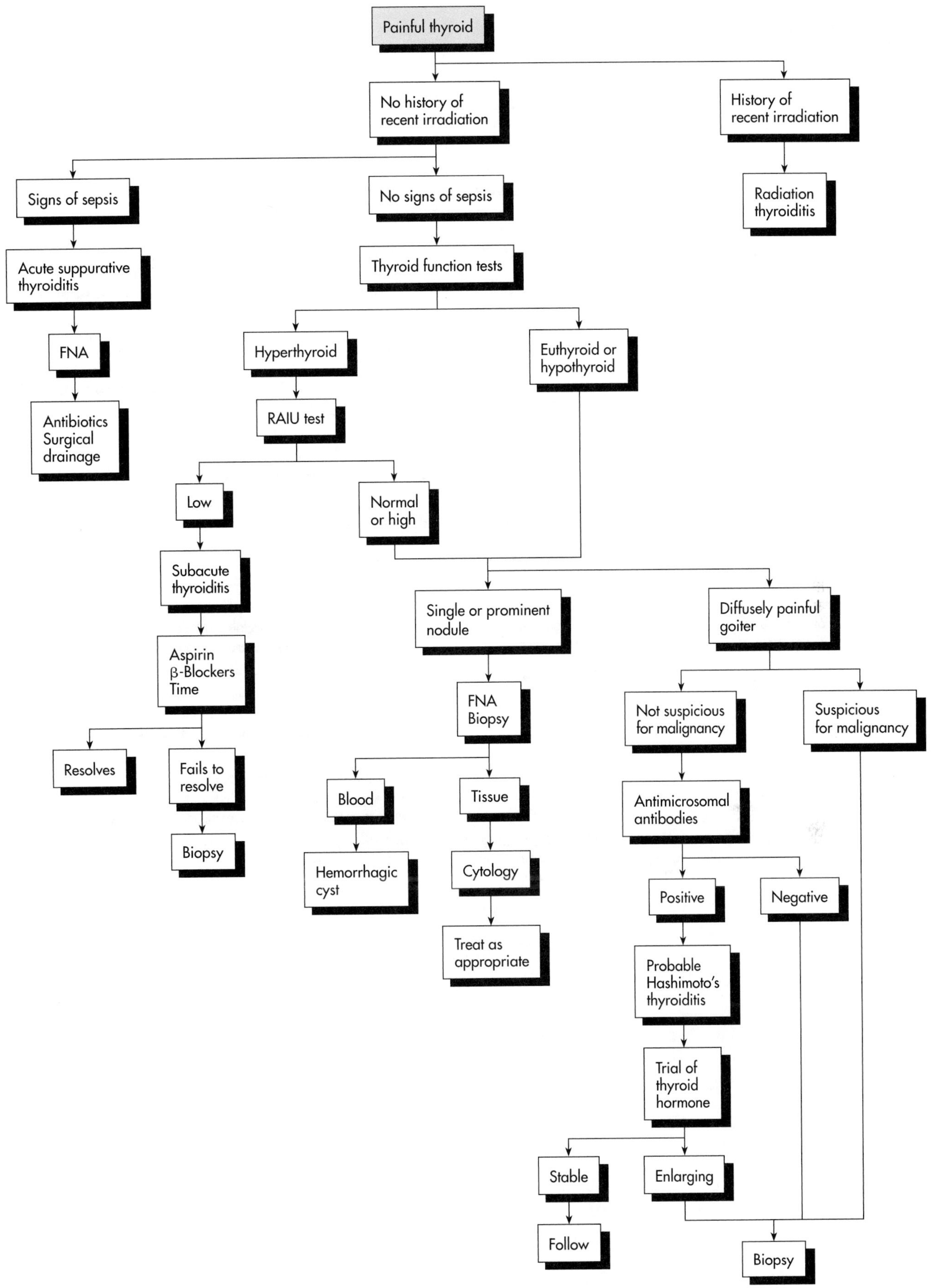

FIGURE 3-213 Painful thyroid. *FNA,* Fine-needle aspiration; *RAIU,* radioactive iodine uptake. (From Greene HL, Johnson WP, Lemcke D [eds]: *Decision making in medicine,* ed 2, St Louis, 1998, Mosby.)

THYROID NODULE

ICD-9CM # 241.0 Nodule, thyroid

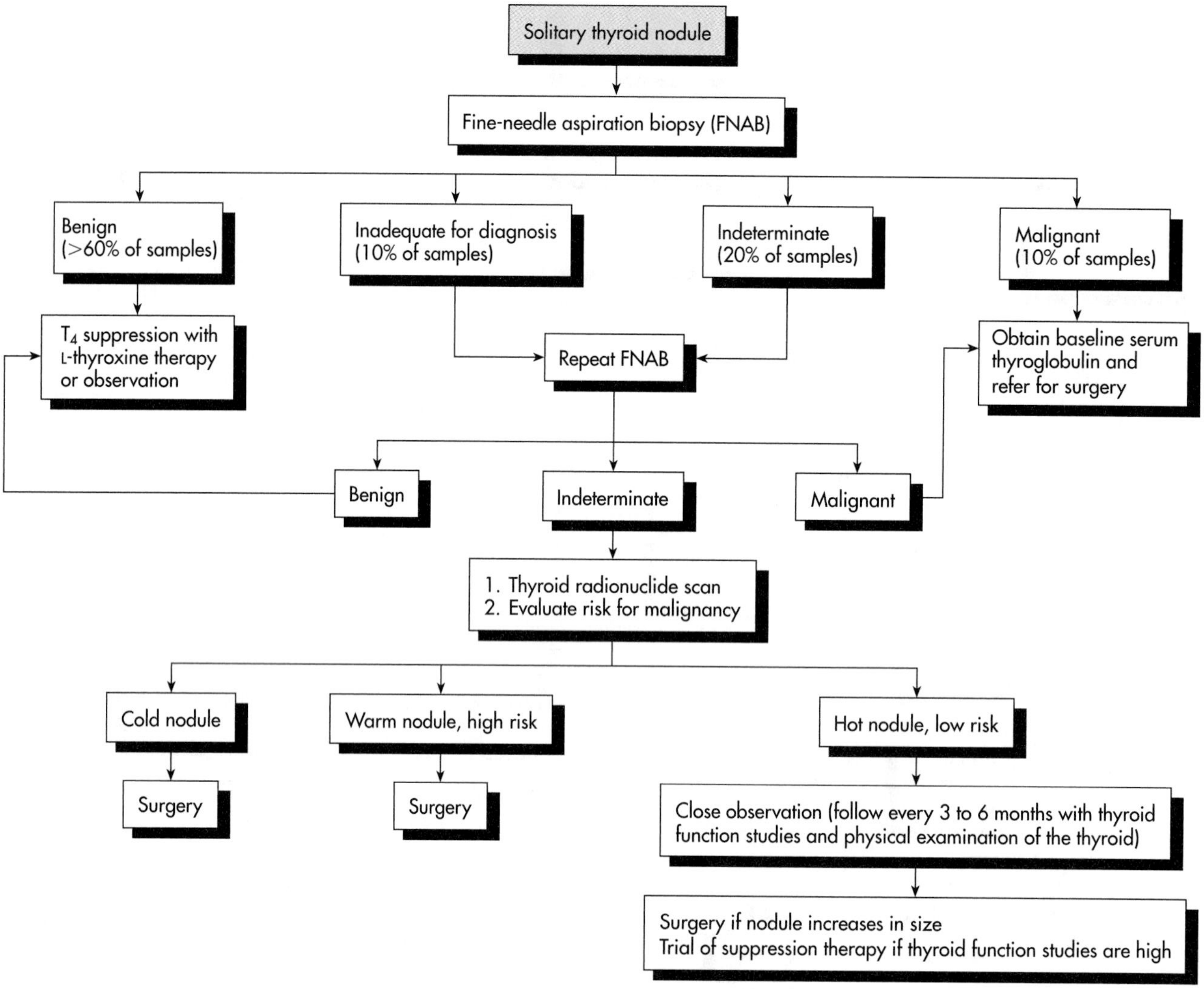

Solitary thyroid nodule

Fine-needle aspiration biopsy (FNAB)

Benign (>60% of samples)

Inadequate for diagnosis (10% of samples)

Indeterminate (20% of samples)

Malignant (10% of samples)

T_4 suppression with L-thyroxine therapy or observation

Repeat FNAB

Obtain baseline serum thyroglobulin and refer for surgery

Benign

Indeterminate

Malignant

1. Thyroid radionuclide scan
2. Evaluate risk for malignancy

Cold nodule

Warm nodule, high risk

Hot nodule, low risk

Surgery

Surgery

Close observation (follow every 3 to 6 months with thyroid function studies and physical examination of the thyroid)

Surgery if nodule increases in size
Trial of suppression therapy if thyroid function studies are high

FIGURE 3-214 Diagnostic evaluation of solitary thyroid nodule. High risk for malignancy: nodule >2 cm, age <40 yr, male sex, regional lymphadenopathy, fixation to adjacent tissues, history of prior head and neck irradiation. (From Ferri F: *Practical guide to the care of the medical patient,* ed 6, St Louis, 2004, Mosby.)

THYROID TESTING

ICD-9CM # V77.0

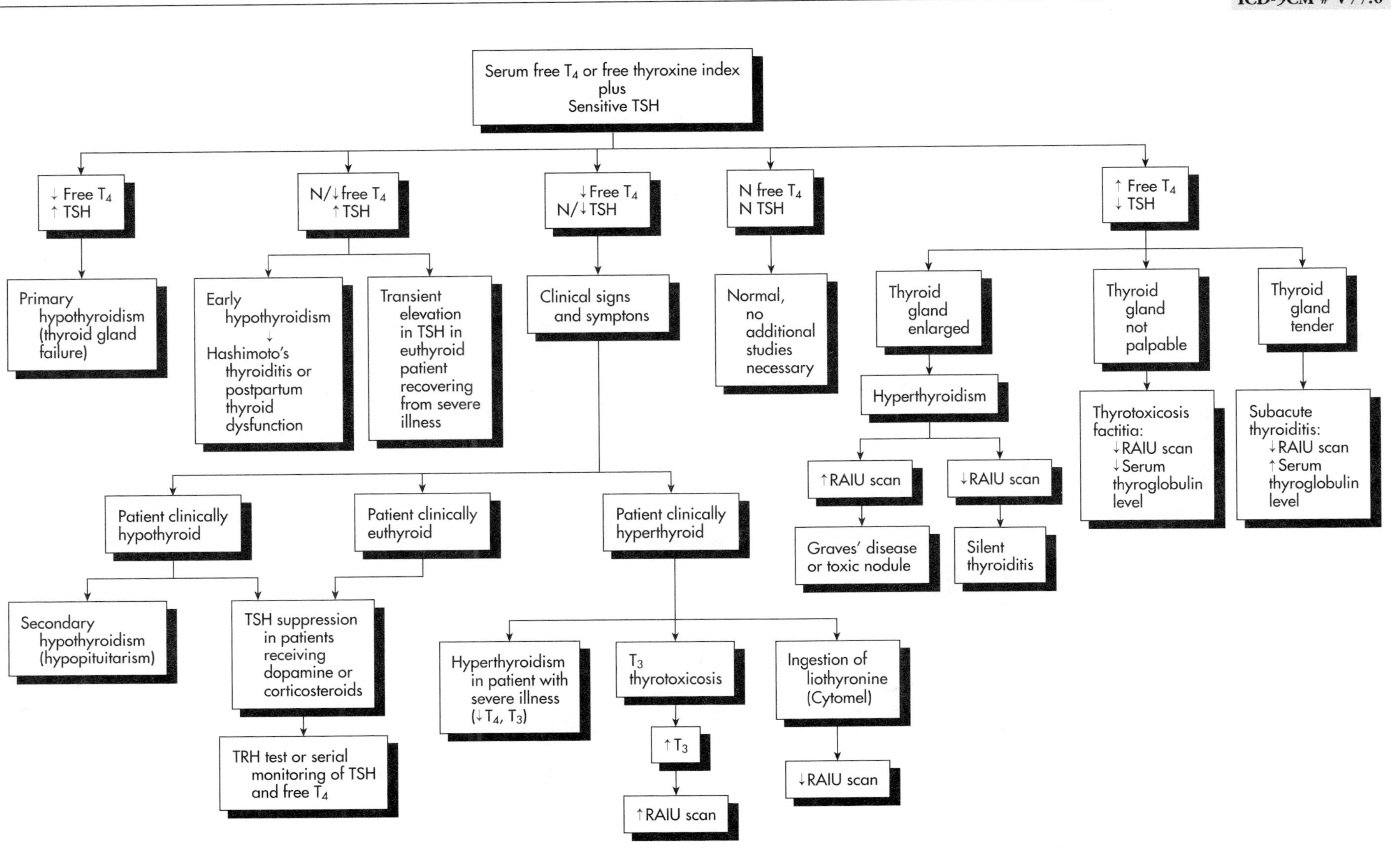

FIGURE 3-215 Diagnostic approach to thyroid testing. *N,* Normal; *RAIU,* radioactive iodine uptake; *TRH,* thyrotropin-releasing hormone; *TSH,* thyroid-stimulating hormone. (From Ferri FF: *Practical guide to the care of the medical patient,* ed 6, St Louis, 2004, Mosby.)

TINNITUS

ICD-9CM # 388.30

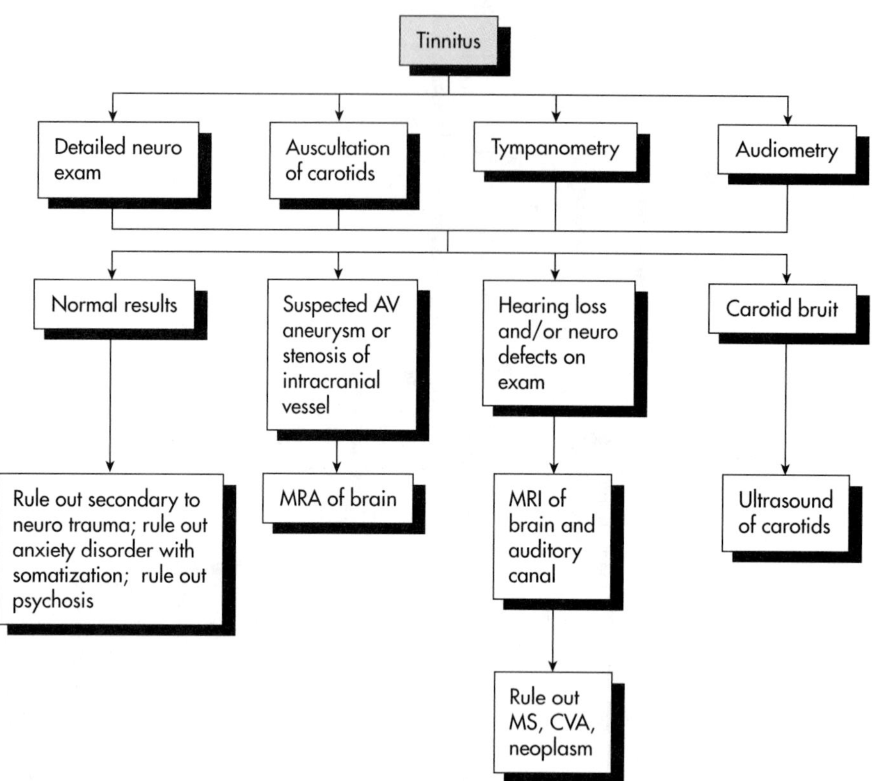

FIGURE 3-216 Tinnitus evaluation. *AV,* Atrioventricular; *CVA,* cerebrovascular accident; *MRA,* magnetic resonance angiography; *MRI,* magnetic resonance imaging; *MS,* multiple sclerosis. (From Ferri FF: *Ferri's best test: a practical guide to clinical laboratory medicine and diagnostic imaging,* Philadelphia, 2004, Elsevier Mosby.)

BOX 3-15 Tinnitus

Diagnostic imaging	**Lab evaluation**
Best Test	***Best Test***
None	None
Ancillary tests	***Ancillary tests***
Carotid Doppler ultrasound	CBC
MRI of brain and auditory canals	Lipid panel
Brain MRA	

From Ferri FF: *Ferri's best test: a practical guide to clinical laboratory medicine and diagnostic imaging,* Philadelphia, 2004, Elsevier Mosby.

CBC, Complete blood count; *MRA,* magnetic resonance angiography; *MRI,* magnetic resonance imaging.

TRANSIENT ISCHEMIC ATTACK

ICD-9CM # 435.9 Unspecified transient cerebral ischemia

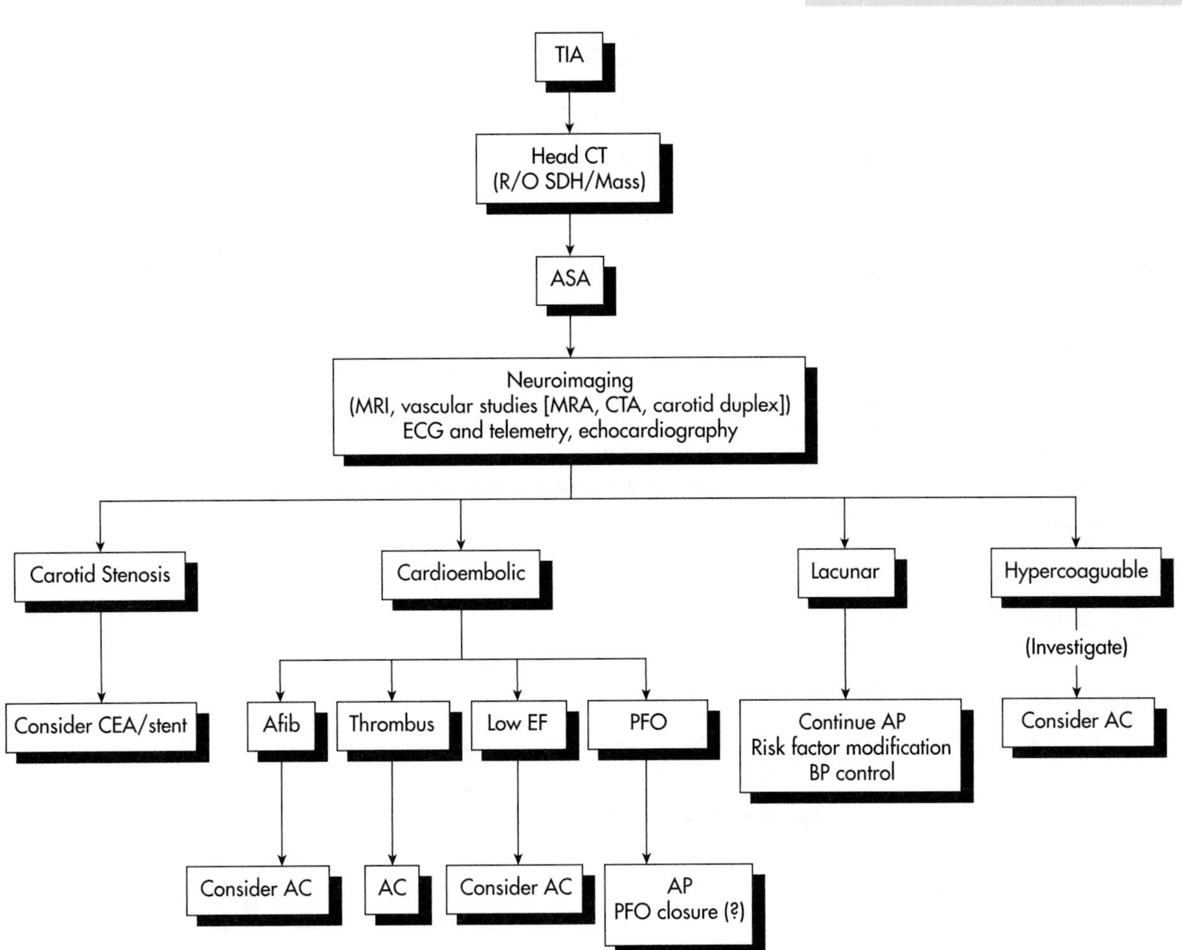

FIGURE 3-217 Transient ischemic attack. *AC,* Anticoagulation; *AP,* antiplatelet; *ASA,* aspirin; *BP,* blood pressure; *CEA,* carotid endarterectomy; *EF,* ejection fraction; *PFO,* patent foramen ovale.

UNCONSCIOUS PATIENT

ICD-9CM # 780.09

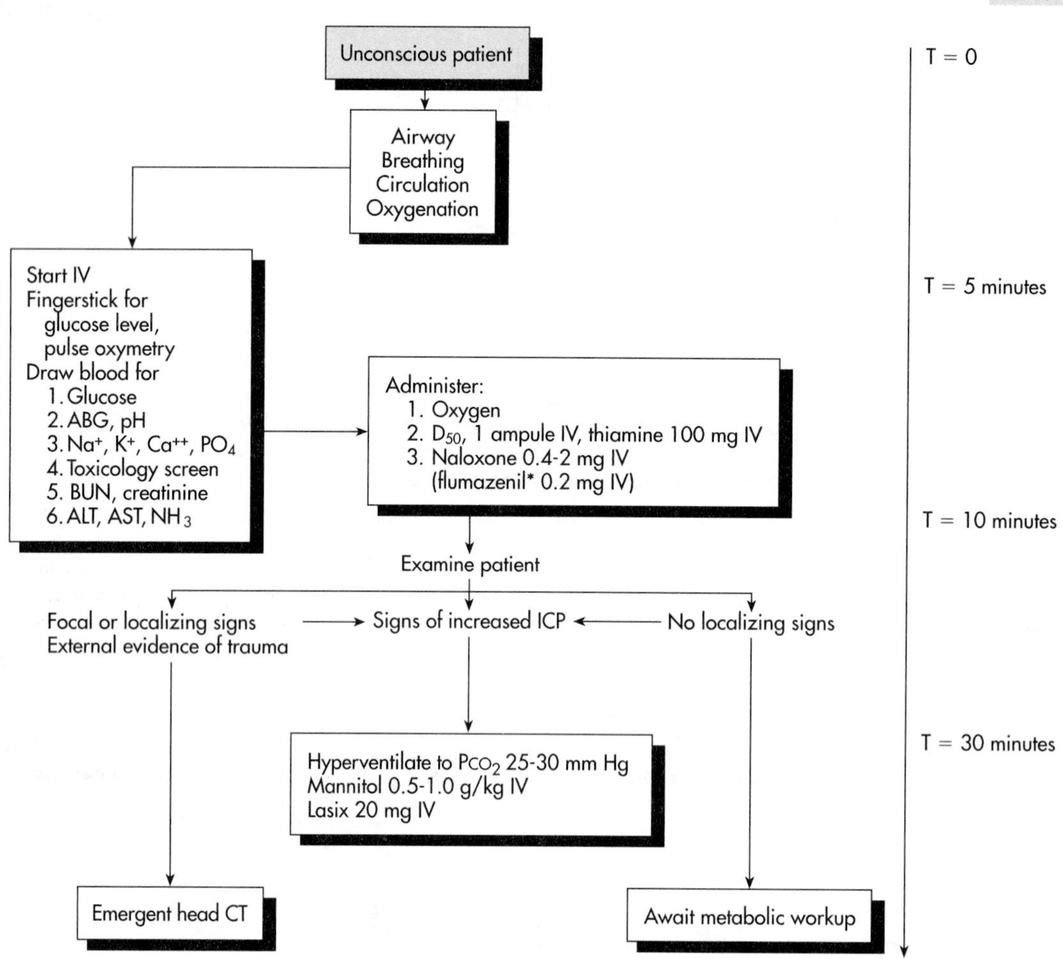

* Use of flumazenil should not be considered routine because it can precipitate seizures in certain subsets of patients.

FIGURE 3-218 Approach to the unconscious patient. *ABG,* Arterial blood gas; *ALT,* alanine aminotransferase; *AST,* aspartate aminotransferase; *BUN,* blood urea nitrogen; *CT,* computed tomography; *ICP,* intracranial pressure. (Modified from Johnson RT, Griffin JW: *Current therapy in neurologic disease,* ed 5, St Louis, 1997, Mosby.)

URETERAL CALCULI

ICD-9CM # 592.9 Urinary calculus

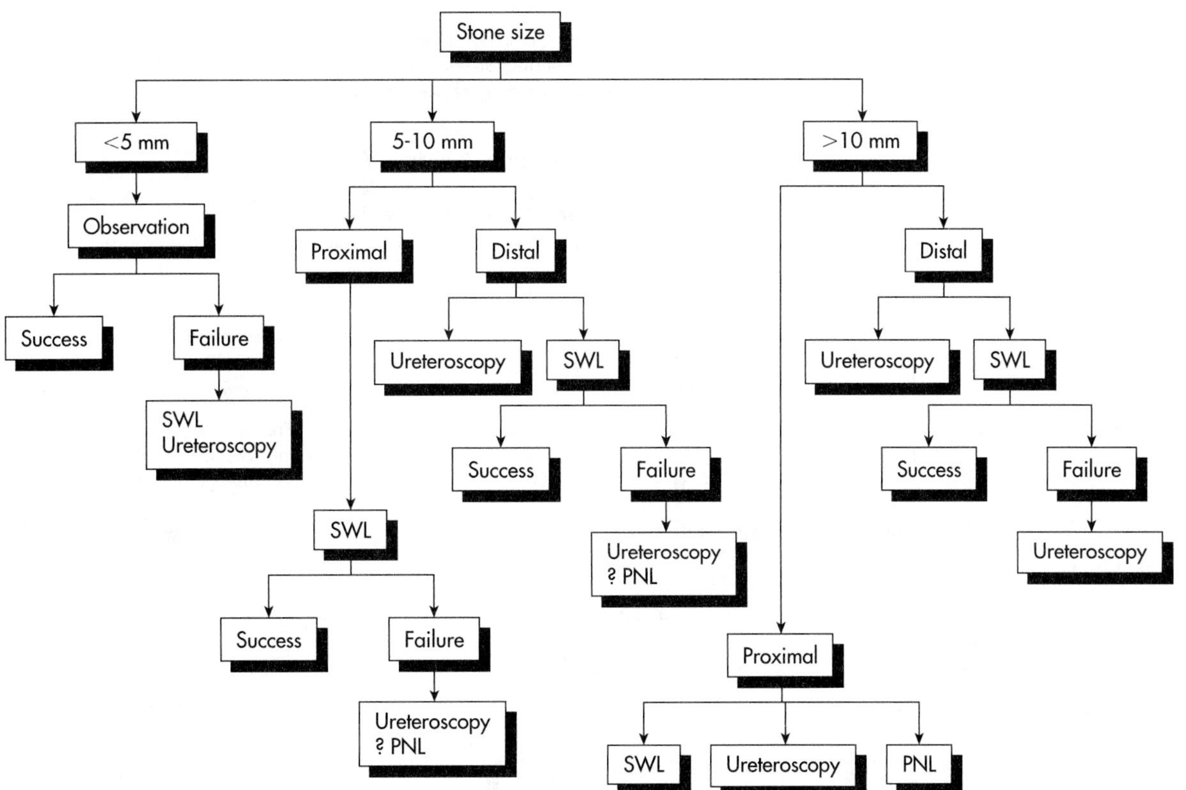

FIGURE 3-219 Management of ureteral calculi. *PNL,* Percutaneous nephrostolithotomy; *SWL,* shock wave lithotripsy. (From Noble J: *Primary care medicine,* ed 3, St Louis, 2001, Mosby.)

URETHRAL DISCHARGE

ICD-9CM # 788.7

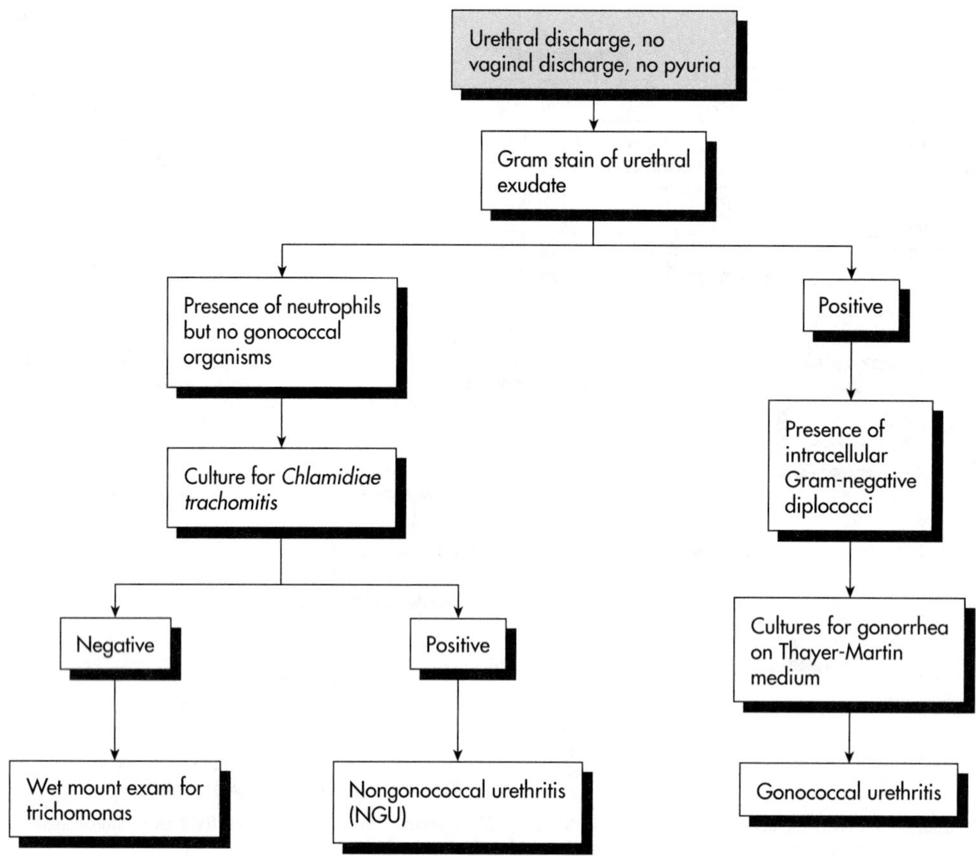

FIGURE 3-220 Urethral discharge.

ICD-9CM # 595.0 Acute cystitis
595.3 Trigonitis
595.2 Chronic cystitis
590.1 Acute pyelonephritis
590.0 Chronic pyelonephritis
590.8 Nonspecific pyelonephritis

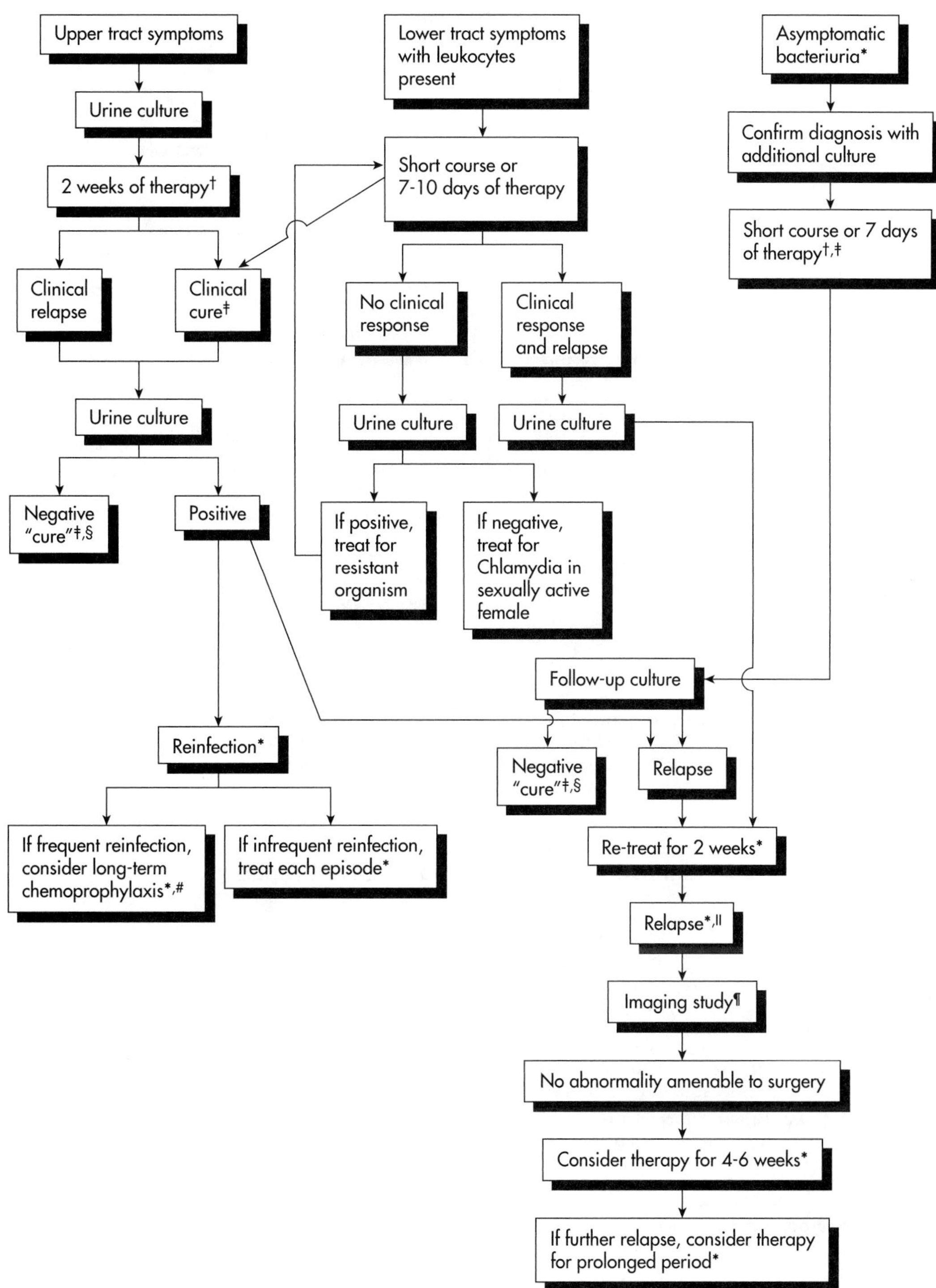

* Consider no therapy in nonpregnant adults without obstructive uropathy or symptoms of urinary tract infection.
† Consider imaging studies in all children and men with correction of significant lesions.
‡ Follow-up culture is required only in pregnancy, in children, and in adults with obstructive uropathy.
§ Obtain follow-up cultures monthly in pregnant women and at 6 weeks and 6 months in children.
|| Evaluate men for chronic bacterial prostatitis.
¶ Delay 2 months postpartum in pregnant women.
\# Consider imaging studies after three to four reinfections in women.

FIGURE 3-221 Approach to the management of urinary tract infection. (From Mandell GL: *Mandell, Douglas, and Bennett's principles and practice of infectious diseases,* ed 5, New York, 2000, Churchill Livingstone.)

URINARY TRACT OBSTRUCTION

ICD-9CM # 599.6

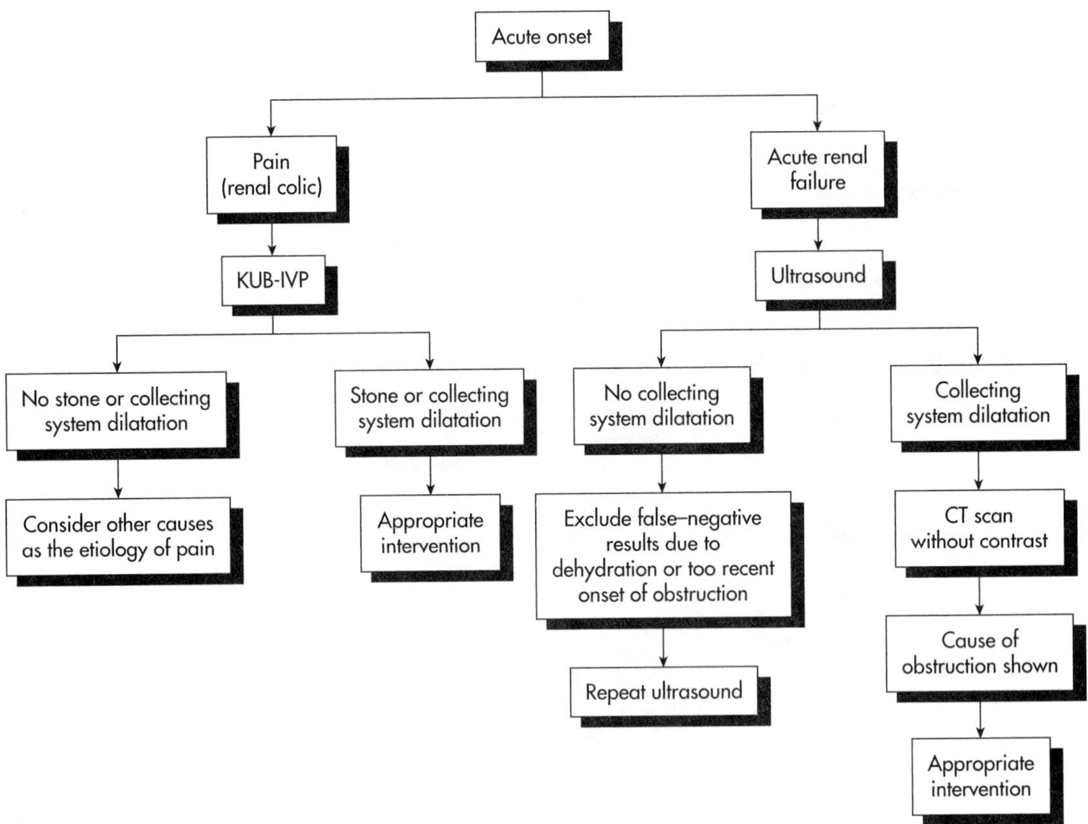

FIGURE 3-222 Scheme of a diagnostic approach to urinary tract obstruction. *CT,* Computed tomography; *IVP,* intravenous pyelography; *KUB,* kidney, ureter, bladder (a flat film of the abdomen without contrast medium). (From Goldman L, Ausiello D [eds]: *Cecil textbook of medicine,* ed 22, Philadelphia, 2004, WB Saunders.)

BOX 3-16 Diagnostic Tests Used in Obstructive Uropathy

Upper Urinary Tract Obstruction
Sonography (ultrasound)
Plain films of the abdomen (KUB)
Excretory or intravenous pyelography
Retrograde pyelography
Isotopic renography
Computed tomography
Magnetic resonance imaging
Pressure flow studies (the Whitaker test)

Lower Urinary Tract Obstruction
Some of the tests listed above
Cystoscopy
Voiding cystourethrogram
Retrograde urethrography
Urodynamic tests
- Debimetry
- Cystometrography
- Electromyography
- Urethral pressure profile

From Klahr S: Obstructive uropathy. In Jacobson HR, Striker GE, Klahr S (eds). *The principles and practice of nephrology,* Toronto, 1991, BC Decker, pp 432-441. Reproduced by permission of Mosby-Year Book.
KUP, Kidneys, ureter, bladder.

URTICARIA

ICD-9CM # 708.8 Other unspecified urticaria

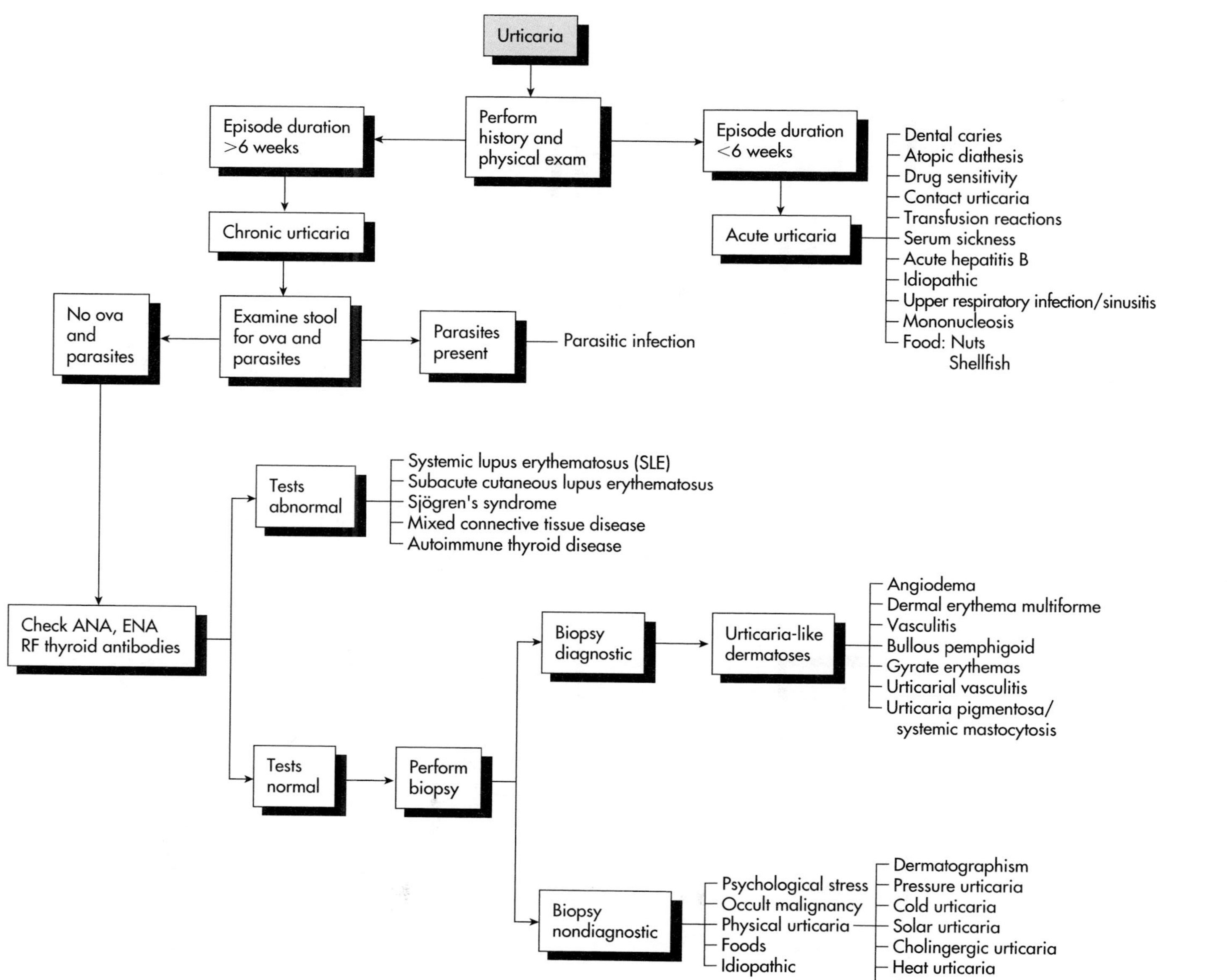

FIGURE 3-223 Evaluation of urticaria. *ANA,* Antibody to nuclear antigens; *ENA,* extractable nuclear antigens; *RF,* rheumatoid factor. (From Healy PM, Jacobson EJ: *Common medical diagnoses,* ed 3, Philadelphia, 2000, WB Saunders.)

VAGINAL DISCHARGE

ICD-9CM # 623.5

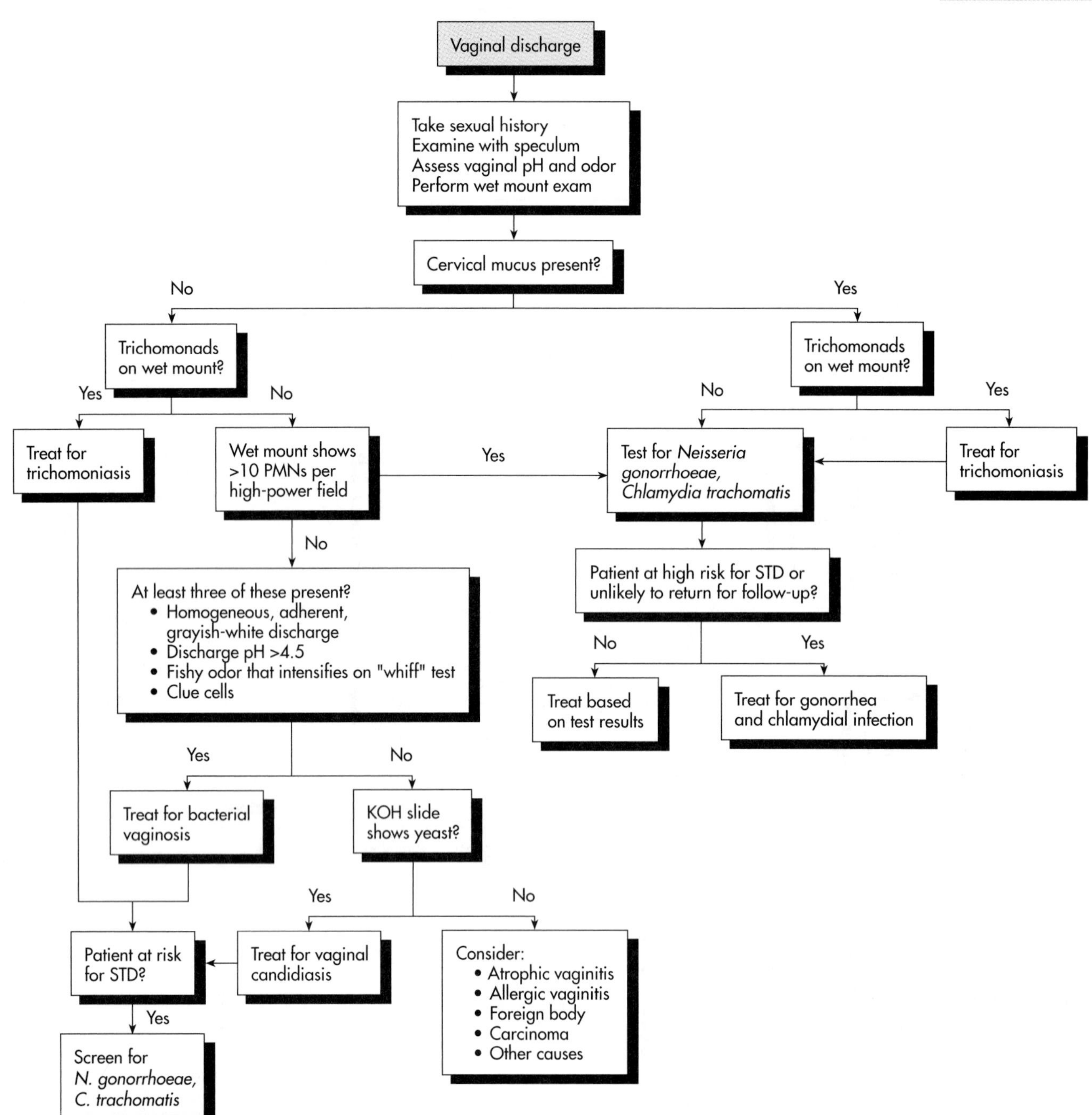

FIGURE 3-224 Evaluation of vaginal discharge. *KOH,* Potassium hydroxide; *PMN,* polymorphonuclear leukocyte; *STD,* sexually transmitted disease. (From Fox KK, Behets FMT: *Postgrad Med* 98:87, 1995.)

VAGINAL PROLAPSE

ICD-9CM # 618.0

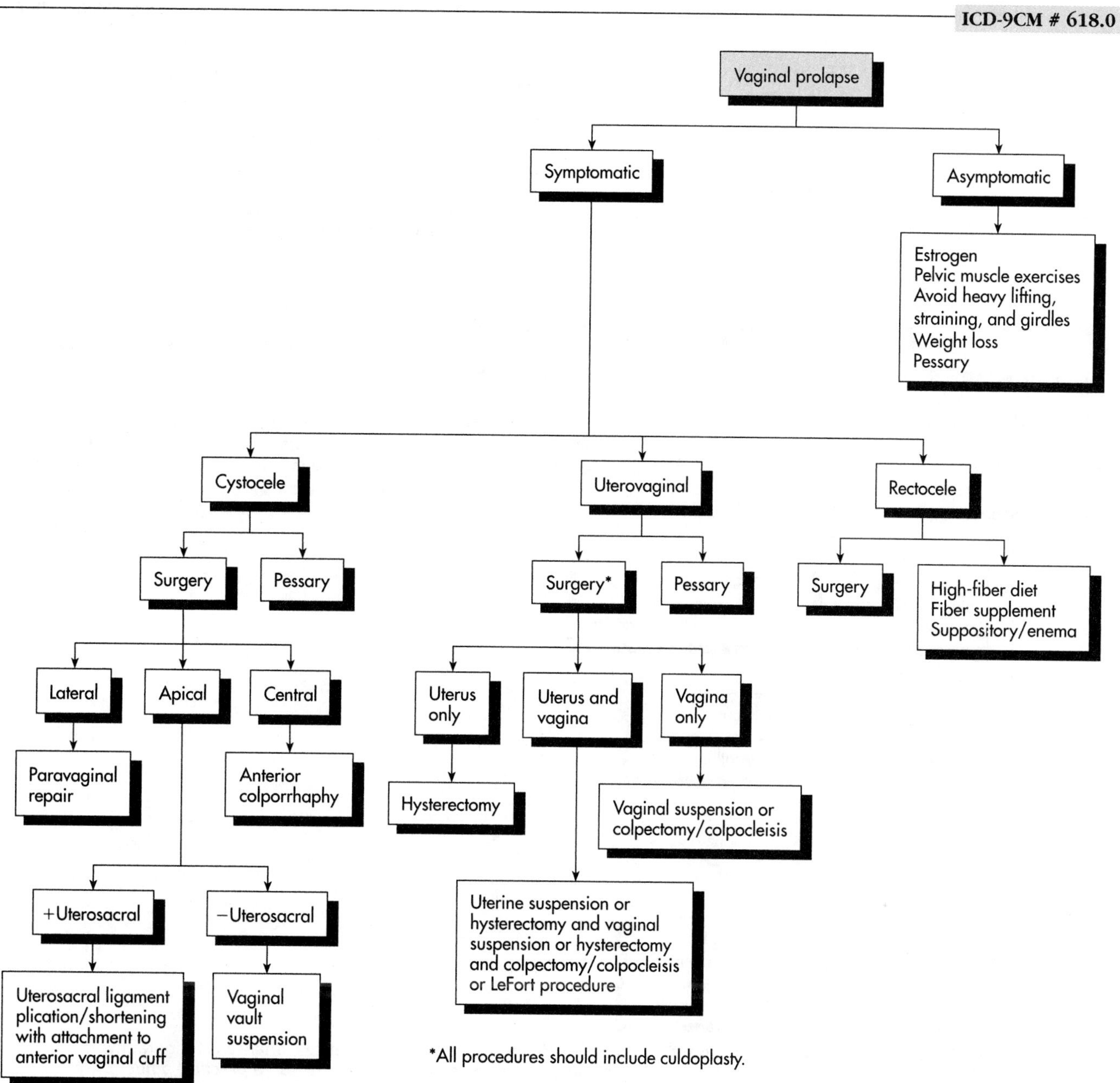

FIGURE 3-225 Management of vaginal prolapse. (From Zuspan FP [ed]: *Handbook of obstetrics, gynecology, and primary care,* St Louis, 1998, Mosby.)

VERTIGO

ICD-9CM # 780.4

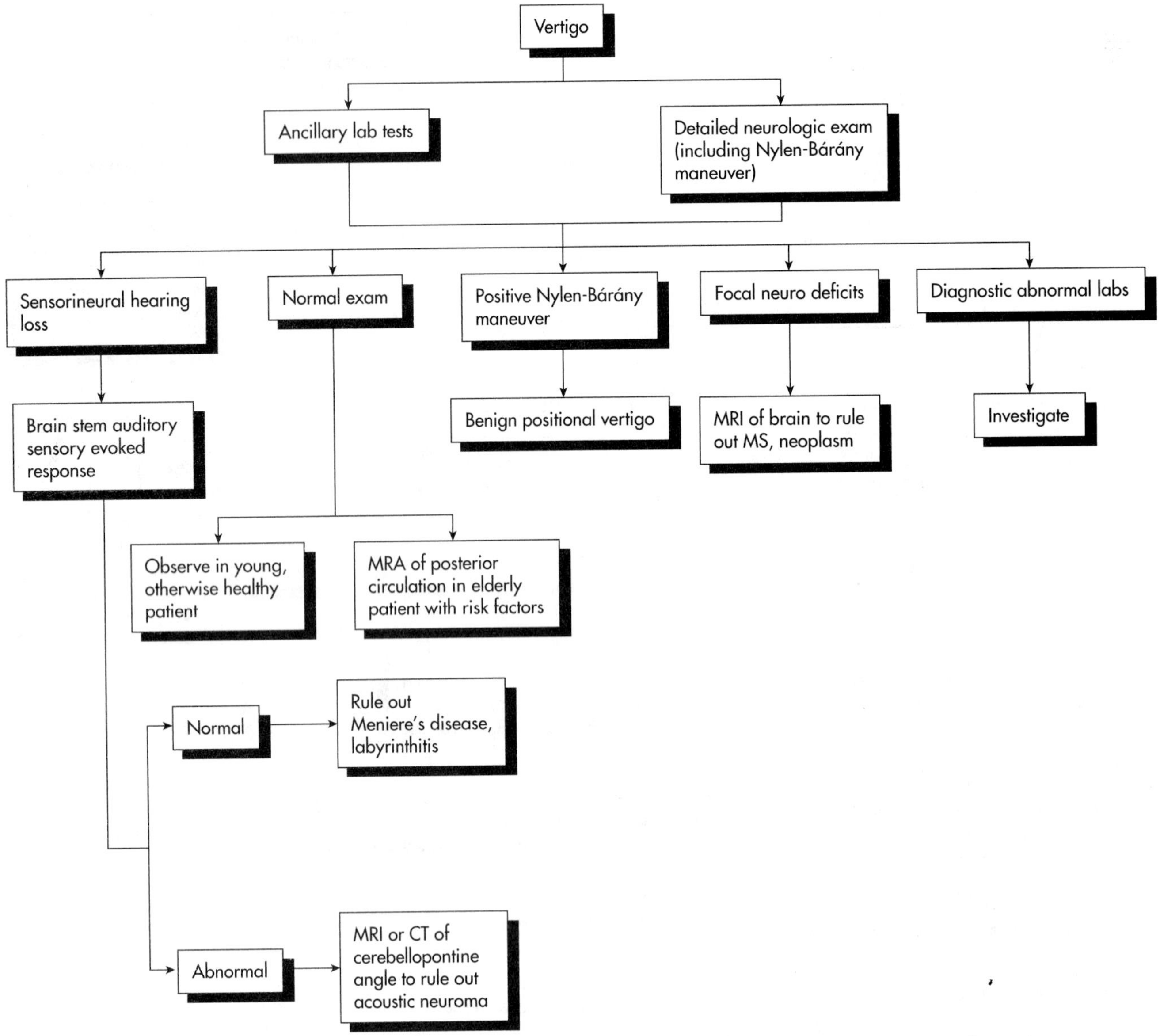

Vertigo

Ancillary lab tests

Detailed neurologic exam (including Nylen-Bárány maneuver)

Sensorineural hearing loss

Normal exam

Positive Nylen-Bárány maneuver

Focal neuro deficits

Diagnostic abnormal labs

Brain stem auditory sensory evoked response

Benign positional vertigo

MRI of brain to rule out MS, neoplasm

Investigate

Observe in young, otherwise healthy patient

MRA of posterior circulation in elderly patient with risk factors

Normal

Rule out Meniere's disease, labyrinthitis

Abnormal

MRI or CT of cerebellopontine angle to rule out acoustic neuroma

FIGURE 3-226 Vertigo evaluation. *CT,* Computed tomography; *MRA,* magnetic resonance arteriography; *MRI,* magnetic resonance imaging; *MS,* multiple sclerosis. (From Ferri FF: *Ferri's best test: a practical guide to clinical laboratory medicine and diagnostic imaging,* Philadelphia, 2004, Elsevier Mosby.)

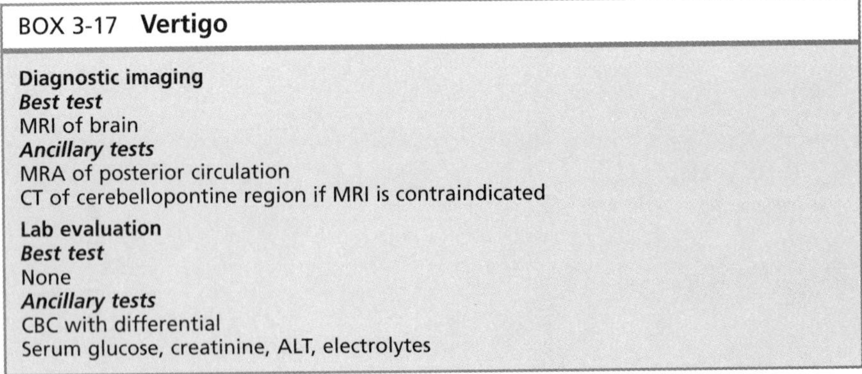

BOX 3-17 **Vertigo**

Diagnostic imaging
Best test
MRI of brain
Ancillary tests
MRA of posterior circulation
CT of cerebellopontine region if MRI is contraindicated

Lab evaluation
Best test
None
Ancillary tests
CBC with differential
Serum glucose, creatinine, ALT, electrolytes

From Ferri FF: *Ferri's best test: a practical guide to clinical laboratory medicine and diagnostic imaging,* Philadelphia, 2004, Elsevier Mosby.

Alt, Alanine aminotransferase; *CBC,* complete blood count; *CT,* computed tomography; *MRA,* magnetic resonance arteriography; *MRI,* magnetic resonance imaging.

VULVAR CANCER

ICD-9CM # 184.4 Vulvar neoplasm

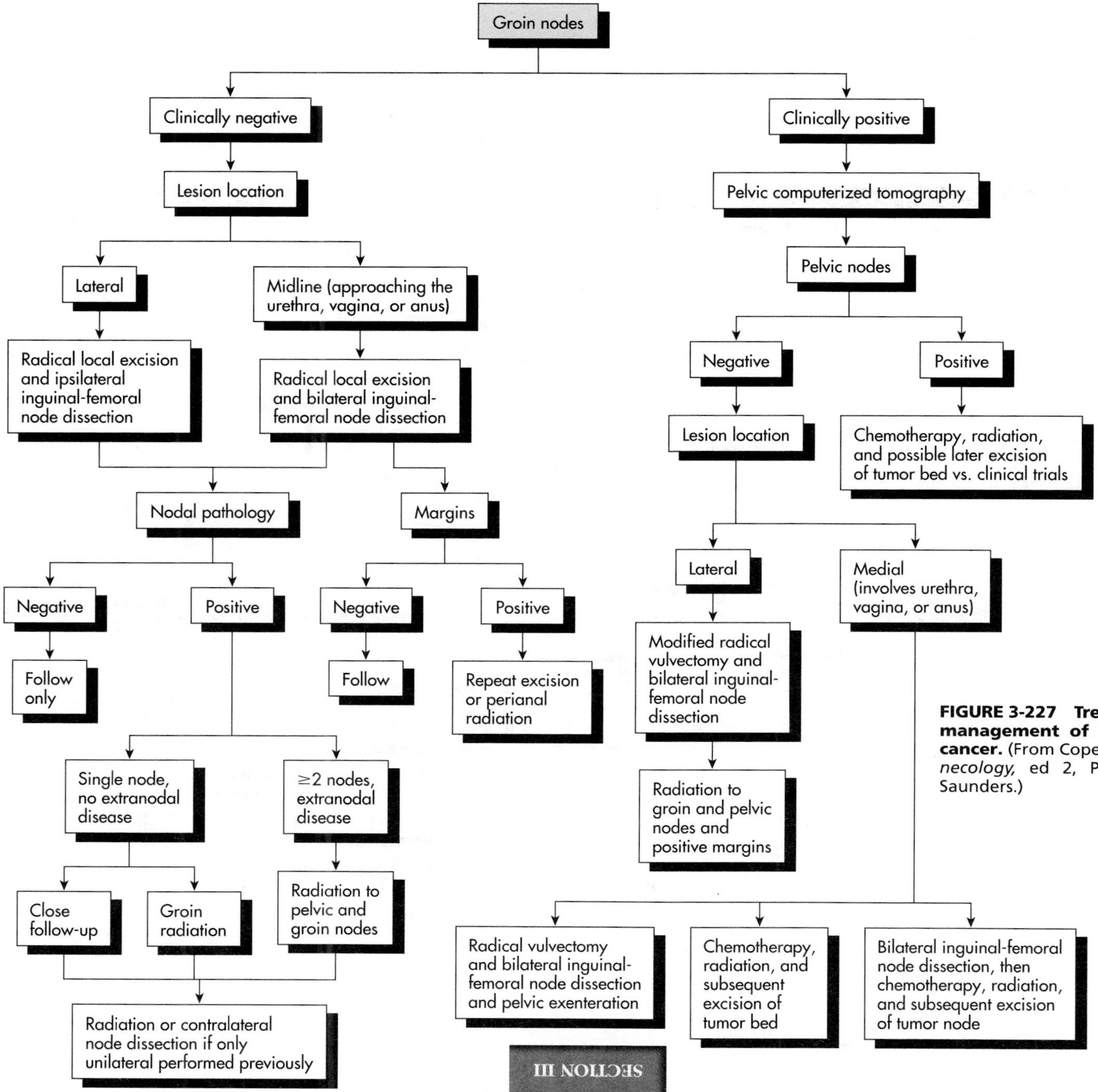

- Groin nodes
  - Clinically negative
    - Lesion location
      - Lateral → Radical local excision and ipsilateral inguinal-femoral node dissection
      - Midline (approaching the urethra, vagina, or anus) → Radical local excision and bilateral inguinal-femoral node dissection
        - Nodal pathology
          - Negative → Follow only
          - Positive
            - Single node, no extranodal disease
              - Close follow-up
              - Groin radiation
            - ≥2 nodes, extranodal disease → Radiation to pelvic and groin nodes
            - → Radiation or contralateral node dissection if only unilateral performed previously
        - Margins
          - Negative → Follow
          - Positive → Repeat excision or perianal radiation
  - Clinically positive
    - Pelvic computerized tomography
      - Pelvic nodes
        - Negative → Lesion location
          - Lateral → Modified radical vulvectomy and bilateral inguinal-femoral node dissection → Radiation to groin and pelvic nodes and positive margins
          - Medial (involves urethra, vagina, or anus)
            - Radical vulvectomy and bilateral inguinal-femoral node dissection and pelvic exenteration
            - Chemotherapy, radiation, and subsequent excision of tumor bed
            - Bilateral inguinal-femoral node dissection, then chemotherapy, radiation, and subsequent excision of tumor node
        - Positive → Chemotherapy, radiation, and possible later excision of tumor bed vs. clinical trials

FIGURE 3-227 Treatment algorithm for management of patients with vulvar cancer. (From Copeland LJ: *Textbook of gynecology,* ed 2, Philadelphia, 2000, WB Saunders.)

WEIGHT GAIN

ICD-9CM # 783.1 Abnormal weight gain
278.00 Obesity

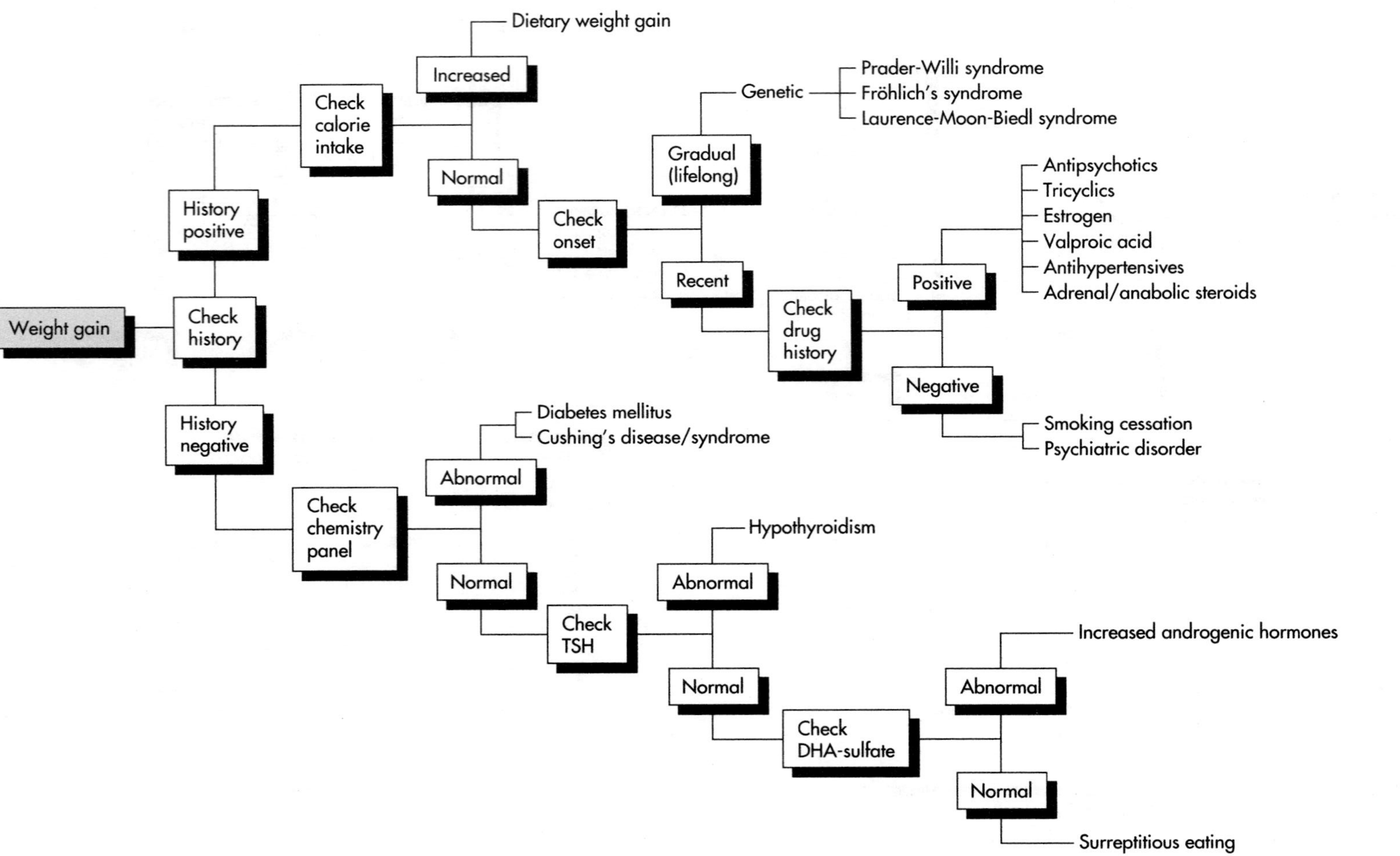

FIGURE 3-228 Weight gain. *DHA,* Dehydroepiandrosterone; *TSH,* thyroid-stimulating hormone. (From Healey PM: *Common medical diagnosis: an algorithmic approach,* ed 3, Philadelphia, 2000, WB Saunders.)

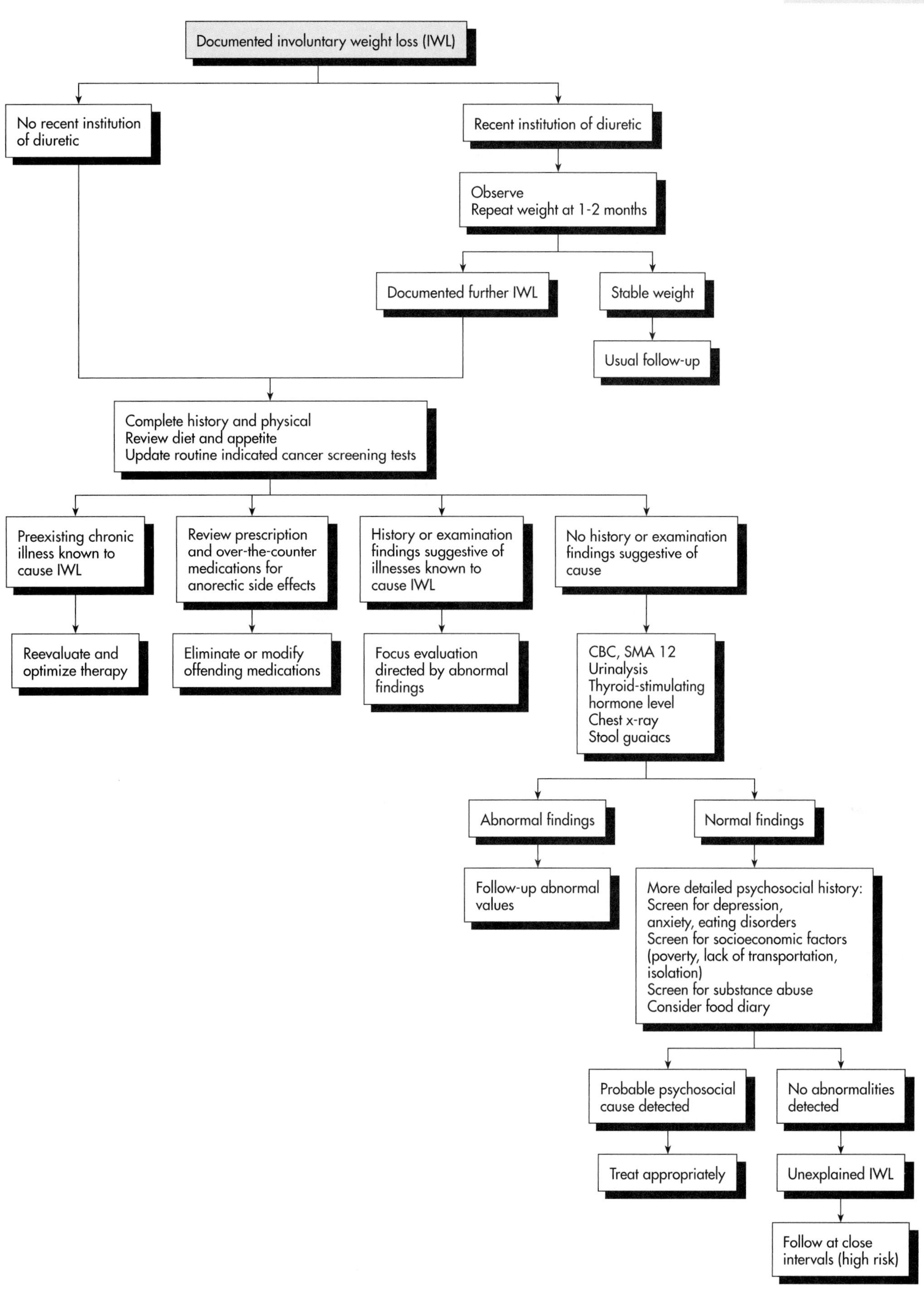

FIGURE 3-229 Involuntary weight loss. *CBC,* Complete blood count. (From Greene HL, Johnson WP, Lemcke D [eds]: *Decision making in medicine,* ed 2, St Louis, 1998, Mosby.)

SECTION IV

Laboratory Tests and Interpretation of Results

This section contains more than 200 commonly performed laboratory tests. In general, the tests are approached with the following format:

1. Laboratory test
2. Normal range in adult patients
3. Common abnormalities, such as positive test, increased or decreased value
4. Causes of abnormal result

The normal ranges may differ slightly, depending on the laboratory. The reader should be aware of the "normal range" of the particular laboratory performing the test. Every attempt has been made to present current laboratory test data, with emphasis on practical considerations.

ACE LEVEL; *see* ANGIOTENSIN-CONVERTING ENZYME

ACETONE (serum or plasma)

Normal: Negative
Elevated in: DKA, starvation, isopropanol ingestion

ACETYLCHOLINE RECEPTOR (ACHR) ANTIBODY

Normal: <0.03 nmol/L
Elevated in: Myasthenia gravis. Changes in AChR concentration correlate with the clinical severity of myasthenia gravis following therapy and during therapy with prednisone and immunosuppressants. False-positive AChR antibody results may be found in patients with Eaton-Lambert syndrome.

ACID-BASE REFERENCE VALUES; *see* Tables 4-1 and 4-2.

TABLE 4-1 Commonly Used Acid-Base Reference Values for Arterial and Venous Plasma or Serum (Averaged from Various Sources)

	ARTERIAL		VENOUS	
	Conventional Units	SI Units*	Conventional Units	SI Units*
pH	7.40 (7.35-7.45)	7.40 (7.35-7.45)	7.37 (7.32-7.42)	7.37 (7.32-7.42)
Pco_2	40 mm Hg (35-45)	5.33 kPa (4.67-6.10)	45 mm Hg (45-50)	6.10 kPa (5.33-6.67)
Po_2	80-100 mm Hg	10.66-13.33 kPa	40 mm Hg (37-43)	5.33 kPa (4.93-5.73)
HCO3 (CO_2 combining power)	24 mEq/L (20-28)	24 mmol/L (20-28)	26 mEq/L (22-30)	26 mmol/L (22-30)
CO_2 content	25 mEq/L (22-28)	25 mmol/L (22-28)	27 mEq/L (24-30)	27 mmol/L (24-30)

From Ravel R: Clinical laboratory medicine, ed 6, St Louis, 1995, Mosby.
*International system.

TABLE 4-2 Summary of Laboratory Findings in Primary Uncomplicated Respiratory and Metabolic Acid-Base Disorders*

Disorder	Pco_2	pH	Base Excess
Acute primary respiratory hypoactivity (respiratory acidosis)	Increase	Decrease	Normal/positive
Acute primary respiratory hyperactivity (respiratory alkalosis)	Decrease	Increase	Normal/negative
Uncompensated metabolic acidosis	Normal	Decrease	Negative
Uncompensated metabolic alkalosis	Normal	Increase	Positive
Partially compensated metabolic acidosis	Decrease	Decrease	Negative
Partially compensated metabolic alkalosis	Increase	Increase	Positive
Chronic primary respiratory hypoactivity (compensated respiratory acidosis)	Increase	Normal	Positive
Fully compensated metabolic alkalosis	Increase	Normal	Positive
Chronic primary respiratory hyperactivity (compensated respiratory alkalosis)	Decrease	Normal	Negative
Fully compensated metabolic acidosis	Decrease	Normal	Negative

From Ravel R: *Clinical laboratory medicine,* ed 6, St Louis, 1995, Mosby.
*Base excess results refer to negative (−) values more than 22 and positive (+) values more than +2.

ACID PHOSPHATASE (serum)

Normal range: 0-5.5 U/L
Elevated in: Carcinoma of prostate, other neoplasms (breast, bone), Paget's disease, osteogenesis imperfecta, malignant invasion of bone, Gaucher's disease, multiple myeloma, myeloproliferative disorders, benign prostatic hypertrophy, prostatic palpation or surgery, hyperparathyroidism, liver disease, chronic renal failure, idiopathic thrombocytopenic purpura, bronchitis

ACID SERUM TEST; *see* HAM TEST

ACTIVATED PARTIAL THROMBOPLASTIN TIME (APTT, aPTT); *see* PARTIAL THROMBOPLASTIN TIME

ALANINE AMINOTRANSFERASE (ALT, SGPT)

Normal range
0-35 U/L
Elevated in
Liver disease (hepatitis, cirrhosis, Reye's syndrome), hepatic congestion, infectious mononucleosis, myocardial infarction, myocarditis, severe muscle trauma, dermatomyositis/polymyositis, muscular dystrophy, drugs (antibiotics, narcotics, antihypertensive agents, heparin, labetalol, statins, NSAIDs, amiodarone, chlorpromazine, phenytoin), malignancy, renal and pulmonary infarction, convulsions, eclampsia, shock liver

ALBUMIN (serum)

Normal range: 4-6 g/dl
Elevated in: Dehydration (relative increase)
Decreased in: Liver disease, nephrotic syndrome, poor nutritional status, rapid IV hydration, protein-losing enteropathies (inflammatory bowel disease), severe burns, neoplasia, chronic inflammatory diseases, pregnancy, oral contraceptives, prolonged immobilization, lymphomas, hypervitaminosis A, chronic glomerulonephritis

ALDOLASE (serum)

Normal range: 0-6 U/L
Elevated in: Muscular dystrophy, rhabdomyolysis, dermatomyositis/polymyositis, trichinosis, acute hepatitis and other liver diseases, myocardial infarction, prostatic carcinoma, hemorrhagic pancreatitis, gangrene, delirium tremens, burns
Decreased in: Loss of muscle mass, late stages of muscular dystrophy

ALDOSTERONE

Normal range: Recumbent: 50-150 ng/L
Upright: 150-300 ng/L
(Highest levels in neonates, decreasing over time to adult levels)
Elevated in: Primary aldosteronism, secondary aldosteronism, pseudoprimary aldosteronism
Decreased in: Patient with hypertension: diabetes mellitus, Turner's syndrome, acute alcohol intoxication, excess secretion of deoxycorticosterone, corticosterone, and 18-hydroxycorticosterone
Patient without hypertension: Addison's disease, hypoaldosteronism resulting from renin deficiency, isolated aldosterone deficiency

ALKALINE PHOSPHATASE (serum)

Normal range: 30-120 U/L
Elevated in:
LIVER AND BILIARY TRACT ORIGIN
Extrahepatic bile duct obstruction
Intrahepatic biliary obstruction
Liver cell acute injury
Liver passive congestion
Drug-induced liver cell dysfunction
Space-occupying lesions
Primary biliary cirrhosis
Sepsis
BONE ORIGIN (OSTEOBLAST HYPERACTIVITY)
Physiologic (rapid) bone growth (childhood and adolescent)
Metastatic tumor with osteoblastic reaction
Fracture healing
Paget's disease of bone
CAPILLARY ENDOTHELIAL ORIGIN
Granulation tissue formation (active)
PLACENTAL ORIGIN
Pregnancy
Some parenteral albumin preparations

OTHER
Thyrotoxicosis
Benign transient hyperphosphatasemia
Primary hyperparathyroidism
Decreased in: Hypothyroidism, pernicious anemia, hypophosphatemia, hypervitaminosis D, malnutrition

ALPHA-1-FETOPROTEIN (serum); *see* α-1 FETOPROTEIN

ALT; *see* ALANINE AMINOTRANSFERASE

ALUMINUM (serum)

Normal range: 0-6 ng/mL
Elevated in: Chronic renal failure on dialysis, parenteral nutrition, industrial exposure

AMMONIA (serum)

Normal range: 10-80 μg/dl
Elevated in: Hepatic failure, hepatic encephalopathy, Reye's syndrome, portacaval shunt, drugs (diuretics, polymyxin B, methicillin)
Decreased in: Drugs (neomycin, lactulose, tetracycline), renal failure

AMYLASE (serum)

Normal range: 0-130 U/L
Elevated in: Acute pancreatitis, pancreatic neoplasm, abscess, pseudocyst, ascites, macroamylasemia, perforated peptic ulcer, intestinal obstruction, intestinal infarction, acute cholecystitis, appendicitis, ruptured ectopic pregnancy, salivary gland inflammation, peritonitis, burns, diabetic ketoacidosis, renal insufficiency, drugs (morphine), carcinomatosis (of lung, esophagus, ovary), acute ethanol ingestion, mumps, prostate tumors, post–endoscopic retrograde cholangiopancreatography, bulimia, anorexia nervosa
Decreased in: Advanced chronic pancreatitis, hepatic necrosis, cystic fibrosis

AMYLASE, URINE; *see* URINE AMYLASE

ANA; *see* ANTINUCLEAR ANTIBODY

ANCA; *see* ANTINEUTROPHIL CYTOPLASMIC ANTIBODY

ANGIOTENSIN-CONVERTING ENZYME (ACE level)

Normal range: <40 nmol/ml/min
Elevated in: Sarcoidosis, primary biliary cirrhosis, alcoholic liver disease, hyperthyroidism, hyperparathyroidism, diabetes mellitus, amyloidosis, multiple myeloma, lung disease (asbestosis, silicosis, berylliosis, allergic alveolitis, coccidioidomycosis), Gaucher's disease, leprosy

ANION GAP

Normal range: 9-14 mEq/L
Elevated in: Lactic acidosis, ketoacidosis (diabetes, alcoholic starvation), uremia (chronic renal failure), ingestion of toxins (paraldehyde, methanol, salicylates, ethylene glycol), hyperosmolar nonketotic coma, antibiotics (carbenicillin)
Decreased in: Hypoalbuminemia, severe hypermagnesemia, IgG myeloma, lithium toxicity, laboratory error (falsely decreased sodium or overestimation of bicarbonate or chloride), hypercalcemia of parathyroid origin, antibiotics (e.g., polymyxin)

ANTICARDIOLIPIN ANTIBODY (ACA)

Normal range: Negative: Test includes detection of IgG, IgM, and IgA antibody to phospholipid, cardiolipin
Present in: Antiphospholipid antibody syndrome, chronic hepatitis C

ANTICOAGULANT; *see* CIRCULATING ANTICOAGULANT

ANTI-DNA

Normal range: Absent
Present in: Systemic lupus erythematosus, chronic active hepatitis, infectious mononucleosis, biliary cirrhosis

ANTIGLOMERULAR BASEMENT ANTIBODY; *see* GLOMERULAR BASEMENT MEMBRANE ANTIBODY

ANTIMITOCHONDRIAL ANTIBODY

Normal range: <1:20 titer
Elevated in: Primary biliary cirrhosis (85% to 95%), chronic active hepatitis (25% to 30%), cryptogenic cirrhosis (25% to 30%)

ANTINEUTROPHIL CYTOPLASMIC ANTIBODY (ANCA)

Positive test: Cytoplasmic pattern (cANCA): positive in Wegener's granulomatosis
Perinuclear pattern (pANCA): positive in inflammatory bowel disease, primary biliary cirrhosis, primary sclerosing cholangitis, autoimmune chronic active hepatitis, crescenteric glomerulonephritis

ANTINUCLEAR ANTIBODY (ANA)

Normal range: <1:20 titer
Positive test: Systemic lupus erythematosus (more significant if titer >1:160), drugs (phenytoin, ethosuximide, primidone, methyldopa, hydralazine, carbamazepine, penicillin, procainamide, chlorpromazine, griseofulvin, thiazides), chronic active hepatitis, age over 60 years (particularly age over 80 years), rheumatoid arthritis, scleroderma, mixed connective tissue disease, necrotizing vasculitis, Sjögren's syndrome, tuberculosis, pulmonary interstitial fibrosis. Table 4-3 describes diseases associated with ANA subtypes. Fig. 4-1 illustrates various fluorescent ANA test patterns.

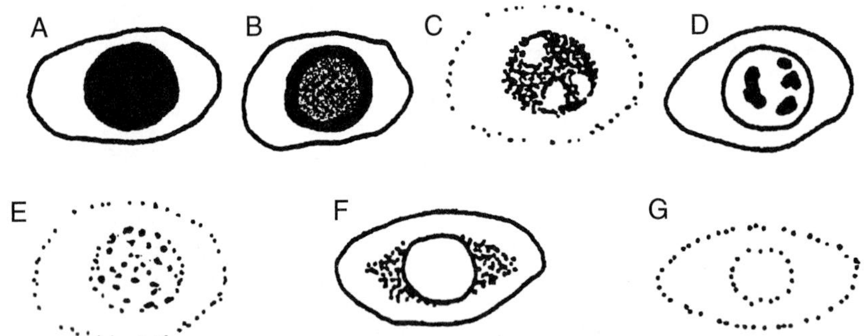

Fig. 4-1 Fluorescent antinuclear antibody test patterns (HEP-2 cells). A, Solid (homogeneous). **B,** Peripheral (rim). **C,** Speckled. **D,** Nucleolar. **E,** Anticentromere. **F,** Antimitochondrial. **G,** Normal (nonreactive). (From Ravel R [ed]: Clinical laboratory medicine, ed 6, St Louis, 1995, Mosby.)

ANTI-RNP ANTIBODY; *see* EXTRACTABLE NUCLEAR ANTIGEN

ANTI-SM (ANTI-SMITH) ANTIBODY; *see* EXTRACTABLE NUCLEAR ANTIGEN

ANTI-SMOOTH MUSCLE ANTIBODY; *see* SMOOTH MUSCLE ANTIBODY

ANTISTREPTOLYSIN O TITER (Streptozyme, ASLO titer)

Normal range for adults: <160 Todd units
Elevated in: Streptococcal upper airway infection, acute rheumatic fever, acute glomerulonephritis, increased levels of β-lipoprotein

NOTE: A fourfold increase in titer between acute and convalescent specimens is diagnostic of streptococcal upper airway infection regardless of the initial titer.

ANTITHROMBIN III

Normal range: 81% to 120% of normal activity; 17-30 mg/dl
Decreased in: Hereditary deficiency of antithrombin III, disseminated intravascular coagulation, pulmonary embolism, cirrhosis, thrombolytic therapy, chronic liver failure, postsurgery, third trimester of pregnancy, oral contraceptives, nephrotic syndrome, IV heparin >3 days, sepsis, acute leukemia, carcinoma, thrombophlebitis
Elevated in: Warfarin drugs, post–myocardial infarction

ARTERIAL BLOOD GASES

Normal range: Po_2: 75-100 mm Hg
Pco_2: 35-45 mm Hg
HCO_3: 24-28 mEq/L
pH: 7.35-7.45
Abnormal values: Acid-base disturbances (see the following)

METABOLIC ACIDOSIS

Metabolic acidosis with increased AG (AG acidosis)
Lactic acidosis
Ketoacidosis (diabetes mellitus, alcoholic ketoacidosis)
Uremia (chronic renal failure)
Ingestion of toxins (paraldehyde, methanol, salicylate, ethylene glycol)
High-fat diet (mild acidosis)

Metabolic acidosis with normal AG (hyperchloremic acidosis)
Renal tubular acidosis (including acidosis of aldosterone deficiency)
Intestinal loss of HCO_3^- (diarrhea, pancreatic fistula)

TABLE 4-3 **Disease-Associated ANA Subtypes**

Nuclear Location	Disease(s)
"Native" DNA (dsDNA, or dsDNA/ssDNA complex)	SLE (60%-70%; range, 35%-75%) —also PSS (5%-55%), MCTD (11%-25%), RA (5%-40%), DM (5%-25%), SS (5%)
sNP	SLE (50%) —also other collagen diseases
DNP (DNA-histone complex)	SLE (52%) —also MCTD (8%), RA (3%)
Histones	Drug-induced SLE (95%) —also SLE (30%), RA (15%-24%)
ENA	
Sm	SLE (30%-40%; range, 28%-40%) —also MCTD (0%-8%)
RNP (U1-RNP)	MCTD (in high titer without any other ANA subtype present: 95%-100%) —also SLE (26%-50%), PSS (11%-22%), RA (10%), SS (3%)
SS-A (Ro)*	SS without RA (60%-70%) —also SLE (26%-50%), neonatal SLE (over 95%), PSS (30%), MCTD (50%), SS with RA (9%), PBC (15%-19%)
SS-B (La)	SS without RA (40%-60%) —also SLE (5%-15%), SS with RA (5%)
Scl-70*	PSS (15%-43%)
Centromere*	CREST syndrome (70%-90%; range 57%-96%) —also PSS (4%-20%), PBC (12%)
Nucleolar	PSS (scleroderma) (54%-90%) —also SLE (25%-26%), RA (9%)
RAP (RANA)	SS with RA (60%-76%) —also SS without RA (5%)
Jo-1	Polymyositis (30%)
PM-1	Polymyositis or PMS/PSS overlap syndrome (60%-90%) —also DM (17%)
ssDNA	SLE (60%-70%) —also CAH, infectious mononucleosis, RA, chronic GN, chronic infections, PBC
Cytoplasmic Location	**Disease(s)**
Mitochondrial	Primary biliary cirrhosis (90%-100%) —also CAH (7%-30%), cryptogenic cirrhosis (30%), acute hepatitis, viral hepatitis (3%), other liver diseases (0%-20%), SLE (5%), SS and PSS (8%)
Microsomal†	Chronic active hepatitis (60%-80%), Hashimoto's thyroiditis (97%)
Ribosomal	SLE (5%-12%)
Smooth muscle‡	Chronic active hepatitis (60%-91%) —also cryptogenic cirrhosis (28%), acute hepatitis, viral hepatitis (5%-87%), infectious mononucleosis (81%), MS (40%-50%), malignancy (67%), PBC (10%-50%)

From Ravel R: *Clinical laboratory medicine,* ed 6, St Louis, 1995, Mosby.
CAH, Chronic active hepatitis; *DM,* dermatomyositis; *GN,* glomerulonephritis; *MS,* multiple sclerosis; *PBC,* primary biliary cirrhosis; *SS,* Sjögren's syndrome.
*Not detected using rat or mouse liver or kidney tissue method.
†Not detected by cultured cell method.
‡Detected by cultured cells but better with rat or mouse tissue.

Carbonic anhydrase inhibitors (e.g., acetazolamide)
Dilutional acidosis (as a result of rapid infusion of bicarbonate-free isotonic saline)
Ingestion of exogenous acids (ammonium chloride, methionine, cystine, calcium chloride)
Ileostomy
Ureterosigmoidostomy
Drugs: amiloride, triamterene, spironolactone, β-blockers

RESPIRATORY ACIDOSIS

Pulmonary disease (COPD, severe pneumonia, pulmonary edema, interstitial fibrosis)
Airway obstruction (foreign body, severe bronchospasm, laryngospasm)
Thoracic cage disorders (pneumothorax, flail chest, kyphoscoliosis)
Defects in muscles of respiration (myasthenia gravis, hypokalemia, muscular dystrophy)
Defects in peripheral nervous system (amyotrophic lateral sclerosis, poliomyelitis, Guillain-Barré syndrome, botulism, tetanus, organophosphate poisoning, spinal cord injury)
Depression of respiratory center (anesthesia, narcotics, sedatives, vertebral artery embolism or thrombosis, increased intracranial pressure)
Failure of mechanical ventilator

METABOLIC ALKALOSIS

It is divided into chloride-responsive (urinary chloride <15 mEq/L) and chloride-resistant forms (urinary chloride level >15 mEq/L)

Chloride-responsive
Vomiting
Nasogastric (NG) suction
Diuretics
Posthypercapnic alkalosis
Stool losses (laxative abuse, cystic fibrosis, villous adenoma)
Massive blood transfusion
Exogenous alkali administration
Chloride-resistant
Hyperadrenocorticoid states (Cushing's syndrome, primary hyperaldosteronism, secondary mineralocorticoidism [licorice, chewing tobacco])
Hypomagnesemia
Hypokalemia
Bartter's syndrome
RESPIRATORY ALKALOSIS
Hypoxemia (pneumonia, pulmonary embolism, atelectasis, high-altitude living)
Drugs (salicylates, xanthines, progesterone, epinephrine, thyroxine, nicotine)
Central nervous system (CNS) disorders (tumor, cerebrovascular accident [CVA], trauma, infections)
Psychogenic hyperventilation (anxiety, hysteria)
Hepatic encephalopathy
Gram-negative sepsis
Hyponatremia
Sudden recovery from metabolic acidosis
Assisted ventilation

ARTHROCENTESIS FLUID

Interpretation of results:

1. **Color:** Normally it is clear or pale yellow; cloudiness indicates inflammatory process or presence of crystals, cell debris, fibrin, or triglycerides.
2. **Viscosity:** Normally it has a high viscosity because of hyaluronate; when fluid is placed on a slide, it can be stretched to a string >2 cm in length before separating (low viscosity indicates breakdown of hyaluronate [lysosomal enzymes from leukocytes] or the presence of edema fluid).
3. **Mucin clot:** Add 1 ml of fluid to 5 ml of a 5% acetic acid solution and allow 1 minute for the clot to form; a firm clot (does not fragment on shaking) is normal and indicates the presence of large molecules of hyaluronic acid (this test is nonspecific and infrequently done).
4. **Glucose:** Normally it approximately equals serum glucose level; a difference of more than 40 mg/dl is suggestive of infection.
5. **Protein:** Total protein concentration is <2.5 g/dl in the normal synovial fluid; it is elevated in inflammatory and septic arthritis.
6. Microscopic examination for crystals
   a. Gout: Monosodium urate crystals
   b. Pseudogout: Calcium pyrophosphate dihydrate crystals

ASLO TITER: *see* ANTISTREPTOLYSIN O TITER

ASPARTATE AMINOTRANSFERASE (AST, SGOT)

Normal range: 0-35 U/L
Elevated in:
HEART
Acute myocardial infarction
Pericarditis (active: some cases)
LIVER
Hepatitis virus, Epstein-Barr, or cytomegalovirus infection
Active cirrhosis
Liver passive congestion or hypoxia
Alcohol or drug-induced liver dysfunction
Space-occupying lesions (active)
Fatty liver (severe)
Extrahepatic biliary obstruction (early)
Drug-induced
SKELETAL MUSCLE
Acute skeletal muscle injury
Muscle inflammation (infectious or noninfectious)
Muscular dystrophy (active)
Recent surgery
Delirium tremens
KIDNEY
Acute injury or damage
Renal infarct

OTHER
Intestinal infarction
Shock
Cholecystitis
Acute pancreatitis
Hypothyroidism
Heparin therapy (60%-80% of cases)

B-TYPE NATRIURETIC PEPTIDE

Normal range: Up to 100pg/mL
Elevated in: Heart failure. This test is useful in the emergency department setting to differentiate heart failure patients from those with chronic obstructive pulmonary disease presenting with dyspnea.

BASOPHIL COUNT

Normal range: 0.4% to 1% of total WBC; 40-100/mm^3
Elevated in: Leukemia, inflammatory processes, polycythemia vera, Hodgkin's lymphoma, hemolytic anemia, after splenectomy, myeloid metaplasia, myxedema
Decreased in: Stress, hypersensitivity reaction, steroids, pregnancy, hyperthyroidism, postirradiation

BILE, URINE; *see* URINE BILE

BILIRUBIN, DIRECT (conjugated bilirubin)

Normal range: 0-0.2 mg/dl
Elevated in: Hepatocellular disease, biliary obstruction, drug-induced cholestasis, hereditary disorders (Dubin-Johnson syndrome, Rotor's syndrome)

BILIRUBIN, INDIRECT (unconjugated bilirubin)

Normal range: 0-1.0 mg/dl
Elevated in: A. Increased bilirubin production (if normal liver, serum unconjugated bilirubin is usually less than 4 mg/100 ml)

1. Hemolytic anemia
   a. Acquired
   b. Congenital
2. Resorption from extravascular sources
   a. Hematomas
   b. Pulmonary infarcts
3. Excessive ineffective erythropoiesis
   a. Congenital (congenital dyserythropoietic anemias)
   b. Acquired (pernicious anemia, severe lead poisoning; if present, bilirubinemia is usually mild)

B. Defective hepatic unconjugated bilirubin clearance (defective uptake or conjugation)

1. Severe liver disease
2. Gilbert's syndrome
3. Crigler-Najjar type I or II
4. Drug-induced inhibition
5. Portacaval shunt
6. Congestive heart failure
7. Hyperthyroidism (uncommon)

BILIRUBIN, TOTAL

Normal range: 0-1.0 mg/dl
Elevated in: Liver disease (hepatitis, cirrhosis, cholangitis, neoplasm, biliary obstruction, infectious mononucleosis), hereditary disorders (Gilbert's disease, Dubin-Johnson syndrome), drugs (steroids, diphenylhydantoin, phenothiazines, penicillin, erythromycin, clindamycin, captopril, amphotericin B, sulfonamides, azathioprine, isoniazid, 5-aminosalicylic acid, allopurinol, methyldopa, indomethacin, halothane, oral contraceptives, procainamide, tolbutamide, labetalol), hemolysis, pulmonary embolism or infarct, hepatic congestion secondary to congestive heart failure

BILIRUBIN, URINE: *see* URINE BILE

BLEEDING TIME (modified Ivy method)

Normal range: 2 to 9 1/2 min
Elevated in: Thrombocytopenia, capillary wall abnormalities, platelet abnormalities (Bernard-Soulier disease, Glanzmann's disease), drugs (aspirin, warfarin, antiinflammatory medications, streptokinase, urokinase, dextran, β-lactam antibiotics, moxalactam), disseminated intravascular coagulation, cirrhosis, uremia, myeloproliferative disorders, von Willebrand's disease

BRCA ANALYSIS

Description of Analysis

Comprehensive BRCA Analysis:

BRCA1: Full sequence determination in both forward and reverse directions of approximately 5500 base pairs comprising 22 coding exons and one noncoding exon (exon 4) and approximately 800 adjacent base pairs in the noncoding intervening sequence (intron). Exon 1, which is noncoding, is not analyzed. The wild-type *BRCA1* gene encodes a protein comprising 1863 amino acids.

BRCA2: Full sequence determination in both forward and reverse directions of approximately 10,200 base pairs comprising 26 coding exons and approximately 900 adjacent base pairs in the noncoding intervening sequence (intron). Exon 1, which is noncoding, is not analyzed. The wild-type *BRCA2* gene encodes a protein comprising 3418 amino acids.

The noncoding intronic regions of *BRCA1* and *BRCA2* that are analyzed do not extend more than 20 base pairs proximal to the 5′ end and 10 base pairs distal to the 3′ end of each exon.

SINGLE-SITE BRACANALYSIS: DNA sequence analysis for a specified mutation in *BRCA1* and/or *BRCA2*.

MULTISITE 3 BRACANALYSIS: DNA sequence analysis of specific portions of *BRCA1* exon 2, *BRCA1* exon 20 and *BRCA2* exon 11 designed to detect only mutations 187delAG and 5385insC in *BRCA1* and 6174delT in *BRCA2*.

Interpretive Criteria

"POSITIVE FOR A DELETERIOUS MUTATION": Includes all mutations (nonsense, insertions, deletions) that prematurely terminate ("truncate") the protein product of *BRCA1* at least 10 amino acids form the C-terminus, or the protein product of *BRCA2* at least 110 amino acids from the C-terminus (based on documentation of deleterious mutations in *BRCA1* and *BRCA2*).

In addition, specific missense mutations and noncoding intervening sequence (IVS) mutations are recognized as deleterious on the basis of data derived from linkage analysis of high-risk families, functional assays, biochemical evidence and/or demonstration of abnormal mRNA transcript processing.

"GENETIC VARIANT, SUSPECTED DELETERIOUS": Includes genetic variants for which the available evidence indicates a likelihood, but not proof, that the mutation is deleterious. The specific evidence supporting such an interpretation will be summarized for individual variants on each such report.

"GENETIC VARIANT, FAVOR POLYMORPHISM": Includes genetic variants for which available evidence indicates that the variant is highly unlikely to contribute substantially to cancer risk. The specific evidence supporting such an interpretation will be summarized for individual variants on each such report.

"GENETIC VARIANT OF UNCERTAIN SIGNIFICANCE": Includes missense mutations and mutations that occur in analyzed intronic regions whose clinical significance has not yet been determined, as well as chain-terminating mutations that truncate *BRCA1* and *BRCA2* distal to amino acid positions 1853 and 3308, respectively.

"NO DELETERIOUS MUTATION DETECTED": Includes nontruncating genetic variants observed at an allele frequency of approximately 1% of a suitable control population (providing that no data suggest clinical significance), as well as all genetic variants for which published data demonstrate absence of substantial clinical significance. Also includes mutations in the protein-coding region that neither alter the amino acid sequence nor are predicted to significantly affect exon splicing, and base pair alterations in noncoding portions of the gene that have been demonstrated to have no deleterious effect on the length or stability of the mRNA transcript.

There may be uncommon genetic abnormalities in *BRCA1* and *BRCA2* that will not be detected by BRCA Analysis. This analysis, however, is believed to rule out the majority of abnormalities in these genes, which are believed responsible for most hereditary susceptibility to breast and ovarian cancer.

"SPECIFIC VARIANT/MUTATION NOT IDENTIFIED": Specific and designated deleterious mutations or variants of uncertain clinical significance are not present in the individual being tested. If one (or rarely two) specific deleterious mutations have been identified in a family member, a negative analysis for the specific mutation(s) indicates that the tested individual is at the general population risk of developing breast or ovarian cancer.

BUN; *see* UREA NITROGEN

C282Y AND H63D MUTATION ANALYSIS

PROCEDURE: Detection of the C282Y and H63D mutations is accomplished by amplification of exons 2 and 4 of the HFE gene on chromosome 6 by polymerase chain reaction (PCR) followed by allele-specific hybridization and chemiluminescent detection of hybridized probes. H63D is viewed by some as a polymorphism rather than a mutation because of its prevalence in the population, because 15% of the individuals affected with hereditary hemochromatosis (HH) are compound heterozygotes for C282Y and H63D and about 1% of patients are H63D homozygotes, which suggests that H63D may be causative in the development of the disorder at reduced penetrance. The test is performed by Quest diagnostics pursuant to a license agreement with Roche Molecular systems, Inc.

INTERPRETATION: Homozygosity for the C282Y mutation has been associated with an increased risk of being affected with hereditary hemochromatosis (HH) compared with the general population. The genotype is observed in 60% to 90% of individuals affected with HH and occurs in less than 1% of the general population. However, approximately 25% of asymptomatic individuals with this genotype do not develop the disorder.

C3; *see* COMPLEMENT C3
C4; *see* COMPLEMENT C4

CALCITONIN (serum)

Normal range: <100 pg/ml
Elevated in: Medullary carcinoma of the thyroid (particularly if level >1500 pg/ml), carcinoma of the breast, apudomas, carcinoids, renal failure, thyroiditis

CALCIUM (serum)

Normal range: 8.8-10.3 mg/dl
ELEVATED
RELATIVELY COMMON
Neoplasia (noncutaneous)
Bone primary
Myeloma
Acute leukemia
Nonbone solid tumors
Breast
Lung
Squamous nonpulmonary
Kidney
Neoplasm secretion of parathyroid hormone-related protein (PTHrP, "ectopic PTH")
Primary hyperparathyroidism
Thiazide diuretics
Tertiary (renal) hyperparathyroidism
Idiopathic
Spurious (artifactual) hypercalcemia
Dehydration
Serum protein elevation
Laboratory technical problem
RELATIVELY UNCOMMON
Neoplasia (less common tumors)
Sarcoidosis
Hyperthyroidism
Immobilization (mostly seen in children and adolescents)
Diuretic phase of acute renal tubular necrosis
Vitamin D intoxication
Milk-alkali syndrome
Addison's disease
Lithium therapy
Idiopathic hypercalcemia of infancy
Acromegaly
Theophylline toxicity
- Table 4-4 describes the laboratory differential diagnosis of hypercalcemia.

DECREASED
Artifactual
Hypoalbuminemia
Hemodilution
Primary hypoparathyroidism
Pseudohypoparathyroidism
Vitamin D–related
Vitamin D deficiency
Malabsorption
Renal failure
Magnesium deficiency
Sepsis
Chronic alcoholism
Tumor lysis syndrome
Rhabdomyolysis
Alkalosis (respiratory or metabolic)
Acute pancreatitis
Drug-induced hypocalcemia
Large doses of magnesium sulfate
Anticonvulsants
Mithramycin
Gentamicin
Cimetidine
- Table 4-5 describes the laboratory differential diagnosis of hypocalcemia.

TABLE 4-4 **Laboratory Differential Diagnosis of Hypercalcemia**

	PLASMA TESTS					URINE TESTS			
Diagnosis	**Ca**	**PO_4**	**PTH**	**25(OH)D**	**$1,25(OH)_2D$**	**cAMP**	**TmP/GFR**	**Ca**	**Comments**
Primary hyperparathyroidism	↑	N/↓	↑	N	N/↑	↑	↓	↑	Parathyroid adenoma most common
MEN I									Parathyroid hyperplasia; also includes pituitary and pancreatic neoplasms
MEN IIa									Parathyroid hyperplasia; also includes medullary thyroid carcinoma and pheochromocytoma
MEN IIb									Parathyroid disease uncommon, primarily medullary thyroid carcinoma and pheochromocytoma
FHH	↑	N	N/↑	N	N	N/↑	N/↓	↓↓	Autosomal dominant inheritance; hypercalcemia present within first decade; benign
Malignancy									
Solid tumor—humoral	↑	N/↓	↓	N	N	↑	↓	↑↑	Primarily epidermoid tumors; PTH-related protein(s) is mediator
Solid tumor—osteolytic	↑	N/↑	↓	N	N	↓	↑	↑↑	
Lymphoma	↑	N/↑	↓	N/↓	↑	↓	↑	↑↑	
Granulomatous disease	↑	N/↑	↓	N/↓	↑↑	↓	↑	↑↑	Sarcoid most common etiology
Vitamin D intoxication	↑	N/↑	↓	↑↑	N	↓	↑	↑↑	
Hyperthyroidism	↑	N	↓	N	N	N	N	↑↑	Plasma concentrations of T4 and/or T_3 are elevated

From Moore WT, Eastman RC: *Diagnostic endocrinology,* ed 2, St Louis, 1996, Mosby.
Ca, Calcium; *cAMP,* cyclic adenosine monophosphate; *FHH,* familial hypocalciuric hypercalcemia; *GFR,* glomerular filtration rate; *MEN,* multiple endocrine neoplasia; *25(OH)D,* 25 hydroxyvitamin D; *PO_4,* phosphate; *PTH,* parathormone; *T_3,* triiodothyronine; *T_4,* thyroxine; *TmP,* renal threshold for phosphorus.

CALCIUM, URINE; *see* URINE CALCIUM

CANCER ANTIGEN 125

Normal range: Less than 1.4%

The cancer antigen 125 (CA 125) test uses an antibody against antigen from tissue culture of an ovarian tumor cell line. Various published evaluations report sensitivity of about 75%-80% in patients with ovarian carcinoma. There is also an appreciable incidence of elevated values in nonovarian malignancies and in certain benign conditions (see below). Test values may transiently increase during chemotherapy.

MALIGNANT

Epithelial ovarian carcinoma, 75%-80% (range 25%-92%, better in serous than mucinous cystadenocarcinoma)
Endometrial carcinoma, 25%-48% (2%-90%)
Pancreatic carcinoma, 59%
Colorectal carcinoma, 20% (15%-56%)
Endocervical adenocarcinoma, 83%
Squamous cervical or vaginal carcinoma, 7%-14%
Lung carcinoma, 32%
Breast carcinoma, 12%-40%
Lymphoma, 35%

BENIGN

Cirrhosis, 40%-80%
Acute pancreatitis, 38%
Acute peritonitis, 75%
Endometriosis, 88%
Acute pelvic inflammation disease, 33%
Pregnancy first trimester, 2%-24%
During menstruation (occasionally)
Renal failure (?frequency)
Normal persons, 0.6%-1.4%

CARBAMAZEPINE (tegretol)

Normal therapeutic range: 4-12 mcg/mL

CARBON MONOXIDE; *see* CARBOXYHEMOGLOBIN

TABLE 4-5 **Laboratory Differential Diagnosis of Hypocalcemia**

	PLASMA TESTS					URINE TESTS					
DIAGNOSIS	**Ca**	**PO4**	**PTH**	**25(OH)D**	**1,25(OH)2D**	**cAMP**	**cAMP AFTER PTH**	**TmP/GFR**	**TmP/GFR AFTER PTH**	**Ca**	**COMMENTS**
Hypoparathyroidism	↓	≠	N/↓	N	↓	↓	↑↑	↑	↓↓	N/↓	Deficiency of PTH
Pseudohypo-parathyroidism											
Type I	↓	↑	↑↑	N	↓	↓	NC	↑	↑	N/↓	Resistance to PTH; patients may have Albright's hereditary osteodystrophy and resistance to multiple hormones
Type II	↓	N	↑↑	N	↓	↓	↑	↑	↑	N/↓	Renal resistance to cAMP
Vitamin D deficiency	↓	N/↓	↑↑	↓↓	N/↓	↑	↑	↓	↓	↓↓	Deficient supply (e.g., nutrition) or absorption (e.g., pancreatic insufficiency) of vitamin D
Vitamin D–dependent rickets											
Type I	↓	N/↓	↑↑	N	↓	↑		↓		↓↓	Deficient activity of renal 25(OH)D-1a-hydroxylase
Type II	↓	N/↓	↑↑	N	↑↑	↑		↓		↓↓	Resistance to 1,25(OH)2D

From Moore WT, Eastman RC: *Diagnostic endocrinology,* ed 2, St Louis, 1996, Mosby.

Ca, Calcium; *cAMP,* cyclic adenosine monophosphate; *FHH,* familial hypocalciuric hypercalcemia; *GFR,* glomerular filtration rate; *MEN,* multiple endocrine neoplasia; *NC,* no change or small increase; *(OH)D,* hydroxycalciferol D; PO_4, phosphate; *PTH,* parathyroid hormone; T_3, triiodothyronine; T_4, thyroxine; *TmP,* renal threshold for phosphorus.

CARBOXYHEMOGLOBIN

Normal range: Saturation of hemoglobin <2%; smokers <9% (coma: 50%; death: 80%)
Elevated in: Smoking, exposure to smoking, exposure to automobile exhaust fumes, malfunctioning gas-burning appliances

CARCINOEMBRYONIC ANTIGEN (CEA)

Normal range: Nonsmokers: 0-2.5 ng/ml
Smokers: 0-5 ng/ml
Elevated in: Colorectal carcinomas, pancreatic carcinomas, and metastatic disease (usually produce higher elevations: >20 ng/ml)
Carcinomas of the esophagus, stomach, small intestine, liver, breast, ovary, lung, and thyroid (usually produce lesser elevations)
Benign conditions (smoking, inflammatory bowel disease, hypothyroidism, cirrhosis, pancreatitis, infections) (usually produce levels <10 ng/ml)

CAROTENE (serum)

Normal range: 50-250 μg/dl
Elevated in: Carotenemia, chronic nephritis, diabetes mellitus, hypothyroidism, nephrotic syndrome, hyperlipidemia
Decreased in: Fat malabsorption, steatorrhea, pancreatic insufficiency, lack of carotenoids in diet, high fever, liver disease

CATECHOLAMINES, URINE; *see* URINE CATECHOLAMINES

CBC; *see* COMPLETE BLOOD COUNT

CD4+ T-LYMPHOCYTE COUNT (CD4+ T-Cells)

Calculated as total WBC × % lymphocytes × % lymphocytes stained with CD4.
This test is used primarily to evaluate immune dysfunction in HIV infection and should be done every 3-6 months in all HIV-infected persons. It is useful as a prognostic indicator and as a criterion for initiating prophylaxis for several opportunistic infections that are sequelae of HIV infection. Progressive depletion of CD4+ T-lymphocytes is associated with an increased likelihood of clinical complications (Table 4-6). Adolescents and adults with HIV are classified as having AIDS if their CD4+ lymphocyte count is under 200/μL and/or if their CD4+ T-lymphocyte percentage is less than 14%. HIV-infected patients whose CD4+ count is less than 200/μL and who acquire certain infectious diseases or malignancies are also classified as having AIDS. Corticosteroids decrease CD4+ T-cell percentage and absolute number.

TABLE 4-6 Relation of CD4 Lymphocyte Counts to the Onset of Certain, HIV-Associated Infections and Neoplasms in North America

CD4 Count (Cells/MM³)*	Opportunistic Infection or Neoplasm	Frequency (%)†
>500	Herpes zoster, polydermatomal	5-10
200-500	*Mycobacterium tuberculosis* infection, pulmonary and extrapulmonary	2-20
	Oral hairy leukoplakia	40-70
	Candida pharyngitis (thrush)	40-70
	Recurrent *Candida* vaginitis	15-30 (F)
	Kaposi's sarcoma, mucocutaneous	15-30 (M)
	Bacterial pneumonia, recurrent	15-20
	Cervical neoplasia	1-2 (F)
100-200	*Pneumocystis carinii* pneumonia	15-60
	Herpes simplex, chronic, ulcerative	5-10
	Histoplasma capsulatum infection, disseminated	0-20
	Kaposi's sarcoma, visceral	3-8 (M)
	Progressive multifocal leukoencephalopathy	2-3
	Lymphoma, non-Hodgkin's	2-5
<100	*Candida* esophagitis	15-20
	Mycobacterium avium-intracellulare, disseminated	25-40
	Toxoplasma gondii encephalitis	5-25
	Cryptosporidium enteritis	2-10
	Cytomegalovirus (CMV) retinitis	20-35
	Cryptococcus neoformans encephalitis	2-5
	CMV esophagitis or colitis	6-12
	Lymphoma, central nervous system	4-8

From Andreoli TE (ed): *Cecil essentials of medicine,* ed 4, Philadelphia, 1997, WB Saunders.
F, Exclusively in women; *HIV,* human immunodeficiency virus; *M,* almost exclusively in men.
*Table indicates CD4 count at which specific infections or neoplasms generally begin to appear. Each infection may recur or progress during the subsequent course of HIV disease.
†Even within the United States, great regional differences in the incidence of specific opportunistic infections are apparent. For example, disseminated histoplasmosis is common in the Mississippi River drainage area, but very rare in individuals who have lived exclusively on the East or West Coast.

CEA; *see* CARCINOEMBRYONIC ANTIGEN

CEREBROSPINAL FLUID (CSF)

Normal range:

Interpretation of results:

1. Appearance of the fluid
   a. Clear: normal.
   b. Yellow color (xanthochromia) in the supernatant of centrifuged CSF within 1 hour or less after collection is usually the result of previous bleeding (subarachnoid hemorrhage); it may also be caused by increased CSF protein, melanin from meningeal melanosarcomas, or carotenoids.
   c. Pinkish color is usually the result of a bloody tap; the color generally clears progressively from tubes 1 to 4 (the supernatant is usually crystal clear in traumatic taps).
   d. Turbidity usually indicates the presence of leukocytes (bleeding introduces approximately 1 WBC/500 RBCs into the CSF).
2. CSF pressure: elevated pressure can be seen with meningitis, meningoencephalitis, pseudotumor cerebri, mass lesions, and intracerebral bleeding.
3. Cell count: in the adult the CSF is normally free of cells (although up to 5 mononuclear cells/mm^3 is considered normal); the presence of granulocytes is never normal.
   a. Neutrophils: seen in bacterial meningitis, early viral meningoencephalitis, and early tuberculosis (TB) meningitis.
   b. Increased lymphocytes: TB meningitis, viral meningoencephalitis, syphilitic meningoencephalitis, fungal meningitis.
4. Protein: serum proteins are generally too large to cross the normal blood-CSF barrier; however, increased CSF protein is seen with meningeal inflammation, traumatic tap, increased CNS synthesis, tissue degeneration, obstruction to CSF circulation, and Guillain-Barré syndrome.
5. Glucose
   a. Decreased glucose is seen with bacterial meningitis, TB meningitis, fungal meningitis, subarachnoid hemorrhage, and some cases of viral meningitis.
   b. A mild increase in CSF glucose can be seen in patients with very elevated serum glucose levels.

Table 4-7, on the following page, describes cerebrospinal fluid findings in central nervous system disorders.

CERULOPLASMIN (serum)

Normal range: 20-35 mg/dl

Elevated in: Pregnancy, estrogens, oral contraceptives, neoplastic diseases (leukemias, Hodgkin's lymphoma, carcinomas), inflammatory states, systemic lupus erythematosus, primary biliary cirrhosis, rheumatoid arthritis

Decreased in: Wilson's disease (values often <10 mg/dl), nephrotic syndrome, advanced liver disease, malabsorption, total parenteral nutrition, Menkes' syndrome

CHLORIDE (serum)

Normal range: 95-105 mEq/L

Elevated in: Dehydration, excessive infusion of normal saline solution, cystic fibrosis (sweat test), hyperparathyroidism, renal tubular disease, metabolic acidosis, prolonged diarrhea, drugs (ammonium chloride administration, acetazolamide, boric acid, triamterene)

Decreased in: Congestive heart failure, syndrome of inappropriate antidiuretic hormone secretion, Addison's disease, vomiting, gastric suction, salt-losing nephritis, continuous infusion of D_5W, thiazide diuretic administration, diaphoresis, diarrhea, burns, diabetic ketoacidosis

CHLORIDE (sweat)

Normal: 0-40 mmol/L

Borderline/indeterminate: 41-60 mmol/L

Consistent with cystic fibrosis: > 60 mmol/L

False low results can occur with edema, excessive sweating, and hypoproteinemia.

CHLORIDE, URINE; *see* URINE CHLORIDE

CHOLESTEROL, HIGH-DENSITY LIPOPROTEIN; *see* HIGH-DENSITY LIPOPROTEIN CHOLESTEROL

CHOLESTEROL, LOW-DENSITY LIPOPROTEIN; *see* LOW-DENSITY LIPOPROTEIN CHOLESTEROL

CHOLESTEROL, TOTAL

Normal range: Varies with age

Generally <200 mg/dl

Elevated in: Primary hypercholesterolemia, biliary obstruction, diabetes mellitus, nephrotic syndrome, hypothyroidism, primary biliary cirrhosis, high-cholesterol diet, pregnancy third trimester, myocardial infarction, drugs (steroids, phenothiazines, oral contraceptives)

TABLE 4-7 **Cerebrospinal Fluid Findings in Central Nervous System Disorders**

Condition	Pressure (mm H_2O)	Leukocytes (mm^3)	Protein (mg/dL)	Glucose (mg/dL)	Comments
Normal	50-80	<5, ≥75% lymphocytes	20-45	>50 (or 75% serum glucose)	
Common Forms of Meningitis					
Acute bacterial meningitis	Usually elevated (100-300)	100-10,000 or more; usually 300-2000; PMNs predominate	Usually 100-500	Decreased, usually <40 (or <66% serum glucose)	Organisms usually seen on Gram stain and recovered by culture. Latex agglutination of CSF usually positive
Partially treated bacterial meningitis	Normal or elevated	5-10,000; PMNs usual but mononuclear cells may predominate if pretreated for extended period of time	Usually 100-500	Normal or decreased	Organisms may be seen on Gram stain. Latex agglutination CSF may be positive. Pretreatment may render CSF sterile
Viral meningitis or meningoencephalitis	Normal or slightly elevated (80-150)	Rarely >1000 cells. Eastern equine encephalitis and lymphocytic choriomeningitis (LCM) may have cell counts of several thousand. PMNs early but mononuclear cells predominate through most of the course	Usually 50-200	Generally normal; may be decreased to <40 in some viral diseases, particularly mumps (15%-20% of cases)	HSV encephalitis is suggested by focal seizures or by focal findings on CT or MRI scans or EEG. Enteroviruses and HSV infrequently recovered from CSF. HSV and enteroviruses may be detected by PCR of CSF
Uncommon Forms of Meningitis					
Tuberculous meningitis	Usually elevated	10-500; PMNs early, but lymphocytes predominate through most of the course	100-3000; may be higher in presence of block	<50 in most cases; decreases with time if treatment is not provided	Acid-fast organisms almost never seen on smear. Organisms may be recovered in culture of large volumes of CSF. *Mycobacterium tuberculosis* may be detected by PCR of CSF
Fungal meningitis	Usually elevated	5-500; PMNs early but mononuclear cells predominate through most of the course. Cryptococcal meningitis may have no cellular inflammatory response	25-500	<50; decreases with time if treatment is not provided	Budding yeast may be seen. Organisms may be recovered in culture. Cryptococcal antigen (CSF and serum) may be positive in cryptococcal infection
Syphilis (acute) and leptospirosis	Usually elevated	50-500; lymphocytes predominate	50-200	Usually normal	Positive CSF serology. Spirochetes not demonstrable by usual techniques of smear or culture; darkfield examination may be positive
Amebic (Naegleria) meningoencephalitis	Elevated	1000-10,000 or more; PMNs predominate	50-500	Normal or slightly decreased	Mobile amebae may be seen by hanging-drop examination of CSF at room temperature

Brain and Parameningeal Abscesses					
Brain abscess	Usually elevated (100-300)	5-200; CSF rarely acellular; lymphocytes predominate; if abscess ruptures into ventricle, PMNs predominate and cell count may reach >100,000	75-500	Normal unless abscess ruptures into ventricular system	No organisms on smear or culture unless abscess ruptures into ventricular system
Subdural empyema	Usually elevated (100-300)	100-5000; PMNs predominate	100-500	Normal	No organisms on smear or culture of CSF unless meningitis also present; organisms found on tap of subdural fluid
Cerebral epidural abscess	Normal to slightly elevated	10-500; lymphocytes predominate	50-200	Normal	No organisms on smear or culture of CSF
Spinal epidural abscess	Usually low, with spinal block	10-100; lymphocytes predominate	50-400	Normal	No organisms on smear or culture of CSF
Chemical (drugs, dermoid cysts, myelography dye)	Usually elevated	100-1000 or more; PMNs predominate	50-100	Normal or slightly decreased	Epithelial cells may be seen within CSF by use of polarized light in some children with dermoids
Noninfectious Causes					
Sarcoidosis	Normal or elevated slightly	0-100; mononuclear	40-100	Normal	No specific findings
Systemic lupus erythematosus with CNS involvement	Slightly elevated	0-500; PMNs usually predominate; lymphocytes may be present	100	Normal or slightly decreased	No organisms on smear or culture. LE preparation may be positive. Positive neuronal and ribosomal P protein antibodies in CSF
Tumor, leukemia	Slightly elevated to very high	0-100 or more; mononuclear or blast cells	50-1000	Normal to decreased (20-40)	Cytology may be positive

From Behrman RE: *Nelson textbook of pediatrics,* ed 16, Philadelphia, 2000, WB Saunders.
CSF, Cerebrospinal fluid; EEG, electroencephalogram; *HSV,* herpes simplex virus; *PCR,* polymerase chain reaction; *PMN,* polymorphonuclear neutrophils.

Decreased in: Starvation, malabsorption, sideroblastic anemia, thalassemia, abetalipoproteinemia, hyperthyroidism, Cushing's syndrome, hepatic failure, multiple myeloma, polycythemia vera, chronic myelocytic leukemia, myeloid metaplasia, Waldenström's macroglobulinemia, myelofibrosis

CHORIONIC GONADOTROPINS, HUMAN (serum)

Normal range, serum: Female, premenopausal: <0.8 IU/L; postmenopausal <3.3 IU/L
Male: <0.7 IU/L
Elevated in: Pregnancy, choriocarcinoma, gestational trophoblastic neoplasia (including molar gestations), placental site trophoblastic tumors; human antimouse antibodies (HAMA) can produce false serum assay for hCG.
The principal use of this test is to diagnose pregnancy. The concentration of hCG increases significantly during the initial 6 weeks of pregnancy. Peak values approaching 100,000 IU/L occur 60-70 days following implantation.
hCG levels generally double every 1-3 days. In patients with concentration <2000 IU/L, an increase of serum hCG <66% after 2 days is suggestive of spontaneous abortion or ruptured ectopic gestation.

CIRCULATING ANTICOAGULANT (lupus anticoagulant)

Normal: Negative
Detected in: Systemic lupus erythematosus, drug-induced lupus, long-term phenothiazine therapy, multiple myeloma, ulcerative colitis, rheumatoid arthritis, postpartum, hemophilia, neoplasms, chronic inflammatory states, AIDS, nephrotic syndrome

NOTE: The name is a misnomer because these patients are prone to hypercoagulability and thrombosis.

CK; *see* CREATINE KINASE

CLOSTRIDIUM DIFFICILE TOXIN ASSAY (stool)

Normal: Negative
Detected in: Antibiotic-associated diarrhea and pseudomembranous colitis

CO; *see* CARBOXYHEMOGLOBIN

COAGULATION FACTORS; *see* Table 4-8 for characteristics of coagulation factors

Factor reference ranges:
V: >10%
VII: >10%
VIII: 50% to 170%
IX: 60% to 136%
X: >10%
XI: 50% to 150%
XII: >30%

- Table 4-9 describes screening laboratory results in coagulation factor deficiencies.

TABLE 4-8 Characteristics of Coagulation Factors

Factor	Descriptive Name	Source	Approximate Half-Life (hr)	Function
I	Fibrinogen	Liver	120	Substrate for fibrin clot (CP)
II	Prothrombin	Liver (VKD)	60	Serine protease (CP)
V	Proaccelerin, labile factor	Liver	12-36	Cofactor (CP)
VII	Serum prothrombin conversion accelerator, proconvertin	Liver (VKD)	6	(?) Serine protease (EP)
VIII	Antihemophilic factor or globulin	Endothelial cells and (?) elsewhere	12	Cofactor (IP)
IX	Plasma thromboplastin component, Christmas factor	Liver (VKD)	24	Serine protease (IP)
X	Stuart-Prower factor	Liver (VKD)	36	Serine protease (CP)
XI	Plasma thromboplastin antecedent	(?) Liver	40-84	Serine protease (IP)
XII	Hageman factor	(?) Liver	50	Serine protease contact activation (IP)
XIII	Fibrin-stabilizing factor	(?) Liver	96-180	Transglutaminase (CP)
Prekallikrein	Fletcher factor	(?) Liver	?	Serine protease contact activation (IP)
High-molecular-weight kininogen	Fitzgerald factor, Flaujeac or Williams factor	(?) Liver	?	Cofactor, contact activation (IP)

From Noble J (ed): *Primary care medicine*, ed 3, St Louis, 2001, Mosby.
CP, Common pathway; *EP*, extrinsic pathway; *IP*, intrinsic pathway; *VKD*, vitamin K dependent.

TABLE 4-9 Screening Laboratory Results in Coagulation Factor Deficiencies

Deficient Factor	Frequency	PT	PTT	TT
I (fibrinogen)	Rare	↑	↑	↑
II (prothrombin)	Very rare	↑	↑	↑
V 1:1,000,000	↑	↑	NL	
VII	1:500,000	↑	NL	NL
VIII	1:5000 (male)	NL	↑	NL
IX	1:30,000 (male)	NL	↑	NL
X 1:500,000	↑	↑	NL	
XI	Rare*	NL	↑	NL
XII† or HMWK† or PK†	Rare	NL	↑	NL
XIII	Rare	NL	NL	NL

From Andreoli TE (ed): *Cecil essentials of medicine,* ed 5, Philadelphia, 2001, WB Saunders.
↑, Increased over normal range; *HMWK,* high-molecular-weight kininogen; *NL,* normal; *PK,* prekallikrein; *PT,* prothrombin time; *PTT,* partial thromboplastin time; *TT,* thrombin time.
*Except in those of Ashkenazi Jewish descent (approximately 4% are heterozygous for factor XI deficiency).
†Not associated with clinical bleeding.

COLD AGGLUTININS TITER

Normal range: <1:32
Elevated in: Primary atypical pneumonia (mycoplasma pneumonia), infectious mononucleosis, CMV infection
Others: hepatic cirrhosis, acquired hemolytic anemia, frostbite, multiple myeloma, lymphoma, malaria

COMPLEMENT

Normal range: C3: 70-160 mg/dl
C4: 20-40 mg/dl
Abnormal values:
DECREASED C3: Active SLE, immune complex disease, acute glomerulonephritis, inborn C3 deficiency, membranoproliferative glomerulonephritis, infective endocarditis, serum sickness, autoimmune/chronic active hepatitis
DECREASED C4: Immune complex disease, active SLE, infective endocarditis, inborn C4 deficiency, hereditary angioedema, hypergammaglobulinemic states, cryobulinemic vasculitis
Table 4-10 describes complement deficiency states.

COMPLETE BLOOD COUNT (CBC)

White blood cells 3200-9800 mm^3 (3.2-9.8 × 10^9/L)
Red blood cells
Male: 4.3-5.9 × 10^6/mm^3 (4.3-5.9 × 10^{12}/L)
Female: 3.5-5 × 10^6/mm^3 (3.5-5 × 10^{12}/L)
Hemoglobin
Male: 13.6-17.7 g/dl (136-172 g/L)
Female: 12-15 g/dl (120-150 g/L)
Hematocrit
Male: 39% to 49% (0.39-0.49)
Female: 33% to 43% (0.33-0.43)
Mean corpuscular volume (MCV): 76-100 μm^3 (76-100 fL)
Mean corpuscular hemoglobin (MCH): 27-33 pg (27-33 pg)
Mean corpuscular hemoglobin concentration (MCHC): 33-37 g/dl (330-370 g/L)
Red blood cell distribution width index (RDW): 11.5% to 14.5%
Platelet count: 130-400 × 10^3/mm^3 (130-400 × 10^9/L)
Differential:
2-6 stabs (bands, early mature neutrophils)
60-70 segs (mature neutrophils)
1-4 eosinophils
0-1 basophils
2-8 monocytes
25-40 lymphocytes

CONJUGATED BILIRUBIN; *see* BILIRUBIN, DIRECT

COOMBS, DIRECT

Normal: Negative
Positive: Autoimmune hemolytic anemia, erythroblastosis fetalis, transfusion reactions, drugs (α-methyldopa, penicillins, tetracycline, sulfonamides, levodopa, cephalosporins, quinidine, insulin)
False positive: May be seen with cold agglutinins

TABLE 4-10 **Complement Deficiency States**

Component	Number of Reported Patients	Mode of Inheritance	Functional Defects	Disease Associations
Classic pathway				
C1qrs	31	ACD	Impaired IC handling, delayed C′ activation, impaired immune response	CVD, 48%; infection (encaps bact), 22%; both, 18%; healthy, 12%
C4	21	ACD		
C2	109	ACD		
Alternative pathway				
D	3	ACD	Impaired C′ activation in absence of specific antibody	Infection (meningococcal), 74%; healthy, 26%
P	70	XL		
Junction of classic and alternative pathways				
C3	19	ACD	Impaired IC handling, opson/phag; granulocytosis, CTX, immune response and absent SBA	CVD, 79%; recurrent infection (encaps bact), 71%
Terminal components				
C5	27	ACD	Impaired CTX; absent SBA	Infection (Neisseria, primarily meningococcal), 58%; CVD, 4%
C6	77	ACD	Absent SBA	Both, 1%
C7	73	ACD		Healthy, 25%
C8	73	ACD		
C9	165	ACD	Impaired SBA	Healthy, 91%; infection, 9%
Plasma proteins regulating C′ activation				
C1-INH	Many	AD Acq	Uncontrolled generation of an inflammatory mediator on C′ activation	Hereditary angioedema
H	13	ACD	Uncontrolled AP activation → low C3	CVD, 40%; CVD plus infection (encaps bact), 40%; healthy, 20%
I	14	ACD	Uncontrolled AP activation → low C3	Infection (encaps bact), 100%
Membrane proteins regulating C′ activation				
Decay-accelerating factor Homologous restriction factor CD59	Many	Acq	Impaired regulation of C3b and C8 deposited on host RBC; PMN, platelets → cell lysis	Paroxysmal nocturnal hemoglobinuria
CR3	>20	ACD	Impaired PMN adhesive functions (i.e., margination), CTX, C3bi-mediated opson/phag	Infection (Staphylococcus aureus, Pseudomonas spp.), 100%
Autoantibodies				
C3 nephritic factors	>59	Acq	Stabilize AP, convertase → low C3	MPGN, 41%; PLD, 25%; infection (encaps bact), 16%; MPGN plus PLD, 10%; PLD plus infection, 5%; MPGN plus PLD plus infection, 3%; MPGN plus infection, 2%
C4 nephritic factor		Acq	Stabilize CP, C3 convertase → low C3	Glomerulonephritis, 50%; CVD, 50%

From Mandell GL: *Mandell, Douglas, and Bennett's principles and practice of infectious diseases,* ed 5, New York, 2000, Churchill Livingstone.
ACD, Autosomal codominant; *Acq,* acquired; *AD,* autosomal dominant; *AP,* alternative pathway; *C′,* complement; *CP,* classic pathway; *CTX,* chemotaxis; *CVD,* collagen-vascular disease; encaps bact, encapsulated bacteria; *IC,* immune complex, *MPGN,* membranoproliferative glomerulonephritis; *PLD,* partial lipodystrophy; *PMN,* polymorphonuclear neutrophil; *RBC,* red blood cells; *SBA,* serum bactericidal activity; *XL,* X-linked.

COOMBS, INDIRECT

Normal: Negative
Positive: Acquired hemolytic anemia, incompatible cross-matched blood, anti-Rh antibodies, drugs (methyldopa, mefenamic acid, levodopa)

COPPER (serum)

Normal range: 70-140 μg/dl (11-22 μmol/L)
Decreased in: Wilson's disease, Menkes' syndrome, malabsorption, malnutrition, nephrosis, total parenteral nutrition, acute leukemia in remission
Elevated in: Aplastic anemia, biliary cirrhosis, systemic lupus erythematosus, hemochromatosis, hyperthyroidism, hypothyroidism, infection, iron deficiency anemia, leukemia, lymphoma, oral contraceptives, pernicious anemia, rheumatoid arthritis

COPPER, URINE; *see* URINE COPPER

CORTISOL, PLASMA

Normal range: Varies with time of collection (circadian variation):
8 AM: 4-19 μg/dl (110-520 nmol/L)
4 PM: 2-15 μg/dl (50-410 nmol/L)
Elevated in: Ectopic adrenocorticotropic hormone production (i.e., oat cell carcinoma of lung), loss of normal diurnal variation, pregnancy, chronic renal failure iatrogenic, stress, adrenal, or pituitary hyperplasia or adenomas
Decreased in: Primary adrenocortical insufficiency, anterior pituitary hypofunction, secondary adrenocortical insufficiency, adrenogenital syndromes

C-PEPTIDE

Elevated in: Insulinoma, sulfonylurea administration
Decreased in: Insulin-dependent diabetes mellitus, factitious insulin administration

CPK; *see* CREATINE KINASE

C-REACTIVE PROTEIN

Normal range: 6.8-820 μg/dl (68-8200 μg/L)
Elevated in: Rheumatoid arthritis, rheumatic fever, inflammatory bowel disease, bacterial infections, myocardial infarction, oral contraceptives, pregnancy third trimester (acute phase reactant), inflammatory and neoplastic diseases

C-REACTIVE PROTEIN, HIGH SENSITIVITY (hs-CRP, Cardio-CRP)

is a new test used as a cardiac risk marker. It is increased in patients with silent atherosclerosis years before a cardiovascular event and is independent of cholesterol level and other lipoproteins. It can be used to help stratify cardiac risk.
Interpretation of results:

Cardio-CRP result (mg/L)	RISK
≤0.6	Lowest risk
0.7-1.1	Low risk
1.2-1.9	Moderate risk
2.0-3.8	High risk
3.9-4.9	Highest risk
≥5.0	Results may be confounded by acute inflammatory disease. If clinically indicated, a repeat test should be performed in 2 or more weeks.

CREATINE KINASE (CK, CPK)

Normal range: 0-130 U/L
Elevated in: Myocardial infarction, myocarditis, rhabdomyolysis, myositis, crush injury/trauma, polymyositis, dermatomyositis, vigorous exercise, muscular dystrophy, myxedema, seizures, malignant hyperthermia syndrome, IM injections, cerebrovascular accident, pulmonary embolism and infarction, acute dissection of aorta
Decreased in: Steroids, decreased muscle mass, connective tissue disorders, alcoholic liver disease, metastatic neoplasms

CREATINE KINASE ISOENZYMES

CK-BB: Elevated in: cerebrovascular accident, subarachnoid hemorrhage, neoplasms (prostate, gastrointestinal tract, brain, ovary, breast, lung), severe shock, bowel infarction, hypothermia, meningitis
CK-MB: Elevated in: myocardial infarction (MI), myocarditis, pericarditis, muscular dystrophy, cardiac defibrillation, cardiac surgery, extensive rhabdomyolysis, strenuous exercise (marathon runners), mixed connective tissue disease, cardiomyopathy, hypothermia

NOTE: CK-MB exists in the blood in two subforms. MB_2 is released from cardiac cells and converted in the blood to MB_1. Rapid assay of CK-MB subforms can detect MI (CK-MB_2 ≥1.0 U/L, with a ratio of CK-MB_2/CK-MB_1 ≥1.5) within 6 hours of onset of symptoms.
Fig. 4-2 illustrates the time course of CK, AST, troponins, and LDH activity after acute MI.
CK-MM: Elevated in: crush injury, seizures, malignant hyperthermia syndrome, rhabdomyolysis, myositis, polymyositis, dermatomyositis, vigorous exercise, muscular dystrophy, IM injections, acute dissection of aorta

CREATININE (serum)

Normal range: 0.6-1.2 mg/dl
Elevated in: Renal insufficiency (acute and chronic), decreased renal perfusion (hypotension, dehydration, congestive heart failure), urinary tract infection, rhabdomyolysis, ketonemia
Drugs (antibiotics [aminoglycosides, cephalosporins], hydantoin, diuretics, methyldopa)

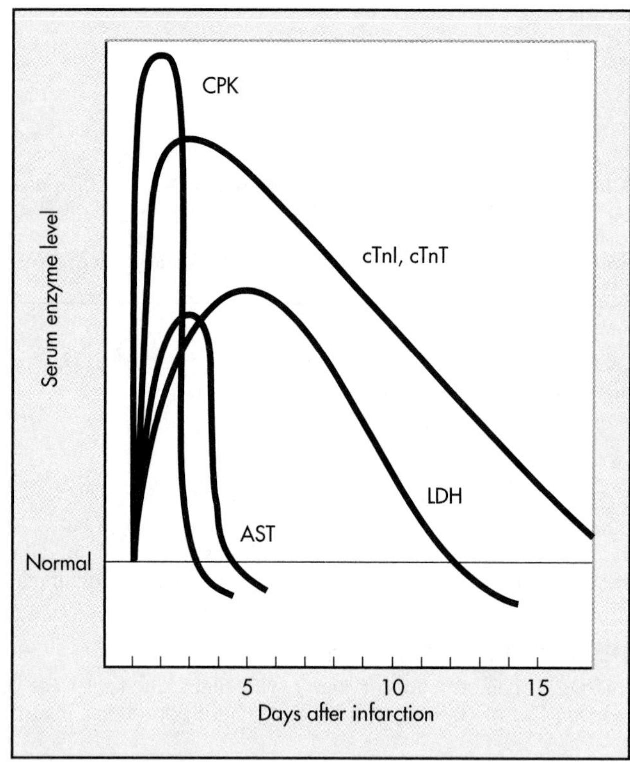

Fig. 4-2 Evaluation of creatine kinase elevation. *CBC,* Complete blood count; *CK,* creatine kinase; *EMG,* electromyography. (From Greene HL, Johnson WP, Lemcke D [eds] : *Decision making in medicine,* ed 2, St Louis, 1998, Mosby.)

Falsely elevated in: Diabetic ketoacidosis, administration of some cephalosporins (e.g., cefoxitin, cephalothin)
Decreased in: Decreased muscle mass (including amputees and older persons), pregnancy, prolonged debilitation

CREATININE CLEARANCE

Normal range: 75-124 ml/min Box 4-1 describes a formula for calculation of creatinine clearance. The Cockcroft-Gault formula to calculate creatinine clearance is described in Box 4-2.
Elevated in: Pregnancy, exercise
Decreased in: Renal insufficiency, drugs (cimetidine, procainamide, antibiotics, quinidine)

CREATININE, URINE; *see* URINE CREATININE

CRYOGLOBULINS (serum)

Normal range: Not detectable
Present in: Collagen-vascular diseases, chronic lymphocytic leukemia, hemolytic anemias, multiple myeloma, Waldenström's macroglobulinemia, chronic active hepatitis, Hodgkin's disease

CRYPTOSPORIDIUM ANTIGEN BY EIA (stool)

Normal range: Not detected
Present in: Cryptosporidiosis

CSF; *see* CEREBROSPINAL FLUID

BOX 4-1 Calculation of the Creatinine Clearance

$Ccr = U_{cr} \times V/P_{cr}$
where C_{cr} = clearance of creatinine (ml/min)
U_{cr} = urine creatinine (mg/dl)
V = volume of urine (ml/min) (for 24-hr volume: divide by 1440)
P_{cr} = plasma creatinine (mg/dl)

Normal range: 95 to 105 ml/min/1.75m^2

BOX 4-2 Cockroft-Gault Formula to Calculate Creatinine Clearance (C_{cr})

$$C_{cr} = \frac{(140 - \text{age in year}) \times (\text{lean body weight in kg})}{S_{cr} \text{ in mg/dl} - 72}$$

For women multiply final value by 0.85

D-DIMER

Normal range: <0. mcg/mL
Elevated in: DVT, pulmonary embolism, high levels of rheumatoid factor, activation of coagulation and fibrolytic system from any cause
D-dimer assay by ELISA assists in the diagnosis of DVT and pulmonary embolism. This test has significant limitations because it can be elevated whenever the coagulation and fibrinolytic systems are activated and can also be falsely elevated with high rheumatoid factor levels.

D-XYLOSE ABSORPTION

Normal range: 21% to 31% excreted in 5 hr
Decreased in: Malabsorption syndrome

D-XYLOSE ABSORPTION TEST

Normal range:
URINE: ≥ 4 g/5 hours (5-hour urine collection in adults > 12 years (25 g dose)
SERUM: ≥ 25 mg/dL (adult, I h, 25 g dose, normal renal function)
Normal results: In patients with malabsorption, normal results suggest pancreatic disease as an etiology of the malabsorption.
Abnormal results: Celiac disease, Crohn's disease, tropical sprue, surgical bowel resection, AIDS. False-positives can occur with decreased renal function, dehydration/hypovolemia, surgical blind loops, decreased gastric emptying, vomiting.

DIGOXIN (LANOXIN)

Normal therapeutic range: 0.5-2 ng/mL
Elevated in: Impaired renal function, excessive dosing, concomitant use of quinidine, amiodarone, verapamil, fluoxetine, nifedipine

DILANTIN; *see* PHENYTOIN

DOPAMINE

Normal range: 0-175 pg/ml
Elevated in: Pheochromocytomas, neuroblastomas, stress, vigorous exercise, certain foods (bananas, chocolate, coffee, tea, vanilla)

ELECTROLYTES, URINE; *see* URINE ELECTROLYTES

ELECTROPHORESIS, HEMOGLOBIN; *see* HEMOGLOBIN ELECTROPHORESIS

ELECTROPHORESIS, PROTEIN; *see* PROTEIN ELECTROPHORESIS

ENA-COMPLEX; *see* EXTRACTABLE NUCLEAR ANTIGEN

ENDOMYSIAL ANTIBODIES

Normal: Not detected
Present in: Celiac disease, dermatitis herpetiformis

EOSINOPHIL COUNT

Normal range: 1%-4% eosinophils (0-440/mm^3)
Elevated in:
HELMINTHIC PARASITES
Ascaris lumbricoides (invasive larval stage)
Hookworms (invasive larval stage)
Strongyloides stercoralis (initial infection and autoinfection)
Trichinosis
Filariasis
Echinococcus granulosus and *E. multilocularis*
Toxocara species
Animal hookworms
Angiostrongylus cantonensis and *A.* costaricensis
Schistosomiasis
Liver flukes
Fasciolopsis buski
Anisakiasis
Capillaria philippinensis
Paragonimus westermani
"Tropical eosinophilia" (unidentified microfilariae)
OTHER INFECTIONS/INFESTATIONS
Pulmonary aspergillosis
Severe scabies

ALLERGIES
Asthma
Hay fever
Drug reactions
Atopic dermatitis
AUTOIMMUNE AND RELATED DISORDERS
Polyarteritis nodosa
Necrotizing vasculitis
Eosinophilic fasciitis
Pemphigus
NEOPLASTIC DISEASES
Hodgkin's disease
Mycosis fungoides
Chronic myelocytic leukemia
Eosinophilic leukemia
Polycythemia vera
Mucin-secreting adenocarcinomas
IMMUNODEFICIENCY STATES
Hyperimmunoglobulin E with recurrent infection
Wiskott-Aldrich syndrome
OTHER
Addison's disease
Inflammatory bowel disease
Dermatitis herpetiformis
Toxic/chemical syndrome
Eosinophilic myalgia syndrome, tryptophan, toxic oil syndrome
Hypereosinophilic syndrome (unknown etiology)

EPINEPHRINE, PLASMA

Normal range: 0-90 pg/ml
Elevated in: Pheochromocytomas, neuroblastomas, stress, vigorous exercise, certain foods (bananas, chocolate, coffee, tea, vanilla), hypoglycemia

EPSTEIN-BARR VIRUS SEROLOGY

Normal range: IgG anti VCA <1:10 or negative
Abnormal: IgG anti VCA >1:10 or positive indicates either current or previous infection
IgM anti VCA >1:10 or positive indicates current or recent infection
Anti-EBNA ≥1.5 or positive indicates previous infection
Table 4-11 and Fig. 4-3 describe test interpretation.

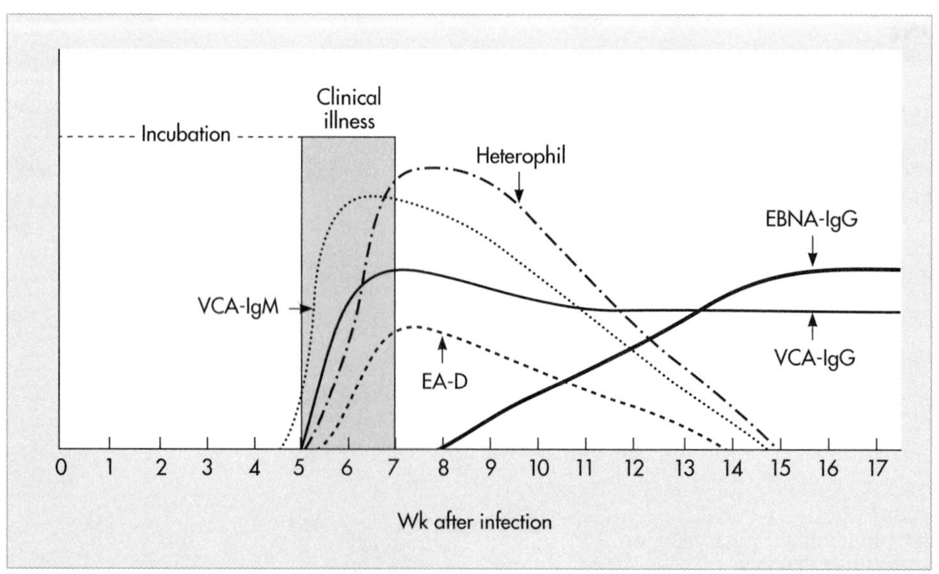

Fig. 4-3 Tests in Epstein-Barr viral infection. See Table 4-19 for abbreviations. (From Ravel R: **Clinical laboratory medicine,** ed 6, St Louis, 1995, Mosby.)

TABLE 4-11 **Antibody Tests in Epstein-Barr Viral Infection**

	Appearance	Peak	Disappears
Heterophil Ab	3-5 days after onset of Sx (range, 0-21 days)	During second wk after onset of Sx (1-4 wk)	2-3 mo after onset of Sx (still found at 1 yr in 20% of cases)
VCA-IgM	Beginning of Sx (1 wk before to 1 wk after Sx begins)	During first wk after onset of Sx (0-21 days)	2-3 mo after onset of Sx (1-6 mo)
VCA-IgG	3 days after onset of Sx (0-2 wk)	During second wk after onset of Sx (1-3 wk)	Decline to lower level, then persists for life
EBNA-IgG	3 wk after onset of Sx (1-4 wk)	8 mo after appearance (3-12 mo)	Lifelong
EA-D	5 days after onset of Sx (during first 1-2 wk after onset of Sx)	14-21 days after onset of Sx (1-4 wk)	9 wk after appearance (2-6 mo)
(EBNA-IgM)	(Same as VCA-IgM)	(Same as VCA-IgM)	(Same as VCA-IgM)

From Ravel R: *Clinical laboratory medicine*, ed 6, St Louis, 1995, Mosby.
Ab, Antibody; *EA*, early antigen; *EBNA*, Epstein-Barr virus nuclear antigen; *Sx*, symptoms; *VCA*, viral capsid antigen.

ERYTHROCYTE SEDIMENTATION RATE (ESR; Westergren)

Normal range: Male: 0-15 mm/hr
Female: 0-20 mm/hr
Elevated in: Collagen-vascular diseases, infections, myocardial infarction, neoplasms, inflammatory states (acute phase reactant), hyperthyroidism, hypothyroidism, rouleaux formation
Decreased in: Sickle cell disease, polycythemia, corticosteroids, spherocytosis, anisocytosis, hypofibrinogenemia, increased serum viscosity

ERYTHROPOIETIN (EP)

Normal: 3.7-16.0 IU/L by radioimmunoassay
Erythropoietin is a glycoprotein secreted by the kidneys that stimulates RBC production by acting on erythroid-committed stem cells.
Increased in: Extremely high: generally seen in patients with severe anemia (Hct <25, <7) such as in cases of aplastic anemia, severe hemolytic anemia, hematologic cancers. Very high: patients with mild to moderate anemia (Hct 25-35, Hb 7-10); high: patients with mild anemia (e.g., AIDS, myelodysplasia). Erythropoietin can be inappropriately elevated in patients with malignant neoplasms, renal cysts, postrenal transplant, meningioma, hemangioblastoma, and leiomyoma.
Decreased in: Renal failure, polycythemia vera, autonomic neuropathy

ESTRADIOL (serum)

Normal range: **FEMALE, PREMENOPAUSAL:** 30-400 pg/mL, depending on phase of menstrual cycle
FEMALE, POSTMENOPAUSAL: 0-30 pg/mL
MALE, ADULT: 10-50 pg/mL
Decreased in: Ovarian failure
Elevated in: Tumors of ovary, testis, adrenal, or nonendocrine sites (rare)

ESTROGEN

Normal range:

Serum:	Males:	20-80 pg/ml
	Females:	Follicular: 60-200 pg/ml
		Luteal: 160-400 pg/ml
		Postmenopausal: <130 pg/ml
Urine:	Males:	4-23 μg/g creatinine
	Females:	Follicular: 7-65 μg/g creatinine
		Midcycle: 32-104 μg/g creatinine
		Luteal: 8-135 μg/g creatinine

Elevated in: Hyperplasia of adrenal cortex, ovarian tumors producing estrogen, granulosa and thecal cell tumors, testicular tumors
Decreased in: Menopause, hypopituitarism, primary ovarian malfunction, anorexia nervosa, hypofunction of adrenal cortex, ovarian agenesis, psychogenic stress, gonadotropin-releasing hormone deficiency

ETHANOL (blood)

Normal range: Negative (values <10 mg/dL are considered negative)
Ethanol is metabolized at 10-25 mg/dL/hour. Levels ≥80 mg/dL are considered evidence of impairment for driving. Fatal blood concentration is considered to be >400 mg/dL.

EXTRACTABLE NUCLEAR ANTIGEN (ENA complex, anti-RNP antibody, anti-Sm, anti-Smith)

Normal: Negative
Present in: Systemic lupus erythematosus, rheumatoid arthritis, Sjögren's syndrome, mixed connective tissue disease

FDP; *see* FIBRIN DEGRADATION PRODUCT

FECAL FAT, QUANTITATIVE (72-hr collection)

Normal range: 2-6 g/24 hr
Elevated in: Malabsorption syndrome

FERRITIN (serum)

Normal range: 18-300 ng/ml
Elevated in: Hyperthyroidism, inflammatory states, liver disease (ferritin elevated from necrotic hepatocytes), neoplasms (neuroblastomas, lymphomas, leukemia, breast carcinoma), iron replacement therapy, hemochromatosis, hemosiderosis
Decreased in: Iron deficiency anemia

α-1 FETOPROTEIN

Normal range: 0-20 ng/ml
Elevated in: Hepatocellular carcinoma (usually values >1000 ng/ml), germinal neoplasms (testis, ovary, mediastinum, retroperitoneum), liver disease (alcoholic cirrhosis, acute hepatitis, chronic active hepatitis), fetal anencephaly, spina bifida, basal cell carcinoma, breast carcinoma, pancreatic carcinoma, gastric carcinoma, retinoblastoma, esophageal atresia

FIBRIN DEGRADATION PRODUCT (FDP)

Normal range: <10 μg/ml
Elevated in: Disseminated intravascular coagulation, primary fibrinolysis, pulmonary embolism, severe liver disease

NOTE: The presence of rheumatoid factor may cause falsely elevated FDP.

FIBRINOGEN

Normal range: 200-400 mg/dl
Elevated in: Tissue inflammation or damage (acute phase protein reactant), oral contraceptives, pregnancy, acute infection, myocardial infarction
Decreased in: Disseminated intravascular coagulation, hereditary afibrinogenemia, liver disease, primary or secondary fibrinolysis, cachexia

FOLATE (folic acid)

Normal range: Plasma: 2-10 ng/ml
Red blood cells: 140-960 ng/ml
Decreased in: Folic acid deficiency (inadequate intake, malabsorption), alcoholism, drugs (methotrexate, trimethoprim, phenytoin, oral contraceptives, Azulfidine), vitamin B_{12} deficiency (defective red cell folate absorption), hemolytic anemia
Elevated in: Folic acid therapy

FOLLICLE-STIMULATING HORMONE (FSH)

Normal range: 5-20 mIU/mL
Elevated in: Menopause, primary gonadal failure, alcoholism, castration, Klinefelter's syndrome, gonadotropin-secreting pituitary hormones
Decreased in: Pregnancy, polycystic ovary disease, anorexia nervosa, anterior pituitary hypofunction

FREE T_4; *see* T_4, FREE

FREE THYROXINE INDEX

Normal range: 1.1-4.3

INCREASED THYROXINE OR FREE THYROXINE VALUES

Laboratory error
Primary hyperthyroidism (T_4/T_3 type)
Severe thyroxine-binding globulin elevation
Excess therapy of hypothyroidism
Excessive dose of levothyroxine
Active thyroiditis (subacute, painless, early active Hashimoto's disease)
Familial dysalbuminemic hyperthyroxinemia (some FT_4 kits, especially analog types)
Peripheral resistance to T_4 syndrome
Amiodarone or propranolol
Postpartum transient toxicosis
Factitious hyperthyroidism
Jod-Basedow (iodine-induced) hyperthyroidism
Severe nonthyroid illness
Acute psychosis (especially paranoid schizophrenia)
T_4 sample drawn 2-4 hr after levothyroxine dose
Struma ovarii

Pituitary thyroid-stimulating hormone–secreting tumor
Certain x-ray contrast media (Telepaque and Oragrafin)
Acute porphyria
Heparin effect (some T_4 and FT_4 kits)
Amphetamine, heroin, methadone, and phencyclidine abuse
Perphenazine or 5-fluorouracil
Antithyroid or anti-IgG heterophil (HAMA) autoantibodies
"T_4" hyperthyroidism
Hyperemesis gravidarum; about 50% of patients
High altitudes

DECREASED THYROXINE OR FREE THYROXINE VALUES

Laboratory error
Primary hypothyroidism
Severe nonthyroid illness*
Lithium therapy
Severe thyroxine-binding globulin decrease (congenital, disease, or drug-induced) or severe albumin decrease*
Dilantin, Depakene, or high-dose salicylate drugs*
Pituitary insufficiency
Large doses of inorganic iodide (e.g., saturated solution of potassium iodide)
Moderate or severe iodine deficiency
Cushing's syndrome
High-dose glucocorticoid drugs
Pregnancy, third trimester (low normal or small decrease)
Addison's disease; some patients (30%)
Heparin effect (a few FT_4 kits)
Desipramine or amiodarone drugs
Acute psychiatric illness

FTA-ABS (serum)

Normal: Nonreactive
Reactive in: Syphilis, other treponemal diseases (yaws, pinta, bejel), SLE, pregnancy

GAMMA-GLUTAMYL TRANSFERASE (gGt); *see* γ-GLUTAMYL TRANSFERASE

GASTRIN (serum)

Normal range: 0-180 pg/ml
Elevated in: Zollinger-Ellison syndrome (gastrinoma), pernicious anemia, hyperparathyroidism, retained gastric antrum, chronic renal failure, gastric ulcer, chronic atrophic gastritis, pyloric obstruction, malignant neoplasms of the stomach, H_2-blockers, omeprazole, calcium therapy, ulcerative colitis, rheumatoid arthritis

GLOMERULAR BASEMENT MEMBRANE (gBm) ANTIBODY

Normal: Negative
Present in: Goodpasture's syndrome

GLUCOSE, FASTING

Normal range: 70-110 mg/dl
Elevated in: Diabetes mellitus, stress, infections, myocardial infarction, cerebrovascular accident, Cushing's syndrome, acromegaly, acute pancreatitis, glucagonoma, hemochromatosis, drugs (glucocorticoids, diuretics [thiazides, loop diuretics]), glucose intolerance
Decreased in: Sulfonylurea therapy, insulin therapy, reactive hypoglycemia (e.g., s/b subtotal gastrectomy), starvation, insulinoma, glycogen storage disorders, severe liver disease or renal disease, ethanol-induced hypoglycemia, mesenchymal tumors that secrete insulin-like hormones

GLUCOSE, POSTPRANDIAL

Normal range: <140 mg/dl
Elevated in: Diabetes mellitus, glucose intolerance
Decreased in: Postgastrointestinal resection, reactive hypoglycemia, hereditary fructose intolerance, galactosemia, leucine sensitivity

GLUCOSE TOLERANCE TEST

Normal values above fasting:
30 min: 30-60 mg/dl
60 min: 20-50 mg/dl
120 min: 5-15 mg/dl
180 min: fasting level or below
Abnormal in: Glucose intolerance, diabetes mellitus, Cushing's syndrome, acromegaly, pheochromocytoma, gestational diabetes

GLUCOSE-6-PHOSPHATE DEHYDROGENASE SCREEN (blood)

Normal: G_6PD enzyme activity detected
Abnormal: If a deficiency is detected, quantitation of G_6PD is necessary; a G_6PD screen may be falsely interpreted as "normal" after an episode of hemolysis because most G_6PD-deficient cells have been destroyed.

γ-GLUTAMYL TRANSFERASE (GGT)

Normal range: 0-30 U/L
Elevated in: Chronic alcoholic liver disease, neoplasms (hepatoma, metastatic disease to the liver, carcinoma of the pancreas), systemic lupus erythematosus, congestive heart failure, trauma, nephrotic syndrome, sepsis, cholestasis, drugs (phenytoin, barbiturates)

GLYCATED (GLYCOSYLATED) HEMOGLOBIN (HbA_{1c})

Normal range: 4.0% to 6.7%
Elevated in: Uncontrolled diabetes mellitus (glycated hemoglobin levels reflect the level of glucose control over the preceding 120 days), lead toxicity, alcoholism, iron deficiency anemia, hypertriglyceridemia
Decreased in: Hemolytic anemias, decreased red blood cell survival, pregnancy, acute or chronic blood loss, chronic renal failure, insulinoma, congenital spherocytosis, hemoglobin S, C, and D diseases

HAM TEST (acid serum test)

Normal: Negative
Positive in: Paroxysmal nocturnal hemoglobinuria
False positive in: Hereditary or acquired spherocytosis, recent transfusion with aged red blood cells, aplastic anemia, myeloproliferative syndromes, leukemia, hereditary dyserythropoietic anemia type II

HAPTOGLOBIN (serum)

Normal range: 50-220 mg/dl
Elevated in: Inflammation (acute phase reactant), collagen-vascular diseases, infections (acute phase reactant), drugs (androgens), obstructive liver disease
Decreased in: Hemolysis (intravascular more than extravascular), megaloblastic anemia, severe liver disease, large tissue hematomas, infectious mononucleosis, drugs (oral contraceptives)

HDL; *see* HIGH-DENSITY LIPOPROTEIN CHOLESTEROL

HELICOBACTER PYLORI (serology, stool antigen)

Normal range: Not detected
Detected in: *H. pylori* infection. Positive serology can indicate current or past infection. Positive stool antigen test indicates acute infection (sensitivity and specificity >90%). Stool testing should be delayed at least 4 weeks after eradication therapy.

HEMATOCRIT

Normal range: Male: 39% to 49%
Female: 33% to 43%
Elevated in: Polycythemia vera, smoking, chronic obstructive pulmonary disease, high altitudes, dehydration, hypovolemia
Decreased in: Blood loss (gastrointestinal, genitourinary) anemia

HEMOGLOBIN

Normal range: Male: 13.6-17.7 g/dl
Female: 12.0-15.0 g/dl
Elevated in: Hemoconcentration, dehydration, polycythemia vera, chronic obstructive pulmonary disease, high altitudes, false elevations (hyperlipemic plasma, white blood cells $>50{,}000/mm^3$), stress
Decreased in: Hemorrhage (gastrointestinal, genitourinary) anemia

HEMOGLOBIN A_{1C}, *see* GLYCATED HEMOGLOBIN

HEMOGLOBIN ELECTROPHORESIS

Normal range:
HbA_1: 95%-98%
HbA_2: 1.5%-3.5%
HbF: <2%
HbC: absent
HbS: absent

HEMOGLOBIN, GLYCATED; *see* GLYCATED HEMOGLOBIN

HEMOGLOBIN, GLYCOSYLATED; *see* GLYCATED HEMOGLOBIN

HEMOGLOBIN, URINE; *see* URINE HEMOGLOBIN

HEMOSIDERIN, URINE; *see* URINE HEMOGLOBIN

HEPATITIS A ANTIBODY

Normal: Negative
Present in: Viral hepatitis A; can be IgM or IgG (if IgM, acute hepatitis A; if IgG, previous infection with hepatitis A)
See Fig. 4-4 for serologic tests in HAV infection.

HAV-IGM ANTIBODY

Appearance
About the same time as clinical symptoms (3-4 wk after exposure, range 14-60 days), or just before beginning of AST/ALT elevation (range 10 days before–7 days after)

Peak
About 3-4 wk after onset of symptoms (1-6 wk)

Becomes Nondetectable
3-4 mo after onset of symptoms (1-6 mo). In a few cases HAV-IgM antibody can persist as long as 12-14 mo.

HAV-TOTAL ANTIBODY

Appearance
About 3 wk after IgM becomes detectable (therefore about the middle of clinical symptom period to early convalescence)

Peak
About 1-2 mo after onset

Becomes Nondetectable
Remains elevated for life, but can slowly fall somewhat

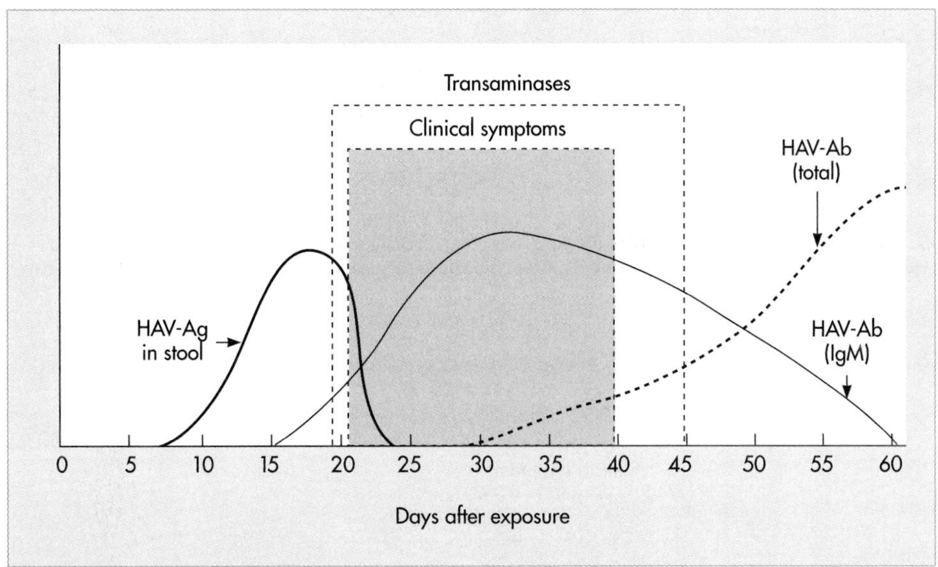

Fig. 4-4 Serologic tests in HAV infection. (From Ravel R: Clinical laboratory medicine, ed 6, St Louis, 1995, Mosby.)

HEPATITIS A VIRAL INFECTION

Best all-purpose test(s) to diagnose acute HAV infection = HAV-Ab (IgM)
Best all-purpose test(s) to demonstrate past HAV infection/immunity = HAV-Ab (total)

HEPATITIS B SURFACE ANTIGEN (HBSAG)

Normal: Not detected
Detected in: Acute viral hepatitis type B, chronic hepatitis B

Appearance
2-6 wk after exposure (range 6 days–6 mo); 5%-15% of patients are negative at onset of jaundice

Peak
1-2 wk before to 1-2 wk after onset of symptoms

Becomes Nondetectable
1-3 mo after peak (range 1 wk-5 mo)

HEPATITIS B VIRAL INFECTION

Figs. 4-5, 4-6, and 4-7 illustrate antigens and antibodies in Hepatitis B Infection.

HB_S

-Ag

HB_SAg: shows current active HBV infection.

Persistence over 6 mo indicates carrier/chronic HBV infection.

HBV nucleic acid probe: present before and longer than HB_SAg.

More reliable marker for increased infectivity than HB_SAg and/or HB_eAg.

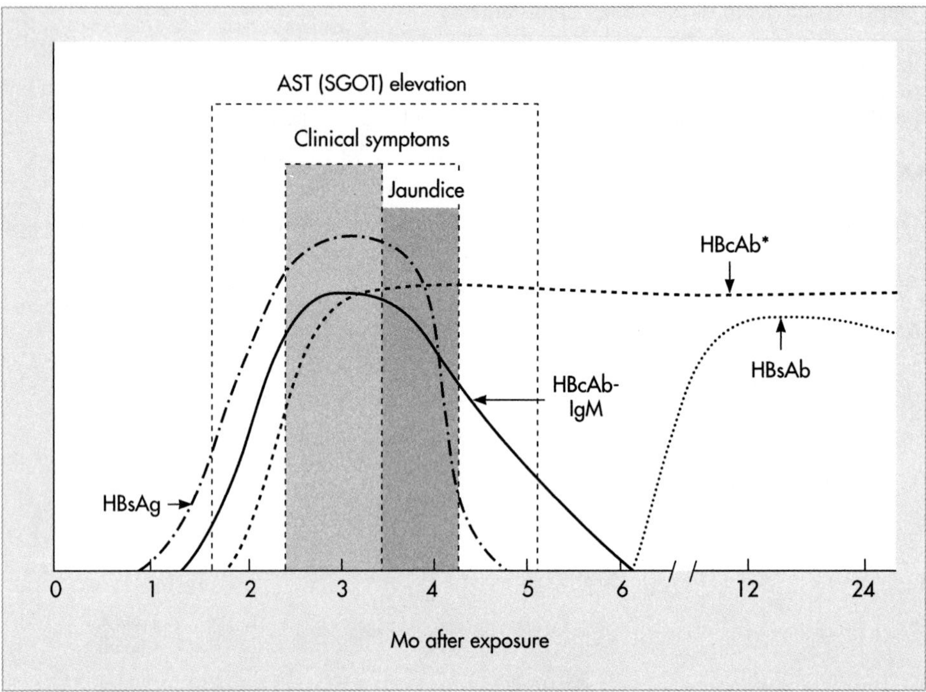

Fig. 4-5 HBV surface antigen-antibody and core antibodies (note "core window"). *HB_CAb = HB_CAb-IgM + HBCAb-IgG (combined). (From Ravel R: *Clinical laboratory medicine,* ed 6, St Louis, 1995, Mosby.)

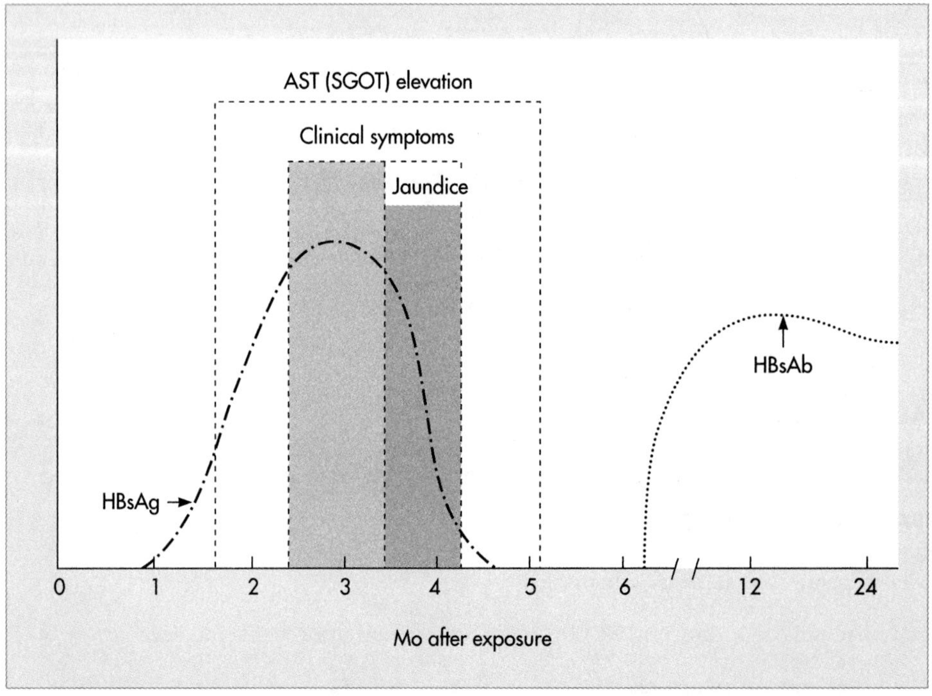

Fig. 4-6 HBV surface antigen and antibody (HB_SAg and HB_SAb-total). (From Ravel R: *Clinical laboratory medicine,* ed 6, St Louis, 1995, Mosby.)

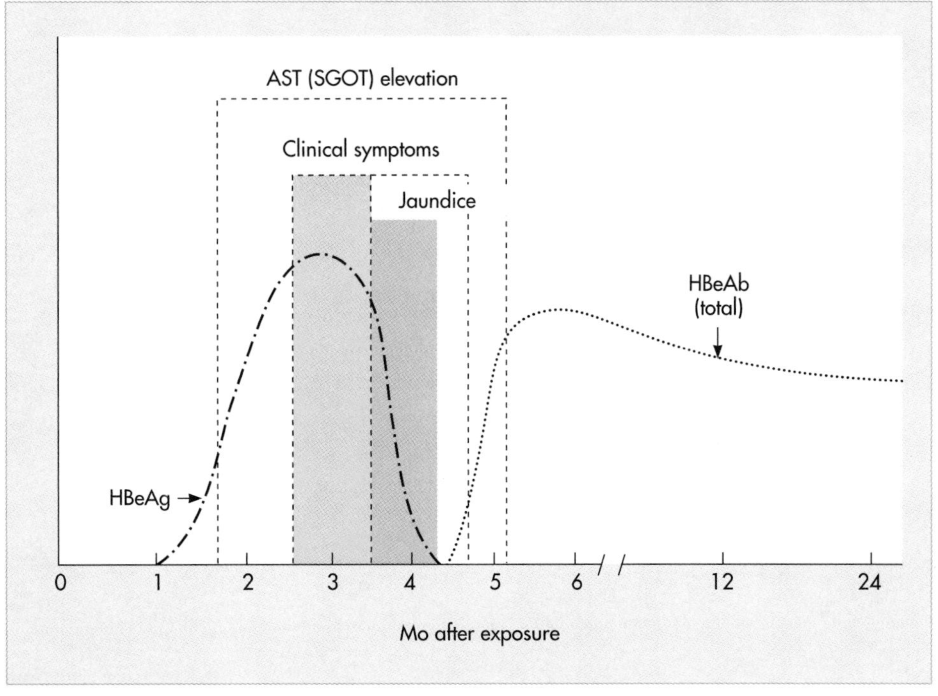

Fig. 4-7 HBV e antigen and antibody. (From Ravel R: *Clinical laboratory medicine,* ed 6, St Louis, 1995, Mosby.)

-Ab
HB$_S$Ab-total: shows previous healed HBV infection and evidence of immunity.
HB$_C$
-Ab
HB$_C$Ab-IgM: shows either acute or very recent infection by HBV.
In convalescent phase of acute HBV, may be elevated when HB$_S$Ag has disappeared (core window).
Negative HB$_C$Ab-IgM with positive HB$_S$Ag suggests either very early acute HBV or carrier/chronic HBV.
HB$_C$Ab-total: only useful to show past HBV infection if HB$_S$Ag and HB$_c$Ab-IgM are both negative.
HB$_E$
-Ag
HB$_e$-AbAg: when present, especially without HB$_e$Ab, suggests increased patient infectivity.
HB$_e$Ab-total: when present, suggests less patient infectivity.

I. HB$_S$Ag positive, HB$_C$Ab negative*
   About 5% (range 0%-17%) of patients with early-stage HBV acute infection (HB$_C$Ab rises later)
II. HB$_S$Ag positive, HB$_C$Ab positive, HB$_S$Ab negative
   a. Most of the clinical symptom stage
   b. Chronic HBV carriers without evidence of liver disease ("asymptomatic carriers")
   c. Chronic HBV hepatitis (chronic persistent type or chronic active type)
III. HB$_S$Ag negative, HB$_C$Ab positive,* HB$_S$Ab negative
   a. Late clinical symptom stage or early convalescence stage (core window)
   b. Chronic HBV infection with HB$_S$Ag below detection levels with current tests
   c. Old previous HBV infection
IV. HB$_S$Ag negative, HB$_C$Ab positive, HB$_S$Ab positive
   a. Late convalescence to complete recovery
   b. Old infection

HEPATITIS C VIRAL INFECTION

Fig. 4-8 illustrates antigens and antibodies in Hepatitis C Infection.
HCV
-Ag
HCV nucleic acid probe: shows current infection by HCV (especially using PCR amplification).
-Ab
HCV-Ab (IgG): current, convalescent, or old HCV infection.
HAV
-Ag
HAV-Ag by EM: shows presence of virus in stool early in infection.
-Ab
HAV-Ab (IgM): current or recent HAV infection.
HAV-Ab (total): convalescent or old HAV infection.

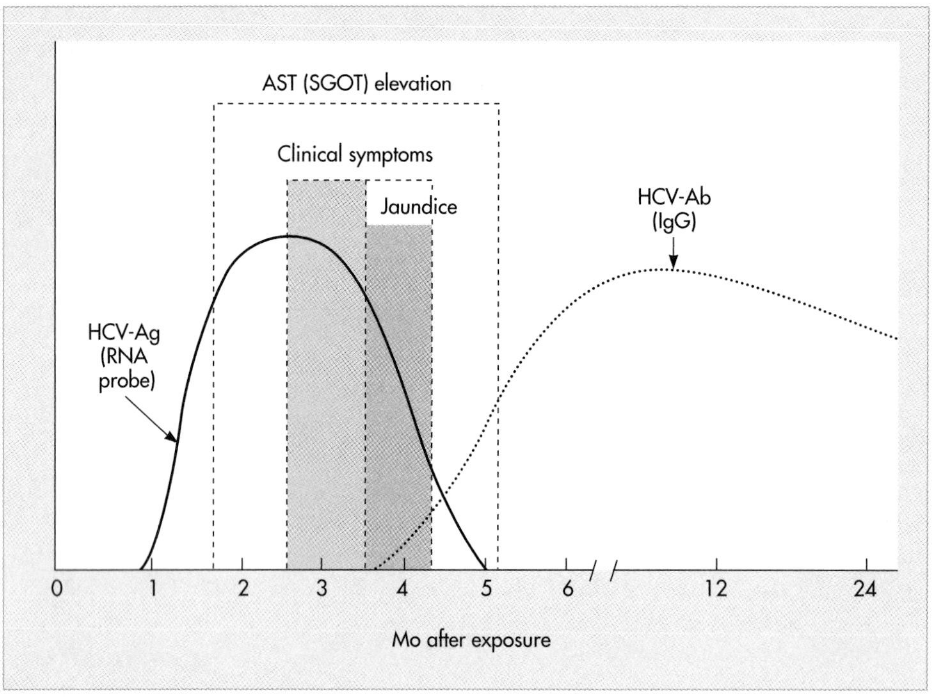

Fig. 4-8 HCV antigen and antibody. (From Ravel R: *Clinical laboratory medicine,* ed 6, St Louis, 1995, Mosby.)

HEPATITIS D VIRAL INFECTION

Fig. 4-9 illustrates antigens and antibodies in Hepatitic D Infection.
Best current all-purpose screening test = ADV-Ab (total)
Best test to differentiate acute from chronic infection = HDV-Ab (IgM)

DELTA HEPATITIS COINFECTION (ACUTE HDV + ACUTE HBV) OR SUPERINFECTION (ACUTE HDV + CHRONIC HBV)

HDV

-Ag

HDV-Ag: shows current infection (acute or chronic) by HDV.
HDV nucleic acid probe: detects antigen before and longer than HDV-Ag by EIA.

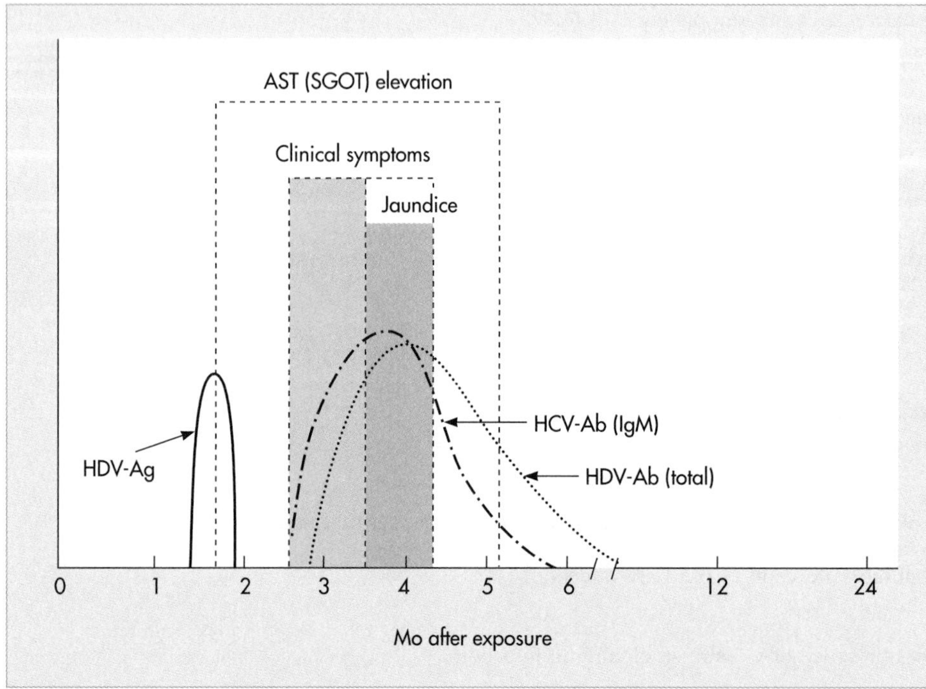

Fig. 4-9 HDV antigen and antibodies. (From Ravel R: *Clinical laboratory medicine,* ed 6, St Louis, 1995, Mosby.)

-Ab

HDV-Ab (IgM): high elevation in acute HDV; does not persist.
Low or moderate elevation in convalescent HDV; does not persist.
Low to high persistent elevation in chronic HDV (depends on degree of cell injury and sensitivity of the assay).
HDV-Ab (total): high elevation in acute HDV; does not persist.
High persistent elevation in chronic HDV.

HDV-AG

Detected by DNA probe, less often by immunoassay
Appearance: Prodromal stage (before symptoms); just at or after initial rise in ALT (about a week after appearance of HB_SAg and about the time HB_CAb-IgM level begins to rise)
Peak: 2-3 days after onset
Becomes nondetectable: 1-4 days (may persist until shortly after symptoms appear)

HDV-AB (IGM)

Appearance: about 10 days after symptoms begin (range 1-28 days)
Peak: about 2 wk after first detection
Becomes nondetectable: about 35 days (range 10-80 days) after first detection (most other IgM antibodies take 3-6 mo to become nondetectable)

HDV-AB (TOTAL)

Appearance: about 50 days after symptoms begin (range 14-80 days); about 5 wk after HDV-Ag (range 3-11 wk)
Peak: About 2 wk after first detection
Becomes nondetectable: about 7 mo after first detection (range 4-14 mo)

HETEROPHIL ANTIBODY

Normal: Negative
Positive in: Infectious mononucleosis

HIGH-DENSITY LIPOPROTEIN (HDL) CHOLESTEROL

Normal range:
Male: 45-70 mg/dl
Female: 45-90 mg/dl
Increased in: Use of gemfibrozil, statins, fenofibrate, nicotinic acid, estrogens, regular aerobic exercise, small (1 oz) daily alcohol intake
Decreased in: Deficiency of apoproteins, liver disease, probucol ingestion, Tangier disease

NOTE: A cholesterol/HDL ratio >4.0 is associated with increased risk of coronary artery disease.

HLA ANTIGENS

Associated disorders: *see* Table 4-12.

TABLE 4-12 **HLA Antigens Associated with Specific Diseases**

Antigen	Condition	Antigen	Condition
HLA-B27	Ankylosing spondylitis	HLA-B8, Dw3	Celiac disease
Reiter's syndrome	HLA-B8, Dw3	Dermatitis herpetiformis	
Psoriatic arthritis	HLA-B8	Myasthenia gravis	
HLA-A10, B18, Dw2	C2 deficiency	HLA-B8	Chronic active hepatitis in children
HLA-A2, B40, Cw3	C4 deficiency	HLA-Drw4	Active chronic hepatitis in adults
HLA-B7, Dw2	Multiple sclerosis	HLA-B13, Bw17	Psoriasis
HLA-A3	Hemochromatosis		

From Cerra FB: *Manual of critical care,* St Louis, 1987, Mosby.

HOMOCYSTEINE, PLASMA

Normal range:
0-30 years: 4.6-8.1 micromol/L
30-59 years: 6.3-11.2 micromol/L (males), 4-5-7.9 micromol/L (females)
> 59 years: 5.8-11.9 micromol/L
Increased: Thrombophilic states, B_6, B_{12}, folic acid, riboflavin deficiency, pregnancy, homocystinuria

NOTE: An increased homocysteine level is an independent risk factor for atherosclerosis.

HUMAN CHORIONIC GONADOTROPIN (HCG)

Normal range: Varies with gestational stage
1st week: 5-50 mU/ml
1-2 wk: 50-550 mU/ml
2-3 wk: up to 5000 mU/ml
3-4 wk: up to 10,000 mU/ml
4-5 wk: up to 50,000 mU/ml
2-3 mo: 10,000-100,000 mU/ml

Elevated in: Normal pregnancy, hydatidiform mole, choriocarcinoma, germ cell tumors of testicle, some non-trophoblastic neoplasms (e.g., neoplasms of cervix, gastrointestinal tract, ovary, lung, breast)

HUMAN IMMUNODEFICIENCY VIRUS ANTIBODY, TYPE 1 (HIV-1)

Normal range: Not detected
Abnormal result: HIV antibodies usually appear in the blood 1-4 mo after infection.
Testing sequence:

1. ELISA is the recommended initial screening test. Sensitivity and specificity are >99%. False-positive ELISA may occur with autoimmune disorders, administration of immune globulin manufactured before 1985 within 6 wk of testing, presence of rheumatoid factor, presence of DLA-DR antibodies in multigravida female, administration of influenza vaccine within 3 mo of testing, hemodialysis, positive plasma reagin test, certain medical disorders (hemophilia, hypergammaglobulinemia, alcoholic hepatitis)
2. A positive ELISA is confirmed with Western blot. False-positive Western blot may result from connective tissue disorders, human leukocyte antigen antibodies, polyclonal gammopathies, hyperbilirubinemia, presence of antibody to another human retrovirus, or cross reaction with other non-virus-derived proteins in healthy persons. Undetermined Western blot may occur in AIDS patients with advanced immunodeficiency (caused by loss of antibodies), and in recent HIV infections.
3. Polymerase chain reaction is used to confirm indeterminate Western blot results or negative results in persons with suspected HIV infection.

Fig. 4-10 describes tests in HIV infection.
Indications for plasma HIV RNA testing are described in Table 4-13.

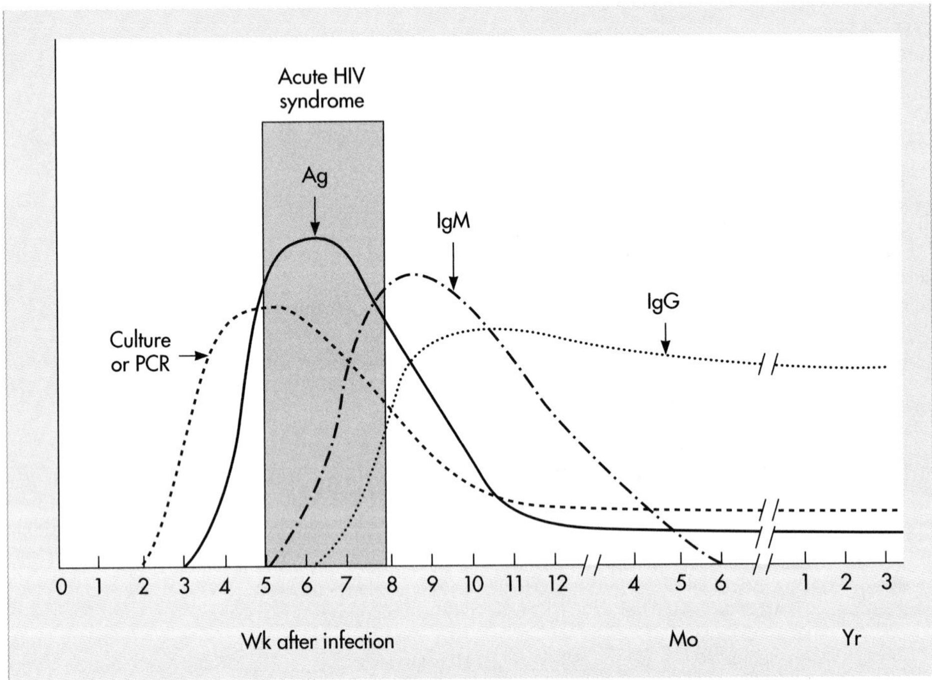

Fig. 4-10 Tests in HIV-1 infection. (From Ravel R: Clinical laboratory medicine, ed 6, St Louis, 1995, Mosby.)

TABLE 4-13 Indications for Plasma HIV RNA Testing*

Clinical Indication	Information	Use
Syndrome consistent with acute HIV infection	Establishes diagnosis when HIV antibody test is negative or indeterminate	Diagnosis†
Initial evaluation of newly diagnosed HIV infection	Baseline viral load "set point"	Decision to start or defer therapy
Every 3-4 mo in patients not on therapy	Changes in viral load	Decision to start therapy
4-8 wk after initiation of anti-retroviral therapy	Initial assessment of drug efficacy	Decision to continue or change therapy
3-4 mo after start of therapy	Maximal effect of therapy	Decision to continue or change therapy
Every 3-4 mo in patients on therapy	Durability of antiretroviral effect	Decision to continue or change therapy
Clinical event or significant decline in CD41 T cells	Association with changing or stable	Decision to continue, initiate, or change

From *MMWR,* vol 47, no RR-5, Apr 24, 1998.
*Acute illness (e.g., bacterial pneumonia, tuberculosis, HSV, PCP) and immunizations can cause increase in plasma HIV RNA for 2-4 wk; viral load testing should not be performed during this time. Plasma HIV RNA results should usually be verified with a repeat determination before starting or making changes in therapy. HIV RNA should be measured using the same laboratory and the same assay.
†Diagnosis of HIV infection determined by HIV RNA testing should be confirmed by standard methods (e.g., Western blot serology) performed 2-4 mo after the initial indeterminate or negative test.

HUMAN IMMUNODEFICIENCY VIRUS TYPE 1 (HIV-1) ANTIGEN (p24), QUALITATIVE (p24 antigen)

Normal range: Negative

This test detects uncomplexed HIV-1 p24 antigen. The core protein p24 is the first detectable protein encoded by the group-specific antigen *(gag)* gene. This protein is a marker for viremia. This test should not be used in place of HIV-1 antibody testing as a screen for HIV-1 infection. HIV-1 p24 may be detectable in the first month of acute HIV-1 infection and generally falls to undetectable levels during the asymptomatic stage of HIV-1 infection. A negative result does not exclude the possibility of infection or exposure to HIV-1. It is recommended that a negative result be followed with repeat testing at least 8 weeks after the original test. This test is used primarily for screening of donated blood and plasma and as an aid for the prognosis of HIV-1 infection.

HUMAN IMMUNODEFICIENCY VIRUS TYPE 1 (HIV-1) VIRAL LOAD

Normal range: HIV-1 RNA, quant. bDNA 3: less than 50 copies/ml or less than 1.7 log copies/ml

This test should be used only in individuals with documented HIV-1 infection for monitoring the progression of infection, response to antiretroviral therapy, and disease prognosis. It is not indicated for diagnosis of HIV infection.

5-HYDROXYINDOLE-ACETIC ACID, URINE; *see* URINE 5-HYDROXYINDOLE-ACETIC ACID

IMMUNE COMPLEX ASSAY

Normal: Negative

Detected in: Collagen-vascular disorders, glomerulonephritis, neoplastic diseases, malaria, primary biliary cirrhosis, chronic acute hepatitis, bacterial endocarditis, vasculitis

IMMUNOGLOBULINS

Normal range:

IgA: 50-350 mg/dl
IgD: <6 mg/dl
IgE: <25 μg/dl
IgG: 800-1500 mg/dl
IgM: 45-150 mg/dl

Elevated in:

IgA: lymphoproliferative disorders, Berger's nephropathy, chronic infections, autoimmune disorders, liver disease
IgE: allergic disorders, parasitic infections, immunologic disorders, IgE myeloma
IgG: chronic granulomatous infections, infectious diseases, inflammation, myeloma, liver disease
IgM: primary biliary cirrhosis, infectious diseases (brucellosis, malaria), Waldenström's macroglobulinemia, liver disease

Decreased in:

IgA: nephrotic syndrome, protein-losing enteropathy, congenital deficiency, lymphocytic leukemia, ataxia-telangiectasia, chronic sinopulmonary disease
IgE: hypogammaglobulinemia, neoplasma (breast, bronchial, cervical), ataxia-telangiectasia
IgG: congenital or acquired deficiency, lymphocytic leukemia, phenytoin, methylprednisolone, nephrotic syndrome, protein-losing enteropathy
IgM: congenital deficiency, lymphocytic leukemia, nephrotic syndrome

INSULIN-LIKE GROWTH FACTOR-1 (IGF-1), SERUM

Normal range:

Age 16-24: 182-780 ng/mL
Age 25-39: 114-492 ng/mL
Age 40-54: 90-360 ng/mL
Age > 55: 71-290 ng/mL

Elevated in: Adolescence, acromegaly, pregnancy, precocious puberty, obesity

Decreased in: Malnutrition, delayed puberty, diabetes mellitus, hypopituitarism, cirrhosis, old age

INTERNATIONAL NORMALIZED RATIO (INR)

The INR is a comparative rating of prothrombin time (PT) ratios. The INR represents the observed PT ratio adjusted by the International Reference Thromboplastin. It provides a universal result indicative of what the patient's PT result would have been if measured using the primary World Health Organization International Reference reagent. For proper interpretation of INR values, the patient should be on stable anticoagulant therapy.

Recommended INR ranges:

Proximal deep vein thrombosis: 2-3
Pulmonary embolism: 2-3
Transient ischemic attacks: 2-3
Atrial fibrillation: 2-3
Mechanical prosthetic valves: 3-4.5
Recurrent venous thromboembolic disease: 3-4.5

IRON-BINDING CAPACITY, TOTAL (TIBC)

Normal range: 250-460 μg/dl
Elevated in: Iron deficiency anemia, pregnancy, polycythemia, hepatitis, weight loss
Decreased in: Anemia of chronic disease, hemochromatosis, chronic liver disease, hemolytic anemias, malnutrition (protein depletion)
Table 4-14 describes TIBC and serum iron abnormalities.

TABLE 4-14 Serum Iron and Total Iron-Binding Capacity Patterns

SI↓	TIBC↓	Chronic diseases Uremia
SI↓	TIBC↑	Chronic iron deficiency anemia Pregnancy in third trimester
SI↑	TIBC↓	Hemachromatosis Iron therapy overload (TIBC may be normal) Hemolytic anemia; thalassemia; lead poisoning; megaloblastic anemia; aplastic, pyridoxine deficiency, or other sideroblastic anemias
SI↑	TIBC↑	Oral contraceptives Acute hepatitis (some report TIBC is low normal) Chronic hepatitis (some patients)
SI↑	TIBC NL	B12 or folate deficiency
SI↓	TIBC NL	Chronic iron deficiency (some patients) Acute infection, surgery, tissue damage
SI NL	TIBC↑	B12/folate deficiency plus iron deficiency

From Ravel R: *Clinical laboratory medicine,* ed 6, St Louis, 1995, Mosby.
NL, Normal; *SI,* serum iron; *TIBC,* total iron-binding capacity.

LACTATE DEHYDROGENASE (LDH)

Normal range: 50-150 U/L
Elevated in: Infarction of myocardium, lung, kidney
Diseases of cardiopulmonary system, liver, collagen, central nervous system
Hemolytic anemias, megaloblastic anemias, transfusions, seizures, muscle trauma, muscular dystrophy, acute pancreatitis, hypotension, shock, infectious mononucleosis, inflammation, neoplasia, intestinal obstruction, hypothyroidism

LACTATE DEHYDROGENASE ISOENZYMES

Normal range:
LDH_1: 22% to 36% (cardiac, red blood cell)
LDH_2: 35% to 46% (cardiac, red blood cell)
LDH_3: 13% to 26% (pulmonary)
LDH_4: 3% to 10% (striated muscle, liver)
LDH_5: 2% to 9% (striated muscle, liver)
Normal ratios:
$LDH_1 < LDH_2$
$LDH_5 < LDH_4$
Abnormal values:
$LDH_1 > LDH_2$: myocardial infarction (can also be seen with hemolytic anemias, pernicious anemia, folate deficiency, renal infarct)
$LDH_5 > LDH_4$: liver disease (cirrhosis, hepatitis, hepatic congestion)

LAP SCORE; *see* LEUKOCYTE ALKALINE PHOSPHATASE

LDH; *see* LACTATE DEHYDROGENASE

LDL; *see* LOW-DENSITY LIPOPROTEIN CHOLESTEROL

LEGIONELLA TITER

Normal:
Negative
Positive in:
Legionnaire's disease (presumptive: ≥1:256 titer; definitive: fourfold titer increase to ≥1:128)

LEUKOCYTE ALKALINE PHOSPHATASE

Normal range: 13-100
Elevated in: Leukemoid reactions, neutrophilia secondary to infections (except in sickle cell crisis—no significant increase in LAP score), Hodgkin's disease, polycythemia vera, hairy cell leukemia, aplastic anemia, Down's syndrome, myelofibrosis
Decreased in: Acute and chronic granulocytic leukemia, thrombocytopenic purpura, paroxysmal nocturnal hemoglobinuria, hypophosphatemia, collagen disorders

LEUKOCYTE COUNT; *see* COMPLETE BLOOD COUNT

LIPASE

Normal range: 0-160 U/L
Elevated in: Acute pancreatitis, perforated peptic ulcer, carcinoma of pancreas (early stage), pancreatic duct obstruction, bowel infarction, intestinal obstruction

LIPOPROTEIN CHOLESTEROL, HIGH-DENSITY; *see* HIGH-DENSITY LIPOPROTEIN CHOLESTEROL

LIPOPROTEIN CHOLESTEROL, LOW-DENSITY; *see* LOW-DENSITY LIPOPROTEIN CHOLESTEROL

LOW-DENSITY LIPOPROTEIN (LDL) CHOLESTEROL

Normal range:
50-130 mg/dl
LDL cholesterol

<100	Optimal
100-129	Near or above optimal
130-159	Borderline high
160-189	High
≥190	Very high

LUPUS ANTICOAGULANT; *see* CIRCULATING ANTICOAGULANT

LUTEINIZING HORMONE

Normal range: 5-25 mIU/ml
Elevated in: Postmenopause, pituitary adenoma, primary gonadal dysfunction, polycystic ovary syndrome
Decreased in: Severe illness, anorexia nervosa, malnutrition, pituitary or hypothalamic impairment, severe stress

LYME DISEASE ANTIBODY TITER

Normal range: Negative
Positive result: Fig. 4-11 illustrates the usual serologic response in Lyme disease.
A serologic test is not necessary or helpful for several days after a tick bite, because it is only 40%-50% sensitive in this stage and a negative test does not rule out the diagnosis.

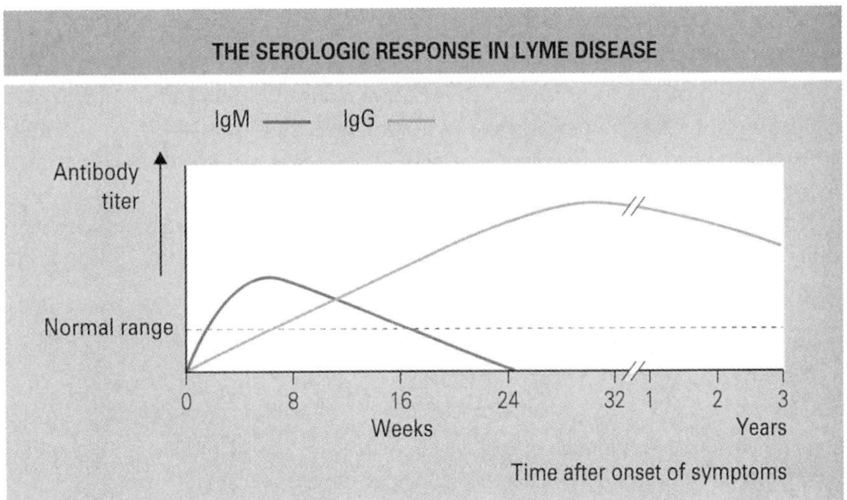

Fig. 4-11 HBV e antigen and antibody. (From Ravel R: *Clinical laboratory medicine,* ed 6, St Louis, 1995, Mosby.)

LYMPHOCYTES

Normal range:

15% to 40%: Total lymphocyte count = 800-2600/mm³
Total T lymphocyte = 800-2200/mm³
CD4 lymphocytes = ≥400/mm³
CD8 lymphocytes = 200-800/mm³
Normal CD4/CD8 ratio is 2.0

Elevated in: Chronic infections, infectious mononucleosis and other viral infections, chronic lymphocytic leukemia, Hodgkin's disease, ulcerative colitis, hypoadrenalism, idiopathic thrombocytopenia

Decreased in: AIDS, bone marrow suppression from chemotherapeutic agents or chemotherapy, aplastic anemia, neoplasms, steroids, adrenocortical hyperfunction, neurologic disorders (multiple sclerosis, myasthenia gravis, Guillain-Barré syndrome)

CD4 lymphocytes are calculated as total white blood cells × % lymphocytes × % lymphocytes stained with CD4. They are decreased in AIDS and other immune dysfunction.

Table 4-15 describes various lymphocyte abnormalities in peripheral blood.

TABLE 4-15 Differential Diagnosis of Abnormal Lymphocytes in Peripheral Blood

Lymphocyte Type	Usual Disease Association	Cytologic Features	Laboratory Features	Clinical Features
Small lymphocyte	Chronic lymphocytic leukemia	B-cell surface markers with low concentration of surface immunoglobulin, CD5 antigen	Hypogammaglobulinemia in 50%; positive direct Coombs' test in 15%; on node biopsy, diffuse, well-differentiated lymphocytic infiltrate	Elderly adults; presentation runs gamut from asymptomatic with lymphocytosis only to bulky disease with adenopathy, splenomegaly, and "packed" bone marrow
Atypical lymphocyte	Infectious mononucleosis, other viral illnesses	Suppressor T-cell markers	Heterophil agglutinin; positive serology for Epstein-Barr virus, cytomegalovirus, toxoplasma, HBsAg	Pharyngitis, fever, adenopathy, rash, splenomegaly, palatal petechiae, jaundice
Plasmacytoid lymphocyte	Waldenström's macroglobulinemia	Cytoplasmic IgM, periodic acid–Schiff (PAS) positivity	IgM paraprotein, rouleaux, cryoglobulins	Adenopathy, splenomegaly, absence of bone lesions, hyperviscosity syndrome, cryopathic phenomena
Lymphoblast	Acute lymphoblastic leukemia (ALL)	Terminal transferase positivity, common ALL antigen, B- or T-precursor markers	Anemia, granulocytopenia, thrombocytopenia, hyperuricemia, diffuse bone marrow infiltration	Peak incidence in childhood, acute onset, bone pain frequent
Lymphosarcoma cell	Lymphocytic lymphoma	B-cell surface markers with high concentration of monoclonal surface immunoglobulin	Nodular or diffuse, poorly differentiated lymphocytic lymphoma on node biopsy, patchy, peritrabecular bone marrow involvement	Middle-aged to older adults, generalized adenopathy, constitutional symptoms
Sézary cell	Cutaneous lymphomas	T-lymphocyte surface markers	Skin biopsy is diagnostic	Exfoliative erythroderma, cutaneous plaques or tumors
Hairy cell	Hairy cell leukemia	B-lymphocyte markers, cytoplasmic projections, tartrate-resistant acid phosphatase, interleukin-2 receptors, CD11 antigen	Pancytopenia	Middle-aged males, moderate to marked splenomegaly without adenopathy
Prolymphocyte	Prolymphocytic leukemia	B-cell surface markers with high concentration of surface immunoglobulin, CD5 negative	Marked lymphocytosis (frequently >100 × 10^9/L)	Elderly adults, massive splenomegaly, minimum adenopathy, poor response to therapy

From Stein JH (ed): *Internal medicine,* ed 5, St Louis, 1998, Mosby.

MAGNESIUM (serum)

Normal range: 1.8-3.0 mg/dl

CAUSES OF HYPERMAGNESEMIA

I. Decreased renal excretion
   A. Renal failure—glomerular filtration rate less than 30 ml/min
   B. Hyperparathyroidism
   C. Hypothyroidism
   D. Addison's disease
   E. Lithium intoxication
   F. Familial hypocalciuric hypercalcemia
II. Other causes: usually in association with decrease in glomerular filtration rate
   A. Endogenous loads
      1. Diabetic ketoacidosis
      2. Severe tissue injury—burns
   B. Exogenous loads
      1. Gastrointestinal
         a. Magnesium-containing laxatives and antacids
         b. High-dose vitamin D analogs
      2. Parenteral: management of toxemia of pregnancy

CAUSES OF HYPOMAGNESEMIA

Alcoholic abuse
Diuretic use
Renal losses
Acute and chronic renal failure
Postobstructive diuresis
Acute tubular necrosis
Chronic glomerulonephritis
Chronic pyelonephritis
Interstitial nephropathy
Renal transplantation
Gastrointestinal losses
Chronic diarrhea
Nasogastric suctioning
Short bowel syndrome
Protein calorie malnutrition
Bowel fistula
Total parenteral nutrition
Acute pancreatitis
Endocrine
Diabetes mellitus
Hyperaldosteronism
Hyperthyroidism
Hyperparathyroidism
Acute intermittent porphyria
Pregnancy
Drugs
Aminoglycosides
Amphotericin
β-Agonists
Cisplatin
Cyclosporine
Diuretics
Foscarnet
Pentamidine
Theophylline
Congenital disorders
Familial hypomagnesemia
Maternal diabetes
Maternal hypothyroidism
Maternal hyperparathyroidism

MEAN CORPUSCULAR VOLUME (MCV)

Normal range: 76-100 μm^3 (76-100 fL)

See Tables 4-16 and 4-17, on the following page, for descriptions of MCV abnormalities.

METANEPHRINES, URINE; *see* URINE METANEPHRINES

TABLE 4-16 **Some Causes of Increased Mean Corpuscular Volume (Macrocytosis)**

Causes	% of all Macrocytosis Patients*	% of Macrocytosis in Each Disease†
Common		
Folate or B_{12} deficiency	20-30 (5-50)‡	80-90 (4-100)
Chronic liver disease	15-20 (6-28)	25-30 (8-65)
Chronic alcoholism	10-12 (3-15)	60 (26-90)
Cytotoxic chemotherapy	10-15 (2-20)	30-40 (13-82)
Cardiorespiratory abnormality	8 (7-9.5)	?
Reticulocytosis	6-7 (0-15)	Depends on severity
Myelodysplastic syndromes	Frequent over age 40 yr	>60 in RAEB and RARS
Unexplained	25 (22.5-27)	—
Normal newborn		
Less Common	<4%	
Noncytotoxic drugs		
Zidovudine		
Phenytoin		30 (14-50)
Azathioprine		
Hypothyroidism		20-30 (8-55)
Chronic leukemia/myelofibrosis		
Radiotherapy for malignancy		
Chronic renal disease (occasional patients)		
Distance-runner macrocytosis (some persons)		
Down syndrome		
Artifactual (e.g., cold agglutinins)		

From Ravel R: *Clinical laboratory medicine,* ed 6, St Louis, 1995, Mosby.
RAEB, Refractory anemia with excessive blasts; RARS, refractory anemia with ring sideroblasts (formerly called IASA, or idiopathic acquired sideroblastic anemia).
*Percentage of all patients with macrocytosis.
†Percentage of patients with each condition listed who have macrocytosis.
‡Numbers in parentheses are literature range.

TABLE 4-17 **Some Causes of Decreased Mean Corpuscular Volume (Microcytosis)**

Common	Less Common
Chronic iron deficiency	Some cases of polycythemia
α- or β-thalassemia (minor)	Some cases of lead poisoning
Anemia of chronic disease	Some cases of congenital spherocytosis
	Some cases of sideroblastic anemia
	Certain abnormal Hbs (Hb E, Hb Lepore)

From Ravel R: *Clinical laboratory medicine,* ed 6, St Louis, 1995, Mosby.

MONOCYTE COUNT

Normal range: 2% to 8%
Elevated in: Viral diseases, parasites, infections, neoplasms, inflammatory bowel disease, monocytic leukemia, lymphomas, myeloma, sarcoidosis
Decreased in: Aplastic anemia, lymphocytic leukemia, glucocorticoid administration

MYOGLOBIN, URINE; *see* URINE MYOGLOBIN

NEUTROPHIL COUNT

Normal range: 50% to 70%
Subsets
Stabs (bands, early mature neutrophils): 2% to 6%
Segs (mature neutrophils): 60% to 70%
Elevated in: Acute bacterial infections, acute myocardial infarction, stress, neoplasms, myelocytic leukemia
Decreased in: Viral infections, aplastic anemias, immunosuppressive drugs, radiation therapy to bone marrow, agranulocytosis, drugs (antibiotics, antithyroidals, clopidogrel), lymphocytic and monocytic leukemias

- Table 4-18 describes various drugs that can cause neutropenia.

NOREPINEPHRINE

Normal range: 0-600 pg/ml
Elevated in: Pheochromocytomas, neuroblastomas, stress, vigorous exercise, certain foods (bananas, chocolate, coffee, tea, vanilla)

TABLE 4-18 Drugs That Cause Neutropenia

Antiarrhythmics
  Tocainide, procainamide, propranolol, quinidine
Antibiotics
  Chloramphenicol, penicillins, sulfonamides, p-aminosalicylic acid (PAS), rifampin, vancomycin, isoniazid, nitrofurantoin
Antimalarials
  Dapsone, quinine, pyrimethamine
Anticonvulsants
  Phenytoin, mephenytoin, trimethadione, ethosuximide, carbamazepine
Hypoglycemic agents
  Tolbutamide, chlorpropamide
Antihistamines
  Cimetidine, brompheniramine, tripelennamine
Antihypertensives
  Methyldopa, captopril
Antiinflammatory agents
  Aminopyrine, phenylbutazone, gold salts, ibuprofen, indomethacin
Antithyroid agents
  Propylthiouracil, methimazole, thiouracil
Diuretics
  Acetazolamide, hydrochlorothiazide, chlorthalidone
Phenothiazines
  Chlorpromazine, promazine, prochlorperazine
Immunosuppressive agents
  Antimetabolites
Cytotoxic agents
  Alkylating agents, antimetabolites, anthracyclines, Vinca alkaloids, cisplatin, hydroxyurea, dactinomycin
Other agents
  Recombinant interferons, allopurinol, ethanol, levamisole, penicillamine, zidovudine, streptokinase, carbamazepine, clopidogrel, ticlopidine

Modified from Goldman L, Ausiello D (eds): *Cecil textbook of medicine,* ed 22, Philadelphia, 2004, WB Saunders.

5′-NUCLEOTIDASE

Normal range: 2-16 IU/L
Elevated in: Biliary obstruction, metastatic neoplasms to liver, primary biliary cirrhosis, renal failure, pancreatic carcinoma, chronic active hepatitis

OSMOLALITY (serum)

Normal range: 280-300 mOsm/kg
It can also be estimated by the following formula:
2([Na] + [K]) + glucose/18+ BuN/2.8
Elevated in: Dehydration, hypernatremia, diabetes insipidus, uremia, hyperglycemia, mannitol therapy, ingestion of toxins (ethylene glycol, methanol, ethanol), hypercalcemia, diuretics
Decreased in: Syndrome of inappropriate diuretic hormone secretion, hyponatremia, overhydration, Addison's disease, hypothyroidism

OSMOLALITY, URINE; *see* URINE OSMOLALITY

PARACENTESIS FLUID

Testing and evaluation of results:

1. Process the fluid as follows:
    a. Tube 1: LDH, glucose, albumin.
    b. Tube 2: protein, specific gravity.
    c. Tube 3: cell count and differential.
    d. Tube 4: save until further notice.
2. Draw serum LDH, protein, albumin.
3. Gram stain, AFB stain, bacterial and fungal cultures, amylase, and triglycerides should be ordered only when clearly indicated; bedside inoculation of blood-culture bottles with ascitic fluid improves sensitivity in detecting bacterial growth.
4. If malignant ascites is suspected, consider a carcinoembryonic antigen level on the paracentesis fluid and cytologic evaluation.
5. In suspected spontaneous bacterial peritonitis (SBP) the incidence of positive cultures can be increased by injecting 10 to 20 ml of ascitic fluid into blood culture bottles.
6. Peritoneal effusion can be subdivided as exudative or transudative based on its characteristics (Section III, Fig 3-21).

7. The serum-ascites albumin gradient (serum albumin level-ascitic fluid albumin level) correlates directly with portal pressure and can also be used to classify ascite. Patients with gradients ≥1.1 g/dl have portal hypertension, and those with gradients <1.1 g/dl do not; the accuracy of this method is >95%.
8. For the differential diagnosis of ascites refer to Section III, Fig. 3-21, on page 1004.
9. An ascitic fluid polymorphonuclear leukocyte count >500/μl is suggestive of SBP.
10. A blood-ascitic fluid albumin gradient.

PARTIAL THROMBOPLASTIN TIME (PTT), ACTIVATED PARTIAL THROMBOPLASTIN TIME (APTT)

Normal range: 25-41 sec
Elevated in: Heparin therapy, coagulation factor deficiency (I, II, V, VIII, IX, X, XI, XII), liver disease, vitamin K deficiency, disseminated intravascular coagulation, circulating anticoagulant, warfarin therapy, specific factor inhibition (PCN reaction, rheumatoid arthritis), thrombolytic therapy, nephrotic syndrome

NOTE: Useful to evaluate the intrinsic coagulation system.

PH, BLOOD

Normal values:
Arterial: 7.35-7.45
Venous: 7.32-7.42
For abnormal values refer to "Arterial Blood Gases."

PH, URINE; *see* URINE PH

PHENOBARBITAL

Normal therapeutic range: 15-30 mcg/mL for epilepsy control

PHENYTOIN (dilantin)

Normal therapeutic range: 10-20 mcg/mL

PHOSPHATASE, ACID; *see* ACID PHOSPHATASE

PHOSPHATASE, ALKALINE; *see* ALKALINE PHOSPHATASE

PHOSPHATE (serum)

Normal range: 2.5-5 mg/dl
DECREASED
Parenteral hyperalimentation
Diabetic acidosis
Alcohol withdrawal
Severe metabolic or respiratory alkalosis
Antacids that bind phosphorus
Malnutrition with refeeding using low-phosphorus nutrients
Renal tubule failure to reabsorb phosphate (Fanconi's syndrome; congenital disorder; vitamin D deficiency)
Glucose administration
Nasogastric suction
Malabsorption
Gram-negative sepsis
Primary hyperthyroidism
Chlorothiazide diuretics
Therapy of acute severe asthma
Acute respiratory failure with mechanical ventilation
INCREASED
Renal failure
Severe muscle injury
Phosphate-containing antacids
Hypoparathyroidism
Tumor lysis syndrome

PLATELET COUNT

Normal range: 130-400 $\times$ $10^3/mm^3$
Elevated in:
REACTIVE THROMBOCYTOSIS
Infections or inflammatory states—vasculitis, allergic reactions, etc.
Surgery and tissue damage—myocardial infarction, pancreatitis, etc.
Postsplenectomy state
Malignancy—solid tumors, lymphoma
Iron deficiency anemia, hemolytic anemia, acute blood loss

Uncertain etiology
Rebound effect after chemotherapy or immune thrombocytopenia
Renal disorders—renal failure, nephrotic syndrome

MYELOPROLIFERATIVE DISORDERS

Chronic myeloid leukemia
Primary thrombocythemia
Polycythemia vera
Idiopathic myelofibrosis

Decreased:

A. Increased destruction
   1. Immunologic
      a. Drugs: quinine, quinidine, digitalis, procainamide, thiazide diuretics, sulfonamides, phenytoin, aspirin, penicillin, heparin, gold, meprobamate, sulfa drugs, phenylbutazone, NSAIDs, methyldopa, cimetidine, furosemide, INH, cephalosporins, chlorpropamide, organic arsenicals, chloroquine
      b. Idiopathic thrombocytopenic purpura
      c. Transfusion reaction: transfusion of platelets with platelet antigen HPA-1a (PL^{A1}) in recipients without PL^{A1}
      d. Fetal/maternal incompatibility
      e. Vasculitis (e.g., systemic lupus erythematosus)
      f. Autoimmune hemolytic anemia
      g. Lymphoreticular disorders (e.g., chronic lymphocytic leukemia)
   2. Nonimmunologic
      a. Prosthetic heart valves
      b. Thrombotic thrombocytopenic purpura
      c. Sepsis
      d. Disseminated intravascular coagulation
      e. Hemolytic-uremic syndrome
      f. Giant cavernous hemangioma
B. Decreased production
   1. Abnormal marrow
      a. Marrow infiltration (e.g., leukemia, lymphoma, fibrosis)
      b. Marrow suppression (e.g., chemotherapy, alcohol, radiation)
   2. Hereditary disorders
      a. Wiskott-Aldrich syndrome: X-linked disorder characterized by thrombocytopenia, eczema, and repeated infections
      b. May-Hegglin anomaly: increased megakaryocytes but ineffective thrombopoiesis
   3. Vitamin deficiencies (e.g., vitamin B_{12}, folic acid)
C. Splenic sequestration, hypersplenism
D. Dilutional, secondary to massive transfusion

POTASSIUM (serum)

Normal range: 3.5-5 mEq/L

CAUSES OF HYPERKALEMIA

I. Pseudohyperkalemia
   A. Hemolysis of sample
   B. Thrombocytosis
   C. Leukocytosis
   D. Laboratory error
II. Increased potassium intake and absorption
   A. Potassium supplements (oral and parenteral)
   B. Dietary—salt substitutes
   C. Stored blood
   D. Potassium-containing medications
III. Impaired renal excretion
   A. Acute renal failure
   B. Chronic renal failure
   C. Tubular defect in potassium secretion
      1. Renal allograft
      2. Analgesic nephropathy
      3. Sickle cell disease
      4. Obstructive uropathy
      5. Interstitial nephritis
      6. Chronic pyelonephritis
      7. Potassium-sparing diuretics
      8. Miscellaneous (lead, systemic lupus erythematosus, pseudohypoaldosteronism)
   D. Hypoaldosteronism
      1. Primary (Addison's disease)
      2. Secondary
         a. Hyporeninemic hypoaldosteronism (type IV RTA)

b. Congenital adrenal hyperplasia
c. Drug-induced
(1) Nonsteroidal antiinflammatory medications
(2) ACE inhibitors
(3) Heparin
(4) Cyclosporine
IV. Transcellular shifts
A. Acidosis
B. Hypertonicity
C. Insulin deficiency
D. Drugs
1. β-blockers
2. Digitalis toxicity
3. Succinylcholine
E. Exercise
F. Hyperkalemic periodic paralysis
V. Cellular injury
A. Rhabdomyolysis
B. Severe intravascular hemolysis
C. Acute tumor lysis syndrome
D. Burns and crush injuries

CAUSES OF HYPOKALEMIA

I. Decreased intake
A. Decreased dietary potassium
B. Impaired absorption of potassium
C. Clay ingestion
D. Kayexalate
II. Increased loss
A. Renal
1. Hyperaldosteronism
a. Primary
1. Conn's syndrome
2. Adrenal hyperplasia
b. Secondary
1. Congestive heart failure
2. Cirrhosis
3. Nephrotic syndrome
4. Dehydration
c. Bartter's syndrome
2. Glycyrrhizic acid (licorice, chewing tobacco)
3. Excessive adrenal corticosteroids
a. Cushing's syndrome
b. Steroid therapy
c. Adrenogenital syndrome
4. Renal tubular defects
a. Renal tubular acidosis
b. Obstructive uropathy
c. Salt-wasting nephropathy
5. Drugs
a. Diuretics
b. Aminoglycosides
c. Mannitol
d. Amphotericin
e. Cisplatin
f. Carbenicillin
B. Gastrointestinal
1. Vomiting
2. Nasogastric suction
3. Diarrhea
4. Malabsorption
5. Ileostomy
6. Villous adenoma
7. Laxative abuse
C. Increased losses from the skin
1. Excessive sweating
2. Burns
III. Transcellular shifts
A. Alkalosis
1. Vomiting

2. Diuretics
3. Hyperventilation
4. Bicarbonate therapy

B. Insulin
1. Exogenous
2. Endogenous response to glucose

C. β_2-Agonists (albuterol, terbutaline, epinephrine)
D. Hypokalemia periodic paralysis
1. Familial
2. Thyrotoxic

IV. Miscellaneous
A. Anabolic state
B. Intravenous hyperalimentation
C. Treatment of megaloblastic anemia
D. Acute mountain sickness

POTASSIUM, URINE; *see* URINE POTASSIUM

PROCAINAMIDE

Normal therapeutic range: 4-10 mcg/mL

PROLACTIN

Normal range: <20 ng/ml
Elevated in: Prolactinomas (level >200 highly suggestive), drugs (phenothiazines, cimetidine, tricyclic antidepressants, metoclopramide, estrogens, antihypertensives [methyldopa], verapamil, haloperidol), postpartum, stress, hypoglycemia, hypothyroidism

PROSTATE-SPECIFIC ANTIGEN (PSA)

Normal range: 0-4 ng/ml
Table 4-19 describes age-specific reference ranges for PSA.
Elevated in: Benign prostatic hypertrophy, carcinoma of prostate, postrectal examination, prostate trauma
Factors affecting serum PSA are described in Table 4-20.

NOTE: Measurement of free PSA is useful to assess the probability of prostate cancer in patients with normal digital rectal examination and total PSA between 4 and 10 ng/ml. In these patients, the global risk of prostate cancer is 25%; however, if the free PSA is >25%, the risk of prostate cancer decreases to 8%, whereas if the free PSA is <10%, the risk of cancer increases to 56%. Free PSA is also useful to evaluate the aggressiveness of prostate cancer. A low free PSA percentage generally indicates a high-grade cancer, whereas a high free PSA percentage is generally associated with a slower growing tumor.
Decreased in: Finasteride therapy, dutasteride therapy, saw palmetto use, bedrest, antiandrogens

TABLE 4-19 **Age-Specific Reference Ranges for PSA**

	SERUM PSA (NG/ML)		
Age (yr)	Whites	Japanese	African American
40-49	0-2.5	0-2.0	0-2.0
50-59	0-3.5	0-3.0	0-4.0
60-69	0-4.5	0-4.0	0-4.5
70-79	0-6.5	0-5.0	0-5.5

From Nseyo UO (ed): *Urology for primary care physicians,* Philadelphia, 1999, WB Saunders.
PSA, Prostate-specific antigen.

TABLE 4-20 **Factors Affecting Serum Prostate-Specific Antigen (PSA)**

Factors Affecting Serum PSA	Duration of Effect
Prostate cell number	Not applicable
Prostate size	Not applicable
Recent ejaculation	6-48 hours
Prostate manipulation	
Vigorous massage	1 week
Cystoscopy	1 week
Prostate biopsy	4-6 weeks
Prostatitis	
Acute	3-6 months
Chronic	Unknown
Prostate cancer	Not applicable
Drugs: finasteride (Proscar)*	3-6 months

From Nseyo UO (ed): *Urology for primary care physicians,* Philadelphia, 1999, WB Saunders.
*Lowers PSA for as long as patient is on the medication.

PROTEIN (serum)

Normal range: 6-8 g/dl
Elevated in: Dehydration, multiple myeloma, Waldenström's macroglobulinemia, sarcoidosis, collagen-vascular diseases
Decreased in: Malnutrition, low-protein diet, overhydration, malabsorption, pregnancy, severe burns, neoplasms, chronic diseases, cirrhosis, nephrosis

PROTEIN ELECTROPHORESIS (serum)

Normal range: Albumin: 60% to 75%
α-1: 1.7% to 5%
α-2: 6.7% to 12.5%
β: 8.3% to 16.3%
γ: 10.7% to 20%
Albumin: 3.6-5.2 g/dl
α-1: 0.1-0.4 g/dl
α-2: 0.4-1 g/dl
β: 0.5-1.2 g/dl
γ: 0.6-1.6 g/dl
Elevated in: Albumin: dehydration
α-1: neoplastic diseases, inflammation
α-2: neoplasms, inflammation, infection, nephrotic syndrome
β: hypothyroidism, biliary cirrhosis, diabetes mellitus
γ: *see* IMMUNOGLOBULINS
Decreased in: Albumin: malnutrition, chronic liver disease, malabsorption, nephrotic syndrome, burns, systemic lupus erythematosus
α-1: emphysema (α-1 antitrypsin deficiency), nephrosis
α-2: hemolytic anemias (decreased haptoglobin), severe hepatocellular damage
β: hypocholesterolemia, nephrosis
γ: *see* IMMUNOGLOBULINS
Fig. 4-12 describes serum protein electrophoretic patterns.

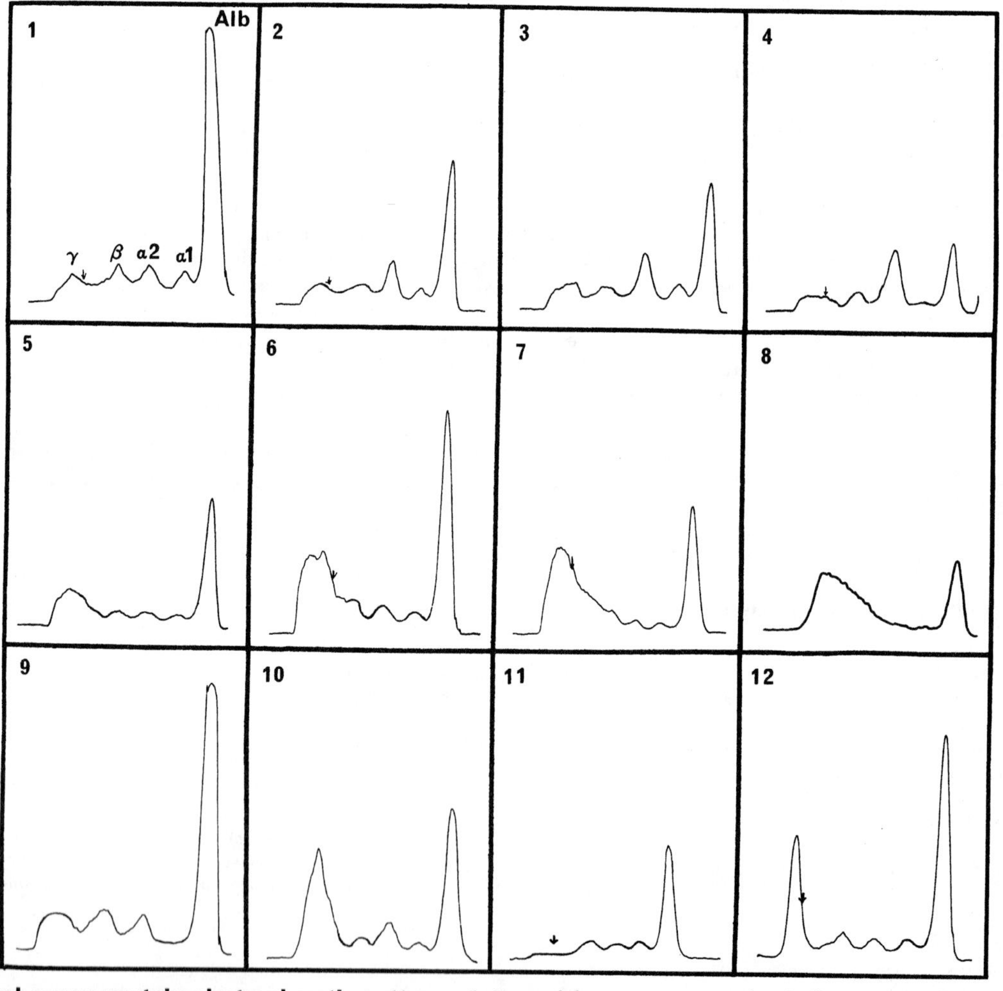

Fig. 4-12 Typical serum protein electrophoretic patterns. *1,* Normal (*arrow* near γ region indicates serum application point). *2,* Acute reaction pattern. *3,* Acute reaction or nephrotic syndrome. *4,* Nephrotic syndrome. *5,* Chronic inflammation, cirrhosis, granulomatous diseases, rheumatoid-collagen group. *6,* Same as 5, but g elevation is more pronounced. There is also partial (but not complete) β-γ fusion. *7,* Suggestive of cirrhosis but could be found in the granulomatous diseases or the rheumatoid-collagen group. *8,* Characteristic pattern of cirrhosis. *9,* α-1 Antitrypsin deficiency with mild γ elevation suggesting concurrent chronic disease. *10,* Same as 5, but the γ elevation is marked. The configuration of the γ peak superficially mimics that of myeloma, but is more broad-based. There are superimposed acute reaction changes. *11,* Hypogammaglobulinemia or light-chain myeloma. *12,* Myeloma, Waldenström's macroglobulinemia, idiopathic or secondary monoclonal gammopathy. (From Ravel R: *Clinical laboratory medicine,* ed 6, St Louis, 1995, Mosby.)

PROTHROMBIN TIME (PT)

Normal range: 10-12 sec
Elevated in: Liver disease, oral anticoagulants (warfarin), heparin, factor deficiency (I, II, V, VII, X), disseminated intravascular coagulation, vitamin K deficiency, afibrinogenemia, dysfibrinogenemia, drugs (salicylate, chloral hydrate, diphenylhydantoin, estrogens, antacids, phenylbutazone, quinidine, antibiotics, allopurinol, anabolic steroids)
Decreased in: Vitamin K supplementation, thrombophlebitis, drugs (glutethimide, estrogens, griseofulvin, diphenhydramine)

PROTOPORPHYRIN (free erythrocyte)

Normal range: 16-36 μg/dl of red blood cells
Elevated in: Iron deficiency, lead poisoning, sideroblastic anemias, anemia of chronic disease, hemolytic anemias, erythropoietic protoporphyria

PSA; *see* PROSTATE-SPECIFIC ANTIGEN

PT; *see* PROTHROMBIN TIME

PTT; *see* PARTIAL THROMBOPLASTIN TIME

RDW; *see* RED BLOOD CELL DISTRIBUTION WIDTH

RED BLOOD CELL (RBC) COUNT

Normal range: Male: 4.3-5.9 × 10^6/mm^3 Female: 3.5-5 × 10^6/mm^3
Elevated in: Polycythemia vera, smokers, high altitude, cardiovascular disease, renal cell carcinoma and other erythropoietin-producing neoplasms, stress, hemoconcentration/dehydration
Decreased in: Anemias, hemolysis, chronic renal failure, hemorrhage, failure of marrow production

RED BLOOD CELL DISTRIBUTION WIDTH (RDW)

Measures variability of red cell size (anisocytosis)
Normal range: 11.5-14.5
Normal RDW and:
ELEVATED MEAN CORPUSCULAR VOLUME (MCV): aplastic anemia, preleukemia
NORMAL MCV: normal, anemia of chronic disease, acute blood loss or hemolysis, chronic lymphocytic leukemia (CLL), chronic myelocytic leukemia, nonanemic enzymopathy or hemoglobinopathy
DECREASED MCV: anemia of chronic disease, heterozygous thalassemia
Elevated RDW and:
ELEVATED MCV: vitamin B_{12} deficiency, folate deficiency, immune hemolytic anemia, cold agglutinins, CLL with high count, liver disease
NORMAL MCV: early iron deficiency, early vitamin B_{12} deficiency, early folate deficiency, anemic globinopathy
DECREASED MCV: iron deficiency, red blood cell fragmentation, HbH disease, thalassemia intermedia

RED BLOOD CELL FOLATE; *see* FOLATE, RED BLOOD CELL

RED BLOOD CELL MASS (volume)

Normal range:
Male: 20-36 ml/kg of body weight (1.15-1.21 L/m^2 body surface area)
Female: 19-31 ml/kg of body weight (0.95-1.00 L/m^2 body surface area)
Elevated in: Polycythemia vera, hypoxia (smokers, high altitude, cardiovascular disease), hemoglobinopathies with high oxygen affinity, erythropoietin-producing tumors (renal cell carcinoma)
Decreased in: Hemorrhage, chronic disease, failure of marrow production, anemias, hemolysis

RED BLOOD CELL MORPHOLOGY; *see* Fig. 4-13

RENIN (SERUM)

Elevated in: Drugs (thiazides, estrogen, minoxidil), chronic renal failure, Bartter's syndrome, pregnancy (normal), pheochromocytoma, renal hypertension, reduced plasma volume, secondary aldosteronism
Decreased in: Adrenocortical hypertension, increased plasma volume, primary aldosteronism, drugs (propranolol, reserpine, clonidine)
Table 4-21 describes typical renin-aldosterone patterns in various conditions.

RETICULOCYTE COUNT

Normal range: 0.5% to 1.5%
Elevated in: Hemolytic anemia (sickle cell crisis, thalassemia major, autoimmune hemolysis), hemorrhage, postanemia therapy (folic acid, ferrous sulfate, vitamin B_{12}), chronic renal failure
Decreased in: Aplastic anemia, marrow suppression (sepsis, chemotherapeutic agents, radiation), hepatic cirrhosis, blood transfusion, anemias of disordered maturation (iron deficiency anemia, megaloblastic anemia, sideroblastic anemia, anemia of chronic disease)

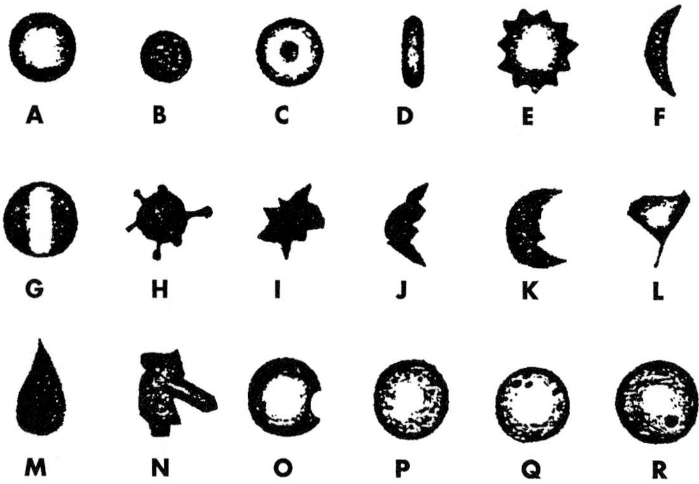

Fig. 4-13 Abnormal red blood cells (RBCs). A, Normal RBC. **B,** Spherocyte. **C,** Target cell. **D,** Elliptocyte. **E,** Echinocyte. **F,** Sickle cell. **G,** Stomatocyte. **H,** Acanthocyte. **I** to **L,** Schistocytes. **M,** Teardrop RBC. **N,** Distorted RBC with Hb C crystal protruding. **O,** Degmacyte. **P,**, Basophilic stippling. **Q,** Pappenheimer bodies. **R,** Howell-Jolly body. (From Ravel R: *Clinical laboratory medicine,* ed 6, St Louis, 1995, Mosby.)

TABLE 4-21 **Typical Renin-Aldosterone Patterns in Various Conditions**

	Plasma Renin	Aldosterone
Primary aldosteronism	Low	High
"Low-renin" essential hypertension	Low	Normal
Cushing's syndrome	Low	Low-normal
Licorice ingestion syndrome	Low	Low
High-salt diet	Low	Low
Oral contraceptives	High	Normal
Cirrhosis	High	High
Malignant hypertension	High	High
Unilateral renal disease	High	High
"High-renin" essential hypertension	High	High
Pregnancy	High	High
Diuretic overuse	High	High
Juxtaglomerular tumor (Bartter's syndrome)	High	High
Low-salt diet	High	High
Addison's disease	High	Low
Hypokalemia	High	Low

From Ravel R: *Clinical laboratory medicine,* ed 6, St Louis, 1995, Mosby.

RHEUMATOID FACTOR

Normal: Negative
Present in titer >1:20
RHEUMATIC DISEASES
Rheumatoid arthritis
Sjögren's syndrome
Systemic lupus erythematosus
Polymyositis/dermatomyositis
Mixed connective tissue disease
Scleroderma
INFECTIOUS DISEASES
Subacute bacterial endocarditis
Tuberculosis
Infectious mononucleosis
Hepatitis
Syphilis
Leprosy
Influenza

MALIGNANCIES
Lymphoma
Multiple myeloma
Waldenström's macroglobulinemia
Postradiation or postchemotherapy
MISCELLANEOUS
Normal adults, especially the elderly
Sarcoidosis
Chronic pulmonary disease (interstitial fibrosis)
Chronic liver disease (chronic active hepatitis, cirrhosis)
Mixed essential cryoglobulinemia
Hypergammaglobulinemic purpura

RNP; *see* EXTRACTABLE NUCLEAR ANTIGEN

SEDIMENTATION RATE; *see* ERYTHROCYTE SEDIMENTATION RATE

SEMEN ANALYSIS

- Table 4-22 describes semen analysis reference ranges.

TABLE 4-22 **Semen Analysis Reference Ranges**

Color	Grayish white
pH	7.3-7.8 (literature range, 7.0-7.8)
Volume	2.0-5.0 ml (literature range, 1.5-6.0 ml)
Sperm count	20-250 million/ml (literature range for upper limit varies from 100-250 million/ml)
Motility	>60% motile <3 hours after specimen is obtained (literature range, >40% to >70%)
% Normal sperm	>60% (literature range, >60% to >70%)
Viscosity	Can be poured from a pipet in droplets rather than a thick strand

From Ravel R (ed): *Clinical laboratory medicine,* ed 6, St Louis, 1995, Mosby.

SGOT; *see* ASPARTATE AMINOTRANSFERASE

SGPT; *see* ALANINE AMINOTRANSFERASE

SMOOTH MUSCLE ANTIBODY

Normal: Negative
Present in: Chronic acute hepatitis (≥1:80), primary biliary cirrhosis (≤1:80), infectious mononucleosis

SODIUM (serum)

Normal range: 135-147 mEq/L
HYPONATREMIA
A. Sodium and water depletion (deficit hyponatremia)
   1. Loss of gastrointestinal secretions with replacement of fluid but not electrolytes
      a. Vomiting
      b. Diarrhea
      c. Tube drainage
   2. Loss from skin with replacement of fluids but not electrolytes
      a. Excessive sweating
      b. Extensive burns
   3. Loss from kidney
      a. Diuretics
      b. Chronic renal insufficiency (uremia) with acidosis
   4. Metabolic loss
      a. Starvation with acidosis
      b. Diabetic acidosis
   5. Endocrine loss
      a. Addison's disease
      b. Sudden withdrawal of long-term steroid therapy
   6. Iatrogenic loss from serous cavities
      a. Paracentesis or thoracentesis
B. Excessive water (dilution hyponatremia)
   1. Excessive water administration
   2. Congestive heart failure
   3. Cirrhosis
   4. Nephrotic syndrome

   5. Hypoalbuminemia (severe)
   6. Acute renal failure with oliguria
C. Inappropriate antidiuretic hormone (IADH) syndrome
D. Intracellular loss (reset osmostat syndrome)
E. False hyponatremia (actually a dilutional effect)
   1. Marked hypertriglyceridemia*
   2. Marked hyperproteinemia*
   3. Severe hyperglycemia

HYPERNATREMIA

Dehydration is the most frequent overall clinical finding in hypernatremia.

1. Deficient water intake (either orally or intravenously)
2. Excess kidney water output (diabetes insipidus, osmotic diuresis)
3. Excess skin water output (excess sweating, loss from burns)
4. Excess gastrointestinal tract output (severe protracted vomiting or diarrhea without fluid therapy)
5. Accidental sodium overdose
6. High-protein tube feedings

STREPTOZYME; *see* ANTI-STREPTOLYSIN O TITER

SUCROSE HEMOLYSIS TEST (sugar water test)

Normal: Absence of hemolysis
Positive in: Paroxysmal nocturnal hemoglobinuria
False positive: autoimmune hemolytic anemia, megaloblastic anemias
False negative: may occur with use of heparin or EDTA

SUDAN III STAIN (qualitative screening for fecal fat)

Normal: Negative. Test should be preceded by diet containing 100-150 g of dietary fat/day for 1 week, avoidance of high-fiber diet, and avoidance of suppositories or oily material before specimen collection.
Positive in: Steatorrhea, use of castor oil or mineral oil droplets

SYNOVIAL FLUID ANALYSIS

Table 4-23 describes the classification and interpretation of synovial fluid analysis.

TABLE 4-23 **Classification and Interpretation of Synovial Fluid Analysis**

Group	Diseases	Appearance	Viscosity	Mucin Clot	WBC/MM³	%PMN	Glucose (mg/dl) (Blood–Synovial Fluid)	Protein (g/dl)
Normal	—	Clear	↑	Firm	<200	<25	<10	<2.5
I (noninflammatory)	Osteoarthritis, aseptic necrosis, traumatic arthritis, erythema nodosum, osteochondritis dissecans	Clear, yellow (may be xanthochromic if traumatic arthritis)	↑	Firm	↑ Up to 10,000	<25	<10	<2.5
II (inflammatory)	Crystal-induced arthritis, rheumatoid arthritis, Reiter's syndrome, collagen-vascular disease, psoriatic arthritis, serum sickness, rheumatic fever	Clear, yellow, turbid	↓	Friable	↑↑ Up to 100,000	40-90	<40	.2.5
III (septic)	Bacterial (staphylococcal, gonococcal, tuberculosis)	Turbid	↓/↑	Friable	↑↑↑ Up to 5 million	40-100	20-100	.2.5

↑, Elevated; ↑↑, markedly high; ↓, decreased; *PMN*, polymorphonuclear leukocytes. Note that there is considerable overlap in the numbers listed above.

T_3 (triiodothyronine)

Normal range: 75-220 ng/dl

Abnormal values:

A. Elevated in hyperthyroidism (usually earlier and to a greater extent than serum T_4).
B. Useful in diagnosing:
   1. T_3 hyperthyroidism (thyrotoxicosis): increased T_3, normal FTI.
   2. Toxic nodular goiter: increased T_3, normal or increased T_4.
   3. Iodine deficiency: normal T_3, possibly decreased T_4.
   4. Thyroid replacement therapy with liothyronine (Cytomel): normal T_4, increased T_3 if patient is symptomatically hyperthyroid.

Not ordered routinely but indicated when hyperthyroidism is suspected and serum free T_4 or FTI inconclusive.

T_3 (triiodothyronine); *see* Table 4-24 for T_3 abnormalities

TABLE 4-24 **Findings in Thyroid Function Tests in Various Clinical Conditions**

Condition	T_4	FT_4I	T_3	FT_3I	TSH	TSI	TRH Stimulation
Hyperthyroidism							
Graves' disease	↑	↑	↑	↑	↓	+	↓
Toxic nodular goiter	↑	↑	↑	↑	↓	−	↓
Pituitary TSH-secreting tumors	↑	↑	↑	↑	↑	−	↓
T3 thyrotoxicosis	N	N	↑	↑	↓	+, −	↓
T4 thyrotoxicosis	↑	↑	N	N	↓	+, −	↓
Hypothyroidism							
Primary	↓	↓	↓	↓	↑	+, −	↑
Secondary	↓	↓	↓	↓	↓, N	−	↓
Tertiary	↓	↓	↓	↓	↓, N	−	N
Peripheral unresponsiveness	↑, N	↑, N	↑, N	↑	↑, N	−	N, ↑

From Tilton RC, Barrows A: Clinical laboratory medicine, St Louis, 1992, Mosby.
N, Normal; ↑, increased; ↓, decreased; +, − variable.

T_3 RESIN UPTAKE (T_3RU)

Normal range:

25% to 35%

Abnormal values:

Increased in hyperthyroidism. T_3 resin uptake (T_3RU or RT_3U) measures the percentage of free T_4 (not bound to protein); it does not measure serum T_3 concentration; T_3RU and other tests that reflect thyroid hormone binding to plasma protein are also known as *thyroid hormone-binding ratios* (THBR).

T_4, SERUM T_4, AND FREE (free thyroxine)

Normal range:

0.8-2.8 ng/dl

Abnormal values:

Serum thyroxine (T_4)

Elevated in:

1. Graves' disease
2. Toxic multinodular goiter
3. Toxic adenoma
4. Iatrogenic and factitious
5. Transient hyperthyroidism.
   a. Subacute thyroiditis
   b. Hashimoto's thyroiditis
   c. Silent thyroiditis
6. Rare causes: hypersecretion of TSH (e.g., pituitary neoplasms), struma ovarii, ingestion of large amounts of iodine in a patient with preexisting thyroid hyperplasia or adenoma (Jod-Basedow phenomenon), hydatidiform mole, carcinoma of thyroid, amiodarone therapy of arrhythmias.

Serum thyroxine test measures both circulating thyroxine bound to protein (represents >99% of circulating T_4) and unbound (free) thyroxine. Values vary with protein binding; changes in the concentration of T_4 secondary to changes in thyroxine-binding globulin (TBG) can be caused by the following:

Increased TBG (↑T_4)	Decreased TBG (↓ T_4)
Pregnancy	Androgens, glucocorticoids
Estrogens	Nephrotic syndrome, cirrhosis
Acute infectious hepatitis	Acromegaly
Oral contraceptives	Hypoproteinemia
Familial	Familial
Fluorouracil, clofibrate, heroin, methadone	Phenytoin, ASA and other NSAIDs, high-dose penicillin, asparaginase
	Chronic debilitating illness

To eliminate the suspected influence of protein binding on thyroxine values, two additional tests are available: T_3 resin uptake and serum free thyroxine.

T_4, FREE (free thyroxine)

Normal range: 0.8-2.8 ng/dl

Elevated in: Graves' disease, toxic multinodular goiter, toxic adenoma, iatrogenic and factitious causes, transient hyperthyroidism

Serum free T_4 directly measures unbound thyroxine. Free T_4 can be measured by equilibrium dialysis (gold standard of free T_4 assays) or by immunometric techniques (influenced by serum levels of lipids, proteins, and certain drugs). The free thyroxine index (FTI) can also be easily calculated by multiplying T_4 times T_3RU and dividing the result by 100; the FTI corrects for any abnormal T_4 values secondary to protein binding: FTI = $T_4 \times T_3RU/100$.

Normal values equal 1.1 to 4.3.

Table 4-2, under "Acid-Base Reference Values," describes additional abnormalities of free T_4.

TEGRETOL; *see* CARBAMAZEPINE; *see* Table 4-24, under "T_3 (triiodothyronine)"

TESTOSTERONE (total testosterone)

Normal range: (Variable with age and sex)

Serum/plasma:	Males: 280-1100 ng/dl
	Females: 15-70 ng/dl
Urine:	Males: 50-135 μg/day
	Females: 2-12 μg/day

Elevated in: Testicular tumors, ovarian masculinizing tumors

Decreased in: Hypogonadism

THEOPHYLLINE

Normal therapeutic range: 10-20 mcg/mL

THORACENTESIS FLUID

Testing and evaluation of results:

1. Pleural effusion fluid should be differentiated in exudate or transudate. The initial laboratory studies should be aimed only at distinguishing an exudate from a transudate.
   a. Tube 1: protein, LDH, albumin.
   b. Tubes 2, 3, 4: save the fluid until further notice. In selected patients with suspected empyema, a pH level may be useful (generally ≤ 7.0). See following for proper procedure to obtain a pH level from pleural fluid.

   NOTE: Do not order further tests until the presence of an exudate is confirmed on the basis of protein and LDH determinations (Section III, Fig. 3-145, on page 1143); however, if the results of protein and LDH determinations cannot be obtained within a reasonable time (resulting in unnecessary delay), additional laboratory tests should be ordered at the time of thoracentesis.
2. A serum/effusion albumin gradient of ≤1.2 g/dl is indicative of exudative effusions, especially in patients with congestive heart failure (CHF) treated with diuretics.
3. Note the appearance of the fluid:
   a. A grossly hemorrhagic effusion can be a result of a traumatic tap, neoplasm, or an embolus with infarction.
   b. A milky appearance indicates either of the following:
      (1) Chylous effusion: caused by trauma or tumor invasion of the thoracic duct; lipoprotein electrophoresis of the effusion reveals chylomicrons and triglyceride levels >115 mg/dl.
      (2) Pseudochylous effusion: often seen with chronic inflammation of the pleural space (e.g., TB, connective tissue diseases).
4. If transudate, consider CHF, cirrhosis, chronic renal failure, and other hypoproteinemic states and perform subsequent workup accordingly.

5. If exudate, consider ordering these tests on the pleural fluid:
   a. Cytologic examination for malignant cells (for suspected neoplasm).
   b. Gram stain, cultures (aerobic and anaerobic), and sensitivities (for suspected infectious process).
   c. AFB stain and cultures (for suspected TB).
   d. pH: a value < 7.0 suggests parapneumonic effusion or empyema; a pleural fluid pH must be drawn anaerobically and iced immediately; the syringe should be prerinsed with 0.2 ml of 1:1000 heparin.
   e. Glucose: a low glucose level suggests parapneumonic effusions and rheumatoid arthritis.
   f. Amylase: a high amylase level suggests pancreatitis or ruptured esophagus.
   g. Perplexing pleural effusions are often a result of malignancy (e.g., lymphoma, malignant mesothelioma, ovarian carcinoma), TB, subdiaphragmatic processes, prior asbestos exposure, and postcardiac injury syndrome.

THROMBIN TIME (TT)

Normal range: 11.3-18.5 sec
Elevated in: Thrombolytic and heparin therapy, disseminated intravascular coagulation, hypofibrinogenemia, dysfibrinogenemia

THYROID-STIMULATING HORMONE (TSH)

Normal range: 2-11 μU/ml

CONDITIONS THAT INCREASE SERUM THYROID-STIMULATING HORMONE VALUES

Laboratory error
Primary hypothyroidism
Synthroid therapy with insufficient dose
Lithium or amiodarone; some patients
Hashimoto's thyroiditis in later stage
Large doses of inorganic iodide (e.g., SSKI)
Severe nonthyroid illness in recovery phase
Iodine deficiency (moderate or severe)
Addison's disease
TSH specimen drawn in evening (peak of diurnal variation)
Pituitary TSH-secreting tumor
Therapy of hypothyroidism (3-6 wk after beginning therapy [range, 1-8 wk]; sometimes longer when pretherapy TSH is over 100 μU/ml)
Acute psychiatric illness
Peripheral resistance to T_4 syndrome
Antibodies (e.g., HAMA) interfering with monoclonal sandwich method of TSH assay
Telepaque (iopanoic acid) and Oragrafin (ipodate) x-ray contrast media
Amphetamines
High altitudes

CONDITIONS THAT DECREASE SERUM THYROID-STIMULATING HORMONE VALUES

Laboratory error
T_4/T_3 toxicosis (diffuse or nodular etiology)
Excessive therapy for hypothyroidism
Active thyroiditis (subacute, painless, or early active Hashimoto's disease)
Multinodular goiter containing areas of autonomy
Severe nonthyroid illness (especially acute trauma, dopamine, or glucocorticoid)
T_3 toxicosis
Pituitary insufficiency
Cushing's syndrome (and some patients on high-dose glucocorticoid)
Jod-Basedow (iodine-induced) hyperthyroidism
Thyroid-stimulating hormone drawn 2-4 hr after levothyroxine dose
Postpartum transient toxicosis
Factitious hyperthyroidism
Struma ovarii
Radioimmunoassay, surgery, or antithyroid drug therapy for hyperthyroidism 4-6 wk (range 2 wk–2 yr) after the treatment
Interleukin-2 drugs (3%-6% of cases) or α-interferon therapy (1% of cases)
Hyperemesis gravidarum
Amiodarone therapy

THYROXINE (T_4)

Normal range: 4-11 μg/dl

TIBC; *see* IRON-BINDING CAPACITY

TRANSFERRIN

Normal range: 170-370 mg/dl
Elevated in: Iron deficiency anemia, oral contraceptive administration, viral hepatitis, late pregnancy
Decreased in: Nephrotic syndrome, liver disease, hereditary deficiency, protein malnutrition, neoplasms, chronic inflammatory states, chronic illness, thalassemia, hemochromatosis, hemolytic anemia

SECTION IV

TRIGLYCERIDES

Normal range: <150 mg/dl
Elevated in: Hyperlipoproteinemias (types I, IIb, III, IV, V), hypothyroidism, pregnancy, estrogens, acute myocardial infarction, pancreatitis, alcohol intake, nephrotic syndrome, diabetes mellitus, glycogen storage disease
Decreased in: Malnutrition, congenital abetalipoproteinemias, drugs (e.g., gemfibrozil, fenofibrate, nicotinic acid, clofibrate)

TRIIODOTHYRONINE; *see* T_3

TROPONINS, SERUM

Normal range: 0-0.4 ng/ml (negative). If there is clinical suspicion of evolving acute MI or ischemic episode, repeat testing in 5-6 hours is recommended.
Indeterminate: 0.05-0.49 ng/ml. Suggest further tests. In a patient with unstable angina and this troponin I level, there is an increased risk of a cardiac event in the near future.
Strong probability of acute MI: ≥0.05 ng/ml
CARDIAC TROPONIN T (CTNT) is a highly sensitive marker for myocardial injury for the first 48 hours after MI and for up to 5-7 days (see Fig. 4-2, under "Creatine Kinase Isoenzymes"). It may be also elevated in renal failure, chronic muscle disease, and trauma.
CARDIAC TROPONIN I (CTNI) is highly sensitive and specific for myocardial injury (≥CK-MB) in the initial 8 hours, peaks within 24 hours and lasts up to 7 days. With progressively higher levels of cTnI, the risk of mortality increases because the amount of necrosis increases.

TSH; *see* THYROID-STIMULATING HORMONE

TT; *see* THROMBIN TIME

TUBERCULIN TEST (PPD)

Abnormal results: *see* Boxes 4-3 and 4-4 for interpretation

BOX 4-3 PPD Reaction Size Considered "Positive" (Intracutaneous 5 TU Mantoux Test at 48 hr)

5 mm or More
HIV infection or risk factors for HIV
Close recent contact with active TB case
Persons with chest x-ray consistent with healed TB

10 mm or More
Foreign-born persons from countries with high TB prevalence in Asia, Africa, and Latin America
IV drug users
Medically underserved low-income population groups (including Native Americans, Hispanics, and blacks)
Residents of long-term care facilities (nursing homes, mental institutions)
Medical conditions that increase risk for TB (silicosis, gastrectomy, undernourished, diabetes mellitus, high-dose corticosteroids or immunosuppression Rx, leukemia or lymphoma, other malignancies)
Employees of long-term care facilities, schools, child-care facilities, health care facilities

15 mm or More
All others not already listed

TB, Tuberculosis; *TU,* tuberculin units.

BOX 4-4 Factors Associated with False-Negative Tuberculin Tests

Technical Errors
Improper administration
Inaccurate reading
Loss of potency of antigen

Patient-Related Factors (Anergy)
Age (elderly)
Nutritional status
Medications—corticosteroids, immunosuppressive agents
Severe tuberculosis
Coexisting diseases
- HIV infection
- Viral illness or vaccination
- Lymphoreticular malignancies
- Sarcoidosis
- Solid tumors

Lepromatous leprosy
Sjögren's syndrome
Ataxia telangiectasia
Uremia
Primary biliary cirrhosis
Systemic lupus erythematosus
Severe systemic disease of any etiology

From Stein JH (ed): *Internal medicine,* ed 4, St Louis, 1994, Mosby.

UNCONJUGATED BILIRUBIN; *see* BILIRUBIN, INDIRECT

UREA NITROGEN, BLOOD (BUN)

Normal range: 8-18 mg/dl
Box 4-5 describes factors affecting BUN level independent of renal function.
Elevated in: Drugs (aminoglycosides and other antibiotics, diuretics, lithium, corticosteroids), dehydration, gastrointestinal bleeding, decreased renal blood flow (shock, congestive heart failure, myocardial infarction), renal disease (glomerulonephritis, pyelonephritis, diabetic nephropathy), urinary tract obstruction (prostatic hypertrophy)

BOX 4-5 Factors Affecting Blood Urea Nitrogen Level Independent of Renal Function

Disproportionate Increase in Blood Urea Nitrogen
Volume depletion "prerenal azotemia"
Gastrointestinal hemorrhage
Corticosteroid or cytotoxic agents
High-protein diet
Obstructive uropathy
Sepsis
Catabolic states tissue breakdown

Disproportionate Decrease in Blood Urea Nitrogen
Low-protein diet
Liver disease

From Andreoli TE (ed): *Cecil essentials of medicine,* ed 5, Philadelphia, 2001, WB Saunders.

Decreased in: Liver disease, malnutrition, pregnancy third trimester, overhydration, acromegaly, celiac disease

URIC ACID (serum)

Normal range: 2-7 mg/dl
Elevated in: Renal failure, gout, excessive cell lysis (chemotherapeutic agents, radiation therapy, leukemia, lymphoma, hemolytic anemia), hereditary enzyme deficiency (hypoxanthine-guanine-phosphoribosyl transferase), acidosis, myeloproliferative disorders, diet high in purines or protein, drugs (diuretics, low doses of ASA, ethambutol, nicotinic acid), lead poisoning, hypothyroidism, Addison's disease, nephrogenic diabetes insipidus, active psoriasis, polycystic kidneys
Decreased in: Drugs (allopurinol, high doses of ASA, probenecid, warfarin, corticosteroid), deficiency of xanthine oxidase, syndrome of inappropriate antidiuretic hormone secretion, renal tubular deficits (Fanconi's syndrome), alcoholism, liver disease, diet deficient in protein or purines, Wilson's disease, hemochromatosis

URINALYSIS

Normal range:
Color: light straw
Appearance: clear
Ketones: absent
pH: 4.5-8 (average, 6)
Protein: absent
Glucose: absent
Specific gravity: 1.005-1.030
Occult blood absent
Microscopic examination:
Red blood cells: 0-5 (high-power field)
White blood cells: 0-5 (high-power field)
Bacteria (spun specimen): absent
Casts: 0-4 hyaline (low-power field)
Abnormalities in the microscopic examination of urine are described in Table 4-25.

TABLE 4-25 Microscopic Examination of the Urine

Finding	Associations
Casts	
Red blood cell	Glomerulonephritis, vasculitis
White blood cell	Interstitial nephritis, pyelonephritis
Epithelial cell	Acute tubular necrosis, interstitial nephritis, glomerulonephritis
Granular	Renal parenchymal disease (nonspecific)
Waxy, broad	Advanced renal failure
Hyaline	Normal finding in concentrated urine
Fatty	Heavy proteinuria
Cells	
Red blood cell	Urinary tract infection, urinary tract inflammation
White blood cell	Urinary tract infection, urinary tract inflammation
Eosinophil	Acute interstitial nephritis
(Squamous) epithelial cell	Contaminants
Crystals	
Uric acid	Acid urine, acute uric acid nephropathy, hyperuricosuria
Calcium phosphate	Alkaline urine
Calcium oxalate	Acid urine, hyperoxaluria, ethylene glycol poisoning
Cystine	Cystinuria
Sulfur	Sulfa-containing antibiotics

From Andreoli TE (ed): *Cecil essentials of medicine,* ed 5, Philadelphia, 2001, WB Saunders.

URINE AMYLASE

Normal range: 35-260 U Somogyi/hr
Elevated in: Pancreatitis, carcinoma of the pancreas

URINE BILE

Normal: Absent
Abnormal: Urine bilirubin: hepatitis (viral, toxic, drug-induced), biliary obstruction
Urine urobilinogen: hepatitis (viral, toxic, drug-induced), hemolytic jaundice, liver cell dysfunction (cirrhosis, infection, metastases)

URINE CALCIUM

Normal range: <250 mg/24 hr
Elevated in: Primary hyperparathyroidism, hypervitaminosis D, bone metastases, multiple myeloma, increased calcium intake, steroids, prolonged immobilization, sarcoidosis, Paget's disease, idiopathic hypercalciuria, renal tubular acidosis
Decreased in: Hypoparathyroidism, pseudohypoparathyroidism, vitamin D deficiency, vitamin D–resistant rickets, diet low in calcium, drugs (thiazide diuretics, oral contraceptives), familial hypocalciuric hypercalcemia, renal osteodystrophy, potassium citrate therapy

URINE CAMP

Elevated in: Hypercalciuria, familial hypocalciuric hypercalcemia, primary hyperparathyroidism, pseudohypoparathyroidism, rickets
Decreased in: Vitamin D intoxication, sarcoidosis

URINE CATECHOLAMINES

Normal range:
Norepinephrine: <100 μg/24 hr
Epinephrine: <10 μg/24 hr
Elevated in: Pheochromocytoma, neuroblastoma, severe stress

URINE CHLORIDE

Normal range: 110-250 mEq/day
Elevated in: Corticosteroids, Bartter's syndrome, diuretics, metabolic acidosis, severe hypokalemia
Decreased in: Chloride depletion (vomiting), colonic villous adenoma, chronic renal failure, renal tubular acidosis

URINE COPPER

Normal range: <40 μg/24 hr

URINE CORTISOL, FREE

Normal range: 10-110 μg/24 hr
Elevated: *see* CORTISOL, plasma

URINE CREATININE (24 HR)

Normal range:
Male: 0.8-1.8 g/day
Female: 0.6-1.6 g/day
NOTE: Useful test as an indicator of completeness of 24 hr urine collection.

URINE EOSINOPHILS

Normal:
Absent
Present:
Interstitial nephritis, acute tubular necrosis, urinary tract infection, kidney transplant rejection, hepatorenal syndrome

URINE GLUCOSE (qualitative)

Normal: Absent
Present in: Diabetes mellitus, renal glycosuria (decreased renal threshold for glucose), glucose intolerance

URINE HEMOGLOBIN, FREE

Normal: Absent
Present in: Hemolysis (with saturation of serum haptoglobin binding capacity and renal threshold for tubular absorption of hemoglobin)

URINE HEMOSIDERIN

Normal: Absent
Present in: Paroxysmal nocturnal hemoglobinuria, chronic hemolytic anemia, hemochromatosis, blood transfusion, thalassemias

URINE 5-HYDROXYINDOLE-ACETIC ACID (urine 5-HIAA)

Normal range: 2-8 mg/24 hr
Elevated in: Carcinoid tumors, after ingestion of certain foods (bananas, plums, tomatoes, avocados, pineapples, eggplant, walnuts), drugs (monoamine oxidase inhibitors, phenacetin, methyldopa, glycerol guaiacolate, acetaminophen, salicylates, phenothiazines, imipramine, methocarbamol, reserpine, methamphetamine)

URINE INDICAN

Normal: Absent
Present in: Malabsorption secondary to intestinal bacterial overgrowth

URINE KETONES (semiquantitative)

Normal: Absent
Present in: Diabetic ketoacidosis, alcoholic ketoacidosis, starvation, isopropanol ingestion

URINE METANEPHRINES

Normal range: 0-2.0 mg/24 hr
Elevated in: Pheochromocytoma, neuroblastoma, drugs (caffeine, phenothiazines, monoamine oxidase inhibitors), stress

URINE MYOGLOBIN

Normal: Absent
Present in: Severe trauma, hyperthermia, polymyositis/dermatomyositis, carbon monoxide poisoning, drugs (narcotic and amphetamine toxicity), hypothyroidism, muscle ischemia

URINE NITRITE

Normal: Absent
Present in: Urinary tract infections

URINE OCCULT BLOOD

Normal: Negative
Positive in: Trauma to urinary tract, renal disease (glomerulonephritis, pyelonephritis), renal or ureteral calculi, bladder lesions (carcinoma, cystitis), prostatitis, prostatic carcinoma, menstrual contamination, hematopoietic disorders (hemophilia, thrombocytopenia), anticoagulants, ASA

URINE OSMOLALITY

Normal range: 50-1200 mOsm/kg
Elevated in: Syndrome of inappropriate antidiuretic hormone secretion, dehydration, glycosuria, adrenal insufficiency, high-protein diet
Decreased in: Diabetes insipidus, excessive water intake, IV hydration with D_5W, acute renal insufficiency, glomerulonephritis

URINE PH

Normal range: 4.6-8 (average 6)
Elevated in: Bacteriuria, vegetarian diet, renal failure with inability to form ammonia, drugs (antibiotics, sodium bicarbonate, acetazolamide)
Decreased in: Acidosis (metabolic, respiratory), drugs (ammonium chloride, methenamine mandelate), diabetes mellitus, starvation, diarrhea

URINE PHOSPHATE

Normal range: 0.8-2.0 g/24 hr
Elevated in: Acute tubular necrosis (diuretic phase), chronic renal disease, uncontrolled diabetes mellitus, hyperparathyroidism, hypomagnesemia, metabolic acidosis, metabolic alkalosis, neurofibromatosis, adult-onset vitamin D–resistant hypophosphatemic osteomalacia
Decreased in: Acromegaly, acute renal failure, decreased dietary intake, hypoparathyroidism, respiratory acidosis

URINE POTASSIUM

Normal range: 25-100 mEq/24 hr
Elevated in: Aldosteronism (primary, secondary), glucocorticoids, alkalosis, renal tubular acidosis, excessive dietary potassium intake
Decreased in: Acute renal failure, potassium-sparing diuretics, diarrhea, hypokalemia

URINE PROTEIN (quantitative)

Normal range: <150 mg/24 hr
Elevated in:
Nephrotic syndrome as a result of primary renal diseases
Malignant hypertension
Malignancies: multiple myeloma, leukemias, Hodgkin's disease

Congestive heart failure
Diabetes mellitus
Systemic lupus erythematosus, rheumatoid arthritis
Sickle cell disease
Goodpasture's syndrome
Malaria
Amyloidosis, sarcoidosis
Tubular lesions: cystinosis
Functional (after heavy exercise)
Pyelonephritis
Pregnancy
Constrictive pericarditis
Renal vein thrombosis
Toxic nephropathies: heavy metals, drugs
Radiation nephritis
Orthostatic (postural) proteinuria
Benign proteinuria: fever, heat or cold exposure

URINE SEDIMENT; *see* Fig. 4-14 for evaluation of common abnormalities

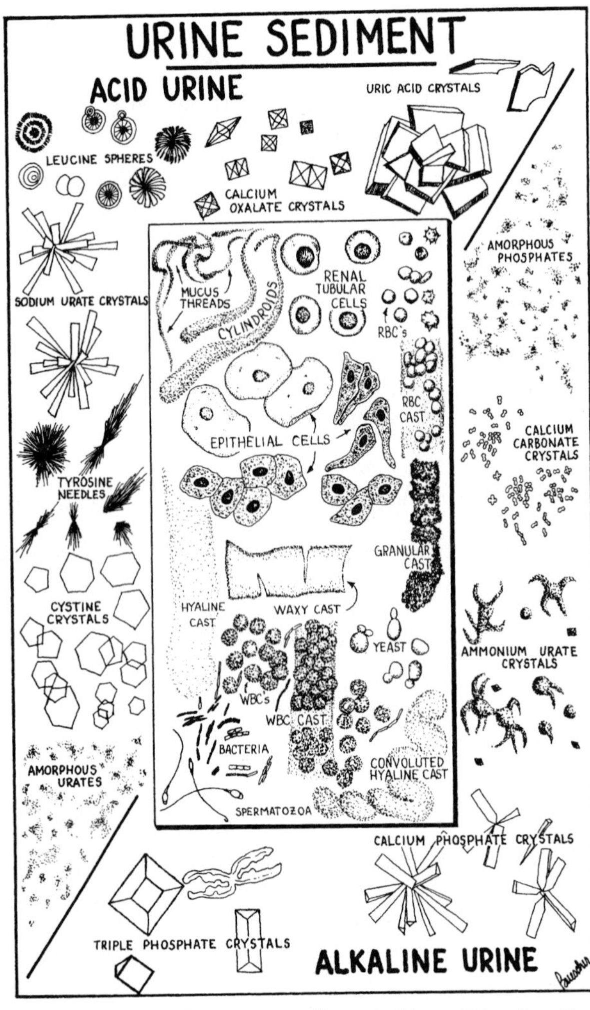

Fig. 4-14 Microscopic examination of urinary sediment. (From Grigorian Greene M: *The Harriet Lane handbook: a manual for pediatric house officers,* ed 12, St Louis, 1991, Mosby.)

URINE SODIUM (QUANTITATIVE)

Normal range: 40-220 mEq/day

Elevated in: Diuretic administration, high sodium intake, salt-losing nephritis, acute tubular necrosis, vomiting, Addison's disease, syndrome of inappropriate antidiuretic hormone secretion, hypothyroidism, congestive heart failure, hepatic failure, chronic renal failure, Bartter's syndrome, glucocorticoid deficiency, interstitial nephritis caused by analgesic abuse, mannitol, dextran, or glycerol therapy, milk-alkali syndrome, decreased renin secretion, postobstructive diuresis

Decreased in: Increased aldosterone, glucocorticoid excess, hyponatremia, prerenal azotemia, decreased salt intake

URINE SPECIFIC GRAVITY

Normal range: 1.005-1.03
Elevated in: Dehydration, excessive fluid losses (vomiting, diarrhea, fever), x-ray contrast media, diabetes mellitus, congestive heart failure, syndrome of inappropriate antidiuretic hormone secretion, adrenal insufficiency, decreased fluid intake
Decreased in: Diabetes insipidus, renal disease (glomerulonephritis, pyelonephritis), excessive fluid intake or IV hydration

URINE VANILLYLMANDELIC ACID (VMA)

Normal range: <6.8 mg/24 hr
Elevated in: Pheochromocytoma, neuroblastoma, ganglioblastoma, drugs (isoproterenol, methocarbamol, levodopa, sulfonamides, chlorpromazine), severe stress, after ingestion of bananas, chocolate, vanilla, tea, coffee
Decreased in: Drugs (monoamine oxidase inhibitors, reserpine, guanethidine, methyldopa)

VDRL

Normal range: Negative
Positive test: Syphilis, other treponemal diseases (yaws, pinta, bejel)

NOTE: A false-positive test may be seen in patients with systemic lupus erythematosus and other autoimmune diseases, infectious mononucleosis, HIV, atypical pneumonia, malaria, leprosy, typhus fever, rat-bite fever, relapsing fever.

NOTE: see Table 4-26 for interpretation of serologic tests for syphilis.

VISCOSITY (serum)

Normal range: 1.4-1.8 relative to water (1.10-1.22 centipoise)
Elevated in: Monoclonal gammopathies (Waldenström's macro-globulinemia, multiple myeloma), hyperfibrinogenemia, systemic lupus erythematosus, rheumatoid arthritis, polycythemia, leukemia

TABLE 4-26 **Interpretation of Serologic Tests fo Syphilis***

FINDING		
Nontreponemal Tests	**Treponemal Tests**	**Interpretation of Finding: Is Syphilis Present?***
Nonreactive	Nonreactive	Early primary syphilis is not ruled out by negative serologic tests. Early syphilis is present in 13%-30% of patients who have a negative microhemagglutination–Treponema pallidum test; in about 30% of patients who present with chancre but have a nonreactive reagin test; and in about 10% of patients who have a negative FTA-ABS test. Late syphilis is present in a very small fraction of patients. Adequately treated syphilis in remote past may produce these results, but treponemal tests usually remain reactive.
	Reactive	Observed in about 10% of patients with chancre. The treponemal tests may turn positive shortly before the reagin tests. Reagin tests repeated after several days are generally positive. In adequately treated early syphilis, the reagin test may return to nonreactive within 1-2 yr, whereas the treponemal tests generally do not. Late syphilis is not ruled out by a negative reagin test. The sensitivity of the reagin tests is lower than that of treponemal tests in untreated late syphilis. In secondary syphilis, rarely, a highly reactive serum appears negative when tested undiluted with a reagin test because flocculation is inhibited by relative antibody excess. Not reported to occur with treponemal tests. Quantitative reagin tests are positive. False-positive treponemal tests occur in 40% of patients with Lyme disease.
Reactive	Nonreactive	Finding is not diagnostic of syphilis but constitutes a classic biologic false-positive reaction.
	borderline (FTA-ABS)	Not diagnostic of syphilis: most patients (90%) with this pattern do not develop clinical or serologic evidence of syphilis. Repeat test is indicated. Chronic borderline results are associated with a variety of conditions other than syphilis.
	Beaded (FTA-ABS)	Not diagnostic of syphilis. Seen with collagen-vascular disease.
	Reactive	Findings diagnostic of syphilis or other treponemal disease. In adequately treated syphilis, one would expect (1) a sustained fourfold drop in titer of reagin test, although reagin test may remain positive after adequate therapy; (2) treponemal tests remain positive after adequate therapy. Concurrent false-positive results on both nontreponemal and treponemal tests could occur in rare instances. It may be impossible to rule out syphilis in an individual with this test profile.

From Stein JH (ed): *Internal medicine,* ed 4, St Louis, 1994, Mosby.
FTA-ABS, Fluorescent treponemal antibody, absorbed.
*Serologic data must always be interpreted in the light of a total clinical evaluation. Diagnosis based on serologic criteria alone is fraught with error. Serologic tests apparently in conflict with clinical diagnosis should be confirmed by repetition or possibly referral to a reference laboratory.

VITAMIN B_{12}

Normal:

190-900 ng/ml

Causes of Vitamin B_{12} deficiency:

1. Pernicious anemia (antibodies against intrinsic factor and gastric parietal cells)
2. Dietary (strict lacto-ovovegetarians, food faddists)
3. Malabsorption (achlorhydria, gastrectomy, ileal resection, pancreatic insufficiency, drugs [omeprazole, cholestyramine])

Falsely low levels occur in patients with severe folate deficiency, in patients using high doses of ascorbic acid, and when cobalamin levels are measured after nuclear medicine studies (radioactivity interferes with cobalamin radioimmunoassay).

Falsely high or normal levels in patients with cobalamin deficiency can occur in severe liver disease and chronic granulocytic leukemia.

The absence of anemia or macrocytosis does not exclude the diagnosis of cobalamin deficiency.

WBC; *see* COMPLETE BLOOD COUNT

WESTERGREN; *see* ERYTHROCYTE SEDIMENTATION RATE

WHITE BLOOD COUNT; *see* COMPLETE BLOOD COUNT

SECTION V

Clinical Preventive Services

PART A
THE PERIODIC HEALTH EXAMINATION*

Age-specific charts, 1315

PART B
IMMUNIZATIONS AND CHEMOPROPHYLAXIS

Childhood immunizations, 1324

Immunizations for adults, 1334

Administration of vaccines and immune globulins, 1346

Endocarditis prophylaxis, 1353

Postexposure prophylaxis to hepatitis B and HIV, 1357

*Data modified from US Preventive Services Task Force: Guide to clinical preventive services: report of the US Preventive Services Task Force, ed 2, Washington, DC, 1996 (revised 2001), US Department of Health and Human Services. Text downloaded from Internet site: http://text.nlm.nih.gov

PART A • THE PERIODIC HEALTH EXAMINATION

Age-Specific Charts

TABLE 5-1 Birth to 10 Years

Interventions considered and recommended for the Periodic Health Examination

Leading causes of death
- Conditions originating in perinatal period
- Congenital anomalies
- Sudden infant death syndrome (SIDS)
- Unintentional injuries (non–motor vehicle)
- Motor vehicle injuries

INTERVENTIONS FOR THE GENERAL POPULATION

Screening

Height and weight
Blood pressure
Vision screen (age 3-4 yr)
Hemoglobinopathy screen (birth)[1]
Phenylalanine level (birth)[2]
T_4 and/or TSH (birth)[3]

Counseling

Injury prevention

Child safety car seats (age <5 yr)
Lap/shoulder belts (age ≥5 yr)
Bicycle helmet; avoid bicycling near traffic
Smoke detector, flame-retardant sleepwear
Hot water heater temperature <120°-130° F
Window/stair guards, pool fence
Safe storage of drugs, toxic substances, firearms, and matches
Syrup of ipecac, poison control phone number
CPR training for parents/caretakers

Diet and exercise

Breast-feeding, iron-enriched formula and foods (infants and toddlers)
Limit fat and cholesterol; maintain caloric balance; emphasize grains, fruits, vegetables (age ≥2 yr)
Regular physical activity*

Substance use

Effects of passive smoking*
Antitobacco message*

Dental health

Regular visits to dental care provider*
Floss, brush with fluoride toothpaste daily*
Advice about baby bottle tooth decay*

Immunizations

Diphtheria-tetanus-pertussis (DTP)[4]
Inactivated poliovirus vaccine (IPV)[5]
Measles-mumps-rubella (MMR)[6]
H. influenzae type b (Hib) conjugate[7]
Hepatitis B[8]
Varicella[9]
Pneumococcal vaccine[10]
Influenza[11]

Chemoprophylaxis

Ocular prophylaxis (birth)

INTERVENTIONS FOR HIGH-RISK POPULATIONS

Population	*Potential Interventions (See detailed high-risk definitions)*
Preterm or low birth weight	Hemoglobin/hematocrit (HR1)
Infants of mothers at risk for HIV	HIV testing (HR2)
Low income; immigrants	Hemoglobin/hematocrit (HR1); PPD (HR3)
TB contacts	PPD (HR3)
Native American/Alaska Native	Hemoglobin/hematocrit (HR1); PPD (HR3); hepatitis A vaccine (HR4); pneumococcal vaccine (HR5)
Travelers to developing countries	Hepatitis A vaccine (HR4)
Residents of long-term care facilities	PPD (HR3); hepatitis A vaccine (HR4); influenza vaccine (HR6)
Certain chronic medical conditions	PPD (HR3); pneumococcal vaccine (HR5); influenza vaccine (HR6)
Increased individual or community lead exposure	Blood lead level (HR7)
Inadequate water fluoridation	Daily fluoride supplement (HR8)
Family hx of skin cancer; nevi; fair skin, eyes, hair	Avoid excess/midday sun, use protective clothing* (HR9)

[1]Whether screening should be universal or targeted to high-risk groups will depend on the proportion of high-risk individuals in the screening area, and other considerations. [2]If done during first 24 hr of life, repeat by age 2 wk. [3]Optimally between day 2 and 6, but in all cases before newborn nursery discharge. [4]2, 4, 6, and 12-18 mo; once between ages 4-6 yr (DTaP may be used at 15 mo and older). [5]2, 4, 6-18 mo; once between ages 4-6 yr. [6]12-15 mo and 4-6 yr. [7]2, 4, 6 and 12-15 mo; no dose needed at 6 mo if PRP-OMP vaccine is used for first 2 doses. [8]Birth, 1 mo, 6 mo; or, 0-2 mo, 1-2 mo later, and 6-18 mo. If not done in infancy: current visit, and 1 and 6 mo later. [9]12-18 mo; or any child without hx of chickenpox or previous immunization. Include information on risk in adulthood, duration of immunity, and potential need for booster doses. [10]The 7-Valent conjugate vaccine (PCV) can be administered at the same time as the other childhood vaccines at a separate site. [11]Influenza vaccine is recommended in children 6 to 23 months of age.
*The ability of clinician counseling to influence this behavior is unproven.

HR1: Infants age 6-12 mo who are living in poverty, black, Native American or Alaska Native, immigrants from developing countries, preterm and low birth weight infants, infants whose principal dietary intake is unfortified cow's milk.

HR2: Infants born to high-risk mothers whose HIV status is unknown. Women at high risk include past or present injection drug use; persons who exchange sex for money or drugs, and their sex partners; injection drug–using, bisexual, or HIV-positive sex partners currently or in past; persons seeking treatment for STDs; blood transfusion during 1978-1985.

HR3: Persons infected with HIV, close contacts of persons with known or suspected TB, persons with medical risk factors associated with TB, immigrants from countries with high TB prevalence, medically underserved low-income populations (including homeless), residents of long-term care facilities.

HR4: Persons ≥2 yr living in or traveling to areas where the disease is endemic and where periodic outbreaks occur (e.g., countries with high or intermediate endemicity; certain Alaska Native, Pacific Island, Native American, and religious communities). Consider for institutionalized children aged ≥2 yr. Clinicians should also consider local epidemiology.

HR5: Immunocompetent persons ≥2 yr with certain medical conditions, including chronic cardiac or pulmonary disease, diabetes mellitus, cochlear implant candidates and recipients, and anatomic asplenia. Immunocompetent persons ≥2 yr living in high-risk environments or social settings (e.g., certain Native American and Alaska Native populations).

HR6: Annual vaccination of children ≥6 mo who are residents of chronic care facilities or who have chronic cardiopulmonary disorders, metabolic diseases (including diabetes mellitus), hemoglobinopathies, immunosuppression, or renal dysfunction.

HR7: Children about age 12 mo who: (1) live in communities in which the prevalence of lead levels requiring individual intervention, including residental lead hazard control or chelation, is high or undefined; (2) live in or frequently visit a home built before 1950 with dilapidated paint or with recent or ongoing renovation or remodeling; (3) have close contact with a person who has an elevated lead level; (4) live near lead industry or heavy traffic; (5) live with someone whose job or hobby involves lead exposure; (6) use lead-based pottery; or (7) take traditional ethnic remedies that contain lead.

HR8: Children living in areas with inadequate water fluoridation (<0.6 ppm).

HR9: Persons with a family history of skin cancer, a large number of moles, atypical moles, poor tanning ability, or light skin, hair, and eye color.

TABLE 5-2 Ages 11-24 Years

Interventions considered and recommended for the Periodic Health Examination	Leading causes of death
	Motor vehicle/other unintentional injuries
	Homicide
	Suicide
	Malignant neoplasms
	Heart diseases

INTERVENTIONS FOR THE GENERAL POPULATION

Screening
Height and weight
Blood pressure[1]
Papanicolaou (Pap) test[2] (females)
Chlamydia screen[3] (females <25 yr)
Lipid panel (in high-risk young adults only)
Rubella serology or vaccination hx[4] (females >12 yr)
Assess for problem drinking

Counseling
Injury prevention
Lap/shoulder belts
Bicycle/motorcycle/ATV helmets*
Smoke detector*
Safe storage/removal of firearms*

Substance use
Avoid tobacco use
Avoid underage drinking and illicit drug use*
Avoid alcohol/drug use while driving, swimming, boating, etc.*

Sexual behavior
STD prevention: abstinence*; avoid high-risk behavior*; condoms/female barrier with spermicide*
Unintended pregnancy: contraception

Diet and exercise
Limit fat and cholesterol; maintain caloric balance; emphasize grains, fruits, vegetables
Adequate calcium intake (females)
Regular physical activity*

Dental health
Regular visits to dental care provider*
Floss, brush with fluoride toothpaste daily

Immunizations
Tetanus-diphtheria (Td) boosters (11-16 yr)
Hepatitis B[5]
MMR (11-12 yr)[6]
Varicella (11-12 yr)[7]
Rubella[4] (females >12 yr)

Chemoprophylaxis
Multivitamin with folic acid (females)

INTERVENTIONS FOR HIGH-RISK POPULATIONS

Population	*Potential Interventions (See detailed high-risk definitions)*
High-risk sexual behavior	RPR/VDRL (HR1); screen for gonorrhea (female) (HR2), HIV (HR3), chlamydia (female) (HR4); hepatitis A vaccine (HR5)
Injection or street drug use	RPR/VDRL (HR1); HIV screen (HR3); hepatitis A vaccine (HR5); PPD (HR6); advice to reduce infection risk (HR7)
TB contacts; immigrants; low income	PPD (HR6)
Native Americans/Alaska Natives	Hepatitis A vaccine (HR5); PPD (HR6); pneumococcal vaccine (HR8)
Travelers to developing countries	Hepatitis A vaccine (HR5)
Certain chronic medical conditions	PPD (HR6); pneumococcal vaccine (HR8); influenza vaccine (HR9)
Settings where adolescents and young adults congregate	Second MMR (HR10)
Susceptible to varicella, measles, mumps	Varicella vaccine (HR11); MMR (HR12)
Blood transfusion between 1975-1985	HIV screen (HR3)
Institutionalized persons; health care/lab workers	Hepatitis A vaccine (HR5); PPD (HR6); influenza vaccine (HR9)
Family hx of skin cancer; nevi; fair skin, eyes, hair	Avoid excess/midday sun, use protective clothing* (HR13)
Prior pregnancy with neural tube defect	Folic acid 4.0 mg (HR14)
Inadequate water fluoridation	Daily fluoride supplement (HR15)

[1]Periodic BP for persons aged ≥21 yr. [2]If sexually active at present or in the past: q ≤3 yr. If sexual history is unreliable, begin Pap tests at age 18 yr. [3]If sexually active. [4]Serologic testing, documented vaccination history, and routine vaccination against rubella (preferably with MMR) are equally acceptable alternatives. [5]If not previously immunized: current visit, 1 and 6 mo later. [6]If no previous second dose of MMR. [7]If susceptible to chickenpox.
*The ability of clinician counseling to influence this behavior is unproven.

HR1: Persons who exchange sex for money or drugs, and their sex partners; persons with other STDs (including HIV); and sexual contacts of persons with active syphilis. Clinicians should also consider local epidemiology.

HR2: Females who have two or more sex partners in the last year; a sex partner with multiple sexual contacts; exchanged sex for money or drugs; or a history of repeated episodes of gonorrhea. Clinicians should also consider local epidemiology.

HR3: Males who had sex with males after 1975; past or present injection drug use; persons who exchange sex for money or drugs, and their sex partners; injection drug–using, bisexual, or HIV-positive sex partner currently or in the past; blood transfusion during 1978-1985; persons seeking treatment for STDs. Clinicians should also consider local epidemiology and consider screening for HIV in general population.

HR4: Sexually active females with multiple risk factors including history of prior STD; new or multiple sex partners; age under 25; nonuse or inconsistent use of barrier contraceptives; cervical ectopy. Clinicians should consider local epidemiology of the disease in identifying other high-risk groups.

HR5: Persons living in, traveling to, or working in areas where the disease is endemic and where periodic outbreaks occur (e.g., countries with high or intermediate endemicity; certain Alaska Native, Pacific Island, Native American, and religious communities); men who have sex with men; injection or street drug users. Vaccine may be considered for institutionalized persons and workers in these institutions, military personnel, and day-care, hospital, and laboratory workers. Clinicians should also consider local epidemiology.

HR6: HIV positive, close contacts of persons with known or suspected TB, health care workers, persons with medical risk factors associated with TB, immigrants from countries with high TB prevalence, medically underserved low-income populations (including homeless), alcoholics, injection drug users, and residents of long-term facilities.

HR7: Persons who continue to inject drugs.

HR8: Immunocompetent persons with certain medical conditions, including chronic cardiac or pulmonary disease, diabetes mellitus, cochlear implants candidates and recipients, and anatomic asplenia. Immunocompetent persons who live in high-risk environments or social settings (e.g., certain Native American and Alaska Native populations).

HR9: Annual vaccination of residents of chronic care facilities; persons with chronic cardiopulmonary disorders, metabolic diseases (including diabetes mellitus), hemoglobinopathies, immunosuppression, or renal dysfunction; and health care providers for high-risk patients.

HR10: Adolescents and young adults in settings where such individuals congregate (e.g., high schools and colleges), if they have not previously received a second dose.

HR11: Healthy persons aged ≥13 yr without a history of chickenpox or previous immunization. Consider serologic testing for presumed susceptible persons aged ≥13 yr.

HR12: Persons born after 1956 who lack evidence of immunity to measles or mumps (e.g., documented receipt of live vaccine on or after the first birthday, laboratory evidence of immunity, or a history of physician-diagnosed measles or mumps).

HR13: Persons with a family or personal history of skin cancer, a large number of moles, atypical moles, poor tanning ability, or light skin, hair, and eye color.

HR14: Women with prior pregnancy affected by neural tube defect who are planning pregnancy.

HR15: Persons aged <17 yr living in areas with inadequate water fluoridation (<0.6 ppm).

TABLE 5-3 Ages 25-64 Years

Interventions considered and recommended for the Periodic Health Examination	Leading causes of death Malignant neoplasms Heart diseases Motor vehicle and other unintentional injuries Human immunodeficiency virus (HIV) infection Suicide and homicide

INTERVENTIONS FOR THE GENERAL POPULATION

Screening

Blood pressure
Height and weight
Lipid panel (men age 35-64, women age 45-64)
Papanicolaou (Pap) test (women)[1]
Fecal occult blood test[2] and/or colonoscopy (≥50 yr)
Mammogram ± clinical breast exam[3] (women 50-69 yr)
Assess for problem drinking
Rubella serology or vaccination hx[4] (women of childbearing age)

Counseling

Substance use

Tobacco cessation
Avoid alcohol/drug use while driving, swimming, boating, etc.*

Diet and exercise

Limit fat and cholesterol; maintain caloric balance; emphasize grains, fruits, vegetables
Adequate calcium intake (women)
Regular physical activity*

Injury prevention

Lap/shoulder belts
Motorcycle/bicycle/ATV helmets*
Smoke detector*
Safe storage/removal of firearms*

Sexual behavior

STD prevention: avoid high-risk behavior*; condoms/female barrier with spermicide*
Unintended pregnancy: contraception

Dental health

Regular visits to dental care provider*
Floss, brush with fluoride toothpaste daily*

Immunizations

Tetanus-diphtheria (Td) boosters
Rubella[4] (women of childbearing age)
Influenza vaccine for people over age 50†

Chemoprophylaxis

Multivitamin with folic acid (women planning or capable of pregnancy)

Discuss hormone prophylaxis (peri- and postmenopausal women)

INTERVENTIONS FOR HIGH-RISK POPULATIONS

Population	*Potential Interventions (See detailed high-risk definitions)*
High-risk sexual behavior	RPR/VDRL (HR1); screen for gonorrhea (female) (HR2), HIV (HR3), chlamydia (female) (HR4); hepatitis B vaccine (HR5); hepatitis A vaccine (HR6)
Injection or street drug use	RPR/VDRL (HR1); HIV screen (HR3); hepatitis B vaccine (HR5); hepatitis A vaccine (HR6); PPD (HR7); advice to reduce infection risk (HR8)
Low income; TB contacts; immigrants; alcoholics	PPD (HR7)
Native Americans/Alaska Natives	Hepatitis A vaccine (HR6); PPD (HR7); pneumococcal vaccine (HR9)
Travelers to developing countries	Hepatitis B vaccine (HR5); hepatitis A vaccine (HR6)
Certain chronic medical conditions	PPD (HR7); pneumococcal vaccine (HR9); influenza vaccine (HR10)
Blood product recipients	HIV screen (HR3); hepatitis B vaccine (HR5)
Susceptible to measles, mumps, or varicella	MMR (HR11); varicella vaccine (HR12)
Institutionalized persons	Hepatitis A vaccine (HR6); PPD (HR7); pneumococcal vaccine (HR9); influenza vaccine (HR10)
Health care/lab workers	Hepatitis B vaccine (HR5); hepatitis A vaccine (HR6); PPD (HR7); influenza vaccine (HR10)
Family hx of skin cancer; fair skin, eyes, hair	Avoid excess/midday sun, use protective clothing* (HR13)
Previous pregnancy with neural tube defect	Folic acid 4.0 mg (HR14)
Cardiovascular risk factors	Lipid panel (HR 15)

[1]Women who are or have been sexually active and who have a cervix: q ≤3 yr. [2]Annually. [3]Mammogram q1-2 yr, or mammogram q1-2 yr with annual clinical breast examination. [4]Serologic testing, documented vaccination history, and routine vaccination (preferably with MMR) are equally acceptable.
*The ability of clinician counseling to influence this behavior is unproven.
†A live attenuated influenza vaccine (LAIV, Flumist) administered intranasally is available for healthy persons 5 to 49 years of age.

HR1: Persons who exchange sex for money or drugs, and their sex partners; persons with other STDs (including HIV); and sexual contacts of persons with active syphilis. Clinicians should also consider local epidemiology.

HR2: Women who exchange sex for money or drugs, or who have had repeated episodes of gonorrhea. Clinicians should also consider local epidemiology.

HR3: Men who had sex with men after 1975; past or present injection drug use; persons who exchange sex for money or drugs, and their sex partners; injection drug–using, bisexual, or HIV-positive sex partner currently or in the past; blood transfusion during 1978-1985; persons seeking treatment for STDs. Clinicians should also consider local epidemiology and consider HIV screening in general population.

HR4: Sexually active women with multiple risk factors including history of STD; new or multiple sex partners; nonuse or inconsistent use of barrier contraceptives; cervical ectopy. Clinicians should also consider local epidemiology.

HR5: Blood product recipients (including hemodialysis patients), persons with frequent occupational exposure to blood or blood products, men who have sex with men, injection drug users and their sex partners, persons with multiple recent sex partners, persons with other STDs (including HIV), travelers to countries with endemic hepatitis B.

HR6: Persons living in, traveling to, or working in areas where the disease is endemic and where periodic outbreaks occur (e.g., countries with high or intermediate endemicity; certain Alaska Native, Pacific Island, Native American, and religious communities); men who have sex with men; injection or street drug users. Consider for institutionalized persons and workers in these institutions, military personnel, and day-care, hospital, and laboratory workers. Clinicians should also consider local epidemiology.

HR7: HIV positive, close contacts of persons with known or suspected TB, health care workers, persons with medical risk factors associated with TB, immigrants from countries with high TB prevalence, medically underserved low-income populations (including homeless), alcoholics, injection drug users, and residents of long-term care facilities.

HR8: Persons who continue to inject drugs.

HR9: Immunocompetent institutionalized persons aged ≥50 yr and immunocompetent persons with certain medical conditions, including chronic cardiac or pulmonary disease, diabetes mellitus, cochlear implants candidates and recipients, and anatomic asplenia. Immunocompetent persons who live in high-risk environments or social settings (e.g., certain Native American and Alaska Native populations).

HR10: Annual vaccination of residents of chronic care facilities; persons with chronic cardiopulmonary disorders, metabolic diseases (including diabetes mellitus), hemoglobinopathies, immunosuppression or renal dysfunction; and health care providers for high-risk patients.

HR11: Persons born after 1956 who lack evidence of immunity to measles or mumps (e.g., documented receipt of live vaccine on or after the first birthday, laboratory evidence of immunity, or a history of physician-diagnosed measles or mumps).

HR12: Healthy adults without a history of chickenpox or previous immunization. Consider serologic testing for presumed susceptible adults.

HR13: Persons with a family or personal history of skin cancer, a large number of moles, atypical moles, poor tanning ability, or light skin, hair, and eye color.

HR14: Women with previous pregnancy affected by neural tube who are planning pregnancy.

HR15: Clinicians should consider a fasting serum lipid panel on a case-by-base basis.

TABLE 5-4 Ages 65 and Older

Interventions considered and recommended for the Periodic Health Examination	Leading causes of death Heart diseases Malignant neoplasms (lung, colorectal, breast) Cerebrovascular disease Chronic obstructive pulmonary disease Pneumonia and influenza

INTERVENTIONS FOR THE GENERAL POPULATION

Screening
Blood pressure
Height and weight
Fecal occult blood test[1] and/or colonoscopy
Mammogram ± clinical breast exam[2] (women ≤69 yr)
Papanicolaou (Pap) test (women)[3]
Vision screening
Assess for hearing impairment
Assess for problem drinking

Counseling
Substance use
Tobacco cessation
Avoid alcohol/drug use while driving, swimming, boating, etc.*
Diet and exercise
Limit fat and cholesterol; maintain caloric balance; emphasize grains, fruits, vegetables
Adequate calcium intake (women)
Regular physical activity*
Injury prevention
Lap/shoulder belts
Motorcycle and bicycle helmets*
Fall prevention*
Safe storage/removal of firearms*
Smoke detector*
Set hot water heater to <120°-130° F
CPR training for household members
Dental health
Regular visits to dental care provider*
Floss, brush with fluoride toothpaste daily*
Sexual behavior
STD prevention: avoid high-risk sexual behavior*; use condoms

Immunizations
Pneumococcal vaccine
Influenza[1]
Tetanus-diphtheria (Td) boosters

Chemoprophylaxis
Discuss hormone prophylaxis (peri- and postmenopausal women)

INTERVENTIONS FOR HIGH-RISK POPULATIONS

Population	*Potential Interventions (See detailed high-risk definitions)*
Institutionalized persons	PPD (HR1); hepatitis A vaccine (HR2); amantadine/rimantadine (HR4)
Chronic medical conditions; TB contacts; low income; immigrants; alcoholics	PPD (HR1)
Persons ≥75 yr, or ≥70 yr with risk factors for falls	Fall prevention intervention (HR5)
Cardiovascular disease risk factors	Consider lipid screening (HR6)
Family hx of skin cancer; nevi; fair skin, eyes, hair	Avoid excess/midday sun, use protective clothing* (HR7)
Native Americans/Alaska Natives	PPD (HR1); hepatitis A vaccine (HR2)
Travelers to developing countries	Hepatitis A vaccine (HR2); hepatitis B vaccine (HR8)
Blood product recipients	HIV screen (HR3); hepatitis B vaccine (HR8)
High-risk sexual behavior	Hepatitis A vaccine (HR2); HIV screen (HR3); hepatitis B vaccine (HR8); RPR/VDRL (HR9)
Injection or street drug use	PPD (HR1); hepatitis A vaccine (HR2); HIV screen (HR3); hepatitis B vaccine (HR8); RPR/VDRL (HR9); advice to reduce infection risk (HR10)
Health care/lab workers	PPD (HR1); hepatitis A vaccine (HR2); amantadine/rimantadine (HR4); hepatitis B vaccine (HR8)
Persons susceptible to varicella	Varicella vaccine (HR11)
Men aged 65 to 75 who have ever smoked	Ultrasound of abdominal aorta (HR12)

[1]Annually. [2]Mammogram q1-2 yr, or mammogram q1-2 yr with annual clinical breast exam. [3]All women who are or have been sexually active and who have a cervix. Consider discontinuation of testing after age 65 yr if previous regular screening with consistently normal results.
*The ability of clinician counseling to influence this behavior is unproven.

HR1: HIV positive, close contacts of persons with known or suspected TB, health care workers, persons with medical risk factors associated with TB, immigrants from countries with high TB prevalence, medically underserved low-income populations (including homeless), alcoholics, injection drug users, and residents of long-term care facilities.

HR2: Persons living in, traveling to, or working in areas where the disease is endemic and where periodic outbreaks occur (e.g., countries with high or intermediate endemicity; certain Alaska Native, Pacific Island, Native American, and religious communities); men who have sex with men; injection or street drug users. Consider for institutionalized persons and workers in these institutions, and day-care, hospital, and laboratory workers. Clinicians should also consider local epidemiology and consider HIV screening in the general population.

HR3: Men who had sex with men after 1975; past or present injection drug use; persons who exchange sex for money or drugs, and their sex partners; injection drug–using, bisexual, or HIV-positive sex partner currently or in the past; blood transfusion during 1978-1985; persons seeking treatment for STDs. Clinicians should also consider local epidemiology.

HR4: Consider for persons who have not received influenza vaccine or are vaccinated late; when the vaccine may be ineffective due to major antigenic changes in the virus; for unvaccinated persons who provide home care for high-risk persons; to supplement protection provided by vaccine in persons who are expected to have a poor antibody response; and for high-risk persons in whom the vaccine is contraindicated.

HR5: Persons aged 75 years and older; or aged 70-74 with one or more additional risk factors including use of certain psychoactive and cardiac medications (e.g., benzodiazepines, antihypertensives); use of ≥4 prescription medications; impaired cognition, strength, balance, or gait. Intensive individualized home-based multifactorial fall prevention intervention is recommended in settings where adequate resources are available to deliver such services.

HR6: Clinicians should consider fasting lipid panel screening on a case-by-case basis for persons aged 65-75, especially in those with additional risk factors (e.g., smoking, diabetes, or hypertension).

HR7: Persons with a family or personal history of skin cancer, a large number of moles, atypical moles, poor tanning ability, or light skin, hair, and eye color.

HR8: Blood product recipients (including hemodialysis patients), persons with frequent occupational exposure to blood or blood products, men who have sex with men, injection drug users and their sex partners, persons with multiple recent sex partners, persons with other STDs (including HIV), travelers to countries with endemic hepatitis B.

HR9: Persons who exchange sex for money or drugs and their sex partners; persons with other STDs (including HIV); and sexual contacts of persons with active syphilis. Clinicians should also consider local epidemiology.

HR10: Persons who continue to inject drugs.

HR11: Healthy adults without a history of chickenpox or previous immunization. Consider serologic testing for presumed susceptible adults.

HR12: Consider ultrasound of abdominal aorta to screen for abdominal aortic aneurysm in all men aged 65 to 75 who have ever smoked.

TABLE 5-5 Pregnant Women*

Interventions considered and recommended for the Periodic Health Examination

INTERVENTIONS FOR THE GENERAL POPULATION

Screening	Offer amniocentesis (15-18 wk)[1] (age ≥35 yr)
First visit	Offer multiple marker testing[1] (15-18 wk)
Blood pressure	Offer serum α-fetoprotein[1] (16-18 wk)
Hemoglobin/hematocrit	*Counseling*
Hepatitis B surface antigen (HBsAg)	Tobacco cessation; effects of passive smoking
RPR/VDRL	Alcohol/other drug use
Chlamydia screen (<25 yr)	Nutrition, including adequate calcium intake
Rubella serology or vaccination history	Encourage breast-feeding
D(Rh) typing, antibody screen	Lap/shoulder belts
Offer CVS (<13 wk)[1] or amniocentesis (15-18 wk)[1] (age ≥35 yr)	Infant safety car seats
Offer hemoglobinopathy screening	STD prevention: avoid high-risk sexual behavior†; use condoms†
Assess for problem or risk drinking	*Chemoprophylaxis*
Offer HIV screening[2]	Multivitamin with folic acid[3]
Follow-up visits	
Blood pressure	
Urine culture (12-16 wk)	

INTERVENTIONS FOR HIGH-RISK POPULATIONS

Population	*Potential Interventions (See detailed high-risk definitions)*
High-risk sexual behavior	Screen for chlamydia (1st visit) (HR1), gonorrhea (1st visit) (HR2), HIV (1st visit) (HR3); HBsAg (3rd trimester) (HR4); RPR/VDRL (3rd trimester) (HR5)
Blood transfusion 1978-1985	HIV screen (1st visit) (HR3)
Injection drug use	HIV screen (HR3); HBsAg (3rd trimester) (HR4); advice to reduce infection risk (HR6)
Unsensitized D-negative women	D(Rh) antibody testing (24-28 wk) (HR7)
Risk factors for Down syndrome	Offer CVS[1] (1st trimester), amniocentesis[1] (15-18 wk) (HR8)
Prior pregnancy with neural tube defect	Offer amniocentesis[1] (15-18 wk), folic acid 4.0 mg[3] (HR9)

[1]Women with access to counseling and follow-up services, reliable standardized laboratories, skilled high-resolution ultrasound, and, for those receiving serum marker testing, amniocentesis capabilities. [2]Universal screening is recommended for areas (states, counties, or cities) with an increased prevalence of HIV infection among pregnant women. In low-prevalence areas, the choice between universal and tangled screening may depend on other considerations. [3]Beginning at least 1 mo before conception and continuing through the first trimester.

*See Tables 5-2 and 5-3 for other preventive services recommended for women of this age group.

†The ability of clinician counseling to influence this behavior is unproven.

HR1: Women with history of STD or new or multiple sex partners. Clinicians should also consider local epidemiology. Chlamydia screen should be repeated in 3rd trimester if at continued risk.

HR2: Women under age 25 with two or more sex partners in the last year, or whose sex partner has multiple sexual contacts; women who exchange sex for money or drugs; and women with a history of repeated episodes of gonorrhea. Clinicians should also consider local epidemiology. Gonorrhea screen should be repeated in the third trimester if at continued risk.

HR3: In areas where universal screening is not performed due to low prevalence of HIV infection, pregnant women with the following individual risk factors should be screened: past or present injection drug use; women who exchange sex for money or drugs; injection drug–using, bisexual, or HIV-positive sex partner currently or in the past; blood transfusion during 1978-1985; persons seeking treatment for STDs.

HR4: Women who are initially HBsAg negative who are at high risk due to injection drug use, suspected exposure to hepatitis B during pregnancy, multiple sex partners.

HR5: Women who exchange sex for money or drugs, women with other STDs (including HIV), and sexual contacts of persons with active syphilis. Clinicians should also consider local epidemiology.

HR6: Women who continue to inject drugs.

HR7: Unsensitized D-negative women.

HR8: Prior pregnancy affected by Down syndrome, advanced maternal age (≥35 yr), known carriage of chromosome rearrangement.

HR9: Women with previous pregnancy affected by neural tube defect.

Childhood Immunizations

TABLE 5-6, A Recommended Childhood Immunization Schedule—United States

Range of Recommended Ages | Catch-Up Vaccination | Preadolescent Assessment

Vaccine ▼ / Age ▶	Birth	1 mo	2 mos	4 mos	6 mos	12 mos	15 mos	18 mos	24 mos	4-6 yrs	11-12 yrs	13-18 yrs
Hepatitis B[1]	Hep B #1 only if mother HBsAg (−)		Hep B #2			Hep B #3					Hep B series	
Diphtheria, tetanus, pertussis[2]			DTaP	DTaP	DTaP		DTaP			DTaP	Td	
Haemophilus influenzae type b[3]			Hib	Hib	Hib	Hib						
Inactivated polio			IPV	IPV		IPV				IPV		
Measles, mumps, rubella[4]						MMR #1				MMR #2	MMR #2	
Varicella[5]							Varicella				Varicella	
Pneumococcal[6]			PCV	PCV	PCV	PCV			PCV	PCV		
Vaccines below this line are for selected populations												
Hepatitis A[7]											Hepatitis A series	
Influenza[8]								Influenza (yearly)				

This schedule indicates the recommended ages for routine administration of currently licensed childhood vaccines for children through age 18 years. Any dose not given at the recommended age should be given at any subsequent visit when indicated and feasible. ▒ Indicates age groups that warrant special effort to administer those vaccines not previously given. Additional vaccines may be licensed and recommended during the year. Licensed combination vaccines may be used whenever any components of the combination are indicated and the vaccine's other components are not contraindicated. Providers should consult the manufacturers' package inserts for detailed recommendations.

1. Hepatitis B vaccine (Hep B). All infants should receive the first dose of hepatitis B vaccine soon after birth and before hospital discharge; the first dose may also be given by age 2 months if the infant's mother is HBsAg-negative. Only monovalent hepatitis B vaccine can be used for the birth dose. Monovalent or combination vaccine containing Hep B may be used to complete the series. Four doses of vaccine may be administered when a birth dose is given. The second dose should be given at least 4 weeks after the first dose, except for combination vaccines, which cannot be administered before age 6 weeks. The third dose should be given at least 16 weeks after the first dose and at least 8 weeks after the second dose. The last dose in the vaccination series (third or fourth dose) should not be administered before age 24 weeks.

Infants born to HBsAg-positive mothers should receive hepatitis B vaccine and 0.5 ml hepatitis B immune globulin (HBIG) within 12 hours of birth at separate sites. The second dose is recommended at age 1-2 months. The last dose in the vaccination series should not be administered before age 6 months. These infants should be tested for HBsAg and anti-HBs at 9-15 months of age.

Infants born to mothers whose HBsAg status is unknown should receive the first dose of the hepatitis B vaccine series within 12 hours of birth. Maternal blood should be drawn as soon as possible to determine the mother's HBsAg status; if the HBsAg test is positive, the infant should receive HBIG as soon as possible (no later than age 1 week). The second dose is recommended at age 1-2 months. The last dose in the vaccination series should not be administered before age 24 weeks.

2. Diphtheria and tetanus toxoids and acellular pertussis vaccine (DTaP). The fourth dose of DTaP may be administered as early as age 12 months, provided 6 months have elapsed since the third dose and the child is unlikely to return at age 15-18 months. **Tetanus and diphtheria toxoids (Td)** is recommended at age 11-12 years if at least 5 years have elapsed since the last dose of tetanus and diphtheria toxoid-containing vaccine. Subsequent routine Td boosters are recommended every 10 years.

3. Haemophilus influenzae type b (Hib) conjugate vaccine. Three Hib conjugate vaccines are licensed for infant use. If PRP-OMP (PedvaxHIB or ComVax [Merck] is administered at ages 2 and 4 months, a dose at age 6 months is not required. DTaP/Hib combination products should not be used for primary immunization in infants at ages 2, 4, or 6 months, but can be used as boosters following any Hib vaccine. The final dose in the series should be given at age $\geq$12 months.

4. Measles, mumps, and rubella vaccine (MMR). The second dose of MMR is recommended routinely at age 4-6 years but may be administered during any visit, provided at least 4 weeks have elapsed since the first dose and that both doses are administered beginning at or after age 12 months. Those who have not previously received the second dose should complete the schedule by the 11- to 12-year-old visit.

5. Varicella vaccine. Varicella vaccine is recommended at any visit at or after age 12 months for susceptible children (i.e., those who lack a reliable history of chickenpox). Susceptible persons aged $\geq$ 13 years should receive two doses, given at least 4 weeks apart.

6. Pneumococcal vaccine. The heptavalent **pneumococcal conjugate vaccine (PCV)** is recommended for all children age 2-23 months. It is also recommended for certain children age 24-59 months. **Pneumococcal polysaccharide vaccine (PPV)** is recommended in addition to PCV for certain high-risk groups. See MMWR 2000;49(RR-9):1-38.

7. Hepatitis A vaccine. Hepatitis A vaccine is recommended for children and adolescents in selected states and regions, and for certain high-risk groups; consult your local public health authority. Children and adolescents in these states, regions, and high-risk groups who have not been immunized against hepatitis A can begin the hepatitis A vaccination series during any visit. The two doses in the series should be administered at least 6 months apart. See MMWR 1999;48(RR-12):1-37.

8. Influenza vaccine. Influenza vaccine is recommended annually for children age $\geq$ 6 months with certain risk factors (including, but not limited to, asthma, cardiac disease, HIV, and diabetes), healthcare workers, and other persons (including household members) in close contact with persons in groups at high risk and can be administered to all others wishing to obtain immunity. In addition, healthy children aged 6-23 months and close contacts of healthy children aged 0-23 months are recommended to receive influenza vaccine. For healthy persons aged 5-49 years, the intranasally administered live, attenuated influenza vaccine (LAIV) is an acceptable alternative to the IM trivalent inactivated influenza vaccine. Children aged $\leq$ 8 years who are receiving influenza vaccine for the first time should receive two doses (separated by at least 4 weeks for TIV and at least 6 weeks for LAIV).

For additional information about vaccines, including precautions and contraindications for immunization and vaccine shortages, please visit the National Immunization Program Web site at www.cdc.gov/nip or call the National Immunization Hotline at 800-232-2522 (English) or 800-232-0233 (Spanish).

Approved by the Advisory Committee on Immunization Practices (www.cdc.gov/nip/acip), the American Academy of Pediatrics (www.aap.org), and the American Academy of Family Physicians (www.aafp.org).

TABLE 5-6, B Catch-up Schedule for Children 4 Months Through 6 Years of Age

	MINIMUM INTERVAL BETWEEN DOSES			
Dose One (Minimum Age)	**Dose One to Dose Two**	**Dose Two to Dose Three**	**Dose Three to Dose Four**	**Dose Four to Dose Five**
DTaP (6 wk)	4 wk	4 wk	6 mo	6 mo[a]
IPV (6 wk)	4 wk	4 wk	4 wk[b]	
Hep B:[c] (birth)	4 wk	8 wk (and 16 wk after first dose)		
MMR (12 mo)	4 wk[d]			
Varicella (12 mo)				
Hib[e] (6 wk)	4 wk: if first dose given at age <12 mo 8 wk (as final dose): if first dose given at age 12 to 14 mo No further doses needed: if first dose given at age ≥15 mo	4 wk[f]: if current age <12 mo 8 wk (as final dose): if current age ≥12 mo and second dose given at age <15 mo No further doses needed: if previous dose given at age ≥15 mo	8 wk (as final dose): this dose only necessary for children aged 12 mo to 5 yr who received three doses before age 12 mo	
PCV[g] (6 wk)	4 wk: if first dose given at age <12 mo and current age <24 mo 8 wk (as final dose): if first dose given at age ≥12 mo or current age 24 to 59 mo No further doses needed: for healthy children if first dose given at age ≥24 mo	4 wk: if current age <12 months 8 wk (as final dose): if current age ≥12 mo No further doses needed: for healthy children if previous dose given at age ≥24 mo	8 wk (as final dose): this dose only necessary for children aged 12 mo to 5 yr who received three doses before age 12 mo	

Approved by the Advisory Committee on Immunization Practices (www.cdc.gov/nip/acip), the American Academy of Pediatrics (www.aap.org), and the American Academy of Family Physicians (www.aafp.org).

DTaP, Diphtheria and tetanus toxoids and acellular pertussis vaccine; *Hib, Haemophilus influenzae* type b vaccine; *IPV,* inactivated polio vaccine; *MMR,* measles-mumps-rubella vaccine; *PCV,* pneumococcal conjugate vaccine.

[a]DTaP: The fifth dose is not necessary if the fourth dose was given after the fourth birthday.

[b]IPV: For children who received an all-IPV or all-OPV series, a fourth dose is not necessary if third dose was given at age ≥4 years. If OPV and IPV were given as part of a series, a total of four doses should be given, regardless of the child's current age.

[c]Hep B: All children and adolescents who have not been immunized against hepatitis B should begin the hepatitis B vaccination series during any visit. Providers should make special efforts to immunize children who were born in, or whose parents were born in, areas of the world where hepatitis B virus infection is moderately or highly endemic.

[d]MMR: The second dose of MMR is recommended routinely at age 4-6 years, but may be given earlier if desired.

[e]Hib: Vaccine is not generally recommended for children aged ≥5 years.

[f]Hib: If current age <12 months and the first two doses were PRP-OMP (PedvaxHIB or ComVax), the third (and final) dose should be given at age 12-15 months and at least 8 weeks after the second dose.

[g]PCV: Vaccine is not generally recommended for children aged ≥5 years.

NOTE: Report adverse reactions to vaccine through the federal Vaccine Adverse Event Reporting System. For information on reporting reactions following vaccines, please visit www.vaers.org or call the 24-hour national toll-free information line 800-822-7967. Report suspected cases of vaccine-preventable diseases to your state or local health department.

TABLE 5-6, C Catch-up Schedule for Children 7 Through 18 Years of Age

MINIMUM INTERVAL BETWEEN DOSES		
Dose One to Dose Two	**Dose Two to Dose Three**	**Dose Three to Booster Dose**
Td: 4 wk	Td: 6 mo	Td*: 6 mo: if first dose given at age <12 mo and current age <11 yr 5 yr: if first dose given at age ≥12 mo and third dose given at age <7 yr and current age ≥11 yr 10 yr: if third dose given at age ≥7 yr
IPV†: 4 wk	IPV†: 4 wk	IPV†
Hep B: 4 wk	Hep B: 8 wk (and 16 wk after first dose)	
MMR: 4 wk		
Varicella‡: 4 wk		

Approved by the Advisory Committee on Immunization Practices (www.cdc.gov/nip/acip), the American Academy of Pediatrics (www.aap.org), and the American Academy of Family Physicians (www.aafp.org).

IPV, Inactivated polio vaccine; *MMR,* measles-mumps-rubella vaccine; *Td,* tetanus-diphtheria (toxoid) vaccine.

*Td: For children 7 to 10 years of age, the interval between the third and booster dose is determined by the age when the first dose was given. For adolescents 11 to 18 years of age, the interval is determined by the age when the third dose was given.

†IPV: Vaccine is not generally recommended for persons aged ≥18 years.

‡Varicella: Give two-dose series to all susceptible adolescents aged ≥13 years.

NOTE: Report adverse reactions to vaccines through the federal Vaccine Adverse Event Reporting System. For information on reporting reactions following vaccines, please visit www.vaers.org or call the 24-hour national toll-free information line 800-822-7967. Report suspected cases of vaccine-preventable diseases to your state or local health department.

TABLE 5-6, D Minimal Age for Initial Childhood Vaccinations and Minimal Interval Between Vaccine Doses by Type of Vaccine[a]

Vaccine Type	Minimal Age for Dose 1	Minimal Interval Between Doses 1 and 2	Minimal Interval Between Doses 2 and 3	Minimal Interval Between Doses 3 and 4
Hepatitis B	Birth	1 mo	2 mo	[b]
DTaP (DT)[c]	6 wk	4 wk	4 wk	6 mo
Combined DTwP–Hibd	6 wk	1 mo	1 mo	6 mo
Hib (primary series)				
HbOC	6 wk	1 mo	1 mo	[d]
PRP-T	6 wk	1 mo	1 mo	[d]
PRP-OMP	6 wk	1 mo	[d]	
Inactivated poliovirus	6 wk	4 wk	4 wk[e]	[f]
Pneumococcal conjugate	6 wk	1 mo	1 mo	[d]
MMR	12 mo[g]	1 mo		
Varicella	12 mo	4 wk		

Modified from *Epidemiology and prevention of vaccine-preventable diseases,* ed 6, Atlanta, 2000, Centers for Disease Control and Prevention.

DTaP (DT), Diphtheria and tetanus toxoids and acellular pertussis vaccine (diphtheria and tetanus toxoids vaccine); *DTwP–Hib,* diphtheria and tetanus toxoids and whole-cell pertussis vaccine–*Haemophilus influenzae* type b conjugate vaccine; *HbOC,* oligosaccharides conjugated to diphtheria CRM197 toxin protein; *MMR,* measles-mumps-rubella vaccine; *PRP-OMP,* polyribosylribitol phosphate polysaccharide conjugated to a meningococcal outer membrane protein; *PRP-T,* polyribosylribitol phosphate polysaccharide conjugated to tetanus toxoid.

[a]The minimal acceptable ages and intervals may not correspond with the optimal recommended ages and intervals for vaccination. For current recommended routine schedules, see the annual Recommended Childhood Immunization Schedule on the facing page.

[b]This final dose of hepatitis B vaccine is recommended at least 4 months after the first dose and no earlier than 6 months of age.

[c]The total number of doses of diphtheria and tetanus toxoids should not exceed six each before the seventh birthday.

[d]The booster doses of Hib and pneumococcal vaccines that are recommended following the primary vaccination series should be administered no earlier than 12 months of age and at least 2 months after the previous dose.

[e]For unvaccinated adults at increased risk of exposure to poliovirus with less than 3 months but more than 2 months available before protection is needed, 3 doses of IPV should be administered at least 1 month apart.

[f]If the third dose is given after the third birthday, the fourth (booster) dose is not needed.

[g]Although the age for measles vaccination may be as young as 6 months in outbreak areas where cases are occurring in children younger than 1 year, children initially vaccinated before the first birthday should be revaccinated at 12-15 months of age and an additional dose of vaccine should be administered at the time of school entry or according to local policy. Doses of MMR or other measles-containing vaccines should be separated by at least 1 month.

TABLE 5-7 Accelerated Schedule of Routine Childhood Immunizations if Necessary for Travel

Vaccine	Routine Schedule	Accelerated Schedule
Diphtheria, tetanus, pertussis	DTaP: 2, 4, 6, 15-18 mo of age	DTaP: 6 wk of age, with 4 wk between 1st, 2nd, and 3rd doses, and 6 mo between 3rd and 4th doses
	DTaP: 4-6 yr of age (booster)	DTaP: 4 yr of age
	dT every 10 yr	dT every 5 yr if at high risk
Poliomyelitis	IPV: at 2 and 4 mo, 6-18 mo, and 4-6 yr	IPV: 6 wk of age, with 1 mo between 1st and 2nd doses and 6 mo between 2nd and 3rd doses
	No additional boosters unless traveling to an endemic area	A single IPV lifetime booster for adolescents and adults who have completed primary immunization
Measles, mumps. rubella	MMR: 12-15 mo of age, with second dose at age 4-6 yr	Two doses at ≥12 mo of age, 4 wk apart
	Not routinely recommended for children <12 mo of age	May give first measles as early as age 6 mo, with additional two doses ≥12 mo of age
Haemophilus influenzae type b	2, 4, 6 (if HbOC or PRP-T), and 12-15 mo	HbOC and PRP-T: 6 wk of age, with 1 mo between the 1st and 2nd and the 2nd and 3rd doses; booster at ≥12 mo of age (≥2 mo from the 3rd dose)
		PRO-OMP: 6 wk of age, with 1 mo between the 1st and 2nd doses; booster at ≥12 mo of age (≥2 mo from the 3rd dose)
Hepatitis B	Birth, 1-2 mo, 6 mo	0, 1, and 4 mo of age
Varicella	12-18 mo of age	12 mo of age (two doses 1 mo apart for persons age ≥13 yr)
Rotavirus	2, 4, 6 mo of age	6 wk of age, with 2nd and 3rd doses each separated by 3 wk

From Behrman RE: *Nelson textbook of pediatrics,* ed 16, Philadelphia, 2000, WB Saunders.

TABLE 5-8 Recommended Immunization Schedule for HIV-Infected Children*

AGE ▶ VACCINE ▼	BIRTH	1 MO	2 MOS	4 MOS	6 MOS	12 MOS	15 MOS	18 MOS	24 MOS	4-6 YRS	11-12 YRS	14-16 YRS
➧ Recommendations for these vaccines are the same as those for immunocompetent children ➧												
Hepatitis B†	Hep B-1											
		Hep B-2			Hep B-3						Hep B‡	
Diphtheria, Tetanus, Pertussis¶			DTaP or DTP	DTaP or DTP	DTaP or DTP		DTaP or DTP			DTaP or DTP	Td	
Haemophilus influenzae type b**			Hib	Hib	Hib	Hib						
➧ Recommendations for these vaccines differ from those for immunocompetent children ➧												
Polio††			IPV	IPV		IPV				IPV		
Measles, Mumps, Rubella§§						MMR	MMR					
Influenza¶¶					Influenza (a dose is required every year)							
*Streptococcus pneumoniae****									Pneumo-coccal			
Varicella						CONTRAINDICATED in all HIV-infected persons						

Modified from *MMWR Morb Mortal Wkly Rep* 46(RR-12), 1997.

NOTE: Modified from the immunization schedule for immunocompetent children. This schedule also applies to children born to HIV-infected mothers whose HIV infection status has not been determined. Once a child is known not to be HIV-infected, the schedule for immunocompetent children applies. This schedule indicates the recommended age for routine administration of currently licensed childhood vaccines. Some combination vaccines are available and may be used whenever administration of all components of the vaccine is indicated. Providers should consult the manufacturers' package inserts for detailed recommendations.

*Vaccines are listed under the routinely recommended ages. Bars indicate range of acceptable ages for vaccination. Shaded bars indicate catch-up vaccination: at 11-12 yrs of age, hepatitis B vaccine should be administered to children not previously vaccinated.

†***Infants born to HBsAg-negative mothers*** should receive 2.5 μg of Merck vaccine (Recombivax HB) or 10 μg of SmithKline Beecham (SB) vaccine (Engerix-B). The 2nd dose should be administered >1 mo after the 1st dose.

Infants born to HBsAg-positive mothers should receive 0.5 ml of hepatitis B immune globulin (HBIG) within 12 hr of birth and either 5 μg of Merck vaccine (Recombivax HB) or 10 μg of SB vaccine (Engerix-B) at a separate site. The 2nd dose is recommended at 1-2 mo of age and the 3rd dose at 6 mo of age.

Infants born to mothers whose HBsAg status is unknown should receive either 5 μg of Merck vaccine (Recombivax HB) or 10 μg of SB vaccine (Engerix-B) within 12 hr of birth. The 2nd dose of vaccine is recommended at 1 mo of age and the 3rd dose at 6 mo of age. Blood should be drawn at the time of delivery to determine the mother's HBsAg status; if it is positive, the infant should receive HBIG as soon as possible (no later than 1 wk of age). The dosage and timing of subsequent vaccine doses should be based upon the mother's HBsAg status.

§Children and adolescents who have not been vaccinated against hepatitis B in infancy may begin the series during any childhood visit. Those who have not previously received three doses of hepatitis B vaccine should initiate or complete the series during the 11- to 12-year-old visit. The 2nd dose should be administered at least 1 mo after the 1st dose, and the 3rd dose should be administered at least 4 mo after the 1st dose and at least 2 mo after the 2nd dose.

¶DTaP (diphtheria and tetanus toxoids and acellular pertussis vaccine) is the preferred vaccine for all doses in the vaccination series, including completion of the series in children who have received > one dose of whole-cell DTP vaccine. Whole-cell DTP is an acceptable alternative to DTaP. The 4th dose of DTaP may be administered as early as 12 mo of age, provided 6 mo have elapsed since the 3rd dose, and if the child is considered unlikely to return at 15-18 mo of age. Td (tetanus and diphtheria toxoids, adsorbed, for adult use) is recommended at 11-12 yr of age if at least 5 yr have elapsed since the last dose of DTP, DTaP, or DT. Subsequent routine Td boosters are recommended every 10 yr.

**Three *H. influenzae* type b (Hib) conjugate vaccines are licensed for infant use. If PRP-OMP (PedvaxHIB [Merck]) is administered at 2 and 4 mo of age, a dose at 6 mo is not required. After the primary series has been completed, any Hib conjugate vaccine may be used as a booster.

††Inactivated poliovirus vaccine (IPV) is the only polio vaccine recommended for HIV-infected persons and their household contacts. Although the 3rd dose of IPV is generally administered at 12-18 mo, the 3rd dose of IPV has been approved to be administered as early as 6 mo of age. Oral poliovirus vaccine (OPV) should NOT be administered to HIV-infected persons or their household contacts.

§§MMR should not be administered to severely immunocompromised children. HIV-infected children without severe immunosuppression should routinely receive their first dose of MMR as soon as possible upon reaching the 1st birthday. Consideration should be given to administering the second dose of MMR vaccine as soon as 1 mo (i.e., minimum 28 days) after the 1st dose, rather than waiting until school entry.

¶¶Influenza virus vaccine should be administered to all HIV-infected children >6 mo of age each year. Children aged 6 mo-8 yr who are receiving influenza vaccine for the first time should receive two doses of split virus vaccine separated by at least 1 mo. In subsequent years, a single dose of vaccine (split virus for persons ≤12 yr of age, whole or split virus for persons >12 yr of age) should be administered each year. The dose of vaccine for children aged 6-35 mo is 0.25 ml; the dose for children aged ≥3 yr is 0.5 ml.

***Pneumococcal vaccine should be administered to HIV-infected children at 24 mo of age. Revaccination should generally be offered to HIV-infected children vaccinated 3-5 yr (children aged ≤10 yr) or >5 yr (children aged >10 yr) earlier.

TABLE 5-9 Immunizations for Immunocompromised Infants and Children

Vaccine	Routine	HIV/AIDS	Severe Immuno-Suppression*	Asplenia	Renal Failure	Diabetes
Routine Infant Immunizations						
DTaP/DTP (DT/T/Td)	Recommended	Recommended	Recommended	Recommended	Recommended	Recommended
IPV	Recommended	Recommended	Recommended	Use as indicated	Use as indicated	Use as indicated
MMR/MR/M/R	Recommended	Recommended/ considered	Contraindicated	Recommended	Recommended	Recommended
Hib	Recommended	Recommended	Recommended	Recommended	Recommended	Recommended
Hepatitis B	Recommended	Recommended	Recommended	Recommended	Recommended	Recommended
Varicella	Recommended	Contraindicated/ considered§	Contraindicated	Contraindicated	Use if indicated	Use if indicated
Rotavirus	Recommended	Contraindicated	Contraindicated	Contraindicated	Use if indicated	Use if indicated
Other Childhood Immunizations						
Pneumococcus†	Use if indicated	Recommended	Recommended	Recommended	Recommended	Recommended
Influenza‡	Use if indicated	Recommended	Recommended	Recommended	Recommended	Recommended

Modified from Centers for Disease Control and Prevention: Recommendations of the Advisory Committee on Immunization Practices (ACIP): Use of vaccines and immune globulins in persons with altered immunity, *MMWR* 42 (RR-4):15, 1993.

*Severe immunosuppression can result from congenital immunodeficiency, HIV infection, leukemia, lymphoma, aplastic anemia, generalized malignancy, alkylating agents, antimetabolites, radiation, or large amounts of corticosteroids.

†Recommended for persons ≥2 yr of age.

‡Not recommended for infants <6 mo of age.

§Varicella vaccine should be considered for asymptomatic or mildly symptomatic HIV-infected children in CDC class N1 or A1 with age-specific CD4+ T-lymphocyte percentages of ≥25%. Eligible children should receive two doses of varicella vaccine with a 3-month interval between doses.

TABLE 5-10 Contraindications to and Precautions in Routine Childhood Vaccinations

True Contraindications and Precautions	Not Contraindications (Vaccines May Be Administered)
General For All Routine Vaccines (DTaP/DTP, OPV, IPV, MMR, Hib, Hepatitis B, Varicella, Rotavirus)	
Contraindications Anaphylactic reaction to a vaccine contraindicates further doses of that vaccine Anaphylactic reaction to a vaccine constituent contraindicates the use of vaccines containing that substance Moderate or severe illnesses with or without a fever	**Not Contraindications** Mild to moderate local reaction (soreness, redness, swelling), after a dose of an injectable antigen Low-grade or moderate fever after a prior vaccine dose Mild acute illness with or without low-grade fever Current antimicrobial therapy Convalescent phase of illness Prematurity (same dose and indications as for normal full-term infants) Recent exposure to an infectious disease History of penicillin or other nonspecific allergies or fact that relatives have such allergies Pregnancy of mother or household contact Unvaccinated household contact
DTaP/DTP	
Contraindications Encephalopathy within 7 days of administration of previous dose of DTaP/DTP **Precautions*** Temperature of ≥40.5° C (105° F) within 48 hr after vaccination with a prior dose of DTaP/DTP and not attributable to another identifiable cause Collapse or shocklike state (hypotonic-hyporesponsive episode) within 48 hr of receiving a prior dose of DTaP/DTP Convulsions within 3 days of receiving a prior dose of DTaP/DTP† Persistent, inconsolable crying lasting ≥3 hr, within 48 hr of receiving a prior dose of DTaP/DTP Guillain-Barré syndrome within 6 wk after a dose‡	**Not Contraindications** Temperature of <40.5° C (105° F) after a previous dose of DTaP/DTP Family history of convulsions† Family history of sudden infant death syndrome Family history of an adverse event after DTaP/DTP administration
OPV	
Contraindications Infection with HIV or a household contact with HIV infection Known immunodeficiency (hematologic and solid tumors; congenital immunodeficiency; long-term immunosuppressive therapy) Immunodeficient household contact **Precaution*** Pregnancy	**Not Contraindications** Breast-feeding Current antimicrobial therapy Mild diarrhea
IPV	
Contraindications Anaphylactic reaction to neomycin, streptomycin, or polymyxin B **Precaution*** Pregnancy	
MMR	
Contraindications Anaphylactic reaction to neomycin or gelatin Pregnancy Known immunodeficiency (hematologic and solid tumors; congenital immunodeficiency; long-term immunosuppressive therapy; HIV infection with evidence of severe immunosuppression)	**Not Contraindications** Tuberculosis or positive PPD test result Simultaneous tuberculin skin testing§ Breast-feeding Pregnancy of mother or household contact of vaccine recipient Immunodeficient family member or household contact HIV infection without evidence of severe immunosuppression Allergic reaction to eggs‖ Nonanaphylactic reactions to neomycin

Continued

TABLE 5-10 **Contraindications to and Precautions in Routine Childhood Vaccinations—cont'd**

Precautions*	
Recent (within 3-11 mo, depending on product and dose) administration of a blood product or immune globulin preparation	
Thrombocytopenia*	
History of thrombocytopenic purpura¶	
HIB	
Contraindications	
None	
Precautions	
None	
HEPATITIS B	
Contraindications	**Not contraindications**
Anaphylactic reaction to common baker's yeast	Pregnancy
Precautions	
None	
VARICELLA	
Contraindications	**Not Contraindications**
Anaphylactic reaction to neomycin or gelatin	Breast-feeding
Pregnancy	Immunodeficiency in a household contact
HIV infection with evidence of severe immunosuppression	HIV infection in a household contact
Known immunodeficiency (hematologic and solid tumors; congenital immunodeficiency; long-term immunosuppressive therapy)	Pregnancy of mother or household contact of vaccine recipient
Precautions*	
Recent (within 3-11 mo, depending on product and dose) administration of a blood product or immune globulin preparation	
Family history of immunodeficiency**	
ROTAVIRUS	
Contraindications	**Not Contraindications**
Hypersensitivity to aminoglycosides, amphotericin B, or monosodium glutamate	Breast-feeding
Moderate or severe febrile illness	Immunodeficiency in a household contact
Known immunodeficiency (hematologic and solid tumors; congenital immunodeficiency; long-term immunosuppressive therapy)	HIV infection in a household contact
Children of HIV-infected mothers, until tests for HIV infection in the infant are negative at ≥2 mo of age by PCR or culture	
Precautions*	
Acute vomiting or diarrhea	

This information is based on the recommendations of the Advisory Committee on Immunization Practices (ACIP) and of the Committee on Infectious Diseases of the American Academy of Pediatrics (AAP). Some recommendations may vary from those in the manufacturer's product label. For more detailed information, health care providers should consult the published recommendations of the ACIP, AAP, the American Academy of Family Physicians (AAFP), and the manufacturer's product label. These guidelines have been adapted and updated from Centers for Disease Control and Prevention: Update: vaccine side effects, adverse reactions, contraindications, and precautions. Recommendations of the Advisory Committee on Immunization Practices (ACIP), *MMWR* 45(RR-12):1, 1996.

DTaP, Diphtheria and tetanus toxoids plus acellular pertussis vaccine; *DTP,* diphtheria, tetanus, and pertussis vaccine; *IPV,* inactivated poliovirus vaccine; *MMR,* measles, mumps, and rubella vaccine; *OPV,* oral poliovirus vaccine; *PCR,* polymerase chain reaction; *PPd,* purified protein derivative; *VZIG,* varicella-zoster immune globulin.

*The events or conditions listed as precautions, although not contraindications, should be carefully reviewed. The benefits and risks of administering a specific vaccine to an individual under the circumstances should be considered. If the risks are believed to outweigh the benefits, the vaccine should be withheld; if the benefits are believed to outweigh the risks (e.g., during an outbreak or foreign travel), the vaccine should be administered. Whether and when to administer DTaP/DTP to children with proven or suspected underlying neurologic disorders should be decided individually. Avoiding administration of certain vaccines to pregnant women is prudent on theoretic grounds. If immediate protection against poliomyelitis is needed, either OPV or IPV is recommended.

†Acetaminophen administered before DTaP or DTP vaccination and thereafter every 4 hr for 24 hr should be considered for children with a personal or family history of convulsions in siblings or parents.

‡The decision to give additional doses of DTaP or DTP should be based on consideration of the benefit of further vaccination vs the risk of recurrence of Guillain-Barré syndrome. For example, completion of the primary vaccination series in children is justified.

§Measles vaccination may temporarily suppress tuberculin skin test reactivity. MMR vaccine may be administered after or on the same day as Mantoux tuberculin skin testing. If MMR has been given recently, the tuberculin test should be postponed until 4-6 wk after administration of MMR.

‖Recent data suggest that most anaphylactic reactions to measles- and mumps-containing vaccines are not associated with hypersensitivity to egg antigens but to other components of the vaccines, such as gelatin. Because the risk of anaphylactic reactions after administration of measles- or mumps-containing vaccines by persons who are allergic to eggs is extremely low, and skin testing with vaccine is not predictive of allergic reactions to these vaccines, skin testing and desensitization are no longer required before administration of MMR vaccine to persons who are allergic to eggs.

¶The decision to vaccinate should be based on consideration of the benefits of immunity to measles, mumps, and rubella vs the risk of recurrence or exacerbation of thrombocytopenia after vaccination, or from natural infections of measles or rubella. In most instances, the benefits of vaccination are much greater than the potential risks and justify giving MMR, particularly in view of the even greater risk of thrombocytopenia after measles or rubella disease. However, if a prior episode of thrombocytopenia occurred in close temporal proximity to vaccination, avoiding a subsequent dose may be prudent.

**Varicella vaccine should not be administered to a member of a household with a family history of immunodeficiency until the immune status of the recipient and other children in the family is documented.

TABLE 5-11 **Vaccines for Children Who Travel**

Vaccine	Description	Dosing	Comments/ Contraindications	LENGTH OF TRAVEL Brief (<2 wk)	Intermediate (2 wk to 3 mo)	Long Term Residential (>3 mo)
Routine						
Polio*	OPV: live attenuated, oral IPV: inactivated, injection	IPV at 2, 4 mo; OPV at 12-18 mo, 4-6 yr; may accelerate to q 4-8 wk × 3 doses	IPV at 2 and 4 mo decreases risk of polio in undiagnosed immunocompromised infants; AAP recommendation may change to IPV only	+	+	+
Diphtheria-tetanus-pertussis*	DPT: D, T toxoid + whole cell P DtaP: DT toxoid + acellular P Td: booster	DtaP recommended at 2, 4, 6, 15-18 mo and 4-6 yr; Td booster at age 12, then q10yr	May accelerate to dose every 4 wk × 3 doses if necessary; decreased incidence of vaccine-related reactions with DTaP	+	+	+
Haemophilus B*	Hib polysaccharide: protein conjugate	0.5 ml IM at 2, 4, 6, 12-15 mo	Typically given as combination with DTaP	+	+	+
Hepatitis B	Recombivax HB: inactivated viral antigen Engerix-B: same	3 doses: 0, 1, 6 mo <11 yr: 0.25 ml IM >11 yr: 0.5 ml IM 3 doses 0, 1, 6 mo <11 yr: 0.5 ml IM >11 yr: 1.0 ml IM	Some protection after just 1 or 2 doses; may accelerate Engerix-B to 0, 1, 2, 12 mo	+	+	+
Measles-mumps-rubella†	Live attenuated viruses	0.25 ml IM at 12-15 mo, then booster at 4-6 or 11-12 yr	May accelerate to 6-12 mo, repeat 1 mo later, then per usual schedule; give at least 2-3 wk before IgG	+	+	+
Varicella	Live attenuated virus	12 mo-12 yr: 0.5 ml SC as single dose >12 yr: 2 doses 4-8 wk apart	Give at least 2-3 wk before IgG; may be given with MMR using different sites; avoid if immunocompromised	+	+	+
Routine for Travel						
Hepatitis A	Havrix: inactive virus (720ELU) Vaqta (24U)	>2 yr: 2 × 0.5 ml doses 6-12 mo apart	Preferred for hepatitis A protection if over age 2 yr Protects in 4 wk after dose 1	+	+	+
Immune globulin (IgG)	Antibodies	<2 yr: 0.02 ml/kg for <3 mo of travel; 0.06 ml/kg q5mo and 3 days before travel	Hepatitis A protection for those under age 2 yr; beware of timing with live virus vaccines			

Consult Centers for Disease Control and Prevention (CDC) for current and specific vaccine recommendations for destination country. From Auerbach PS: *Wilderness medicine,* ed 4, St Louis, 2001, Mosby.

+, Recommended; ±, consider; *AAP,* American Academy of Pediatrics; *DTaP,* diphtheria and tetanus toxoids plus acellular pertussis vaccine; *IM,* intramuscularly; *q,* every; *SC,* subcutaneously.

TABLE 5-11 **Vaccines for Children Who Travel—cont'd**

Vaccine	Description	Dosing	Comments/ Contraindications	LENGTH OF TRAVEL Brief (<2 wk)	Intermediate (2 wk to 3 mo)	Long Term Residential (>3 mo)
Required or Geographically Indicated						
Yellow fever	Live virus	>9 mo: 0.5 ml SC at least 10 days before departure; booster q10yr	Required for parts of sub-Saharan Africa, of tropical South America; may give at 4-9 mo if traveling to epidemic area; under 9 mo: risk of vaccine-related encephalitis	+	+	+
Typhoid	Heat inactivated	6 mo-2 yr: 2 × 0.25 ml SC 4 wk apart, booster q3yr	Fever, pain with heat killed: significantly fewer side effects with ViCPS and Ty21a; important for Latin America, Asia, Africa; vaccine not a substitute for eating and drinking cleanly	±	+	+
	ViCPS: polysaccharide	2-6 yr: 0.5 ml IM × 1 booster q2yr				
	Ty21a: oral live attenuated	>6 yr: 1 capsule q 2 days × 4; booster q 5 yr				
Meningococcal	Serogroups A, C, Y, W-135: polysaccharide	>2 years: 0.5 ml SC; booster in 1 yr if 1st dose after age 4 yr, otherwise in 5 yr	Use for central Africa, Saudi Arabia for the Hajj, Nepal, and epidemic areas; minimal efficacy under age 2 yr	±	±	±
Japanese encephalitis	Inactivated virus	1-3 yr: 0.5 ml SC at 0, 7, 14-30 days >3 years: 1.0 ml SC at 0, 7, 14-30 days Last dose >10 days before travel	Indicated for parts of India and rural Asia if stay >1 mo; no safety data for under age 1 yr; high rate of hypersensitivity	±	±	+
Cholera	Inactivated bacteria	>6 mo: 0.2 ml SC	Vaccine of questionable efficacy; not recommended by CDC or WHO; do not use under 6 mo			
Lyme disease	LYMErix: antigenic protein*	>15 yr: 0.5 ml IM at 0, 1, 12 mo	Indicated for frequent, prolonged exposure to Lyme-endemic area, not brief exposures			
Extended Stay						
Rabies	HDCV: human diploid cell	1 ml IM in deltoid muscle at 0, 7, 21-28 days if >1 mo stay	If exposed and immunized: give vaccine, 1 ml IM at 0, 3 days If exposed and unimmunized: give rabies Ig (RIG), 20 IU/kg half at site and half IM; give vaccine, 1 ml IM at 0, 3, 7, 14, 28 days	±	+	+

*Not readily available.

TABLE 5-12 Schedule for Catch-Up Administration of PCV (Prevnar) in Unvaccinated Infants and Children

Age at First Dose	Primary Series	Booster Dose
2-6 mo	Three doses, 2 mo apart*	One dose at 12-15 mo†
7-11 mo	Two doses, 2 mo apart*	One dose at 12-15 mo†
12-23 mo	Two doses, 2 mo apart	—
24-59 mo		
Healthy children	One dose	—
Children with sickle cell disease, asplenia, HIV infection, chronic illness, or immunocompromising condition‡	Two doses, 2 mo apart	—

Modified from *MMWR Morb Mortal Wkly Rep* 49(RR-9):24, 2000.
HIV, Human immunodeficiency virus; *PCV,* pneumococcal conjugate vaccine.
*For the primary series in children vaccinated before 12 mo of age, the minimum interval between doses is 4 wk.
†The booster dose should be administered at least 8 wk after the primary series is completed.
‡Recommendations do not include children who have undergone bone marrow transplant.

TABLE 5-13 Administration Schedule for PCV (Prevnar) When a Lapse in Immunization Has Occurred

Age at Presentation (months)	Previous PCV Immunization History	Recommended Regimen
7 to 11	One dose	One dose at 7 to 11 mo followed by a booster at 12 to 15 mo with a minimal interval of 2 mo
	Two doses	One dose at 7 to 11 mo followed by a booster at 12 to 15 mo with a minimal interval of 2 mo
12 to 23	One dose before 12 mo	Two doses at least 2 mo apart
	Two doses before 12 mo	One dose at least 2 mo following the most recent dose
24 to 59	Any incomplete schedule	One dose*

Modified from *MMWR Morb Mortal Wkly Rep* 49(RR-9):24, 2000.
PCV, Pneumococcal conjugate vaccine.
*Children with certain chronic illnesses or immunosuppressing conditions should receive two doses at least 2 mo apart.

TABLE 5-14 Using PPV in High-Risk Children 2 Years and Older Who Have Been Immunized with PCV (Prevnar)

Health Status	PPV Schedule	Revaccinate With PPV
Healthy	None	No
Sickle cell disease, anatomic or functional asplenia, HIV-infection, immunocompromising conditions	1 dose PPV given at least 2 mo after PCV	Yes*
Chronic illness	1 dose PPV given at least 2 mo after PCV	No

Modified from *MMWR Morb Mortal Wkly Rep* 49(RR-9):24, 2000.
HIV, Human immunodeficiency virus; *PCV,* pneumococcal conjugate vaccine; *PPV,* pneumococcal polysaccharide vaccine.
* If patient is older than 10 yr, a single revaccination should be given at least 5 yr after previous dose; if patient is 10 yr or younger, revaccinate 3 to 5 yr after previous dose. Regardless of when administered, a second dose of PPV should not be given less than 3 yr following the previous PPV dose.

TABLE 5-15, A Recommended Adult Immunization Schedule—United States

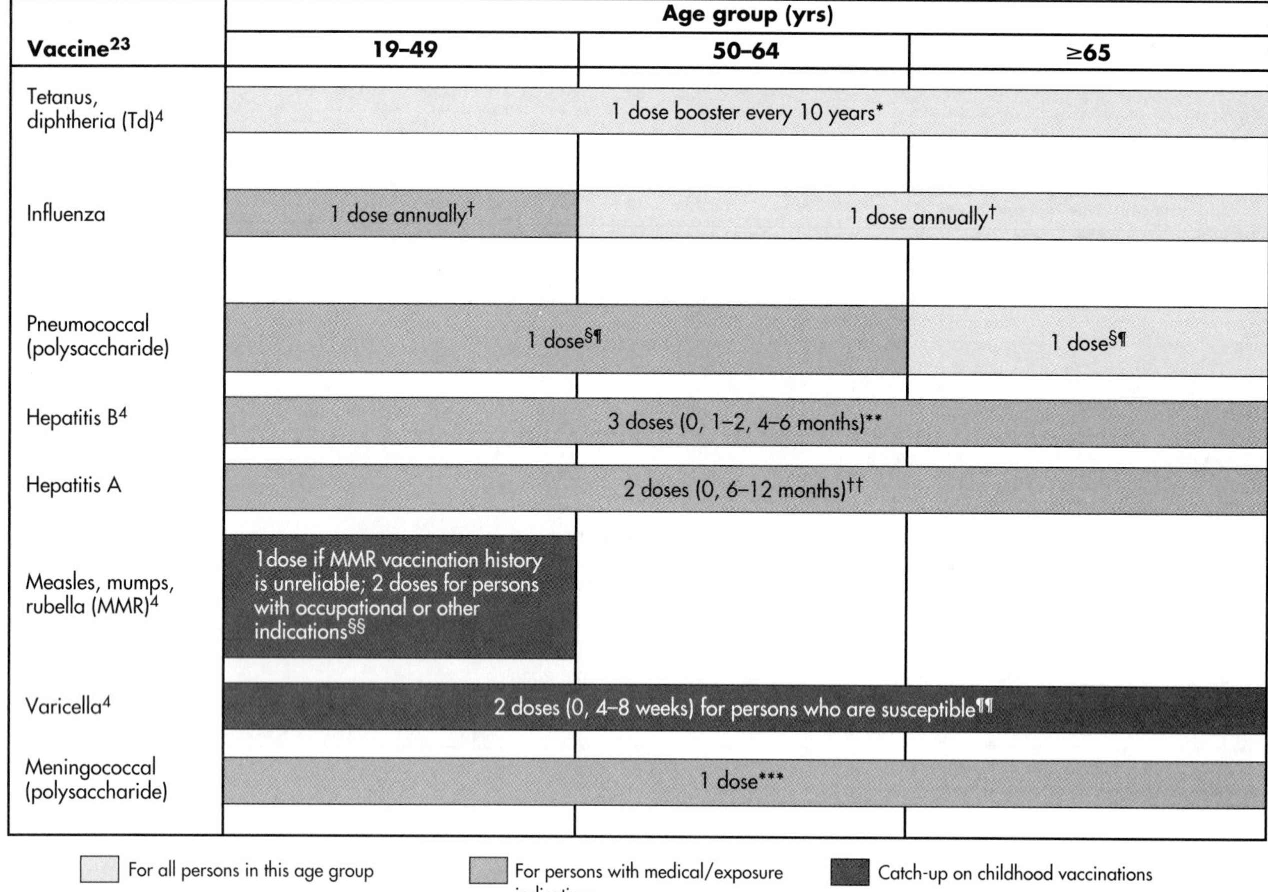

Vaccine[2,3]	Age group (yrs) 19–49	50–64	≥65
Tetanus, diphtheria (Td)[4]	1 dose booster every 10 years*		
Influenza	1 dose annually†	1 dose annually†	
Pneumococcal (polysaccharide)	1 dose§¶		1 dose§¶
Hepatitis B[4]	3 doses (0, 1–2, 4–6 months)**		
Hepatitis A	2 doses (0, 6–12 months)††		
Measles, mumps, rubella (MMR)[4]	1 dose if MMR vaccination history is unreliable; 2 doses for persons with occupational or other indications§§		
Varicella[4]	2 doses (0, 4–8 weeks) for persons who are susceptible¶¶		
Meningococcal (polysaccharide)	1 dose***		

For all persons in this age group — For persons with medical/exposure indications — Catch-up on childhood vaccinations

[1]Approved by the Advisory Committee on Immunization Practices and accepted by the American College of Obstetricians and Gynecologists (ACOG) and the American Academy of Family Physicians (AAFP).

[2]This schedule indicates recommended age groups for routine administration of currently licensed vaccines for persons aged ≥19 years. Licensed combination vaccine may be used whenever any components of the combination are indicated and the vaccine's other components are not contraindicated. Health-care providers should consult manufacturers' package inserts for detailed recommendations.

[3]Additional information regarding these vaccines and contraindications for vaccination is available from the National Immunization Hotline (telephone, 800-232-2522 [English] or 800-232-0233 [Spanish] or at http://www.cdc.gov/nip.

[4]Covered by the Vaccine Injury Compensation Program. Information on how to file a claim is available at http://www.hrsa.gov/osp/vicp or by telephone, 800-338-2382. Vaccine injury claims are filed with U.S. Court of Federal Claims, 717 Madison Place, N.W., Washington, D.C. 20005; telephone, 202-219-9657.

***Tetanus and diphtheria (Td).** Adults, including pregnant women with uncertain histories of a complete primary vaccination series, should receive a primary series of Td. A primary series for adults is 3 doses: the first 2 doses administered at least 4 weeks apart and the third dose, 6–12 months after the second. Administer 1 dose if the person received the primary series and the last vaccination was ≥10 years previously. In addition, information is available regarding administration of Td as prophylaxis in wound management (*1*). The American College of Physicians Task Force on Adult Immunization supports a second option for Td use in adults: a single Td booster at age 50 years for persons who have completed the full pediatric series, including the teenage/young adult booster.

†**Influenza vaccination.** *Medical indications:* chronic disorders of the cardiovascular or pulmonary systems including asthma; chronic metabolic diseases including diabetes mellitus, renal dysfunction, hemoglobinopathies, or immunosuppression (including immunosuppression caused by medications or by human immunodeficiency virus [HIV]) requiring medical follow-up or hospitalization during the preceding year; women who will be in the second or third trimester of pregnancy during the influenza season. *Occupational indications:* health-care workers (HCWs). *Other indications:* residents of nursing homes and other long-term-care facilities; persons likely to transmit influenza to persons at high risk (e.g., in-home caregivers to persons with medical indications; household contact and out-of-home caregivers for children aged ≤23 months, or children with asthma or other indicator conditions for influenza vaccination; household members and caregivers for elderly and adults with high-risk conditions); and anyone who wishes to be vaccinated. For healthy persons age 5-49 years without high-risk conditions, either the inactivated vaccine or the intranasally administered influenza vaccine (FluMist™) may be administered (*2,3*).

§**Pneumococcal polysaccharide vaccination.** *Medical indications:* chronic disorders of the pulmonary system, excluding asthma, cardiovascular diseases, diabetes mellitus, chronic liver diseases (including liver disease as a result of alcohol abuse [e.g., cirrhosis]), chronic renal failure or nephrotic syndrome, functional or anatomic asplenia (e.g., sickle cell disease or splenectomy), immunosuppressive conditions (e.g., congenital immunodeficiency, HIV infection, leukemia, lymphoma, multiple myeloma, Hodgkins disease, generalized malignancy, and organ or bone marrow transplantation), chemotherapy with alkylating agents, antimetabolites, or long-term systemic corticosteroids. *Geographic/other indications:* Alaska Natives and certain American Indian populations. *Other indications:* residents of nursing homes and other long-term-care facilities (*4*).

¶**Revaccination with pneumococcal polysaccharide vaccine.** One-time revaccination after 5 years for persons with chronic renal failure or nephrotic syndrome, functional or anatomic asplenia (e.g., sickle cell disease or splenectomy), immunosuppressive conditions (e.g., congenital immunodeficiency, HIV infection, leukemia, lymphoma, multiple myeloma, Hodgkins disease, generalized malignancy, and organ or bone marrow transplantation), chemotherapy with alkylating agents, antimetabolites, or long-term systemic corticosteroids. For persons aged ≥65 years, one-time revaccination if they were vaccinated ≥5 years previously and were aged <65 years at the time of primary vaccination (*4*).

****Hepatitis B (HepB) vaccine.** *Medical indications:* hemodialysis patients, patients who receive clotting-factor concentrates. *Occupational indications:* HCWs and public-safety workers who have exposure to blood in the workplace, persons in training in schools of medicine, dentistry, nursing, laboratory technology, and other allied health professions. *Behavioral indications:* injection-drug users, persons with more than one sex partner during the previous 6 months, persons with a recently acquired sexually transmitted disease (STD), all clients in STD clinics, men who have sex with men (MSM). *Other indications:* household contacts and sex partners of persons with chronic Hepatitis B virus (HBV) infection, clients and staff of institutions for the developmentally disabled, international travelers to countries with high or intermediate prevalence of chronic HBV infection for >6 months, and inmates of correctional facilities (*5*).

††**Hepatitis A (HepA) vaccine.** For the combined HepA-HepB vaccine, use 3 doses (at 0, 1, and 6 months). *Medical indications:* persons with clotting-factor disorders or chronic liver disease. *Behavioral indications:* MSM, users of injecting and noninjecting illegal drugs. *Occupational indications:* persons working with Hepatitis A virus (HAV)-infected primates or with HAV in a research laboratory setting. *Other indications:* persons traveling to or working in countries that have high or intermediate endemicity of HAV (*6*).

§§**Measles, Mumps, Rubella (MMR) vaccination.** *Measles component:* adults born before 1957 might be considered immune to measles. Adults born in or after 1957 should receive at least 1 dose of MMR unless they have a medical contraindication, documentation of at least 1 dose, or other acceptable evidence of immunity. A second dose of MMR is recommended for adults who 1) were exposed recently to measles or were in an outbreak setting, 2) were previously vaccinated with killed measles vaccine, 3) were vaccinated with an unknown vaccine during 1963–1967, 4) are students in postsecondary educational institutions, 5) work in health-care facilities, or 6) plan to travel internationally. *Mumps component:* 1 dose of MMR should be adequate for protection. *Rubella component:* Administer 1 dose of MMR to women whose rubella vaccination history is unreliable and counsel women to avoid becoming pregnant for 4 weeks after vaccination. For women of childbearing age, regardless of birth year, routinely determine rubella immunity and counsel women regarding congenital rubella syndrome. Do not vaccinate pregnant women or those planning to become pregnant in the next 4 weeks. If pregnant and susceptible, vaccinate as early in the postpartum period as possible (*7*).

¶¶**Varicella vaccination.** Recommended for all persons who do not have reliable clinical history of varicella infection, or serologic evidence of varicella zoster virus (VZV) infection who might be at high risk for exposure or transmission. This includes HCWs and family contacts of immunocompromised persons, those who live or work in environments where transmission is likely (e.g., teachers of young children, day-care employees, and residents and staff members in institutional settings), persons who live or work in environments where VZV transmission can occur (e.g., college students, inmates and staff members of correctional institutions, and military personnel) adolescents and adults living in households with children, women who are not pregnant but who might become pregnant in the future, and international travelers who are not immune to infection. Do not vaccinate pregnant women or those planning to become pregnant in the next 4 weeks. If a woman is pregnant and susceptible, vaccinate as early in the postpartum period as possible. Approximately 95% of U.S.-born adults are immune to VZV (*8,9*).

*****Meningococcal vaccine (quadrivalent polysaccharide for serogroups A, C, Y, and W-135).** Consider vaccination for persons with medical indications: adults with terminal complement component deficiencies or with anatomic or functional asplenia. Other indications: travelers to countries where meningitis is hyperendemic or epidemic (e.g., the "meningitis belt" of sub-Saharan Africa, Mecca, or Saudi Arabia). Revaccination at 3–5 years may be indicated for persons at high risk for infection (e.g., persons residing in areas in which disease is epidemic). Counsel college freshmen, particularly those who live in dormitories, regarding meningococcal disease and the vaccine so that they can make an educated decision about receiving the vaccination (*10*). The American Academy of Family Physicians recommends that colleges provide education on meningococcal infection and vaccination and offer it to those who are interested. Physicians need not initiate discussion of the meningococcal quadrivalent polysaccharide vaccine as part of routine medical care.

References

1. CDC. Diphtheria, tetanus, and pertussis: recommendations for vaccine use and other preventive measures. Recommendations of the Immunization Practices Advisory Committee (ACIP). MMWR 1991;40(No. RR-10).
2. CDC. Prevention and control of influenza: recommendations of the Advisory Committee for Immunization Practices. MMWR 2003;52(No. RR-8).
3. CDC. Using live, attenuated influenza vaccine for prevention and control of influenza: supplemental recommendations of the Advisory Committee on Immunization Practices (ACIP). MMWR 2003;52(No. RR-13).
4. CDC. Prevention of pneumococcal disease: recommendations of the Advisory Committee on Immunization Practices (ACIP). MMWR 1997;47(No. RR-8).
5. CDC. Hepatitis B virus: a comprehensive strategy for eliminating transmission in the United States through universal childhood vaccination. Recommendations of the Immunization Practices Advisory Committee (ACIP). MMWR 1991;40(No. RR-13).
6. CDC. Prevention of hepatitis A through active or passive immunization: recommendations of the Advisory Committee on Immunization Practices (ACIP). MMWR 1999;48(No. RR-12).
7. CDC. Measles, mumps, and rubella—vaccine use and strategies for elimination of measles, rubella, and congenital rubella syndrome and control of mumps: recommendations of the Advisory Committee on Immunization Practices (ACIP) MMWR 1998;47(No. RR-8).
8. CDC. Prevention of varicella: recommendations of the Advisory Committee on Immunization Practices (ACIP). MMWR 1996;45(No. RR-11).
9. CDC. Prevention of varicella: updated recommendations of the Advisory Committee on Immunization Practices (ACIP). MMWR 1999;48(No. RR-6).
10. CDC. Prevention and control of meningococcal disease and meningococcal disease and college students: recommendations of the Advisory Committee on Immunization Practices (ACIP). MMWR 2000;49(No. RR-7).
11. *MMRW Morb Mortal Wkly Rep* 52, 2003.

TABLE 5-15, B Recommended Adult Immunization Schedule for Adults with Medical Conditions—United States

	Vaccine						
Medical condition	**Tetanus-diptheria (Td)***	**Influenza†**	**Pneumococcal (polysaccharide)§¶**	**Hepatitis B****	**Hepatitis A††**	**Measles, mumps, rubella (MMR)§§**	**Varicella¶¶**
Pregnancy		A					
Diabetes, heart disease, chronic pulmonary disease, and chronic liver disease, including chronic alcoholism		B	C		D		
Congenital immunodeficiency, leukemia, lymphoma, generalized malignancy, therapy with alkylating agents, antimetabolites, radiation, or large amounts of corticosteroids			E				F
Renal failure/end-stage renal disease and patients receiving hemodialysis or clotting factor concentrates			E	G			
Asplenia, including elective splenectomy and terminal complement-component deficiencies		H	E,I,J				
Human immunodeficiency virus (HIV) infection			E,K			L	

For all persons in this group — For persons with medical/exposure indications — Catch-up on childhood vaccinations — Contraindicated

From *MMWR Morb Mortal Wkly Rep* 52, 2003.

A. For women without chronic diseases/conditions, vaccinate if pregnancy will be at second or third trimester during influenza season. For women with chronic diseases/conditions, vaccinate at any time during the pregnancy.

B. Although chronic liver disease and alcoholism are not indicator conditions for influenza vaccination, administer 1 dose annually if the patient is aged >50 years, has other indications for influenza vaccine, or requests vaccination.

C. Asthma is an indicator condition for influenza but not for pneumococcal vaccination.

D. For all persons with chronic liver disease.

E. For persons aged <65 years, revaccinate once after ≥5 years have elapsed since initial vaccination.

F. Persons with impaired humoral but not cellular immunity may be vaccinated (*9*).

G. For hemodialysis patients use special formulation of vaccine (40 μg/mL) or two 1.0 mL 20 μg doses administered at one site. Vaccinate early in the course of renal disease. Assess antibody titers to hepatitis B surface antigen (anti-HBs) levels annually. Administer additional doses if anti-HBs levels decline to ≤10 mIU/mL.

H. No data have been reported specifically on risk for severe or complicated influenza infections among persons with asplenia. However, influenza is a risk factor for secondary bacterial infections that might cause severe disease in asplenics.

I. Administer meningococcal vaccine and consider *Haemophilus influenzae* type b vaccine.

J. In the event of elective splenectomy, vaccinate >2 weeks before surgery.

K. Vaccinate as close to diagnosis as possible when CD4 cell counts are highest.

L. Withhold MMR or other measles-containing vaccines from HIV-infected persons with evidence of severe immunosuppression.

Please refer to Table 15-5A for footnote explanations.

TABLE 5-16 **Immunizations During Pregnancy**

Immuno-biologic Agent	Risk From Disease to Pregnant Woman	Risk From Disease to Fetus or Neonate	Type of Immunizing Agent	Risk from Immunizing Agent to Fetus	Indications for Immunization During Pregnancy	Dose Schedule	Comments
Live Virus Vaccines							
Measles	Significant morbidity, low mortality; not altered by pregnancy	Significant increase in abortion rate; may cause malformations	Live attenuated virus vaccine	None confirmed	Contraindicated (see immune globulins)	Single dose SC, preferably as measles-mumps-rubella*	Vaccination of susceptible women should be part of postpartum care
Mumps	Low morbidity and mortality; not altered by pregnancy	Probable increased rate of abortion in first trimester	Live attenuated virus vaccine	None confirmed	Contraindicated	Single dose SC, preferably as measles-mumps-rubella	Vaccination of susceptible women should be part of postpartum care
Poliomyelitis	No increased incidence in pregnancy, but may be more severe if it does occur	Anoxic fetal damage reported; 50% mortality in neonatal disease	Live attenuated virus (oral polio vaccine [OPV]) and enhanced, potency inactivated virus (e-IPV) vaccine†	None confirmed	Not routinely recommended for women in U.S., except persons at increased risk of exposure	*Primary:* Two doses of e-IPV SC at 4-8 wk intervals and a third dose 6-12 mo after the second dose *Immediate protection:* One dose OPV orally (in out-break setting)	Vaccine indicated for susceptible pregnant women traveling in endemic areas or in other high-risk situations
Rubella	Low morbidity and mortality; not altered by pregnancy	High rate of abortion and congenital rubella syndrome	Live attenuated virus vaccine	None confirmed	Contraindicated	Single dose SC, preferably as measles-mumps-rubella	Teratogenicity of vaccine is theoretic, not confirmed to date; vaccination of susceptible women should be part of postpartum care
Yellow fever	Significant morbidity and mortality; not altered by pregnancy	Unknown	Live attenuated virus vaccine	Unknown	Contraindicated except if exposure is unavoidable	Single dose SC	Postponement of travel preferable to vaccination, if possible

Continued

TABLE 5-16 **Immunizations During Pregnancy—cont'd**

Immunobiologic Agent	Risk From Disease to Pregnant Woman	Risk From Disease to Fetus or Neonate	Type of Immunizing Agent	Risk from Immunizing Agent to Fetus	Indications for Immunization During Pregnancy	Dose Schedule	Comments
Inactivated Virus Vaccines							
Influenza	Possible increase in morbidity and mortality during epidemic of new antigenic strain	Possible increased abortion rate; no malformations confirmed	Inactivated virus vaccine	None confirmed	Women with serious underlying diseases; public health authorities to be consulted for current recommendation	One dose IM every year	
Rabies	Near 100% fatality; not altered by pregnancy	Determined by maternal disease	Killed virus vaccine	Unknown	Indications for prophylaxis not altered by pregnancy; each case considered individually	Public health authorities to be consulted for indications, dosage, and route of administration	
Hepatitis B	Possible increased severity during third trimester	Possible increase in abortion rate and prematurity; neonatal hepatitis can occur; high risk of newborn carrier state	Recombinant vaccine	None reported	Preexposure and postexposure for women at risk of infection	Three- or four-dose series IM	Used with hepatitis B immune globulin for some exposures; exposed newborn needs vaccination as soon as possible
Inactivated Bacterial Vaccines							
Cholera	Significant morbidity and mortality; more severe during third trimester	Increased risk of fetal death during third-trimester maternal illness	Killed bacterial vaccine	None confirmed	Indications not altered by pregnancy; vaccination recommended only in unusual outbreak situations	Single dose SC or IM, depending on manufacturer's recommendations when indicated	
Plague	Significant morbidity and mortality; not altered by pregnancy	Determined by maternal disease	Killed bacterial vaccine	None reported	Selective vaccination of exposed persons	Public health authorities to be consulted for indications, dosage, and route of administration	
Pneumococcus	No increased risk during pregnancy; no increase in severity of disease	Unknown	Polyvalent polysaccharide vaccine	No data available on use during pregnancy	Indications not altered by pregnancy; vaccine used only for high-risk individuals	In adults, one SC or IM dose only; consider repeat dose in 6 yr for high-risk individuals	

Typhoid	Significant morbidity and mortality; not altered by pregnancy	Unknown	Killed or live attenuated oral bacterial vaccine	None confirmed	Not recommended routinely except for close, continued exposure or travel to endemic areas	*Killed; Primary:* Two injections SC at least 4 wk apart *Booster:* Single dose SC or ID (depending on type of product used) every 3 yr *Oral; Primary:* Four doses on alternate days *Booster:* Schedule not yet determined	
Toxoids							
Tetanus, diphtheria	Severe morbidity; tetanus mortality 30%, diphtheria mortality 10%; unaltered by pregnancy	Neonatal tetanus mortality 60%	Combined tetanus-diphtheria toxoids preferred: adult tetanus-diphtheria formulation	None confirmed	Lack of primary series, or no booster within past 10 yr	*Primary:* Two doses IM at 1-2 mo interval with a third dose 6-12 mo after the second *Booster:* Single dose IM every 10 yr, after completion of primary series	Updating of immune status should be part of antepartum care
Specific Immune Globulins							
Hepatitis B	Possible increased severity during third trimester	Possible increase in abortion rate and prematurity; neonatal hepatitis can occur; high risk of carriage in newborn	Hepatitis B immune globulin	None reported	Postexposure prophylaxis	Depends on exposure; consult Immunization Practices Advisory Committee recommendations	Usually given with HBV vaccine; exposed newborn needs immediate postexposure prophylaxis

Continued

TABLE 5-16 **Immunizations During Pregnancy—cont'd**

Immunobiologic Agent	Risk From Disease to Pregnant Woman	Risk From Disease to Fetus or Neonate	Type of Immunizing Agent	Risk from Immunizing Agent to Fetus	Indications for Immunization During Pregnancy	Dose Schedule	Comments
Specific Immune Globulins—cont'd							
Rabies	Near 100% fatality; not altered by pregnancy	Determined by maternal disease	Rabies immune globulin	None reported	Postexposure prophylaxis	Half dose at injury site, half dose in deltoid	Used in conjunction with rabies killed virus vaccine
Tetanus	Severe morbidity; mortality 21%	Neonatal tetanus mortality 60%	Tetanus immune globulin	None reported	Postexposure prophylaxis	One dose IM	Used in conjunction with tetanus toxoid
Varicella	Possible increase in severe varicella pneumonia	Can cause congenital varicella with increased mortality in neonatal period; very rarely causes congenital defects	Varicella-zoster immune globulin (obtained from the American Red Cross)	None reported	Can be considered for healthy pregnant women exposed to varicella to protect against maternal, not congenital, infection	One dose IM within 96 hr of exposure	Indicated also for newborns of mothers who developed varicella within 4 days before delivery or 2 days after delivery; approximately 90%-95% of adults are immune to varicella; not indicated for prevention of congenital varicella
Standard Immune Globulins							
Hepatitis A	Possible increased severity during third trimester	Probable increase in abortion rate and prematurity; possible transmission to neonate at delivery if mother is incubating the virus or is acutely ill at that time	Standard immune globulin		Postexposure prophylaxis	0.02 ml/kg IM in one dose of immune globulin	Immune globulin should be given as soon as possible and within 2 wk of exposure; infants born to mothers who are incubating the virus or are acutely ill at delivery should receive one dose of 0.5 ml as soon as possible after birth
Measles	Significant morbidity, low mortality; not altered by pregnancy	Significant increase in abortion rate; may cause malformations	Standard immune globulin		Postexposure prophylaxis	0.25 ml/kg IM in one dose of immune globulin, up to 15 ml	Unclear if it prevents abortion; must be given within 6 days of exposure

From *ACOG Technical Bulletin,* No 160, Oct 1991.
ID, Intradermally; *IM,* intramuscularly; *PO,* orally; *SC,* subcutaneously.
*Two doses necessary for adequate vaccination of students entering institutions of higher education, newly hired medical personnel, and international travelers.
†Inactivated polio vaccine recommended for nonimmunized adults at increased risk.
From *ACOG Technical Bulletin,* No 160, Oct 1991.

TABLE 5-17 **Immunizing Agents and Immunization Schedules for Health-Care Workers (HCWs)***

Generic Name	Primary Schedule and Booster(s)	Indications	Major Precautions and Contraindications	Special Considerations
Immunizing Agents Strongly Recommended for Health-Care Workers				
Hepatitis B (HB) recombinant vaccine	Two doses IM 4 wk apart; third dose 5 mo after second; booster doses not necessary.	**Preexposure:** HCWs at risk for exposure to blood or body fluids.	Based on limited data no risk of adverse effects to developing fetuses is apparent. Pregnancy should *not* be considered a contraindication to vaccination of women. Previous anaphylactic reaction to common baker's yeast is a contraindication to vaccination.	The vaccine produces neither therapeutic nor adverse effects on HBV-infected persons. Prevaccination serologic screening is not indicated for persons being vaccinated because of occupational risk. HCWs who have contact with patients or blood should be tested 1-2 mo after vaccination to determine serologic response.
Hepatitis B immune globulin (HBIG)	0.06 ml/kg IM as soon as possible after exposure. A second dose of HBIG should be administered 1 mo later if the HB vaccine series has not been started.	**Postexposure** prophylaxis: For persons exposed to blood or body fluids containing HBsAg and who are not immune to HBV infection—0.06 ml/kg IM as soon as possible (but no later than 7 days after exposure).		
Influenza vaccine (inactivated whole-virus and split-virus vaccines)	Annual vaccination with current vaccine. Administered IM.	HCWs who have contact with patients at high risk for influenza or its complications; HCWs who work in chronic care facilities; HCWs with high-risk medical conditions or who are aged ≥65 yr.	History of anaphylactic hypersensitivity to egg ingestion.	No evidence exists of risk to mother or fetus when the vaccine is administered to a pregnant woman with an underlying high-risk condition. Influenza vaccination is recommended during second and third trimesters of pregnancy because of increased risk for hospitalization.
Measles live-virus vaccine	One dose SC; second dose at least 1 mo later.	HCWs† born during or after 1957 who do not have documentation of having received two doses of live vaccine on or after the first birthday **or** a history of physician-diagnosed measles or serologic evidence of immunity. Vaccination should be considered for all HCWs who lack proof of immunity, including those born before 1957.	Pregnancy; immunocompromised persons‡, including HIV-infected persons who have evidence of severe immunosuppression; anaphylaxis after gelatin ingestion or administration of neomycin; recent administration of immune globulin.	MMR is the vaccine of choice if recipients are likely to be susceptible to rubella and/or mumps as well as to measles. Persons vaccinated during 1963-1967 with a killed measles vaccine alone, killed vaccine followed by live vaccine, or with a vaccine of unknown type should be revaccinated with two doses of live measles virus vaccine.

Modified from *MMWR Morb Mortal Wkly Rep* 46(RR-18), 1998.

HBsAg, Hepatitis B surface antigen; *HBV,* hepatitis B virus; *HIV,* human immunodeficiency virus; *IM,* intramuscular; *MMR,* measles, mumps, rubella vaccine; *SC,* subcutaneous.

*Persons who provide health care to patients or work in institutions that provide patient care (e.g., physicians, nurses, emergency medical personnel, dental professionals and students, medical and nursing students, laboratory technicians, hospital volunteers, and administrative and support staff in health-care institutions).

†All HCWs (i.e., medical or nonmedical, paid or volunteer, full time or part time, student or nonstudent, with or without patient-care responsibilities) who work in health-care institutions (e.g., inpatient and outpatient, public and private) should be immune to measles, rubella, and varicella.

‡Persons immunocompromised because of immune deficiency diseases, HIV infection, leukemia, lymphoma or generalized malignancy or immunosuppressed as a result of therapy with corticosteroids, alkylating drugs, antimetabolites, or radiation.

Continued

TABLE 5-17 Immunizing Agents and Immunization Schedules for Health-Care Workers (HCWs)*—cont'd

Generic Name	Primary Schedule and Booster(s)	Indications	Major Precautions and Contraindications	Special Considerations
Mumps live-virus vaccine	One dose SC; no booster	HCWs† believed to be susceptible can be vaccinated. Adults born before 1957 can be considered immune.	Pregnancy; immunocompromised persons‡; history of anaphylactic reaction after gelatin ingestion or administration of neomycin	MMR is the vaccine of choice if recipients are likely to be susceptible to measles and rubella as well as to mumps.
Hepatitis A vaccine	Two doses of vaccine either 6-12 mo apart (HAVRIX), or 6 mo apart (VAQTA)	Not routinely indicated for HCWs in the United States. Persons who work with HAV-infected primates or with HAV in a research laboratory setting should be vaccinated.	History of anaphylactic hypersensitivity to alum or, for HAVRIX, the preservative 2-phenoxyethanol. The safety of the vaccine in pregnant women has not been determined; the risk associated with vaccination should be weighed against the risk for hepatitis A in women who may be at high risk for exposure to HAV.	
Meningococcal polysaccharide vaccine (tetravalent A, C, W135, and Y)	One dose in volume and by route specified by manufacturer; need for boosters unknown	Not routinely indicated for HCWs in the United States.	The safety of the vaccine in pregnant women has not been evaluated; it should not be administered during pregnancy unless the risk for infection is high.	
Typhoid vaccine, IM, SC, and oral	IM vaccine: One 0.5-ml dose, booster 0.5 ml every 2 yr. SC vaccine: two 0.5 ml doses, ≥4 wk apart, booster 0.5 ml SC or 0.1 ID every 3 yr if exposure continues *Oral vaccine:* Four doses on alternate days. The manufacturer recommends revaccination with the entire four-dose series every 5 yr	Workers in microbiology laboratories who frequently work with *Salmonella typhi*	Severe local or systemic reaction to a previous dose. Ty21a (oral) vaccine should not be administered to immunocompromised persons† or to persons receiving antimicrobial agents.	Vaccination should not be considered an alternative to the use of proper procedures when handling specimens and cultures in the laboratory.
Vaccinia vaccine (smallpox)	One dose administered with a bifurcated needle; boosters administered every 10 yr	Laboratory workers who directly handle cultures with vaccinia, recombinant vaccinia viruses, or orthopox viruses that infect humans	The vaccine is contraindicated in pregnancy, in persons with eczema or a history of eczema, and in immunocompromised persons† and their household contacts.	Vaccination may be considered for HCWs who have direct contact with contaminated dressings or other infectious material from volunteers in clinical studies involving recombinant vaccinia virus.

*Persons who provide health care to patients or work in institutions that provide patient care (e.g., physicians, nurses, emergency medical personnel, dental professionals and students, medical and nursing students, laboratory technicians, hospital volunteers, and administrative and support staff in health-care institutions).

†All HCWs (i.e., medical or nonmedical, paid or volunteer, full time or part time, student or nonstudent, with or without patient-care responsibilities) who work in health-care institutions (e.g., inpatient and outpatient, public and private) should be immune to measles, rubella, and varicella.

‡Persons immunocompromised because of immune deficiency diseases, HIV infection, leukemia, lymphoma or generalized malignancy or immunosuppressed as a result of therapy with corticosteroids, alkylating drugs, antimetabolites, or radiation.

TABLE 5-17 **Immunizing Agents and Immunization Schedules for Health-Care Workers (HCWs)*—cont'd**

Generic Name	Primary Schedule and Booster(s)	Indications	Major Precautions and Contraindications	Special Considerations
Other Vaccine-Preventable Diseases				
Tetanus and diphtheria (toxoids [Td])	Two IM doses 4 wk apart; third dose 6-12 mo after second dose; booster every 10 yr	All adults	Except in the first trimester, pregnancy is not a precaution. History of a neurologic reaction or immediate hypersensitivity reaction after a previous dose. History of severe local (Arthus-type) reaction after a previous dose. Such persons should not receive further routine or emergency doses of Td for 10 yr.	Tetanus prophylaxis in wound management‡
Pneumococcal polysaccharide vaccine (23 valent)	One dose, 0.5 ml, IM or SC; revaccination recommended for those at highest risk ≥5 yr after the first dose	Adults who are at increased risk of pneumococcal disease and its complications because of underlying health conditions; older adults, especially those age ≥65 who are healthy	The safety of vaccine in pregnant women has not been evaluated; it should not be administered during pregnancy unless the risk for infection is high. Previous recipients of any type of pneumococcal polysaccharide vaccine who are at highest risk for fatal infection or antibody loss may be revaccinated ≥5 yr after the first dose.	
Rubella live-virus vaccine	One dose SC; no booster	Indicated for HCWs,† both men and women, who do not have documentation of having received live vaccine on or after their first birthday **or** laboratory evidence of immunity. Adults born before 1957, **except women who can become pregnant,** can be considered immune.	Pregnancy; immunocompromised persons†; history of anaphylactic reaction after administration of neomycin	The risk for rubella vaccine–associated malformations in the offspring of women pregnant when vaccinated or who become pregnant within 3 mo after vaccination is negligible. Such women should be counseled regarding the theoretic basis of concern for the fetus. MMR is the vaccine of choice if recipients are likely to be susceptible to measles or mumps, as well as to rubella.
Varicella zoster live-virus vaccine	Two 0.5-ml doses SC 4-8 wk apart if ≥13 yr of age	Indicated for HCWs† who do not have either a reliable history of varicella or serologic evidence of immunity	Pregnancy, immunocompromised persons,‡ history of anaphylactic reaction following receipt of neomycin or gelatin. Avoid salicylate use for 6 wk after vaccination.	Vaccine is available from the manufacturer for certain patients with acute lymphocytic leukemia (ALL) in remission. Because 71%-93% of persons without a history of varicella are immune, serologic testing before vaccination is likely to be cost-effective.

Modified from *MMWR Morb Mortal Wkly Rep* 46(RR-18), 1998.

Continued

TABLE 5-17 **Immunizing Agents and Immunization Schedules for Health-Care Workers (HCWs)*—cont'd**

Generic Name	Primary Schedule and Booster(s)	Indications	Major Precautions and Contraindications	Special Considerations
Varicella-zoster immune globulin (VZIG)	Persons <50 kg: 125 μ/10 kg IM; persons ≥50 kg: 625 μ§	Persons known or likely to be susceptible (particularly those at high risk for complications, e.g., pregnant women) who have close and prolonged exposure to a contact case or to an infectious hospital staff worker or patient		Serologic testing may help in assessing whether to administer VZIG. If use of VZIG prevents varicella disease, patient should be vaccinated subsequently.
BCG Vaccination				
Bacille Calmette Guérin (BCG) vaccine (tuberculosis)	One percutaneous dose of 0.3 ml; no booster dose recommended	Should be considered only for HCWs in areas where multidrug tuberculosis is prevalent, a strong likelihood of infection exists, and where comprehensive infection control precautions have failed to prevent TB transmission to HCWs	Should not be administered to immunocompromised persons,‡ pregnant women	In the United States tuberculosis-control efforts are directed toward early identification, treatment of cases, and preventive therapy with isoniazid.
Other Immunobiologics That Are or May Be Indicated for Health-Care Workers				
Immune globulin (hepatitis A)	**Postexposure**—One IM dose of 0.02 ml/kg administered ≤2 wk after exposure	Indicated for HCWs exposed to feces of infectious patients	Contraindicated in persons with IgA deficiency; do not administer within 2 wk after MMR vaccine, or 3 wk after varicella vaccine. Delay administration of MMR vaccine for ≥3 mo and varicella vaccine ≥5 mo after administration of IG	Administer in large muscle mass (deltoid, gluteal).

§Some experts recommend 125 μ/10 kg regardless of total body weight.

TABLE 5-18 **Recommendations for Persons with Medical Conditions Requiring Special Vaccination Considerations**

Condition	Td	MMR	Varicella	HBV	HAV	Pneumovax[a]	Influenza[b]	HbCV	Meningococcal	IPV	Other live vaccines[c]	Other Killed Vaccines[d]
HIV infection	Rou	Rou/Contr[e]	Contr[f]	Rou[g]	Rou	Rec	Rec	Cons	Rou	Rou	Contr	Rou
Severe immuno-compromise[h]	Rou	Contr	Contr[f]	Rou[g]	Rou	Rec	Rec	Rou[i]	Rou	Rou	Contr	Rou
Renal failure	Rou	Rou	Rou	Rec[g]	Rou	Rec	Rec	Rou	Rou	Rou	Rou	Rou
Diabetes	Rou	Rou	Rou	Rou	Rou	Rec	Rec	Rou	Rou	Rou	Rou	Rou
Chronic liver disease	Rou	Rou	Rou	Rou	Rec	Rec	Rec	Rou	Rou	Rou	Rou	Rou
Cardiac disease	Rou	Rou	Rou	Rou	Rou	Rec	Rec	Rou	Rou	Rou	Rou	Rou
Pulmonary disease	Rou	Rou	Rou	Rou	Rou	Rec	Rec	Rou	Rou	Rou	Rou	Rou
Alcoholism	Rou	Rou	Rou	Rou	Rou	Rec	Rec	Rou	Rou	Rou	Rou	Rou
Functional/anatomic asplenia	Rou	Rou	Rou	Rou	Rou	Rec[j]	Rec	Rec[j]	Rec[j]	Rou	Rou	Rou
Terminal complement deficiency	Rou	Rou	Rou	Rou	Rou	Rou	Rou	Rou	Rec	Rou	Rou	
Clotting factor disorders	Rou	Rou	Rou	Rec	Rec	Rou	Rou	Rou	Rou	Rou	Rou	Rou

Modified and updated from *MMWR Morb Mortal Wkly Rep* 42(RR-4):16 and 17, 1993.

Cons, Consider vaccination; *Contr,* contraindicated; *Rec,* recommended; *Rou,* routine as outlined for all adults.

[a]Pneumovax should be repeated in 5 years for patients in whom vaccine is recommended. Asthma without chronic obstructive pulmonary disease is not an indication for the vaccine.

[b]Influenza vaccine should also be given to caregivers and household members.

[c]Includes bacille Calmette-Guérin, vaccinia, oral typhoid, yellow fever (if exposure cannot be avoided, persons with HIV can be given yellow fever vaccine; see text).

[d]Includes rabies (check postvaccination titers in HIV or severely immunocompromised persons), Lyme, inactivated typhoid, cholera, plague, and anthrax.

[e]For asymptomatic, nonseverely immunocompromised persons with human immunodeficiency virus (HIV), MMR can be used; it is contraindicated in severely immunocompromised persons. MMR can be considered in symptomatic HIV patients without severe immunocompromise.

[f]Varicella can be given to household members and caregivers, but if varicella-like rash develops after vaccination, contact should be avoided.

[g]Recommended for persons with severe chronic renal failure approaching or already receiving dialysis, and higher doses should be given. Antibody titers should be measured after vaccination in these patients and in those with HIV or severe immunocompromise (who may require higher doses) to ensure adequate response. Yearly titers should be measured in dialysis patients.

[h]Severe immunocompromise can result from congenital immunodeficiency, leukemia, lymphoma, malignancy, organ transplant, chemotherapy, radiation therapy, or high-dose corticosteroids.

[i]Only for persons with Hodgkin's disease.

[j]Give at least 2 weeks in advance of elective splenectomy.

TABLE 5-19, A **Recommended and Minimum Ages and Intervals Between Vaccine Doses**[a]

Vaccine and Dose Number	Recommended Age for This Dose	Minimum Age for This Dose	Recommended Interval to Next Dose	Minimum Interval to Next Dose
Hepatitis B1[b]	Birth-2 mo	Birth	1-4 mo	4 wk
Hepatitis B2	1-4 mo	4 wk	2-17 mo	8 wk
Hepatitis B3[c]	6-18 mo	6 mo[d]	—	—
Diphtheria and tetanus toxoids and acellular pertussis (DTaP)1	2 mo	6 wk	2 mo	4 wk
DTaP2	4 mo	10 wk	2 mo	4 wk
DTaP3	6 mo	14 wk	6-12 mo	6 mo[d,e]
DTaP4	15-18 mo	12 mo	3 yr	6 mo[d]
DTaP5	4-6 yr	4 yr	—	—
Haemophilus influenzae, type b (Hib)1[b,f]	2 mo	6 wk	2 mo	4 wk
Hib2	4 mo	10 wk	2 mo	4 wk
Hib3[g]	6 mo	14 wk	6-9 mo	8 wk
Hib4	12-15 mo	12 mo	—	—
Inactivated poliovirus vaccine (IPV)1	2 mo	6 wk	2 mo	4 wk
IPV2	4 mo	10 wk	2-14 mo	4 wk
IPV3	6-18 mo	14 wk	3.5 yr	4 wk
IPV4	4-6 yr	18 wk	—	—
Pneumococcal conjugate vaccine (PCV)1[f]	2 mo	6 wk	2 mo	4 wk
PCV2	4 mo	10 wk	2 mo	4 wk
PCV3	6 mo	14 wk	6 mo	8 wk
PCV4	12-15 mo	12 mo	—	—
Measles, mumps, and rubella (MMR)[i]	12-15 mo[h]	12 mo	3-5 yr	4 wk
MMR2	4-6 yr	13 mo	—	—
Varicella[i]	12-15 mo	12 mo	4 wk[i]	4 wk[i]
Hepatitis A1	≥2 yr	2 yr	6-18 mo[d]	6 mo[d]
Hepatitis A2	≥30 mo	30 mo	—	—
Influenza[j]	—	6 mo[d]	1 mo	4 wk
Pneumococcal polysaccharide (PPV)1	—	2 yr	5 yr[k]	5 yr
PPV2	—	7 yr[k]	—	—

From *MMWR Morb Mortal Wkly Rep* 51 (RR-2), 2002.

[a]Combination vaccines are available. Using licensed combination vaccines is preferred over separate injections of their equivalent component vaccines (Source: *MMWR* 48[RR-5]:5, 1999). When administering combination vaccines, the minimum age for administration is the oldest age for any of the individual components; the minimum interval between doses is equal to the greatest interval of any of the individual antigens.

[b]A combination hepatitis B-Hib vaccine is available (Comvax(r), manufactured by Merck Vaccine Division). This vaccine should not be administered to infants aged <6 weeks because of the Hib component.

[c]Hepatitis B3 should be administered ≥8 weeks after Hepatitis B2 and 16 weeks after Hepatitis B1, and it should not be administered before age 6 months.

[d]Calendar months.

[e]The minimum interval between DTaP3 and DTaP4 is recommended to be ≥6 months. However, DTaP4 does not need to be repeated if administered ≥4 months after DTaP3.

[f]For Hib and PCV, children receiving the first dose of vaccine at age ≥7 months require fewer doses to complete the series (see *MMWR* 40[RR-1]:1-7, 1991 and *MMWR* 49[RR-9]:1-35, 2000).

[g]For a regimen of only polyribosylribitol phosphate-meningococcal outer membrane protein (PRP-OMP, PedvaxHib(r), manufactured by Merck), a dose administered at age 6 months is not required.

[h]During a measles outbreak, if cases are occurring among infants aged <12 months, measles vaccination of infants aged ≥6 months can be undertaken as an outbreak control measure. However, doses administered at age <12 months should not be counted as part of the series (Source: *MMWR* 47[RR-8]:1-57), 1998).

[i]Children aged 12 months-13 years require only one dose of varicella vaccine. Persons aged ≥13 years should receive two doses separated by ≥4 weeks.

[j]Two doses of inactivated influenza vaccine, separated by 4 weeks, are recommended for children aged 6 months-9 years who are receiving the vaccine for the first time. Children aged 6 months-9 years who have previously received influenza vaccine and persons aged ≥9 years require only one dose per influenza season.

[k]Second doses of PPV are recommended for persons at highest risk for serious pneumococcal infection and those who are likely to have a rapid decline in pneumococcal antibody concentration. Revaccination 3 years after the previous dose can be considered for children at highest risk for severe pneumococcal infection who would be aged <10 years at the time of revaccination (see *MMWR* 46[RR-8]:1-24, 1997).

TABLE 5-19, B Guidelines for Spacing of Live and Inactivated Antigens

Antigen Combination	Recommended Minimum Interval Between Doses
≥2 inactivated	None; can be administered simultaneously or at any interval between doses
Inactivated and live	None; can be administered simultaneously or at any interval between doses
≥2 live parenteral*	4-week minimum interval, if not administered simultaneously

From *MMWR Morb Mortal Wkly Rep* 51(RR-2), 2002.

*Live oral vaccines (e.g., Ty21a typhoid vaccine, oral polio vaccine) can be administered simultaneously or at any interval before or after inactivated or live parenteral vaccines.

TABLE 5-19, C Guidelines for Administering Antibody-Containing Products* and Vaccines

Simultaneous Administration

Combination	Recommended Minimum Interval Between Doses
Antibody-containing products and inactivated antigen	None; can be administered simultaneously at different sites or at any time between doses
Antibody-containing products and live antigen	Should not be administered simultaneously,† if simultaneous administration of measles-containing vaccine or varicella vaccine is unavoidable, administer at different sites and revaccinate or test for seroconversion after the recommended interval

Nonsimultaneous Administration

Product Administered		
First	**Second**	**Recommended Minimum Interval Between Doses**
Antibody-containing products	Inactivated antigen	None
Inactivated antigen	Antibody-containing products	None
Antibody-containing products	Live antigen	Dose-related‡
Live antigen	Antibody-containing products	2 weeks

From *MMWR Morb Mortal Wkly Rep* 51(RR-2), 2002.

*Blood products containing substantial amounts of immunoglobulin, including intramuscular and intravenous immune globulin, specific hyperimmune globulin (e.g., hepatitis B immune globulin, tetanus immune globulin, varicella zoster immune globulin, and rabies immune globulin), whole blood, packed red cells, plasma, and platelet products.

†Yellow fever and oral Ty21a typhoid vaccines are exceptions to these recommendations. These live attenuated vaccines can be administered at any time before, after, or simultaneously with an antibody-containing product without substantially decreasing the antibody response.

‡The duration of interference of antibody-containing products with the immune response to the measles component of measles-containing vaccine, and possibly varicella vaccine, is dose-related.

TABLE 5-20 Suggested Intervals Between Administration of Antibody-Containing Products for Different Indications and Measles-Containing Vaccine and Varicella Vaccine*

Product/Indication	Dose, Including mg Immunoglobulin G (IgG)/kg Body Weight*	Recommended Interval Before Measles or Varicella Vaccination (mo)
Respiratory syncytial virus immune globulin (IG) monoclonal antibody (Synagis™)†	15 mg/kg intramuscularly (IM)	None
Tetanus IG	250 units (10 mg IgG/kg) IM	3
Hepatitis A IG		
Contact prophylaxis	0.02 mL/kg (3.3 mg IgG/kg) IM	3
International travel	0.06 mL/kg (10 mg IgG/kg) IM	3
Hepatitis B IG	0.06 mL/kg (10 mg IgG/kg) IM	3
Rabies IG	20 IU/kg (22 mg IgG/kg) IM	4
Varicella IG	125 units/10 kg (20-40 mg IgG/kg) IM, maximum 625 units	5
Measles prophylaxis IG		
Standard (i.e., nonimmunocompromised) contact	0.25 mL/kg (40 mg IgG/kg) IM	5
Immunocompromised contact	0.50 mL/kg (80 mg IgG/kg) IM	6
Blood transfusion		
Red blood cells (RBCs), washed	10 mL/kg negligible IgG/kg intravenously (IV)	None
RBCs, adenine-saline added	10 mL/kg (10 mg IgG/kg) IV	3
Packed RBCs (hematocrit 65%)‡	10 mL/kg (60 mg IgG/kg) IV	6
Whole blood (hematocrit 35%-50%)‡	10 mL/kg (80-100 mg IgG/kg) IV	6
Plasma/platelet products	10 mL/kg (160 mg IgG/kg) IV	7
Cytomegalovirus intravenous immune globulin (IGIV)	150 mg/kg maximum	6
Respiratory syncytial virus prophylaxis IGIV	750 mg/kg	9
IGIV		
Replacement therapy for immune deficiencies§	300-400 mg/kg IV§	8
Immune thrombocytopenic purpura	400 mg/kg IV	8
Immune thrombocytopenic purpura	1000 mg/kg IV	10
Kawasaki disease	2 g/kg IV	11

From *MMWR Morb Mortal Wkly Rep* 51(RR-2), 2002.

*This table is not intended for determining the correct indications and dosages for using antibody-containing products. Unvaccinated persons might not be fully protected against measles during the entire recommended interval, and additional doses of immune globulin or measles vaccine might be indicated after measles exposure. Concentrations of measles antibody in an immune globulin preparation can vary by manufacturer's lot. Rates of antibody clearance after receipt of an immune globulin preparation might vary also. Recommended intervals are extrapolated from an estimated half-life of 30 days for passively acquired antibody and an observed interference with the immune response to measles vaccine for 5 months after a dose of 80 mg IgG/kg (Source: Mason W. Takahashi M, Schneider T. Presented at the 32nd meeting of the Interscience Conference on Antimicrobial Agents and Chemotherapy, Los Angeles, Calif., October 1992).

†Contains antibody only to respiratory syncytial virus.

‡Assumes a serum IgG concentration of 16 mg/mL.

§Measles and varicella vaccination is recommended for children with asymptomatic or mildly symptomatic human immunodeficiency virus (HIV) infection but is contraindicated for persons with severe immunosuppression from HIV or any other immunosuppressive disorder.

TABLE 5-21 Guide to Contraindications and Precautions[a] to Commonly Used Vaccines

Vaccine	True Contraindications and Precautions[a]	Untrue (Vaccines Can be Administered)
General for all vaccines, including diphtheria and tetanus toxoids and acellular pertussis vaccine (DTaP); pediatric diphtheria-tetanus toxoid (DT); adult tetanus-diphtheria toxoid (Td); inactivated poliovirus vaccine (IPV); measles-mumps-rubella vaccine (MMR); *Haemophilus influenzae* type b vaccine (Hib); hepatitis A vaccine; hepatitis B vaccine; varicella vaccine; pneumococcal conjugate vaccine (PCV); influenza vaccine; and pneumococcal polysaccharide vaccine (PPV)	**Contraindications** Serious allergic reaction (e.g., anaphylaxis) after a previous vaccine dose Serious allergic reaction (e.g., anaphylaxis) to a vaccine component **Precautions** Moderate or severe acute illness with or without fever	Mild acute illness with or without fever Mild to moderate local reaction (i.e., swelling, redness, soreness); low-grade or moderate fever after previous dose Lack of previous physical examination in well-appearing person Current antimicrobial therapy Convalescent phase of illness Premature birth (hepatitis B vaccine is an exception in certain circumstances)[b] Recent exposure to an infectious disease History of penicillin allergy, other nonvaccine allergies, relatives with allergies, receiving allergen extract immunotherapy
DTaP	**Contraindications** Severe allergic reaction after a previous dose or to a vaccine component Encephalopathy (e.g., coma, decreased level of consciousness; prolonged seizures) within 7 days of administration of previous dose of DTP or DTaP Progressive neurologic disorder, including infantile spasms, uncontrolled epilepsy, progressive encephalopathy; defer DTaP until neurologic status clarified and stabilized **Precautions** Fever of >40.5° C ≤48 hr after vaccination with a previous dose of DTP or DTaP Collapse or shock-like state (i.e., hypotonic hyporesponsive episode) ≤48 hr after receiving a previous dose of DTP/DTaP Seizure ≤days of receiving a previous dose of DTP/DTaP[c] Persistent, inconsolable crying lasting ≥3 hr ≤48 hours after receiving a previous dose of DTP/DTaP Moderate or severe acute illness with or without fever	Temperature of <40.5° C, fussiness or mild drowsiness after a previous dose of diphtheria toxoid-tetanus toxoid-pertussis vaccine (DTP)/DTaP Family history of seizures[c] Family history of sudden infant death syndrome Family of history of an adverse event after DTP or DTaP administration Stable neurologic conditions (e.g., cerebral palsy, well-controlled convulsions, developmental delay)
DT, Td	**Contraindications** Severe allergic reaction after a previous dose or to a vaccine component **Precautions** Guillain-Barré syndrome ≤6 wk after previous dose of tetanus toxoid-containing vaccine Moderate or severe acute illness with or without fever	
IPV	**Contraindications** Severe allergic reaction to previous dose or vaccine component **Precautions** Pregnancy Moderate or severe acute illness with or without fever	
MMR[d]	**Contraindications** Severe allergic reaction after a previous dose or to a vaccine component Pregnancy Known severe immunodeficiency (e.g., hematologic and solid tumors; congenital immunodeficiency; long-term immunosuppressive therapy,[e] or severely symptomatic human immunodeficiency virus [HIV] infection) **Precautions** Recent (≤11 mo) receipt of antibody-containing blood product (specific interval depends on product) History of thrombocytopenia or thrombocytopenic purpura Moderate or severe acute illness with or without fever	Positive tuberculin skin test Simultaneous TB skin testing[f] Breast-feeding Pregnancy of recipient's mother or other close or household contact Recipient is child-bearing-age female Immunodeficient family member or household contact Asymptomatic or mildly symptomatic HIV infection Allergy to eggs

Continued

TABLE 5-21 **Guide to Contraindications and Precautions[a] to Commonly Used Vaccines—cont'd**

Vaccine	True Contraindications and Precautions[a]	Untrue (Vaccines Can be Administered)
Hib	**Contraindications** Severe allergic reaction after a previous dose or to a vaccine component Age <6 wk **Precaution** Moderate or severe acute illness with or without fever	
Hepatitis B	**Contraindications** Severe allergic reaction after a previous dose or to a vaccine component **Precautions** Infant weighing <2000 g[b] Moderate or severe acute illness with or without fever	Pregnancy Autoimmune disease (e.g., systemic lupus erythematosus or rheumatoid arthritis)
Hepatitis A	**Contraindications** Severe allergic reaction after a previous dose or to a vaccine component **Precautions** Pregnancy Moderate or severe acute illness with or without fever	
Varicella[d]	**Contraindications** Severe allergic reaction after a previous dose or to a vaccine component Substantial suppression of cellular immunity Pregnancy **Precautions** Recent (≤11 mo) receipt of antibody-containing blood product (specific interval depends on product) Moderate or severe acute illness with or without fever	Pregnancy of recipient's mother or other close or household contact Immunodeficient family member of household contact[g] Asymptomatic or mildly symptomatic HIV infection Humoral immunodeficiency (e.g., agammaglobulinemia)
PCV	**Contraindications** Severe allergic reaction after a previous dose or to a vaccine component **Precaution** Moderate or severe acute illness with or without fever	
Influenza	**Contraindications** Severe allergic reaction to previous dose or vaccine component, including egg protein **Precautions** Moderate or severe acute illness with or without fever	Nonsevere (e.g., contact) allergy to latex or thimerosal Concurrent administration of Coumadin or aminophylline
PPV	**Contraindications** Severe allergic reaction after a previous dose or to a vaccine component **Precaution** Moderate or severe acute illness with or without fever	

From *MMWR Morb Mortal Wkly Rep* 51(RR-2), 2002.

[a]Events or conditions listed as precautions should be reviewed carefully. Benefits and risks of administering a specific vaccine to a person under these circumstances should be considered. If the risk from the vaccine is believed to outweigh the benefit, the vaccine should not be administered. If the benefit of vaccination is believed to outweigh the risk, the vaccine should be administered. Whether and when to administer DTaP to children with proven or suspected underlying neurologic disorders should be decided on a case-by-case basis.

[b]Hepatitis B vaccination should be deferred for infants weighing <2000 g if the mother is documented to be hepatitis B surface antigen (HbsAg)-negative at the time of the infant's birth. Vaccination can commence at chronological age 1 month. For infants born to HbsAg-positive women, hepatitis B immunoglobulin and hepatitis B vaccine should be administered at or soon after birth regardless of weight. See text for details.

[c]Acetaminophen or other appropriate antipyretic can be administered to children with a personal or family history of seizures at the time of DTaP vaccination and every 4-6 hours for 24 hours thereafter to reduce the possibility of postvaccination fever (Source: American Academy of Pediatrics, In Pickering LK, ed, *Red Book: Report of the Committee on Infectious Diseases,* 25th ed. Elk Grove Village, IL, 2000, American Academy of Pediatrics.

[d]MMR and varicella vaccines can be administered on the same day. If not administered on the same day, these vaccines should be separated by ≥28 days.

[e]Substantially immunosuppressive steroid dose is considered to be ≥2 weeks of daily receipt of 20 mg or 2 mg/kg body weight of prednisone or equivalent.

[f]Measles vaccination can suppress tuberculin reactivity temporarily. Measles-containing vaccine can be administered on the same day as tuberculin skin testing. If testing cannot be performed until after the day of MMR vaccination, the test should be postponed for ≥4 weeks after the vaccination. If an urgent need exists to skin test, do so with the understanding that reactivity might be reduced by the vaccine.

[g]If a vaccinee experiences a presumed vaccine-related rash 7-25 days after vaccination, avoid direct contact with immunocompromised persons for the duration of the rash.

TABLE 5-22 **Vaccinations for International Travel**

Disease*	Areas Affected†	Prophylaxis Recommended	Ideal Time Between Last Vaccine Dose and Travel
Tetanus	All	All travelers; vaccine series/booster.	Probably 30 days for series Anamnestic response to booster
Measles	All	Born after 1956; ensure immunity by antibody titer, diagnosed measles, or two doses of vaccine.	As MMR, 7-14 days
Rubella	All	Born after 1956 and any female of childbearing age; rubella titer or one dose of vaccine.	As MMR, 7-14 days
Mumps	All	Born after 1956; ensure immunity by antibody titer, diagnosed mumps, or one dose of vaccine.	As MMR, 7-14 days
Varicella	All	All travelers; antibody titer, reported illness, or vaccine series.	7-14 days
Hepatitis B	5%-20% of population are carriers in Africa, Middle East except Israel, all Southeast Asia, Amazon basin, Haiti, and Dominican Republic; 1%-5% of population are carriers in south-central and southwest Asia, Israel, Japan, Americas, Russia, and eastern and southern Europe.	Travelers for more than 6 mo in close contact with population or for less time but with high-risk activities (close household contact, seeking dental or medical care, sex); vaccine series.	Probably 30 days
Hepatitis A	Developing countries.	Travelers to rural areas; eating and drinking in settings of poor sanitation; vaccine or pooled immune globulin (IG).	Vaccine, 30 days Pooled IG, 2 days
Influenza	Tropics throughout the year; southern hemisphere from April to September.	Travelers for whom vaccine is otherwise indicated; give current vaccine and revaccinate in fall as usual.	7-14 days
Meningococcus*	Sub-Saharan Africa "belt" (Senegal to Ethiopia) from December to June; required for pilgrims to Saudi Arabia during Haj; epidemics reported in other African nations, India, Nepal, and Mongolia.	All travelers; vaccine.	7-10 days
Rabies	Endemic dog rabies exists in Mexico, El Salvador, Guatemala, Peru, Colombia, Ecuador, India, Nepal, Philippines, Sri Lanka, Thailand, and Vietnam.	Travelers staying for more than 30 days or at high risk of exposure to domestic or wild animals; vaccine series/booster.	7-14 days
Poliomyelitis	Developing countries not in western hemisphere; at risk all year in tropics; in temperate zones, incidence increases in summer and fall.	All travelers; vaccine series/booster.	Parenteral vaccine series, 28 day (see text) Anamnestic response to booster

Continued

TABLE 5-22 **Vaccinations for International Travel—cont'd**

Disease*	Areas Affected†	Prophylaxis Recommended	Ideal Time Between Last Vaccine Dose and Travel
Typhoid fever	Many countries in Asia, Africa, Central America, and South America.	Travelers with prolonged stay in rural areas with poor sanitation; vaccine series/booster.	Oral vaccine, 7 days Parenteral vaccine, probably 14 days
Yellow fever*	North and central South America, forest-savannah zones of Africa; some countries in Africa, Asia, and Middle East require travelers from endemic areas to be vaccinated.	All travelers; vaccine/booster at approved yellow fever vaccination center.	10 days
Japanese encephalitis	Seasonally in most areas of Asia, Indian subcontinent, and western Pacific islands; in temperate zones, incidence increases in summer and early fall; in tropics, year-round incidence.	Travelers staying for more than 30 days in high-risk rural areas; staying outdoors during transmission season; vaccine series.	10 days
Cholera*	Certain undeveloped countries.	If required by local authorities, one dose usually suffices; primary series only for those living in high-risk areas under poor sanitary conditions or those with compromised gastric defense mechanisms (achlorhydria, antacid therapy, previous ulcer surgery); booster every 6 mo.	Probably 30 days
Plague	Africa, Asia, and Americas in rural mountainous or upland areas.	Travelers whose research or field activities bring them in contact with rodents; vaccine series/booster; consider taking tetracycline (500 mg four times a day) for chemoprophylaxis (inferred from clinical experience in treating plague).	Probably 30 days

From Noble J: *Primary care medicine,* ed 3, St Louis, 2001, Mosby.

*Only yellow fever vaccine is required for entry by any country; cholera vaccine may be required by some local authorities; and meningococcus vaccine is required for pilgrims to Mecca, Saudia Arabia, during Haj. However, it is important to follow CDC recommendations for all vaccines to prevent disease. If a required vaccine is contraindicated or withheld for any reason, attempts should be made to obtain a waiver from the country's consulate or embassy.

†Because areas affected can change, and for more specific details, consult CDC's traveler's hotline.

TABLE 5-23 Recommended Schedule of Hepatitis B Immunoprophylaxis to Prevent Perinatal Transmission

Population Group	Vaccine Dose*	Age of Infant
Infants born to HBsAg-positive mothers	First dose	Birth (within 12 hr)
	HBIG†	Birth (within 12 hr)
	Second dose	1 mo
	Third dose	6 mo‡
Infants born to mothers not screened for HBsAg§	First dose	Birth (within 12 hr)
	HBIG‡	If mother is HBsAg positive, administer HBIG to infant as soon as possible, not later than 1 wk after birth
	Second dose	1-2 mo‖
	Third dose	6 mo‡

Modified from *MMWR Morb Mortal Wkly Rep* 40(RR-13):12, 1991.
HbsAg, Hepatitis B surface antigen; *HBIG,* hepatitis B immune globulin.
*See Table 5-20 for appropriate vaccine dose.
†HBIG is given in a dose of 0.5 ml, administered intramuscularly at a site different from that used for vaccine.
‡If four-dose schedule (Engerix-B) is used, the third dose is administered at 2 mo of age and the fourth dose at 12-18 mo.
§First vaccine dose is the same as the dose for an HBsAg-positive mother (see Table 5-20). If mother is HBsAg positive, continue that dose; if mother is HBsAg negative, use appropriate dose from Table 5-20.
‖Infants of women who are HBsAg negative can be vaccinated at 2 mo of age.

TABLE 5-24 Recommended Doses of Currently Licensed Hepatitis B Vaccines

Population Group	Recombivax HB* Dose in μg (Dose in ml)	Engerix-B* Dose in mg (Dose in ml)
Infants of HbsAg-negative mothers and children <11 yr	2.5 (0.25)	10 (0.5)
Infants of HbsAg-positive mothers; prevention of perinatal infection	5 (0.5)	10 (0.5)
Children and adolescents 11-19 yr	5 (0.5)	20 (1.0)
Adults ≥20 yr	10 (1.0)	20 (1.0)
Dialysis patients and other immunocompromised persons	40†	40‡

Modified from *MMWR Morb Mortal Wkly Rep* 40(RR-13):7, 1991.
*Both vaccines are routinely administered in a three-dose series at 0, 1, and 6 mo. Engerix-B is also licensed for a four-dose series administered at 0, 1, 2, and 12 mo.
†Special formulation.
‡Two 1.0-ml doses administered at one site in a four-dose schedule at 0, 1, 2, and 6 mo.

ENDOCARDITIS PROPHYLAXIS

BOX 5-1 Cardiac Conditions Associated with Endocarditis

Endocarditis Prophylaxis Recommended

High-Risk Category

Prosthetic cardiac valves, including bioprosthetic and homograft valves
Previous bacterial endocarditis
Complex cyanotic congenital heart disease (e.g., single ventricle states, transposition of the great arteries, tetralogy of Fallot)
Surgically constructed systemic pulmonary shunts or conduits

Moderate-Risk Category

Most other congenital cardiac malformations (other than above and below)
Acquired valvar dysfunction (e.g., rheumatic heart disease)
Hypertrophic cardiomyopathy
Mitral valve prolapse with valvar regurgitation and/or thickened leaflets

Endocarditis Prophylaxis Not Recommended

Negligible-Risk Category (No Greater Risk Than the General Population)

Isolated secundum atrial septal defect
Surgical repair of atrial septal defect, ventricular defect, or patent ductus arteriosus (without residua beyond 6 mos)
Previous coronary artery bypass graft surgery
Mitral valve prolapse without valvar regurgitation
Physiologic, functional, or innocent heart murmurs
Previous Kawasaki disease without valvar dysfunction
Previous rheumatic fever without valvar dysfunction
Cardiac pacemakers (intravascular and epicardial) and implanted defibrillators

From Dajani AS et al: *JAMA* 277:1794-1801, 1997.

BOX 5-2 Dental Procedures and Endocarditis Prophylaxis

Endocarditis Prophylaxis Recommended*
Dental extractions
Periodontal procedures including surgery, scaling and root planing, probing, and recall maintenance
Dental implant placement and reimplantation of avulsed teeth
Endodontic (root canal) instrumentation of surgery only beyond the apex
Subgingival placement of antibiotic fibers or strips
Initial placement of orthodontic bands—but not brackets
Intraligamentary local anesthetic injections
Prophylactic cleaning of teeth or implants where bleeding is anticipated

Endocarditis Prophylaxis Not Recommended
Restorative dentistry† (operative and prosthodontic) with or without retraction cord‡
Local anesthetic injections (nonintraligamentary)
Intracanal endodontic treatment; postplacement and buildup
Placement of rubber dams
Postoperative suture removal
Placement of removable prosthodontic or orthodontic appliances
Taking of oral impressions
Fluoride treatments
Taking of oral radiographs
Orthodontic appliance adjustment
Shedding of primary teeth

From Dajani AS et al: *JAMA* 277:1794-1801, 1997.
*Prophylaxis is recommended for patients with high- and moderate-risk cardiac conditions.
†This includes restoration of decayed teeth (filling cavities) and replacement of missing teeth.
‡Clinical judgment may indicate antibiotic use in selected circumstances that may create significant bleeding.

BOX 5-3 Other Procedures and Endocarditis Prophylaxis

Endocarditis Prophylaxis Recommended
Respiratory tract
Tonsillectomy and/or adenoidectomy
Surgical operations that involve respiratory mucosa
Bronchoscopy with a rigid bronchoscope
Gastrointestinal Tract*
Sclerotherapy for esophageal varices
Esophageal stricture dilation
Endoscopic retrograde cholangiography* with biliary obstruction
Biliary tract surgery
Surgical operations that involve intestinal mucosa
Genitourinary Tract
Prostatic surgery
Cystoscopy
Urethral dilation

Endocarditis Prophylaxis Not Recommended
Respiratory Tract
Endotracheal intubation
Bronchoscopy with a flexible bronchoscope, with or without biopsy†
Tympanostomy tube insertion
Gastrointestinal Tract
Transesophageal echocardiography†
Endoscopy with or without gastrointestinal biopsy†
Genitourinary Tract
Vaginal hysterectomy†
Vaginal delivery†
Cesarean section
In uninfected tissue:
- Urethral catheterization
- Uterine dilation and curettage
- Therapeutic abortion
- Sterilization procedures
- Insertion or removal of intrauterine devices

Other
Cardiac catheterization, including balloon angioplasty
Implanted cardiac pacemakers, implanted defibrillators, and coronary stents
Incision or biopsy of surgically scrubbed skin
Circumcision

From Dajani AS et al: *JAMA* 277:1794-1801, 1997.
*Prophylaxis is recommended for high-risk patients; optional for medium-risk patients.
†Prophylaxis is optional for high-risk patients.

TABLE 5-25 Prophylactic Regimens for Dental, Oral, Respiratory Tract, or Esophageal Procedures

Situation	Agent	Regimen*
Standard general prophylaxis	Amoxicillin	Adults: 2.0 g; children: 50 mg/kg orally (PO) 1 hr before procedure
Unable to take oral medications	Ampicillin	Adults: 2.0 g intramuscularly (IM) or intravenously (IV); children: 50 mg/kg IM or IV within 30 min before procedure
Allergic to penicillin	Clindamycin	Adults: 600 mg; children: 20 mg/kg PO 1 hr before procedure
	or	
	Cephalexin† or cefadroxil†	Adults: 2.0 g; children: 50 mg/kg PO 1 hr before procedure
	or	
	Azithromycin or clarithromycin	Adults: 500 mg; children: 15 mg/kg PO 1 hr before procedure
Allergic to penicillin and unable to take oral medications	Clindamycin	Adults: 600 mg; children: 20 mg/kg IV within 30 min of procedure
	or	
	Cefazolin†	Adults 1.0 g; children: 25 mg/kg IM or IV within 30 min of procedure

From Dajani AS et al: *JAMA* 277:1794-1801, 1997.
*Total children's dose should not exceed adult dose.
†Cephalosporins should not be used in individuals with immediate-type hypersensitivity reaction (urticaria, angioedema, or anaphylaxis) to penicillins.

TABLE 5-26 Prophylactic Regimens for Genitourinary/Gastrointestinal (Excluding Esophageal) Procedures

Situation	Agents*	Regimen†
High-risk patients	Ampicillin plus gentamicin	Adults: ampicillin 2.0 g intramuscularly (IM) or intravenously (IV) plus gentamicin 1.5 mg/kg (not to exceed 120 mg) within 30 min of starting the procedure; 6 hr later, ampicillin 1 g IM/IV or amoxicillin 1 g orally (PO)
		Children: ampicillin 50 mg/kg IM or IV (not to exceed 2.0 g) plus gentamicin 1.5 mg/kg within 30 min of starting the procedure; 6 hr later, ampicillin 25 g/kg IM/IV or amoxicillin 25 mg/kg PO
High-risk patients allergic to ampicillin	Vancomycin plus gentamicin	Adults: vancomycin 1.0 g IV over 1-2 hr plus gentamicin 1.5 mg/kg IV/IM (not to exceed 120 mg); complete injection/infusion within 30 min of starting the procedure
		Children: vancomycin 20 mg/kg IV over 1-2 hr plus gentamicin 1.5 mg/kg IV/IM; complete injection/infusion within 30 min of starting the procedure
Moderate-risk patients	Amoxicillin or ampicillin	Adults: amoxicillin 2.0 g PO 1 hr before procedure, or ampicillin 2.0 g IV/IV within 30 min of starting the procedure
		Children: amoxicillin 50 mg/kg PO 1 hr before procedure, or ampicillin 50 mg/kg IM/IV within 30 min of starting the procedure
Moderate-risk patients allergic to ampicillin/amoxicillin	Vancomycin	Adults: vancomycin 1.0 g IV over 1-2 hr; complete infusion within 30 min of starting the procedure
		Children: vancomycin 20 mg/kg IV over 1-2 hr; complete infusion within 30 min of starting the procedure

From Dajani AS et al: *JAMA* 277:1794-1801, 1997.
*Total children's dose should not exceed adult dose.
†No second dose of vancomycin or gentamicin is recommended.

TABLE 5-27 **Recommended Daily Dosage of Influenza Antiviral Medications for Treatment and Prophylaxis**

	AGE GROUPS				
Antiviral Agent	**1 to 6 Years**	**7 to 9 Years**	**10 to 12 Years**	**13 to 64 Years**	**65 Years and Older**
Amantadine[a]					
Treatment	5 mg per kg per day up to 150 mg in two divided doses[b]	5 mg per kg per day up to 150 mg in two divided doses[b]	100 mg bid[c]	100 mg bid[c]	100 mg or less per day
Prophylaxis	5 mg per kg per day up to 150 mg in two divided dosesb	5 mg per kg per day up to 150 mg in two divided doses[b]	100 mg bid[c]	100 mg bid[c]	100 mg or less per day
Rimantadine[d]					
Treatment[e]	NA	NA	NA	100 mg bid[c]	100 or 200[f] mg per day
Prophylaxis	5 mg per kg per day up to 150 mg in two divided doses[b]	5 mg per kg per day up to 150 mg in two divided doses[b]	100 mg bid[c]	100 mg bid[c]	100 or 200[f] mg per day
Zanamivir[g,h]					
Treatment	NA	10 mg bid	10 mg bid	10 mg bid	10 mg bid
Oseltamivir					
Treatment[i]	Dose varies by child's weight[j]	Dose varies by child's weight[j]	Dose varies by child's weight[j]	75 mg bid	75 mg bid
Prophylaxis	NA	NA	NA	75 mg per day	75 mg per day

From *MMWR Morb Mortal Wkly Rep* 50(RR-4):1, 2001.
NA, Not applicable.
[a]The drug package insert should be consulted for dosage recommendations for administering amantadine to persons with creatinine clearance of 50 mL or less per min per 1.73m^2.
[b]5 mg per kg of amantadine or rimantadine syrup = 1 tsp/22 lb.
[c]Children 10 yr of age or older who weigh less than 40 kg (88 lb) should be administered amantadine or rimantadine at a dosage of 5 mg per kg per day.
[d]A reduction in dosage to 100 mg per day of rimantadine is recommended for persons who have severe hepatic dysfunction or those with creatinine clearance of 10 ml or less per min. Other persons with less severe hepatic or renal dysfunction taking 100 mg per day of rimantadine should be observed closely, and the dosage should be reduced or the drug discontinued, if necessary.
[e]Only approved for treatment in adults.
[f]Elderly residents of nursing homes should be administered only 100 mg per day of rimantadine. A reduction in dosage of 100 mg per day should be considered for all persons 65 yr of age or older if they experience side effects when taking 200 mg per day.
[g]Zanamivir is administered via inhalation by using a plastic device included in the package with the medication. Patients will benefit from instruction and demonstration of correct use of the device.
[h]Zanamivir is not approved for prophylaxis.
[i]A reduction in the dose of oseltamivir is recommended for persons with creatinine clearance of less than 30 ml per min.
[j]The dose recommendation for children who weigh less than 15 kg (33 lb) is 30 mg bid; for children weighing 15 to 23 kg (33 to 50.6 lb), the dose is 45 mg bid; for children weighing 23 to 40 kg (50.6 to 88 lb), the dose is 60 mg bid; and for children weighing more than 40 kg (88 lb), the dose is 75 mg bid.

TABLE 5-28 **Recommended Postexposure Prophylaxis for Exposure to Hepatitis B Virus**

Vaccination and Antibody Response Status of Exposed Workers*	TREATMENT: Source HBsAg Positive	Source HBsAg Negative	Source Unknown or Not Available for Testing
Unvaccinated	HBIG† × 1 and initiate HB vaccine series‡	Initiate HB vaccine series	Initiate HB vaccine series
Previously vaccinated			
Known responder§	No treatment	No treatment	No treatment
Known nonresponderi	HBIG × 1 and initiate revaccination or HBIG × 2¶	No treatment	If known high-risk source, treat as if source were HBsAg positive
Antibody response unknown	Test exposed person for anti-HBs¶ 1. If adequate,§ no treatment is necessary 2. If inadequate,‖ administer HBIG × 1 and vaccine booster	No treatment	Test exposed person for anti-HBs 1. If adequate,‡ no treatment is necessary 2. If inadequate,‡ administer vaccine booster and recheck titer in 1-2 mo

Anti-HBs, Antibody to HBsAg; *HB,* hepatitis B; *HBIG,* hepatitis B immune globulin; *HBsAg,* hepatitis B surface antigen.
*Persons who have previously been infected with HBV are immune to reinfection and do not require postexposure prophylaxis.
†Hepatitis B immune globulin; dose is 0.06 ml/kg intramuscularly.
‡Hepatitis B vaccine.
§A responder is a person with adequate levels of serum antibody to HBsAg (i.e., anti-HBs ≥10 mIU/ml).
‖A nonresponder is a person with inadequate response to vaccination (i.e., serum anti-HBs <10 mIU/ml).
¶The option of giving one dose of HBIG and reinitiating the vaccine series is preferred for nonresponders who have not completed a second 3-dose vaccine series. For persons who previously completed a second vaccine series but failed to respond, two doses of HBIG are preferred.

TABLE 5-29 **Recommended HIV Postexposure Prophylaxis for Percutaneous Injuries**

	INFECTION STATUS OF SOURCE				
Exposure Type	HIV-Positive Class 1*	HIV-Positive Class 2*	Source of Unknown HIV Status†	Unknown Source‡	HIV-Negative
Less severe§	Recommend basic 2-drug PEP	Recommend expanded 3-drug PEP	Generally, no PEP warranted; however, consider basic 2-drug PEP‖ for source with HIV risk factors††	Generally, no PEP warranted; however, consider basic 2-drug PEP‖ in settings where exposure to HIV-infected persons is likely	No PEP warranted
More severe#	Recommend expanded 3-drug PEP	Recommend expanded 3-drug PEP	Generally, no PEP warranted; however, consider basic 2-drug PEP‖ for source with HIV risk factors¶	Generally, no PEP warranted; however, consider basic 2-drug PEP‖ in settings where exposure to HIV-infected persons is likely	No PEP warranted

HIV, Human immunodeficiency virus; *PEP,* postexposure prophylaxis (see Box 5-7).
*HIV-Positive, Class 1—asymptomatic HIV infection or known low viral load (e.g., <1500 RNA copies/ml). HIV-Positive, class 2—symptomatic HIV infection, acquired immunodeficiency syndrome, acute seroconversion, or known high viral load. If drug resistance is a concern, obtain expert consultation. Initiation of PEP should not be delayed pending expert consultation, and, because expert consultation alone cannot substitute for face-to-face counseling, resources should be available to provide immediate evaluation and follow-up care for all exposures.
†Source of unknown HIV status (e.g., deceased source person with no samples available for HIV testing).
‡Unknown source (e.g., a needle from a sharps disposal container).
§Less severe (e.g., solid needle and superficial injury).
‖The designation "consider PEP" indicates that PEP is optional and should be based on an individualized decision between the exposed person and the treating clinician.
¶If PEP is offered and taken and the source is later determined to be HIV-negative, PEP should be discontinued.
#More severe (e.g., large-bore hollow needle, deep puncture, visible blood on device, or needle used in patient's artery or vein).

TABLE 5-30 **Recommended HIV Postexposure Prophylaxis for Mucous Membrane Exposures and Nonintact Skin[a] Exposures**

	INFECTION STATUS OF SOURCE				
Exposure Type	**HIV-Positive Class 1[b]**	**HIV-Positive Class 2[b]**	**Source of Unknown HIV Status[c]**	**Unknown Source[d]**	**HIV-Negative**
Small volume[e]	Consider basic 2-drug PEP[f]	Recommend basic 2-drug PEP	Generally, no PEP warranted; however, consider basic 2-drug PEP[f] for source with HIV risk factors[g]	Generally, no PEP warranted; however, consider basic 2-drug PEP[f] in settings where exposure to HIV-infected persons is likely	No PEP warranted
Large volume[h]	Recommend basic 2-drug PEP	Recommend expanded 3-drug PEP	Generally, no PEP warranted; however, consider basic 2-drug PEP[f] for source with HIV risk factors[g]	Generally, no PEP warranted; however, consider basic 2-drug PEP[f] in settings where exposure to HIV-infected persons is likely	No PEP warranted

HIV, Human immunodeficiency virus; *PEP,* postexposure prophylaxis (see Box 5-7).
[a]For skin exposures, follow-up is indicated only if there is evidence of compromised skin integrity (e.g., dermatitis, abrasion, or open wound).
[b]HIV-Positive, Class 1—asymptomatic HIV infection or known low viral load (e.g., <1,500 RNA copies/mL). HIV-Positive, Class 2—symptomatic HIV infection, acquired immunodeficiency syndrome, acute seroconversion, or known high viral load. If drug resistance is a concern, obtain expert consultation. Initiation of PEP should not be delayed pending expert consultation, and, because expert consultation alone cannot substitute for face-to-face counseling, resources should be available to provide immediate evaluation and follow-up care for all exposures.
[c] Source of unknown HIV status (e.g., deceased source person with no samples available for HIV testing).
[d]Unknown source (e.g., splash from inappropriately disposed blood).
[e]Small volume (i.e., a few drops).
[f]The designation, "consider PEP," indicates that PEP is optional and should be based on an individualized decision between the exposed person and the treating clinician.
[g]If PEP is offered and taken and the source is later determined to be HIV-negative, PEP should be discontinued.
[h]Large volume (i.e., major blood splash).

BOX 5-4 **Situations for Which Expert* Consultation for HIV Postexposure Prophylaxis Is Advised**

- Delayed (i.e., later than 24-36 hr) exposure report
  - — the interval after which there is no benefit from postexposure prophylaxis (PEP) is undefined
- Unknown source (e.g., needle in sharps disposal container or laundry)
  - — decide use of PEP on a case-by-case basis
  - — consider the severity of the exposure and the epidemiologic likelihood of HIV exposure
  - — do not test needles or other sharp instruments for HIV
- Known or suspected pregnancy in the exposed person
  - — does not preclude the use of optimal PEP regimens
  - — do not deny PEP solely on the basis of pregnancy
- Resistance of the source virus to antiretroviral agents
  - — influence of drug resistance on transmission risk is unknown
  - — selection of drugs to which the source person's virus is unlikely to be resistant is recommended, if the source person's virus is known or suspected to be resistant to ≥1 of the drugs considered for the PEP regimen
  - — resistance testing of the source person's virus at the time of the exposure is not recommended
- Toxicity of the initial PEP regimen
  - — adverse symptoms, such as nausea and diarrhea are common with PEP
  - — symptoms often can be managed without changing the PEP regimen by prescribing antimotility and/or antiemetic agents
  - — modification of dose intervals (i.e., administering a lower dose of drug more frequently throughout the day, as recommended by the manufacturer), in other situations, might help alleviate symptoms

HIV, Human immunodeficiency virus.
*Local experts and/or the National Clinicians' Postexposure Prophylaxis Hotline (PEPline [1-888-448-4911]).

BOX 5-5 Occupational Exposure Management Resources

National Clinicians' Postexposure Prophylaxis Hotline (PEPline) Run by University of California–San Francisco/San Francisco General Hospital staff; supported by the Health Resources and Services Administration Ryan White CARE Act, HIV/AIDS Bureau, AIDS Education and Training Centers, and CDC.	Phone: (888) 448-4911 Internet: http://www.ucsf.edu/hivcntr
Needlestick! A website to help clinicians manage and document occupational blood and body fluid exposures. Developed and maintained by the University of California, Los Angeles (UCLA), Emergency Medicine Center, UCLA School of Medicine, and funded in party by CDC and the Agency for Healthcare Research and Quality.	Internet: http://www.needlestick.mednet.ucla.edu
Hepatitis Hotline	Phone: (888) 443-7232 Internet: http://www.cdc.gov/ncidod/diseases/hepatitis/index.htm
Reporting to CDC: Occupationally acquired HIV infections and failures of PEP.	Phone: (800) 893-0485
HIV Antiretroviral Pregnancy Registry	Phone: (800) 258-4263 Fax: (800) 800-1052 Address: 1410 Commonwealth Drive Suite 215 Wilmington, NC 28405 Internet: http://www.glaxowellcome.com/preg_reg/antiretroviral
Food and Drug Administration Report unusual or severe toxicity to antiretroviral agents.	Phone: (800) 332-1088 Address: MedWatch HF-2, FDA 5600 Fishers Lane Rockville, MD 20857 Internet: http://www.fda.gov/medwatch
HIV/AIDS Treatment Information Service	Internet: http://www.hivatis.org

BOX 5-6 Management of Occupational Blood Exposures

Provide immediate care to the exposure site:
- Wash wounds and skin with soap and water
- Flush mucous membranes with water

Determine risk associated with exposure:
- Type of fluid (e.g., blood, visibly bloody fluid, other potentially infectious fluid or tissue, and concentrated virus)
- Type of exposure (i.e., percutaneous injury, mucous membrane or nonintact skin exposure, and bites resulting in blood exposure)

Evaluate exposure source:
- Assess the risk of infection using available information
- Test known sources for HBsAg, anti-HCV, and HIV antibodies (consider using rapid testing)
- For unknown sources, assess risk of exposure to HBV, HCV, or HIV infection
- Do not test discarded needles or syringes for virus contamination

Evaluate the exposed person:
- Assess immune status for HBV infection (i.e., by history of hepatitis B vaccination and vaccine response)

Give PEP for exposures posing risk of infection transmission:
- HBV: See Table 5-28
- HCV: PEP not recommended
- HIV: See Tables 5-29 and 5-30
  - — Initiate PEP as soon as possible, preferably within hours of exposure
  - — Offer pregnancy testing to all women of childbearing age not known to be pregnant
  - — Seek expert consultation if viral resistance is suspected
  - — Administer PEP for 4 wk if tolerated

Perform follow-up testing and provide counseling:
- Advise exposed persons to seek medical evaluation for any acute illness occurring during follow-up

HBV exposures
- Perform follow-up anti-HBs testing in persons who receive hepatitis B vaccine
  - — Test for anti-HBs 1-2 mo after last dose of vaccine
  - — Anti-HBs response to vaccine cannot be ascertained if HBIG was received in the previous 3-4 mo

HCV exposures
- Perform baseline and follow-up testing for anti-HCV and alanine aminotransferase (ALT) 4-6 mo after exposures
- Perform HCV RNA at 4-6 wk if earlier diagnosis of HCV infection desired
- Confirm repeatedly reactive anti-HCV enzyme immunoassays (EIAs) with supplemental tests

HIV exposures
- Perform HIV-antibody testing for at least 6 mo postexposure (e.g., at baseline, 6 wk, 3 mo, and 6 mo)
- Perform HIV antibody testing if illness compatible with an acute retroviral syndrome occurs
- Advise exposed persons to use precautions to prevent secondary transmission during the follow-up period
- Evaluate exposed persons taking PEP within 72 hr after exposure and monitor for drug toxicity for at least 2 wk

HBIG, Hepatitis B immune globulin; *HBsAg,* hepatitis B surface antigen; *HBV,* hepatitis B virus; *HCV,* hepatitis C virus; *HIV,* human immunodeficiency virus; *PEP,* post-exposure prophylaxis; *RNA,* ribonucleic acid.

BOX 5-7 **Basic and Expanded HIV Postexposure Prophylaxis Regimens**

Basic Regimen

- **Zidovudine (Retrovir; ZDV; AZT) and Lamivudine (Epivir; 3TC); available as Combivir**
  - — ZDV: 600 mg per day, in two or three divided doses
  - — 3TC: 150 mg bid

Advantages
- — ZDV is associated with decreased risk of HIV transmission in the CDC case-control study of occupational HIV infection
- — ZDV has been used more than the other drugs for PEP in HCP
- — Serious toxicity is rare when used for PEP
- — Side effects are predictable and manageable with antimotility and antiemetic agents
- — Probably a safe regimen for pregnant HCP
- — Can be given as a single tablet (Combivir) bid

Disadvantages
- — Side effects are common and might result in low adherence
- — Source patient virus might have resistance to this regimen
- — Potential for delayed toxicity (oncogenic/teratogenic) is unknown

Alternative Basic Regimens

- **Lamivudine (3TC) and Stavudine (Zerit; d4T)**
  - — 3TC: 150 mg bid
  - — d4T: 40 mg (if body weight is <60 kg, 30 mg) bid

Advantages
- — Well tolerated in patients with HIV infection, resulting in good adherence
- — Serious toxicity appears to be rare
- — Twice daily dosing might improve adherence

Disadvantages
- — Source patient virus might be resistant to this regimen
- — Potential for delayed toxicity (oncogenic/teratogenic) is unknown

- **Didanosine (Videx, chewable/dispersable buffered tablet; Videx EC, delayed-release capsule; ddl) and Stavudine (d4T)**
  - — ddl: 400 mg (if body weight is <60 kg, 125 mg bid) daily, on an empty stomach
  - — d4T: 40 mg (if body weight is <60 kg, 30 mg bid) bid

Advantages
- — Likely effective against HIV strains from source patients who are taking ZDV and 3TC

Disadvantages
- — ddl is difficult to administer and unpalatable.
- — Chewable/dispersable buffered tablet formulation of ddl interferes with absorption of some drugs (e.g., quinolone antibiotics, and indinavir).
- — Serious toxicity (e.g., neuropathy, pancreatitis, or hepatitis) can occur. Fatal and nonfatal pancreatitis has occurred in HIV-positive, treatment-naive patients. Patients taking ddl and d4T should be carefully assessed and closely monitored for pancreatitis, lactic acidosis, and hepatitis.
- — Side effects are common; anticipate diarrhea and low adherence.
- — Potential for delayed toxicity (oncogenic/teratogenic) is unknown.

Expanded Regimen

Basic regimen plus one of the following:

- **Indinavir (Crixivan; IDV)**
  - — 800 mg every 8 hr, on an empty stomach

Advantages
- — Potent HIV inhibitor

Disadvantages
- — Serious toxicity (e.g., nephrolithiasis) can occur; must take 8 glasses of fluid per day
- — Hyperbilirubinemia common; must avoid this drug during late pregnancy
- — Requires acid for absorption and cannot be taken simultaneously with ddl in chewable/dispersable buffered tablet formulation (doses must be separated by at least 1 hr)
- — Concomitant use of astemizole, terfenadine, dihydroergotamine, ergotamine, ergonovine, methylergonovine, rifampin, cisapride, St. John's Wort, lovastatin, simvastatin, pimozide, midazolam, or triazolam is not recommended
- — Potential for delayed toxicity (oncogenic/teratogenic) is unknown

- **Nelfinavir (Viracept; NFV)**
  - — 750 mg tid, with meals or snack, or
  - — 1250 mg bid, with meals or snack

Advantages
- — Potent HIV inhibitor
- — Twice dosing per day might improve adherence

Disadvantages
- — Concomitant use of astemizole, terfenadine, dihydroergotamine, ergotamine, ergonovine, methylergonovine, rifampin, cisapride, St. John's Wort, lovastatin, simvastatin, pimozide, midazolam, or triazolam is not recommended
- — Might accelerate the clearance of certain drugs, including oral contraceptives (requiring alternative or additional contraceptive measures for women taking these drugs)
- — Potential for delayed toxicity (oncogenic/teratogenic) is unknown

- **Efavirenz (Sustiva; EFV)**
  - — 600 mg daily, at bedtime

Continued

BOX 5-7 Basic and Expanded HIV Postexposure Prophylaxis Regimens—cont'd

Advantages
- — Does not require phosphorylation before activation and might be active earlier than other antiretroviral agents (NOTE: this might be only a theoretical advantage of no clinical benefit)
- — One dose daily might improve adherence

Disadvantages
- — Drug is associated with rash (early onset) that can be severe and might rarely progress to Stevens-Johnson syndrome.
- — Differentiating between early drug-associated rash and acute seroconversion can be difficult and cause extraordinary concern for the exposed person.
- — Nervous system side effects (e.g., dizziness, somnolence, insomnia, and/or abnormal dreaming) are common. Severe psychiatric symptoms are possible (dosing before bedtime might minimize these side effects).
- — Should not be used during pregnancy because of concerns about teratogenicity.
- — Concomitant use of astemizole, cisapride, midazolam, triazolam, ergot derivatives, or St. John's Wort is not recommended because inhibition of the metabolism of these drugs could create the potential for serious and/or life-threatening adverse events (e.g., cardiac arrhythmias, prolonged sedation, or respiratory depression).
- — Potential for oncogenic toxicity is unknown.

- **Abacavir (Ziagen; ABC); available as Trizivir, a combination of ZDV, 3TC, and ABC**
  - — 300 mg bid

Advantages
- — Potent HIV inhibitor
- — Well tolerated in patients with HIV infection

Disadvantages
- — Severe hypersensitivity reactions can occur, usually within the first 6 wk of treatment
- — Potential for delayed toxicity (oncogenic/teratogenic) is unknown

Antiretroviral Agents for Use as PEP Only with Expert Consultation

- Retonavir (Norvir; RTV)

Disadvantages
- — Difficult to take (requires dose escalation)
- — Poor tolerability
- — Many drug interactions

- **Saquinavir (Fortovase, soft-gel formulation; SQV)**

Disadvantages
- — Bioavailability is relatively poor, even with new formulation

- **Amprenavir (Agenerase; AMP)**

Disadvantages
- — Dosage consists of eight large pills taken bid
- — Many drug interactions

- **Delavirdine (Rescriptor; DLV)**

Disadvantages
- — Drug is associated with rash (early onset) that can be severe and progress to Stevens-Johnson syndrome
- — Many drug interactions

- **Lopinavir/Ritonavir (Kaletra)**
  - — 400/100 mg bid

Advantages
- — Potent HIV inhibitor
- — Well tolerated in patients with HIV infection

Disadvantages
- — Concomitant use of flecainide, propafenone, astemizole, terfenadine, dihydroergotamine, ergotamine, ergonovine, methylergonovine, rifampin, cisapride, St. John's Wort, lovastatin, simvastatin, pimozide, midazolam, or triazolam is not recommended because inhibition of the metabolism of these drugs could create the potential for serious and/or life-threatening adverse events (e.g., cardiac arrhythmias, prolonged sedation, or respiratory depression)
- — May accelerate the clearance of certain drugs, including oral contraceptives (requiring alternative or additional contraceptive measures for women taking these drugs)
- — Potential for delayed toxicity (oncogenic/teratogenic) is unknown

Antiretroviral Agents Generally Not Recommended for Use as PEP

- **Nevirapine (Viramune; NVP)**
  - — 200 mg daily for 2 wk, then 200 mg bid

Disadvantages
- — Associated with severe hepatotoxicity (including at least one case of liver failure requiring liver transplantation in an exposed person taking PEP)
- — Associated with rash (early onset) that can be severe and progress to Stevens-Johnson syndrome
- — Differentiating between early drug-associated rash and acute seroconversion can be difficult and cause extraordinary concern for the exposed person
- — Concomitant use of St. John's Wort is not recommended because this might result in suboptimal antiretroviral drug concentrations

Definitions of Complementary/Alternative Therapies

Acupuncture Thin needles are inserted superficially on the skin at locations throughout the body. These points are located along "channels" of energy. Heat can be applied by burning (moxibustion), electric current (electroacupuncture), or pressure (acupressure). Healing is proposed by the restoration of a balance of energy flow called *Qi*. Another explanation suggests that, possibly, the stimulation activates endorphin receptors.

Alexander Technique A body work technique in which rebalancing of "postural sets" (i.e., physical alignment) is taught by mentally focusing on the way correct alignments should look and feel and through verbal and tactile guidance by the practitioner.

Antineoplastons Naturally occurring peptides, amino acid derivatives, and carboxylic acids are proposed to control neoplastic cell growth using the patient's own "biochemical defense system," which works jointly with the immune system.

Applied Kinesiology A form of treatment that uses nutrition, physical manipulation, vitamins, diets, and exercise to restore and energize the body. Weak muscles are proposed to be a source of dysfunctional health.

Aromatherapy A form of herbal medicine that uses various oils from plants. Route of administration can be through absorption in the skin or inhalation. The action of antiviral and antibacterial agents is proposed to aid in healing. The aromatic biochemical structures of certain herbs are thought to act in areas of the brain related to past experiences and emotions (e.g., limbic system).

Ayurveda A major health system that emphasizes a preventive approach to health by focusing on an inner state of harmony and spiritual realization for self-healing. Includes special types of diets, herbs, and mineral parts and changes based on a system of constitutional categories in lifestyle. The use of enemas and purgation is to cleanse the body of excess toxins.

Biofeedback A mind-body therapy procedure in which sensors are placed on the body to measure muscle, heart rate, and sweat responses or neural activity. Information is provided by visual, auditory, or body-muscle cell activation so as to teach either to increase or decrease physiologic activity which, when reconstituted, is proposed to improve health problems (e.g., pain, anxiety, or high blood pressure). In some cases, relaxation exercises complement this procedure.

Brachytherapy Ionizing radiation therapy with the source applied to the surface of the body or located a short distance from the treated area.

Bristol Cancer Help Center (BCHC) Diet A stringent diet of raw and partly cooked vegetables with proteins from soy; claimed to enhance the quality of life and attitude toward illness in cancer patients.

Cell Therapy Healthy cellular material from fetuses, embryos, or organs of animals is directly injected into human patients to stimulate healing in dysfunctional organs. May also include blood transfusions or bone marrow transplantations.

Chelation Therapy Involves the removal—through intravenous infusion of a chelating agent (synthetic amino acid ethylenediamine tetraacetic acid [EDTA])—of metal, toxins, lead, mercury, nickel, copper, cadmium, and plaque as a way to treat certain diseases (e.g., cardiovascular). Ancillary treatments include the use of vitamins, changes in diet, and exercise.

Cognitive Therapy Psychologic therapy in which the major focus is on altering and changing irrational beliefs through a type of "socratic" dialogue and self-evaluation of certain illogical thoughts. Conditioning and learning are important components of this therapy.

Craniosacral Therapy A form of gentle manual manipulation used for diagnosis and for making corrections in a system made up of cerebrospinal fluid, cranial and dural membranes, cranial bones, and sacrum. This system is proposed to be dynamic with its own physiologic frequency. Through touch and pressure, tension is proposed to be reduced and cranial rhythms normalized, leading to improvement in health and disease.

Dance Therapy A movement-based therapy that aids in promoting feeling and awareness. The goal is to integrate body, mind, and self-esteem. It uses different parts of the body such as fingers, wrists, and arms to respond to music.

Diathermy The use of high-frequency electrical currents as a form of physical therapy and in surgical procedures. The term *diathermy,* derived from the Greek words *dia* and *therma,* literally means "heating through." The three forms of diathermy used by physical therapists are short-wave, ultrasound, and microwave.

Dimethylaminoethanol (DMAE) Pharmacologic therapy that uses a natural substance found in certain foods and the

From Spencer JW: *Complementary/alternative medicine: an evidence-based approach,* St Louis, 1999, Mosby.

human brain. It is a precursor to the transmitter acetylcholine. It is proposed to have a stimulant effect on the central nervous system if used as a supplement.

Electrochemical Treatment (ECT) A method using direct current to treat cancer. It involves inserting platinum electrodes into tumors and applying a constant voltage of less than 10 V to produce a 40- to 80-mA current between the anodes and cathodes for 30 minutes to several hours.

Electroencephalographic Normalization Gross neural activity is recorded from the scalp as an electroencephalogram (EEG) to assist in "restoring a balance in health" by training patients to produce more uniform and consistent EEG frequencies throughout certain or all areas of the brain (occipital, frontal, temporal, and parietal).

Environmental Medicine A practice of medicine in which the major focus is on cause-and-effect relationships in health. Evaluations are made of factors such as eating and living habits and types of air breathed. Testing in the patient's own environment is performed to determine what precipitators are present that may be related to disease or other health problems. A treatment protocol is developed from this information.

Eye Movement Desensitization and Reprocessing (EMDR) A technique that proposes to remove painful memories by behavioral techniques. Rhythmic, multisaccadic eye movements are produced by allowing the patient to track and follow a moving object while imaging a stressful memory or event. By using deconditioning, including verbal interaction with the therapist, the painful memory is extinguished and health improved.

Feldenkrais Method A bodywork technique in which its founder used the integration of physics, judo, and yoga. The practitioner directs sequences of movement using verbal or hands-on techniques or teaches a system of self-directed exercise to treat physical impairments through the learning of new movement patterns.

Hallucinogens The use of lysergic acid diethylamide (LSD) to produce at certain doses anticraving for certain illicit drugs such as cocaine, or ibogaine, a stimulant, to assist in developing tolerance and decreasing symptoms of dependence.

Hatha Yoga The branch of yoga practice that involves physical exercise, breathing practices, and movement. These exercises are designed to have a salutary effect on posture, flexibility, and strength, and are intended ultimately to prepare the body to remain still for long periods of meditation.

Hellerwork A bodywork technique that treats and improves proper body alignment through the development of a more complete awareness of the physical body. The goal is to realign fascia for improvement in standing, sitting, and breathing using "body energy," verbal feedback, and changing emotions and attitudes.

Herbal Medicine Herbs are used to treat various health conditions. Herbal medicine is a major form of treatment for more than 70% of the world's population.

Homeopathy A form of treatment in which substances (minerals, plant extracts, chemicals, or disease-producing germs), which in sufficient doses would produce a set of illness symptoms in healthy individuals, are given in microdoses to produce a "cure" of those same symptoms. The *symptom* is not thought to be part of the illness but part of a curative process.

Hydergine A phytotherapeutic method that combines extracts from the ergot fungus. Originally proposed to be used as an antihypertensive agent.

Hydrazine Sulfate A pharmacologic treatment proposed to treat certain cancers.

Hyperbaric Oxygen A therapy in which 100% oxygen is given at or above atmospheric pressure. An increase in oxygen in the tissue is proposed to increase blood circulation and improve healing and health and influence the course of disease.

Hyperthermia The use of various heating methods (such as electromagnetic therapy) to produce temperature elevations of a few degrees in cells and tissues, leading to a proposed antitumor effect. This is often used in conjunction with radiotherapy or chemotherapy for cancer treatment.

Immunoaugmentative Therapy A cancer treatment that proposes that cancer cells can be arrested by the use of four different blood proteins; this approach is also proposed to restore the immune system. Can be used as an adjunctive therapy.

Jin Shin Jyutsu A bodywork technique that uses specific "healing points" at the body surface, which are proposed to overlie energy flowing (Qi). The therapist's fingers are used to "redirect, balance, and provide a more efficient energy flow" to and throughout the body.

Laetrile A pharmacologic treatment using apricot pits that has been proposed to treat certain cancers.

Light Therapy Natural light or light of specified wavelengths is used to treat disease. This may include ultraviolet light, colored light, or low-intensity laser light. The eye generally is the initial entry point for the light because of its direct connection to the brain.

Magnetic Therapy Magnets are placed directly on the skin, stimulating living cells and increasing blood flow by ionic currents that are created from polarities on the magnets. Both acute and chronic health conditions are suggested to be treatable by this procedure.

Manual Manipulation A group of therapies with different assumptions and, in part, different areas of treatment. The major focus includes both stimulation and body manipulation, which are proposed to improve health or arrest disease, or both. Includes soft-tissue manipulation through stroking, kneading, friction, and vibration. Types include *massage,* adjustment of the spinal column *(chiropractic),* and tissue and musculoskeletal *(osteopathic)* manipulation.

Mediterranean Diet A diet that is thought to provide optimal distribution of daily caloric intake of different nutrients and includes 50% to 60% carbohydrates, 30% fats, and 10% proteins. The diet is derived from the eating habits of people in the Mediterranean area, who were shown to have reduced rates of cardiovascular disease.

Mind-Body Therapies A group of therapies that emphasize using the mind or brain in conjunction with the body to assist healing. Mind-body therapies can involve varying degrees of levels of consciousness, including *hypnosis,* in which selective attention is used to induce a specific altered state (trance) for memory retrieval, relaxation, or suggestion; *visual imagery,* in which the focus is on a target visual stimulus; *yoga,* which involves integration of posture and controlled breathing, relaxation, and/or meditation; *relaxation,* which includes lighter levels of altered states of consciousness through indirect or direct focus; and *meditation,* in which there is an intentional use of posture, concentration, contemplation, and visualization.

Muscle Energy Technique A manual therapy with components of both passive mobilization and muscle reeducation. Diagnosis of somatic dysfunction is performed by the practitioner after which the patient is guided to provide corrective muscle contraction. This is followed by further testing and correction.

Music Therapy The use of music either in an active or passive mode. Proposed to help allow for the expression of feelings, which helps to reduce stress. Other types of "vibratory" sounds can be used mainly to reduce stress, anxiety, and pain.

Native American Therapies Therapies used by many Native American Indian tribes, including their own healing herbs and ceremonies that use components with a spiritual emphasis.

Naturopathy A major health system that includes practices that emphasize diet, nutrition, homeopathy, acupuncture, herbal medicine, manipulation, and various mind-body therapies. Focal points include self-healing and treatment through changes in lifestyle and emphasis on health prevention.

Neuroelectric Therapy Transcranial or cranial neuroelectric stimulation (TENS), once called "electrosleep"; originally used in the 1950s to treat insomnia. In a typical TENS session, surface electrodes are placed in the mastoid region (behind the ear) and, similar to electroacupuncture, stimulated using a low-amperage, low-frequency alternating current. It has been suggested that TENS stimulates endogenous neurotransmitters such as endorphins that produce symptomatic relief.

Ornish Diet A life-choice program based on eating a vegetarian diet containing less than 10% fat. The diet is high in complex carbohydrates and fiber. Animal products and oils are avoided.

Orthomolecular Therapy A therapeutic approach that uses naturally occurring substances within the body, such as proteins, fat, and water, that promote restoration or balance (or both) by using vitamins, minerals, or other forms of nutrition to subsequently treat disease or promote healing, or both.

Oslo Diet An eating plan that emphasizes increased intake of fish and reduced total fat intake. Diet is combined with regular endurance exercise.

Pilates An educational and exercise approach using the proper body mechanics, movements, truncal and pelvic stabilization, coordinated breathing, and muscle contractions to promote strengthening. Attention is paid to the entire musculoskeletal system.

Piracetam A pharmacologic treatment proposed to be useful in the treatment of dementia. Uses a cyclic relative of the transmitter gamma-aminobutyric acid (GABA).

Prayer The use of prayer(s) that are offered to "some higher being" or authority to heal and/or arrest disease. May be practiced by the individual patient, by groups, or by other(s) with or without the patient's knowledge (e.g., intercessory).

Pritkin Diet A weight management plan that is based on a vegetarian framework. Meals are low in fat, high in fiber, and high in complex carbohydrates.

Qi Gong A form of Chinese exercise-stimulation therapy that proposes to improve health by redirecting mental focus, breathing, coordination, and relaxation. The goal is to "rebalance" the body's own healing capacities by activating proposed electrical or energetic currents that flow along meridians located throughout the body. These meridians, however, do not follow conventional nerve or muscle pathways. In Chinese medical training and practice this therapy includes "external Qi," which is energy transmitted from one person to another so as to heal.

Raja Yoga Yoga practice that includes all of the other forms of yoga practice. The practitioner is instructed to follow moral directives, physical exercises, breathing exercises, meditation, devotion, and service to others to facilitate religious awakening.

Reconstructive Therapy A nonsurgical therapy for arthritis that involves the injection of nutritional substances into the supporting tissues around an injured joint. The intent is to cause the dilation of blood vessels, which will allow fibroblasts to form around the injury and begin the healing process.

Reflexology A bodywork technique that uses reflex points on the hands and feet. Pressure is applied at points that correspond to various body parts, to eliminate blockages thought to produce pain or disease. The goal is to bring the body into balance.

Reiki Comes from the Japanese word meaning "universal life force energy." The practitioner serves as a conduit for healing energy directed into the body or energy field of the recipient without physical contact with the body.

Restricted Environmental Stimulation Therapy (REST) A procedure that uses a completely sensory-deprived environment to increase physical or mental healing through a nonreactive state.

Rolfing A bodywork technique that involves the myofascia. The body is realigned by using the hands to apply a deep pressure and friction that allows more sufficient posture, movement, and the "release" of emotions from the body.

Shark Cartilage A cancer therapy that proposes that shark cartilage can interrupt blood supply to a tumor(s) and subsequently "starve" it of any nutrients by using the antiangiogenic properties and other substances contained in the cartilage.

Shiatsu A bodywork technique involving finger pressure at specific points on the body mainly to balance "energy" in the body. The major focus is on prevention by keeping the body healthy. The therapy uses more than 600 points on the skin that are proposed to be connected to pathways through which energy flows. A Japanese form of acupressure.

T'ai Chi A technique that uses slow, purposeful motor-physical movements of the body to control and achieve a more balanced physiologic and psychologic state.

Therapeutic Riding A form of animal-assisted therapy in which either passive or active movements are produced to aid in approximating the human gait. In certain cases, physiotherapeutic exercises are performed.

Therapeutic Touch A body energy field technique in which hands are passed over the body without actually touching to recreate and change proposed "energy imbalances" for restoring innate healing forces. Verbal interaction between patient and therapist helps to maximize effects.

Traditional Chinese Medicine An ancient form of medicine that focuses on prevention and secondarily treats disease with an emphasis on maintaining balance through the body by stimulating a constant, smooth-flowing Qi energy. Herbs, acupuncture, massage, diet, and exercise are also used.

Trager Psychophysical Integration A bodywork technique in which the practitioner enters a meditative state and guides the client through gentle, light, rhythmic, nonintrusive movements. "Mentastics" exercises using self-healing movements are taught to the clients.

Transcranial Electrostimulation Pulsed electrical stimulation of 50 microamperes or less is applied between two electrodes attached to the ear. The stimulation is proposed to activate endogenous opioid activity, which may assist in the treatment of certain health problems such as substance abuse and physical pain.

Twelve-Step Program A program such as Alcoholics Anonymous that is based on a series of 12 steps, or tasks, that participants are asked to complete. As members progress through the 12 steps, they are expected to gain courage to attempt personal change and develop a greater acceptance of themselves. Programs emphasize the group process through the sharing of stories and experiences and through social interactions with other group members. Most 12-step programs incorporate a spiritual component and ask members to turn their lives over to a higher power.

The definitions listed above are not complete; for additional information, the interested reader should consult books such as Micozzi's *Fundamentals of complementary and alternative medicine* and Spencer JW: *Complementary/alternative medicine: an evidence-based approach*.

Commonly Used Herbals with Documented or Suspected Risks

Commonly Used Herbals with Documented or Suspected Risks

Herbal	Plant Source	Common Use	Comments
Aconite (Monkshood)	*Aconitum napellus*	Analgesic, antipyretic, wound healing	Side effects include cardiac arrhythmia and respiratory paralysis.
Aloe (internally)	*Aloe barbadenis, Aloe vera,* various Aloe species	Constipation, general tonic, wound healing	Side effects include gastrointestinal (GI) cramping, diarrhea, nephritis, hypokalemia, albuminuria, and hematuria with chronic use.
Borage	*Borago officinalis*	Antidiarrheal, diuretic	Contains low levels of pyrrolizidine alkaloids (lycopsamine, amabiline, thesinine) that are potentially hepatotoxic and carcinogenic.
Calamus	*Acorus calamus*	Antipyretic, digestive aid	Some calamus species contain beta asarone, which may be carcinogenic.
Chaparral	*Larrea tridentata*	Anticancer	Case reports of liver toxicity have been associated with use.
Coltsfoot	*Tussilago farfara*	Antitussive, demulcent	Contains pyrrolizidine alkaloids that are potentially hepatotoxic and carcinogenic.
Comfrey	*Symphytum officinale,* various Symphytum species	Bruises, sprains, wound healing	Contains pyrrolizidine alkaloids that are potentially hepatotoxic and carcinogenic.
Ephedra (Ma-huang)	*Ephedra sinica,* various *Ephedra* species	Appetite suppressant, bronchodilator, athletic performance enhancement (often combined with caffeine-containing herbals)	Side effects include insomnia, irritability, GI disturbances, urinary retention, and tachycardia. Misuse can lead to hypertension and arrhythmias.
Germander	*Teucrium chamaedrys*	Appetite suppressant	Contains diterpneoid derivatives that are potentially hepatotoxic.
Licorice	*Glycyrrhiza glabra*	Antiulcer, expectorant	Should only be used in small doses for short duration (<4 wk). With high doses, hypertension, hypokalemia, and sodium and water retention may occur.
Life root	*Senecio aureus*	Emmenagogue	Contains pyrrolizidine alkaloids that are potentially hepatotoxic and carcinogenic.
Pokeroot	*Phytolacca americana*	Anticancer, antirheumatic	Contains a saponin mixture, phytolaccatoxin, and PWM (a proteinaceous mitogen), which can cause gastroenteritis, hypotension, and diminished respiration.
Sassafras	*Sassafras albidum*	Antirheumatic, antispasmodic, stimulant	Contains the volatile oil safrole, which is potentially carcinogenic.
Yohimbe	*Pausinystalia yohimbe*	Impotence	Side effects include anxiety, nervousness, nausea, vomiting, and tachycardia.

From Novey DW: *A clinician's guide to complementary & alternative medicine,* St Louis, 2000, Mosby.

Commonly Used Herbal Medicines

Herbal Medicine	Scientific Name	Common Use	Potential Interactions	Potential Adverse Effects	Contraindications
Aloe vera (external only)	*Aloe barbendenis, Aloe vera,* various Aloe species	External: first-degree burns, cuts, abrasions	None known	Contact dermatitis	May delay healing of deep vertical (surgical) wounds
Arnica (external only)	*Arnica montana*	External: wound healing, inflammation	None known	Contact dermatitis; can damage skin with prolonged use	None unknown
Astragalus (or Tragacanth)	*Astragalus membranaceus*	Colds, flu, minor infections; hyperlipidemia, hyperglycemia (unproven)	None known	None known	None known
Bearberry	*Arctostaphylos uva-ursi*	Urinary tract inflammation	Any substance that acidifies the urine	Nausea and vomiting	Pregnancy, lactation, children under age 12 yr
Bilberry	*Vaccinium myrtillus*	Atherosclerosis, bruising, diarrhea, local inflammation of mucous membranes	Anticoagulants and antiplatelet drugs (possible)	Excessive consumption of berries; constipation	None known
Black cohosh	*Cimicifuga racemosa*	Dysmenorrhea, menopausal symptoms, premenstrual syndrome	None known	Gastric discomfort, dizziness, nervous system and visual disturbances, hypotension, bradycardia, increased perspiration	Pregnancy, lactation
Blessed thistle	*Centaurea enedictus*	Appetite stimulant, dyspepsia	None known	Allergies	Allergies to blessed thistle
Blue cohosh	*Caulophyllum thalictroides*	Menstrual difficulties; uterine stimulant	None known	Hypertension, respiratory stimulation, stimulation of intestinal motility	Should not be used without medical supervision; pregnancy, lactation, in children
Calendula	*Calendula officinalis*	External: wound healing	None known	None known	None known
Cascara sagrada	*Rhamnus purshiana*	Constipation	With chronic use due to potassium loss: cardiac glycoside, thiazide diuretics, corticosteroids, licorice root	Abdominal cramps	Intestinal obstruction, acute intestinal inflammation
Cat's claw	*Unicaria tomentosa, U. guianesis*	Cancer (anecdotal)	None known	None known	None known
Cayenne (Capsicum)	*Capsicum frutescens*	External: muscle spasms, chronic pain associated with herpes zoster, trigeminal neuralgia, surgical trauma	None known	Local burning sensation, hypersensitivity reaction	Injured skin, allergy
Chamomile	*Matricaria recutita* (formerly *M. chamomile, Chamomile recutita)*	External: skin and mucous membrane inflammation; internal: GI spasm and GI inflammatory disease	May delay concomitant drug absorption from the gut	Allergies (rare)	Allergies to chamomile (and other herbs of the daisy family); avoid in pregnancy

Cranberry	*Vaccinium macrocarpon*	Prevention of urinary tract infection	None known	Overuse: diarrhea	None known
Dandelion	*Tanaxacum officinale*	Appetite stimulant, dyspepsia	None known	Contact dermatitis, gastric discomfort	None known
Devil's claw	*Arpagophytum procumbens*	Appetite stimulant, supportive therapy for degenerative disorder of the locomotor system	None known	None known	Gastric and duodenal ulcers; gallstone (use only after consultation with health care provider)
Dong-quai	*Angelica sinensis*	CNS stimulant, suppression of immune system, analgesia, uterus stimulant (effectiveness is controversial)	Contains courmarin derivatives, monitor with warfarin; possible synergism with calcium channel blockers	Photosensitivity; lowers blood pressure, possible CNS stimulation; possible carcinogenic (contains safrole)	Pregnancy
Echinacea	*Echinacea angustifolia, E. pallida, E. purpurea*	Supportive therapy for colds and flu	None known	Local tingling and numbing sensation with fresh juice	Long-term use not recommended; progressive systemic illness such as tuberculosis, leucosis, collagenosis, multiple sclerosis, AIDS and HIV infection, and other autoimmune diseases; allergy to plants in the daisy family
Eleuthero	*Eleutherococcus senticosus*	Improvement in well-being	Digitalis glycosides	High doses: irritability, insomnia, anxiety; skin eruptions, headache, diarrhea, hypertension, pericardial pain in rheumatic heart disease	Similar to ginseng
Evening primrose	*Oenothera biennis*	Hyperlipidemia, atopic eczema	None known	Nausea, GI disturbances, headache	None known
Eyebright	*Eyphrasia officinalis*	Topical: conjunctivitis, eye irritations	None known	None known; cannot be recommended because of risk of potential contamination with homemade, nonsterile preparations	See "Potential Adverse Effects"
Fenugreek	*Trigonella foenum-graecum*	External: inflammation; internal: appetite stimulant	None known	Skin reactions with repeated external application	None known
Feverfew	*Tanacetum parthenium*	Migraine prophylaxis	Anticoagulants, antiplatelet drugs, thrombolytics	Mouth ulceration with chewing leaves, oral irritation, GI disturbances, increase in heart rate	Allergy to feverfew and other plants in the daisy family; pregnancy
Fo-ti	*Polygonum multiforum*	Rejuvenation, decreased liver and kidney function, insomnia, hyperlipidemia, immunosuppression, antimicrobial	None known	None known	Pregnancy

Continued

Commonly Used Herbal Medicines—cont'd

Herbal Medicine	Scientific Name	Common Use	Potential Interactions	Potential Adverse Effects	Contraindications
Garlic	*Allium sativum*	Hyperlipidemia; other uses: antibacterial, anticancer, antifungal, antihypertensive, anti-inflammatory agent, hypoglycemic	Anticoagulants, antiplatelet drugs	GI disturbances, garlic odor; may increase insulin level, producing decrease in blood glucose; high dose: anemia	Pregnancy and lactation
Ginger	*Zingiber officinale*	Dyspepsia, prevention of motion sickness	Anticoagulants, antiplatelet drugs; calcium channel blocker (possible)	None; GI irritation and discomfort with high dose	Gallstones (use only after consultation with health care provider); pregnancy (controversial)
Ginkgo	*Ginkgo biloba*	Symptomatic treatment of age-related organic brain syndrome, peripheral arterial occlusive disease (stage II of Fontaine), SSRI-induced sexual dysfunction, tinnitus, vertigo	Anticoagulants, antiplatelet drugs, thrombolytics	GI upset, headache, allergic skin reaction; cases of spontaneous bleeding have been reported	None known
Ginseng	*Panax ginseng, P. quinquefolia*	Improvement in well-being	Anticoagulants, antiplatelet drugs, thrombolytics; may potentiate MAOIs; stimulants (including caffeine), antipsychotic drugs, hormone therapy	High dose: breast tenderness, nervousness, excitation; estrogenic effects in women, hypotension, hypertension	Chronic use (should use 2 wk on and 2 wk off); acute illnesses, any form of hemorrhage; pregnancy and lactation
Goldenseal	*Hydrastis canadensi*	Inflammation of mucous membranes (unproven); does not mask illegal drugs in urine drug screens	May interfere with the ability of colon to manufacture B vitamins and may decrease their absorption; heparin (possible)	Hypoglycemia	Pregnancy and lactation
Gotu kola	*Centella asiatica* (formerly *Hydrocotyle asiatica)*	External: wound healing	None known	Hypersensitivity	None known
Grape seed	*Vitis vinifera*	Antioxidant	None known	None known	None known
Hawthorn	*Crataegus* spp.	Congestive heart failure; stage II of NYHA	Cardiotonic drugs, antihypertensive drugs	High dose: hypotension and sedation; nausea, fatigue, sweating, rash; none	Pregnancy, lactation
Horse chestnut	*Aeculus hippocastanum*	Chronic venous insufficiency	None known	GI disturbances, nausea, pruritus	None known
Hyssop	*Hyssopus officinalis*	Pharyngitis, expectorant	None known	None known	None known
Kava-kava	*Piper methysticum*	Anxiety, restlessness, sleep induction	Potentiation of CNS depressants and alcohol	Chronic use: kavaism with dry, flaking, discolored skin and reddened eyes; numbness of mouth with chewing, CNS depression	Pregnancy, nursing, endogenous depression

Licorice	*Glycyrrhiza glabra*	Gastric/duodenal ulcers	Due to potassium loss; digitalis glycosides, thiazide diuretics, corticosteroids, licorice	With prolonged use and with high doses: mineralocorticoid effects including sodium and water retention, hypokalemia, myoglobinuria	Gall bladder disease, kidney disease, pheochromocytoma and other adrenal tumors, diseases that cause low serum potassium livers, fasting, anorexia, bulimia, untreated hypothyroidism
Marshmallow	*Althaea officinalis*	Ingestion, irritation of oral and pharyngeal mucosa	May delay absorption of other drugs taken simultaneously	None known	None known
Milkthistle	*Silbum marianum*	Dyspepsia, supportive therapy for toxic liver damage	None known	Mild diarrhea	None known
Passion flower	*Passiflora incarnata*	Anxiety, insomnia (unproven)	None known	None known; may have MAOI activity	None known
Pau d'arco	*Tabebuia impetiginosa*	Cancer	Vitamin K	Chronic use: anemia	Bleeding disorders
Peppermint	*Mentha X piperita*	External: myalgia and neuralgia; internal: GI spasms, nausea, inflammation of oral mucosa	External: irritation of mucous membranes; overuse: heartburn, relaxation of esophageal sphincter	External: contact dermatitis; internal: mouth irritation, muscle tremor, hypersensitivity reaction, heartburn, bradycardia	Obstruction of bile ducts, gallbladder inflammation, severe liver damage, pregnancy
Plantain	*Plantago major*	External: inflammation of skin; internal: cough, oral and pharyngeal mucosa inflammation	None known	None known	None known
Pygeum	*Pygeum africanum*	Benign prostatic hyperplasia	None known	GI disturbance	None known
Saw palmetto	*Serenoa repens*	Benign prostatic hyperplasia, stages I and II	Hormone therapy	GI disturbance	Pregnancy, lactation, children, breast cancer
Slippery elm	*Scutellaria lateriflora*	Pharyngitis, GI inflammatory disorders	None known	Contact dermatitis	None known
St. John's wort	*Hypericum perforatum*	External: oil preparation for mild wounds and burns; internal: mild to moderate depression	MAOIs; SSRIs and other antidepressants, sympathomimetics	Possible photosensitization, GI disturbance	Pregnancy and lactation
Stinging nettle	*Urtica dionica*	Benign prostatic hyperplasia	None known	Allergy	Pregnancy; cardiac and renal dysfunction
Tea tree	*Melaleuca alternifolia*	External: bacteriostatic	None known	Allergic contact dermatitis	None known
Tumeric	*Curuma longa*	Dyspepsia	None known	None known	Obstruction of bile passages
Valerian	*Valeriana officinalis*	Restlessness, sleeping disorders	Possible with CNS depressants and alcohol	Strong, disagreeable odor; headache, excitability, cardiac disturbances, rare morning drowsiness	None known
Vitex (or chaste tree berry)	*Vitex agnus-castus*	Menstrual disorders	May interfere with dopamine-receptor antagonists	GI disturbances, itching, urticaria	None known

AIDS, Acquired immunodeficiency syndrome; *CNS*, central nervous system; *GI*, gastrointestinal; *HIV*, human immunodeficiency virus; *MAOI*, monoamine oxidase inhibitor; *NYHA*, New York Heart Association; *SSRI*, selective serotonin reuptake inhibitors.

Drug/Herb Interactions

The table that follows lists known drug/herb interactions for herbs included in this book. The pharmaceuticals and drug classes that are known to interact with herbal products are listed in the first column in alphabetical order, beside the names of the herbs with which they interact.

The reader should not assume that an herbal product not included here may be taken safely with a given drug or class of drugs. Research into herbal products is changing constantly, and new interactions are becoming known every day. Caution is always necessary when using herbal products, particularly when the client is taking them concurrently with pharmaceuticals.

From Skidmore-Roth L: *Mosby's Handbook of Herbs & Natural Supplements,* St Louis, 2004, Mosby.

Drug/Drug Classes	Herb	Interaction
ACE inhibitors	Pill-bearing spurge	May ↑ hypotension, do not use concurrently
ACE inhibitors	Pineapple	May antagonize ACE inhibitor actions, do not use concurrently
ACE inhibitors	Yohimbe	May ↓ or block actions of these drugs, do not use concurrently
ACE inhibitors	St. John's wort	May lead to severe photosensitivity, do not use concurrently
Acetazolamide	Quinine	When used with acetazolamide may lead to toxicity, do not use concurrently
Adenosine	Guarana	May ↓ the adenosine response
Alcohol	Betel palm	↑ effects of alcohol
Alcohol	Catnip	May enhance the effects of alcohol
Alcohol	Chamomile	May ↑ the effects of alcohol
Alcohol	Clary	↑ the action of alcohol
Alcohol	Corkwood	May ↑ anticholinergic effect
Alcohol	Goldenseal	May ↑ the effects of alcohol
Alcohol	Hops	↑ CNS effects
Alcohol	Jamaican dogwood	↑ effects of alcohol, do not use concurrently
Alcohol	St. John's wort	May ↑ MAO inhibition, do not use concurrently
Alcohol	Lavender	↑ sedation when used with lavender, do not use concurrently
All medications	Fenugreek	May cause reduced absorption of all medications used concurrently
All medications	Glucomanan	May ↓ the absorption of all medications if taken concurrently; separate dosages by at least 2 hours
All medications	Kaolin	↓ absorption of all drugs
All medications	Karaya gum	↓ absorption of all drugs
All medications	Pectin	↓ absorption of all drugs, vitamins, and minerals if taken concurrently
All oral medications	Flax	Absorption may ↓ if taken concurrently
All oral medications	Ginger	May ↑ absorption of all medications taken orally
All oral medications	Guar gum	May ↓ the absorption of all oral medications
All oral medications	Marshmallow	May ↓ absorption of oral medications, do not use concurrently
All oral medications	Mullein	May ↓ absorption of oral medications
Alpha-adrenergic blockers	Yohimbe	May result in ↑ toxicity, do not use concurrently
Alpha-adrenergic blockers	Butcher's broom	May ↓ action of alpha-adrenergic blockers
Alpha-adrenergic blockers	Capsicum peppers	May ↓ the action of alpha-adrenergic blockers
Aluminium salts	Quinine	May cause ↓ absorption of quinine
Amantadine	Jimsonweed	↑ antocholinergic effects
Amphetamines	Eucalyptus	May ↓ the effectiveness of amphetamines
Amphetamines	Rauwolfia	May cause ↓ pressor effects, do not use concurrently
Amphetamines	St. John's wort	May cause serotonin syndrome
Amphetamines	Khat	↑ action
Analgesics	Cola tree	May ↑ the effect of analgesics
Anesthetics	Ephedra	Causes ↑ arrhythmias when used with halothane anesthetics
Antacids	Jimsonweed	↓ action of jimsonweed
Antacids	Buckthorn	May ↓ the action of buckthorn if taken within 1 hour of the herb
Antacids	Cascara sagrada	May ↓ the action of cascara if taken within 1 hour of the herb

Continued

Drug/Drug Classes	Herb	Interaction
Antacids	Castor	To prevent decreased absorption of castor, do not take within 1 hour of antacids
Antacids	Chinese rhubarb	May ↓ the effectiveness of Chinese rhubarb if taken within 1 hour of the herb
Antacids	Green tea	May ↓ the therapeutic effects of green tea
Antianginals	Blue cohosh	May ↓ the action of antianginals, causing chest pain
Antianxiety agents	Cowslip	May ↑ the effect of antianxiety agents
Antiarrhythmics	Buckthorn	Chronic buckthorn use can cause hypokalemia and enhance the effects of antiarrhythmics
Antiarrhythmics	Khat	↑ action
Antiarrhythmics	Broom	May ↑ the effect of antiarrhythmics
Antiarrhythmics	Cascara sagrada	Chronic cascara use can cause hypokalemia and enhance the effects of antiarrhythmics
Antiarrhythmics	Chinese rhubarb	Chronic use of Chinese rhubarb can cause hypokalemia and enhance the effects of antiarrhythmics
Antiarrhythmics	Figwort	May ↑ the effects of antiarrhythmics
Antiarrhythmics	Fumitory	May ↑ the effects of antiarrhythmics
Antiarrhythmics	Goldenseal	May ↑ the effects of antiarrhythmics
Antiarrhythmics	Horehound	↑ serotonin effect, do not use concurrently
Antiarrhythmics	Licorice	↑ cardiac effects of antiarrhythmics, do not use concurrently
Antiarrhythmics	Aconite	↑ toxicity
Antibiotics	Acidophilus	Do not use concurrently
Anticholinergics	Jaborandi tree	When taken internally may ↓ effects of anticholinergics
Anticholinergics	Butterbur	May enhance the effects of anticholinergics
Anticholinergics	Jimsonweed	↑ effects of anticholinergics
Anticholinergics	Pill-bearing spurge	May ↓ effects of anticholinergic, do not use concurrently
Anticoagulants	Agrimony	May ↓ clotting times
Anticoagulants	Alfalfa	May prolong bleeding
Anticoagulants	Angelica	May prolong bleeding
Anticoagulants	Bilberry	May ↑ action of anticoagulants
Anticoagulants	Black haw	↑ the action of anticoagulants
Anticoagulants	Bogbean	May ↑ risk of bleeding
Anticoagulants	Buchu	Can ↑ the action of anticoagulants, causing bleeding
Anticoagulants	Chamomile	May interfere with the actions of anticoagulants
Anticoagulants	Chondroitin	Can cause ↑ bleeding
Anticoagulants	Coenzyme q10	May ↓ the action of anticoagulants
Anticoagulants	Fenugreek	Risk of ↑ bleeding when used concurrently
Anticoagulants	Feverfew	May ↑ anticoagulant effects
Anticoagulants	Garlic	May ↑ bleeding when used concurrently
Anticoagulants	Ginger	May ↑ risk of bleeding when taken concurrently
Anticoagulants	Ginkgo	↑ risk of bleeding
Anticoagulants	Ginseng	May ↓ the action of anticoagulants
Anticoagulants	Goldenseal	May ↓ the effects of anticoagulants
Anticoagulants	Horse chestnut	↑ risk of severe bleeding, do not use concurrently
Anticoagulants	Irish moss	↑ effects of anticoagulants, do not use concurrently
Anticoagulants	Kelp	May pose ↑ risk of bleeding, do not use concurrently
Anticoagulants	Kelpware	May pose ↑ risk of bleeding, do not use concurrently
Anticoagulants	Khella	↑ risk of bleeding when used with anticoagulants, do not use concurrently
Anticoagulants	Lovage	May ↑ effects of anticoagulants, do not use concurrently
Anticoagulants	Lungwort	May ↑ effects of anticoagulants, do not use concurrently
Anticoagulants	Lysine	Use of large amounts of lysine causes ↑ aminoglycoside toxicity, do not use concurrently
Anticoagulants	Meadowsweet	May ↑ risk of bleeding, do not use concurrently
Anticoagulants	Motherwort	May cause ↑ risk of bleeding, do not use concurrently
Anticoagulants	Mugwort	May cause ↑ risk of bleeding, do not use concurrently
Anticoagulants	Nettle	May ↓ effect of anticoagulants, do not use concurrently
Anticoagulants	Parsley	Large amounts may interfere with anticoagulation therapy
Anticoagulants	Pau d'arco	May result in ↑ risk of bleeding, do not use concurrently
Anticoagulants	Pill-bearing spurge	May ↑ effects of anticoagulants, do not use concurrently
Anticoagulants	Pineapple	May ↑ bleeding time when used with anticoagulants, do not use concurrently
Anticoagulants	Poplar	May ↑ bleeding time when used with anticoagulants, do not use concurrently
Anticoagulants	Prickly ash	May ↑ bleeding time when used with anticoagulants, do not use concurrently
Anticoagulants	Quinine	May ↑ action of anticoagulants, do not use concurrently
Anticoagulants	Safflower	May potentiate anticoagulant action, do not use concurrently
Anticoagulants	Saw palmetto	May potentiate anticoagulant effect of salicylants, do not use concurrently
Anticoagulants	Senega	May ↑ bleeding time, do not use concurrently
Anticoagulants	Tonka bean	May result in ↑ risk of bleeding, do not use concurrently
Anticoagulants	Turmeric	May result in ↑ risk of bleeding, do not use concurrently
Anticoagulants	Wintergreen	May cause ↑ risk of bleeding, do not use concurrently
Anticoagulants	Yarrow	May result in ↑ risk of bleeding, do not use concurrently
Anticoagulants, oral	Dong quai	May ↑ the effects of oral anticoagulants
Anticonvulsants	Ginkgo	May ↓ the anticonvulsant effect
Anticonvulsants	Ginseng	May provide an additive anticonvulsant action when taken concurrently
Anticonvulsants	Sage	May ↓ action of anticonvulsants, do not use concurrently
Antidepressants	Hops	↑ CNS effects
Antidepressants	Sam-e	Combining with antidepressants may lead to serotonin syndrome, do not use concurrently

Drug/Drug Classes	Herb	Interaction
Antidepressants	St. John's wort	Combined with these drugs may lead to severe photosensitivity, do not use concurrently
Antidiabetics	Alfalfa	May potentiate hypoglycemic action
Antidiabetics	Aloe	When taken internally may ↑ effects of antidiabetics
Antidiabetics	Blue cohosh	May ↓ the action of antidiabetics
Antidiabetics	Burdock	↑ hypoglycemic effect can occur
Antidiabetics	Elecampane	May ↓ blood glucose
Antidiabetics	Ephedra	May ↑ blood glucose
Antidiabetics	Eyebright	May ↑ the effects of antidiabetics when taken internally
Antidiabetics	Glucosamine	May ↑ the hypoglycemic effects of oral antidiabetics
Antidiabetics	Goat's rue	May ↑ the hypoglycemic effects of oral antidiabetics
Antidiabetics	Gotu kola	May ↓ the effectiveness of antidiabetics
Antidiabetics	Horehound	Enhance hypoglycemia, do not use concurrently
Antidiabetics	Horse chestnut	↑ hypoglycemic effects
Antidiabetics	Jambul	↑ effects of antidiabetics, do not use concurrently
Antidiabetics	Myrrh	May cause ↑ hypoglycemic effects, do not use concurrently
Antidiabetics	Myrtle	May cause ↑ hypoglycemic effects, do not use concurrently
Antidiabetics	Senega	May ↓ effects of antidiabetics, do not use concurrently
Antidiabetics	Raspberry	May ↑ hypoglycemia, monitor blood glucose levels
Antidiabetics	Siberian ginseng	May ↑ levels of antidiabetics, do not use concurrently
Antidiabetics, oral	Bay	May ↑ hypoglycemic effects
Antidiabetics, oral	Bee pollen	↓ effectiveness of antidiabetics, ↑ hyperglycemia
Antidiabetics, oral	Bilberry	May ↑ hypoglycemia
Antidiabetics, oral	Coenzyme q10	Oral antidiabetics may ↓ the action of coenzyme Q10 and deplete endogenous stores
Antidiabetics, oral	Coriander	May ↑ the effects of oral antidiabetics
Antidiabetics, oral	Dandelion	May ↑ the effects of oral antidiabetics
Antidiabetics, oral	Eucalyptus	May alter the effectiveness of antidiabetics
Antidiabetics, oral	Fenugreek	Hypoglycemial is possible when used concurrently
Antidiabetics, oral	Garlic	Because of hypoglycemic effects of garlic, oral antidiabetic dosages may need to be adjusted
Antidiabetics, oral	Ginseng	May ↑ the hypoglycemic effects of oral antidiabetics
Antidiabetics, oral	Glucomanan	May ↑ the hypoglycemic effects of oral antidiabetics
Antidiabetics, oral	Gymnema	May ↑ the action of oral antidiabetics
Antidiarrheals	Nutmeg	May be potentiated, monitor for constipation
Antidysrhythmics	Aloe	When taken internally may ↑ effects of antidysrhythmics
Antidysrhythmics	Coltsfoot	May antagonize antidysrhythmics
Antidysrhythmics	Devil's claw	Use cautiously because of possible inotropic and chronotropic effects
Antifungals	Gossypol	Concurrent use may cause nephrotoxicity
Antifungals, azole	Goldenseal	May slow the metabolism of azole antifungals
Antifungals, azole	Licorice	May ↑ levels of azole antifungals, do not use concurrently
Antiglaucoma agents	Betel palm	↓ effects of antiglaucoma agents
Antihistamines	Lavender	↑ sedation when used with lavender, do not use concurrently
Antihistamines	Khat	↑ action
Antihistamines	Corkwood	May ↑ anticholinergic effect
Antihistamines	Hops	↑ CNS effects
Antihistamines	Jamaican dogwood	May produce ↑ effect, do not use concurrently
Antihypertensives	Khat	↑ action
Antihypertensives	Aconite	↑ toxicity
Antihypertensives	Astragalus	May ↑ or ↓ action of antihypertensives
Antihypertensives	Barberry	May ↑ antihypertensive action
Antihypertensives	Betony	May ↑ action of antihypertensives
Antihypertensives	Black cohosh	↑ action of antihypertensives
Antihypertensives	Blood root	May ↑ hypotensive effects
Antihypertensives	Blue cohosh	↓ the action of antihypertensives and ↑ blood pressure
Antihypertensives	Broom	May ↑ the effect of antihypertensives
Antihypertensives	Burdock	May ↑ hypotensive effects
Antihypertensives	Cat's claw	May ↑ the hypotensive effects of antihypertensives
Antihypertensives	Coltsfoot	May antagonize antihypertensives
Antihypertensives	Dandelion	May ↑ the effects of antihypertensives
Antihypertensives	Goldenseal	May ↑ the effects of antihypertensives
Antihypertensives	Guarana	May ↓ the effects of antihypertensives
Antihypertensives	Hawthorn	May ↑ hypotension when used concurrently
Antihypertensives	Irish moss	↑ effects of antihypertensives, do not use concurrently
Antihypertensives	Jamaican dogwood	↑ effects of antihypertensive, do not use concurrently
Antihypertensives	Kelp	↑ hypotensive effects, do not use concurrently
Antihypertensives	Khella	↑ hypotension when used with antihypertensives, do not use concurrently
Antihypertensives	Licorice	May cause ↑ hypokalemia, do not use concurrently
Antihypertensives	Mistletoe	May cause ↑ hypotensive effect of antihypertensives, do not use concurrently
Antihypertensives	Queen Anne's lace	↑ hypotension when used with antihypertensives, use together cautiously
Antihypertensives	Rue	May cause ↑ vasodilation, do not use concurrently
Antihypertensives	Yarrow	May result in ↑ hypotension, do not use concurrently
Antilipidemics	Glucomanan	May ↑ the action of antilipidemics
Antilipidemics	Gotu kola	May ↓ the effectiveness of antilipidemics

Continued

Drug/Drug Classes	Herb	Interaction
Antimigraine agents	Butterbur	May enhance the effects of antimigraine agents
Antineoplastics	Yew	May cause ↑ myelosuppression, do not use concurrently
Antiparkinson agents	Kava	↑ symptoms of parkinsonism, do not use concurrently
Antiplatelet agents	Bilberry	May cause antiaggregation of platelets
Antiplatelet agents	Bogbean	May ↑ risk of bleeding
Antiplatelet agents	Dong quai	May ↑ the effects of antiplatelet agents
Antiplatelet agents	Feverfew	May ↑ the action of antiplatelet agents
Antiplatelet agents	Ginger	May ↑ risk of bleeding when taken concurrently
Antiplatelet agents	Saw palmetto	May lead to ↑ bleeding, do not use concurrently
Antiplatelet agents	Ginkgo	↑ risk of bleeding
Antipsychotics	Hops	↑ CNS effects
Antipsychotics	Kava	May result in neuroleptic disorder
Antiretrovirals	St. John's wort	When taken PO in combination with indinavir may ↓ the antiretroviral action.
Ascorbic acid	Chromium	Both chromium and ascorbic acid absorption ↑ when taken concurrently
Aspirin	Bilberry	May ↑ the anticoagulation action of aspirin
Aspirin	Bogbean	May ↑ risk of bleeding
Aspirin	Horse chestnut	↑ risk of severe bleeding, do not use concurrently
Atropine	Black root	Forms an insoluble complex with atropine; do not use concurrently
Barbiturates	Eucalyptus	May ↓ the effectiveness of barbiturates
Barbiturates	Jamaican dogwood	↑ effects of barbiturates, do not use concurrently
Barbiturates	Kava	↑ sedation
Barbiturates	Pill-bearing spurge	May ↑ effects of barbiturates, do not use concurrently
Barbiturates	Lemon balm	May potentiate the sedative effects of bariturates
Belladonna alkaloids	Mayapple	May ↓ laxative effects of mayapple, do not use concurrently
Benzodiazepines	Coffee	↓ the effect of benzodiazepines
Benzodiazepines	Cola tree	May ↓ the effect of cola tree products
Benzodiazepines	Goldenseal	May slow the metabolism of benzodiazepines
Benzodiazepines	Kava	↑ sedation and coma, do not use concurrently
Benzodiazepines	Melatonin	May ↑ anxiolytic effects of benzodiazepines, use cautiously
Beta-blockers	Betel palm	↑ action of beta-blockers
Beta-blockers	Butterbur	May enhance the effects of beta-blockers
Beta-blockers	Coenzyme q10	Beta-blockers may ↓ the action of coenzyme Q10 and deplete endogenous stores
Beta-blockers	Coffee	Caffeine in coffee ↑ blood pressure in those taking beta-blockers
Beta-blockers	Cola tree	May ↑ blood pressure when used with beta-blockers
Beta-blockers	Ephedra	Causes ↑ hypertension when used with beta-blockers
Beta-blockers	Figwort	May ↑ the effects of beta-blockers
Beta-blockers	Fumitory	May ↑ the effects of beta-blockers
Beta-blockers	Goldenseal	May ↑ the effects of beta-blockers
Beta-blockers	Guarana	May ↑ the effects of beta-blockers
Beta-blockers	Jaborandi tree	When used internally may ↑ adverse cardiovascular reactions, do not use concurrently
Beta-blockers	Khat	↑ action
Beta-blockers	Lily of the valley	May ↑ effects, do not use concurrently
Beta-blockers	Motherwort	May cause ↓ heart rate, do not use concurrently
Bethanechol	Jaborandi tree	When used internally, cholinergic effects ↑
Bronchodilators	Coffee	Large amounts of coffee may ↑ the action of some bronchodilators
Bronchodilators	Green tea	Large amounts of green tea ↑ the action of some bronchodilators
Bronchodilators	Guarana	May ↑ the action of bronchodilators
Caffeine	Creatine	May ↓ the effects of creatine
Calcitonin	Yellow dock	May cause ↑ hypocalcemia, do not use concurrently
Calcium supplements	Shark cartilage	May lead to ↑ calcium levels
Calcium-channel blockers	Khat	↑ action
Calcium-channel blockers	Lily of the valley	May ↑ effects, do not use concurrently
Calcium-channel blockers	Burdock	May ↑ hypotensive effects
Calcium-channel blockers	Goldenseal	May slow the metabolism of calcium-channel blockers
Calcium-channel blockers	Khella	↑ hypotension when used with calcium-channel blockers, do not use concurrently
Calcium-channel blockers	Barberry	May ↑ effect of calcium-channel blockers
Calcium-channel blockers	Betel palm	↑ action of calcium-channel blockers
Carbamazepine	Plantain	May ↓ effects of carbamazepine, do not use concurrently
Carbidopa	Octacosanol	May cause dyskinesia when used with carbidopa/levodopa, do not use concurrently
Cardiac agents	Squill	May ↑ effect of cardiac agents, causing life-threatening toxicity, do not use concurrently
Cardiac agents	Plantain	May ↑ effect of cardiac agents, do not use concurrently
Cardiac agents	Rauwolfia	May result in ↑ hypotension, do not use concurrently
Cardiac glycosides	Khat	↑ action
Cardiac glycosides	Lily of the valley	May ↑ effects, do not use concurrently
Cardiac glycosides	Aconite	↑ toxicity

Drug/Drug Classes	Herb	Interaction
Cardiac glycosides	Aloe	When taken internally may ↑ effects of cardiac glycosides
Cardiac glycosides	Betel palm	↑ action of cardiac glycosides
Cardiac glycosides	Beth root	May ↓ effects of cardiac glycosides
Cardiac glycosides	Black root	Forms an insoluble complex with cardiac glycosides; do not use concurrently
Cardiac glycosides	Broom	May ↑ the effect of cardiac glycosides
Cardiac glycosides	Buckthorn	Chronic buckthorn use can cause hypokalemia and enhance the effects of cardiac glycosides
Cardiac glycosides	Cascara sagrada	Chronic cascara use can cause hypokalemia and enhance the effects of cardiac glycosides
Cardiac glycosides	Chinese rhubarb	Chronic use of Chinese rhubarb can cause hypokalemia and enhance the effects of cardiac glycosides
Cardiac glycosides	Condurango	Absorption of digitoxin and digoxin may be ↓ when taken concurrently
Cardiac glycosides	Figwort	May ↑ the action of figwort
Cardiac glycosides	Fumitory	May ↑ the effects of cardiac glycosides
Cardiac glycosides	Goldenseal	May ↓ the effects of cardiac glycosides
Cardiac glycosides	Hawthorn	May ↑ the effects of cardiac glycosides
Cardiac glycosides	Horsetail	↑ toxicity and ↑ hypokalemia
Cardiac glycosides	Licorice	May cause ↑ toxicity and ↑ hypokalemia, do not use concurrently.
Cardiac glycosides	Mistletoe	May cause ↓ cardiac function, do not use concurrently
Cardiac glycosides	Motherwort	May cause ↓ heart rate, do not use concurrently
Cardiac glycosides	Night-blooming cereus	May ↑ actions of cardiac glycosides, do not use concurrently
Cardiac glycosides	Oleander	May cause fatal digitalis toxicity, do not use concurrently
Cardiac glycosides	Queen anne's lace	May ↑ cardiac depression, do not use concurrently
Cardiac glycosides	Quinine	May ↑ action of cardiac glycosides, do not use concurrently
Cardiac glycosides	Rauwolfia	Will cause severe bradycardia, do not use together
Cardiac glycosides	Rue	May cause ↑ inotropic effects, do not use concurrently
Cardiac glycosides	Senna	Chronic use may potentiate cardiac glycosides
Cardiac glycosides	Siberian ginseng	May ↑ levels of cardiac glycosides, do not use concurrently
Cardiac medications	Kudzu	Enhance effects of cardiac medications, do not use concurrently
Central nervous system depressants	Yarrow	May cause ↑ sedation, do not use concurrently
Central nervous system depressants	Goldenseal	May ↑ the effects of central nervous system depressants
Central nervous system depressants	Hawthorn	May ↑ the sedative effects of central nervous system depressants
Central nervous system depressants	Kava	↑ sedation, do not use concurrently
Central nervous system depressants	Mistletoe	May cause ↑ sedation, do not use concurrently
Central nervous system depressants	Passion flower	May cause ↑ sedation, do not use concurrently
Central nervous system depressants	Peyote	May ↑ effect of other CNS drugs, do not use concurrently
Central nervous system depressants	Hops	↑ CNS effects
Central nervous system depressants	Lemon balm	May potentiate the sedative effects of CNS depressants
Central nervous system depressants	Rauwolfia	May cause ↑ CNS depression, do not use concurrently
Central nervous system depressants	Skullcap	May potentiate sedation of CNS depressants, do not use concurrently
Central nervous system depressants	Senega	May cause ↑ CNS effects, do not use concurrently
Central nervous system depressants	Valerian	May ↑ effects of CNS depressants, do not use concurrently
Central nervous system depressants	Poppy	↑ CNS depression when use with CNS depressants, do not use concurrently
Central nervous system depressants	Nettle	May lead to ↑ CNS depression
Central nervous system depressants	Pokeweed	May ↑ action of CNS depressants, do not use concurrently
Central nervous system depressants	Yerba mate	May produce antagonistic effect, do not use concurrently
Central nervous system depressants	Queen Anne's lace	↑ action of CNS depressants, use together cautiously
Central nervous system stimulants	Squill	May ↑ effects of CNS stimulants, do not use concurrently
Central nervous system stimulants	Yerba mate	May ↑ effects CNS stimulants, use together cautiously
Central nervous system stimulants	Yohimbe	May result in ↑ CNS stimulation, do not use concurrently
Cerebral stimulants	Horsetail	↑ CNS effects, do not use concurrently
Cerebral stimulants	Melatonin	May have a synergistic effect and exacerbate insomnia, do not use concurrently

Continued

Drug/Drug Classes	Herb	Interaction
Cholinergics, ophthalmic	Jaborandi tree	When used internally cholinergic effects ↑
Cholinesterase inhibitors	Pill-bearing spurge	May ↑ effects of cholinesterase inhibitors
Ciprofloxacin	Fennel	Affects the absorption, distribution, and elimination of ciprofloxacin; dosages should be separated by at least 2 hours
Clonidine	Capsicum peppers	May ↓ the antihypertensive effects of clonidine
Contraceptives, oral	Alfalfa	May alter action
Contraceptives, oral	Black cohosh	May ↑ effects
Contraceptives, oral	Chaste tree	May interfere with the action of oral contraceptives
Contraceptives, oral	St. John's wort	When combined with oral contraceptives, may lead to severe photosensitivity, do not use concurrently
Corticosteroids	Buckthorn	Hypokalemia can result from use of buckthorn with corticosteroids
Corticosteroids	Cascara sagrada	Hypokalemia may result from concurrent use
Corticosteroids	Chinese rhubarb	Chronic use of Chinese rhubarb can cause hypokalemia and enhance the effects of corticosteroids
Corticosteroids	Licorice	May ↑ effects of corticosteroids, do not use concurrently
Corticosteroids	Perilla	May augment the effects of corticosteroids, do not use concurrently
CYP2A6, drugs metabolized by	Condurango	Use condurango with caution
CYP3A4, drugs metabolized by	Wild cherry	May slow metabolism, do not use concurrently
CYP450, drugs metabolized by	Myrtle	Do not use concurrently
CYP450, drugs metabolized by	Pennyroyal	Do not use concurrently with drugs metabolized by CYP450
CYP450, drugs metabolized by	Hops	↓ CYP450 levels
CYP450, drugs metabolized by	Milk thistle	Should not be used together
CYP450, drugs metabolized by	Black pepper	Avoid concurrent use
CYP450, drugs metabolized by	Condurango	Use condurango with caution, especially in clients with hepatic disorders
Decongestants	Khat	↑ action
Dhea	Melatonin	May ↓ cytokine production, do not use concurrently
Disulfiram	Pill-bearing spurge	Do not use concurrently
Disulfiram	Senna	Do not use with disulfiram
Diuretics	Yellow dock	May cause ↑ hypocalcemia, do not use concurrently
Diuretics	Bearberry	Concurrent use may lead to electrolyte loss, primarily hypokalemia
Diuretics	Cucumber	May ↑ the diuretic effect of other diuretics
Diuretics	Dandelion	May ↑ diuresis, leading to fluid loss and electrolyte imbalances
Diuretics	Gossypol	Concurrent use may cause severe hypokalemia
Diuretics	Horsetail	↑ effects of diuretics, do not use concurrently
Diuretics	Khella	↑ hypotension when used with diuretics, do not use concurrently
Diuretics	Licorice	May cause ↑ hypokalemia, do not use concurrently
Diuretics	Nettle	May ↑ effects of diuretics, resulting in dehydration and hypokalemia, do not use concurrently
Diuretics	Queen Anne's lace	↑ hypotension, use together cautiously
Diuretics	Yerba mate	May ↑ effects of diuretics, do not use concurrently
Diuretics, loop	St. John's wort	May lead to severe photosensitivity, do not use concurrently
Diuretics, loop	Aloe	When taken internally may ↑ effects of loop diuretics
Diuretics, thiazide	St. John's wort	May lead to severe photosensitivity, do not use concurrently
Diuretics, thiazide	Aloe	When taken internally may ↑ effects of thiazide diuretics
Diuretics, thiazide	Buckthorn	Hypokalemia can result from use of buckthorn with thiazide diuretics
Diuretics, thiazide	Cascara sagrada	Hypokalemia may result from concurrent use
Diuretics, thiazide	Chinese rhubarb	Chronic use of Chinese rhubarb can cause hypokalemia and enhance the effects of thiazide diuretics
Econazole vaginal cream	Echinacea	May ↓ the action of this cream
Electrolyte solutions	Agar	↑ dehydration
Emetics	Horehound	Granisetron and ondansetron ↑ serotonin effect, do not use concurrently
Ephedrine	Rauwolfia	May cause ↓ pressor effects, do not use concurrently
Epinephrine	Rauwolfia	May cause ↓ pressor effects, do not use concurrently
Ergots	Horehound	↑ serotonin effect, do not use concurrently
Estrogens	Alfalfa	May alter action
Estrogens	Hops	↑ hormonal levels
Furoquinolones	Cola tree	May ↑ the effect of cola tree products
Glucocorticoids	Squill	May ↑ effects of glucocorticoids, do not use concurrently
Glucose	Creatine	May ↑ the storage of creatine in muscle tissue

Drug/Drug Classes	Herb	Interaction
Guanethidine	Ephedra	May ↓ the effect of guanethidine
Hepatotoxic agents	Black root	Avoid concurrent use
HMG-coa reductase inhibitors	Coenzyme Q10	HMG-coa reductase inhibitors may ↓ the action of coenzyme Q10 and deplete endogenous stores
Hormone replacement therapy	Black cohosh	May alter the effects of other hormone replacement therapies
Hormone replacement therapy	Dhea	DHEA may interfere with estrogen and androgen therapy
Hormones	Saw palmetto	May antagonize hormone therapy, do not use concurrently
Hormones (animal)	Cat's claw	May interact with hormones made from animal products
Hypnotics	Clary	↑ the action of hypnotics
Hypoglycemics, oral	Bitter melon	May ↑ effects of oral hypoglycemics
Immune serum	Safflower	May cause ↑ immunosuppression, do not use concurrently
Immunomodulators	Echinacea	May ↓ the effects of immunosuppressants; should not be used immediately before, during, or after transplant surgery
Immunostimulants	Cat's claw	Do not use concurrently
Immunosuppressants	Ginseng	May diminish the effect of immunosuppressants; do not use before, during, or after transplant surgery
Immunosuppressants	Schisandra	May ↓ effectiveness of immunosuppressants, avoid use before, during, or after transplant surgery
Immunosuppressants	Safflower	May cause ↑ immunosuppression, do not use concurrently
Immunosuppressants	Mistletoe	May stimulate immunity, do not use concurrently
Immunosuppressants	St. John's wort	Rejection of transplanted hearts has occurred when taken PO with cyclosporine. Other immunosuppressants may have same interaction in this and other transplants
Immunosuppressants	Saw palmetto	May ↑ or ↓ immunostimulant effects, do not use concurrently
Immunosuppressants	Skullcap	May ↓ effects of immunosuppressants, do not use concurrently
Immunosuppressants	Turmeric	May ↓ effectiveness of immunosuppressants, do not use concurrently
Immunosuppressants	Maitake	May ↓ effects of immunosuppressants, do not use immediately before, during, or after transplant surgery.
Insulin	Basil	May ↑ hypoglycemic effects
Insulin	Bay	May ↑ hypoglycemic effects
Insulin	Bee pollen	↓ effectiveness of insulin, ↑ hyperglycemia
Insulin	Bilberry	May significantly ↓ blood sugar levels—monitor carefully
Insulin	Cat's claw	May interact with insulin
Insulin	Dandelion	May ↑ the effects of insulin
Insulin	Eucalyptus	May alter the effectiveness of insulin
Insulin	Garlic	Because of hypoglycemic effects of garlic, insulin dosages may need to be adjusted
Insulin	Ginseng	May ↑ the hypoglycemic effects of insulin
Insulin	Glucomanan	May ↑ the hypoglycemic effects of insulin
Insulin	Guar gum	May delay glucose absorption when used concurrently; insulin dose may need to be decreased
Insulin	Gymnema	May ↑ the action of insulin
Interferon	Astragalus	May prevent or shorten upper respiratory infections
Interleukin-2	Astragalus	May ↑ or ↓ effect of drugs such as interleukin-2
Ipecac	Mayapple	May ↓ laxative effects of mayapple, do not use concurrently
Iron salts	Bilberry	Interferes with iron absorption
Iron salts	Chromium	↓ chromium absorption when taken concurrently
Iron salts	Condurango	Iron absorption may be ↓
Iron salts	Ground ivy	May ↓ the absorption of iron salts
Iron salts	Hawthorn	May ↓ the absorption of iron salts; separate dosages by at least 2 hours
Iron salts	Hops	↓ absorption of iron salts
Iron salts	Horehound	↓ absorption of iron salts
Iron salts	Horse chestnut	↓ absorption of iron salts
Iron salts	Lady's mantle	↓ absorption of iron salts
Iron salts	Lavender	↓ absorption of iron salts
Iron salts	Lemon balm	↓ absorption of iron salts
Iron salts	Marshmallow	May ↓ absorption of iron salts
Iron salts	Meadowsweet	May ↓ absorption of iron salts
Iron salts	Mistletoe	May ↓ absorption of iron salts
Iron salts	Motherwort	May ↓ absorption of iron salts
Iron salts	Nettle	May interfere with absorption of iron salts
Iron salts	Oak	May ↓ absorption of iron salts
Iron salts	Plantain	May ↓ absorption of iron salts
Iron salts	Poplar	May ↓ absorption of iron salts
Iron salts	Prickly ash	May ↓ absorption of iron salts
Iron salts	Raspberry	May ↓ absorption of iron salts
Iron salts	Sage	May ↓ absorption of iron salts
Iron salts	Slippery elm	May ↓ absorption of iron salts
Iron salts	Squill	May ↓ absorption of iron salts
Iron salts	Valerian	May interfere with absorption of iron salts
Iron salts	Witch hazel	May ↓ absorption of iron salts
Iron salts	Yellow dock	May ↓ absorption of iron salts
Isoproterenol	Rauwolfia	May cause ↓ pressor effects, do not use concurrently

Continued

Drug/Drug Classes	Herb	Interaction
Kanamycin	Siberian ginseng	May ↑ action of kanamycin
Laxatives	Flax	May ↑ the action of laxatives
Laxatives	Senna	Additive effect can occur, do not use concurrently
Laxatives	Squill	May ↑ effects of laxatives, do not use concurrently
Levodopa	Octacosanol	May cause dyskinesia when used with carbidopa/levodopa, do not use concurrently
Levodopa	Rauwolfia	↓ effect of levodopa, with ↑ extrapyramidal motor symptoms
Lithium	Coffee	↓ levels of lithium
Lithium	Cola tree	May ↓ the effect of cola tree products
Lithium	Dandelion	Toxicity may occur if used concurrently
Lithium	Goldenrod	May result in dehydration and lithium toxicity
Lithium	Horsetail	Dehydration and lithium toxicity
Lithium	Juniper	Dehydration and lithium toxicity
Lithium	Nettle	May result in dehydration, lithium toxicity
Lithium	Parsley	May lead to dehydration, lithium toxicity
Lithium	Plantain	May ↓ effects of lithium, do not use concurrently
Magnesium	Melatonin	↑ inhibition of N-methyl-D-aspartate receptors, do not use concurrently
Magnesium	Quinine	May cause ↓ absorption of quinine
MAOIs	Khat	↑ action
MAOIs	Betel palm	May ↑ chance of hypertensive crisis
MAOIs	Butcher's broom	May ↑ action of MAOIs and precipitate a hypertensive crisis
MAOIs	Cacao tree	May ↑ the vasopressor effect of MAOIs
MAOIs	Capsicum peppers	May precipitate hypertensive crisis
MAOIs	Coffee	Large amounts of coffee should be avoided; hypertensive actions may occur
MAOIs	Cola tree	May ↑ blood pressure when used with phenelzine and tranylcypromine
MAOIs	Ephedra	Hypertensive crisis can occur when used concurrently
MAOIs	Galanthamine	Hypertensive crisis may occur
MAOIs	Ginkgo	May ↑ action of MAOIs
MAOIs	Ginseng	Concurrent use may result in manic-like syndrome
MAOIs	Green tea	Large amounts of green tea taken concurrently with MAOIs can cause hypertensive crisis
MAOIs	Guarana	Large amounts of guarana taken with MAOIs can result in hypertensive crisis
MAOIs	Jimsonweed	↑ anticholinergic effects
MAOIs	Night-blooming cereus	May ↑ cardiac effects, do not use concurrently
MAOIs	Nutmeg	May be potentiated, do not use concurrently
MAOIs	Parsley	When used with tricyclics or SSRIs may lead to serotonin syndrome, do not use concurrently
MAOIs	Passion flower	May cause ↑ MAOI activity, do not use concurrently
MAOIs	Rauwolfia	May cause excitation and/or hypertension, do not use concurrently
MAOIs	St. John's wort	May ↑ MAO inhibition, do not use concurrently
MAOIs	Valerian	May negate therapeutic effects of MAOIs, do not use concurrently
MAOIs	Yohimbe	May ↑ effects of MAOIs, do not use concurrently
Methyldopa	Capsicum peppers	May ↓ the antihypertensive effects of methyldopa
Minerals	Allspice	May interfere with absorption of minerals
Minerals	Pipsissewa	Should be taken 2 hrs before or after pipsissewa
Mithramycin	Yellow dock	May cause ↑ hypocalcemia, do not use concurrently
Morphine	Oats	May ↓ effect of morphine, do not use concurrently
Neuromuscular blockers	Quinine	May ↑ action of neuromuscular blockers, do not use concurrently
Nicotine	Lobelia	↑ effects of nicotine-containing products, do not use concurrently
Nicotine	Oats	May ↓ hypertensive effects of nicotine
Norepinephrine	Rauwolfia	May cause ↓ pressor effects, do not use concurrently
NSAIDs	Bearberry	May ↑ effect of NSAIDs
NSAIDs	Bilberry	May ↑ action of NSAIDs
NSAIDs	Bogbean	May ↑ risk of bleeding
NSAIDs	Chondroitin	Can cause ↑ bleeding
NSAIDs	Gossypol	Concurrent use may result in gastrointestinal distress and gastrointestinal tissue damage
NSAIDs	St. John's wort	When combined may lead to severe photosensitivity, do not use concurrently
NSAIDs	Turmeric	May result in ↑ risk of bleeding, do not use concurrently
NSAIDs	Saw palmetto	May lead to ↑ bleeding time, do not use concurrently
NSAIDs, topical	Jaborandi tree	Jaborandi tree action ↓ when used with topical NSAIDs, do not use concurrently
Opioids	Lavender	↑ sedation when used with lavender, do not use concurrently
Opioids	Parsley	May cause serotonin syndrome, do not use concurrently
Opioids	Corkwood	May ↑ anticholinergic effect
Opioids	Jamaican dogwood	↑ effects of opioids, do not use concurrently
Oxytocics	Ephedra	Causes severe hypertension when used with oxytocics
Paroxetine	St. John's wort	↑ sedation
Phenothiazines	Coenzyme q10	Some phenothiazines may ↓ the action of coenzyme Q10 and deplete endogenous stores
Phenothiazines	Corkwood	May ↑ anticholinergic effect
Phenothiazines	Ephedra	Tachycardia may result if used concurrently

Drug/Drug Classes	Herb	Interaction
Phenothiazines	Evening primrose oil	May cause seizures
Phenothiazines	Jimsonweed	↓ action of phenothiazines
Phenothiazines	Yohimbe	May result in ↑ toxicity, do not use concurrently
Phenytoin	Yellow dock	May cause ↑ hypocalcemia, do not use concurrently
Phenytoin	Valerian	May negate therapeutic effects of meds containing phenytoin, do not use concurrently
Plasma, fresh	Cat's claw	May interact with fresh plasma
Potassium-wasting drugs	Aloe	When taken internally may ↑ effects of potassium-wasting drugs
Psychoanaleptic agents	Cola tree	May ↑ the effects of psychoanaleptic agents
Psychotropic agents	Nutmeg	May be potentiated, do not use concurrently
Radioactive isotopes	Bugleweed	Can interfere with the action of radioactive isotopes
Salicylates	Horse chestnut	↑ risk of severe bleeding, do not use concurrently
Salicylates	Chondroitin	Can cause ↑ bleeding
Salicylates	Cola tree	May ↑ the effect of cola tree products
Salicylates	Gossypol	Concurrent use may result in tissue damage
Salicylates	Irish moss	↑ risk of bleeding, do not use concurrently
Salicylates	Pansy	May ↑ actions of salicylates
Scopolamine	Black root	Forms an insoluble complex with scopolamine; do not use concurrently
Sedative/hypnotics	Lavender	↑ sedation when used with lavender, do not use concurrently
Sedative/hypnotics	Cowslip	May ↑ the effect of sedative/hypnotics
Sedative/hypnotics	Catnip	May enhance the effects of sedatives
Sedative/hypnotics	Chamomile	May ↑ the effects of sedatives
Sedatives/hypnotics	Black cohosh	May ↑ hypotensive effects
Sodium bicarbonate	Quinine	May lead to toxicity, do not use concurrently
SSRIs	St. John's wort	Serotonin syndrome and an additive effect may occur. Concurrent use may lead to coma, do not use concurrently
SSRIs	Yohimbe	May cause ↑ CNS stimulation, do not use together
Statins	Goldenseal	May slow the metabolism of statins
Stimulants	Ginseng	Overstimulation may occur with concurrent use
Stimulants	Siberian ginseng	Concurrent use is not recommended, overstimulation may occur
Succinylcholine	Melatonin	↑ blocking properties of succinylcholine, do not use concurrently
Sumatriptan	Horehound	↑ serotonin effect, do not use concurrently
Sympathomimetics	Ephedra	↑ the effect of sympathomimetics and causes hypertension
Sympathomimetics	Rauwolfia	Will ↑ blood pressure, do not use concurrently
Sympathomimetics	Yohimbe	↑ yohimbe toxicity, do not use concurrently
Systemic steroids	Aloe	When taken internally may ↑ effects of systemic steroids
Tannic acids	Agar	↑ dehydration
Thyroid hormones	Soy	May interfere with thyroid hormone absorption, do not use concurrently
Thyroid hormones	Kelpware	May ↓ effects of thyroid hormones, do not use concurrently
Thyroid hormones	Spirulina	High iodine content of spirulina may ↓ action of thyroid hormones, do not use concurrently
Thyroid preparations	Bugleweed	Can interfere with the action of thyroid preparations
Thyroid preparations	Agar	Avoid concurrent use because of high iodine content in agar
Tolbutamide	Angelica	May delay elimination of tolbutamide
Toxoids	Safflower	May cause ↑ immunosuppression, do not use concurrently
Trazodone	St. John's wort	May cause serotonin syndrome
Tricyclic antidepressants	Coenzyme q10	Tricyclic antidepressants ay ↓ the action of coenzyme Q10 and deplete endogenous stores
Tricyclic antidepressants	Jimsonweed	↑ anticholinergic effects when jimsonweed used with tricyclics
Tricyclic antidepressants	Yohimbe	May result in ↑ hypertension, doses may need to be ↓
Tricyclic antidepressants	Corkwood	May ↑ anticholinergic effect
Tricyclic antidepressants	Ephedra	Hypertensive crisis can occur when used concurrently
Urinary alkalizers	Ephedra	↑ the effect of urinary alkalizers
Urine acidifiers	Bearberry	May inactivate bearberry
Vaccines	Safflower	May cause ↑ immunosuppression, do not use concurrently
Vaccines (passive)	Cat's claw	May interact with passive vaccines composed of animal sera
Vitamin B	Goldenseal	May ↓ absorption of vitamin B
Warfarin	Acidophilus	↓ warfarin action
Warfarin	Anise	May ↑ action of warfarin
Warfarin	Valerian	May negate therapeutic effects of warfarin, do not use concurrently
Xanthines	Cacao tree	May ↓ the metabolism of xanthines such as theophylline
Xanthines	Coffee	Large amounts of coffee ↑ the action of xanthines such as theophylline
Xanthines	Cola tree	May ↑ the action of xanthines
Xanthines	Ephedra	Causes ↑ central nervous system stimulation
Xanthines	Green tea	Large amounts of green tea ↑ the action of xanthines
Xanthines	Guarana	May ↑ pulse rate, blood pressure, and arrhythmias when taken concurrently
Zinc	Chromium	↓ chromium absorption when taken concurrently
Zinc	Melatonin	↑ inhibition of NMDA receptors, do not use concurrently

Continued

APPENDIX 4

Herbal Resources

The following is a sampling of online resources that provide current, reliable information about herbal products, their uses, and their health effects. Some are consumer oriented, and others are intended for health professionals. The names of the sponsoring organizations' home pages are arranged alphabetically. URLs are provided for each individual site, or for the Internet portal through which the site may be accessed.

AGRICOLA (AGRICultural OnLine Access):
http://www.nal.usda.gov/ag98/

Alternative Herbal Index: Provides alphabetized monographs for more than 100 commonly used herbs, including information on usage, chemistry, interactions, and dosage, as well as a symptom-to-herb checker. http://onhealth.webmd.com/alternative/resource/herbs/index.asp

Alternative Medicine Home Page, from the University of Pittsburgh: A compendium of resources to herbal and other alternative medicine information, broken into several categories. Each category includes a brief description of the linked material. Categories include:

- Databases
- Internet resources (divided into subject areas)
- Mailing lists & newsgroups
- AIDS and HIV
- Practitioner's directories
- Related resources
- Government resources
- Pennsylvania resources

http://www.pitt.edu/cbw/altm.html

American Botanical Council:
http://www.herbalgram.org/

American Herbal Pharmacopoeia:
http://www.herbal-ahp.org/

American Herbalists Guild:
http://www.americanherbalistsguild.com/

American Society of Pharmacognosy:
http://www.phcog.org/

British Herbal Medicine Association:
http://www.ex.ac.uk/phytonet/bhma.html

Dr. Duke's Phytochemical and Ethnobotanical Databases, from the Agricultural Research Service: A database of medicinal plants that allows the user to search by either common or scientific name. Provides information about the individual phytochemical components in each species, their biological actions, and relevant references.
http://www.ars-grin.gov/duke/plants.html

European Scientific Cooperative on Phytotherapy (ESCOP):
http://www.escop.com/

Herb Research Foundation (HRF): Contains an herbal question-and-answer column, an interface that allows the user to submit questions to the HRF foundation staff, herb news, herb references, and information about setting up media outreach and public education programs about safe and appropriate herb use. The HRF is a nonprofit research and education organization whose stated mission is to improve world health through the informed use of herbs. Some services are available free of charge, while others, such as custom botanical literature research and document delivery, involve a fee.
http://www.herbs.org

Herbal Abstract Page: A compendium of links to Medline and other abstracts of articles about Western herbal and traditional Chinese medical therapies and their documented effects on human health.
http://www.seanet.com/?vettf/Medline4.htm

Medicine, from MedlinePlus:
http://www.nlm.nih.gov/medlineplus/herbalmedicine.html

Herbs for Health, from About.com: Offers a variety of consumer information about American Indian herbs, Ayurvedic medicinal products, Chinese herbs, ethnobotany, and Western herbs, along with daily updates on herbs and other alternative medicine issues in the news. Provides numerous links to other sites for information about herbs and alternative medicine.
http://herbsforhealth.about.com/

Rocky Mountain Herbal Institute: Provides searchable general information about Chinese herbalism; describes continuing education courses available in Chinese herbal sciences and environmental health to medical and health professionals. Provides a free, searchable database of 220 Chinese herbs and related sample course materials.
http://www.rmhiherbal.org/

RxList Alternatives, from allnurses.com: Provides searchable user monographs and frequently-asked-questions lists for commonly used Western herbs, Chinese herbal remedies, and homeopathic remedies.
http://www.rxlist.com/alternative.htm

Southwest School of Botanical Medicine: A comprehensive list of files containing botanical illustrations, including digitized

From Skidmore-Roth L: Mosby's *Handbook of Herbs & Natural Supplements,* St Louis, 2004, Mosby.

photographs, color prints, lithographs, engravings, line drawings, and wood prints. Includes both .jpeg and .gif file formats.
http://www.swsbm.com/HOMEPAGE/HomePage.html

United States Pharmacopoeia (USP): Under "Dietary Supplements," includes detailed information on the status of USP-NF Botanical Monograph Development Project.
http://www.usp.org/

World Health Organization Herbal Monographs: Under "Development," see the entry for *Alternative Medicine Home Page, from the University of Pittsburgh*.
http://www.who.int/medicines/library/trm/medicinalplants/monographs.shtml

Relaxation Techniques

Relaxation Techniques

Relaxation Technique	Summary	Further Resources
Breathing exercise	This is the foundation of most relaxation techniques. Have patients place one hand on the chest and the other on the abdomen. Instruct them to take a slow, deep breath, as if they were sucking in all the air in the room. While doing this, the hand on the abdomen should rise higher than the hand on the chest. This promotes diaphragmatic breathing that increases alveolar expansion in the bases of the lungs. Have them hold the breath for a count of 7 and then exhale. Exhalation should take twice as long as inhalation. Repeat this for a total of five breaths, and encourage patients to do this three times a day.	*Conscious Breathing* by Gay Hendricks is one of many good resources on using breathing for relaxation and health.
Meditation		
Transcendental/The relaxation response	To prevent distracting thoughts, the subject repeats a mantra (a word or sound) over and over again while sitting in a comfortable position. If a distracting thought comes to mind, it is accepted and let go, with the mind focusing again on the mantra.	www.mindbody.harvard.edu or *The Relaxation Response* by Herbert Benson; www.tm.org for information on transcendental meditation
Mindful meditation	This represents the philosophy of living in the present or in the moment. The *body scan* is one technique where the subject uses breathing to obtain a relaxed state while lying or sitting. The mind progressively focuses on different parts of the body, where it feels any and all sensations intentionally but nonjudgmentally before moving on to another part of the body. A patient with back pain may focus on the quality and characteristics of the pain as if to better understand it and bring it under control.	*Full Catastrophe Living* by Jon Kabat-Zinn describes this technique in full and the program for stress reduction at the University of Massachusetts Medical Center.
Centering prayer	This is a form similar to transcendental meditation that has a more religious foundation. The subject repeats a "sacred word" similar to a mantra. As thoughts come to mind, they are accepted and let go, clearing the mind to become more centered on the spirit within, as if the mind's preoccupied thoughts are the layers of an onion that are peeled away, allowing better understanding of the spirit at the core.	www.Centeringprayer.com; look under "method of centering prayer" for a nondenominational discussion.

From Rakel RE (ed): *Principles of family practice*, ed 6, Philadelphia, 2002, WB Saunders.

Continued

Relaxation Techniques—cont'd

Relaxation Technique	Summary	Further Resources
Progressive muscle relaxation (PMR)	A form of relaxation in which the subject is attuned to the difference in feeling when the muscles are tensed and then relaxed. In a comfortable position, start by tensing the whole body from head to toe. While doing this, notice the feelings of tightness. Take a deep breath in and as you let it out, let the tension release and the muscles relax. This is then followed by progressive tension and relaxation throughout the body. One may start by clenching the fists and then tensing the arms, shoulders, chest, abdomen, hips, legs, and so on, with each step followed by relaxation.	www.uaex.edu/publications/pub/fshei28.htm is a good review of PMR as well as other relaxation exercises. It is sponsored by the University of Arkansas. *You Must Relax* is a book by the founder of this technique, Edmund Jacobson.
Visualization/Self-hypnosis	The subject uses visualization to recruit images that create a relaxed state. For example, if a person is anxious, visualizing images of a place and a time that were peaceful and comforting would help induce relaxation. This is best used in conjunction with a breathing exercise.	There are many audiocassettes that can guide people through a visualization "script" that can result in relaxation. Emmett Miller is one well-known author.
Autogenic training	This induces a physiologic response by using simple phrases. For example, "My legs are heavy and warm" is meant to increase the blood flow to this area, resulting in relaxation. This is done progressively from head to toe with the use of deep breathing and repetition of the phrase. After completing this, focus attention on any body part that may still be tense, and then focus the breath and phrase to that area until the whole body is relaxed.	The British Autogenic Society at www.autogenictherapy.org.uk is a good resource for more information.
Exercise/Movement		
Aerobic	While performing an aerobic exercise, focus attention on a phrase, sound, word, or prayer and passively disregard other thoughts that may enter the mind. Some may focus on their breathing, saying to themselves, "In" with inhalation and "Out" with exhalation, or repeating "one-two, one-two" with each step they take with jogging. Doing this will help the mind focus, preventing other thoughts that may cause tension.	*Beyond the Relaxation Response* by Herbert Benson includes discussion of his research on inducing the relaxation response while exercising.
Yoga	This has been practiced for thousands of years in India. In America, it has been divided into three aspects: breathing (pranayama yoga), bodily postures or asanas (hatha yoga), and meditation to maintain balance and health. Regular practice induces relaxation.	For the following therapies, it is best to encourage your patients to take a class at a local community center or gym and to pick up an introductory book at a library or bookstore.
Tai chi	An ancient Chinese martial art that uses slow, graceful movements combined with inner mindfulness and breathing techniques to help bring balance between the mind and body.	See above.
Qi gong	A traditional Chinese practice that uses movement, meditation, and controlled breathing to balance the body's vital energy force, chi.	See above.

From Rakel RE (ed): *Principles of family practice,* ed 6, Philadelphia, 2002, WB Saunders.

INDEX

Bolded page numbers indicate principal textual treatment. Page numbers followed by f indicate figures; t, tables; b, boxes.

B

C

D

E

F

G

H

J

K

N

O

Q

R

S

T

U

W

NEUROLOGY

OPHTHALMOLOGY

ORTHOPEDICS

OTORHINOLARYNGOLOGY (ENT)

CURRENT LAW STATUTES ANNOTATED
1985

VOLUME FOUR

AUSTRALIA AND NEW ZEALAND
The Law Book Company Ltd.
Sydney : Melbourne : Perth

CANADA AND U.S.A.
The Carswell Company Ltd.
Agincourt, Ontario

INDIA
N. M. Tripathi Private Ltd.
Bombay
and
Eastern Law House Private Ltd.
Calcutta and Delhi

M.P.P. House
Bangalore

ISRAEL
Steimatzky's Agency Ltd.
Jerusalem : Tel Aviv : Haifa

MALAYSIA : SINGAPORE : BRUNEI
Malayan Law Journal (Pte.) Ltd.
Singapore

PAKISTAN
Pakistan Law House
Karachi